# 2010
# STANDARD POSTAGE
# STAMP CATALOGUE

## ONE HUNDRED AND SIXTY-SIXTH EDITION IN SIX VOLUMES

## VOLUME 3
### COUNTRIES OF THE WORLD
### G-I

| | |
|---|---|
| EDITOR | James E. Kloetzel |
| ASSOCIATE EDITOR | William A. Jones |
| ASSISTANT EDITOR /NEW ISSUES & VALUING | Martin J. Frankevicz |
| ASSISTANT EDITOR | Charles Snee |
| VALUING ANALYST | Steven R. Myers |
| ADMINISTRATIVE ASSISTANT/IMAGE COORDINATOR | Beth L. Brown |
| DESIGN MANAGER | Teresa M. Wenrick |
| ADVERTISING | Phyllis Stegemoller |
| CIRCULATION / PRODUCT PROMOTION MANAGER | Tim Wagner |
| VICE PRESIDENT/EDITORIAL AND PRODUCTION | Steve Collins |
| PRESIDENT | William Fay |

Released June 2009
Includes New Stamp Listings through the June 2009 *Scott Stamp Monthly* Catalogue Update

Copyright© 2009 by

## *Scott Publishing Co.*

911 Vandemark Road, Sidney, OH 45365-0828
A division of AMOS PRESS, INC., publishers of *Scott Stamp Monthly, Linn's Stamp News, Coin World* and *Coin World's Coin Values.*

# Table of Contents

See Volume 1 for United States, United Nations and Countries of the World A-B
See Volume 2, 4 through 6 for Countries of the World, C-F, J-Z.

Volume 2: C-F
Volume 4: J-O
Volume 5: P-Sl
Volume 6: So-Z

# Scott Publishing Co.

**SCOTT** 911 VANDEMARK ROAD, SIDNEY, OHIO 45365  937-498-0802

Dear Scott Catalogue User:

### A time of uncertainty.

We all know that economies worldwide are weak. As part of that situation, demand for most products is soft. From all information we can gather, it appears that the market for stamps is a bit stronger than most, and for that we can be grateful. Having just returned from the Westpex stamp show in San Francisco, I can personally vouch for the fact that a well-organized, well-run show can result in high attendance and serious interest on the part of buyers. This show is always a joy to attend, and this year's version did not seem to show the least downturn in interest or activity. However, let's be honest. Unless you have the rarest of the rare or the highest possible grade of a stamp, the market in general is not lively. Most stamps are holding their own, but just barely.

As a result of these circumstances, collectors and dealers will find that many fewer values have changed in this 2010 Volume 3 edition of the *Scott Standard Postage Stamp Catalogue* compared to the record number of changes that were seen in last year's edition. There are certainly value changes, almost 21,000 of them, but this is fewer than half as many changes as were made in the 2009 Volume 3.

### Where are the value changes in the 2010 Volume 3?

Leading the way in Volume 3 with more than 6,200 value changes is Germany, including German Occupation and German Offices Abroad issues. There are also many significant value changes in Indian States. The Convention States show 1,798 value changes, while the Feudatory States record 3,671 changes. Other countries with large numbers of changes are Hungary (2,111), Italy (1,635), Guadeloupe (629) and Indo-China (551). Almost every country in Volume 3 shows some value changes, though smaller numbers than the examples cited.

Value changes in Germany tend to be numerous for the entire stamp-issuing period, but the majority of the changes are small, being in the 5 percent to 15 percent range. The 1872 ¼gr violet Imperial Eagle, Scott 1, moves to $87.50 used from $85 last year, but the scarcer 7kr ultramarine stamp from the same set, Scott 10, climbs to $2,350 unused and $87.50 used, from $2,000 unused and $82.50 used in the 2009 Volume 3. While a majority of value changes in Germany show generally modest upward movement, values of the issues of the last few years show decreases, reflecting currency conversion considerations.

Germany value changes continue through the semi-postals and the air post issues. The 1935 Ostropa souvenir sheet of four, Scott B68, moves to $825 unused from just $700 last year, and the 1930 2m and 4m South America Flight Zeppelin stamps, Scott C38-C39, rise modestly to $240 each unused and $300 each used, from $230 each unused and $290 each used in 2009. The mint, never-hinged set jumps to $2,625 from $2,550.

The Convention States and Feudatory States of India have been thoroughly reviewed this year, and the review has resulted in a great many value changes, many of them significant increases. In Chamba, many stamps double in value, and some stamps rise in value even more. Some values for singles and sets in never-hinged condition have been added.

Value increases in the Feudatory States are similar to those in the Convention States, with very significant value jumps noted in many areas. Collectors of these areas of India philately will definitely want to examine closely all of the value and editorial changes in this 2010 Volume 3.

In Hungary, imperforate sets are noted in footnotes where they occur, and perhaps the most notable value changes in the country are for these imperforates. Values often have risen dramatically in this 2010 edition. Additionally, many new notes with values have been added for imperforates not previously listed. Collectors of specialized Hungary will want to check both the new imperforate listings and the new values for all the imperforates.

The regular Hungary issues show very occasional value changes in the issues after the 1920s, with many more changes in the 1990-2006 period.

In Italy, virtually all stamps show upward value adjustments through the 1950s. The first stamp of the country, the 1862 10c bister, Scott 17, moves to $8,000 unused and $325 used, from $6,500 unused and $290 used last year. There are also numerous value changes, modestly upward, in Trieste.

### We are close to completing our all-color image project.

Collectors may remember that color images began appearing in the Scott catalogs for the first time in October 2004, when the 2005 *Scott Specialized Catalogue of United States Stamps and Covers* was published for the first time in color. That was followed by the *Scott Classic Specialized Catalogue* of 2005. Then, with the 2006 Standard catalogues, Volumes 1-6, the entire Scott catalogue line appeared in color.

We began scanning stamps from the Scott reference collection in early 2001, and these images (in black and white) started appearing in the 2002 catalogues. Later in 2001, we were blessed by the appearance of a philatelic angel who loaned us, during a period of many months, his entire 400-volume collection of worldwide mint stamps. That angel was Dr. Hsien-ming Meng, an Ohio collector within easy driving distance from our Sidney, Ohio, offices. Between the Scott reference collection and Dr. Meng's collection, we soon approached 90 percent to 100 percent completion in color scans for country after country.

Many other collectors and dealers have helped in the last few years, and we now show close to 100 percent of the stamps in the catalogues in full color. Those who have helped with this project have sent color scans or the actual stamps that were needed.

And we thank all the others who continue to send in scans or stamps. Remember, if you see a Scott image of a stamp in black and white, we probably need a color scan. Any help you can provide will be appreciated. Just call or write us for details concerning what must be done.

We now have begun a new project of replacing images of stamps that are not in an appropriate condition for the catalogues or are in need of color correction. Hundreds of scans already have been replaced, and many more will be in coming years.

### Final thoughts.

On the editorial side, two new major numbers, Scott 36 and 45, have been added to Ifni. New booklet pane and complete booklet listings have been added to Guernsey and Isle of Man. And there are numerous new minor-number listings added in the Indian Feudatory State of Alwar, where part-perforate varieties have been listed, and in Bhopal, where errors such as imperforates, part perforates, double printings, omitted overprints or doubled overprints have been added, as well as some laid paper varieties. Also in the Feudatory States, many varieties have been added to the listings of Cochin, Hyderabad, Indore, Jaipur, Kishangarh, Rajasthan, Sirmoor and Soruth. See the Volume 3 Number Additions, Deletions & Changes listing on page 1335 for these and other changes.

Especially in uncertain economic times such as these, a hobby is a great gift. Happy collecting.

*James E. Kloetzel*

James E. Kloetzel/Catalogue Editor

# Acknowledgments

Our appreciation and gratitude go to the following individuals who have assisted us in preparing information included in this year's Scott Catalogues. Some helpers prefer anonymity. These individuals have generously shared their stamp knowledge with others through the medium of the Scott Catalogue.

Those who follow provided information that is in addition to the hundreds of dealer price lists and advertisements and scores of auction catalogues and realizations that were used in producing the catalogue values. It is from those noted here that we have been able to obtain information on items not normally seen in published lists and advertisements. Support from these people goes beyond data leading to catalogue values, for they also are key to editorial changes.

A special acknowledgment to Liane and Sergio Sismondo of The Classic Collector for their extraordinary assistance and knowledge sharing that has aided in the preparation of this year's Standard and Classic Specialized Catalogues.

A. R. Allison (Orange Free State Study Circle)
Roland Austin
Robert Ausubel (Great Britain Collectors Club)
Jack Hagop Barsoumian (International Stamp Co.)
Tim Bartshe
William Batty-Smith
Jules K. Beck (Latin American Philatelic Society)
Vladimir Berrio-Lemm
John Birkinbine II
John D. Bowman (Carriers and Locals Society)
Joshua Buchsbayew (Cherrystone Auctions)
Bernard Bujnak
Timothy Bryan Burgess
Mike Bush (Joseph V. Bush, Inc.)
Tina & John Carlson (JET Stamps)
Carlson Chambliss
Richard A. Champagne (Richard A. Champagne, Inc.)
Henry Chlanda
Richard Clever
Ray Cobb
Leroy P. Collins III (United Postal Stationery Society)
Laurie Conrad
Frank D. Correl
Tony L. Crumbley (Carolina Coin & Stamp, Inc.)
Stephen R. Datz
Tony Davis
Charles Deaton
Bob Dumaine
Sister Theresa Durand
Mark Eastzer (Markest Stamp Co.)
Esi Ebrani (Iran Philatelic Study Circle)
Paul G. Eckman
Marty Farber
George Fedyk
Leon Finik (Loral Stamps)
Henry Fisher
Robert A. Fisher
Jeffrey M. Forster
Ken Fowler
Robert S. Freeman
Ernest E. Fricks (France & Colonies Philatelic Society)
Bob Genisol (Sultan Stamp Center)
Michael A. Goldman (Regency Superior, Ltd.)
Daniel E. Grau
Andy Green
Jan E. Gronwall

Joe Hahn (Associated Collectors of El Salvador)
Bruce Hecht (Bruce L. Hecht Co.)
Clifford O. Herrick (Fidelity Trading Co.)
Peter Hoffman
George W. Holschauer (Colonial Stamp Company)
Armen Hovsepian
Philip J. Hughes (Croatian Philatelic Society)
Doug Iams
Michael Jaffe (Michael Jaffe Stamps, Inc.)
N. M. Janoowalla
Stephen Joe (International Stamp Service)
John Kardos (The Stamp Gallery)
Allan Katz (Ventura Stamp Co.)
Stanford M. Katz
Patricia A. Kaufmann
William V. Kriebel
Dr. Ingert (Ihor) Kuzych-Berlzovsky
Michael Lenard
John R. Lewis (The William Henry Stamp Co.)
William A. Litle
Pedro Llach (Filatelia Llach S.L.)
George Luzitano
Dennis Lynch
Robert L. Markovits (Quality Investors, Ltd.)
Marilyn R. Mattke
William K. McDaniel
Mark S. Miller (India Study Circle)
Allen Mintz (United Postal Stationery Society)
William E. Mooz
Gary M. Morris (Pacific Midwest Co.)
Peter Mosiondz, Jr.
Bruce M. Moyer (Moyer Stamps & Collectibles)
Gary Nelson
Dr. Marwan Nusair
Robert Odenweller (AIEP)
Albert Olejnik
Dr. Everett L. Parker
Mark Parren
John E. Pearson (Pittwater Philatelic Service)
John Pedneault
Michael O. Perry
Donald J. Peterson (International Philippine Philatelic Society)
Stanley M. Piller (Stanley M. Piller & Associates)
Todor Drumev Popov
Peter W. W. Powell
Stephen Radin (Albany Stamp Co.)
Siddique Mahmudur Rahman
Dr. Reuben A. Ramkissoon
Ghassan D. Riachi

Peter A. Robertson
Omar Rodriquez
Michael Rogers (Michael Rogers, Inc.)
Michael Ruggiero
Mehrdad Sadri (Persiphila)
Richard H. Salz
Alex Schauss (Schauss Philatelics)
Jacques C. Schiff, Jr. (Jacques C. Schiff, Jr., Inc.)
Bernard Seckler (Fine Arts Philatelists)
Guy Shaw
Charles F. Shreve (Spink Shreves Galleries)
Sergio & Liane Sismondo (The Classic Collector)
Jay Smith
Frank J. Stanley, III
Philip & Henry Stevens (postalstationery.com)
Jerry Summers
Scott R. Trepel (Siegel Auction Galleries)
Steve Unkrich
Philip T. Wall
Kristian Wang
Richard A. Washburn
Giana Wayman
William R. Weiss, Jr. (Weiss Philatelics)
Ed Wener (Indigo)
Hans A. Westphal
Don White (Dunedin Stamp Centre)
Kirk Wolford (Kirk's Stamp Company)
Robert F. Yacano (K-Line Philippines)
Ralph Yorio
Val Zabijaka
Michal Zika
John P. Zuckerman (Siegel Auction Galleries)
Alfonsa G. Zulueta, Jr.

# Addresses, Telephone Numbers, Web Sites, E-Mail Addresses of General & Specialized Philatelic Societies

Collectors can contact the following groups for information about the philately of the areas within the scope of these societies, or inquire about membership in these groups. Aside from the general societies, we limit this list to groups that specialize in particular fields of philately, particular areas covered by the Scott Standard Postage Stamp Catalogue, and topical groups. Many more specialized philatelic society exist than those listed below. These addresses are updated yearly, and they are, to the best of our knowledge, correct and current. Groups should inform the editors of address changes whenever they occur. The editors also want to hear from other such specialized groups not listed.

Unless otherwise noted all website addresses begin with http://

American Philatelic Society
100 Match Factory Place
Bellefonte PA 16823-1367
Ph: (814) 933-3803
www.stamps.org
E-mail: apsinfo@stamps.org

American Stamp Dealers
Association, Inc.
Joe Savarese
3 School St. Suite #205
Glen Cove NY 11542
Ph: (516) 759-7000
www.asdaonline.com
E-mail: asda@erols.com

National Stamp Dealers Association
Dick Keiser, president
2916 NW Bucklin Hill Rd #136
Silverdale WA 98383-8514
Ph: (800) 875-6633
www.nsdainc.org
E-mail: gail@nsdainc.org

International Society of Worldwide
Stamp Collectors
Joanne Berkowitz, MD
PO Box 19006
Sacramento CA 95819
www.iswsc.org
E-mail: executivedirector@iswsc.org

Royal Philatelic Society
41 Devonshire Place
London, United Kingdom, W1G 6JY
www.rpsl.org.uk
E-mail: secretary@rpsl.org.uk

Royal Philatelic Society of Canada
PO Box 929, Station Q
Toronto, ON, Canada, M4T 2P1
Ph: (888) 285-4143
www.rpsc.org
E-mail: info@rpsc.org

Young Stamp Collectors of America
Janet Houser
100 Match Factory Place
Bellefonte PA 16823-1367
Ph: (814) 933-3820
www.stamps.org/ysca/intro.htm
E-mail: ysca@stamps.org

**Groups focusing on fields or aspects found in worldwide philately (some may cover U.S. area only)**

American Air Mail Society
Stephen Reinhard
PO Box 110
Mineola NY 11501
www.americanairmailsociety.org
E-mail: sreinhard1@optonline.net

American First Day Cover Society
Douglas Kelsey
PO Box 16277
Tucson AZ 85732-6277
Ph: (520) 321-0880
www.afdcs.org
E-mail: afdcs@aol.com

American Revenue Association
Eric Jackson
PO Box 728
Leesport PA 19533-0728
Ph: (610) 926-6200
www.revenuer.org
E-mail: eric@revenuer.com

American Topical Association
Ray E. Cartier
PO Box 57
Arlington TX 76004-0057
Ph: (817) 274-1181
americantopicalassn.org
E-mail: americantopical@msn.com

Christmas Seal & Charity Stamp
Society
John Denune
234 East Broadway
Granville OH 43023
Ph: (740) 587-0276
http://cscss.home.att.net
E-mail: jdenune@roadrunner.com

Errors, Freaks and Oddities
Collectors Club
Stan Raugh
4217 Eighth Ave.
Temple PA 19560
Ph: (717) 445-9420 Nor. Am. Phone
No.
www.efocc.org
E-mail: ddprice98@hotmail.com

First Issues Collectors Club
Clark Buchi
P.O. Box 453
Brentwood TN 37024-0453
www.firstissues.org
E-mail: orders@firstissues.org

International Society of Reply
Coupon Collectors
Peter Robin
PO Box 353
Bala Cynwyd PA 19004
E-mail: peterrobin@verizon.net

The Joint Stamp Issues Society
Pascal LeBlond
60-600 Rue Cormier
Gatineau, QC, Canada, J9H 6B4
jointissues.ovh.org
E-mail: jointissues@yahoo.com

National Duck Stamp Collectors
Society
Anthony J. Monico
PO Box 43
Harleysville PA 19438-0043
www.ndscs.org
E-mail: ndscs@hwcn.org

No Value Identified Club
Albert Sauvanet
Le Clos Royal B, Boulevard des Pas
Enchantes
St. Sebastien-sur Loire, France, 44230
E-mail: alain.vailly@irin.univ nantes.fr

The Perfins Club
Jerry Hejduk
PO Box 490450.
Leesburg FL 34749-0450
Ph: (352) 326-2117
E-mail: flprepers@comcast.net

Postage Due Mail Study Group
John Rawlins
13, Longacre
Chelmsford
United Kingdom, CM1 3BJ
E-mail: john.rawlins2@ukonline.co.uk.

Post Mark Collectors Club
Beverly Proulx
7629 Homestead Drive
Baldwinsville NY 13027
Ph: (315) 638-0532
www.postmarks.org
E-mail: stampdance@tweny.rr.com

Postal History Society
Kalman V. Illyefalvi
869 Bridgewater Drive
New Oxford PA 17350-8206
Ph: (717) 624-5941
www.stampclubs.com
E-mail: kalphyl@juno.com

Precancel Stamp Society
Jerry Hejduk
PO Box 490450.
Leesburg FL 34749-0450
Ph: (352) 326-2117
www.precancels.com
E-mail: psspromosec@comcast.net

United Postal Stationery Society
Stuart Leven
1445-50 Foxworthy Ave. #187
San Jose, CA 95118-1119
www.upss.org
E-mail: poststat@gmail.com

United States Possessions Philatelic
Society
Geoffrey Brewster
6453 E. Stallion Rd.
Paradise Valley AZ 85253
Ph: (480) 607-7184

**Groups focusing on U.S. area philately as covered in the Standard Catalogue**

Canal Zone Study Group
Richard H. Salz
60 27th Ave.
San Francisco CA 94121-1026

Carriers and Locals Society
John D. Bowman
PO Box 74
Grosse Ile MI 48138
www.pennypost.org
E-mail: jbowman@stx.rr.net

Confederate Stamp Alliance
Gen. Francis J. Crown
PO Box 278
Capshaw AL 35742-0278
Ph. (302) 422-2656
www.csalliance.org
E-mail: csaas@knology.net

Hawaiian Philatelic Society
Kay H. Hoke
PO Box 10115
Honolulu HI 96816-0115
Ph: (808) 521-5721

Plate Number Coil Collectors Club
Ronald E. Maifeld
PO Box 54622
Cincinnati OH 45254-0622
Ph: (513) 231-4208
www.pnc3.org
E-mail: president@pnc3.org

Ryukyu Philatelic Specialist Society
Laura Edmonds, Secy.
PO Box 240177
Charlotte NC 28224-0177
Ph: (704) 519-5157
www.ryukyustamps.org
E-mail: secretary@ryukyustamps.org

United Nations Philatelists
Blanton Clement, Jr.
P.O. Box 146
Morrisville PA 19067-0146
www.unpi.com
E-mail: bclemjr@yahoo.com

United States Stamp Society
Executive Secretary
PO Box 6634
Katy TX 77491-6631
www.usstamps.org
E-mail: webmaster@usstamps.org

U.S. Cancellation Club
Roger Rhoads
6160 Brownstone Ct.
Mentor OH 44060
www.geocities.com/athens/2088/
uscchome.htm
E-mail: rrrhoads@aol.com

U.S. Philatelic Classics Society
Rob Lund
2913 Fulton
Everett WA 98201-3733
www.uspcs.org
E-mail: membershipchairman@uspcs.org

**Groups focusing on philately of foreign countries or regions**

Aden & Somaliland Study Group
Gary Brown
PO Box 106
Briar Hill, Victoria, Australia, 3088
E-mail: garyjohn951@optushome.com.au

American Society of Polar
  Philatelists (Antarctic areas)
Alan Warren
PO Box 39
Exton PA 19341-0039
Ph: (847) 421-7655
www.polarphilatelists.org
E-mail: cjenner00@yahoo.com

Andorran Philatelic Study Circle
D. Hope
17 Hawthorn Dr.
Stalybridge, Cheshire, United
Kingdom, SK15 1UE
http://apsc.free.fr
E-mail: apsc@free.fr

Australian States Study Circle of
  The Royal Sydney Philatelic Club
Ben Palmer
GPO 1751
Sydney, N.S.W., Australia, 2001

Austria Philatelic Society
Ralph Schneider
PO Box 23049
Belleville IL 62223
Ph: (618) 277-6152
www.austriaphilatelicsociety.com
E-mail: rsstamps@aol.com

American Belgian Philatelic Society
Edward de Bary
11 Wakefield Dr. Apt. 2105
Asheville NC 28803
E-mail: belgam@charter.net

Bechuanalands and Botswana Society
Neville Midwood
69 Porlock Lane
Furzton, Milton Keynes, United
Kingdom, MK4 1JY
www.nevsoft.com
E-mail: bbsoc@nevsoft.com

Bermuda Collectors Society
Thomas J. McMahon
PO Box 1949
Stuart FL 34995
www.bermudacollectorssociety.org
E-mail: science29@comcast.net

Brazil Philatelic Association
William V. Kriebel
1923 ManningSt.
Philadelphia PA 19103-5728
Ph: (215) 735-3697
E-mail: kriebewv@drexel.edu

British Caribbean Philatelic Study
  Group
Dr. Reuben A. Ramkissoon
3011 White Oak Lane
Oak Brook IL 60523-2513
Ph: (630) 963-1439
www.bcpsg.com
E-mail: rramkissoon@juno.com

The King George VI Collectors
  Society (British Commonwealth)
John Shaw
17 Balcaskie Road, Eltham
London, United Kingdom, SE9 1HQ
www.kg6.info

British North America Philatelic
  Society (Canada & Provinces)
H. P. Jacobi
6-2168 150A St.
Surrey, B.C., Canada, V4A 9W4
www.bnaps.org
E-mail: pjacobi@shaw.ca

British West Indies Study Circle
W. Clary Holt
PO Drawer 59
Burlington NC 27216
Ph: (336) 227-7461

Burma Philatelic Study Circle
Michael Whittaker
1, Ecton Leys, Hillside
Rugby, Warwickshire, United Kingdom,
CV22 5SL
E-mail: whittaker2004@ntlworld.com

Ceylon Study Group
R. W. P. Frost
42 Lonsdale Road, Cannington
Bridgewater, Somerset, United
Kingdom, TA5 2JS
E-mail: rodney.frost@tiscali.co.uk

Channel Islands Specialists Society
Moira Edwards
86, Hall Lane, Sandon,
Chelmsford, United Kingdom, CM2
7RQ
www.ciss1950.org.uk
E-mail: am012e5360@blueyonder.co.uk

China Stamp Society
Paul H. Gault
PO Box 20711
Columbus OH 43220
www.chinastampsociety.org
E-mail: secretary@chinastampsociety.org

Colombia/Panama Philatelic Study
  Group (COPAPHIL)
Thomas P. Myers
7411 Old Post Road #1
Lincoln NE 68506
www.copaphil.org
E-mail: tpmphil@hotmail.com

Association Filatelic de Costa Rica
Giana Wayman
c/o Interlink 102, PO Box 52-6770
Miami, FL 33152
E-mail: scotland@racsa.co.cr

Society for Costa Rica Collectors
Dr. Hector R. Mena
PO Box 14831
Baton Rouge LA 70808
www.socorico.org
E-mail: hrmena@aol.com

Cuban Philatelic Society of America
Ernesto Cuesta
PO Box 34434
Bethesda MD 20827
www.philat.com/cpsa
E-mail: ecuesta@philat.com

Cyprus Study Circle
Colin Dear
10 Marne Close, Wem
Shropshire, United Kingdom, SY4 5YE
www.cyprusstudycircle.org/index.htm
E-mail: colindear@talktalk.net.

Society for Czechoslovak Philately
Phil Rhoade
905 E. Oakside St.
South Bend IN 46614
www.csphilately.org
E-mail: philip.rhoade@mnsu.edu

Danish West Indies Study Unit of
  the Scandinavian Collectors Club
Arnold Sorensen
7666 Edgedale Drive
Newburgh IN 47630
Ph: (812) 853-2653
dwistudygroup.com
E-mail: valbydwi@hotmail.com

East Africa Study Circle
Jonathan Smalley
1 Lincoln Close
Tweeksbury, United Kingdom, B91
1AE
easc.org.uk
E-mail: jpasmalley@tiscali.co.uk

Egypt Study Circle
Mike Murphy
109 Chadwick Road
London, United Kingdom, SE15 4PY
Dick Wilson: North American Agent
egyptstudycircle.org.uk
E-mail: egyptstudycircle@hotmail.com

Estonian Philatelic Society
Juri Kirsimagi
29 Clifford Ave.
Pelham NY 10803
Ph: (914) 738-3713

Ethiopian Philatelic Society
Ulf Lindahl
21 Westview Place
Riverside CT 06878
Ph: (203) 866-3540
home.comcast.net/~fbheiser/ethiopia5.
htm
E-mail: ulindahl@optonline.net

Falkland Islands Philatelic Study
  Group
Carl J. Faulkner
Williams Inn, On-the-Green
Williamstown MA 01267-2620
www.fipsg.org.uk
Ph: (413) 458-9371

Faroe Islands Study Circle
Norman Hudson
28 Enfield Road
Ellesmere Port, Cheshire, United
Kingdom, CH65 8BY
www.faroeislandssc.org.
E-mail: jntropics@hotmail.com

Former French Colonies Specialist
  Society
BP 628
75367 Paris, Cedex 08, France
www.colfra.com
E-mail: clubcolfra@aol.com

France & Colonies Philatelic Society
Edward Grabowski
111 Prospect St., 4C
Westfield NJ 07090
www.drunkenboat.net/frandcol/
E-mail: edjjg@alum.mit.edu

Germany Philatelic Society
PO Box 6547
Chesterfield MO 63006
www.gps.nu

Gibraltar Study Circle
David R. Stirrups
34 Glamis Drive
Dundee, United Kingdom, DD2 1QP
E-mail: drstirrups@dundee.ac.uk

Great Britain Collectors Club
Timothy Bryan Burgess
3547 Windmill Way
Concord CA 94518
www.gbstamps.com/gbcc
E-mail: Pennyred@earthlink.net

International Society of Guatemala
  Collectors
Jaime Marckwordt
449 St. Francis Blvd.
Daly City CA 94015-2136
www.guatemalastamps.com

Hellenic Philatelic Society of
  America (Greece and related
  areas)
Dr. Nicholas Asimakopulos
541 Cedar Hill Ave.
Wyckoff NJ 07481
Ph: (201) 447-6262
E-mail: nick1821@aol.com

Haiti Philatelic Society
Ubaldo Del Toro
5709 Marble Archway
Alexandria VA 22315
www.haitiphilately.org
E-mail: u007ubi@aol.com

Hong Kong Stamp Society
Dr. An-Min Chung
3300 Darby Rd. Cottage 503
Haverford PA 19041-1064

Society for Hungarian Philately
Robert Morgan
2201 Roscomare Rd.
Los Angeles CA 90077-2222
www.hungarianphilately.org
E-mail: h.alan.hoover@hungarianphilately.
org

India Study Circle
John Warren
PO Box 7326
Washington DC 20044
Ph: (202) 564-6876
www.indiastudycircle.org
E-mail: warren.john@epa.gov

Indian Ocean Study Circle
Mrs. S. Hopson
Field Acre, Hoe Benham
Newbury, Berkshire, United Kingdom,
RG20 8PD

Society of Indo-China Philatelists
Ron Bentley
2600 North 24th Street
Arlington VA 22207
www.sicp.org
E-mail: ron.bentley@verizon.net

Iran Philatelic Study Circle
Mehdi Esmaili
PO Box 750096
Forest Hills NY 11375
www.iranphilatelic.org
E-mail: m.esmaili@earthlink.net

Eire Philatelic Association (Ireland)
David J. Brennan
PO Box 704
Bernardsville NJ 07924
eirephilatelicassoc.org
E-mail: brennan704@aol.com

Society of Israel Philatelists
Paul S. Aufrichtig
300 East 42nd St.
New York NY 10017

Italy and Colonies Study Circle
Andrew DíAnneo
1085 Dunweal Lane
Calistoga CA 94515
www.icsc.pwp.blueyonder.co.uk
E-mail: audanneo@napanet.net

International Society for Japanese
  Philately
Kenneth Kamholz
PO Box 1283
Haddonfield NJ 08033
www.isjp.org
E-mail: isjp@isjp.org

Korea Stamp Society
John E. Talmage
PO Box 6889
Oak Ridge TN 37831
www.pennfamily.org/KSS-USA
E-mail: jtalmage@usit.net

Latin American Philatelic Society
Jules K. Beck
30 1/2 Street #209
St. Louis Park MN 55426-3551

Liberian Philatelic Society
William Thomas Lockard
PO Box 106
Wellston OH 45692
Ph: (740) 384-2020
E-mail: tlockard@zoomnet.net

Liechtenstudy USA (Liechtenstein)
Paul Tremaine
PO Box 601
Dundee OR 97115-0601
Ph: (503) 538-4500
www.liechtenstudy.org
E-mail: editor@liechtenstudy.org

Lithuania Philatelic Society
John Variakojis
3715 W. 68th St.
Chicago IL 60629
Ph: (773) 585-8649
www.withgusto.org/lps/index.htm
E-mail: variakojis@earthlink.net

Luxembourg Collectors Club
Gary B. Little
7319 Beau Road
Sechelt, BC, Canada, V0N 3A8
http://lcc.luxcentral.com
E-mail: gary@luxcentral.com

Malaya Study Group
David Tett
PO Box 34
Wheathampstead, Herts, United
Kingdom, AL4 8JY
www.m-s-g/org/uk
E-mail: davidtett@aol.com

Malta Study Circle
Alec Webster
50 Worcester Road
Sutton, Surrey,
United Kingdom, SM2 6QB
E-mail: alecwebster50@hotmail.com

Mexico-Elmhurst Philatelic Society
International
David Pietsch
PO Box 50997
Irvine CA 92619-0997
E-mail: mepsi@msn.com

Society for Moroccan and Tunisian
Philately
206, bld. Pereire
75017 Paris, France
members.aol.com/Jhaik5814
E-mail: splm206@aol.com

Natal and Zululand Study Circle
Dr. Guy Dillaway
PO Box 181
Weston MA 02493
www.nzsc.demon.co.uk

Nepal & Tibet Philatelic Study
Group
Roger D. Skinner
1020 Covington Road
Los Altos CA 94024-5003
Ph: (650) 968-4163
fuchs-online.com/ntpsc/
E-mail: colinhepper@hotmail.co.uk

American Society for Netherlands
Philately
Hans Kremer
50 Rockport Ct.
Danville CA 94526
Ph: (925) 820-5841
www.angelfire.com/ca2/asnp
E-mail: hkremer@usa.net

New Zealand Society of Great Britain
Keith C. Collins
13 Briton Crescent
Sanderstead, Surrey, United Kingdom,
CR2 0JN
www.cs.stir.ac.uk/~rgc/nzsgb
E-mail: rgc@cs.stir.ac.uk

Nicaragua Study Group
Erick Rodriguez
11817 S.W. 11th St.
Miami FL 33184-2501
clubs.yahoo.com/clubs/nicara-
guastudygroup
E-mail: nsgsec@yahoo.com

Society of Australasian Specialists/
Oceania
Henry Bateman
PO Box 4862
Monroe LA 71211-4862
Ph: (800) 571-0293 members.aol.
com/stampsho/saso.html
E-mail: hbateman@jam.rr.com

Orange Free State Study Circle
J. R. Stroud
28 Oxford St.
Burnham-on-sea, Somerset, United
Kingdom, TA8 1LQ
orangefreestatephilately.org.uk
E-mail: richardstroudph@gofast.co.uk

Pacific Islands Study Circle
John Ray
24 Woodvale Avenue
London, United Kingdom, SE25 4AE
www.pisc.org.uk
E-mail: info@pisc.org.uk

Pakistan Philatelic Study Circle
Jeff Siddiqui
PO Box 7002
Lynnwood WA 98046
E-mail: jeffsiddiqui@msn.com

Centro de Filatelistas
Independientes de Panama
Vladimir Berrio-Lemm
Apartado 0823-02748
Plaza Concordia Panama, Panama
E-mail: panahistoria@gmail.com

Papuan Philatelic Society
Steven Zirinsky
PO Box 49, Ansonia Station
New York NY 10023
Ph: (718) 706-0616
www.communigate.co.uk/york/pps
E-mail: szirinsky@cs.com

International Philippine Philatelic
Society
Donald J. Peterson
7408 Alaska Ave., NW
Washington DC 20012
Ph: (202) 291-6229
www.theipps.info
E-mail: dpeterson@comcast.net

Pitcairn Islands Study Group
Dr. Everett L. Parker
719 Moosehead Lake Rd.
Greenville ME 04441-3626
Ph: (336) 475-4558
www.pisg.net
E-mail: nalweller@aol.com

Plebiscite-Memel-Saar Study Group
of the German Philatelic Society
Clay Wallace
100 Lark Court
Alamo CA 94507
E-mail: clayw1@sbcglobal.net

Polonus Philatelic Society (Poland)
Chris Kulpinski
9350 E. Palm Tree Dr.
Scottsdale AZ 85255
Ph: (480) 585-7114
www.polonus.org
E-mail: ctk@kulpinski.net

International Society for
Portuguese Philately
Clyde Homen
1491 Bonnie View Rd.
Hollister CA 95023-5117
www.portugalstamps.com
E-mail: cjh1491@sbcglobal.net

Rhodesian Study Circle
William R. Wallace
PO Box 16381
San Francisco CA 94116
www.rhodesianstudycircle.org.uk
E-mail: bwall8rscr@earthlink.net

Rossica Society of Russian Philately
Edward J. Laveroni
P.O. Box 320997
Los Gatos CA 95032-0116
www.rossica.org
E-mail: ed.laveroni@rossica.org

St. Helena, Ascension & Tristan Da
Cunha Philatelic Society
Dr. Everett L. Parker
719 Moosehead Lake Rd.
Greenville ME 04441-3626
Ph: (207) 695-3163
ourworld.compuserve.com/homep-
ages/ ST_HELENA_ASCEN_TDC
E-mail: eparker@hughes.net

St. Pierre & Miquelon Philatelic
Society
James R. (Jim) Taylor
2335 Paliswood Rd. SW
Calgary, AB, T2V 3P6, Canada

Associated Collectors of El Salvador
Joseph D. Hahn
1015 Old Boalsburg Rd. Apt G-5
State College PA 16801-6149
www.elsalvadorphilately.org
E-mail: joehahn2@yahoo.com

Fellowship of Samoa Specialists
Donald Mee
23 Leo Street
Christchurch, 8051, New Zealand
www.samoaexpress.org
E-mail: donanm@xtra.co.nz

Sarawak Specialistsí Society
Stu Leven
PO Box 24764
San Jose CA 95154-4764
Ph: (408) 978-0193
www.britborneostamps.org.uk
E-mail: stulev@ix.netcom.com

Scandinavian Collectors Club
Donald B. Brent
PO Box 13196
El Cajon CA 92020
www.scc-online.org
E-mail: dbrent47@sprynet.com

Slovakia Stamp Society
Jack Benchik
PO Box 555
Notre Dame IN 46556

Philatelic Society for Greater
Southern Africa
Alan Hanks
34 Seaton Drive
Aurora, ON, L4G 2KI, Canada
Ph: (905) 727-6993
www.psgsa.thestampweb.com
Email: alan.hanks@sympatico.ca

Spanish Philatelic Society
Robert H. Penn
1108 Walnut Drive
Danielsville PA 18038
Ph: (610) 767-6793

Sudan Study Group
c/o North American Agent
Richard S. Wilson
53 Middle Patent Road
Bedford NY 10506
www.sudanphilately.co.uk
E-mail: dadu1@verizon.net

American Helvetia Philatelic
Society (Switzerland,
Liechtenstein)
Richard T. Hall
PO Box 15053
Asheville NC 28813-0053
www.swiss-stamps.org
E-mail: secretary2@swiss-stamps.org

Tannu Tuva Collectors Society
Ken Simon
513 Sixth Ave. So.
Lake Worth FL 33460-4507
Ph: (561) 588-5954
www.tuva.tk
E-mail: yurttuva@yahoo.com

Society for Thai Philately
H. R. Blakeney
PO Box 25644
Oklahoma City OK 73125
E-mail: HRBlakeney@aol.com

Transvaal Study Circle
J. Woolgar
PO Box 379
Gravesend, DA11 9EW, United
Kingdom
www.transvaal.org.uk

Ottoman and Near East Philatelic
Society (Turkey and related areas)
Bob Stuchell
193 Valley Stream Lane
Wayne PA 19087
www.oneps.org
E-mail: rstuchell@msn.com

Ukrainian Philatelic & Numismatic
Society
George Slusarczuk
PO Box 303
Southfields NY 10975-0303
www.upns.org
E-mail: Yurko@frontiernet.net

Vatican Philatelic Society
Sal Quinonez
1 Aldersgate, Apt. 1002
Riverhead NY 11901-1830
Ph: (516) 727-6426
www.vaticanphilately.org

British Virgin Islands Philatelic
Society
Giorgio Migliavacca
PO Box 7007
St. Thomas VI 00801-0007
www.islandsun.com/FEATURES/
bviphil9198.html
E-mail: issun@candwbvi.net

West Africa Study Circle
Dr. Peter Newroth
Suite 603
5332 Sayward Hill Crescent
Victoria, BC, Canada, V8Y 3H8
www.wasc.org.uk/

Western Australia Study Group
Brian Pope
PO Box 423
Claremont, Western Australia,
Australia, 6910

Yugoslavia Study Group of the
Croatian Philatelic Society
Michael Lenard
1514 North 3rd Ave.
Wausau WI 54401
Ph: (715) 675-2833
E-mail: mjlenard@aol.com

## Topical Groups

**Americana Unit**
Dennis Dengel
17 Peckham Rd.
Poughkeepsie NY 12603-2018
www.americanaunit.org
E-mail: info@americanaunit.org

**Astronomy Study Unit**
John Budd
29203 Coharie Loop
San Antonio FL 33576-4643
Ph: (978) 851-8283
E-mail: jwgbudd@earthlink.net

**Bicycle Stamp Club**
Norman Batho
358 Iverson Place
East Windsor NJ 08520
Ph: (609) 448-9547
members.tripod.com/~bicyclestamps
E-mail: normbatho@worldnet.att.net

**Biology Unit**
Alan Hanks
34 Seaton Dr.
Aurora, ON, Canada, L4G 2K1
Ph: (905) 727-6993

**Bird Stamp Society**
Graham Horsman
23 A East Main Street
Blackburn West Lothian
Scotland, EH47 7QR, United Kingdom
www.bird-stamps.org/bss
E-mail: graham_horsman7@msn.com

**Canadiana Study Unit**
John Peebles
PO Box 3262, Station ìAî
London, ON, Canada, N6A 4K3
E-mail: john.peebles@sympatico.ca

**Captain Cook Study Unit**
Brian P. Sandford
173 Minuteman Dr.
Concord MA 01742-1923
www.captaincooksociety.com
E-mail: US@captaincooksociety.com

**Casey Jones Railroad Unit**
Donald Kesler
709 NW 35th Place
Lawton OK 73505-5121
www.uqp.de/cjr/index.htm
E-mail: normaned@rochester.rr.com

**Cats on Stamps Study Unit**
Mary Ann Brown
3006 Wade Rd.
Durham NC 27705
www.catsonstamps.org
E-mail: mabrown@nc.rr.com

**Chemistry & Physics on Stamps Study Unit**
Dr. Roland Hirsch
20458 Water Point Lane
Germantown MD 20874
www.cpossu.org
E-mail: rfhirsch@cpossu.org

**Chess on Stamps Study Unit**
Anne Kasonic
7625 County Road #153
Interlaken NY 14847
E-mail: akasonic@capital.net

**Christmas Philatelic Club**
Linda Lawrence
312 Northwood Drive
Lexington KY 40505
www.hwcn.org/link/cpc
E-mail: stamplinda@aol.com

**Christopher Columbus Philatelic Society**
Donald R. Ager
PO Box 71
Hillsboro NH 03244-0071
http://ccps.maphist.nl/
Ph: (603) 464-5379
E-mail: megnddon@tds.net

**Collectors of Religion on Stamps**
Verna Shackleton
425 North Linwood Avenue #110
Appleton WI 54914
www://my.vbe.com/~cmfourl/coros1.htm
E-mail: corosec@sbcglobal.net

**Dogs on Stamps Study Unit**
Morris Raskin
202A Newport Rd.
Monroe Township NJ 08831
Ph: (609) 655-7411
www.dossu.org
E-mail: mraskin@cellurian.com

**Earthís Physical Features Study Group**
Fred Klein
515 Magdalena Ave.
Los Altos CA 94024
epfsu.jeffhayward.com

**Ebony Society of Philatelic Events and Reflections (African-American topicals)**
Manuel Gilyard
800 Riverside Drive, Ste 4H
New York NY 10032-7412
www.esperstamps.org
E-mail: gilyardmani@aol.com

**Europa Study Unit**
Donald W. Smith
PO Box 576
Johnstown PA 15907-0576
www.europanews.emperors.net
E-mail: eunity@aol.com or donsmith65@msn.com

**Fine & Performing Arts**
Deborah L. Washington
6922 So. Jeffery Boulevard
#7 - North
Chicago IL 60649
E-mail: brasslady@comcast.net

**Fire Service in Philately**
Brian R. Engler, Sr.
726 1/2 W. Tilghman St.
Allentown PA 18102-2324
Ph: (610) 433-2782
www.firestamps.com

**Gay & Lesbian History on Stamps Club**
Joe Petronie
PO Box 190842
Dallas TX 75219-0842
www.glhsc.org
E-mail: glhsc@aol.com

**Gems, Minerals & Jewelry Study Unit**
George Young
PO Box 632
Tewksbury MA 01876-0632
Ph: (978) 851-8283
www.rockhounds.com/rockshop/gmjsuapp.txt
E-mail: george-young@msn.com

**Graphics Philately Association**
Mark H Winnegrad
PO Box 380
Bronx NY 10462-0380
www.graphics-stamps.org
E-mail: indybruce1@yahoo.com

**Journalists, Authors & Poets on Stamps**
Ms. Lee Straayer
P.O. Box 6808
Champaign IL 61826
E-mail: lstraayer@dcbnet.com

**Lighthouse Stamp Society**
Dalene Thomas
8612 West Warren Lane
Lakewood CO 80227-2352
Ph: (303) 986-6620
www.lighthousestampsociety.org
E-mail: dalene@lighthousestampsociety.org

**Lions International Stamp Club**
John Bargus
108-2777 Barry Rd. RR 2
Mill Bay, BC, Canada, V0R 2P2
Ph: (250) 743-5782

**Mahatma Gandhi On Stamps Study Circle**
Pramod Shivagunde
Pratik Clinic, Akluj
Solapur, Maharashtra, India, 413101
E-mail: drnanda@bom6.vsnl.net.in

**Mask Study Unit**
Carolyn Weber
1220 Johnson Drive, Villa 104
Ventura CA 93003-0540
E-mail: cweber@venturalink.net

**Masonic Study Unit**
Stanley R. Longenecker
930 Wood St.
Mount Joy PA 17552-1926
Ph: (717) 653-1155
E-mail: natsco@usa.net

**Mathematical Study Unit**
Estelle Buccino
5615 Glenwood Rd.
Bethesda MD 20817-6727
Ph: (301) 718-8898
www.math.ttu.edu/msu/
E-mail: m.strauss@ttu.edu

**Medical Subjects Unit**
Dr. Frederick C. Skvara
PO Box 6228
Bridgewater NJ 08807
E-mail: fcskvara@optonline.net

**Mourning Stamps and Covers Club**
John Hotchner
PO Box 1125
Falls Church VA 22041-0125
E-mail: jmhstamp@ix.netcom.com

**Napoleonic Age Philatelists**
Ken Berry
7513 Clayton Dr.
Oklahoma City OK 73132-5636
Ph: (405) 721-0044
www.nap-stamps.org
E-mail: krb2@earthlink.net

**Old World Archeological Study Unit**
Caroline Scannel
11 Dawn Drive
Smithtown NY 11787-1761
www.owasu.org
E-mail: editor@owasu.org

**Petroleum Philatelic Society International**
Dr. Chris Coggins
174 Old Bedford Road
Luton, England, LU2 7HW, United Kingdom
E-mail: WAMTECH@Luton174.fsnet.co.uk

**Philatelic Computing Study Group**
Robert de Violini
PO Box 5025
Oxnard CA 93031-5025
www.pcsg.org
E-mail: dviolini@adelphia.net

**Philatelic Lepidopteristsí Association**
Alan Hanks
34 Seaton Dr.
Aurora, ON, Canada, L4G 2K1
Ph: (905) 727-6933
E-mail: alan.hanks@sympatico.ca

**Rotary on Stamps Unit**
Gerald L. Fitzsimmons
105 Calla Ricardo
Victoria TX 77904
rotaryonstamps.org
E-mail: glfitz@suddenlink.net

**Scouts on Stamps Society International**
Lawrence Clay
PO Box 6228
Kennewick WA 99336
Ph: (509) 735-3731
www.sossi.org
E-mail: rfrank@sossi.org

**Ships on Stamps Unit**
Les Smith
302 Conklin Avenue
Penticton, BC, Canada, V2A 2T4
Ph: (250) 493-7486
www.shipsonstamps.org
E-mail: lessmith440@shaw.ca

**Space Unit**
Carmine Torrisi
PO Box 780241
Maspeth NY 11378
Ph: (718) 386-7882
stargate.1usa.com/stamps/
E-mail: ctorrisi1@nyc.rr.com

**Sports Philatelists International**
Margaret Jones
5310 Lindenwood Ave.
St. Louis MO 63109-1758
www.sportstamps.org

**Stamps on Stamps Collectors Club**
Alf Jordan
156 West Elm Street
Yarmouth ME 04096
www.stampsonstamps.org
E-mail: ajordan1@maine.rr.com

**Textile Unit**
John C. Monson
1062 Bramblewood Dr.
Castle Rock CO 80108-3643
www.caratex.com
E-mail: textilerama@mindspring.com

**Windmill Study Unit**
Walter J. Hollien
PO Box 346
Long Valley NJ 07853-0346
Ph: (862) 812-0030
E-mail: whollien@earthlink.net

**Wine On Stamps Study Unit**
Bruce L. Johnson
115 Raintree Drive
Zionsville IN 46077
www.wine-on-stamps.org
E-mail: indybruce@yahoo.com

**Women on Stamps Study Unit**
Hugh Gottfried
2232 26th St.
Santa Monica CA 90405-1902
E-mail: hgottfried@adelphia.net

**Zeppelin Collectors Club**
Cheryl Ganz
PO Box 77196
Washington DC 20013
www.americanairmailsociety.org

# Expertizing Services

The following organizations will, for a fee, provide expert opinions about stamps submitted to them. Collectors should contact these organizations to find out about their fees and requirements before submitting philatelic material to them. The listing of these groups here is not intended as an endorsement by Scott Publishing Co.

## General Expertizing Services

American Philatelic Expertizing
 Service (a service of the
 American Philatelic Society)
100 Match Factory Place
Bellefonte PA 16823-1367
Ph: (814) 237-3803
Fax: (814) 237-6128
www.stamps.org
E-mail: ambristo@stamps.org
Areas of Expertise: Worldwide

B. P. A. Expertising, Ltd.
PO Box 137
Leatherhead, Surrey, United Kingdom
KT22 0RG
E-mail: sec.bpa@tcom.co.uk
Areas of Expertise: British
Commonwealth, Great Britain,
Classics of Europe, South America and
the Far East

Philatelic Foundation
70 West 40th St., 15th Floor
New York NY 10018
Ph: (212) 221-6555
Fax: (212) 221-6208
www.philatelicfoundation.org
E-mail:philatelicfoundation@verizon.net
Areas of Expertise: U.S. & Worldwide

Professional Stamp Experts
PO Box 6170
Newport Beach CA 92658
Ph: (877) STAMP-88
Fax: (949) 833-7955
www.collectors.com/pse
E-mail: pseinfo@collectors.com
Areas of Expertise: Stamps and
covers of U.S., U.S. Possessions,
British Commonwealth

Royal Philatelic Society Expert
 Committee
41 Devonshire Place
London, United Kingdom W1N 1PE
www.rpsl.org.uk/experts.html
E-mail: experts@rpsl.org.uk
Areas of Expertise: All

## Expertizing Services Covering Specific Fields Or Countries

China Stamp Society Expertizing
 Service
1050 West Blue Ridge Blvd
Kansas City MO 64145
Ph: (816) 942-6300
E-mail: hjmesq@aol.com
Areas of Expertise: China

Confederate Stamp Alliance
 Authentication Service
Gen. Frank Crown, Jr.
PO Box 278
Capshaw AL 35742-0396
Ph: (302) 422-2656
Fax: (302) 424-1990
www.csalliance.org
E-mail: csaas@knology.net
Areas of Expertise: Confederate stamps
and postal history

Errors, Freaks and Oddities
 Collectors Club
 Expertizing Service
138 East Lakemont Dr.
Kingsland GA 31548
Ph: (912) 729-1573
Areas of Expertise: U.S. errors, freaks
and oddities

Estonian Philatelic Society
 Expertizing Service
39 Clafford Lane
Melville NY 11747
Ph: (516) 421-2078
E-mail: esto4@aol.com
Areas of Expertise: Estonia

Hawaiian Philatelic Society
 Expertizing Service
PO Box 10115
Honolulu HI 96816-0115
Areas of Expertise: Hawaii

Hong Kong Stamp Society
 Expertizing Service
PO Box 206
Glenside PA 19038
Fax: (215) 576-6850
Areas of Expertise: Hong Kong

International Association of
 Philatelic Experts
United States Associate members:

Paul Buchsbayew
119 W. 57th St.
New York NY 10019
Ph: (212) 977-7734
Fax: (212) 977-8653
Areas of Expertise: Russia, Soviet
Union

William T. Crowe
(see Professional Stamp Experts)
Areas of Expertise: United States

John Lievsay
(see American Philatelic Expertizing
Service and Philatelic Foundation)
Areas of Expertise: France

Robert W. Lyman
P.O. Box 348
Irvington on Hudson NY 10533
Ph and Fax: (914) 591-6937
Areas of Expertise: British North
America, New Zealand

Robert Odenweller
P.O. Box 401
Bernardsville, NJ 07924-0401
Ph and Fax: (908) 766-5460
Areas of Expertise: New Zealand,
Samoa to 1900

Alex Rendon
P.O. Box 323
Massapequa NY 11762
Ph and Fax: (516) 795-0464
Areas of Expertise: Bolivia,
Colombia, Colombian States

Sergio Sismondo
10035 Carousel Center Dr.
Syracuse NY 13290-0001
Ph: (315) 422-2331
Fax: (315) 422-2956
Areas of Expertise: British East
Africa, Camerouns,
Cape of Good Hope, Canada, British
North America

International Society for Japanese
 Philately Expertizing Committee
32 King James Court
Staten Island NY 10308-2910
Ph: (718) 227-5229
Areas of Expertise: Japan and
related areas, except WWII Japanese
Occupation issues

International Society for
 Portuguese Philately Expertizing
 Service
PO Box 43146
Philadelphia PA 19129-3146
Ph: (215) 843-2106
Fax: (215) 843-2106
E-mail: s.s.washburne@worldnet.att.
net
Areas of Expertise: Portugal and
Colonies

Mexico-Elmhurst Philatelic Society
 International Expert Committee
PO Box 1133
West Covina CA 91793
Areas of Expertise: Mexico

Ukrainian Philatelic & Numismatic
 Society Expertizing Service
30552 Dell Lane
Warren MI 48092-1862
Ph: (810) 751-5754
Areas of Expertise: Ukraine, Western
Ukraine

V. G. Greene Philatelic Research
 Foundation
P.O. Box 204, Station Q
Toronto, ON, Canada M4T 2M1
Ph: (416) 921-2073
Fax: (416) 921-1282
E-mail: vggfoundation@on.aibn.com
www.greenefoundation.ca
Areas of Expertise: British North
America

# Information on Catalogue Values, Grade and Condition

## Catalogue Value

The Scott Catalogue value is a retail value; that is, an amount you could expect to pay for a stamp in the grade of Very Fine with no faults. Any exceptions to the grade valued will be noted in the text. The general introduction on the following pages and the individual section introductions further explain the type of material that is valued. The value listed for any given stamp is a reference that reflects recent actual dealer selling prices for that item.

Dealer retail price lists, public auction results, published prices in advertising and individual solicitation of retail prices from dealers, collectors and specialty organizations have been used in establishing the values found in this catalogue. Scott Publishing Co. values stamps, but Scott is not a company engaged in the business of buying and selling stamps as a dealer.

Use this catalogue as a guide for buying and selling. The actual price you pay for a stamp may be higher or lower than the catalogue value because of many different factors, including the amount of personal service a dealer offers, or increased or decreased interest in the country or topic represented by a stamp or set. An item may occasionally be offered at a lower price as a "loss leader," or as part of a special sale. You also may obtain an item inexpensively at public auction because of little interest at that time or as part of a large lot.

Stamps that are of a lesser grade than Very Fine, or those with condition problems, generally trade at lower prices than those given in this catalogue. Stamps of exceptional quality in both grade and condition often command higher prices than those listed.

Values for pre-1900 unused issues are for stamps with approximately half or more of their original gum. Stamps with most or all of their original gum may be expected to sell for more, and stamps with less than half of their original gum may be expected to sell for somewhat less than the values listed. On rarer stamps, it may be expected that the original gum will be somewhat more disturbed than it will be on more common issues. Post-1900 unused issues are assumed to have full original gum. From breakpoints in most countries' listings, stamps are valued as never hinged, due to the wide availability of stamps in that condition. These notations are prominently placed in the listings and in the country information preceding the listings. Some countries also feature listings with dual values for hinged and never-hinged stamps.

## Grade

A stamp's grade and condition are crucial to its value. The accompanying illustrations show examples of Very Fine stamps from different time periods, along with examples of stamps in Fine to Very Fine and Extremely Fine grades as points of reference. When a stamp seller offers a stamp in any grade from fine to superb without further qualifying statements, that stamp should not only have the centering grade as defined, but it also should be free of faults or other condition problems.

**FINE** stamps (illustrations not shown) have designs that are quite off center, with the perforations on one or two sides very close to the design but not quite touching it. There is white space between the perforations and the design that is minimal but evident to the unaided eye. Imperforate stamps may have small margins, and earlier issues may show the design just touching one edge of the stamp design. Very early perforated issues normally will have the perforations slightly cutting into the design. Used stamps may have heavier than usual cancellations.

**FINE-VERY FINE** stamps will be somewhat off center on one side, or slightly off center on two sides. Imperforate stamps will have two margins of at least normal size, and the design will not touch any edge. For perforated stamps, the perfs are well clear of the design, but are still noticeably off center. *However, early issues of a country may be printed in such a way that the design naturally is very close to the edges. In these cases, the perforations may cut into the design very slightly.* Used stamps will not have a cancellation that detracts from the design.

**VERY FINE** stamps will be just slightly off center on one or two sides, but the design will be well clear of the edge. The stamp will present a nice, balanced appearance. Imperforate stamps will be well centered within normal-sized margins. *However, early issues of many countries may be printed in such a way that the perforations may touch the design on one or more sides. Where this is the case, a boxed note will be found defining the centering and margins of the stamps being valued.* Used stamps will have light or otherwise neat cancellations. This is the grade used to establish Scott Catalogue values.

**EXTREMELY FINE** stamps are close to being perfectly centered. Imperforate stamps will have even margins that are slightly larger than normal. Even the earliest perforated issues will have perforations clear of the design on all sides.

**Scott Publishing Co. recognizes that there is no formally enforced grading scheme for postage stamps, and that the final price you pay or obtain for a stamp will be determined by individual agreement at the time of transaction.**

## Condition

*Grade* addresses only centering and (for used stamps) cancellation. *Condition* refers to factors other than grade that affect a stamp's desirability.

Factors that can increase the value of a stamp include exceptionally wide margins, particularly fresh color, the presence of selvage, and plate or die varieties. Unusual cancels on used stamps (particularly those of the 19th century) can greatly enhance their value as well.

Factors other than faults that decrease the value of a stamp include loss of original gum, regumming, a hinge remnant or foreign object adhering to the gum, natural inclusions, straight edges, and markings or notations applied by collectors or dealers.

Faults include missing pieces, tears, pin or other holes, surface scuffs, thin spots, creases, toning, short or pulled perforations, clipped perforations, oxidation or other forms of color changelings, soiling, stains, and such man-made changes as reperforations or the chemical removal or lightening of a cancellation.

## Grading Illustrations

On the following two pages are illustrations of various stamps from countries appearing in this volume. These stamps are arranged by country, and they represent early or important issues that are often found in widely different grades in the marketplace. The editors believe the illustrations will prove useful in showing the margin size and centering that will be seen on the various issues.

In addition to the matters of margin size and centering, collectors are reminded that the very fine stamps valued in the Scott catalogues also will possess fresh color and intact perforations, and they will be free from defects.

Examples shown are computer-manipulated images made from single digitized master illustrations.

## Stamp Illustrations Used in the Catalogue

It is important to note that the stamp images used for identification purposes in this catalogue may not be indicative of the grade of stamp being valued. Refer to the written discussion of grades on this page and to the grading illustrations on the following two pages for grading information.

Fine-Very Fine

SCOTT
CATALOGUES
VALUE
STAMPS IN
THIS GRADE
Very Fine

Extremely Fine

Fine-Very Fine

SCOTT
CATALOGUES
VALUE
STAMPS IN
THIS GRADE
Very Fine

Extremely Fine

Fine-Very Fine →

**SCOTT CATALOGUES VALUE STAMPS IN THIS GRADE**

Very Fine →

Extremely Fine →

Fine-Very Fine →

**SCOTT CATALOGUES VALUE STAMPS IN THIS GRADE**

Very Fine →

Extremely Fine →

For purposes of helping to determine the gum condition and value of an unused stamp, Scott Publishing Co. presents the following chart which details different gum conditions and indicates how the conditions correlate with the Scott values for unused stamps. Used together, the Illustrated Grading Chart on the previous pages and this Illustrated Gum Chart should allow catalogue users to better understand the grade and gum condition of stamps valued in the Scott catalogues.

| Gum Categories: | MINT N.H. | ORIGINAL GUM (O.G.) | | | | NO GUM |
|---|---|---|---|---|---|---|
| | Mint Never Hinged *Free from any disturbance* | Lightly Hinged *Faint impression of a removed hinge over a small area* | Hinge Mark or Remnant *Prominent hinged spot with part or all of the hinge remaining* | Large part o.g. *Approximately half or more of the gum intact* | Small part o.g. *Approximately less than half of the gum intact* | No gum *Only if issued with gum* |
| Commonly Used Symbol: | ★★ | ★ | ★ | ★ | ★ | (★) |
| Pre-1900 Issues (Pre-1881 for U.S.) | *Very fine pre-1900 stamps in these categories trade at a premium over Scott value* | | | Scott Value for "Unused" | | Scott "No Gum" listings for selected unused classic stamps |
| From 1900 to break-points for listings of never-hinged stamps | Scott "Never Hinged" listings for selected unused stamps | Scott Value for "Unused" (Actual value will be affected by the degree of hinging of the full o.g.) | | | | |
| From breakpoints noted for many countries | Scott Value for "Unused" | | | | | |

**Never Hinged (NH; ★★):** A never-hinged stamp will have full original gum that will have no hinge mark or disturbance. The presence of an expertizer's mark does not disqualify a stamp from this designation.

**Original Gum (OG; ★):** Pre-1900 stamps should have approximately half or more of their original gum. On rarer stamps, it may be expected that the original gum will be somewhat more disturbed than it will be on more common issues. Post-1900 stamps should have full original gum. Original gum will show some disturbance caused by a previous hinge(s) which may be present or entirely removed. The actual value of a post-1900 stamp will be affected by the degree of hinging of the full original gum.

**Disturbed Original Gum:** Gum showing noticeable effects of humidity, climate or hinging over more than half of the gum. The significance of gum disturbance in valuing a stamp in any of the Original Gum categories depends on the degree of disturbance, the rarity and normal gum condition of the issue and other variables affecting quality.

**Regummed (RG; (★)):** A regummed stamp is a stamp without gum that has had some type of gum privately applied at a time after it was issued. This normally is done to deceive collectors and/or dealers into thinking that the stamp has original gum and therefore has a higher value. A regummed stamp is considered the same as a stamp with none of its original gum for purposes of grading.

# Understanding the Listings

On the opposite page is an enlarged "typical" listing from this catalogue. Below are detailed explanations of each of the highlighted parts of the listing.

**1 Scott number** — Scott catalogue numbers are used to identify specific items when buying, selling or trading stamps. Each listed postage stamp from every country has a unique Scott catalogue number. Therefore, Germany Scott 99, for example, can only refer to a single stamp. Although the Scott catalogue usually lists stamps in chronological order by date of issue, there are exceptions. When a country has issued a set of stamps over a period of time, those stamps within the set are kept together without regard to date of issue. This follows the normal collecting approach of keeping stamps in their natural sets.

When a country issues a set of stamps over a period of time, a group of consecutive catalogue numbers is reserved for the stamps in that set, as issued. If that group of numbers proves to be too few, capital-letter suffixes, such as "A" or "B," may be added to existing numbers to create enough catalogue numbers to cover all items in the set. A capital-letter suffix indicates a major Scott catalogue number listing. Scott uses a suffix letter only once. Therefore, a catalogue number listing with a capital-letter suffix will not also be found with the same letter (lower case) used as a minor-letter listing. If there is a Scott 16A in a set, for example, there will not also be a Scott 16a. However, a minor-letter "a" listing may be added to a major number containing an "A" suffix (Scott 16Aa, for example).

Suffix letters are cumulative. A minor "b" variety of Scott 16A would be Scott 16Ab, not Scott 16b.

There are times when a reserved block of Scott catalogue numbers is too large for a set, leaving some numbers unused. Such gaps in the numbering sequence also occur when the catalogue editors move an item's listing elsewhere or have removed it entirely from the catalogue. Scott does not attempt to account for every possible number, but rather attempts to assure that each stamp is assigned its own number.

Scott numbers designating regular postage normally are only numerals. Scott numbers for other types of stamps, such as air post, semipostal, postal tax, postage due, occupation and others have a prefix consisting of one or more capital letters or a combination of numerals and capital letters.

**2 Illustration number** — Illustration or design-type numbers are used to identify each catalogue illustration. For most sets, the lowest face-value stamp is shown. It then serves as an example of the basic design approach for other stamps not illustrated. Where more than one stamp use the same illustration number, but have differences in design, the design paragraph or the description line clearly indicates the design on each stamp not illustrated. Where there are both vertical and horizontal designs in a set, a single illustration may be used, with the exceptions noted in the design paragraph or description line.

When an illustration is followed by a lower-case letter in parentheses, such as "A2(b)," the trailing letter indicates which overprint or surcharge illustration applies.

Illustrations normally are 70 percent of the original size of the stamp. An effort has been made to note all illustrations not illustrated at that percentage. Virtually all souvenir sheet illustrations are reduced even more. Overprints and surcharges are shown at 100 percent of their original size if shown alone, but are 70 percent of original size if shown on stamps. In some cases, the illustration will be placed above the set, between listings or omitted completely. Overprint and surcharge illustrations are not placed in this catalogue for purposes of expertizing stamps.

**3 Paper color** — The color of a stamp's paper is noted in italic type when the paper used is not white.

**4 Listing styles** — There are two principal types of catalogue listings: major and minor.

Major listings are in a larger type style than minor listings. The catalogue number is a numeral that can be found with or without a capital-letter suffix, and with or without a prefix.

Minor listings are in a smaller type style and have a small-letter suffix (if the listing immediately follows that of the major number) may [only] the letter. These listings identify a variety of the major item.

Examples include perforation, color, watermark or printing method differences, multiples (some souvenir sheets, booklet panes and se-tenant combinations), and singles of multiples.

Examples of major number listings include 16, 28A, B97, C13A, 10N5, and 10N6A. Examples of minor numbers are 16a and C13Ab.

**5 Basic information about a stamp or set** — Introducing each stamp issue is a small section (usually a line listing) of basic information about a stamp or set. This section normally includes the date of issue, method of printing, perforation, watermark and, sometimes, some additional information of note. *Printing method, perforation and watermark apply to the following sets until a change is noted.* Stamps created by overprinting or surcharging previous issues are assumed to have the same perforation, watermark, printing method and other production characteristics as the original. Dates of issue are as precise as Scott is able to confirm and often reflect the dates on first-day covers, rather than the actual date of release.

**6 Denomination** — This normally refers to the face value of the stamp; that is, the cost of the unused stamp at the post office at the time of issue. When a denomination is shown in parentheses, it does not appear on the stamp. This includes the non-denominated stamps of the United States, Brazil and Great Britain, for example.

**7 Color or other description** — This area provides information to solidify identification of a stamp. In many recent cases, a description of the stamp design appears in this space, rather than a listing of colors.

**8 Year of issue** — In stamp sets that have been released in a period that spans more than a year, the number shown in parentheses is the year that stamp first appeared. Stamps without a date appeared during the first year of the issue. Dates are not always given for minor varieties.

**9 Value unused and Value used** — The Scott catalogue values are based on stamps that are in a grade of Very Fine unless stated otherwise. Unused values refer to items that have not seen postal, revenue or any other duty for which they were intended. Pre-1900 unused stamps that were issued with gum must have at least most of their original gum. Later issues are assumed to have full original gum. From breakpoints specified in most countries' listings, stamps are valued as never hinged. Stamps issued without gum are noted. Modern issues with PVA or other synthetic adhesives may appear ungummed. Unused self-adhesive stamps are valued as appearing undisturbed on their original backing paper. Values for used self-adhesive stamps are for examples either on piece or off piece. For a more detailed explanation of these values, please see the "Catalogue Value," "Condition" and "Understanding Valuing Notations" sections elsewhere in this introduction.

In some cases, where used stamps are more valuable than unused stamps, the value is for an example with a contemporaneous cancel, rather than a modern cancel or a smudge or other unclear marking. For those stamps that were released for postal and fiscal purposes, the used value represents a postally used stamp. Stamps with revenue cancels generally sell for less.

Stamps separated from a complete se-tenant multiple usually will be worth less than a pro-rated portion of the se-tenant multiple, and stamps lacking the attached labels that are noted in the listings will be worth less than the values shown.

**10 Changes in basic set information** — Bold type is used to show any changes in the basic data given for a set of stamps. These basic data categories include perforation gauge measurement, paper type, printing method and watermark.

**11 Total value of a set** — The total value of sets of three or more stamps issued after 1900 are shown. The set line also notes the range of Scott numbers and total number of stamps included in the grouping. The actual value of a set consisting predominantly of stamps having the minimum value of twenty cents may be less than the total value shown. Similarly, the actual value or catalogue value of se-tenant pairs or of blocks consisting of stamps having the minimum value of twenty cents may be less than the catalogue values of the component parts.

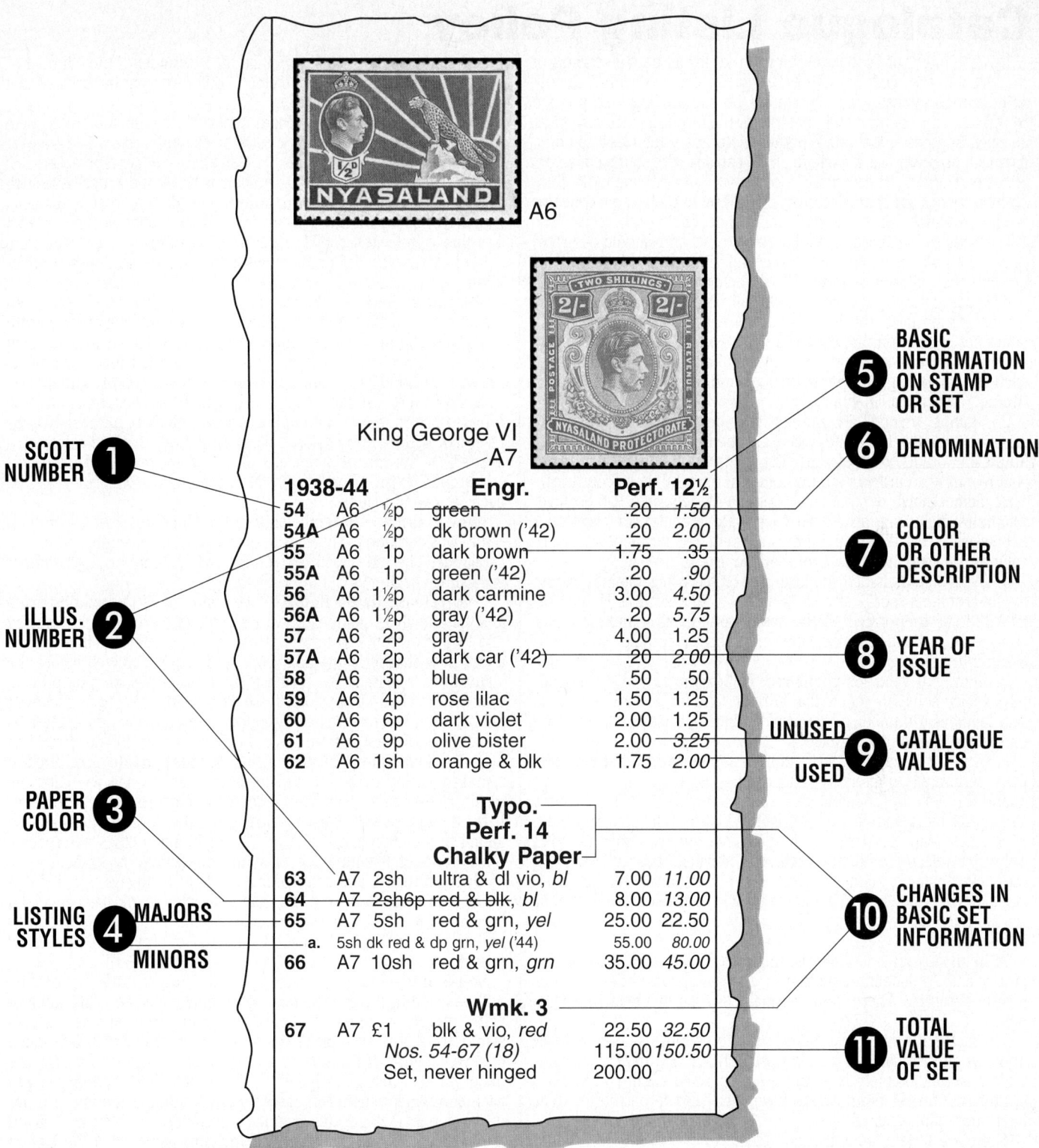

A6

King George VI
A7

SCOTT NUMBER **1**

ILLUS. NUMBER **2**

PAPER COLOR **3**

LISTING STYLES **4**   MAJORS

MINORS

**5** BASIC INFORMATION ON STAMP OR SET

**6** DENOMINATION

**7** COLOR OR OTHER DESCRIPTION

**8** YEAR OF ISSUE

UNUSED **9** CATALOGUE VALUES
USED

**10** CHANGES IN BASIC SET INFORMATION

**11** TOTAL VALUE OF SET

| 1938-44 | | | Engr. | Perf. 12½ | |
|---|---|---|---|---|---|
| **54** | A6 | ½p | green | .20 | *1.50* |
| **54A** | A6 | ½p | dk brown ('42) | .20 | *2.00* |
| **55** | A6 | 1p | dark brown | 1.75 | *.35* |
| **55A** | A6 | 1p | green ('42) | .20 | *.90* |
| **56** | A6 | 1½p | dark carmine | 3.00 | *4.50* |
| **56A** | A6 | 1½p | gray ('42) | .20 | *5.75* |
| **57** | A6 | 2p | gray | 4.00 | *1.25* |
| **57A** | A6 | 2p | dark car ('42) | .20 | *2.00* |
| **58** | A6 | 3p | blue | .50 | *.50* |
| **59** | A6 | 4p | rose lilac | 1.50 | *1.25* |
| **60** | A6 | 6p | dark violet | 2.00 | *1.25* |
| **61** | A6 | 9p | olive bister | 2.00 | *3.25* |
| **62** | A6 | 1sh | orange & blk | 1.75 | *2.00* |

**Typo.**
**Perf. 14**
**Chalky Paper**

| | | | | | |
|---|---|---|---|---|---|
| **63** | A7 | 2sh | ultra & dl vio, *bl* | 7.00 | *11.00* |
| **64** | A7 | 2sh6p | red & blk, *bl* | 8.00 | *13.00* |
| **65** | A7 | 5sh | red & grn, *yel* | 25.00 | *22.50* |
| **a.** | | | 5sh dk red & dp grn, *yel* ('44) | 55.00 | *80.00* |
| **66** | A7 | 10sh | red & grn, *grn* | 35.00 | *45.00* |

**Wmk. 3**

| | | | | | |
|---|---|---|---|---|---|
| **67** | A7 | £1 | blk & vio, *red* | 22.50 | *32.50* |
| | | | *Nos. 54-67 (18)* | 115.00 | *150.50* |
| | | | Set, never hinged | 200.00 | |

# Catalogue Listing Policy

It is the intent of Scott Publishing Co. to list all postage stamps of the world in the *Scott Standard Postage Stamp Catalogue*. The only strict criteria for listing is that stamps be decreed legal for postage by the issuing country and that the issuing country actually have an operating postal system. Whether the primary intent of issuing a given stamp or set was for sale to postal patrons or to stamp collectors is not part of our listing criteria. Scott's role is to provide basic comprehensive postage stamp information. It is up to each stamp collector to choose which items to include in a collection.

It is Scott's objective to seek reasons why a stamp should be listed, rather than why it should not. Nevertheless, there are certain types of items that will not be listed. These include the following:

1. Unissued items that are not officially distributed or released by the issuing postal authority. If such items are officially issued at a later date by the country, they will be listed. Unissued items consist of those that have been printed and then held from sale for reasons such as change in government, errors found on stamps or something deemed objectionable about a stamp subject or design.

2. Stamps "issued" by non-existent postal entities or fantasy countries, such as Nagaland, Occusi-Ambeno, Staffa, Sedang, Torres Straits and others. Also, stamps "issued" in the names of legitimate, stamp-issuing countries that are not authorized by those countries.

3. Semi-official or unofficial items not required for postage. Examples include items issued by private agencies for their own express services. When such items are required for delivery, or are valid as prepayment of postage, they are listed.

4. Local stamps issued for local use only. Postage stamps issued by governments specifically for "domestic" use, such as Haiti Scott 219-228, or the United States non-denominated stamps, are not considered to be locals, since they are valid for postage throughout the country of origin.

5. Items not valid for postal use. For example, a few countries have issued souvenir sheets that are not valid for postage. This area also includes a number of worldwide charity labels (some denominated) that do not pay postage.

6. Intentional varieties, such as imperforate stamps that look like their perforated counterparts and are usually issued in very small quantities. Also, other egregiously exploitative issues such as stamps sold for far more than face value, stamps purposefully issued in artificially small quantities or only against advance orders, stamps awarded only to a selected audience such as a philatelic bureau's standing order customers, or stamps sold only in conjunction with other products. All of these kinds of items are usually controlled issues and/or are intended for speculation. These items normally will be included in a footnote.

7. Items distributed by the issuing government only to a limited group, club, philatelic exhibition or a single stamp dealer or other private company. These items normally will be included in a footnote.

The fact that a stamp has been used successfully as postage, even on international mail, is not in itself sufficient proof that it was legitimately issued. Numerous examples of so-called stamps from non-existent countries are known to have been used to post letters that have successfully passed through the international mail system.

There are certain items that are subject to interpretation. When a stamp falls outside our specifications, it may be listed along with a cautionary footnote.

A number of factors are considered in our approach to analyzing how a stamp is listed. The following list of factors is presented to share with you, the catalogue user, the complexity of the listing process.

**Additional printings** — "Additional printings" of a previously issued stamp may range from an item that is totally different to cases where it is impossible to differentiate from the original. At least a minor number (a small-letter suffix) is assigned if there is a distinct change in stamp shade, noticeably redrawn design, or a significantly different perforation measurement. A major number (numeral or numeral and capital-letter combination) is assigned if the editors feel the "additional printing" is sufficiently different from the original that it constitutes a different issue.

**Commemoratives** — Where practical, commemoratives with the same theme are placed in a set. For example, the U.S. Civil War Centennial set of 1961-65 and the Constitution Bicentennial series of 1989-90 appear as sets. Countries such as Japan and Korea issue such material on a regular basis, with an announced, or at least predictable, number of stamps known in advance. Occasionally, however, stamp sets that were released over a period of years have been separated. Appropriately placed footnotes will guide you to each set's continuation.

**Definitive sets** — Blocks of numbers generally have been reserved for definitive sets, based on previous experience with any given country. If a few more stamps were issued in a set than originally expected, they often have been inserted into the original set with a capital-letter suffix, such as U.S. Scott 1059A. If it appears that many more stamps than the originally allotted block will be released before the set is completed, a new block of numbers will be reserved, with the original one being closed off. In some cases, such as the U.S. Transportation and Great Americans series, several blocks of numbers exist. Appropriately placed footnotes will guide you to each set's continuation.

**New country** — Membership in the Universal Postal Union is not a consideration for listing status or order of placement within the catalogue. The index will tell you in what volume or page number the listings begin.

**"No release date" items** — The amount of information available for any given stamp issue varies greatly from country to country and even from time to time. Extremely comprehensive information about new stamps is available from some countries well before the stamps are released. By contrast some countries do not provide information about stamps or release dates. Most countries, however, fall between these extremes. A country may provide denominations or subjects of stamps from upcoming issues that are not issued as planned. Sometimes, philatelic agencies, those private firms hired to represent countries, add these later-issued items to sets well after the formal release date. This time period can range from weeks to years. If these items were officially released by the country, they will be added to the appropriate spot in the set. In many cases, the specific release date of a stamp or set of stamps may never be known.

**Overprints** — The color of an overprint is always noted if it is other than black. Where more than one color of ink has been used on overprints of a single set, the color used is noted. Early overprint and surcharge illustrations were altered to prevent their use by forgers.

**Se-tenants** — Connected stamps of differing features (se-tenants) will be listed in the format most commonly collected. This includes pairs, blocks or larger multiples. Se-tenant units are not always symmetrical. An example is Australia Scott 508, which is a block of seven stamps. If the stamps are primarily collected as a unit, the major number may be assigned to the multiple, with minors going to each component stamp. In cases where continuous-design or other unit se-tenants will receive significant postal use, each stamp is given a major Scott number listing. This includes issues from the United States, Canada, Germany and Great Britain, for example.

# Special Notices

## Classification of stamps

The *Scott Standard Postage Stamp Catalogue* lists stamps by country of issue. The next level of organization is a listing by section on the basis of the function of the stamps. The principal sections cover regular postage, semi-postal, air post, special delivery, registration, postage due and other categories. Except for regular postage, catalogue numbers for all sections include a prefix letter (or number-letter combination) denoting the class to which a given stamp belongs. When some countries issue sets containing stamps from more than one category, the catalogue will at times list all of the stamps in one category (such as air post stamps listed as part of a postage set).

The following is a listing of the most commonly used catalogue prefixes.

### Prefix... Category
C .......Air Post
M.......Military
P ........Newspaper
N .......Occupation - Regular Issues
O .......Official
Q .......Parcel Post
J .........Postage Due
RA .....Postal Tax
B ........Semi-Postal
E ........Special Delivery
MR ....War Tax

Other prefixes used by more than one country include the following:
H .......Acknowledgment of Receipt
I .........Late Fee
CO.....Air Post Official
CQ.....Air Post Parcel Post
RAC...Air Post Postal Tax
CF......Air Post Registration
CB .....Air Post Semi-Postal
CBO...Air Post Semi-Postal Official
CE .....Air Post Special Delivery
EY......Authorized Delivery
S ........Franchise
G .......Insured Letter
GY .....Marine Insurance
MC ....Military Air Post
MQ....Military Parcel Post
NC.....Occupation - Air Post
NO.....Occupation - Official
NJ ......Occupation - Postage Due
NRA...Occupation - Postal Tax
NB .....Occupation - Semi-Postal
NE .....Occupation - Special Delivery
QY .....Parcel Post Authorized Delivery
AR .....Postal-fiscal
RAJ ....Postal Tax Due
RAB ...Postal Tax Semi-Postal
F ........Registration
EB......Semi-Postal Special Delivery
EO .....Special Delivery Official
QE .....Special Handling

## New issue listings

Updates to this catalogue appear each month in the *Scott Stamp Monthly* magazine. Included in this update are additions to the listings of countries found in the *Scott Standard Postage Stamp Catalogue* and the *Specialized Catalogue of United States Stamps*, as well as corrections and updates to current editions of this catalogue.

From time to time there will be changes in the final listings of stamps from the *Scott Stamp Monthly* to the next edition of the catalogue. This occurs as more information about certain stamps or sets becomes available.

The catalogue update section of the *Scott Stamp Monthly* is the most timely presentation of this material available. Annual subscriptions to the *Scott Stamp Monthly* are available from Scott Publishing Co., Box 828, Sidney, OH 45365-0828.

## Number additions, deletions & changes

A listing of catalogue number additions, deletions and changes from the previous edition of the catalogue appears in each volume. See Catalogue Number Additions, Deletions & Changes in the table of contents for the location of this list.

## Understanding valuing notations

The *minimum catalogue value* of an individual stamp or set is 20 cents. This represents a portion of the cost incurred by a dealer when he prepares an individual stamp for resale. As a point of philatelic-economic fact, the lower the value shown for an item in this catalogue, the greater the percentage of that value is attributed to dealer mark up and profit margin. In many cases, such as the 20-cent minimum value, that price does not cover the labor or other costs involved with stocking it as an individual stamp. The sum of minimum values in a set does not properly represent the value of a complete set primarily composed of a number of minimum-value stamps, nor does the sum represent the actual value of a packet made up of minimum-value stamps. Thus a packet of 1,000 different common stamps — each of which has a catalogue value of 20-cents — normally sells for considerably less than 200 dollars!

The *absence of a retail value* for a stamp does not necessarily suggest that a stamp is scarce or rare. A dash in the value column means that the stamp is known in a stated form or variety, but information is either lacking or insufficient for purposes of establishing a usable catalogue value.

Stamp values in *italics* generally refer to items that are difficult to value accurately. For expensive items, such as those priced at $1,000 or higher, a value in italics indicates that the affected item trades very seldom. For inexpensive items, a value in italics represents a warning. One example is a "blocked" issue where the issuing postal administration may have controlled one stamp in a set in an attempt to make the whole set more valuable. Another example is an item that sold at an extreme multiple of face value in the marketplace at the time of its issue.

One type of warning to collectors that appears in the catalogue is illustrated by a stamp that is valued considerably higher in used condition than it is as unused. In this case, collectors are cautioned to be certain the used version has a genuine and contemporaneous cancellation. The type of cancellation on a stamp can be an important factor in determining its sale price. Catalogue values do not apply to fiscal, telegraph or non-contemporaneous postal cancels, unless otherwise noted.

Some countries have released back issues of stamps in canceled-to-order form, sometimes covering as much as a 10-year period. The Scott Catalogue values for used stamps reflect canceled-to-order material when such stamps are found to predominate in the marketplace for the issue involved. Notes frequently appear in the stamp listings to specify which items are valued as canceled-to-order, or if there is a premium for postally used examples.

Many countries sell canceled-to-order stamps at a marked reduction of face value. Countries that sell or have sold canceled-to-order stamps at *full* face value include United Nations, Australia, Netherlands, France and Switzerland. It may be almost impossible to identify such stamps if the gum has been removed, because official government canceling devices are used. Postally used copies of these items on cover, however, are usually worth more than the canceled-to-order stamps with original gum.

## Abbreviations

Scott Publishing Co. uses a consistent set of abbreviations throughout this catalogue to conserve space, while still providing necessary information.

## COLOR ABBREVIATIONS

| | | |
|---|---|---|
| amb .amber | crim .crimson | ol .....olive |
| anil ..aniline | cr .....cream | olvn .olivine |
| ap ....apple | dk ....dark | org ...orange |
| aqua.aquamarine | dl .....dull | pck...peacock |
| az.....azure | dp ....deep | pnksh pinkish |
| bis....bister | db ....drab | Prus .Prussian |
| bl .....blue | emer emerald | pur...purple |
| bld ...blood | gldn .golden | redsh reddish |
| blk ...black | grysh grayish | res....reseda |
| bril...brilliant | grn...green | ros ...rosine |
| brn...brown | grnsh greenish | ryl ....royal |
| brnsh brownish | hel ...heliotrope | sal ....salmon |
| brnz .bronze | hn ...henna | saph .sapphire |
| brt....bright | ind ....indigo | scar ..scarlet |
| brnt..burnt | int....intense | sep ...sepia |
| car ...carmine | lav....lavender | sien ..sienna |
| cer ...cerise | lem ..lemon | sil.....silver |
| chlky chalky | lil .....lilac | sl......slate |
| cham chamois | lt......light | stl.....steel |
| chnt .chestnut | mag..magenta | turq..turquoise |
| choc.chocolate | man .manila | ultra.ultramarine |
| chr...chrome | mar ..maroon | Ven ..Venetian |
| cit ....citron | mv ...mauve | ver ...vermilion |
| cl .....claret | multi multicolored | vio ...violet |
| cob...cobalt | mlky milky | yel....yellow |
| cop...copper | myr ..myrtle | yelsh yellowish |

When no color is given for an overprint or surcharge, black is the color used. Abbreviations for colors used for overprints and surcharges include: "(B)" or "(Blk)," black; "(Bl)," blue; "(R)," red; and "(G)," green.

Additional abbreviations in this catalogue are shown below:

| | |
|---|---|
| Adm............. | Administration |
| AFL............. | American Federation of Labor |
| Anniv. ......... | Anniversary |
| APS............. | American Philatelic Society |
| Assoc. ......... | Association |
| ASSR.......... | Autonomous Soviet Socialist Republic |
| b. ............... | Born |
| BEP............. | Bureau of Engraving and Printing |
| Bicent. ........ | Bicentennial |
| Bklt............. | Booklet |
| Brit. ........... | British |
| btwn........... | Between |
| Bur............. | Bureau |
| c. or ca........ | Circa |
| Cat.............. | Catalogue |
| Cent............ | Centennial, century, centenary |
| CIO............. | Congress of Industrial Organizations |
| Conf............ | Conference |
| Cong........... | Congress |
| Cpl............. | Corporal |
| CTO............ | Canceled to order |
| d. ............... | Died |
| Dbl............. | Double |
| EKU............ | Earliest known use |
| Engr. ........... | Engraved |
| Exhib. ......... | Exhibition |
| Expo. ......... | Exposition |
| Fed. ........... | Federation |
| GB ............. | Great Britain |
| Gen............ | General |
| GPO........... | General post office |
| Horiz.......... | Horizontal |
| Imperf......... | Imperforate |
| Impt........... | Imprint |

| | |
|---|---|
| Intl............. | International |
| Invtd. ......... | Inverted |
| L ................ | Left |
| Lieut., lt. ..... | Lieutenant |
| Litho. ......... | Lithographed |
| LL ............. | Lower left |
| LR ............. | Lower right |
| mm ............ | Millimeter |
| Ms. ............ | Manuscript |
| Natl............ | National |
| No. ............ | Number |
| NY ............. | New York |
| NYC........... | New York City |
| Ovpt. ......... | Overprint |
| Ovptd......... | Overprinted |
| P ............... | Plate number |
| Perf............ | Perforated, perforation |
| Phil............ | Philatelic |
| Photo. ......... | Photogravure |
| PO ............. | Post office |
| Pr. ............. | Pair |
| P.R. ............ | Puerto Rico |
| Prec. .......... | Precancel, precanceled |
| Pres........... | President |
| PTT........... | Post, Telephone and Telegraph |
| Rio ............ | Rio de Janeiro |
| Sgt. ........... | Sergeant |
| Soc............ | Society |
| Souv........... | Souvenir |
| SSR ........... | Soviet Socialist Republic, see ASSR |
| St. ............. | Saint, street |
| Surch. ........ | Surcharge |
| Typo........... | Typographed |
| UL ............. | Upper left |
| Unwmkd..... | Unwatermarked |
| UPU........... | Universal Postal Union |
| UR ............ | Upper Right |
| US............. | United States |
| USPOD ...... | United States Post Office Department |
| USSR......... | Union of Soviet Socialist Republics |
| Vert........... | Vertical |
| VP ............. | Vice president |
| Wmk.......... | Watermark |
| Wmkd........ | Watermarked |
| WWI.......... | World War I |
| WWII......... | World War II |

# Examination

Scott Publishing Co. will not comment upon the genuineness, grade or condition of stamps, because of the time and responsibility involved. Rather, there are several expertizing groups that undertake this work for both collectors and dealers. Neither will Scott Publishing Co. appraise or identify philatelic material. The company cannot take responsibility for unsolicited stamps or covers sent by individuals.

All letters, E-mails, etc. are read attentively, but they are not always answered due to time considerations.

# How to order from your dealer

When ordering stamps from a dealer, it is not necessary to write the full description of a stamp as listed in this catalogue. All you need is the name of the country, the Scott catalogue number and whether the desired item is unused or used. For example, "Japan Scott 422 unused" is sufficient to identify the unused stamp of Japan listed as "422 A206 5y brown."

# Basic Stamp Information

A stamp collector's knowledge of the combined elements that make a given stamp issue unique determines his or her ability to identify stamps. These elements include paper, watermark, method of separation, printing, design and gum. On the following pages each of these important areas is briefly described.

## Paper

Paper is an organic material composed of a compacted weave of cellulose fibers and generally formed into sheets. Paper used to print stamps may be manufactured in sheets, or it may have been part of a large roll (called a web) before being cut to size. The fibers most often used to create paper on which stamps are printed include bark, wood, straw and certain grasses. In many cases, linen or cotton rags have been added for greater strength and durability. Grinding, bleaching, cooking and rinsing these raw fibers reduces them to a slushy pulp, referred to by paper makers as "stuff." Sizing and, sometimes, coloring matter is added to the pulp to make different types of finished paper.

After the stuff is prepared, it is poured onto sieve-like frames that allow the water to run off, while retaining the matted pulp. As fibers fall onto the screen and are held by gravity, they form a natural weave that will later hold the paper together. If the screen has metal bits that are formed into letters or images attached, it leaves slightly thinned areas on the paper. These are called watermarks.

When the stuff is almost dry, it is passed under pressure through smooth or engraved rollers - dandy rolls - or placed between cloth in a press to be flattened and dried.

Stamp paper falls broadly into two types: wove and laid. The nature of the surface of the frame onto which the pulp is first deposited causes the differences in appearance between the two. If the surface is smooth and even, the paper will be of fairly uniform texture throughout. This is known as *wove paper*. Early papermaking machines poured the pulp onto a continuously circulating web of felt, but modern machines feed the pulp onto a cloth-like screen made of closely interwoven fine wires. This paper, when held to a light, will show little dots or points very close together. The proper name for this is "wire wove," but the type is still considered wove. Any U.S. or British stamp printed after 1880 will serve as an example of wire wove paper.

Closely spaced parallel wires, with cross wires at wider intervals, make up the frames used for what is known as *laid paper*. A greater thickness of the pulp will settle between the wires. The paper, when held to a light, will show alternate light and dark lines. The spacing and the thickness of the lines may vary, but on any one sheet of paper they are all alike. See Russia Scott 31-38 for examples of laid paper.

*Batonne*, from the French word meaning "a staff," is a term used if the lines in the paper are spaced quite far apart, like the printed ruling on a writing tablet. Batonne paper may be either wove or laid. If laid, fine laid lines can be seen between the batons.

*Quadrille* is the term used when the lines in the paper form little squares. *Oblong quadrille* is the term used when rectangles, rather than squares, are formed. See Mexico-Guadalajara Scott 35-37 for examples of oblong quadrille paper.

Paper also is classified as thick or thin, hard or soft, and by color if dye is added during manufacture. Such colors may include yellowish, greenish, bluish and reddish.

Brief explanations of other types of paper used for printing stamps, as well as examples, follow.

**Pelure** — Pelure paper is a very thin, hard and often brittle paper that is sometimes bluish or grayish in appearance. See Serbia Scott 169-170.

**Native** — This is a term applied to handmade papers used to produce some of the early stamps of the Indian states. Stamps printed on native paper may be expected to display various natural inclusions that are normal and do not negatively affect value. Japanese paper, originally made of mulberry fibers and rice flour, is part of this group. See Japan Scott 1-18.

**Manila** — This type of paper is often used to make stamped envelopes and wrappers. It is a coarse-textured stock, usually smooth on one side and rough on the other. A variety of colors of manila paper exist, but the most common range is yellowish-brown.

**Silk** — Introduced by the British in 1847 as a safeguard against counterfeiting, silk paper contains bits of colored silk thread scattered throughout. The density of these fibers varies greatly and can include as few as one fiber per stamp or hundreds. U.S. revenue Scott R152 is a good example of an easy-to-identify silk paper stamp.

Silk-thread paper has uninterrupted threads of colored silk arranged so that one or more threads run through the stamp or postal stationery. See Great Britain Scott 5-6 and Switzerland Scott 14-19.

**Granite** — Filled with minute cloth or colored paper fibers of various colors and lengths, granite paper should not be confused with either type of silk paper. Austria Scott 172-175 and a number of Swiss stamps are examples of granite paper.

**Chalky** — A chalk-like substance coats the surface of chalky paper to discourage the cleaning and reuse of canceled stamps, as well as to provide a smoother, more acceptable printing surface. Because the designs of stamps printed on chalky paper are imprinted on what is often a water-soluble coating, any attempt to remove a cancellation will destroy the stamp. *Do not soak these stamps in any fluid.* To remove a stamp printed on chalky paper from an envelope, wet the paper from underneath the stamp until the gum dissolves enough to release the stamp from the paper. See St. Kitts-Nevis Scott 89-90 for examples of stamps printed on this type of chalky paper.

**India** — Another name for this paper, originally introduced from China about 1750, is "China Paper." It is a thin, opaque paper often used for plate and die proofs by many countries.

**Double** — In philately, the term double paper has two distinct meanings. The first is a two-ply paper, usually a combination of a thick and a thin sheet, joined during manufacture. This type was used experimentally as a means to discourage the reuse of stamps.

The design is printed on the thin paper. Any attempt to remove a cancellation would destroy the design. U.S. Scott 158 and other Banknote-era stamps exist on this form of double paper.

The second type of double paper occurs on a rotary press, when the end of one paper roll, or web, is affixed to the next roll to save time feeding the paper through the press. Stamp designs are printed over the joined paper and, if overlooked by inspectors, may get into post office stocks.

**Goldbeater's Skin** — This type of paper was used for the 1866 issue of Prussia, and was a tough, translucent paper. The design was printed in reverse on the back of the stamp, and the gum applied over the printing. It is impossible to remove stamps printed on this type of paper from the paper to which they are affixed without destroying the design.

**Ribbed** — Ribbed paper has an uneven, corrugated surface made by passing the paper through ridged rollers. This type exists on some copies of U.S. Scott 156-165.

Various other substances, or substrates, have been used for stamp manufacture, including wood, aluminum, copper, silver and gold foil, plastic, and silk and cotton fabrics.

Wove | Laid | Granite

Quadrille | Oblong Quadrille | Laid Batonne

## Watermarks

Watermarks are an integral part of some papers. They are formed in the process of paper manufacture. Watermarks consist of small designs, formed of wire or cut from metal and soldered to the surface of the mold or, sometimes, on the dandy roll. The designs may be in the form of crowns, stars, anchors, letters or other characters or symbols. These pieces of metal - known in the paper-making industry as "bits" - impress a design into the paper. The design sometimes may be seen by holding the stamp to the light. Some are more easily seen with a watermark detector. This important tool is a small black tray into which a stamp is placed face down and dampened with a fast-evaporating watermark detection fluid that brings up the watermark image in the form of dark lines against a lighter background. These dark lines are the thinner areas of the paper known as the watermark. Some watermarks are extremely difficult to locate, due to either a faint impression, watermark location or the color of the stamp. There also are electric watermark detectors that come with plastic filter disks of various colors. The disks neutralize the color of the stamp, permitting the watermark to be seen more easily.

**Multiple watermarks of Crown Agents and Burma**

**Watermarks of Uruguay, Vatican City and Jamaica**

WARNING: Some inks used in the photogravure process dissolve in watermark fluids (Please see the section on Soluble Printing Inks). Also, see "chalky paper."

Watermarks may be found normal, reversed, inverted, reversed and inverted, sideways or diagonal, as seen from the back of the stamp. The relationship of watermark to stamp design depends on the position of the printing plates or how paper is fed through the press. On machine-made paper, watermarks normally are read from right to left. The design is repeated closely throughout the sheet in a "multiple-watermark design." In a "sheet watermark," the design appears only once on the sheet, but extends over many stamps. Individual stamps may carry only a small fraction or none of the watermark.

"Marginal watermarks" occur in the margins of sheets or panes of stamps. They occur on the outside border of paper (ostensibly outside the area where stamps are to be printed). A large row of letters may spell the name of the country or the manufacturer of the paper, or a border of lines may appear. Careless press feeding may cause parts of these letters and/or lines to show on stamps of the outer row of a pane.

## Soluble Printing Inks

WARNING: Most stamp colors are permanent; that is, they are not seriously affected by short-term exposure to light or water. Many colors, especially of modern inks, fade from excessive exposure to light. There are stamps printed with inks that dissolve easily in water or in fluids used to detect watermarks. Use of these inks was intentional to prevent the removal of cancellations. Water affects all aniline inks, those on so-called safety paper and some photogravure printings - all such inks are known as *fugitive colors. Removal from paper of such stamps requires care and alternatives to traditional soaking.*

## Separation

"Separation" is the general term used to describe methods used to separate stamps. The three standard forms currently in use are perforating, rouletting and die-cutting. These methods are done during the stamp production process, after printing. Sometimes these methods are done on-press or sometimes as a separate step. The earliest issues, such as the 1840 Penny Black of Great Britain (Scott 1), did not have any means provided for separation. It was expected the stamps would be cut apart with scissors or folded and torn. These are examples of imperforate stamps. Many stamps were first issued in imperforate formats and were later issued with perforations. Therefore, care must be observed in buying single imperforate stamps to be certain they were issued imperforate and are not perforated copies that have been altered by having the perforations trimmed away. Stamps issued imperforate usually are valued as singles. However, imperforate varieties of normally perforated stamps should be collected in pairs or larger pieces as indisputable evidence of their imperforate character.

### PERFORATION

The chief style of separation of stamps, and the one that is in almost universal use today, is perforating. By this process, paper between the stamps is cut away in a line of holes, usually round, leaving little bridges of paper between the stamps to hold them together. Some types of perforation, such as hyphen-hole perfs, can be confused with roulettes, but a close visual inspection reveals that paper has been removed. The little perforation bridges, which project from the stamp when it is torn from the pane, are called the teeth of the perforation.

As the size of the perforation is sometimes the only way to differentiate between two otherwise identical stamps, it is necessary to be able to accurately measure and describe them. This is done with a perforation gauge, usually a ruler-like device that has dots or graduated lines to show how many perforations may be counted in the space of two centimeters. Two centimeters is the space universally adopted in which to measure perforations.

**Perforation gauge**

perce en arc                    perce en lignes

perce en points                 oblique roulette

perce en scie                   perce serpentin

To measure a stamp, run it along the gauge until the dots on it fit exactly into the perforations of the stamp. If you are using a graduated-line perforation gauge, simply slide the stamp along the surface until the lines on the gauge perfectly project from the center of the bridges or holes. The number to the side of the line of dots or lines that fit the stamp's perforation is the measurement. For example, an "11" means that 11 perforations fit between two centimeters. The description of the stamp therefore is "perf. 11." If the gauge of the perforations on the top and bottom of a stamp differs from that on the sides, the result is what is known as *compound perforations.* In measuring compound perforations, the gauge at top and bottom is always given first, then the sides. Thus, a stamp that measures 11 at top and bottom and 10 1/2 at the sides is "perf. 11 x 10 1/2." See U.S. Scott 632-642 for examples of compound perforations.

Stamps also are known with perforations different on three or all four sides. Descriptions of such items are clockwise, beginning with the top of the stamp.

A perforation with small holes and teeth close together is a "fine perforation." One with large holes and teeth far apart is a "coarse perforation." Holes that are jagged, rather than clean-cut, are "rough perforations." *Blind perforations* are the slight impressions left by the perforating pins if they fail to puncture the paper. Multiples of stamps showing blind perforations may command a slight premium over normally perforated stamps.

The term *syncopated perfs* describes intentional irregularities in the perforations. The earliest form was used by the Netherlands from 1925-33, where holes were omitted to create distinctive patterns. Beginning in 1992, Great Britain has used an oval perforation to help prevent counterfeiting. Several other countries have started using the oval perfs or other syncopated perf patterns.

A new type of perforation, still primarily used for postal stationery, is known as microperfs. Microperfs are tiny perforations (in some cases hundreds of holes per two centimeters) that allows items to be intentionally separated very easily, while not accidentally breaking apart as easily as standard perforations. These are not currently measured or differentiated by size, as are standard perforations.

## ROULETTING

In rouletting, the stamp paper is cut partly or wholly through, with no paper removed. In perforating, some paper is removed. Rouletting derives its name from the French roulette, a spur-like wheel. As the wheel is rolled over the paper, each point makes a small cut. The number of cuts made in a two-centimeter space determines the gauge of the roulette, just as the number of perforations in two centimeters determines the gauge of the perforation.

The shape and arrangement of the teeth on the wheels varies. Various roulette types generally carry French names:

*Perce en lignes* - rouletted in lines. The paper receives short, straight cuts in lines. This is the most common type of rouletting. See Mexico Scott 500.

*Perce en points* - pin-rouletted or pin-perfed. This differs from a small perforation because no paper is removed, although round, equidistant holes are pricked through the paper. See Mexico Scott 242-256.

*Perce en arc* and *perce en scie* - pierced in an arc or saw-toothed designs, forming half circles or small triangles. See Hanover (German States) Scott 25-29.

*Perce en serpentin* - serpentine roulettes. The cuts form a serpentine or wavy line. See Brunswick (German States) Scott 13-18.

Once again, no paper is removed by these processes, leaving the stamps easily separated, but closely attached.

## DIE-CUTTING

The third major form of stamp separation is die-cutting. This is a method where a die in the pattern of separation is created that later cuts the stamp paper in a stroke motion. Although some standard stamps bear die-cut perforations, this process is primarily used for self-adhesive postage stamps. Die-cutting can appear in straight lines, such as U.S. Scott 2522, shapes, such as U.S. Scott 1551, or imitating the appearance of perforations, such as New Zealand Scott 935A and 935B.

# Printing Processes

## ENGRAVING (Intaglio, Line-engraving, Etching)

**Master die** — The initial operation in the process of line engraving is making the master die. The die is a small, flat block of softened steel upon which the stamp design is recess engraved in reverse.

**Master die**

Photographic reduction of the original art is made to the appropriate size. It then serves as a tracing guide for the initial outline of the design. The engraver lightly traces the design on the steel with his graver, then slowly works the design until it is completed. At various points during the engraving process, the engraver hand-inks the die and makes an impression to check his progress. These are known as progressive die proofs. After completion of the engraving, the die is hardened to withstand the stress and pressures of later transfer operations.

**Transfer roll**

**Transfer roll** — Next is production of the transfer roll that, as the name implies, is the medium used to transfer the subject from the master die to the printing plate. A blank roll of soft steel, mounted on a mandrel, is placed under the bearers of the transfer press to allow it to roll freely on its axis. The hardened die is placed on the bed of the press and the face of the transfer roll is applied to the die, under pressure. The bed or the roll is then rocked back and forth under increasing pressure, until the soft steel of the roll is forced into every engraved line of the die. The resulting impression on the roll is known as a "relief" or a "relief transfer." The engraved image is now positive in appearance and stands out from the steel. After the required number of reliefs are "rocked in," the soft steel transfer roll is hardened.

Different flaws may occur during the relief process. A defective relief may occur during the rocking in process because of a minute piece of foreign material lodging on the die, or some other cause. Imperfections in the steel of the transfer roll may result in a breaking away of parts of the design. This is known as a relief break, which will show up on finished stamps as small, unprinted areas. If a damaged relief remains in use, it will transfer a repeating defect to the plate. Deliberate alterations of reliefs sometimes occur. "Altered reliefs" designate these changed conditions.

**Plate** — The final step in pre-printing production is the making of the printing plate. A flat piece of soft steel replaces the die on the bed of the transfer press. One of the reliefs on the transfer roll is positioned over this soft steel. Position, or layout, dots determine the correct position on the plate. The dots have been lightly marked on

the plate in advance. After the correct position of the relief is determined, the design is rocked in by following the same method used in making the transfer roll. The difference is that this time the image is being transferred from the transfer roll, rather than to it. Once the design is entered on the plate, it appears in reverse and is recessed. There are as many transfers entered on the plate as there are subjects printed on the sheet of stamps. It is during this process that double and shifted transfers occur, as well as re-entries. These are the result of improperly entered images that have not been properly burnished out prior to rocking in a new image.

Modern siderography processes, such as those used by the U.S. Bureau of Engraving and Printing, involve an automated form of rocking designs in on preformed cylindrical printing sleeves. The same process also allows for easier removal and re-entry of worn images right on the sleeve.

**Transferring the design to the plate**

Following the entering of the required transfers on the plate, the position dots, layout dots and lines, scratches and other markings generally are burnished out. Added at this time by the siderographer are any required *guide lines, plate numbers* or other *marginal markings*. The plate is then hand-inked and a proof impression is taken. This is known as a plate proof. If the impression is approved, the plate is machined for fitting onto the press, is hardened and sent to the plate vault ready for use.

On press, the plate is inked and the surface is automatically wiped clean, leaving ink only in the recessed lines. Paper is then forced under pressure into the engraved recessed lines, thereby receiving the ink. Thus, the ink lines on engraved stamps are slightly raised, and slight depressions (debossing) occur on the back of the stamp. Prior to the advent of modern high-speed presses and more advanced ink formulations, paper had to be dampened before receiving the ink. This sometimes led to uneven shrinkage by the time the stamps were perforated, resulting in improperly perforated stamps, or misperfs. Newer presses use drier paper, thus both *wet* and *dry printings* exist on some stamps.

**Rotary Press** — Until 1914, only flat plates were used to print engraved stamps. Rotary press printing was introduced in 1914, and slowly spread. Some countries still use flat-plate printing.

After approval of the plate proof, older *rotary press plates* require additional machining. They are curved to fit the press cylinder. "Gripper slots" are cut into the back of each plate to receive the "grippers," which hold the plate securely on the press. The plate is then hardened. Stamps printed from these bent rotary press plates are longer or wider than the same stamps printed from flat-plate presses. The stretching of the plate during the curving process is what causes this distortion.

**Re-entry** — To execute a re-entry on a flat plate, the transfer roll is re-applied to the plate, often at some time after its first use on the press. Worn-out designs can be resharpened by carefully burnishing out the original image and re-entering it from the transfer roll. If the original impression has not been sufficiently removed and the transfer roll is not precisely in line with the remaining impression, the resulting double transfer will make the re-entry obvious. If the registration is true, a re-entry may be difficult or impossible to distinguish. Sometimes a stamp printed from a successful re-entry is identified by having a much sharper and clearer impression than its neighbors. With the advent of rotary presses, post-press re-entries were not possible. After a plate was curved for the rotary press, it was impossible to make a re-entry. This is because the plate had already been bent once (with the design distorted).

However, with the introduction of the previously mentioned modern-style siderography machines, entries are made to the pre-formed cylindrical printing sleeve. Such sleeves are dechromed and softened. This allows individual images to be burnished out and re-entered on the curved sleeve. The sleeve is then rechromed, resulting in longer press life.

**Double Transfer** — This is a description of the condition of a transfer on a plate that shows evidence of a duplication of all, or a portion of the design. It usually is the result of the changing of the registration between the transfer roll and the plate during the rocking in of the original entry. Double transfers also occur when only a portion of the design has been rocked in and improper positioning is noted. If the worker elected not to burnish out the partial or completed design, a strong double transfer will occur for part or all of the design.

It sometimes is necessary to remove the original transfer from a plate and repeat the process a second time. If the finished re-worked image shows traces of the original impression, attributable to incomplete burnishing, the result is a partial double transfer.

With the modern automatic machines mentioned previously, double transfers are all but impossible to create. Those partially doubled images on stamps printed from such sleeves are more than likely re-entries, rather than true double transfers.

**Re-engraved** — Alterations to a stamp design are sometimes necessary after some stamps have been printed. In some cases, either the original die or the actual printing plate may have its "temper" drawn (softened), and the design will be re-cut. The resulting impressions from such a re-engraved die or plate may differ slightly from the original issue, and are known as "re-engraved." If the alteration was made to the master die, all future printings will be consistently different from the original. If alterations were made to the printing plate, each altered stamp on the plate will be slightly different from each other, allowing specialists to reconstruct a complete printing plate.

**Dropped Transfers** — If an impression from the transfer roll has not been properly placed, a dropped transfer may occur. The final stamp image will appear obviously out of line with its neighbors.

**Short Transfer** — Sometimes a transfer roll is not rocked its entire length when entering a transfer onto a plate. As a result, the finished transfer on the plate fails to show the complete design, and the finished stamp will have an incomplete design printed. This is known as a "short transfer." U.S. Scott No. 8 is a good example of a short transfer.

## TYPOGRAPHY (Letterpress, Surface Printing, Flexography, Dry Offset, High Etch)

Although the word "Typography" is obsolete as a term describing a printing method, it was the accepted term throughout the first century of postage stamps. Therefore, appropriate Scott listings in this catalogue refer to typographed stamps. The current term for this form of printing, however, is "letterpress."

As it relates to the production of postage stamps, letterpress printing is the reverse of engraving. Rather than having recessed areas trap the ink and deposit it on paper, only the raised areas of the design are inked. This is comparable to the type of printing seen by inking and using an ordinary rubber stamp. Letterpress includes all printing where the design is above the surface area, whether it is wood, metal or, in some instances, hardened rubber or polymer plastic.

For most letterpress-printed stamps, the engraved master is made in much the same manner as for engraved stamps. In this instance, however, an additional step is needed. The design is transferred to another surface before being transferred to the transfer roll. In this way, the transfer roll has a recessed stamp design, rather than one done in relief. This makes the printing areas on the final plate raised, or relief areas.

For less-detailed stamps of the 19th century, the area on the die not used as a printing surface was cut away, leaving the surface area raised. The original die was then reproduced by stereotyping or electrotyping. The resulting electrotypes were assembled in the required number and format of the desired sheet of stamps. The plate used in printing the stamps was an electroplate of these assembled electrotypes.

Once the final letterpress plates are created, ink is applied to the raised surface and the pressure of the press transfers the ink impression to the paper. In contrast to engraving, the fine lines of letterpress are impressed on the surface of the stamp, leaving a debossed surface. When viewed from the back (as on a typewritten page), the corresponding line work on the stamp will be raised slightly (embossed) above the surface.

## PHOTOGRAVURE (Gravure, Rotogravure, Heliogravure)

In this process, the basic principles of photography are applied to a chemically sensitized metal plate, rather than photographic paper. The design is transferred photographically to the plate through a halftone, or dot-matrix screen, breaking the reproduction into tiny dots. The plate is treated chemically and the dots form depressions, called cells, of varying depths and diameters, depending on the degrees of shade in the design. Then, like engraving, ink is applied to the plate and the surface is wiped clean. This leaves ink in the tiny cells that is lifted out and deposited on the paper when it is pressed against the plate.

Gravure is most often used for multicolored stamps, generally using the three primary colors (red, yellow and blue) and black. By varying the dot matrix pattern and density of these colors, virtually any color can be reproduced. A typical full-color gravure stamp will be created from four printing cylinders (one for each color). The original multicolored image will have been photographically separated into its component colors.

Modern gravure printing may use computer-generated dot-matrix screens, and modern plates may be of various types including metal-coated plastic. The catalogue designation of Photogravure (or "Photo") covers any of these older and more modern gravure methods of printing.

For examples of the first photogravure stamps printed (1914), see Bavaria Scott 94-114.

## LITHOGRAPHY (Offset Lithography, Stone Lithography, Dilitho, Planography, Collotype)

The principle that oil and water do not mix is the basis for lithography. The stamp design is drawn by hand or transferred from engraving to the surface of a lithographic stone or metal plate in a greasy (oily) substance. This oily substance holds the ink, which will later be transferred to the paper. The stone (or plate) is wet with an acid fluid, causing it to repel the printing ink in all areas not covered by the greasy substance.

Transfer paper is used to transfer the design from the original stone or plate. A series of duplicate transfers are grouped and, in turn, transferred to the final printing plate.

**Photolithography** — The application of photographic processes to lithography. This process allows greater flexibility of design, related to use of halftone screens combined with line work. Unlike photogravure or engraving, this process can allow large, solid areas to be printed.

**Offset** — A refinement of the lithographic process. A rubber-covered blanket cylinder takes the impression from the inked lithographic plate. From the "blanket" the impression is *offset* or transferred to the paper. Greater flexibility and speed are the principal reasons offset printing has largely displaced lithography. The term "lithography" covers both processes, and results are almost identical.

### EMBOSSED (Relief) Printing

Embossing, not considered one of the four main printing types, is a method in which the design first is sunk into the metal of the die. Printing is done against a yielding platen, such as leather or linoleum. The platen is forced into the depression of the die, thus forming the design on the paper in relief. This process is often used for metallic inks.

Embossing may be done without color (see Sardinia Scott 4-6); with color printed around the embossed area (see Great Britain Scott 5 and most U.S. envelopes); and with color in exact registration with the embossed subject (see Canada Scott 656-657).

### HOLOGRAMS

For objects to appear as holograms on stamps, a model exactly the same size as it is to appear on the hologram must be created. Rather than using photographic film to capture the image, holography records an image on a photoresist material. In processing, chemicals eat away at certain exposed areas, leaving a pattern of constructive and destructive interference. When the phororesist is developed, the result is a pattern of uneven ridges that acts as a mold. This mold is then coated with metal, and the resulting form is used to press copies in much the same way phonograph records are produced.

A typical reflective hologram used for stamps consists of a reproduction of the uneven patterns on a plastic film that is applied to a reflective background, usually a silver or gold foil. Light is reflected off the background through the film, making the pattern present on the film visible. Because of the uneven pattern of the film, the viewer will perceive the objects in their proper three-dimensional relationships with appropriate brightness.

The first hologram on a stamp was produced by Austria in 1988 (Scott 1441).

### FOIL APPLICATION

A modern tecnique of applying color to stamps involves the application of metallic foil to the stamp paper. A pattern of foil is applied to the stamp paper by use of a stamping die. The foil usually is flat, but it may be textured. Canada Scott 1735 has three different foil applications in pearl, bronze and gold. The gold foil was textured using a chemical-etch copper embossing die. The printing of this stamp also involved two-color offset lithography plus embossing.

### COMBINATION PRINTINGS

Sometimes two or even three printing methods are combined in producing stamps. In these cases, such as Austria Scott 933 or Canada 1735 (described in the preceding paragraph), the multiple-printing technique can be determined by studying the individual characteristics of each printing type. A few stamps, such as Singapore Scott 684-684A, combine as many as three of the four major printing types (lithography, engraving and typography). When this is done it often indicates the incorporation of security devices against counterfeiting.

### INK COLORS

Inks or colored papers used in stamp printing often are of mineral origin, although there are numerous examples of organic-based pigments. As a general rule, organic-based pigments are far more subject to varieties and change than those of mineral-based origin.

The appearance of any given color on a stamp may be affected by many aspects, including printing variations, light, color of paper, aging and chemical alterations.

Numerous printing variations may be observed. Heavier pressure or inking will cause a more intense color, while slight interruptions in the ink feed or lighter impressions will cause a lighter appearance. Stamps printed in the same color by water-based and solvent-based inks can differ significantly in appearance. This affects several stamps in the U.S. Prominent Americans series. Hand-mixed ink formulas (primarily from the 19th century) produced under different conditions (humidity and temperature) account for notable color variations in early printings of the same stamp (see U.S. Scott 248-250, 279B, for example). Different sources of pigment can also result in significant differences in color.

Light exposure and aging are closely related in the way they affect stamp color. Both eventually break down the ink and fade colors, so that a carefully kept stamp may differ significantly in color from an identical copy that has been exposed to light. If stamps are exposed to light either intentionally or accidentally, their colors can be faded or completely changed in some cases.

Papers of different quality and consistency used for the same stamp printing may affect color appearance. Most pelure papers, for example, show a richer color when compared with wove or laid papers. See Russia Scott 181a, for an example of this effect.

The very nature of the printing processes can cause a variety of differences in shades or hues of the same stamp. Some of these shades are scarcer than others, and are of particular interest to the advanced collector.

# Luminescence

All forms of tagged stamps fall under the general category of luminescence. Within this broad category is fluorescence, dealing with forms of tagging visible under longwave ultraviolet light, and phosphorescence, which deals with tagging visible only under shortwave light. Phosphorescence leaves an afterglow and fluorescence does not. These treated stamps show up in a range of different colors when exposed to UV light. The differing wavelengths of the light activates the tagging material, making it glow in various colors that usually serve different mail processing purposes.

Intentional tagging is a post-World War II phenomenon, brought about by the increased literacy rate and rapidly growing mail volume. It was one of several answers to the problem of the need for more automated mail processes. Early tagged stamps served the purpose of triggering machines to separate different types of mail. A natural outgrowth was to also use the signal to trigger machines that faced all envelopes the same way and canceled them.

Tagged stamps come in many different forms. Some tagged stamps have luminescent shapes or images imprinted on them as a form of security device. Others have blocks (United States), stripes, frames (South Africa and Canada), overall coatings (United States), bars (Great Britain and Canada) and many other types. Some types of tagging are even mixed in with the pigmented printing ink (Australia Scott 366, Netherlands Scott 478 and U.S. Scott 1359 and 2443).

The means of applying taggant to stamps differs as much as the intended purposes for the stamps. The most common form of tagging is a coating applied to the surface of the printed stamp. Since the taggant ink is frequently invisible except under UV light, it does not interfere with the appearance of the stamp. Another common application is the use of phosphored papers. In this case the paper itself either has a coating of taggant applied before the stamp is printed, has taggant applied during the papermaking process (incorporating it into the fibers), or has the taggant mixed into the coating of the paper. The latter method, among others, is currently in use in the United States.

Many countries now use tagging in various forms to either expedite mail handling or to serve as a printing security device against counterfeiting. Following the introduction of tagged stamps for public use in 1959 by Great Britain, other countries have steadily joined the parade. Among those are Germany (1961); Canada and Denmark (1962); United States, Australia, France and Switzerland (1963); Belgium and Japan (1966); Sweden and Norway (1967); Italy (1968); and Russia (1969). Since then, many other countries have begun using forms of tagging, including Brazil, China, Czechoslovakia, Hong Kong, Guatemala, Indonesia, Israel, Lithuania, Luxembourg, Netherlands, Penrhyn Islands, Portugal, St. Vincent, Singapore, South Africa, Spain and Sweden to name a few.

In some cases, including United States, Canada, Great Britain and Switzerland, stamps were released both with and without tagging. Many of these were released during each country's experimental period. Tagged and untagged versions are listed for the aforementioned countries and are noted in some other countries' listings. For at least a few stamps, the experimentally tagged version is worth far more than its untagged counterpart, such as the 1963 experimental tagged version of France Scott 1024.

In some cases, luminescent varieties of stamps were inadvertently created. Several Russian stamps, for example, sport highly fluorescent ink that was not intended as a form of tagging. Older stamps, such as early U.S. postage dues, can be positively identified by the use of UV light, since the organic ink used has become slightly fluorescent over time. Other stamps, such as Austria Scott 70a-82a (varnish bars) and Obock Scott 46-64 (printed quadrille lines), have become fluorescent over time.

Various fluorescent substances have been added to paper to make it appear brighter. These optical brightners, as they are known, greatly affect the appearance of the stamp under UV light. The brightest of these is known as Hi-Brite paper. These paper varieties are beyond the scope of the Scott Catalogue.

Shortwave UV light also is used extensively in expertizing, since each form of paper has its own fluorescent characteristics that are impossible to perfectly match. It is therefore a simple matter to detect filled thins, added perforation teeth and other alterations that involve the addition of paper. UV light also is used to examine stamps that have had cancels chemically removed and for other purposes as well.

# Gum

The Illustrated Gum Chart in the first part of this introduction shows and defines various types of gum condition. Because gum condition has an important impact on the value of unused stamps, we recommend studying this chart and the accompanying text carefully.

The gum on the back of a stamp may be shiny, dull, smooth, rough, dark, white, colored or tinted. Most stamp gumming adhesives use gum arabic or dextrine as a base. Certain polymers such as polyvinyl alcohol (PVA) have been used extensively since World War II.

The *Scott Standard Postage Stamp Catalogue* does not list items by types of gum. The *Scott Specialized Catalogue of United States Stamps* does differentiate among some types of gum for certain issues.

Reprints of stamps may have gum differing from the original issues. In addition, some countries have used different gum formulas for different seasons. These adhesives have different properties that may become more apparent over time.

Many stamps have been issued without gum, and the catalogue will note this fact. See, for example, United States Scott 40-47. Sometimes, gum may have been removed to preserve the stamp. Germany Scott B68, for example, has a highly acidic gum that eventually destroys the stamps. This item is valued in the catalogue with gum removed.

# Reprints and Reissues

These are impressions of stamps (usually obsolete) made from the original plates or stones. If they are valid for postage and reproduce obsolete issues (such as U.S. Scott 102-111), the stamps are *reissues*. If they are from current issues, they are designated as *second, third,* etc., *printing*. If designated for a particular purpose, they are called *special printings*.

When special printings are not valid for postage, but are made from original dies and plates by authorized persons, they are *official reprints*. *Private reprints* are made from the original plates and dies by private hands. An example of a private reprint is that of the 1871-1932 reprints made from the original die of the 1845 New Haven, Conn., postmaster's provisional. *Official reproductions* or imitations are made from new dies and plates by government authorization. Scott will list those reissues that are valid for postage if they differ significantly from the original printing.

The U.S. government made special printings of its first postage stamps in 1875. Produced were official imitations of the first two stamps (listed as Scott 3-4), reprints of the demonetized pre-1861 issues (Scott 40-47) and reissues of the 1861 stamps, the 1869 stamps and the then-current 1875 denominations. Even though the official imitations and the reprints were not valid for postage, Scott lists all of these U.S. special printings.

Most reprints or reissues differ slightly from the original stamp in some characteristic, such as gum, paper, perforation, color or watermark. Sometimes the details are followed so meticulously that only a student of that specific stamp is able to distinguish the reprint or reissue from the original.

# Remainders and Canceled to Order

Some countries sell their stock of old stamps when a new issue replaces them. To avoid postal use, the *remainders* usually are canceled with a punch hole, a heavy line or bar, or a more-or-less regular-looking cancellation. The most famous merchant of remainders was Nicholas F. Seebeck. In the 1880s and 1890s, he arranged printing contracts between the Hamilton Bank Note Co., of which he was a director, and several Central and South American countries. The contracts provided that the plates and all remainders of the yearly issues became the property of Hamilton. Seebeck saw to it that ample stock remained. The "Seebecks," both remainders and reprints, were standard packet fillers for decades.

Some countries also issue stamps *canceled-to-order (CTO)*, either in sheets with original gum or stuck onto pieces of paper or envelopes and canceled. Such CTO items generally are worth less than postally used stamps. In cases where the CTO material is far more prevalent in the marketplace than postally used examples, the catalogue value relates to the CTO examples, with postally used examples noted as premium items. Most CTOs can be detected by the presence of gum. However, as the CTO practice goes back at least to 1885, the gum inevitably has been soaked off some stamps so they could pass as postally used. The normally applied postmarks usually differ slightly from standard postmarks, and specialists are able to tell the difference. When applied individually to envelopes by philatelically minded persons, CTO material is known as *favor canceled* and generally sells at large discounts.

# Cinderellas and Facsimiles

*Cinderella* is a catch-all term used by stamp collectors to describe phantoms, fantasies, bogus items, municipal issues, exhibition seals, local revenues, transportation stamps, labels, poster stamps and many other types of items. Some cinderella collectors include in their collections local postage issues, telegraph stamps, essays and proofs, forgeries and counterfeits.

A *fantasy* is an adhesive created for a nonexistent stamp-issuing authority. Fantasy items range from imaginary countries (Occusi-Ambeno, Kingdom of Sedang, Principality of Trinidad or Torres Straits), to non-existent locals (Winans City Post), or nonexistent transportation lines (McRobish & Co.'s Acapulco-San Francisco Line).

On the other hand, if the entity exists and could have issued stamps (but did not) or was known to have issued other stamps, the items are considered *bogus* stamps. These would include the Mormon postage stamps of Utah, S. Allan Taylor's Guatemala and Paraguay inventions, the propaganda issues for the South Moluccas and the adhesives of the Page & Keyes local post of Boston.

*Phantoms* is another term for both fantasy and bogus issues.

*Facsimiles* are copies or imitations made to represent original stamps, but which do not pretend to be originals. A catalogue illustration is such a facsimile. Illustrations from the Moens catalogue of the last century were occasionally colored and passed off as stamps. Since the beginning of stamp collecting, facsimiles have been made for collectors as space fillers or for reference. They often carry the word "facsimile," "falsch" (German), "sanko" or "mozo" (Japanese), or "faux" (French) overprinted on the face or stamped on the back. Unfortunately, over the years a number of these items have had fake cancels applied over the facsimile notation and have been passed off as genuine.

## Forgeries and Counterfeits

Forgeries and counterfeits have been with philately virtually from the beginning of stamp production. Over time, the terminology for the two has been used interchangeably. Although both forgeries and counterfeits are reproductions of stamps, the purposes behind their creation differ considerably.

Among specialists there is an increasing movement to more specifically define such items. Although there is no universally accepted terminology, we feel the following definitions most closely mirror the items and their purposes as they are currently defined.

*Forgeries* (also often referred to as *Counterfeits*) are reproductions of genuine stamps that have been created to defraud collectors. Such spurious items first appeared on the market around 1860, and most old-time collections contain one or more. Many are crude and easily spotted, but some can deceive experts.

An important supplier of these early philatelic forgeries was the Hamburg printer Gebruder Spiro. Many others with reputations in this craft included S. Allan Taylor, George Hussey, James Chute, George Forune, Benjamin & Sarpy, Julius Goldner, E. Oneglia and L.H. Mercier. Among the noted 20th-century forgers were Francois Fournier, Jean Sperati and the prolific Raoul DeThuin.

Forgeries may be complete replications, or they may be genuine stamps altered to resemble a scarcer (and more valuable) type. Most forgeries, particularly those of rare stamps, are worth only a small fraction of the value of a genuine example, but a few types, created by some of the most notable forgers, such as Sperati, can be worth as much or more than the genuine. Fraudulently produced copies are known of most classic rarities and many medium-priced stamps.

In addition to rare stamps, large numbers of common 19th- and early 20th-century stamps were forged to supply common stamps to the early packet trade. Many can still be easily found. Few new philatelic forgeries have appeared in recent decades. Successful imitation of well-engraved work is virtually impossible. It has proven far easier to produce a fake by altering a genuine stamp than to duplicate a stamp completely.

*Counterfeit* (also often referred to as *Postal Counterfeit* or *Postal Forgery*) is the term generally applied to reproductions of stamps that have been created to defraud the government of revenue. Such items usually are created at the time a stamp is current and, in some cases, are hard to detect. Because most counterfeits are seized when the perpetrator is captured, postal counterfeits, particularly used on cover, are usually worth much more than a genuine example to spe-cialists. The first postal counterfeit was of Spain's 4-cuarto carmine of 1854 (the real one is Scott 25). Apparently, the counterfeiters were not satisfied with their first version, which is now very scarce, and they soon created an engraved counterfeit, which is common. Postal counterfeits quickly followed in Austria, Naples, Sardinia and the Roman States. They have since been created in many other countries as well, including the United States.

An infamous counterfeit to defraud the government is the 1-shilling Great Britain "Stock Exchange" forgery of 1872, used on telegraph forms at the exchange that year. The stamp escaped detection until a stamp dealer noticed it in 1898.

## Fakes

*Fakes* are genuine stamps altered in some way to make them more desirable. One student of this part of stamp collecting has estimated that by the 1950s more than 30,000 varieties of fakes were known. That number has grown greatly since then. The widespread existence of fakes makes it important for stamp collectors to study their philatelic holdings and use relevant literature. Likewise, collectors should buy from reputable dealers who guarantee their stamps and make full and prompt refunds should a purchased item be declared faked or altered by some mutually agreed-upon authority. Because fakes always have some genuine characteristics, it is not always possible to obtain unanimous agreement among experts regarding specific items. These students may change their opinions as philatelic knowledge increases. More than 80 percent of all fakes on the philatelic market today are regummed, reperforated (or perforated for the first time), or bear forged overprints, surcharges or cancellations.

Stamps can be chemically treated to alter or eliminate colors. For example, a pale rose stamp can be re-colored to resemble a blue shade of high market value. In other cases, treated stamps can be made to resemble missing color varieties. Designs may be changed by painting, or a stroke or a dot added or bleached out to turn an ordinary variety into a seemingly scarcer stamp. Part of a stamp can be bleached and reprinted in a different version, achieving an inverted center or frame. Margins can be added or repairs done so deceptively that the stamps move from the "repaired" into the "fake" category.

Fakers have not left the backs of the stamps untouched either. They may create false watermarks, add fake grills or press out genuine grills. A thin India paper proof may be glued onto a thicker backing to create the appearance an issued stamp, or a proof printed on cardboard may be shaved down and perforated to resemble a stamp. Silk threads are impressed into paper and stamps have been split so that a rare paper variety is added to an otherwise inexpensive stamp. The most common treatment to the back of a stamp, however, is regumming.

Some in the business of faking stamps have openly advertised foolproof application of "original gum" to stamps that lack it, although most publications now ban such ads from their pages. It is believed that very few early stamps have survived without being hinged. The large number of never-hinged examples of such earlier material offered for sale thus suggests the widespread extent of regumming activity. Regumming also may be used to hide repairs or thin spots. Dipping the stamp into watermark fluid, or examining it under long-wave ultraviolet light often will reveal these flaws.

Fakers also tamper with separations. Ingenious ways to add margins are known. Perforated wide-margin stamps may be falsely represented as imperforate when trimmed. Reperforating is commonly done to create scarce coil or perforation varieties, and to eliminate the naturally occurring straight-edge stamps found in sheet margin positions of many earlier issues. Custom has made straight-edged stamps less desirable. Fakers have obliged by perforating straight-edged stamps so that many are now uncommon, if not rare.

Another fertile field for the faker is that of overprints, surcharges and cancellations. The forging of rare surcharges or overprints began in the 1880s or 1890s. These forgeries are sometimes difficult to detect, but experts have identified almost all. Occasionally, overprints or cancellations are removed to create non-overprinted stamps or seemingly unused items. This is most commonly done by removing a manuscript cancel to make a stamp resemble an unused example. "SPECIMEN" overprints may be removed by scraping and repainting to create non-overprinted varieties. Fakers use inexpensive revenues or pen-canceled stamps to generate unused stamps for further faking by adding other markings. The quartz lamp or UV lamp and a high-powered magnifying glass help to easily detect removed cancellations.

The bigger problem, however, is the addition of overprints, surcharges or cancellations - many with such precision that they are very difficult to ascertain. Plating of the stamps or the overprint can be an important method of detection.

Fake postmarks may range from many spurious fancy cancellations to a host of markings applied to transatlantic covers, to adding normally appearing postmarks to definitives of some countries with stamps that are valued far higher used than unused. With the increased popularity of cover collecting, and the widespread interest in postal history, a fertile new field for fakers has come about. Some have tried to create entire covers. Others specialize in adding stamps, tied by fake cancellations, to genuine stampless covers, or replacing less expensive or damaged stamps with more valuable ones. Detailed study of postal rates in effect at the time a cover in question was mailed, including the analysis of each handstamp used during the period, ink analysis and similar techniques, usually will unmask the fraud.

## Restoration and Repairs

Scott Publishing Co. bases its catalogue values on stamps that are free of defects and otherwise meet the standards set forth earlier in this introduction. Most stamp collectors desire to have the finest copy of an item possible. Even within given grading categories there are variances. This leads to a controversial practice that is not defined in any universal manner: stamp *restoration*.

There are broad differences of opinion about what is permissible when it comes to restoration. Carefully applying a soft eraser to a stamp or cover to remove light soiling is one form of restoration, as is washing a stamp in mild soap and water to clean it. These are fairly accepted forms of restoration. More severe forms of restoration include pressing out creases or removing stains caused by tape. To what degree each of these is acceptable is dependent upon the individual situation. Further along the spectrum is the freshening of a stamp's color by removing oxide build-up or the effects of wax paper left next to stamps shipped to the tropics.

At some point in this spectrum the concept of *repair* replaces that of restoration. Repairs include filling thin spots, mending tears by reweaving or adding a missing perforation tooth. Regumming stamps may have been acceptable as a restoration or repair technique many decades ago, but today it is considered a form of fakery.

Restored stamps may or may not sell at a discount, and it is possible that the value of individual restored items may be enhanced over that of their pre-restoration state. Specific situations dictate the resultant value of such an item. Repaired stamps sell at substantial discounts from the value of sound stamps.

# Terminology

**Booklets** — Many countries have issued stamps in small booklets for the convenience of users. This idea continues to become increasingly popular in many countries. Booklets have been issued in many sizes and forms, often with advertising on the covers, the panes of stamps or on the interleaving.

The panes used in booklets may be printed from special plates or made from regular sheets. All panes from booklets issued by the United States and many from those of other countries contain stamps that are straight edged on the sides, but perforated between. Others are distinguished by orientation of watermark or other identifying features. Any stamp-like unit in the pane, either printed or blank, that is not a postage stamp, is considered to be a *label* in the catalogue listings.

Scott lists and values booklet panes. Modern complete booklets also are listed and valued. Individual booklet panes are listed only when they are not fashioned from existing sheet stamps and, therefore, are identifiable from their sheet stamp counterparts.

Panes usually do not have a used value assigned to them because there is little market activity for used booklet panes, even though many exist used and there is some demand for them.

**Cancellations** — The marks or obliterations put on stamps by postal authorities to show that they have performed service and to prevent their reuse are known as cancellations. If the marking is made with a pen, it is considered a "pen cancel." When the location of the post office appears in the marking, it is a "town cancellation." A "postmark" is technically any postal marking, but in practice the term generally is applied to a town cancellation with a date. When calling attention to a cause or celebration, the marking is known as a "slogan cancellation." Many other types and styles of cancellations exist, such as duplex, numerals, targets, fancy and others. See also "precancels," below.

**Coil Stamps** — These are stamps that are issued in rolls for use in dispensers, affixing and vending machines. Those coils of the United States, Canada, Sweden and some other countries are perforated horizontally or vertically only, with the outer edges imperforate. Coil stamps of some countries, such as Great Britain and Germany, are perforated on all four sides and may in some cases be distinguished from their sheet stamp counterparts by watermarks, counting numbers on the reverse or other means.

**Covers** — Entire envelopes, with or without adhesive postage stamps, that have passed through the mail and bear postal or other markings of philatelic interest are known as covers. Before the introduction of envelopes in about 1840, people folded letters and wrote the address on the outside. Some people covered their letters with an extra sheet of paper on the outside for the address, producing the term "cover." Used airletter sheets, stamped envelopes and other items of postal stationery also are considered covers.

**Errors** — Stamps that have some major, consistent, unintentional deviation from the normal are considered errors. Errors include, but are not limited to, missing or wrong colors, wrong paper, wrong watermarks, inverted centers or frames on multicolor prin' inverted or missing surcharges or overprints, double impres' missing perforations, unintentionally omitted tagging and others. Factually wrong or misspelled information, if it appears on all examples of a stamp, are not considered errors in the true sense of the word. They are errors of design. Inconsistent or randomly appearing items, such as misperfs or color shifts, are classified as freaks.

**Color-Omitted Errors** — This term refers to stamps where a missing color is caused by the complete failure of the printing plate to deliver ink to the stamp paper or any other paper. Generally, this is caused by the printing plate not being engaged on the press or the ink station running dry of ink during printing.

**Color-Missing Errors** — This term refers to stamps where a color or colors were printed somewhere but do not appear on the finished stamp. There are four different classes of color-missing errors, and the catalog indicates with a two-letter code appended to each such listing what caused the color to be missing. These codes are used only for the United States' color-missing error listings.

**FO** = A *foldover* of the stamp sheet during printing may block ink from appearing on a stamp. Instead, the color will appear on the back of the foldover (where it might fall on the back of the selvage or perhaps on the back of the stamp or another stamp). FO also will be used in the case of foldunders, where the paper may fold underneath the other stamp paper and the color will print on the platen.

**EP** = A piece of *extraneous paper* falling across the plate or stamp paper will receive the printed ink. When the extraneous paper is removed, an unprinted portion of stamp paper remains and shows partially or totally missing colors.

**CM** = A misregistration of the printing plates during printing will result in a *color misregistration*, and such a misregistraion may result in a color not appearing on the finished stamp.

**PS** = A *perforation shift* after printing may remove a color from the finished stamp. Normally, this will occur on a row of stamps at the edge of the stamp pane.

**Measurements** – When measurements are given in the Scott catalogues for stamp size, grill size or any other reason, the first measurement given is always for the top and bottom dimension, while the second measurement will be for the sides (just as perforation gauges are measured). Thus, a stamp size of 15mm x 21mm will indicate a vertically oriented stamp 15mm wide at top and bottom, and 21mm tall at the sides. The same principle holds for measuring or counting items such as U.S. grills. A grill count of 22x18 points (B grill) indicates that there are 22 grill points across by 18 grill points down.

**Overprints and Surcharges** — Overprinting involves applying wording or design elements over an already existing stamp. Overprints can be used to alter the place of use (such as "Canal Zone" on U.S. stamps), to adapt them for a special purpose ("Porto" on Denmark's 1913-20 regular issues for use as postage due stamps, Scott J1-J7) or to commemorate a special occasion (United States Scott 647-648).

A *surcharge* is a form of overprint that changes or restates the face value of a stamp or piece of postal stationery.

Surcharges and overprints may be handstamped, typeset or, occasionally, lithographed or engraved. A few hand-written overprints and surcharges are known.

**Personalized Stamps** — In 1999, Australia issued stamps with se-tenant labels that could be personalized with pictures of the customer's choice. Other countries quickly followed suit, with some offering to print the selected picture on the stamp itself within a frame that was used exclusively for personalized issues. As the picture used on these stamps or labels vary, listings for such stamps are for *any* picture within the common frame (or any picture on a se-tenant label), be it a "generic" image or one produced especially for a customer, almost invariably at a premium price.

**Precancels** — Stamps that are canceled before they are placed in the mail are known as precancels. Precanceling usually is done to expedite the handling of large mailings and generally allow the affected mail pieces to skip certain phases of mail handling.

In the United States, precancellations generally identified the point of origin; that is, the city and state. This information appeared across the face of the stamp, usually centered between parallel lines. More recently, bureau precancels retained the parallel lines, but the city and state designations were dropped. Recent coils have a service inscription that is present on the original printing plate. These show the mail service paid for by the stamp. Since these stamps are not intended to receive further cancellations when used as intended, they are considered precancels. Such items often do not have parallel lines as part of the precancellation.

In France, the abbreviation *Affranchts* in a semicircle together with the word *Postes* is the general form of precancel in use. Belgian precancellations usually appear in a box in which the name of the city appears. Netherlands precancels have the name of the city enclosed between concentric circles, sometimes called a "lifesaver." Precancellations of other countries usually follow these patterns, but may be any arrangement of bars, boxes and city names.

Precancels are listed in the Scott catalogues only if the precancel changes the denomination (Belgium Scott 477-478); if the precanceled stamp is different from the non-precanceled version (such as untagged U.S. precancels); or if the stamp exists only precanceled (France Scott 1096-1099, U.S. Scott 2265).

**Proofs and Essays** — Proofs are impressions taken from an approved die, plate or stone in which the design and color are the same as the stamp issued to the public. Trial color proofs are impressions taken from approved dies, plates or stones in colors that vary from the final version. An essay is the impression of a design that differs in some way from the issued stamp. "Progressive die proofs" generally are considered to be essays.

**Provisionals** — These are stamps that are issued on short notice and intended for temporary use pending the arrival of regular issues. They usually are issued to meet such contingencies as changes in government or currency, shortage of necessary postage values or military occupation.

During the 1840s, postmasters in certain American cities issued stamps that were valid only at specific post offices. In 1861, postmasters of the Confederate States also issued stamps with limited validity. Both of these examples are known as "postmaster's provisionals."

**Se-tenant** — This term refers to an unsevered pair, strip or block of stamps that differ in design, denomination or overprint.

Unless the se-tenant item has a continuous design (see U.S. Scott 1451a, 1694a) the stamps do not have to be in the same order as shown in the catalogue (see U.S. Scott 2158a).

**Specimens** — The Universal Postal Union required member nations to send samples of all stamps they released into service to the International Bureau in Switzerland. Member nations of the UPU received these specimens as samples of what stamps were valid for postage. Many are overprinted, handstamped or initial-perforated "Specimen," "Canceled" or "Muestra." Some are marked with bars across the denominations (China-Taiwan), punched holes (Czechoslovakia) or back inscriptions (Mongolia).

Stamps distributed to government officials or for publicity purposes, and stamps submitted by private security printers for official approval, also may receive such defacements.

The previously described defacement markings prevent postal use, and all such items generally are known as "specimens."

**Tete Beche** — This term describes a pair of stamps in which one is upside down in relation to the other. Some of these are the result of intentional sheet arrangements, such as Morocco Scott B10-B11. Others occurred when one or more electrotypes accidentally were placed upside down on the plate, such as Colombia Scott 57a. Separation of the tete-beche stamps, of course, destroys the tete beche variety.

# Pronunciation Symbols

ə .... banana, collide, abut

ˈə, ˌə .... humdrum, abut

ə .... immediately preceding \l\, \n\, \m\, \ŋ\, as in battle, mitten, eaten, and sometimes open \ˈō-pᵊm\, lock and key \-ᵊŋ-\; immediately following \l\, \m\, \r\, as often in French table, prisme, titre

ər .... further, merger, bird

ˈər- 
ˈə-r .... as in two different pronunciations of hurry \ˈhər-ē, ˈhə-rē\

a .... mat, map, mad, gag, snap, patch

ā .... day, fade, date, aorta, drape, cape

ä .... bother, cot, and, with most American speakers, father, cart

ȧ .... father as pronounced by speakers who do not rhyme it with bother; French patte

au̇ .... now, loud, out

b .... baby, rib

ch .... chin, nature \ˈnā-chər\

d .... did, adder

e .... bet, bed, peck

ˈē, ˌē .... beat, nosebleed, evenly, easy

ē .... easy, mealy

f .... fifty, cuff

g .... go, big, gift

h .... hat, ahead

hw .... whale as pronounced by those who do not have the same pronunciation for both whale and wail

i .... tip, banish, active

ī .... site, side, buy, tripe

j .... job, gem, edge, join, judge

k .... kin, cook, ache

k̲ .... German ich, Buch; one pronunciation of loch

l .... lily, pool

m .... murmur, dim, nymph

n .... no, own

ⁿ .... indicates that a preceding vowel or diphthong is pronounced with the nasal passages open, as in French un bon vin blanc \œ̃ⁿ -bōⁿ -vaⁿ -bläⁿ\

ŋ .... sing \ˈsiŋ\, singer \ˈsiŋ-ər\, finger \ˈfiŋ-gər\, ink \ˈiŋk\

ō .... bone, know, beau

ȯ .... saw, all, gnaw, caught

œ .... French boeuf, German Hölle

œ̄ .... French feu, German Höhle

ȯi .... coin, destroy

p .... pepper, lip

r .... red, car, rarity

s .... source, less

sh .... as in shy, mission, machine, special (actually, this is a single sound, not two); with a hyphen between, two sounds as in grasshopper \ˈgras-ˌhä-pər\

t .... tie, attack, late, later, latter

th .... as in thin, ether (actually, this is a single sound, not two); with a hyphen between, two sounds as in knighthood \ˈnīt-ˌhu̇d\

t̲h̲ .... then, either, this (actually, this is a single sound, not two)

ü .... rule, youth, union \ˈyün-yən\, few \ˈfyü\

u̇ .... pull, wood, book, curable \ˈkyu̇r-ə-bəl\, fury \ˈfyu̇r-ē\

ue .... German füllen, hübsch

ue̅ .... French rue, German fühlen

v .... vivid, give

w .... we, away

y .... yard, young, cue \ˈkyü\, mute \ˈmyüt\, union \ˈyün-yən\

ʸ .... indicates that during the articulation of the sound represented by the preceding character the front of the tongue has substantially the position it has for the articulation of the first sound of yard, as in French digne \dēnʸ\

z .... zone, raise

zh .... as in vision, azure \ˈa-zhər\ (actually, this is a single sound, not two); with a hyphen between, two sounds as in hogshead \ˈhȯgz-ˌhed, ˈhägz-\

\ .... slant line used in pairs to mark the beginning and end of a transcription: \ˈpen\

ˈ .... mark preceding a syllable with primary (strongest) stress: \ˈpen-mən-ˌship\

ˌ .... mark preceding a syllable with secondary (medium) stress: \ˈpen-mən-ˌship\

- .... mark of syllable division

( ) .... indicate that what is symbolized between is present in some utterances but not in others: factory \ˈfak-t(ə-)rē\

÷ .... indicates that many regard as unacceptable the pronunciation variant immediately following: cupola \ˈkyü-pə-lə, ÷-ˌlō\

# Currency Conversion

| Country | Dollar | Pound | S Franc | Yen | HK $ | Euro | Cdn $ | Aus $ |
|---|---|---|---|---|---|---|---|---|
| Australia | 1.5738 | 2.2809 | 1.3572 | 0.0175 | 0.2030 | 2.0154 | 1.2835 | — |
| Canada | 1.2262 | 1.7771 | 1.0574 | 0.0136 | 0.1581 | 1.5702 | — | 0.7791 |
| European Union | 0.7809 | 1.1318 | 0.6734 | 0.0087 | 0.1007 | — | 0.6368 | 0.4962 |
| Hong Kong | 7.7542 | 11.238 | 6.6870 | 0.0863 | — | 9.9298 | 6.3238 | 4.9271 |
| Japan | 89.839 | 130.20 | 77.474 | — | 11.586 | 115.05 | 73.266 | 57.084 |
| Switzerland | 1.1596 | 1.6806 | — | 0.0129 | 0.1495 | 1.4850 | 0.9457 | 0.7368 |
| United Kingdom | 0.6900 | — | 0.5950 | 0.0077 | 0.0890 | 0.8836 | 0.5627 | 0.4384 |
| United States | — | 1.4493 | 0.8624 | 0.0111 | 0.1290 | 1.2806 | 0.8155 | 0.6354 |

| Country | Currency | U.S. $ Equiv. |
|---|---|---|
| Gabon | Community of French Africa (CFA) franc | .0020 |
| Gambia | dalasy | .0387 |
| Georgia | lari | .6003 |
| Germany | euro | 1.2806 |
| Ghana | cedi | .7461 |
| Gibraltar | pound | 1.4493 |
| Great Britain | pound | 1.4493 |
| Alderney | pound | 1.4493 |
| Guernsey | pound | 1.4493 |
| Jersey | pound | 1.4493 |
| Isle of Man | pound | 1.4493 |
| Greece | euro | 1.2806 |
| Greenland | Danish krone | .1718 |
| Grenada | East Caribbean dollar | .3724 |
| Grenada Grenadines | East Caribbean dollar | .3724 |
| Guatemala | quetzal | .1259 |
| Guinea | franc | .0002 |
| Guinea-Bissau | CFA franc | .0020 |
| Guyana | dollar | .0049 |
| Haiti | gourde | .0252 |
| Honduras | lempira | .0530 |
| Hong Kong | dollar | .1290 |
| Hungary | forint | .0043 |
| Iceland | krona | .0088 |
| India | rupee | .0205 |
| Indonesia | rupiah | .0001 |
| Iraq | dinar | .0009 |
| Ireland | euro | 1.2806 |
| Israel | shekel | .2461 |
| Italy | euro | 1.2806 |
| Ivory Coast | CFA franc | .0020 |

*Source: **Wall Street Journal** Jan. 31, 2009. Figures reflect values as of Jan. 30, 2009.*

# scott**mounts**

For stamp presentation unequaled in beauty and clarity, insist on ScottMounts. Made of 100% inert polystyrol foil, ScottMounts protect your stamps from the harmful effects of dust and moisture. Available in your choice of clear or black backs, ScottMounts are center-split across the back for easy insertion of stamps and feature crystal clear mount faces. Double layers of gum assure stay-put bonding on the album page. Discover the quality and value ScottMounts have to offer. ScottMounts are available from your favorite stamp dealer or direct from:

**SCOTT.**

Scott Publishing Co.
1-800-572-6885
P.O. Box 828 Sidney OH 45365-0828
www.amosadvantage.com

Discover the quality and value ScottMounts have to offer.
For a complete list of ScottMount sizes visit www.amosadvantage.com

## AMOS
PUBLISHING

Publishers of:
Coin World, Linn's Stamp News and Scott Publishing Co.

# COMMON DESIGN TYPES

Pictured in this section are issues where one illustration has been used for a number of countries in the Catalogue. Not included in this section are overprinted stamps or those issues which are illustrated in each country.

## EUROPA
### Europa, 1956

The design symbolizing the cooperation among the six countries comprising the Coal and Steel Community is illustrated in each country.

Belgium.................................496-497
France..................................805-806
Germany...............................748-749
Italy......................................715-716
Luxembourg..........................318-320
Netherlands...........................368-369

### Europa, 1958

"E" and
Dove — CD1

European Postal Union at the service of European integration.

#### 1958, Sept. 13

Belgium.................................527-528
France..................................889-890
Germany...............................790-791
Italy......................................750-751
Luxembourg..........................341-343
Netherlands...........................375-376
Saar.....................................317-318

### Europa, 1959

6-Link Enless
Chain — CD2

#### 1959, Sept. 19

Belgium.................................536-537
France..................................929-930
Germany...............................805-806
Italy......................................791-792
Luxembourg..........................354-355
Netherlands...........................379-380

### Europa, 1960

19-Spoke
Wheel
CD3

First anniverary of the establishment of C.E.P.T. (Conference Europeenne des Administrations des Postes et des Telecommunications.) The spokes symbolize the 19 founding members of the Conference.

#### 1960, Sept.

Belgium.................................553-554
Denmark........................................379
Finland..................................376-377
France..................................970-971
Germany...............................818-820
Great Britain.........................377-378
Greece..........................................688
Iceland.................................327-328

Ireland..................................175-176
Italy......................................809-810
Luxembourg..........................374-375
Netherlands...........................385-386
Norway..........................................387
Portugal................................866-867
Spain....................................941-942
Sweden.................................562-563
Switzerland...........................400-401
Turkey.............................1493-1494

### Europa, 1961

19 Doves
Flying as
One — CD4

The 19 doves represent the 19 members of the Conference of European Postal and Telecommunications Administrations C.E.P.T.

#### 1961-62

Belgium.................................572-573
Cyprus..................................201-203
France.............................1005-1006
Germany...............................844-845
Great Britain.........................383-384
Greece..................................718-719
Iceland.................................340-341
Italy......................................845-846
Luxembourg..........................382-383
Netherlands...........................387-388
Spain...............................1010-1011
Switzerland...........................410-411
Turkey.............................1518-1520

### Europa, 1962

Young Tree
with 19
Leaves
CD5

The 19 leaves represent the 19 original members of C.E.P.T.

#### 1962-63

Belgium.................................582-583
Cyprus..................................219-221
France.............................1045-1046
Germany...............................852-853
Greece..................................739-740
Iceland.................................348-349
Ireland..................................184-185
Italy......................................860-861
Luxembourg..........................386-387
Netherlands...........................394-395
Norway.................................414-415
Switzerland...........................416-417
Turkey.............................1553-1555

### Europa, 1963

Stylized
Links,
Symbolizing
Unity — CD6

#### 1963, Sept.

Belgium.................................598-599
Cyprus..................................229-231
Finland..........................................419
France.............................1074-1075
Germany...............................867-868
Greece..................................768-769
Iceland.................................357-358
Ireland..................................188-189
Italy......................................880-881
Luxembourg..........................403-404
Netherlands...........................416-417
Norway.................................441-442
Switzerland...................................429
Turkey.............................1602-1603

### Europa, 1964

Symbolic
Daisy — CD7

5th anniversary of the establishment of C.E.P.T. The 22 petals of the flower symbolize the 22 members of the Conference.

#### 1964, Sept.

Austria..........................................738
Belgium.................................614-615
Cyprus..................................244-246
France.............................1109-1110
Germany...............................897-898
Greece..................................801-802
Iceland.................................367-368
Ireland..................................196-197
Italy......................................894-895
Luxembourg..........................411-412
Monaco.................................590-591
Netherlands...........................428-429
Norway..........................................458
Portugal................................931-933
Spain...............................1262-1263
Switzerland...........................438-439
Turkey.............................1628-1629

### Europa, 1965

Leaves and
"Fruit"
CD8

#### 1965

Belgium.................................636-637
Cyprus..................................262-264
Finland..........................................437
France.............................1131-1132
Germany...............................934-935
Greece..................................833-834
Iceland.................................375-376
Ireland..................................204-205
Italy......................................915-916
Luxembourg..........................432-433
Monaco.................................616-617
Netherlands...........................438-439
Norway.................................475-476
Portugal................................958-960
Switzerland...................................469
Turkey.............................1665-1666

### Europa, 1966

Symbolic
Sailboat — CD9

#### 1966, Sept.

Andorra, French.............................172
Belgium.................................675-676
Cyprus..................................275-277
France.............................1163-1164
Germany...............................963-964
Greece..................................862-863
Iceland.................................384-385
Ireland..................................216-217
Italy......................................942-943
Liechtenstein................................415
Luxembourg..........................440-441
Monaco.................................639-640
Netherlands...........................441-442
Norway.................................496-497
Portugal................................980-982
Switzerland...........................477-478
Turkey.............................1718-1719

### Europa, 1967

Cogwheels
CD10

#### 1967

Andorra, French.....................174-175
Belgium.................................688-689
Cyprus..................................297-299
France.............................1178-1179
Germany...............................969-970
Greece..................................891-892
Iceland.................................389-390
Ireland..................................232-233
Italy......................................951-952
Liechtenstein................................420
Luxembourg..........................449-450
Monaco.................................669-670
Netherlands...........................444-447
Norway.................................504-505
Portugal................................994-996
Spain...............................1465-1466
Switzerland...................................482
Turkey...........................B120-B121

### Europa, 1968

Golden Key
with
C.E.P.T.
Emblem
CD11

#### 1968

Andorra, French.....................182-183
Belgium.................................705-706
Cyprus..................................314-316
France.............................1209-1210
Germany...............................983-984
Greece..................................916-917
Iceland.................................395-396
Ireland..................................242-243
Italy......................................979-980
Liechtenstein................................442
Luxembourg..........................466-467
Monaco.................................689-691
Netherlands...........................452-453
Portugal.............................1019-1021
San Marino....................................687
Spain.........................................1526
Turkey.............................1775-1776

### Europa, 1969

"EUROPA"
and "CEPT"
CD12

Tenth anniversary of C.E.P.T.

#### 1969

Andorra, French.....................188-189
Austria..........................................837
Belgium.................................718-719
Cyprus..................................326-328
Denmark.......................................458
Finland..........................................483
France.............................1245-1246
Germany...............................996-997
Great Britain.................................585
Greece..................................947-948
Iceland.................................406-407
Ireland..................................270-271
Italy..................................1000-1001
Liechtenstein................................453
Luxembourg..........................474-475
Monaco.................................722-724
Netherlands...........................475-476
Norway.................................533-534
Portugal.............................1038-1040
San Marino...........................701-702
Spain.........................................1567
Sweden.................................814-816

Switzerland................................500-501
Turkey...................................1799-1800
Vatican.....................................470-472
Yugoslavia ...........................1003-1004

### Europa, 1970

Interwoven Threads CD13

### 1970

Andorra, French ......................196-197
Belgium....................................741-742
Cyprus .....................................340-342
France.................................1271-1272
Germany..............................1018-1019
Greece ..............................985, 987
Iceland.....................................420-421
Ireland......................................279-281
Italy.....................................1013-1014
Liechtenstein ...............................470
Luxembourg..............................489-490
Monaco.....................................768-770
Netherlands...............................483-484
Portugal ...............................1060-1062
San Marino................................729-730
Spain ........................................1607
Switzerland................................515-516
Turkey ...................................1848-1849
Yugoslavia ...........................1024-1025

### Europa, 1971

"Fraternity, Cooperation, Common Effort" CD14

### 1971

Andorra, French ......................205-206
Belgium....................................803-804
Cyprus .....................................365-367
Finland........................................504
France.........................................1304
Germany..............................1064-1065
Greece ...............................1029-1030
Iceland.....................................429-430
Ireland......................................305-306
Italy.....................................1038-1039
Liechtenstein ...............................485
Luxembourg..............................500-501
Malta........................................425-427
Monaco.....................................797-799
Netherlands...............................488-489
Portugal ...............................1094-1096
San Marino................................749-750
Spain ...................................1675-1676
Switzerland................................531-532
Turkey ...................................1876-1877
Yugoslavia ...........................1052-1053

### Europa, 1972

Sparkles, Symbolic of Communications CD15

### 1972

Andorra, French ......................210-211
Andorra, Spanish ............................62
Belgium....................................825-826
Cyprus .....................................380-382
Finland......................................512-513
France.........................................1341
Germany..............................1089-1090
Greece ...............................1049-1050
Iceland.....................................439-440
Ireland......................................316-317
Italy.....................................1065-1066
Liechtenstein ...............................504
Luxembourg..............................512-513
Malta........................................450-453
Monaco.....................................831-832

Netherlands...............................494-495
Portugal ...............................1141-1143
San Marino................................771-772
Spain .........................................1718
Switzerland................................544-545
Turkey ...................................1907-1908
Yugoslavia ...........................1100-1101

### Europa, 1973

Post Horn and Arrows CD16

### 1973

Andorra, French ......................219-220
Andorra, Spanish ............................76
Belgium....................................839-840
Cyprus .....................................396-398
Finland.........................................526
France.........................................1367
Germany..............................1114-1115
Greece ...............................1090-1092
Iceland.....................................447-448
Ireland......................................329-330
Italy.....................................1108-1109
Liechtenstein ...........................528-529
Luxembourg..............................523-524
Malta........................................469-471
Monaco.....................................866-867
Netherlands...............................504-505
Norway......................................604-605
Portugal ...............................1170-1172
San Marino................................802-803
Spain .........................................1753
Switzerland................................580-581
Turkey ...................................1935-1936
Yugoslavia ...........................1138-1139

### Europa, 2000

CD17

### 2000

Albania..................................2621-2622
Andorra, French ...........................522
Andorra, Spanish ...........................262
Armenia...................................610-611
Austria.........................................1814
Azerbaijan...............................698-699
Belarus........................................350
Belgium........................................1818
Bosnia & Herzegovina (Moslem) ....358
Bosnia & Herzegovina (Serb) ........111-112
Croatia.....................................428-429
Cyprus.........................................959
Czech Republic ..........................3120
Denmark......................................1189
Estonia.........................................394
Faroe Islands................................376
Finland.........................................1129
Aland Islands................................166
France.........................................2771
Georgia....................................228-229
Germany...............................2086-2087
Gibraltar..................................837-840
Great Britain (Guernsey)..........805-809
Great Britain (Jersey)..............935-936
Great Britain (Isle of Man) ............883
Greece .........................................1959
Greenland.....................................363
Hungary.................................3699-3700
Iceland.........................................910
Ireland....................................1230-1231
Italy.........................................2349
Latvia.........................................504
Liechtenstein .............................1178
Lithuania......................................668
Luxembourg.................................1035
Macedonia....................................187
Malta.....................................1011-1012
Moldova........................................355
Monaco...................................2161-2162
Poland.........................................3519
Portugal .......................................2358
Portugal (Azores)...........................455
Portugal (Madeira)..........................208

Romania.......................................4370
Russia.........................................6589
San Marino...................................1480
Slovakia.........................................355
Slovenia........................................424
Spain .........................................3036
Sweden.........................................2394
Switzerland...................................1074
Turkey .........................................2762
Turkish Rep. of Northern Cyprus....500
Ukraine.........................................379
Vatican City ...................................1152

The Gibraltar stamps are similar to the stamp illustrated, but none have the design shown above. All other sets listed above include at least one stamp with the design shown, but some include stamps with entirely different designs. Bulgaria Nos. 4131-4132 and Yugoslavia Nos. 2485-2486 are Europa stamps with completely different designs.

### PORTUGAL & COLONIES
#### Vasco da Gama

Fleet Departing CD20

Fleet Arriving at Calicut — CD21

Embarking at Rastello CD22

Muse of History CD23

San Gabriel, da Gama and Camoens CD24

Archangel Gabriel, the Patron Saint CD25

Flagship San Gabriel — CD26

Vasco da Gama — CD27

Fourth centenary of Vasco da Gama's discovery of the route to India.

### 1898

Azores ....................................93-100
Macao.......................................67-74
Madeira.....................................37-44
Portugal ................................147-154
Port. Africa....................................1-8
Port. Congo...............................75-98
Port. India...............................189-196
St. Thomas & Prince Islands ...170-193
Timor........................................45-52

#### Pombal
#### POSTAL TAX
#### POSTAL TAX DUES

Marquis de Pombal — CD28

Planning Reconstruction of Lisbon, 1755 — CD29

Pombal Monument, Lisbon — CD30

Sebastiao Jose de Carvalho e Mello, Marquis de Pombal (1699-1782), statesman, rebuilt Lisbon after earthquake of 1755. Tax was for the erection of Pombal monument. Obligatory on all mail on certain days throughout the year. Postal Tax Dues are inscribed "Multa."

### 1925

Angola ............. RA1-RA3, RAJ1-RAJ3
Azores ........... RA9-RA11, RAJ2-RAJ4
Cape Verde ...... RA1-RA3, RAJ1-RAJ3
Macao.............. RA1-RA3, RAJ1-RAJ3
Madeira............. RA1-RA3, RAJ1-RAJ3
Mozambique..... RA1-RA3, RAJ1-RAJ3
Nyassa.............. RA1-RA3, RAJ1-RAJ3
Portugal ....... RA11-RA13, RAJ2-RAJ4
Port. Guinea ..... RA1-RA3, RAJ1-RAJ3
Port. India........ RA1-RA3, RAJ1-RAJ3
St. Thomas & Prince
Islands ............. RA1-RA3, RAJ1-RAJ3
Timor ............... RA1-RA3, RAJ1-RAJ3

Vasco da Gama CD34

Mousinho de Albuquerque CD35

Dam CD36

Prince Henry the Navigator CD37

Affonso de Albuquerque CD38

Plane over Globe CD39

### 1938-39

Angola .........................274-291, C1-C9
Cape Verde .................234-251, C1-C9
Macao.......................289-305, C7-C15
Mozambique.................270-287, C1-C9
Port. Guinea .................233-250. C1-C9
Port. India...................439-453, C1-C8
St. Thomas & Prince
Islands ... 302-319, 323-340, C1-C18
Timor.........................223-239, C1-C9

### Lady of Fatima

Our Lady of the Rosary, Fatima, Portugal — CD40

**1948-49**

Angola .....................................315-318
Cape Verde ....................................266
Macao...........................................336
Mozambique..............................325-328
Port. Guinea ...................................271
Port. India ....................................480
St. Thomas & Prince Islands .........351
Timor ..........................................254

A souvenir sheet of 9 stamps was issued in 1951 to mark the extension of the 1950 Holy Year. The sheet contains: Angola No. 316, Cape Verde No. 266, Macao No. 336, Mozambique No. 325, Portuguese Guinea No. 271, Portuguese India Nos. 480, 485, St. Thomas & Prince Islands No. 351, Timor No. 254. The sheet also contains a portrait of Pope Pius XII and is inscribed "Encerramento do Ano Santo, Fatima 1951." It was sold for 11 escudos.

### Holy Year

Church Bells and Dove CD41

Angel Holding Candelabra CD42

Holy Year, 1950.

**1950-51**

Angola .....................................331-332
Cape Verde ...............................268-269
Macao.......................................339-340
Mozambique..............................330-331
Port. Guinea ...............................273-274
Port. India ...............490-491, 496-503
St. Thomas & Prince Islands ...353-354
Timor .......................................258-259

A souvenir sheet of 8 stamps was issued in 1951 to mark the extension of the Holy Year. The sheet contains: Angola No. 331, Cape Verde No. 269, Macao No. 340, Mozambique No. 331, Portuguese Guinea No. 275, Portuguese India No. 490, St. Thomas & Prince Islands No. 354, Timor No. 258, some with colors changed. The sheet contains doves and is inscribed 'Encerramento do Ano Santo, Fatima 1951.' It was sold for 17 escudos.

### Holy Year Conclusion

Our Lady of Fatima — CD43

Conclusion of Holy Year. Sheets contain alternate vertical rows of stamps and labels bearing quotation from Pope Pius XII, different for each colony.

**1951**

Angola ..........................................357
Cape Verde ....................................270
Macao...........................................352
Mozambique....................................356
Port. Guinea ...................................275
Port. India ....................................506
St. Thomas & Prince Islands .........355
Timor ..........................................270

### Medical Congress

CD44

First National Congress of Tropical Medicine, Lisbon, 1952. Each stamp has a different design.

**1952**

Angola ..........................................358
Cape Verde ....................................287
Macao...........................................364
Mozambique....................................359
Port. Guinea ...................................276
Port. India ....................................516
St. Thomas & Prince Islands .........356
Timor ..........................................271

### Postage Due Stamps

CD45

**1952**

Angola .....................................J37-J42
Cape Verde ..............................J31-J36
Macao.......................................J53-J58
Mozambique..............................J51-J56
Port. Guinea ...............................J40-J45
Port. India ...............................J47-J52
St. Thomas & Prince Islands ...J52-J57
Timor .......................................J31-J36

### Sao Paulo

Father Manuel da Nobrega and View of Sao Paulo — CD46

Founding of Sao Paulo, Brazil, 400th anniv.

**1954**

Angola ..........................................385
Cape Verde ....................................297
Macao...........................................382
Mozambique....................................395
Port. Guinea ...................................291
Port. India ....................................530
St. Thomas & Prince Islands .........369
Timor ..........................................279

### Tropical Medicine Congress

CD47

Sixth International Congress for Tropical Medicine and Malaria, Lisbon, Sept. 1958. Each stamp shows a different plant.

**1958**

Angola ..........................................409
Cape Verde ....................................303
Macao...........................................392
Mozambique....................................404
Port. Guinea ...................................295
Port. India ....................................569
St. Thomas & Prince Islands .........371
Timor ..........................................289

### Sports

CD48

Each stamp shows a different sport.

**1962**

Angola .....................................433-438
Cape Verde ...............................320-325
Macao.......................................394-399
Mozambique..............................424-429
Port. Guinea ...............................299-304
St. Thomas & Prince Islands ...374-379
Timor .......................................313-318

### Anti-Malaria

Anopheles Funestus and Malaria Eradication Symbol — CD49

World Health Organization drive to eradicate malaria.

**1962**

Angola ..........................................439
Cape Verde ....................................326
Macao...........................................400
Mozambique....................................430
Port. Guinea ...................................305
St. Thomas & Prince Islands .........380
Timor ..........................................319

### Airline Anniversary

Map of Africa, Super Constellation and Jet Liner — CD50

Tenth anniversary of Transportes Aereos Portugueses (TAP).

**1963**

Angola ..........................................490
Cape Verde ....................................327
Mozambique....................................434
Port. Guinea ...................................318
St. Thomas & Prince Islands .........381

### National Overseas Bank

Antonio Teixeira de Sousa — CD51

Centenary of the National Overseas Bank of Portugal.

**1964, May 16**

Angola ..........................................509
Cape Verde ....................................328
Port. Guinea ...................................319
St. Thomas & Prince Islands .........382
Timor ..........................................320

### ITU

ITU Emblem and the Archangel Gabriel — CD52

International Communications Union, Cent.

**1965, May 17**

Angola ..........................................511
Cape Verde ....................................329
Macao...........................................402
Mozambique....................................464
Port. Guinea ...................................320
St. Thomas & Prince Islands .........383
Timor ..........................................321

### National Revolution

CD53

40th anniv. of the National Revolution. Different buildings on each stamp.

**1966, May 28**

Angola ..........................................525
Cape Verde ....................................338
Macao...........................................403
Mozambique....................................465
Port. Guinea ...................................329
St. Thomas & Prince Islands .........392
Timor ..........................................322

### Navy Club

CD54

Centenary of Portugal's Navy Club. Each stamp has a different design.

**1967, Jan. 31**

Angola .....................................527-528
Cape Verde ...............................339-340
Macao.......................................412-413
Mozambique..............................478-479
Port. Guinea ...............................330-331
St. Thomas & Prince Islands ...393-394
Timor .......................................323-324

### Admiral Coutinho

CD55

Centenary of the birth of Admiral Carlos Viegas Gago Coutinho (1869-1959), explorer and aviation pioneer. Each stamp has a different design.

**1969, Feb. 17**

Angola ..........................................547
Cape Verde ....................................355
Macao...........................................417
Mozambique....................................484
Port. Guinea ...................................335
St. Thomas & Prince Islands .........397
Timor ..........................................335

### Administration Reform

Luiz Augusto Rebello da Silva — CD56

Centenary of the administration reforms of the overseas territories.

**1969, Sept. 25**

Angola .............................................549
Cape Verde ....................................357
Macao .............................................419
Mozambique ...................................491
Port. Guinea ...................................337
St. Thomas & Prince Islands .........399
Timor ..............................................338

### Marshal Carmona

CD57

Birth centenary of Marshal Antonio Oscar Carmona de Fragoso (1869-1951), President of Portugal. Each stamp has a different design.

**1970, Nov. 15**

Angola .............................................563
Cape Verde ....................................359
Macao .............................................422
Mozambique ...................................493
Port. Guinea ...................................340
St. Thomas & Prince Islands .........403
Timor ..............................................341

### Olympic Games

CD59

20th Olympic Games, Munich, Aug. 26-Sept. 11. Each stamp shows a different sport.

**1972, June 20**

Angola .............................................569
Cape Verde ....................................361
Macao .............................................426
Mozambique ...................................504
Port. Guinea ...................................342
St. Thomas & Prince Islands .........408
Timor ..............................................343

### Lisbon-Rio de Janeiro Flight

CD60

50th anniversary of the Lisbon to Rio de Janeiro flight by Arturo de Sacadura and Coutinho, March 30-June 5, 1922. Each stamp shows a different stage of the flight.

**1972, Sept. 20**

Angola .............................................570
Cape Verde ....................................362
Macao .............................................427
Mozambique ...................................505
Port. Guinea ...................................343
St. Thomas & Prince Islands .........409
Timor ..............................................344

### WMO Centenary

WMO Emblem — CD61

Centenary of international meterological cooperation.

**1973, Dec. 15**

Angola .............................................571
Cape Verde ....................................363
Macao .............................................429
Mozambique ...................................509
Port. Guinea ...................................344
St. Thomas & Prince Islands .........410
Timor ..............................................345

### FRENCH COMMUNITY
**Upper Volta can be found under Burkina Faso in Vol. 1**
**Madagascar can be found under Malagasy in Vol. 3**
### Colonial Exposition

People of French Empire CD70

Women's Heads CD71

France Showing Way to Civilization CD72

"Colonial Commerce" CD73

International Colonial Exposition, Paris.

**1931**

Cameroun ...............................213-216
Chad .........................................60-63
Dahomey ................................97-100
Fr. Guiana .............................152-155
Fr. Guinea .............................116-119
Fr. India ................................100-103
Fr. Polynesia ...........................76-79
Fr. Sudan ..............................102-105
Gabon ...................................120-123
Guadeloupe ..........................138-141
Indo-China ............................140-142
Ivory Coast .............................92-95
Madagascar ..........................169-172
Martinique .............................129-132
Mauritania ...............................65-68
Middle Congo ..........................61-64
New Caledonia .......................176-179
Niger ........................................73-76
Reunion .................................122-125
St. Pierre & Miquelon ...........132-135
Senegal .................................138-141
Somali Coast .........................135-138
Togo .......................................254-257
Ubangi-Shari ............................82-85
Upper Volta ..............................66-69
Wallis & Futuna Isls. ...............85-88

### Paris International Exposition
### Colonial Arts Exposition

"Colonial Resources"
CD74          CD77

Overseas Commerce CD75

Exposition Building and Women CD76

"France and the Empire" CD78

Cultural Treasures of the Colonies CD79

Souvenir sheets contain one imperf. stamp.

**1937**

Cameroun ..............................217-222A
Dahomey ................................101-107
Fr. Equatorial Africa ..............27-32, 73
Fr. Guiana .............................162-168
Fr. Guinea .............................120-126
Fr. India ................................104-110
Fr. Polynesia .........................117-123
Fr. Sudan ..............................106-112
Guadeloupe ..........................148-154
Indo-China ............................193-199
Inini ..............................................41
Ivory Coast ...........................152-158
Kwangchowan .............................132
Madagascar ..........................191-197
Martinique .............................179-185
Mauritania ................................69-75
New Caledonia .......................208-214
Niger ........................................72-83
Reunion .................................167-173
St. Pierre & Miquelon ...........165-171
Senegal .................................172-178
Somali Coast .........................139-145
Togo .......................................258-264
Wallis & Futuna Isls. ..................89

### Curie

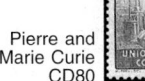

Pierre and Marie Curie CD80

40th anniversary of the discovery of radium. The surtax was for the benefit of the Intl. Union for the Control of Cancer.

**1938**

Cameroun ........................................ B1
Cuba ...........................................B1-B2
Dahomey ......................................... B2
France ...........................................B76
Fr. Equatorial Africa ...................... B1
Fr. Guiana ....................................... B3
Fr. Guinea ....................................... B2
Fr. India ......................................... B6
Fr. Polynesia .................................. B5
Fr. Sudan ........................................ B1
Guadeloupe .................................... B3

Indo-China ..................................... B14
Ivory Coast ..................................... B2
Madagascar .................................... B2
Martinique ...................................... B2
Mauritania ...................................... B3
New Caledonia ................................ B4
Niger ............................................... B1
Reunion .......................................... B4
St. Pierre & Miquelon ..................... B3
Senegal ........................................... B3
Somali Coast .................................. B2
Togo ................................................ B1

### Caillie

Rene Caillie and Map of Northwestern Africa — CD81

Death centenary of Rene Caillie (1799-1838), French explorer. All three denominations exist with colony name omitted.

**1939**

Dahomey ................................108-110
Fr. Guinea .............................161-163
Fr. Sudan ..............................113-115
Ivory Coast ...........................160-162
Mauritania .............................109-111
Niger ........................................84-86
Senegal .................................188-190
Togo .......................................265-267

### New York World's Fair

Natives and New York Skyline CD82

**1939**

Cameroun ...............................223-224
Dahomey ................................111-112
Fr. Equatorial Africa .................78-79
Fr. Guiana .............................169-170
Fr. Guinea .............................164-165
Fr. India ................................111-112
Fr. Polynesia .........................124-125
Fr. Sudan ..............................116-117
Guadeloupe ..........................155-156
Indo-China ............................203-204
Inini .........................................42-43
Ivory Coast ...........................163-164
Kwangchowan .......................121-122
Madagascar ..........................209-210
Martinique .............................186-187
Mauritania .............................112-113
New Caledonia .......................215-216
Niger ........................................87-88
Reunion .................................174-175
St. Pierre & Miquelon ...........205-206
Senegal .................................191-192
Somali Coast .........................179-180
Togo .......................................268-269
Wallis & Futuna Isls. ...............90-91

### French Revolution

Storming of the Bastille CD83

French Revolution, 150th anniv. The surtax was for the defense of the colonies.

**1939**

Cameroun ..................................B2-B6
Dahomey ...................................B3-B7
Fr. Equatorial Africa ..........B4-B8, CB1
Fr. Guiana ........................B4-B8, CB1
Fr. Guinea .................................B3-B7
Fr. India ..................................B7-B11
Fr. Polynesia ..................B6-B10, CB1
Fr. Sudan ..................................B2-B6
Guadeloupe ..............................B4-B8
Indo-China ...................B15-B19, CB1
Inini ...........................................B1-B5
Ivory Coast ...............................B3-B7

Kwangchowan ...........................B1-B5
Madagascar ...................B3-B7, CB1
Martinique ............................B3-B7
Mauritania ...........................B4-B8
New Caledonia .................B5-B9, CB1
Niger .................................B2-B6
Reunion .........................B5-B9, CB1
St. Pierre & Miquelon..............B4-B8
Senegal ........................B4-B8, CB1
Somali Coast .......................B3-B7
Togo .................................B2-B6
Wallis & Futuna Isls. ...............B1-B5

Plane over Coastal Area CD85

All five denominations exist with colony name omitted.

### 1940

Dahomey ...............................C1-C5
Fr. Guinea ..............................C1-C5
Fr. Sudan ...............................C1-C5
Ivory Coast ............................C1-C5
Mauritania .............................C1-C5
Niger.....................................C1-C5
Senegal ............................C12-C16
Togo......................................C1-C5

### Defense of the Empire

Colonial Infantryman — CD86

### 1941

Cameroun...................................B13B
Dahomey ..................................B13
Fr. Equatorial Africa .....................B8B
Fr. Guiana ................................B10
Fr. Guinea ................................B13
Fr. India ..................................B13
Fr. Polynesia .............................B12
Fr. Sudan ................................B12
Guadeloupe ...............................B10
Indo-China ..............................B19B
Inini .......................................B7
Ivory Coast ...............................B13
Kwangchowan .............................B7
Madagascar ...............................B9
Martinique ................................B9
Mauritania ...............................B14
New Caledonia ...........................B11
Niger .....................................B12
Reunion ...................................B11
St. Pierre & Miquelon....................B8B
Senegal ...................................B14
Somali Coast ..............................B9
Togo......................................B10B
Wallis & Futuna Isls. ......................B7

### Colonial Education Fund

CD86a

### 1942

Cameroun....................................CB3
Dahomey ...................................CB4
Fr. Equatorial Africa ......................CB5
Fr. Guiana ................................CB4
Fr. Guinea ................................CB4

Fr. India ...................................CB3
Fr. Polynesia .............................CB4
Fr. Sudan ................................CB4
Guadeloupe ...............................CB3
Indo-China ...............................CB5
Inini ......................................CB3
Ivory Coast ...............................CB4
Kwangchowan .............................CB4
Malagasy ..................................CB5
Martinique ................................CB3
Mauritania ...............................CB4
New Caledonia ............................CB4
Niger .....................................CB4
Reunion ...................................CB4
St. Pierre & Miquelon.....................CB3
Senegal ...................................CB5
Somali Coast .............................CB3
Togo......................................CB3
Wallis & Futuna ..........................CB3

Cross of Lorraine & Four-motor Plane CD87

### 1941-5

Cameroun................................C1-C7
Fr. Equatorial Africa .............C17-C23
Fr. Guiana ...........................C9-C10
Fr. India ...............................C1-C6
Fr. Polynesia .........................C3-C9
Fr. West Africa ......................C1-C3
Guadeloupe ...........................C1-C2
Madagascar.........................C37-C43
Martinique ............................C1-C2
New Caledonia ......................C7-C13
Reunion ............................C18-C24
St. Pierre & Miquelon...............C1-C7
Somali Coast.........................C1-C7

Transport Plane CD88

Caravan and Plane CD89

### 1942

Dahomey ...............................C6-C13
Fr. Guinea .............................C6-C13
Fr. Sudan .............................C6-C13
Ivory Coast ...........................C6-C13
Mauritania............................C6-C13
Niger ...................................C6-C13
Senegal .............................C17-C25
Togo.....................................C6-C13

### Red Cross

Marianne CD90

The surtax was for the French Red Cross and national relief.

### 1944

Cameroun...................................B28
Fr. Equatorial Africa ......................B38
Fr. Guiana ................................B12
Fr. India ..................................B14
Fr. Polynesia .............................B13
Fr. West Africa ............................B1
Guadeloupe ...............................B12
Madagascar ...............................B15
Martinique ................................B11
New Caledonia ............................B13
Reunion ...................................B15
St. Pierre & Miquelon.....................B13
Somali Coast ..............................B13

Wallis & Futuna Isls. ......................B9

### Eboue

CD91

Felix Eboue, first French colonial administrator to proclaim resistance to Germany after French surrender in World War II.

### 1945

Cameroun................................296-297
Fr. Equatorial Africa ...............156-157
Fr. Guiana ...........................171-172
Fr. India ..............................210-211
Fr. Polynesia.........................150-151
Fr. West Africa ........................15-16
Guadeloupe ..........................187-188
Madagascar..........................259-260
Martinique ...........................196-197
New Caledonia .......................274-275
Reunion .............................238-239
St. Pierre & Miquelon...............322-323
Somali Coast.........................238-239

### Victory

Victory — CD92

European victory of the Allied Nations in World War II.

### 1946, May 8

Cameroun......................................C8
Fr. Equatorial Africa .......................C24
Fr. Guiana ..................................C11
Fr. India .....................................C7
Fr. Polynesia.................................C10
Fr. West Africa ...............................C4
Guadeloupe ...................................C3
Indo-China ..................................C19
Madagascar..................................C44
Martinique ....................................C3
New Caledonia ...............................C14
Reunion .....................................C25
St. Pierre & Miquelon........................C8
Somali Coast..................................C8
Wallis & Futuna Isls. .........................C1

### Chad to Rhine

Leclerc's Departure from Chad — CD93

Battle at Cufra Oasis — CD94

Tanks in Action, Mareth — CD95

Normandy Invasion — CD96

Entering Paris — CD97

Liberation of Strasbourg — CD98

"Chad to the Rhine" march, 1942-44, by Gen. Jacques Leclerc's column, later French 2nd Armored Division.

### 1946, June 6

Cameroun.................................C9-C14
Fr. Equatorial Africa ...............C25-C30
Fr. Guiana ...........................C12-C17
Fr. India .............................C8-C13
Fr. Polynesia........................C11-C16
Fr. West Africa .....................C5-C10
Guadeloupe ...........................C4-C9
Indo-China ..........................C20-C25
Madagascar..........................C45-C50
Martinique ...........................C4-C9
New Caledonia ......................C15-C20
Reunion ............................C26-C31
St. Pierre & Miquelon...............C9-C14
Somali Coast.........................C9-C14
Wallis & Futuna Isls. ................C2-C7

### UPU

French Colonials, Globe and Plane — CD99

Universal Postal Union, 75th anniv.

### 1949, July 4

Cameroun.....................................C29
Fr. Equatorial Africa .......................C34
Fr. India ....................................C17
Fr. Polynesia.................................C20
Fr. West Africa ..............................C15
Indo-China ..................................C26
Madagascar..................................C55
New Caledonia ...............................C24
St. Pierre & Miquelon........................C18
Somali Coast.................................C18
Togo.........................................C18
Wallis & Futuna Isls. ........................C10

## Tropical Medicine

Doctor Treating Infant CD100

The surtax was for charitable work.

### 1950

| | |
|---|---|
| Cameroun | B29 |
| Fr. Equatorial Africa | B39 |
| Fr. India | B15 |
| Fr. Polynesia | B14 |
| Fr. West Africa | B3 |
| Madagascar | B17 |
| New Caledonia | B14 |
| St. Pierre & Miquelon | B14 |
| Somali Coast | B14 |
| Togo | B11 |

## Military Medal

Medal, Early Marine and Colonial Soldier — CD101

Centenary of the creation of the French Military Medal.

### 1952

| | |
|---|---|
| Cameroun | 332 |
| Comoro Isls. | 39 |
| Fr. Equatorial Africa | 186 |
| Fr. India | 233 |
| Fr. Polynesia | 179 |
| Fr. West Africa | 57 |
| Madagascar | 286 |
| New Caledonia | 295 |
| St. Pierre & Miquelon | 345 |
| Somali Coast | 267 |
| Togo | 327 |
| Wallis & Futuna Isls. | 149 |

## Liberation

Allied Landing, Victory Sign and Cross of Lorraine — CD102

Liberation of France, 10th anniv.

### 1954, June 6

| | |
|---|---|
| Cameroun | C32 |
| Comoro Isls. | C4 |
| Fr. Equatorial Africa | C38 |
| Fr. India | C18 |
| Fr. Polynesia | C22 |
| Fr. West Africa | C17 |
| Madagascar | C57 |
| New Caledonia | C25 |
| St. Pierre & Miquelon | C19 |
| Somali Coast | C19 |
| Togo | C19 |
| Wallis & Futuna Isls. | C11 |

## FIDES

Plowmen CD103

Efforts of FIDES, the Economic and Social Development Fund for Overseas Possessions

(Fonds d' Investissement pour le Developpement Economique et Social). Each stamp has a different design.

### 1956

| | |
|---|---|
| Cameroun | 326-329 |
| Comoro Isls. | 43 |
| Fr. Equatorial Africa | 189-192 |
| Fr. Polynesia | 181 |
| Fr. West Africa | 65-72 |
| Madagascar | 292-295 |
| New Caledonia | 303 |
| St. Pierre & Miquelon 350 | |
| Somali Coast | 268 |
| Togo | 331 |

## Flower

CD104

Each stamp shows a different flower.

### 1958-9

| | |
|---|---|
| Cameroun | 333 |
| Comoro Isls. | 45 |
| Fr. Equatorial Africa | 200-201 |
| Fr. Polynesia | 192 |
| Fr. So. & Antarctic Terr. | 11 |
| Fr. West Africa | 79-83 |
| Madagascar | 301-302 |
| New Caledonia | 304-305 |
| St. Pierre & Miquelon | 357 |
| Somali Coast | 270 |
| Togo | 348-349 |
| Wallis & Futuna Isls. | 152 |

## Human Rights

Sun, Dove and U.N. Emblem CD105

10th anniversary of the signing of the Universal Declaration of Human Rights.

### 1958

| | |
|---|---|
| Comoro Isls. | 44 |
| Fr. Equatorial Africa | 202 |
| Fr. Polynesia | 191 |
| Fr. West Africa | 85 |
| Madagascar | 300 |
| New Caledonia | 306 |
| St. Pierre & Miquelon | 356 |
| Somali Coast | 274 |
| Wallis & Futuna Isls. | 153 |

## C.C.T.A.

CD106

Commission for Technical Cooperation in Africa south of the Sahara, 10th anniv.

### 1960

| | |
|---|---|
| Cameroun | 335 |
| Cent. Africa | 3 |
| Chad | 66 |
| Congo, P.R. | 90 |
| Dahomey | 138 |
| Gabon | 150 |
| Ivory Coast | 180 |
| Madagascar | 317 |
| Mali | 9 |
| Mauritania | 117 |
| Niger | 104 |
| Upper Volta | 89 |

## Air Afrique, 1961

Modern and Ancient Africa, Map and Planes — CD107

Founding of Air Afrique (African Airlines).

### 1961-62

| | |
|---|---|
| Cameroun | C37 |
| Cent. Africa | C5 |
| Chad | C7 |
| Congo, P.R. | C5 |
| Dahomey | C17 |
| Gabon | C5 |
| Ivory Coast | C18 |
| Mauritania | C17 |
| Niger | C22 |
| Senegal | C31 |
| Upper Volta | C4 |

## Anti-Malaria

CD108

World Health Organization drive to eradicate malaria.

### 1962, Apr. 7

| | |
|---|---|
| Cameroun | B36 |
| Cent. Africa | B1 |
| Chad | B1 |
| Comoro Isls. | B1 |
| Congo, P.R. | B3 |
| Dahomey | B15 |
| Gabon | B4 |
| Ivory Coast | B15 |
| Madagascar | B19 |
| Mali | B1 |
| Mauritania | B16 |
| Niger | B14 |
| Senegal | B16 |
| Somali Coast | B15 |
| Upper Volta | B1 |

## Abidjan Games

CD109

Abidjan Games, Ivory Coast, Dec. 24-31, 1961. Each stamp shows a different sport.

### 1962

| | |
|---|---|
| Chad | 83-84 |
| Cent. Africa | 19-20 |
| Congo, P.R. | 103-104 |
| Gabon | 163-164, C6 |
| Niger | 109-111 |
| Upper Volta | 103-105 |

## African and Malagasy Union

Flag of Union CD110

First anniversary of the Union.

### 1962, Sept. 8

| | |
|---|---|
| Cameroun | 373 |
| Cent. Africa | 21 |

| | |
|---|---|
| Chad | 85 |
| Congo, P.R. | 105 |
| Dahomey | 155 |
| Gabon | 165 |
| Ivory Coast | 198 |
| Madagascar | 332 |
| Mauritania | 170 |
| Niger | 112 |
| Senegal | 211 |
| Upper Volta | 106 |

## Telstar

Telstar and Globe Showing Andover and Pleumeur-Bodou — CD111

First television connection of the United States and Europe through the Telstar satellite, July 11-12, 1962.

### 1962-63

| | |
|---|---|
| Andorra, French | 154 |
| Comoro Isls. | C7 |
| Fr. Polynesia | C29 |
| Fr. So. & Antarctic Terr. | C5 |
| New Caledonia | C33 |
| Somali Coast | C31 |
| St. Pierre & Miquelon | C26 |
| Wallis & Futuna Isls. | C17 |

## Freedom From Hunger

World Map and Wheat Emblem CD112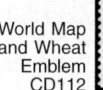

U.N. Food and Agriculture Organization's "Freedom from Hunger" campaign.

### 1963, Mar. 21

| | |
|---|---|
| Cameroun | B37-B38 |
| Cent. Africa | B2 |
| Chad | B2 |
| Congo, P.R. | B4 |
| Dahomey | B16 |
| Gabon | B5 |
| Ivory Coast | B16 |
| Madagascar | B21 |
| Mauritania | B17 |
| Niger | B15 |
| Senegal | B17 |
| Upper Volta | B2 |

## Red Cross Centenary

CD113

Centenary of the International Red Cross.

### 1963, Sept. 2

| | |
|---|---|
| Comoro Isls. | 55 |
| Fr. Polynesia | 205 |
| New Caledonia | 328 |
| St. Pierre & Miquelon | 367 |
| Somali Coast | 297 |
| Wallis & Futuna Isls. | 165 |

### African Postal Union, 1963

UAMPT Emblem, Radio Masts, Plane and Mail CD114

Establishment of the African and Malagasy Posts and Telecommunications Union.

**1963, Sept. 8**

| | |
|---|---|
| Cameroun | C47 |
| Cent. Africa | C10 |
| Chad | C9 |
| Congo, P.R. | C13 |
| Dahomey | C19 |
| Gabon | C13 |
| Ivory Coast | C25 |
| Madagascar | C75 |
| Mauritania | C22 |
| Niger | C27 |
| Rwanda | 36 |
| Senegal | C32 |
| Upper Volta | C9 |

### Air Afrique, 1963

Symbols of Flight — CD115

First anniversary of Air Afrique and inauguration of DC-8 service.

**1963, Nov. 19**

| | |
|---|---|
| Cameroun | C48 |
| Chad | C10 |
| Congo, P.R. | C14 |
| Gabon | C18 |
| Ivory Coast | C26 |
| Mauritania | C26 |
| Niger | C35 |
| Senegal | C33 |

### Europafrica

Europe and Africa Linked — CD116

Signing of an economic agreement between the European Economic Community and the African and Malagasy Union, Yaounde, Cameroun, July 20, 1963.

**1963-64**

| | |
|---|---|
| Cameroun | 402 |
| Chad | C11 |
| Cent. Africa | C12 |
| Congo, P.R. | C16 |
| Gabon | C19 |
| Ivory Coast | 217 |
| Niger | C43 |
| Upper Volta | C11 |

### Human Rights

Scales of Justice and Globe CD117

15th anniversary of the Universal Declaration of Human Rights.

**1963, Dec. 10**

| | |
|---|---|
| Comoro Isls. | 58 |
| Fr. Polynesia | 206 |
| New Caledonia | 329 |
| St. Pierre & Miquelon | 368 |
| Somali Coast | 300 |
| Wallis & Futuna Isls. | 166 |

### PHILATEC

Stamp Album, Champs Elysees Palace and Horses of Marly CD118

Intl. Philatelic and Postal Techniques Exhibition, Paris, June 5-21, 1964.

**1963-64**

| | |
|---|---|
| Comoro Isls. | 60 |
| France | 1078 |
| Fr. Polynesia | 207 |
| New Caledonia | 341 |
| St. Pierre & Miquelon | 369 |
| Somali Coast | 301 |
| Wallis & Futuna Isls. | 167 |

### Cooperation

CD119

Cooperation between France and the French-speaking countries of Africa and Madagascar.

**1964**

| | |
|---|---|
| Cameroun | 409-410 |
| Cent. Africa | 39 |
| Chad | 103 |
| Congo, P.R. | 121 |
| Dahomey | 193 |
| France | 1111 |
| Gabon | 175 |
| Ivory Coast | 221 |
| Madagascar | 360 |
| Mauritania | 181 |
| Niger | 143 |
| Senegal | 236 |
| Togo | 495 |

### ITU

Telegraph, Syncom Satellite and ITU Emblem CD120

Intl. Telecommunication Union, Cent.

**1965, May 17**

| | |
|---|---|
| Comoro Isls. | C14 |
| Fr. Polynesia | C33 |
| Fr. So. & Antarctic Terr. | C8 |
| New Caledonia | C40 |
| New Hebrides | 124-125 |
| St. Pierre & Miquelon | C29 |
| Somali Coast | C36 |
| Wallis & Futuna Isls. | C20 |

### French Satellite A-1

Diamant Rocket and Launching Installation — CD121

Launching of France's first satellite, Nov. 26, 1965.

**1965-66**

| | |
|---|---|
| Comoro Isls. | C15-C16 |
| France | 1137-1138 |
| Fr. Polynesia | C40-C41 |
| Fr. So. & Antarctic Terr. | C9-C10 |
| New Caledonia | C44-C45 |
| St. Pierre & Miquelon | C30-C31 |
| Somali Coast | C39-C40 |
| Wallis & Futuna Isls. | C22-C23 |

### French Satellite D-1

D-1 Satellite in Orbit — CD122

Launching of the D-1 satellite at Hammaguir, Algeria, Feb. 17, 1966.

**1966**

| | |
|---|---|
| Comoro Isls. | C17 |
| France | 1148 |
| Fr. Polynesia | C42 |
| Fr. So. & Antarctic Terr. | C11 |
| New Caledonia | C46 |
| St. Pierre & Miquelon | C32 |
| Somali Coast | C49 |
| Wallis & Futuna Isls. | C24 |

### Air Afrique, 1966

Planes and Air Afrique Emblem — CD123

Introduction of DC-8F planes by Air Afrique.

**1966**

| | |
|---|---|
| Cameroun | C79 |
| Cent. Africa | C35 |
| Chad | C26 |
| Congo, P.R. | C42 |
| Dahomey | C42 |
| Gabon | C47 |
| Ivory Coast | C32 |
| Mauritania | C57 |
| Niger | C63 |
| Senegal | C47 |
| Togo | C54 |
| Upper Volta | C31 |

### African Postal Union, 1967

Telecommunications Symbols and Map of Africa — CD124

Fifth anniversary of the establishment of the African and Malagasy Union of Posts and Telecommunications, UAMPT.

**1967**

| | |
|---|---|
| Cameroun | C90 |
| Cent. Africa | C46 |
| Chad | C37 |
| Congo, P.R. | C57 |
| Dahomey | C61 |
| Gabon | C58 |
| Ivory Coast | C34 |
| Madagascar | C85 |
| Mauritania | C65 |
| Niger | C75 |
| Rwanda | C1-C3 |
| Senegal | C60 |
| Togo | C81 |
| Upper Volta | C50 |

### Monetary Union

Gold Token of the Ashantis, 17-18th Centuries — CD125

West African Monetary Union, 5th anniv.

**1967, Nov. 4**

| | |
|---|---|
| Dahomey | 244 |
| Ivory Coast | 259 |
| Mauritania | 238 |
| Niger | 204 |
| Senegal | 294 |
| Togo | 623 |
| Upper Volta | 181 |

### WHO Anniversary

Sun, Flowers and WHO Emblem CD126

World Health Organization, 20th anniv.

**1968, May 4**

| | |
|---|---|
| Afars & Issas | 317 |
| Comoro Isls. | 73 |
| Fr. Polynesia | 241-242 |
| Fr. So. & Antarctic Terr. | 31 |
| New Caledonia | 367 |
| St. Pierre & Miquelon | 377 |
| Wallis & Futuna Isls. | 169 |

### Human Rights Year

Human Rights Flame — CD127

**1968, Aug. 10**

| | |
|---|---|
| Afars & Issas | 322-323 |

Comoro Isls. ............................76
Fr. Polynesia............................243-244
Fr. So. & Antarctic Terr. ...........32
New Caledonia..........................369
St. Pierre & Miquelon...............382
Wallis & Futuna Isls. ...............170

## 2nd PHILEXAFRIQUE

CD128

Opening of PHILEXAFRIQUE, Abidjan, Feb. 14. Each stamp shows a local scene and stamp.

### 1969, Feb. 14

Cameroun....................................C118
Cent. Africa .................................C65
Chad............................................C48
Congo, P.R..................................C77
Dahomey.....................................C94
Gabon..........................................C82
Ivory Coast ..........................C38-C40
Madagascar.................................C92
Mali.............................................C65
Mauritania...................................C80
Niger...........................................C104
Senegal ......................................C68
Togo............................................C104
Upper Volta.................................C62

### Concorde

Concorde in Flight CD129

First flight of the prototype Concorde supersonic plane at Toulouse, Mar. 1, 1969.

### 1969

Afars & Issas ...............................C56
Comoro Isls. ................................C29
France..........................................C42
Fr. Polynesia...............................C50
Fr. So. & Antarctic Terr. ..............C18
New Caledonia.............................C63
St. Pierre & Miquelon...................C40
Wallis & Futuna Isls. ...................C30

### Development Bank

Bank Emblem — CD130

African Development Bank, fifth anniv.

### 1969

Cameroun....................................499
Chad............................................217
Congo, P.R..................................181-182
Ivory Coast .................................281
Mali.............................................127-128
Mauritania...................................267
Niger...........................................220
Senegal ......................................317-318
Upper Volta.................................201

### ILO

ILO Headquarters, Geneva, and Emblem — CD131

Intl. Labor Organization, 50th anniv.

### 1969-70

Afars & Issas ...............................337
Comoro Isls. ................................83
Fr. Polynesia...............................251-252
Fr. So. & Antarctic Terr. ..............35
New Caledonia.............................379
St. Pierre & Miquelon...................396
Wallis & Futuna Isls. ...................172

### ASECNA

Map of Africa, Plane and Airport CD132

10th anniversary of the Agency for the Security of Aerial Navigation in Africa and Madagascar (ASECNA, Agence pour la Securite de la Navigation Aerienne en Afrique et a Madagascar).

### 1969-70

Cameroun....................................500
Cent. Africa .................................119
Chad............................................222
Congo, P.R..................................197
Dahomey.....................................269
Gabon..........................................260
Ivory Coast .................................287
Mali.............................................130
Niger...........................................221
Senegal ......................................321
Upper Volta.................................204

### U.P.U. Headquarters

CD133

New Universal Postal Union headquarters, Bern, Switzerland.

### 1970

Afars & Issas ...............................342
Algeria .........................................443
Cameroun....................................503-504
Cent. Africa .................................125
Chad............................................225
Comoro Isls. ................................84
Congo, P.R..................................216
Fr. Polynesia...............................261-262
Fr. So. & Antarctic Terr. ..............36
Gabon..........................................258
Ivory Coast .................................295
Madagascar.................................444
Mali.............................................134-135
Mauritania...................................283
New Caledonia.............................382
Niger...........................................231-232
St. Pierre & Miquelon...................397-398
Senegal ......................................328-329
Tunisia ........................................535
Wallis & Futuna Isls. ...................173

### De Gaulle

CD134

First anniversay of the death of Charles de Gaulle, (1890-1970), President of France.

### 1971-72

Afars & Issas ...............................356-357
Comoro Isls. ................................104-105
France..........................................1322-1325
Fr. Polynesia...............................270-271
Fr. So. & Antarctic Terr. ..............52-53
New Caledonia.............................393-394
Reunion ................................377, 380
St. Pierre & Miquelon...................417-418
Wallis & Futuna Isls. ...................177-178

### African Postal Union, 1971

UAMPT Building, Brazzaville, Congo — CD135

10th anniversary of the establishment of the African and Malagasy Posts and Telecommunications Union, UAMPT. Each stamp has a different native design.

### 1971, Nov. 13

Cameroun....................................C177
Cent. Africa .................................C89
Chad............................................C94
Congo, P.R..................................C136
Dahomey.....................................C146
Gabon..........................................C120
Ivory Coast .................................C47
Mauritania...................................C113
Niger...........................................C164
Rwanda .......................................C8
Senegal ......................................C105
Togo............................................C166
Upper Volta.................................C97

### West African Monetary Union

African Couple, City, Village and Commemorative Coin — CD136

West African Monetary Union, 10th anniv.

### 1972, Nov. 2

Dahomey.....................................300
Ivory Coast .................................331
Mauritania...................................299
Niger...........................................258
Senegal ......................................374
Togo............................................825
Upper Volta.................................280

### African Postal Union, 1973

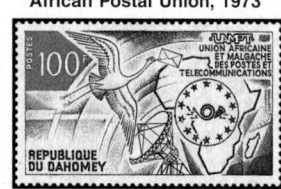

Telecommunications Symbols and Map of Africa — CD137

11th anniversary of the African and Malagasy Posts and Telecommunications Union (UAMPT).

### 1973, Sept. 12

Cameroun....................................574
Cent. Africa .................................194
Chad............................................294
Congo, P.R..................................289
Dahomey.....................................311
Gabon..........................................320
Ivory Coast .................................361
Madagascar.................................500
Mauritania...................................304
Niger...........................................287

Rwanda .......................................540
Senegal ......................................393
Togo............................................849
Upper Volta.................................297

### Philexafrique II — Essen

CD138

CD139

Designs: Indigenous fauna, local and German stamps. Types CD138-CD139 printed horizontally and vertically se-tenant in sheets of 10 (2x5). Label between horizontal pairs alternately commemorates Philexafrique II, Libreville, Gabon, June 1978, and 2nd International Stamp Fair, Essen, Germany, Nov. 1-5.

### 1978-1979

Benin...........................................C285-C286
Central Africa ..............................C200-C201
Chad............................................C238-C239
Congo Republic............................C245-C246
Djibouti........................................C121-C122
Gabon..........................................C215-C216
Ivory Coast .................................C64-C65
Mali.............................................C356-C357
Mauritania...................................C185-C186
Niger...........................................C291-C292
Rwanda .......................................C12-C13
Senegal ......................................C146-C147

-------

## BRITISH COMMONWEALTH OF NATIONS

The listings follow established trade practices when these issues are offered as units by dealers. The Peace issue, for example, includes only one stamp from the Indian state of Hyderabad. The U.P.U. issue includes the Egypt set. Pairs are included for those varieties issues with bilingual designs se-tenant.

### Silver Jubilee

Windsor Castle and King George V CD301

Reign of King George V, 25th anniv.

### 1935

Antigua ........................................77-80
Ascension....................................33-36
Bahamas .....................................92-95
Barbados .....................................186-189
Basutoland...................................11-14
Bechuanaland Protectorate..........117-120
Bermuda......................................100-103
British Guiana...............................223-226
British Honduras...........................108-111
Cayman Islands............................81-84
Ceylon.........................................260-263
Cyprus.........................................136-139
Dominica......................................90-93
Falkland Islands...........................77-80
Fiji...............................................110-113
Gambia ........................................125-128
Gibraltar.......................................100-103
Gilbert & Ellice Islands.................33-36

Gold Coast .............................108-111
Grenada ...............................124-127
Hong Kong ............................147-150
Jamaica ...............................109-112
Kenya, Uganda, Tanganyika .......42-45
Leeward Islands .....................96-99
Malta .................................184-187
Mauritius ............................204-207
Montserrat .............................85-88
Newfoundland........................226-229
Nigeria ................................34-37
Northern Rhodesia ...................18-21
Nyasaland Protectorate..............47-50
St. Helena ...........................111-114
St. Kitts-Nevis ......................72-75
St. Lucia .............................91-94
St. Vincent ..........................134-137
Seychelles ...........................118-121
Sierra Leone .........................166-169
Solomon Islands ......................60-63
Somaliland Protectorate..............77-80
Straits Settlements .................213-216
Swaziland .............................20-23
Trinidad & Tobago ....................43-46
Turks & Caicos Islands ..............71-74
Virgin Islands........................69-72

The following have different designs but are included in the omnibus set:

Great Britain...........................226-229
Offices in Morocco ...... 67-70, 226-229,
  422-425, 508-510
Australia.................................152-154
Canada...................................211-216
Cook Islands ...........................98-100
India....................................142-148
Nauru....................................31-34
New Guinea .............................46-47
New Zealand ............................199-201
Niue ....................................67-69
Papua ...................................114-117
Samoa ...................................163-165
South Africa.............................68-71
Southern Rhodesia ....................33-36
South-West Africa ....................121-124

249 stamps

### Coronation

Queen Elizabeth and King George VI CD302

**1937**

Aden .....................................13-15
Antigua ..................................81-83
Ascension................................37-39
Bahamas ................................97-99
Barbados ...............................190-192
Basutoland...............................15-17
Bechuanaland Protectorate.....121-123
Bermuda ................................115-117
British Guiana..........................227-229
British Honduras.......................112-114
Cayman Islands.........................97-99
Ceylon ..................................275-277
Cyprus ..................................140-142
Dominica................................94-96
Falkland Islands ........................81-83
Fiji .....................................114-116
Gambia ..................................129-131
Gibraltar................................104-106
Gilbert & Ellice Islands...............37-39
Gold Coast .............................112-114
Grenada .................................128-130
Hong Kong .............................151-153
Jamaica .................................113-115
Kenya, Uganda, Tanganyika .......60-62
Leeward Islands .......................100-102
Malta ...................................188-190
Mauritius ...............................208-210
Montserrat ..............................89-91
Newfoundland..........................230-232
Nigeria .................................50-52
Northern Rhodesia ....................22-24
Nyasaland Protectorate...............51-53
St. Helena .............................115-117
St. Kitts-Nevis ........................76-78
St. Lucia ...............................107-109
St. Vincent .............................138-140
Seychelles .............................122-124
Sierra Leone ...........................170-172
Solomon Islands .......................64-66
Somaliland Protectorate..............81-83
Straits Settlements ...................235-237

Swaziland ...............................24-26
Trinidad & Tobago .....................47-49
Turks & Caicos Islands ..............75-77
Virgin Islands...........................73-75

The following have different designs but are included in the omnibus set:

Great Britain............................234
Offices in Morocco .......... 82, 439, 514
Canada..................................237
Cook Islands ...........................109-111
Nauru....................................35-38
Newfoundland..........................233-243
New Guinea .............................48-51
New Zealand ............................223-225
Niue .....................................70-72
Papua ...................................118-121
South Africa..............................74-78
Southern Rhodesia ....................38-41
South-West Africa ....................125-132

202 stamps

### Peace

King George VI and Parliament Buildings, London CD303

Return to peace at the close of World War II.

**1945-46**

Aden .....................................28-29
Antigua ..................................96-97
Ascension................................50-51
Bahamas ................................130-131
Barbados ...............................207-208
Bermuda ...............................131-132
British Guiana..........................242-243
British Honduras.......................127-128
Cayman Islands.........................112-113
Ceylon ..................................293-294
Cyprus ..................................156-157
Dominica................................112-113
Falkland Islands ........................97-98
Falkland Islands Dep.............1L9-1L10
Fiji .....................................137-138
Gambia ..................................144-145
Gibraltar................................119-120
Gilbert & Ellice Islands...............52-53
Gold Coast .............................128-129
Grenada .................................143-144
Jamaica .................................136-137
Kenya, Uganda, Tanganyika .......90-91
Leeward Islands .......................116-117
Malta ...................................206-207
Mauritius ...............................223-224
Montserrat ..............................104-105
Nigeria .................................71-72
Northern Rhodesia ....................46-47
Nyasaland Protectorate...............82-83
Pitcairn Island..........................9-10
St. Helena .............................128-129
St. Kitts-Nevis ........................91-92
St. Lucia ...............................127-128
St. Vincent .............................152-153
Seychelles .............................149-150
Sierra Leone ...........................186-187
Solomon Islands .......................80-81
Somaliland Protectorate..............108-109
Trinidad & Tobago .....................62-63
Turks & Caicos Islands ..............90-91
Virgin Islands...........................88-89

The following have different designs but are included in the omnibus set:

Great Britain............................264-265
  Offices in Morocco .............523-524
Aden
 Kathiri State of Seiyun.............12-13
 Qu'aiti State of Shihr and Mukalla .....
  .........................................12-13
Australia.................................200-202
Basutoland...............................29-31
Bechuanaland Protectorate......137-139
Burma...................................66-69
Cook Islands ...........................127-130
Hong Kong .............................174-175
India....................................195-198
 Hyderabad ..........................51
New Zealand ............................247-257
Niue .....................................90-93
Pakistan-Bahawalpur .................O16
Samoa ...................................191-194
South Africa.............................100-102
Southern Rhodesia ....................67-70

South-West Africa ...................153-155
Swaziland ...............................38-40
Zanzibar................................222-223

164 stamps

### Silver Wedding

King George VI and Queen Elizabeth

CD304    CD305

**1948-49**

Aden .....................................30-31
 Kathiri State of Seiyun..............14-15
 Qu'aiti State of Shihr and Mukalla .....
  .........................................14-15
Antigua ..................................98-99
Ascension................................52-53
Bahamas ................................148-149
Barbados ...............................210-211
Basutoland...............................39-40
Bechuanaland Protectorate......147-148
Bermuda ...............................133-134
British Guiana..........................244-245
British Honduras.......................129-130
Cayman Islands.........................116-117
Cyprus ..................................158-159
Dominica................................114-115
Falkland Islands ........................99-100
Falkland Islands Dep............1L11-1L12
Fiji .....................................139-140
Gambia ..................................146-147
Gibraltar................................121-122
Gilbert & Ellice Islands...............54-55
Gold Coast .............................142-143
Grenada .................................145-146
Hong Kong .............................178-179
Jamaica .................................138-139
Kenya, Uganda, Tanganyika .......92-93
Leeward Islands .......................118-119
Malaya
 Johore ..............................128-129
 Kedah...............................55-56
 Kelantan............................44-45
 Malacca.............................1-2
 Negri Sembilan .....................36-37
 Pahang..............................44-45
 Penang..............................1-2
 Perak................................99-100
 Perlis................................1-2
 Selangor............................74-75
 Trengganu..........................47-48
Malta ...................................223-224
Mauritius ...............................229-230
Montserrat ..............................106-107
Nigeria .................................73-74
North Borneo ..........................238-239
Northern Rhodesia ....................48-49
Nyasaland Protectorate...............85-86
Pitcairn Island..........................11-12
St. Helena .............................130-131
St. Kitts-Nevis ........................93-94
St. Lucia ...............................129-130
St. Vincent .............................154-155
Sarawak.................................174-175
Seychelles .............................151-152
Sierra Leone ...........................188-189
Singapore ..............................21-22
Solomon Islands .......................82-83
Somaliland Protectorate..........110-111
Swaziland ...............................48-49
Trinidad & Tobago .....................64-65
Turks & Caicos Islands ..............92-93
Virgin Islands...........................90-91
Zanzibar................................224-225

The following have different designs but are included in the omnibus set:

Great Britain............................267-268
 Offices in Morocco..... 93-94, 525-526
Bahrain .................................62-63
Kuwait ..................................82-83
Oman ...................................25-26
South Africa............................106
South-West Africa ....................159

138 stamps

### U.P.U.

Mercury and Symbols of Communications — CD306

Plane, Ship and Hemispheres — CD307

Mercury Scattering Letters over Globe CD308

U.P.U. Monument, Bern CD309

Universal Postal Union, 75th anniversary.

**1949**

Aden .....................................32-35
 Kathiri State of Seiyun..............16-19
 Qu'aiti State of Shihr and Mukalla .....
  .........................................16-19
Antigua ..................................100-103
Ascension................................57-60
Bahamas ................................150-153
Barbados ...............................212-215
Basutoland...............................41-44
Bechuanaland Protectorate......149-152
Bermuda ...............................138-141
British Guiana..........................246-249
British Honduras.......................137-140
Brunei ..................................79-82
Cayman Islands.........................118-121
Cyprus ..................................160-163
Dominica................................116-119
Falkland Islands ........................103-106
Falkland Islands Dep............1L14-1L17
Fiji .....................................141-144
Gambia ..................................148-151
Gibraltar................................123-126
Gilbert & Ellice Islands...............56-59
Gold Coast .............................144-147
Grenada .................................147-150
Hong Kong .............................180-183
Jamaica .................................142-145
Kenya, Uganda, Tanganyika .......94-97
Leeward Islands .......................126-129
Malaya
 Johore ..............................151-154
 Kedah...............................57-60
 Kelantan............................46-49
 Malacca.............................18-21
 Negri Sembilan .....................59-62
 Pahang..............................46-49
 Penang..............................23-26
 Perak................................101-104
 Perlis................................3-6
 Selangor............................76-79
 Trengganu..........................49-52
Malta ...................................225-228
Mauritius ...............................231-234
Montserrat ..............................108-111
New Hebrides, British ..............62-65
New Hebrides, French .............79-82
Nigeria .................................75-78
North Borneo ..........................240-243
Northern Rhodesia ....................50-53
Nyasaland Protectorate...............87-90
Pitcairn Islands........................13-16
St. Helena .............................132-135
St. Kitts-Nevis ........................95-98
St. Lucia ...............................131-134
St. Vincent .............................170-173

Sarawak..........................176-179
Seychelles.....................153-156
Sierra Leone..................190-193
Singapore...........................23-26
Solomon Islands...............84-87
Somaliland Protectorate...112-115
Southern Rhodesia ...........71-72
Swaziland ...........................50-53
Tonga..................................87-90
Trinidad & Tobago ............66-69
Turks & Caicos Islands ...101-104
Virgin Islands....................92-95
Zanzibar...........................226-229

The following have different designs but are included in the omnibus set:

Great Britain................276-279
  Offices in Morocco.................546-549
Australia................................223
Bahrain...............................68-71
Burma...............................116-121
Ceylon.............................304-306
Egypt...............................281-283
India................................223-226
Kuwait.................................89-92
Oman...................................31-34
Pakistan-Bahawalpur  26-29, O25-O28
South Africa....................109-111
South-West Africa ..........160-162

319 stamps

### University

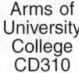

Arms of University College CD310

Alice, Princess of Athlone CD311

1948 opening of University College of the West Indies at Jamaica.

### 1951

Antigua ..........................104-105
Barbados .......................228-229
British Guiana.................250-251
British Honduras............141-142
Dominica........................120-121
Grenada.........................164-165
Jamaica..........................146-147
Leeward Islands ............130-131
Montserrat .....................112-113
St. Kitts-Nevis................105-106
St. Lucia.........................149-150
St. Vincent.....................174-175
Trinidad & Tobago ...........70-71
Virgin Islands...................96-97

28 stamps

### Coronation

Queen Elizabeth II — CD312

### 1953

Aden.......................................47
  Kathiri State of Seiyun.................28
  Qu'aiti State of Shihr and Mukalla .....
  .............................................28
Antigua ...............................106
Ascension..............................61
Bahamas.............................157
Barbados.............................234
Basutoland.............................45
Bechuanaland Protectorate...153
Bermuda.............................142
British Guiana......................252
British Honduras.................143
Cayman Islands...................150

Cyprus ................................167
Dominica.............................141
Falkland Islands .................121
Falkland Islands Dependencies ....1L18
Fiji......................................145
Gambia...............................152
Gibraltar..............................131
Gilbert & Ellice Islands..........60
Gold Coast.........................160
Grenada.............................170
Hong Kong.........................184
Jamaica..............................153
Kenya, Uganda, Tanganyika ...101
Leeward Islands .................132
Malaya
  Johore..............................155
  Kedah.................................82
  Kelantan.............................71
  Malacca..............................27
  Negri Sembilan....................63
  Pahang...............................71
  Penang................................27
  Perak................................126
  Perlis..................................28
  Selangor............................101
  Trengganu...........................74
Malta...................................241
Mauritius.............................250
Montserrat ..........................127
New Hebrides, British ...........77
Nigeria..................................79
North Borneo.......................260
Northern Rhodesia ...............60
Nyasaland Protectorate..........96
Pitcairn ................................19
St. Helena ..........................139
St. Kitts-Nevis....................119
St. Lucia.............................156
St. Vincent.........................185
Sarawak.............................196
Seychelles..........................172
Sierra Leone.......................194
Singapore.............................27
Solomon Islands...................88
Somaliland Protectorate.......127
Swaziland .............................54
Trinidad & Tobago ...............84
Tristan da Cunha...................13
Turks & Caicos Islands ........118
Virgin Islands.....................114

The following have different designs but are included in the omnibus set:

Great Britain...................313-316
  Offices in Morocco.................579-582
Australia.........................259-261
Bahrain.............................92-95
Canada...............................330
Ceylon................................317
Cook Islands ..................145-146
Kuwait............................113-116
New Zealand ..................280-284
Niue...............................104-105
Oman.................................52-55
Samoa............................214-215
South Africa.......................192
Southern Rhodesia ...............80
South-West Africa ..........244-248
Tokelau Islands .....................4

106 stamps

### Royal Visit 1953
Separate designs for each country for the visit of Queen Elizabeth II and the Duke of Edinburgh.

### 1953

Aden.......................................62
Australia.........................267-269
Bermuda.............................163
Ceylon................................318
Fiji......................................146
Gibraltar..............................146
Jamaica..............................154
Kenya, Uganda, Tanganyika ...102
Malta...................................242
New Zealand ..................286-287

13 stamps

### West Indies Federation

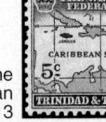

Map of the Caribbean CD313

Federation of the West Indies, April 22, 1958.

### 1958

Antigua ..........................122-124
Barbados .......................248-250
Dominica........................161-163
Grenada.........................184-186
Jamaica..........................175-177
Montserrat .....................143-145
St. Kitts-Nevis................136-138
St. Lucia.........................170-172
St. Vincent.....................198-200
Trinidad & Tobago ...........86-88

30 stamps

### Freedom from Hunger

Protein Food CD314

U.N. Food and Agricultural Organization's "Freedom from Hunger" campaign.

### 1963

Aden.......................................65
Antigua ...............................133
Ascension..............................89
Bahamas.............................180
Basutoland.............................83
Bechuanaland Protectorate...194
Bermuda.............................192
British Honduras.................179
British Honduras.................271
Brunei.................................100
Cayman Islands...................168
Dominica.............................181
Falkland Islands .................146
Fiji......................................198
Gambia...............................172
Gibraltar..............................161
Gilbert & Ellice Islands..........76
Grenada.............................190
Hong Kong.........................218
Malta...................................291
Mauritius.............................270
Montserrat ..........................150
New Hebrides, British ...........93
North Borneo.......................296
Pitcairn ................................35
St. Helena ..........................173
St. Lucia.............................179
St. Vincent.........................201
Sarawak.............................212
Seychelles..........................213
Solomon Islands.................109
Swaziland ...........................108
Tonga.................................127
Tristan da Cunha...................68
Turks & Caicos Islands ........138
Virgin Islands.....................140
Zanzibar.............................280

37 stamps

### Red Cross Centenary

Red Cross and Elizabeth II CD315

### 1963

Antigua ..........................134-135
Ascension.........................90-91
Bahamas.........................183-184
Basutoland........................84-85
Bechuanaland Protectorate...195-196
Bermuda.........................193-194
British Guiana.................272-273
British Honduras............180-181
Cayman Islands...............169-170
Dominica........................182-183
Falkland Islands .............147-148
Fiji...................................203-204
Gambia...........................173-174
Gibraltar.........................162-163
Gilbert & Ellice Islands......77-78
Grenada.........................191-192
Hong Kong.....................219-220
Jamaica..........................203-204

Malta...............................292-293
Mauritius.........................271-272
Montserrat .....................151-152
New Hebrides, British .......94-95
Pitcairn Islands.................36-37
St. Helena .....................174-175
St. Kitts-Nevis................143-144
St. Lucia.........................180-181
St. Vincent.....................202-203
Seychelles......................214-215
Solomon Islands..............110-111
South Arabia ........................1-2
Swaziland .......................109-110
Tonga..............................134-135
Tristan da Cunha...............69-70
Turks & Caicos Islands .....139-140
Virgin Islands..................141-142

70 stamps

### Shakespeare

Shakespeare Memorial Theatre, Stratford-on-Avon — CD316

400th anniversary of the birth of William Shakespeare.

### 1964

Antigua ...............................151
Bahamas.............................201
Bechuanaland Protectorate......197
Cayman Islands...................171
Dominica.............................184
Falkland Islands .................149
Gambia...............................192
Gibraltar..............................164
Montserrat .........................153
St. Lucia.............................196
Turks & Caicos Islands .......141
Virgin Islands......................143

12 stamps

### ITU

ITU Emblem CD317

Intl. Telecommunication Union, cent.

### 1965

Antigua ..........................153-154
Ascension.........................92-93
Bahamas.........................219-220
Barbados .......................265-266
Basutoland......................101-102
Bechuanaland Protectorate...202-203
Bermuda.........................196-197
British Guiana.................293-294
British Honduras............187-188
Brunei.............................116-117
Cayman Islands...............172-173
Dominica........................185-186
Falkland Islands .............154-155
Fiji...................................211-212
Gibraltar.........................167-168
Gilbert & Ellice Islands......87-88
Grenada.........................205-206
Hong Kong.....................221-222
Mauritius.........................291-292
Montserrat .....................157-158
New Hebrides, British ......108-109
Pitcairn Islands.................52-53
St. Helena .....................180-181
St. Kitts-Nevis................163-164
St. Lucia.........................197-198
St. Vincent.....................224-225
Seychelles......................218-219
Solomon Islands..............126-127
Swaziland .......................115-116
Tristan da Cunha...............85-86
Turks & Caicos Islands .....142-143
Virgin Islands..................159-160

64 stamps

## Intl. Cooperation Year

ICY
Emblem
CD318

### 1965

Antigua ...............................155-156
Ascension .............................94-95
Bahamas .........................222-223
Basutoland.......................103-104
Bechuanaland Protectorate..204-205
Bermuda...........................199-200
British Guiana...................295-296
British Honduras...............189-190
Brunei ..............................118-119
Cayman Islands.................174-175
Dominica...........................187-188
Falkland Islands ...............156-157
Fiji ....................................213-214
Gibraltar............................169-170
Gilbert & Ellice Islands.........104-105
Grenada............................207-208
Hong Kong .......................223-224
Mauritius...........................293-294
Montserrat ........................176-177
New Hebrides, British .........110-111
New Hebrides, French .........126-127
Pitcairn Islands.....................54-55
St. Helena ........................182-183
St. Kitts-Nevis ..................165-166
St. Lucia ...........................199-200
Seychelles ........................220-221
Solomon Islands................143-144
South Arabia .......................17-18
Swaziland..........................117-118
Tristan da Cunha..................87-88
Turks & Caicos Islands ..........144-145
Virgin Islands....................161-162

64 stamps

## Churchill Memorial

Winston
Churchill
and St.
Paul's,
London,
During Air
Attack
CD319

### 1966

Antigua ............................157-160
Ascension .............................96-99
Bahamas .........................224-227
Barbados ..........................281-284
Basutoland........................105-108
Bechuanaland Protectorate......206-209
Bermuda...........................201-204
British Antarctic Territory...........16-19
British Honduras...............191-194
Brunei ..............................120-123
Cayman Islands.................176-179
Dominica...........................189-192
Falkland Islands ...............158-161
Fiji ....................................215-218
Gibraltar............................171-174
Gilbert & Ellice Islands.........106-109
Grenada............................209-212
Hong Kong .......................225-228
Mauritius...........................295-298
Montserrat ........................178-181
New Hebrides, British .........112-115
New Hebrides, French .........128-131
Pitcairn Islands.....................56-59
St. Helena ........................184-187
St. Kitts-Nevis ..................167-170
St. Lucia ...........................201-204
St. Vincent ........................241-244
Seychelles ........................222-225
Solomon Islands................145-148
South Arabia .......................19-22
Swaziland..........................119-122
Tristan da Cunha..................89-92
Turks & Caicos Islands ..........146-149
Virgin Islands....................163-166

136 stamps

## Royal Visit, 1966

Queen
Elizabeth
II and
Prince
Philip
CD320

Caribbean visit, Feb. 4 - Mar. 6, 1966.

### 1966

Antigua ............................161-162
Bahamas .........................228-229
Barbados ..........................285-286
British Guiana...................299-300
Cayman Islands.................180-181
Dominica...........................193-194
Grenada............................213-214
Montserrat ........................182-183
St. Kitts-Nevis ..................171-172
St. Lucia ...........................205-206
St. Vincent ........................245-246
Turks & Caicos Islands ..........150-151
Virgin Islands....................167-168

26 stamps

## World Cup Soccer

Soccer
Player
and Jules
Rimet
Cup
CD321

World Cup Soccer Championship, Wembley, England, July 11-30.

### 1966

Antigua ............................163-164
Ascension ...........................100-101
Bahamas .........................245-246
Bermuda...........................205-206
Brunei ..............................124-125
Cayman Islands.................182-183
Dominica...........................195-196
Fiji ....................................219-220
Gibraltar............................175-176
Gilbert & Ellice Islands.........125-126
Grenada............................230-231
New Hebrides, British .........116-117
New Hebrides, French .........132-133
Pitcairn Islands.....................60-61
St. Helena ........................188-189
St. Kitts-Nevis ..................173-174
St. Lucia ...........................207-208
Seychelles ........................226-227
Solomon Islands................167-168
South Arabia .......................23-24
Tristan da Cunha..................93-94

42 stamps

## WHO Headquarters

World Health Organization
Headquarters, Geneva — CD322

### 1966

Antigua ............................165-166
Ascension ...........................102-103
Bahamas .........................247-248
Brunei ..............................126-127
Cayman Islands.................184-185
Dominica...........................197-198
Fiji ....................................224-225
Gibraltar............................180-181
Gilbert & Ellice Islands.........127-128
Grenada............................232-233
Hong Kong .......................229-230
Montserrat ........................184-185
New Hebrides, British .........118-119
New Hebrides, French .........134-135
Pitcairn Islands.....................62-63
St. Helena ........................190-191
St. Kitts-Nevis ..................177-178
St. Lucia ...........................209-210

St. Vincent........................247-248
Seychelles ........................228-229
Solomon Islands................169-170
South Arabia .......................25-26
Tristan da Cunha...................99-100

46 stamps

## UNESCO Anniversary

"Education" — CD323

"Science" (Wheat ears & flask enclosing globe). "Culture" (lyre & columns). 20th anniversary of the UNESCO.

### 1966-67

Antigua ............................183-185
Ascension ...........................108-110
Bahamas .........................249-251
Barbados ..........................287-289
Bermuda...........................207-209
Brunei ..............................128-130
Cayman Islands.................186-188
Dominica...........................199-201
Gibraltar............................183-185
Gilbert & Ellice Islands.........129-131
Grenada............................234-236
Hong Kong .......................231-233
Mauritius...........................299-301
Montserrat ........................186-188
New Hebrides, British .........120-122
New Hebrides, French .........136-138
Pitcairn Islands.....................64-66
St. Helena ........................192-194
St. Kitts-Nevis ..................179-181
St. Lucia ...........................211-213
St. Vincent ........................249-251
Seychelles ........................230-232
Solomon Islands................171-173
South Arabia .......................27-29
Swaziland..........................123-125
Tristan da Cunha...............101-103
Turks & Caicos Islands ..........155-157
Virgin Islands....................176-178

84 stamps

## Silver Wedding, 1972

Queen Elizabeth II and Prince
Philip — CD324

Designs: borders differ for each country.

### 1972

Anguilla.............................161-162
Antigua ............................295-296
Ascension ...........................164-165
Bahamas .........................344-345
Bermuda...........................296-297
British Antarctic Territory...........43-44
British Honduras...............306-307
British Indian Ocean Territory ......48-49
Brunei ..............................186-187
Cayman Islands.................304-305
Dominica...........................352-353
Falkland Islands ...............223-224
Fiji ....................................328-329
Gibraltar............................292-293
Gilbert & Ellice Islands.........206-207
Grenada............................466-467
Hong Kong .......................271-272
Montserrat ........................286-287
New Hebrides, British .........169-170
Pitcairn Islands.................127-128
St. Helena ........................271-272
St. Kitts-Nevis ..................257-258
St. Lucia ...........................328-329
St.Vincent ........................344-345
Seychelles ........................309-310
Solomon Islands................248-249
South Georgia .....................35-36

Tristan da Cunha...............178-179
Turks & Caicos Islands ..........257-258
Virgin Islands....................241-242

60 stamps

## Princess Anne's Wedding

Princess Anne
and Mark
Phillips — CD325

Wedding of Princess Anne and Mark Phillips, Nov. 14, 1973.

### 1973

Anguilla.............................179-180
Ascension ...........................177-178
Belize ...............................325-326
Bermuda...........................302-303
British Antarctic Territory............60-61
Cayman Islands.................320-321
Falkland Islands ...............225-226
Gibraltar............................305-306
Gilbert & Ellice Islands.........216-217
Hong Kong .......................289-290
Montserrat ........................300-301
Pitcairn Island...................135-136
St. Helena ........................277-278
St. Kitts-Nevis ..................274-275
St. Lucia ...........................349-350
St. Vincent ........................358-359
St. Vincent Grenadines ...................1-2
Seychelles ........................311-312
Solomon Islands................259-260
South Georgia .....................37-38
Tristan da Cunha...............189-190
Turks & Caicos Islands ..........286-287
Virgin Islands....................260-261

44 stamps

## Elizabeth II Coronation Anniv.

CD326

CD327

CD328

Designs: Royal and local beasts in heraldic form and simulated stonework. Portrait of Elizabeth II by Peter Grugeon. 25th anniversary of coronation of Queen Elizabeth II.

### 1978

Ascension ................................229
Barbados .................................474
Belize .......................................397
British Antarctic Territory...............71
Cayman Islands..........................404
Christmas Island ..........................87
Falkland Islands ........................275
Fiji ...........................................384
Gambia .....................................380
Gilbert Islands ...........................312
Mauritius..................................464
New Hebrides, British ..................258
St. Helena ................................317
St. Kitts-Nevis ..........................354
Samoa .....................................472

Solomon Islands..............................368
South Georgia ................................51
Swaziland ......................................302
Tristan da Cunha............................238
Virgin Islands.................................337

20 sheets

### Queen Mother Elizabeth's 80th Birthday

CD330

Designs: Photographs of Queen Mother Elizabeth. Falkland Islands issued in sheets of 50; others in sheets of 9.

**1980**

Ascension.........................................261
Bermuda...........................................401
Cayman Islands.................................443
Falkland Islands ..............................305
Gambia.............................................412
Gibraltar...........................................393
Hong Kong .......................................364
Pitcairn Islands.................................193
St. Helena ........................................341
Samoa...............................................532
Solomon Islands...............................426
Tristan da Cunha...............................277

12 stamps

### Royal Wedding, 1981

Prince Charles and Lady Diana — CD331

CD331a

Wedding of Charles, Prince of Wales, and Lady Diana Spencer, St. Paul's Cathedral, London, July 29, 1981.

**1981**

Antigua ............................................623-625
Ascension.........................................294-296
Barbados...........................................547-549
Barbuda............................................497-499
Bermuda...........................................412-414
Brunei...............................................268-270
Cayman Islands.................................471-473
Dominica...........................................701-703
Falkland Islands ..............................324-326
Falkland Islands Dep...........1L59-1L61
Fiji....................................................442-444
Gambia.............................................426-428
Ghana...............................................759-761
Grenada............................................1051-1053
Grenada Grenadines.............440-443
Hong Kong .......................................373-375
Jamaica ............................................500-503
Lesotho.............................................335-337
Maldive Islands.................................906-908
Mauritius...........................................520-522
Norfolk Island ..........................280-282
Pitcairn Islands.................................206-208
St. Helena ........................................353-355
St. Lucia ...........................................543-545
Samoa...............................................558-560
Sierra Leone.....................................509-517
Solomon Islands...............................450-452
Swaziland .........................................382-384
Tristan da Cunha.....................294-296
Turks & Caicos Islands ......486-488
Caicos Island ...................................8-10
Uganda .............................................314-316
Vanuatu ............................................308-310
Virgin Islands....................................406-408

### Princess Diana

CD332

CD333

Designs: Photographs and portrait of Princess Diana, wedding or honeymoon photographs, royal residences, arms of issuing country. Portrait photograph by Clive Friend. Souvenir sheet margins show family tree, various people related to the princess. 21st birthday of Princess Diana of Wales, July 1.

**1982**

Antigua ............................................663-666
Ascension.........................................313-316
Bahamas ..........................................510-513
Barbados...........................................585-588
Barbuda............................................544-546
British Antarctic Territory.............92-95
Cayman Islands.................................486-489
Dominica...........................................773-776
Falkland Islands ..............................348-351
Falkland Islands Dep...........1L72-1L75
Fiji....................................................470-473
Gambia.............................................447-450
Grenada............................................1101A-1105
Grenada Grenadines.............485-491
Lesotho.............................................372-375
Maldive Islands.................................952-955
Mauritius...........................................548-551
Pitcairn Islands.................................213-216
St. Helena ........................................372-375
St. Lucia ...........................................591-594
Sierra Leone.....................................531-534
Solomon Islands...............................471-474
Swaziland .........................................406-409
Tristan da Cunha......................310-313
Turks and Caicos Islands......530A-534
Virgin Islands....................................430-433

### 250th anniv. of first edition of Lloyd's List (shipping news publication) & of Lloyd's marine insurance.

CD335

Designs: First page of early edition of the list; historical ships, modern transportation or harbor scenes.

**1984**

Ascension.........................................351-354
Bahamas ..........................................555-558
Barbados...........................................627-630
Cayes of Belize .........................10-13
Cayman Islands.................................522-525
Falkland Islands ..............................404-407
Fiji....................................................509-512
Gambia.............................................519-522
Mauritius...........................................587-590
Nauru................................................280-283
St. Helena ........................................412-415
Samoa...............................................624-627
Seychelles ........................................538-541
Solomon Islands...............................521-524
Vanuatu ............................................368-371
Virgin Islands....................................466-469

### Queen Mother 85th Birthday

CD336

Designs: Photographs tracing the life of the Queen Mother, Elizabeth. The high value in each set pictures the same photograph taken of the Queen Mother holding the infant Prince Henry.

**1985**

Ascension.........................................372-376
Bahamas ..........................................580-584
Barbados...........................................660-664
Bermuda...........................................469-473
Falkland Islands ..............................420-424
Falkland Islands Dep.......1L92-1L96
Fiji....................................................531-535
Hong Kong .......................................447-450
Jamaica ............................................599-603
Mauritius...........................................604-608
Norfolk Island ..........................364-368
Pitcairn Islands.................................253-257
St. Helena ........................................428-432
Samoa...............................................649-653
Seychelles ........................................567-571
Solomon Islands...............................543-547
Swaziland .........................................476-480
Tristan da Cunha.....................372-376
Vanuatu ............................................392-396
Zil Elwannyen Sesel ...............101-105

### Queen Elizabeth II, 60th Birthday

CD337

**1986, April 21**

Ascension.........................................389-393
Bahamas ..........................................592-596
Barbados...........................................675-679
Bermuda...........................................499-503
Cayman Islands.................................555-559
Falkland Islands ..............................441-445
Fiji....................................................544-548
Hong Kong .......................................465-469
Jamaica ............................................620-624
Kiribati..............................................470-474
Mauritius...........................................629-633
Papua New Guinea ...................640-644
Pitcairn Islands.................................270-274
St. Helena ........................................451-455
Samoa...............................................670-674
Seychelles ........................................592-596
Solomon Islands...............................562-566
South Georgia ..........................101-105
Swaziland .........................................490-494
Tristan da Cunha.....................388-392
Vanuatu ............................................414-418
Zambia..............................................343-347
Zil Elwannyen Sesel ...............114-118

### Royal Wedding

Marriage of Prince Andrew and Sarah Ferguson — CD338

**1986, July 23**

Ascension.........................................399-400
Bahamas ..........................................602-603
Barbados...........................................687-688
Cayman Islands.................................560-561
Jamaica ............................................629-630
Pitcairn Islands.................................275-276
St. Helena ........................................460-461
St. Kitts.............................................181-182

Seychelles ........................................602-603
Solomon Islands...............................567-568
Tristan da Cunha.....................397-398
Zambia..............................................348-349
Zil Elwannyen Sesel ...............119-120

### Queen Elizabeth II, 60th Birthday

Queen Elizabeth II & Prince Philip, 1947 Wedding Portrait — CD339

Designs: Photographs tracing the life of Queen Elizabeth II.

**1986**

Anguilla.............................................674-677
Antigua .............................................925-928
Barbuda............................................783-786
Dominica...........................................950-953
Gambia.............................................611-614
Grenada............................................1371-1374
Grenada Grenadines.............749-752
Lesotho.............................................531-534
Maldive Islands.................................1172-1175
Sierra Leone.....................................760-763
Uganda .............................................495-498

### Royal Wedding, 1986

CD340

Designs: Photographs of Prince Andrew and Sarah Ferguson during courtship, engagement and marriage.

**1986**

Antigua .............................................939-942
Barbuda............................................809-812
Dominica...........................................970-973
Gambia.............................................635-638
Grenada............................................1385-1388
Grenada Grenadines.............758-761
Lesotho.............................................545-548
Maldive Islands.................................1181-1184
Sierra Leone.....................................769-772
Uganda .............................................510-513

### Lloyds of London, 300th Anniv.

CD341

Designs: 17th century aspects of Lloyds, representations of each country's individual connections with Lloyds and publicized disasters insured by the organization.

**1986**

Ascension.........................................454-457
Bahamas ..........................................655-658
Barbados...........................................731-734
Bermuda...........................................541-544
Falkland Islands ..............................481-484
Liberia...............................................1101-1104
Malawi..............................................534-537
Nevis................................................571-574
St. Helena ........................................501-504
St. Lucia ...........................................923-926
Seychelles ........................................649-652
Solomon Islands...............................627-630

South Georgia .......................131-134
Trinidad & Tobago ..................484-487
Tristan da Cunha....................439-442
Vanuatu ............................485-488
Zil Elwannyen Sesel................146-149

### Moon Landing, 20th Anniv.

CD342

Designs: Equipment, crew photographs, spacecraft, official emblems and report profiles created for the Apollo Missions. Two stamps in each set are square in format rather than like the stamp shown; see individual country listings for more information.

**1989**

Ascension Is. ...........................468-472
Bahamas .............................674-678
Belize ...............................916-920
Kiribati.............................517-521
Liberia..............................1125-1129
Nevis...............................586-590
St. Kitts............................248-252
Samoa ..............................760-764
Seychelles ..........................676-680
Solomon Islands.....................643-647
Vanuatu ............................507-511
Zil Elwannyen Sesel................154-158

### Queen Mother, 90th Birthday

CD343              CD344

Designs: Portraits of Queen Elizabeth, the Queen Mother. See individual country listings for more information.

**1990**

Ascension Is. ...........................491-492
Bahamas .............................698-699
Barbados ............................782-783
British Antarctic Territory..........170-171
British Indian Ocean Territory .......106-107
Cayman Islands......................622-623
Falkland Islands .....................524-525
Kenya...............................527-528
Kiribati.............................555-556
Liberia..............................1145-1146
Pitcairn Islands......................336-337
St. Helena ..........................532-533
St. Lucia ...........................969-970
Seychelles ..........................710-711
Solomon Islands.....................671-672
South Georgia ......................143-144
Swaziland ...........................565-566
Tristan da Cunha....................480-481
Zil Elwannyen Sesel................171-172

### Queen Elizabeth II, 65th Birthday, and Prince Philip, 70th Birthday

CD345

CD346

Designs: Portraits of Queen Elizabeth II and Prince Philip differ for each country. Printed in sheets of 10 + 5 labels (3 different) between. Stamps alternate, producing 5 different triptychs.

**1991**

Ascension Is. .........................505-506
Bahamas .............................730-731
Belize ...............................969-970
Bermuda ............................617-618
Kiribati.............................571-572
Mauritius ...........................733-734
Pitcairn Islands......................348-349
St. Helena ..........................554-555
St. Kitts............................318-319
Samoa ..............................790-791
Seychelles ..........................723-724
Solomon Islands.....................688-689
South Georgia ......................149-150
Swaziland ...........................586-587
Vanuatu ............................540-541
Zil Elwannyen Sesel................177-178

### Royal Family Birthday, Anniversary

CD347

Queen Elizabeth II, 65th birthday, Charles and Diana, 10th wedding anniversary: Various photographs of Queen Elizabeth II, Prince Philip, Prince Charles, Princess Diana and their sons William and Henry.

**1991**

Antigua .............................1446-1455
Barbuda.............................1229-1238
Dominica ...........................1328-1337
Gambia .............................1080-1089
Grenada ............................2006-2015
Grenada Grenadines...........1331-1340
Guyana .............................2440-2451
Lesotho.............................871-875
Maldive Islands.....................1533-1542
Nevis...............................666-675
St. Vincent..........................1485-1494
St. Vincent Grenadines .........769-778
Sierra Leone ........................1387-1396
Turks & Caicos Islands ..........913-922
Uganda .............................918-927

### Queen Elizabeth II's Accession to the Throne, 40th Anniv.

CD348

CD349

Various photographs of Queen Elizabeth II with local Scenes.

**1992 - CD348**

Antigua .............................1513-1518
Barbuda.............................1306-1309
Dominica ...........................1414-1419
Gambia .............................1172-1177
Grenada ............................2047-2052
Grenada Grenadines...........1368-1373

Lesotho.............................881-885
Maldive Islands....................1637-1642
Nevis...............................702-707
St. Vincent.........................1582-1587
St. Vincent Grenadines ...........829-834
Sierra Leone ........................1482-1487
Turks and Caicos Islands.......978-987
Uganda .............................990-995
Virgin Islands.......................742-746

**1992 - CD349**

Ascension Islands ...................531-535
Bahamas .............................744-748
Bermuda ............................623-627
British Indian Ocean Territory .......119-123
Cayman Islands......................648-652
Falkland Islands.....................549-553
Gibraltar ............................605-609
Hong Kong ..........................619-623
Kenya...............................563-567
Kiribati.............................582-586
Pitcairn Islands......................362-366
St. Helena ..........................570-574
St. Kitts............................332-336
Samoa ..............................805-809
Seychelles ..........................734-738
Solomon Islands.....................708-712
South Georgia ......................157-161
Tristan da Cunha....................508-512
Vanuatu ............................555-559
Zambia .............................561-565
Zil Elwannyen Sesel................183-187

### Royal Air Force, 75th Anniversary

CD350

**1993**

Ascension ...........................557-561
Bahamas .............................771-775
Barbados ............................842-846
Belize ...............................1003-1008
Bermuda ............................648-651
British Indian Ocean Territory ........136-140
Falkland Is. .........................573-577
Fiji .................................687-691
Montserrat ..........................830-834
St. Kitts............................351-355

### Royal Air Force, 80th Anniv.

Design CD350 Re-inscribed

**1998**

Ascension ...........................697-701
Bahamas .............................907-911
British Indian Ocean Terr .........198-202
Cayman Islands......................754-758
Fiji .................................814-818
Gibraltar ............................755-759
Samoa ..............................957-961
Turks & Caicos Islands ........1258-1265
Tuvalu ..............................763-767
Virgin Islands.......................879-883

### End of World War II, 50th Anniv.

CD351

### LEST WE FORGET

CD352

**1995**

Ascension ...........................613-617
Bahamas .............................824-828
Barbados ............................891-895
Belize ...............................1047-1050
British Indian Ocean Territory ........163-167
Cayman Islands......................704-708
Falkland Islands .....................634-638
Fiji .................................720-724
Kiribati.............................662-668
Liberia..............................1175-1179
Mauritius ...........................803-805
St. Helena ..........................646-654
St. Kitts............................389-393
St. Lucia ...........................1018-1022
Samoa ..............................890-894
Solomon Islands.....................799-803
South Georgia & S. Sandwich Is. .........198-200
Tristan da Cunha....................562-566

### UN, 50th Anniv.

CD353

**1995**

Bahamas .............................839-842
Barbados ............................901-904
Belize ...............................1055-1058
Jamaica .............................847-851
Liberia..............................1187-1190
Mauritius ...........................813-816
Pitcairn Islands......................436-439
St. Kitts............................398-401
St. Lucia ...........................1023-1026
Samoa ..............................900-903
Tristan da Cunha....................568-571
Virgin Islands.......................807-810

### Queen Elizabeth, 70th Birthday

CD354

**1996**

Ascension ...........................632-635
British Antarctic Territory..........240-243
British Indian Ocean Territory ........176-180
Falkland Islands.....................653-657
Pitcairn Islands......................446-449
St. Helena ..........................672-676
Samoa ..............................912-916
Tokelau .............................223-227
Tristan da Cunha....................576-579
Virgin Islands.......................824-828

## Diana, Princess of Wales (1961-97)

CD355

**1998**

| | |
|---|---|
| Ascension | 696 |
| Bahamas | 901A-902 |
| Barbados | 950 |
| Belize | 1091 |
| Bermuda | 753 |
| Botswana | 659-663 |
| British Antarctic Territory | 258 |
| British Indian Ocean Terr. | 197 |
| Cayman Islands | 752A-753 |
| Falkland Islands | 694 |
| Fiji | 819-820 |
| Gibraltar | 754 |
| Kiribati | 719A-720 |
| Namibia | 909 |
| Niue | 706 |
| Norfolk Island | 644-645 |
| Papua New Guinea | 937 |
| Pitcairn Islands | 487 |
| St. Helena | 711 |
| St. Kitts | 437A-438 |
| Samoa | 955A-956 |
| Seychelles | 802 |
| Solomon Islands | 866-867 |
| South Georgia & S. Sandwich Islands | 220 |
| Tokelau | 252B-253 |
| Tonga | 980 |
| Niuafo'ou | 201 |
| Tristan da Cunha | 618 |
| Tuvalu | 762 |
| Vanuatu | 719 |
| Virgin Islands | 878 |

## Wedding of Prince Edward and Sophie Rhys-Jones

CD356

**1999**

| | |
|---|---|
| Ascension | 729-730 |
| Cayman Islands | 775-776 |
| Falkland Islands | 729-730 |
| Pitcairn Islands | 505-506 |
| St. Helena | 733-734 |
| Samoa | 971-972 |
| Tristan da Cunha | 636-637 |
| Virgin Islands | 908-909 |

## 1st Manned Moon Landing, 30th Anniv.

CD357

**1999**

| | |
|---|---|
| Ascension | 731-735 |
| Bahamas | 942-946 |
| Barbados | 967-971 |
| Bermuda | 778 |
| Cayman Islands | 777-781 |

| | |
|---|---|
| Fiji | 853-857 |
| Jamaica | 889-893 |
| Kirbati | 746-750 |
| Nauru | 465-469 |
| St. Kitts | 460-464 |
| Samoa | 973-977 |
| Solomon Islands | 875-879 |
| Tuvalu | 800-804 |
| Virgin Islands | 910-914 |

## Queen Mother's Century

CD358

**1999**

| | |
|---|---|
| Ascension | 736-740 |
| Bahamas | 951-955 |
| Cayman Islands | 782-786 |
| Falkland Islands | 734-738 |
| Fiji | 858-862 |
| Norfolk Island | 688-692 |
| St. Helena | 740-744 |
| Samoa | 978-982 |
| Solomon Islands | 880-884 |
| South Georgia & South Sandwich Islands | 231-235 |
| Tristan da Cunha | 638-642 |
| Tuvalu | 805-809 |

## Prince William, 18th Birthday

CD359

**2000**

| | |
|---|---|
| Ascension | 755-759 |
| Cayman Islands | 797-801 |
| Falkland Islands | 762-766 |
| Fiji | 889-893 |
| South Georgia and South Sandwich Islands | 257-261 |
| Tristan da Cunha | 664-668 |
| Virgin Islands | 925-929 |

## Reign of Queen Elizabeth II, 50th Anniv.

CD360

**2002**

| | |
|---|---|
| Ascension | 790-794 |
| Bahamas | 1033-1037 |
| Barbados | 1019-1023 |
| Belize | 1152-1156 |
| Bermuda | 822-826 |
| British Antarctic Territory | 307-311 |
| British Indian Ocean Territory | 239-243 |
| Cayman Islands | 844-848 |
| Falkland Islands | 804-808 |
| Gibraltar | 896-900 |
| Jamaica | 952-956 |
| Nauru | 491-495 |
| Norfolk Island | 758-762 |
| Papua New Guinea | 1019-1023 |
| Pitcairn Islands | 552 |
| St. Helena | 788-792 |
| St. Lucia | 1146-1150 |
| Solomon Islands | 931-935 |
| South Georgia & So. Sandwich Is. | 274-278 |
| Swaziland | 706-710 |
| Tokelau | 302-306 |
| Tonga | 1059 |

| | |
|---|---|
| Niuafo'ou | 239 |
| Tristan da Cunha | 706-710 |
| Virgin Islands | 967-971 |

## Queen Mother Elizabeth (1900-2002)

CD361

**2002**

| | |
|---|---|
| Ascension | 799-801 |
| Bahamas | 1044-1046 |
| Bermuda | 834-836 |
| British Antarctic Territory | 312-314 |
| British Indian Ocean Territory | 245-247 |
| Cayman Islands | 857-861 |
| Falkland Islands | 812-816 |
| Nauru | 499-501 |
| Pitcairn Islands | 561-565 |
| St. Helena | 808-812 |
| St. Lucia | 1155-1159 |
| Seychelles | 830 |
| Solomon Islands | 945-947 |
| South Georgia & So. Sandwich Isls. | 281-285 |
| Tokelau | 312-314 |
| Tristan da Cunha | 715-717 |
| Virgin Islands | 979-983 |

## Head of Queen Elizabeth II

CD362

**2003**

| | |
|---|---|
| Ascension | 822 |
| Bermuda | 865 |
| British Antarctic Territory | 322 |
| British Indian Ocean Territory | 261 |
| Cayman Islands | 878 |
| Falkland Islands | 828 |
| St. Helena | 820 |
| South Georgia & South Sandwich Islands | 294 |
| Tristan da Cunha | 731 |
| Virgin Islands | 1003 |

## Coronation of Queen Elizabeth II, 50th Anniv.

CD363

**2003**

| | |
|---|---|
| Ascension | 823-825 |
| Bahamas | 1073-1075 |
| Bermuda | 866-868 |
| British Antarctic Territory | 323-325 |
| British Indian Ocean Territory | 262-264 |
| Cayman Islands | 879-881 |
| Jamaica | 970-972 |
| Kiribati | 825-827 |
| Pitcairn Islands | 577-581 |
| St. Helena | 821-823 |
| St. Lucia | 1171-1173 |
| Tokelau | 320-322 |
| Tristan da Cunha | 732-734 |
| Virgin Islands | 1004-1006 |

## Prince William, 21st Birthday

CD364

**2003**

| | |
|---|---|
| Ascension | 826 |
| British Indian Ocean Territory | 265 |
| Cayman Islands | 882-884 |
| Falkland Islands | 829 |
| South Georgia & South Sandwich Islands | 295 |
| Tokelau | 323 |
| Tristan da Cunha | 735 |
| Virgin Islands | 1007-1009 |

# British Commonwealth of Nations

## Dominions, Colonies, Territories, Offices and Independent Members

Comprising stamps of the British Commonwealth and associated nations.

A strict observance of technicalities would bar some or all of the stamps listed under Burma, Ireland, Kuwait, Nepal, New Republic, Orange Free State, Samoa, South Africa, South-West Africa, Stellaland, Sudan, Swaziland, the two Transvaal Republics and others but these are included for the convenience of collectors.

## 1. Great Britain

Great Britain: Including England, Scotland, Wales and Northern Ireland.

## 2. The Dominions, Present and Past

### AUSTRALIA
The Commonwealth of Australia was proclaimed on January 1, 1901. It consists of six former colonies as follows:

| | |
|---|---|
| New South Wales | Victoria |
| Queensland | Tasmania |
| South Australia | Western Australia |

The following islands and territories are, or have been, administered by Australia: Australian Antarctic Territory, Christmas Island, Cocos (Keeling) Islands, Nauru, New Guinea, Norfolk Island, Papua.

### CANADA
The Dominion of Canada was created by the British North America Act in 1867. The following provinces were former separate colonies and issued postage stamps:

| | |
|---|---|
| British Columbia and | Newfoundland |
| Vancouver Island | Nova Scotia |
| New Brunswick | Prince Edward Island |

### FIJI
The colony of Fiji became an independent nation with dominion status on Oct. 10, 1970.

### GHANA
This state came into existence Mar. 6, 1957, with dominion status. It consists of the former colony of the Gold Coast and the Trusteeship Territory of Togoland. Ghana became a republic July 1, 1960.

### INDIA
The Republic of India was inaugurated on January 26, 1950. It succeeded the Dominion of India which was proclaimed August 15, 1947, when the former Empire of India was divided into Pakistan and the Union of India. The Republic is composed of about 40 predominantly Hindu states of three classes: governor's provinces, chief commissioner's provinces and princely states. India also has various territories, such as the Andaman and Nicobar Islands.

The old Empire of India was a federation of British India and the native states. The more important princely states were autonomous. Of the more than 700 Indian states, these 43 are familiar names to philatelists because of their postage stamps.

### CONVENTION STATES

| | |
|---|---|
| Chamba | Jhind |
| Faridkot | Nabha |
| Gwalior | Patiala |

### NATIVE FEUDATORY STATES

| | |
|---|---|
| Alwar | Jammu |
| Bahawalpur | Jammu and Kashmir |
| Bamra | Jasdan |
| Barwani | Jhalawar |
| Bhopal | Jhind (1875-76) |
| Bhor | Kashmir |
| Bijawar | Kishangarh |
| Bundi | Las Bela |
| Bussahir | Morvi |
| Charkhari | Nandgaon |
| Cochin | Nowanuggur |
| Dhar | Orchha |
| Duttia | Poonch |
| Faridkot (1879-85) | Rajpeepla |
| Hyderabad | Sirmur |
| Idar | Soruth |
| Indore | Travancore |
| Jaipur | Wadhwan |

### NEW ZEALAND
Became a dominion on September 26, 1907. The following islands and territories are, or have been, administered by New Zealand:

| | |
|---|---|
| Aitutaki | Ross Dependency |
| Cook Islands (Rarotonga) | Samoa (Western Samoa) |
| Niue | Tokelau Islands |
| Penrhyn | |

### PAKISTAN
The Republic of Pakistan was proclaimed March 23, 1956. It succeeded the Dominion which was proclaimed August 15, 1947. It is made up of all or part of several Moslem provinces and various districts of the former Empire of India, including Bahawalpur and Las Bela. Pakistan withdrew from the Commonwealth in 1972.

### SOUTH AFRICA
Under the terms of the South African Act (1909) the self-governing colonies of Cape of Good Hope, Natal, Orange River Colony and Transvaal united on May 31, 1910, to form the Union of South Africa. It became an independent republic May 3, 1961.

Under the terms of the Treaty of Versailles, South-West Africa, formerly German South-West Africa, was mandated to the Union of South Africa.

### SRI LANKA (CEYLON)
The Dominion of Ceylon was proclaimed February 4, 1948. The island had been a Crown Colony from 1802 until then. On May 22, 1972, Ceylon became the Republic of Sri Lanka.

## 3. Colonies, Past and Present; ControlledTerritory and Independent Members of the Commonwealth

| | |
|---|---|
| Aden | Bechuanaland |
| Aitutaki | Bechuanaland Prot. |
| Antigua | Belize |
| Ascension | Bermuda |
| Bahamas | Botswana |
| Bahrain | British Antarctic Territory |
| Bangladesh | British Central Africa |
| Barbados | British Columbia and |
| Barbuda | Vancouver Island |
| Basutoland | British East Africa |
| Batum | British Guiana |

British Honduras
British Indian Ocean Territory
British New Guinea
British Solomon Islands
British Somaliland
Brunei
Burma
Bushire
Cameroons
Cape of Good Hope
Cayman Islands
Christmas Island
Cocos (Keeling) Islands
Cook Islands
Crete,
  British Administration
Cyprus
Dominica
East Africa & Uganda
  Protectorates
Egypt
Falkland Islands
Fiji
Gambia
German East Africa
Gibraltar
Gilbert Islands
Gilbert & Ellice Islands
Gold Coast
Grenada
Griqualand West
Guernsey
Guyana
Heligoland
Hong Kong
Indian Native States
  (see India)
Ionian Islands
Jamaica
Jersey

Kenya
Kenya, Uganda & Tanzania
Kuwait
Labuan
Lagos
Leeward Islands
Lesotho
Madagascar
Malawi
Malaya
  Federated Malay States
  Johore
  Kedah
  Kelantan
  Malacca
  Negri Sembilan
  Pahang
  Penang
  Perak
  Perlis
  Selangor
  Singapore
  Sungei Ujong
  Trengganu
Malaysia
Maldive Islands
Malta
Man, Isle of
Mauritius
Mesopotamia
Montserrat
Muscat
Namibia
Natal
Nauru
Nevis
New Britain
New Brunswick
Newfoundland
New Guinea

New Hebrides
New Republic
New South Wales
Niger Coast Protectorate
Nigeria
Niue
Norfolk Island
North Borneo
Northern Nigeria
Northern Rhodesia
North West Pacific Islands
Nova Scotia
Nyasaland Protectorate
Oman
Orange River Colony
Palestine
Papua New Guinea
Penrhyn Island
Pitcairn Islands
Prince Edward Island
Queensland
Rhodesia
Rhodesia & Nyasaland
Ross Dependency
Sabah
St. Christopher
St. Helena
St. Kitts
St. Kitts-Nevis-Anguilla
St. Lucia
St. Vincent
Samoa
Sarawak
Seychelles
Sierra Leone
Solomon Islands
Somaliland Protectorate
South Arabia
South Australia
South Georgia

Southern Nigeria
Southern Rhodesia
South-West Africa
Stellaland
Straits Settlements
Sudan
Swaziland
Tanganyika
Tanzania
Tasmania
Tobago
Togo
Tokelau Islands
Tonga
Transvaal
Trinidad
Trinidad and Tobago
Tristan da Cunha
Trucial States
Turks and Caicos
Turks Islands
Tuvalu
Uganda
United Arab Emirates
Victoria
Virgin Islands
Western Australia
Zambia
Zanzibar
Zululand

**POST OFFICES IN
FOREIGN COUNTRIES**
Africa
  East Africa Forces
  Middle East Forces
Bangkok
China
Morocco
Turkish Empire

# Colonies, Former Colonies, Offices, Territories Controlled by Parent States

## Belgium
Belgian Congo
Ruanda-Urundi

## Denmark
Danish West Indies
Faroe Islands
Greenland
Iceland

## Finland
Aland Islands

## France

### COLONIES PAST AND PRESENT, CONTROLLED TERRITORIES
Afars & Issas, Territory of
Alaouites
Alexandretta
Algeria
Alsace & Lorraine
Anjouan
Annam & Tonkin
Benin
Cambodia (Khmer)
Cameroun
Castellorizo
Chad
Cilicia
Cochin China
Comoro Islands
Dahomey
Diego Suarez
Djibouti (Somali Coast)
Fezzan
French Congo
French Equatorial Africa
French Guiana
French Guinea
French India
French Morocco
French Polynesia (Oceania)
French Southern & Antarctic Territories
French Sudan
French West Africa
Gabon
Germany
Ghadames
Grand Comoro
Guadeloupe
Indo-China
Inini
Ivory Coast
Laos
Latakia
Lebanon
Madagascar
Martinique
Mauritania
Mayotte
Memel
Middle Congo
Moheli
New Caledonia
New Hebrides
Niger Territory
Nossi-Be
Obock
Reunion
Rouad, Ile
Ste.-Marie de Madagascar
St. Pierre & Miquelon
Senegal
Senegambia & Niger
Somali Coast
Syria
Tahiti
Togo
Tunisia
Ubangi-Shari
Upper Senegal & Niger
Upper Volta
Viet Nam
Wallis & Futuna Islands

### POST OFFICES IN FOREIGN COUNTRIES
China
Crete
Egypt
Turkish Empire
Zanzibar

## Germany

### EARLY STATES
Baden
Bavaria
Bergedorf
Bremen
Brunswick
Hamburg
Hanover
Lubeck
Mecklenburg-Schwerin
Mecklenburg-Strelitz
Oldenburg
Prussia
Saxony
Schleswig-Holstein
Wurttemberg

### FORMER COLONIES
Cameroun (Kamerun)
Caroline Islands
German East Africa
German New Guinea
German South-West Africa
Kiauchau
Mariana Islands
Marshall Islands
Samoa
Togo

## Italy

### EARLY STATES
Modena
Parma
Romagna
Roman States
Sardinia
Tuscany
Two Sicilies
    Naples
    Neapolitan Provinces
    Sicily

### FORMER COLONIES, CONTROLLED TERRITORIES, OCCUPATION AREAS
Aegean Islands
    Calimno (Calino)
    Caso
    Cos (Coo)
    Karki (Carchi)
    Leros (Lero)
    Lipso
    Nisiros (Nisiro)
    Patmos (Patmo)
    Piscopi
    Rodi (Rhodes)
    Scarpanto
    Simi
    Stampalia
Castellorizo
Corfu
Cyrenaica
Eritrea
Ethiopia (Abyssinia)
Fiume
Ionian Islands
    Cephalonia
    Ithaca
    Paxos
Italian East Africa
Libya
Oltre Giuba
Saseno
Somalia (Italian Somaliland)
Tripolitania

### POST OFFICES IN FOREIGN COUNTRIES
"ESTERO"*
Austria
China
    Peking
    Tientsin
Crete
Tripoli
Turkish Empire
    Constantinople
    Durazzo
    Janina
Jerusalem
Salonika
Scutari
Smyrna
Valona

*Stamps overprinted "ESTERO" were used in various parts of the world.

## Netherlands
Aruba
Netherlands Antilles (Curacao)
Netherlands Indies
Netherlands New Guinea
Surinam (Dutch Guiana)

## Portugal

### COLONIES PAST AND PRESENT, CONTROLLED TERRITORIES
Angola
Angra
Azores
Cape Verde
Funchal
Horta
Inhambane
Kionga
Lourenco Marques
Macao
Madeira
Mozambique
Mozambique Co.
Nyassa
Ponta Delgada
Portuguese Africa
Portuguese Congo
Portuguese Guinea
Portuguese India
Quelimane
St. Thomas & Prince Islands
Tete
Timor
Zambezia

## Russia

### ALLIED TERRITORIES AND REPUBLICS, OCCUPATION AREAS
Armenia
Aunus (Olonets)
Azerbaijan
Batum
Estonia
Far Eastern Republic
Georgia
Karelia
Latvia
Lithuania
North Ingermanland
Ostland
Russian Turkestan
Siberia
South Russia
Tannu Tuva
Transcaucasian Fed. Republics
Ukraine
Wenden (Livonia)
Western Ukraine

## Spain

### COLONIES PAST AND PRESENT, CONTROLLED TERRITORIES
Aguera, La
Cape Juby
Cuba
Elobey, Annobon & Corisco
Fernando Po
Ifni
Mariana Islands
Philippines
Puerto Rico
Rio de Oro
Rio Muni
Spanish Guinea
Spanish Morocco
Spanish Sahara
Spanish West Africa

### POST OFFICES IN FOREIGN COUNTRIES
Morocco
Tangier
Tetuan

# Dies of British Colonial Stamps

DIE A                                    DIE B

DIE I                                    DIE II

**DIE A:**
1. The lines in the groundwork vary in thickness and are not uniformly straight.
2. The seventh and eighth lines from the top, in the groundwork, converge where they meet the head.
3. There is a small dash in the upper part of the second jewel in the band of the crown.
4. The vertical color line in front of the throat stops at the sixth line of shading on the neck.

**DIE B:**
1. The lines in the groundwork are all thin and straight.
2. All the lines of the background are parallel.
3. There is no dash in the upper part of the second jewel in the band of the crown.
4. The vertical color line in front of the throat stops at the eighth line of shading on the neck.

**DIE I:**
1. The base of the crown is well below the level of the inner white line around the vignette.
2. The labels inscribed "POSTAGE" and "REVENUE" are cut square at the top.
3. There is a white "bud" on the outer side of the main stem of the curved ornaments in each lower corner.
4. The second (thick) line below the country name has the ends next to the crown cut diagonally.

DIE Ia.                    DIE Ib.
1 as die II.               1 and 3 as die II.
2 and 3 as die I.          2 as die I.

**DIE II:**
1. The base of the crown is aligned with the underside of the white line around the vignette.
2. The labels curve inward at the top inner corners.
3. The "bud" has been removed from the outer curve of the ornaments in each corner.
4. The second line below the country name has the ends next to the crown cut vertically.

---

Wmk. 1          Wmk. 2          Wmk. 3          Wmk. 4
Crown and C C   Crown and C A   Multiple Crown  Multiple Crown
                                and C A         and Script C A

Wmk. 4a          Wmk. 314
                 St. Edward's Crown
                 and C A Multiple

Wmk. 373          Wmk. 384

Wmk. 406

# British Colonial and Crown Agents Watermarks

Watermarks 1 to 4, 314, 373, 384 and 406, common to many British territories, are illustrated here to avoid duplication.

The letters "CC" of Wmk. 1 identify the paper as having been made for the use of the Crown Colonies, while the letters "CA" of the others stand for "Crown Agents." Both Wmks. 1 and 2 were used on stamps printed by De La Rue & Co.

Wmk. 3 was adopted in 1904; Wmk. 4 in 1921; Wmk. 314 in 1957; Wmk. 373 in 1974; Wmk. 384 in 1985; Wmk 406 in 2008.

In Wmk. 4a, a non-matching crown of the general St. Edwards type (bulging on both sides at top) was substituted for one of the Wmk. 4 crowns which fell off the dandy roll. The non-matching crown occurs in 1950-52 printings in a horizontal row of crowns on certain regular stamps of Johore and Seychelles, and on various postage due stamps of Barbados, Basutoland, British Guiana, Gold Coast, Grenada, Northern Rhodesia, St. Lucia, Swaziland and Trinidad and Tobago. A variation of Wmk. 4a, with the non-matching crown in a horizontal row of crown-CA-crown, occurs on regular stamps of Bahamas, St. Kitts-Nevis and Singapore.

Wmk. 314 was intentionally used sideways, starting in 1966. When a stamp was issued with Wmk. 314 both upright and sideways, the sideways varieties usually are listed also – with minor numbers. In many of the later issues, Wmk. 314 is slightly visible.

Wmk. 373 is usually only faintly visible.

# MINKUS
## Album Series

The Minkus album line is now available through Amos Hobby Publishing.
The supplement schedule is listed below. Pages are punched to fit 2 or 3-ring binders.
Sold as page units only. Binders, slipcases and labels sold separately.
For more information album contents visit our web site at www.amosadvantage.com.

**FEBRUARY**
Global Part 1
Global Part 2
All American Regular & Commemoratives

**MARCH**
All American Part 3 United Nations
U.N Singles
U.N. Imprint Blocks
U.N. Postal Stationery

**APRIL**
All American Part 2 Postal Stationery
All American Part 4 Booklet Panes
All American Part 5 Sheetlets
All American Part 7 Postal Cards
U.S. Commemoratives
U.S. Plate Blocks
U.S. Regular Issues
U.S. Booklet Panes
U.S. Postal Stationery
U.S. Sheetlets

**MAY**
Albania
Austria
Bulgaria
Canada
Croatia
France
French Andorra
Germany
Gibraltar
Great Britain, Ireland
Guernsey, Jersey, Isle Of Man
Hong Kong
Ireland
Monaco
Romania
Serbia & Montenegro
Singapore
Slovenia

**JUNE**
Denmark
Egypt
Finland
Greece
Israel Singles
Israel Plate Blocks
Israel Tab Singles
Korea
Liechtenstein
Norway
Sweden
Switzerland

**JULY**
Bangladesh
India
Italy
Japan
Pakistan
People's Republic of China
Portugal/Azores/Maderia
San Marino
Spain
Sri Lanka
Thailand
Vatican City

**AUGUST**
Armenia
Azerbaijan
Belarus
Belgium
Czech Republic & Slovakia
Georgia
Hungary
Kazakhstan
Kyrgyzstan
Latvia, Lithuania, Estonia
Luxembourg
Moldova
Netherlands
Poland
Russia
Tajikistan
Turkmenistan
Ukraine
Uzbekistan

**SEPTEMBER**
Argentina
Australia
Brazil
Chile
Colombia
Dominican Republic
Haiti
Mexico
New Zealand
Venezuela

**DECEMBER**
All American Part 6 Plate No. Coils
U.S. Plate No. Coils

# AMOS
## ADVANTAGE

911 Vandemark Road
Sidney OH 45365
1-800-572-6885
www.amosadvantage.com

# GABON

ga-'bōⁿ

LOCATION — West coast of Africa, at the equator
GOVT. — Republic
AREA — 102,089 sq. mi.
POP. — 1,225,853 (1999 est.)
CAPITAL — Libreville

Gabon originally was under the control of French West Africa. In 1886, it was united with French Congo. In 1904, Gabon was granted a certain degree of colonial autonomy which prevailed until 1934, when it merged with French Equatorial Africa. Gabon Republic was proclaimed November 28, 1958.

100 Centimes = 1 Franc

Catalogue values for unused stamps in this country are for Never Hinged items, beginning with Scott 148 in the regular postage section, Scott B4 in the semi-postal section, Scott C1 in the airpost section, Scott CB1 in the airpost semi-postal section, Scott J34 in the postage due section, and Scott O1 in the officials section.

## Watermark

Wmk. 385

Stamps of French Colonies of 1881-86 Handstamp Surcharged in Black:

a    b

**1886    Unwmk.    Perf. 14x13½**

| 1 | A9 (a) | 5c on 20c red, grn | 525.00 | 525.00 |
| 2 | A9 (b) | 10c on 20c red, grn | 525.00 | 525.00 |
| 3 | A9 (b) | 25c on 20c red, grn | 87.50 | 65.00 |
| e. | | 56 dots around "GAB" | 6,250. | 1,900. |
| 4 | A9 (b) | 50c on 15c bl | 1,450. | 2,000. |
| 5 | A9 (b) | 75c on 15c bl | 1,800. | 2,200. |

Nos. 1-3 exist with double surcharge of numeral; No. 3 with "GAB" double or inverted, or with "25" double.
On Nos. 3 and 5 the surcharge slants down; on No. 4 it slants up. The number of dots varies.
Counterfeits of Nos. 1-15 exist.

Handstamp Surcharged in Black — c

**15**

**1888-89**

| 6 | A9 | 15c on 10c blk, lav | 5,600. | 1,400. |
| 7 | A9 | 15c on 1fr brnz grn, straw | 2,250. | 1,100. |
| 8 | A9 | 25c on 5c grn, grnsh | 1,500. | 275. |
| 9 | A9 | 25c on 10c blk, lav | 5,800. | 1,800. |
| 10 | A9 | 25c on 75c car, rose | 3,400. | 1,800. |

Official reprints exist.

Postage Due Stamps of French Colonies Handstamp Surcharged in Black — d

**1889    Imperf.**

| 11 | D1 | 15c on 5c black | 300.00 | 250.00 |
| 12 | D1 | 15c on 30c black | 5,000. | 3,700. |
| 13 | D1 | 25c on 20c black | 125.00 | 95.00 |

Nos. 11 and 13 exist with "GABON," "TIMBRE" or "25" double; "TIMBRE" or "15" omitted, etc.

A8

**1889    Typeset**

| 14 | A8 | 15c blk, rose | 1,800. | 1,200. |
| 15 | A8 | 25c blk, green | 1,200. | 925. |

Ten varieties of each. Nos. 14-15 exist with "GAB" inverted or omitted, and with small "f" in "Francaise."

Navigation and Commerce — A9

**1904-07    Typo.    Perf. 14x13½**
**Name of Colony in Blue or Carmine**

| 16 | A9 | 1c blk, lil bl | 1.10 | .95 |
| a. | | "GABON" double | 250.00 | |
| 17 | A9 | 2c brn, buff | 1.25 | 1.10 |
| 18 | A9 | 4c claret, lav | 2.00 | 1.50 |
| 19 | A9 | 5c yellow green | 2.75 | 2.25 |
| 20 | A9 | 10c rose | 9.50 | 7.50 |
| 21 | A9 | 15c gray | 10.50 | 7.50 |
| 22 | A9 | 20c red, grn | 15.00 | 11.50 |
| 23 | A9 | 25c blue | 12.50 | 7.50 |
| 24 | A9 | 30c yel brn | 15.00 | 15.00 |
| 25 | A9 | 35c blk, yel ('06) | 21.00 | 21.00 |
| 26 | A9 | 40c red, straw | 25.00 | 19.00 |
| 27 | A9 | 45c blk, gray grn ('07) | 45.00 | 45.00 |
| 28 | A9 | 50c brn, az | 20.00 | 20.00 |
| 29 | A9 | 75c dp vio, org | 25.00 | 25.00 |
| 30 | A9 | 1fr brnz grn, straw | 40.00 | 35.00 |
| 31 | A9 | 2fr vio, rose | 95.00 | 80.00 |
| 32 | A9 | 5fr lil, lav | 150.00 | 125.00 |
| | | Nos. 16-32 (17) | 490.60 | 424.80 |

Perf. 13½x14 stamps are counterfeits.
For surcharges see Nos. 72-84.

Fang Warrior — A10    Fang Woman — A12

Libreville A11

Inscribed: "Congo Français"

**1910    Perf. 13½x14**

| 33 | A10 | 1c choc & org | 1.90 | 1.90 |
| 34 | A10 | 2c black & choc | 2.50 | 2.50 |
| 35 | A10 | 4c vio & dp bl | 2.50 | 2.50 |
| 36 | A10 | 5c ol gray & grn | 4.00 | 4.00 |
| 37 | A10 | 10c red & car | 5.75 | 5.75 |
| 38 | A10 | 20c choc & dk vio | 7.50 | 7.50 |
| 39 | A11 | 25c dp bl & choc | 8.00 | 8.00 |
| 40 | A11 | 30c gray blk & red | 36.00 | 36.00 |
| 41 | A11 | 35c dk vio & grn | 24.00 | 24.00 |
| 42 | A11 | 40c choc & ultra | 30.00 | 30.00 |
| 43 | A11 | 45c carmine & vio | 47.50 | 47.50 |
| 44 | A11 | 50c bl grn & gray | 72.50 | 72.50 |
| 45 | A11 | 75c org & choc | 120.00 | 120.00 |
| 46 | A12 | 1fr dk brn & bis | 120.00 | 120.00 |
| 47 | A12 | 2fr carmine & brn | 325.00 | 325.00 |
| 48 | A12 | 5fr blue & choc | 325.00 | 325.00 |
| | | Nos. 33-48 (16) | 1,132. | 1,132. |

Inscribed: "Afrique Equatoriale"

**1910-22**

| 49 | A10 | 1c choc & org | .30 | .30 |
| 50 | A10 | 2c black & choc | .30 | .30 |
| a. | | 2c gray black & deep olive | .50 | .55 |
| 51 | A10 | 4c vio & dp bl | .50 | .50 |
| 52 | A10 | 5c ol gray & grn | .80 | .50 |
| 53 | A10 | 5c gray blk & ocher ('22) | 1.10 | 1.25 |
| 54 | A10 | 10c red & car | 1.25 | 1.00 |
| 55 | A10 | 10c yel grn & bl grn ('22) | 1.10 | 1.25 |
| 56 | A10 | 15c brn vio & rose ('18) | .80 | .65 |
| 57 | A10 | 20c ol brn & dk vio | 14.50 | 10.00 |
| 58 | A11 | 25c dp bl & choc | 1.00 | .90 |
| 59 | A11 | 25c Prus bl & blk ('22) | 1.50 | 1.50 |
| 60 | A11 | 30c gray blk & red | 1.50 | 1.50 |
| 61 | A11 | 30c rose & red ('22) | 1.75 | 1.75 |
| 62 | A11 | 35c dk vio & grn | 1.10 | 1.10 |
| 63 | A11 | 40c choc & ultra | 1.50 | 1.25 |
| 64 | A11 | 45c carmine & vio | 1.40 | 1.40 |
| 65 | A11 | 45c blk & red ('22) | 2.10 | 2.10 |
| 66 | A11 | 50c bl grn & gray | 1.75 | 1.60 |
| 67 | A11 | 50c dk bl & bl ('22) | 1.25 | 1.25 |
| 68 | A11 | 75c org & choc | 6.00 | 6.00 |
| 69 | A12 | 1fr dk brn & bis | 3.25 | 3.25 |
| 70 | A12 | 2fr car & brn | 5.50 | 5.50 |
| 71 | A12 | 5fr blue & choc | 9.00 | 9.00 |
| | | Nos. 49-71 (23) | 59.25 | 53.85 |

For overprints & surcharges see #85-119, B1-B3.

Stamps of 1904-07 Surcharged in Black or Carmine

**1912**

| 72 | A9 | 5c on 2c brn, buff | 1.40 | 1.40 |
| 73 | A9 | 5c on 4c cl, lav (C) | 1.40 | 1.40 |
| 74 | A9 | 5c on 15c gray (C) | 1.25 | 1.25 |
| 75 | A9 | 5c on 20c red, grn | 1.10 | 1.10 |
| 76 | A9 | 5c on 25c bl (C) | 1.25 | 1.25 |
| 77 | A9 | 5c on 30c pale brn (C) | 1.40 | 1.40 |
| 78 | A9 | 10c on 40c red, straw | 1.40 | 1.40 |
| 79 | A9 | 10c on 45c blk, gray grn (C) | 1.40 | 1.40 |
| 80 | A9 | 10c on 50c brn, az (C) | 1.50 | 1.50 |
| 81 | A9 | 10c on 75c dp vio, org (C) | 1.50 | 1.50 |
| 82 | A9 | 10c on 1fr brnz grn, straw (C) | 1.50 | 1.50 |
| 83 | A9 | 10c on 2fr vio, rose | 1.60 | 1.60 |
| a. | | Inverted surcharge | 325.00 | 325.00 |
| 84 | A9 | 10c on 5fr lil, lav | 4.50 | 4.50 |
| | | Nos. 72-84 (13) | 21.20 | 21.20 |

Two spacings between the surcharged numerals are found on Nos. 72 to 84. For detailed listings, see the Scott Classic Specialized Catalogue of Stamps and Covers.

Stamps of 1910-22 Overprinted in Black, Blue or Carmine

On A10, A12

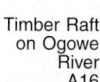

On A11

**1924-31**

| 85 | A10 | 1c brown & org | .30 | .40 |
| 86 | A10 | 2c blk & choc (Bl) | .50 | .60 |
| 87 | A10 | 4c violet & ind | .30 | .30 |
| 88 | A10 | 5c gray blk & ocher | .45 | .45 |
| 89 | A10 | 10c yel grn & bl grn | 1.00 | 1.00 |
| a. | | Double overprint (Bk & Bl) | 160.00 | |
| 90 | A10 | 10c dk bl & brn ('26) (C) | .40 | .40 |
| 91 | A10 | 15c brn vio & rose (Bl) | 1.00 | 1.00 |
| 92 | A10 | 15c rose & brn vio ('31) (Bl) | 1.25 | 1.25 |
| 93 | A10 | 20c ol brn & dk vio (C) | 1.00 | 1.00 |
| a. | | Inverted overprint | 160.00 | 160.00 |
| 94 | A11 | 25c Prus bl & blk (C) | .80 | .80 |
| 95 | A11 | 30c rose & red (Bl) | .80 | .80 |
| 96 | A11 | 30c blk & org ('26) | 1.00 | 1.00 |
| 97 | A11 | 30c dk grn & bl grn ('28) | 1.10 | 1.10 |
| 98 | A11 | 35c dk vio & grn (Bl) | .75 | .75 |
| 99 | A11 | 40c choc & ultra (C) | .75 | .75 |
| 100 | A11 | 45c blk & red (Bl) | 1.50 | 1.50 |
| 101 | A11 | 50c dk bl & bl (C) | 1.00 | 1.00 |
| 102 | A11 | 50c car & grn ('26) | 1.10 | 1.10 |
| 103 | A11 | 65c dp bl & red org ('28) | 4.50 | 4.00 |
| 104 | A11 | 75c org & brn (Bl) | 2.00 | 2.00 |
| 105 | A11 | 90c brn red & rose ('30) | 2.75 | 2.75 |
| 106 | A12 | 1fr dk brn & bis | 1.75 | 1.75 |
| 107 | A12 | 1.10fr dl grn & rose red ('28) | 7.00 | 6.50 |
| 108 | A12 | 1.50fr pale bl & dk bl ('30) | 1.25 | 1.25 |
| 109 | A12 | 2fr rose & brn | 2.10 | 2.25 |
| 110 | A12 | 3fr red vio ('30) | 10.50 | 8.25 |
| 111 | A12 | 5fr dp bl & choc | 6.50 | 6.50 |
| | | Nos. 85-111 (27) | 54.85 | 50.45 |

Types of 1924-31 Issues Surcharged with New Values in Black or Carmine

**1925-28**

| 112 | A12 | 65c on 1fr ol grn & brn | 1.10 | 1.10 |
| 113 | A12 | 85c on 1fr ol grn & brn | 1.25 | 1.25 |
| 114 | A11 | 90c on 75c brn red & cer ('27) | 1.60 | 1.60 |
| 115 | A12 | 1.25fr on 1fr dk bl & ultra ('27) | .90 | .90 |
| 116 | A12 | 1.50fr on 1fr lt bl & dk bl ('27) | 1.60 | 1.60 |
| 117 | A12 | 3fr on 5fr mag & ol brn | 9.25 | 8.00 |
| 118 | A12 | 10fr on 5fr org brn & grn ('27) | 15.00 | 13.00 |
| 119 | A12 | 20fr on 5fr red vio & org red ('27) | 16.00 | 14.50 |
| | | Nos. 112-119 (8) | 46.70 | 41.95 |

Bars cover the old denominations on #114-119.

Common Design Types pictured following the introduction.

**Colonial Exposition Issue**
Common Design Types

**1931    Perf. 12½**
**Name of Country in Black**

| 120 | CD70 | 40c dp green | 3.75 | 3.75 |
| 121 | CD71 | 50c violet | 3.75 | 3.75 |
| 122 | CD72 | 90c red orange | 3.75 | 3.75 |
| 123 | CD73 | 1.50fr dull blue | 5.75 | 5.75 |
| | | Nos. 120-123 (4) | 17.00 | 17.00 |

Timber Raft on Ogowe River A16

Count Savorgnan de Brazza — A17

Village of
Setta
Kemma
A18

**1932-33      Photo.      Perf. 13x13½**
| | | | | |
|---|---|---|---|---|
|124|A16|1c brown violet|.25|.25|
|125|A16|2c blk, *rose*|.25|.25|
|126|A16|4c green|.30|.30|
|127|A16|5c grnsh blue|.55|.55|
|128|A16|10c red, *yel*|.55|.55|
|129|A16|15c red, *grn*|.65|.60|
|130|A16|20c deep red|.65|.60|
|131|A16|25c brown red|.65|.50|
|132|A17|30c yellow grn|2.00|1.60|
|133|A17|40c brown vio|2.10|1.00|
|134|A17|45c blk, *dl grn*|3.00|2.00|
|135|A17|50c red brown|1.60|1.00|
|136|A17|65c Prus blue|6.00|5.75|
|137|A17|75c blk, *red org*|3.75|2.75|
|138|A17|90c rose red|3.75|2.75|
|139|A17|1fr yel grn, *bl*|26.50|22.50|
|140|A18|1.25fr dp vio ('33)|2.00|1.60|
|141|A18|1.50fr dull blue|9.50|6.00|
|142|A18|1.75fr dp green ('33)|2.10|1.60|
|143|A18|2fr brn red|47.50|35.00|
|144|A18|3fr yel grn, *bl*|5.50|4.00|
|145|A18|5fr red brown|13.50|11.00|
|146|A18|10fr blk, *red org*|30.00|27.50|
|147|A18|20fr dk violet|47.50|40.00|
| |*Nos. 124-147 (24)*|210.15|169.65|

See French Equatorial Africa No. 192 for stamp inscribed "Gabon" and "Afrique Equatoriale Francaise."

Catalogue values for all unused stamps in this section, from this point to the end of the section, are for **Never Hinged** items.

**Republic**

Prime Minister
Leon
Mba — A19

Flag & Map of
Gabon & UN
Emblem — A20

**Unwmk.**
**1959, Nov. 28      Engr.      Perf. 13**
|148|A19|15fr shown| |.40|.20|
|149|A19|25fr Mba, profile| |.40|.20|

Proclamation of the Republic, 1st anniv.

**Imperforates**
Most Gabon stamps from 1959 onward exist imperforate in issued and trial colors, and also in small presentation sheets in issued colors.

**C.C.T.A. Issue**
Common Design Type
**1960, May 21      Engr.      Perf. 13**
|150|CD106|50fr vio brn & Prus bl|1.10|1.10|

**1961, Feb. 9**
|151|A20|15fr multi|.35|.20|
|152|A20|25fr multi|.55|.20|
|153|A20|85fr multi|1.90|1.10|
| |*Nos. 151-153 (3)*|2.80|1.50|

Gabon's admission to United Nations.

Combretum
A21

1fr, 5fr, Tulip tree, vert. 2fr, 3fr, Yellow cassia.

**1961, July 4      Unwmk.      Perf. 13**
|154|A21|50c rose red & grn|.20|.20|
|155|A21|1fr sl grn, red & bis|.20|.20|
|156|A21|2fr dk grn & yel|.40|.20|
|157|A21|3fr ol grn & yel|.60|.55|
|158|A21|5fr multi|.75|.60|
|159|A21|10fr grn & rose red|.80|.60|
| |*Nos. 154-159 (6)*|2.95|2.35|

President Leon
Mba — A22

**1962**                                         **Engr.**
|160|A22|15fr indigo, car & grn|.30|.20|
|161|A22|20fr brn blk, car & grn|.50|.20|
|162|A22|25fr brn, car & grn|.55|.20|
| |*Nos. 160-162 (3)*|1.35|.60|

**Abidjan Games Issue**
Common Design Type
**1962, July 21      Photo.      Perf. 12½x12**
|163|CD109|20fr Foot race, start|.75|.50|
|164|CD109|50fr Soccer|1.25|1.00|
| |*Nos. 163-164,C6 (3)*|5.75|3.75|

**African-Malgache Union Issue**
Common Design Type
**1962, Sept. 8      Perf. 12½x12**
|165|CD110|30fr emer, bluish grn, red & gold|1.60|1.25|

Captain
Ntchorere
and Flags
of France
and
Gabon
A23

**1962, Nov. 23      Perf. 12**
|166|A23|80fr multi|1.60|1.10|

Capt. Ntchorere, who died for France, 6/7/40.

Waves
Around
Globe
A23a

Design: 100fr, Orbit patterns around globe.

**1963, Sept. 19      Photo.      Perf. 12½**
|167|A23a|25fr ultra, grn & org|.55|.55|
|168|A23a|100fr grn, ultra & red brn|2.10|1.75|

Issued to publicize space communications.

UNESCO
Emblem,
Scales and
Tree
A23b

**1963, Dec. 10      Engr.      Perf. 13**
|169|A23b|25fr grn, dk gray & red brn|.60|.20|

15th anniv. of the Universal Declaration of Human Rights.

Barograph
and WMO
Emblem
A23c

**1964, Mar. 23      Unwmk.      Perf. 13**
|170|A23c|25fr ol bis, sl grn & ultra|.90|.60|

UN's 4th World Meteorological Day, Mar. 23.

Arms of
Gabon — A24

**1964, June 15   Photo.   Perf. 13x12½**
|171|A24|25fr ocher & multi|.90|.45|

Tarpon
A25

Designs: 60fr, Gorilla, vert. 80fr, Buffalo.

**1964, July 15      Engr.      Perf. 13**
|172|A25|30fr brn red, bl & blk|1.25|.70|
|173|A25|60fr brn, grn & brn red|2.25|.90|
|174|A25|80fr dk bl, grn & red brn|2.40|1.25|
| |*Nos. 172-174 (3)*|5.90|2.85|

**Cooperation Issue**
Common Design Type
**1964, Nov. 7**
|175|CD119|25fr gray, dk brn & lt bl|.90|.60|

Dissotis
Rotundifolia — A26

5fr, Gloriosa superba. 15fr, Eulophia horsfallii.

**1964, Nov. 16  Photo.  Perf. 12x12½**
**Flowers in Natural Colors**
|176|A26|3fr deep grn|.35|.20|
|177|A26|5fr green|.70|.35|
|178|A26|15fr dark brn|1.10|.75|
| |*Nos. 176-178 (3)*|2.15|1.30|

Sun and
IQSY
Emblem
A27

**1965, Feb. 25      Perf. 12½x12**
|179|A27|85fr multi|1.60|.80|

International Quiet Sun Year, 1964-65.

Morse
Telegraph
A28

**1965, May 17      Engr.      Perf. 13**
|180|A28|30fr multi|.90|.60|

Cent. of the ITU.

Manganese
Crusher,
Moanda
A29

Design: 60fr, Uranium mining, Mounana.

**1965, June 15      Unwmk.      Perf. 13**
|181|A29|15fr brt bl, pur & red|.55|.30|
|182|A29|60fr brn, brt bl & red|1.90|.90|

Issued to publicize Gabon's mineral wealth.

Field Ball — A30        Okoukoue
Dance — A31

**1965, July 15      Engr.      Perf. 13**
|183|A30|25fr brt grn, blk & red|.90|.60|

1st African Games, Brazzaville, 7/18-25. See #C35.

**1965, Sept. 15      Perf. 13**
Design: 60fr, Mukudji dance.
|184|A31|25fr brn, grn & yel|.55|.20|
|185|A31|60fr blk, dk red & brn|1.75|.90|

Abraham
Lincoln
A32

**1965, Sept. 28  Photo.  Perf. 12½x13**
|186|A32|50fr vio bl, blk, gold & buff|1.00|.50|

Centenary of death of Abraham Lincoln.

Old & New
Post Offices
and Mail
Transport
A33

**1965, Dec. 18      Engr.      Perf. 13**
|187|A33|30fr bl, brt grn & choc|.90|.70|

Issued for Stamp Day, 1965.

Balumbu
Mask — A34

Intl. Negro Arts Festival, Dakar, Senegal, Apr. 1-24:

10fr, Fang ancestral figure, Byeri. 25fr, Fang mask. 30fr, Okuyi mask, Myene. 85fr, Bakota leather mask.

**1966, Apr. 18  Photo.  Perf. 12x12½**
|188|A34|5fr red, brn, blk & buff|.30|.20|
|189|A34|10fr brt grnsh bl, dk brn & yel|.35|.30|
|190|A34|25fr multicolored|1.00|.35|
|191|A34|30fr mar, yel & blk|1.25|.70|
|192|A34|85fr multicolored|3.00|1.60|
| |*Nos. 188-192 (5)*|5.90|3.15|

WHO Headquarters, Geneva — A35

**1966, May 3   Photo.   Perf. 12½x13**
193 A35 50fr org yel, ultra & blk   1.40  .60
   Inauguration of the WHO Headquarters, Geneva.

Mother Learning to Write — A36     Soccer Player — A37

**1966, June 22  Photo.   Perf. 12x12½**
194 A36 30fr multi   .90  .45
   UNESCO literacy campaign.

**1966, July 15   Engr.   Perf. 13**
Design: 90fr, Player facing left.
195 A37 25fr brn, grn & ultra   .80  .20
196 A37 90fr ultra & dk pur   2.50 1.25
   Nos. 195-196,C45 (3)   6.30 2.70
   8th World Cup Soccer Championship, Wembley, England, July 11-30.

Timber Industry — A38

Economic development: 85fr, Offshore oil rigs.

**1966, Aug. 17   Perf. 13**
197 A38 20fr red brn, lil & dk grn   .80  .50
198 A38 85fr dk brn, brt bl & brt grn   4.00 1.60

Woman with Children at Bank Window A39

**1966, Sept. 23   Engr.   Perf. 13**
199 A39 25fr brt bl, vio brn & sl grn   1.00  .50
   Issued to publicize Savings Banks.

Scouts Around Campfire A40

50fr, Boy Scout pledging ceremony, vert.

**1966, Oct. 17   Engr.   Perf. 13**
200 A40 30fr sl bl, car & dk brn   1.00  .60
201 A40 50fr Prus bl, brn red & dk brn   1.60  .70
   Issued to honor Gabon's Boy Scouts.

Sikorsky S-43 Hydroplane and Map of West Africa A41

**1966, Dec. 17  Photo.   Perf. 12½x12**
202 A41 30fr multi   2.10 1.25
   Stamp Day and for the 30th anniv. of the 1st air-mail service from Libreville to Port Gentil.

Hippopotami — A42

Animals: 2fr, African crocodiles. 3fr, Water chevrotain. 5fr, Chimpanzees. 10fr, Elephants. 20fr, Leopards.

**1967, Jan. 5   Photo.   Perf. 13x14**
203 A42  1fr multi   .20  .20
204 A42  2fr multi   .45  .20
205 A42  3fr multi   .45  .20
206 A42  5fr multi   .50  .20
207 A42 10fr multi   2.00  .80
208 A42 20fr multi   4.00  .80
   Nos. 203-208 (6)   7.60 2.40

Lions International Emblem — A43

50fr, Lions emblem, map of Gabon and globe.

**1967, Jan. 14   Perf. 12½x13**
209 A43 30fr multicolored   .80  .20
210 A43 50fr blue & multi   1.40  .80
a.   Strip of 2, #209-210 + label   3.25 1.75
   50th anniv. of Lions Intl.

Carnival Masks — A44

**1967, Feb. 4   Photo.   Perf. 12x12½**
211 A44 30fr brn, yel bis & bl   1.10  .45
   Libreville Carnival, Feb. 4-7.

"Transportation" and Tourist Year Emblem — A45

**1967, Feb. 15   Perf. 12½x13**
212 A45 30fr multi   1.10  .45
   International Tourist Year, 1967.

Olympic Diving Tower, Mexico City — A46     Symbolic of Atomic Energy Agency — A47

   1968 Olympic Games: 30fr, Sun, snow crystals and Olympic rings. 50fr, Ice skating rink and view of Grenoble.

**1967, Mar. 18   Engr.   Perf. 13**
213 A46 25fr dk vio, grnsh bl & ultra   .75  .40
214 A46 30fr grn, red lil & mar   1.10  .50
215 A46 50fr ultra, grn & brn   1.75 1.10
   Nos. 213-215 (3)   3.60 2.00

**1967, Apr. 15   Engr.   Perf. 13**
216 A47 30fr red brn, dk grn & ultra   1.00  .20
   International Atomic Energy Agency.

Pope Paul VI, Papal Arms and Libreville Cathedral A48

**1967, June 1   Engr.   Perf. 13**
217 A48 30fr ultra, grn & blk   1.10  .50
   "Populorum progressio" encyclical by Pope Paul VI concerning underdeveloped countries.

Flags, Tree, Logger, Map of Gabon and Mask — A49

**1967, June 24   Engr.   Perf. 13**
218 A49 30fr multi   1.00  .50
   EXPO '67, International Exhibition, Montreal, Apr. 28-Oct. 27, 1967.

**Europafrica Issue, 1967**

Map of Europe and Africa and Products A50

**1967, July 18   Photo.   Perf. 12½x12**
219 A50 50fr multi   1.50  .60

UN Emblem, Women and Child A51

**1967, Aug. 10   Engr.   Perf. 13**
220 A51 75fr brt blue, dk brn & emer   1.90  .80
   United Nations Commission for Women.

19th Century Mail Ships — A52

Design: No. 222, Modern mail ships.

**1967, Nov. 17   Photo.   Perf. 12½**
221 A52 30fr multi   1.90  .95
222 A52 30fr multi   1.90  .95
a.   Pair, #221-222   5.00 5.00
   Stamp Day. No. 222a has continuous design.

Draconea Fragrans — A53

Trees: 10fr, Pycnanthus angolensis. 20fr, Disthemonanthus benthamianus.

**1967, Dec. 5   Engr.   Perf. 13**
   **Size: 22x36mm**
223 A53  5fr bl, emer & brn   1.00  .35
224 A53 10fr grn, dk grn & bl   1.10  .55
225 A53 20fr rose red, grn & ol   1.60  .90
   Nos. 223-225,C61-C62 (5)   9.30 4.80
   For booklet pane see No. C62a.

WHO Regional Office A54

**1968, Apr. 8   Engr.   Perf. 13**
226 A54 20fr multi   1.00  .50
   20th anniv. of the WHO.

Dam, Power Station and UNESCO Emblem A55

**1968, June 18   Engr.   Perf. 13**
227 A55 15fr lake, org & Prus bl   .70  .40
   Hydrological Decade (UNESCO), 1965-74.

Pres. Albert Bernard Bongo — A56

30fr, Pres. Bongo & arms of Gabon in background.

**1968, June 24  Photo.   Perf. 12x12½**
228 A56 25fr grn, buff & blk   .65  .20
229 A56 30fr rose lil, lt bl & blk   .75  .20

Tanker, Refinery, and Map of Area Served — A56a

**1968, July 30   Photo.   *Perf. 12½***
230  A56a 30fr multi                    1.00  .50
Port Gentil (Gabon) Refinery opening, 6/12/68.

Open Book, Child and UNESCO Emblem A57

**1968, Sept. 10   Engr.   *Perf. 13***
231  A57 25fr vio bl, dl red & brn     1.60  .20
Issued for International Literacy Day.

A58                    A60

A59

**1968, Oct. 15   Engr.   *Perf. 13***
232  A58 20fr Coffee                   1.60  .75
233  A58 40fr Cacao                    2.50 1.10

**1968, Nov. 23   Engr.   *Perf. 13***
234  A59 30fr "La Junon"               2.00  .70
Issued for Stamp Day.

**1968, Dec. 10**
Lawyer, globe and human rights flame.
235  A60 20fr blk, bl grn & car         .70  .45
International Human Rights Year.

Okanda Gap — A61

Designs: 15fr, Barracuda. 25fr, Kinguele Waterfall, vert. 30fr, Sitatunga trophies, vert.

**1969, Mar. 28   Photo.**
236  A61 10fr brn, bl & sl grn          .35  .20
237  A61 15fr brn red, emer & ind 2.50  .50
238  A61 20fr bl, pur & ol              .75  .30
239  A61 30fr multi                    1.60  .70
    Nos. 236-239 (4)                   5.20 1.75
Year of African Tourism, 1969.

Mvet (Musical Instrument) A62

Musical Instruments: 30fr, Ngombi harp. 50fr, Ebele and Mbe drums. 100fr, Medzang xylophone.

**1969, June 6   Engr.   *Perf. 13***
240  A62 25fr plum, ol & dp car         .50  .20
241  A62 30fr red brn, ol & dk brn      .50  .20
242  A62 50fr plum, ol & dp car        1.10  .65
243  A62 100fr red brn, ol & dk brn    2.40 1.00
  a.  Min. sheet of 4, #240-243        6.50 6.50
    Nos. 240-243 (4)                   4.50 2.05

Aframomum Polyanthum (Zingiberaceae) A63

Tree of Life A64

African Plants: 2fr, Chlamydocola chlamydantha (Sterculiaceae). 5fr, Costus dinklagei (Zingiberaceae). 10fr, Cola rostrata (Sterculiaceae). 20fr, Dischistocalyx grandifolius (Acanthaceae).

**1969, July 15   Photo.   *Perf. 12x12½***
244  A63 1fr multi                      .20  .20
245  A63 2fr lt ol & multi              .20  .20
246  A63 5fr multi                      .20  .20
247  A63 10fr slate & multi            1.10  .20
248  A63 20fr yel & multi              1.75  .70
    Nos. 244-248 (5)                   3.45 1.50

**1969, Aug. 17   Photo.**
249  A64 25fr multi                     .60  .50
National renovation.

Drilling for Oil on Land — A65

Workers and ILO Emblem — A66

Design: 50fr, Offshore drilling station.

**1969, Sept. 13   *Perf. 12x12½***
250  A65 25fr multi                     .20  .20
251  A65 50fr multi                    2.10  .20
  a.  Strip of 2, #250-251 + label     3.00 3.00
20th anniv. of the ELF-SPAFE oil operations in Gabon.

**1969, Oct. 29   Engr.   *Perf. 13***
252  A66 30fr bl, sl grn & dp car       .90  .45
50th anniv. of the ILO.

Arms of Port Gentil — A67

Coats of Arms: 20fr, Lambarene. 30fr, Libreville.

**1969, Nov. 19   Photo.   *Perf. 12***
253  A67 20fr red, gold, sil & blk     1.00  .20
254  A67 25fr bl, blk & gold           1.40  .20
255  A67 30fr bl & multi               1.60  .80
    Nos. 253-255 (3)                   4.00 1.20
See Nos. 267-269, 291-293, 321-326, 340-348, 409-417, 492-501.

Canoe Mail Transport A68

**1969, Dec. 18   Engr.   *Perf. 13***
256  A68 30fr brt grn, grnsh bl & red brn   1.25  .80
Issued for Stamp Day 1969.

Satellite, Globe, TV Screen and ITU Emblem A69

**1970, May 17   Engr.   *Perf. 13***
257  A69 25fr dk bl, dk red brn & blk .90  .60
International Telecommunications Day.

**UPU Headquarters Issue**
Common Design Type
**1970, May 20   Engr.   *Perf. 13***
258  CD133 30fr brt grn, brt rose lil & brn  1.10  .55

Geisha and African Drummer A70

**1970, May 27   Photo.   *Perf. 12½x12***
259  A70 30fr ultra & multi           1.10  .60
EXPO '70 Intl. Exhibition, Osaka, Japan, 3/15-9/13.

**ASECNA Issue**
Common Design Type
**1970, Aug. 26   Engr.   *Perf. 13***
260  CD132 100fr brt grn & bl grn 2.00  .95

UN Emblem, Globe, Dove and Charts A71

**1970, Oct. 24   Photo.   *Perf. 12½x12***
261  A71 30fr Prus bl & multi          .90  .60
25th anniversary of the United Nations.

Bushbucks A72

Designs: 15fr, Pels scaly-tailed flying squirrel. 25fr, Gray-cheeked monkey, vert. 40fr, African golden cat. 60fr, Sevaline genet.

**1970, Dec. 14   Photo.   *Perf. 12½x13***
262  A72 5fr yel grn & multi           .60  .40
263  A72 15fr red org & blk            .95  .55
264  A72 25fr vio & multi             1.75  .80
265  A72 40fr red & multi             2.75 1.10
266  A72 60fr bl & multi              4.75 2.10
    Nos. 262-266 (5)                  10.80 4.95

Coats of Arms Type of 1969
20fr, Mouila. 25fr, Bitam. 30fr, Oyem.

**1971, Feb. 16   Photo.   *Perf. 12***
267  A67 20fr ver, blk, sil & gold     .90  .20
268  A67 25fr emer, gold & blk        1.00  .20
269  A67 30fr emer, gold, blk & red   1.25  .20
    Nos. 267-269 (3)                   3.15  .60

Men of Four Races and Emblem — A73

**1971, Mar. 21   Engr.   *Perf. 13***
270  A73 40fr multi                    .90  .45
Intl. year against racial discrimination.

Map of Africa and Telecommunications System — A74

**1971, Apr. 30   Photo.   *Perf. 13***
271  A74 30fr org & multi              .90  .45
Pan-African telecommunications system.

Charaxes Smaragdalis — A75

Butterflies: 10fr, Euxanthe crossleyi. 15fr, Epiphora rectifascia. 25fr, Imbrasia bouvieri.

**1971, May 26   Photo.   *Perf. 13***
272  A75 5fr yel & multi              2.40  .80
273  A75 10fr bl & multi              5.00 1.00
274  A75 15fr grn & multi             9.00 1.10
275  A75 25fr ol & multi             11.50 2.00
    Nos. 272-275 (4)                  27.90 4.90

Hertzian Center, Nkol Ogoum A76

**1971, June 17   Engr.   *Perf. 13***
276  A76 40fr grn, blk & dk car       1.10  .70
3rd World Telecommunications Day.

Mother Nursing Child A77

**1971, Aug. 17   Engr.   *Perf. 13***
277  A77 30fr lil rose, sep & ocher    .90  .45
Gabonese social security system, 15th anniv.

UN Headquarters and Emblem — A78

**1971, Sept. 30   Photo.   *Perf. 13***
278  A78 30fr red & multi              .90  .45
10th anniv. of Gabon's admission to the UN.

Large
Egret — A79

Birds: 40fr, African gray parrot. 50fr, Woodland Kingfisher. 75fr, Cameroon bareheaded rock-fowl. 100fr, Gold Coast touraco.

| | | | | |
|---|---|---|---|---|
| **1971, Oct. 12** | | **Litho.** | **Perf. 13** | |
| 279 | A79 | 30fr multi | 2.25 | 1.10 |
| 280 | A79 | 40fr multi | 3.00 | 1.50 |
| 281 | A79 | 50fr multi | 3.25 | 1.60 |
| 282 | A79 | 75fr multi | 4.50 | 2.10 |
| 283 | A79 | 100fr multi | 6.25 | 2.50 |
| | *Nos. 279-283 (5)* | | 19.25 | 8.80 |

Asystasia
Volgeliana
A80

Designs: Flowers of Acanthus Family after paintings by Noel Hallé.

| | | | | |
|---|---|---|---|---|
| **1972, Apr. 4** | | **Photo.** | **Perf. 13** | |
| 284 | A80 | 5fr pale cit & multi | .20 | .20 |
| 285 | A80 | 10fr multi | .50 | .20 |
| 286 | A80 | 20fr multi | .75 | .50 |
| 287 | A80 | 30fr lil rose & multi | 1.10 | .70 |
| 288 | A80 | 40fr dk grn & multi | 1.90 | 1.00 |
| 289 | A80 | 65fr red & multi | 3.25 | 1.40 |
| | *Nos. 284-289 (6)* | | 7.70 | 4.00 |

Louis
Pasteur — A81

| | | | | |
|---|---|---|---|---|
| **1972, May 15** | | **Engr.** | **Perf. 13** | |
| 290 | A81 | 80fr dp org, pur & grn | 1.25 | .60 |

Sesquicentennial of the birth of Louis Pasteur (1822-1895), scientist and bacteriologist.

Arms Type of 1969

30fr, Franceville. 40fr, Makokou. 60fr, Tchibanga.

| | | | | |
|---|---|---|---|---|
| **1972, June 2** | | **Photo.** | **Perf. 12** | |
| 291 | A67 | 30fr sil & multi | .75 | .20 |
| 292 | A67 | 40fr grn & multi | 1.25 | .50 |
| 293 | A67 | 60fr blk, grn & sil | 1.60 | .75 |
| | *Nos. 291-293 (3)* | | 3.10 | 1.45 |

Globe and Telecommunications
Symbols — A81a

| | | | | |
|---|---|---|---|---|
| **1972, July 25** | | | **Perf. 13x12½** | |
| 294 | A81a | 40fr blk, yel & org | .90 | .45 |

4th World Telecommunications Day.

Nat King
Cole — A82

Black American Jazz Musicians: 60fr, Sidney Bechet. 100fr, Louis Armstrong.

| | | | | |
|---|---|---|---|---|
| **1972, Sept. 1** | | **Photo.** | **Perf. 13x13½** | |
| 295 | A82 | 40fr bl & multi | 1.60 | .35 |
| 296 | A82 | 60fr org & multi | 2.40 | .70 |
| 297 | A82 | 100fr multi | 4.00 | 1.10 |
| | *Nos. 295-297 (3)* | | 8.00 | 2.15 |

Blanding's
Rear-fanged
Snake — A83

Designs: 2fr, Beauty snake. 3fr, Eggeating snake. 15fr, Striped ground snake. 25fr, Jameson's mamba. 50fr, Gabon viper.

| | | | | |
|---|---|---|---|---|
| **1972, Oct. 2** | | **Litho.** | **Perf. 13** | |
| 298 | A83 | 1fr lem & multi | .20 | .20 |
| 299 | A83 | 2fr red brn & multi | .20 | .20 |
| 300 | A83 | 3fr brn org & multi | .50 | .20 |
| 301 | A83 | 15fr multi | 1.90 | .50 |
| 302 | A83 | 25fr grn & multi | 3.75 | .55 |
| 303 | A83 | 50fr multi | 5.75 | 1.00 |
| | *Nos. 298-303 (6)* | | 12.30 | 2.65 |

See Nos. 330-332, 354-357.

Dr. Armauer G. Hansen, Lambarene
Leprosarium — A84

| | | | | |
|---|---|---|---|---|
| **1973, Jan. 28** | | **Engr.** | **Perf. 13** | |
| 304 | A84 | 30fr Prus grn, sl grn & brn | 1.25 | .55 |

Centenary of the discovery of the Hansen bacillus, the cause of leprosy.

Charaxes
Candiope — A85

Designs: Various butterflies.

| | | | | |
|---|---|---|---|---|
| **1973, Feb. 23** | | **Litho.** | **Perf. 13** | |
| 305 | A85 | 10fr shown | 2.50 | .40 |
| 306 | A85 | 15fr Eunica pechueli | 3.00 | .40 |
| 307 | A85 | 25fr Cyrestis camillus | 5.00 | .85 |
| 308 | A85 | 30fr Charaxes castor | 6.75 | 1.25 |
| 309 | A85 | 40fr Charaxes ameliae | 8.00 | 1.75 |
| 310 | A85 | 50fr Pseudacrea boisduvali | 8.75 | 2.10 |
| | *Nos. 305-310 (6)* | | 34.00 | 6.75 |

Balloon of Santos-Dumont,
1901 — A86

History of Aviation: 1fr, Montgolfier's balloon, 1783, vert. 3fr, Octave Chanute's biplane, 1896. 4fr, Clement Ader's Plane III, 1897. 5fr, Louis Bleriot crossing the Channel, 1909. 10fr, Fabre's hydroplane, 1910.

| | | | | |
|---|---|---|---|---|
| **1973, May 3** | | **Engr.** | **Perf. 13** | |
| 311 | A86 | 1fr grn, sl grn & dk red | .20 | .20 |
| 312 | A86 | 2fr sl grn & brt bl | .20 | .20 |
| 313 | A86 | 3fr bl, sl & org | .20 | .20 |
| 314 | A86 | 4fr lil & dk pur | .75 | .20 |
| 315 | A86 | 5fr slate grn & org | 1.10 | .35 |
| 316 | A86 | 10fr rose lil & Prus bl | 4.55 | 1.65 |
| | *Nos. 311-316 (6)* | | 4.55 | 1.65 |

| | | | |
|---|---|---|---|
| **1977** | | **Coil Stamp** | |
| 316A | A86 | 10fr aqua | 3.50 .20 |

No. 316A has red control numbers on back of every 10th stamp.

INTERPOL
Emblem — A87

| | | | | |
|---|---|---|---|---|
| **1973, June 26** | | **Engr.** | **Perf. 13** | |
| 317 | A87 | 40fr magenta & ultra | .90 | .40 |

50th anniversary of the International Criminal Police Organization (INTERPOL).

Earth
Station "2
Decembre"
A88

| | | | | |
|---|---|---|---|---|
| **1973, July 2** | | **Engr.** | **Perf. 13** | |
| 318 | A88 | 40fr slate grn, bl & brn | .90 | .40 |

Party Headquarters, Libreville — A89

| | | | | |
|---|---|---|---|---|
| **1973, Aug. 17** | | | **Photo.** | |
| 319 | A89 | 30fr multi | .90 | .20 |

**African Postal Union Issue**
Common Design Type

| | | | | |
|---|---|---|---|---|
| **1973, Sept. 12** | | **Engr.** | **Perf. 13** | |
| 320 | CD137 | 100fr red lil, pur & bl | 1.25 | .75 |

Arms Type of 1969

5fr, Gamba. 10fr, Ogowe-Lolo. 15fr, Fougamou. 30fr, Kango. 40fr, Booue. 60fr, Koula-Moutou.

| | | | | |
|---|---|---|---|---|
| **1973-74** | | **Photo.** | **Perf. 12** | |
| 321 | A67 | 5fr bl & multi ('74) | .65 | .20 |
| 322 | A67 | 10fr blk, red & gold ('74) | .65 | .20 |
| 323 | A67 | 15fr grn & multi ('74) | .90 | .20 |
| 324 | A67 | 30fr red & multi | 1.60 | .35 |
| 325 | A67 | 40fr red & multi | 1.90 | .55 |
| 326 | A67 | 60fr emer & multi | 3.00 | .70 |
| | *Nos. 321-326 (6)* | | 8.70 | 2.20 |

Issued #321-323, 2/13; #324-326, 10/4.

St. Teresa of
Lisieux — A90

40fr, St. Teresa and Jesus carrying cross.

| | | | | |
|---|---|---|---|---|
| **1973, Dec. 4** | | **Photo.** | **Perf. 13** | |
| 327 | A90 | 30fr blk & multi | .90 | .20 |
| 328 | A90 | 40fr blk & multi | 1.10 | .35 |

St. Teresa of the Infant Jesus (Thérèse Martin, 1873-97), Carmelite nun.

Human Rights
Flame — A91

| | | | | |
|---|---|---|---|---|
| **1973, Dec. 10** | | | **Engr.** | |
| 329 | A91 | 20fr grn, red & ultra | .60 | .20 |

25th anniversary of the Universal Declaration of Human Rights.

Wildlife Type of 1972

Monkeys: 40fr, Mangabey. 60fr, Cercopithecus cephus. 80fr, Mona monkey.

| | | | | |
|---|---|---|---|---|
| **1974, Mar. 20** | | **Litho.** | **Perf. 14** | |
| 330 | A83 | 40fr gray grn & multi | 1.50 | .65 |
| 331 | A83 | 60fr lt bl & multi | 2.40 | .80 |
| 332 | A83 | 80fr lil rose & multi | 4.00 | 1.25 |
| | *Nos. 330-332 (3)* | | 7.90 | 2.70 |

Ogowe
River at
Lambarene
A93

50fr, Cape Estérias. 75fr, Poubara rope bridge.

| | | | | |
|---|---|---|---|---|
| **1974, July 30** | | **Photo.** | **Perf. 13x13½** | |
| 333 | A93 | 30fr multi | .60 | .20 |
| 334 | A93 | 50fr multi | .80 | .20 |
| 335 | A93 | 75fr multi | 1.75 | .90 |
| | *Nos. 333-335 (3)* | | 3.15 | 1.30 |

Manioc
A94

Design: 50fr, Palms and dates.

| | | | | |
|---|---|---|---|---|
| **1974, Nov. 13** | | **Photo.** | **Perf. 13x12½** | |
| 336 | A94 | 40fr org red & multi | .90 | .30 |
| 337 | A94 | 50fr bister & multi | 1.10 | .30 |

**UDEAC Issue**

Presidents and Flags of Cameroun, CAR, Congo, Gabon and Meeting Center — A95

| | | | | |
|---|---|---|---|---|
| **1974, Dec. 8** | | **Photo.** | **Perf. 13** | |
| 338 | A95 | 40fr multi | .70 | .30 |

See No. C156.

Hôtel du Dialogue — A96

| | | | | |
|---|---|---|---|---|
| **1975, Jan. 20** | | **Photo.** | **Perf. 13** | |
| 339 | A96 | 50fr multi | .90 | .45 |

Opening of Hôtel du Dialogue.

### Arms Type of 1969

5fr, Ogowe-Ivindo. 10fr, Moabi. #342, Moanda. #343, Nyanga. 25fr, Mandji. #345, Mekambo. #346, Omboué. 60fr, Minvoul. 90fr, Mayumba.

| **1975-77** | | **Photo.** | | **Perf. 12** |
|---|---|---|---|---|
| 340 | A67 | 5fr red & multi | .20 | .20 |
| 341 | A67 | 10fr gold & multi | .20 | .20 |
| 342 | A67 | 15fr red, sil & blk | .45 | .20 |
| 343 | A67 | 15fr bl & multi | .35 | .20 |
| 344 | A67 | 25fr grn & multi | .45 | .20 |
| 345 | A67 | 50fr blk, gold & red | 1.40 | .35 |
| 346 | A67 | 50fr multi | 1.50 | .60 |
| 347 | A67 | 60fr multi | 1.40 | .60 |
| 348 | A67 | 90fr multi | 1.90 | .75 |
| | | *Nos. 340-348 (9)* | 7.85 | 3.30 |

Issued: #340-342, Jan. 21, 1975; #343-345, Aug. 17, 1976; #346-348, July 12, 1977.

Map of Africa with Lion's Head, and Lions Emblem — A97

| **1975, May 2** | | **Typo.** | | **Perf. 13** |
|---|---|---|---|---|
| 349 | A97 | 50fr grn & multi | | .90 .30 |

Lions Club 17th congress, District 403, Libreville.

Hertzian Wave Transmitter Network, Map of Gabon A98

| **1975, July 8** | | **Engr.** | | **Perf. 13** |
|---|---|---|---|---|
| 350 | A98 | 40fr multi | | .90 .60 |

City and Rural Women, Car, Train and Building — A99

| **1975, July 22** | | **Engr.** | | **Perf. 13** |
|---|---|---|---|---|
| 351 | A99 | 50fr car, bl & brn | | 2.10 .80 |

International Women's Year 1975.

Scoutmaster Ange Mba, Emblems and Rope — A100

Design: 50fr, Hand holding rope, Scout, camp, Boy Scout and Nordjamb 75 emblems.

| **1975, July 29** | | | | |
|---|---|---|---|---|
| 352 | A100 | 40fr multi | .60 | .30 |
| 353 | A100 | 50fr grn, red & dk brn | .90 | .40 |

Nordjamb 75, 14th Boy Scout Jamboree, Lillehammer, Norway, July 29-Aug. 7.

### Wildlife Type of 1972

Fish: 30fr, Lutjanus goreensis. 40fr, Galeoides decadactylus. 50fr, Sardinella aurita. 120fr, Scarus hoefleri.

| **1975, Sept. 22** | | **Litho.** | | **Perf. 14** |
|---|---|---|---|---|
| 354 | A83 | 30fr multi | .75 | .30 |
| 355 | A83 | 40fr multi | 1.10 | .50 |
| 356 | A83 | 50fr multi | 1.75 | .50 |
| 357 | A83 | 120fr multi | 3.25 | 1.25 |
| | | *Nos. 354-357 (4)* | 6.85 | 2.55 |

Agro-Industrial Complex — A102

| **1975, Dec. 15** | | **Litho.** | | **Perf. 12½** |
|---|---|---|---|---|
| 358 | A102 | 60fr multi | | 1.00 .50 |

Inauguration of Agro-Industrial Complex, Franceville.

Tchibanga Bridge — A103

Bridges of Gabon: 10fr, Mouila. 40fr, Kango. 50fr, Lambaréné, vert.

| **1976, Jan. 30** | | **Engr.** | | **Perf. 13** |
|---|---|---|---|---|
| 359 | A103 | 5fr multi | .20 | .20 |
| 360 | A103 | 10fr multi | .35 | .20 |
| 361 | A103 | 40fr multi | .80 | .30 |
| 362 | A103 | 50fr multi | 1.10 | .45 |
| | | *Nos. 359-362 (4)* | 2.45 | 1.15 |

Telephones 1876 and 1976, Satellite, A. G. Bell — A104

| **1976, Mar. 10** | | **Engr.** | | **Perf. 13** |
|---|---|---|---|---|
| 363 | A104 | 60fr dk bl, grn & sl grn | | .90 .40 |

Centenary of first telephone call by Alexander Graham Bell, Mar. 10, 1876.

Msgr. Jean Remy Bessieux — A105

| **1976, Apr. 30** | | **Engr.** | | **Perf. 13** |
|---|---|---|---|---|
| 364 | A105 | 50fr grn, bl & sepia | | .90 .45 |

Death centenary of Msgr. Bessieux.

Athletes, Torch, Map of Africa, Games Emblem — A106

| **1976, June 25** | | **Photo.** | | **Perf. 13x12½** |
|---|---|---|---|---|
| 365 | A106 | 50fr multi | | .70 .20 |
| 366 | A106 | 50fr org & multi | | .90 .30 |

First Central African Games (Zone 5), Libreville, June-July.

Motobécane, France — A107

Motorcycles: 5fr, Bultaco, Spain. 10fr, Suzuki, Japan. 20fr, Kawasaki, Japan. 100fr, Harley-Davidson, US.

| **1976, July 20** | | **Litho.** | | **Perf. 12½** |
|---|---|---|---|---|
| 367 | A107 | 3fr multi | .40 | .25 |
| 368 | A107 | 5fr org & multi | .40 | .25 |
| 369 | A107 | 10fr bl & multi | .70 | .30 |
| 370 | A107 | 20fr multi | 1.25 | .30 |
| 371 | A107 | 100fr car & multi | 4.50 | 1.00 |
| | | *Nos. 367-371 (5)* | 7.25 | 2.10 |

Rice A108

| **1976, Oct. 15** | | **Litho.** | | **Perf. 13x13½** |
|---|---|---|---|---|
| 372 | A108 | 50fr shown | | .90 .35 |
| 373 | A108 | 60fr Pepper plants | | 1.10 .55 |

| **1977, Apr. 22** | | **Litho.** | | **Perf. 13x13½** |
|---|---|---|---|---|

50fr, Banana plantation. 60fr, Peanut market.

| 374 | A108 | 50fr multi | | .90 .35 |
|---|---|---|---|---|
| 375 | A108 | 60fr multi | | 1.10 .55 |

Telecommunications Emblem and Telephone — A109

| **1977, May 17** | | | | **Perf. 13** |
|---|---|---|---|---|
| 376 | A109 | 60fr multi | | .90 .50 |

World Telecommunications Day.

View of Oyem A110

50fr, Cape Lopez. 70fr, Lebamba Cave.

| **1977, June 9** | | **Litho.** | | **Perf. 12½** |
|---|---|---|---|---|
| 377 | A110 | 50fr multi | .70 | .30 |
| 378 | A110 | 60fr multi | .75 | .40 |
| 379 | A110 | 70fr multi | .85 | .45 |
| | | *Nos. 377-379 (3)* | 2.30 | 1.15 |

Conference Hall — A111

| **1977, June 23** | | **Photo.** | | **Perf. 13x12½** |
|---|---|---|---|---|
| 380 | A111 | 100fr multi | | 1.40 .75 |

Meeting of the OAU, Libreville.

Arms of Gabon — A112

| **1977** | | **Engr.** | | **Perf. 13** |
|---|---|---|---|---|
| | | **Size: 23x36mm** | | |
| 381 | A112 | 50fr blue | 1.25 | .50 |
| | | **Size: 17x23mm** | | |
| 382 | A112 | 60fr orange | 1.10 | .50 |
| *a.* | | Booklet pane of 5 | 6.00 | |
| 383 | A112 | 80fr red | 1.60 | .65 |
| | | *Nos. 381-383 (3)* | 3.95 | 1.65 |

#381 issued in coils; #382 in booklets only.
Issued: #381-382, June 23; #383, Sept.

Modern Buildings, Libreville — A113

| **1977, Aug. 17** | | **Litho.** | | **Perf. 12** |
|---|---|---|---|---|
| 387 | A113 | 50fr multi | | .90 .20 |

National Festival 1977.

Paris to Vienna, 1902 — A114

Renault Automobiles: 10fr, Coupé 1 2 CV, 1921. 30fr, Torpédo Scaphandrier, 1925. 40fr, Reinastella 40 CV, 1929. 100fr, Nerva Grand Sport, 1937. 150fr, Voiturette 1 CV, 1899. 200fr, Alpine Renault V6, 1977.

| **1977, Aug 30** | | **Engr.** | | **Perf. 13** |
|---|---|---|---|---|
| 388 | A114 | 5fr multi | .50 | .35 |
| 389 | A114 | 10fr multi | .50 | .35 |
| 390 | A114 | 30fr multi | 1.25 | .50 |
| 391 | A114 | 40fr multi | 2.10 | .60 |
| 392 | A114 | 100fr multi | 5.25 | 2.25 |
| | | *Nos. 388-392 (5)* | 9.60 | 4.05 |

#### Miniature Sheet

| 393 | | Sheet of 2 + label | 18.00 | 18.00 |
|---|---|---|---|---|
| *a.* | | A114 150fr multi | 5.25 | 5.25 |
| *b.* | | A114 200fr multi | 7.00 | 7.00 |

Louis Renault, French automobile pioneer, birth centenary. Nos. 383a-393b are perf. on 3 sides, without perforation between stamps and center label showing dark brown portrait of Renault.
See Nos. 395-400.

Globe A115

| **1978, Feb. 21** | | **Engr.** | | **Perf. 13x12½** |
|---|---|---|---|---|
| 394 | A115 | 80fr multi | | .90 .60 |

World Leprosy Day.

### Automobile Type of 1977

Citroen Cars: 10fr, Cabriolet, 1922. 50fr, Taxi, 1927. 60fr, Berline, 1932. 80fr, Berline, 1934. 150fr, Torpedo, 1919. 200fr, Berline, 1948. 250fr, Pallas, 1975.

| **1978, May 9** | | **Engr.** | | **Perf. 13** |
|---|---|---|---|---|
| 395 | A114 | 10fr multi | .80 | .35 |
| 396 | A114 | 50fr multi | 1.50 | .45 |
| 397 | A114 | 60fr multi | 2.50 | .95 |

| | | | |
|---|---|---|---|
| 398 | A114 80fr multi | 2.50 | .95 |
| 399 | A114 200fr multi | 6.75 | 2.25 |
| | Nos. 395-399 (5) | 14.05 | 4.95 |

**Miniature Sheet**

| | | | |
|---|---|---|---|
| 400 | Sheet of 2 | 18.00 | 18.00 |
| a. | A114 150fr multi | 5.25 | 5.25 |
| b. | A114 250fr multi | 7.00 | 7.00 |

Andre Citroen (1878-1935), automobile designer and manufacturer.

Ndjole on Ogowe River — A116

Views: 40fr, Lambarene lake district. 50fr, Owendo Harbor.

**1978, May 17    Litho.    Perf. 12½**

| | | | |
|---|---|---|---|
| 401 | A116 30fr multi | .40 | .20 |
| 402 | A116 40fr multi | .70 | .20 |
| 403 | A116 50fr multi | .90 | .35 |
| | Nos. 401-403 (3) | 2.00 | .75 |

Sternotomis Mirabilis — A117

Anti- Apartheid Emblem — A118

Various Coleopteras.

**1978, June 21  Photo.   Perf. 12½x13**

| | | | |
|---|---|---|---|
| 404 | A117 20fr multi | .75 | .30 |
| 405 | A117 60fr multi | 3.00 | .65 |
| 406 | A117 75fr multi | 3.75 | .75 |
| 407 | A117 80fr multi | 4.50 | 1.25 |
| | Nos. 404-407 (4) | 12.00 | 2.95 |

**1978, July 25    Engr.    Perf. 13**

| | | | |
|---|---|---|---|
| 408 | A118 80fr multi | .90 | .60 |

**Arms Type of 1969**

**1978-80        Photo.        Perf. 12**

| | | | |
|---|---|---|---|
| 409 | A67 5fr Oyem | .20 | .20 |
| 410 | A67 5fr Ogowe-Maritime ('79) | .20 | .20 |
| 411 | A67 10fr Lastoursville ('79) | .20 | .20 |
| 412 | A67 10fr Haut-Ogooue ('80) | .20 | .20 |
| 413 | A67 15fr M'Bigou ('79) | .20 | .20 |
| 414 | A67 20fr Estuaire ('80) | .20 | .20 |
| 415 | A67 30fr Bitam ('80) | .20 | .20 |
| 416 | A67 40fr Okondja | 1.10 | .20 |
| 417 | A67 60fr Mimongo | 1.60 | .40 |
| | Nos. 409-417 (9) | 4.10 | 2.00 |

A119

**1978, Oct. 24    Engr.    Perf. 13**

| | | | |
|---|---|---|---|
| 419 | A119 80fr multi | 1.10 | .65 |

UNESCO campaign to save the Acropolis.

Penicillin Formula, — A120

**1978, Nov. 21    Engr.    Perf. 13**

| | | | |
|---|---|---|---|
| 420 | A120 90fr multi | 2.40 | 1.10 |

Alexander Fleming's discovery of antibiotics, 50th anniversary.

The Visitation — A121

80fr, Massacre of the Innocents. Woodcarvings from St. Michael's Church, Libreville.

**1978, Dec. 15                  Photo.**

| | | | |
|---|---|---|---|
| 421 | A121 60fr gold & multi | .90 | .40 |
| 422 | A121 80fr gold & multi | 1.10 | .50 |

Christmas 1978. See Nos. 437-438.

Train and Map A122

**1978, Dec. 27    Litho.    Perf. 12½**

| | | | |
|---|---|---|---|
| 423 | A122 60fr multi | 1.50 | .60 |

Inauguration of Trans-Gabon Railroad, Libreville to Njolé.

A123

Pre-Olympic Year (Kremlin Towers, Olympic Emblem, Ancestral Figure and): 80fr, Long jump, vert. 100fr, Yachts.

**1979, May 15    Engr.    Perf. 13**

| | | | |
|---|---|---|---|
| 424 | A123 60fr multi | .60 | .30 |
| 425 | A123 80fr multi | .75 | .40 |
| 426 | A123 100fr multi | .95 | .55 |
| a. | Miniature sheet of 3, #424-426 | 3.75 | 3.75 |
| | Nos. 424-426 (3) | 2.30 | 1.25 |

Rowland Hill, Messenger and Gabon No. O9 — A124

Allamanda Schottii A125

Designs: 80fr, Bakota mask and tulip tree flowers, vert. 150fr, Pigeon, UPU emblem, truck and canoe. No. 430b, Gloriosa superba. No. 430c, Phaeomeria magnifica, vert. No. 430d, Berlinia bracteosa, vert.

**1979, June 8    Photo.    Perf. 13**

| | | | |
|---|---|---|---|
| 427 | A124 50fr multi | 1.10 | 1.10 |
| 428 | A124 80fr multi | 2.00 | 1.25 |

**Engr.**

| | | | |
|---|---|---|---|
| 429 | A124 150fr multi | 3.25 | 2.00 |
| | Nos. 427-429 (3) | 6.35 | 4.35 |

**Souvenir Sheet**

**Photo.                Perf. 14**

| | | | |
|---|---|---|---|
| 430 | Sheet of 4 | 10.00 | 10.00 |
| a. | A125 100fr multicolored | 1.90 | |
| b. | A125 100fr multicolored | 1.90 | |
| c. | A125 100fr multicolored | 1.90 | |
| d. | A125 100fr multicolored | 1.90 | |

Philexafrique II, Libreville, June 8-17. Nos. 427-429 each printed in sheets of 10 with 5 labels showing exhibition emblem. No. 427 also commemorates Sir Rowland Hill (1795-1879), originator of penny postage. No. 430 has label with exhibition emblem.

IYC Emblem, Globe, Child with Bird — A126

**1979, June 15    Engr.    Perf. 13**

| | | | |
|---|---|---|---|
| 431 | A126 100fr multi | 1.40 | .70 |

International Year of the Child.

"TELECOM 79" — A127

**1979, Sept. 18  Litho.  Perf. 13x12½**

| | | | |
|---|---|---|---|
| 432 | A127 80fr multi | 1.00 | .40 |

3rd World Telecommunications Exhibition, Geneva, Sept. 20-26.

Sugar Cane Harvest — A128

**1979, Oct. 9    Photo.    Perf. 12½x13**

| | | | |
|---|---|---|---|
| 433 | A128 25fr shown | .45 | .20 |
| 434 | A128 30fr Yams | .65 | .20 |

Judo Throw — A129

**1979, Oct. 23    Engr.    Perf. 13**

| | | | |
|---|---|---|---|
| 435 | A129 40fr multi | 1.60 | .55 |

World Judo Championships, Paris, Dec.

Mother and Child, Map of Congo River Basin — A130

**1979, Dec. 2    Litho.    Perf. 12**

| | | | |
|---|---|---|---|
| 436 | A130 200fr multi | 2.50 | .80 |

Medical Week, Dec. 2-9.

**Christmas Type of 1978**

Wood Carvings, St. Michael's Church, Libreville: 60fr, Flight into Egypt. 80fr, The Circumcision.

**1979, Dec. 12    Photo.    Perf. 13**

| | | | |
|---|---|---|---|
| 437 | A121 60fr multi | .90 | .40 |
| 438 | A121 80fr multi | 1.10 | .40 |

Pres. Omar Bongo — A131

**1979-80    Litho.    Perf. 12½**

| | | | |
|---|---|---|---|
| 439 | A131 60fr multi | .90 | .40 |
| 440 | A131 80fr multi | 2.50 | 1.25 |

Bongo's 44th birthday (#439); re-election and inauguration (#440). Issued: 60fr, 12/30/79; 80fr, 2/27/80.

OPEC, 20th Anniv. — A132

**1980, Mar. 27  Litho.  Perf. 13½x13**

| | | | |
|---|---|---|---|
| 441 | A132 50fr multi | 1.10 | .35 |

Donguila Church — A133

**1980 Apr. 3    Litho.    Perf. 12½**

| | | | |
|---|---|---|---|
| 442 | A133 60fr shown | .65 | .30 |
| 443 | A133 80fr Bizengobibere Church | .85 | .35 |

Easter 1980.

De Brazza
(1852-1905),
Map of Gabon
with Franceville
A134

**1980, June 30    Litho.    Perf. 12½**
444 A134 165fr multi                    2.50 1.10

Franceville Foundation centenary, founded
by Savorgnan De Brazza.

20th Anniversary of
Independence — A135

**1980, Aug. 17    Photo.    Perf. 13**
445 A135 60fr Leon Mba and
Omar Bongo                      .90   .25

World Tourism Conference, Manila,
Sept. 27 — A136

**1980, Sept. 10                    Engr.**
446 A136 80fr multi                    .90   .35

20th
Anniversary
of OPEC
A137

**1980, Sept. 15    Litho.    Perf. 12½**
447 A137 90fr shown                    1.00   .40
448 A137 120fr Men Holding
OPEC emblem,
vert.                           1.50   .60

Pseudochelidon
Eurystomina
A138

**1980, Oct. 15    Photo.    Perf. 14x14½**
449 A138 50fr shown                    3.00   .80
450 A138 60fr Merops nubicus           3.50  1.10
451 A138 80fr Pitta angolensis         4.75  1.60
452 A138 150fr Scotopelia peli         7.50  2.75
Nos. 449-452 (4)                      18.75  6.25

Statue of Bull,
Bizangobibere
Church — A139

**1980, Dec. 10    Photo.    Perf. 14x14½**
453 A139 60fr shown                    .75   .35
454 A139 80fr Male statue              1.25   .55
Christmas 1980.

Heinrich von
Stephan — A140

**1981, Jan. 7    Engr.    Perf. 13**
455 A140 90fr brn & dk brn             .90   .35
Von Stephan (1831-97), UPU founder.

13th Anniversary of National
Renovation Movement — A141

**1981, Mar. 12    Litho.    Perf. 13x12½**
456 A141 60fr multi                    .70   .25

Lion Statue,
Bizangobibere
A142

**1981, Apr. 12    Photo.    Perf. 14x14½**
457 A142 75fr multi                    .90   .40
458 A142 100fr multi                   1.10   .55
Easter 1981.

Port Gentil Lions
Club
Banner — A143

**1981, May 1    Litho.    Perf. 12½**
459 A143 60fr shown                    .75   .25
460 A143 75fr District 403             .85   .30
461 A143 80fr Libreville Coco-
tiers                          1.10   .35
462 A143 100fr Libreville Hibiscus                            1.40   .40

463 A143 165fr Ekwata                  2.10   .70
464 A143 200fr Haut-Ogooue             2.40   .90
Nos. 459-464 (6)                       8.60  2.90

Lions International, 23rd Congress of District 403, Libreville, May 1-3.

13th World Telecommunications
Day — A144

**1981, May 17    Photo.    Perf. 13**
465 A144 125fr multi                   1.60   .55

Unity, Work
and Justice
A145

R.P. Klaine
(Missionary), 70th
Death Anniv.
A146

**1981-96?    Photo.    Perf. 13**
466 A145 5fr beige & blk               .20   .20
467 A145 10fr pale lil & blk           .20   .20
468 A145 15fr brt yel grn &
blk                            .20   .20
469 A145 20fr pink & blk               .20   .20
470 A145 25fr vio & blk                .20   .20
471 A145 40fr red org & blk            .45   .20
472 A145 50fr bluish grn & blk         .55   .20
473 A145 75fr bis brn & blk            .70   .25
473A A145 90fr lt bl & blk ('83)       .70   .25
474 A145 100fr yel & blk               1.00   .40
474A A145 125fr grn & blk ('83)        1.10   .35
474B A145 150fr brt pink & blk
('86)                          1.25   .40
474C A145 175fr grnish bl & blk
('96)                          .55   .55
Nos. 466-474B (12)                     6.75  3.05
See Nos. 862-871.

**1981, July 2                    Litho.**
90fr, Archbishop Walker, 110th birth anniv.
475 A146 70fr multi                    .80   .30
476 A146 90fr multi                    1.25   .35

Map of Gabon
and Scout
Sign — A147

Intl. Year of the
Disabled — A148

**1981, July 16                    Perf. 12½**
477 A147 75fr multi                    1.00   .35

4th Pan-African Scouting Congress,
Abidjan, Aug.

No. 477 Overprinted: DAKAR / 28e
CONFERENCE / MONDIALE DU /
SCOUTISME

**1981, July 23**
478 A147 75fr multi                    1.50   .45

28th World Scouting Conf., Dakar, Aug.

**1981, Aug. 6    Engr.    Perf. 13**
479 A148 100fr multi                   1.10   .45

Hypolimnas
Salmacis
A149

**1981, Sept. 10    Litho.    Perf. 14½x14**
480 A149 75fr shown                    1.75   .45
481 A149 100fr Euphaedra
themis                         2.10   .70
482 A149 150fr Amauris niavi-
us                             3.00  1.10
483 A149 250fr Cymothoe lu-
casi                           5.00  1.75
Nos. 480-483 (4)                      11.85  4.00

Paul as
Harlequin, by
Pablo Picasso
(1881-1973)
A150

**1981, Sept. 25    Perf. 14½x13½**
484 A150 500fr multi                   7.00  2.50

World Food Day — A151

**1981, Oct. 16    Engr.    Perf. 13**
485 A151 350fr multi                   4.00  1.60

Traditional
Hairstyle — A152

Designs: Various hairstyles.

**1981, Nov. 12    Litho.    Perf. 14½x15**
| | | | |
|---|---|---|---|
| **486** | A152 | 75fr multi | 1.10 | .55 |
| **487** | A152 | 100fr multi | 1.25 | .50 |
| **488** | A152 | 125fr multi | 1.90 | .80 |
| **489** | A152 | 200fr multi | 3.00 | 1.10 |
| *a.* | | Souvenir sheet of 4, #486-489 | 7.50 | 7.50 |
| | | *Nos. 486-489 (4)* | 7.25 | 2.95 |

See Nos. 609A-609B, 676.

Christmas
1981
A153

Designs: Children's drawings.

**1981, Dec. 10    Perf. 14½x14**
| | | | | |
|---|---|---|---|---|
| **490** | A153 | 75fr Girls dancing | .90 | .35 |
| **491** | A153 | 100fr Dinner | 1.25 | .50 |

### Arms Type of 1969
**Perf. 12, 13 (#495-497)**

**1982-92**                         **Photo.**
| | | | | |
|---|---|---|---|---|
| **492** | A67 | 75fr Moyen-Ogooue | .70 | .20 |
| **493** | A67 | 90fr Cocobeach | .90 | .25 |
| **494** | A67 | 100fr Woleu-N'tem | 1.00 | .25 |
| **495** | A67 | 100fr Lambarene | .90 | .30 |
| **496** | A67 | 100fr Port Gentil District | .90 | .35 |
| **497** | A67 | 100fr Medouneu | .90 | .35 |
| **498** | A67 | 125fr Mouila | 1.25 | .35 |
| **499** | A67 | 135fr N'Djole | 1.40 | .40 |
| **500** | A67 | 150fr N'Gounie | 1.50 | .40 |
| **501** | A67 | 160fr Leconi | 1.40 | .60 |
| | | *Nos. 492-501 (10)* | 10.85 | 3.45 |

Issued: #492, 494, 500, 1/13/82; #493, 498, 499, 8/7/84; #496, 4/17/91; #497, 8/12/82.

A154

**1982, Feb. 16    Litho.    Perf. 13**
| | | | | |
|---|---|---|---|---|
| **502** | A154 | 100fr multi | 2.40 | 1.10 |

Visit of Pope John Paul II, Feb. 17-19.

A155

**1982, Mar. 31    Engr.    Perf. 13**
| | | | | |
|---|---|---|---|---|
| **503** | A155 | 75fr black | .80 | .30 |

Alfred de Musset (1810-1857), writer.

Merchant
Navy Ships
A156

**1982, Apr. 7    Litho.    Perf. 14½x14**
| | | | | |
|---|---|---|---|---|
| **504** | A156 | 75fr Timber carrier | .75 | .30 |
| **505** | A156 | 100fr Freighter | 1.00 | .40 |
| **506** | A156 | 200fr Oil tanker | 2.00 | .85 |
| | | *Nos. 504-506 (3)* | 3.75 | 1.55 |

See Nos. 588, 599.

TB Bacillus Centenary — A157

**1982, Apr. 24    Litho.    Perf. 13**
| | | | | |
|---|---|---|---|---|
| **507** | A157 | 100fr multi | 1.60 | .50 |

PHILEXFRANCE
'82 Stamp
Exhibition, Paris,
June 11-
21 — A158

**1982, Apr. 28    Perf. 12½**
| | | | | |
|---|---|---|---|---|
| **508** | A158 | 100fr Rope bridge | .85 | .40 |
| **509** | A158 | 200fr Sculptured head | 1.90 | .55 |
| *a.* | | Pair, #508-509 + label | 4.00 | 2.75 |

14th World Telecommunications
Day — A159

**1982, May 17    Perf. 13**
| | | | | |
|---|---|---|---|---|
| **510** | A159 | 75fr multi | .90 | .40 |

1982 World
Cup — A160

Designs: Various soccer players.

**1982, May 19    Perf. 14x14½**
| | | | | |
|---|---|---|---|---|
| **511** | A160 | 100fr multi | 1.00 | .40 |
| **512** | A160 | 125fr multi | 1.10 | .45 |
| **513** | A160 | 200fr multi | 2.10 | .75 |
| *a.* | | Souvenir sheet of 3, #511-513, perf. 14½ | 5.00 | 5.00 |
| | | *Nos. 511-513 (3)* | 4.20 | 1.60 |

For overprints see Nos. 516-518.

2nd UN Conf. on Peaceful Uses of
Outer Space, Vienna, Aug. 9-
21 — A161

**1982, July 7    Engr.    Perf. 13**
| | | | | |
|---|---|---|---|---|
| **514** | A161 | 250fr Satellites | 2.75 | 1.25 |

White
Carnations
A162

Designs: Various carnations.

**1982, June 9    Photo.    Perf. 14½x14**
| | | | | |
|---|---|---|---|---|
| **515** | | Strip of 3 | 5.00 | 4.25 |
| *a.* | A162 | 75fr multi | .90 | .45 |
| *b.* | A162 | 100fr multi | 1.10 | .50 |
| *c.* | A162 | 175fr multi | 2.25 | 1.00 |

Nos. 511-513a Overprinted in Red
with Semi-Finalists or Finalists

**1982, Aug. 19    Litho.    Perf. 14x14½**
| | | | | |
|---|---|---|---|---|
| **516** | A160 | 100fr multi | 1.00 | .45 |
| **517** | A160 | 125fr multi | 1.10 | .45 |
| **518** | A160 | 200fr multi | 2.10 | .75 |
| *a.* | | Souvenir sheet of 3 | 5.00 | 5.00 |
| | | *Nos. 516-518 (3)* | 4.20 | 1.55 |

Italy's victory in 1982 World Cup.

Phyllonotus
Duplex
A163

**1982, Sept. 22    Perf. 14½x14**
| | | | | |
|---|---|---|---|---|
| **519** | A163 | 75fr shown | 1.25 | .45 |
| **520** | A163 | 100fr Chama crenulata | 1.50 | .55 |
| **521** | A163 | 125fr Cardium hians | 2.10 | .75 |
| | | *Nos. 519-521 (3)* | 4.85 | 1.75 |

Okouyi
Mask — A164

**1982, Oct. 13    Litho.    Perf. 14x14½**
| | | | | |
|---|---|---|---|---|
| **522** | A164 | 75fr shown | .65 | .30 |
| **523** | A164 | 100fr Ondoumbo reliquary | 1.10 | .40 |
| **524** | A164 | 150fr Tsogho statuette | 1.90 | .55 |
| **525** | A164 | 250fr Fang bellows | 2.75 | .95 |
| | | *Nos. 522-525 (4)* | 6.40 | 2.20 |

Christmas
1982 — A165

**1982, Dec. 15    Litho.    Perf. 14x14½**
| | | | | |
|---|---|---|---|---|
| **526** | A165 | 100fr St. Francis Xavier Church | .90 | .35 |

Trans-Gabon Railroad
Inauguration — A166

**1983, Jan. 18    Perf. 12½**
| | | | | |
|---|---|---|---|---|
| **527** | A166 | 75fr multi | 2.00 | .50 |

5th African Highway Conference,
Libreville, Feb. 6-11 — A167

**1983, Feb. 2    Perf. 13**
| | | | | |
|---|---|---|---|---|
| **528** | A167 | 100fr multi | .90 | .35 |

15th Anniv. of Natl.
Renewal — A168

Provincial Symbols: a. Bakota mask, Ogowe Ivindo. b. Butterfly, Ogowe Lolo. c. Buffalo, Nyanga. d. Isogho hairdo, Ngounie. e. Tarpon, Ogowe Maritime. f. Manganese, Haut Ogowe. g. Crocodiles, Moyen Ogowe. h. Coffee plant. i. Epitorium trochiformis.

**1983, Mar. 12    Litho.    Perf. 13x13½**
| | | | | |
|---|---|---|---|---|
| **529** | | Strip of 9 + label | 15.00 | 12.50 |
| *a.* | A168 | 75fr multi | .95 | .40 |
| *b.* | A168 | 90fr multi | 1.10 | .45 |
| *c.* | A168 | 90fr multi | 1.10 | .45 |
| *d.* | A168 | 100fr multi | 1.25 | .55 |
| *e.* | A168 | 125fr multi | 1.50 | .70 |
| *f.* | A168 | 125fr multi | 1.50 | .70 |
| *g.* | A168 | 125fr multi | 1.50 | .70 |
| *h.* | A168 | 135fr multi | 1.75 | .80 |
| *i.* | A168 | 135fr multi | 1.75 | .80 |

25th Anniv. of Intl. Maritime
Org. — A169

**1983, Mar. 17    Perf. 13**
| | | | | |
|---|---|---|---|---|
| **530** | A169 | 125fr multi | 1.25 | .50 |

Pelican
A170

**1983, Apr. 20    Litho.    Perf. 15x14½**
| | | | | |
|---|---|---|---|---|
| **531** | A170 | 90fr Water musk deer | .90 | .35 |
| **532** | A170 | 125fr shown | 1.25 | .45 |
| **533** | A170 | 225fr Elephant | 3.25 | .85 |
| **534** | A170 | 400fr Iguana | 4.50 | 1.50 |
| *a.* | | Souv. sheet of 4, #531-534 | 16.00 | 16.00 |
| | | *Nos. 531-534 (4)* | 9.90 | 3.15 |

25th Anniv.
of UN
Economic
Commission
for Africa
A171

**1983, Apr. 29    Litho.    Perf. 12½**
| | | | | |
|---|---|---|---|---|
| **535** | A171 | 125fr multi | 1.25 | .50 |

15th World Telecommunications
Day — A172

**1983, May 17    Litho.    Perf. 13**
536  A172  90fr multi                1.40   .55
537  A172  90fr multi                1.40   .55
  a.    Pair, #536-537              4.00  4.00
Denomination of No. 536 in lower right, No. 537, upper left.

Nkoltang Earth Satellite
Station — A173

**1983, July 2**
538  A173  125fr multi               1.25   .50
10th anniv. of station; WCY.

Ivindo River Rapids — A174

**1983, Sept. 7    Engr.    Perf. 13**
539  A174  90fr shown                 .85   .35
540  A174  125fr Ogooue River       1.40   .60
541  A174  185fr Wonga Wongue
              Preserve                2.00   .80
542  A174  350fr Coastal view       3.75  1.50
       Nos. 539-542 (4)             8.00  3.25

Hand Drum,
Mahongwe
A175

Harmful
Insects — A176

**1983, Oct. 12    Litho.    Perf. 14x14½**
543  A175  90fr shown                 .90   .35
544  A175  125fr Okoukoue dancer    1.40   .45
545  A175  135fr Four-stringed fid-
              dle                     1.50   .60
546  A175  260fr Ndoumou dancer     3.00  1.10
       Nos. 543-546 (4)             6.80  2.50

**1983, Nov. 9**
547  A176  90fr Glossinidae         1.60   .80
548  A176  125fr Belonogaster
              junceus                 1.90  1.10
549  A176  300fr Aedes aegypti      4.00  1.60
550  A176  350fr Mylabris           5.00  2.10
       Nos. 547-550 (4)            12.50  5.60

Christmas
1983 — A177

Wood Carvings, St. Michael's Church,
Libreville.

**Perf. 14½x13½**
**1983, Dec. 14    Litho.**
551  A177  90fr Adultress            .80   .35
552  A177  125fr Good Samaritan     1.40   .65

Boeing 737, No. 202 — A178

**1984, Jan. 12    Perf. 13x12½**
553  A178  125fr shown              1.50   .40
554  A178  225fr Lufthansa jet,
              Germany No.
              C2                     3.00   .70
  a.    Pair, #553-554 + label      5.50  4.75
19th World UPU Congress, Hamburg, June 19-26.

3rd Anniv. of Africa 1 Radio
Transmitter — A179

**1984, Feb. 7    Litho.    Perf. 12½**
555  A179  125fr multi              1.25   .35

Local
Flowers — A180

Various flowers.

**1984, Apr. 18    Litho.    Perf. 14x15**
556  A180  90fr multi               1.40   .45
557  A180  125fr multi              1.60   .55
558  A180  135fr multi              2.10   .65
559  A180  350fr multi              4.50  1.60
       Nos. 556-559 (4)             9.60  3.25

Fruit Trees
A181

**1984, Mar. 1    Litho.    Perf. 14½x14**
560  A181  90fr Coconut            1.40   .45
561  A181  100fr Papaya            1.40   .55
562  A181  125fr Mango             1.90   .65
563  A181  250fr Banana            3.75   .85
       Nos. 560-563 (4)            8.45  2.50

World Telecommunications
Day — A182

**1984, May 17    Perf. 13x13½**
564  A182  125fr multi             1.25   .45

Black Jazz
Musicians
A183

**1984, July 5    Perf. 12½**
565  A183  90fr Lionel Hampton     1.75   .70
566  A183  125fr Charlie Parker    2.40   .70
567  A183  260fr Erroll Garner     3.75  1.75
       Nos. 565-567 (3)            7.90  3.15

View of Medouneu — A184

**1984, Sept. 1    Litho.    Perf. 13**
568  A184  90fr shown              .95   .40
569  A184  125fr Canoes, Ogooue
              River                 1.50   .55
570  A184  165fr Railroad          2.50  1.25
       Nos. 568-570 (3)            4.95  2.20

15th World UPU
Day — A185

**1984, Oct. 9    Litho.    Perf. 13½**
571  A185  125fr UPU emblem,
              globe, mail           1.40   .50

40th Anniv., International Civil Aviation
Organization — A186

**1984, Dec. 1    Litho.    Perf. 13½**
572  A186  125fr Icarus            1.40   .50

Masks — A186a

**1984, Oct. 30    Litho.    Perf. 14x15**
572A  A186a  90fr Kouele            —     —
572B  A186a  125fr Eventail Pou-
               nou                   —     —
572C  A186a  150fr Reliquaire
               Mahongoue            —     —
572D  A186a  250fr Kota du Sud      —     —

Christmas — A187

**1984, Dec. 14    Litho.    Perf. 12½**
573  A187  90fr St. Michael's
              Church Libreville     .90   .45
574  A187  125fr St. Michael's, diff. 1.40  .65
  a.    Pair, #573-574             3.00  2.50

World Leprosy Day — A188

**1985, Jan. 27    Litho.    Perf. 12½**
575  A188  125fr Hospital, Libreville 1.50  .55

International Youth Year — A189

**1985, Feb. 6    Litho.    Perf. 13x12½**
576  A189  125fr Silhouttes, wreath 1.40  .50

Birds
A190

**1984    Litho.    Perf. 15x14**
577  A190  90fr Crowned crane      1.10   .60
578  A190  125fr Hummingbird       1.75   .75
579  A190  150fr Toucan            2.40   .90
       Nos. 577-579 (3)            5.25  2.25

Silhouettes,
Emblem — A191

**1985, Mar. 20    Perf. 12½**
580  A191  125fr brt ultra, red & bl 1.40  .50
Cultural and Technical Cooperation Agency,
15th anniv.

Wildlife
A192

**1985, Apr. 17    Perf. 15x14**
581  A192  90fr Aulacode           1.60   .40
582  A192  100fr Porcupine         1.60   .40
583  A192  125fr Giant pangolin    2.10  1.10
584  A192  350fr Antelope          5.50  2.10
  a.    Souvenir sheet of 4, #581-
          584                      13.00 13.00
       Nos. 581-584 (4)           10.80  4.00

Georges
Damas
Aleka,
Composer
A193

**1985, Apr. 30**     *Perf. 13*
585 A193 90fr Portrait, La Con-
     corde score     1.10 .35

A194

A195

**1985, May 17**     *Perf. 13½*
586 A194 125fr multi     1.40 .50
   World Telecommunications Day. ITU, 120th
anniv.

**1985, June 9**
587 A195 90fr Emblem     1.10 .60
   J.O.C., 30th anniv.

Merchant Navy Ships Type of 1982
**1985, July 1**     *Perf. 15x14*
588 A156 185fr Freighter Mpassa 2.10 .80

Posts and Telecommunications
Administration, 20th Anniv. — A196

**1985, July 25**     *Perf. 13*
589 A196 90fr Headquarters     1.10 .50

President
Bongo — A197

**1985, Aug. 17**     *Perf. 14*
590 A197 250fr multi     3.50 1.60
591 A197 500fr multi     7.75 4.00
  *a.* Pair, #590-591 + 3 labels   14.00 14.00
        *Imperf*
     **Size: 120x90mm**
592 A197 1000fr View of Libre-
     ville     14.00 14.00
   *Nos. 590-592 (3)*     25.25 19.60
   Natl. Independence, 25th anniv.
   No. 592 has non-denominated vignettes of
Nos. 590-591.

Org. of Petroleum
Exporting
Countries, 25th
Anniv. — A198

**1985, Sept. 25**     *Perf. 13½*
593 A198 350fr multi     4.00 1.90

Intl. Center of the Bantu
Civilizations — A199

**1985, Nov. 16**    Litho.    *Perf. 15x14*
594 A199 185fr multi     2.00 .95

St. Andrew's
Church, Libreville
— A199a

Design: 125fr, Church interior, horiz.

    *Perf. 14x15, 15x14*
**1985, Dec.**          Litho.
594A A199a 90fr multicolored    —
594B A199a 125fr multicolored    —
   Christmas.

UNESCO, 25th Anniv. — A200

**1986, Jan. 5**    Litho.    *Perf. 12½*
595 A200 100fr multi     1.10 .45

A201

**1986, May 1**    Litho.    *Perf. 13½*
596 A201 150fr multi     1.75 .60
   Rotary Intl. District 915, 4th conf.

A202

**1986, June 16**    Litho.    *Perf. 12½*
597 A202 150fr multi     1.75 .60
   Natl. Week of Cartography, Libreville, June
16-20.

Coffee Flowers, Berries,
Beans — A203

**1986, Aug. 27**    Litho.    *Perf. 12½*
598 A203 125fr multi     2.00 .90
   Organization of African and Madagascar
Coffee Producers, 25th anniv.

Merchant Navy Ships Type of 1982
**1986, June 24**    Litho.    *Perf. 15x14*
599 A156 250fr Merchantman
     L'Abanga     3.00 1.25

Natl. Postage Stamp, Cent. — A205

**1986, July 10**     *Perf. 13½x14½*
600 A205 500fr Boats, No. 4    7.00 3.50

Flowering
Plants — A206

**1986, July 23**     *Perf. 14½x15*
601 A206 100fr Allamanda neri-
     ifolia     1.25 .50
602 A206 150fr Musa cultivar    1.90 .80
603 A206 160fr Dissotis decum-
     bens     2.10 .85
604 A206 350fr Campylos-
     permum laeve     4.75 2.10
   *Nos. 601-604 (4)*     10.00 4.25

Butterflies
A207

**1986, Sept. 18**    Litho.    *Perf. 15x14*
605 A207 150fr Machaon     2.50 1.00
606 A207 290fr Urania     5.00 1.75

St. Pierre
Church,
Libreville
A208

**1986, Dec. 23**    Litho.    *Perf. 15x14½*
607 A208 500fr multi     5.00 2.10
   Christmas.

Trans-Gabon Railway from Owendo to
Franceville, Inauguration — A209

**1986, Dec. 30**     *Perf. 13*
608 A209 90fr multi     1.40 .50
     **Souvenir Sheet**
609 A209 250fr multi     4.50 4.50

Traditional Hairstyles Type of 1981
**1986**    Litho.    *Perf. 14x15*
609A A152 100fr black, gray &
     yellow     *150.00 7.50*
609B A152 150fr tan, black &
     red brown     5.00 1.50

Fish
A210

**1987, Jan. 15**     *Perf. 15x14½*
610 A210 90fr Adioryx bas-
     tatus     1.25 .50
611 A210 125fr Scarus boefleri 1.75 .70
612 A210 225fr Cephala-
     canthus
     volitans     2.25 1.10
613 A210 350fr Dasyatis
     marmorata     3.50 1.75
  *a.* Souv. sheet of 4, Nos. 610-
     613     13.00 13.00
   *Nos. 610-613 (4)*     8.75 4.05
   No. 613a issued Oct. 1987.

Raoul Follereau
(1903-1977)
A211

**1987, Jan. 23**     *Perf. 12½*
614 A211 125fr multi     1.75 .85
   World Leprosy Day.

Pres. Bongo Accepting the 1986 Dag
Hammarskjold Peace Prize — A212

**1987, Mar. 31     Litho.     Perf. 13**
615  A212  125fr multi                    1.25  .60

World Telecommunications
Day — A213

**1987, May 17     Litho.     Perf. 13½**
616  A213  90fr multi                     1.10  .40

Lions Club of
Gabon, 30th
Anniv. — A214

**1987, July 18     Litho.     Perf. 12x12½**
617  A214  90fr multi                     1.10  .40

Pierre de
Coubertin, Father
of the Modern
Olympics
A215

**1987, Aug. 29**
618  A215  200fr multi                    2.00  .85

Lions Club Intl.,
70th
Anniv. — A216

**1987, Oct. 1**
619  A216  165fr multi                    1.75  .65

World Post
Day — A217

**1987, Oct. 9     Litho.     Perf. 13½**
620  A217  125fr multi                    1.25  .50

Seashells
A218

**1987, Oct.          Perf. 15x14**
621  A218  90fr Natica fanel              .90  .30
622  A218  125fr Natica fulminea
                  cruentata             1.25  .45
  a.    Souv. sheet of 2, Nos. 621-622   6.00  6.00

Intl. Year of Shelter for the
Homeless — A219

**1987, Oct. 5          Perf. 12½**
623  A219  90fr multi                    1.10  .40

Solidarity with the
South West
African Peoples'
Organization
(SWAPO) — A220

St. Anna of
Odimba
Mission — A221

**1987, Sept. 15   Litho.   Perf. 14½x15**
624  A220  225fr Pres. Bongo,
                  SWAPO leader  2.10  .95

**1987, Nov. 2          Perf. 13½**
625  A221  90fr multi                    1.00  .30

Universal Child Immunization — A222

**1987, Nov. 16        Perf. 15x14½**
626  A222  100fr multi                   1.25  .40

20th Anniv. of
the
Presidency of
Omar Bongo
A223

**1987, Dec. 2          Perf. 14½x13½**
627  A223  1000fr multi         10.00  5.50

Christmas
A224

**1987, Dec. 15        Perf. 15x14½**
628  A224  90fr St. Therese
              Church, Oyem   1.00  .30

1988 Winter Olympics,
Calgary — A225

**1987, Dec. 30        Perf. 13½x14½**
629  A225  125fr multi                   1.25  .50

Medicinal
Plants — A226

**1988, Jan. 26   Litho.   Perf. 14x15**
630  A226  90fr Cassia oc-
              cidentalis          1.10  .55
631  A226  125fr Tabernanthe
              iboga               1.60  .55
632  A226  225fr Cassia alata     2.75  1.10
633  A226  350fr Anthocleista
              schweinfurthii      5.50  2.75
  a.   Miniature sheet of 4, #630-
              633                12.00  12.00
       Nos. 630-633 (4)         10.95  4.95

World Wildlife Fund — A227

African forest elephant, *Loxodonta africana
cyclotis.*

**1988, Feb. 29   Litho.   Perf. 13½**
634  A227  25fr multi              2.25  .85
635  A227  40fr multi, diff.       3.00  1.60
636  A227  50fr multi, diff.       5.00  1.90
637  A227  100fr multi, diff.      8.50  3.25
       Nos. 634-637 (4)           18.75  7.60

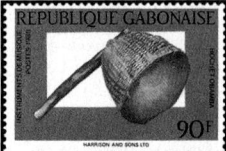

Traditional Musical
Instruments — A228

**1988, Feb. 17          Perf. 14**
638  A228  90fr Obamba
              hochet            1.25  .65
639  A228  100fr Fang sanza,
              vert.             1.50  .65
640  A228  125fr Mitsogho harp,
              vert.             1.60  .85
641  A228  165fr Fang xylo-
              phone             2.50  .95
  a.    Souv. sheet of 4, Nos. 638-
              641                7.50  7.50
       Nos. 638-641 (4)         6.85  3.10

World Cup Rugby — A229

**Perf. 13½x14½**
**1987, June 10          Litho.**
642  A229  350fr multi           4.25  1.90

Delta Post Office Inauguration — A230

**1988, Mar. 9**
643  A230  90fr multi            1.00  .30

World Telecommunications
Day — A231

**1988, May 17          Perf. 13½**
644  A231  125fr multi           1.25  .45

Storming of the Bastille, July 14,
1789 — A232

**1988, May 30   Litho.   Perf. 13**
645  A232  125fr multi           1.60  .50
       PHILEXFRANCE '89.

Intl. Fund for Agricultural Development
(IFAD), 10th Anniv. — A233

**1988, June 20**          **Perf. 13½**
646 A233 350fr multi          4.25 1.60

Intl. Red Cross and Red Crescent
Organizations, 125th Anniv. — A234

**1988, July 15    Litho.    Perf. 12½**
647 A234 125fr multi          1.25  .45

1988
Summer
Olympics,
Seoul
A235

**1988, Sept. 17    Litho.    Perf. 15x14**
648  A235  90fr  Tennis          1.00  .35
649  A235  100fr  Swimming       1.00  .45
650  A235  350fr  Running        3.75 1.60
651  A235  500fr  Hurdles        5.75 2.00
  a.    Souv. sheet of 4, #648-651   13.00 13.00
  Nos. 648-651 (4)               11.50 4.40

World
Post
Day
A236

**1988, Oct. 9          Perf. 13½**
652 A236 125fr blk, brt yel & brt
             blue             1.25  .45

Christmas
A237

**1988, Dec. 20    Litho.    Perf. 15x14**
653 A237 200fr Medouneu
             Church          2.00  .70

Natica
Fanel —
A237a

**1988          Litho.    Perf. 15x14**
653A A237a 90fr shown      25.00 5.00
653B A237a 125fr Natica sp.  30.00 7.50
  c.    Souv. sheet of 2, #653A-
             653B              —   —

A238

A239

**1989, Feb. 21          Perf. 13½**
654 A238 175fr multi          1.50  .60
Chaine des Rotisseurs in Gabon, 10th anniv.

**1989, Mar. 6    Litho.    Perf. 13½**
655 A239 125fr multi          1.40  .55
Rabi Kounga oil field. See No. 707.

Traditional Games — A240

**Perf. 13½x14½**
**1989, Mar. 20          Litho.**
656 A240 90fr multicolored    1.10  .55

Birds — A241

**1989, Apr. 17    Litho.    Perf. 14x15**
657 A241 100fr White-tufted
             bittern          1.00  .35
658 A241 175fr Gabon gray
             parakeet         1.50  .65
659 A241 200fr Pygmy hornbill  1.90  .70
660 A241 500fr Pope's martin   4.75 2.10
  a.    Souv. sheet of 4, Nos. 657-
             660              12.00 12.00
  Nos. 657-660 (4)            9.15 3.80

See Nos. 750-753.

A242

**1989, Apr. 27          Perf. 13**
661 A242 125fr multi          1.25  .45
8th Convention of Lions Intl. District 403,
Libreville, Apr. 27-29.

World Telecommunications
Day — A243

**1989, May 17    Wmk. 385    Perf. 13½**
662 A243 300fr multi          3.25 1.10

PHILEXFRANCE '89 — A244

Symbols of the French revolution, 1789.

**Wmk. 385**
**1989, July 7    Litho.    Perf. 13**
663 A244 175fr multi          2.10  .80

French Revolution, Bicent. — A245

**1989, July 14**
664 A245 500fr multi          6.50 3.25

Fruit — A246

**Perf. 14½x15**
**1989, May 30    Litho.    Unwmk.**
665 A246  90fr Coconuts       1.00  .45
666 A246 125fr Cabosse        1.50  .50
667 A246 175fr Pineapple      2.25  .80
668 A246 250fr Breadfruit     2.75 1.25
  a.    Souv. sheet of 4, #665-668   8.50 8.50
  Nos. 665-668 (4)            7.50 3.00

AIMF, 10th Anniv. — A247

**1989, July 27    Litho.    Perf. 13**
669 A247 100fr multi          1.25  .50

African
Development
Bank, 25th
Anniv. — A248

**1989, Aug. 2    Litho.    Perf. 13**
670 A248 100fr multi          1.00  .40

Apples and Oranges, by Cezanne
(1839-1906) — A249

**Perf. 13½x14½**
**1989, June 22          Litho.**
671 A249 500fr multicolored   6.00 3.25

1990 World Cup Soccer
Championships, Italy — A250

Various athletes.

**Perf. 15x14½**
**1989, Aug. 23    Litho.    Unwmk.**
672 A250 100fr shown          .95  .35
673 A250 175fr multi, diff.   1.75  .65
674 A250 300fr multi, diff.   3.00 1.25
675 A250 500fr multi, diff.   4.75 1.90
  a.    Souv. sheet of 4, #672-675  11.00 11.00
  Nos. 672-675 (4)            10.45 4.15

Traditional Hair Style Type of 1981
**1989, Sept. 16          Perf. 14½x15**
676 A152 175fr gray, black & vio  2.00  .85

Post Day — A252

**1989, Sept. 10    Litho.    Perf. 12**
**Granite Paper**
677 A252 175fr multicolored   1.75  .80

Postal Service, 125th Anniv. (in
1987) — A255

**Perf. 13½x14½**
**1989          Litho.    Unwmk.**
681 A255 90fr multicolored   11.00 2.75
Dated 1988.

St. Louis Church, Port Gentil A256

**1989, Dec. 15 Litho. Perf. 15x14**
682 A256 100fr multicolored 1.00 .40
Christmas. See Nos. 725-726, 757.

L'Ogooue', N'Gomo A256a

**1989 Litho. Perf. 15x14**
682A A256a 100fr multicolored —

Libreville Coat of Arms — A257

**Wmk. 385**
**1990, Mar. 12 Litho. Perf. 13½**
683 A257 100fr multicolored 1.10 .55

World Health Day — A258

**1990, Apr. 7 Litho. Perf. 13**
684 A258 400fr multicolored 4.50 2.10

Souvenir Sheet

Prehistoric Tools A259

**1990, Feb. 14 Litho. Perf. 15x14**
685 Sheet of 4 30.00 30.00
a. A259 100fr Hand axe 1.25 .60
b. A259 175fr Knife blade 2.10 1.40
c. A259 300fr Arrowhead 3.75 1.50
d. A259 400fr Double bladed hand axe 6.25 4.50
See Nos. 727-730.

Souvenir Sheet

Fauna — A260
Illustration reduced.

**1990, Apr. 13 Perf. 14**
686 A260 Sheet of 4 14.00 14.00
a. 100fr Cercopitheque 1.40 .70
b. 175fr Potamocherus Porcus 2.40 1.60
c. 200fr Antelope 3.00 1.75
d. 500fr Mandrill 7.00 4.00

First Postage Stamps, 150th Anniv. — A261

**1991, Jan. 9 Litho. Perf. 13½x14½**
687 A261 500fr multicolored 7.00 3.50

Independence, 30th Anniv. — A263

**1990, Aug. 17 Litho. Perf. 13**
693 A263 100fr multicolored 1.10 .50

Mushrooms — A263a
Various mushrooms.

**1990 Litho. Perf. 15x14**
693A A263a 100fr multicolored 6.00 1.10
693B A263a 175fr multicolored 12.00 2.25
693C A263a 300fr multicolored 17.50 4.25
693D A263a 500fr multicolored 24.50 6.50
Nos. 693A-693D (4) 60.00 14.10

Organization of Petroleum Exporting Countries (OPEC), 30th anniv. — A264

**1990, Sept. 19 Litho. Perf. 13**
694 A264 200fr multicolored 2.00 1.00

1990 World Cup Soccer Championships, Italy — A264a

**1990, June 8 Litho. Perf. 15x14**
694A A264a 100fr Goalie making save 1.00 .50
694B A264a 175fr Four players, ball 1.75 .80
694D A264a 500fr Player celebrating 4.75 2.25

A 300fr stamp and a souvenir sheet containing 694A-694D, with the 300fr value, exist. The editors would like to examine examples.

A265

**1990, Oct. 9 Perf. 13½**
695 A265 175fr blue, yel & blk 2.00 1.00
World Post Day.

Traditional Bwiti Dancer A265a

**1990 Litho. Perf. 15x14**
695A A265a 100fr Ndjembe dancers —
695B A265a 175fr shown —

Flowers A266

**1991, Jan. 9 Litho. Perf. 15x14**
696 A266 100fr Frangipanier 1.25 .60
697 A266 175fr Boule de feu 2.10 1.00
698 A266 200fr Flamboyant 2.40 1.10
699 A266 300fr Rose de porcelaine 3.75 1.75
a. Souvenir sheet of 4, #696-699 10.00 10.00
Nos. 696-699 (4) 9.50 4.45

Petroglyphs — A267

**1991, Feb. 26 Litho. Perf. 15x14**
700 A267 100fr Lizard figure 1.00 .50
701 A267 175fr Triangular figure 1.75 .90
702 A267 300fr Incused lines 3.25 1.50
703 A267 500fr Concentric circles, circles in lines 5.50 2.50
a. Souvenir sheet of 4, #700-703 75.00 75.00
Nos. 700-703 (4) 11.50 5.40

Rubber Trees — A268

**1991, Mar. 20 Litho. Perf. 14x15**
705 A268 100fr multicolored 1.00 .45

World Telecommunications Day — A269

**1991, May 17 Litho. Perf. 13½**
706 A269 175fr multicolored 1.90 .95

**Rabi Kounga Oil Field Type of 1989**
**1991 Litho. Perf. 13½**
707 A239 175fr multicolored 150.00

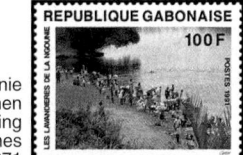

Ngounie Women Washing Clothes A271

**1991, July 17 Litho. Perf. 13½**
708 A271 100fr multicolored 1.00 .45

A272

A273
Designs: Craftsmen.

## 1991, June 19 — Perf. 14x15
| | | | | |
|---|---|---|---|---|
| 709 | A272 | 100fr Basket maker | 1.10 | .55 |
| 710 | A272 | 175fr Wood carver | 1.90 | .95 |
| 711 | A272 | 200fr Weaver | 2.25 | 1.10 |
| 712 | A272 | 500fr Thatch maker | 5.75 | 2.75 |
| | | Nos. 709-712 (4) | 11.00 | 5.35 |

## 1991, Aug. 18  Litho.  Perf. 14x15
Gabonese Medals: 100fr, Equatorial Knight's Star. 175fr, Equatorial Officer's Star. 200fr, Equatorial Commander's Star.

### Gray Background
| | | | | |
|---|---|---|---|---|
| 713 | A273 | 100fr multicolored | 1.00 | .50 |
| 714 | A273 | 175fr multicolored | 1.75 | .90 |
| 715 | A273 | 200fr multicolored | 2.00 | 1.00 |
| | | Nos. 713-715 (3) | 4.75 | 2.40 |

See Nos. 735-737.

Fishing in Gabon A274

## 1991, Sept. 18 — Perf. 15x14
| | | | | |
|---|---|---|---|---|
| 716 | A274 | 100fr Bow-net fishing | 1.10 | .55 |
| 717 | A274 | 175fr Trammel fishing | 1.60 | .95 |
| 718 | A274 | 200fr Net fishing | 2.10 | 1.10 |
| 719 | A274 | 300fr Seine fishing | 3.25 | 1.75 |
| a. | | Souvenir sheet of 4, #716-719 | 9.50 | 9.50 |
| | | Nos. 716-719 (4) | 8.05 | 4.35 |

World Post Day — A275

Termite Mounds — A276

## 1991, Oct. 9 — Perf. 13½
| | | | | |
|---|---|---|---|---|
| 720 | A275 | 175fr blue & multi | 2.00 | .95 |

See Nos. 749, 786.

## 1991, Nov. 6 — Perf. 14x15
| | | | | |
|---|---|---|---|---|
| 721 | A276 | 100fr Phallic | 1.50 | .60 |
| 722 | A276 | 175fr Cathedral | 2.50 | 1.00 |
| 723 | A276 | 200fr Mushroom | 3.00 | 1.10 |
| 724 | A276 | 300fr Arboreal | 4.00 | 1.75 |
| | | Nos. 721-724 (4) | 11.00 | 4.45 |

### Church Type of 1989

## 1991, Dec. 18  Litho.  Perf. 15x14
| | | | | |
|---|---|---|---|---|
| 725 | A256 | 100fr Church of Makokou | 1.00 | .40 |
| 726 | A256 | 100fr Church of Dibwangui | 1.00 | .40 |

Christmas. No. 725 inscribed 1990.

### Prehistoric Tools Type of 1990
Pottery: 100fr, Neolithic pot. 175fr, Bottle, 8th cent. 200fr, Vase, 8th cent. 300fr, Vase, 8th cent, diff.

## 1992, Jan. 9  Litho.  Perf. 14x15
| | | | | |
|---|---|---|---|---|
| 727 | A259 | 100fr multi, vert. | 1.10 | .40 |
| 728 | A259 | 175fr multi, vert. | 1.90 | .75 |
| 729 | A259 | 200fr multi, vert. | 2.50 | .85 |
| 730 | A259 | 300fr multi, vert. | 3.00 | 1.25 |
| a. | | Sheet of 4, #727-730 | 9.50 | 9.50 |
| | | Nos. 727-730 (4) | 8.50 | 3.25 |

Occupations A277

## 1992, Feb. 5
| | | | | |
|---|---|---|---|---|
| 731 | A277 | 100fr Basket maker | 1.10 | .55 |
| 732 | A277 | 175fr Blacksmith | 1.90 | .95 |
| 733 | A277 | 200fr Boat builder | 2.10 | 1.10 |
| 734 | A277 | 300fr Hairdresser | 3.25 | 1.75 |
| a. | | Souvenir sheet of 4, #731-734 | 9.50 | 9.50 |
| | | Nos. 731-734 (4) | 8.35 | 4.35 |

No. 734a issued Feb. 9.

### Gabonese Medals Type of 1991
Designs: 100fr, Equatorial Grand Officer's Star. 175fr, Grand Cross of Dignity and Equatorial Star. 200fr, Order of Merit.

## 1992, Mar. 18  Litho.  Perf. 14x15
### Aquamarine Background
| | | | | |
|---|---|---|---|---|
| 735 | A273 | 100fr multicolored | .95 | .50 |
| 736 | A273 | 175fr multicolored | 1.90 | .90 |
| 737 | A273 | 200fr multicolored | 2.25 | 1.00 |
| | | Nos. 735-737 (3) | 5.10 | 2.40 |

A278

A279

## 1992, Apr. 19 — Perf. 13
| | | | | |
|---|---|---|---|---|
| 738 | A278 | 500fr multicolored | 6.00 | 3.00 |

Konrad Adenauer (1876-1967), German Statesman.

## 1992, May 17 — Perf. 13½
| | | | | |
|---|---|---|---|---|
| 739 | A279 | 175fr multicolored | 2.00 | .95 |

World Telecommunications Day.

Butterflies A280

## 1992, June 10  Litho.  Perf. 15x14
| | | | | |
|---|---|---|---|---|
| 740 | A280 | 100fr Graphium policenes | 1.75 | 1.00 |
| 741 | A280 | 175fr Acraea egina | 2.75 | 1.50 |

A281

A282

## 1992, July 25 — Perf. 14x15
| | | | | |
|---|---|---|---|---|
| 742 | A281 | 100fr Cycling | 1.10 | .55 |
| 743 | A281 | 175fr Boxing | 2.00 | 1.00 |
| 744 | A281 | 200fr Pole vault | 2.25 | 1.10 |
| | | Nos. 742-744 (3) | 5.35 | 2.65 |

1992 Summer Olympics, Barcelona.

## 1992, Sept. 16  Litho.  Perf. 14x15
Tribal masks.
| | | | | |
|---|---|---|---|---|
| 745 | A282 | 100fr Fang | 1.00 | .50 |
| 746 | A282 | 175fr Mpongwe | 1.90 | .95 |
| 747 | A282 | 200fr Kwele | 2.10 | 1.00 |
| 748 | A282 | 300fr Pounou | 3.25 | 1.60 |
| a. | | Souvenir sheet of 4, #745-748 | 9.50 | 9.50 |
| | | Nos. 745-748 (4) | 8.25 | 4.05 |

### World Post Day Type of 1991
Inscribed 1992

## 1992, Oct. 9  Litho.  Perf. 13½
| | | | | |
|---|---|---|---|---|
| 749 | A275 | 175fr bl grn & multi | 2.00 | .95 |

### Bird Type of 1989

## 1992, Nov. 4  Litho.  Perf. 14x15
| | | | | |
|---|---|---|---|---|
| 750 | A241 | 100fr African owl | 2.50 | .95 |
| 751 | A241 | 175fr Coliou strie | 4.00 | 1.50 |
| 752 | A241 | 200fr Vulture | 5.00 | 2.10 |
| 753 | A241 | 300fr Giant kingfisher | 9.00 | 2.75 |
| a. | | Souvenir sheet of 4, #750-753 | 27.50 | 27.50 |
| | | Nos. 750-753 (4) | 20.50 | 7.25 |

Cattle A283

Various scenes of cattle in pasture.

## 1992, Dec. 10 — Perf. 15x14
| | | | | |
|---|---|---|---|---|
| 754 | A283 | 100fr multicolored | 1.00 | .50 |
| 755 | A283 | 175fr multicolored | 1.75 | .90 |
| 756 | A283 | 200fr multicolored | 2.00 | 1.00 |
| | | Nos. 754-756 (3) | 4.75 | 2.40 |

### Church Type of 1989

## 1992, Dec. 16
| | | | | |
|---|---|---|---|---|
| 757 | A256 | 100fr Tchibanga Church | 1.00 | .40 |

Christmas.

Intl. Conference on Nutrition, Rome — A284

## 1992, Dec. 20 — Perf. 13½
| | | | | |
|---|---|---|---|---|
| 758 | A284 | 100fr multicolored | 1.00 | .40 |

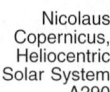

Shells A285

## 1993, Jan. 6  Litho.  Perf. 15x14
| | | | | |
|---|---|---|---|---|
| 759 | A285 | 100fr Pugilina | .90 | .40 |
| 760 | A285 | 175fr Conus pulcher | 1.90 | .70 |
| 761 | A285 | 200fr Fusinus | 2.25 | .80 |
| 762 | A285 | 300fr Cymatium | 3.50 | 1.25 |
| a. | | Souvenir sheet, #759-762 | 12.00 | 12.00 |
| | | Nos. 759-762 (4) | 8.55 | 3.15 |

World Leprosy Day A286

## 1993, Jan. 28 — Perf. 13½
| | | | | |
|---|---|---|---|---|
| 763 | A286 | 175fr multicolored | 2.00 | .95 |

Fernan-Vaz Mission A287

## 1993, Feb. 3 — Perf. 15x14
| | | | | |
|---|---|---|---|---|
| 764 | A287 | 175fr multicolored | 2.40 | 1.00 |

Chappe's Semaphore Telegraph, Bicent. — A288

Designs: 100fr, Claude Chappe (1763-1805), engineer and inventor. 175fr, Chappe's signaling device and code. 200fr, Emile Baudot (1845-1903), devising telegraph code, early telegraph equipment. 300fr, Modern satellite, electronic chip and fiber optics.

## 1993, Mar. 10  Litho.  Perf. 13½
| | | | | |
|---|---|---|---|---|
| 765 | A288 | 100fr multicolored | 1.00 | .50 |
| 766 | A288 | 175fr multicolored | 1.75 | .90 |
| 767 | A288 | 200fr multicolored | 2.00 | 1.10 |
| 768 | A288 | 300fr multicolored | 3.25 | 1.60 |
| a. | | Souvenir sheet of 4, #765-768 | 9.50 | 9.50 |
| | | Nos. 765-768 (4) | 8.00 | 4.10 |

Albert Schweitzer's Arrival in Lambarene, 80th Anniv. — A289

## 1993, Apr. 6  Litho.  Perf. 13
| | | | | |
|---|---|---|---|---|
| 769 | A289 | 500fr multicolored | 6.00 | 2.75 |
| a. | | Booklet pane of 1 | 6.50 | |

### Booklet Stamps
### Size: 26x37mm
### Perf. 13½
| | | | | |
|---|---|---|---|---|
| 770 | A289 | 250fr Feeding chickens | 2.75 | 1.40 |
| a. | | Booklet pane of 4 | 16.00 | |
| 771 | A289 | 250fr Holding babies | 2.75 | 1.40 |
| a. | | Booklet pane of 4 | 16.00 | |
| | | Nos. 769-771 (3) | 11.50 | 5.55 |

Booklet containing one of each pane sold for 3000fr. Value $40.

Nicolaus Copernicus, Heliocentric Solar System A290

## 1993, May 5  Litho.  Perf. 15x14
| | | | | |
|---|---|---|---|---|
| 772 | A290 | 175fr multicolored | 1.60 | .75 |

Polska '93.

A291

A292

**1993, May 17**      *Perf. 13½*
773 A291 175fr multicolored    1.60   .75

World Telecommunications Day.

**1993, June 9**    **Litho.**    *Perf. 14*
Traditional Wine Making: 100fr, Still. 175fr, Extracting juice from palm roots. 200fr, Man in palm tree.

| | | | | |
|---|---|---|---|---|
| 774 | A292 | 100fr multicolored | 1.00 | .45 |
| 775 | A292 | 175fr multicolored | 1.60 | .80 |
| 776 | A292 | 200fr multicolored | 1.90 | .95 |
| a. | | Souvenir sheet of 3, #774-776 | 6.00 | 6.00 |
| | | Nos. 774-776 (3) | 4.50 | 2.20 |

Crustaceans — A293

**1993, July 21**   **Litho.**   *Perf. 15x14*

| | | | | |
|---|---|---|---|---|
| 777 | A293 | 100fr Spiny lobster | 1.10 | .60 |
| 778 | A293 | 175fr Violin crab | 1.75 | .95 |
| 779 | A293 | 200fr Crayfish | 2.25 | 1.10 |
| 780 | A293 | 300fr Spider crab | 3.25 | 1.60 |
| | | Nos. 777-780 (4) | 8.35 | 4.25 |

Paris '94 — A294

**1993, Aug. 10**    **Litho.**    *Perf. 13*
781 A294 100fr multicolored    1.10   .50

Animal Traps A295

**1993, Sept. 15**   **Litho.**   *Perf. 15x14*

| | | | | |
|---|---|---|---|---|
| 782 | A295 | 100fr Squirrel | 1.10 | .20 |
| 783 | A295 | 175fr Small game | 1.75 | .55 |
| 784 | A295 | 200fr Large game | 1.90 | .90 |
| 785 | A295 | 300fr Palm rat | 3.25 | 1.40 |
| a. | | Souvenir sheet of 4, #782-785 | 6.00 | 6.00 |
| | | Nos. 782-785 (4) | 8.00 | 3.05 |

World Post Day Type of 1991
Inscribed 1993

**1993, Oct. 9**      *Perf. 13½*
786 A275 175fr yellow & multi    1.60   .75

Making Bamboo
Toys — A296

**1993, Oct. 20**      *Perf. 11½*
787 A296 100fr multicolored    1.10   .55

Tourism
A297

**1993, Nov. 16**

| | | | | |
|---|---|---|---|---|
| 788 | A297 | 100fr Leconi Canyon | 1.00 | .20 |
| 789 | A297 | 175fr La Lope Valley | 1.60 | .50 |

Christmas
A298

**1993, Dec. 20**      *Perf. 15x14*
790 A298 100fr Catholic Mission,
         Mandji    1.10   .55

Provincial
Map — A299

**1994**      **Litho.**      *Perf. 14½*

| | | | | |
|---|---|---|---|---|
| 791 | A299 | 5fr yellow & multi | .20 | .20 |
| 792 | A299 | 10fr multicolored | .20 | .20 |
| 793 | A299 | 25fr multi | .20 | .20 |
| 795 | A299 | 75fr violet & multi | .40 | .25 |
| 796 | A299 | 100fr pink & multi | .70 | .30 |
| 797 | A299 | 175fr blue & multi | 1.00 | .45 |

Issued: 5fr, 75fr, 100fr, 1/28/94.

Numbers have been reserved for 2 additional values in this set released between 1993 and 1994. The editors would like to examine the other stamps.

Vision of Gabon's Future — A300

**1994, Oct. 5**    **Litho.**    *Perf. 14½*
798 A300 500fr multicolored    *3.00 1.50*

1994 World Cup Soccer
Championships, US — A301

Designs: a, 100fr, Hands on soccer ball. b, 175fr, Two players, ball in air. c, 200fr, Legs of players. d, 300fr, Player, ball.

**1994, Apr. 5**      *Perf. 15x14*
799 A301 Sheet of 4, #a.-d.    30.00 15.00

UN, 50th
Anniv. —
A301a

**1995, July 5**   **Litho.**   *Perf. 11¾x11½*
799E A301a 500fr multi    2.00 2.00

Prehistoric Wildlife — A302

No. 800: a, Sordes. b, Diplodocus (d-e, g-h). c, Eudimorphodon (b). d, Dimetrodon (a). e, Anuroenathus. f, Deinonychus, pachycephalosaurus (e). g, Triceratops (j). h, Hadrosaur (i, k-l). i, Genus Meganeura. j, Longisquama. k, Oviraptor. l, Monoclonius.

No. 801: a, Pistosaurus (d-e, h). b, Pteranodon (c). c, Coelophysis. d, Xenacanthus (g). e, Ischyodus (f, h-i). f, Placochelys. g, Dunkleosteus (j). h, Cymbospondylus (i). i, Enchodus. j, Paracybeloides (k). k, Nautiliod (h). l, Palaeospondylus.

No. 802: a, Tyrannosaurus rex (d). b, Apatosaurus (a, d-e). c, Dimorphodon. d, Stegasaurus (a, e). e, Archaeopteryx. f, Protoceratops. g, Ichthyosaur. h, Phobosuchus, deltoptychius. i, Parasaurolophus (f). j, Scapanorhynchus (g). k, Spathobathis, plesiosaurus (j, l). l, Cladoselacho.

**1995, Sept. 4**    **Litho.**    *Perf. 14*

| | | | | |
|---|---|---|---|---|
| 800 | A302 | 125fr Sheet of 12, #a.-l. | 9.00 | 4.50 |
| 801 | A302 | 225fr Sheet of 12, #a.-l. | 15.00 | 7.50 |
| 802 | A302 | 260fr Sheet of 12, #a.-l. | 17.50 | 8.75 |
| | | Nos. 800-802 (3) | 41.50 | 20.75 |

Singapore '95 (#800).

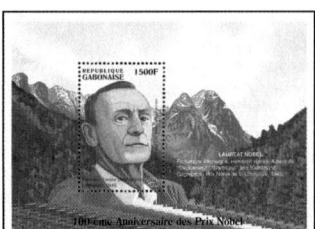

Nobel Prize Fund Established,
Cent. — A303

No. 803 — Nobel Prize recipients: a, Walter H. Brattain, physics, 1956. b, Carl F. Cori, medicine, 1947. c, Gerty T. Cori, medicine, 1947. d, Owen Chamberlain, physics, 1959. e, Christian Anfinsen, chemistry, 1972. f, George de Hevesy, chemistry, 1943. g, Kenichi Fukui, chemistry, 1981. h, Élie Wiesel, peace, 1986. i, Carl F. Braun, physics, 1909.

No. 804: a, Georg Wittig, chemistry, 1979. b, Charles Dawes, peace, 1925. c, Frederic Mistral, literature, 1904. d, Juan Jimenez, literature, 1956. e, Michael S. Brown, medicine, 1985. f, Guglielmo Marconi, physics, 1909. g, Werner Forssmann, medicine, 1956. h, Francis W. Aston, chemistry, 1922. i, Martin Ryle, physics, 1974.

No. 805: a, Leon Jouhaux, peace, 1951. b, Rudolf L. Mossbauer, physics, 1961. c, George Seferis, literature, 1963. d, James Chadwick, physics, 1935. e, Aung San Suu Kyi, peace, 1991. f, John H. Nothrop, chemistry, 1946. g, Eduard Buchner, chemistry, 1907. h, Hans A. Bethe, physics, 1967. i, Nils Dalen, physics, 1912.

No. 806, 1500fr, Hermann Hesse, literature, 1946. No. 807, 1500fr, Albert Schweitzer, peace, 1952. No. 808, 1500fr, Nelson Mandela, peace, 1993.

**1995, Oct. 18**    **Litho.**    *Perf. 14*

| | | | | |
|---|---|---|---|---|
| 803 | A303 | 125fr Sheet of 9, #a.-i. | 6.75 | 3.25 |
| 804 | A303 | 225fr Sheet of 9, #a.-i. | 9.00 | 6.00 |
| 805 | A303 | 260fr Sheet of 9, #a.-i. | 14.00 | 7.00 |
| | | Nos. 803-805 (3) | 29.75 | 16.25 |

**Souvenir Sheets**

| | | | | |
|---|---|---|---|---|
| 806-808 | A303 | Set of 3 | 27.00 | 27.00 |

Monseigneur
Bessieux (1803-
76), Evangelist
A306

**1995, Dec. 25**    **Litho.**    *Perf. 13*
811 A306 500fr multicolored    2.75 1.40

Louis Pasteur
(1822-95),
Microbiologist —
A306a

**1995**      **Litho.**      *Perf. 14¼x14¾*
811A A306a 500fr multi    — —

Food and
Agriculture
Organization,
50th Anniv.
— A306b

**1995**      **Litho.**      *Perf. 11¾*
811B A306b 500fr multi    — —

Mbigou Rock
Sculptor — A306c

**1995**      **Litho.**      *Perf. 14¼x14¾*
811C A306c 500fr multi    2.40 2.40

**Miniature Sheet of 8**

World
War II,
50th
Anniv.
A307

No. 812: a, German generals planning attack. b, Afrika Korps troops ride tanks into El Agheila. c, German artillary fires on British positions in Tobruk. d, British soldiers surrender. e, British soldiers break siege of Tobruk. f, Allies advancing though barbed wire, El Alamein. g, German tanks retreat to Tunis. h, German tank surrenders.

**1996, Jan. 29**      *Perf. 14*
812 A307 125fr Sheet of 8, #a.-h.
          + label    6.50 2.75

World War II, 50th Anniv. A308

No. 813: a, Pres. Franklin D. Roosevelt. b, Pres. Harry S Truman. c, Gen. George Marshall.
1000fr, Flags of US, Great Britain, USSR.

**1996, Jan. 26    Litho.    Perf. 14**
813  A308  225fr Strip of 3, #a.-c. 4.50 4.50
**Souvenir Sheet**
814  A308  1000fr multicolored   6.50 6.50
No. 813 was issued in sheets of 9 stamps.

Dogs — A309

No. 815: a, Dalmatian. b, Basset hound. c, Harrier. d, German Shepherd. e, Bernese bouvier. f, Pug. g, West highland white terrier. h, Akita.

**1996, May 13    Litho.    Perf. 14**
815  A309  125fr Sheet of 8, #a.-h. 6.00 6.00
China '96 Philatelic Exhibition.

St. Pius X Catholic Mission, 10th Anniv. A310

Mgr. Marcel Lefebvre, interior of mission.

**1996, Mar. 4    Perf. 13½**
816  A310  100fr yellow & multi   .75  .20
817  A310  125fr blue & multi     .95  .45

Rotary, Intl. A311

Rotary emblem and: 125fr, UN flag. 225fr, Natl. flag of Gabon. 260fr, Rotary, Intl. flag. 1500fr, Olympic flag.

**1996, July 3    Litho.    Perf. 14**
818-820  A311  Set of 3   4.00 3.00
**Souvenir Sheet**
821  A311  1500fr multicolored   9.00 9.00

Boy Scouts — A312

Designs: 125fr, Scout sign. 225fr, Constructing a lean-to. 260fr, Camping. 1500fr, Lord Baden-Powell.

**1996, July 15**
822-824  A312  Set of 3   4.00 3.25
**Souvenir Sheet**
825  A312  1500fr multicolored   9.00 9.00

Cercopithecus Solatus — A313

**1996, Mar. 6    Perf. 13½x13**
826  A313  500fr multicolored   2.75 1.60

Fight Against AIDS — A314

**1996, Apr. 3    Perf. 13½x13**
827  A314  500fr multicolored   2.75 1.60

Shells — A315

Designs: 100fr, Fusinus caparti. 260fr, Hexaplex rosarium. 500fr, Conus pulcher, horiz.

**1996    Perf. 13½x13, 13x13½**
828-830  A315  Set of 3   5.00 3.50

1996 Summer Olympic Games, Atlanta A316

**1996, May 8    Perf. 11½**
831  A316  225fr Boxing   1.25  .75
832  A316  500fr Relay race   2.50 1.60

Campaign Against Use of Illegal Drugs A317

**1996, Aug. 6    Litho.    Perf. 11½**
833  A317  500fr multicolored   2.75 1.25

Contemporary Paintings, by H. Moundounga A318

**1996, Sept. 10**
834  A318  100fr Girl   .65  .20
835  A318  125fr Three faces   .85  .40
836  A318  225fr Eyes   1.50  .75
a.    Souvenir sheet, #834-836   3.25 3.25
Nos. 834-836 (3)   3.00 1.35

Souvenir Sheet

Temple in Winter — A319

**1996, May 13    Litho.    Perf. 14**
837  A319  500fr multicolored   4.50 2.25
China '96 Philatelic Exhibition, No. 837 was not available until March 1997.

Environmental Protection — A320

Endangered species: 100fr, Galago alleni, vert. 125fr, Perodicticus potto. 225fr, Orycteropus afer. 260fr, Manis gigantea.

**1996, June 5    Perf. 13½**
838-841  A320  Set of 4   4.50 3.25

Children's Paintings A321

Designs: 100fr, Woman's arms encircling world, vert. 125fr, People forming circle around animals. 225fr, Slaughtering of elephants, vert.

**1996, Dec. 25    Litho.    Perf. 11½**
842-844  A321  Set of 3   1.75 1.25
Dated 1996.

Traditional Houses A322

Designs: 100fr, Mud & stick cabin. 125fr, Pygmy hut. 225fr, Bark-sided cabins. 260fr, Wood-sided cabins.

**1996, Nov. 6**
845-848  A322  Set of 4   4.50 2.75
a.    Souvenir sheet, #845-848   5.00 5.00

A323          A324

**1996, Oct. 10**
849  A323  500fr multicolored   2.00 1.25
Investiture of Pres. Nelson Mandela, 3rd anniv.

**1997, Apr. 9    Litho.    Perf. 14**
UNICEF, 50th Anniv.: No. 850: a, Boy holding cup. b, Girl holding cup. c, Boy eating.

1500fr, Boy holding plate.
850  A324  260fr Sheet of 3, #a.-c.   4.00 4.00
**Souvenir Sheet**
851  A324  1500fr multicolored   8.50 8.50

UNESCO, 50th Anniv. A325

No. 852, 225fr: a, Kyoto, Japan. b, Puma, Los Katios Natl. Park, Colombia. c, Abu Simbel Monument, Egypt. d, Old Rauma, Finland. e, Rotunda, City of Vicenza, Italy. f, Homes, China. g, Port of Salvador, Brazil. h, Delos Ruins, Greece.
No. 853, 225fr: a, Fasil Ghebbi Monument, Gondar Region, Ethiopia. b, Victoria Falls, Zambia. c, Zambezi Plains, Chewore Safari Areas, Zimbabwe. d, Nature Reserve, Niger. e, Banc D'Arguin Natl. Park, Mauritania. f, Gorée Island, Senegal. g, Djémila Ruins, Algeria. h, Mosque, Medina of Fez, Morocco.
1000fr, Terracotta warriors, Mausoleum of first Qin Emperor, China.

**1997, Apr. 16**
**Sheets of 8, #a-h, + Label**
852-853  A325  Set of 2   18.00 18.00
**Souvenir Sheet**
854  A325  1000fr multicolored   6.50 6.50

City Arms — A326

**1997, Mar. 12    Litho.    Perf. 11½x12**
855  A326  100fr N'Dendé   .65  .20
856  A326  125fr Libreville   .85  .35
857  A326  225fr Mitzic   1.50  .80
Nos. 855-857 (3)   3.00 1.35

Return of Hong Kong to China — A327

Designs: 125fr, Skyline. 225fr, Skyline, diff. 260fr, Skyline at night, horiz. 500fr, Skyline at night, Deng Xiaoping (1904-97), horiz.

**1997, July 1    Perf. 14**
858-861  A327  Set of 4   6.00 4.00
Nos. 858-859 were each issued in sheets of 4. Nos. 860-861 are 59x28mm and were issued in sheets of 3.

**Unity, Work and Justice Type of 1981**
**1994-95    Litho.    Perf. 11¾**
**Granite Paper**
862  A145  5fr green blue & black   .20  .20
863  A145  10fr orange & black   .20  .20
864  A145  25fr grey lilac & black   .20  .20
865  A145  50fr salmon & black   .20  .20
866  A145  75fr tan & blk   .20  .20
867  A145  100fr pink & black   .20  .20
868  A145  125fr yellow green & black   .45  .35
869  A145  175fr yellow & black   .55  .40

| | | | |
|---|---|---|---|
| 870 | A145 225fr green & black | .70 | .55 |
| 871 | A145 260fr lt blue & black | .80 | .60 |

*Nos. 862-871 (10)*  3.70  3.10

Issued: 50fr, 125fr, 9/30/95; others, 9/20/94.

Paintings — A328

**1995, Oct. 10     Litho.     Perf. 14**

| | | | |
|---|---|---|---|
| 872 | A328 100fr Woman | 1.00 | .45 |
| 873 | A328 125fr Stylized women | 1.50 | .65 |
| 873A | A328 225fr Masked Face | 2.00 | 1.10 |

Raponda Walker, 25th Death Anniv. — A329

Masks — A330

**1995, June 7     Perf. 13½**

| | | | |
|---|---|---|---|
| 874 | A329 500fr multicolored | 7.50 | — |

**1995**

| | | | |
|---|---|---|---|
| 875 | A330 100fr Bateke | 2.50 | — |
| 876 | A330 125fr Bavili | 2.50 | |
| 877 | A330 225fr Fang | 2.50 | |
| 878 | A330 260fr Bandjabi | 2.50 | |

Shells A331

**1995**

| | | | |
|---|---|---|---|
| 879 | A331 100fr Cymbium glans | | — |
| 880 | A331 125fr Muricidae murey | | — |
| 880A | A331 225fr Siliquaria | — | — |
| 881 | A331 260fr Strombus latus | | — |

The editors suspect that additional stamps may have been issued in this set and would like to examine any examples.

Saint-Exupery French Cultural Center — A332

**1996     Perf. 13x13½**

| | | | |
|---|---|---|---|
| 883 | A332 100fr black & multi | | — |
| 884 | A332 125fr blue & multi | | — |
| 885 | A332 225fr red & multi | | — |

Inter-Continental Hotel, 50th Anniv. — A333

**1996     Perf. 13½**

| | | | |
|---|---|---|---|
| 886 | A333 125fr creme & blue | | — |
| 886A | A333 225fr lt yel & blue | 1.00 | — |

Early Post Offices — A333a

**1996, July 20     Litho.     Perf. 12x11½**

| | | | |
|---|---|---|---|
| 886B | A333a 100fr Port Gentil, 1917 | 1.00 | .50 |
| 886C | A333a 125fr Cap-Lopez, 1888 | 1.00 | .65 |
| 886D | A333a 225fr Libreville, 1862 | 1.45 | 1.10 |

The editors would like to examine any examples of stamps from this set heretofore unlisted.

Flowers, Butterflies, Moths, Insects — A334

Designs, vert: 125fr, Rubra tigridia pauonia, pieridae. 225fr, Acraeidae, strelitzia reginae. 260fr, Zautedeschia aethiopica, zonabris oculata. 500fr, Bee orchid, iron prominent moth caterpillar.

No. 891, 260fr: a, Liliaceae. b, Macrophylla, phoebis philea. c, Theaceae amugashita. d, Lilium american cultivars, vanessa atalanta. e, Hybrids, hippodamia convergens. f, Sibine stimulea, iridaceae.

No. 892, 260fr: a, Kalmialati. b, G. gandavensis, calopteryx maculata. c, Narcissus pseudonarcisus. d, Ipheton uniflorum, Tlemaris thysbe. e, Rudbackia hirta. f, Tritida grandiflora, danaus plexippus.

No. 893, 1500fr, Papilion zellicaon, geranium pelargonium, vert. No. 894, 1500fr, Anax jumus, gladstoniana, vert.

**1997, Aug. 11     Litho.     Perf. 14**

| | | | |
|---|---|---|---|
| 887-890 | A334 Set of 4 | 7.00 | 4.50 |

**Sheets of 6, #a-f**

| | | | |
|---|---|---|---|
| 891-892 | A334 Set of 2 | 20.00 | 20.00 |

**Souvenir Sheets**

| | | | |
|---|---|---|---|
| 893-894 | A334 Set of 2 | 18.00 | 18.00 |

Protection of Indigenous Animals — A335

Designs: 100fr, Dendrohyrax arboreus. 125fr, Galago elegantulus. 225fr, Stephanoaetus coronatus.

**1997, June 5     Perf. 13½x13**

| | | | |
|---|---|---|---|
| 895-897 | A335 Set of 3 | 3.00 | 2.00 |
| 897a | Souvenir sheet of 3, #895-897 | 1.75 | 1.75 |

Gabonese Art — A336

Designs: 100fr, Droits de Creatures, vert. 125fr, Ambassadeur, vert. 225fr, Hallucinations.

**1997, May 8     Perf. 13½x13, 13x13½**

| | | | |
|---|---|---|---|
| 898-900 | A336 Set of 3 | 1.50 | 1.00 |
| 900a | Souvenir sheet of 1, #900 | .80 | .80 |

Air Gabon, 20th Anniv. A337

**1997, June 1     Perf. 13x13½**

| | | | |
|---|---|---|---|
| 901 | A337 125fr multicolored | .90 | .50 |
| 902 | A337 225fr multicolored | 1.60 | .80 |

First ACP Summit, Libreville — A338

**1997     Litho.     Perf. 13½x13**

| | | | |
|---|---|---|---|
| 903 | A338 225fr multicolored | 1.40 | .70 |

Lions Club in Gabon, 40th Anniv. — A339

**1997, Oct. 8     Perf. 13½x13**

| | | | |
|---|---|---|---|
| 904 | A339 225fr multicolored | 1.40 | .70 |

AIPLF, 30th Anniv. A340

**1997, Oct. 30     Perf. 12x11½**

| | | | |
|---|---|---|---|
| 905 | A340 260fr multicolored | 1.40 | .65 |

Paul Gondjout, 1st Pres. of the Natl. Assembly — A341

**1997, Nov. 11     Perf. 14x14½**

| | | | |
|---|---|---|---|
| 906 | A341 500fr multicolored | 2.75 | 1.25 |

Heinrich von Stephan (1831-97) — A342

**1997, Nov. 17     Perf. 11½x12**

| | | | |
|---|---|---|---|
| 907 | A342 500fr multicolored | 2.75 | 1.25 |

Princess Diana (1961-97) — A343

No. 908: a, 500fr. b, 300fr. c, 260fr. d, 225fr. e, f, 125fr.
3000fr, Diana in white dress.

**1998, Feb. 10     Litho.     Perf. 13½**

| | | | |
|---|---|---|---|
| 908 | A343 Sheet of 6, #a-f. | 10.00 | 10.00 |

**Souvenir Sheet**

| | | | |
|---|---|---|---|
| 909 | A343 3000fr multicolored | 15.00 | 15.00 |

District Arms — A344

Designs: 100fr, Akieni. 125fr, Pana. 225fr, Lebamba.

**1998, June 4     Litho.     Perf. 13½x13**

| | | | |
|---|---|---|---|
| 910-912 | A344 Set of 3 | 3.00 | 1.50 |

Traditional Tools A345

Designs: 100fr, Yanghe. 125fr, Ikanga. 225fr, Ivedili.

**1997, Nov. 5     Litho.     Perf. 14**

| | | | |
|---|---|---|---|
| 913-915 | A345 Set of 3 | 3.00 | 1.90 |

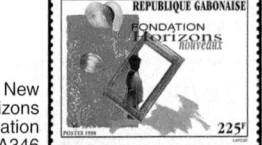

New Horizons Foundation A346

**1998     Litho.     Perf. 13x13½**

| | | | |
|---|---|---|---|
| 916 | A346 225fr multicolored | 1.40 | .70 |

Protected Animals — A347

Designs: 100fr, Hippopotamus amphibius. 125fr, Sylvicapra grimmia. 225fr, Pelecanus rufescens.

**1998     Perf. 13½x13**

| | | | |
|---|---|---|---|
| 917 | A347 100fr multicolored | .65 | .35 |
| 918 | A347 125fr multicolored | .95 | .65 |
| 919 | A347 225fr multicolored | 1.25 | .75 |
| a. | Souvenir sheet, #917-919 | 3.25 | 3.25 |

1998 World Cup Soccer Championships, France — A348

Various soccer plays, country flags in background: 100fr, 125fr, 225fr, 260fr.

**1998, July 10 Litho. Perf. 13½x13**
920-923 A348 Set of 4    4.75 2.75
*923a*   Sheet of 4, #920-923   5.00 5.00

ACCT, 26th Anniv. — A349

**1998**
924 A349 260fr multicolored   1.40 .65

Elimination of Land Mines — A350

**1998 Litho. Perf. 11½x12**
925 A350 260fr multicolored   1.60 .80

Gandhi — A351

**1998**
926 A351 260fr multicolored   1.60 .80

Mother Teresa (1910-97) — A352

**1998**
927 A352 500fr multicolored   2.75 1.40

Deng Xiaoping (1904-97) — A353

**1998**
928 A353 500fr multicolored   2.75 1.40

Intl. Year of the Ocean A354

**1999 Litho. Perf. 11½**
929 A354 125fr multicolored   1.60 .85
Dated 1998.

Wooden Tools — A355

**1999**
930 A355 100fr Mortier   .70 .55
931 A355 125fr Pilon   1.00 .80
Dated 1998.

Universal Declaration of Human Rights A356

**1999**
932 A356 225fr multicolored   1.40 .80
Dated 1998.

Space Exploration — A357

Designs: No. 933, 225fr, Gemini 7. No. 934, 225fr, Skylab. No. 935, 225fr, Atlas Moon Explorer. No. 936, 225fr, Space Shuttle.
No. 937: a, Venera 4. b, TDRS. c, Sputnik II. d, Zond II. e, Untethered walk. f, Intelsat 6. g, Luna 16. h, Sputnik III. i, Vostok V. j, Lunar explorer. k, 2nd lunar landing. l, Conrad and Surveyor.
No. 938: a, Sputnik. b, Mariner 2. c, Apollo 11 Lunar Module. d, Gemini 7. e, Mir. f, Atlas Moon Explorer. g, Space Shuttle Orbit. h, Hubbell. i, Soyuz. j, Apollo 11 re-entry. k, Skylab. l, Venture Star.
No. 939: a, Lunar landing II. b, Gemini 7. c, Venture Star. d, Hubbell.
No. 940, 1500fr, Shuttle launch. No. 941, 1500fr, Untethered walk. No. 942, 1500fr, Apollo II. No. 943, 1500fr, Lunar landing module.

**1999, Apr. 30 Litho. Perf. 14**
933-936 A357 Set of 4   3.75 2.00
937 A357 100fr Sheet of 12,
    #a.-l.   6.00 6.00
938 A357 125fr Sheet of 12,
    #a.-l.   8.50 8.50
**Sheet of 4**
939 A357 225fr Sheet of 4,
    #a.-d.   4.00 4.00
**Souvenir Sheets**
940-943 A357 Set of 4   35.00 35.00
Moon landing, 30th anniv.

Traditional Weapons — A358

Designs: 100fr, Sagaie. 125fr, Arbalète. 225fr, Couteau et jet.

**1999 Perf. 13**
944-946 A358 Set of 3   3.00 1.60

Folklore — A358a

Designs: 125fr, Mitsogho reliquary.

**1999 Litho. Perf. 13¼**
946A A358a 125fr multi   —
The editors suspect that additional stamps may have been issued in this set and would like to examine any examples.

Democracy A359

**1999 Litho. Perf. 11¾**
947 A359 100fr multicolored   1.00 .50

UPU, 125th Anniv. A360

Designs: 100fr, People, map. 225fr, Emblem, letters, vert. 260fr, Great Wall of China, vert.

**1999**
948 A360 100fr multicolored   .60 .40
949 A360 225fr multicolored   1.00 .75
950 A360 260fr multicolored   1.50 1.00
    *Nos. 948-950 (3)*   3.10 2.15

Manufacture of Aspirin, Cent. — A361

**1999**
951 A361 225fr multicolored   1.40 .70

Mushrooms — A361a

Designs: 100fr, Amanite panthère. 125fr, Basidomycetes, horiz. 225fr, Basidomycetes, diff., horiz. 260fr, Amanite tue-mouches.

**1999 Litho. Perf. 13¼x13, 13x13¼**
951A-951D A361a Set of 4   5.50 5.50

PhilexFrance '99 — A362

**1999, July 2 Litho. Perf. 13**
952 A362 225fr multi   2.00 1.40
No. 952 has a holographic image. Soaking in water may affect hologram.

Central African Economic and Monetary Community Days — A364

Map of Africa and: 125fr, Circle of member's flags. 225fr, Rows of member's flags.

**1999 Litho. Perf. 14½**
954-955 A364 Set of 2   2.40 2.40

Pope John XXIII, St. Peter's Basilica A365

**1999 Litho. Perf. 11¾**
956 A365 100fr multi   .75 .75
Announcement of 2nd Vatican Council, 40th anniv., Christmas.

**Unity, Work and Justice Type of 1981**
**1999 Litho. Perf. 11¾**
**Granite Paper**
959 A145 40fr lil & blk   .20 .20

Shells A365a

Designs: 100fr, Harpa doris. 125fr, Thais haemastoma. 225fr, Cassis tessellata.

**1999, June 25 Litho. Perf. 13x13½**
964-966 A365a Set of 3   4.00 4.00

Fish A365b

Designs: 100fr, Epinephelus marginatus, mugil cephalus. 125fr, Brycinus macrolepidotus. 225fr, Oreochromis schwebischi. 260fr, Pomadasys peroteti, caranx hippos, ethmalosa fimbriata.

**1999**
967-970 A365b Set of 4   5.50 5.50

Expo 2000, Hanover A366

**Perf. 11¾x11½**
**2000, Feb. 16**     **Litho.**
971   A366   225fr multi     1.60   1.60

Protected Animals A367

Designs: 125fr, Haliaetus vocifer. 225fr, Panthera pardus. 260fr, Panthera leo.

**2000, June 5**
972-974   A367   Set of 3     4.00   4.00

Events of the 20th Century A368

Designs: 100fr, Universal Declaration of Human Rights, vert. 125fr, World War II. 225fr, First man on the moon.

**Perf. 11½x11¾, 11¾x11½**
**2000, July 20**     Set of 3
975-977   A368   Set of 3     3.00   3.00

Scientific Achievements of the 20th Century — A369

Designs: 100fr, Microprocessor, 1971. 125fr, Nuclear reactor, 1942. 225fr, Structure of DNA, 1953.

**2000**     **Perf. 11¾x11½**
978-980   A369   Set of 3     3.00   3.00

Tourism A370

100fr, Pygmy village. 125fr, Lake region. 225fr, Poubara Waterfall. 260fr, Mt. Brazza.

**2000**     **Perf. 13x13½**
981-984   A370   Set of 4     4.75   4.75

Y2K Bug — A371

**2000, Dec. 11**     **Perf. 11½x11¾**
985   A371   225fr multi     1.40   1.40

Dr. Albert Schweitzer (1875-1965) A372

**2000, Jan. 14**     **Perf. 13¼x13**
986   A372   260fr multi     1.60   1.60

A373

Trains — A374

Designs: No. 987, 100fr, Japanese Hikari trains. 125fr, Hungarian Bo-Bo electric locomotive. No. 989, 500fr, Pakistani electric locomotive. No. 990, 500fr, Belgian locomotive.

No. 991: a, 100fr, Korean Bo-Bo locomotive. b, 100fr, Moroccan electric locomotive. c, 100fr, Spanish electric locomotive. d, 500fr, Yugoslavian Type J2-441. e, 500fr, Chinese electric locomotive. f, 500fr, Norwegian Type E115.

No. 992: a, 100fr, Portuguese Diesel-electric locomotive. b, 100fr, Japanese mag-lev train. c, 100fr, Long Island Railroad diesel car. d, 500fr, German Type 103. e, 500fr, Romanian Co-Co locomotive. f, 500fr, English HST.

No. 993, 1500fr, English train "The Advanced." No. 994, 1500fr, French TGV 001. No. 995, 1500fr, Austrian Transalpine train. No. 996, 1500fr, Stourbridge Lion. No. 997, 1500fr, Puffing Billy, vert. No. 998, 1500fr, Union Pacific 4-8-8-4 Big Boy, vert. No. 999, French TGV, vert.

Illustration A374 reduced.

**Perf. 13¼x13¾, 13¾x13¼**
**2000, Dec. 10**     **Litho.**
987-990   A373   Set of 4     6.00   6.00
**Sheets of 6, #a-f**
991-992   A373   Set of 2     20.00   20.00
**Souvenir Sheets**
993-995   A373   Set of 3     24.00   24.00
996-999   A374   Set of 4     30.00   30.00

A375

Prehistoric Animals — A376

Designs: No. 1000, 100fr, Archaeopteryx. No. 1001, 100fr, Velociraptor, vert. No. 1002, 125fr, Torosaurus. No. 1003, 125fr, Corythosaurus, vert. No. 1004, 125fr, Pachycephalosaurus, vert. No. 1005, 500fr, Parasaurolophus.

No. 1006, 100fr, Pterodactylus. No. 1007, 125fr, Allosaurus. No. 1008, 125fr, Struthiomimus, vert. No. 1009, 225fr, Psittacosaurus,

vert. No. 1010, 260fr, Parasauraolophus, vert. No. 1011, 500fr, Acanthostega.

No. 1012: a, 125fr, Camarasaurus. b, 125fr, Rhamphorhynchus. c, 125fr, Saltasaurus. d, 225fr, Camptosaurus. e, 225fr, Megalosaurus. f, 225fr, Allosaurus. g, 260fr, Anchisaurus. h, 260fr, Dilophosaurus. i, 260fr, Massospondylus.

No. 1013: a, 100fr, Stegosaurus. b, 100fr, Pteranodon. c, 100fr, Carnotaurus. d, 125fr, Iguanodon. e, 125fr, Pentaceratops. f, 125fr, Styracosaurus. g, 500fr, Deinonychus. h, 500fr, Stegoceras. i, 500fr, Struthiomimus.

No. 1014: a, 125fr, Volcano. b, 125fr, Pterodactylus. c, 125fr, Dimorphodon. d, 125fr, Alamosaurus. e, 225fr, Psittacosaurus. f, 225fr, Deinonychus. g, 225fr, Dromiceiomimus. h, 225fr, Yangchuanosaurus. i, 260fr, Protorosaurus. j, 260fr, Triceratops. k, 260fr, Daspletosaurus. l, 260fr, Pentaceratops.

No. 1015: a, 125fr, Brachiosaurus. b, 125fr, Scaphognathus. c, 125fr, Mountain and sun. d, 125fr, Pteranodon. e, 225fr, Tyrannosaurus. f, 225fr, Ichthyosaurus. g, 225fr, Macroplata. h, 225fr, Dilophosaurus. i, 500fr, Stegosaurus. j, 500fr, Thecodontosaurus. k, 500fr, Saltosaurus. l, 500fr, Pachyrhinosaurus.

No. 1016, 225fr: a, Tyrannosaurus. b, Criorhynchus. c, Pterodactylus. d, Albertosaurus. e, Dromiceiomimus. f, Opisthocoelicaudia. g, Brachiosaurus. h, Pachycephalosaurus. i, Parasaurolophus. j, Edmontosaurus. k, Pentaceratops. l, Corythosaurus.

No. 1017, 260fr: a, Peteinosaurus. b, Volcanoes. c, Acanthostega. d, Ceresiosaurus. e, Pliosaur. f, Stethacanthus. g, Ichthyosaur. h, Pholidogaster. i, Gerrothorax. j, Diplocaulus. k, Mixosaurus. l, Echinoceras raricostatum.

No. 1018, 1500fr, Tyrannosaurus Rex. No. 1019, 1500fr, Arrhinoceratops. No. 1020, 1500fr, Argentinosaurus, vert. No. 1021, 1500fr, Cetiosaurus, vert. No. 1022, 1500fr, Archaeopteryx. No. 1023, Saltasaurus, vert.

**2000, Dec. 20**
1000-1005   A375   Set of 6    8.00   8.00
1006-1011   A376   Set of 6    8.00   8.00
**Sheets of 9, #a-i**
1012-1013   A375   Set of 2    20.00   20.00
**Sheets of 12, #a-l**
1014-1015   A375   Set of 2    30.00   30.00
1016-1017   A376   Set of 2    30.00   30.00
**Souvenir Sheets**
1018-1021   A375   Set of 4    30.00   30.00
1022-1023   A376   Set of 2    16.00   16.00

No. 1021 contains one 42x56mm stamp.

**Train Type of 2000 and**

A377

Designs: 100fr, German Type 201. No. 1025, 225fr, German Type 112. No. 1026, 225fr, ICT. No. 1027, 260fr, ICE. No. 1028, 260fr, French Electric BB9004. No. 1029, 260fr, French Type 232U 4-8-2. No. 1030, 500fr, French Type 241C 4-8-2 "Mountain." No. 1031, 500fr, German TEE.

No. 1032: a, 125fr, German Type 41. b, 125fr, Type 39. c, 125fr, German Type 10. d, 500fr, German Type 99. e, 500fr, German Type 58. f, 500fr, German Type 44.

No. 1033: a, 225fr, German Type 229. b, 225fr, Type 152. c, 225fr, German Type 101. d, 500fr, German Type 250. e, 500fr, German Type 232. f, 500fr, Type 216.

No. 1034: a, 125fr, Prussian Type P8 4-6-0. b, 125fr, Bavarian Type S3/6 4-6-2. c, 125fr, German Type 01 4-6-2. d, 500fr, German Electric "Crocodile." e, 500fr, Swiss Electric Type Be 4/6. f, 500fr, Swiss Electric Type Ae 6/6.

No. 1035: a, 125fr, Stirling 8ft Single 4-2-2 "No. 1," UK. b, 125fr, Greeley Pacific Type A3 4-6-2 "Flying Scotsman," UK. c, 125fr, Stanier Coronation Type 4-6-2 "Coronation Scot," UK. d, 500fr, Baldwin 4-4-0 "The General," US. e, 500fr, Class J1 Hudson 4-8-4, US. f, "Super Chief" Diesel-electric, US.

No. 1036, 1500fr, Type 91. No. 1037, 1500fr, Type 57. No. 1038, Greeley Pacific Type A4 4-6-2 "Silver Link," UK. No. 1039, J Type 4-8-4, US.

**Perf. 13¼x13½, 13½x13¼**
**2000?**     **Litho.**
1024-1027   A374   Set of 4    4.00   4.00
1028-1031   A377   Set of 4    8.00   8.00
**Sheets of 6, #a-f**
1032-1033   A374   Set of 2    20.00   20.00
1034-1035   A377   Set of 2    19.00   19.00

**Souvenir Sheets**
1036-1037   A374   Set of 2    16.00   16.00
1038-1039   A377   Set of 2    16.00   16.00

Nos. 1038-1039 each contain one 56x42mm stamp.

Raponda Walker Foundation A378

**2000**     **Litho.**     **Perf. 11½**
1039A   A378   225fr multi    1.10   1.10

End of the Millennium A379

**2000**
1039B   A379   225fr multi    1.20   1.20

**Scientific Achievements of the 20th Century Type of 2000**

Designs: 100fr, Isolation of insulin, 1921. 125fr, Invention of television, 1921. 225fr, Invention of the calculator, 1951.

**Perf. 11¾x11½**
**2000, Nov. 28**     **Litho.**
1040-1042   A369   Set of 3    3.00   3.00

Mengane Dancers A380

**2001**     **Litho.**     **Perf. 11¾**
1043   A380   100fr multi    .30   .30
**Souvenir Sheet**

No. 1045: a, 100fr, Mengane. b, 130fr, Maghouba. c, 225fr, Ndjobi.

1045   A380   Sheet of 3, #a-c    2.25   2.25

Two additional stamps may have been issued in this set. The editors would like to examine any examples.

Flowers — A381

Design: 225fr, Strophantus gratus. 260fr, Spathodea campanulata.

**2001**     **Litho.**     **Perf. 11¾**
1048   A381   225fr multi    —   —
1049   A381   260fr multi    —   —

Two additional stamps were issued in this set. The editors would like to examine any examples.

Gabon Poste Emblem A382

Color of denomination: 125fr, Green. 225fr, Blue.

**2003, Apr. 5**    **Litho.**    **Perf. 13x13¼**
1050-1051   A382   Set of 2    1.75   1.75

Orchids — A383

Designs: 100fr, Plectrelmintus caudatus.
125fr, Eulophia. 225fr, Jacinthe d'eau.

**2004, Feb. 20**          **Perf. 13¼x13**
1052-1054  A383  Set of 3          2.25  2.25
1054a   Souvenir sheet, #1052-1054   2.75  2.75

Cooperation Between Gabon and
People's Republic of China, 30th
Anniv. — A384

No. 1055: a, 125fr, Chinese Prime Minister
Wen Jiabao, Gabon Pres. Omar Bongo and
flags. b, 225fr, Coats of arms of People's
Republic of China and Gabon.
Illustration reduced.

**2004, Apr. 20**          **Perf. 12**
1055  A384  Horiz. pair, #a-b      1.75  1.75

FIFA (Fédération Internationale de
Football Association), Cent. — A385

Background color: 125fr, Blue. 225fr, Green.

**2004, Apr. 24**  **Litho.**  **Perf. 13x13¼**
1058-1059  A385  Set of 2         1.75  1.75

Biodiversity — A386

Designs: 100fr, Hyperolius kuligae. 125fr,
Chameleon, vert. 225fr, Merops malimbicus.
260fr, Owl.

**2004, June 5**  **Perf. 13x13¼, 13¼x13**
1060-1063  A386  Set of 4         3.50  3.50

Rotary International, Cent. — A387

**2005, Feb. 23**  **Litho.**  **Perf. 13x13¼**
1064  A387  125fr multi          .60  .60

---

Souvenir Sheet

Lake Evaro — A388

Illustration reduced.

**2005**      **Litho.**      **Perf. 13¾x13½**
1066  A388  225fr multi         .85  .85
**Souvenir Sheet**
1067  A388  500fr multi         1.90  1.90

Soccer
Players
and Flag
A390

**2005**      **Litho.**      **Perf. 13x13¼**
1069  A390  225fr multi         .85  .85
No. 1069 issued in sheets of 4.

Central African
Network of
Protected
Areas — A391

**2007, July**   **Litho.**      **Perf. 13¼**
1070  A391  500fr multi         2.10  2.10

---

## SEMI-POSTAL STAMPS

No. 37 Surcharged in
Red

**1916**      **Unwmk.**      **Perf. 13½x14**
B1  A10  10c + 5c red & car     30.00  30.00
a.   Double surcharge           200.00  225.00
**Same Surcharge on No. 54 in Red**
B2  A10  10c + 5c red & car     37.50  37.50
a.   Double surcharge           200.00  225.00

---

No. 54 Surcharged in
Red

**1917**
B3  A10  10c + 5c red & car     1.75  1.75

Catalogue values for unused
stamps in this section, from this
point to the end of the section, are
for Never Hinged items.

**Republic**
**Anti-Malaria Issue**
Common Design Type
**1962, Apr. 7**  **Engr.**  **Perf. 12½x12**
B4  CD108  25fr + 5fr yel grn   1.00  1.00
WHO drive to eradicate malaria.

**Freedom from Hunger Issue**
Common Design Type
**1963, Mar. 21**  **Unwmk.**  **Perf. 13**
B5  CD112  25fr + 5fr dk red, grn
& brn                            1.00  1.00

Red Cross — SP1

**1997, May 8**  **Litho.**  **Perf. 13½x13**
B6  SP1  150fr +75fr multi      1.40  1.10

---

## AIR POST STAMPS

Catalogue values for unused
stamps in this section are for
Never Hinged items.

Dr. Albert Schweitzer — AP1

**Unwmk.**
**1960, July 23**  **Engr.**  **Perf. 13**
C1  AP1  200fr grn, dl red brn
& ultra                          7.50  3.75
For surcharge see No. C11.

Workmen Felling Tree — AP2

**1960, Oct. 8**
C2  AP2  100fr red brn, grn & blk  4.50  1.90
5th World Forestry Cong., Seattle, WA, Aug.
29-Sept. 10.

---

**Olympic Games Issue**
French Equatorial Africa No. C37
Surcharged in Red Like Chad No. C1

AP2a

**1960, Dec. 15**
C3  AP2a  250fr on 500fr grnsh
blk, blk &
slate                           10.00  10.00
17th Olympic Games, Rome, 8/25-9/11.

Lyre-tailed Honey Guide — AP3

**1961, May 30**          **Perf. 13**
C4  AP3  50fr sl grn, red brn &
ultra                            4.75  1.60
See Nos. C14-C17.

**Air Afrique Issue**
Common Design Type
**1962, Feb. 17**  **Engr.**  **Perf. 13**
C5  CD107  500fr sl grn, blk &
bis                             13.00  7.00

Long
Jump — AP3a

**1962, July 21  Photo.  Perf. 12x12½**
C6  AP3a  100fr dk & lt bl, brn &
blk                              3.75  2.25
Issued to publicize the Abidjan Games.

Breguet 14, 1928 — AP4

Development of air transport: 20fr, Dragon
biplane transport. 60fr, Caravelle jet. 85fr,
Rocket-propelled aircraft.

**1962, Sept. 4**     **Engr.**     **Perf. 13**
C7  AP4  10fr dl red brn & sl    .75   .20
C8  AP4  20fr dk bl, sl & ocher  1.10  .45
C9  AP4  60fr dk sl grn, blk &
brn                              2.75  1.00
C10  AP4  85fr dk bl, blk & org  2.75  1.60
a.   Souv. sheet of 4, #C7-C10   11.00  11.00
Nos. C7-C10 (4)                   7.35  3.25
Gabon's 1st phil. exhib., Libreville, Sept. 2-9.

No. C1 Surcharged in Red:
"100F/JUBILE GABONAIS/1913-1963"
**1963, Apr. 18**
C11  AP1  100fr on 200fr         4.00  2.10
50th anniv. of Dr. Albert Schweitzer's arrival
in Gabon.

Post Office, Libreville — AP5

**1963, Apr. 28  Photo.  *Perf. 13x12***
C12 AP5 100fr multi                    1.90 1.00

**African Postal Union Issue**
Common Design Type

**1963, Sept. 8  Unwmk.  *Perf. 12½***
C13 CD114 85fr brt car, ocher &
red                                    1.90  .80

Bird Type of 1961

Birds: 100fr, Johanna's sunbird. 200fr, Blue-headed bee-eater, vert. 250fr, Crowned hawk-eagle, vert. 500fr, Narina trogon, vert.

**1963-64  Engr.  *Perf. 13***
C14 AP3 100fr dk grn, vio bl &
car                                    3.75 1.25
C15 AP3 200fr ol, vio bl & red         8.00 3.00
C16 AP3 250fr grn, blk & dk
brn ('64)                             15.00 4.00
C17 AP3 500fr multi                   15.00 7.00
    Nos. C14-C17 (4)                  41.75 15.25

**1963 Air Afrique Issue**
Common Design Type

**1963, Nov. 19  Photo.  *Perf. 13x12***
C18 CD115 50fr lt vio, gray, blk &
grn                                    1.60  .65

**Europafrica Issue**
Common Design Type

**1963, Nov. 30  *Perf. 12x13***
C19 CD116 50fr vio, yel & dk brn   1.60  .75

**Chiefs of State Issue**

Map and Presidents of Chad, Congo, Gabon and CAR AP5a

**1964, June 23  *Perf. 12½***
C20 AP5a 100fr multi                   2.10  .90
    See note after Central African Republic No. C19.

**Europafrica Issue, 1964**

Globe and Emblems of Industry and Agriculture — AP6

**1964, July 20  *Perf. 12x13***
C21 AP6 50fr red, olive & blue     1.60  .75
    See note after Cameroun No. 402.

Start of Race — AP7

Athletes (Greek): 50fr, Massage at gymnasium, vert. 100fr, Anointing with oil before game, vert. 200fr, Four athletes.

**1964, July 30  Engr.  *Perf. 13***
C22 AP7 25fr sl grn, dk brn &
org                                    1.00  .45
C23 AP7 50fr dk brn, sl grn &
org brn                                1.60  .60
C24 AP7 100fr vio bl, ol grn &
dk brn                                 3.00 1.10
C25 AP7 200fr dk brn, mag &
org red                                5.25 3.00
a.  Min. sheet of 4, #C22-C25        14.00 14.00
    Nos. C22-C25 (4)                 10.85 5.15
18th Olympic Games, Tokyo, Oct. 10-25.

Communications Symbols — AP7a

**1964, Nov. 2  Litho.  *Perf. 12½x13***
C26 AP7a 25fr lt grn, dk brn & lt
red brn                                 .90  .20
    See note after Chad No. C19.

John F. Kennedy (1917-63) — AP8

**1964, Nov. 23  Photo.  *Perf. 12½***
C27 AP8 100fr grn, org & blk           2.25 1.50
a.  Souv. sheet of 4                  11.00 11.00

Telephone Operator, Nurse and Police Woman — AP9

**1964, Dec. 5  Engr.  *Perf. 13***
C28 AP9 50fr car, bl & chocolate   1.40  .40
    Social evolution of Gabonese women.

World Map and ICY Emblem — AP10

**1965, Mar. 25  Unwmk.  *Perf. 13***
C29 AP10 50fr org, Prus bl &
grnsh bl                               1.40  .70
    International Cooperation Year.

Merchant Ship, 17th Century — AP11

25fr, Galleon, 16th cent., vert. 85fr, Frigate, 18th cent., vert. 100fr, Brig, 19th cent.

**1965, Apr. 22  Photo.  *Perf. 13***
C30 AP11 25fr lilac & multi            1.25  .55
C31 AP11 50fr yellow & multi           2.75  .80
C32 AP11 85fr multi                    4.75 1.75
C33 AP11 100fr multi                   6.25 2.10
    Nos. C30-C33 (4)                  15.00 5.20

Red Cross Nurse Carrying Sick Child — AP12

**1965, June 25  Engr.  *Perf. 13***
C34 AP12 100fr brn, slate grn &
red                                    2.25  .75
    Issued for the Gabonese Red Cross.

Women's Basketball AP13

**1965, July 15  Unwmk.***
C35 AP13 100fr sep, red org &
brt lil                                2.75  .90
    African Games, Brazzaville, July 18-25.

Maps of Europe and Africa — AP14

**1965, July 26  Photo.  *Perf. 13x12***
C36 AP14 50fr multi                    1.90  .65
    See note after Cameroun No. 421.

Pres. Leon Mba AP15

**1965, Aug. 17  *Perf. 12½***
C37 AP15 25fr multi                     .90  .50
    Fifth anniversary of independence.

Sir Winston Churchill and Microphones — AP16

**1965, Sept. 28  Photo.  *Perf. 12½***
C38 AP16 100fr gold, blk & bl          2.50 1.10
    Sir Winston Spencer Churchill (1874-1965), statesman and World War II leader.

Dr. Albert Schweitzer — AP17

Embossed on Gold Foil
***Die-cut Perf. 14½, Approx.***
**1965, Dec. 4**
C39 AP17 1000fr gold                  75.00 75.00
    Dr. Albert Schweitzer (1875-1965), medical missionary, theologian and musician.

Pope John XXIII and St. Peter's — AP18

**1965, Dec. 10  Photo.  *Perf. 13x12½***
C40 AP18 85fr multi                    1.75 1.10
    Issued in memory of Pope John XXIII.

Anti-Malaria Treatment AP19

**1966, Apr. 8  Photo.  *Perf. 12½***
C41 AP19 50fr shown                    1.25  .75
a.  Min. sheet of 4                    8.75 8.75
C42 AP19 100fr First aid               2.75 1.10
a.  Min. sheet of 4                   14.00 14.00
    Issued for the Red Cross.

Diamant Rocket, A-1 Satellite and Map of Africa — AP20

90fr, FR-1 satellite, Diamant rocket and earth.

**1966, May 18  Engr.  *Perf. 13***
C43 AP20 30fr dk pur, brt bl &
red brn                                 .85  .45
C44 AP20 90fr brt lil, red & pur       2.00  .80
    French achievements in space.

Soccer and World Map — AP21

**1966, July 15    Engr.    Perf. 13**
C45 AP21 100fr slate & brn red    3.00 1.25
8th World Soccer Cup Championship, Wembley, England, July 11-30.

Symbols of Industry and Transportation AP22

**1966, July 26    Photo.    Perf. 12x13**
C46 AP22 50fr multi    1.50 .65
3rd anniv. of the economic agreement between the European Economic Community and the African and Malgache Union.

**Air Afrique Issue, 1966**
Common Design Type
**1966, Aug. 31    Photo.    Perf. 13**
C47 CD123 30fr org, blk & gray    1.00 .60

Student and UNESCO Emblem — AP23

**1966, Nov. 4    Engr.    Perf. 13**
C48 AP23 100fr dl bl, ocher & blk    2.25 .85
20th anniv. of UNESCO.

Libreville Airport — AP24

**1966, Nov. 21    Engr.    Perf. 13**
C49 AP24 200fr dp bl & red brn    5.00 1.50
Inauguration of Libreville Airport.

Farman 190 — AP25

Planes: 300fr, De Havilland Heron. 500fr, Potez 56.

**1967, Apr. 1    Engr.    Perf. 13**
C50 AP25 200fr ultra, lil & bl grn    5.25 1.75
C51 AP25 300fr brn, lil & brt bl    8.75 2.10
C52 AP25 500fr brn car, dk grn
    & indigo    14.00 4.75
    *Nos. C50-C52 (3)*    28.00 8.60
For surcharge see No. C128.

Planes, Runways and ICAO Emblem — AP26

**1967, May 19    Engr.    Perf. 13**
C53 AP26 100fr plum, brt bl &
    yel grn    2.50 1.10
International Civil Aviation Organization.

Blood Donor and Bottles — AP27

100fr, Human heart and transfusion apparatus.

**1967, June 26    Photo.    Perf. 12½**
C54 AP27 50fr ocher, red &
    sl    1.75 .65
    a.    Souvenir sheet of 4    9.75 9.75
C55 AP27 100fr yel grn, red &
    gray    3.50 1.25
    a.    Souvenir sheet of 4    15.00 15.00
Issued for the Red Cross. Nos. C54a, C55a each contain 2 vertical tête bêche pairs.

Jamboree Emblem and Symbols of Orientation AP28

**1967, Aug. 1    Engr.    Perf. 13**
Design: 100fr, Jamboree emblem, maps and Scouts of Africa and America.
C56 AP28 50fr multi    1.60 .80
C57 AP28 100fr brt grn, dp car &
    bl    2.40 1.60
12th Boy Scout World Jamboree, Farragut State Park, Idaho, Aug. 1-9.

**African Postal Union Issue, 1967**
Common Design Type
**1967, Sept. 9    Engr.    Perf. 13**
C58 CD124 100fr dl bl, ol & red
    brn    2.25 .95

Mission Church — AP29

**1967, Oct. 18    Engr.    Perf. 13**
C59 AP29 100fr brt bl, dk grn &
    blk    2.75 1.25
125th anniv. of the arrival of American Protestant missionaries in Baraka-Libreville.

UN Emblem, Sword, Book and People — AP30

**1967, Nov. 7    Photo.    Perf. 13**
C60 AP30 60fr dk red, vio bl & bis    1.10 .65
UN Commission on Human Rights.

**Tree Type of Regular Issue**
Designs: 50fr, Baillonella toxisperma. 100fr, Aucoumea klaineana.
**1967, Dec. 5    Engr.    Perf. 13**
**Size: 26½x47½mm**
C61 A53 50fr grn, brt bl & brn    2.10 1.10
C62 A53 100fr multi    3.50 1.90
    a.    Bklt. pane of 5, #223-225,
        C61-C62 with gutter btwn.    10.00 10.00

Konrad Adenauer AP31

**1968, Feb. 20    Photo.    Perf. 12½**
C63 AP31 100fr blk, dl org &
    red    3.25 1.10
    a.    Souvenir sheet of 4    13.00 13.00
Issued in memory of Konrad Adenauer (1876-1967), chancellor of West Germany (1949-63). No. C63a includes 1967 CEPT (Europa) emblem.

Madonna of the Rosary by Murillo AP32

90fr, Christ in Bonds, by Luis de Morales. 100fr, St. John on Patmos, by Juan Mates.
**1968, July 9    Photo.    Perf. 12½x12**
C64 AP32 60fr multi    1.40 .55
C65 AP32 90fr multi    2.00 .95
C66 AP32 100fr multi, horiz.    2.25 1.10
    *Nos. C64-C66 (3)*    5.65 2.60
See #C77, C102-C104, C132-C133, C146-C148.

**Europafrica Issue**

Stylized Knot — AP32a

**1968, July 23    Photo.    Perf. 13**
C67 AP32a 50fr yel brn, emer &
    lt ultra    1.10 .45
See note after Congo Republic No. C69.

Support for Red Cross — AP33

50fr, Distribution of Red Cross gifts.

**1968, Aug. 13**
C68 AP33 50fr multi    1.40 .65
C69 AP33 100fr multi    3.25 1.40
    a.    Bklt. pane of 2, #C68, C69 with
        gutter btwn.    7.50 7.50
Issued for the Red Cross.

High Jump — AP34

**1968, Sept. 3    Engr.**
C70 AP34 25fr shown    .85 .50
C71 AP34 30fr Bicycling, vert.    1.00 .55
C72 AP34 100fr Judo, vert.    2.75 1.25
C73 AP34 200fr Boxing    5.00 2.10
    a.    Bklt. pane of 4, #C70-C71,
        C72-C73 with gutter btwn.    13.00 13.00
    *Nos. C70-C73 (4)*    9.60 4.40
Issued to publicize the 19th Summer Olympic Games, Mexico City, Oct. 12-27.

Pres. Mba, Flag and Arms of Gabon AP35

Embossed on Gold Foil
**1968, Nov. 28    Perf. 14½**
C74 AP35 1000fr gold, grn, yel
    & dk bl    30.00 30.00
Death of Pres. Léon Mba (1902-67), 1st anniv.

Pres. Bongo, Maps of Gabon and Owendo Harbor — AP36

**1968, Dec. 16    Photo.    Perf. 12½**
C75 AP36 25fr shown    1.60 .20
C76 AP36 30fr Owendo Harbor    1.60 .20
    a.    Strip of 2, #C75-C76 + label    3.75 3.75
Laying of the foundation stone for Owendo Harbor, June 24, 1968.

**PHILEXAFRIQUE Issue**
Painting Type of 1968
Design: 100fr, The Convent of St. Mary of the Angels, by Francois Marius Granet.
**1969, Jan. 8    Photo.    Perf. 12½x12**
C77 AP32 100fr multi    4.75 4.75
Issued to publicize PHILEXAFRIQUE Philatelic Exhibition in Abidjan, Feb. 14-23. Printed with alternating brown label.

Mahatma Gandhi — AP37

Portraits: 30fr, John F. Kennedy. 50fr, Robert F. Kennedy. 100fr, Martin Luther King, Jr.

**1969, Jan. 15**  **Perf. 12½**
| | | | | |
|---|---|---|---|---|
| C78 | AP37 | 25fr pink & blk | .75 | .45 |
| C79 | AP37 | 30fr lt yel grn & blk | .75 | .45 |
| C80 | AP37 | 50fr lt bl & blk | 1.10 | .45 |
| C81 | AP37 | 100fr brt rose lil & blk | 2.25 | .90 |
| a. | | Souv. sheet of 4, #C78-C81 | 6.00 | 6.00 |
| | | Nos. C78-C81 (4) | 4.85 | 2.25 |

Issued to honor exponents of non-violence.

**2nd PHILEXAFRIQUE Issue**
**Common Design Type**
**1969, Feb. 14**  **Engr.**  **Perf. 13**
| | | | | |
|---|---|---|---|---|
| C82 | CD128 | 50fr grn, ind & red brn | 2.25 | 2.25 |

Battle of Rivoli, by Henri Philippoteaux — AP39

100fr, The Oath of the Army, by Jacques Louis David. 250fr, Napoleon with the Children on the Terrace in St. Cloud, by Louis Ducis.

**1969, Apr. 23  Photo.**  **Perf. 12½x12**
| | | | | |
|---|---|---|---|---|
| C83 | AP39 | 50fr brn & multi | 2.25 | 1.10 |
| C84 | AP39 | 100fr grn & multi | 2.75 | 2.40 |
| C85 | AP39 | 250fr lil & multi | 12.00 | 7.00 |
| | | Nos. C83-C85 (3) | 17.00 | 10.50 |

Birth bicentenary of Napoleon I.

Red Cross Plane, Nurse and Biafran Children — AP40

20fr, Dispensary, ambulance & supplies. 25fr, Physician & nurse in children's ward. 30fr, Dispensary & playing children.

**1969, June 20  Photo.**  **Perf. 14x13½**
| | | | | |
|---|---|---|---|---|
| C86 | AP40 | 15fr lt ultra, dk brn & red | .80 | .20 |
| C87 | AP40 | 20fr emer, blk, brn & red | .75 | .45 |
| C88 | AP40 | 25fr grnsh bl, dk brn & red | .75 | .45 |
| C89 | AP40 | 30fr org yel, dk brn & red | 1.10 | .45 |
| | | Nos. C86-C89 (4) | 3.40 | 1.55 |

Red Cross help for Biafra.
A souvenir sheet contains four stamps similar to Nos. C86-C89, but lithographed and rouletted 13x13½. Gray margin with red inscription and Red Cross. Size: 118x75mm. Sold in cardboard folder. Value $4.

Astronauts and Lunar Landing Module, Apollo 11 — AP41

**Embossed on Gold Foil**
**1969, July 25  Die-cut Perf. 10½x10**
| | | | |
|---|---|---|---|
| C90 | AP41 | 1000fr gold | 26.00 26.00 |

See note after Algeria No. 427.

African and European Heads and Symbols — AP42

Icarus and Sun — AP43

**Europafrica Issue, 1970**
**1970, June 5  Photo.**  **Perf. 12x13**
| | | | |
|---|---|---|---|
| C91 | AP42 | 50fr multi | 1.25 .50 |

**1970, June 10  Engr.**  **Perf. 13**

Designs: 100fr, Leonardo da Vinci's flying man, 1519. 200fr, Jules Verne's space shell approaching moon, 1865.
| | | | | |
|---|---|---|---|---|
| C92 | AP43 | 25fr ultra, red & org | .75 | .45 |
| C93 | AP43 | 100fr ocher, plum & sl grn | 1.90 | .95 |
| C94 | AP43 | 200fr gray, ultra & dk car | 4.50 | 1.90 |
| a. | | Min. sheet of 3, #C92-C94 | 8.00 | 8.00 |
| | | Nos. C92-C94 (3) | 7.15 | 3.30 |

UAMPT Emblem AP44

**Embossed on Gold Foil**
**1970, June 18  Die-cut Perf. 12½**
| | | | |
|---|---|---|---|
| C95 | AP44 | 200fr gold, yel grn & bl | 4.25 2.40 |

Meeting of the Afro-Malagasy Union of Posts & Telecommuncations (UAMPT), Libreville, 6/17-23.

Throwing Knives AP45

Gabonese Weapons: 30fr, Assegai and crossbow, vert. 50fr, War knives, vert. 90fr, Dagger and sheath.

**1970, July 10  Engr.**  **Perf. 13**
| | | | | |
|---|---|---|---|---|
| C96 | AP45 | 25fr multi | .60 | .35 |
| C97 | AP45 | 30fr multi | .80 | .40 |
| C98 | AP45 | 50fr multi | 1.00 | .50 |
| C99 | AP45 | 90fr multi | 2.40 | .90 |
| a. | | Min. sheet of 4, #C96-C99 | 6.50 | 6.50 |
| | | Nos. C96-C99 (4) | 4.80 | 2.15 |

Japanese Masks, Mt. Fuji and Torii at Miyajima — AP46

**Embossed on Gold Foil**
**1970, July 31  Die-cut Perf. 10**
| | | | |
|---|---|---|---|
| C100 | AP46 | 1000fr multi | 25.00 25.00 |

Issued to publicize EXPO '70 International Exhibition, Osaka, Japan, Mar. 15-Sept. 13.

Pres. Albert Bernard Bongo — AP47

**Lithographed; Gold Embossed**
**1970, Aug. 17**  **Perf. 12½**
| | | | |
|---|---|---|---|
| C101 | AP47 | 200fr multi | 5.00 2.25 |

10th anniversary of independence.

**Painting Type of 1968**

Paintings: 50fr, Portrait of a Young Man, School of Raphael. 100fr, Portrait of Jeanne d'Aragon, by Raphael. 200fr, Madonna with Blue Diadem, by Raphael.

**1970, Oct. 16  Photo.**  **Perf. 12½x12**
| | | | | |
|---|---|---|---|---|
| C102 | AP32 | 50fr multi | 1.10 | .50 |
| C102A | AP32 | 100fr blue & multi | 2.40 | .95 |
| C102B | AP32 | 200fr brown & multi | 4.75 | 2.50 |
| | | Nos. C102-C102B (3) | 8.25 | 3.95 |

Raphael (1483-1520).

**Miniature Sheets**

Sikorsky S-32 — AP47a

Hugo Junkers — AP47b

**1970, Dec. 5  Litho.**  **Perf. 12**
| | | | |
|---|---|---|---|
| C103 | | Sheet of 8 | 10.00 10.00 |
| a. | AP47a | 15fr shown | |
| b. | AP47a | 25fr Fokker "Southern Cross" | |
| c. | AP47a | 40fr Dornier DO-18 | |
| d. | AP47a | 60fr Dornier DO-X | |
| e. | AP47a | 80fr Breguet "Bizerte" | |
| f. | AP47a | 125fr Douglas "Cloudster" | |

| | | | | |
|---|---|---|---|---|
| g. | AP47a | 150fr De Havilland DH-2 | | |
| h. | AP47a | 200fr Vickers "Vimi" | | |
| C104 | | Sheet of 4 | 17.00 | 17.00 |
| b. | AP47b | 200fr shown | | |
| c. | AP47b | 300fr Claude Dornier | | |
| c. | AP47b | 400fr Anthony Fokker | | |
| d. | AP47b | 500fr Igor Sikorsky | | |

**Imperf**
| | | | | |
|---|---|---|---|---|
| C105 | | Sheet of 8 | 10.00 | 10.00 |
| a. | AP47a | 10fr Dornier "Spatz" | | |
| b. | AP47a | 20fr Douglas DC-3 | | |
| c. | AP47a | 30fr Dornier DO-7 "Wal" | | |
| d. | AP47a | 50fr Sikorsky S-38 | | |
| e. | AP47a | 75fr De Havilland "Moth" | | |
| f. | AP47a | 100fr Supermarine "Spitfire" | | |
| g. | AP47a | 125fr Breguet XIX | | |
| h. | AP47a | 150fr Fokker "Universal" | | |

**Size: 80x90mm**
| | | | | |
|---|---|---|---|---|
| C106 | AP47b | 1000fr Claude Dornier | 17.00 | 17.00 |

Claude Dornier (1884-1969), aviation pioneer. No. C104 exists imperf. Value $17.

Presidents Bongo and Pompidou — AP48

**1971, Feb. 11**  **Photo.**  **Perf. 13**
| | | | |
|---|---|---|---|
| C107 | AP48 | 50fr multi | 2.25 1.10 |

Visit of Georges Pompidou, Pres. of France.

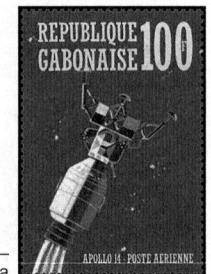

Apollo 14 — AP48a

**1971, Feb. 19**  **Perf. 14**
**Yellow Inscriptions**
| | | | |
|---|---|---|---|
| C108 | 15fr Lift off | .20 | .20 |
| C108A | 25fr Achieving orbit | .45 | .30 |
| C108B | 40fr Lunar module descent | .80 | .60 |
| C108C | 55fr Lunar landing | 1.00 | .65 |
| C108D | 75fr Lunar liftoff | 1.50 | 1.00 |
| C108E | 120fr Earth re-entry | 2.50 | 1.50 |
| | Nos. C108-C108E (6) | 6.45 | 4.25 |

**Souvenir Sheet**
| | | | |
|---|---|---|---|
| C108F | Sheet of 2 | 7.50 | 4.25 |
| g. | AP48a 100fr Modules attached | 3.00 | 1.75 |
| h. | AP48a 100fr like #C108E | 3.00 | 1.75 |

Nos. C108-C108F exist imperf. with white inscriptions. Same values.

Flowers and Plane — AP49

25fr, Carnations. 40fr, Roses. 55fr, Daffodils. 75fr, Orchids. 120fr, Tulips.

**1971, May 7  Litho.**  **Perf. 13½x14**
| | | | | |
|---|---|---|---|---|
| C109 | AP49 | 15fr yellow & multi | .45 | .20 |
| C109A | AP49 | 25fr multi | .70 | .20 |
| C109B | AP49 | 40fr pink & multi | 1.10 | .40 |
| C109C | AP49 | 55fr blue & multi | 1.40 | .45 |

| | | | | |
|---|---|---|---|---|
| **C110** | AP49 | 75fr multi | 2.40 | .60 |
| **C111** | AP49 | 120fr green & multi | 3.00 | .85 |
| *a.* | | Souv. sheet of 2, #C110-C111 | 6.00 | 6.00 |
| | | *Nos. C109-C111 (6)* | 9.05 | 2.70 |

"Flowers by air."

Napoleon's Death Mask AP50

Designs: 200fr, Longwood, St. Helena, by Jacques Marchand, horiz. 500fr, Sarcophagus in Les Invalides, Paris.

**1971, May 12       Photo.       Perf. 13**

| | | | | |
|---|---|---|---|---|
| **C112** | AP50 | 100fr gold & multi | 3.00 | .70 |
| **C113** | AP50 | 200fr gold & multi | 5.00 | .80 |
| **C114** | AP50 | 500fr gold & multi | 12.00 | 3.25 |
| | | *Nos. C112-C114 (3)* | 20.00 | 4.75 |

Napoleon Bonaparte (1769-1821).

### Souvenir Sheet

Charles de Gaulle — AP51

Designs: 40fr, President de Gaulle. 80fr, General de Gaulle. 100fr, Quotation.

**1971, June 18       Photo.       Perf. 12½**

| | | | | |
|---|---|---|---|---|
| **C115** | AP51 | Sheet of 5 | 11.00 | 11.00 |
| *a.* | | 40fr dark red & multi | .95 | .95 |
| *b.* | | 80fr dark green & multi | .95 | .95 |
| *c.* | | 100fr green, brown & yel | 2.50 | 2.50 |

In memory of Gen. Charles de Gaulle (1890-1970), Pres. of France.
For surcharge see No. C126.

Red Crosses AP52

**1971, June 29**

| | | | | |
|---|---|---|---|---|
| **C116** | AP52 | 50fr multicolored | 1.40 | .40 |

For the Red Cross of Gabon.
For surcharge see No. C143.

Uranium — AP53

**1971, July 20    Photo.    Perf. 13x12½**

| | | | | |
|---|---|---|---|---|
| **C117** | AP53 | 85fr shown | 7.00 | 3.50 |
| **C118** | AP53 | 90fr Manganese | 8.00 | 4.00 |

Landing Module over Moon — AP54

### Embossed on Gold Foil

**1971, July 30       Die-cut Perf. 10**

| | | | | |
|---|---|---|---|---|
| **C119** | AP54 | 1500fr multi | 30.00 | 30.00 |

Apollo 11 and 15 US moon missions.

### African Postal Union Issue, 1971
### Common Design Type

Design: 100fr, Bakota copper mask and UAMPT building, Brazzaville, Congo.

**1971, Nov. 13    Photo.    Perf. 13x13½**

| | | | | |
|---|---|---|---|---|
| **C120** | CD135 | 100fr bl & multi | 2.00 | .70 |

Ski Jump and Miyajima Torii AP55

130fr, Speed skating and Japanese temple.

**1972, Jan. 31       Engr.       Perf. 13**

| | | | | |
|---|---|---|---|---|
| **C121** | AP55 | 40fr hn brn, sl grn & vio bl | 1.25 | .35 |
| **C122** | AP55 | 130fr hn brn, sl grn & vio bl | 3.25 | .75 |
| *a.* | | Souvenir sheet of 2, #C121-C122 + label | 5.00 | 5.00 |

11th Winter Olympic Games, Sapporo, Japan, Feb. 3-13.

The Basin and Grand Canal, by Vanvitelli — AP56

Paintings: 70fr, Rialto Bridge, by Canaletto (erroneously inscribed Caffi), vert. 140fr, Santa Maria della Salute, by Vanvitelli, vert.

**1972, Feb. 7       Photo.       Perf. 13**

| | | | | |
|---|---|---|---|---|
| **C123** | AP56 | 60fr gold & multi | 2.50 | .70 |
| **C124** | AP56 | 70fr gold & multi | 3.75 | 1.00 |
| **C125** | AP56 | 140fr gold & multi | 7.25 | 1.50 |
| | | *Nos. C123-C125 (3)* | 13.50 | 3.20 |

UNESCO campaign to save Venice.

### No. C115 Surcharged in Brown and Gold
### Souvenir Sheet

**1972, Feb. 11       Perf. 12½**

| | | | | |
|---|---|---|---|---|
| **C126** | AP51 | Sheet of 5 | 20.00 | 20.00 |
| *a.* | | 60fr on 40fr multi | 2.75 | 2.75 |
| *b.* | | 120fr on 80fr multi | 4.00 | 4.00 |
| *c.* | | 180fr on 100fr multi | 8.25 | 8.25 |

Publicity for the erection of a memorial for Charles de Gaulle. Nos. C126a-C126b have surcharge and Cross of Lorraine in gold, 2 bars obliterating old denomination in brown; No. C126c has surcharge, cross and bars in brown. Two Lorraine Crosses and inscription (MEMORIAL DU GENERAL DE GAULLE) in brown added in margin.

Hotel Inter-Continental, Libreville — AP57

**1972, Feb. 26       Engr.       Perf. 13**

| | | | | |
|---|---|---|---|---|
| **C127** | AP57 | 40fr bl, sl grn & org brn | 1.10 | .35 |

### No. C51 Surcharged

**1972, Mar. 3**

| | | | | |
|---|---|---|---|---|
| **C128** | AP25 | 50fr on 300fr multi | 1.00 | .30 |

Official visit of the Grand Master of the Knights of Malta, March 3.

Discobolus, by Alcamenes AP58

Designs: 100fr, Doryphoros, by Polycletus. 140fr, Borghese gladiator, by Agasias.

**1972, May 10       Engr.       Perf. 13**

| | | | | |
|---|---|---|---|---|
| **C129** | AP58 | 30fr rose cl & gray | .90 | .40 |
| **C130** | AP58 | 100fr rose cl & gray | 1.90 | .50 |
| **C131** | AP58 | 140fr rose cl & gray | 2.50 | .70 |
| *a.* | | Min. of sheet of 3, #C129-C131 | 6.50 | 6.50 |
| | | *Nos. C129-C131 (3)* | 5.30 | 1.60 |

20th Olympic Games, Munich, 8/26-9/10.
For surcharges see Nos. C134-C136.

### Painting Type of 1968

Paintings: 30fr, Adoration of the Magi, by Peter Brueghel, the Elder. 40fr, Madonna and Child, by Marco Basaiti.

**1972, Oct. 30       Photo.       Perf. 13**

| | | | | |
|---|---|---|---|---|
| **C132** | AP32 | 30fr gold & multi | 1.10 | .20 |
| **C133** | AP32 | 40fr gold & multi | 1.60 | .20 |

Christmas 1972.

### Nos. C129-C131 Surcharged with New Value, Two Bars and Names of Athletes

**1972, Dec. 5       Engr.       Perf. 13**

| | | | | |
|---|---|---|---|---|
| **C134** | AP58 | 40fr on 30fr | 1.10 | .35 |
| **C135** | AP58 | 120fr on 100fr | 2.00 | .65 |
| **C136** | AP58 | 170fr on 140fr | 3.25 | 1.00 |
| | | *Nos. C134-C136 (3)* | 6.35 | 2.00 |

Gold medal winners in 20th Olympic Games: Daniel Morelon, France, Bicycling (C134); Kipchoge Keino, Kenya, steeplechase (C135); Mark Spitz, US, swimming (C136).

Globe with Space Orbits, Simulated Stamps — AP59

**1973, Feb. 20       Photo.       Perf. 13**

| | | | | |
|---|---|---|---|---|
| **C137** | AP59 | 100fr multi | 2.25 | .50 |
| *a.* | | Souv. sheet of 4, perf. 12x12½ | 25.00 | 25.00 |

PHILEXGABON 1973, Phil. Exhib., Libreville, Feb. 19-26. No. C137a exists imperf.

DC10-30 "Libreville" over Libreville Airport — AP60

**1973, Mar. 19       Typo.       Perf. 13**

| | | | | |
|---|---|---|---|---|
| **C138** | AP60 | 40fr blue & multi | 2.25 | .50 |

Kinguélé Hydroelectric Station — AP61

Design: 40fr, Kinguélé Dam.

**1973, June 19       Engr.       Perf. 13**

| | | | | |
|---|---|---|---|---|
| **C139** | AP61 | 30fr slate grn & dk ol | .80 | .20 |
| **C140** | AP61 | 40fr slate grn, dk ol & bl | 1.10 | .20 |
| *a.* | | Strip of 2, #C139-C140 + label | 2.75 | 1.25 |

Hydroelectric installations at Kinguélé.

M'Bigou Stone Sculpture, Woman's Head — AP62

Design: 200fr, Sculpture, man's head.

**1973, July 5**

| | | | | |
|---|---|---|---|---|
| **C141** | AP62 | 100fr blk, bl & grn | 3.25 | .70 |
| **C142** | AP62 | 200fr grn, sep & sl grn | 3.75 | 1.25 |

### No. C116 Surcharged with New Value, 2 Bars, and Overprinted in Ultramarine: "SECHERESSE SOLIDARITE AFRICAINE"

**1973, Aug. 16       Photo.       Perf. 12½**

| | | | | |
|---|---|---|---|---|
| **C143** | AP52 | 100fr on 50fr multi | 2.25 | .65 |

African solidarity in drought emergency.

Astronauts and Lunar Rover on
Moon — AP63

**1973, Sept. 6    Engr.    *Perf. 13***
C144 AP63 500fr multi              10.00 4.00
Apollo 17 US moon mission, 12/7-19/73.

Presidents Houphouet Boigny (Ivory
Coast) and De Gaulle — AP64

**1974, Apr. 30    Engr.    *Perf. 13***
C145 AP64 40fr rose lilac & indigo 2.25  .55
30th anniv. of the Conf. of Brazzaville.

Painting Type of 1968

Impressionist Paintings: 40fr, Pleasure
Boats, by Claude Monet, horiz. 50fr, Ballet
Dancer, by Edgar Degas. 130fr, Young Girl
with Flowers, by Auguste Renoir.

**1974, June 11    Photo.    *Perf. 13***
C146 AP32  40fr gold & multi       3.50  .50
C147 AP32  50fr gold & multi       5.50  .70
C148 AP32 130fr gold & multi       8.75 1.10
   *Nos. C146-C148 (3)*        17.75 2.30

Astronaut on
Moon, Eagle and
Emblems
AP65

**1974, July 20    Engr.    *Perf. 13***
C149 AP65 200fr multi               3.00  .90
First men on the moon, 5th anniversary.

UPU
Emblem,
Letters,
Pigeon
AP66

UPU cent.: 300fr, UPU emblem, letters,
pigeons, diff.

**1974, Oct. 9    Engr.    *Perf. 13***
C150 AP66 150fr lt bl & Prus bl    2.50  .90
C151 AP66 300fr org & claret       5.00 1.75

Space
Docking,
US and
USSR
Crafts
AP67

**1974, Oct. 23    Engr.    *Perf. 13***
C152 AP67 1000fr grn, red & sl   11.00 5.25
Russo-American space cooperation.
For overprint see No. C169.

Soccer and Games Emblem — AP68

Designs: Soccer actions.

**1974, Oct. 25**
C153 AP68  40fr grn, red & brn     .70  .20
C154 AP68  65fr red, brn & grn    1.00  .35
C155 AP68 100fr grn, red & brn    1.50  .60
  *a.* Souv. sheet of 3, #C153-C155
    + 3 labels                  4.50 4.50
   *Nos. C153-C155 (3)*        3.20 1.15
World Cup Soccer Championship, Munich,
June 13-July 7.

**UDEAC Issue**

Presidents and Flags of Cameroun,
CAR, Gabon and Congo — AP68a

**1974, Dec. 8    Photo.    *Perf. 13***
C156 AP68a 100fr gold & multi     1.25  .45

Annunciation, Tapestry, 15th
Century — AP69

Christmas: 40fr, Visitation from 15th century tapestry, Notre Dame de Beaune, vert.

**1974, Dec. 11**
C157 AP69 40fr gold & multi       1.10  .30
C158 AP69 50fr gold & multi       1.25  .35

Dr. Schweitzer and Lambarene
Hospital — AP70

**1975, Jan. 14    Engr.    *Perf. 13***
C159 AP70 500fr multi             9.00 3.00
Dr. Albert Schweitzer (1875-1965), medical
missionary, birth centenary.

Crucifixion, by
Bellini — AP71

Paintings: 150fr, Resurrection, Burgundian
School, c. 1500.

**1975, Apr. 8    Photo.    *Perf. 13½***
   **Size: 26x45mm**
C160 AP71 140fr gold & multi      2.10  .60
   **Size: 36x48mm**
   ***Perf. 13***
C161 AP71 150fr gold & multi      2.50  .70
Easter 1975.

Marc Seguin Locomotive,
1829 — AP72

Locomotives: 25fr, The Iron Duke, 1847.
40fr, Thomas Rogers, 1895. 50fr, The Soviet
272, 1934.

**1975, Apr. 8    Engr.    *Perf. 13***
C162 AP72 20fr multi              1.60  .40
C163 AP72 25fr multi              2.25  .40
C164 AP72 40fr multi              2.75  .65
C165 AP72 50fr lil & multi        3.50  .75
   *Nos. C162-C165 (4)*       10.10 2.20

Swimming Pool, Montreal Olympic
Games' Emblem — AP73

Designs: 150fr, Boxing ring and emblem.
300fr, Stadium, aerial view, and emblem.

**1975, Sept. 30    Litho.    *Perf. 13x12½***
C166 AP73 100fr multi             1.50  .30
C167 AP73 150fr multi             1.90  .60
C168 AP73 300fr multi             3.75 1.10
  *a.* Min. sheet of 3, #C166-C168  8.00 8.00
   *Nos. C166-C168 (3)*        7.15 2.00
Pre-Olympic Year 1975.

No. C152 Surcharged in Violet Blue:
"JONCTION / 17 Juillet 1975"

**1975, Oct. 20    Engr.    *Perf. 13***
C169 AP67 1000fr multi           11.00 4.50
Apollo-Soyuz link-up in space, July 17, 1975.

Annunciation, by Maurice
Denis — AP74

Painting: 50fr, Virgin and Child with Two
Saints, by Fra Filippo Lippi.

**1975, Dec. 9    Photo.    *Perf. 13***
C170 AP74 40fr gold & multi       1.25  .40
C171 AP74 50fr gold & multi       1.60  .55
Christmas 1975.

Concorde and
Globe — AP75

**1975, Dec. 29    Engr.    *Perf. 13***
C172 AP75 500fr bl, vio bl & red 11.00 3.75
For overprint see No. C198.

No. C172 Surcharged
**1976, Jan. 21**
C173 AP75 1000fr on 500fr        20.00 8.00
Nos. C172-C173 for the 1st commercial
flight of supersonic jet Concorde from Paris to
Rio, Jan. 21.

Slalom and Olympic Games
Emblem — AP76

Design: 250fr, Speed skating and Winter
Olympic Games emblem.

**1976, Apr. 22    Engr.    *Perf. 13***
C174 AP76 100fr blk, bl & red     1.50  .40
C175 AP76 250fr blk, bl & red     3.25 1.40
  *a.* Souvenir sheet           6.50 6.50
12th Winter Olympic Games, Innsbruck,
Austria, Feb. 4-15. No. C175a contains 100fr
and 250fr stamps in continuous design with
additional inscription and skier between, but
without perforations between the design
elements.
Size of perforated area: 125x27mm; size of
sheet: 169x90mm.

Jesus
Between
the Thieves
AP77

Design: 130fr, St. Thomas putting finger
into wounds of Jesus. Both designs after
wood carvings in Church of St. Michael,
Libreville.

**1976, Apr. 28    Litho.    *Perf. 12½x13***
C176 AP77 120fr multi             1.60  .65
C177 AP77 130fr multi             2.25  .95
Easter 1976. See #C188-C189, C220-C221.

Boston Tea Party — AP78

Designs: 150fr, Battle of New York. 200fr, Demolition of statue of George III.

| 1976, May 3 | Engr. | Perf. 13 | |
|---|---|---|---|
| C178 | AP78 100fr multi | 1.25 | .50 |
| C179 | AP78 150fr multi | 2.25 | .70 |
| C180 | AP78 200fr multi | 2.75 | .80 |
| a. | Triptych, #C178-C180 + 2 labels | 8.50 | 3.00 |

American Bicentennial.

Nos. C178-C180 Overprinted: "4 JUILLET 1976"

| 1976, July 4 | Engr. | Perf. 13 | |
|---|---|---|---|
| C181 | AP78 100fr multi | 1.25 | .50 |
| C182 | AP78 150fr multi | 2.25 | .70 |
| C183 | AP78 200fr multi | 2.75 | .80 |
| a. | Triptych, #C181-C183 + 2 labels | 8.50 | 3.00 |

Independence Day.

Running — AP79

200fr, Soccer. 260fr, High jump.

| 1976, July 27 | Litho. | Perf. 12½ | |
|---|---|---|---|
| C184 | AP79 100fr multi | 1.10 | .35 |
| C185 | AP79 200fr multi | 2.50 | .65 |
| C186 | AP79 260fr multi | 3.25 | .90 |
| a. | Souv. sheet of 3, #C184-C186, perf. 13 | 8.00 | 3.75 |
| | Nos. C184-C186 (3) | 6.85 | 1.90 |

21st Olympic Games, Montreal, Canada, July 17-Aug. 1.

Presidents Giscard d'Estaing and Bongo — AP80

| 1976, Aug. 5 | Photo. | Perf. 13 | |
|---|---|---|---|
| C187 | AP80 60fr blue & multi | 1.25 | .30 |

Visit of Pres. Valèrie Giscard d'Estaing of France.

Sculpture Type of 1976

Christmas: 50fr, Presentation at the Temple. 60fr, Nativity. Designs after wood Carvings in Church of St. Michael, Libreville.

| 1976, Dec. 6 | Litho. | Perf. 12½x13 | |
|---|---|---|---|
| C188 | AP77 50fr multi | 1.00 | .20 |
| C189 | AP77 60fr multi | 1.10 | .35 |

Oklo Fossil Reactor — AP81

| 1976, Dec. 15 | Litho. | Perf. 13 | |
|---|---|---|---|
| C190 | AP81 60fr red & multi | 1.10 | .30 |

The Last Supper, by Juste de Gand — AP82

100fr, The Deposition, by Nicolas Poussin.

| 1977, Mar. 25 | Litho. | Perf. 12½ | |
|---|---|---|---|
| C191 | AP82 50fr gold & multi | 1.10 | .20 |
| C192 | AP82 100fr gold & multi | 2.25 | .65 |

Easter 1977.

Air Gabon Plane and Insigne — AP83

| 1977, June 3 | Litho. | Perf. 12½ | |
|---|---|---|---|
| C193 | AP83 60fr multi | 1.10 | .30 |

Air Gabon's first intercontinental route.

Beethoven, Piano and Score — AP84

| 1977, June 15 | Engr. | Perf. 13 | |
|---|---|---|---|
| C194 | AP84 260fr slate | 3.50 | .95 |

Ludwig van Beethoven (1770-1827).

Lindbergh and Spirit of St. Louis — AP85

| 1977, Sept. 13 | Engr. | Perf. 13 | |
|---|---|---|---|
| C195 | AP85 500fr multi | 8.50 | 2.75 |

Charles A. Lindbergh's solo transatlantic flight from NY to Paris, 50th anniv.

Soccer — AP86

| 1977, Oct. 18 | Photo. | Perf. 13x12½ | |
|---|---|---|---|
| C196 | AP86 250fr multi | 3.25 | 1.10 |

Elimination games, World Soccer Cup, Buenos Aires, 1978.

Viking on Mars AP87

| 1977, Nov. 17 | Engr. | Perf. 13 | |
|---|---|---|---|
| C197 | AP87 1000fr multi | 13.00 | 3.50 |

Viking, US space probe.

No. C172 Overprinted: "PARIS NEW-YORK / PREMIER VOL / 22.11.77"

| 1977, Nov. 22 | Engr. | Perf. 13 | |
|---|---|---|---|
| C198 | AP75 500fr multi | 11.00 | 2.50 |

Concorde, 1st commercial flight, Paris to NYC.

Lion Hunt, by Rubens — AP88

Rubens Paintings: 80fr, Hippopotamus Hunt. 200fr, Head of Black Man, vert.

| 1977, Nov. 24 | Litho. | Perf. 13 | |
|---|---|---|---|
| C199 | AP88 60fr gold & multi | 1.10 | .35 |
| C200 | AP88 80fr gold & multi | 1.25 | .45 |
| C201 | AP88 200fr gold & multi | 3.50 | 1.10 |
| a. | Souv. sheet of 3, #C199-C201 | 8.00 | 4.00 |
| | Nos. C199-C201 (3) | 5.85 | 1.90 |

Peter Paul Rubens (1577-1640).

Adoration of the Kings, by Rubens — AP89

Design: 80fr, Flight into Egypt, by Rubens.

| 1977, Dec. 15 | Litho. | Perf. 12½ | |
|---|---|---|---|
| C202 | AP89 60fr gold & multi | 1.10 | .30 |
| C203 | AP89 80fr gold & multi | 1.25 | .45 |

Christmas 1977; Peter Paul Rubens.

Paul Gauguin, Self-Portrait AP90

150fr, Flowers in vase and Maori statuette.

| 1978, Feb. 8 | Litho. | Perf. 12½x12 | |
|---|---|---|---|
| C204 | AP90 150fr multi | 3.00 | .60 |
| C205 | AP90 300fr multi | 5.50 | 1.10 |

Paul Gauguin (1848-1903), French painter.

Pres. Bongo, Map of Gabon, Plane and Train AP91

Lithographed; Gold Embossed

| 1978, Mar. 12 | | Perf. 12½ | |
|---|---|---|---|
| C206 | AP91 500fr multi | 7.00 | 1.75 |

10th anniversary of national renewal.

Soccer and Argentina '78 Emblem — AP92

Argentina '78 Emblem and: 120fr, Three soccer players. 200fr, Jules Rimet Cup, vert.

| 1978, July 18 | Engr. | Perf. 13 | |
|---|---|---|---|
| C207 | AP92 100fr red, grn & brn | 1.10 | .20 |
| C208 | AP92 120fr grn, red & brn | 1.25 | .40 |
| C209 | AP92 200fr brn & red | 2.40 | .55 |
| a. | Min. sheet of 3, #C207-C209 | 6.50 | 3.00 |
| | Nos. C207-C209 (3) | 4.75 | 1.15 |

11th World Cup Soccer Championship, Argentina, June 1-25.

Nos. C207-C209a Overprinted in Ultramarine or Black:
a. ARGENTINE / HOLLANDE / 3-1
b. BRESIL / ITALIE / 2-1
c. CHAMPION / DU MONDE 1978 / ARGENTINE

| 1978, July 21 | Engr. | Perf. 13 | |
|---|---|---|---|
| C210 | AP92(a) 100fr multi | 1.00 | .30 |
| C211 | AP92(b) 120fr multi | 1.25 | .40 |
| C212 | AP92(c) 200fr multi | 2.10 | .65 |
| a. | Min. sheet of 3 (Bk) | 6.00 | 6.00 |
| | Nos. C210-C212 (3) | 4.35 | 1.35 |

Argentina's World Cup victory.

Albrecht Dürer (age 13), Self-portrait AP93

Design: 250fr, Lucas de Leyde, by Dürer.

| 1978, Sept. 15 | Engr. | Perf. 13 | |
|---|---|---|---|
| C213 | AP93 100fr red brn & slate | 1.40 | .30 |
| C214 | AP93 250fr blk & red brn | 3.75 | .80 |

Dürer (1474-1528), German painter.

Philexafrique II-Essen Issue
Common Design Types

Designs: No. C215, Gorilla and Gabon No. 280. No. C216, Stork and Saxony No. 1.

| 1978, Nov. 1 | Litho. | Perf. 13x12½ | |
|---|---|---|---|
| C215 | CD138 100fr multi | 2.75 | 1.40 |
| C216 | CD139 100fr multi | 2.75 | 1.40 |
| a. | Pair, #C215-C216 + label | 8.00 | 3.75 |

#C216a exists with two different labels: one for PHILEXAFRIQUE II and one for ESSEN '78.

Wright
Brothers
and Flyer
AP94

**1978, Dec. 19      Engr.      Perf. 13**
C217  AP94  380fr multi                    5.00  1.10
75th anniversary of 1st powered flight.

Pope John
Paul II
AP95

Design: 200fr, Popes Paul VI and John Paul
I, St. Peter's Basilica and Square, horiz.

**1979, Jan. 24      Litho.      Perf. 12½**
C218  AP95  100fr multi                    2.50  .35
C219  AP95  200fr multi                    5.50  .80

Sculpture Type of 1976

Easter: 100fr, Disciples recognizing Jesus
in the breaking of the bread. 150fr, Jesus
appearing to Mary Magdalene. Designs after
wood carvings in Church of St. Michael,
Libreville.

**1979, Apr. 10      Litho.      Perf. 12½x13**
C220  AP77  100fr multi                    1.25  .45
C221  AP77  150fr multi                    2.25  .65

Capt. Cook
and Ships
AP96

**1979, July 10      Engr.      Perf. 13**
C222  AP96  500fr multi                    7.00  2.00
Capt. James Cook (1728-1779), explorer,
death bicentenary.

Flags and Map of England and
France, Bleriot, Bleriot XI — AP97

Aviation Retrospect: 1000fr, Astronauts
walking on moon (gold embossed inset).

**Perf. 12½x12, 12**
**1979, Aug. 8      Litho.**
C223  AP97  250fr multi                    3.25  1.00
C224  AP97  1000fr multi                  11.00  3.75
1st flight over English Channel, 70th anniv.;
Apollo 11 moon landing, 10th anniv.

Rotary Emblem,
Map of Africa,
Head — AP98

**1979, Sept. 25      Photo.      Perf. 13**
C225  AP98  80fr multi                     1.10  .35
Rotary International, 75th anniversary.

Eugene Jamot,
Tsetse
Fly — AP99

**1979, Nov. 23      Engr.      Perf. 13**
C226  AP99  300fr multi                    5.00  1.50
Eugene Jamot (1879-1937), discoverer of
sleeping sickness cure.

Bobsledding,
Lake Placid '80
Emblem
AP100

**1980, Feb. 25      Litho.      Perf. 12½**
C227  AP100  100fr shown                   1.00  .40
C228  AP100  200fr Ski jump                2.10  .75
  a.    Souv. sheet of 2, #C227-
        C228                               4.00  1.90
13th Winter Olympic Games, Lake Placid,
NY, Feb. 12-24.

Jean Ingres
AP101

**1980, May 14      Engr.      Perf. 13**
C229  AP101  100fr shown                   1.50  .50
C230  AP101  200fr Jacques Of-
                 fenbach               3.00  .95
C231  AP101  360fr Gustave
                 Flaubert             4.50  1.75
      Nos. C229-C231 (3)                   9.00  3.20

12th World Telecommunications
Day — AP102

**1980, May 17      Litho.      Perf. 12½**
C232  AP102  80fr multi                    1.10  .35

Costes, Bellonte and Plane — AP103

Design: 1000fr, Mermoz, sea plane.

**1980, July 16      Engr.      Perf. 13**
C233  AP103  165fr multi                   1.60  .70
C234  AP103  1000fr multi                 11.00  4.50
1st North Atlantic crossing, 50th anniv.; 1st
South Atlantic air mail service, 50th anniv.

Running,
Moscow '80
Emblem
AP104

**1980, July 25                      Litho.**
C235  AP104  50fr shown                    .55  .20
C236  AP104  100fr Pole vault             1.10  .45
C237  AP104  250fr Boxing                 2.90  1.00
  a.    Souv. sheet of 3, #C235-
        C237                               8.50  4.00
      Nos. C235-C237 (3)                   4.55  1.65
22nd Summer Olympic Games, Moscow,
July 19-Aug. 3.

**Nos. C235-C237a Overprinted in Red,
Brown, Ultramarine or Black**

50fr: YIFTER (Eth.) / NYAMBUI (Tanz.) /
MAANINKA (Finl.) / 5000 Metres
100fr: KOZIAKIEWICZ (Pol.) / (record du
monde) / VOLKOV (Urss) et / SLUSARSKI
(Pol.)
250fr: WELTERS / ALDAMA (Cuba) /
MUGABI (Oug.) / KRUBER (Rda) / et
SZCZERDA (Pol.)

**1980, Sept. 25      Litho.      Perf. 13**
C238  AP104  50fr (R, vert. &
                 horiz.)             .50  .20
C239  AP104  100fr (Br)                    .95  .40
C240  AP104  250fr (U)                    2.50  .85
  a.    Souv. sheet of 3 (Blk)             8.50  4.00
      Nos. C238-C240 (3)                   3.95  1.45

Pres.
Charles de
Gaulle
AP105

**1980, Nov. 9      Photo.      Perf. 13**
C241  AP105  100fr shown                   1.25  .35
C242  AP105  200fr Pres. & Mrs.
                 de Gaulle          2.40  .70
  a.    Souv. sheet of 2, #C241-
        C242                               6.50  3.25
Pres. Charles de Gaulle (1890-1970).

AP106

**1981, Feb. 19      Litho.      Perf. 13**
C243  AP106  60fr Soccer Play-
                 ers                  .65  .20
C244  AP106  190fr Soccer player          2.10  .75
ESPANA '82 World Cup Soccer
Championship.

AP107

**1981, Mar. 26      Litho.      Perf. 13**
Spacecraft and Astronauts: 250fr, Yuri
Gagarin. 500fr, Alan B. Shepard.
C245  AP107  150fr multi                   1.40  .55
C246  AP107  250fr multi                   2.40  .85
C247  AP107  500fr multi                   4.75  1.75
  a.    Souv. sheet of 3, #C245-
        C247, perf. 12½               9.00  4.50
      Nos. C245-C247 (3)                   8.55  3.15
200th anniv. of discovery of Uranus by Wil-
liam Herschel (1738-1822).

Map of Africa
and Emblems
AP108

**1981, June 1      Litho.      Perf. 12½**
C248  AP108  100fr multi                   1.00  .40
Electric Power Distribution Union, 7th Con-
gress, Libreville, June 1-5.

D-51 Steam Locomotive, Japan, and
SNCF Turbotrain TGV-001,
France — AP109

200th Birth Anniv. of George Stephenson:
100fr, B&O Mallet 7100, US, Prussian T3
steam locomotive. 350fr, Stephenson and his
Rocket, BB Alsthom electric locomotive, Central Africa.

**1981, June 4      Engr.      Perf. 13**
C249  AP109  75fr multi                    .95  .35
C250  AP109  100fr multi                   1.40  .45
C251  AP109  350fr multi                   4.50  1.50
  a.    Souvenir sheet of 3                6.50  3.25
      Nos. C249-C251 (3)                   6.85  2.30
#C251a contains #C249-C251 in changed
colors.

No. C251a Overprinted in 1 line
across 3 stamps: 26 fevrier 1981-
Record du monde de vitesse 380 km
a l'heure
**Souvenir Sheet**
**1981, June 13    Engr.    *Perf. 13***
C252 AP109   Sheet of 3      6.50 3.25
New world railroad speed record, set Feb.
26.

Intl. Letter Writing
Week, Oct. 9-
16 — AP110

**1981, Oct. 9    Photo.    *Perf. 13***
C253 AP110 200fr multi          2.25  .90

**Souvenir Sheet**

22nd Anniv. of
Independence — AP110a

Illustration reduced.

**1982      Typo.      *Perf. 13x12½***
**Self-Adhesive**
C253A AP110a 2000fr multi     40.00 40.00
Printed on wood.

Still Life with a Mandolin, by George
Braque (1882-1963) — AP111

Design:  350fr, Boy Blowing Bubbles, by
Edouard Manet (1832-1883), vert.

***Perf. 13x12½, 12½x13***
**1982, Oct. 5                Litho.**
C254 AP111 300fr multi         3.75 1.10
C255 AP111 350fr multi         6.00 1.25

Pre-olympic
Year — AP112

Manned Flight
Bicentenary
AP113

**1983, Feb. 16    Litho.    *Perf. 13***
C256 AP112 90fr  Gymnast        .70  .30
C257 AP112 350fr  Wind surfing  4.00 1.10

**1983, June 1    Engr.    *Perf. 13***
Balloons.
C258 AP113 100fr  Transatlantic
                  flight, 5th an-
                  niv.          1.10  .40
C259 AP113 125fr  Montgolfiere,
                  1783          1.25  .45
C260 AP113 350fr  Rozier's bal-
                  loon, 1783    4.00 1.50
     Nos. C258-C260 (3)         6.35 2.35

Lady with
Unicorn, by
Raphael
(1483-1520)
AP114

**1983, June 19              *Perf. 12½x13***
C261 AP114 1000fr multi       12.00 5.25

1984 Winter Olympics — AP115

**1984, Feb. 8    Litho.    *Perf. 12½***
C262 AP115 125fr  Hockey        1.40  .20
C263 AP115 350fr  Figure skaters 3.75  .70
          See No. C268.

Paris-Libreville-Paris Air Race, Mar.
15-28 — AP116

**1984, Mar. 15    Litho.    *Perf. 13x12½***
C264 AP116 500fr  Planes, em-
                  blem          5.00  .85

The Racetrack, by Edgar
Degas — AP117

**1984, Mar. 21              *Perf. 13***
C265 AP117 500fr multi        8.00 1.25

1984 Summer
Olympics
AP118

Hamburg '84 Philatelic
Exhibition — AP119

Illustration AP119 reduced.

**1984, May 31    Litho.    *Perf. 12½***
C266 AP118  90fr  Basketball     .80  .20
C267 AP118 125fr  Running       1.25  .20

**Souvenir Sheet**
Nos. C262-C263, C266-C267 with
Added Inscriptions
**1984, Oct. 3    Litho.    *Perf. 13***
C268           Sheet of 4       7.50 3.50
  a.   AP118 90fr MEDAILLE D'OR:
         U.S.A.                   .65  .20
  b.   AP118 125fr MEDAILLE D'OR:
         KORIR                    .95  .20
  c.   AP115 125fr Hockey sur glace:
         U.R.S.S.                 .95  .20
  d.   AP115 350fr Danse couple: J.
         Torvill-C. Dean         2.75  .55

**Souvenir Sheet**
**1984      Typo.      *Perf. 13x12½***
**Self-Adhesive**
C268A     AP119 1000fr multi   21.00 21.00
Printed on wood.

Dr. Albert
Schweitzer
(1875-1965) —
AP119a

**1985, Sept. 5    Litho.    *Perf. 12½***
C269 AP119a 350fr multi        4.75  .70

Flags of
Gabon, UN
AP120

**1985, Sept. 20**
C270 AP120 225fr multi         2.50  .40
Admission of Gabon to UN, 25th anniv.

Central Post Office, Libreville, UPU
and Gabon Postal Emblems — AP121

**1985, Oct. 9**
C271 AP121 300fr multi         3.50  .60
World Post Day.

UN, 40th
Anniv. — AP122

**1985, Oct. 24    Litho.    *Perf. 12½***
C272 AP122 350fr multi         4.25  .70

PHILEXAFRICA '85, Lome,
Togo — AP123

**1985, Oct. 30              *Perf. 13***
C273 AP123 100fr  Scout camp-
                  site          2.00  .20
C274 AP123 150fr  Telecommuni-
                  cations,
                  transporta-
                  tion          3.50  .50
  a.   Pair, #C273-C274 + label 6.50 2.00

Gabon's Gift to
the UN — AP124

Design:  Mother and Child, carved wood
statue, and UN emblem.

**1986, Mar. 15    Litho.    *Perf. 13½***
C275 AP124 350fr multi         4.25 1.10

Lastour Arriving in Gabon — AP125

**1986, Mar. 25   Litho.      Perf. 12½**
C276  AP125 100fr multi             1.50   .45
Lastoursville, cent.

World Telecommunications
Day — AP126

**1986, May 17              Perf. 13½**
C277  AP126 300fr multi             3.00   .95

1986 World Cup Soccer
Championships, Mexico — AP127

**1986, May 31              Perf. 12½**
C278  AP127 100fr Goal              1.00   .35
C279  AP127 150fr Dribbling, re-
               ligious carv-
               ing                  1.50   .45
C280  AP127 250fr Players,
               map, soccer
               cup                  2.50   .80
C281  AP127 350fr Stadium,
               flags               3.25  1.10
   a.     Souv. sheet of 4, #C278-
               C281                10.00  4.75
   Nos. C278-C281 (4)               8.25  2.70
For overprints see Nos. C283-C286.

World Post
Day — AP128

**1986, Oct. 9    Litho.      Perf. 12½**
C282  AP128 500fr multi             5.00  1.50

Nos. C278-C281 Ovptd. "ARGENTINA
3 -R.F.A 2" in One or Two Lines in
Red

**1986, Oct. 23   Litho.      Perf. 12½**
C283  AP127 100fr multi             1.00   .35
C284  AP127 150fr multi             1.50   .45
C285  AP127 250fr multi             2.50   .80
C286  AP127 350fr multi             3.25  1.10
   Nos. C283-C286 (4)               8.25  2.70

The
Renewal,
19th Anniv.
AP129

**1987, Mar. 12   Litho.      Perf. 13**
C287  AP129 500fr multi             6.50  2.00

Konrad Adenauer
(1876-1967),
West German
Chancellor
AP130

**1987, Apr. 15             Perf. 12x12½**
C288  AP130 300fr mar, chlky bl
               & blk                4.50  1.25

Schweitzer and Medical
Settlement — AP131

**1988, Apr. 17   Litho.      Perf. 12½x12**
C289  AP131 500fr multi             6.50  2.25
   Dr. Albert Schweitzer (1875-1965), missionary physician and founder of the hospital
and medical settlement, Lambarene, Gabon.

Port Gentil Refinery, 20th
Anniv. — AP132

**1988, Sept. 1   Litho.      Perf. 13½**
C290  AP132 350fr multi             4.00  1.75

De Gaulle's Call for French
Resistance, 50th Anniv. — AP133

**1990, June 18   Litho.      Perf. 13**
C291  AP133 500fr multicolored      7.50  2.50

Port of Marseilles by J. B. Jongkind
(1819-1891) — AP134

**1991, Feb. 9    Litho.      Perf. 13**
C292  AP134 500fr multicolored      6.00  2.75

Discovery of America, 500th
Anniv. — AP135

**1992, Oct. 12   Litho.      Perf. 13**
C293  AP135 500fr multicolored      5.50  2.50

Antoine de Saint-Exupery (1900-
44) — AP136

**1994             Litho.      Perf. 13**
C294  AP136 500fr multicolored     *3.25 1.60*

Opening of the Channel
Tunnel — AP137

**1994**
C295  AP137 500fr multicolored     *3.00 1.50*

---

### AIR POST SEMI-POSTAL STAMPS

Catalogue values for unused
stamps in this section are for
Never Hinged items.

Ramses II Paying Homage to Four
Gods, Wadi-es-Sabua — SPAP1

**Unwmk.**
**1964, Mar. 9    Engr.       Perf. 13**
CB1  SPAP1 10fr + 5fr dk bl & bis
               brn                  1.00  1.00
CB2  SPAP1 25fr + 5fr dk car
               rose & vio bl        1.25  1.25
CB3  SPAP1 50fr + 5fr sl grn &
               claret               2.10  2.10
   Nos. CB1-CB3 (3)                 4.35  4.35

UNESCO world campaign to save historic
monuments in Nubia.

---

## POSTAGE DUE STAMPS

Postage Due Stamps of
France Overprinted

**1928             Unwmk.      Perf. 14x13½**
J1   D2  5c  light blue             .35   .35
J2   D2  10c gray brown             .35   .35
J3   D2  20c olive green           1.00  1.00
J4   D2  25c bright rose           1.10  1.10
J5   D2  30c light red             1.60  1.60
J6   D2  45c blue green            1.75  1.75
J7   D2  50c brown violet          3.00  3.00
J8   D2  60c yellow brown          3.00  3.00
J9   D2  1fr red brown             3.00  3.00
J10  D2  2fr orange red            4.75  4.75
J11  D2  3fr bright violet         5.50  5.50
   Nos. J1-J11 (11)               25.40 25.40

Chief Makoko,              Count
de Brazza's               Savorgnan de
Aide — D3                 Brazza — D4

**1930             Typo.       Perf. 13½x14**
J12  D3  5c  dk bl & olive         1.25  1.25
J13  D3  10c dk red & brn          1.40  1.40
J14  D3  20c green & brn           1.90  1.90
J15  D3  25c lt bl & brn           1.90  1.90
J16  D3  30c bis brn & Prus bl     2.75  2.75
J17  D3  45c Prus bl & ol          4.50  4.50
J18  D3  50c red vio & brn         4.75  4.75
J19  D3  60c gray lil & bl blk     9.00  9.00
J20  D4  1fr bis brn & bl blk     12.50 12.50
J21  D4  2fr violet & brn         16.00 16.00
J22  D4  3fr dp red & brn         18.00 18.00
   Nos. J12-J22 (11)              73.95 73.95

Fang Woman — D5

**1932             Photo.      Perf. 13x13½**
J23  D5  5c  dk bl, *bl*             .95   .95
J24  D5  10c red brown             1.10  1.10
J25  D5  20c chocolate             1.75  1.75
J26  D5  25c yel grn, *bl*         1.75  1.75
J27  D5  30c car rose              2.10  2.10
J28  D5  45c red org, *yel*        7.75  7.75
J29  D5  50c dk violet             2.50  2.50
J30  D5  60c dull blue             3.75  3.75
J31  D5  1fr blk, *red org*        9.00  9.00
J32  D5  2fr dark green           10.00 10.00
J33  D5  3fr rose lake             9.25  9.25
   Nos. J23-J33 (11)              49.90 49.90

Catalogue values for unused
stamps in this section, from this
point to the end of the section, are
for Never Hinged items.

### Republic

Pineapple — D6

**Unwmk.**
**1962, Dec. 10   Engr.       Perf. 11**
J34  D6  50c shown                  .20   .20
J35  D6  50c Mangoes                .20   .20
   a.  Pair, #J34-J35                     .35

| | | | | |
|---|---|---|---|---|
| J36 | D6 | 1fr Avocados | .20 | .20 |
| J37 | D6 | 1fr Tangerines | .20 | .20 |
| a. | | Pair, #J36-J37 | .35 | |
| J38 | D6 | 2fr Coconuts | .20 | .20 |
| J39 | D6 | 2fr Grapefruit | .20 | .20 |
| a. | | Pair, #J38-J39 | .35 | |
| J40 | D6 | 5fr Oranges | .35 | .35 |
| J41 | D6 | 5fr Papaya | .35 | .35 |
| a. | | Pair, #J40-J41 | .80 | |
| J42 | D6 | 10fr Breadfruit | .75 | .75 |
| J43 | D6 | 10fr Guavas | .75 | .75 |
| a. | | Pair, #J42-J43 | 1.90 | |
| J44 | D6 | 25fr Lemons | .90 | .90 |
| J45 | D6 | 25fr Bananas | .90 | .90 |
| a. | | Pair, #J44-J45 | 2.25 | |
| | | Nos. J34-J45 (12) | 5.20 | 5.20 |

Pairs se-tenant at the base.

Charaxes
Candiope — D7

Butterflies: 10fr, Charaxes ameliae. 25fr, Cyrestis camillus. 50fr, Charaxes castor. 100fr, Pseudacrea boisduvali.

**1978, July 4        Litho.        Perf. 13**

| | | | | |
|---|---|---|---|---|
| J46 | D7 | 5fr multi | .30 | .20 |
| J47 | D7 | 10fr multi | .30 | .20 |
| J48 | D7 | 25fr multi | .65 | .30 |
| J49 | D7 | 50fr multi | 1.25 | .50 |
| J50 | D7 | 100fr multi | 2.00 | .95 |
| | | Nos. J46-J50 (5) | 4.50 | 2.15 |

### OFFICIAL STAMPS

Catalogue values for unused stamps in this section are for Never Hinged items.

Map of                     Flag of
Gabon — O1              Gabon — O2

Designs: 25fr, 30fr, Flag of Gabon. 50fr, 85fr, 100fr, 200fr, Coat of Arms.

**1968        Unwmk.     Photo.     Perf. 14**

| | | | | |
|---|---|---|---|---|
| O1 | O1 | 1fr olive & multi | .20 | .20 |
| O2 | O1 | 2fr multi | .20 | .20 |
| O3 | O1 | 5fr lilac & multi | .20 | .20 |
| O4 | O1 | 10fr emer & multi | .20 | .20 |
| O5 | O1 | 25fr brn & multi | .50 | .20 |
| O6 | O1 | 30fr org & multi | .50 | .20 |
| O7 | O1 | 50fr multi | .95 | .20 |
| O8 | O1 | 85fr multi | 1.75 | .35 |
| O9 | O1 | 100fr yel & multi | 2.10 | .45 |
| O10 | O1 | 200fr gray & multi | 4.00 | 1.10 |
| | | Nos. O1-O10 (10) | 10.60 | 3.30 |

**1971-84        Typo.        Perf. 13x14**

| | | | | |
|---|---|---|---|---|
| O11 | O2 | 5fr multi ('81) | .20 | .20 |
| O12 | O2 | 10fr multi | .20 | .20 |
| O13 | O2 | 20fr multi ('81) | .20 | .20 |
| O14 | O2 | 25fr multi ('84) | .25 | .20 |
| O15 | O2 | 30fr multi ('78) | .40 | .20 |
| O16 | O2 | 40fr multi ('72) | .75 | .25 |
| O17 | O2 | 50fr multi ('76) | .85 | .20 |
| O18 | O2 | 60fr multi ('77) | 1.10 | .25 |
| O19 | O2 | 75fr multi ('81) | .75 | .20 |
| O20 | O2 | 80fr multi ('77) | 1.50 | .40 |
| O21 | O2 | 100fr multi ('77) | 1.25 | .25 |
| O22 | O2 | 500fr multi ('78) | 6.25 | 1.25 |
| | | Nos. O11-O22 (12) | 13.70 | 3.80 |

## GAMBIA

'gam-bē-ə

LOCATION — Extending inland from the mouth of the Gambia River on the west coast of Africa
GOVT. — Republic in British Commonwealth
AREA — 4,068 sq. mi.
POP. — 1,087,000 (1995 est.)
CAPITAL — Banjul

The British Crown Colony and Protectorate of Gambia became independent in 1965 and a republic in 1970.

12 Pence = 1 Shilling
100 Bututs = 1 Dalasy (1971)

Catalogue values for unused stamps in this country are for Never Hinged items, beginning with Scott 144.

Queen Victoria
A1          A2

**Typographed and Embossed**
**1869, Jan.     Unwmk.     Imperf.**

| | | | | |
|---|---|---|---|---|
| 1 | A1 | 4p pale brown | 525. | 225. |
| a. | | 4p brown | 575. | 210. |
| 2 | A1 | 6p deep blue | 550. | 225. |
| a. | | 6p blue | 625. | 210. |
| b. | | 6p pale blue | 3,000. | 1,250. |

**1874, Aug.                    Wmk. 1**

| | | | | |
|---|---|---|---|---|
| 3 | A1 | 4p pale brown | 450. | 225. |
| a. | | 4p brown | 425. | 210. |
| 4 | A1 | 6p blue | 375. | 210. |
| a. | | 6p deep blue | 325. | 225. |
| b. | | Panel sloping down from left to right | 700. | 400. |

The name panel sloping down variety is from a top left corner position. A top left corner position exists with a less noticeable sloping of the panel down from right to left; it is worth less.

**1880, June                    Perf. 14**

| | | | | |
|---|---|---|---|---|
| 5 | A1 | ½p orange | 11.00 | 19.00 |
| 6 | A1 | 1p maroon | 5.25 | 7.00 |
| 7 | A1 | 2p rose | 30.00 | 12.50 |
| 8 | A1 | 3p ultra | 75.00 | 37.50 |
| 9 | A1 | 4p brown | 250.00 | 18.50 |
| 10 | A1 | 6p blue | 100.00 | 52.50 |
| a. | | Panel sloping down from left to right | 275.00 | 175.00 |
| 11 | A1 | 1sh green | 275.00 | 150.00 |
| | | Nos. 5-11 (7) | 746.25 | 297.00 |

The watermark on Nos. 5-11 exists both upright and sideways.
See footnote following No. 4.

**1886-87                    Wmk. 2 Sideways**

| | | | | |
|---|---|---|---|---|
| 12 | A1 | ½p gray grn | 3.75 | 2.50 |
| 13 | A1 | 1p rose car ('87) | 6.50 | 9.00 |
| a. | | 1p maroon | | 17,250. |
| 14 | | 2p deep orange | 2.25 | 9.25 |
| b. | | 2p orange | 12.00 | 5.75 |
| 15a | A1 | 2½p ultramarine ('87) | 5.25 | 2.25 |
| 16 | A1 | 3p gray | 7.75 | 17.00 |
| 17 | A1 | 4p dp brown | 10.00 | 2.25 |
| 18 | A1 | 6p slate green | 12.50 | 52.50 |
| a. | | 6p pale olive green | 82.50 | 62.50 |
| b. | | 6p bronze green | 32.50 | 62.50 |
| c. | | As "a," panel sloping down from left to right | 200.00 | 160.00 |
| d. | | As "b," panel sloping down from left to right | 70.00 | 110.00 |
| 19 | A1 | 1sh violet | 3.75 | 20.00 |
| a. | | 1sh purple | 6.25 | 22.50 |
| | | Nos. 12-19 (8) | 51.75 | 114.75 |

See footnote following No. 4.

**1898, Jan.     Typo.     Wmk. 2**

| | | | | |
|---|---|---|---|---|
| 20 | A2 | ½p gray green | 3.25 | 2.00 |
| 21 | A2 | 1p carmine rose | 2.50 | .85 |
| 22 | A2 | 2p brn org & pur | 7.00 | 4.00 |
| 23 | A2 | 2½p ultramarine | 2.25 | 2.75 |
| 24 | A2 | 3p red vio & ultra | 26.00 | 14.00 |
| 25 | A2 | 4p brown & ultra | 11.50 | 35.00 |
| 26 | A2 | 6p ol grn & car rose | 12.00 | 32.50 |
| 27 | A2 | 1sh vio & green | 37.50 | 77.50 |
| | | Nos. 20-27 (8) | 102.00 | 168.60 |

King Edward VII — A3

**1902-05                    Perf. 14**

| | | | | |
|---|---|---|---|---|
| 28 | A3 | ½p green | 3.50 | 2.75 |
| 29 | A3 | 1p car rose | 4.50 | 1.10 |
| 30 | A3 | 2p org & pur | 3.75 | 2.25 |
| 31 | A3 | 2½p br blue ('05) | 32.50 | 20.00 |
| 32 | A3 | 3p red vio & ultra | 14.00 | 4.00 |

| | | | | |
|---|---|---|---|---|
| 33 | A3 | 4p brn & ultra | 3.75 | 27.50 |
| 34 | A3 | 6p ol grn & rose | 6.25 | 14.00 |
| 35 | A3 | 1sh bluish vio & green | 47.50 | 92.50 |
| 36 | A3 | 1sh6p grn & red, yel | 8.00 | 21.00 |
| 37 | A3 | 2sh black & org | 55.00 | 70.00 |
| 38 | A3 | 2sh6p pur & brn, yel | 17.50 | 70.00 |
| 39 | A3 | 3sh red & grn, yel | 22.50 | 70.00 |
| | | Nos. 28-39 (12) | 218.75 | 395.10 |

Numerals of 5p, 7½p, 10p, 1sh6p, 2sh, 2sh6p and 3sh of type A3 are in color on plain tablet.
Issued: 1p, 3/13; ½p, 3p, 4/19; 2p, 2½p, 4p, 6p, 1sh, 2sh, 6/14; 1sh6p, 2sh6p, 3sh, 4/6/05.
For surcharges, see Nos. 65-66.

**1904-09                    Wmk. 3**

| | | | | |
|---|---|---|---|---|
| 41 | A3 | ½p green | 5.25 | .35 |
| 42 | A3 | 1p car rose | 5.25 | .20 |
| a. | | 1p carmine ('09) | 8.00 | .20 |
| 43 | A3 | 2p org & pur ('06) | 14.00 | 2.50 |
| 44 | A3 | 2p gray ('09) | 1.90 | 12.50 |
| 45 | A3 | 2½p ultramarine | 7.00 | 5.50 |
| 46 | A3 | 3p red vio & ultra | 8.50 | 2.25 |
| 47 | A3 | 3p vio, yel ('09) | 4.00 | 1.10 |
| 48 | A3 | 4p brn & ultra ('06) | 20.00 | 45.00 |
| 49 | A3 | 4p blk & red, yel ('09) | 1.40 | .75 |
| 50 | A3 | 5p gray & black | 16.00 | 22.50 |
| 51 | A3 | 5p grn & vio ('09) | 1.75 | 1.40 |
| 52 | A3 | 6p orn & rose ('06) | 20.00 | 62.50 |
| 53 | A3 | 6p dull vio ('09) | 2.50 | 2.50 |
| 54 | A3 | 7½p blue grn & red | 12.50 | 42.50 |
| 55 | A3 | 7½p brn & ultra ('09) | 2.75 | 2.75 |
| 56 | A3 | 10p ol bis & red | 24.00 | 35.00 |
| 57 | A3 | 10p ol grn & car rose ('09) | 2.75 | 8.00 |
| 58 | A3 | 1sh violet & grn | 25.00 | 55.00 |
| 59 | A3 | 1sh blk, grn ('09) | 3.75 | 20.00 |
| 60 | A3 | 1sh 6p vio & grn ('09) | 16.00 | 70.00 |
| 61 | A3 | 2sh black & org | 80.00 | 100.00 |
| 62 | A3 | 2sh vio & bl, bl ('09) | 16.00 | 22.50 |
| 63 | A3 | 2sh 6p blk & red, bl ('09) | 24.00 | 22.50 |
| 64 | A3 | 3sh yel & grn ('09) | 26.00 | 55.00 |
| | | Nos. 41-64 (24) | 340.30 | 592.30 |

Nos. 38-39 Surcharged in Black:

a                          b

Type a (I) — The word "PENNY" is 5mm from the horizontal bars.
Type a (II) — "PENNY" is 4mm from the bars.

**1906, Apr.                    Wmk. 2**

| | | | | |
|---|---|---|---|---|
| 65 | A3 | ½p on 2sh6p, type I | 57.50 | 70.00 |
| a. | | Type II | 62.50 | 75.00 |
| 66 | A3 | 1p on 3sh | 62.50 | 35.00 |
| a. | | Double surcharge | 2,150. | 5,750. |

King George V — A4

**1912-22                    Wmk. 3**

| | | | | |
|---|---|---|---|---|
| 70 | A4 | ½p green | 2.00 | 1.75 |
| 71 | A4 | 1p carmine | 2.75 | 2.00 |
| a. | | 1p scarlet | 4.25 | 1.00 |
| 72 | A4 | 1½p ol brn & grn | .60 | .35 |
| 73 | A4 | 2p gray | .60 | 3.25 |
| 74 | A4 | 2½p dp br blue | 4.50 | 3.50 |
| 75 | A4 | 3p violet, yel | .60 | .35 |
| 76 | A4 | 4p blk & red, yel | 1.10 | 11.50 |
| 77 | A4 | 5p orange & vio | 1.10 | 2.25 |
| 78 | A4 | 6p dl vio & red violet | 1.10 | 2.75 |
| 79 | A4 | 7½p brn & ultra | 1.40 | 7.50 |
| 80 | A4 | 10p ol grn & car rose | 2.25 | 20.00 |
| 81 | A4 | 1sh blk, green | 2.25 | 1.10 |
| a. | | 1sh black, emerald | 1.10 | 22.50 |
| 82 | A4 | 1sh6p vio & green | 12.50 | 11.50 |
| 83 | A4 | 2sh vio & bl, bl | 4.00 | 7.00 |
| 84 | A4 | 2sh6p blk & red, bl | 3.75 | 16.00 |
| 85 | A4 | 3sh red & green | 9.75 | 30.00 |
| 86 | A4 | 5sh grn & red, yel ('22) | 92.50 | 150.00 |
| | | Nos. 70-86 (17) | 142.75 | 270.80 |

Numerals of 1½p, 5p, 7½p, 10p, 1sh6p, 2sh, 2sh6p, 3sh, 4sh and 5sh of type A3 are in color on colorless tablet. No. 86 is on chalky paper.

**1921-22                    Wmk. 4**

| | | | | |
|---|---|---|---|---|
| 87 | A4 | ½p green | .35 | 20.00 |
| 88 | A4 | 1p carmine | 1.10 | 5.75 |
| 89 | A4 | 1½p ol grn & bl grn | 1.40 | 15.00 |
| 90 | A4 | 2p gray | 1.10 | 2.50 |
| 91 | A4 | 2½p ultramarine | .60 | 7.00 |
| 92 | A4 | 5p org & violet | 2.00 | 18.00 |
| 93 | A4 | 6p dl vio & red vio | 2.00 | 20.00 |
| 94 | A4 | 7½p brn & ultra | 2.25 | 35.00 |
| 95 | A4 | 10p yel grn & car rose | 8.00 | 17.00 |
| 96 | A4 | 4sh blk & red ('22) | 85.00 | 150.00 |
| | | Nos. 87-96 (10) | 103.80 | 290.25 |

No. 96 is on chalky paper.

George V and           George V — A6
Elephant — A5

**1922-27     Engr.     Wmk. 4**
**Head and Shield in Black**

| | | | | |
|---|---|---|---|---|
| 102 | A5 | ½p green | .65 | .65 |
| 103 | A5 | 1p brown | .90 | .20 |
| 104 | A5 | 1½p carmine | .95 | .20 |
| 105 | A5 | 2p gray | 1.10 | 3.75 |
| 106 | A5 | 2½p orange | 1.10 | 12.50 |
| 107 | A5 | 3p ultramarine | 1.10 | .35 |
| 108 | A5 | 4p car, org ('27) | 6.25 | 22.50 |
| 109 | A5 | 5p yellow green | 2.40 | 11.50 |
| 110 | A5 | 6p claret | 1.50 | .35 |
| 111 | A5 | 7½p vio, yel ('27) | 8.00 | 62.50 |
| 112 | A5 | 10p blue | 5.50 | 20.00 |
| 113 | A6 | 1sh vio, org ('24) | 2.75 | 1.40 |
| 114 | A6 | 1sh6p blue | 12.50 | 16.00 |
| 115 | A6 | 2sh vio, blue | 4.50 | 4.75 |
| 116 | A6 | 2sh6p dark green | 5.00 | 11.00 |
| 117 | A6 | 3sh aniline vio | 13.50 | 55.00 |
| a. | | 3sh black purple | 240.00 | 475.00 |
| 118 | A6 | 4sh brown | 6.25 | 18.00 |
| 119 | A6 | 5sh dk grn, yel ('26) | 13.50 | 42.50 |
| 120 | A6 | 10sh yellow green | 80.00 | 110.00 |
| | | Nos. 102-120 (19) | 167.45 | 393.00 |

**1922, Sept. 1                    Wmk. 3**
**Head & Shield in Black**

| | | | | |
|---|---|---|---|---|
| 121 | A5 | 4p carmine, yel | 3.00 | 3.50 |
| 122 | A5 | 7½p violet, yel | 3.75 | 7.50 |
| 123 | A6 | 1sh violet, orange | 10.50 | 26.00 |
| 124 | A6 | 5sh dk green, yel | 45.00 | 140.00 |
| | | Nos. 121-124 (4) | 62.25 | 177.00 |

Common Design Types pictured following the introduction.

**Silver Jubilee Issue**
Common Design Type

**1935, May 6     Wmk. 4     Perf. 11x12**

| | | | | |
|---|---|---|---|---|
| 125 | CD301 | 1½p carmine & bl | .60 | .70 |
| 126 | CD301 | 3p ultra & brn | .75 | 1.25 |
| 127 | CD301 | 6p ol grn & lt bl | 1.40 | 4.00 |
| 128 | CD301 | 1sh brn vio & ind | 4.50 | 8.50 |
| | | Nos. 125-128 (4) | 7.25 | 14.45 |
| | | Set, never hinged | 16.00 | |

**Coronation Issue**
Common Design Type

**1937, May 12                    Perf. 11x11½**

| | | | | |
|---|---|---|---|---|
| 129 | CD302 | 1p brown | .20 | .80 |
| 130 | CD302 | 1½p dark carmine | .20 | .40 |
| 131 | CD302 | 3p deep ultra | .50 | 1.10 |
| | | Nos. 129-131 (3) | .90 | 2.30 |
| | | Set, never hinged | 1.60 | |

King George VI
and Elephant
Badge of
Gambia — A7

**1938-46                    Perf. 12**

| | | | | |
|---|---|---|---|---|
| 132 | A7 | ½p bl grn & blk | .20 | .80 |
| 133 | A7 | 1p brn & red vio | .20 | .55 |
| 134 | A7 | 1½p rose red & brn lake | .25 | 2.25 |
| 134A | A7 | 1½p gray black & ultra ('44) | .20 | 1.75 |
| 135 | A7 | 2p gray black & ultra | 3.00 | 3.75 |
| 135A | A7 | 2p rose red & brn lake ('43) | .65 | 2.50 |
| 136 | A7 | 3p blue & brt bl | .40 | .20 |

## GAMBIA

**Perf. 13½x14**

**1969, Dec. 15    Litho.    Unwmk.**
| | | | | |
|---|---|---|---|---|
| 241 | A19 | 2p pink, org red & blk | .85 | .20 |
| 242 | A19 | 1sh buff, dl yel & blk | .85 | .20 |
| 243 | A19 | 1sh6p lt bl, ultra & blk | 1.00 | 1.25 |
| | | Nos. 241-243 (3) | 2.70 | 1.65 |

35th anniversary of pioneer air services.

Runner, Flag and Arms of Gambia A20

**1970, July 16    Perf. 14½x14**
**Flag in Red, Blue & Green**
| | | | | |
|---|---|---|---|---|
| 244 | A20 | 1p pink & brown | .20 | .20 |
| 245 | A20 | 1sh ultra & brown | .20 | .20 |
| 246 | A20 | 5sh green & brown | .40 | .40 |
| | | Nos. 244-246 (3) | .80 | .80 |

9th Commonwealth Games, Edinburgh, Scotland, July 16-25.

Pres. Jawara and State House A21

Republic Day, Apr. 24, 1970: 1sh, Pres. Sir Dauda Kairaba Jawara, vert. 1sh6p, Pres. Jawara and Gambia flag, vert.

**1970, Nov. 2    Litho.    Perf. 14**
| | | | | |
|---|---|---|---|---|
| 247 | A21 | 2p gray & multi | .20 | .20 |
| 248 | A21 | 1sh multicolored | .20 | .20 |
| 249 | A21 | 1sh6p pink & multi | .70 | .70 |
| | | Nos. 247-249 (3) | 1.10 | 1.10 |

Methodist Church, Georgetown — A22

Designs: 1sh, Map of Africa and cross, vert. 1sh6p, John Wesley.

**1971, Apr. 16    Unwmk.    Perf. 14**
| | | | | |
|---|---|---|---|---|
| 250 | A22 | 2p multicolored | .20 | .20 |
| 251 | A22 | 1sh vio blue & multi | .20 | .20 |
| 252 | A22 | 1sh6p green & multi | .60 | .60 |
| | | Nos. 250-252 (3) | 1.00 | 1.00 |

Establishment of Methodist Mission, 150th anniv.

Yellowfin Tuna A23

Fish from Gambian Waters: 4b, Peters' mormyrid. 6b, Tropical two-wing flying fish. 8b, African sleeper goby. 10b, Yellowtail snapper. 13b, Rock hind. 25b, West African eel cat. 38b, Tiger shark. 50b, Electric catfish. 63b, Swamp eel. 1.25d, Smalltooth sawfish. 2.50d, Barracuda. 5d, Brown bullhead.

**1971, July 1    Litho.    Perf. 14**
**Fish in Natural Colors**
| | | | | |
|---|---|---|---|---|
| 253 | A23 | 2b blue | .20 | .20 |
| 254 | A23 | 4b lemon | .20 | .20 |
| 255 | A23 | 6b lt blue green | .20 | .20 |
| 256 | A23 | 8b orange brown | .20 | .20 |
| 257 | A23 | 10b lt Prus blue | .20 | .20 |
| 258 | A23 | 13b orange yel | .20 | .20 |
| 259 | A23 | 25b green | .35 | .50 |
| 260 | A23 | 38b brick red | .40 | .55 |
| 261 | A23 | 50b Prus blue | .70 | .80 |
| 262 | A23 | 63b bister | .85 | 1.60 |
| 263 | A23 | 1.25d yel green | 1.50 | 3.25 |
| 264 | A23 | 2.50d deep rose | 3.00 | 5.50 |
| 265 | A23 | 5d ultramarine | 5.50 | 9.50 |
| | | Nos. 253-265 (13) | 13.50 | 22.90 |

Mungo Park, Scottish Landscape, Map of Gambia Basin — A24

Map of Gambia River Basin and: 25b, Park traveling in dugout canoe. 37b, Park's death under attack at Busa Rapids.

**Perf. 13½x14**

**1971, Sept. 10    Litho.    Unwmk.**
| | | | | |
|---|---|---|---|---|
| 270 | A24 | 4b ultra & multi | .40 | .20 |
| 271 | A24 | 25b yel green & multi | 1.25 | .45 |
| 272 | A24 | 37b brick red & multi | 2.10 | 2.50 |
| | | Nos. 270-272 (3) | 3.75 | 3.15 |

Mungo Park (1771-1806), Scottish explorer of the Gambia and Niger Rivers.

Radio Gambia and Pres. Jawara A25

Designs: 25b, Map showing area reached by Radio Gambia. 37b, Like 4b.

**1972, July 1    Perf. 14**
| | | | | |
|---|---|---|---|---|
| 273 | A25 | 4b black & dull yel | .20 | .20 |
| 274 | A25 | 25b black, blue & red | .20 | .25 |
| 275 | A25 | 37b black & yel green | .40 | .75 |
| | | Nos. 273-275 (3) | .80 | 1.20 |

Radio Gambia, 10th anniv., May 1.

High Jump A26

**1972, Aug. 31    Perf. 13½**
| | | | | |
|---|---|---|---|---|
| 276 | A26 | 4b emerald & multi | .20 | .20 |
| 277 | A26 | 25b lt ultra & multi | .20 | .20 |
| 278 | A26 | 37b red & multi | .60 | .60 |
| | | Nos. 276-278 (3) | 1.00 | 1.00 |

20th Olympic Games, Munich, 8/26-9/11.

Mandingo Woman — A27

Designs: 25b, Musician playing Mandingo 21-stringed lute (kora). 37b, Map of Mali empire and area of Mandingo language.

**1972, Oct. 18    Litho.    Perf. 14x14½**
| | | | | |
|---|---|---|---|---|
| 279 | A27 | 2b rose red & multi | .20 | .20 |
| 280 | A27 | 25b lt ultra & multi | .30 | .30 |
| 281 | A27 | 37b emerald & multi | .50 | .50 |
| | | Nos. 279-281 (3) | 1.00 | 1.00 |

International Conference on Mandingo Studies, London, June 30-July 3.

Ship Model with Lanterns A28

Christmas: 2b, Lighted ship (lantern) carried by boys.

**1972, Dec. 1    Litho.    Perf. 13x13½**
| | | | | |
|---|---|---|---|---|
| 282 | A28 | 2b violet & multi | .20 | .20 |
| 283 | A28 | 1.25d blue & multi | .80 | .80 |

Peanuts, FAO Emblem — A29

**1973, Mar. 31    Litho.    Perf. 14½x14**
| | | | | |
|---|---|---|---|---|
| 284 | A29 | 2b red & multi | .20 | .20 |
| 285 | A29 | 25b lt blue & multi | .25 | .25 |
| 286 | A29 | 37b emerald & multi | .40 | .40 |
| | | Nos. 284-286 (3) | .85 | .85 |

Freedom from Hunger, 2nd UN development campaign.

Planting and Drying Rice — A30

Oil Palms — A31

Cassava A32

**1973, Apr. 30    Perf. 14½x14**
| | | | | |
|---|---|---|---|---|
| 287 | A30 | 2b shown | .20 | .20 |
| 288 | A30 | 25b Sorghum (Guinea corn) | .20 | .20 |
| 289 | A30 | 37b Rice crop | .40 | .30 |

**1973, July 16**
| | | | | |
|---|---|---|---|---|
| 290 | A31 | 2b shown | .20 | .20 |
| 291 | A31 | 25b Limes | .25 | .25 |
| 292 | A31 | 37b Oil palm fruits | .55 | .45 |

**1973, Oct. 15**
| | | | | |
|---|---|---|---|---|
| 293 | A32 | 2b shown | .20 | .20 |
| 294 | A32 | 50b Cotton | .55 | .45 |
| | | Nos. 287-294 (8) | 2.55 | 2.25 |

Gambian agriculture.

OAU Emblem — A33

**1973, Nov. 1    Unwmk.    Perf. 13½x13**
| | | | | |
|---|---|---|---|---|
| 295 | A33 | 4b green, yel & black | .20 | .20 |
| 296 | A33 | 25b dp mag, yel & black | .25 | .25 |
| 297 | A33 | 37b blue, yel & black | .25 | .25 |
| | | Nos. 295-297 (3) | .70 | .70 |

10th anniv. of the OAU.

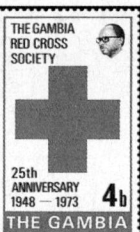

Red Cross — A34

**Perf. 14½x14**

**1973, Nov. 30    Wmk. 314**
| | | | | |
|---|---|---|---|---|
| 298 | A34 | 4b red & black | .20 | .20 |
| 299 | A34 | 25b ultra, red & black | .25 | .25 |
| 300 | A34 | 37b emer, red & black | .30 | .30 |
| | | Nos. 298-300 (3) | .75 | .75 |

25th anniv. of Gambia Red Cross Soc.

Flag of Gambia and Arms of Banjul — A35

**Perf. 13½x13**

**1973, Dec. 17    Litho.    Unwmk.**
| | | | | |
|---|---|---|---|---|
| 301 | A35 | 4b yel green & multi | .20 | .20 |
| 302 | A35 | 25b ver & multi | .25 | .25 |
| 303 | A35 | 37b lt ultra & multi | .25 | .25 |
| | | Nos. 301-303 (3) | .70 | .70 |

Change of name of Bathurst to Banjul and of St. Mary's Island to Banjul Island.

UPU Emblem — A36

**1974, Aug. 24    Litho.    Perf. 13½x13**
| | | | | |
|---|---|---|---|---|
| 304 | A36 | 4b lilac & multi | .20 | .20 |
| 305 | A36 | 37b blue & multi | .55 | .55 |

Centenary of Universal Postal Union.

Churchill at Harrow — A37

Churchill in Uniform of 4th Hussars — A38

Designs: 50b, Churchill as Prime Minister.

**1974, Nov. 30    Litho.    Perf. 13½**
| | | | | |
|---|---|---|---|---|
| 306 | A37 | 4b multicolored | .20 | .20 |
| 307 | A38 | 37b multicolored | .30 | .20 |
| 308 | A38 | 50b multicolored | .50 | .65 |
| | | Nos. 306-308 (3) | 1.00 | 1.10 |

Sir Winston Churchill (1874-1965).

WPY Emblem, Races of Man A39

Symbolic Designs and WPY Emblem: 37b, Races multiplying and dividing like atom. 50b, World population.

**1974, Dec. 16    Litho.    Perf. 14**
| | | | | |
|---|---|---|---|---|
| 309 | A39 | 4b multicolored | .20 | .20 |
| 310 | A39 | 37b multicolored | .20 | .20 |
| 311 | A39 | 50b multicolored | .25 | .25 |
| | | Nos. 309-311 (3) | .65 | .65 |

World Population Year.

Dr. Schweitzer and Hospital,
Lambarene — A40

50b, Dr. Schweitzer examining patient.
1.25d, Dr. Schweitzer in boat on Ogowe River.

**1975, Jan. 14    Litho.    Perf. 14**
| | | | | |
|---|---|---|---|---|
| 312 | A40 | 10b multicolored | .20 | .20 |
| 313 | A40 | 50b multicolored | .65 | .25 |
| 314 | A40 | 1.25d multicolored | 1.40 | .75 |
| | | Nos. 312-314 (3) | 2.25 | 1.20 |

Dr. Albert Schweitzer (1875-1965), medical
missionary, birth centenary.

Peace
Dove
A41

10b, Gambia flag. 50b, Gambia coat of
arms. 1.25d, Map of Gambia & Gambia River.

**1975, Feb. 18    Perf. 13**
| | | | | |
|---|---|---|---|---|
| 315 | A41 | 4b multicolored | .20 | .20 |
| 316 | A41 | 10b multicolored | .20 | .20 |
| 317 | A41 | 50b multicolored | .20 | .20 |
| 318 | A41 | 1.25d multicolored | .30 | .30 |
| | | Nos. 315-318 (4) | .90 | .90 |

10th anniversary of independence.

Public Services              David, by
Graph, A.D.B.              Michelangelo
Emblem                          A43
A42

African Development Bank Emblem and:
50b, Plant symbolizing growth of Africa, fed by
Development Bank. 1.25d, A.D.B. emblem
surrounded by symbols of water, education,
roads and hospitals.

**1975, Mar. 31    Litho.    Perf. 14**
| | | | | |
|---|---|---|---|---|
| 319 | A42 | 10b multicolored | .20 | .20 |
| 320 | A42 | 50b multicolored | .25 | .25 |
| 321 | A42 | 1.25d multicolored | .45 | .45 |
| | | Nos. 319-321 (3) | .90 | .90 |

African Development Bank, 10th anniv.

**1975, Nov. 14    Perf. 14½**

Bas-reliefs by Michelangelo: 50b, Madonna
of the Steps. 1.25d, Battle of the Centaurs,
horiz.

| | | | | |
|---|---|---|---|---|
| 322 | A43 | 10b dull blue & multi | .20 | .20 |
| 323 | A43 | 50b sepia & multi | .35 | .35 |
| 324 | A43 | 1.25d green & multi | .90 | .90 |
| | | Nos. 322-324 (3) | 1.45 | 1.45 |

Michelangelo Buonarroti (1475-1564), Italian painter, sculptor and architect.

Gambia
High
School
A44

Designs: 50b, Pupil in laboratory and school
emblem. 1.50d, School emblem.

**1975, Nov. 17**
| | | | | |
|---|---|---|---|---|
| 325 | A44 | 10b multicolored | .20 | .20 |
| 326 | A44 | 50b multicolored | .20 | .20 |
| 327 | A44 | 1.50d multicolored | .50 | .50 |
| | | Nos. 325-327 (3) | .90 | .90 |

Gambia High School, centenary.

Teacher
and IWY
Emblem
A45

IWY: 10b, Women planting rice. 50b, Nurse
holding baby. 1.50d, Woman traffic officer.

**1975, Dec. 15    Litho.    Perf. 14½**
| | | | | |
|---|---|---|---|---|
| 328 | A45 | 4b yellow & multi | .20 | .20 |
| 329 | A45 | 10b multicolored | .20 | .20 |
| 330 | A45 | 50b multicolored | .35 | .20 |
| 331 | A45 | 1.50d blue & multi | .60 | .30 |
| | | Nos. 328-331 (4) | 1.35 | .90 |

Woman
Golfer
A46

Designs: 50b, Golfer addressing ball. 1.50d,
Golfer finishing iron shot.

**1976, Feb. 18    Litho.    Perf. 14½**
| | | | | |
|---|---|---|---|---|
| 332 | A46 | 10b multicolored | 1.25 | .20 |
| 333 | A46 | 50b multicolored | 2.50 | .35 |
| 334 | A46 | 1.50d multicolored | 3.75 | 1.40 |
| | | Nos. 332-334 (3) | 7.50 | 1.95 |

11th anniversary of independence.

American
Militiaman — A47

American Bicent.: 50b, Continental Army
soldier. 1.25d, Declaration of Independence.

**1976, May 15    Litho.    Perf. 14x13½**
| | | | | |
|---|---|---|---|---|
| 335 | A47 | 25b multicolored | .25 | .20 |
| 336 | A47 | 50b multicolored | .50 | .40 |
| 337 | A47 | 1.25d multicolored | .90 | .90 |
| a. | | Souvenir sheet of 3, #335-337 | 2.50 | 4.00 |
| | | Nos. 335-337 (3) | 1.65 | 1.50 |

Mother and Child,
Christmas
Decoration — A48

**1976, Oct. 28    Litho.    Perf. 14**
| | | | | |
|---|---|---|---|---|
| 338 | A48 | 10b lt ultra & multi | .20 | .20 |
| 339 | A48 | 50b rose & multi | .20 | .20 |
| 340 | A48 | 1.25d yel grn & multi | .50 | .40 |
| | | Nos. 338-340 (3) | .90 | .80 |

Christmas.

Serval Cat and Wildlife Fund
Emblem — A49

Designs: 25b, Harnessed antelope. 50b,
Sitatunga. 1.25d, Leopard.

**1976, Nov. 29    Perf. 13½x14**
| | | | | |
|---|---|---|---|---|
| 341 | A49 | 10b multicolored | 12.00 | .50 |
| 342 | A49 | 25b multicolored | 15.00 | .50 |
| 343 | A49 | 50b multicolored | 27.50 | 1.00 |
| 344 | A49 | 1.25d multicolored | 50.00 | 10.00 |
| a. | | Souvenir sheet of 4, #341-344 | 125.00 | 20.00 |
| | | Nos. 341-344 (4) | 104.50 | 12.00 |

Abuko Nature Reserve.

Queen's Visit, 1961 — A50

Designs: 50b, The spurs and jeweled sword.
1.25d, The oblation of the sword.

**1977, Feb. 7    Litho.    Perf. 13½x14**
| | | | | |
|---|---|---|---|---|
| 345 | A50 | 25b multicolored | .20 | .20 |
| 346 | A50 | 50b multicolored | .20 | .20 |
| 347 | A50 | 1.25d multicolored | .50 | .50 |
| | | Nos. 345-347 (3) | .90 | .90 |

25th anniv. of the reign of Elizabeth II.

Festival
Emblem
and
Weaver
A51

**1977, Jan. 12    Litho.    Perf. 14**
| | | | | |
|---|---|---|---|---|
| 348 | A51 | 25b multicolored | .20 | .20 |
| 349 | A51 | 50b multicolored | .30 | .30 |
| 350 | A51 | 1.25d multicolored | .75 | .75 |
| a. | | Souvenir sheet of 3, #348-350 | 2.75 | 3.50 |
| | | Nos. 348-350 (3) | 1.25 | 1.25 |

2nd World Black and African Festival,
Lagos, Nigeria, Jan. 15-Feb. 12.

Stone
Circles,
near
Kuntaur
A52

Tourism: 50b, Ruins of Fort on James
Island. 1.25d, Mungo Park Monument.

**1977, Feb. 18    Litho.    Perf. 14½**
| | | | | |
|---|---|---|---|---|
| 351 | A52 | 25b multicolored | .20 | .20 |
| 352 | A52 | 50b multicolored | .30 | .30 |
| 353 | A52 | 1.25d multicolored | .75 | .75 |
| | | Nos. 351-353 (3) | 1.25 | 1.25 |

Clerodendrum Splendens — A53

Flowers and Shrubs: 4b, White water lily.
6b, Fireball lily. 8b, Mussaenda elegans. 10b,
Broad-leaved ground orchid. 13b, Fiber plant.
25b, False kapok. 38b, Baobab. 50b, Coral
tree. 63b, Gloriosa lily. 1.25d, Bell-flowered
mimosa. 2.50d, Kindin dolo. 5d, African tulip
tree. 6b, 8b, 10b, 13b, 25b, 38b, 1.25d, 2.50d,
vertical.

**1977, July 1    Litho.    Perf. 14½**
| | | | | |
|---|---|---|---|---|
| 354 | A53 | 2b multicolored | .20 | .20 |
| 355 | A53 | 4b multicolored | .20 | .25 |
| 356 | A53 | 6b multicolored | .20 | .25 |
| 357 | A53 | 8b multicolored | .20 | .20 |
| 358 | A53 | 10b multicolored | 2.25 | .25 |
| 359 | A53 | 13b yellow & multi | 1.75 | 1.75 |
| a. | | Pale olive background | 3.50 | 4.50 |
| 360 | A53 | 25b multicolored | .20 | .20 |
| 361 | A53 | 38b multicolored | .25 | .70 |
| 362 | A53 | 50b multicolored | .40 | .55 |
| 363 | A53 | 63b multicolored | .45 | .75 |
| 364 | A53 | 1.25d multicolored | .70 | 1.90 |
| 365 | A53 | 2.50d multicolored | .75 | 1.90 |
| 366 | A53 | 5d multicolored | 1.10 | 3.00 |
| | | Nos. 354-366 (13) | 8.65 | 11.90 |

For surcharges see Nos. 390A-390C.

Crowned Crane,              Madonna, Flight
Nile Crocodile,              into Egypt, by
Bush Buck — A54              Rubens — A55

Designs: 25b, Banjul Declaration, excerpt,
flag colors. 50b, Banjul Declaration. 1.25d,
Climbing lily, butterfly and moth.

**1977, Oct. 15    Litho.    Perf. 14**
| | | | | |
|---|---|---|---|---|
| 367 | A54 | 10b lt blue & black | .20 | .20 |
| 368 | A54 | 25b multicolored | .50 | .20 |
| 369 | A54 | 50b multicolored | .95 | .25 |
| 370 | A54 | 1.25d red & black | 3.00 | .75 |
| | | Nos. 367-370 (4) | 4.65 | 1.40 |

Banjul Declaration, for the conservation of
flora and fauna, Feb. 18, 1977.

**1977, Dec. 15    Litho.    Perf. 14x13½**

Rubens Paintings: 25b, Education of Mary
by St. Ann. 50b, Child's head. 1d, Madonna
surrounded by saints.

| | | | | |
|---|---|---|---|---|
| 371 | A55 | 10b multicolored | .20 | .20 |
| 372 | A55 | 25b multicolored | .25 | .25 |
| 373 | A55 | 50b multicolored | .55 | .35 |
| 374 | A55 | 1d multicolored | 1.00 | 1.00 |
| | | Nos. 371-374 (4) | 2.00 | 1.80 |

Peter Paul Rubens (1577-1640). Nos. 371-
374 printed in sheets of 5 stamps and decorative label.

Dome of the Rock, Jerusalem — A56

**1978, Jan. 3    Litho.    Perf. 14½**
| | | | | |
|---|---|---|---|---|
| 375 | A56 | 8b olive green & multi | .60 | .30 |
| 376 | A56 | 25b red & multi | 2.50 | 1.25 |

Palestinian fighters and their families.

Walking on
Greased
Pole — A57

Verreaux's Eagle Owl — A58

Designs: 50b, Pillow fight on greased pole. 1.25d, Rowers in long boat.

**1978, Feb. 18**     *Perf. 14*
377 A57 10b multicolored   .20 .20
378 A57 50b multicolored   .30 .20
379 A57 1.25d multicolored   .50 .50
    *Nos. 377-379 (3)*   1.00 .90

Independence Regatta celebrating 13th anniversary of independence.

**Elizabeth II Coronation Anniversary Issue**
Souvenir Sheet
Common Design Types
**1978, Apr. 15**   **Litho.**   *Perf. 15*
380   Sheet of 6   1.50 1.50
  *a.* CD326 1d White grayhound of Richmond   .30 .30
  *b.* CD327 1d Elizabeth II   .30 .30
  *c.* CD328 1d Lion   .30 .30

No. 380 contains 2 se-tenant strips of Nos. 380a-380c, separated by horizontal gutter with commemorative and descriptive inscriptions.

**1978, Oct. 28**   **Litho.**   *Perf. 14x13½*
Birds of Prey and Wildlife Fund Emblem: 25b, Lizard buzzard. 50b, West African harrier hawk. 1.25d, Long-crested hawk eagle.
381 A58 20b multicolored   20.00 .75
382 A58 25b multicolored   20.00 .75
383 A58 50b multicolored   30.00 3.00
384 A58 1.25d multicolored   45.00 11.00
    *Nos. 381-384 (4)*   115.00 15.50

Abuko Nature Reserve.

MV Lady Wright A59

New river vessels: 25b, River vessel Lady Chilel Jawara. 1d, Cross section of Lady Chilel Jawara.

**1978, Dec. 1**   **Litho.**   *Perf. 14½*
385 A59 8b multicolored   .20 .20
386 A59 25b multicolored   .40 .30
387 A59 1d multicolored   1.40 1.25
    *Nos. 385-387 (3)*   2.00 1.75

Motorized Police A60

**1979, Feb. 18**   **Litho.**   *Perf. 14*
388 A60 10b shown   .90 .20
389 A60 50b Fire engine   1.60 .30
390 A60 1.25d Ambulance   2.50 1.00
    *Nos. 388-390 (3)*   5.00 1.50

14th anniversary of independence.

Nos. 359, 363-364 Surcharged
**1979**   **Litho.**   *Perf. 14½*
390A A53 25b on 13b multi   .25 .35
390B A53 25b on 63b multi   .20 .20
390C A53 25b on 1.25d multi   .20 .20
    *Nos. 390A-390C (3)*   .65 .75

Issued: #390A, 3/5; others, 3/26.

Ramsgate Sands, by William P. Frith — A61

Designs: 10b, 25b, IYC emblem and details from painting shown on 1d. 25b, vert.

**1979, May 25**   **Litho.**   *Perf. 14*
**Size: 38x21mm, 21x38mm**
391 A61 10b multicolored   .20 .20
392 A61 25b multicolored   .20 .20
**Size: 56x21mm**
393 A61 1d multicolored   .85 .85
    *Nos. 391-393 (3)*   1.25 1.25

International Year of the Child.

Gambia No. 15, Maltese Cross Postmark A62

Gambian Stamps and Maltese Cross Postmark: 25b, #1. 50b, #208. 1.25d, #125.

**1979, Aug. 16**   **Litho.**   *Perf. 14½*
394 A62 10b multicolored   .20 .20
395 A62 25b multicolored   .20 .20
396 A62 50b multicolored   .20 .30
397 A62 1.25d multicolored   .50 .70
  *a.* Souvenir sheet of 1   1.25 1.40
    *Nos. 394-397 (4)*   1.10 1.40

Sir Rowland Hill (1795-1879), originator of penny postage.

Abuko Earth Station, Construction — A63

Telecommunications: 50b, Newly opened station. 1d, Intelsat satellites orbiting earth.

**1979, Sept. 20**   **Litho.**   *Perf. 14*
398 A63 25b multicolored   .20 .20
399 A63 50b multicolored   .30 .30
400 A63 1d multicolored   .50 .50
    *Nos. 398-400 (3)*   1.00 1.00

Apollo 11 Lift-off — A64

**1979, Oct. 17**   **Litho.**   *Perf. 14*
401 A64 25b shown   .20 .20
402 A64 38b Orbiting moon   .25 .25
403 A64 50b Splashdown   .55 .55
  *a.* Souvenir booklet   5.00
  *b.* Pane, 2 each 25b, 38b, 50b   1.90
  *c.* Pane of 1 (2d Lunar module)   1.75
    *Nos. 401-403 (3)*   1.00 1.00

Apollo 11 moon landing, 10th anniversary. No. 403a contains Nos. 403b-403c printed on peelable, self-adhesive paper backing with Apollo 11 emblems on back. Stamps and panes are die-cut and have 1 to 3 sides rouletted 9½.

Large Spotted Acraea, Wildlife Fund Emblem — A65

Wildlife Fund Emblem and Butterflies: 50b, Yellow pansy. 1d, Veined swallowtail. 1.25d, Foxy charaxes.

**1980, Jan. 3**   **Litho.**   *Perf. 13½x14*
404 A65 25b multicolored   15.00 .50
405 A65 50b multicolored   20.00 1.00
406 A65 1d multicolored   32.50 2.50
407 A65 1.25d multicolored   35.00 3.00
  *a.* Souvenir sheet of 4, #404-407   120.00 20.00
    *Nos. 404-407 (4)*   102.50 7.00

Abuko Nature Reserve.

Steam Launch "Vampire" — A66

**1980, May 6**   **Litho.**   *Perf. 14½*
408 A66 10b shown   .20 .20
409 A66 25b "Lady Denham"   .40 .20
**Perf. 13½x14½**
**Size: 49x21mm**
410 A66 50b "Mansa Kila Ba"   .60 .50
411 A66 1.25d "Prince of Wales"   .80 .85
    *Nos. 408-411 (4)*   2.00 1.75

London 80 Intl. Stamp Exhib., May 6-14. For surcharge see No. 497A.

**Queen Mother Elizabeth Birthday Issue**
Common Design Type
**1980, Aug. 4**   **Litho.**   *Perf. 14*
412 CD330 67b multicolored   .40 .50

Phoenician Trading Vessel — A67

**1980, Oct. 2**   **Litho.**   *Perf. 14½*
413 A67 8b shown   .20 .20
414 A67 67b Egyptian seagoing ship   .80 .60
415 A67 75b Portuguese caravel   .90 .70
416 A67 1d Spanish galleon   1.10 .90
    *Nos. 413-416 (4)*   3.00 2.40

Virgin and Child, by Francesco de Mura — A68

Christmas: 67b, Praying Virgin with Crown of Stars, by Correggio. 75b, Rest on the Flight, after Correggio.

**1980, Dec. 18**   **Litho.**   *Perf. 14*
417 A68 8b multicolored   .20 .20
418 A68 67b multicolored   .25 .25
419 A68 75b multicolored   .40 .40
    *Nos. 417-419 (3)*   .85 .85

New Atlantic Hotel, Conference Emblem — A69

**1981, Feb. 18**   **Litho.**   *Perf. 14*
420 A69 25b shown   .20 .20
421 A69 75b Ancient stone circle   .40 .40
422 A69 85b Conference emblem   .55 .55
    *Nos. 420-422 (3)*   1.15 1.15

World Tourism Conference, Manila, Sept. 27 and 16th anniversary of independence.

13th World Telecomunications Day — A70

**1981, May 17**   **Litho.**   *Perf. 14*
423 A70 50b No. 399   .50 .35
424 A70 50b No. 313   .50 .35
425 A70 85b ITU, WHO emblems   .85 .60
    *Nos. 423-425 (3)*   1.85 1.30

**Royal Wedding Issue**
Common Design Type
**1981, July 22**   **Litho.**   *Perf. 13½x13*
426 CD331 75b Bouquet   .25 .25
427 CD331 1d Charles   .35 .35
428 CD331 1.25d Couple   .40 .40
    *Nos. 426-428 (3)*   1.00 1.00

For surcharges see Nos. 439, 497C.

Planting Rice Seedlings A71

**1981, Sept. 4**   **Litho.**   *Perf. 14*
429 A71 10b shown   .20 .20
430 A71 50b Spraying   .30 .35
431 A71 85b Winnowing and drying   .50 .55
    *Nos. 429-431 (3)*   1.00 1.10

West African Rice Development Assoc., 10th anniv.

Abuko Nature Reserve A72

Designs: Wildlife Fund emblem and reptiles.

**1981, Nov. 17**   **Litho.**   *Perf. 14*
432 A72 40b Bosc's monitor   30.00 .75
433 A72 60b Dwarf crocodile   22.50 1.50
434 A72 80b Royal python   40.00 2.50
435 A72 85b Chameleon   45.00 3.00
    *Nos. 432-435 (4)*   137.50 7.75

30th Anniv. of West African Examinations Council — A73

**1982, Mar. 16**   **Litho.**   *Perf. 14*
436 A73 60b Test room   .60 .40
437 A73 85b 1st high school   .75 .55
438 A73 1.10d Council office   1.00 .75
    *Nos. 436-438 (3)*   2.35 1.70

No. 426 Surcharged
**1982, Apr. 19 Litho. Perf. 13½x13**
439 CD331 60b on 75b multi 1.50 2.00

Scouting Year A74

**1982, May Perf. 14**
440 A74 85b Tree planting 2.75 1.00
441 A74 1.25d Woodworking 3.00 1.75
442 A74 1.27d Baden-Powell 3.50 2.50
Nos. 440-442 (3) 9.25 5.25

1982 World Cup A75

**1982, June 13 Litho. Perf. 14**
443 A75 10b Team .20 .20
444 A75 1.10d Players 1.75 .75
445 A75 1.25d Stadium 1.75 .80
446 A75 1.55d Cup 2.00 1.00
a. Souvenir sheet of 4, #443-446 6.75 6.75
Nos. 443-446 (4) 5.70 2.75

For surcharge see No. 497B.

**Princess Diana Issue**
Common Design Type
**1982, July 1 Perf. 14½x14**
447 CD333 10b Arms .20 .20
448 CD333 85b Diana .65 .65
449 CD333 1.10d Wedding .85 .85
450 CD333 2.50d Portrait 1.75 1.75
Nos. 447-450 (4) 3.45 3.45

For surcharge see No. 479D.

Economic Community of West African States Development A76

Designs: 10b, Yundum Experimental Farm. 60b, Banjul/Kaolack Microwave Tower. 90b, Soap Factory, Denton Bridge Banjul. 1.25d, Control Tower, Yundum.

**1982, Nov. 5 Litho. Perf. 14x14½**
451 A76 10b multicolored .35 .20
452 A76 60b multicolored 2.40 2.40
453 A76 90b multicolored 2.40 3.25
454 A76 1.25d multicolored 3.25 3.75
Nos. 451-454 (4) 8.40 9.60

Kassina Cassinoides — A77

**1982, Dec. Litho. Perf. 14**
455 A77 10b shown 3.00 .20
456 A77 20b Hylarana galamensis 5.25 .45
457 A77 85b Euphlyctis occipitalis 8.75 4.50
458 A77 2d Kassina senegalensis 12.00 12.00
Nos. 455-458 (4) 29.00 17.15

A78

**1983, Mar. 14 Wmk. 373 Perf. 12**
459 A78 10b Globe showing Gambia .20 .20
460 A78 60b Batik cloth .25 .35
461 A78 1.10d Bagging peanuts .45 .60
462 A78 2.10d Flag .70 1.10
Nos. 459-462 (4) 1.60 2.25

Commonwealth Day.

Sisters of St. Joseph of Cluny Centenary — A79

**1983, Apr. 8 Litho. Perf. 14**
463 A79 10b Founder Anne Marie Javouhey, vert. .20 .20
464 A79 85b Javouhey with children, house .50 .50

River Boats A80

**1983, July 11 Litho. Perf. 14**
465 A80 1b Canoes .20 .20
466 A80 2b Upstream ferry .20 .20
467 A80 3b Dredging vessel .20 .20
468 A80 4b Harbor launch .20 .20
469 A80 5b Freighter .20 .20
470 A80 10b 60-foot launch .20 .20
471 A80 20b Multi-purpose vessel .20 .20
472 A80 30b Large sailing canoe .20 .20
473 A80 40b Passenger-cargo ferry .20 .20
474 A80 50b Cargo liner, diff. .25 .25
475 A80 75b Fishing boats .45 .50
476 A80 1d Peanut river train .55 .60
477 A80 1.25d Groundnutter .70 .85
478 A80 2.50d Banjul-Barra ferry 1.50 2.25
479 A80 5d Binlang Bolong 3.25 4.75
480 A80 10d Passenger-cargo ferry, diff. 6.00 8.50
Nos. 465-480 (16) 14.50 19.50

For overprints see Nos. 523-524.

World Communications Year — A81

**1983, Oct. 10**
481 A81 10b Local ferry .20 .20
482 A81 85b GPO telex, Banjul .95 .80
483 A81 90b Radio Gambia 1.10 .90
484 A81 1.10d Loading mail, Yundum Airport 1.25 1.10
Nos. 481-484 (4) 3.50 3.00

Osprey, Breeding Range A82

Designs: Birds, Maps of Europe and Africa.

**1983, Sept. 12 Litho. Perf. 14**
485 A82 10b multicolored 3.75 .65
486 A82 60b multicolored 6.50 4.25
487 A82 85b multicolored 7.50 4.75
488 A82 1.10d multicolored 8.25 7.25
Nos. 485-488 (4) 26.00 16.90

Raphael, 500th Birth Anniv. A83

Details from St. Paul Preaching at Athens.

**1983, Nov. 1 Litho. Perf. 14**
489 A83 60b multicolored .65 .65
490 A83 85b multicolored .85 .85
491 A83 1d multicolored .90 .90
Nos. 489-491 (3) 2.40 2.40

**Souvenir Sheet**
492 A83 2d multi, vert. 2.00 1.50

Manned Flight, 200th Anniv. A84

Flown covers and: 60b, Montgolfier Balloon. 85b, British Caledonian Aircraft. 96b, Junkers Airplane. 1.25d, Lunar module. 4d, Zeppelin.

**1983, Dec. 12 Litho. Perf. 14**
493 A84 60b multicolored .35 .35
494 A84 85b multicolored .45 .45
a. Bklt. pane, 2 each #493, 494 2.75
495 A84 90b multicolored .45 .45
496 A84 1.25d multicolored .50 .50
a. Bklt. pane, 2 each #495, 496 4.50
Nos. 493-496 (4) 1.75 1.75

**Souvenir Sheet**
497 A84 4d multicolored 8.00 8.00

No. 497 issued in booklet containing Nos. 497, 494a, 496a.

Nos. 411, 445, 428 and 449 Surcharged with Black Bars and New Value
**Perfs. as before**
**1983, Dec. 14 Litho.**
497A A66 1.50d on 1.25d, #411
497B A75 1.50d on 1.25d, #445
497C CD331 2d on 1.25d, #428
497D CD333 2d on 1.10d, #449

The status of Nos. 497A-497D is questioned.

Easter A85

Various Disney characters painting Easter eggs.

**1984, Apr. 15 Litho. Perf. 11**
498 A85 1b multicolored .25 .20
499 A85 2b multicolored .25 .20
500 A85 3b multicolored .25 .20
501 A85 4b multicolored .25 .20
502 A85 5b multicolored .25 .20
503 A85 10b multicolored .25 .20
504 A85 60b multicolored .55 .45
505 A85 90b multicolored .85 .70
506 A85 5d multicolored 3.50 3.00
Nos. 498-506 (9) 6.40 5.35

**Souvenir Sheet**
**Perf. 14**
507 A85 5d multicolored 6.75 6.75

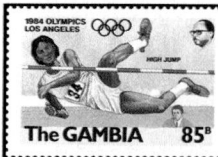

1984 Summer Olympics A86

**1984, Mar. 30 Litho. Perf. 14**
508 A86 60b Shot put, vert. .30 .30
509 A86 85b High jump .45 .45
510 A86 90b Wrestling, vert. .45 .45
511 A86 1d Gymnastics, vert. .50 .50
512 A86 1.25d Swimming .60 .60
513 A86 2d Diving 1.00 1.00
Nos. 508-513 (6) 3.30 3.30

**Souvenir Sheet**
514 A86 5d Yachting, vert. 3.75 3.75

For overprints see Nos. 570-576.

Nile Crododile A87

**1984, May 23**
515 A87 4b Young hatching 4.00 .75
516 A87 6b Adult carrying young 4.00 .75
517 A87 90b Adult 27.50 5.00
518 A87 1.50d Adult, diff. 32.50 6.00
Nos. 515-518 (4) 68.00 12.50

**Souvenir Sheet**
As Nos. 515-518, without WWF emblem.
518A A87 Sheet of 4 9.50 6.00
b.-e. each single 2.25 1.50

**Lloyd's List Issue**
Common Design Type
**1984, June 1 Litho. Perf. 14**
519 CD335 60b Banjul Port .90 .60
520 CD335 85b Bulk cargo carrier 1.10 .90
521 CD335 90b Sinking of the Dagomba 1.10 1.10
522 CD335 1.25d 19th-cent. frigate 2.00 1.90
Nos. 519-522 (4) 5.10 4.50

Nos. 478-479 Overprinted: "19th UPU / CONGRESS HAMBURG"
**1984, June 19 Litho. Perf. 14**
523 A80 2.50d multicolored 1.60 1.75
524 A80 5d multicolored 3.00 3.50

1984 Summer Olympics A88

**1984, July 28 Litho. Perf. 14**
525 A88 60b Running .50 .40
526 A88 85b Long jump .65 .55
527 A88 90b Running, diff. .65 .55
528 A88 1.25d Long jump, diff. .85 .70
Nos. 525-528 (4) 2.65 2.20

Gambia-South America Transatlantic Flight, 50th Anniv. — A89

**1984, Nov. 1 Litho. Perf. 14**
529 A89 60b Graf Zeppelin D-LZ127 1.60 1.10
530 A89 85b Dornier Wal on S.S. Westfalen 2.40 1.90
531 A89 90b Dornier DO-18 D-ABYM 2.75 2.75
532 A89 1.25d Dornier Wal D-2069 2.75 3.00
Nos. 529-532 (4) 9.50 8.75

**Butterflies A90**

**1984, Nov. 27**
| | | | | |
|---|---|---|---|---|
| 533 | A90 | 10b Antanartia hippomene | .40 | .25 |
| 534 | A90 | 85b Pseudacraea eurytus | 1.10 | 1.00 |
| 535 | A90 | 90b Charaxes lactitinctus | 1.10 | 1.00 |
| 536 | A90 | 3d Graphium pylades | 3.00 | 4.25 |
| | | Nos. 533-536 (4) | 5.60 | 6.50 |

**Souvenir Sheets**
| | | | | |
|---|---|---|---|---|
| 537 | A90 | 5d Eurema hapale | 14.50 | 14.50 |

**Marine Life — A90a**

**1984, Nov. 27**
| | | | | |
|---|---|---|---|---|
| 538 | A90a | 55b Penaeus duorarum | .50 | .35 |
| 539 | A90a | 75b Caretta caretta | .75 | .50 |
| 540 | A90a | 1.50d Physalia | 1.10 | 1.00 |
| 541 | A90a | 2.35d Uca pugilator | 2.10 | 1.90 |
| | | Nos. 538-541 (4) | 4.45 | 3.75 |

**Souvenir Sheets**
| | | | | |
|---|---|---|---|---|
| 542 | A90a | 5d Cowrie snail | 6.50 | 6.50 |

**UN Child Survival Campaign A91**

**1985, Feb. 27**
| | | | | |
|---|---|---|---|---|
| 543 | A91 | 10b Oral rehydration therapy | .20 | .20 |
| 544 | A91 | 85b Growth monitoring | .50 | .50 |
| 545 | A91 | 1.10d Breast-feeding | .65 | .65 |
| 546 | A91 | 1.50d Universal immunization | .75 | .75 |
| | | Nos. 543-546 (4) | 2.10 | 2.10 |

**UN Decade for Women A92**

Design: 1d, 1.25d, Woman working in office.

**1985, Mar. 11**
| | | | | |
|---|---|---|---|---|
| 547 | A92 | 60b multicolored | .35 | .35 |
| 548 | A92 | 85b multicolored | .50 | .50 |
| 549 | A92 | 1d multicolored | .65 | .65 |
| 550 | A92 | 1.25d multicolored | .70 | .70 |
| | | Nos. 547-550 (4) | 2.20 | 2.20 |

**Audubon Birth Bicent. — A93    Queen Mother, 85th Birthday — A94**

Illustrations of North American bird species by John J. Audubon (1785-1851).

**1985, July 15**
| | | | | |
|---|---|---|---|---|
| 551 | A93 | 60b Cathartes aura | 2.10 | 1.00 |
| 552 | A93 | 85b Anhinga anhinga | 2.50 | 1.75 |
| 553 | A93 | 1.50d Butoroides striatus | 2.75 | 3.75 |
| 554 | A93 | 5d Aix sponsa | 4.75 | 6.25 |
| | | Nos. 551-554 (4) | 12.10 | 12.75 |

**Souvenir Sheet**
| | | | | |
|---|---|---|---|---|
| 555 | A93 | 10d Gavia immer | 10.50 | 10.50 |

**1985, July 24**
| | | | | |
|---|---|---|---|---|
| 556 | A94 | 85b Inspecting troops | .50 | .50 |
| 557 | A94 | 3d Portrait | 1.50 | 1.50 |
| 558 | A94 | 5d Portrait, diff. | 2.75 | 2.75 |
| | | Nos. 556-558 (3) | 4.75 | 4.75 |

**Souvenir Sheet**
| | | | | |
|---|---|---|---|---|
| 559 | A94 | 10d On parade with Prince Charles | 5.75 | 5.75 |

**Life on the Mississippi, by Mark Twain (1835-1910) — A95**

Walt Disney characters. The 60b, 85b, 2.35d, 5d and No. 569 show scenes from "Faithful John" by the brothers Grimm.

**1985, Oct. 30**
| | | | | |
|---|---|---|---|---|
| 560 | A95 | 60b Portrait | .85 | .85 |
| 561 | A95 | 85b Treasure | 1.10 | 1.10 |
| 562 | A95 | 1.50d Helm of Calamity Jane | 2.25 | 2.25 |
| 563 | A95 | 2d Antebellum Mansion, Missouri Shore | 2.50 | 2.50 |
| 564 | A95 | 2.35d Music | 2.50 | 2.50 |
| 565 | A95 | 2.50d Measuring Channel Depth, Natchez | 3.00 | 3.00 |
| 566 | A95 | 3d Card Game aboard the Gold Dust | 3.25 | 3.25 |
| 567 | A95 | 5d Statue | 4.25 | 4.25 |
| | | Nos. 560-567 (8) | 19.70 | 19.70 |

**Souvenir Sheet**
| | | | | |
|---|---|---|---|---|
| 568 | A95 | 10d Landing, St. Louis | 11.00 | 11.00 |
| 569 | A95 | 10d Goofy | 11.00 | 11.00 |

**Nos. 508-514 Ovptd. "GOLD MEDALIST" or "GOLD MEDAL," Name of Winner and Country**

60b, Claudia Losch, West Germany, women's shot put. 85b, Ulrike Meyfarth, West Germany, women's high jump. 90b, Pasquale Passarelli, West Germany, 126-pound Greco-Roman wrestling. 1d, Li Ning, China, men's gymnastic floor exercises. 1.25d, Michael Gross, West Germany, men's 100-meter butterfly and 200-meter freestyle swimming. 2d, Sylvie Bernier, Canada, women's springboard diving. 5d, US, Star Class yachting.

**1985, Nov. 11    Perf. 14**
| | | | | |
|---|---|---|---|---|
| 570 | A86 | 60b multicolored | .65 | .30 |
| 571 | A86 | 85b multicolored | .85 | .40 |
| 572 | A86 | 90b multicolored | .85 | .45 |
| 573 | A86 | 1d multicolored | .85 | .50 |
| 574 | A86 | 1.25d multicolored | 1.25 | .65 |
| 575 | A86 | 2d multicolored | 1.60 | 1.00 |
| | | Nos. 570-575 (6) | 6.05 | 3.30 |

**Souvenir Sheet**
| | | | | |
|---|---|---|---|---|
| 576 | A86 | 5d multicolored | 3.00 | 3.00 |

**UN 40th Anniv. A97**

Views of Banjul.

**1985, Nov. 15**
| | | | | |
|---|---|---|---|---|
| 577 | A97 | 85b Independence Stadium | 1.00 | 1.00 |
| 578 | A97 | 2d Central Bank | 2.40 | 2.40 |
| 579 | A97 | 4d Port | 5.00 | 5.00 |
| 580 | A97 | 6d Oyster Creek Bridge | 7.50 | 7.50 |
| | | Nos. 577-580 (4) | 15.90 | 15.90 |

Natl. independence, 20th anniv.

**UN FAO, 40th Anniv. A98**

**1985, Nov. 15**
| | | | | |
|---|---|---|---|---|
| 581 | A98 | 60b Corn | .95 | .95 |
| 582 | A98 | 1.10d Paddy | 1.90 | 1.90 |
| 583 | A98 | 3d Cow, calf | 5.50 | 5.50 |
| 584 | A98 | 5d Fruit | 8.50 | 8.50 |
| | | Nos. 581-584 (4) | 16.85 | 16.85 |

**Diocese of Gambia and Guinea, 50th Anniv. A99**

Designs: 60b, Fishermen, Fotoba, Guinea. 85b, St. Mary's Primary School, Banjul. 1.10d, St. Mary's Cathedral, Banjul. 1.50d, Mobile Dispensary at Christy, Kunda, 1935-45.

**1985, Dec. 24**
| | | | | |
|---|---|---|---|---|
| 585 | A99 | 60b multicolored | .40 | .30 |
| 586 | A99 | 85b multicolored | .65 | .45 |
| 587 | A99 | 1.10d multicolored | .70 | .60 |
| 588 | A99 | 1.50d multicolored | 1.10 | .90 |
| | | Nos. 585-588 (4) | 2.85 | 2.25 |

**Girl Guides, 75th Anniv. — A100    Christmas — A101**

**1985, Dec. 27**
| | | | | |
|---|---|---|---|---|
| 589 | A100 | 60b Application, horiz. | .40 | .40 |
| 590 | A100 | 85b 2nd Bathurst, horiz. | .60 | .60 |
| 591 | A100 | 1.50d Lady Baden-Powell | 1.25 | 1.25 |
| 592 | A100 | 5d Rosamond Fowlis, leader | 4.00 | 4.00 |
| | | Nos. 589-592 (4) | 6.25 | 6.25 |

**Souvenir Sheet**
| | | | | |
|---|---|---|---|---|
| 593 | A100 | 10d Guides | 7.75 | 7.75 |

**1985, Dec. 27    Perf. 15**

Painting details: 60b, Virgin and Child, by Dirck Bouts (c. 1400-1475). 85b, The Annunciation, by Robert Campin (c. 1378-1444). 1.50d, Adoration of the Shepherds, by Gerard David (c. 1460-1523). 5d, The Nativity, by Gerard David. 10d, Adoration of the Magi, by Hieronymus Bosch (1450-1516).

| | | | | |
|---|---|---|---|---|
| 594 | A101 | 60b multicolored | .30 | .30 |
| 595 | A101 | 85b multicolored | .45 | .45 |
| 596 | A101 | 1.50d multicolored | .90 | .90 |
| 597 | A101 | 5d multicolored | 1.75 | 1.75 |
| | | Nos. 594-597 (4) | 3.40 | 3.40 |

**Souvenir Sheet**
| | | | | |
|---|---|---|---|---|
| 598 | A101 | 10d multicolored | 6.00 | 6.00 |

**Intl. Youth Year A102**

**1985, Dec. 31    Perf. 14**
| | | | | |
|---|---|---|---|---|
| 599 | A102 | 60b Mother's helper | .30 | .30 |
| 600 | A102 | 85b Wrestling | .45 | .45 |
| 601 | A102 | 1.10d Griot storyteller | .60 | .60 |
| 602 | A102 | 1.50d Crocodile pool | .90 | .90 |
| | | Nos. 599-602 (4) | 2.25 | 2.25 |

**Souvenir Sheet**
| | | | | |
|---|---|---|---|---|
| 603 | A102 | 5d Cow herder | 3.25 | 3.25 |

**Halley's Comet — A104**

Designs: 10b, Maria Mitchell (1818-1889), American astronomer, Kitt Peak Natl. Observatory, Papago Indian Reservation, Arizona. 20b, Apollo 11, Neil Armstrong steps on moon, 1969. 75b, Skylab 4, Kohoutek Comet, 1973. 1d, NASA Infrared Astronomical Satellite, 1983. 2d, Comet sighting, 1577, Turkish art. No. 609, NASA Intl. Cometary Explorer satellite. No. 610, Comet.

**1986, Mar.**
| | | | | |
|---|---|---|---|---|
| 604 | A103 | 10b multicolored | .40 | .20 |
| 605 | A103 | 20b multicolored | .75 | .20 |
| 606 | A103 | 75b multicolored | 1.10 | .55 |
| 607 | A103 | 1d multicolored | 1.40 | .80 |
| 608 | A103 | 2d multicolored | 2.10 | 1.40 |
| 609 | A103 | 5d multicolored | 5.75 | 5.00 |
| | | Nos. 604-609 (6) | 11.50 | 8.15 |

**Souvenir Sheet**
| | | | | |
|---|---|---|---|---|
| 610 | A104 | 10d multicolored | 9.00 | 9.00 |

For overprints see Nos. 650-656.

**Queen Elizabeth II, 60th Birthday**
**Common Design Type**

Designs: 1d, Royal family at Royal Tournament, 1936. 2.50d, Christening, 1983. No. 613, State visit to West Germany, 1978. No. 614, At Balmoral, 1935.

**1986, Apr. 21**
| | | | | |
|---|---|---|---|---|
| 611 | CD339 | 1d lt yel bis & blk | .55 | .40 |
| 612 | CD339 | 2.50d pale green & multi | 1.10 | .75 |
| 613 | CD339 | 10d dl lil & multi | 3.50 | 3.00 |
| | | Nos. 611-613 (3) | 5.15 | 4.15 |

**Souvenir Sheet**
| | | | | |
|---|---|---|---|---|
| 614 | CD339 | 10d tan & black | 4.25 | 4.25 |

**1986 World Cup Soccer Championships, Mexico — A105**

**1986, May 2**
| | | | | |
|---|---|---|---|---|
| 615 | A105 | 75b Block | .65 | .60 |
| 616 | A105 | 1d Kneeling the ball | .90 | .85 |
| 617 | A105 | 2.50d Kick | 2.75 | 2.50 |
| 618 | A105 | 10d Heading the ball | 7.00 | 7.00 |
| | | Nos. 615-618 (4) | 11.30 | 10.95 |

**Souvenir Sheet**
| | | | | |
|---|---|---|---|---|
| 619 | A105 | 10d Goalie catching ball | 11.50 | 11.50 |

For overprints see Nos. 639-643.

**AMERIPEX '86 — A106**

Exhibition emblem, automobiles and flags: 25b, 1986 Mercedes 500, Germany. 75b, 1935 Cord 810, US. 1d, 1957 Borgward Isabella Coupe, Germany. 1.25d, 1985-6 Lamborghini Countach, Italy. 2d, 1955 Ford

Thunderbird, US. 2.25d, 1956 Citroen DS19, France. 5d, 1936 Bugatti Atlante, France. 10d, 1936 Horch 853, Germany. No. 628, 1913 Benz 8/20, Germany. No. 629, 1924 Steiger 10/50, Germany.

**1986, May 22**      *Perf. 15*
| | | | | |
|---|---|---|---|---|
| **620** | A106 | 25b | multi | .20 .20 |
| **621** | A106 | 75b | multi | .45 .35 |
| **622** | A106 | 1d | multi | .70 .55 |
| **623** | A106 | 1.25d | multi | .75 .65 |
| **624** | A106 | 2d | multi | .90 *1.00* |
| **625** | A106 | 2.25d | multi | .90 *1.10* |
| **626** | A106 | 5d | multi | 1.75 *2.50* |
| **627** | A106 | 10d | multi | 3.75 *4.25* |
| | | *Nos. 620-627 (8)* | | 9.40 *10.60* |

**Souvenir Sheets**
| | | | | |
|---|---|---|---|---|
| **628** | A106 | 12d | multi | 8.25 8.25 |
| **629** | A106 | 12d | multi | 8.25 8.25 |

Karl Benz automobile cent.

Statue of Liberty, Cent. A107

Statue and famous emigrants: 20b, John Jacob Astor (1763-1848), financier. 1d, Jacob Riis (1849-1914), journalist. 1.25d, Igor Sikorsky (1889-1972), aeronautics engineer. 5d, Charles Boyer (1899-1978), actor. 10d, Statue, vert.

**1986, June 10**      *Perf. 14*
| | | | | |
|---|---|---|---|---|
| **630** | A107 | 20b | multicolored | .20 .20 |
| **631** | A107 | 1d | multicolored | .70 .70 |
| **632** | A107 | 1.25d | multicolored | .80 .80 |
| **633** | A107 | 5d | multicolored | 3.25 3.25 |
| | | *Nos. 630-633 (4)* | | 4.95 4.95 |

**Souvenir Sheet**
| | | | | |
|---|---|---|---|---|
| **634** | A107 | 10d | multicolored | 6.25 6.25 |

**Royal Wedding Issue, 1986**
**Common Design Type**

1d, Engagement of Prince Andrew and Sarah Ferguson. 2.50d, Andrew. 4d, Andrew in flight uniform, other helicopter pilot. 7d, Couple, diff.

**1986, July 23**
| | | | | |
|---|---|---|---|---|
| **635** | CD340 | 1d | multi | .60 .60 |
| **636** | CD340 | 2.50d | multi | 1.40 1.40 |
| **637** | CD340 | 4d | multi | 2.25 2.25 |
| | | *Nos. 635-637 (3)* | | 4.25 4.25 |

**Souvenir Sheet**
| | | | | |
|---|---|---|---|---|
| **638** | CD340 | 7d | multi | 5.00 5.00 |

Nos. 615-619 Overprinted "WINNERS / Argentina 3 / W. Germany 2" in Gold

**1986, Sept. 16**    **Litho.**    *Perf. 14*
| | | | | |
|---|---|---|---|---|
| **639** | A105 | 75b | multicolored | .40 .40 |
| **640** | A105 | 1d | multicolored | .60 .60 |
| **641** | A105 | 2.50d | multicolored | 1.50 1.50 |
| **642** | A105 | 10d | multicolored | 5.50 5.50 |
| | | *Nos. 639-642 (4)* | | 8.00 8.00 |

**Souvenir Sheet**
| | | | | |
|---|---|---|---|---|
| **643** | A105 | 10d | multicolored | 7.25 7.25 |

Christmas, STOCKHOLMIA '86 — A108

Disney characters mailing letters in various countries.

**1986, Nov. 4**      *Perf. 11*
| | | | | |
|---|---|---|---|---|
| **644** | A108 | 1d | Great Britain | 1.25 .50 |
| **645** | A108 | 1.25d | United States | 1.40 .70 |
| **646** | A108 | 2d | France | 2.25 1.25 |
| **647** | A108 | 2.35d | Australia | 2.50 1.40 |
| **648** | A108 | 5d | Germany | 3.25 2.00 |
| | | *Nos. 644-648 (5)* | | 10.65 5.85 |

**Souvenir Sheet**
| | | | | |
|---|---|---|---|---|
| **649** | A108 | 10d | Sweden | 10.00 10.00 |

Nos. 604-610 Ovptd. with Halley's Comet Logo in Silver

**1986, Oct. 21**    **Litho.**    *Perf. 14*
| | | | | |
|---|---|---|---|---|
| **650** | A103 | 10b | multicolored | .25 .20 |
| **651** | A103 | 20b | multicolored | .70 .20 |
| **652** | A103 | 75b | multicolored | 1.10 .50 |
| **653** | A103 | 1d | multicolored | 1.25 .60 |
| **654** | A103 | 2d | multicolored | 1.60 *1.50* |
| **655** | A103 | 10d | multicolored | 4.75 4.50 |
| | | *Nos. 650-655 (6)* | | 9.65 7.50 |

**Souvenir Sheet**
| | | | | |
|---|---|---|---|---|
| **656** | A104 | 10d | multicolored | 5.75 5.75 |

Marc Chagall (1887-1985), Artist A109

Paintings, ceramicware, sculpture: 75b, Snowing. 85b, The Boat, 1957. 1d, Maternity, 1913. 1.25d, The Flute Player. 2.35d, Lovers and the Beast, 1957. 4d, Fishes at Saint Jean. 5d, Entering the Ring, 1968. 10d, Three Acrobats, 1956. No. 665, The Sabbath. No. 666, The Cattle Driver.

**1987, Feb. 6**      **Litho.**
| | | | | |
|---|---|---|---|---|
| **657** | A109 | 75b | multi | .50 .25 |
| **658** | A109 | 85b | multi | .60 .30 |
| **659** | A109 | 1d | multi | .70 .40 |
| **660** | A109 | 1.25d | multi | .90 .50 |
| **661** | A109 | 2.35d | multi | 1.50 .80 |
| **662** | A109 | 4d | multi | 2.25 1.25 |
| **663** | A109 | 5d | multi | 2.75 1.50 |
| **664** | A109 | 10d | multi | 4.50 2.50 |

**Sizes: 110x95mm, 110x68mm**
*Imperf*
| | | | | |
|---|---|---|---|---|
| **665** | A109 | 12d | multi | 7.00 7.00 |
| **666** | A109 | 12d | multi | 7.00 7.00 |
| | | *Nos. 657-666 (10)* | | 27.70 21.50 |

Musical Instruments — A110

Various instruments from the Mandingo Empire.

**1987, Jan. 21**    **Litho.**    *Perf. 15*
| | | | | |
|---|---|---|---|---|
| **667** | A110 | 75b | Bugarab, tabala | .20 .20 |
| **668** | A110 | 1d | Balaphong, fiddle | .40 .30 |
| **669** | A110 | 1.25d | Bolongbato, konting | .50 .35 |
| **670** | A110 | 10d | Koras | 2.50 *2.50* |
| | | *Nos. 667-670 (4)* | | 3.60 3.35 |

**Souvenir Sheet**
| | | | | |
|---|---|---|---|---|
| **671** | A110 | 12d | Sabarrs | 3.75 *3.75* |

Nos. 669-670 vert.
For overprints see Nos. 750, 856-860.

America's Cup A111

**1987, Apr. 3**      *Perf. 14*
| | | | | |
|---|---|---|---|---|
| **672** | A111 | 20b | America, 1851 | .20 .20 |
| **673** | A111 | 1d | Courageous, 1974 | .45 .45 |
| **674** | A111 | 2.50d | Volunteer, 1887 | 1.10 1.10 |
| **675** | A111 | 10d | Intrepid, 1967 | 4.50 4.50 |
| | | *Nos. 672-675 (4)* | | 6.25 6.25 |

**Souvenir Sheet**
| | | | | |
|---|---|---|---|---|
| **676** | A111 | 12d | Australia II, 1983 | 6.50 6.50 |

For overprint see No. 751.

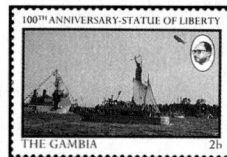

Statue of Liberty, Cent. A112

Photographs of restoration and unveiling in 1986.

**1987, Apr. 9**      **Litho.**
| | | | | |
|---|---|---|---|---|
| **677** | A112 | 1b | Shoulder, torch | .20 .20 |
| **678** | A112 | 2b | Operation Sail flotilla | .20 .20 |
| **679** | A112 | 3b | Tall ship, ships | .20 .20 |
| **680** | A112 | 5b | Luxury liner, aircraft carrier | .20 .20 |
| **681** | A112 | 50b | Statue's coiffure | .55 .55 |
| **682** | A112 | 75b | Coiffure, diff. | .80 .80 |
| **683** | A112 | 1d | Workmen scaling statue | .95 .95 |
| **684** | A112 | 1.25d | Back of statue | 1.10 1.10 |
| **685** | A112 | 10d | Front of Statue | 5.75 5.75 |
| **686** | A112 | 12d | Side of statue | 6.00 6.00 |
| | | *Nos. 677-686 (10)* | | 15.95 15.95 |

Nos. 677, 681-686 vert.

Flowers from Abuko Nature Reserve — A113

75b, Lantana camara. 1d, Clerodendrum thomsoniae. 1.50d, Haemanthus multiflorus. 1.70d, Gloriosa simplex. 1.75d, Combretum microphyllum. 2.25d, Eulophia guineensis. 5d, Erythrina senegalensis. 15d, Dichrostachys glomerata.
#691, Costus spectabilis. #691A, Strophanthus preussii.

**1987, May 25**
| | | | | |
|---|---|---|---|---|
| **687** | A113 | 75b | multi | .20 .20 |
| **687A** | A113 | 1d | multi | .25 .25 |
| **688** | A113 | 1.50d | multi | .45 .40 |
| **688A** | A113 | 1.70d | multi | .50 .45 |
| **689** | A113 | 1.75d | multi | .50 .45 |
| **689A** | A113 | 2.25d | multi | .70 .60 |
| **689B** | A113 | 5d | multi | 1.60 1.40 |
| **690** | A113 | 15d | multi | 3.75 *3.75* |
| | | *Nos. 687-690 (8)* | | 7.95 7.50 |

**Souvenir Sheets**
| | | | | |
|---|---|---|---|---|
| **691** | A113 | 15d | shown | 3.75 *3.75* |
| **691A** | A113 | 15d | multi | 3.75 *3.75* |

#691-691A are continuous designs.
For overprint see No. 752.

CAPEX '87 A115

Various buses.

**1987, June 15**
| | | | | |
|---|---|---|---|---|
| **692** | A115 | 20b | multi, vert. | .60 .20 |
| **693** | A115 | 75b | multi | .80 .25 |
| **694** | A115 | 1d | multi | 2.10 .75 |
| **695** | A115 | 10d | multi, vert. | 4.25 2.00 |
| | | *Nos. 692-695 (4)* | | 7.75 3.20 |

**Souvenir Sheet**
| | | | | |
|---|---|---|---|---|
| **696** | A115 | 12d | multi | 7.75 7.75 |

For overprint see No. 749.

1988 Summer Olympics, Seoul A116

**1987, July 3**
| | | | | |
|---|---|---|---|---|
| **697** | A116 | 50b | Women's basketball | .20 .20 |
| **698** | A116 | 1d | Volleyball | .65 .30 |
| **699** | A116 | 3d | Field hockey | 1.25 .90 |
| **700** | A116 | 10d | Handball | 4.00 3.00 |
| | | *Nos. 697-700 (4)* | | 6.10 4.40 |

**Souvenir Sheet**
| | | | | |
|---|---|---|---|---|
| **701** | A116 | 15d | Soccer | 5.75 5.75 |

Nos. 697-698 vert.

A117

The Twelve Days of Christmas, Medieval Counting Song — A118

Designs: 20b, Partridge in a pear tree. 40b, 2 turtle doves. 60b, 3 French hens. 75b, 4 calling birds. 1d, 5 golden rings. 1.25d, 6 geese a-laying. 1.50d, 7 swans a-swimming. 2d, 8 maids a-milking. 3d, 9 ladies dancing. 5d, 10 lords a-leaping. 10d, 11 pipers piping. 12d, 12 drummers drumming.

**Miniature Sheet**

**1987, Nov. 2**    **Litho.**    *Perf. 14*
| | | | | |
|---|---|---|---|---|
| **702** | | Sheet of 12 | | 16.00 16.00 |
| a. | A117 | 20b | multicolored | .20 .20 |
| b. | A117 | 40b | multicolored | .20 .20 |
| c. | A117 | 60b | multicolored | .20 .20 |
| d. | A117 | 75b | multicolored | .20 .20 |
| e. | A117 | 1d | multicolored | .40 .40 |
| f. | A117 | 1.25d | multicolored | .45 .45 |
| g. | A117 | 1.50d | multicolored | .70 .60 |
| h. | A117 | 2d | multicolored | .90 .75 |
| i. | A117 | 3d | multicolored | 1.50 1.25 |
| j. | A117 | 5d | multicolored | 2.25 1.90 |
| k. | A117 | 10d | multicolored | 4.00 3.50 |
| l. | A117 | 12d | multicolored | 5.00 4.25 |

**Souvenir Sheet**
| | | | | |
|---|---|---|---|---|
| **703** | A118 | 15d | multi | 5.75 *5.75* |

16th Boy Scout Jamboree, Australia, 1987-88 A119

**1987, Nov. 9**
| | | | | |
|---|---|---|---|---|
| **704** | A119 | 75b | Singing around campfire | .20 .20 |
| **705** | A119 | 1d | Nature study, African katydid | .70 .30 |
| **706** | A119 | 1.25d | Bird watching, red-tailed tropicbird | .95 .40 |
| **707** | A119 | 12d | Boarding bus | 6.75 3.50 |
| | | *Nos. 704-707 (4)* | | 8.60 4.40 |

**Souvenir Sheet**
| | | | | |
|---|---|---|---|---|
| **708** | A119 | 15d | Nature study | 8.75 8.75 |

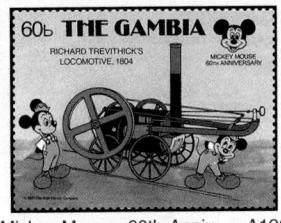

Mickey Mouse, 60th Anniv. — A120

Disney animated characters and historic locomotives: 60b, Richard Trevithick's locomotive, 1804. 75b, Empire State Express 999, 1893. 1d, George Stephenson's Rocket, 1829. 1.25d, Santa Fe Mountain 2-10-2, 1920. 2d, Class GG-1 Pennsylvania, 1933. 5d, Stourbridge Lion, 1829. 10d, Best Friend of Charleston, 1830. 12d, M10001 Union Pacific, 1934. No. 717, Tres Grande Vitesse-SNCF, 1981, France. No. 718, The General, Western & Atlantic, 1855.

**1987, Dec. 9     Litho.     Perf. 14x13½**
| | | | | |
|---|---|---|---|---|
| 709 | A120 | 60b multicolored | .20 | .20 |
| 710 | A120 | 75b multicolored | .25 | .25 |
| 711 | A120 | 1d multicolored | .50 | .30 |
| 712 | A120 | 1.25d multicolored | .60 | .40 |
| 713 | A120 | 2d multicolored | .90 | .60 |
| 714 | A120 | 5d multicolored | 2.25 | 1.50 |
| 715 | A120 | 10d multicolored | 4.50 | 3.00 |
| 716 | A120 | 12d multicolored | 5.00 | 3.50 |
| | *Nos. 709-716 (8)* | | 14.20 | 9.75 |

**Souvenir Sheets**
| | | | | |
|---|---|---|---|---|
| 717 | A120 | 15d multicolored | 7.25 | 7.25 |
| 718 | A120 | 15d multicolored | 7.25 | 7.25 |

Fauna and Flora A121

**1988, Feb. 9     Litho.     Perf. 15**
| | | | | |
|---|---|---|---|---|
| 719 | A121 | 50b Duiker, acacia | .20 | .20 |
| 720 | A121 | 75b Red-billed hornbill, casuarina | .20 | .20 |
| 721 | A121 | 90b West African dwarf crocodile, rice | .25 | .25 |
| 722 | A121 | 1d Leopard, papyrus | .25 | .25 |
| 723 | A121 | 1.25d Crested cranes, millet | .35 | .35 |
| 724 | A121 | 2d Waterbuck, baobab tree | .55 | .55 |
| 725 | A121 | 3d Oribi, Senegal palm | .80 | .80 |
| 726 | A121 | 5d Hippopotamus, papaya | 1.40 | 1.40 |
| | *Nos. 719-726 (8)* | | 4.00 | 4.00 |

**Souvenir Sheets**
| | | | | |
|---|---|---|---|---|
| 727 | A121 | 12d Great white pelican | 2.50 | 2.50 |
| 728 | A121 | 12d Red-throated bee-eater | 2.50 | 2.50 |

Nos. 720, 722, 724, 726 and 728 vert.

40th Wedding Anniv. of Queen Elizabeth II and Prince Philip — A122

**1988, Mar. 15     Perf. 14**
| | | | | |
|---|---|---|---|---|
| 729 | A122 | 75b Wedding portrait, 1947 | .20 | .20 |
| 730 | A122 | 1d Couple at leisure | .25 | .25 |
| 731 | A122 | 3d Wedding portrait, diff. | 1.00 | 1.00 |
| 732 | A122 | 10d Couple, c. 1987 | 3.50 | 3.50 |
| | *Nos. 729-732 (4)* | | 4.95 | 4.95 |

**Souvenir Sheet**
| | | | | |
|---|---|---|---|---|
| 733 | A122 | 15d Wedding party | 3.50 | 3.50 |

1988 Summer Olympics, Seoul A123

**1988, May 3     Litho.     Perf. 14**
| | | | | |
|---|---|---|---|---|
| 734 | A123 | 1d Archery, vert. | .20 | .20 |
| 735 | A123 | 1.25d Boxing, vert. | .20 | .20 |
| 736 | A123 | 5d Gymnastics, vert. | 1.50 | 1.25 |
| 737 | A123 | 10d 100-Meter sprint | 3.50 | 2.50 |
| | *Nos. 734-737 (4)* | | 5.40 | 4.15 |

**Souvenir Sheet**
| | | | | |
|---|---|---|---|---|
| 738 | A123 | 15d Award ceremony, Olympic stadium | 4.00 | 4.00 |

Anniversaries & Events — A124

Designs: 50b, Red Cross flag. 75b, Friendship 7, piloted by John Glenn, 1963. 1d, British Airways Concorde jet. 1.25d, Spirit of St. Louis, piloted by Charles Lindbergh, 1927. 2d, X-15, piloted by Major William Knight, 1967. 3d, Bell X-1, piloted by Capt. Charles Yeager, 1947. 10d, Spanish galleon, British warship, 1588. 12d, The Titanic. No. 747, Kangaroo and joey. No. 748, Cathedral, modern church, vert.

**1988, May 15**
| | | | | |
|---|---|---|---|---|
| 739 | A124 | 50b multicolored | .90 | .75 |
| 740 | A124 | 75b multicolored | .90 | .75 |
| 741 | A124 | 1d multicolored | 1.60 | 1.25 |
| 742 | A124 | 1.25d multicolored | 1.60 | 1.25 |
| 743 | A124 | 2d multicolored | 2.00 | 1.25 |
| 744 | A124 | 3d multicolored | 2.50 | 2.25 |
| 745 | A124 | 10d multicolored | 6.75 | 5.50 |
| 746 | A124 | 12d multicolored | 7.75 | 6.50 |
| | *Nos. 739-746 (8)* | | 24.00 | 20.00 |

**Souvenir Sheets**
| | | | | |
|---|---|---|---|---|
| 747 | A124 | 15d multicolored | 4.75 | 4.75 |
| 748 | A124 | 15d multicolored | 4.75 | 4.75 |

Intl. Red Cross, 125th anniv. (50b); first American in space, 25th anniv. in 1987 (75b); 1st London-New York scheduled Concorde flight, 10th anniv. in 1987 (1d); first solo transatlantic flight, 60th anniv. in 1987 (1.25d); fastest speed flown, 6.72 Mach, 20th anniv. in 1987 (2d); 1st supersonic flight, 40th anniv. in 1987 (3d); defeat of the Spanish Armada, 400th anniv. (10d); maiden voyage of the Titanic, 75th anniv. in 1987 (12d); founding of Australia, bicentennial (No. 747); and founding of Berlin, 750th anniv. in 1987 (No. 748).

Nos. 694, 670, 675 and 690 Ovptd. for Philatelic Exhibitions

a

b

c

d

**1988, Apr. 19     Litho.     Perf. 14, 15**
| | | | | |
|---|---|---|---|---|
| 749 | A115(a) | 1d multi | .50 | .50 |
| 750 | A110(b) | 10d multi | 3.50 | 3.50 |
| 751 | A111(c) | 10d multi | 3.50 | 3.50 |
| 752 | A113(d) | 15d multi | 4.50 | 4.50 |
| | *Nos. 749-752 (4)* | | 12.00 | 12.00 |

Paintings by Titian A125

Designs: 25b, Emperor Charles V, 1549. 50b, St. Margaret and the Dragon, 1565. 60b, Ranuccio Farnese, 1542. 75b, Tarquin and Lucretia, 1570. 1d, The Knight of Malta, c. 1550. 5d, Spain Succouring Faith, 1571. 10d, Doge Francesco Venier, 1555. 12d, Doge Grimani Before the Faith, c. 1555-1576. No. 761, Jealous Husband, 1511. No. 762, Venus Blindfolding Cupid, 1560.

**1988, July 7     Litho.     Perf. 13½x14**
| | | | | |
|---|---|---|---|---|
| 753 | A125 | 25b multicolored | .20 | .20 |
| 754 | A125 | 50b multicolored | .50 | .50 |
| 755 | A125 | 60b multicolored | .55 | .55 |
| 756 | A125 | 75b multicolored | .80 | .80 |
| 757 | A125 | 1d multicolored | .90 | .90 |
| 758 | A125 | 5d multicolored | 3.00 | 3.00 |
| 759 | A125 | 10d multicolored | 5.00 | 5.00 |
| 760 | A125 | 12d multicolored | 5.75 | 5.75 |
| | *Nos. 753-760 (8)* | | 16.70 | 16.70 |

**Souvenir Sheets**
| | | | | |
|---|---|---|---|---|
| 761 | A125 | 15d multicolored | 4.25 | 4.25 |
| 762 | A125 | 15d multicolored | 4.25 | 4.25 |

Tribute to John F. Kennedy A126

**1988, Sept. 1     Litho.     Perf. 14**
| | | | | |
|---|---|---|---|---|
| 763 | A126 | 75b Sailing | .20 | .20 |
| 764 | A126 | 1d Peace Corps enactment | .35 | .35 |
| 765 | A126 | 1.25d Public address, vert. | .45 | .45 |
| 766 | A126 | 12d Grave, Arlington Natl. Cemetery | 3.25 | 3.25 |
| | *Nos. 763-766 (4)* | | 4.25 | 4.25 |

**Souvenir Sheet**
| | | | | |
|---|---|---|---|---|
| 767 | A126 | 15d Kennedy, vert. | 4.75 | 4.75 |

Entertainers — A127

20b, Emmett Lee Kelly (1898-1979), clown. 1d, Gambia Natl. Ensemble. 1.25d, Jackie Gleason (1916-87), comedian, & The Honeymooners cast. 1.50d, Stan Laurel (1890-1965) & Oliver Hardy (1892-1957), film comedy team. 2.50d, Yul Brynner (c. 1920-85), actor. 3d, Cary Grant (1904-86), actor. 10d, Danny Kaye (1918-87), comedian, actor. 20d, Charlie Chaplin (1889-1977), comedian, actor. #776,

Harpo (1893-1964), Chico (1891-1961), Zeppo (1901-79) & Groucho (1890-1977) Marx, comedy team. #777, Fred Astaire (1899-1987) & Rita Hayworth (1918-87), dancers & film stars. #768-775 vert.

**1988, Nov. 9     Litho.**
| | | | | |
|---|---|---|---|---|
| 768 | A127 | 20b multi | .20 | .20 |
| 769 | A127 | 1d multi | .50 | .50 |
| 770 | A127 | 1.25d multi | .60 | .60 |
| 771 | A127 | 1.50d multi | .65 | .65 |
| 772 | A127 | 2.50d multi | 1.10 | 1.10 |
| 773 | A127 | 3d multi | 1.40 | 1.40 |
| 774 | A127 | 10d multi | 4.50 | 4.50 |
| 775 | A127 | 12d multi | 8.00 | 8.00 |
| | *Nos. 768-775 (8)* | | 16.95 | 16.95 |

**Souvenir Sheets**
| | | | | |
|---|---|---|---|---|
| 776 | A127 | 15d multi | 7.75 | 7.75 |
| 777 | A127 | 15d multi | 7.75 | 7.75 |

Kelly's name is spelled incorrectly; Brynner's and Grant's dates are incorrect.

Zeppelin LZ7 Deutschland, 1910 — A128

Transportation innovations: 50b, Stephenson's Locomotion, 1825. 75b, General Motors Sun Racer, 1987. 1d, Sprague's Premiere, 1888. 1.25d, Gold Rush bicycle, 1986. 2.50d, 1st Liquid-fuel rocket, invented by Robert Goddard, 1925. 10d, Orukter Amphibolos, 1805. 12d, Sovereign of the Seas, 1988. No. 786, USS Nautilus, 1954, vert. No. 787, Fulton's Nautilus, early 19th cent.

**1988, Nov. 21     Litho.     Perf. 14**
| | | | | |
|---|---|---|---|---|
| 778 | A128 | 25b multi | .65 | .25 |
| 779 | A128 | 50b multi | 1.10 | .40 |
| 780 | A128 | 75b multi | 1.25 | .55 |
| 781 | A128 | 1d multi | 1.75 | .70 |
| 782 | A128 | 1.25d multi | 1.75 | .75 |
| 783 | A128 | 2.50d multi | 2.75 | 1.25 |
| 784 | A128 | 10d multi | 6.75 | 3.50 |
| 785 | A128 | 12d multi | 7.75 | 4.00 |
| | *Nos. 778-785 (8)* | | 23.75 | 11.40 |

**Souvenir Sheets**
| | | | | |
|---|---|---|---|---|
| 786 | A128 | 15d multi | 6.00 | 6.00 |
| 787 | A128 | 15d multi | 6.00 | 6.00 |

Discovery of America, 500th Anniv. (in 1992) A129

Designs: 50b, Caravel, Henry the Navigator (1394-1460), Prince of Portugal, and coat of arms, vert. 75b, Jesse Ramsden's sextant, map of Africa, arms, vert. 1d, Hour glass, 15th cent., and map, vert. 1.25d, Henry and Vasco da Gama, vert. 2.50d, Da Gama and 15th cent. caravel, vert. 5d, Mungo Park (1771-1806), Scottish explorer, arms and map of Gambia River. 10d, Map of west African coast, 1563. 12d, Portuguese caravel, arms. No. 796, Caravel off the Gambian coast, 15th cent., vert. No. 797, European ship off Gambian coast, 15th cent., vert.

**1988, Dec. 1     Litho.     Perf. 14**
| | | | | |
|---|---|---|---|---|
| 788 | A129 | 50b multi | .95 | .95 |
| 789 | A129 | 75b multi | 1.10 | 1.10 |
| 790 | A129 | 1d multi | 1.50 | 1.50 |
| 791 | A129 | 1.25d multi | 1.75 | 1.75 |
| 792 | A129 | 2.50d multi | 2.25 | 2.25 |
| 793 | A129 | 5d shown | 3.75 | 3.75 |
| 794 | A129 | 10d multi | 6.25 | 6.25 |
| 795 | A129 | 12d multi | 6.50 | 6.50 |
| | *Nos. 788-795 (8)* | | 24.05 | 24.05 |

**Souvenir Sheets**
| | | | | |
|---|---|---|---|---|
| 796 | A129 | 15d multi | 6.00 | 6.00 |
| 797 | A129 | 15d multi | 6.00 | 6.00 |

Space Achievements — A130

Galileo and: 50b, Futuristic aerospace plane and Ernst Mach (1838-1916), Austrian physicist, vert. 75b, OAO III astronomical satellite and Niels Bohr (1885-1962), Danish physicist and Nobel laureate in 1922, vert. 1d, NASA space shuttle, future space station and Robert Goddard (1882-1945), American rocket scientist. 1.25d, Flyby of probe past Jupiter, 1979, and Edward Barnard (1857-1923), American astronomer who discovered Jupiter's 5th satellite in 1892. 2d, Hubble Space Telescope and George Hale (1868-1938), American astronomer, vert. 3d, Precision measurement of the distance between the Earth and the Moon by laser and Albert A. Michelson (1852-1931), Nobel laureate in 1907 for research on the speed of light. 10d, HEAO-2 Einstein orbital satellite and Albert Einstein, vert. 20d, Voyager, 1st circumnavigation of the world without refueling, 1987, and the Wright Brothers. No. 806, Moon Ganymede passing the Great Red Spot on Jupiter. No. 807, Apollo and Neil Armstrong, 1st man on the Moon, July 20, 1969, vert.

**1988, Dec. 12**      *Perf. 14*

| | | | | |
|---|---|---|---|---|
| 798 | A130 | 50b multi | .20 | .20 |
| 799 | A130 | 75b multi | .20 | .20 |
| 800 | A130 | 1d multi | .55 | .55 |
| 801 | A130 | 1.25d multi | .75 | .75 |
| 802 | A130 | 2d multi | 1.10 | 1.10 |
| 803 | A130 | 3d multi | 1.75 | 1.75 |
| 804 | A130 | 10d multi | 4.50 | 4.50 |
| 805 | A130 | 20d multi | 8.00 | 8.00 |
| | *Nos. 798-805 (8)* | | 17.05 | 17.05 |

**Souvenir Sheets**

| | | | | |
|---|---|---|---|---|
| 806 | A130 | 15d multi | 5.50 | 5.50 |
| 807 | A130 | 15d multi | 5.50 | 5.50 |

350th anniv. of the publication of Discourses, by Galileo.

Army Day
A131

**1989, Feb. 10**    Litho.    *Perf. 14*

| | | | | |
|---|---|---|---|---|
| 808 | A131 | 75b Troops on parade | .20 | .20 |
| 809 | A131 | 1d Regimental flags | .30 | .30 |
| 810 | A131 | 1.25d Drummer, vert. | .45 | .45 |
| 811 | A131 | 10d Atlantic Shooting Cup winner, vert. | 2.75 | 2.75 |
| 812 | A131 | 15d Assault course, vert. | 4.50 | 4.50 |
| 813 | A131 | 20d 105-mm gun | 5.00 | 5.00 |
| | *Nos. 808-813 (6)* | | 13.20 | 13.20 |

**Miniature Sheet**

Mickey Mouse, 60th Anniv. (in 1988) — A132

Mickey Mouse through the years: a, 1928. b, 1931. c, 1936. d, 1955. e, 1947. f, 1940. g, 1960. h, 1976. i, 1988. 15d, Birthday party.

**1989, Apr. 6**    Litho.    *Perf. 13x13½*

| | | | | |
|---|---|---|---|---|
| 814 | A132 | Sheet of 9 | 12.00 | 12.00 |
| *a.-i.* | | 2d any single | 1.10 | 1.10 |

**Size: 139x110mm**

*Imperf*

| | | | | |
|---|---|---|---|---|
| 815 | A132 | 15d multi | 8.00 | 8.00 |

---

Easter
A133

Paintings by Rubens: 50b, Le Coup de Lance, 1620. 75b, The Flagellation of Christ, 1617. 1d, The Lamentation for Christ, c. 1617. 1.25d, Descent from the Cross, c. 1611. 2d, The Holy Trinity, c. 1620. 5d, The Doubting Thomas. 10d, Lamentation over Christ, 1614. 12d, Lamentation over Christ with the Virgin and St. John, c. 1613. No. 824, The Last Supper, c. 1631. No. 825, The Raising of the Cross, c. 1610.

**1989, Apr. 14**    *Perf. 13½x14*

| | | | | |
|---|---|---|---|---|
| 816 | A133 | 50b multi | .20 | .20 |
| 817 | A133 | 75b multi | .25 | .25 |
| 818 | A133 | 1d multi | .35 | .35 |
| 819 | A133 | 1.25d multi | .50 | .50 |
| 820 | A133 | 2d multi | .80 | .80 |
| 821 | A133 | 5d multi | 1.75 | 1.75 |
| 822 | A133 | 10d multi | 3.00 | 3.00 |
| 823 | A133 | 12d multi | 3.50 | 3.50 |
| | *Nos. 816-823 (8)* | | 10.35 | 10.35 |

**Souvenir Sheets**

| | | | | |
|---|---|---|---|---|
| 824 | A133 | 15d multi | 4.25 | 4.25 |
| 825 | A133 | 15d multi | 4.25 | 4.25 |

Indigenous Birds — A134

**1989, Apr. 24**      *Perf. 14*

| | | | | |
|---|---|---|---|---|
| 826 | A134 | 20b African emerald cuckoo | .80 | .25 |
| 827 | A134 | 60b Gray-headed bush shrike | .95 | .40 |
| 828 | A134 | 75b Crowned crane | 1.10 | .45 |
| 829 | A134 | 1d Secretary bird | 1.10 | .45 |
| 830 | A134 | 2d Red-billed hornbill | 1.40 | .75 |
| 831 | A134 | 5d Superb sunbird | 3.50 | 1.90 |
| 832 | A134 | 10d Little owl | 7.50 | 3.75 |
| 833 | A134 | 12d Bateleur eagle | 8.50 | 4.50 |
| | *Nos. 826-833 (8)* | | 24.85 | 12.45 |

**Souvenir Sheets**

| | | | | |
|---|---|---|---|---|
| 834 | A134 | 15d Red-billed fire finch | 7.00 | 7.00 |
| 835 | A134 | 15d Ostriches | 7.00 | 7.00 |

Indigenous Butterflies — A135

**1989, May 15**

| | | | | |
|---|---|---|---|---|
| 836 | A135 | 50b Papilio antimachus | .20 | .20 |
| 837 | A135 | 75b Euphaedra neophron | .25 | .25 |
| 838 | A135 | 1d Aterica rabena | .40 | .40 |
| 839 | A135 | 1.25d Salamis parhassus | .90 | .90 |
| 840 | A135 | 5d Precis rhadama | 2.75 | 2.75 |
| 841 | A135 | 10d Papilio demodocus | 5.00 | 5.00 |
| 842 | A135 | 12d Charaxes etesippe | 5.75 | 5.75 |
| 843 | A135 | 15d Danaus formosa | 7.25 | 7.25 |
| | *Nos. 836-843 (8)* | | 22.50 | 22.50 |

**Souvenir Sheets**

| | | | | |
|---|---|---|---|---|
| 844 | A135 | 15d Euphaedra ceres | 8.75 | 8.75 |
| 845 | A135 | 15d Cymothoe pluto | 8.75 | 8.75 |

---

Trains of Africa
A136

Designs: 50b, Nigerian coal train, 1959. 75b, 14A Class 2-6-6-2 Garratt. 1d, British (Pacific) in Sudan. 1.25d, American 0-8-0, 1925. 5d, Scottish 4-8-2, 1955. 7d, Scottish 4-8-2, 1926. 10d, British 4-6-0. 12d, American-made 2-6-0 in Ghana. No. 854, British 2-8-2 Class 25 facing forward, vert. No. 855, Class 25 facing left, vert.

**1989, June 15**    Litho.    *Perf. 14*

| | | | | |
|---|---|---|---|---|
| 846 | A136 | 50b multi | .20 | .20 |
| 847 | A136 | 75b multi | .25 | .25 |
| 848 | A136 | 1d multi | .65 | .65 |
| 849 | A136 | 1.25d multi | .90 | .90 |
| 850 | A136 | 5d multi | 2.75 | 2.75 |
| 851 | A136 | 7d multi | 3.00 | 3.00 |
| 852 | A136 | 10d multi | 5.25 | 5.25 |
| 853 | A136 | 12d multi | 6.00 | 6.00 |
| | *Nos. 846-853 (8)* | | 19.00 | 19.00 |

**Souvenir Sheets**

| | | | | |
|---|---|---|---|---|
| 854 | A136 | 15d multi | 6.75 | 6.75 |
| 855 | A136 | 15d multi | 6.75 | 6.75 |

Nos. 667-671 Ovptd.
"PHILEXFRANCE / '89"

**1989, June 23**    Litho.    *Perf. 15*

| | | | | |
|---|---|---|---|---|
| 856 | A110 | 75b multi | .25 | .25 |
| 857 | A110 | 1d multi | .30 | .30 |
| 858 | A110 | 1.25d multi | .45 | .45 |
| 859 | A110 | 10d multi | 2.00 | 2.00 |
| | *Nos. 856-859 (4)* | | 3.00 | 3.00 |

**Souvenir Sheet**

| | | | | |
|---|---|---|---|---|
| 860 | A110 | 12d multi | 3.50 | 3.50 |

Paintings by Japanese Artists
A137

Paintings by Hiroshige unless noted otherwise: 50b, Sparrow and Bamboo. 75b, Peonies and a Canary, by Hokusai. 1d, Crane and Marsh Grasses. 1.25d, Crossbill and Thistle, by Hokusai. 2d, Cuckoo and Azalea, by Hokusai. 5d, Parrot on a Pine Branch. 10d, Mandarin Ducks in a Stream. 12d, Bullfinch and Drooping Cherry, by Hokusai. No. 869, Tit and Peony, horiz. No. 870, Peony and Butterfly, by Shigenobu, horiz.

**1989, July 7**    *Perf. 13½x14, 14x13½*

| | | | | |
|---|---|---|---|---|
| 861 | A137 | 50b multi | .20 | .20 |
| 862 | A137 | 75b multi | .30 | .30 |
| 863 | A137 | 1d multi | .55 | .55 |
| 864 | A137 | 1.25d multi | .65 | .65 |
| 865 | A137 | 2d multi | 1.00 | 1.00 |
| 866 | A137 | 5d multi | 2.50 | 2.50 |
| 867 | A137 | 10d multi | 5.00 | 5.00 |
| 868 | A137 | 12d multi | 5.50 | 5.50 |
| | *Nos. 861-868 (8)* | | 15.70 | 15.70 |

**Souvenir Sheets**

| | | | | |
|---|---|---|---|---|
| 869 | A137 | 15d multi | 6.25 | 6.25 |
| 870 | A137 | 15d multi | 6.25 | 6.25 |

1990 World Cup Soccer Championships, Italy — A138

Various athletes and Italian landmarks: 75b, Rialto Bridge, Venice. 1.25d, The Baptistery, Pisa. 5d, Casino San Remo. 12d, The Colosseum, Rome. No. 875, St. Mark's Cathedral, Venice. No. 876, Piazza Colonna, Rome.

---

**1989, Aug 25**      *Perf. 14*

| | | | | |
|---|---|---|---|---|
| 871 | A138 | 75b multi | .55 | .55 |
| 872 | A138 | 1.25d multi | .70 | .70 |
| 873 | A138 | 7d multi | 3.25 | 3.25 |
| 874 | A138 | 12d multi | 5.50 | 5.50 |
| | *Nos. 871-874 (4)* | | 10.00 | 10.00 |

**Souvenir Sheets**

| | | | | |
|---|---|---|---|---|
| 875 | A138 | 15d multi | 6.50 | 6.50 |
| 876 | A138 | 15d multi | 6.50 | 6.50 |

Medicinal Plants — A139

**1989, Sept. 18**    Litho.    *Perf. 14*

| | | | | |
|---|---|---|---|---|
| 877 | A139 | 20b *Vitex doniana* | .20 | .20 |
| 878 | A139 | 50b *Ricinus communis* | .20 | .20 |
| 879 | A139 | 75b *Palisota hirsuta* | .20 | .20 |
| 880 | A139 | 1d *Smilax kraussiana* | .50 | .50 |
| 881 | A139 | 1.25d *Aspilia africana* | .55 | .55 |
| 882 | A139 | 5d *Newbouldia laevis* | 2.25 | 2.25 |
| 883 | A139 | 8d *Monodora tenuifolia* | 3.50 | 3.50 |
| 884 | A139 | 10d *Gossypium arboreum* | 4.25 | 4.25 |
| | *Nos. 877-884 (8)* | | 11.65 | 11.65 |

**Souvenir Sheets**

| | | | | |
|---|---|---|---|---|
| 885 | A139 | 15d *Kigelia africana* | 6.75 | 6.75 |
| 886 | A139 | 15d *Spathodea campanulata* | 6.75 | 6.75 |

Fish
A140

**1989, Oct. 19**    Litho.    *Perf.*

| | | | | |
|---|---|---|---|---|
| 887 | A140 | 20b Lookdown | .20 | .20 |
| 888 | A140 | 75b Boarfish | .70 | .70 |
| 889 | A140 | 1d Gray triggerfish | .75 | .75 |
| 890 | A140 | 1.25d Skipjack tuna | .90 | .90 |
| 891 | A140 | 2d Bermuda chub | 1.25 | 1.25 |
| 892 | A140 | 4d Atlantic manta | 2.40 | 2.40 |
| 893 | A140 | 5d Striped mullet | 3.00 | 3.00 |
| 894 | A140 | 10d Ladyfish | 4.25 | 4.25 |
| | *Nos. 887-894 (8)* | | 13.45 | 13.45 |

**Souvenir Sheets**

| | | | | |
|---|---|---|---|---|
| 895 | A140 | 15d Porcupinefish | 8.25 | 8.25 |
| 896 | A140 | 15d Shortfin makos | 8.25 | 8.25 |

**Souvenir Sheet**

The White House, Washington, D.C. — A141

**1989, Nov. 17**    Litho.    *Perf. 14*

| | | | | |
|---|---|---|---|---|
| 897 | A141 | 10d multicolored | 3.50 | 3.50 |

World Stamp Expo '89.

World Stamp Expo '89, Washington,
D.C. — A142

Disney characters riding carousel horses:
20b, Daniel Muller Indian pony. 50b, Her-
schell-Spillman steed. 75b, Gustav Dentzel
stander. 1d, Muller armored stander. 1.25d,
Jumper from the Smithsonian Collection. 2d,
Illion "American Beauty." 8d, Zalar jumper.
10d, Parker buckling. No. 906, Philadelphia
Tobaggan Co. Carousel, Elitch Gardens, Denver, CO. No. 907, PTC Roman chariot.

**1989, Nov. 29    Litho.    Perf. 14x13½**

| | | | | |
|---|---|---|---|---|
| 898 | A142 | 20b multicolored | .70 | .20 |
| 899 | A142 | 50b multicolored | 1.10 | .30 |
| 900 | A142 | 75b multicolored | 1.25 | .40 |
| 901 | A142 | 1d multicolored | 1.25 | .50 |
| 902 | A142 | 1.25d multicolored | 1.40 | .75 |
| 903 | A142 | 2d multicolored | 1.90 | 1.00 |
| 904 | A142 | 8d multicolored | 5.50 | 3.00 |
| 905 | A142 | 10d multicolored | 5.50 | 3.25 |
| | | Nos. 898-905 (8) | 18.60 | 9.40 |

**Souvenir Sheets**

| | | | | |
|---|---|---|---|---|
| 906 | A142 | 12d multicolored | 7.75 | 7.75 |
| 907 | A142 | 12d multicolored | 7.75 | 7.75 |

Nobel Prize Winners for Physiology
and Great Medical Pioneers — A143

20b, Charles Nicolle (1866-1936), France,
1928 Prize, discovered transmission of typhus
by body lice. 50b, Paul Ehrlich (1854-1915),
Germany, 1908 Prize, immunology research.
75b, Selman Waksman (1888-1973), Russian-
American, 1952 Prize, discovered antibiotic
streptomycin, used to treat tuberculosis. 1d,
Edward Jenner (1749-1823), Great Britain,
discovered smallpox vaccine. 1.25d, Robert
Koch (1843-1910), 1905 Prize, isolated the
tubercle bacillus. 5d, Sir Alexander Fleming
(1881-1955), Scotland, 1945 Prize, developed
penicillin. 8d, Max Theiler (1899-1972), US,
1951 Prize, developed yellow fever vaccine.
10d, Louis Pasteur (1822-95), France, proved
the germ theory of infection.
#916, C-9 Nightingale Aeromedical Airlift.
#917, Hughes Vicking helicopter used in airlift.

**1989, Dec. 12    Perf. 14**

| | | | | |
|---|---|---|---|---|
| 908 | A143 | 20b multicolored | .45 | .25 |
| 909 | A143 | 50b multicolored | .85 | .40 |
| 910 | A143 | 75b multicolored | 1.10 | .50 |
| 911 | A143 | 1d multicolored | 1.10 | .60 |
| 912 | A143 | 1.25d multicolored | 1.25 | .70 |
| 913 | A143 | 5d multicolored | 2.75 | 1.60 |
| 914 | A143 | 8d multicolored | 4.25 | 2.50 |
| 915 | A143 | 10d multicolored | 5.50 | 3.25 |
| | | Nos. 908-915 (8) | 17.25 | 9.80 |

**Souvenir Sheets**

| | | | | |
|---|---|---|---|---|
| 916 | A143 | 15d multicolored | 6.25 | 6.25 |
| 917 | A143 | 15d multicolored | 6.25 | 6.25 |

Orchids — A144

**1989, Dec. 18    Perf. 14**

| | | | | |
|---|---|---|---|---|
| 918 | A144 | 20b Bulbophyllum lepidum | .30 | .30 |
| 919 | A144 | 75b Tridactyle tridactylites | .75 | .75 |
| 920 | A144 | 1d Vanilla imperialis | 1.10 | 1.10 |
| 921 | A144 | 1.25d Oeceoclades maculata | 1.25 | 1.25 |
| 922 | A144 | 2d Polystachya affinis | 1.75 | 1.75 |

| | | | | |
|---|---|---|---|---|
| 923 | A144 | 4d Ancistrochilus rothschildianus | 3.00 | 3.00 |
| 924 | A144 | 5d Angraecum distichum | 3.50 | 3.50 |
| 925 | A144 | 10d Liparis guineensis | 5.50 | 5.50 |
| | | Nos. 918-925 (8) | 17.15 | 17.15 |

**Souvenir Sheets**

| | | | | |
|---|---|---|---|---|
| 926 | A144 | 15d Eulophia guineensis | 7.75 | 7.75 |
| 927 | A144 | 15d Plectrelminthus caudatus | 7.75 | 7.75 |

Christmas — A145

Disney characters and classic automobiles:
20b, 1922 Pierce Arrow. 50b, 1919 Spyker.
75b, 1929 Packard. 1d, 1920 Daimler. 1.25d,
1924 Hispano Suiza. 2d, Opel Laubfrosch,
1924-27. 10d, 1927 Vauxhall 30/98. 12d, 1923
Peerless. No. 936, 1930 Bentley Super-
charged, Santa Claus. No. 937, 1928 Stutz
Blackhawk Speedster, picnic.

**1989, Dec. 19    Litho.    Perf. 14**

| | | | | |
|---|---|---|---|---|
| 928 | A145 | 20b multicolored | .65 | .20 |
| 929 | A145 | 50b multicolored | .95 | .35 |
| 930 | A145 | 75b multicolored | 1.10 | .45 |
| 931 | A145 | 1d multicolored | 1.25 | .50 |
| 932 | A145 | 1.25d multicolored | 1.40 | .70 |
| 933 | A145 | 2d multicolored | 1.50 | .90 |
| 934 | A145 | 10d multicolored | 5.00 | 3.00 |
| 935 | A145 | 12d multicolored | 5.50 | 3.25 |
| | | Nos. 928-935 (8) | 17.35 | 9.35 |

**Souvenir Sheets**

| | | | | |
|---|---|---|---|---|
| 936 | A145 | 15d multicolored | 8.75 | 8.75 |
| 937 | A145 | 15d multicolored | 8.75 | 8.75 |

Wimbledon          1st Moon
Tennis             Landing, 20th
Champions          Anniv. (in 1989)
A146               A147

**1990, Jan. 2    Litho.    Perf. 15x14½**

| | | | | |
|---|---|---|---|---|
| 938 | A146 | 20b John Newcombe | .20 | .20 |
| 939 | A146 | 20b G.W. Hillyard | .20 | .20 |
| a. | | Pair, #938-939 | .30 | .30 |
| 940 | A146 | 50b Roy Emerson | .20 | .20 |
| 941 | A146 | 50b Dorothy Chambers | .20 | .20 |
| a. | | Pair, #940-941 | .30 | .30 |
| 942 | A146 | 75b Donald Budge | .20 | .20 |
| 943 | A146 | 75b Suzanne Lenglen | .20 | .20 |
| a. | | Pair, #942-943 | .45 | .45 |
| 944 | A146 | 1d Laurence Doherty | .25 | .25 |
| 945 | A146 | 1d Helen Wills Moody | .25 | .25 |
| a. | | Pair, #944-945 | .55 | .55 |
| 946 | A146 | 1.25d Bjorn Borg | .40 | .40 |
| 947 | A146 | 1.25d Maureen Connolly | .40 | .40 |
| a. | | Pair, #946-947 | .85 | .85 |
| 948 | A146 | 4d Jean Borotra | 1.25 | 1.25 |
| 949 | A146 | 4d Maria Bueno | 1.25 | 1.25 |
| a. | | Pair, #948-949 | 2.75 | 2.75 |
| 950 | A146 | 5d Anthony Wilding | 1.50 | 1.50 |
| 951 | A146 | 5d Louise Brough | 1.50 | 1.50 |
| a. | | Pair, #950-951 | 3.25 | 3.25 |
| 952 | A146 | 7d Fred Perry | 2.00 | 2.00 |
| 953 | A146 | 7d Margaret Court | 2.00 | 2.00 |
| a. | | Pair, #952-953 | 4.50 | 4.50 |
| 954 | A146 | 10d Bill Tilden | 2.75 | 2.75 |
| 955 | A146 | 10d Billie Jean King | 2.75 | 2.75 |
| a. | | Pair, #954-955 | 6.25 | 6.25 |

| | | | | |
|---|---|---|---|---|
| 956 | A146 | 12d Rod Laver | 3.00 | 3.00 |
| 957 | A146 | 12d Martina Navratilova | 3.00 | 3.00 |
| a. | | Pair, #956-957 | 6.75 | 6.75 |
| | | Nos. 938-957 (20) | 23.50 | 23.50 |

**Souvenir Sheets**

| | | | | |
|---|---|---|---|---|
| 958 | A146 | 15d Rod Laver, diff. | 7.25 | 7.25 |
| 959 | A146 | 15d Martina Navratilova, diff. | 7.25 | 7.25 |

**1990, Feb. 16    Perf. 14**

Designs: 20b, Eagle lunar module descending, horiz. 50b, Apollo 11 liftoff. 75b, Astronaut
descending ladder, horiz. 1d, Astronaut, US
flag over Sea of Tranquillity, horiz. 1.25d, Mission emblem. 1.75d, Crew, horiz. 8d, Lunar
module, Sea of Tranquillity, horiz. 12d, Recovery of command module Columbia after
splashdown. No. 968, Neil Armstrong
returning to Eagle. No. 969, View of Earth.

| | | | | |
|---|---|---|---|---|
| 960 | A147 | 20b multicolored | .25 | .25 |
| 961 | A147 | 50b multicolored | .70 | .25 |
| 962 | A147 | 75b multicolored | 1.10 | .35 |
| 963 | A147 | 1d multicolored | 1.25 | .40 |
| 964 | A147 | 1.25d multicolored | 1.25 | .50 |
| 965 | A147 | 1.75d multicolored | 1.60 | .75 |
| 966 | A147 | 8d multicolored | 4.75 | 2.25 |
| 967 | A147 | 12d multicolored | 6.00 | 2.75 |
| | | Nos. 960-967 (8) | 16.90 | 7.50 |

**Souvenir Sheets**

| | | | | |
|---|---|---|---|---|
| 968 | A147 | 15d multicolored | 5.75 | 5.75 |
| 969 | A147 | 15d multicolored | 5.75 | 5.75 |

**Miniature Sheet**

Birds of
Africa
A148

No. 970: a, White-faced owl. b, Village
weaver. c, Red-throated bee eater. d, Brown
harrier eagle. e, Red bishop. f, Scarlet-
chested sunbird. g, Red-billed hornbill. h,
Mosque swallow. i, White-faced tree duck. j,
African fish eagle. k, Great white pelican. l,
Carmine bee eater. m, Hadada ibis. n, Crocodile plover. o, Yellow-bellied sunbird. p, African
skimmer. q, Woodland kingfisher. r, Jacana. s,
Pygmy goose. t, Hamerkop.

**1990, Apr. 12    Litho.    Perf. 14**

| | | | | |
|---|---|---|---|---|
| 970 | | Sheet of 20 | 21.00 | 21.00 |
| a.-t. | | A148 1.25d any single | 1.00 | 1.00 |

RAF
World War
II Fighter
Planes
A149

Designs: 10b, Bristol Blenheim Mk-1. 20b,
Battle. 50b, Blenheim 4. 60b, Wellington 1C.
75b, Whitley 5. 1d, Hampden Mk-1. 1.25d,
Spitfire 1A and Hurricane 1. 2d, Avro
Manchester. 3d, Stirling. 5d, Handley Page
Halifax B-2. 10d, Lancaster B-3. 12d, Mos-
quito B-4. No. 983, Lancaster B-3 over
Hamburg. No. 984, Spitfire 1, Battle of Britain.

**1990, Apr. 18    Perf. 14**

| | | | | |
|---|---|---|---|---|
| 971 | A149 | 10b multicolored | .25 | .20 |
| 972 | A149 | 20b multicolored | .70 | .20 |
| 973 | A149 | 50b multicolored | .90 | .30 |
| 974 | A149 | 60b multicolored | 1.10 | .30 |
| 975 | A149 | 75b multicolored | 1.10 | .35 |
| 976 | A149 | 1d multicolored | 1.25 | .35 |
| 977 | A149 | 1.25d multicolored | 1.50 | .40 |
| 978 | A149 | 2d multicolored | 1.75 | .40 |
| 979 | A149 | 3d multicolored | 2.10 | .90 |
| 980 | A149 | 5d multicolored | 2.75 | 1.25 |
| 981 | A149 | 10d multicolored | 5.00 | 2.50 |
| 982 | A149 | 12d multicolored | 6.25 | 3.00 |
| | | Nos. 971-982 (12) | 24.65 | 10.15 |

**Souvenir Sheets**

| | | | | |
|---|---|---|---|---|
| 983 | A149 | 15d multicolored | 7.00 | 7.00 |
| 984 | A149 | 15d multicolored | 7.00 | 7.00 |

Independence,
25th
Anniv. — A150

Designs: 3d, Sir Dawda Jawara, President.
12d, Jet and map showing airport. 18d,
National arms.

**1990, June 5    Litho.    Perf. 14**

| | | | | |
|---|---|---|---|---|
| 985 | A150 | 1d multicolored | .20 | .20 |
| 986 | A150 | 3d multicolored | 1.10 | 1.10 |
| 987 | A150 | 12d multicolored | 5.75 | 5.75 |
| | | Nos. 985-987 (3) | 7.05 | 7.05 |

**Souvenir Sheet**

| | | | | |
|---|---|---|---|---|
| 988 | A150 | 18d multicolored | 6.25 | 6.25 |

Baobab
Tree
A151

**1990, June 14    Litho.    Perf. 14**

| | | | | |
|---|---|---|---|---|
| 989 | A151 | 5b shown | .20 | .20 |
| 990 | A151 | 10b Woodcarving | .20 | .20 |
| 991 | A151 | 20b Pres. Jawara | .20 | .20 |
| 992 | A151 | 50b Map | .20 | .20 |
| 993 | A151 | 75b Batik fabric | .20 | .20 |
| 994 | A151 | 1d Bakau Beach Resort | .25 | .25 |
| 995 | A151 | 1.25d Tendaba Camp | .30 | .30 |
| 996 | A151 | 2d Shrimp industry | .45 | .45 |
| 997 | A151 | 5d Peanut oil mill | .75 | .75 |
| 998 | A151 | 10d Pottery, kora | 1.50 | 1.50 |
| 999 | A151 | 15d Ansellia africana orchid | 3.75 | 3.75 |
| 1000 | A151 | 30d Ancient stone rings, Euryphene gambiae | 6.25 | 6.25 |
| | | Nos. 989-1000 (12) | 14.25 | 14.25 |

Nos. 990, 999 vert.

Penny
Black,
150th
Anniv.
A152

**1990, June 18**

| | | | | |
|---|---|---|---|---|
| 1001 | A152 | 1.25d brt bl & blk | .90 | .35 |
| 1002 | A152 | 12d dark red & blk | 6.00 | 3.50 |

**Souvenir Sheet**

| | | | | |
|---|---|---|---|---|
| 1003 | A152 | 15d sil, bis & blk | 7.75 | 7.75 |

Mickey Visits England — A153

Walt Disney characters at: 20b, 10 Downing
Street. 50b, Trafalgar Square. 75b, Cliffs of
Dover. 1d, Tower of London. 5d, Hampton
Court Palace. 8d, Magdalen Tower, Oxford
University. 10d, Old London Bridge. 12d,
Rosetta Stone, British Museum. No. 1012,
Picadilly Circus. No. 1013, Houses of Parlia-
ment and Big Ben on the River Thames.

**1990, June 19    Perf. 14x13½**

| | | | | |
|---|---|---|---|---|
| 1004 | A153 | 20b multicolored | .20 | .20 |
| 1005 | A153 | 50b multicolored | .20 | .20 |
| 1006 | A153 | 75b multicolored | .75 | .75 |
| 1007 | A153 | 1d multicolored | .75 | .75 |
| 1008 | A153 | 5d multicolored | 3.00 | 3.00 |
| 1009 | A153 | 8d multicolored | 3.50 | 3.50 |

| | | | | |
|---|---|---|---|---|
| **1010** | A153 | 10d multicolored | 4.50 | 4.50 |
| **1011** | A153 | 12d multicolored | 5.50 | 5.50 |
| | | *Nos. 1004-1011 (8)* | 18.40 | 18.40 |

**Souvenir Sheets**

| | | | | |
|---|---|---|---|---|
| **1012** | A153 | 18d multicolored | 9.50 | 9.50 |
| **1013** | A153 | 18d multicolored | 9.50 | 9.50 |

Stamp World London '90. Nos. 1004-1005, 1007, 1009 vert.

A154

**1990, July 19**          ***Perf. 14***

| | | | | |
|---|---|---|---|---|
| **1014** | A154 | 6d Girl facing left | 1.75 | 1.75 |
| **1015** | A154 | 6d Young girl, diff. | 1.75 | 1.75 |
| **1016** | A154 | 6d Seated in chair | 1.75 | 1.75 |
| | *a.* | A154 Strip of 3, #1014-1016 | 6.25 | 6.25 |

**Souvenir Sheet**

| | | | | |
|---|---|---|---|---|
| **1017** | A154 | 18d like No. 1014 | 5.75 | 5.75 |

A156                    A157

Players from participating countries.

**1990, Sept. 24**          Litho.          ***Perf. 14***

| | | | | |
|---|---|---|---|---|
| **1018** | A156 | 1d Italy | .45 | .45 |
| **1019** | A156 | 1.25d Argentina | .55 | .55 |
| **1020** | A156 | 3d Costa Rica | 1.25 | 1.25 |
| **1021** | A156 | 5d UAE | 2.00 | 2.00 |
| | | *Nos. 1018-1021 (4)* | 4.25 | 4.25 |

**Souvenir Sheets**

| | | | | |
|---|---|---|---|---|
| **1022** | A156 | 18d Holland | 8.75 | 8.75 |
| **1023** | A156 | 18d Romania | 8.75 | 8.75 |

World Cup Soccer Championships, Italy.

**1990, Nov. 1**          Litho.          ***Perf. 14***

| | | | | |
|---|---|---|---|---|
| **1024** | A157 | 20b Men's discus | .20 | .20 |
| **1025** | A157 | 50b Men's 100-meter race | .20 | .20 |
| **1026** | A157 | 75b Women's 400-meter race | .20 | .20 |
| **1027** | A157 | 1d Men's 200-meter race | .55 | .55 |
| **1028** | A157 | 1.25d Rhythmic gymnastics | .45 | .45 |
| **1029** | A157 | 3d Soccer | 1.60 | 1.60 |
| **1030** | A157 | 10d Men's marathon | 5.25 | 5.25 |
| **1031** | A157 | 12d Tornado class sailing | 6.25 | 6.25 |
| | | *Nos. 1024-1031 (8)* | 14.70 | 14.70 |

**Souvenir Sheets**

| | | | | |
|---|---|---|---|---|
| **1032** | A157 | 15d Parade of flags | 7.50 | 7.50 |
| **1033** | A157 | 15d Stadium, card section | 7.50 | 7.50 |

1992 Summer Olympics, Barcelona.

Christmas A158

Entire paintings or different details from: 20b, 7d, The Annunciation with St. Emidius by Crivelli. 50b, The Annunciation by Campin. 75b, The Solly Madonna by Raphael. 1.25d, The Tempi Madonna by Raphael. 2d, Madonna of the Linen Window by Raphael. 10d, The Orleans Madonna by Raphael. 15d,

Madonna and Child by Crivelli. No. 1042, The Niccolini-Cowper Madonna by Raphael.

**1990, Dec. 24**          Litho.          ***Perf. 13½x14***

| | | | | |
|---|---|---|---|---|
| **1034** | A158 | 20b multicolored | .20 | .20 |
| **1035** | A158 | 50b multicolored | .20 | .20 |
| **1036** | A158 | 75b multicolored | .20 | .20 |
| **1037** | A158 | 1.25d multicolored | .65 | .65 |
| **1038** | A158 | 2d multicolored | 1.00 | 1.00 |
| **1039** | A158 | 7d multicolored | 3.25 | 3.25 |
| **1040** | A158 | 10d multicolored | 4.00 | 4.00 |
| **1041** | A158 | 15d multicolored | 5.75 | 5.75 |
| | | *Nos. 1034-1041 (8)* | 15.25 | 15.25 |

**Souvenir Sheet**

| | | | | |
|---|---|---|---|---|
| **1042** | A158 | 15d multicolored | 9.00 | 9.00 |

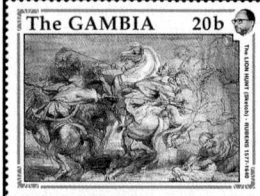

Peter Paul Rubens (1577-1640), Painter — A159

Entire paintings or different details from: 20b, 75b, 10d, No. 1054, The Lion Hunt. 1d, 1.25d, 3d, 15d, The Tiger Hunt. 5d, No. 1055, The Boar Hunt. No. 1056, The Crocodile and Hippopotamus Hunt. No. 1057, Saint George Slays the Dragon, vert.

**1990, Dec. 24**          Litho.          ***Perf. 14x13½***

| | | | | |
|---|---|---|---|---|
| **1046** | A159 | 20b multicolored | .20 | .20 |
| **1047** | A159 | 75b multicolored | .20 | .20 |
| **1048** | A159 | 1d multicolored | .40 | .40 |
| **1049** | A159 | 1.25d multicolored | .55 | .55 |
| **1050** | A159 | 3d multicolored | 1.25 | 1.25 |
| **1051** | A159 | 5d multicolored | 1.90 | 1.90 |
| **1052** | A159 | 10d multicolored | 3.25 | 3.25 |
| **1053** | A159 | 15d multicolored | 4.50 | 4.50 |
| | | *Nos. 1046-1053 (8)* | 12.25 | 12.25 |

**Souvenir Sheets**

| | | | | |
|---|---|---|---|---|
| **1054** | A159 | 15d multicolored | 5.25 | 5.25 |
| **1055** | A159 | 15d multicolored | 5.25 | 5.25 |
| **1056** | A159 | 15d multicolored | 5.25 | 5.25 |
| **1057** | A159 | 15d multicolored | 5.25 | 5.25 |

World Summit for Children A160

**1991, Jan. 7**          Litho.          ***Perf. 14***

| | | | | |
|---|---|---|---|---|
| **1058** | A160 | 1d multicolored | .80 | .80 |

Intl. Literacy Year — A161

Walt Disney characters in "The Sword in the Stone": No. 1059a, Wart and Sir Kay. b, Merlin reading book. c, Wart learning geography. d, Wart writing on blackboard. e, Wart as bird, Madam Mim. f, Merlin and Madam Mim. g, Mim as dragon. h, Wart pulling sword from stone. i, Wart as King of England. No. 1060, Merlin, Wart in forest, vert. No. 1061, Knight trying to remove sword from stone, vert.

**1991, Feb. 14**          Litho.          ***Perf. 14x13½***

| | | | | |
|---|---|---|---|---|
| **1059** | A161 | 3d Sheet of 9, #a-i | 16.00 | 16.00 |

**Souvenir Sheets**

| | | | | |
|---|---|---|---|---|
| **1060** | A161 | 20d multicolored | 10.50 | 10.50 |
| **1061** | A161 | 20d multicolored | 10.50 | 10.50 |

Miniature Sheets

Wildlife A162

No. 1062: a, Bebearia senegalensis. b, Graphium ridleyanus. c, Precis antilope. d, Charaxes ameliae. e, Addax. f, Sassaby. g, Civet. h, Green monkey. i, Spurwing goose. j, Red-billed hornbill. k, Osprey. l, Glossy ibis. m, Egyptian plover. n, Golden-tailed woodpecker. o, Green woodhoopoe. p, Gaboon viper.

No. 1063: a, Red-billed firefinch. b, Leaflove. c, Piacpiac. d, Emerald cuckoo. e, Red colobus monkey. f, African elephant. g, Duiker. h, Giant eland. i, Oribi. j, West African dwarf crocodile. k, Crowned crane. l, Jackal. m, Yellow-throated longclaw. n, Abyssinian ground hornbill. o, Papilio hesperus. p, Papilio antimachus.

No. 1064: a, Martial eagle. b, Red-cheeked cordon-bleu. c, Red bishop. d, Great white pelican. e, Patas monkey. f, Vervet monkey. g, Roan antelope. h, Western hartebeest. i, Waterbuck. j, Warthog. k, Spotted hyena. l, Olive baboon. m, Palla decius. n, Acraea pharsalus. o, Neptidopsis ophione. p, Acraea caecilia.

No. 1065, African spoonbill, vert. No. 1066, Lion, vert. No. 1067, Buffalo weaver, vert.

**1991, May 31**          Litho.          ***Perf. 14***

| | | | | |
|---|---|---|---|---|
| **1062** | A162 | 1d Sheet of 16, | | |
| | | #a.-p. | 6.50 | 6.50 |
| **1063** | A162 | 1.50d Sheet of 16, | | |
| | | #a.-p. | 9.50 | 9.50 |
| **1064** | A162 | 5d Sheet of 16, | | |
| | | #a.-p. | 30.00 | 30.00 |
| | | *Nos. 1062-1064 (3)* | 46.00 | 46.00 |

**Souvenir Sheets**

| | | | | |
|---|---|---|---|---|
| **1065** | A162 | 18d multicolored | 6.50 | 6.50 |
| **1066** | A162 | 18d multicolored | 6.50 | 6.50 |
| **1067** | A162 | 18d multicolored | 6.50 | 6.50 |

Butterflies — A163

Designs: 20b, Papilio dardanus. 50b, Bematistes poggei. 1d, Vanessa cardui. 1.50d, Amphicallia tigris. 3d, Hypolimnes dexithea. 8d, Acraea egina. 10d, Salmis temora. 15d, Precis octavia. No. 1076, Danaus chrysippus. No. 1077, Charaxes jasius. No. 1078, Papilio demodocus. No. 1079, Papilio nireus.

**1991, June 1**          Litho.          ***Perf. 14***

| | | | | |
|---|---|---|---|---|
| **1068** | A163 | 20b multicolored | .20 | .20 |
| **1069** | A163 | 50b multicolored | .20 | .20 |
| **1070** | A163 | 1d multicolored | .40 | .40 |
| **1071** | A163 | 1.50d multicolored | .70 | .70 |
| **1072** | A163 | 3d multicolored | 1.40 | 1.40 |
| **1073** | A163 | 8d multicolored | 3.50 | 3.50 |
| **1074** | A163 | 10d multicolored | 4.25 | 4.25 |
| **1075** | A163 | 15d multicolored | 6.50 | 6.50 |
| | | *Nos. 1068-1075 (8)* | 17.15 | 17.15 |

**Souvenir Sheets**

| | | | | |
|---|---|---|---|---|
| **1076** | A163 | 18d multicolored | 6.50 | 6.50 |
| **1077** | A163 | 18d multicolored | 6.50 | 6.50 |
| **1078** | A163 | 18d multicolored | 6.50 | 6.50 |
| **1079** | A163 | 18d multicolored | 6.50 | 6.50 |

While Nos. 1078-1079 have same release date as Nos. 1068-1077, the dollar value of Nos. 1078-1079 were lower when they were released.

**Royal Family Birthday, Anniversary**
Common Design Type

**1991, Aug. 12**          Litho.          ***Perf. 14***

| | | | | |
|---|---|---|---|---|
| **1080** | CD347 | 20b multi | .20 | .20 |
| **1081** | CD347 | 50b multi | .20 | .20 |
| **1082** | CD347 | 75b multi | .20 | .20 |
| **1083** | CD347 | 1d multi | .50 | .50 |
| **1084** | CD347 | 1.25d multi | .65 | .65 |
| **1085** | CD347 | 1.50d multi | .80 | .80 |
| **1086** | CD347 | 12d multi | 6.00 | 6.00 |
| **1087** | CD347 | 15d multi | 7.50 | 7.50 |
| | | *Nos. 1080-1087 (8)* | 16.05 | 16.05 |

**Souvenir Sheets**

| | | | | |
|---|---|---|---|---|
| **1088** | CD347 | 18d Elizabeth, Philip | 5.25 | 5.25 |
| **1089** | CD347 | 18d Diana, sons, Charles | 7.50 | 7.50 |

20b, 75b, 1.50d, 15d, No. 1089, Charles and Diana, 10th wedding anniversary. Others, Queen Elizabeth II, 65th birthday.

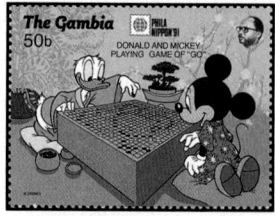

Phila Nippon '91 — A164

Walt Disney characters playing Japanese games and sports: 50b, Donald Duck and Mickey Mouse playing Go. 75b, Morty, Ferdie and Pete sumo wrestling. 1d, Minnie Mouse, Clarabelle, Daisy Duck playing battledore and shuttlecock. 1.25d, Goofy, Mickey at Okinawa bullfight, vert. 5d, Mickey as a Hawk Hunter Tagari, vert. 7d, Mickey, Minnie, and Donald play Jan-Ken-Pon, vert. 10d, Goofy as archer. 15d, Morty, Ferdie fly Japanese kites, vert. No. 1098, Goofy batting in Japanese baseball game, vert. No. 1099, Mickey, Scrooge McDuck playing Japanese football, vert. No. 1100, Mickey fly fishing, vert. No. 1101, Mickey climbing Mt. Fuji, vert.

***Perf. 14x13½, 13½x14***          Litho.

| | | | | |
|---|---|---|---|---|
| **1090** | A164 | 50b multicolored | .20 | .20 |
| **1091** | A164 | 75b multicolored | .20 | .20 |
| **1092** | A164 | 1d multicolored | .50 | .50 |
| **1093** | A164 | 1.25d multicolored | .60 | .60 |
| **1094** | A164 | 5d multicolored | 2.25 | 2.25 |
| **1095** | A164 | 7d multicolored | 3.00 | 3.00 |
| **1096** | A164 | 10d multicolored | 4.50 | 4.50 |
| **1097** | A164 | 15d multicolored | 6.50 | 6.50 |
| | | *Nos. 1090-1097 (8)* | 17.75 | 17.75 |

**Souvenir Sheets**

| | | | | |
|---|---|---|---|---|
| **1098** | A164 | 20d multicolored | 5.75 | 5.75 |
| **1099** | A164 | 20d multicolored | 5.75 | 5.75 |
| **1100** | A164 | 20d multicolored | 5.75 | 5.75 |
| **1101** | A164 | 20d multicolored | 5.75 | 5.75 |

Intl. Literacy Year — A165

Walt Disney characters in scenes from Rudyard Kipling's "Just So Stories": 50b, How the Whale Got His Throat. 75b, How the Camel Got His Hump. 1d, How the Leopard Got His Spots. 1.25d, The Elephant's Child. 1.50d, Singsong of Old Man Kangaroo. 7d, The Crab that Played with the Sea. 10d, The Cat that Walked by Himself. 15d, The Butterfly that Stamped. No. 1110, How the Alphabet was Made, vert. No. 1111, The Beginning of the Armadillos. No. 1112, How the First Letter was Written, vert. No. 1113, How the Rhinoceros Got His Skin.

**1991, Aug. 28**          Litho.          ***Perf. 14x13½***

| | | | | |
|---|---|---|---|---|
| **1102** | A165 | 50b multicolored | .20 | .20 |
| **1103** | A165 | 75b multicolored | .20 | .20 |
| **1104** | A165 | 1d multicolored | .50 | .50 |
| **1105** | A165 | 1.25d multicolored | .65 | .65 |
| **1106** | A165 | 1.50d multicolored | .70 | .70 |
| **1107** | A165 | 7d multicolored | 3.50 | 3.50 |
| **1108** | A165 | 10d multicolored | 5.00 | 5.00 |
| **1109** | A165 | 15d multicolored | 7.50 | 7.50 |
| | | *Nos. 1102-1109 (8)* | 18.25 | 18.25 |

**Souvenir Sheets**

***Perf. 13½x14, 14x13½***

| | | | | |
|---|---|---|---|---|
| **1110** | A165 | 20d multicolored | 7.00 | 7.00 |
| **1111** | A165 | 20d multicolored | 7.00 | 7.00 |
| **1112** | A165 | 20d multicolored | 7.00 | 7.00 |
| **1113** | A165 | 20d multicolored | 7.00 | 7.00 |

Train Cabooses — A166

No. 1114: a, Steel cupola, Canadian Pacific. b, Four-wheel, Cumberland and Pennsylvania. c, Mexican slim gauge. d, All steel cupola, Northern Pacific. e, Four-wheel, Morristown & Erie. f, Streamlined cupola, Burlington Northern. g, Caboose coach, McCloud River. h, Wide vision, Santa Fe. i, Wide vision, Frisco.
No. 1115: a, Narrow gauge, Oahu Railway. b, Standard brake-van, British Railways. c, Wide view steel, Union Pacific. d, Four-wheel, Belt Railway of Chicago. e, Four-wheel, McCloud River. f, Logging, Angelina County Lumber Co. g, Narrow gauge, Coahuila & Zacatecas. h, Three-foot gauge, United Railways of Yucatan. i, Steel cupola, Rio Grande.
No. 1116: a, Four-wheel, Colorado & Southern. b, Transfer, Santa Fe. c, Wooden cupola, Canadian National. d, Transfer steel, Union Pacific. e, Caboose coach, Virginia & Truckee. f, Standard brake-van, British. g, Narrow gauge, Intl. Railways of Central America. h, Steel cupola, Northern Pacific. i, Wood, Burlington Northern.
No. 1117, Pennsylvania electric, vert. No. 1118, Unidentified caboose, trainman with flag, vert. No. 1119, Unidentified green wooden caboose behind yellow freight car.

**1991, Sept. 12**       *Perf. 14x13½*
**Sheets of 9**

| | | | | |
|---|---|---|---|---|
| 1114 | A166 | 1d Sheet of 9, #a.-i. | 4.75 | 4.75 |
| 1115 | A166 | 2d Sheet of 9, #a.-i. | 6.00 | 6.00 |
| 1116 | A166 | 1.50d Sheet of 9, #a.-i. | 4.75 | 4.75 |
| | | Nos. 1114-1116 (3) | 15.50 | 15.50 |

**Souvenir Sheets**
*Perf. 12x13, 13x12*

| | | | | |
|---|---|---|---|---|
| 1117 | A166 | 20d multicolored | 6.00 | 6.00 |
| 1118 | A166 | 20d multicolored | 6.00 | 6.00 |
| 1119 | A166 | 20d multicolored | 6.00 | 6.00 |

While Nos. 1115-1116 and 1118-1119 have the same issue date as Nos. 1114 and 1117, the dollar value of Nos. 1115-1116 and 1118-1119 was lower when they were released.

Fish — A167

**1991, Oct. 28**   **Litho.**   *Perf. 14x14½*

| | | | | |
|---|---|---|---|---|
| 1120 | A167 | 20b Tiger shark | .25 | .25 |
| 1121 | A167 | 25b Common jewel fish | .25 | .25 |
| 1122 | A167 | 50b Five spot fish | .45 | .45 |
| 1123 | A167 | 75b Smalltooth sawfish | .45 | .45 |
| 1124 | A167 | 1d Five spot ti-lapia | .45 | .45 |
| 1125 | A167 | 1.25d Dwarf jewel fish | .55 | .55 |
| 1126 | A167 | 1.50d Five spot jewel fish | .65 | .65 |
| 1127 | A167 | 3d Bumphead | 1.00 | 1.00 |
| 1128 | A167 | 10d Egyptian mouth-brooder | 3.25 | 3.25 |
| 1129 | A167 | 15d Burton's mouth-brooder | 4.50 | 4.50 |
| | | Nos. 1120-1129 (10) | 11.80 | 11.80 |

**Souvenir Sheets**

| | | | | |
|---|---|---|---|---|
| 1130 | A167 | 18d Great barracuda | 10.50 | 10.50 |
| 1131 | A167 | 18d Yellowtail snapper | 10.50 | 10.50 |

While Nos. 1120-1122, 1125, 1129-1131 have the same issue date as Nos. 1123-1124, 1126-1128 the dollar value of Nos. 1120-1122, 1125, 1129-1130 was lower when they were released.

Hummel Figurines — A168

20b, #1141a, Girl and boy waving handkerchiefs. 75b, #1140a, Boy and girl under umbrella. 1d, #1140b, Two girls wearing scarfs. 1.50d, #1140c, Girl and boy in window with flower box. 2.50d, #1141b, Two girls with basket. 5d, #1141c, Boy wearing long pants, boy wearing shorts. 10d, #1141d, Two girls on fence. 15d, #1140d, Boy with stick, girl with bag.

**1991, Nov. 4**    **Litho.**    *Perf. 14*

| | | | | |
|---|---|---|---|---|
| 1132 | A168 | 20b multicolored | .20 | .20 |
| 1133 | A168 | 75b multicolored | .20 | .20 |
| 1134 | A168 | 1d multicolored | .25 | .25 |
| 1135 | A168 | 1.50d multicolored | .50 | .50 |
| 1136 | A168 | 2.50d multicolored | .70 | .70 |
| 1137 | A168 | 5d multicolored | 1.50 | 1.50 |
| 1138 | A168 | 10d multicolored | 3.00 | 3.00 |
| 1139 | A168 | 15d multicolored | 4.50 | 4.50 |
| | | Nos. 1132-1139 (8) | 10.85 | 10.85 |

**Souvenir Sheets**

| | | | | |
|---|---|---|---|---|
| 1140 | A168 | 4d Sheet of 4, #a.-d. | 5.00 | 5.00 |
| 1141 | A168 | 5d Sheet of 4, #a.-d. | 6.25 | 6.25 |

Paintings by Vincent Van Gogh A169

Designs: 20b, The Old Cemetery Tower at Nuenen in the Snow, horiz. 25b, Head of a Peasant Woman with White Cap. 50b, The Green Parrot. 75b, Vase with Carnations. 1d, Vase with Red Gladioli. 1.25b, Beach at Scheveningen in Calm Weather, horiz. 1.50d, Boy Cutting Grass with a Sickle, horiz. 2d, Coleus Plant in a Flowerpot. 3d, Self-portrait, spring-summer 1887. 4d, Self-portrait. 5d, Self-portrait, diff. 6d, Self-portrait, spring 1887. 8d, Still Life with a Bottle, Two Glasses, Cheese and Bread. 10d, Still Life with Cabbage, Clogs and Potatoes, horiz. 12d, Montmartre: The Street Lamps. 15d, Head of a Peasant Woman with Brownish Cap. No. 1158, Arles: View From the Wheat Fields. No. 1159, Autumn Landscape. No. 1160, Montmartre: Quarry, The Mills, horiz. No. 1161, The Potato Eaters, horiz.

*Perf. 13½x14, 14x13½*
**1991, Dec. 5**          **Litho.**

| | | | | |
|---|---|---|---|---|
| 1142 | A169 | 20b multicolored | .25 | .25 |
| 1143 | A169 | 25b multicolored | .25 | .25 |
| 1144 | A169 | 50b multicolored | .25 | .25 |
| 1145 | A169 | 75b multicolored | .25 | .25 |
| 1146 | A169 | 1d multicolored | .35 | .35 |
| 1147 | A169 | 1.25d multicolored | .45 | .45 |
| 1148 | A169 | 1.50d multicolored | .55 | .55 |
| 1149 | A169 | 2d multicolored | .65 | .65 |
| 1150 | A169 | 3d multicolored | .90 | .90 |
| 1151 | A169 | 4d multicolored | 1.25 | 1.25 |
| 1152 | A169 | 5d multicolored | 1.50 | 1.50 |
| 1153 | A169 | 6d multicolored | 2.00 | 2.00 |
| 1154 | A169 | 8d multicolored | 2.75 | 2.75 |
| 1155 | A169 | 10d multicolored | 3.25 | 3.25 |
| 1156 | A169 | 12d multicolored | 4.25 | 4.25 |
| 1157 | A169 | 15d multicolored | 4.50 | 4.50 |

**Size: 127x102mm**
*Imperf*

| | | | | |
|---|---|---|---|---|
| 1158 | A169 | 20d multicolored | 6.25 | 6.25 |
| 1159 | A169 | 20d multicolored | 6.25 | 6.25 |
| 1160 | A169 | 20d multicolored | 6.25 | 6.25 |
| 1161 | A169 | 20d multicolored | 6.25 | 6.25 |
| | | Nos. 1142-1161 (20) | 48.40 | 48.40 |

While Nos. 1142-1143, 1146, 1148, 1150, 1153, 1155-1156, 1160-1161 have the same issue date as Nos. 1144-1145, 1147, 1149, 1151-1152, 1154, 1157-1159, the dollar value of Nos. 1142-1143, 1146, 1148, 1150, 1153, 1155-1156, 1160-1161 was lower when they were released.

Christmas A170

Paintings by Fra Angelico: 20b, The Madonna of Humility. 50b, Madonna and Child with Angels. 75b, The Virgin and Child with Angels. 1d, Annunciation. 1.25d, Presentation in the Temple. 5d, Annunciation, diff. 10d, Madonna della Stella. 15d, Naming of St. John the Baptist. No. 1170, Annunciation and Adoration of the Magi. No. 1171, Coronation of the Virgin.

**1991, Dec. 23**        *Perf. 12*

| | | | | |
|---|---|---|---|---|
| 1162 | A170 | 20b multicolored | .20 | .20 |
| 1163 | A170 | 50b multicolored | .20 | .20 |
| 1164 | A170 | 75b multicolored | .20 | .20 |
| 1165 | A170 | 1d multicolored | .30 | .30 |
| 1166 | A170 | 1.25d multicolored | .45 | .45 |
| 1167 | A170 | 5d multicolored | 1.60 | 1.60 |
| 1168 | A170 | 10d multicolored | 3.00 | 3.00 |
| 1169 | A170 | 15d multicolored | 4.50 | 4.50 |
| | | Nos. 1162-1169 (8) | 10.45 | 10.45 |

**Souvenir Sheets**
*Perf. 14½*

| | | | | |
|---|---|---|---|---|
| 1170 | A170 | 20d multicolored | 6.25 | 6.25 |
| 1171 | A170 | 20d multicolored | 6.25 | 6.25 |

**Queen Elizabeth II's Accession to the Throne, 40th Anniv.**
Common Design Type

**1992, Feb. 6**    **Litho.**    *Perf. 14*

| | | | | |
|---|---|---|---|---|
| 1172 | CD348 | 20b multicolored | .20 | .20 |
| 1173 | CD348 | 50b multicolored | .20 | .20 |
| 1174 | CD348 | 1d multicolored | .35 | .35 |
| 1175 | CD348 | 15d multicolored | 6.25 | 6.25 |
| | | Nos. 1172-1175 (4) | 7.00 | 7.00 |

**Souvenir Sheets**

| | | | | |
|---|---|---|---|---|
| 1176 | CD348 | 20d Queen at left, yacht | 6.25 | 6.25 |
| 1177 | CD348 | 20d Queen at right, boat | 6.25 | 6.25 |

Famous Blues Musicians — A171

**1992, Feb. 12**        *Perf. 14*

| | | | | |
|---|---|---|---|---|
| 1178 | A171 | 20b Son House | .25 | .25 |
| 1179 | A171 | 25b W. C. Handy | .25 | .25 |
| 1180 | A171 | 50b Muddy Waters | .45 | .45 |
| 1181 | A171 | 75b Lightnin Hopkins | .65 | .65 |
| 1182 | A171 | 1d Ma Rainey | .70 | .70 |
| 1183 | A171 | 1.25d Mance Lipscomb | .80 | .80 |
| 1184 | A171 | 1.50d Mahalia Jackson | .90 | .90 |
| 1185 | A171 | 2d Ella Fitzgerald | 1.00 | 1.00 |
| 1186 | A171 | 3d Howlin Wolf | 1.25 | 1.25 |
| 1187 | A171 | 5d Bessie Smith | 2.00 | 2.00 |
| 1188 | A171 | 7d Leadbelly | 2.75 | 2.75 |
| 1189 | A171 | 10d Joe Willie Wilkins | 4.25 | 4.25 |
| | | Nos. 1178-1189 (12) | 15.25 | 15.25 |

**Souvenir Sheets**

| | | | | |
|---|---|---|---|---|
| 1190 | A171 | 20d Gambian string drummer | 7.50 | 7.50 |
| 1191 | A171 | 20d Elvis Presley | 7.50 | 7.50 |
| 1192 | A171 | 20d Billie Holiday | 7.50 | 7.50 |

While all stamps have the same issue date the dollar value of some was lower when they actually were released.

A172

Papal Visit, 1992 — A172a

Designs: 1d, Pope John Paul II. 1.25d, Pope, Pres. Dwada Jawara. 20d, Flags, Papal arms. 25d, Pope at Mass.
Illustration A172a reduced.

**1992, Feb. 23**    **Litho.**    *Perf. 14*

| | | | | |
|---|---|---|---|---|
| 1193 | A172 | 1d multicolored | .65 | .65 |
| 1194 | A172 | 1.25d multicolored | .80 | .80 |
| 1195 | A172 | 20d multicolored | 7.25 | 7.25 |
| | | Nos. 1193-1195 (3) | 8.70 | 8.70 |

**Souvenir Sheet**

| | | | | |
|---|---|---|---|---|
| 1196 | A172 | 25d multicolored | 11.00 | 11.00 |

**Embossed**
*Perf. 12*
**Without Gum**
**Size: 65x43mm**

| | | | |
|---|---|---|---|
| 1196A | A172a | 50d gold | 25.00 |

No. 1196A was not available until late 1993, exists imperf on large card.

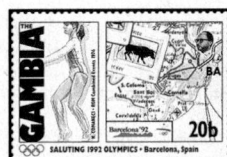

1992 Summer Olympics, Barcelona A173

20b, Map & Nadia Comaneci, gymnastics, Romania, 1976. 50b, D. Moorcraft, 5000 meters, Great Britain, 1984. 75b, M. Nemeth, javelin, Hungary, 1976. 1d, J. Pedraza, 20k walking, Mexico, 1968. 1.25d, Map, Spanish Arms & flag, Yachting soling class, Brazil, 1984. 1.50d, Spanish building, Field hockey, East Germany, 1984. 12d, Map & Michael Jordan, basketball, US, 1984. 15d, V. Borzov, 100 meters, USSR, 1972. #1201, Flamenco dancer, vert. #1206, Map & Bull.

**1992, Mar. 6**    **Litho.**    *Perf. 14*

| | | | | |
|---|---|---|---|---|
| 1197 | A173 | 20b multicolored | .20 | .20 |
| 1198 | A173 | 50b multicolored | .30 | .30 |
| 1199 | A173 | 75b multicolored | .40 | .40 |
| 1200 | A173 | 1d multicolored | .50 | .50 |
| 1201 | A173 | 1.25d multicolored | .70 | .70 |
| 1202 | A173 | 1.50d multicolored | .75 | .75 |
| 1203 | A173 | 12d multicolored | 4.00 | 4.00 |
| 1204 | A173 | 15d multicolored | 6.00 | 6.00 |
| | | Nos. 1197-1204 (8) | 12.85 | 12.85 |

**Souvenir Sheet**

| | | | | |
|---|---|---|---|---|
| 1205 | A173 | 20d multicolored | 7.25 | 7.25 |
| 1206 | A173 | 20d multicolored | 7.25 | 7.25 |

While Nos. 1197, 1201-1203, 1206 have the same issue date as Nos. 1198-1200, 1204-1205, the value of Nos. 1197, 1201-1203, 1206 was lower when they were released.

Easter A174

Paintings: 20b, Christ Presented to the People, by Rembrandt. 50b, Christ Carrying the Cross, by Mathias Grunewald. 75b, The Crucifixion, by Mathias Grunewald. 1d, The Crucifixion, by Rubens. 1.25d, The Road to Calvary, (detail), by Tintoretto. 1.50d, The Road to Calvary (entire), by Tintoretto. 15d, The Crucifixion, by Masaccio. 20d, Descent from the Cross (detail), by Rembrandt. No. 1215, Crowning with Thorns (detail), by Titian. No. 1216, Crowning with Thorns, by Anthony Van Dyck.

**1992, Apr. 16    Litho.    Perf. 13½**
| | | | | |
|---|---|---|---|---|
| 1207 | A174 | 20b multicolored | .20 | .20 |
| 1208 | A174 | 50b multicolored | .25 | .20 |
| 1209 | A174 | 75b multicolored | .25 | .20 |
| 1210 | A174 | 1d multicolored | .35 | .25 |
| 1211 | A174 | 1.25d multicolored | .55 | .35 |
| 1212 | A174 | 1.50d multicolored | .65 | .40 |
| 1213 | A174 | 15d multicolored | 4.50 | 4.50 |
| 1214 | A174 | 20d multicolored | 5.75 | 5.75 |
| | | *Nos. 1207-1214 (8)* | 12.50 | 11.85 |

**Souvenir Sheets**
| | | | | |
|---|---|---|---|---|
| 1215 | A174 | 25d multicolored | 7.50 | 7.50 |
| 1216 | A174 | 25d multicolored | 7.50 | 7.50 |

World Columbian Stamp Expo, Chicago — A175

Walt Disney characters in Chicago: 50b, Mickey at Navy pier. 1d, Mickey floats by Wrigley Building. 1.25d, Donald graduates from University of Chicago. 12d, Goofy at Chicago's Adler Planetarium. No. 1221, Goofy above Chicago at the Hancock Center, horiz.

**1992, Apr. 8    Litho.    Perf. 13½x14**
| | | | | |
|---|---|---|---|---|
| 1217 | A175 | 50b multicolored | .25 | .25 |
| 1218 | A175 | 1d multicolored | .50 | .50 |
| 1219 | A175 | 1.25d multicolored | .75 | .75 |
| 1220 | A175 | 12d multicolored | 6.00 | 6.00 |
| | | *Nos. 1217-1220 (4)* | 7.50 | 7.50 |

**Souvenir Sheet**
**Perf. 14x13½**
| | | | | |
|---|---|---|---|---|
| 1221 | A175 | 18d multicolored | 9.00 | 9.00 |

No. 1220 has name spelled "Alder."

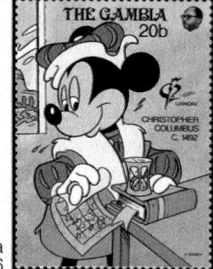

Granada '92 — A176

Mickey Mouse as Columbus: 20b, With map. 75b, Ideas rejected. 1.50d, Explores America. 15d, Returns to Spain. No. 1231, Embarks for America.

**1992, Apr. 8    Perf. 13½x14**
| | | | | |
|---|---|---|---|---|
| 1227 | A176 | 20b multicolored | .60 | .60 |
| 1228 | A176 | 75b multicolored | .90 | .90 |
| 1229 | A176 | 1.50d multicolored | 1.25 | 1.25 |
| 1230 | A176 | 15d multicolored | 6.25 | 6.25 |
| | | *Nos. 1227-1230 (4)* | 9.00 | 9.00 |

**Souvenir Sheet**
| | | | | |
|---|---|---|---|---|
| 1231 | A176 | 18d multicolored | 9.00 | 9.00 |

Flowers — A177

**1992, July 21    Litho.    Perf. 14**
| | | | | |
|---|---|---|---|---|
| 1237 | A177 | 20b Hibiscus | .20 | .20 |
| 1238 | A177 | 50b Calabash nutmeg | .25 | .25 |
| 1239 | A177 | 75b Silk cotton tree | .35 | .35 |
| 1240 | A177 | 1d Oncoba | .45 | .45 |
| 1241 | A177 | 1.25d Paintbrush plant | .55 | .55 |
| 1242 | A177 | 1.50d Tree gardenia | .65 | .65 |
| 1243 | A177 | 2d Glory bower | .80 | .80 |
| 1244 | A177 | 5d Ashanti blood | 1.75 | 1.75 |
| 1245 | A177 | 10d African peach | 2.75 | 2.75 |
| 1246 | A177 | 12d Butterfly bush | 3.00 | 3.00 |
| 1247 | A177 | 15d Crepe ginger | 3.75 | 3.75 |
| 1248 | A177 | 18d Spider tresses | 4.00 | 4.00 |
| | | *Nos. 1237-1248 (12)* | 18.50 | 18.50 |

**Souvenir Sheets**
| | | | | |
|---|---|---|---|---|
| 1249 | A177 | 20d Water lily | 5.75 | 5.75 |
| 1250 | A177 | 20d Bougainvillea | 5.75 | 5.75 |
| 1251 | A177 | 20d Baobab tree | 5.75 | 5.75 |
| 1252 | A177 | 20d Climbing pea | 5.75 | 5.75 |

While Nos. 1240, 1242, 1244, 1247, 1250 have the same release date as Nos. 1237, 1241, 1243, 1248-1249, their values in relation to the dollar were higher when they were released.

Riverboats — A178

Riverboat and waterway: 20b, Joven Antonia, Gambia River. 50b, Dresden, Elbe River. 75b, Medway Queen, Medway River. 1d, Lady Wright, Gambia River. 1.25d, Devin, Vltava River. 1.50d, Lady Chilel, Gambia River. 5d, Robert Fulton, Hudson River. 10d, Coonawarra, Murray River. 12d, Nakusp, Columbia River. 15d, Lucy Ashton, Firth of Clyde. No. 1263, Rudesheim, Rhine River. No. 1264, City of Cairo, Mississippi River.

**1992, Aug. 3    Litho.    Perf. 14**
| | | | | |
|---|---|---|---|---|
| 1253 | A178 | 20b multicolored | .20 | .20 |
| 1254 | A178 | 50b multicolored | .25 | .25 |
| 1255 | A178 | 75b multicolored | .35 | .35 |
| 1256 | A178 | 1d multicolored | .45 | .45 |
| 1257 | A178 | 1.25d multicolored | .60 | .60 |
| 1258 | A178 | 1.50d multicolored | .75 | .75 |
| 1259 | A178 | 5d multicolored | 1.90 | 1.90 |
| 1260 | A178 | 10d multicolored | 3.00 | 3.00 |
| 1261 | A178 | 12d multicolored | 3.25 | 3.25 |
| 1262 | A178 | 15d multicolored | 4.25 | 4.25 |
| | | *Nos. 1253-1262 (10)* | 15.00 | 15.00 |

**Souvenir Sheets**
| | | | | |
|---|---|---|---|---|
| 1263 | A178 | 20d multicolored | 7.50 | 7.50 |
| 1264 | A178 | 20d multicolored | 7.50 | 7.50 |

**Miniature Sheet**

World War II in the Pacific — A179

Designs: a, USS Pennsylvania. b, Japanese attack begins. c, USS Ward sinking Japanese submarine. d, Ford Naval Air Station under attack. e, News bulletin announcing attack. f, Front page of Honolulu Star-Bulletin. g, Japanese invade Guam. h, US recovers Wake Island. i, Doolittle raids Japan from USS Hornet. j, Battle of Midway.

**1992    Litho.    Perf. 14½x15**
| | | | | |
|---|---|---|---|---|
| 1265 | A179 | 2d Sheet of 10, #a.-j. | 18.00 | 18.00 |

1992 Summer Olympics, Barcelona — A180

Designs: 20b, Women's double sculls. 50b, Kayak, vert. 75b, Women's precision rapid-fire shooting. 1d, Judo, vert. 1.25d, Javelin, vert. 1.50d, Gymnastics, vault, vert. 3d, Windsurfing, vert. 5d, High jump. No. 1274, Women's 200-meter backstroke. No. 1275, Table tennis.

**1992, Aug. 10    Litho.    Perf. 14**
| | | | | |
|---|---|---|---|---|
| 1266 | A180 | 20b multicolored | .25 | .25 |
| 1267 | A180 | 50b multicolored | .45 | .45 |
| 1268 | A180 | 75b multicolored | .65 | .65 |
| 1269 | A180 | 1d multicolored | .70 | .70 |
| 1270 | A180 | 1.25d multicolored | .80 | .80 |
| 1271 | A180 | 1.50d multicolored | 1.00 | 1.00 |
| 1272 | A180 | 3d multicolored | 1.50 | 1.50 |
| 1273 | A180 | 5d multicolored | 2.25 | 2.25 |
| | | *Nos. 1266-1273 (8)* | 7.60 | 7.60 |

**Souvenir Sheets**
| | | | | |
|---|---|---|---|---|
| 1274 | A180 | 18d multicolored | 5.00 | 5.00 |
| 1275 | A180 | 18d multicolored | 5.00 | 5.00 |

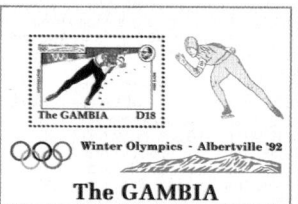

1992 Winter Olympics, Albertville — A181

Designs: 2d, Downhill skiing, vert. 10d, Four-man bobsled, vert. 12d, Ski jumping, vert. 15d, Slalom skiing. No. 1280, 18d, Men's 500-meter speedskating. No. 1281, 18d, Pairs figure skating, vert.

**1992, Aug. 10    Litho.    Perf. 14**
| | | | | |
|---|---|---|---|---|
| 1276-1279 | A181 | Set of 4 | 20.00 | 20.00 |

**Souvenir Sheets**
| | | | | |
|---|---|---|---|---|
| 1280-1281 | A181 | Set of 2 | 11.50 | 11.50 |

Dinosaurs — A182

20b, Dryosaurus. 25b, Saurolophus. 50b, #1291, Allosaurus. 75b, Fabrosaurus. 1d, Deinonychus. 1.25d, #1292A, Cetiosaurus. 1.50d, Camptosaurus. 2d, #1292, Ornithosuchus. 3d, Spinosaurus. 5d, Ornithomimus. 10d, Kentrosaurus. 12d, Schlermochus.

**1992, Sept. 21    Litho.    Perf. 14**
| | | | | |
|---|---|---|---|---|
| 1283 | A182 | 20b multi | .45 | .45 |
| 1284 | A182 | 25b multi | .45 | .45 |
| 1284A | A182 | 50b multi | .55 | .55 |
| 1284B | A182 | 75b multi | .65 | .65 |
| 1284C | A182 | 1d multi | .65 | .65 |
| 1285 | A182 | 1.25d multi | .80 | .80 |
| 1286 | A182 | 1.50d multi | .80 | .80 |
| 1286A | A182 | 2d multi | .80 | .80 |
| 1287 | A182 | 3d multi | .90 | .90 |
| 1288 | A182 | 5d multi | 1.50 | 1.50 |
| 1289 | A182 | 10d multi | 2.75 | 2.75 |
| 1290 | A182 | 12d multi | 3.25 | 3.25 |
| | | *Nos. 1283-1290 (12)* | 13.55 | 13.55 |

**Souvenir Sheets**
| | | | | |
|---|---|---|---|---|
| 1291 | A182 | 25d multi | 8.00 | 8.00 |
| 1292 | A182 | 25d multi | 8.00 | 8.00 |
| 1292A | A182 | 25d multi | 8.00 | 8.00 |

Genoa '92.

Walt Disney's Goofy, 60th Anniv. — A183

Scenes from Disney cartoon films: 50b, Orphan's Benefit, 1934, 1941. 75b, Moose Hunters, 1937. 1d, Mickey's Amateurs, 1937. 1.25d, Lonesome Ghosts, 1937. 5d, Boat Builders, 1938. 7d, The Whalers, 1938. 10d, Goofy and Wilbur, 1939. 15d, Saludos Amigos, 1941. No. 1301, The Band Concert, 1935, vert. No. 1302, Goofy today, vert.

**1992    Litho.    Perf. 14x13½**
| | | | | |
|---|---|---|---|---|
| 1293 | A183 | 50b multicolored | .45 | .45 |
| 1294 | A183 | 75b multicolored | .65 | .65 |
| 1295 | A183 | 1d multicolored | .80 | .80 |
| 1296 | A183 | 1.25d multicolored | .80 | .80 |
| 1297 | A183 | 5d multicolored | 2.10 | 2.10 |
| 1298 | A183 | 7d multicolored | 2.75 | 2.75 |
| 1299 | A183 | 10d multicolored | 3.00 | 3.00 |
| 1300 | A183 | 15d multicolored | 3.75 | 3.75 |
| | | *Nos. 1293-1300 (8)* | 14.30 | 14.30 |

**Souvenir Sheets**
**Perf. 13½x14**
| | | | | |
|---|---|---|---|---|
| 1301 | A183 | 20d multicolored | 9.00 | 9.00 |
| 1302 | A183 | 20d multicolored | 9.00 | 9.00 |

Discovery of America, 500th Anniv. A184

5d, Santa Maria. 12d, Pinta, Santa Maria, and Nina. 18d, Tree branch, green-winged macaw.

**1992, Oct.    Litho.    Perf. 14**
| | | | | |
|---|---|---|---|---|
| 1303 | A184 | 5d multi | 2.00 | 2.00 |
| 1304 | A184 | 12d multi | 3.00 | 3.00 |

**Souvenir Sheet**
| | | | | |
|---|---|---|---|---|
| 1305 | A184 | 18d multi, vert. | 6.50 | 6.50 |

Golf — A186

Pres. Jarwara playing golf and: 20b, Map, flag of Australia. 1d, Trophy, Gambian flag. 1.50d, Gambian flag. 2d, Map, flag of Japan. 3d, Map, flag of US. 5d, Trophy, 1985, Gambian flag (small portrait only). #1312, Map, flag of Scotland. 12d, Map, flag of Italy. #1312B, Pres. Jawara about to tee off. #1312C, Gambian flag (small portrait).

**1992    Litho.    Perf. 14**
| | | | | |
|---|---|---|---|---|
| 1306 | A186 | 20b multi | .45 | .45 |
| 1307 | A186 | 1d multi | 1.00 | 1.00 |
| 1308 | A186 | 1.50d multi | 1.25 | 1.25 |
| 1309 | A186 | 2d multi | 1.50 | 1.50 |
| 1310 | A186 | 3d multi | 2.00 | 2.00 |
| 1311 | A186 | 5d multi | 2.75 | 2.75 |
| 1312 | A186 | 10d multi | 4.00 | 4.00 |
| 1312A | A186 | 12d multi | 4.75 | 4.75 |
| | | *Nos. 1306-1312A (8)* | 17.70 | 17.70 |

**Souvenir Sheets**
| | | | | |
|---|---|---|---|---|
| 1312B | A186 | 10d multi | 9.00 | 9.00 |
| 1312C | A186 | 18d multi, horiz. | 9.00 | 9.00 |

No. 1306, Royal Melbourne Golf Course, Australia. No. 1309, Shinonoseki Golf Course, Japan. No. 1310, US Open, Pebble Beach. No. 1312, St. Andrew's Golf Course, Scotland. No. 1312A, Italian Open, Monticello, Milan.
Issued: 20b, 2d, 5d, #1312, 1312B, Dec. 8; others, Oct.

**Souvenir Sheet**

Ellis Island, New York City — A187

**1992, Oct. 28    Litho.    Perf. 14**
| | | | | |
|---|---|---|---|---|
| 1313 | A187 | 18d multicolored | 6.50 | 6.50 |

Postage Stamp Mega Event '92, New York City.

Christmas
A188

Details or entire paintings: 50b, The Holy Family, by Raphael. 75b, Madonna and Child with St. Elizabeth and the Infant St. John (Small Holy Family), by Raphael. 1d, The Holy Family as the Little Holy Family, by Raphael. 1.25d, Escape to Egypt, by Broederlam. 1.50d, Flight Into Egypt, by Isenbrant. No. 1319, The Flight into Egypt, by Cosimo Tura. No. 1320, Flight into Egypt, by Master of Hoogstraelen. No. 1321, The Holy Family, by El Greco. 4d, The Holy Family, by Bernard Van Orley. 5d, Holy Family with Infant Jesus Sleeping, by Charles Le Brun. 10d, Rest on the Flight to Egypt, by Gentileschi. 12d, Rest on the Flight to Egypt, by Orazio Gentileschi. No. 1326, The Holy Family, by Giorgione. No. 1327, Rest on the Flight to Egypt, by Simone Cantarino. No. 1328, The Flight to Egypt, by Vittore Carpaccio.

**1992, Nov. 3    Litho.    Perf. 13½x14**

| | | | | |
|---|---|---|---|---|
| 1314 | A188 | 50b multicolored | .25 | .25 |
| 1315 | A188 | 75b multicolored | .35 | .35 |
| 1316 | A188 | 1d multicolored | .45 | .45 |
| 1317 | A188 | 1.25d multicolored | .60 | .60 |
| 1318 | A188 | 1.50d multicolored | .60 | .60 |
| 1319 | A188 | 2d multicolored | .85 | .85 |
| 1320 | A188 | 2d multicolored | .85 | .85 |
| 1321 | A188 | 2d multicolored | .85 | .85 |
| 1322 | A188 | 4d multicolored | 1.50 | 1.50 |
| 1323 | A188 | 5d multicolored | 1.90 | 1.90 |
| 1324 | A188 | 10d multicolored | 3.25 | 3.25 |
| 1325 | A188 | 12d multicolored | 3.50 | 3.50 |
| | | Nos. 1314-1325 (12) | 14.95 | 14.95 |

**Souvenir Sheets**

| | | | | |
|---|---|---|---|---|
| 1326 | A188 | 25d multicolored | 5.25 | 5.25 |
| 1327 | A188 | 25d multicolored | 5.25 | 5.25 |
| 1328 | A188 | 25d multicolored | 5.25 | 5.25 |

A189    A190

A191

A192

A193

A194

Anniversaries and Events — A195

Designs: No. 1329, Ariane 4 rocket. No. 1330, Berlin airlift, Konrad Adenauer. No. 1331, LZ127 Graf Zeppelin. 6d, Jentink's duiker. 7d, World map. 9d, Wolfgang Amadeus Mozart. No. 1335, America's Cup yacht Enterprise, 1930. No. 1336, Imperial parrot. No. 1337, Lions Intl. emblem. No. 1338, American Space shuttle. 15d, Prisoners of war returning home, Adenauer. 18d, First rigid airship, LZ1. No. 1341, European Space Agency's Hermes space shuttle. No. 1342, Scene from "The Marriage of Figaro." No. 1343, Face of Adenauer. No. 1344, Count Ferdinand von Zeppelin. No. 1345, Earth as seen from space.

**1992-93    Litho.    Perf. 14**

| | | | | |
|---|---|---|---|---|
| 1329 | A189 | 2d multicolored | .80 | .80 |
| 1330 | A191 | 2d multicolored | .90 | .90 |
| 1331 | A191 | 2d multicolored | .80 | .80 |
| 1332 | A192 | 6d multicolored | 2.50 | 2.50 |
| 1333 | A193 | 7d multicolored | 3.00 | 3.00 |
| 1334 | A190 | 9d multicolored | 5.00 | 5.00 |
| 1335 | A194 | 10d multicolored | 3.75 | 3.75 |
| 1336 | A192 | 10d multicolored | 3.25 | 3.25 |
| 1337 | A195 | 10d multicolored | 2.75 | 2.75 |
| 1338 | A189 | 12d multicolored | 3.00 | 3.00 |
| 1339 | A191 | 15d multicolored | 4.50 | 4.50 |
| 1340 | A191 | 18d multicolored | 4.50 | 4.50 |
| | | Nos. 1329-1340 (12) | 34.75 | 34.75 |

**Souvenir Sheets**

| | | | | |
|---|---|---|---|---|
| 1341 | A189 | 18d multicolored | 7.00 | 7.00 |
| 1342 | A190 | 18d multicolored | 7.00 | 7.00 |
| 1343 | A191 | 18d multicolored | 7.00 | 7.00 |
| 1344 | A191 | 18d multicolored | 7.00 | 7.00 |
| 1345 | A192 | 18d multicolored | 7.00 | 7.00 |

Intl. Space Year (#1329, 1338, 1341). Wolfgang Amadeus Mozart, bicent. of death (#1334, 1342). Konrad Adenauer, 25th anniv. of death (#1330, 1339, 1343). Count Zeppelin, 75th anniv. of death (#1331, 1340, 1344). Earth Summit, Rio de Janiero (#1332, 1336, 1345). Intl. Conf. on Nutrition, Rome (#1333). America's Cup yacht race (#1335). Lions Intl., 75th anniv. (#1337).

Issued: #1333, 1335, 1339, 1343, 1/93; others, 12/92.

Peace Corps, 25th Anniv. A196

**1993, Feb.**

| | | | | |
|---|---|---|---|---|
| 1346 | A196 | 2d multicolored | 1.50 | 1.50 |

Elvis Presley, 15th Anniv. of Death (in 1992) — A197

No. 1347: a, Portrait. b, With guitar. c, Holding microphone.

**1993**

| | | | | |
|---|---|---|---|---|
| 1347 | A197 | 3d Strip of 3, #a.-c. | 3.25 | 3.25 |

Miniature Sheets

Baseball Films — A198

No. 1348 — Movie and stars: a, Casey at the Bat, Wallace Beery, 1927, Elliott Gould, 1986. b, Babe Comes Home, Anna Q. Nilsson, Babe Ruth, 1927. c, Elmer the Great, Joe E. Brown, 1933. d, The Naughty Nineties, Bud Abbott and Lou Costello, 1945. e, Take Me Out to the Ball Game, Frank Sinatra, Gene Kelly, Esther Williams, 1949. f, Damn Yankees, Tab Hunter, Gwen Verdon, 1958. g, The Pride of St. Louis, Dan Dailey, 1952. h, Brewster's Millions, John Candy, Richard Pryor, 1985.

No. 1349: a, The Jackie Robinson Story, Jackie Robinson, Ruby Dee, 1950. b, Bang the Drum Slowly, Robert DeNiro, 1973. c, The Bingo Long Traveling All-Stars & Motor Kings, James Earl Jones, Billy Dee Williams, 1976. d, Bull Durham, Kevin Costner, Susan Sarandon, 1988. e, Eight Men Out, eight actors, 1988. f, Field of Dreams, Ray Liotta, 1989. g, Major League, Charlie Sheet, 1989. h, Mr. Baseball, Tom Selleck, 1992.

No. 1350, The Babe, John Goodman, 1992. No. 1351, The Natural, Robert Redford. No. 1351A, The Winning Team, Ronald Reagan. No. 351B, A League of Their Own, Tom Hanks, Madonna.

**1993, Mar. 25    Litho.    Perf. 13**

| | | | | |
|---|---|---|---|---|
| 1348 | A198 | 3d Sheet of 8, #a.-h. | 8.50 | 8.50 |
| 1349 | A198 | 3d Sheet of 8, #a.-h. | 8.50 | 8.50 |

**Souvenir Sheet**

| | | | | |
|---|---|---|---|---|
| 1350 | A198 | 20d multi | 5.75 | 5.75 |
| 1351 | A198 | 20d multi, vert. | 5.75 | 5.75 |
| 1351A | A198 | 20d multi | 5.75 | 5.75 |
| 1351B | A198 | 20d multi, vert. | 5.75 | 5.75 |

Miniature Sheets

Louvre Museum, Bicent. — A199

Details from paintings, by Jacques-Louis David (1748-1825): Nos. 1352a-b, Oath of the Horatii (diff. details). c, The Love of Paris & Helen. d, Rape of the Sabine Women. e, Leonidas of Thermopylae. f-h, Napoleon Crowning Josephine (left, center, right).

Details from paintings, by Antoine (c. 1588-1648) and Louis (1593-1648) Le Nain: No. 1353a, Inside Home of Peasants. b-c, The Tobacco Smokers (diff. details). d, The Cart. e, Peasants' Meal. f-g, Interior Portraits (diff. details). h, The Forge.

Details or entire paintings, by Leonardo Da Vinci: No. 1354a, St. John the Baptist. b, Virgin of the Rocks. c, Bacchus. d, Woman from the Court of Milan. e, The Virgin of the Rocks

(detail). f, Mona Lisa. g, Mona Lisa (detail of hands). h, Two Horsemen, Study of the Horse. No. 1355, Allegory of Victory, by Mathieu Le Nain (1607-1677). No. 1356, The Artist and Her Daughter, by Elisabeth Vigee-Lebrun (1755-1842).

**1993, Jan. 7    Litho.    Perf. 12**

| | | | | |
|---|---|---|---|---|
| 1352 | A199 | 3d Sheet of 8, #a.-h. | 8.00 | 8.00 |
| 1353 | A199 | 3d Sheet of 8, #a.-h. | 8.00 | 8.00 |
| 1354 | A199 | 3d Sheet of 8, #a.-h. | 8.00 | 8.00 |

**Souvenir Sheets**
**Perf. 14½**

| | | | | |
|---|---|---|---|---|
| 1355 | A199 | 20d multicolored | 8.75 | 8.75 |
| 1356 | A199 | 20d multicolored | 8.75 | 8.75 |

#1355-1356 each contain one 55x88mm stamp.

Miniature Sheet

Animals of West Africa — A200

No. 1358: a, Giraffe. b, Baboon. c, Caracal. d, Large-spotted genet. e, Bushbuck. f, Red-fronted gazelle. g, Red-flanked duiker. h, Cape buffalo. i, African civet. j, Side-striped jackal. k, Ratel. l, Striped polecat.

No. 1359: a, Vervet. b, Blackish-green guenon. c, Long-tailed pangolin. d, Leopard. e, Elephant. f, Hunting dog. g, Spotted hyena. h, Lion. i, Hippopotamus. j, Nile crocodile. k, Aardvark. l, Warthog.

**1993, Apr. 5    Litho.    Perf. 14**

| | | | | |
|---|---|---|---|---|
| 1358 | A200 | 2d Sheet of 12, #a.-l. | 10.50 | 10.50 |
| 1359 | A200 | 5d Sheet of 12, #a.-l. | 15.00 | 15.00 |

**Souvenir Sheet**

| | | | | |
|---|---|---|---|---|
| 1360 | A200 | 20d like #1359b | 9.00 | 9.00 |

No. 1360 printed in continuous design with black frameline around stamp. A number has been reserved for an additional value in this set.

Long-Tailed Pangolin — A201

Pangolin in various positions on tree limb.

**1993, Apr. 5**

| | | | | |
|---|---|---|---|---|
| 1362 | A201 | 1.25d multicolored | .75 | .75 |
| 1363 | A201 | 1.50d multicolored | 1.00 | 1.00 |
| 1364 | A201 | 2d multicolored | 1.25 | 1.25 |
| 1365 | A201 | 5d multicolored | 3.00 | 3.00 |
| | | Nos. 1362-1365 (4) | 6.00 | 6.00 |

**Souvenir Sheet**

| | | | | |
|---|---|---|---|---|
| 1366 | A201 | 20d like #1363 | 7.50 | 7.50 |

World Wildlife Federation.

Birds
A202    A203

Designs: 1.25d, Osprey. 1.50d, Egyptian vulture, horiz. 2d, Martial eagle. 3d, Ruppell's griffon vulture, horiz. 5d, Auger buzzard. 8d,

Greater kestrel. 10d, Secretary bird. 15d, Bateleur eagle, horiz.

No. 1375a, Rose-ringed parakeet. b, Variable sunbird. c, Red-billed hornbill. d, Red-billed fire-finch. e, Common go-away bird. f, Crimson-breasted shrike. g, Gray-headed bush-shrike. h, Nicator. i, Egyptian plover. j, Congo peacock. k, Greater painted snipe. l, Crowned crane.

#1376, Verreaux's eagle. #1377, Tawny owl.

| 1993, Apr. 15 | Litho. | | Perf. 14 | |
|---|---|---|---|---|
| 1367 | A202 | 1.25d multicolored | 1.00 | 1.00 |
| 1368 | A202 | 1.50d multicolored | 1.25 | 1.25 |
| 1369 | A202 | 2d multicolored | 1.50 | 1.50 |
| 1370 | A202 | 3d multicolored | 2.00 | 2.00 |
| 1371 | A202 | 5d multicolored | 2.25 | 2.25 |
| 1372 | A202 | 8d multicolored | 3.00 | 3.00 |
| 1373 | A202 | 10d multicolored | 3.00 | 3.00 |
| 1374 | A202 | 15d multicolored | 4.25 | 4.25 |
| | | Nos. 1367-1374 (8) | 18.25 | 18.25 |
| 1375 | A203 | 2d Sheet of 12, #a.-l. | 21.00 | 21.00 |

**Souvenir Sheets**

| 1376 | A202 | 20d multicolored | 9.00 | 9.00 |
|---|---|---|---|---|
| 1377 | A202 | 20d multicolored | 9.00 | 9.00 |

#1376-1377 each contain 1 56x42mm stamp.

Aviation Anniversaries — A204

Designs: No. 1379, Guyot balloon, 1785, vert. No. 1380, Dr. Hugo Eckener, zeppelin LZ3 in flight. No. 1381, Sopwith Snipe. No. 1382, Eckener, LZ3 moored to ground. 8d, Eckener, Graf Zeppelin. 10d, Balloon, Comte D'Artois, 1785, vert. 15d, Royal Aircraft Factory S.E.5. No. 1386, Avro 504K. No. 1387, Eckener, LZ3 in flight, diff. No. 1388, Blanchard's flying ship, 1785, vert.

| 1993, May | Litho. | | Perf. 14 | |
|---|---|---|---|---|
| 1379 | A204 | 2d multicolored | .80 | .80 |
| 1380 | A204 | 2d multicolored | .80 | .80 |
| 1381 | A204 | 5d multicolored | 1.50 | 1.50 |
| 1382 | A204 | 5d multicolored | 1.50 | 1.50 |
| 1383 | A204 | 8d multicolored | 2.50 | 2.50 |
| 1384 | A204 | 10d multicolored | 2.75 | 2.75 |
| 1385 | A204 | 15d multicolored | 3.75 | 3.75 |
| | | Nos. 1379-1385 (7) | 13.60 | 13.60 |

**Souvenir Sheets**

| 1386 | A204 | 20d multicolored | 8.50 | 8.50 |
|---|---|---|---|---|
| 1387 | A204 | 20d multicolored | 8.50 | 8.50 |
| 1388 | A204 | 20d multicolored | 8.50 | 8.50 |

Dr. Hugo Eckener, 125th birth anniv. (#1380, 1382, 1383, 1387). Royal Air Force, 75th anniv. (#1381, 1385, 1386).
Nos. 1379, 1384, 1388 are airmail.

Miniature Sheet

Coronation of Queen Elizabeth II, 40th Anniv. A205

Designs: a, 2d, Official coronation photograph. b, 5d, Orb and Scepter. c, 8d, Winston Churchill. d, 10d, Queen during Trooping of the Color.
20d, Portrait, by Joe King, 1972.

| 1993, June 2 | | Perf. 13½x14 | |
|---|---|---|---|
| 1389 | A205 | Sheet of 8, 2 each #a.-d. | 18.00 18.00 |

**Souvenir Sheet**
**Perf. 14**

| 1390 | A205 | 20d multicolored | 9.50 | 9.50 |
|---|---|---|---|---|

No. 1390 contains one 28x42mm stamp.

Miniature Sheet

A206

No. 1391 — Benz Automobiles: a, 1894 Benz Velo. b, 1894 Benz. c, 1885 Benz. d, 1905 Benz Mannheim. e, 1892 Benz. f, 1900 Benz, blue. g, 1911 Benz. h, 1893 Benz Velo. i, 1900 Benz, black. j, 1900 Benz, red. k, 1911 Benz, front view. l, 1885 Benz, rear view.
No. 1393, 20d, 1900 Benz, diff.
No. 1392 — Ford automobiles: a, Henry Ford, age 30, 1910 Model T. b, 1896, green seat. c, Henry Ford with Barney Oldfield and 1902 racing car, 999. d, 1896, Henry Ford with bicycle. e, 1903 Model A. f, 1908 Model T, top down. g, 1908 Model T, top up. h, 1906 Model K. i, 1931 Model A. j, 1906 Model A. k, 1906 Model N. l, 1905 Model F.
No. 1393, 1900 Benz, diff. No. 1394, 1896 Ford with red seat.

| 1993, June 7 | | Perf. 14 | |
|---|---|---|---|
| 1391 | A206 | 2d Sheet of 12, #a.-l. | 8.50 8.50 |
| 1392 | A206 | 2d Sheet of 12, #a.-l. | 8.50 8.50 |

**Souvenir Sheets**

| 1393 | A206 | 20d multicolored | 7.00 | 7.00 |
|---|---|---|---|---|
| 1394 | A206 | 20d multicolored | 7.00 | 7.00 |

1st Benz 4-wheel automobile, cent. (#1391, 1993).
1st engine by Henry Ford, cent. (#1392, 1994).

Miniature Sheets

Entertainers — A207

No. 1395: a, Buddy Holly. b, Otis Redding. c, Bill Haley. d, Dinah Washington. e, Musical instruments. f, Ritchie Valens. g, Clyde McPhatter. h, Elvis Presley.
No. 1396: a-d, Various pictures of Madonna.
No. 1397: a-i, Various pictures of Elvis Presley.
No. 1398: a-i, Various pictures of Marilyn Monroe.

| 1993, July 26 | | Litho. | Perf. 14 | |
|---|---|---|---|---|
| 1395 | A207 | 3d Sheet of 8, #a.-h. | 14.00 | 14.00 |
| 1396 | A207 | 3d Sheet of 9, #a.-i. | 14.00 | 14.00 |
| 1397 | A207 | 3d Sheet of 9, #a.-i. | 14.00 | 14.00 |
| 1398 | A207 | 3d Sheet of 9, #a.-i. | 14.00 | 14.00 |
| | | Nos. 1395-1398 (4) | 56.00 | 56.00 |

Cats and Dogs A208

No. 1399 — Cats, Siamese. b, Colorpoint longhair. c, Burmese. d, Birman. e, Snowshoe. f, Tonkinese. g, Foreign shorthair. h, Balinese. i, Oriental shorthair. j, Foreign shorthair, diff. k, Colorpoint longhair, diff. l, Colorpoint longhair, diff.
Dogs: No. 1400a, Shih tzu. b, Skye terrier. c, Berner laufhund. d, Boxer. e, Welsh corgi (Queen Elizabeth II). f, Dumfrieshire. g, Lurcher. h, Welsh corgi (Princess Anne). i, Pekinese. j, Papillon. k, Otterhound. l, Pug.
No. 1401, Colorpoint longhair, diff. No. 1402, Burmese, vert. No. 1403, Long-haired dachshund. No. 1404, Cairn terrier.

| 1993, Sept. 13 | Litho. | | Perf. 14 | |
|---|---|---|---|---|
| 1399 | A208 | 2d Sheet of 12, #a.-l. | 16.00 | 16.00 |
| 1400 | A208 | 2d Sheet of 12, #a.-i. | 15.00 | 15.00 |

**Souvenir Sheets**

| 1401 | A208 | 20d multicolored | 7.50 | 7.50 |
|---|---|---|---|---|
| 1402 | A208 | 20d multicolored | 7.50 | 7.50 |
| 1403 | A208 | 20d multicolored | 7.50 | 7.50 |
| 1404 | A208 | 20d multicolored | 7.50 | 7.50 |

Taipei '93 — A209

Designs: No. 1405, Fawang Si Pagoda, Song Shan Mt., Henan. No. 1406, Wanshoubao Pagoda, Shashi. No. 1407, Red Pavilion, Shibaozhai. No. 1408, Songyue Si Pagoda, Song Shan Mt., Henan. No. 1409, Bond Center, Hong Kong. No. 1410, Tianning Si Pagoda, Beijing. No. 1411, Xuanzhuang Pagoda, Xian, Shenxi. No. 1412, Forbidden City, Beijing.
No. 1413 — Tang Dynasty funerary objects: a, Camel. b, Horse and female rider. c, Camel, diff. d, Yellow-glazed horse. e, Camel, diff. f, Horse with saddle.
No. 1414 — Pottery: a, Vase. b, Small wine cup. c, Fahua type Mei-ping vase. d, Urn vase, export ware. e, Tureen. f, Lidded Potiche.
No. 1415, Standing Buddhas, Hallway of Upper Huayan Si Temple, Datong. No. 1416, Seated Buddha, Main Hall, Shanhua Si Temple, Datong.

| 1993, Sept. 27 | Litho. | | Perf. 14 | |
|---|---|---|---|---|
| 1405 | A209 | 20b multicolored | .25 | .25 |
| 1406 | A209 | 20b multicolored | .25 | .25 |
| 1407 | A209 | 2d multicolored | .90 | .90 |
| 1408 | A209 | 2d multicolored | .90 | .90 |
| 1409 | A209 | 5d multicolored | 2.00 | 2.00 |
| 1410 | A209 | 5d multicolored | 2.00 | 2.00 |
| 1411 | A209 | 15d multicolored | 4.00 | 4.00 |
| 1412 | A209 | 15d multicolored | 4.00 | 4.00 |
| | | Nos. 1405-1412 (8) | 14.30 | 14.30 |

**Miniature Sheets**

| 1413 | A209 | 5d Sheet of 6, #a.-f. | 17.00 | 17.00 |
|---|---|---|---|---|
| 1414 | A209 | 5d Sheet of 6, #a.-f. | 17.00 | 17.00 |

**Souvenir Sheets**

| 1415 | A209 | 18d multicolored | 7.00 | 7.00 |
|---|---|---|---|---|
| 1416 | A209 | 18d multicolored | 7.00 | 7.00 |

**With Bangkok '93 Emblem**

No. 1417, Sanctuary of Prasat Phanom Wan. No. 1418, Lai Kham Vihan, Chiang Mai. No. 1419, Spirit Shrine, Bangkok. No. 1420, Walking Buddha, Wat Phra Si Ratana Mahathat. No. 1421, Buddha, Sukhothai's Wat Mahathat. No. 1422, Gopura of Prasat Phanom Rung. No. 1423, Prang of Prasat Hin Phimai. No. 1424, Slender Chedis, Wat Yai Chai, Mongkon.
No. 1425 — Thai painting: a, Early Fruit Stand. b, Scene in Chinese Style, Wat Bovornivet. c, Buddha Descends from Tauatimsa. d, Sang Thong Tales, Lai Kham Vihan. e, The Damned in Hell, Wah Suthat. f, King Sanjaya Travels on Elephant, Wat Suwannaram.
No. 1426 — Thai Buddha sculpture: a, U Thong C, 14th-15th cent. b, Adorned Seated, 17th cent. c, Phra Chai, 19th cent. d, Bronze, 14th cent. e, U Thong A, bronze. f, Crowned, 14th-15th cent.
No. 1427, Ceramics, horiz. No. 1428, Character in Khon, dance drama.

**1993**

| 1417 | A209 | 20b multicolored | .25 | .25 |
|---|---|---|---|---|
| 1418 | A209 | 20b multicolored | .25 | .25 |
| 1419 | A209 | 2d multicolored | .90 | .90 |
| 1420 | A209 | 2d multicolored | .90 | .90 |
| 1421 | A209 | 5d multicolored | 2.00 | 2.00 |
| 1422 | A209 | 5d multicolored | 2.00 | 2.00 |
| 1423 | A209 | 15d multicolored | 4.00 | 4.00 |
| 1424 | A209 | 15d multicolored | 4.00 | 4.00 |
| | | Nos. 1417-1424 (8) | 14.30 | 14.30 |

**Miniature Sheets**

| 1425 | A209 | 5d Sheet of 6, #a.-f. | 17.00 | 17.00 |
|---|---|---|---|---|
| 1426 | A209 | 5d Sheet of 6, #a.-f. | 17.00 | 17.00 |

**Souvenir Sheets**

| 1427 | A209 | 18d multicolored | 7.00 | 7.00 |
|---|---|---|---|---|
| 1428 | A209 | 18d multicolored | 7.00 | 7.00 |

**With Indopex '93 Emblem**

Designs: No. 1429, Pura Taman Ayun (garden temple), Mengwi, Bali. No. 1430, Natl. monument with statue of Prince Diponegoro, Jakarta. No. 1431, Candi Jawi, East Java. No. 1432, Guardian at Singosari Palace, East Java. No. 1433, Monument of Irian Jaya, (liberation), Jakarta. No. 1434, Central Temple, Prambanan complex, Lara Djonggrang. No. 1435, "Date of the Year Temple," Panataran complex, East Java. No. 1436, Brahma & Siva Temples, Loro Jonggrang, Java.
No. 1437 — Masks: a, Telek Luh. b, Jero Gde. c, Barong Macan. d, Monkey. e, Mata Gde. f, Jauk Kras.
No. 1438 — Paintings: a, Tree Mask, Soedibio, 1978. b, Dry Lizard, Hendra Gunawan, 1977. c, The Corn Eater, Sudjana Kerton, 1988. d, Night Watchman, Djoko Pekik, 1988. e, Hunger, Kerton, 1984. f, Arje Player, Soedjojono, 1971.
No. 1439, Stone carving, Brahma & Gods, Borobudur, Java, horiz. No. 1440, Effigies of the Dead, Torajaland, horiz.

| 1993, Sept. 27 | Litho. | | Perf. 14 | |
|---|---|---|---|---|
| 1429 | A209 | 20b multicolored | .25 | .25 |
| 1430 | A209 | 20b multicolored | .25 | .25 |
| 1431 | A209 | 2d multicolored | .90 | .90 |
| 1432 | A209 | 2d multicolored | .90 | .90 |
| 1433 | A209 | 5d multicolored | 2.00 | 2.00 |
| 1434 | A209 | 5d multicolored | 2.00 | 2.00 |
| 1435 | A209 | 15d multicolored | 4.00 | 4.00 |
| 1436 | A209 | 15d multicolored | 4.00 | 4.00 |
| | | Nos. 1429-1436 (8) | 14.30 | 14.30 |

**Miniature Sheets**

| 1437 | A209 | 5d Sheet of 6, #a.-f. | 16.00 | 16.00 |
|---|---|---|---|---|
| 1438 | A209 | 5d Sheet of 6, #a.-f. | 16.00 | 16.00 |

**Souvenir Sheets**

| 1439 | A209 | 18d multicolored | 7.00 | 7.00 |
|---|---|---|---|---|
| 1440 | A209 | 18d multicolored | 7.00 | 7.00 |

Miniature Sheet

Casey at the Bat — A210

Nos. 1441-1443: Characters and scenes from Disney's animated film Casey at the Bat.

| 1993, Oct. 25 | Litho. | | Perf. 14x13½ | |
|---|---|---|---|---|
| 1441 | A210 | 2d Sheet of 9, #a.-i. | 12.00 | 12.00 |

**Souvenir Sheets**

| 1442 | A210 | 20d multicolored | 8.00 | 8.00 |
|---|---|---|---|---|

**Perf. 13½x14**

| 1443 | A210 | 20d multi, vert. | 8.00 | 8.00 |
|---|---|---|---|---|

Picasso — A211

Paintings: 2d, Woman with a Comb, 1906. 5d, The Mirror, 1932. 7d, Woman on a Pillow, 1969. 18d, The Three Dancers, 1925.

| 1993, Oct. 7 | Litho. | | Perf. 14 | |
|---|---|---|---|---|
| 1444-1446 | A211 | Set of 3 | 5.25 | 5.25 |

**Souvenir Sheet**

| 1447 | A211 | 18d multicolored | 7.00 | 7.00 |
|---|---|---|---|---|

Copernicus
A212

5d, Early astronomical instrument. 10d, Telescope.

**1993, Oct. 7** **Perf. 14**
1448-1449 A212 Set of 2    5.00 5.00
**Souvenir Sheet**
**Perf. 12x13**
1450 A212 18d Copernicus    7.00 7.00

Polska '93
A213

Paintings: 2d, Pont-Neuf, Paris, by Rudzka-Cybisowa, 1932. No. 1452, 10d, Honegger's Liturgical Symphony, by Bogusz, 1973. No. 1453, 10d, Niedzica castle. 18d, When You Enter Here, Whisper My Name Soundlessly, by Waniek, 1973.

**1993, Oct. 7** **Perf. 14**
1451-1453 A213 Set of 3    7.25 7.25
**Souvenir Sheet**
1454 A213 18d multicolored    7.00 7.00

1994 World Cup
Soccer
Championships,
US — A214

Players, country: 1.25d, Hannich, Hungary; Stopyra, France. 1.50d, Labd, Morocco; Lineker, England. 2d, Segota, Canada; Morozov, Russia. 3d, Roger Milla, Cameroun. 5d, Rodax, Australia; Weiss, Czech Republic. 10d, Claesen, Belgium; Bossis & Amoros, France. 12d, Candida, Brazil; Ramirez, Costa Rica. 15d, Silva, Brazil; Platini, France. No. 1463, Muller, Brazil; McDonald, Ireland, horiz. No. 1463A, Buchwald and Matthaeus, Germany; Maradona, Argentina, horiz.

**1993, Nov. 22** **Perf. 13½x14**
1455 A214 1.25d multi    .65 .65
1456 A214 1.50d multi    .70 .70
1457 A214 2d multi    1.00 1.00
1458 A214 3d multi    1.75 1.75
1459 A214 5d multi    2.50 2.50
1460 A214 10d multi    3.75 3.75
1461 A214 12d multi    4.00 4.00
1462 A214 15d multi    5.00 5.00
    Nos. 1455-1462 (8)    19.35 19.35
**Souvenir Sheets**
**Perf. 13**
1463 A214 25d multi    9.00 9.00
1463A A214 25d multi    9.00 9.00

Christmas
A215

Designs: No. 1464, 25b, No. 1467, 2d, No. 1471, 15d, Details or entire painting, Adoration of the Magi, by Rubens.

Details or entire woodcut by Durer: No. 1465, 1d, Holy Family with Joachim & Anna. No. 1466, 1.50d, The Annunciation, Life of the Virgin. No. 1468, 2d, The Virgin Mary Worshipped by Albrecht Bonstetten. No. 1469, 7d, Virgin on a Throne, Crowned by an Angel. No. 1470, 10d, The Holy Family with Two Angels in a Portico (detail).
No. 1472, 20d, Adoration of the Magi, by Rubens. No. 1473, 20d, The Holy Family with Two Angels in a Portico, (entire), by Durer, horiz.

**1993, Dec. 1** **Perf. 13½x14, 14x13½**
1464-1471 A215 Set of 8    16.00 16.00
**Souvenir Sheets**
1472-1473 A215 Set of 2    14.00 14.00

Fine
Art — A216

Paintings by Rembrandt: 50b, A Man in a Cap. No. 1476, Man with a Gold Helmet. 7d, A Franciscan Monk. 15d, The Apostle Paul. 20d, Dr. Tulp Demonstrating the Anatomy of the Arm, horiz.
Paintings by Matisse: 1.50d, Portrait of Pierre Matisse. No. 1477, Portrait of Auguste Pellerin (II). 5d, Andre Derain. 12d, The Young Sailor (II). No. 1483, Pianist and Checker Players, horiz.

**1993, Dec. 15** **Perf. 13½x14**
1474 A216 50b multicolored    .70 .70
1475 A216 1.50d multicolored    1.10 1.10
1476 A216 2d multicolored    1.25 1.25
1477 A216 2d multicolored    1.25 1.25
1478 A216 5d multicolored    2.50 2.50
1479 A216 7d multicolored    3.25 3.25
1480 A216 12d multicolored    4.00 4.00
1481 A216 15d multicolored    5.00 5.00
    Nos. 1474-1481 (8)    19.05 19.05
**Souvenir Sheets**
**Perf. 14x13½**
1482 A216 20d multicolored    8.50 8.50
1483 A216 20d multicolored    8.50 8.50

Winter
Sports
A217

Disney characters portraying sports: 50b, Ski ballet. 75b, Pairs figure skating. 1d, Speed skating. 1.25d, Biathlon. 4d, 4-Man bobsled. 5d, Luge. 7d, Figure skating. 10d, Downhill skiing. 15d, Ice hockey.
No. 1493, 20d, Cross country skiing. No. 1494, 20d, Mogul skiing.

**1993, Dec. 20** **Perf. 13½x14**
1484-1492 A217 Set of 9    18.00 18.00
**Souvenir Sheets**
1493-1494 A217 20d Set of 2    15.00 15.00

A218

Hong Kong '94 — A219

Stamps, painting, Spring Garden-1846, by M. Bruce: No. 1495, Hong Kong #357, left detail. No. 1496, Right detail, #1000.
No. 1497 — Museum of Qin Figures, Shaanxi Province, Tomb of First Emperor: a, Qin warriors, horses. b, Warrior in battle dress. c, Armor clad warrior. d, Chariot driver. e, Dog. f, Qin warriors.
No. 1498, Show emblem, Hong Kong #253, vert.

**1994, Feb. 18** **Litho.** **Perf. 14**
1495 A218 1.50d multicolored    .80 .40
1496 A218 1.50d multicolored    .80 .40
  a. Pair, #1495-1496    2.00 1.50
1497 A219 1.50d Sheet of 6, #a.-f.    5.00 5.00
**Souvenir Sheet**
1498 A218 20d multicolored    5.75 5.75

Nos. 1495-1496 issued in sheets of 5 pairs. No. 1496a is a continuous design.
New Year 1994 (Year of the Dog) (#1497e, #1498).

New Year
1994 (Year
of the Dog)
A220

Disney characters: 25b, Pluto the Racer. 50b, Fifi. 75b, Pluto, Jr. 1.25d, Goofy and Bowser. 1.50d, Butch. 2d, Toliver. 3d, Ronnie. 5d, Primo. 8d, Pluto's kid brother. 10d, Army mascot. 12d, Pluto and Dinah's pups. 18d, Bent Tail, Junior.
#1511, Pluto, Dinah. #1512, Eega Beeva, Dog Pflip, Goofy, horiz. #1513, Dinah's pups, Pluto.

**1994, Apr. 11** **Litho.** **Perf. 13½x14**
1499-1510 A220 Set of 12    22.50 22.50
**Souvenir Sheets**
1511 A220 20d multicolored    6.50 6.50
**Perf. 14x13½, 13½x14**
1512 A220 20d multicolored    6.50 6.50
1513 A220 20d multicolored    6.50 6.50

Orchids
A221

Designs: 1d, Oeceoclades maculata. 1.25d, Angraecum distichum. 2d, Plectrelminthus caudatus. 5d, Tridactyle tridactylites. 8d, Bulbophyllum lepidum. 10d, Angraecum eburneum. 12d, Eulophia guineensis. 15d, Angraecum eichleranum.
No. 1522, Ancistrochilus rothschildianus. No. 1523, Vanilla imperialis.

**1994, May 1** **Perf. 14**
1514 A221 1d multicolored    .30 .30
1515 A221 1.25d multicolored    .30 .30
1516 A221 2d multicolored    .50 .50
1517 A221 5d multicolored    1.25 1.25
1518 A221 8d multicolored    2.10 2.10
1519 A221 10d multicolored    2.50 2.50

1520 A221 12d multicolored    3.00 3.00
1521 A221 15d multicolored    3.75 3.75
    Nos. 1514-1521 (8)    13.70 13.70
**Souvenir Sheets**
1522 A221 25d multicolored    7.50 7.50
1523 A221 25d multicolored    7.50 7.50

Easter
A222

Disney characters celebrate Easter: No. 1524, 25b, No. 1527, 4d, No. 1529, 8d, No. 1531, 12d, Ludwig von Drake. No. 1525, 50b, Minnie Mouse, Daisy Duck. No. 1526, 3d, Mickey Mouse. No. 1528, 5d, Donald Duck. No. 1530, 10d, Goofy.
No. 1532, 20d, Von Drake. No. 1533, 20d, Mickey, Minnie.

**1994, Apr. 11** **Litho.** **Perf. 13½x14**
1524-1531 A222 Set of 8    19.00 19.00
**Souvenir Sheets**
1532-1533 A222 Set of 2    15.00 15.00

Miniature Sheets of 6 or 8

Sierra
Club,
Cent.
A223

No. 1534, 5d — Various views of: a-b, Prince William Sound. c-d, The Serengeti. e-f, Ross Island.
No. 1535, 5d: a-c, Briksdal Fjord, vert. d-f, Yosemite, vert.
No. 1536, 5d: a-b, Tibetan Plateau, vert. c-d, Yellowstone, vert. e, Ross Island, vert. f, The Serengeti, vert. g, Mount Erebus, vert. h, Ansel Adams Wilderness, vert.
No. 1537, 5d: a-b, Ansel Adams Wilderness. c-d, Mount Erebus. e, Prince William Sound. f, Yellowstone. g, Tibetan Plateau. h, Sierra Club emblem.

**1994, Apr. 25** **Perf. 14**
**Sheets of 6, #a-f**
1534-1535 A223 Set of 2    24.00 24.00
**Sheets of 8, #a-h**
1536-1537 A223 Set of 2    30.00 30.00

Paintings
of Cats
A224

No. 1538, 5d: a, The Arena, by Harold Weston. b, Cat Killing a Bird, by Picasso. c, Cat and Butterfly, by Hokusai. d, Winter: Cat on a Cushion, by Steinlen. e, Rattown Tigers, by Prang. f, Cat on the Floor, by Steinlen. g, Cat and Kittens, by Prang. i, Little White Kittens into Mischief, by Ives. j, Cat Bathing, by Hiroshige. k, Playtime, by Tuck. l, Summer: Cat on a Balustrade, by Steinlen.
No. 1539, 5d, vert.: a, Girl with a Kitten, by Perronneau. b, Still Life with Cat and Fish, by Chardin. c, Tinkle a Cat. d, Naughty Puss! e, Cats, by Steinlen. f, Girl in Red with Cat and Dog, by Phillips. g, Cat, Butterfly and Begonia, by Haronobu. h, Cat and Kitten, by Higgins. i, Woman with a Cat, by Renoir. j, Minnie from Outskirts of Village, by Thrall. k, The Fisher, by Tuck. l, Artist and His Family, by Vaenius.
No. 1540, 20d, The Morning Rising, by Lepicie. No. 1541, 20d, The Graham Children, by Hogarth, vert.

**1994, July 11** **Litho.** **Perf. 14**
**Sheets of 12, #a-l**
1538-1539 A224 Set of 2    50.00 50.00
**Souvenir Sheets**
1540-1541 A224 Set of 2    14.50 14.50

Monkeys — A225

Designs: 1d, Patas. 1.50d, Collared mangabey. 2d, Black and white colobus. 5d, Mona. 8d, Kirk's colobus. 10d, Vervet. 12d, Red colobus. 15d, Guinea baboon.

Heads of: No. 1550, 25d, Collared mangabey. No. 1551, 25d, Guinea baboon.

**1994, Aug. 1    Litho.    *Perf. 14***
1542-1549 A225    Set of 8   17.50 17.50
        **Souvenir Sheets**
1550-1551 A225 25d Set of 2   19.00 19.00

D-Day, 50th Anniv. A226

Designs: 50b, Free Dutch sloop Soema joins attack. 75b, HMS Belfast fires on beach defenses. 1d, USS Texas hits Point Du Hoc. 2d, Free French cruiser George Leygues. 20d, HMS Ramillies.

**1994, Aug. 16**
1552-1555 A226    Set of 4    4.50 4.50
        **Souvenir Sheet**
1556 A226   20d multicolored   7.00 7.00

First Manned Moon Landing, 25th Anniv. A227

No. 1557: a, Yuri Gagarin. b, Valentina Tereshkova. c, Ham (chimpanzee). d, Alexei Leonov. e, Neil Armstrong. f, Svetlana Y. Savitskaya. g, Marc Garneau. h, Vladimir Komarov. i, Ulf Merbold.

30d, Neil Armstrong, Edwin "Buzz" Aldrin, Michael Collins at press conference.

**1994, Aug. 16**
1557 A227  2d Sheet of 9,
      #a.-i.        9.00 9.00
        **Souvenir Sheet**
1558 A227  30d multicolored   11.00 11.00

A228

PHILAKOREA '94 — A229

Designs: 50b, Kungnakchon Hall, Naejangsa. 2d, Kettle of Popchusa. 3d, Pomun Tourist Resort.

Paper screen panels, episode from Sanguozhi, 18th cent. Choson Dynasty: a, Warriors on horseback. b, Soldiers atop fort. c, Shooting with bows and arrows. d, Bowing before horse & rider. e, Fight on horseback. f,

---

h, Charging on horses. g, Trudging through valley. i, j, Living peacefully.
20d, Traditional tombstone guardian, Taenung, vert.

**1994, Aug. 16  *Perf. 14, 13½ (#1562)***
1559-1561 A228  Set of 3   2.00 2.00
**1562** A229  1d Sheet of 10, #a.-
        j.        6.75 6.75
        **Souvenir Sheet**
1563 A228  20d multicolored   8.00 8.00

A230

Intl. Olympic Committee, Cent. — A231

Designs: 1.50d, Daley Thompson, Great Britain, decathalon, 1980, 1984. 5d, Heide Marie Rosendohl, Germany, long jump, 1972. 20d, Team Sweden, ice hockey, 1994.

**1994, Aug. 16    *Perf. 14***
1564 A230  1.50d multicolored  .65 .65
1565 A230  5d multicolored  2.00 2.00
        **Souvenir Sheet**
1566 A231  20d multicolored   7.75 7.75

Butterflies A232

Designs: 1d, Mylothris rhodope. 1.25d, Iolaphilus menas. 2d, Neptis nemetes. 5d, Antanartia delius. 8d, Acraea caecilia. 10d, Papilio nireus. 12d, Pipilio menestheus. 15d, Iolaphilus julus.

No. 1575, 25d, Colotis evippe. No. 1576, 25d, Bematistes epaea.

**1994, Aug. 18    *Perf. 14***
1567-1574 A232  Set of 8  16.00 16.00
        **Souvenir Sheets**
1575-1576 A232  Set of 2   17.00 17.00

1994 World Cup Soccer Championships, US — A233

Designs: 50b, Bobby Charlton, England. 75b, Ferenc Puskas, Hungary. 1d, Paolo Rossi, Italy. 2d, Biri Biri, Gambian playing for Spain. 3d, Diego Maradona, Argentina. 8d, Johan Cruyff, Netherlands. 10d, Franz Beckenbauer, Germany. 15d, Thomas Dooley, US.

No. 1585, 25d, Pele, Brazil. No. 1586, 25d, Gordon Banks, England.

**1994, Sept. 1**
1577-1584 A233  Set of 8  15.00 15.00
        **Souvenir Sheets**
1585-1586 A233  Set of 2   18.00 18.00

---

Mushrooms A234

No. 1587, 5d: a, Agaricus campestris. b, Lepista nuda. c, Podaxis pistillaris. d, Oudemansiella radicata. e, Schizophyllum commune. f, Chlorophyllum molybdites. g, Hypholoma fasciculare. h, Mycena pura. i, Ganoderma lucidum.

No. 1588, 5d: a, Suillus luteus. b, Bolbitius vitellinus. c, Clitocybe nebularis. d, Omphalotus olearius. e, Auricularia auricula. f, Macrolepiota rhacodes. g, Volvariella volvacea. h, Psilocybe coprophila. i, Suillus granulatus.

No. 1589, 20d, Cyathus striatus. No. 1590, 20d, Leucoagaricus naucina.

**1994, Sept. 30**
    **Sheets of 9, #a-i**
1587-1588 A234  Set of 2  25.00 25.00
        **Souvenir Sheets**
1589-1590 A234  Set of 2  16.00 16.00

Christmas A235

French paintings: 50b, Expectant Madonna with St. Joseph, by unknown artist. 75b, Rest of the Holy Family, by Louis Le Nain. 1d, Rest on the Flight into Egypt, by Antoine Watteau. No. 1594, 2d, Noon, by Claude Lorrain. No. 1595, 2d, Rest on the Flight into Egypt, by Francois Boucher. No. 1596, 2d, Rest on the Flight into Egypt, by Jean-Honore Fragonard. 10d, The Holy Family, by Nicolas Poussin. 12d, Mystical Marriage of St. Catherine, by Pierre-Francois Mignard.

No. 1599, 25d, The Nativity by Torchlight, by Louis Le Nain. No. 1600, 25d, Adoration of the Shepherds, by Mathieu Le Nain.

**1994, Dec. 5  Litho.  *Perf. 13½x14***
1591-1598 A235  Set of 8  13.00 13.00
        **Souvenir Sheets**
1599-1600 A235  Set of 2  16.00 16.00

Marilyn Monroe (1926-62), Actress — A236

No. 1601: a-i, Various portraits.
No. 1602, 25d, Wearing red dress. No. 1603, 25d, Wearing long, dangling earrings.

**1995, Jan. 8  Litho.  *Perf. 14***
1601 A236  4d Sheet of 9, #a.-
        i.        12.00 12.00
        **Souvenir Sheets**
1602-1603 A236  Set of 2  13.00 13.00

---

Elvis Presley (1935-77), Entertainer A237

No. 1604: a, As child. b, Singing, later years. c, With mother. d, With wife, Priscilla. e, With gold medallion. f, Wearing army uniform. g, Singing, younger years. h, Wearing hat. i, With daughter, Lisa Marie.

**1995, Jan. 8**
1604 A237  4d Sheet of 9, #a.-
        i.        10.50 10.50

Dinosaurs A238

No. 1605: a, Pteranodon. b, Archaeopteryx. c, Rhamphorhynchus. d, Ornithomimus. e, Stegosaurus. f, Heterodontosaurus. g, Lystrosaurus. h, Euoplocephalus. i, Coelophysis. j, Staurilosaurus. k, Giantoperis. l, Diarthrognathus.

No. 1606: a, Archaeopteryx, diff. b, Vangehuanosaurus. c, Ceolophysis, diff. d, Plateosaurus. e, Baryonyx. f, Ornitholestes. g, Dryosaurus. h, Estemmenosuchus. i, Macroplata. j, Shonisaurus. k, Muraeonosaurus. l, Archelon.

20d, Bactrosaurus. 22d, Tyrannosaurus, vert. No. 1609, 25d, Triceratops, vert. No. 1610, 25d, Spinosaurus.

**1995      Litho.    *Perf. 14***
1605 A238  2d Sheet of 12,
        #a.-l.    11.00 11.00
1606 A238  3d Sheet of 12,
        #a.-l.    11.00 11.00
        **Souvenir Sheets**
1607 A238  20d multi    7.50 7.50
1608 A238  22d multi    7.50 7.50
1609-1610 A238  Set of 2  15.00 15.00

New Year 1995 (Year of the Boar) — A239

No. 1611: Stylized boars with Chinese inscriptions in: a, Green. b, Blue violet. c, White. d, Black.
10d, Three boars.

**1995, May 4    *Perf. 14½***
1611 A239  3d Sheet of 4, #a.-d. 3.50 3.50
        **Souvenir Sheet**
1612 A239  10d multicolored   3.50 3.50

Water Birds A240

Designs: 2d, Great white egret. 8d, Hammerkop. 10d, Shoveler. 12d, Crowned crane.
No. 1617: a, Pintail. b, Fulvous tree duck (a). c, Garganey. d, White-faced tree duck. e, White-backed duck. f, Egyptian goose. g, Pigmy goose. h, Little bittern (k). i, Redshank. j, Ringed plover. k, Black-winged stilt. l, Squacco heron (k).
No. 1618, 25d, Ferruginous duck. No. 1619, 25d, Moorhen.

**1995, May 8    *Perf. 14***
1613-1616 A240  Set of 4  10.00 10.00

**1617** A240 3d Sheet of 12,
    #a.-l.             11.00 11.00
**Souvenir Sheets**
**1618-1619** A240 Set of 2    16.50 16.50

ECOWAS — A241

Designs: 2d, Free movement of people in Gambia. 5d, Captain Yaya AJJ Jammeh, Chairman of Arm Force Provisional Ruling Council, Head of State.

**1995, May 30    Litho.    Perf. 14**
**1620** A241 2d multicolored    .60 .60
**1621** A241 5d multicolored    1.50 1.50

Marine Life
A242

No. 1622, vert: a, Multicolored parrot fish. b, Sparisoma viride. c, Queen parrot fish. d, Bicolor parrot fish.
No. 1623: a, Leatherback turtle. b, Tiger shark. c, Surgeon fish. d, Emperor angelfish. e, Blue parro fish. f, Triggerfish. g, Sea horse. h, Lionfish. i, Moray eel. j, Red fin butterflyfish. k, Octopus. l, Ray.
No. 1624, 25d, Holacanthus ciliaris. No. 1625, 25d, Angelichthys isabelita.

**1995, June 20**
**1622** A242 8d Strip of 4, #a.-d.  10.00 10.00
**1623** A242 3d Sheet of 12,
    #a.-l.             10.00 10.00
**Souvenir Sheets**
**1624-1625** A242 Set of 2    19.00 19.00

UN, 50th Anniv. — A243

No. 1626: a, 3d, Girls. b, 5d, Woman helping girl at blackboard. c, 8d, Girl writing on blackboard.
25d, Nurse holding baby on scales.

**1995, July 6**
**1626** A243    Strip of 3, #a.-c.    3.50 3.50
**Souvenir Sheet**
**1627** A243 25d multicolored    6.50 6.50

World War II Motion Pictures
A244

No. 1628 — Movie stars: a, Peter Lawford. b, Gene Tierney, Dana Andrews. c, Groucho, Gummo Marx. d, James Stewart. e, Chico, Harpo Marx. f, Tyrone Power. g, Cary Grant, Ingrid Bergman. h, Veronica Lake.
Motion pictures: No. 1629, 25d, A Lady Fights Back. No. 1630, 25d, Desert Victory.

**1995, July 6**
**1628** A244 3d Sheet of 8, #a.-
    h. + label         12.00 12.00
**Souvenir Sheets**
**1629-1630** A244    Set of 2    14.50 14.50

VJ Day, 50th Anniv.
A245

No. 1631: a, Fairey Firefly. b, Fairey Barracuda II. c, Vickers Supermarine Seafire II. d, HMS Repulse. e, HMS Illustrious. f, HMS Exeter.
25d, Bomber being shot down by 3-stack cruiser.

**1995, Aug. 1**
**1631** A245 5d Sheet of 6,
    #a.-f. + label    11.00 11.00
**Souvenir Sheet**
**1632** A245 25d multicolored    9.00 9.00

A246              A247

Carrying sacks of grain: No. 1633a, 3d, Woman in pink. b, 5d, Two people. c, 8d, Man. 25d, Fisherman with net.

**1995, Aug. 1    Litho.    Perf. 14**
**1633** A246    Strip of 3, #a.-c.  3.75 3.75
**Souvenir Sheet**
**1634** A246 25d multicolored    6.50 6.50
FAO, 50th Anniv. No. 1633 is a continuous design.

**1995, Aug. 1**
Nobel Prize Winners: 2d, Kenichi Fukui, chemistry, 1981. 3d, Gustav Stresemann, peace, 1929. 5d, Thomas Mann, literature, 1929. 8d, Albert Schweitzer, peace, 1952. 12d, Leo Esaki, physics, 1973. 15d, Lech Walsea, peace, 1983.
No. 1635: a, Marie Curie, chemistry, 1911. b, Adolf Butenandt, chemistry, 1939. c, Tonegawa Susumu, medicine, 1987. d, Nelly Sachs, literature, 1966. e, Kawabata Yasunari, literature, 1968. f, Yukawa Hideki, physics, 1949. g, Paul Ehrlich, medicine, 1908. h, Sato Eisaku, peace, 1974. i, Carl von Ossietzky, peace, 1935.
25d, Willy Brandt, peace, 1971.

**1634A-1634F** A247  Set of 6  11.00 11.00
**1635** A247    5d Sheet of 9,
    #a.-i.           12.50 12.50
**Souvenir Sheet**
**1636** A247 25d multicolored    7.00 7.00

Rotary Intl., 90th Anniv.
A248

Designs: 15d, Paul Haris, Rotary emblem. 20d, Natl. flag, Rotary emblem.

**1995, Aug. 1**
**1637** A248 15d multicolored    3.50 3.50
**Souvenir Sheet**
**1638** A248 20d multicolored    5.75 5.75

Miniature Sheets of 3

1995 Boy Scout Jamboree, Holland — A249

No. 1639 — How to tie the lariat: a, First step. b, Second step. c, Completed.
No. 1640 — How to tie bowline: a, 12d, First step. b, 10d, Second step. c, 5d, Completed.
No. 1641, 25d, Bowline used to lift injured scout. No. 1642, 25d, Hitch used in lifesaving lift.

**1995, Aug. 1**
**1639** A249 2d Sheet of 3, #a.-
    c.               2.00 2.00
**1640** A249    Sheet of 3, #a.-
    c.               8.50 8.50
**Souvenir Sheets**
**1641-1642** A249  Set of 2    13.00 13.00

Queen Mother, 95th Birthday
A250

No. 1643: a, Drawing. b, Bright blue hat, dress. c, Formal portrait. d, Green hat, dress. 25d, Pale blue & white dress, blue hat.

**1995, Aug. 1    Perf. 13½x14**
**1643** A250    5d Strip or block of
    4, #a.-d.          5.00 5.00
**Souvenir Sheet**
**1644** A250 25d multicolored    6.25 6.25
No. 1643 was issued in sheets of 8 stamps.
Nos. 1643-1644 exist with black frame and overprint in sheet margin "In Memoriam 1900-2002" in one or two lines.

1996 Summer Olympics, Atlanta
A251

Designs: 1d, Bruce Jenner, US, decathlon. 1.25d, Greg Louganis, US, diving. 1.50d, Michael Gross, Germany 50-meter butterfly. 2d, Vasily Alexeev, USSR, weight lifting. 3d, Patrick Ewing, US, Juan Antonio Corbalan, Spain, basketball. 5d, Men's volleyball, US v. Brazil. 10d, John Svenden, West Germany, Armando Fernandez, US, water polo. 15d, Pertti Karppinen, Finland, single sculls.
No. 1653, vert: a, Stefano Cerioni, Italy, fencing. b, Alberto Covo, Italy, 10,000-meter run. c, Mary Lou Retton, US, women's gymnastics. d, Vladimir Artemov, USSR, men's gymnastics. e, Florence Griffith-Joyner, US, 400-meter relay. f, Brazil, soccer. g, Nelson Valis, US, 1000-meter sprint cycling. h, Cheryl Miller, US, women's basketball.
No. 1654, 25d, Karen Stives, US, equestrian. No. 1655, 25d, Edwin Moses, US, 400-meter hurdles, vert.

**1995, Aug. 17**
**1645-1652** A251  Set of 8  11.00 11.00
**1653** A251 3d Sheet of 8, #a.-
    h.               7.00 7.00
**Souvenir Sheets**
**1654-1655** A251  Set of 2    15.50 15.50
Volleyball, cent. (#1650).

Rotary, Intl., 90th Anniv., 1995 Boy Scout Jamboree, Holland — A252

Designs: 2d, Gambia Rotary contributing to education. No. 1657, 5d, Wood Badge course, Yundum, 1980. No. 1658, 5d, M.J.E. Sambou, organizing scout commissioner, vert.

**1995, Sept. 5**
**1656-1658** A252  Set of 3    4.00 4.00

Flowers — A253

Designs: 2d, Zantedeschia rehmannii. 5d, Euadenia eminens. 10d, Passiflora vitifolia. 15d, Dietes grandiflora.
No. 1663, 3d: a, Canarina abyssinica. b, Nerine bowdenii. c, Zantedeschia aethiopica. d, Aframomum sceptrum. e, Schotia brachypetala. f, Catharanthus roseus. g, Protea grandiceps. h, Plumbago capensis. i, Uncarina grandidieri.
No. 1664, 3d: a, Kigelia africana. b, Hibiscus schizopetalus. c, Dombeya mastersii. d, Agapanthus orientalis. e, Strelitzia reginae. f, Spathodea campanulata. g, Rhodolaena bakeriana. h, Gazania rigens. i, Ixianthes retzioides.
No. 1665, 25d, Eulophia quartiniana. No. 1666, 25d, Gloriosa simplex.

**1995, Oct. 2    Litho.    Perf. 14**
**1659-1662** A253  Set of 4    8.00 8.00
**Sheets of 9, #a-i**
**1663-1664** A253  Set of 2    14.50 14.50
**Souvenir Sheets**
**1665-1666** A253  Set of 2    15.00 15.00

SOS Children's Villages
A254

Designs: No. 1667, 2d, Children playing near houses. No. 1668, 2d, Aid worker with child, vert. 5d, Children.

**1995, Oct. 9    Litho.    Perf. 14**
**1667-1669** A254 Set of 3    2.75 2.75

Entertainers
A255

No. 1670: a, Roy Orbison. b, Mick Jagger. c, Bruce Springsteen. d, Jimi Hendrix. e, Bill Haley. f, Gene Vincent. g, Buddy Holly. h, Jerry Lee Lewis. i, Chuck Berry.
No. 1671: a-i, Various pictures of James Dean.
No. 1672, 25d, James Dean. No. 1673, 25dElvis Presley.

**1995, Dec. 1    Litho.    Perf. 13½x14**
**1670** A255 3d Sheet of 9, #a.-
    i.              10.00 10.00
**1671** A255 3d Sheet of 9, #a.-
    i.              9.00 9.00
**Souvenir Sheets**
**1672-1673** A255  Set of 2    19.00 19.00
Motion pictures, cent. (#1671-1672).

Christmas
A256

Details or entire paintings: 75b, Madonna of the, Valley. 1d, Madonna, by Giotto. 2d, The Flight into Egypt, by Luca Giordano. 5d, The Epiphany, by Bondone. 8d, Virgin & Child, by Burgkmair. 12d, Madonna, by Bellini.
No. 1680, 25d, Mother and Child, by Rubens. No. 1681, 25d, The Christ, by Carpaccio.

**1995, Dec. 18**
1674-1679 A256   Set of 6        11.00 11.00
**Souvenir Sheets**
1680-1681 A256   Set of 2        18.00 18.00

Banjul Intl.
Airport
A257

Denominations: 1d, 2d, 3d, 5d.

**1995, Dec. 21   Litho.      Perf. 14**
1682-1685 A257   Set of 4         4.00 4.00

UPU, 121st
Anniv. — A258

Denominations: 1d, 2d, 3d, 7d.

**1995, Dec. 21**
1686-1689 A258   Set of 4         4.00 4.00

Marine
Life
A259

Designs: 2d, Commerson's dolphin. 5d, Narwhal. 8d, True's beaked whale. 10d, Rough-toothed dolphin.
No. 1694, 3d — Dolphins:a, Northern rightwhale. b, Spotted. c, Common. d, Pacific white-sided. e. Atlantic humpbacked. f, Atlantic white-sided. g, White-beaked. h, Striped. i, Risso's.
No. 1695, 3d — Whales: a, Bryde's. b, Sperm. c, Humpback. d, Sei. e, Blue. f, Gray. g, Fin. h, Killer. i, Right.
No. 1696, 25d, Beluga, clymene dolphin. No. 1697, 25d, Bowhead whale, dall's porpoise, blue shark.

**1995, Dec. 22**
1690-1693 A259   Set of 4         6.75 6.75
**Sheets of 9, #a-i**
1694-1695 A259   Set of 2        14.50 14.50
**Souvenir Sheets**
1696-1697 A259   Set of 2        15.50 15.50

Cowboys and American
Indians — A260

Disney characters portraying Amerian Indians or in western scenes: 15b, Pete, Seminole. 20b, Donald, Chinook. 25b, Huey, Dewey, Louie, Blackfoot. 30b, Sharp shooter Minnie. 40b, Bull-riding Donald. 50b, Cattle-branding Mickey. 2d, Donald, Tlingit. 3d, Bronco-busting Mickey. 12d, Trick-roping Grandma Duck. No. 1707, 15d, Goofy the ranch hand. No. 1708, 15d, Mickey, Pomo. 20d, Minnie, Goofy, Navaho.
No. 1710, 25d, Minnie, Massachusetts Tribe. No. 1711, 25d, Pluto singing, vert. No.

1712, 25d, Donald with rope around neck, vert. No. 1712, 25d, Minnie, Shoshoni, vert.

**1995, Dec. 22       Perf. 14x13½**
1698-1709 A260   Set of 12       21.00 21.00
**Souvenir Sheets**
1710-1713 A260   Set of 4        32.50 32.50

New Year 1996
(Year of the
Rat) — A261

No. 1714 — Various stylized rats: a, 63b. b, 75b. c, 1.50d. d, 4d.
No. 1715a, Like #1714a. b, Like #1714d. c, Like #1714c. d, Like #1714b.
No. 1716, Two rats.

**1996, Jan. 2                  Perf. 14½**
1714 A261   Strip of 4, #a.-d.       1.50 1.50
1715 A261   3d Sheet of 4, #a.-d.    2.75 2.75
**Souvenir Sheet**
1716 A261   10d multicolored         5.00 5.00
#1714 issued in sheets of 16 stamps.

Paintings
from
Metropolitan
Museum of
Art — A262

No. 1717, 4d: a, Don Tiburcio Pérez y Cuervo, by Goya. b, Jean Antoine Moltedo, by J.A.D. Ingres. c, The Letter, by Corot. d, General Etienne Maurice Gerard, by J.L. David. e, Portrait of the Artist, by Van Gogh. f, Joseph Henri Altés, by Degas. g, Princess de Broglie, by Ingres. h, Lady at the Table, by Cassatt.
No. 1718, 4d: a, Broken Eggs, by Greuze. b, Johann Joachim Winckelmann, by Mengs. c, Col. George K.H. Coussmaker, by Reynolds. d, Self Portrait with Pupils, by Labille-Guiard. e, Courtesan Holding a Fan, by Utamaro. f, The Woodgatherers, by Gainsborough. g, Mr. Grace D. Elliott, by Gainsborough. h, The Drummond Children, by Raeburn.
No. 1719, 4d: a, Sunflowers, by Monet. b, Still Life with Pansies, by Fantin-Latour. c, Parisians Enjoying the Park, by Monet. d, La Mére Larchevêque, by Pissarro. e, Rue de L'Epicerie, Rouen, by Pissarro. f, The Abduction of Rebecca, by Delacroix. g, Daughter, Abraham-Ben-Chimol, by Delacroix. h, Christ on Lake of Gennesaret, by Delacroix.
No. 1720, 4d: a, Henry Frederick, Prince of Wales, by Peake. b, Saints Peter, Martha, Mary & Leonard, by Correggio. c, Marriage Feast at Cana, by Juan de Flandes. d, Portrait of one of Wedigh Family, by Holbein. e, Guilluame Budé, by Clouet. f, Portrait of a Cardinal, by El Greco. g, St. Jerome as a Cardinal, by El Greco. h, Portrait of a Man, by Titian.
No. 1721, 25d, The Harvesters, by Bruegel. No. 1722, 25d, The Creation of the World and the Expulsion from Paradise, by Giovanni de Paolo. No. 1723, 25d, Henry IV at the Battle of Ivry, by Rubens. No. 1724, 25d, The Israelites Gathering Manna in the Desert, by Rubens.

**1996, Jan. 29   Litho.   Perf. 13½x14**
**Sheets of 8, #a-h**
1717-1720 A262   Set of 4        40.00 40.00
**Souvenir Sheets**
**Perf. 14**
1721-1724 A262   Set of 4        29.00 29.00
Nos. 1721-1724 each contain one 85x57mm stamp.
No. 1723 is actually in the Uffizi Gallery in Florence; No. 1724 in the Los Angeles County Museum of Art.

Traditional
Fire
Dance
A263

Designs: 1d, Blowing fire from mouth, vert. 2d, Like 1d, diff. 3d, Holding sticks of fire at leg, vert. 7d, Holding out two sticks of fire.

**1996, Jan. 29     Litho.      Perf. 14**
1725-1728 A263   Set of 4         3.50 3.50

Disney Characters Performing Good
Deeds — A264

Designs: 1d, Community blood drive. 4d, Adopt-a-pet. 5d, Christmas giving for the needy. 10d, Teaching outdoor skills. 15d, Teaching reading. 20d, Volunteer fire fighters.
No. 1735, 25d, Highway volunteers. No. 1736, 25d, Counting whales.

**1996, Apr. 12   Litho.   Perf. 13½x14**
1729-1734 A264   Set of 6        12.00 12.00
**Souvenir Sheets**
1735-1736 A264   Set of 2        11.00 11.00

Bruce Lee (1940-
73), Martial Arts
Expert — A265

No. 1737: Various portraits. 25d, In fighting stance.

**1996, Apr. 1      Litho.      Perf. 14**
1737 A265   3d Sheet of 9, #a.-i.   7.50 7.50
**Souvenir Sheet**
1738 A265   25d multicolored        6.25 6.25
China '96, 9th Asian Intl. Philatelic Exhibition (#1737).

African
Wildlife
A266

15d, African civet.
No. 1740: a, Roan antelope. b, Lesser bush baby. c, Leopard. d, Guinea forest red colobus. e, Kob. f, Common eland.
No. 1741: a, African buffalo. b, Topi. c, Vervet. d, Hippopotamus. e, Waterbuck. f, Senegal chameleon. g, Western green mamba. h, Slender snouted crocodile (i). i, Adanson's mud turtle.
No. 1742, 25d, Lion. No. 1743, 25d, Chimpanzee.

**1996, Apr. 15      Litho.      Perf. 14**
1739 A266   15d multicolored       3.50 3.50
1740 A266   3d Block of 6, #a.-f.  4.25 4.25
1741 A266   4d Sheet of 9, #a.-i.  7.25 7.25
**Souvenir Sheets**
1742-1743 A266   Set of 2        13.50 13.50
No. 1740 issued in sheets of 12 stamps.

Queen
Elizabeth II,
70th
Birthday
A267

No. 1744: a, Portrait wearing blue dress. b, Wearing white dress, crown. c, Younger picture, crown.
25d, Buckingham Palace, horiz.

**1996, May 9   Litho.   Perf. 13½x14**
1744 A267   8d Strip of 3, #a.-c.   5.25 5.25
**Souvenir Sheet**
**Perf. 14x13½**
1745 A267   25d multicolored        6.50 6.50
No. 1744 was issued in sheets of 9 stamps with each strip in a different order.

Classic
Cars and
Fire
Engines
A268

No. 1746, 4d — Classic cars: a, 1912 Fiat Tipo 510, Italy. b, 1936 Toyota Model 4B Phaeton, Japan. c, 1924 NAG C4B, Germany. d, 1903 Cadillac, US. e, 1925 Bentley, Great Britain. f, 1909 Renault Model AX, France.
No. 1747, 4d — Fire engines: a, 1850 Pumper Hose Cart, US. b, 1891 Steam Fire Engine, US. c, 1864 Lausitzer, Germany. d, 1902 Chemical Engine, Great Britain. e, 1904 Motor Fire Engine, Great Britain. f, 1860 Colonia No. 5, Germany.
No. 1748, 25d, 1917 Mitsubishi Model A, Japan. No. 1749, 25d, 1865 Amoskeag steamer, US.

**1996, May 27                 Perf. 14**
**Sheets of 6, #a-f**
1746-1747 A268   Set of 2        12.00 12.00
**Souvenir Sheets**
1748-1749 A268   Set of 2        13.00 13.00

Euro '96, 1996 European Soccer
Championships, England — A269

Team pictures: No. 1750, 2d, Bulgaria. No. 1751, 2d, Croatia. No. 1752, 2d, Czech Republic. No. 1753, 2d, Denmark. No. 1754, 2d, England. No. 1755, 2d, France. No. 1756, 2d, Germany. No. 1757, 2d, Holland. No. 1758, 2d, Italy. No. 1759, 2d, Portugal. No. 1760, 2d, Romania. No. 1761, 2d, Russia. No. 1762, 2d, Scotland. No. 1763, 2d, Spain. No. 1764, 2d, Switzerland. No. 1765, 2d, Turkey.
No. 1766, 25d,Hristo Stoitchkov, Bulgaria, vert. No. 1767, 25d, Davor Suker, Croatia, vert. No. 1768, 25d, Pavel Hapal, Czech Republic. No. 1769, 25d, 1992 Denmark team, European championship winners. No. 1770, 25d, Bryan Robson, England, vert. No. 1771, 25d, 1984 Championship cup won by French team, vert. No. 1772, 25d, Jüegen Klinsmann, Germany. No. 1773, 25d, Ruud Gullit, Holland, vert. No. 1774, 25d, Roberto Baggio, Italy, vert. No. 1775, 25d, Eusebio, Portugal, vert. No. 1776, 25d, Gheorge Hagi, Romania, vert. No. 1777, 25d, Oleg Salenko, Russia, vert.No. 1778, 25d, Gary McAllister, Scotland, vert. No. 1779, 25d, Juan Goikoetxea, Spain, vert. No. 1780, 25d, Christophe Ohrel, Switzerland, vert. No. 1781, 25d, Hami Mandirali, Turkey, vert.

**1996, June 8 Litho. Perf. 14**
1750-1765 A269 Set of 16 12.50 12.50
**Souvenir Sheets**
1766-1781 A269 Set of 16 120.00 120.00

Nos. 1750-1765 each exist in miniature sheets of 8 + 1 label.
See Nos. 1808-1819.

1996 Summer Olympic Games, Atlanta — A270

1912 Olympics, Stockholm: 1d, Ray Ewry, standing high jump. 2d, Fanny Durack, free-style swimming. 5d, Stadium, scenes in Stocholm. 10d, Jim Thorpe, decathlon, pentathlon.

No. 1786, 3d — Winners in past Olympics: a, Japanese volleyball team, 1964. b, Li Neng, floor exercises, 1984. c, Sergei Bubka, pole vault, 1988. d, Nadia Comaneci, all around gymnastics, 1976. e, Edwin Moses, 400-meter hurdles, 1984. f, Vitaly Shcherbo, all around gymnastics, 1992. g, Evelyn Ashford, 100-meters, 1984. h, Muhammad Ali, light heavy-weight boxing, 1960. i, Carl Lewis, C. Smith, 400-meters relay, 1984.

No. 1787, 3d — 1992 Olympians: a, Fu Mingxia, platform diving. b, Heike Henkel, high jump. c, Spanish soccer team. d, Jackie Joyner-Kersee, heptathlon. e, Tatiana Gutsu, all around gymnastics. f, Michael Johnson, 400-meters. g, Lin Li, 200-meter individual medley. h, Gail Devers, 100-meters. i, Mike Powell, long jump.

No. 1788, 25d, Michael Gross, swimming, 1984, 1988, horiz. No. 1789, 25d, Ulrike Meyfarth, high jump, 1972, 1984.

**1996, July 18 Litho. Perf. 14**
1782-1785 A270 Set of 4 3.50 3.50
**Sheets of 9, #a-i**
1786-1787 A270 Set of 2 10.00 10.00
**Souvenir Sheets**
1788-1789 A270 Set of 2 11.00 11.00

Jerusalem, 3000th Anniv. — A271

Designs: 1.50d, Roman costume, Pillar of Absalem. 2d, Turkish costume, Gate of Mercy. 3d, Greek costume, Church of the Holy Sepulcher. 10d, Western Wall of the Temple Mount, Hasidic costume.
25d, Emblem, King David Tower, vert.

**1996, July 25**
1790-1793 A271 Set of 4 3.75 3.75
**Souvenir Sheet**
1794 A271 25d multicolored 5.50 5.50

Radio, Cent. A272

Designs: 1d, Glenn Miller. 4d, Louis Armstrong. 5d, Nat King Cole. 10d, Andrews Sisters.
25d, Harry S Truman.

**1996, July 25 Perf. 13½x14**
1795-1798 A272 Set of 4 5.25 5.25
**Souvenir Sheet**
1799 A272 25d multicolored 5.75 5.75

UNICEF, 50th Anniv. — A273

Designs: 63b, Boy holding shoes. 3d, Girl receiving vaccination. 8d, Boy with soup ladle. 10d, Girl with blanket. 25d, Boy receiving vaccination, horiz.

**1996, July 25 Perf. 14**
1800-1803 A273 Set of 4 4.50 4.50
**Souvenir Sheet**
1804 A273 25d multicolored 5.50 5.50

A274 A275

No. 1805: a, John F. Kennedy. b, Jacqueline Kennedy Onassis. c, Willy Brandt. d, Marilyn Monroe. e, Mao Tse Tung. f, Sung Ching Ling. g, Charles de Gaulle. h, Marlene Dietrich.
Nos. 1806-1807: Various portraits of Jacqueline Kennedy Onassis (1929-94).

**1996, Aug. 22**
1805 A274 5d Sheet of 8,
#a.-h. 11.00 11.00
1806 A275 5d Sheet of 9,
#a.-i. 13.00 13.00
**Souvenir Sheet**
1807 A274 25d multicolored 6.25 6.25

**Nos. 1751-1752, 1754, 1756, 1758, 1761, 1767-1768, 1770, 1772, 1774, 1777 With Added Inscriptions**

**1996, Aug. 26**
1808-1813 A269 Set of 6 3.50 3.50
**Souvenir Sheets**
1814-1819 A269 Set of 6 37.50 37.50

Nos. 1808-1813, each of which are 2d stamps, were issued in sheets of 8 + 1 label. Inscriptions on Nos. 1808-1813 and in sheet margins of Nos. 1814-1819, each of which are 25d stamps, show date of game, teams competing, and final score. Margin of the miniature sheets show additional information about individual games, and name of Germany as winner.

Team or team player shown as follows: Croatia (#1808, 1814), Czech Republic (#1809, 1815), England (#1810, 1816), Germany (#1811, 1817), Italy (#1812, 1818), Russia (#1813, 1819).

Richard Petty, NASCAR Driving Champion A276

No. 1820: a, 1969 Ford. b, Richard Petty. c, 1978 Dodge Magnum. d, 1987 Pontiac. e, 1989 Pontiac. f, 1975 Dodge Daytona.
25d, 1972 Plymouth.

**1996, Aug. 27**
1820 A276 5d Sheet of 6, #a.-f. 7.75 7.75
**Souvenir Sheet**
1821 A276 25d multicolored 5.50 5.50
No. 1821 contains one 85x28mm stamp.

Elvis Presley's 1st "Hit" Year, 40th Anniv. A277

Designs: Various portraits.

**1996, Sept. 8 Litho. Perf. 13½x14**
1822 A277 5d Sheet of 6, #a.-f. 7.50 7.50

Supermarine S6B's Schneider Trophy Victory, 65th Anniv. — A278

No. 1823 — Spitfire aircraft: a, PR XIX, Royal Swedish Air Force. b, MK VB, US Army Air. c, MK VC, French Air Force. d, MK VB, Soviet Air Force. e, MK IXE, Netherlands East Indies Air Force. f, MK IXE, Israeli Defense Force. g, MK VIII, Royal Australian Air Force. h, MK VB, Turkish Air Force. i, PR XI, Royal Danish Air Force.

No. 1823J: k, K5054, first prototype aircraft. l, K9787, first production aircraft. m, MK 1A, "Battle of Britain." n, LF MK IXE, D-Day invasion markings. o, MK XII, first "Griffon" engined model. p, MK XIVC, SEAC markings. q, PR XIX, Royal Swedish Air Force. r, PR MK XIX. s, FMK 22/24 final variant.

No. 1824, The Supermarine S.6B S1595. No. 1824A, Supermarine S.6B S1595 seaplane.

**1996, Sept. 13 Litho. Perf. 14**
1823 A278 4d Sheet of 9, #a.-i. 8.00 8.00
1823J A278 4d Sheet of 9, #k.-s. 8.00 8.00
**Souvenir Sheets**
1824 A278 25d multicolored 5.50 5.50
1824A A278 25d multicolored 5.50 5.50

Bob Dylan, Singer — A279

**1996, Sept. 8 Litho. Perf. 14**
1825 A279 5d multicolored 1.75 1.75
Issued in sheets of 16.

Birds — A280

Designs: 50b, Egyptian plover. 63b, Painted snipe. 75b, Golden-breasted bunting. 1d, Bateleur. 1.50d, Didric cuckoo. 2d, European turtle dove. 3d, Village weaver. 4d, European roller. 5d, Cut-throat. 10d, Hoopoe. 15d, White-faced scops-owl. 20d, Narina trogan. 25d, Pied kingfisher. 30d, Common kestrel.

**1996, Oct. 22 Litho. Perf. 14**
1826 A280 50b multicolored .20 .20
1827 A280 63b multicolored .20 .20
1828 A280 75b multicolored .20 .20
1829 A280 1d multicolored .25 .25
1830 A280 1.50d multicolored .30 .30
1831 A280 2d multicolored .45 .45

1832 A280 3d multicolored .65 .65
1833 A280 4d multicolored .90 .90
1834 A280 5d multicolored 1.10 1.10
1835 A280 10d multicolored 2.25 2.25
1836 A280 15d multicolored 3.25 3.25
1837 A280 20d multicolored 4.50 4.50
1838 A280 25d multicolored 5.50 5.50
1839 A280 30d multicolored 6.50 6.50
Nos. 1826-1839 (14) 26.25 26.25
See Nos. 1898-1900.

Christmas A281

Details of painting, Assumption of the Madonna, by Titian: 1d, Watching assumption, cherub, clouds. 1.50d, Cherubs. 2d, Cherub. 3d, Cherub holding up cloud, outstretched arms below. 10d, People watching assumption. 15d, Cherubs pointing.
No. 1846, 25d, Madonna and Child with Two Angels, by Filippo Lippi, horiz. No. 1847, 25d, Virgin and Child with Infant St. John, by Raphael.

**1996, Nov. 18 Perf. 13½x14**
1840-1845 A281 Set of 6 7.25 7.25
**Souvenir Sheets**
1846-1847 A281 Set of 2 11.00 11.00

Sylvester Stallone in Movie, "Rocky" — A282

**1996, Nov. 21 Litho. Perf. 14**
1848 A282 10d multicolored 2.25 2.25
Issued in sheets of 3.

Development Projects — A283

Designs: No. 1849, 63b, No. 1852, 2d, Arch 22, vert. 1d, Tractor, rice development project. 1.50d, Worker in rice paddy, vert. 3d, Banjul Intl. Airport Terminal Building. 5d, Chamoi Bridge.
20d, Workers in rice paddy. 25d, Statue in front of Arch 22, vert.

**1996 Litho. Perf. 14**
1849-1854 A283 Set of 6 3.00 3.00
**Souvenir Sheets**
1855 A283 20d multicolored 4.50 4.50
1856 A283 25d multicolored 5.50 5.50

New Year 1997 (Year of the Ox) — A284

Nos. 1857-1858 — Various stylized oxen, background color: a, 63b, orange. b, 75b, purple. c, 1.50d, blue green. d, 4d, yellow orange. All stamps in No. 1858 are 3d.
10d, Ox with baby lying on its back.

**1997, Jan. 16**      **Perf. 15**
1857 A284   Strip of 4, #a.-d.   1.50 1.50
1858 A284   3d Sheet of 4, #a.-d.   2.75 2.75

**Souvenir Sheet**
**Perf. 14**
1859 A284   10d multicolored   3.00 3.00

No. 1859 contains one 43x29mm stamp.

Mickey's Journey to the West — A285

Nos. 1860-1861: a-f, Scenes from Disney's "Monkey King."

No. 1862, Donald, Mickey, vert. No. 1863, Wu-Kong Sun (The Monkey King), monkeys, Mickey. No. 1864, Mickey, Intelligent Tortoise, Master San Tang. No. 1865, Mickey, Minnie obtaining Buddhist scriptures.

**1997, Jan. 28**     **Perf. 14x13½**
1860 A285   2d Sheet of 6, #a.-f.   5.50 5.50
  g.   No. 1860 overprinted   5.50 5.50
1861 A285   3d Sheet of 6, #a.-f.   6.25 6.25
  g.   No. 1861 overprinted   7.00 7.00

**Souvenir Sheets**
1862 A285   5d multi   5.00 5.00
  a.   With marginal overprint   5.00 5.00
1863 A285   10d multi   5.00 5.00
  a.   With marginal overprint   5.00 5.00
1864 A285   10d multi   5.00 5.00
  a.   With marginal overprint   5.00 5.00
1865 A285   15d multi   5.00 5.00
  a.   With marginal overprint   5.00 5.00

Nos. 1860g, 1861g are overprinted in red in sheet margin: "70TH ANNIVERSARY OF MICKEY & MINNIE," and in black with "Happy Birthday," Mickey Mouse, and "1998" in emblem. Nos. 1862a, 1863a, 1864a, 1865a are overprinted in black in sheet margin with just "Happy Birthday" emblem.

Souvenir Sheet

Deng Xiaoping — A286

No. 1867, Like #1866.
Illustration reduced.

**1996, May 13**    **Litho.**    **Perf. 13**
1866 A286   5d shown   5.25 5.25

**Litho. & Embossed**
**Die Cut Perf. 9**
**Size: 95x56mm**
1867 A286   300d gold

China '96. Nos. 1866-1867 were not available until March 1997.

Jackie Chan, Action Film Actor — A287

A287a

Various portraits.
Illustration reduced.

**1997, Feb. 12**      **Perf. 14**
1868 A287   4d Sheet of 8, #a.-h.   8.00 8.00

**Souvenir Sheet**
1869 A287   25d multi, horiz.   7.00 7.00

**Litho. & Embossed**
**Die Cut Perf. 9**
**Without Gum**
1869A A287a   300d gold & multi

Endangered Species — A288

No. 1870, 1.50d: a, Clouded leopard. b, Audouin's gull. c, Leatherback turtle. d, White-eared pheasant. e, Kakapo. f, Right whale. g, Black-footed ferret. h, Dwarf lemur. i, Peacock pheasant. j, Brown hyena. k, Cougar. l, Gharial. m, Monk seal. n, Mountain gorilla. o, Blyth's tragopan. p, Malayan tapir. q, Black rhinoceros. r, Polar bear. s, Red colobus. t, Tiger.

No. 1871, 1.50d: a, Arabian oryx. b, Baiji. c, Ruffed lemur. d, California condor. e, Blue-headed quail-dove. f, Numbat. g, Congo peacock. h, White uakari. i, Eskimo curlew. j, Gouldian finch. k, Coelacanth. l, Toucan barbet. m, Snow leopard. n, Queen Alexandra's birdwing. o, Dalmatian pelican. p, Chaco tortoise. q, Medong catfish. r, Helmeted hornbill. s, White-eyed river martin. t, Fluminense swallowtail.

No. 1872, 25d, Giant panda. No. 1873, 25d, Humpback whale. No. 1874, 25d, Japanese crane.

**1997, Feb. 24**
**Sheets of 20, #a-t**
1870-1871 A288   Set of 2   17.50 17.50

**Souvenir Sheets**
1872-1874 A288   Set of 3   19.00 19.00

Hong Kong '97 (Nos. 1870-1871).

Jungle Book — A289

No. 1875: a, Monkey facing right. b, Bear. c, Elephant. d, Monkey facing left. e, Panther, butterfly. f, Buffalo. g, Mandrill. h, Tiger. i, Wolf. j, Cobra. k, Mongoose. l, Child's face, flower.

**1997**
1875 A289   3d Sheet of 12, #a.-l.   8.75 8.75

Mushrooms — A290

Designs: 1d, Polyporus squamosus. 3d, Armillaria tabescens. 5d, Collybia velutipes. 10d, Sarcoscypha coccinea.

No. 1880, vert: a, Amanita caesarea. b, Lepiota procera. c, Hygophorus psittacinus. d, Russula xerampelina. e, Laccaria amethystina. f, Coprinus micaceus. g, Boletus edulis. h, Morchella esculenta. i, Otidea auricula. 25d, Volvariella bombycina.

**1997, Mar. 10**    **Litho.**    **Perf. 14**
1876-1879 A290   Set of 4   4.75 4.75
1880 A290   4d Sheet of 9, #a.-i.   8.00 8.00

**Souvenir Sheet**
1881 A290   25d multicolored   7.00 7.00

UNESCO, 50th Anniv. — A291

World Heritage sites: 1d, Horyu-Ji, Japan. 2d, Great Wall, China. 3d, City of Ayutthaya, Thailand. 4d, Ascension Convent, Santa Maria, Philippines. 10d, Dragons, Komodo Natl. Park, Indonesia. 15d, Timbuktu, Mali.

No. 1888, 4d, vert. — Various sites in Japan: a, g, h. Kyoto. b, Himeji-Jo. c, d, Horyu-Ji. e, f, Yakushima.

No. 1889, 4d, vert. — Various sites in China: a, b, c, Mogao Caves. d, e, Great Wall. f, g, h, Imperial Palace.

No. 1890, 4d, vert. — Various sites: a, Mt. Nimba Strict Nature Reserve, Guinea. b, Banc D'Argun Natl. Park, Mauritania. c, Marrakesh, Morocco. d, Ichkeul Natl. Park, Tunisia. e, Mali. f, Salonga Natl. Park, Zaire. g, Timgad, Algeria. h, Benin.

No. 1891, 5d — Various sites in Germany: a, b, c, Bamberg. d, e, Maulbronn.

No. 1892, 5d — Various sites in Greece: a, d, e, Ruins in Delphi. b, c, City of Rhodes.

No. 1893, 5d — Various sites in Japan: a, b, Shirakami-Sanchi. c, d, e, Himeji-Jo.

No. 1894, 25d, Cloisters, Santa Maria de Alcobaca, Portugal. No. 1895, 25d, Kyoto, Japan. No. 1896, 25d, Ruins of Kilwa Kisiwani, Tanzania. No. 1897, 25d, Plitvice Lakes Natl. Park, Croatia.

**1997, Mar. 24**
1882-1887 A291   Set of 6   7.75 7.75
**Sheets of 8, #a-h, + Label**
1888-1890 A291   Set of 3   21.00 21.00
**Sheets of 5, #a-e, + Label**
1891-1893 A291   Set of 3   16.50 16.50
**Souvenir Sheets**
1894-1897 A291   each   22.00 22.00

**Bird Type of 1996**

Designs: 40d, Temminck's courser. 50d, European bee-eater. 100d, Green-winged teal.

**1997, Mar. 25**    **Litho.**    **Perf. 14**
1898 A280   40d multicolored   8.00 8.00
1899 A280   50d multicolored   10.00 10.00
1900 A280   100d multicolored   20.00 20.00
    Nos. 1898-1900 (3)   38.00 38.00

Disney's 101 Dalmatians — A293

No. 190, vert.1: a, Dipstick. b, Fidget. c, Jewel. d, Lucky. e, Two-Tone. f, Wizzer.

No. 1902: a-i, Various "Playful Puppies."

No. 1903: a-i, Various "Mischievous puppies."

No. 1904, 25d, Hiding under sheep. No. 1905, 25d, Cruella. No. 1906, 25d, Looking at picture. No. 1907, 25d, Distributing mail, vert. No. 1908, 25d, Into paint. No. 1909, 25d, Playing video game.

**1997, May 1**    **Perf. 13½x14, 14x13½**
1901 A293   50b Sheet of 6, #a.-f.   2.75 2.75
1902 A293   2d Sheet of 9, #a.-i.   4.75 4.75
1903 A293   3d Sheet of 9, #a.-i.   7.50 7.50
**Souvenir Sheets**
1904-1909 A293   Set of 6   45.00 45.00

Minnie Thru the Years — A294

No. 1910 — Minnie in various scenes dated: a, 1928. b, 1933. c, 1934. d, 1937. e, 1938. f, 1941. g, 1950. h, 1990. i, 1997. 25d, 1987.

**1997, May 1**     **Perf. 13½x14**
1910 A294   4d Sheet of 9, #a.-i.   12.00 12.00

**Souvenir Sheet**
1911 A294   25d multicolored   9.75 9.75

Juventus (World Club Soccer Champions), Cent. — A295

No. 1912: a, Juventus, 1897. b, Player from early years, emblems. c, Giampiero Boniperti. d, Roberto Bettega. e, European/ South American Cup, 1996. f, Drawing in celebration of cent.

**1997, May 9**    **Litho.**    **Perf. 14x13½**
1912 A295   5d Sheet of 6, #a.-f.   6.25 6.25

Queen Elizabeth II, Prince Philip, 50th Wedding Anniv. A296

No. 1913: a, Queen. b, Royal Arms. c, Queen, Prince Philip. d, Queen holding flowers, Prince saluting. e, Royal Yacht Britannia. f, Prince Philip.
20d, Queen in red hat.

**1997, May 20**      **Perf. 14**
1913 A296   4d Sheet of 6, #a.-f.   5.25 5.25
**Souvenir Sheet**
1914 A296   20d multicolored   4.25 4.25

Paul P. Harris (1868-1947), Founder of Rotary Intl. — A297

Rotary emblem, portrait of Harris and: 10d, Tree of friendship planted by Sydney W. Pascall, Rotary Pres. 1931-32.
25d, Emblem, preserve planet earth.

**1997, May 20**    **Litho.**    **Perf. 14**
1915 A297   10d multicolored   2.00 2.00
**Souvenir Sheet**
1916 A297   25d multicolored   5.25 5.25

Heinrich von Stephan (1831-97), Founder of UPU
A298

No. 1917 — Portrait of von Stephan and: a, Otto von Bismarck. b, UPU emblem. c, Two-horse team and wagon, Boston, 1900. 25d, Hamburg-Lübeck postilion, 1828.

**1997, May 20**
1917 A298 5d Sheet of 3, #a.-c. 3.50 3.50
**Souvenir Sheet**
1918 A298 25d multicolored 5.75 5.75
PACIFIC 97.

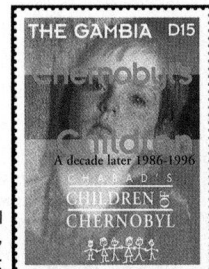

Chernobyl Disaster, 10th Anniv.
A299

Designs: No. 1919, Chabad's Children of Chernobyl. No. 1920, UNESCO.

**1997, May 20 Litho. Perf. 13½x14**
1919 A299 15d multicolored 3.00 3.00
1920 A299 15d multicolored 3.00 3.00

Grimm's Fairy Tales
A300

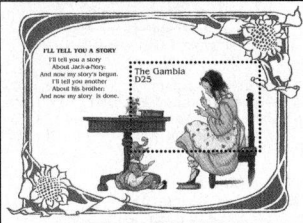

Mother Goose — A301

No. 1921 — Scenes from "Little Red Riding Hood": a, Grandmother's house. b, Little Red Riding Hood. c, Wolf.
No. 1922, Little Red Riding Hood, wolf, horiz. No. 1923, Girl seated on chair from "I'll Tell You a Story."

**1997, May 20 Perf. 13½x14**
1921 A300 10d Sheet of 3, #a.-c. 6.00 6.00
**Souvenir Sheet**
**Perf. 14x13½**
1922 A300 10d multicolored 4.50 4.50
**Perf. 14**
1923 A301 25d multicolored 5.25 5.25

Paintings, by Hiroshige (1797-1858)
A302

No. 1924, 4d: a, Morning Glory and Cricket. b, Dragonfly and Begonia. c, Two Ducks Swimming among Reeds. d, A Black-Naped Oriole Perched on a Stem of Rose Mallow. e, A Pheasant on a Snow-covered Pine. f, A Cuckoo Flying through the Rain.
No. 1925, 4d: a, An Egret among Rushes. b, Peacock and Peonies. c, Three Wild Geese Flying across the Moon. d, A Cock in the Snow. e, A Pheasant and Bracken. f, Peonies.
No. 1926, 4d: a, Sparrow and Bamboo. b, Mandarin Ducks on an Icy Pond with Brown Leaves Falling. c, Blossoming Plum Tree. d, Java Sparrow and Magnolia. e, Chinese Bellflowers and Miscanthus. f, A Small Black Bird Clinging to a Tendril of Ivy.
No. 1927, 4d: a, Sparrows and Camellia in Snow. b, Parrot on a Branch of Pine. c, A Long-tailed Blue Bird on a Branch of Flowering Plum. d, Sparrow and Bamboo. e, Bird in a Tree. f, A Wild Duck Swimming beneath Snow-laden Reeds.
No. 1928, 5d: a, Kingfisher above a Yellow-flowered Water Plant. b, Wagtail and Roses. c, A Mandarin Duck on a Snowy Bank. d, A Japanese White-eye on a Persimmon Branch. e, Sparrows and Camellia in Snow. f, Kingfisher and Moon above a Yellow-flowered Water Plant.
No. 1929, 5d: a, Sparrow and Bamboo. b, Birds Flying over Waves. c, Blossoming Plum Tree with Full Moon. d, Kingfisher and Iris. e, A Blue-and-white Flycatcher on a Hibiscus Flower. f, Mandarin Ducks in Snowfall.
Unidentified paintings of: No. 1930, 25d, Falcon on perch. No. 1931, 25d, Two birds seated on branch. No. 1932, 25d, Kingfisher above iris. No. 1933, 25d, Like #1925c. No. 1934, 25d, Bird on grapevine. No. 1935, 25d, Small bird in flowering tree.

**1997, May 20 Perf. 14**
**Sheets of 6, #a-f**
1924-1926 A302 Set of 3 15.00 15.00
1927-1929 A302 Set of 3 19.00 19.00
**Souvenir Sheets**
1930-1935 A302 Set of 6 33.00 33.00

Return of Hong Kong & Macao to China — A303

No. 1936: a, Signing of joint declaration on question of Macao, 1987. b, Deng Xiaoping sharing toast with Portugal's Prime Minister Anibal Cavaco Silva after signing declaration. c, Deng Xiaoping, Britain's Prime Minister Margaret Thatcher sharing toast after signing Sino-British Declaration, 1984. d, Signing of the Sino-British Joint Declaration on question of Hong Kong, 1984.
No. 1937: a, Sir Henry Pottinger, 1st governor of Hong Kong, 1841-44, Hong Kong Island ceded to Britain, 1843. b, Sir Hercules Robinson, governor 1859-65, Kowloon ceded to Britain, 1860. c, Sir Henry Blake, governor 1898-1903, New Territories leased to Britain, 1899.
No. 1938: a, Ships in harbor, Sir Henry Pottinger. b, Suspension bridge, Chris Patten, governor of Hong Kong, 1992-1997. c, Skyline at night, C.H. Tung, first Chinese chief executive, 1997.
No. 1939: a, Signing of Treaty of Nanking, 1842. b, Signing of Japanese surrender document, 1945. c, Signing of Sino-British Joint Declaration on question of Hong Kong, 1984, diff.
Illustration reduced.

**1997, July 1**
1936 A303 3d Sheet of 4, #a.-d. 2.75 2.75
1937 A303 4d Sheet of 3, #a.-c. 2.75 2.75
1938 A303 5d Sheet of 3, #a.-c. 3.25 3.25
1939 A303 6d Sheet of 3, #a.-c. 3.75 3.75

Wonders of the World — A304

Designs: 63b, Great Mosque at Samarra, Iraq, vert. (24x38mm). 75b, Moai stone faces, Easter Island. 1d, Golden Gate Bridge, San Francisco. 1.50d, Statue of Liberty, New York, vert. (24x38mm). 2d, Parthenon, Greece. 3d, Pyramid of the Sun, Teotihuacán, Mexico.
No. 1946, 5d: a, Rock of Gibraltar. b, St. Peter's Basilica, Vatican City. c, Santa Sophia, Istanbul. d, Gateway Arch, St. Louis. e, Great Wall of China. f, Carcassonne, France.
No. 1947, 5d: a, Stonehenge, England. b, Hughes HK-1 Hercules "Spruce Goose" airplane. c, Hoverspeed catamaran, Great Britain. d, Jet powered "Thrust 2." e, Djoser Step Pyramid, Egypt. f, Mallard steam locomotive.
No. 1948, 25d, Grand Canyon of the Colorado River, Arizona. No. 1949, 25d, Mt. Everest, Nepal. No. 1950, 25d, Washington Monument, Washington, DC.

**1997, July 15**
1940-1945 A304 Set of 6 3.75 3.75
**Sheets of 6, #a-f**
1946-1947 A304 Set of 2 12.50 12.50
**Souvenir Sheets**
1948-1950 A304 Set of 3 15.00 15.00

1993 Winter Olympics, Nagano
A305

Designs: 5d, Downhill skiing. 10d, Luge. 15d, Speed skating. 20d, Ice hockey.
No. 1955, 5d: a, Luge, diff. b, Ice hockey (goalie). c, 4-man bobsled. d, Ski jumping. e, Curling. f, Women's figure skating. g, Speed skating, diff. h, Biathlon. i, Downhill skiing, diff.
No. 1956, 5d, vert: a, 2-man bobsled. b, Free-style skiing. c, Ski jumping, diff. d, Downhill skiing, diff. e, Women's figure skating, diff. f, Slalom skiing. g, Pairs figure skating. h, Cross-country skiing. i, Ski jumping, diff.
No. 1957, 25d, Female figure skater, vert. No. 1958, 25d, 2-man bobsled, diff.

**1997, July 21 Litho. Perf. 14**
1951-1954 A305 Set of 4 11.00 11.00
**Sheets of 9, #a-i**
1955-1956 A305 Set of 2 21.00 21.00
**Souvenir Sheets**
1957-1958 A305 Set of 2 12.00 12.00

Cats
A306

Designs: 63b, Scottish fold. 1.50d, American curl. 2d, British bi-color. 3d, Devon rex. 6d, Silver tabby 20d, Abyssinian.
No. 1965: a, Burmilla. b, Blue Burmese. c, Korat. d, British tabby. e, Foreign white. f, Somali.
No. 1966, 25d, Cornish rex. No. 1967, 25d, Siamese.

**1997, Aug. 12**
1959-1964 A306 Set of 6 8.75 8.75
1965 A306 5d Sheet of 6, #a.-
f. 8.00 8.00
**Souvenir Sheets**
1966-1967 A306 Set of 2 12.50 12.50

Dinosaurs
A307

Designs: 50b, Coelophysis, ornitholestes. 63b, Spinosaurus. 75b, Kentrosaurus. 1d, Ceratosaurus. 1.50d, Stygimoloch. 2d, Troodon. 3d, Velociraptor. 4d, Triceratops. 5d, Protoceratops. 10d, Ornithomimus. 15d, Stegosaurus. 20d, Ankylosaurus saichania.
No. 1980, 4d: a, Anurognathus. b, Pteranodon. c, Pterosaurus. d, Saltasaurus. e, Agathaumus. f, Stegosaurus. g, Albertosaurus libratus. h, 4 Lesothosaurus. i, 7 Lesothosaurus.
No. 1981, 5d: a, Tarbosaurus bataar. b, Brachiosaurus. c, Styracosasaurus. d, Baryonyx. e, Coelophysis. f, Carnotaurus. g, Compsognathus longipes. h, Compsognathus-elegant jaw. i, Stenonychosaurus.
No. 1982, 25d, Deinonychus. No. 1983, 25d, Seismosaurus.

**1997, June 23 Litho. Perf. 14**
1968-1979 A307 Set of 12 17.50 17.50
**Sheets of 9, #a-i**
1980-1981 A307 Set of 2 13.50 13.50
**Souvenir Sheets**
1982-1983 A307 Set of 2 13.00 13.00
No. 1982 contains one 50x38mm stamp. No. 1983 contains one 89x28mm stamp.

Dogs
A308

Designs: 75b, Dalmatian. 1d, Rottweiler. 3d, Newfoundland. 4d, Great Dane. 10d, Old English sheepdog. 15d, Queensland heeler.
No. 1990: a, Akita. b, Welsh corgi. c, German shepherd. d, St. Bernard. e, Bullmastiff. f, Malamute.
No. 1991, 25d, Doberman pinscher. No. 1992, 25d, Boxer.

**1997, Aug. 12**
1984-1989 A308 Set of 6 8.75 8.75
1990 A308 5d Sheet of 6, #a.-
f. 8.00 8.00
**Souvenir Sheets**
1991-1992 A308 Set of 2 12.50 12.50

1998 World Cup Soccer Championships, France — A309

Winning teams: 1d, Uruguay, 1950. 1.50d, W. Germany, 1954. 2d, Brazil, 1970. 3d, Brazil, 1962. 5d, Italy, 1938. 10d, Uruguay, 1930.
No. 1999, 4d: a, Brazil, 1994. b, Argentina, 1986. c, Brazil, 1970. d, Italy, 1934. e, Uruguay, 1958. f, England, 1966. g, Brazil, 1962. h, W. Germany, 1990.
No. 2000, 4d: a, Mario Kempes, Argentina, 1978. b, Ademir, Brazil, 1950. c, Muller, W. Germany, 1970. d, Lineker, England, 1986. e, Eusebio, Portugal, 1966. f, Schillaci, Italy, 1990. g, Lata, Poland, 1974. h, Rossi, Italy, 1982.
No. 2001, 4d, vert: a, Kinkladze, Georgia. b, Shearer, England. c, Dani, Portugal. d, Weah, Liberia. e, Ravanelli, Italy. f, Raducioiu, Romania. g, Peter Schmeichel, Denmark. h, Bergkamp, Holland.
No. 2002, 4d, vert: a, Moore, England, 1966. b, Fritzwalter, W. Germany, 1954. c, Beckenbauer, W. Germany, 1974. d, Zoff, Italy, 1982. e, Maradona, Argentina, 1986. f, Passarella, Argentina, 1978. g, Matthäus, W. Germany, 1990. h, Dunga, Brazil, 1994.
No. 2003, 25d, Pele, Brazil. No. 2004, 25d, Eusebio, Portugal. No. 2005, 25d, Juninho, Brazil. No. 2006, 25d, Philippe Albert, Belgium.

**1997, Sept. 4** *Perf. 14x13½, 13½x14*
1993-1998 A309 Set of 6    5.00 5.00
**Sheets of 8, #a-h, + Label**
1999-2002 A309 Set of 4   30.00 30.00
**Souvenir Sheets**
2003-2006 A309 Set of 4   25.00 25.00

Sea Birds
A310

Designs: 5d, Red-legged cormorant. 10d, Roseate tern. 15d, Blue-footed booby. 20d, Sanderling.
No. 2011: a, Brown pelican. b, Galapagos penguin. c, Red billed tropic bird. d, Little tern. e, Dunlin. f, Kittiwake. g, Atlantic puffin. h, Wandering albatross. i, Masked booby. j, Glaucous winged gull. k, Artic tern. l, Piping plover.
No. 2012, 23d, Osprey. No. 2013, 23d, Long-tailed skua.

**1997, Aug. 4**   Litho.   *Perf. 14*
2007-2010 A310 Set of 4   11.00 11.00
2011 A310 3d Sheet of 12, #a.-l.    9.50 9.50
**Souvenir Sheets**
2012-2013 A310 Set of 2   9.00 9.00

A311

Diana, Princess of Wales (1961-97) — A312

Various portraits.

**1997, Nov. 26**   Litho.   *Perf. 14*
2014 A311 10d Sheet of 4, #a.-d. 8.50 8.50
**Souvenir Sheet**
2015 A312 25d multicolored   5.75 5.75

Christmas
A313

Entire paintings or details: 1d, Angel, by Rembrandt. 1.50d, Initiation into the Rites of

Dionysus, in Villa dei Misteri, Pompeii. 2d, Pair of Erotes with Purple Cloaks. 3d, The Ecstasy of Saint Teresa, by Gianlorenzo Bernini (carving). 5d, Annunciation, by Mathias Grunewald. 10d, Angel Playing the Organ, by Stefan Lochner.
No. 2022, 25d, The Rest on the Flight into Egypt, by Caravaggio. No. 2023, 25d, Education of Cupid, by Titian.

**1997, Dec. 8**
2016-2021 A313 Set of 6   8.25 8.25
**Souvenir Sheets**
2022-2023 A313 Set of 2   10.50 10.50

New Year 1998
(Year of the Tiger) — A314

No. 2024 — Various stylized tigers with: a, Yellow brown background. b, Purple background. c, Brown background. d, Orange background.
10d, Tiger, landscape.

**1998, Jan. 5**   Litho.   *Perf. 14½*
2024 A314 3d Sheet of 4, #a.-d. 2.75 2.75
**Souvenir Sheet**
*Perf. 14*
2025 A314 10d multicolored   2.75 2.75
No. 2025 contains one 38x24mm stamp.

Trains
A315

No. 2026, 5d: a, Electric Train, Scotland. b, Beaconsfield, China. c, TGV, France. d, People Mover, England. e, ICE train, Germany. f, Montmartre Funicular, France.
No. 2027, 5d: a, SD70 Burlington Northern, US. b, Mallard, England. c, Baldwin 4-8-0, Peru. d, Sweden Rail. e, Rack Train, Amberawa-Java. f, Beyer-Peacock, Pakistan.
No. 2028, 25d, Monorail, England. No. 2029, 25d, Southern Pacific, US.

**1998, May 19**   Litho.   *Perf. 14*
**Sheets of 6, #a-f**
2026-2027 A315 Set of 2   14.00 14.00
**Souvenir Sheets**
2028-2029 A315 Set of 2   10.50 10.50

Flowers
A316

Designs, vert: 75b, Daffodil. 1.50d, Transvaal daisy. 3d, Torchlily. 4d, Ancistrochilus rothschildianus. 10d, Polystachya vulcanica. 15d, Gladiolus.
No. 2036: a, Adenium multiflorum. b, Huernia namaquensis. c, Gloriosa superba. d, Strelitzia reginae. e, Passiflora mollissima. f, Bauhinia variegata.
No. 2037, 25d, Aerangis rhodosticta, vert. No. 2038, 25d, Ansella gigantea, vert.

**1998, June 2**   Litho.   *Perf. 14*
2030-2035 A316 Set of 6   8.50 8.50
2036 A316 5d Sheet of 6, #a.-f.    7.50 7.50
**Souvenir Sheets**
2037-2038 A316 Set of 2   12.00 12.00

Historical Aircraft
A317

No. 2039, 5d: a, Short Type 38, 1913. b, Fokker F.VII B 3m, 1925. c, Junkers F-13,

1919. d, Pitcairn "Mailwing," 1927. e, Douglas, 1920. f, Curtiss "Condor," 1934.
No. 2040, 5d: a, Wright Brothers, 1903. b, Curtiss, 1910. c, Farman, 1907. d, Bristol, 1911. e, Antoinette, 1908. f, Sopwith "Bat Boat," 1912.
No. 2041, 25d, Albatross, 1913. No. 2042, 25d, Boeing 247, 1932.

**1998, June 10**
**Sheets of 6, #a-f**
2039-2040 A317 Set of 2   15.00 15.00
**Souvenir Sheets**
2041-2042 A317 Set of 2   12.00 12.00
No. 2041-2042 each contain one 85x28mm stamp.

Disney's "Mulan"
A318

Characters from the animated movie — No. 2043: a, Mulan. b, Mushu. c, Little Brother. d, Cri-Kee. e, Grandmother Fa. f, Fa Li. g, Fa Zhou. h, Mulan and Khan.
No. 2044: a, Mulan riding Khan. b, Shang. c, Chi Fu. d, Chien-Po. e, Yao. f, Ling. g, Shan-Yu. h, Mulan, Shang & Mushu.
No. 2045, 25d, Mulan. No. 2046, 25d, Mulan riding Khan, diff. No. 2047, 25d, Mulan jumping in air. No. 2048, 25d, Mulan looking at Shang (in margin).

**1998, July 1**   Litho.   *Perf. 13½x14*
2043 A318 4d Sheet of 8, #a.-h. 11.00 11.00
2044 A318 5d Sheet of 8, #a.-h. 11.50 11.50
**Souvenir Sheets**
2045-2048 A318 Set of 4   30.00 30.00

Ferrari Automobiles — A318a

No. 2048A: c, 365 GTB/4. d, Daytona. e, 1966 275 GTB.
25d, 365 GTB/4, diff.
Illustration reduced.

**1998, Oct. 29**   Litho.   *Perf. 14*
2048A A318a 10d Sheet of 3, #c-e    5.75 5.75
**Souvenir Sheet**
*Perf. 13¾x14¼*
2048B A318a 25d multi   5.00 5.00
No. 2048A contains three 39x25mm stamps.

Famous People — A319    Sinking of the Titanic — A320

No. 2049, 4d — Jazz musicians: a, Sidney Bechet (1897-1959). b, Bechet playing clarinet. c, "Duke" Ellington conducting band. d, Ellington (1899-1974). e, Louis Armstrong (1900-71). f, Armstrong playing trumpet. g, Charlie "Bird" Parker playing saxophone. h, Parker (1920-55).

No. 2050, 4d —2:49 PM 12/6/2007 Composers: a, Cole Porter (1893-1964). b, "Born to Dance," by Porter. c, "Porgy and Bess," by George Gershwin. d, Gershwin (1898-1937). e, Richard Rodgers (1902-79) & Oscar Hammerstein II (1895-1960). f, "The King and I," by Rodgers & Hammerstein. g, "West Side Story," by Leonard Bernstein. h, Bernstein (1918-90).
No. 2051, 25d, Ella Fitzgerald (1917-96). No. 2052, 25d, Irving Berlin (1888-1989), "Oh How I Hate to Get Up in the Morning."

**1998, Oct. 12**   Litho.   *Perf. 14*
**Sheets of 8, #a-h**
2049-2050 A319 Set of 2   15.00 15.00
**Souvenir Sheets**
2051-2052 A319 Set of 2   14.00 14.00
Nos. 2049b-2049c, 2049f-2049g, 2050b-2050c, 2050f-2050g are 53x38mm.

**1998, Oct. 25**
No. 2053: a, Capt. Edward J. Smith. b, Molly Brown. c, News of the disaster breaks. d, Benjamin Guggenheim. e, Isidor Strauss. f, Ida Strauss.
No. 2054, 25d, Picture of ship on postcard. No. 2055, 25d, Ship sinking. No. 2056, 25d, Remains of ship lying on bottom of ocean years later.
2053 A320 5d Sheet of 6, #a.-f.    8.25 8.25
**Souvenir Sheets**
2054-2056 A320 Set of 3   19.00 19.00

Diana, Princess of Wales (1961-97)
A321

**1998, Oct. 29**   *Perf. 14½x14*
2057 A321 10d multicolored   2.00 2.00
Issued in sheets of 6.

Pablo Picasso (1881-1973) — A322

Paintings: 3d, Death of Casagemas, 1901. 5d, Seated Woman, 1920, vert. 10d, Mother and Child, 1907, vert.
25d, Child Playing with a Toy Truck, 1953, vert.

**1998, Oct. 29**   *Perf. 14½*
2058-2060 A322 Set of 3   3.50 3.50
**Souvenir Sheet**
2061 A322 25d multicolored   5.00 5.00

A323     A324

No. 2062 — Mahatma Gandhi (1869-1948): a, Age 62, 1932. b, Age 60, 1930, with Sarojini Naidu. c, Age 61, 1931, spinning yarn. d, Age 47, 1916.
25d, Age 61, 1931.

**1998, Oct. 29**   *Perf. 14*
2062 A323 10d Sheet of 4, #a.-d. 7.50 7.50
**Souvenir Sheet**
2063 A323 25d multicolored   5.00 5.00
Nos. 2062b-2062c are 53x39mm.

## 1998

Ships: 2d, Chinese Junk. 3d, HMS Victory. 10d, County Class Destroyer. 15d, Viking Longboat.

No. 2068, 5d, horiz: a, HMS Dreadnought. b, Truxton Class Cruiser. c, Queen Mary. d, Canberra. e, Queen Elizabeth. f, Queen Elizabeth 2.

No. 2069, 5d: a, Santa Maria. b, Mary Rose. c, Mayflower. d, Ark Royal. e, HMS Beagle. f, HMS Bounty.

No. 2070, 25d, Cutty Sark. No. 2071, 25d, Sovereign of the Seas.

| 2064-2067 | A324 | Set of 4 | 6.00 | 6.00 |

**Sheets of 6, #a-f**

| 2068-2069 | A324 | Set of 2 | 12.00 | 12.00 |

**Souvenir Sheets**

| 2070-2071 | A324 | Set of 2 | 10.00 | 10.00 |

No. 2070 contains one 42x56mm stamp; No. 2071, one 56x42mm stamp.

1998 World Scouting Jamboree, Chile — A325

No. 2072: a, Scout handclasp. b, Small boat sailing. c, Scout salute.
No. 2073, Lord Robert Baden-Powell.

**1998, Oct. 29    Litho.    Perf. 14**
| 2072 | A325 | 10d Sheet of 3, #a.-c. | 6.00 | 6.00 |

**Souvenir Sheet**
| 2073 | A325 | 25d multicolored | 5.00 | 5.00 |

Royal Air Force, 80th Anniv. A326

No. 2074, 5d: a, Sepecat Jaguar GR1. b, BAe Harrier GR7. c, Panavia Tornado GR1 firing Sidewinder AIM 9-L missle. d, Panavia Tornado GR1 on afterburner.

No. 2075, 5d: a, Sepecat Jaguar GR1A in low visibility gray finish. b, Panavia Tornado GR1A. c, Sepecat Jaguar GR1A in Bosnia theater camouflage finish. d, BAe Hawk 200.

No. 2076, 7d: a, Panavia Tornado GR1 flying left. b, BAe Hawk TIA. c, Sepecat Jaguar GR1A. d, Panavia Tornado GR1 flying right.

No. 2077, 20d, Eurofighters. No. 2078, 25d, Biplane, hawk's head. No. 2079, 25d, Lightning, Eurofighter. No. 2080, 25d, Biplane, hawk in flight. No. 2081, 25d, Lancaster, Eurofighter. No. 2082, 25d, Biplane, hawk perched.

**1998, Oct. 29**
**Sheets of 4, #a-d**
| 2074-2076 | A326 | Set of 3 | 13.50 | 13.50 |

**Souvenir Sheets**
| 2077-2082 | A326 | Set of 6 | 29.00 | 29.00 |

Paintings by Eugène Delacroix (1798-1863) — A327

No. 2083, 4d: a, Mule Drivers from Tetuan. b, Encampment of Arab Mule Drivers. c, An Orange Seller. d, The Banks of the River. e, View of Tangier from the Seashore. f, Arab Horses Fighting in a Stable. g, Horses at the Trough. h, The Combat of the Giaour and Hassan.

No. 2084, 4d, vert: a, Moroccan from Tangier Standing. b, A Man of Tangier. c, Young Arab Standing with a Rifle. d, Moroccan Chieftan. e, Jewish Bride of Tangiers. f, Seated Jewess from Morocco. g, A seated Arab. h, Young Arab Seated by a Wall.

No. 2085, 4d: a, Turk Seated on a Sofa Smoking. b, View of Tangier from North African and Spanish Album. c, The Spanish Coast at Salobrena from North African and Spanish Album. d, The Aissaouas. e, Sea View from the Heights of Dieppe. f, An Arab Fantasy. g, Arab Comic Fantasy. h, An Arab Camp at Night.

Details: No. 2086, 25d, Self-portrait, vert. No. 2087, 25d, Two Women of Algiers in Their Apartment. No. 2088, 25d, Massacre of Chios.

**1998, Oct. 29**
**Sheets of 8, #a-h**
| 2083-2085 | A327 | Set of 3 | 19.50 | 19.50 |

**Souvenir Sheets**
| 2086-2088 | A327 | Set of 3 | 15.00 | 15.00 |

Christmas — A328

Designs: 1d, Beagle in sock. 2d, Giraffe, wreath. 3d, Rainbow bee eater, ribbon, ornament. 4d, Adult deer. 5d, Fawn. 10d, Irish red and white setter in package.
No. 2095, 25d, Brown classic tabby kitten. No. 2096, 25d, Basset hound, rough collie.

**1998, Nov. 23**
| 2089-2094 | A328 | Set of 6 | 5.00 | 5.00 |

**Souvenir Sheets**
| 2095-2096 | A328 | Set of 2 | 10.00 | 10.00 |

New Year 1999 (Year of the Rabbit) — A329

No. 2097 — Stylized rabbits, background color: a, Olive brown. b, Green blue. c, Red brown. d, Pale orange.

**1999, Jan. 4    Litho.    Perf. 14½**
| 2097 | A329 | 3d Sheet of 4, #a.-d. | 2.40 | 2.40 |

**Souvenir Sheet**
| 2098 | A329 | 10d multicolored | 2.00 | 2.00 |

No. 2098 contains one 39x24mm stamp.

Disney's Jungle Book A330

No. 2099: a, Mowgli, King Louie (bear). b, Mowgli, snake. c, Flunky Monkey. d, Monkey singing. e, Girl. f, Mowgli, Flunky Monkey. g, Mowgli, buzzards. h, Shere Khan (tiger).
No. 2100, 25d, Baby elephant, horiz. No. 2101, 25d, King Louie, horiz.

**1999, Mar. 11  Litho.   Perf. 13½x14**
| 2099 | A330 | 5d Sheet of 8, #a.-h. | 7.50 | 7.50 |

**Souvenir Sheets**
| 2100-2101 | A330 | Set of 2 | 10.00 | 10.00 |

Australia '99, World Stamp Expo A331

No. 2102, 6d — African butterflies: a, Golden piper. b, Citrus swallowtail. c, Azure

hairstreak. d, Two-tailed pasha. e, Blue pansy. f, African leaf butterfly.
No. 2103, 6d: a, Plain tiger. b, Blue swallowtail. c, Papilio mnesheus. d, Common opal. e, Forest green. f, Boisduval's false acraea.
No. 2104, 25d, Pirate butterfly, vert. No. 2105, 25d, Two-tailed pasha, vert.

**1999, Apr. 12    Litho.    Perf. 14**
**Sheets of 6, #a-f**
| 2102-2103 | A331 | Set of 2 | 13.00 | 13.00 |

**Souvenir Sheets**
| 2104-2105 | A331 | Set of 2 | 10.00 | 10.00 |

Wedding of Prince Edward and Sophie Rhys-Jones A332

No. 2106 — Various portraits of couple showing Sophie with: a, Blue collar. b, Long hair. c, Red collar.
25d, Couple, horiz.

**1999, June 19   Litho.   Perf. 13½**
| 2106 | A332 | 10d Sheet of 3, #a.-c. | 5.50 | 5.50 |

**Souvenir Sheet**
| 2107 | A332 | 25d multicolored | 5.00 | 5.00 |

IBRA '99, World Philatelic Exhibition, Nuremberg — A333

Exhibition emblem, Adler 2-3-2 steam engine and: 4d, Samoa #104d. 5d, Samoa #55.
Emblem, sailing ship Friedrech August and: 10d, Samoa #64, #65. 15d, Samoa #67. 25d, Cover with Samoa #67 (part), 68.
Illustration reduced.

**1999, July 6         Perf. 14x14¼**
| 2108-2111 | A333 | Set of 4 | 6.75 | 6.75 |

**Souvenir Sheet**
| 2112 | A333 | 25d multicolored | 5.00 | 5.00 |

No. 2112 contains one 60x40mm stamp.

Apollo 11 Moon Landing, 30th Anniv. — A334

No. 2113: a, Bell X-14A VTOL aircraft. b, Lunar landing prototype rig. c, Early prototype lander. d, Zero gravity training. e, Jet pack training. f, Lunar lander pilot training.
No. 2114, 25d, Apollo 11 Eagle, horiz. No. 2115, 25d, Apollo 11 splash down, horiz.

**1999, July 6         Perf. 14**
| 2113 | A334 | 6d Sheet of 6, #a.-f. | 6.50 | 6.50 |

**Souvenir Sheets**
| 2114-2115 | A334 | Set of 2 | 10.00 | 10.00 |

PhilexFrance '99, World Philatelic Exhibition — A335

Early railroads: No. 2116, 25d, Road-railer carriage. No. 2117, 25d, 2-2-2 Passenger locomotive, 1846.
Illustration reduced.

**1999, July 6         Perf. 13¾**
| 2116-2117 | A335 | Set of 2 | 10.00 | 10.00 |

Roots Homecoming Festival — A336

Designs: 1d, Cannon, Freedom Post, Juffureh. 2d, Fort Bullen, Barra. 3d, James Fort Island.

**1999, June 21   Litho.   Perf. 14**
| 2118-2120 | A336 | Set of 3 | 1.10 | 1.10 |

UN Rights of the Child, 10th Anniv. — A337

No. 2121 — Children: a, With head down on table. b, Drinking from cup. c, Drawing on paper.
25d, Child smiling under umbrella.

**1999, July 6**
| 2121 | A337 | 10d Sheet of 3, #a.-c. | 5.75 | 5.75 |

**Souvenir Sheet**
| 2122 | A337 | 25d multicolored | 5.00 | 5.00 |

Johann Wolfgang von Goethe (1749-1832), Poet — A338

No. 2123: a, Faust quaffs the spirit's nectar. b, Portraits of Goethe and Friedrich von Schiller (1759-1805). c, Faust contemplates mortality.
25d, Portrait of Goethe, vert.

**1999, July 6**
| 2123 | A338 | 15d Sheet of 3, #a.-c. | 8.50 | 8.50 |

**Souvenir Sheet**
| 2124 | A338 | 25d multicolored | 5.00 | 5.00 |

Paintings by
Hokusai
(1760-1849)
A339

No. 2125, 5d — Details or entire paintings:
a, Bunshosei. b, Overthrower of Castles,
Overthrower of Nations. c, Bee on Wild Rose.
d, Sei Shonagon. e, Kuan-Yu. f, The Fifth
Month.
No. 2126, 5d: a, Exotic Beauty. b, Wind (2
people). c, Dancing Monkey. d, Lady and
Maiden on an Outing. e, Wind (3 people). f,
Courtesan with Fan.
No. 2127, 25d, People on the Balcony of
Sazaido. No. 2128, 25d, Caocao before the
Battle of Chibi.

**1999, July 6**      **Perf. 13¾**
**Sheets of 6, #a-f**
2125-2126 A339 Set of 2   12.00 12.00
**Souvenir Sheets**
2127-2128 A339 Set of 2   10.00 10.00

Sea Birds
A340

Designs: 2d, American oystercatcher. 3d,
Blue-footed booby. 10d, Western gull. 15d,
Brown pelican.
No. 2133, 4d: a, Atlantic puffin. b, Red-tailed
tropicbird. c, Reddish egret. d, Laughing gull.
e, Great white egret. f, Northern gannet. g,
Forster's tern. h, Great cormorant. i, Razor bill.
No. 2134, 4d: a, Adélie penguin. b, Black
skimmer. c, Erect-crested penguin. d, Heer-
man's gull. e, Glaucous-winged gull. f, Layson
albatross. g, White pelican. h, Tufted puffin. i,
Black guillemot.
No. 2135: a, Razor bill. b, Shelduck. c,
Sandwich tern. d, Arctic skua. e, Gannet. f,
Common gull.
No. 2136, 25d, Pelicans. No. 2137, 25d,
California gull. No. 2138, 25d, Gentoo
penguin.

**1999, Aug. 1**      **Perf. 14**
2129-2132 A340 Set of 4   5.50 5.50
**Sheets of 9, #a-i**
2133-2134 A340 Set of 2   14.50 14.50
2135 A340 5d Sheet of 6, #a-
f   9.75 9.75
**Souvenir Sheets**
2136-2138 A340 Set of 3   15.00 15.00
Nos. 2135-2138 have continuous designs.

Prehistoric Animals — A341

No. 2139, 3d: a, Diatryma. b, Pteranodon. c,
Stegodon. d, Icaronycteris. e, Archaeopteryx.
f, Chasmatosaurus. g, Tytthostonyx. h, Hyae-
nodon. i, Uintatherium. j, Hesperocyon. k,
Ambelodon. l, Indricotherium.
No. 2140, 3d: a, Carnotaurus. b,
Quetzalcoatlus. c, Peteinosaurus. d, Pre-
nocephale. e, Hesperornis. f, Coelophysis. g,
Camptosaurus. h, Panderichthys. i,
Garudimimus. j, Cacops. k, Ichthyostega. l,
Scutellosaurus.
No. 2141, 25d, Lepisosteus. No. 2142, 25d,
Sabertooth cat. No. 2143, 25d, Deinonychus.
No. 2144, 25d, Microceratops.

**1999, Aug. 1**
**Sheets of 12, #a-l**
2139-2140 A341 Set of 2   13.00 13.00
**Souvenir Sheets**
2141-2144 A341 Set of 4   20.00 20.00

Queen Mother,
100th Birthday (in
2000) — A342

No. 2145: a, Duchess of York, Princess Elizabeth, 1928. b, Lady Elizabeth Bowles-Lyon,
1923. c, Queen Elizabeth, 1946. d, Queen
Mother, Prince Harry.
25d, Queen Mother celebrating 89th birthday, 1989.

**1999, Aug. 4**
2145 A342 10d Sheet of 4, #a.-d.
+ label   7.25 7.25
**Souvenir Sheet**
**Perf. 13¾**
2146 A342 25d multicolored   5.00 5.00
No. 2146 contains one 38x51mm stamp.
Margins of sheets are embossed.

Orchids — A343

Designs: 2d, Sophrocattleya. 3d, Cattleya.
4d, Brassolaeliocattleya. 5d, Brassoepiden-
drum. 10d, Sophrolaeliocattleya. 15d,
Iwanagaara.
No. 2153, 6d: a, Brassolaeliocattleya (yellow). b, Cattleytonia. c, Laeliocattleya (yellow).
d, Miltonia. e, Cattleya forbesii. f, Odontoglossum cervantesii.
No. 2154, 6d: a, Lycaste macrobulbon. b,
Laeliocattleya (red). c, Brassocattleya (pink).
d, Cattleya, diff. e, Brassocattleya (speckled).
f, Brassolaeliocattleya (yellow & red).
No. 2155, 25d, Unnamed. No. 2156, 25d,
Brassolaeliocattleya (white & red).

**1999, Aug. 1**      **Perf. 14**
2147-2152 A343 Set of 6   7.25 7.25
**Sheets of 6, #a-f**
2153-2154 A343 Set of 2   14.00 14.00
**Souvenir Sheets**
2155-2156 A343 Set of 2   10.00 10.00

Marine
Fauna
A344

Designs: 1d, Sea gull. 1.50d, Portuguese
man-of-war. 5d, Walrus. 10d, Manatee.
No. 2161, 3d: a, Anglefish. b, Leafy sea
dragon. c, Hawksbill turtle. d, Mandarin fish. e,
Candy cane sea star. f, Plate coral. g, Butterflyfish. h, Coral polyp. i, Hermit crab. j, Strawberry shrimp. k, Giant blue clam. l, Sea
cucumber.
No. 2162, 3d: a, Whale shark. b, Gray reef
shark. c, New ZEngland octopus. d, Puffer
fish. e, Lionfish. f, Squid. g, Chambered nautilus. h, Clown fish. i, Moray eel. j, Spiny lobster.
k, Sotted ray. l, Clown anemone.
25d, Common dolphin.

**1999, Aug. 1**
2157-2160 A344 Set of 4   3.50 3.50
**Sheets of 12, #a-l**
2161-2162 A344 Set of 2   13.00 13.00
2163 A343 25d multicolored   5.00 5.00

Galapagos Islands Marine
Fauna — A345

No. 2164: a, Swallow-tailed gull. b, Frigate
bird. c, Red-footed booby. d, Galapagos hawk.
e, Great blue heron. f, Masked booby. g, Bottlenose dolphins. h, Black grunts. i, Surgeonfish. j, Stingray. k, Pilot whales. l, Pacific
green sea turtle. m, Shark. n, Sea lion. o,
Marine iguana. p, Pacific manta ray. q, Moorish idol. r, Galapagos penguin. s, Silver grunts.
t, Sea urchin. u, Wrasse. v, Almaco
amberjack. w, Blue-chin parrotfish. x, Yellow
sea urchin. y, Lobster. z, Grouper. aa, Scorpionfish. ab, Squirrelfish. ac, Octopus. ad,
King angelfish. ae, Horned shark. af,
Galapagos hogfish. ag, Puffer fish. ah, Moray
eel. ai, Orange tube corals. aj, Whitestripe
chromis. ak, Longnose hawkfish. al, Sea
cucumber. am, Spotted hawkfish. an, Zebra
moray eel.
25d, Emperor penguins.

**1999, Aug. 1**
2164 A345 1.50d Sheet of 40,
#a.-an.   14.00 14.00
**Souvenir Sheet**
2165 A345 25d multicolored   5.00 5.00

Souvenir Sheet

1999 Return of Macao to People's
Republic of China — A346

No. 2166: a, Temple of A-ma. b, Border
gate. c, Ruins of St. Paul's Cathedral.
Illustration reduced.

**1999, Aug. 20**     **Litho.**     **Perf. 14**
2166 A346 7d Sheet of 3, #a-c   4.00 4.00

Space Exploration
A347

Designs: 1d, Telstar I, horiz. 1.50d, Skylab.
2d, Mars 3 orbiter and lander. 3d, COBE. 10d,
Astronaut Bruce McCandless. 15d, Apollo 13.
No. 2173, 6d: a, German V-2 rocket. b,
Delta Straight 8. c, Ariane 4. d, Mercury on
Atlas rocket. e, Saturn 1B. f, Cassini.
No. 2174, 6d, horiz.: a, Mariner 4. b, Viking
Mars orbiter and lander. c, Giotto. d, Luna 9. e,
Voyager. f, Galileo.
No. 2175, 6d, horiz.: a, Soviet Vostok 1. b,
Apollo command and service modules. c,
Mecury capsule. d, Apollo 16 lunar module. e,
Gemini 8. f, Soviet Soyuz.
No. 2176, 25d, Apollo-Soyuz, horiz. No.
2177, 25d, Mars Pathfinder, horiz.

**1999**
2167-2172 A347 Set of 6   6.25 6.25
**Sheets of 6, #a-f**
2173-2175 A347 Set of 3   19.50 19.50
2176-2177 A347 Set of 2   10.00 10.00
#2176-2177 contain one 57x43mm stamp.

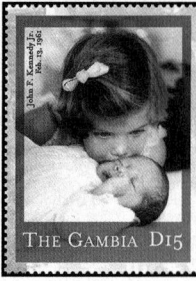

John F.
Kennedy, Jr.
(1960-99)
A348

No. 2178: a, In 1961. b, In 1970s. c, In
1997.

**1999, Dec. 7**
2178 A348 15d Sheet of 3, #a.-c.   7.75 7.75

Flowers — A349

Various flower photographs making up a
photomosaic of Princess Diana.

**1999, Dec. 31**    **Litho.**    **Perf. 13¾**
2179 A349 3d Sheet of 8, #a.-h.   5.00 5.00
See No. 2290.

Millennium
A350

No. 2180, 3d — Highlights of 1450-1500: a,
Da Vinci designs 1st flying machine. b,
Gutenberg prints the Bible. c, 1st book in color
printed. d, Ivan III becomes Grand Prince of
Moscow. e, Ottomans capture Constantinople.
f, Ming emperors rebuild Great Wall of China.
g, Lorenzo de Medici begins rule in Florence.
h, Henry VII becomes first Tudor king of
England. i, Vasco da Gama sails to India. j,
Aragon and Castile unite. k, Birth of Desider-
ius Erasmus. l, Cabot explores No. America.
m, Henry VI wages War of the Roses. n,
Bartholomeu Dias discovers Cape of Good
Hope. o, Matthias Corvinus (Hunyadi)
becomes king of Hungary. p, Columbus sails
to America (60x40mm). q, Girolamo Savonarola burned at stake.
No. 2181, 3d — Highlights of 1900-1910: a,
Max Planck develops quantum theory. b, Graf
Ferdinand von Zeppelin constructs first airship. c, Marconi sends 1st transatlantic message. d, Queen Victoria dies. e, 1st Nobel
Prize. f, Boer War ends. g, Wright Brothers'
1st flight. h, 1st teddy bears made in Germany. i, Work begins on Panama Canal. j,
Einstein develops theory of relativity. k, 1905
revolution in Russia. l, San Francisco earthquake. m, Color photography developed by
Louis Lumière. n, Picasso paints "Les Demoiselles d'Avignon." o, Peary reaches North
Pole. p, Model T appears (60x40mm). q, 1st
kibbutz founded in Holy Land.

**2000, Feb. 1**     **Perf. 12¾x12½**
**Sheets of 17, #a-q**
2180-2181 A350 Set of 2   23.00 23.00
Inscriptions are misspelled on several
stamps on No. 2181.

New Year 2000
(Year of the
Dragon)
A351

No. 2182 — Various dragons and Chinese characters with background colors: a, Blue green. b, Brownish gray. c, Red orange (purple dragon). d, Orange.
15d, Dull orange.

**2000, Feb. 5**      *Perf. 14x14½*
2182 A351 5d Sheet of 4, #a.-d. 4.25 4.25
**Souvenir Sheet**
*Perf. 14*
2183 A351 15d multi     3.00 3.00
No. 2183 contains one 42x28mm stamp.

African Wildlife
A352

Designs: 50b, Indri. 75b, Nubian ibex. 1d, Grevy's zebra, vert. 2d, Bongo, vert. 3d, White rhinoceros. 4d, Lesser galago. 5d, Okapi, vert. 10d, Mhorr gazelle, vert.
No. 2192, 5d: a, Giant sable antelope. b, Greater kudu. c, Somali wild ass. d, Dorcas gazelle. e, Addax. f, Pelzeln's gazelle.
No. 2193, 6d: a, Cheetah. b, Chimpanzee. c, Angwantibo. d, Black rhinoceros. e, Bontebok. f, Giant eland.
No. 2194, 7d: a, Mountain gorilla. b, Black-faced impala. c, Crowned lemur. d, Long-tailed ground roller. e, Brown hyena. f, Mountain zebra.
No. 2195, 7d: a, Sacred ibis. b, Mauritius kestrel. c, Barbary leopard. d, Radiated tortoise. e, Pygmy hippopotamus. f, Bald ibis.
No. 2196, 25d, Aye-aye. No. 2197, 25d, Black lechwe, vert. No. 2198, 25d, Nile crocodile. No. 2199, 25d, African elephant.

**2000, Feb. 18**      *Perf. 14*
2184-2191 A352 Set of 8    4.50 4.50
**Sheets of 6, #a.-f.**
2192-2195 A352 Set of 4   29.00 29.00
**Souvenir Sheets**
2196-2199 A352 Set of 4   23.00 23.00
AmeriStamp Expo, Portland, Ore. (#2194).

The Three Stooges — A353

No. 2200: a, Curly pulling Moe's hair. b, Curly caught in wringer. c, Curly, Moe with drill. d, Moe pulling Larry's hair. e, Moe, f, Moe sticking finger in Curly's nose. g, Stooges pointing. h, Skull biting Curly's nose. i, Shemp.
No. 2201, 25d, Larry with crown. No. 2202, 25d, Curly on telephone, vert.

**2000, Jan. 14**   Litho.    *Perf. 13¼*
2200 A353 5d Sheet of 9, #a.-
    i.        11.50 11.50
**Souvenir Sheets**
2201-2202 A353 Set of 2   10.50 10.50

I Love Lucy — A354

No. 2203: a, Lucy on sofa. b, Lucy, Ricky. c, Fred, Lucy, and Ethel. d, Lucy standing. e, Lucy, Ricky embracing. f, Lucy looking in mirror. g, Lucy with fists clenched. h, Lucy, Ricky on sofa. i, Lucy and Ethel.
No. 2204, 25d, Lucy, Ricky embracing, vert. No. 2205, 25d, Lucy looking in mirror, vert.

**2000, Jan. 14**   Litho.    *Perf. 13¼*
2203 A354 5d Sheet of 9, #a.-
    i.        11.50 11.50
**Souvenir Sheets**
2204-2205 A354 Set of 2   10.50 10.50

Betty Boop
A355

No. 2206: a, In green and yellow outfit. b, In red dress. c, In red shirt and blue jeans. d, In green and brown outfit. e, Seated in chair. f, In orange shirt and blue jeans. g, In fur coat. h, In pink dress. i, With dumbbell and water bottle.
No. 2207, 25d, In yellow flowered dress. No. 2208, 25d, In bathtub.

**2000, Jan. 14**   Litho.    *Perf. 13¼*
2206 A355 5d Sheet of 9, #a.-
    i.        11.50 11.50
**Souvenir Sheets**
2207-2208 A355 Set of 2   10.50 10.50

Paintings of Anthony Van Dyck — A356

No. 2209: a, Samson and Delilah, c. 1619-20. b, Samson and Delilah sketch, 1618-20. c, Samson and Delilah, c. 1628-30.
No. 2210, 5d: a, The Adoration of the Shepherds. b, The Rest on the Flight to Egypt, The Virgin of the Partridges. c, Suffer the Little Children to Come Unto Me. d, Christ and the Moneychangers. e, Feast at the House of Simon the Pharisee. f, The Lamentation Over the Dead Christ.
No. 2211, 5d, vert.: a, Anton Giulo Brignole-Sale. b, Paolina Adorno Brignole-Sale. c, Battina Balbi Durazzo. d, Portrait of a Man of the Cattaneo Family. e, Portrait of a Woman. f, Elena Grimaldi Cattaneo.
No. 2212, 5d, vert.: a, A Genoese Senator. b, A Seated Gentlewoman. c, The Senator's Wife. d, A Genoese Lady, The Marchesa Balbi. e, Polyxena Spinola, Marchesa de Legones. f, Agostino Pallavicini.
No. 2213, 5d, vert.: a, Prince Rupert of the Palatinate. b, William II of Nassau and Orange. c, Prince Charles Louis of the Palatinate. d, Prince Rupert, Count Palatine. e, The Princess Mary. f, Prince Charles Louis, Count Palatine.
No. 2214, 5d, vert.: a, Sir George Villiers and Lady Katherine Manners as Adonis and Venus. b, Lady Mary Villiers with Lord Arran. c, Rachel de Ruvigny, Countess Southampton as Fortune. d, Venus at Forge of Vulcan. e, Daedalus and Icarus. f, The Clipping of Cupid's Wing.
No. 2215, 25d, A Man with His Son. No. 2216, 25d, Prince Charles Louis, Elector Palatine and His Brother, Prince Rupert of the Palatinate, vert. No. 2217, 25d, Venetia, Lady Digby, as Prudence, vert. No. 2218, 25d, Drunken Silenus, vert. No. 2219, 25d, Portrait of a Genoese Lady, vert. No. 2220, 25d, Charles II as Prince of Wales, vert. No. 2221, 25d, William II, Prince of Orange, and His Bride, Mary, Princess Royal of England, vert. No. 2222, 25d, The Three Eldest Children of Charles I, vert.

**2000, May 1**      *Perf. 13¾*
2209 A356 5d Sheet of 3, #a.-
    c.        3.00 3.00
**Sheets of 6, #a.-f.**
2210-2214 A356 Set of 5   30.00 30.00
**Souvenir Sheets**
2215-2222 A356 Set of 8   47.50 47.50

Papal Visits — A357

No. 2223, 6d — 1991-92 Visits: a, Portugal. b, Poland. c, Hungary. d, Brazil. e, Senegal. f, Gambia. g, Guinea. h, Angola. i, Sao Tomé. j, Dominican Republic.
No. 2224, 6d — 1993 Visits: a, Benin. b, Uganda. c, Sudan. d, Albania. e, Spain. f, Jamaica. g, Mexico. h, United States. i, Lithuania. j, Latvia.
No. 2225, 6d — 1993-95 Visits: a, Estonia. b, Croatia. c, Philippines. d, Papua New Guinea. e, Australia. f, Sri Lanka. g, Czech Republic. h, Belgium. i, Slovakia. j, Cameroon.
No. 2226, 6d — 1995-96 Visits: a, South Africa. b, Kenya. c, United States. d, United Nations. e, Guatemala. f, Nicaragua. g, El Salvador. h, Venezuela. i, Tunisia. j, Slovenia.
No. 2227, 6d — 1996-98 Visits: a, Germany. b, Hungary. c, France, 1996. d, Bosnia. e, Czech Republic. f, Lebanon. g, Poland. h, France, 1997. i, Brazil. j, Cuba.
No. 2228, 6d — 1998-99 Visits: a, Nigeria. b, Austria. c, Croatia. d, Mexico. e, United States. f, Romania. g, Poland. h, Slovenia. i, India. j, Georgia.
No. 2229, 25d, Pope rekindles Eternal Flame. No. 2230, 25d, Pope blesses Holy Land. No. 2231, 25d, Pope places prayer on Western Wall. No. 2232, 25d, Pope assisted by Israeli president and prime minister. No. 2233, 25d, Pope prays at Western Wall. No. 2234, 25d, Pope receives Bible from chief rabbis. No. 2235, 25d, Pope touches bowl of soil. No. 2236, 25d, Pope at Yad Vashem, horiz.

**2000, May 15**   Litho.    *Perf. 13¾*
**Sheets of 10, #a.-j, + 2 labels**
2223-2228 A357 Set of 6   63.00 63.00
**Souvenir Sheets**
*Perf. 14½x14¾, 14¾x14½ (#2236)*
2229-2236 A357 Set of 8   36.00 36.00
Stamps from Nos. 2223-2228 are 28x47mm.

Mushrooms
A358

Designs: 4d, Morel. 5d, Chanterelle. 15d, Knight cap. 20d, Spindle.
No. 2241, 7d: a, Yellow parasol. b, Mottle-gill. c, Poplar field cap. d, Caesar's. e, Flame shield-cap. f, Lilac bonnet.
No. 2242, 7d: a, Common puffball. b, Earth star. c, Silky volvar. d, Stump puffball. e, Spindle-stemmed bolete. f, Fox-orange cort.
No. 2243, 25d, Red-stemmed tough shank. No. 2244, 25d, St. George's.

**2000, May 15**      *Perf. 14*
2237-2240 A358 Set of 4   7.75 7.75
**Sheets of 6, #a.-f.**
2241-2242 A358 Set of 2   15.00 15.00
**Souvenir Sheets**
2243-2244 A358 Set of 2   9.00 9.00

First Zeppelin Flight, Cent. — A359

No. 2245: a, LZ-10. b, LZ-127. c, LZ-129. 25d, LZ-130.

**2000, May 1**   Litho.    *Perf. 14*
2245 A359 15d Sheet of 3, #a-c 7.75 7.75
**Souvenir Sheet**
2246 A359 25d multi    4.50 4.50
No. 2246 contains one 50x38mm stamp.

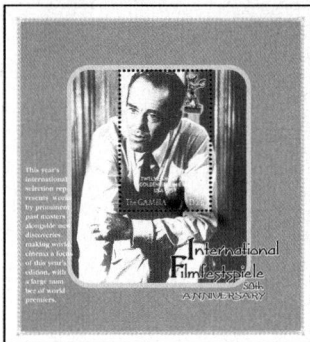

Prince William, 18th Birthday — A360

No. 2247: a, As child. b, In sweater. c, In suit, with flowers. d, In suit.
25d, With Prince Harry.

**2000, May 1**      *Perf. 14*
2247 A360 7d Sheet of 4, #a-d 5.00 5.00
**Souvenir Sheet**
*Perf. 13¾*
2248 A360 25d multi    4.50 4.50
No. 2248 contains one 38x50mm stamp.

Berlin Film Festival, 50th Anniv. — A361

No. 2249: a, Pane. Amore e Fantasia. b, Richard III. c, Smultronstället (Wild Strawberries). d, The Defiant Ones. e, The Living Desert. f, A Bout de Souffle.
25d, Twelve Angry Men.

**2000, May 1**      *Perf. 14*
2249 A361 7d Sheet of 6, #a-f 7.25 7.25
**Souvenir Sheet**
2250 A361 25d multi    4.50 4.50

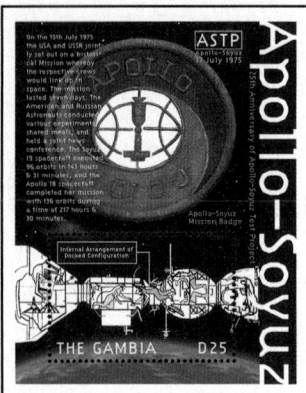

Apollo-Soyuz Mission, 25th Anniv. — A362

No. 2251: a, Donald K. Slayton. b, Thomas P. Stafford. c, Vance D. Brand. 25d, Diagram of docked spacecraft.

**2000, May 1**
2251 A362 15d Sheet of 3, #a-c   7.75 7.75
**Souvenir Sheet**
2252 A362 25d multi   4.50 4.50

**Souvenir Sheet**

2000 Summer Olympics, Sydney — A363

No. 2253: a, Paavo Nurmi. b, Basketball. c, Panathenian Stadium, Athens and Greek flag. d, Ancient Greek chariot racing.

**2000, May 1**
2253 A363 6d Sheet of 4, #a-d   4.25 4.25

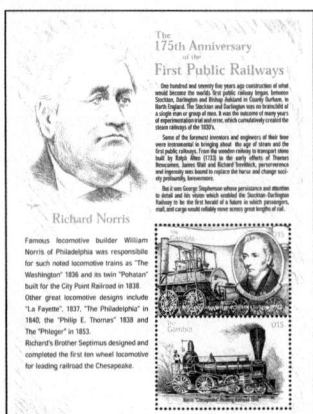

Public Railways, 175th Anniv. — A364

No. 2254: a, Locomotion No. 1, George Stephenson. b, Chesapeake.

**2000, May 1**
2254 A364 15d Sheet of 2, #a-b   5.25 5.25

**Souvenir Sheet**

Johann Sebastian Bach (1685-1750) — A365

**2000, May 1**
2255 A365 25d multi   4.50 4.50

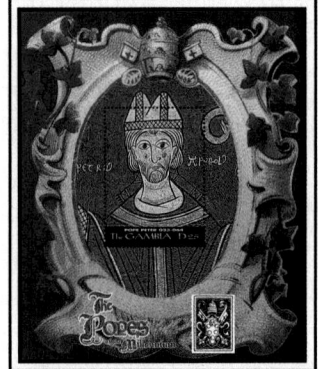

Popes — A366

No. 2256, 7d: a, Pope Felix IV, 526-30. b, Gelasius I, 492-96. c, Gregory I, 590-604. d, Gregory IX, 1227-41. e, Gregory XII, 1406-15. f, Honorius III, 1216-27.
No. 2257, 7d: a, Gregory XIII, 1572-85. b, Urban II, 1088-99. c, Sixtus I, 115-125. d, Pius IX, 1846-78. e, Pius IV, 1559-65. f, Paschal I, 817-24.
No. 2258, 7d: a, Alexander VII, 1655-67. b, Benedict XI, 1303-04. c, Calixtus III, 1455-58. d, Celestine V, 1294. e, Clement IX, 1667-69. f, Fabian, 236-50.
No. 2259, 25d, Peter, 33-64. No. 2260, 25d, Damasus I, 366-384. No. 2261, 25d, John I, 523-526.

**2000, July 26   Litho.   Perf. 13¾**
**Sheets of 6, #a-f**
2256-2258 A366   Set of 3   21.00 21.00
**Souvenir Sheets**
2259-2261 A366   Set of 3   13.00 13.00

Butterflies — A367

Designs: 1.50d, Amphicalia tigris. 2d, Myrina silenus. 3d, Chrysiridia madagascarensis. 5d, Papilionidae. 10d, Dasiothia medea.

**2000, Aug. 7   Perf. 14¾x14**
2262 A367 1.50d multi   .20 .20
2263 A367 2d multi   .35 .35
2264 A367 3d multi   .50 .50
2265 A367 5d multi   .80 .80
2266 A367 10d multi   1.60 1.60
  Nos. 2262-2266 (5)   3.45 3.45

Nos. 2264-2266 exist dated 2003.
See Nos. 2436-2439, 2452-2452B, 2699.

**Souvenir Sheet**

Albert Einstein (1879-1955) — A368

**2000, May 1   Litho.   Perf. 14¼**
2267 A368 25d multi   4.00 4.00

Space — A369

No. 2268, 7d: a, Uhuru. b, Rosat. c, I.U.E. d, Astro E. e, Exosat. f, Chandra.
No. 2269, 7d, vert.: a, Helios. b, Solar Max. c, SOHO. d, O.S.O. e, Special rocket launch. f, I.M.P.
No. 2270, 25d, XMM. No. 2271, 25d, Cassini Huygens.

**2000, May 1   Perf. 14**
**Sheets of 6, #a-f**
2268-2269 A369   Set of 2   12.50 12.50
**Souvenir Sheets**
2270-2271 A369   Set of 2   7.50 7.50

The Stamp Show 2000, London; World Stamp Expo 2000, Anaheim.

Monarchs — A370

No. 2272: a, Charles I of Great Britain, 1625-49. b, Clovis III, king of the Franks (691-95).
No. 2273, 7d: a, Charles II of France, 885-887. b, Catherine de Medici of France, 1547-59. c, Boris Godunov of Russia, 1598-1605. d, Basil III of Russia, 1505-33. e, Anne of Great Britain, 1702-14. f, Charles IX of France, 1560-74.
No. 2274, 7d: a, James IV of Scotland, 1488-1513. b, James V of Scotland, 1513-42. c, James VI of Scotland, 1567-1625. d, Mary of Scotland, 1542-67. e, Mary of Great Britain, 1689-94. f, Elizabeth II, of Great Britain, 1952-present.
No. 2275, 25d, James Francis Edward Stuart. No. 2276, 25d, James IV of Scotland. No. 2277, 25d, Bahadur Shah of India, 1837-57.
Illustration reduced.

**2000, July 26   Perf. 13¾**
2272 A370 7d Sheet of 2, #a-b   2.10 2.10
**Sheets of 6, #a-f**
2273-2274 A370   Set of 2   12.50 12.50
**Souvenir Sheets**
2275-2277 A370   Set of 3   11.00 11.00

Puppies — A371

Designs: 1d, West Highland terrier. 1.50d, Bernese mountain dog. 3d, Yorkshire terrier. 4d, West Highland terrrier, diff. 10d, Chow chow. 15d, Poodle.
No. 2284: a, Border collie (brown and white). b, Border collie (black, brown and white). c, Yorkshire terrier. d, German shepherd. e, Beagle. f, Spaniel.

**2000, Aug. 7   Perf. 14¼**
2278-2283 A371   Set of 6   5.25 5.25
2284 A371 7d Sheet of 6, #a-f   6.25 6.25
**Souvenir Sheet**
2285 A371 25d Boxer   3.50 3.50

The Stamp Show 2000, London (Nos. 2284-2285).

Cats — A372

No. 2286, 4d: a, Egyptian mau. b, Singapura. c, American shorthair. d, Cornish rex. e, Birman. f, Scottish fold. g, Turkish angora. h, Turkish van.
No. 2287, 5d: a, Ragdoll. b, Bombay. c, Korat. d, Somali. e, British shorthair. f, American curl. g, Maine coon cat. h, Like No. 2286h.
No. 2288, 25d, Cat and kitten. No. 2289, 25d, Cat.

**2000, Aug. 7**
**Sheets of 8, #a-h**
2286-2287 A372   Set of 2   10.50 10.50
**Souvenir Sheets**
2288-2289 A372   Set of 2   7.50 7.50

The Stamp Show 2000, London.

**Flower Photomosaic Type of 1999 and**

Queen Mother, 100th Birthday — A373

Designs: No. 2090, Various flower photographs making up a photomosaic of the Queen Mother. No. 2290I: Various photos of religious scenes making up a photomosaic of Pope John Paul II.
Illustration reduced.

**2000, Aug. 7   Litho.   Perf. 13¾**
2290 A349 5d Sheet of 8, #a-h   6.00 6.00
2290I A349 6d Sheet of 8, #j-q   7.50 7.50

**Litho. & Embossed**
**Without Gum**
**Die Cut 9x8¾**

2291 A373 85d multi

Issued: Nos. 2290, 2291 8/7. No. 2290I, 8/8.

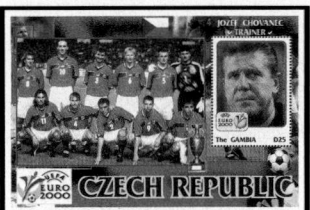

European Soccer
Championships — A374

No. 2292, horiz. — Czech Republic: a, Nedved. b, Team photo. c, Maier. d, Antonin Panenka. e, Selessin Stadium, Liege. f, Patrik Berger.

No. 2293, horiz. — England: a, Alan Shearer. b, Team photo. c, David Seaman. d, Sol Campbell. e, Philips Stadium, Eindhoven. f, Southgate.

No. 2294, horiz. — Norway: a, Leonardsen. b, Team photo. c, Mykland. d, Solbakken. e, Rekdal.

No. 2295, horiz. — Slovenia: a, Aleksander Knavs. b, Team photo. c, Zlatko Zahovic. d, Ales Ceh. e, Stade Communal, Charleroi. f, Miran Pavlin.

No. 2296, horiz. — Sweden: a, Ljungberg. b, Team photo. c, Andersson. d, Nilsson. e, Schwarz.

No. 2297, horiz. — Turkey: a, Yalcin. b, Team photo. c, Buruk. d, Erdem. e, King Baudouin Stadium. f, Korkut.

No. 2298, 25d, Czech Republic coach, Jozef Chovanec. No. 2299, 25d, England coach Kevin Keegan. No. 2300, 25d, Norway coach Nils-Johan Semb. No. 2301, 25d, Slovenia coach Srecko Katanec. No. 2302, 25d, Sweden coaches, Söderberg and Lagerbäck. No. 2303, 25d, Turkey coach Mustafa Denizli. Illustration reduced.

**2000, Aug. 7    Litho.    Perf. 13¾**
| 2292 | A374 | 7d Sheet of 6, #a-f | 6.25 | 6.25 |
| 2293 | A374 | 7d Sheet of 6, #a-f | 6.25 | 6.25 |
| 2294 | A374 | 7d Sheet of 6, #a-e, 2292e | 6.25 | 6.25 |
| 2295 | A374 | 7d Sheet of 6, #a-f | 6.25 | 6.25 |
| 2296 | A374 | 7d Sheet of 6, #a-e, 2293e | 6.25 | 6.25 |
| 2297 | A374 | 7d Sheet of 6, #a-f | 6.25 | 6.25 |
| | | Nos. 2292-2297 (6) | 37.50 | 37.50 |

**Souvenir Sheets**
| 2298-2303 | A374 | Set of 6 | 22.50 | 22.50 |

Paintings of
Birds — A375

Designs: 1.50d, A White Pheasant and Other Fowl in a Classical Landscape, by Abraham Bisschop. 3d, Salmon-crested Cockatoo, by Bartolomeo Bimbi. 4d, A Great Bustard Cock and Other Birds, by Ludger Tom Ring. 15d, A Great Black-backed Gull and Other Birds, by Jokob Bogdani.

No. 2308, 5d: a, Peacocks, Hens and Mouse, by Tobias Stranover. b, Lady in a Red Jacket Feeding a Parrot, by Frans van Mieris. c, Birds by a Pool, by Melchior de Hondecoeter. d, Ganymede and the Eagle, by Peter Paul Rubens. e, Leda and the Swan, by Cesare de Sesto. f, Ducks and Ducklings at the Foot of a Tree in a Mediterranean Landscape, by Adriaen van Oolen. g, Portrait of the Falconer Robert Cheseman Carrying a Hooded Falcon, by Hans Holbein. h, A Golden Pheasant on a Stone Plinth, with Other Birds, by Jacobus Vonck.

No. 2309, 5d, horiz.: a, Still Life of Birds, by Caravaggio (hanging dead birds, basket). b, Turkeys with Young and Rock Doves, by Johan Wenzel Peter. c, The Threatened Swan, by Jan Asselyn. d, Still Life of Fruit and Birds in a Landscape, by Jakab Bogdany. e, Mobbing the Owl, by Tobias Stranover (owl at right, other birds). f, A Concert of Birds, by Hondecoeter (owl, cockatoo at center). g, Owls and Young Ones, by William Tomkins. h, Birds by a Stream, by Jean Baptiste Oudry.

No. 2310, 25d, The King Eagle Pursued to the Sun, by Philip Reinagle. No. 2311, 25d, Still Life of Birds, by Georg Flegl, horiz.

**2000, Oct. 2    Perf. 13½**
| 2304-2307 | A375 | Set of 4 | 3.50 | 3.50 |

**Sheets of 8, #a-h**
| 2308-2309 | A375 | Set of 2 | 12.00 | 12.00 |

**Souvenir Sheets**
| 2310-2311 | A375 | Set of 2 | 7.50 | 7.50 |

Descriptions of paintings are in margins on Nos. 2308-2311.

Paintings from the Prado — A376

No. 2312, 6d: a, The Madonna of the Fish, by Raphael. b, The Holy Family with a Lamb, by Raphael. c, The Madonna of the Stair, by Andrea del Sarto. d, Moneychanger from The Moneychanger and his Wife, by Marinus van Reymerswaele. e, Madonna and Child by Jan Gossaert. f, Wife from The Moneychanger and his Wife.

No. 2313, 6d: a, Bearded man from St. Benedict's Supper, by Juan Andres Ricci. b, Our Lady of the Immaculate Conception, by Francisco de Zurbarán. c, Monk with candle from St. Benedict's Supper. d, The Penitient Magdalen, by José de Ribera. e, Christ as Man of Sorrows, by Antonion de Pereda. f, St. Jerome, by Pereda.

No. 2314, 6d: a, Children with a Shell, by Bartolomé Esteban Murillo. b, Our Lady of the Immaculate Conception, by Murillo. c, The Good Shepherd, by Murillo. d, Woman with red headdress from The Parasol, by Francisco de Goya. e, A Rural Gift, by Ramon Bayeu. f, Woman with blue headdress from The Parasol.

No. 2315, 6d: a, Queen Isabella Farnese, by Jean Ranc. b, Young Woman Seen from the Back, by Jean-Baptiste Greuze. c, Charles III as a Child, by Ranc. d, James Bourdieu, by Sir Joshua Reynolds. e, Dr. Isaac Henrique Sequeira, by Thomas Gainsborough. f, Portrait of a Clergyman, by Reynolds.

No. 2316, 6d: a, Portrait of a Young Woman, by Zacarias González Velázquez. b, The Painter Francisco de Goya, by Vicente Lopez Portaña. c, Portrait of a Girl, by Rafael Tejeo Diaz. d, Mary, from The Nativity, by Federico Barocci. e, Madonna and Child with St. John, by Correggio. f, Jesus, from The Nativity.

No. 2317, 6d: a, St. Andrew, by Francisco Rizi. b, Christ Crucified, by Diego Velázquez. c, St. Onuphrius, by Francisco Collantes. d, Charles II, by Juan Carreño de Miranda. e, St. Sebastian, by Carreño de Miranda. f, Peter Ivanovich Potemkin, by Carreño de Miranda.

No. 2318, 25d, The Defense of Cádiz Against the English, by Zurbarán. No. 2319, 25d, The Surrender of Juliers, by Jusepe Leonardo. No. 2320, 25d, The Holy Family with a Bird, by Murillo. No. 2321, 25d, Danäe, by Titian, horiz. No. 2322, 25d, Venus and Adonis, by Paolo Veronese, horiz. No. 2323, 25d, Jacob's Dream, by Ribera.

**2000, Oct. 6    Perf. 12x12¼, 12¼x12**
**Sheets of 6, #a-f**
| 2312-2317 | A376 | Set of 6 | 32.50 | 32.50 |

**Souvenir Sheets**
| 2318-2323 | A376 | Set of 6 | 22.50 | 22.50 |

Espana 2000, Intl. Philatelic Exhibition.

Battle of Britain, 60th Anniv. — A377

No. 2324, 5d, horiz.: a, Hurricane downing German BF109. b, Spitfire over River Thames. c, Flight Lt. Denys E. Gilliam attacking German Dornier 217 planes. d, Hurricanes heading to intercept Luftwaffe bombers. e, Hurricanes returning to Croydon. f, G.A. Langley in combat with BF109. g, Bristol Blenheim IV over English Channel. h, Spitfires taking off from Hornchurch.

No. 2325, 5d, horiz.: a, Plane from 29th Blenheim Squadron heading to Norwegian coast. b, Luftwaffe pilot Helmut Wick downs RAF pilot John Cock. c, Spitfire downs Dornier 217 off Dover. d, Bristol Beaufighter IIF on patrol. e, Bolton-Paul Defiants intercept Luftwaffe bombers. f, Spitfire in dogfite with German Stuka JU-87 divebomber. g, Spitfire and Hurricane fly over London and River Thames. h, Gloster Gladiator.

No. 2326, 25d, Group Captain Frank Carey. No. 2327, 25d, German Commander Adolf Joseph Ferdinand Galland.

**2000, Oct. 16    Perf. 14**
**Sheets of 8, #a-h**
| 2324-2325 | A377 | Set of 2 | 12.00 | 12.00 |

**Souvenir Sheets**
| 2326-2327 | A377 | Set of 2 | 7.50 | 7.50 |

Composers — A378

No. 2328, 7d: a, Antonio Vivaldi. b, Giacomo Puccini. c, Franz Joseph Haydn. d, Leopold Stokowski. e, Felix Mendelssohn. f, Gaetano Donizetti.

No. 2329, 7d: a, Witold Lutoslawski. b, William Sterndale Bennett. c, Wolfgang Amadeus Mozart. d, Ludwig van Beethoven. e, Sergei Rachmaninoff. f, Peter Ilich Tchaikovsky.

No. 2330, 25d, Manuel de Falla. No. 2331, 25d, Fréderic Chopin. Illustration reduced.

**2000, Oct. 2    Litho.    Perf. 13¾x13¼**
**Sheets of 6, #a-f**
| 2328-2329 | A378 | Set of 2 | 12.50 | 12.50 |

**Souvenir Sheets**
| 2330-2331 | A378 | Set of 2 | 7.50 | 7.50 |

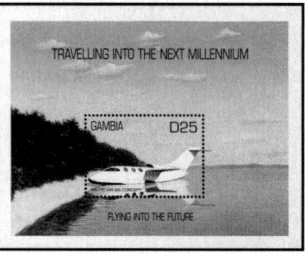

Transportation of the Future — A379

No. 2332 — Automobiles: b, Mazda RX-Evolv. c, Isuzu Kai. d, Ford 021C. e, Pontiac GTO. f, Chevrolet CERV III. g, Toyota Will VI.

No. 2333 — Aircraft: a, Blended wing body, BWB-1. b, Boeing 767-400 ERX. c, Lockheed concept. d, Boeing X. e, American National Aerospace plane X-30 concept. f, Hotol taking off from Russian AN-225.

No. 2334 — Trains: a, Maglev train MLU-002. b, Magnetic rail car. c, Monorail above ground concept. d, Seattle Monorail. e, Monorail above cabin concept. f, Monorail concept.

No. 2335 — Watercraft: h, Pendolare concept boat. i, Planesail boat. j, Airfoil concept. k, Ferry Sea Coaster concept. l, Shinaitoku Matu new sail technology. m, Supersport luxury yacht concept.

No. 2335G, 25d, Nautic Air 400 concept. No. 2335H, 25d, Maglev train. No. 2335I, 25d, Honda Sprocket concept. No. 2335J, 25d, Triton, US Coast Guard concept. Illustration reduced.

**2000, Oct. 2    Perf. 14**
**Sheets of 6, #a-f**
| 2332 | A379 | 7d Sheet of 6, #b-g | 6.25 | 6.25 |
| 2333 | A379 | 7d Sheet of 6, #a-f | 6.25 | 6.25 |
| 2334 | A379 | 8d Sheet of 6, #a-f | 6.50 | 6.50 |
| 2335 | A379 | 8d Sheet of 6, #h-m | 7.50 | 7.50 |

**Souvenir Sheets**
| 2335G-2335J | A379 | Set of 4 | 15.00 | 15.00 |

Nos. 2335 and 2335A contain one 56x41mm stamp.

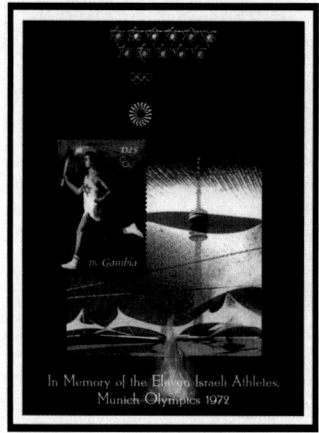

Massacre of Israeli Olympic Athletes, 1972 — A380

No. 2336, horiz.: a, Moshe Weinberg. b, Eliezer Halffin. c, Mark Slavin. d, Ze'ev Friedman. e, Joseph Romano. f, Kahat Shor. g, David Berger. h, Joseph Gottfreund. i, Andrei Schpitzer. j, Amitsur Shapira. k, Yaakov Springer. l, Olympic poster.

**2000, Nov. 9**
| 2336 | A380 | 4d Sheet of 12, #a-l | 7.25 | 7.25 |

**Souvenir Sheet**
| 2337 | A380 | 25d Torchbearer | 4.00 | 4.00 |

Ships
A381

Designs: 5d, Spanish Armada. 10d, Brazilian river gunboat Colombo. 15d, Russian Navy mine carrier Jenissel. 20d, Japanese battleship Yamato.

No. 2342, 7d: a, British first-rate battleship, 18th cent. b, Spanish galleon, 16th cent. c, Russian four-masted barque, 20th cent. d, Henri Grace à Dieu with flag on stern, 16th cent. e, Frontispiece of John Dee's Arte of Navigation, 16th cent. f, British ironclad, 19th cent.

No. 2343, 7d: a, Chinese junk, 18th cent. b, Two-masted cog, 15th cent. c, Henri Grace à Dieu, no flag on stern, 16th cent. d, St. Brendan and monks at sea, 16th cent. e, Figurehead. f, British carrack, 16th cent.

No. 2344, 25d, Challenger, 19th cent. No. 2345, 25d, Golden Hind, 16th cent.

**2000, Oct. 2    Litho.    Perf. 14**
| 2338-2341 | A381 | Set of 4 | 7.25 | 7.25 |

**Sheets of 6, #a-f**
| 2342-2343 | A381 | Set of 2 | 12.00 | 12.00 |

**Souvenir Sheets**
| 2344-2345 | A381 | Set of 2 | 7.25 | 7.25 |

Birds — A382

No. 2346, 7d, vert.: a, Pied flycatcher. b, Blackcap. c, Stonechat. d, Nightingale. e, Black-headed tchagra. f, Yellow wagtail.
No. 2347, 7d, vert.: a, Gray parrot. b, Great spotted cuckoo. c, Bar-tailed trogon. d, African hobby. e, Green turaco. f, Trumpeter hornbill.
No. 2348, 7d, vert.: a, Yellow-rumped tinkerbird. b, Greater honeyguide. c, Hoopoe. d, European roller. e, Carmine bee-eater. f, White-throated bee-eater.
#2349, 25d, European bee-eater. #2350, 25d, Bateleur. #2351, 25d, Secretary bird.
Illustration reduced.

**2000, Oct. 2**     *Perf. 13¾x13¼*
**Sheets of 6, #a-f**
2346-2348 A382   Set of 3    17.50 17.50
**Souvenir Sheets**
2349-2351 A382   Set of 3    10.50 10.50

Ferrari Automobiles — A383

Designs: 4d, 3335P. 5d, 5125. 10d, 312P. 25d, 330P4.

**2000, Nov. 15**     *Perf. 14*
2352-2355 A383   Set of 4    6.25 6.25

12th Classic Automobile Marathon — A384

No. 2356, 5d: a, Morgan. b, Rover. c, Marmon. d, Rolls Royce Silver Cloud. e, Rolls Royce Phantom. f, Mercedes 680S. g, Mercedes 74. h, Invicta.
No. 2357, 5d: a, Allard. b, Ford coupe. c, Citroen Pilot. d, Packard (white). e, Austin A90. f, Bentley. g, Packard (red). h, Aston Martin.
No. 2358, 25d, Cadillac. No. 2359, 25d, Morris Minor.

**2000, Nov. 15**
**Sheets of 8, #a-h**
2356-2357 A384   Set of 2    11.50 11.50
**Souvenir Sheets**
2358-2359 A384   Set of 2    7.25 7.25

Queen Mother, 100th Birthday — A385

**2000, Aug. 7**     Litho.     *Perf. 14*
2360 A385 7d multi    1.00 1.00
Printed in sheets of 6.

The Horse in Art A386

Designs: 4d, At Full Stretch, by John Skeaping. 5d, The Burton, by Lionel Edwards. 10d, A Game of Polo, by Li Lin. 15d, St. George and the Dragon, by Raphael, vert.
No. 2365, 7d: a, Horses Emerging From the Sea, by Eugène Delacroix. b, The Ninth Duke of Marlborough on a Grey Horse, by Sir Alfred Munnings. c, Ovid in Exile Amongst the Scythians, by Delacroix. d, Early Morning Gallop, by Skeaping. e, Mare and Foal, by Munnings. f, Detail from Three-a-side Polo at Simla, by Edwards.
No. 2366, 7d, vert.: a, A Lady Hawking, by E. J. H. Vernet. b, Captain Robert Orme, by Sir Joshua Reynolds. c, Napoleon Crossing the Alps, by Jacques-Louis David. d, Nobby Gray, by Munnings. e, Amateur Jockeys Near a Carriage, by Edgar Degas. f, Detail from Three-a-side Polo at Simla, diff.
No. 2367, 25d, The Reckoning, by George Morland. No. 2368, 25d, One of the Family, by Frederic G. Cotman.

**2000, Oct. 2**
2361-2364 A386   Set of 4    5.00 5.00
**Sheets of 6, #a-f**
2365-2366 A386   Set of 2    12.00 12.00
**Souvenir Sheets**
2367-2368 A386   Set of 2    7.25 7.25

New Year 2001 (Year of the Snake) — A387

No. 2369: a, Vermilion background. b, Purple background. c, Dark blue background. d, Light green background.

**2001, Jan. 2**
2369 A387   4d Sheet of 4, #a-d   2.40 2.40
**Souvenir Sheet**
2370 A387   15d Snake    2.25 2.25

Rijksmuseum, Amsterdam, Bicent. (in 2000) — A388

No. 2371, 7d, vert.: a, Vessels in a Strong Wind, by Jan Porcellis. b, Seascape in the Morning, by Simon de Vlieger. c, Travelers at a Country Inn, by Isaack van Ostade. d, Orpheus with Animals in a Landscape, by Aelbert Cuyp. e, Italian With a Mountain Plateau, by Cornelis van Poelenburch. f, Boatmen and hill from Boatman Moored on a Lake Shore, by Adam Pynacker.
No. 2372, 7d, vert.: a, Cow, boatmen and sailboat from Boatmen Moored on a Lake Shore. b, The Ford in the River, by Jan Baptist Weenix. c, Two Horses Near a Gate in a Meadow, by Paulus Potter. d, Cows and Sheep at a Stream, by Karel Dujardin. e, Violin player from The Duet, by Cornelis Saftleven. f, Lute player from The Duet.
No. 2373, 7d, vert.: a, Teapot from Still Life With Turkey Pie, by Pieter Claesz. b, Bouquet of Flowers in a Vase, by Ambrosius Bosschaert. c, Vase from Still Life With Flowers, Fruit and Shells, by Balthasar van der Ast. d, Flowers and fruit from Still Life With Flowers, Fruit and Shells. e, Tulips in a Vase, by Hans Boulenger. f, Laid Table With Cheese and Fruit, by Floris van Dijck.
No. 2374, 7d, vert.: a, Turkey, from Still Life With Turkey Pie. b, Still Life With Gilt Goblet, by Willem Claesz Heda. c, Still Life With Lobster and Nautilus Cup, by Jan Davidsz de Heem. d, Bacchanal, by Moses van Uyttenbroeck. e, The Anatomy Lesson of Dr. Nicolaes Tulp, by Rembrandt. f, Johannes Lutma, by Jacob Backer.
No. 2375, 7d, vert.: a, The Meagre Company, by Frans Hals and Pieter Codde. b, The Twins Clara and Aelbert de Bray, by Salomon de Bray. c, Self-portrait, by Ferdinand Bol. d, Ambulatory of the New Church in Delft, with the Tomb of Willem the Silent, by Gerard Houckgeest. e, View of the Tomb of Willem in the New Church in Delft, by Emanuel de Witte. f, Mountainous Landscape, by Hercules Segers.
No. 2376, 7d, vert.: a, Lute player from Gallant Company by Codde. b, Men and archway from Gallant Company. c, Man on bended knee from The Marriage of Willem van Loon and Margaretha Bas, by Jan Miense Molenaer. d, Crowd from The Marriage of Willen van Loon and Margaretha Bas. e, Woman in black robe from The Marriage of Willem van Loon and Margaretha Bas. f, Johanna Le Maire, by Nicolaes Eliasz Pickenoy.
No. 2377, 25d, The Fall of Man, by Cornelis van Haarlem. No. 2378, 25d, The Art Gallery of Jan Gildemeester Jansz, by Jan Ekels II. No. 2379, 25d, View of the Nieuwe Kerk and the Rear of the Town Hall in Amsterdam, by Isaak Outwater. No. 2380, 25d, The Spendthrift, by Cornelis Troost. No. 2381, 25d, Morning Ride on the Beach, by Anton Mauve. No. 2382, 25d, Meadow Landscape With Cattle, by Willen Roelofs.

**2001, Jan. 15**     *Perf. 13¾*
**Sheets of 6, #a-f**
2371-2376 A388   Set of 6    35.00 35.00
**Souvenir Sheets**
2377-2382 A388   Set of 6    22.50 22.50

The Wizard of Oz, Cent. (in 2000) — A389

No. 2383, 7d: a, Witch of the North. b, Poppies. c, Dorothy's house. d, Witch of the East. e, Dorothy. f, The Wizard.
No. 2384, 7d: a, Witch's wolf. b, Witch's forest. c, Witch's monkeys. d, Dorothy in poppies. e, Queen Mouse. f, Witch and evil bees.
No. 2385, 7d: a, Cowardly Lion. b, Land of Oz. c, Tin Man. d, Scarecrow. e, Toto. f, Munchkins.
No. 2386, 27d, Green Maiden. No. 2387, 27d, Gate keeper. No. 2388, 27d, Dorothy at crossroads, horiz.

**2001, Jan. 30**
**Sheets of 6, #a-f**
2383-2385 A389   Set of 3    17.50 17.50
**Souvenir Sheets**
2386-2388 A389   Set of 3    11.50 11.50

History of the Theater — A390

No. 2389, 6d: a, Terra cotta statue. b, Tragic masks of King Priam. c, Euripides. d, Terra cotta statues of actors portraying drunks. e, Scene from Chinese play. f, Indian actors. g, Scene from Noh play, Japan. h, Scene from Clytemnestra.
No. 2390, 6d: a, William Shakespeare. b, Johann Wolfgang von Goethe. c, Moliere. d, Henrik Ibsen. e, George Bernard Shaw. f, Anton Chekhov. g, Sholom Aleichem. h, Tennessee Williams.
No. 2391, 25d, Sarah Bernhardt, vert. No. 2392, 25d, John Barrymore, vert.

**2001, Jan. 30**     *Perf. 14*
**Sheets of 8, #a-h**
2389-2390 A390   Set of 2    14.00 14.00
**Souvenir Sheet**
2391-2392 A390   Set of 2    7.25 7.25

Pokémon — A391

No. 2393: a, Beedrill. b, Arbok. c, Machop. d, Vileplume. e, Clefairy. f, Poliwhirl.

| 2001, Feb. 1 | | | Perf. 13¾ | |
|---|---|---|---|---|
| 2393 | A391 | 7d Sheet of 6, #a-f | 6.00 | 6.00 |
| **Souvenir Sheet** | | | | |
| 2394 | A391 | 25d Articuno | 3.50 | 3.50 |

Orchids — A392

Designs: 1.50d, Encyclia alata. 2d, Dendrobium lasiantherum. 3d, Cymbidiella pardalina. No. 2398, 4d, Cymbidium lowianum. 5d, Cypripedium irapeanum. 15d, Doritis pulcherrima.

No. 2401: a, Epidendrum pseudepidendrum. b, Eriopsis biloba. c, Masdevallia coccinea. d, Odontoglossum lindleyanum. e, Oerstedella wallisii. f, Paphiopedilum acmodontum. g, Laelia rubescens. h, Huntleya wallisii. i, Lycaste longiscapa. j, Maxillaria variabilis. k, Mexicoa ghiesbrechtiana. l, Miltoniopsis phalaenopsis.

No. 2402: a, Sobralia candida. b, Phragmipedium basseae. c, Phaius tankervilleae. d, Vanda rothchildiana. e, Telipogon pulchera. f, Rossioglossum insleayi.

No. 2403, 25d, Chaubardia heteroclita. No. 2404, 25d, Cychnoches loddigesii. No. 2405, 25d, Cattleya dowiana.

| 2001, Feb. 1 | | Litho. | Perf. 14 | |
|---|---|---|---|---|
| 2395-2400 | A392 | Set of 6 | 6.00 | 6.00 |
| 2401 | A392 | 4d Sheet of 12, #a-l | 9.25 | 9.25 |
| 2402 | A392 | 7d Sheet of 6, #a-f | 8.25 | 8.25 |
| **Souvenir Sheets** | | | | |
| 2403-2405 | A392 | Set of 3 | 15.00 | 15.00 |

Hong Kong 2001 Stamp Exhibition (Nos. 2401-2405).

Medicinal Plants — A393

Designs: 3d, Pokeweed. 5d, Bay laurel. 10d, Coltsfoot. 15d, Marshmallow.

No. 2410, 8d, vert.: a, Restharrow. b, White willow. c, Sweet serge. d, Passion flower. e, Rosemary. f, Pepper.

No. 2411, 8d, vert.: a, Succory. b, Dandelion. c, Garlic. d, Hemp agrimony. e, Star thistle. f, Cypress.

No. 2412, 25d, Arbutus, vert. No. 2413, 25d, Olive, vert.

| 2001, Mar. 1 | | | | |
|---|---|---|---|---|
| 2406-2409 | A393 | Set of 4 | 6.25 | 6.25 |
| **Sheets of 6, #a-f** | | | | |
| 2410-2411 | A393 | Set of 2 | 19.00 | 19.00 |
| **Souvenir Sheets** | | | | |
| 2412-2413 | A393 | Set of 2 | 9.50 | 9.50 |

Japanese Art — A394

Designs: 1d, Mount Fuji and Tea Fields, by Matsuoka Eikyu. 2d, One heron from Herons and Flowers, by Okamoto Shuki. No. 2416, 3d, Two herons from Herons and Flowers. No. 2417, 3d, The Realm of Gods in Yingzhou, by Tomioka Tessai. No. 2418, 4d, Peach Blossom Spring in Wuling, by Tessai. No. 2419, 4d, Egret, by Takeuchi Seiho. No. 2420, 5d, Spring Colors of the Lake and Mountains, by Shoda Gyokan. No. 2421, 5d, Sparrows, by Seiho. No. 2422, 10d, Red Lotus and White Goose, by Goun Saku. No. 2423, 10d, Portrait of Ushiwakamaru, by Kano Osanobu. 15d, Woman Selling Flowers, by Ito Shoha. 20d, The Sound of the Ocean, by Matsumoto Ichiyo.

No. 2426, 5d — Birds and Flowers of the Twelve Months, by Sakai Hoitsu: a, Red and white flowers, bird on branch. b, Yellow flowers, bird flying. c, White flowers, bird on branch. d, Blue flowers. e, Sun, white and blue flowers. f, Red and white flowers.

No. 2427, 5d — Birds and Flowers of the Twelve Months, by Hoitsu: a, Insect in sky, red pink and white flowers. b, Blue irises. c, Red, white light blue flowers. d, Fruit on tree. e, Bird standing in water. f, Snow-covered tree.

No. 2428, 7d — Birds and Flowers, by Soga Chokuan: a, White flowers. b, Rooster at R. c, Roosters at L, red flower at R. d, Rooster at R, white flowers. e, Birds in sky. f, Roosters at L and R, white and red flowers. g, Roosters at L and R. Rooster at L, tree and red flowers.

No. 2429, 7d — The Four Accomplishments, by Kaiho Yusho: a, Table. b, Two people near tree. c, Rock and hill. d, Two people. e, Rock and tree. f, One person. g, Three people. h, Three people, table.

No. 2430 — Book of Lacquer Paintings, by Shibata Zeshin: a, Flower. b, Birds. c, Butterfly on flower. d, Lobster.

No. 2431, 30d, Untitled painting (Yanagibashi at Ryogoku), by Utagawa Kuniyoshi, horiz. No. 2432, 30d, Poppies, by Tsuchida Bakusen, horiz. No. 2433, 30d, Puppies and Morning Glories, by Yamaguchi Soken, horiz. No. 2434, 30d, Deep Pool, by Nishimura Goun, horiz. No. 2435, 30d, Spring Farming Near a Riverside Village, by Mori Getsujo, horiz.

| 2001, Apr. 17 | | | | |
|---|---|---|---|---|
| 2414-2425 | A394 | Set of 12 | 16.00 | 16.00 |
| **Sheets of 6, #a-f** | | | | |
| 2426-2427 | A394 | Set of 2 | 11.50 | 11.50 |
| **Sheets of 8, #a-h** | | | | |
| 2428-2429 | A394 | Set of 2 | 22.50 | 22.50 |
| 2430 | A394 | 10d Sheet of 4, #a-d | 7.75 | 7.75 |
| **Imperf.** | | | | |
| **Size: 118x88mm** | | | | |
| 2431-2435 | A394 | Set of 5 | 29.00 | 29.00 |

Nos. 2428-2430 contain 28x42mm stamps. Phila Nippon '01, Japan.

**Butterflies Type of 2000**

Designs: 7d, Salamis temora. 8d, Cyrestus camillus. 20d, Papilio demodocus. 25d, Danaus chrysippus.

| 2001 | | | Perf. 14¾x14 | |
|---|---|---|---|---|
| 2436-2439 | A367 | Set of 4 | 11.50 | 11.50 |

No. 2439 exists dated 2003.

**I Love Lucy Type of 2000**

No. 2440: a, Lucy singing. b, Lucy with tambourine. c, Lucy with Ricky and Ethel. d, Lucy. e, Ethel and Ricky at piano. f, Ethel and Ricky on bench. g, Lucy at typewriter. h, Ethel singing. i, Lucy on bench.

No. 2441, 25d, Like #2440a, vert. No. 2442, 25d, Like #2440d, vert.

| 2001 | | | Perf. 13¾ | |
|---|---|---|---|---|
| 2440 | A354 | 5d Sheet of 9, #a-i | 8.75 | 8.75 |
| **Souvenir Sheets** | | | | |
| 2441-2442 | A354 | Set of 2 | 9.50 | 9.50 |

Horses — A395

No. 2443, 7d, Head of: a, Akhal-Teke. b, Palomino. c, Kladruber. d, Paint Horse. e, Pinto. f, Kabardin.

No. 2444, 7d, horiz: a, Akhal-Teke. b, Kladruber. c, Palomino. d, Pinto. e, Paint Horse. f, Kabardin.

| 2001 | | Litho. | Perf. 14 | |
|---|---|---|---|---|
| **Sheets of 6, #a-f** | | | | |
| 2443-2444 | A395 | Set of 2 | 11.50 | 11.50 |
| **Souvenir Sheet** | | | | |
| 2445 | A395 | 25d Palomino | 3.50 | 3.50 |

**Three Stooges Type of 2000**

No. 2446: a, Shemp as angel. b, Larry, Moe, Shemp, wearing feathered hats. c, Moe, Shemp and Larry wearing hospital uniforms. d, Larry with hammer, Shemp with gun, Moe. e, Moe, Larry, Shemp with woman. f, Moe and Shemp wearing tams. g, Moe, Larry, wagon wheel. h, Shemp, Moe, Larry in bus driver uniforms. i, Shemp hitting Larry and Moe.

No. 2447, 25d, Curly with telephone, skull, vert. No. 2448, 25d, Shemp on Moe's back, vert.

| 2001 | | | Perf. 13¾ | |
|---|---|---|---|---|
| 2446 | A353 | 5d Sheet of 9, #a-i | 6.25 | 6.25 |
| **Souvenir Sheets** | | | | |
| 2447-2448 | A353 | Set of 2 | 7.00 | 7.00 |

**I Love Lucy Type of 2000**

No. 2449 : a, Lucy crawling on building ledge. b, Lucy standing against wall, arms outstretched. c, Lucy in apartment. d, Lucy reclining on ledge. e, Lucy with hand on forehead. f, Lucy reclining against wall. g, Ricky, bound and gagged Lucy. h, Lucy on sofa. i, Lucy, robber.

No. 2450, 25d, Lucy, robber, vert. No. 2451, 25d, Bound and gagged Lucy, seated Ethel, vert.

| 2001 | | | | |
|---|---|---|---|---|
| 2449 | A354 | 5d Sheet of 9, #a-i | 6.25 | 6.25 |
| **Souvenir Sheets** | | | | |
| 2450-2451 | A354 | Set of 2 | 7.00 | 7.00 |

**Butterfly Type of 2000**

| 2001 | | | Perf. 14¾x14 | |
|---|---|---|---|---|
| 2452 | A367 | 50d Coeliades forestan | 7.00 | 7.00 |
| 2452A | A367 | 75d Ornithoptera alexandrae | 10.00 | 10.00 |
| 2452B | A367 | 100d Morpho cypris | 14.00 | 14.00 |

Queen Victoria (1819-1901) — A396

No. 2453, horiz.: a, Reading speech from throne. b, Benjamin Disraeli. c, Riding in procession from Parliament.

| 2001, Apr. 26 | | | Perf. 14 | |
|---|---|---|---|---|
| 2453 | A396 | 15d Sheet of 3, #a-c | 6.25 | 6.25 |
| **Souvenir Sheet** | | | | |
| 2454 | A396 | 25d Portrait | 3.50 | 3.50 |

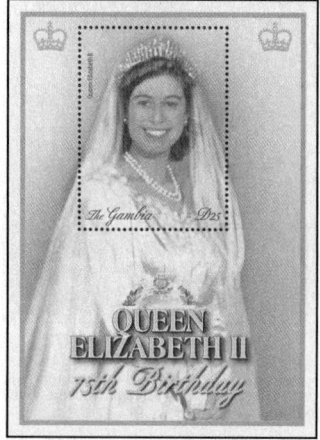

Queen Elizabeth II, 75th Birthday — A397

No. 2456: a, In uniform. b, In pink hat. c, Wearing crown, facing R. d, Wearing crown, facing L.

| 2001, Apr. 26 | | | Perf. 14 | |
|---|---|---|---|---|
| 2455 | A397 | 15d Sheet of 4, #a-d | 8.25 | 8.25 |
| **Souvenir Sheet** | | | | |
| 2456 | A397 | 25d In wedding dress | 3.50 | 3.50 |

Flowers — A398

Designs: 1d, Disa uniflora. 4d, Monodora myristica. 6d, Clappertonia ficifolia. 20d, Calanthe rosea.

No. 2461, 7d: a, Vanilla planifolia. b, Strelitzia reginae. c, Gladiolus cardinalis. d, Arctotis venusta. e, Protea obtusifolia. f, Geissorhiza rochensis.

No. 2462, 7d: a, Canarina abyssinica. b, Amorphophallus abyssinicus. c, Calanthe rosea, diff. d, Gloriosa simplex. e, Clappertonia ficifolia, diff. f, Ansellia gigantea.

No. 2463, 25d, Arctotis venusta, diff. No. 2464, 25d, Geissorhiza rochensis, horiz.

| 2001, Mar. 1 | | Litho. | Perf. 14 | |
|---|---|---|---|---|
| 2457-2460 | A398 | Set of 4 | 4.75 | 4.75 |
| **Sheets of 6, #a-f** | | | | |
| 2461-2462 | A398 | Set of 2 | 12.50 | 12.50 |
| **Souvenir Sheets** | | | | |
| 2463-2464 | A398 | Set of 2 | 7.50 | 7.50 |

Photomosaic of Queen Elizabeth II — A399

**2001, Apr. 26**
2465 A399 8d multi 1.10 1.10

Printed in sheets of 8, with and without marginal inscription "In Celebration of the 50th Anniversary of H. M. Queen Elizabeth II's Accession to the Throne.'

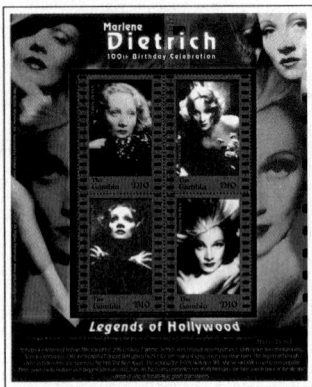

Marlene Dietrich — A400

No. 2466: a, With head on forearm. b, With bare shoulder. c, With arms crossed. d, Wearing hat.

**2001, Apr. 26** **Perf. 13¾**
2466 A400 10d Sheet of 4, #a-d 5.75 5.75

Mao Zedong (1893-1976) — A401

No. 2467: a, In 1935. b, In 1949. c, In 1951. 25d, In 1928.

**2001, Apr. 26** **Perf. 14**
2467 A401 15d Sheet of 3, #a-c 6.25 6.25
**Souvenir Sheet**
2468 A401 25d multi 3.50 3.50

Giuseppe Verdi (1813-1901), Opera Composer — A402

No. 2469: a, Verdi with gray hair. b, Score and perfromers from La Traviata. c, Score and performer from Aida. d, Verdi with brown hair. 25d, Verdi and scores of Don Carlos and Rigoletto.

**2001, Apr. 26**
2469 A402 10d Sheet of 4, #a-d 5.75 5.75
**Souvenir Sheet**
2470 A402 25d multi 3.50 3.50

Monet Paintings — A403

No. 2471, horiz.: a, Madame Monet on the Sofa. b, The Picnic. c, The Luncheon. d, Jean Monet on His Mechanical Horse. 25d, La Japonaise.

**2001, Apr. 26** **Perf. 13¾**
2471 A403 10d Sheet of 4, #a-d 5.75 5.75
**Souvenir Sheet**
2472 A403 25d multi 3.50 3.50

Toulouse-Lautrec Paintings — A404

No. 2473: a, At Le Rat Mort. b, The Milliner. c, Messaline. 25d, Napoleon.

**2001, Apr. 26**
2473 A404 7d Sheet of 3, #a-c 3.00 3.00
**Souvenir Sheet**
2474 A404 25d multi 3.50 3.50

Orchids — A405

Designs: 3d, Orchis morio. 4d, Fulophia speciosa. 5d, Angraecum leonis. 15d, Oeceoclades maculata.
No. 2479, 8d: a, Ceratostylis retisquama. b, Rangaeris rhipsalisocia. c, Phaius hybrid. d, Disa hybrid. e, Disa uniflora. f, Angraecum leonis.
No. 2480, 8d, horiz.: a, Satyrium erectum. b, Aeranthes grandiose. c, Aerangis somasticta. d, Polystachya bella. e, Eulophia guineensis. f, Disa blackii.
No. 2482, 25d, Disa kirstenbosch pride.

**2001, June 15** **Perf. 14**
2475-2478 A405 Set of 4 4.00 4.00

**Sheets of 6, #a-f**
2479-2480 A405 Set of 2 13.00 13.00
**Souvenir Sheets**
2482 A405 multi 3.50 3.50

Belgica 2001 Intl. Stamp Exhibition, Brussels (#2479-2480).
A 25d souvenir sheet, similar to No. 2482, depicting Aerangis curnowiana, was prepared but not issued.

SOS Children's Village A406

**2001, July 2**
2483 A406 10d multi 1.40 1.40

Flora & Fauna A407

Designs: 2d, Hoopoe. 3d, Great spotted cuckoo. 4d, Plain tiger butterfly. 5d, Zebra duiker. 10d, Sooty managbey. 20d, Greater kudu.
No. 2490, 8d: a, Hippopotamus. b, Elephant. c, Parusta simplex. d, Gray heron. e, Charaxes imperialis. f, Gloriosa simplex.
No. 2491, 8d: a, Alpine swift. b, Blotched genet. c, Thomas' galago. d, Carmine bee-eater. e, Tree pangolin. f, Campbell's monkey.
No. 2492, 8d: a, Gray parrot. b, Rachel's weaver. c, European bee-eater. d, River kingfisher. e, Red river hog. f, Bushbuck.
No. 2493, 8d: a, Blue diadem butterfly. b, Fire-footed rope squirrel. c, Clappertonia ficifolia. d, Costus spectabilis. e, African migrant butterfly. f, Giant African snail.
No. 2494, 25d, Long-tailed pangolin, vert. No. 2495, 25d, Eurasian kestrel, vert.

**2001, July 16**
2484-2489 A407 Set of 6 6.00 6.00
**Sheets of 6, #a-f**
2490-2493 A407 Set of 4 26.00 26.00
**Souvenir Sheets**
2494-2495 A407 Set of 2 7.00 7.00

A408

Ducks and Geese — A409

Designs: 2d, Blue-winged teal. No. 2497, 3d, Red-crested pochard. No. 2498, 4d, Falcated teal. No. 2499, 5d, Mandarin duck. No. 2500, 10d, King eider. 15d, Hooded merganser.
No. 2502, 3d, Wood duck. No. 2503, 4d, Mallard. No. 2504, 5d, Barrow's goldeneye. No. 2505, 10d, Bufflehead.
No. 2506, 7d, horiz.: a, Barrow's goldeneye. b, Harlequin duck. c, Pintail. d, Black-bellied whistling duck. e, Cinnamon teal. f, Surf scoter.
No. 2507, 7d, horiz.: a, Black scoter. b, Black duck. c, Green-winged teal. d, Bufflehead. e, Red-breasted merganser. f, Fulvous whistling duck.
No. 2508, 8d: a, European wigeon. b, Mallard. c, Garganey. d, Pintail, diff. e, Shoveler. f, Green-winged teal.
No. 2509, 8d: a, Black duck. b, Bufflehead. c, Cinnamon teal, diff. d, Goldeneye. e, Ruddy shelduck. f, Ferruginous duck.
No. 2510, 8d: a, Masked duck. b, Old squaw. c, Ring-necked duck. d, Harlequin duck, diff. e, Redhead. f, Canvasback.

No. 2511, 25d, American wigeon. No. 2512, 25d, Wood duck. No. 2513, 25d, Baikal teal. No. 2514, 25d, Green-winged teal, horiz. No. 2515, 25d, Canada geese, horiz.

**2001, July 16**
2496-2501 A408 Set of 6 5.25 5.25
2502-2505 A409 Set of 4 3.00 3.00
**Sheets of 6, #a-f**
2506-2507 A409 Set of 2 11.00 11.00
2508-2510 A408 Set of 3 19.00 19.00
**Souvenir Sheets**
2511-2513 A408 Set of 3 10.00 10.00
2514-2515 A409 Set of 2 6.50 6.50

Cetaceans — A410

No. 2516, 7d: a, Killer whale (denomination at UR). b, Sperm whale (denomination at UR). c, Strap-toothed whale. d, Humpback whale. e, Southern right whale. f, Beluga.
No. 2517, 7d: a, Killer whale (denomination at LR). b, Sperm whale (denomination at LR). c, Narwhal. d, Gray whale. e, Blue whale. f, Northern right whale.
No. 2518, 25d, Killer whale. No. 2519, 25d, Humpback whale.

**2001, July 16** **Sheets of 6, #a-f**
2516-2517 A410 Set of 2 11.00 11.00
**Souvenir Sheets**
2518-2519 A410 Set of 2 6.50 6.50

A411

Trains A412

Designs: 2d, Rheingold Express. No. 2521, 10d, Amtrak train. No. 2522, 15d, The Blue Train. 20d, Cisalpino.
4d, Eurostar. No. 2525, 7d, Mallard. No. 2526, 10d, Rocket. No. 2527, TGV.
No. 2528, 7d: a, Eurostar, diff. b, Flying Hamburger. c, Coast Starlight. d, Tres Grande Vitesse. e, Golden Arrow. f, Shinkanzen "Max."
No. 2529, 7d: a, Siliguri to Darjeeling, India train. b, California Zephyr. c, Flying Scotsman. d, Trans-Siberian Express. e, Indian-Pacific. f, Thunersee.
No. 2530, 8d: a, Le Shuttle. b, Nord Express. c, 2-6-0, Switzerland. d, Duchess. e, Balkan Express. f, Class 44 2-10-0, Germany.
No. 2531, 8d: a, 7029 Clun Castle. b, Puffing Billy. c, ICE Electric. d, 4-4-2 S, Belgium. e, 2-8-2, Germany. f, PLM Coupe-Vents.
No. 2532, 25d, Cape Town to Victoria Falls train. No. 2533, 25d, The Southerner. No. 2534, 25d, Stanier Class 5 4-6-0. No. 2535, 25d, Flying Scotsman, diff.

**2001, July 31** **Perf. 14**
2520-2523 A411 Set of 4 6.25 6.25
2524-2527 A412 Set of 4 5.00 5.00
**Sheets of 6, #a-f**
2528-2529 A411 Set of 2 11.00 11.00
2530-2531 A412 Set of 2 13.00 13.00
**Souvenir Sheets**
2532-2533 A411 Set of 2 6.50 6.50
2534-2535 A412 Set of 2 6.50 6.50

British Royal Navy — A413

Designs: 3d, St. Andrew, 1600s. 4d, Fleet maneuvers, 1914. 10d, HMS Illustrious, 1899. 15d, Battle of North Foreland, 1666.

No. 2540, 7d, horiz.: a, Mary Rose, 1512. b, Attack off Quebec, 1759. c, Armada campaign, 1588. d, Battle of Scheveningen, 1653. e, Blanche captures La Pique, 1795. f, Embarkation at Dover, 1520.

No. 2541, 7d, horiz. — Battles: a, Quiberon Bay, 1759. b, Barfleur, 1692. c, Nile, 1798. d, Trafalgar, 1805. e, Jutland, 1916. f, Camperdown, 1797.

No. 2542, 7d, horiz.: a, Battle of Navarino, 1827. b, Sinking of Eurydice, 1878. c, HMS Pantaloon captures Borboleta, 1845. d, Dardanelles, 1915. e, HMS Pickle captures Bolodora, 1829. f, HMS Invincible and Inflexible, Battle of the Falklands, 1914.

No. 2543, 25d, Ark Royal, 1582, horiz. No. 2544, 25d, Sovereign of the Seas, 1637, horiz.

| | | | |
|---|---|---|---|
| **2001, Sept. 6** | | | **Litho.** |
| 2536-2539 | A413 | Set of 4 | 4.25 4.25 |
| **Sheets of 6, #a-f** | | | |
| 2540-2542 | A413 | Set of 3 | 17.00 17.00 |
| **Souvenir Sheets** | | | |
| 2543-2544 | A413 | Set of 2 | 6.50 6.50 |

2002 World Cup Soccer Championships, Japan and Korea — A414

Jules Rimet Trophy and: 2d, Netherlands flag and player. 3d, Argentina flag and player. 4d, Ibaraki Kashima Stadium, Japan, horiz. 5d, George Best and Northern Ireland flag. 10d, Dino Zoff and Italian flag. 15d, Poster for 1938 tournament, France.

25d, Pat Bonner making save for Ireland.

| | | | |
|---|---|---|---|
| **2001, Sept. 6** | | | |
| 2545-2550 | A414 | Set of 6 | 5.25 5.25 |
| **Souvenir Sheet** | | | |
| 2551 | A414 | 25d multi | 3.25 3.25 |

No. 2551 contains one 56x42mm stamp.

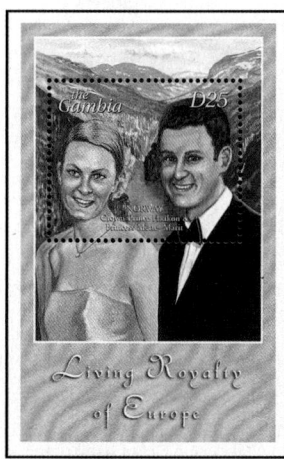

European Royalty — A415

No. 2552: a, King Harald V, Queen Sonja, Norway. b, Queen Margrethe II, Denmark. c, King Carl XVI Gustaf and Queen Silvia, Sweden. d, King Juan Carlos, Queen Sofia, Spain. e, Queen Beatrix, Netherlands. f, King Albert II, Queen Paola, Belgium.

No. 2553, 25d, Crown Prince Haakon, Princess Mette-Marit, Norway. No. 2554, 25d, King Juan Carlos, Spain, vert.

| | | | |
|---|---|---|---|
| **Perf. 14¼x14½, 14½x14¼** | | | |
| **2001, Nov. 15** | | | |
| 2552 | A415 | 7d Sheet of 6, #a-f | 5.50 5.50 |
| **Souvenir Sheets** | | | |
| 2553-2554 | A415 | Set of 2 | 6.25 6.25 |

**Queen Mother Type of 1999**

No. 2555: a, Duchess of York, Princess Elizabeth, 1928. b, Lady Elizabeth Bowes-Lyon, 1923. c, Queen Elizabeth, 1946. d, Queen Mother, Prince Harry.

40d, Queen Mother celebrating 89th birthday, 1989.

| | | | |
|---|---|---|---|
| **2001, Dec. 13** | | | **Perf. 14** |
| 2555 | A342 | 15d Sheet of 4, #a-d + label | 7.75 7.75 |
| **Souvenir Sheet** | | | |
| **Perf. 13¾** | | | |
| 2556 | A342 | 40d multi | 5.00 5.00 |

No. 2556 contains one 38x50mm stamp.

Oriental Actors and Actresses — A416

No. 2557, 15d: a, Alex Fong. b, William So. c, Flora Chan. d, Rain Li.

No. 2558, 15d — Kelly Chen: a, Close-up. b, As child, with cherry. c, On swing. d, As child, with hand above eyes.

No. 2559, 15d — Jacky Cheung: a, At L, laughing, looking to R. b, Looking forward, mouth open. c, At R, laughing, looking L. d, Looking forward, mouth closed.

No. 2560, 15d — Andy Hui, and Chinese characters at: a, L (pink suit). b, R (yellow suit). c, L (yellow suit). d, R (pink suit).

No. 2561, 15d — Miriam Yeung, with roses and petals at: a, LR. b, LL. c, UR. d, UL.

| | | | |
|---|---|---|---|
| **2001, Nov. 5** | **Litho.** | **Perf. 13¾x13¼** | |
| **Sheets of 4, #a-d** | | | |
| 2557-2561 | A416 | Set of 5 | 37.50 37.50 |

New Year 2002 (Year of the Horse) — A417

No. 2562 — Denomination at: a, UR. b, UL. c, LR. d, LL.

20d, African zebra.

| | | | |
|---|---|---|---|
| **2001, Dec. 26** | | | **Perf. 13** |
| 2562 | A417 | 6d Miniature sheet of 4, #a-d | 3.00 3.00 |
| **Souvenir Sheet** | | | |
| **Perf. 12½x13** | | | |
| 2563 | A417 | 20d multi | 2.25 2.25 |

No. 2563 contains one 68x31mm triangular stamp.

Jacqueline Kennedy Onassis (1929-94) — A418

No. 2564: a, As baby. b, At age 6. c, Engagement to J.F.K. d, In wedding gown, 1955. e, In 1960. f, In 1980.

30d, At wedding to Aristotle Onassis.

| | | | |
|---|---|---|---|
| **2002, Jan. 24** | | | **Perf. 14** |
| 2564 | A418 | 7d Sheet of 6, #a-f | 5.50 5.50 |
| **Souvenir Sheet** | | | |
| 2565 | A418 | 30d multi | 4.00 4.00 |

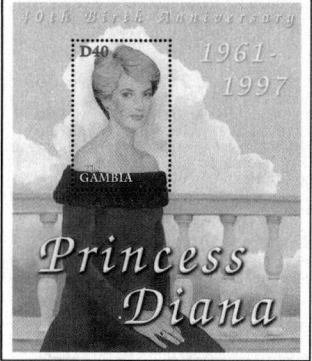

Princess Diana (1961-97) — A419

No. 2566 — Diana and: a, Coral rose. b, White rose. c, Yellow rose. d, Purple rose.

40d, Portrait.

| | | | |
|---|---|---|---|
| **2002, Jan. 24** | | | |
| 2566 | A419 | 15d Sheet of 4, #a-d | 7.75 7.75 |
| **Souvenir Sheet** | | | |
| 2567 | A419 | 40d multi | 5.25 5.25 |

Moths A420

Designs: 2d, Tiger moth. 3d, Hawk moth. No. 2570, 10d, Pericopid moth. 15d, Spurge hawk.

No. 2572, 10d (50x38mm): a, Sloane's urania. b, Saturniid moth. c, Black witch moth. d, Burnet moth on plant. e, Day-flying moth. f, Lime hawk moth.

No. 2573, 10d (50x38mm): a, Emperor moth. b, Millar's tiger. c, Hawk moth, diff. d, Phrygionis privignara. e, Burnet moth, waterfall. f, Urania leilus.

No. 2574, 40d, Emerald moth. No. 2575, 40d, Red under-wing moth, vert.

| | | | |
|---|---|---|---|
| **Perf. 14, 13¾ (#2572-2573)** | | | |
| **2002, Jan. 24** | | | |
| 2568-2571 | A420 | Set of 4 | 4.00 4.00 |
| **Sheets of 6, #a-f** | | | |
| 2572-2573 | A420 | Set of 2 | 15.00 15.00 |
| **Souvenir Sheets** | | | |
| 2574-2575 | A420 | Set of 2 | 10.00 10.00 |

United We Stand — A421

| | | | |
|---|---|---|---|
| **2002, Feb. 6** | | | **Perf. 13¾x13¼** |
| 2576 | A421 | 20d multi | 2.50 2.50 |

Issued in sheets of 4.

Reign of Queen Elizabeth II, 50th Anniv. — A422

No. 2577: a, With beige hat. b, With red hat. c, With blue hat. d, Near vehicle.

40d, Wearing uniform.

| | | | |
|---|---|---|---|
| **2002, Feb. 6** | | | **Perf. 14½** |
| 2577 | A422 | 15d Sheet of 4, #a-d | 7.50 7.50 |
| **Souvenir Sheet** | | | |
| 2578 | A422 | 40d multi | 5.00 5.00 |

A423

Orchids — A424

No. 2579, vert.: a, Machu piechu. b, Masdevallia copper angel. c, Masdevallia hirtzi. d, Tuakau canoy.

No. 2580: a, Eriopsis sceptrum. b, Sarcanthopsis muellem. c, Bougainville white. d, Telipogon klotzchianus.

No. 2581, 7d: a, Richard Mueller. b, Colmanara wildcat. c, Cycnoches chlorochilon. d, Vanda coerylea. e, Disa blackii. f, Unnamed.

No. 2582, 7d: a, Seagulls beaulu queen. b, Hazel Boyd. c, Costa Rica. d, Dendrobium infudibulum. e, Disa hybrid. f, Chysis.

No. 2583, 7d: a, Spathoglottis portusfinschii. b, Dendrobium macrophyllum. c, Grammaneis ellisii. d, Stanhopea wardii. e,

Dendrobium nindi. f, Dendrobium williamsianum.

No. 2584, 7d: a, Seutieama steeli. b, Dendrobium inaequale. c, Dendrobium lasiathera. d, Calypso bulbosa. e, Vanda hindsii. f, Dendrobium violaceoflavens.

No. 2585, 8d, horiz.: a, Phaleonopsis rosenstomii. b, Cypripedium guttatum. c, Cypripedium reginae. d, Dendrobium engae. e, Diplocaulobium hydrophilum. f, Dendrobium cuthbertsonii.

No. 2586, 25d, Dendrobium nobile. No. 2587, 25d, Ancidium alliance, vert.

No. 2588, 25d, Menadenium labiosum. No. 2589, 25d, Dendrobium spectabile. No. 2590, 25d, Dendrobium canaliculatum, horiz.

**2001, June 15      Litho.      Perf. 14**
2579  A423   7d Sheet of 4, #a-
                    d                    2.75  2.75
2580  A424  10d Sheet of 4, #a-
                    d                    4.00  4.00
**Sheets of 6, #a-f**
2581-2582  A423   Set of 2    8.50  8.50
2583-2585  A424   Set of 3   12.50 12.50
**Souvenir Sheets**
2586-2587  A423   Set of 2    5.00  5.00
2588-2590  A424   Set of 3    7.50  7.50

Nos. 2579-2590 were not available until 2002. Belgica 2001 Intl. Stamp Exhibition (#2579).

Wildlife
A425

Designs: 2d, Martial eagle. 4d, Lion. 5d, Aardvark. 10d, Lion cub, vert.

No. 2595, 7d: a, Lion cub. b, Water buffalo. c, Topi. d, Hyena. e, Secretary bird. f, Genet.

No. 2596, 7d: a, Reedbuck. b, Hippopotamus. c, Waterbuck and malachite kingfisher. d, Hoopoe. e, White pelican. f, Waterbuck.

No. 2597, 25d, Hippopotamus. No. 2598, 25d, Crocodile.

**2001, July 16**
2591-2594  A425   Set of 4    2.10  2.10
**Sheets of 6, #a-f**
2595-2596  A425   Set of 2    8.50  8.50
**Souvenir Sheets**
2597-2598  A425   Set of 2    5.00  5.00

Nos. 2591-2598 were not available until 2002.

Pres. Theodore Roosevelt (1858-
1919) — A426

No. 2599: a, Wearing hat and uniform. b, Close-up. c, With hand on chair. d, Wearing hat and neckerchief.
40d, Close-up, diff.

**2002, Jan. 24**
2599  A426  15d Sheet of 4, #a-d  7.75  7.75
**Souvenir Sheet**
2600  A426  40d multi            5.25  5.25

Betty
Boop — A427

No. 2602, 40d, With gray ribbon in hair, horiz. No. 2603, 40d, With ice cream sundae.

**2002, Feb. 13                Perf. 13¾**
2601  A427   7d shown           .90   .90
**Souvenir Sheets**
2602-2603  A427   Set of 2   10.00 10.00

No. 2601 was issued in sheets of 9.

Shirley Temple in "Little Miss
Broadway" — A428

No. 2604, horiz.: a, With man and old woman. b, Close-up. c, Waving. d, Holding man's tie. e, At hotel desk with men. f, Woman watching Temple point to tooth.

No. 2605: a, Dancing with young man. b, Dancing with old man with hat. c, Sitting with boy. d, Holding hands with old man.

30d, Wearing tiara and dancing with young man.

**2002, Feb. 13**
2604  A428   8d Sheet of 6, #a-f  6.00  6.00
2605  A428  10d Sheet of 4, #a-d  5.00  5.00
**Souvenir Sheet**
2606  A428  30d multi            4.00  4.00

2002 Winter
Olympics, Salt
Lake City — A429

Designs: No. 2607, 20d, Curling. No. 2608, 20d, Ski jumping.

**2002, Mar. 18              Perf. 14**
2607-2608  A429   Set of 2    5.00  5.00
   a.  Souvenir sheet, #2607-2608  5.00  5.00

Chiune Sugihara,
Japanese Diplomat
Who Saved Jews in
World War
II — A430

**2002, Apr. 29            Perf. 13½x13¼**
2609  A430  10d multi           1.25  1.25
Printed in sheets of 4.

Intl. Year of Mountains — A431

No. 2610: a, Winkler Tower, Italy. b, Mt. Huanstan Chico, Peru. c, Hodaka Mountains, Japan. d, Mustagh Ata, Kashmir.
40d, Mt. Myoko, Japan.

**2002, July 1              Perf. 13¼x13½**
2610  A431  15d Sheet of 4, #a-d  7.25  7.25
**Souvenir Sheet**
2611  A431  40d multi            4.75  4.75

2002 World Cup Soccer
Championships, Japan and
Korea — A432

Players, dates and locations of matches — No. 2612, 9d: a, France v. Senegal. b, Uruguay v. Denmark. c, France v. Uruguay. d, Denmark v. Senegal. e, Denmark v. France. f, Senegal v. Uruguay.

No. 2613, 9d: a, Paraguay v. South Africa. b, Spain v. Slovenia. c, Spain v. Paraguay. d, South Africa v. Slovenia. e, South Africa v. Spain. f, Slovenia v. Paraguay.

No. 2614, 9d: a, Brazil v. Turkey. b, China v. Costa Rica. c, Brazil v. China. d, Costa Rica v. Turkey. e, Costa Rica v. Brazil. f, Turkey v. China.

No. 2615, 9d: a, South Korea v. Poland. b, US v. Portugal. c, South Korea v. US. d, Portugal v. Poland. e, Portugal v. South Korea. f, Poland v. US.

No. 2616, 9d: a, Germany v. Saudi Arabia. b, Ireland v. Cameroun. c, Germany v. Ireland. d, Cameroun v. Saudi Arabia. e, Cameroun v. Germany. f, Saudi Arabia v. Ireland.

No. 2617, 9d: a, England v. Sweden. b, Argentina v. Nigeria. c, Sweden v. Nigeria. d, Argentina v. England. e, Sweden v. Argentina. f, Nigeria v. England.

No. 2618, 9d: a, Croatia v. Mexico. b, Italy v. Ecuador. c, Italy v. Croatia. d, Mexico v. Ecuador. e, Mexico v. Italy. f, Ecuador v. Croatia.

No. 2619, 9d: a, Japan v. Belgium. b, Russia v. Tunisia. c, Japan v. Russia. d, Tunisia v. Belgium. e, Tunisia v. Japan. f, Belgium v. Russia.

Stadia and dates of matches between — No. 2620, 20d: a, France v. Senegal. b, Uruguay v. Denmark.

No. 2621, 20d: a, France v. Uruguay. b, Denmark v. Senegal.

No. 2622, 20d: a, Denmark v. France. b, Senegal v. Uruguay.

No. 2623, 20d: a, Paraguay v. South Africa. b, Spain v. Slovenia.

No. 2624, 20d: a, Spain v. Paraguay. b, South Africa v. Slovenia.

No. 2625, 20d: a, South Africa v. Spain. b, Slovenia v. Paraguay.

No. 2626, 20d: a, Brazil v. Turkey. b, China v. Costa Rica.

No. 2627, 20d: a, Brazil v. China. b, Costa Rica v. Turkey.

No. 2628, 20d: a, Costa Rica v. Brazil. b, Turkey v. China.

No. 2629, 20d: a, South Korea v. Poland. b, US v. Portugal.

No. 2630, 20d: a, South Korea v. US. b, Portugal v. Poland.

No. 2631, 20d: a, Portugal v. South Korea. b, Poland v. US.

No. 2632, 20d: a, Germany v. Saudi Arabia. b, Ireland v. Cameroun.

No. 2633, 20d: a, Germany v. Ireland. b, Cameroun v. Saudi Arabia.

No. 2634, 20d: a, Cameroun v. Germany. b, Saudi Arabia v. Ireland.

No. 2635, 20d: a, England v. Sweden. b, Argentina v. Nigeria.

No. 2636, 20d: a, Sweden v. Nigeria. b, Argentina v. England.

No. 2637, 20d: a, Sweden v. Argentina. b, Nigeria v. England.

No. 2638, 20d: a, Croatia v. Mexico. b, Italy v. Ecuador.

No. 2639, 20d: a, Italy v. Croatia. b, Mexico v. Ecuador.

No. 2640, 20d: a, Mexico v. Italy. b, Ecuador v. Croatia.

No. 2641, 20d: a, Japan v. Belgium. b, Russia v. Tunisia.

No. 2642, 20d: a, Japan v. Russia. b, Tunisia v. Belgium.

No. 2643, 20d: a, Tunisia v. Japan. b, Belgium v. Russia.

**2002, July 1              Perf. 13¼**
**Sheets of 6, #a-f**
2612-2619  A432   Set of 8   52.50 52.50
**Souvenir Sheets**
2620-2643  A432   Set of 24  110.00 110.00

See Nos. 2654-2656 for sheets with match results.

Popeye — A433

No. 2644, 10d: a, Popeye on cross-country skis. b, Popeye ski jumping. c, Popeye slaloming. d, Popeye snowboarding.

No. 2645, 10d: a, Swee'Pea on sled. b, Olive Oyl on skis. c, Brutus. d, Wimpy on ice skates.

No. 2646, 25d, Popeye and Olive in bobsled. No. 2647, 25d, Brutus playing hockey. No. 2648, 25d, Olive on ice skates. No. 2649, 25d, Popeye speed skating, horiz.

**2002, June 17      Litho.      Perf. 14**
**Sheets of 6, #a-f**
2644-2645  A433   Set of 2    9.25  9.25
**Souvenir Sheets**
2646-2649  A433   Set of 4   12.00 12.00

20th World Scout Jamboree,
Thailand — A434

No. 2650: a, Scout with bugle. b, Scout making fire. c, Scout fishing.
40d, Scout tying knot.

**2002, July 1              Perf. 13½x13¼**
2650  A434  15d Sheet of 3, #a-c  5.25  5.25
**Souvenir Sheet**
2651  A434  40d multi            4.75  4.75

Intl. Year of Ecotourism — A435

No. 2652: a, Bird-of-Paradise flower. b, Goliath heron. c, Baobab tree. d, Roan antelope. e, Red tip butterfly. f, Egyptian cobra.
No. 2653, Yellow-billed stork.

**2002, July 1**
2652 A435 9d Sheet of 6, #a-d    6.25 6.25
**Souvenir Sheet**
2653 A435 9d multi    1.00 1.00

**Nos. 2616, 2617 and 2619 Redrawn
With Match Scores**

No. 2654, 9d: a, Germany 8, Saudi Arabia 0. b, Ireland 1, Cameroun 1. c, Germany 1, Ireland 1. d, Cameroun 1, Saudi Arabia 0. e, Cameroun 0, Germany 2. f, Saudi Arabia 0, Ireland 3
No. 2655, 9d: a, England 1, Sweden 1. b, Argentina 1, Nigeria 0. c, Sweden 2, Nigeria 1. d, Argentina 0, England 1. e, Sweden 1, Argentina 1. f, Nigeria 0, England 0.
No. 2656, 9d: a, Japan 2, Belgium 2. b, Russia 2, Tunisia 0. c, Japan 1, Russia 0. d, Tunisia 1, Belgium 1. e, Japan 2, Tunisia 0. f, Belgium 3, Russia 2.

**2002, July 15**    **Perf. 13¼**
**Sheets of 6, #a-f**
2654-2656 A432    Set of 3    19.00 19.00

Elvis Presley
(1935-77)
A436

**2002, Aug. 19**    **Perf. 13½x13¾**
2657 A436 5d multi    .55 .55

Things from the Netherlands — A437

---

Lighthouses
of
Holland

Netherlands Lighthouses — A438

Netherlands Postage Stamps, 150th
Anniv. — A439

Women's Traditional Costumes of the
Netherlands — A440

No. 2658: a, Farm. b, Porcelain. c, Building. d, Ice skaters. e, Cheese, flowers and wooden shoes. f, Prince Willem-Alexander and his bride.
No. 2659: a, Den Helder. b, Terschelling. c, Maasvlakte. d, Ijmuiden. e, Westkapelle. f, Breskens.
No. 2660: a, Netherlands #1. b, Netherlands #B72. c, Netherlands #279. d, Netherlands #586. e, Netherlands #620. f, Netherlands #1108a.
No. 2661: a, Woman from Friesland (plaid headdress). b, Back of woman from Utrecht. c, Woman and child from Noord-Holland.

**2002, Aug. 30**    **Perf. 13½x13¼**
2658 A437 10d Sheet of 6, #a-f    6.50 6.50
2659 A438 10d Sheet of 6, #a-f    6.50 6.50
**Perf. 13¼x13½**
2660 A439 10d Sheet of 6, #a-f    6.50 6.50
**Perf. 13¼**
2661 A440 20d Sheet of 3, #a-c    6.50 6.50
Amphilex 2002 Intl. Stamp Exhibition, Amsterdam.

Marine Mammals and Flowers — A441

No. 2662, 10d: a, Blue whale. b, Pan-tropical spotted dolphin. c, Killer whale. d, Minke whale. e, Sperm whale. f, Pilot whale.

---

No. 2663, 10d: a, Juba-jamba. b, Devil's tongue. c, Rattle box. d, Vernonia purpurea. e, Seaside purslane. f, Fireball lily.
No. 2664, 50d, Humpback whale. No. 2665, 50d, Cape weed, swamp arum, vert.

**2002, Sept. 23**    **Perf. 14**
**Sheets of 6, #a-f**
2662-2663 A441    Set of 2    11.50 11.50
**Souvenir Sheets**
2664-2665 A441    Set of 2    10.00 10.00

A442

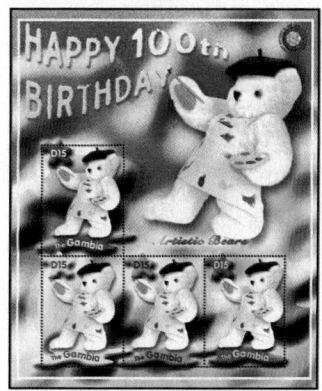

Teddy Bears, Cent. — A443

No. 2666: a, Bear with green feathered cap. b, Bear with beer stein. c, Bear with flower bouquet. d, Bear with mountain hat.
No. 2667 — Color of denomination and country name: a, White. b, Red violet. c, Blue violet. d, Green.

**2002, Oct. 21**    **Perf. 14**
2666 A442 15d Sheet of 4, #a-d    6.00 6.00
**Perf. 14¼**
2667 A443 15d Sheet of 4, #a-d    6.00 6.00

Christmas — A444

Designs: 3d, Madonna of Loreto, by Perugino. 5d, Madonna della Consolazione, by Perugino. 7d, Adoration of the Shepherds, by Perugino. 15d, Transfiguration of Christ, by Giovanni Bellini. 35d, Adoration of the Magi, by Perugino.
45d, Christ Blessing, by Bellini.

**2002, Nov. 4**    **Perf. 14**
2668-2672 A444    Set of 5    6.25 6.25
**Souvenir Sheet**
2673 A444 45d multi    4.50 4.50

---

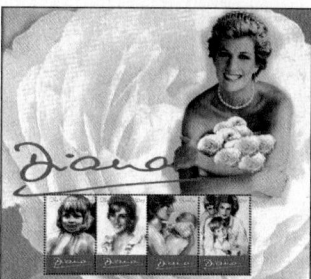

Princess Diana (1961-97) — A445

No. 2674, 15d — With red panel at bottom: a, As child. b, Wearing tiara. c, Holding baby. d, With children.
No. 2675, 15d: a, Wearing red hat. b, Wearing red and white hat. c, Wearing white gown. d, Wearing black gown and choker.

**2002, Nov. 18**
**Sheets of 4, #a-d**
2674-2675 A445    Set of 2    11.50 11.50

**Souvenir Sheet**

Gold-banded Forester
Butterfly — A446

**2002**    **Litho.**    **Perf. 14**
2676 A446 60d multi    5.75 5.75

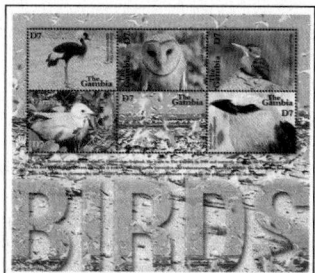

Birds — A447

No. 2677: a, Black-crowned crane. b, Barn owl. c, African pygmy kingfisher. d, Audouin's gull. e, Royal tern. f, Blue-bellied roller.

**2002**
2677 A447 7d Sheet of 6, #a-f    4.25 4.25

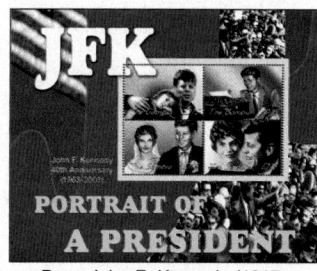

Pres. John F. Kennedy (1917-63) — A448

No. 2678, 15d: a, With daughter Caroline. b, At typewriter. c, At wedding to Jacqueline. d, With Jacqueline.
No. 2679, 15d, vert: a, In naval uniform. b, As child. c, Wearing shirt with open collar. d, At microphone.

**2002, Nov. 8**
**Sheets of 4, #a-d**
2678-2679 A448    Set of 2    11.50 11.50

A449

Trains
A450

Designs: 2d, Paris, Lyon & Mediterranean Railway. 3d, Zugspitz rack train, Germany. No. 2682, 10d, Austrian State Railway Class 210. 15d, State Railway of Saxony.

4d, 1922 Great Britain Class A1 4-6-2. 5d, 1957 Tee four car train. No. 2686, 7d, 1928 German Rheingold Mitropa car. 8d, 1900 German Gerda 4-4-0.

No. 2688, 7d: a, French Natl. Railway Series 68. b, French Natl. Railway Mistral. c, Prussian State Railway. d, Austrian Southern Railway. e, Paris-Orleans Railway. f, German Federal Railway E10.

No. 2689, 7d: a, Royal Prussian Union Railway. b, Austrian Federal Railway. c, German Rugen steam locomotive. d, Rh B Ge 2/4 electric locomotive. e, Panoramic Express, Switzerland. f, Brunig steam engine, Swiss Natl. Railway.

No. 2690, 10d: a, 1813 Puffing Billy, Great Britain. b, Adler, Germany, 1836. c, 1906 German 4-6-0. d, Class 132 Co-Co, Germany.

No. 2691, 10d: a, 1832 Brother Jonathan 4-2-0, US. b, Medoc Class 2-4-0, Germany and Switzerland, 1857. c, 1908 German Class S 3/6 4-6-2. d, 1959 German Class VT 11.5.

No. 2692, 10d: a, 1843 Beuth 2-2-2, Germany. b, 1852 Crampton 4-2-0, France. c, 1932 Sut 877 Flying Hamburger, Germany. d, 1970 Class 103.1 Co-Co, Germany.

No. 2693, 25d, German Federal Railway V200. No. 2694, 25d, German Federal Railway Trans-Europe Express.

No. 2695, 25d, 1953 VT10.5, Germany. No. 2696, 25d,1973 Class ET 403 four-car electric, Germany.

**2002**

| | | | | |
|---|---|---|---|---|
| 2680-2683 | A449 | Set of 4 | 2.75 | 2.75 |
| 2684-2687 | A450 | Set of 4 | 2.40 | 2.40 |

**Sheets of 6, #a-f**

| | | | | |
|---|---|---|---|---|
| 2688-2689 | A449 | Set of 2 | 8.00 | 8.00 |

**Sheets of 4, #a-d**

| | | | | |
|---|---|---|---|---|
| 2690-2692 | A450 | Set of 3 | 11.50 | 11.50 |

**Souvenir Sheets**

| | | | | |
|---|---|---|---|---|
| 2693-2694 | A449 | Set of 2 | 5.00 | 5.00 |
| 2695-2696 | A450 | Set of 2 | 5.00 | 5.00 |

Charles A. Lindbergh (1902-74), Aviator — A451

No. 2697, 15d: a, As child, with dog. b, As young man, brown violet background. c, With aviator goggles. d, Anne Morrow Lindbergh.

No. 2698, 15d: a, As child. b, As young man, blue background. c, Wearing uniform. d, Wearing suit and tie.

**2002, Nov. 18    Litho.    Perf. 14**
**Sheets of 4, #a-d**

| | | | | |
|---|---|---|---|---|
| 2697-2698 | A451 | Set of 2 | 11.50 | 11.50 |

**Butterfly Type of 2000**

Designs: 4d, Amphicalia tigris.

**2003, Jan. 14    Perf. 14¾x14**

| | | | | |
|---|---|---|---|---|
| 2699 | A367 | 4d multi | .40 | .40 |

New Year 2003 (Year of the Ram) — A452

No. 2697: a, Tan background, brown ram. b, Purple background. c, Brown background, orange ram. d, Orange background, purple and red ram.

**2003, Jan. 27    Perf. 13¾**

| | | | | |
|---|---|---|---|---|
| 2701 | A452 | 10d Sheet of 4, #a-d | 3.50 | 3.50 |

A453

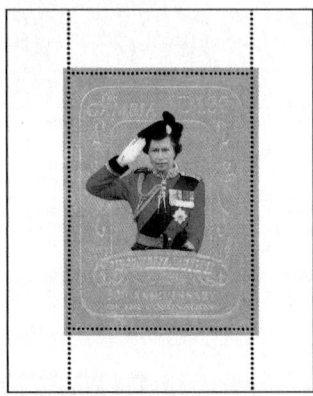

Coronation of Queen Elizabeth II, 50th Anniv. — A454

No. 2702: a, Wearing tiara. b, Wearing blue hat. c, Wearing cape and hat.

**2003    Litho.    Perf. 14**

| | | | | |
|---|---|---|---|---|
| 2702 | A453 | 20d Sheet of 3, #a-c | 5.50 | 5.50 |

**Souvenir Sheet**

| | | | | |
|---|---|---|---|---|
| 2703 | A453 | 45d shown | 4.25 | 4.25 |

**Miniature Sheet**
**Litho. & Embossed**
**Perf. 13¼x13**

| | | | | |
|---|---|---|---|---|
| 2704 | A454 | 130d shown | 10.50 | 10.50 |

Issued: Nos. 2702-2703, 5/13; 130d, 2/24.

Art by Yoshitoshi Taiso (1839-92)
A455

Designs: 5d, Concubine Washing Her Hands Under an Ornate Faucet. 10d, Housewife in an Inner Chamber Fanning a Fire. 15d, Geisha Catching a Firefly. 25d, A Young Geisha Dressed as an Elegant Young Man While Taking Part in the Niwaka Celebration.

No. 2709: a, Music Teacher Playing on a Samisen. b, An "Okamisan," or Proprietress of a Tea House, at Work. c, A City Merchant's Widow Absorbed in a Novelette. d, Busy Young Waitress Preoccupied With Her Responsibilities.

45d, A "Saikun," or Wife of a Government Official, Lighting an Oil Lamp.

**2003, Mar. 10    Litho.    Perf. 14¼**

| | | | | |
|---|---|---|---|---|
| 2705-2708 | A455 | Set of 4 | 4.75 | 4.75 |
| 2709 | A455 | 20d Sheet of 4, #a-d | 6.50 | 6.50 |

**Souvenir Sheet**

| | | | | |
|---|---|---|---|---|
| 2710 | A455 | 45d multi | 4.00 | 4.00 |

Paintings by the Cranachs
A456

Paintings by Lucas Cranach the Elder (1472-1553) or Lucas Cranach the Younger (1515-86) (Y): 5d, Portrait of Johannes Scheyring. 7d, Rudolph Agricola. 10d, Portrait Head of a Gentleman (Y). 20d, Hans von Lindau (Y).

No. 2715: a, Margravine Elizabeth von Ansbach (Y). b, Elector Joachim II of Brandenburg (Y). c, Portrait of a Nobleman (Y). d, Portrait of a Noblewoman (Y).

40d, The Ill-matched Couple.

**2003, Mar. 10**

| | | | | |
|---|---|---|---|---|
| 2711-2714 | A456 | Set of 4 | 3.50 | 3.50 |
| 2715 | A456 | 15d Sheet of 4, #a-d | 5.00 | 5.00 |

**Souvenir Sheet**

| | | | | |
|---|---|---|---|---|
| 2716 | A456 | 40d multi | 3.25 | 3.25 |

Paintings by Wassily Kandinsky (1866-1944) — A457

Designs: 2d, Composition X. 4d, Arrow Towards the Circle. 5d, Yellow-Red-Blue. 7d, Accompanied Middle. 10d, In Blue. 20d, Round and Pointed.

No. 2723, vert.: a, Picture with Archer. b, Light. c, Picture in the Picture. d, White Stroke.

No. 2724, 45d, Improvisation XIX. No. 2725, 45d, On the Points.

**2003, Mar. 10    Perf. 14¼**

| | | | | |
|---|---|---|---|---|
| 2717-2722 | A457 | Set of 6 | 4.25 | 4.25 |
| 2723 | A457 | 15d Sheet of 4, #a-d | 5.00 | 5.00 |

**Size: 97x78mm**
**Imperf**

| | | | | |
|---|---|---|---|---|
| 2724-2725 | A457 | Set of 2 | 7.50 | 7.50 |

A458

Astronauts Killed In Space Shuttle Columbia Accident — A459

No. 2726, 15d — Michael P. Anderson: a, Columbia crew, brown background, country name at UL. b, Anderson and jet. c, Shuttle lifting off. d, Shuttle in orbit, Space Station.

No. 2727, 15d — Kalpana Chawla: a, Like No. 2726a, country name at LL. b, Shuttle being transported by jet. c, Shuttle glowing in re-entry. d, Chawla, astronaut spacewalking.

No. 2728, 15d — Laurel Blair Salton Clark: a, Like No. 2727a, green and red background. b, Shuttle in orbit, moon in background. c, Shuttle on launch pad. d, Clark and jet.

No. 2729, 15d — Ilan Ramon: a, Columbia crew, purple and yellow background. b, Ramon in jet. c, Shuttle with engines firing at launch pad. d, Shuttle in orbit.

No. 2730: a, Mission Specialist David M. Brown. b, Commander Rick D. Husband. c, Mission Specialist 4 Laurel Blair Salton Clark. d, Mission Specialist 4 Kalpana Chawla. e, Payload Commander, Michael P. Anderson. f, Pilot William C. McCool. g, Payload Specialist 4 Ilan Ramon.

**2003, Apr. 7    Perf. 14¼**
**Sheets of 4, #a-d**

| | | | | |
|---|---|---|---|---|
| 2726-2729 | A458 | Set of 4 | 21.00 | 21.00 |

**Souvenir Sheet**

| | | | | |
|---|---|---|---|---|
| 2730 | A459 | 10d Sheet of 7, #a-g | 6.00 | 6.00 |

A460

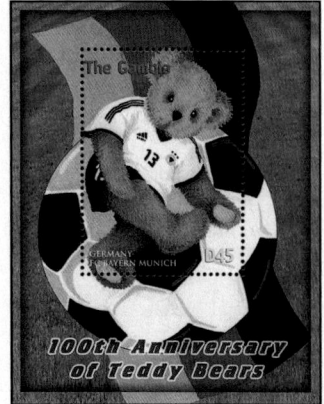

Teddy Bears — A461

No. 2732, 15d — Bears with flags and soccer uniforms of: a, England. b, Brazil. c, Germany. d, Spain.
No. 2733, 15d — Bears with soccer uniforms of German teams: a, Schalke 04. b, FC Bayern Munich. c, Bayer Leaerkusen. d, Hertha Berlin.
No. 2734, 45d, FC Bayern Munich, white uniform. No. 2735, 45d, FC Bayern Munich red uniform, horiz.

**2003      Embroidered      Imperf.**
**Self-Adhesive (#2731)**
2731  A460  150d shown            14.00 14.00
**Sheets of 4, #a-d**
**Litho.**
**Perf. 13¼**
2732-2733  A461   Set of 2        11.00 11.00
**Souvenir Sheets**
2734-2735  A461   Set of 2         8.25  8.25
Issued: No. 2731, Apr.; Nos. 2732-2735, 7/1.
No. 2731 was issued in sheets of 4.

Prince William, 21st Birthday — A462

No. 2736: a, Wearing suit, no tie. b, Wearing suit and tie. c, Wearing blue shirt, no suit. 45d, Wearing polo uniform.

**2003, May 13    Litho.    Perf. 14**
2736  A462  20d Sheet of 3, #a-c   5.50  5.50
**Souvenir Sheet**
2737  A462  45d multi              4.25  4.25

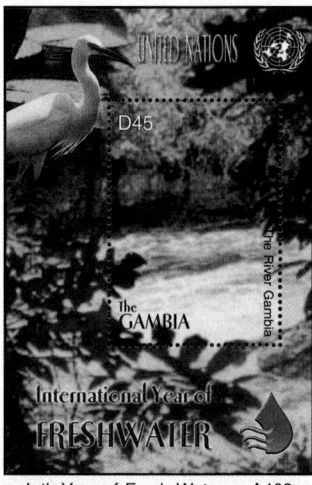

Intl. Year of Fresh Water — A463

No. 2738 — Gambia River: a, Foliage at top. b, Foliage at top, silhouette of far shore at center. c, Trees at right.
45d, Gambia River rapids.

**2003, July 1              Perf. 13¼**
2738  A463  20d Sheet of 3, #a-c   5.50  5.50
**Souvenir Sheet**
2739  A463  45d multi              4.25  4.25

Tour de France Bicycle Race, Cent. — A464

No. 2740, 15d: a, Henri Pelissier, 1923. b, Ottavio Bottecchia, 1924. c, Bottecchia, 1925. d, Lucien Buysse, 1926.
No. 2741, 15d: a, Nicholas Frantz, 1927. b, Frantz, 1928. c, Maurice de Waele, 1929. d, André Leducq, 1930.
No. 2742, 15d: a, Antonin Magne, 1931. b, Leducq, 1932. c, Georges Speicher, 1933. d, Magne, 1934.

**2003, July 1              Perf. 13¼**
**Sheets of 4, #a-d**
2740-2742  A464   Set of 3        17.00 17.00

General Motors Automobiles — A465

No. 2743, 15d — Cadillacs: a, 1937 Series 60. b, 1927 La Salle. c, 1930 V-16. d, 1931 V-16 Convertible.
No. 2744, 15d — Corvettes: a, 1960 Shark. b, 1964 Sting Ray Convertible. c, 1956 Convertible. d, 1967.
No. 2745, 45d, 1954 Cadillac Eldorado. No. 2746, 45d, 1964 Corvette Sting Ray.

**2003, July 1          Perf. 13¼x13½**
**Sheets of 4, #a-d**
2743-2744  A465   Set of 2        11.00 11.00
**Souvenir Sheets**
2745-2746  A465   Set of 2         8.25  8.25

History of Aviation — A466

No. 2747, 15d: a, First powered flight by Wright Brothers, 1903. b, Goupil, first full-size triplane, 1908. c, Deutschland LZ-7, first commercial airship, 1909. d, Lt. Col. Richard Byrd's flight over North Pole, 1926.
No. 2748, 15d: a, Granville Gee Bee, world speed record, 1932. b, Boeing 247D with all-metal construction retractable landing gear, 1933. c, Douglas DC-3, 1935. d, Amelia Earhart's solo flight from Hawaii to California, 1935.
No. 2749, 15d: a, First solar powered flight, by MacCready Solar Challenger, 1981. b, Voyager 2 space probe explores Saturn, 1981. c, Space Shuttle Columbia, 1981. d, First nonstop non-refueled around the world flight, by Voyager, 1986.
No. 2750, 40d, Vought V-173 Short Takeoff and Landing research airplane, 1942. No. 2751, 40d, Pioneer 10 space probe, 1972. No. 2752, 40d, AD-1 scissors-wing SST, 1979.

**2003, July 14              Perf. 14**
**Sheets of 4, #a-d**
2747-2749  A466   Set of 3        17.00 17.00
**Souvenir Sheets**
2750-2752  A466   Set of 3        11.00 11.00

Ferrari Race Cars — A467

Designs: 2d, 126 C2. 3d, 312 T2. 5d, 312 T4. 7d, 126 C3. 10d, F399. 15d, F1-2000. 20d, F2001. 25d, F2002.

**2003, July 28              Perf. 14¼**
2753-2760  A467   Set of 8         6.50  6.50

Circus Performers — A468

No. 2761, 15d: a, Francesco Caroli. b, Lou Jacobs. c, Frankie Saluto. d, Gingernut.
No. 2762, 15d: a, Evgeny Maranogli. b, Saby. c, Colonel Joe. d, Puma.

**2003, Sept. 1              Perf. 14**
**Sheets of 4, #a-d**
2761-2762  A468   Set of 2        10.00 10.00

**Marine Mammals and Flowers Type of 2002**

No. 2763 — Insects and flowers: a, Colored shield-backed bug, Waltheria indica. b, Dragonfly, Red mangrove. c, Cotton stainer bug, Baissea multiflora. d, Harpagomantis. Mimosa pigra. e, Katydid, Coia cordifolia. f, African grasshopper, Urena labata.
50d, Giant swallowtail butterfly, Ipomoea cairica.

**2003              Perf. 14**
2763  A441  10d Sheet of 6, #a-f   4.50  4.50
**Souvenir Sheet**
2764  A441  50d multi              4.00  4.00

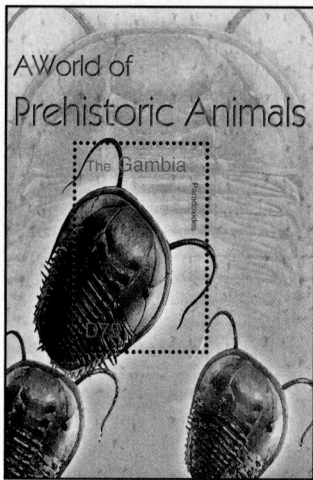

A World of Prehistoric Animals

Prehistoric Animals — A469

No. 2765, 30d: a, Peteinosaurus. b, Pachycephalosaurus. c, Ichthyosaur. d, Anomalocaris.
No. 2766, 30d, horiz.: a, Criorhynchus. b, Seismosaurus. c, Triceratops. d, Stegosaurus.
No. 2767, 75d, Paradoxides. No. 2768, 75d, Edmontosaurus, horiz.

**2003, Nov. 4    Litho.    Perf. 14**
**Sheets of 4, #a-d**
2765-2766  A469   Set of 2        17.00 17.00
**Souvenir Sheets**
2767-2768  A469   Set of 2        10.50 10.50

Christmas — A470

Paintings: 3d, Madonna of the Grand Duke, by Raphael. 5d, Madonna della Impannata, by Raphael. 7d, Adoration of the Magi, by Filippo Lippi. 60d, Adoration in the Woods, by Lippi. 75d, Madonna del Carmelo, by Giambattista Tiepolo.

**2003, Nov. 17              Perf. 14¼**
2769-2772  A470   Set of 4         5.50  5.50
**Souvenir Sheet**
2773  A470  75d multi              5.50  5.50

Leo Diamond — A471

**2003, Nov. 18          Perf. 13¼x13½**
2774  A471  15d multi              1.10  1.10
**Souvenir Sheet**
2775  A471  60d multi              4.50  4.50
No. 2774 issued in sheets of six.

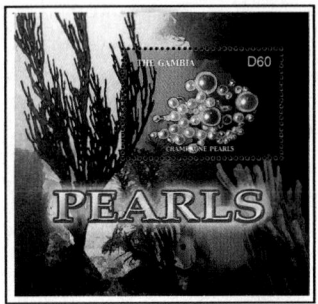

Pearls — A472

No. 2776: a, South Sea pearls. b, Mabe pearls. c, Pinctada maxima. d, Australian pearls. e, Pearls on ocean floor. f, South Sea white pearls.
  60d, Champagne pearls.

**2003, Nov. 18**
2776  A472  15d Sheet of 6, #a-f    6.50  6.50
**Souvenir Sheet**
2777  A472  60d multi               4.50  4.50

James Cagney (1899-1986) — A473

No. 2778: a, With solid tie. b, With hat. c, With gun. d, With lapel handkerchief. e, With plaid tie. f, With woman.

**2003**                               *Perf. 14*
2778  A473  10d Sheet of 6, #a-d    4.50  4.50

Clark Gable (1901-60) — A474

No. 2779: a, Wearing tuxedo and bow tie, hand showing. b, Wearing suit and tie, no mustache, no hand showing. c, Wearing tuxedo and bow tie, no hand showing. d, Wearing suit and tie, hand showing. e, Wearing suit and solid tie, with mustache. f, Wearing suit and striped tie, with mustache.

**2003**
2779  A474  10d Sheet of 6, #a-f    4.50  4.50

Diamonds — A475

No. 2780: a, Rough diamonds. b, Yellow diamonds. c, Pink diamonds. d, Blue diamonds. e, White diamonds. f, Green diamonds.
  75d, Champagne diamonds.

---

*Perf. 13¼x13½*
**2003, Nov. 18**                    **Litho.**
2780  A475  20d Sheet of 6, #a-f    8.00  8.00
**Souvenir Sheet**
2781  A475  75d multi               5.00  5.00

Minerals — A476

No. 2782: a, Stilbite. b, Smoky quartz. c, Lapis lazuli. d, Amethyst. e, Black opals. f, Rubies.
  60d, Quartz.

**2003, Nov. 18**
2782  A476  15d Sheet of 6, #a-f    6.00  6.00
**Souvenir Sheet**
2783  A476  60d multi               4.00  4.00

New Year 2004 (Year of the Monkey) — A477

No. 2784: a, Monkey with white and brown face, white ears. b, Monkey with white and blue gray face. c, Monkey with white and brown face. d, Monkey with orange and white face.

**2004, Jan. 5**                     *Perf. 13¼*
2784  A477  15d Sheet of 4, #a-d    4.50  4.50

Paintings by Xu Beihong (1895-1953) — A478

No. 2785, vert.: a, Four Magpies. b, Cormorants. c, Under the Banyan Tree. d, Citrus Tree. e, Double Happiness. f, Rooster in Bamboo Garden.
  No. 2786: a, Bird on the Kapok Tree. b, Twin Pines.

**2004, Jan. 21  Litho.  *Perf. 13½x13¼***
2785  A478  10d Sheet of 6, #a-f    4.00  4.00
*Perf. 13¼*
2786  A478  25d Sheet of 2, #a-b    3.50  3.50
  2004 Hong Kong Stamp Expo. No. 2785 contains six 28x42mm stamps.

---

FIFA (Fédération Internationale de Football Association), Cent. — A479

FIFA cups: No. 2787, 10d, World Cup. No. 2788, 10d, Jules Rimet Cup. No. 2789, 10d, Women's World Cup. No. 2790, 10d, Under 17 World Championship Cup. No. 2791, 10d, Under 19 Women's World Championship Cup. No. 2792, 10d, Club World Championship Cup. No. 2793, 10d, Confederations Cup. No. 2794, 10d, World Youth Championship Cup. No. 2795, 10d, Fustal (Indoor Soccer) World Championship Cup.

**2004, Feb. 16**                    *Perf. 13¼*
2787-2795  A479     Set of 9        6.25  6.25

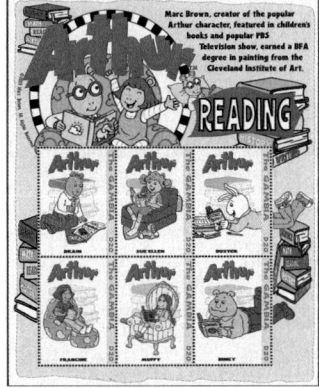

Arthur and Friends — A480

No. 2796 — Characters reading: a, Brain. b, Sue Ellen. c, Buster. d, Francine. e, Muffy. f, Binky.
  No. 2797, 30d: a, Brain playing clarinet. b, Francine playing banjo. c, Buster playing flute. d, Sue Ellen playing violin.
  No. 2798, 30d: a, Brain playing bass. b, Francine playing drum. c, Buster playing tuba. d, Sue Ellen playing saxophone.

**2004, Feb. 16**
2796  A480   20d Sheet of 6,
                        #a-f        8.25  8.25
**Sheets of 4, #a-d**
2797-2798  A480   Set of 2         16.50  16.50

Concorde and Queen Elizabeth 2 — A481

---

Concorde — A482

No. 2800, 25d — Concorde 216 G-BOAF and: a, British flag, with dots of blue at UR. b, British flag, no dots at UR, c, Clouds.
  No. 2801, 25d — Concorde 216 G-BOAF and: a, Statue of Liberty. b, Field of US flag. c, Stripes of US flag.
  No. 2802, 25d — Concorde 213 F-BTSD and: a, Top of Eiffel Tower. b, French flag, middle part of Eiffel Tower. c, French flag, first and second landings of Eiffel Tower.

**2004, Feb. 17**                    *Perf. 14*
2799  A481  60d multi               4.25  4.25
**Sheets of 3, #a-c**
*Perf. 13¼x13½*
2800-2802  A482     Set of 3       15.50  15.50

Paintings in the Hermitage, St. Petersburg, Russia — A483

No. 2803, vert.: a, Portrait of a Gentleman, by Domenico Capriolo. b, Sybil, by Dosso Dossi. c, A Woman in a Turban, by Anne-Louis Girodet-Trioson. d, Portrait of a Gentleman, by Ambrosius Holbein.
  75d, Husband and Wife, by Lorenzo Lotto.

**2004, Feb. 17**                    *Perf. 13¼*
2803  A483  30d Sheet of 4, #a-d    8.25  8.25
*Imperf*
2804  A483  75d multi               5.25  5.25
  St. Petersburg, 300th anniv. No. 2803 contains four 37x50mm stamps.

Paintings by Pablo Picasso — A484

No. 2805, vert.: a, Girl in Chemise. b, Portrait of Jacinto Salvadó as Harlequin. c, Tumblers. d, Woman with a Crow.
  75d, The Siesta.

**2004, Feb. 17**                    *Perf. 13¼*
2805  A484  30d Sheet of 4, #a-d    8.25  8.25
*Imperf*
2806  A484  75d multi               5.25  5.25
  No. 2805 contains four 37x50mm stamps.

Paintings by Norman Rockwell — A485

No. 2807: a, Detail of 1957 Saturday Evening Post Illustration. b, Girl at Mirror. c, After the Prom. d, The Prom Dress.
75d, Losing the Game.

**2004, Feb. 17**          **Perf. 13¼**
2807  A485  30d Sheet of 4, #a-d    8.25  8.25
     **Souvenir Sheet**
2808  A485  75d multi               5.25  5.25

Paintings by
Kunichika
Toyohara
(1835-1900)
A486

Designs: 10d, The Actor Kikugoro Onoe V as Moronao with the Late Sojuro Nakamura I as Hangan Enya. 15d, The Actor Kikugoro Onoe V as Kunimoto Shinohara with Danjuro Ichikawa IX as Takamori. 20d, The Actor Kikugoro Onoe V as Kansuke Yamamoto with Sadanji Ichikawa I as Daizo Ushikubo. 35d, The Actor Kikugoro Onoe V as the Ghost Seigen with Fukusuke Nakamura IV as Sakurahime.
No. 2813: a, The Actor Sadanji Ichikawa I as the Fishmonger Fukashichi. b, The Actor Sadanji Ichikawa I as Umeomaru. c, The Actor Kuzo Ichikawa III as Shihei Fujiwara. d, The Actor Shikan Nakamura IV as Motome.
75d, The Actor Udanji Ichikawa as Saihei Koya (Ozawa Keifu Tomofusa), horiz.

**2004, Feb. 17**
2809-2812  A486  Set of 4           5.50  5.50
2813  A486  30d Sheet of 4, #a-d    8.25  8.25
     **Souvenir Sheet**
2814  A486  75d multi               5.25  5.25

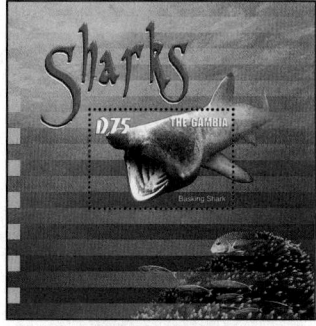

Sharks — A487

No. 2815: a, Lemon shark. b, Nurse shark. c, Leopard shark. d, Starry smoothhound sharks.
75d, Basking shark.

**2004, Mar. 8**          **Perf. 13¼x13½**
2815  A487  30d Sheet of 4, #a-d    8.25  8.25
     **Souvenir Sheet**
2816  A487  75d multi               5.25  5.25

Cats — A488

No. 2817, vert.: a, Black and white bicolor American shorthair. b, Brown and white Sphinx. c, Copper-eyed white Persian. d, Blue mackerel tabby Oriental longhair.
75d, Copper-eyed cameo Persian.

**2004, Mar. 8**          **Perf. 13½x13¼**
2817  A488  30d Sheet of 4, #a-d    8.25  8.25
     **Souvenir Sheet**
     **Perf. 13¼x13½**
2818  A488  75d multi               5.25  5.25

Dogs — A489

No. 2819, vert.: a, Bracco. b, Shih tzu. c, Boston terrier. d, Chihuahua.
75d, Borzoi.

**2004, Mar. 8**          **Perf. 13½x13¼**
2819  A489  30d Sheet of 4, #a-d    8.25  8.25
     **Souvenir Sheet**
     **Perf. 13¼x13½**
2820  A489  75d multi               5.25  5.25

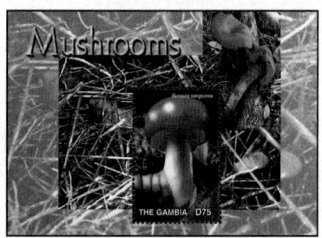

Mushrooms — A490

No. 2821, 30d: a, Hydrocybe conica. b, Laccaria fraterna. c, Gomphus clavatus. d, Hydrocybe psittacina.
No. 2822, 30d, horiz.: a, Steel blue entoloma. b, Caged stinkhorn. c, Flowerpot depiota. d, Singeri depiota.
75d, Russula sanguinea.

**Perf. 13½x13¼, 13¼x13½**
**2004, Mar. 8**
     **Sheets of 4, #a-d**
2821-2822  A490  Set of 2          16.50 16.50
     **Souvenir Sheet**
2823  A490  75d multi               5.25  5.25

Orchid Cacti — A491

No. 2824, 30d: a, Echinocerus. b, Harrisia. c, Stapelia. d, Matucana.
No. 2825, 30d: a, Epiphyllum crenatum. b, Isopogon latifolius. c, Banksia ericifolia. d, Echinopsis.
75d, Epiphyllum.

**2004, Mar. 8**          **Perf. 13¼x13½**
     **Sheets of 4, #a-d**
2824-2825  A491  Set of 2          16.50 16.50
     **Souvenir Sheet**
2826  A491  75d multi               5.25  5.25

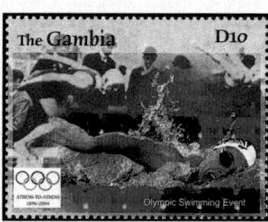

European Soccer Championships, Portugal — A492

No. 2827 — Teams from: a, Bulgaria. b, Croatia. c, Czech Republic. d, Denmark. e, England. f, France. g, Germany. h, Greece. i, Italy. j, Latvia. k, Netherlands. l, Portugal (no country name). m, Russia. n, Spain. o, Sweden. p, Switzerland.
No. 2828, vert.: a, Angelo Domenghini. b, Dragan Dzajic. c, Luigi Riva. d, Stadio Olimpico.
65d, 1968 champions, Italy.

**Perf. 13¼, 13½x13¼ (#2828)**
**2004, Mar. 26**
2827  A492  6d Sheet of 16, #a-p   6.75  6.75
2828  A492  25d Sheet of 4, #a-d   7.00  7.00
     **Souvenir Sheet**
2829  A492  65d multi              4.50  4.50
No. 2828 contains four 28x42mm stamps.

2004 Summer Olympics, Athens — A493

Designs: 10d, Swimming. 15d, Henri de Baillet-Latour (1876-1942), Intl. Olympic Committee President, vert. 20d, Gold medal of 1896 Olympics, vert. 30d, Pentathlon.

**2004, Apr. 19**          **Perf. 13¼**
2830-2833  A493  Set of 4          5.25  5.25

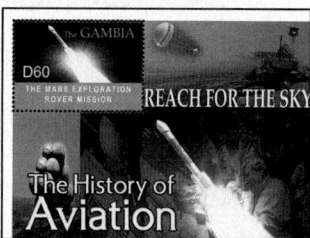

Trains, Bridges, Tunnels and Stations — A494

No. 2834, 12d: a, Mallard locomotive. b, North British 4-8-2T locomotive. c, Russian P36 4-8-4 locomotive. d, Forth Rail Bridge. e, Lune Viaduct. f, Lambley Viaduct. g, Alston Arches Viaduct. h, Royal Albert Bridge. i, Blackfriar's Bridge.
No. 2835, 12d: a, City of Truro train. b, Sharp Stewart 4-4-0 locomotive. c, Indian Railways WT Class locomotive. d, Charing Cross Station. e, Linlithgow Station. f, Hellifield Station. g, Kings Cross Station. h, Paddington Station. i, Victoria Station.
No. 2836, 12d: a, Virgin Pendolino train. b, Mountain Class Garratt locomotive. c, 2-8-8-4 No. 227 locomotive. d, Kilsby Tunnel. e, Box Tunnel. f, Willersley Tunnel. g, Stansted Airport Tunnel. h, Clayton Tunnel. i, Severn Tunnel.
No. 2837, 65d, West Highland Line train. No. 2838, 65d, Darjeeling-Himalaya train. No. 2839, 65d, Eurostar.

**2004, Apr. 19**          **Perf. 13¼x13½**
     **Sheets of 9, #a-i**
2834-2836  A494  Set of 3         22.50 22.50
     **Souvenir Sheets**
2837-2839  A494  Set of 3         13.50 13.50

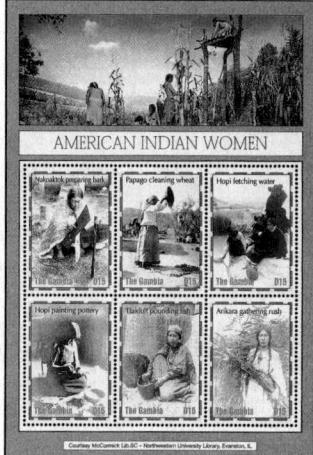

American Indians — A495

No. 2840: a, Nakoaktok preparing bark. b, Papago cleaning wheat. c, Hopi fetching water. d, Hopi painting pottery. e, Tlakluit pounding fish. f, Arikara gathering rush.
No. 2841, horiz.: a, Apsaroke Indians and teepee. b, Pigean Indians. c, Apsaroke Indians. d, Sioux chiefs.

**2004, May 3**          **Perf. 14¼x14¾**
2840  A495  15d Sheet of 6, #a-f   6.25  6.25
     **Perf. 13¾**
2841  A495  30d Sheet of 4, #a-d   8.25  8.25
No. 2841 contains four 38x30mm stamps.

History of Aviation — A496

No. 2842: a, Leonardo da Vinci. b, Count Ferdinand von Zeppelin. c, William E. Boeing. d, Capt. John Cunningham. e, Capt. Edwin C. Musick. f, Capt. Jock Lowe. g, William Lear. h, Jenny Murray.
60d, Mars Rover mission.

**2004, May 3**          **Perf. 14**
2842  A496  12d Sheet of 8, #a-h   6.75  6.75
     **Souvenir Sheet**
2843  A496  60d multi              4.25  4.25

A497

Marilyn Monroe (1926-62) — A498

No. 2844: a, Wearing necklace. b, No necklace.

No. 2845 — Background color: a, Orange. b, Green. c, Bright lilac rose. d, Bright yellow. e, Bright blue. f, Bright red. g, Dull blue. h, Bright yellow green. i, Blue green. j, Yellow. k, Red orange. l, Purple. m, Red lilac. n, Light blue. o, Dark blue. p, Rose pink.

No. 2846 — Black background and: a, Hand on face. b, Wearing necklace. c, Wearng red dress. d, Wearing blouse with collar.

**2004, May 3**                    **Perf. 14**
2844  A497   25d Pair, #a-b          3.50  3.50
2845  A498   7d Sheet of 16, #a-p    7.75  7.75
2846  A498   25d Sheet of 4, #a-d    7.00  7.00

No. 2844 was printed in sheets containing two pairs.

D-Day, 60th Anniv. A499

Designs: 7d, Jim Wallwork, 6th Airborne Division. 10d, Major Gen. Richard Gale. 15d, Winston Churchill. 30d, J.K. "Paddy" Byrne, 197th Typhoon Squadron.

No. 2851, 25d: a, Bombers over coast of Normandy. b, RAF Mitchell bomber dropping bombs. c, British Horsa gliders behind enemy lines. d, Paratroopers dropping into Normandy.

No. 2852, 25d: a, British paratroopers prepare for mission. b, British paratroopers secure Pegasus Bridge. c, American paratroopers drop into Sainte-Mère-Eglise area. d, American paratroopers enter town of Sainte-Mère-Eglise.

No. 2853, 60d, RAF bombers under construction. No. 2854, 60d, Troops disembarking from landing craft.

**2004, May 3**                         **Litho.**
2847-2850  A499   Set of 4 +
                   labels            4.25   4.25
**Sheets of 4, #a-d**
2851-2852  A499                     14.00  14.00
**Souvenir Sheets**
2853-2854  A499   Set of 2           8.25   8.25

Election of Pope John Paul II, 25th Anniv. (in 2003) — A500

No. 2855 — Pope in: a, 1988. b, 1989. c, 1990. d, 1991. e, 1992. f, 1993. g, 1994. h, 1995. i, 1996. j, 1997. k, 1998. l, 1999. m, 2000. n, 2001. o, 2002.
No. 2856 — Pope in: a, 1978. b, 1979. c, 1980. d, 1981. e, 1982. f, 1983. g, 1984. h, 1985. i, 1986. j, 1987.

**2004, May 13**              **Perf. 13½x13¼**
2855  A500  7d Sheet of 15, #a-o  7.25  7.25
2856  A500  10d Sheet of 10, #a-j 6.75  6.75

American Lighthouses A501

Designs: 25d, Tybee Island, Georgia. 30d, Old Cape Henry, Virginia. 35d, Morris Island, South Carolina. 40d, Hillsboro Inlet, Florida. 50d, Cape Lookout, North Carolina.

**2004, May 27**              **Perf. 14¾x14¼**
2857-2861  A501   Set of 5    12.50  12.50

Gambian postal authorities have declared the following items as "illegal:"

Sheet of nine 25d stamps: Oceans;

Sheets of six 25d stamps: Birds of Prey with Rotary emblem, Orchids with Rotary emblem, New Cinema, Vincent van Gogh Paintings, Monuments of Egypt, Fire Engines;

Sheets of four 25d stamps: Pope John Paul II, Nude Art, Great Composers, Lighthouses with Rotary emblem, Aircraft with Rotary emblem, Actresses, Pin-up Art;

Sheet of three 25d stamps: Polar Birds with Rotary emblem;

Sheets of two 25d stamps: Prehistoric World, Chinese New Year, Looney Tunes, Games and Sports.

Paintings by Joan Miró A502

Designs: 20d, Woman, 1934, pastel on paper. 25d, Woman, 1934, pastel and pencil on emery paper. 35d, Self-portrait. No. 2865, 75d, Man with Pipe.

No. 2866: a, Portrait IV. b, Seated Woman. c, Painting on Ingres Paper. d, Portrait II.

No. 2867, 75d, Composition with Personages in the Burning Forest, horiz. No. 2868, 75d, Bird, horiz.

**2004, Feb. 17**   **Litho.**   **Perf. 13¼**
2862-2865  A502   Set of 4    11.00  11.00
2866  A502  30d Sheet of 4,
                   #a-d        8.25   8.25

**Size: 100x80mm**
**Imperf**
2867-2868  A502   Set of 2    10.50  10.50

**Souvenir Sheet**

Deng Xiaoping (1904-97), Chinese Leader — A503

**2004, May 3**                    **Perf. 13½**
2869  A503  75d multi                5.25  5.25

**Miniature Sheet**

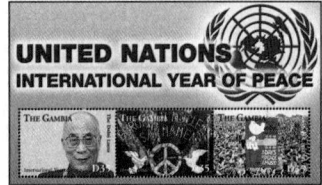

Intl. Year of Peace — A504

No. 2870: a, Dalai Lama. b, European nuclear disarmament banner. c, Woodstock music festival.

**2004, May 3**                    **Perf. 14**
2870  A504  35d Sheet of 3, #a-c    7.25  7.25

**Miniature Sheet**

Rare and Famous Postage Stamps — A505

No. 2871: a, British Guiana #13. b, Great Britain #1. c, United States #85A. d, United States #C3a. e, United States #1.

**2004, June 24**                   **Perf. 13**
2871  A505  20d Sheet of 5, #a-e,
                   + label          6.75  6.75

Flowers — A506

Designs: 1d, Babiana rubrocyanaea. 2d, Protea. 3d, Lithops bromfieldii. 5d, Saintpaulia ionantha. 6d, Monopsis lutea. 7d, Dudleya lanceolata. 9d, Euphorbia punicea. 10d, Oxalis violacea. 25d, Helichrysum bracteatum. 50d, Senecio obovatus. 75d, Mesembryanthemum acinaciforme. 100d, Montbretia crocosmiiflora. 200d, Gladiolus colvillei.

**2004, July 1**              **Perf. 14¾x14**
2872  A506   1d multi          .20    .20
2873  A506   2d multi          .20    .20
2874  A506   3d multi          .20    .20
2875  A506   5d multi          .35    .35
2876  A506   6d multi          .40    .40
2877  A506   7d multi          .50    .50
2878  A506   9d multi          .60    .60
2879  A506   10d multi         .70    .70
2880  A506   25d multi        1.75   1.75
2881  A506   50d multi        3.50   3.50
2882  A506   75d multi        5.00   5.00
2883  A506   100d multi       6.75   6.75
2884  A506   200d multi      13.50  13.50
  Nos. 2872-2884 (13)       33.65  33.65

A507

First Elvis Presley Record, 50th Anniv. — A508

Various portraits of Elvis Presley.

**2004, Aug. 2**                    **Perf. 13¼**
2885  A507  12d Sheet of 9, #a-i    7.50  7.50
2886  A508  12d Sheet of 9, #a-i    7.50  7.50

**Miniature Sheet**

George Herman "Babe" Ruth (1895-1948), Baseball Player — A509

No. 2887: a, Swinging, legs spread apart. b, Standing. c, Swinging, legs together. d, Holding bat.

**2004, Sept. 3**                   **Perf. 13½**
2887  A509  25d Sheet of 4, #a-d    6.75  6.75

Pres. Ronald Reagan (1911-2004) — A510

No. 2888: a, With wife, Nancy and Pope John Paul II. b, With Israeli Prime Minister Shimon Peres.

No. 2889: a, With window in background. b, Before microphones. c, Holding glass.

**2004, Oct. 13**
2888 A510 15d Pair, #a-b    2.10 2.10
2889 A510 15d Vert. strip of 3,      #a-c    3.25 3.25

No. 2888 was printed in sheets of three pairs. No. 2889 was printed in sheets of two strips.

FIFA (Fédération Internationale de Football Association), Cent. — A511

No. 2890: a, Dixie Dean. b, Ruud Gullit. c, Karl-Heinz Rummenigge. d, Luis Enrique Martinez.
65d, Pele.

**2004, Oct. 27**     *Perf. 12¾x12½*
2890 A511 25d Sheet of 4, #a-d   7.00 7.00
**Souvenir Sheet**
2891 A511 65d multi        4.50 4.50

National Basketball Association Players — A512

Designs: No. 2892, 10d, Darko Milicic, Detroit Pistons. No. 2893, 10d, Chris Kaman, Los Angeles Clippers. No. 2894, 10d, Andrei Kirilenko, Utah Jazz. No. 2895, 10d, T. J. Ford, Milwaukee Bucks.

**2004**              *Perf. 14*
2892-2895 A512 Set of 4    2.75 2.75

Issued: No. 2892, 11/2; Nos. 2893-2894, 11/3; No. 2895, 11/6. Each stamp printed in sheets of 12.

Ocean Liners — A513

Designs: 7d, Bremen. 10d, RMS Queen Mary. 15d, Queen Mary II. 20d, RMS Queen Elizabeth 2. 25d, Britannic. 35d, RMS Majestic.
90d, RMS Aquitania.

**2004, Nov. 5**        *Perf. 14¼*
2896-2901 A513 Set of 6    7.75 7.75
**Souvenir Sheet**
2902 A513 90d multi       6.25 6.25

**Miniature Sheet**

Elvis Presley and Teddy Bears — A514

No. 2903: a, Presley in dark red suit. b, Teddy bear, plaid sleeve in background. c, Presley with guitar. d, Teddy bear, dark red suit in background. e, Presley in pink suit and tie. f, Teddy bear, guitar in background.

**2004, Nov. 29**        *Perf. 14*
2903 A514 20d Sheet of 6, #a-f   8.25 8.25

THE GAMBIA D7   Christmas A515

Designs: 7d, Greek Madonna, by Giovanni Bellini. 10d, Madonna in the Church, by Jan van Eyck. 20d, Conestabile Madonna, by Raphael. 25d, Madonna and Child, by Sandro Botticelli. 65d, Madonna and Child with Chancellor Rolin, by van Eyck.

**2004, Dec. 13**       *Perf. 12*
2904-2907 A515 Set of 4    4.25 4.25
**Souvenir Sheet**
2908 A515 65d multi       4.50 4.50

Pres. Ronald Reagan (1911-2004) — A516

No. 2909, 25d: a, With Margaret Thatcher, 1986. b, With Pope John Paul II, 1982. c, Signing Missing Children's Act and Victim Witness Protection Act, 1992. d, With wife, Nancy, 1987.
No. 2910, 25d, horiz.: a, First Family, 1982. b, Signing treaty with Mikhail Gorbachev, 1987. c, Assassination attempt, 1981. d, With Deng Xiaoping, 1984.
60d, Portrait.

**2004, Oct. 13**   *Litho.*    *Perf. 14*
**Sheets of 4, #a-d**
2909-2910 A516 Set of 2   14.00 14.00
**Souvenir Sheet**
2911 A516 60d multi     4.25   4.25

**Lighthouse Type of 2004**

Designs: 5d, Isla de Flores Lighthouse, Uruguay. 7d, Punta Brava Lighthouse, Uruguay. 15d, Boston Lighthouse, US. No. 2911D, 20d, Cabo Polonio Lighthouse, Uruguay. No. 2911E, 20d, Bass Harbor Head Lighthouse, US. 45d, Punta del Este Lighthouse, Uruguay. 60d, Portland Head Lighthouse, US.

**2004**     *Litho.*     *Perf. 14¾x14*
2911A-2911G A501   Set of 7 12.00 12.00

Elvis Presley (1935-77) — A517

No. 2912, 15d: a, Standing, with guitar, 1956. b, Wearing army hat, 1957. c, Holding guitar, 1968. d, Holding guitar, 1970. e, Playing guitar, 1972. f, Singing, 1973.
No. 2913, 15d: a, Seated, with guitar, 1956. b, With guitar, 1958. c, Playing guitar, 1964. d, Playing drums, 1966. e, On horse, 1968. f, Playing guitar, 1969.

**2005, Jan. 8**
**Sheets of 6, #a-f**
2912-2913 A517 Set of 2   12.50 12.50

New Year 2005 (Year of the Rooster) A518

Paintings by Xu Beihong: 10d, Rooster. 40d, Black Rooster, horiz.

**2005, Jan.**        *Perf. 11½*
2914 A518 10d multi       .70   .70
**Souvenir Sheet**
2915 A518 40d multi     2.75 2.75

No. 2914 printed in sheets of 4. No. 2915 contains one 46x36mm stamp.

**Basketball Players Type of 2004**

Designs: No. 2916, 25d, Steve Nash, Dallas Mavericks. No. 2917, 25d, Shaquille O'Neal, Los Angeles Lakers.

**2005, Feb. 10**        *Perf. 14*
2916-2917 A512 Set of 2   3.50 3.50

Both players were on different teams when stamps were released.

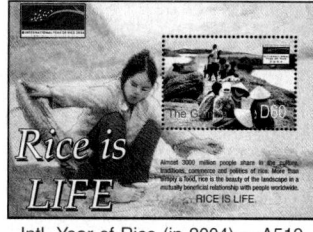

Intl. Year of Rice (in 2004) — A519

No. 2918, vert.: a, Rice terraces. b, Woman holding rice plants. c, Two people holding rice plants.
60d, Rice farmers.

**2005, Feb. 10**
2918 A519 30d Sheet of 3, #a-c   6.25 6.25
**Souvenir Sheet**
2919 A519 60d multi     4.25 4.25

The Gambia D1   Butterflies — A520

Designs: 1d, Belenois solilucis. 2d, Colotis evippe. 3d, Acraea cepheus. 5d, Bebearia senegalensis. 6d, Danaus chrysippus. 7d, Papilio dardanus. 10d, Graphium agamedes. 15d, Papilio hesperus. 25d, Charaxes boueti. 30d, Cymothoe egesta. 50d, Amauris albimaculata. 75d, Charaxes lucretius. 100d, Papilio zalmoxis. 200d, Papilio antimachus.

*Perf. 13¼x13½, 14¾x14¼ (7d, 30d)*
**2005, Apr. 4**

| | | | | |
|---|---|---|---|---|
| 2920 | A520 | 1d multi | .20 | .20 |
| 2921 | A520 | 2d multi | .20 | .20 |
| 2922 | A520 | 3d multi | .20 | .20 |
| 2923 | A520 | 5d multi | .35 | .35 |
| 2924 | A520 | 6d multi | .40 | .40 |
| 2924A | A520 | 7d multi | .50 | .50 |
| 2925 | A520 | 10d multi | .70 | .70 |
| 2926 | A520 | 15d multi | 1.00 | 1.00 |
| 2927 | A520 | 25d multi | 1.75 | 1.75 |
| 2927A | A520 | 30d multi | 2.10 | 2.10 |
| 2928 | A520 | 50d multi | 3.50 | 3.50 |
| 2929 | A520 | 75d multi | 5.25 | 5.25 |
| 2929A | A520 | 100d multi | 7.00 | 7.00 |
| 2929B | A520 | 200d multi | 14.00 | 14.00 |
| *Nos. 2920-2929B (14)* | | | 37.15 | 37.15 |

Battle of Trafalgar, Bicent. — A521

Designs: 5d, Santisima Trinidad. 10d, Victory firing at French flagship Bucentaure, horiz. 15d, Lord Horatio Nelson. 30d, French sailors from the Redoubtable boarding Victory. 60d, Vice-admiral Horatio Nelson.

**2005, Apr. 4**       *Perf. 14*
2930-2933 A521 Set of 4   4.25 4.25
**Souvenir Sheet**
2934 A521 60d multi     4.25 4.25

**Souvenir Sheet**

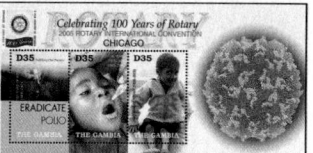

Rotary International, Cent. — A522

No. 2935: a, "Eradicate Polio," child receiving polio vaccine. b, Child receiving polio vaccine, diff. c, Child seated.

**2005, Apr. 4**
2935 A522 35d Sheet of 3, #a-c   7.25 7.25

Blondie, by Dean Young and Denis LeBrun — A523

No. 2936, 40d: a, "I have a date with Cookie." b, "Wait one second, please." c, "Wow, Cookie! I didn't know your family was wealth enough to have a chauffeur!"
No. 2937, 40d: a, "Listen up, everybody. . ." b, "Then after he leaves you can get back to normal." c, "I want to see this place humming with activity and enthusiasm!"

**2005, Apr. 4**       *Perf. 13¼*
**Sheets of 3, #a-c**
2936-2937 A523 Set of 2   17.00 17.00

World Cup Soccer Championships,
75th Anniv. — A524

No. 2938 — Brazilian flag and scenes from
1950 World Cup: a, 1950 Uruguay team. b,
Goal from Uruguay-Brazil championship
game. c, Maracaná Municipal Stadium, Brazil.
d, Alcide Edgardo Ghiggia.
   60d, 1950 Uruguay team, diff.

**2005, Apr. 4**       **Perf. 14¼**
2938 A524 25d Sheet of 4, #a-d   7.00 7.00
**Souvenir Sheet**
2939 A524 60d multi       4.25 4.25

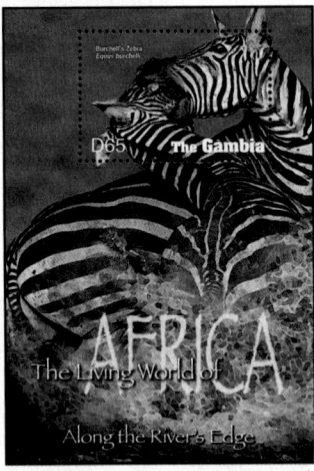

African Fauna — A525

No. 2940, 25d: a, African fish eagle. b,
Hummingbird hawkmoth. c, Nile crocodile. d,
Blue wildebeest.
   No. 2941, 25d: a, Bateleur eagle. b, Green
mamba. c, Chimpanzee. d, Yellow pansy
butterfly.
   No. 2942, 25d: a, Jackass penguins. b,
Leatherback turtle. c, Scaevola thunbergii. d,
Cancrid crab.
   No. 2943, 25d: a, Mediterranean monk seal.
b, Horned boxfish. c, Scorpion fish. d,
Cnidarians.
   No. 2944, Burchell's zebra. No. 2945, 65d,
Greater galago. No. 2946, 65d, Bottlenose
dolphin, vert. No. 2947, 65d, Gerbera daisies,
vert.

**2005, Apr. 4**       **Perf. 13¼x13½**
**Sheets of 4, #a-d**
2940-2943 A525 Set of 4    28.00 28.00
**Souvenir Sheets**
2944-2947 A525 Set of 4    18.00 18.00

Hans Christian Andersen (1805-75),
Author — A526

No. 2942, horiz.: a, The Ugly Duckling. b,
The Little Match Girl. c, The Rose Tree
Regiment.
   60d, The Emperor's New Clothes.

**2005, Apr. 4**       **Perf. 14**
2948 A526 35d Sheet of 3, #a-c   7.25 7.25
**Souvenir Sheet**
2949 A526 60d multi       4.25 4.25

Wedding of Prince
Charles and
Camilla Parker
Bowles — A527

Various photos of couple with oval color of:
No. 2950, 2d, Brown. No. 2951, 2d, Purple.
No. 2952, 2d, Red brown.

**2005, Apr. 9**       **Perf. 13½**
2950-2952 A527   Set of 3    .45 .45
Each stamp printed in sheets of 4.

Friedrich von Schiller (1759-1805),
Writer — A528

No. 2953: a, Statue of Schiller. b, Painting of
Schiller. c, Bust of Schiller.
   60d, Cameo of Schiller.

**2005, Apr. 4**   **Litho.**    **Perf. 14**
2953 A528 35d Sheet of 3, #a-c   7.25 7.25
**Souvenir Sheet**
2954 A528 60d multi       4.25 4.25

Miniature Sheet

End of World War II, 60th
Anniv. — A529

No. 2955 — Prince Bernhard of the Netherlands: a, And Prime Minister Pieter Ger-
brandy. b, And Queen Wilhelmina. c, And
Generals Bernard Montgomery and Hendrik
Kruls. d, And people of Nimwegen. e, At German surrender. f, Returning home with family.

**2005, Apr. 14**   **Litho.**   **Perf. 12¾**
2955 A529 12d Sheet of 6, #a-f   5.00 5.00

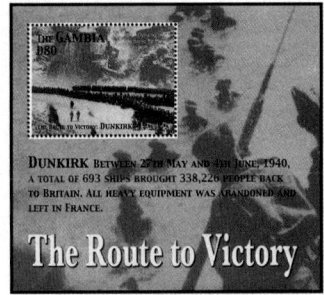

End of World War II, 60th
Anniv. — A530

No. 2956, 20d — Dunkirk: a, Germans
advance across France. b, Anthony C. Bartley.
c, Ships and boats. d, Rescued soldiers.
   No. 2957, 20d — D-Day: a, Allied troops hit
the beaches of Normandy. b, Germans blast
Sword Beach. c, Allied troops advance inland.
d, Germans begin to surrender.
   No. 2958, 80d, Operation Dynamo. No.
2959, 80d, Royal Navy lands on Gold Beach.

**2005, May 9**      **Perf. 13¼x13½**
**Sheets of 4, #a-d**
2956-2957 A530   Set of 2   11.50 11.50
**Souvenir Sheets**
2958-2959 A530   Set of 2   11.50 11.50

Souvenir Sheet

Expo 2005, Aichi, Japan — A531

No. 2960: a, Mt. Kilimanjaro. b, Lion. c,
Splitting of the Red Sea. d, Astronaut on
Moon.

**2005, May 16**       **Perf. 12**
2960 A531 15d Sheet of 4, #a-d   4.25 4.25

Pope John Paul II
(1920-2005) and
Mother Teresa
(1910-97) — A532

**2005, June 1**       **Perf. 14**
2961 A532 30d multi     2.10 2.10
Printed in sheets of 6.

Maimonides (1135-1204) — A533

No. 2962: a, Denomination in white. b,
Denomination in red.
Illustration reduced.

**2005, July 12**       **Perf. 12**
2962 A533 25d Pair, #a-b    3.75 3.75
Printed in sheets of 2 pairs.

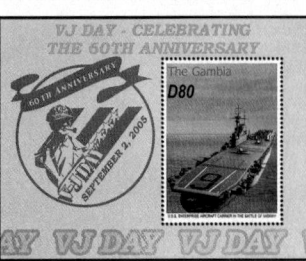

VJ Day, 60th Anniv. — A534

No. 2963, horiz. — Paintings by Jean Mas-
terly: a, B-29 Flies Over the Missouri. b, Enola
Gay Over Hiroshima. c, Dogfight Over the
Pacific. d, Hellcat Fury Engages the Enemy.
   80d, USS Enterprise Aircraft Carrier in the
Battle of Midway.

**2005, July 12**       **Perf. 12¾**
2963 A534 25d Sheet of 4, #a-d   7.25 7.25
**Souvenir Sheet**
2964 A534 80d multi       5.75 5.75
No. 2963 contains four 40x31mm stamps.

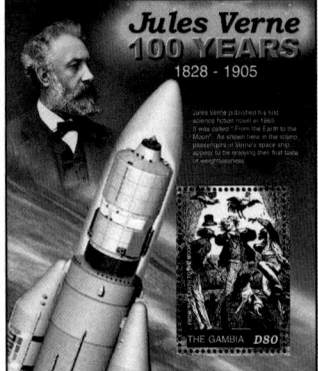

Jules Verne (1828-1905),
Writer — A535

No. 2965, horiz.: a, Hungary #C287. b,
Monaco #1100. c, France #770.
   80d, Scene from "From the Earth to the
Moon."

**2005, July 12**
2965 A535 35d Sheet of 3, #a-c   7.75 7.75
**Souvenir Sheet**
2966 A535 80d multi       5.75 5.75

Souvenir Sheet

Albert Einstein (1879-1955),
Physicist — A536

No. 2967: a, Einstein, country name in red.
b, Einstein, country name in white. c, Israel
#117.

**2005, July 28**
2967 A536 35d Sheet of 3, #a-c   7.75 7.75

American
First Day
Cover
Society,
50th
Anniv.
A537

**2005, July 29**
2968 A537 25d multi       1.90 1.90

## Souvenir Sheet

Taipei 2005 Stamp Exhibition — A538

No. 2969: a, Presidential Palace, Taipei. b, Chiang Kai-Shek Memorial, Taipei. c, Queen's Head, Yehliu. d, National Palace Museum, Taipei.

| 2005, Aug. 19 | | Perf. 14 | |
|---|---|---|---|
| 2969 A538 35d Sheet of 4, #a-d | | 10.00 | 10.00 |

First Europa Stamps, 50th Anniv. (in 2006) A539

Designs: 35d, Mailman, Luxembourg #318. 40d, Stars, "50," France #806. 50d, Map of Europe, France #805.

| 2005, Oct. 20 | | | |
|---|---|---|---|
| 2970-2972 A539 | Set of 3 | 9.00 | 9.00 |
| 2972a | Souvenir sheet, #2970-2972 + label | 9.00 | 9.00 |

Election of Pope Benedict XVI — A540

| 2005, Nov. 15 | | Perf. 13½ | |
|---|---|---|---|
| 2973 A540 35d multi | | 2.50 | 2.50 |

Printed in sheets of 4.

Pope John Paul II (1920-2005) A541

Pope John Paul II: No. 2974, 40d, Looking right. No. 2975, 40d, With arm raised. No. 2976, 40d, With hand to face. No. 2977, 40d, Praying with four men at side. No. 2978, 40d, Surrounded by praying clergymen. No. 2979, With praying hands of other people. No. 2980, 40d, Wearing miter, with crowd. No. 2981, 40d, Praying at church. No. 2982, 40d, With arms outstretched at church. No. 2983, 40d, Praying with rosary. No. 2984, 40d, Holding crucifix, round globe. No. 2985, 40d, Holding crucifix, oval world map. No. 2986, 40d, Holding crucifix, and at doorway. No. 2987, 40d, With crucifix at side of face. No. 2988, 40d, Holding crucifix in front of his face. No. 2989, 40d, Holding crucifix, with other arm raised. No. 2990, 40d, With crucifix, Papal arms. No. 2991, 40d, With Good Shepherd. No. 2992, 40d, Holding child. No. 2993, 40d, With UN emblem. No. 2994, 40d, Being assisted.

No. 2995, 80d, Bowing with crucifix. No. 2996, 80d, Wearing miter in front of church. No. 2997, 80d, With kneeling bishop. No. 2998, 80d, Holding microphone. No. 2999, 80d, With raised hands, Papal arms. No. 3000, 80d, With Virgin Mary.

**Embossed on Metal**
| 2005 | | Die Cut Perf. 12½ | |
|---|---|---|---|

**Self-Adhesive**
**Silver-Colored Metal**
| 2974-2994 A541 Set of 21 | | 60.00 | 60.00 |
|---|---|---|---|

**Gold-Colored Metal**
| 2995-3000 A541 Set of 6 | | 35.00 | 35.00 |
|---|---|---|---|

## Miniature Sheet

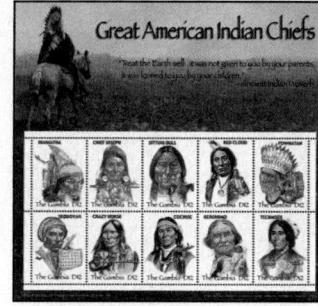

American Indian Chiefs — A542

No. 3001: a, Hiawatha. b, Chief Joseph. c, Sitting Bull. d, Red Cloud. e, Powhatan. f, Sequoyah. g, Crazy Horse. h, Cochise. i, Geronimo. j, Tecumseh.

| 2005, Nov. 15 | Litho. | Perf. 13½ | |
|---|---|---|---|
| 3001 A542 12d Sheet of 10, #a-j | | 8.50 | 8.50 |

Christmas — A543

Designs: 7d, The Annunciation, by Lorenzo di Credi. 10d, The Holy Family, by di Credi. 25d, The Adoration of the Magi, by Filippo Lippi. 30d, Marriage of St. Catherine, by Lippi. 65d, The Annunciation, by Fra Angelico.

| 2005, Dec. 19 | | Perf. 13½x¼ | |
|---|---|---|---|
| 3002-3005 A543 Set of 4 | | 5.00 | 5.00 |

**Souvenir Sheet**
| 3006 A543 65d multi | | 4.50 | 4.50 |
|---|---|---|---|

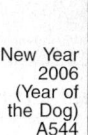

New Year 2006 (Year of the Dog) A544

| 2006, Jan. 3 | | Perf. 13¼ | |
|---|---|---|---|
| 3007 A544 15d multi | | 1.10 | 1.10 |

Printed in sheets of 4.

Elvis Presley (1935-77) — A545

Illustration reduced.

| ***Serpentine Die Cut 7¾*** | | | |
|---|---|---|---|
| **2006, Jan. 24** | **Litho. & Embossed** | | |
| 3008 A545 200d multi | | 14.50 | 14.50 |

Children's Drawings — A546

No. 3009, 25d — Cats: a, Kitty, by Raquel Bobolia. b, Jaguar, by Megan Albe. c, Quazy

Jaguar, by Nick Abrams. d, Chelsy Cheetah, by Carly Bowerman.
No. 3010, 25d — Reptiles: a, Stripey, by Christopher Bowerman. b, Sea Turtle, by Tyler Overton. c, Hungry Lizard, by Jessica Shutt. d, Frogs, by Elyse Bobczynski.
No. 3011, 25d — Flowers: a, Three Flowers, by Lauren Van Way. b, Blossoms, by Michelle Malachowsky. c, Flower Pot, by Van Way. d, Red Flower Pot, by Anne Wilks.

| 2006, Jan. 24 | Litho. | Perf. 13¼ | |
|---|---|---|---|
| **Sheets of 4, #a-d** | | | |
| 3009-3011 A546 Set of 3 | | 22.00 | 22.00 |

Queen Elizabeth II, 80th Birthday — A547

No. 3012: a, Wearing military uniform. b, At coronation. c, On Time Magazine cover. d, Wearing wedding gown.
65d, Wearing robe and crown.

| 2006, Feb. 27 | | Perf. 13¼ | |
|---|---|---|---|
| 3012 A547 30d Sheet of 4, #a-d | | 8.50 | 8.50 |

**Souvenir Sheet**
**Perf. 12**
| 3013 A547 65d multi | | 4.75 | 4.75 |
|---|---|---|---|

Worldwide Fund for Nature (WWF) — A548

No. 3014 — Black-crowned crane: a, Head. b, Standing on one leg. c, Birds in wild. d, Chick.

| 2006, Feb. 27 | | Perf. 12¾ | |
|---|---|---|---|
| 3014 A548 30d Block or strip of 4, #a-d | | 8.50 | 8.50 |
| e. | Souvenir sheet, 2 each #3014a-3014d | 17.00 | 17.00 |

2006 Winter Olympics, Turin A549

Designs: No. 3015, Norway #1048. No. 3015A, Poster for 1992 Albertville Winter Olympics. 15d, Norway #1047. No. 3017,

Poster for 2002 Salt Lake City Winter Olympics. No. 3017A, France #B611, horiz. 25d, Poster for 1994 Lillehammer Winter Olympics.

| 2006, Mar. 23 | | | Perf. 13¼ | | |
|---|---|---|---|---|---|
| 3015 | A549 10d multicolored | | | .75 | .75 |
| 3015A | A549 10d multi | | | .75 | .75 |
| 3016 | A549 15d multicolored | | | 1.10 | 1.10 |
| 3017 | A549 20d multicolored | | | 1.40 | 1.40 |
| 3017A | A549 20d multi | | | 1.40 | 1.40 |
| 3018 | A549 25d multicolored | | | 1.75 | 1.75 |
| | Nos. 3015-3018 (6) | | | 7.15 | 7.15 |

Marilyn Monroe (1926-62), Actress — A550

| 2006, Apr. 6 | | | |
|---|---|---|---|
| 3019 A550 30d multi | | 2.10 | 2.10 |

Printed in sheets of 4.

Dr. Martin Luther King, Jr. (1929-68), Civil Rights Activist — A551

| 2006, May 27 | | Perf. 11½x12 | |
|---|---|---|---|
| 3020 A551 40d multi | | 3.00 | 3.00 |

Printed in sheets of 3.

## Miniature Sheet

American Philatelic Society, 120th Anniv. — A552

No. 3021 — United States stamps: a, #1120. b, #E14. c, #114. d, #C3. e, #894. f, #E2. g, #294. h, #Q2.

| 2006, May 27 | | Perf. 13¼ | |
|---|---|---|---|
| 3021 A552 17d Sheet of 8, #a-h | | 9.75 | 9.75 |

Washington 2006 World Philatelic Exhibition.

## Souvenir Sheet

Ludwig Durr (1878-1956), Engineer, and Zeppelins — A553

No. 3022 — Durr and: a, Zeppelin NT. b, Zeppelin ZR-3 (U.S.S. Los Angeles). c, Zeppelin ZRS (U.S.S. Macon).

| 2006, June 22 | | Perf. 12¾ | |
|---|---|---|---|
| 3022 A553 40d Sheet of 3, #a-c | | 8.75 | 8.75 |

74 GAMBIA

## Souvenir Sheet

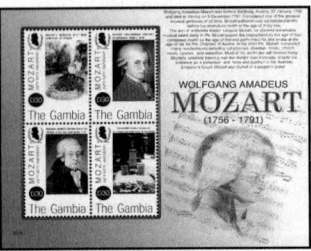

Wolfgang Amadeus Mozart (1756-91), Composer — A554

No. 3023: a, Mozart's Memorial, Vienna. b, Portrait of Mozart, by Barbara Kraft. c, Portrait of Mozart by unknown artist. d, Mozart family graves, Salzburg.

**2006, June 22**
3023 A554 30d Sheet of 4, #a-d    8.75 8.75

Rembrandt (1606-69), Painter A555

Details from paintings: 10d, Jacob Blessing the Sons of Joseph. 12d, Jacob Blessing the Sons of Joseph, diff. 15d, Jacob Blessing the Sons of Joseph, diff. No. 3027, 25d, Jacob Wrestling with the Angel.

No. 3028, 25d — The Staalmeesters: a, Man wearing hat, leaning to right, "Rembrandt" in white. b, Man wearing hat, "Rembrandt" in white. c, Man without hat, "Rembrandt" in white. d, Man wearing hat, "Rembrandt" in black.

No. 3029, 25d: a, Young Girl at Open Half-Door. b, Self-portrait, 1632-39. c, Self-portrait, 1640. d, Portrait of a Young Woman.

No. 3030, 25d — A Married Couple with Their Children: a, Man. b, Child, "Rembrandt" in white. c, Child, "Rembrandt" in black. d, Woman.

No. 3031, 65d — A Polish Nobleman. No. 3032, 65d, The Knight with the Falcon. No. 3033, 65d, A Young Woman in Fancy Dress. No. 3034, 65d, Portrait of a Lady with a Lap Dog.

**2006, Aug. 23    Litho.    Perf. 14¼**
3024-3027 A555    Set of 4    4.50  4.50
**Sheets of 4, #a-d**
3028-3030 A555    Set of 3    22.00 22.00
**Imperf**
**Size: 76x106mm**
3031-3034 A555    Set of 4    18.50 18.50

Queen Juliana of the Netherlands A556

**2006, July 24    Litho.    Perf. 13¼**
3035 A556 15d multi    1.10 1.10
Printed in sheets of 6.

Princess Maxima of the Netherlands — A557

No. 3036: a, Head. b, Head and torso.

**2006, Dec. 6**
3036 A557 30d Pair, #a-b    4.50 4.50
Printed in sheets containing 3 of each stamp.

Christmas — A558

Designs: No. 3037, 25d, Gingerbread man. 30d, Christmas tree. 45d, Bell. 50d, Mittens.
No. 3041: a, 15d, Gingerbread man. b, 18d, Christmas tree. c, 25d, Bell.

**2006, Dec. 8    Perf. 14**
3037-3040 A558    Set of 4    11.00 11.00
**Souvenir Sheet**
3041 A558    Sheet of 4,
    #3041a-3041c,
    3040    7.75 7.75

## Miniature Sheet

2006 World Cup Soccer Championships, Germany — A559

No. 3042 — World Cup and soccer ball with flag of: a, 10d, Australia. b, 20d, Germany. c, 25d, Sweden. d, 30d, Brazil.

**2006, Dec. 20    Perf. 13¼**
3042 A559    Sheet of 4, #a-d    6.25 6.25

Concorde A560

No. 3043, 15d: a, Concorde arriving at Filton. b, Concorde G-BOAF in flight.
No. 3044, 15d: a, Concorde taking off from Toulouse. b, Concorde test pilot Andre Turcat.

**2006, Dec. 20    Perf. 13¼x13½**
**Pairs, #a-b**
3043-3044 A560    Set of 2    4.50 4.50
Nos. 3043-3044 were each printed in sheets containing three pairs.

Space Achievements — A561

No. 3045, 20d — Various views of Mars Reconnaissance Orbiter.
No. 3046, 20d — Space Shuttle Columbia: a, Columbia attached to rocket boosters in flight. b, Lift-off of Columbia. c, Shuttle mission simulator. d, Mission control. e, Capt. John W. Young. f, Capt. Robert L. Crippen.
No. 3047, 25d — Giotto Comet Probe: a, Halley's Comet. b, Giotto Comet Probe, green and orange lines. c, Giotto Comet Probe. d, Comet and Giotto Comet Probe.
No. 3048, 25d — Viking 1: a, Viking 1 in flight. b, Viking 1 on Mars, text in black, denomination at UL. c, Viking 1 on Mars, text in black, denomination at UR. d, Viking 1 on Mars, "Viking 1" in white.
No. 3049, 65d, Venus Express. No. 3050, 65d, Hayabusa spacecraft. No. 3051, 65d, Luna 9, vert. No. 3052, 65d, Space Shuttle Discovery returns to space, vert.

**2006, Dec. 20    Perf. 14**
**Sheets of 6, #a-f**
3045-3046 A561    Set of 2    17.50 17.50
**Sheets of 4, #a-d**
3047-3048 A561    Set of 2    14.50 14.50
**Souvenir Sheets**
3049-3052 A561    Set of 4    19.00 19.00

New Year 2007 (Year of the Pig) A562

**2007, Feb. 15    Perf. 13x13½**
3053 A562 20d multi    1.50 1.50
Printed in sheets of 4.

Scouting, Cent. A563

Knot in: 30d, Green. 65d, Orange.

**2007, Feb. 15    Perf. 13¼**
3054 A563 30d multi    2.25 2.25
**Souvenir Sheet**
3055 A563 65d multi    4.75 4.75
No. 3054 printed in sheets of 4.

## Miniature Sheets

Programs of Pres. John F. Kennedy — A564

No. 3056, 25d — Peace Corps: a, Kennedy greeting Peace Corps volunteers at White House. b, R. Sargent Shriver, first director of Peace Corps. c, Kennedy signing executive order creating Peace Corps. d, Kennedy greeting Peace Corps volunteers.
No. 3057, 25d — Alliance for Progress: a, Kennedy in rocking chair. b, Kennedy and Cabinet. c, Volunteer Ida Shoatz in Peru. d, Kennedy speaking at University of Michigan.

**2007, Feb. 15    Perf. 12¾**
**Sheets of 4, #a-d**
3056-3057 A564    Set of 2    14.50 14.50

Betty Boop — A565

No. 3058 — Betty Boop: a, With hands at side. b, Holding flowers. c, With dog biting swimsuit. d, Wearing long red dress. e, With hands clasped. f, Holding top hat and cane.
No. 3059 — Betty Boop in: a, Red. b, Purple.

**2007, Feb. 15    Litho.**
3058 A565 15d Sheet of 6, #a-f    6.50 6.50
**Souvenir Sheet**
3059 A565 40d Sheet of 2, #a-b    6.00 6.00

Pope Benedict XVI — A566

**2007, May 1    Perf. 13¼**
3060 A566 12d multi    .90 .90
Printed in sheets of 8.

Intl. Polar Year — A567

No. 3061 — Penguin: a, At bongo drums. b, With lei and grass skirt. c, At drum set. d, With purple guitar. e, At microphone. f, With yellow and orange guitar.
65d, Penguin in chair at table.

**2007, May 1**           **Litho.**
3061 A567 15d Sheet of 6, #a-f   6.75   6.75

**Souvenir Sheet**
3062 A567 65d multi       4.75   4.75

Wedding of Queen Elizabeth II and
Prince Philip, 60th Anniv. — A568

No. 3063, vert. — Photos of Queen and
Prince: a, On wedding day, gray brown frame.
b, As older couple, gray brown frame. c, As
older couple, close-up. d, On wedding day,
pink frame. e, On wedding day, blue gray
frame. f, As older couple, blue gray frame.
65d, Queen and Prince, diff.

**2007, May 1**
3063 A568 15d Sheet of 6, #a-f   6.75   6.75

**Souvenir Sheet**
3064 A568 65d multi       4.75   4.75

Princess Diana (1961-97) — A569

No. 3065, vert. — Diana wearing: a, Tiara,
close-up. b, Light blue dress, close-up. c,
Maroon dress, close-up. d, Tiara, from distance. e, Light blue dress, from distance. f,
Maroon dress, from distance.
No. 3066, vert. — Diana wearing: a, Blue
and white hat. b, Lilac and purple hat. c, Black
dress. d, Red and white hat.
65d, Painting of Diana.

**2007, May 1**
3065 A569 15d Sheet of 6, #a-f   6.75   6.75
3066 A569 25d Sheet of 4, #a-d   7.50   7.50

**Souvenir Sheet**
3067 A569 65d multi       4.75   4.75

1986 Halley's Comet Merchandising
Emblem — A570

No. 3068: a, Light olive green frame. b, Light
blue frame. c, Violet black frame. d, Brown
frame.
65d, Black background.

**2007, June 20**         **Perf. 13¼**
3068 A570 20d Sheet of 4, #a-d   6.00   6.00

**Souvenir Sheet**
3069 A570 65d black       5.00   5.00

Ferrari Automobiles, 60th
Anniv. — A571

No. 3070: a, 1970 512 S. b, 1996 F 310. c,
1950 195 S. d, 1965 275 P2. e, 1980 Mondial
8. f, 1975 312 T. g, 1952 500 F2. h, 1986 GTB
Turbo.

**2007, June 20**      **Perf. 13½x13¼**
3070 A571 12d Sheet of 8, #a-h   7.25   7.25

Paintings by Qi Baishi (1864-
1957) — A572

No. 3071: a, Autumn Leaves and Magpie. b,
Camellias. c, Pomegranates. d, Mynahs and
Amaranthus.
65d, Magpie and Plum Blossoms.

**2007, July 16**         **Perf. 12½**
3071 A572 25d Sheet of 4, #a-d   8.25   8.25

**Souvenir Sheet**
**Perf. 11¼x11½**
3072 A572 65d multi       5.50   5.50

First Helicopter Flight, Cent. — A573

No. 3073: a, UH-1B/C. b, S-65/RH-53B. c,
UH-1. d, BK 117. e, Autogyro. f, AS-61.
65d, AH-1 Huey Cobra.

**2007, July 16**         **Perf. 13¼**
3073 A573 15d Sheet of 6, #a-f   7.50   7.50

**Souvenir Sheet**
3074 A573 65d multi       5.50   5.50

Wives of United States Presidents and
First Ladies — A574

No. 3075: a, Martha Washington. b, Abigail
Adams. c, Dolley Madison. d, Elizabeth
Monroe. e, Louisa Adams. f, Emily Donelson.
g, Angelica Van Buren. h, Anna Harrison. i,
Letitia Tyler. j, Julia Tyler. k, Sarah Polk. l, Mar-
garet Taylor. m, Abigail Fillmore. n, Jane
Pierce. o, Eagle, flags, White House.
No. 3076: a, Harriet Johnston. b, Mary Lin-
coln. c, Eliza Johnson. d, Julia Grant. e, Lucy
Hayes. f, Lucretia Garfield. g, Mary Arthur
McElroy. h, Frances Cleveland. i, Caroline
Harrison. j, Ida McKinley. k, Edith Roosevelt. l,
Helen Taft. m, Ellen Wilson. n, Edith Wilson.
No. 3077: a, Florence Harding. b, Grace
Coolidge. c, Lou Hoover. d, Eleanor
Roosevelt. e, Bess Truman. f, Mamie Eisen-
hower. g, Jacqueline Kennedy. h, Lady Bird
Johnson. i, Pat Nixon. j, Betty Ford. k,
Rosalynn Carter. l, Nancy Reagan. m, Bar-
bara Bush. n, Hillary Clinton. o, Laura Bush.
No. 3078, 65d, Martha Washington. No.
3079, 65d, Abigail Adams. No. 3080, 65d,
Martha Jefferson. No. 3081, 65d, Martha
Washington Jefferson Randolph. No. 3082,
65d, Dolley Madison. No. 3083, 65d, Elizabeth
Monroe. No. 3084, 65d, Louisa Adams. No.
3085, 65d, Rachael Jackson. No. 3086, 65d,
Emily Donelson. No. 3087, 65d, Hannah Van
Buren. No. 3088, 65d, Angelica Van Buren.
No. 3089, 65d, Anna Harrison. No. 3090, 65d,
Letitia Tyler. No. 3091, 65d, Priscilla Tyler. No.
3092, 65d, Julia Tyler. No. 3093, 65d, Sarah
Polk. No. 3094, 65d, Margaret Taylor. No.
3095, 65d, Mary Taylor. No. 3096, 65d, Abigail
Fillmore. No. 3097, 65d, Jane Pierce. No.
3098, 65d, Harriet Johnston. No. 3099, 65d,
Mary Lincoln. No. 3100, 65d, Eliza Johnson.
No. 3101, 65d, Julia Grant. No. 3102, 65d,
Lucy Hayes. No. 3103, 65d, Lucretia Garfield.
No. 3104, 65d, Ellen Arthur. No. 3105, 65d,
Mary Arthur McElroy. No. 3106, 65d, Frances
Cleveland. No. 3107, 65d, Caroline Harrison.
No. 3108, 65d, Mary Lord Harrison. No. 3109,
65d, Ida McKinley. No. 3110, 65d, Edith
Roosevelt. No. 3111, 65d, Helen Taft. No.
3112, 65d, Ellen Wilson. No. 3113, 65d, Edith
Wilson. No. 3114, 65d, Florence Harding. No.
3115, 65d, Grace Coolidge. No. 3116, 65d,
Lou Hoover. No. 3117, 65d, Eleanor
Roosevelt. No. 3118, 65d, Bess Truman. No.
3119, 65d, Mamie Eisenhower. No. 3120, 65d,
Jacqueline Kennedy. No. 3121, 65d, Lady Bird
Johnson. No. 3122, 65d, Pat Nixon. No. 3123,
65d, Betty Ford. No. 3124, 65d, Rosalynn
Carter. No. 3125, 65d, Nancy Reagan. No.
3126, 65d, Barbara Bush. No. 3127, 65d, Hillary Clinton. No. 3128, 65d, Laura Bush.

**2007**                 **Perf. 13¼**
3075 A574 10d Sheet of 15,
      #a-o,         12.50   12.50
3076 A574 10d Sheet of 15,
      #a-n,
      3075o       12.50   12.50
3077 A574 10d Sheet of 15,
      #a-o        12.50   12.50
   Nos. 3075-3077 (3)   37.50   37.50

**Souvenir Sheets**
3078-3128 A574   Set of 51 350.00 350.00
3078a         Perf. 14¼    6.75    6.75

Issued: Nos. 3075-3077, 7/31. Nos. 3078-
3128, 10/24. Nos. 3075-3077 each contain fifteen 25x37mm stamps.
No. 3078a was not issued in a souvenir
sheet.

---

**Miniature Sheet**

Pres. Gerald R. Ford (1913-
2006) — A575

No. 3129 — Ford: a, With wife, Betty. b, At
Presidential inauguration ceremony. c, With
Betty, Pres. Richard Nixon and Pat Nixon. d,
At 90th birthday celebration.

**2007, Aug. 9**   **Litho.**   **Perf. 13¼**
3129 A575 25d Sheet of 4, #a-d   8.25   8.25

**Miniature Sheet**

Elvis Presley (1935-77) — A576

No. 3130 — Presley, guitar and background
color of: a, Green. b, Tan. c, Orange. d, Black
(white suit). e, Brown. f, Black (black jacket).

**2007, Sept. 6**
3130 A576 15d Sheet of 6, #a-f   7.75   7.75

**Miniature Sheets**

Intl. Holocaust Remembrance
Day — A577

No. 3131, 14d — United Nations diplomats
and delegates: a, Ronaldo Mota Sardenberg,
Brazil. b, Alisher Vohidov, Uzbekistan. c, Mar-
tin Belinga-Eboutou, Cameroun. d, Fernand
Poukre-Kono, Central African Republic. e,
Heraldo Muñoz, Chile. f, Wang Guangya,
China. g, Elbio O. Rosselli, Uruguay. h, Shashi
Tharoor, Undersecretary General.
No. 3132, 14d: a, Basile Ikouebe, Republic
of the Congo. b, Saul Weisleder, Costa Rica.
c, Alcicle Djedje, Ivory Coast. d, Andreas D.
Mavroiannis, Cyprus. e, Martin Palous, Czech
Republic. f, Atoki Ileka, Democratic Republic
of the Congo. g, Crispin S. Gregoire, Domi-
nica. h, Parfait Onanga-Anyanga, Ambassador
and Special Advisor of the 61st UN General
Assembly.
No. 3133, 14d: a, Hoya Rashed Al-Khalifa,
President of 61st UN General Assembly. b,
Denis Dangue Rewaka, Gabon. c, Crispin
Grey-Johnson, Gambia. d, Irakli Alasania,
Georgia. e, Nana Effah-Apenteng, Ghana. f,
Adamantios Vassilakis, Greece. g, Jorge Skin-
ner-Klee Arenales, Guatemala. h, Jean-Mau-
rice Ripert, France.
No. 3134, 14d: a, Hilari G. Davide, Jr., Phil-
ippines. b, Andrzej Towpik, Poland. c, Joao
Manuel Guerra Salgueiro, Portugal. d, Alexei
Tulbure, Moldova. e, Mihnea I. Motoc,
Romania. f, Vitaly I. Churkin, Russia. g,
Joseph Nsengimana, Rwanda. h, Augustine P.
Mahiga, Tanzania.

**2007, Nov. 28**   **Litho.**   **Perf. 13½**
         **Sheets of 8, #a-h**
3131-3134 A577   Set of 4    41.00   41.00

2008 Summer Olympics,
Beijing — A578

**Die Cut Perf. 8½x8¼**
**2007, Nov. 29    Litho. & Embossed**
**Without Gum**
**3135** A578 40d multi                    3.75 3.75

Christmas
A579

Designs: 25d, Girl at manger scene. 30d,
Children eating holiday dishes. 45d, Boy with
Madonna and Child sculptures. 50d, Christ-
mas celebrations with music.

**2007, Dec. 3    Litho.    Perf. 12**
**3136-3139** A579    Set of 4    14.00 14.00

Souvenir Sheet

Breast Cancer Prevention — A580

**2007, Dec. 10    Perf. 14**
**3140** A580 65d multi                    6.00 6.00

America's
Cup Yacht
Races
A581

No. 3141 — Various yachts with wide
panels in: a, Blue. b, Yellow orange. c, Red. d,
Orange.

**2007, Dec. 28    Perf. 13¼**
**3141**        Strip of 4    6.75 6.75
  *a.*  A581 10d multi        .85    .85
  *b.*  A581 15d multi      1.40  1.40
  *c.*  A581 20d multi      1.75  1.75
  *d.*  A581 30d multi      2.75  2.75

Miniature Sheet

National Basketball Association
Players — A582

No. 3142: a, Carmelo Anthony, Denver Nug-
gets. b, Kobe Bryant, Los Angeles Lakers. c,
Vince Carter, New Jersey Nets. d, Allen Iver-
son, Denver Nuggets. e, LeBron James,
Cleveland Cavaliers. f, Yao Ming, Houston
Rockets. g, Steve Nash, Phoenix Suns. h,
Shaquille O'Neal, Miami Heat. i, Dwayne
Wade, Miami Heat.

**2007, Dec. 28    Perf. 13¼**
**3142** A582 10d Sheet of 9, #a-i    8.25 8.25

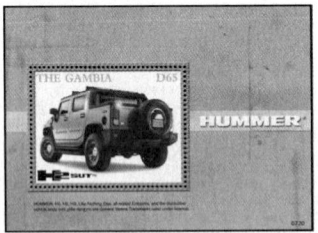

Hummer Vehicles — A583

No. 3143: a, H2 on road, denomination in
white. b, H2 on road, denomination in black. c,
H2, white background. d, H2 on rocks.
65d, H2 SUT.

**2007, Dec. 28    Perf. 13½**
**3143** A583 25d Sheet of 4, #a-d    9.00 9.00
**Souvenir Sheet**
**3144** A583 65d multi                    6.00 6.00

New Year
2008 (Year
of the Rat)
A584

**2008, Jan. 28    Litho.    Perf. 12**
**3145** A584 30d multi                    2.75 2.75
Printed in sheets of 4.

2008 Taipei Intl. Stamp
Exhibition — A585

No. 3146, horiz. — Taipei landmarks: a,
Temple and garden. b, Dr. Sun Yat-sen Memorial Hall. c, Natl. Opera House. d, Temple.
45d, Lover's Bridge, Tamsui.

**2008, Apr. 11    Perf. 13¼**
**3146** A585 12d Sheet of 4, #a-d    5.00 5.00
**Souvenir Sheet**
**Perf. 13¼x13½**
**3147** A585 45d multi                    4.50 4.50
No. 3146 contains four 42x28mm stamps.

Pioneer Satellites — A586

No. 3148: a, Pioneer 1 in orbit, Moon in
background. b, Pioneer 1 in nose cone. c, Pio-
neer 1.
No. 3149, horiz.: a, Technicians and Pioneer
3. b, Pioneer 3 in orbit. c, Pioneer 3 on launch
pad.
No. 3150: a, Pioneer 1 on launch pad. b,
Pioneer 1 in orbit, diff.
No. 3151: a, Pioneer 3. b, Pioneer 3 in orbit,
Moon in background.
No. 3152, Pioneer 1, horiz. No. 3153, Pio-
neer 3, horiz.

**2008, Apr. 11    Perf. 13¼**
**3148** A586 15d Horiz. strip of 3,
              #a-c                    4.50 4.50
**3149** A586 15d Vert. strip of 3,
              #a-c                    4.50 4.50
**3150** A586 20d Pair, #a-b          4.00 4.00
**3151** A586 20d Pair, #a-b          4.00 4.00
**Souvenir Sheets**
**3152** A586 65d multi                    6.50 6.50
**Perf. 13¼x13½**
**3153** A586 65d multi                    6.50 6.50
No. 3153 contains one 51x38mm stamp.
Nos. 3148-3151 were issued in sheets containing two strips or pairs.

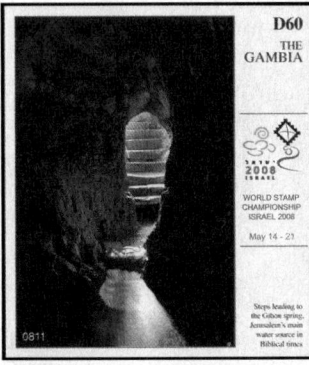

2008 World Stamp Championship,
Israel — A587

Illustration reduced.

**2008, May 14    Imperf.**
**3154** A587 60d multi                    5.75 5.75

Miniature Sheet

Seven Wonders of the Ancient
World — A588

No. 3155: a, Mausoleum of Maussollos,
Halicarnassus. b, Colossus of Rhodes. c, Tip
of Giant Pyramid, Giza. d, Hanging Gardens of
Babylon. e, Sphinx and Giant Pyramid. f,
Lighthouse of Alexandria. g, Statue of Zeus,
Olympia. h, Temple of Artemis, Ephesus.

**2008, May 16    Perf. 13¼**
**3155** A588 12d Sheet of 8, #a-h    9.25 9.25

Miniature Sheet

Elvis Presley (1935-77) — A589

No. 3156 — Presley: a, Wearing striped
jacket. b, With acoustic guitar. c, With arms on
knee. d, With electric guitar.

**2008, May 16**
**3156** A589 25d Sheet of 4, #a-d    9.50 9.50

Miniature Sheet

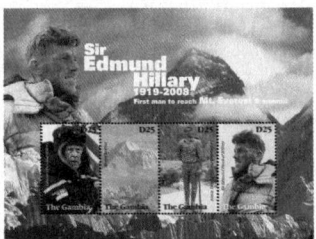

Sir Edmund Hillary (1919-2008),
Mountaineer — A590

No. 3157: a, Hillary and flag. b, Mt. Everest.
c, Statue of Hillary. d, Hillary as young man.

**2008, May 16**
**3157** A590 25d Sheet of 4, #a-d    9.50 9.50

Miniature Sheet

2008 Summer Olympics,
Beijing — A591

No. 3158: a, Suzanne Lenglen, 1920 Tennis
gold medalist. b, Duke Kahanamoku, 1920

Swimming gold medalist. c, Nedo Nadi, 1920 Fencing gold medalist. d, Olympic rings and text "Olympex 2008."

**2008, May 28**     *Perf. 12*
3158 A591 10d Sheet of 4, #a-d   4.00 4.00

Visit of Pope Benedict XVI to United States — A592

**2008, June 12**     *Perf. 13¼*
3159 A592 25d multi     2.40 2.40
Printed in sheets of 4.

Presidential Monuments
Mount Rushmore National Memorial

United States Landmarks — A593

No. 3160, vert.: a, Grant's Tomb, New York. b, Jefferson Memorial, Washington, DC. c, Kennedy Eternal Flame, Arlington, Virginia. d, Capitol, Washington, DC. e, Lincoln Memorial, Washington, DC. f, Washington Monument, Washington, DC.
65d, Mount Rushmore, South Dakota.

**2008, June 12**
3160 A593 15d Sheet of 6, #a-f   8.50 8.50
**Souvenir Sheet**
3161 A593 65d multi     6.25 6.25

Muhammad Ali, Boxer — A594

No. 3162, 25d — Ali : a, With white trunks, fists in front of chest. b, Seated. c, With white trunks, arm extended. d, Wearing drawstring shorts.
No. 3163, 25d, horiz. — Ali: a, Behind microphone. b, With hand on chin. c, With fist raised. d, Running.
No. 3164, 65d, Head of Ali in color. No. 3165, 65d, Head of Ali in black and white.

**2008, July 21**     *Perf. 11½*
**Sheets of 4, #a-d**
3162-3163 A594   Set of 2   19.00 19.00
**Souvenir Sheets**
*Perf. 13¼*
3164-3165 A594   Set of 2   12.50 12.50
No. 3162 contains four 30x40mm stamps. No. 3163 contains four 40x30mm stamps.

Gambia Coat of Arms — A595

Illustration reduced.

**2008, Sept. 15   Litho.   *Perf. 14x15***
3166 A595 40d blk & mar + label 3.50 3.50
Printed in sheets of 8 stamps + 8 labels.

**Miniature Sheet**

Marilyn Monroe (1926-62), Actress — A596

No. 3167 — Monroe: a, Facing forward, eyes open. b, Facing left. c, Facing right. d, Facing forward, eyes shut.

**2008, Sept. 22**     *Perf. 13¼*
3167 A596 25d Sheet of 4, #a-d   8.50 8.50

---

# GEORGIA

ˈjor-jə

LOCATION — South of Russia, bordering on the Black Sea and occupying the entire western part of Trans-Caucasia
GOVT. — Republic
AREA — 26,900 sq. mi.
POP. — 5,066,499 (1999 est.)
CAPITAL — Tbilisi (Tiflis)

Georgia was formerly a province of the Russian Empire and later a part of the Transcaucasian Federation of Soviet Republics. Stamps of Georgia were replaced in 1923 by those of Transcaucasian Federated Republics.
On Mar. 1, 1994, Georgia joined the Commonwealth of Independent States.

100 Kopecks = 1 Ruble
100 Kopecks = 1 Coupon (1993)
100 Tetri = 1 Lari (Sept. 25, 1995)

> **Catalogue values for unused stamps in this country are for Never Hinged items, beginning with Scott 75 in the regular postage section, and Scott B10 in the semi-postal section.**

---

**Tiflis**
A 6k local stamp, imperforate and embossed without color on white paper, was issued in November, 1857, at Tiflis by authority of the viceroy. The square design shows a coat of arms.

**National Republic**

St. George
A1       A2

| | | | *Perf. 11½, Imperf.* | |
|---|---|---|---|---|
| **1919** | | **Litho.** | **Unwmk.** | |
| 12 | A1 | 10k blue | .35 | .35 |
| 13 | A1 | 40k red orange | .35 | .35 |
| *a.* | | Tête bêche pair | 50.00 | 50.00 |
| 14 | A1 | 50k emerald | .35 | .35 |
| 15 | A1 | 60k red | .35 | .35 |
| 16 | A1 | 70k claret | .35 | .35 |
| 17 | A2 | 1r orange brown | .35 | .35 |
| | | *Nos. 12-17 (6)* | 2.10 | 2.10 |

Queen Thamar — A3

| | | | *Perf. 11½, Imperf.* | |
|---|---|---|---|---|
| **1920** | | | | |
| 18 | A3 | 2r red brown | .35 | .45 |
| 19 | A3 | 3r gray blue | .35 | .55 |
| 20 | A3 | 5r orange | .35 | 1.10 |
| | | *Nos. 18-20 (3)* | 1.05 | 2.10 |

Nos. 12-20 with parts of design inverted, sideways or omitted are fraudulent varieties.
Overprints meaning "Day of the National Guard, 12, 12, 1920" (5 lines) and "Recognition of Independence, 27, 1, 1921" (4 lines) were applied, probably in Italy, to remainders taken by government officials who fled when Russian forces occupied Georgia.
"Constantinople" and new values were unofficially surcharged on stamps of 1919-20 by a consul in Turkey.

**Soviet Socialist Republic**

Soldier with Flag — A5     Peasant Sowing Grain — A6

Industry and Agriculture — A7

| | | **Unwmk.** | *Perf. 11½* | |
|---|---|---|---|---|
| **1922** | | | | |
| 26 | A5 | 500r rose | 4.00 | 3.25 |
| 27 | A6 | 1000r bister brown | 4.00 | 3.25 |
| 28 | A7 | 2000r slate | 7.00 | 6.00 |
| 29 | A7 | 3000r brown | 7.00 | 6.00 |
| 30 | A7 | 5000r green | 7.00 | 6.00 |
| | | *Nos. 26-30 (5)* | 29.00 | 24.50 |

Forgeries exist of Nos. 26-30.
Nos. 26 to 30 exist imperforate but were not so issued. Value for set, $100.

**Nos. 26-30 Handstamped with New Values in Violet**

| | | | | |
|---|---|---|---|---|
| **1923** | | | | |
| 36 | A6 | 10,000r on 1000r | 5.50 | 5.50 |
| *a.* | | Black surcharge | 20.00 | 25.00 |
| *b.* | | 20000r on 1000r | 200.00 | |
| 37 | A7 | 15,000r on 2000r, blk surch. | 5.25 | 7.50 |
| *a.* | | Violet surcharge | 30.00 | 30.00 |
| 38 | A5 | 20,000r on 500r | 5.00 | 7.50 |
| *a.* | | Black surcharge | 15.00 | 7.50 |
| 39 | A7 | 40,000r on 5000r | 4.50 | 4.50 |
| *a.* | | Black surcharge | 15.00 | 15.00 |
| 40 | A7 | 80,000r on 3000r | 5.00 | 7.50 |
| *a.* | | Black surcharge | 15.00 | 17.50 |
| | | *Nos. 36-40 (5)* | 25.25 | 32.50 |

There were two types of the handstamped surcharges, with the numerals 5½mm and 6½mm high. The impressions are often too indistinct to measure or even to distinguish the numerals.
Double and inverted surcharges exist, as is usual with handstamps.

**Printed Surcharge in Black**

| | | | | |
|---|---|---|---|---|
| 43 | A6 | 10,000r on 1000r | 6.00 | 6.25 |
| 44 | A7 | 15,000r on 2000r | 4.00 | 4.00 |
| 45 | A5 | 20,000r on 500r | 2.00 | 2.00 |

| | | | | |
|---|---|---|---|---|
| 46 | A7 | 40,000r on 5000r | 4.00 | 3.75 |
| 47 | A7 | 80,000r on 3000r | 4.00 | 4.00 |
| | | *Nos. 43-47 (5)* | 20.00 | 20.00 |

Nos. 43, 45, 46 and 47 exist imperforate but were not so issued. Value \$25 each.

Russian Stamps of 1909-18 Handstamp Surcharged

Type I surcharge measures 20x5½mm.
Type II surcharge measures 22x7¼mm.

| | | | *Perf. 14½x15* | |
|---|---|---|---|---|
| **1923** | | | | |
| 48 | A14 | 10,000r on 7k lt bl | 200.00 | 200.00 |
| 49 | A11 | 15,000r on 15k red brn & bl (I) | 14.00 | 14.00 |
| *a.* | | Type II | 12.00 | 12.00 |

**Type I Surcharge Handstamped on Armenia No. 141**

| | | | | |
|---|---|---|---|---|
| 50 | A11 | 15,000r on 5r on 15k red brn & bl | 200.00 | 500.00 |
| *a.* | | Type II | 200.00 | 500.00 |
| | | *Nos. 48-50 (3)* | 414.00 | 714.00 |

Russian Stamps and Types of 1909-18 Surcharged in Dark Blue or Black

| | | | *Perf. 11½, 14½x15* | |
|---|---|---|---|---|
| **1923** | | | | |
| 51 | A14 | 75,000r on 1k org | 3.00 | 4.25 |
| *a.* | | Imperf. | 100.00 | 125.00 |
| 52 | A14 | 200,000r on 5k cl | 4.00 | 5.00 |
| 53 | A8 | 300,000r on 20k bl & car (Bk) | 4.00 | 5.00 |
| *a.* | | Dark blue surcharge | 70.00 | 100.00 |
| 54 | A14 | 350,000r on 3k red | 7.00 | 8.00 |
| *a.* | | Imperf. | 7.00 | 7.25 |
| | | *Imperf* | | |
| 55 | A14 | 700,000r on 2k grn | 7.00 | 10.00 |
| *a.* | | Perf. 14½x15 | 27.50 | 32.50 |
| | | *Nos. 51-55 (5)* | 25.00 | 32.25 |

> **Catalogue values for unused stamps in this section, from this point to the end of the section, are for Never Hinged items.**

**Republic**

Admission to UN, 1st Anniv. A20

Map, flag, UN emblem.

| | | | | |
|---|---|---|---|---|
| **1993, July 31** | | **Litho.** | *Perf. 13¼* | |
| 73 | A20 | 25r green & multi | .60 | .60 |
| 74 | A20 | 50r brown & multi | 1.00 | 1.00 |
| 75 | A20 | 100r violet & multi | 1.60 | 1.60 |
| *a.* | | Souvenir sheet of 3, #73-75 + label | 3.75 | 3.75 |
| | | *Nos. 73-75 (3)* | 3.20 | 3.20 |

For overprint, see Nos. 327-328.

Natl. Arms, Flag — A21     Fresco, 18th Cent. — A22

Apostle Simon, 11th Cent. — A23

Three Women, by Lado Gudiashvili A24

**1993, Oct. 11    Photo.    Perf. 12x11½**
76    A21    50k multicolored    .35    .35
**Litho.**
**Perf. 12x12½**
77    A22    50k multicolored    .40    .40
78    A23    1c multicolored    .75    .75
79    A24    1c multicolored    1.00    1.00
　　　Nos. 76-79 (4)    2.50    2.50

Nos. 76, 78-79 dated 1992.
For surcharges see Nos. 80-83, 93-95.

Surcharged in Claret, Black, or Blue

**1994, May 31    Photo.    Perf. 12x11½**
80    A21    5000c on 50k #76 (C)    .35    .35
**Litho.**
**Perf. 12x12½**
81    A22    5000c on 50k #77
　　　　　(Blk)    .35    .35
82    A23    10,000c on 1c #78 (Bl)    .50    .50
83    A24    10,000c on 1c #79 (C)    .50    .50
　　　Nos. 80-83 (4)    1.70    1.70

Size and location of surcharge varies.

Places of Worship — A25

30c, Mtskheta Church. 40c, Gelati Church. 50c, Nikortsminda Church. 60c, Ikorta Church. 70c, Samtavisi Church. 80c, Bolnisi Zion Synagogue. 90c, Gremi Citadel Church.

**1993, Oct. 11    Litho.    Perf. 13½**
84    A25    30c blue    .40    .40
85    A25    40c red brown    .50    .50
86    A25    50c olive brown    .60    .60
87    A25    60c rose carmine    .75    .75
88    A25    70c rose lake    .80    .85
89    A25    80c green    .95    .95
90    A25    90c slate    1.10    1.10
　　　Nos. 84-90 (7)    5.10    5.15

See Nos. 111-120.

Niko Nikoladze (1843-1928) — A26

**1994, May 31    Litho.    Perf. 13½**
91    A26    150c black & gold    .85    .85

UPU, 120th Anniv. A27

**1994, May 30**
92    A27    200c multicolored    1.00    1.00

Nos. 77-79 Surcharged in Green or Red

**1994    Litho.    Perf. 12x12½**
93    A22    200c on 50k #77    .50    .50
94    A23    300c on 1c #78 (R)    .55    .55
95    A24    500c on 1c #79    1.10    1.10
　　　Nos. 93-95 (3)    2.15    2.15

Set exists with inverted surcharges. Value $10.

A27a

**1994, Oct. 9    Litho.    Perf. 14**
95A    A27a    100c shown    1.25    1.25
95B    A27a    200c Monument    3.00    3.00

All Georgian Congress.

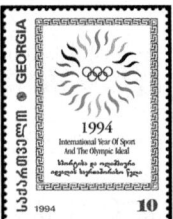

A28

**1995, Mar. 28    Litho.    Perf. 14½**
Georgia Natl. Olympic Committee: 10c, Intl. year of sport & Olympic ideal. 15c, Olympic congress, cent. 20c, Intl. Olympic Committee, cent. 25c, Olympic truce.

96-99    A28    Set of 4    4.75    4.75

Dated 1994.

Paintings by Niko Piromanashvili (1862-1918) — A29

#100, Three Princes Carousing on the Grass. #101, Still life. #102, Georgian Woman with a Tambourine, vert. #103, Bear on a Moonlit Night, vert. #104, Woman with a Tankard of Beer, vert. #105, Deer, vert. #106, Fisherman, vert. #107, Giraffe, vert. #108, Boy on a Donkey, vert. #109, Brooder with Chicks. #110, Family Picnicking.

**1995, Mar. 29    Litho.    Perf. 14**
100-109    A29    20c Set of 10    9.75    9.75
**Souvenir Sheet**
110    A29    100c multicolored    6.25    6.25

Churches Type of 1993

10c    20c

400c

1c, #120, Metechi, 1278-1289. 2c, #117, Alaverdi, 11th cent. 3c, #116, Dranda, 8th cent. #114, Sveti-Zchoveli, 1010-1019. #115, Kumurdo, 964. #118, Anauri, 17th cent. #119, Bitschvinta, 10th cent.

**1995    Litho.    Perf. 14**
**Size: 25½x39mm**
111    A25    1c black & violet    1.60    1.60
112    A25    2c black & sepia    1.60    1.60
113    A25    3c black & red brn    1.60    1.60
114    A25    10c black & violet    1.60    1.60
115    A25    10c black & sepia    1.60    1.60
116    A25    10c black & grn blue    1.60    1.60
117    A25    20c black & slate    1.60    1.60
118    A25    20c black & olive grn    1.60    1.60
119    A25    400c black & org brn    1.60    1.60
120    A25    400c black & red brn    1.60    1.60
　　　Nos. 111-120 (10)    16.00    16.00

Paolo Iashvili (1894-1937) — A30

**1995, Apr. 1**
125    A30    300c multicolored    1.25    1.25

Prehistoric Animals — A31

#126, Brontosaurus. #127, Saurolophus. #128, Scolosaurus. #129, Triceratops. #130, Parasaurolophus. #131, Ceratosaurus. #132, Deinonichus. #133, Tyrannosaurus. #134, Stegosaurus.
　#135: a, Pterodactylus (d). b, Rhamphophynghus (c, e). c, Pteranodon. d, Spinosaurus. e, Tyrannosaurus (f, h, i). f, Velociraptor. g, Monoklonius. h, Ornithomimus. i, Mastodon.
100c, Deinonychus.

**1995    Litho.    Perf. 14**
126-134    A31    15c Set of 9    6.25    6.25
**Miniature Sheet of 9**
135    A31    15c #a.-i.    7.25    7.25
**Souvenir Sheet**
136    A31    100c multicolored    5.25    5.25
　　　Issued: #126-134, 5/12.

UNESCO World Heritage Sites A32

100c, Bagrati Cathedral. 500c, Jvari of Mtskhetha.

**1995, Aug. 30    Litho.    Perf. 14**
137    A32    100c multi    1.00    1.00
**Souvenir Sheet**
138    A32    500c multi, vert.    5.25    5.25

Miniature Sheet

Wildlife Painting A33

Design: #a.-p., Various animals and birds.

**1995, Aug. 4**
139    A33    15c Sheet of 16, #a.-p.    9.25    9.25

Miniature Sheets of 16

Birds A34

Designs: Each 15t: Nos. 140a-140p, Various songbirds. Nos. 141a-141p, Various raptors.
Each 100t: No. 142, Songbird. No. 143, Owl.

**1996, Feb. 26    Litho.    Perf. 14**
140-141    A34    Set of 2    22.50    22.50
**Souvenir Sheets**
142-143    A34    Set of 2    12.50    12.50

Miniature Sheet

Fauna and Flora A35

a, Stork's head. b, Stork's body (a, f), berries. c, Snake (d, g, h). d, Moth. e, Lizard. f, Songbirds. g, Insect, flowers. h, Bee on flower. i, Butterfly, flower. j, Frog, lily (f). k, Snail. l, Turtle (p). m, Lobster. n, Sea plant, eel (o). o, Fish. p, Salamander.

**1996, Mar. 14    Litho.    Perf. 14**
144    A35    10t Sheet of 16, #a.-
　　　p.    10.00    10.00

Dinosaurs — A36

Illustration reduced.

**1996, Apr. 24    Litho.    Perf. 14**
**145** A36 10t Sheet of 9, #a.-i.    7.25 7.25

Intl. Olympic Committee, Cent. — A37

Georgian Olympians, landmarks from earlier Summer Olympic Games: 1t, Helsinki, 1952. 2t, Melbourne, 1956. 3t, Rome, 1960. 4t, Tokyo, 1964. 5t, Mexico City, 1968. 6t, Munich, 1972. 7t, Montreal, 1976. 8t, Moscow, 1980. 9t, Seoul, 1988. 10t, Barcelona, 1992. Early Greek: 50t, Wrestlers. 70t, Runner.

**1996, Aug. 16    Litho.    Perf. 14**
**146-155** A37    Set of 10    7.00 7.00
**Souvenir Sheets**
**156** A37 50t multicolored    6.50 6.50
**157** A37 70t multicolored    7.50 7.50

Olymphilex '96 (#157).

Paintings — A38

Designs: 10t, Citizens of Paris, by Lado Gudiashvili. 20t, Abstract, by Wassily Kandinsky. 30t, Still Life, by David Kakabadze. 50t, Three Painters, by Shalva Kikodze.
80t, Portrait of Niko Pirosmani, by Pablo Picasso.

**1996, Aug. 2    Litho.    Perf. 14**
**158** A38 10t multicolored    .40 .40
**159** A38 20t multicolored    .70 .70
**160** A38 30t multicolored    1.00 1.00
**161** A38 50t multicolored    1.40 1.40
**Size: 72x90mm**
**Imperf**
**162** A38 80t multicolored    3.00 3.00
Nos. 158-162 (5)    6.50 6.50

A39

**1996, Dec. 25    Litho.    Perf. 13x14**
**163** A39 30t Anton I (1720-88)    1.25 1.25

Ivan Javakhishvili (1876-1940), Writer — A40

**1997, Mar. 6    Perf. 14**
**164** A40 50t multicolored    1.40 1.40

UN, 50th Anniv. A41

**1997, Mar. 5    Litho.    Perf. 14**
**165** A41 30t purple & blue    1.40 1.40
**166** A41 125t red & blue    4.00 4.00

Dogs — A42

Designs: 10t, Rottweiler. 30t, Gordon setter. 50t, St. Bernard. 60t, English bulldog. 70t, Caucasian sheep dog.
125t, Caucasian sheep dog, diff.

**1997, June 2    Litho.    Perf. 14**
**167** A42 10t multicolored    .30 .30
**168** A42 30t multicolored    .70 .70
**169** A42 50t multicolored    1.25 1.25
**170** A42 60t multicolored    1.60 1.60
**171** A42 70t multicolored    2.00 2.00
*a.* Sheet of 6, #167-172    9.25
Nos. 167-171 (5)    5.85 5.85
**Souvenir Sheet**
**172** A42 125t multicolored    3.50 3.50

No. 171a contains stamp from No. 172 without the continuous design. Issued: 2/27/98.

Animated Film Characters — A43

Designs: a, 20t, Two mice talking. b, 30t, Man in bed. c, 40t, Balloons, bear, girl on cloud. d, 50t, Animals dancing, tree. e, 60t, Duck dressed as woman, tree.

**1997, July 15    Litho.    Perf. 14**
**173** A43 Strip of 5, #a.-e.    6.25 6.25

Georgian Women's Team, Winners of 1996 World Chess Olympiad — A44

No. 174: a, Maia Chiburdanidze, Nona Gaprindashvili, Nana Ioseliani, Nino Gurieli, 1992 winners. b, Chiburdanidze, Ioseliani, Ketevan Arakhamia, Gurieli, 1994 winners. c, Chiburdanidze, Ioseliani, Arakhamia, Gurieli, 1996 winners.
No. 175: a, 20t, Vice-Champion Nana Alexandria, 1975, 1981. b, 40t, Chiburdanidze, 1978, 1981 (Vice-Champion), 1984, 1986, 1991. c, 20t, Ioseliani, 1988, 1993. d, 50t, Gaprindashvili, 1962, 1965, 1969, 1972, 1975 (Vice-Champion).

**1997, July 21    Litho.    Imperf.**
**174** A44 30t Sheet of 3, #a.-d.+
      label    3.00 3.00
**175** A44    Sheet of 4, #a.-d.    4.00 4.00
Nos. 174-175 have simulated perforations.

A45

1998 Winter Olympic Games, Nagano A46

Stylized skier — #176: a, 20t. b, 30t. c, 40t. d, 50t.
Early hand-made winter apparel, equipment — No. 177: a, 20t, Snow shoe, hat, gloves. b, 30t, Scarf, snow shoe. c, 40t, Sled, gloves. d, 50t, Scarf, snow shoe.
No. 178, Stylized skier, diff. No. 179, Man's feet with snow shoes.

**1998, Feb. 8    Litho.    Perf. 14**
**176** A45    Sheet of 4, #a.-d.    3.75 3.75
**177** A46    Sheet of 4, #a.-d.    3.75 3.75
**Souvenir Sheets**
**178** A45 70t multicolored    2.25 2.25
**179** A46 70t multicolored    2.25 2.25

Moscow '97 — A47

Tiflis local postage stamp of 1857.

**1997, Oct. 17    Litho.    Perf. 13x14**
**180** A47 80t multicolored    2.25 2.25
**Souvenir Sheet**
**181** A47 1 l multicolored    2.75 2.75

Prince Vakhushti Bagrationi (1696-1758) — A48

40t, Map of Georgia, 1745, portrait. 80t, Portrait.

**1997, Oct. 9**
**182** A48 40t multi    1.00 1.00
**183** A48 80t multi, vert.    2.00 2.00

World Delphic Congress — A49

40t, Symbols of education, art & music, 1st World Junior Delphics. 80t, Building on mountaintop, 2nd World Delphic Cong.

**1997, Nov. 24    Litho.    Perf. 14**
**184** A49 40t multicolored    1.10 1.10
**185** A49 80t multicolored    2.00 2.00

Voyage of Jason and the Argonauts A50

Plate and Vase Paintings: a, 30t, Greek galley from Rhodes, terracotta plate, 700-650BC. b, 40t, Preparation for Battle, vase painting, 460BC. c, 50t, Boreades, Phineus & Harpy, vase painting, 6th cent. d, 60t, Punishment of King Amicus, vase painting, 420-400BC. e, 70t, Argonauts in Colchis, vase painting, 4th cent. BC. f, 80t, The Dragon Vomiting Jason, vase painting, 490-485BC.

**1998, June 23    Litho.    Perf. 13x13½**
**186** A50 Sheet of 6, #a.-f.    8.50 8.50

Independence, 80th Anniv. — A51

**1998, Dec. 25    Litho.    Perf. 14**
**187** A51 80t multicolored    2.50 2.50

Horses A52

Various breeds.

**1998, Dec. 22**
**188** A52 10t multicolored    .50 .50
**189** A52 40t multicolored    1.50 1.50
**190** A52 70t multicolored    2.50 2.50
**191** A52 80t multicolored    3.00 3.00
Nos. 188-191 (4)    7.50 7.50
**Souvenir Sheet**
**Imperf**
**192** A52 100t multicolored    4.25 4.25
No. 192 has simulated perfs.

Locomotives — A53

Various locomotives built at Tbilisi Locomotives Works.

**1998, Dec. 24**
**193** A53 10t multicolored    .40 .40
**194** A53 30t multicolored    1.10 1.10
**195** A53 40t multicolored    1.40 1.40

| | | | |
|---|---|---|---|
| 196 | A53 | 50t multicolored | 1.60 1.60 |
| 197 | A53 | 80t multicolored | 2.75 2.75 |
| | | Nos. 193-197 (5) | 7.25 7.25 |

**Souvenir Sheet**

| | | | |
|---|---|---|---|
| 198 | A53 | 100t multicolored | 4.00 4.00 |

Europa
A54

**1998, Dec. 31   Litho.   Perf. 13x12¾**

| | | | |
|---|---|---|---|
| 199 | A54 | (80t) Berikaoba | 2.50 2.50 |
| 200 | A54 | (100t) Chiakokonoba | 3.25 3.25 |

Wildlife
A55

10t, Vormela peregusna guld. 40t, Hyaena hyaena. 80t, Ursus arctos syriacus. 100t, Capra aegagrus erxleber.

**1999, Feb.   Litho.   Perf. 14x13½**

| | | | |
|---|---|---|---|
| 201 | A55 | 10t multicolored | .40 .40 |
| 202 | A55 | 40t multicolored | 1.25 1.25 |
| 203 | A55 | 80t multicolored | 2.50 2.50 |
| | | Nos. 201-203 (3) | 4.15 4.15 |

**Souvenir Sheet**
*Imperf*

| | | | |
|---|---|---|---|
| 204 | A55 | 100t multicolored | 3.25 3.25 |

Dated 1998. No. 204 has simulated perfs.

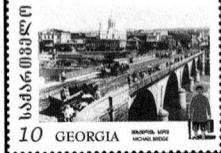

Ancient and Modern Bridges of Tbilisi
A56

Bridges: a, 10t, Michael. b, 40t, Saarbruken. c, 50t, N. Baratashvili. d, 60t, Mukhrani. e, 70t, Avlabari. f, 80t, Metekhi.

**1999, Feb.   Perf. 13½x14**

| | | | |
|---|---|---|---|
| 205 | A56 | Sheet of 6, #a.-f. | 9.25 9.25 |

Mustela Lutreola, Worldwide Fund for Wildlife
A57

**1999, Apr. 27   Litho.   Perf. 13x12¾**

| | | | |
|---|---|---|---|
| 206 | A57 | (10t) Standing in water | 1.60 1.60 |
| 207 | A57 | (20t) Feeding | 1.60 1.60 |
| 208 | A57 | (30t) Two standing | 1.60 1.60 |
| 209 | A57 | (60t) In burrow | 1.60 1.60 |
| a. | | Block of 4, #206-209 | 8.00 8.00 |

Nos. 206-209 were issued in sheets of 10 of each denomination and as se-tenant blocks of 4 in sheets of 20. The stamps from the se-tenant sheets have thicker lettering in the country and Latin names. Singles from the se-tenant sheets of 20 and from the individual sheetlets of 10 are of equal value.

Europa — A58

(80t), Batsara-Babaneury Reserve. (100t), Lagodekhy Reserve.

**1999, Apr. 28   Litho.   Perf. 12¾x13**

| | | | |
|---|---|---|---|
| 210 | A58 | (80t) multi | 2.50 2.50 |
| 211 | A58 | (100t) multi | 3.00 3.00 |

Council of Europe, 50th Anniv. — A59

**1999, Nov.   Litho.   Perf. 12¾**

| | | | |
|---|---|---|---|
| 212 | A59 | 50t shown | 1.50 1.50 |
| 213 | A59 | 80t Latin letters | 2.00 2.00 |

Georgian Olympic Committee, 10th Anniv.
A60

**1999, Nov.   Perf. 13¾**

| | | | |
|---|---|---|---|
| 214 | A60 | 20t multi | .85 .85 |
| 215 | A60 | 50t multi | 1.90 1.90 |

Butterflies
A61

Designs: 10t, Iphiclides podalirius. 20t, Parnassius apollo. 50t, Colias aurorina herrich-schaffer. 80t, Tomares romanovi.

**1999, Nov.**

| | | | |
|---|---|---|---|
| 216 | A61 | 10t multi | .50 .50 |
| 217 | A61 | 20t multi | .85 .85 |
| 218 | A61 | 50t multi | 1.60 1.60 |
| 219 | A61 | 80t multi | 3.25 3.25 |
| | | Nos. 216-219 (4) | 6.20 6.20 |

UPU, 125th Anniv. — A62

**1999, Nov.   Perf. 13¼x13½**

| | | | |
|---|---|---|---|
| 220 | A62 | 20t shown | .75 .75 |
| 221 | A62 | 80t Letter writer | 2.75 2.75 |

Trucks
A63

**1999, Dec.   Perf. 13¾**
**Color of Truck**

| | | | |
|---|---|---|---|
| 222 | A63 | 20t green | .50 .50 |
| 223 | A63 | 40t red & yellow | .95 .95 |
| 224 | A63 | 50t blue & white | 1.40 1.40 |
| 225 | A63 | 80t red & white | 2.10 2.10 |
| | | Nos. 222-225 (4) | 4.95 4.95 |

**Souvenir Sheet**

| | | | |
|---|---|---|---|
| 226 | A63 | 100t red | 3.50 3.50 |

**Souvenir Sheet**

Svaneti, World Heritage Site — A64

**1999, Dec.   Perf. 12¾**

| | | | |
|---|---|---|---|
| 227 | A64 | 100t multi | 3.50 3.50 |

**Europa, 2000**
Common Design Type

Denominations: 80t, 100t.

**2000, Mar. 31   Litho.   Perf. 12¾x13**

| | | | |
|---|---|---|---|
| 228-229 | CD17 | Set of 2 | 8.50 8.50 |

Scenes from "The Knight in a Tiger's Skin," by Shota Rustaveli
A65

Denominations: 10t, 20t, 30t, 50t, 60t.

**2000, May 8   Perf. 14¼x13¾**

| | | | |
|---|---|---|---|
| 230-234 | A65 | Set of 5 | 5.25 5.25 |

**Souvenir Sheet**

| | | | |
|---|---|---|---|
| 235 | A65 | 80t multi + label | 4.25 4.25 |

Nos. 230-235 also issued imperf. Value, set $10.

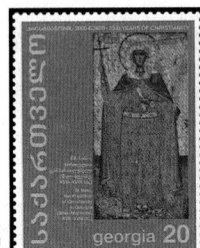

Christianity, 2000th Anniv. — A66

Icons: 20t, St. Nino the Preacher. 50t, The Savior. 80t, The Virgin Hodigitria.

**2000, May 10   Perf. 13¾**

| | | | |
|---|---|---|---|
| 236-238 | A66 | Set of 3 | 4.50 4.50 |

**Souvenir Sheet**

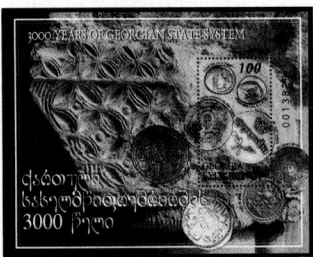

Georgian State System, 3000th Anniv. — A67

Illustration reduced.

**2000, May 11   Perf. 13**

| | | | |
|---|---|---|---|
| 239 | A67 | 100t multi | 3.50 3.50 |

Fish — A68

Various fish: 10t, 20t, 30t, 50t, 80t.

**2000, May 12   Perf. 13¾x13¼**

| | | | |
|---|---|---|---|
| 240-244 | A68 | Set of 5 | 7.25 7.25 |

David Saradjishvili (1848-1911), Brandy Maker
A69

**2000, Sept. 20   Litho.   Perf. 14¼x14**

| | | | |
|---|---|---|---|
| 245 | A69 | 80t multi | 2.10 2.10 |

2000 Summer Olympics, Sydney — A70

No. 246: a, 20t, Runner at left. b, 50t, Runner at center. c, 80t, Runner at right. Illustration reduced.

**2000 Sept. 20   Perf. 13¾**

| | | | |
|---|---|---|---|
| 246 | A70 | Strip of 3, #a-c | 5.25 5.25 |

Millennium — A71

No. 247: a, 20t, "1999." b, 50t, "2000." c, 80t, "2001." Illustration reduced.

**2000, Sept. 20**

| | | | |
|---|---|---|---|
| 247 | A71 | Strip of 3, #a-c | 3.75 3.75 |

Joint Georgia-Russia Space Reflector Project — A72

Designs: 20t, Astronauts at work. 80t, Reflector.

**2000, Dec. 11   Litho.   Perf. 13¾**

| | | | |
|---|---|---|---|
| 248-249 | A72 | Set of 2 | 3.50 3.50 |

Human Rights in Europe, 50th Anniv.
A73

Denomination colors: 50t, Orange brown. 80t, Blue.

**2000, Dec. 12          Perf. 14¼x14**
250-251 A73   Set of 2                    3.50 3.50

Mushrooms A74

Designs: 10t, Cantharellus cibarius. 20t, Agaricus campestris. 30t, Armillariella mella. 50t, Russula adusta. 80t, Cortinarus violaceus.

**2000, Dec. 14          Perf. 13¼x13½**
252-256 A74   Set of 5                    6.25 6.25

UN High Commissioner for Refugees, 50th Anniv. — A75

**2000, Dec. 14          Perf. 13½x14**
257 A75 50t multi                         1.50 1.50

**Houses of Worship Type of 1993**
Unidentified buildings. Colors: 10t, Brown. 50t, Blue.

**2000, Dec. 18          Perf. 13¼x13**
**Size: 24x32mm**
258-259 A25   Set of 2                    2.10 2.10

Writers — A76

Designs: 30t, Alexander Kazbegi (1848-93). 40t, Jakob Gogebashvili (1840-1912). 50t, Vadja Pshavela (1861-1915). 70t, Akaki Tsereteli (1840-1915). 80t, Ilia Chavchavadze (1837-1907).

**2000, Dec. 19          Perf. 13¼x13¾**
260-264 A76   Set of 5                    6.50 6.50

Alexander Kartveli (1896-1977), Aircraft Designer — A77

Designs: 10t, P-47D Thunderbolt. 20t, F-84. 80t, F-105D Thunderchief.

**2000, Dec. 20          Perf. 13¾x14**
265-267 A77   Set of 3                    4.00 4.00
**Souvenir Sheet**
**Perf. 13**
268 A77 100t Portrait, vert.              3.50 3.50

Fire Fighting Service, 175th Anniv. — A78

**2000, Dec. 24          Perf. 13¾x14**
269 A78 50t multi                         1.50 1.50

Europa — A79

Designs: 40t, Ritsa Lake. 80t, Borjomi Park.

**2001, Sept. 10   Litho.   Perf. 12½x13**
270-271 A79   Set of 2                    5.75 5.75
a. Booklet pane, 2 each #270-271, perf. 12½x13 on 3 sides   11.00
Booklet, #271a                            12.00

Great Silk Route A80

**2001, Sept. 20          Perf. 13x12½**
272 A80 20t shown                          .90  .90
**Souvenir Sheet**
273 A80 80t Like 20t, no emblem           3.50 3.50

Kutaisi Synagogue — A81

**2001, Sept. 13   Litho.   Perf. 13x14**
274 A81 140t multi                        4.50 4.50

First Europe-Asia Chess Match — A82

**2001, Sept. 18   Litho.   Perf. 13¾**
275 A82 1 l multi                         3.00 3.00

Poets — A83

No. 276: a, Taras Shevchenko (1814-61), Ukrainian poet. b, Akaki Tsereteli (1840-1915), Georgian poet.

**2001, Dec. 19          Perf. 13**
276 A83 50t Horiz. pair, #a-b             3.75 3.75
See Ukraine No. 445.

Georgian National Ballet — A84

Designs: 30t, Dancers Iliko Sukhishvili (1907-85) and Nino Ramishvili (1910-2000), sketch for dance "Mtiuluri." 50t, Dancers, sketch for dance "Samaya." 80t, Sukhishvili, Ramishvili, and sketch for dance "Jeirani."

**2002, Feb. 11          Perf. 13½x13¼**
277-279 A84   Set of 3                    5.25 5.25

Port of Poti, 140th Anniv. — A85

No. 280: a, Map, ship (black and white photograph). b, Mobile container crane, containers. c, Ship and tugboat, cargo hauler. d, Cargo hauler, small boat, container crane lifting container (black and white photograph). e, Ship, cargo hauler (black and white photograph). f, Cargo hauler, large ship.

**2002, Feb. 11          Perf. 13¼x13½**
280 A85 30t Sheet of 6, #a-f             6.25 6.25

A86

Ashot Kurapatatl Opiza — A87

**2002, Feb. 11          Perf. 13¼x13½**
281 A86 100t blue                         3.00 3.00
**Perf. 13¼**
282 A87 5 l brown                        11.00 11.00

Europa — A88

Designs: 40t, Georgian Circus. 80t, Tbilisi Circus.

**2002, Mar. 22          Perf. 13½x13¼**
283-284 A88   Set of 2                    5.75 5.75
a. Booklet pane, 2 each #283-284, perf. 13½x13¼ on 3 sides   12.50
Booklet, #284a                            13.50

Convention on Status of Refugees, 50th Anniv. — A89

**2002, May 15   Litho.   Perf. 13¼**
285 A89 50t multi                         1.75 1.75

Dinamo Tbilisi, Winner of 1981 European Soccer Cup — A90

**2002, Sept. 23          Perf. 13¾**
286 A90 20t multi                         1.25 1.25

Year of Dialogue Among Civilizations A91

**2002, Sept. 23          Perf. 13x13¾**
287 A91 40t multi                         1.60 1.60

Intl. Federation of Stamp Dealers Associations, 50th Anniv. — A92

**2002, Sept. 23          Perf. 13¼x13**
288 A92 100t No. 12                       3.50 3.50

Fighter Aircraft A93

Designs: 30t, SU-25 Scorpio. 80t, MiG 21U.

**2002, Sept. 23          Perf. 13¾x13**
289-290 A93   Set of 2                    4.25 4.25

Traditional Costumes A94

Men and women in various costumes: 20t, 30t, 50t.

**2002, Sept. 23          Perf. 13¾**
291-293 A94   Set of 3                    4.00 4.00

Church
Murals
A95

Murals from: 10t, 14th cent., vert. 30t, 16th-
17th cent. 80t, 18th cent., vert.

**Perf. 13½x13, 13x13½**
**2002, Sept. 23**
294-296 A95    Set of 3                4.75 4.75

Pectoral
Crosses
A96

Designs: 10t, Crucifixion, 10th cent. 20t,
Cross from Martvili, 7th-9th cent. 50t, Cross
from Martvili, 10th cent. 80t, Cross of King
Tamari, 12th cent.

**2002, Sept. 23**                    **Perf. 14¼x14**
297-300 A96    Set of 4                6.00 6.00

Flowers — A97

Designs: 20t, Bellflower. 30t, Caucasia rhododendron. 50t, Anemone. 80t, Marsh
marigold.

**2003, Sept. 23**                    **Perf. 13x13¾**
301-304 A97    Set of 4                6.50 6.50

Souvenir Sheet

Alexandre Dumas (Père) (1802-70),
French Novelist — A98

**2002, Sept. 23**                    **Perf. 14x13¾**
305 A98 120t multi                     4.75 4.75

Europa — A99

Poster art: 40t, Three men and donkey. 80t,
Four people.

---

**2003, Mar. 10**           **Perf. 13½x13¼**
306-307 A99    Set of 2                6.00 6.00
*307a*    Booklet pane, 2 each #306-
          307, perf. 13½x13¼ on 3
          sides                       11.50    —
          Complete booklet, #307a     12.00

Souvenir Sheet

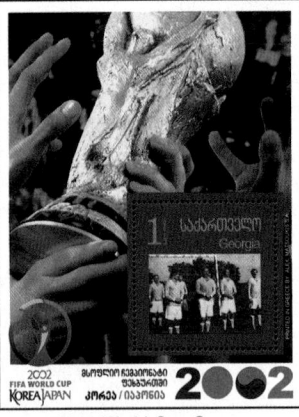

2002 World Cup Soccer
Championships, Japan and
Korea — A100

**2003, Apr. 25**                     **Perf. 13¾**
308 A100 1 l multi                     3.50 3.50

Souvenir Sheet

Paleontology — A101

No. 309: a, Stylized drawing of ancient
European man. b, Skull.

**2003, Apr. 25**                     **Perf. 12¾**
309 A101 60t Sheet of 2, #a-b         4.25 4.25

Margin of No. 309 has "1700000 YEARS
OLD" overprinted in red brown on silver oval
that is an overprint over an inscription that
reads "17000000 YEARS OLD". Examples
exist without the red brown overprint.

Youth — A102

**2003, June 20    Litho.    Perf. 14x14¼**
310 A102 50t multi                     1.50 1.50

Women
for Peace
A103

**2003, June 20**                   **Perf. 13¾x13**
311 A103 50t multi                     1.50 1.50

---

Zoo                    Minerals — A105
Animals — A104

Animals at Tbilisi Zoo: 20t, Elephant. 30t,
Wolf. 40t, Ostrich. 50t, Bear.

**2003, Aug. 25**                     **Perf. 14x13¾**
312-315 A104   Set of 4                4.75 4.75
*315a*    Miniature sheet, 2 each
          #312-315                    10.00 10.00
No. 315a was sold in a booklet cover but
unattached, and is comprised of two tete-
beche blocks of Nos. 312-315.

**2003, Aug. 25**                     **Perf. 13¼x13**
Minerals: 10t, Rock crystal. 20t, Agate with
amethyst. 30t, Orpiment rose. 50t, Realgar
with orpiment.
316-319 A105   Set of 4                3.75 3.75
*319a*    Miniature sheet, 2 each #316-
          319                          8.00 8.00
No. 319a was sold in a booklet cover but
unattached, and is composed of two tete-
beche blocks of Nos. 316-319.

Fruit — A106

Designs: 10t, Prunus spinosa. 20t,
Laurocerasus officinalis. 30t, Cydonia
oblonga. 50t, Punica granatum. 80t, Pyrus
caucasica.

**2003, Aug. 25**                     **Perf. 14x13¾**
320-324 A106   Set of 5                6.00 6.00

Souvenir Sheet

Old Tbilisi, by Elene Akhvlediani
(1901-75) — A107

**2003, Aug. 25**
325 A107 80t multi                     3.00 3.00

Souvenir Sheet

Self-portrait, by Vincent van Gogh
(1853-90) — A108

**2003, Aug. 25**                     **Perf. 13x12¾**
326 A108 100t multi                    4.00 4.00

Nos. 73, 75a Overprinted

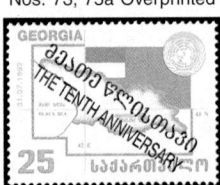

---

**2003, Oct. 6    Litho.    Perf. 13¼**
327 A20 25t green & multi               .85 .85
**Souvenir Sheet**
328    Sheet, #327, 328a, 328b        6.00 6.00
*a.*   A20 50t brown & multi           1.60 1.60
*b.*   A20 100t violet & multi         3.50 3.50

First postage stamps, 10th anniv.

Intl.
Association of
Academies of
Science, 10th
Anniv. — A109

**2003, Nov. 28**                   **Perf. 13¾x13¼**
329 A109 30t multi                     1.10 1.10

East-West Energy Corridor — A110

**2003, Nov. 28**                   **Perf. 13¼x13¾**
330 A110 80t multi                     2.00 2.00

Tourism — A111

Designs: 10t, Skiers, Bakuriani. 20t, Caves,
Vardzia. 30t, Harbor, Batum. 50t, Lake Ritsa.

**2003, Nov. 28**                   **Perf. 13¾x13¼**
331-334 A111   Set of 4                3.50 3.50
*334a*    Booklet pane, 2 each #331-
          334                          6.50    —
          Complete booklet, #334a      7.00
No. 334a is composed of two tete-beche
blocks of Nos. 331-334.

Grapes
A112

Designs: 10t, Aladasturi. 20t, Rkhatsiteli.
30t, Ojaleshi. 50t, Goruli Mtsvane. 80t, Alek-
sandrouli (Khvanchkhara).

**2003, Nov. 28**
335-339 A112   Set of 5                7.00 7.00

Europa
A113

Designs: 40t, Merry Christmas. 80t, Happy
Easter.

**2004, Jan. 28  Litho.  Perf. 13¼x13½**
340-341  A113  Set of 2      5.75  5.75
341a  Booklet pane, 4 each #340-
341, perf. 13¼x13½ on 2
or 3 sides                    20.00   —
Complete booklet, #341a      22.50

Georgi
Tsereteli
(1904-73),
Direcetor
of Institute
of Oriental
Studies
A114

**2004, Nov. 5  Litho.  Perf. 13¼x13¾**
342  A114  30t multi         1.10  1.10

Souvenir Sheet

Rose Revolution, 1st Anniv. — A115

No. 343: a, Crowd with flags. b, Protestors with flag sprayed with water.

**2004, Nov. 5  Perf. 13¼x13**
343  A115  50t Sheet of 2, #a-b   5.00  5.00

FIFA (Fédération
Internationale de
Football
Association),
Cent. — A116

Caricatures of soccer players: 20t, Boris Paichadze. 30t, Avtandil Gogoberidze. 50t, Mikheil Meskhi. 80t, David Kipiani.

**2004, Nov. 5  Perf. 13¾x13¼**
344-347  A116  Set of 4      6.75  6.75

2004 Summer Olympics,
Athens — A117

Sculptures of athletes by: 20t, B. Skhulukhia. 30t, V. Cherkezishvili. 50t, N. Jikia. 80t, L. Vardosanidze.

**2004, Nov. 5  Perf. 13¼x13¾**
348-351  A117  Set of 4      6.75  6.75

Ancient
Jewelry — A118

Designs: 20t, Belt and buckle, 3rd-4th cent. 30t, Necklace and belt buckle, 3rd-4th cent. 40t, Necklace and pins, 2000-1500 B.C. 80t, Necklace, 5th cent. B.C., double-voluted pins, 3rd millennium B.C.

**2004, Nov. 5**
352-355  A118  Set of 4      6.50  6.50

UNESCO
World
Heritage
Sites
A119

Designs: 20t, Ushguli. 30t, Bagrati. 50t, Gelati. 60t, Samtavro. 70t, Svetitskhoveli. 80t, Jvari.

**2004, Nov. 5  Litho.  Perf. 14x13¼**
356-361  A119  Set of 6      8.00  8.00

Flag of
Georgia
A120

**2005, Feb. 11  Litho.  Perf. 14x13¼**
362  A120  50t multi        1.90  1.90

Europa — A121

Loaves of bread and: 20t, Girl. 80t, Bakers.

**2005, May 27  Perf. 14x13¾**
363  A121  20t multi        1.25  1.25
364  A121  80t multi        4.75  4.75

**Booklet Stamps**
**Size: 29x41mm**
**Perf. 13¾ on 2, 3 or 4 Sides**
365  A121  20t multi        1.25  1.25
366  A121  80t multi        4.75  4.75
a.  Booklet pane, 2 each #365-366   12.50   —
b.  Booklet pane, 3 each #365-366   19.00   —
Complete booklet, #366a, 366b       32.50

Rabbi Abraam
Khvoles — A122

**2005, June 1  Perf. 12**
367  A122  1 l multi        3.75  3.75

2008
Summer
Olympics,
Beijing
A123

**2005, Dec. 28  Litho.  Perf. 12**
368  A123  80t multi        3.25  3.25

2006 World Cup
Soccer
Championships,
Germany — A124

**2005, Dec. 28**
369  A124  100t multi       3.75  3.75

Georgian
Ballet — A125

Designs: 40t, V. Tsiguadze. 50t, V. Chabukiani.

**2005, Dec. 28**
370-371  A125  Set of 2     3.50  3.50

Orchids — A126

Designs: 20t, Dactylorhiza euxina. 40t, Dactylorhiza iberica. 50t, Oprys caucasica. 80t, Orchis caucasica.

**2005, Dec. 28**
372-375  A126  Set of 4     6.75  6.75

Theaters — A127

Designs: No. 376, 30t, Georgian Drama Theater, Batumi. No. 377, 30t, Georgian Drama Theater, Kutaisi. No. 378, 30t, Abkhazian Drama Theater, Sukhumi. No. 379, 30t, Georgian Academic Theater, Tbilisi. No. 380, 30t, Georgian Drama Theater, Tbilisi. No. 381, 30t, Georgian Opera and Ballet Theater, Tbilisi. No. 382, 30t, Armenian Drama Theater, Tbilisi. No. 383, 30t, Ossetian Drama Theater, Tskhinvali.

**2005, Dec. 28**
376-383  A127  Set of 8     9.00  9.00

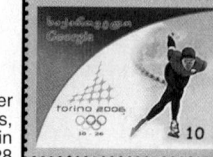

2006 Winter
Olympics,
Turin
A128

Designs: 10t, Speed skating. 20t, Biathlon. 30t, Ski jumping. 40t, Figure skating. 80t, Downhill skiing.

**2005, Dec. 29**
384-388  A128  Set of 5     6.75  6.75

Souvenir Sheet

Tbilisi Funicular, Cent. — A129

**2005, Dec. 30**
389  A129  100t multi       3.75  3.75

Europa
Stamps,
50th
Anniv.
A130

Designs: 10t, Various Georgian Europa stamps. 20t, Person inserting postcard in mail slot. 30t, France #805, Germany #748, magnifying glass, newspaper. 40t, Earth in ripped newspaper wrapper.
No. 394, 80t, Like 10t. No. 395, 80t, Like 20t. No. 396, 80t, Like 30t. No. 397, 80t, Like 40t.

**2006, Jan. 30  Perf. 12¾x13**
390-393  A130  Set of 4     4.00  4.00
**Souvenir Sheets**
394-397  A130  Set of 4     12.50  12.50

Europa — A131

Stars and: 20t, People holding flags. 80t, Earth, Georgian flag.

**Perf. 13½x13¼**
**2006, June 30  Litho.**
398-399  A131  Set of 2     2.60  2.60
399a  Booklet pane, 4 each #398-
399, perf. 13½x13¼ on 3
sides                         21.00   —
Complete booklet, #399a      21.00

No. 399a contains two tete-beche pairs of Nos. 398-399.

Nos. 365-366
Overprinted

**Perf. 13¾ on 2, 3 or 4 Sides**
2006, Oct. 23          Litho.
402 A121 20t multi                    .75    .75
403 A121 80t multi                   3.25   3.25
  *a.* Sheet of 4, 2 each #402-403    8.00   8.00
  *b.* Sheet of 6, 3 each #402-403   12.00  12.00
Europa stamps, 50th anniv. Nos. 403a and 403b are Nos. 366a and 366b removed from the booklet and overprinted on the stamps and margin.

No. 79
Surcharged
in Gray and
Silver

**Method and Perf. As Before**
2006, Nov. 2
404 A24 10t on 1c #79               .40    .40

Nikola Tesla (1856-1943), Electrical Engineer, and Wireless Transmission Tower — A132

2006, Nov. 15   Litho.   **Perf. 12x12¼**
405 A132 50t multi                 1.50   1.50

Souvenir Sheet

Georgian Wild West Show
Horsemen — A133

2007, Jan. 25   Litho.   **Perf. 12¼**
406 A133 100t multi                3.00   3.00

Tbilisi State
University,
Cent.
A134

2007, Jan. 25   Litho.   **Perf. 12¼x12**
407 A134 40t multi                 1.10   1.10

Prince
David
Guramishvili
(1705-92),
Poet
A135

2007, July 11          **Perf. 13¾x13¼**
408 A135 50t multi                 1.40   1.40

2006 Chess
Olympics,
Turin
A136

2007, July 11
409 A136 200t multi                5.25   5.25

Famous
Men
A137

Designs: No. 410, Rembrandt (1606-69), painter. No. 411, Wolfgang Amadeus Mozart (1756-91), composer.

2007, July 11          **Perf. 13¾x13¼**
410 A137 100t multi                2.50   2.50

**Perf. 13¾x14**
**Size: 39x27mm**
411 A137 100t multi                2.50   2.50

Worldwide Fund
for Nature
(WWF) — A138

Aquila clanga: 30t, In flight. 40t, On branch. 50t, With prey. 60t, Head.

2007, July 11          **Perf. 13¼x13¾**
412-415 A138   Set of 4            4.50   4.50

Eagles — A139

Designs: 10t, Aquila rapax. 30t, Haliaeetus albicilla. 50t, Circaetus gallicus. 70t, Aquila chryaetus.

2007, July 11
416-419 A139   Set of 4            4.50   4.50

Georgian
Military
A140

Designs: 20t, Tanks. 30t, Soldiers. 40t, Ship. 50t, Helicopters.

2007, July 11          **Perf. 14¼x14**
420-423 A140   Set of 4            3.50   3.50

Ancient Ships
A141

Various ships: 20t, 30t, 50t, 70t.

2007, July 11
424-427 A141   Set of 4            4.50   4.50

Souvenir Sheets

Guns from National Museum — A142

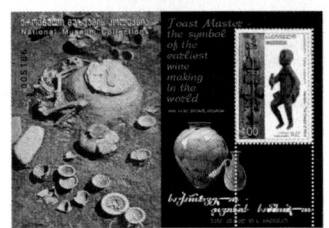

Sculpture from National
Museum — A143

No. 428 — Various guns with background color of: a, Yellow. b, Buff. c, Light blue. d, Light green.

2007, July 11          **Perf. 13x13¼**
428 A142  50t Sheet of 4, #a-d     5.00   5.00
429 A143 100t multi                2.50   2.50

Souvenir Sheet

Magician, Cards and Dove — A144

**Perf. 13¼x13¾**
2008, Mar. 14                      Litho.
430 A144 1 l multi                 3.25   3.25

Europa — A145

Designs: 90t, Scouts in boat and near tent. 1 l, Scouts around campfire.

2008, Mar. 14          **Perf. 14x13¾**
431-432 A145   Set of 2            5.75   5.75
  *432a* Booklet pane, 4 each #431-432   23.00  —
         Complete booklet, #432a        23.00  —
Scouting, cent. (in 2007). No. 432a contains two tete-beche pairs of Nos. 431-432.

Diplomatic
Relations
Between
Georgia and
Japan, 15th
Anniv. (in
2007) — A146

2008, Mar. 14   Litho.   **Perf. 13¾**
433 A146 1 l multi                 3.25   3.25
Dated 2007.

Mountains
A147

Designs: 20t, Mt. Ushba. 30t, Mt. Ushba, diff. 50t, Mt. Kazbeg. 70t, Mt. Shkhara.

2008          Litho.   **Perf. 13¼x13¾**
434-437 A147   Set of 4            6.25   6.25
Issued: 30t, 6/1; others, 3/14. Bottom panel with mountain name on No. 435 was overprinted in silver and black to correct inscription. No. 435 was not issued without overprint.

---

**SEMI-POSTAL STAMPS**

SP1          SP2

SP3          SP4

Surcharge in Red or Black
1922          Unwmk.   **Perf. 11½**
B1 SP1 1000r on 50r vio (R)        .50   3.00
B2 SP2 3000r on 100r brn
        red                        .50   3.00
B3 SP3 5000r on 250r gray
        grn                        .50   3.00
B4 SP4 10,000r on 25r blue
        (R)                        .50   3.00
  *Nos. B1-B4 (4)*                2.00  12.00
Nos. B1-B4 exist imperf but were not so issued. Values slightly more than perforated examples.

Georgian Natl.
Olympic
Committee
SP10

1994, May 27   Litho.   **Perf. 13½**
B10 SP10 100c +50c multi           1.10   1.10

UNICEF, 50th Anniv. SP11

Children's paintings: 20t+5t, People on ladder above rainbow, vert. 30t+10t, Animal character.

### *Perf. 13x14, 14x13*

| | | | | |
|---|---|---|---|---|
| **1996, Dec. 20** | | | **Litho.** | |
| B11 | SP11 | 20t +5t multi | 1.40 | 1.40 |
| B12 | SP11 | 30t +10t multi | 1.90 | 1.90 |

In Remembrance of Sept. 11, 2001 Terrorist Attacks — SP12

| | | | | |
|---|---|---|---|---|
| **2001, Dec. 31 Litho.** | | | ***Perf. 13x13¼*** | |
| B13 | SP12 | 30t +10t multi | 1.60 | 1.60 |
| **Souvenir Sheet** | | | | |
| B14 | SP12 | 120t +10t multi | 5.50 | 5.50 |

# GERMAN EAST AFRICA

ˈjər-mən ˈēst ˈa-fri-kə

LOCATION — In East Africa, bordering on the Indian Ocean
GOVT. — German Colony
AREA — 384,180 sq. mi.
POP. — 7,680,132 (1913)
CAPITAL — Dar-es Salaam

Following World War I, the greater part of this German Colonial possession was mandated to Great Britain. The British ceded to the Belgians the provinces of Ruanda and Urundi (Belgian East Africa). The Kionga triangle was awarded to the Portuguese and became part of the Mozambique Colony. The remaining area became the British Mandated Territory of Tanganyika.

64 Pesa = 1 Rupee
100 Heller = 1 Rupee (1905)
100 Centimes = 1 Franc (1916)
12 Pence = 1 Shilling (1916)
100 Cents = 1 Rupee (1917)
12 Pence = 1 Shilling 100 Cents = 1 Rupee (1917)

Stamps of Germany Surcharged in Black

Nos. 1-5          Nos. 6-10

| | | | | |
|---|---|---|---|---|
| **1893** | **Unwmk.** | | ***Perf. 13½x14½*** | |
| **Surcharge 15¼mm long** | | | | |
| 1 | A9 | 2pes on 3pf brown | 45.00 | 57.50 |
| 2 | A9 | 3pes on 5pf green | 52.50 | 57.50 |
| 3 | A10 | 5pes on 10pf car | 45.00 | 29.00 |
| **Surcharge 16¼mm long** | | | | |
| 4 | A10 | 10pes on 20pf ultra | 32.50 | 16.00 |
| **Surcharge 16¾mm long** | | | | |
| 5 | A10 | 25pes on 50pf red brn | 45.00 | 32.50 |
| *Nos. 1-5 (5)* | | | 220.00 | 192.50 |

The surcharge also comes 16¾mm on #1; 14¼ or 16¼mm on #2-3; 17½mm on #5. See the *Scott Classic Catalogue* for listings of these spacings.

---

**1896**

| | | | | |
|---|---|---|---|---|
| 6 | A9 | 2pes on 3pf dk brn | 2.00 | 37.50 |
| a. | | 2pes on 3pf light brown | 28.00 | 45.00 |
| b. | | 2pes on 3pf grayish brown | 11.50 | 11.50 |
| c. | | 2pes on 3pf reddish brown | 105.00 | 200.00 |
| 7 | A9 | 3pes on 5pf green | 2.50 | 4.50 |
| 8 | A10 | 5pes on 10pf car | 2.50 | 4.50 |
| 9 | A10 | 10pes on 20pf ultra | 5.25 | 5.25 |
| 10 | A10 | 25pes on 50pf red brn | 23.00 | 28.00 |
| *Nos. 6-10 (5)* | | | 35.25 | 79.75 |

A5

Kaiser's Yacht "Hohenzollern" — A6

| | | | | |
|---|---|---|---|---|
| **1900** | | **Typo.** | ***Perf. 14*** | |
| 11 | A5 | 2p brown | 2.75 | 1.60 |
| 12 | A5 | 3p green | 2.75 | 2.00 |
| 13 | A5 | 5p carmine | 3.25 | 2.50 |
| 14 | A5 | 10p ultra | 5.25 | 5.00 |
| 15 | A5 | 15p org & blk, *sal* | 5.25 | 6.50 |
| 16 | A5 | 20p lake & blk | 7.50 | 15.00 |
| 17 | A5 | 25p pur & blk, *sal* | 7.50 | 15.00 |
| 18 | A5 | 40p lake & blk, *rose* | 9.00 | 23.00 |
| **Engr.** | | | | |
| ***Perf. 14½x14*** | | | | |
| 19 | A6 | 1r claret | 20.00 | 57.50 |
| 20 | A6 | 2r yellow green | 10.00 | 90.00 |
| 21a | A6 | 3r red & slate | 120.00 | 200.00 |
| *Nos. 11-21a (11)* | | | 193.25 | 418.10 |

### Value in Heller

| | | | | |
|---|---|---|---|---|
| **1905** | | **Typo.** | ***Perf. 14*** | |
| 22 | A5 | 2½h brown | 4.00 | 1.75 |
| 23 | A5 | 4h dk olive green | 16.50 | 5.75 |
| a. | | 4h green | 15.00 | 2.00 |
| b. | | 4h dark yellowish green | 29.00 | 20.00 |
| 24 | A5 | 7½h carmine | 15.00 | 1.60 |
| 25 | A5 | 15h ultra | 24.00 | 6.00 |
| a. | | 15h violet blue | 50.00 | 16.00 |
| 26 | A5 | 20h org & blk, *yel* | 15.00 | 16.00 |
| 27 | A5 | 30h lake & blk | 15.00 | 6.00 |
| 28 | A5 | 45h pur & blk | 29.00 | 37.50 |
| 29 | A5 | 60h lake & blk, *rose* | 37.50 | 100.00 |
| *Nos. 22-29 (8)* | | | 156.00 | 174.60 |

| | | | | |
|---|---|---|---|---|
| **1905-16** | | **Wmk. Lozenges (125)** | | |
| 31 | A5 | 2½h brown ('06) | 1.00 | 1.00 |
| 32 | A5 | 4h green ('06) | 1.00 | .65 |
| b. | | Booklet pane of 4 + 2 labels | 45.00 | |
| c. | | Booklet pane of 5 + label | 400.00 | |
| 33 | A5 | 7½h car ('06) | 1.10 | 1.60 |
| b. | | Booklet pane of 4 + 2 labels | 45.00 | |
| c. | | Booklet pane of 5 + label | 400.00 | |
| 34 | A5 | 15h dk blue ('08) | 2.25 | 1.50 |
| 35 | A5 | 20h org & blk, *yel* ('11) | 2.50 | 20.00 |
| 36 | A5 | 30h lake & blk ('09) | 2.60 | 8.25 |
| 37 | A5 | 45h pur & blk ('06) | 5.75 | 57.50 |
| 38 | A5 | 60h lake & blk, *rose* | 30.00 | 200.00 |
| **Engr.** | | | | |
| ***Perf. 14½x14*** | | | | |
| 39 | A6 | 1r red ('16) | 15.00 | 25,000. |
| 40 | A6 | 2r yellow green | | |
| 41 | A6 | 3r car & slate ('08) | 50.00 | 250.00 |
| a. | | 3r red & blackish green ('08) | 100.00 | 400.00 |
| *Nos. 31-41 (11)* | | | 161.20 | |

No. 40 was never placed in use.
The frame of No. 41a fluoresces bright orange under ultra-violet light.
Forged cancellations are found on #35-39, 41.

In early 1916, German East African authorities ordered supplies of provisional stamps, printed by the press of the Evangelical Mission in Wuga. Three values in denominations most

---

urgently needed were produced in March, but before they could be issued, new stocks of regular stamps were received from Germany. To prevent their capture by the British, the provisionals were buried until 1922, when they were retrieved by the German government and sold at auction. Because of their long storage in the tropical climate, 90-95% of the stamps were destroyed and those surviving are usually brittle and somewhat faded.

Values: 2½h violet brown, $57.50; 7½h, carmine, $25; 1r pink, $1,400.

---

## OCCUPATION STAMPS

### Issued Under Belgian Occupation

Stamps of Belgian Congo, 1915, Handstamped "RUANDA" in Black or Blue

| | | | |
|---|---|---|---|
| **1916** | **Unwmk.** | ***Perf. 13½ to 15*** | |
| N1 | A29 | 5c green & blk | 25.00 |
| N2 | A30 | 10c carmine & blk | 25.00 |
| N3 | A21 | 15c blue grn & blk | 50.00 |
| N4 | A31 | 25c blue & blk | 25.00 |
| N5 | A23 | 40c brown red & blk | 25.00 |
| N6 | A24 | 50c brown lake & blk | 35.00 |
| N7 | A25 | 1fr olive bis & blk | 180.00 |
| N8 | A27 | 5fr ocher & blk | 2,750. |
| *Nos. N1-N7 (7)* | | | 365.00 |

Stamps of Belgian Congo, 1915, Handstamped "URUNDI" in Black or Blue

| | | | |
|---|---|---|---|
| N9 | A29 | 5c green & blk | 25.00 |
| N10 | A30 | 10c carmine & blk | 25.00 |
| N11 | A21 | 15c bl grn & blk | 50.00 |
| N12 | A31 | 25c blue & blk | 25.00 |
| N13 | A23 | 40c brn red & blk | 25.00 |
| N14 | A24 | 50c brn lake & blk | 35.00 |
| N15 | A25 | 1fr ol bis & blk | 180.00 |
| N16 | A27 | 5fr ocher & blk | 2,750. |
| *Nos. N9-N15 (7)* | | | 365.00 |

Stamps of Belgian Congo overprinted "Karema," "Kigoma" and "Tabora" were not officially authorized.
Nos. N1-N16 exist with forged overprint.

Stamps of Belgian Congo, 1915, Overprinted in Dark Blue

| | | | | |
|---|---|---|---|---|
| **1916** | | ***Perf. 12½ to 15*** | | |
| N17 | A29 | 5c green & blk | .75 | .25 |
| b. | | Inverted overprint | 175.00 | — |
| N18 | A30 | 10c carmine & blk | 1.00 | .40 |
| N19 | A21 | 15c bl grn & blk | .75 | .25 |
| N20 | A31 | 25c blue & blk | 6.50 | 1.50 |
| N21 | A23 | 40c brn red & blk | 14.00 | 5.50 |
| N22 | A24 | 50c brn lake & blk | 17.50 | 5.50 |
| N23 | A25 | 1fr olive bis & blk | 3.00 | .65 |
| N24 | A27 | 5fr ocher & blk | 3.00 | 1.40 |
| *Nos. N17-N24 (8)* | | | 46.50 | 15.45 |

Nos. N17-N18, N20-N22 Surcharged in Black or Red

| | | | | |
|---|---|---|---|---|
| **1922** | | | | |
| N25 | A24 | 5c on 50c brn lake & blk | .50 | .40 |
| N26 | A29 | 10c on 5c grn & blk (R) | .50 | .35 |
| N27 | A23 | 25c on 40c brn red & blk (R) | 3.00 | 1.75 |
| N28 | A30 | 30c on 10c car & blk | .50 | .25 |
| N29 | A31 | 50c on 25c bl & blk (R) | .50 | .25 |
| *Nos. N25-N29 (5)* | | | 5.00 | 3.00 |

No. N25 has the surcharge at each side.

---

### Issued Under British Occupation

Stamps of Nyasaland Protectorate, 1913-15 Overprinted

| | | | | |
|---|---|---|---|---|
| **1916** | | **Wmk. 3** | ***Perf. 14*** | |
| N101 | A3 | ½p green | 1.75 | 9.50 |
| a. | | Double overprint (R & Bk) | | |
| N102 | A3 | 1p carmine | 1.75 | 3.75 |
| N103 | A3 | 3p violet, *yel* | 14.00 | 20.00 |
| a. | | Double overprint | 26,000. | |
| N104 | A3 | 4p scar & blk, *yel* | 37.50 | 47.50 |
| N105 | A3 | 1sh black, *green* | 50.00 | 60.00 |
| *Nos. N101-N105 (5)* | | | 105.00 | 140.75 |

"N.F." stands for "Nyasaland Force."

---

Stamps of East Africa and Uganda, 1912-14, Overprinted in Black or Red

| | | | | |
|---|---|---|---|---|
| **1917** | | | | |
| N106 | A3 | 1c black (R) | .20 | .95 |
| N107 | A3 | 3c blue green | .20 | .20 |
| N108 | A3 | 6c carmine | .20 | .20 |
| N109 | A3 | 10c brown orange | .60 | .70 |
| a. | | Inverted overprint | | |
| N110 | A3 | 12c gray | .60 | 2.50 |
| N111 | A3 | 15c ultramarine | 1.20 | 3.50 |
| N112 | A3 | 25c scar & blk, *yel* | .90 | 4.00 |
| N113 | A3 | 50c violet & blk | 1.20 | 3.75 |
| N114 | A3 | 75c blk, *bl grn,* olive back (R) | 1.20 | 5.25 |
| a. | | 75c black, *emerald* (R) | 3.75 | 52.50 |

Overprinted

| | | | | |
|---|---|---|---|---|
| N115 | A4 | 1r blk, *green* (R) | 3.50 | 8.00 |
| a. | | 1r black, *emerald* (R) | 9.50 | 65.00 |
| N116 | A4 | 2r blk & red, *bl* | 13.00 | 52.50 |
| N117 | A4 | 3r gray grn & vio | 15.00 | 95.00 |
| N118 | A4 | 4r grn & red, *yel* | 20.00 | 105.00 |
| N119 | A4 | 5r dl vio & ultra | 45.00 | 105.00 |
| N120 | A4 | 10r grn & red, *grn* | 105.00 | 375.00 |
| a. | | 10r grn & red, *emerald* | 130.00 | 450.00 |
| N121 | A3 | 20r vio & blk, *red* | 225.00 | 475.00 |
| N122 | A3 | 50r gray grn & red | 575.00 | 950.00 |
| *Nos. N106-N120 (15)* | | | 207.80 | 761.55 |

See Tanganyika for "G.E.A." overprints on stamps inscribed "East Africa and Uganda Protectorates" with watermark 4.

---

### SEMI-POSTAL STAMPS

#### Issued under Belgian Occupation

Semi-Postal Stamps of Belgian Congo, 1918, Overprinted

| | | | | |
|---|---|---|---|---|
| **1918** | | **Unwmk.** | ***Perf. 14, 15*** | |
| NB1 | A29 | 5c + 10c grn & bl | .50 | .50 |
| NB2 | A30 | 10c + 15c car & bl | .50 | .50 |
| NB3 | A21 | 15c + 20c bl grn & bl | .50 | .50 |
| NB4 | A31 | 25c + 25c dp & pale bl | .50 | .50 |
| NB5 | A23 | 40c + 40c brn red & bl | .75 | .75 |
| NB6 | A24 | 50c + 50c brn lake & bl | 1.00 | 1.00 |
| NB7 | A25 | 1fr + 1fr ol bis & bl | 2.75 | 2.75 |

| | | | | |
|---|---|---|---|---|
| NB8 | A27 | 5fr + 5fr ocher & bl | 8.50 | 8.50 |
| NB9 | A28 | 10fr + 10fr grn & bl | 70.00 | 70.00 |
| | | *Nos. NB1-NB9 (9)* | 85.00 | 85.00 |

The letters "A.O." are the initials of "Afrique Orientale" (East Africa).

## GERMAN NEW GUINEA

'jər-mən 'nü 'gi-nē

LOCATION — A group of islands in the west Pacific Ocean, including a part of New Guinea and adjacent islands of the Bismarck Archipelago.
GOVT. — German Protectorate
AREA — 93,000 sq. mi.
POP. — 601,427 (1913)
CAPITAL — Herbertshohe (later Kokopo)

The islands were occupied by Australian troops during World War I and renamed "New Britain." By covenant of the League of Nations they were made a mandated territory of Australia in 1920. The old name of "New Guinea" has since been restored. Postage stamps were issued under all regimes. For other listings see New Britain (1914-15), North West Pacific Islands (1915-22) and New Guinea in Vol. 4.

100 Pfennig = 1 Mark

Stamps of Germany Overprinted in Black

A3

Kaiser's Yacht "Hohenzollern" — A4

| | | **1901** | **Typo.** | **Perf. 14** | |
|---|---|---|---|---|---|
| 7 | A3 | 3pf brown | | 1.25 | 1.25 |
| 8 | A3 | 5pf green | | 7.50 | 1.25 |
| 9 | A3 | 10pf carmine | | 25.00 | 2.75 |
| 10 | A3 | 20pf ultra | | 1.50 | 2.75 |
| 11 | A3 | 25pf org & blk, *yel* | | 1.75 | 16.00 |
| 12 | A3 | 30pf org & blk, *sal* | | 1.75 | 20.00 |
| 13 | A3 | 40pf lake & blk | | 1.75 | 23.00 |
| 14 | A3 | 50pf pur & blk, *sal* | | 2.00 | 20.00 |
| 15 | A3 | 80pf lake & blk, *rose* | | 3.75 | 27.50 |

| | | **Engr.** | | | |
|---|---|---|---|---|---|
| | | **Perf. 14½x14** | | | |
| 16 | A4 | 1m carmine | | 4.00 | 52.50 |
| 17 | A4 | 2m blue | | 6.00 | 77.50 |
| 18 | A4 | 3m black vio | | 7.50 | 150.00 |
| 19 | A4 | 5m slate & car | | 190.00 | 500.00 |
| | | *Nos. 7-19 (13)* | | 253.75 | 894.50 |

Fake cancellations exist on Nos. 10-19.
The stamps of German New Guinea overprinted "G.R.I." and new values in British currency were all used in New Britain and are listed under that country as Nos. 1-29C, O1-2.

A5

A6

| | | **Wmk. Lozenges (125)** | | | |
|---|---|---|---|---|---|
| **1914-19** | | **Typo.** | | **Perf. 14** | |
| 20 | A3 | 3pf brown ('19) | | | .80 |
| 21 | A5 | 5pf green | | | 1.60 |
| 22 | A5 | 10pf carmine | | | 1.60 |

| | | **Engr.** | | | |
|---|---|---|---|---|---|
| | | **Perf. 14½x14** | | | |
| 23 | A6 | 5m slate & carmine | | | 32.50 |
| | | *Nos. 20-23 (4)* | | | 36.50 |

Nos. 20-23 were never placed in use.
Nos. 21-23 have "NEUGUINEA" as one word without a hyphen.

## GERMAN SOUTH WEST AFRICA

'jər-mən 'sauth 'west 'a-fri-kə

LOCATION — In southwest Africa, bordering on the South Atlantic
GOVT. — German Colony
AREA — 322,450 sq. mi. (1913)
POP. — 94,372 (1913)
CAPITAL — Windhoek

The Colony was occupied by South African troops during World War I and in 1920 was mandated to the Union of

| | | **1897-99** | **Unwmk.** | **Perf. 13½x14½** | |
|---|---|---|---|---|---|
| 1 | A9 | 3pf brown | | 8.25 | 10.00 |
| *a.* | | 3pf reddish brown ('99) | | 115.00 | 200.00 |
| *b.* | | 3pf yellow brown ('99) | | 31.00 | 57.50 |
| 2 | A9 | 5pf green | | 4.00 | 5.75 |
| 3 | A10 | 10pf carmine | | 6.50 | 9.00 |
| 4 | A10 | 20pf ultra | | 9.00 | 14.00 |
| 5 | A10 | 25pf orange ('98) | | 29.00 | 52.50 |
| *a.* | | Inverted overprint | | *2,750.* | |
| 6 | A10 | 50pf red brown | | 32.50 | 50.00 |
| | | *Nos. 1-6 (6)* | | 89.25 | 141.25 |

South Africa by the League of Nations. See South West Africa in Vol. 6.

100 Pfennig = 1 Mark

Stamps of Germany Overprinted

| | | **1897** | **Unwmk.** | **Perf. 13½x14½** | |
|---|---|---|---|---|---|
| 1 | A9 | 3pf dark brown | | 8.25 | 11.50 |
| *a.* | | 3pf yellow brown | | 50.00 | 2,800. |
| 2 | A9 | 5pf green | | 4.50 | 4.00 |
| 3 | A10 | 10pf carmine | | 21.00 | 20.00 |
| 4 | A10 | 20pf ultra | | 5.75 | 5.25 |
| 5 | A10 | 25pf orange | | 225.00 | 29,000. |
| 6 | A10 | 50pf red brown | | 225.00 | |

Nos. 5 and 6 were prepared for issue but were not sent to the Colony.

Overprinted "Deutsch-Südwestafrika"

| | | **1899** | | | |
|---|---|---|---|---|---|
| 7 | A9 | 3pf dark brown | | 4.00 | 21.00 |
| *a.* | | 3pf reddish brown | | 52.50 | 160.00 |
| *b.* | | 3pf yellow brown | | 7.00 | 12.00 |
| 8 | A9 | 5pf green | | 3.25 | 2.60 |
| 9 | A10 | 10pf carmine | | 3.25 | 3.25 |
| 10 | A10 | 20pf ultra | | 11.50 | 15.00 |
| 11 | A10 | 25pf orange | | 350.00 | 400.00 |
| 12 | A10 | 50pf red brown | | 11.50 | 10.50 |

Kaiser's Yacht "Hohenzollern"
A3          A4

| | | **1900** | **Typo.** | **Perf. 14** | |
|---|---|---|---|---|---|
| 13 | A3 | 3pf brown | | 4.00 | 1.50 |
| 14 | A3 | 5pf green | | 20.00 | .80 |
| 15 | A3 | 10pf carmine | | 14.00 | .80 |
| 16 | A3 | 20pf ultra | | 30.00 | 1.50 |
| 17 | A3 | 25pf org & blk, *yel* | | 1.50 | 5.25 |
| 18 | A3 | 30pf org & blk, *sal* | | 57.50 | 2.75 |
| 19 | A3 | 40pf lake & blk | | 1.75 | 3.25 |
| 20 | A3 | 50pf pur & blk, *sal* | | 2.10 | 2.10 |
| 21 | A3 | 80pf lake & blk, *rose* | | 2.10 | 9.00 |

| | | **Engr.** | | | |
|---|---|---|---|---|---|
| | | **Perf. 14½x14** | | | |
| 22 | A4 | 1m carmine | | 110.00 | 30.00 |
| 23 | A4 | 2m blue | | 30.00 | 37.50 |
| 24 | A4 | 3m black vio | | 32.50 | 50.00 |
| 25 | A4 | 5m slate & car | | 200.00 | 160.00 |
| | | *Nos. 13-25 (13)* | | 505.45 | 304.45 |

| | | **Wmk. Lozenges (125)** | | | |
|---|---|---|---|---|---|
| **1906-19** | | **Typo.** | | **Perf. 14** | |
| 26 | A3 | 3pf dk brn ('07) | | .80 | 3.75 |
| 27 | A3 | 5pf green | | .80 | 1.40 |
| *b.* | | Bklt. pane of 6 (2 #27, 4 #28) | | 40.00 | |
| *c.* | | Booklet pane of 5 + label | | 160.00 | |
| 28 | A3 | 10pf lt rose | | 1.00 | 1.40 |
| *b.* | | Booklet pane of 5 + label | | 400.00 | |
| 29 | A3 | 20pf ultra ('11) | | 1.00 | 3.75 |
| 30 | A3 | 30pf org & blk, *cream*('11) | | 16.00 | 52.50 |

| | | **Engr.** | | | |
|---|---|---|---|---|---|
| | | **Perf. 14½x14** | | | |
| 31 | A4 | 1m carmine ('12) | | 12.50 | 70.00 |
| 32 | A4 | 2m blue ('11) | | 12.50 | 70.00 |
| 33 | A4 | 3m blk vio ('19) | | 14.00 | |
| *a.* | | 3m gray violet | | 40.00 | |
| 34 | A4 | 5m slate & car | | 32.50 | 300.00 |
| *a.* | | 5m slate & rose red | | 52.50 | |
| | | *Nos. 26-34 (9)* | | 91.10 | |

Nos. 33, 33a, 34a were never placed in use.
Forged cancellations are found on #30-32, 34.

## GERMAN STATES

'jər-mən 'stāts

### Watermarks

Wmk. 92 — 17mm wide    Wmk. 93 — 14mm wide

Wmk. 94 — Horiz. Wavy Lines Wide Apart

Wmk. 95v — Vert. Wavy Lines Close Together

Wmk. 95h — Horiz. Wavy Lines Close Together    Wmk. 102 — Post Horn

Wmk. 116 — Crosses and Circles

Wmk. 128 — Wavy Lines

Wmk. 130 — Wreath of Oak Leaves    Wmk. 148 — Small Flowers

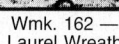
Wmk. 162 —
Laurel Wreath

Wmk. 192 —
Circles

## BADEN

LOCATION — In southwestern Germany
GOVT. — Grand Duchy
AREA — 5,817 sq. mi.
POP. — 1,432,000 (1864)
CAPITAL — Karlsruhe (principal city)

Baden was a member of the German Confederation. In 1870 it became part of the German Empire.

60 Kreuzer = 1 Gulden

Values for unused stamps are for examples with original gum as defined in the catalogue introduction except for Nos. 1-9 which are valued without gum. Very fine examples of Nos. 1-9 will have one or two margins touching the framelines due to the very narrow spacing of the stamps on the plates. Stamps with margins clear of the framelines on all four sides are scarce and sell for considerably more.

A1

**1851-52    Unwmk.    Typo.    Imperf.**

| | | | | |
|---|---|---|---|---|
| 1 | A1 | 1kr blk, *dk buff* | 250.00 | 210.00 |
| 2 | A1 | 3kr blk, *yellow* | 125.00 | 12.50 |
| 3 | A1 | 6kr blk, *yel grn* | 400.00 | 40.00 |
| 4 | A1 | 9kr blk, *lil rose* | 80.00 | 24.00 |
| | | Nos. 1-4 (4) | 855.00 | 286.50 |

**Thin Paper (First Printing, 1851)**

| | | | | |
|---|---|---|---|---|
| 1a | A1 | 1kr black, *buff* | 1,825. | 675.00 |
| 2a | A1 | 3kr black, *orange* | 625.00 | 30.00 |
| 3a | A1 | 6kr blk, *blue green* | 2,000. | 75.00 |
| 4a | A1 | 9kr black, *deep rose* | 2,550. | 140.00 |
| 4b | A1 | 9kr blk, *bl grn* (error) | | 1,300,000. |

**1853-58**

| | | | | |
|---|---|---|---|---|
| 6 | A1 | 1kr black | 150.00 | 22.50 |
| a. | | Tête bêche gutter pair | | 45,000. |
| 7 | A1 | 3kr black, *green* | 150.00 | 6.00 |
| 8 | A1 | 3kr black, *bl* ('58) | 625.00 | 30.00 |
| a. | | Printed on both sides | | |
| 9 | A1 | 6kr black, *yellow* | 240.00 | 24.00 |
| | | Nos. 6-9 (4) | 1,165. | 82.50 |

*Reissues (1865) of Nos. 1, 2, 3, 6, 7 and 8 exist on thick paper and No. 9 on thin paper; the color of the last is brighter than that of the original.*

Coat of Arms
A2        A3

**1860-62    Perf. 13½**

| | | | | |
|---|---|---|---|---|
| 10 | A2 | 1kr black | 72.50 | 22.50 |
| 12 | A2 | 3kr ultra ('61) | 80.00 | 16.00 |
| a. | | 3kr Prussian blue | 275.00 | 50.00 |
| 13 | A2 | 6kr red org ('61) | 95.00 | 60.00 |
| a. | | 6kr yellow orange ('62) | 175.00 | 72.50 |
| 14 | A2 | 9kr rose ('61) | 240.00 | 160.00 |
| | | Nos. 10-14 (4) | 487.50 | 258.50 |

Copies of Nos. 10-14 and 18 with all perforations intact sell for considerably more.

---

**1862    Perf. 10**

| | | | | |
|---|---|---|---|---|
| 15 | A2 | 1kr black | 57.50 | 72.50 |
| a. | | 1kr silver gray | | 6,600. |
| 16 | A2 | 6kr prussian blue | 110.00 | 62.50 |
| 17 | A2 | 9kr brown | 82.50 | 67.50 |
| a. | | 9kr dark brown | 350.00 | 275.00 |

**Perf. 13½**

| | | | | |
|---|---|---|---|---|
| 18 | A3 | 3kr rose | 2,500. | 310.00 |

**1862-65    Perf. 10**

| | | | | |
|---|---|---|---|---|
| 19 | A3 | 1kr black ('64) | 45.00 | 12.00 |
| a. | | 1kr silver gray | | 2,100. |
| 20 | A3 | 3kr rose | 45.00 | 1.60 |
| a. | | Imperf. | 100,000. | 40,000. |
| 22 | A3 | 6kr ultra ('65) | 7.50 | 22.50 |
| a. | | 6kr Prussian blue ('64) | 575.00 | 65.00 |
| 23 | A3 | 9kr brown ('64) | 14.00 | 25.00 |
| a. | | 9kr bister | 375.00 | 90.00 |
| b. | | Printed on both sides | | 6,500. |
| 24 | A3 | 18kr green | 375.00 | 575.00 |
| 25 | A3 | 30kr deep orange | 27.50 | 1,300. |
| a. | | 30kr yellow orange | 140.00 | 2,200. |

Forged cancellations are known on #25, 28a.

A4

**1868**

| | | | | |
|---|---|---|---|---|
| 26 | A4 | 1kr green | 4.00 | 4.50 |
| 27 | A4 | 3kr rose | 2.25 | 1.50 |
| 28 | A4 | 7kr dull blue | 19.00 | 32.50 |
| a. | | 7kr sky blue | 42.50 | 92.50 |
| | | Nos. 26-28 (3) | 25.25 | 38.50 |

The postage stamps of Baden were superseded by those of the German Empire on Jan. 1, 1872, but Official stamps were used during the year 1905.

---

**Stamps of the Baden sector of the French Occupation Zone of Germany, issued in 1947-49, are listed under Germany, Occupation Issues.**

---

## RURAL POSTAGE DUE STAMPS

RU1

**1862    Unwmk.    Perf. 10**
**Thin Paper**

| | | | | |
|---|---|---|---|---|
| LJ1 | RU1 | 1kr blk, *yellow* | 4.00 | 275.00 |
| a. | | Thick paper | 140.00 | 575.00 |
| LJ2 | RU1 | 3kr blk, *yellow* | 2.25 | 110.00 |
| a. | | Thick paper | 110.00 | 375.00 |
| LJ3 | RU1 | 12kr blk, *yellow* | 26.00 | 20,000. |
| a. | | Half used as 6kr on cover | | 25,000. |
| b. | | Quarter used as 3kr on cover | | — |
| | | Nos. LJ1-LJ3 (3) | 32.25 | 20,385. |

On #LJ3, "LAND-POST" is a straight line. Paper of #LJ1a, LJ2a is darker yellow. Forged cancellations abound on #LJ1-LJ3.

---

## OFFICIAL STAMPS
See Germany Nos. OL16-OL21.

---

## BAVARIA

LOCATION — In southern Germany
GOVT. — Kingdom
AREA — 30,562 sq. mi. (1920)
POP. — 7,150,146 (1919)
CAPITAL — Munich

Bavaria was a member of the German Confederation and became part of the German Empire in 1870. After World War I, it declared itself a republic. It lost its postal autonomy on Mar. 31, 1920.

60 Kreuzer = 1 Gulden

100 Pfennig = 1 Mark (1874)

Values for unused stamps are for examples with original gum as defined in the catalogue introduction. Unused examples of the 1849-78 issues without gum sell for about 50-60% of the figures quoted.

A1

Broken Circle — A1a

**1849    Unwmk.    Typo.    Imperf.**

| | | | | |
|---|---|---|---|---|
| 1 | A1 | 1kr black | 725.00 | 1,825. |
| a. | | 1kr deep black | 2,175. | 2,900. |
| b. | | Tête bêche pair | 125,000. | |

**With Silk Thread**

| | | | | |
|---|---|---|---|---|
| 2 | A1a | 3kr blue | 45.00 | 2.25 |
| a. | | 3kr greenish blue | 45.00 | 2.25 |
| b. | | 3kr deep blue | 45.00 | 2.25 |
| 3 | A1a | 6kr brown | 6,500. | 190.00 |

No. 1 exists with silk thread, from a single proof sheet. Value about $4,000.

Complete circle — A2

Coat of Arms — A3

**1850-58    With Silk Thread**

| | | | | |
|---|---|---|---|---|
| 4 | A2 | 1kr pink | 90.00 | 19.00 |
| 5 | A2 | 6kr brown | 40.00 | 5.50 |
| a. | | Half used as 3kr on cover | | 15,750. |
| 6 | A2 | 9kr yellow green | 60.00 | 13.00 |
| a. | | 9kr blue green ('53) | 6,250. | 150.00 |
| 7 | A2 | 12kr red ('58) | 125.00 | 125.00 |
| 8 | A2 | 18kr yellow ('54) | 110.00 | 190.00 |
| | | Nos. 4-8 (5) | 425.00 | 352.50 |

---

**1862**

| | | | | |
|---|---|---|---|---|
| 9 | A2 | 1kr yellow | 60.00 | 17.50 |
| 10 | A1a | 3kr rose | 140.00 | 2.25 |
| a. | | 3kr carmine | 45.00 | 4.75 |
| 11 | A2 | 6kr blue | 65.00 | 8.75 |
| a. | | 6kr ultra | 2,200. | 7,600. |
| b. | | Half used as 3kr on cover | | 10,000. |
| 12 | A2 | 9kr bister | 90.00 | 13.00 |
| 13 | A2 | 12kr yellow grn | 82.50 | 60.00 |
| a. | | Half used as 6kr on cover | | 32,000. |
| 14 | A2 | 18kr ver red | 875.00 | 140.00 |
| a. | | 18kr pale red | 140.00 | 450.00 |
| | | Nos. 9-14 (6) | 1,322. | 241.50 |

No. 11a was not put in use.

**1867-68    Embossed**

| | | | | |
|---|---|---|---|---|
| 15 | A3 | 1kr yellow grn | 60.00 | 8.75 |
| a. | | 1kr dark blue green | 275.00 | 40.00 |
| 16 | A3 | 3kr rose | 60.00 | 1.40 |
| a. | | Printed on both sides | | 4,500. |
| 17 | A3 | 6kr blue | 42.50 | 17.00 |
| a. | | Half used as 3kr on cover | | 75,000. |
| 18 | A3 | 6kr bister ('68) | 72.50 | 45.00 |
| a. | | Half used as 3kr on cover | | 32,000. |
| 19 | A3 | 7kr ultra ('68) | 375.00 | 11.50 |
| 20 | A3 | 9kr bister | 42.50 | 30.00 |
| 21 | A3 | 12kr lilac | 325.00 | 90.00 |
| 22 | A3 | 18kr red | 125.00 | 150.00 |
| | | Nos. 15-22 (8) | 1,102. | 353.65 |

The paper of the 1867-68 issues often shows ribbed or laid lines.

**1870-72    Wmk. 92    Perf. 11½**
**Without Silk Thread**

| | | | | |
|---|---|---|---|---|
| 23 | A3 | 1kr green | 11.00 | 1.25 |
| 24 | A3 | 3kr rose | 22.50 | .70 |
| 25 | A3 | 6kr bister | 30.00 | 27.50 |
| 26 | A3 | 7kr ultra | 2.75 | 3.25 |
| a. | | 7kr Prussian blue | 19.00 | 11.00 |
| 27 | A3 | 9kr pale brn ('72) | 4.25 | 3.50 |
| 28 | A3 | 10kr yellow | 4.50 | 12.50 |
| 29 | A3 | 12kr lilac | 1,100. | 4,125. |
| 30 | A3 | 18kr dull brick red | 8.75 | 12.50 |
| a. | | 18kr dark brick red | 110.00 | 62.50 |

The paper of the 1870-75 issues frequently appears to be laid with the lines either close or wide apart.
See Nos. 33-37.
*Reprints exist.*

**Wmk. 93**

| | | | | |
|---|---|---|---|---|
| 23a | A3 | 1kr | 92.50 | 8.75 |
| 24a | A3 | 3kr | 90.00 | 2.25 |
| 25a | A3 | 6kr | 150.00 | 65.00 |
| 26b | A3 | 7kr | 125.00 | 32.50 |
| 27a | A3 | 9kr | 250.00 | 450.00 |
| 28a | A3 | 10kr | 225.00 | 325.00 |
| 29a | A3 | 12kr | 325.00 | 1,000. |
| 30a | A3 | 18kr dull brick red | 375.00 | 150.00 |
| c. | | 18kr dark brick red | 250.00 | 225.00 |

A4

A5

**1874-75    Wmk. 92    Imperf.**

| | | | | |
|---|---|---|---|---|
| 31 | A4 | 1m violet | 575.00 | 72.50 |

**Perf. 11½**

| | | | | |
|---|---|---|---|---|
| 32 | A4 | 1m violet ('75) | 190.00 | 45.00 |

See Nos. 46-47, 54-57, 73-76.

**1875    Wmk. 94**

| | | | | |
|---|---|---|---|---|
| 33 | A3 | 1kr green | .65 | 22.50 |
| 34 | A3 | 3kr rose | .65 | 4.00 |
| 35 | A3 | 7kr ultra | 3.25 | 250.00 |
| 36 | A3 | 10kr yellow | 27.50 | 250.00 |
| 37 | A3 | 18kr red | 22.50 | 57.50 |
| | | Nos. 33-37 (5) | 54.55 | 584.00 |

False cancellations exist on #29, 29a, 33-37.

**1876-78    Embossed    Perf. 11½**

| | | | | |
|---|---|---|---|---|
| 38 | A5 | 3pf lt green | 27.50 | 1.40 |
| 39 | A5 | 5pf dk green | 72.50 | 10.00 |
| 40 | A5 | 5pf lilac ('78) | 140.00 | 18.00 |
| 41 | A5 | 10pf rose | 140.00 | .55 |
| 42 | A5 | 20pf ultra | 150.00 | 2.75 |
| 43 | A5 | 25pf yellow brn | 140.00 | 5.00 |
| 44 | A5 | 50pf scarlet | 47.50 | 4.75 |
| 45 | A5 | 50pf brown ('78) | 725.00 | 25.00 |
| 46 | A4 | 1m violet | 1,750. | 82.50 |
| 47 | A4 | 2m orange | 19.00 | 7.25 |

The paper of the 1876-78 issue often shows ribbed lines.
See Nos. 48-53, 58-72. For overprints and surcharge see Nos. 237, O1-O5.

**1881-1906    Wmk. 95v    Perf. 11½**

| | | | | |
|---|---|---|---|---|
| 48 | A5 | 3pf green | 11.50 | .45 |
| a. | | Imperf. | 375.00 | 1,800. |
| 49 | A5 | 5pf lilac | 17.00 | 1.25 |
| 50 | A5 | 10pf carmine | 11.00 | .40 |
| a. | | Imperf. | 375.00 | 1,800. |

| | | | | |
|---|---|---|---|---|
| 51 | A5 | 20pf ultra | 13.00 | .65 |
| 52 | A5 | 25pf yellow brn | 110.00 | 3.25 |
| 53 | A5 | 50pf deep brown | 140.00 | 3.25 |
| 54 | A4 | 1m rose lilac ('00) | 2.25 | 1.40 |
| a. | | 1m red lilac, toned paper | 62.50 | 3.00 |
| 55 | A4 | 2m orange ('01) | 3.25 | 4.50 |
| a. | | Toned paper ('90) | 72.50 | 10.00 |
| 56 | A4 | 3m olive gray ('00) | 18.00 | 22.50 |
| a. | | White paper ('06) | 140.00 | 500.00 |
| 57 | A4 | 5m yellow grn ('00) | 18.00 | 22.50 |
| a. | | White paper ('06) | 140.00 | 375.00 |
| | | Nos. 48-57 (10) | 344.00 | 60.15 |

Nos. 56-57 are on toned paper. A 2m lilac was not regularly issued.

| 1888-1900 | | Wmk. 95h | Perf. 14½ | |
|---|---|---|---|---|
| 58 | A5 | 2pf gray ('00) | 1.50 | .45 |
| 59 | A5 | 3pf green | 9.25 | 2.10 |
| 60 | A5 | 3pf brown ('00) | .20 | .40 |
| 61 | A5 | 5pf lilac | 22.50 | 3.25 |
| 62 | A5 | 5pf dk green ('00) | .20 | .40 |
| 63 | A5 | 10pf carmine | .30 | .40 |
| 64 | A5 | 20pf ultra | .30 | .40 |
| 65 | A5 | 25pf yellow brn | 27.50 | 6.00 |
| 66 | A5 | 25pf orange ('00) | .35 | .55 |
| 67 | A5 | 30pf olive grn ('00) | .40 | .70 |
| 68 | A5 | 40pf yellow ('00) | .40 | .95 |
| 69 | A5 | 50pf dp brown | 57.50 | 3.25 |
| 70 | A5 | 50pf maroon ('00) | .35 | 1.40 |
| 71 | A5 | 80pf lilac ('00) | 2.25 | 4.00 |
| | | Nos. 58-71 (14) | 123.00 | 24.25 |

Nos. 59, 61, 65, 69 and 70 are on toned paper; Nos. 67-68 on white.

**Toned Paper**

| | | | | |
|---|---|---|---|---|
| 58a | A5 | 2pf ('90) | 11.00 | 3.50 |
| 60a | A5 | 3pf ('90) | 9.25 | .40 |
| 62a | A5 | 5pf ('90) | 9.25 | .40 |
| 63a | A5 | 10pf | 6.00 | .40 |
| b. | | 10pf imperf | 72.50 | 175.00 |
| 64a | A5 | 20pf | 8.75 | 1.25 |
| 66a | A5 | 25pf ('90) | 15.00 | 1.50 |
| 70a | A5 | 50pf ('90) | 45.00 | 2.10 |
| 71a | A5 | 80pf ('99) | 27.50 | 8.25 |

| 1911 | | | Wmk. 95v | |
|---|---|---|---|---|
| 72 | A5 | 5pf dark green | .60 | 8.50 |

| 1911 | | Wmk. 95h | Perf. 11½ | |
|---|---|---|---|---|
| 73 | A4 | 1m rose lilac | 4.00 | 27.50 |
| 74 | A4 | 2m orange | 17.00 | 37.50 |
| 75 | A4 | 3m olive gray | 17.00 | 57.50 |
| 76 | A4 | 5m pale yel grn | 17.00 | 57.50 |
| | | Nos. 73-76 (4) | 55.00 | 180.00 |

See note after No. 91 concerning used values.

A6        A7

Prince
Regent
Luitpold
A8

| | | Perf. 14x14½ | | |
|---|---|---|---|---|
| 1911 | | Wmk. 95h | Litho. | |
| 77 | A6 | 3pf brn, gray brn | .20 | .20 |
| a. | | "911" for "1911" | 275.00 | 275.00 |
| 78 | A6 | 5pf dk grn, grn | .20 | .20 |
| a. | | Tête bêche pair | 4.50 | 10.50 |
| b. | | Booklet pane of 4 + 2 labels | 100.00 | 150.00 |
| c. | | Bklt. pane of 5 + label | 225.00 | 375.00 |
| d. | | Bklt. pane of 6 | 35.00 | |
| 79 | A6 | 10pf scar, buff | .20 | .20 |
| a. | | Tête bêche pair | 5.75 | 62.50 |
| b. | | "911" for "1911" | 15.00 | 15.00 |
| d. | | Booklet pane of 5 + label | 65.00 | 30.00 |
| 80 | A6 | 20pf dp bl, bl | 1.90 | .75 |
| 81 | A6 | 25pf vio brn, buff | 2.90 | 1.10 |

| | | Perf. 11½ | | |
|---|---|---|---|---|
| | | Wmk. 95v | | |
| 82 | A7 | 30pf org buff, buff | 1.50 | .90 |
| 83 | A7 | 40pf ol grn, buff | 3.00 | .90 |
| 84 | A7 | 50pf cl, gray brn | 2.50 | 1.40 |
| 84A | A7 | 60pf dk grn, buff | 2.50 | 1.40 |
| 85 | A7 | 80pf vio, gray brn | 8.75 | 4.75 |
| 86 | A8 | 1m brn, gray brn | 2.50 | 1.25 |
| 87 | A8 | 2m grn, grn | 2.50 | 6.25 |
| 88 | A8 | 3m lake, buff | 12.50 | 35.00 |
| 89 | A8 | 5m dk bl, buff | 11.00 | 25.00 |
| 90 | A8 | 10m org, yel | 22.50 | 42.50 |
| 91 | A8 | 20m blk brn, yel | 19.00 | 20.00 |
| | | Nos. 77-91 (16) | 93.65 | 141.80 |

90th birthday of Prince Regent Luitpold. All values exist in 2 types except #84A. Nos. 77-84, 85-91 exist imperf.

---

**Used values:** Nos. 73-76 and 77-91 often were canceled en masse for accounting purposes. These cancels are perfectly clear, and used values are for stamps canceled thus. Postally used examples are worth about twice as much.

Prince Regent
Luitpold — A9

| 1911, June 10 | | | Unwmk. | |
|---|---|---|---|---|
| 92 | A9 | 5pf grn, yel & blk | .45 | .90 |
| b. | | Horiz. pair, imperf. btwn. | 140.00 | 225.00 |
| 93 | A9 | 10pf rose, yel & blk | .70 | 1.40 |
| b. | | Pair, imperf. between | 140.00 | 225.00 |

Silver Jubilee of Prince Regent Luitpold.

A10       A11

King Ludwig III

A12       A13

| | | Perf. 14x14½ | | |
|---|---|---|---|---|
| 1914-20 | | Wmk. 95h | Photo. | |
| 94 | A10 | 2pf gray ('18) | .20 | 1.25 |
| 95 | A10 | 3pf brown | .20 | 1.25 |
| 96 | A10 | 5pf yellow grn | 1.10 | 1.40 |
| a. | | 5pf dark green | 1.10 | 1.40 |
| b. | | Tête bêche pair | 3.00 | 10.00 |
| c. | | Booklet pane of 5 + 1 label | 13.00 | 50.00 |
| 97 | A10 | 7½pf dp green ('16) | .20 | 1.40 |
| a. | | Tête bêche pair | 1.90 | 6.00 |
| b. | | Booklet pane of 6 | 12.50 | |
| 98 | A10 | 10pf vermilion | 1.40 | 1.40 |
| a. | | Tête bêche pair | 3.00 | 10.00 |
| b. | | Booklet pane of 5 + 1 label | 13.00 | 50.00 |
| 99 | A10 | 10pf car rose ('16) | .20 | 1.25 |
| 100 | A10 | 15pf ver ('16) | .20 | 1.25 |
| a. | | Tête bêche pair | 1.90 | 6.00 |
| b. | | Booklet pane of 5 + 1 label | 5.50 | 19.00 |
| 101 | A10 | 15pf car ('20) | 1.50 | 27.50 |
| 102 | A10 | 20pf blue | .20 | 1.25 |
| 103 | A10 | 25pf gray | .20 | 1.25 |
| 104 | A10 | 30pf orange | .80 | 1.25 |
| 105 | A10 | 40pf olive grn | .20 | 1.40 |
| 106 | A10 | 50pf red brn | .20 | 1.40 |
| 107 | A10 | 60pf blue grn | .80 | 1.40 |
| 108 | A10 | 80pf violet | .20 | 1.40 |

| | | Perf. 11½ | | |
|---|---|---|---|---|
| | | Wmk. 95v | | |
| 109 | A11 | 1m brown | .20 | 1.40 |
| 110 | A11 | 2m violet | .20 | 2.50 |
| 111 | A11 | 3m scarlet | .30 | 5.00 |

| | | Wmk. 95h | | |
|---|---|---|---|---|
| 112 | A12 | 5m deep blue | .40 | 10.00 |
| 113 | A12 | 10m yellow grn | 1.40 | 50.00 |
| 114 | A12 | 20m brown | 2.50 | 72.50 |
| | | Nos. 94-114 (21) | 12.60 | 187.45 |

See #117-135. For ovpts. and surcharges see #115, 136-175, 193-236, B1-B3.

Used Values
of Nos. 94-275, B1-B3 are for postally used stamps, which abound, sell for same prices as unused.

No. 94 Surcharged

| 1916 | | Wmk. 95h | Perf. 14x14½ | |
|---|---|---|---|---|
| 115 | A13 | 10pf on 2pf gray | .20 | .85 |
| a. | | Double surcharge | | |

Ludwig III Types of 1914-20

| 1916-20 | | | Imperf. | |
|---|---|---|---|---|
| 117 | A10 | 2pf gray | .20 | 10.00 |
| 118 | A10 | 3pf brown | .20 | 12.00 |
| 119 | A10 | 5pf pale yel grn | .20 | 12.00 |

---

| | | | | |
|---|---|---|---|---|
| 120 | A10 | 7½pf dp green | .20 | 10.00 |
| a. | | Tête bêche pair | 3.25 | 6.00 |
| 121 | A10 | 10pf car rose | .20 | 10.00 |
| 122 | A10 | 15pf vermilion | .20 | 10.00 |
| a. | | Tête bêche pair | 3.25 | 6.00 |
| 123 | A10 | 20pf blue | .20 | 12.00 |
| 124 | A10 | 25pf gray | .20 | 12.00 |
| 125 | A10 | 30pf orange | .20 | 12.00 |
| 126 | A10 | 40pf olive grn | .20 | 12.00 |
| 127 | A10 | 50pf red brown | .20 | 12.00 |
| 128 | A10 | 60pf dark green | .20 | 13.00 |
| 129 | A10 | 80pf violet | .20 | 13.00 |
| 130 | A11 | 1m brown | .35 | 13.00 |
| 131 | A11 | 2m violet | .35 | 13.00 |
| 132 | A11 | 3m scarlet | .45 | 22.50 |
| 133 | A12 | 5m deep blue | .75 | 30.00 |
| 134 | A12 | 10m yellow green | 1.25 | 57.50 |
| 135 | A12 | 20m brown | 1.75 | 90.00 |
| | | Nos. 117-135 (19) | 7.50 | 374.00 |

Stamps and Type of 1914-20
Overprinted:

a            b

**Wmk. 95h or 95v**

| 1919 | | | Perf. 14x14½ | |
|---|---|---|---|---|
| | | Overprint "a" | | |
| 136 | A10 | 3pf brown | .20 | 1.00 |
| 137 | A10 | 5pf yellow grn | .20 | 1.00 |
| 138 | A10 | 7½pf deep green | .20 | 1.00 |
| 139 | A10 | 10pf car rose | .20 | 1.00 |
| 140 | A10 | 15pf vermilion | .20 | 1.00 |
| 141 | A10 | 20pf blue | .20 | 1.00 |
| 142 | A10 | 25pf gray | .20 | 1.00 |
| 143 | A10 | 30pf orange | .20 | 1.00 |
| 144 | A10 | 35pf orange | .20 | 1.90 |
| a. | | Without overprint | 100.00 | |
| 145 | A10 | 40pf olive grn | .20 | 1.10 |
| 146 | A10 | 50pf red brown | .20 | 1.10 |
| 147 | A10 | 60pf dark green | .20 | 1.10 |
| 148 | A10 | 75pf red brown | .20 | .95 |
| a. | | Without overprint | 22.50 | 225.00 |
| 149 | A10 | 80pf violet | .20 | 1.25 |

| | | Perf. 11½ | | |
|---|---|---|---|---|
| | | Overprint "a" | | |
| 150 | A11 | 1m brown | .20 | 1.10 |
| 151 | A11 | 2m violet | .20 | 1.25 |
| 152 | A11 | 3m scarlet | .40 | 3.50 |

| | | Overprint "b" | | |
|---|---|---|---|---|
| 153 | A12 | 5m deep blue | .90 | 10.00 |
| 154 | A12 | 10m yellow green | .95 | 37.50 |
| 155 | A12 | 20m dk brown | 1.50 | 37.50 |
| | | Nos. 136-155 (20) | 6.95 | 106.25 |

Inverted overprints exist on Nos. 137-143, 145-147, 149. Value, each $15.
Double overprints exist on Nos. 137, 139, 143, 145, 150. Values, $30-$75.

| | | Imperf | | |
|---|---|---|---|---|
| | | Overprint "a" | | |
| 156 | A10 | 3pf brown | .20 | 13.00 |
| 157 | A10 | 5pf pale yel grn | .20 | 13.00 |
| 158 | A10 | 7½pf dp green | .20 | 13.00 |
| 159 | A10 | 10pf car rose | .20 | 13.00 |
| 160 | A10 | 15pf vermilion | .20 | 13.00 |
| 161 | A10 | 20pf blue | .20 | 13.00 |
| 162 | A10 | 25pf gray | .20 | 13.00 |
| 163 | A10 | 30pf orange | .20 | 13.00 |
| 164 | A10 | 35pf orange | .20 | 17.00 |
| a. | | Without overprint | 13.00 | |
| 165 | A10 | 40pf olive grn | .20 | 13.00 |
| 166 | A10 | 50pf red brown | .20 | 13.00 |
| 167 | A10 | 60pf dk green | .20 | 13.00 |
| 168 | A10 | 75pf red brown | .20 | 17.00 |
| a. | | Without overprint | 190.00 | |
| 169 | A10 | 80pf violet | .20 | 17.00 |
| 170 | A11 | 1m brown | .20 | 20.00 |
| 171 | A11 | 2m violet | .40 | 22.50 |
| 172 | A11 | 3m scarlet | .55 | 35.00 |

| | | Overprint "b" | | |
|---|---|---|---|---|
| 173 | A12 | 5m deep blue | .75 | 42.50 |
| 174 | A12 | 10m yellow grn | .95 | 60.00 |
| 175 | A12 | 20m brown | 1.90 | 60.00 |
| | | Nos. 156-175 (20) | 7.55 | 434.00 |

Stamps of Germany
1906-19 Overprinted

---

| 1919 | | Wmk. 125 | Perf. 14, 14½ | |
|---|---|---|---|---|
| 176 | A22 | 2½pf gray | .20 | .90 |
| 177 | A16 | 3pf brown | .20 | .90 |
| 178 | A16 | 5pf green | .20 | .90 |
| 179 | A22 | 7½pf orange | .20 | .95 |
| 180 | A16 | 10pf carmine | .20 | 1.25 |
| 181 | A22 | 15pf dk violet | .20 | 1.00 |
| a. | | Double overprint | 375.00 | 1,050. |
| 182 | A16 | 20pf ultra | .20 | .90 |
| 183 | A16 | 25pf org & blk, yel | .20 | 1.25 |
| 184 | A22 | 35pf red brown | .20 | 1.40 |
| 185 | A16 | 40pf lake & blk | .20 | 1.40 |
| 186 | A16 | 75pf green & blk | .35 | 1.90 |
| 187 | A16 | 80pf lake & blk, rose | .35 | 2.50 |
| 188 | A17 | 1m car rose | .75 | 4.00 |
| 189 | A21 | 2m dull blue | 1.10 | 8.00 |
| 190 | A19 | 3m gray violet | 1.10 | 10.50 |
| 191 | A20 | 5m slate & car | 1.10 | 10.50 |
| a. | | Inverted overprint | 3,575. | |
| | | Nos. 176-191 (16) | 6.75 | 48.25 |

Bavarian Stamps of 1914-16
Overprinted:

c            d

**Wmk. 95h or 95v**

| 1919-20 | | | Perf. 14x14½ | |
|---|---|---|---|---|
| | | Overprint "c" | | |
| 193 | A10 | 3pf brown | .20 | 1.25 |
| 194 | A10 | 5pf yellow grn | .20 | .95 |
| 195 | A10 | 7½pf dp green | .20 | 13.00 |
| 196 | A10 | 10pf car rose | .20 | .95 |
| 197 | A10 | 15pf vermilion | .20 | .95 |
| 198 | A10 | 20pf blue | .20 | .95 |
| 199 | A10 | 25pf gray | .20 | 1.25 |
| 200 | A10 | 30pf orange | .20 | 1.25 |
| 201 | A10 | 40pf olive grn | .20 | 11.50 |
| 202 | A10 | 50pf red brown | .20 | 1.50 |
| 203 | A10 | 60pf dk green | .20 | 11.50 |
| 204 | A10 | 75pf olive bister | .35 | 11.50 |
| 205 | A10 | 80pf violet | .20 | 3.00 |

| | | Perf. 11½ | | |
|---|---|---|---|---|
| | | Overprint "c" | | |
| 206 | A11 | 1m brown | .20 | 2.25 |
| 207 | A11 | 2m violet | .20 | 4.25 |
| 208 | A11 | 3m scarlet | .35 | 6.00 |

| | | Overprint "d" | | |
|---|---|---|---|---|
| 209 | A12 | 5m deep blue | .60 | 14.50 |
| 210 | A12 | 10m yellow grn | 1.25 | 30.00 |
| 211 | A12 | 20m dk brown | 1.90 | 50.00 |
| | | Nos. 193-211 (19) | 7.25 | 166.55 |

| | | Imperf | | |
|---|---|---|---|---|
| | | Overprint "c" | | |
| 212 | A10 | 3pf brown | .20 | 10.00 |
| 213 | A10 | 5pf pale yel grn | .20 | 10.00 |
| 214 | A10 | 7½pf deep green | .20 | 22.50 |
| 215 | A10 | 10pf car rose | .20 | 10.00 |
| 216 | A10 | 15pf vermilion | .20 | 10.00 |
| 217 | A10 | 20pf blue | .20 | 10.00 |
| a. | | Double overprint | 50.00 | |
| 218 | A10 | 25pf gray | .20 | 10.00 |
| 219 | A10 | 30pf orange | .20 | 11.50 |
| 220 | A10 | 40pf olive grn | .20 | 11.50 |
| 221 | A10 | 50pf red brn | .20 | 11.50 |
| 222 | A10 | 60pf dk green | .20 | 11.50 |
| 223 | A10 | 75pf olive bis | .20 | 30.00 |
| a. | | Without overprint | 5.00 | |
| 224 | A10 | 80pf violet | .20 | 11.50 |
| 225 | A11 | 1m brown | .20 | 18.00 |
| 226 | A11 | 2m violet | .20 | 18.00 |
| 227 | A11 | 3m scarlet | .45 | 22.50 |

| | | Overprint "d" | | |
|---|---|---|---|---|
| 228 | A12 | 5m deep blue | .60 | 32.50 |
| 229 | A12 | 10m yellow grn | 1.25 | 57.50 |
| 230 | A12 | 20m brown | 1.75 | 90.00 |
| | | Nos. 212-230 (19) | 7.05 | 408.50 |

Ludwig Type of 1914,
Printed in Various
Colors and
Surcharged

| 1919 | | | Perf. 11½ | |
|---|---|---|---|---|
| 231 | A11 | 1.25m on 1m yel grn | .20 | 1.25 |
| 232 | A11 | 1.50m on 1m orange | .20 | 2.75 |
| 233 | A11 | 2.50m on 1m gray | .35 | 5.25 |
| | | Nos. 231-233 (3) | .75 | 9.25 |

**1920**                                                      *Imperf.*
**234** A11 1.25m on 1m yel grn          .20    30.00
  *a.*  Without surcharge          325.00
**235** A11 1.50m on 1m org              .20    30.00
  *a.*  Without surcharge           6.50
**236** A11 2.50m on 1m gray             .35    30.00
  *a.*  Without surcharge           6.50
    *Nos. 234-236 (3)*             .75    90.00

No. 60 Surcharged in
Dark Blue

**1920**                                          *Perf. 14½*
**237** A5 20pf on 3pf brown             .20     1.25
  *a.*  Inverted surcharge        6.50    26.00
  *b.*  Double surcharge         80.00   190.00

Plowman                  "Electricity"
A14                      Harnessing
                         Light to a
                         Water Wheel
                         A15

Sower — A16              Madonna and
                        Child — A17

von Kaulbach's
"Genius" — A18

TWENTY PFENNIG
Type I — Foot of "2" turns downward.
Type II — Foot of "2" turns upward.

**1920**    **Wmk. 95h**   *Perf. 14x14½*
                               *Typo.*
**238** A14 5pf yellow grn      .20    1.00
**239** A14 10pf orange         .20    1.00
**240** A14 15pf carmine        .20    1.00
**241** A15 20pf violet (I)     .20    1.00
  *a.*  20pf violet (II)         8.00   1,150.
**242** A15 30pf dp blue        .20    1.10
**243** A15 40pf brown          .20    1.10
**244** A16 50pf vermilion      .20    1.25
**245** A16 60pf blue green     .20    1.90
**246** A16 75pf lilac rose     .20    1.90
      *Perf. 12x11½*
       **Wmk. 95v**
**247** A17 1m car & gray       .35    1.90
**248** A17 1¼m ultra & ol
       bis              .20    1.90
**249** A17 1½m dk grn &
       gray             .20    2.75
**250** A17 2½m blk & gray      .20   12.00
      *Perf. 11½x12*
       **Wmk. 95h**
**251** A18 3m pale blue        .45   11.50
**252** A18 5m orange           .45   11.50
**253** A18 10m deep
       green            .75   22.50
**254** A18 20m black          1.25   30.00
    *Nos. 238-254 (17)*   5.65  105.30

     **Imperf. Pairs**
*238a* A14 5pf yellow grn     55.00   350.00
*239a* A14 10pf orange       125.00
*241b* A15 20pf violet (I)    55.00
*243a* A15 40pf brown        110.00
*244a* A16 50pf vermilion     32.50
*245a* A16 60pf blue green    37.50
*246a* A16 75pf lilac rose    37.50
*247a* A17 1m car & gray       6.50    26.00
*248a* A17 1¼m ultra & ol bis  6.50    26.00
*249a* A17 1½m dk grn &
       gray             6.50    26.00
*250a* A17 2½m blk & gray     11.50    65.00
*251a* A18 3m pale blue       11.50    65.00
*252a* A18 5m orange          11.50    65.00
*253a* A18 10m deep green     11.50    65.00
*254a* A18 20m black          11.50    65.00

     *Perf. 12x11½*
**1920**   **Litho.**   **Wmk. 95v**
**255** A17 2½m black & gray    .40    30.00
  On No. 255 the background dots are small, hazy and irregularly spaced. On No. 250 they are large, clear, round, white and regularly spaced in rows. The backs of the typo. stamps usually show a raised impression of parts of the design.

Stamps and Types of
Preceding Issue
Overprinted

**1920**
**256** A14 5pf yellow green    .20    1.10
  *a.*  Inverted overprint        26.00
  *b.*  Imperf., pair           37.50   375.00
**257** A14 10pf orange         .20    1.10
  *a.*  Imperf., pair           37.50   375.00
**258** A14 15pf carmine        .20    1.10
**259** A15 20pf violet         .20    1.10
  *a.*  Inverted overprint        26.00   650.00
  *b.*  Double overprint        13.00
  *c.*  Imperf., pair           50.00
**260** A15 30pf deep blue      .20    1.10
  *a.*  Inverted overprint        26.00
  *b.*  Imperf., pair           50.00   375.00
**261** A15 40pf brown          .20    1.10
  *a.*  Inverted overprint        26.00   450.00
  *b.*  Imperf., pair           50.00
**262** A16 50pf vermilion      .20    1.90
**263** A16 60pf blue green     .20    1.00
**264** A16 75pf lilac rose     .35    4.00
**265** A16 80pf dark blue      .35    2.25
  *a.*  Without overprint       100.00
  *b.*  Imperf., pair           50.00

Overprinted in Black
or Red

**266** A17 1m car & gray       .35    1.75
  *a.*  Imperf., pair           50.00   375.00
  *b.*  Inverted overprint        47.50
**267** A17 1¼m ultra & ol bis  .35    1.75
  *a.*  Imperf., pair           47.50
**268** A17 1½m dk grn &
       gray            .40    2.75
  *a.*  Imperf., pair           47.50
**269** A17 2m vio & ol bis     .60    3.25
  *a.*  Without overprint        32.50
  *b.*  Imperf., pair           50.00
**270** A17 2½m (#250) (R)      .20    2.25
  *c.*  Imperf., pair           50.00
**270A** A17 2½m (#255) (R)     .45    80.00
  *c.*  Imperf., pair           50.00

Overprinted

**271** A18 3m pale blue       2.25    7.25
**272** A18 4m dull red        2.75    8.50
  *a.*  Without overprint        47.50
**273** A18 5m orange          2.25    8.00
**274** A18 10m dp green       2.75   10.00
**275** A18 20m black          5.00   10.50
    *Nos. 256-275 (21)*  19.65  151.75

  Nos. 256-275 were available for postage through all Germany, but were used almost exclusively in Bavaria.

### SEMI-POSTAL STAMPS

Regular Issue of 1914-
20 Surcharged in Black

**1919**   **Wmk. 95h**   *Perf. 14x14½*
**B1** A10 10pf + 5pf car rose   .35    1.50
  *a.*  Inverted surcharge       26.00    65.00
  *b.*  Surcharge on back        50.00
  *c.*  Imperf., pair           325.00

**B2** A10 15pf + 5pf ver        .35    1.50
  *a.*  Inverted surcharge       26.00    65.00
  *b.*  Imperf., pair           190.00
**B3** A10 20pf + 5pf blue       .35    1.90
  *a.*  Inverted surcharge       26.00    65.00
  *b.*  Imperf., pair           375.00
    *Nos. B1-B3 (3)*      1.05    4.90
  Surtax was for wounded war veterans.

### POSTAGE DUE STAMPS

D1                       D2

    With Silk Thread
**1862**   **Typeset**   **Unwmk.**   *Imperf.*
**J1** D1 3kr black           125.00   325.00
  *a.*  "Empfange"              375.00  1,000.

    Without Silk Thread
**1870**   **Typo.**   **Wmk. 93**   *Perf. 11½*
**J2** D1 1kr black            10.00   725.00
  *a.*  Wmk. 92                 45.00  1,650.
**J3** D1 3kr black            10.00   450.00
  *a.*  Wmk. 92                 45.00   875.00

Type of 1876 Regular Issue
Overprinted in Red
"Vom Empfänger zahlbar"

**1876**                         **Wmk. 94**
**J4** D2 3pf gray             14.00   350.00
**J5** D2 5pf gray             10.00    17.00
**J6** D2 10pf gray            3.25     1.25
    *Nos. J4-J6 (3)*     27.25   368.25

**1883**                         **Wmk. 95v**
**J7** D2 3pf gray             82.50    92.50
**J8** D2 5pf gray             55.00    60.00
**J9** D2 10pf gray            2.25      .55
  *a.*  "Empfanper"            140.00   140.00
  *b.*  "zahlhar"               72.50    72.50
  *c.*  Imperf.                 87.50
    *Nos. J7-J9 (3)*    139.75   153.05

**1895-1903**   **Wmk. 95h**   *Perf. 14½*
**J10** D2 2pf gray             .60     1.40
**J11** D2 3pf gray             .55     2.50
**J12** D2 5pf gray (′03)      1.00     1.75
**J13** D2 10pf gray (′03)      .60      .90
    *Nos. J10-J13 (4)*   2.75    6.55

**1888**
    **Rose-toned Paper**
*J10a* D2 2pf gray            1.90     4.50
*J11a* D2 3pf gray            2.50     2.25
  *b.*  Inverted overprint              2,200.
*J12a* D2 5pf gray            2.50     2.50
*J13a* D2 10pf gray           2.50     1.10
  *b.*  As "a," double overprint        2,200.
    *Nos. J10a-J13a (4)*  9.40   10.35

  No. J13b was used at Pirmasens.

Surcharged in Red in Each Corner
**1895**
**J14** D2 2pf on 3pf gray              44,000.
  At least six stamps exist, all used in Aichach.

### OFFICIAL STAMPS

  Nos. 77-81, 84, 95-96, 98-99, 102 perforated with a large E were issued for official use in 1912-16.

Regular Issue of 1888-
1900 Overprinted

**1908**   **Wmk. 95h**   *Perf. 14½*
**O1** A5 3pf dk brown (R)      .75     3.25
**O2** A5 5pf dk green (R)      .20      .20
**O3** A5 10pf carmine (G)      .20      .20
**O4** A5 20pf ultra (R)        .35      .50
**O5** A5 50pf maroon          3.25     6.00
    *Nos. O1-O5 (5)*    4.75   10.15

  Nos. O1-O5 were issued for the use of railway officials. "E" stands for "Eisenbahn."

Coat of
Arms — O1

**1916-17**   **Typo.**   *Perf. 11½*
**O6** O1 3pf bister brn        .20      .50
**O7** O1 5pf yellow orn        .20      .50
**O8** O1 7½pf grn, *grn*       .20      .40
**O9** O1 7½pf grn (′17)        .20      .35
**O10** O1 10pf deep rose       .20      .35
**O11** O1 15pf red, *buff*     .30      .40
**O12** O1 15pf red (′17)       .20      .50
**O13** O1 20pf dp bl, *bl*    1.25     1.90
**O14** O1 20pf dp blue (′17)   .20      .35
**O15** O1 25pf gray            .20      .40
**O16** O1 30pf orange          .20      .40
**O17** O1 60pf dark green      .20      .40
**O18** O1 1m dl vio, *gray*    .55     1.90
**O19** O1 1m maroon (′17)     1.90   450.00
    *Nos. O6-O19 (14)*   6.00  458.35

    Used Values
of Nos. O6-O69 are for postally used stamps. Canceled-to-order stamps, which abound, sell for same prices as unused.

Official Stamps
and Type of 1916-
17 Overprinted

**1918**
**O20** O1 3pf bister brn       .20    10.00
**O21** O1 5pf yellow green     .20     1.00
**O22** O1 7½pf gray green      .20    10.00
**O23** O1 10pf deep rose       .20     1.00
**O24** O1 15pf red             .20     1.00
**O25** O1 20pf blue            .20     1.00
**O26** O1 25pf gray            .20     1.00
**O27** O1 30pf orange          .20     1.00
**O28** O1 35pf orange          .20     1.00
**O29** O1 50pf olive gray      .20     1.25
**O30** O1 60pf dark green      .20    10.00
**O31** O1 75pf red brown       .35     2.75
**O32** O1 1m dl vio, *gray*    .75    10.00
**O33** O1 1m maroon           3.00   325.00
    *Nos. O20-O33 (14)*  6.30  376.00

O2                       O3

O4

**1920**   **Typo.**   *Perf. 14x14½*
**O34** O2 5pf yellow grn       .20     5.00
**O35** O2 10pf orange          .20     5.00
**O36** O2 15pf carmine         .20     5.00
**O37** O2 20pf violet          .20     5.00
**O38** O2 30pf dark blue       .20     6.50
**O39** O2 40pf bister          .20     6.50
     *Perf. 14½x14*
     **Wmk. 95v**
**O40** O3 50pf vermilion       .20    20.00
**O41** O3 60pf blue green      .20     8.50
**O42** O3 70pf dk violet       .20    22.50
  *a.*  Imperf., pair           26.00
**O43** O3 75pf deep rose       .20    29.00
**O44** O3 80pf dull blue       .20    29.00
**O45** O3 90pf olive green     .20    40.00
**O46** O4 1m dark brown        .20    35.00
  *a.*  Imperf., pair           72.50
**O47** O4 1¼m green            .20    50.00
**O48** O4 1½m vermilion        .20    52.50
  *a.*  Imperf., pair           25.00
**O49** O4 2½m deep blue        .20    60.00
  *a.*  Imperf., pair           72.50
**O50** O4 3m dark red          .20    72.50
  *a.*  Imperf., pair           20.00
**O51** O4 5m black            1.50    90.00
  *a.*  Imperf., pair           72.50
    *Nos. O34-O51 (18)*  4.90  542.00

Stamps of Preceding Issue Overprinted

**1920, Apr. 1**

| | | | | | |
|---|---|---|---|---|---|
| O52 | O2 | 5pf yellow green | | .20 | 2.75 |
| a. | | Imperf., pair | | 26.00 | |
| O53 | O2 | 10pf orange | | .20 | 1.50 |
| O54 | O2 | 15pf carmine | | .20 | 1.50 |
| O55 | O2 | 20pf violet | | .20 | 1.25 |
| O56 | O2 | 30pf dark blue | | .20 | 1.10 |
| O57 | O2 | 40pf bister | | .20 | 1.10 |
| O58 | O3 | 50pf vermilion | | .20 | 1.10 |
| a. | | Imperf., pair | | 26.00 | |
| O59 | O3 | 60pf blue green | | .20 | 1.10 |
| O60 | O3 | 70pf dark violet | | 1.50 | 2.25 |
| O61 | O3 | 75pf deep rose | | .35 | 1.10 |
| O62 | O3 | 80pf dull blue | | .20 | 1.10 |
| O63 | O3 | 90pf olive green | | 1.25 | 2.75 |

**Similar Ovpt., Words 8mm apart**

| | | | | | |
|---|---|---|---|---|---|
| O64 | O4 | 1m dark brown | | .20 | 1.10 |
| a. | | Imperf., pair | | 26.00 | |
| O65 | O4 | 1¼m green | | .20 | 1.10 |
| O66 | O4 | 1½m vermilion | | .20 | 1.10 |
| O67 | O4 | 2½m deep blue | | .20 | 1.10 |
| a. | | Imperf., pair | | 37.50 | |
| O68 | O4 | 3m dark red | | .20 | 1.10 |
| O69 | O4 | 5m black | | 8.00 | 25.00 |
| | | *Nos. O52-O69 (18)* | | 13.90 | 49.10 |

Nos. O52-O69 could be used in all parts of Germany, but were almost exclusively used in Bavaria.

---

# BERGEDORF

LOCATION — In northern Germany.
POP. — 2,989 (1861)

Originally Bergedorf belonged jointly to the Free City of Hamburg and the Free City of Lübeck. In 1867 it was purchased by Hamburg.

16 Schillings = 1 Mark

---

Values for unused stamps are for examples with original gum as defined in the catalogue introduction. Stamps without gum sell for about 40% of the figures quoted. Values for used stamps are for examples canceled with parallel bars. Stamps bearing dated town postmarks sell for more.

A1

A2

Combined Arms of Lübeck and Hamburg — A3

A4

A5

**1861-67    Unwmk.    Litho.    Imperf.**

| | | | | | |
|---|---|---|---|---|---|
| 1 | A1 | ½s blk, *pale bl* | | 37.50 | 575.00 |
| a. | | ½s black, *blue* ('67) | | 110.00 | 4,400. |
| 2 | A3 | 1s blk, *white* | | 37.50 | 300.00 |
| a. | | Tête bêche pair, vertical | | 225.00 | |
| b. | | Tête bêche pair, horiz. | | 300.00 | |
| 3 | A4 | 1½s blk, *yellow* | | 17.50 | 1,100. |
| a. | | Tête bêche pair | | 125.00 | |
| 4 | A2 | 3s blue, *pink* | | 22.50 | 1,450. |
| 5 | A5 | 4s blk, *brown* | | 22.50 | 1,825. |
| | | *Nos. 1-5 (5)* | | 137.50 | 5,250. |

Counterfeit cancellations are plentiful.
No. 3 exists in a tête bêche gutter pair. Value, unused $325.
The ½s on violet and 3s on rose, listed previously, as well as a 1s and 1½s on thick paper and 4s on light rose brown, come from proof sheets and were never placed in use. A 1½ "SCHILLINGE" (instead of SCHILLING) also exists only as a proof.

REPRINTS

---

½ SCHILLING
There is a dot in the upper part of the right branch of "N" of "EIN." The upper part of the shield is blank or almost blank. The horizontal bar of "H" in "HALBER" is generally defective.
1 SCHILLING
The "1" in the corners is generally with foot. The central horizontal bar of the "E" of "EIN" is separated from the vertical branch by a black line. The "A" of "POSTMARKE" has the horizontal bar incomplete or missing. The horizontal bar of the "H" of "SCHILLING" is separated from the vertical branches by a dark line at each side, sometimes the bar is missing.
1½ SCHILLINGE
There is a small triangle under the right side of the tower, exactly over the "R" of "POSTMARKE."
3 SCHILLINGE
The head of the eagle is not shaded. The horizontal bar of the second "E" of "BERGEDORF" is separated from the vertical branch by a thin line. There is generally a colored dot in the lower half of the "S" of "POSTMARKE."
4 SCHILLINGE
The upper part of the shield is blank or has two or three small dashes. In most of the reprints there is a diagonal dash across the wavy lines of the groundwork at the right of "I" and "E" of "VIER."
Reprints, value $1 each.

These stamps were superseded by those of the North German Confederation in 1868.

---

# BREMEN

LOCATION — In northwestern Germany
AREA — 99 sq. mi.
POP. — 122,402 (1871)

Bremen was a Free City and member of the German Confederation. In 1870 it became part of the German Empire.

22 Grote = 10 Silbergroschen

Values for unused stamps are for examples with original gum as defined in the catalogue introduction. Stamps without gum sell for about 50-60% of the figures quoted.

Coat of Arms — A1

THREE GROTE

I        II        III

Type I — The central part of the scroll below the word Bremen is crossed by one vertical line.
Type II — The center of the scroll is crossed by two vertical lines.
Type III — The center of the scroll is crossed by three vertical lines.

**1855    Unwmk.    Litho.    Imperf.**
**Horizontally Laid Paper**

| | | | | |
|---|---|---|---|---|
| 1 | A1 | 3gr black, *blue* | 175.00 | 275.00 |

**Vertically Laid Paper**

| | | | | |
|---|---|---|---|---|
| 1A | A1 | 3gr black, *blue* | 350.00 | 550.00 |

No. 1 can be found with parts of a papermaker's watermark, consisting of lilies. Value: unused $900; used $1,250.
See Nos. 9-10.

A2

A3

FIVE GROTE

Type I — The shading at the left of the ribbon containing "funf Grote" runs downward from the shield.
Type II — The shading at the left of the ribbon containing "funf Grote" runs upward.

---

**1856-60    Wove Paper**

| | | | | |
|---|---|---|---|---|
| 2 | A2 | 5gr blk, *rose* | 150.00 | 300.00 |
| a. | | Printed on both sides | | |
| b. | | "Marken" (not issued) | 11.00 | |
| 3 | A2 | 7gr blk, *yel* ('60) | 225.00 | 650.00 |
| 4 | A3 | 5sgr green ('59) | 275.00 | 300.00 |
| a. | | Chalky paper | 50.00 | 1,500. |
| b. | | 5sgr yellow green | 125.00 | 300.00 |

See Nos. 6, 8, 12-13, 15.

A4

A5

**1861-63    Serpentine Roulette**

| | | | | |
|---|---|---|---|---|
| 5 | A4 | 2gr orange ('63) | 275.00 | 1,800. |
| a. | | 2gr red orange | 700.00 | 3,000. |
| b. | | Chalky paper | 350.00 | 2,800. |
| 6 | A2 | 5gr blk, *rose* ('62) | 200.00 | 175.00 |
| a. | | Horiz. pair, imperf between | | — |
| 7 | A5 | 10gr black | 700.00 | 850.00 |
| 8 | A3 | 5sgr yellow green ('63) | 1,100. | 175.00 |
| a. | | Chalky paper | 600.00 | 425.00 |
| b. | | 5sgr green | 925.00 | 210.00 |

See Nos. 11, 14.

**1863**
**Horizontally (H) or Vertically (V) Laid Paper**

| | | | | |
|---|---|---|---|---|
| 9 | A1 | 3gr blk, *blue* (V) | 350.00 | 550.00 |
| a. | | 3gr black, *blue* (H) | 1,100. | 2,900. |

**1866-67    Perf. 13**

| | | | | |
|---|---|---|---|---|
| 10 | A1 | 3gr black, *blue* | 72.50 | 300.00 |

**Wove Paper**

| | | | | |
|---|---|---|---|---|
| 11 | A4 | 2gr orange | 62.50 | 225.00 |
| a. | | 2gr red orange | 275.00 | 500.00 |
| b. | | Horiz. pair, imperf. btwn. | 2,800. | |
| 12 | A2 | 5gr blk, *rose* | 110.00 | 275.00 |
| a. | | Horiz. pair, imperf. btwn. | 1,250. | |
| 13 | A2 | 7gr blk, *yel* ('67) | 125.00 | 4,000. |
| 14 | A5 | 10gr black ('67) | 175.00 | 1,000. |
| 15 | A3 | 5sgr green | 125.00 | 3,750. |
| a. | | 5sgr yellow green | 450.00 | 175.00 |
| b. | | As "a," chalky paper | 450.00 | 225.00 |

The stamps of Bremen were superseded by those of the North German Confederation on Jan. 1, 1868.

---

# BRUNSWICK

## BRUNSWICK

LOCATION — In northern Germany
GOVT. — Duchy
AREA — 1,417 sq. mi.
POP. — 349,367 (1880)
CAPITAL — Brunswick

Brunswick was a member of the German Confederation and, in 1870 became part of the German Empire.

12 Pfennigs = 1 Gutegroschen

30 Silbergroschen (Groschen) = 24 Gutegroschen = 1 Thaler

Values for unused stamps are for examples with original gum as defined in the catalogue introduction except for Nos. 1-3 which are valued without gum. Nos. 1-3 with original gum sell for much higher prices, and Nos. 4-26 without gum sell for about 50-60% of the figures quoted.

The "Leaping Saxon Horse" — A1

The ½gr has white denomination and "Gr" in right oval.

**1852    Unwmk.    Typo.    Imperf.**

| | | | | |
|---|---|---|---|---|
| 1 | A1 | 1sgr rose | 1,800. | 275.00 |
| 2 | A1 | 2sgr blue | 1,275. | 225.00 |
| a. | | Half used as 1sgr on cover | | — |
| 3 | A1 | 3sgr vermilion | 1,300. | 225.00 |

See Nos. 4-11, 13-22.

---

**1853-63    Wmk. 102**

| | | | | |
|---|---|---|---|---|
| 4 | A1 | ¼ggr blk, *brn* ('56) | 725.00 | 225.00 |
| 5 | A1 | ⅓sgr black ('56) | 125.00 | 290.00 |
| 6 | A1 | ½gr blk, *grn* ('63) | 21.00 | 210.00 |
| 7 | A1 | 1sgr blk, *orange* | 350.00 | 50.00 |
| a. | | 1sgr black, *orange buff* | | 57.50 |
| 8 | A1 | 1sgr blk, *yel* ('61) | 350.00 | 45.00 |
| a. | | Diagonal half used as ½sgr on cover | | 18,000. |
| 9 | A1 | 2sgr blk, *blue* | 290.00 | 50.00 |
| a. | | Diagonal half used as 1sgr on cover | | 8,750. |
| b. | | Vertical half used as 1sgr on cover | | 18,000. |
| 10 | A1 | 3sgr blk, *rose* | 450.00 | 72.50 |
| 11 | A1 | 3sgr rose ('62) | 550.00 | 190.00 |

A3

A4

**1857**

| | | | | |
|---|---|---|---|---|
| 12 | A3 | Four ¼ggr blk, *brn* ('57) | 37.50 | 90.00 |
| a. | | Four ¼gr blk, *yel brown* | — | 190.00 |

The bister on white paper was not issued. Value $6.

**1864    Serpentine Roulette 16**

| | | | | |
|---|---|---|---|---|
| 13 | A1 | ⅓sgr black | 450.00 | 2,100. |
| 14 | A1 | ½gr blk, *green* | 190.00 | 3,000. |
| 15 | A1 | 1sgr blk, *yellow* | 2,850. | 1,425. |
| 16 | A1 | 1sgr yellow | 375.00 | 125.00 |
| 17 | A1 | 2sgr blk, *blue* | 375.00 | 325.00 |
| a. | | Half used as 1sgr on cover | | 11,000. |
| 18 | A1 | 3sgr rose | 725.00 | 475.00 |

**Rouletted 12**

| | | | | |
|---|---|---|---|---|
| 20 | A1 | 1sgr blk, *yellow* | | 11,000. |
| 21 | A1 | 1sgr yellow | 600.00 | 325.00 |
| 22 | A1 | 3sgr rose | | 2,500. |

#13, 16, 18, 21-22 are on white paper. Faked roulettes of Nos. 13-22 exist.

**1865    Serpentine Roulette**
**Embossed    Unwmk.**

| | | | | |
|---|---|---|---|---|
| 23 | A4 | ⅓gr black | 25.00 | 325.00 |
| 24 | A4 | 1gr carmine | 2.25 | 45.00 |
| 25 | A4 | 2gr ultra | 8.25 | 110.00 |
| a. | | 2gr gray blue | 8.25 | 110.00 |
| c. | | Half used as 1sgr on cover | | 17,600. |
| 26 | A4 | 3gr brown | 6.50 | 125.00 |
| | | *Nos. 23-26 (4)* | 42.00 | 605.00 |

Faked cancellations of Nos. 5-26 exist.

**Imperf., Pair**

| | | | | |
|---|---|---|---|---|
| 23a | A4 | ½gr | | 90.00 |
| 24a | A4 | 1gr | | 27.50 |
| 25b | A4 | 2gr | | 77.50 |
| 26a | A4 | 3gr | | 90.00 |

Stamps of Brunswick were superseded by those of the North German Confederation on Jan. 1, 1868.

---

# HAMBURG

LOCATION — Northern Germany
GOVT. — Free City
AREA — 160 sq. mi.
POP. — 453,869 (1880)
CAPITAL — Hamburg

Hamburg was a member of the German Confederation and became part of the German Empire in 1870.

16 Schillings = 1 Mark

Values for unused stamps are for examples with original gum as defined in the catalogue introduction. Stamps without gum sell for about 50-60% of the figures quoted.

Value Numeral on Arms — A1

**1859    Typo.    Wmk. 128    Imperf.**

| | | | | |
|---|---|---|---|---|
| 1 | A1 | ½s black | 85.00 | 550.00 |
| 2 | A1 | 1s brown | 85.00 | 72.50 |
| 3 | A1 | 2s red | 85.00 | 92.50 |
| 4 | A1 | 3s blue | 85.00 | 110.00 |

| | | | | |
|---|---|---|---|---|
| 5 | A1 | 4s yellow green | 65.00 | 1,300. |
| a. | | 4s green | 110.00 | 1,150. |
| b. | | Double impression | | |
| 6 | A1 | 7s orange | 80.00 | 35.00 |
| 7 | A1 | 9s yellow | 175.00 | 1,700. |

See Nos. 13-21.

A2        A3

**1864**             **Litho.**

| | | | | |
|---|---|---|---|---|
| 9 | A2 | 1¼s gray | 77.50 | 72.50 |
| a. | | 1¼s lilac | 150.00 | 85.00 |
| b. | | 1¼s red lilac | 125.00 | 72.50 |
| c. | | 1¼s blue | 425.00 | 850.00 |
| d. | | 1¼s greenish gray | 110.00 | 92.50 |
| 12 | A3 | 2½s rose | 125.00 | 125.00 |

See Nos. 22-23.
*The 1¼s and 2½s have been reprinted on watermarked and unwatermarked paper.*

**1864-65**    **Typo.**    **Perf. 13½**

| | | | | |
|---|---|---|---|---|
| 13 | A1 | ½s black | 5.50 | 10.00 |
| a. | | Horiz. pair, imperf between | 65.00 | |
| 14 | A1 | 1s brown | 11.00 | 15.00 |
| a. | | Half used as ½s on cover | | 16,000. |
| b. | | Horiz. pair, imperf between | 450.00 | 650.00 |
| 15 | A1 | 2s red | 13.00 | 20.00 |
| 17 | A1 | 3s ultra | 32.50 | 30.00 |
| a. | | Imperf., pair | 140.00 | |
| b. | | Horiz. pair, imperf vert. | | |
| c. | | 3s blue | 42.50 | 29.00 |
| 18 | A1 | 4s green | 8.75 | 16.50 |
| 19 | A1 | 7s orange | 140.00 | 100.00 |
| 20 | A1 | 7s violet ('65) | 9.25 | 16.00 |
| a. | | Imperf., pair | 275.00 | |
| 21 | A1 | 9s yellow | 22.50 | 1,700. |
| a. | | Vert. pair, imperf. btwn. | 375.00 | |

**Litho.**

| | | | | |
|---|---|---|---|---|
| 22 | A2 | 1¼s lilac | 72.50 | 11.00 |
| a. | | 1¼s red lilac | 72.50 | 11.00 |
| b. | | 1¼s violet | 72.50 | 8.75 |
| 23 | A3 | 2½s yellow grn | 110.00 | 26.00 |
| a. | | 2½s blue green | 110.00 | 27.50 |

*The 1¼s has been reprinted on watermarked and unwatermarked paper; the 2½s on unwatermarked paper.*

A4        A5

*Rouletted 10*

**1866**    **Unwmk.**    **Embossed**

| | | | | |
|---|---|---|---|---|
| 24 | A4 | 1¼s violet | 37.50 | 32.50 |
| a. | | 1¼s red violet | 72.50 | 72.50 |
| 25 | A5 | 1½s rose | 7.25 | 125.00 |

*Reprints:*
*1¼s: The rosettes between the words of the inscription have a well-defined open circle in the center of the originals, while in the reprints this circle is filled up.*
*In the upper part of the top of the "g" of "Schilling", there is a thin vertical line which is missing in the reprints.*
*The two lower lines of the triangle in the upper left corner are of different thicknesses in the originals while in the reprints they are of equal thickness.*
*The labels at the right and left containing the inscriptions are 2¾mm in width in the originals while they are 2½mm in reprints.*
*1½s: The originals are printed on thinner paper than the reprints. This is easily seen by turning the stamps over, when on the originals the color and impression will clearly show through, which is not the case in the reprints.*
*The vertical stroke of the upper part of the "g" in Schilling is very short on the originals, scarcely crossing the top line, while in the reprints it almost touches the center of the "g".*
*The lower part of the "g" of Schilling in the originals, barely touches the inner line of the frame, in some stamps it does not touch it at all, while in the reprints the whole stroke runs into the inner line of the frame.*

A6

**1867**    **Typo.**    **Wmk. 128**    **Perf. 13½**

| | | | | |
|---|---|---|---|---|
| 26 | A6 | 2½s dull green | 10.00 | 65.00 |
| a. | | 2½s dark green | 52.50 | 80.00 |
| b. | | Imperf., pair | 225.00 | |
| c. | | Horiz. pair, imperf between | 80.00 | |

Forged cancellations exist on almost all stamps of Hamburg, especially on Nos. 4, 7, 21 and 25.
Nos. 1-23 and 26 exist without watermark, but they come from the same sheets as the watermarked stamps.
The stamps of Hamburg were superseded by those of the North German Confederation on Jan. 1, 1868.

---

# HANOVER

LOCATION — Northern Germany
GOVT. — Kingdom
AREA — 14,893 sq. mi.
POP. — 3,191,000
CAPITAL — Hanover

Hanover was a member of the German Confederation and became in 1866 a province of Prussia.

10 Pfennigs = 1 Groschen
24 Gute Groschen = 1 Thaler
30 Silbergroschen = 1 Thaler (1858)

Values for unused stamps are for examples with original gum as defined in the catalogue introduction. Stamps without gum sell for about 50-60% of the figures quoted.

Coat of Arms
A1        A2

**Wmk. Square Frame**

**1850**    **Rose Gum**    **Typo.**    **Imperf.**

| | | | | |
|---|---|---|---|---|
| 1 | A1 | 1g g blk, *gray bl* | 3,400. | 40.00 |

See Nos. 2, 11.
*The reprints have white gum and no watermark.*

**1851-55**          **Wmk. 130**

| | | | | |
|---|---|---|---|---|
| 2 | A1 | 1g g blk, *gray grn* | 80.00 | 5.25 |
| a. | | 1g g black, *yellow green* | 775.00 | 26.00 |
| 3 | A2 | ¹⁄₁₀th blk, *salmon* | 100.00 | 42.50 |
| a. | | ¹⁄₁₀th black, *crimson* ('55) | 100.00 | 42.50 |
| b. | | Bisect on cover | | |
| 5 | A2 | ¹⁄₁₅th blk, *gray bl* | 150.00 | 65.00 |
| a. | | Bisect on cover | | |
| 6 | A2 | ¹⁄₁₀th blk, *yellow* | 190.00 | 55.00 |
| a. | | ¹⁄₁₀th black, *orange* | 190.00 | 50.00 |
| | | Nos. 2-6 (4) | 520.00 | 167.75 |

Bisects Nos. 3b, 5a, 12a and 13a were used for ½g.
See Nos. 8, 12-13.
*The ¹⁄₁₀th has been reprinted on unwatermarked paper, with white gum.*

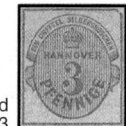

Crown and
Numeral — A3

**1853**          **Wmk. 130**

| | | | | |
|---|---|---|---|---|
| 7 | A3 | 3pf rose | 400.00 | 250.00 |

See Nos. 9, 16-17, 25.
*The reprints of No. 7 have white gum.*

**Fine Network in Second Color**

**1855**          **Unwmk.**

| | | | | |
|---|---|---|---|---|
| 8 | A2 | ¹⁄₁₀th black & org | 190.00 | 125.00 |
| a. | | ¹⁄₁₀th black & yellow | 325.00 | 190.00 |

No. 8 with olive yellow network and other values with fine network are essays.

**Large Network in Second Color**

**1856-57**

| | | | | |
|---|---|---|---|---|
| 9 | A3 | 3pf rose & blk | 250.00 | 225.00 |
| a. | | 3pf rose & gray | 325.00 | 300.00 |
| 11 | A1 | 1g g black & grn | 65.00 | 6.50 |
| 12 | A2 | ¹⁄₁₀th black & rose | 125.00 | 26.00 |
| a. | | Bisect on cover | | 13,500. |

| | | | | |
|---|---|---|---|---|
| 13 | A2 | ¹⁄₁₅th black & blue | 100.00 | 60.00 |
| a. | | Bisect on cover | | 6,500. |
| 14 | A2 | ¹⁄₁₀th blk & org ('57) | 650.00 | 45.00 |

*The reprints have white gum, and the network does not cover all the outer margin.*

**Without Network**

**1859-63**

| | | | | |
|---|---|---|---|---|
| 16 | A3 | 3pf pink | 110.00 | 82.50 |
| a. | | 3pf carmine rose | 65.00 | 72.50 |
| 17 | A3 | 3pf grn (Drei Zehntel) ('63) | 325.00 | 775.00 |

Examples of No. 25 with rouletting trimmed off sometimes pretend to be No. 17. Minimum size of No. 17 acknowledged as genuine: 21½x24½mm.
*The reprints of No. 16 have pink gum instead of red; the extremities of the banderol point downward instead of outward.*

Crown and     King George
Post          V — A8
Horn — A7

**1859-61**          **Imperf.**

| | | | | |
|---|---|---|---|---|
| 18 | A7 | ½g black ('60) | 140.00 | 160.00 |
| a. | | Rose gum | 325.00 | 275.00 |
| 19 | A8 | 1g rose | 3.00 | 2.00 |
| a. | | 1g vio rose | 16.50 | 16.50 |
| b. | | 1g carmine | 65.00 | 26.00 |
| c. | | Half used as ½g on cover | | 10,000. |
| 20 | A8 | 2g ultra | 16.00 | 26.00 |
| a. | | Half used as 1g on cover | | 7,000. |
| 22 | A8 | 3g yellow | 200.00 | 50.00 |
| a. | | 3g orange yellow | 110.00 | 77.50 |
| 23 | A8 | 3g brown ('61) | 22.50 | 40.00 |
| a. | | One third used as 1g on cover | | — |
| 24 | A8 | 10g green ('61) | 200.00 | 725.00 |

*Reprints of ½g are on thick toned paper with yellowish gum. Originals are on white paper with rose or white gum. Reprints exist tête bêche.*
*Reprints of 3g yellow and 3g brown have white or pinkish gum. Originals have rose or orange gum.*

**1864**    **White Gum**    **Perce en Arc 16**

| | | | | |
|---|---|---|---|---|
| 25 | A3 | 3pf grn (Drei Zehntel) | 26.00 | 50.00 |
| 26 | A7 | ½g black | 225.00 | 225.00 |
| 27 | A8 | 1g rose | 6.50 | 2.50 |
| 28 | A8 | 2g ultra | 100.00 | 175.00 |
| a. | | Half used as 1g on cover | | — |
| 29 | A8 | 3g brown | 60.00 | 60.00 |
| | | Nos. 25-29 (5) | 417.50 | 512.50 |

*Reprints of 3g are percé en arc 13½.*

**Rose Gum**

| | | | | |
|---|---|---|---|---|
| 25a | A3 | 3pf green | 65.00 | 65.00 |
| 26a | A7 | ½g black | 400.00 | 375.00 |
| 27a | A8 | 1g rose | 32.50 | 20.00 |
| 29a | A8 | 3g brown | 975.00 | 975.00 |

The stamps of Prussia superseded those of Hanover on Oct. 1, 1866.

---

# LUBECK

LOCATION — Situated on an arm of the Baltic Sea between the former German States of Holstein and Mecklenburg.
GOVT. — Free City and State
AREA — 115 sq. mi.
POP. — 136,413
CAPITAL — Lubeck

Lubeck was a member of the German Confederation and became part of the German Empire in 1870.

16 Schillings = 1 Mark

Values for Nos. 1-7 unused are for stamps without gum. Stamps with gum sell for about twice the figures quoted. Values for Nos. 8-14 unused are for examples with original gum as defined in the catalogue introduction. Nos. 8-14 without gum sell for about 50-60% of the figures quoted.

Coat of Arms — A1

**1859**    **Litho.**    **Wmk. 148**    **Imperf.**

| | | | | |
|---|---|---|---|---|
| 1 | A1 | ½g gray lilac | 400.00 | 1,700. |
| 2 | A1 | 1s orange | 400.00 | 1,700. |
| 3 | A1 | 2s brown | 17.00 | 200.00 |
| a. | | Value in words reads "ZWEI EIN HALB" | 325.00 | 6,000. |
| 4 | A1 | 2½s rose | 35.00 | 750.00 |
| 5 | A1 | 4s green | 16.00 | 500.00 |

**1862**          **Unwmk.**

| | | | | |
|---|---|---|---|---|
| 6 | A1 | ½s lilac | 12.00 | 1,300. |
| 7 | A1 | 1s yellow orange | 21.00 | 1,300. |

*The reprints of the 1859-62 issues are unwatermarked and printed in bright colors.*

A2        A3

**1863**        **Rouletted 11½**
**Eagle embossed**

| | | | | |
|---|---|---|---|---|
| 8 | A2 | ½s green | 32.50 | 52.50 |
| 9 | A2 | 1s orange | 100.00 | 125.00 |
| a. | | Rouletted 10 | 160.00 | 400.00 |
| 10 | A2 | 2s rose | 20.00 | 45.00 |
| 11 | A2 | 2½s ultra | 90.00 | 325.00 |
| 12 | A2 | 4s bister | 40.00 | 85.00 |
| | | Nos. 8-12 (5) | 282.50 | 632.50 |

*The reprints are imperforate and without embossing.*

**1864**    **Litho.**    **Imperf.**

| | | | | |
|---|---|---|---|---|
| 13 | A3 | 1¼s dark brown | 32.50 | 72.50 |
| a. | | 1¼s reddish brown | 21.00 | 125.00 |

A4

**1865**        **Rouletted 11½**
**Eagle embossed**

| | | | | |
|---|---|---|---|---|
| 14 | A4 | 1½s red lilac | 21.00 | 65.00 |

*The reprints are imperforate and without embossing.*
Counterfeit cancellations are found on #1-14.
The stamps of Lübeck were superseded by those of the North German Confederation on Jan. 1, 1868.

---

# MECKLENBURG-SCHWERIN

LOCATION — In northern Germany, bordering on the Baltic Sea.
GOVT. — Grand Duchy
AREA — 5,065 sq. mi. (approx.)
POP. — 674,000 (approx.)
CAPITAL — Schwerin

Mecklenburg-Schwerin was a member of the German Confederation and became part of the German Empire in 1870.

48 Schillings = 1 Thaler

Values for unused stamps are for examples with original gum as defined in the catalogue introduction. Stamps without gum sell for about 70% of the figures quoted.

Coat of Arms
A1                    A2

| 1856 | | Unwmk. | Typo. | Imperf. |
|---|---|---|---|---|
| 1 | A1 | Four ¼s red | 125.00 | 100.00 |
| a. | | ¼s red | 12.50 | 10.00 |
| 2 | A2 | 3s orange yellow | 82.50 | 45.00 |
| 3 | A2 | 5s blue | 190.00 | 225.00 |
| | | Nos. 1-3 (3) | 397.50 | 370.00 |

See Nos. 4, 6-8.

A3

| 1864-67 | | | Rouletted 11½ | |
|---|---|---|---|---|
| 4 | A1 | Four ¼s red | 2,250. | 1,500. |
| a. | | ¼s red | 140.00 | 200.00 |
| 5 | A3 | Four ¼s red | 52.50 | 42.50 |
| a. | | ¼s red | 6.75 | 6.75 |
| 6 | A2 | 2s gray lil ('67) | 125.00 | 1,350. |
| a. | | 2s red violet ('66) | 200.00 | 200.00 |
| 7 | A2 | 3s org yel, wide margin ('67) | 35.00 | 250.00 |
| a. | | Narrow margin ('65) | 140.00 | 100.00 |
| 8 | A2 | 5s bister brn | 125.00 | 200.00 |
| a. | | Thick paper | 190.00 | 275.00 |

The overall size of #7, including margin, is 24½x24½mm. That of #7a is 23½x23mm.
Counterfeit cancellations exist on those stamps valued higher used than unused.
These stamps were superseded by those of the North German Confederation on Jan. 1, 1868.

## MECKLENBURG-STRELITZ

LOCATION — In northern Germany, divided by Mecklenburg-Schwerin.
GOVT. — Grand Duchy
AREA — 1,131 sq. mi.
POP. — 106,347
CAPITAL — Neustrelitz

Mecklenburg-Strelitz was a member of the German Confederation and became part of the German Empire in 1870.

30 Silbergroschen = 48 Schillings = 1 Thaler

Values for unused stamps are for examples with original gum as defined in the catalogue introduction. Stamps without gum sell for about 50% of the figures quoted.

Coat of Arms
A1                    A2
Rouletted 11½

| 1864 | | Unwmk. | | Embossed |
|---|---|---|---|---|
| 1 | A1 | ¼sg orange | 150.00 | 2,000. |
| a. | | ¼sg yellow orange | 275.00 | 3,400. |
| 2 | A1 | ⅓sg green | 67.50 | 1,150. |
| a. | | ⅓sg dark green | 125.00 | 2,000. |
| 3 | A1 | 1sch violet | 225.00 | 2,700. |
| 4 | A2 | 1sg rose | 125.00 | 160.00 |
| 5 | A2 | 2sg ultra | 35.00 | 675.00 |
| 6 | A2 | 3sg bister | 27.50 | 1,100. |

Counterfeit cancellations abound.
These stamps were superseded by those of the North German Confederation in 1868.

## OLDENBURG

LOCATION — In northwestern Germany, bordering on the North Sea.
GOVT. — Grand Duchy
AREA — 2,482 sq. mi.

POP. — 483,042 (1910)
CAPITAL — Oldenburg

Oldenburg was a member of the German Confederation and became part of the German Empire in 1870.

30 Silbergroschen = 1 Thaler
30 Groschen = 1 Thaler

Values for unused stamps are for examples with original gum as defined in the catalogue introduction. Stamps without gum sell for about 50% of the figures quoted.

A1                    A2

| 1852-55 | | Unwmk. | Litho. | Imperf. |
|---|---|---|---|---|
| 1 | A1 | ⅟30th blk, blue | 325.00 | 26.00 |
| 2 | A1 | ⅟15th blk, rose | 525.00 | 30.00 |
| 3 | A1 | ⅟10th blk, yellow | 750.00 | 82.50 |
| 4 | A2 | ⅓sgr blk, grn ('55) | 1,100. | 900.00 |

There are three types of Nos. 1 and 2.

A3                    A4

| 1859 | | | | |
|---|---|---|---|---|
| 5 | A3 | ½g blk, green | 2,200. | 2,650. |
| 6 | A3 | 1g blk, blue | 600.00 | 35.00 |
| 7 | A3 | 2g blk, rose | 800.00 | 500.00 |
| 8 | A3 | 3g blk, yellow | 800.00 | 500.00 |
| a. | | "OLBENBURG" | 1,200. | 1,000. |

See Nos. 10, 13-15.

| 1861 | | | | |
|---|---|---|---|---|
| 9 | A4 | ¼g orange | 250.00 | 3,300. |
| 10 | A3 | ⅓g green | 375.00 | 700.00 |
| a. | | ⅓g bluish green | 375.00 | 700.00 |
| b. | | ⅓g moss green | 1,400. | 2,300. |
| c. | | "OLDEIBURG" | 600.00 | 1,000. |
| d. | | "Dritto" | 600.00 | 1,000. |
| e. | | "Drittd" | 600.00 | 1,000. |
| f. | | Printed on both sides | | 5,000. |
| 12 | A4 | ½g redsh brn | 350.00 | 400.00 |
| a. | | ½g dark brown | 350.00 | 400.00 |
| 13 | A3 | 1g blue | 175.00 | 125.00 |
| a. | | 1g gray blue | 375.00 | 200.00 |
| b. | | Printed on both sides | | 3,750. |
| 14 | A3 | 2g red | 350.00 | 350.00 |
| 15 | A3 | 3g yellow | 350.00 | 325.00 |
| a. | | "OLDEIBURG" | 600.00 | 600.00 |
| b. | | Printed on both sides | | 5,000. |

Forged cancellations are found on Nos. 9, 10, 12 and their minor varieties.

Coat of Arms — A5

| 1862 | | Embossed | Rouletted 11½ | |
|---|---|---|---|---|
| 16 | A5 | ⅓g green | 150.00 | 150.00 |
| 17 | A5 | ½g orange | 150.00 | 80.00 |
| a. | | ½g orange red | 190.00 | 110.00 |
| 18 | A5 | 1g rose | 92.50 | 11.50 |
| 19 | A5 | 2g ultra | 150.00 | 37.50 |
| 20 | A5 | 3g bister | 175.00 | 40.00 |

| 1867 | | | Rouletted 10 | |
|---|---|---|---|---|
| 21 | A5 | ⅓g green | 19.00 | 450.00 |
| 22 | A5 | ½g orange | 19.00 | 300.00 |
| 23 | A5 | 1g rose | 8.00 | 37.50 |
| a. | | Half used as ½g on cover | | — |
| 24 | A5 | 2g ultra | 8.00 | 325.00 |
| 25 | A5 | 3g bister | 20.00 | 250.00 |
| | | Nos. 21-25 (5) | 74.00 | 1,362. |

Forged cancellations are found on #21-25.
The stamps of Oldenburg were replaced by those of the North German Confederation on Jan. 1, 1868.

## PRUSSIA

LOCATION — The greater part of northern Germany.
GOVT. — Independent Kingdom
AREA — 134,650 sq. mi.
POP. — 40,165,219 (1910)
CAPITAL — Berlin

Prussia was a member of the German Confederation and became part of the German Empire in 1870.

12 Pfennigs = 1 Silbergroschen
60 Kreuzer = 1 Gulden (1867)

Values for unused stamps are for examples with original gum as defined in the catalogue introduction. Stamps without gum sell for about 50% of the figures quoted.

King Frederick William IV
A1                    A2

| 1850-56 | | Engr. Wmk. 162 Imperf. | | |
|---|---|---|---|---|
| | | **Background of Crossed Lines** | | |
| 1 | A1 | 4pf yel grn ('56) | 100.00 | 65.00 |
| a. | | 4pf dark green | 150.00 | 110.00 |
| 2 | A1 | 6pf (½sg) red org | 80.00 | 45.00 |
| 3 | A2 | 1sg black, rose | 75.00 | 8.00 |
| a. | | 1sg black, bright red | 18,750. | 400.00 |
| 4 | A2 | 2sg black, blue | 100.00 | 14.50 |
| a. | | Half used as 1sg on cover | | — |
| 5 | A2 | 3sg black, yellow | 100.00 | 12.50 |
| a. | | 3sg black, orange buff | 300.00 | 30.00 |
| | | Nos. 1-5 (5) | 455.00 | 145.00 |

See Nos. 10-13.
Reprints exist on watermarked and unwatermarked paper.

A3                    A4

Solid Background

| 1857 | | Typo. | | Unwmk. |
|---|---|---|---|---|
| 6 | A3 | 1sg rose | 290.00 | 32.50 |
| a. | | 1sg carmine rose | 325.00 | 45.00 |
| 7 | A3 | 2sg blue | 1,175. | 80.00 |
| a. | | 2sg dark blue | 1,600. | 110.00 |
| b. | | Half used as 1sg on cover | | — |
| 8 | A3 | 3sg orange | 140.00 | 37.50 |
| a. | | 3sg yellow | 1,450. | 87.50 |
| b. | | 3sg deep orange | 725.00 | 110.00 |
| | | Nos. 6-8 (3) | 1,605. | 150.00 |

The reprints of Nos. 6-8 inclusive have a period instead of a colon after "SILBERGR."

Background of Crossed Lines

| 1858-60 | | | | Typo. |
|---|---|---|---|---|
| 9 | A4 | 4pf green | 65.00 | 32.50 |
| | | **Engr.** | | |
| 10 | A1 | 6pf (½sg) org ('59) | 175.00 | 140.00 |
| a. | | 6pf (½sg) brick red | 260.00 | 180.00 |
| | | **Typo.** | | |
| 11 | A2 | 1sg rose | 30.00 | 2.50 |
| 12 | A2 | 2sg blue | 100.00 | 16.00 |
| a. | | 2sg dark blue | 140.00 | 37.50 |
| b. | | Half used as 1sg on cover | | — |
| 13 | A2 | 3sg orange | 87.50 | 13.00 |
| a. | | 3sg yellow | 125.00 | 16.00 |
| | | Nos. 9-13 (5) | 457.50 | 204.00 |

Coat of Arms
A6                    A7

| 1861-65 | | Embossed | Rouletted 11½ | |
|---|---|---|---|---|
| 14 | A6 | 3pf red lilac ('67) | 25.00 | 40.00 |
| a. | | 3pf red violet ('65) | 300.00 | 250.00 |
| 15 | A6 | 4pf yellow green | 9.50 | 9.50 |
| a. | | 4pf green | 37.50 | 50.00 |

| 16 | A6 | 6pf orange | 11.00 | 13.00 |
|---|---|---|---|---|
| a. | | 6pf vermilion | 110.00 | 60.00 |
| 17 | A7 | 1sg rose | 3.00 | .75 |
| 18 | A7 | 2sg ultra | 11.00 | 1.40 |
| a. | | 2sg blue | 375.00 | 27.50 |
| 20 | A7 | 3sg bister | 8.00 | 1.75 |
| a. | | 3sg gray brown ('65) | | 27.50 |
| | | Nos. 14-20 (6) | 67.50 | 66.40 |

A8                    A9

**Typographed in Reverse on Paper Resembling Goldbeater's Skin**

| 1866 | | | Rouletted 10 | |
|---|---|---|---|---|
| 21 | A8 | 10sg rose | 87.50 | 95.00 |
| 22 | A9 | 30sg blue | 100.00 | 200.00 |

Perfect examples of #21-22 are extremely rare.

A10

| 1867 | | Embossed | Rouletted 16 | |
|---|---|---|---|---|
| 23 | A10 | 1kr green | 22.50 | 40.00 |
| 24 | A10 | 2kr orange | 37.50 | 87.50 |
| 25 | A10 | 3kr rose | 18.50 | 25.00 |
| 26 | A10 | 6kr ultra | 18.50 | 40.00 |
| 27 | A10 | 9kr bister brown | 25.00 | 45.00 |
| | | Nos. 23-27 (5) | 122.00 | 237.50 |

Imperforate stamps of the above sets are proofs.
The stamps of Prussia were superseded by those of the North German Confederation on Jan. 1, 1868.

OFFICIAL STAMPS
See Germany Nos. OL1-OL15.

## SAXONY

LOCATION — In central Germany
GOVT. — Kingdom
AREA — 5,787 sq. mi.
POP. — 2,500,000 (approx.)
CAPITAL — Dresden

Saxony was a member of the German Confederation and became a part of the German Empire in 1870.

10 Pfennigs = 1 Neu-Groschen
30 Neu-Groschen = 1 Thaler

Values for unused stamps are for examples with original gum as defined in the catalogue introduction. Stamps without gum sell for about 50-60% of the figures quoted.

A1

| 1850 | | Unwmk. | Typo. | Imperf. |
|---|---|---|---|---|
| 1 | A1 | 3pf brick red | 5,800. | 5,250. |
| a. | | 3pf cherry red | 8,750. | 13,250. |
| b. | | 3pf brown red | 8,750. | 9,500. |

Coat of          Frederick
Arms — A2        Augustus
                 II — A3

| 1851 | | | | |
|---|---|---|---|---|
| 2 | A2 | 3pf green | 100.00 | 87.50 |
| a. | | 3pf yellow green | 1,350. | 600.00 |

Nos. 2 and 2a are valued with the margin just touching the design in one or two places.

Stamps with margins all around sell considerably higher.

**1851-52**            **Engr.**

| | | | | |
|---|---|---|---|---|
| 3 | A3 | ½ng black, *gray* | 65.00 | 11.00 |
| *a.* | | *½ng pale blue (error)* | *19,000.* | |
| 5 | A3 | 1ng black, *rose* | 87.50 | 8.75 |
| 6 | A3 | 2ng black, *pale bl* | 240.00 | 50.00 |
| 7 | A3 | 2ng blk, *dk bl('52)* | 650.00 | 45.00 |
| 8 | A3 | 3ng black, *yellow* | 150.00 | 18.50 |
| | | *Nos. 3-8 (5)* | 1,192. | 133.25 |

King John I — A4

**1855-60**

| | | | | |
|---|---|---|---|---|
| 9 | A4 | ½ng black, *gray* | 8.75 | 2.25 |
| *a.* | | *"1½" at left or right* | — | — |
| 10 | A4 | 1ng black, *rose* | 8.75 | 2.25 |
| 11 | A4 | 2ng black, *dark blue* | 17.50 | 11.00 |
| *a.* | | *2ng black, blue* | *65.00* | *30.00* |
| 12 | A4 | 3ng black, *yellow* | 19.00 | 7.25 |
| 13 | A4 | 5ng ver ('56) | 80.00 | 50.00 |
| *a.* | | *5ng orange brown ('60)* | *225.00* | *300.00* |
| *b.* | | *5ng deep brown ('57)* | *650.00* | *175.00* |
| 14 | A4 | 10ng blue ('56) | 200.00 | 200.00 |

The ½ng is found in 3 types, the 1ng in 2. In 1861 the 5ng and 10ng were printed on hard, brittle, translucent paper.

A5            A6

**Typo.; Arms Embossed**

**1863**            **Perf. 13**

| | | | | |
|---|---|---|---|---|
| 15 | A5 | 3pf blue green | 1.60 | 37.50 |
| *a.* | | *3pf yellow green* | *55.00* | *72.50* |
| 16 | A5 | ½ng orange | .90 | 1.75 |
| *a.* | | *½ng red orange* | *22.50* | *4.50* |
| 17 | A6 | 1ng rose | 1.00 | 2.00 |
| *a.* | | *Vert. pair, imperf. between* | *225.00* | |
| *b.* | | *Horiz. pair, imperf. between* | *375.00* | |
| 18 | A6 | 2ng blue | 2.25 | 5.00 |
| *a.* | | *2ng dark blue* | *11.00* | *25.00* |
| 19 | A6 | 3ng red brown | 2.50 | 8.75 |
| *a.* | | *3ng bister brown* | *22.50* | *7.25* |
| 20 | A6 | 5ng dull violet | 30.00 | 45.00 |
| *a.* | | *5ng gray violet* | *10.00* | *450.00* |
| *b.* | | *5ng gray blue* | *30.00* | *72.50* |
| *c.* | | *5ng slate* | *22.50* | *250.00* |

The stamps of Saxony were superseded on Jan. 1, 1868, by those of the North German Confederation.

---

# SCHLESWIG-HOLSTEIN

LOCATION — In northern Germany.
GOVT. — Duchies
AREA — 7,338 sq. mi.
POP. — 1,519,000 (approx.)
CAPITAL — Schleswig

Schleswig-Holstein was an autonomous territory from 1848 to 1851 when it came under Danish rule. In 1864, it was occupied by Prussia and Austria, and in 1866 it became a province of Prussia.

16 Schillings = 1 Mark

Values for unused stamps are for examples with original gum as defined in the catalogue introduction. Stamps without gum sell for about 50% of the figures quoted.

Coat of Arms — A1

**Typographed; Arms Embossed**

**1850**    **Unwmk.**    **Imperf.**
**With Silk Threads**

| | | | | |
|---|---|---|---|---|
| 1 | A1 | 1s dl bl & grnsh bl | 300.00 | 5,250. |
| *a.* | | *1s Prussian blue* | *675.00* | |
| 2 | A1 | 2s rose & pink | 525.00 | 6,650. |
| *a.* | | *2s deep rose & rose* | *675.00* | |
| *b.* | | *Double embossing* | *2,900.* | |

Forged cancellations are found on Nos. 1-2, 5-7, 9, 16 and 19.

A2            A3

**1865**   **Typo.**   **Rouletted 11½**

| | | | | |
|---|---|---|---|---|
| 3 | A2 | ½s rose | 32.50 | 40.00 |
| 4 | A2 | 1¼s green | 16.00 | 19.00 |
| 5 | A3 | 1⅓s red lilac | 40.00 | 110.00 |
| 6 | A2 | 2s ultra | 45.00 | 210.00 |
| 7 | A3 | 4s bister | 60.00 | 1,200. |
| | | *Nos. 3-7 (5)* | 193.50 | 1,579. |

**Schleswig**

A4            A5

**1864**   **Typo.**   **Rouletted 11½**

| | | | | |
|---|---|---|---|---|
| 8 | A4 | 1¼s green | 40.00 | 18.50 |
| 9 | A4 | 4s carmine | 87.50 | 450.00 |

**1865**          **Rouletted 10, 11½**

| | | | | |
|---|---|---|---|---|
| 10 | A4 | ½s green | 30.00 | 50.00 |
| 11 | A4 | 1¼s red lilac | 50.00 | 22.50 |
| *a.* | | *1¼s gray lilac ('67)* | *225.00* | *67.50* |
| *b.* | | *Half of #11a used as ½s on cover* | | *30,000.* |
| 12 | A5 | 1⅓s rose | 27.50 | 60.00 |
| 13 | A4 | 2s ultra | 27.50 | 60.00 |
| 14 | A4 | 4s bister | 30.00 | 75.00 |
| | | *Nos. 10-14 (5)* | 165.00 | 267.50 |

**Holstein**

A6            A7

Type I — Small lettering in frame. Wavy lines in spandrels close together.
Type II — Small lettering in frame. Wavy lines wider apart.
Type III — Larger lettering in frame and no periods after "H R Z G." Wavy lines as II.

**1864**   **Litho.**   **Imperf.**

| | | | | |
|---|---|---|---|---|
| 15 | A6 | 1¼s bl & gray, I | 47.50 | 50.00 |
| *a.* | | *Half used as ½s on cover* | | *9,250.* |
| 16 | A6 | 1¼s bl & gray, II | 725.00 | 3,000. |
| *a.* | | *Half used as ½s on cover* | | *23,000.* |
| 17 | A6 | 1¼s bl & gray, III | 45.00 | 55.00 |
| *a.* | | *Half used as ½s on cover* | | *7,750.* |

**1864**   **Typo.**   **Rouletted 8**

| | | | | |
|---|---|---|---|---|
| 18 | A7 | 1¼s blue & rose | 37.50 | 18.50 |
| *a.* | | *Half used as ½s on cover* | | *1,900.* |

A8

**1865**          **Rouletted 8**

| | | | | |
|---|---|---|---|---|
| 19 | A8 | ½s green | 60.00 | 87.50 |
| 20 | A8 | 1¼s red lilac | 45.00 | 22.50 |
| 21 | A8 | 2s blue | 47.50 | 45.00 |
| | | *Nos. 19-21 (3)* | 152.50 | 155.00 |

A9            A10

**1865-66**      **Rouletted 7 and 8**

| | | | | |
|---|---|---|---|---|
| 22 | A9 | 1¼s red lilac ('66) | 65.00 | 22.50 |
| *a.* | | *Half used as ½s on cover* | | *23,000.* |
| 23 | A10 | 1⅓s carmine | 55.00 | 40.00 |
| 24 | A9 | 2s blue ('66) | 125.00 | 140.00 |
| 25 | A10 | 4s bister | 50.00 | 72.50 |
| | | *Nos. 22-25 (4)* | 295.00 | 275.00 |

These stamps were superseded by those of North German Confederation on Jan. 1, 1868.

---

# THURN AND TAXIS

A princely house which, prior to the formation of the German Empire, enjoyed the privilege of a postal monopoly. These stamps were superseded on July 1, 1867, by those of Prussia, followed by those of the North German Postal District on Jan. 1, 1868, and later by stamps of the German Empire on Jan. 1, 1872.

Values are for stamps with four complete margins just clear of the framelines. Stamps with margins just touching the framelines on one or two sides are worth approximately 60% of the values quoted. Stamps with four large margins are rare and command premiums of up to 500% over the values quoted.

Values for unused stamps are for examples with original gum as defined in the catalogue introduction. Stamps without gum sell for about 50% of the figures quoted.

## NORTHERN DISTRICT
30 Silbergroschen or Groschen = 1 Thaler

A1            A2

**1852-58**  **Unwmk.**  **Typo.**  **Imperf.**

| | | | | |
|---|---|---|---|---|
| 1 | A1 | ¼sgr blk, *red brn('54)* | 275.00 | 67.50 |
| 2 | A1 | ⅓sgr blk, *buff('58)* | 125.00 | 275.00 |
| 3 | A1 | ½sgr blk, *green* | 750.00 | 42.50 |
| 4 | A1 | 1sgr blk, *dk bl* | 1,375. | 160.00 |
| 5 | A1 | 1sgr blk, *lt bl('53)* | 825.00 | 35.00 |
| 6 | A1 | 2sgr blk, *rose* | 875.00 | 37.50 |
| *a* | | *Half used as 1sgr on cover* | | *6,000.* |
| 7 | A1 | 3sgr blk, *brownish yellow* | 1,000. | 32.50 |
| *a.* | | *3sgr blk, pale orange yellow* | *875.00* | *50.00* |

Reprints of Nos. 1-12, 15-20, 23-24, were made in 1910. They have "ND" in script on the back. Value, $6 each.

**1859-60**

| | | | | |
|---|---|---|---|---|
| 8 | A1 | ¼sgr red ('60) | 72.50 | 82.50 |
| 9 | A1 | ½gr green | 300.00 | 125.00 |
| 10 | A1 | 1sgr blue | 300.00 | 57.50 |
| 11 | A1 | 2sgr rose ('60) | 160.00 | 110.00 |
| 12 | A1 | 3sgr red brn ('60) | 160.00 | 140.00 |
| 13 | A2 | 5sgr lilac | 1.90 | 400.00 |
| 14 | A2 | 10sgr orange | 2.75 | 1,000. |

Excellent forged cancellations exist on Nos. 13 and 14. For reprints, see note after No. 7.

**1862-63**

| | | | | |
|---|---|---|---|---|
| 15 | A1 | ¼sgr black ('63) | 35.00 | 82.50 |
| 16 | A1 | ⅓sgr green ('63) | 50.00 | 275.00 |
| 17 | A1 | ½sgr orange yellow | 110.00 | 65.00 |
| 18 | A1 | 1sgr rose ('63) | 72.50 | 45.00 |
| 19 | A1 | 2sgr blue ('63) | 57.50 | 125.00 |
| 20 | A1 | 3sgr bister ('63) | 27.50 | 65.00 |
| | | *Nos. 15-20 (6)* | 352.50 | 657.50 |

For reprints, see note after No. 7.

**1865**          **Rouletted**

| | | | | |
|---|---|---|---|---|
| 21 | A1 | ¼sgr black | 7.50 | 400.00 |
| 22 | A1 | ⅓sgr green | 11.00 | 275.00 |
| 23 | A1 | ½sgr yellow | 24.00 | 37.50 |
| 24 | A1 | 1sgr rose | 24.00 | 27.50 |
| 25 | A1 | 2sgr blue | 1.50 | 75.00 |
| 26 | A1 | 3sgr bister | 2.75 | 30.00 |
| | | *Nos. 21-26 (6)* | 70.75 | 845.00 |

For reprints, see note after No. 7.

**1866**      **Rouletted in Colored Lines**

| | | | | |
|---|---|---|---|---|
| 27 | A1 | ¼sgr black | 1.50 | 2,600. |
| 28 | A1 | ⅓sgr green | 1.50 | 1,300. |
| 29 | A1 | ½sgr yellow | 1.50 | 1,300. |
| 30 | A1 | 1sgr rose | 1.50 | 125.00 |
| *a.* | | *Horizontal pair without rouletting between* | *140.00* | *1,450.* |
| *b.* | | *Half used as ½sgr on cover* | | *50,000.* |
| 31 | A1 | 2sgr blue | 1.50 | 1,300. |
| 32 | A1 | 3sgr bister | 1.50 | 375.00 |
| | | *Nos. 27-32 (6)* | 9.00 | 5,975. |

Forged cancellations on Nos. 2, 13-14, 15-16, 21-22, 25-32 are plentiful.

## SOUTHERN DISTRICT

A1            A2

**1852-53**    **Unwmk.**    **Imperf.**

| | | | | |
|---|---|---|---|---|
| 42 | A1 | 1kr blk, *lt grn* | 250.00 | 21.00 |
| 43 | A1 | 3kr blk, *dk bl* | 950.00 | 65.00 |
| 44 | A1 | 3kr blk, *bl ('53)* | 825.00 | 21.00 |
| 45 | A1 | 6kr blk, *rose* | 1,325. | 14.50 |
| 46 | A1 | 9kr blk, *brownish yellow* | 875.00 | 21.00 |
| *a.* | | *9kr blk, pale orange yellow* | *775.00* | *50.00* |

Reprints of Nos. 42-50, 53-56 were made in 1910. Each has "ND" in script on the back. Value, each $6.

**1859**

| | | | | |
|---|---|---|---|---|
| 47 | A1 | 1kr green | 25.00 | 17.50 |
| 48 | A1 | 3kr blue | 600.00 | 32.50 |
| 49 | A1 | 6kr rose | 600.00 | 87.50 |
| 50 | A1 | 9kr yellow | 600.00 | 125.00 |
| 51 | A2 | 15kr blue | 2.75 | 210.00 |
| 52 | A2 | 30kr orange | 2.75 | 575.00 |

Forged cancellations exist on Nos. 51 and 52. For reprints, see note after No. 46.

**1862**

| | | | | |
|---|---|---|---|---|
| 53 | A1 | 3kr rose | 14.50 | 45.00 |
| 54 | A1 | 6kr blue | 14.50 | 45.00 |
| 55 | A1 | 9kr bister | 14.50 | 45.00 |
| | | *Nos. 53-55 (3)* | 43.50 | 135.00 |

For reprints, see note after No. 46.

**1865**          **Rouletted**

| | | | | |
|---|---|---|---|---|
| 56 | A1 | 1kr green | 10.50 | 13.00 |
| 57 | A1 | 3kr rose | 17.00 | 6.50 |
| 58 | A1 | 6kr blue | 1.25 | 20.00 |
| 59 | A1 | 9kr bister | 1.90 | 22.50 |
| | | *Nos. 56-59 (4)* | 30.65 | 62.00 |

For reprint of No. 56, see note after No. 46.

**1867**      **Rouletted in Colored Lines**

| | | | | |
|---|---|---|---|---|
| 60 | A1 | 1kr green | 1.10 | 22.50 |
| 61 | A1 | 3kr rose | 1.10 | 20.00 |
| 62 | A1 | 6kr blue | 1.10 | 32.50 |
| 63 | A1 | 9kr bister | 1.10 | 32.50 |
| | | *Nos. 60-63 (4)* | 4.40 | 107.50 |

Forged cancellations exist on Nos. 51-52, 58-63.

The Thurn & Taxis Stamps, Northern and Southern Districts, were replaced on July 1, 1867, by those of Prussia.

---

# WURTTEMBERG

LOCATION — In southern Germany
GOVT. — Kingdom
AREA — 7,530 sq. mi.
POP. — 2,580,000 (approx.)
CAPITAL — Stuttgart

Württemberg was a member of the German Confederation and became a part of the German Empire in 1870. It gave up its postal autonomy on March

31, 1902, but official stamps were issued until 1923.

16 Kreuzer = 1 Gulden
100 Pfennigs = 1 Mark (1875)

Values for unused stamps are for examples with original gum as defined in the catalogue introduction. Unused stamps without gum of Nos. 1-46 sell for about 60-70% of the figures quoted. Unused stamps without gum of Nos. 47-54 sell for about 50% of the figures quoted.

A1      A1a

**1851-52   Unwmk.   Typo.   *Imperf.***

| No. | Type | Description | Un | Used |
|---|---|---|---|---|
| 1 | A1 | 1kr blk, *buff* | 1,000. | 100.00 |
| a. | | 1kr black, *straw* | 3,500. | 500.00 |
| 2 | A1 | 3kr blk, *yellow* | 275.00 | 6.00 |
| a. | | 3kr black, *orange* | 3,000. | 300.00 |
| 4 | A1 | 6kr blk, *yel grn* | 1,350. | 32.50 |
| a. | | 6kr black, *blue green* | 2,600. | 50.00 |
| 5 | A1 | 9kr blk, *rose* | 4,700. | 32.50 |
| 6 | A1a | 18kr blk, *dl vio* ('52) | 1,400. | 650.00 |

*On the "reprints" the letters of "Württemberg" are smaller, especially the first "e"; the right branch of the "r's" of Württemberg runs upward in the reprints and downward in the originals.*

Coat of Arms — A2

**With Orange Silk Threads**
**Typographed and Embossed**
**1857**

| 7 | A2 | 1kr yellow brown | 550.00 | 65.00 |
|---|---|---|---|---|
| a. | | 1kr dark brown | 1,000. | 225.00 |
| 9 | A2 | 3kr yellow orange | 300.00 | 7.50 |
| 10 | A2 | 6kr green | 550.00 | 60.00 |
| 11 | A2 | 9kr carmine rose | 1,300. | 60.00 |
| 12 | A2 | 18kr blue | 2,400. | 1,150. |

Very fine examples of Nos. 7-12 with have one or two margins touching, but not cutting, the frameline.
See Nos. 13-46, 53.
*The reprints have red or yellow silk threads and are printed 2mm apart, while the originals are ¾mm apart.*

**1859   Without Silk Threads**

| 13 | A2 | 1kr brown | 600.00 | 100.00 |
|---|---|---|---|---|
| a. | | 1kr dark brown | 1,900. | 675.00 |
| 15 | A2 | 3kr yellow org | 250.00 | 7.50 |
| 16 | A2 | 6kr green | 9,250. | 100.00 |
| 17 | A2 | 9kr car rose | 1,200. | 60.00 |
| 18 | A2 | 18kr dark blue | 2,900. | 1,700. |

*The colors of the reprints are brighter; they are also printed 2mm apart instead of 1¼mm.*

**1860      *Perf. 13½***

| 19 | A2 | 1kr brown | 1,050. | 125.00 |
|---|---|---|---|---|
| 20 | A2 | 3kr yellow org | 300.00 | 8.75 |
| 21 | A2 | 6kr green | 3,000. | 100.00 |
| 22 | A2 | 9kr carmine | 1,150. | 125.00 |

**1861      Thin Paper**

| 23 | A2 | 1kr brown | 550.00 | 150.00 |
|---|---|---|---|---|
| a. | | 1kr black brown | 675.00 | 175.00 |
| 25 | A2 | 3kr yellow org | 67.50 | 30.00 |
| 26 | A2 | 6kr green | 275.00 | 60.00 |
| 27 | A2 | 9kr rose | 750.00 | 160.00 |
| a. | | 9kr claret | 825.00 | 225.00 |
| 29 | A2 | 18kr dark blue | 1,500. | 1,200. |

Examples of Nos. 23-29 with all perforations intact sell for considerably more.

**1862      *Perf. 10***

| 30 | A2 | 1kr black brown | 300.00 | 275.00 |
|---|---|---|---|---|
| 31 | A2 | 3kr yellow orange | 450.00 | 35.00 |
| 32 | A2 | 6kr green | 300.00 | 125.00 |
| 33 | A2 | 9kr claret | 3,000. | 625.00 |

**1863**

| 34 | A2 | 1kr yellow grn | 40.00 | 12.50 |
|---|---|---|---|---|
| a. | | 1kr green | 375.00 | 87.50 |

| 36 | A2 | 3kr rose | 300.00 | 4.50 |
|---|---|---|---|---|
| a. | | 3kr dark claret | 1,500. | 250.00 |
| 37 | A2 | 6kr blue | 140.00 | 52.50 |
| 39 | A2 | 9kr yellow brn | 750.00 | 160.00 |
| a. | | 9kr red brown | 250.00 | 50.00 |
| b. | | 9kr black brown | 1,125. | 175.00 |
| 40 | A2 | 18kr orange | 1,125. | 375.00 |

**1865-68      *Rouletted 10***

| 41 | A2 | 1kr yellow grn | 40.00 | 8.75 |
|---|---|---|---|---|
| a. | | 1kr dark green | 575.00 | 300.00 |
| 42 | A2 | 3kr rose | 40.00 | 2.75 |
| a. | | 3kr claret | 1,900. | 2,250. |
| 43 | A2 | 6kr blue | 250.00 | 47.50 |
| 44 | A2 | 7kr slate bl ('68) | 925.00 | 125.00 |
| 45 | A2 | 9kr bister brn ('66) | 1,500. | 110.00 |
| a. | | 9kr red brown | 1,150. | 100.00 |
| 46 | A2 | 18kr orange ('67) | 1,700. | 1,000. |

A3

**1869-73      Typo. & Embossed**

| 47 | A3 | 1kr yellow grn | 29.00 | 1.90 |
|---|---|---|---|---|
| 48 | A3 | 2kr orange | 160.00 | 125.00 |
| 49 | A3 | 3kr rose | 14.50 | 1.25 |
| 50 | A3 | 7kr blue | 62.50 | 17.50 |
| 51 | A3 | 9kr lt brn ('73) | 75.00 | 37.50 |
| 52 | A3 | 14kr orange | 80.00 | 45.00 |
| a. | | 14kr lemon yellow | 1,400. | 1,400. |
| | | Nos. 47-52 (6) | 421.00 | 228.15 |

See No. 54.

**1873      *Imperf.***

| 53 | A2 | 70kr red violet | 1,700. | 3,750. |
|---|---|---|---|---|
| a. | | 70kr violet | 2,900. | 5,250. |

Nos. 53 and 53a have single or double lines of fine black dots printed in the gutters between the stamps.

**1874      *Perf. 11½x11***

| 54 | A3 | 1kr yellow green | 100.00 | 37.50 |
|---|---|---|---|---|

A4      A5

**1875-1900      Typo.**

| 55 | A4 | 2pf sl gray ('94) | 1.60 | .75 |
|---|---|---|---|---|
| 56 | A4 | 3pf green | 17.00 | 1.25 |
| 57 | A4 | 3pf brn ('90) | .65 | .55 |
| a. | | Imperf. pair | 125.00 | |
| 58 | A4 | 5pf violet | 7.00 | .65 |
| 59 | A4 | 5pf grn ('90) | 1.25 | .55 |
| a. | | 5pf blue green | 250.00 | 24.00 |
| b. | | Imperf., pair | 125.00 | |
| 60 | A4 | 10pf carmine | 1.00 | .65 |
| a. | | 10pf rose | 67.50 | .75 |
| b. | | Imperf., pair | 67.50 | |
| 61 | A4 | 20pf ultra | 1.00 | .65 |
| a. | | 20pf dull blue | 1.00 | .65 |
| b. | | Imperf., pair | 125.00 | |
| 62 | A4 | 25pf red brn | 100.00 | 8.25 |
| 63 | A4 | 25pf orange ('90) | 2.40 | 1.00 |
| a. | | Imperf., pair | 125.00 | |
| 64 | A4 | 30pf org & blk ('00) | 2.75 | 3.25 |
| 65 | A5 | 40pf dp rose & blk ('00) | 3.25 | 4.75 |
| 66 | A4 | 50pf gray | 700.00 | 35.00 |
| 67 | A4 | 50pf gray grn | 52.50 | 4.00 |
| 68 | A4 | 50pf pur brn ('90) | 2.40 | .75 |
| a. | | 50pf red brown | 325.00 | 42.50 |
| 69 | A4 | 2m yellow | 775.00 | 210.00 |
| 70 | A4 | 2m ver, *buff* ('79) | 1,900. | 110.00 |
| 71 | A5 | 2m org & blk ('83) | 7.75 | 8.25 |
| | | Telegraph cancel | | 2.75 |
| a. | | 2m yellow & black | 350.00 | 47.50 |
| b. | | Imperf., pair | 125.00 | |
| | | Telegraph cancel | | 21.00 |
| 72 | A5 | 5m bl & blk ('81) | 37.50 | *140.00* |
| | | Telegraph cancel | | 62.50 |
| a. | | Double impression of figure of value | 160.00 | |

No. 70 has "Unverkäuflich" (not for sale) printed on its back to remind postal clerks that it, like No. 69, was for their use and not to be sold to the public.
The regular postage stamps of Württemberg were superseded by those of the German Empire in 1902. Official stamps were in use until 1923.

---

## WURTTEMBERG OFFICIAL STAMPS

### For the Communal Authorities

O1

***Perf. 11½x11***

**1875-1900   Typo.   Unwmk.**

| O1 | O1 | 2pf slate gray ('00) | 1.25 | .75 |
|---|---|---|---|---|
| O2 | O1 | 3pf brown ('96) | 1.25 | .65 |
| O3 | O1 | 5pf violet | 35.00 | 1.25 |
| a. | | Imperf., pair | | 3,750. |
| O4 | O1 | 5pf blue grn ('90) | 1.25 | .75 |
| a. | | Imperf., pair | 47.50 | |
| O5 | O1 | 10pf rose | 7.00 | 1.25 |
| a. | | Imperf., pair | 82.50 | |
| O6 | O1 | 25pf orange ('00) | 21.00 | 4.00 |
| | | Nos. O1-O6 (6) | 66.75 | 8.65 |

See Nos. O12-O32. For overprints and surcharges see Nos. O7-O11, O40-O52, O59-O93.

### Used Values

When italicized, used values for Nos. O7-O183 are for favor-canceled stamps. Postally used stamps command a premium.

Stamps of Previous Issues Overprinted in Black

**1906, Jan. 30**

| O7 | O1 | 2pf slate gray | 37.50 | 67.50 |
|---|---|---|---|---|
| O8 | O1 | 3pf dk brown | 14.00 | 10.00 |
| O9 | O1 | 5pf green | 4.00 | 2.75 |
| O10 | O1 | 10pf deep rose | 4.00 | 3.00 |
| O11 | O1 | 25pf orange | 42.50 | 67.50 |
| | | Nos. O7-O11 (5) | 102.00 | 150.75 |

Centenary of Kingdom of Württemberg.
Nos. O7-O11 also exist imperf but it is doubtful if they were ever issued in that condition.
Value Nos. O7-O11 canceled-to-order, $26.00.

**1906-21      Wmk. 116**

| O12 | O1 | 2pf slate gray | 3.25 | .20 |
|---|---|---|---|---|
| O13 | O1 | 2½pf gray blk ('16) | .55 | .20 |
| O14 | O1 | 3pf dk brown | .65 | .20 |
| O15 | O1 | 5pf green | .65 | .20 |
| O16 | O1 | 7½pf orange ('16) | .55 | .20 |
| O17 | O1 | 10pf dp rose | .65 | .20 |
| O18 | O1 | 10pf orange ('21) | .20 | .20 |
| O19 | O1 | 15pf yellow brn ('16) | 1.25 | .20 |
| O20 | O1 | 15pf dk violet ('17) | .65 | .20 |
| O21 | O1 | 20pf dp ultra ('11) | 1.25 | .20 |
| O22 | O1 | 20pf dp green ('21) | .20 | .20 |
| O23 | O1 | 25pf orange | .65 | .20 |
| O24 | O1 | 25pf brn & blk ('17) | .95 | .20 |
| O25 | O1 | 35pf brown ('19) | 1.25 | .65 |
| O26 | O1 | 40pf rose red ('21) | .20 | .20 |
| O27 | O1 | 50pf rose lake ('11) | 12.00 | .20 |
| O28 | O1 | 50pf vio brn ('21) | .20 | .20 |
| O29 | O1 | 60pf olive grn ('21) | .35 | .20 |
| O30 | O1 | 1.25m emerald ('21) | .20 | .20 |
| O31 | O1 | 2m gray ('21) | .20 | .20 |
| O32 | O1 | 3m brown ('21) | .35 | .20 |
| | | Nos. O12-O32 (21) | 26.20 | 4.65 |

No. O24 contains solid black numerals.
Nos. O12-O32 exist imperf. Value, each pair, $6-$16.

O3

***Perf. 14½x14***

**1916, Oct. 6   Typo.   Unwmk.**

| O33 | O3 | 2½pf slate | 1.25 | *1.25* |
|---|---|---|---|---|
| O34 | O3 | 7½pf yellow brn | 1.25 | *1.25* |
| O35 | O3 | 10pf car rose | 1.25 | *1.25* |
| O36 | O3 | 15pf yellow brn | 1.25 | *1.25* |
| O37 | O3 | 20pf blue | 1.25 | *1.25* |
| O38 | O3 | 25pf gray blk | 3.25 | *1.25* |
| O39 | O3 | 50pf red brown | 7.00 | *1.25* |
| | | Nos. O33-O39 (7) | 16.50 | *8.75* |

25th year of the reign of King Wilhelm II.

Stamps of 1900-06 Surcharged

***Perf. 11½x11***

**1916, Sept. 10      Wmk. 116**

| O40 | O1 | 25pf on 25pf orange | 2.75 | *.65* |
|---|---|---|---|---|
| a. | | Without wmk. | 27.50 | |

No. O13 Surcharged in Blue

**1919      Wmk. 116**

| O42 | O1 | 2pf on 2½pf gray blk | .65 | *.40* |
|---|---|---|---|---|

Official Stamps of 1906-19 Overprinted

**1919**

| O43 | O1 | 2½pf gray blk | .35 | *.55* |
|---|---|---|---|---|
| O44 | O1 | 3pf dk brown | 10.00 | *.55* |
| O45 | O1 | 5pf green | .35 | *.55* |
| O46 | O1 | 7½pf orange | .65 | *.55* |
| O47 | O1 | 10pf rose | .35 | *.55* |
| O48 | O1 | 15pf purple | .35 | *.55* |
| O49 | O1 | 20pf ultra | .35 | *.55* |
| O50 | O1 | 25pf brown & blk | .35 | *.55* |
| O51 | O1 | 35pf brown | 4.00 | *.55* |
| O52 | O1 | 50pf red brown | 4.75 | *.55* |
| | | Nos. O43-O52 (10) | 21.50 | *5.50* |

Stag — O4

**Wmk. 192**

**1920, Mar. 19   Litho.   *Perf. 14½***

| O53 | O4 | 10pf maroon | 1.00 | *1.25* |
|---|---|---|---|---|
| O54 | O4 | 15pf brown | 1.00 | *1.25* |
| O55 | O4 | 20pf indigo | 1.00 | *1.25* |
| O56 | O4 | 30pf deep green | 1.00 | *1.25* |
| O57 | O4 | 50pf yellow | 1.00 | *1.25* |
| O58 | O4 | 75pf bister | 2.00 | *1.25* |
| | | Nos. O53-O58 (6) | 7.00 | *7.50* |

Official Stamps of 1906-19 Overprinted

***Perf. 11½x11***

**1920, Apr. 1      Wmk. 116**

| O59 | O1 | 5pf green | 3.25 | 8.75 |
|---|---|---|---|---|
| O60 | O1 | 10pf deep rose | 2.00 | 4.00 |
| O61 | O1 | 15pf dp violet | 2.00 | 4.00 |
| O62 | O1 | 20pf ultra | 3.25 | 7.75 |
| a. | | Wmk. 192 | 4.00 | 7.75 |
| O63 | O1 | 50pf red brown | 4.00 | 15.00 |
| | | Nos. O59-O63 (5) | 14.50 | 40.00 |

Nos. O59 to O63 were available for official postage throughout all Germany but were used almost exclusively in Württemberg.

Stamps of 1917-21 Surcharged in Black, Red or Blue

**1923**

| O64 | O1 | 5m on 10pf orange | .20 | *.20* |
|---|---|---|---|---|
| O65 | O1 | 10m on 15pf dp violet | .20 | *.20* |
| O66 | O1 | 12m on 40pf rose red | .20 | *.20* |
| O67 | O1 | 20m on 10pf orange | .20 | *.20* |
| O68 | O1 | 25m on 20pf green | .20 | *.20* |
| O69 | O1 | 40m on 20pf green | .20 | *.20* |
| O70 | O1 | 50m on 60pf olive grn | .20 | *.20* |

Surcharged

| | | | | |
|---|---|---|---|---|
| O71 | O1 | 60m on 1.25m emer-ald | .20 | .20 |
| O72 | O1 | 100m on 40pf rose red | .20 | .20 |
| O73 | O1 | 200m on 2m gray (R) | .20 | .20 |
| O74 | O1 | 300m on 50pf red brn (Bl) | .20 | .20 |
| O75 | O1 | 400m on 3m brn (Bl) | .20 | .20 |
| O76 | O1 | 1000m on 60pf ol grn | .20 | .25 |
| O77 | O1 | 2000m on 1.25m emer-ald | .20 | .25 |
| | | Nos. O64-O77 (14) | 2.80 | 2.90 |

Abbreviations:
Th = (Tausend) Thousand
Mil = (Million) Million
Mlrd = (Milliarde) Billion

Surcharged

**1923**

| | | | | |
|---|---|---|---|---|
| O78 | O1 | 5th m on 10pf orange | .20 | .35 |
| O79 | O1 | 20th m on 40pf rose red | .20 | .35 |
| O80 | O1 | 50th m on 15pf violet | .20 | .35 |
| O81 | O1 | 75th m on 2m gray | 1.25 | .35 |
| O82 | O1 | 100th m on 20pf green | .20 | .35 |
| O83 | O1 | 250th m on 3m brown | .20 | .35 |

Surcharged

| | | | | |
|---|---|---|---|---|
| O84 | O1 | 1mil m on 60pf ol grn | 1.00 | .35 |
| O85 | O1 | 2mil m on 50pf red brn | .20 | .35 |
| O86 | O1 | 5mil m on 1.25m emer | .20 | .35 |

Surcharged

| | | | | |
|---|---|---|---|---|
| O87 | O1 | 4 mlrd m on 50pf red brn | 2.40 | .35 |
| O88 | O1 | 10 mlrd m on 3m brn | 2.40 | .35 |
| | | Nos. O78-O88 (11) | 8.45 | 3.85 |

No. O23 Surcharged with New Values
in Rentenpfennig as

**1923, Dec.**

| | | | | |
|---|---|---|---|---|
| O89 | O1 | 3pf on 25pf orange | .35 | .35 |
| O90 | O1 | 5pf on 25pf orange | .35 | .35 |
| O91 | O1 | 10pf on 25pf orange | .35 | .35 |
| O92 | O1 | 20pf on 25pf orange | .35 | .35 |
| O93 | O1 | 50pf on 25pf orange | .65 | .35 |
| | | Nos. O89-O93 (5) | 2.05 | 1.75 |

**For the State Authorities**

O6

**Perf. 11½x11**

**1881-1902** Typo. Unwmk.

| | | | | |
|---|---|---|---|---|
| O94 | O6 | 2pf sl gray ('96) | 1.25 | 1.00 |
| O95 | O6 | 3pf green | 21.00 | 3.25 |
| O96 | O6 | 3pf dk brown ('90) | 1.25 | .65 |
| O97 | O6 | 5pf violet | 5.25 | 1.25 |
| O98 | O6 | 5pf green ('90) | 2.00 | .65 |
| O99 | O6 | 10pf rose | 3.25 | 1.00 |

| | | | | |
|---|---|---|---|---|
| O100 | O6 | 20pf ultra | .75 | 1.00 |
| O101 | O6 | 25pf brown | 32.50 | 6.25 |
| O102 | O6 | 25pf orange ('90) | 5.25 | .75 |
| O103 | O6 | 30pf org & blk ('02) | 1.25 | 1.60 |
| O104 | O6 | 40pf dp rose & blk ('90) | 1.25 | 1.60 |
| O105 | O6 | 50pf gray grn | 7.00 | 7.75 |
| O106 | O6 | 50pf maroon ('91) | 1.25 | 2.75 |
| a. | | 50pf red brown ('90) | 200.00 | 1,450. |
| O107 | O6 | 1m yellow | 62.50 | 160.00 |
| O108 | O6 | 1m violet ('90) | 6.25 | 14.00 |
| | | Nos. O94-O108 (15) | 152.00 | 203.50 |

See #O119-O135. For overprints & surcharges see #O109-O118, O146-O164, O176-O183.

Overprinted in Black

**1906**

| | | | | |
|---|---|---|---|---|
| O109 | O6 | 2pf slate gray | 27.50 | 5.25 |
| O110 | O6 | 3pf dk brown | 5.25 | 5.25 |
| O111 | O6 | 5pf green | 4.00 | 5.25 |
| O112 | O6 | 10pf dp rose | 4.00 | 5.25 |
| O113 | O6 | 20pf ultra | 4.00 | 5.25 |
| O114 | O6 | 25pf orange | 8.25 | 5.25 |
| O115 | O6 | 30pf org & blk | 8.25 | 5.25 |
| O116 | O6 | 40pf dp rose & blk | 32.50 | 5.25 |
| O117 | O6 | 50pf red brown | 32.50 | 5.25 |
| O118 | O6 | 1m purple | 62.50 | 5.25 |
| | | Nos. O109-O118 (10) | 188.75 | 52.50 |

Cent. of the kingdom of Wüttemberg.
Nos. O109 to O118 are also found imperforate, but it is doubtful if they were ever issued in that condition.

**1906-19** Wmk. 116

| | | | | |
|---|---|---|---|---|
| O119 | O6 | 2pf slate gray | .40 | .20 |
| O120 | O6 | 2½pf gray blk ('16) | .45 | .20 |
| O121 | O6 | 3pf dk brown | .40 | .20 |
| O122 | O6 | 5pf green | .40 | .20 |
| O123 | O6 | 7½pf orange ('16) | .45 | .20 |
| O124 | O6 | 10pf deep rose | .40 | .20 |
| O125 | O6 | 15pf yel brn ('16) | .45 | .20 |
| O126 | O6 | 15pf purple ('17) | .65 | .30 |
| O127 | O6 | 20pf ultra | .55 | .20 |
| O128 | O6 | 25pf orange | .40 | .20 |
| O129 | O6 | 25pf brn & blk ('17) | .35 | .20 |
| O130 | O6 | 30pf org & blk | .35 | .20 |
| O131 | O6 | 35pf brown ('19) | 1.25 | 2.75 |
| O132 | O6 | 40pf dp rose & blk | .40 | .20 |
| O133 | O6 | 50pf red brown | .40 | .20 |
| O134 | O6 | 1m purple | 2.00 | .20 |
| O135 | O6 | 1m sl & blk ('17) | 2.00 | .65 |
| | | Nos. O119-O135 (17) | 11.30 | 6.50 |

King Wilhelm II — O8

**1916** Unwmk. Typo. Perf. 14

| | | | | |
|---|---|---|---|---|
| O136 | O8 | 2½pf slate | .65 | .60 |
| O137 | O8 | 7½pf orange | .65 | .60 |
| O138 | O8 | 10pf carmine | .65 | .60 |
| O139 | O8 | 15pf yellow brn | .65 | .60 |
| O140 | O8 | 20pf blue | .65 | .60 |
| O141 | O8 | 25pf gray blk | 1.25 | .60 |
| O142 | O8 | 30pf green | 1.25 | .60 |
| O143 | O8 | 40pf claret | 2.00 | .60 |
| O144 | O8 | 50pf red brn | 2.75 | .60 |
| O145 | O8 | 1m violet | 2.75 | .60 |
| | | Nos. O136-O145 (10) | 13.25 | 6.00 |

25th year of the reign of King Wilhelm II.

Stamps of 1890-1906
Surcharged

**1916-19** Wmk. 116 Perf. 11½x11

| | | | | |
|---|---|---|---|---|
| O146 | O6 | 25pf on 25pf orange | 24.00 | .65 |
| a. | | Without watermark | 32.50 | 9,250. |
| O147 | O6 | 50pf on 50pf red brn | 1.25 | .75 |
| a. | | Inverted surcharge | 32.50 | |

Beware of fake cancels on No. O146a.

No. O120 Surcharged
in Blue

**1919** Wmk. 116

| | | | | |
|---|---|---|---|---|
| O149 | O6 | 2pf on 2½pf gray blk | 1.25 | 1.25 |

Official Stamps of
1890-1919 Overprinted

**1919**

| | | | | |
|---|---|---|---|---|
| O150 | O6 | 2½pf gray blk | .45 | .35 |
| O151 | O6 | 3pf dk brown | 7.00 | .65 |
| a. | | Without watermark | 47.50 | |
| O152 | O6 | 5pf green | .35 | .35 |
| O153 | O6 | 7½pf orange | .35 | .35 |
| O154 | O6 | 10pf rose | .35 | .35 |
| O155 | O6 | 15pf purple | .35 | .25 |
| O156 | O6 | 20pf ultra | .35 | .35 |
| O157 | O6 | 25pf brn & blk | .35 | .35 |
| a. | | Inverted overprint | 82.50 | 160.00 |
| O158 | O6 | 30pf org & blk | .65 | .35 |
| a. | | Inverted overprint | 225.00 | 350.00 |
| O159 | O6 | 35pf brown | .45 | .35 |
| O160 | O6 | 40pf rose & blk | .45 | .35 |
| O161 | O6 | 50pf claret | .65 | .55 |
| O162 | O6 | 1m slate & blk | .75 | .65 |
| | | Nos. O150-O162 (13) | 12.50 | 5.25 |

Nos. O151, O151a
Surcharged in Carmine

**1920** Wmk. 116

| | | | | |
|---|---|---|---|---|
| O164 | O6 | 75pf on 3pf dk brn | 1.00 | 1.00 |
| a. | | Without watermark | 67.50 | 14.50 |

View of
Stuttgart
O9

10pf, 50pf, 2.50m, 3m, View of Stuttgart.
15pf, 75pf, View of Ulm. 20pf, 1m, View of Tubingen. 30pf, 1.25m, View of Ellwangen.

**Wmk. 192**
**1920, Mar. 25** Typo. Perf. 14½

| | | | | |
|---|---|---|---|---|
| O166 | O9 | 10pf maroon | .55 | 1.00 |
| O167 | O9 | 15pf brown | .55 | 1.00 |
| O168 | O9 | 20pf indigo | .55 | 1.00 |
| O169 | O9 | 30pf blue grn | .55 | 1.00 |
| O170 | O9 | 50pf yellow | .55 | 1.00 |
| O171 | O9 | 75pf bister | .55 | 1.00 |
| O172 | O9 | 1m orange red | .55 | 1.00 |
| O173 | O9 | 1.25m dp violet | .55 | 1.00 |
| O174 | O9 | 2.50m dark ultra | 1.25 | 1.00 |
| O175 | O9 | 3m yellow grn | 2.00 | 1.00 |
| | | Nos. O166-O175 (10) | 7.65 | 10.00 |

Official Stamps of
1906-19 Overprinted

**1920** Wmk. 116 Perf. 11½x11

| | | | | |
|---|---|---|---|---|
| O176 | O6 | 5pf green | 2.00 | 3.25 |
| O177 | O6 | 10pf deep rose | 1.25 | 2.75 |
| O178 | O6 | 15pf purple | 1.25 | 2.75 |
| O179 | O6 | 20pf ultra | 1.25 | 1.25 |
| a. | | Wmk. 192 | 100.00 | 275.00 |
| O180 | O6 | 30pf orange & blk | 1.25 | 3.25 |
| O181 | O6 | 40pf dp rose & blk | 1.25 | 2.75 |
| O182 | O6 | 50pf red brown | 1.25 | 3.25 |
| O183 | O6 | 1m slate & blk | 2.00 | 7.00 |
| | | Nos. O176-O183 (8) | 11.50 | 26.25 |

The note after No. O63 will also apply to Nos. O176-O183.

# NORTH GERMAN CONFEDERATION

Northern District
30 Groschen = 1 Thaler
Southern District
60 Kreuzer = 1 Gulden
Hamburg
16 Schillings = 1 Mark

Values for unused stamps are for examples with original gum as defined in the catalogue introduction. Stamps without gum sell for about 50% of the figures quoted.

A1                    A2

*Rouletted 8½ to 10, 11 to 12½ and Compound*

**1868** Typo. Unwmk.

| | | | | |
|---|---|---|---|---|
| 1 | A1 | ¼gr violet | 25.00 | 15.00 |
| 2 | A1 | ⅓gr green | 30.00 | 3.00 |
| 3 | A1 | ½gr orange | 30.00 | 2.25 |
| 4 | A1 | 1gr rose | 18.50 | .90 |
| b. | | Half used as ½gr on cover | | |
| 5 | A1 | 2gr ultra | 75.00 | 1.50 |
| 6 | A1 | 5gr bister | 75.00 | 7.50 |
| 7 | A2 | 1kr green | 32.50 | 7.50 |
| 8 | A2 | 2kr orange | 52.50 | 50.00 |
| 9 | A2 | 3kr rose | 32.50 | 1.90 |
| 10 | A2 | 7kr ultra | 150.00 | 9.50 |
| 11 | A2 | 18kr bister | 32.50 | 60.00 |
| | | Nos. 1-11 (11) | 553.50 | 159.05 |

See Nos. 13-23.

**Imperf**

| | | | | |
|---|---|---|---|---|
| 1a | A1 | ¼gr red lilac | 190.00 | — |
| 2a | A1 | ⅓gr green | 90.00 | — |
| 3a | A1 | ½gr orange | 140.00 | — |
| 4a | A1 | 1gr rose | 75.00 | — |
| 5a | A1 | 2gr ultra | 250.00 | — |
| 6a | A1 | 5gr bister | 250.00 | — |
| 7a | A2 | 1kr green | 67.50 | 110.00 |
| 8a | A2 | 2kr orange | 190.00 | 90.00 |
| 9a | A2 | 3kr rose | 75.00 | 95.00 |
| 10a | A2 | 7kr ultra | 325.00 | 625.00 |
| 11a | A2 | 18kr bister | 325.00 | 625.00 |

A3

**1868**

| | | | | |
|---|---|---|---|---|
| 12 | A3 | (½s) lilac brown | 100.00 | 50.00 |
| d. | | Imperf | 200.00 | |

See No. 24.

**1869** Perf. 13½x14

| | | | | |
|---|---|---|---|---|
| 13 | A1 | ¼gr lilac | 13.00 | 14.50 |
| a. | | ¼gr red violet | 22.50 | 17.50 |
| 14 | A1 | ⅓gr green | 4.75 | 1.50 |
| 15 | A1 | ½gr orange | 4.75 | 1.50 |
| 16 | A1 | 1gr rose | 3.75 | 1.00 |
| 17 | A1 | 2gr ultra | 6.50 | 1.10 |
| 18 | A1 | 5gr bister | 8.00 | 7.25 |
| 19 | A2 | 1kr green | 11.50 | 7.25 |
| 20 | A2 | 2kr orange | 37.50 | 100.00 |
| 21 | A2 | 3kr rose | 6.50 | 1.90 |
| 22 | A2 | 7kr ultra | 10.00 | 8.00 |
| 23 | A2 | 18kr bister | 140.00 | 1,600. |
| | | Nos. 13-23 (11) | 246.25 | 1,744. |

Counterfeit cancels exist on No. 23.

**1869**

| | | | | |
|---|---|---|---|---|
| 24 | A3 | (½s) dull violet brown | 4.50 | 7.25 |

A4                    A5

**Perf. 14x13½**

| | | | | |
|---|---|---|---|---|
| 25 | A4 | 10gr gray | 290.00 | 360.00 |
| | | Pen cancellation | | 60.00 |
| 26 | A5 | 30gr blue | 225.00 | 925.00 |
| | | Pen cancellation | | 125.00 |

Counterfeit cancels exist on No. 26.

See Germany designs A2, A3 and A8 for similar stamps.

## OFFICIAL STAMPS

O1

| 1870 | | Unwmk. | Typo. | Perf. 14½x14 | |
|------|------|--------|-------|-------|-------|
| O1 | O1 | ¼gr | black & buff | 26.00 | 40.00 |
| O2 | O1 | ⅓gr | black & buff | 8.75 | 18.50 |
| O3 | O1 | ½gr | black & buff | 2.50 | 3.00 |
| O4 | O1 | 1gr | black & buff | 2.50 | .90 |
| O5 | O1 | 2gr | black & buff | 6.50 | 3.75 |
| O6 | O1 | 1kr | black & gray | 30.00 | 240.00 |
| O7 | O1 | 2kr | black & gray | 72.50 | 1,250. |
| O8 | O1 | 3kr | black & gray | 22.50 | 45.00 |
| O9 | O1 | 7kr | black & gray | 40.00 | 250.00 |
| | | Nos. O1-O9 (9) | | 211.25 | 1,851. |

Counterfeit cancels exist on Nos. O6-O9.
   The stamps of the North German Confederation were replaced by those of the German Empire on Jan. 1, 1872.

# collecting accessories

### Hawid Glue Pen*

A simple, safe method for sealing top-cut mounts at the open edge. Simply run pen along open edge of mount, press and cut off excess mount film.

| ITEM | RETAIL |
|------|--------|
| SG622 | $7.95 |

### Hawid Mounting Gum

Solvent free adhesive that can be safely used to glue mounts back on album page.

| ITEM | RETAIL |
|------|--------|
| SG603 | $4.95 |

*Use glue pen and mounting gum at own risk. Not liable for any damage to mount contents from adhesive products.*

### Scott/Linn's Multi Gauge

"The best peforation gauge in the world just got better!" The gauge used by the Scott Editorial staff to perf stamps for the Catalogue has been improved. Not only is the Scott/Linn's gauge graduated in tenths, each division is marked by thin lines to assist collectors in gauging stamp to the tenth. The Scott/Linn's Multi-Gauge is a perforation gauge, cancellation gauge, zero-center ruler and millimeter ruler in one easy-to-use instrument. It's greate for measuring multiples and stamps on cover.

| ITEM | DESCRIPTION | RETAIL |
|------|-------------|--------|
| LIN01 | Multi-Gauge | $6.95 |

### Rotary Mount Cutter

German engineered mount cutter delivers precise and accurate cuts. The metal base features cm-measurements across the top and down both sides. The rotary cutter has an exchangeable, self-sharpening blade that rotates within a plastic casing, safely insuring perfectly straight and rectangular cuts.

| ITEM | DESCRIPTION | RETAIL |
|------|-------------|--------|
| 980RMC | Mount Cutter | $74.00 |

### Stamp Tongs

Avoid messy fingerprints and damage to your stamps when you use these finely crafted instruments.

| ITEM | | RETAIL |
|------|---|--------|
| ACC181 | 120 mm Spade Tip w/case | $4.25 |
| ACC182 | 120 mm Spoon Tip w/case | $4.25 |
| ACC183 | 155 mm Point Tip w/case | $8.95 |
| ACC184 | 120mm Cranked Tip w/case | $4.95 |

ACC184
ACC181
ACC182
ACC183

These accessories and others are available from your favorite stamp dealer or direct from:

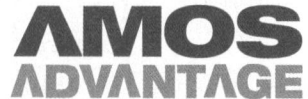

## AMOS ADVANTAGE

1-800-572-6885
P.O. Box 828, Sidney OH 45365-0828
www.amosadvantage.com

# GERMANY

ˈjər-mə-nē

LOCATION — In northern Europe bordering on the Baltic and North Seas
AREA — 182,104 sq. mi. (until 1945)
POP. — 67,032,242 (1946)
CAPITAL — Berlin

In 1949 the Russian occupied areas became a separate country, the German Democratic Republic. The country was reunified Oct. 3, 1990.

30 Silbergroschen or Groschen = 1 Thaler

60 Kreuzer = 1 Gulden

100 Pfennigs = 1 Mark (1875)

100 Pfennigs = 1 Deutsche Mark (1948)

100 Cents = 1 Euro (2002)

---

**Catalogue values for unused stamps in this country are for Never Hinged items, beginning with Scott 722 in the regular postage section, Scott B338 in the semi-postal section, Scott C61 in the airpost section, Scott 9N103 in the Berlin regular postage section and Scott 9NB12 in the Berlin semi-postal section.**

---

## Watermarks

Wmk. 48 — Diagonal Zigzag Lines

Wmk. 116 — Crosses and Circles

Wmk. 125 — Lozenges

Wmk. 126 — Network

Wmk. 127 — Quatrefoils

Wmk. 192 — Circles

Wmk. 223 — Eagle

Wmk. 237 — Swastikas

Wmk. 241 — Cross

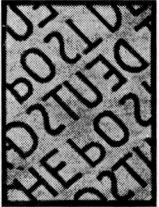

Wmk. 284 — "DEUTSCHE POST" Multiple

Wmk. 285 — Marbleized Pattern

Wmk. 286 — D P Multiple

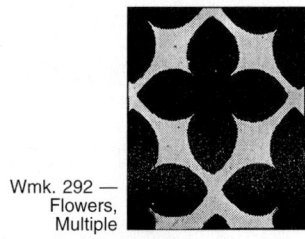

Wmk. 292 — Flowers, Multiple

Wmk. 295 — B P and Zigzag Lines

Wmk. 304 — DBP and Rosettes Multiple

## Empire

Values for unused stamps are for examples with original gum as defined in the catalogue introduction. Any exceptions are specifically mentioned.

Imperial Eagle — A1

### Typographed, Center Embossed

| | | | | |
|---|---|---|---|---|
| **1872** | | **Unwmk.** | **Perf. 13½x14½** | |
| | | **Eagle with small shield** | | |
| 1 | A1 | ¼gr violet | 190.00 | 87.50 |
| 2 | A1 | ⅓gr green | 450.00 | 37.50 |
| a. | | Imperf. | | |
| 3 | A1 | ½gr red orange | 950.00 | 37.50 |
| a. | | ½gr orange yellow | 1,100. | 45.00 |
| 4 | A1 | 1gr rose | 300.00 | 5.25 |
| a. | | Imperf. | | |
| b. | | Half used as ½gr on cover | | 47,500. |
| 5 | A1 | 2gr ultra | 1,600. | 14.50 |
| a. | | Imperf. | | 8,750. |
| 6 | A1 | 5gr bister | 875.00 | 87.50 |
| a. | | Imperf. | | 10,000. |
| 7 | A1 | 1kr green | 650.00 | 52.50 |
| 8 | A1 | 2kr orange | 37.50 | 160.00 |
| a. | | 2kr red orange | 600.00 | 300.00 |
| 9 | A1 | 3kr rose | 1,750. | 12.50 |
| 10 | A1 | 7kr ultra | 2,350. | 87.50 |
| 11 | A1 | 18kr bister | 475.00 | 375.00 |

Values for imperforates are for copies postmarked at Leipzig (⅓gr), Coblenz (1gr), Hoengen (2gr) and Leutersdorf (5gr).

A2          A3

| | | | | |
|---|---|---|---|---|
| **1872** | | **Typo.** | **Perf. 14½x13½** | |
| 12 | A2 | 10gr gray | 52.50 | 2,400. |
| | | Pen cancellation | | 150.00 |
| 13 | A3 | 30gr blue | 105.00 | 2,500. |
| | | Pen cancellation | | 525.00 |

For similar designs see A8, North German Confederation A4, A5.

A4          A5

### Center Embossed

| | | | | |
|---|---|---|---|---|
| **1872** | | | **Perf. 13½x14½** | |
| | | **Eagle with large shield** | | |
| 14 | A4 | ¼gr violet | 72.50 | 95.00 |
| 15 | A4 | ⅓gr yellow green | 32.50 | 14.50 |
| a. | | ½gr blue green | 125.00 | 110.00 |
| 16 | A4 | ½gr orange | 37.50 | 8.00 |
| a. | | Imperf. | | |
| 17 | A4 | 1gr rose | 42.50 | 1.90 |
| a. | | Imperf. | | 15,500. |
| b. | | Half used as ½gr on cover | | 35,000. |
| 18 | A4 | 2gr ultra | 19.00 | 4.25 |
| 19 | A4 | 2½gr orange brn | 1,800. | 55.00 |
| a. | | 2½gr lilac brown | 4,100. | 325.00 |
| 20 | A4 | 5gr bister | 29.00 | 29.00 |
| a. | | Imperf. | | 5,750. |
| 21 | A4 | 1kr yellow green | 32.50 | 25.00 |
| a. | | 1kr blue green | 350.00 | 400.00 |
| 22 | A4 | 2kr orange | 475.00 | 1,900. |
| 23 | A4 | 3kr rose | 22.50 | 3.50 |
| 24 | A4 | 7kr ultra | 29.00 | 65.00 |
| 25 | A4 | 9kr red brown | 275.00 | 225.00 |
| a. | | 9kr lilac brown | 1,400. | 450.00 |
| 26 | A4 | 18kr bister | 32.50 | 1,750. |

Values for Nos. 17a and 20a are for stamps postmarked at Potsdam (1gr), Damgarten or Anklam (5gr).

#14-26 with embossing inverted are fraudulent.

**1874**

### Brown Surcharge

| | | | | |
|---|---|---|---|---|
| 27 | A5 | 2½gr on 2½gr brn | 37.50 | 40.00 |
| 28 | A5 | 9kr on 9kr brown | 65.00 | 450.00 |

A6          A7

"Pfennige"

| | | | | |
|---|---|---|---|---|
| **1875-77** | | | | **Typo.** |
| 29 | A6 | 3pf blue green | 55.00 | 5.25 |
| 30 | A6 | 5pf violet | 97.50 | 3.75 |

### Center Embossed

| | | | | |
|---|---|---|---|---|
| 31 | A7 | 10pf rose | 40.00 | 1.50 |
| 32 | A7 | 20pf ultra | 450.00 | 1.50 |
| 33 | A7 | 25pf red brown | 475.00 | 18.00 |
| 34 | A7 | 50pf gray | 1,500. | 11.00 |
| 35 | A7 | 50pf ol gray ('77) | 1,650. | 12.50 |

See Nos. 37-42. For surcharges see Offices in Turkey Nos. 1-6.

A8

**1875-90 Typo. Perf. 14½x13½**

36 A8 2m brownish pur
('90) 65.00 3.50
*a.* 2m purple 375.00 125.00
*b.* 2m dull vio pur ('89) 1,400. 60.00

No. 36a used is valued as a stamp with cds cancel dated between Jan. 1875 and Nov. 17, 1884.

Types of 1875-77, "Pfennig" without
final "e"

**1880-83 Perf. 13½x14½**

37 A6 3pf yel green 3.00 1.25
*a.* Imperf.
38 A6 5pf violet 1.50 1.25

**Center Embossed**

39 A7 10pf red 8.00 1.25
*a.* Imperf. 325.00
40 A7 20pf brt ultra 6.00 1.25
41 A7 25pf dull rose brn 15.00 5.25
*a.* 25pf red brown, thick paper
('83) 190.00 6.00
42 A7 50pf dp grayish ol grn 7.50 1.25
*a.* 50pf olive green 210.00 1.25
*Nos. 37-42 (6)* 41.00 11.50

Values for Nos. 37-42 are for stamps on thin paper. Those on thick paper sell for considerably more.

A9

A10

**1889-1900 Perf. 13½x14½**

45 A9 2pf gray ('00) .50 .75
*a.* "REIGHSPOST" 55.00 140.00
Never hinged 175.00
46 A9 3pf brown 2.25 1.10
*a.* 3pf yellow brown 9.00 3.75
*b.* Imperf. 160.00
Never hinged 375.00
*c.* 3pf reddish brown 110.00 8.00
47 A9 5pf blue green 1.40 1.10
48 A10 10pf carmine 1.75 1.10
*a.* Imperf. 225.00
Never hinged 650.00
49 A10 20pf ultra 7.50 1.10
*a.* 20pf Prus blue 375.00 110.00
50 A10 25pf orange ('90) 30.00 1.50
*a.* Imperf. 190.00
Never hinged 625.00
51 A10 50pf chocolate 26.00 1.10
*a.* 50pf copper brown 375.00 9.75
*b.* Imperf. 325.00
Never hinged 425.00
*Nos. 45-51 (7)* 69.40 7.75
Set, never hinged 265.00

For surcharges and overprints see Offices in China Nos. 1-6, 16, Offices in Morocco 1-6, Offices in Turkey 8-12.

Germania — A11

**1900, Jan. 1 Perf. 14**

52 A11 2pf gray .85 .50
*a.* Imperf. 350.00
Never hinged 1,600.
53 A11 3pf brown .85 1.00
*a.* Imperf. 350.00
Never hinged 1,600.
54 A11 5pf green 1.00 .60
55 A11 10pf carmine 1.75 .75
*a.* Imperf. 45.00
Never hinged 100.00
56 A11 20pf ultra 7.50 .60
57 A11 25pf orange & blk,
*yel* 13.50 4.50
58 A11 30pf orange & blk,
*sal* 18.50 .85
59 A11 40pf lake & black 22.50 1.25
60 A11 50pf pur & blk, *sal* 22.50 1.00
61 A11 80pf lake & blk, *rose* 37.50 2.25
*Nos. 52-61 (10)* 126.45 13.30
Set, never hinged 795.00

Early printings of Nos. 57-61 had "REICH-SPOST" in taller and thicker letters than on the ordinary stamps.

For surcharges see Nos. 65B, Offices in China 17-32, Offices in Morocco 7-15, 32A, Offices in Turkey 13-20, 25-27.

**"REICHSPOST" Larger**

57a A11 25pf 1,800. 4,500.
58a A11 30pf 1,800. 4,500.
59a A11 40pf 1,800. 4,500.
60a A11 50pf 1,800. 4,500.
61a A11 80pf 1,800. 4,500.

General Post
Office in
Berlin — A12

"Union of
North and
South
Germany"
A13

Unveiling
Kaiser
Wilhelm I
Memorial,
Berlin — A14

Wilhelm II
Speaking at
Empire's
25th
Anniversary
Celebration
A15

Two types of 5m:
I — "5" is thick; "M" has slight serifs.
II — "5" thinner; "M" has distinct serifs.

**Engr. Perf. 14½x14**

62 A12 1m carmine rose 100.00 1.90
Never hinged 400.00
*a.* Imperf. 2,600.
63 A13 2m gray blue 75.00 6.75
Never hinged 450.00
64 A14 3m black violet 97.50 45.00
Never hinged 600.00
65 A15 5m slate & car, I 1,250. 2,100.
Never hinged 4,500.
*d.* Red and white retouched 325.00 350.00
Never hinged 1,350.
*e.* White only retouched 600.00 600.00
Never hinged 1,650.
65A A15 5m slate & car, II 325.00 375.00
Never hinged 1,350.

Nos. 62-65 exist perf. 11½.
The vignette and frame of No. 65 usually did not align perfectly during printing. Red paint was used to retouch the vignette and/or white paint was used to retouch the inner frame.
No. 62a is without gum.
For surcharges see Offices in China Nos. 33-36A, Offices in Morocco 16-19A, Offices in Turkey 21-24B, 28-30.

Half of No. 54 Handstamp
Surcharged in Violet  **3PF**

**1901 Perf. 14**

65B A11 3pf on half of 5pf 9,750. 7,500.
Never hinged 26,500.

This provisional was produced aboard the German cruiser Vineta. The purser, with the ship commander's approval, surcharged and bisected 300 5pf stamps so the ship's post office could meet the need for a 3pf (printed matter rate). The crew wanted to send home U.S. newspapers reporting celebrations of the Kaiser's birthday.
Forgeries exist and improper usages as well.

A16

**1902 Typo.**

65C A16 2pf gray 1.50 .60
66 A16 3pf brown .75 1.00
*a.* "DFUTSCHES" 9.75 40.00
Never hinged 30.00
67 A16 5pf green 2.25 1.00
68 A16 10pf carmine 7.25 1.00
69 A16 20pf ultra 3.00 1.00
70 A16 25pf org & blk, *yel* 45.00 2.10
71 A16 30pf org & blk, *sal* 52.50 .60
72 A16 40pf lake & blk 67.50 1.00
73 A16 50pf pur & blk, *buff* 67.50 1.10

74 A16 80pf lake & blk,
*rose* 150.00 2.75
*Nos. 65C-74 (10)* 424.25 12.15
Set, never hinged 1,900.

Nos. 65C-74 exist imperf. Value, set $2,000.
See Nos. 80-91, 118-119, 121-132, 169, 174, 210. For surcharges see Nos. 133-136, B1, Offices in China 37-42, 47-52, Offices in Morocco 20-28, 33-41, 45-53, Offices in Turkey 31-38, 43-50, 55-59.

A17

A18

A19

A20

**Perf. 14, 14¼-14½**
**Engr.**

75 A17 1m carmine rose 240.00 2.75
*a.* Imperf. 900.00
76 A18 2m gray blue 82.50 97.50
77 A19 3m black violet 75.00 18.00
*a.* Imperf. 900.00
78 A20 5m slate & car 210.00 18.00
*a.* Imperf. 900.00

See Nos. 92, 94-95, 102, 111-113. For surcharges see Nos. 115-116, Offices in China 43, 45-46, 53, 55-56, Offices in Morocco 29, 31-32, 42, 44, 54, 56-57, Offices in Turkey 39, 41-42, 51, 53-54.

A21

79 A21 2m gray blue 120.00 5.00
*a.* Imperf. 900.00 —
Never hinged 2,500.
*Nos. 75-79 (5)* 727.50 141.25
Set, never hinged 3,125.

See Nos. 93, 114. For surcharges see Nos. 117, Offices in China 44, 54, Offices in Morocco 30, 43, 55, Offices in Turkey 40, 52.

**1905-19 Typo. Wmk. 125 Perf. 14**

80 A16 2pf gray 1.60 2.60
81 A16 3pf brown .60 1.40
82 A16 5pf green
(shades) .60 1.40
*b.* Bklt. pane of 5 + label
('11) 250.00 500.00
Never hinged 500.00
*c.* Bklt. pane of 4 + 2 labels
('10) 400.00 800.00
Never hinged 800.00
*d.* Bklt. pane of 2 + 4 labels
('12) 250.00 500.00
Never hinged 500.00
*e.* Bklt. pane, #82 + 5 #83
('17) 75.00 190.00
Never hinged 190.00
*f.* Bklt. pane, 2 #82 + 4 #83
('20) 21.00 50.00
Never hinged 50.00
*g.* Bklt. pane, 4 #82 + 2 #83
('19) 21.00 50.00
Never hinged 50.00
83 A16 10pf red .60 1.40
*b.* Bklt. pane of 5 + label
('10) 325.00 650.00
Never hinged 650.00
*c.* Bklt. pane of 4 + 2 labels
('12) 300.00 625.00
Never hinged 625.00
*d.* 10pf carmine red 2.00 1.50
Never hinged
84 A16 20pf blue vio
('18) .75 1.40
*a.* 20pf light blue 13.00 3.75
Never hinged 52.50

*b.* 20pf ultramarine 8.00 1.50
Never hinged 92.50
*c.* Imperf. 625.00 2,750.
Never hinged 1,750.
*d.* Half used as 10pf on
cover 700.00
85 A16 25pf org & blk,
*yel* .60 1.40
86 A16 30pf org & blk,
*buff* .60 1.40
*a.* 30pf org & blk, *cr* 26.00 90.00
Never hinged 82.50
87 A16 40pf lake & black 1.00 1.40
88 A16 50pf pur & blk,
*buff* .60 1.40
89 A16 60pf magenta 1.50 1.40
*a.* 60pf red violet 22.50 13.50
Never hinged 67.50
90 A16 75pf green & blk
('19) .25 2.25
91 A16 80pf lake & blk,
*rose* 1.10 1.90

**Perf. 14½ (25x17 holes)**
**Engr.**

92 A17 1m carmine
rose 2.25 2.25
93 A21 2m brt blue 5.25 4.75
*a.* 2m gray blue 42.50 52.50
Never hinged 140.00
94 A19 3m violet gray 2.25 4.25
*b.* 3m black-brown violet 11.50 26.00
Never hinged 26.00
95 A20 5m slate & car 1.90 4.75
*a.* Center inverted 45,000. 65,000.
*Nos. 80-95 (16)* 21.45 35.35
Set, never hinged 52.50

Pre-war printings of Nos. 80-91 have brighter colors and white instead of yellow gum. They sell for considerably more than the wartime printings which are valued here. No. 80 exists only from a pre-war printing.
Nos. 92-95 exist only from a wartime printing. The 1m-5m also exist perf 14¼-13¾ (26x17 holes) in both pre-war and wartime printings. Both of these printings are much more expensive than Nos. 92-95. See the *Scott Classic Specialized Catalogue* for detailed listings.
Labels in No. 82c contain an "X." The version with advertising is worth 3 times as much. No. 82f has three 10pf stamps in the top row. The version with 3 on the bottom row is worth 4 times as much.
No. 84d was used at Field Post Office No. 107 in 1915, and at Field Post Office No. 766 during 1917.

Surcharged and overprinted stamps of designs A16-A22 are listed under Allenstein, Belgium, Danzig, France, Latvia, Lithuania, Marienwerder, Memel, Poland, Romania, Saar and Upper Silesia.

A22

**1916-19 Typo.**

96 A22 2pf lt gray ('18) .25 3.25
97 A22 2½pf lt gray .25 1.90
98 A22 7½pf red orange .30 2.25
*b.* Bklt. pane, 4 #98 + 2 #100 110.00 275.00
Never hinged 275.00
*c.* Bklt. pane, 2 #98 + 4 #99 125.00 300.00
Never hinged 300.00
*d.* Bklt. pane, 2 #98 + 4 #100 110.00 275.00
Never hinged 275.00
*e.* Bklt. pane, 2 #82 + 4 #98 37.50 90.00
Never hinged 90.00
*f.* 7½pf yellow orange 3.25 2.25
99 A22 15pf yellow brown 3.00 2.25
100 A22 15pf dk violet ('17) .20 1.90
*b.* Bklt. pane, 4 #82 + 2 #100 110.00 275.00
Never hinged 275.00
*c.* Bklt. pane, 2 #83 + 4 #100 82.50 210.00
Never hinged 210.00
101 A22 35pf red brown
('19) .20 1.25
*Nos. 96-101 (6)* 4.20 12.80
Set, never hinged 13.50

See No. 120. For surcharge see No. B2.
Nos. 98e and 100c have the 2 stamps first in the bottom row.

Type of 1902

**1920 Engr. Wmk. 192 Perf. 14½**

102 A19 3m black violet 1,875. 3,750.
Never hinged 4,500.

| | | | | |
|---|---|---|---|---|
| 3 A64 | 15pf maroon ('34) | .30 | .35 |
| 4 A64 | 20pf brt blue ('34) | .45 | .35 |
| 5 A64 | 25pf ultra ('34) | .45 | .35 |
| 6 A64 | 30pf olive grn ('34) | .75 | .35 |
| 6 A64 | 40pf red violet ('34) | .75 | .35 |
| 6 A64 | 50pf dk grn & blk ('34) | 3.00 | .35 |
| A64 | 60pf claret & blk ('34) | .75 | .35 |
| A64 | 80pf dk bl & blk ('36) | 2.25 | 1.25 |
| A64 | 100pf org & blk ('34) | 3.00 | 1.10 |
| | Nos. 415-431 (17) | 13.30 | 7.60 |
| | Set, never hinged | 100.00 | |

Karl
ers — A66

Swastika, Sun
and
Nuremberg
Castle — A70

ns: 3pf, Franz Adolf E. Lüderitz. 6pf,
stav Nachtigal. 25pf, Hermann von
ann.

| June 30 | Perf. 13x13½ | | |
|---|---|---|---|
| 6 | 3pf brown & choc | 2.25 | 6.00 |
| 6 | 6pf dk grn & choc | 1.10 | 1.50 |
| 6 | 12pf dk car & choc | 1.75 | 1.50 |
| 6 | 25pf brt blue & choc | 9.00 | 20.00 |
| | Nos. 432-435 (4) | 14.10 | 29.00 |
| | never hinged | 149.00 | |

in remembrance of the lost colonies
any.

denburg Memorial Issue
Type of 1932
With Black Border

| pt. 4 | | Perf. 14 | |
|---|---|---|---|
| | 3pf olive bister | .75 | .45 |
| | 5pf brt green | .75 | .55 |
| | 6pf dk green | 1.40 | .45 |
| | 8pf vermilion | 2.25 | .45 |
| | 12pf deep carmine | 2.25 | .45 |
| | 25pf ultra | 6.75 | 8.25 |
| | Nos. 436-441 (6) | 14.15 | 10.60 |
| | ever hinged | 120.00 | |

| pt. 1 | | Photo. | |
|---|---|---|---|
| | 6pf dark green | 3.00 | .60 |
| | 2pf dark carmine | 3.75 | .60 |
| | er hinged | 63.50 | |

Congress at Nuremberg.
exist. Value never hinged, each.

German
Eagle
A72

| 26 | Typo. | Wmk. 237 | |
|---|---|---|---|
| | dark green | 3.00 | .60 |
| | dark carmine | 3.25 | .60 |
| | hinged | 63.50 | |

mark the Saar Plebiscite.

Germania
Welcoming
Home the
Saar
A74

| | | | |
|---|---|---|---|
| een | | 2.50 | .60 |
| armine | | 4.50 | .60 |
| ged | | 82.50 | |

the birth of von Schiller.

---

| 1935, Jan. 16 | | Photo. | |
|---|---|---|---|
| 448 A74 | 3pf brown | .35 | 1.10 |
| 449 A74 | 6pf dark green | .35 | .75 |
| 450 A74 | 12pf lake | 1.75 | .75 |
| 451 A74 | 25pf dark blue | 7.25 | 8.25 |
| | Nos. 448-451 (4) | 9.70 | 10.85 |
| | Set, never hinged | 92.50 | |

Return of the Saar to Germany.

German
Soldier
A75

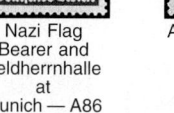

Wreath and
Swastika
A76

| 1935, Mar. 15 | | | |
|---|---|---|---|
| 452 A75 | 6pf dark green | .75 | 1.50 |
| 453 A75 | 12pf copper red | .75 | 1.50 |
| | Set, never hinged | 15.75 | |

Issued to commemorate War Heroes' Day.

| 1935, Apr. 26 | | Unwmk. | |
|---|---|---|---|
| 454 A76 | 6pf dark green | .75 | 1.40 |
| 455 A76 | 12pf crimson | .90 | 1.40 |
| | Set, never hinged | 18.00 | |

Young Workers' Professional Competitions.

Heinrich
Schütz — A77

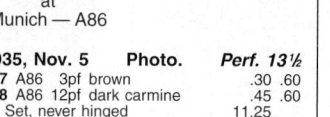

"The
Eagle" — A80

| | Wmk. Swastikas (237) | | |
|---|---|---|---|
| 1935, June 21 | Engr. | Perf. 14 | |
| 456 A77 | 6pf shown | .45 | .50 |
| 457 A77 | 12pf Bach | .65 | .50 |
| 458 A77 | 25pf Handel | 1.10 | .90 |
| | Nos. 456-458 (3) | 2.20 | 1.90 |
| | Set, never hinged | 24.00 | |

Schutz-Bach-Handel celebration.

| 1935, July 10 | | Perf. 14 | |
|---|---|---|---|

Designs: 12pf, Modern express train. 25pf,
"The Hamburg Flyer." 40pf, Streamlined
locomotive.

| 459 A80 | 6pf dark green | .90 | .60 |
|---|---|---|---|
| 460 A80 | 12pf copper red | .90 | .60 |
| 461 A80 | 25pf ultra | 5.00 | 1.75 |
| 462 A80 | 40pf red violet | 8.25 | 1.75 |
| | Nos. 459-462 (4) | 15.05 | 4.70 |
| | Set, never hinged | 102.00 | |

Centenary of railroad in Germany.
Exist imperf. Value, $225 each.

Otto von
Guericke
A90

Symbolical of
Municipalities
A91

| 1936, May 4 | | | |
|---|---|---|---|
| 472 A90 | 6pf dark green | .30 | .45 |
| | Never hinged | 1.20 | |

250th anniv. of the death of the German
inventor, Otto von Guericke, May 11, 1686.

| 1936, June 3 | | | |
|---|---|---|---|
| 473 A91 | 3pf dark brown | .20 | .30 |
| 474 A91 | 6pf deep green | .20 | .30 |
| 475 A91 | 12pf lake | .30 | .50 |
| 476 A91 | 25pf dark ultra | .50 | 1.00 |
| | Nos. 473-476 (4) | 1.20 | 2.10 |
| | Set, never hinged | 15.00 | |

6th Intl. Cong. of Municipalities, June 7-13.

Bugler of Hitler
Youth Movement
A84

Eagle and
Swastika over
Nuremberg
A85

| 1935, July 25 | | Photo. | |
|---|---|---|---|
| 463 A84 | 6pf deep green | 1.10 | 2.25 |
| 464 A84 | 15pf brown lake | 1.50 | 2.50 |
| | Set, never hinged | 18.75 | |

Hitler Youth Meeting.

| 1935, Aug. 30 | | Engr. | |
|---|---|---|---|
| 465 A85 | 6pf gray green | .75 | .35 |
| 466 A85 | 12pf dark carmine | 1.90 | .35 |
| | Set, never hinged | 15.00 | |

1935 Nazi Congress at Nuremberg.

---

Nazi Flag
Bearer and
Feldherrnhalle
at
Munich — A86

Airplane — A87

| 1935, Nov. 5 | | Photo. | Perf. 13½ |
|---|---|---|---|
| 467 A86 | 3pf brown | .30 | .60 |
| 468 A86 | 12pf dark carmine | .45 | .60 |
| | Set, never hinged | 11.25 | |

12th anniv. of the 1st Hitler "Putsch" at
Munich, Nov. 9, 1923.

| 1936, Jan. 6 | | | |
|---|---|---|---|
| 469 A87 | 40pf sapphire | 5.25 | 3.00 |
| | Never hinged | 42.50 | |

10th anniv. of the Lufthansa air service.

Gottlieb
Daimler — A88

Carl
Benz — A89

| 1936, Feb. 15 | | Perf. 14 | |
|---|---|---|---|
| 470 A88 | 6pf dark green | .50 | .75 |
| 471 A89 | 12pf copper red | .50 | .75 |
| | Set, never hinged | 12.00 | |

The 50th anniv. of the automobile; Intl. Automobile and Motorcycle Show, Berlin.

Cathedral
Island
A96

Hermann
Goering
Stadium
A97

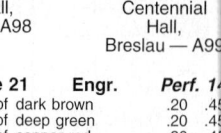

Town Hall,
Breslau — A98

Centennial
Hall,
Breslau — A99

| 1938, June 21 | | Engr. | Perf. 14 |
|---|---|---|---|
| 486 A96 | 3pf dark brown | .20 | .45 |
| 487 A97 | 6pf deep green | .20 | .45 |
| 488 A98 | 12pf copper red | .30 | .45 |
| 489 A99 | 15pf violet brown | .60 | .75 |
| | Nos. 486-489 (4) | 1.30 | 2.10 |
| | Set, never hinged | 12.00 | |

16th German Gymnastic and Sports Festival held at Breslau, July 23-31, 1938.

Nazi Emblem — A100

| 1939, Apr. 4 | | Photo. | Wmk. 237 |
|---|---|---|---|
| 490 A100 | 6pf dark green | 1.10 | 3.75 |
| 491 A100 | 12pf deep carmine | 1.50 | 3.75 |
| | Set, never hinged | 18.75 | |

Young Workers' Professional Competitions.

St. Mary's
Church — A101

The Kran
Danzig —

---

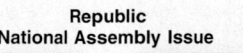

Shield
Bearer — A94

German and
Austrian
Carrying Nazi
Flag — A95

| 1937, Mar. 3 | | Engr. | Unwmk. |
|---|---|---|---|
| 481 A94 | 3pf brown | .20 | .30 |
| 482 A94 | 6pf green | .20 | .30 |
| 483 A94 | 12pf carmine | .50 | .60 |
| | Nos. 481-483 (3) | .90 | 1.20 |
| | Set, never hinged | 11.00 | |

The Reich's Air Protection League.

| Wmk. Swastikas (237) | | | |
|---|---|---|---|
| 1938, Apr. 8 | Photo. | Perf. 14x13½ | |
| Size: 23x28mm | | | |
| 484 A95 | 6pf dark green | .20 | .45 |
| | Never hinged | 1.00 | |

| Unwmk. | | Perf. 12½ | |
|---|---|---|---|
| Size: 21½x26mm | | | |
| 485 A95 | 6pf deep green | .20 | .50 |
| | Never hinged | 1.10 | |

Union of Austria and Germany.

---

## Republic
### National Assembly Issue

A23

A24

Rebuilding
Germany — A25

Designs: A23, Live Stump of Tree Symbolizing that Germany will Survive her Difficulties.
A24, New Shoots from Oak Stump Symbolical
of New Government.

| | Perf. 13x13½ | | |
|---|---|---|---|
| 1919-20 | Unwmk. | Typo. | |
| 105 A23 | 10pf carmine rose | .20 | 1.50 |
| 106 A24 | 15pf choc & blue | .20 | 1.50 |
| 107 A25 | 25pf green & red | .20 | 1.50 |
| 108 A25 | 30pf red vio & red ('20) | .20 | 1.50 |
| | Nos. 105-108 (4) | .80 | 6.00 |
| | Set, never hinged | 2.65 | |

"1019" instead of "1919" is the result of broken type.

### Types of 1902

| | Perf. 15x14½ | | |
|---|---|---|---|
| 1920 | Wmk. 125 | Offset | |
| 111 A17 | 1m red | 1.90 | 2.25 |
| 112 A17 | 1.25m green | 1.50 | 1.75 |
| 113 A17 | 1.50m yellow brown | .45 | 1.75 |
| 114 A21 | 2.50m lilac rose | .45 | 2.25 |
| a. | 2.50m magenta | 1.50 | 12.00 |
| b. | 2.50m brown lilac | .60 | 2.75 |
| | Nos. 111-114 (4) | 4.30 | 8.00 |
| | Set, never hinged | 14.00 | |

Nos. 111, 112 and 113 differ from the illustration in many minor respects. The numerals
of Nos. 75 and 92 are outlined, with shaded
background. Those of No. 111 are plain, with
solid background and flags have been added
to the top of the building, at right and left.

### Types of 1902 Surcharged

| 1920 | Engr. | Perf. 14½ | |
|---|---|---|---|
| 115 A17 | 1.25m on 1m green | .40 | 6.00 |
| 116 A17 | 1.50m on 1m org brn | .30 | 6.75 |
| 117 A21 | 2.50m on 2m lilac rose | 8.75 | 200.00 |
| | Nos. 115-117 (3) | 9.45 | |
| | Set, never hinged | 25.00 | |

### Germania Types of 1902-16

| 1920 | Typo. | Perf. 14, 14½ | |
|---|---|---|---|
| 118 A16 | 5pf brown | .20 | 1.90 |
| 119 A16 | 10pf orange | .20 | 1.50 |
| a. | Tête bêche pair | .90 | 5.75 |
| | Never hinged | 2.25 | |
| d. | Bklt. pane, 4 #119 + 2 #123 | 2.40 | 13.00 |
| | Never hinged | 6.00 | |
| 120 A22 | 15pf violet brn | .20 | 1.90 |
| a. | Imperf. | 67.50 | |
| | Never hinged | 190.00 | |
| c. | Bklt. pane, 4 #84 + 2 #120 | 7.25 | 17.00 |
| | Never hinged | 17.00 | |
| 121 A16 | 20pf green | .20 | 2.25 |
| a. | Imperf. | | 1,200. |
| 123 A16 | 30pf dull blue | .20 | 1.50 |
| a. | Tête bêche pair | .90 | 6.75 |
| | Never hinged | 2.25 | |
| d. | Bklt. pane, 2 #123 + 4 #124 | 2.40 | 13.00 |
| | Never hinged | 6.00 | |
| 124 A16 | 40pf carmine rose | .20 | 1.90 |
| a. | Tête bêche pair | .90 | 6.75 |
| | Never hinged | 2.25 | |
| b. | Imperf. | 150.00 | 900.00 |
| | Never hinged | 375.00 | |
| d. | Bklt. pane, 2 #124 + 4 #126 | 4.50 | 42.50 |
| | Never hinged | 11.50 | |

---

| 125 A16 | 50pf red lilac | .60 | 1.90 |
|---|---|---|---|
| 126 A16 | 60pf olive green | .20 | 1.60 |
| a. | Tête bêche pair | .70 | 9.75 |
| | Never hinged | 1.75 | |
| c. | Imperf. | 160.00 | |
| | Never hinged | 425.00 | |
| 127 A16 | 75pf red violet | .60 | 1.90 |
| 128 A16 | 80pf blue violet | .20 | 2.25 |
| a. | Imperf. | 190.00 | |
| | Never hinged | 450.00 | |
| 129 A16 | 1m violet & grn | .20 | 2.25 |
| a. | Imperf. | 77.50 | |
| 130 A16 | 1¼m ver & mag | .60 | 1.50 |
| 131 A16 | 2m carmine & bl | .60 | 1.50 |
| 132 A16 | 4m black & rose | .20 | 2.25 |
| | Nos. 118-132 (14) | 4.00 | 26.50 |
| | Set, never hinged | 10.50 | |

### Stamps of 1920 Surcharged:

No. 133

No. 135

Nos. 134, 136

| 1921, Aug. | | | |
|---|---|---|---|
| 133 A16 | 1.60m on 5pf | .20 | 2.25 |
| 134 A16 | 3m on 1¼m | .20 | 2.25 |
| 135 A16 | 5m on 75pf (G) | .20 | 2.25 |
| 136 A16 | 10m on 75pf | .40 | 2.25 |
| | Nos. 133-136 (4) | 1.00 | 9.00 |
| | Set, never hinged | 3.50 | |

In 1920 the current stamps of Bavaria
were overprinted "Deutsches Reich". These
stamps were available for postage throughout Germany, but because
they were used almost exclusively in
Bavaria, they are listed among the
issues of that state.

Iron Workers
A27

Miners
A28

Farmers
A29

Post Horn
A30

Plowing
A32

A26

Numeral of
Value — A31

---

| | Wmk. Lozenges (125) | | |
|---|---|---|---|
| 1921 | Typo. | Perf. 14 | |
| 137 A26 | 5pf claret | .20 | 1.75 |
| 138 A26 | 10pf olive green | .20 | 1.90 |
| a. | Tête bêche pair | .85 | 21.00 |
| b. | Bklt. pane, 5 #138 + 1 #141 | 4.50 | 60.00 |
| | Never hinged | 11.50 | |
| 139 A26 | 15pf grnsh blue | .20 | 1.60 |
| 140 A26 | 25pf dark brown | .20 | 1.60 |
| 141 A26 | 30pf blue green | .20 | 1.60 |
| a. | Tête bêche pair | .70 | 19.00 |
| b. | Bklt. pane, 2 #124 + 4 #141 | 5.00 | 42.50 |
| | Never hinged | 12.00 | |
| 142 A26 | 40pf red orange | .20 | 1.40 |
| 143 A26 | 50pf violet | .30 | 1.60 |
| 144 A27 | 60pf red violet | .20 | 1.40 |
| 145 A27 | 80pf carmine rose | .20 | 5.25 |
| 146 A28 | 100pf yellow grn | .30 | 1.90 |
| 147 A28 | 120pf ultra | .20 | 1.90 |
| 148 A29 | 150pf orange | .20 | 1.90 |
| 149 A29 | 160pf slate grn | .20 | 8.25 |
| 150 A30 | 2m dp vio & rose | .40 | 3.50 |
| 151 A30 | 3m red & yel | .40 | 15.00 |
| 152 A30 | 4m dp grn & yel grn | .20 | 3.50 |

| 1922-23 | | | |
|---|---|---|---|
| SIX MARKS: | | | |
| Type I — Numerals upright. | | | |
| Type II — Numerals leaning toward the right and slightly thinner. | | | |
| EIGHT MARKS: | | | |
| Type I — Numerals 2½mm wide with thick strokes. | | | |
| Type II — Numerals 2mm wide with thinner strokes. | | | |

| 153 A31 | 5m orange | .30 | 2.25 |
|---|---|---|---|
| 154 A31 | 10m carmine rose | .50 | 2.50 |
| 155 A32 | 20m indigo & grn | 1.10 | 2.75 |
| a. | Green background inverted | 190.00 | 900.00 |
| | Never hinged | 675.00 | |
| | Nos. 137-155 (19) | 5.70 | 61.25 |
| | Set, never hinged | 16.00 | |

See Nos. 156-209, 211, 222-223, 225, 227.
For surcharges and overprints see Nos. 241-
245, 247-248, 261-262, 273-276, B6-B7, O24.

| 1922 | Litho. | Perf. 14½x14 | |
|---|---|---|---|
| 156 A31 | 100m brown vio, buff | .20 | 1.40 |
| 157 A31 | 200m rose, buff | .20 | 1.40 |
| 158 A31 | 300m green, buff | .20 | 1.40 |
| a. | Imperf. | 110.00 | |
| 159 A31 | 400m bls brn, buff | .50 | 2.25 |
| 160 A31 | 500m orange, buff | .20 | 1.40 |
| | Nos. 156-160 (5) | 1.30 | 7.85 |
| | Set, never hinged | 3.40 | |

### Postally Used vs. CTO

Values quoted for canceled copies of
the 1921-1923 issues are for postally
used stamps. These bring higher prices
than the plentiful canceled-to-order
specimens made by applying genuine
handstamps to remainders. C.T.O.
examples sell for about the same price
as unused stamps. Certification of postal usage by competent authorities is
necessary.

| 1921-22 | Typo. | Wmk. 126 | |
|---|---|---|---|
| 161 A26 | 5pf claret | .75 | 200.00 |
| 162 A26 | 10pf olive grn | 6.75 | 175.00 |
| 163 A26 | 15pf grnsh blue | .55 | 210.00 |
| 164 A26 | 25pf dark brown | .20 | 3.00 |
| 165 A26 | 30pf blue green | .85 | 300.00 |
| 166 A26 | 40pf red orange | .20 | 3.75 |
| 167 A26 | 50pf violet ('21) | .20 | 1.50 |
| 168 A27 | 60pf red violet | .20 | 20.00 |
| 169 A16 | 75pf red violet | .35 | 2.25 |
| 170 A27 | 75pf deep ultra | .20 | 3.00 |
| 171 A27 | 80pf car rose | .40 | 55.00 |
| 172 A28 | 120pf olive green | .20 | 1.50 |
| a. | Imperf. | 60.00 | 1,500. |
| | Never hinged | 150.00 | |

---

| 173 A28 | 120pf ultra | .70 | 110.00 |
|---|---|---|---|
| 174 A16 | 1¼m ver & mag | .55 | 3.75 |
| 175 A29 | 150pf orange | .20 | 1.40 |
| a. | Imperf. | 37.50 | |
| | Never hinged | 110.00 | |
| 176 A29 | 160pf slate green | .70 | 160.00 |
| 177 A30 | 2m violet & rose | .20 | 1.40 |
| 178 A30 | 3m red & yel ('21) | .20 | 1.40 |
| a. | Imperf. | 37.50 | 375.00 |
| | Never hinged | 110.00 | |
| 179 A30 | 4m dp grn & yel grn | .20 | 1.40 |
| 180 A30 | 5m org & yel | .30 | 1.90 |
| a. | Imperf. | 140.00 | |
| 181 A30 | 10m car & pale rose | .30 | 1.50 |
| a. | Pale rose (background) omitted | 45.00 | 975.00 |
| 182 A30 | 20m violet & org | .20 | 2.50 |
| 183 A30 | 30m brown & yel | .20 | 1.50 |
| 184 A30 | 50m dk green & vio | .20 | 1.50 |
| | Nos. 161-184 (24) | 14.80 | 1,263. |
| | Set, never hinged | 37.50 | |

| 1922-23 | | | |
|---|---|---|---|
| 185 A30 | 2m blue violet | .20 | 1.50 |
| a. | Imperf. | 140.00 | |
| 186 A30 | 3m red | .20 | 1.50 |
| 187 A30 | 4m dark green | .20 | 1.50 |
| a. | Imperf. | 30.00 | |
| 188 A30 | 5m orange | .20 | 1.50 |
| a. | Imperf. | 110.00 | |
| 189 A30 | 6m dark blue (II) | .20 | 1.50 |
| a. | 6m dark blue (I) | .20 | 1.90 |
| | Imperf. | 110.00 | |
| 190 A30 | 8m olive green (I) | .20 | 1.50 |
| a. | 8m olive green (II) | .40 | 37.50 |
| 191 A30 | 20m dk violet ('23) | .20 | 1.50 |
| 192 A30 | 30m pur brn ('23) | .20 | 7.25 |
| 193 A30 | 40m lt green | .20 | 1.90 |

| | Engr. | | |
|---|---|---|---|
| 194 A30 | 5m orange | .25 | 1.50 |
| a. | Imperf. | 140.00 | |
| 195 A31 | 10m carmine rose | .55 | 2.25 |
| 196 A32 | 20m indigo & grn | .20 | 3.50 |
| a. | Imperf. | 175.00 | |
| b. | Green background inverted | 32.50 | 400.00 |
| | Nos. 185-196 (12) | 2.80 | 26.90 |
| | Set, never hinged | 8.85 | |

| 1922-23 | Litho. | Perf. 14½x14 | |
|---|---|---|---|
| 198 A31 | 50m indigo | .20 | 1.50 |
| 199 A31 | 100m brn vio, buff ('23) | .20 | 1.40 |
| 200 A31 | 200m rose, buff ('23) | .20 | 1.90 |
| 201 A31 | 300m grn, buff ('23) | .20 | 1.50 |
| 202 A31 | 400m bis brn, buff ('23) | .20 | 1.50 |
| 203 A31 | 500m org, buff ('23) | .20 | 1.50 |
| 204 A31 | 1000m gray ('23) | .20 | 1.50 |
| 205 A31 | 2000m blue ('23) | .35 | 1.90 |
| 206 A31 | 3000m brown ('23) | .20 | 2.75 |
| 207 A31 | 4000m violet ('23) | .20 | 1.50 |
| a. | Imperf. | 37.50 | 190.00 |
| | Never hinged | 110.00 | |

208 A31 5000m gray grn ('23) .30 1.50
a. Imperf. 52.50 225.00
   Never hinged 150.00
209 A31 100,000m ver ('23) .20 1.40
a. Imperf. 52.50 225.00
   Never hinged 150.00
   Nos. 198-209 (12) 2.65 19.85
   Set, never hinged 5.35

**1920-22    Wmk. 127    Typo.**
210 A16 1¼m ver & mag 450.00 725.00
    Never hinged 1,150.
211 A30 50m grn & vio ('22) 1.10 775.00
    Never hinged 3.25

Wmk. 127 was intended for use only in printing revenue stamps.

Arms of Munich — A33

**Wmk. Network (126)**
**1922, Apr. 22    Typo.    Perf. 13x13½**
212 A33 1¼m claret .20 1.90
213 A33 2m dark violet .20 1.90
214 A33 3m vermilion .20 1.90
215 A33 4m deep blue .20 1.90

**Wmk. Lozenges (125)**
216 A33 10m brown, buff .55 2.75
217 A33 20m lilac rose, pink 3.25 11.50
    Nos. 212-217 (6) 4.60 21.85
    Set, never hinged 14.70
Munich Industrial Fair.

Type of 1921 and

Miners — A34        A35

**1922-23    Wmk. 126    Perf. 14**
221 A34 5m orange .20 13.00
222 A29 10m dull blue ('22) .20 1.50
223 A29 12m vermilion ('22) .20 1.50
224 A34 20m red lilac .20 1.50
225 A29 25m olive brown .20 1.50
226 A34 30m olive green .20 2.25
227 A29 40m green .20 1.50
228 A34 50m grnsh blue .35 110.00
229 A35 100m violet .20 1.50
230 A35 200m carmine rose .20 1.50
231 A35 300m green .20 1.40
232 A35 400m dark brown .20 5.75
233 A35 500m red orange .20 6.00
234 A35 1000m slate .20 1.40
    Nos. 221-234 (14) 2.95 150.30
    Set, never hinged 6.50
The 50m was issued only in vertical coils.
Nos. 222-223 exist imperf.
For surcharges and overprints see Nos. 246, 249-260, 263-271, 277, 310, B5, O22-O23, O25-O28.

Wartburg Castle — A36

Cathedral of Cologne — A37

**1923    Engr.**
237 A36 5000m deep blue .30 2.75
a. Imperf. 300.00 750.00
   Never hinged 1,100.
238 A37 10,000m brn ol .30 3.75
   Set, never hinged 1.50

Abbreviations:
Th = (Tausend) Thousand
Mil = (Million) Million
Mlrd = (Milliarde) Billion

A38

**1923    Typo.**
238A A38 5th m grnsh blue .20 17.00
a. Imperf. 90.00
   Never hinged 240.00
239 A38 50th m bister .20 1.50
a. Imperf. 22.50 3,750.
   Never hinged 60.00
240 A38 75th m dark violet .20 11.00
   Nos. 238A-240 (3) .60 29.50
   Set, never hinged 1.10
For surcharges see Nos. 272, 278.

Stamps and Types of 1922-23 Surcharged in Black, Blue, Green or Brown with Bars over Original Value

**Wmk. Lozenges (125)**
**1923    Perf. 14**
241 A26 8th m on 30pf .20 1.50
a. "8" inverted 21.00 325.00
   Never hinged 60.00

**Wmk. Network (126)**
242 A26 5th m on 40pf .20 1.60
242A A26 8th m on 40pf 16.00 6,000.
243 A29 15th m on 40m .20 1.50
244 A29 20th m on 12m .20 1.50
a. Inverted surcharge 110.00 1,000.
245 A29 20th m on 25m .20 2.25
246 A35 20th m on 200m .20 2.25
a. Inverted surcharge 57.50 750.00
   Never hinged 150.00
247 A29 25th m on 10m .20 14.50
248 A30 30th m on 10m dp bl .20 1.40
a. Inverted surcharge 67.50
   Never hinged 175.00
249 A35 30th m on 200m pale bl (Bl) .20 1.50
a. Without surcharge 110.00
   Never hinged 225.00
250 A35 75th m on 300m yel grn .20 14.50
a. Imperf. 45.00
   Never hinged 125.00
251 A35 75th m on 400m yel grn .20 1.90
a. Without surcharge 110.00
   Never hinged 225.00
252 A35 75th m on 1000m yel grn .20 1.90
a. Without surcharge 110.00
   Never hinged 225.00
253 A35 100th m on 100m .20 2.25
a. Double surcharge 37.50 450.00
   Never hinged 97.50
b. Inverted surcharge 14.50
   Never hinged 37.50
254 A35 100th m on 400m bluish grn (G) .20 1.40
a. Imperf. 50.00 525.00
   Never hinged 110.00
b. Without surcharge 110.00
   Never hinged 225.00
255 A35 125th m on 1000m sal .20 1.90
256 A35 250th m on 200m .20 5.25
a. Inverted surcharge 35.00
   Never hinged 90.00
b. Double surcharge 52.50
   Never hinged 140.00
257 A35 250th m on 300m dp grn .20 17.00
a. Inverted surcharge 35.00
   Never hinged 90.00
258 A35 250th m on 400m .20 19.00
a. Inverted surcharge 26.00
   Never hinged 75.00
259 A35 250th m on 500m pink .20 1.50
a. Imperf. 52.50 675.00
   Never hinged 125.00

260 A35 250th m on 500m red org .20 19.00
a. Double surcharge 30.00 975.00
   Never hinged 75.00
b. Inverted surcharge 30.00
   Never hinged 82.50
261 A26 800th m on 5pf lt grn (G) .20 4.25
a. Imperf. 35.00 150.00
   Never hinged 90.00
262 A26 800th m on 10pf lt grn (G) .20 5.00
a. Imperf. 30.00
   Never hinged 90.00
263 A35 800th m on 200m .20 75.00
a. Double surcharge 75.00 975.00
   Never hinged 190.00
b. Inverted surcharge 37.50
   Never hinged 110.00
264 A35 800th m on 300m lt grn (G) .20 5.00
a. Black surcharge 47.50
265 A35 800th m on 400m dk brn .20 14.50
a. Inverted surcharge 42.50
   Never hinged 110.00
b. Double surcharge 75.00
   Never hinged 190.00
266 A35 800th m on 400m lt grn (G) .20 3.75
267 A35 800th m on 500m lt grn (G) .20 1,500.
a. 800th m on 500m red org (Bk) 37.50
268 A35 800th m on 1000m lt grn (G) .20 1.50
269 A35 2mil m on 200m rose red .20 1.50
a. 2mil m on 200m car rose (#230) 1,250.
   Never hinged 2,850.
270 A35 2mil m on 300m dp .20 2.10
a. Inverted surcharge 42.50
   Never hinged 110.00
b. Double surcharge 75.00
   Never hinged 190.00
271 A35 2mil m on 500m dl rose .20 6.50
272 A38 2mil m on 5th m dl rose .20 1.50
b. Imperf. 42.50 125.00
Nos. 264a, 267a were not put in use.

**Serrate Roulette 13½**
273 A26 400th m on 15pf bis (Br) .20 4.50
a. Imperf. 52.50 275.00
   Never hinged 125.00
274 A26 400th m on 25pf bis (Br) .20 4.50
a. Imperf. 90.00 275.00
   Never hinged 225.00
275 A26 400th m on 30pf bis (Br) .20 4.50
a. Imperf. 45.00 110.00
   Never hinged 110.00
276 A26 400th m on 40pf bis (Br) .20 4.50
a. Imperf. 45.00 —
   Never hinged 110.00
277 A35 2mil m on 200m rose red .45 150.00
278 A38 2mil m on 5th m dull rose .20 9.00
Nos. 241-278 (39) 23.85 7,910.
Set, never hinged 51.00
Nos. 272-276 exist without surcharge. Value each, $150 unused, $375 never hinged.

A39        A39a

The stamps of types A39 and A39a usually have the value darker than the rest of the design.

**1923    Wmk. 126    Perf. 14**
280 A39 500th m brown .20 2.75
281 A39 1mil m grnsh bl .20 1.60
a. Imperf. 52.50 350.00
   Never hinged 125.00
282 A39 2mil m dull vio .20 20.00
284 A39 4mil m yel grn .20 1.50
a. Value double 57.50
   Never hinged 140.00
b. Imperf. 42.50
   Never hinged 97.50
285 A39 5mil m rose .20 1.50
286 A39 10mil m red .20 1.50
a. Value double 50.00 125.00
   Never hinged 125.00

287 A39 20mil m ultra .20 1.90
288 A39 30mil m red brn .20 9.25
289 A39 50mil m dull ol grn .20 1.90
a. Imperf. 52.50 350.00
   Never hinged 125.00
b. Value inverted 45.00
290 A39 100mil m gray .20 1.50
291 A39 200mil m bis brn .20 1.50
a. Imperf. 42.50
   Never hinged 97.50
293 A39 500mil m ol grn .20 1.40
294 A39a 1mlrd m choc .30 1.90
295 A39a 2mlrd m pale brn & grn .20 1.90
296 A39a 5mlrd m yellow & brn .20 1.50
297 A39a 10mlrd m ap grn & grn .20 1.50
a. Imperf. 45.00 275.00
   Never hinged 110.00
298 A39a 20mlrd m bluish grn & brn .20 1.90
299 A39a 50mlrd m bl & dp bl .20 35.00
    Nos. 280-299 (18) 3.70 90.00
    Set, never hinged 18.75
The variety "value omitted" exists on Nos. 280-281, 284-287, 290-291, 293-294, 296, 298-299 and 307. Values $30 to $150 hinged, $75 to $350 never hinged.
See Nos. 301-309. For surcharges and overprints see Nos. 311-321, O40-O46.

**Serrate Roulette 13½**
301 A39 10mil m red .55 45.00
302 A39 20mil m ultra .55 300.00
303 A39 50mil m dull grn .55 6.00
304 A39 200mil m bis brn .55 11.50
305 A39a 1mlrd m choc .55 7.50
306 A39a 2mlrd m pale brn & grn .55 3.50
307 A39a 5mlrd m yel & brn .75 2.25
308 A39a 20mlrd m bluish grn & brn .75 11.00
309 A39a 50mlrd m bl & dp bl 1.90 675.00
    Nos. 301-309 (9) 6.70 1,061.
    Set, never hinged 18.50

**Stamps and Types of 1923 Surcharged with New Values**
**1923    Perf. 14**
310 A35 1mlrd m on 100m vio .20 29.00
a. Inverted surcharge 110.00
   Never hinged 300.00
b. Deep reddish purple 60.00 3,600.
   Never hinged 150.00
311 A39 5mlrd m on 2mil m .20 125.00
a. Inverted surcharge 19.00
   Never hinged 57.50
b. Double surcharge 45.00
   Never hinged 110.00
312 A39 5mlrd m on 4mil m .20 22.50
a. Inverted surcharge 37.50 1,200.
   Never hinged 97.50
b. Double surcharge 37.50
   Never hinged 97.50
313 A39 5mlrd m on 10mil m .20 2.75
a. Inverted surcharge 19.00 1,100.
   Never hinged 57.50
b. Double surcharge 37.50
   Never hinged 97.50
314 A39 10mlrd m on 20mil m .20 4.50
a. Double surcharge 45.00
   Never hinged 125.00
b. Inverted surcharge 26.00
   Never hinged 45.00
315 A39 10mlrd m on 50mil m .20 4.50
a. Inverted surcharge 19.00 900.00
   Never hinged 57.50
b. Double surcharge 45.00
   Never hinged 125.00
316 A39 10mlrd m on 100mil m .20 7.50
a. Inverted surcharge 26.00 1,500.
   Never hinged 75.00
b. Double surcharge 45.00
   Never hinged 125.00
    Nos. 310-316 (7) 1.40 195.75
    Set, never hinged 22.50
No. 310b was issued in Bavaria only and is known as the Hitler provisional. Excellent forgeries exist.

**Serrate Roulette 13½**
319 A39 5mlrd m on 10mil m 1.90 190.00
a. Inverted surcharge 26.00 1,100.
   Never hinged 67.50
b. Double surcharge 45.00
   Never hinged 110.00
320 A39 10mlrd m on 20mil m 5.00 110.00
321 A39 10mlrd m on 50mil m 1.90 37.50
a. Inverted surcharge 26.00 1,100.
   Never hinged 67.50
    Nos. 319-321 (3) 8.80 337.50
    Set, never hinged 22.50

A40        German Eagle — A41

**1923**
323 A40 3pf brown .35 .20
324 A40 5pf dark green .35 .20
325 A40 10pf carmine .35 .20
326 A40 20pf deep ultra .95 .35
327 A40 50pf orange 2.75 1.00
328 A40 100pf brn vio 8.25 1.10
    Nos. 323-328 (6) 13.00 3.05
    Set, never hinged 80.00
For overprints see Nos. O47-O52.

**Imperf.**
323a A40 3pf 125.00 275.00
324a A40 5pf 110.00
325a A40 10pf 110.00 190.00
326a A40 20pf 140.00 225.00
327a A40 50pf 800.00 —
328a A40 100pf 175.00 —
    Nos. 323a-328a (6) 1,460. 690.00
    Set, never hinged 3,100.

**Value Omitted**
323b A40 3pf 160.00 300.00
324b A40 5pf 160.00 300.00
325b A40 10pf 160.00
326b A40 20pf 160.00
327b A40 50pf 160.00
328b A40 100pf 160.00
    Nos. 323b-328b (6) 960.00 600.00
    Set, never hinged 2,250.

**1924    Wmk. 126**
330 A41 3pf lt brown .30 .35
331 A41 5pf lt green .30 .35
332 A41 10pf vermilion .30 .35
333 A41 20pf dull blue 1.90 .35
334 A41 30pf rose lilac 1.90 .45
335 A41 40pf olive green 13.00 .75
336 A41 50pf orange 13.50 1.10
    Nos. 330-336 (7) 31.25 3.70
    Set, never hinged 275.00
The values above 5pf have "Pf" in the upper right corner.
For overprints see Nos. O53-O61.

**Imperf.**
330a A41 3pf 140.00 375.00
331a A41 5pf 175.00 375.00
332a A41 10pf 225.00
333a A41 20pf 160.00
334a A41 30pf 160.00
335a A41 50pf 190.00
    Nos. 330a-335a (6) 1,050. 750.00
    Set, never hinged 2,475.

Rheinstein Castle — A43

View of Cologne A44

Marienburg Castle — A45

**1924    Engr.    Wmk. 126**
337 A43 1m green 10.50 2.25
338 A44 2m blue 18.00 2.00
339 A45 3m claret 21.00 5.25
    Nos. 337-339 (3) 49.50 9.50
    Set, never hinged 153.75
See No. 387.

Dr. Heinrich von Stephan
A46        A47

**1924-28    Typo.**
340 A46 10pf dark green .55 .30
341 A46 20pf dark blue 1.25 .60
342 A47 60pf red brown 3.75 .75
a. Chalky paper ('28) 21.00 13.50
343 A47 80pf slate 9.75 1.50
    Nos. 340-343 (4) 15.30 3.15
    Set, never hinged 77.75
Universal Postal Union, 50th anniversary. No. 340 exists imperf. Value $325.

Traffic Wheel — A48

German Eagle Watching Rhine Valley — A49

**1925, May 30    Perf. 13½x13**
345 A48 5pf deep green 3.00 5.25
346 A48 10pf vermilion 3.75 9.75
    Set, never hinged 38.00
German Traffic Exhibition, Munich, May 30-Oct. 11, 1925.

**1925    Perf. 14**
347 A49 5pf green .45 .35
348 A49 10pf vermilion 1.10 .35
349 A49 20pf deep blue 4.50 1.00
    Nos. 347-349 (3) 6.05 1.70
    Set, never hinged 35.00
1000 years' union of the Rhineland with Germany.

Speyer Cathedral
A50

**1925, Sept. 11    Engr.**
350 A50 5m dull green 32.50 14.50
    Never hinged 125.00

Johann Wolfgang von Goethe — A51

Designs: 3pf, 25pf, Goethe. 5pf, Friedrich von Schiller. 8pf, 20pf, Ludwig van Beethoven. 10pf, Frederick the Great. 15pf, Immanuel Kant. 30pf, Gotthold Ephraim Lessing. 40pf, Gottfried Wilhelm Leibnitz. 50pf, Johann Sebastian Bach. 80pf, Albrecht Durer.

**1926-27    Typo.    Perf. 14**
351 A51 3pf olive brown .60 .30
352 A51 3pf bister ('27) 1.10 .30
353 A51 5pf dark green 1.10 .30
b. 5pf light green ('27) 1.10 .30
   Never hinged 7.50
354 A51 8pf blue grn ('27) 1.10 .30
355 A51 10pf carmine 1.10 .30
356 A51 15pf vermilion 2.25 .30
a. Booklet pane of 8 + 2 labels 275.00
   Never hinged 675.00
357 A51 20pf myrtle grn 10.50 1.10
358 A51 25pf blue 3.50 .90
359 A51 30pf olive grn 6.50 .50
360 A51 40pf dp violet 11.50 .55
361 A51 50pf brown 14.50 7.50
362 A51 80pf chocolate 30.00 4.75
    Nos. 351-362 (12) 83.75 17.10
    Set, never hinged 865.00
Nos. 351-354, 356 and 357 exist imperf. See Scott Classic Specialized Catalogue of Stamps & Covers for detailed listing.

**1930, June 30**
385 A51 8pf dark green 1.10 .90
386 A61 15pf carmine rose 1.10 .90
    Set, never hinged 15.00
Issued in commemoration of the final evacuation of the Rhineland by the Allied forces.

View of Cologne A63

**1930    Engr.    Wmk. 126**
**Inscribed: "Reichsmark"**
387 A63 2m dark blue 29.00 14.00
    Never hinged 100.00
A type of design A43 in green exists with "Reichsmark" instead of "Mark." It was not issued, though some examples are known in private hands.

**1927, Oct. 10**
363 A51 8pf blue green 17.00 62.50
364 A51 15pf vermilion 17.00 62.50
365 A51 25pf blue 17.00 62.50
    Nos. 363-365 (3) 51.00 187.50
    Set, never hinged 180.00

"I.A.A." stands for "Internationales Arbeitsamt," (Intl. Labor Bureau), an agency of the League of Nations. Issued in connection with a meeting of the I.A.A. in Berlin, Oct. 10-15, 1927, they were on sale to the public.

Traffic Wheel — A48    German Eagle Watching Rhine Valley — A49

Pres. Friedrich Ebert A60        Pres. Paul von Hindenburg A61

Pres. von Hindenburg A64

**1928-32    Typo.    Perf. 14**
366 A60 3pf bister .20 .60
367 A61 3pf lt blue ('31) .75 1.25
a. Tête bêche pair 4.75 9.00
b. Bklt. pane of 9 + label 35.00 90.00
   Never hinged 9.00
368 A61 5pf lt green .40 .60
a. Tête bêche pair 4.25 9.00
b. Imperf. 9.00
   Never hinged 250.00
c. Bklt. pane of 6 + 4 labels 22.50 60.00
   Never hinged 60.00
d. Bklt. pane, 4 #368 + 6 #369 35.00 90.00
   Never hinged 90.00
369 A60 6pf lt olive grn ('32) .75 .65
a. Bklt. pane, 2 #369 + 8 #373 55.00 135.00
   Never hinged 135.00
370 A60 8pf dark green .20 .60
a. Bklt. pane of 6 3.75 7.50
   Never hinged 7.50
371 A60 10pf vermilion 2.00 2.25
372 A60 10pf red violet ('30) .95 .75
373 A61 12pf orange ('32) 1.10 .65
a. Tête bêche pair 11.00 22.50
   Never hinged 22.50
374 A61 15pf car rose .60 .60
a. Tête bêche pair 7.75 15.00
   Never hinged 15.00
b. Bklt. pane 6 + 4 labels 27.50 67.50
   Never hinged 67.50
375 A60 20pf Prus green 6.25 3.75
a. Imperf. 300.00
   Never hinged 600.00
376 A60 20pf gray ('30) 6.00 .75
377 A61 25pf blue 7.50 .90
378 A60 30pf olive green 5.00 .90
379 A61 40pf violet 13.00 .90
380 A60 45pf orange 9.00 3.00
381 A60 50pf brown 9.00 2.50
382 A60 60pf orange brn 11.50 3.00
383 A61 80pf chocolate 21.00 6.75
384 A61 80pf yel bis ('30) 9.00 2.75
    Nos. 366-384 (19) 104.20 33.15
    Set, never hinged 1,080.

Stamps of 1928 Overprinted

Nos. 354, 356 and 358 Overprinted

42...
42...
42...
42...
42...
429...
430...
431...

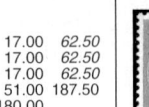
Pres. von Hindenburg A64

**1932, Oct. 1    Typo.**
391 A64 4pf blue
392 A64 5pf brt green
393 A64 12pf dp orange
394 A64 15pf dk red
395 A64 25pf ultra
396 A64 40pf violet
397 A64 50pf brown
    Nos. 391-397 (7)
    Set, never hinged
85th birthday of Pres. von Hindenburg. See Nos. 401-431, 43... and overprints see Fra... bourg #N1-16 and Pola...

**1933, Apr. 12**
398 A65 6pf dk green
a. Tête bêche pair
   Never hinged
b. Bklt. pane of 9 + label
   Never hinged
399 A65 12pf carmin...
a. Tête bêche pair
b. Bklt. pane of 5 +...
   Never hinged
400 A65 25pf ultra...
    Nos. 398-400...

**1933**
401 A64 3pf ol...
402 A64 4pf d...
403 A64 6pf d...
404 A64 8pf d...
a. Bklt. pane...
   Never hinged
405 A64 10pf...
406 A64 12pf...
a. Bklt. pane...
   #406
   Never hinged
407 A64 15p...
408 A64 20p...
409 A64 30p...
410 A64 40p...
411 A64 50p...
412 A64 80p...
413 A64 100...
414 A64 100...
    Nos. 4...

**1933-36**
415 A64 Bklt...
a.
   Neve
   Bklt.
b.
   Neve

**1934, S...**
436 A6...
437 A6...
438 A6...
439 A6...
440 A6...
441 A6...
    Nos...

**1934, S...**
442 A70 1...
443 A70 12...
    Set, ne...
Imperfs...
Naz...
$750...

Allegory... "Saar Belo... to German... A71

**1934, Aug...**
444 A71 6...
445 A72 12...
    Set, ne...
Issued to...

Friedrich von Schiller A73

**1934, Nov. 5**
446 A73 6pf g...
447 A73 12pf c...
    Set, never h...
175th anniv. o...

Celebration...
Issued...
of Germa...

Hindenbu...

Hir...

Pe...

**1939, Sept. 18**
492 A101　6pf dark green　　.20　.60
493 A102　12pf orange red　　.30　.75
Set, never hinged　　　　3.75

Unification of Danzig with the Reich.

Johannes Gutenberg and Library at Leipzig — A103

6pf, "High House," Leipzig. 12pf, Old Town Hall, Leipzig. 25pf, View of Leipzig Fair.

Inscribed "Leipziger Messe"
**Perf. 10½**

**1940, Mar. 3　　Photo.　Unwmk.**
494 A103　3pf dark brown　　.20　.45
495 A103　6pf dk gray green　.20　.45
496 A103　12pf henna brown　.20　.45
497 A103　25pf ultra　　　　.50　1.10
Nos. 494-497 (4)　　1.10　2.45
Set, never hinged　　　7.50

Leipzig Fair.

House of Nations, Leipzig — A107

6pf, Concert Hall, Leipzig. 12pf, Leipzig Fair Office. 25pf, Railroad Terminal, Leipzig.

Inscribed: "Reichsmesse Leipzig, 1941"

**1941, Mar. 1　　　　Perf. 14x13½**
498 A107　3pf brown　　　.20　.75
499 A107　6pf green　　　.20　.75
500 A107　12pf dark red　.30　.90
501 A107　25pf bright blue　.65　1.50
Nos. 498-501 (4)　　1.35　3.90
Set, never hinged　　8.00

Leipzig Fair.

Fashion Allegory — A111　Vienna Fair Hall — A112

"Burgtheater" Ā113　Monument to Prince Eugene A114

**1941, Mar. 8　　　　Perf. 13½x14**
502 A111　3pf dark red brown　.20　.50
503 A112　6pf brt blue grn　.20　.50
504 A113　12pf scarlet　　.20　.60
505 A114　25pf bright blue　.55　1.50
Nos. 502-505 (4)　1.15　3.10
Set, never hinged　　10.00

Vienna Fair.

A115　　Adolf Hitler — A116

**1941-44　　Typo.　Perf. 14**
**Size: 18½x22½mm**
506 A115　1pf gray black　.20　.30
　a.　Bklt. pane, 4 #506 + 4 #509　1.10　2.50
　　Never hinged　　2.50
507 A115　3pf lt brown　.20　.30
　a.　Bklt. pane, 6 #507 + 2 #510　1.20　3.00
　　Never hinged　3.00
508 A115　4pf slate　.20　.30
　a.　Bklt. pane, 4 #508, 2 #511 + 2 labels　1.00　2.50
　　Never hinged　2.50
509 A115　5pf dp yellow grn　.20　.30
510 A115　6pf purple　.20　.30
　a.　Bklt. pane of 7 + label　7.75　19.00
　　Never hinged　19.00
511 A115　8pf red　.20　.30
511A A115　10pf dk brown ('42)　.20　.45
511B A115　12pf carmine ('42)　.20　.45

**Engr.**
512 A115　10pf dark brown　.35　.30
513 A115　12pf brt carmine　.35　.30
　a.　Bklt. pane of 6 + 2 labels　3.25　7.50
　　Never hinged　7.50
514 A115　15pf brown lake　.20　.30
515 A115　16pf peacock green　.20　1.50
516 A115　20pf blue　.20　.35
517 A115　24pf orange brown　.20　1.50

**Size: 21½x26mm**
518 A115　25pf brt ultra　.20　.45
519 A115　30pf olive green　.20　.45
520 A115　40pf brt red vio　.20　.45
521 A115　50pf myrtle green　.20　.45
522 A115　60pf dk red brown　.20　.45
523 A115　80pf indigo　.20　.45
524 A116　1m dk slate grn ('44)　.40　5.25
　a.　Perf. 12½ ('42)　1.25　6.00
525 A116　2m violet ('44)　.90　5.25
　a.　Perf. 12½ ('42)　1.40　6.00

**Perf. 12½**
526 A116　3m cop red ('42)　1.25　15.00
　a.　Perf. 14 ('44)　2.00　9.00
527 A116　5m dark blue ('42)　2.25　47.50
　a.　Perf. 14 ('44)　3.50　13.00
Nos. 506-527 (24)　9.10　82.70
Set, #506-527, never hinged　23.00
Set, #524a-527a, never hinged　40.00

Nos. 507, 510, 511, 511A, 511B, 520, 524-526 exist imperf.
For surcharge see No. MQ3. For overprints see Russia Nos. N9-N48.

Storm Trooper Emblem A117　Adolf Hitler A118

**1942, Aug. 8　　Photo.　Perf. 14**
528 A117　6pf purple　.20　.75
　　Never hinged　.75

War Effort Day of the Storm Troopers.

**1944　　　　　　　Engr.**
529 A118　42pf bright green　.20　2.00
　　Never hinged　.30

Exists imperf. Value $375.

A119

**1946　Typo.　Wmk. 284　Perf. 14**
**Size: 18x22mm**
530 A119　1pf black　.20　3.00
531 A119　2pf black　.20　.20
532 A119　3pf yellow brn　.20　3.25
533 A119　4pf slate　.20　4.50
534 A119　5pf yellow grn　.20　.60
535 A119　6pf purple　.20　.20
536 A119　8pf dp ver　.20　.20
537 A119　10pf chocolate　.20　.20
538 A119　12pf bright red　.20　.20
539 A119　12pf slate gray　.20　.20
　a.　Bklt. pane, 5 #539 + 3 #542　.90　90.00
　　Never hinged　18.00
540 A119　15pf violet brn　.20　6.75
541 A119　15pf lt yel grn　.20　.20
542 A119　15pf slate green　.20　.20
543 A119　20pf lt blue　.20　.20
544 A119　24pf orange brn　.20　.20

545 A119　25pf brt ultra　.20　6.00
546 A119　25pf orange yel　.20　1.20
547 A119　30pf olive　.20　.20
548 A119　40pf red violet　.20　.20
549 A119　42pf emerald　.75　30.00
550 A119　45pf brt red　.20　.30
551 A119　50pf dk ol grn　.20　.20
552 A119　60pf brown red　.20　.20
553 A119　75pf deep ultra　.20　.20
554 A119　80pf dark blue　.20　.20
555 A119　84pf emerald　.20　.20
**Size: 24½x29½mm**
556 A119　1m olive green　.20　.20
　　Nos. 530-556 (27)　59.20
Set, never hinged　5.25

Imperf. examples of Nos. 543, 544 and 548 are usually from the souvenir sheet No. B295. Most other denominations exist imperf.
For overprints see Nos. 585A-599, 9N64, 10N17-10N21.

Planting Olive A120　Sower A121

Laborer A122　Reaping Wheat A123

Germany Reaching for Peace — A124　Heinrich von Stephan — A125

**1947-48　　　　　　Perf. 14**
557 A120　2pf brown blk　.20　.35
558 A120　6pf purple　.20　.20
559 A121　8pf red　.20　.35
560 A121　10pf yel grn ('48)　.20　.35
561 A122　12pf gray　.20　.20
562 A120　15pf choc ('48)　.20　3.75
563 A123　16pf dk bl grn　.20　.35
564 A121　20pf blue　.20　1.10
565 A123　24pf brown org　.20　.35
566 A122　25pf orange yel　.20　1.10
567 A122　30pf red ('48)　.20　3.00
568 A121　40pf red vio　.20　.35
569 A123　50pf ultra ('48)　.20　2.00
571 A122　60pf red brn ('48)　.20　.75
　a.　60pf brown red　.35
572 A122　80pf dark blue　.20　1.10
573 A123　84pf emerald　.20　1.90

**Engr.**
574 A124　1m olive　.20　.35
575 A124　2m dk brown vio　.20　1.10
576 A124　3m copper red　.20　10.00
577 A124　5m dk blue ('48)　.75　40.00
　　Nos. 557-577 (20)　68.65
Set, never hinged　5.25

Used examples of Nos. 576-577 with expertized postal cancellations sell for much more.
For overprints see Nos. 600-633, 9N1-9N34, 9N65-9N67, 10N1-10N16.

**1947, May 15　　　　Litho.**
578 A125　24pf orange brown　.20　1.50
579 A125　75pf dark blue　.20　1.50
Set, never hinged　.45

50th anniv. of the death of Heinrich von Stephan, 1st postmaster general of the German Empire.

**Leipzig Fair Issues**
Type of Semi-Postal Stamp of 1947

12pf, Maximilian I granting charter, 1497. 75pf, Estimating and collecting taxes, 1365.

**Perf. 13½x13**
**1947, Sept. 2　Litho.　Wmk. 284**
580 SP252　12pf carmine　.20　1.90
581 SP252　75pf dk vio blue　.20　2.50
Set, never hinged　.45

Type of Semi-Postal Stamp of 1947, Dated 1948

50pf, Merchants at customs barrier, 1388. 84pf, Arranging stocks of merchandise, 1433.

**1948, Mar. 2　　　　Engr.**
582 SP252　50pf deep blue　.20　1.50
583 SP252　84pf green　.20　2.25
Set, never hinged　.45

Exist imperf. Value, each, $450.

**Hanover Fair Issue**

Weighing Goods for Export — A126

**1948, May 22　　Typo.　Perf. 14**
584 A126　24pf deep carmine　.20　1.50
585 A126　50pf ultra　.20　2.25
　c.　Pair, #584-585　2.10　15.00
　　Pair, never hinged　5.50
Set, never hinged　.45

**For Use in the United States and British Zones**
Stamps of Germany 1946-47 Overprinted in Black

a　　　　　　b

Overprint Type "a" on 1946 Numeral Issue

**1948　　Wmk. 284　　Perf. 14**
585A A119　2pf black　2.25　32.50
585B A119　8pf dp ver　5.25　62.50
586 A119　10pf chocolate　.30　4.75
586A A119　12pf bright red　3.75　52.50
586B A119　12pf slate gray　67.50　550.00
586C A119　15pf violet brn　3.75　52.50
587 A119　15pf lt yel grn　1.25　16.00
587A A119　16pf slate green　21.00　200.00
587B A119　24pf orange brn　37.50　210.00
587C A119　25pf brt ultra　7.50　62.50
588 A119　25pf orange yel　.60　8.25
589 A119　30pf olive　.60　8.25
589A A119　40pf red violet　27.50　210.00
590 A119　45pf brt red　.90　8.25
591 A119　50pf dk olive grn　.90　8.25
592 A119　75pf dp ultra　2.25　24.00
593 A119　84pf emerald　2.25　24.00
　　Nos. 585A-593 (17)　185.05
Set, never hinged　375.00

**Same, Overprinted Type "b"**
593A A119　2pf black　10.50　67.50
593B A119　8pf dp ver　18.00　140.00
593C A119　10pf chocolate　16.50　140.00
593D A119　12pf bright red　5.25　67.50
593E A119　12pf slate gray　140.00　1,000.
593F A119　15pf violet brown　5.25　47.50
594 A119　15pf lt yel grn　.35　8.25
594A A119　16pf slate grn　20.00　160.00
594B A119　24pf org brn　21.00　210.00
594C A119　25pf brt ultra　6.00　62.50
594D A119　25pf orange yel　19.00　200.00
595 A119　30pf olive　.60　6.75
595A A119　40pf red violet　27.50　250.00
596 A119　45pf bright red　1.25　12.00
597 A119　50pf dk ol grn　1.25　12.00
598 A119　75pf dp ultra　1.40　12.00
599 A119　84pf emerald　1.40　13.00
　　Nos. 593A-599 (17)　295.25
Set, never hinged　600.00

Nine other denominations of type A119 (1, 3, 4, 5, 6, 20, 42, 60 and 80pf) were also overprinted with types "a" and "b." These overprints were not authorized, but the stamps were sold at post offices and tolerated for postal use. Forgeries exist.
The overprints on Nos. 585A-599 have been extensively counterfeited.

**Overprint Type "a" on Stamps and Types of 1947 Pictorial Issue**
600 A120　2pf brown black　.20　.45
601 A120　6pf purple　.20　.45
602 A121　8pf dp vermilion　.20　.45
603 A121　10pf yellow green　.20　.45
604 A122　12pf slate gray　.20　.45
605 A120　15pf chocolate　3.00　15.00

| | | | | |
|---|---|---|---|---|
| 606 | A123 | 16pf dk blue green | .60 | 2.25 |
| 607 | A121 | 20pf blue | .20 | .90 |
| 608 | A123 | 24pf brown orange | .20 | .45 |
| 609 | A120 | 25pf orange yellow | .20 | .45 |
| 610 | A122 | 30pf red | 1.10 | 4.50 |
| 611 | A121 | 40pf red violet | .30 | 1.10 |
| 612 | A123 | 50pf ultra | .35 | .90 |
| 614 | A122 | 60pf red brown | .35 | .90 |
| a. | | 60pf brown red | 22.50 | 225.00 |
| | | Never hinged | 60.00 | |
| 615 | A122 | 80pf dark blue | .60 | 2.25 |
| 616 | A123 | 84pf emerald | 1.90 | 6.00 |
| | | Nos. 600-616 (16) | 9.80 | 36.95 |
| | | Set, never hinged | 22.50 | |

### Same, Overprinted Type "b"

| | | | | |
|---|---|---|---|---|
| 617 | A120 | 2pf brown black | .35 | 1.40 |
| 618 | A120 | 6pf purple | .35 | 1.40 |
| 619 | A121 | 8pf red | .35 | 1.40 |
| 620 | A121 | 10pf yellow green | .20 | .45 |
| 621 | A122 | 12pf gray | .35 | 1.50 |
| 622 | A120 | 15pf chocolate | .20 | .65 |
| 623 | A123 | 16pf dk blue green | .65 | 2.25 |
| 624 | A121 | 20pf blue | .20 | .45 |
| 625 | A123 | 24pf brown orange | .30 | 1.50 |
| 626 | A120 | 25pf orange yel | 3.50 | 15.00 |
| 627 | A122 | 30pf red | .20 | .65 |
| 628 | A121 | 40pf red violet | .20 | .60 |
| 629 | A123 | 50pf ultra | .20 | .60 |
| 631 | A122 | 60pf red brown | .20 | .65 |
| a. | | 60pf brown red | 1.10 | 3.75 |
| | | Never hinged | 2.25 | |
| 632 | A122 | 80pf dark blue | .20 | .65 |
| 633 | A123 | 84pf emerald | .45 | 1.40 |
| | | Nos. 617-633 (16) | 7.90 | 30.55 |
| | | Set, never hinged | 18.00 | |

Most of Nos. 585A-633 exist with inverted and double overprints.

Frankfurt Town Hall A127 / Our Lady's Church, Munich A128

Cologne Cathedral A129 / Brandenburg Gate, Berlin A130

Holsten Gate, Lübeck — A131

Two types of mark values:
Type I — Four horiz. lines in stairs.
Type II — Seven horizontal lines.

### Perf. 11½x11, 11

| 1948-51 | | Litho. | Wmk. 286 | |
|---|---|---|---|---|
| 634 | A127 | 2pf black | .20 | .45 |
| a. | | Perf. 14 | 1.10 | 4.75 |
| 635 | A128 | 4pf orange brown | .20 | .45 |
| a. | | Perf. 14 | 2.75 | .90 |
| 636 | A128 | 5pf blue | .20 | .45 |
| a. | | Perf. 14 | .75 | .45 |
| 637 | A128 | 6pf orange brown | .20 | .60 |
| 638 | A128 | 6pf orange | .20 | .45 |
| a. | | Perf. 14 | 6.00 | 4.50 |
| 639 | A127 | 8pf orange yel | .20 | .45 |
| 640 | A128 | 8pf dk slate blue | .20 | .45 |
| 641 | A129 | 10pf green | .20 | .45 |
| a. | | Perf. 14 | .75 | .45 |
| 642 | A128 | 15pf orange | .90 | 4.50 |
| 643 | A127 | 15pf violet | .50 | .45 |
| a. | | Perf. 14 | 4.50 | .45 |
| 644 | A127 | 16pf bluish green | .30 | .60 |
| 645 | A127 | 20pf blue | .45 | 3.00 |
| 646 | A130 | 20pf carmine | .30 | .60 |
| a. | | Perf. 14 | 1.90 | .45 |
| 647 | A130 | 24pf carmine | .20 | .45 |
| 648 | A129 | 25pf vermilion | .45 | .45 |
| a. | | Perf. 14 | 27.50 | 160.00 |
| 649 | A130 | 30pf blue | .60 | .45 |
| a. | | Perf. 14 | 11.00 | .45 |
| 650 | A128 | 30pf scarlet | 1.10 | 5.25 |
| 651 | A129 | 40pf rose lilac | .75 | .45 |
| a. | | Perf. 14 | 7.50 | .45 |
| 652 | A130 | 50pf ultra | .60 | 1.90 |
| 653 | A128 | 50pf bluish green | .75 | .45 |
| a. | | Perf. 14 | 67.50 | .45 |
| 654 | A129 | 60pf violet brn | 30.00 | .45 |
| a. | | Perf. 14 | 1.10 | .45 |

---

| | | | | |
|---|---|---|---|---|
| 655 | A130 | 80pf red violet | 1.25 | .45 |
| a. | | Perf. 14 | 45.00 | .45 |
| 656 | A128 | 84pf rose violet | .75 | 6.00 |
| 657 | A129 | 90pf rose lilac | 1.25 | .45 |
| a. | | Perf. 14 | 65.00 | .50 |

#### Perf. 11, 11x11½

| | | | | |
|---|---|---|---|---|
| 658 | A131 | 1m yellow grn (I) | 15.00 | .60 |
| a. | | Perf. 14 (II) ('51) | 60.00 | .45 |
| b. | | Perf. 11 (II) | 19.00 | .45 |
| 659 | A131 | 2m violet (I) | 13.50 | .60 |
| a. | | Type II | 22.50 | .45 |
| 660 | A131 | 3m car rose (I) | 15.00 | 2.50 |
| a. | | Type II | 75.00 | 1.00 |
| 661 | A131 | 5m blue (I) | 22.50 | 21.00 |
| a. | | Type II | 90.00 | 3.25 |
| | | Nos. 634-661 (28) | 107.75 | 54.35 |
| | | Set, never hinged | 260.00 | |
| | | Set, 634a-658a, never hinged | 550.00 | |
| | | Set, 658b-661a, never hinged | 375.00 | |

Imperforates of many values exist.
Specialists collect Nos. 634-661 with watermark in four positions: upright, D's facing left; upright, D's facing right; sideways, D's facing up; sideways, D's facing down.
Two types of perforation: line and comb. Nos. 634-657 are found both perf. 11 and 11½x11.

Herman Hildebrant Wedigh — A132

### Wmk. 116

| 1949, Apr. 22 | | Engr. | Perf. 14 | |
|---|---|---|---|---|
| 662 | A132 | 10pf green | 1.10 | 2.25 |
| 663 | A132 | 20pf carmine rose | 1.10 | 2.25 |
| 664 | A132 | 30pf blue | 1.50 | 3.00 |
| a. | | Sheet of 3, #662-664 | 32.50 | 180.00 |
| | | Sheet, never hinged | 82.50 | |
| | | Nos. 662-664 (3) | 3.70 | 7.50 |
| | | Set, never hinged | 7.50 | |

Hanover Export Fair, 1949.
No. 664a sold for 1 mark.

### Federal Republic
AREA — 95,520 sq. mi.
POP. — 62,040,000 (1974 est.)
CAPITAL — Bonn

"Reconstruction" A133 / Bavaria Stamp A134

| 1949, Sept. 7 | | Litho. | Wmk. 286 | |
|---|---|---|---|---|
| 665 | A133 | 10pf blue green | 15.00 | 21.00 |
| 666 | A133 | 20pf rose carmine | 17.50 | 24.00 |
| | | Set, never hinged | | |

Opening of the first Federal Assembly.
Exist imperf. Value, each $475.

### Wmk. 285

| 1949, Sept. 30 | | Litho. | Perf. 14 | |
|---|---|---|---|---|

Design: 30pf, Bavaria 6kr.

| | | | | |
|---|---|---|---|---|
| 667 | A134 | 20pf red & dull blue | 19.00 | 37.50 |
| 668 | A134 | 30pf dull blue & choc | 32.50 | 60.00 |
| | | Set, never hinged | 90.00 | |

Cent. of German postage stamps. See No. B309.

Heinrich von Stephan, General Post Office and Guild House, Bern A135

| 1949, Oct. 9 | | | Wmk. 286 | |
|---|---|---|---|---|
| 669 | A135 | 30pf ultra | 21.00 | 37.50 |
| | | Never hinged | 60.00 | |

75th anniv. of the UPU.

---

Numeral and Post Horn — A136

| 1951-52 | | Typo. | Wmk. 295 | |
|---|---|---|---|---|
| 670 | A136 | 2pf yellow grn | .35 | .95 |
| 671 | A136 | 4pf yellow brn | .35 | .30 |
| a. | | Booklet pane, 3 #671 + 3 #673 + 4 #677 | 110.00 | 450.00 |
| | | Never hinged | 450.00 | |
| 672 | A136 | 5pf dp rose vio | 1.90 | .30 |
| 673 | A136 | 6pf orange | 4.50 | 3.00 |
| 674 | A136 | 8pf gray | 5.25 | 7.50 |
| 675 | A136 | 10pf dk green | .75 | .30 |
| a. | | Booklet pane, 4 #675 + 5 #677 + label | 110.00 | 450.00 |
| | | Never hinged | 450.00 | |
| 676 | A136 | 15pf purple | 10.00 | .95 |
| 677 | A136 | 20pf carmine | .75 | .30 |
| 678 | A136 | 25pf rose lake | 22.50 | 4.75 |

#### Engr.
#### Size: 20x24½mm

| | | | | |
|---|---|---|---|---|
| 679 | A136 | 30pf blue | 13.00 | .45 |
| 680 | A136 | 40pf rose lilac ('52) | 32.50 | .45 |
| 681 | A136 | 50pf blue gray ('52) | 45.00 | .45 |
| 682 | A136 | 60pf brown ('52) | 32.50 | .45 |
| 683 | A136 | 70pf dp yel ('52) | 135.00 | 14.00 |
| 684 | A136 | 80pf carmine ('52) | 150.00 | 1.90 |
| 685 | A136 | 90pf yel grn ('52) | 150.00 | 2.25 |
| | | Nos. 670-685 (16) | 604.35 | 38.30 |
| | | Set, never hinged | 1,875. | |

Imperfs. exist of #671, 673, 675, 681 & 684.

W. K. Roentgen A137 / Mona Lisa A138

| 1951, Dec. 10 | | | | |
|---|---|---|---|---|
| 686 | A137 | 30pf blue | 30.00 | 18.00 |
| | | Never hinged | 72.50 | |

50th anniv. of the awarding of the Nobel prize in physics to Wilhelm K. Roentgen.

### Wmk. 285

| 1952, Apr. 15 | | Litho. | Perf. 13½ | |
|---|---|---|---|---|
| 687 | A138 | 5pf multicolored | .75 | 1.10 |
| | | Never hinged | 2.00 | |

500th anniv. of the birth of Leonardo da Vinci.

N. A. Otto — A139 / Martin Luther — A140

### Wmk. 295

| 1952, July 25 | | Engr. | Perf. 14 | |
|---|---|---|---|---|
| 688 | A139 | 30pf deep blue | 15.00 | 15.00 |
| | | Never hinged | 29.00 | |

75th anniv. of the four-cycle gas engine.

| 1952, July 25 | | | | |
|---|---|---|---|---|
| 689 | A140 | 10pf green | 4.00 | 4.75 |
| | | Never hinged | 13.50 | |

Issued to publicize the Lutheran World Federation Assembly, Hanover, 1952.

---

Freighter Off Heligoland A141 / Carl Schurz A142

| 1952, Sept. 6 | | | | |
|---|---|---|---|---|
| 690 | A141 | 20pf red | 6.25 | 5.75 |
| | | Never hinged | 15.00 | |

Return of Heligoland, Mar. 1, 1952.

### Wmk. 285

| 1952, Sept. 17 | | Litho. | Perf. 13½ | |
|---|---|---|---|---|
| 691 | A142 | 20pf blue, blk & brn org | 6.25 | 7.50 |
| | | Never hinged | 19.00 | |

Centenary of Carl Schurz's arrival in America.

Thurn and Taxis Postilion A143

Philipp Reis — A144

| 1952, Oct. 25 | | | | |
|---|---|---|---|---|
| 692 | A143 | 10pf multicolored | 3.00 | 2.00 |
| | | Never hinged | 7.50 | |

1st Thurn and Taxis stamp, cent.

| 1952, Oct. 27 | | Photo. | Perf. 14 | |
|---|---|---|---|---|
| 693 | A144 | 30pf blue | 18.00 | 15.00 |
| | | Never hinged | 45.00 | |

75 years of telephone service in Germany.

"Prevent Traffic Accidents" — A145

| 1953, Mar. 30 | | Litho. | Wmk. 285 | |
|---|---|---|---|---|
| 694 | A145 | 20pf blk, red & bl grn | 6.25 | 4.50 |
| | | Never hinged | 16.50 | |

Justus von Liebig — A146 / Red Cross and Compass — A147

| 1953, May 12 | | Engr. | Wmk. 295 | |
|---|---|---|---|---|
| 695 | A146 | 30pf dark blue | 14.50 | 22.50 |
| | | Never hinged | 45.00 | |

150th anniv. of the birth of Justus von Liebig, chemist.

#### Perf. 14x13½

| 1953, May 8 | | Litho. | Wmk. 285 | |
|---|---|---|---|---|
| 696 | A147 | 10pf dp ol grn & red | 4.50 | 6.75 |

125th anniv. of the birth of Henri Dunant, founder of the Red Cross.

War Prisoner and Barbed Wire — A148 | Train and Hand Signal — A149

**Typographed and Embossed**
**1953, May 9      Unwmk.      Perf. 14**
697  A148  10pf gray & black    1.90  .35
    Never hinged                6.00
Issued in memory of the prisoners of war.

**Wmk. 295**
**1953, June 20    Engr.      Perf. 14**
Designs: 10pf, Pigeon and planes. 20pf, Automobiles and traffic signal. 30pf, Ship, barges and buoy.
698  A149  4pf brown       2.25   3.75
699  A149  10pf deep green  4.50   6.00
700  A149  20pf red        5.75   9.75
701  A149  30pf deep ultra 17.50  22.50
    Nos. 698-701 (4)       30.00  42.00
    Set, never hinged      77.50
Exhibition of Transport and Communications, Munich, 1953.

Pres. Theodor Heuss — A150

**1954-60      Typo.      Perf. 14**
**Size: 18½x22mm**
702  A150  2pf citron     .20   .20
  a.  Booklet pane, 5 #702, 4 #704 + label ('55)  22.50  110.00
      Never hinged        42.50
  b.  Booklet pane, 3 #702, 6 #704 + label ('56)  3.75  60.00
      Never hinged        7.50
  c.  Booklet pane, 3 #702, 1 #707, 5 #708 + label ('56)  7.50  75.00
      Never hinged        16.50
703  A150  4pf orange brn  .20   .20
704  A150  5pf rose lilac  .20   .20
  a.  Booklet pane, 2 #704, 7 #708 + label ('55)  22.50  110.00
      Never hinged        42.50
705  A150  6pf lt brown    .20   .75
706  A150  7pf bluish green .20   .30
707  A150  8pf gray        .20   .60
708  A150  10pf green      .20   .20
  a.  Booklet pane, 4 #708, 5 #710 + label ('55)  22.50  110.00
      Never hinged        42.50
709  A150  15pf ultra      .20   .45
710  A150  20pf dk car rose .20   .20
711  A150  25pf red brown   .30   .60
**Engr.**
**Size: 19½x24mm**
712  A150  30pf blue       4.50   4.50
713  A150  40pf red violet 1.90   .30
714  A150  50pf gray       67.50  .45
715  A150  60pf red brown  15.00  .60
716  A150  70pf olive      4.50   1.90
717  A150  80pf deep rose   .75   4.50
718  A150  90pf deep green 4.50   2.25
**Size: 24½x29½mm**
719  A150  1m olive green   .50   .30
720  A150  2m lt vio blue   .75   1.10
721  A150  3m deep plum    1.90   2.25
    Nos. 702-721 (20)     103.90 21.85
    Set, never hinged     275.00
Coils and sheets of 100 were issued of the 5, 7, 10, 15, 20, 25, 40 and 70pf. Every fifth coil stamp has a control number on the back.
Printings of Nos. 704, 706, 708-711 and 708b were made on fluorescent paper beginning in 1960.
Nos. 702, 709, 714 exist imperf. Value about $425 each.
See Nos. 737b, 755-761.

Catalogue values for unused stamps in this section, from this point to the end of the section, are for Never hinged items.

Paul Ehrlich and Emil von Behring — A151

15th Century Printer — A152

**Wmk. 285**
**1954, Mar. 13    Litho.      Perf. 13½**
722  A151  10pf dark green 11.00  3.75
Centenary of the births of Paul Ehrlich and Emil von Behring, medical researchers. Exists imperf. Value $1,000.

**1954, May 5    Typo.      Wmk. 295**
723  A152  4pf chocolate   1.10   .60
500th anniversary of the publication of Gutenberg's 42-line Bible. Design from woodcut by Jost Amman.

Bishop's Miter and Sword — A153 | Carl F. Gauss — A154

**Engraved; Center Embossed**
**1954, June 5   Unwmk.   Perf. 13½x14**
724  A153  20pf gray & red  8.00   4.50
Martyrdom of Saint Boniface, 1200th anniv.

**Wmk. 295**
**1955, Feb. 23    Engr.      Perf. 14**
725  A154  10pf deep green  5.00   .60
Cent. of the death of Carl Friedrich Gauss, mathematician.

A155 | A156

**Wmk. 304**
**1955, May 7    Litho.      Perf. 13½**
726  A155  10pf green      5.00   1.50
Cent. of the birth of Oskar von Miller, electrical engineer.

**Engraved and Embossed**
**1955, May 9   Unwmk.   Perf. 13½x14**
727  A156  40pf blue      16.50   5.50
Friedrich von Schiller, poet, 150th death anniv.

1906 Automobile A157

**Wmk. 304**
**1955, June 1    Typo.      Perf. 13½**
728  A157  20pf red & black 10.50  5.00
German postal motor-bus service, 50th anniv.

Arms of Baden-Württemberg A158 | Globe and Atomic Symbol A159

**Perf. 13x13½**
**1955, June 15    Litho.      Wmk. 295**
729  A158  7pf lemon, blk & brn red   4.00   4.50
730  A158  10pf lemon, blk & grn      6.50   6.50
  a.  Value omitted    475.00  450.00
Baden-Württemberg Exhibition, Stuttgart, 1955.

**1955, June 24  Photo.   Perf. 13½x14**
731  A159  20pf rose brown 10.50  1.10
Issued to encourage scientific research.

Orb and Symbols of Battle — A160

**Photogravure and Embossed**
**Perf. 14x13½**
**1955, Aug. 10      Unwmk.**
732  A160  20pf red lilac  9.00   3.75
Issued in honor of Augsburg and the millenium of the Battle on the Lechfeld.

Family in Flight — A161

Railroad Signal, Tracks — A162

**1955, Aug. 2    Engr.      Wmk. 304**
733  A161  20pf brown lake  3.75   .50
Ten years of German expatriation. See No. 930.

**Perf. 13½x14**
**1955, Oct. 5    Litho.      Wmk. 304**
734  A162  20pf red & black 10.00  2.50
European Timetable conf. at Wiesbaden, Oct. 5-15, 1955.

A163

A164

Stifter monument and sylized Trees.
**1955, Oct. 22      Engr.**
735  A163  10pf dark green  3.75  2.50
150th anniv. of the birth of Adalbert Stifter, poet.

**Lithographed and Embossed**
**Perf. 14x13½**
**1955, Oct. 24      Unwmk.**
736  A164  10pf UN emblem   3.75  4.50
United Nations Day, Oct. 24, 1955.

Numeral A165 | Numeral and Signature A166

**1955-58  Wmk. 304  Typo.  Perf. 14**
737  A165  1pf gray        .20   .20
**Wmk. 295**
737A A165 1pf gray ('58)   7.75  19.00
  b.  Bklt. pane of 10 (#707, 2 each #737A, #704, #708, 3 #710)  22.50  52.50
No. 737A was issued only in the booklet pane, No. 737b. No. 737 was issued on fluorescent paper in 1963.

**1956, Jan. 7    Engr.    Wmk. 304**
738  A166  20pf dark red   6.75  2.75
125th anniv. of the birth of Heinrich von Stephan, co-founder of the UPU.

Clavichord
A167

**1956, Jan. 27** **Litho.**
739 A167 10pf dull lilac .75 .35
200th anniv. of the birth of Wolfgang Amadeus Mozart, composer.

Heinrich Heine, Poet, Death Cent. — A168

*Perf. 13x13½*
**1956, Feb. 17** **Wmk. 295**
740 A168 10pf ol grn & blk 2.75 3.00

Old Buildings, Lüneburg A169

**Wmk. 304**
**1956, May 2** **Engr.** *Perf. 14*
741 A169 20pf dull red 7.50 8.25
Millenary of Lüneburg.

Olympic Rings A170 / Robert Schumann A171

**1956, June 9** *Perf. 13½x14*
742 A170 10pf slate green .80 .60
Issued to publicize the Olympic year, 1956.

**1956, July 28** **Litho.** **Unwmk.**
743 A171 10pf citron, blk & red .65 .45
Schumann, composer, death cent.

Synod Emblem — A172 / Thomas Mann — A173

*Perf. 13½x13*
**1956, Aug. 8** **Wmk. 304**
744 A172 10pf green 3.50 3.75
745 A172 20pf brown carmine 4.00 5.25
Meeting of German Protestants (Evangelical Synod), Frankfurt-on-Main, Aug. 8-12.

**1956, Aug. 11** **Engr.** *Perf. 13½x14*
746 A173 20pf pale rose vio 3.00 2.10
1st anniv. of the death of Thomas Mann, novelist.

Maria Laach Abbey — A174 / "Rebuilding Europe" — A175

**1956, Aug. 24** **Photo.** *Perf. 13x13½*
747 A174 20pf brn lake & gray 2.25 2.00
800th anniv. of the dedication of the Maria Laach Abbey.

**Europa Issue, 1956**
**1956, Sept. 15** **Engr.** *Perf. 14*
748 A175 10pf green 1.00 .20
749 A175 40pf blue 6.00 .95
Issued to symbolize the cooperation among the six countries comprising the Coal and Steel Community.

Plan of Cologne Cathedral and Hand — A176

**1956, Aug. 29** **Litho.** *Perf. 13x13½*
750 A176 10pf gray grn & red brn 2.75 2.50
77th meeting of German Catholics, Cologne, Aug. 29.

Map of the World and Policeman's Hand — A177

**1956, Sept. 1** *Perf. 13½x13*
751 A177 20pf red org, grn & blk 3.00 2.50
Issued on the occasion of the International Police Show, Essen, Sept. 1-23.

Pigeon Holding Letter — A178

**1956, Oct. 27** **Engr.** *Perf. 14*
752 A178 10pf green 1.50 .65
Issued to publicize the Day of the Stamp.

Cemetery Crosses — A179

**1956, Nov. 17** *Perf. 14x13½*
753 A179 10pf slate 1.50 .65
Issued to commemorate the people of Germany who died during WWII and to promote the Society for the Care of Military Cemeteries.

Saar Coat of Arms — A180

**1957, Jan. 2** **Litho.** *Perf. 13x13½*
754 A180 10pf bluish grn & brn .45 .45
Return of the Saar to Germany. See Saar #262.

**Heuss Type of 1954**
**1956-57** **Wmk. 304** **Engr.** *Perf. 14*
**Size: 18½x22mm**
755 A150 30pf slate green .40 .60
756 A150 40pf lt ultra 1.90 .30
757 A150 50pf olive .95 .30
758 A150 60pf lt brown 3.25 .45
759 A150 70pf violet 10.00 .45
760 A150 80pf red orange 5.25 1.90
761 A150 90pf bluish green 16.50 .95
Nos. 755-761 (7) 38.25 4.95

Nos. 755-756 were printed on both ordinary and fluorescent paper; Nos. 757-761 only on ordinary paper. Issue dates: 40pf, 1956. Others, 1957.
The 40pf and 70pf were also issued in coils. Every fifth coil stamp has control number on back.

Heinrich Hertz — A181

**1957, Feb. 22** **Litho.** *Perf. 14*
762 A181 10pf lt green & blk 1.25 .50
Heinrich Hertz, physicist, birth cent.

Paul Gerhardt — A182

**1957, May 18** **Engr.**
763 A182 20pf carmine lake .50 .50
350th anniv. of the birth of Paul Gerhardt, Lutheran clergyman and hymn writer.

Tulip and Post Horn — A183

**1957, June 8**
764 A183 20pf red orange .50 .50
Flora & Philately Exhib., Cologne, June 8-10.

Arms of Aschaffenburg, 1332 — A184

*Perf. 13½x13*
**1957, June 15** **Wmk. 304**
765 A184 20pf dp salmon & blk .50 .50
1000th anniv. of the founding of the Abbey and town of Aschaffenburg.

Scholars (Sapiens Manuscript) A185

**1957, June 24** *Perf. 13½x13*
766 A185 10pf blk, bl grn & red org .40 .40
Founding of Freiburg University, 500th anniv.

Modern Passenger Freighter — A186

**1957, June 25** *Perf. 13½x14*
767 A186 15pf brt blue, blk & red 1.10 1.00
Merchant Marine Day, June 25.

Liebig Laboratory A187

**1957, July 3** **Engr.** *Perf. 14x13½*
768 A187 10pf dark green .40 .40
350th anniv. of the Justus Liebig School at Ludwig University, Giessen.

Albert Ballin — A188

*Perf. 13½x14*
**1957, Aug. 15** **Litho.** **Wmk. 304**
769 A188 20pf dk car rose & blk 1.25 .45
Cent. of the birth of Albert Ballin, founder of the Hamburg-America Steamship Line.

Television Screen — A189

**1957, Aug. 23** **Engr.** *Perf. 14x13½*
770 A189 10pf blue vio & grn .40 .40
Issued to publicize the television industry.

**Europa Issue, 1957**

"United Europe" A190

**Lithographed; Tree Embossed**
**1957-58** **Unwmk.** *Perf. 14x13½*
771 A190 10pf yel grn & lt bl .35 .20
a. Imperf. 300.00 300.00
772 A190 40pf dk bl & lt bl 3.75 .35
**Wmk. 304**
772A A190 10pf yel grn & lt bl 5.50 8.25
Nos. 771-772A (3) 9.60 8.80
A united Europe for peace and prosperity. Issued: #771-772, 9/16; #772A, 8/1958.

Water Lily — A191

European Robin — A192

**Wmk. 304**
**1957, Oct. 4     Litho.     Perf. 14**
773 A191 10pf yel grn & org yel     .35  .45
774 A192 20pf multicolored     .55  .45

Protection of wild animals and plants.

Carrier Pigeons — A193

Baron vom Stein — A194

**1957, Oct. 5**
775 A193 20pf dp car & blk     .85  .50

Intl. Letter Writing Week, Oct. 6-12.

**1957, Oct. 26     Engr.     Perf. 13½x14**
776 A194 20pf red     1.50  .60

200th anniv. of the birth of Baron Heinrich Friedrich vom und zum Stein, Prussian statesman.

Leo Baeck — A195

Landschaft Building, Stuttgart — A196

**1957, Nov. 2**
777 A195 20pf dark red     1.50  .60

1st anniv. of the death of Rabbi Leo Baeck of Berlin.

**Perf. 13x13½**
**1957, Nov. 16     Litho.     Wmk. 304**
778 A196 10pf dk grn & yel grn     .80  .50

500th anniversary of the Wurttemberg Landtag (Assembly).

Coach — A197

"Max and Moritz" — A198

**1957, Nov. 26     Engr.     Perf. 14**
779 A197 10pf olive green     .75  .50

Centenary of the death of Joseph V. Eichendorff, poet.

**1958, Jan. 9     Litho.     Perf. 13½x13**

Design: 20pf, Wilhelm Busch.

780 A198 10pf lt ol grn & blk     .20  .20
781 A198 20pf red & black     .75  .60

50th anniv. of the death of Wilhelm Busch, humorist.

"Prevent Forest Fires" — A199

**1958, Mar. 5     Perf. 14**
782 A199 20pf brt red & blk     .65  .50

Rudolf Diesel A200

**1958, Mar. 18     Engr.     Perf. 14**
783 A200 10pf dk blue grn     .40  .40

Centenary of the birth of Rudolf Diesel, inventor.

Giraffe and Lion — A201

View of Old Munich — A202

**Perf. 13x13½**
**1958, May 7     Litho.     Wmk. 304**
784 A201 10pf brt yel grn & blk     .50  .40

Zoo at Frankfort on the Main, cent. Exists imperf. Value $225.

**1958, May 22     Engr.     Perf. 14x13½**
785 A202 20pf dark red     .50  .40

800th anniversary of Munich.

Market Cross, Trier — A203

Heraldic Eagle 5m Coin — A204

**1958, June 3**
786 A203 20pf dark red & black     .50  .40

Millennium of the market of Trier (Treves).

**1958, June 20     Litho.     Perf. 13x13½**
787 A204 20pf red & black     .60  1.40

10th anniv. of the German currency reform. Exists imperf. Value $300.

Turner Emblem and Oak Leaf A205

Schulze-Delitzsch A206

**Perf. 13½x14**
**1958, July 21     Wmk. 304**
788 A205 10pf gray, blk & dl grn     .35  .45

150 years of German Turners and on the occasion of the 1958 Turner festival.

**1958, Aug. 29     Engr.     Perf. 13½x14**
789 A206 10pf yellow green     .45  .35

150th anniv. of the birth of Hermann Schulze-Delitzsch, founder of German trade organizations.

---

Common Design Types pictured following the introduction.

---

**Europa Issue, 1958**
**Common Design Type**
**1958, Sept. 13     Litho.**
**Size: 24½x30mm**
790 CD1 10pf yel grn & blue     .35  .20
791 CD1 40pf lt blue & red     3.00  .35

Nicolaus Cusanus (Nikolaus Krebs) A207

Pres. Theodor Heuss A208

**1958, Dec. 3     Litho.     Perf. 14x13½**
792 A207 20pf dk car rose & blk     .45  .35

500th anniv. of the Cusanus Hospice at Kues, founded by Cardinal Nicolaus (1401-64). Exists imperf. Value $300.

**1959     Wmk. 304     Perf. 14**
793 A208 7pf blue green     .20  .20
794 A208 10pf green     .40  .20
795 A208 20pf dk car rose     .40  .20
**Engr.**
796 A208 40pf blue     12.00  .90
797 A208 70pf deep purple     3.50  .75
Nos. 793-797 (5)     16.50  2.25

Nos. 793-795 were issued in sheets of 100 and in coils. Every fifth coil stamp has a control number on the back.

An experimental booklet containing one pane of 10 of No. 794 was sold at Darmstadt in 1960. Value $750.

Jakob Fugger — A209

Adam Riese — A210

**1959, Mar. 6     Perf. 13½x13½**
798 A209 20pf dk red & black     .40  .45

500th anniversary of the birth of Jakob Fugger the Rich, businessman and banker.

**1959, Mar. 28     Perf. 13½x13**
799 A210 10pf ol grn & blk     .40  .45

Adam Riese (c. 1492-1559), arithmetic teacher, 400th death anniversary.

Alexander von Humboldt — A211

Buildings, Buxtehude A212

**1959, May 6     Engr.     Perf. 13½x14**
800 A211 40pf blue     1.60  1.25

Alexander von Humboldt (1769-1859), naturalist and geographer, death centenary.

**1959, June 20     Litho.     Perf. 14**
801 A212 20pf lt blue, ver & blk     .40  .40

Millennium of town of Buxtehude.

Holy Coat of Trier — A213

**Lithographed; Coat Embossed**
**1959, July 18     Wmk. 304     Perf. 14**
802 A213 20pf dull cl, buff & blk     .40  .40

Showing of the seamless robe of Christ at the Cathedral of Trier, July 19-Sept. 20.

Synod Emblem — A214

**1959, Aug. 12     Litho.**
803 A214 10pf grn, brt vio & blk     .30  .30

Meeting of German Protestants (Evangelical Synod), Munich, Aug. 12-16.

## Souvenir Sheet

A215

Portraits: 10pf, George Friedrich Handel. 15pf, Louis Spohr. 20pf, Ludwig van Beethoven. 25pf, Joseph Haydn. 40pf, Felix Mendelssohn-Bartholdy.

**Perf. 14x13½**

| | | | | |
|---|---|---|---|---|
| **1959, Sept. 8** | | **Engr.** | **Wmk. 304** | |
| **804** A215 | Sheet of 5 | | 24.00 | 50.00 |
| a. | 10pf deep green | | 3.00 | 5.50 |
| b. | 15pf blue | | 3.00 | 5.50 |
| c. | 20pf dark carmine | | 3.00 | 3.75 |
| d. | 25pf brown | | 3.00 | 7.50 |
| e. | 40pf dark blue | | 3.00 | 5.50 |

Opening of Beethoven Hall in Bonn and to honor various anniversaries of German composers.

### Europa Issue, 1959
Common Design Type

| | | | | |
|---|---|---|---|---|
| **1959, Sept. 19** | **Litho.** | **Perf. 13½x14** | | |
| **Size: 24x29½mm** | | | | |
| **805** CD2 | 10pf olive green | | .30 | .20 |
| **806** CD2 | 40pf dark blue | | 1.60 | .40 |

Uprooted Oak Emblem — A216

| | | | | |
|---|---|---|---|---|
| **1960, Apr. 7** | | **Perf. 13½x13** | | |
| **807** A216 | 10pf grn, blk & lil | | .20 | .20 |
| **808** A216 | 40pf bl, blk & org | | 2.10 | 2.10 |

World Refugee Year, 7/1/59-6/30/60.

Philipp Melanchthon A217

Symbols of Christ's Sufferings A218

| | | | | |
|---|---|---|---|---|
| **1960, Apr. 19** | | **Perf. 13½x14** | | |
| **809** A217 | 20pf dk car rose & blk | | 1.25 | 1.10 |

400th anniversary of the death of Philipp Melanchthon, co-worker of Martin Luther in the German Reformation.

| | | | | |
|---|---|---|---|---|
| **1960, May 17** | | **Perf. 14x13½** | | |
| **810** A218 | 10pf Prus grn, gray & ocher | | .30 | .30 |

1960 Passion Play, Oberammergau, Bavaria.

Dove, Chalice and Crucifix — A219

| | | | | |
|---|---|---|---|---|
| **1960, July 30** | **Engr.** | **Perf. 14x13½** | | |
| **811** A219 | 10pf dull green | | .55 | .45 |
| **812** A219 | 20pf maroon | | .75 | .75 |

37th Eucharistic World Congress, Munich.

Wrestlers and Olympic Rings — A220

Sport scenes from Greek urns: 10pf, Sprinters. 20pf, Discus and Javelin throwers. 40pf, Chariot race.

| | | | | |
|---|---|---|---|---|
| **1960, Aug. 8** | | **Wmk. 304** | | |
| **813** A220 | 7pf red brown | | .20 | .20 |
| **814** A220 | 10pf olive green | | .40 | .20 |
| **815** A220 | 20pf vermilion | | .40 | .20 |
| **816** A220 | 40pf dark blue | | 1.25 | 1.25 |
| | Nos. 813-816 (4) | | 2.25 | 1.85 |

17th Olympic Games, Rome, 8/25-9/11.

Hildesheim Cathedral, Miters, Cross and Crosier — A221

| | | | | |
|---|---|---|---|---|
| **1960, Sept. 6** | **Engr.** | **Perf. 13½x14** | | |
| **817** A221 | 20pf claret | | .75 | .45 |

St. Bernward (960-1022) and St. Godehard (960-1038), bishops.

### Europa Issue, 1960
Common Design Type

| | | | | |
|---|---|---|---|---|
| **1960, Sept. 19** | | **Wmk. 304** | | |
| **Size: 30x25mm** | | | | |
| **818** CD3 | 10pf ol grn & yel grn | | .20 | .20 |
| **819** CD3 | 20pf brt red & lt red | | .75 | .20 |
| **820** CD3 | 40pf bl & lt bl | | 1.25 | .75 |
| | Nos. 818-820 (3) | | 2.20 | 1.15 |

George C. Marshall A222        Steam Locomotive A223

| | | | | |
|---|---|---|---|---|
| **1960, Oct. 15** | **Litho.** | **Perf. 13x13½** | | |
| **821** A222 | 40pf dp blue & blk | | 2.50 | 2.10 |

Issued to honor George C. Marshall, US general and statesman.

| | | | | |
|---|---|---|---|---|
| **1960, Dec. 7** | | **Perf. 13½x14** | | |
| **822** A223 | 10pf ol bis & blk | | .30 | .35 |

125th anniversary of German railroads.

St. George — A224

| | | | | |
|---|---|---|---|---|
| | **Wmk. 304** | | | |
| **1961, Apr. 23** | **Engr.** | **Perf. 14** | | |
| **823** A224 | 10pf green | | .20 | .30 |

Honoring Boy Scouts of the world on St. George's Day (patron saint of Boy Scouts).

Albrecht Dürer — A225

Portraits: 5pf, Albertus Magnus. 7pf, St. Elizabeth of Thuringia. 8pf, Johann Gutenberg. 15pf, Martin Luther. 20pf, Johann Sebastian Bach. 25pf, Balthasar Neumann. 30pf, Immanuel Kant. 40pf, Gotthold Ephraim

Lessing. 50pf, Johann Wolfgang von Goethe. 60pf, Friedrich von Schiller. 70pf, Ludwig van Beethoven. 80pf, Heinrich von Kleist. 90pf, Prof. Franz Oppenheimer. 1m, Annette von Droste-Hülshoff. 2m, Gerhart Hauptmann.

| | | | | |
|---|---|---|---|---|
| **1961-64** | **Typo.** | **Perf. 14** | | |
| **Fluorescent or Ordinary Paper** | | | | |
| **824** A225 | 5pf olive | | .20 | .20 |
| b. | Tête bêche pair ('63) | | .50 | .90 |
| **825** A225 | 7pf dark bister | | .20 | .20 |
| **826** A225 | 8pf lilac | | .20 | .35 |
| **827** A225 | 10pf olive green | | .20 | .20 |
| b. | Tête bêche pair | | .50 | 1.50 |
| **828** A225 | 15pf blue | | .35 | .75 |
| b. | Tête bêche pair ('63) | | .90 | 2.10 |
| **829** A225 | 20pf dk red | | .35 | .30 |
| b. | Tête bêche pair ('63) | | .60 | 1.90 |
| **830** A225 | 25pf orange brn | | .20 | .20 |

| | | | | |
|---|---|---|---|---|
| **Engr.** | | | | |
| **831** A225 | 30pf gray | | .20 | .20 |
| **832** A225 | 40pf blue | | .20 | .20 |
| **833** A225 | 50pf red brown | | .35 | .20 |
| **834** A225 | 60pf dk car rose ('62) | | .35 | .20 |
| **835** A225 | 70pf grnsh black | | .20 | .20 |
| a. | 70pf deep green | | .60 | .20 |
| **836** A225 | 80pf brown | | .40 | .40 |
| **837** A225 | 90pf yel ol ('64) | | .35 | .30 |
| **838** A225 | 1m violet blue | | .50 | .20 |
| **839** A225 | 2m yel grn ('62) | | 3.00 | .50 |
| | Nos. 824-839 (16) | | 7.25 | 4.60 |

Nos. 824-825, 827-830, 832, 834-835, 835a were issued in coils as well as in sheets. Every fifth coil stamp has a black control number on the back.

Nos. 824-839, including booklet panes and tête bêche pairs, were printed on fluorescent paper. Nos. 824-829 and 832 were also printed on ordinary paper.

Gottlieb Daimler's Car of 1886 and Signature A226

Design: 20pf, Carl Benz's 3-wheel car of 1886 and signature.

| | | | | |
|---|---|---|---|---|
| **1961, July 3** | | **Litho.** | | |
| **840** A226 | 10pf green & blk | | .20 | .20 |
| **841** A226 | 20pf brick red & blk | | .35 | .30 |

75 years of motorized traffic.

Messenger, Nuremberg, 18th Century — A227        Cathedral, Speyer — A228

### Photogravure and Engraved

| | | | | |
|---|---|---|---|---|
| **1961, Aug. 31** | **Wmk. 304** | **Perf. 14** | | |
| **842** A227 | 7pf brown red & blk | | .20 | .30 |

Issued to publicize the exhibition "The Letter in Five Centuries," Nuremberg.

| | | | | |
|---|---|---|---|---|
| **1961, Sept. 2** | | **Engr.** | | |
| **843** A228 | 20pf vermilion | | .30 | .45 |

900th anniversary of Speyer Cathedral.

### Europa Issue, 1961
Common Design Type

| | | | | |
|---|---|---|---|---|
| **1961, Sept. 18** | | **Litho.** | | |
| **Size: 28½x18½mm** | | | | |
| **844** CD4 | 10pf olive green | | .20 | .20 |
| **845** CD4 | 40pf violet blue | | .35 | .50 |

No. 844 was printed on both ordinary and fluorescent paper.

Reis Telephone A229

| | | | | |
|---|---|---|---|---|
| **1961, Oct. 26** | **Engr.** | **Perf. 14** | | |
| **846** A229 | 10pf green | | .30 | .35 |

Cent. of the demonstration of the 1st telephone by Philipp Reis.

Wilhelm Emanuel von Ketteler — A230

| | | | | |
|---|---|---|---|---|
| **1961, Dec. 22** | | **Litho.** | | |
| **847** A230 | 10pf olive grn & blk | | .30 | .35 |

Sesquicentennial of the birth of von Ketteler, Bishop of Mainz and pioneer in social development.

### Fluorescent Paper

was introduced for all stamps, starting with No. 848. Of the stamps before No. 848, those issued on both ordinary and fluorescent paper include Nos. 704, 706, 708-711, 737, 755-756, 824-829, 832, 844. Those issued only on fluorescent paper (up to No. 848) include Nos. 708b, 830-831, 833-839 and 842.

Drusus Stone and Old View of Mainz — A231

Notes and Tuning Fork — A232

| | | | | |
|---|---|---|---|---|
| **1962, May 10** | **Engr.** | **Wmk. 304** | | |
| **848** A231 | 20pf deep claret | | .30 | .35 |

The 2000th anniversary of Mainz.

| | | | | |
|---|---|---|---|---|
| **1962, July 12** | **Litho.** | **Perf. 14** | | |
| **849** A232 | 20pf red & black | | .30 | .45 |

Issued to show appreciation of choral singing. The music is from the choral movement for three voices "In dulci jubilo" from "Musae Sioniae" by Michael Praetorius.

"Faith, Thanksgiving, Service" A233

| | | | | |
|---|---|---|---|---|
| **1962, Aug. 22** | **Engr.** | **Unwmk.** | | |
| **850** A233 | 20pf magenta | | .30 | .45 |

79th meeting of German Catholics, Hanover, Aug. 22-29.

Open Bible, Chrismon and Chalice — A234

| | | | | |
|---|---|---|---|---|
| **1962, Sept. 11** | **Litho.** | **Wmk. 304** | | |
| **851** A234 | 20pf vermilion & blk | | .30 | .45 |

Württemberg Bible Society, 150th anniv.

## Europa Issue, 1962
### Common Design Type

**1962, Sept. 17**     **Engr.**
**Size: 28x23mm**

| 852 | CD5 | 10pf green | .20 | .20 |
| 853 | CD5 | 40pf blue | .40 | .35 |

"Bread for the World" — A235

### Lithographed and Embossed
**1962, Nov. 23**     **Perf. 14**

854 A235 20pf brown red & blk   .30 .45

Issued in connection with the Advent Collection of the Protestant Church in Germany.

Mother and Child Receiving Gift Parcel — A236

**1963, Feb. 9**     **Engr.**

855 A236 20pf dark carmine   .20 .35

Issued to express gratitude to the American organizations, CRALOG (Council of Relief Agencies Licensed to Operate in Germany) and CARE (Cooperative for American Remittances to Everywhere), for help during 1946-1962.

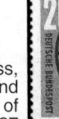

Globe, Cross, Seeds and Stalks of Wheat — A237

Checkered Lily — A238

### Lithographed and Engraved
**1963, Feb. 27**    **Wmk. 304**   **Perf. 14**

856 A237 20pf gray, blk & red   .20 .35

German Catholic "Misereor" (I have compassion) campaign against hunger and illness.

**1963, Apr. 28**     **Litho.**    **Unwmk.**

Flowers: 15pf, Lady's slipper. 20pf, Columbine. 40pf, Beach thistle.

| 857 | A238 | 10pf multicolored | .20 | .20 |
| 858 | A238 | 15pf multicolored | .20 | .20 |
| 859 | A238 | 20pf multicolored | .20 | .20 |
| 860 | A238 | 40pf multicolored | .35 | .35 |
| | | Nos. 857-860 (4) | .95 | .95 |

Flora and Philately Exhibition, Hamburg.

Heidelberg Catechism A239

**1963, May 2**     **Litho. & Engr.**

861 A239 20pf dp org, brn org & blk   .30 .35

400th anniv. of the Heidelberg Catechism, containing the doctrine of the reformed church.

Cross of Golgotha, Darkened Sun and Moon — A240

**1963, May 4**    **Litho.**    **Wmk. 304**

862 A240 10pf grn, dp car, blk & vio   .20 .30

Consecration of the Regina Martyrum Church, Berlin-Plötzensee, in memory of the victims of Nazism.

Arms of 18 Participating Countries, Paris Conference, 1863 — A241

Map Showing New Railroad Link, German and Danish Flags — A242

**1963, May 7**     **Engr.**

863 A241 40pf violet blue   .40 .50

1st Intl. Postal Conf., Paris, 1863, cent.

**1963, May 14**    **Litho.**    **Unwmk.**

864 A242 20pf multi   .30 .30

Inauguration of the "Bird Flight Line" railroad link between Germany and Denmark.

Cross — A243

### Lithographed and Embossed
**1963, May 24**    **Unwmk.**    **Perf. 14**

865 A243 20pf magenta, red & yel   .20 .30

Cent. of the founding of the Intl. Red Cross in connection with the German Red Cross cent. celebrations, Munster, May 24-26.

Synod Emblem and Crown of Barbed Wire — A244

**Perf. 13½x13**
**1963, July 24**    **Litho.**    **Wmk. 304**

866 A244 20pf dp orange & blk   .30 .35

Meeting of German Protestants (Evangelical Synod), Dortmund, July 24-28.

### Europa Issue, 1963
### Common Design Type

**1963, Sept. 14**     **Engr.**    **Perf. 14**
**Size: 28x23½mm**

| 867 | CD6 | 15pf green | .25 | .30 |
| 868 | CD6 | 20pf red | .20 | .20 |

Old Town Hall, Hanover A245

State Capitals: #870, Hamburg harbor, 775th anniv. #871, North Ferry pier, Kiel. #872, National Theater, Munich. #873, Fountain & building, Wiesbaden. #874, Reichstag Building,Berlin. #875, Gutenberg Museum, Mainz. #876, Jan Wellem (Johann Wilhelm II, 1658-1716) statue, Dusseldorf. #877, City Hall, Bonn. #878, City Hall, Bremen. #879, View of Stuttgart. #879A, Ludwig's Church, Saarbrucken.

**1964-65**    **Litho.**    **Unwmk.**    **Perf. 14**

| 869 | A245 | 20pf gray, blk & red | .20 | .30 |
| 870 | A245 | 20pf multicolored | .20 | .30 |
| 871 | A245 | 20pf multicolored | .20 | .30 |
| 872 | A245 | 20pf multicolored | .20 | .30 |
| 873 | A245 | 20pf multicolored | .20 | .30 |
| 874 | A245 | 20pf blue, blk, & grn | .20 | .30 |
| 875 | A245 | 20pf multicolored | .20 | .30 |
| 876 | A245 | 20pf multicolored | .20 | .30 |
| 877 | A245 | 20pf multi ('65) | .20 | .30 |
| 878 | A245 | 20pf multi ('65) | .20 | .30 |
| 879 | A245 | 20pf multi ('65) | .20 | .30 |
| 879A | A245 | 20pf multi ('65) | .20 | .30 |
| | | Nos. 869-879A (12) | 2.40 | 3.60 |

View of Ottobeuren Abbey — A246

### Lithographed and Engraved
**1964, May 29**     **Perf. 14**

880 A246 20pf pink, red & blk   .20 .30

Ottobeuren Benedictine Abbey, 1200th anniv.

Pres. Heinrich Lübke — A247

Sophie Scholl — A248

**1964, July 1**    **Litho.**    **Perf. 14**

| 881 | A247 | 20pf carmine | .20 | .20 |
| 882 | A247 | 40pf ultra | .20 | .30 |

Lübke's re-election. See Nos. 974-975.

**1964, July 20**     **Litho. & Engr.**

Designs: No. 884, Ludwig Beck. No. 885, Dietrich Bonhoeffer. No. 886, Alfred Delp. No. 887, Karl Friedrich Goerdeler. No. 888, Wilhelm Leuschner. No. 889, Count James von Moltke. No. 890, Count Claus Schenk von Stauffenberg.

| 883 | A248 | 20pf blue gray & blk | .60 | 1.10 |
| 884 | A248 | 20pf blue gray & blk | .60 | 1.10 |
| 885 | A248 | 20pf blue gray & blk | .60 | 1.10 |
| 886 | A248 | 20pf blue gray & blk | .60 | 1.10 |
| 887 | A248 | 20pf blue gray & blk | .60 | 1.10 |
| 888 | A248 | 20pf blue gray & blk | .60 | 1.10 |
| 889 | A248 | 20pf blue gray & blk | .60 | 1.10 |
| 890 | A248 | 20pf blue gray & blk | .60 | 1.10 |
| | | Nos. 883-890 (8) | 4.80 | 8.80 |

Issued to honor the German resistance to the Nazis, 1943-45. Printed in sheet of eight, containing one each of Nos. 883-890, se-tenant. Size: 148x105mm. The stamps were valid; the sheet was not, though widely used.

John Calvin — A249

Benzene Ring, Kekulé's Formula — A250

**1964, Aug. 3**    **Litho.**    **Perf. 14**

891 A249 20pf red & black   .20 .30

Issued to honor the meeting of the International Union of the Reformed Churches in Germany, Frankfort on the Main, Aug. 3-13.

**1964, Aug. 14**    **Unwmk.**    **Perf. 14**

Designs: 15pf, Cerenkov radiation, reactor in operation. 20pf, German gas engine.

| 892 | A250 | 10pf dk brn, brt grn & blk | .20 | .20 |
| 893 | A250 | 15pf brt grn, ultra & blk | .20 | .20 |
| 894 | A250 | 20pf red, grn & blk | .20 | .20 |
| | | Nos. 892-894 (3) | .60 | .60 |

Progress in science and technology: 10pf, centenary of benzene formula by August Friedrich Kekulé; 15pf, 25 years of nuclear fission, Hahn and Strassmann; 20pf, centenary of German internal combustion engine, Nikolaus August Otto and Eugen Langen.

Ferdinand Lasalle — A251

Radiating Sun — A252

**1964, Aug. 31**     **Litho.**

895 A251 20pf slate bl & blk   .20 .30

Cent. of the death of Ferdinand Lasalle, a founder of the German Labor Movement.

**1964, Sept. 2**    **Engr.**    **Wmk. 304**

896 A252 20pf gray & red   .20 .30

80th meeting of German Catholics, Stuttgart, Sept. 2-6. The inscription from Romans 12:2: ". . . be ye transformed through the renewing of your mind."

### Europa Issue, 1964
### Common Design Type

**1964, Sept. 14**    **Litho.**    **Unwmk.**
**Size: 23x29mm**

| 897 | CD7 | 15pf yellow grn & lil | .20 | .20 |
| 898 | CD7 | 20pf rose & lilac | .20 | .20 |

Judo — A253

**1964, Oct. 10**

899 A253 20pf multicolored   .20 .30

18th Olympic Games, Tokyo, Oct. 10-25.

Prussian Eagle — A254

## Lithographed and Embossed
**1964, Oct. 30     Unwmk.     Perf. 14**
900  A254  20pf brown org & blk      .20    .30

250 years of the Court of Accounts in Germany, founded as the Royal Prussian Upper Chamber of Accounts.

John F. Kennedy
(1917-63)
A255

Castle Gate,
Ellwangen
A256

**1964, Nov. 21     Engr.     Wmk. 304**
901  A255  40pf dark blue      .30    .30

**1964-66     Typo.     Unwmk.**
Designs: (German buildings through 12 centuries): 10pf, Wall pavilion, Zwinger, Dresden. 15pf, Tegel Castle, Berlin. 20pf, Portico, Lorsch. 40pf, Trifels Fortress, Palatinate. 60pf, Treptow Gate, Neubrandenburg. 70pf, Osthofen Gate, Soest. 80pf, Elling Gate, Weissenburg.

903  A256  10pf brown ('65)      .20    .20
904  A256  15pf dk green ('65)      .20    .20
  b.     Tête bêche pair ('65)      1.10   1.25
905  A256  20pf brown red ('65)      .20    .20
  b.     Tête bêche pair ('66)      1.10   1.50

**Engr.**
908  A256  40pf violet bl ('65)      .20    .20
909  A256  50pf olive bister      .40    .20
910  A256  60pf rose red      .95    .35
911  A256  70pf dark green ('65)      1.25   .35
912  A256  80pf chocolate      .95    .35
      Nos. 903-912 (8)      4.35   2.05

Nos. 903-905, 908, 910-912 were issued in sheets of 100 and in coils. Every fifth coil stamp has a black control number on the back.

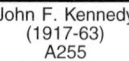

Illustrations from
the Works of
Matthias
Claudius
A257

Otto von Bismarck
by Franz von
Lenbach — A258

**1965, Jan. 21     Engr.     Perf. 14**
917  A257  20pf black & red      .20    .30

150th anniv. of the death of Matthias Claudius, poet and editor of the "Wandsbecker Bothe." Exists imperf. Value $225.

**1965, Apr. 1     Litho.     Perf. 14**
918  A258  20pf black & dull red      .20    .30

Prince Otto von Bismarck (1815-1898), Prussian statesman and 1st chancellor of the German Empire.
Exists imperf. Value $750.

Jet Plane and
Space
Capsule — A259

Bouquet of
Flowers — A260

---

Designs: 5pf, Traffic lights and signs. 10pf, Communications satellite and ground station. 15pf, Old and new post buses. 20pf, Semaphore telegraph and telecommunication tower. 40pf, Old and new railroad engines. 70pf, Sailing ship and ocean liner.

**1965**
919  A259  5pf gray & multi      .20    .30
920  A259  10pf multicolored      .20    .30
921  A259  15pf multicolored      .20    .30
922  A259  20pf maroon & multi      .20    .30
923  A259  40pf dk blue & multi      .20    .30
924  A259  60pf dull vio, yel & lt bl      .20    .30
925  A259  70pf multicolored      .30    .30
      Nos. 919-925 (7)      1.50   2.10

Intl. Transport and Communications Exhib., Munich, June 25-Oct. 30. No. 924 also for the 10th anniv. of the reopening of air service by Lufthansa. Issued: 60pf, 4/1; others, 6/25.
No. 919 exists imperf. Value $225.

**1965, May 1     Litho.**
926  A260  15pf multicolored      .20    .20

75th anniv. of May Day celebration in Germany.

ITU
Emblem — A261

Adolph
Kolping — A262

**1965, May 17     Unwmk.     Perf. 14**
927  A261  40pf dp blue & blk      .30    .35
Cent. of the ITU.

**1965, May 26     Typo.**
928  A262  20pf black, gray & red      .20    .30

Kolping (1813-65). founder of the Catholic Unions of Journeymen, the Kolpingwork.

Rescue
Ship — A263

**1965, May 29     Litho. & Engr.**
929  A263  20pf red & black      .20    .30
Cent. of the German Sea Rescue Service.

Type of 1955 dated "1945-1965"
**Perf. 14x13½**
**1965, July 28     Engr.     Wmk. 304**
930  A161  20pf gray      .20    .30
20 years of German expatriation.

Synod Emblem and
Labyrinth — A264

## Lithographed and Engraved
**Perf. 13½x14**
**1965, July 28     Unwmk.**
931  A264  20pf dp bl, grnsh bl &
            blk      .20    .30

12th meeting of German Protestants (Evangelical Synod), Cologne, July 28-Aug. 1.

---

Waves and
Stuttgart
Television
Tower — A265

**1965, July 28     Litho.     Perf. 13½x13**
932  A265  20pf dp bl, blk & brt
            pink      .20    .30

Issued to publicize the German Radio Exhibition, Stuttgart, Aug. 27-Sept. 5.

Stamps of
Thurn
and Taxis,
1852-59
A266

**1965, Aug. 28     Perf. 14**
933  A266  20pf multicolored      .20    .30

125th anniv. of the introduction of postage stamps in Great Britain.

### Europa Issue, 1965
Common Design Type
**Perf. 14x13½**
**1965, Sept. 27     Engr.     Wmk. 304**
Size: 28x23mm
934  CD8  15pf green      .20    .20
935  CD8  20pf dull red      .20    .20

Nordertor,
Flensburg
A267

Brandenburg
Gate
A268

Designs: 5pf, Berlin Gate, Stettin. 10pf, Wall Pavilion, Zwinger, Dresden. 20pf, Portico, Lorsch. 40pf, Trifels Fortress, Palatinate. 50pf, Castle Gate, Ellwangen. 60pf, Treptow Gate, Neubrandenburg. 70pf, Osthofen Gate, Soest. 80pf, Elling Gate, Weissenburg. 90pf, Zschocke Ladies' Home, Königsberg. 1m, Melanchthon House, Wittenberg. 1.10m, Trinity Hospital, Hildesheim. 1.30m, Tegel Castle, Berlin. 2m, Löwenberg, Town Hall, interior view.

**1966-69     Unwmk.     Engr.     Perf. 14**
936  A267  5pf olive      .20    .20
937  A267  10pf dk brn ('67)      .20    .20
939  A267  20pf dk grn ('67)      .20    .20
940  A267  30pf yellow green      .20    .20
941  A267  30pf red ('67)      .20    .20
942  A267  40pf olive bis ('67)      .30    .30
943  A267  50pf blue ('67)      .40    .20
944  A267  60pf dp org ('67)      2.50   1.50
945  A267  70pf slate grn ('67)      1.10   .20
946  A267  80pf red brown
            ('67)      2.10   1.50
947  A267  90pf black      .75    .30
948  A267  1m dull blue      .75    .20
949  A267  1.10m red brown      .75    .35
950  A267  1.30m green ('69)      2.10   1.40
951  A267  2m purple      2.10   .60
      Nos. 936-951 (15)      13.85   7.55

**1966-68     Typo.     Perf. 14**
952  A268  10pf chocolate      .20    .20
  a.     Bklt. pane, 4 #952, 2 #953, 4
         #954 ('67)      3.75   15.00
  b.     Tête bêche pair      .65    .75
  c.     Bklt. pane, 2 #952, 4 #953      2.25   7.50
953  A268  20pf deep green      .30    .20
  a.     Tête bêche pair ('68)      .90    1.25
  b.     Bklt. pane, 2 #953, 2 #954      1.50   6.00
954  A268  30pf red      .30    .20
  a.     Tête bêche pair ('68)      .95    1.40
955  A268  50pf dark blue      1.25   .35
956  A268  100pf dark blue ('67)      9.75   .60
      Nos. 952-956 (5)      11.80   1.55

Nos. 952-956 were issued in sheets of 100 and in coils. Every fifth coil stamp has a black control number on the back.

---

Nathan
Söderblom
A269

Cardinal von
Galen
A270

**1966, Jan. 15     Litho.     Perf. 13x13½**
959  A269  20pf dull lilac & blk      .20    .30

Soderblom (1866-1931),Swedish Protestant theologian, who worked for the union of Christian churches and received 1930 Nobel Peace Prize.

**1966, Mar. 22     Litho.     Perf. 14**
960  A270  20pf dp lil rose, sal
            pink & blk      .20    .30

Clemens August Cardinal Count von Galen (1878-1946), anti-Nazi Bishop of Munster.

"The Miraculous
Draught" — A271

G. W.
Leibniz — A272

**1966, July 13     Litho.     Perf. 14**
961  A271  30pf dp orange & blk      .20    .30

81st meeting of German Catholics, Bamberg, July 13-17.

**1966, Aug. 24     Unwmk.     Perf. 14**
962  A272  30pf rose car, pink &
            blk      .20    .30

Gottfried Wilhelm Leibniz (1646-1716), philosopher and mathematician.

### Europa Issue, 1966
Common Design Type
**1966, Sept. 24     Perf. 14**
Size:  23x28½mm
963  CD9  20pf multicolored      .25    .30
964  CD9  30pf multicolored      .20    .20

Diagram of
Three-Phase
Transmission
A273

UNICEF Emblem
A274

**1966, Sept. 28     Litho.**
965  A273  20pf shown      .20    .20
966  A273  30pf Dynamo      .20    .20

Progress in science and technology: 20pf, 75th anniv. of three-phase power transmission; 30pf, cent.y of discovery by Werner von Siemens of the dynamoelectric principle.

**1966, Oct. 24     Litho.     Perf. 14**
967  A274  30pf red, blk & gray      .20    .30

Awarding of the 1965 Nobel Peace Prize to UNICEF.

Werner von
Siemens (1816-
92), Electrical
Engineer and
Inventor — A275

**1966, Dec. 13     Engr.     Perf. 14**
968  A275  30pf maroon      .20    .30

Europa Issue, 1967
**Common Design Type**
**1967, May 2** **Photo.** *Perf. 14*
**Size: 23x28mm**
969 CD10 20pf multi .30 .30
970 CD10 30pf multi .20 .25

Franz von Taxis — A276
"Peace Is Among Us" — A277

**Lithographed and Engraved**
**1967, June 3** *Perf. 14*
971 A276 30pf dp orange & blk .20 .30

450th anniv. of the death of Franz von Taxis, founder of the Taxis (Thurn and Taxis) postal system.

**1967, June 21**
972 A277 30pf brt pink & blk .20 .30

13th meeting of German Protestants (Evangelical Synod), Hanover, June 21-25.

Friedrich von Bodelschwingh A278

*Perf. 13½x13*
**1967, July 1** **Litho.** **Unwmk.**
973 A278 30pf redsh brown & blk .20 .30

Cent. of Bethel Institution (for the incurable). Friedrich von Bodelschwingh (1877-1946), manager of Bethel (1910-46) & son of the founder.

Lübke Type of 1964
**1967, Oct. 14** **Litho.** *Perf. 14*
974 A247 30pf carmine .20 .30
975 A247 50pf ultra .35 .35

Re-election of President Heinrich Lübke.

The Wartburg, Eisenach A279

**1967, Oct. 31** **Engr.** *Perf. 14*
976 A279 30pf red .30 .35

450th anniversary of the Reformation.

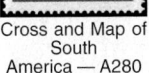

Cross and Map of South America — A280
Koenig Printing Press — A281

**1967, Nov. 17** **Photo.** *Perf. 14*
977 A280 30pf multicolored .20 .30

"Adveniat," aid movement of German Catholics for the Latin American church.

**1968, Jan. 12** **Litho.** *Perf. 14*
Designs: 20pf, Zinc sulfide and lead sulfide crystals. 30pf, Schematic diagram of a microscope.
978 A281 10pf multicolored .20 .20
979 A281 20pf multicolored .20 .20
980 A281 30pf multicolored .20 .20
*Nos. 978-980 (3)* .60 .60

Progress in science and technology: 10pf, 150th anniv. of the Koenig printing press; 20pf, 1000th anniv. of mining in the Harz Mountains; 30pf, cent. of scientific microscope construction.

Symbols of Various Crafts A282

**1968, Mar. 8** **Litho.** *Perf. 14*
981 A282 30pf multicolored .30 .35

Traditions and progress of the crafts. Exists imperf. Value $250.

Souvenir Sheet

Adenauer, Churchill, de Gasperi and Schuman — A283

Portraits: 10pf, Winston S. Churchill. 20pf, Alcide de Gasperi. 30pf, Robert Schuman. 50pf, Konrad Adenauer.

**1968, Apr. 19** **Litho.** *Perf. 14*
**Black Inscriptions**
982 A283 Sheet of 4 2.25 2.25
a. 10pf dark red brown .50 .30
b. 20pf green .50 .35
c. 30pf dark red .50 .50
d. 50pf bright blue .50 .75

1st anniv. of the death of Konrad Adenauer (1876-1967), chancellor of West Germany (1949-63), and honoring leaders in building a united Europe.

Europa Issue, 1968
Common Design Type
**1968, Apr. 29** **Photo.**
**Size: 29x24½mm**
983 CD11 20pf green, yel & brn *.25* *.30*
984 CD11 30pf car, yel & brn .20 .20

Karl Marx (1818-83) A284

**Lithgraphed and Engraved**
**1968, Apr. 29** *Perf. 14*
985 A284 30pf red, black & gray .20 .30

Pierre de Coubertin — A285

**1968, June 6** **Unwmk.** *Perf. 14*
986 A285 30pf lilac & dk pur .30 .30
*Nos. 986,B434-B437 (5)* 2.20 2.30

19th Olympic Games, Mexico City, 10/12-27.

Opening Bars, "Die Meistersinger von Nurnberg," by Wagner — A286

**Lithographed and Photogravure**
**1968, June 21**
987 A286 30pf gray, blk & fawn .20 .30

Cent. of the 1st performance of Richard Wagner's "Die Meistersinger von Nurnberg."

Konrad Adenauer (1876-1967) A287

**1968, July 19** **Litho.** *Perf. 14*
988 A287 30pf dp orange & blk .30 .30

Cross and Dove in Center of Universe A288

**1968, July 19** **Litho. & Engr.**
989 A288 20pf brt grn, bl blk & yel .20 .30

Issued to publicize the 82nd meeting of German Catholics, Essen, Sept. 4-8.

North German Confederation Nos. 4 and 10 — A289

**1968, Sept. 5** **Engr.** *Perf. 14*
990 A289 30pf cop red, gray vio & blk .20 .30

Cent. of the stamps of the North German Confederation.

Arrows Symbolizing Determination A290
Human Rights Flame A291

**1968, Sept. 26** **Photo.** *Perf. 14*
991 A290 30pf multi .20 .30

Centenary of the German trade unions.

**1968, Dec. 10** **Photo.** *Perf. 14*
992 A291 30pf multicolored .20 .30

International Human Rights Year.

Junkers 52 A292

Design: 30pf, Boeing 707.
**1969, Feb. 6** **Litho.** *Perf. 14*
993 A292 20pf green & multi .40 .20
994 A292 30pf red & multi .60 .20

50th anniv. of German airmail service.

Five-pointed Star — A293

**1969, Apr. 28** **Litho.** *Perf. 13½x13*
995 A293 30pf red & multi .45 .30

50th anniv. of the ILO.

**Europa Issue, 1969**
Common Design Type
**1969, Apr. 28** **Photo.** *Perf. 14*
**Size: 29x23mm**
996 CD12 20pf green, blue & yel .30 .20
997 CD12 30pf red brn, yel & blk .35 .20

Heraldic Eagles of Federal and Weimar Republics A294

**1969, May 23** **Photo.** *Perf. 14*
998 A294 30pf red, black & gold .90 .45

German Basic Law, 20th anniv., and the proclamation of the Weimar Constitution, 50th anniv.

Crosses — A295

**1969, June 4** **Litho. & Engr.**
999 A295 30pf dk violet bl & cream .45 .30

German War Graves Commission, 50th anniv.

Seashore A296

**1969, June 4** *Perf. 14*
1000 A296 10pf shown .20 .20
1001 A296 20pf Foothills .60 .35
1002 A296 30pf Mountains .30 .20
1003 A296 50pf Riverbed .90 .50
*Nos. 1000-1003 (4)* 2.00 1.25

Issued to publicize Nature Protection.

"Hungry for Justice" — A297

**1969, July 7** **Litho.** *Perf. 14*
1004 A297 30pf multicolored .45 .30

14th meeting of German Protestants (Evangelical Synod), Stuttgart, July 16-20.

Electromagnetic Field — A298

**1969, Aug. 11      Litho.      Perf. 14**
1005 A298 30pf red & multi          .45   .30
Issued to publicize the German Radio Exhibition, Stuttgart, Aug. 29-Sept. 7.

Maltese Cross — A299

**1969, Aug. 11      Perf. 13x13½**
1006 A299 30pf red & black          .45   .30
Maltese Relief Service, founded 1955, world-wide activities in social services, first aid and disaster assistance.

**Souvenir Sheet**

Marie Juchacz, Marie-Elisabeth Lüders and Helene Weber — A300

**1969, Aug. 11      Engr.      Perf. 14**
1007 A300    Sheet of 3          .90   .65
  a.    10pf olive                 .20   .20
  b.    20pf dark green            .20   .20
  c.    30pf lake                  .20   .20

50th anniv. of universal women's suffrage, Marie Juchacz (1879-1956), Marie-Elisabeth Lüders (1878-1966) and Helene Weber (1881-1962) were members of the German Reichstag.

Bavaria No. 16 — A301

**1969, Sept. 4      Litho. & Embossed**
1008 A301 30pf gray & rose          .45   .30
23rd meeting of the Federation of German Philatelists, Sept. 6, the 70th Philatelists' Day, Sept. 7, and the phil. exhib. "120 Years of Bavarian Stamps" in Garmish-Partenkirchen, Sept. 4-7.

Brine Pipe Line — A302

**1969, Sept. 4      Litho.      Perf. 13½x13**
1009 A302 20pf multicolored         .45   .30
350th anniversary of the Brine Pipe Line from Traunstein to Bad Reichenhall.

Rothenburg ob der Tauber — A303

**Lithographed and Engraved**
**1969, Sept. 4      Perf. 14**
1010 A303 30pf dark red & blk       .45   .30
See #1047-1049, 1067-1069A, 1106-1110.

Pope John XXIII      Mahatma Gandhi
(1881-1963)          (1869-1948)
A304                 A305

**1969, Oct. 2      Engr.      Perf. 13½x14**
1011 A304 30pf dark red             .35   .30

**1969, Oct. 2      Litho.**
1012 A305 20pf yellow grn & blk     .30   .30

Ernst Moritz          Ludwig van
Arndt                 Beethoven
A306                  A307

**1969, Nov. 13      Litho. & Engr.**
1013 A306 30pf gray & maroon        .35   .30
Arndt (1769-1860), historian, poet and member of German National Assembly.

**1970, Mar. 20      Perf. 13½x14**
Portraits: 20pf, Georg Wilhelm Hegel (1770-1831), philosopher. 30pf, Friedrich Hölderlin (1770-1843), poet.
1014 A307 10pf pale vio & blk       .75   .20
1015 A307 20pf olive & blk          .35   .20
1016 A307 30pf rose & blk           .35   .20
  Nos. 1014-1016 (3)               1.45   .60

Saar No. 171 A308

**1970, Apr. 29  Photo.  Perf. 14x13½**
1017 A308 30pf blk, red & gray
             grn                    .35   .30
Issued to publicize the SABRIA National Stamp Exhibition, Saarbrucken, Apr. 29-May 4. No. 1017 was issued Apr. 29 at the SABRIA post office in Saarbrucken, on May 4 throughout Germany.

**Europa Issue, 1970**
Common Design Type
**1970, May 4      Engr.      Perf. 14x13½**
Size: 28x23mm
1018 CD13 20pf green                .30   .20
1019 CD13 30pf red                  .35   .20

Münchhausen on His Severed Horse — A309

**1970, May 11      Litho.      Perf. 13½x13**
1020 A309 20pf multicolored         .35   .30
Soldier and storyteller Count Hieronymus C. F. von Münchhausen (1720-97).

Seagoing Vessel and Underpass A310

Nurse Assisting Elderly Woman — A311

**1970, June 18      Litho.      Perf. 14**
1021 A310 20pf multicolored         .35   .30
North Sea-Baltic Sea Canal, 75th anniv.

**1970                              Photo.**
5pf, Welder (industrial protection). 10pf, Mountain climbers (rescuer bringing down casualty). 30pf, Fireman. 50pf, Stretcher bearer, casualty & ambulance. 70pf, Rescuer & drowning boy.
1022 A311  5pf dull blue & multi    .20   .20
1023 A311 10pf brown & multi        .20   .20
1024 A311 20pf green & multi        .30   .20
1025 A311 30pf red & multi          .75   .20
1026 A311 50pf blue & multi         .75   .35
1027 A311 70pf green & multi        .90   .75
  Nos. 1022-1027 (6)               3.10  1.90

Honoring various voluntary services. Issued: 20pf, 30pf, 6/18; others, 9/21.

Pres. Gustav           Cross Seen
Heinemann              through Glass
A312                   A313

**1970-73           Engr.           Perf. 14**
1028  A312   5pf dark gray         .20   .20
1029  A312  10pf brown             .20   .20
1030  A312  20pf green             .20   .20
1030A A312  25pf dp yellow
                  grn              .30   .20
1031  A312  30pf red brown         .30   .20
1032  A312  40pf brown org         .30   .20
1033  A312  50pf dark blue        1.40   .20
1034  A312  60pf blue              .50   .20
1035  A312  70pf dark brown        .65   .30
1036  A312  80pf slate grn         .65   .30
1037  A312  90pf magenta          1.25  1.10
1038  A312   1m olive              .90   .30
1038A A312 110pf olive gray       1.00   .60
1039  A312 120pf ocher            1.10   .75
1040  A312 130pf ocher            1.25   .75
1040A A312 140pf dk blue grn      1.40   .90
1041  A312 150pf purple           1.40   .60
1042  A312 160pf orange           2.00  1.00
1042A A312 170pf orange           1.60   .60
1043  A312 190pf deep claret      2.25   .75
1044  A312   2m deep violet       1.75   .35
  Nos. 1028-1044 (21)            20.60  9.90

Issued: 5pf, 1m, 7/23/70; 10, 20pf, 10/23/70; 30, 90pf, 2m, 1/7/71; 40, 50, 70, 80pf, 4/8/71; 60pf, 6/25/71; 25pf, 8/27/71; 120, 160pf, 3/8/72; 130pf, 6/20/72; 150pf, 7/5/72; 170pf, 9/11/72; 110, 140, 190pf, 1/16/73.

**1970, Aug. 25                    Litho.**
1045 A313 20pf emerald & yellow     .30   .20
Issued to publicize the world mission of Catholic missionaries who bring the Gospel to all peoples.

Cross           Comenius
A314            A315

**1970, Sept. 4      Perf. 13x13½**
1046 A314 20pf multicolored         .30   .30
Issued to publicize the 83rd meeting of German Catholics, Trier, Sept. 9-13.

**Town Type of 1969**
Designs: No. 1047, View of Cochem and Moselle River. No. 1048, Cathedral and view of Freiburg im Breisgau. No. 1049, View of Oberammergau.

**1970              Litho.           Perf. 14**
1047 A303 20pf apple grn & blk      .45   .30
1048 A303 20pf green & dk brn       .45   .30
1049 A303 30pf dp orange & blk      .45   .30
  Nos. 1047-1049 (3)               1.35   .90
Issued: #1047, 9/21; #1048, 11/4; #1049, 5/11.

**1970, Nov. 12      Perf. 13½x14**
1050 A315 30pf dark red & blk       .45   .30
John Amos Comenius (1592-1670), theologian and educator.

Friedrich Engels — A316

Imperial Eagle, 1872 — A317

**1970, Nov. 27      Litho.      Perf. 14**
1051 A316 50pf red & vio blue      1.40   .75
Engels (1820-95), socialist, collaborator with Marx.

**1971, Jan. 18      Litho.      Perf. 13½x14**
1052 A317 30pf multicolored        1.40   .30
Centenary of the German Empire.

Friedrich Ebert (Germany No. 378) — A318

Molecule Diagram Textile Pattern — A319

**1971, Jan. 18                    Perf. 13**
1053 A318 30pf red brn, ol & blk   1.40   .30
Ebert (1871-1925), 1st Pres. of the German Republic.

**1971, Feb. 18      Litho.      Perf. 13½x13**
1054 A319 20pf brt grn, red & blk   .30   .20
Synthetic textile fiber research, 125th anniversary.

School Crossing — A320

Signal to Pass — A321

Traffic Signs: 20pf, Proceed with caution. 30pf, Stop. 50pf, Pedestrian crossing.

**1971, Feb. 18          Perf. 14**
1055  A320  10pf black, ultra & red   .20   .20
1056  A320  20pf black, red & grn    .30   .20
1057  A320  30pf black, gray & red   .45   .20
1058  A320  50pf black, ultra & red  .75   .45
      Nos. 1055-1058 (4)            1.70  1.05

New traffic rules, effective Mar. 1, 1971.

**1971, Apr. 16    Photo.    Perf. 14**
Traffic Signs: 10pf, Warning signal. 20pf, Drive at right. 30pf, "Observe pedestrian crossings."
1059  A321  5pf blue, blk & car      .20   .20
1060  A321  10pf multicolored        .20   .20
1061  A321  20pf brt grn, blk &
            car                      .35   .20
1062  A321  30pf carmine &
            multi                    .65   .20
      Nos. 1059-1062 (4)            1.40   .80

New traffic rules, effective Mar. 1, 1971.

Luther Facing Charles V, Woodcut by Rabus — A322

Thomas à Kempis — A323

**1971, Mar. 18          Perf. 14**
1063  A322  30pf red & black         .60   .30

450th anniversary of the Diet of Worms.

**Europa Issue, 1971**
**Common Design Type**
**1971, May 3    Photo.    Perf. 14**
**Size: 28½x23mm**
1064  CD14  20pf green, gold & blk   .30   .20
1065  CD14  30pf dp car, gold & blk  .30   .20

**1971, May 3          Engr.**
1066  A323  30pf red & black         .50   .30

500th anniversary of the death of Thomas à Kempis (1379-1471), Augustinian monk, author of "The Imitation of Christ."

**Town Type of 1969**
20pf, View of Goslar. #1068, View of Nuremberg. #1069, Heligoland. 40pf, Heidelberg.

**1971-72    Litho. & Engr.    Perf. 14**
1067  A303  20pf brt green & blk     .45   .35
1068  A303  30pf vermilion & blk     .45   .30
1069  A303  30pf lt grn & blk
            ('72)                    .45   .20
1069A A303  40pf orange & blk
            ('72)                    .50   .20
      Nos. 1067-1069A (4)           1.85  1.05

Issued: 20pf, 9/15; #1068, 5/21; #1069, 1069A, 10/20.

Dürer's Signature A324

**1971, May 21          Engr.**
1070  A324  30pf copper red & blk   1.25   .30

500th anniversary of the birth of Albrecht Dürer (1471-1528), painter and engraver.

Congress Emblem — A325

Illustration from New Astronomy, by Kepler — A326

**1971, May 28    Litho.    Perf. 13½x13**
1071  A325  30pf red, orange & blk   .45   .30

Ecumenical Meeting at Pentecost of the German Evangelical and Catholic Churches, Augsburg, June 2-5.

**1971, June 25    Photo.    Perf. 14**
1072  A326  30pf brt car, gold & blk  .50   .30

Johannes Kepler (1571-1630), astronomer.

Dante Alighieri — A327

"Matches Cause Fires" — A328

**1971, Sept. 3    Engr.    Perf. 14**
1073  A327  10pf black               .20   .20

650th anniversary of the death of Dante Alighieri (1265-1321), poet.

**1971-74        Typo.        Perf. 14**
Designs: 10pf, Broken ladder. 20pf, Hand and circular saw. 25pf, "Alcohol and automobile." 30pf, Safety helmets prevent injury. 40pf, Defective plug. 50pf, Nail sticking from board. 60pf, 70pf, Traffic safety (ball rolling before car). 1m, Hoisted cargo. 1.50m, Fenced-in open manhole.
1074  A328  5pf orange             .20   .20
  a.    Bklt. pane, 2 each #1074,
        1077-1079 ('74)           5.25  11.00
1075  A328  10pf dark brown        .20   .20
  a.    Bklt. pane, 4 #1075, 2
        #1078                      3.00  3.00
  b.    Bklt. pane, 2 each #1075-
        1076, 1078-1079 ('75)      5.25  11.00
  c.    Bklt. pane, 2 each #1079,
        1075, 1078, 1076          13.50  16.50
1076  A328  20pf purple            .30   .20
1077  A328  25pf green             .40   .20
1078  A328  30pf dark red          .35   .20
1079  A328  40pf rose claret       .35   .20
1080  A328  50pf Prus blue        1.90   .20
1081  A328  60pf violet blue      1.10   .45
1082  A328  70pf green & vio
            bl                    1.10   .30
1083  A328  100pf olive           1.60   .20
1085  A328  150pf red brown       5.00  1.10
      Nos. 1074-1085 (11)        12.50  3.45

Accident prevention.
Issued in sheets of 100 and in coils. Every fifth coil stamp has a control number on the back.
Issued: 25pf, 60pf, 9/10; 5pf, 10/29; 10pf, 30pf, 3/8/72; 40pf, 6/20/72; 20pf, 100pf, 7/5/72; 150pf, 9/11/72; 50pf, 1/16/73; 70pf, 6/5/73.

Deaconesses A329

Senefelder's Lithography Press — A330

**1972, Jan. 20    Litho.    Perf. 13x13½**
1087  A329  25pf green, blk & gray   .45   .30

Wilhelm Löhe (1808-1872), founder of the Deaconesses Training Institute at Neuendettelsau.

**1972, Apr. 14    Litho.    Perf. 13½x13**
1088  A330  25pf multicolored        .45   .30

175th anniv. of the invention of the lithographic printing process by Alois Senefelder in 1796.

**Europa Issue 1972**
**Common Design Type**
**1972, May 2    Photo.    Perf. 13½x14**
**Size: 23x29mm**
1089  CD15  25pf yel grn, dk bl &
            yel                      .35   .20
1090  CD15  30pf pale rose, dk &
            lt bl                    .50   .25

Lucas Cranach, by Dürer A331

Archer in Wheelchair A332

**Lithographed and Engraved**
**1972, May 18          Perf. 14**
1091  A331  25pf green, buff & blk   .50   .30

Cranach (1472-1553), painter and engraver.

**1972, July 18    Litho.    Perf. 14**
1092  A332  40pf yel, blk & red brn  .60   .30

21st Stoke-Mandeville Games for the Paralyzed, Heidelberg, Aug. 1-10.

Kurt Schumacher A333

Post Horn and Decree — A334

**1972, Aug. 18    Litho. & Engr.**
1093  A333  40pf red & black        1.25   .30

Schumacher (1895-1952), 1st chairman of the German Social Democratic Party.

**1972, Aug. 18          Photo.**
1094  A334  40pf gold, car & blk     .80   .30

Centenary of the German Postal Museum, Berlin. Design shows page from Heinrich von Stephan's decree establishing the museum.

Open Book — A335

Music by Heinrich Schütz — A336

**1972, Sept. 11   Photo.   Perf. 13x13½**
1095  A335  40pf red & multi         .60   .30

International Book Year 1972.

**Lithographed and Engraved**
**1972, Sept. 29          Perf. 14**
1096  A336  40pf multicolored        .75   .30

300th anniversary of the death of Heinrich Schütz (1585-1672), composer.

Carnival Dancers A337

**1972, Nov. 10    Litho.    Perf. 14**
1097  A337  40pf red & multi         .90   .30

Cologne Carnival sesquicentennial.

Heinrich Heine (1797-1856), Poet — A338

**1972, Dec. 13    Litho.    Perf. 14**
1098  A338  40pf rose, blk & red     .90   .30

"Bread for the World" A339

**1972, Dec. 13    Photo.    Perf. 14**
1099  A339  30pf green & red         .45   .45

14th "Bread for the World-Developing Peace" campaign of the Protestant Church in Germany.

Würzburg Cathedral, 13th Century Seal — A340

**1972, Dec. 13          Litho.**
1100  A340  40pf dp car, lil rose &
            blk                      .50   .30

Synod 72, meeting of Catholic bishoprics, Würzburg.

Colors of France and Germany
Interlaced — A340a

**1973, Jan. 22    Litho.    Perf. 14**
**Size: 51x28mm**
1101 A340a 40pf multicolored        1.25   .30
10th anniversary of the Franco-German
Cooperation Treaty.

Meteorological
Map — A341

**1973, Feb. 19    Litho.    Perf. 14**
1102 A341 30pf multicolored        .35   .30
Cent. of intl. meteorological cooperation.

Radio Tower
and "Interpol"
A342

**1973, Feb. 19    Perf. 13½x13**
1103 A342 40pf blk & red        .45   .30
50th anniversary of International Criminal
Police Organization (INTERPOL).

Nicolaus Copernicus and Solar
System — A343

**1973, Feb. 19    Perf. 14**
1104 A343 40pf blk & red        1.25   .30

Festival
Poster — A344

**1973, Mar. 15    Photo.    Perf. 14**
1105 A344 40pf multicolored        .45   .30
German Turner Festival, Stuttgart, 6/12-17.

Town Type of 1969

Designs: 30pf, Saarbrücken. No. 1107, Ship
in Hamburg Harbor. No. 1108, Rüdesheim.
No. 1109, Aachen. No. 1110, Ships, Bremen
Harbor.

**1973    Lithographed and Engraved**
1106 A303 30pf yel grn & blk        .60   .20
1107 A303 40pf red & blk        .90   .20
1108 A303 40pf org & blk        .75   .20
1109 A303 40pf brn red & blk        .60   .20
1110 A303 40pf red & blk        .60   .20
    Nos. 1106-1110 (5)        3.45   1.00
Issued: #1107-1108, 3/15; others 10/19.

---

**Europa Issue 1973**
Common Design Type
**1973, Apr. 30    Photo.    Perf. 13½x14**
**Size: 38½x21mm**
1114 CD16 30pf grn, lt grn & yel        .35   .20
1115 CD16 40pf dp mag, lil & yel        .50   .20

**1973, May 25    Litho.    Perf. 14**
1116 A345 40pf red, blk & brn        .50   .30
Maximilian Kolbe (1894-1941), Polish priest
who died in Auschwitz and was beatified in
1971.

"R" for               "Not by Bread
Roswitha — A346      Alone" — A347

**1973, May 25**
1117 A346 40pf red, blk & yel        .50   .30
Millenary of the death of Roswitha of
Gandersheim, Germany's first poetess.

**1973, May 25    Photo.**
1118 A347 30pf multicolored        .35   .20
15th meeting of German Protestants (Evangelical Synod), Dusseldorf, June 27-July 1.

Environment Emblem and
"Waste" — A348

30pf, "Water." 40pf, "Noise." 70pf, "Air."

**1973, June 5    Litho.**
1119 A348 25pf multicolored        .35   .20
1120 A348 30pf multicolored        .40   .20
1121 A348 40pf org & multi        .75   .20
1122 A348 70pf ultra & multi        1.25   .65
    Nos. 1119-1122 (4)        2.75   1.25
International environment protection and
Environment Day, June 5.

Reconstructed
Model of
Schickard's
Calculator
A349

**1973, June 12**
1123 A349 40pf org & multi        .45   .40
350th anniv. of the calculator built by Prof.
Wilhelm Shickard, University of Tubingen.

Otto Wels
(1873-1939),
Leader of
German Social
Democratic
Party — A350

**1973, Sept. 14    Litho.    Perf. 14**
1124 A350 40pf magenta & lilac        .50   .30

---

Lubeck Cathedral — A351

**1973, Sept. 14    Litho. & Engr.**
1125 A351 40pf blk & multi        .90   .30
800th anniversary of Lubeck Cathedral.

Emblems
from UN
and
German
Flags
A352

**1973, Sept. 21    Litho.**
1126 A352 40pf multicolored        1.25   .30
Germany's admission to the UN.

Radio and
Speaker,
1923 — A353

**1973, Oct. 19    Photo.    Perf. 14**
1127 A353 30pf brt grn & multi        .35   .20
50 years of German broadcasting.

Luise Otto-
Peters
A354

**1974, Jan. 15    Litho. & Engr.**
1128 A354 40pf shown        .60   .45
1129 A354 40pf Helene Lange        .60   .45
1130 A354 40pf Gertrud Bäumer        .60   .45
1131 A354 40pf Rosa Luxemburg        .60   .45
    Nos. 1128-1131 (4)        2.40   1.80
Honoring German women writers and leaders in political and women's movements.

Drop of
Blood
and
Police
Car Light
A355

**1974, Feb. 15    Photo.    Perf. 14**
1132 A355 40pf carmine & ultra        .80   .30
Blood donor service in conjunction with
accident emergency service.

Handicapped People — A356

**1974, Feb. 15    Litho.    Perf. 14**
1133 A356 40pf red & blk        .80   .30
Rehabilitation of the handicapped.

---

Thomas
Aquinas
Teaching
A357

**1974, Feb. 15**
1134 A357 40pf blk & red        .50   .30
St. Thomas Aquinas (1225-1274), scholastic philosopher.

Girls under Trees, by August
Macke — A358

Paintings: No. 1135, Deer in Red, by Franz
Marc. 40pf, Portrait in Blue, by Alexej von
Jawlensky, vert. 50pf, Pechstein (man)
Asleep, by Erich Heckel, vert. 70pf, "Big Still-
life," by Max Beckmann. 120pf, Old Farmer, by
Ernst Ludwig Kirchner, vert.

**1974    Photo.**
1135 A358 30pf multicolored        .50   .20
1136 A358 30pf multicolored        .60   .20
1137 A358 40pf multicolored        .60   .20
1138 A358 50pf multicolored        .65   .20
1139 A358 70pf multicolored        .90   .75
1140 A358 120pf multicolored        1.75   1.50
    Nos. 1135-1140 (6)        5.00   3.05
German expressionist painters.
Issued: #1135, 1137, Feb. 15; #1136, 1138,
Aug. 16; #1139-1140, Oct. 29.

Young Man, by          Immanuel Kant
Lehmbruck              A360
A359

Europa: 40pf, Kneeling Woman, by Wilhelm
Lehmbruck.

**1974, Apr. 17    Litho.    Perf. 14**
1141 A359 30pf multicolored        .35   .20
1142 A359 40pf multicolored        .50   .25

**1974    Litho. and Engr.    Perf. 14**
1143 A360 40pf Klopstock        .50   .20
        **Engr.**
1144 A360 90pf shown        1.90   .45
Friedrich Gottlieb Klopstock (1724-1803),
poet, and Immanuel Kant (1724-1804),
philosopher.
Issue dates: 40pf, May 15; 90pf, Apr. 17.

Souvenir Sheet

Federal Eagle and Flag — A361

**1974, May 15    Litho. & Embossed**
1145 A361 40pf gray & multi        1.25   1.90
Federal Republic of Germany, 25th anniv.

Soccer and Games Emblem A362

Design: 40pf, Three soccer players.

**1974, May 15**     **Litho.**
1146 A362 30pf grn & multi    .80   .20
1147 A362 40pf org & multi   1.60   .20

World Cup Soccer Championship, Munich, June 13-July 7.

Crowned Cross Emblem of Diaconate A363

Landscape A364

**1974, May 15**
1148 A363 40pf multicolored    .45   .30

125th anniversary of the Diaconal Association of the German Protestant Church.

**1974, May 15**
1149 A364 30pf multicolored    .35   .30

To promote hiking and youth hostels.

Broken Bars of Prison Window A365

**1974, July 16**   **Litho.**   **Perf. 14x13½**
1150 A365 70pf violet bl & blk   .95   .45

"Amnesty International," an organization for the protection of the rights of political, non-violent, prisoners.

Hans Holbein, Self-portrait A366

**Lithographed and Engraved**
**1974, July 16**     **Perf. 13½x14**
1151 A366 50pf multicolored    .75   .30

Hans Holbein the Elder (c. 1470-1524), painter.

Man and Woman Looking at Moon, by Friedrich — A367

**1974, Aug. 16**   **Photo.**   **Perf. 14**
1152 A367 50pf multicolored    .95   .30

Caspar David Friedrich (1774-1840), German Romantic painter.

Swiss and German 19th Century Mail Boxes — A368

**1974, Oct. 29**   **Litho.**   **Perf. 14**
1153 A368 50pf red & multi   1.25   .35

Centenary of Universal Postal Union.

Mothers and Foundation Emblem — A369

**1975, Jan. 15**   **Litho.**   **Perf. 13**
1154 A369 50pf multicolored    .65   .30

Convalescent Mothers' Foundation, 25th anniversary.

Annette Kolb (1875-1967), Writer — A370

German women writers: 40pf, Ricarda Huch (1864-1947), writer. 50pf, Else Lasker-Schüler (1869-1945), poetess. 70pf, Gertrud von Le Fort (1876-1971), writer.

**Lithographed and Engraved**
**1975, Jan. 15**     **Perf. 14**
1155 A370 30pf brown & multi   .60   .30
1156 A370 40pf multicolored    .50   .30
1157 A370 50pf claret & multi   .50   .30
1158 A370 70pf blue & multi    .90   .90
     Nos. 1155-1158 (4)   2.50   1.80

Dr. Albert Schweitzer — A371

Design: 40pf, Hans Böckler.

**1975**            **Engr.**
1159 A371 40pf grn & blk    .65   .30
1160 A371 70pf bl & blk   1.90   .75

Böckler (1875-1951), German Workers' Union leader, and of Dr. Albert Schweitzer (1875-1965), medical missionary. Issued: 40pf, Feb. 14; 70pf, Jan. 15.

Head, by Michelangelo A372

Plan of St. Peter's, Rome A373

**1975, Feb. 14**   **Photo.**   **Perf. 14**
1161 A372 70pf vio bl & blk   1.40   1.25

Michelangelo Buonarroti (1475-1564), Italian sculptor, painter and architect.

**1975, Feb. 14**
1162 A373 50pf red & multi    .65   .30

Holy Year 1975, the "Year of Reconciliation."

Ice Hockey A374

**1975, Feb. 14**     **Litho.**   **Perf. 14**
1163 A374 50pf bl & multi    .95   .30

Ice Hockey World Championship, Munich and Düsseldorf, Apr. 3-19.

Concentric Group, by Oskar Schlemmer — A375

Europa: 50pf, Bauhaus Staircase, painting by Oskar Schlemmer (1888-1943) and CEPT emblem.

**1975, Apr. 15**     **Litho. & Engr.**
1164 A375 40pf gray & multi    .45   .20
1165 A375 50pf gray & multi    .70   .20

Eduard Mörike, Weather Vane, Quill and Signature A376

**1975, May 15**
1166 A376 40pf multicolored    .40   .20

Eduard Mörike (1804-75), pastor and poet.

Joust, from Jousting Book of William IV A377

**1975, May 15**   **Photo.**   **Perf. 14**
1167 A377 50pf multicolored    .90   .30

500th anniv. of the Wedding of Landshut, (last Duke of Landshut married the daughter of King of Poland, now a yearly local festival).

Cathedral of Mainz A378

**1975, May 15**     **Litho. & Engr.**
1168 A378 40pf multicolored    .90   .30

Millennium of the Cathedral of Mainz.

View of Neuss, Woodcut A379

Satellite A380

**1975, May 15**
1169 A379 50pf multicolored    .60   .30

500th anniv. of the unsuccessful siege of Neuss by Duke Charles the Bold of Burgundy.

**1975-82**     **Engr.**    **Perf. 14**
1170 A380 5pf Shown       .20   .20
1171 A380 10pf Electric train    .20   .20
1172 A380 20pf Old Weser
              lighthouse      .20   .20
1173 A380 30pf Rescue heli-
              copter        .20   .20
1174 A380 40pf Space shut-
              tle             .30   .20
1175 A380 50pf Radar station   .40   .20
1176 A380 60pf X-ray ma-
              chine         .50   .20
1177 A380 70pf Shipbuilding   .60   .20
1178 A380 80pf Tractor      .65   .20
1179 A380 100pf Bituminous
              coal excava-
              tor             .75   .20
1180 A380 110pf Color TV
              camera     1.50   .60
1181 A380 120pf Chemical
              plant        .95   .30
1182 A380 130pf Brewery   1.90   .60
1183 A380 140pf Heating
              plant,
              Licterfelde   1.10   .40
1184 A380 150pf Power shovel   2.40   .75
1185 A380 160pf Blast furnace   1.50   .60
1186 A380 180pf Payloader   1.90   .75
1187 A380 190pf As #1184   2.25   .60
1188 A380 200pf Oil drilling   1.60   .30
1189 A380 230pf Frankfurt Air-
              port         2.75   .90
1190 A380 250pf Airport    3.25   1.40
1191 A380 300pf Electro. RR   3.75   1.40
1192 A380 500pf Effelsberg ra-
              dio tele-
              scope     4.00   1.10
   Nos. 1170-1192 (23)   32.85   11.70

Issued: 40, 50, 100pf, 5/15; 10, 30, 70pf, 8/14; 80, 120, 160pf, 10/15; 5, 140, 200pf, 11/14; 20, 500pf, 2/17/76; 60pf, 11/16/78; 230pf, 5/17/79; 150, 180pf, 7/12/79; 110, 130, 300pf, 6/16/82; 190, 250pf, 7/15/82.

Market and Town Hall, Alsfeld A381

#1197, Plönlein Corner, Siebers Tower and Kobolzeller Gate, Rothenburg. #1198, Town Hall (Steipe), Trier. #1199, View of Xanten.

**1975, July 15**     **Litho. & Engr.**
1196 A381 50pf multicolored    .75   .50
1197 A381 50pf multicolored    .75   .50
1198 A381 50pf multicolored    .75   .50
1199 A381 50pf multicolored    .75   .50
     Nos. 1196-1199 (4)   3.00   2.00

European Architectural Heritage Year.

Three Stages of Drug Addiction A382

**1975, Aug. 14**   **Photo.**   **Perf. 14**
1200 A382 40pf multicolored    .40   .30

Fight against drug abuse.

Matthias Erzberger A383

**1975, Aug. 14**       **Engr.**
1201 A383 50pf red & black    .60   .30

Erzberger (1875-1921), statesman, signer of Compiègne Armistice (1918) at end of World War I.

Sign of Royal
Prussian Post,
1776 — A384

**1975, Aug. 14**                          **Litho.**
1202 A384 10pf blue & multi          .35  .20
 Stamp Day, 1975, and 76th German Philatelists' Day, Sept. 21.

Souvenir Sheet

Gustav Stresemann, Ludwig Quidde,
Carl von Ossietzky — A385

**1975, Nov. 14    Engr.    Perf. 14**
1203 A385 Sheet of 3              1.90  1.90
*a.-c.*    50pf, single stamp          .60   .50
 German winners of Nobel Peace Prize. No.
1203 has litho. marginal inscription.

Olympic Rings,
Symbolic
Mountains
A386

**1976, Jan. 5          Litho. & Engr.**
1204 A386 50pf red & multi          .90  .30
 12th Winter Olympic Games, Innsbruck,
Austria, Feb. 4-15.

Konrad
Adenauer — A387

**1976, Jan. 5                       Engr.**
1205 A387 50pf dark slate green  1.75  .30
 Konrad Adenauer (1876-1967), Chancellor
(1949-63).

Books by Hans
Sachs — A388

**1976, Jan. 5                      Litho.**
1206 A388 40pf multicolored         .60  .30
 Hans Sachs (1494-1576), poet (meistersinger), 400th death anniversary.

Junkers F 13,
1926 — A389

**1976, Jan. 5**
1207 A389 50pf multicolored         .90  .30
 Lufthansa, 50th anniversary.

German
Eagle — A390

**1976, Feb. 17    Photo.    Perf. 14**
1208 A390 50pf red, blk & gold      .75  .30
 Federal Constitutional Court, 25th anniv.

"EG"
A391

**1976, Apr. 6     Photo.     Perf. 14**
1209 A391 40pf red & multi          .75  .30
 European Coal and Steel Community, 25th
anniversary.

Wuppertal
Suspension
Train — A392

**1976, Apr. 6                      Litho.**
1210 A392 50pf multicolored         .75  .30
 Wuppertal suspension railroad, 75th anniv.

Girl Selling Trinkets
and Prints — A393

 Europa: 50pf, Boy selling copperplate prints,
and CEPT emblem. Ludwigsburg china figurines, c. 1765.

**1976, May 13                     Photo.**
1211 A393 40pf olive & multi        *.40* .20
1212 A393 50pf scarlet & multi      *.60* .20

Dr. Carl
Sonnenschein
A394

**1976, May 13                     Litho.**
1213 A394 50pf carmine & multi     .60  .30
 Sonnenschein (1876-1929), Roman Catholic clergyman and social reformer.

Weber Conducting "Freischutz" in
Covent Garden — A395

**1976, May 13**
1214 A395 50pf red brown & blk     .75  .30
 Carl Maria von Weber (1786-1826), composer, 150th death anniversary.

Hymn, by Paul
Gerhardt
A396

**1976, May 13          Engr. & Litho.**
1215 A396 40pf multicolored        .40 .20
 Gerhardt (1607-76), Lutheran hymn writer.

Carl
Schurz,
American
Flag,
Capitol
A397

**1976, May 13                     Litho.**
1216 A397 70pf multicolored        .95  .35
 American Bicentennial.

Modern
Stage
A398

**1976, July 14         Litho.     Perf. 14**
1217 A398 50pf multicolored       1.25  .30
 Bayreuth Festival, centenary.

Bronze
Ritual
Chariot c.
1000
B.C.
A399

 Archaeological Treasures: 40pf, Celtic gold
vessel, 5th-4th centuries B.C. 50pf, Celtic silver torque, 2nd-1st centuries B.C. 120pf,
Roman cup with masks, 1st century A.D.

**1976, July 14**
1218 A399  30pf multicolored        .35  .30
1219 A399  40pf multicolored        .50  .30
1220 A399  50pf multicolored        .75  .45
1221 A399 120pf multicolored       1.60 1.60
    Nos. 1218-1221 (4)             3.20 2.65

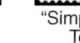

Golden Plover              "Simplicissimus
A400                          Teutsch"
                                 A401

**1976, Aug. 17**
1222 A400 50pf multicolored       1.00  .30
 Protection of birds.

**1976, Aug. 17**
1223 A401 40pf multicolored       1.00  .30
 Johann Jacob Christoph von Grimmelshausen, 300th birth anniversary; author of
the "Adventures of Simplicissimus Teutsch."

Imperial Post             Caroline Neuber
Emblem, Höchst                  as
am Main, 18th             Medea — A403
Cent. — A402

**1976, Oct. 14       Litho.     Perf. 14**
1224 A402 10pf brown & multi       .30 .20
 Stamp Day.

**1976, Nov. 16                    Photo.**
 German Actresses: 40pf, Sophie Schröder
(1781-1868) as Sappho. 50pf, Louise Dumont
(1862-1932) as Hedda Gabler. 70pf, Hermine
Körner (1878-1960) as Lady Macbeth.
1225 A403 30pf multicolored         .40  .20
1226 A403 40pf multicolored         .40  .20
1227 A403 50pf multicolored         .60  .30
1228 A403 70pf multicolored        1.00  .90
    Nos. 1225-1228 (4)             2.40 1.60

Palais de l'Europe, Strasbourg — A404

**1977, Jan. 13       Engr.     Perf. 14**
1229 A404 140pf green & blk       1.60 .50
 Inauguration of the new Council of Europe
Headquarters, Jan. 28.

Scenes from Till          Pfaueninsel
Eulenspiegel                 Castle
A405                          A406

**1977, Jan. 13                    Litho.**
1230 A405 50pf multicolored        .50  .30
 Till Eulenspiegel (d. 1350), roguish fool and
hero, his adventures reported in book of same
name.

## 1977-79    Typo.    Perf. 14

| | | |
|---|---|---|
| 1231 A406 10pf Glucksburg | .20 | .20 |
| a. Bklt. pane, 4 #1231, 2 each #1234, 1236 | 4.00 | 6.75 |
| b. Bklt. pane, 4 #1231, 2 #1234, 2 #1310 | 2.50 | 3.00 |
| c. Bklt. pane, 4 #1231, 2 #1310, 2 #1312 | 6.00 | 6.25 |
| d. Bklt. pane, 2 each #1231, 1234, 1310-1311 | 9.00 | 13.50 |
| 1232 A406 20pf Shown | .20 | .20 |
| 1233 A406 25pf Gemen | .35 | .20 |
| 1234 A406 30pf Ludwigstein | .30 | .20 |
| 1235 A406 40pf Eltz | .50 | .20 |
| 1236 A406 50pf Neuschwan- stein | .55 | .20 |
| 1237 A406 60pf Marksburg | .75 | .20 |
| 1238 A406 70pf Mespelbrunn | .75 | .20 |
| 1239 A406 90pf Vischer- enburg | 1.10 | .35 |
| 1240 A406 190pf Pfaueninsel | 1.90 | .75 |
| 1240A A406 200pf Burresheim | 2.25 | .75 |
| 1241 A406 210pf Schwanen- burg | 3.00 | 1.10 |
| 1242 A406 230pf Lichtenberg | 3.00 | 1.10 |
| *Nos. 1231-1242 (13)* | 14.85 | 5.65 |

See Nos. 1308-1315.
Issued in sheets of 100 and in coils. Every fifth coil stamp has control number on the back.
Issued: 60, 200pf, 1/13; 40, 190pf, 2/16; 10, 30pf, 4/14; 50, 70pf, 5/17; 230pf, 11/16/78; 25, 90pf, 1/11/79; 20, 210pf, 2/14/79.

### Souvenir Sheet

German Art Nouveau — A407

Designs: 30pf, Floral ornament. 70pf, Athena, poster by Franz von Stuck. 90pf, Chair, c. 1902.

## 1977, Feb. 16    Litho.    Perf. 14

| | | |
|---|---|---|
| 1243 A407 Sheet of 3 | 2.00 | 1.50 |
| a. 30pf multicolored | .30 | .20 |
| b. 70pf multicolored | .55 | .50 |
| c. 90pf multicolored | .90 | .70 |

1st German Art Nouveau Exhib., 75th anniv.

Jean Monnet A408

## 1977, Feb. 16

1244 A408 50pf black & yellow    .60 .30

Jean Monnet (1888-1979), French proponent of unification of Europe, became first Honorary Citizen of Europe in Apr. 1976.

Flower Show Emblem A409

Gauss Plane of Complex Numbers A410

## 1977, Apr. 14

1245 A409 50pf green & multi    .80 .30

25th Federal Horticultural Show, Stuttgart, Apr. 29-Oct. 23.

## 1977, Apr. 14

1246 A410 40pf silver & multi    1.25 .30

Carl Friedrich Gauss (1777-1855), mathematician, 200th birth anniversary.

---

Barbarossa Head, Cappenberg Reliquary — A411

## 1977, Apr. 14

1247 A411 40pf multicolored    1.25 .30

Staufer Year 1977. "Time of the Hohenstaufen" Exhibition, Stuttgart, Mar. 25-June 5, in connection with the 25th anniversary of Baden-Wurttemberg.

Rhön Highway A412

Europa: 50pf, Rhine, Siebengebirge and train.

## 1977, May 7    Litho. & Engr.

| | | |
|---|---|---|
| 1248 A412 40pf brt green & blk | .70 | .25 |
| 1249 A412 50pf brt red & blk | .70 | .25 |

Rubens, Self-portrait A413

Ulm Cathedral A414

## 1977, May 17    Engr.

1250 A413 30pf brown black    .80 .30

Peter Paul Rubens (1577-1640), Flemish painter, 400th birth anniversary.

## 1977, May 17    Litho. & Engr.

1251 A414 40pf blue & sepia    .50 .30

600th anniversary of Ulm Cathedral.

Madonna, Oldest Rector's Seal A415

Landgrave Philipp, Great Seal of University A416

## 1977, May 17    Photo.

| | | |
|---|---|---|
| 1252 A415 50pf indigo & org red | .75 | .30 |
| 1253 A416 50pf indigo & org red | .75 | .30 |

Mainz University, 500th anniv. (No. 1252); Marburg University, 450th anniv. (No. 1253).

Morning, by Runge — A417

## 1977, July 13    Litho.    Perf. 14

1254 A417 60pf blue & multi    .75 .35

Philipp Otto Runge (1777-1810), painter.

---

Bishop Ketteler's Coat of Arms — A418

## 1977, July 13

1255 A418 50pf multicolored    .60 .30

Wilhelm Emmanuel von Ketteler (1811-1877), Bishop of Mainz, Reichstag member and social reformer, death centenary.

Fritz von Bodelschwingh A419

## 1977, July 13    Litho. & Engr.

1256 A419 50pf multicolored    .75 .30

Pastor Fritz von Bodelschwingh (1877-1946), manager of Bethel Institute (for the incurable sick), birth centenary.

Jesus as Teacher, Great Seal of University — A420

## 1977, Aug. 16    Photo.

1257 A420 50pf multicolored    .90 .30

Tübingen University, 500th anniversary.

Golden Hat, Schifferstadt, Bronze Age — A421

## 1977, Aug. 16    Litho.

Archaeological heritage: 120pf, Gilt helmet, from Prince's Tomb, Krefeld-Gellep. 200pf, Bronze Centaur's head, Schwarzenacker.

| | | |
|---|---|---|
| 1258 A421 30pf multicolored | .40 | .30 |
| 1259 A421 120pf multicolored | 1.50 | 1.10 |
| 1260 A421 200pf multicolored | 2.00 | 1.60 |
| *Nos. 1258-1260 (3)* | 3.90 | 3.00 |

Telephone Operator and Switchboard, 1881 — A422

## 1977, Oct. 13    Litho.    Perf. 14

1261 A422 50pf multicolored    1.00 .30

German telephone centenary.

---

Arms of Hamburg, Post Emblem, c. 1861 — A423

Wilhelm Hauff — A424

## 1977, Oct. 13

1262 A423 10pf multicolored    .35 .20

Stamp Day.

## 1977, Nov. 10    Photo.    Perf. 14

1263 A424 40pf multicolored    .40 .20

Wilhelm Hauff (1802-1827), writer and fabulist, 150th death anniversary.

Traveling Surgeon A425

Book Cover, by Alexander Schröder A426

## 1977, Nov. 10    Litho.

1264 A425 50pf multicolored    .75 .30

Dr. Johann Andreas Eisenbarth (1663-1727), traveling surgeon and adventurer.

## 1978, Jan. 12    Litho.    Perf. 14

1265 A426 50pf multicolored    .60 .30

Rudolf Alexander Schröder (1878-1962), writer, designer, Lutheran minister.

"Refugees" — A427

## 1978, Jan. 12    Photo.

1266 A427 50pf multicolored    .60 .30

Friedland Aid Society for displaced Germans, 20th anniversary.

### Souvenir Sheet

Gerhart Hauptmann, Hermann Hesse, Thomas Mann — A428

## 1978, Feb. 16    Litho.    Perf. 14

| | | |
|---|---|---|
| 1267 A428 Sheet of 3 | 1.75 | 1.40 |
| a. 30pf multicolored | .35 | .25 |
| b. 50pf multicolored | .50 | .30 |
| c. 70pf multicolored | .70 | .50 |

German winners of Nobel Literature Prize.

Martin Buber (1878-1965), Writer and Philosopher A429

1978, Feb. 16

1268 A429 50pf multicolored .60 .30

Museum Tower and Observatory — A430

1978, Apr. 13 Litho. *Perf. 14*

1269 A430 50pf multicolored .60 .30

German Museum for Natural Sciences and Technology, Munich, 75th anniversary.

Old City Halls A431

Europa: 40pf, Bamberg. 50pf, Regensburg. 70pf, Esslingen on Neckar.

Lithographed and Engraved

1978, May 22 *Perf. 14*

1270 A431 40pf multicolored	*.50*	*.20*
1271 A431 50pf multicolored	*.85*	*.20*
1272 A431 70pf multicolored	*.95*	*.45*
Nos. 1270-1272 (3)	2.30	.85

Pied Piper of Hamelin A432

1978, May 22 Litho.

1273 A432 50pf multicolored .75 .30

The Pied Piper led 130 children of Hamelin away never to be seen again.

Janusz Korczak — A433

Fossil Bat — A434

1978, July 13 Litho. *Perf. 14*

1274 A433 90pf multicolored 1.00 .50

Dr. Janusz Korczak (1878-1942), physician, educator, proponent of children's rights.

1978, July 13

200pf, Eohippus (primitive horse), horiz.

1275 A434 80pf multicolored 1.40 1.40

1276 A434 200pf multicolored 1.50 1.50

Archaeological heritage from Messel open-cast mine, c. 50 million years old.

Parliament, Bonn — A435

1978, Aug. 17 Litho. *Perf. 14*

1277 A435 70pf multicolored 1.10 .35

65th Interparliamentary Conf., Bonn, Sept. 3-14.

A436

Rose Window, Freiburg Cathedral.

1978, Aug. 17

1278 A436 40pf multicolored .40 .30

85th Congress of German Catholics, Freiburg, Sept. 13-17.

A437

1978, Aug. 17

Brentano as Butterfly, by Luise Duttenhofer.

1279 A437 30pf multicolored .40 .30

Clemens Brentano (1778-1842), poet.

A438

1978, Aug. 17

1280 A438 50pf multicolored .75 .30

European Human Rights Convention, 25th anniversary.

Baden Posthouse Sign, c. 1825 — A439

Saxony No. 1 with "World Philatelic Movement" Cancel — A440

1978, Oct. 12 Litho. *Perf. 14*

1281 A439 40pf multicolored	.40	.20
1282 A440 50pf multicolored	.40	.20
a. Pair, #1281-1282	1.10	1.25

Stamp Day and German Philatelists' Meeting, Frankfurt am Main, Oct. 12-15.

Easter at Walchensee, by Lovis Corinth — A441

Impressionist Paintings: 70pf, Horseman on Shore, by Max Liebermann, vert. 120pf, Lady with Cat, by Max Slevogt, vert.

1978, Nov. 16 Photo. *Perf. 14*

1283 A441 50pf multicolored	.55	.45
1284 A441 70pf multicolored	.85	.60
1285 A441 120pf multicolored	1.50	1.40
Nos. 1283-1285 (3)	2.90	2.45

Child and Building A442

1979, Jan. 11 Photo.

1286 A442 60pf black & rose .90 .30

International Year of the Child and 20th anniv. of Declaration of Children's Rights.

Agnes Miegel — A443

Film — A444

1979, Feb. 14 Photo. *Perf. 14*

1287 A443 60pf multicolored .60 .30

Agnes Miegel (1879-1964), poet.

1979, Feb. 14 Litho.

1288 A444 50pf black & green .75 .30

25th German Short-Film Festival, Oberhausen, Apr. 23-28.

Parliament Benches in Flag Colors of Members — A445

1979, Feb. 14

1289 A445 50pf multicolored .90 .30

European Parliament, first direct elections, June 7-10, 1979.

Emblems of Road Rescue Services A446

1979, Feb. 14

1290 A446 50pf multicolored .75 .30

A447

Europa: 50pf, Telegraph office, 1863. 60pf, Post Office window, 1854.

1979, May 17 Litho. *Perf. 14*

1291 A447 50pf multicolored	*.60*	.20
1292 A447 60pf multicolored	*.75*	.20

A448

1979, May 17 Photo.

1293 A448 60pf red & black .85 .30

Anne Frank (1929-45), author, Nazi victim.

First Electric Train, 1879 Berlin Exhibition A449

1979, May 17 Litho.

1294 A449 60pf multicolored .90 .30

Intl. Transportation Exhib., Hamburg.

Hand Setting Radio Dial A450

1979, July 12 Litho. *Perf. 14*

1295 A450 60pf multicolored .85 .30

World Administrative Radio Conference, Geneva, Sept. 24-Dec. 1.

Moses Receiving Tablets of the Law, by Lucas Cranach — A451

1979, July 12 Litho. & Engr.

1296 A451 50pf black & blue grn .90 .30

450th anniv. of Martin Luther's Catechism.

Cross and Charlemagne's Emblem — A452

1979, July 12 Litho. & Embossed

1297 A452 50pf multicolored .60 .30

1979 pilgrimage to Aachen.

Hildegard von Bingen with Manuscript A453

1979, Aug. 9 Litho.

1298 A453 110pf multicolored 1.10 .50

Hildegard von Bingen, Benedictine nun, mystic and writer, 800th death anniversary.

Diagram of Einstein's Photoelectric
Effect — A454

Designs: No. 1300, Otto Hahn's diagram of
the splitting of the uranium nucleus. No. 1301,
Max von Laue's atom arrangement in crystals.

**1979, Aug. 9**                      **Photo.**
1299  A454  60pf multicolored        .75   .35
1300  A454  60pf multicolored       1.50   .35
1301  A454  60pf multicolored        .75   .35
      Nos. 1299-1301 (3)            3.00  1.05

Birth centenaries of German Nobel Prize
winners: Albert Einstein, physics, 1921; Otto
Hahn, chemistry, 1944; Max von Laue, physics, 1914.

Pilot on
Board — A455

**Lithographed and Engraved**
**1979, Oct. 11**                   **Perf. 14**
1302  A455  60pf multicolored        .60   .30

Three centuries of pilots' regulations.

Birds in Garden, by Paul Klee — A456

**1979, Nov. 14**                    **Photo.**
1303  A456  90pf multicolored        .90   .50

Paul Klee (1879-1940), Swiss artist.

Mephistopheles
and
Faust — A457

**1979, Nov. 14**                    **Litho.**
1304  A457  60pf multicolored       1.10   .30

Doctor Johannes Faust.

Energy
Conservation
A458

**1979, Nov. 14**                 **Perf. 13x13½**
1305  A458  40pf multicolored        .60   .30

Castle Type A406 of 1977-79
**1979-82**         **Typo.**       **Perf. 14**
1308      35pf Lichtenstein          .50   .30
1309      40pf Wolfsburg             .45   .20
1310      50pf Inzlingen             .60   .20
1311      60pf Rheydt                .65   .30
1312      80pf Wilhelmsthal          .95   .20
1313     120pf Charlottenburg       1.50   .50
1314     280pf Ahrensburg           3.25   .50
1315     300pf Herrenhausen         3.75   .35
         Nos. 1308-1315 (8)        11.65  2.55

Issued: 60pf, 11/14; 40pf, 50pf, 2/14/80;
35pf, 80pf, 300pf, 6/16/82; 120pf, 280pf,
7/15/82.

Iphigenia, by Anselm
Feuerbach — A459

**1980, Jan. 10**                    **Litho.**
1321  A459  50pf multicolored       1.00   .30

Anselm Feuerbach (1829-1880), historical
and portrait painter.

Flags of
NATO
and
Members
A460

**1980, Jan. 10**
1322  A460  100pf multicolored      1.60   .75

Germany's membership in NATO, 25th anniv.

Osnabruck, 1,200th
Anniversary — A461

**1980, Jan. 10**               **Litho. & Engr.**
1323  A461  60pf multicolored        .75   .30

Götz von
Berlichingen,
Painting on
Glass — A462

**1980, Jan. 10**                    **Litho.**
1324  A462  60pf multicolored        .75   .30

Götz von Berlichingen (1480-1562), knight.

Duden Dictionary, Old and New
Editions — A463

**1980, Jan. 14**
1325  A463  60pf multicolored        .75   .30

Konrad Duden's German Language Dictionary, centenary of publication.

German Association for Public and
Private Social Welfare
Centenary — A464

**1980, Apr. 10**
1326  A464  60pf multicolored        .75   .30

A465

Emperor Frederick I (Barbarossa) and Sons,
Welf Chronicles, 12th century.

**1980, Apr. 10**
1327  A465  60pf multicolored       1.00   .30

Imperial Diet of Geinhausen, 800th anniv.

A466

**1980, May 8**        **Litho.**    **Perf. 14**

Europa: 50pf, Albertus Magnus (1193-
1280), saint and doctor of the Church. 60pf,
Gottfried Wilhelm Leibniz (1646-1716),
philosopher.

1328  A466  50pf multicolored        .75   .25
1329  A466  60pf multicolored        .75   .25

Confession of
Augsburg,
Engraving,
1630 — A467

**1980, May 8**
1330  A467  50pf multicolored        .60   .30

Reading of Confession of Augsburg to
Charles V (first official creed of Lutheran
Church), 450th anniversary.

Nature
Preserves
A468

**1980, May 8**                      **Photo.**
1331  A468  40pf multicolored       1.00   .30

Oscillogram Pulses and Ear — A469

**Lithographed and Embossed**
**1980, July 10**                   **Perf. 14**
1332  A469  90pf multicolored       1.10   .35

16th Intl. Cong. for the Training and Education of the Hard of Hearing, Hamburg, 8/4-8.

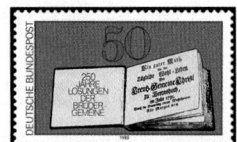

Book of Daily Bible Readings, Title
Page, 1731
A470

**1980, July 10**                    **Litho.**
1333  A470  50pf multicolored        .60   .30

Moravian Brethren's Book of Daily Bible
Readings, 250th edition.

St. Benedict of
Nursia, 1500th
Birth
Anniv. — A471

**1980, July 10**               **Perf. 13x13½**
1334  A471  50pf multicolored        .60   .30

Helping
Hand — A472

**1980, Aug. 14**               **Litho. & Engr.**
1335  A472  60pf multicolored        .75   .30

Dr. Friedrich Joseph Haass (1780-1853),
physician and philanthropist.

Marie von Ebner-
Eschenbach (1830-
1916),
Writer — A473

**1980, Aug. 14**                    **Photo.**
1336  A473  60pf multicolored        .75   .30

Ship's
Rigging
A474

**1980, Aug. 14**                    **Litho.**
1337  A474  60pf multicolored       1.50   .30

Gorch Fock (pen name of Johan Kinau)
(1880-1916), poet and dramatist.

Hoeing, Pressing Grapes, Wine Cellar,
14th Century Woodcuts
A475

**1980, Oct. 9**       **Litho.**    **Perf. 14**
1338  A475  50pf multicolored        .75   .30

Wine production in Central Europe, 2000th
anniversary.

Setting Final Stone
in South Tower,
Cologne
Cathedral — A476

**1980, Oct. 9**
1339  A476  60pf multicolored       1.50   .30

Completion of Cologne Cathedral, cent.

Landscape with Fir Trees, by
Altdorfer — A477

**Lithographed and Engraved**
**1980, Nov. 13**    *Perf. 14*
1340 A477 40pf multicolored   .60 .30
Albrecht Altdorfer (1480-1538), painter and engraver.

Elly Heuss-Knapp A478

**1981, Jan. 15**    *Photo.*
1341 A478 60pf multicolored   .75 .30
Elly Heuss-Knapp (1881-1951), founded Elly Heuss-Knapp Foundation (Rest and Recuperation for Mothers).

International Year of the Disabled — A479

**1981, Jan. 15**    *Litho.*
1342 A479 60pf multicolored   .75 .30

European Urban Renaissance — A480

**1981, Jan. 15**    *Litho. & Engr.*
1343 A480 60pf multicolored   .85 .30

Georg Philipp Telemann, Title Page of "Singet dem Herrn" Cantata — A481

**1981, Feb. 12**    *Photo.*
1344 A481 60pf multicolored   .75 .30
Georg Telemann (1681-1767), composer.

Foreign Guest Worker Integration — A482

**1981, Feb. 12**    *Litho.*
1345 A482 50pf multicolored   .85 .30

Preservation of the Environment A483

**1981, Feb. 12**
1346 A483 60pf multicolored   1.25 .30

European Patent Office Centenary A484

**1981, Feb. 12**
1347 A484 60pf multicolored   .75 .30

A485

**1981, Feb. 12**    *Perf. 13x13½*
1348 A485 40pf Chest scintigram   .60 .30
Early examination for the prevention of cancer.

A486

**1981, May 7**    *Litho.*   *Perf. 14*
50pf, South German couple dancing in regional costumes. 60pf, Northern couple.
1349 A486 50pf multicolored   .60 .20
1350 A486 60pf multicolored   .70 .20
Europa.

19th German Protestant Convention, Hamburg, June 17-21 — A487

**1981, May 7**    *Photo.*
1351 A487 50pf multicolored   .75 .30

A488

**1981, May 7**    *Litho.*
1352 A488 60pf Altar figures   .75 .30
Tilman Riemenschneider (1460-1531), sculptor, 450th death anniversary.

A489

**1981, July 16**    *Litho.*   *Perf. 14*
1353 A489 110pf multicolored   1.60 .50
Georg von Neumayer polar research station.

Energy Conservation Research — A490

**1981, July 16**
1354 A490 50pf Solar generator   .95 .30

Wildlife Protection A491

**1981, July 16**
1355 A491 60pf Baby coot   1.25 .30

Cooperation in Third World Development — A492

**1981, July 16**
1356 A492 90pf multicolored   1.25 .45

Wilhelm Raabe (1831-1910), Poet — A493

**1981, Aug. 13**    *Litho. & Engr.*
1357 A493 50pf dk green & green   .75 .30

Statement of Constitutional Freedom (Fundamental Concept of Democracy) — A494

**1981, Aug. 13**    *Litho.*   *Perf. 14*
1358 A494 40pf shown   .85 .20
1359 A494 50pf Separation of powers   .85 .20
1360 A494 60pf Sovereignty of the people   1.25 .20
Nos. 1358-1360 (3)   2.95 .60

A495

People by Mailcoach, lithograph, 1855.
**1981, Oct. 8**    *Litho.*
1361 A495 60pf multicolored   1.25 .30
Stamp Day, Oct. 25.

A496

**1981, Nov. 12**    *Litho.*   *Perf. 14*
1362 A496 100pf multicolored   1.40 .45
Antarctic Treaty, 20th anniv.

St. Elizabeth of Thuringia, 750th Anniv. of Death — A497

**1981, Nov. 12**
1363 A497 50pf multicolored   1.00 .30

Karl von Clausewitz, by W. Wach — A498

**1981, Nov. 12**    *Photo.*
1364 A498 60pf multicolored   1.00 .30
Prussian general and writer, (1780-1831).

Social Insurance Centenary — A499

**1981, Nov. 12**
1365 A499 60pf multicolored   .85 .30

Pear-shaped Pot with Lid, 1715 — A500

**1982, Jan. 13**    *Litho.*
1366 A500 60pf multicolored   .85 .30
Johann Friedrich Bottger (1682-1719), originator of Dresden china, 300th birth anniv.

Energy Conservation — A501

**1982, Jan. 13**
1367 A501 60pf multicolored   .85 .30

A502

Illustration from The Town Band of Bremen (folktale).

**1982, Jan. 13**
1368 A502 40pf red & black .60 .30

A503

**1982, Feb. 18** Photo.
1369 A503 60pf multicolored 2.25 .30

Johann Wolfgang von Goethe (1749-1832), by Georg Melchior Kraus, 1776.

Robert Koch (1843-1910), Discoverer of Tubercle Bacillus, (1882) — A504

**1982, Feb. 18**
1370 A504 50pf multicolored 2.50 .30

Die Fromme Helene, by Wilhelm Busch (1832-1908) A505

**1982, Apr. 15** Litho. Perf. 13½x14
1371 A505 50pf multicolored 1.00 .30

Europa 1982 A506

**1982, May 5** Litho. Perf. 14
1372 A506 50pf Hambach Meeting sesquicentennial .90 .25
1373 A506 60pf Treaties of Rome, 1957-1982 1.10 .25

Kiel Regatta Week Centenary — A507

**1982, May 5**
1374 A507 60pf multicolored 1.00 .30

Young Men's Christian Assoc. (YMCA) Centenary — A508

**1982, May 5**
1375 A508 50pf multicolored .75 .30

"Don't Drink and Drive" A509

**1982, July 15** Photo.
1376 A509 80pf red & black 1.00 .30

25th Anniv. of German Lepers' Org. — A510

**1982, July 15** Photo.
1377 A510 80pf multicolored 1.00 .30

Prevent Water Pollution A511

**1982, July 15**
1378 A511 120pf multicolored 2.50 .35

Urea Model and Synthesis Formula A512

**1982, Aug. 12** Photo.
1379 A512 50pf multicolored .90 .30

Friedrich Wohler (1800-1882), chemist, discoverer of organic chemistry.

St. Francis Preaching to the Birds, by Giotto — A513

**1982, Aug. 12** Litho.
1380 A513 60pf multicolored .90 .30

800th birth anniv. of St. Francis of Assisi and 87th German Catholics Cong., Dusseldorf, 9/1-5.

James Franck, Max Born — A514

**1982, Aug. 12** Litho. & Engr.
1381 A514 80pf multicolored 1.25 .30

James Franck (1882-1964) and Max Born (1882-1970), Nobel Prize physicists, developed quantum theory.

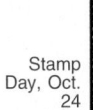

Stamp Day, Oct. 24 A515

**1982, Oct. 14** Photo. Perf. 14
1382 A515 80pf Poster 1.40 .30

400th Anniv. of the Gregorian Calendar — A516

Design: Calendar illumination, by Johannes Rasch, 1586.

**1982, Oct. 14** Litho.
1383 A516 60pf multicolored .90 .30

A517

Presidents: a, Theodor Heuss, 1949-59. b, Heinrich Lubke, 1959-69. c, Gustav Heinemann, 1969-74. d, Walter Scheel, 1974-79. e, Karl Carstens, 1979-84.

**1982, Nov. 10**
1384 Sheet of 5 5.00 4.50
a.-e. A517 80pf, single stamp .75 .75

A518

**1983, Jan. 13** Litho. Perf. 14
1385 A518 80pf gray & black 1.50 .45

Edith Stein (d. 1942), philospher and Carmelite Nun.

Persecution and Resistance, 1933-1945 — A519

**1983, Jan. 13**
1386 A519 80pf multicolored 1.50 .45

Light Space Modulator, 1930 — A520

Walter Gropius (1883-1969), Founder of Bauhaus Architecture: 60pf, Sanctuary, zinc lithograph, 1942. 80pf, Bauhaus Archives, Berlin, 1979.

**1983, Feb. 8**
1387 A520 50pf multicolored .75 .30
1388 A520 60pf multicolored 1.10 .30
1389 A520 80pf multicolored 1.25 .30
 Nos. 1387-1389 (3) 3.10 .90

Federahannes, Swabian-Alemannic Carnival — A521

**1983, Feb. 8**
1390 A521 60pf multicolored 1.00 .30

4th Intl. Horticultural Show, Munich, Apr. 28-Oct. 9 — A522

**1983, Apr. 12** Litho. Perf. 14
1391 A522 60pf multicolored 1.00 .30

Europa 1983 A523

Discoveries: 60pf, Printing press by Johannes Guttenburg. 80pf, Electromagnetic waves by Heinrich Hertz.

**1983, May 5** Litho. Perf. 14
1392 A523 60pf Movable type 1.90 .35
1393 A523 80pf Resonant circuit, electric flux lines 1.10 .35

Johannes Brahms (1833-1897), Composer A524

**1983, May 5** Photo.
1394 A524 80pf multicolored 1.50 .45

Franz Kafka (1883-1924), Writer — A525

**1983, May 5**
1395 A525 80pf Signature, Tyn Church, Prague 1.50 .45

Beer Pureness Law, 450th Anniv. A526

**1983, May 5** Litho.
1396 A526 80pf Brewers, engraving, 1677 1.50 .45

300th Anniv. of Immigration to US — A527

**1983, May 5** Litho. & Engr.
1397 A527 80pf Concord 1.60 .45

See US No. 2040.

Children and Road Safety A528

**1983, July 14** Litho. Perf. 14
1398 A528 80pf multicolored 1.50 .45

50th Intl.
Auto
Show,
Frankfurt,
Sept. 15-
25
A529

**1983, July 14**
1399  A529  60pf multicolored          .75   .30

Otto
Warburg — A530

**1983, Aug. 11   Photo.   Perf. 14**
1400  A530  50pf multicolored          .90   .45
   Warburg (1883-1970), pioneer of modern
biochemistry, 1931 Nobel prize winner in
medicine.

Christoph Martin
Wieland (1733-
1813),
Poet — A531

**1983, Aug. 11          Litho.**
1401  A531  80pf multicolored         1.25   .45

10th Anniv. of UN
Membership — A532

**1983, Aug. 11          Photo.**
1402  A532  80pf multicolored         1.60   .45

Rauhe Haus Orphanage
Sesquicentennial — A533

**1983, Aug. 11          Litho.**
1403  A533  80pf multicolored         1.25   .45

Survey and Measuring Maps — A534

**1983, Aug. 11**
1404  A534  120pf multicolored        1.60   .50
   Intl. Union of Geodesy and Geophysics
Gen. Assembly, Hamburg, Aug. 15-26.

Stamp
Day — A535

**1983, Oct. 13   Litho.   Perf. 13½**
1405  A535  80pf Postrider            1.40   .45

Martin Luther
(1483-1546)
A536

**1983, Oct. 13          Perf. 14**
1406  A536  80pf Engraving by G.
              Konig                    2.25   .45

Customs Union
Sesquicentennial — A537

**1983, Nov. 10**
1407  A537  60pf multicolored         1.60   .30

Territorial Authorities (Federation,
Land, Communities) — A538

**1983, Nov. 10          Litho.**
1408  A538  80pf multicolored         1.60   .45

Trier,
2000th
Anniv.
A539

**1984, Jan. 12   Litho. & Engr.**
1409  A539  80pf Black Gate, 175
              A.D.                     1.60   .45

Philipp Reis (1834-
1874) Physicist and
Inventor — A540

**1984, Jan. 12          Litho.**
1410  A540  80pf multicolored         1.60   .45

Gregor Mendel (1822-1884), Basic
Laws of Heredity — A541

**1984, Jan. 12          Litho.**
1411  A541  50pf multicolored         1.00   .30

500th Anniv. of
Michelstadt Town
Hall — A542

**1984, Feb. 16          Litho.**
1412  A542  60pf multicolored         1.00   .30

350th Anniv. of Oberammergau
Passion Play — A543

**1984, Feb. 16          Photo.**
1413  A543  60pf multicolored         1.00   .30

Second
Election of
Parliament,
June
17 — A544

**1984, Apr. 12   Litho.   Perf. 13½**
1414  A544  80pf multicolored         1.75   .50

Europa (1959-
1984)
A545

**1984, May 8    Photo.    Perf. 14**
1415  A545  60pf multicolored         1.25   .35
1416  A545  80pf multicolored         1.25   .35

A546

**1984, May 8          Engr.**
1417  A546  60pf multicolored          .75   .30
   Nursery Rhyme Illustration, by Ludwig
Richter (1803-84).

A547

**1984, May 8**
1418  A547  80pf Statue, 1693         1.25   .45
   St. Norbert von Xanten (1080-1134).

Barmer Theological Declaration, 50th
Anniv. — A548

**1984, May 8          Litho.**
1419  A548  80pf Cross, text          1.25   .45

Souvenir Sheet

1984 UPU
Congress
A549

**1984, June 19   Litho.   Perf. 14**
1420      Sheet of 3                  3.50  2.75
   *a.* A549 60pf Letter sorting, 19th
        cent.                          .60   .50
   *b.* A549 80pf Scanner              .90   .75
   *c.* A549 120pf H. von Stephan,
        founder                       1.50  1.40

City of Neuss
Bimillennium
A550

**1984, June 19      Litho. & Engr.**
1421  A550  80pf Tomb of Oclatius     1.25   .45

Friedrich
Wilhelm Bessel
(1784-1846),
Astronomer
A551

**1984, June 19**
1422  A551  80pf Bessel function
              diagram                 1.25   .45

88th German
Catholic
Convention,
Munich, July 4-
8 — A552

**1984, June 19          Photo.**
1423  A552  60pf Pope Pius XII        1.00   .30

Town Hall,
Duderstadt — A553

**1984, Aug. 21   Litho.   Perf. 14**
1424  A553  60pf multicolored          .90   .30

Medieval
Document,
Computer — A554

**1984, Aug. 21**
1425  A554  70pf multicolored         1.25   .45
   10th Intl. Archives Congress, Bonn.

German Electron Synchrotron (DESY)
Research Center, Hamburg — A555

**1984, Aug. 21          Photo.**
1426  A555  80pf multicolored         1.60   .45

Schleswig-Holstein Canal
Bicentenary — A556

**1984, Aug. 21** Litho.
1427 A556 80pf Knoop lock 1.50 .45

Stamp
Day
A557

**1984, Oct. 18** Litho. *Perf. 14*
1428 A557 80pf Imperial Taxis
Posthouse, Augs-
burg 1.60 .45

Anti-smoking Campaign — A558

**1984, Nov. 8** Litho.
1429 A558 60pf Match, text 1.00 .30

Equal Rights for
Men and
Women — A559

**1984, Nov. 8**
1430 A559 80pf Male & female
symbols 1.50 .45

Peace and Understanding — A560

**1984, Nov. 8**
1431 A560 80pf Text 1.25 .45

Augsburg, 2000th Anniv. — A561

**1985, Jan. 10** Litho.
1432 A561 80pf Roman Emperor
Augustus, Aug-
sburg buildings 1.50 .35

Philipp Jakob
Spener, Religious
Leader (1635-1705)
A562

**1985, Jan. 10** Litho.
1433 A562 80pf multicolored 1.25 .45

Deutches Wortebuch — A563

**1985, Jan. 10** Litho.
1434 A563 80pf Bros. Grimm, text 1.60 .45

Romano
Guardini,
Theologist
(1885-1968)
A564

**1985, Jan. 10** Litho.
1435 A564 80pf multicolored 1.25 .45

Market and Coinage Rights in Verden,
1000th Anniv.
A565

**1985, Feb. 21** Litho.
1436 A565 60pf multicolored 1.60 .30

German-Danish Border Areas and
Flags — A566

**1985, Feb. 21**
1437 A566 80pf multicolored 1.75 .60
Bonn-Copenhagen declarations on mutual
minorities, 30th anniv.

Johann Peter
Hebel (1760-
1826),
Poet — A567

**1985, Apr. 16** Litho.
1438 A567 80pf multicolored 1.25 .45

Egon Erwin
Kisch (1885-
1948),
Journalist
A568

**1985, Apr. 16** Litho.
1439 A568 60pf Kisch using telephone 1.00 .30

Europa
1985 — A569

European Music Year: 60pf, Georg Friedrich
Handel. 80pf, Johann Sebastian Bach.

**1985, May 7** Photo.
1440 A569 60pf Portrait of Handel 1.50 .35
1441 A569 80pf Portrait of Bach 1.50 .35

Dominikus
Zimmermann
(1685-1766),
Architect — A570

**1985, May 7** Photo.
1442 A570 70pf Stucco column 1.10 .45

St. George's
Cathedral,
750th
Anniv. — A571

**1985, May 7** Litho. *Perf. 14*
1443 A571 60pf Cathedral,
Limburg .90 .45

Father Josef Kentenich (1885-
1968) — A572

**1985, May 7** Litho.
1444 A572 80pf Portrait 1.25 .45

Forest
Conservation
A573

**1985, July 16** Litho. *Perf. 14*
1445 A573 80pf Clock, forest 1.75 .45

Intl. Youth
Year
A574

**1985, July 16** *Perf. 14*
1446 A574 60pf Scouts, scouting
and IYY em-
blems 1.00 .45
30th World Scouting Conf., Munich, 7/15-19.

Frankfurt Stock Exchange, 400th
Anniv. — A575

Design: Bourse, est. 1879, and Frankfurt
Eagle, the exchange emblem.

**1985, Aug. 13** *Perf. 14x14½*
1447 A575 80pf multicolored 1.50 .45

The
Sunday
Walk, by
Carl
Spitzweg
(1808-85)
A576

**1985, Aug. 13**
1448 A576 60pf multicolored 1.60 .45

Fritz Reuter (1810-
1874), Dialect
Author — A577

**1985, Oct. 15** Litho. *Perf. 14*
1449 A577 80pf Portrait, manuscript 1.75 .45

Departure of the 1st Train from
Nuremberg to Furth, 1835 — A578

**1985, Nov. 12** Litho. *Perf. 14x14½*
1450 A578 80pf Adler locomotive 1.75 .45
Founder Johannes Scharrer (1785-1844),
German Railways 150th anniv.

Reintegration of
German World War
II Refugees, 40th
Anniv. — A579

**1985, Nov. 12** *Perf. 14*
1451 A579 80pf multicolored 1.75 .45

Natl.
Armed
Forces,
30th
Anniv.
A580

**1985, Nov. 12** *Perf. 14x14½*
1452 A580 80pf Iron Cross, natl.
colors 2.50 .45

Benz Tricycle, Saloon Car, 1912, and
Modern Automobile — A581

**1986, Jan. 16** Litho. *Perf. 14*
1453 A581 80pf multicolored 1.75 .45
Automobile cent.

Bad
Hersfeld,
1250th
Anniv.
A582

**1986, Feb. 13** Litho. *Perf. 14*
1454 A582 60pf multicolored 1.25 .45

Bach Contata,
Detail, by Oskar
Kokoschka (1886-
1980)
A583

**1986, Feb. 13**
1455 A583 80pf Self portrait 1.25 .45

Halley's Comet A584

**1986, Feb. 13**
1456  A584  80pf multicolored                1.75  .50

Europa 1986 A585

Details from Michelangelo's David: 60pf, Mouth (pure water). 80pf, Nose, (pure air).

**1986, May 5          Photo.          Perf. 14**
1457  A585  60pf multicolored              *1.25  .35*
1458  A585  80pf multicolored              *1.25  .35*

St. Johannis Monastery, Walsrode — A586

**1986, May 5          Litho. & Engr.**
1459  A586  60pf multicolored                1.25  .45
Monastery millennium and town of Walsrode, 603rd anniv.

King Ludwig II of Bavaria (1845-1886), Neuschwanstein Castle — A587

**1986, May 5          Litho.**
1460  A587  60pf multicolored                2.10  .45

Karl Barth (1886-1968), Protestant Theologian A588

**1986, May 5          Engr.**
1461  A588  80pf blk, dk red & red lil       1.40  .45

Religion, Science, Friendship and Fatherland — A589

**1986, May 5          Litho.**
1462  A589  80pf multicolored                1.40  .45
Union of German Catholic Students, 100th assembly, Frankfurt, June 12-15.

Carl Maria von Weber (1786-1826), Mass in E-flat Major — A590

**1986, June 20          Litho.          Perf. 14**
1463  A590  80pf multicolored                1.75  .45

Franz Liszt and Signature A591

**1986, June 20**
1464  A591  80pf dk blue & dk org            1.75  .45

Intl. Peace Year A592

**1986, June 20**
1465  A592  80pf multicolored                1.60  .45

Souvenir Sheet

Reichstag, Berlin — A593

Historic buildings: b, Koening Museum, Bonn. c, Parliament, Bonn.

**1986, June 20**
1466      Sheet of 3                         3.75  3.25
a.-c.  A593 80pf, any single                 1.00  1.00

European Satellite Technology — A594

Design: TV-SAT/TDF-1 over Europe.

**1986, June 20**
1467  A594  80pf multicolored                1.90  .50

Augsburg Cathedral Stained Glass Window A595

**1986, Aug. 14          Perf. 14**
1468  A595  80pf multicolored                1.90  .45
Monuments protection.

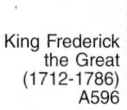

King Frederick the Great (1712-1786) A596

**1986, Aug. 14**
1469  A596  80pf multicolored                2.50  .45

German Skat Congress, Cent. — A597

**1986, Aug. 14**
1470  A597  80pf Tournament card             1.75  .45

Organization for Economic Cooperation and Development, 25th Anniv. — A598

**1986, Aug. 14**
1471  A598  80pf multicolored                1.40  .45

Heidelberg University, 600th Anniv. — A599

**1986, Oct. 16          Litho.**
1472  A599  80pf multicolored                1.60  .45

Stagecoach, Stamps from 1975-1984 — A600

**1986, Oct. 16**
1473  A600  80pf multicolored                1.60  .45
Stamp Day, 50th Anniv.

A601          A602

**1986, Nov. 13          Litho.          Perf. 14**
1474  A601  70pf multicolored                1.00  .45
Mary Wigman (1886-1973), dancer.

**1986-91          Engr.          Perf. 14**
Famous Women: 5pf, Emma Ihrer (1857-1911), politician, labor leader. 10pf, Paula Modersohn-Becker (1876-1907), painter. 20pf, Cilly Aussem (1909-63), tennis champion. 30pf, Kathe Kollwitz (1867-1945), painter, graphic artist. 40pf, Maria Sibylla Merian (1647-1717), naturalist, painter. 50pf, Christine Teusch (1888-1968), minister of education and cultural affairs. 60pf, Dorothea Erxleben (1715-62), physician. 70pf, Elisabet Boehm (1859-1943), social organizer. 80pf, Clara Schumann (1819-96), pianist, composer. 100pf, Therese Giehse (1898-1975), actress. 120pf, Elisabeth Selbert (1896-1986), politician. 130pf, Lise Meitner (1878-1968), physicist. 140pf, Cecile Vogt (1875-1962), neurologist. 150pf, Sophie Scholl (1921-43), member of anti-Nazi resistance. 170pf, Hannah Arendt (1906-75), American political scientist. 180pf, Lotte Lehmann (1888-1976), soprano. 200pf, Bertha von Suttner (1843-1914), 1905 Nobel Peace Prize winner. 240pf, Mathilde Franziska Anneke, (1817-84), American author. 250pf, Queen Louise of Prussia (1776-1810). 300pf, Fanny Hensel (1805-47), composer-conductor. 350pf, Hedwig Dransfeld (1871-1925), women's rights activist. 500pf, Alice Salomon (1872-1948), feminist and social activist.

1475  A602  5pf multi                         .20   .20
1476  A602  10pf multi                        .20   .20
1477  A602  20pf multi                        .75   .35
1478  A602  30pf multi                        .35   .30
1479  A602  40pf multi                        .75   .20
1480  A602  50pf multi                        .75   .20
1481  A602  60pf multi                        .90   .20
1482  A602  70pf multi                       1.10   .60
1483  A602  80pf multi                        .90   .20
1484  A602  100pf multi                      1.10   .35
1485  A602  120pf multi                      1.50   .90
1486  A602  130pf multi                      2.25   .75
1487  A602  140pf multi                      2.60  1.40
1488  A602  150pf multi                      3.00  1.40

1489  A602  170pf multi                      1.90  1.10
1490  A602  180pf multi                      2.25  1.10
1491  A602  200pf multi                      1.90   .75
1492  A602  240pf multi                      2.60  1.90
1493  A602  250pf multi                      3.75  1.90
1493A A602  300pf multi                      2.25  1.10
1494  A602  350pf multi                      4.00  2.25
1494A A602  500pf multi                      5.00  3.00
      *Nos. 1475-1494A (22)*                40.00 20.35

Issued: 50pf, 80pf, 11/18; 40pf, 60pf, 9/17/87; 120pf, 11/7/87; 10pf, 4/14/88; 20pf, 130pf, 5/5/88; 100pf, 170pf, 240pf, 350pf, 11/10/88; 500pf, 1/12/89; 5pf, 2/9/89; 180pf, 250pf, 7/13/89; 140pf, 300pf, 8/10/89; 30pf, 70pf, 1/8/91; 150pf, 200pf, 2/14/91.
See #1723/1735, 2188-2197, Berlin #9N516-9N532.

Advent Collection for Church Projects in Latin America, 25th Anniv. A603

**1986, Nov. 13          Litho.          Perf. 14**
1495  A603  80pf multicolored                1.00  .45

Berlin, 750th Anniv. — A604

**1987, Jan. 15          Litho.**
1496  A604  80pf multicolored                2.00  .60

Archbishop's Residence at Wurzburg, 1719-44 A605

**1987, Jan. 15          Photo.**
1497  A605  80pf multicolored                1.50  .45
Balthasar Neumann (1687-1753), Baroque architect.

Ludwig Erhard (1897-1977), Economist, Chancellor 1963-66 A606

**1987, Jan. 15**
1498  A606  80pf multicolored                1.75  .35

1987 Census — A607

**1987, Jan. 15          Litho.**
1499  A607  80pf Federal Eagle               1.60  .45

Clemenswerth Hunting Castle, 250th Anniv. — A608

**1987, Feb. 12          Litho.**
1500  A608  60pf multicolored                1.25  .45

Joseph von Fraunhofer (1787-1826), Optician, Physicist — A609

**1987, Feb. 12**     **Litho. & Engr.**
1501 A609 80pf Light spectrum diagram    1.25 .45

Karl May (1842-1912), Novelist — A610

**1987, Feb. 12**     **Photo.**
1502 A610 80pf Apache Chief Winnetou    1.40 .45

Papal Arms, Madonna and Child, Buildings in Kevelaer — A611

**1987, Apr. 9**     **Litho.**
1503 A611 80pf multicolored    1.60 .45
State visit of Pope John Paul II, Apr. 30-May 4; 17th Marian and 10th Mariological World Congress, Kevelaer, Sept. 11-20.

German Choral Soc., 125th Anniv. A612

**1987, Apr. 9**
1504 A612 80pf multicolored    1.40 .45

Europa 1987 A613

Modern architecture: 60pf, German Pavilion, designed by Ludwig Mies van der Rohe, 1928 World's Fair, Barcelona. 80pf, Kohlbrand Bridge, 1974, Hamburg, designed by Thyssen Engineering.

**1987, May 5**     **Litho.**
1505 A613 60pf multicolored    *1.25 .35*
1506 A613 80pf multicolored    *1.50 .35*

Organ Pipes, Signature A614

**1987, May 5**
1507 A614 80pf multicolored    1.00 .45
Dietrich Buxtehude (c. 1637-1707), composer.

Wilhelm Kaisen (1887-1979), Bremen City Senate President — A615

**1987, May 5**
1508 A615 80pf multicolored    1.40 .45

Johann Albrecht Bengel (1687-1752), Lutheran Theologian — A616

**1987, May 5**     **Photo.**    *Perf. 14*
1509 A616 80pf multicolored    1.25 .45

Kurt Schwitters (1887-1948), Artist — A617

**1987, May 5**     **Litho.**
1510 A617 80pf multicolored    1.25 .45

Rotary Intl. Convention, Munich, June 7-10 — A618

**1987, May 5**     **Photo.**
1511 A618 70pf multicolored    1.40 .45

Dulmen's Wild Horses, Merfelder Bruch Nature Reserve A619

**1987, May 5**
1512 A619 60pf multicolored    1.60 .45
European Environmental Conservation Year.

Bishopric of Bremen, 1200th Anniv. A620

Design: Charlemagne, Bremen Cathedral, city arms, Bishop Willehad.

**1987, July 16**     **Litho.**    *Perf. 14*
1513 A620 80pf multicolored    1.25 .45

7th European Rifleman's Festival, Lippstadt, Sept. 12-13 — A621

**1987, Aug. 20**     **Litho.**    *Perf. 14*
1514 A621 80pf multicolored    1.25 .45

Stamp Day — A622

**1987, Oct. 15**     **Litho.**
1515 A622 80pf Postmen, 1897    1.25 .85

Historic Sites and Objects — A623

Designs: 5pf, Brunswick Lion. 10pf, Frankfurt Airport. 20pf, No. 1526, Queen Nefertiti of Egypt, bust, Egyptian Museum, Berlin. 30pf, Corner tower, Celle Castle, 14th cent. 33pf, 120pf, Schleswig Cathedral. 38pf, 280pf, Statue of Roland, Bremen. 40pf, Chile House, Hamburg. 41pf, 170pf, Russian church, Wiesbaden. 45pf, Rastatt Castle. 50pf, Filigree tracery on spires, Freiburg Cathedral. 60pf, Bavaria Munich, bronze statue above the Theresienwiese, Hall of Fame. No. 1527, Heligoland. 80pf, Entrance to Zollern II coal mine, Dortmund. 90pf, 140pf, Bronze flagon from Reinheim. 100pf, Altotting Chapel, Bavaria. 200pf, Magdeburg Cathedral. 300pf, Hambach Castle. 350pf, Externsteine Bridge near Horn-Bad Meinberg. 400pf, Opera House, Dresden. 450pf, New Gate, Neubrandenburg. 500pf, State Theatre, Cottbus. 700pf, German Theater, Berlin.

| | | **1987-96** | **Typo.** | **Perf. 14** | |
|---|---|---|---|---|---|
| 1515A | A623 | 5pf | multi | .20 | .20 |
| 1516 | A623 | 10pf | multi | .20 | .20 |
| 1517 | A623 | 20pf | multi | .30 | .20 |
| 1518 | A623 | 30pf | multi | .50 | .20 |
| 1519 | A623 | 33pf | tmulti | .45 | .30 |
| 1520 | A623 | 38pf | multi | .75 | .45 |
| 1521 | A623 | 40pf | multi | .30 | .30 |
| 1522 | A623 | 41pf | multi | .50 | .35 |
| 1523 | A623 | 45pf | multi | .45 | .35 |
| 1524 | A623 | 50pf | multi | .50 | .20 |
| 1525 | A623 | 60pf | multi | .75 | .20 |
| 1526 | A623 | 70pf | multi | .70 | .20 |
| 1527 | A623 | 70pf | multi | .45 | .30 |
| 1528 | A623 | 80pf | multi | .75 | .20 |
| a. | | Bklt. pane, 4 10pf, 2 50pf, 2 80pf ('89) | | 3.75 | 4.00 |
| b. | | Bklt. pane, 2 each 20pf, 80pf | | 4.00 | 5.50 |
| 1529 | A623 | 90pf | rnulti | 1.25 | 1.50 |
| 1530 | A623 | 100pf | multi | 1.50 | .30 |
| a. | | Bklt. pane, 2 each 10, 60, 80, 100pf | | 7.50 | 9.00 |
| b. | | Bklt. pane, 2 each 20, 50, 80, 100pf | | 5.75 | 9.75 |
| c. | | Booklet pane, 10 #1530 | | 19.00 | 16.00 |
| | | Complete booklet, #1530c | | 22.50 | |
| d. | | Booklet pane, 4 #1516, 2 each #1524, 1528, 1530 | | 6.00 | 7.50 |
| | | Complete booklet, #1530d | | 7.00 | |
| 1531 | A623 | 120pf | multi | 1.50 | .50 |
| 1532 | A623 | 140pf | multi | 1.75 | .60 |
| 1533 | A623 | 170pf | multi | 2.50 | .75 |
| 1534 | A623 | 200pf | lmulti | 2.25 | .65 |
| 1535 | A623 | 280pf | multi | 3.75 | 1.90 |
| 1536 | A623 | 300pf | multi | 2.60 | .45 |
| 1537 | A623 | 350pf | multi | 3.00 | .60 |
| 1538 | A623 | 400pf | multi | 3.75 | .60 |
| 1539 | A623 | 450pf | multi | 5.00 | .50 |
| 1540 | A623 | 500pf | multi | 5.00 | 1.40 |
| 1540A | A623 | 700pf | multi | 8.00 | 3.00 |
| | | *Nos. 1515A-1540A (27)* | | 48.65 | 16.40 |

Issued: 30, 50, 60, 80pf, 11/6/87; 10, 300pf, 1/14/88; 120pf, #1526, 7/14/88; 40, 90, 280pf, 8/11/88; 20, 33, 38, 140pf, 1/12/89; 100, 350pf, 2/9/89; 5pf, 2/15/90; 45p, #1527, 6/21/90; 170pf, 6/4/91; 400pf, 10/10/91; 450pf, 8/13/92; 200pf, 4/15/93; 500pf, 6/17/93; 41pf, 8/12/93; 700pf, 9/16/93; #1530b, 11/9/94; #1530d, 8/14/96.
See #1655-1663, 1838-60, Berlin #9N543-9N557.

Christoph Willibald Gluck (1714-1787), Composer, and Score from the Opera Armide — A624

**1987, Nov. 6**     *Perf. 14*
1541 A624 60pf car lake & dk gray    1.00 .35

Gerhart Hauptmann (1862-1946), Playwright — A625

**1987, Nov. 6**     **Litho.**
1542 A625 80pf black & brick red    1.50 .45

German Agro Action Organization, 125th Anniv. — A626

**1987, Nov. 6**     **Photo.**
1543 A626 80pf Rice field    1.50 .45

Mainz Carnival, 150th Anniv. — A627

**1988, Jan. 14**     **Litho.**    *Perf. 14*
1544 A627 60pf Jester    1.00 .45

Jacob Kaiser (1888-1961), Labor Leader — A628

**1988, Jan. 14**     **Litho. & Engr.**
1545 A628 80pf black    1.00 .45

Franco-German Cooperation Treaty, 25th Anniv. — A629

**1988, Jan. 14**
1546 A629 80pf Adenauer, De Gaulle    1.60 .60
See France No. 2086.

Beatification of Edith Stein and Rupert Mayer by Pope John Paul II in 1987 — A630

**1988, Jan. 14**     **Photo.**
1547 A630 80pf brown, blk & ver    1.25 .45

A631

Woodcut (detail) by Ludwig Richter.

**1988, Feb. 18**     Litho.
1548 A631 60pf multicolored   1.25 .45

Woodcut inspired by poem Solitude of the Green Woods, by Baron Joseph von Eichendorff (1788-1857).

A632

**1988, Feb. 18**     Photo.
1549 A632 80pf dk red & brn blk 1.50 .45

Arthur Schopenhauer (1788-1860), philosopher.

Friedrich Wilhelm Raiffeisen (1818-1888), Economist — A633

**1988, Feb. 18**     Litho.
1550 A633 80pf black & brt yel grn 1.60 .45

The German Raiffeisen Assoc., an agricultural cooperative credit soc., was founded by Raiffeisen.

Ulrich Reichsritter von Hutten (1488-1523), Humanist — A634

Design: Detail from an engraving published with Hutten's Conquestiones.

**1988, Apr. 14**    Litho. & Engr.
1551 A634 80pf multicolored   1.25 .50

Europa 1988 A635

Transport and communication: 60pf, Airbus A320. 80pf, Integrated Services Digital Network (ISDN) system.

**1988, May 5**     Litho.
1552 A635 60pf multicolored   1.00 .35
1553 A635 80pf multicolored   1.00 .35

City of Dusseldorf, 700th Anniv. — A636

**1988, May 5**
1554 A636 60pf multicolored   1.25 .45

Cologne University, 600th Anniv. — A637

**1988, May 5**
1555 A637 80pf multicolored   1.25 .45

Jean Monnet (1888-1979), French Statesman A638

**1988, May 5**
1556 A638 80pf multicolored   1.25 .45

Theodor Storm (1817-1888), Poet, Novelist — A639

**1988, May 5**
1557 A639 80pf multicolored   1.25 .45

German Volunteer Service, 25th Anniv. — A640

**1988, May 5**
1558 A640 80pf multicolored   1.25 .45

Town of Meersburg, Millennium — A641

**1988, July 14**   Litho.   Perf. 14
1559 A641 60pf multicolored   .90 .45

Leopold Gmelin (1788-1853), Chemist A642

**1988, July 14**   Litho. & Engr.
1560 A642 80pf multicolored   1.00 .45

Vernier Scale as a Symbol of Precision and Quality — A643

**1988, July 14**     Litho.
1561 A643 140pf multicolored   1.90 .90

Made in Germany.

August Bebel (1840-1913), Founder of the Social Democratic Party — A644

**1988, Aug. 11**     Photo.
1562 A644 80pf multicolored   1.40 .45

Intl. Red Cross, 125th Anniv. — A645

**1988, Oct. 13**   Litho. & Engr.
1563 A645 80pf scarlet & black   1.40 .45

Stamp Day — A646

**1988, Oct. 13**     Litho.
1564 A646 20pf Carrier pigeon   .60 .35

1st Nazi Pogrom, Nov. 9, 1938 A647

Star, "Remembering is the secret of redemption," & burning synagogue in Baden-Baden.

**1988, Oct. 13**     Photo.
1565 A647 80pf dull pale pur & blk   1.00 .45

Postage Stamps for Bethel, Cent. A648

**1988, Nov. 10**     Litho.
1566 A648 60pf multicolored   1.10 .45

The Postage Stamps for Bethel program was founded by Pastor Friedrich V. Bodelschwingh to employ disabled residents of Bethel.

Samaritan Association of Workers (ASB) Rescue Service, Cent. — A649

**1988, Nov. 10**
1567 A649 80pf multicolored   1.10 .45

Bonn Bimillennium — A650

**1989, Jan. 12**     Litho.
1568 A650 80pf multicolored   1.50 .65

Bonn as capital of the federal republic, 40th anniv.

Bluxao I, 1955, by Willi Baumeister (1889-1955) — A651

**1989, Jan. 12**
1569 A651 60pf multicolored   1.00 .45

Misereor and Brot fur die Welt, 30th Annivs. A652

**1989, Jan. 12**     Photo.
1570 A652 80pf Barren and verdant soil   1.10 .45

Church organizations helping Third World nations to become self-sufficient in food production.

Cats in the Attic, Woodcut by Gerhard Marcks (1889-1981) — A653

**1989, Feb. 9**   Litho.   Perf. 14
1571 A653 60pf multicolored   1.00 .45

European Parliament 3rd Elections, June 18 — A654

Flags of member nations.

**1989, Apr. 20**     Litho.
1572 A654 100pf multicolored   1.90 .90

Europa 1989 A655

**1989, May 5**
1573 A655 60pf Kites   1.00 .30
1574 A655 100pf Puppets   1.50 .35

Hamburg Harbor, 800th Anniv. A656

**1989, May 5**
1575 A656 60pf multicolored    1.40   .45

Cosmas Damian Asam (1686-1739), Painter, Architect A657

**1989, May 5       Litho. & Engr.**
1576 A657 60pf Fresco    .75   .45

Federal Republic of Germany, 40th Anniv. — A658

**1989, May 5       Photo.**
1577 A658 100pf Natl. crest, flag, presidents' signatures    1.75   .65

Council of Europe, 40th Anniv. — A659

**1989, May 5       Perf. 14**
1578 A659 100pf Parliamentary Assembly, stars    1.60   .75

Franz Xaver Gabelsberger (1789-1849), Inventor of a German Shorthand — A660

**1989, May 5       Litho.**
1579 A660 100pf multicolored    1.60   .60

Sts. Kilian, Colman and Totnan (d. 689), Martyred Missionaries, and Clover — A661

**1989, June 15       Litho.**
1580 A661 100pf multicolored    1.50   .60
See Ireland No. 748.

Friedrich Silcher (1789-1860), Composer, and *Lorelai* Score — A662

**1989, June 15**
1581 A662 80pf multicolored    1.00   .45

Social Security Pension Insurance, Cent. — A663

**1989, June 15**
1582 A663 100pf dull ultra, bl & ver    1.50   .50

Friedrich List (1789-1846), Economist — A664

**1989, July 13   Engr.   Perf. 14**
1583 A664 170pf black & dark red    2.25   .90

*Summer Evening*, 1905, by Heinrich Vogler — A665

**1989, July 13       Litho.**
1584 A665 60pf multicolored    .85   .45
Worpswede Artists' Village, cent.

A666

**1989, July 13       Photo.**
1585 A666 100pf slate grn, blk & gray    1.10   .50
Reverend Paul Schneider (d. 1939), martyr of Buchenwald concentration camp.

A667

**1989, Aug. 10       Litho.**
1586 A667 60pf multicolored    1.25   .45
Frankfurt Cathedral, 750th anniv.

Child Welfare A668

**1989, Aug. 10       Perf. 14**
1587 A668 100pf multicolored    1.40   .50

Trade Union of the Mining and Power Industries, Cent. — A669

**1989, Aug. 10       Perf. 14**
1588 A669 100pf multicolored    1.25   .50

Reinhold Maier (1889-1971), Politician A670

**1989, Oct. 12       Litho.**
1589 A670 100pf multicolored    1.40   .50

Restoration of St. James Church Organ, Constructed by Arp Schnitger, 1689 — A671

**1989, Nov. 16**
1590 A671 60pf multicolored    1.25   .45

Speyer, 2000th Anniv. A672

**1990, Jan. 12   Litho.   Perf. 14x14½**
1591 A672 60pf multicolored    1.25   .45

A673

Design: *The Young Post Rider*, an Engraving by Albrecht Durer.

**Litho. & Engr.**
**1990, Jan. 12       Perf. 14**
1592 A673 100pf buff, vio brn & gray    2.00   .60
Postal communications in Europe, 500th anniv. See Austria No. 1486, Belgium No. 1332, Berlin 9N584, and DDR No. 2791.

A674

**1990, Jan. 12       Litho.**
1593 A674 100pf multicolored    1.25   .60
Riesling Vineyards, 500th anniv.

Addition of Lubeck to the UNESCO World Heritage List, 1987 A675

**1990, Jan. 12       Litho. & Engr.**
1594 A675 100pf multicolored    1.25   .60

Seal of Col. Spittler, 1400, and Teutonic Order Heraldic Emblem A676

**1990, Feb. 15       Litho.**
1595 A676 100pf multicolored    1.50   .60
Teutonic Order, 800th anniv.

Seal of Frederick II and Galleria Reception Hall at the Frankfurt Fair A677

**1990, Feb. 15**
1596 A677 100pf multicolored    1.50   .60
Granting of fair privileges to Frankfurt by Frederick II, 750th anniv.

Youth Science and Technology Competition, 25th Anniv. — A678

**1990, Feb. 15**
1597 A678 100pf multicolored    1.50   .60

Nature and Environmental Protection — A679

**1990, Feb. 15**
1598 A679 100pf North Sea    1.60   .60

Labor Day, Cent. A680

**1990, Apr. 19   Photo.   Perf. 14**
1599 A680 100pf dark red & blk   1.25   .60

German Assoc. of Housewives, 75th
Anniv. — A681

**1990, Apr. 19**                        **Litho.**
1600  A681  100pf multicolored          1.25   .60

Europa
A682

Post offices in Frankfurt am Main: 60pf,
Thurn and Taxis Palace. 100pf, Modern Giro
office.

**1990, May 3**                          **Litho.**
1601  A682  60pf multicolored            *1.10   .50*
1602  A682  100pf multicolored           *1.50   .50*

German Students' Fraternity, 175th
Anniv. — A683

**1990, May 3**                    **Litho. & Engr.**
1603  A683  100pf multicolored           1.60   .60

Intl. Telecommunication Union, 125th
Anniv. — A684

**1990, May 3**                          **Litho.**
1604  A684  100pf multicolored           1.25   .60

German Life Boat Institution, 125th
Anniv. — A685

**1990, May 3**
1605  A685  60pf multicolored            1.25   .50

Wilhelm
Leuschner
(1890-1944),
Politician
A686

**1990, May 3**                    **Litho. & Engr.**
1606  A686  100pf lt gray violet         1.50   .60

Rummelsberg Diaconal Institution,
Cent. — A687

**1990, May 3**                          **Litho.**
1607  A687  100pf multicolored           1.25   .60

Charter of German Expellees, 40th
Anniv. — A688

**1990, June 21**                        **Photo.**
1608  A688  100pf multicolored           1.50   .50

Intl. Chamber of Commerce, 30th
Universal Congress — A689

**1990, June 21**                        **Litho.**
1609  A689  80pf multicolored            1.25   .75

Matthias
Claudius
(1740-1815),
Writer — A691

**1990, Aug. 9**                         **Litho.**
1611  A691  100pf multicolored           1.40   .45

**Reunified Germany**
AREA — 137,179 sq. mi.
POP. — 82,087,361 (1999 est.)
CAPITAL — Berlin

German Reunification — A692

**1990, Oct. 3    Litho.    Perf. 14**
1612  A692  50pf black, red & yel  1.10  .35
1613  A692  100pf black, red & yel  1.50  .50

First Postage Stamps, 150th
Anniv. — A693

**1990, Oct. 11**                        **Litho.**
1614  A693  100pf multicolored           1.40   .45

Heinrich Schliemann (1822-1890),
Archaeologist — A694

**1990, Oct. 11**
1615  A694  60pf multicolored            1.25   .45
       See Greece No. 1705.

Kathe Dorsch
(1912-1957),
Actress — A695

**1990, Nov. 6**                         **Photo.**
1616  A695  100pf red & violet           1.40   .60

Opening of Berlin
Wall, 1st
Anniv. — A696

**1990, Nov. 6    Photo.    Perf. 14**
1617  A696  50pf shown              1.10   .70
1618  A696  100pf Brandenburg
            Gate                    1.50   .70
            **Souvenir Sheet**
1619        Sheet of 2              3.00  3.25
   a.   A696  50pf like No. 1617    1.10   .90
   b.   A696  100pf like No. 1618   1.50  1.10
Rainbow continuous on stamps from #1619.

Pharmacy
Profession,
750th
Anniv. — A697

**1991, Jan. 8**                         **Litho.**
1620  A697  100pf multicolored           1.50   .60

Hanover,
750th
Anniv. — A698

**1991, Jan. 8**
1621  A698  60pf multicolored            1.25   .45

Brandenburg Gate,
Bicentennial — A699

**1991, Jan. 8**                   **Litho. & Engr.**
1622  A699  100pf gray, dk bl &
            red                          1.75   .45

A700

**1991, Jan. 8**                         **Photo.**
1623  A700  60pf multicolored            1.00   .45
   Erich Buchholz (1891-1972), painter and
architect.

A701

**1991, Jan. 8**                         **Litho.**
1624  A701  100pf multicolored           1.25   .60
   Walter Eucken (1891-1950), economist.

25th Intl.
Tourism
Exchange,
Berlin — A702

**1991, Jan. 8**
1625  A702  100pf multicolored           1.40   .45

Souvenir Sheet

World Bobsled Championships,
Altenberg — A703

**1991, Jan. 8          Perf. 12½x13**
1626  A703  100pf multicolored           1.75  2.00

Friedrich Spee von Langenfeld (1591-
1635), Poet — A704

**1991, Feb. 14    Litho.    Perf. 14**
1627  A704  100pf multicolored           1.40   .45

A705

**1991, Feb. 14**
1628  A705  100pf multicolored           1.40   .45
   Ludwig Windthorst (1812-1891), politician.

A706

**1991, Mar. 12**
1629 A706 60pf multicolored    1.00  .45
Jan von Werth (1591-1652), general.

Flowers
A707

**1991, Mar. 12**          *Perf. 13*
1630 A707 30pf Schweizer
          mannschild          .40  .30
1631 A707 50pf Wulfens primel
          (primula)           .55  .50
1632 A707 80pf Sommerenzian
          (gentian)           .90  .35
1633 A707 100pf Preiselbeere
          (cranberry)        1.25  .35
1634 A707 350pf Alpenedelweiss 4.00 3.00
     Nos. 1630-1634 (5)       7.10 4.50

Battle of
Legnica,
750th
Anniv.
A708

**Litho. & Engr.**
**1991, Apr. 9**          *Perf. 14*
1635 A708 100pf multicolored  1.50  .90
See Poland No. 3019.

Choral
Singing
Academy
of Berlin,
Bicent.
A709

**1991, Apr. 9**
1636 A709 100pf multicolored  1.40  .60

Lette Foundation, 125th
Anniv. — A710

**1991, Apr. 9**          Photo.
1637 A710 100pf multicolored  1.40  .45

Historic
Aircraft
A711

**1991, Apr. 9**
1638 A711 30pf Junkers F13,
          1930               .35  .35
1639 A711 50pf Grade Eindeck-
          er, 1909           .55  .30
1640 A711 100pf Fokker FIII,
          1922              1.50  .35
1641 A711 165pf Graf Zeppelin
          LZ 127, 1928      2.25 2.00
     Nos. 1638-1641 (4)     4.65 3.00

Europa
A712

Satellites: 60pf, ERS-1. 100pf, Copernicus.

**1991, May 2**  Litho.  *Perf. 14*
1642 A712 60pf multicolored  1.10  .45
1643 A712 100pf multicolored 2.00  .45

Town
Charters,
700th
Anniv. — A713

Design: Arms of Bernkastel, Mayen,
Montabaur, Saarburg, Welschbillig, and
Wittlich.

**1991, May 2**
1644 A713 60pf multicolored  1.00  .45

Max Reger (1873-1916),
Composer — A714

**1991, May 2**
1645 A714 100pf multicolored 1.50  .45

Inter-City
Express
Railway
A715

**1991, May 2**
1646 A715 60pf multicolored  1.00  .45

18th World Gas Congress,
Berlin — A716

Designs: 60pf, Wilhelm August Lampadius
(1772-1842), chemist. 100pf, Gas street lamp.

**1991, June 4**  Litho.  *Perf. 13x12½*
1647 A716 60pf lt blue & black  .75  .30
1648 A716 100pf lt blue & black 1.10 .45
  a.   Pair, #1647-1648 + label 2.40 2.40

Sea Birds — A717

Designs: 60pf, Kampflaufer, Philomachus
pugnax. 80pf, Zwergseeschwalbe, Sterna
albifrons. 100pf, Ringelgans, Branta bernicla.
140pf, Seeadler, Haliaeetus albicilla.

**1991, June 4**  Litho.  *Perf. 14*
1649 A717 60pf multicolored   .75  .45
1650 A717 80pf multicolored  1.10  .75
1651 A717 100of multicolored 1.10  .75
1652 A717 140pf multicolored 2.10 1.50
     Nos. 1649-1652 (4)      5.05 3.45

Paul Wallot (1841-1912),
Architect — A718

**Litho. & Engr.**
**1991, June 4**          *Perf. 14*
1653 A718 100pf multicolored 1.50  .45

Historic Sites Type of 1987

Designs: No. 1655, Frankfurt Airport. No.
1656, Wernigerode Town Hall. 60pf, Munich,
Bavaria. 80pf, Zech Zollern II Dortmund. No.
1663, Wallfahrtskapelle Alloting. No. 1664,
Schwerin Castle. 110pf, Regensburg Stone
Bridge.

***Die Cut perf 10¼x10¾ on 3 sides***
***(#1656, 1664, 1666), Die Cut Imperf***
**1991-2001**              Litho.
**Self-Adhesive**
1655 A623 10pf multi      1.00 1.40
1656 A623 10pf multi      2.25 1.90
1659 A623 60pf multi      1.00 1.40
1661 A623 80pf multi      1.00 1.00
1663 A623 100pf multi     1.25 1.25
  a.   Bklt. pane, 2 each #1655,
       1659, 1661, 1663   8.25 8.25
1664 A623 100pf multi     2.25 2.25
1666 A623 110pf multi     2.25 2.25
  a.   Booklet, 2 each #1656,
       1664, 8 #1666     25.00 25.00
     Nos. 1655-1666 (7)  11.00 11.45

Issued: #1655, 1659, 1661, 1663, June 4.
Nos. 1656, 1664, 110pf, 5/25/01. Nos.
1655, 1659, 1661, 1663 issued on
peelable paper backing serving as booklet
cover.

Dragonflies
A719

50pf, #1671, Libellula depressa. #1672,
70pf, Sympetrum sanguineum. #1673, 80pf,
Cordulegaster boltonii. #1674, 100pf, Aeshna
viridis.

**1991, July 9**  Photo.  *Perf. 14*
1670 A719 50pf multicolored  .65  .30
1671 A719 60pf multicolored 1.25  .60
1672 A719 60pf multicolored 1.25  .60
1673 A719 60pf multicolored 1.25  .60
1674 A719 60pf multicolored 1.25  .60
  a.   Block of 4, #1671-1674 5.50 5.50
1675 A719 70pf multicolored 1.00  .75
1676 A719 80pf multicolored 1.10  .75
1677 A719 100pf multicolored 1.25 .75
     Nos. 1670-1677 (8)     9.00 4.95

Traffic
Safety
A720

**1991, July 9**          Litho.
1678 A720 100pf multicolored 1.50  .60

Geneva Convention
on Refugees, 40th
Anniv. — A721

**1991, July 9**
1679 A721 100pf blk, gray & pink 1.40 .45

Intl. Radio Exhibition, Berlin — A722

**1991, July 9**
1680 A722 100pf multicolored 1.40  .45

Reinold von Thadden-Trieglaff (1891-
1976), Founder of German Protestant
Convention — A723

**1991, Aug. 8**  Litho.  *Perf. 14*
1681 A723 100pf multicolored 1.40  .45

August Heinrich Hoffman von
Fallersleben (1798-1874), Poet and
Philologist — A724

**1991, Aug. 8**
1682 A724 100pf multicolored 1.40  .45
German national anthem, 150th anniv.

3-Phase Energy Transmission,
Cent. — A725

**1991, Aug. 8**
1683 A725 170pf multicolored 2.25 1.10

Rhine-Ruhr Harbor, Duisburg, 275th
Anniv. — A726

**1991, Sept. 12**  Litho.  *Perf. 14*
1684 A726 100pf multicolored 1.40  .45

Souvenir Sheet

Theodor Korner (1791-1813),
Poet — A727

**1991, Sept. 12**      *Perf. 13x12½*
1685 A727   Sheet of 2     2.25   2.25
   a.     60pf Sword and pen    1.10   1.10
   b.     100pf Portrait      1.10   1.10

Hans Albers
(1891-1960),
Actor — A728

**1991, Sept. 12**    **Photo.**    *Perf. 14*
1686 A728   100pf multicolored    1.75   .45

Postman,
Spreewald
Region
A729

**1991, Oct. 10**    **Litho.**    *Perf. 14*
1687 A729   100pf multicolored    1.40   .45
        Stamp Day.

Bird
Monument by
Max
Ernst — A730

**1991, Oct. 10**
1688 A730   100pf multicolored    1.40   .45

Sorbian
Legends
A731

**1991, Nov. 5**        *Perf. 13*
1689 A731   60pf Fiddler, water
              sprite          .90   .45
1690 A731   100pf Midday woman,
              woman from
              Nochten      1.40   .45

         **Souvenir Sheet**

Wolfgang Amadeus Mozart, Death
Bicent. — A732

**1991, Nov. 5**    **Litho.**    *Perf. 14*
1691 A732   100pf multicolored    2.25   2.25

Otto Dix (1891-
1969),
Painter — A733

Designs: 60pf, Portrait of the Dancer Anita
Berber. 100pf, Self-portrait.

---

**1991, Nov. 5**    **Photo.**    *Perf. 14*
1692 A733   60pf multicolored    .75   .45
1693 A733   100pf multicolored    1.50   .45

Julius Leber
(1891-1945),
Politician
A734

**1991, Nov. 5**        **Litho.**
1694 A734   100pf black & red    1.40   .45

Nelly Sachs (1891-
1970),
Writer — A735

**1991, Nov. 5**
1695 A735   100pf violet      1.40   .45

City of
Koblenz,
2000th
Anniv.
A736

**1992, Jan. 9**     *Perf. 13x12½*
1696 A736   60pf multicolored    1.50   .50

Terre Des
Hommes Child
Welfare
Organization,
25th
Anniv. — A737

**1992, Jan. 9**    **Litho.**    *Perf. 14*
1697 A737   100pf multicolored    1.50   .60

Martin
Niemoller
(1892-1984),
Theologian
A738

**1992, Jan. 9**
1698 A738   100pf multicolored    1.10   .45

Coats of Arms
of States of
the Federal
Republic of
Germany
A739

**1992-94**           *Perf. 13½*
1699   100pf Baden-Wurttem-
              berg         1.40   .65
1700   100pf Bavaria      1.40   .65
1701   100pf Berlin        1.40   .65
1702   100pf Brandenburg    1.40   .65
1703   100pf Bremen       1.40   .65
1704   100pf Hamburg      1.40   .65
1705   100pf Hesse        1.40   .65
1706   100pf Mecklenburg-
              Western Pomera-
              nia          1.40   .65
1707   100pf Lower Saxony    1.40   .65
1708   100pf North Rhine -
              Westphalia    1.40   .65
1709   100pf Rhineland-Palati-
              nate        1.40   .65
1710   100pf Saar         1.40   .65
1711   100pf Saxony       1.40   .65
1712   100pf Saxony-Anhalt   1.40   .65

---

1713   100pf Schleswig-Holstein   1.40   .65
1714   100pf Thuringia       1.40   .65
    *Nos. 1699-1714 (16)*    22.40 10.40

        See #B818.
   Issued: #1699, 1/9/92; #1700, 3/12/92;
#1701, 6/11/92; #1702, 7/16/92; #1703,
8/13/92; #1704, 9/10/92; #1705. 3/11/93;
#1706, 6/17/93; #1707, 7/15/93; #1708,
8/12/93; #1709, 9/16/93; #1710, 1/13/94;
#1711, 3/10/94; #1712, 6/16/94; #1713,
7/14/94; #1714, 9/8/94.

     Famous Women Type of 1986

   80pf, Rahel Varnhagen von Ense (1771-
1833), pioneer in women's movement. No.
1724, Elisabeth Schwarzhaupt (1901-86), politician. No. 1725, Louise Henriette of Orange
(1627-67), mother of Frederick, King of Prussia. No. 1726, Grethe Weiser (1903-70),
actress. No. 1727, Marlene Dietrich (1901-92),
actress. No. 1728, Käte Strobel (1907-96),
government minister. No. 1729, Marie-Elisabeth Lüders (1878-1966), politician. No. 1730,
Marieluise Fleisser (1901-74), writer. No.
1731, Maria Probst (1902-67), politician. No.
1732, Nelly Sachs (1891-1970), writer. 400pf,
Charlotte von Stein (1742-1827), confidant of
Goethe. 440pf, Gret Palucca (1902-93),
dancer. 450pf, Hedwig Courths-Mahler (1867-
1950), novelist.

**1992-2000**      **Engr.**     *Perf. 14*
1723   A602   80pf blue &
              brown      .85   .45
1724   A602   100pf green & org
              brown    1.00   .75
1725   A602   100pf violet & bis-
              ter        .85   .45
1726   A602   100pf ol bis & bl
              grn        .85   .75
1727   A602   110pf vio & dk
              brn     1.00   .60
1728   A602   110pf ol & red brn   .90   .75
1729   A602   220pf grn bl & vio
              bl     1.90   1.75
1730   A602   220pf grn & brn   1.60   1.60
1731   A602   300pf deep blue
              & brown   2.25   1.90
1732   A602   300pf brn & vio   2.10   2.10
1733   A602   400pf lake & blk   4.50   3.25
1734   A602   440pf dp vio & dk
              car     4.25   5.00
1735   A602   450pf brt blue &
              blue    5.00   3.75
    *Nos. 1723-1735 (13)*   27.05 23.10

   Issued: 400pf, 1/9/92; 450pf, 6/11/92; 80pf,
#1725, 10/13/94; #1727, 8/14/97; #1729,
8/28/97; #1724, #1731, 10/16/97; 440pf,
10/8/98; #1726, 11/9/00; Nos. 1730,
1732, 1/11/01.

Arthur
Honegger
(1892-1955),
Composer
A740

**1992, Feb. 6**    **Photo.**    *Perf. 14*
1736 A740   100pf sepia & black   1.50   .65

Ferdinand von Zeppelin (1838-1917),
Airship Builder — A741

**1992, Feb. 6**         **Litho.**
1737 A741   165pf multicolored   2.25   1.25

City of
Kiel,
750th
Anniv.
A742

**1992, Mar. 12**
1738 A742   60pf multicolored    1.00   .50

---

Konrad
Adenauer
A743

**1992, Mar. 12**         **Photo.**
1739 A743   100pf black & dull org   1.75   .50

Ernst Jakob
Renz (1815-
1892), Circus
Director — A744

**1992, Mar. 12**         **Litho.**
1740 A744   100pf multicolored   1.40   .50

Berlin
Sugar
Institute,
125th
Anniv.
A745

**1992, Mar. 12**      *Perf. 13x12½*
1741 A745   100pf multicolored   1.40   .65

Johann Adam Schall von Bell (1592-
1666), Astronomer and
Missionary — A746

**1992, Apr. 9**   **Litho.**   *Perf. 13x12½*
1742 A746   140pf multicolored   2.00   1.00

Erfurt, Capital
of Thuringia,
1250th
Anniv. — A747

**1992, May 7**    **Litho.**    *Perf. 14*
1743 A747   60pf multicolored    1.00   .50

Discovery of
America,
500th
Anniv. — A748

Europa: 60pf, Woodcut illustrating letters
from Columbus, 1493. 100pf, Rene de
Laudonniere and Chief Athore by Jacques le
Moyne de Morgues, 1564.

**1992, May 7**         *Perf. 13½*
1744 A748   60pf multicolored    *.85*   *.40*
1745 A748   100pf multicolored   *1.50*   *.45*

A749

**1992, May 7**      *Perf. 13*
1746 A749 100pf multicolored    1.40   .50
Order of Merit, 150th anniv.

A750

**1992, May 7**   **Litho.**   *Perf. 14*
1747 A750 100pf multicolored    1.40   .60
St. Ludgerus, 1250th birth anniv.

Adam Riese (1492-1559),
Mathematician — A751

**1992, May 7**
1748 A751 100pf multicolored    1.40   .60

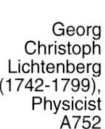

Georg
Christoph
Lichtenberg
(1742-1799),
Physicist
A752

**1992, June 11**   **Litho.**   *Perf. 14*
1749 A752 100pf multicolored    1.40   .60

20th Century Paintings — A753

Designs: 60pf, Landscape with a Horse, by
Franz Marc (1880-1916). 100pf, Fashion
Shop, by August Macke (1887-1914). 170pf,
Murnau with a Rainbow, by Vassily Kandinsky
(1866-1944).

**1992, June 11**   **Litho.**   *Perf. 14*
1750 A753 60pf multicolored    .75   .60
1751 A753 100pf multicolored    1.25   .60
1752 A753 170pf multicolored    2.00   1.60
    *Nos. 1750-1752 (3)*    4.00   2.80
    See Nos. 1878-1880.

Leipzig
Botanical
Garden
A754

**1992, July 16**   **Litho.**   *Perf. 13x12½*
1753 A754 60pf multicolored    1.00   .50

Family
Living — A755

**1992, July 16**      *Perf. 13½*
1754 A755 100pf multicolored    1.50   .50

17th World Congress on Home
Economics, Hanover — A756

**1992, July 16**   **Photo.**   *Perf. 14*
1755 A756 100pf multicolored    1.50   .60

Egid Quirin Asam
(1692-1750),
Architect and
Sculptor — A757

**1992, Aug. 13**   **Litho.**   *Perf. 14*
1756 A757 60pf multicolored    1.00   .50

German
State
Opera,
Berlin,
250th
Anniv.
A758

**1992, Aug. 13**
1757 A758 80pf multicolored    1.25   .50

Federation of
German Amateur
Theaters,
Cent. — A759

**1992, Aug. 13**
1758 A759 100pf multicolored    1.50   .50

Construction
of First Globe
by Martin
Behaim, 500th
Anniv. — A760

**1992, Sept. 10**      *Perf. 13½*
1759 A760 60pf multicolored    1.25   .50

Opening of Main-Danube
Canal — A761

**1992, Sept. 10**      *Perf. 14*
1760 A761 100pf multicolored    1.25   .50

Werner
Bergengruen
(1892-1964),
Writer — A762

**1992, Sept. 10**
1761 A762 100pf blk, bl & gray    1.25   .50

Jewelry & Watch
Industries in
Pforzheim, 225th
Anniv. — A763

**1992, Sept. 10**
1762 A763 100pf multicolored    1.25   .50

Balloon
Post — A764

**1992, Oct. 15**   **Litho.**   *Perf. 14*
1763 A764 100pf multicolored    1.50   .60
    Stamp Day.

Hugo Distler
(1908-1942),
Composer
A765

**1992, Oct. 15**
1764 A765 100pf violet & black    1.50   .50

Association of German Plant and
Machine Builders, Cent. — A766

**1992, Oct. 15**   **Litho. & Engr.**
1765 A766 170pf multicolored    2.00   1.00

Single
European
Market
A767

**1992, Nov. 5**   **Litho.**   *Perf. 14*
1766 A767 100pf multicolored    1.60   .60

Jochen Klepper
(1903-1942),
Writer — A768

**Litho. & Engr.**

**1992, Nov. 5**      *Perf. 14*
1767 A768 100pf multicolored    1.50   .50

A769

**1992, Nov. 5**      **Photo.**
1768 A769 100pf sepia & black    1.50   .50
Werner von Siemens (1816-1892), electrical
engineer.

A770

**1992, Nov. 5**      **Litho.**
1769 A770 100pf multicolored    1.50   .50
Gebhard Leberecht von Blucher (1742-
1819), Commander of Prussian Army.

City of Munster,
1200th
Anniv. — A771

**1993, Jan. 14**   **Litho.**   *Perf. 14*
1770 A771 60pf multicolored    1.00   .50

Sir Isaac
Newton,
Scientist
A772

**1993, Jan. 14**      **Litho. & Engr.**
1771 A772 100pf multicolored    1.25   .50

North German Naval Observatory,
Hamburg, 125th Anniv. — A773

**1993, Jan. 14**   **Litho.**   *Perf. 13x12½*
1772 A773 100pf multicolored    1.25   .50

Health and Safety
in
Workplace — A774

**1993, Jan. 14**   **Photo.**   *Perf. 14*
1773 A774 100pf blk, yel & bl    1.25   .50

Association of
German
Electrical
Engineers,
Cent. — A775

**1993, Jan. 14**
1774 A775 170pf multicolored    1.90   1.00

Leipzig Gewandhaus Orchestra, 250th
Anniv. — A776

**1993, Feb. 11   Litho.   Perf. 13x12½**
1775  A776  100pf black & gold         1.25   .50

St. John of Nepomuk, 600th Death
Anniv. — A777

**1993, Mar. 11**
1776  A777  100pf multicolored         1.25   .50

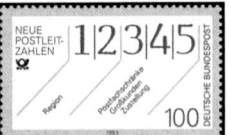

New
Postal
Codes
A778

**1993, Mar. 11                  Perf. 14**
1777  A778  100pf multicolored         1.50   .50

20th Century German
Paintings — A779

Designs: No. 1778, Cafe, by George Grosz
(1893-1959). No. 1779, Sea and Sun, by Otto
Pankok (1893-1966). No. 1780, Audience, by
A. Paul Weber (1893-1980).

**1993, Mar. 11**
1778  A779  100pf multicolored         1.25   .75
1779  A779  100pf multicolored         1.25   .75
1780  A779  100pf multicolored         1.25   .75
       Nos. 1778-1780 (3)              3.75  2.25

See Nos. 1863-1865, 1922-1924.

Benedictine Abbeys of Maria Laach
and Bursfelde, 900th Anniv. — A780

**Litho. & Engr.**
**1993, Apr. 15                  Perf. 14**
1781  A780  80pf multicolored          1.25   .50

5th Intl. Horticultural Show,
Stuttgart — A781

**1993, Apr. 15   Litho.   Perf. 13x12½**
1782  A781  100pf multicolored         1.25   .50

Contemporary Art — A782

Europa: 80pf, Storage Place, by Joseph
Beuys (1921-1986). 100pf, Homage to the
Square, by Joseph Albers (1888-1976).

**1993, May 5   Litho.   Perf. 13½x14**
1783  A782  80pf multicolored          1.25   .60
1784  A782  100pf multicolored         1.25   .60

Dahlwitz Hoppegarten (Hippodrome),
Berlin, 125th Anniv. — A783

**1993, May 5   Litho.   Perf. 14**
1785  A783  80pf multicolored          1.00   .60

Lake Constance Steamer
Hohentwiel — A784

**1993, May 5                   Photo.**
1786  A784  100pf multicolored         1.25   .50

See Austria No. 1618, Switzerland No. 931.

Schulpforta School
for Boys, 450th
Anniv. — A785

**1993, May 5                    Litho.**
1787  A785  100pf multicolored         1.25   .50

Coburger
Convent,
125th
Anniv.
A786

**1993, May 5   Litho. & Engr.**
1788  A786  100pf black, green &
            red                        1.25   .50

City of
Potsdam,
1000th
Anniv.
A787

**1993, June 17   Litho.   Perf. 13x12½**
1789  A787  80pf multicolored          1.25   .50

German UNICEF Committee, 40th
Anniv. — A788

**1993, June 17                  Litho.**
1790  A788  100pf multicolored         1.25   .50

Friedrich Holderlin
(1770-1843),
Writer — A789

**1993, June 17   Photo.   Perf. 14**
1791  A789  100pf multicolored         1.25   .50

Hans Fallada
(1893-1947),
Novelist — A790

**1993, July 15**
1792  A790  100pf multicolored         1.25   .50

Scenic Regions in Germany — A791

**1993-96        Litho.       Perf. 14**
**Denominations 100pf**
1793  A791  Rugen Island         1.10   .65
1794  A791  Harz Mountains       1.10   .65
1795  A791  Rhon Mountains       1.10   .65
1796  A791  Bavarian Alps        1.10   .75
1797  A791  Ore Mountains        1.10   .75
1798  A791  Main River Valley    1.10   .75
1799  A791  Mecklenburg lake
            district             1.10   .75
1800  A791  Franconian Swit-
            zerland              1.00   .75
1801  A791  Upper Lusatia        1.00   .75
1802  A791  Sauerland            1.00   .75
1803  A791  Havel River, Ber-
            lin                  1.00   .75
1804  A791  Holstein Switzer-
            land                 1.00   .75
1805  A791  Saale                1.00   .75
1806  A791  Spreewald            1.00   .75
1807  A791  Eifel                1.00   .75
       Nos. 1793-1807 (15)      15.70 10.95

Issued: #1793-1795, 7/15/93; #1796-1799,
7/14/94; #1800-1803, 7/6/95; #1804-1807,
4/11/96.
See #1938, 1974-1976, 2072-2073.

Mathias Klotz (1653-1743), Violin
Maker — A792

**1993, Aug. 12   Litho.   Perf. 13x12½**
1808  A792  80pf multicolored          1.00   .45

Heinrich
George (1893-
1946),
Actor — A793

**1993, Aug. 12                  Perf. 14**
1809  A793  100pf multicolored         1.25   .50

Intl. Radio Exhibition, Berlin — A794

**1993, Aug. 12**
1810  A794  100pf multicolored         1.25   .50

Hans Leip
(1893-1983),
Poet and
Painter
A795

**1993, Sept. 16   Litho.   Perf. 13**
1811  A795  100pf red, black &
            blue                       1.50   .50

Birger Forell
(1893-1958),
Swedish
Priest — A796

**1993, Sept. 16                 Perf. 14**
1812  A796  100pf multicolored         1.50   .70

**Souvenir Sheet**

For the Children — A797

**1993, Sept. 16**
1813  A797  100pf multicolored         1.50  1.50

Peter I. Tchaikovsky (1840-93),
Composer — A798

**1993, Oct. 14**
1814  A798  80pf multicolored          1.25   .50

Max Reinhardt
(1873-1943),
Theatrical
Director — A799

**1993, Oct. 14**
1815 A799 100pf buff, black &
red                1.50   .50

St. Hedwig of
Silesia, 750th
Death
Anniv. — A800

**1993, Oct. 14**
1816 A800 100pf multicolored   1.50   .50
See Poland No. 3176.

Paracelsus (1493-
1541), Physician,
Teacher — A801

**Litho. & Engr.**
**1993, Nov. 10**          **Perf. 14**
1817 A801 100pf multicolored   1.50   .50

Claudio Monteverdi (1567-1643),
Composer — A802

**1993, Nov. 10   Litho.   Perf. 13x12½**
1818 A802 100pf multicolored   1.50   .50

Willy Brandt
(1913-92),
Statesman
A803

**1993, Nov. 10**          **Perf. 14**
1819 A803 100pf multicolored   1.75   .90

Staade,
1000th
Anniv.
A804

**Litho. & Engr.**
**1994, Jan. 13**          **Perf. 14**
1820 A804 80pf multicolored   1.00   .50

Intl. Year
of the
Family
A805

**1994, Jan. 13**          **Litho.**
1821 A805 100pf multicolored   1.25   .65

Heinrich Hertz (1857-94),
Physicist — A806

**1994, Jan. 13**      **Perf. 13x12½**
1822 A806 200pf multicolored   2.25  1.00

Frankfurt
Am Main,
1200th
Anniv.
A807

**1994, Feb. 10**
1823 A807 80pf multicolored   1.00   .50

Fulda,
1250th
Anniv.
A808

**1994, Mar. 10**          **Perf. 14**
1824 A808 80pf multicolored   1.00   .50

German Women's Associations,
German Women's Council,
Cent. — A809

**1994, Mar. 10**      **Perf. 13x12½**
1825 A809 100pf black, red &
yellow             1.25   .60

Fourth European Parliamentary
Elections — A810

**1994, Mar. 10**          **Perf. 14**
1826 A810 100pf multicolored   1.50   .65

Foreigners in Germany: Living
Together — A811

**1994, Mar. 10**
1827 A811 100pf multicolored   1.25   .65

Church of
Our Lady,
Munich,
500th
Anniv.
A812

**1994, Apr. 14   Litho.   Perf. 14**
1828 A812 100pf multicolored   1.50   .75

Europa
A813

Designs: 80pf, Ohm's Law, by Georg Simon
Ohm. 100pf, Quantum theory, by Max Planck.

**1994, May 5**           **Photo.**
1829 A813  80pf multicolored   *1.00*  *.45*
1830 A813 100pf multicolored   *1.00*  *.45*

Souvenir Sheet

Carl Hagenbeck (1844-1913), Circus
Director, Animal Trainer, and Berlin
Zoo, 150th Anniv. — A814

Designs: a, Hagenbeck, circus animals, zoo
entrance. b, Zoo entrance, animals.

**1994, May 5**           **Litho.**
1831 A814   Sheet of 2          3.25  4.00
   *a.*    100pf multicolored   1.00   .95
   *b.*    200pf multicolored   2.00  2.00

Hans Pfitzner
(1869-1949),
Composer,
Conductor — A815

**1994, May 5**
1832 A815 100pf multicolored   1.25   .60

Spandau
Fortress,
400th
Anniv.
A816

**1994, June 16   Litho.   Perf. 14**
1833 A816 80pf multicolored   1.00   .50

Herzogsagmuhle, Social Welfare
Organization, Cent. — A817

**1994, June 16**          **Perf. 13**
1834 A817 100pf blue, yel & blk  1.25   .60

Emperor Frederick
II (1194-1250)
A818

**1994, June 16**      **Perf. 13½x14**
1835 A818 400pf multicolored   4.25  3.25

Souvenir Sheet

Attempt to Assassinate Hitler, 50th
Anniv. — A819

**1994, July 20   Litho.   Perf. 14**
1836 A819 100pf multicolored   1.50  1.50

**Historic Sites Type of 1987**

No. 1838, Wernigerode Town Hall. No.
1839, Böttcherstrasse, Bremen. No. 1840,
Berus Monument, Überherrn. No. 1841,
Wilhelmshöhe Hillside Park, Kassel. No. 1842,
Kirchheim Castle. No. 1843, St. Reinoldi
Church, Dortmund. No. 1844, Goethe-Schiller
Monument, Weimar. No. 1845, Schwerin Castle, Wei-
mar. No. 1846, Bellevue Castle, Berlin. No.
1847, EXPO 2000, Hanover. No. 1848,
Regensburg Stone Bridge. No. 1849, Brühl's
Terrace, Dresden. No. 1850, St. Nikolai
Cathedral, Greifswald. No. 1851, Grimma
Town Hall. No. 1852, Wartburg Castle, Eisen-
ach. No. 1853, Town hall, Bremen. No. 1854,
Cologne Cathedral. No. 1855, Holsten Gate,
Lübeck. No. 1856, Heidelberg Castle. No.
1857, Town Hall, Suhl-Heinrichs. No. 1858,
Speyer Cathedral. No. 1859, St. Michael's
Church, Hamburg. No. 1860, Hildesheim Town
Hall.

| | | | Perf. 14 | |
|---|---|---|---|---|
| **1994-2001** | | **Typo.** | | |
| 1838 | A623 | 10pf multi | .45 | .20 |
| 1839 | A623 | 20pf dk bl & brn org | .35 | .35 |
| 1840 | A623 | 47pf green & gray | .55 | .45 |
| 1841 | A623 | 47pf dk grn & gray | .45 | .45 |
| 1842 | A623 | 50pf vio brn & beige | .75 | .50 |
| 1843 | A623 | 80pf dull grn & sepia | .75 | .60 |
| 1844 | A623 | 100pf blue & black | .80 | .75 |
| *a.* | | Booklet pane of 10 | 9.00 | 9.00 |
| | | Complete booklet, #1844a | 9.00 | 9.00 |
| 1845 | A623 | 100pf multi | 1.10 | 1.10 |
| 1846 | A623 | 110pf dark gray & buff | 1.00 | .35 |
| *a.* | | Booklet pane of 10 | 11.50 | 11.50 |
| | | Complete booklet, #1846a | 11.50 | |
| 1847 | A623 | 110pf org & bl | 1.10 | .50 |
| *a.* | | Booklet pane of 10 | 13.50 | 13.50 |
| | | Complete booklet, #1847a | 13.50 | |
| 1848 | A623 | 110pf multi | 1.10 | .75 |
| *a.* | | Booklet pane of 10 | 12.50 | 12.50 |
| | | Booklet, #1848a | 13.50 | |
| 1849 | A623 | 220pf grn & blk | 1.60 | .75 |
| 1850 | A623 | 220pf multi | 2.25 | 1.90 |
| 1851 | A623 | 300pf brn & ind | 2.25 | 2.00 |
| 1852 | A623 | 400pf vio brn & beige | 4.50 | 3.00 |
| 1853 | A623 | 440pf mul- ticolored | 4.25 | 3.25 |
| 1854 | A623 | 440pf blk & gray | 5.00 | 3.25 |
| 1855 | A623 | 510pf red brn & ind | 5.00 | 3.75 |
| 1856 | A623 | 510pf brn & bis brn | 5.50 | 4.25 |
| 1857 | A623 | 550pf mul- ticolored | 5.25 | 2.10 |
| 1858 | A623 | 640pf rose brn & gray bl | 6.75 | 2.25 |
| 1859 | A623 | 690pf blk & grn | 7.25 | 2.50 |
| 1860 | A623 | 720pf dk gray & lil | 7.50 | 5.50 |
| | *Nos. 1838-1860 (23)* | | 65.50 | 40.50 |

Issued: 550pf, 8/11/94; 640pf, 8/10/95;
690pf, 6/13/96; 47pf, 7/17/97; #1846, #1849,
#1853, 8/14/97; #1844, #1855, 8/28/97;
#1847, 9/10/98; 10pf, #1848, 300pf, 9/28/00;
#1845, 1/11/01. #1841, 80pf, 4/5/01. 720pf,
7/2/01. #1850, #1854, 8/9/01. 50pf, #1852,
9/5/01. 20pf, #1856, 11/8/01.

Johann Gottfried Herder (1744-1803), Theologian A820

**1994, Aug. 11** **Photo.** *Perf. 14*
1862 A820 80pf multicolored 1.00 .50

Paintings Type of 1993

Designs: 100pf, Maika, by Christian Schad. 200pf, Landscape, by Erich Heckel. 300pf, Couple Lying on Grass, by Gabriele Munter.

**1994, Aug. 11** **Litho.** *Perf. 14*
1863 A779 100pf multicolored 1.00 .60
1864 A779 200pf multicolored 2.00 1.50
1865 A779 300pf multicolored 3.00 2.40
 Nos. 1863-1865 (3) 6.00 4.50

Ethnological Museum, Leipzig, 125th Anniv. — A821

**1994, Sept. 8** **Litho.** *Perf. 13x12½*
1866 A821 80pf multicolored 1.00 .50

Hermann von Helmholtz (1821-94), Scientist — A822

**Litho. & Engr.**
**1994, Sept. 8** *Perf. 13½x14*
1867 A822 100pf multicolored 1.40 .50

Willi Richter (1894-1972), Politician, Labor Leader — A823

**1994, Sept. 8** **Litho.**
1868 A823 100pf multicolored 1.25 .50

Souvenir Sheet

For the Children — A824

**1994, Sept. 8** *Perf. 14*
1869 A824 100pf multicolored 1.50 1.50

Hans Sachs (1494-1576), Singer & Poet — A825

**1994, Oct. 13** **Engr.** *Perf. 13½x14*
1870 A825 100pf olive & maroon 1.25 .60

St. Wolfgang (924-94), Bishop of Regensburg A826

**1994, Oct. 13** **Litho.** *Perf. 14*
1871 A826 100pf multicolored 1.25 .60

Mail Delivery, Spreewald Region, c. 1900 — A827

**1994, Oct. 13**
1872 A827 100pf multicolored 1.25 .60

Stamp Day.

Quedlinburg, 1000th Anniv. — A828

**Litho. & Engr.**
**1994, Nov. 9** *Perf. 14*
1873 A828 80pf multicolored 1.00 .50

Opening of the Berlin Wall, 5th Anniv. A829

**1994, Nov. 9** **Litho.** *Perf. 13x12½*
1874 A829 100pf black, org & yel 1.25 .60

Natl. Assoc. for Preservation of German Graves Abroad, 75th Anniv. — A830

**1994, Nov. 9** *Perf. 14*
1875 A830 100pf black & red 1.25 .60

Theodore Fontane (1819-98), Poet — A831

**1994, Nov. 9** *Perf. 13½x14*
1876 A831 100pf multicolored 1.25 .60

Baron Friedrich von Steuben (1730-94) A832

**1994, Nov. 9** *Perf. 14*
1877 A832 100pf multicolored 1.25 .60

Paintings Type of 1992

Designs: 100pf, The Water Tower in Bremen, by Franz Radziwill. 200pf, Still Life

with a Cat, by Georg Schrimpf. 300pf, An Estate in Dangast, by Karl Schmidt-Rottluff.

**1995, Jan. 12** **Litho.** *Perf. 14*
1878 A753 100pf multicolored 1.00 .50
1879 A753 200pf multicolored 2.00 1.50
1880 A753 300pf multicolored 3.00 2.25
 Nos. 1878-1880 (3) 6.00 4.25

Province of Gera, 1000th Anniv. — A833

**1995, Jan. 12** *Perf. 13½x13*
1881 A833 80pf multicolored .90 .50

Diet of Worms, 500th Anniv. A834

**1995, Jan. 12** *Perf. 13x12½*
1882 A834 100pf multicolored 1.00 .60

Frederick William of Brandenburg, the Great Elector (1620-88) A835

**1995, Feb. 9** **Litho.** *Perf. 14*
1883 A835 300pf multicolored 3.25 2.10

Conf. of General Convention on Climate, Berlin — A836

**1995, Mar. 9** **Litho.** *Perf. 14*
1884 A836 100pf multicolored 1.00 .60

W.K. Roentgen (1845-1923) — A837

**1995, Mar. 9**
1885 A837 100pf multicolored 1.00 .60

Carolo-Wilhelmina Technical University, Braunschweig, 250th Anniv. — A838

**1995, Mar. 9**
1886 A838 100pf multicolored 1.00 .60

Former State of Mecklenburg, 1000th Anniv. — A839

**1995, Mar. 9**
1887 A839 100pf multicolored 1.00 .60

City of Regensburg, 750th Anniv. — A840

**1995, Apr. 6** **Litho.** *Perf. 14*
1888 A840 80pf multicolored .90 .50

Freedom of Expression A841

**1995, Apr. 6** **Photo.**
1889 A841 100pf multicolored 1.00 .60

Dietrich Bonhoeffer (1906-45), Protestant Theologian — A842

**1995, Apr. 6**
1890 A842 100pf multicolored 1.00 .60

Johann Conrad Schlaun (1695-1773), Architect A843

**1995, Apr. 6** **Litho.** *Perf. 13*
1891 A843 200pf multicolored 2.00 1.60

Vincent Conferences in Germany, 150th Anniv. — A844

**1995, May 5** **Litho.** *Perf. 14*
1892 A844 100pf multicolored 1.00 .65

Schiller Society, Cent. — A845

**1995, May 5** **Photo.**
1893 A845 100pf multicolored 1.00 .60

End of World War II, 50th Anniv. — A846

Designs: No. 1894, End of the war. 200pf, Moving towards United Europe.
 No. 1896, Liberation of concentration camps. No. 1897: a, Destruction of buildings. b, Refugees.

GERMANY

135

**1995, May 5**    **Litho.**    *Perf. 14*
**1894** A846 100pf red & black    *1.00*   .55
**1895** A846 200pf bl, gray, yel &
    blk      *2.00* 1.00

**Souvenir Sheets**
**1896** A846 100pf multicolored   1.10 *1.50*
**1897**    Sheet of 2     2.25 *2.50*
  *a.-b.*   A846 100pf any single   1.10 1.10

Europa (#1894-1895).

Kiel Canal, Cent. — A847

**1995, June 8**    **Litho.**    *Perf. 14*
**1898** A847 80pf multicolored    .90 .50

UN, 50th Anniv. — A848

**1995, June 8**
**1899** A848 100pf gold, lil & gray   1.00 .60

Radio, Cent. A849

**1995, June 8**
**1900** A849 100pf Marconi, wireless apparatus   1.25 .80

See Ireland Nos. 973-974, Italy 2038-2039, San Marino Nos. 1336-1337, Vatican City Nos. 978-979.

Carl Orff (1895-1982), Composer — A850

**1995, July 6**    **Litho.**    *Perf. 13x13½*
**1901** A850 100pf multicolored   1.00 .60

Henry the Lion, Duke of Bavaria (1129-95) A851

**1995, July 6**       *Perf. 14*
**1902** A851 400pf multicolored   3.75 3.00

Kaiser Wilhelm Memorial Church, Berlin, Cent. — A852

**1995, Aug. 10**    **Photo.**    *Perf. 14*
**1903** A852 100pf multicolored   1.00 .60

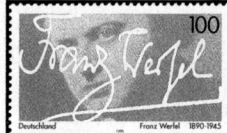

Franz Werfel (1890-1945), Author — A853

**1995, Aug. 10**       **Litho.**
**1904** A853 100pf multicolored   1.00 .60

Franz Josef Strauss (1915-88), Politician A854

**1995, Sept. 6**   **Photo.**   *Perf. 14x13½*
**1905** A854 100pf multicolored   1.10 .75

**Souvenir Sheet**

German Film, Cent. — A855

Illustration reduced.

**1995, Sept. 6**       *Perf. 14*
**1906** A855   Sheet of 3    4.00 *4.75*
  *a.*   80pf Metropolis    .75 .75
  *b.*   100pf Little Superman   .90 .90
  *c.*   200pf The Sky Over Berlin   2.10 2.10

Kurt Schumacher (1895-1952), Politician A856

**1995, Oct. 12**    **Litho.**    *Perf. 13*
**1907** A856 100pf multicolored   1.00 .60

**Souvenir Sheet**

For the Children — A857

Illustration reduced.

**1995, Oct. 12**       *Perf. 14*
**1908** A857 100pf multicolored   1.25 *1.50*

Leopold von Ranke (1795-1886), Historian A858

**1995, Nov. 9**    **Litho.**    *Perf. 14*
**1909** A858 80pf multicolored   .85 .50

Paul Hindemith (1895-1963), Composer A859

**1995, Nov. 9**
**1910** A859 100pf multicolored   1.00 .60

Nobel Prize Fund Established, Cent. — A860

**1995, Nov. 9**    **Litho. & Engr.**
**1911** A860 100pf Nobel, last will   1.25 .90

See Sweden Nos. 2155-2158.

CARE, 50th Anniv. A861

**1995, Nov. 9**   **Litho.**   *Perf. 13x12½*
**1912** A861 100pf multicolored   1.00 .60

Victims of a Divided Germany, 1945-89 A862

**1995, Nov. 9**       *Perf. 14*
**1913** A862 100pf Berlin Wall   1.00 .60

Borussia Dortmund, Soccer Champions — A863

**1995, Dec. 6**    **Photo.**    *Perf. 14*
**1914** A863 100pf multicolored   1.25 .75

Children's Missionary Work in Germany, Cent. — A864

**1996, Jan. 11**    **Litho.**    *Perf. 14*
**1915** A864 100pf multicolored   .95 .65

Friedrich von Bodelschwingh (1877-1946), Protestant Theologian A865

**1996, Jan. 11**       *Perf. 13½*
**1916** A865 100pf black & red   .95 .65

Martin Luther (1483-1546), Theologian A866

**1996, Feb. 8**    **Litho.**    *Perf. 14*
**1917** A866 100pf multicolored   1.00 .80

Philipp Franz von Siebold (1796-1866), Physician and Diplomat — A867

**1996, Feb. 17**       *Perf. 13x12½*
**1918** A867 100pf multicolored   1.00 .80

Cathedral Square, Halberstadt, 1000th Anniv. — A868

**1996, Mar. 7**    **Litho.**    *Perf. 13*
**1919** A868 80pf multicolored   .80 .45

August Cardinal Graf von Galen (1878-1946) A869

**1996, Mar. 7**       *Perf. 13½*
**1920** A869 100pf bl, gray & bis   .95 .60

Giovanni Battista Tiepolo (1696-1770), Painter — A870

**1996, Mar. 7**       *Perf. 13*
**1921** A870 200pf multicolored   2.00 1.40

**20th Century German Paintings Type of 1993**

Designs: 100pf, Sitting Female Nude, by Max Pechstein (1881-1955). 200pf, Abstract For Wilhelm Runge, by Georg Muche (1895-1987). 300pf, Still Life with Guitar, Book and Vase, by Helmut Kolle (1899-1931).

**1996, Mar. 7**       *Perf. 14*
**1922** A779 100pf multicolored   1.10 .90
**1923** A779 200pf multicolored   2.40 1.75
**1924** A779 300pf multicolored   2.50 2.50
  *Nos. 1922-1924 (3)*    6.00 5.15

## Souvenir Sheet

### For the Children — A871

Illustration reduced.

**1996, Apr. 11     Litho.     *Perf. 14***
1925 A871 100pf Racing mes-
senger                         1.10  1.40

### Famous Women — A872

Europa: 80pf, Self-portrait, by Paula Modersohn-Becker (1876-1907). 100pf, Self-portrait,
by Käthe Kollwitz (1867-1945).

**1996, May 3**
1926 A872  80pf multicolored     *1.00  .35*
1927 A872 100pf red & black      *1.00  .75*

Freising's
Right to
Hold
Markets,
1000th
Anniv.
A873

**1996, May 3**
1928 A873 100pf multicolored     1.00  .65

Wolfgang Borchert (1921-47),
Writer — A874

**1996, May 3     *Perf. 13***
1929 A874 100pf multicolored     1.00  .65

Ruhr Festival, Recklinghausen, 50th
Anniv. — A875

**1996, May 3**
1930 A875 100pf multicolored     1.00  .65

German
Theater
Assoc., 150th
Anniv. — A876

**1996, May 3     Photo.     *Perf. 14***
1931 A876 200pf multicolored     2.00 1.10

---

Academy of
Arts in Berlin,
300th Anniv.
A877

**1996, June 13     Litho.     *Perf. 13***
1932 A877 100pf multicolored     1.00  .65

Gottfried Wilhelm Leibniz (1646-1716),
Mathematician, Philosopher — A878

**1996, June 13     *Perf. 14***
1933 A878 100pf multicolored     1.00  .65

City of
Heidelberg,
800th
Anniv. — A879

**1996, July 18     Litho.     *Perf. 14***
1934 A879 100pf multicolored     1.00  .65
   Complete booklet, 10 #1934   10.00

UNICEF,
50th
Anniv.
A880

**1996, July 18**
1935 A880 100pf multicolored     1.00  .65

Ludwig Thoma
(1867-1921),
Satirist
A881

**1996, July 18     *Perf. 13x13½***
1936 A881 100pf multicolored     1.00  .65

### Souvenir Sheet

German
Natl.
Parks
A882

**1996, July 18     *Perf. 14***
1937    Sheet of 3              6.50  6.50
   **a.** A882 100pf Coastal     1.00  1.00
   **b.** A882 200pf Mudflat     1.75  1.75
   **c.** A882 300pf Sea-inlet   2.75  2.75

Scenic Regions Type of 1993

"Gendarmenmarkt," central district of Berlin.

**1996, Aug. 14     Litho.     *Perf. 14***
1938 A791 100pf multicolored     1.00  .65

---

Assoc. of German Philatelists, 50th
Anniv. — A883

**1996, Aug. 14     Photo.     *Perf. 14***
1939 A883 100pf multicolored     1.00  .65

Paul Lincke
(1866-1946),
Musician,
Composer
A884

**1996, Aug. 14     Litho.     *Perf. 13***
1940 A884 100pf multicolored     1.00  .65

UNESCO
World Cultural
Heritage
A885

Design: Closed blast furnace, Völklingen.

**1996, Aug. 14     *Perf. 13½***
1941 A885 100pf multicolored     1.00  .65

German Civil
Code,
Cent. — A886

**1996, Aug. 14**
1942 A886 300pf multicolored     3.00 2.25

Borussia
Dortmund,
Champion
Soccer
Club — A887

**1996, Aug. 27**
1943 A887 100pf multicolored     1.00  .65

Life
Without
Drugs
A888

**1996, Sept. 12     Photo.     *Perf. 14***
1944 A888 100pf multicolored     1.00  .65

UNESCO
World
Cultural
Heritage
A889

Design: Old Town, Bamberg

**1996, Sept. 12     Litho.     *Perf. 14***
1945 A889 100pf multicolored     1.00  .65

---

Homeopathic
Medicine,
Bicent. — A890

Samuel    Hahnemann    (1755-1843),
physician.

**1996, Sept. 12     Litho.     *Perf. 14***
1946 A890 400pf multicolored     4.00 3.00

Anton
Bruckner
(1824-96),
Composer
A891

**1996, Oct. 9     Litho.     *Perf. 13***
1947 A891 100pf multicolored     1.00  .65

Donaueschingen Music Festival, 75th
Anniv. — A892

**1996, Oct. 18     Litho.     *Perf. 13½***
1948 A892 100pf multicolored     1.00  .65

Baron Ferdinand von Mueller (1825-
96), Botanist — A893

**Litho. & Engr.**
**1996, Oct. 18     *Perf. 14***
1949 A893 100pf multicolored     1.00  .65
   See Australia No. 1566.

Carl
Zuckmayer
(1896-1977),
Playwright
A894

**1996, Nov. 14     Litho.     *Perf. 13***
1950 A894 100pf red, gray & blue 1.00  .65

Carlo Schmid (1896-1979), Politician,
Scholar & Writer — A895

**1996, Dec. 3     Photo.     *Perf. 14***
1951 A895 100pf multicolored     1.00  .65

Franz Schubert (1797-1828), Composer A896

**1997, Jan. 16    Litho.    Perf. 14**
1952 A896 100pf multicolored    1.00    .65

Sepp Herberger (1897-1977), Soccer Coach — A897

**1997, Jan. 16**
1953 A897 100pf multicolored    1.00    .65

Traffic Safety for Children A898

**1997, Jan. 16**
1954 A898 100pf multicolored    1.00    .65
See No. 1979.

Philipp Melanchthon (1497-1560), Protestant Reformer A899

**1997, Feb. 4    Litho.    Perf. 14**
1955 A899 100pf multicolored    1.00    .65

Cologne Carnival, 175th Anniv. — A900

**1997, Feb. 4**
1956 A900 100pf multicolored    1.00    .65

Chancellor Ludwig Erhard (1897-1977) A901

**1997, Feb. 4    Photo.**
1957 A901 100pf multicolored    1.00    .65

Leipzig Fair, 500th Anniv. A902

**1997, Mar. 6    Perf. 13x12½**
1958 A902 100pf red, sil & blue    1.00    .65

German Architecture after 1945 — A903

Building, architect: a, Berlin Philharmonic, by Hans Scharoun. b, New National Gallery, Berlin, by Ludwig Mies van der Rohe. c, St. Mary, Queen of Peace Church, Neviges, by Gottfried Böhm. d, German Pavilion, 1967 World's Fair, Montreal, by Frei Otto.

**1997, Mar. 6    Litho.    Perf. 14**
1959    A903    Sheet of 4    4.50    4.50
a.-d.    100pf any single    1.00    1.00

City of Straubing, 1100th Anniv. — A904

**1997, Mar. 10    Perf. 13x12½**
1960 A904 100pf multicolored    1.00    .65

Heinrich von Stephan (1831-97) — A905

**1997, Apr. 8    Litho.    Perf. 14**
1961 A905 100pf multicolored    1.00    .65

Augustusburg and Falkenlust Castles, UNESCO World Heritage Sites — A906

**1997, Apr. 8**
1962 A906 100pf multicolored    1.00    .65

Idar-Oberstein Gem & Jewelry Industry, 500th Anniv. — A907

**1997, Apr. 8    Perf. 13½**
1963 A907 300pf multicolored    3.25    2.25

St. Adalbert (956-997) — A908

**1997, Apr. 23    Engr.    Perf. 14**
1964 A908 100pf deep violet    1.00    .65
See Poland #3337, Czech Republic #3012, Hungary #3569, Vatican City #1040.

Stories and Legends A909

Europa: 80pf, Fisherman and his Wife. 100pf, Rübezahl of Riesengebirge (Giant Mountains).

**1997, May 5    Litho.    Perf. 14**
1965 A909 80pf multicolored    1.00    .60
1966 A909 100pf multicolored    1.00    .75

Sister Cities Movement, 50th Anniv. — A910

**1997, May 5**
1967 A910 100pf multicolored    1.10    .65

Souvenir Sheet

Society for Protection of German Forests, 50th Anniv. — A911

**1997, May 5**
1968 A911    Sheet of 2    3.25    3.25
a.    100pf multicolored    1.10    1.10
b.    200pf multicolored    2.00    2.00

Fr. Sebastian Kneipp (1821-97), Hydrotherapist A912

**1997, June 9    Perf. 13**
1969 A912 100pf multicolored    1.00    .65

Marshall Plan, 50th Anniv. A913

**1997, June 9    Perf. 13**
1970 A913 100pf multicolored    1.10    .65

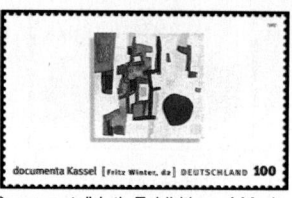

"Documenta" Intl. Exhibition of Modern Art, Kassel — A914

Designs: a, Composition, by Fritz Winter, 1956. b, Mouth No. 15, by Tom Wesselmann, 1968. c, Quathlamba, by Frank Stella, 1964. d, Video sculpture, Beuys/Bois, by Nam June Paik.

**1997, June 20    Litho.    Perf. 14**
1971 A914 100pf Sheet of 4, #a.-d.    4.25    4.25

Müngsten Bridge, Cent. — A915

**1997, June 20    Litho.    Perf. 13½**
1972 A915 100pf multicolored    1.00    .65

Souvenir Sheet

For the Children — A916

Illustration reduced.

**1997, July 17    Photo.    Perf. 13½**
1973 A916 100pf multicolored    1.10    1.40

Scenic Regions Type of 1993

#1974, Bavarian Forest. #1975, Lüneburg Heath. #1976, North German Moorland.

**1997, Aug. 28    Litho.    Perf. 14**
1974 A791 110pf multicolored    1.10    .90
1975 A791 110pf multicolored    1.10    .90
1976 A791 110pf multicolored    1.10    .90
Nos. 1974-1976 (3)    3.30    2.70

Centenary of Rudolf Diesel's Engine A917

**1997, Aug. 28    Perf. 13**
1977 A917 300pf blue & gray    3.00    2.25

Cultivation of Potatoes in Germany,
350th Anniv. — A918

**1997, Sept. 17**   **Litho.**   *Perf. 13*
1978 A918 300pf multicolored          3.00 2.25

Traffic Safety for Children Type

**1997, Oct. 9**   **Litho.**   *Perf. 14*
1979 A898 10pf like #1954             .20 .20

Felix Mendelssohn-Bartholdy (1809-
47), Composer — A919

**1997, Oct. 9**                *Perf. 13x13½*
1980 A919 110pf multicolored          1.10 .75

FC Bayern Munchen, 1997 German
Soccer Champions — A920

**1997, Oct. 16**   **Photo.**   *Perf. 14*
1981 A920 110pf multicolored          1.10 .75

Third Saar-Lorraine-Luxembourg
Summit — A921

**1997, Oct. 16**                      **Litho.**
1982 A921 110pf multicolored          1.10 .75
See Luxembourg #972, France #2613.

Charitable Assoc. of the German
Catholic Church, Cent. — A922

**1997, Nov. 6**   **Photo.**   *Perf. 14*
1983 A922 110pf multicolored          1.10 .75

Heinrich Heine
(1797-1856),
Poet — A923

**1997, Nov. 6**   **Litho.**   *Perf. 13*
1984 A923 110pf multicolored          *1.25  .75*
   No. 1984 was sold in sheets of 10. It was
withdrawn from sale 11/18/97, because runes
associated with Nazi Germany were printed
on the decorative selvage of the sheet. Value
of withdrawn sheet of 10, $35. It was again
placed on sale in sheets with runes removed.

Gerhard
Tersteegen
(1697-1769),
Author of
Religious
Hymns,
Booklets
A924

**1997, Nov. 6**                      *Perf. 14*
1985 A924 110pf multicolored          1.10 .75

Thomas Dehler (1897-1967),
Politician — A925

**1997, Nov. 6**
1986 A925 110pf multicolored          1.10 .75

Cistercian
Monastery
Maulbronn,
UNESCO
World
Heritage
Site — A926

**1998, Jan. 22**   **Litho.**   *Perf. 14*
1987 A926 100pf multicolored          1.10 .75

Glienicke
Bridge,
Berlin — A927

**1998, Jan. 22**
1988 A927 110pf multicolored          1.10 .75

City of
Nördlingen,
1100th
Anniv. — A928

**1998, Jan. 22**
1989 A928 110pf multicolored          1.10 .75
   a.    Booklet pane of 10          11.50
         Complete booklet, #1989a +
         20 self-adhesive labels      12.00

Bertolt Brecht
(1898-1956),
Playwright
A929

**1998, Feb. 5**
1990 A929 110pf multicolored          1.10 .75

Max Planck Society for Advancement
of Science, 50th Anniv. — A930

**1998, Feb. 5**
1991 A930 110pf multicolored          1.10 .75

Town of Bad Frankenhausen, 1000th
Anniv. — A931

**1998, Mar. 12**   **Litho.**   *Perf. 13*
1992 A931 110pf multicolored          1.10 .75

Peace of Westphalia, End of Thirty
Years' War, 350th Anniv. — A932

**1998, Mar. 12**                      *Perf. 14*
1993 A932 110pf black & red           1.10 .75

German State Parliament
Buildings — A933

   Designs: No. 1994, Baden-Württemberg.
No. 1995, Bavaria. No. 1996, Chamber of
Deputies, Berlin. No. 1997, Brandenburg.

**1998, Mar. 12**
1994 A933 110pf multicolored          1.25 .75
1995 A933 110pf multicolored          1.25 .75
1996 A933 110pf multicolored          1.25 .75
1997 A933 110pf multicolored          1.25 .75
   *Nos. 1994-1997 (4)*              5.00 3.00
See Nos 2027, 2029-2031, 2074-2076.

Hildegard von
Bingen (1098-
1179),
Christian
Mystic — A934

**1998, Apr. 16**
1998 A934 100pf multicolored          1.00 .75

Cistercian Abbey of St. Marienstern,
Panschwitz-Kuckau, 750th
Anniv. — A935

**1998, Apr. 16**                *Perf. 13x12½*
1999 A935 110pf multicolored          1.10 .75

Souvenir Sheet

For the Children — A936

Illustration reduced.

**1998, Apr. 16**                      *Perf. 14*
2000 A936 110pf multicolored          1.25 1.25

Bayreuth Opera, 250th Anniv. — A937

Illustration reduced.

**1998, Apr. 16**                      *Perf. 13½*
2001 A937 300pf multicolored          3.25 2.40

Ernst Jünger
(1895-1998),
Writer — A938

**1998, Apr. 22**                      *Perf. 14*
2002 A938 110pf multicolored          1.10 .75

German Rural
Women's
Assoc.
A939

**1998, May 7**   **Litho.**   *Perf. 13*
2003 A939 110pf multicolored          1.10 .75

Europa and German
Reunification
Day — A940

**1998, May 7**                *Perf. 14½x14*
2004 A940 110pf multicolored          1.10 .75

## Souvenir Sheet

German Constitution — A941

Designs: a, Parliamentary Council, Bonn, 1948, convening to draw up constitution. b, Natl. Assembly, St. Paul's Church, Frankfurt, 1848, electing pan-German constitutional Parliament.

**1998, May 7**          *Perf. 14*
**2005** A941   Sheet of 2          3.50 3.50
  *a.*   110pf multicolored          1.00 1.00
  *b.*   220pf multicolored          2.00 2.00

Congress of German Catholics, 150th Anniv. — A942

**1998, June 10  Litho.   *Perf. 13x13½***
**2006** A942 110pf multicolored     1.25  .70

Deutsche Mark, 50th Anniv. — A943

**1998, June 19**          *Perf. 13*
**2007** A943 110pf multicolored     1.25  .90

German Cultivation of Hops — A944

**1998, July 16  Litho.   *Perf. 13***
**2008** A944 110pf multicolored     1.10  .75

Founding of the European Central Bank, Frankfurt am Main — A945

**1998, July 16  Photo.   *Perf. 14***
**2009** A945 110pf multicolored     1.10  .70

## Souvenir Sheet

Saxon Switzerland Natl. Park — A945a

Illustration reduced.

**1998, July 16     Litho.     *Perf. 14***
**2009A** A945a   Sheet of 2          3.50 3.50
  *b.*   110pf multicolored          1.00 1.00
  *c.*   220pf multicolored          2.00 2.00

1998 Intl. Congress of Mathematicians, Berlin — A946

**1998, Aug. 20  Photo.   *Perf. 14x13½***
**2010** A946 110pf multicolored     1.10  .75

Grube Messel Fossil Beds A947

Würzburg Palace, Germany — A948

UNESCO World Heritage Sites: No. 2013, Puning Temple, Chengde, People's Republic of China.

**1998, Aug. 20  Litho.   *Perf. 13x12½***
**2011** A947 100pf multicolored     1.00  .65
          *Perf. 13½x14*
**2012** A948 110pf multicolored     1.10  .70
**2013** A948 110pf multicolored     1.10  .70
See China People's Republic #2887-2888.

## Souvenir Sheet

20th Cent. German Design — A949

Designs: a, Glassware, by Peter Behrens, 1910. b, Teapot, by Marianne Brandt, 1924. c, Desk lamp, by Wilhelm Wagenfeld, 1924. d, "Wassily" chair, by Marcel Breuer, 1926.

**1998, Aug. 20**          *Perf. 14*
**2014**   Sheet of 4          4.75 4.75
  *a.-d.* A949 110pf any single     1.10 1.10
See No. 2051.

Manfred Hausmann (1898-1986), Author — A950

**1998, Sept. 10  Litho.   *Perf. 14***
**2015** A950 110pf multicolored     1.10  .75

A951

**1998, Sept. 10**
**2016** A951 110pf multicolored     1.10  .75
Team 1 FC Kaiserslautern, 1998 German soccer champions.

Prevent Child Abuse — A952

**1998, Sept. 10**
**2017** A952 110pf black & red     1.10  .75

Francke Charitable Institutions, Halle, 300th Anniv. — A953

**1998, Sept. 10**          *Perf. 13*
**2018** A953 110pf Building     1.10  .75

Mail Boat, "Hiorten" A954

**1998, Oct. 8   Litho.   *Perf. 14***
**2019** A954 110pf multicolored     1.10  .75
Stamp Day.

Telephone Help Lines for People in Distress — A955

**1998, Oct. 8**          *Perf. 13x12½*
**2020** A955 110pf multicolored     1.10  .75

Günther Ramin (1898-1956), Organist, Choir Leader — A956

**1998, Oct. 8   Photo.   *Perf. 14x14½***
**2021** A956 300pf multicolored     3.00 2.25

Saxony State Orchestra, Dresden, 450th Anniv. — A957

**1998, Nov. 12  Litho.   *Perf. 14***
**2022** A957 300pf multicolored     3.00 2.25

Universal Delcaration of Human Rights, 50th Anniv. — A958

**1998, Nov. 12**          *Perf. 13x12½*
**2023** A958 110pf multicolored     1.10  .75
See No. B848.

Weimar, 1999 European City of Culture, 1100th Anniv. — A959

**1999, Jan. 14  Litho.   *Perf. 14***
**2024** A959 100pf multicolored     1.10  .80
  *a.*   Booklet pane of 10    12.50 12.50
        Complete booklet, #2024a +
        20 labels                  12.50
The self-adhesive labels are part of the booklet cover.

International Year of the Elderly A960

**1999, Jan. 14**          *Perf. 13*
**2025** A960 110pf multicolored     1.10  .80

Katharina von Bora (1499-1552), Wife of Martin Luther, from Painting by Lucas Cranach A961

**1999, Jan. 14**          *Perf. 14*
**2026** A961 110pf multicolored     1.10  .80

**State Parliaments Type of 1998**
The Hessian Parliament.

**1999, Jan. 14**
**2027** A933 110pf multicolored     1.10  .80

Erich Kästner (1899-1974), Writer — A963

**1999, Feb. 18  Litho.   *Perf. 13***
**2028** A963 300pf multicolored     3.00 2.40

## State Parliaments Type of 1998

Buildings: No. 2029, Hamburg. No. 2030, Mecklenburg-Western Pomerania. No. 2031, Bremen City Parliament.

| 1999 | Litho. | | Perf. 14 | |
|------|--------|---|----------|---|
| 2029 | A933 110pf multicolored | | 1.10 | .80 |
| 2030 | A933 110pf multicolored | | 1.10 | .80 |
| 2031 | A933 110pf multicolored | | 1.10 | .80 |
| | *Nos. 2029-2031 (3)* | | 3.30 | 2.40 |

Issued: #2029-2030, 3/11; #2031, 4/27.

NATO, 50th Anniv. A963a

**1999, Mar. 11**      **Photo.**
2032 A963a 110pf multicolored    1.10 .80

Fraunhofer Society, 50th Anniv. — A964

**1999, Mar. 11**     **Litho.**    *Perf. 13*
2033 A964 110pf multicolored    1.10 .80

Expo 2000, Hanover A965

**1999, Apr. 27**
2034 A965 110pf multicolored    1.10 .80
See No. 2083.

German Automobile Club, Cent. — A966

**1999, Apr. 27**      **Photo.**
2035 A966 110pf multicolored    1.10 .80

German Cancer Relief Organization, 25th Anniv. — A967

**1999, Apr. 27**     **Litho.**    *Perf. 13*
2036 A967 110pf multicolored    1.10 .80

Knights of St. John of Jerusalem and Knights of Malta, 900th Anniv. — A968

**1999, May 4**
2037 A968 110pf multicolored    1.10 .80

---

Berlin Airlift, 1948-49 A969

**1999, May 4**      **Photo.**    *Perf. 14*
2038 A969 110pf multicolored    1.10 .80

Council of Europe, 50th Anniv. — A970

**1999, May 4**     **Litho.**    *Perf. 13*
2039 A970 110pf multicolored    1.10 .80

**Souvenir Sheet**

Berchtesgaden Natl. Park — A971

**1999, May 4**      *Perf. 14*
2040 A971 110pf multicolored    *1.40 1.60*

Europa.

**Souvenir Sheet**

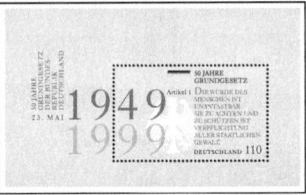

Basic Law, 50th Anniv. — A972

Illustration reduced.

**1999, May 21**     **Litho.**    *Perf. 14*
2041 A972 110pf multicolored    1.25 1.25

**Souvenir Sheet**

Federal Republic of Germany, 50th Anniv. — A973

Scenes from 1949, 1999: a, Leaders gathering, session of Parliament. b, Child carrying wood, child picking flower. c, Building "The Wall," people walking where "The Wall" has been removed. d, Soldiers, government assembly.

**1999, May 21**
2042    Sheet of 4      4.50 4.50
   *a.-d.* A973 110pf any single    1.10 1.10

---

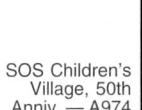

SOS Children's Village, 50th Anniv. — A974

**1999, June 10**   **Litho.**   *Perf. 13¾x14*
2043 A974 110pf multicolored    1.10 .75

Paderborn Bishopric, 1200th Anniv. — A975

**1999, June 10**      *Perf. 14*
2044 A975 110pf multicolored    1.10 .75

Johann Strauss, the Younger (1825-99) A976

**1999, June 10**   **Photo.**   *Perf. 13¾*
2045 A976 300pf multicolored    3.25 2.25

Dominikus-Ringeisen Institution, Ursberg, 115th Anniv. — A977

**1999, July 15**      **Litho.**
2046 A977 110pf multicolored    1.10 .75

Pres. Gustav Heinemann (1899-1976) A978

**1999, July 15**
2047 A978 110pf multicolored    1.10 .75

Cultural Foundation of the Federal States — A979

Sculpture: 110pf, Old Woman Smiling, by Ernst Barlach (1870-1938). 220pf, Bust of a Thinker, by Wilhelm Lehmbruck (1881-1919).

**1999, July 15**    **Photo.**    *Perf. 14*
2048 A979 110pf multicolored    1.25 .80
2049 A979 220pf multicolored    2.10 1.50

---

First Peace Conference in The Hague, Cent. — A980

**1999, July 15**   **Litho.**   *Perf. 13¼x13*
2050 A980 300pf multicolored    3.25 2.10

## 20th Cent. German Design Type of 1998
### Souvenir Sheet

Designs: a, HF1 Television set, by Herbert Hirche, 1958. b, Knife, fork, spoon and teaspoon, by Peter Raacke, 1959. c, Pearl bottle, by Günter Kupetz, 1969. d, "Transrapid," Maglev train, by Alexander Neumeister, 1982.

**1999, Aug. 12**    **Litho.**    *Perf. 14*
### Souvenir Sheet
2051    Sheet of 4      4.50 4.50
   *a.-d.* A949 110pf any single    1.10 1.10

Johann Wolfgang von Goethe (1749-1832), Poet — A981

**1999, Aug. 12**      *Perf. 13¾*
2052 A981 110pf multicolored    1.10 .80

**Souvenir Sheet**

For the Children — A982

Illustration reduced.

**1999, Aug. 12**      *Perf. 13¼*
2053 A982 110pf multicolored    1.10 1.10

Bayern München, 1999 German Soccer Champions — A983

**1999, Sept. 16**    **Litho.**    *Perf. 14*
2054 A983 110pf multicolored    1.10 .80

Federal Association of German Book Traders Peace Prize, 50th Anniv. — A984

**1999, Sept. 16**   **Photo.**   *Perf. 13¾*
2055 A984 110pf multicolored    1.10 .80

Richard Strauss (1864-1949), Composer A985

**1999, Sept. 16    Litho.    *Perf. 13¼***
2056  A985 300pf multicolored    3.25 2.40

Göltzsch Valley Bridge A986

**1999, Oct. 14    Litho.    *Perf. 14***
2057  A986 110pf multicolored    1.10  .80

German Federation of Trade Unions, 50th Anniv. — A987

**1999, Oct. 14**
2058  A987 110pf red & black    1.10  .80

Endangered Species A988

**1999, Nov. 4    Litho.    *Perf. 13¾***
2059  A988 100pf Large horse-shoe bat    1.00  .80

EXPO 2000, Hanover A989

**2000, Jan. 13    Litho.    *Perf. 14x14¼***
2060  A989 100pf multi    1.10  .80
See No. 2094.

Holy Year 2000 — A990

**2000, Jan. 13    *Perf. 13¾***
2061  A990 110pf multi    1.10  .80

Completion of Aachen Cathedral, 1200th Anniv. — A991

**2000, Jan. 13**
2062  A991 110pf Charlemagne    1.10  .80

German Soccer Assoc., Cent. — A992

**2000, Jan. 13    Photo.**
2063  A992 110pf multi    1.10  .80
Value is for stamp with surrounding selvage.

Herbert Wehner (1906-90), Politician A993

**2000, Jan. 13**
2064  A993 110pf multi    1.10  .80

Albert Schweitzer (1875-1965), Humanitarian A994

**2000, Jan. 13    Litho.    *Perf. 14x13¾***
2065  A994 110pf multi    1.10  .80

Prevention of Violence Against Women — A995

**2000, Jan. 13    *Perf. 14***
2066  A995 110pf multi    1.10  .80

Berlin Intl. Film Festival, 50th Anniv. A996

**2000, Feb. 17    Litho.    *Perf. 14***
2067  A996 100pf multi    1.00  .80

Johannes Gutenberg (c. 1400-1468) A997

**2000, Feb. 17    *Perf. 13¾***
2068  A997 110pf red & black    1.10  .80

Friedrich Ebert (1871-1925), President of German Reich — A998

**2000, Feb. 17    Photo.**
2069  A998 110pf multi    1.25  .80

Düsseldorf Carnival, 175th Anniv. — A999

**2000, Feb. 17    Litho.    *Perf. 13x13½***
2070  A999 110pf multi    1.10  .80

Kurt Weill (1900-50), Composer — A1000

**2000, Feb. 17    *Perf. 14***
2071  A1000 300pf multi    3.25 2.40

**Scenic Regions Type of 1993**
Design: #2072, Passau. #2073, Saar River bend, Mettlach.

**2000    Litho.    *Perf. 13¾x14***
2072  A791 110pf multi    1.25  .80
2073  A791 110pf multi    1.25  .80
Issued: No. 2072, 3/16.

**State Parliament Building Type**
#2074, Lower Saxony. #2075, North Rhine-Westphalia. #2076, Rhineland-Palatinate. #2077, Saarland.

**2000    Litho.    *Perf. 13¾x14***
2074  A933 110pf multi    1.10  .80
2075  A933 110pf multi    1.10  .80
2076  A933 110pf multi    1.10  .80
    ***Perf. 14***
2077  A933 110pf multi    1.10  .80
    Nos. 2074-2077 (4)    4.40 3.20
Issued: #2074, 3/16; #2075, 4/13; #2076, 8/14; #2077, 11/9.

Pinwheel A1001

**2000, Mar. 16    Litho.    *Perf. 13¾***
2078  A1001 110pf multi    1.25  .80

Souvenir Sheet

Hainich National Park — A1002

Illustration reduced.

**2000, Mar. 16    *Perf. 13¼***
2079  A1002 110pf multi    1.25 1.25

Blue Wonder Bridge, Dresden A1003

**2000, Apr. 13    Litho.    *Perf. 13¼***
2080  A1003 100pf multi    1.10  .75

**Cultural Foundation Type of 1999**
Designs: 110pf, The Expulsion from Paradise, sculpture by Leonhard Kern. 220pf, Silver table fountain, 1652-53, by Melchior Gelb.

**2000, Apr. 13    *Perf. 14x14¼***
2081  A979 110pf multi    1.25  .75
2082  A979 220pf multi    2.10 1.60

**Expo 2000 Type of 1999**
**2000, Apr. 13    *Die Cut Perf. 11***
**Booklet Stamp**
**Self-Adhesive**
2083  A965 110pf multi    4.00 3.75
a.    Booklet pane of 10    42.50
No. 2083a is a complete booklet.

Griefswald, 750th Anniv. — A1004

**Litho. & Engr.**
**2000, Apr. 13    *Perf. 14x14¼***
2084  A1004 110pf multi    1.10  .80

Nikolaus Ludwig von Zinzendorf (1700-60), Religious Leader A1005

**2000, May 12    Photo.    *Perf. 13¾***
2085  A1005 110pf multi    1.10  .75

**Europa, 2000**
Common Design Type
**2000, May 12    Litho.    *Perf. 13¾***
2086  CD17 110pf multi    1.40  .80
**Booklet Stamp**
**Self-Adhesive**
***Die Cut Perf. 10¾***
2087  CD17 110pf multi    1.50 1.25
a.    Complete booklet of 10    17.50

Einkommende Zeitungen, First Daily Newspaper, 350th Anniv. — A1006

**2000, June 8    Litho.    *Perf. 13¾x14***
2088  A1006 110pf multi    1.10  .80

Chambers of Handicrafts in Germany, Cent. — A1007

**2000, June 8    *Perf. 14***
2089  A1007 300pf gray & org    3.25 2.40

Zugspitze Weather Station,
Cent. — A1008

**2000, July 13   Litho.   *Perf. 13¾x14***
2090 A1008 100pf multi     1.10   .80

Federal Disaster Relief Organization,
50th Anniv. — A1009

**2000, July 13       *Perf. 14***
2091 A1009 110pf multi     1.25   .80

Johann
Sebastian
Bach (1685-
1750)
A1010

**2000, July 13       *Perf. 13¼***
2092 A1010 110pf multi     1.10   .80

First Zeppelin
Flight,
Cent. — A1011

**2000, July 13**
2093 A1011 110pf multi     1.25   .80

### Expo 2000 Type of 2000

110pf, Expo emblem, Earth, fingerprint.

**2000, Aug. 14   Litho.   *Perf. 14x14¼***
2094 A989 110pf multi     1.25   .80

Friedrich
Nietzsche
(1844-1900),
Philosopher
A1012

**2000, Aug. 14       *Perf. 13¼***
2095 A1012 110pf multi     1.25   .80

Ernst Wiechert
(1887-1950),
Writer
A1013

**2000, Aug. 14       *Perf. 13¾***
2096 A1013 110pf multi     1.25   .80

"For You" — A1014

**2000, Sept. 14   Litho.   *Perf. 13x13¼***
2097 A1014 100pf multi     1.00   .80

### Souvenir Sheet

For the Children — A1015

**2000, Sept. 14     *Perf. 13¾x14***
2098 A1015 110pf multi     1.25   1.25

Adolph
Kolping (1813-
65)
A1016

**2000, Sept. 14       *Perf. 13¼***
2099 A1016 110pf multi     1.25   .80

Kolping Society, 150th anniv.

Federal
Court of
Justice,
50th
Anniv.
A1017

### Litho. & Engr.
**2000, Sept. 14     *Perf. 14x14¼***
2100 A1017 110pf multi     1.25   .80

Bernhard Nocht Institute for Tropical
Medicine, Cent. — A1018

**2000, Sept. 14   Litho.   *Perf. 13¾x14***
2101 A1018 300pf multi     3.25   2.50

Reunification
of Germany,
10th Anniv.
A1019

**2000, Sept. 28       *Perf. 13¼***
2102 A1019 110pf multi     1.10   .80

Stamp
Day — A1020

**2000, Oct. 12   Litho.   *Perf. 13x13¼***
2103 A1020 110pf multi     1.10   .80

Rainer Maria Rilke
(1875-1926),
Poet — A1021

**2000, Nov. 9   Litho.   *Perf. 13¼x13½***
2104 A1021 110pf multi     1.10   .80

Arnold Bode
(1900-77),
Artist — A1022

**2000, Nov. 9       *Perf. 13¼***
2105 A1022 110pf red & black     1.10   .80

Leonhart
Fuchs (1501-
66), Botanist
A1023

**2001, Jan. 11   Litho.   *Perf. 13¾***
2106 A1023 100pf multi     1.25   .70

Kingdom
of
Prussia,
300th
Anniv.
A1024

**2001, Jan. 11       *Perf. 14***
2107 A1024 110pf multi     1.40   1.00

Association of Disabled War Veterans,
50th Anniv. — A1025

**2001, Jan. 11   Photo.   *Perf. 14***
2108 A1025 110pf multi     1.40   1.00

Youth Helpline Federation — A1026

**2001, Jan. 11   Litho.   *Perf. 13¾x14***
2109 A1026 110pf multi     1.40   1.00

Albert Lortzing
(1801-51),
Opera
Composer
A1027

**2001, Jan. 11       *Perf. 13¾***
2110 A1027 110pf multi     1.40   1.00

Martin Bucer
(1491-1551),
Theologian
A1028

**2001, Feb. 8   Litho.   *Perf. 13¾***
2111 A1028 110pf multi     1.40   1.00

Johann
Heinrich Voss
(1751-1826),
Translator of
Greek
Classics
A1029

**2001, Feb. 8       *Perf. 13¼***
2112 A1029 300pf multi     3.75   2.75

### State Parliament Type of 1998

Design: No. 2113, Saxony. No. 2114, Saxony-Anhalt. No. 2115, Schleswig-Holstein. No. 2116, Thuringia.

| | | | | |
|---|---|---|---|---|
| **2001** | | **Litho.** | ***Perf. 13¾x14*** | |
| 2113 | A933 | 110pf multi | 1.40 | 1.00 |
| 2114 | A933 | 110pf multi | 1.40 | 1.00 |
| 2115 | A933 | 110pf multi | 1.40 | 1.00 |
| 2116 | A933 | 110pf multi | 1.40 | 1.00 |
| | | *Nos. 2113-2116 (4)* | 5.60 | 4.00 |

Issued: No. 2113, 3/8/01. No. 2114, 5/10. No. 2115, 7/12. No. 2116, 9/5.

Erich Ollenhauer (1901-63),
Politician — A1030

**2001, Mar. 8   Litho.   *Perf. 14***
2117 A1030 110pf multi     1.40   1.00

Karl Arnold
(1901-58),
Politician
A1031

**2001, Mar. 8**     *Perf. 13¼*
2118 A1031 110pf multi    1.40 1.00

Federal
Border
Police, 50th
Anniv.
A1032

**2001, Mar. 8**   Litho.   *Perf. 13¾*
2119 A1032 110pf multi    1.40 1.00

Rendsburg Railway Bridge — A1033

**2001, Apr. 5**   Litho.   *Perf. 14*
2120 A1033 100pf multi    1.25 .95

Folk Music — A1034

**2001, Apr. 5**    *Perf. 13x13½*
2121 A1034 110pf multi    1.40 1.00

"Post!"
A1035

**2001, Apr. 5**   Photo.   *Perf. 14*
2122 A1035 110pf multi    1.40 1.00

Goethe Institute, 50th Anniv. — A1036

**2001, Apr. 5**    Litho.
2123 A1036 300pf multi    3.75 2.75

Endangered Species — A1037

Designs: No. 2124, Mountain gorilla. No. 2125, Indian rhinoceros.

**2001, May 10**   Litho.   *Perf. 14*
2124 A1037 110pf multi    1.40 1.00
2125 A1037 110pf multi    1.40 1.00
See Nos. 2132-2133.

Europa
A1038

**2001, May 10**    *Perf. 13¾*
2126 A1038 110pf multi    1.25 1.00

Werner Egk (1901-83),
Composer — A1039

**2001, May 10**    *Perf. 14*
2127 A1039 110pf multi    1.40 1.00

St. Catherine's Monastery, 750th
Anniv., Oceanographic Museum, 50th
Anniv. — A1040

**2001, June 13**   Litho.   *Perf. 13x13½*
2128 A1040 110pf multi    1.40 1.00

Catholic Court
Church,
Dresden,
250th Anniv.
A1041

**2001, June 13**    *Perf. 13¼*
2129 A1041 110pf multi    1.40 1.00

Canzow
Village
Church
A1042

**2001, July 12**   Photo.   *Perf. 14x14¼*
2130 A1042 110pf multi    1.40 1.00
Conservation of sacred monuments.

Souvenir Sheet

Health — A1043

No. 2131: a, Hand (circulatory diseases). b, Chest (cancer). c, Abdomen (infectious diseases). d, Head (depression).

**2001, July 12**   Litho.   *Perf. 13x13½*
2131 A1043 Sheet of 4    5.00 5.00
a.-d.   110pf Any single    1.25 1.25

**Endangered Species Type of 2001**
*Die Cut Perf. 11¼x11*
**2001, July 12**    Litho.
**Booklet Stamps**
**Self-Adhesive**
2132 A1037 110pf Like #2124   1.40 1.40
2133 A1037 110pf Like #2125   1.40 1.40
a.   Booklet, 5 each #2132-2133   20.00

Furth Dragon
Lancing
Festival
A1044

**2001, Aug. 9**   Litho.   *Perf. 13¼*
2134 A1044 100pf multi    1.25 .95

Himmelsberg Lime Tree Natural
Monument — A1045

**2001**    *Perf. 13¾x14*
2135 A1045 110pf multi    1.40 1.00
**Die Cut Perf. 9¾x10½**
2135A A1045 110pf multi    2.25 1.10
b.   Booklet of 20    47.50
Issued: No. 2135, 8/9; No. 2135A, 9/13.

Lifelong
Learning
A1046

**2001, Aug. 9**    *Perf. 14*
2136 A1046 110pf multi    1.40 1.00

Federal Constitutional Court, 50th
Anniv. — A1047

**2001, Sept. 5**
2137 A1047 110pf multi    1.40 1.00

First World Congress of Union
Network International — A1048

**2001, Sept. 5**    *Perf. 13x13½*
2138 A1048 110pf multi    1.40 1.00

Opening of
Jewish
Museum,
Berlin — A1049

**2001, Sept. 5**   Photo.   *Perf. 13¾*
2139 A1049 110pf multi    1.40 1.00

Souvenir Sheet

For Children — A1050

**2001, Sept. 5**   Litho.   *Perf. 13¾x14*
2140 A1050 110pf multi    1.40 1.00

"For You" — A1051

**2001, Oct. 11**    *Perf. 13x13¼*
2141 A1051 110pf multi    1.40 1.00

Werner
Heisenberg
(1901-76),
Physicist
A1052

**2001, Nov. 8**   Litho.   *Perf. 13¾*
2142 A1052 300pf multi    3.75 2.75

Souvenir Sheet

German Antarctic Expeditions,
Cent. — A1053

Expedition vessels: a, Gauss. b, Polarstern.

**2001, Nov. 8**    *Perf. 13¾x14*
2143 A1053 Sheet of 2, #a-b   3.75 3.75
a.   110pf multi    1.25 1.25
b.   220pf multi    2.50 2.50

Introduction of
the Euro, Jan.
1 — A1054

**2002, Jan. 10**   Litho.   *Perf. 13¾*
2144 A1054 56c multi    1.50 .50

### Coil Stamp
**Self-Adhesive**
2144A A1054 56c multi     3.25 2.40

Hans von Dohnanyi (1902-45), Documenter of Nazi Atrocities A1055

**2002, Jan. 10**    Photo.
2145 A1055 56c multi    1.75 1.40
2145A A1055 56c multi    *900.00* —
No. 2145A has "2002" in upper right corner and colored face and name. Approximately 320 small panes of 10 of No. 2145A were accidentally mixed in with approved stock of No. 2145 and sold over post office counters.

Bautzen, 1000th Anniv. A1056

**2002, Jan. 10**    Litho.
2146 A1056 56c multi    1.50 .80

***Die Cut Perf. 11***
**Litho.**
**Booklet Stamp**
**Self-Adhesive**
2146A A1056 56c multi    2.40 1.90
   b.   Booklet of 10    24.00

More Tolerance — A1057

**2002, Jan. 10**    *Perf. 13¾x14*
2147 A1057 56c multi    1.50 .80

Adolph Freiherr Knigge (1762-96), Writer — A1058

**2002, Feb. 7**    Litho.    *Perf. 13¾*
2148 A1058 56c multi    1.50 .80

Berlin Subway System, Cent. — A1059

**2002, Feb. 7**    *Perf. 13¼*
2149 A1059 56c multi    1.50 .80

Johann Christoph Schuster's Mechanical Calculator — A1060

**2002, Mar. 7**    Litho.    *Perf. 14*
2150 A1060 56c multi    1.50 .80
Cultural Foundation of the Federal States.

Deggendorf, 1000th Anniv. — A1061

**2002, Mar. 7**
2151 A1061 56c multi    1.50 .80

Ecksberg Foundation for the Mentally Handicapped, 150th Anniv. — A1062

**Litho. & Engr.**
**2002, Apr. 4**    *Perf. 14x13¾*
2152 A1062 56c multi    1.50 .80

Freemason's Museum, Cent. — A1063

**2002, Apr. 4**    Litho.    *Perf. 14*
2153 A1063 56c multi    1.50 .80

Baden-Württemberg, 50th Anniv. — A1064

**2002, Apr. 4**    *Perf. 13¼*
2154 A1064 56c multi    1.50 .80

"Post" — A1065

**2002, Apr. 4**    *Perf. 13x13½*
2155 A1065 56c multi    1.50 .80

Federal Employment Services, 50th Anniv. — A1066

**2002, Apr. 4**    *Perf. 14*
2156 A1066 153c black & red    4.25 2.40

### Voss Type of 2001
***Die Cut Perf. 10¼***
**2002, Apr. 4**    Litho.
### Coil Stamp
**Self-Adhesive**
2157 A1029 €1.53 multi    4.25 2.75
Dated 2001. No. 2157 was sold only for euro currency.

Europa A1067

**2002**    Litho.    *Perf. 13¼*
2158 A1067 56c multi    1.50 .80

**Self-Adhesive Coil Stamp**
***Die Cut Perf. 10¼***
2158A A1067 56c multi    2.40 2.00
Issued: No. 2158, 5/2; No. 2158A, 7/4.

Garden Kingdom of Dessau-Wörlitz, UNESCO World Heritage Site — A1068

**2002**    *Perf. 13¾x14*
2159 A1068 56c multi    1.50 .80

**Booklet Stamp**
**Self-Adhesive**
2159A A1068 56c multi    1.50 .80
   b.   Booklet of 20    30.00
Issued: No. 2159, 5/2; No. 2159A, 8/8.

Halle-Wittenberg University, 500th Anniv. — A1069

**2002, May 2**    *Perf. 14*
2160 A1069 56c multi    1.50 .80

Children's Church, 150th Anniv. A1070

**2002, May 2**    *Perf. 13¼*
2161 A1070 56c multi    1.50 .80

### Souvenir Sheet

Documenta 11 Art Exhibition — A1071

**2002, May 2**    *Perf. 13¾x14*
2162 A1071 56c multi    1.50 .80

2002 World Cup Soccer Championships, Japan and Korea — A1072

No. 2163: a, Flags, soccer ball and field (28mm diameter). b, Soccer players, years of German championships. Illustration reduced.

**2002, May 2**    *Perf. 13¾*
2163 A1072 Horiz. pair    3.00 2.25
   a.-b.   56c Any single    1.50 .95
See Argentina No. 2184, Brazil No. 2840, France No. 2891, Italy No. 2526 and Uruguay No. 1946.

Albrecht Daniel Thaer (1752-1828), Agronomist — A1073

**2002, May 2**    *Perf. 13x13½*
2164 A1073 225c multi    6.25 3.50

Yellow Feather in Red, by Ernst Wilhelm Nay (1902-68) — A1074

**2002, June 6**    Litho.    *Perf. 13¾x14*
2165 A1074 56c multi    1.50 .80

Endangered Species — A1075

Designs: 51c, Desmoulins whorl snail. 56c, Freshwater pearl mussel.

**2002, June 6**    *Perf. 14x14¼*
2166 A1075 51c multi    1.40 .80
2167 A1075 56c multi    1.50 .80
See Czech Republic No. 3173.

World Hunger Help — A1076

**2002, July 4**    Litho.    *Perf. 13¾x14*
2168 A1076 51c multi    1.40 .80

Natl. Germanic Museum, 150th
Anniv. — A1077

**2002, July 4**
2169 A1077 56c multi    1.50 .80

Hermann Hesse (1877-1962),
Writer — A1078

**2002, July 4**      *Perf. 14*
2170 A1078 56c multi    1.50 .80

**Souvenir Sheet**

Hochharz Natl. Park — A1079

**2002, July 4**      *Perf. 13¾x14*
2171 A1079 56c multi    1.60 1.00

Josef Felder
(1900-2000),
Politician,
Journalist
A1080

**2002, Aug. 8**    **Litho.**    *Perf. 13*
2172 A1080 56c multi    1.50 .80

Volunteer
Fire
Brigades
A1081

**2002, Aug. 8**      *Perf. 14*
2173 A1081 56c multi    1.50 .80

Museum Island, Berlin, UNESCO
World Heritage Site
A1082

**Litho. & Engr.**
**2002, Aug. 8**      *Perf. 13¾x14*
2174 A1082 56c blk & Prus blue 1.50 .80

Communications Museum,
Berlin — A1083

**2002, Aug. 8**    **Litho.**    *Perf. 14*
2175 A1083 153c multi    4.25 2.40

Foundation Walls of Roman Villa
Bathhouse, Wurmlingen — A1084

**2002, Sept. 5**    **Litho.**    *Perf. 13¾x14*
2176 A1084 51c multi    1.40 .70

Rotes Elisabeth-Ufer, by Ernst Ludwig
Kirchner (1880-1938) — A1085

**2002, Sept. 5**
2177 A1085 112c multi    3.25 1.60

**Souvenir Sheet**

For Children — A1086

**2002, Sept. 5**      *Perf. 13x13½*
2178 A1086 56c multi    1.50 1.00

Heinrich von
Kleist (1777-
1811),
Writer — A1087

**2002, Oct. 10**    **Litho.**    *Perf. 13*
2179 A1087 56c multi    1.50 .80

Eugen
Jochum
(1902-87),
Conductor
A1088

**2002, Oct. 10**      *Perf. 14x14¼*
2180 A1088 56c multi    1.50 .80

Otto von Guericke (1602-86),
Physicist — A1089

**2002, Oct. 10**      *Perf. 14*
2181 A1089 153c multi    4.25 2.25

Federal Agency
for Civic
Education, 50th
Anniv.
A1090

**2002, Nov. 7**    **Litho.**    *Perf. 13¼*
2182 A1090 56c blk, red & org 1.50 .80

German Television, 50th
Anniv. — A1091

**2002, Nov. 7**      *Perf. 14*
2183 A1091 56c multi    1.50 .80

Halle Market Church, by Lyonel
Feininger (1871-1956) — A1092

**2002, Dec. 5**   **Litho.**   *Perf. 13¾x14*
2184 A1092 55c multi    1.50 .80

**Famous Women Type of 1986 With
Euro Denominations Only**

Designs: 45c, Annette von Droste-Hülshoff
(1797-1848), poet. 55c, Hildegard Knef (1925-
2002), actress. €1, Marie Juchacz (1879-
1956), politician. €1.44, Esther von Kirchbach
(1894-1946), writer.

**2002-03**    **Engr.**    *Perf. 14*
2185 A602   45c ol grn & Prus
        bl    1.25 .65
2186 A602   55c car & blk    1.50 .80
2187 A602   €1 dk bl & claret 2.75 1.40
2188 A602   €1.44 dk bl & ocher 4.00 2.10
     Nos. 2185-2188 (4)    9.50 4.95

Issued: 45c, 55c, €1.44, 12/27/02; €1,
1/16/03.

**Historic Sites Type of 1987 With
Euro Denominations Only**

Designs: 25c, Prince's Residence, Arolsen.
40c, Bach Statue, Leipzig. 44c, Berlin Philharmonic Hall. 45c, Tönninger Packhaus (Warehouse, Tönning). 55c, Old Opera House,
Frankfurt. €1, Porta Nigra, Trier. €1.44, Birthplace of Ludwig van Beethoven, Bonn. €1.60,
Bauhaus, Dessau. €1.80, Stuttgart Staatsgalerie. €2, Equestrian statue, Bamberg.
€2.20, Monument to Theodor Fontane,
Neuruppin. €2.60, Barque "Seute Deern,"
Bremerhaven. €4.10, Gabled houses,
Wismar.

**Typo., Litho. (#2209, 2213)**
**2002-04**      *Perf. 14*
2199 A623   5c olive & turq   .20 .20
2200 A623   25c multi    .70 .35
2201 A623   40c pur & grn   1.10 .60
2202 A623   44c blk & yel   1.25 .60
2203 A623   45c gray blk & brick
        red    1.25 .60
2204 A623   55c blk & yel   1.50 .75
2205 A623   €1 blk & greenish
        gray    2.75 1.40
2206 A623   €1.44 gray grn &
        pink    4.00 2.00
2207 A623   €1.60 slate & org 4.50 2.25

2208 A623   €1.80 dull grn &
        brn    5.00 2.50
2209 A623   €2 brn blk &
        lake    5.50 2.75
2210 A623   €2.20 blue blk &
        gray bl    6.25 3.50
2211 A623   €2.60 blue & red 7.25 3.75
2212 A623   €4.10 bl grn & red
        vio    11.50 6.00

**Self-Adhesive**
*Die Cut Perf. 10¼x11*
**Photo.**
2213 A623 €1.44 Like #2206   4.00 2.00
**Coil Stamp**
**Litho.**
2214 A623 55c blk & yel    2.00 1.00
**Booklet Stamps**
*Die Cut Perf. 10¼x11 on 3 Sides*
2215 A623 45c gray blk & brick
        red    1.60 .80
2216 A623 55c blk & yel    2.00 1.00
  a.    Booklet 4 #2215, 8 #2216 20.00
     Nos. 2199-2216 (18)   62.35 32.05

Issued: 44c, 45c, 55c, €1, €1.60, 12/27/02;
€1.44, €2.20, 1/16/03; €1.80, €2, 2/13/03;
€2.60, €4.10, 3/6/03; No. 2213, June 2003.
25c, 40c, 1/8/04; 5c, 2/5/04.

Kronach, 1000th Anniv. — A1093

**2003, Jan. 16**    **Litho.**    *Perf. 14*
2222 A1093 45c multi    1.25 .65

Georg Elser
(1903-45),
Failed Assassin
of
Hitler — A1094

**2003, Jan. 16**      *Perf. 13¼*
2223 A1094 55c multi    1.50 .80

Treaty for
German-French
Cooperation,
40th Anniv.
A1095

**2003, Jan. 16**      *Perf. 13¾*
2224 A1095 55c multi    1.50 .80

Bible Year
A1096

**2003, Jan. 16**      *Perf. 14x14¼*
2225 A1096 55c multi    1.50 .80

Proun 30t, by El Lissitzky (1890-
1941) — A1097

**2003, Jan. 16**
2226 A1097 144c multi    4.00 2.10

Cultural Foundation of the Federal States.

Rose
A1098

**2003, Feb. 13**    Litho.    *Perf. 14*
2227   A1098   55c multi     1.50   .80

**Booklet Stamp**
**Self-Adhesive**
*Die Cut Perf. 10x10¼*
2228   A1098   55c multi     1.50   .80
   *a.*    Booklet pane of 10    15.00

Junger Argentinier, by Max
Beckmann — A1099

Composition, by Adolf Hölzel — A1100

**2003, Feb. 13**     *Perf. 13¾x14*
2229   A1099   55c multi    1.50   .80
2230   A1100   100c multi    2.75 1.40

**Souvenir Sheet**

Boys' Choirs — A1101

No. 2231: a, Thomanerchor Leipzig. b, Dredner Kreuzchor. c, Regensburger Domspatzen.

**2003, Feb. 13**    *Perf. 14x14¼*
2231   A1101   Sheet of 3    5.50 3.25
   *a.*    45c multi     1.25   .80
   *b.*    55c multi     1.50   .80
   *c.*    100c multi    2.75 1.40

Cologne Cathedral, UNESCO World Heritage Site — A1102

**2003, Mar. 6**     *Perf. 13¼*
2232   A1102   55c multi    1.50   .80

**Self-Adhesive**
**Coil Stamp**
2233   A1102   55c multi    1.50   .80

Intl. Horticultural Exhibition 2003, Rostock A1103

**2003, Apr. 10**    Litho.    *Perf. 13¼*
2234   A1103   45c multi    1.25   .70

German Museum, Munich, Cent. A1104

**2003, Apr. 10**   Photo.   *Perf. 14x14¼*
2235   A1104   55c multi    1.50   .80

Deutsche Welle Radio, 50th
Anniv. — A1105

**2003, Apr. 10**    Litho.    *Perf. 14*
2236   A1105   55c multi    1.50   .80

German Society for the Protection of Children, 50th Anniv. A1106

**2003, Apr. 10**     *Perf. 13¼*
2237   A1106   55c multi    1.50   .80

Reinhold Schneider (1903-58), Writer — A1107

**2003, May 8**    Litho.    *Perf. 13¼*
2238   A1107   55c multi    1.50   .80

Ecumenical Church Conference, Berlin — A1108

**2003, May 8**     *Perf. 14*
2239   A1108   55c multi    1.50   .80

Justus von Liebig (1803-73), Chemist — A1109

**2003, May 8**
2240   A1109   55c multi    1.50   .80

German General Automobile Club, Cent. — A1110

**2003, May 8**     *Perf. 13¼x13½*
2241   A1110   55c multi    1.50   .80

Europa — A1111

**2003, May 8**
2242   A1111   55c multi    *1.50*   *.80*

Hans Jonas (1903-93), Philosopher — A1112

**2003, May 8**     *Perf. 13¾x14*
2243   A1112   220c multi    6.25 3.25

Five Digit Postal Codes, 10th Anniv. A1113

**2003, June 12**    Litho.    *Perf. 14*
2244   A1113   55c multi    1.50   .80

Salzach River Bridge, Laufen, Germany - Oberndorf, Austria, Cent. — A1114

**2003, June 12**
2245   A1114   55c multi    1.50   .80

**Booklet Stamp**
**Self-Adhesive**
2245A   A1114   55c multi    1.50   .80
   *b.*    Booklet pane of 20    30.00

See Austria No. 1922.

**Souvenir Sheet**

Unteres Odertal National Park — A1115

**2003, June 12**     *Perf. 13x13½*
2246   A1115   55c multi    1.50 1.00

German Music Council, 50th Anniv. A1116

**2003, June 12**     *Perf. 14*
2247   A1116   144c multi    4.00 2.10

**Self-Adhesive**
**Booklet Stamp**
*Die Cut Perf. 11¼x11*
2247A   A1116   144c multi    4.00 2.10
   *b.*    Booklet pane of 10    40.00

Issued: No. 2247, 6/12/03; No. 2247A, 1/8/04.

Scenic Regions in Germany — A1117

**2003**    Litho.    *Perf. 13x13½*
2248   A1117   55c Ruhr Region    1.50   .80

Issued: No. 2248, 7/10. This is an expanding set. Numbers have been reserved for additional items.

Andreas Hermes (1878-1964), Politician — A1118

**2003, July 10**   Photo.   *Perf. 14x14¼*
2258   A1118   55c multi    1.50   .80

Petrified Forest, Chemnitz A1119

**2003, Aug. 7**    Litho.    *Perf. 13¼*
2259   A1119   144c multi    4.00 2.10

**City Views**

Market, Munich A1120

Buildings in Old City, Görlitz — A1121

**2003, Aug. 7**    Litho.    *Perf. 13¼*
2260   A1120   45c multi    1.25   .65
       *Perf. 13x13½*
2261   A1121   55c multi    1.50   .80

**Self-Adhesive**
**Booklet Stamp**
*Die Cut Perf. 11x 10¾*
2261A   A1120   45c multi    1.40   .55
   *b.*    Booklet pane of 10    14.00

Issued: Nos. 2260, 2261, 8/7/03; No. 2261A, 1/8/04.

Theodor W. Adorno (1903-69), Philosopher — A1122

**2003, Sept. 11**     *Perf. 14*
2262   A1122   55c multi    1.50   .80

Bietigheim Enzviadukt, 150th
Anniv. — A1123

**2003, Sept. 11**          **Perf. 13x13½**
2263 A1123 55c multi          1.50   .80

Souvenir Sheet

For Children — A1124

**2003, Sept. 11**          **Perf. 13¾x14**
2264 A1124 55c multi          1.50   .80

Mailbox
A1125

**2003, Oct. 9    Litho.    Perf. 13¼**
2265 A1125 55c multi          1.50   .80

German Lifesaving
Association — A1126

**2003, Oct. 9**           **Perf. 13¾**
2266 A1126 144c multi          4.00  2.10

Opera House, Dresden, by Gottfried
Semper (1803-79), Architect — A1127

**2003, Nov. 13   Litho.   Perf. 13x13½**
2267 A1127 55c multi          1.50   .80

German Catholic Women's
Organization, Cent. — A1128

**2003, Nov. 13**          **Perf. 14**
2268 A1128 55c multi          1.50   .80

---

Ratification of Maastricht Treaty, 10th
Anniv. — A1129

**2003, Nov. 13**
2269 A1129 55c multi          1.50   .80

Landshut, 800th Anniv. — A1130

**2004, Jan. 8    Litho.    Perf. 14**
2270 A1130 45c multi          1.25   .65

Schleswig,
1200th Anniv.
A1131

**2004, Jan. 8**           **Perf. 13¼**
2271 A1131 55c multi          1.50   .80

Arnstadt,
1300th Anniv.
A1132

**2004, Feb. 5    Litho.    Perf. 13¼**
2272 A1132 55c multi          1.50   .80

Greetings — A1133

**2004, Feb. 5**           **Perf. 14**
2273 A1133 55c multi          1.50   .80

Joseph Schmidt (1904-42),
Singer — A1134

**2004, Mar. 11    Litho.    Perf. 14**
2274 A1134 55c multi          1.50   .80

Paul Ehrlich (1854-1915) and Emil von
Behring (1854-1917),
Physicians — A1135

**2004, Mar. 11**
2275 A1135 144c multi          4.00  2.10

---

Souvenir Sheet

Classical Theater — A1136

No. 2276: a, Premiere of *William Tell*, by
Friedrich von Schiller, bicent. b, Premiere of
*Faust*, by Johann Wolfgang von Goethe, 150th
anniv.

**2004, Mar. 11**          **Perf. 13¾**
2276 A1136    Sheet of 2     4.00  2.10
a.     45c multi              1.25   .65
b.     100c multi            2.75  1.40

Bauhaus World Heritage Sites,
Weimar and Dessau — A1137

**2004, Apr. 7    Litho.    Perf. 14**
2277 A1137 55c multi          1.50   .80

White
Stork
A1138

**2004, Apr. 7**
2278 A1138 55c multi          1.50   .80

Kurt Georg
Kiesinger
(1904-88),
Chancellor
A1139

**2004, Apr. 7**          **Perf. 13¾**
2279 A1139 55c multi          1.50   .80

Electric Light
Bulb of
Heinrich
Göbel, 150th
Anniv.
A1140

**2004, Apr. 7**
2280 A1140 220c red & blue    6.25  3.25

Europa
A1141

**2004, May 6    Litho.    Perf. 13¼**
2281 A1141 45c multi          1.25   .65

---

Expansion of
the European
Union
A1142

**2004, May 6**
2282 A1142 55c multi          1.50   .80

St. Boniface
of Mainz (c.
675-754)
A1143

**2004, May 6**          **Perf. 13¾**
2283 A1143 55c multi          1.50   .80

Reinhard Schwarz-Schilling (1904-85),
Composer — A1144

**2004, May 6**          **Perf. 14**
2284 A1144 55c multi          1.50   .80

Ludwigsburg Castle, 300th
Anniv. — A1145

**2004, May 6**
2285 A1145 144c multi          4.00  2.10

Wattenmeer
National
Park — A1146

**2004, June 3    Litho.    Perf. 13**
2286 A1146 55c multi          1.50   .80

German -
Russian Youth
Meeting
A1147

**2004, June 3**          **Perf. 13¾**
2287 A1147 55c multi          1.50   .80
See Russia No. 6845.

Transatlantic Speed Record-Breaking
Voyage of the Steamship "Bremen,"
75th Anniv. — A1148

**2004, July 8    Litho.    Perf. 14**
2288   A1148  55c multi               1.50   .80
**Booklet Stamp**
**Self-Adhesive**
2288A  A1148  55c multi               1.50   .80
b.     Booklet pane of 20           30.00

Ludwig
Feuerbach
(1804-72),
Philosopher
A1149

**2004, July 8                      Perf. 13¾**
2289   A1149  144c multi             4.00  2.10

Lighthouses
A1150

**2004, July 8**
2290   A1150  45c Griefswalder
                     Oie            1.25   .65
2291   A1150  55c Roter Sand        1.50   .80
**Die Cut Perf. 10¼**
**Coil Stamp**
**Self-Adhesive**
2291A  A1150  55c Roter Sand        1.50   .80
       See Nos. 2344-2345B, 2491-2494.

Memorial
Church,
Speyer, Cent.
A1151

**2004, Aug. 12    Litho.    Perf. 13¾**
2292   A1151  55c multi              1.50   .80

Camellia — A1152

**2004, Aug. 12                     Perf. 14**
2293   A1152  55c multi              1.50   .80
**Booklet Stamp**
**Self-Adhesive**
**Die Cut Perf. 10x10¼**
2294   A1152  55c multi              1.50   .80
a.     Booklet pane, 5 each #2228,
                     2294          15.00

Engelbert Humperdinck (1854-1921),
Composer — A1153

**2004, Sept. 9      Litho.     Perf. 14**
2295   A1153  45c multi              1.25   .65

Eduard Mörike (1804-75),
Poet — A1154

**2004, Sept. 9**
2296   A1154  55c multi              1.50   .80

For Children
A1155

**2004, Sept. 9                     Perf. 13¾**
2297   A1155  55c multi              1.50   .80

Egon Eiermann (1904-70),
Architect — A1156

**2004, Sept. 9                     Perf. 14**
2298   A1156  100c multi             2.75  1.40

Federal Social
Court, 50th
Anniv.
A1157

**Litho. & Embossed**
**2004, Sept. 9                     Perf. 13¾**
2299   A1157  144c multi             4.00  2.10

Dornier
Do X
A1158

**2004, Oct. 7      Litho.     Perf. 14**
2300   A1158  55c multi              1.50   .80
       Stamp Day.

Winter
Scene
A1159

**2004, Nov. 4**
2301   A1159  55c multi              1.50   .80

International Space Station — A1160

**2004, Nov. 4**
2302   A1160  55c multi              1.50   .80

The Secret, by Felix Nussbaum (1904-
44) — A1161

**2004, Nov. 4**
2303   A1161  55c multi              1.50   .80

Forchheim,
1200th Anniv.
A1162

**2005, Jan. 3      Litho.     Perf. 13¼**
2304   A1162  45c multi              1.25   .65

Adoration of
the Magi, St.
Clara's
Church,
Cologne
A1163

**2005, Jan. 3**
2305   A1163  55c multi              1.50   .80
       See No. 2509.

Sculpture of
Celtic Prince
Found in
Glauberg
A1164

**2005, Jan. 3                      Perf. 13¾**
2306   A1164  144c multi             4.00  2.10

Flowers — A1165

Designs: 5c, Krokus (crocus). 10c, Tulpe
(tulip). 20c, Tagetes (marigold). 25c, Malve
(mallow). 35c, Dahlie (dahlia). 40c, Leber-
blümchen (hepatica). 45c, Margerite (daisy).
50c, Aster. 55c, Klatschmohn (red poppy).
65c, Sonnenhut (rudbeckia). 70c,
Kartaüsernelke (clusterhead pink). 90c,
Narzisse (narcissus). 95c, Sonnenblume (sunflower). 100c, Tränendes herz (Bleeding
heart). 145c, Schwertlilie (iris). 220c, Edelweiss. 390c, Feuerlilie (tiger lily). 430c, Ritter-
sporn (larkspur).

**2005-06      Litho.          Perf. 14**
2307   A1165   5c multi               .20   .20
2308   A1165  10c multi               .30   .20
2309   A1165  20c multi               .55   .30
a.     Miniature sheet, 4 each
       #2307-2308, 2 each
       #2309                         2.75  2.75
2310   A1165  25c multi               .70   .40
2311   A1165  35c multi              1.00   .50
2312   A1165  40c multi              1.10   .55
2313   A1165  45c multi              1.25   .65
2314   A1165  50c multi              1.40   .70
2315   A1165  55c multi              1.50   .80
2316   A1165  65c multi              1.75   .90
2317   A1165  70c multi              2.00   .95
2318   A1165  90c multi              2.50  1.25
2319   A1165  95c multi              2.75  1.40
2320   A1165  100c multi             2.75  1.40
2321   A1165  145c multi             4.00  2.10
2322   A1165  220c multi             6.25  3.00
2323   A1165  390c multi            11.00  5.50
2324   A1165  430c multi            12.00  6.25
       Nos. 2307-2324 (18)          53.00 27.05
**Coil Stamp**
**Self-Adhesive**
**Die Cut Perf. 10¼x10**
2325   A1165  25c multi               .70   .40
2326   A1165  35c multi              1.00   .55
2326A  A1165  55c multi              1.50   .80
2326B  A1165  90c multi              2.50  1.40
a.     Booklet pane of 10          25.00

Issued: 95c, 430c, 1/3. 45c, 4/7. #2310, 50c,
6/2. 20c, #2315, 7/7. 5c, 8/11.10c, 40c, 9/8/
#2326A, 7/7. #2325, 35c, 90c, 145c, 1/2/06.
65c, 3/2/06. 70c, 220c, 4/13/06. 390c, 5/4/06.
100c, 7/13/06. #2309a, 3/1/07.

Advertising
Pillars, 150th
Anniv.
A1166

**2005, Feb. 10     Litho.     Perf. 13¾**
2327   A1166  55c multi              1.50   .80

Berlin
Cathedral,
Cent.
A1167

**2005, Feb. 10                     Perf. 13**
2328   A1167  95c multi              2.75  1.40
**Booklet Stamp**
**Self-Adhesive**
**Die Cut Perf. 11**
2329   A1167  95c multi              2.75  1.40
a.     Booklet pane of 10          27.50

Bonn-Copenhagen Declaration, 50th
Anniv. — A1168

**2005, Mar. 3                      Perf. 14**
2330   A1168  55c multi              1.50   .80
       See Denmark No. 1322.

Resumption of Regulated Civil
Aviation, 50th Anniv. — A1169

**2005, Mar. 3**
2331  A1169  155c multi          4.25  2.25

Postal Workers
A1170

Designs: No. 2332, Postman on bicycle. No.
2333, Postman on snowy hillside.

**2005, Mar. 3**              *Perf. 13¾*
2332  A1170  55c multi          1.50  .80
2333  A1170  55c multi          1.50  .80

Mittelland Canal, Cent. — A1171

**2005, Apr. 7**   **Litho.**   *Perf. 14*
2334  A1171  45c multi          1.25  .80

Bavarian
Forest
National
Park — A1172

**2005, Apr. 7**              *Perf. 13¾*
2335  A1172  55c multi          1.50  .80

Hans Christian
Andersen
(1805-75),
Author — A1173

**2005, Apr. 7**              *Perf. 14*
2336  A1173  144c multi         4.00  2.10

**Coil Stamp**
**Self-Adhesive**
*Die Cut Perf. 10¼*

2336A  A1173  144c multi        4.00  2.10

Founding of
Die Brücke
Expressionist
Group, Cent.
A1174

**2005, May 12**   **Litho.**   *Perf. 13¾*
2337  A1174  55c buff, blk & red   1.50  .80

Paris Treaty,
50th Anniv.
A1175

**2005, May 12**
2338  A1175  55c black & red     1.50  .80

Friedrich von Schiller Year — A1176

**2005, May 12**              *Perf. 14*
2339  A1176  55c multi          1.50  .80

Pope John Paul II (1920-
2005) — A1177

**2005, May 12**
2340  A1177  55c multi          1.50  .80

Europa
A1178

**2005, May 12**
2341  A1178  55c multi         *1.50   .80*

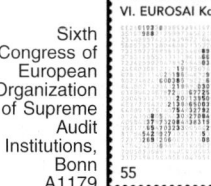

Sixth
Congress of
European
Organization
of Supreme
Audit
Institutions,
Bonn
A1179

**2005, June 2**   **Litho.**   *Perf. 13¾*
2342  A1179  55c multi          1.50  .80

20th
World
Youth
Day
A1180

**2005, June 2**              *Perf. 14*
2343  A1180  55c multi          1.50  .80

See Vatican City No. 1298.

**Lighthouse Type of 2004**
Designs: Nos. 2344, 2345B, Brunsbüttel,
Jetty 1. No. 2345A, Griefswalde Oie. 55c,
Westerheversand.

**2005, July 7**   **Litho.**   *Perf. 13¾*
2344   A1150  45c multi         1.25  .65
2345   A1150  55c multi         1.50  .80

**Booklet Stamps**
**Self-Adhesive**
*Die Cut Perf. 10¾*

2345A  A1150  45c multi         1.25  .65
2345B  A1150  45c multi         1.25  .65
  c.    Booklet pane, 5 each
        #2345A-2345B           12.50

Albert Einstein's Theory of Relativity,
Cent. — A1181

**2005, July 7**              *Perf. 14*
2346  A1181  55c multi          1.50  .80

**Souvenir Sheet**

Prussian Castles and
Gardens — A1182

**2005, July 7**          *Perf. 13x13½*
2347  A1182  220c multi         6.25  3.25

**Self-Adhesive**
**Booklet Stamp**
*Die Cut Perf. 11*

2347A  A1182  220c multi        6.25  3.25
  b.    Booklet pane of 10     57.50  —
      Issued: #2347, 7/7. #2347A, 11/3.

**Postal Workers Type of 2005**
Designs: No. 2348, Postman on punt. No.
2349, Postman with handcart.

**2005, Aug. 11**  **Litho.**  *Perf. 13¾*
2348  A1170  55c multi          1.50  .80
2349  A1170  55c multi          1.50  .80

German
Friends of
Nature, Cent.
A1183

**2005, Aug. 11**             *Perf. 13¼*
2350  A1183  144c multi         4.00  2.10

Magdeburg, 1200th Anniv. — A1184

**2005, Sept. 8**  **Litho.**  *Perf. 14*
2351  A1184  55c multi          1.50  .80

For Children — A1185

**2005, Sept. 8**
2352  A1185  55c multi          1.50  .80

Peace of
Augsburg,
450th Anniv.
A1186

**2005, Sept. 8**             *Perf. 13¾*
2353  A1186  55c multi          1.50  .80

See No. 2508.

Max Schmeling (1905-2005),
Boxer — A1187

**2005, Sept. 8**             *Perf. 14*
2354  A1187  55c multi          1.50  .80

Dedication of Rebuilt Church of Our
Lady, Dresden — A1188

**2005, Oct. 13**  **Litho.**  *Perf. 14*
2355  A1188  55c multi          1.50  .80

Adalbert
Stifter (1805-
68), Writer
A1189

**2005, Oct. 13**            *Perf. 13¾*
2356  A1189  95c multi          2.75  1.40

St. Leonhard's
Day
Procession,
Bad
Tölz — A1190

**2005, Nov. 3**   **Litho.**  *Perf. 13¼*
2357  A1190  45c multi          1.25  .65

Federal Armed
Forces, 50th
Anniv.
A1191

**2005, Nov. 3**             *Perf. 13¾*
2358  A1191  55c multi          1.50  .80

Diplomatic Relations With Israel, 40th Anniv. A1192

**2005, Nov. 3**
2359 A1192 55c multi        1.50   .80
See Israel No. 1619.

Awarding of Nobel Peace Prize to Bertha von Suttner, Cent. — A1193

**2005, Nov. 3**        *Perf. 14*
2360 A1193 55c multi        1.50   .80

Awarding of Nobel Physiology or Medicine Prize to Robert Koch, Cent. — A1194

**2005, Nov. 3**        *Perf. 13¼*
2361 A1194 144c multi        4.00  2.10

Halle, 1200th Anniv. A1195

**2006, Jan. 2**   *Litho.*   *Perf. 14*
2362 A1195 45c multi        1.25   .65

Winter A1196

**2005, Jan. 2**   *Litho.*   *Perf. 14*
2363 A1196 55c multi        1.50   .80

Spring A1197

**2006, Apr. 13**   *Litho.*   *Perf. 14*
2364 A1197 55c multi        1.50   .80

Summer — A1198

**2006, July 13**   *Litho.*   *Perf. 14*
2365 A1198 55c multi        1.50   .80

Autumn — A1199

**2006, Oct. 5**   *Litho.*   *Perf. 14*
2366 A1199 55c multi        1.50   .80

Wolfgang Amadeus Mozart (1756-91), Composer A1200

**2006, Jan. 2**   *Litho.*   *Perf. 13¼*
2367 A1200 55c multi        1.50   .80

Golden Bull of Emperor Charles IV — A1201

**2006, Jan. 2**        *Perf. 14*
2368 A1201 145c multi        4.00  2.10
**Self-Adhesive**
**Booklet Stamp**
*Die Cut Perf. 10*
2369 A1201 145c multi        4.00  2.10
   *a.*   Booklet pane of 10        40.00

St. Michael's Church, Schwäbisch Hall, 850th Anniv. — A1202

**2006, Feb. 9**   *Litho.*   *Perf. 14*
2370 A1202 55c multi        1.50   .80

Frisian Council, 50th Anniv. A1203

**2006, Feb. 9**
2371 A1203 90c multi        2.50  1.40

Ingolstadt, 1200th Anniv. A1204

**2006, Mar. 2**   *Litho.*   *Perf. 13¼*
2372 A1204 55c multi        1.50   .80

Karl Friedrich Schinkel (1781-1841), Architect — A1205

**2006**        *Perf. 14*
2373 A1205 55c multi        1.50   .80
**Coil Stamp**
**Self-Adhesive**
*Die Cut Perf. 10x10¼*
2373A A1205 55c multi        1.50   .80
   Issued: No. 2373, 3/2. No. 2373A, 7/13.

Care for the Blind — A1206

**Litho. & Embossed**
**2006, Mar. 2**        *Perf. 13x13½*
2374 A1206 55c black & gray        1.50   .80
   Berlin School for the Blind, 200th Anniv., Nikolaus Care Foundation, 150th Anniv.

Pres. Johannes Rau (1931-2006) — A1207

**2006, Mar. 2**   *Litho.*   *Perf. 14*
2375 A1207 55c multi        1.50   .80

Viadrina Universtiy, Frankfurt an der Oder, 500th Anniv. A1208

**Litho. & Embossed**
**2006, Apr. 13**        *Perf. 13¾*
2376 A1208 55c multi        1.50   .80

Self-Portrait in Fur Coat, by Albrecht Dürer A1209

**2006, Apr. 13**        *Litho.*
2377 A1209 145c multi        4.00  2.10

Upper Middle Rhine Valley UNESCO World Heritage Site — A1210

**2006, May 4**   *Litho.*   *Perf. 13¾*
2378 A1210 55c multi        1.50   .80

**Self-Adhesive**
**Booklet Stamp**
*Die Cut Perf. 11*
2379 A1210 55c multi        1.50   .80
   *a.*   Booklet pane of 10        15.00

Europa A1211

**2006, May 4**        *Perf. 14*
2380 A1211 55c multi        1.50   .80

Gerd Bucerius (1906-95), Publisher and Politician — A1212

**2006, May 4**
2381 A1212 85c multi        2.40  1.25

Stefan Andres (1906-70), Writer — A1213

**2006, June 8**
2382 A1213 55c multi        1.50   .80

John Augustus Roebling (1806-69), Bridge Designer — A1214

**2006, June 8**        *Perf. 14*
2383 A1214 145c multi        4.00  2.10
**Self-Adhesive**
**Coil Stamp**
*Die Cut Perf. 11*
2384 A1214 145c multi        4.00  2.10

Standardized Motor Vehicle Identification, Cent. — A1215

**2006, July 13**   *Litho.*   *Perf. 14*
2385 A1215 45c multi        1.25   .65

Burghausen Castle, Burghausen — A1216

**2006, July 13**
2386 A1216 55c multi        1.50   .80

Saskia van Uylenburgh, by Rembrandt (1606-69) A1217

**2006, July 13**     **Perf. 13¾**
2387 A1217 70c multi    2.00 1.00

See Netherlands No. 1253. The design of No. 2387 was reproduced without the permission of the German authorities in a Netherlands booklet pane that also contains a similar Netherlands stamp.

Discovery of Neanderthal Man Bones, 150th Anniv. — A1218

**2006, Aug. 10**   **Litho.**   **Perf. 14**
2388 A1218 220c multi    6.00 3.25

Souvenir Sheet

Black Forest — A1219

**2006, Aug. 10**    **Perf. 13¾**
2389 A1219 55c multi    1.50 .80

**Lighthouses Type of 2004**
Designs: 45c, Neuland. 55c, Hohe Weg.

**2006, Aug. 10**    **Perf. 13¾**
2390 A1150 45c multi    1.25 .65
2391 A1150 55c multi    1.50 .80

"Captain of Köpenick" A1220

**2006, Sept. 7**   **Litho.**   **Perf. 13¼**
2392 A1220 55c multi    1.50 .80

Theft of town funds and arrest of mayor in Köpenick by petty thief Friedrich Wilhelm Voigt, who masqueraded as an army officer, cent.

For Children A1221

**2006, Sept. 7**
2393 A1221 55c multi    1.50 .80

Hanseatic League, 650th Anniv. — A1222

**Litho. & Engr.**
**2006, Sept. 7**    **Perf. 14**
2394 A1222 70c multi    2.00 1.00

See Sweden No. 2541

Stamp Day A1223

**2006, Oct. 5**   **Litho.**   **Perf. 14**
2395 A1223 55c multi    1.50 .80

Hannah Arendt (1906-75), Political Scientist — A1224

**2006, Oct. 5**    **Perf. 13¾x14**
2396 A1224 145c multi    4.00 2.10

**Seasons Types of 2006**
**Die Cut Perf. 14**
**2006, Nov. 9**    **Litho.**
**Booklet Stamps**
**Self-Adhesive**
2397 A1197 55c Spring    1.50 .80
2398 A1198 55c Summer    1.50 .80
2399 A1199 55c Autumn    1.50 .80
2400 A1196 55c Winter    1.50 .80
a.   Booklet pane, 5 each #2397-2400    30.00

Eugen Bolz (1881-1945), Politician A1225

**2006, Nov. 9**    **Perf. 13¾**
2401 A1225 45c multi    1.25 .65

Joseph Cardinal Höffner (1906-87) A1226

**2006, Nov. 9**    **Perf. 13¼**
2402 A1226 55c multi    1.50 .80

Werner Forssmann (1904-79), 1956 Physiology or Medicine Nobel Laureate — A1227

**2006, Nov. 9**    **Perf. 14**
2403 A1227 90c multi    2.50 1.40

**Flowers Type of 2005**
Designs: 25c, Gartennelke (carnation). 55c, Gartenrose (rose). 200c, Goldmohn (California poppy).

**2006-08**    **Litho.**   **Perf. 14**
2405 A1165 25c multi    .70 .35
2407 A1165 55c multi    1.75 .85
2416 A1165 200c multi    5.50 2.75

**Self-Adhesive**
**Coil Stamps**
**Die Cut Perf. 10¼x10**
2419 A1165 25c multi    .70 .35
2420 A1165 55c multi    1.75 .85

**Booklet Stamps**
2421 A1165 65c multi    1.75 .85
a.   Booklet pane of 5 + 5 etiquettes    8.75
2422 A1165 70c multi    1.90 .95
a.   Booklet pane of 5 + 5 etiquettes    9.50

Issued: 200c, 11/9/06; 55c, 6/12/08. 25c, 10/9/08. No. 2419, 10/9/08; No. 2420, 6/12/08; Nos. 2421-2422, 1/2/09.

Fürth, 1000th Anniv. A1228

**2007, Jan. 2**   **Litho.**   **Perf. 13¼**
2424 A1228 45c multi    1.25 .65

**Booklet Stamp**
**Self-Adhesive**
**Die Cut Perf. 11**
2425 A1228 45c multl    1.25 .65
a.   Booklet pane of 10    12.50

Germany, 2007 President of the European Union A1229

**Litho. & Embossed**
**2007, Jan. 2**    **Perf. 13¾**
2426 A1229 55c multi    1.50 .80

Bamberg Bishopric, 1000th Anniv. A1230

**2007, Jan. 2**   **Litho.**   **Perf. 13¼**
2427 A1230 55c multi    1.50 .80

Admission of Saarland into Federal Republic, 50th Anniv. — A1231

**2007, Jan. 2**    **Perf. 14**
2428 A1231 55c multi    1.50 .80

**Booklet Stamp**
**Self-Adhesive**
**Die Cut Perf. 10x10¼**
2428A A1231 55c multi    1.50 .80
b.   Booklet pane of 10    15.00

Wankel Rotary Engine, 50th Anniv. — A1232

**2007, Jan. 2**
2429 A1232 145c multi    4.00 2.10

Johann Christian Senckenberg (1707-72), Founder of Hospital, Frankfurt am Main — A1233

**2007, Feb. 8**   **Litho.**   **Perf. 14**
2430 A1233 90c multi    2.50 1.40

Munich Jewish Center A1234

**2007, Mar. 1**   **Litho.**   **Perf. 14**
2431 A1234 55c multi    1.50 .80

Paul Gerhardt (1607-76), Hymn Writer — A1235

**2007, Mar. 1**
2432 A1235 55c multi    1.50 .80

The Unearthing of the Cross, by Adam Elsheimer A1236

**2007, Mar. 1**    **Perf. 13¼**
2433 A1236 55c multi    1.50 .80

Rome Treaty, 50th Anniv. A1237

**2007, Mar. 1**                              *Perf. 13¾*
2434  A1237  55c multi                    1.50  .80

Leaders of Anti-Nazi Resistance Movement — A1238

**2007, Mar. 1**                          *Perf. 13¾x14*
2435  A1238  55c multi                    1.50  .80
Claus Schenk Graf von Stauffenberg (1907-44), Hitler assassination plotter, and Helmuth James Graf von Moltke (1907-45), founding member of Kreisau Circle resistance group.

Pope Benedict XVI, 80th Birthday — A1239

**2007, Apr. 12**      **Litho.**          *Perf. 14*
2436  A1239  55c multi                    1.50  .80

Letter Writing A1240

**2007, Apr. 12**                          *Perf. 13¾*
2437  A1240  55c  Boy writing letter  1.50  .80
2438  A1240  55c  Boy mailing let-
              ter                         1.50  .80
See Nos. 2454-2455.

Publication of World Map of Martin Waldseemuller, 500th Anniv. — A1241

**Litho. & Engr.**
**2007, Apr. 12**                          *Perf. 14*
2439  A1241  220c multi                   6.00  3.25

Europa A1242

**2007, May 3**       **Litho.**           *Perf. 14*
2440  A1242  45c multi                    1.25  .65
Scouting, cent.

Bellevue Palace, Presidential Residence — A1243

**2007, May 3**
2441  A1243  55c multi                    1.50  .80
**Coil Stamp**
**Self-Adhesive**
*Die Cut Perf. 10x10¼*
2441A  A1243  55c multi                   1.50  .80

Moyland Castle, 700th Anniv. — A1244

**2007, May 3**
2442  A1244  85c multi                    2.40  1.25

Hambacher Fest, 175th Anniv. — A1245

**2007, May 3**                            *Perf. 14*
2443  A1245  145c multi                   4.00  2.00
**Booklet Stamp**
**Self-Adhesive**
*Die Cut Perf. 10x10¼*
2444  A1245  145c multi                   4.00  2.00
    a.    Booklet pane of 10             40.00

Karl Valentin (1882-1948), Writer A1246

**2007, June 14**    **Litho.**            *Perf. 13¾*
2445  A1246  45c multi                    1.25  .65

Paul Klinger (1907-71), Film Actor A1247

**2007, June 14**
2446  A1247  55c multi                    1.50  .80

**Lighthouses Type of 2004**
Designs: 45c, Bremerhaven Oberfeuer. 55c, Hörnum.

**2007, July 12**                          *Perf. 13¾*
2447  A1150  45c multi                    1.25  .65
2448  A1150  55c multi                    1.50  .80

UNESCO World Heritage Sites — A1248

Designs: 65c, Historic Center of Riga, Latvia. 70c, Historic Centers of Straslund and Wismar, Germany.

**2007, July 12**                          *Perf. 14*
2449  A1248  65c multi                    1.90  .95
2450  A1248  70c multi                    2.00  1.00
See Latvia Nos. 679-680.

Saale Valley Dam and Lake Bleiloch, 75th Anniv. — A1249

**2007, Aug. 9**     **Litho.**            *Perf. 14*
2451  A1249  55c multi                    1.50  .80

German Federal Bank, 50th Anniv. A1250

**2007, Aug. 9**
2452  A1250  55c multi                    1.50  .80

Kaiser Wilhelm Bridge, Wilhelmshaven, Cent. — A1251

**2007, Aug. 9**              **Litho. & Engr.**
2453  A1251  145c multi                   4.00  2.00

**Letter Writing Type of 2007**
Designs: No. 2454, Postman delivering letter to woman. No. 2455, Woman reading letter.

**2007, Sept. 20**   **Litho.**            *Perf. 13¾*
2454  A1240  55c multi                    1.60  .80
2455  A1240  55c multi                    1.60  .80

For Children — A1252

**2007, Sept. 20**                         *Perf. 14*
2456  A1252  55c multi                    1.60  .80

Science Advisory Committee, 50th Anniv. — A1253

**2007, Sept. 20**
2457  A1253  90c multi                    2.60  1.40

German Work Federation (Architecture Group), Cent. A1254

**2007, Oct. 11**    **Litho.**            *Perf. 13¼*
2458  A1254  55c multi                    1.60  .80

**Souvenir Sheet**

Frontiers of the Roman Empire UNESCO World Heritage Site — A1255

**2007, Oct. 11**                          *Perf. 14*
2459  A1255  55c multi                    1.60  .80

Heinrich Friedrich Carl Freiherr vom und zum Stein (1757-1831), Prussian Statesman — A1256

**2007, Oct. 11**                          *Perf. 13¾x14*
2460  A1256  145c multi                   4.00  2.10

St. Elizabeth of Hungary (1207-31) A1257

**2007, Nov. 8**     **Litho.**            *Perf. 13¾*
2461  A1257  55c multi                    1.60  .80

Astrid Lindgren (1907-2002), Writer — A1258

**Litho. & Engr.**
**2007, Nov. 8**                           *Perf. 13¾x14*
2462  A1258  100c multi                   2.75  1.40
See Sweden No. 2572.

Brandenburg Gate, Designed by Carl Gotthard Langhans (1732-1808) — A1259

**2007, Dec. 27**    **Litho.**            *Perf. 14*
2463  A1259  55c multi                    1.60  .80

## Self-Adhesive
## Booklet Stamp
*Die Cut Perf. 10x10¼*

2464 A1259 55c multi      1.60   .80
*a.*    Booklet pane of 10    16.00

Reichenau Monastic Island UNESCO World Heritage Site — A1260

**2008, Jan. 2**    Litho.    *Perf. 13*
2465 A1260 45c multi     1.40   .70

## Booklet Stamp
## Self-Adhesive
*Die Cut Perf. 10¾*

2466 A1260 45c multi     1.40   .70
*a.*    Booklet pane of 10    14.00

Heinrich Zille (1858-1929), Illustrator A1261

**2008, Jan. 2**     *Perf. 13¾*
2467 A1261 55c multi    1.60   .80

Federal Cartel Office, 50th Anniv. A1262

**2008**     *Perf. 14*
2468 A1262 90c multi    2.50 1.40

## Booklet Stamp
## Self-Adhesive
*Die Cut Perf. 11¼x11*

2468A A1262 90c multi    3.00 1.50
*b.*    Booklet pane of 10    30.00

Issued: No. 2468, 1/2; No. 2468A, 3/13.

Eichstätt, 1100th Anniv. A1263

**2008, Jan. 2**     *Perf. 13¾*
2469 A1263 145c multi    4.00 2.10

## Coil Stamp
## Self-Adhesive
*Die Cut Perf. 10¼*

2469A A1263 145c multi    4.25 2.10

Wenzel Jamnitzer (1508-85), Goldsmith — A1264

**2008, Jan. 2**    *Perf. 13¾x14*
2470 A1264 220c multi    6.00 3.25

"Congratulations" — A1265

"All the Best" A1266

**2008, Feb. 7**     *Perf. 14*
2471 A1265 55c multi    1.60   .80
2472 A1266 55c multi    1.60   .80

Carl Spitzweg (1808-85), Painter A1267

**2008, Feb. 7**    Litho.    *Perf. 13¾*
2473 A1267 55c multi    1.60   .80

## Coil Stamp
## Self-Adhesive
*Die Cut Perf. 10¼*

2474 A1267 55c multi    1.60   .80

Village Church, Bochum-Stiepel, 1000th Anniv. — A1268

**2008, Feb. 7**    Litho.    *Perf. 13¾*
2475 A1268 145c multi    4.00 2.10

Helmut Käutner (1908-80), Film Director — A1269

**2008, Mar. 13**    Litho.    *Perf. 14*
2476 A1269 55c multi    1.75   .85

Frankfurt Zoo, 150th Anniv. A1270

**2008, Mar. 13**     *Perf. 13¼*
2477 A1270 65c multi    2.10 1.10

Seebach Bird Sanctuary, Cent. — A1271

**2008, Apr. 10**    Litho.    *Perf. 14*
2478 A1271 45c multi    1.50   .75

Johann Hinrich Wichern (1808-81), Theologian — A1272

**2008, Apr. 10**
2479 A1272 55c multi    1.75   .85

Max Planck (1858-1947), Physicist A1273

**2008, Apr. 10**     *Perf. 13¾*
2480 A1273 55c multi    1.75   .85

Oskar Schindler (1908-74), Industrialist Who Saved Jews From Holocaust — A1274

**2008, Apr. 10**     *Perf. 14x14¼*
2481 A1274 145c multi    4.75 2.40

First International Match of German Soccer Team, Cent. A1275

**2008, Apr. 10**     *Perf. 13¾*
2482 A1275 170c multi    5.50 2.75

Christoffel Blind Mission, Cent. — A1276

**2008, May 8**    Litho.    *Perf. 13x13½*
2483 A1276 55c multi    1.75   .85

## Greetings Types of 2008 and

"Kind Regards" — A1277

"Thank You" A1278

**2008, May 8**     *Perf. 14*
2484 A1277 55c multi    1.75   .85
2485 A1278 55c multi    1.75   .85

## Booklet Stamps
## Self-Adhesive
*Die Cut Perf. 14*

2486 A1277 55c multi    1.75   .85
2487 A1265 55c multi    1.75   .85
2488 A1266 55c multi    1.75   .85
2489 A1278 55c multi    1.75   .85
*a.*    Booklet pane of 20, 5 each #2486-2489    35.00
   Nos. 2486-2489 (4)    7.00 3.40

Europa (#2484, 2486).

Honorary Offices — A1279

**2008, June 12**    Litho.    *Perf. 14*
2490 A1279 55c multi    1.75   .85

## Lighthouses Type of 2004

Designs: No. 2491, 45c, Warnemünde. Nos. 2492, 2494, 55c, Amrum. No. 2493, 55c, Hörnum.

**2008, July 3**    Litho.    *Perf. 13¾*
2491 A1150 45c multi    1.40   .70
2492 A1150 55c multi    1.75   .85

## Booklet Stamps
## Self-Adhesive
*Die Cut Perf. 11*

2493 A1150 55c multi    1.75   .85
2494 A1150 55c multi    1.75   .85
*a.*    Booklet pane of 10, 5 each #2493-2494    17.50

Drachenfels Railway, 125th Anniv. — A1280

**2008, July 3**     *Perf. 14*
2495 A1280 45c multi    1.40   .70

Franz Kafka (1883-1924), Writer — A1281

**2008, July 3**
2496 A1281 55c black    1.75   .85

Self-portrait With Model, by Lovis Corinth (1858-1925) — A1282

**2008, July 3**           *Perf. 13x13½*
2497  A1282 145c multi                4.75 2.40

Training Ship Gorch Fock, 50th Anniv. A1283

**2008, Aug. 7    Litho.    *Perf. 13¼***
2498  A1283 55c multi                 1.75   .85

Joachim Ringelnatz (1883-1934), Writer and Painter A1284

**2008, Aug. 7**                *Perf. 13¾*
2499  A1284 85c pur & black           2.60 1.40

Hermann Schulze-Delitzsch (1808-83), Economist — A1285

**2008, Aug. 7**                  *Perf. 14*
2500  A1285 90c multi                 2.75 1.40

Stamp Day — A1286

**2008, Sept. 4    Litho.    *Perf. 13¼***
2501  A1286 55c multi                 1.60   .80

For Children A1287

**2008, Sept. 4**               *Perf. 14*
2502  A1287 55c multi                 1.60   .80

Old Rhine Bridge, Bad Sackingen, Germany - Stein, Switzerland — A1288

**2008, Sept. 4**
2503  A1288 70c multi                 2.00 1.00
   See Switzerland No. 1319.

Gallimarkt (Livestock Market) of Leer, 500th Anniv. — A1289

**2008, Oct. 9    Litho.    *Perf. 14***
2504  A1289 45c multi                 1.25   .60

Nebra Sky Disk A1290

**2008, Oct. 9**
2505  A1290 55c multi                 1.50   .75

Lorenz Werthmann (1858-1921), Founder of Caritas Charity A1291

**2008, Oct. 9**               *Perf. 13¾*
2506  A1291 55c multi                 1.50   .75

First Powered Flight Over Germany, by Hans Grade, Cent. — A1292

**2008, Oct. 9**                  *Perf. 14*
2507  A1292 145c multi                4.00 2.00

### Peace of Augsburg and Adoration of the Magi Types of 2005
*Die Cut Perf. 11¼*

**2008, Nov. 1                      Litho.**
**Booklet Stamps**
**Self-Adhesive**
2508  A1186 55c multi                 1.40   .70
2509  A1163 55c multi                 1.40   .70
  *a.*   Booklet pane of 10, 5 each
           #2508-2509                 14.00

Lebenshilfe (Organization for the Mentally Handicapped), 50th Anniv. — A1293

**2008, Nov. 13**                *Perf. 14*
2510  A1293 55c multi                 1.40   .70

A Heart for Children Charity, 30th Anniv. A1294

**2008, Nov. 13**               *Perf. 13¼*
2511  A1294 55c black & red           1.40   .70

Nils Holgersson on Goose A1295

**2008, Nov. 13**               *Perf. 13¾*
2512  A1295 100c multi                2.60 1.25
   Selma Lagerlöf (1858-1940), author of *Nils Holgersson's Wonderful Journey Through Sweden.*

Frankenberg City Hall, 500th Anniv. A1296

**2009, Jan. 2    Litho.    *Perf. 13¾***
2513  A1296 45c multi                 1.25   .60

**Booklet Stamp**
**Self-Adhesive**
*Die Cut Perf. 10¾*
2514  A1296 45c multi                 1.25   .60
  *a.*   Booklet pane of 10          12.50

Misereor and Bread for the World Charities, 50th Anniv. — A1297

**2009, Jan. 2**                 *Perf. 14*
2515  A1297 55c multi                 1.50   .75

Tangermünde, 1000th Anniv. — A1298

**2009, Jan. 2**                 *Perf. 14*
2516  A1298 90c multi                 2.40 1.25

Pres. Theodor Heuss (1884-1963) A1299

**2009, Jan. 2**                *Perf. 13¾*
2517  A1299 145c multi                4.00 2.00

Heinz Erhardt (1909-79), Comedian
A1300

**2009, Feb. 12    Litho.    Perf. 13¾**
2518 A1300 55c multi                1.40    .70

Felix Mendelssohn Bartholdy (1809-47), Composer
A1301

**2009, Feb. 12              Perf. 13¼**
2519 A1301 65c multi                1.75    .85

Munich Propylaea, by Architect Leo von Klenze (1784-1864)
A1302

**2009, Feb. 12              Perf. 13¾**
2520 A1302 70c multi                1.90    .95

Der Feuervogel (Firebird), Woodcut by Helmut Andreas Paul Grieshaber (1909-81)
A1303

**2009, Feb. 12              Perf. 13¼**
2521 A1303 165c multi              4.25    2.10

## SEMI-POSTAL STAMPS

### Issues of the Republic

Regular Issue of 1906-17 Surcharged

**1919, May 1    Wmk. 125    Perf. 14**
B1 A16 10pf + 5pf car red          .45    4.50
B2 A22 15pf + 5pf dk vio           .45    4.50
    Set, never hinged                     2.75

The surtax was for the war wounded.

"Planting Charity" — SP1          Feeding the Hungry — SP2

**1922, Dec. 11    Litho.    Wmk. 126**
B3 SP1 6m + 4m ultra & brn        .20   22.50
B4 SP1 12m + 8m red org & bl
        gray                       .20   22.50
    Set, never hinged                    1.50

---

Nos. 221, 225 and 196 Surcharged

**1923, Feb. 19**
B5 A34 5m + 100m                   .20    9.00
B6 A29 25m + 500m                  .20   22.50
  a.   Inverted surcharge         95.00
        Never hinged             190.00
B7 A32 20m + 1000m                2.10   87.50
  a.   Inverted surcharge        975.00  3,750.
        Never hinged            2,100.
  b.   Green background inverted 260.00  1,200.
        Never hinged             400.00
        Nos. B5-B7 (3)             2.50  119.00
    Set, never hinged              5.40

Note following No. 160 applies to #B1-B7.

**1924, Feb. 25    Typo.    Perf. 14½x15**
Designs: 10pf+30pf, Giving drink to the thirsty. 20pf+60pf, Clothing the naked. 50pf+1.50m, Healing the sick.
B8 SP2 5pf + 15pf dk
        green                     1.10    2.60
B9 SP2 10pf + 30pf vermil-
        ion                       1.10    2.60
B10 SP2 20pf + 60pf dk blue       6.00    7.50
B11 SP2 50pf + 1.50m red
        brn                      22.50   60.00
        Nos. B8-B11 (4)          30.70   72.70
    Set, never hinged            123.00

The surtax was used for emergency aid. See No. B58.

Arms of Prussia — SP6

**1925, Dec. 15              Perf. 14**
**Inscribed: "1925"**
B12 SP6 5pf + 5pf shown           .50    1.90
B13 SP6 10pf + 10pf Bava-
        ria                      1.10    1.90
B14 SP6 20pf + 20pf Saxo-
        ny                       6.00   13.50
  a.   Bklt. pane of 2 + 2 labels 190.00  600.00
        Never hinged             500.00
        Nos. B12-B14 (3)          7.60   17.30
    Set, never hinged            33.40

**1926, Dec. 1**
**Inscribed: "1926"**
B15 SP6 5pf + 5pf Wurt-
        temberg                  1.00    2.25
B16 SP6 10pf + 10pf Baden        1.50    3.00
  a.   Bklt. pane of 6 + 2 labels 77.50  190.00
        Never hinged             190.00
B17 SP6 25pf + 25pf Thurin-
        gia                     11.00   19.00
B18 SP6 50pf + 50pf Hesse       40.00   95.00
        Nos. B15-B18 (4)        53.50  119.25
    Set, never hinged           170.00

See Nos. B23-B32.

Pres. Paul von Hindenburg — SP13

**1927, Sept. 26              Photo.**
B19 SP13 8pf dark green          .90    1.50
  a.   Bklt. pane, 4 #B19, 3
        #B20 + label            45.00  110.00
        Never hinged           110.00
B20 SP13 15pf scarlet            .90    2.25
B21 SP13 25pf deep blue         6.00   21.00
B22 SP13 50pf bister brown      9.75   24.00
        Nos. B19-B22 (4)       17.55   48.75
    Set, never hinged           79.40

80th birthday of Pres. Hindenburg. The stamps were sold at double face value. The surtax was given to a fund for War Invalids.

Arms Type of 1925

Design: 8pf+7pf, Mecklenberg-Schwerin.

---

**1928, Nov. 15              Typo.**
**Inscribed: "1928"**
B23 SP6 5pf + 5pf
              Hamburg            .50    3.75
B24 SP6 8pf + 7pf multi          .50    3.75
  a.   Bklt. pane, 4 #B24, 3 #B25
        + label                110.00  275.00
        Never hinged           275.00
B25 SP6 15pf + 15pf Olden-
        burg                     .75    3.75
B26 SP6 25pf + 25pf Bruns-
        wick                    9.00   47.50
B27 SP6 50pf + 50pf Anhalt     45.00   90.00
        Nos. B23-B27 (5)       55.75  148.75
    Set, never hinged          181.35

**1929, Nov. 4**
Coats of Arms: 8pf+4pf, Lippe-Detmold. 25pf+10pf, Mecklenburg-Strelitz. 50pf+40pf, Schaumburg-Lippe.
**Inscribed: "1929"**
B28 SP6 5pf + 2pf Bremen         .60    1.50
  a.   Bklt. pane of 6 + 2 labels 12.50  32.50
        Never hinged            32.50
B29 SP6 8pf + 4pf multi          .60    1.50
  a.   Bklt. pane, 4 #B29, 3 #B30
        + label                 40.00  100.00
        Never hinged           100.00
B30 SP6 15pf + 5pf Lubeck        .75    1.50
B31 SP6 25pf + 10pf multi      11.00   45.00
B32 SP6 50pf + 40pf choc,
        ocher & red            40.00   90.00
  a.   "PE" for "PF"           150.00  400.00
        Never hinged           450.00
        Nos. B28-B32 (5)       52.95  139.50
    Set, never hinged          180.00

Cathedral of Aachen — SP24          Brandenburg Gate, Berlin — SP25

Castle of Marienwerder SP26          Statue of St. Kilian and Marienburg Fortress at Würzburg SP27

Souvenir Sheet
**Wmk. 223**
**1930, Sept. 12    Engr.    Perf. 14**
B33   Sheet of 4               375.00  1,500.
        Never hinged          1,100.
  a.   SP24 8pf + 4pf dark green 26.00  90.00
        Never hinged            67.50
  b.   SP25 15pf + 5pf carmine  26.00  90.00
        Never hinged            67.50
  c.   SP26 25pf + 10p dark blue 26.00  90.00
        Never hinged            67.50
  d.   SP27 50pf + 40pf dark brown 26.00  90.00
        Never hinged            67.50

Intl. Phil. Exhib., Berlin, Sept. 12-21, 1930. No. B33 is watermarked Eagle on each stamp and "IPOSTA"-"1930" in the margins. Size: approximately 105x150. Each holder of an admission ticket was entitled to purchase one sheet. The ticket cost 1m and the sheet 1.70m (face value 98pf, charity 59pf, special paper 13pf).
   The margin of the souvenir sheet is ungummed.

Types of International Philatelic Exhibition Issue
**1930, Nov. 1              Wmk. 126**
B34 SP24 8 + 4pf dp green        .40    .75
  a.   Bklt. pane of 7 + label  19.00  50.00
        Never hinged            50.00
  b.   Bklt. pane, 3 #B34, 4
        #B35 + label            25.00  60.00
        Never hinged            60.00
B35 SP25 15 + 5pf car            .45    1.10
B36 SP26 25 + 10pf dk blue      7.50   22.50
B37 SP27 50 + 40pf dp brn      21.00   82.50
        Nos. B34-B37 (4)       29.35  106.85
    Set, never hinged          103.30

The surtax was for charity.

---

The Zwinger at Dresden SP28          Breslau City Hall SP29

Heidelberg Castle SP30          Holsten Gate, Lübeck SP31

**1931, Nov. 1**
B38 SP28 8 + 4pf dk green        .30    1.00
  a.   Bklt. pane of 7 + label  15.00  35.00
        Never hinged            40.00
  b.   Bklt. pane, 3 #B38, 4
        #B39 + label            25.00  57.50
        Never hinged            57.50
B39 SP29 15 + 5pf carmine        .45    1.00
B40 SP30 25 + 10pf dk green     7.50   22.50
B41 SP31 50 + 40pf dp
        brown                  32.50   75.00
        Nos. B38-B41 (4)       40.75   99.50
    Set, never hinged          159.35

The surtax was for charity.

Nos. B38-B39 Surcharged

**1932, Feb. 2**
B42 SP28 6 + 4pf on 8+4pf       4.50    9.75
B43 SP29 12 + 3pf on 15+5pf     5.00   11.00
    Set, never hinged           41.25

Wartburg Castle — SP32          Stolzenfels Castle — SP33

Nuremberg Castle — SP34          Lichtenstein Castle — SP35

Marburg Castle — SP36

**1932, Nov. 1              Engr.**
B44 SP32 4 + 2pf lt blue         .30    .50
  a.   Bklt. pane, 5 #B44, 5 #B45 11.00  27.50
        Never hinged            27.50
B45 SP33 6 + 4pf olive grn       .30    .50
B46 SP34 12 + 3pf lt red         .50    1.00
  b.   Bklt. pane of 8 + 2 labels 11.00  27.50
        Never hinged            27.50
B47 SP35 25 + 10pf dp blue      7.50   17.00
B48 SP36 40 + 40pf brown
        vio                    27.50   60.00
        Nos. B44-B48 (5)       36.10   79.00
    Set, never hinged          140.25

The surtax was for charity.

"Tannhäuser" SP37

Designs: 4pf+2pf, "Der Fliegende Hollander." 5pf+2pf, "Das Rheingold." 6pf+4pf, "Die Meistersinger." 8pf+4pf, "Die Walkure."

12pf+3pf, "Siegfried." 20pf+10pf, "Tristan und Isolde." 25pf+15pf, "Lohengrin." 40pf+35pf, "Parsifal."

## Wmk. Swastikas (237)

### 1933, Nov. 1     Perf. 13½x13

| | | | | |
|---|---|---|---|---|
| B49 | SP37 | 3 + 2pf bister brn | 1.90 | 4.75 |
| B50 | SP37 | 4 + 2pf dk blue | 1.40 | 1.90 |
| b. | | Bklt. pane, 5 #B50, 5 #B52 | 65.00 | 160.00 |
| | | Never hinged | 160.00 | |
| B51 | SP37 | 5 + 2pf brt green | 3.75 | 6.00 |
| B52 | SP37 | 6 + 4pf gray grn | 1.40 | 1.50 |
| B53 | SP37 | 8 + 4pf dp orange | 1.90 | 3.50 |
| b. | | Bklt. pane, 5 #B53, 4 #B53, 4 #B54 + label | 77.50 | 190.00 |
| | | Never hinged | 190.00 | |
| B54 | SP37 | 12 + 3pf brown red | 1.90 | 1.75 |
| B55 | SP37 | 20 + 10pf blue | 150.00 | 190.00 |
| B56 | SP37 | 25 + 15pf ultra | 24.00 | 37.50 |
| B57 | SP37 | 40 + 35pf magenta | 110.00 | 125.00 |
| | | Nos. B49-B57 (9) | 296.25 | 371.90 |
| | | Set, never hinged | 2,208. | |

### Perf. 13½x14

| | | | | |
|---|---|---|---|---|
| B50a | SP37 | 4 + 2pf dark blue | 1.10 | 3.00 |
| B52a | SP37 | 6 + 4pf gray green | 1.10 | 4.75 |
| B53a | SP37 | 8 + 4pf deep orange | 1.90 | 3.75 |
| B54a | SP37 | 12 + 3pf brown red | 2.25 | 6.25 |
| B55a | SP37 | 20 + 10pf blue | 110.00 | 97.50 |
| | | Nos. B50a-B55a (5) | 116.35 | 115.25 |
| | | Set, never hinged | 765.00 | |

### Types of Semi-Postal Stamps of 1924 Issue Overprinted "1923-1933"
### Souvenir Sheet

### 1933, Nov. 29    Typo.    Perf. 14½

| | | | | |
|---|---|---|---|---|
| B58 | | Sheet of 4 | 1,350. | 9,750. |
| | | Never hinged | 5,250. | |
| a. | SP2 | 5 + 15pf dark green | 75.00 | 300.00 |
| b. | SP2 | 10 + 30pf vermilion | 75.00 | 300.00 |
| c. | SP2 | 20 + 60pf dark blue | 75.00 | 300.00 |
| d. | SP2 | 50pf + 1.50m dk brown | 75.00 | 300.00 |
| | | Any single, never hinged | 190.00 | |

The Swastika watermark covers the four stamps and above them appears a further watermark "10 Jahre Deutsche Nothilfe" and "1923-1933" below. Sheet size: 208x148mm.

The margin of the souvenir sheet is ungummed.

Businessman SP46      Judge SP54

Designs: 4pf+2pf, Blacksmith. 5pf+2pf, Mason. 6pf+4f, Miner. 8pf+4pf, Architect. 12pf+3pf, Farmer. 20pf+10pf, Agricultural Chemist. 25pf+15pf, Sculptor.

### 1934, Nov. 5    Engr.    Perf. 13x13½

| | | | | |
|---|---|---|---|---|
| B59 | SP46 | 3 + 2pf brown | .75 | 1.00 |
| B60 | SP46 | 4 + 2pf black | .75 | 1.00 |
| a. | | Bklt. pane, 5 #B60, 5 #B62 | 18.00 | 45.00 |
| | | Never hinged | 45.00 | |
| B61 | SP46 | 5 + 2pf green | 6.00 | 7.50 |
| B62 | SP46 | 6 + 4pf dull grn | .45 | .50 |
| B63 | SP46 | 8 + 4pf org brn | .75 | 1.00 |
| a. | | Bklt. pane, 5 #B63, 4 #B64 + label | 30.00 | 75.00 |
| | | Never hinged | 75.00 | |
| B64 | SP46 | 12 + 3pf henna brn | .45 | .50 |
| B65 | SP46 | 20 + 10pf Prus blue | 15.00 | 21.00 |
| B66 | SP46 | 25 + 15pf ultra | 15.00 | 21.00 |
| B67 | SP54 | 40 + 35pf plum | 45.00 | 67.50 |
| | | Nos. B59-B67 (9) | 84.15 | 121.00 |
| | | Set, never hinged | 417.00 | |

### Souvenir Sheet

SP55

---

| | | | | |
|---|---|---|---|---|
| B68 | SP55 | Sheet of 4 | 825.00 | 700.00 |
| a. | | 3pf red brown | 32.50 | 37.50 |
| b. | | 6pf dark green | 32.50 | 37.50 |
| c. | | 12pf dark carmine | 32.50 | 37.50 |
| d. | | 25pf dark blue | 32.50 | 37.50 |

### 1935, June 23    Wmk. 241    Perf. 14

Watermarked cross on each stamp and "OSTROPA 1935" in the margins of the sheet. Size: 148x104mm. 1.70m was the price of a ticket of admission to the Intl. Exhib., Königsberg, June 23-July 3, 1935.

Because the gum on No. B68 contains sulphuric acid and tends to damage the sheet, most collectors prefer to remove it. **Catalogue unused values are for sheet and singles without gum.**

East Prussia SP59     Skating SP69

Designs (Costumes of Various Sections of Germany): 4pf+3pf, Silesia. 5pf+3pf, Rhineland. 6pf+4pf, Lower Saxony. 8pf+4pf, Brandenburg. 12pf+6pf, Black Forest. 15pf+10pf, Hesse. 25pf+15pf, Upper Bavaria. 30pf+20pf, Friesland. 40pf+35pf, Franconia.

### Wmk. Swastikas (237)

### 1935, Oct. 4    Perf. 14x13½

| | | | | |
|---|---|---|---|---|
| B69 | SP59 | 3 + 2pf dk brown | .20 | .25 |
| a. | | Bklt. pane, 4 #B69, 5 #B74 + label | 15.00 | 37.50 |
| | | Never hinged | 37.50 | |
| B70 | SP59 | 4 + 3pf gray | 1.00 | 1.25 |
| B71 | SP59 | 5 + 3pf emerald | .20 | .65 |
| a. | | Bklt. pane, 5 #B71, 5 #B72 | 4.75 | 11.00 |
| | | Never hinged | 11.00 | |
| B72 | SP59 | 6 + 4pf dk green | .20 | .25 |
| B73 | SP59 | 8 + 4pf yel brn | 1.75 | 1.10 |
| B74 | SP59 | 12 + 6pf dk car | .20 | .25 |
| B75 | SP59 | 15 + 10pf red brn | 4.00 | 5.00 |
| B76 | SP59 | 25 + 15pf ultra | 7.00 | 5.00 |
| B77 | SP59 | 30 + 20pf olive brn | 8.75 | 16.00 |
| B78 | SP59 | 40 + 35pf plum | 8.75 | 12.00 |
| | | Nos. B69-B78 (10) | 31.30 | 41.75 |
| | | Set, never hinged | 160.00 | |

### 1935, Nov. 25    Perf. 13½

12+6pf, Ski jump. 25+15pf, Bobsledding.

| | | | | |
|---|---|---|---|---|
| B79 | SP69 | 6 + 4pf green | .65 | .45 |
| B80 | SP69 | 12 + 4pf carmine | 1.25 | .80 |
| B81 | SP69 | 25 + 15pf ultra | 6.00 | 7.00 |
| | | Nos. B79-B81 (3) | 7.90 | 8.25 |
| | | Set, never hinged | | |

Winter Olympic Games held in Bavaria, Feb. 6-16, 1936.

### 1936, May 8

Designs: 3pf+2pf, Horizontal bar. 4pf+3pf, Diving. 6pf+4pf, Soccer. 8pf+4pf, Throwing javelin. 12pf+6pf, Torch runner. 15pf+10pf, Fencing. 25pf+15pf, Sculling. 40pf+35pf, Equestrian.

| | | | | |
|---|---|---|---|---|
| B82 | SP69 | 3 + 2pf brown | .20 | .25 |
| a. | | Bklt. pane, 5 #B82, 5 #B86 | 8.00 | 20.00 |
| | | Never hinged | 20.00 | |
| B83 | SP69 | 4 + 3pf indigo | .20 | .50 |
| a. | | Bklt. pane, 5 #B83, 5 #B84 | 8.00 | 20.00 |
| | | Never hinged | 20.00 | |
| B84 | SP69 | 6 + 4pf green | .20 | .25 |
| B85 | SP69 | 8 + 4pf red org | 3.00 | 1.25 |
| B86 | SP69 | 12 + 6pf carmine | .25 | .25 |
| B87 | SP69 | 15 + 10pf brn vio | 4.50 | 3.00 |
| B88 | SP69 | 25 + 15pf ultra | 3.00 | 3.25 |
| B89 | SP69 | 40 + 35pf violet | 5.25 | 7.00 |
| | | Nos. B82-B89 (8) | 16.60 | 15.75 |
| | | Set, never hinged | 110.00 | |

Summer Olympic Games, Berlin, 8/1-16/36. See Nos. B91-B92.

### Souvenir Sheet

Horse Race — SP80

### 1936, June 22    Wmk. 237    Perf. 14

| | | | | |
|---|---|---|---|---|
| B90 | SP80 | 42pf brown | 7.50 | 13.50 |
| | | Never hinged | | |

A surtax of 1.08m was to provide a 100,000m sweepstakes prize. Wmk. 237 appears on the stamp, with "Munchen Riem 1936" watermarked on sheet margin.

For overprint see No. B105.

---

### Type of 1935
### Souvenir Sheets

### 1936, Aug. 1    Perf. 14x13½

| | | | | |
|---|---|---|---|---|
| B91 | SP69 | Sheet of 4 | 26.00 | 47.50 |
| B92 | SP69 | Sheet of 4 | 26.00 | 47.50 |
| | | Set, never hinged | 85.00 | |

11th Olympic Games, Berlin. No. B91 contains Nos. B82-B84, B89. No. B92 contains Nos. B85-B88.

Wmk. 237 appears on each stamp with "XI Olympische Spiele-Berlin 1936" watermarked on sheet margin. Sold for 1m each.

Frontier Highway, Munich — SP81

Designs: 4pf+3pf, Ministry of Aviation. 5pf+3pf, Nuremberg Memorial. 6pf+4pf, Bridge over the Saale, Saxony. 8pf+4pf, Germany Hall, Berlin. 12pf+6pf, German Alpine highway. 15pf+10pf, Fuhrer House, Munich. 25pf+15pf, Bridge over the Mangfall. 40pf+35pf, Museum of German Art, Munich.

### Perf. 13½x14

### 1936, Sept. 21     Unwmk.

| | | | | |
|---|---|---|---|---|
| B93 | SP81 | 3pf + 2pf blk brn | .20 | .25 |
| a. | | Bklt. pane, 4 #B93 + 5 #B98 + label | 10.00 | 24.00 |
| | | Never hinged | 24.00 | |
| B94 | SP81 | 4pf + 3pf black | .20 | .55 |
| B95 | SP81 | 5pf + 3pf brt grn | .20 | .25 |
| a. | | Bklt. pane, 5 #B95, 5 #B96) | 3.75 | 9.75 |
| | | Never hinged | 9.75 | |
| B96 | SP81 | 6pf + 4pf dk grn | .20 | .25 |
| B97 | SP81 | 8pf + 4pf brown | .70 | .25 |
| B98 | SP81 | 12pf + 6pf brn car | .20 | .25 |
| B99 | SP81 | 15pf + 10pf vio brn | 2.75 | 3.25 |
| B100 | SP81 | 25pf + 15pf indigo | 1.90 | 3.25 |
| B101 | SP81 | 40pf + 35pf rose vio | 3.00 | 5.00 |
| | | Nos. B93-B101 (9) | 9.35 | 14.30 |
| | | Set, never hinged | 60.15 | |

### Souvenir Sheets

Adolf Hitler — SP90

### Wmk. 237

### 1937, Apr. 5    Photo.    Perf. 14

| | | | | |
|---|---|---|---|---|
| B102 | SP90 | Sheet of 4 | 18.00 | 10.50 |
| | | Never hinged | 52.50 | |
| a. | | 6pf dark green | 1.10 | 1.50 |
| | | Never hinged | | |

48th birthday of Adolf Hitler. Sold for 1m. See #B103-B104. For overprint see #B106.

### 1937, Apr. 16     Imperf.

| | | | | |
|---|---|---|---|---|
| B103 | SP90 | Sheet of 4 | 37.50 | 22.50 |
| | | Never hinged | 165.00 | |
| a. | | 6pf dark green | 2.25 | 3.00 |
| | | Never hinged | | |

German Natl. Phil. Exhib., Berlin, June 16-18, 1937 and the Phil. Exhib. of the Stamp Collectors Group of the Strength Through Joy Organization at Hamburg, Apr. 17-20, 1937. Sold at the Exhib. post offices for 1.50m.

### No. B102 with Marginal Inscriptions
### Perf. 14 and Rouletted

### 1937, June 10     Wmk. 237

| | | | | |
|---|---|---|---|---|
| B104 | SP90 | Sheet of 4 | 37.50 | 67.50 |
| | | Never hinged | 240.00 | |
| a. | | 6pf dark grn + 25pf label | 3.00 | 6.75 |
| | | Never hinged | 9.75 | |

No. B104 inscribed in the margin beside each stamp "25 Rpf. einschliesslich Kulturspende" in three lines.

The sheets were rouletted to allow for separation of each stamp with its component label. Sold at the post office as individual stamps with labels attached or in complete sheets.

---

### Souvenir Sheet No. B90 Overprinted in Red

### 1937, Aug. 1     Perf. 14

| | | | | |
|---|---|---|---|---|
| B105 | SP80 | 42pf brown | 60.00 | 97.50 |
| | | Never hinged | 150.00 | |

4th running of the "Brown Ribbon" horse race at the Munich-Riem Race Course, Aug. 1, 1937.

### Souvenir Sheet No. B104 Overprinted in Black on Each Stamp

### Perf. 14 and Rouletted

### 1937, Sept. 3     Wmk. 237

| | | | | |
|---|---|---|---|---|
| B106 | SP90 | Sheet of 4 | 75.00 | 45.00 |
| | | Never hinged | 250.00 | |
| a. | | 6pf dark grn + 25pf label | 4.50 | 5.50 |
| | | Never hinged | 13.50 | |

1937 Nazi Congress at Nuremburg.

Lifeboat — SP91

Designs: 4pf+3pf, Lightship "Elbe I." 5pf+3pf, Fishing smacks. 6pf+4pf, Steamer. 8pf+4pf, Sailing vessel. 12pf+6pf, The "Tannenberg." 15pf+10pf, Sea-Train "Schwerin." 25pf+15pf, S. S. Hamburg. 40pf+35pf, S. S. Bremen.

### Perf. 13½

### 1937, Nov. 4    Engr.    Unwmk.

| | | | | |
|---|---|---|---|---|
| B107 | SP91 | 3pf + 2pf dk brwn | .20 | .30 |
| a. | | Bklt. pane, 4 #B107 + 5 #B112 + label | 14.50 | |
| B108 | SP91 | 4pf + 3pf black | 1.00 | .80 |
| B109 | SP91 | 5pf + 3pf yel grn | .20 | .30 |
| a. | | Bklt. pane, 5 #B109, 5 #B110 | 6.00 | |
| B110 | SP91 | 6pf + 4pf bl grn | .20 | .30 |
| B111 | SP91 | 8pf + 4pf orange | .60 | 1.25 |
| B112 | SP91 | 12pf + 6pf car lake | .20 | .20 |
| B113 | SP91 | 15pf + 10pf vio brn | 1.25 | 3.75 |
| B114 | SP91 | 25pf + 15pf ultra | 3.00 | 3.75 |
| B115 | SP91 | 40pf + 35pf red vio | 5.00 | 7.50 |
| | | Nos. B107-B115 (9) | 11.65 | 18.15 |
| | | Set, never hinged | 83.55 | |

No. B115 actually pictures the S.S. Europa.

Youth Carrying Torch and Laurel — SP100     Adolf Hitler — SP101

### Wmk. 237

### 1938, Jan. 28    Photo.    Perf. 14

| | | | | |
|---|---|---|---|---|
| B116 | SP100 | 6 + 4pf dk green | .90 | 1.90 |
| B117 | SP100 | 12 + 8pf brt car | .90 | 1.90 |
| | | Set, never hinged | 15.00 | |

Assumption of power by the Nazis, 5th anniv.

### 1938, Apr. 13    Engr.    Unwmk.

| | | | | |
|---|---|---|---|---|
| B118 | SP101 | 12 + 38pf copper red | 1.90 | 2.25 |
| | | Never hinged | 9.75 | |

Hitler's 49th birthday.

Horsewoman
SP102

**1938, July 20**
B119 SP102 42 + 108pf dp
brn 21.00 *45.00*
Never hinged 110.00

5th "Brown Ribbon" at Munich.

Adolf Hitler
SP103

Theater at
Saarbrücken
SP104

**1938, Sept. 1**
B120 SP103 6 + 19pf deep grn 2.25 *3.75*
Never hinged 15.00

1938 Nazi Congress at Nuremberg. The surtax was for Hitler's National Culture Fund.

**1938, Oct. 9    Photo.    Wmk. 237**
B121 SP104 6 + 4pf blue grn .90 *1.90*
B122 SP104 12 + 8pf dk car 1.90 *2.50*
Set, never hinged 19.00

Inauguration of the theater of the District of Saarpfalz at Saarbrücken. The surtax was for Hitler's National Culture Fund.

Castle of
Forchtenstein
SP105

Designs (scenes in Austria and various flowers): 4pf+3pf, Flexenstrasse in Vorarlberg. 5pf+3pf, Zell am See, Salzburg. 6pf+4pf, Grossglockner. 8pf+4pf, Ruins of Aggstein. 12pf+6pf, Prince Eugene Monument, Vienna. 15pf+10pf, Erzberg. 25pf+15pf, Hall, Tyrol. 40pf+35pf, Braunau.

**Unwmk.**
**1938, Nov. 18    Engr.    Perf. 14**
B123 SP105 3 + 2pf olive brn .20 *.30*
a.   Bklt. pane, 4 #B123, 5
     #B128 + label 9.25 24.00
     Never hinged 24.00
B124 SP105 4 + 3pf indigo 1.50 1.25
B125 SP105 5 + 3pf emerald .20 *.30*
a.   Bklt. pane, 5 #B125, 5
     #B126 3.25 *7.50*
     Never hinged 7.50
B126 SP105 6 + 4pf dk grn .20 *.20*
B127 SP105 8 + 4pf red org 1.50 1.25
B128 SP105 12 + 6pf dk car .20 *.30*
B129 SP105 15 + 10pf dp cl 2.75 *4.00*
B130 SP105 25 + 15pf dk blue 2.50 *4.00*
B131 SP105 40 + 35pf plum 5.75 *7.00*
     Nos. B123-B131 (9) 14.80 *18.60*
Set, never hinged 74.80

The surtax was for "Winter Help."

Sudeten
Couple — SP114

**1938, Dec. 2    Photo.    Wmk. 237**
B132 SP114 6 + 4pf blue grn 1.10 *2.50*
B133 SP114 12 + 8pf dk car 2.25 *3.00*
Set, never hinged 30.00

Annexation of the Sudeten Territory. The surtax was for Hitler's National Culture Fund.

Early Types of
Automobiles
SP115

**1939**

Designs: 12pf+8pf, Racing cars. 25pf+10pf, Modern automobile.

B134 SP115 6 + 4pf dk grn 3.50 3.50
B135 SP115 12 + 8pf brt car 3.50 3.50
B136 SP115 25 + 10pf dp blue 5.75 *6.00*
     Nos. B134-B136 (3) 12.75 *13.00*
Set, never hinged 82.50

Berlin Automobile and Motorcycle Exhibition. The surtax was for Hitler's National Culture Fund. For overprints see #B141-B143.

Adolf Hitler
SP118

Exhibition
Building
SP119

**Unwmk.**
**1939, Apr. 13    Engr.    Perf. 14**
B137 SP118 12 + 38pf carmine 1.50 *4.00*
Never hinged 8.25

Hitler's 50th birthday. The surtax was for Hitler's National Culture Fund.

**1939, Apr. 22    Photo.    Perf. 12½**
B138 SP119 6 + 4pf dk green 1.00 *2.50*
B139 SP119 15 + 5pf dp plum 1.00 *2.50*
Set, never hinged 12.75

Horticultural Exhib. held at Stuttgart. Surtax for Hitler's National Culture Fund.

Adolf
Hitler — SP120

**Perf. 14x13½**
**1939, Apr. 28    Wmk. 237**
B140 SP120 6 + 19pf black brn 3.25 *9.00*
Never hinged 18.00

Day of National Labor. The surtax was for Hitler's National Culture Fund.
See No. B147.

Nos. B134-B136
Overprinted in
Black

**1939, May 18    Perf. 14**
B141 SP115 6 + 4pf dk
     green 18.00 *26.00*
B142 SP115 12 + 8pf brt car 18.00 *26.00*
B143 SP115 25 + 10pf dp
     blue 18.00 *26.00*
     Nos. B141-B143 (3) 54.00 *78.00*
Set, never hinged 210.00

Nurburgring Auto Races, 5/21, 7/23/39.

Racehorse
"Investment"
and Jockey
SP121

**1939, June 18    Engr.    Unwmk.**
B144 SP121 25 + 50pf ultra 15.00 15.00
Never hinged 60.00

70th anniv. of the German Derby. The surtax was divided between Hitler's National Culture Fund and the race promoters.

Man Holding
Rearing
Horse — SP122

"Venetian Woman"
by Albrecht
Dürer — SP123

**1939, July 12**
B145 SP122 42 + 108pf dp
     brown 15.00 *24.00*
Never hinged 60.00

6th "Brown Ribbon" at Munich.

**1939, July 12    Photo.    Wmk. 237**
B146 SP123 6 + 19pf dk green 5.25 *9.75*
Never hinged 26.00

Day of German Art. The surtax was used for Hitler's National Culture Fund.

Hitler Type of 1939
Inscribed "Reichsparteitag 1939"
**1939, Aug. 25    Perf. 14x13½**
B147 SP120 6 + 19pf black brn 3.50 *9.00*
Never hinged 18.00

1939 Nazi Congress at Nuremberg.

Meeting in
German
Hall, Berlin
SP124

Designs: 4pf+3pf, Meeting of postal and telegraph employees. 5pf+3pf, Professional competitions. 6pf+4pf, 6pf+9pf, Professional camp. 8pf+4pf, 8pf+12pf, Gold flag competitions. 10pf+5pf, Awarding prizes. 12&+6pf, 12pf+18pf, Automobile race. 15pf+10pf, Sports. 16pf+10pf, 16pf+24pf, Postal police. 20pf+10pf, 20pf+30pf, Glider workshops. 24pf+10pf, 24pf+36pf, Mail coach. 25pf+15pf, Convalescent home, Konigstein.

**Perf. 13½x14**
| | | Unwmk. | Photo. |
|---|---|---|---|
| **1939-41** | | | |
| B148 | SP124 | 3 + 2pf bister brn | 1.50 *4.50* |
| B149 | SP124 | 4 + 3pf slate blue | 1.50 *4.50* |
| B150 | SP124 | 5 + 3pf brt bl grn | .45 *1.25* |
| B151 | SP124 | 6 + 4pf myrtle grn | .55 *1.10* |
| B151A | SP124 | 6 + 9pf dk grn ('41) | .55 *1.25* |
| B152 | SP124 | 8 + 4pf dp orange | .55 *1.25* |
| B152A | SP124 | 8 + 12pf hn brn ('41) | .80 *1.00* |
| B153 | SP124 | 10 + 5pf dk brown | .45 *1.60* |
| B154 | SP124 | 12 + 6pf rose brown | .60 *1.60* |
| B154A | SP124 | 12 + 18pf dk car rose ('41) | .80 *1.00* |
| B155 | SP124 | 15 + 10pf dp red lilac | .45 *1.60* |
| B156 | SP124 | 16 + 10pf slate grn | .45 *1.60* |
| B156A | SP124 | 16 + 24pf black ('41) | .80 *3.25* |
| B157 | SP124 | 20 + 10pf ultra | .60 *1.60* |
| B157A | SP124 | 20 + 30pf ultra ('41) | .80 *3.25* |
| B158 | SP124 | 24 + 10pf ol grn | 1.50 *3.25* |
| B158A | SP124 | 24 + 36pf pur ('41) | 2.50 *9.00* |

B159 SP124 25 + 15pf dk
     blue 1.50 *2.60*
     Nos. B148-B159 (18) 16.35 *45.20*
Set, never hinged 110.00

The surtax was used for Hitler's National Culture Fund and the Postal Employees' Fund. See Nos. B273, B275-B277.

Elbogen
Castle — SP136

Buildings: 4pf+3pf, Drachenfels on the Rhine. 5pf+3pf, Kaiserpfalz at Goslar. 6pf+4pf, Clocktower at Graz. 8pf+4pf, Town Hall, Frankfurt. 12pf+6pf, Guild House, Klagenfurt. 15pf+10pf, Ruins of Schreckenstein Castle. 25pf+15pf, Fortress of Salzburg. 40pf+35pf, Castle of Hohentwiel.

**1939    Unwmk.    Engr.    Perf. 14**
B160 SP136 3 + 2pf dk brn .20 *.40*
a.   Bklt. pane, 4 #B160, 5
     #B165 + label 9.25 24.00
     Never hinged 24.00
B161 SP136 4 + 3pf gray blk 1.40 1.75
B162 SP136 5 + 3pf emerald .20 *.50*
a.   Bklt. pane, 5 #B162, 5
     #B163 4.00 *9.75*
     Never hinged 9.75
B163 SP136 6 + 4pf slate grn .20 *.35*
B164 SP136 8 + 4pf red org 1.40 1.40
B165 SP136 12 + 6pf dk car .20 *.35*
B166 SP136 15 + 10pf brn vio 2.10 *4.25*
B167 SP136 25 + 15pf ultra 1.60 *4.25*
B168 SP136 40 + 35pf rose
     vio 2.25 *5.75*
     Nos. B160-B168 (9) 9.55 *19.00*
Set, never hinged 45.00

Hall of Honor at
Chancellery,
Berlin — SP145

**1940, Mar. 28**
B169 SP145 24 + 76pf dk grn 6.00 *17.00*
Never hinged 27.50

2nd National Stamp Exposition, Berlin.

Child Greeting
Hitler — SP146

**Perf. 14x13½**
**1940, Apr. 10    Photo.    Wmk. 237**
B170 SP146 12 + 38pf cop red 1.50 *5.50*
Never hinged 11.00

51st birthday of Adolf Hitler.

Armed Warrior
SP147

Horseman
SP148

**1940, Apr. 30    Unwmk.    Perf. 14**
B171 SP147 6 + 4pf sl grn & lt
     grn .30 *1.25*
     Never hinged 1.00

Issued to commemorate May Day.

**Perf. 14x13½**
**1940, June 22    Wmk. 237**
B172 SP148 25 + 100pf dp ul-
     tra 3.50 *10.50*
     Never hinged 20.00

Blue Ribbon race, Hamburg, June 30, 1940. Surtax for Hitler's National Culture Fund.

Chariot
SP149

**Unwmk.**

**1940, July 20    Engr.    Perf. 14**
B173 SP149 42 + 108pf brown    22.50  *26.00*
  Never hinged    90.00

7th "Brown Ribbon" at Munich.
The surtax was for Hitler's National Culture Fund and the promoters of the race.

View of Malmedy
SP150

Design: 12pf+8pf, View of Eupen.

**Perf. 14x13½**

**1940, July 25    Photo.    Wmk. 237**
B174 SP150  6 + 4pf dk green    .65  *2.75*
B175 SP150 12 + 8pf org red    .65  *2.75*
  Set, never hinged    8.25

Issued on the occasion of the reunion of Eupen-Malmedy with the Reich.

Rocky Cliffs of Heligoland
SP152

Artushof in Danzig — SP153

**1940, Aug. 9    Unwmk.**
B176 SP152 6 + 94pf brt bl
    grn & red org    4.00  *11.00*
  Never hinged    22.50

Heligoland's 50th year as part of Germany.

**1940, Nov. 5    Engr.    Perf. 14**
Buildings: 4pf+3pf, Town Hall, Thorn. 5pf+3pf, Castle at Kaub. 6pf+4pf, City Theater, Poznan. 8pf+4pf, Castle at Heidelberg. 12pf+6pf, Porta Nigra Trier. 15pf+10pf, New German Theater, Prague. 25pf+15pf, Town Hall, Bremen. 40pf+35pf, Town Hall, Munster.

B177 SP153  3 + 2pf dk brn    .20  *.35*
  a.    Bkt. pane, 4 #B177 + 5
        #B182 + label    7.50  *19.00*
      Never hinged    19.00
B178 SP153  4 + 3pf bluish
        blk    .45  *.80*
B179 SP153  5 + 3pf yel grn    .20  *.50*
  a.    Bkt. pane, 5 #B179, 5
        #B180    3.75  *9.25*
      Never hinged    9.25
B180 SP153  6 + 4pf dk grn    .20  *.30*
B181 SP153  8 + 4pf dp org    .90  *.75*
B182 SP153 12 + 6pf carmine    .20  *.30*
B183 SP153 15 + 10pf dk vio
        brn    .90  *2.50*
B184 SP153 25 + 15pf dp ultra    1.25  *2.50*
B185 SP153 40 + 35pf red lil    2.50  *6.00*
  Nos. B177-B185 (9)    6.80  *14.00*
  Set, never hinged    32.00

von Behring
SP162

Postilion
SP163

**1940, Nov. 26    Photo.**
B186 SP162  6 + 4pf dp green    .45  *1.50*
B187 SP162 25 + 10pf brt ultra    .90  *2.25*
  Set, never hinged    11.00

Dr. Emil von Behring (1854-1917), bacteriologist.

**1941, Jan. 12    Perf. 14x13½**
B188 SP163 6 +24pf dp green    .75  *2.25*
  Never hinged    5.00

Postage Stamp Day. The surtax was for Hitler's National Culture Fund.

Benito Mussolini and Adolf Hitler
SP164

**Perf. 13½x14**

**1941, Jan. 30    Wmk. 237**
B189 SP164 12 + 38pf rose brn    .50  *2.50*
  Never hinged    5.25

Issued as propaganda for the Rome-Berlin Axis. The surtax was for Hitler's National Culture Fund.

Adolf Hitler — SP165          Race Horse — SP166

**1941, Apr. 17    Perf. 14x13½**
B190 SP165 12 + 38pf dk red    1.10  *3.00*
  Never hinged    7.50

52nd birthday of Adolf Hitler. The surtax was for Hitler's National Culture Fund.

**Perf. 13½x14**

**1941, June 20    Engr.    Unwmk.**
B191 SP166 25 + 100pf sapphire    2.75  *7.50*
  Never hinged    13.00

Issued in commemoration of the Blue Ribbon race held at Hamburg, June 29, 1941.

Amazons
SP167

**1941, July 20    Perf. 14**
B192 SP167 42 + 108pf brown    1.75  *4.50*
  Never hinged    8.25

8th "Brown Ribbon" at Munich.

Brandenburg Gate, Berlin — SP168

**1941, Sept. 9**
B193 SP168 25 + 50pf dp ultra    1.75  *5.50*
  Never hinged    10.00

Issued in honor of the Berlin races.

Marburg
SP169          Veldes
SP170

Pettau — SP171          Triglav — SP172

**1941, Sept. 29    Photo.**
B194 SP169  3 + 7pf brown    .70  *2.00*
B195 SP170  6 + 9pf purple    .55  *2.00*
B196 SP171 12 + 13pf rose
        brn    .70  *2.40*
B197 SP172 25 + 15pf dk blue    1.40  *1.75*
  Nos. B194-B197 (4)    3.35  *8.15*
  Set, never hinged    16.00

Annexation of Styria and Carinthia.

View from Belvedere Palace, Vienna — SP173

Belvedere Gardens, Vienna
SP174

**1941, Sept. 16    Engr.**
B198 SP173 12 + 8pf dp red    .65  *2.25*
B199 SP174 15 + 10pf violet    .65  *2.50*
  Set, never hinged    9.75

Issued to commemorate the Vienna Fair.

Mozart — SP175

**1941, Nov. 28**
B200 SP175  6 + 4pf dk rose vio    .20  *.60*
  Never hinged    .75

Wolfgang Amadeus Mozart (1756-91).

Philatelist
SP176

**1942, Jan. 11    Photo.**
B201 SP176  6 + 24pf dp purple    .50  *2.75*
  Never hinged    .75

To commemorate Stamp Day.

Soldier's Head — SP177

**1942, Mar. 10    Perf. 14x13½**
B202 SP177 12 + 38pf slate blk    .30  *1.50*
  Never hinged    1.60

To commemorate Hero Memorial Day.

Adolf Hitler — SP178

**1942, Apr. 13**
B203 SP178 12 + 38pf lake    1.50  *6.00*
  Never hinged    11.00

To commemorate Hitler's 53rd birthday.

Racing Three-year-old
SP179

**1942, June 16    Engr.    Perf. 14**
B204 SP179 25 + 100pf dk bl    4.50  *11.00*
  Never hinged    16.50

73rd Hamburg Derby.

Race Horses
SP180

**1942, July 14**
B205 SP180 42 + 108pf brown    1.50  *5.25*
  Never hinged    7.50

9th "Brown Ribbon" at Munich.

Lüneburg Lion and Nuremberg Betrothal Cup — SP181

**1942, Aug. 8    Photo.    Perf. 14x13½**
B206 SP181  6 + 4pf copper red    .20  *1.50*
B207 SP181 12 + 88pf green    .50  *2.25*
  Set, never hinged    3.00

10th anniv. of the German Goldsmiths' Society and the 1st Goldsmiths' Day in Germany.

Henlein Monument, Nuremberg — SP182

**1942, Aug. 29    Perf. 14**
B208 SP182  6 + 24pf rose vio    .45  *1.50*
  Never hinged    1.60

400th anniversary of the death of Peter Henlein, inventor of the pocket watch.

Postilion and Map of Europe
SP183

Postilion and Globe — SP184

Postilion SP185

**Perf. 13½x14, 14x13½**

**1942, Oct. 12**          **Photo.**
B209 SP183   3 + 7pf dull blue    .25 *1.50*

**Engr.**
B210 SP184   6 + 14pf ultra & dp
         brn       .35 *1.50*
B211 SP185 12 + 38pf rose red
         & dp brn    .50 *2.50*
    *Nos. B209-B211 (3)*   1.10 *5.50*
    Set, never hinged    3.75

European Postal Congress, Vienna.

Nos. B209 to B211 Overprinted in Black

**1942, Oct. 19**
B212 SP183   3 + 7pf      .65 *2.50*
B213 SP184   6 + 14pf     .65 *2.50*
B214 SP185 12 + 38pf     .90 *4.50*
    *Nos. B212-B214 (3)*   2.20 *9.50*
    Set, never hinged    7.50

To commemorate the signing of the European postal-telegraph agreement at Vienna.

Mail Coach SP186

**1943, Jan. 10**          **Engr.**
B215 SP186   6 + 24pf gray, brn
         & yel       .20 *.90*
                    .75

To commemorate Stamp Day. The surtax went to Hitler's National Culture Fund.

Brandenburg Gate SP187     Nazi Emblem SP188

**1943, Jan. 26**          **Photo.**
B216 SP187 54 + 96pf cop red   .45 *2.25*
    Never hinged             1.90

10th anniversary of the assumption of power by the Nazis.

**1943, Jan. 26**
B217 SP188   3 + 2pf olive bister   .20 *.90*
    Never hinged             .60

Used to secure special philatelic cancellations.

Submarine SP189

Designs: 4pf+3pf, Schutz-Staffel Troops. 5pf+4pf, Motorized marksmen. 6pf+9pf, Signal Corps. 8pf+7pf, Engineer Corps. 12pf+8pf, Grenade assault. 15pf+10pf, Heavy artillery. 20pf+14pf, Anti-aircraft units in action. 25pf+15pf, Dive bombers. 30pf+30pf, Paratroops. 40pf+40pf, Tank. 50pf+50pf, Speed boat.

**1943, Mar. 21**          **Engr.**
B218 SP189   3 + 2pf dk brn    .35 *1.25*
B219 SP189   4 + 3pf brown    .35 *1.25*
B220 SP189   5 + 4pf dk grn    .35 *1.25*
B221 SP189   6 + 9pf dp violet   .35 *1.25*
B222 SP189   8 + 7pf brn org    .35 *1.25*
B223 SP189 12 + 8pf car lake   .35 *1.25*
B224 SP189 15 + 10pf vio brn   .35 *1.25*
B225 SP189 20 + 14pf slate bl   .35 *1.25*
B226 SP189 25 + 15pf indigo   .35 *1.25*
B227 SP189 30 + 30pf green    .55 *1.90*
B228 SP189 40 + 40pf red lil    .55 *1.90*
B229 SP189 50 50pf grnsh blk   .80 *3.00*
    *Nos. B218-B229 (12)*   5.05 *18.05*
    Set, never hinged    17.00

Army Day and Hero Memorial Day. Nos. B220 and B224 exist imperf. Value, each $75.

Nazi Flag and Children SP201

**1943, Mar. 26**          **Photo.**
B230 SP201   6 + 4pf dk green   .20 *.90*
    Never hinged             .85

To commemorate the Day of Youth Obligation when all German boys and girls had to take an oath of allegiance to Hitler.

Adolf Hitler SP202

**1943, Apr. 13**
B231 SP202   3 + 7pf brown
         blk        .45 *1.50*
B232 SP202   6 + 14pf dk grn   .45 *1.50*
B233 SP202   8 + 22pf dk
         chlky bl    .45 *1.50*
B234 SP202 12 + 38pf cop red   .45 *1.50*
B235 SP202 24 + 76pf vio brn   .95 *3.50*
B236 SP202 40 + 160pf dk ol
         grn       .95 *3.50*
    *Nos. B231-B236 (6)*   3.70 *13.00*
    Set, never hinged    9.75

Hitler's 54th birthday. No. B231 exists imperf. Value $100.

Reich Labor Service Corpsmen
SP203        SP204

Designs: 6pf+14pf, Corpsman chopping. 12pf+18pf, Corpsman with implements.

**1943, June 26**          **Engr.**
B237 SP203   3 + 7pf bis brn   .20 *.75*
B238 SP204   5 + 10pf pale ol
         grn       .20 *.50*
B239 SP204   6 + 14pf dp blue   .20 *.50*
B240 SP204 12 + 18pf dk red   .35 *1.40*
    *Nos. B237-B240 (4)*   .95 *3.15*
    Set, never hinged    2.40

Anniversary of Reich Labor Service. Nos. B237-B238, B240 exist imperf. Values: Nos. B237-B238, $45 each; No. B240, $60.

Rosegger's Birthplace, Upper Styria — SP207

Peter Rosegger SP208

**Perf. 13½x14, 14x13½**

**1943, July 27**          **Photo.**
B241 SP207   6 + 4pf green    .20 *.90*
B242 SP208 12 + 8pf copper red   .20 *.90*
    Set, never hinged    1.50

Centenary of the birth of Peter Rosegger, Austrian writer.

Hunter SP209

**1943, July 27**          **Engr.**
B243 SP209 42 + 108pf brown   .20 *1.25*
    Never hinged             .90

10th "Brown Ribbon" at Munich. No. B243 exists imperf. Value $200.

Race Horse — SP210

**1943, Aug. 14**
B244 SP210   6 + 4pf vio blk   .20 *1.25*
B245 SP210 12 + 88pf dk car   .20 *1.25*
    Set, never hinged    1.60

Grand Prize of the Freudenau, the Vienna race track, Aug. 15, 1943.

Mother and Children — SP211

**1943, Sept. 1**
B246 SP211 12 + 38pf dark red   .20 *1.25*
    Never hinged             .80

10th anniversary of Winter Relief.

St. George in Gold — SP212

**1943, Oct. 1**
B247 SP212   6 + 4pf dk ol grn   .20 *.75*
B248 SP212 12 + 88pf vio brn   .20 *1.10*
    Set, never hinged    1.10

German Goldsmiths' Society.

Ancient Lübeck — SP213

**1943, Oct. 24**          **Photo.**
B249 SP213 12 + 8pf copper red   .20 *1.10*
    Never hinged             .65

Hanseatic town of Lubeck, 800th anniv. No. B249 exists imperf. Value, $110.

"And Despite All, You Were Victorious" SP214

**1943, Nov. 5**
B250 SP214 24 + 26pf henna   .20 *1.10*
    Never hinged             .80

20th anniv. of the Nazis' Munich beer-hall putsch and to honor those who died for the Nazi movement. No. B250 exists imperf; value, $100.

Dr. Robert Koch — SP215

**1944, Jan. 25**    **Engr.**    **Unwmk.**
B251 SP215 12 + 38pf sepia   .20 *1.10*
    Never hinged             .75

Centenary of the birth of the bacteriologist, Robert Koch (1843-1910).

Hitler and Nazi Emblems SP216

**1944, Jan. 29**          **Photo.**
B252 SP216 54 + 96pf yel brn   .25 *1.25*
    Never hinged             .80

Assumption of power by the Nazis, 11th anniv.

Airport Scene — SP217

Seaplane SP218

Plane Seen from Above — SP219

**Perf. 14x13½, 13½x14**

**1944, Feb. 11**   **Photo.**   **Unwmk.**

| | | | | |
|---|---|---|---|---|
| B252A | SP217 | 6 + 4pf dk grn | .20 | 1.10 |
| B252B | SP218 | 12 + 8pf maroon | .20 | 1.10 |
| B252C | SP219 | 42 + 108pf dp slate bl | .30 | 2.25 |

Nos. B252A-B252C (3)   .70   4.45
Set, never hinged   2.40

25th anniv. of German air mail. The surtax was for the National Culture Fund.

Infant's Crib — SP220

6pf+4pf, Public nurse. 12pf+8pf, "Mother & Child" clinic. 15pf+10pf, Expectant mothers.

**1944, Mar. 2**

| | | | | |
|---|---|---|---|---|
| B253 | SP220 | 3 + 2pf dk brn | .20 | .50 |
| B254 | SP220 | 6 + 4pf dk grn | .20 | .50 |
| B255 | SP220 | 12 + 8pf dp car | .20 | .50 |
| B256 | SP220 | 15 + 10pf vio brn | .20 | .65 |

Nos. B253-B256 (4)   .80   2.15
Set, never hinged   1.25

10th anniv. of "Mother and Child" aid.

Assault Boat — SP221

**1944, Mar. 11**

Designs: 4pf+3pf, Chain-wheel vehicle. 5pf+3pf, Paratroops. 6pf+4pf, Submarine officer. 8pf+4pf, Schutz-Staffel grenade throwers. 10pf+5pf, Searchlight. 12pf+6pf, Infantry. 15pf+10pf, Self-propelled gun. 16pf+10pf, Speed boat. 20pf+10pf, Sea raider. 24pf+10pf, Railway artillery. 25pf+15pf, Rockets. 30pf+20pf, Mountain trooper.

**Inscribed: "Grossdeutsches Reich"**

| | | | | |
|---|---|---|---|---|
| B257 | SP221 | 3 + 2pf yel brn | .20 | 1.25 |
| B258 | SP221 | 4 + 3pf royal bl | .20 | .70 |
| B259 | SP221 | 5 + 3pf dp yel grn | .20 | .60 |
| B260 | SP221 | 6 + 4pf dp vio | .20 | .60 |
| B261 | SP221 | 8 + 4pf org ver | .20 | .70 |
| B262 | SP221 | 10 + 5pf chocolate | .20 | .60 |
| B263 | SP221 | 12 + 6pf carmine | .20 | .60 |
| B264 | SP221 | 15 + 10pf dp claret | .20 | .70 |
| B265 | SP221 | 16 + 10pf dk bl grn | .20 | 1.25 |
| B266 | SP221 | 20 + 10pf brt bl | .20 | 1.50 |
| B267 | SP221 | 24 + 10pf dl org brn | .20 | 1.50 |
| B268 | SP221 | 25 + 15pf vio bl | .80 | 4.00 |

| | | | | |
|---|---|---|---|---|
| B269 | SP221 | 30 + 20pf olive grn | .80 | 4.00 |

Nos. B257-B269 (13)   3.80   18.00
Set, never hinged   14.00

To commemorate Hero Memorial Day.

Flora Statue in Fulda's Schloss Garden — SP234

**1944, Mar. 11**

| | | | | |
|---|---|---|---|---|
| B270 | SP234 | 12 + 38pf dp brown | .20 | .90 |
| | | Never hinged | | .60 |

1,200th anniversary of town of Fulda.

Adolf Hitler — SP235

**1944, Apr. 14**   **Engr.**   **Unwmk.**

| | | | | |
|---|---|---|---|---|
| B271 | SP235 | 54 + 96pf rose car | .30 | 1.75 |
| | | Never hinged | | 1.25 |

To commemorate Hitler's 55th birthday.

Type of 1939-41 and

Woman Mail Carrier SP236

Field Post in the East — SP237

Designs: 8pf+12pf, Mail coach. 16pf+24pf, Automobile race. 20pf+30pf, Postal police. 24pf+36pf, Glider workshops.

**1944, May 3**   **Photo.**
**Designs measure 29½x24½mm**

| | | | | |
|---|---|---|---|---|
| B272 | SP236 | 6 + 9pf vio bl | .20 | .75 |
| B273 | SP124 | 8 + 12pf gray blk | .20 | .75 |
| B274 | SP237 | 12 + 18pf dp plum | .20 | .75 |
| B275 | SP124 | 16 + 24pf dk grn | .20 | .75 |

| | | | | |
|---|---|---|---|---|
| B276 | SP124 | 20 + 30pf blue | .20 | 1.40 |
| B277 | SP124 | 24 + 36pf dk pur | .20 | 1.40 |

Nos. B272-B277 (6)   1.20   5.80
Set, never hinged   2.50

Surtax for the Postal Employees' Fund.

Soldier and Tirolese Rifleman — SP238

**1944, July**

| | | | | |
|---|---|---|---|---|
| B278 | SP238 | 6 + 4pf dp grn | .20 | .80 |
| B279 | SP238 | 12 + 8pf brn lake | .20 | .80 |

Set, never hinged   .75

7th National Shooting Matches at Innsbruck.

Albert I, Duke of Prussia — SP239

**1944, July**

| | | | | |
|---|---|---|---|---|
| B280 | SP239 | 6 + 4pf dk bl grn | .25 | 1.25 |
| | | Set, never hinged | | .75 |

400th anniv. of Albert University, Königsberg.

Labor Corps Girl SP240

Labor Corpsman SP241

**1944, June**   **Engr.**

| | | | | |
|---|---|---|---|---|
| B281 | SP240 | 6 + 4pf green | .20 | .60 |
| B282 | SP241 | 12 + 8pf carmine | .20 | .65 |

Set, never hinged   .80

Issued to honor an exhibit of the Reich Labor Service.

Race Horse and Foal — SP242

**1944, July 23**   **Perf. 14x13½**

| | | | | |
|---|---|---|---|---|
| B283 | SP242 | 42 + 108pf brown | .25 | 2.00 |
| | | Never hinged | | 1.10 |

11th "Brown Ribbon" at Munich.

Race Horse's Head in Oak Wreath — SP243

**1944, Aug.**   **Photo.**   **Perf. 14**

| | | | | |
|---|---|---|---|---|
| B284 | SP243 | 6 + 4pf Prus green | .20 | 1.10 |
| B285 | SP243 | 12 + 88pf car lake | .20 | 1.10 |

Set, never hinged   1.10

Vienna Grand Prize Race.

Nautilus Cup in Green Vault, Dresden — SP244

**1944, Sept. 11**

| | | | | |
|---|---|---|---|---|
| B286 | SP244 | 6 + 4pf dk green | .20 | 1.10 |
| B287 | SP244 | 12 + 88pf car brn | .20 | 1.10 |

Set, never hinged   1.10

German Goldsmiths' Society. No. B287 exists imperf. Value \$175.

Post Horn and Letter — SP245

**1944, Oct. 2**

| | | | | |
|---|---|---|---|---|
| B288 | SP245 | 6 + 24pf dk green | .20 | 1.25 |
| | | Never hinged | | .65 |

To commemorate Stamp Day.

Eagle and Serpent — SP246

**1944, Nov. 9**

| | | | | |
|---|---|---|---|---|
| B289 | SP246 | 12 + 8pf rose red | .20 | 1.25 |
| | | Never hinged | | .75 |

21st anniv. of the Munich putsch.

Count Anton Günther — SP247

**1945, Jan. 6**   **Typo.**   **Perf. 13½x14**

| | | | | |
|---|---|---|---|---|
| B290 | SP247 | 6 + 14pf brown vio | .20 | 1.25 |
| | | Never hinged | | .75 |

600th anniv. of municipal law in Oldenburg. Exists imperf. Value, \$75.

People's Army — SP248

**1945, Feb.**   **Photo.**   **Perf. 14x13½**

| | | | | |
|---|---|---|---|---|
| B291 | SP248 | 12 + 8pf rose car | .30 | 2.25 |
| | | Never hinged | | 1.25 |

Proclamation of the People's Army (Volkssturm) in East Prussia to fight the Russians.

Elite Storm Trooper (S. S.) — SP249

Storm Trooper (S. A.) — SP250

**1945, Apr. 21**     *Perf. 13½x14*

| | | | |
|---|---|---|---|
| B292 | SP249 12 + 38pf brt car | 7.50 | 900.00 |
| B293 | SP250 12 + 38pf brt car | 7.50 | 900.00 |
| | Set, never hinged | 65.00 | |

12th anniv. of the assumption of power by the Nazis. Nos. B292-B293 were on sale in Berlin briefly before the collapse of that city. Exist imperf unused. Value same as perf. Forged cancels abound. Certificates of authenticity mandatory for used examples.

### Souvenir Sheets

SP251

### Wmk. 284

**1946, Dec. 8**    **Typo.**    *Perf. 14*

| | | | |
|---|---|---|---|
| B294 | SP251 Sheet of 3 | 19.00 | 140.00 |
| | Never hinged | 45.00 | |

*Imperf*

| | | | |
|---|---|---|---|
| B295 | SP251 Sheet of 3 | 19.00 | 175.00 |
| | Never hinged | 45.00 | |
| a. | A119 20pf light blue | 3.75 | 19.00 |
| b. | A119 24pf orange brown | 3.75 | 19.00 |
| c. | A119 40pf red violet | 3.75 | 19.00 |

No. B294 contains Nos. 543, 544 and 548. Nos. B294-B295 sold for 5m each. Surtax for refugees and the aged.

Leipzig Proclaimed Market Place, 1160 — SP252

Design: 60pf+40pf, Foreign merchants displaying their wares, 1268.

### Wmk. 48

**1947, Mar. 5**    **Engr.**    *Perf. 13*

| | | | |
|---|---|---|---|
| B296 | SP252 24 +26pf chestnut brn | .20 | 4.75 |
| B297 | SP252 60 + 40pf dp vio blue | .20 | 4.75 |
| | Set, never hinged | 1.50 | |

1947 Leipzig Fairs.
No. B296 exists imperf. Value $150.
See Nos. 580-583, 10NB1-10NB2, 10NB4-10NB5, 10NB12-10NB13 and German Democratic Republic Nos. B15-B16.

Madonna SP254      Cathedral Towers SP255

Designs: 12pf+8pf, Three Kings. 24pf+16pf, Cologne Cathedral.

### Wmk. 286

**1948, Aug. 15**    **Typo.**    *Perf. 11*

| | | | |
|---|---|---|---|
| B298 | SP254 6 + 4pf org brn | .30 | .75 |
| a. | "1948-1248" | 4.75 | 19.00 |
| | Never hinged | 11.50 | |
| B299 | SP254 12 + 8pf grnsh blue | .70 | 1.90 |
| a. | "1948-1948" | 6.25 | 22.50 |
| | Never hinged | 15.00 | |
| B300 | SP254 24 + 16pf car | 1.40 | 3.50 |
| B301 | SP255 50 + 50pf blue | 3.25 | 9.00 |
| | Nos. B298-B301 (4) | 5.65 | 15.15 |
| | Set, never hinged | 10.50 | |

700th anniv. of the laying of the cornerstone of Cologne Cathedral. The surtax was to aid in its reconstruction.

---

Specialists collect Nos. B298-B301 with watermark in four positions: upright, D's facing left; upright, D's facing right; sideways, D's facing up; sideways, D's facing down. Two types of perforation: line and comb.

Brandenburg Gate, Berlin SP256      Bicycle Racers SP257

*Perf. 10½x11½, 11*

**1948, Dec.**      Litho.

| | | | |
|---|---|---|---|
| B302 | SP256 10 + 5pf green | 3.00 | 7.50 |
| B303 | SP256 20 + 10pf rose car | 3.00 | 7.50 |
| | Set, never hinged | 11.50 | |

The surtax was for aid to Berlin.

### Wmk. 116

**1949, May 15**    **Engr.**    *Perf. 14*

| | | | |
|---|---|---|---|
| B304 | SP257 10 + 5pf green | 1.90 | 6.00 |
| B305 | SP257 20 + 10pf brn org | 4.50 | 16.50 |
| | Set, never hinged | 16.50 | |

1949 Bicycle Tour of Germany.

Goethe at Rome — SP258

Goethe — SP259

30pf+15pf, Goethe portrait facing left.

**1949, Aug. 15**

| | | | |
|---|---|---|---|
| B306 | SP258 10 + 5pf green | .90 | 3.00 |
| B307 | SP259 20 + 10pf red | 1.40 | 5.25 |
| B308 | SP259 30 + 15pf blue | 7.50 | 24.00 |
| | Nos. B306-B308 (3) | 9.80 | 32.25 |
| | Set, never hinged | 32.50 | |

Bicentenary of the birth of Johann Wolfgang von Goethe.
The surtax was for the reconstruction of Goethe House, Frankfurt-on-Main.

### Federal Republic

Bavaria Stamp of 1849 SP260    St. Elisabeth SP261

**1949, Sept. 30**    **Litho.**    **Wmk. 285**

| | | | |
|---|---|---|---|
| B309 | SP260 10 + 2pf grn & blk | 7.25 | 22.50 |
| | Never hinged | 13.00 | |

Centenary of German postage stamps.

**1949, Dec. 14**    **Engr.**    **Wmk. 286**

Designs: 10pf+5pf, Paracelsus. 20pf+10pf, F. W. A. Froebel. 30pf+15pf, J. H. Wichern.

| | | | |
|---|---|---|---|
| B310 | SP261 8 + 2pf brn vio | 8.50 | 22.50 |
| B311 | SP261 10 + 5pf yel grn | 6.25 | 11.50 |
| B312 | SP261 20 + 10pf red | 6.25 | 11.50 |

---

| | | | |
|---|---|---|---|
| B313 | SP261 30 + 15pf vio bl | 32.50 | 100.00 |
| | Nos. B310-B313 (4) | 53.50 | 145.50 |
| | Set, never hinged | 125.00 | |

The surtax was for welfare organizations.

Seal of Johann Sebastian Bach — SP262

Frescoes from Marienkirche SP263

**1950, July 28**      *Perf. 14*

| | | | |
|---|---|---|---|
| B314 | SP262 10 + 2pf dk grn | 22.50 | 42.50 |
| B315 | SP262 20 + 3pf dk car | 26.00 | 50.00 |
| | Set, never hinged | 120.00 | |

Bicentenary of the death of Bach.

**1951, Aug. 30**    **Photo.**    **Wmk. 286**
### Center in Gray

| | | | |
|---|---|---|---|
| B316 | SP263 10 + 5pf green | 27.50 | 67.50 |
| B317 | SP263 20 + 5pf brn lake | 32.50 | 75.00 |
| | Set, never hinged | 180.00 | |

Construction of Marienkirche, Lübeck, 700th anniv.
The surtax aided in its reconstruction.

Stamps Under Magnifying Glass — SP264    St. Vincent de Paul — SP265

### Wmk. 295

**1951, Sept. 14**    **Typo.**    *Perf. 14*

| | | | |
|---|---|---|---|
| B318 | SP264 10 + 2pf multi | 15.00 | 45.00 |
| B319 | SP264 20 + 3pf multi | 15.00 | 45.00 |
| | Set, never hinged | 82.50 | |

Natl. Philatelic Exposition, Wuppertal, 1951.

**1951, Oct. 23**      Engr.

Portraits: 10pf+3pf, Friedrich von Bodelschwingh. 20pf+5pf, Elsa Brandstrom. 30pf+10pf, Johann Heinrich Pestalozzi.

| | | | |
|---|---|---|---|
| B320 | SP265 4 + 2pf brown | 4.25 | 9.00 |
| B321 | SP265 10 + 3pf green | 6.25 | 7.50 |
| B322 | SP265 20 + 5pf rose red | 6.25 | 7.50 |
| B323 | SP265 30 + 10pf dp blue | 47.50 | 110.00 |
| | Nos. B320-B323 (4) | 64.25 | 134.00 |
| | Set, never hinged | 130.00 | |

The surtax was for charitable purposes.

Nuremberg Madonna SP266    Boy Hikers and Youth Hostel SP267

---

**1952, Aug. 9**

| | | | |
|---|---|---|---|
| B324 | SP266 10 + 5pf green | 7.50 | 18.00 |
| | Never hinged | 15.00 | |

Centenary of the founding of the Germanic National Museum, Nuremberg. The surtax was for the museum.

**1952, Sept. 17**      *Perf. 13½x14*

Design: 20pf+3pf, Girls and Hostel.

| | | | |
|---|---|---|---|
| B325 | SP267 10 + 2pf green | 9.25 | 20.00 |
| B326 | SP267 20 + 3pf dp car | 9.25 | 20.00 |
| | Set, never hinged | 37.50 | |

The surtax was to aid the youth program of the Federal Republic.

Elizabeth Fry SP268    Owl and Cogwheel SP269

10pf+5pf, Dr. Carl Sonnenschein. 20pf+10pf, Theodor Fliedner. 30pf+10pf, Henri Dunant.

**1952, Oct. 1**

| | | | |
|---|---|---|---|
| B327 | SP268 4 + 2pf org brn | 3.25 | 6.00 |
| B328 | SP268 10 + 5pf green | 3.25 | 6.00 |
| B329 | SP268 20 + 10pf brn car | 6.75 | 12.00 |
| B330 | SP268 30 + 10pf dp blue | 35.00 | 82.50 |
| | Nos. B327-B330 (4) | 48.25 | 106.50 |
| | Set, never hinged | 120.00 | |

The surtax was for welfare organizations.

**1953, May 7**    **Wmk. 295**    *Perf. 14*

| | | | |
|---|---|---|---|
| B331 | SP269 10 + 5pf dp grn | 13.00 | 30.00 |
| | Never hinged | 27.50 | |

50th anniv. of the founding of the German Museum in Munich.

Thurn and Taxis Palace Gate — SP270    August Hermann Francke — SP271

Design: 20pf+3pf, Telecommunications Bldg., Frankfurt-on-Main.

### Wmk. 285

**1953, July 29**    **Litho.**    *Perf. 13½*

| | | | |
|---|---|---|---|
| B332 | SP270 10 + 2pf yel grn, bl & fawn | 8.25 | 25.00 |
| B333 | SP270 20 + 3pf fawn, blk & gray | 8.25 | 25.00 |
| | Set, never hinged | 47.50 | |

The surtax was for the International Stamp Exhibition, Frankfurt-on-Main, 1953.

### Wmk. 295

**1953, Nov. 2**    **Engr.**    *Perf. 14*

Designs: 10pf+5pf, Sebastian Kneipp. 20pf+10pf, Dr. Johann Christian Senckenberg. 30pf+10pf, Fridtjof Nansen.

| | | | |
|---|---|---|---|
| B334 | SP271 4 + 2pf choc | 1.75 | 7.50 |
| B335 | SP271 10 + 5pf bl grn | 3.00 | 7.50 |
| B336 | SP271 20 + 10pf red | 5.00 | 11.00 |
| B337 | SP271 30 + 10pf blue | 20.00 | 67.50 |
| | Nos. B334-B337 (4) | 29.75 | 93.50 |
| | Set, never hinged | 77.50 | |

The surtax was for welfare organizations.

> **Catalogue values for unused stamps in this section, from this point to the end of the section, are for Never Hinged items.**

Käthe
Kollwitz — SP272

Carrier Pigeon
and Magnifying
Glass — SP273

Portraits: 10pf+5pf, Lorenz Werthmann.
20pf+10pf, Johann Friedrich Oberlin.
40pf+10pf, Bertha Pappenheim.

**1954, Dec. 28          Perf. 13½x14**
B338 SP272  7pf + 3pf brown    3.00   3.00
B339 SP272 10pf + 5pf green    1.50   1.50
B340 SP272 20pf + 10pf red     7.50   4.50
B341 SP272 40pf + 10pf blue   32.50  40.00
     Nos. B338-B341 (4)        44.50  49.00

The surtax was for welfare organizations.

**1955, Sept. 14  Wmk. 304   Perf. 14**
20pf+3pf, Post horn and stamp tongs.
B342 SP273 10pf + 2pf green    4.50   5.75
B343 SP273 20pf + 3pf red     10.50  13.50

WESTROPA, 1955, philatelic exhibition at
Dusseldorf. The surtax aided the Society of
German Philatelists.

Amalie
Sieveking — SP274

Portraits: 10pf+5pf, Adolph Kolping.
20pf+10pf, Dr. Samuel Hahnemann.
40pf+10pf, Florence Nightingale.

**1955, Nov. 15          Photo. & Litho.**
B344 SP274  7 + 3pf olive bis   3.00   3.00
B345 SP274 10 + 5pf dk green    2.25   1.50
B346 SP274 20 + 10pf red org    2.25   1.50
B347 SP274 40 + 10pf grnsh
              blue             30.00  37.50
     Nos. B344-B347 (4)        37.50  43.50

Surtax for independent welfare organizations.

Boy and
Geometrical
Designs
SP275

Design: 10pf+5pf, Girl playing flute.

**Unwmk.**
**1956, July 21  Litho.      Perf. 14**
B348 SP275  7pf + 3pf multi    1.90   3.00
B349 SP275 10pf + 5pf multi    6.50   7.50

The surtax was for the Youth Hostel
Organization.

The Midwife
SP276

10+5pf, Ignaz Philipp Semmelweis.
20+10pf, The mother. 40+10pf, The children's
nurse.

**1956, Oct. 1                    Photo.**
**Design and Inscription in Black**
B350 SP276  7pf + 3pf org
              brn             1.50   2.25
B351 SP276 10pf + 5pf green   1.10    .75
B352 SP276 20pf + 10pf brt
              red             1.10    .75

---

B353 SP276 40pf + 10pf brt
              blue           15.00  15.00
     Nos. B350-B353 (4)      18.70  18.75

Issued to honor Ignaz Philipp Semmelweis,
the discoverer of the cause of puerperal fever.
Surtax for independent welfare organizations.

Children
Leaving
SP277

Design: 20pf+10pf, Child arriving.

**1957, Feb. 1  Litho.    Perf. 13½x13**
B354 SP277 10pf + 5pf gray grn
              & red org      1.10   1.90
B355 SP277 20pf + 10pf red org
              & lt bl        2.75   3.75

The surtax was for vacations for the children
of Berlin.

Young
Miner — SP278

20pf+10pf, "A
Hunter from the
Palatinate."
SP279

10+5pf, Miner with drill. 20+10pf, Miner &
conveyor. 40+10pf, Miner & coal elevator.

**1957, Oct. 1  Wmk. 304    Perf. 14**
B356 SP278  7pf + 3pf bis brn
              & blk         1.10   1.50
B357 SP278 10pf + 5pf blk &
              yel grn         .75    .75
B358 SP278 20pf + 10pf black
              & red         1.10    .75
B359 SP278 40pf + 10pf black
              & blue       16.50  18.00
     Nos. B356-B359 (4)    19.45  21.00

Surtax for independent welfare organizations.

**1958, Apr. 1                   Litho.**
"The Fox who Stole the Goose"
B360 SP279 10pf + 5pf brn red,
              grn & blk      1.50   1.90
B361 SP279 20pf + 10pf multi  3.00   3.50

The surtax was to finance young peoples'
study trips to Berlin.

Friedrich Wilhelm
Raiffeisen
SP280

Dairy Maid
SP281

Designs: 20pf+10pf, Girl picking grapes.
40pf+10pf, Farmer with pitchfork.

**1958, Oct. 1  Wmk. 304    Perf. 14**
B362 SP280  7pf + 3pf gldn
              brn & dk
              brn            .45    .45
B363 SP281 10pf + 5pf grn,
              red & yel      .45    .45
B364 SP281 20pf + 10pf red,
              yel & bl       .45    .45
B365 SP281 40pf + 10pf blue
              & ocher       6.00   7.25
     Nos. B362-B365 (4)     7.35   8.60

Surtax for independent welfare organizations.

---

Stamp of Hamburg,
1859 — SP282

Design: 20pf+10pf, Stamp of Lübeck, 1859.

**1959          Engr.        Wmk. 304**
B366 SP282 10pf + 5pf yel green
              & brown         .25    .60
  a.   10pf + 5pf green & brown   .75   2.10
B367 SP282 20pf + 10pf red org
              & red brn       .25    .65
  a.   20pf + 10pf maroon & red
              brown          1.10   2.10

"Interposta" Philatelic Exhibition, Hamburg,
May 22-31, 1959 for the cent. of the 1st
stamps of Hamburg and Lübeck.
The surtax on #B366, B367 was for vacations for the children of Berlin.
Issued: #B366-B367, 8/22; #B366a-B367a,
5/22.

Girl Giving
Bread to Beggar
SP283

Jacob and
Wilhelm Grimm
SP284

Designs (from "Star Dollars" fairy tale):
10pf+5pf, Girl giving coat to boy, 20pf+10pf,
Star-Money from Heaven.

**1959, Oct. 1        Litho.     Perf. 14**
B368 SP283  7pf + 3pf brown &
              yel             .25    .35
B369 SP283 10pf + 5pf green &
              yel             .25    .35
B370 SP283 20pf + 10pf brick
              red & yel       .30    .35
B371 SP284 40pf + 10pf bl, blk,
              ocher & emer   3.00   4.50
     Nos. B368-B371 (4)      3.80   5.55

Surtax for independent welfare organizations.

Little Red
Riding Hood
and the
Wolf — SP285

Various Scenes from Little Red Riding
Hood.

**1960, Oct. 1  Wmk. 304    Perf. 14**
B372 SP285  7pf + 3pf brn ol,
              red & blk      .45    .45
B373 SP285 10pf + 5pf grn, red
              & blk          .45    .35
B374 SP285 20pf + 10pf brick
              red, emer &
              blk            .45    .35
B375 SP285 40pf + 20pf brt bl,
              red & blk     2.25   3.75
     Nos. B372-B375 (4)     3.60   4.90

Surtax for independent welfare organizations.

**1961, Oct. 2**
Various Scenes from Hansel and Gretel.
B376 SP285  7pf + 3pf multi   .20    .30
B377 SP285 10pf + 5pf multi   .20    .30
B378 SP285 20pf + 10pf multi  .20    .30
B379 SP285 40pf + 20pf multi 1.00   1.75
     Nos. B376-B379 (4)      1.60   2.65

Surtax for independent welfare organizations.
See B384-B387, B392-B395, B400-B403.

---

Fluorescent Paper
was introduced for semipostal
stamps, starting with No. B380.

---

Apollo — SP286

Hoopoe — SP287

10pf+5pf, Camberwell beauty. 20pf+10pf,
Tortoise-shell. 40pf+20pf, Tiger swallowtail.

**Wmk. 304**
**1962, May 25  Litho.     Perf. 14**
**Butterflies in Natural Colors, Black
Inscriptions**
B380 SP286  7pf + 3pf bis brn   .35    .60
B381 SP286 10pf + 5pf brt green .35    .60
B382 SP286 20pf + 10pf dp crim  .75   1.10
B383 SP286 40pf + 20pf brt blue 1.10  1.90
     Nos. B380-B383 (4)        2.55   4.20

Issued for the benefit of young people.
Nos. B381-B383 exist without watermark.
Value, each $900 unused, $975 used.

Fairy Tale Type of 1960
Scenes from Snow White (Schnee-
wittchen).

**1962, Oct. 10                 Perf. 14**
B384 SP285  7pf + 3pf multi    .20    .25
B385 SP285 10pf + 5pf multi    .20    .25
B386 SP285 20pf + 10pf multi   .20    .25
B387 SP285 40pf + 20pf multi   .80   1.25
     Nos. B384-B387 (4)       1.40   2.00

Surtax for independent welfare organizations.

**1963, June 12  Unwmk.    Perf. 14**
Birds: 15pf+5pf, European golden oriole.
20pf+10pf, Bullfinch. 40pf+20pf, European
kingfisher.
B388 SP287 10pf + 5pf multi    .45    .60
B389 SP287 15pf + 5pf multi    .35    .60
B390 SP287 20pf + 10pf multi   .35    .60
B391 SP287 40pf + 20pf multi  1.60   2.40
     Nos. B388-B391 (4)       2.75   4.20

Issued for the benefit of young people.

Fairy Tale Type of 1960
Various Scenes from the Grimm Brothers'
"The Wolf and the Seven Kids."

**1963, Sept. 23                Litho.**
B392 SP285 10pf + 5pf multi    .20    .25
B393 SP285 15pf + 5pf multi    .20    .25
B394 SP285 20pf + 10pf multi   .20    .25
B395 SP285 40pf + 20pf multi   .60   1.10
     Nos. B392-B395 (4)       1.20   1.85

Surtax for independent welfare organizations.

Herring
SP288

Fish: 15pf+5pf, Rosefish. 20pf+10pf, Carp.
40pf+20pf, Cod.

**1964, Apr. 10  Unwmk.    Perf. 14**
B396 SP288 10pf + 5pf multi    .20    .30
B397 SP288 15pf + 5pf multi    .20    .30
B398 SP288 20pf + 10pf multi   .35    .45
B399 SP288 40pf + 20pf multi   .95   1.90
     Nos. B396-B399 (4)       1.70   2.95

Issued for the benefit of young people.

Fairy Tale Type of 1960
Various Scenes from Sleeping Beauty
(Dornroschen).

**1964, Oct. 6    Litho.    _Perf. 14_**
| | | | |
|---|---|---|---|
| B400 | SP285 | 10pf + 5pf multi | .20 | .25 |
| B401 | SP285 | 15pf + 5pf multi | .20 | .25 |
| B402 | SP285 | 20pf + 10pf multi | .20 | .25 |
| B403 | SP285 | 40pf + 20pf multi | .35 | .90 |
| | _Nos. B400-B403 (4)_ | .95 | 1.65 |

Surtax for independent welfare organizations.

Woodcock
SP289

**1965, Apr. 1    Unwmk.    _Perf. 14_**
Birds: 15pf+5pf, Ring-necked pheasant.
20pf+10pf, Black grouse. 40pf+20pf,
Capercaillie.

| | | | |
|---|---|---|---|
| B404 | SP289 | 10pf + 5pf multi | .20 | .30 |
| B405 | SP289 | 15pf + 5pf multi | .20 | .30 |
| B406 | SP289 | 20pf + 10pf multi | .20 | .30 |
| B407 | SP289 | 40pf + 20pf multi | .30 | .90 |
| | _Nos. B404-B407 (4)_ | .90 | 1.80 |

Issued for the benefit of young people.

Cinderella
Feeding
Pigeons
SP290

Various Scenes from Cinderella.

**1965, Oct. 6    Litho.    _Perf. 14_**
| | | | |
|---|---|---|---|
| B408 | SP290 | 10pf + 5pf multi | .20 | .25 |
| B409 | SP290 | 15pf + 5pf multi | .20 | .25 |
| B410 | SP290 | 20pf + 10pf multi | .20 | .25 |
| B411 | SP290 | 40pf + 20pf multi | .45 | .65 |
| | _Nos. B408-B411 (4)_ | 1.05 | 1.40 |

Surtax for independent welfare organizations.
See Nos. B418-B421, B426-B429.

Roe
Deer — SP291

**1966, Apr. 22    Litho.    _Perf. 14_**
Designs: 20pf+10pf, Chamois. 30pf+15pf,
Fallow deer. 50pf+25pf, Red deer.

| | | | |
|---|---|---|---|
| B412 | SP291 | 10pf + 5pf multi | .25 | .25 |
| B413 | SP291 | 20pf + 10pf multi | .25 | .25 |
| B414 | SP291 | 30pf + 15pf multi | .25 | .30 |
| B415 | SP291 | 50pf + 25pf multi | .60 | .90 |
| | _Nos. B412-B415 (4)_ | 1.35 | 1.70 |

Issued for the benefit of young people.
See Nos. B422-B425.

Prussian Letter
Carrier — SP292

Design: 30pf+15pf, Bavarian mail coach.

**1966    Litho.    _Perf. 14_**
| | | | |
|---|---|---|---|
| B416 | SP292 | 30pf + 15pf multi | .35 | .65 |
| B417 | SP292 | 50pf + 25pf multi | .50 | .65 |

Meeting of the Federation Internationale de
Philatélie (FIP), Munich, Sept. 26-29, and
stamp exhibition, Municipal Museum, Sept.
24-Oct. 1. The surcharge was for the Foundation for the Promotion of Philately and Postal
History.
Issued: #B416, 9/24; #B417, 7/13.

Fairy Tale Type of 1965
Various Scenes from The Princess and the
Frog.

**1966, Oct. 5    Litho.    _Perf. 14_**
| | | | |
|---|---|---|---|
| B418 | SP290 | 10pf + 5pf multi | .20 | .25 |
| B419 | SP290 | 20pf + 10pf multi | .20 | .25 |
| B420 | SP290 | 30pf + 15pf multi | .20 | .25 |
| B421 | SP290 | 50pf + 25pf multi | .45 | .90 |
| | _Nos. B418-B421 (4)_ | 1.05 | 1.65 |

Surtax for independent welfare organizations.

Animal Type of 1966
10pf+5pf, Rabbit. 20pf+10pf, Ermine.
30pf+15pf, Hamster. 50pf+25pf, Red fox.

**1967, Apr. 4    Litho.    _Perf. 14_**
| | | | |
|---|---|---|---|
| B422 | SP291 | 10pf + 5pf multi | .20 | .30 |
| B423 | SP291 | 20pf + 10pf multi | .25 | .30 |
| B424 | SP291 | 30pf + 15pf multi | .45 | .60 |
| B425 | SP291 | 50pf + 25pf multi | .95 | 1.50 |
| | _Nos. B422-B425 (4)_ | 1.85 | 2.70 |

Issued for the benefit of young people.

Fairy Tale Type of 1965
Various Scenes from Frau Holle.

**1967, Oct. 3    Litho.    _Perf. 14_**
| | | | |
|---|---|---|---|
| B426 | SP290 | 10pf + 5pf multi | .20 | .25 |
| B427 | SP290 | 20pf + 10pf multi | .20 | .25 |
| B428 | SP290 | 30pf + 15pf multi | .20 | .25 |
| B429 | SP290 | 50pf + 25pf multi | .60 | 1.10 |
| | _Nos. B426-B429 (4)_ | 1.20 | 1.85 |

Surtax for independent welfare organizations.

Wildcat
SP293

Animals: 20pf+10pf, Otter. 30pf+15pf,
Badger. 50pf+25pf, Beaver.

**1968, Feb. 2    Photo.    Unwmk.**
| | | | |
|---|---|---|---|
| B430 | SP293 | 10pf + 5pf multi | .25 | .45 |
| B431 | SP293 | 20pf + 15pf multi | .35 | .75 |
| B432 | SP293 | 30pf + 15pf multi | .50 | 1.00 |
| B433 | SP293 | 50pf + 25pf multi | 1.90 | 3.00 |
| | _Nos. B430-B433 (4)_ | 3.00 | 5.20 |

The surtax was for the benefit of young
people.

Olympic Games Type of Regular Issue
10pf+5pf, Karl-Friedrich Freiherr von
Langen, equestrian. 20pf+10pf, Rudolf Harbig,
runner. 30pf+15pf, Helene Mayer, fencer.
50pf+25pf, Carl Diem, sports organizer.

**Lithographed and Engraved**
**1968, June 6    Unwmk.    _Perf. 14_**
| | | | |
|---|---|---|---|
| B434 | A285 | 10 + 5pf olive & dk brn | .30 | .30 |
| B435 | A285 | 20 + 10pf dp emer & dk grn | .30 | .30 |
| B436 | A285 | 30 + 15pf dp rose & dk red | .50 | .50 |
| B437 | A285 | 50 + 25pf brt bl & dk bl | .80 | .90 |
| | _Nos. B434-B437 (4)_ | 1.90 | 2.00 |

The surtax was for the Foundation for the
Promotion of the 1972 Olympic Games in
Munich.

Doll, c.
1878 — SP294

Pony — SP295

Various 19th Cent. Dolls. #B438-B440 are
from Germanic Natl. Museum, Nuremberg;
#B441 is from Altona Museum, Hamburg.

**1968, Oct. 3    Litho.    _Perf. 14_**
| | | | |
|---|---|---|---|
| B438 | SP294 | 10pf + 5pf multi | .20 | .25 |
| B439 | SP294 | 20pf + 10pf multi | .20 | .25 |
| B440 | SP294 | 30pf + 15pf multi | .25 | .25 |
| B441 | SP294 | 50pf + 25pf multi | .60 | .90 |
| | _Nos. B438-B441 (4)_ | 1.25 | 1.65 |

Surtax for independent welfare organizations.

**1969, Feb. 6    Litho.    _Perf. 14_**
Horses: 20pf+10pf, Work horse. 30pf+15pf,
Hotblood. 50pf+25pf, Thoroughbred.

| | | | |
|---|---|---|---|
| B442 | SP295 | 10pf + 5pf multi | .30 | .45 |
| B443 | SP295 | 20pf + 10pf multi | .30 | .45 |
| B444 | SP295 | 30pf + 15pf multi | .50 | .75 |
| B445 | SP295 | 50pf + 25pf multi | 1.60 | 1.50 |
| | _Nos. B442-B445 (4)_ | 2.70 | 3.15 |

Surtax for the benefit of young people.

SP296          SP297

Olympic Rings and: 10pf+5pf, Track.
20pf+10pf, Hockey. 30pf+15pf, Archery.
50pf+25pf, Sailing.

**1969, June 4    Photo.    _Perf. 14_**
| | | | |
|---|---|---|---|
| B446 | SP296 | 10pf + 5pf dk brn & lem | .20 | .20 |
| B447 | SP296 | 20pf + 10pf bl grn & emer | .35 | .30 |
| B448 | SP296 | 30pf + 15pf mag & dp lil rose | .50 | .45 |
| B449 | SP296 | 50pf + 25pf dp bl & brt bl | 1.10 | .90 |
| | _Nos. B446-B449 (4)_ | 2.15 | 1.85 |

1972 Olympic Games in Munich. The surtax
was for the German Olympic Committee.

**1969, Oct. 2    Litho.    _Perf. 13½x14_**
Tin Toys: 10pf+5pf, Locomotive. 20pf+10pf,
Gardener. 30pf+15pf, Bird seller. 50pf+25pf,
Knight on horseback.

| | | | |
|---|---|---|---|
| B450 | SP297 | 10pf + 5pf multi | .20 | .20 |
| B451 | SP297 | 20pf + 10pf multi | .25 | .25 |
| B452 | SP297 | 30pf + 15pf multi | .30 | .30 |
| B453 | SP297 | 50pf + 25pf multi | .85 | 1.10 |
| | _Nos. B450-B453 (4)_ | 1.60 | 1.85 |

Surtax for independent welfare organizations.

Tin Toy Type of 1969 Inscribed:
"Weihnachtsmarke 1969"
Christmas: 10pf+5pf, Jesus in Manger.

**1969, Nov. 13    _Perf. 13½x14_**
| | | | |
|---|---|---|---|
| B454 | SP297 | 10pf + 5pf multi | .30 | .30 |

Heinrich von
Rugge — SP298

Minnesingers: 20pf+10pf, Wolfram von
Eschenbach. 30pf+15pf, Walther von Metz.
50pf+25pf, Walther von der Vogelweide.

**1970, Feb. 5    Photo.    _Perf. 13½x14_**
| | | | |
|---|---|---|---|
| B455 | SP298 | 10pf + 5pf multi | .35 | .30 |
| B456 | SP298 | 20pf + 10pf multi | .60 | .35 |
| B457 | SP298 | 30pf + 15pf multi | .75 | .60 |
| B458 | SP298 | 50pf + 25pf multi | 1.60 | 1.50 |
| | _Nos. B455-B458 (4)_ | 3.30 | 2.75 |

Surtax was for benefit of young people.

Residenz
(Palace),
Munich
SP299

Munich Buildings: 20pf+10pf, Propylaea.
30pf+15pf, Glyptothek. 50pf+25pf, Bavaria
Statue and Colonnade.

**1970, June 5    Engr.    _Perf. 14_**
| | | | |
|---|---|---|---|
| B459 | SP299 | 10pf + 5pf olive bis | .20 | .20 |
| B460 | SP299 | 20pf + 10pf dk bl grn | .45 | .30 |
| B461 | SP299 | 30pf + 15pf carmine | .60 | .45 |
| B462 | SP299 | 50pf + 25pf dk blue | 1.00 | .90 |
| | _Nos. B459-B462 (4)_ | 2.25 | 1.85 |

The surtax was for the Foundation for the
Promotion of the 1972 Olympic Games in
Munich.

Jester — SP300        King
                      Caspar — SP301

Puppets: 20pf+10pf, "Hanswurst."
30pf+15pf, Clown. 50pf+25pf, Harlequin.

**1970, Oct. 6    Litho.    _Perf. 13½x14_**
| | | | |
|---|---|---|---|
| B463 | SP300 | 10pf + 5pf multi | .25 | .25 |
| B464 | SP300 | 20pf + 10pf multi | .25 | .30 |
| B465 | SP300 | 30pf + 15pf multi | .35 | .35 |
| B466 | SP300 | 50pf + 25pf multi | .90 | .95 |
| | _Nos. B463-B466 (4)_ | 1.75 | 1.85 |

Surtax for independent welfare organizations.

**1970, Nov. 12**
Christmas: 10pf+5pf, Rococo Angel, from
Ursuline Sisters' Convent, Innsbruck.

| | | | |
|---|---|---|---|
| B467 | SP300 | 10pf + 5pf multi | .30 | .25 |

**1971, Feb. 5    Litho.    _Perf. 14_**
Children's Drawings: 20pf+10pf, Flea.
30pf+15pf, Puss-in-Boots. 50pf+25pf, Snake.

| | | | |
|---|---|---|---|
| B468 | SP301 | 10pf + 5pf multi | .30 | .30 |
| B469 | SP301 | 20pf + 10pf multi | .35 | .35 |
| B470 | SP301 | 30pf + 15pf multi | .60 | .60 |
| B471 | SP301 | 50pf + 25pf multi | 1.00 | 1.00 |
| | _Nos. B468-B471 (4)_ | 2.25 | 2.25 |

Surtax for the benefit of young people.

Ski                    Women Churning
Jump — SP302           Butter — SP303

20pf+10pf, Figure skating. 30pf+15pf,
Downhill skiing. 50pf+25pf, Ice hockey.

"1971" at Lower Right

**1971, June 4    Litho.    _Perf. 14_**
| | | | |
|---|---|---|---|
| B472 | SP302 | 10pf + 5pf brn org & blk | .25 | .20 |
| B473 | SP302 | 20pf + 10pf green & blk | .45 | .30 |
| B474 | SP302 | 30pf + 15pf rose red & blk | .60 | .60 |
| B475 | SP302 | 50pf + 25pf blue & blk | 1.50 | 1.50 |
| a. | Souvenir sheet of 4 | 3.00 | 2.50 |
| b. | 10pf + 5pf brown org & blk | .25 | .20 |
| c. | 20pf + 10pf green & black | .45 | .30 |
| d. | 30pf + 15pf rose red & black | .80 | .60 |
| e. | 50pf + 25pf blue & black | 1.50 | 1.25 |
| | _Nos. B472-B475 (4)_ | 2.80 | 2.60 |

Olympic Games 1972.
#B475a contains #B475b-B475e which lack
the small date ("1971") at lower right.

**1971, Oct. 5    Litho.    _Perf. 14_**
Wooden Toys: 25pf+10pf, Horseback rider.
30pf+15pf, Nutcracker. 60pf+30pf, Dovecot.

| | | | |
|---|---|---|---|
| B476 | SP303 | 20pf + 10pf multi | .20 | .20 |
| B477 | SP303 | 25pf + 10pf multi | .20 | .20 |
| B478 | SP303 | 30pf + 15pf multi | .45 | .45 |
| B479 | SP303 | 60pf + 30pf multi | 1.25 | 1.25 |
| | _Nos. B476-B479 (4)_ | 2.10 | 2.10 |

Surtax for independent welfare organizations.

**1971, Nov. 11**

Christmas: Christmas angel with lights.

**B480** SP303 20pf + 10pf multi          .45    .35

Ducks Crossing
Road — SP304

Olympic Rings and
Wrestling — SP305

Designs: 25pf+10pf, Hunter chasing deer
and rabbits. 30pf+15pf, Girl protecting birds
from cat. 60pf+30pf, Boy annoying swans.

**1972, Feb. 4     Litho.      Perf. 14**

| | | | |
|---|---|---|---|
| **B481** | SP304 20pf + 10pf multi | .50 | .45 |
| **B482** | SP304 25pf + 10pf multi | .40 | .30 |
| **B483** | SP304 30pf + 15pf multi | .75 | .75 |
| **B484** | SP304 60pf + 30pf multi | 1.50 | 1.50 |
| | *Nos. B481-B484 (4)* | 3.15 | 3.00 |

Animal protection. Surtax for the benefit of
young people.

**1972, June 5     Photo.      Perf. 14**

25pf+10pf, Sailing. 30pf+15pf, Gymnastics.
60pf+30pf, Swimming.

| | | | |
|---|---|---|---|
| **B485** | SP305 20pf + 10pf multi | .45 | .35 |
| **B486** | SP305 25pf + 10pf multi | .45 | .35 |
| **B487** | SP305 30pf + 15pf multi | .45 | .35 |
| **B488** | SP305 60pf + 30pf multi | 1.60 | 1.50 |
| | *Nos. B485-B488 (4)* | 2.95 | 2.55 |

20th Olympic Games, Munich, Aug. 26
Sept. 10. See No. B490.

**Souvenir Sheet**

Olympic Games Site,
Munich — SP306

**1972, July 5     Litho.      Perf. 14**

| | | | | |
|---|---|---|---|---|
| **B489** | SP306 | Sheet of 4 | 5.00 | 5.00 |
| *a.* | | 25pf + 10pf Gymnastics women's | 1.10 | 1.10 |
| *b.* | | 30pf + 15pf Soccer stadium | 1.10 | 1.10 |
| *c.* | | 40pf + 20pf Tent and lake | 1.10 | 1.10 |
| *d.* | | 70pf + 35pf Television tower, vert. | 1.10 | 1.10 |

20th Olympic Games, Munich. Surcharge
was for the Foundation for the Promotion of
the Munich Olympic Games.

**Olympic Games Type of 1972
Souvenir Sheet**

**1972, Aug. 18     Litho.      Perf. 14**

| | | | | |
|---|---|---|---|---|
| **B490** | | Sheet of 4 | 4.50 | 4.50 |
| *a.* | SP305 25pf + 5pf Long jump, women's | | .45 | .45 |
| *b.* | SP305 30pf + 10pf Basketball | | 1.25 | 1.25 |
| *c.* | SP305 40pf + 10pf Discus, women's | | 1.60 | 1.60 |
| *d.* | SP305 70pf + 10pf Canoeing | | .80 | .80 |
| *e.* | Bklt. pane of 4, #B490a-B490d | | 8.00 | 8.00 |

20th Olympic Games, Munich.

Knight — SP307

Adoration of the
Kings — SP308

**1972, Oct. 5**

| | | | |
|---|---|---|---|
| **B491** | SP307 25pf + 10pf shown | .30 | .30 |
| **B492** | SP307 30pf + 15pf Rook | .30 | .25 |
| **B493** | SP307 40pf + 20pf Queen | .50 | .25 |
| **B494** | SP307 70pf + 35pf King | 1.90 | 1.75 |
| | *Nos. B491-B494 (4)* | 3.00 | 2.55 |

19th cent. chess pieces made by Faience
Works, Gien, France; now in Hamburg
Museum. Surtax for independent welfare
organizations.

**1972, Nov. 10                              Litho.**

**B495** SP308 30pf + 15pf multi          .65    .45

Christmas 1972.

Osprey
SP309

Hesse-Kassel
SP310

Birds of Prey: 30pf+15pf, Buzzard.
40pf+20pf, Red kite. 70pf+35pf, Montagu's
harrier.

**1973, Feb. 6     Photo.      Perf. 14**

| | | | |
|---|---|---|---|
| **B496** | SP309 25pf + 10pf multi | .90 | .75 |
| **B497** | SP309 30pf + 15pf multi | 1.10 | .90 |
| **B498** | SP309 40pf + 20pf multi | 1.50 | 1.40 |
| **B499** | SP309 70pf + 35pf multi | 3.50 | 3.50 |
| | *Nos. B496-B499 (4)* | 7.00 | 6.55 |

Surtax was for benefit of young people.

**1973, Apr. 5     Litho.      Perf. 14**

Posthouse Signs: No. B501, Prussia. No.
B502a, Württemberg. No. B502b, Bavaria.

| | | | |
|---|---|---|---|
| **B500** | SP310 40pf + 20pf multi | .65 | .65 |
| **B501** | SP310 70pf + 35pf multi | 1.25 | 1.25 |

**Souvenir Sheet**

| | | | | |
|---|---|---|---|---|
| **B502** | | Sheet of 2 | 4.25 | 4.25 |
| *a.* | SP310 40pf + 20pf multi | | .90 | .90 |
| *b.* | SP310 70pf + 35pf multi | | 1.50 | 1.50 |

IBRA München 1973 International Philatelic
Exhibition, Munich, May 11-20. No. B502 sold
for 2.20 mark.

French Horn, 19th
Century — SP311

Christmas
Star — SP312

Musical Instruments: 30pf+15pf, Pedal
piano, 18th century. 40pf+20pf, Violin, 18th
century. 70pf+35pf, Pedal harp, 18th century.

**1973, Oct. 5     Litho.      Perf. 14**

| | | | |
|---|---|---|---|
| **B503** | SP311 25pf + 10pf multi | .50 | .30 |
| **B504** | SP311 30pf + 15pf multi | .60 | .30 |
| **B505** | SP311 40pf + 20pf multi | .75 | .45 |
| **B506** | SP311 70pf + 35pf multi | 1.90 | 1.50 |
| | *Nos. B503-B506 (4)* | 3.75 | 2.55 |

Surtax was for independent welfare
organizations.

**1973, Nov. 9                 Litho. & Engr.**

**B507** SP312 30pf + 15pf multi          .60    .45

Christmas 1973.

Young
Builder — SP313

30+15pf, Girl in national costume. 40+20pf,
Boy studying. 70+35pf, Girl with microscope.

**1974, Apr. 17     Photo.      Perf. 14**

| | | | |
|---|---|---|---|
| **B508** | SP313 25pf + 10pf multi | .50 | .45 |
| **B509** | SP313 30pf + 15pf multi | .90 | .75 |
| **B510** | SP313 40pf + 20pf multi | 1.50 | 1.40 |
| **B511** | SP313 70pf + 35pf multi | 2.75 | 2.25 |
| | *Nos. B508-B511 (4)* | 5.65 | 4.85 |

Surtax was for benefit of young people.

Campion — SP314

**1974, Oct. 15     Litho.      Perf. 14**

Flowers: 40pf+20pf, Foxglove. 50pf+25pf,
Mallow. 70pf+35pf, Bellflower.

| | | | |
|---|---|---|---|
| **B512** | SP314 30pf + 15pf multi | .30 | .30 |
| **B513** | SP314 40pf + 20pf multi | .40 | .30 |
| **B514** | SP314 50pf + 25pf multi | .45 | .40 |
| **B515** | SP314 70pf + 35pf multi | 1.25 | 1.25 |
| | *Nos. B512-B515 (4)* | 2.40 | 2.25 |

Surtax was for independent welfare
organizations.

**1974, Oct. 29**

Christmas: 40pf+20pf, Advent decoration.

**B516** SP314 40pf + 20pf multi          .75    .50

Diesel Locomotive Class
218 — SP315

Locomotives: 40pf+20pf, Electric engine
Class 103. 50pf+25pf, Electric rail motor train
Class 403. 70pf+35pf, Magnetic suspension
train "Transrapid" (model).

**1975, Apr. 15     Litho.      Perf. 14**

| | | | |
|---|---|---|---|
| **B517** | SP315 30pf + 15pf multi | .45 | .40 |
| **B518** | SP315 40pf + 20pf multi | .70 | .60 |
| **B519** | SP315 50pf + 25pf multi | .95 | .90 |
| **B520** | SP315 70pf + 35pf multi | 1.60 | 1.50 |
| | *Nos. B517-B520 (4)* | 3.70 | 3.40 |

Surtax was for benefit of young people.

Edelweiss
SP316

Basketball
SP317

Alpine Flowers: 40pf+20pf, Trollflower.
50pf+25pf, Alpine rose. 70pf+35pf,
Pasqueflower.

**1975, Oct. 15     Litho.      Perf. 14**

| | | | |
|---|---|---|---|
| **B521** | SP316 30pf + 15pf multi | .35 | .30 |
| **B522** | SP316 40pf + 20pf multi | .35 | .30 |
| **B523** | SP316 50pf + 25pf multi | .60 | .45 |
| **B524** | SP316 70pf + 35pf multi | 1.40 | 1.40 |
| | *Nos. B521-B524 (4)* | 2.70 | 2.45 |

Surtax was for independent welfare
organizations.

**1975, Nov. 14**

Christmas: Snow rose.

**B525** SP316 40pf + 20pf multi          .75    .75

**1976, Apr. 6     Litho.      Perf. 14**

Designs: 40pf+20pf, Rowing. 50pf+25pf,
Gymnastics, women's. 70pf+35pf, Volleyball.

| | | | |
|---|---|---|---|
| **B526** | SP317 30pf + 15pf multi | .45 | .35 |
| **B527** | SP317 40pf + 20pf multi | .80 | .60 |
| **B528** | SP317 50pf + 25pf multi | 1.00 | .90 |
| **B529** | SP317 70pf + 35pf multi | 1.40 | 1.25 |
| | *Nos. B526-B529 (4)* | 3.65 | 3.10 |

Youth training for Olympic Games. Surtax
was for benefit of young people.

Swimmer and Olympic Rings — SP318

30pf+15pf, Hockey. 50pf+25pf, High jump.
70pf+35pf, Rowing, coxed four.

**1976, Apr. 6**

| | | | |
|---|---|---|---|
| **B530** | SP318 40pf + 20pf multi | .75 | .45 |
| **B531** | SP318 50pf + 25pf multi | 1.00 | .75 |

**Souvenir Sheet**

| | | | | |
|---|---|---|---|---|
| **B532** | | Sheet of 2 | 2.00 | 2.00 |
| *a.* | SP318 30pf + 15pf multi | | .75 | .50 |
| *b.* | SP318 70pf + 35pf multi | | 1.00 | .85 |

21st Olympic Games, Montreal, Canada,
July 17-Aug. 1. The surtax was for the German
Sports Aid Foundation.

Phlox
SP319

Flowers: 40pf+20pf, Marigolds. 50pf+25pf,
Dahlias. 70pf+35pf, Pansies.

**1976, Oct. 14     Litho.      Perf. 14**

| | | | |
|---|---|---|---|
| **B533** | SP319 30pf + 15pf multi | .45 | .35 |
| **B534** | SP319 40pf + 20pf multi | .60 | .50 |
| **B535** | SP319 50pf + 25pf multi | .65 | .60 |
| **B536** | SP319 70pf + 35pf multi | 1.10 | 1.10 |
| | *Nos. B533-B536 (4)* | 2.80 | 2.55 |

Surtax was for independent welfare
organizations.

## Souvenir Sheet

Nativity, Window, Frauenkirche, Esslingen — SP320

**1976, Nov. 16      Litho. & Engr.**
B537 SP320 50pf + 25pf multi      .90  .75
Christmas 1976.

Wapen von Hamburg, c. 1730 SP321

Historic Ships: 40pf+20pf, Preussen, 5-master, 1902. 50pf+25pf, Bremen, 1929. 70pf+35pf, Freighter Sturmfels, 1972.

**1977, Apr. 14      Litho.      Perf. 14**
B538 SP321 30pf + 15pf multi      .50  .50
B539 SP321 40pf + 20pf multi      .65  .60
B540 SP321 50pf + 25pf multi      .90  .80
B541 SP321 70pf + 35pf multi    1.25 1.25
   Nos. B538-B541 (4)             3.30 3.15

Surtax was for benefit of young people.

Caraway — SP322

Meadow Flowers: 40pf+20pf, Dandelion. 50pf+25pf, Red clover. 70pf+35pf, Meadow sage.

**1977, Oct. 13      Litho.      Perf. 14**
B542 SP322 30pf + 15pf multi      .35  .30
B543 SP322 40pf + 20pf multi      .45  .35
B544 SP322 50pf + 25pf multi      .50  .45
B545 SP322 70pf + 35pf multi    1.00 1.10
   Nos. B542-B545 (4)             2.30 2.20

Surtax was for independent welfare organizations.
See Nos. B553-B556.

## Souvenir Sheet

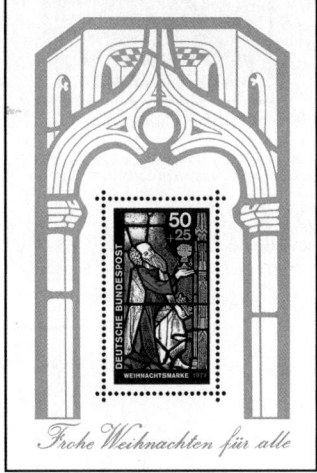

King Caspar Offering Gold, Window, St. Gereon's, Cologne — SP323

**1977, Nov. 10**
B546 SP323 50pf + 25pf multi      .80  .75
Christmas 1977.

Giant Slalom SP324

Design: No. B548, Steeplechase.

**1978      Litho.      Perf. 14**
B547 SP324 50pf + 25pf multi    1.40 1.10
B548 SP324 70pf + 35pf multi    3.00 2.75

Issued: #B547, Jan. 12, #B548, Apr. 13.
Surtax was for the German Sports Foundation.

Balloon Ascent, Oktoberfest, Munich, 1820 — SP325

Designs: 40pf+20pf, Airship LZ 1, 1900. 50pf+25pf, Bleriot monoplane, 1909. 70pf+35pf, Grade monoplane, 1909.

**1978, Apr. 13      Litho.      Perf. 14**
B549 SP325 30pf + 15pf multi      .50  .45
B550 SP325 40pf + 20pf multi      .70  .60
B551 SP325 50pf + 25pf multi      .90  .80
B552 SP325 70pf + 35pf multi    1.10 1.10
   Nos. B549-B552 (4)             3.20 2.95

Surtax was for benefit of young people.

### Flower Type of 1977

Woodland Flowers: 30pf+15pf, Arum. 40pf+20pf, Weaselsnout. 50pf+25pf, Turk's-cap lily. 70pf+35pf, Liverwort.

**1978, Oct. 12      Litho.      Perf. 14**
B553 SP322 30pf + 15pf multi      .35  .30
B554 SP322 40pf + 20pf multi      .50  .40
B555 SP322 50pf + 25pf multi      .75  .65
B556 SP322 70pf + 35pf multi    1.00 1.00
   Nos. B553-B556 (4)             2.60 2.35

Surtax was for independent welfare organizations.

## Souvenir Sheet

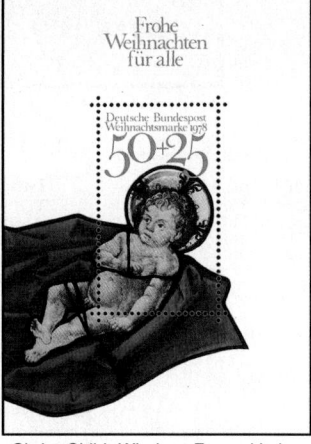

Christ Child, Window, Frauenkirche, Munich — SP326

**1978, Nov. 16      Litho.      Perf. 14**
B557 SP326 50pf + 25pf multi      .75  .75
Christmas 1978.

Dornier Wal, 1922 SP327

Airplanes: 50pf+25pf, Heinkel HE70, 1932. 60pf+30pf, Junkers W33 Bremen, 1928. 90pf+45pf, Focke-Wulf FW61, 1936.

**1979, Apr. 5      Litho.      Perf. 14**
B558 SP327 40pf + 20pf multi      .50  .50
B559 SP327 50pf + 25pf multi      .75  .75
B560 SP327 60pf + 30pf multi      .90  .90
B561 SP327 90pf + 45pf multi    1.25 1.25
   Nos. B558-B561 (4)             3.40 3.40

Surtax was for benefit of young people.
See Nos. B570-B573.

Handball SP328

Design: 90pf+45pf, Canoeing.

**1979, Apr. 5**
B562 SP328 60pf + 30pf multi      .90  .80
B563 SP328 90pf + 45pf multi    1.40 1.25

Surtax was for German Sports Foundation.

Post House Sign, Altheim, Saar, 1754 — SP329

**1979, Oct. 11      Litho.      Perf. 14**
B564 SP329 60pf + 30pf multi    1.10 1.10

Stamp Day. Surtax was for Foundation of Promotion of Philately and Postal History. Issued in sheet of 10.

Red Beech SP330

Woodland Plants: 50pf+25pf, English oak. 60pf+30pf, Hawthorn. 90pf+45pf, Mountain pine.

**1979, Oct. 11      Litho.      Perf. 14**
B565 SP330 40pf + 20pf multi      .45  .45
B566 SP330 50pf + 25pf multi      .60  .60
B567 SP330 60pf + 30pf multi      .70  .70
B568 SP330 90pf + 45pf multi    1.25 1.25
   Nos. B565-B568 (4)             3.00 3.00

Surtax was for independent welfare organizations.

Nativity, Medieval Manuscript SP331

**1979, Nov. 14      Litho.      Perf. 13½**
B569 SP331 60pf + 30pf multi      .90  .90
Christmas 1979.

### Aviation Type of 1979

40+20pf, FS 24 Phoenix, 1957. 50+25pf, Lockheed Super Constellation, 1950. 60+30pf, Airbus A300, 1972. 90+45pf, Boeing 747, 1969.

**1980, Apr. 10      Litho.      Perf. 14**
B570 SP327 40 + 20pf multi       .35  .35
B571 SP327 50 + 25pf multi       .60  .60
B572 SP327 60 + 30pf multi       .80  .80
B573 SP327 90 + 45pf multi     1.25 1.25
   Nos. B570-B573 (4)             3.00 3.00

Surtax was for benefit of young people.

Soccer SP332

Designs: 60pf+30pf, Equestrian. 90pf+45pf, Cross-country skiing.

**1980, May 8      Photo.      Perf. 14**
B574 SP332 50 + 25pf multi       .50  .45
B575 SP332 60 + 30pf multi       .75  .60
B576 SP332 90 + 45pf multi     1.40 1.40
   Nos. B574-B576 (3)             2.65 2.45

Surtax was for German Sports Foundation.

Ceratocephalus — SP333

Wildflowers: 50pf+25pf, Climbing meadow pea. 60pf+30pf, Corn cockle. 90pf+45pf, Grape hyacinth.

**1980, Oct. 9      Litho.      Perf. 14**
B577 SP333 40 + 20pf multi       .50  .45
B578 SP333 50 + 25pf multi       .65  .60
B579 SP333 60 + 30pf multi       .75  .75
B580 SP333 90 + 45pf multi     1.25 1.25
   Nos. B577-B580 (4)             3.15 3.05

Surtax was for independent welfare organizations.

Post House Sign, 1754, Altheim, Saar — SP334

**1980, Nov. 13      Litho.      Perf. 14**
B581 SP334 60 + 30pf multi       .75  .65

49th FIP Congress (Federation Internationale de Philatelie), Essen, Nov. 12-13.

Nativity, Altomunster Manuscript, 12th Century
SP335

1980, Nov. 13 *Perf. 14x13½*

B582 SP335 60 + 30pf multi 1.00 .90

Christmas 1980.

Borda Circle, 1800 — SP336

Historic Optical Instruments: 50pf+25pf, Reflecting telescope, 1770. 60pf+30pf, Binocular microscope, 1860. 90pf+45pf, Octant, 1775.

1981, Apr. 10 **Litho.** *Perf. 13½*

B583 SP336 40 + 20pf multi .50 .35
B584 SP336 50 + 25pf multi .90 .75
B585 SP336 60 + 30pf multi .90 .75
B586 SP336 90 + 45pf multi 1.25 1.25
Nos. B583-B586 (4) 3.55 3.10

Surtax was for benefit of young people.

Rowing
SP337

1981, Apr. 10 *Perf. 14*

B587 SP337 60 + 30pf shown .90 .75
B588 SP337 90 + 45pf Gliding 1.40 1.25

Surtax was for the German Sports Foundation.

Water Nut — SP338

Endangered Species: 50pf+25pf, Floating heart. 60pf+30pf, Water gillyflower. 90pf+45pf, Water lobelia.

1981, Oct. 8 **Litho.**

B589 SP338 40 + 20pf multi .45 .35
B590 SP338 50 + 25pf multi .60 .50
B591 SP338 60 + 30pf multi .75 .75
B592 SP338 90 + 45pf multi 1.40 1.40
Nos. B589-B592 (4) 3.20 3.00

Surtax was for independent welfare organizations.

Nativity, 19th Cent. Painting
SP339

1981, Nov. 12 **Litho.**

B593 SP339 60 + 30pf multi 1.00 .85

Christmas 1981.

Antique Cars
SP340

Designs: 40+20pf, Benz, 1886. 50+25pf, Mercedes, 1913. 60+30pf, Hanomag, 1925. 90+45pf, Opel Olympia, 1937.

1982, Apr. 15 **Litho.**

B594 SP340 40 + 20pf multi .50 .45
B595 SP340 50 + 25pf multi .65 .60
B596 SP340 60 + 30pf multi .90 .75
B597 SP340 90 + 45pf multi 1.50 1.60
Nos. B594-B597 (4) 3.55 3.40

Surtax was for benefit of young people.

Jogging
SP341

1982, Apr. 15 **Litho.**

B598 SP341 60 + 30pf shown .90 .80
B599 SP341 90 + 45pf Archery 1.40 1.25

Surtax was for the German Sports Foundation.

Tea-rose Hybrid — SP342

60+30pf, Floribunda. 80f+40pf, Bourbon rose. 120+60pf, Polyantha hybrid.

1982, Oct. 14 **Litho.** *Perf. 14*

B600 SP342 50 + 20pf multi .50 .45
B601 SP342 60 + 30pf multi .65 .60
B602 SP342 80 + 40pf multi 1.10 1.00
B603 SP342 120 + 60pf multi 1.50 1.50
Nos. B600-B603 (4) 3.75 3.55

Surtax was for independent welfare organizations.

Christmas
SP343

1982, Nov. 10

Designs: Nativity, Oak altar, St. Peter's Church, Hamburg, 1380.

B604 SP343 80 + 40pf multi 1.50 1.00

Historic Motorcycles — SP344

Designs: 50pf+20pf, Daimler-Maybach, 1885. 60pf+30pf, NSU, 1901. 80pf+40pf, Megola-Sport, 1922. 120pf+60pf, BMW, 1936.

1983, Apr. 12 **Litho.** *Perf. 14*

B605 SP344 50 + 20pf multi .50 .45
B606 SP344 60 + 30pf multi .65 .60
B607 SP344 80 + 40pf multi 1.25 1.10
B608 SP344 120 + 60pf multi 1.75 1.60
Nos. B605-B608 (4) 4.15 3.75

Surtax was for benefit of young people.

1983 Sports Championships — SP345

80+40pf, Gymnastics Festival. 120+60pf, Modern Pentathlon World Championships.

1983, Apr. 12

B609 SP345 80 + 40pf multi 1.10 .95
B610 SP345 120 + 60pf multi 1.75 1.60

Surtax was for German Sports Foundation.

Swiss Androsace
SP346

60+30pf, Krain groundsel. 80+40pf, Fleischer's willow herb. 120+60pf, Alpine sowthistle.

1983, Oct. 13 **Litho.** *Perf. 14*

B611 SP346 50 + 20pf multi .50 .45
B612 SP346 60 + 30pf multi .65 .60
B613 SP346 80 + 40pf multi 1.25 1.10
B614 SP346 120 + 60pf multi 1.75 1.60
Nos. B611-B614 (4) 4.15 3.75

Surtax was for welfare organizations.

Christmas
SP347

1983, Nov. 10 **Litho.**

B615 SP347 80 + 40pf Carolers 1.60 1.25

Surtax was for free welfare work.

Insects — SP348

1984, Apr. 12 **Litho.**

Designs: 50pf+20pf, Trichodes apoarius. 60pf+30pf, Vanessa atalanta. 80pf+40pf, Apis mellifera. 120pf+60pf, Chrysotoxum festivum.

B616 SP348 50 + 20pf multi .60 .50
B617 SP348 60 + 30pf multi 1.10 1.00
B618 SP348 80 + 40pf multi 1.50 1.40
B619 SP348 120 + 60pf multi 2.10 2.10
Nos. B616-B619 (4) 5.30 5.00

Surtax was for German Youth Stamp Foundation.

Women's Discus
SP349

Olympic Sports: 80pf+40pf, Rhythmic gymnastics. 120pf+60pf, Wind surfing.

1984, Apr. 12

B620 SP349 60 + 30pf multi 1.00 .75
B621 SP349 80 + 40pf multi 1.40 1.25
B622 SP349 120 + 60pf multi 2.75 2.50
Nos. B620-B622 (3) 5.15 4.50

Surtax was for German Sports Foundation.

Orchids
SP350

Designs: 50pf+20pf, Aceras anthropophorum. 60pf+30pf, Orchis ustulata. 80pf+40pf, Limodorum abortivum. 120+60pf, Dactylorhiza sambucina.

1984, Oct. 18 **Litho.** *Perf. 14*

B623 SP350 50 + 20pf multi .75 .65
B624 SP350 60 + 30pf multi .75 .65
B625 SP350 80 + 40pf multi 1.10 1.00
B626 SP350 120 + 60pf multi 2.25 2.25
Nos. B623-B626 (4) 4.85 4.55

Surtax was for welfare organizations.

Christmas 1984 — SP351

1984, Nov. 8 **Litho.**

B627 SP351 80pf + 40pf St. Martin 1.40 1.25

Surtax was for welfare organizations.

Bowling
SP352

1985, Feb. 21 **Photo.**

B628 SP352 80pf + 40pf multi 1.25 1.00
B629 SP352 120pf + 60pf Kayaking 2.00 1.75

Surtax was for German Sports Foundation.

Antique Bicycles
SP353

50pf+20pf, Draisienne, 1817. 60pf+30pf, NSU Germania, 1886. 80pf+40pf, Crossframe, 1887. 120pf+60pf, Adler tricycle, 1888.

1985, Apr. 16 **Litho.**

B630 SP353 50pf + 20pf multi .75 .75
B631 SP353 60pf + 30pf multi .90 .90
B632 SP353 80pf + 40pf multi 1.25 1.25
B633 SP353 120pf + 60pf multi 2.40 2.40
Nos. B630-B633 (4) 5.30 5.30

Surtax was for benefit of young people. Each stamp shows the Intl. Youth Year emblem.

MOPHILA '85, Hamburg, Sept. 11-15
SP354

1985, Aug. 13 **Litho.** *Perf. 14x14½*

B634 SP354 60 + 20pf Coachman, horses 2.25 1.90
B635 SP354 80 + 20pf Stagecoach 2.25 1.90
a. Pair, #B634-B635 6.00 5.25

Surtax for the benefit of the Philatelic & Postal History Foundation. No. B635a has continuous design.

SP355

Various ornamental borders, medieval prayer book, Prussian State Library, Berlin.

**1985, Oct. 15    Litho.    Perf. 14**
B636 SP355 50pf + 20pf multi    .70    .60
B637 SP355 60pf + 30pf multi    .85    .75
B638 SP355 80pf + 40pf multi    1.10    1.00
B639 SP355 120pf + 60pf multi    1.90    1.90
    Nos. B636-B639 (4)    4.55    4.25

Surtax for welfare organizations.

Christmas
1985 — SP356

Woodcut: The Birth of Christ, by Hans Baldung Grien (1485-1545), Freiburg Cathedral High Altar.

**1985, Nov. 12    Litho.    Perf. 14**
B640 SP356 80pf + 40pf multi    1.40    1.40

Surtax for welfare organizations.

European World Sports
Championships — SP357

**1986, Feb. 13    Litho.    Perf. 14**
B641 SP357 80 + 40pf Running    1.50    1.50
B642 SP357 120 + 55pf Bobsledding    2.25    2.25

Surtax for the Natl. Sports Promotion Foundation.

Vocational Training — SP358

**1986, Apr. 10**
B643 SP358 50 + 25pf Optician    1.00    .90
B644 SP358 60 + 30pf Mason    1.10    1.00
B645 SP358 70 + 35pf Beautician    1.40    1.25
B646 SP358 80 + 40pf Baker    1.90    1.75
    Nos. B643-B646 (4)    5.40    4.90

Surtax for German Youth Stamp Foundation.

Glassware in
German
Museums — SP359

**1986, Oct. 16    Litho.**
B647 SP359 50 + 25pf Ornamental flask, c. 300    .70    .60
B648 SP359 60 + 30pf Goblet, c. 1650    .90    .80
B649 SP359 70 + 35pf Imperial eagle tankard, c. 1662    1.00    .90
B650 SP359 80 + 40pf Engraved goblet, c. 1720    1.25    1.10
    Nos. B647-B650 (4)    3.85    3.40

Surtax for public welfare organizations.

Christmas
SP360

Adoration of the Infant Jesus, Ortenberg Altarpiece, c. 1430, Hesse Museum, Darmstadt.

**1986, Nov. 13    Litho.    Perf. 14**
B651 SP360 80 + 40pf multi    1.40    1.25

Surtax for public welfare organizations.

World Championships — SP361

**1987, Feb. 12    Litho.**
B652 SP361 80 + 40pf Sailing    1.25    1.25
B653 SP361 120 + 55pf Cross-country skiing    2.10    2.10

Surtax for the benefit of the national Sports Promotion Foundation.

Youth in
Industry
SP362

**1987, Apr. 9    Litho.**
B654 SP362 50 + 25pf Plumber    1.10    1.10
B655 SP362 60 + 30pf Dental technician    1.40    1.40
B656 SP362 70 + 35pf Butcher    1.50    1.50
B657 SP362 80 + 40pf Bookbinder    2.00    2.00
    Nos. B654-B657 (4)    6.00    6.00

Surtax for youth organizations.

Gold and
Silver
Artifacts
SP363

**1987, Oct. 15**
B658 SP363 50 + 25pf Roman bracelet, 4th cent.    1.10    1.10
B659 SP363 60 + 30pf Gothic buckle, 6th cent.    1.10    1.10
B660 SP363 70 + 35pf Merovingian disk fibula, 7th cent.    1.10    1.10
B661 SP363 80 + 40pf Purse-shaped reliquary, 8th cent.    1.50    1.50
    Nos. B658-B661 (4)    4.80    4.80

Surtax for welfare organizations sponsoring free museum exhibitions.

Christmas
SP364

Illustration from Book of Psalms, 13th cent., Bavarian Natl. Museum: Birth of Christ.

**1987, Nov. 6**
B662 SP364 80 + 40pf multi    1.50    1.25

Surtax for public welfare organizations.

Sports
SP365

**1988, Feb. 18    Litho.**
B663 SP365 60 + 30pf Soccer    1.10    1.10
B664 SP365 80 + 40pf Tennis    1.90    1.90
B665 SP365 120 + 55pf Diving    2.25    2.25
    Nos. B663-B665 (3)    5.25    5.25

Surtax for Stiftung Deutsche Sporthilfe, a foundation for the promotion of sports in Germany.

Rock
Stars
SP366

#B666, Buddy Holly (1936-59). #B667, Elvis Presley (1935-77). #B668, Jim Morrison (1943-71). #B669, John Lennon (1940-80).

**1988, Apr. 14    Litho.    Perf. 14**
B666 SP366 50 + 25pf multi    1.10    1.10
B667 SP366 60 + 30pf multi    2.75    2.75
B668 SP366 70 + 35pf multi    1.50    1.50
B669 SP366 80 + 40pf multi    2.40    2.40
    Nos. B666-B669 (4)    7.75    7.75

Surtax for German Youth Stamp Foundation.

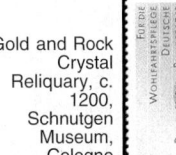

Gold and Rock
Crystal
Reliquary, c.
1200,
Schnutgen
Museum,
Cologne
SP367

Gold and silver artifacts: No. B671, Bust of Charlemagne, 14th cent., Aachen cathedral. No. B672, Crown of Otto III, 10th cent., Essen cathedral. No. B673, Flower bouquet, c. 1620, Schmuck Museum, Pforzheim.

**1988, Oct. 13    Litho.**
B670 SP367 50 + 25pf multi    .60    .60
B671 SP367 60 + 30pf multi    .95    .95
B672 SP367 70 + 35pf multi    .95    .95
B673 SP367 80 + 40pf multi    1.40    1.40
    Nos. B670-B673 (4)    3.90    3.90

Surtax for welfare organizations.

Christmas
SP368

Illumination from The Gospel Book of Henry the Lion, Helmarshausen, 1188, Prussian Cultural Museum, Bavaria: Adoration of the Magi.

**1988, Nov. 10    Litho.**
B674 SP368 80 + 40pf multi    1.40    1.25

Surtax for public welfare organizations.

World Championship Sporting Events
Hosted by Germany — SP369

**1989, Feb. 9    Litho.**
B675 SP369 100pf + 50pf Table tennis    2.00    2.00
B676 SP369 140pf + 60pf Gymnastics    3.00    3.00

Surtax for the Natl. Sports Promotion Foundation.

IPHLA Philatelic Literature Exhibition,
Frankfurt, Apr. 19-23 — SP370

**1989, Apr. 20    Litho.**
B677 SP370 100 + 50pf multi    2.75    2.75

Surtax benefited the Foundation for the Promotion of Philately and Postal History.

Circus
SP371

**1989, Apr. 20**
B678 SP371 60 + 30pf Elephants    1.75    1.75
B679 SP371 70 + 30pf Bareback rider    2.10    2.10
B680 SP371 80 + 35pf Clown    3.00    3.00
B681 SP371 100 + 50pf Caravans, big top    4.50    4.50
    Nos. B678-B681 (4)    11.35    11.35

Surtax for natl. youth welfare organizations.

Mounted
Courier of
Thurn and
Taxis, 18th
Cent.
SP372

History of mail carrying: No. B683, Hamburg postal service messenger, 1808. No. B684, Bavarian mail coach, c. 1900.

**1989, Oct. 12    Litho.**
B682 SP372 60 + 30pf multi    1.10    1.10
B683 SP372 80 + 35pf multi    1.90    1.90
B684 SP372 100 + 50pf multi    2.50    2.50
    Nos. B682-B684 (3)    5.50    5.50

Surtax for the benefit of Free Welfare Work.

Christmas
SP373

Wood carvings by Veit Stoss in St. Lawrence's Church, Nuremburg, 1517-18.

**1989, Nov. 16    Litho.**
B685 SP373 60 + 30pf Angel    1.25    1.10
B686 SP373 100 + 50pf Adoration of the Kings    1.60    1.50

Surtax for benefit of the Federal Working Assoc. of Free Welfare Work.

Popular
Sports
SP374

**1990, Feb. 15    Litho.**
B687 SP374 100 + 50pf Handball    2.50    2.50
B688 SP374 140 + 60pf Physical fitness    3.00    3.00

Surtax for the Natl. Sports Promotion Foundation.

*Max and Moritz*, by Wilhelm Busch, 125th Anniv. SP375

**1990, Apr. 19                     Litho.**
B689  SP375  60 + 30pf Widow
                        Bolte              .80  .80
B690  SP375  70 + 30pf Max      1.25 1.25
B691  SP375  80 + 35pf Max and
                        Moritz             1.60 1.60
B692  SP375  100 + 50pf Max and
                        Moritz, diff.      2.00 2.00
       *Nos. B689-B692 (4)*        5.65 5.65
    Surcharge for the German Youth Stamp
Foundation.

**Souvenir Sheet**

Dusseldorf '90 — SP376

Illustration reduced.

**1990, June 21                     Litho.**
B693  SP376  Sheet of 6        17.00 19.00
   a.           100pf + 50pf multi   2.75  2.75
    Surtax for the Foundation for Promotion of
Philately and Postal History. 10th Intl. Philatelic Exhibition of Youth and 11th Natl. Philatelic Exhibition of Youth.

Post and
Telecommunications — SP377

    Designs: 60pf+30pf, Postal vehicle, 1900.
80pf+35pf, Telephone exchange, 1890.
100pf+50pf, Post office, 1900.

**1990, Sept. 27  Litho.  Perf. 13½x14**
B694  SP377  60pf + 30pf multi    .90  .90
B695  SP377  80pf + 35pf multi   1.40 1.40
B696  SP377  100pf + 50pf multi  2.00 2.00
       *Nos. B694-B696 (3)*        4.30 4.30
    Surtax for welfare organizations.

Christmas
SP378

**1990, Nov. 6                     Litho.  Perf. 14**
B697  SP378  50pf + 20pf shown    .90  .90
B698  SP378  60pf + 30pf Smok-
                        ing manikin       1.00 1.00
B699  SP378  70pf + 30pf Nut-
                        cracker            1.40 1.40
B700  SP378  100pf + 50pf Angel,
                        diff.              2.25 2.25
       *Nos. B697-B700 (4)*        5.55 5.55
    Surtax for welfare organizations.

Sports
SP379

**1991, Feb. 14           Litho.  Perf. 14**
B701  SP379  70 +30pf Weight
                        lifting            1.50 1.50
B702  SP379  100 +50pf Cycling   1.50 1.50
B703  SP379  140 +60pf Basket-
                        ball               2.25 2.25
B704  SP379  170 +80pf Wrestling 2.25 2.25
       *Nos. B701-B704 (4)*        7.50 7.50
    Surtax for the Foundation for the Promotion
of Sports.

Endangered
Butterflies
SP380

    #B705, Alpen gelbling, alpine sulphur.
#B706, Grosser eisvogel, Viceroy. #B707,
Grosser schillerfalter, purple emperor. #B708,
Blauschillernder beuerfalter, bluish copper.
#B709,Schwalben-schwanz,    swallowtail.
#B710, Alpen apollo, alpine apollo. #B711,
Hochmoor gelbling, moor sulphur. #B712,
Grosser feuerfalter, large copper.

**1991, Apr. 9        Litho.     Perf. 13½**
B705  SP380  30 +15pf multi       .50  .50
B706  SP380  50 +25pf multi       .60  .60
B707  SP380  60 +30pf multi      1.10 1.10
B708  SP380  70 +30pf multi      1.25 1.25
B709  SP380  80 +35pf multi      1.50 1.50
B710  SP380  90 +45pf multi      2.00 2.00
B711  SP380  100 +50pf multi     2.50 2.50
B712  SP380  140 +60pf multi     3.00 3.00
       *Nos. B705-B712 (8)*      12.45 12.45
    Surtax for German Youth Stamp Foundation.
See Nos. B728-B732.

**Souvenir Sheet**

Otto Lilienthal's First Glider Flight,
Cent. — SP381

**1991, July 9            Litho.     Perf. 14**
B713  SP381  100pf +50pf multi   3.00 3.00
    Surtax benefited Foundation of Philately
and Postal History.

Post Offices
SP382

    30pf+15pf, Bethel. 60pf+30pf, Budingen
postal station. 70pf+30pf, Stralsund.

80pf+35pf, Lauscha. 100pf+50pf, Bonn.
140pf+60pf, Weilburg.

**1991, Oct. 10           Litho.     Perf. 14**
B714  SP382  30pf +15pf multi    .50  .50
B715  SP382  60pf +30pf multi   1.00 1.00
B716  SP382  70pf +30pf multi   1.25 1.25
B717  SP382  80pf +35pf multi   1.50 1.50
B718  SP382  100pf +50pf multi  2.00 2.00
B719  SP382  140pf +60pf multi  2.50 2.50
       *Nos. B714-B719 (6)*      8.75 8.75

Christmas
SP383

    Paintings by Martin Schongauer (c. 1450-
1491): 60pf+30pf, Angel of the Annunciation.
70pf+30pf, The Annunciation. 80pf+35pf,
Angel. 100pf+50pf, Nativity.

**1991, Nov. 5            Litho.     Perf. 14**
B720  SP383  60pf +30pf multi   1.00 1.00
B721  SP383  70pf +30pf multi   1.25 1.25
B722  SP383  80pf +35pf multi   2.25 2.25
B723  SP383  100pf +50pf multi  3.00 3.00
       *Nos. B720-B723 (4)*      7.50 7.50
    Surtax for Federal Working Association of
Free Welfare Work.

Olympic
Sports
SP384

**1992, Feb. 6            Litho.     Perf. 14**
B724  SP384  60pf +30pf Wo-
                        men's fenc-
                        ing                .90  .90
B725  SP384  80pf +40pf Rowing
                        coxed eights      1.10 1.10
B726  SP384  100pf +50pf
                        Dressage          2.25 2.25
B727  SP384  170pf +80pf Men's
                        slalom skiing     3.50 3.50
       *Nos. B724-B727 (4)*      7.75 7.75

**Endangered Butterfly Type of 1991**

    60+30pf, Purpurbar. 70+30pf, Labkraut
schwarmer. 80+40pf, Silbermonch. 100+50pf,
Schwarzer bar. 170+80pf, Rauschbeeren-
fleckenspanner.

**1992, Apr. 9            Litho.     Perf. 13½**
B728  SP380  60pf +30pf multi   1.50 1.50
B729  SP380  70pf +30pf multi   1.75 1.75
B730  SP380  80pf +40pf multi   2.25 2.25
B731  SP380  100pf +50pf multi  2.50 2.50
B732  SP380  170pf +80pf multi  2.75 2.75
       *Nos. B728-B732 (5)*     10.75 10.75
    Surtax for German Youth Stamp Foundation.

Preservation
of Tropical
Rain Forests
SP385

**1992, June 11           Litho.     Perf. 13**
B733  SP385  100pf +50pf multi  1.75 1.75

Antique Clocks
SP386

    Antique clocks: 60pf+30pf, Turret, c. 1400.
70pf+30pf, Astronomical geographical mantel-
piece, 1738. 80pf+40pf, Fluted, c. 1790.
100pf+50pf, Figurine, c. 1580. 170pf+80pf,
Table, c. 1550.

**1992, Oct. 15           Litho.     Perf. 14**
B734  SP386  60pf +30pf multi   1.10 1.10
B735  SP386  70pf +30pf multi   1.40 1.40
B736  SP386  80pf +40pf multi   1.40 1.40
B737  SP386  100pf +50pf multi  1.75 1.75
B738  SP386  170pf +80pf multi  2.50 2.50
       *Nos. B734-B738 (5)*      8.15 8.15
    Surtax for welfare organizations.

Christmas
SP387

    Carvings from Church of St. Anne,
Annaberg-Buchholz, by Franz Maidburg: 60pf
+ 30pf, Adoration of the Magi. 100pf + 50pf,
The Nativity.

**1992, Nov. 5**
B739  SP387  60pf +30pf multi   1.00  .90
B740  SP387  100pf +50pf multi  1.75 1.50
    Surtax for benefit of free welfare work.

Sports
SP388

    Designs: 60pf+30pf, Olympic ski jump,
Garmisch-Partenkirchen. 80pf+40pf, Olympic
Park, Munich. 100pf+50pf, Olympic Stadium,
Berlin. 170pf+80pf, Olympic harbor, Kiel.

**1993, Feb. 11           Litho.     Perf. 13½**
B741  SP388  60pf +30pf multi   1.50 1.50
B742  SP388  80pf +40pf multi   2.00 2.00
B743  SP388  100pf +50pf multi  2.50 2.50
B744  SP388  170pf +80pf multi  3.00 3.00
       *Nos. B741-B744 (4)*      9.00 9.00
    Surtax for Natl. Sports Promotion
Foundation.

Beetles
SP389

    Designs: No. B745, Alpenbock (Alpine saw-
yer). No. B746, Rosenkafer (rose chafer). No.
B747, Hirschkafer (stag beetle). No. B748,
Sandlaufkafer (tiger beetle). 200pf + 50pf,
Maikafer (cockchafer).

**1993, Apr. 15           Litho.     Perf. 14**
B745  SP389  80pf +40pf multi   1.60 1.60
B746  SP389  80pf +40pf multi   1.60 1.60
B747  SP389  100pf +50pf multi  2.00 2.00
B748  SP389  100pf +50pf multi  2.00 2.00
B749  SP389  200pf +50pf multi  3.25 3.25
       *Nos. B745-B749 (5)*     10.45 10.45
    Surtax for German Youth Stamp Foundation.

Stamp
Day — SP390

**1993, Sept. 16   Litho.   Perf. 13½x14**
B750  SP390  100pf +50pf multi     1.60  1.60

Surtax for the Foundation for Promotion of
Philately and Postal History.

Traditional
Costumes
SP391

Costumes from: No. B751, Rugen, Mecklenburg, Western Pomerania. No. B752, Fohr,
Schleswig-Holstein. No. B753, Schwalm,
Hesse. No. B754, Oberndorf, Bavaria. 200pf +
40pf, Ernstroda, Thuringia.

**1993, Oct. 14            Perf. 14**
B751  SP391   80pf +40pf multi     1.50  1.50
B752  SP391   80pf +40pf multi     1.50  1.50
B753  SP391  100pf +50pf multi     1.75  1.75
B754  SP391  100pf +50pf multi     1.75  1.75
B755  SP391  200pf +40pf multi     3.00  3.00
       *Nos. B751-B755 (5)*         9.50  9.50

Surtax for welfare organizations. See Nos.
B768-B772.

Christmas
SP392

Wings of high altar in choir of Blaubeuren
Monastery: 80pf+40pf, Adoraration of Magi.
100pf+50pf, Nativity.

**1993, Nov. 10     Litho.     Perf. 14**
B756  SP392   80pf +40pf multi     1.00   .90
B757  SP392  100pf +50pf multi     1.90  1.75

Surtax for welfare organizations.

Figure Skating
SP393

Sports: #B759, Olympic Flame. #B760,
Soccer ball, World Cup Trophy. 200pf+80pf,
Skiier.

**1994, Feb. 10    Litho.    Perf. 14x13½**
B758  SP393   80pf +40pf multi     1.40  1.40
B759  SP393  100pf +50pf multi     1.60  1.60
B760  SP393  100pf +50pf multi     1.60  1.60
B761  SP393  200pf +80pf multi     2.75  2.75
       *Nos. B758-B761 (4)*         7.35  7.35

1994 Winter Olympics, Lillehammer
(#B758). Intl. Olympic Committee, Cent.
(#B759). 1994 World Cup Soccer Championships, US (#B760). 1994 Paralympics, Lillehammer (#B761).

Heinrich
Hoffmann
(1809-94),
Physician,
Writer of
Children's
Books
SP394

Characters from "Slovenly Peter:" No. B762,
Little Pauline. No. B763, Johnny Head-in-the-
air. No. B764, Slovenly Peter. No. B765,
Naughty Frederick. 200pf+80pf, The Fidget.

**1994, Apr. 14     Litho.     Perf. 13½**
B762  SP394   80pf +40pf multi     1.25  1.25
B763  SP394   80pf +40pf multi     1.25  1.25
B764  SP394  100pf +50pf multi     1.50  1.50
B765  SP394  100pf +50pf multi     1.50  1.50
B766  SP394  200pf +80pf multi     2.75  2.75
       *Nos. B762-B766 (5)*         8.25  8.25

Surtax for German Youth Stamp Foundation.

Environmental
Protection
SP395

**1994, June 16      Litho.      Perf. 13**
B767  SP395  100pf +50pf blk &
                 grn               1.60  1.60

Traditional Costume Type 1993

Costumes from: No. B768, Buckeburg. No.
B769, Halle an der Saale. No. B770, Hoyer-
swerda. No. B771, Minden. 200pf+70pf,
Betzingen.

**1994, Oct. 13     Litho.     Perf. 13½**
B768  SP391   80pf +40pf multi     1.25  1.25
B769  SP391   80pf +40pf multi     1.25  1.25
B770  SP391  100pf +50pf multi     1.75  1.75
B771  SP391  100pf +50pf multi     1.75  1.75
B772  SP391  200pf +70pf multi     2.75  2.75
       *Nos. B768-B772 (5)*         8.75  8.75

Surtax for welfare organizations.

Christmas
SP396

Paintings by Hans Memling: 80pf+40pf,
Adoration of the Magi. 100pf+50pf, Nativity
Scene.

**1994, Nov. 9     Litho.     Perf. 13½**
B773  SP396   80pf +40pf multi     1.25  1.10
B774  SP396  100pf +50pf multi     1.75  1.60

Sports
SP397

**1995, Feb. 9     Photo.     Perf. 13½**
B775  SP397   80pf +40pf Rowing 1.25  1.25
B776  SP397  100pf +50pf Gym-
                 nastics           1.50  1.50
B777  SP397  100pf +50pf Boxing 1.50  1.50
B778  SP397  200pf +80pf Volley-
                 ball              3.00  3.00
       *Nos. B775-B778 (4)*         7.25  7.25

World Kayaking Championships, Duisburg
(#B775). Intl. Gymnastics Festival, Berlin
(#B776). World Amateur Boxing Champion-
ships, Berlin (#B777). Volleyball, cent.
(#B778).

Dogs
SP398

#B779, Munsterlander. #B780, Schnauzer.
#B781, German shepherd. #B782, Wire
haired dachshund. 200pf+80pf, Wolf spitz.

**1995, June 8     Litho.     Perf. 13½**
B779  SP398   80pf +40pf multi     1.25  1.25
B780  SP398   80pf +40pf multi     1.25  1.25
B781  SP398  100pf +50pf multi     1.60  1.60
B782  SP398  100pf +50pf multi     1.60  1.60
B783  SP398  200pf +80pf multi     2.75  2.75
       *Nos. B779-B783 (5)*         8.45  8.45

Surtax for benefit of German Youth Stamp
Foundation. See Nos. B792-B796.

Stamp
Day — SP399

**1995, Sept. 6     Litho.     Perf. 13**
B784  SP399  200pf +100pf multi    3.00  3.00

Surtax for Foundation for Promotion of Philately and Postal History.

Farmhouses — SP400

#B785, Eifel region. #B786, Saxony. #B787,
Lower Germany. #B788, Upper Bavaria.
200pf+70pf, Mecklenburg.

**1995, Oct. 12     Litho.     Perf. 14**
B785  SP400   80pf +40pf multi     1.25  1.25
B786  SP400   80pf +40pf multi     1.25  1.25
B787  SP400  100pf +50pf multi     1.60  1.60
B788  SP400  100pf +50pf multi     1.60  1.60
B789  SP400  200pf +70pf multi     2.75  2.75
       *Nos. B785-B789 (5)*         8.45  8.45

Surtax for welfare organizations.
See Nos. B802-B806.

Christmas
SP401

Stained glass windows, Augsburg Cathedral: 80pf+40pf, Annunciation. 100pf+50pf,
Nativity.

**1995, Nov. 9     Litho.     Perf. 14**
B790  SP401   80pf +40pf multi     1.25  1.10
B791  SP401  100pf +50pf multi     1.75  1.60

Surtax for welfare organizations.

Dog Type of 1995

#B792, Borzoi. #B793, Chow chow. #B794,
St. Bernard. #B795, Collie. 200pf+80pf,
Briard.

**1996, Feb. 8     Litho.     Perf. 13½**
B792  SP398   80pf +40pf multi     1.25  1.25
B793  SP398   80pf +40pf multi     1.25  1.25
B794  SP398  100pf +50pf multi     1.60  1.60
B795  SP398  100pf +50pf multi     1.60  1.60
B796  SP398  200pf +80pf multi     2.50  2.50
       *Nos. B792-B796 (5)*         8.20  8.20

Surtax for benefit of German Youth Stamp
Foundation.

Modern
Olympic
Games, Cent.
SP402

Olympic champions: 80pf+40pf, Carl
Schuhmann (1869-1946), pommel horse. No.
B798, Annie Hübler Horn (1885-1976), pairs
figure skating. No. B799, Josef Neckermann
(1912-92), equestrian. 200pf+80pf, Alfred
Flatow (1869-1942), Gustav Felix Flatow
(1875-1945), gymnastics.

**1996, June 13     Photo.     Perf. 13½**
B797  SP402   80pf +40pf multi     1.25  1.25
B798  SP402  100pf +50pf multi     1.60  1.60
B799  SP402  100pf +50pf multi     1.60  1.60
B800  SP402  200pf +80pf multi     2.75  2.75
       *Nos. B797-B800 (4)*         7.20  7.20

Preservation of Tropical
Habitats — SP403

**1996, July 18     Photo.     Perf. 14**
B801  SP403  100pf +50pf multi     1.50  1.50

Farmhouse Type of 1995

Location: No. B802, Spree Forest. No.
B803, Thuringia. No. B804, Black Forest. No.
B805, Westphalia. 200pf+70pf, Schleswig-
Holstein.

**1996, Oct. 9     Litho.     Perf. 14**
B802  SP400   80pf +40pf multi     1.25  1.25
B803  SP400   80pf +40pf multi     1.25  1.25
B804  SP400  100pf +50pf multi     1.50  1.50
B805  SP400  100pf +50pf multi     1.50  1.50
B806  SP400  200pf +70pf multi     2.50  2.50
       *Nos. B802-B806 (5)*         8.00  8.00

Christmas
SP404

Illuminated pages from Henry II's book of
pericopes (Gospels), 11th cent.: 80pf+40pf,
Adoration of the Magi. 100pf+50pf, Nativity.

**1996, Nov. 14     Litho.     Perf. 14**
B807  SP404   80pf +40pf multi     1.25  1.10
B808  SP404  100pf +50pf multi     1.50  1.40

Surtax for welfare organizations.

Sports
SP405

**1997, Feb. 4     Litho.     Perf. 14x13½**
B809  SP405   80pf +40pf Aer-
                 obics             1.25  1.25
B810  SP405  100pf +50pf Inline
                 skating           1.60  1.60
B811  SP405  100pf +50pf Street-
                 ball              1.60  1.60
B812  SP405  200pf +80pf Free
                 climbing          2.50  2.50
       *Nos. B809-B812 (4)*         6.95  6.95

Horses
SP406

**1997, June 9      Litho.      *Perf.* 14**
B813 SP406  80pf + 40pf Rhe-
                      no-German
                      draft            1.25 1.25
B814 SP406  80pf + 40pf
                      Shetland po-
                      ny               1.25 1.25
B815 SP406 100pf + 50pf Frie-
                      sian             1.50 1.50
B816 SP406 100pf + 50pf
                      Haflinger        1.50 1.50
B817 SP406 200pf + 80pf Hano-
                      verian           3.00 3.00
       *Nos. B813-B817 (5)*       8.50 8.50

Arms Type of 1992 Redrawn and
Inscribed
"Hochwasserhilfe 1997" and
"DEUTSCHLAND"

**1997, Aug. 19      Litho.      *Perf. 13½***
B818 A739 110pf +90pf like
                      #1702            2.00 2.00

Souvenir Sheet

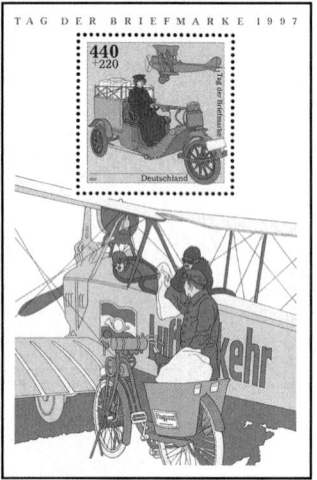

Stamp Day — SP407

Illustration reduced.

**1997, Sept. 17      Litho.      *Perf.* 14**
B819 SP407 440pf +220pf multi   6.75 6.75

Mills — SP408

Designs: 100pf+50pf, Black Forest. No.
B821, Hesse. No. B822, Windmill, lower
Rhine. No. B823, Scoop windmill, Schleswig-
Holstein. 220pf+80pf, Dutch windmill.

**1997, Oct. 9      Litho.      *Perf. 13½x14***
**Background Color**
B820 SP408 100pf +50pf grn    1.75  1.75
B821 SP409 110pf +50pf brn    1.75  1.75
B822 SP408 110pf +50pf blue   1.75  1.75
B823 SP408 110pf +50pf yel    1.75  1.75
B824 SP408 220pf +80pf pink   3.00  3.00
       *Nos. B820-B824 (5)*      10.00 10.00

---

Christmas
SP409

**1997, Nov. 6      Litho.      *Perf.* 14**
B825 SP409 100pf +50pf Magi       1.40 1.25
B826 SP409 110pf +50pf Nativity   1.60 1.50
Surtax for Federal Assoc. of Free Welfare
Work in Bonn.

Sports
SP410

1998 Sporting events: 100pf+50pf, World
Cup Soccer Championships, France. No.
B828, Winter Olympic Games, Nagano. No.
B829, Rowing Championships, Cologne.
300pf+100pf, Winter Paralympics, Nagano.

**1998, Feb. 5      Photo.      *Perf.* 14**
B827 SP410 100pf +50pf multi    1.50  1.50
B828 SP410 110pf +50pf multi    1.75  1.75
B829 SP410 110pf +50pf multi    1.75  1.75
B830 SP410 300pf +100pf
                      multi            4.25  4.25
       *Nos. B827-B830 (4)*      9.25  9.25

Environmental Protection — SP411

**1998, May 7      Litho.      *Perf.* 14**
B831 SP411 110pf +50pf multi    1.60 1.60

Cartoon
Figures
SP412

#B832, Mouse, Little Yellow Duck, Elephant.
#833, Sandman. #834, Maja the Bee. #835,
Captain Bluebear. #836, Pumuckl.

**1998, June 10      Litho.      *Perf.* 14**
B832 SP412 100pf +50pf multi    1.50  1.50
B833 SP412 100pf +50pf multi    1.50  1.50
B834 SP412 110pf +50pf multi    1.75  1.75
B835 SP412 110pf +50pf multi    1.75  1.75
B836 SP412 220pf +50pf multi    3.50  3.50
       *Nos. B832-B836 (5)*      10.00 10.00
Surtax for the German Youth Stamp
Foundation.

Welfare
Stamps
SP413

Birds: 100pf+50pf, Hen-harrier. No. B838,
Great bustard. No. B839, White-eyed duck.
No. B840, Sedge warbler. 220pf+80pf, Wood-
chat shrike.

**1998, Oct. 8      Litho.      *Perf.* 14**
**Background Colors**
B837 SP413 100pf +50pf tan    1.50  1.50
B838 SP413 110pf +50pf gray
                      grn              1.75  1.75

---

B839 SP413 110pf +50pf gray
                      blue             1.75  1.75
B840 SP413 110pf +50pf blue
                      grn              1.75  1.75
B841 SP413 220pf +80pf lilac    3.50  3.50
       *Nos. B837-B841 (5)*     10.25 10.25

Christmas
SP414

**1998, Nov. 12**
B842 SP414 100pf +50pf Shep-
                      herds            1.50 1.40
B843 SP414 110pf +50pf Holy
                      Child            1.75 1.60

Racing
Sports
SP415

**1999, Feb. 18      Photo.      *Perf.* 14**
B844 SP415 100pf +50pf Bi-
                      cycles           1.75  1.75
B845 SP415 110pf +50pf Cars   1.75  1.75
B846 SP415 110pf +50pf Hor-
                      ses              1.75  1.75
B847 SP415 300pf +100pf
                      Motorcycles      3.75  3.75
       *Nos. B844-B847 (4)*      9.00  9.00

**Declaration of Human Rights Type
of 1998**
Inscribed "KOSOVO-HILFE 1999"

**1999, Apr. 27      Litho.      *Perf.* 14**
B848 A958 110pf +100pf multi   2.25 2.25
Sutax for aid to refugees from Kosovo.

Souvenir Sheet

IBRA '99, Intl. Stamp Exhibition,
Nuremberg — SP416

Design: Bavaria #1 & Saxony #1.
Illustration reduced.

**1999, Apr. 27           *Perf. 13½***
B849 SP416 300pf +110pf multi   4.50 4.50
German postage stamps, 150th anniv.

Cartoons
SP417

#B850, The Little Polar Bear. #B851, Rudi
the Crow. #B852, Mecki (hedgehog). #B853,
Twipsy, mascot of Expo 2000, Hanover.
220pf+80pf, Tabaluga (green dragon).

**1999, June 10      Litho.      *Perf. 13¾***
B850 SP417 100pf +50pf multi    1.75  1.75
B851 SP417 100pf +50pf multi    1.75  1.75
B852 SP417 110pf +50pf multi    2.00  2.00
B853 SP417 110pf +50pf multi    2.00  2.00
B854 SP417 220pf +80pf multi    2.50  2.50
       *Nos. B850-B854 (5)*     10.00 10.00
Surtax for the German Youth Stamp
Foundation.

---

The Cosmos — SP418

#B855, Andromeda galaxy. #B856, Cygnus
constellation. #B857, X-ray image of exploding
star. #B858, Collision of Comet Shoemaker-
Levy 9 and Jupiter. 300pf + 100pf, Gamma ray
image of entire sky, satellite.

**1999, Oct. 14      Litho.      *Perf.* 14**
B855 SP418 100pf +50pf multi    1.50  1.50
B856 SP418 100pf +50pf multi    1.50  1.50
B857 SP418 110pf +50pf multi    1.75  1.75
B858 SP418 110pf +50pf multi    1.75  1.75
B859 SP418 300pf +100pf
                      multi            3.50  3.50
       *Nos. B855-B859 (5)*     10.00 10.00
Surtax for the Federal Association of Free
Welfare Work. Nos. B858-B859 have a
holographic image. Soaking in water may
affect hologram.

Christmas
SP419

**1999, Nov. 4      Litho.      *Perf. 13¾***
B860 SP419 100pf +50pf Angel    1.60 1.40
B861 SP419 110pf +50pf Manger   1.75 1.50

Sports — SP420

Ancient art and: 100pf + 50pf, Swimmer.
No. B863, Gymnast. No. B864, Sprinters.
300pf + 100pf, Hands.

**2000, Feb. 17      Litho.      *Perf. 13¾x14***
B862 SP420 100pf + 50pf multi   1.60 1.60
B863 SP420 110pf + 50pf multi   1.75 1.75
B864 SP420 110pf + 50pf multi   1.75 1.75
B865 SP420 300pf + 100pf multi  4.25 4.25
       *Nos. B862-B865 (4)*      9.35 9.35
Surtax was for German Sports Federation.

Environmental Protection — SP421

**2000, May 12   Litho.   *Perf. 13¾x14***
B866 SP421 110pf +50pf multi    1.75 1.75

Expo 2000, Hanover — SP422

#B867, 4 backpackers. #B868, Crowd.
#B869, Map of Africa, words "see, come, hear,
feel." #B870, Eye. #B871, Abstract with Chinese characters. #B872, Abstract.

**2000, June 8   Litho.   Perf. 13¾x14**
| | | | | |
|---|---|---|---|---|
| B867 | SP422 | 100pf +50pf multi | 1.50 | 1.50 |
| B868 | SP422 | 100pf +50pf multi | 1.50 | 1.50 |
| B869 | SP422 | 110pf +50pf multi | 1.60 | 1.60 |
| B870 | SP422 | 110pf +50pf multi | 1.60 | 1.60 |
| B871 | SP422 | 110pf +50pf multi | 1.60 | 1.60 |
| B872 | SP422 | 300pf +100pf | | |
| | | multi | 4.25 | 4.25 |
| *Nos. B867-B872 (6)* | | | 12.05 | 12.05 |

Surtax for German Youth Stamp Foundation.

Actors and Actresses — SP423

#B873, Curd Jürgens (1915-82). #B874, Lilli Palmer (1914-86). #B875, Heinz Rühmann (1902-94). #B876, Romy Schneider (1938-82). #B877, Gert Fröbe (1913-88).

**2000, Oct. 12   Litho.   Perf. 14**
| | | | | |
|---|---|---|---|---|
| B873 | SP423 | 100pf +50pf multi | 1.50 | 1.50 |
| B874 | SP423 | 100pf +50pf multi | 1.50 | 1.50 |
| B875 | SP423 | 110pf +50pf multi | 1.75 | 1.75 |
| B876 | SP423 | 110pf +50pf multi | 1.75 | 1.75 |
| B877 | SP423 | 300pf +100pf | | |
| | | multi | 4.00 | 4.00 |
| *Nos. B873-B877 (5)* | | | 10.50 | 10.50 |

Surtax was for Federal Association of Welfare Work.

Christmas SP424

Designs: 100pf+50pf, Birth of Christ, by Conrad von Soest. 110pf+50pf, Nativity scene.

**2000, Nov. 9   Litho.   Perf. 13¾**
| | | | | |
|---|---|---|---|---|
| B878 | SP424 | 100pf +50pf multi | 1.50 | 1.40 |
| B879 | SP424 | 110pf +50pf multi | 1.75 | 1.60 |

Surtax for the Federal Association of Voluntary Welfare Work.
See Spain Nos. 3071-3072.

Sports — SP425

Designs: 100pf+50pf, Sports for schools. No. B881, Sports for the disabled. No. B882, Popular and leisure sports. 300pf+100pf, Sports for senior citizens.

**2001, Feb. 8   Litho.   Perf. 13¾x14**
| | | | | |
|---|---|---|---|---|
| B880 | SP425 | 100pf +50pf multi | 1.90 | 1.90 |
| B881 | SP425 | 110pf +50pf multi | 2.00 | 2.00 |
| B882 | SP425 | 110pf +50pf multi | 2.00 | 2.00 |
| B883 | SP425 | 300pf +100pf | | |
| | | multi | 4.75 | 4.75 |
| *Nos. B880-B883 (4)* | | | 10.65 | 10.65 |

Surtax for German Sports Federation.

Wuppertal Suspension Railway — SP426

**2001, Mar. 8**
| | | | | |
|---|---|---|---|---|
| B884 | SP426 | 110pf +50pf multi | 2.00 | 2.00 |

Surtax for the Foundation for Promotion of Philately and Postal History.

Characters from Children's Stories SP427

Designs: No. B885, Pinocchio. No. B886, Pippi Longstockings. No. B887, Jim Knopf. No. B888, Heidi. 300pf +100pf, Tom Sawyer and Huckleberry Finn.

**2001, June 13   Litho.   Perf. 13¾**
| | | | | |
|---|---|---|---|---|
| B885 | SP427 | 100pf +50pf multi | 1.90 | 1.90 |
| B886 | SP427 | 100pf +50pf multi | 1.90 | 1.90 |
| B887 | SP427 | 110pf +50pf multi | 2.00 | 2.00 |
| B888 | SP427 | 110pf +50pf multi | 2.00 | 2.00 |
| B889 | SP427 | 300pf +100pf | | |
| | | multi | 4.75 | 4.75 |
| *Nos. B885-B889 (5)* | | | 12.55 | 12.55 |

Surtax for the German Youth Stamp Foundation.

Film Stars SP428

Designs: No. B890, Marilyn Monroe. No. B891, Charlie Chaplin. No. B892, Film reel. No. B893, Greta Garbo. 300pf+100pf, Jean Gabin.

**2001, Oct. 11   Litho.   Perf. 14**
| | | | | |
|---|---|---|---|---|
| B890 | SP428 | 100pf +50pf multi | 1.90 | 1.90 |
| *a.* | | Perf. 13x13¼x13½x13¼ | 1.90 | 1.90 |
| B891 | SP428 | 100pf +50pf multi | 1.90 | 1.90 |
| *a.* | | Perf. 13½x13¼ | 1.90 | 1.90 |
| B892 | SP428 | 110pf +50pf multi | 2.00 | 2.00 |
| *a.* | | Perf. 13½x13¼ | 2.00 | 2.00 |
| B893 | SP428 | 110pf +50pf multi | 2.00 | 2.00 |
| *a.* | | Perf. 13x13¼ | 2.00 | 2.00 |
| B894 | SP428 | 300pf +100pf | | |
| | | multi | 4.75 | 4.75 |
| *a.* | | Perf. 13x13¼ | 4.75 | 4.75 |
| *b.* | | Booklet pane, #B890a-B894a | 11.50 | 11.50 |
| | | Booklet, #B894b | 11.50 | |
| *Nos. B890-B894 (5)* | | | 12.55 | 12.55 |

Surtax for the Federal Association of Voluntary Welfare Work.

A stamp picturing Audrey Hepburn originally was to have been included in this set but was withdrawn. It was never officially issued, nor were any examples sold over post office counters. However, 30 examples from the original printing were not recovered and destroyed as ordered by the post office. Four of the stamps have been found used on German mail.

Christmas SP429

Designs: 100pf+50pf, Madonna and Child, by Alfredo Roldán. 110pf+50pf, Adoration of the Shepherds, by José de Ribera.

**2001, Nov. 8   Litho.   Perf. 13¼**
| | | | | |
|---|---|---|---|---|
| B895 | SP429 | 100pf +50pf multi | 1.90 | 1.90 |
| B896 | SP429 | 110pf +50pf multi | 2.00 | 2.00 |
| *a.* | | Souvenir sheet (see footnote) | 5.50 | 5.50 |

No. B896a contains Nos. B895-B896 and lithographed and perf. 13¼ examples of Spain Nos. 3123-3124. No. B896a sold for 4.45m.
See Spain Nos. 3123-3124.

Intl. Year of Mountains — SP430

**2002, Jan. 10   Litho.   Perf. 14**
| | | | | |
|---|---|---|---|---|
| B897 | SP430 | 56c +26c multi | 2.00 | 2.00 |

Winter Olympic Sports — SP431

Designs: 51c+26c, Biathlon. No. B899, 56c+26c, Ski jumping. No. B900, 56c+26c, Speed skating. 153c+51c, Luge.

**2002, Feb. 7   Litho.   Perf. 13¾x14**
| | | | | |
|---|---|---|---|---|
| B898 | SP431 | 51c +26c multi | 1.90 | 1.90 |
| B899 | SP431 | 56c +26c multi | 2.00 | 2.00 |
| B900 | SP431 | 56c +26c multi | 2.00 | 2.00 |
| B901 | SP431 | 153c +51c multi | 4.75 | 4.75 |
| *a.* | | Booklet pane, #B898-B901 | 10.50 | 10.50 |
| | | Booklet, #B901a | 10.50 | |
| *Nos. B898-B901 (4)* | | | 10.65 | 10.65 |

Surtax for German Sports Promotion Foundation.

Toys and Games SP432

Designs: No. B902, Chess pieces. No. B903, Toy truck. No. B904, Doll. No. B905, Teddy bear. 153c+51c, Toy train.

**2002, June 6   Litho.   Perf. 13¾**
| | | | | |
|---|---|---|---|---|
| B902 | SP432 | 51c +26c multi | 1.90 | 1.90 |
| B903 | SP432 | 51c +26c multi | 1.90 | 1.90 |
| B904 | SP432 | 56c +26c multi | 2.00 | 2.00 |
| B905 | SP432 | 56c +26c multi | 2.00 | 2.00 |
| B906 | SP432 | 153c +51c multi | 4.75 | 4.75 |
| *Nos. B902-B906 (5)* | | | 12.55 | 12.55 |

Surtax for German Youth Stamp Foundation.

**Environmental Protection Type of 1998 Inscribed "Hochwasserhilfe 2002"**

**2002, Aug. 30   Litho.   Perf. 13x13½**
| | | | | |
|---|---|---|---|---|
| B907 | SP411 | 56c +44c multi | 2.40 | 2.40 |

Surtax for flood victims relief.

Christmas SP433

Details from paintings by Rogier van der Weyden: 51c+26c, Annunciation to the Virgin. 56c+26c, Miraflores Altarpiece.

**2002, Nov. 7   Litho.   Perf. 13¾**
| | | | | |
|---|---|---|---|---|
| B908 | SP433 | 51c +26c multi | 2.00 | 2.00 |
| B909 | SP433 | 56c +26c multi | 2.00 | 2.00 |

Surtax for Federal Working Party on Independent Welfare.

Automobiles — SP434

Designs: 45c+20c, 1960 BMW Isetta 300. No. B911, 55c+25c, 1961 VEB Sachsenring Trabant P50. No. B912, 55c+25c, 1949 Volkswagen Beetle. No. B913, 55c+25c, 1954 Mercedes-Benz 300 SL. 144c+56c, 1957 Borgward Isabella Coupe.

**2002, Dec. 5   Litho.   Perf. 14**
| | | | | |
|---|---|---|---|---|
| B910 | SP434 | 45c +20c multi | 1.60 | 1.60 |
| B911 | SP434 | 55c +25c multi | 1.90 | 1.90 |
| B912 | SP434 | 55c +25c multi | 1.90 | 1.90 |
| B913 | SP434 | 55c +25c multi | 1.90 | 1.90 |
| B914 | SP434 | 144c +56c multi | 4.25 | 4.25 |
| *Nos. B910-B914 (5)* | | | 12.30 | 12.30 |

Surtax for Federal Working Party on Independent Welfare.

2006 World Cup Soccer Championships, Germany — SP435

Designs: 45c+20c, Player kicking ball. No. B916, Player heading ball. No. B917, Four children playing soccer. No. B918, Fan celebrating. 144c+56c, Child and adult playing soccer.

**2003, Mar. 6   Litho.   Perf. 13x13½**
| | | | | |
|---|---|---|---|---|
| B915 | SP435 | 45c +20c multi | 1.40 | 1.40 |
| B916 | SP435 | 55c +25c multi | 1.75 | 1.75 |
| B917 | SP435 | 55c +25c multi | 1.75 | 1.75 |
| B918 | SP435 | 55c +25c multi | 1.75 | 1.75 |
| B919 | SP435 | 144c +56c multi | 4.50 | 4.50 |
| *Nos. B915-B919 (5)* | | | 11.15 | 11.15 |

Surtax for German Sports Promotion Foundation.

First East-to-West Non-Stop Transatlantic Flight, 75th Anniv. SP436

**2003, Apr. 10   Perf. 13¾**
| | | | | |
|---|---|---|---|---|
| B920 | SP436 | 144c +56c multi | 4.25 | 4.25 |

Surtax for German Organization for the Enhancement of Philately and Postal History.

June 17, 1953 Uprising in East Germany, 50th Anniv. SP437

**2003, June 12   Photo.   Perf. 14x14¼**
| | | | | |
|---|---|---|---|---|
| B921 | SP437 | 55c +25c multi | 1.90 | 1.90 |

### Souvenir Sheet

Father and Son, Cartoons by Ehrich Ohser — SP438

No. B922: a, Father and son running in same direction. b, Father and son falling. c, Son running, father seated. d, Father and son running in different directions. e, Father and son with arms extended.

**2003, July 10   Litho.   *Perf. 13x13½***

| | | | |
|---|---|---|---|
| B922 | SP438 | Sheet of 5 | 11.50 11.50 |
| a. | | 45c +20c multi | 1.50 1.50 |
| b.-d. | | 55c +25c any single | 1.75 1.75 |
| e. | | 144c +56c multi | 4.50 4.50 |

#### Automobile Type of 2002

Designs: 45c+20c, Wartburg 311 Coupe. No. B924, Olympia Rekord P1. No. B925, 356 B Coupe. No. 926, 55c+25c, Taunus 17 M P3. 144c+56c, Auto Union 1000 S.

**2003, Oct. 9   Litho.   *Perf. 14***

| | | | |
|---|---|---|---|
| B923 | SP434 | 45c +20c multi | 1.50 1.50 |
| B924 | SP434 | 55c +25c multi | 1.90 1.90 |
| B925 | SP434 | 55c +25c multi | 1.90 1.90 |
| B926 | SP434 | 55c +25c multi | 1.90 1.90 |
| B927 | SP434 | 144c +56c multi | 4.50 4.50 |
| | *Nos. B923-B927 (5)* | | 11.70 11.70 |

Christmas SP439

Designs: 45c+20c, Adoration of the Shepherds. 55c+25c, Holy Family.

**2003, Nov. 13   Litho.   *Perf. 13¾***

| | | | |
|---|---|---|---|
| B928 | SP439 | 45c +20c multi | 1.50 1.50 |
| B929 | SP439 | 55c +25c multi | 1.90 1.90 |

Wind Energy SP440

**2004, Jan. 8   Litho.   *Perf. 13¾***

| | | | |
|---|---|---|---|
| B930 | SP440 | 55c +25c multi | 2.10 2.10 |

Sporting Events and Anniversaries — SP441

Designs: 45c+20c, European Soccer Championships, June 12-July 4, 2004. No. B932, Summer Olympic Games, Athens, Greece. No. B933, Paralympics, Athens, Greece. No. B934, First German World Cup Championship, 50th anniv. 144c+56c, FIFA (Fédération Internationale de Football Association), cent.

**2004, Feb. 5   Litho.   *Perf. 13x13½***

| | | | |
|---|---|---|---|
| B931 | SP441 | 45c +20c multi | 1.75 1.75 |
| B932 | SP441 | 55c +25c multi | 2.10 2.10 |
| B933 | SP441 | 55c +25c multi | 2.10 2.10 |
| B934 | SP441 | 55c +25c multi | 2.10 2.10 |
| B935 | SP441 | 144c +56c multi | 5.25 5.25 |
| | *Nos. B931-B935 (5)* | | 13.30 13.30 |

Cats — SP442

Designs: 45c+20c, Two cats playing with ball of string. No. B937, Cat, two kittens playing with ball. No. B938, Kitten on cat. No. B939, Cat licking paw. 144c+56c, Two cats sleeping.

**2004, June 3   Litho.   *Perf. 13¾x14***

| | | | |
|---|---|---|---|
| B936 | SP442 | 45c +20c multi | 1.60 1.60 |
| B937 | SP442 | 55c +25c multi | 1.90 1.90 |
| B938 | SP442 | 55c +25c multi | 1.90 1.90 |
| B939 | SP442 | 55c +25c multi | 1.90 1.90 |
| B940 | SP442 | 144c +56c multi | 4.75 4.75 |
| | *Nos. B936-B940 (5)* | | 12.05 12.05 |

Landscapes — SP443

Designs: 45c+20c, Iceberg and pack ice. No. B942, Mountains and clouds. No. B943, Islands. No. B944, Sand dunes. 144c+56c, Tree tops.

**2004, Oct. 7   Litho.   *Perf. 14***

| | | | |
|---|---|---|---|
| B941 | SP443 | 45c +20c multi | 1.60 1.60 |
| B942 | SP443 | 55c +25c multi | 2.00 2.00 |
| B943 | SP443 | 55c +25c multi | 2.00 2.00 |
| B944 | SP443 | 55c +25c multi | 2.00 2.00 |
| B945 | SP443 | 144c +56c multi | 5.00 5.00 |
| | *Nos. B941-B945 (5)* | | 12.60 12.60 |

Christmas SP444

Paintings by Peter Paul Rubens: 45c+20c, The Flight Into Egypt. 55c+25c, Adoration of the Magi.

**2004, Nov. 4          *Perf. 13¾***

| | | | |
|---|---|---|---|
| B946 | SP444 | 45c +20c multi | 1.75 1.75 |
| B947 | SP444 | 55c +25c multi | 2.10 2.10 |

See Belgium Nos. 2051-2053.

Sports — SP445

Designs: 45c+20c, Soccer fans, mascot of 2006 World Cup Soccer Championships. No. B949, Soccer players, soccer ball globe. No. B950, Gymnasts, Brandenburg Gate, Berlin. No. B951, Ski jumper and ski jump. 144c+56c, Fencers, Leipzig Arena.

**2005, Feb. 10   Litho.   *Perf. 13¾x14***

| | | | |
|---|---|---|---|
| B948 | SP445 | 45c +20c multi | 1.75 1.75 |
| B949 | SP445 | 55c +25c multi | 2.10 2.10 |
| B950 | SP445 | 55c +25c multi | 2.10 2.10 |
| B951 | SP445 | 55c +25c multi | 2.10 2.10 |
| B952 | SP445 | 144c +56c multi | 5.25 5.25 |
| | *Nos. B948-B952 (5)* | | 13.30 13.30 |

2006 World Cup Soccer Championships (Nos. B948-B949), Intl. Gymnastics Exhibition, Berlin (No. B950), Nordic Skiing World Championships, Oberstdorf (No. B951), Fencing World Championships, Leipzig (No. B952).

Stamp Day SP446

**2005, May 12   Litho.   *Perf. 14***

| | | | |
|---|---|---|---|
| B953 | SP446 | 55c +25c multi | 2.10 2.10 |

Sailing Ships — SP447

Designs: 45c+20c, Greif. No. B955, Rickmer Rickmers. No. B956, Passat. No. B957, Grossherzogin Elisabeth. 144c+56c, Deutschland.

**2005, June 2   Litho.   *Perf. 13¾x14***

| | | | |
|---|---|---|---|
| B954 | SP447 | 45c +20c multi | 1.60 1.60 |
| B955 | SP447 | 55c +25c multi | 2.00 2.00 |
| B956 | SP447 | 55c +25c multi | 2.00 2.00 |
| B957 | SP447 | 55c +25c multi | 2.00 2.00 |
| B958 | SP447 | 144c +56c multi | 5.00 5.00 |
| | *Nos. B954-B958 (5)* | | 12.60 12.60 |

Christmas SP448

Paintings by Stefan Lochner: 45c+20c, Adoration of the Child. 55c+25c, Madonna and Child in Rose Garden.

**2005, Nov. 3   Litho.   *Perf. 13¾***

| | | | |
|---|---|---|---|
| B959 | SP448 | 45c +20c multi | 1.60 1.60 |
| B960 | SP448 | 55c +25c multi | 1.90 1.90 |

Butterflies — SP449

Designs: 45c+20c, Zitronenfalter. No. B962, Russischer Bär. Nos. B963, B965, Tagpfauenauge. 145c+55c, Weisser Waldportier.

**2005, Dec. 1   Litho.   *Perf. 14***

| | | | |
|---|---|---|---|
| B961 | SP449 | 45c +20c multi | 1.60 1.60 |
| B962 | SP449 | 55c +25c multi | 1.90 1.90 |
| B963 | SP449 | 55c +25c multi | 1.90 1.90 |
| B964 | SP449 | 145c +55c multi | 4.75 4.75 |
| | *Nos. B961-B964 (5)* | | 10.15 10.15 |

**Self-Adhesive Booklet Stamp**
***Die Cut Perf. 11***

| | | | |
|---|---|---|---|
| B965 | SP449 | 55c +25c multi | 2.25 2.25 |
| a. | | Booklet pane of 10 | 22.50 |

Protection of the Ozone Layer — SP450

**2006, Jan. 2          *Perf. 14***

| | | | |
|---|---|---|---|
| B966 | SP450 | 55c +25c multi | 2.50 2.50 |

Sports — SP451

Designs: 45c+20c, Crowd waving German flags, stadium lights. No. B968, Stadium exterior, blurred athlete. No. B969, Stadium interior, players holding World Cup. No. B970, Horse and rider, rider's leg. 145c+55c, Emblem of 2006 World Cup Soccer Championships, blurred picture of soccer player kicking ball.

**2006, Feb. 9   Litho.   *Perf. 13x13½***

| | | | |
|---|---|---|---|
| B967 | SP451 | 45c +20c multi | 1.60 1.60 |
| B968 | SP451 | 55c +25c multi | 1.90 1.90 |
| B969 | SP451 | 55c +25c multi | 1.90 1.90 |
| B970 | SP451 | 55c +25c multi | 1.90 1.90 |
| B971 | SP451 | 145c +55c multi | 4.75 4.75 |
| a. | | Souvenir sheet, #B967-B969, B971 | 12.00 12.00 |
| | *Nos. B967-B971 (5)* | | 12.05 12.05 |

2006 World Cup Soccer Championships (Nos. B967-B969, B971), World Equestrian Championships, Aachen (No. B970).
No. B971a issued 5/4.

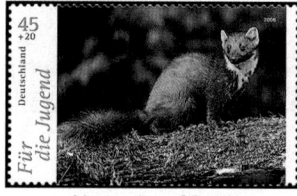

Mammals — SP452

Designs: 45c+20c, Pine marten. No. B973, Doe and fawn. No. B974, Hares. No. B975, Squirrel. 145c+55c, Wild pig and piglets.

**2006, June 8   Litho.   *Perf. 14***

| | | | |
|---|---|---|---|
| B972 | SP452 | 45c +20c multi | 1.75 1.75 |
| B973 | SP452 | 55c +25c multi | 2.10 2.10 |
| B974 | SP452 | 55c +25c multi | 2.10 2.10 |
| B975 | SP452 | 55c +25c multi | 2.10 2.10 |
| B976 | SP452 | 145c +55c multi | 5.25 5.25 |
| | *Nos. B972-B976 (5)* | | 13.30 13.30 |

Surtax for the German Youth Stamp Foundation.

Trains — SP453

Designs: 45c+20c, Fliegender Hamburger (VT 877). No. B978, Trans Europ Express (VT 11.5). Nos. B979, B981, InterCityExpress (ET403). 145c+55c, Henschel-Wegmann train (61 001).

**2006, Oct. 5   Litho.   *Perf. 13¾x14***

| | | | |
|---|---|---|---|
| B977 | SP453 | 45c +20c multi | 1.75 1.75 |
| B978 | SP453 | 55c +25c multi | 2.00 2.00 |
| B979 | SP453 | 55c +25c multi | 2.00 2.00 |
| B980 | SP453 | 145c +55c multi | 5.00 5.00 |
| | *Nos. B977-B980 (4)* | | 10.75 10.75 |

**Booklet Stamp**
**Self-Adhesive**
*Die Cut Perf. 11*

B981 SP453 55c +25c multi   2.50  2.50
a.   Booklet pane of 10   25.00

Christmas — SP454

15th Cent. altarpiece art by Meister Francke: 45c+20c, Nativity. 55c+25c, Adoration of the Magi.

**2006, Nov. 9   Litho.   Perf. 14**
B982 SP454 45c +20c multi   1.75  1.75
B983 SP454 55c +25c multi   2.00  2.00

SP455

Designs: 45c+20c, Canoe World Championships. No. B985, Handball World Championships. No. B986, Gymnastics World Championships. 145c+55c, Modern Pentathlon World Championships.

**2007   Litho.   Perf. 13x13½**
B984 SP455 45c +20c multi   1.75  1.75
B985 SP455 55c +25c multi   2.10  2.10
B986 SP455 55c +25c multi   2.10  2.10
B987 SP455 145c +55c multi  5.25  5.25
a.   Souvenir sheet, #B984-B987   12.00  12.00
Nos. B985-B987 (3)   9.45  9.45

Issued: B985, 1/2. B984, B986-B987, 2/8. B987a, 5/3.

**Souvenir Sheet**

Graf Zeppelin and Itinerary of Flight to South America — SP456

**Litho. & Engr.**
**2007, Mar. 1   Perf. 14x14¼**
B988 SP456 170c +70c multi   6.50  6.50

Stamp Day.

**Souvenir Sheet**

Hans Huckelbein, der Unglücksrabe, by Wilhelm Busch — SP457

No. B989: a, Bird eating berry jam. b, Bird standing in jam. c, Bird tipping pan of jam. d, Bird dirtying clean laundry.

**2007, June 14   Litho.   Perf. 13¼**
B989 SP457   Sheet of 4   12.00  12.00
a.   45c +20c multi   1.75  1.75
b.-c.   55c +25c either single   2.10  2.10
d.   145c +55c multi   5.50  5.50

Christmas
SP458

Designs: 45c+20c, Magi. 55c+25c, Madonna and Child, donkey and bull.

**2007, Nov. 8   Litho.   Perf. 13¼**
B990 SP458 45c +20c multi   1.90  1.90
B991 SP458 55c +25c multi   2.40  2.40

Adult and Juvenile Animals — SP459

Designs: 45c+20c, Guinea pigs. Nos. B993, B996, Horses. No. B994, Dogs. 145c+55c, Rabbits.

**2007, Dec. 27   Photo.   Perf. 13¾x14**
B992 SP459 45c +20c multi   1.90  1.90
B993 SP459 55c +25c multi   2.40  2.40
B994 SP459 55c +25c multi   2.40  2.40
B995 SP459 145c +55c multi  6.00  6.00
Nos. B992-B995 (4)   12.70  12.70

**Self-Adhesive**
**Booklet Stamp**
*Die Cut Perf. 11*

B996 SP459 55c +25c multi   2.50  2.50
a.   Booklet pane of 10   25.00

Sports Championships — SP460

Designs: 45c+20c, World Gliding Championships, Berlin. No. B998, Chess Olympiad, Dresden. No. B999, European Soccer Championships, Austria and Switzerland. 145c+55c, 2008 Summer Olympics, Beijing.

**Perf. 13¼x13½**
**2008, Mar. 13   Litho.**
B997 SP460 45c +20c multi   2.10  2.10
B998 SP460 55c +25c multi   2.50  2.50
B999 SP460 55c +25c multi   2.50  2.50
B1000 SP460 145c +55c multi  6.25  6.25
Nos. B997-B1000 (4)   13.35  13.35

Knut, Polar Bear Cub in Berlin Zoo SP461

**2008, Apr. 10   Litho.   Perf. 14**
B1001 SP461 55c +25c multi   2.60  2.60

Aircraft — SP462

Designs: 45c+20c, Dornier Do J Wal. No. B1003, Junkers Ju 52. Nos. B1004, B1006, Airbus A380. 145c+55c, Messerschmitt-Bölkow-Blohm BO 105 helicopter.

**2008, June 12   Litho.   Perf. 14**
B1002 SP462 45c +20c multi   2.00  2.00
B1003 SP462 55c +25c multi   2.50  2.50
B1004 SP462 55c +25c multi   2.50  2.50
B1005 SP462 145c +55c multi  6.25  6.25
Nos. B1002-B1005 (4)   13.25  13.25

**Self-Adhesive**
*Die Cut Perf. 11*
B1006 SP462 55c +25c multi   2.50  2.50
a.   Booklet pane of 10   25.00

**Miniature Sheet**

Dinosaurs — SP463

No. B1007: a, Triceratops. b, Diplodocus. c, Tyrannosaurus rex. d, Plateosaurus.

**2008, Sept. 4   Litho.   Perf. 13x13½**
B1007 SP463   Sheet of 4   12.50  12.50
a.   45c +20c multi   1.90  1.90
b.-c.   55c +25c Either single   2.40  2.40
d.   145c +55c multi   5.75  5.75

Christmas
SP464

Designs: 45c+20c, Nativity, by Albrecht Dürer. 55c+25c, Adoration of the Magi, by Raphael, horiz.

**2008, Nov. 13   Litho.   Perf. 14**
B1008 SP464 45c +20c multi   1.75  1.75
B1009 SP464 55c +25c multi   2.10  2.10

See Vatican City Nos. 1399-1401.

Atmospheric Phenomena — SP465

Designs: 45c+20c, Rainbow. Nos. B1011, B1014, Clouds. No. B1012, Aurora borealis. 145c+55c, Lightning.

**2009, Jan. 2   Litho.   Perf. 14**
B1010 SP465 45c +20c multi   1.75  1.75
B1011 SP465 55c +25c multi   2.25  2.25
B1012 SP465 55c +25c multi   2.25  2.25
B1013 SP465 145c +55c multi  5.50  5.50
Nos. B1010-B1013 (4)   11.75  11.75

**Booklet Stamp**
**Self-Adhesive**
*Die Cut Perf. 11*

B1014 SP465 55c +25c multi   2.25  2.25
a.   Booklet pane of 10   22.50

**AIR POST STAMPS**

**Issues of the Republic**

Post Horn with Wings — AP1

Biplane
AP2

**Perf. 15x14½**
**1919, Nov. 10   Typo.   Unwmk.**
C1 AP1 10pf orange   .20  2.50
C2 AP2 40pf dark green   .20  3.00
a.   Imperf.   1,875.
Set, never hinged   1.10

No. C2a is ungummed.

Carrier Pigeon AP3

German Eagle AP4

**1922-23   Wmk. 126   Perf. 14, 14½**
**Size: 19x23mm**
C3 AP3 25(pf) chocolate   .45  18.00
C4 AP3 40(pf) orange   .35  24.00
C5 AP3 50(pf) violet   .20  8.25
C6 AP3 60(pf) carmine   .50  20.00
C7 AP3 80(pf) blue grn   .35  20.00

**Perf. 13x13½**
**Size: 22x28mm**
C8 AP3 1m dk grn & pale grn   .20  3.75
C9 AP3 2m lake & gray   .20  3.75
C10 AP3 3m dk blue & gray   .20  4.50
C11 AP3 5m red org & yel   .20  3.75
C12 AP3 10m vio & rose ('23)   .20  10.50
C13 AP3 25m brn & yel ('23)   .20  8.50
C14 AP3 100m ol grn & rose ('23)   .20  7.25
Nos. C3-C14 (12)   3.25  132.25
Set, never hinged   11.50

**1923**
C15 AP3 5m vermilion   .20  45.00
C16 AP3 10m violet   .20  10.50
C17 AP3 25m dark brown   .20  10.50
C18 AP3 100m olive grn   .20  11.00
C19 AP3 200m deep blue   .20  32.50
a.   Imperf.   60.00
Nos. C15-C19 (5)   1.00  109.50
Set, never hinged   2.25

Issued: #C15-C18, June 1. #C19, July 25. Note following #160 applies to #C1-C19.

**1924, Jan. 11   Perf. 14**
**Size: 19x23mm**
C20 AP3 5(pf) yellow grn   1.25  1.50
C21 AP3 10(pf) carmine   1.25  1.75
C22 AP3 20(pf) violet blue   6.75  5.25
C23 AP3 50(pf) orange   11.00  24.00
C24 AP3 100(pf) dull violet   30.00  55.00
C25 AP3 200(pf) grnsh blue   55.00  75.00
C26 AP3 300(pf) gray   97.50 100.00
a.   Imperf.   1,425.
Nos. C20-C26 (7)   202.75 262.50
Set, never hinged   1,153.

**1926-27**
C27 AP4 5pf green   .75  .90
C28 AP4 10pf rose red   .75  .90
b.   Tête bêche pair   92.50 200.00
Never hinged   200.00
d.   Bklt. pane 10 (6 No. C28 + 4 No. C29)   55.00 150.00
Never hinged   150.00
C29 AP4 15pf lilac rose ('27)   1.60  1.40
a.   Double impression   1,375.
C30 AP4 20pf dull blue   1.60  1.90
a.   Tête bêche pair   92.50 200.00
Never hinged   200.00
b.   Bklt. pane 4 (4 No. C30 + 6 labels)   62.50 150.00
Never hinged   150.00
c.   Bklt. pane 5 (5 No. C30 + 5 labels)   200.00 500.00
Never hinged   500.00
C31 AP4 50pf brown org   18.00  5.25
C32 AP4 1m black & salmon   18.00  6.00
C33 AP4 2m black & blue   18.00  22.50
C34 AP4 3m black & ol grn   52.50  82.50
Nos. C27-C34 (8)   111.20 121.35
Set, never hinged   835.00

"Graf Zeppelin" Crossing Ocean — AP5

**1928-31**         **Photo.**
| | | | | |
|---|---|---|---|---|
| C35 | AP5 | 1m carmine ('31) | 25.00 | 32.50 |
| C36 | AP5 | 2m ultra | 37.50 | 52.50 |
| C37 | AP5 | 4m black brown | 27.50 | 35.00 |
| | | *Nos. C35-C37 (3)* | 90.00 | 120.00 |
| | | Set, never hinged | 400.00 | |

Issued: 2m, 4m, Sept. 20. 1m, May 8.
For overprints see Nos. C40-C45.

AP6

**1930, Apr. 19**         **Wmk. 126**
| | | | | |
|---|---|---|---|---|
| C38 | AP6 | 2m ultra | 240.00 | 300.00 |
| C39 | AP6 | 4m black brown | 240.00 | 300.00 |
| | | Set, never hinged | 2,625. | |

First flight of Graf Zeppelin to South America. Nos. C38-C39 exist with watermark vertical or horizontal.
Counterfeits exist of Nos. C38-C45.

Nos. C35-C37 Overprinted in Brown

**1931, July 15**
| | | | | |
|---|---|---|---|---|
| C40 | AP5 | 1m carmine | 110.00 | 110.00 |
| C41 | AP5 | 2m ultra | 160.00 | 200.00 |
| C42 | AP5 | 4m black brown | 400.00 | 675.00 |
| | | *Nos. C40-C42 (3)* | 670.00 | 985.00 |
| | | Set, never hinged | 3,050. | |

Polar flight of Graf Zeppelin.

Nos. C35-C37 Overprinted

**1933, Sept. 25**
| | | | | |
|---|---|---|---|---|
| C43 | AP5 | 1m carmine | 750.00 | 375.00 |
| C44 | AP5 | 2m ultra | 75.00 | 190.00 |
| C45 | AP5 | 4m black brown | 75.00 | 190.00 |
| | | *Nos. C43-C45 (3)* | 900.00 | 755.00 |
| | | Set, never hinged | 3,000. | |

Graf Zeppelin flight to Century of Progress International Exhibition, Chicago.

Swastika Sun, Globe and Eagle — AP7

Otto Lilienthal — AP8

Design: 3m, Count Ferdinand von Zeppelin.

**Perf. 14, 13½x13**
**1934, Jan. 21**     **Typo.**     **Wmk. 237**
| | | | | |
|---|---|---|---|---|
| C46 | AP7 | 5(pf) brt green | .75 | .55 |
| C47 | AP7 | 10(pf) brt carmine | .75 | .75 |
| C48 | AP7 | 15(pf) ultra | 1.25 | 1.25 |
| C49 | AP7 | 20(pf) dull blue | 2.25 | 1.60 |
| C50 | AP7 | 25(pf) brown | 3.50 | 1.50 |

| | | | | |
|---|---|---|---|---|
| C51 | AP7 | 40(pf) red violet | 6.75 | 1.10 |
| C52 | AP7 | 50(pf) dk green | 12.00 | .75 |
| C53 | AP7 | 80(pf) orange yel | 3.75 | 3.75 |
| C54 | AP7 | 100(pf) black | 6.00 | 2.75 |
| C55 | AP8 | 2m green & blk | 16.50 | 19.00 |
| C56 | AP8 | 3m blue & blk | 30.00 | 42.50 |
| | | *Nos. C46-C56 (11)* | 83.50 | 75.50 |
| | | Set, never hinged | 520.00 | |

"Hindenburg" — AP10

**Perf. 14, 14½x14**
**1936, Mar. 16**         **Engr.**
| | | | | |
|---|---|---|---|---|
| C57 | AP10 | 50pf dark blue | 18.00 | .75 |
| C58 | AP10 | 75pf dull green | 19.00 | 1.10 |

The note concerning gum after No. B68 also applies to Nos. C57-C58.
**Unused values are for stamps without gum.**

Count Zeppelin — AP11

Airship Gondola — AP12

**1938, July 5**    **Unwmk.**    **Perf. 13½**
| | | | | |
|---|---|---|---|---|
| C59 | AP11 | 25pf dull blue | 2.25 | 1.25 |
| C60 | AP12 | 50pf green | 3.50 | 1.25 |
| | | Set, never hinged | 42.00 | |

Count Ferdinand von Zeppelin (1838-1917), airship inventor and builder.

> **Catalogue values for unused stamps in this section, from this point to the end of the section, are for Never Hinged items.**

## Federal Republic

Lufthansa Emblem AP13

**Perf. 13½x13**
**1955, Mar. 31**   **Litho.**   **Wmk. 295**
| | | | | |
|---|---|---|---|---|
| C61 | AP13 | 5pf lilac rose & blk | 1.00 | .75 |
| C62 | AP13 | 10pf green & blk | 1.25 | 1.25 |
| C63 | AP13 | 15pf blue & blk | 7.50 | 5.75 |
| C64 | AP13 | 20pf red & blk | 21.00 | 7.50 |
| | | *Nos. C61-C64 (4)* | 30.75 | 15.25 |

Re-opening of German air service, Apr. 1.

## MILITARY AIR POST STAMP

Junkers 52 Transport MAP1

**1942**    **Unwmk.**    **Typo.**    **Perf. 13½**
| | | | | |
|---|---|---|---|---|
| MC1 | MAP1 | ultramarine | .20 | .30 |
| | | Never hinged | .45 | |
| *a.* | | Rouletted | .20 | .60 |
| | | Never hinged | .45 | |

## MILITARY PARCEL POST STAMPS

Nazi Emblem — MPP1

**1942**    **Unwmk.**    **Typo.**    **Perf. 13½**
          **Size: 28x23mm**
| | | | | |
|---|---|---|---|---|
| MQ1 | MPP1 | red brown | .20 | .45 |
| | | Never hinged | .45 | |
| *a.* | | Rouletted | .20 | .45 |
| | | Never hinged | .45 | |

**1944**    **Size: 22½x18mm**    **Perf. 14**
| | | | | |
|---|---|---|---|---|
| MQ2 | MPP1 | bright green | .45 | 2.25 |
| | | Never hinged | 1.10 | |

No. 520 Overprinted in Black

**1944**                **Engr.**
| | | | | |
|---|---|---|---|---|
| MQ3 | A115 | on 40pf brt red vio | .45 | 3.50 |
| | | Never hinged | 1.10 | |

Forged surcharges exist.
Used values for Nos. MQ1-MQ3 are for CTO examples. Postally used stamps are scarce and sell for much more.

## OFFICIAL STAMPS

### Issues of the Republic

In 1920 the Official Stamps of Bavaria and Wurttemberg then current were overprinted "Deutsches Reich" and made available for official use in all parts of Germany. They were, however, used almost exclusively in the two states where they originated and we have listed them among the issues of those states.

O1

O2

O3

O4

O5

O6

O7

O8

O9

O10

O11

O12

## 1920-21 Typo. Wmk. 125 Perf. 14

| | | | | | |
|---|---|---|---|---|---|
| O1 | O1 | 5pf deep green | | .90 | 13.50 |
| O2 | O2 | 10pf car rose | | .20 | 1.60 |
| O3 | O2 | 10pf orange ('21) | | .50 | 450.00 |
| O4 | O3 | 15pf violet brn | | .20 | 2.25 |
| a. | | Imperf. ('21) | | 750.00 | 750.00 |
| O5 | O4 | 20pf deep ultra | | .20 | 1.90 |
| O6 | O5 | 30pf org, buff | | .20 | 1.90 |
| O7 | O6 | 40pf carmine | | .20 | 1.90 |
| O8 | O7 | 50pf violet, buff | | .20 | 1.90 |
| O9 | O8 | 60pf red brown ('21) | | .20 | 1.90 |
| O10 | O9 | 1m red, buff | | .20 | 1.90 |
| O11 | O10 | 1.25m dk bl, yel | | .20 | 2.25 |
| O12 | O11 | 2m dark blue | | 4.25 | 3.00 |
| O13 | O12 | 5m brown, yel | | .20 | 3.00 |
| | | Nos. O1-O13 (13) | | 7.65 | 487.00 |
| | | Set, never hinged | | 25.60 | |

The value of No. O4a is for a stamp postmarked at Bautzen.

See No. O15. For surcharges see Nos. O29-O33, O35-O36, O38.

---

### Postally Used vs. CTO

Values quoted for canceled examples of Nos. O1-O46 are for postally used stamps. See note after No. 160.

O13

O14

O15

## Wmk. 126, 125 (#O16-O17)

### 1922-23

| | | | | | |
|---|---|---|---|---|---|
| O14 | O13 | 75pf dark blue | | .20 | 7.50 |
| O15 | O11 | 2m dark blue | | .20 | 1.50 |
| a. | | Imperf. | | 97.50 | |
| O16 | O14 | 3m brown, rose | | .20 | 1.50 |
| O17 | O15 | 10m dk grn, rose | | .20 | 1.50 |
| O18 | O15 | 10m dk grn, rose | | .20 | 9.00 |
| O19 | O15 | 20m dk bl, rose | | .20 | 1.50 |
| O20 | O15 | 50m vio, rose | | .20 | 1.50 |
| O21 | O15 | 100m rose red, rose | | .20 | 1.50 |
| | | Nos. O14-O21 (8) | | 1.60 | 25.50 |
| | | Set, never hinged | | 4.50 | |

Issue date: #O18-O21, 1923. Nos. O20-O21 exist imperf.

For surcharges see Nos. O34, O37, O39.

---

### Regular Issue of 1923 Overprinted

a

### 1923

| | | | | | |
|---|---|---|---|---|---|
| O22 | A34 | 20m red lilac | | .30 | 7.50 |
| O23 | A34 | 30m olive grn | | .20 | 32.50 |
| O24 | A29 | 40m green | | .20 | 3.00 |
| O25 | A35 | 200m car rose | | .20 | 1.50 |
| O26 | A35 | 300m green | | .20 | 1.50 |
| O27 | A35 | 400m dk brn | | .20 | 1.50 |
| O28 | A35 | 500m red orange | | .20 | 1.50 |
| | | Nos. O22-O28 (7) | | 1.50 | 49.00 |
| | | Set, never hinged | | 4.50 | |

---

## Official Stamps of 1920-23 Surcharged with New Values
### Abbreviations:
### Th=(Tausend) Thousand
### Mil=(Million) Million
### Mlrd=(Milliarde) Billion

### 1923     Wmk. 125

| | | | | | |
|---|---|---|---|---|---|
| O29 | O12 | 5th m on 5m | | .20 | 3.00 |
| a. | | Inverted surcharge | | 50.00 | |
| | | Never hinged | | 110.00 | |
| O30 | O5 | 20th m on 30pf | | .20 | 3.00 |
| a. | | Inverted surcharge | | 55.00 | |
| | | Never hinged | | 125.00 | |
| b. | | Imperf. | | 60.00 | |
| | | Never hinged | | 150.00 | |
| O31 | O3 | 100th m on 15pf | | .20 | 3.00 |
| a. | | Imperf. | | 60.00 | |
| | | Never hinged | | 150.00 | |
| b. | | Inverted surcharge | | 50.00 | |
| | | Never hinged | | 110.00 | |
| O32 | O2 | 250th m on 10pf car rose | | .20 | 3.00 |
| a. | | Double surcharge | | 37.50 | |
| | | Never hinged | | 90.00 | |
| O33 | O5 | 800th m on 30pf | | .60 | 300.00 |

### Official Stamps and Types of 1920-23 Surcharged with New Values
### Wmk. 126

| | | | | | |
|---|---|---|---|---|---|
| O34 | O15 | 75th m on 50m | | .20 | 3.00 |
| a. | | Inverted surcharge | | 50.00 | |
| | | Never hinged | | 110.00 | |
| O35 | O3 | 400th m on 15pf brn | | .20 | 27.50 |
| O36 | O5 | 800th m on 30pf org, buff | | .20 | 4.50 |
| O37 | O13 | 1 mil m on 75pf | | .20 | 37.50 |
| O38 | O2 | 2 mil m on 10pf car rose | | .30 | 3.75 |
| a. | | Imperf. | | 90.00 | |
| | | Never hinged | | 210.00 | |
| O39 | O15 | 5 mil m on 100m | | .20 | 5.75 |
| | | Nos. O29-O39 (11) | | 2.70 | 394.00 |
| | | Set, never hinged | | 5.00 | |

The 10, 15 and 30 pfennig are not known with this watermark and without surcharge.

### #290-291, 295-299 Overprinted Type "a"

### 1923

| | | | | | |
|---|---|---|---|---|---|
| O40 | A39 | 100 mil m | | .20 | 150.00 |
| O41 | A39 | 200 mil m | | .20 | 150.00 |
| O42 | A39a | 2 mlrd m | | .20 | 110.00 |
| O43 | A39a | 5 mlrd m | | .20 | 82.50 |
| O44 | A39a | 10 mlrd m | | 3.00 | 140.00 |
| O45 | A39a | 20 mlrd m | | 3.75 | 150.00 |
| O46 | A39a | 50 mlrd m | | 1.90 | 200.00 |
| | | Nos. O40-O46 (7) | | 9.45 | 982.50 |
| | | Set, never hinged | | 32.50 | |

### Same Overprint on Nos, 323-328, Values in Rentenpfennig

### 1923

| | | | | | |
|---|---|---|---|---|---|
| O47 | A40 | 3pf brown | | .20 | .75 |
| O48 | A40 | 5pf dk green | | .20 | .75 |
| a. | | Inverted overprint | | 92.50 | 175.00 |
| | | Never hinged | | 175.00 | |
| O49 | A40 | 10pf carmine | | .20 | .75 |
| a. | | Inverted overprint | | 80.00 | 175.00 |
| | | Never hinged | | 150.00 | |
| b. | | Imperf. | | 60.00 | |
| | | Never hinged | | 150.00 | |
| O50 | A40 | 20pf dp ultra | | .60 | 1.10 |
| O51 | A40 | 50pf orange | | .60 | 1.50 |
| O52 | A40 | 100pf brown vio | | 3.75 | 7.50 |
| | | Nos. O47-O52 (6) | | 5.55 | 12.35 |
| | | Set, never hinged | | 25.00 | |

### Same Overprint On Issues of 1924

### 1924

| | | | | | |
|---|---|---|---|---|---|
| O53 | A41 | 3pf lt brown | | .35 | 2.25 |
| a. | | Inverted overprint | | 60.00 | 300.00 |
| | | Never hinged | | 300.00 | |
| O54 | A41 | 5pf lt green | | .20 | .75 |
| a. | | Imperf. | | 75.00 | |
| | | Never hinged | | 225.00 | |
| b. | | Inverted overprint | | 110.00 | |
| | | Never hinged | | 300.00 | |
| O55 | A41 | 10pf vermilion | | .20 | .75 |
| O56 | A41 | 20pf blue | | .20 | .75 |
| O57 | A41 | 30pf rose lilac | | .75 | .75 |
| O58 | A41 | 40pf olive green | | .75 | .75 |
| O59 | A41 | 50pf orange | | 6.75 | 3.75 |
| O60 | A47 | 60pf red brown | | 1.50 | 3.75 |
| O61 | A47 | 80pf slate | | 6.75 | 32.50 |
| | | Nos. O53-O61 (9) | | 17.45 | 46.00 |
| | | Set, never hinged | | 60.00 | |

O16

---

Swastika — O17

### 1927-33     Perf. 14

| | | | | | |
|---|---|---|---|---|---|
| O62 | O16 | 3pf bister | | .30 | .75 |
| O63 | O16 | 4pf lt bl ('31) | | .50 | .90 |
| O64 | O16 | 4pf blue ('33) | | 6.75 | 13.50 |
| O65 | O16 | 5pf green | | .20 | .75 |
| O66 | O16 | 6pf pale ol grn ('32) | | .75 | .90 |
| O67 | O16 | 8pf dk grn | | .30 | .75 |
| O68 | O16 | 10pf carmine | | 7.50 | 6.00 |
| O69 | O16 | 10pf ver ('29) | | 15.00 | 19.00 |
| O70 | O16 | 10pf red vio ('30) | | .45 | .90 |
| a. | | Never hinged | | 150.00 | |
| | | Never hinged | | 375.00 | |
| O71 | O16 | 10pf choc ('33) | | 2.50 | 9.00 |
| O72 | O16 | 12pf org ('32) | | .50 | .90 |
| O73 | O16 | 15pf vermilion | | 1.75 | .90 |
| O74 | O16 | 15pf car ('29) | | .45 | .90 |
| O75 | O16 | 20pf Prus grn | | 7.50 | 3.00 |
| O76 | O16 | 20pf gray ('30) | | 2.25 | 1.10 |
| O77 | O16 | 30pf olive grn | | .90 | .90 |
| O78 | O16 | 40pf violet | | .75 | .90 |
| O79 | O16 | 60pf red brn ('28) | | 1.10 | 1.90 |
| | | Nos. O62-O79 (18) | | 49.45 | 62.95 |
| | | Set, never hinged | | 200.00 | |

### 1934, Jan. 18     Wmk. 237

| | | | | | |
|---|---|---|---|---|---|
| O80 | O17 | 3pf bister | | .75 | 1.10 |
| O81 | O17 | 4pf dull blue | | .30 | .90 |
| O82 | O17 | 5pf brt green | | .20 | 1.10 |
| O83 | O17 | 6pf dk green | | .20 | .90 |
| a. | | Imperf. | | 150.00 | |
| | | Never hinged | | 375.00 | |
| O84 | O17 | 8pf vermilion | | 2.25 | .90 |
| O85 | O17 | 10pf chocolate | | .30 | 7.50 |
| O86 | O17 | 12pf brt carmine | | 2.25 | 1.50 |
| a. | | Unwmkd. | | 5.00 | 7.00 |
| O87 | O17 | 15pf claret | | .90 | 9.00 |
| O88 | O17 | 20pf light blue | | .45 | 1.50 |
| O89 | O17 | 30pf olive grn | | .90 | 1.50 |
| O90 | O17 | 40pf red violet | | .90 | 1.50 |
| O91 | O17 | 50pf orange yel | | 1.40 | 3.75 |
| | | Nos. O80-O91 (12) | | 10.80 | 31.15 |
| | | Set, never hinged | | 40.00 | |

### 1942     Unwmk.     Perf. 14

| | | | | | |
|---|---|---|---|---|---|
| O92 | O17 | 3pf bister brn | | .30 | .65 |
| O93 | O17 | 4pf dull blue | | .30 | .65 |
| O94 | O17 | 5pf deep olive | | .30 | 3.00 |
| O95 | O17 | 6pf deep violet | | .30 | .65 |
| O96 | O17 | 8pf vermilion | | .30 | .65 |
| O97 | O17 | 10pf chocolate | | .30 | .60 |
| O98 | O17 | 12pf rose car | | .30 | 1.25 |
| a. | | Wmk. 237 | | 1.50 | 13.50 |
| O99 | O17 | 15pf brown car | | 2.40 | 12.00 |
| O100 | O17 | 20pf light blue | | .30 | 1.30 |
| O101 | O17 | 30pf olive grn | | .30 | 1.30 |
| O102 | O17 | 40pf red violet | | .30 | 1.30 |
| O103 | O17 | 50pf dk green | | 2.25 | 7.25 |
| | | Nos. O92-O103 (12) | | 7.65 | 30.90 |
| | | Set, never hinged | | 35.00 | |

---

## LOCAL OFFICIAL STAMPS

### For Use in Prussia

("Nr. 21" refers to the district of Prussia) — LO1

### 1903 Unwmk. Typo. Perf. 14, 14½

| | | | | | |
|---|---|---|---|---|---|
| OL1 | LO1 | 2pf slate | | .90 | 3.75 |
| OL2 | LO1 | 3pf bister brn | | .90 | 3.75 |
| OL3 | LO1 | 5pf green | | .30 | .50 |
| OL4 | LO1 | 10pf carmine | | .30 | .50 |
| OL5 | LO1 | 20pf ultra | | .30 | .50 |
| OL6 | LO1 | 25pf org & blk, yel | | .30 | 1.60 |
| OL7 | LO1 | 40pf lake & blk | | .35 | 1.90 |
| OL8 | LO1 | 50pf pur & blk, sal | | .35 | 1.90 |
| | | Nos. OL1-OL8 (8) | | 3.70 | 14.40 |
| | | Set, never hinged | | 9.10 | |

LO2

LO3

---

LO4

LO5

LO6

LO7

LO8

### 1920 Typo. Wmk. 125 Perf. 14

| | | | | | |
|---|---|---|---|---|---|
| OL9 | LO2 | 5pf green | | .20 | 3.00 |
| OL10 | LO3 | 10pf carmine | | .70 | 1.50 |
| OL11 | LO4 | 15pf vio brn | | .20 | 1.50 |
| OL12 | LO5 | 20pf dp ultra | | .20 | 1.40 |
| OL13 | LO6 | 30pf org, buff | | .20 | 1.40 |
| OL14 | LO7 | 50pf brn lil, buff | | .30 | 1.50 |
| OL15 | LO8 | 1m red, buff | | 8.25 | 3.75 |
| | | Nos. OL9-OL15 (7) | | 10.05 | 14.05 |
| | | Set, never hinged | | 35.00 | |

### For Use in Baden

LO9

### 1905 Unwmk. Typo. Perf. 14, 14½

| | | | | | |
|---|---|---|---|---|---|
| OL16 | LO9 | 2pf gray blue | | 52.50 | 75.00 |
| OL17 | LO9 | 3pf brown | | 6.00 | 10.50 |
| OL18 | LO9 | 5pf green | | 4.25 | 7.50 |
| OL19 | LO9 | 10pf rose | | .75 | 2.10 |
| OL20 | LO9 | 20pf blue | | 1.50 | 3.00 |
| OL21 | LO9 | 25pf org & blk, yel | | 35.00 | 52.50 |
| | | Nos. OL16-OL21 (6) | | 100.00 | 150.60 |
| | | Set, never hinged | | 850.00 | |

---

## NEWSPAPER STAMPS

Newsboy and Globe — N1

### Wmk. Swastikas (237)
### 1939, Nov. 1 Photo. Perf. 14

| | | | | | |
|---|---|---|---|---|---|
| P1 | N1 | 5pf green | | .60 | 5.25 |
| P2 | N1 | 10pf red brown | | .60 | 5.25 |
| | | Set, never hinged | | 4.50 | |

---

## POSTAL TAX STAMPS

On November 28, 1948, the "Notopfer Berlin" ("Berlin emergency levy") was enacted by the West German authorities to raise funds to subsidize civilian operations in West Berlin. Part of this levy was a 2pf surtax on virtually all types of internal mail in West Germany, except that of the military governments and foreign consulates and surface mail to Berlin. Initially applied to the Bizone (American and British administration), this levy was later extended to the French zone of occupation, and was continued by the Federal Republic of Germany after its formation in Sept. 1949.

From Dec. 1, 1948, until the expiration of the levy on March 31, 1956, most mail was required to carry one of the "Notopfer" tax stamps.

 PT1

## 1948        Wmk. 286        Typo.
*Imperf*

RA1 PT1 2pf dk blue .25 .25
 Never hinged .55

### Compound Perf 12 and 14

RA2 PT1 2pf dk blue .30 .30
 Never hinged 1.25

No. RA2 also exists perf 9-10, 11, 11¼x11, 11½, compund 11½ and 12, 12x11½, 13½x11½ and rouletted, some of which were produced by local post offices or by private parties.
Issued: RA1, 12/1; RA2, 12/15.
Illustration PT1 actual size.

## 1948-50        Wmk. 285        Typo.
*Imperf*

RA3 PT1 2pf dk blue 15.00 1.50
 Never hinged 50.00

### Compound Perf 12 and 14

RA4 PT1 2pf dk blue ('49) .60 .25
 Never hinged 2.25

No. RA4 also exists perf 9½, 11, 11¼x11, 11½, 12, 12x11, 12x13½, 12¼ and rouletted, some of which were produced by local post offices or by private parties.

### Wmk. 285

1950, June 10    Litho.    *Perf. 14*

RA5 PT1 2pf dk blue .25 .25
 .45

1955, Aug. 8        Wmk. 295

RA6 PT1 2pf dk blue .25 .25
 Never hinged .45

---

## FRANCHISE STAMPS

For use by the National Socialist German Workers' Party

Party Emblem — F1

## 1938    Typo.    Wmk. 237    *Perf. 14*

S1 F1 1pf black .70 3.00
S2 F1 3pf bister .70 1.90
S3 F1 4pf dull blue .70 1.50
S4 F1 5pf brt green .40 1.50
S5 F1 6pf dk green .40 1.50
S6 F1 8pf vermilion 2.75 1.50
S7 F1 12pf brt car 4.50 1.50
S8 F1 16pf gray .65 9.00
S9 F1 24pf citron 1.00 4.75
S10 F1 30pf olive grn 1.00 7.50
S11 F1 40pf red violet 1.00 11.00
 *Nos. S1-S11 (11)* 13.80 44.65
 Set, never hinged 120.00

## 1942        Unwmk.

S12 F1 1pf gray blk .70 3.50
S13 F1 3pf bister brn .30 .55
S14 F1 4pf dk gray blue .30 .55
S15 F1 5pf gray green .30 3.50
S16 F1 6pf violet .30 .55
S17 F1 8pf deep orange .30 .55
 a. Imperf. 95.00
 Never hinged 190.00
S18 F1 12pf carmine .30 .55
S19 F1 16pf blue green 3.25 16.00
S20 F1 24pf yellow brn .50 1.00
S21 F1 30pf dp olive grn .50 1.75
S22 F1 40pf light rose vio .55 2.25
 *Nos. S12-S22 (11)* 7.30 30.75
 Set, never hinged 25.00

---

# GERMAN OCCUPATION STAMPS

100 Centimes = 1 Franc
100 Pfennig = 1 Mark

## Issued under Belgian Occupation

Belgian Stamps of 1915-20 Overprinted

### Perf. 11½, 14, 14½

1919-21        Unwmk.

1N1 A46 1c orange .30 .45
1N2 A46 2c chocolate .30 .45
1N3 A46 3c gray blk ('21) .30 1.90
1N4 A46 5c green .60 .90
1N5 A46 10c carmine 1.25 1.90
1N6 A46 15c purple .60 .90
1N7 A46 20c red violet .90 1.25
1N8 A46 25c blue 1.10 1.50
1N9 A54 25c dp blue ('21) 3.75 8.25

Overprinted

1N10 A47 35c brn org & blk 1.10 1.25
1N11 A48 40c green & blk 1.10 1.90
1N12 A49 50c car rose & blk 5.50 9.00
1N13 A56 65c cl & blk ('21) 3.00 10.50
1N14 A50 1fr violet 21.00 19.00
1N15 A51 2fr slate 35.00 37.50
1N16 A52 5fr deep blue 8.25 10.00
1N17 A53 10fr brown 55.00 55.00
 *Nos. 1N1-1N17 (17)* 139.05 161.65
 Set, never hinged 450.00

Belgian Stamps of 1915 Surcharged

Nos. 1N18-     Nos. 1N23-1N24
1N22

### Black Surcharge

1920

1N18 A46 5pf on 5c green .40 .35
1N19 A46 10pf on 10c car .50 .45
1N20 A46 15pf on 15c pur .70 .70
1N21 A46 20pf on 20c red vio .70 1.00
1N22 A46 30pf on 25c blue 1.10 1.25

### Red Surcharge

1N23 A49 75pf on 50c car rose & blk 15.00 15.00
1N24 A50 1m25pf on 1fr violet 21.00 21.00
 *Nos. 1N18-1N24 (7)* 39.40 39.75
 Set, never hinged 110.00

### EUPEN ISSUE

Belgian Stamps of 1915-20 Overprinted:

Nos. 1N25-     Nos. 1N37-1N41
1N36

1920-21        *Perf. 11½, 14, 14½*

1N25 A46 1c orange .30 .40
1N26 A46 2c chocolate .30 .40
1N27 A46 3c gray blk ('21) .45 1.40
1N28 A46 5c green .45 .90
1N29 A46 10c carmine .75 1.25
1N30 A46 15c purple 1.10 1.25
1N31 A46 20c red violet 1.25 1.40
1N32 A46 25c blue 1.10 1.90
1N33 A54 25c dp blue ('21) 3.50 9.50
1N34 A47 35c brn org & blk 1.50 1.90

---

1N35 A48 40c green & blk 1.75 2.25
1N36 A49 50c car rose & blk 5.00 7.25
1N37 A56 65c cl & blk ('21) 2.75 11.00
1N38 A50 1fr violet 20.00 19.00
1N39 A51 2fr slate 32.50 30.00
1N40 A52 5fr deep blue 10.50 11.00
1N41 A53 10fr brown 45.00 50.00
 *Nos. 1N25-1N41 (17)* 128.20 150.80
 Set, never hinged 325.00

### MALMEDY ISSUE
Belgian Stamps of 1915-20 Overprinted:

Nos. 1N42-     Nos. 1N51-1N53
1N50

Nos. 1N54-1N58

1920-21

1N42 A46 1c orange .25 .40
1N43 A46 2c chocolate .25 .40
1N44 A46 3c gray blk ('21) .35 1.60
1N45 A46 5c green .45 .90
1N46 A46 10c carmine .70 1.25
1N47 A46 15c purple 1.10 1.40
1N48 A46 20c red violet 1.50 1.90
1N49 A46 25c blue 1.25 1.90
1N50 A54 25c dp blue ('21) 3.50 8.75
1N51 A47 35c brn org & blk 1.50 2.25
1N52 A48 40c grn & blk 1.50 2.25
1N53 A49 50c car rose & blk 6.00 7.25
1N54 A56 65c cl & blk ('21) 2.75 11.00
1N55 A50 1fr violet 20.00 17.00
1N56 A51 2fr slate 32.50 30.00
1N57 A52 5fr deep blue 10.50 17.00
1N58 A53 10fr brown 45.00 55.00
 *Nos. 1N42-1N58 (17)* 129.10 160.25
 Set, never hinged 325.00

### OCCUPATION POSTAGE DUE STAMPS

Belgian Postage Due Stamps of 1919-20, Overprinted

1920        Unwmk.        *Perf. 14½*

1NJ1 D3 5c green .75 1.10
1NJ2 D3 10c carmine 1.50 1.90
1NJ3 D3 20c gray green 3.00 4.50
1NJ4 D3 30c bright blue 3.00 4.50
1NJ5 D3 50c gray 15.00 15.00
 *Nos. 1NJ1-1NJ5 (5)* 23.25 27.00
 Set, never hinged 57.50

Belgian Postage Due Stamps of 1919-20, Overprinted

1NJ6 D3 5c green 1.50 1.10
1NJ7 D3 10c carmine 3.00 1.90
1NJ8 D3 20c gray green 10.50 11.50
1NJ9 D3 30c bright blue 6.00 8.25
1NJ10 D3 50c gray 12.00 11.00
 *Nos. 1NJ6-1NJ10 (5)* 33.00 33.75
 Set, never hinged 82.50

---

### A. M. G. ISSUE

**Issued jointly by the Allied Military Government of the US and Great Britain, for civilian use in areas under Allied occupation.**

---

 OS1

Type I. Thick paper, white gum.
Type II. Medium paper, yellow gum.
Type III. Medium paper, white gum.

### Perf. 11, 11½ and Compound
1945-46        Litho.        Unwmk.
### Type III, Brunswick Printing
#### Size: 19-19½x22-22½mm

3N1 OS1 1pf slate gray .20 5.00
3N2 OS1 3pf dull lilac .20 1.10
3N3 OS1 4pf lt gray .20 1.50
3N4 OS1 5pf emerald .20 4.00
3N5 OS1 6pf yellow .20 1.10
3N6 OS1 8pf orange 2.00 37.50
3N7 OS1 10pf yel brn .20 1.50
3N8 OS1 12pf rose vio .20 .90
3N9 OS1 15pf rose car .20 3.00
3N10 OS1 16pf dp Prus grn .20 13.50
3N11 OS1 20pf blue .20 3.00
3N12 OS1 24pf chocolate .20 13.50
3N13 OS1 25pf brt ultra .20 13.50
#### Size: 21½x25mm
3N14 OS1 30pf olive .20 1.90
3N15 OS1 40pf dp mag .20 2.50
3N16 OS1 42pf green .20 2.25
3N17 OS1 50pf slate grn .20 15.00
3N18 OS1 60pf vio brn .50 19.00
3N19 OS1 80pf bl blk 15.00 300.00
#### Size: 25x29½mm
3N20 OS1 1m dk ol grn ('46) 2.50 500.00
 *Nos. 3N1-3N20 (20)* 23.20 939.75
 Set, never hinged 50.00

Most of Nos. 3N1-3N20 exist imperforate and part-perforate.

### Type I, Washington Printing
#### Size: 19-19½x22-22½mm
#### Perf. 11

3N2a OS1 3pf lilac .20 1.90
3N3a OS1 4pf light gray .20 1.50
3N4a OS1 5pf emerald .20 .35
3N5a OS1 6pf yellow .20 .35
3N6a OS1 8pf deep orange .20 .35
3N7a OS1 10pf brown .20 .35
3N8a OS1 12pf rose violet .25 .35
3N9a OS1 15pf cerise .20 1.50
3N13a OS1 25pf bright ultra .20 1.50
 *Nos. 3N2a-3N13a (9)* 1.85 8.15
 Set, never hinged 2.50

### Type II, London Printing
#### Size: 19-19½x22-22½mm
#### Photo.
#### Perf. 14, 14½ and Compound

3N2b OS1 3pf lilac .20 .60
3N3b OS1 4pf light gray .20 .60
3N4b OS1 5pf deep emerald .20 15.00
3N5b OS1 6pf orange yellow .20 .60
3N6b OS1 8pf dark orange .20 3.75
3N8b OS1 12pf rose violet .20 .60
 *Nos. 3N2b-3N8b (6)* 1.20 21.15
 Set, never hinged 2.00

---

### ISSUED UNDER FRENCH OCCUPATION

Coats of Arms

Rhine          Palatinate
Province        District
OS3            OS4

Saarland        Württemberg
OS5            OS6

Baden
OS7

Johann
Wolfgang von
Goethe
OS8

Friedrich von
Schiller — OS9

Heinrich
Heine — OS10

### Perf. 14x13½

| 1945-46 | | Unwmk. | | Typo. |
|---|---|---|---|---|
| 4N1 | OS3 | 1pf blk, grn & lem | .20 | .25 |
| 4N2 | OS4 | 3pf dk red, blk & dl yel | .20 | .20 |
| 4N3 | OS6 | 5pf brn, blk & org yel | .20 | .20 |
| 4N4 | OS7 | 8pf brn, yel & red | .20 | .20 |
| 4N5 | OS3 | 10pf brn, grn & lem | 6.50 | 52.50 |
| 4N6 | OS4 | 12pf red, blk & org yel | .20 | .20 |
| 4N7 | OS5 | 15pf blk, ultra & red ('46) | .20 | .25 |
| 4N8 | OS6 | 20pf red, org yel & blk | .20 | .20 |
| 4N9 | OS5 | 24pf blk, dp ultra & red ('46) | .20 | .20 |
| 4N10 | OS7 | 30pf blk, org yel & red | .20 | .25 |

### Perf. 13
### Engr.

| 4N11 | OS8 | 1m lilac brn | .70 | 18.00 |
|---|---|---|---|---|
| 4N12 | OS9 | 2m dp bl ('46) | .45 | 52.50 |
| 4N13 | OS10 | 5m dl red brn ('46) | .55 | 67.50 |
| | | Nos. 4N1-4N13 (13) | 10.00 | 192.50 |
| | | Set, never hinged | 20.00 | |

Exist imperf. Value for set of 13, $475 mint never hinged.

### BADEN

Johann Peter
Hebel
OS1

Girl of
Constance
OS2

Hans Baldung
Grien — OS3

Rastatt
Castle — OS4

Black
Forest
Scene
OS5

---

Cathedral of
Freiburg — OS6

| 1947 | | Unwmk. | Photo. | Perf. 14 |
|---|---|---|---|---|
| 5N1 | OS1 | 2pf gray | .20 | .30 |
| 5N2 | OS2 | 3pf brown | .20 | .30 |
| 5N3 | OS3 | 10pf slate blue | .20 | .30 |
| 5N4 | OS1 | 12pf dk green | .20 | .30 |
| 5N5 | OS2 | 15pf purple | .20 | .35 |
| 5N6 | OS4 | 16pf olive green | .20 | 1.50 |
| 5N7 | OS3 | 20pf blue | .20 | .35 |
| 5N8 | OS2 | 24pf crimson | .20 | .30 |
| 5N9 | OS2 | 45pf cerise | .20 | .90 |
| 5N10 | OS1 | 60pf deep orange | .20 | .30 |
| 5N11 | OS3 | 75pf brt blue | .20 | 1.90 |
| 5N12 | OS3 | 84pf blue green | .20 | 1.90 |
| 5N13 | OS6 | 1m dark brown | .20 | .75 |
| | | Nos. 5N1-5N13 (13) | | 9.45 |
| | | Set, never hinged | | 2.25 |

Festival
Headdress
OS7

Grand
Duchess
Stephanie
OS8

### 1948

| 5N14 | OS1 | 2pf dp orange | .20 | .30 |
|---|---|---|---|---|
| 5N15 | OS2 | 6pf violet brn | .20 | .30 |
| 5N16 | OS7 | 8dpf blue green | .25 | 1.10 |
| 5N17 | OS3 | 10pf dark brown | .20 | .30 |
| 5N18 | OS1 | 12pf crimson | .20 | .30 |
| 5N19 | OS2 | 15pf blue | .25 | .60 |
| 5N20 | OS4 | 16dpf violet | .35 | 1.90 |
| 5N21 | OS3 | 20dpf brown | 1.50 | .95 |
| 5N22 | OS4 | 24pf dark green | .25 | .30 |
| 5N23 | OS7 | 30pf cerise | .55 | 1.10 |
| 5N24 | OS8 | 50pf brt blue | .55 | .30 |
| 5N25 | OS1 | 60dpf gray | 1.90 | .60 |
| 5N26 | OS5 | 84dpf rose brn | 2.75 | 4.50 |
| 5N27 | OS6 | 1dm brt blue | 2.75 | 4.50 |
| | | Nos. 5N14-5N27 (14) | 11.90 | 17.05 |
| | | Set, never hinged | 26.50 | |

### Without "PF"

| 1948-49 | | | | |
|---|---|---|---|---|
| 5N28 | OS1 | 2(pf) dp orange | .35 | .55 |
| 5N29 | OS4 | 4(pf) violet | .25 | .45 |
| 5N30 | OS2 | 5(pf) blue | .35 | .60 |
| 5N31 | OS2 | 6(pf) violet brn | 11.50 | 13.50 |
| 5N32 | OS7 | 8(pf) rose brn | .35 | 1.00 |
| 5N33 | OS3 | 10(pf) dark green | 1.60 | .55 |
| 5N37 | OS3 | 20(pf) cerise | .65 | .35 |
| 5N38 | OS4 | 40(pf) brown | 30.00 | 75.00 |
| 5N39 | OS1 | 80(pf) red | 3.75 | 6.00 |
| 5N40 | OS5 | 90(pf) rose brn | 29.00 | 75.00 |
| | | Nos. 5N28-5N40 (10) | 77.80 | 173.00 |
| | | Set, never hinged | 150.00 | |

Constance Cathedral and Insel
Hotel — OS9

Type I. Frameline thick and straight. Inscriptions thick. Shading dark. Upper part of "B" narrow.
Type II. Frameline thin and zigzag. Inscriptions fine. Shading light. Upper part of "B" wide.

### 1949, June 22

| 5N41 | OS9 | 30pf dark blue (I) | 9.00 | 65.00 |
|---|---|---|---|---|
| | | Never hinged | 20.00 | |
| a. | | Type II | 250.00 | 1,450. |
| | | Never hinged | 475.00 | |

Issued to publicize the International Engineering Congress, Constance, 1949.

---

Conradin
Kreutzer — OS10

### 1949, Aug. 27

| 5N42 | OS10 | 10pf dark green | 1.50 | 7.50 |
|---|---|---|---|---|
| | | Never hinged | | 3.00 |

Conradin Kreutzer (1780-1849), composer.

Stagecoach — OS11

Design: 20pf, Post bus, trailer and plane.

### 1949, Sept. 17

| 5N43 | OS11 | 10pf green | 2.25 | 10.50 |
|---|---|---|---|---|
| 5N44 | OS11 | 20pf red brown | 2.25 | 10.50 |
| | | Set, never hinged | 9.00 | |

Centenary of German postage stamps.

Globe, Olive Branch
and Post
Horn — OS12

### 1949, Oct. 4

| 5N45 | OS12 | 20pf dark red | 2.75 | 10.50 |
|---|---|---|---|---|
| 5N46 | OS12 | 30pf deep blue | 2.75 | 9.00 |
| | | Set, never hinged | 10.00 | |

75th anniv. of the UPU.

---

### OCCUPATION SEMI-POSTAL STAMPS

Arms of
Baden
OSP1

Cornhouse,
Freiburg
OSP2

### Perf. 13½x14
### 1949, Feb. 25    Photo.    Unwmk.
### Cross in Red

| 5NB1 | OSP1 | 10 + 20pf green | 8.50 | 75.00 |
|---|---|---|---|---|
| 5NB2 | OSP1 | 20 + 40pf lilac | 8.50 | 75.00 |
| 5NB3 | OSP1 | 30 + 60pf blue | 8.50 | 75.00 |
| 5NB4 | OSP1 | 40 + 80pf gray | 8.50 | 75.00 |
| a. | | Sheet of 4, #5NB1-5NB4, imperf. | 110.00 | 1,350. |
| | | Nos. 5NB1-5NB4 (4) | 34.00 | 300.00 |
| | | Set, never hinged | 75.00 | |

The surtax was for the Red Cross.
No. 5NB4a measures 90x101mm. and has no gum.

### 1949, Feb. 24    Perf. 14

10pf+20pf, Cathedral tower. 20pf+30pf, Trumpeting angel. 30pf+50pf, Fish pool.

| 5NB5 | OSP2 | 4 + 16pf dk vio | 5.25 | 35.00 |
|---|---|---|---|---|
| 5NB6 | OSP2 | 10 + 20pf dk grn | 5.25 | 35.00 |
| 5NB7 | OSP2 | 20 + 30pf car | 5.25 | 35.00 |
| 5NB8 | OSP2 | 30 + 50pf blue | 6.75 | 45.00 |
| a. | | Sheet of 4, #5NB5-5NB8 | 26.00 | 210.00 |
| | | Never hinged | 52.50 | |
| b. | | As "a," imperf. | 26.00 | 210.00 |
| | | Never hinged | 52.50 | |
| | | Nos. 5NB5-5NB8 (4) | 22.50 | 150.00 |
| | | Set, never hinged | 55.00 | |

The surtax was for the reconstruction of historical monuments in Freiburg.

---

Carl Schurz at
Rastatt
OSP3

Goethe
OSP4

### 1949, Aug. 23

| 5NB9 | OSP3 | 10 + 5pf green | 4.75 | 29.00 |
|---|---|---|---|---|
| 5NB10 | OSP3 | 20 + 10pf cer | 4.75 | 29.00 |
| 5NB11 | OSP3 | 30 + 15pf blue | 5.50 | 29.00 |
| | | Nos. 5NB9-5NB11 (3) | 15.00 | 87.00 |
| | | Set, never hinged | 29.00 | |

Centenary of the surrender of Rastatt.

### 1949, Aug. 12

Various Portraits.

| 5NB12 | OSP4 | 10 + 5pf green | 3.50 | 19.00 |
|---|---|---|---|---|
| 5NB13 | OSP4 | 20 + 10pf cer | 3.50 | 19.00 |
| 5NB14 | OSP4 | 30 + 15pf blue | 5.25 | 45.00 |
| | | Nos. 5NB12-5NB14 (3) | 12.25 | 83.00 |
| | | Set, never hinged | 26.00 | |

Johann Wolfgang von Goethe (1749-1832).

---

### RHINE PALATINATE

Beethoven
OS1

Wilhelm E. F.
von Ketteler
OS2

Girl Carrying
Grapes
OS3

Porta Nigra,
Trier
OS4

Karl Marx
OS5

"Devil's Table",
Near
Pirmasens
OS6

Street Corner,
St. Martin
OS7

Cathedral of
Worms
OS8

Cathedral of
Mainz
OS9

Statue of
Johann
Gutenberg
OS10

Gutenfels and Pfalzgrafenstein Castles
on Rhine — OS11

Statue of
Charlemagne
OS12

**1947-48    Unwmk.    Photo.    Perf. 14**

| | | | | |
|---|---|---|---|---|
| 6N1 | OS1 | 2pf gray | .20 | .30 |
| 6N2 | OS2 | 3pf dk brown | .20 | .30 |
| 6N3 | OS3 | 10pf slate blue | .20 | .30 |
| 6N4 | OS4 | 12pf green | .20 | .30 |
| 6N5 | OS5 | 15pf purple | .20 | .30 |
| 6N6 | OS6 | 16pf lt ol grn | .20 | 1.10 |
| 6N7 | OS7 | 20pf brt blue | .20 | .30 |
| 6N8 | OS8 | 24pf crimson | .20 | .30 |
| 6N9 | OS10 | 30pf cerise ('48) | .20 | 2.25 |
| 6N10 | OS9 | 45pf cerise | .20 | .60 |
| 6N11 | OS9 | 50pf blue ('48) | .20 | 2.25 |
| 6N12 | OS1 | 60pf dp orange | .20 | .30 |
| 6N13 | OS10 | 75pf blue | .20 | .60 |
| 6N14 | OS11 | 84pf green | .20 | 1.40 |
| 6N15 | OS12 | 1m brown | .20 | .75 |
| | *Nos. 6N1-6N15 (15)* | | | 11.35 |
| | Set, never hinged | | 2.25 | |

Exist imperf. Value for set, $525 mint never hinged.

**1948**

| | | | | |
|---|---|---|---|---|
| 6N16 | OS1 | 2pf dp orange | .20 | .30 |
| 6N17 | OS2 | 6pf violet brn | .20 | .30 |
| 6N18 | OS4 | 8dpf blue green | .25 | 1.10 |
| 6N19 | OS3 | 10pf dk brown | .25 | .30 |
| 6N20 | OS4 | 12pf crim rose | .25 | .30 |
| 6N21 | OS5 | 15pf blue | .60 | .60 |
| 6N22 | OS6 | 16dpf dk violet | .30 | 1.40 |
| 6N23 | OS7 | 20dpf brown | 1.40 | .60 |
| 6N24 | OS8 | 24pf green | .25 | .30 |
| 6N25 | OS9 | 30pf cerise | .45 | .35 |
| 6N26 | OS10 | 50pf brt blue | .75 | .35 |
| 6N27 | OS1 | 60dpf gray | 3.75 | .35 |
| 6N28 | OS11 | 84dpf rose brown | 1.90 | 5.50 |
| 6N29 | OS12 | 1dm brt blue | 3.00 | 5.75 |
| | *Nos. 6N16-6N29 (14)* | | 13.55 | 17.50 |
| | Set, never hinged | | 26.00 | |

Exist imperf. Value for set, $500 mint never hinged.

**Types of 1947 Without "PF"**

**1948-49**

| | | | | |
|---|---|---|---|---|
| 6N30 | OS1 | 2(pf) dp org | .30 | .35 |
| 6N31 | OS6 | 4(pf) vio ('49) | .30 | .35 |
| 6N32 | OS5 | 5(pf) blue ('49) | .35 | .60 |
| 6N33 | OS2 | 6(pf) vio brn | 13.50 | 15.00 |
| 6N33A | OS4 | 8(pf) rose brn ('49) | 30.00 | 375.00 |
| 6N34 | OS3 | 10(pf) dk grn | .35 | .35 |
| *a.* | | Imperf. | 55.00 | 190.00 |
| | | Never hinged | 110.00 | |
| 6N35 | OS7 | 20(pf) cerise | .35 | .35 |
| 6N36 | OS8 | 40(pf) brn ('49) | 1.40 | 3.75 |
| 6N37 | OS4 | 80(pf) red ('49) | 1.50 | 5.00 |
| 6N38 | OS11 | 90(pf) rose brn ('49) | 2.25 | 15.00 |
| | *Nos. 6N30-6N38 (10)* | | 50.30 | 415.75 |
| | Set, never hinged | | 110.00 | |

**Type of Baden, 1949**

Designs as in Baden.

**1949, Sept. 17**

| | | | | |
|---|---|---|---|---|
| 6N39 | OS11 | 10pf green | 4.25 | 19.00 |
| 6N40 | OS11 | 20pf red brown | 4.25 | 19.00 |
| | Set, never hinged | | 16.50 | |

**UPU Type of Baden, 1949**

**1949, Oct. 4**

| | | | | |
|---|---|---|---|---|
| 6N41 | OS12 | 20pf dark red | 3.00 | 11.50 |
| 6N42 | OS12 | 30pf deep blue | 3.00 | 9.75 |
| | Set, never hinged | | 10.50 | |

---

## OCCUPATION SEMI-POSTAL STAMPS

St. Martin — OSP1

Design: 30pf+50pf, St. Christopher.

**1948    Unwmk.    Photo.    Perf. 14**

| | | | | |
|---|---|---|---|---|
| 6NB1 | OSP1 | 20pf + 30pf dp cl | .60 | 57.50 |
| 6NB2 | OSP1 | 30pf + 50pf dp bl | .60 | 57.50 |
| | Set, never hinged | | 3.00 | |

The surtax was to aid victims of an explosion at Ludwigshafen.

**Type of Baden, 1949, Showing Arms of Rhine Palatinate**

**1949, Feb. 25    Perf. 13½x14**

**Cross in Red**

| | | | | |
|---|---|---|---|---|
| 6NB3 | OSP1 | 10pf + 20pf grn | 7.75 | 82.50 |
| 6NB4 | OSP1 | 20pf + 40pf lil | 7.75 | 82.50 |
| 6NB5 | OSP1 | 30pf + 60pf bl | 7.75 | 82.50 |
| 6NB6 | OSP1 | 40pf + 80pf gray | 7.75 | 82.50 |
| *a.* | | Sheet of 4, #6NB3-6NB6, imperf. | 82.50 | 1,050. |
| | *Nos. 6NB3-6NB6 (4)* | | 31.00 | 330.00 |
| | Set, never hinged | | 65.00 | |

The surtax was for the Red Cross. #6NB6a measures 90x100mm and has no gum.

**Goethe Type of Baden, 1949**

Various Portraits.

**1949, Aug. 12**

| | | | | |
|---|---|---|---|---|
| 6NB7 | OSP4 | 10pf + 5pf green | 2.25 | 18.00 |
| 6NB8 | OSP4 | 20pf + 10pf cerise | 2.25 | 18.00 |
| 6NB9 | OSP4 | 30pf + 15pf blue | 4.50 | 42.50 |
| | *Nos. 6NB7-6NB9 (3)* | | 9.00 | 78.50 |
| | Set, never hinged | | 22.50 | |

---

## WURTTEMBERG

Friedrich von
Schiller
OS1

Castle of
Bebenhausen
OS2

Friedrich
Hölderlin
OS3

Town Gate of
Wangen
(Allgäu)
OS4

Lichtenstein
Castle — OS5

Zwiefalten
Church — OS6

**1947-48    Unwmk.    Photo.    Perf. 14**

| | | | | |
|---|---|---|---|---|
| 8N1 | OS1 | 2pf gray ('48) | .20 | .60 |
| 8N2 | OS3 | 3pf brown ('48) | .20 | .30 |
| 8N3 | OS4 | 10pf slate bl ('48) | .20 | .35 |
| 8N4 | OS1 | 12pf dk green | .20 | .25 |
| 8N5 | OS3 | 15pf purple ('48) | .20 | .45 |
| 8N6 | OS2 | 16pf ol grn ('48) | .20 | 1.00 |
| 8N7 | OS4 | 20pf blue ('48) | .20 | 1.00 |
| 8N8 | OS2 | 24pf crimson | .20 | .30 |
| 8N9 | OS3 | 45pf cerise | .20 | 1.00 |
| 8N10 | OS1 | 60pf dp org ('48) | .20 | .75 |
| 8N11 | OS4 | 75pf brt blue | .20 | 1.10 |
| 8N12 | OS5 | 84pf blue grn | .20 | 1.40 |
| 8N13 | OS6 | 1m dk brown | .20 | 1.10 |
| | *Nos. 8N1-8N13 (13)* | | | 9.60 |
| | Set, never hinged | | 2.25 | |

Nos. 8N4 and 8N10 exist imperf. Value, each $37.50, mint never hinged.

Waldsee
OS7

Ludwig
Uhland
OS8

**1948**

| | | | | |
|---|---|---|---|---|
| 8N14 | OS1 | 2pf dp orange | .20 | .35 |
| 8N15 | OS3 | 6pf violet brn | .20 | .30 |
| 8N16 | OS7 | 8dpf blue grn | .35 | 1.75 |
| 8N17 | OS4 | 10pf dk brown | .20 | .35 |
| 8N18 | OS1 | 12pf crimson | .20 | .30 |
| 8N19 | OS3 | 15pf blue | .30 | .35 |
| 8N20 | OS2 | 16dpf dk violet | .35 | 1.60 |
| 8N21 | OS4 | 20dpf brown | .75 | .75 |
| 8N22 | OS2 | 24pf dk green | .45 | .60 |
| 8N23 | OS7 | 30pf cerise | .60 | .60 |
| 8N24 | OS8 | 50pf dull blue | .95 | .60 |
| 8N25 | OS1 | 60dpf gray | 5.75 | .60 |
| 8N26 | OS5 | 84dpf rose brn | 1.50 | 3.75 |
| 8N27 | OS6 | 1dm brt blue | 1.50 | 3.75 |
| | *Nos. 8N14-8N27 (14)* | | 13.30 | 15.65 |
| | Set, never hinged | | 26.00 | |

Nos. 8N14, 8N17, 8N22-8N23 exist imperf. Value, each $35, mint never hinged.

**Without "PF"**

**1948-49**

| | | | | |
|---|---|---|---|---|
| 8N28 | OS1 | 2(pf) dp orange | .35 | .60 |
| 8N29 | OS2 | 4(pf) violet | 1.10 | .35 |
| 8N30 | OS3 | 5(pf) blue | 3.00 | 2.25 |
| 8N31 | OS3 | 6(pf) vio brown | 3.00 | 5.75 |
| 8N32 | OS7 | 8(pf) rose brn | 3.00 | 2.25 |
| 8N33 | OS4 | 10(pf) dk green | 3.00 | .35 |
| 8N34 | OS4 | 20(pf) cerise | 3.00 | .35 |
| 8N35 | OS2 | 40(pf) brown | 9.75 | 37.50 |
| 8N36 | OS1 | 80(pf) red | 19.00 | 37.50 |
| 8N37 | OS5 | 90(pf) rose brn | 30.00 | 97.50 |
| | *Nos. 8N28-8N37 (10)* | | 75.20 | 184.40 |
| | Set, never hinged | | 150.00 | |

Nos. 8N29 and 8N31 exist imperf. Value, respectively $75 and $57.50, mint never hinged.

**Type of Baden, 1949**

Designs as in Baden.

**1949, Sept. 17**

| | | | | |
|---|---|---|---|---|
| 8N38 | OS11 | 10pf green | 3.50 | 12.00 |
| 8N39 | OS11 | 20pf red brown | 3.50 | 12.00 |
| | Set, never hinged | | 11.50 | |

**UPU Type of Baden, 1949**

**1949, Oct. 4**

| | | | | |
|---|---|---|---|---|
| 8N40 | OS12 | 20pf dark red | 2.25 | 9.75 |
| 8N41 | OS12 | 30pf deep blue | 2.25 | 9.00 |
| | Set, never hinged | | 9.75 | |

## OCCUPATION SEMI-POSTAL STAMPS

**Type of Baden, 1949**

Design: Arms of Württemberg.

**Perf. 13½x14**

**1949, Feb. 25    Photo.    Unwmk.**

**Cross in Red**

| | | | | |
|---|---|---|---|---|
| 8NB1 | OSP1 | 10 + 20pf grn | 16.00 | 90.00 |
| 8NB2 | OSP1 | 20 + 40pf lilac | 16.00 | 90.00 |
| 8NB3 | OSP1 | 30 + 60pf blue | 16.00 | 90.00 |
| 8NB4 | OSP1 | 40 + 80pf gray | 16.00 | 90.00 |
| *a.* | | Sheet of 4, imperf. | 110.00 | 1,350. |
| | *Nos. 8NB1-8NB4 (4)* | | 64.00 | 360.00 |
| | Set, never hinged | | 120.00 | |

The surtax was for the Red Cross.
No. 8NB4a measures 90x100mm and contains one each of Nos. 8NB1 to 8NB4, with red inscription in upper margin and no gum.

View of
Isny
OSP1

Design: 20pf+6pf, Skier and village.

**Wmk. 116**

**1949, Feb. 11    Typo.    Perf. 14**

| | | | | |
|---|---|---|---|---|
| 8NB5 | OSP1 | 10 + 4pf dull green | 2.75 | 19.00 |
| 8NB6 | OSP1 | 20 + 6pf red brown | 2.75 | 19.00 |
| | Set, never hinged | | 11.00 | |

Issued to commemorate the 1948-49 German Ski Championship at Isny im Allgau.

Gustav
Werner — OSP2

**1949, Sept. 4**

| | | | | |
|---|---|---|---|---|
| 8NB7 | OSP2 | 10 + 5pf bl grn | 2.25 | 12.00 |
| 8NB8 | OSP2 | 20 + 10pf claret | 2.25 | 12.00 |
| | Set, never hinged | | 9.00 | |

Cent. of the founding of Gustav Werner's "Christianity in Action" and "House of Brotherhood."

**Goethe Type of Baden, 1949**

Various Portraits.

**1949, Aug. 12**

| | | | | |
|---|---|---|---|---|
| 8NB9 | OSP4 | 10 + 5pf green | 3.75 | 19.00 |
| 8NB10 | OSP4 | 20 + 10pf cerise | 5.50 | 26.00 |
| 8NB11 | OSP4 | 30 + 15pf blue | 5.50 | 37.50 |
| | *Nos. 8NB9-8NB11 (3)* | | 14.75 | 82.50 |
| | Set, never hinged | | 26.00 | |

---

## OCCUPATION POSTAL TAX STAMPS

### Wohnungsbau Issues

During July 1-December 31, 1949, a postal tax was levied on most categories of mail, with proceeds going to the 'Social Housing' (*Socialen Wohnungsbau*) program, which provided interest-free loans for housing construction and renovation intended to provide housing for economically-disadvantaged families.

Germany Nos. RA1, RA2, RA4 Overprinted in Red

Illustration actual size.

**Overprint 18.7mm wide**

**Wmk. 286**

**1949, July 1    Typo.    Imperf.**

| | | | | |
|---|---|---|---|---|
| 8NRA1 | PT1 | 2pf dk blue | 225.00 | 425.00 |
| | | Never hinged | 550.00 | |

**Compound Perf 12, 14**

| | | | | |
|---|---|---|---|---|
| 8NRA2 | PT1 | 2pf dk blue | 15.00 | 2.75 |
| | | Never hinged | 37.50 | |

**Overprint 16.5 mm wide**

**1949, July 22    Wmk. 285    Perf. 12¼**

| | | | | |
|---|---|---|---|---|
| 8NRA3 | PT1 | 2pf dk blue | 3.75 | 1.75 |
| | | Never hinged | 9.00 | |

OSPT1

**1949    Perf. 12¼**

| | | | | |
|---|---|---|---|---|
| 8NRA4 | OSPT1 | 2pf yellow | .20 | 1.00 |
| | | Never hinged | .50 | |
| *a.* | | 2pf yellow orange | 13.50 | 15.00 |

| | | | |
|---|---|---|---|
| | Never hinged | 30.00 | |
| *b.* | 2pf orange | .20 | 1.00 |
| | Never hinged | .50 | |

Issued: No. 4a, 8/19; No. 4, 8/22. No. 4b, 8/25. No. 4c, 10/4.
Illustration OSPT1 actual size.

---

## BERLIN

**Issued for Use in the American, British and French Occupation Sectors of Berlin**
Germany Nos. 557-569, 571-573
Overprinted Diagonally in Black

a

### Wmk. 284

| | | | | |
|---|---|---|---|---|
| **1948, Sept. 1** | | **Typo.** | | **Perf. 14** |
| 9N1 | A120 | 2pf brown blk | .45 | 4.50 |
| 9N2 | A120 | 6pf purple | .30 | 4.50 |
| 9N3 | A121 | 8pf red | .30 | 4.50 |
| 9N4 | A121 | 10pf yellow grn | .25 | 1.10 |
| 9N5 | A122 | 12pf gray | .25 | 1.10 |
| 9N6 | A120 | 15pf chocolate | 4.75 | 67.50 |
| 9N7 | A121 | 16pf dk blue grn | .35 | 1.60 |
| 9N8 | A121 | 20pf blue | 2.25 | 6.75 |
| 9N9 | A123 | 24pf brown org | .25 | .45 |
| 9N10 | A122 | 25pf orange yel | 6.75 | 52.50 |
| 9N11 | A122 | 30pf red | 1.00 | 7.50 |
| 9N12 | A121 | 40pf red violet | 1.10 | 7.50 |
| 9N13 | A123 | 50pf ultra | 2.50 | 30.00 |
| 9N14 | A122 | 60pf red brown | .75 | .45 |
| 9N15 | A122 | 80pf dark blue | 2.00 | 26.00 |
| 9N16 | A123 | 84pf emerald | 5.25 | 97.50 |

Germany Nos. 574-577 Overprinted
Diagonally in Black

b

### Engr.

| | | | | |
|---|---|---|---|---|
| 9N17 | A124 | 1m olive | 20.00 | 150.00 |
| 9N18 | A124 | 2m dk brown vio | 22.50 | 475.00 |
| 9N19 | A124 | 3m copper red | 26.00 | 675.00 |
| 9N20 | A124 | 5m dark blue | 30.00 | 675.00 |
| | *Nos. 9N1-9N20 (20)* | | 127.00 | 2,288. |
| | Set, never hinged | | 350.00 | |

Forged overprints and cancellations are found on Nos. 9N1-9N20.

Stamps of Germany 1947-48 with "a"
Overprint in Red

| | | | | |
|---|---|---|---|---|
| **1948-49** | | **Wmk. 284** | **Typo.** | **Perf. 14** |
| 9N21 | A120 | 2pf brn blk ('49) | .75 | 1.90 |
| 9N22 | A120 | 6pf purple ('49) | 4.50 | 1.90 |
| 9N23 | A121 | 8pf red ('49) | 19.00 | 4.50 |
| 9N24 | A121 | 10pf yellow grn | .75 | .60 |
| 9N25 | A120 | 15pf chocolate | 1.60 | 1.90 |
| 9N26 | A121 | 20pf blue | .75 | .75 |
| 9N27 | A120 | 25pf org yel ('49) | 32.50 | 45.00 |
| 9N28 | A122 | 30pf red ('49) | 30.00 | 4.75 |
| 9N29 | A121 | 40pf red vio ('49) | 30.00 | 13.50 |
| 9N30 | A123 | 50pf ultra ('49) | 30.00 | 7.50 |
| 9N31 | A122 | 60pf red brown | 3.75 | .60 |
| 9N32 | A122 | 80pf dk bl ('49) | 42.50 | 9.00 |

**With "b" Overprint in Red**

### Engr.

| | | | | |
|---|---|---|---|---|
| 9N33 | A124 | 1m olive | 225.00 | 450.00 |
| 9N34 | A124 | 2m dk brn vio | 100.00 | 225.00 |
| | *Nos. 9N21-9N34 (14)* | | 521.10 | 766.90 |
| | Set, never hinged | | 1,300. | |

Forgeries exist of the overprints on Nos. 9N21-9N34. No. 9N33 exists imperf.

---

A1

Statue of Heinrich von Stephan — A2

| | | | | |
|---|---|---|---|---|
| **1949, Apr. 9** | | **Litho.** | | **Perf. 14** |
| 9N35 | A1 | 12pf gray | 5.75 | 9.00 |
| 9N36 | A1 | 16pf blue green | 11.00 | 19.00 |
| 9N37 | A1 | 24pf orange brn | 7.50 | .75 |
| 9N38 | A1 | 50pf brown olive | 55.00 | 45.00 |
| 9N39 | A1 | 60pf brown red | 65.00 | 37.50 |
| 9N40 | A2 | 1m olive | 30.00 | 140.00 |
| 9N41 | A2 | 2m brown violet | 37.50 | 90.00 |
| | *Nos. 9N35-9N41 (7)* | | 211.75 | 341.25 |
| | Set, never hinged | | 750.00 | |

75th anniv. of the UPU.

Brandenburg Gate,
Berlin — A3

Tempelhof
Airport — A4

Designs: 4pf, 8pf, 40pf, Schoeneberg, Rudolf Wilde Square. 5pf, 25pf, 5m, Tegel Castle. 6pf, 50pf, Reichstag Building. 10pf, 30pf, Cloisters, Kleist Park. 15pf, Tempelhof Airport. 20pf, 80pf, 90pf, Polytechnic College, Charlottenburg. 60pf, National Gallery. 2m, Gendarmen Square. 3m, Brandenburg Gate.

| | | | | |
|---|---|---|---|---|
| **1949** | | **Typo.** | | **Wmk. 284** |
| | | **Size: 22x18mm** | | |
| 9N42 | A3 | 1pf black | .20 | .35 |
| *a.* | | Bklt. pane 5 + label | 9.00 | 22.50 |
| | | Never hinged | 22.50 | |
| *b.* | | Tête bêche | .35 | 1.25 |
| | | Never hinged | 1.00 | |
| 9N43 | A3 | 4pf yellow brn | .20 | .35 |
| *a.* | | Bklt. pane 5 + label | 9.00 | 22.50 |
| | | Never hinged | 22.50 | |
| *b.* | | Tête bêche | .95 | 2.40 |
| | | Never hinged | 1.90 | |
| 9N44 | A3 | 5pf blue green | .20 | .35 |
| 9N45 | A3 | 6pf red violet | .35 | 1.50 |
| 9N46 | A3 | 8pf red orange | .35 | 1.50 |
| 9N47 | A3 | 10pf yellow grn | .35 | .35 |
| *a.* | | Bklt. pane 5 + label | 65.00 | 175.00 |
| | | Never hinged | 140.00 | |
| 9N48 | A4 | 15pf chocolate | 3.75 | .90 |
| 9N49 | A3 | 20pf red | 1.50 | .35 |
| *a.* | | Bklt. pane 5 + label | 65.00 | 175.00 |
| | | Never hinged | 140.00 | |
| 9N50 | A3 | 25pf orange | 7.50 | 1.10 |
| 9N51 | A3 | 30pf violet bl | 3.50 | 1.25 |
| *a.* | | Imperf. | 675.00 | |
| | | Never hinged | 1,350. | |
| 9N52 | A3 | 40pf lake | 4.50 | 1.10 |
| 9N53 | A3 | 50pf olive | 4.50 | .35 |
| 9N54 | A3 | 60pf red brown | 15.00 | .35 |
| 9N55 | A3 | 80pf dark blue | 3.00 | 1.10 |
| 9N56 | A3 | 90pf emerald | 3.00 | 1.50 |

### Engr.
**Size: 29¼-29¾x24-24½mm**

| | | | | |
|---|---|---|---|---|
| 9N57 | A4 | 1m olive | 5.50 | 1.10 |
| 9N58 | A4 | 2m brown vio | 15.00 | 1.50 |
| 9N59 | A4 | 3m henna brn | 67.50 | 15.00 |
| 9N60 | A4 | 5m deep blue | 45.00 | 15.00 |
| | *Nos. 9N42-9N60 (19)* | | 180.90 | 45.00 |
| | Set, never hinged | | 700.00 | |

See Nos. 9N101-9N102, 9N108-9N110.

Goethe and
"Iphigenie" — A5

---

Statue of Atlas,
New York — A6

Designs (Goethe and scenes from his works): 20pf, "Reineke Fuchs." 30pf, "Faust."

| | | | | |
|---|---|---|---|---|
| **1949, July 29** | | **Litho.** | | **Perf. 14** |
| 9N61 | A5 | 10pf green | 42.50 | 65.00 |
| 9N62 | A5 | 20pf carmine | 42.50 | 75.00 |
| 9N63 | A5 | 30pf ultra | 7.50 | 50.00 |
| | *Nos. 9N61-9N63 (3)* | | 92.50 | 190.00 |
| | Set, never hinged | | 300.00 | |

Bicentenary of the birth of Johann Wolfgang von Goethe.

Germany Nos. 550, 565, 572 and 576
Surcharged "BERLIN" and New Value
in Dark Green

| | | | | |
|---|---|---|---|---|
| **1949, Aug. 1** | | | | **Typo.** |
| 9N64 | A119 | 5pf on 45pf | 1.10 | .35 |
| 9N65 | A123 | 10pf on 24pf | 3.25 | .35 |
| 9N66 | A122 | 20pf on 80pf | 19.00 | 16.50 |
| | | **Engr.** | | |
| 9N67 | A124 | 1m on 3m | 45.00 | 17.00 |
| | *Nos. 9N64-9N67 (4)* | | 68.35 | 34.20 |
| | Set, never hinged | | 250.00 | |

| | | | | |
|---|---|---|---|---|
| **1950, Oct. 1** | | **Engr.** | | **Wmk. 116** |
| 9N68 | A6 | 20pf dk carmine | 35.00 | 40.00 |
| | | Never hinged | 90.00 | |

European Recovery Plan.

Albert
Lortzing — A7

Freedom Bell,
Berlin — A8

| | | | | |
|---|---|---|---|---|
| **1951, Apr. 22** | | | | |
| 9N69 | A7 | 20pf red brown | 20.00 | 52.50 |
| | | Never hinged | 52.50 | |

Centenary of the death of Albert Lortzing, composer.

| | | | | |
|---|---|---|---|---|
| **1951** | | | | **Perf. 14** |
| 9N70 | A8 | 5pf chocolate | .75 | 7.50 |
| 9N71 | A8 | 10pf deep green | 3.75 | 22.50 |
| 9N72 | A8 | 20pf rose red | 2.25 | 19.00 |
| 9N73 | A8 | 30pf blue | 19.00 | 67.50 |
| 9N74 | A8 | 40pf rose violet | 5.50 | 37.50 |
| | *Nos. 9N70-9N74 (5)* | | 31.25 | 154.00 |
| | Set, never hinged | | 87.50 | |

### Re-engraved

| | | | | |
|---|---|---|---|---|
| **1951-52** | | | | |
| 9N75 | A8 | 5pf olive bis ('52) | .75 | 1.90 |
| 9N76 | A8 | 10pf yellow grn | 2.25 | 3.75 |
| 9N77 | A8 | 20pf brt red | 10.50 | 16.50 |
| 9N78 | A8 | 30pf blue ('52) | 24.00 | 50.00 |
| 9N79 | A8 | 40pf dp car ('52) | 10.50 | 15.00 |
| | *Nos. 9N75-9N79 (5)* | | 48.00 | 87.15 |
| | Set, never hinged | | 110.00 | |

Bell clapper moved from left to right. Imprint "L. Schnell" in lower margin.
No. 9N76 exists imperf. Value, $575 unused, $1,100 mint never hinged.
See Nos. 9N94-9N98.

Ludwig van
Beethoven — A9

Olympic
Symbols — A10

| | | | | |
|---|---|---|---|---|
| **1952, Mar. 26** | | **Engr.** | | **Unwmk.** |
| 9N80 | A9 | 30pf blue | 16.00 | 30.00 |
| | | Never hinged | 42.50 | |

125th anniversary of the death of Ludwig van Beethoven.

---

| | | | | |
|---|---|---|---|---|
| **1952, June 20** | | **Litho.** | | **Wmk. 116** |
| 9N81 | A10 | 4pf yellow brown | .35 | 1.90 |
| 9N82 | A10 | 10pf green | 3.75 | 15.00 |
| 9N83 | A10 | 20pf rose red | 6.75 | 26.00 |
| | *Nos. 9N81-9N83 (3)* | | 10.85 | 42.90 |
| | Set, never hinged | | 27.50 | |

Pre-Olympic Festival Day, June 20, 1952.

Carl Friedrich
Zelter — A11

Arms Breaking
Chains — A12

Portraits: 5pf, Otto Lilienthal. 6pf, Walter Rathenau. 8pf, Theodor Fontane. 10pf, Adolph von Menzel. 15pf, Rudolf Virchow. 20pf, Werner von Siemens. 25pf, Karl Friedrich Schinkel. 30pf, Max Planck. 40pf, Wilhelm von Humboldt.

| | | | | |
|---|---|---|---|---|
| **1952-53** | | **Engr.** | | **Wmk. 284** |
| 9N84 | A11 | 4pf brown | .20 | .55 |
| 9N85 | A11 | 5pf dp blue ('53) | .35 | .55 |
| 9N86 | A11 | 6pf choc ('53) | 2.00 | 9.75 |
| 9N87 | A11 | 8pf henna brn ('53) | .75 | 2.25 |
| 9N88 | A11 | 10pf deep green | 1.10 | .55 |
| 9N89 | A11 | 15pf purple ('53) | 5.25 | 15.00 |
| 9N90 | A11 | 20pf brown red | .75 | .75 |
| 9N91 | A11 | 25pf dp olive ('53) | 16.00 | 6.75 |
| 9N92 | A11 | 30pf brn vio ('53) | 5.50 | 9.75 |
| 9N93 | A11 | 40pf black ('53) | 6.75 | 3.00 |
| | *Nos. 9N84-9N93 (10)* | | 38.65 | 48.90 |
| | Set, never hinged | | 140.00 | |

Bell Type of 1951-1952
Second Re-engraving

| | | | | |
|---|---|---|---|---|
| **1953** | | **Wmk. 284** | | **Perf. 14** |
| 9N94 | A8 | 5pf brown | .35 | 1.00 |
| 9N95 | A8 | 10pf deep green | 1.10 | 1.50 |
| 9N96 | A8 | 20pf brt red | 3.00 | 3.00 |
| 9N97 | A8 | 30pf blue | 5.00 | 12.00 |
| 9N98 | A8 | 40pf rose violet | 21.00 | 37.50 |
| | *Nos. 9N94-9N98 (5)* | | 30.45 | 55.00 |
| | Set, never hinged | | 77.50 | |

Bell clapper hangs straight down. Marginal imprint omitted.
For overprint & surcharge see #9N106, 9NB17.

| | | | | |
|---|---|---|---|---|
| **1953, Aug. 17** | | | | **Typo.** |
| | | Design: 30pf, Brandenburg Gate. | | |
| 9N99 | A12 | 20pf black | 1.25 | 1.50 |
| 9N100 | A12 | 30pf dp carmine | 9.00 | 30.00 |
| | Set, never hinged | | 37.50 | |

Strike of East German workers, 6/17/53.

Similar to Type of 1949

Designs: 4pf, Exposition halls. 20pf, Olympic Stadium, Berlin.

| | | | | |
|---|---|---|---|---|
| **1953-54** | | **Wmk. 284** | | **Perf. 14** |
| 9N101 | A3 | 4pf yellow brn ('54) | 1.75 | 5.00 |
| 9N102 | A3 | 20pf red | 22.50 | 2.50 |
| | Set, never hinged | | 70.00 | |

> **Catalogue values for unused stamps in this section, from this point to the end of the section, are for Never Hinged items.**

Allied Council
Building — A13

| | | | | |
|---|---|---|---|---|
| **1954, Jan. 25** | | | | **Litho.** |
| 9N103 | A13 | 20pf red | 8.25 | 4.50 |

Four Power Conference, Berlin, 1954.

Prof. Ernst
Reuter (1889-
1953), Mayor of
Berlin (1948-53)
A14

**1954, Jan. 18**    **Engr.**    **Wmk. 284**
9N104 A14 20pf chocolate    8.25 1.90
See No. 9N174.

Ottmar
Mergenthaler
and
Linotype — A15

**1954, May 11**
9N105 A15 10pf dk blue grn    2.75 2.75
Cent. of the birth of Ottmar Mergenthaler.

No. 9N96
Overprinted in
Black

**1954, July 17**    **Perf. 13½x14**
9N106 A8 20pf bright red    4.25 5.25
Issued to publicize the West German presidential election held in Berlin July 17, 1954.

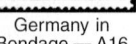

Germany in
Bondage — A16

Richard
Strauss — A17

**1954, July 20**    **Typo.**
9N107 A16 20pf car & gray    5.25 5.25
10th anniv. of the attempted assassination of Adolf Hitler.

### Similar to Type of 1949

Designs: 7pf, Exposition halls. 40pf, Memorial library. 70pf, Hunting lodge, Grunewald.

**1954**    **Wmk. 284**    **Perf. 14**
9N108 A3 7pf aqua    5.50 1.50
9N109 A3 40pf rose lilac    9.00 3.00
9N110 A3 70pf olive green    105.00 21.00
   Nos. 9N108-9N110 (3)    119.50 25.50
   Set, hinged    50.00

**1954, Sept. 18**    **Engr.**
9N111 A17 40pf violet blue    11.00 3.75
5th anniv. of the death of Richard Strauss, composer.

Early
Forge — A18

**1954, Sept. 25**
9N112 A18 20pf reddish brown    7.50 1.90
Centenary of the death of August Borsig, industrial leader.

M. S. Berlin and
Arms of
Berlin — A19

**1955, Mar. 12**    **Wmk. 284**
9N113 A19 10pf Prus green    1.10 .75
9N114 A19 25pf violet blue    7.25 4.25
Issued to publicize the resumption of shipping under West German ownership.

Wilhelm
Furtwängler — A20

**Perf. 13½x14**
**1955, Sept. 17**    **Unwmk.**
9N115 A20 40pf ultra    21.00 21.00
Issued to honor the conductor Wilhelm Furtwängler and to publicize the Berlin Music Festival, September 1955.

Arms of Berlin
A21      A22

**1955, Oct. 17**    **Litho.**    **Wmk. 304**
9N116 A21 10pf red, org yel & blk    .35 .75
9N117 A21 20pf red, org yel & blk    5.25 9.00
Meeting of the German Bundestag in Berlin, Oct. 17-22, 1955.

**1956, Mar. 16**
9N118 A22 10pf red, ocher & blk    1.10 .75
9N119 A22 25pf red, ocher & blk    4.50 4.50
Meeting of the German Bundesrat in Berlin Mar. 16, 1956.

Radio Station, Berlin (A23
has no top inscription. A24
has top inscription.)
A23      A24

Free University
A25

Monument of the
Great Elector
Frederick William
A26

Designs: 1pf, 3pf, Brandenburg Gate. 5pf, General Post Office. 8pf, City Hall, Neukölln. 10pf, Kaiser Wilhelm Memorial Church. 15pf, Airlift memorial. 25pf, Lilienthal Monument. 30pf, Pfaueninsel Castle. 40pf, Charlottenburg Castle. 50pf, Reuter power plant. 60pf, Chamber of Commerce and Industry and Stock Exchange. 70pf, Schiller Theater. 3m, Congress Hall.

**Typo.; Litho. (3pf, #9N122)**
**1956-63**    **Wmk. 304**    **Perf. 14**
9N120 A25 1pf gray ('57)    .25 .20
9N120A A25 3pf brt pur ('63)    .25 .20
9N121 A25 5pf rose lil ('57)    .25 .20
9N122 A25 7pf blue green    8.25 2.40
9N123 A24 7pf blue green    .25 .20
9N124 A24 8pf gray    .45 .35
9N125 A24 8pf red org ('59)    .30 .30
9N126 A24 10pf emerald    .25 .20
9N127 A24 15pf chlky blue    .45 .25
9N128 A25 20pf rose car    .45 .20
9N129 A24 25pf dull red brn    .45 .45

     **Engr.**
9N130 A24 30pf gray grn ('57)    .90 .90
9N131 A25 40pf lt ultra ('57)    9.00 7.50
9N132 A24 50pf olive    .90 .90
9N133 A25 60pf lt brn ('57)    .90 .90
9N134 A25 70pf violet    24.00 13.50
9N135 A26 1m olive    1.90 2.25

**Size: 29x24½mm**
9N136 A25 3m rose cl ('58)    5.25 22.50
   Nos. 9N120-9N136 (18)    54.45 53.40

No. 9N120 exists on both ordinary and fluorescent paper; No. 9N120A on fluorescent paper only; others on ordinary paper.

Engineers' Society
Emblem — A27

Paul
Lincke — A28

**1956, May 12**    **Engr.**    **Perf. 14**
9N140 A27 10pf dark green    1.90 1.50
9N141 A27 20pf dark red    4.25 5.00
Cent. of Soc. of German Civil Engineers.

**1956, Sept. 3**
9N142 A28 20pf dark red    2.50 2.75
Death of Paul Lincke, composer, 10th anniv.

Radio Station,
Berlin-Nikolassee
A29

Spandau,
1850 — A30

**1956, Sept. 15**
9N143 A29 25pf brown    6.00 9.00
German Industrial Fair, Berlin, Sept. 15-30.

**1957, Mar. 7**
9N144 A30 20pf gray ol & brn red    .60 .75
725th anniversary of Spandau.

Hansa Model
Town and
"B" — A31

Designs: 20pf, View of exposition grounds and "B." 40pf, Auditorium and "B."

**1957**    **Engr.**
9N145 A31 7pf violet brown    .20 .20
9N146 A31 20pf carmine    .75 .75
9N147 A31 40pf violet blue    1.90 2.25
   Nos. 9N145-9N147 (3)    2.85 3.20
Intl. Building Show, Berlin, 7/6-9/29/57.

Friedrich Karl von
Savigny, Law
Teacher — A32

Uta Statue,
Naumburg
Cathedral — A33

Portraits: 7pf, Theodor Mommsen, historian. 8pf, Heinrich Zille, painter. 10pf, Ernst Reuter, mayor of Berlin. 15pf, Fritz Haber, chemist. 20pf, Friedrich Schleiermacher, theologian. 25pf, Max Reinhardt, theatrical director. 40pf, Alexander von Humboldt, naturalist and geographer. 50pf, Christian Daniel Rauch, sculptor.

**1957-59**    **Wmk. 304**    **Perf. 14**
**Portraits in Brown**
9N148 A32 7pf blue grn ('58)    .20 .25
9N149 A32 8pf gray ('58)    .20 .25
9N150 A32 10pf green ('58)    .20 .25
9N151 A32 15pf dark blue    .35 .75
9N152 A32 20pf carmine ('58)    .20 .25
9N153 A32 25pf magenta    .80 1.00
9N154 A32 30pf olive green    2.10 2.50
9N155 A32 40pf blue ('59)    .80 1.00
9N156 A32 50pf olive    3.75 6.50
   Nos. 9N148-9N156 (9)    8.60 12.75
Issued to honor famous men of Berlin. See No. 9NB19.

**1957, Aug. 6**
9N157 A33 25pf brown red    .90 1.10
Issued to publicize the annual meeting of the East German Culture Society in Berlin.

"Unity and
Justice and
Liberty" — A34

Postilion 1897-
1925 — A35

**1957, Oct. 15**    **Litho.**
9N158 A34 10pf multicolored    .30 .75
9N159 A34 20pf multicolored    2.25 3.00
1st meeting of the 3rd German Bundesrat, Berlin, 10/15.

**1957, Oct. 23**    **Wmk. 304**    **Perf. 14**
9N160 A35 20pf multicolored    .75 .90
Issued for Stamp Day and BEPHILA stamp exhibition, Berlin, Oct. 23-27.

World Veterans'
Federation
Emblem — A36

Christ and the
Cosmos — A37

**1957, Oct. 28**
9N161 A36 20pf bl grn, ol grn & yel .90 .75

7th General Assembly of the World Veterans' Federation, Berlin, Oct. 24-Nov. 1.

**1958, Aug. 13**
9N162 A37 10pf lt bl grn & blk .35 .60
9N163 A37 20pf rose lilac & blk 1.00 1.50

Issued in honor of the 78th German Catholics Meeting, Berlin, Aug. 13-17.

Prof. Otto Suhr (1894-1957), Mayor of Berlin (1955-57) A38

**1958, Aug. 30   Engr.   Perf. 14**
9N164 A38 20pf rose red 1.10 2.00

Pres. Heuss Type of Germany, 1959
**Litho., Engraved (40pf, 70pf)**
**1959**
9N165 A208 7pf blue green .20 .35
9N166 A208 10pf green .25 .35
9N167 A208 20pf dk car rose .50 .35
9N168 A208 40pf blue 2.25 4.50
9N169 A208 70pf dull purple 8.25 10.50
Nos. 9N165-9N169 (5) 11.45 16.05

Nos. 9N168-9N169 were issued in sheets of 100 and in coils. Every fifth coil stamp has a control number on the back.

Aerial Bridge to Berlin — A39

Globe and Brandenburg Gate — A40

**1959, May 12   Engr.**
9N170 A39 25pf maroon & blk .60 .45

10th anniversary of Berlin Airlift.

**1959, June 18   Litho.   Perf. 14**
9N171 A40 20pf lt blue & red .85 .45

Issued to publicize the 14th International Municipal Congress, Berlin, June 18-23.

Friedrich von Schiller (1759-1805), Poet — A41

**1959, Nov. 10   Engr.   Wmk. 304**
9N172 A41 20pf dull red & brn .35 .45

Dr. Robert Koch (1843-1910), Bacteriologist A42

Hans Böckler (1875-1951), Labor Leader — A43

**1960, May 27   Perf. 14**
9N173 A42 20pf rose lake .35 .45

Mayor Type of 1954

Portrait: Dr. Walther Carl Rudolf Schreiber, Mayor of Berlin, 1953-54.

**1960, June 30   Wmk. 304   Perf. 14**
9N174 A14 20pf brown car .50 .65

**1961, Feb. 16   Litho.   Perf. 14**
9N175 A43 20pf dk brick red & blk .30 .35

Hans Böckler (1875-1951), labor leader.

**Fluorescent Paper**
**was introduced for all stamps,**
**starting with No. 9N176, and includ-**
**ing Nos. 9N120 and 9N120A.**

Albrecht Dürer — A44

Portraits: 5pf, Albertus Magnus. 7pf, St. Elizabeth of Thuringia. 8pf, Johann Gutenberg. 15pf, Martin Luther. 20pf, Johann Sebastian Bach. 25pf, Balthasar Neumann. 30pf, Immanuel Kant. 40pf, Gotthold Ephraim Lessing. 50pf, Johann Wolfgang von Goethe. 60pf, Friedrich von Schiller. 70pf, Ludwig van Beethoven. 80pf, Heinrich von Kleist. 1m, Annette von Droste-Hülshoff. 2m, Gerhart Hauptmann.

**1961-62   Typo.   Wmk. 304**
9N176 A44 5pf olive .20 .20
9N177 A44 7pf dk bister .20 .35
9N178 A44 8pf lilac .20 .35
9N179 A44 10pf olive green .20 .25
  b.  Tête bêche pair 1.10 2.25
9N180 A44 15pf blue .20 .35
9N181 A44 20pf dark red .20 .25
9N182 A44 25pf orange brn .20 .35

**Engr.**
9N183 A44 30pf gray .25 .50
9N184 A44 40pf blue .50 .95
9N185 A44 50pf red brown .35 .95
9N186 A44 60pf dk car rose ('62) .35 1.10
9N187 A44 70pf green .50 1.10
9N188 A44 80pf brown 3.00 7.50
9N189 A44 1m violet blue 1.40 3.50
9N190 A44 2m yel grn ('62) 1.75 5.00
Nos. 9N176-9N190 (15) 9.50 22.75

Nos. 9N176-9N182, 9N184 and 9N187 were issued in sheets and in coils. Every fifth coil stamp has a black control number on the back.

Louise Schroeder A45

**1961, June 3   Engr.   Perf. 14**
9N192 A45 20pf dark brown .35 .35

Issued to honor Louise Schroeder, acting mayor of Berlin (1947-1948).

Synod Emblem & St. Mary's Church — A46

Design: 20pf, Emblem and Kaiser Wilhelm Memorial Church.

**1961, July 19   Litho.   Wmk. 304**
9N193 A46 10pf green & vio .25 .25
9N194 A46 20pf rose claret & vio .25 .25

10th meeting of German Protestants (Evangelical Synod), Berlin, July 19-23.

Berlin Bear with Record, TV Set & Radio Tower — A47

**1961, Aug. 3   Engr.**
9N195 A47 20pf brn red & dk brn .30 .30

German Radio, Television and Phonograph Exhibition, Berlin, Aug. 25-Sept. 3.

Berlin, 1650 — A48

Views of Old Berlin: 10pf, Spree and Waisenbrücke (Orphans' Bridge). 15pf, Mauer Street, 1780. 20pf, Berlin Palace, 1703. 25pf, Potsdam Square, 1825. 40pf, Portico, Bellevue Palace, 1800. 50pf, Fischer Bridge, 1830. 60pf, Halle Gate, 1880. 70pf, Parochial Church, 1780. 80pf, University, 1825. 90pf, Opera House, 1780. 1m, Grunewald Lake, 1790.

**1962-63   Wmk. 304   Perf. 14**
9N196 A48 7pf dk gray & gldn brn .20 .20
9N197 A48 10pf grn & dk gray .20 .20
9N198 A48 15pf bluish gray & dk bl ('63) .20 .20
9N199 A48 20pf org brn & sep .20 .20
9N200 A48 25pf ol & gray ('63) .20 .25
9N201 A48 40pf bluish gray & ultra .25 .40
9N202 A48 50pf gray & dk brn ('63) .40 .40
9N203 A48 60pf gray & car rose ('63) .45 .45
9N204 A48 70pf gray & lilac .45 .45
9N205 A48 80pf dk gray & dk red ('63) .55 .70
9N206 A48 90pf sep & brn org ('63) .60 .75
9N207 A48 1m ol gray & dp grn .70 1.10
Nos. 9N196-9N207 (12) 4.40 5.30

Gelber Hund, 1912, and Boeing 707 — A49

**1962, Sept. 12   Litho.**
9N208 A49 60pf brt blue & blk .55 .55

50th anniv. of German airmail service.

Berlin Bear and Radio Tower — A50

**1963, July 24   Unwmk.   Perf. 14**
9N209 A50 20pf bl, vio bl & gray .30 .30

German Radio, Television and Phonograph Exhibition, Berlin, Aug. 30-Sept. 8.

Schöneberg City Hall, John F. Kennedy Place, Berlin — A51

**1964, May 30   Engr.   Wmk. 304**
9N210 A51 20pf dk brn, cr .30 .30

700th anniv. of the Schöneberg district of Berlin. The Senate and House of Representatives of West Berlin meet at Schöneberg City Hall.

Lübke Type of Germany, 1964
**1964, July 1   Litho.   Unwmk.**
9N211 A247 20pf carmine .20 .20
9N212 A247 40pf ultra .35 .35
See Nos. 9N263-9N264.

Capitals Type of Germany
Design: Reichstag Building, Berlin.

**1964, Sept. 14   Litho.   Perf. 14**
9N213 A245 20pf blue, blk & grn .35 .35

Kennedy Type of Germany
**1964, Nov. 21   Engr.   Wmk. 304**
9N214 A255 40pf dark blue .45 .55

Castle Gate, Ellwangen — A52

Designs (German buildings through 12 centuries): 10pf, Wall pavilion, Zwinger, Dresden. 15pf, Tegel Castle, Berlin. 20pf, Portico, Lorsch. 40pf, Trifels Fortress, Palatinate. 60pf, Treptow Gate, Neubrandenburg. 70pf, Osthofen Gate, Soest. 80pf, Elling Gate, Weissenburg.

**1964-65   Typo.   Unwmk.**
9N215 A52 10pf brown ('65) .20 .25
  b.  Tête bêche pair .45 2.00
9N216 A52 15pf dk green ('65) .20 .25
9N217 A52 20pf brn red ('65) .20 .25

**Engr.**
9N218 A52 40pf vio bl ('65) .60 1.10
9N219 A52 50pf olive bis 1.40 1.50
9N220 A52 60pf rose red .95 1.10
9N221 A52 70pf dk green ('65) 1.90 3.50
9N222 A52 80pf chocolate 1.90 1.50
Nos. 9N215-9N222 (8) 7.35 9.45

Nos. 9N215-9N218, 9N221 were issued in sheets of 100 and in coils. Every fifth coil stamp has a black control number on the back.

Kaiser Wilhelm Memorial Church A53   Nordertor, Flensburg A54

The New Berlin: 15pf, German Opera House, horiz. 20pf, Philharmonic Hall, horiz. 30pf, Jewish Community Center, horiz. 40pf, Regina Martyrum memorial, horiz. 50pf, Ernst Reuter Square, horiz. 60pf, Europa Center. 70pf, School of Engineering, horiz. 90pf, City Highway. 90pf, Planetarium and observatory, horiz. 1m, Schaeferberg radio tower, Wannsee. 1.10m, University clinic, Steglitz, horiz.

**Engraved and Lithographed**
**1965-66   Unwmk.   Perf. 14**
9N223 A53 10pf multi .20 .20
9N224 A53 15pf multi .20 .20
9N225 A53 20pf multi .20 .20
9N226 A53 30pf multi ('66) .20 .20
9N227 A53 40pf multi ('66) .25 .25
9N228 A53 50pf multi .25 .30
9N229 A53 60pf multi ('66) .30 .35
9N230 A53 70pf multi ('66) .45 .45
9N231 A53 80pf multi .45 .45
9N232 A53 90pf multi ('66) .55 .75

| | | | | |
|---|---|---|---|---|
| 9N233 | A53 | 1m multi ('66) | .55 | .90 |
| 9N234 | A53 | 1.10m multi ('66) | .55 | .95 |
| | | Nos. 9N223-9N234 (12) | 4.15 | 5.20 |

**1966-69　　　　Engr.　　　Perf. 14**

5pf, Berlin Gate, Stettin. 8pf, Castle, Kaub on the Rhine. 10pf, Wall Pavilion, Zwinger, Dresden. 20pf, Portico, Lorsch. 40pf, Trifels Fortress, Palatinate. 50pf, Castle Gate, Ellwangen. 60pf, Treptow Gate, Neubrandenburg. 70pf, Osthofen Gate, Soest. 80pf, Elling Gate, Weissenburg. 90pf, Zschocke Ladies' Home, Königsberg. 1m, Melanchthon House, Wittenberg. 1.10m, Trinity Hospital, Hildesheim. 1.30m, Tegel Castle, Berlin. 2m, Löwenberg Town Hall, interior view.

| | | | | |
|---|---|---|---|---|
| 9N235 | A54 | 5pf olive | .20 | .20 |
| 9N236 | A54 | 8pf car rose | .20 | .20 |
| 9N237 | A54 | 10pf dk brn ('67) | .20 | .20 |
| 9N238 | A54 | 20pf dk grn ('67) | .20 | .20 |
| 9N239 | A54 | 30pf yellow grn | .25 | .25 |
| 9N240 | A54 | 30pf red ('67) | .25 | .20 |
| 9N241 | A54 | 40pf ol bis ('67) | .55 | .75 |
| 9N242 | A54 | 50pf blue ('67) | .35 | .45 |
| 9N243 | A54 | 60pf dp org ('67) | 1.50 | 1.90 |
| 9N244 | A54 | 70pf sl grn ('67) | .75 | .75 |
| 9N245 | A54 | 80pf red brn ('67) | .95 | 1.60 |
| 9N246 | A54 | 90pf black | .50 | .75 |
| 9N247 | A54 | 1m dull blue | .50 | .75 |
| 9N248 | A54 | 1.10m red brn | 1.40 | 1.40 |
| 9N249 | A54 | 1.30m green ('69) | 2.25 | 2.25 |
| 9N250 | A54 | 2m purple | 2.25 | 1.90 |
| | | Nos. 9N235-9N250 (16) | 12.30 | 13.75 |

Brandenburg Gate Type of Germany

**1966-70　　　Typo.　　　Perf. 14**

| | | | | |
|---|---|---|---|---|
| 9N251 | A268 | 10pf chocolate | .20 | .20 |
| a. | | Bklt. pane of 10 (4 #9N251, 2 #9N252, 4 #9N253) | 6.75 | 12.00 |
| b. | | Tête bêche pair | .90 | 1.10 |
| c. | | Bklt. pane of 6 (4 #9N251, 2 #9N253) ('70) | 3.00 | 4.50 |
| 9N252 | A268 | 20pf dp green | .20 | .20 |
| a. | | Bklt. pane of 4 (2 #9N252, 2 #9N253) ('70) | 2.25 | 3.00 |
| 9N253 | A268 | 30pf red | .20 | .20 |
| a. | | Tête bêche pair | 1.10 | 1.40 |
| 9N254 | A268 | 50pf dk blue | .55 | .35 |
| 9N255 | A268 | 100pf dk blue ('67) | 4.25 | 4.25 |
| | | Nos. 9N251-9N255 (5) | 5.40 | 5.20 |

Nos. 9N251-9N255 were issued in sheets of 100 and in coils. Every fifth coil stamp has a black control number on the back.

A55　　　　　　　A56

Designs: 10pf, Young Man, by Conrat Meit, 1520. 20pf, The Great Elector Friedrich Wilhelm (1640-88), head from monument by Andreas Schlüter. 30pf, The Evangelist Mark, by Tilman Riemenschneider. 50pf, Head of "Victory" from Brandenburg Gate, by Gottfried Schadow, 1793. 1m, Madonna, by Joseph Anton Feuchtmayer. 1.10m, Jesus and John, wood sculpture, anonymous, c. 1320.

**1967　　　　　　Engr.　　　Perf. 14**

| | | | | |
|---|---|---|---|---|
| 9N256 | A55 | 10pf sepia & lemon | .20 | .20 |
| 9N257 | A55 | 20pf sl grn & bluish gray | .20 | .20 |
| 9N258 | A55 | 30pf brown & olive | .20 | .20 |
| 9N259 | A55 | 50pf black & gray | .35 | .35 |
| 9N260 | A55 | 1m blue & chlky blue | .75 | .75 |

**Size: 22x40mm**

| | | | | |
|---|---|---|---|---|
| 9N261 | A55 | 1.10m brown & buff | 1.10 | 1.50 |
| | | Nos. 9N256-9N261 (6) | 2.80 | 3.20 |

Issued to publicize Berlin art treasures.

**1967, July 19　　　Litho. and Engr.**

Berlin Radio Tower and Television Screens

| | | | | |
|---|---|---|---|---|
| 9N262 | A56 | 30pf multicolored | .30 | .35 |

25th German Radio, Television and Phonograph Exhibition, Berlin, Aug. 25-Sept. 3.

Lübke Type of Germany, 1964

**1967, Oct. 14　　　　　　　Litho.**

| | | | | |
|---|---|---|---|---|
| 9N263 | A247 | 30pf carmine | .20 | .25 |
| 9N264 | A247 | 50pf ultra | .35 | .45 |

Old Court　　　　　Turners'
Building (Berlin　　Emblem — A58
Museum) — A57

**1968, Mar. 16　　　Engr.　　　Perf. 14**

| | | | | |
|---|---|---|---|---|
| 9N265 | A57 | 30pf black | .30 | .35 |

500th anniv. of the Berlin Court of Appeal.

**1968, Apr. 29　　　Litho.　　　Perf. 14**

| | | | | |
|---|---|---|---|---|
| 9N266 | A58 | 20pf gray, blk & red | .30 | .35 |

Issued to publicize the German Turner Festival, Berlin, May 28-June 3.

Newspaper Vendor
by Christian
Wilhelm
Allers — A59

19th Century Berliners: 5pf, Hack, by Heinrich Zille, horiz. No. 9N269, Horse omnibus, coachman and passengers, 1890, by C. W. Allers. No. 9N270, Cobbler's apprentice, by Franz Kruger. No. 9N271, Cobbler, by Adolph von Menzel. No. 9N272, Blacksmiths, by Paul Meyerheim. No. 9N273, Three Ladies, by Franz Kruger. 50pf, Strollers at Brandenburg Gate, by Christian W. Allers.

**1969　　　　　　Engr.　　　Perf. 14**

| | | | | |
|---|---|---|---|---|
| 9N267 | A59 | 5pf black | .20 | .20 |
| 9N268 | A59 | 5pf dp brown | .20 | .20 |
| 9N269 | A59 | 10pf brown | .20 | .20 |
| 9N270 | A59 | 20pf dk olive grn | .20 | .20 |
| 9N271 | A59 | 20pf green | .20 | .20 |
| 9N272 | A59 | 30pf dk red brown | .60 | .45 |
| 9N273 | A59 | 30pf red brown | .60 | .45 |
| 9N274 | A59 | 50pf ultra | 1.50 | 1.75 |
| | | Nos. 9N267-9N274 (8) | 3.70 | 3.65 |

Souvenir Sheet

Berlin Zoo Animals — A60

Designs: 10pf, Orangutan family. 20pf, White pelicans. 30pf, Gaur and calf. 50pf, Zebra and foal.

**Engraved and Lithographed**

**1969, June 4　　　　　　Perf. 14**

| | | | | |
|---|---|---|---|---|
| 9N275 | A60 | Sheet of 4 | 1.90 | 1.90 |
| a. | | 10pf bister & black | .45 | .45 |
| b. | | 20pf light green & black | .45 | .45 |
| c. | | 30pf lilac rose & black | .45 | .45 |
| d. | | 50pf blue & black | .45 | .45 |

125th anniversary of the Berlin Zoo. The sheet was sold with a 20pf surtax for the benefit of the Zoo.

Australian　　　　　Joseph
Postman — A61　　　Joachim — A62

Designs: 20pf, African telephone operator. 30pf, Middle East telecommunications engineer. 50pf, Loading mail on plane.

**1969, July 21　　　Litho.　　　Perf. 14**

| | | | | |
|---|---|---|---|---|
| 9N276 | A61 | 10pf olive & apple grn | .20 | .20 |
| 9N277 | A61 | 20pf dk brn, bis & brn | .25 | .25 |
| 9N278 | A61 | 30pf vio blk & bis | .25 | .25 |
| 9N279 | A61 | 50pf dk blue & blue | 1.25 | 1.25 |
| | | Nos. 9N276-9N279 (4) | 2.25 | 2.30 |

20th Congress of the Post Office Trade Union Federation, Berlin, July 7-11.

**1969, Sept. 12　　　Photo.　　　Perf. 14**

Design: 50pf, Alexander von Humboldt, painting by Joseph Stieler.

| | | | | |
|---|---|---|---|---|
| 9N280 | A62 | 30pf multicolored | .55 | .45 |
| 9N281 | A62 | 50pf multicolored | .90 | 1.25 |

Cent. of the Berlin Music School and honoring its 1st director, Joseph Joachim (1831-1907), violinist, conductor and composer; Alexander von Humboldt (1769-1859), naturalist and explorer.

**1970, Jan. 7**

Theodor Fontane, painting by Hanns Fechner.

| | | | | |
|---|---|---|---|---|
| 9N282 | A62 | 20pf multicolored | .35 | .30 |

150th anniv. of the birth of Theodor Fontane (1819-1898), poet and writer.
See No. 9N303.

Film　　　　　Symbols of
Frame — A63　Dance, Theater &
　　　　　　　　Art — A64

**1970, June 18　　　Photo.　　　Perf. 14**

| | | | | |
|---|---|---|---|---|
| 9N283 | A63 | 30pf multicolored | .45 | .55 |

20th International Film Festival.

President Heinemann Type of
Germany Inscribed "Berlin"

**1970-73　　　　Engr.　　　Perf. 14**

| | | | | |
|---|---|---|---|---|
| 9N284 | A312 | 5pf dk gray | .20 | .20 |
| 9N285 | A312 | 8pf olive bis | .70 | .90 |
| 9N286 | A312 | 10pf brown | .20 | .20 |
| 9N286A | A312 | 15pf olive | .20 | .25 |
| 9N287 | A312 | 20pf green | .20 | .20 |
| 9N288 | A312 | 25pf dp yel grn | .90 | .55 |
| 9N289 | A312 | 30pf red brown | .95 | .55 |
| 9N290 | A312 | 40pf brown org | .55 | .25 |
| 9N291 | A312 | 50pf dark blue | .55 | .55 |
| 9N292 | A312 | 60pf blue | .90 | .55 |
| 9N293 | A312 | 70pf dk brown | .70 | .60 |
| 9N294 | A312 | 80pf slate grn | .90 | .90 |
| 9N295 | A312 | 90pf magenta | 1.75 | 2.25 |
| 9N296 | A312 | 1m olive | .90 | .70 |
| 9N296A | A312 | 110pf olive gray | 1.10 | 1.10 |
| 9N297 | A312 | 120pf ocher | 1.10 | .90 |
| 9N298 | A312 | 130pf ocher | 1.60 | 1.50 |
| 9N298A | A312 | 140pf dk blue grn | 1.60 | 1.50 |
| 9N299 | A312 | 150pf purple | 1.60 | .75 |
| 9N300 | A312 | 160pf orange | 2.25 | 1.90 |
| 9N300A | A312 | 170pf orange | 1.60 | 1.60 |
| 9N300B | A312 | 190pf dp claret | 1.90 | 2.75 |
| 9N301 | A312 | 2m dp violet | 1.90 | 1.40 |
| | | Nos. 9N284-9N301 (23) | 24.25 | 21.70 |

Issued: 5pf, 1m, 7/23; 10, 20pf, 10/23; 30, 90pf, 2m, 1/7/71; 8, 40, 50, 70, 80pf, 4/8/71; 60pf, 6/25/71; 25pf, 8/27/71; 120, 160pf, 3/8/72; 15, 130pf, 6/20/72; 150pf, 7/5/72; 170pf, 9/11/72; 110, 140, 190pf, 1/16/73.

**1970, Sept. 4　　　Litho.　　　Perf. 13½x14**

| | | | | |
|---|---|---|---|---|
| 9N302 | A64 | 30pf gray & multi | .55 | .55 |

20th Berlin Festival Weeks.

Portrait Type of 1969

30pf, Leopold von Ranke, by Julius Schrage.

**1970, Oct. 23　　　Photo.　　　Perf. 13½x14**

| | | | | |
|---|---|---|---|---|
| 9N303 | A62 | 30pf multicolored | .45 | .35 |

175th anniversary of the birth of Leopold von Ranke (1795-1886), historian.

Imperial Eagle Type of Germany

**1971, Jan. 18　　　Litho.　　　Perf. 13½x14**

| | | | | |
|---|---|---|---|---|
| 9N304 | A317 | 30pf org, red, gray & blk | .55 | .55 |

Metropolitan Train, 1932 — A65

5pf, Suburban train, 1925. 10pf, Street cars, 1890. 20pf, Horsedrawn trolley. 50pf, Street car, 1950. 1m, Subway train, 1971.

**1971　　　　　　Litho.　　　Perf. 14**

| | | | | |
|---|---|---|---|---|
| 9N305 | A65 | 5pf multicolored | .20 | .20 |
| 9N306 | A65 | 10pf multicolored | .20 | .20 |
| 9N307 | A65 | 20pf multicolored | .25 | .25 |
| 9N308 | A65 | 30pf multicolored | .45 | .35 |
| 9N309 | A65 | 50pf multicolored | 1.60 | 1.40 |
| 9N310 | A65 | 1m multicolored | 1.90 | 1.90 |
| | | Nos. 9N305-9N310 (6) | 4.60 | 4.30 |

Issued: 30pf, 1m, Jan. 18; others, May 3.

Bagpipe Player, by
Dürer — A66

**1971, May 21　　　Engr.　　　Perf. 14**

| | | | | |
|---|---|---|---|---|
| 9N311 | A66 | 10pf black & brown | .45 | .30 |

500th anniversary of the birth of Albrecht Dürer (1471-1528), painter and engraver.

Score from 2nd Brandenburg Concerto
and Bach — A67

**1971, July 14　　　Litho.　　　Perf. 14**

| | | | | |
|---|---|---|---|---|
| 9N312 | A67 | 30pf buff, brn & slate | .70 | .60 |

250th anniv. of 1st performance of Johann Sebastian Bach's 2nd Brandenburg Concerto.

A68　　　　　　　　A69

**1971, July 14　　　　　　　Photo.**

Telecommunications tower, Berlin.

| | | | | |
|---|---|---|---|---|
| 9N313 | A68 | 30pf dk blue, blk & car | .75 | .60 |

Intl. Broadcasting Exhibition, Berlin.

**1971, Aug. 27**

| | | | | |
|---|---|---|---|---|
| 9N314 | A69 | 25pf multicolored | .55 | .40 |

Hermann von Helmholtz (1821-94), scientist. See Nos. 9N332-9N333, 9N341.

Souvenir Sheet

Racing Cars — A70

**1971, Aug. 27　　　Litho.　　　Perf. 14**

| | | | | |
|---|---|---|---|---|
| 9N315 | A70 | Sheet of 4 | 1.50 | 1.50 |
| a. | | 10pf Opel racer | .20 | .20 |
| b. | | 25pf Auto Union racer | .25 | .20 |

**c.** 30pf Mercedes-Benz SSKL,
1931 .35 .20
**d.** 60pf Mercedes and Auto
Union cars racing on North
embankment .60 .60

50th anniversary of Avus Race Track.

### Accident Prevention Type of Germany

5pf, "Matches cause fires." 10pf, Broken ladder. 20pf, Hand & circular saw. 25pf, "Alcohol & automobile." 30pf, Safety helmets prevent injury. 40pf, Defective plug. 50pf, Nail sticking from board. 60pf, 70pf, Traffic safety (ball rolling before car). 100pf, Hoisted cargo. 150pf, Fenced-in open manhole.

| | | **1971-73** | **Typo.** | **Perf. 14** | |
|---|---|---|---|---|---|
| 9N316 | A328 | 5pf orange | | .25 | .30 |
| 9N317 | A328 | 10pf dk | | | |
| | | brown | | .20 | .20 |
| **a.** | | Bklt. pane, 2 each | | | |
| | | #9N317-9N318, | | | |
| | | 9N320-9N321 ('74) | | 7.00 | 7.50 |
| 9N318 | A328 | 20pf purple | | .25 | .25 |
| 9N319 | A328 | 25pf green | | .35 | .60 |
| 9N320 | A328 | 30pf dark | | | |
| | | red | | .35 | .30 |
| 9N321 | A328 | 40pf rose cl | | .35 | .40 |
| 9N322 | A328 | 50pf Prus | | | |
| | | blue | | 1.90 | 1.10 |
| 9N323 | A328 | 60pf violet | | | |
| | | blue | | 1.90 | 2.25 |
| 9N323A | A328 | 70pf green & | | | |
| | | vio bl | | 1.40 | 1.00 |
| 9N324 | A328 | 100pf olive | | 1.90 | 1.10 |
| 9N325 | A328 | 150pf red | | | |
| | | brown | | 5.75 | 6.75 |
| | | *Nos. 9N316-9N325 (11)* | | 14.60 | 14.25 |

Issued in sheets of 100 and coils. Every fifth coil stamp has a control number on the back. Issued: 25pf, 60pf, 9/10; 5pf, 10/29; 10pf, 30pf, 3/8/72; 40pf, 6/20/72; 20pf, 100pf, 7/5/72; 150pf, 9/11/72; 50pf, 1/16/73; 70pf, 6/5/73.

Microscope and Metal Slide — A71    Friedrich Gilly, by Gottfried Schadow — A72

| **1971, Oct. 26** | **Photo.** | **Perf. 14** | |
|---|---|---|---|
| 9N326 A71 | 30pf multicolored | .45 | .35 |

Materials Testing Laboratory centenary.

| **1972, Feb. 4** | **Engr.** | **Perf. 14** | |
|---|---|---|---|
| 9N327 A72 | 30pf black & blue | .55 | .35 |

Friedrich Gilly (1772-1800), sculptor.

Grunewaldsee, by Alexander von Riesen — A73

Paintings of Berlin Lakes: 25pf, Wannsee, by Max Liebermann. 30pf, Schlachtensee, by Walter Leistikow.

| **1972, Apr. 14** | **Photo.** | **Perf. 14** | |
|---|---|---|---|
| 9N328 A73 | 10pf blue & multi | .20 | .20 |
| 9N329 A73 | 25pf green & multi | .55 | .55 |
| 9N330 A73 | 30pf black & multi | .95 | .60 |
| | *Nos. 9N328-9N330 (3)* | 1.70 | 1.35 |

A74      A75

| **1972, May 18** | | | |
|---|---|---|---|
| 9N331 A74 | 60pf violet & blk | 1.00 | 1.00 |

E. T. A. Hoffmann (1776-1822), writer and composer. (Portrait by Wilhelm Hensel.)

### Portrait Type of 1971

Designs: No. 9N332, Max Liebermann (1847-1935), self-portrait. No. 9N333, Karl August, Duke of Hardenberg (1750-1822), Prussian statesman, by J. H. W. Tischbein.

| **1972** | **Photo.** | **Perf. 14** | |
|---|---|---|---|
| 9N332 A69 | 40pf multicolored | .70 | .45 |
| 9N333 A69 | 40pf multicolored | .60 | .45 |

Issued: #9N332, July 18; #9N333, Nov. 10.

| **1972, Oct. 20** | **Engr. & Litho.** | | |
|---|---|---|---|
| 9N334 A75 | 20pf Stamp-printing press | .45 | .30 |

Stamp Day 1972, and for the 5th National Youth Philatelic Exhib., Berlin, Oct. 26-29.

Streetcar, 1907 A76

#9N336, Double-decker bus, 1919. #9N337, Double-decker bus, 1925. #9N338, Electrobus, 1933. #9N339, Double-decker bus, 1970. #9N340, Elongated bus, 1973.

| **1973, Apr. 30** | **Litho.** | **Perf. 14** | |
|---|---|---|---|
| 9N335 A76 | 20pf gray & multi | .35 | .30 |
| 9N336 A76 | 30pf gray & multi | .75 | .45 |
| 9N337 A76 | 40pf gray & multi | 1.10 | .70 |

| **1973, Sept. 14** | | | |
|---|---|---|---|
| 9N338 A76 | 20pf gray & multi | .35 | .30 |
| 9N339 A76 | 30pf gray & multi | 1.10 | .45 |
| 9N340 A76 | 40pf gray & multi | 1.10 | .70 |
| | *Nos. 9N335-9N340 (6)* | 4.75 | 2.90 |

Public transportation in Berlin.

### Portrait Type of 1971

Design: 40pf, Ludwig Tieck (1773-1853), poet and writer, by Carl Christian Vogel von Vogelstein.

| **1973, May 25** | **Photo.** | **Perf. 14** | |
|---|---|---|---|
| 9N341 A69 | 40pf multicolored | .70 | .40 |

Johann Joachim Quantz (1697-1773), Flutist and Composer — A77

| **1973, June 12** | **Engr.** | **Perf. 14** | |
|---|---|---|---|
| 9N342 A77 | 40pf black | .75 | .60 |

**Souvenir Sheet**

50 Years of Broadcasting — A78

| **1973, Aug. 23** | **Litho.** | **Perf. 14** | |
|---|---|---|---|
| 9N343 A78 | Sheet of 4 | 3.75 | 3.75 |
| **a.** | A78 20pf Speaker, set, 1926 | .90 | .60 |
| **b.** | A78 30pf Hans Bredow | .90 | .90 |
| **c.** | A78 40pf Girl, TV, tape recorder | .90 | .90 |
| **d.** | A78 70pf TV camera | .90 | 1.25 |

50 years of German broadcasting. Sold for 1.80m.

Georg W. von Knobelsdorff A79

Gustav R. Kirchhoff — A80

275th anniversary of the birth of Georg Wenzelslaus von Knobelsdorff (1699-1753), architect.

| **1974, Feb. 15** | **Engr.** | **Perf. 14** | |
|---|---|---|---|
| 9N344 A79 | 20pf chocolate | .45 | .30 |

275th anniversary of the birth of Georg Wenzelslaus von Knobelsdorff (1699-1753), architect.

| **1974, Feb. 15** | **Litho. & Engr.** | | |
|---|---|---|---|
| 9N345 A80 | 30pf gray & dk grn | .35 | .35 |

Sesquicentennial of the birth of Gustav Robert Kirchhoff (1824-1887), physicist.

Airlift Memorial, Allied Flags — A81

| **1974, Apr. 17** | **Photo.** | **Perf. 14** | |
|---|---|---|---|
| 9N346 A81 | 90pf multicolored | 2.25 | 1.50 |

End of the Allied airlift into Berlin, 25th anniv.

Adolf Slaby and Waves — A82

| **1974, Apr. 17** | **Litho.** | **Perf. 14** | |
|---|---|---|---|
| 9N347 A82 | 40pf black & red | .55 | .40 |

125th anniversary of the birth of Adolf Slaby (1849-1913), radio pioneer.

School Seal Showing Athena and Hermes — A83

| **1974, July 13** | **Photo.** | **Perf. 14** | |
|---|---|---|---|
| 9N348 A83 | 50pf multicolored | .70 | .45 |

400th anniversary of the Gray Brothers' School, a secondary Franciscan school.
0

Berlin-Tegel Airport — A84

**Lithographed and Engraved**
| **1974, Oct. 15** | | **Perf. 14** | |
|---|---|---|---|
| 9N349 A84 | 50pf multicolored | 1.00 | .60 |

Opening of Berlin-Tegel Airport and Terminal, Nov. 1, 1974.

Venus, by F. E. Meyer, c. 1775 — A85    Gottfried Schadow — A86

Berlin Porcelain: 40pf, "Astronomy," by W. C. Meyer, c. 1772. 50pf, "Justice," by J. G. Müller, c. 1785.

| **1974, Oct. 29** | **Litho.** | **Perf. 14** | |
|---|---|---|---|
| 9N350 A85 | 30pf carmine & multi | .55 | .45 |
| 9N351 A85 | 40pf carmine & multi | .60 | .55 |
| 9N352 A85 | 50pf carmine & multi | .70 | .70 |
| | *Nos. 9N350-9N352 (3)* | 1.85 | 1.70 |

| **1975, Jan. 15** | **Engr.** | **Perf. 14** | |
|---|---|---|---|
| 9N353 A86 | 50pf maroon | .75 | .55 |

Johann Gottfried Schadow (1764-1850), sculptor.

S.S. Princess Charlotte A87

Ships: 40pf, S.S. Siegfried. 50pf, S.S. Sperber. 60pf, M.S. Vaterland. 70pf, M.S. Moby Dick.

| **1975, Feb. 14** | **Litho.** | **Perf. 14** | |
|---|---|---|---|
| 9N354 A87 | 30pf gray & multi | .60 | .30 |
| 9N355 A87 | 40pf olive & multi | .60 | .30 |
| 9N356 A87 | 50pf ultra & multi | 1.10 | .30 |
| 9N357 A87 | 60pf red brn & multi | 1.10 | .70 |
| 9N358 A87 | 70pf dk blue & multi | 1.50 | 1.40 |
| | *Nos. 9N354-9N358 (5)* | 4.90 | 3.40 |

Berlin passenger ships

### Industry Type of Germany

| **1975-82** | **Engr.** | **Perf. 14** | | |
|---|---|---|---|---|
| | **Design A380** | | | |
| 9N359 | 5pf Symphonie satellite | | .20 | .20 |
| 9N360 | 10pf Electric train | | .20 | .20 |
| 9N361 | 20pf Old Weser lighthouse | | .20 | .20 |
| 9N362 | 30pf Rescue helicopter | | .35 | .20 |
| 9N363 | 40pf Space shuttle | | .50 | .25 |
| 9N364 | 50pf Radar station | | .50 | .20 |
| 9N365 | 60pf X-ray machine | | .80 | .35 |
| 9N366 | 70pf Shipbuilding | | .90 | .45 |
| 9N367 | 80pf Tractor | | .90 | .25 |
| 9N368 | 100pf Coal excavator | | .90 | .45 |
| 9N368A | 110pf TV camera | | 1.40 | 1.10 |
| 9N369 | 120pf Chemical plant | | 1.25 | .90 |
| 9N369A | 130pf Brewery | | 2.25 | 1.10 |
| 9N370 | 140pf Heating plant | | 1.25 | 1.25 |
| 9N371 | 150pf Power shovel | | 3.00 | 1.10 |
| 9N372 | 160pf Blast furnace | | 2.90 | 1.25 |
| 9N373 | 180pf Payloader | | 3.00 | 1.90 |
| 9N373A | 190pf As #9N371 | | 3.00 | 2.10 |
| 9N374 | 200pf Oil drill platform | | 1.60 | .45 |
| 9N375 | 230pf Frankfurt airport | | 2.40 | 1.90 |
| 9N375A | 250pf Airport | | 4.00 | 2.10 |
| 9N375B | 300pf Electric railroad | | 4.00 | 2.10 |
| 9N376 | 500pf Radio telescope | | 5.75 | 3.75 |
| | *Nos. 9N359-9N376 (23)* | | 41.25 | 23.75 |

Issued: 40, 50, 100pf, 5/15; 10, 30, 70pf, 8/14; 80, 120, 160pf, 10/15; 5, 140, 200pf, 11/14; 20, 500pf, 2/17/76; 60pf, 11/16/78; 230pf, 5/17/79; 150, 180pf, 7/12/79; 110, 130, 300pf, 6/16/82; 190, 250pf, 7/15/82.

Ferdinand Sauerbruch — A88

**Lithographed and Engraved**
**1975, May 15          Perf. 13½x14**
**9N379** A88 50pf dull red & dk brn    .75    .55
Ferdinand Sauerbruch (1875-1951) surgeon, birth centenary.

Gymnasts' Emblem — A89

**1975, May 15     Photo.     Perf. 14**
**9N380** A89 40pf green, gold & blk    .55    .35
6th Gymnaestrada, Berlin, July 1-5.

Lovis Corinth (1858-1925), Self-portrait, 1900 — A90

**1975, July 15     Photo.     Perf. 14**
**9N381** A90 50pf multicolored    .75    .55

Architecture Type of Germany
Houses, Naunynstrasse, Berlin-Kreuzberg.

**1975, July 15     Litho. & Engr.**
**9N382** A381 50pf multicolored    .75    .60
European Architectural Heritage Year.

Paul Löbe and Reichstag A92

**1975, Nov. 14     Engr.     Perf. 14**
**9N383** A92 50pf copper red    .75    .55
Paul Löbe (1875-1967), president of German Parliament 1920-1932, birth centenary.

Grain — A93

**1976, Jan. 5     Photo.     Perf. 14**
**9N384** A93 70pf green & yellow    .75    .60
Green Week International Agricultural Exhibition, Berlin, 50th anniversary.

Hockey A94

**1976, May 13     Engr.     Perf. 14**
**9N385** A94 30pf green    .70    .35
Women's World Hockey Championships.

Treble Clef — A95

**1976, May 13          Photo.**
**9N386** A95 40pf multicolored    .75    .45
German Choir Festival.

Berlin Fire Brigade Emblem — A96

**1976, May 13          Litho.**
**9N387** A96 50pf red & multi    1.25    .75
Berlin Fire Brigade, 125th anniversary.

Sailboat on Havel River — A97

Berlin Views: 40pf, Spandau Castle. 50pf, Tiergarten.

**1976, Nov. 16     Engr.     Perf. 14**
**9N388** A97 30pf blue & blk    .55    .35
**9N389** A97 40pf brown & blk    .75    .35
**9N390** A97 50pf green & blk    .85    .35
    Nos. 9N388-9N390 (3)    2.15    1.05
See Nos. 9N422-9N424.

Castle Type of Germany
**1977-79     Typo.     Perf. 14**
10pf, Glücksburg. 20pf, 190pf, Pfaueninsel. 25pf, Gemen. 30pf, Ludwigstein. 40pf, Eltz. 50pf, Neuschwanstein. 60pf, Marksburg. 70pf, Mespelbrunn. 90pf, Vischering. 200pf, Bürresheim. 210pf, Schwanenburg. 230pf, Lichtenberg.

**9N391** A406  10pf gray blue    .20    .20
  a.  Bklt. pane, 4 #9N391, 2
    each #9N394, 9N396    8.00    10.50
  b.  Bklt. pane, 4 #9N391, 2
    #9N394, 2 #9N440    4.00    6.75
  c.  Bklt. pane, 4 #9N391, 2
    #9N440, 2 #9N442    8.75    15.00
  d.  Bklt. pane, 2 each
    #9N391, 9N394, 9N440-
    9N441    15.00    22.50
**9N392** A406  20pf orange    .20    .20
**9N393** A406  25pf crimson    .35    .35
**9N394** A406  30pf olive    .25    .20
**9N395** A406  40pf blue green    .30    .20
**9N396** A406  50pf rose car    .55    .25
**9N397** A406  60pf brown    .95    .45
**9N398** A406  70pf blue    .95    .45
**9N399** A406  90pf dark blue    .85    .75
**9N400** A406  190pf red brown    1.40    1.40
**9N401** A406  200pf green    1.40    1.40
**9N402** A406  210pf red brown    2.00    1.50
**9N403** A406  230pf dark green    2.00    1.50
    Nos. 9N391-9N403 (13)    11.40    8.85

Issued in sheets of 100 and coils. Every fifth coil stamp has a control number on the back.
Issued: 60pf, 200pf, 1/13; 40pf, 190pf, 2/16; 10pf, 20pf, 30pf, 4/14; 50pf, 70pf, 5/17; 230pf, 11/16/78; 25pf, 90pf, 1/11/79; 210pf, 2/14/79.
See Nos. 9N438-9N445.

Eugenie d'Alton, by Rausch — A98

**1977, Jan. 13     Photo.     Perf. 14**
**9N404** A98 50pf violet black    .75    .55
Christian Daniel Rausch (1777-1857), sculptor, birth bicentenary.

Eduard Gaertner (1801-77), Painter — A99

**1977, Feb. 16          Litho. & Engr.**
**9N405** A99 40pf lt grn, grn & blk    .55    .35

Fountain, by Georg Kolbe — A100

**1977, Apr. 14     Photo.     Perf. 14**
**9N406** A100 30pf dark olive    .55    .35
Georg Kolbe (1877-1947), sculptor.

"Bear each other's burdens" A101

**1977, May 17     Litho.     Perf. 14**
**9N407** A101 40pf green blk & yel    .55    .35
17th meeting of German Protestants (Evangelical Synod), Berlin.

Patent Office, Berlin-Kreuzberg — A102

**1977, July 13          Litho. & Engr.**
**9N408** A102 60pf gray & red    1.50    .65
Centenary of German patent laws.

Telephones, 1905 and 1977 A103

Painting by George Grosz (1893-1959) A104

**1977, July 13          Litho.**
**9N409** A103 50pf multicolored    1.75    1.00
International Broadcasting Exhibition, Berlin, Aug. 26-Sept. 4, and centenary of telephone in Germany.

**1977, July 13**
**9N410** A104 70pf multicolored    .90    .90
15th European Art Exhibition, Berlin, Aug. 14-Oct. 16.

Rhinecanthus Aculeatus — A105

Designs: 30pf, Paddlefish. 40pf, Tortoise. 50pf, Rhinoceros iguana. Designs include statue of iguanodon from Aquarium entrance.

**1977, Aug. 16     Photo.     Perf. 14**
**9N411** A105 20pf multicolored    .45    .45
**9N412** A105 30pf multicolored    .70    .60
**9N413** A105 40pf multicolored    .95    .75
**9N414** A105 50pf multicolored    1.40    .90
    Nos. 9N411-9N414 (4)    3.50    2.70
25th anniv. of the reopening of Berlin Aquarium.

Walter Kollo (1878-1940), Composer — A106

**1978, Jan. 12     Engr.     Perf. 14**
**9N415** A106 50pf brn, red & dk brn    1.00    .65

Chamber of Commerce Emblem — A107

**1978, Apr. 13     Engr.     Perf. 14**
**9N416** A107 90pf dk blue & red    1.25    1.25
American Chamber of Commerce in Germany, 75th anniversary.

Albrecht von Graefe — A108

**1978, May 22     Engr.     Perf. 14**
**9N417** A108 30pf red brn & blk    .55    .35
Dr. von Graefe (1828-70) ophthalmologist.

Friedrich Ludwig Jahn — A109

**1978, July 13     Engr.     Perf. 14**
**9N418** A109 50pf dk carmine    .75    .55
Friedrich Ludwig Jahn (1778-1852), founder of organized gymnastics.

Swimmers — A110

**1978, Aug. 17    Litho.    Perf. 14**
9N419 A110 40pf multicolored    1.00    .80
3rd World Swimming Championships, Berlin, Aug. 18-28.

The Boat, by Karl Hofer — A111

**1978, Oct. 12    Photo.    Perf. 14**
9N420 A111 50pf multicolored    .75    .60
Karl Hofer (1878-1955), painter.

National
Library
A112

**1978, Nov. 16    Engr.    Perf. 14**
9N421 A112 90pf red & olive    1.40    .95
Opening of new National Library building.

Views Type of 1976

Berlin Views: 40pf, Belvedere, Charlottenburg Castle. 50pf, Shell House on Landwehr Canal. 60pf, Village Church, Alt-Lichtenrade.

**1978, Nov. 16**
9N422 A97 40pf green & blk    .60    .35
9N423 A97 50pf lilac & blk    .75    .60
9N424 A97 60pf brown & blk    .90    .70
Nos. 9N422-9N424 (3)    2.25 1.65

International
Conference
Center — A113

**Photogravure and Engraved**
**1979, Feb. 14    Perf. 14**
9N425 A113 60pf multicolored    1.10    .65
Opening of Intl. Conference Center in Berlin.

A114    A115

**1979, May 17    Litho.    Perf. 14**
9N426 A114 60pf German eagles 1.40 1.00
Cent. of German Natl. Printing Bureau.

**1979, July 12    Photo.    Perf. 14**
9N427 A115 60pf TV screen, emblem    1.00    .75
Intl. Broadcasting Exhibition, Berlin.

Target
and
Arrows
A116

**1979, July 12**
9N428 A116 50pf multicolored    .75    .55
World Archery Championships, Berlin.

Moses
Mendelssohn
A117

**1979, Aug. 9    Engr.    Perf. 14**
9N429 A117 90pf black    1.25    .75
Mendelssohn (1729-86), philosopher.

Gas
Lamp — A118

Historic Street Lanterns: 40pf, Carbon arc lamp. 50pf, Hanging gas lamps. 60pf, 5-armed candelabra.

**1979, Aug. 9    Litho.**
9N430 A118 10pf multicolored    .35    .20
9N431 A118 40pf multicolored    .75    .60
9N432 A118 50pf multicolored    1.10    .60
9N433 A118 60pf multicolored    1.10 1.00
Nos. 9N430-9N433 (4)    3.30 2.40
300 years of street lighting in Berlin.

Orchid
A119

**1979, Aug. 9**
9N434 A119 50pf multicolored    .85    .55
Botanical Gardens, Berlin, 300th anniv.

Berlin Poster
Columns, 125th
Anniversary
A120

**Lithographed and Engraved**
**1979, Nov. 14    Perf. 14**
9N435 A120 50pf multicolored    1.40    .75

Castle Type of Germany

**1979-82    Typo.    Perf. 14**
9N438 A406 35pf Lichtenstein    .30    .30
9N439 A406 40pf Wolfsburg    .55    .30
9N440 A406 50pf Inzlingen    .60    .30
9N441 A406 60pf Rheydt    .90    .45
9N442 A406 80pf Wilhelmsthal    .60    .30
9N443 A406 120pf Charlottenburg    1.00    .90
9N444 A406 280pf Ahrensburg    3.50 2.25
9N445 A406 300pf Herrenhausen    3.50 2.25
Nos. 9N438-9N445 (8)    10.95 7.05

Issued: 60pf, 11/14; 40pf, 50pf, 2/14/80; 35pf, 80pf, 30pf, 6/16/82; 120pf, 280pf, 7/15/82.

World Map
Showing
Continental
Drift — A121

**1980, Feb. 14    Litho.    Perf. 14**
9N451 A121 60pf multicolored    1.40 1.00
Alfred Wegener (1880-1930), geophysicist and meteorologist; founded theory of continental drift.

German Catholics
Day — A122

Cardinal Count Preysing (1880-1950).

**1980, May 8    Engr.    Perf. 14**
9N452 A122 50pf blk & car rose    .75    .55

Prussian
Museum,
Berlin, 150th
Anniv. — A123

Designs: 40pf, Angel, enamel medallion, 12th cent. 60pf, Monks Reading, oak sculpture, by Ernest Barlach (1870-1938).

**1980, July 10    Litho.    Perf. 14**
9N453 A123 40pf multicolored    .75    .45
9N454 A123 60pf multicolored    1.00    .60

Von Steuben
Leading
Troops — A124

**1980, Aug. 14    Litho.    Perf. 14**
9N455 A124 40pf multicolored    1.00    .55
Friedrich Wilhelm von Steuben (1730-94).

Robert Stolz
(1880-1975),
Composer
A125

**1980, Aug. 14**
9N456 A125 60pf dk blue & bis    1.00    .75

Lilienthal
Memorial — A126

Designs: 50pf, Grosse Neugierde Memorial, 1835. 60pf, Lookout tower, Grunewald Memorial to Kaiser Wilhelm I.

**1980, Nov. 13    Engr.    Perf. 14**
9N457 A126 40pf dk green & blk    .75    .35
9N458 A126 50pf brown & blk    .80    .75
9N459 A126 60pf dk blue & blk    1.25    .75
Nos. 9N457-9N459 (3)    2.80 1.85

Von Gontard and Kleist Park
Colonnades, Berlin — A127

**1981, Jan. 15    Litho.    Perf. 14**
9N460 A127 50pf multicolored    .90    .60
Karl Philipp von Gontard (1731-91), architect.

Achim von Arnim
(1781-1831),
Poet — A128

**1981, Jan. 15    Engr.**
9N461 A128 60pf dark green    .90    .60

Adelbert von
Chamisso (1781-
1838),
Poet — A129

**1981, Jan. 15    Litho.**
9N462 A129 60pf brn & gldn brn    .90    .60

Berlin-Kreuzberg,
Liberation
Monument,
1813 — A130

**1981, Feb. 12    Engr.    Perf. 14**
9N463 A130 40pf brown    1.10    .75
Karl Friedrich Schinkel (1781-1841), architect, 400th anniversary of birth.

Arts and Science
Medal, Awarded
1842-1933 — A131

**1981, July 16    Litho.    Perf. 14**
9N464 A131 40pf multicolored    .75    .55
"Prussia—an attempt at a balance" exhibition.

Amor and
Psyche, by
Reinhold Begas
(1831-1911)
A132

**1981, July 16    Photo.**
9N465 A132 50pf multicolored    .75    .55

186 GERMAN OCCUPATION STAMPS

Intl. Telecommunications
Exhibition — A133

**1981, July 16**       **Litho.**
9N466 A133 60pf multicolored   1.25   .75

Peter Beuth (1781-
1853),
Constitutional Law
Expert — A134

**Lithographed and Engraved**
**1981, Nov. 12**      **Perf. 14**
9N467 A134 60pf gold & black   .75   .60

Nijinsky, by Georg
Kolbe,
1914 — A135

20th Century Sculptures: 60pf, Mother
Earth II, by Ernst Barlach, 1920. 90pf, Flora
Kneeling, by Richard Scheibe, 1930.

**1981, Nov. 12**      **Photo.**
9N468 A135 40pf multicolored   .55   .35
9N469 A135 60pf multicolored   .90   .60
9N470 A135 90pf multicolored   1.25 1.00
   *Nos. 9N468-9N470 (3)*   2.70 1.95

750th
Anniv. of
Spandau
A136

**Lithographed and Engraved**
**1982, Feb. 18**      **Perf. 14**
9N471 A136 60pf multicolored   1.25   .90

Berlin Philharmonic
Centenary — A137

**Lithographed and Embossed**
**1982, Apr. 15**      **Perf. 14**
9N472 A137 60pf multicolored   1.10   .60

Salzburg
Emigration to
Prussia, 250th
Anniv. — A138

**& 1982, May 5**      **Litho.**   **Engr.**
9N473 A138 50pf multicolored   .75   .55

Italian Stone Carriers, by Max
Pechstein — A139

80pf, Two Girls Bathing, by Otto Mueller.

**1982, July 15**     **Litho.**    **Perf. 14**
9N474 A139 50pf multicolored   .90   .70
9N475 A139 80pf multicolored   1.40 1.00

Villa Borsig — A140

**1982, Nov. 10**    **Engr.**    **Perf. 14**
9N476 A140 50pf shown   1.10   .70
9N477 A140 60pf Sts. Peter and
     Paul Church   1.10   .80
9N478 A140 80pf Villa von der
     Heydt   1.50   .90
   *Nos. 9N476-9N478 (3)*   3.70 2.40

State Theater, Charlottenburg,
1790 — A141

**1982, Nov. 10**     **Litho. & Engr.**
9N479 A141 80pf multicolored   1.60 1.10
Carl Gotthard Langhans (1732-1808),
architect.

A142          A142a

Various street pumps and fire hydrants,
1900.

**1983, Jan. 13**    **Litho.**    **Perf. 14**
9N480 A142 50pf multi   1.10   .75
9N481 A142 60pf multi   1.40   .75
9N482 A142 80pf multi   1.60 1.25
9N483 A142 120pf multi   2.25 2.00
   *Nos. 9N480-9N483 (4)*   6.35 4.75

**1983, Feb. 8**    **Engr.**    **Perf. 14**
9N484 A142a 80pf dark brown   1.75 1.40
Berlin-Koblenz Telegraph Service
sesquicentennial.

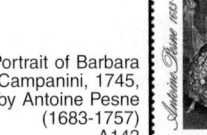

Portrait of Barbara
Campanini, 1745,
by Antoine Pesne
(1683-1757)
A143

**1983, May 5**    **Photo.**    **Perf. 14**
9N485 A143 50pf multicolored   .90   .65

Joachim Ringelnatz
(1883-1934),
Painter and
Writer — A144

**1983, July 14**    **Litho.**    **Perf. 14**
9N486 A144 50pf Silhouette   1.00   .75

Intl. Radio Exhibition, Sept. 2-
11 — A145

**1983, July 14**
9N487 A145 80pf Nipkow's pho-
     totelegraphy
     diagram   1.60 1.25

Ancient
Artwork, Berlin
Museum
A146

30pf, Bust of Queen Cleopatra VII, 69-30
B.C. 50pf, Statue of Egyptian Couple, Giza,
2400 B.C. 60pf, Stone God with Beaded Turban, Mexico, 300 B.C. 80pf, Enamel Plate,
16th cent.

**1984, Jan. 12**    **Litho.**    **Perf. 14**
9N488 A146 30pf multicolored   1.00   .75
9N489 A146 50pf multicolored   1.40 1.00
9N490 A146 60pf multicolored   1.75 1.40
9N491 A146 80pf multicolored   2.25 1.60
   *Nos. 9N488-9N491 (4)*   6.40 4.75

Electricity
Centenary — A147

Design: Allegorical figure holding light bulb
(symbol of electric power).

**1984, May 8**    **Litho.**    **Perf. 14**
9N492 A147 50pf black & org   .90   .65

Conference
Emblem — A148

**1984, May 8**
9N493 A148 60pf multicolored   1.10   .75
European Ministers of Culture, 4th Conf.

Erich Klausener
(1885-1934),
Chairman of
Catholic
Action — A149

**1984, May 8**   **Engr.**   **Perf. 14x13½**
9N494 A149 80pf dark green   1.10   .75

Alfred Brehm (1829-1884),
Zoologist — A150

**Lithographed and Engraved**
**1984, Apr. 18**      **Perf. 14**
9N495 A150 80pf Brehm, white
     stork   1.90 1.25

Ernst Ludwig Heim
(1747-1834),
Botanist — A151

**1984, Aug. 21**   **Engr.**    **Perf. 14**
9N496 A151 50pf brown & blk   1.10   .75

Sunflowers, by Karl
Schmidt-Rottluff
(1884-1976)
A152

**1984, Nov. 8**    **Litho.**    **Perf. 14**
9N497 A152 60pf multi   1.10   .75

Bettina von Arnim
(1785-1859),
Writer — A153

**1985, Feb. 21**     **Litho. & Engr.**
9N498 A153 50pf multicolored   1.00   .80

Wilhelm von
Humboldt
(1767-1835),
Statesman
A154

**1985, Feb. 21**       **Engr.**
9N499 A154 80pf blue, blk & red   1.50 1.25

1985 Berlin
Horticultural
Show — A155

**1985, Apr. 16**    **Litho.**    **Perf. 14**
9N500 A155 80pf Symbolic flower   1.40 1.10

Berlin
Bourse,
300th
Anniv.
A156

**1985, May 7**     **Litho. & Engr.**
9N501 A156 50pf multicolored   1.10   .80

Otto Klemperer (1885-1973),
Conductor — A157

**1985, May 7**       **Engr.**
9N502 A157 60pf dp blue violet   1.40 1.10

Telefunken Camera, 1936 — A158

**1985, July 16    Litho.    Perf. 14**
9N503 A158 80pf multicolored    1.90  1.50

German Television, 50th anniv., Intl. Telecommunications Exhibition, Berlin.

9th World
Gynecological
Congress — A159

Design: Emblem of the Intl. Federation for
Gynecology and birth aid.

**1985, July 16    Photo.    Perf. 13½x14**
9N504 A159 60pf pale yel, ap grn
& dp grn    1.10  .80

Edict of
Potsdam,
300th
Anniv.
A160

**Lithographed and Engraved**
**1985, Oct. 15    Perf. 14**
9N505 A160 50pf dk bluish lilac    .90  .70

Kurt Tucholsky
(1890-1935),
Novelist,
Journalist — A161

**1985, Nov. 12    Litho.    Perf. 14**
9N506 A161 80pf multi    1.75  1.10

Wilhelm Furtwangler (1886-1954),
Composer — A162

Score from Sonata in D Sharp.

**Lithographed and Engraved**
**1986, Jan. 16    Perf. 14**
9N507 A162 80pf multi    1.90  1.60

Ludwig Mies van der Rohe (1886-
1969), Architect — A163

**1986, Feb. 13**
9N508 A163 50pf multi    1.10  1.25

New Natl. Gallery, Berlin.

16th European Communities
Day — A164

**1986, Apr. 10    Litho.    Perf. 14**
9N509 A164 60pf Flags    .95  1.00

Leopold von         Gottfried Benn
Ranke (1795-        (1886-1956),
1886),              Writer and
Historian — A165    Physician — A166

**1986, May 5    Litho.**
9N510 A165 80pf brn blk & tan    1.75  1.40
**Engr.**
9N511 A166 80pf brt blue    1.75  1.40

Portals and
Gateways
A167

**1986, June 20    Litho. & Engr.**
9N512 A167 50pf Charlottenburg
Gate    1.50  1.25
9N513 A167 60pf Gryphon Gate,
Glienicke Cas-
tle    1.50  1.25
9N514 A167 80pf Elephant Gate,
Berlin Zoo    1.75  1.75
Nos. 9N512-9N514 (3)    4.75  4.25

King Frederick
the
Great — A168

Painting: The Flute Concert (detail), by
Adolph von Menzel.

**1986, Aug. 14    Litho.    Perf. 14**
9N515 A168 80pf multicolored    1.75  1.40

**Famous Women Type of Germany**

Designs: 5pf, Emma Ihrer (1857-1911), politician, labor leader. 10pf, Paula Modersohn-
Becker (1876-1907), painter. 20pf, Cilly Aussem (1909-63), tennis champion. 40pf, Maria
Sibylla Merian. 50pf, Christine Teusch. 60pf,
Dorothea Erxleben (1715-62), physician. 80pf,
Clara Schumann. 100pf, Therese Giehse
(1898-1975), actress. 130pf, Lise Meitner
(1878-1968), physicist. 140pf, Cecile Vogt
(1875-1962), neurologist. 170pf, Hannah
Arendt (1906-75), American political scientist.
180pf, Lotte Lehmann (1888-1976), soprano.
240pf, Mathilde Franziska Anneke, (1817-84),
American author. 250pf, Queen Louise of
Prussia (1776-1810). 300pf, Fanny Hensel
(1805-1847), composer-conductor. 350pf,
Hedwig Dransfeld (1871-1925), women's
rights activist. 500pf, Alice Salomon (1872-
1948), feminist and social activist.

**1986-89    Engr.    Perf. 14**
**Type A602**
9N516    5pf bluish gray &
org brn    .35  1.50
9N517    10pf vio & yel brn    .35  1.40
9N518    20pf lake & Prus bl    1.50  3.75
9N519    40pf dp bl & dk lil
rose    1.25  3.75
9N520    50pf gray ol & Prus
bl    1.90  2.50
9N521    60pf dp vio &
grnsh blk    .75  3.75
9N522    80pf dk grn & lt red
brn    1.10  2.25
9N523    100pf dk red &
grnsh blk    1.50  1.50

9N524    130pf Prus bl & dk
vio    3.50  11.00
9N525    140pf blk & dk ol bis    3.75  11.00
9N526    170pf gray grn & dk
brn    2.25  9.00
9N527    180pf bl & brn vio    3.50  11.00
9N528    240pf Prus bl & yel
brn    3.00  13.00
9N529    250pf dp lil rose &
dp bl    7.25  19.00
9N530    300pf dk vio & sage
grn    7.50  19.00
9N531    350pf gray grn &
lake    5.25  15.00
9N532    500pf slate grn & brt
ver    8.25  32.50
Nos. 9N516-9N532 (17)    52.95  160.90

Issued: 50pf, 80pf, 11/1/86; 40pf, 9/17/87;
10pf, 4/4/88; 20pf, 130pf, 5/5/88; 60pf, 100pf,
170pf, 240pf, 350pf, 11/10/88; 500pf, 1/12/89;
5pf, 2/9/89; 180pf, 250pf, 7/13/89; 140pf,
300pf, 8/10/89.

**Berlin 750th Anniv. Type of Germany**

Designs: a, Berlin, 1650, engraving by Caspar Merian. b, Charlottenburg Castle, c. 1830.
c, AEG Company turbine construction building, by architect Walter Behrens, 1909. d, Philharmonic Concert Hall and Chamber Music
Rooms on the Kemperplatz, 1987.

**1987, Jan. 15    Litho.    Perf. 14**
9N536 A604 80pf like #1496    1.90  1.50

**Souvenir Sheet**
**Perf. 14x14½**
9N537    Sheet of 4    4.25  4.25
a.    A604 40pf multicolored    .90  .75
b.    A604 50pf multicolored    .90  .75
c.    A604 60pf multicolored    .90  .90
d.    A604 80pf multicolored    1.00  1.25

No. 9N537 contains four 43x25mm stamps.

Louise Schroeder
(1887-1957),
Politican — A169

**1987, Feb. 12    Engr.    Perf. 14**
9N538 A169 50pf sep & dk red    1.10  1.10

Settlement of
Bohemians at
Rixdorf, 250th
Anniv. — A170

Bohemian refugees, bas-relief detail from
monument to King Friedrich Wilhelm I of Prussia, 1912.

**1987, May 5    Litho. & Engr.**
9N539 A170 50pf sep & pale
gray grn    .80  .90

1987 Intl. Architecture
Exhibition — A171

**1987, May 5    Litho.    Perf. 14x14½**
9N540 A171 80pf lt ultra, sil & blk  1.40 1.10

14th Int'l. Botanical
Congress — A172

**1987, July 16    Litho.    Perf. 14**
9N541 A172 60pf multicolored    .90  1.00

Int'l.
Radio
Exhibition
A173

**1987, Aug. 20**
9N542 A173 80pf Gramophone,
compact disc    1.25  .95

**Historic Sites and Objects Type of
Germany**

Designs: 5pf, Brunswick Lion. 10pf, Frankfurt Airport. 20pf, No. 9N550, Queen Nefertiti,
bust, Egyptian Museum, Berlin. 30pf, Corner
tower, Celle Castle, 14th cent. 40pf, Chile
House, Hamburg. 50pf, Filigree tracery on
spires, Freiburg Cathedral. 60pf, Bavaria
Munich, bronze statue above the Theresienwiese, Hall of Fame. No. 9N551, Heligoland. 80pf, Entrance to Zollern II, coal mine,
Dortmund. 100pf, Altotting Chapel, Bavaria.
120pf, Schleswig Cathedral. 140pf, Bronze
flagon from Reinheim. 300pf, Hambach Castle. 350pf, Externsteine Bridge near Horn-Bad
Meinberg.

**1987-90    Typo.    Perf. 14**
**Type A623**
9N543    5pf Prus bl & gray    .30  .45
9N544    10pf lt chalky bl &
slate bl    .35  .35
9N545    20pf dull blue & tan    .35  .75
9N546    30pf aqua & org brn    .95  .95
9N547    40pf ultra, dk red
brn & org red    1.25  2.10
9N548    50pf ultra & yel brn    1.50  1.10
9N549    60pf cob & pale gray    1.50  1.10
9N550    70pf dull bl & fawn    1.50  2.50
9N551    70pf vio bl & henna
brn    2.10  4.50
9N552    80pf cob & pale gray    1.50  1.10
a.    Bkt. pane of 8 (4 10pf, 2
50pf, 2 80pf) ('89)    22.50  52.50
9N553    100pf brt bluish grn &
olive bis    1.10  1.50
a.    Bkt. pane of 8 (2 each 10pf,
60pf, 80pf, 100pf)    45.00  90.00
9N554    120pf brn org & lt
grnsh bl    2.25  3.50
9N555    140pf tan & lt grn    2.25  4.25
9N556    300pf dk red brn &
tan    4.50  4.50
9N557    350pf brt ultra & ol
bis    4.50  7.50
Nos. 9N543-9N557 (15)    25.90  36.15

Issued: 30pf, 50pf, 60pf, 80pf, 11/6/87; 10pf,
300pf, 1/14/88; #9N550, 120pf, 7/14/88; 20pf,
140pf, 1/12/89; 100pf, 350pf, 2/9/89; 5pf,
2/15/90; #9N551, 6/21/90.

European
Culture — A175

**1988, Jan. 14    Litho.    Perf. 14**
9N568 A175 80pf Berlin Bear    1.90  1.90

Urania
Science
Museum,
Cent.
A176

**1988, Feb. 18**
9N569 A176 50pf multicolored    1.40  1.25

A177

Design: Thoroughbred Foal, bronze sculpture by Renee Sintenis (1888-1965).

**1988, Feb. 18**
9N570 A177 60pf multicolored    .90  .90

Design: The Great Elector with Family in Berlin Castle Gardens.

**1988, May 5　　　Litho. & Engr.**
9N571　A178　50pf multicolored　　1.10　1.10
The Great Elector of Brandenburg (d. 1688).

Intl. Monetary Fund and World Bank Congress, Berlin — A179

**1988, Aug. 11　　　　　Litho.**
9N572　A179　70pf multicolored　　1.10　1.00

Berlin-Potsdam Railway, 150th Anniv. — A180

**1988, Oct. 13　　　　　Litho.**
9N573　A180　10pf multicolored　　.65　.45

The Collector, 1913, by Ernst Barlach (1870-1938) A181

**1988, Oct. 13**
9N574　A181　40pf multicolored　　.70　.55

Berlin Airlift, 40th Anniv. — A182

**1989, May 5　　Photo.　　Perf. 14**
9N575　A182　60pf multicolored　　1.10　1.25

13th Intl. Congress of the Supreme Audit Office, Berlin A183

**1989, May 5　　　　　Litho.**
9N576　A183　80pf multicolored　　1.40　1.40

Ernst Reuter (1889-1953), Mayor of Berlin — A184

---

**Litho. & Engr.**
**1989, July 13　　　　Perf. 14x14½**
9N577　A184　100pf multicolored　　1.90　1.60

Intl. Radio Exhibition, Berlin — A185

**1989, July 13　　　　　Litho.**
9N578　A185　100pf multicolored　　1.60　1.50

Plans of the Zoological Gardens, Berlin, and Designer Peter Joseph Lenne (1789-1866) — A186

**Litho. & Engr.**
**1989, Aug. 10　　　　　Perf. 14**
9N579　A186　60pf multicolored　　1.50　1.25

Carl von Ossietzky (1889-1938), Awarded Nobel Peace Prize of 1935 — A187

**1989, Aug. 10　　　　　Photo.**
9N580　A187　100pf multicolored　　1.75　1.60

450th Anniv. of the Reformation A188

Design: Nikolai Church, Spandau District.

**1989, Oct. 12　　　　　Litho.**
9N581　A188　60pf multicolored　　.95　.85

French Gymnasium, 300th Anniv. — A189

School from 1701 to 1873 and frontispiece of *Leges Gymnasie Gallici,* published in 1689.

**1989, Oct. 12　　　Litho. & Engr.**
9N582　A189　40pf multicolored　　.95　.85

*Journalists,* 1925, by Hannah Hoch (1889-1978) — A190

**1989, Oct. 12　　Litho.　　Perf. 13½**
9N583　A190　100pf multicolored　　1.90　1.50

---

**European Postal Service 500th Anniv. Type**
**Litho. & Engr.**
**1990, Jan. 12　　　　　Perf. 14**
9N584　A673　100pf The Young
　　　　　　　Post Rider　　2.50　2.10
　See Austria No. 1486, Belgium No. 1332, Germany No. 1592, and DDR No. 2791.

Public Transportation, 250th Anniv. — A191

**1990, Jan. 12　　　　　Litho.**
9N585　A191　60pf multicolored　　1.90　1.50

Ernst Rudorff (1840-1916), Conservationist — A192

**1990, Jan. 12**
9N586　A192　60pf multicolored　　1.90　1.50

People's Free Theater Organization, Cent. — A193

**1990, Feb. 15　　　　　Perf. 13½**
9N587　A193　100pf multicolored　　2.00　1.90

Parliament House, 40th Anniv. — A194

**1990, Feb. 15　　　　Perf. 14x14½**
9N588　A194　100pf multicolored　　2.75　1.90

Bicent. of the Invention of the Barrel Organ — A195

**1990, May 3　　Litho.　　Perf. 14**
9N589　A195　100pf multicolored　　2.00　1.75

90th German Catholics Day — A196

**1990, May 3**
9N590　A196　60pf multicolored　　1.75　1.60

---

German Pharmaceutical Society, Cent. — A197

**1990, Aug. 9　　Litho.　　Perf. 14**
9N591　A197　100pf multicolored　　3.75　3.00

Adolph Diesterweg (1790-1866), Educator — A198

**1990, Sept. 27**
9N592　A198　60pf multicolored　　2.75　2.75

　Stamps for Berlin were discontinued Oct. 3, 1990, when Germany and the German Democratic Republic merged. The stamps remained valid until Dec. 31, 1991.

---

**OCCUPATION SEMI-POSTAL STAMPS**

Offering Plate and Berlin Bear — SP1

**Wmk. 284**
**1949, Dec. 1　　Litho.　　Perf. 14**
9NB1　SP1　10 + 5pf grn　　35.00　160.00
9NB2　SP1　20 + 5pf car　　35.00　160.00
9NB3　SP1　30 + 5pf blue　　37.50　225.00
　a.　Souv. sheet of 3,
　　　#9NB1-9NB3　　500.00　2,100.
　　　Never hinged　　900.00
　Nos. 9NB1-9NB3 (3)　　107.50　545.00
　　　Set, never hinged　　375.00

　The surtax was for Berlin victims of currency devaluation.

Harp and Laurel Branch — SP2　　"Singing Angels" — SP3

**1950, Oct. 29　　Engr.　　Wmk. 116**
9NB4　SP2　10 + 5pf grn　　16.00　35.00
9NB5　SP3　30 + 5pf dk sl bl　　32.50　90.00
　　　Set, never hinged　　140.00

　The surtax was to aid in reestablishing the Berlin Philharmonic Orchestra.

Young Stamp Collectors — SP4　　Kaiser Wilhelm Memorial Church — SP5

**1951, Oct. 7　　　　　Perf. 14**
9NB6　SP4　10 + 3pf grn　　10.50　30.00
9NB7　SP4　20 + 2pf brn red　　13.50　37.50
　　　Set, never hinged　　52.50

　Stamp Day, Berlin, Oct. 7, 1951.

**1953, Aug. 9**       **Wmk. 284**

Design: 20pf+10pf, 30pf+15pf, Ruins of Kaiser Wilhelm Memorial Church.

| | | | |
|---|---|---|---|
| 9NB8 | SP5 4 + 1pf choc | .20 | 15.00 |
| 9NB9 | SP5 10 + 5pf green | .75 | 42.50 |
| 9NB10 | SP5 20 + 10pf car | 1.40 | 42.50 |
| 9NB11 | SP5 30 + 15pf dp bl | 6.00 | 97.50 |
| *Nos. 9NB8-9NB11 (4)* | | 8.35 | 197.50 |
| Set, never hinged | | | 22.50 |

The surtax was to aid in reconstructing the church.

---

**Catalogue values for unused stamps in this section, from this point to the end of the section, are for Never Hinged items.**

---

Prussian Postilion — SP6

Prussian Field Postilion — SP7

**1954, Aug. 4**   **Litho.**   **Wmk. 284**
9NB12 SP6 20 + 10pf multi    15.00  30.00

National Stamp Exhibition, Berlin, Aug. 4-8.

*Perf. 13½x14*

**1955, Oct. 27**       **Wmk. 304**
9NB13 SP7 25 + 10pf multi    6.00  13.50

The surtax was for the benefit of philately.

St. Otto, Bishop of Bamberg — SP8

Statues: 10pf+5pf, St. Hedwig, Duchess of Silesia. 20pf+10pf, St. Peter.

**1955, Nov. 26**   **Engr.**   *Perf. 14*

| | | | |
|---|---|---|---|
| 9NB14 | SP8 7 + 3pf brown | .75 | 2.75 |
| 9NB15 | SP8 10 + 5pf gray grn | 1.40 | 3.00 |
| 9NB16 | SP8 20 + 10pf rose lil | 1.90 | 3.75 |
| *Nos. 9NB14-9NB16 (3)* | | 4.05 | 9.50 |

25th anniv. of the Bishopric of Berlin. The surtax was for the reconstruction of destroyed churches throughout the bishopric.

Bell Type of 1951 Surcharged

*Perf. 13½x14*

**1956, Aug. 9**       **Wmk. 284**
9NB17 OS8 20pf + 10pf citron    2.50  3.00

The surtax was for help for flood victims.

Postrider of Brandenburg, 1700 — SP9

Ludwig Heck — SP10

---

**Wmk. 304**

**1956, Oct. 26**   **Litho.**   *Perf. 14*
9NB18 SP9 25pf + 10pf multi    2.50  3.50

The surtax was for the benefit of philately.

**1957, Sept. 7**   **Engr.**   *Perf. 13½x14*
9NB19 SP10 20pf + 10pf red & dk brn    .75  .90

Dr. Ludwig Heck, zoologist and long-time director of the Berlin Zoo. The surtax was for the Zoo.

Elly Heuss-Knapp and Relaxing Mothers SP11

Boy at Window — SP12

**1957, Nov. 30**       *Perf. 14*
9NB20 SP11 20pf + 10pf dk red    1.40  2.40

The surtax was for welfare work among mothers.

**1960, Sept. 15**   **Litho.**   **Wmk. 304**

Designs: 10pf+5pf, Girl going to school. 20pf+10pf, Girl with flower and mountains. 40pf+20pf, Boy at seashore.

| | | | |
|---|---|---|---|
| 9NB21 | SP12 7pf + 3pf dk brn & brn | .20 | .30 |
| 9NB22 | SP12 10pf + 5pf ol grn & slate grn | .20 | .30 |
| 9NB23 | SP12 20pf + 10pf dk car & brn blk | .55 | .55 |
| 9NB24 | SP12 40pf + 20pf bl & ind | 1.25 | 3.75 |
| *Nos. 9NB21-9NB24 (4)* | | 2.20 | 4.90 |

The surtax was for vacations for the children of Berlin.

---

**Fluorescent Paper was introduced for semipostal stamps, starting with Nos. 9NB25-9NB28.**

---

**Fairy Tale Type of 1960**

Various Scenes from Sleeping Beauty.

**1964, Oct. 6**   **Unwmk.**   *Perf. 14*

| | | | |
|---|---|---|---|
| 9NB25 | SP285 10pf + 5pf multi | .20 | .20 |
| 9NB26 | SP285 15pf + 5pf multi | .20 | .20 |
| 9NB27 | SP285 20pf + 10pf multi | .40 | .20 |
| 9NB28 | SP285 40pf + 20pf multi | .55 | .90 |
| *Nos. 9NB25-9NB28 (4)* | | 1.35 | 1.50 |

The surtax was for independent welfare organizations.

---

**Beginning with 9NB25-9NB28 semipostals are types of Germany inscribed "Berlin" except Nos. 9NB129-9NB131.**

---

**Bird Type of 1965**

Birds: 10pf+5pf, Woodcock. 15pf+5pf, Ringnecked pheasant. 20pf+10pf, Black grouse. 40pf+20pf, Capercaillie.

**1965, Apr. 1**   **Litho.**   *Perf. 14*

| | | | |
|---|---|---|---|
| 9NB29 | SP289 10pf + 5pf multi | .20 | .20 |
| 9NB30 | SP289 15pf + 5pf multi | .20 | .20 |
| 9NB31 | SP289 20pf + 10pf multi | .20 | .20 |
| 9NB32 | SP289 40pf + 20pf multi | .50 | .75 |
| *Nos. 9NB29-9NB32 (4)* | | 1.10 | 1.35 |

Issued for the benefit of young people.

**Fairy Tale Type of 1965**

Various Scenes from Cinderella.

**1965, Oct. 6**   **Litho.**   *Perf. 14*

| | | | |
|---|---|---|---|
| 9NB33 | SP290 10pf + 5pf multi | .20 | .20 |
| 9NB34 | SP290 15pf + 5pf multi | .20 | .20 |
| 9NB35 | SP290 20pf + 10pf multi | .20 | .20 |
| 9NB36 | SP290 40pf + 20pf multi | .50 | .75 |
| *Nos. 9NB33-9NB36 (4)* | | 1.10 | 1.35 |

The surtax was for independent welfare organizations.

---

**Animal Type of 1966**

10pf+5pf, Roe deer. 20pf+10pf, Chamois. 30pf+15pf, Fallow deer. 50pf+25pf, Red deer.

**1966, Apr. 22**   **Litho.**   *Perf. 14*

| | | | |
|---|---|---|---|
| 9NB37 | SP291 10pf + 5pf multi | .20 | .20 |
| 9NB38 | SP291 20pf + 10pf multi | .20 | .20 |
| 9NB39 | SP291 30pf + 15pf multi | .25 | .25 |
| 9NB40 | SP291 50pf + 25pf multi | .55 | .75 |
| *Nos. 9NB37-9NB40 (4)* | | 1.20 | 1.40 |

Issued for the benefit of young people.

**Fairy Tale Type of 1965**

Various Scenes from The Princess and the Frog.

**1966, Oct. 5**   **Litho.**   *Perf. 14*

| | | | |
|---|---|---|---|
| 9NB41 | SP290 10pf + 5pf multi | .20 | .20 |
| 9NB42 | SP290 20pf + 10pf multi | .20 | .20 |
| 9NB43 | SP290 30pf + 15pf multi | .35 | .60 |
| 9NB44 | SP290 50pf + 25pf multi | .45 | .70 |
| *Nos. 9NB41-9NB44 (4)* | | 1.20 | 1.30 |

Surtax for independent welfare organizations.

**Animal Type of 1966**

10pf+5pf, Rabbit. 20pf+10pf, Ermine. 30pf+15pf, Hamster. 50pf+25pf, Red fox.

**1967, Apr. 4**       **Unwmk.**

| | | | |
|---|---|---|---|
| 9NB45 | SP291 10pf + 5pf multi | .20 | .25 |
| 9NB46 | SP291 20pf + 10pf multi | .20 | .25 |
| 9NB47 | SP291 30pf + 15pf multi | .35 | .90 |
| 9NB48 | SP291 50pf + 25pf multi | 1.00 | 1.40 |
| *Nos. 9NB45-9NB48 (4)* | | 1.75 | 2.20 |

Issued for the benefit of young people.

**Fairy Tale Type of 1965**

Various Scenes from Frau Holle.

**1967, Oct. 3**   **Litho.**   *Perf. 14*

| | | | |
|---|---|---|---|
| 9NB49 | SP290 10pf + 5pf multi | .20 | .25 |
| 9NB50 | SP290 20pf + 10pf multi | .20 | .25 |
| 9NB51 | SP290 30pf + 15pf multi | .20 | .35 |
| 9NB52 | SP290 50pf + 25pf multi | .55 | .75 |
| *Nos. 9NB49-9NB52 (4)* | | 1.15 | 1.60 |

The surtax was for independent welfare organizations.

**Animal Type of 1968**

Animals: 10pf+5pf, Wildcat. 20pf+10pf, Otter. 30pf+15pf, Badger. 50pf+25pf, Beaver.

**1968, Feb. 2**   **Photo.**   *Perf. 14*

| | | | |
|---|---|---|---|
| 9NB53 | SP293 10pf + 5pf multi | .25 | .45 |
| 9NB54 | SP293 20pf + 10pf multi | .30 | .45 |
| 9NB55 | SP293 30pf + 15pf multi | .55 | .90 |
| 9NB56 | SP293 50pf + 25pf multi | 1.60 | 2.10 |
| *Nos. 9NB53-9NB56 (4)* | | 2.70 | 3.90 |

Surtax for benefit of young people.

**Doll Type of 1968**

Various 19th century dolls in sitting position.

**1968, Oct. 3**   **Litho.**   *Perf. 14*

| | | | |
|---|---|---|---|
| 9NB57 | SP294 10pf + 5pf multi | .20 | .25 |
| 9NB58 | SP294 20pf + 10pf multi | .20 | .25 |
| 9NB59 | SP294 30pf + 15pf multi | .20 | .35 |
| 9NB60 | SP294 50pf + 25pf multi | .60 | .75 |
| *Nos. 9NB57-9NB60 (4)* | | 1.20 | 1.60 |

The surtax was for independent welfare organizations.

**Horse Type of 1969**

Horses: 10pf+5pf, Pony. 20pf+10pf, Work horse. 30pf+15pf, Hotblood. 50pf+25pf, Thoroughbred.

**1969, Feb. 6**   **Litho.**   *Perf. 14*

| | | | |
|---|---|---|---|
| 9NB61 | SP295 10pf + 5pf multi | .20 | .30 |
| 9NB62 | SP295 20pf + 10pf multi | .30 | .55 |
| 9NB63 | SP295 30pf + 15pf multi | .45 | .75 |
| 9NB64 | SP295 50pf + 25pf multi | 1.25 | 1.50 |
| *Nos. 9NB61-9NB64 (4)* | | 2.20 | 3.10 |

Surtax for benefit of young people.

**Tin Toy Type of 1969**

Tin Toys: 10pf+5pf, Coach. 20pf+10pf, Woman feeding chickens. 30pf+15pf, Woman grocer. 50pf+25pf, Postilion on horseback.

**1969, Oct. 2**   **Litho.**   *Perf. 13½x14*

| | | | |
|---|---|---|---|
| 9NB65 | SP297 10pf + 5pf multi | .20 | .20 |
| 9NB66 | SP297 20pf + 10pf multi | .20 | .20 |
| 9NB67 | SP297 30pf + 15pf multi | .35 | .35 |
| 9NB68 | SP297 50pf + 25pf multi | 1.00 | 1.00 |
| *Nos. 9NB65-9NB68 (4)* | | 1.75 | 1.75 |

The surtax was for independent welfare organizations.

---

**Animal Type of 1966**

10pf+5pf, Roe deer. 20pf+10pf, Chamois. 30pf+15pf, Fallow deer. 50pf+25pf, Red deer.

**1969, Nov. 13**   **Litho.**   *Perf. 13½x14*

Christmas: 10pf+5pf, The Three Kings.

9NB69 SP297 10pf + 5pf multi    .35  .30

**Minnesinger Type of 1970**

Minnesingers (and their Ladies): 10pf+5pf, Heinrich von Stretlingen. 20pf+10pf, Meinloh von Sevelingen. 30pf+15pf, Burkhart von Hohenfels. 50pf+25pf, Albrecht von Johansdorf.

**1970, Feb. 5**   **Photo.**   *Perf. 13½x14*

| | | | |
|---|---|---|---|
| 9NB70 | SP298 10pf + 5pf multi | .20 | .25 |
| 9NB71 | SP298 20pf + 10pf multi | .35 | .45 |
| 9NB72 | SP298 30pf + 15pf multi | .55 | .60 |
| 9NB73 | SP298 50pf + 25pf multi | 1.25 | 1.40 |
| *Nos. 9NB70-9NB73 (4)* | | 2.35 | 2.70 |

Surtax for benefit of young people.

**Puppet Type of 1970**

10pf+5pf, "Kasperl." 20pf+10pf, Polichinelle. 30pf+5pf, Punch. 50pf+25pf, Pulcinella.

**1970, Oct. 6**   **Litho.**   *Perf. 13½x14*

| | | | |
|---|---|---|---|
| 9NB74 | SP300 10pf + 5pf multi | .20 | .20 |
| 9NB75 | SP300 20pf + 10pf multi | .25 | .25 |
| 9NB76 | SP300 30pf + 15pf multi | .55 | .45 |
| 9NB77 | SP300 50pf + 25pf multi | .90 | 1.10 |
| *Nos. 9NB74-9NB77 (4)* | | 1.90 | 2.00 |

Surtax for independent welfare organizations.

**1970, Nov. 12**

Christmas: 10pf+5pf, Rococo angel, from Ursuline Sisters' Convent, Innsbruck.

9NB78 SP300 10pf + 5pf multi    .30  .30

**Drawings Type of 1971**

Children's Drawings: 10pf+5pf, Fly. 20pf+10pf, Fish. 30pf+15pf, Porcupine. 50pf+25pf, Cock. All stamps horizontal.

**1971, Feb. 5**   **Litho.**   *Perf. 14*

| | | | |
|---|---|---|---|
| 9NB79 | SP301 10pf + 5pf multi | .30 | .30 |
| 9NB80 | SP301 20pf + 10pf multi | .30 | .30 |
| 9NB81 | SP301 30pf + 15pf multi | .45 | .50 |
| 9NB82 | SP301 50pf + 25pf multi | 1.25 | 1.40 |
| *Nos. 9NB79-9NB82 (4)* | | 2.30 | 2.50 |

Surtax for the benefit of young people.

**Wooden Toy Type of 1971**

Wooden Toys: 10pf+5pf, Movable dolls in box. 25pf+10pf, Knight on horseback. 30pf+15pf, Jumping jack. 60pf+30pf, Nurse rocking babies.

**1971, Oct. 5**

| | | | |
|---|---|---|---|
| 9NB83 | SP303 10pf + 5pf multi | .20 | .25 |
| 9NB84 | SP303 25pf + 10pf multi | .25 | .35 |
| 9NB85 | SP303 30pf + 15pf multi | .55 | .55 |
| 9NB86 | SP303 60pf + 30pf multi | 1.00 | 1.10 |
| *Nos. 9NB83-9NB86 (4)* | | 2.00 | 2.25 |

**1971, Nov. 11**

Christmas: Christmas angel with candles.

9NB87 SP303 10pf + 5pf multi    .35  .35

**Animal Protection Type of 1972**

10pf+5pf, Boy trying to rob bird's nest. 25pf+10pf, Girl with kittens to be drowned. 30pf+15pf, Watch dog & man with whip. 60pf+30pf, Hedgehog & deer passing before car at night.

**1972, Feb. 4**

| | | | |
|---|---|---|---|
| 9NB88 | SP304 10pf + 5pf multi | .20 | .20 |
| 9NB89 | SP304 25pf + 10pf multi | .30 | .30 |
| 9NB90 | SP304 30pf + 15pf multi | .55 | .55 |
| 9NB91 | SP304 60pf + 30pf multi | 1.25 | 1.25 |
| *Nos. 9NB88-9NB91 (4)* | | 2.30 | 2.30 |

Surtax for the benefit of young people.

**Chess Type of 1972**

**1972, Oct. 5**   **Litho.**   *Perf. 14*

| | | | |
|---|---|---|---|
| 9NB92 | SP307 20pf + 10 Knight | .30 | .30 |
| 9NB93 | SP307 30pf + 15 Rook | .45 | .45 |
| 9NB94 | SP307 40pf + 20 Queen | 1.25 | 1.25 |
| 9NB95 | SP307 70pf + 35 King | 1.75 | 1.75 |
| *Nos. 9NB92-9NB95 (4)* | | 3.75 | 3.75 |

Surtax for independent welfare organizations.

**Christmas Type of 1972**

Design: 20pf+10pf, Holy Family.

**1972, Nov. 10**   **Litho.**   *Perf. 14*
9NB96 SP308 20pf + 10pf multi    .55  .45

**Bird Type of 1973**

Birds of Prey: 20pf+10pf, Goshawk. 30pf+15pf, Peregrine falcon. 40pf+20pf, Sparrow hawk. 70pf+35pf, Golden eagle.

**1973, Feb. 6          Photo.          *Perf. 14***
9NB97    SP309  20pf + 10pf multi    .50   .50
9NB98    SP309  30pf + 15pf multi    .75   .75
9NB99    SP309  40pf + 20pf multi   1.00  1.00
9NB100   SP309  70pf + 35pf multi   1.75  1.75
       *Nos. 9NB97-9NB100 (4)*       4.00  4.00

Surtax was for benefit of young people.

### Instrument Type of 1973

Musical Instruments: 20+10pf, Hurdygurdy, 17th cent. 30+15pf, Drum, 16th cent. 40+20pf, Archlute, 18th cent. 70+35pf, Organ, 16th cent.

**1973, Oct. 5          Litho.          *Perf. 14***
9NB101   SP311  20pf + 10pf multi    .35   .35
9NB102   SP311  30pf + 15pf multi    .75   .75
9NB103   SP311  40pf + 20pf multi    .90   .90
9NB104   SP311  70pf + 35pf multi   1.25  1.25
       *Nos. 9NB101-9NB104 (4)*      3.25  3.25

Surtax was for independent welfare organizations.

### Star Type of 1973

Christmas: 20pf+10pf, Christmas star.

**1973, Nov. 9          Litho. & Engr.**
9NB105   SP312  20pf + 10pf multi    .55   .55

### Youth Type of 1974

Designs: 20pf+10pf, Boy photographing. 30pf+15pf, Boy athlete. 40pf+20pf, Girl violinist. 70pf+35pf, Nurse's aid.

**1974, Apr. 17          Photo.          *Perf. 14***
9NB106   SP313  20pf + 10pf multi    .35   .45
9NB107   SP313  30pf + 15pf multi    .40   .45
9NB108   SP313  40pf + 20pf multi    .90  1.00
9NB109   SP313  70pf + 35pf multi   1.25  1.40
       *Nos. 9NB106-9NB109 (4)*      2.90  3.30

Surtax was for benefit of young people.

### Flower Type of 1974

Designs: 30pf+15pf, Spring bouquet. 40pf+20pf, Autumn bouquet. 50pf+25pf, Roses. 70pf+35pf, Winter flowers. All horiz.

**1974, Oct. 15          Litho.          *Perf. 14***
9NB110   SP314  30pf + 15pf multi    .40   .40
9NB111   SP314  40pf + 20pf multi    .85   .85
9NB112   SP314  50pf + 25pf multi    .85   .85
9NB113   SP314  70pf + 35pf multi   1.25  1.25
       *Nos. 9NB110-9NB113 (4)*      3.35  3.35

Surtax was for independent welfare organizations.

**1974, Oct. 29**

Christmas: Christmas bouquet, horiz.

9NB114   SP314  30pf + 15pf multi    .75   .85

### Locomotive Type of 1975

Steam Locomotives: 30pf+15pf, Dragon. 40pf+20pf, Class 89 (70-75). 50pf+25pf, Class O50. 70pf+35pf, Class O10.

**1975, Apr. 15          Litho.          *Perf. 14***
9NB115   SP315  30pf + 15pf multi    .75   .60
9NB116   SP315  40pf + 20pf multi    .75   .75
9NB117   SP315  50pf + 25pf multi   1.50  1.25
9NB118   SP315  70pf + 35pf multi   2.25  2.25
       *Nos. 9NB115-9NB118 (4)*      5.25  4.85

Surtax was for benefit of young people.

### Flower Type of 1975

Alpine Flowers: 30pf+15pf, Yellow gentian. 40pf+20pf, Arnica. 50pf+25pf, Cyclamen. 70pf+35pf, Blue gentian.

**1975, Oct. 15          Litho.          *Perf. 14***
9NB119   SP316  30pf + 15pf multi    .55   .55
9NB120   SP316  40pf + 20pf multi    .45   .45
9NB121   SP316  50pf + 25pf multi    .60   .60
9NB122   SP316  70pf + 35pf multi   1.00  1.00
       *Nos. 9NB119-9NB122 (4)*      2.60  2.60

Surtax was for independent welfare organizations.

**1975, Nov. 14**

Christmas: 30pf+15pf, Snow heather.

9NB123   SP316  30pf + 15pf multi    .75   .75

### Sports Type of 1976

30+15pf, Shot put, women's. 40+20pf, Hockey. 50+25pf, Handball. 70+35pf, Swimming.

**1976, Apr. 6          Litho.          *Perf. 14***
9NB124   SP317  30pf + 15pf multi    .75   .70
9NB125   SP317  40pf + 20pf multi    .75   .70
9NB126   SP317  50pf + 25pf multi    .75   .80
9NB127   SP317  70pf + 35pf multi   1.50  1.60
       *Nos. 9NB124-9NB127 (4)*      3.75  3.80

Youth training for Olympic Games. The surtax was for the benefit of young people.

Iris — SP13

Flowers: 40pf+20pf, Wallflower. 50pf+25pf, Dahlia. 70pf+35pf, Larkspur.

**1976, Oct. 14          Litho.          *Perf. 14***
9NB128   SP13   30pf + 15pf           .35   .35
9NB129   SP13   40pf + 20pf           .40   .40
9NB130   SP13   50pf + 25pf           .75   .75
9NB131   SP13   70pf + 35pf          1.00  1.00
       *Nos. 9NB128-9NB131 (4)*      2.50  2.50

Surtax was for independent welfare organizations.

### Souvenir Sheet
### Christmas Type of 1976

Christmas: 30pf+15pf, Annunciation to the Shepherds, stained-glass window, Frauenkirche, Esslingen.

**1976, Nov. 16          Litho. & Engr.**
9NB132   SP320  30pf + 15pf multi    .75   .65

### Ship Type of 1977

Historic Ships: 30pf+15pf, Bremer Kogge, c. 1380. 40pf+20pf, Helena Sloman, 1850. 50pf+25pf, Passenger ship, Cap Polonio, 1914. 70pf+35pf, Freighter Widar, 1971.

**1977, Apr. 14          Litho.          *Perf. 14***
9NB133   SP321  30pf + 15pf           .45   .45
9NB134   SP321  40pf + 20pf           .70   .70
9NB135   SP321  50pf + 25pf           .95   .95
9NB136   SP321  70pf + 35pf          1.40  1.40
       *Nos. 9NB133-9NB136 (4)*      3.50  3.50

Surtax was for benefit of young people.

### Flower Type of 1977

Meadow Flowers: 30pf+15pf, Daisy. 40pf+20pf, Cowslip. 50pf+25pf, Sainfoin. 70pf+35pf, Forget-me-not.

**1977, Oct. 13          Litho.          *Perf. 14***
9NB137   SP322  30pf + 15pf           .30   .30
9NB138   SP322  40pf + 20pf           .55   .55
9NB139   SP322  50pf + 25pf           .75   .75
9NB140   SP322  70pf + 35pf          1.10  1.10
       *Nos. 9NB137-9NB140 (4)*      2.70  2.70

Surtax was for independent welfare organizations.
See Nos. 9NB148-9NB151.

### Souvenir Sheet
### Christmas Type of 1977

30pf+15pf, Virgin and Child, stained-glass window, Sacristy of St. Gereon Basilica, Cologne.

**1977, Nov. 10**
9NB141   SP323  30pf + 15pf multi    .75   .75

### Aviation Type of 1978

Designs: 30pf+15pf, Montgolfier balloon, 1783. 40pf+20pf, Lilienthal's glider, 1891. 50pf+25pf, Wright brothers' plane, 1909. 70pf+35pf, Etrich/Rumpler Taube, 1910.

**1978, Apr. 13          Litho.          *Perf. 14***
9NB142   SP325  30pf + 15pf           .35   .45
9NB143   SP325  40pf + 20pf           .55   .60
9NB144   SP325  50pf + 25pf           .70   .75
9NB145   SP325  70pf + 35pf          1.25  1.25
       *Nos. 9NB142-9NB145 (4)*      2.85  3.05

Surtax was for benefit of young people.

### Sports Type of 1978

50+25pf, Bicycling. 70+35pf, Fencing.

**1978, Apr. 13          Litho.          *Perf. 14***
9NB146   SP324  50pf + 25pf           .90   .60
9NB147   SP324  70pf + 35pf          1.25  1.00

Surtax was for German Sports Foundation.

### Flower Type of 1977

Woodland Flowers: 30pf+15pf, Solomon's-seal. 40pf+20pf, Wood primrose. 50pf+25pf, Cephalanthera rubra (orchid). 70pf+35pf, Bugle.

**1978, Oct. 12          Litho.          *Perf. 14***
9NB148   SP322  30pf + 15pf           .45   .45
9NB149   SP322  40pf + 20pf           .55   .55
9NB150   SP322  50pf + 25pf           .75   .75
9NB151   SP322  70pf + 35pf          1.10  1.10
       *Nos. 9NB148-9NB151 (4)*      2.85  2.85

Surtax was for independent welfare organizations.

### Souvenir Sheet
### Christmas Type of 1978

Christmas: 30pf+15pf, Adoration of the Kings, stained glass window, Frauenkirche, Munich.

**1978, Nov. 16          Litho.          *Perf. 14***
9NB152   SP326  30pf + 15pf multi    .75   .75

### Aviation Type of 1979

Airplanes: 40pf+20pf, Vampyr, 1921. 50pf+25pf, Junkers JU52/3M, 1932. 60pf+30pf, Messerschmitt BF/ME 108, 1934. 90pf+45pf, Douglas DC3, 1935.

**1979, Apr. 5          Litho.          *Perf. 14***
9NB153   SP327  40pf + 20pf           .55   .55
9NB154   SP327  50pf + 25pf           .75   .75
9NB155   SP327  60pf + 30pf           .95   .95
9NB156   SP327  90pf + 45pf          1.50  1.50
       *Nos. 9NB153-9NB156 (4)*      3.75  3.75

Surtax was for benefit of young people.

### Sports Type of 1979

60pf+30pf, Runners. 90pf+45pf, Archers.

**1979, Apr. 5**
9NB157   SP328  60pf + 30pf           .90   .95
9NB158   SP328  90pf + 45pf          1.25  1.25

Surtax was for German Sports Foundation.

### Plant Type of 1979

Woodland Plants: 40pf+20pf, Larch. 50pf+25pf, Hazelnut. 60pf+30pf, Horse chestnut. 90pf+45pf, Blackthorn.

**1979, Oct. 11          Litho.          *Perf. 14***
9NB159   SP330  40pf + 20pf           .60   .45
9NB160   SP330  50pf + 25pf           .75   .70
9NB161   SP330  60pf + 30pf          1.00   .95
9NB162   SP330  90pf + 45pf          1.40  1.25
       *Nos. 9NB159-9NB162 (4)*      3.75  3.35

Surtax was for independent welfare organizations.

### Christmas Type of 1979

Christmas: Nativity, medieval manuscript, Cistercian Abbey, Altenberg.

**1979, Nov. 14          Litho.          *Perf. 13½***
9NB163   SP331  40pf + 20pf multi    .90   .75

### Aviation Type of 1979

Designs: 40pf+20pf, Vickers Viscount, 1950. 50pf+25pf, Fokker 27 Friendship, 1955. 60pf+30pf, Sud Aviation Caravelle, 1955. 90pf+45pf, Sikorsky-55, 1949.

**1980, Apr. 10          Litho.          *Perf. 14***
9NB164   SP327  40 + 20pf multi      .75   .75
9NB165   SP327  50 + 25pf multi      .80   .80
9NB166   SP327  60 + 30pf multi     1.00  1.00
9NB167   SP327  90 + 45pf multi     1.50  1.50
       *Nos. 9NB164-9NB167 (4)*      4.05  4.05

Surtax was for benefit of young people.

### Sports Type of 1980

Designs: 50pf+25pf, Javelin. 60pf+30pf, Weight lifting. 90pf+45pf, Water polo.

**1980, May 8          Photo.          *Perf. 14***
9NB168   SP332  50 + 25pf multi      .75   .75
9NB169   SP332  60 + 30pf multi      .75   .75
9NB170   SP332  90 + 45pf multi     1.10  1.10
       *Nos. 9NB168-9NB170 (3)*      2.60  2.60

Surtax was for German Sports Foundation.

### Wildflower Type of 1980

Wildflowers: 40pf+20pf, Orlaya. 50pf+25pf, Yellow gagea. 60pf+30pf, Summer pheasant's eye. 90pf+45pf, Small-flowered Venus' looking-glass.

### Flower Type of 1977

**1980, Oct. 9          Litho.          *Perf. 14***
9NB171   SP333  40 + 20pf multi      .80   .80
9NB172   SP333  50 + 25pf multi      .90   .90
9NB173   SP333  60 + 30pf multi      .90   .90
9NB174   SP333  90 + 45pf multi     1.50  1.50
       *Nos. 9NB171-9NB174 (4)*      4.10  4.10

Surtax was for independent welfare organizations.

### Christmas Type of 1980

Christmas: 40pf+20pf, Annunciation to the Shepherds, from Altomunster manuscript, 12th century.

**1980, Nov. 13  Litho.  *Perf. 14x13½***
9NB175   SP335  40 + 20pf multi      .90   .80

### Optical Instrument Type of 1981

40pf+20pf, Theodolite, 1810. 50pf+25pf, Equatorial telescope, 1820. 60pf+30pf, Microscope, 1790. 90pf+45pf, Sextant, 1830.

**1981, Apr. 10          Litho.          *Perf. 13½***
9NB176   SP336  40 + 20pf multi      .60   .60
9NB177   SP336  50 + 25pf multi      .80   .80
9NB178   SP336  60 + 30pf multi     1.00  1.00
9NB179   SP336  90 + 45pf multi     1.60  1.60
       *Nos. 9NB176-9NB179 (4)*      4.00  4.00

Surtax for benefit of young people.

### Sports Type of 1981

Designs: 60pf+30pf, Women's gymnastics. 90pf+45pf, Cross-county running.

**1981, Apr. 10          *Perf. 14***
9NB180   SP337  60 + 30pf multi      .90   .75
9NB181   SP337  90 + 45pf multi     1.40  1.10

Surtax for the German Sports Foundation.

### Plant Type of 1981

40pf+20pf, Common bistort. 50pf+25pf, Pedicularis sceptrum-carolinum. 60pf+30pf, Gladiolus palustris. 90pf+45pf, Iris sibirica.

**1981, Oct. 8          Litho.**
9NB182   SP338  40 + 20pf multi      .75   .75
9NB183   SP338  50 + 25pf multi      .80   .75
9NB184   SP338  60 + 30pf multi      .90   .75
9NB185   SP338  90 + 45pf multi     1.75  1.50
       *Nos. 9NB182-9NB185 (4)*      4.20  3.75

Surtax was for independent welfare organizations.

### Christmas Type of 1981

Adoration of the Kings, 19th cent. painting.

**1981, Nov. 12          Litho.**
9NB186   SP339  40 + 20pf multi      .90   .60

### Antique Car Type of 1982

Designs: 40pf+20pf, Daimler, 1889. 50pf+25pf, Wanderer, 1911. 60pf+30pf, Adler limousine, 1913. 90pf+45pf, DKW-F, 1931.

**1982, Apr. 15          Litho.**
9NB187   SP340  40 + 20pf multi      .75   .75
9NB188   SP340  50 + 25pf multi      .80   .80
9NB189   SP340  60 + 30pf multi     1.00  1.00
9NB190   SP340  90 + 45pf multi     1.60  1.60
       *Nos. 9NB187-9NB190 (4)*      4.15  4.15

Surtax was for benefit of young people.

### Sports Type of 1982

60pf+30pf, Sprinting. 90pf+45pf, Volleyball.

**1982, Apr. 15          Litho.**
9NB191   SP341  60 + 30pf multi      .95   .75
9NB192   SP341  90 + 45pf multi     1.40  1.00

Surtax was for the German Sports Foundation.

### Flower Type of 1982

Designs: 50pf+25pf, Floribunda grandiflora. 60pf+30pf, Tea-rose hybrid, diff. 80pf+40pf, Floribunda, diff. 120pf+60pf, Miniature rose.

**1982, Oct. 14          Litho.          *Perf. 14***
9NB193   SP342  50 + 20pf multi     1.00  1.00
9NB194   SP342  60 + 30pf multi     1.10   .90
9NB195   SP342  80 + 40pf multi     1.50  1.50
9NB196   SP342  120 + 60pf multi    2.40  2.40
       *Nos. 9NB193-9NB196 (4)*      6.00  5.70

Surtax was for independent welfare organizations.

### Christmas Type of 1982

Christmas: Adoration of the Kings, Oak altar, St. Peter's Church, Hamburg, 1380.

**1982, Nov. 10**
9NB197   SP343  50 + 20pf multi      .90   .75

## Motorcycle Type of 1983

Designs: 50pf+20pf, Hildebrand & Wolfmuller, 1894. 60pf+30pf, Wanderer, 1908. 80pf+40pf, DKW-Lomos, 1922. 120pf+60pf, Mars, 1925.

**1983, Apr. 12**  Litho.  *Perf. 14*
| | | | | |
|---|---|---|---|---|
| 9NB198 | SP344 | 50 + 20pf multi | .75 | .55 |
| 9NB199 | SP344 | 60 + 30pf multi | 1.10 | .95 |
| 9NB200 | SP344 | 80 + 40pf multi | 1.25 | .95 |
| 9NB201 | SP344 | 120 + 60pf multi | 3.00 | 2.50 |
| *Nos. 9NB198-9NB201 (4)* | | | 6.10 | 4.95 |

Surtax was for benefit of young people.

## Sports Type of 1983

Designs: 80pf+40pf, European Latin American Dance Championship. 120pf+60pf, World Hockey Championship.

**1983, Apr. 12**
| | | | | |
|---|---|---|---|---|
| 9NB202 | SP345 | 80 + 40pf multi | 1.50 | 1.10 |
| 9NB203 | SP345 | 120 + 60pf multi | 2.25 | 1.90 |

Surtax was for German Sports Foundation.

## Flower Type of Germany

Designs: 50pf+20pf, Mountain wildflower. 60pf+30pf, Alpine auricula. 80pf+40pf, Little primrose. 120pf+60pf, Einsele's aquilegia.

**1983, Oct. 13**  Litho.  *Perf. 14*
| | | | | |
|---|---|---|---|---|
| 9NB204 | SP346 | 50 + 20pf multi | .70 | .70 |
| 9NB205 | SP346 | 60 + 30pf multi | 1.00 | 1.00 |
| 9NB206 | SP346 | 80 + 40pf multi | 1.75 | 1.75 |
| 9NB207 | SP346 | 120 + 60pf multi | 2.75 | 2.75 |
| *Nos. 9NB204-9NB207 (4)* | | | 6.20 | 6.20 |

Surtax was for welfare organizations.

## Christmas Type of Germany

**1983, Nov. 10**  Litho.
| | | | | |
|---|---|---|---|---|
| 9NB208 | SP347 | 50 + 20pf Nativity | .90 | .80 |

Surtax was for free welfare work.

## Insect Type of 1984

Designs: 50pf+20pf, Trichius fasciatus. 60pf+30pf, Agrumenia carniolioa. 80pf+40pf, Bombus terrestris. 120pf+60pf, Eristalis tenax.

**1984, Apr. 12**  Litho.
| | | | | |
|---|---|---|---|---|
| 9NB209 | SP348 | 50 + 20pf multi | 1.00 | .65 |
| 9NB210 | SP348 | 60 + 30pf multi | 1.00 | .80 |
| 9NB211 | SP348 | 80 + 40pf multi | 2.10 | 1.25 |
| 9NB212 | SP348 | 120 + 60pf multi | 2.50 | 2.50 |
| *Nos. 9NB209-9NB212 (4)* | | | 6.60 | 5.20 |

Surtax was for German Youth Stamp Foundation.

## Olympic Type of 1984

Women's Events: 60pf+30pf, Hurdles. 80pf+40pf, Cycling. 120pf+60pf, Kayak.

**1984, Apr. 12**
| | | | | |
|---|---|---|---|---|
| 9NB213 | SP349 | 60 + 30pf multi | 1.50 | 1.00 |
| 9NB214 | SP349 | 80 + 40pf multi | 1.90 | 1.00 |
| 9NB215 | SP349 | 120 + 60pf multi | 2.75 | 2.75 |
| *Nos. 9NB213-9NB215 (3)* | | | 6.15 | 4.75 |

Surtax was for German Sports Foundation.

## Orchid Type of 1984

50+20pf, Listera cordata. 60+30pf, Ophrys insectifera. 80pf+40pf, Epipactis palustris. 120pf+60pf, Ophrys coriophora.

**1984, Oct. 18**  Litho.  *Perf. 14*
| | | | | |
|---|---|---|---|---|
| 9NB216 | SP350 | 50 + 20pf multi | 1.25 | 1.10 |
| 9NB217 | SP350 | 60 + 30pf multi | 1.75 | 1.10 |
| 9NB218 | SP350 | 80 + 40pf multi | 3.00 | 2.50 |
| 9NB219 | SP350 | 120 + 60pf multi | 4.50 | 4.00 |
| *Nos. 9NB216-9NB219 (4)* | | | 10.50 | 8.70 |

Surtax was for welfare organizations.

## Christmas Type of 1984

**1984, Nov. 8**  Litho.
| | | | | |
|---|---|---|---|---|
| 9NB220 | SP351 | 50 + 20pf St. Nicholas | 1.10 | 1.10 |

Surtax was for welfare organizations.

## Sport Type of 1985

**1985, Feb. 21**  Photo.
| | | | | |
|---|---|---|---|---|
| 9NB221 | SP352 | 80 + 40pf Basketball | 1.40 | 1.40 |
| 9NB222 | SP352 | 120 + 40pf Table Tennis | 2.25 | 2.25 |

Surtax was for German Sport Foundation.

## Bicycle Type of 1985

50pf+20pf, Bussing bicycle, 1868. 60pf+30pf, Child's tricycle, 1885. 80pf+40pf, Jaray bicycle, 1925. 120pf+60pf, Opel racer, 1925.

**1985, Apr. 16**  Litho.
| | | | | |
|---|---|---|---|---|
| 9NB223 | SP353 | 50 + 20pf multi | 1.10 | 1.10 |
| 9NB224 | SP353 | 60 + 30pf multi | 1.10 | 1.10 |
| 9NB225 | SP353 | 80 + 40pf multi | 1.50 | 1.50 |
| 9NB226 | SP353 | 120 + 60pf multi | 3.50 | 3.50 |
| *Nos. 9NB223-9NB226 (4)* | | | 7.20 | 7.20 |

Surtax was for benefit of young people. Each stamp also shows the International Youth Year emblem.

## Prayer Book Type of 1985

**1985, Oct. 15**  Litho.  *Perf. 14*
| | | | | |
|---|---|---|---|---|
| 9NB227 | SP355 | 50 + 20pf multi | 1.10 | 1.10 |
| 9NB228 | SP355 | 60 + 30pf multi | 1.50 | 1.50 |
| 9NB229 | SP355 | 80 + 40pf multi | 1.50 | 1.50 |
| 9NB230 | SP355 | 120 + 60pf multi | 2.25 | 2.25 |
| *Nos. 9NB227-9NB230 (4)* | | | 6.35 | 6.35 |

Surtax for welfare organizations.

## Christmas Type of 1985

Woodcut: Worship of the Kings, Epiphany Altar, Frieburg Cathedral, by Hans Baldung Grien (1485-1545).

**1985, Nov. 12**  Litho.  *Perf. 14*
| | | | | |
|---|---|---|---|---|
| 9NB231 | SP356 | 50 + 20pf multi | 1.25 | 1.00 |

Surtax for welfare organizations.

## European Sports Championships Type of 1986

**1986, Feb. 13**  Litho.  *Perf. 14*
| | | | | |
|---|---|---|---|---|
| 9NB232 | SP357 | 80 + 40pf Swimming | 1.60 | 1.60 |
| 9NB233 | SP357 | 120 + 55pf Show jumping | 2.25 | 2.25 |

Surtax for the Natl. Sports Promotion Foundation.

## Vocational Training Type of 1986

**1986, Apr. 10**
| | | | | |
|---|---|---|---|---|
| 9NB234 | SP358 | 50 + 25pf Glazier | 1.10 | 1.25 |
| 9NB235 | SP358 | 60 + 30pf Mechanic | 1.50 | 1.60 |
| 9NB236 | SP358 | 70 + 35pf Tailor | 1.50 | 1.60 |
| 9NB237 | SP358 | 80 + 40pf Carpenter | 1.90 | 1.90 |
| *Nos. 9NB234-9NB237 (4)* | | | 6.00 | 6.35 |

Surtax for German Youth Stamp Foundation.

## Glassware Type of 1986

**1986, Oct. 16**  Litho.  *Perf. 13x13½*
| | | | | |
|---|---|---|---|---|
| 9NB238 | SP359 | 50 + 25pf Cantharus, 1st cent. | 1.10 | 1.10 |
| 9NB239 | SP359 | 60 + 30pf Tumbler, c. 200 | 1.50 | 1.50 |
| 9NB240 | SP359 | 70 + 35pf Jug, 3rd cent. | 1.50 | 1.50 |
| 9NB241 | SP359 | 80 + 40pf Diatreta, 4th cent. | 1.90 | 1.90 |
| *Nos. 9NB238-9NB241 (4)* | | | 6.00 | 6.00 |

Surtax for public welfare organizations.

## Christmas Type of 1986

Christmas: Adoration of the Magi, Ortenberg Altarpiece, c. 1420.

**1986, Nov. 13**  Litho.  *Perf. 14*
| | | | | |
|---|---|---|---|---|
| 9NB242 | SP360 | 50 + 25pf multi | .90 | .80 |

Surtax for public welfare organizations.

## Sports Championships Type of 1987

**1987, Feb. 12**  Litho.
| | | | | |
|---|---|---|---|---|
| 9NB243 | SP361 | 80 + 40pf Gymnastics | 1.50 | 1.50 |
| 9NB244 | SP361 | 120 + 55pf Judo | 2.25 | 2.25 |

Surtax for the benefit of the national Sports Promotion Foundation.

## Industry Type of 1987

**1987, Apr. 9**  Litho.
| | | | | |
|---|---|---|---|---|
| 9NB245 | SP362 | 50 + 25pf Cooper | 1.10 | 1.10 |
| 9NB246 | SP362 | 60 + 30pf Stonemason | 1.10 | 1.10 |
| 9NB247 | SP362 | 70 + 35pf Furrier | 1.50 | 1.50 |
| 9NB248 | SP362 | 80 + 40pf Painter | 1.50 | 1.50 |
| *Nos. 9NB245-9NB248 (4)* | | | 5.20 | 5.20 |

Surtax for youth organizations.

## Gold and Silver Artifacts Type of 1987

**1987, Oct. 15**
| | | | | |
|---|---|---|---|---|
| 9NB249 | SP363 | 50 + 25pf Bonnet ornament, 5th cent. | .75 | .90 |
| 9NB250 | SP363 | 60 + 30pf Athena plate, 1st cent. B.C. | 1.10 | 1.25 |
| 9NB251 | SP363 | 70 + 35pf Armilla armlet, c. 1180 | 1.40 | 1.50 |
| 9NB252 | SP363 | 80 + 40pf Snake bracelet, 300 B.C. | 1.60 | 1.75 |
| *Nos. 9NB249-9NB252 (4)* | | | 4.85 | 5.40 |

Surtax for welfare organizations sponsoring free museum exhibitions.

## Christmas Type of 1987

Illustration from Book of Psalms, 13th cent., Bavarian Natl. Museum: Adoration of the Magi.

**1987, Nov. 6**
| | | | | |
|---|---|---|---|---|
| 9NB253 | SP364 | 50 + 25pf multi | .90 | .80 |

Surtax for public welfare ogranizations.

## Sports Type of 1988

**1988, Feb. 18**  Litho.
| | | | | |
|---|---|---|---|---|
| 9NB254 | SP365 | 60 + 30pf Trapshooting | 1.60 | 1.50 |
| 9NB255 | SP365 | 80 + 40pf Figure skating | 1.60 | 1.50 |
| 9NB256 | SP365 | 120 + 55pf Hammer throw | 2.10 | 2.10 |
| *Nos. 9NB254-9NB256 (3)* | | | 5.30 | 5.10 |

## Music Type of 1988

No. 9NB257, Piano terzet. No. 9NB258, Wind quintet. No. 9NB259, Guitar, mandolin, recorder. No. 9NB260, Children's choir.

**1988, Apr. 14**  Litho.  *Perf. 14*
| | | | | |
|---|---|---|---|---|
| 9NB257 | SP366 | 50 +25pf multi | 1.25 | 1.25 |
| 9NB258 | SP366 | 60 +30pf multi | 1.60 | 1.60 |
| 9NB259 | SP366 | 70 +35pf multi | 1.60 | 1.60 |
| 9NB260 | SP366 | 80 +40pf multi | 2.50 | 2.50 |
| *Nos. 9NB257-9NB260 (4)* | | | 6.95 | 6.95 |

Surtax for German Youth Stamp Foundation.

## Artifacts Type of 1988

#9NB261, Brooch, c. 1700, Schmuck Jewelry Museum, Pforzheim. #9NB262, Lion, 1540, Kunstgewerbe Museum, Berlin. #9NB263, Lidded goblet, 1536, Kunstgewerbe Museum. #9NB264, Cope clasp, c. 1400, Aachen cathedral.

**1988, Oct. 13**  Litho.
| | | | | |
|---|---|---|---|---|
| 9NB261 | SP367 | 50 +25pf multi | 1.10 | 1.25 |
| 9NB262 | SP367 | 60 +30pf multi | 1.25 | 1.40 |
| 9NB263 | SP367 | 75 +35pf multi | 1.40 | 1.50 |
| 9NB264 | SP367 | 80 +40pf multi | 1.60 | 1.75 |
| *Nos. 9NB261-9NB264 (4)* | | | 5.35 | 5.90 |

Surtax for welfare organizations.

## Christmas Type of 1988

Illumination from The Gospel Book of Henry the Lion, Helmarshausen, 1188, Prussian Cultural Museum, Bavaria: Angels announce the birth of Christ to the shepherds.

**1988, Nov. 10**  Litho.
| | | | | |
|---|---|---|---|---|
| 9NB265 | SP368 | 50 +25pf multi | 1.40 | 1.25 |

Surtax for public welfare organizations.

## Sports Type of 1989

**1989, Feb. 9**  Litho.
| | | | | |
|---|---|---|---|---|
| 9NB266 | SP369 | 100 +50pf Volleyball | 2.50 | 2.50 |
| 9NB267 | SP369 | 140 +60pf Hockey | 3.25 | 3.25 |

Surtax for the Natl. Sports Promotion Foundation.

## Circus Type of 1989

**1989, Apr. 20**  Litho.
| | | | | |
|---|---|---|---|---|
| 9NB268 | SP371 | 60 +30pf Tamer and tigers | 1.60 | 1.60 |
| 9NB269 | SP371 | 70 +30pf Trapeze artists | 2.10 | 2.10 |
| 9NB270 | SP371 | 80 +35pf Seals | 3.00 | 3.00 |
| 9NB271 | SP371 | 100 +50pf Jugglers | 3.25 | 3.25 |
| *Nos. 9NB268-9NB271 (4)* | | | 9.95 | 9.95 |

Surtax for natl. youth welfare organizations.

## Mail Carrying Type of 1989

#9NB272, Messenger, 15th cent. #9NB273, Brandenburg mail wagon, c. 1700. #9NB274, Prussian postal workers, 19th cent.

**1989, Oct. 12**  Litho.
| | | | | |
|---|---|---|---|---|
| 9NB272 | SP372 | 60 +30pf multi | 2.50 | 2.50 |
| 9NB273 | SP372 | 80 +35pf multi | 3.25 | 3.00 |
| 9NB274 | SP372 | 100 +50pf multi | 4.00 | 4.00 |
| *Nos. 9NB272-9NB274 (3)* | | | 9.75 | 9.50 |

Surtax for the benefit of Free Welfare Work.

## Christmas Type of 1989

**1989, Nov. 16**  Litho.
| | | | | |
|---|---|---|---|---|
| 9NB275 | SP373 | 40 +20pf Angel | 1.25 | 1.25 |
| 9NB276 | SP373 | 60 +30pf Nativity | 2.10 | 2.10 |

Surtax for the benefit of the Federal Working Assoc. of Free Welfare Work.

## Sports Type of 1990

Designs: No. 9NB277, Water polo. No. 9NB278, Wheelchair basketball.

**1990, Feb. 15**  Litho.
| | | | | |
|---|---|---|---|---|
| 9NB277 | SP374 | 100 +50pf multi | 3.25 | 3.25 |
| 9NB278 | SP374 | 140 +60pf multi | 5.50 | *6.25* |

Surtax for the Natl. Sports Promotion Foundation.

## *Max and Moritz* Type of 1990

**1990, Apr. 19**  Litho.
| | | | | |
|---|---|---|---|---|
| 9NB279 | SP375 | 60 +30pf Max, Moritz | 1.60 | *1.90* |
| 9NB280 | SP375 | 70 +30pf Max, Moritz, diff. | 2.50 | *2.75* |
| 9NB281 | SP375 | 80 +35pf Moritz | 2.50 | *2.75* |
| 9NB282 | SP375 | 100 +50pf Bug, Uncle | 2.50 | *2.75* |
| *Nos. 9NB279-9NB282 (4)* | | | 9.10 | 10.15 |

Surcharge for the German Youth Stamp Foundation.

## Post and Telecommunications Type

Designs: 60pf + 30pf, Railway mail car, 1900. 80pf + 35pf, Telephone installation, 1900. 100pf + 50pf, Mail truck, 1900.

**1990, Sept. 27**  Litho.  *Perf. 13½x14*
| | | | | |
|---|---|---|---|---|
| 9NB283 | SP377 | 60 +30pf multi | 2.10 | 2.10 |
| 9NB284 | SP377 | 80 +35pf multi | 3.00 | 3.00 |
| 9NB285 | SP377 | 100 +50pf multi | 4.00 | 4.00 |
| *Nos. 9NB283-9NB285 (3)* | | | 9.10 | 9.10 |

Surtax for welfare organizations.

## GERMAN OFFICES ABROAD

### OFFICES IN CHINA

100 Pfennings = 1 Mark
100 Cents = 1 Dollar (1905)

Stamps of Germany,
1889-90, Overprinted in
Black at 56 degree
Angle

| 1898 | Unwmk. | | Perf. 13½x14½ | |
|---|---|---|---|---|
| 1 | A9 | 3pf dark brown | 5.25 | 5.00 |
| a. | | 3pf yellow brown | 9.00 | 12.00 |
| b. | | 3pf reddish ocher | 37.50 | 125.00 |
| 2 | A9 | 5pf green | 2.75 | 2.25 |
| 3 | A10 | 10pf carmine | 5.75 | 6.25 |
| 4 | A10 | 20pf ultramarine | 17.00 | 16.00 |
| 5 | A10 | 25pf orange | 32.50 | 30.00 |
| 6 | A10 | 50pf red brown | 16.00 | 12.50 |
| | | Nos. 1-6 (6) | 79.25 | 72.00 |

#### Overprinted at 45 degree Angle

| 1c | A9 | 3pf yellow brown | 125.00 | 23,000. |
|---|---|---|---|---|
| 1d | A9 | 3pf reddish ocher | 175.00 | |
| e. | | 3pf gray brown | 1,400. | |
| 2a | A9 | 5pf green | 11.50 | 12.50 |
| 3a | A10 | 10pf carmine | 14.00 | 10.50 |
| 4a | A10 | 20pf ultramarine | 12.50 | 10.50 |
| 5a | A10 | 25pf orange | 50.00 | 60.00 |
| 6a | A10 | 50pf red brown | 20.00 | 16.00 |

Value for No. 1c used is for a stamp with
small 1898 Shanghai cancel. Examples with
other cancellations or later Shanghai cancels
sell for about half the value quoted.

### Foochow Issue

Nos. 3 and 3a
Handstamp Surcharged

| 1900 | | | | |
|---|---|---|---|---|
| 16 | A10 | 5pf on 10pf, #3 | 525.00 | 900.00 |
| a. | | On No. 3a | 600.00 | 850.00 |

For similar 5pf surcharges on 10pf carmine,
see Tsingtau Issue, Kiauchau.

### Tientsin Issue

German Stamps of
1900 Issue
Handstamped

| 1900 | | | | |
|---|---|---|---|---|
| 17 | A11 | 3pf brown | 575.00 | 750.00 |
| 18 | A11 | 5pf green | 375.00 | 350.00 |
| 19 | A11 | 10pf carmine | 900.00 | 850.00 |
| 20 | A11 | 20pf ultra | 750.00 | 900.00 |
| 21 | A11 | 30pf org & blk, sal | 6,500. | 6,500. |
| 22 | A11 | 50pf pur & blk, sal | 30,000. | 16,000. |
| 23 | A11 | 80pf lake & blk, rose | 4,500. | 4,500. |

This handstamp is known inverted and
double on most values.
Excellent faked handstamps are plentiful.

### Regular Issue

German Stamps of
1900 Overprinted

A14

---

A15

#### Overprinted Horizontally in Black

| 1901 | | | Perf. 14, 14½ | |
|---|---|---|---|---|
| 24 | A11 | 3pf brown | 1.50 | 1.50 |
| a. | | 3pf light red brown | 35.00 | 35.00 |
| 25 | A11 | 5pf green | 1.50 | 1.10 |
| 26 | A11 | 10pf carmine | 2.50 | 1.10 |
| 27 | A11 | 20pf ultra | 3.25 | 1.50 |
| 28 | A11 | 25pf org & blk, yel | 9.00 | 16.00 |
| 29 | A11 | 30pf org & blk, sal | 9.00 | 13.00 |
| 30 | A11 | 40pf lake & blk | 9.00 | 8.50 |
| 31 | A11 | 50pf pur & blk, sal | 9.00 | 8.50 |
| 32 | A11 | 80pf lake & blk, rose | 11.00 | 11.00 |

#### Overprinted in Black or Red

| 33 | A12 | 1m car rose | 26.00 | 32.50 |
|---|---|---|---|---|
| 34 | A13 | 2m gray blue | 27.50 | 30.00 |
| 35 | A14 | 3m blk vio (R) | 45.00 | 65.00 |
| 36 | A15 | 5m slate & car, I | 450.00 | 600.00 |
| b. | | Red and/or white re-touched | 210.00 | 300.00 |
| 36A | A15 | 5m slate & car, II | 210.00 | 300.00 |
| | | Nos. 24-36A (14) | 814.25 | 1,089. |

See note after Germany No. 65A for information on retouches on No. 36. For description of the 5m Type I and Type II, see note
above Germany No. 62.

#### Surcharged on German Stamps of 1902 in Black or Red

a

b

c

| 1905 | | | | |
|---|---|---|---|---|
| 37 | A16(a) | 1c on 3pf | 2.90 | 3.25 |
| 38 | A16(a) | 2c on 5pf | 2.90 | 1.40 |
| 39 | A16(a) | 4c on 10pf | 5.00 | 1.40 |
| 40 | A16(a) | 10c on 20pf | 2.90 | 1.75 |
| 41 | A16(a) | 20c on 40pf | 20.00 | 15.00 |
| 42 | A16(a) | 40c on 80pf | 32.50 | 13.00 |
| 43 | A17(b) | ½d on 1m | 15.00 | 19.00 |

---

| 44 | A21(b) | 1d on 2m | 17.50 | 21.00 |
|---|---|---|---|---|
| 45 | A19(c) | 1½d on 3m (R) | 15.00 | 45.00 |
| 46 | A20(b) | 2½d on 5m | 110.00 | 300.00 |
| | | Nos. 37-46 (10) | 223.70 | 413.30 |

#### Surcharged on German Stamps of 1905 in Black or Red

| 1906-13 | | | Wmk. 125 | |
|---|---|---|---|---|
| 47 | A16(a) | 1c on 3pf | .40 | 1.25 |
| 48 | A16(a) | 2c on 5pf | .40 | 1.25 |
| 49 | A16(a) | 4c on 10pf | .40 | 1.25 |
| 50 | A16(a) | 10c on 20pf | .85 | 5.75 |
| 51 | A16(a) | 20c on 40pf | .90 | 3.50 |
| 52 | A16(a) | 40c on 80pf | 1.10 | 50.00 |
| 53 | A17(b) | ½d on 1m | 6.00 | 37.50 |
| 54 | A21(b) | 1d on 2m | 7.50 | 37.50 |
| 55 | A19(c) | 1½d on 3m (R) | 7.50 | 110.00 |
| 56 | A20(b) | 2½d on 5m | 29.00 | 65.00 |
| | | Nos. 47-56 (10) | 54.05 | 313.00 |

Forged cancellations exist.

---

### OFFICES IN MOROCCO

100 Centimos = 1 Peseta

Stamps of Germany
Surcharged in Black

| 1899 | Unwmk. | | Perf. 13½x14½ | |
|---|---|---|---|---|
| 1 | A9 | 3c on 3pf dk brn | 3.00 | 2.10 |
| 2 | A9 | 5c on 5pf green | 3.00 | 2.40 |
| 3 | A10 | 10c on 10pf car | 7.50 | 6.25 |
| 4 | A10 | 25c on 20pf ultra | 18.00 | 15.00 |
| 5 | A10 | 30c on 25pf orange | 26.00 | 32.50 |
| 6 | A10 | 60c on 50pf red brn | 22.50 | 37.50 |
| | | Nos. 1-6 (6) | 80.00 | 95.75 |

Before Nos. 1-6 were issued, the same six
basic stamps of Germany's 1889-1900 issue
were overprinted "Marocco" diagonally without
the currency-changing surcharge line, but
were not issued. Value, $750.

German Stamps of
1900 Surcharged

A12

A13

---

A14

A15

#### Black or Red Surcharge

| 1900 | | | Perf. 14, 14½ | |
|---|---|---|---|---|
| 7 | A11 | 3c on 3pf brn | 1.25 | 1.75 |
| 8 | A11 | 5c on 5pf grn | 1.50 | 1.10 |
| 9 | A11 | 10c on 10pf car | 2.00 | 1.10 |
| 10 | A11 | 25c on 20pf ultra | 2.75 | 2.75 |
| 11 | A11 | 30c on 25pf org & blk, yel | 9.00 | 15.00 |
| 12 | A11 | 35c on 30pf org & blk, sal | 6.75 | 6.25 |
| 13 | A11 | 50c on 40pf lake & blk | 6.75 | 6.25 |
| 14 | A11 | 60c on 50pf pur & blk, sal | 14.00 | 32.50 |
| 15 | A11 | 1p on 80pf lake & blk, rose | 11.00 | 11.00 |
| 16 | A12 | 1p25c on 1m car rose | 32.50 | 45.00 |
| 17 | A13 | 2p50c on 2m gray bl | 37.50 | 57.50 |
| 18 | A14 | 3p75c on 3m blk vio (R) | 45.00 | 65.00 |
| 19 | A15 | 6p25c on 5m sl & car, type I | 375.00 | 500.00 |
| b. | | Red and/or white re-touched | 200.00 | 325.00 |
| 19A | A15 | 6p25c on 5m sl & car, type II | 210.00 | 275.00 |
| | | Nos. 7-19A (14) | 755.00 | 1,020. |

A 1903 printing of Nos. 8, 16-18 and 19A
differs in the "M" and "t" of the surcharge. Values are for 1900 printing: Nos. 8, 16-18. 1903
printing: No. 19A.

See note after Germany No. 65A for information on retouches on No. 19. For description of the 5m Type I and Type II, see note
above Germany No. 62.

#### German Stamps of 1902 Surcharged in Black or Red

a

b

c

| 1905 | | | | |
|---|---|---|---|---|
| 20 | A16(a) | 3c on 3pf | 2.75 | 2.75 |
| 21 | A16(a) | 5c on 5pf | 4.75 | 1.10 |
| 22 | A16(a) | 10c on 10pf | 8.25 | 1.10 |
| 23 | A16(a) | 25c on 20pf | 19.00 | 3.00 |
| 24 | A16(a) | 30c on 25pf | 6.75 | 5.50 |
| 25 | A16(a) | 35c on 30pf | 10.00 | 5.50 |
| 26 | A16(a) | 50c on 40pf | 9.50 | 7.75 |
| 27 | A16(a) | 60c on 50pf | 21.00 | 24.00 |
| 28 | A16(a) | 1p on 80pf | 21.00 | 19.00 |
| 29 | A17(b) | 1p25c on 1m | 52.50 | 37.50 |
| 30 | A21(b) | 2p50c on 2m | 95.00 | 150.00 |
| 31 | A19(c) | 3p75c on 3m (R) | 42.50 | 55.00 |
| 32 | A20(b) | 6p25c on 5m | 150.00 | 210.00 |
| | | Nos. 20-32 (13) | 443.00 | 522.20 |

#### Surcharged on Germany No. 54

| 32A | A11(a) | 5c on 5pf | 8.00 | 24.00 |
|---|---|---|---|---|

## German Stamps of 1905 Surcharged

| **1906-11** | | | **Wmk. 125** | |
|---|---|---|---|---|
| 33 | A16(a) | 3c on 3pf | 8.75 | 2.10 |
| 34 | A16(a) | 5c on 5pf | 6.50 | 1.10 |
| 35 | A16(a) | 10c on 10pf | 6.50 | 1.10 |
| 36 | A16(a) | 25c on 20pf | 16.00 | 6.00 |
| 37 | A16(a) | 30c on 25pf | 19.00 | 8.75 |
| 38 | A16(a) | 35c on 30pf | 16.00 | 9.75 |
| 39 | A16(a) | 50c on 40pf | 32.50 | 150.00 |
| 40 | A16(a) | 60c on 50pf | 25.00 | 17.00 |
| 41 | A16(a) | 1p on 80pf | 140.00 | 275.00 |
| 42 | A17(b) | 1p25c on 1m | 62.50 | 175.00 |
| 43 | A21(b) | 2p50c on 2m | 62.50 | 175.00 |
| 44 | A20(b) | 6p25c on 5m | 125.00 | 325.00 |
| | *Nos. 33-44 (12)* | | 520.25 | 1,145. |

Excellent forgeries exist of No. 41.

### Surcharge Spelled "Marokko" in Black or Red

| **1911** | | | | |
|---|---|---|---|---|
| 45 | A16(a) | 3c on 3pf | .55 | .70 |
| 46 | A16(a) | 5c on 5pf | .55 | 1.00 |
| 47 | A16(a) | 10c on 10pf | .55 | 1.10 |
| 48 | A16(a) | 25c on 20pf | .65 | 1.40 |
| 49 | A16(a) | 30c on 25pf | 1.50 | 16.00 |
| 50 | A16(a) | 35c on 30pf | 1.50 | 8.75 |
| 51 | A16(a) | 50c on 40pf | 1.25 | 5.25 |
| 52 | A16(a) | 60c on 50pf | 1.50 | 37.50 |
| 53 | A16(a) | 1p on 80pf | 1.60 | 24.00 |
| 54 | A17(b) | 1p25c on 1m | 2.75 | 65.00 |
| 55 | A21(b) | 2p50c on 2m | 5.25 | 47.50 |
| 56 | A19(c) | 3p75c on 3m (R) | 7.00 | 225.00 |
| 57 | A20(b) | 6p25c on 5m | 19.00 | 325.00 |
| | *Nos. 45-57 (13)* | | 43.65 | 758.20 |

Forged cancellations exist.

---

## OFFICES IN THE TURKISH EMPIRE

---

Unused values for Nos. 1-6 are for stamps with original gum. Stamps without gum sell for about one-third of the figures quoted.

### 40 Paras = 1 Piaster

A1

A2

### German Stamps of 1880-83 Surcharged in Black or Blue

| **1884** | | **Unwmk.** | **Perf. 13½x14½** | |
|---|---|---|---|---|
| 1 | A1 | 10pa on 5pf dull vio | 55.00 | 32.50 |
| 2 | A2 | 20pa on 10pf rose | 80.00 | 80.00 |
| 3 | A2 | 1pi on 20pf ultra (Bk) | 65.00 | 5.25 |
| 4 | A2 | 1pi on 20pf ultra (Bl) | 2,250. | 72.50 |
| 5 | A2 | 1¼pi on 25pf brn | 190.00 | 250.00 |
| 6 | A2 | 2½pi on 50pf gray grn | 100.00 | 80.00 |
| a. | | 2½pi on 50pf deep olive grn | 275.00 | 210.00 |
| | *Nos. 1-6 (6)* | | 2,740. | 520.25 |

There are two types of the surcharge on the 1¼pi and 2½pi stamps, the difference being in the spacing between the figures and the word "PIASTER."

There are re-issues of these stamps which vary only slightly from the originals in overprint measurements.

A3

A4

A5

### German Stamps of 1889-1900 Surcharged in Black

| **1889** | | | | |
|---|---|---|---|---|
| 8 | A3 | 10pa on 5pf grn | 3.75 | 4.00 |
| 9 | A4 | 20pa on 10pf car | 8.00 | 2.75 |
| 10 | A4 | 1pi on 20pf ultra | 5.50 | 2.40 |
| 11 | A5 | 1¼pi on 25pf org | 24.00 | 20.00 |

| 12 | A5 | 2½pi on 50pf choc | 37.50 | 24.00 |
|---|---|---|---|---|
| a. | | 2½pi on 50pf copper brown | 200.00 | 125.00 |
| | *Nos. 8-12 (5)* | | 78.75 | 53.15 |

### German Stamps of 1900 Surcharged

A12

A13

A14

A15

| **1900** | | | **Perf. 14, 14½** | |
|---|---|---|---|---|
| | | | **Black or Red Surcharge** | |
| 13 | A11 | 10pa on 5pf grn | 1.75 | 1.75 |
| 14 | A11 | 20pa on 10pf car | 2.25 | 2.10 |
| 15 | A11 | 1pi on 20pf ultra | 4.75 | 1.90 |
| 16 | A11 | 1¼pi on 25pf org & blk, yel | 6.50 | 3.50 |
| 17 | A11 | 1½pi on 30pf org & blk, sal | 6.50 | 4.75 |
| 18 | A11 | 2pi on 40pf lake & blk | 6.50 | 4.75 |
| 19 | A11 | 2½pi on 50pf pur & blk, sal | 11.00 | 13.50 |
| 20 | A11 | 4pi on 80pf lake & blk, rose | 14.00 | 13.50 |
| 21 | A12 | 5pi on 1m car rose | 40.00 | 40.00 |
| 22 | A13 | 10pi on 2m gray bl | 35.00 | 45.00 |
| 23 | A14 | 15pi on 3m blk vio (R) | 50.00 | 110.00 |
| 24 | A15 | 25pi on 5m sl & car, type I | 350.00 | 675.00 |
| a. | | Double surcharge | | 11,000. |
| d. | | Red and/or white re-touched | 175.00 | 250.00 |
| 24B | A15 | 25pi on 5m sl & car, type II | 210.00 | 375.00 |
| c. | | Double surcharge | | 9,750. |
| | *Nos. 13-24B (13)* | | 738.25 | 1,290. |

See note after Germany #65A for information on retouches on #24. For description of the 5m Type I & Type II, see note above Germany #62.

### German Stamps of 1900 Surcharged in Black

| **1903-05** | | | | |
|---|---|---|---|---|
| 25 | A11 | 10pa on 5pf green | 9.50 | 13.50 |
| 26 | A11 | 20pa on 10pf car | 30.00 | 19.00 |
| 27 | A11 | 1pi on 20pf ultra | 8.75 | 7.25 |

| 28 | A12 | 5pi on 1m car rose | 140.00 | 95.00 |
|---|---|---|---|---|
| 29 | A13 | 10pi on 2m bl ('05) | 160.00 | 275.00 |
| 30 | A15 | 25pi on 5m sl & car | 190.00 | 550.00 |
| a. | | Double surcharge | | 9,000. |
| | *Nos. 25-30 (6)* | | 538.25 | 959.75 |

The 1903-05 surcharges may be easily distinguished from those of 1900 by the added bar at the top of the letter "A."

### German Stamps of 1902 Surcharged in Black or Red

a

b

| **1905** | | | **Unwmk.** | |
|---|---|---|---|---|
| 31 | A16(a) | 10pa on 5pf | 3.50 | 2.50 |
| 32 | A16(a) | 20pa on 10pf | 8.00 | 3.25 |
| 33 | A16(a) | 1pi on 20pf | 19.00 | 2.00 |
| 34 | A16(a) | 1¼pi on 25pf | 9.50 | 8.00 |
| 35 | A16(a) | 1½pi on 30pf | 14.00 | 16.00 |
| 36 | A16(a) | 2pi on 40pf | 22.50 | 16.00 |
| 37 | A16(a) | 2½pi on 50pf | 9.50 | 22.50 |
| 38 | A16(a) | 4pi on 80pf | 27.50 | 17.50 |
| 39 | A17(b) | 5pi on 1m | 47.50 | 40.00 |
| 40 | A21(b) | 10pi on 2m | 40.00 | 47.50 |
| 41 | A19(b) | 15pi on 3m (R) | 47.50 | 55.00 |
| 42 | A20(b) | 25pi on 5m | 240.00 | 550.00 |
| | *Nos. 31-42 (12)* | | 488.50 | 780.25 |

### German Stamps of 1905 Surcharged in Black or Red

| **1906-12** | | | **Wmk. 125** | |
|---|---|---|---|---|
| 43 | A16(a) | 10pa on 5pf | 2.40 | .65 |
| 44 | A16(a) | 20pa on 10pf | 4.75 | .75 |
| 45 | A16(a) | 1pi on 20pf | 6.50 | .75 |
| 46 | A16(a) | 1¼pi on 25pf | 13.00 | 13.00 |
| 47 | A16(a) | 1½pi on 30pf | 13.00 | 10.00 |
| 48 | A16(a) | 2pi on 40pf | 5.25 | 1.75 |
| 49 | A16(a) | 2½pi on 50pf | 9.50 | 17.50 |
| 50 | A16(a) | 4pi on 80pf | 15.00 | 22.50 |
| 51 | A17(b) | 5pi on 1m | 35.00 | 32.50 |
| 52 | A21(b) | 10pi on 2m | 35.00 | 47.50 |
| 53 | A19(b) | 15pi on 3m (R) | 40.00 | 475.00 |
| 54 | A20(b) | 25pi on 5m | 32.50 | 80.00 |
| | *Nos. 43-54 (12)* | | 211.90 | 701.90 |

### German Stamps of 1905 Surcharged Diagonally in Black

| **1908** | | | | |
|---|---|---|---|---|
| 55 | A16 | 5c on 5pf | 1.60 | 2.75 |
| 56 | A16 | 10c on 10pf | 2.75 | 4.75 |
| 57 | A16 | 25c on 20pf | 6.50 | 25.00 |
| 58 | A16 | 50c on 40pf | 27.50 | 60.00 |
| 59 | A16 | 100c on 80pf | 50.00 | 65.00 |
| | *Nos. 55-59 (5)* | | 88.35 | 157.50 |

Forged cancellations exist on #37, 53-54, 57-59.

# GERMAN DEMOCRATIC REPUBLIC

LOCATION — Eastern Germany
GOVT. — Republic
AREA — 41,659 sq. mi.
POP. — 16,701,500 (1983)
CAPITAL — Berlin (Soviet sector)

100 Pfennigs = 1 Deutsche Mark (East)

100 Pfennigs = 1 Mark of the Deutsche Notenbank (MDN) (1965)

100 Pfennigs = 1 Mark of the National Bank (M) (1969)

100 Pfennigs = 1 Deutsche Mark (West) (1990)

Catalogue values for unused stamps in this country are for Never Hinged items, beginning with Scott 48 in the regular postage section, Scott B14 in the semipostal section, Scott C1 in the airpost section, and Scott O1 official section.

**Watermarks**

Watermark 292, see Germany.

Wmk. 297 —
DDR and Post Horn

Wmk. 313 —
Quatrefoil and DDR

## FOR USE IN ALL PROVINCES IN THE RUSSIAN ZONE

When the mark was revalued in June, 1948, a provisional overprint, consisting of various city and town names and post office or zone numerals, was applied by hand in black, violet or blue at innumerable post offices to their stocks.

Germany Nos. 557 to 573 Overprinted in Black

**1948, July 3    Wmk. 284    Perf. 14**

| | | | | |
|---|---|---|---|---|
| 10N1 | A120 | 2pf brown blk | .20 | .20 |
| 10N2 | A120 | 6pf purple | .20 | .30 |
| 10N3 | A121 | 8pf red | .20 | .30 |
| 10N4 | A121 | 10pf yellow grn | .20 | .30 |
| 10N5 | A122 | 12pf gray | .20 | .30 |
| 10N6 | A120 | 15pf choco-late | .20 | .30 |

---

| | | | | |
|---|---|---|---|---|
| 10N7 | A123 | 16pf dk blue grn | .20 | .50 |
| 10N8 | A121 | 20pf blue | .20 | .30 |
| 10N9 | A123 | 24pf brown org | .20 | .25 |
| 10N10 | A120 | 25pf orange yel | .20 | .25 |
| 10N11 | A122 | 30pf red | .25 | .30 |
| 10N12 | A121 | 40pf red violet | .20 | .30 |
| 10N13 | A123 | 50pf ultra | .20 | .65 |
| 10N14 | A122 | 60pf red brown | .25 | .65 |
| a. | | 60pf brown red | 30.00 | 100.00 |
| 10N15 | A122 | 80pf dark blue | .65 | .80 |
| 10N16 | A122 | 84pf emerald | .65 | 1.10 |
| | *Nos. 10N1-10N16 (16)* | | 4.20 | 6.80 |
| | Set, never hinged | | 10.00 | |

Same Overprint on Numeral Stamps of Germany, 1946

**1948, Sept.**

| | | | | |
|---|---|---|---|---|
| 10N17 | A119 | 5pf yellow grn | .20 | .70 |
| 10N18 | A119 | 30pf olive | .40 | 2.00 |
| 10N19 | A119 | 45pf brt red | .20 | .80 |
| 10N20 | A119 | 75pf deep ultra | .20 | .80 |
| 10N21 | A119 | 84pf emerald | .40 | 1.60 |
| | *Nos. 10N17-10N21 (5)* | | 1.40 | 5.90 |
| | Set, never hinged | | 3.50 | |

Nos 10N1-10N21 all exist with inverted overprint, and majority with double overprint.

Same Overprint on Berlin-Brandenburg Nos. 11N1-11N7

**Unwmk.**

**1948, Sept.    Litho.    Perf. 14**

| | | | | |
|---|---|---|---|---|
| 10N22 | OS1 | 5pf green | .20 | .65 |
| a. | | Serrate roulette | .20 | .65 |
| 10N23 | OS1 | 6pf violet | .20 | .65 |
| 10N24 | OS1 | 8pf red | .20 | .65 |
| 10N25 | OS1 | 10pf brown | .20 | .65 |
| 10N26 | OS1 | 12pf rose | .20 | 1.20 |
| 10N27 | OS1 | 20pf blue | .20 | 1.00 |
| 10N28 | OS1 | 30pf olive | .20 | 1.20 |
| | *Nos. 10N22-10N28 (7)* | | 1.40 | 6.00 |
| | Set, never hinged | | 2.75 | |

The overprint made #10N22-10N28 valid for postage throughout the Russian Zone.

Gerhard Hauptmann — OS2

Designs: 2pf, 20pf, Käthe Kollwitz. 40pf, Gerhard Hauptmann. 8pf, 50pf, Karl Marx. 10pf, 84pf, August Bebel. 12pf, 30pf, Friedrich Engels. 15pf, 60pf, G. W. F. Hegel. 16pf, 25pf, Rudolf Virchow. 24pf, 80pf, Ernst Thälmann.

**Perf. 13x12½**

**1948    Typo.    Wmk. 292**

| | | | | |
|---|---|---|---|---|
| 10N29 | OS2 | 2pf gray | .25 | .80 |
| 10N30 | OS2 | 6pf violet | .25 | .80 |
| 10N31 | OS2 | 8pf red brn | .25 | .80 |
| 10N32 | OS2 | 10pf blue grn | .20 | .80 |
| 10N33 | OS2 | 12pf blue | 1.60 | .80 |
| 10N34 | OS2 | 15pf brown | .20 | 1.60 |
| 10N35 | OS2 | 16pf turquoise | .20 | .80 |
| 10N36 | OS2 | 20pf maroon | .20 | 1.00 |
| 10N37 | OS2 | 24pf carmine | 1.60 | .80 |
| 10N38 | OS2 | 25pf olive grn | .40 | 1.60 |
| 10N39 | OS2 | 30pf red | 1.25 | 1.60 |
| 10N40 | OS2 | 40pf red violet | 1.25 | 1.60 |
| 10N41 | OS2 | 50pf dk ultra | .25 | 1.60 |
| 10N42 | OS2 | 60pf dull green | 1.60 | 1.60 |
| 10N43 | OS2 | 80pf dark blue | .50 | 1.00 |
| 10N44 | OS2 | 84pf brown lake | 1.10 | 2.75 |
| | *Nos. 10N29-10N44 (16)* | | 11.10 | 19.95 |
| | Set, never hinged | | 35.00 | |

See German Democratic Republic #122-136.

Karl Liebknecht and Rosa Luxemburg OS3

**Perf. 13½x13**

**1949, Jan. 15    Litho.    Wmk. 292**

| | | | | |
|---|---|---|---|---|
| 10N45 | OS3 | 24pf rose | .20 | .70 |
| | Never hinged | | .40 | |

30th anniv. of the death of Karl Liebknecht and Rosa Luxemburg, German socialists.

---

Dove and Laurel — OS4

**1949**

| | | | | |
|---|---|---|---|---|
| 10N46 | OS4 | 24pf carmine rose | .50 | 2.00 |
| | Never hinged | | 1.00 | |

Overprinted in Black: "3. Deutscher Volkskongress 29.-30. Mai 1949"

**1949, May 29**

| | | | | |
|---|---|---|---|---|
| 10N47 | OS4 | 24pf carmine rose | .65 | 3.00 |
| | Never hinged | | 2.00 | |

Nos. 10N46 and 10N47 were issued for the 3rd German People's Congress.

---

# GERMAN DEMOCRATIC REPUBLIC

Catalogue values for unused stamps in this section, from this point to the end of the section, are for Never Hinged items.

## Canceled to Order

The government stamp agency started in 1949 to sell canceled sets of new issues.

Used values are for CTO's for Nos. 48-2831, except for souvenir sheets, which are valued as postally used.

Pigeon, Letter and Globe A5

**Wmk. Flowers Multiple (292)**

**1949, Oct. 9    Litho.    Perf. 13½**

| | | | | |
|---|---|---|---|---|
| 48 | A5 | 50pf lt blue & dk blue | 12.00 | 10.50 |

75th anniv. of the UPU.

Letter Carriers — A6

Skier — A7

**1949, Oct. 27      Perf. 13**

| | | | | |
|---|---|---|---|---|
| 49 | A6 | 12pf blue | 8.50 | 10.00 |
| 50 | A6 | 30pf red | 12.50 | 17.50 |

"Day of the International Postal Workers' Trade Union," October 27-29, 1949.

**1950, Mar. 2      Perf. 13**

| | | | | |
|---|---|---|---|---|
| 51 | A7 | 12pf shown | 6.50 | 4.00 |
| 52 | A7 | 24pf Skater | 8.00 | 6.50 |

1st German Winter Sport Championship Matches, Schierke, 1950.

Globe and Sun — A8

**1950, May 1      Typo.**

| | | | | |
|---|---|---|---|---|
| 53 | A8 | 30pf deep carmine | 20.00 | 16.00 |

60th anniv. of Labor Day.

---

A9

Pres. Wilhelm Pieck — A10

**1950-51    Wmk. 292    Perf. 13x12½**

| | | | | |
|---|---|---|---|---|
| 54 | A9 | 12pf dark blue | 22.50 | 1.75 |
| 55 | A9 | 24pf red brown | 32.50 | 1.00 |

**Perf. 13x13½**

| | | | | |
|---|---|---|---|---|
| 56 | A10 | 1m olive green | 32.50 | 5.75 |

**Litho.**

| | | | | |
|---|---|---|---|---|
| 57 | A10 | 2m red brown | 19.00 | 4.25 |

**Engr.**

| | | | | |
|---|---|---|---|---|
| 57A | A10 | 5m deep blue ('51) | 7.00 | 1.50 |
| | *Nos. 54-57A (5)* | | 113.50 | 14.25 |

See Nos. 113-117, 120-121.

Leonhard Euler — A11

Miner — A12

Portraits: 5pf, Alexander von Humboldt. 6pf, Theodor Mommsen. 8pf, Wilhelm von Humboldt. 10pf, H. L. F. von Helmholtz. 12pf, Max Planck. 16pf, Jacob Grimm. 20pf, W. H. Nernst. 24pf, Gottfried von Leibnitz. 50pf, Adolf von Harnack.

**Wmk. 292**

**1950, July 10    Litho.    Perf. 12½**

| | | | | |
|---|---|---|---|---|
| 58 | A11 | 1pf gray | 5.00 | 1.60 |
| 59 | A11 | 5pf dp green | 5.75 | 5.00 |
| 60 | A11 | 6pf purple | 11.50 | 5.00 |
| 61 | A11 | 8pf orange brn | 18.00 | 11.50 |
| 62 | A11 | 10pf dk gray grn | 16.00 | 11.50 |
| 63 | A11 | 12pf dk blue | 15.00 | 3.25 |
| 64 | A11 | 16pf Prus blue | 20.00 | 20.00 |
| 65 | A11 | 20pf violet brn | 18.00 | 16.50 |
| 66 | A11 | 24pf red | 20.00 | 3.25 |
| 67 | A11 | 50pf dp ultra | 30.00 | 21.00 |
| | *Nos. 58-67 (10)* | | 159.25 | 98.60 |
| | Set, hinged | | 50.00 | |

250th anniv. of the founding of the Academy of Science, Berlin.
See Nos. 352-354.

**1950, Sept. 1      Perf. 13**

Design: 24pf, Smelting copper.

| | | | | |
|---|---|---|---|---|
| 68 | A12 | 12pf blue | 6.00 | 7.50 |
| 69 | A12 | 24pf dark red | 9.00 | 8.25 |

750th anniv. of the opening of the Mannsfeld copper mines.

Symbols of a Democratic Vote — A13

Hand Between Dove and Tank — A14

**1950, Sept. 28**

| | | | | |
|---|---|---|---|---|
| 70 | A13 | 24pf brown red | 16.00 | 6.00 |

Publicizing the election of Oct. 15, 1950.

**1950, Dec. 15   Litho.   *Perf. 13***

Designs show hand shielding dove from: 8pf, Exploding shell. 12pf, Atomic explosion. 24pf, Cemetery.

| | | | | |
|---|---|---|---|---|
| 71 | A14 | 6pf violet blue | 4.00 | 3.25 |
| 72 | A14 | 8pf brown | 4.00 | 1.50 |
| 73 | A14 | 12pf blue | 5.75 | 3.25 |
| 74 | A14 | 24pf red | 5.75 | 1.50 |
| | | *Nos. 71-74 (4)* | 19.50 | 9.50 |

Issued to publicize the "Fight for Peace."

Tobogganing A15

Design: 24pf, Ski jump.

**1951, Feb. 3   Litho.   *Perf. 13***

| | | | | |
|---|---|---|---|---|
| 76 | A15 | 12pf blue | 8.25 | 7.50 |
| 77 | A15 | 24pf rose | 10.50 | 9.00 |

Issued to publicize the second Winter Sports Championship Matches at Oberhof.

A16

**1951, Mar. 4   Wmk. 292   *Perf. 13***

| | | | | |
|---|---|---|---|---|
| 78 | A16 | 24pf rose carmine | 17.50 | 14.00 |
| 79 | A16 | 50pf violet blue | 17.50 | 14.00 |

Issued to publicize the 1951 Leipzig Fair.

Pres. Wilhelm Pieck and Pres. Boleslaw Bierut Shaking Hands Across Oder-Neisse Frontier — A17

**1951, Apr. 22   *Perf. 13***

| | | | | |
|---|---|---|---|---|
| 80 | A17 | 24pf scarlet | 21.00 | 19.00 |
| 81 | A17 | 50pf blue | 21.00 | 19.00 |

Visit of Pres. Boleslaw Bierut of Poland to the Russian Zone of Germany.

Mao Tse-tung A18

Redistribution of Chinese Land — A19

**1951, June 27   *Perf. 13***

| | | | | |
|---|---|---|---|---|
| 82 | A18 | 12pf dark green | 90.00 | 27.50 |
| 83 | A19 | 24pf deep carmine | 115.00 | 35.00 |
| 84 | A18 | 50pf violet blue | 90.00 | 35.00 |
| | | *Nos. 82-84 (3)* | 295.00 | 97.50 |
| | | Set, hinged | 150.00 | |

Issued to publicize East Germany's friendship toward Communist China.

Boy Raising Flag A20    5-Year Plan Symbolism A21

Design: 24pf, 50pf, Girls dancing.

**1951, Aug. 3**
**Grayish Paper, Except 30pf**

| | | | | |
|---|---|---|---|---|
| 85 | A20 | 12pf choc & org brn | 12.00 | 8.00 |
| 86 | A20 | 24pf dk car & yel grn | 12.00 | 5.00 |
| 87 | A20 | 30pf dk bl grn & org brn, *cit* | 14.50 | 10.00 |
| 88 | A20 | 50pf vio bl & dk car | 14.50 | 10.00 |
| | | *Nos. 85-88 (4)* | 53.00 | 33.00 |

3rd World Youth Festival, Berlin, 1951.

**1951, Sept. 2   Typo.   Wmk. 292**

| | | | | |
|---|---|---|---|---|
| 89 | A21 | 24pf multicolored | 5.00 | 3.00 |

East Germany's Five-Year Plan.

Karl Liebknecht — A22

Father and Children with Stamp Collection A23

**1951, Oct. 7   Litho.   *Perf. 13½x13***

| | | | | |
|---|---|---|---|---|
| 90 | A22 | 24pf red & blue gray | 5.00 | 2.50 |

Karl Liebknecht, socialist, 80th birth anniv.

**1951, Oct. 28   *Perf. 13***

| | | | | |
|---|---|---|---|---|
| 91 | A23 | 12pf deep blue | 5.50 | 3.00 |

Stamp Day, Oct. 28, 1951.

Stalin and Wilhelm Pieck A24

Design: 12pf, Pavel Bykov and Erich Wirth.

**1951**

| | | | | |
|---|---|---|---|---|
| 92 | A24 | 12pf deep blue | 5.00 | 4.00 |
| 93 | A24 | 24pf red | 5.00 | 5.50 |

Month of East German-Soviet friendship. Issue dates: 12pf, Dec. 15, 24pf, Dec. 1.

Winter Sports Championship Matches, Oberhof, 1952 — A25

Design: 12pf, Skier. 24pf, Ski jump.

**1952, Jan. 12   Wmk. 292**

| | | | | |
|---|---|---|---|---|
| 94 | A25 | 12pf blue green | 4.50 | 3.00 |
| 95 | A25 | 24pf deep blue | 4.50 | 3.00 |

Ludwig van Beethoven, 125th Death Anniv. — A26

**1952, Mar. 26   *Perf. 13½***

Design: 12pf, Beethoven full face.

| | | | | |
|---|---|---|---|---|
| 96 | A26 | 12pf bl gray & vio bl | 2.00 | .75 |
| 97 | A26 | 24pf gray & red brn | 2.75 | 1.00 |

See Nos. 100-102.

Cyclists — A27

Klement Gottwald — A28

**1952, May 5   Photo.   *Perf. 13x13½***

| | | | | |
|---|---|---|---|---|
| 98 | A27 | 12pf blue | 3.75 | 1.80 |

5th International Bicycle Peace Race, Warsaw-Berlin-Prague.

**1952, May 1**

| | | | | |
|---|---|---|---|---|
| 99 | A28 | 24pf violet blue | 3.00 | 2.50 |

Friendship between German Democratic Republic and Czechoslovakia.

**Type of 1952**

Portraits: 6pf, G. F. Handel. 8pf, Albert Lortzing. 50pf, C. M. von Weber.

**1952, July 5   Litho.   Wmk. 297**

| | | | | |
|---|---|---|---|---|
| 100 | A26 | 6pf brn buff & choc | 2.25 | 1.50 |
| 101 | A26 | 8pf pink & dp rose pink | 3.00 | 2.75 |
| 102 | A26 | 50pf bl gray & dp bl | 3.00 | 3.00 |
| | | *Nos. 100-102 (3)* | 8.25 | 7.25 |

Victor Hugo — A29

Portraits: 20pf, Leonardo da Vinci. 24pf, Nicolai Gogol. 35pf, Avicenna.

**Wmk. 292**

**1952, Aug. 11   Photo.   *Perf. 13***

| | | | | |
|---|---|---|---|---|
| 103 | A29 | 12pf brown | 3.25 | 4.75 |
| 104 | A29 | 20pf green | 3.25 | 4.75 |
| 105 | A29 | 24pf rose | 3.25 | 4.75 |
| 106 | A29 | 35pf blue | 4.75 | 6.50 |
| | | *Nos. 103-106 (4)* | 14.50 | 20.75 |

Machine, Globe and Dove — A30

**1952, Sept. 7   Wmk. 297   *Perf. 13***

| | | | | |
|---|---|---|---|---|
| 108 | A30 | 24pf red | 2.25 | 1.00 |
| 109 | A30 | 35pf deep blue | 2.25 | 2.00 |

Issued to publicize the 1952 Leipzig Fair.

Friedrich Ludwig Jahn — A31

**1952, Oct. 15   Litho.**

| | | | | |
|---|---|---|---|---|
| 110 | A31 | 12pf blue | 2.10 | 1.25 |

Jahn (1778-1852), introduced gymnastics to Germany, and was a politician.

Halle University — A32

**1952, Oct. 18   Photo.**

| | | | | |
|---|---|---|---|---|
| 111 | A32 | 24pf green | 2.25 | 1.00 |

450th anniv. of the founding of Halle University, Wittenberg.

Stamp, Flags, Wreath, Dove and Hammer — A33

**1952, Oct. 26**

| | | | | |
|---|---|---|---|---|
| 112 | A33 | 24pf red brown | 2.50 | 1.25 |

Stamp Day, Oct. 26, 1952.

**Pieck Types of 1950**
**Perf. 13x12½**

**1952-53   Wmk. 297   Typo.**

| | | | | |
|---|---|---|---|---|
| 113 | A9 | 5pf blue green | 10.00 | 2.75 |
| 114 | A9 | 12pf dark blue | 26.00 | 1.50 |
| 115 | A9 | 24pf red brown | 24.00 | 1.25 |

**Perf. 13x13½**

| | | | | |
|---|---|---|---|---|
| 116 | A10 | 1m olive green | 32.50 | 16.00 |

**Litho.   *Perf. 13***

| | | | | |
|---|---|---|---|---|
| 117 | A10 | 2m red brown ('53) | 27.50 | 3.25 |
| | | *Nos. 113-117 (5)* | 120.00 | 24.75 |
| | | Set, hinged | 35.00 | |

Globe, Dove and St. Stephen's Cathedral — A34

Pres. Wilhelm Pieck — A35

**1952, Dec. 8   Photo.   *Perf. 13***

| | | | | |
|---|---|---|---|---|
| 118 | A34 | 24pf brt carmine | 1.60 | *2.50* |
| 119 | A34 | 35pf deep blue | 1.60 | *4.00* |

Issued to publicize the Congress of Nations for Peace, Vienna, Dec. 12-19, 1952.

**1953   *Perf. 13x13½***

| | | | | |
|---|---|---|---|---|
| 120 | A35 | 1m olive | 14.00 | .50 |
| *a.* | | 1m dark olive | 22.50 | 2.50 |
| 121 | A35 | 2m red brown | 10.00 | .50 |

See Nos. 339-340, 532.

## Portrait Types of Russian Occupation, 1948

Designs as before.

*Perf. 13x12½*

| 1953 | | Typo. | | Wmk. 297 | |
|---|---|---|---|---|---|
| **122** | OS2 | 2pf gray | | 2.50 | *3.00* |
| **123** | OS2 | 6pf purple | | 2.50 | 1.75 |
| **124** | OS2 | 8pf red brown | | 1.75 | 1.75 |
| **125** | OS2 | 10pf blue grn | | 3.50 | 3.00 |
| **126** | OS2 | 15pf brown | | 11.50 | 11.50 |
| **127** | OS2 | 16pf turquoise | | 4.25 | 3.00 |
| **128** | OS2 | 20pf maroon | | 7.50 | 1.50 |
| **129** | OS2 | 25pf olive grn | | 180.00 | *200.00* |
| **130** | OS2 | 30pf red | | 13.00 | 7.50 |
| **131** | OS2 | 40pf red violet | | 3.50 | 2.50 |
| **132** | OS2 | 50pf dk ultra | | 22.00 | 16.00 |
| **133** | OS2 | 60pf dull green | | 4.25 | 2.50 |
| **134** | OS2 | 80pf dark blue | | 6.00 | 1.75 |
| *a.* | | Varnish coating, dark ultramarine | | 11.00 | 7.50 |
| **135** | OS2 | 80pf crimson | | 11.00 | 7.50 |
| **136** | OS2 | 84pf brown lake | | 50.00 | *65.00* |
| | | *Nos. 122-136 (15)* | | 323.25 | 328.25 |
| | | Set, hinged | | 100.00 | |

"Industry" and Red Flag — A36

Marx and Engels — A37

Karl Marx Speaking — A38

Karl Marx Medallion — A39

Designs: 12pf, Spasski tower and communist flag. 16pf, Marching workers. 24pf, Portrait of Karl Marx. 35pf, Marx addressing audience. 48pf, Karl Marx and Friedrich Engels. 60pf, Red banner above heads and shoulders of workers.

| 1953 | | Photo. | | Perf. 13 | |
|---|---|---|---|---|---|
| **137** | A36 | 6pf grnsh gray & red | | 1.50 | .35 |
| **138** | A37 | 10pf grnsh gray & dk brn | | 4.00 | .75 |
| **139** | A36 | 12pf grn, dp plum & dk grn | | 1.10 | .50 |
| **140** | A37 | 16pf vio bl & dk car | | 3.00 | 1.75 |
| **141** | A38 | 20pf brown & buff | | 1.50 | .75 |
| **142** | A38 | 24pf brown & red | | 3.00 | .75 |
| **143** | A36 | 35pf dp pur & cr | | 3.00 | 2.50 |
| **144** | A36 | 48pf dk ol grn & red brn | | 2.25 | .75 |
| *a.* | | Souvenir sheet of 6 | | 100.00 | *150.00* |
| | | Hinged | | 35.00 | |
| **145** | A37 | 60pf vio brn & red | | 3.75 | 2.50 |
| **146** | A39 | 84pf blue & brown | | 3.25 | 1.75 |
| *a.* | | Souvenir sheet of 4 | | 100.00 | *150.00* |
| | | Hinged | | 35.00 | |
| | | *Nos. 137-146 (10)* | | 26.35 | 12.35 |

No. 144a contains one each of the denominations in types A36 and A38. Perf. and imperf.

No. 146a contains one each of the denominations in types A37 and A39. Perf. and imperf.

---

Maxim Gorky — A40

Bicycle Racers — A41

**1953, Mar. 28**

| **147** | A40 | 35pf brown | | .35 | .25 |
|---|---|---|---|---|---|

**1953, May 2    Wmk. 297    Perf. 13**

24pf, 60pf, Different views of bicycle race.

| **148** | A41 | 24pf bluish green | | 2.50 | 2.00 |
|---|---|---|---|---|---|
| **149** | A41 | 35pf deep ultra | | 1.25 | 1.25 |
| **150** | A41 | 60pf chocolate | | 1.60 | 1.60 |
| | | *Nos. 148-150 (3)* | | 5.35 | 4.85 |

6th International Bicycle Peace Race.

Heinrich von Kleist A42

Woman Mariner A43

20pf, Evangelical Marienkirche. 24pf, Sailboat on Oder River. 35pf, City Hall, Frankfurt-on-Oder.

**1953, July 6    Litho.**

| **151** | A42 | 16pf chocolate | | 1.60 | *2.00* |
|---|---|---|---|---|---|
| **152** | A42 | 20pf blue green | | 1.00 | *1.60* |
| **153** | A42 | 24pf rose red | | 1.60 | *2.00* |
| **154** | A42 | 35pf violet blue | | 1.60 | *2.50* |
| | | *Nos. 151-154 (4)* | | 5.80 | 8.10 |

700th anniversary of the founding of Frankfurt-on-Oder.

**1953    Litho.    Perf. 13x12½**

Designs: 1pf, Coal miner. 6pf, German and Soviet workers. 8pf, Mother teaching Marxist principles. 10pf, Machinists. 12pf, Worker, peasant and intellectual. 15pf, Teletype operator. 16pf, Steel worker. 20pf, Bad Elster. 24pf, Stalin Boulevard. 25pf, Locomotive building. 30pf, Dancing couple. 35pf, Sports Hall, Berlin. 40pf, Laboratory worker. 48pf, Zwinger Castle, Dresden. 60pf, Launching ship. 80pf, Agricultural workers. 84pf, Dove and East German family.

| **155** | A43 | 1pf black brown | | 1.60 | .20 |
|---|---|---|---|---|---|
| **156** | A43 | 5pf emerald | | 2.00 | .20 |
| **157** | A43 | 6pf violet | | 2.00 | .20 |
| **158** | A43 | 8pf orange brn | | 2.75 | .20 |
| **159** | A43 | 10pf blue green | | 2.00 | .20 |
| **160** | A43 | 12pf blue | | 2.00 | .20 |
| **161** | A43 | 15pf purple | | 3.25 | .20 |
| **162** | A43 | 16pf dk violet | | 5.00 | .20 |
| **163** | A43 | 20pf olive | | 4.75 | .20 |
| **163A** | A43 | 24pf carmine | | 8.75 | .20 |
| **164** | A43 | 25pf dk green | | 6.25 | .20 |
| **165** | A43 | 30pf dp car | | 6.25 | .20 |
| **166** | A43 | 35pf violet bl | | 19.00 | .20 |
| **167** | A43 | 40pf rose red | | 16.00 | .20 |
| **168** | A43 | 48pf rose red | | 16.00 | .20 |
| **169** | A43 | 60pf deep blue | | 16.00 | .20 |
| **170** | A43 | 80pf aqua | | 17.50 | .20 |
| **171** | A43 | 84pf chocolate | | 16.00 | .20 |
| | | *Nos. 155-171 (18)* | | 147.10 | 3.60 |
| | | Set, hinged | | 40.00 | |

See Nos. 187-204, 227-230A, 330-338, 476-482. For surcharges see #216-223A.

Used values of Nos. 155-171 are for cto reprints with printed cancellations. The reprints differ slightly from originals in design and shade.

Power Shovel — A44

Design: 35pf, Road-building machine.

**1953, Aug. 29    Photo.    Perf. 13**

| **172** | A44 | 24pf red brown | | 2.25 | 2.00 |
|---|---|---|---|---|---|
| **173** | A44 | 35pf deep green | | 3.25 | 2.50 |

The 1953 Leipzig Fair.

---

G. W. von Knobelsdorff and Berlin State Opera House — A45

Design: 35pf, Balthasar Neumann and Wurzburg bishop's palace.

**1953, Sept. 16    Perf. 13x12½**

| **174** | A45 | 24pf cerise | | 1.50 | 1.50 |
|---|---|---|---|---|---|
| **175** | A45 | 35pf dk slate blue | | 2.00 | 1.50 |

200th anniv. of the deaths of G. W. von Knobelsdorff and Balthasar Neumann, architects.

Lucas Cranach — A46

Nurse Applying Bandage — A47

**1953, Oct. 16    Perf. 13x13½**

| **176** | A46 | 24pf brown | | 3.25 | 1.50 |
|---|---|---|---|---|---|

400th anniversary of the death of Lucas Cranach (1472-1553), painter.

**Perf. 13½x13**

**1953, Oct. 23    Wmk. 297**

| **177** | A47 | 24pf brown & red | | 2.50 | 1.50 |
|---|---|---|---|---|---|

Issued to honor the Red Cross.

Mail Delivery — A48

Lion and Lioness — A49

**1953, Oct. 25    Photo.**

| **178** | A48 | 24pf blue gray | | 3.25 | .60 |
|---|---|---|---|---|---|

Stamp Day, Oct. 24, 1953.

**1953, Nov. 2    Perf. 13x13½**

| **179** | A49 | 24pf olive brown | | 1.75 | .50 |
|---|---|---|---|---|---|

75th anniversary of Leipzig Zoo.

Thomas Muntzer and Attackers A50

16pf, H. F. K. vom Stein. 20pf, Ferdinand von Schill leading cavalry. 24pf, G. L. Blucher and battle scene. 35pf, Students fighting for National Unity. 48pf, Revolution of 1848.

**1953, Nov.    Photo.    Perf. 13x12½**

| **180** | A50 | 12pf brown | | 1.50 | .60 |
|---|---|---|---|---|---|
| **181** | A50 | 16pf dp brown | | 1.50 | .60 |
| **182** | A50 | 20pf dk car rose | | 1.50 | .40 |
| **183** | A50 | 24pf deep blue | | 1.50 | .40 |

---

| **184** | A50 | 35pf dk green | | 2.50 | 1.60 |
|---|---|---|---|---|---|
| **185** | A50 | 48pf dk brown | | 2.50 | 1.25 |
| | | *Nos. 180-185 (6)* | | 11.00 | 4.85 |

Issued to honor German patriots.

Franz Schubert — A51

Gotthold E. Lessing — A52

**1953, Nov. 13    Perf. 13½x13**

| **186** | A51 | 48pf brt orange brn | | 2.75 | 1.50 |
|---|---|---|---|---|---|

Death of Franz Schubert, 125th anniv.

## Types of 1953 Redrawn

Designs as before.

| 1953-54 | | Typo. | | Perf. 13x12½ | |
|---|---|---|---|---|---|
| **187** | A43 | 1pf black brn | | .80 | .20 |
| **188** | A43 | 5pf emerald | | 3.50 | .20 |
| *a.* | | Bklt. pane, 3 #188 + 3 #227 | | 24.00 | 24.00 |
| *b.* | | Bklt. pane, 3 #188 + 3 #228 | | 24.00 | 24.00 |
| **189** | A43 | 6pf purple | | 4.00 | .20 |
| **190** | A43 | 8pf orange brn | | 5.00 | .20 |
| **191** | A43 | 10pf blue grn | | 32.50 | .20 |
| **192** | A43 | 12pf grnsh blue | | 5.50 | .20 |
| **193** | A43 | 15pf brt vio ('54) | | 20.00 | .20 |
| **194** | A43 | 16pf dk purple | | 6.00 | .20 |
| **195** | A43 | 20pf olive ('54) | | 85.00 | .20 |
| **196** | A43 | 24pf carmine | | 6.25 | .20 |
| **197** | A43 | 25pf dk bl grn | | 4.00 | .20 |
| **198** | A43 | 30pf dp carmine | | 5.00 | .20 |
| **199** | A43 | 35pf dp vio bl | | 5.50 | .20 |
| **200** | A43 | 40pf rose red ('54) | | 12.00 | .20 |
| **201** | A43 | 48pf rose vio | | 11.00 | .20 |
| **202** | A43 | 60pf blue | | 17.50 | .20 |
| **203** | A43 | 80pf aqua | | 4.00 | .20 |
| **204** | A43 | 84pf chocolate | | 20.00 | .20 |
| | | *Nos. 187-204 (18)* | | 247.55 | 3.60 |
| | | Set, hinged | | 60.00 | |

Nos. 155-171 were printed from screened halftones, and shading consists of dots. Shading in lines without screen on Nos. 187-204. Designers' and engravers' names added below design on all values except 6, 12, 16 and 35pf. There are many other minor differences.

See note on used values after No. 171.

**1954, Jan. 20    Photo.    Perf. 13**

| **205** | A52 | 20pf dark green | | 2.00 | .90 |
|---|---|---|---|---|---|

225th anniversary of the birth of G. E. Lessing, dramatist.

Dove Over Conference Table — A53

Joseph V. Stalin — A54

**1954, Jan. 25    Perf. 12½x13**

| **206** | A53 | 12pf blue | | 1.75 | .75 |
|---|---|---|---|---|---|

Four Power Conference, Berlin, 1954.

**1954, Mar. 5    Typo.    Perf. 13x12½**

| **207** | A54 | 20pf gray, dk brn & red org | | 2.50 | .75 |
|---|---|---|---|---|---|

1st anniv. of the death of Joseph V. Stalin.

Cyclists A55

Design: 24pf, Cyclists passing farm.

**1954, Apr. 30**     **Photo.**
208 A55 10pf brown   1.20 .75
209 A55 24pf dull green   2.00 1.20

7th International Bicycle Peace Race.

Dancers — A56     Fritz
Reuter — A57

Design: 24pf, Boy, two girls and flag.

**1954, June 3**     **Perf. 13**
210 A56 12pf emerald   1.00 .75
211 A56 24pf rose brown   1.00 .75

Issued to publicize the 2nd German youth meeting for peace, unity and freedom.

**1954, July 12**
212 A57 24pf sepia   1.75 1.00

Death of Fritz Reuter, writer, 80th anniv.

Ernst
Thälmann — A58

**1954, Aug. 18**     **Perf. 13½x13**
213 A58 24pf red org & indigo   1.00 .65

10th anniv. of the death of Ernst Thälmann (1886-1944), Communist leader.

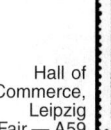

Hall of
Commerce,
Leipzig
Fair — A59

**1954, Sept. 4**     **Perf. 13x13½**
214 A59 24pf dark red   .85 .45
215 A59 35pf gray blue   .85 .60

Issued to publicize the 1954 Leipzig Fair.

**Redrawn Types of 1953-54
Surcharged with New Value and "X"
in Black**

**1954**     **Typo.**     **Perf. 13x12½**
216 A43 5pf on 6pf purple   1.00 .20
217 A43 5pf on 8pf org brn   1.40 .20
218 A43 10pf on 12pf grnsh bl   1.00 .20
219 A43 15pf on 16pf dk pur   1.00 .20
220 A43 20pf on 24pf car   1.10 .20
221 A43 40pf on 48pf rose vio   3.00 .20
222 A43 50pf on 60pf blue   3.00 .20
223 A43 70pf on 84pf choc   10.00 .20
    Nos. 216-223 (8)   21.50 1.60

See note on used values after No. 171.

**No. 163A Surcharged with New
Value and "X" in Black**

**1955**     **Litho.**
223A A43 20pf on 24pf car   .80 .25

Counterfeit surcharges exist on other values of the lithographed set (Nos. 155-171).

Pres.
Wilhelm
Pieck and
Flags
A60

**1954, Oct. 6**     **Photo.**
224 A60 20pf brown   2.25 .90
225 A60 35pf greenish blue   2.25 1.00

5th anniv. of the founding of the German Democratic Republic.

---

Cologne
Cathedral,
Leipzig
Monument and
Unissued Stamp
Design — A61

**1954, Oct. 23**     **Perf. 13x13½**
226 A61 20pf brt car rose   1.50 .75
   a.   Souvenir sheet, imperf.   50.00 40.00

Stamp Day. No. 226a has frame and inscription in blue. Size: 60x80mm.

**Redrawn Types of 1953-54**

Designs: 10pf, Worker, peasant and intellectual. 15pf, Steelworker. 20pf, Stalin Boulevard. 40pf, Zwinger Castle, Dresden. 50pf, Launching ship. 70pf, Dove and East German family.

**1955**     **Typo.**     **Perf. 13x12½**
227 A43 10pf blue   2.00 .20
   a.   Bklt. pane, 4 #227 + 2 #228
227B A43 15pf violet   2.40 .20
228 A43 20pf carmine   1.75 .20
229 A43 40pf rose violet   3.75 .20
230 A43 50pf deep blue   6.25 .20
230A A43 70pf chocolate   8.50 .20
    Nos. 227-230A (6)   24.65 1.20

See note on used values after No. 171. .

Soviet Pavilion,
Leipzig Spring
Fair — A62

Women of
Three
Nations — A63

Design: 35pf, Chinese pavilion.

**Perf. 13x13½**
**1955, Feb. 21**    **Photo.**    **Wmk. 297**
231 A62 20pf rose violet   1.20 .75
232 A62 35pf violet blue   1.40 .75

Issued to publicize the Leipzig Spring Fair.

**1955, Mar. 1**     **Perf. 13x13½**
233 A63 10pf green   1.00 .35
234 A63 20pf red   1.00 .35

International Women's Day, 45th year.

Workers' Demonstration — A64

**1955, Mar. 15**     **Perf. 13x12½**
235 A64 10pf black & red   1.00 .75

Intl. Trade Union Conference, Apr., 1955.

A65     A66

Monument to the Victims of Fascism.

---

**1955, Apr. 9**     **Perf. 13½x13**
236 A65 10pf violet blue   .80 .75
237 A65 20pf cerise   1.10 1.20
   a.   Souv. sheet of 2, #236-237, imperf.   15.00 19.00

No. 237a sold for 50pf.

**1955, Apr. 15**     **Perf. 12½x13**
Russian War Memorial, Berlin.
238 A66 20pf lilac rose   1.25 .75

Nos. 236-238 issued for 10th anniv. of liberation, No. 237a for reconstruction of natl. memorial sites.

Cyclists — A67     Friedrich von
Schiller — A68

**1955**    **Wmk. 297**    **Perf. 13½x13**
239 A67 10pf blue green   1.00 .45
240 A67 20pf car rose   1.25 .50

8th International Bicycle Peace Race, Prague-Berlin-Warsaw.

Starting with the 1955 issues, commemorative stamps which are valued in italics were sold on a restricted basis.

**1955, Apr. 20**
Various Portraits of Schiller.
241 A68 5pf dk gray grn   *2.75* *2.25*
242 A68 10pf brt blue   .40 .20
243 A68 20pf chocolate   .40 .20
   a.   Souv. sheet, #241-243, imperf.   24.00 24.00
    Nos. 241-243 (3)   *3.55* *2.65*

150th anniv. of the death of Friedrich von Schiller, poet.
No. 243a sold for 50pf.

Karl Liebknecht — A69

Portraits: 10pf, August Bebel. 15pf, Franz Mehring. 20pf, Ernst Thalmann. 25pf, Clara Zetkin. 40pf, Wilhelm Liebknecht. 60pf, Rosa Luxemburg.

**1955, June 20**    **Photo.**    **Perf. 13x12½**
244 A69 5pf blue green   .30 .20
245 A69 10pf deep blue   .40 .20
246 A69 15pf violet   *5.50* *2.25*
247 A69 20pf red   .40 .20
248 A69 25pf slate   .40 .20
249 A69 40pf rose carmine   2.10 .20
250 A69 60pf dk brown   .40 .20
    Nos. 244-250 (7)   *9.50* *3.45*

Issued to honor German communists.

Optical
Goods — A70

Design: 20pf, Pottery and china.

**1955, Aug. 29**    **Photo.**    **Perf. 13x13½**
253 A70 10pf dark blue   .50 .25
254 A70 20pf slate green   .50 .25

Issued to publicize the 1955 Leipzig Fair.

---

Farmer Receiving
Deed — A71

Harvesters
A72

10pf, Construction of new farm community.

**1955, Sept. 3**   **Perf. 13½x13, 13x13½**
255 A71 5pf dull green   *4.75* *3.50*
256 A71 10pf ultra   .65 .20
257 A72 20pf lake   .65 .20
    Nos. 255-257 (3)   *6.05* *3.90*

10th anniv. of the Land-Reform Program.

Man Holding
Badge of
Peoples'
Solidarity — A73

Engels at "First
International,"
1864 — A74

**Perf. 13½x13**
**1955, Oct. 10**     **Wmk. 297**
258 A73 10pf dark blue   .60 .25

10th anniv. of the "Peoples' Solidarity."

**1955, Nov. 7**     **Perf. 13½x13**

Designs: 10pf, Marx and Engels writing the Communist Manifesto. 15pf, Engels as newspaper editor. 20pf, Friedrich Engels. 30pf, Friedrich Engels. 70pf, Engels on the barricades in 1848.

259 A74 5pf Prus blue & olive   .35 .20
260 A74 10pf dk blue & yel   .70 .20
261 A74 15pf dk green & ol   .70 .20
262 A74 20pf brn vio & org   1.40 .20
263 A74 30pf org brn & lt bl   *8.50* *6.50*
264 A74 70pf gray grn & rose   2.50 .20
   a.   Souvenir sheet of 6, #259-264   62.50 75.00
    Nos. 259-264 (6)   14.15 7.55

Friedrich Engels, 135th birth anniv.

Cathedral at
Magdeburg
A75

Georgius
Agricola
A76

German Buildings: 10pf, German State Opera. 15pf, Old City Hall, Leipzig. 20pf, City Hall, Berlin. 30pf, Cathedral at Erfurt. 40pf, Zwinger at Dresden.

**1955, Nov. 14**
265 A75 5pf black brown   .75 .30
266 A75 10pf gray green   .75 .30
267 A75 15pf purple   .75 .30
268 A75 20pf carmine   .75 .75
269 A75 30pf dk red brown   10.00 10.00
270 A75 40pf indigo   1.50 .75
    Nos. 265-270 (6)   14.50 12.40

For surcharges see Nos. B29-B30.

**1955, Nov. 21**     **Wmk. 297**
271 A76 10pf brown   .60 .35

400th anniv. of the death of Georgius Agricola, mineralogist and scholar.

Paintings in Dresden Gallery — A77

Mozart — A78

Famous Paintings: 5pf, Portrait of a Young Man, by Dürer. 10pf, Chocolate Girl, by Liotard. 15pf, Portrait of a Boy, by Pinturicchio. 20pf, Self-portrait with Saskia, by Rembrandt. 40pf, Girl with Letter, by Vermeer. 70pf, Sistine Madonna, by Raphael.

**1955, Dec. 15      Perf. 13½x13**
272  A77  5pf dk red brown      .65    .20
273  A77  10pf chestnut         .65    .20
274  A77  15pf pale purple     29.00  16.00
275  A77  20pf brown            .65    .20
276  A77  40pf olive green      .65    .25
277  A77  70pf deep blue       1.60    .50
      Nos. 272-277 (6)         33.20  17.35

Issued to publicize the return of famous art works to the Dresden Art Gallery.
See Nos. 355-360, 439-443.

**1956, Jan. 27      Photo.**
Designs: 20pf, Portrait facing left.
278  A78  10pf gray green      10.00  6.00
279  A78  20pf copper brown    3.50  1.00

200th anniv. of the birth of Wolfgang Amadeus Mozart, composer.

Flag and Schoenefeld Airport, Berlin — A79

Lufthansa Plane A80

Designs: 15pf, Plane facing right. 20pf, Plane facing down and left.

**1956, Feb. 1      Perf. 13x12½**
280  A79  5pf multicolored     12.00  6.25
281  A80  10pf gray green       .70    .20
282  A80  15pf dull blue        .70    .20
283  A80  20pf brown red        .70    .20
      Nos. 280-283 (4)         14.10   6.85

Issued to commemorate the opening of passenger service of the German Lufthansa.

Heinrich Heine — A81

Railroad Cranes — A82

Design: 20pf, Heine (different portrait.)

**1956, Feb. 17      Perf. 13½x13**
284  A81  10pf Prus green      11.50  4.25
285  A81  20pf dark red         2.50   .40

Cent. of the death of Heinrich Heine, poet.

**1956, Feb. 26      Perf. 13x13½**
286  A82  20pf brown red        .50    .25
287  A82  35pf violet blue      .75    .45

Issued to publicize the Leipzig Spring Fair.

Ernst Thälmann A83

**1956, Apr. 16   Litho.   Perf. 13x13½**
288  A83  20pf black olive & red      .60    .35
  a.  Souvenir sheet of 1, imperf   10.00  18.00

Birth of Ernst Thälmann, 70th anniv.
No. 288a was sold at double face value. The proceeds were used for national memorials at former concentration camps.

Wheel, Hand and Olive Branch — A84

City Hall and Old Market — A85

Design: 20pf, Wheel and coats of arms of Warsaw, Berlin, Prague.

**Perf. 13½x12½**
**1956, Apr. 30      Wmk. 297**
289  A84  10pf lt green         .60    .35
290  A84  20pf brt carmine      .60    .25

9th International Bicycle Peace Race, Warsaw-Berlin-Prague, May 1-15, 1956.

**1956, June 1**
Designs: 20pf, Hofkirche and Elbe Bridge. 40pf, Technical College.
291  A85  10pf green            .25    .20
292  A85  20pf carmine rose     .25    .20
293  A85  40pf brt purple      1.75   1.75
      Nos. 291-293 (3)         2.25   2.15

750th anniversary of Dresden.

Worker Holding Cogwheel Emblem — A86

**1956, June 30      Perf. 13½x13**
294  A86  20pf rose red         .45    .20

10th anniversary of nationalized industry.

Robert Schumann (Music by Schubert) A87

**1956, July 20      Perf. 13x13½**
295  A87  10pf brt green       1.75    .95
296  A87  20pf rose red        1.10    .20

Centenary of the death of Robert Schumann, composer. See Nos. 303-304.

Soccer Players — A88

Thomas Mann — A89

Designs: 10pf, Javelin Thrower. 15pf, Women Hurdlers. 20pf, Gymnast.

**1956, July 25      Perf. 13½x13**
297  A88  5pf green            .20    .20
298  A88  10pf dk vio blue     .20    .20
299  A88  15pf red violet     2.10    .70
300  A88  20pf rose red        .20    .20
      Nos. 297-300 (4)        2.70   1.30

Second Sports Festival, Leipzig, Aug. 2-5.

**1956, Aug. 13      Wmk. 297**
301  A89  20pf bluish black   1.00    .40

Death of Thomas Mann, novelist, 1st anniv.

Jakub Bart Cisinski — A90

Robert Schumann (Music by Schumann) A91

**1956, Aug. 20      Photo.**
302  A90  50pf claret         1.00    .40

Birth centenary of Jakub Bart Cisinski, poet.

**1956, Oct. 8      Perf. 13x13½**
303  A91  10pf brt green      4.50   1.75
304  A91  20pf rose red       2.50    .25

See Nos. 295, 296.

Lace — A92

Olympic Rings, Laurel and Torch — A93

Design: 20pf, Sailboat.

**1956, Sept. 1   Typo.   Perf. 13½x13**
305  A92  10pf green & blk    .30    .25
306  A92  20pf rose red & blk .30    .25

Leipzig Fair, Sept. 2-9.

**1956, Sept. 28      Litho.**
Design: 35pf, Classic javelin thrower.
307  A93  20pf brown red      .40    .20
308  A93  35pf slate blue     .60    .25

16th Olympic Games at Melbourne, Nov. 22-Dec. 8, 1956.

Post Runner of 1450 — A94

Greifswald University Seal — A95

**1956, Oct. 27**
309  A94  20pf red            .45    .20

Issued to publicize the Day of the Stamp.

**1956, Oct. 17      Perf. 13x13½**
310  A95  20pf magenta        .45    .20

500th anniv. of Greifswald University.

Ernst Abbe — A96

Zeiss Works, Jena A97

Portrait: 25pf, Carl Zeiss.

**Perf. 12½x13, 13x12½**
**1956, Nov. 9   Photo.   Wmk. 297**
311  A96  10pf dark green     .20    .20
312  A97  20pf brown red      .20    .20
313  A96  25pf bluish black   .35    .25
      Nos. 311-313 (3)        .75    .65

Carl Zeiss Optical Works, Jena, 110th anniv.

Chinese Girl with Flowers — A98

Designs: 10pf, Negro woman and child. 25pf, European man and dove.

**1956, Dec. 10   Litho.   Perf. 13**
314  A98  5pf ol, pale lem   1.25    .70
315  A98  10pf brown, pink    .20    .20
316  A98  25pf vio bl, pale vio bl  .20  .20
      Nos. 314-316 (3)       1.65   1.10

Issued for Human Rights Day.

Elephants A99

**1956, Dec. 14   Photo.   Perf. 13x12½**
**Design in Gray**
317  A99  5pf shown          .20    .20
318  A99  10pf Flamingoes     .20    .20
319  A99  15pf White rhinoceros  4.25  2.25
320  A99  20pf Mouflon        .20    .20
321  A99  25pf Bison          .20    .20
322  A99  30pf Polar bear     .20    .20
      Nos. 317-322 (6)       5.25   3.25

Issued to publicize the Berlin Zoo.

Freighter A100

Design: 25pf, Electric Locomotive.

**1957, Mar. 1   Litho.   Wmk. 313**
323  A100  20pf rose red      .25    .20
324  A100  25pf bright blue   .25    .20

Leipzig Spring Fair.

Silver Thistle A101

10pf, Emerald lizard. 20pf, Lady's-slipper.

**1957, Apr. 12     Photo.     Wmk. 313**
| 325 | A101 | 5pf chocolate | .20 | .20 |
| 326 | A101 | 10pf dk slate grn | 2.25 | 2.00 |
| 327 | A101 | 20pf red brown | .20 | .20 |
| | | Nos. 325-327 (3) | 2.65 | 2.40 |

Nature Conservation Week, Apr. 14-20.

Children at
Play — A102

20pf, Friedrich Froebel and Children.

**1957, Apr. 18     Litho.     Perf. 13**
| 328 | A102 | 10pf dk slate grn & ol | 1.20 | .80 |
| 329 | A102 | 20pf black & brown red | .20 | .20 |

175th anniv. of the birth of Friedrich Froebel, educator.

### Redrawn Types of 1953

Designs: 5pf, Woman mariner. 10pf, Worker, peasant and intellectual. 15pf, Steel worker. 20pf, Stalin Boulevard. 25pf, Locomotive building. 30pf, Dancing couple. 40pf, Zwinger Castle, Dresden. 50pf, Launching ship. 70pf, Dove and East German family.

Imprint: "E. Gruner K. Wolf"
No imprint on 10pf, 15pf
**Perf. 13x12½, 14**

**1957-58     Typo.     Wmk. 313**
| 330 | A43 | 5pf emerald | .20 | .20 |
| a. | | Bklt. pane, 3 #330 + 3 #331b | 25.00 | |
| b. | | Bklt. pane, 3 #330 + 3 #333 | 25.00 | |
| c. | | Booklet pane of 6 | 2.00 | |
| 331 | A43 | 10pf blue ('58) | .20 | .20 |
| a. | | Bklt. pane, 4 #331b + 2 #333 | 40.00 | |
| b. | | Perf. 13x12½ | 5.00 | .20 |
| 332 | A43 | 15pf violet ('58) | .20 | .20 |
| a. | | Perf. 13x12½ | .30 | .20 |
| 333 | A43 | 20pf carmine | .30 | .20 |
| a. | | Bklt. pane, 5 #333 + 1 #477 | 2.00 | |
| 334 | A43 | 25pf bluish green | .30 | .20 |
| 335 | A43 | 30pf dull red | .75 | .20 |
| 336 | A43 | 40pf rose violet | 1.10 | .20 |
| 337 | A43 | 50pf bright blue | 1.40 | .20 |
| 338 | A43 | 70pf chocolate | 1.60 | .20 |

See Nos. 476-482.

### Pieck Type of 1953
**Photo.     Perf. 13x13½**
| 339 | A35 | 1m dk olive grn ('58) | 2.25 | .25 |
| 340 | A35 | 2m red brown ('58) | 4.50 | .30 |
| | | Nos. 330-340 (11) | 12.80 | 2.35 |

No. 334 comes only perf 13x12½. Nos 330-333 and 335-338 come both perf 13x12½ and perf 14.

Bicycle Race
Route — A103

**1957, Apr. 30     Litho.     Wmk. 313**
| 346 | A103 | 5pf orange | .30 | .20 |

Issued to publicize the 10th International Bicycle Peace Race, Prague-Berlin-Warsaw.

Steam
Shovel
A104

Miner — A105

Design: 20pf, Coal conveyor.

---

**Perf. 13x12½, 13½x13 (25pf)**
**1957, May 3**
| 347 | A104 | 10pf green | .20 | .20 |
| 348 | A104 | 20pf redsh brown | .20 | .20 |
| 349 | A105 | 25pf blue violet | 2.25 | .75 |
| | | Nos. 347-349 (3) | 2.65 | 1.15 |

Issued in honor of the coal mining industry.

Henri
Dunant
and
Globe
A106

25pf, Henri Dunant facing right and globe.

**1957, May 7     Photo.     Perf. 13x12½**
| 350 | A106 | 10pf green, red & blk | .25 | .20 |
| 351 | A106 | 25pf brt blue, red & blk | .25 | .20 |

Tenth Red Cross world conference.

### Portrait Type of 1950, Redrawn

Portraits: 5pf, Joachim Jungius. 10pf, Leonhard Euler. 20pf, Heinrich Hertz.

**1957, June 7     Litho.**
| 352 | A11 | 5pf brown | 1.50 | .50 |
| 353 | A11 | 10pf green | .20 | .20 |
| 354 | A11 | 20pf henna brown | .20 | .20 |
| | | Nos. 352-354 (3) | 1.90 | .90 |

Issued to honor famous German scientists.

### Painting Type of 1955.

Famous Paintings: 5pf, Holy Family, by Mantegna. 10pf, The Dancer Campani, by Carriera. 15pf, Portrait of Morette, by Holbein. 20pf, The Tribute Money, by Titian. 25pf, Saskia with Red Flower, by Rembrandt. 40pf, Young Street Bearer, by Piazetta.

**Perf. 13½x13**
**1957, June 26     Photo.     Wmk. 313**
| 355 | A77 | 5pf dk brown | .30 | .20 |
| 356 | A77 | 10pf lt yellow grn | .30 | .20 |
| 357 | A77 | 15pf brown olive | .30 | .20 |
| 358 | A77 | 20pf rose brown | .30 | .20 |
| 359 | A77 | 25pf deep claret | .30 | .20 |
| 360 | A77 | 40pf dk blue gray | 4.50 | 1.50 |
| | | Nos. 355-360 (6) | 6.00 | 2.50 |

Clara
Zetkin — A107

**1957, July 5     Perf. 13½x13**
| 361 | A107 | 10pf dk green & red | .60 | .25 |

Centenary of the birth of Clara Zetkin, politician and founder of the socialist women's movement.

Bertolt
Brecht — A108

**1957, Aug. 14     Perf. 13½x13**
| 362 | A108 | 10pf dark green | .30 | .20 |
| 363 | A108 | 25pf deep blue | .40 | .20 |

Brecht (1898-1956), playwright and poet.

Congress
Emblem — A109

Fair
Emblem — A110

**1957, Aug. 23     Litho.**
| 364 | A109 | 20pf brt red & black | .50 | .25 |

4th Intl. Trade Union Congress, Leipzig, Oct. 4-15.

---

**1957, Aug. 30     Wmk. 313**
| 365 | A110 | 20pf crimson & ver | .25 | .20 |
| 366 | A110 | 25pf brt blue & lt blue | .30 | .20 |

Issued to publicize the 1957 Leipzig Fair.

Savings
Book — A111

Postrider,
1563 — A112

**1957, Oct. 10     Perf. 13½x13**
| 367 | A111 | 10pf grn & blk, gray | .75 | .45 |
| 368 | A111 | 20pf rose car & blk, gray | .30 | .30 |

Issued to publicize "Savings Weeks."

**1957, Oct. 25     Wmk. 313**
| 369 | A112 | 5pf black, pale sepia | .50 | .20 |

Issued for the Day of the Stamp.

Sputnik I
A113

Storming of the
Winter Palace
A114

20pf, Stratospheric balloon above clouds. 25pf, Ship with plumb line exploring deep sea.

**1957-58     Perf. 12½x13**
| 370 | A113 | 10pf blue black | .35 | .20 |
| 371 | A113 | 20pf car rose ('58) | .50 | .20 |
| 372 | A113 | 25pf brt blue ('58) | 1.90 | .95 |
| | | Nos. 370-372 (3) | 2.75 | 1.35 |

IGY. The 10pf also for the launching of the 1st artificial satellite.

**1957, Nov. 7     Photo.**
| 373 | A114 | 10pf yellow grn & red | .25 | .20 |
| 374 | A114 | 25pf brt blue & red | .25 | .20 |

40th anniv. of the Russian Revolution.

Guenther
Ramin — A115

Dove and
Globe — A116

Portrait: 20pf, Hermann Abendroth.

**Perf. 13½x13**
**1957, Nov. 22     Litho.     Wmk. 313**
| 375 | A115 | 10pf yellow grn & blk | 1.00 | .60 |
| 376 | A115 | 20pf red orange & blk | .20 | .20 |

Ramin (1898-1956) and Abendroth (1883-1956), musicians, on the 1st anniv. of their death.

**1958, Feb. 27     Perf. 13½x13**
| 377 | A116 | 20pf rose red | .25 | .20 |
| 378 | A116 | 25pf blue | .30 | .20 |

Issued to publicize the 1958 Leipzig Fair.

---

Radio
Tower,
Morse
Code and
Post Horn
A117

Design: 20pf, Radio tower and small post horn.

**1958, Mar. 6     Perf. 13x12½**
| 379 | A117 | 5pf gray & blk | .75 | .45 |
| 380 | A117 | 20pf crim rose & dk red | .35 | .20 |

Conf. of Postal Ministers of Communist countries, Moscow, Dec. 3-17, 1957.

Sketch by
Zille — A118

Symbolizing
Quantum
Theory — A119

Design: 20pf, Self-portrait of Zille.

**1958, Mar. 20     Perf. 13½x13**
| 381 | A118 | 10pf green & gray | 2.40 | 1.00 |
| 382 | A118 | 20pf dp car & gray | .55 | .20 |

Centenary of the birth of Heinrich Zille, artist.

**1958, Apr. 23     Litho.**

Design: 20pf, Max Planck.

| 383 | A119 | 10pf gray green | 1.10 | .75 |
| 384 | A119 | 20pf magenta | .35 | .20 |

Centenary of the birth of Max Planck, physicist.

Prize
Cow — A120

10pf, Mowing machine. 20pf, Beet harvester.

**Perf. 13x13½**
**1958, June 4     Wmk. 313**
**Size: 28x23mm**
| 385 | A120 | 5pf gray & blk | 2.25 | 1.00 |

**Size: 39x22mm**
**Perf. 13x12½**
| 386 | A120 | 10pf brt green | .35 | .20 |
| 387 | A120 | 20pf rose red | .35 | .20 |
| | | Nos. 385-387 (3) | 2.95 | 1.40 |

6th Agricultural Show, Markkleeberg.

Charles
Darwin — A121

**1958, June 19     Perf. 13½x13**

Portrait: 20pf, Carl von Linné.

| 388 | A121 | 10pf green & black | 1.25 | .75 |
| 389 | A121 | 20pf dk red & black | .20 | .20 |

Cent. of Darwin's theory of evolution and the bicent. of Linné's botanical system.

Seven Towers of
Rostock and
Ships — A122

Congress Emblem — A123

10pf, Ship at pier. 25pf, Ships in harbor.

**1958** Perf. 13½x13
390 A122 10pf emerald .20 .20
391 A122 20pf red orange .40 .25
392 A122 25pf lt blue 1.00 1.00
Nos. 390-392 (3) 1.60 1.45

Establishment of Rostock as a seaport.
Issue dates: 20pf, July 5; 10pf and 25pf, Nov. 24.
For overprint see No. 500.

**1958, June 25** Perf. 13x13½
393 A123 10pf rose red .35 .20

5th congress of the Socialist Party of the German Democratic Republic (SED).

Mare and Foal A124

Designs: 10pf, Trotter. 20pf, Horse race.

**1958, July 22 Photo.** Perf. 13x12½
394 A124 5pf black brown 2.25 1.75
395 A124 10pf dark olive green .20 .20
396 A124 20pf dark red brown .20 .20
Nos. 394-396 (3) 2.65 2.15

Grand Prize of the DDR, 1958.

Jan Amos Komensky (Comenius) A125

Design: 20pf, Teacher and pupils, 17th cent.

**1958, Aug. 7 Litho.** Perf. 13x13½
397 A125 10pf brt bl grn & blk 1.50 .75
398 A125 20pf org brn & blk .20 .20

University Seal A126

Design: 20pf, Schiller University, Jena.

**1958, Aug. 19** Perf. 13x12½
399 A126 5pf gray & black 1.25 .75
400 A126 20pf dark red & gray .30 .20

Friedrich Schiller University in Jena, 400th anniv.

Soldier on Obstacle Course — A127

Arms Breaking A-Bomb — A128

Design: 20pf, Spartacist emblem. 25pf, Marching athletes, map and flag.

**Perf. 13½x13**
**1958, Sept. 19 Litho. Wmk. 313**
401 A127 10pf emerald & brn 1.50 .70
402 A127 20pf brown red & yel .20 .20
403 A127 25pf lt blue & red .20 .20
Nos. 401-403 (3) 1.90 1.10

1st Spartacist Sports Meet of Friendly Armies, Leipzig, Sept. 20-28.

**1958, Sept. 19** Perf. 13x13½
404 A128 20pf rose red .20 .20
405 A128 25pf blue .40 .20

People's fight against atomic death.

Woman and Leipzig Railroad Station A129

Design: 25pf, Woman in Persian lamb coat and old City Hall, Leipzig.

**1958, Aug. 29** Perf. 13x12½
406 A129 10pf green, brn & blk .20 .20
407 A129 25pf blue & black .30 .20

Issued to publicize the 1958 Leipzig Fair.

Post Wagon, 17th Century A130

Design: 20pf, Mail train and plane.

**1958, Oct. 23** Wmk. 313
408 A130 10pf green 1.75 .80
409 A130 20pf lake .35 .20

Issued for the Day of the Stamp.

Brandenburg Gate, Berlin — A131

Head from Greek Tomb — A132

**1958, Nov. 29** Perf. 13x13½
410 A131 20pf rose red .35 .20
411 A131 25pf dark blue 2.50 1.50

Issued to commemorate 10 years of democratic city administration of Berlin.

**1958, Dec. 2** Perf. 13½x13
20pf, Giant's head from Pergamum frieze.
412 A132 10pf blue grn & blk 1.25 .70
413 A132 20pf dp rose & black .20 .20

Return of art treasures from Russia. See #484-486.

Negro and Caucasian Men — A133

Design: 25pf, Chinese and Caucasian girls.

**1958, Dec. 10** Perf. 13x12½
414 A133 10pf brt blue grn & blk .20 .20
415 A133 25pf blue & black 1.75 .80

10th anniv. of the signing of the Universal Declaration of Human Rights.

Worker and Soldier — A134

Otto Nuschke — A135

**1958, Nov. 7** Perf. 12½x13
416 A134 20pf blk, ver & dl pur 10.00 14.00

40th anniv. of the Revolution of Nov. 7. (Stamp inscribed Nov. 9.) Withdrawn from sale on day of issue.

**Perf. 13½x13**
**1958, Dec. 27** Wmk. 313
417 A135 20pf red .30 .20

First anniversary of the death of Otto Nuschke, vice president of the republic.

Communist Newspaper, "The Red Flag" — A136

**1958, Dec. 30** Perf. 13x12½
418 A136 20pf red .35 .25

German Communist Party, 40th anniv.

Rosa Luxemburg Addressing Crowd — A137

20pf, Karl Liebknecht addressing crowd.

**Perf. 13x13½**
**1959, Jan. 15** Wmk. 313
419 A137 10pf blue green 2.00 .90
420 A137 20pf henna brn & blk .20 .20

40th anniversary of the death of Rosa Luxemburg and Karl Liebknecht.

Gewandhaus, Leipzig — A138

President Wilhelm Pieck — A139

Design: 25pf, Opening theme of Mendelssohn's A Major symphony.

**1959, Feb. 28 Engr.** Perf. 14
421 A138 10pf green, grnsh .35 .25
422 A138 25pf blue, bluish 1.50 2.00

150th anniversary of the birth of Felix Mendelssohn-Bartholdy, composer.

**1959, Jan. 3 Photo.** Perf. 13½x13
423 A139 20pf henna brown .45 .20

83rd birthday of President Wilhelm Pieck. See No. 511.

"Black Pump" Plant A140

Design: 25pf, Photographic equipment.

**1959, Feb. 28 Litho.** Perf. 13x12½
424 A140 20pf carmine rose .20 .20
425 A140 25pf lt ultra .35 .20

1959 Leipzig Spring Fair.

Boy and Girl — A141

Statue of Handel, Halle — A142

**1959, Apr. 2** Perf. 13½x13
426 A141 10pf blk, lt grn 1.50 .75
427 A141 20pf blk, salmon .20 .20

5 years of the Youth Consecration ceremony.

**1959, Apr. 27** Wmk. 313
20pf, Handel by Thomas Hudson, 1749.
428 A142 10pf bluish grn & blk 1.60 .80
429 A142 20pf rose & blk .20 .20

Bicentenary of the death of George Frederick Handel, composer.

Alexander von Humboldt and Central American View — A143

Post Horn — A144

Design: 20pf, Portrait and Siberian view.

**1959, May 6**
430 A143 10pf bluish grn 1.25 .75
431 A143 20pf rose .30 .20

Centenary of the death of Alexander von Humboldt, naturalist and geographer.

**1959, May 30** Perf. 13½x13
432 A144 20pf scar, yel & blk .20 .20
433 A144 25pf lt bl, yel & blk .75 .60

Conference of socialist postal ministers.

Gray Heron A145

10pf, Bittern. 20pf, Lily of the valley & butterfly. 25pf, Beaver. 40pf, Pussy willows and bee.

**1959, June 26** Perf. 13x12½
434 A145 5pf lt bl, blk & lil .20 .20
435 A145 10pf grnsh bl, dk brn & org .20 .20
436 A145 20pf org red, grn & vio .20 .20
437 A145 25pf lilac, yel & blk .35 .20
438 A145 40pf gray bl, yel & blk 5.50 2.50
Nos. 434-438 (5) 6.45 3.30

Issued to publicize wildlife protection.

**Painting Type of 1955.**

Famous Paintings: 5pf, Portrait, by Angelica Kauffmann. 10pf, The Lady Lace Maker, by Gabriel Metsu. 20pf, Mademoiselle Lavergne, by Liotard. 25pf, Old Woman with Brazier, by Rubens. 40pf, Young Man in Black Coat, by Hals.

**1959, June 29  Photo.  *Perf. 13½x13***
| | | | | |
|---|---|---|---|---|
| 439 | A77 | 5pf olive | .20 | .20 |
| 440 | A77 | 10pf green | .20 | .20 |
| 441 | A77 | 20pf dp org | .20 | .20 |
| 442 | A77 | 25pf chestnut | .35 | .20 |
| 443 | A77 | 40pf dp magenta | 5.50 | 1.90 |
| | | *Nos. 439-443 (5)* | 6.45 | 2.70 |

Great Cormoran — A146

Youths of Three Races — A147

Birds: 10pf, Black Stork. 15pf, Eagle owl. 20pf, Black grouse. 25pf, Hoopoe. 40pf, Peregrine falcon.

***Perf. 13x13½***
**1959, July 2  Litho.  Wmk. 313**
**Designs in Black**
| | | | | |
|---|---|---|---|---|
| 444 | A146 | 5pf yellow | .20 | .20 |
| 445 | A146 | 10pf lt green | .20 | .20 |
| 446 | A146 | 15pf pale violet | 4.75 | 2.10 |
| 447 | A146 | 20pf deep pink | .20 | .20 |
| 448 | A146 | 25pf blue | .20 | .20 |
| 449 | A146 | 40pf vermilion | .20 | .20 |
| | | *Nos. 444-449 (6)* | 5.75 | 3.10 |

Protection of native birds.

**1959, July 25  *Perf. 12½x13, 13x12½***

25pf, Swedish girl kissing African girl, horiz.
| | | | | |
|---|---|---|---|---|
| 450 | A147 | 20pf crimson | .20 | .20 |
| 451 | A147 | 25pf bright blue | .75 | .45 |

7th World Youth Festival, Vienna, 7/26-8/14.

Glass Tea Service A148

Design: 25pf, Distilling apparatus, vert.

**1959, Sept. 1  *Perf. 13x12½, 12½x13***
| | | | | |
|---|---|---|---|---|
| 452 | A148 | 10pf bluish green | .20 | .20 |
| 453 | A148 | 25pf bright blue | 1.75 | .75 |

75 years of Jena glassware.

Lunik 2 Hitting Moon — A149

**1959, Sept. 21  *Perf. 13½x13***
| | | | | |
|---|---|---|---|---|
| 454 | A149 | 20pf rose red | .60 | .30 |

Landing of the Soviet rocket Lunik 2 on the moon, Sept. 13, 1959.

New Buildings, Leipzig, Globe and Fair Emblem A150

**1959, Aug. 17  *Perf. 13x12½***
| | | | | |
|---|---|---|---|---|
| 455 | A150 | 20pf gray & rose | .35 | .25 |

1959 Leipzig Fall Fair.

Flag and Harvester — A151

Johannes R. Becher — A152

10pf, Fritz Heckert rest home. 15pf, Zwinger, Dresden. 20pf, Steelworker. 25pf, Chemist. 40pf, Central Stadium, Leipzig. 50pf, Woman tractor driver. 60pf, Airplane. 70pf, Merchant ship. 1m, 1st atomic reactor of the DDR.

**1959, Oct. 6  *Perf. 13½x13***
**Flag in Black, Red & Orange Yellow**
**Inscription and Design in Black &**
**Red**
| | | | | |
|---|---|---|---|---|
| 456 | A151 | 5pf yellow | .20 | .20 |
| 457 | A151 | 10pf gray | .20 | .20 |
| 458 | A151 | 15pf citron | .20 | .20 |
| 459 | A151 | 20pf gray | .20 | .20 |
| 460 | A151 | 25pf lt gray olive | .20 | .20 |
| 461 | A151 | 40pf citron | .20 | .20 |
| 462 | A151 | 50pf salmon | .20 | .20 |
| 463 | A151 | 60pf pale bluish grn | .20 | .20 |
| 464 | A151 | 70pf pale grnsh yel | .20 | .20 |
| 465 | A151 | 1m bister brn | .30 | .25 |
| | | *Nos. 456-465 (10)* | 2.10 | 2.05 |

German Democratic Republic, 10th anniv.

**1959, Oct. 28  Litho.  *Perf. 13x13½***
| | | | | |
|---|---|---|---|---|
| 466 | A152 | 20pf red & slate | 1.20 | .70 |

1st anniversary of the death of Johannes R. Becher, writer.

Printed with alternating yellow labels. The label carries in blue a verse from the national anthem and Becher's signature.

Schiller's Home, Weimar — A153

Post Rider and Mile Stone, 18th Century — A154

Design: 20pf, Friedrich von Schiller.

**1959, Nov. 10  Engr.  *Perf. 14***
| | | | | |
|---|---|---|---|---|
| 467 | A153 | 10pf dull green, *grnsh* | 1.40 | .75 |
| 468 | A153 | 20pf lake, *pink* | .50 | .20 |

Birth of Friedrich von Schiller, 200th anniv.

**1959, Nov. 17  Litho.  *Perf. 13½x13***

Design: 20pf, Motorized mailman.
| | | | | |
|---|---|---|---|---|
| 469 | A154 | 10pf green | 1.25 | .70 |
| 470 | A154 | 20pf dk car rose | .20 | .20 |

Issued for the Day of the Stamp.

Red Squirrels A155

**1959, Nov. 27  *Perf. 13x12½***
| | | | | |
|---|---|---|---|---|
| 471 | A155 | 5pf shown | .35 | .20 |
| 472 | A155 | 10pf Hares | .45 | .20 |
| 473 | A155 | 20pf Roe deer | .45 | .20 |
| 474 | A155 | 25pf Red deer | .50 | .20 |
| 475 | A155 | 40pf Lynx | 9.50 | 2.50 |
| | | *Nos. 471-475 (5)* | 11.25 | 3.30 |

**Redrawn Types of 1953**
**Without Imprint**
***Perf. 14, 13x12½ (#477)***
**1959-60  Wmk. 313  Typo.**
| | | | | |
|---|---|---|---|---|
| 476 | A43 | 5pf emerald | .20 | .20 |
| 477 | A43 | 10pf lt bl grn *(Machinists)* | .20 | .20 |
| a. | | Perf. 14 | 1.00 | .20 |
| b. | | Bklt. pane of 6 #477a | 6.00 | |
| 478 | A43 | 20pf carmine | .25 | .20 |
| a. | | Se-tenant with DEBRIA label | .95 | .20 |
| 479 | A43 | 30pf dull red | .20 | .20 |
| 480 | A43 | 40pf rose violet | .20 | .20 |
| 481 | A43 | 50pf brt blue | .25 | .20 |
| 482 | A43 | 70pf choc ('60) | .25 | .20 |
| | | *Nos. 476-482 (7)* | 1.55 | 1.40 |

No. 478a was issued Sept. 3, 1959, to commemorate the 2nd German Stamp Exhibition, Berlin. Sheet contains 60 stamps, 40 labels.
Two other stamps without imprint are Nos. 331-332.

**Type of 1958 and**

Pergamum Altar of Zeus — A156

Designs: 5pf, Head of an Attic goddess, 580 B.C. 10pf, Head of a princess from Tell el Amarna, 1360 B.C. 20pf, Bronze figure from Toprak-Kale (Armenia), 7th century B.C.

**1959, Dec. 29  Litho.  *Perf. 13½x13***
| | | | | |
|---|---|---|---|---|
| 484 | A132 | 5pf yellow & black | .20 | .20 |
| 485 | A132 | 10pf bluish grn & blk | .20 | .20 |
| 486 | A132 | 20pf rose & black | .20 | .20 |
| 487 | A156 | 25pf lt blue & blk | .80 | .55 |
| | | *Nos. 484-487 (4)* | 1.40 | 1.15 |

Boxing — A157

10pf, Sprinters. 20pf, Ski jump. 25pf, Sailboat.

***Perf. 13x13½***
**1960, Jan. 27  Wmk. 313**
| | | | | |
|---|---|---|---|---|
| 488 | A157 | 5pf brown & ocher | 4.50 | 1.75 |
| 489 | A157 | 10pf green & ocher | .20 | .20 |
| 490 | A157 | 20pf car & ocher | .20 | .20 |
| 491 | A157 | 25pf ultra & ocher | .20 | .20 |
| | | *Nos. 488-491 (4)* | 5.10 | 2.35 |

1960 Winter and Summer Olympic Games.

Technical Fair, North Entrance A158

Design: 25pf, "Ring" Fair building.

**1960, Feb. 17  *Perf. 13x12½***
| | | | | |
|---|---|---|---|---|
| 492 | A158 | 20pf red & gray | .20 | .20 |
| 493 | A158 | 25pf lt blue & gray | .20 | .20 |

1960 Leipzig Spring Fair.

Purple Foxglove A159

Lenin A160

Medicinal Plants: 10pf, Camomile. 15pf, Peppermint. 20pf, Poppy. 40pf, Dog rose.

**1960, Apr. 7  *Perf. 12½x13***
| | | | | |
|---|---|---|---|---|
| 494 | A159 | 5pf grn, gray & car rose | .25 | .20 |
| 495 | A159 | 10pf citron, gray & grn | .25 | .20 |
| 496 | A159 | 15pf fawn, gray & grn | .25 | .20 |
| 497 | A159 | 20pf grnsh bl, gray & vio | .25 | .20 |
| 498 | A159 | 40pf brn, gray, grn & red | 4.50 | 1.75 |
| | | *Nos. 494-498 (5)* | 5.50 | 2.55 |

**1960, Apr. 22  Engr.  *Perf. 14***
| | | | | |
|---|---|---|---|---|
| 499 | A160 | 20pf lake | .35 | .20 |

90th anniversary of the birth of Lenin.

**No. 390 Overprinted:**
**"Inbetriebnahme des**
**Hochseehafens 1.Mai 1960"**
**1960, Apr. 28  Litho.  *Perf. 13½x13***
| | | | | |
|---|---|---|---|---|
| 500 | A122 | 10pf emerald | .40 | .30 |

Inauguration of the seaport Rostock.

Russian Soldier and Liberated Prisoner — A161

**1960, May 5  Litho.  *Perf. 13x13½***
| | | | | |
|---|---|---|---|---|
| 501 | A161 | 20pf rose red | .35 | .25 |

15th anniv. of Germany's liberation from fascism.

Model of Vacation Ship — A162

Designs: 25pf, Ship before Leningrad.

***Perf. 13½x13***
**1960, June 23  Wmk. 313**
| | | | | |
|---|---|---|---|---|
| 502 | A162 | 5pf slate, cit & blk | .20 | .20 |
| 503 | A162 | 25pf blk, yel & ultra | 4.00 | 4.00 |
| | | *Nos. 502-503,B58-B59 (4)* | 4.65 | 4.60 |

Launching of the trade union (FDGB) vacation ship, June 25, 1960.

Masked Dancer in Porcelain A163

Lenin Monument, Eisleben A164

Meissen porcelain: 10pf, Plate with Meissen mark and date. 15pf, Otter. 20pf, Potter. 25pf, Coffee pot.

**1960, July 28  *Perf. 12½x13***
| | | | | |
|---|---|---|---|---|
| 504 | A163 | 5pf blue & orange | .25 | .20 |
| 505 | A163 | 10pf blue & emerald | .25 | .20 |
| 506 | A163 | 15pf blue & purple | 3.25 | 3.25 |
| 507 | A163 | 20pf blue & orange red | .25 | .20 |
| 508 | A163 | 25pf blue & apple grn | .25 | .20 |
| | | *Nos. 504-508 (5)* | 4.25 | 4.05 |

Meissen porcelain works, 250th anniv.

## Perf. 13x13½

**1960, July 2**　　**Wmk. 313**

Design: 20pf, Thälmann monument, gift for Pushkin, USSR.

**509** A164 10pf dark green　.25　.20
**510** A164 20pf bright red　.25　.20

### Pieck Type of 1959

**1960, Sept. 10　Litho.　Perf. 13½x13**
**511** A139 20pf black　.40　.25
　　a. 　Souv. sheet of 1, imperf.　1.25　1.50

Pres. Wilhelm Pieck (1876-1960).

Modern Postal Trucks A165

Design: 25pf, Railroad mail car, 19th cent.

**1960, Oct. 6**　　**Perf. 13x12½**
**512** A165 20pf car rose, blk & yel　.25　.20
**513** A165 25pf blue, gray & blk　2.75　1.20

Issued for the Day of the Stamp, 1960.

New Opera House, Leipzig A166

Design: 25pf, Car, sailboat, tent, campers.

**1960, Aug. 29**　　**Wmk. 313**
**514** A166 20pf rose brn & gray　.25　.20
**515** A166 25pf blue & grysh brn　.30　.25

1960 Leipzig Fall Fair.

Hans Burkmair Medal, 1518 A167

Neidhardt von Gneisenau A168

25pf, Dancing Peasants by Albrecht Dürer.

**1960, Oct. 20　Litho.　Perf. 12½x13**
**516** A167 20pf buff, grn & ocher　.20　.20
**517** A167 25pf lt blue & blk　1.50　1.50

400th anniv. of the Dresden Art Gallery.

**1960, Oct. 27　Perf. 13x12½, 12½x13**

20pf, Neidhardt von Gneisenau, horiz.

**518** A168 20pf dk car & blk　.20　.20
**519** A168 25pf ultra　1.25　1.25

200th anniversary of the birth of Count August Neidhardt von Gneisenau, Prussian Field Marshal.

Rudolf Virchow A169

Humboldt University, Berlin — A170

---

10pf, Robert Koch. 25pf, Wilhelm & Alexander von Humboldt medal. 40pf, Wilhelm Griesinger.

**1960, Nov. 4　Litho.　Perf. 13x12½**
**520** A169 5pf ocher & blk　.20　.20
**521** A169 10pf green & blk　.20　.20
**522** A170 20pf cop red, gray & blk　.20　.20
**523** A170 25pf brt blue & blk　.20　.20
**524** A169 40pf car rose & blk　2.25　1.20
　　Nos. 520-524 (5)　3.05　2.00

Nos. 520, 521, 524 for the 250th anniv. of the Charité (hospital), Berlin; Nos. 522-523 the 150th anniv. of Humboldt University, Berlin. Nos. 520 and 523, and Nos. 521 and 522 are printed se-tenant.

Scientist and Chemical Formula — A171

Designs: 10pf, Chemistry worker (fertilizer). 20pf, Woman worker (automobile). 25pf, Laboratory assistant (synthetic fabrics).

### Perf. 13x13½

**1960, Nov. 10**　　**Wmk. 313**
**525** A171 5pf dk red & gray　.20　.20
**526** A171 10pf orange & brt grn　.20　.20
**527** A171 20pf blue & red　.20　.20
**528** A171 25pf yellow & ultra　1.60　1.60
　　Nos. 525-528 (4)　2.20　2.20

Day of the Chemistry Worker.

"Young Socialists' Express" A172

20pf, Sassnitz Harbor station & ferry. 25pf, Diesel locomotive & 1835 "Adler."

### Perf. 13x13½; 13x12½ (20pf)

**1960, Dec. 5**
**Sizes: 10pf, 25pf, 28x23mm; 20pf, 38½x22mm**

**529** A172 10pf emerald & blk　.25　.20
**530** A172 20pf red & blk　.25　.20
**531** A172 25pf blue & blk　4.50　2.75
　　Nos. 529-531 (3)　5.00　3.15

125th anniv. of German railroads. No. 530 exists imperf. Value $3.50.

### Pieck Type of 1953 with Dates Added

**1961, Jan. 3　Photo.　Perf. 13x13½**
**532** A35 20pf henna brn & blk　.35　.25

Issued on the 85th anniversary of the birth of Pres. Wilhelm Pieck (1876-1960).

380 Kilovolt Switch A173

Lilienstein A174

Design: 25pf, Leipzig Press Center.

**1961, Mar. 3　Litho.　Perf. 13½x13**
**533** A173 10pf brt grn & dk gray　.30　.20
**534** A173 25pf vio blue & dk gray　.30　.20

Leipzig Spring Fair of 1961.

**1961**　　**Typo.**　　**Perf. 14**

Designs: 5pf, Rudelsburg on Saale. 10pf, Wartburg. No. 538, City Hall, Wernigerode. 25pf, Brocken, Harz Mts., horiz.

**535** A174 5pf gray　.20　.20
**536** A174 10pf blue green　.20　.20
**537** A174 25pf red brown　.20　.20

---

**538** A174 20pf dull red　.20　.20
**539** A174 25pf dark blue　.20　.20
　　Nos. 535-539 (5)　1.00　1.00

Issued: #538, 25pf, 3/14; 5pf, 10pf, #537, 6/22.

Trawler — A176

Designs: 20pf, Fishermen. 25pf, S.S. Robert Koch. 40pf, Cannery worker.

**1961, Apr. 4　Engr.　Wmk. 313**
**545** A176 10pf gray green　.20　.20
**546** A176 20pf claret　.20　.20
**547** A176 25pf slate　.20　.20
**548** A176 40pf dull violet　2.00　1.20
　　Nos. 545-548 (4)　2.60　1.80

Deep-sea fishing industry.

Vostok 1 Leaving Earth A177

Designs: 20pf, Cosmonaut in capsule. 25pf, Parachute landing of capsule.

**1961, Apr.　Litho.　Perf. 13x12½**
**549** A177 10pf lt blue grn & red　1.00　.60
**550** A177 20pf red　1.00　.60
**551** A177 25pf lt blue　4.00　4.00
　　Nos. 549-551 (3)　6.00　5.20

1st man in space, Yuri A. Gagarin, 4/12/61. Issue dates: 10pf, Apr. 18; others, Apr. 20.

Zebra A178

Dresden Zoo cent.: 20pf, Black-and-white colobus monkeys.

**1961, May 9**
**552** A178 10pf green & blk　4.50　4.50
**553** A178 20pf lilac rose & blk　.75　.25

Engels, Marx, Lenin and Crowd — A179

**1961, Apr. 20　Litho.　Perf. 13½x13**
**554** A179 20pf red　.45　.25

15th anniversary of Socialist Unity Party of Germany (SED).

Stag Leap — A180

Designs: 20pf, Arabesque. 25pf, Exercise on parallel bars, horiz.

**1961, June 3　Perf. 13½x13, 13x13½**
**555** A180 10pf blue green　.20　.20
**556** A180 20pf rose pink　.20　.20
**557** A180 25pf brt blue　5.00　3.50
　　Nos. 555-557 (3)　5.40　3.90

3rd Europa Cup for Women's Gymnastics.

---

Salt Miners and Castle Giebichenstein — A181

20pf, Chemist and "Five Towers" of Halle.

**1961, June 22**　　**Perf. 13x12½**
**558** A181 10pf blk, grn & yel　2.40　1.00
**559** A181 20pf blk, dk red & yel　.20　.20

1000th anniv. of the founding of Halle.

Kayak Slalom A182

10pf, Canoe. 20pf, Two seater canoe.

**1961, July 6　Litho.　Wmk. 313**
**560** A182 5pf gray & Prus bl　2.75　2.00
**561** A182 10pf gray & slate grn　.20　.20
**562** A182 20pf gray & dk car rose　.20　.20
　　Nos. 560-562 (3)　3.15　2.40

Canoe Slalom and Rapids World Championships.

Target Line Casting A183

Design: 20pf, River fishing.

**1961, July 21**
**563** A183 10pf green & blue　2.25　1.50
**564** A183 20pf dk red brn & blue　.35　.20

World Fishing Championships, Dresden.

Tulip — A184

"Alte Waage," Historical Building, Leipzig — A185

**1961, Sept. 13　Photo.　Perf. 14**
**565** A184 10pf shown　.35　.20
**566** A184 25pf Dahlia　.35　.20
**567** A184 40pf Rose　8.00　8.00
　　Nos. 565-567 (3)　8.70　8.40

Intl. Horticulture Exhibition, Erfurt.

### Perf. 13½x13

**1961, Aug. 23　Litho.　Wmk. 313**

Design: 25pf, Old Exchange Building.

**568** A185 10pf citron & bl grn　.20　.20
**569** A185 25pf lt blue & ultra　1.00　.25

1961 Leipzig Fall Fair. See Nos. 595-597.

Liszt's Hand, French Sculpture — A186

Television
Camera and
Screen — A187

Designs: 5pf, Liszt and Hector Berlioz. 20pf, Franz Liszt, medallion by Ernst Rietschel, 1852. 25pf, Liszt and Frederic Chopin.

**1961, Oct.-Nov.      Engr.      Perf. 14**
570 A186  5pf gray            .25   .20
571 A186  10pf blue green     1.75  1.75
572 A186  20pf dull red        .25   .20
573 A186  25pf chalky blue    2.25  2.25
     Nos. 570-573 (4)         4.50  4.40
150th anniversary of the birth of Franz Liszt, composer.

**1961, Oct. 25      Perf. 13x13½**
Design: 20pf, Microphone and radio dial.
574 A187  10pf brt green & blk  1.50  1.50
575 A187  20pf brick red & blk   .20   .20
     Issued for Stamp Day, 1961.

Maj. Gherman Titov and Young
Pioneers — A188

10pf, Titov in Leipzig, vert. 15pf, Titov in spaceship. 20pf, Titov & Walter Ulbricht. 25pf, Spaceship Vostok 2. 40pf, Titov & Ulbricht in Berlin.

**1961, Dec. 11      Litho.      Perf. 13½**
576 A188  5pf carmine & vio   .25   .20
577 A188  10pf olive grn & car .25   .20
578 A188  15pf blue & lilac   7.50  7.50
579 A188  20pf blue & car rose .25   .20
580 A188  25pf carmine & blue  .25   .20
581 A188  40pf car & dk blue  1.25   .30
     Nos. 576-581 (6)         9.75  8.60
Visit of Russian Maj. Gherman Titov to the German Democratic Republic.

Chairman Walter
Ulbricht — A189

**1961-67  Wmk. 313  Typo.  Perf. 14**
**Size: 17x21mm**
582   A189  5pf slate          .20   .20
  a.    Booklet pane of 8      9.25 13.00
583   A189  10pf brt green     .20   .20
  a.    Booklet pane of 8      5.25  8.75
584   A189  15pf red lilac     .25   .20
585   A189  20pf dark red      .30   .20
586   A189  25pf dull bl ('63) .30   .20
587   A189  30pf car rose
              ('63)            .20   .20
588   A189  40pf brt vio ('63) .20   .20
589   A189  50pf ultra ('63)   .20   .20
589A  A189  60pf dp yel grn
              ('64)            .30   .20
590   A189  70pf red brn ('63) .20   .20
590A  A189  80pf brt blue ('67).40   .40

**Engr.**
**Size: 24x28½mm**
590B  A189  1dm dull grn ('63) .75   .35
590C  A189  2dm brown ('63)   1.50   .50
     Nos. 582-590C (13)       5.10  3.25
See #751-752, 1112A-1114A, 1483. Currency abbreviation is "DM" on #590B-590C, "MDN" on #751-752, "M" on #1113-1114A.

Red Ants
A190

**1962, Feb. 16      Photo.**
591 A190  5pf shown          3.25  4.00
592 A190  10pf Weasels        .20   .20
593 A190  20pf Shrews         .20   .20
594 A190  40pf Bat            .50   .30
     Nos. 591-594 (4)        4.15  4.70
     See Nos. 663-667.

**Type of 1961**
Buildings: 10pf, "Coffee Tree House." 20pf, Gohlis Castle. 25pf, Romanus House.

**1962, Feb. 22  Litho.  Perf. 13x13½**
595 A185  10pf olive grn & brn .20   .20
596 A185  20pf orange red &
              blk              .30   .20
597 A185  25pf brt blue & brn  .75   .50
     Nos. 595-597 (3)         1.25   .90
     Leipzig Spring Fair of 1962.

Air
Defense
A191

Designs: 10pf, Motorized infantry. 20pf, Soldier and worker as protectors. 25pf, Sailor and destroyer escort. 40pf, Tank and tankman.

**1962, Mar. 1      Perf. 13x12½**
598 A191  5pf light blue      .20   .20
599 A191  10pf bright green    .20   .20
600 A191  20pf red            .20   .20
601 A191  25pf ultra          .25   .25
602 A191  40pf brown         1.50  1.00
     Nos. 598-602 (5)        2.35  1.85
National People's Army, 6th anniv.

Cyclists and Hradcany,
Prague — A192

25pf, Cyclist, East Berlin City Hall and dove.

**1962, Apr. 26  Litho.  Wmk. 313**
603 A192  10pf multicolored   .20   .20
604 A192  25pf multicolored  1.25  1.00
     Nos. 603-604,B89 (3)    1.65  1.40
15th International Bicycle Peace Race, Berlin-Warsaw-Prague.

Johann Gottlieb
Fichte — A193

10pf, Fichte's birthplace in Rammenau.

**1962, May 17      Perf. 13x13½**
605 A193  10pf brt green & blk 1.25  1.25
606 A193  20pf vermilion & blk .20   .20
Bicentenary of the birth of Johann Gottlieb Fichte, philosopher.

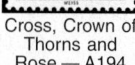

Cross, Crown of
Thorns and
Rose — A194

George Dimitrov
at Reichstag Trial,
Leipzig — A195

**1962, June 7      Perf. 12½x13**
607 A194  20pf red & black    .20   .20
608 A194  25pf brt blue & blk 1.10   .65
20th anniversary of the destruction of Lidice in Czechoslovakia by the Nazis.

**1962, June 18      Photo.      Perf. 14**
20pf, Dimitrov as Premier of Bulgaria.
609 A195  5pf blue grn & blk  .50   .30
610 A195  20pf car rose & blk .20   .20
  a.    Pair, #609-610, + label 5.00 30.00
George Dimitrov, (1882-1949), communist leader and premier of the Bulgarian Peoples' Republic.
Nos. 609-610 also printed se-tenant, divided by a label inscribed with a Dimitrov quotation.

Corn
Planter
A196

20pf, Milking machine. 40pf, Combine harvester.

**1962, June 26  Litho.  Perf. 13x12½**
611 A196  10pf multicolored   .20   .20
612 A196  20pf multicolored   .20   .20
613 A196  40pf yel, grn & dk red 1.50 1.25
     Nos. 611-613 (3)        1.90  1.65
10th Agricultural Exhibition, Markkleeberg.

Map of Baltic
Sea and
Emblem — A197

Designs: 20pf, Hotel, Rostock, vert. 25pf, Cargo ship "Frieden" in Rostock harbor.

**Perf. 13x13½, 13½x13 (20pf)**
**1962, July 2      Wmk. 313**
614 A197  10pf bluish grn & ultra .20 .20
615 A197  20pf dk red & yellow  .20  .20
616 A197  25pf blue & bister   2.25  2.25
     Nos. 614-616 (3)         2.65  2.65
5th Baltic Sea Week, Rostock, July 7-15.

Brandenburg Gate,
Berlin — A198

**1962, July 17      Perf. 13½x13**
#618 Heads of youths of three races. #619, Peace dove. #620, National Theater, Helsinki.
617 A198  5pf multicolored   2.25  2.25
618 A198  5pf multicolored   2.25  2.25
619 A198  20pf multicolored  2.25  2.25
620 A198  20pf multicolored  2.25  2.25
  a.    Block of 4, #617-620 13.00 13.00
     Nos. 617-620,B90-B91 (6) 9.60 9.40
8th Youth Festival for Peace and Friendship, Helsinki, July 28-Aug. 6, 1962.
No. 620a forms the festival flower emblem.

Free Style
Swimming
A199

Designs: 10pf, Back stroke. 25pf, Butterfly stroke. 40pf, Breast stroke. 70pf, Water polo.

**1962, Aug. 7  Litho.  Perf. 13x13½**
**Design in Greenish Blue**
621 A199  5pf orange         .20   .20
622 A199  10pf grnsh blue    .20   .20
623 A199  20pf ultra         .20   .20
624 A199  40pf brt violet   1.10  1.10
625 A199  70pf red brown     .20   .20
  a.    Block of 6, #621-625, B92 2.25 2.25
     Nos. 621-625,B92 (6)    2.10  2.10
10th European Swimming Championships, Leipzig, Aug. 18-25.
Nos. 621-625, B92 each printed in sheets of 50, No. 625a in sheet of 60.

Municipal Store,
Leipzig — A200

**Engr. & Photo.**
**1962, Aug. 28  Wmk. 313  Perf. 14**
Buildings: 20pf, Mädler Passage. 25pf, Leipzig Air Terminal and plane.
626 A200  10pf black & emer-
              ald             .20   .20
627 A200  20pf black & red    .25   .20
628 A200  25pf black & blue   .75   .60
     Nos. 626-628 (3)        1.20  1.00
     Leipzig Fall Fair of 1962.

"Transportation and
Communication" — A201

**1962, Oct. 3  Litho.  Perf. 13½x13**
629 A201  5pf light blue & black  .30  .20
10th anniv. of the Friedrich List Transportation College.

**Souvenir Sheet**

ERSTER GRUPPENFLUG IM KOSMOS

WOSTOK III 11.8.1962, 9.30 Uhr, bis 15.8.1962, 7.55 Uhr (MEZ)
WOSTOK IV 12.8.1962, 9.02 Uhr, bis 15.8.1962, 8.01 Uhr (MEZ)

Pavel R. Popovich, Andrian G.
Nikolayev and Space
Capsules — A202

**1962, Sept. 13  Wmk. 313  Imperf.**
630 A202  70pf dk blue, lt grn
              & yel          2.25  3.50
1st Russian group space flight of Vostoks III and IV, Aug. 11-13, 1962.

DDR
Television
Signal
A203

Young
Collectors
and World
Map — A204

**1962, Oct. 25      Perf. 13½x13**
631 A203  20pf green & gray   .20   .20
632 A204  40pf brt pink & blk 1.50  1.50
No. 631 for the 10th anniv. of television in the German Democratic Republic; No. 632 is for Stamp Day.

Gerhart
Hauptmann
A205

**1962, Nov. 15**     *Perf. 13x13½*
633 A205 20pf red & black     .35   .20
   Centenary of the birth of Gerhart
Hauptmann, playwright.

**Souvenir Sheet**

Russian Space Flights and
Astronauts — A206

**1962, Dec. 28**   **Litho.**   *Perf. 12½x13*
634 A206   Sheet of 8     30.00 30.00
  *a.*   5pf yellow     1.50   1.50
  *b.*   10pf emerald     1.50   1.50
  *c.*   15pf magenta     3.00   3.00
  *d.*   20pf red     3.00   3.00
  *e.*   25pf greenish blue     3.00   3.00
  *f.*   30pf red brown     3.00   3.00
  *g.*   40pf crimson     1.50   1.50
  *h.*   50pf ultramarine     1.50   1.50

   Issued to show the development of Russian
space flights from Sputnik 1 to Vostoks 3 and
4, and to honor the Russian astronauts
Gagarin, Titov, Nikolayev and Popovich.

Pierre de
Coubertin — A207

   Design: 25pf, Stadium and Olympic rings.

**1963, Jan. 2**     *Perf. 13½x13*
635 A207 20pf carmine & gray    .20   .20
636 A207 25pf blue & bister    1.50   1.50
   Baron Pierre de Coubertin, organizer of the
modern Olympic Games, birth cent.

Congress
Emblem, Flag
with Marx,
Engels and
Lenin — A208

**1963, Jan. 15**     *Perf. 13x13½*
637 A208 10pf yel, org, red & blk    .30   .20
   6th congress of Socialist Unity Party of Germany (SED).

World Map and Exterminator — A209

   Designs: 25pf, Map, cross and staff of Aesculapius. 50pf, Map, cross, mosquito.

**1963, Feb. 6**     *Perf. 13x12½*
638 A209 20pf dp org, dk red
        & blk     .20   .20
639 A209 25pf multicolored     .20   .20
640 A209 50pf multicolored     1.10   1.10
   *Nos. 638-640 (3)*     1.50   1.50

   WHO drive to eradicate malaria.

Silver Fox
A210

   Design: 25pf, Karakul.

**1963, Feb. 14**   **Photo.**   *Perf. 14*
641 A210 20pf rose & black     .20   .20
642 A210 25pf blue & black     1.40   1.40
   Intl. Fur Auctions, Leipzig, 2/14-15, 4/21-24.

Barthels House,
Leipzig — A211

   Designs: 20pf, New Leipzig City Hall. 25pf,
Belltower Building.

**Engr. & Photo.**
**1963, Feb. 26**   **Wmk. 313**   *Perf. 14*
643 A211 10pf black & citron    .20   .20
644 A211 20pf black & red org    .30   .20
645 A211 25pf black & blue    1.10   1.10
   *Nos. 643-645 (3)*    1.60   1.50

   1963 Leipzig Spring Fair.

**Souvenir Sheet**
   On March 12, 1963, a souvenir sheet
publicizing "Chemistry for Peace and
Socialism" was issued. It contains two
imperforate stamps, 50pf and 70pf,
printed on ungummed synthetic tissue.
Size: 105x74mm. Value $3.75.

Richard Wagner and "The Flying
Dutchman" — A213

   Portrait & Scene from Play: 5pf, Johann
Gottfried Seume (1763-1810). 10pf, Friedrich
Hebbel (1813-63). 20pf, Georg Büchner
(1813-37).

**1963, Apr. 9**   **Litho.**   *Perf. 13x12½*
647 A213   5pf brt citron & blk    .20   .20
648 A213 10pf brt green & blk    .20   .20
649 A213 20pf orange & blk    .20   .20
650 A213 25pf dull blue & blk    1.50   1.50
   *Nos. 647-650 (4)*    2.10   2.10

   Anniversaries of German dramatists and the
150th anniv. of the birth of Richard Wagner,
composer.

First Aid
Station
A214

   Design: 20pf, Ambulance and hospital.

**1963, May 14**     **Wmk. 313**
651 A214 10pf multicolored    1.00   1.00
652 A214 20pf red, blk & gray    .20   .20
   Centenary of International Red Cross.

Eugene Pottier,
Writer — A215

25pf, Pierre-Chretien Degeyter, composer.

**1963, June 18**     *Perf. 13x13½*
653 A215 20pf vermilion & blk    .20   .20
654 A215 25pf vio blue & blk    1.00   1.00
   75th anniv. of the communist song "The
International."

A216

   No. 655, Valentina Tereshkova, Vostok 6.
No. 656, Valeri Bykovski, Vostok 5.

**1963, July 18**   **Photo.**   *Perf. 13½*
655    20pf blue, blk & gray bl   .75   .20
656    20pf blue, blk & gray bl   .75   .20
  *a.* A216 Pair, #655-656    1.50   .40
   Space flights of Valeri Bykovski, June 14-19,
and Valentina Tereshkova, 1st woman cosmonaut, June 16-19, 1963.

Motorcyclist in
"Motocross" at
Apolda — A217

**Engr. & Photo.**
**1963, July 30**     *Perf. 14*
  20pf, Motorcyclist at Sachsenring, horiz.
25pf, 2 motorcyclists at Sachsenring, horiz.

**Size: 23x28mm**
657 A217 10pf lt grn & dk grn    3.00 3.00
**Size: 48½x21mm**
658 A217 20pf rose & dk red    .25   .20
659 A217 25pf lt blue & dk blue    .25   .20
   *Nos. 657-659 (3)*    3.50 3.40

   Motorcycle World Championships.

Monument at
Treblinka
A218

   *Perf. 13x13½*
**1963, Aug. 20**   **Litho.**   **Wmk. 313**
660 A218 20pf brick red & dk blue   .30   .20
   Erection of a memorial at Treblinka (Poland)
concentration camp.

Globe, Car and
Train — A219

**1963, Aug. 27**     *Perf. 13½x13*
   Design: No. 662, Globe, plane and bus.

661 A219 10pf multicolored    .65   .20
662 A219 10pf multicolored    .65   .20
  *a.*   Pair, #661-662    2.00   .40
   Issued to publicize the 1963 Leipzig Fall Fair.

**Fauna Type of 1962**
   10pf, Stag beetle. 20pf, Fire salamander.
30pf, Pond turtle. 50pf, Green toad. 70pf,
Hedgehogs.

**1963, Sept. 10**   **Photo.**   *Perf. 14*
663 A190 10pf emer, brn & blk    .20   .20
664 A190 20pf crimson, blk & yel    .20   .20
665 A190 30pf multicolored    .20   .20
666 A190 50pf multicolored    3.00 3.00
667 A190 70pf claret brn, brn &
        bis     .50   .50
   *Nos. 663-667 (5)*    4.10 4.10

Neidhardt von Gneisenau and
Gebhard Leberecht von
Blücher — A220

   Designs: 10pf, Cossacks and home guard,
Berlin. 20pf, Ernst Moritz Arndt and Baron
Heinrich vom Stein. 25pf, Lützow's volunteers
before battle. 40pf, Gerhard von Scharnhorst
and Prince Mikhail I. Kutuzov.

**1963, Oct. 10**   **Litho.**   *Perf. 13½x13*
**Center in Tan and Black**
668 A220   5pf brt yellow    .20   .20
669 A220 10pf emerald    .20   .20
670 A220 20pf dp orange    .20   .20
671 A220 25pf dp ultra    .20   .20
672 A220 40pf dark red    2.00   .75
   *Nos. 668-672 (5)*    2.80 1.55

   150th anniversary of War of Liberation.

Valentina
Tereshkova and
Space
Craft — A221

Burning
Synagogue and
Star of David in
Chains — A222

   #674, Tereshkova and map of DDR, vert.
#675, Yuri A. Gagarin and map of DDR, vert.
25pf, Tereshkova in space capsule.

**1963**     *Perf. 13½x13, 13x13½*
**Size: 28x28mm (10pf, 25pf);**
**28x37mm (20pf)**
673 A221 10pf ultra & green    .20   .20
674 A221 20pf red, blk & ocher    .20   .20
675 A221 20pf red, grn & ocher    .20   .20
676 A221 25pf orange & blue    3.50 1.75
   *Nos. 673-676 (4)*    4.10 2.35

   Visit of astronauts Valentina Tereshkova &
Yuri A. Gagarin to the German Democratic
Republic.

   *Perf. 13½x13*
**1963, Nov. 8**     **Wmk. 313**
677 A222 10pf multicolored    .30   .20

   25th anniv. of the "Crystal Night," the start of
the systematic persecution of the Jews in Germany. Inscribed: "Never again Crystal Night."

Letter
Sorting
Machine
A223

   Design: 20pf, Mechanized mail loading.

**1963, Nov. 25**     *Perf. 13x12½*
678 A223 10pf multicolored    1.60   1.60
679 A223 20pf multicolored    .20   .20

   Issued for Stamp Day.

Ski Jump and Olympic Rings A224

**1963, Dec. 16   Litho.   Perf. 13½x13**

| | | | | |
|---|---|---|---|---|
| 680 | A224 | 5pf shown | .20 | .20 |
| 681 | A224 | 10pf Start | .20 | .20 |
| 682 | A224 | 25pf Landing | 2.00 | 2.00 |
| | Nos. 680-682,B111 (4) | | 2.60 | 2.60 |

9th Winter Olympic Games, Innsbruck, Jan. 29-Feb. 9, 1964.

Admiral — A225

Butterflies: 15pf, Alpine Apollo. 20pf, Swallowtail. 25pf, Postilion. 40pf, Great fox.

**Wmk. 313**

**1964, Jan. 15   Photo.   Perf. 14**
**Butterflies in Natural Colors**

| | | | | |
|---|---|---|---|---|
| 683 | A225 | 10pf citron & blk | .35 | .20 |
| 684 | A225 | 15pf pale violet & blk | .35 | .20 |
| 685 | A225 | 20pf lt brick red & blk | .35 | .20 |
| 686 | A225 | 25pf lt blue & dk brn | .35 | .20 |
| 687 | A225 | 40pf lt ultra & blk | 5.25 | 1.75 |
| | Nos. 683-687 (5) | | 6.65 | 2.55 |

William Shakespeare — A226

20pf, Quadriga, Brandenburg Gate, Berlin. 25pf, Keystone, History Museum (Zeughaus), Berlin.

**1964, Feb. 6   Litho.   Perf. 13x12½**

| | | | | |
|---|---|---|---|---|
| 688 | A226 | 20pf rose & dk blue | .25 | .20 |
| 689 | A226 | 25pf lt blue & mag | .25 | .20 |
| 690 | A226 | 40pf lt vio & dk bl grn | 1.20 | .80 |
| | Nos. 688-690 (3) | | 1.70 | 1.20 |

200th anniv. of the birth of the sculptor Johann Gottfried Schadow (20pf); 300th anniv. of the birth of the sculptor Andreas Schlüter (25pf); 400th anniv. of the birth of William Shakespeare, dramatist (40pf).

Electrical Engineering Exhibit — A227

20pf, Bräunigkes Court, exhibition hall, 1700.

**Perf. 13x13½**
**1964, Feb. 26   Wmk. 313**

| | | | | |
|---|---|---|---|---|
| 691 | A227 | 10pf brt green & blk | 2.25 | .25 |
| 692 | A227 | 20pf red & black | 2.25 | .25 |
| a. | Block, 1 each #661-662 + 2 labels | | 18.00 | 1.00 |

Leipzig Spring Fair, Mar. 1-10, 1964.

Khrushchev and Inventors — A228

Youth Training for Leadership A229

40pf, Khrushchev, Tereshkova & Gagarin.

**1964, May 15   Perf. 13x13½**

| | | | | |
|---|---|---|---|---|
| 693 | A228 | 25pf blue | .25 | .20 |
| 694 | A228 | 40pf lilac & grnsh blk | 2.50 | 1.50 |

Issued in honor of Premier Nikita S. Khrushchev of the Soviet Union.

**1964, May 13   Litho.**

Designs: 20pf, Young athletes. 25pf, Accordion player and girl with flowers.

**Center in Black**

| | | | | |
|---|---|---|---|---|
| 695 | A229 | 10pf ultra, mag & emer | .20 | .20 |
| 696 | A229 | 20pf emer, ultra & mag | .20 | .20 |
| 697 | A229 | 25pf magenta, emer & ultra | 1.50 | .60 |
| | Nos. 695-697 (3) | | 1.90 | 1.00 |

German Youth Meeting, Berlin.

Television Antenna and Puppets — A230

Children's Day: Various characters from children's television programs.

**1964, June 1   Perf. 13x13½**

| | | | | |
|---|---|---|---|---|
| 698 | A230 | 5pf multicolored | .20 | .20 |
| 699 | A230 | 10pf multicolored | .20 | .20 |
| 700 | A230 | 15pf multicolored | .20 | .20 |
| 701 | A230 | 20pf multicolored | .20 | .20 |
| 702 | A230 | 40pf multicolored | 1.40 | 1.40 |
| | Nos. 698-702 (5) | | 2.20 | 2.20 |

Woman as Educator and Portrait of Jenny Marx — A231

Designs: 25pf, Women in industry and transistor diagram. 70pf, Women in agriculture.

**Perf. 13½x13**
**1964, June 26   Litho.   Wmk. 313**

| | | | | |
|---|---|---|---|---|
| 703 | A231 | 20pf crimson, gray & yel | .30 | .20 |
| 704 | A231 | 25pf lt blue, gray & red | .90 | .75 |
| 705 | A231 | 70pf emerald, gray & yel | .30 | .20 |
| | Nos. 703-705 (3) | | 1.50 | 1.15 |

Congress of Women of the German Democratic Republic, June 25-27.

Bicycling A232

Diving — A233

**Litho. & Engr.**

**1964, July 15   Perf. 14**

| | | | | |
|---|---|---|---|---|
| 706 | A232 | 5pf shown | .20 | .20 |
| 707 | A232 | 10pf Volleyball | .20 | .20 |
| 708 | A232 | 20pf Judo | .20 | .20 |
| 709 | A232 | 25pf Woman diver | .20 | .20 |
| 710 | A232 | 70pf Equestrian | 1.50 | 1.50 |
| | Nos. 706-710,B118 (6) | | 2.60 | 2.50 |

**Litho.**
**Perf. 13x13½**

| | | | | |
|---|---|---|---|---|
| 711 | A233 | 10pf shown | 2.25 | 2.25 |
| 712 | A233 | 10pf Volleyball | 2.25 | 2.25 |
| 713 | A233 | 10pf Bicycling | 2.25 | 2.25 |
| 714 | A233 | 10pf Judo | 2.25 | 2.25 |
| a. | Block of 6, #711-714, B119-B120 | | 20.00 | 20.00 |

18th Olympic Games, Tokyo, Oct. 10-25, 1964. See Nos. B118-B120. No. 714a printed in 2 horiz. rows (1st: #711, B119, #712. 2nd: #713, B120, #714). The Olympic rings extend over the 6 stamps.

Monument, Leningrad A234

**1964, Aug. 8   Litho.   Perf. 13x13½**

| | | | | |
|---|---|---|---|---|
| 715 | A234 | 25pf brt blue, blk & yel | .90 | .20 |

Issued to honor the victims of the siege of Leningrad, Sept. 1941-Jan. 1943.

Bertha von Suttner — A235

**1964, Sept. 1   Perf. 14**

| | | | | |
|---|---|---|---|---|
| 716 | A235 | 20pf red & black | .20 | .20 |
| 717 | A235 | 25pf ultra & black | .20 | .20 |
| 718 | A235 | 50pf lilac & black | 1.00 | .65 |
| | Nos. 716-718 (3) | | 1.40 | 1.05 |

Issued to promote World Peace.

Medieval Glazier and Goblet — A236

Designs: 20pf, Frederic Joliot Curie. 50pf, Carl von Ossietzky.

**1964, Sept. 3   Perf. 14**

15pf, Jena glass for chemical industry.

| | | | | |
|---|---|---|---|---|
| 719 | A236 | 10pf lt ultra & multi | .50 | .20 |
| 720 | A236 | 15pf red & multi | .50 | .20 |
| a. | Pair, #719-720 + label | | 2.00 | .45 |

Issued for the Leipzig Fall Fair, 1964.

Handstamp of First Socialist International, 1864 — A237

**1964, Sept. 16   Photo.   Wmk. 313**

| | | | | |
|---|---|---|---|---|
| 721 | A237 | 20pf orange red & blk | .20 | .20 |
| 722 | A237 | 25pf dull blue & blk | .60 | .50 |

Centenary of First Socialist International.

Stamp of 1955 (Dürer's Portrait of Young Man) — A238

**1964, Sept. 23   Litho.   Perf. 13x13½**

| | | | | |
|---|---|---|---|---|
| 723 | A238 | 50pf gray & dk red brn | 1.60 | 1.10 |
| | Nos. 723,B124-B125 (3) | | 2.15 | 1.55 |

Natl. Stamp Exhibition, Berlin, Oct. 3-18.

Coal Transport A239

#724, Navigation. #725, Flag & new Berlin buildings. #727, Chemist. #728, Soldier. #729, Farm woman & cows. #730, Steel worker. #731, Woman scientist & lecture hall. #732, Heavy industry. #733, Optical industry. #734, Consumer goods (woman examining cloth). #735, Foreign trade, Leipzig fair emblem. #736, Buildings industry. #737, Sculptor. #738, Woman skier.

**Perf. 13½x13**
**1964, Oct. 6   Litho.   Wmk. 313**

| | | | | |
|---|---|---|---|---|
| 724 | A239 | 10pf blue & multi | .30 | .20 |
| 725 | A239 | 10pf blue & multi | .30 | .20 |
| 726 | A239 | 10pf gray & multi | .30 | .20 |
| 727 | A239 | 10pf red & multi | .30 | .20 |
| 728 | A239 | 10pf blue & multi | .30 | .20 |
| 729 | A239 | 10pf yel grn & multi | .30 | .20 |
| 730 | A239 | 10pf red & multi | .30 | .20 |
| 731 | A239 | 10pf red & multi | .30 | .20 |
| 732 | A239 | 10pf gray & multi | .30 | .20 |
| 733 | A239 | 10pf gray & multi | .30 | .20 |
| 734 | A239 | 10pf blue & multi | .30 | .20 |
| 735 | A239 | 10pf blue & multi | .30 | .20 |
| 736 | A239 | 10pf yel grn & multi | .30 | .20 |
| 737 | A239 | 10pf yel grn & multi | .30 | .20 |
| 738 | A239 | 10pf blue & multi | .30 | .20 |
| | Nos. 724-738 (15) | | 4.50 | 3.00 |

German Democratic Republic, 15th anniv. A souvenir sheet contains 15 imperf. stamps similar to #724-738. Size: 210x287mm. Value, $45.

For surcharge see No. B134.

Man from Mönchgut, Rügen — A240

**1964, Nov. 25   Photo.   Perf. 14**

Regional Costumes: No. 740, Woman from Mönchgut, Rügen. No. 741, Man from Spreewald. No. 742, Woman from Spreewald. No. 743, Man from Thuringia. No. 744, Woman from Thuringia.

| | | | | |
|---|---|---|---|---|
| 739 | A240 | 5pf multicolored | 7.00 | 4.25 |
| 740 | A240 | 5pf multicolored | 7.00 | 4.25 |
| a. | Pair, #739-740 | | 25.00 | 10.00 |
| 741 | A240 | 10pf multicolored | 1.75 | .90 |
| 742 | A240 | 10pf multicolored | 1.75 | .90 |
| a. | Pair, #741-742 | | 7.50 | 3.00 |
| 743 | A240 | 20pf multicolored | 1.75 | .90 |
| 744 | A240 | 20pf multicolored | 1.75 | .90 |
| a. | Pair, #739-740 | | 7.50 | 3.00 |
| | Nos. 739-744 (6) | | 21.00 | 12.10 |

Printed in checkerboard arrangement. See Nos. 859-864.

## Souvenir Sheets

Exploration of Ionosphere — A241

Designs: 40pf, Exploration of sun activities. 70pf, Exploration of radiation belt.

**1964, Dec. 29　Litho.　Perf. 13½x13**

| | | | | |
|---|---|---|---|---|
| 745 | A241 | 25pf vio bl & yel | 5.50 | 6.00 |
| 746 | A241 | 40pf vio bl, yel & red | 2.75 | 3.00 |
| 747 | A241 | 70pf dp grn, vio bl & yel | 2.75 | 3.00 |
| | | Nos. 745-747 (3) | 11.00 | 12.00 |

Intl. Quiet Sun Year, 1964-65.

Albert Schweitzer as Physician A242

August Bebel — A243

Designs (Schweitzer): 20pf, As fighter against war and atom bomb. 25pf, At the organ with score of Organ Prelude by Bach.

**Wmk. 313**

**1965, Jan. 14　Photo.　Perf. 14**

| | | | | |
|---|---|---|---|---|
| 748 | A242 | 10pf emerald, blk & bis | .35 | .20 |
| 749 | A242 | 20pf crimson, blk & bis | .35 | .20 |
| 750 | A242 | 25pf blue, blk & bis | 3.00 | 1.50 |
| | | Nos. 748-750 (3) | 3.70 | 1.90 |

90th birthday of Dr. Albert Schweitzer, medical missionary.

### Ulbricht Type of 1961-63
Currency in "Mark of the Deutsche Notenbank" (MDN)

**1965, Feb. 10　　　Engr.**
**Size: 24x28½mm**

| | | | | |
|---|---|---|---|---|
| 751 | A189 | 1mdn dull green | .45 | .35 |
| 752 | A189 | 2mdn brown | .50 | .40 |

See note below Nos. 590B-590C.

**1965　　Photo.　Perf. 14**

10pf, Wilhelm Conrad Roentgen. #753A, Adolph von Menzel. 25pf, Wilhelm Külz. 40pf, Erich Weinert. 50pf, Dante Alighieri.

| | | | | |
|---|---|---|---|---|
| 753 | A243 | 10pf dk brn, yel & emer | .35 | .20 |
| 753A | A243 | 10pf dk brn, yel & org | .65 | .20 |
| 754 | A243 | 20pf ol brn, red & buff | .35 | .20 |
| 754A | A243 | 25pf ol brn, yel & bl | .80 | .20 |
| 754B | A243 | 40pf ol brn, buff & car rose | .45 | .20 |
| 755 | A243 | 50pf dk brn, yel & org | 1.60 | .20 |
| | | Nos. 753-755 (6) | 4.20 | 1.20 |

Roentgen (1845-1923), physicist, discoverer of X-rays. Sesquicentennial of the birth of Adolph von Menzel, painter and graphic artist.

---

Bebel, labor leader (1840-1913). 90th anniv. of the birth of Wilhelm Külz, politician. 75th anniv. of the birth of Erich Weinert, poet. Alighieri (1265-1321), Italian poet.
　Issued: #753, 3/24; #753A, 12/8; 20pf, 2/22; 25pf, 7/5; 40pf, 7/28; 50pf, 4/15.

A244　　　　A245

Designs: 10pf, Gold Medal, Leipzig Fair. 15pf, Obverse of medal, arms of German Democratic Republic. 25pf, Chemical plant.

**1965, Feb. 25　　　Wmk. 313**

| | | | | |
|---|---|---|---|---|
| 756 | A244 | 10pf lilac rose & gold | .20 | .20 |
| 757 | A244 | 15pf lilac rose & gold | .20 | .20 |
| 758 | A244 | 25pf lilac, yel & gold | .50 | .20 |
| | | Nos. 756-758 (3) | .90 | .60 |

1965 Leipzig Spring Fair; 800th anniv. of the Fair.

**1965, Mar. 24**

Designs: 10pf, Giraffe. 25pf, Common iguana, horiz. 30pf, White-tailed gnu.

| | | | | |
|---|---|---|---|---|
| 759 | A245 | 10pf green & gray | .20 | .20 |
| 760 | A245 | 25pf dk vio bl & gray | .25 | .20 |
| 761 | A245 | 30pf brown & gray | 1.75 | 1.00 |
| | | Nos. 759-761 (3) | 2.20 | 1.40 |

10th anniversary of Berlin Zoo.

Col. Pavel Belyayev and Lt. Col. Alexei Leonov A246

25pf, Lt. Col. Leonov floating in space.

**Perf. 13½x13**

**1965, Apr. 15　Litho.　Wmk. 313**

| | | | | |
|---|---|---|---|---|
| 762 | A246 | 10pf red | .30 | .20 |
| 763 | A246 | 25pf dk ultra | 2.00 | 1.25 |

Space flight of Voskhod 2 and the first man walking in space, Lt. Col. Alexel Leonov.

Boxing Glove and Laurel Wreath — A247

**1965, Apr. 27　Photo.　Perf. 14**

| | | | | |
|---|---|---|---|---|
| 764 | A247 | 20pf blk, red & gold | .75 | .60 |

16th European Boxing Championship, Berlin, May, 1965. See No. B126.

Walter Ulbricht and Erich Weinert Distributing "Free Germany" Leaflets on the Eastern Front — A248

50pf, Liberation of concentration camps. 60pf, Russian soldiers raising flag on Reichstag, Berlin. 70pf, Political demonstration.

---

**1965, May 5　　Photo.　Perf. 14**
**Flags in Red, Black & Yellow**

| | | | | |
|---|---|---|---|---|
| 765 | A248 | 40pf blue grn & red | .25 | .20 |
| 766 | A248 | 50pf dull blue & red | .25 | .20 |
| 767 | A248 | 60pf brown & red | 2.50 | 1.40 |
| 768 | A248 | 70pf vio blue & red | .25 | .20 |
| | | Nos. 765-768,B127-B131 (9) | 4.50 | 3.00 |

20th anniv. of liberation from fascism.

Radio Tower and Globe A249

ITU Emblem and Frequency Diagram A250

40pf, Workers & broadcasting equipment.

**1965, May 12　Litho.　Perf. 12½x13**

| | | | | |
|---|---|---|---|---|
| 769 | A249 | 20pf dk car rose & blk | .30 | .20 |
| 770 | A249 | 40pf vio bl & blk | 1.40 | .35 |

20th anniv. of the German Democratic broadcasting system.

**1965, May 17**

25pf, ITU emblem & telephone diagram.

| | | | | |
|---|---|---|---|---|
| 771 | A250 | 20pf olive, yel & blk | .35 | .20 |
| 772 | A250 | 25pf vio, pale vio & blk | 1.90 | .35 |

Cent. of the ITU.

Emblem of Free German Trade Union — A251

Hemispheres with Crowd of Workers — A252

**1965, June 10　Photo.　Perf. 14**

| | | | | |
|---|---|---|---|---|
| 773 | A251 | 20pf red & gold | .35 | .20 |
| 774 | A252 | 25pf gold, blue & blk | 1.10 | .30 |

20th anniv. of the Free German Trade Union (FDGB) and of the World Organization of Trade Unions.

Symbols of Industry — A253

Marx and Lenin — A254

Designs: 20pf, Red Tower. 25pf, City Hall.

**1965, June 16**

| | | | | |
|---|---|---|---|---|
| 775 | A253 | 10pf gold & emerald | .25 | .20 |
| 776 | A253 | 20pf gold & crimson | .25 | .20 |
| 777 | A253 | 25pf gold & brt blue | .90 | .30 |
| | | Nos. 775-777 (3) | 1.40 | .70 |

800th anniv. of Chemnitz (Karl Marx City).

**1965, June 21　Litho.　Perf. 13½x13**

| | | | | |
|---|---|---|---|---|
| 778 | A254 | 20pf red, black & gold | .50 | .20 |

6th Conference of Postal Ministers of Communist Countries, Peking, June 21-July 15.

---

"Alte Waage" and New Building, Leipzig — A255

25pf, Old City Hall. 40pf, Opera House & General Post Office. 70pf, Hotel "Stadt Leipzig."

**Unwmk.**

**1965, Aug. 25　　Photo.　Perf. 14**

| | | | | |
|---|---|---|---|---|
| 781 | A255 | 10pf gold, cl brn & ultra | .20 | .20 |
| a. | | Souv. sheet of 2, #781, 784 | 3.00 | 3.00 |
| 782 | A255 | 25pf gold, brn, & ocher | .20 | .20 |
| a. | | Souv. sheet of 2, #782-783 | 2.50 | 2.50 |
| 783 | A255 | 40pf gold, brn, ocher & yel grn | .25 | .20 |
| 784 | A255 | 70pf gold & ultra | 1.80 | .60 |
| | | Nos. 781-784 (4) | 2.45 | 1.20 |

800th anniv. of the City of Leipzig. No. 781a sold for 90pf; No. 782a for 80pf. The souvenir sheets were issued Sept. 4, 1965.

Cameras A256

Equestrian A257

Leipzig Fall Fair: 15pf, Electric guitar and organ. 25pf, Microscope.

**1965, Sept. 9　　　Perf. 14**

| | | | | |
|---|---|---|---|---|
| 785 | A256 | 10pf green, blk & gold | .25 | .20 |
| 786 | A256 | 15pf multicolored | .25 | .20 |
| 787 | A256 | 25pf multicolored | .70 | .20 |
| | | Nos. 785-787 (3) | 1.20 | .60 |

**Perf. 13½x13**

**1965, Sept. 15　Litho.　Unwmk.**

| | | | | |
|---|---|---|---|---|
| 789 | A257 | 10pf shown | .25 | .20 |
| 790 | A257 | 10pf Swimmer | .25 | .20 |
| 791 | A257 | 10pf Runner | 2.10 | 2.10 |
| | | Nos. 789-791,B135-B136 (5) | 3.10 | 2.90 |

Intl. Modern Pentathlon Championships, Leipzig.

Alexei Leonov and Brandenburg Gate — A258

Memorial Monument, Putten — A259

Designs: No. 793, Pavel Belyayev and Berlin City Hall. 25pf, Leonov floating in space and space ship.

**Wmk. 313**

**1965, Nov. 1　Litho.　Perf. 14**
**Size: 23½x28½mm**

| | | | | |
|---|---|---|---|---|
| 792 | A258 | 20pf blue, sil & red | .45 | .45 |
| 793 | A258 | 20pf blue, sil & red | .45 | .45 |

## Size: 51x28½mm

794 A258 25pf blue, sil & red    .45  .45
   *a.*   Strip of 3, #792-794   2.90  2.90

Visit of the Russian astronauts to the German Democratic Republic.

**1965, Nov. 19**     **Perf. 13x13½**
795 A259 25pf brt bl, pale yel & blk  .60  .20

Issued in memory of the victims of a Nazi attack on Putten, Netherlands, Sept. 30, 1944.

Furnace A260

After old woodcuts: 15pf, Ore miners. 20pf, Proustite crystals. 25pf, Sulphur crystals.

**Perf. 13x12½**
**1965, Nov. 11**   **Litho.**   **Unwmk.**
796 A260 10pf black & multi  .25  .20
797 A260 15pf black & multi  .55  .55
798 A260 20pf black & multi  .25  .20
799 A260 25pf black & multi  .25  .20
   Nos. 796-799 (4)   1.30  1.15

Mining Academy in Freiberg, bicent.

Red Kite A261     Otto Grotewohl A262

Birds: 10pf, Lammergeier. 20pf, Buzzard. 25pf, Kestrel. 40pf, Northern goshawk. 70pf, Golden eagle.

**1965, Dec. 8**   **Photo.**   **Perf. 14**
**Gold Frame**
800 A261 5pf orange & blk  .20  .20
801 A261 10pf emer, brn & blk  .20  .20
802 A261 20pf car, red brn & blk  .25  .20
803 A261 25pf blue, red brn & blk  .25  .20
804 A261 40pf lilac, blk & dk red  .35  .20
805 A261 70pf brn, blk & yel  3.50  1.75
   Nos. 800-805 (6)   4.75  2.75

**1965, Dec. 14**   **Photo.**   **Wmk. 313**
806 A262 20pf black  .70  .20

Issued in memory of Otto Grotewohl (1894-1964), prime minister (1949-1964).

### Souvenir Sheet

Spartacus Letter, Karl Liebknecht and Rosa Luxemburg — A263

**1966, Jan. 3**     **Unwmk.**
807 A263  Sheet of 2   1.90  4.00
   *a.*  20pf red & black  .35  .35
   *b.*  50pf red & black  .35  .35

50th anniv. of the natl. conf. of the Spartacus organization.

Tobogganing, Women's Singles A264

20pf, Men's doubles. 25pf, Men's singles.

---

**Perf. 13½x13**
**1966, Jan. 25**   **Litho.**   **Unwmk.**
808 A264 10pf citron & dp grn  .20  .20
809 A264 20pf car rose & dk vio bl  .20  .20
810 A264 25pf blue & dk blue  1.10  .60
   Nos. 808-810 (3)   1.50  1.00

10th Intl. Tobogganing Championships, Friedrichroda, Feb. 8-13.

Electronic Computer A265

Design: 15pf, Drill and milling machine.

**1966, Feb. 24**     **Perf. 13x12½**
811 A265 10pf multicolored  .25  .20
812 A265 15pf multicolored  .85  .25

Leipzig Spring Fair, 1966.

Jan Arnost Smoler and Linden Leaf — A266

Soldier and National Gallery, Berlin — A267

25pf, House of the Sorbs, Bautzen, Saxony.

**1966, Mar. 1**     **Perf. 13x13½**
813 A266 20pf brt bl, blk & brt red  .20  .20
814 A266 25pf brt red, blk & brt bl  .55  .35

Smoler (1816-84), philologist of the Sorbian language. The Sorbs are a small group of slavic people in Saxony.

### Wmk. 313
**1966, Mar. 1**   **Photo.**   **Perf. 14**

Designs (Soldier and): 10pf, Brandenburg Gate. 20pf, Factory. 25pf, Combine.

815 A267 5pf ol gray, blk & yel  .20  .20
816 A267 10pf ol gray, blk & yel  .20  .20
817 A267 20pf ol gray, blk & yel  .20  .20
818 A267 25pf ol gray, blk & yel  1.00  .60
   Nos. 815-818 (4)   1.60  1.20

National People's Army, 10th anniversary.

Luna 9 on Moon — A268

Medal for Scholarship — A269

**1966, Mar. 7**     **Unwmk.**
819 A268 20pf multicolored  1.90  .30

1st soft landing on the moon by Luna 9, 2/3/66.

**1966, Mar. 7**   **Litho.**   **Perf. 13½x13**
820 A269 20pf multicolored  .55  .20

20th anniv. of the State Youth Organization.

---

Traffic Signs — A270

Traffic safety: 15pf, Automobile and child with scooter. 25pf, Bicyclist and signaling hand. 50pf, Motorcyclist, ambulance and glass of beer.

**1966, Mar. 28**   **Litho.**   **Perf. 13**
821 A270 10pf dk & lt bl, red & blk  .20  .20
822 A270 15pf brt grn, citron & blk  .20  .20
823 A270 25pf ol bis, brt bl & blk  .20  .20
824 A270 50pf car, yel, gray & blk  .90  .60
   Nos. 821-824 (4)   1.50  1.20

Marx, Lenin and Crowd — A271

Designs: 5pf, Party emblem and crowd, vert. 15pf, Marx, Engels and title page of Communist Manifesto, vert. 20pf, Otto Grotewohl and Wilhelm Pieck shaking hands, and Party emblem, vert. 25pf, Chairman Walter Ulbricht receiving flowers.

**1966, Mar. 31**   **Photo.**   **Perf. 14**
825 A271 5pf multicolored  .20  .20
826 A271 10pf multicolored  .20  .20
827 A271 15pf green & blk  .20  .20
828 A271 20pf dk carmine & blk  .25  .20
829 A271 25pf multicolored  1.50  .85
   Nos. 825-829 (5)   2.35  1.65

20th anniversary of Socialist Unity Party of Germany (SED).

WHO Headquarters, Geneva — A272

**Perf. 13x12½**
**1966, Apr. 26**   **Litho.**   **Unwmk.**
830 A272 20pf multicolored  .35  .25

Inauguration of WHO Headquarters, Geneva.

Rügen Island, Königsstuhl — A273

National Parks: 10pf, Spree River woodland. 20pf, Saxon Switzerland. 25pf, Dunes at Westdarss. 30pf, Thale in Harz, Devil's Wall. 50pf, Feldberg Lakes, Mecklenburg.

**Perf. 13x12½**
**1966, May 17**   **Litho.**   **Unwmk.**
831 A273 10pf multicolored  .20  .20
832 A273 15pf multicolored  .20  .20
833 A273 20pf multicolored  .20  .20
834 A273 25pf multicolored  .25  .20
835 A273 30pf multicolored  1.60  .75
836 A273 50pf multicolored  .25  .20
   Nos. 831-836 (6)   2.70  1.75

Plauen Lace — A274

---

Various Lace Designs.

**1966, May 26**     **Perf. 13x13½**
837 A274 10pf green & lt green  .20  .20
838 A274 20pf dk blue & lt blue  .20  .20
839 A274 25pf brown red & ver  .25  .20
840 A274 50pf dk vio & bluish lil  2.10  .85
   Nos. 837-840 (4)   2.75  1.45

Rhododendron A275

Parachutist Landing on Target — A276

Flowers: 20pf, Lilies of the Valley. 40pf, Dahlias. 50pf, Cyclamen.

**Photo. & Engr.**
**1966**       **Perf. 14x13½**
841 A275 20pf multicolored  .20  .20
842 A275 25pf multicolored  .25  .20
843 A275 40pf multicolored  .30  .20
844 A275 50pf multicolored  3.50  3.50
   Nos. 841-844 (4)   4.25  4.10

Intl. Flower Show, Erfurt.
Issued: 20pf, Aug. 16; others, June 28.

**1966, July 12**   **Litho.**   **Perf. 12½x13**

15pf, Group parachute jump. 20pf, Free fall.

845 A276 10pf blue, blk & ol  .20  .20
846 A276 15pf multicolored  .50  .50
847 A276 20pf sky blue, blk & ol  .20  .20
   Nos. 845-847 (3)   .90  .90

8th Intl. Parachute Championships, Leipzig.

Hans Kahle, Song of German Fighters and Medal of Spanish Republic — A277

15pf, Hans Beimler and street fighting in Madrid.

**1966, July 15**   **Photo.**   **Perf. 14**
848 A277 5pf multicolored  .25  .20
849 A277 15pf multicolored  .25  .20
   Nos. 848-849, B137-B140 (6)   2.35  1.90

German fighters in the Spanish Civil War.

Television Set A278

Design: 15pf, Electric typewriter.

**Perf. 13x12½**
**1966, Aug. 29**   **Litho.**   **Unwmk.**
850 A278 10pf brt grn, blk & gray  .60  .20
851 A278 15pf red, blk & gray  1.40  .20

1966 Leipzig Fall Fair.

Women's Doubles Kayak
Race — A279

**1966, Aug. 16**
852 A279 15pf brt blue & multi　1.00　.75
7th Canoe World Championships, Berlin.
See No. B141.

Oradour sur Glane　Emblem of the
Memorial and　Committee for
French Flag　Health
A280　Education
　A281

*Perf. 13x13½*
**1966, Sept. 9**　　　　**Wmk. 313**
853 A280 25pf ultra, blk & red　.35　.25
Issued in memory of the victims of the Nazi
attack on Oradour, France, June 10, 1944.

**1966, Sept. 13**　　　*Perf. 14*
5pf, Symbolic blood donor & recipient, horiz.
854 A281　5pf brt green & red　.25　.20
855 A281 40pf brt blue & red　1.60　.40
　Nos. 854-855,B142 (3)　2.20　.80
Blood donations and health education.

Weight
Lifter — A282

*Perf. 13½x13*
**1966, Sept. 22　Litho.　Unwmk.**
856 A282 15pf lt brown & blk　1.40 1.10
Intl. and European Weight Lifting Championships, Berlin. See No. B143.

Congress
Hall — A283

Emblem — A284

**1966, Oct. 10**　　*Perf. 13*
857 A283 10pf multicolored　.45　.35
858 A284 20pf dk blue & yellow　.20　.20
6th Cong. of the Intl. Organ. of Journalists,
Berlin.

**Costume Type of 1964**
Regional Costumes: 5pf, Woman from
Altenburg. No. 860, Man from Altenburg. No.
861, Woman from Mecklenburg. 15pf, Man
from Mecklenburg. 20pf, Woman from Magdeburg area. 30pf, Man from Magdeburg area.

**1966, Oct. 25　Photo.　*Perf. 14***
859 A240　5pf multicolored　.35　.20
860 A240 10pf multicolored　.35　.20
　a.　Pair, #859-860　1.00　.75
861 A240 10pf lt green & multi　.35　.20
862 A240 15pf lt green & multi　.35　.20
　a.　Pair, #861-862　1.00　.75
863 A240 20pf yellow & multi　1.90 1.25
864 A240 30pf yellow & multi　1.90 1.25
　a.　Pair, #863-864　4.25 3.00
　Nos. 859-864 (6)　5.20 3.30
Printed in checkerboard arrangement.

Megalamphodus
Megalopterus — A285

Various Tropical Fish in Natural Colors.

**1966, Nov. 8　Litho.　*Perf. 13x12½***
865 A285　5pf lt blue & gray　.20　.20
866 A285 10pf blue & indigo　.20　.20
867 A285 15pf citron & blk　2.25 1.50
868 A285 20pf green & blk　.20　.20
869 A285 25pf ultra & blk　.25　.20
870 A285 40pf emerald & blk　.30　.20
　Nos. 865-870 (6)　3.40 2.50

Map of Oil Pipeline and Oil
Field — A286

Design: 25pf, Map of oil pipelines and "Walter Ulbricht" Leuna chemical factory.

**1966, Nov. 8**　　*Perf. 13½x13*
871 A286 20pf red & black　.20　.20
872 A286 25pf blue & black　.75　.30
Chemical industry.

Detail from Ishtar Gate, Babylon, 580
B.C. — A287

Designs from Babylon c. 580 B.C.: 20pf,
Mythological animal from Ishtar Gate. 25pf,
Lion facing right and ornaments, vert. 50pf,
Lion facing left and ornaments, vert.

*Perf. 13½x14, 14x13½*
**1966, Nov. 23**　　**Photo.**
873 A287 10pf multicolored　.20　.20
874 A287 20pf multicolored　.20　.20
875 A287 25pf multicolored　.20　.20
876 A287 50pf multicolored　.55　.80
　Nos. 873-876 (4)　1.15 1.40
Near East Museum, Berlin.

Wartburg,　Gentian — A289
Thuringia — A288

Design: 25pf, Wartburg, Palace.

**1966, Nov. 23　Litho.　*Perf. 13x13½***
877 A288 20pf olive　.20　.20
878 A288 25pf violet brown　.55　.25
　Nos. 877-878,B145 (3)　.95　.65
900th anniv. (in 1967) of the Wartburg (castle) near Eisenach, Thuringia.

**1966, Dec. 8　Litho.　*Perf. 12½x13***
Protected Flowers: 20pf, Cephalanthera
rubra (orchid). 25pf, Mountain arnica.

**Black Background**
879 A289 10pf yel, grn & bl　.20　.20
880 A289 20pf yel, grn & red　.25　.20
881 A289 25pf red, yel & grn　1.25　.70
　Nos. 879-881 (3)　1.70 1.10

Son Leaving
Home — A290

City Hall,
Stralsund — A291

Various Scenes from Fairy Tale "The Table,
the Ass and the Stick."

**1966, Dec. 8**　　*Perf. 13½x13*
882 A290　5pf multicolored　.25　.25
883 A290 10pf multicolored　.25　.25
884 A290 20pf multicolored　.60　.60
885 A290 25pf multicolored　.60　.60
886 A290 30pf multicolored　.25　.25
887 A290 50pf multicolored　.25　.25
　a.　Sheet of 6, #882-887　2.75 2.75
See Nos. 968-973, 1063-1068, 1087-1092,
1176-1181, 1339-1344.

*Perf. 14x13½, 13½x14*
**1967, Jan. 24**　　**Photo.**
Buildings: 5pf, Wörlitz Castle, horiz. 15pf,
Chorin Convent. 20pf, Ribbeck House, Berlin,
horiz. 25pf, Moritzburg, Zeitz. 40pf, Old City
Hall, Potsdam.
888 A291　5pf multicolored　.20　.20
889 A291 10pf multicolored　.20　.20
890 A291 15pf multicolored　.25　.20
891 A291 20pf multicolored　.25　.20
892 A291 25pf multicolored　.25　.20
893 A291 40pf multicolored　1.00　.65
　Nos. 888-893 (6)　2.15 1.65
See Nos. 1018, 1020, 1071-1076.

Rifle Shooting, Prone — A292

Designs: 20pf, Shooting on skis. 25pf, Relay
race with rifles on skis.

**1967, Feb. 15　Litho.　*Perf. 13x12½***
894 A292 10pf Prus bl gray & brt
　　　　　pink　.20　.20
895 A292 20pf sl grn, brt bl & grn　.20　.20
896 A292 25pf ol grn, ol & grnsh
　　　　　bl　.65　.35
　Nos. 894-896 (3)　1.05　.75
World Biathlon Championships (skiing and
shooting), Altenberg, Feb. 15-19.

Circular Knitting
Machine — A293

Mother and
Child — A294

Design: 15pf, Zeiss telescope and galaxy.

**1967, Mar. 2**　　*Perf. 13½x13*
897 A293 10pf dull mag & brt grn　.20　.20
898 A293 15pf ultra & gray　.75　.25
Leipzig Spring Fair of 1967.

**1967, Mar. 7**　　*Perf. 13x13½*
Design: 25pf, Working women.
899 A294 20pf rose brn, red & gray　.25　.20
900 A294 25pf dk bl, brt bl & brn　.60　.50
20th anniv. of the Democratic Women's
Federation of Germany.

Marx, Engels, Lenin and Electronic
Control Center — A295

Designs (Portraits and): 5pf, Farmer driving
combine. No. 903, Students and teacher.
15pf, Family. No. 905, Soldier, sailor and aviator. No. 906, Ulbricht among workers. 25pf,
Soldier, sailor, aviator and factories. 40pf,
Farmers with modern equipment. Nos. 901,
903-905 are vertical.

**1967**　　**Photo.**　　*Perf. 14*
901 A295　5pf multicolored　.20　.20
902 A295 10pf multicolored　.20　.20
903 A295 10pf multicolored　.20　.20
904 A295 15pf multicolored　.35　.35
905 A295 20pf multicolored　.20　.20
906 A295 20pf multicolored　.20　.20
907 A295 25pf multicolored　.20　.20
908 A295 40pf multicolored　.40　.45
　Nos. 901-908 (8)　1.95 2.00
7th congress of Socialist Unity Party of Germany (SED), Apr. 17.
Issued: #902, 906-908 3/22; #901, 903-905,
4/6.

Tahitian Women, by Paul
Gauguin — A296

Paintings from Dresden Gallery: 20pf,
Young Woman, by Ferdinand Hodler. 25pf,
Peter in the Zoo, by H. Hakenbeck. 30pf,
Venetian Episode (woman feeding pigeons),
by R. Bergander. 50pf, Grandmother and
Granddaughter, by J. Scholtz. 70pf, Cairn in
the Snow, by Caspar David Friedrich.

**1967, Mar. 29**
909 A296 20pf multi, vert.　.20　.20
910 A296 25pf multi, vert.　.20　.20
911 A296 30pf multi, vert.　.20　.20
912 A296 50pf multi　.20　.20
913 A296 50pf multi, vert.　1.50 1.10
914 A296 70pf multi　.30　.20
　Nos. 909-914 (6)　2.60 2.10

Barn Owl — A297

Protected Birds: 10pf, Eurasian crane. 20pf, Peregrine falcon. 25pf, Bullfinches. 30pf, European kingfisher. 40pf, European roller.

**1967, Apr. 27    Photo.    Perf. 14**
**Birds in Natural Colors**

| | | | |
|---|---|---|---|
| 915 | A297 | 5pf gray blue | .20 .20 |
| 916 | A297 | 10pf gray blue | .20 .20 |
| 917 | A297 | 20pf gray blue | .20 .20 |
| 918 | A297 | 25pf gray blue | .20 .20 |
| 919 | A297 | 30pf gray blue | 3.50 1.75 |
| 920 | A297 | 40pf gray blue | .30 .20 |
| | | Nos. 915-920 (6) | 4.60 2.75 |

Arms of Warsaw, Berlin and Prague A298

Design: 25pf, Bicyclists and doves.

**Perf. 13x12½**
**1967, May 10    Litho.    Wmk. 313**

| | | | |
|---|---|---|---|
| 921 | A298 | 10pf org, blk & lil | .20 .20 |
| 922 | A298 | 25pf lt bl & dk car | .40 .30 |

20th Intl. Bicycle Peace Race, Berlin-Warsaw-Prague.

Cat A299

Children's Drawings: 10pf, Snow White and the Seven Dwarfs. 15pf, Fire truck. 20pf, Cock. 25pf, Flowers in vase. 30pf, Children playing ball.

**1967, June 1    Unwmk.**

| | | | |
|---|---|---|---|
| 923 | A299 | 5pf multicolored | .20 .20 |
| 924 | A299 | 10pf black & multi | .20 .20 |
| 925 | A299 | 15pf dk blue & multi | .20 .20 |
| 926 | A299 | 20pf orange & multi | .20 .20 |
| 927 | A299 | 25pf multicolored | .20 .20 |
| 928 | A299 | 30pf multicolored | 1.00 .60 |
| | | Nos. 923-928 (6) | 2.00 1.60 |

Issued for International Children's Day.

Girl with Straw Hat, by Salomon Bray — A300    Exhibition Emblem and Map of DDR — A301

Paintings: 5pf, Three Horsemen, by Rubens, horiz. 10pf, Girl Gathering Grapes, by Gerard Dou. 20pf, Spring Idyl, by Hans Thoma, horiz. 25pf, Wilhelmine Schroder-Devrient, by Karl Begas. 50pf, The Four Evangelists, by Jacob Jordaens.

**1967, June 7    Photo.    Perf. 14**

| | | | |
|---|---|---|---|
| 929 | A300 | 5pf lt & dk gray | .20 .20 |
| 930 | A300 | 10pf lt red brn & red brn | .20 .20 |
| 931 | A300 | 20pf lt & dp yel grn | .20 .20 |
| 932 | A300 | 25pf pale rose & rose lil | .20 .20 |

| | | | |
|---|---|---|---|
| 933 | A300 | 40pf pale grn & ol grn | .20 .20 |
| 934 | A300 | 50pf tan & sepia | 1.40 .85 |
| | | Nos. 929-934 (6) | 2.40 1.85 |

Issued to publicize paintings missing from museums since World War II.

**Perf. 12½x13**
**1967, June 14    Litho.    Unwmk.**
935 A301 20pf dk grn, ocher & red    .30 .20

15th Agricultural Exhib., Markkleeberg.

Marie Curie — A302

German Playing Cards — A303

Portraits: 5pf, Georg Herwegh, poet. 20pf, Käthe Kollwitz. 25pf, Johann J. Winckelmann, archaeologist. 40pf, Theodor Storm, writer.

**1967    Engr.    Perf. 14**

| | | | |
|---|---|---|---|
| 936 | A302 | 5pf brown | .25 .20 |
| 937 | A302 | 10pf dark blue | .25 .20 |
| 938 | A302 | 20pf dull red | .25 .20 |
| 939 | A302 | 25pf gray | .25 .20 |
| 940 | A302 | 40pf slate green | .75 .50 |
| | | Nos. 936-940 (5) | 1.75 1.30 |

150th anniv. of the birth of Herwegh, Winckelmann and Storm, and the birth centenaries of Curie and Kollwitz.

**1967, July 18    Photo.**

Designs: Various German playing cards.

| | | | |
|---|---|---|---|
| 941 | A303 | 5pf red & multi | .20 .20 |
| 942 | A303 | 10pf green & multi | .20 .20 |
| 943 | A303 | 20pf multicolored | .25 .20 |
| 944 | A303 | 25pf multicolored | 4.75 2.25 |
| | | Nos. 941-944 (4) | 5.40 2.85 |

Mare and Foal A304

Horses: 10pf, Stallion. 20pf, Horse race finish. 50pf, Colts, vert.

**Perf. 13½x13, 13x13½**
**1967, Aug. 15    Litho.    Unwmk.**

| | | | |
|---|---|---|---|
| 945 | A304 | 5pf multicolored | .20 .20 |
| 946 | A304 | 10pf org, blk & dk brn | .20 .20 |
| 947 | A304 | 20pf blue & multi | .25 .20 |
| 948 | A304 | 25pf multicolored | 3.00 1.75 |
| | | Nos. 945-948 (4) | 3.65 2.35 |

Thoroughbred Horse Show of Socialist Countries, Hoppegarten, Berlin.

Small Electrical Appliances — A305

Leipzig Fall Fair: 15pf, Woman's fur coat and furrier's trademark.

Max Reichpietsch and Warship — A306

15pf, Albin Köbis, warship. 20pf, Sailors marching with red flag, warship.

**1967, Aug. 8    Photo.    Unwmk.**
949 A305 10pf brt bl, blk & yel    .35 .20
950 A305 15pf yellow, brn & blk    .80 .30

**1967, Sept. 5    Litho.    Perf. 13½x13**
**Bluish Paper**

| | | | |
|---|---|---|---|
| 951 | A306 | 10pf dk blue, gray & red | .20 .20 |
| 952 | A306 | 15pf dk blue, gray & red | 1.10 .40 |
| 953 | A306 | 20pf dk blue, gray & red | .35 .20 |
| | | Nos. 951-953 (3) | 1.65 .80 |

50th anniv. of the sailors' uprising at Kiel.

Monument at Kragujevac A307

**1967, Sept. 20    Perf. 13x13½**
954 A307 25pf dk red, yel & blk    .65 .25

Issued in memory of the victims of the Nazis at Kragujevac, Yugoslavia, Oct. 21, 1941.

Worker and Symbols of Electrification — A308

Communist Emblem and: 5pf, Worker, Communist newspaper masthead. 15pf, Russian War Memorial, Berlin-Treptow. 20pf, Russian and German soldiers, coat of arms. 40pf, Lenin, cruiser Aurora.

**1967, Oct. 6    Photo.    Perf. 14x14½**

| | | | |
|---|---|---|---|
| 955 | A308 | 5pf multicolored | .20 .20 |
| 956 | A308 | 10pf multicolored | .20 .20 |
| 957 | A308 | 15pf multicolored | .20 .20 |
| 958 | A308 | 20pf multicolored | .30 .20 |
| 959 | A308 | 40pf multicolored | 2.25 1.40 |
| a. | | Souvenir sheet of 2 | 2.00 2.50 |
| | | Nos. 955-959 (5) | 3.15 2.20 |

50th anniv. of the Russian October Revolution. No. 959a contains 2 imperf. stamps similar to Nos. 958-959 with simulated perforations. It commemorates the Red October Jubilee Stamp Exhibition, Karl-Marx-Stadt, Oct. 6-15. Sold for 85pf.

Martin Luther, by Lucas Cranach — A309    Young Inventors and Fair Emblem — A310

Designs: 25pf, Luther's House, Wittenberg, horiz. 40pf, Castle Church, Wittenberg.

**Engraved and Photogravure**
**1967, Oct. 17    Perf. 14**

| | | | |
|---|---|---|---|
| 960 | A309 | 20pf black & rose lilac | .20 .20 |
| 961 | A309 | 25pf black & blue | .20 .20 |
| 962 | A309 | 40pf black & lemon | 2.10 .60 |
| | | Nos. 960-962 (3) | 2.50 1.00 |

450th anniversary of the Reformation.

**1967, Nov. 15    Unwmk.    Perf. 14**

Designs: No. 964, Boy's and girl's heads and emblem of the Free German Youth Organization. 25pf, Young workers receiving awards, and medal.

**Size: 23x28½mm**
963 A310 20pf multicolored    .45 .30
964 A310 20pf multicolored    .45 .30

**Size: 51x28½mm**
965 A310 25pf multicolored    .45 .30
a.    Strip of 3, #963-965    3.75 3.75

Issued to publicize the 10th Masters of Tomorrow Fair, Leipzig, Nov. 15-26.

Goethe House, Weimar A311

Design: 25pf, Schiller House, Weimar.

**1967, Nov. 27    Litho.    Perf. 13x12½**
966 A311 20pf gray, blk & brn    .25 .20
967 A311 25pf citron, dk grn & brn    1.40 .40

Honoring German classical humanism.

**Fairy Tale Type of 1966**
Various Scenes from King Drosselbart.

**1967, Nov. 27    Perf. 13½x13**

| | | | |
|---|---|---|---|
| 968 | A290 | 5pf multicolored | .20 .20 |
| 969 | A290 | 10pf multicolored | .20 .20 |
| 970 | A290 | 15pf multicolored | .75 .60 |
| 971 | A290 | 20pf multicolored | .75 .60 |
| 972 | A290 | 25pf multicolored | .20 .20 |
| 973 | A290 | 30pf multicolored | .20 .20 |
| a. | | Sheet of 6, #968-973 | 5.00 5.00 |

Farmers, Stables and Silos — A312

**Perf. 13x12½**
**1967, Dec. 6    Litho.    Unwmk.**
974 A312 10pf multicolored    .30 .20

1st agricultural co-operatives, 15th anniv.

Nutcracker and Figurines — A313    Speed Skating — A314

20pf, Candle holders: angel and miner.

**1967, Dec. 6    Photo.    Perf. 13½x14**
975 A313 10pf green & multi    .60 .35
976 A313 20pf red & multi    .20 .20

Issued to publicize local handicrafts of the Erzgebirge in Saxony (Ore Mountains).

**Perf. 13½x13**
**1968, Jan. 17    Litho.    Unwmk.**

Sport and Olympic Rings: 15pf, Slalom. 20pf, Ice hockey. 25pf, Figure skating, pair. 30pf, Long-distance skiing.

| | | | |
|---|---|---|---|
| 977 | A314 | 5pf blue, dk bl & red | .20 .20 |
| 978 | A314 | 15pf multicolored | .20 .20 |
| 979 | A314 | 20pf grnsh bl, dk bl & red | .20 .20 |
| 980 | A314 | 25pf multicolored | .20 .20 |

**981** A314 30pf grnsh bl, vio bl &
      red              3.00 1.00
    *Nos. 977-981,B146 (6)*     4.00 2.00
10th Winter Olympic Games, Grenoble, France, Feb. 6-18.

Actinometer, Sun and Potsdam Meteorological Observatory A315

Designs: 20pf, Antenna, Cloud Formation and Map of Europe. 25pf, Weather influence on farming (fields by day and night, produce).

**1968, Jan. 24**      **Perf. 13½x13**
    **Size: 23x28mm**
**982** A315 10pf brt mag, org & blk   .35  .25
    **Size: 50x28mm**
**983** A315 20pf multicolored      .35  .25
    **Size: 23x28mm**
**984** A315 25pf olive, blk & yel   .35  .25
   *a.*   Strip of 3, #982-984   4.00 4.00
75th anniversary of the Meteorological Observatory in Potsdam.

Venus 4 Interplanetary Station — A316

Design: 25pf, Earth satellites Kosmos 186 and 188 orbiting earth.

**1968, Jan. 24**   **Photo.**   **Perf. 14**
**985** A316 20pf multicolored     .20  .20
**986** A316 25pf multicolored     1.00  .40
Russian space explorations.

Fighters of The Underground A317

20pf, "The Liberation." 25pf, "The Partisans."

**1968, Feb. 21**   **Photo.**   **Perf. 14x13½**
**987** A317 10pf black & multi   .20  .20
**988** A317 20pf black & multi   .20  .20
**989** A317 25pf black & multi   .40  .25
    *Nos. 987-989 (3)*     .80  .65

The designs are from the stained glass window triptych by Walter Womacka in the Sachsenhausen Memorial Museum.

Diesel Locomotive — A318

Design: 15pf, Refrigerator fishing ship.

**1968, Feb. 29**         **Perf. 14**
**990** A318 10pf multicolored     .30  .20
**991** A318 15pf multicolored     .85  .30
The 1968 Leipzig Spring Fair.

Woman from Hoyerswerda A319

Maxim Gorky and View of Gorky A320

Sorbian Regional Costumes: 20pf, Woman from Schleife. 40pf, Woman from Crostwitz. 50pf, Woman from Spreewald.

**1968, Mar. 14**
**992** A319 10pf citron & multi   .20  .20
**993** A319 20pf fawn & multi   .20  .20
**994** A319 40pf blue grn & multi   .25  .20
**995** A319 50pf green & multi   2.40  .75
    *Nos. 992-995 (4)*     3.05 1.35

**1968, Mar. 14**           **Engr.**
25pf, Stormy petrel and toppling towers.
**996** A320 20pf brown & rose car   .20  .20
**997** A320 25pf brown & rose car   .45  .25
Maxim Gorky (1868-1936), Russian writer.

Ring-necked Pheasants A321

15pf, Gray partridges. 20pf, Mallards. 25pf, Graylag geese. 30pf, Wood pigeons. 40pf, Hares.

**1968, Mar. 26**   **Litho.**   **Perf. 13½x13**
**998** A321 10pf gray & multi   .20  .20
**999** A321 15pf gray & multi   .20  .20
**1000** A321 20pf gray & multi   .20  .20
**1001** A321 25pf gray & multi   .25  .20
**1002** A321 30pf gray & multi   .30  .20
**1003** A321 40pf gray & multi   2.75 4.00
    *Nos. 998-1003 (6)*     3.90 5.00

Karl Marx — A322     Fritz Heckert — A323

Designs: 10pf, Title page of the "Communist Manifesto." 25pf, Title page of "Das Kapital."

**1968, Apr. 25**   **Photo.**   **Perf. 14**
**1004** A322 10pf yel grn & blk   .25  .25
**1005** A322 20pf mag, yel & blk   .25  .25
**1006** A322 25pf lem, blk & red
           brn         .25  .25
   *a.*   Strip of three   1.50 3.00
   *b.*   Souvenir sheet of 3   1.00 3.00

Karl Marx (1818-83). Nos. 1004-1006 are printed se-tenant. No. 1006a contains 3 imperf. stamps similar to Nos. 1004-1006 with simulated perforations.

**1968, Apr. 25**
Design: 20pf, Young workers, new apartment buildings and Congress emblem.
**1007** A323 10pf multicolored   .20  .20
**1008** A323 20pf multicolored   .25  .25
7th Congress of the Free German Trade Unions.

"Right to Work" — A324

Designs: 10pf, "Right to Live," tree and globe. 25pf, "Right for Peace," dove and sun.

**1968, May 8**   **Litho.**   **Perf. 13½x13**
**1009** A324  5pf maroon & pink   .20  .20
**1010** A324 10pf brn ol & ol bister   .20  .20
**1011** A324 25pf Prus bl & lt bl   .65  .40
    *Nos. 1009-1011 (3)*     1.05  .80
International Human Rights Year.

Angler A325

Designs: No. 1013, Rowing (woman). No. 1014, High jump (woman).

          **Unwmk.**
**1968, June 6**   **Photo.**   **Perf. 14**
**1012** A325 20pf ol grn, sl bl & dk
           red       .75  .65
**1013** A325 20pf Prus bl, dk bl &
           ol        .20  .20
**1014** A325 20pf cop red, dp cl &
           bl        .20  .20
    *Nos. 1012-1014 (3)*     1.15 1.05
World angling championships, Gustrow (#1012); European women's rowing championships, Berlin (#1013); 2nd European youth athletic competition, Leipzig (#1014).

Brandenburg Gate, Torch — A326     Youth Festival Emblem — A327

Design: 25pf, Stadium and torch.

**1968, June 20**   **Litho.**   **Perf. 13½x13**
**1015** A326 10pf multicolored   .20  .20
**1016** A326 25pf multicolored   .85  .40
2nd Children's and Youths' Spartakiad, Berlin.

**1968, June 20**
**1017** A327 25pf multicolored   .70  .35
9th Youth Festival for Peace & Friendship, Sofia.
See No. B148.

        **Type of 1967 and**

Moritzburg Castle, Dresden — A328

Buildings: 10pf, City Hall, Wernigerode. 25pf, City Hall, Greifswald. 30pf, Sanssouci Palace, Potsdam.

**1968, June 25**   **Photo.**   **Perf. 13½x14**
**1018** A291 10pf multicolored   .20  .20
**1019** A328 20pf multicolored   .20  .20
**1020** A291 25pf multicolored   .20  .20
**1021** A328 30pf multicolored   .60  .60
    *Nos. 1018-1021 (4)*     1.20 1.20

Walter Ulbricht and Arms of Republic A329

      **Photo. & Engr.**
**1968, June 27**         **Perf. 14**
**1022** A329 20pf org, dp car & blk   .55  .20
75th birthday of Walter Ulbricht, chairman of the Council of State, Communist party secretary and deputy prime minister.

Old Rostock and Arms A330

Design: 25pf, Historic and modern buildings, 1968, and arms of Rostock.

**1968, July 9**         **Photo.**
**1023** A330 20pf multicolored   .20  .20
**1024** A330 25pf multicolored   .50  .40
750th anniv. of Rostock and to publicize the 11th Baltic Sea Week.

Karl Landsteiner, M.D. (1868-1943) A331

"Trener" Stunt Plane — A332

Portraits: 15pf, Emanuel Lasker (1868-1941), chess champion and writer. 20pf, Hanns Eisler (1898-1962), composer. 25pf, Ignaz Semmelweis, M.D. (1818-1865). 40pf, Max von Pettenkofer (1818-1901), hygienist.

**1968, July 17**   **Engr.**   **Perf. 14**
**1025** A331 10pf gray green   .20  .20
**1026** A331 15pf black     .20  .20
**1027** A331 20pf brown     .20  .20
**1028** A331 25pf gray blue   .20  .20
**1029** A331 40pf rose lake   .70  .70
    *Nos. 1025-1029 (5)*     1.50 1.50

**1968, Aug. 13**   **Litho.**   **Perf. 12½x13**
25pf, 2 "Trener" stunt planes in parallel flight.
**1030** A332 10pf multicolored   .20  .20
**1031** A332 25pf blue & multi   .45  .35

Peasant Woman, by Wilhelm Leibl — A333

Paintings from Dresden Gallery: 10pf, "On the Beach," by Walter Womacka, horiz. 15pf, Mountain Farmers Mowing, by Albin Egger-Lienz, horiz. 40pf, The Artist's daughter, by Venturelli. 50pf, High School Girl, by Michaelis. 70pf, Girl with Guitar, by Castelli.

    **Perf. 14x13½, 13½x14**
**1968, Aug. 20**         **Photo.**
**1032** A333 10pf multicolored   .20  .20
**1033** A333 15pf multicolored   .20  .20
**1034** A333 20pf multicolored   .20  .20
**1035** A333 40pf multicolored   .35  .20

| | | | | |
|---|---|---|---|---|
| 1036 | A333 | 50pf multicolored | .35 | .20 |
| 1037 | A333 | 70pf multicolored | 1.90 | .95 |
| | | Nos. 1032-1037 (6) | 3.20 | 1.95 |

Model Trains — A334

**1968, Aug. 29**    **Perf. 14x13½**

| | | | | |
|---|---|---|---|---|
| 1038 | A334 | 10pf lt ultra, red & blk | .30 | .25 |

The 1968 Leipzig Fall Fair.

Spremberg Dam — A335

Designs: 10pf, Pöhl Dam, vert. 15pf, Ohra Dam, vert. 20pf, Rappbode Dam.

**Perf. 13x12½, 12½x13**

**1968, Sept. 11**      **Litho.**

| | | | | |
|---|---|---|---|---|
| 1039 | A335 | 5pf multicolored | .20 | .20 |
| 1040 | A335 | 10pf multicolored | .20 | .20 |
| 1041 | A335 | 15pf multicolored | .35 | .35 |
| 1042 | A335 | 20pf multicolored | .25 | .20 |
| | | Nos. 1039-1042 (4) | 1.00 | .95 |

Issued to publicize dams built since 1945.

Runner A336

Designs: 25pf, Woman gymnast, vert. 40pf, Water polo, vert. 70pf, Sculling.

**1968, Sept. 18**    **Photo.**    **Perf. 14**

| | | | | |
|---|---|---|---|---|
| 1043 | A336 | 5pf multicolored | .20 | .20 |
| 1044 | A336 | 25pf multicolored | .20 | .20 |
| 1045 | A336 | 40pf multicolored | .20 | .20 |
| 1046 | A336 | 70pf blue & multi | 1.25 | 1.00 |
| | | Nos. 1043-1046,B149-B150 (6) | 2.25 | 2.00 |

19th Olympic Games, Mexico City, 10/12-27.

Monument, Fort Breendonk, Belgium — A337

**1968, Oct. 10**    **Litho.**    **Perf. 13x13½**

| | | | | |
|---|---|---|---|---|
| 1047 | A337 | 25pf multicolored | .35 | .20 |

Issued in memory of the victims of the Nazis at the Fort Breendonk Concentration Camp.

Tiger Beetle — A338

**1968, Oct. 16**      **Perf. 13½x13**

Insects: 15pf, Ground beetle (Cychrus caraboides). 20pf, Ladybug. 25pf, Ground beetle (Carabus arcensis hrbst.). 30pf, Hister beetle. 40pf, Checkered beetle.

| | | | | |
|---|---|---|---|---|
| 1048 | A338 | 10pf yellow & multi | .20 | .20 |
| 1049 | A338 | 15pf bluish lil & blk | .20 | .20 |
| 1050 | A338 | 20pf multicolored | .20 | .20 |
| 1051 | A338 | 25pf lt lilac & blk | 1.90 | 1.50 |
| 1052 | A338 | 30pf lt green, blk & red | .25 | .20 |
| 1053 | A338 | 40pf pink & black | 3.00 | 2.50 |
| | | Nos. 1048-1053 (6) | 3.00 | 2.50 |

Lenin and Letter to Spartacists — A339

Designs: 20pf, Workers, soldiers and sailors with masthead and slogans. 25pf, Karl Liebknecht and Rosa Luxemburg.

**1968, Oct. 29**    **Litho.**    **Perf. 13x12½**

| | | | | |
|---|---|---|---|---|
| 1054 | A339 | 10pf lemon, red & blk | .20 | .20 |
| 1055 | A339 | 20pf lemon, red & blk | .20 | .20 |
| 1056 | A339 | 25pf lemon, red & blk | .45 | .35 |
| | | Nos. 1054-1056 (3) | .85 | .75 |

November Revolution in Germany, 50th anniv.

Cattleya — A340

Orchids: 10pf, Paphiopedilum albertianum. 15pf, Cattleya fabia. 20pf, Cattleya aclandiae. 40pf, Sobralia macrantha. 50pf, Dendrobium alpha.

**1968, Nov. 12**    **Photo.**    **Perf. 13**

**Flowers in Natural Colors**

| | | | | |
|---|---|---|---|---|
| 1057 | A340 | 5pf bluish lilac | .20 | .20 |
| 1058 | A340 | 10pf green | .20 | .20 |
| 1059 | A340 | 15pf bister | .20 | .20 |
| 1060 | A340 | 20pf green | .20 | .20 |
| 1061 | A340 | 40pf light brown | .25 | .20 |
| 1062 | A340 | 50pf gray | 1.60 | 1.10 |
| | | Nos. 1057-1062 (6) | 2.65 | 2.10 |

**Fairy Tale Type of 1966**

Various Scenes from Puss in Boots.

**1968, Nov. 27**    **Litho.**    **Perf. 13½x13**

| | | | | |
|---|---|---|---|---|
| 1063 | A290 | 5pf multicolored | .20 | .20 |
| 1064 | A290 | 10pf multicolored | .20 | .20 |
| 1065 | A290 | 15pf multicolored | .90 | .75 |
| 1066 | A290 | 20pf multicolored | .90 | .75 |
| 1067 | A290 | 25pf multicolored | .20 | .20 |
| 1068 | A290 | 30pf multicolored | .20 | .20 |
| a. | | Sheet of 6, #1063-1068 | 5.00 | 7.50 |

Young Pioneers A341

Design: 15pf, Five Young Pioneers.

**1968, Dec. 3**      **Perf. 13x13½**

| | | | | |
|---|---|---|---|---|
| 1069 | A341 | 10pf blue & multi | .20 | .20 |
| 1070 | A341 | 15pf multicolored | .60 | .25 |

20th anniv. of the founding of the Ernst Thalmann Young Pioneers' organization.

**Buildings Type of 1967**

Buildings: 5pf, City Hall, Tangermunde. 10pf, German State Opera, Berlin. 20pf, Wall Pavilion, Dresden. 25pf, Burgher's House, Luckau. 30pf, Rococo Palace, Dornburg. 40pf, "Stockfish" House, Erfurt.

**1969, Jan. 1**    **Photo.**    **Perf. 14**

| | | | | |
|---|---|---|---|---|
| 1071 | A291 | 5pf multi | .20 | .20 |
| 1072 | A291 | 10pf multi, horiz. | .20 | .20 |
| 1073 | A291 | 20pf multi | .20 | .20 |
| 1074 | A291 | 25pf multi | .75 | .65 |
| 1075 | A291 | 30pf multi, horiz. | .20 | .20 |
| 1076 | A291 | 40pf multi | .25 | .20 |
| | | Nos. 1071-1076 (6) | 1.80 | 1.65 |

Martin Andersen Nexö, Danish Writer — A342

Portraits: 20pf, Otto Nagel (1894-1967), painter. 25pf, Alexander von Humboldt (1769-1859), naturalist, traveler, statesman. 40pf, Theodor Fontane (1819-1898), writer.

**1969, Feb. 5**    **Engr.**    **Perf. 14**

| | | | | |
|---|---|---|---|---|
| 1077 | A342 | 10pf grnsh black | .20 | .20 |
| 1078 | A342 | 20pf deep brown | .20 | .20 |
| 1079 | A342 | 25pf violet blue | .75 | .30 |
| 1080 | A342 | 40pf brown | .20 | .20 |
| | | Nos. 1077-1080 (4) | 1.35 | .90 |

Issued to honor famous men.

Be Attentive and Considerate! — A343

10pf, Watch ahead! (car, truck & traffic signal). 20pf, Watch railroad crossings! (train & car at crossing). 25pf, If in doubt don't pass! (cars & truck).

**1969, Feb. 18**    **Litho.**    **Perf. 13x13½**

| | | | | |
|---|---|---|---|---|
| 1081 | A343 | 5pf lt blue & multi | .20 | .20 |
| 1082 | A343 | 10pf yellow & multi | .20 | .20 |
| 1083 | A343 | 20pf pink & multi | .20 | .20 |
| 1084 | A343 | 25pf multicolored | .45 | .30 |
| | | Nos. 1081-1084 (4) | 1.05 | .90 |

Traffic safety campaign.

Combine — A344

Leipzig Spring Fair: 15pf, Planeta-Variant offset printing press.

**1969, Feb. 26**    **Photo.**    **Perf. 14**

| | | | | |
|---|---|---|---|---|
| 1085 | A344 | 10pf multicolored | .20 | .20 |
| 1086 | A344 | 15pf crimson, blk & bl | .25 | .20 |

Jorinde and Joringel A345

Various Scenes from Fairy Tale "Jorinde and Joringel."

**1969, Mar. 18**    **Litho.**    **Perf. 13½x13**

| | | | | |
|---|---|---|---|---|
| 1087 | A345 | 5pf black & multi | .20 | .20 |
| 1088 | A345 | 10pf black & multi | .20 | .20 |
| 1089 | A345 | 15pf black & multi | .45 | .45 |
| 1090 | A345 | 20pf black & multi | .45 | .45 |
| 1091 | A345 | 25pf black & multi | .20 | .20 |
| 1092 | A345 | 30pf black & multi | .20 | .20 |
| a. | | Sheet of 6, #1087-1092 | 2.25 | 2.25 |

See Nos. 1176-1181.

Spring Snowflake A346

Red Cross, Crescent, Lion and Sun Emblems A347

Protected Plants: 10pf, Adonis. 15pf, Globeflowers. 20pf, Garden Turk's-cap. 25pf, Button snakeroot. 30pf, Dactylorchis latifolia.

**1969, Apr. 4**    **Photo.**    **Perf. 14**

| | | | | |
|---|---|---|---|---|
| 1093 | A346 | 5pf green & multi | .20 | .20 |
| 1094 | A346 | 10pf green & multi | .20 | .20 |
| 1095 | A346 | 15pf green & multi | .20 | .20 |
| 1096 | A346 | 20pf green & multi | .20 | .20 |
| 1097 | A346 | 25pf green & multi | 2.40 | 1.25 |
| 1098 | A346 | 30pf green & multi | .30 | .20 |
| | | Nos. 1093-1098 (6) | 3.50 | 2.25 |

**1969, Apr. 23**    **Litho.**    **Perf. 12½x13**

Design: 15pf, Large Red Cross, Red Crescent and Lion and Sun Emblems.

| | | | | |
|---|---|---|---|---|
| 1099 | A347 | 10pf gray, red & yel | .25 | .20 |
| 1100 | A347 | 15pf multicolored | 1.10 | .35 |

League of Red Cross Societies, 50th anniv.

Conifer Nursery A348

Erythrite from Schneeberg A349

10pf, Forests as natural resources (timber & resin). 20pf, Forests as regulators of climate. 25pf, Forests as recreation areas (tents along lake).

**1969, Apr. 23**

| | | | | |
|---|---|---|---|---|
| 1101 | A348 | 5pf multicolored | .25 | .20 |
| 1102 | A348 | 10pf multicolored | .25 | .20 |
| 1103 | A348 | 20pf multicolored | .25 | .20 |
| 1104 | A348 | 25pf multicolored | 1.60 | .70 |
| | | Nos. 1101-1104 (4) | 2.35 | 1.30 |

Prevention of forest fires.

**1969, May 21**    **Photo.**    **Perf. 13½x14**

Minerals: 10pf, Fluorite from Halsbrücke. 15pf, Galena from Neudorf. 20pf, Smoky quartz from Lichtenberg. 25pf, Calcite from Niederrabenstein. 50pf, Silver from Freiberg.

| | | | | |
|---|---|---|---|---|
| 1105 | A349 | 5pf tan & multi | .20 | .20 |
| 1106 | A349 | 10pf multicolored | .20 | .20 |
| 1107 | A349 | 15pf gray & multi | .20 | .20 |
| 1108 | A349 | 20pf lemon & multi | .20 | .20 |
| 1109 | A349 | 25pf multicolored | .75 | .55 |
| 1110 | A349 | 50pf lt blue & multi | .25 | .20 |
| | | Nos. 1105-1110 (6) | 1.80 | 1.55 |

Women and Symbols of Agriculture, Science and Industry — A350

Design: 25pf, Woman's head and symbols.

**1969, May 28**    **Engr.**    **Perf. 14**

| | | | | |
|---|---|---|---|---|
| 1111 | A350 | 20pf dk red & blue | .20 | .20 |
| 1112 | A350 | 25pf blue & dk red | .85 | .30 |

2nd Women's Congress of the German Democratic Republic.

## Ulbricht Type of 1961-67

**1969-71 Wmk. 313 Typo. *Perf. 14***
**Size: 17x21mm**

1112A A189 35pf Prus blue
('71) .30 .30

**Unwmk.**
**Engr.**
**Size: 24x28½mm**

1113 A189 1m dull green .35 .35
1114 A189 2m brown .45 .45
*Nos. 1112A-1114 (3)* 1.10 1.10

See note below Nos. 590B-590C.

### Coil Stamp

**1970, Jan. 20 Typo. Wmk. 313**
**Size: 17x21mm**

1114A A189 1m olive .75 3.00

Emblem of DDR
Philatelic
Society — A351

Worker
Protecting
Children — A352

**1969, June 4 Photo. Unwmk.**
1115 A351 10pf red, gold & ultra .30 .20

National Philatelic Exhibition "20 Years DDR," Magdeburg, Oct. 31-Nov. 9.

**1969, June 4 Litho. *Perf. 13***

25pf, Workers of various races. 20pf+5pf, Berlin buildings: Brandenburg Gate, Council of State, Soviet Cenotaph, Town Hall Tower, Television Tower, Teachers' Building & Hall.

**Size: 23x28mm**
1116 A352 10pf lemon & multi .55 .60

**Size: 50x28mm**
1117 A352 20pf + 5pf multi .55 .60

**Size: 23x28mm**
1118 A352 25pf lemon & multi .55 .60
*a.* Strip of 3, #1116-1118 2.75 2.75

Intl. Peace Meeting, Berlin. The surtax on No. 1117 was for the Peace Council of the German Democratic Republic.

Opening Ceremony before Battle of
Leipzig Monument — A353

15pf, Parading athletes & stadium. 25pf, Running, hurdling, javelin & flag waving. 30pf, Presentation of colors before old Leipzig Town Hall.

**Photo. & Engr.**
**1969, June 18 *Perf. 14***
1119 A353 5pf multi & black .20 .20
1120 A353 15pf multi & black .20 .20
1121 A353 25pf multi & black 1.40 .50
1122 A353 30pf multi & black .20 .20
*Nos. 1119-1122,B152-B153 (6)* 2.40 1.50

5th German Gymnastic and Sports Festival, Leipzig.

Pierre de
Coubertin, by
Wieland
Forster — A354

Knight — A355

Design: 25pf, Coubertin column, Memorial Grove, Olympia.

**1969, June 6 *Perf. 14x13½***
1123 A354 10pf black & lt blue .20 .20
1124 A354 25pf black & sal pink .70 .45

Revival of the Olympic Games, 75th anniv.

**1969, July 29 Photo. *Perf. 14***

#1126, Bicycle wheel. #1127, Volleyball.

1125 A355 20pf red, gold & dk brn .25 .20
1126 A355 20pf green, gold & red .25 .20
1127 A355 20pf multicolored .25 .20
*Nos. 1125-1127 (3)* .75 .60

16th Students' Chess World Championships, Dresden (No. 1125); Indoor Bicycle World Championships, Erfurt (No. 1126); 2nd Volleyball World Cup (No. 1127).

Merchandise
A356

**1969, Aug. 27 Litho. *Perf. 12½x13***
1128 A356 10pf multicolored .25 .20

Leipzig Fall Fair, Aug. 31-Sept. 7, 1969.

Television Tower,
Berlin — A358

People and Flags — A359

Designs: 20pf, Sphere of Television Tower and TV test picture. No. 1144, Television Tower and TV test picture.

**1969, Oct. 6 *Perf. 14***
1142 A358 10pf multicolored .20 .20
1143 A358 20pf multicolored .25 .20

**Souvenir Sheets**
1144 A358 1m dk blue & multi 1.25 3.00

**Perf. 13x12½**
1145 A359 1m red & multi 1.20 2.10

No. 1144 contains one 21½x60mm stamp.

Cathedral, Otto von Guericke
Monument and Hotel International,
Magdeburg — A360

**1969, Oct. 28 Litho. *Perf. 13x12½***
1146 A360 20pf multicolored .20 .20

Natl. Postage Stamp Exhibition in honor of the 20th anniv. of the German Democratic Republic, Magdeburg. Oct. 31-Nov. 9. See No. B154.

UFI
Emblem — A361

**1969, Oct. 28 *Perf. 13x13½***
1147 A361 10pf multicolored .20 .20
1148 A361 15pf multicolored 1.40 .35

36th UFI Congress (Union des Foires Internationales), Leipzig, Oct. 28-30.

Memorial Monument, Copenhagen-
Ryvangen — A362

Rostock University
Seal and
Building — A363

**1969, Oct. 28 *Perf. 13***
1149 A362 25pf multicolored .60 .20

Issued in memory of the victims of the Nazis in Denmark.

**1969, Nov. 12 *Perf. 12½x13***

Design: 15pf, Steam turbine, curve and Rostock University emblem.

1150 A363 10pf brt blue & multi .25 .20
1151 A363 15pf violet & multi 1.10 .25

550th anniversary of Rostock University.

ILO
Emblem — A364

Mold for
Christmas
Cookies — A365

**1969, Nov. 12 *Perf. 13½x14***
1152 A364 20pf dp green & silver .20 .20
1153 A364 25pf lil rose & silver 1.40 .30

50th anniv. of the ILO.

**1969, Nov. 25 Litho. *Perf. 13½x13***

50pf, Negro couple, shaped spice cookie.

1154 A365 10pf dull org, bl & red brn .90 .75
1155 A365 50pf lt blue & multi 1.50 1.25
*a.* Pair, #1154-1155 5.50 4.75
*Nos. 1154-1155,B155 (3)* 2.70 2.30

Folk art of Lusatia.

Antonov
An-24
A366

Planes: 25pf, Ilyushin Il-18. 30pf, Tupolev Tu-134. 50pf, Mi-8 helicopter.

**1969, Dec. 2 *Perf. 13x12½***
1156 A366 20pf blue, red & blk .20 .20
1157 A366 25pf vio, red & blk 1.00 .80
1158 A366 30pf ultra, red & blk .20 .20
1159 A366 50pf olive, red & blk .25 .20
*Nos. 1156-1159 (4)* 1.65 1.40

---

**1969, Sept. 23 Photo. *Perf. 14***
1129 A357 10pf Rostock .20 .20
1130 A357 10pf Neubrandenburg .20 .20
1131 A357 10pf Potsdam .20 .20
1132 A357 10pf Eisenhüttenstadt .20 .20
1133 A357 10pf Hoyerswerda .20 .20
1134 A357 10pf Magdeburg .20 .20
1135 A357 10pf Halle-Neustadt .20 .20
1136 A357 10pf Suhl .20 .20
1137 A357 10pf Dresden .20 .20
1138 A357 10pf Leipzig .20 .20
1139 A357 10pf Karl-Marx-Stadt .20 .20
1140 A357 10pf Berlin .20 .20
*Nos. 1129-1140 (12)* 2.40 2.40

**Souvenir Sheet**
1141 A357 1m multicolored 1.60 4.00

#1129-1141, 1142-1145 for 20th anniv. of the German Democratic Republic. No. 1141 contains one 29x52mm stamp.

1m, DDR Arms, Town Hall, Marienkirche and Television Tower, Berlin, vert.

Arms of
Republic
and View
of
Rostock
A357

Siberian Teacher, by D. K. Sveshnikov A367

Russian Paintings from Dresden Gallery of Modern Masters: 10pf, Steelworker, by V. A. Serov. 20pf, Still Life, by E. A. Aslamasjan. 25pf, Hot Day (boats on river), by J. D. Romas. 40pf, Spring is Coming (young woman and snow-covered street), by L. V. Kabatchek. 50pf, Man on River Bank, by V. J. Makovskij.

**1969, Dec. 10    Photo.    Perf. 13**
| | | | | |
|---|---|---|---|---|
| 1160 | A367 | 5pf gray & multi | .20 | .20 |
| 1161 | A367 | 10pf gray & multi | .20 | .20 |
| 1162 | A367 | 20pf gray & multi | .20 | .20 |
| 1163 | A367 | 25pf gray & multi | .90 | .90 |
| 1164 | A367 | 40pf gray & multi | .25 | .20 |
| 1165 | A367 | 50pf gray & multi | .25 | .20 |
| | | Nos. 1160-1165 (6) | 2.00 | 1.90 |

Ernst Barlach (1870-1938), Sculptor and Writer — A368

Portraits: 10pf, Johann Gutenberg (1400-68). 15pf, Kurt Tucholsky (1890-1935), writer. 20pf, Ludwig van Beethoven. 25pf, Friedrich Hölderlin (1770-1843), poet. 40pf, Georg Wilhelm Friedrich Hegel (1770-1831), philosopher.

**1970, Jan. 20    Engr.    Perf. 14**
| | | | | |
|---|---|---|---|---|
| 1166 | A368 | 5pf blue violet | .25 | .20 |
| 1167 | A368 | 10pf gray brown | .25 | .20 |
| 1168 | A368 | 15pf violet blue | .25 | .20 |
| 1169 | A368 | 20pf rose lilac | .30 | .20 |
| 1170 | A368 | 25pf blue green | 1.90 | .50 |
| 1171 | A368 | 40pf rose claret | .30 | .20 |
| | | Nos. 1166-1171 (6) | 3.25 | 1.50 |

Rabbit — A369

**1970, Feb. 5    Photo.    Perf. 13½x14**
| | | | | |
|---|---|---|---|---|
| 1172 | A369 | 10pf shown | .20 | .20 |
| 1173 | A369 | 20pf Red fox | .20 | .20 |
| 1174 | A369 | 25pf Mink | 2.40 | 1.60 |
| 1175 | A369 | 40pf Hamster | .30 | .20 |
| | | Nos. 1172-1175 (4) | 3.10 | 2.20 |

525th International Fur Auctions, Leipzig.

**Fairy Tale Type of 1969**

Various Scenes from Fairy Tale "Little Brother and Sister."

**1970, Feb. 17    Litho.    Perf. 13½x13**
| | | | | |
|---|---|---|---|---|
| 1176 | A345 | 5pf lilac & multi | .20 | .20 |
| 1177 | A345 | 10pf lilac & multi | .20 | .20 |
| 1178 | A345 | 15pf lilac & multi | .40 | .35 |
| 1179 | A345 | 20pf lilac & multi | .40 | .35 |
| 1180 | A345 | 25pf lilac & multi | .20 | .20 |
| 1181 | A345 | 30pf lilac & multi | .20 | .20 |
| a. | | Sheet of 6, #1176-1181 | 3.00 | 2.25 |

Telephone Coordinating Station — A370

15pf, High voltage testing transformer, vert.

**1970, Feb. 24    Perf. 13x12½, 12½x13**
| | | | | |
|---|---|---|---|---|
| 1182 | A370 | 10pf multicolored | .20 | .20 |
| 1183 | A370 | 15pf multicolored | .45 | .25 |

Leipzig Spring Fair, Mar. 1-10, 1970.

Horseman's Tombstone (700 A.D.) — A371

Treasures from the Halle Museum: 20pf, Helmet (500 A.D.). 25pf, Bronze basin (1000 B.C.). 40pf, Clay drum (2500 B.C.).

**1970, Mar. 3    Photo.    Perf. 13**
| | | | | |
|---|---|---|---|---|
| 1184 | A371 | 10pf dp grn, gray & dk brn | .20 | .20 |
| 1185 | A371 | 20pf multicolored | .20 | .20 |
| 1186 | A371 | 25pf yellow & multi | .60 | .80 |
| 1187 | A371 | 40pf multicolored | .20 | .20 |
| | | Nos. 1184-1187 (4) | 1.20 | 1.40 |

Lenin and Clara Zetkin — A372

Designs: 10pf, Lenin, "ISKRA" (newspaper's name), composing frame and printing press. 25pf, Lenin and title page of German edition of "State and Revolution." 40pf, Lenin statue, Eisleben. 70pf, Lenin monument and Lenin Square, Berlin. 1m, Lenin portrait, vert.

**Photogravure and Engraved**

**1970, Apr. 16    Perf. 14**
| | | | | |
|---|---|---|---|---|
| 1188 | A372 | 10pf multicolored | .20 | .20 |
| 1189 | A372 | 20pf multicolored | .20 | .20 |
| 1190 | A372 | 25pf multicolored | 1.60 | .75 |
| 1191 | A372 | 40pf multicolored | .20 | .20 |
| 1192 | A372 | 70pf multicolored | .30 | .20 |
| | | Nos. 1188-1192 (5) | 2.50 | 1.55 |

**Souvenir Sheet**
| | | | | |
|---|---|---|---|---|
| 1193 | A372 | 1m dk carmine & multi | 1.50 | 6.00 |

Sea Kale — A373

Protected Plants: 20pf, European pasque-flower. 25pf, Fringed gentian. 30pf, Galeate orchis. 40pf, Marsh tea. 70pf, Round-leaved wintergreen.

**1970, Apr. 28    Photo.**
| | | | | |
|---|---|---|---|---|
| 1194 | A373 | 10pf multicolored | .20 | .20 |
| 1195 | A373 | 20pf violet & multi | .20 | .20 |
| 1196 | A373 | 25pf multicolored | 1.50 | 1.50 |
| 1197 | A373 | 30pf multicolored | .20 | .20 |
| 1198 | A373 | 40pf multicolored | .25 | .20 |
| 1199 | A373 | 70pf multicolored | .30 | .20 |
| | | Nos. 1194-1199 (6) | 2.65 | 2.50 |

Red Army Soldier Raising Flag over Berlin Reichstag A374

**1970, May 5    Litho.    Perf. 13x13½**

20pf, Spasski Tower, Kremlin; State Council Building, Berlin; coats of arms of USSR and DDR, newspaper clipping about friendship treaty with USSR. 25pf, Mutual Economic Aid Building, Moscow, flags of member countries. 70pf, Memorial monument, Buchenwald.

| | | | | |
|---|---|---|---|---|
| 1200 | A374 | 10pf multi | .25 | .20 |
| 1201 | A374 | 20pf multi | .25 | .20 |
| 1202 | A374 | 25pf multi | 1.10 | .35 |
| | | Nos. 1200-1202 (3) | 1.60 | .75 |

**Souvenir Sheet**
| | | | | |
|---|---|---|---|---|
| 1203 | A374 | 70pf multi, horiz. | 1.50 | 4.00 |

25th anniv. of liberation from Fascism.

Shortwave Antenna, RBI Emblem and Globe — A375

Grain and Globe — A376

15pf, Berlin Radio Station, emblems of Radio Berlin Intl. (RBI), Radio DDR & Radio Germany.

**1970, May 13    Litho.    Perf. 13½x13**
**Size: 23x28mm**
| | | | | |
|---|---|---|---|---|
| 1204 | A375 | 10pf ap grn, vio bl & bl | .50 | .50 |

**Size: 50x28mm**
| | | | | |
|---|---|---|---|---|
| 1205 | A375 | 15pf vio bl, dp rose & ap grn | .75 | .75 |
| a. | | Pair, #1204-1205 | 3.25 | 2.00 |

DDR broadcasting system, 25th anniv.

**1970, May 19**

25pf, House of Culture, Dresden, and grain.
| | | | | |
|---|---|---|---|---|
| 1206 | A376 | 20pf vio bl, yel & bl | .65 | .65 |
| 1207 | A376 | 25pf vio bl, yel & bl | .65 | .65 |
| a. | | Strip of 2, #1206-1207 + label | 4.00 | 4.00 |

Issued to publicize the 5th World Cereal and Bread Congress, Dresden, May 24-29.

Fritz Heckert Medal A377

Design: 25pf, Globes and "FSM."

**1970, June 9    Perf. 13x12½**
| | | | | |
|---|---|---|---|---|
| 1208 | A377 | 20pf red, yel & brn | .20 | .20 |
| 1209 | A377 | 25pf red, bl & yel | .55 | .40 |

25th anniv. of the Free German Trade Union and of the World Organization of Trade Unions.

Traffic Policeman — A378

Designs: 10pf, Young Pioneers congratulating police woman. 15pf, Volga police car. 20pf, Railroad policeman with radio-telephone. 25pf, River police in Volga wing-type boat.

**1970, June 23    Litho.    Perf. 13x12½**
| | | | | |
|---|---|---|---|---|
| 1210 | A378 | 5pf ocher & multi | .25 | .20 |
| 1211 | A378 | 10pf green & multi | .25 | .20 |
| 1212 | A378 | 15pf ultra & multi | .25 | .20 |
| 1213 | A378 | 20pf multicolored | .25 | .20 |
| 1214 | A378 | 25pf multicolored | 1.90 | .30 |
| | | Nos. 1210-1214 (5) | 2.90 | 1.10 |

25th anniversary of the People's Police.

Gods Amon, Shu and Tefnut — A379

Designs from Lion Temple in Musawwarat: 15pf, Head of King Arnekhamani. 20pf, Cow from cattle frieze. 25pf, Head of Prince Arka. 30pf, Head of God Arensnuphis, vert. 40pf, Elephants and prisoners of war. 50pf, Lion God Apedemak.

**Perf. 13½x14, 14x13½**
**1970, June 23    Photo.**
| | | | | |
|---|---|---|---|---|
| 1215 | A379 | 10pf multicolored | .20 | .20 |
| 1216 | A379 | 15pf multicolored | .20 | .20 |
| 1217 | A379 | 20pf multicolored | .20 | .20 |
| 1218 | A379 | 25pf multicolored | .70 | .70 |
| 1219 | A379 | 30pf multicolored | .20 | .20 |
| 1220 | A379 | 40pf multicolored | .20 | .20 |
| 1221 | A379 | 50pf multicolored | .20 | .20 |
| | | Nos. 1215-1221 (7) | 1.90 | 1.90 |

Archaeological work in the Sudan by the Humboldt University, Berlin.

Arms and Flags of DDR and Poland — A380

**1970, July 1    Litho.    Perf. 13x12½**
| | | | | |
|---|---|---|---|---|
| 1222 | A380 | 20pf multicolored | .30 | .20 |

20th anniversary of the Görlitz Agreement concerning the Oder-Neisse border.

Culture Association Emblem — A381

Athlete on Pommel Horse — A382

Design: 25pf, Johannes R. Becher medal.

**1970, July 1    Photo.    Perf. 14**
| | | | | |
|---|---|---|---|---|
| 1223 | A381 | 10pf ultra, sil & brn | 1.60 | 1.60 |
| 1224 | A381 | 25pf ultra, gold & brn | 1.60 | 1.60 |
| a. | | Strip of 2, #1223-1224 + label | 8.25 | 8.25 |

25th anniv. of the German Kulturbund.

**1970, July 1    Perf. 14x13½**
| | | | | |
|---|---|---|---|---|
| 1225 | A382 | 10pf blk, yel & brn red | .20 | .20 |

Issued to publicize the 3rd Children's and Youths' Spartakiad. See No. B156.

Meeting of the American, British and Russian Delegations — A383

10pf, Cecilienhof Castle. 20pf, "Potsdam Agreement" in German, English, French & Russian.

**1970, July 28    Litho.    Perf. 13**
**Size: 23x28mm**
| | | | | |
|---|---|---|---|---|
| 1226 | A383 | 10pf blk, cit & red | .25 | .20 |
| 1227 | A383 | 20pf blk, cit & red | .25 | .20 |

## Size: 77x28mm

| 1228 | A383 25pf red & blk | .25 | .20 |
|---|---|---|---|
| a. | Strip of 3, #1226-1228 | 1.40 | 2.75 |

25th anniv. of the Potsdam Agreement among the Allies concerning Germany at the end of WWII.

Men's Pocket and Wrist Watches — A384

**1970, Aug. 25  Photo.  Perf. 13½x14**

| 1229 | A384 10pf ultra, blk & gold | .30 | .20 |
|---|---|---|---|

Leipzig Fall Fair, 1970.

Theodor Neubauer and Magnus Poser — A385

"Homeland" from Soviet Cenotaph, Berlin-Treptow A386

**1970, Sept. 2  Perf. 13x12½, 12½x13**

| 1230 | A385 20pf dk bl, car & pale grn | .20 | .20 |
|---|---|---|---|
| 1231 | A386 25pf dp car, pale bl | .25 | .20 |

Issued in memory of fighters against "fascism and imperialistic wars."

Competition Map and Compass — A387

Design: 25pf, Competition map and runner at 3 different stations.

**1970, Sept. 15  Litho.  Perf. 13x12½**

| 1232 | A387 10pf yellow & multi | .20 | .20 |
|---|---|---|---|
| 1233 | A387 25pf yellow & multi | 1.00 | .25 |

World Orienting Championships.

Mother and Child, by Käthe Kollwitz — A388

Works of Art: 10pf, Forest Worker Scharf's Birthday, by Otto Nagel. 20pf, Portrait of a Girl, by Otto Nagel. 25pf, No More War, (Woman with raised arm) by Käthe Kollwitz. 40pf, Head from Gustrow Memorial, by Ernst Barlach. 50pf, The Flutist, by Ernst Barlach.

**Photo.; Litho. (25pf, 30pf)**
**1970, Sept. 22          Perf. 14x13½**

| 1234 | A388 10pf multicolored | .20 | .20 |
|---|---|---|---|
| 1235 | A388 20pf multicolored | .20 | .20 |
| 1236 | A388 25pf pink & dk brn | .75 | .95 |
| 1237 | A388 30pf sal & blk | .20 | .20 |
| 1238 | A388 40pf yel & blk | .20 | .20 |
| 1239 | A388 50pf yel & blk | .25 | .20 |
| | Nos. 1234-1239 (6) | 1.80 | 1.95 |

Issued in memory of the artists Otto Nagel, Käthe Kollwitz and Ernst Barlach.

The Little Trumpeter A389

**1970, Oct. 1          Photo.**

| 1240 | A389 10pf dp ultra, brn & org | .20 | .30 |
|---|---|---|---|

2nd Natl. Youth Stamp Exhib., Karl-Marx-Stadt, Oct. 4-11. The design shows the memorial in Halle for Fritz Weineck, trumpeter for the Red War Veterans' Organization. See No. B160.

Emblem with Flags of East Block Nations — A390

**1970, Oct. 1  Litho.  Perf. 13x12½**

| 1241 | A390 10pf carmine & multi | .20 | .20 |
|---|---|---|---|
| 1242 | A390 20pf multicolored | .25 | .25 |

Issued to publicize the Brothers in Arms maneuvers of the East Bloc countries in the territory of the German Democratic Republic.

Musk Ox — A391

Berlin Zoo: 15pf, Shoebill. 20pf, Addax. 25pf, Malayan sun bear.

**1970, Oct. 6          Photo.          Perf. 14**

| 1243 | A391 10pf blue & multi | .30 | .20 |
|---|---|---|---|
| 1244 | A391 15pf green & multi | .30 | .20 |
| 1245 | A391 20pf org & multi | .55 | .30 |
| 1246 | A391 25pf multicolored | 5.00 | 5.00 |
| | Nos. 1243-1246 (4) | 6.15 | 5.70 |

UN Headquarters and Emblem — A392

**1970, Oct. 20          Photo.          Perf. 13**

| 1247 | A392 20pf ultra & multi | .55 | .25 |
|---|---|---|---|

25th anniversary of the United Nations.

Friedrich Engels
A393

Epiphyllum
A394

20pf, Friedrich Engels and Karl Marx. 25pf, Engels and title page of his polemic against Dühring.

**Photogravure and Engraved**
**1970, Nov. 24          Perf. 14**

| 1248 | A393 10pf ver, gray & blk | .25 | .20 |
|---|---|---|---|
| 1249 | A393 20pf ver, dk grn & blk | .25 | .20 |
| 1250 | A393 25pf ver, dk car rose & blk | 1.10 | .60 |
| | Nos. 1248-1250 (3) | 1.60 | 1.00 |

Friedrich Engels (1820-1895), socialist, collaborator with Karl Marx.

**1970, Dec. 2          Photo.          Perf. 14**

Flowering Cactus Plants: 10pf, Astrophytum myriostigma. 15pf, Echinocereus salm-dyckianus. 20pf, Selenicereus grandiflorus. 25pf, Hamatocactus setispinus. 30pf, Mamillaria boolii.

| 1251 | A394 5pf multicolored | .20 | .20 |
|---|---|---|---|
| 1252 | A394 10pf dk blue & multi | .20 | .20 |
| 1253 | A394 15pf multicolored | .20 | .20 |
| 1254 | A394 20pf multicolored | .20 | .20 |
| 1255 | A394 25pf dk blue & multi | 1.50 | 1.50 |
| 1256 | A394 30pf purple & multi | .20 | .20 |
| | Nos. 1251-1256 (6) | 2.50 | 2.50 |

### Souvenir Sheet

Ludwig van Beethoven — A395

**1970, Dec. 10          Engr.          Perf. 14**

| 1257 | A395 1m gray | 1.50 | 3.00 |
|---|---|---|---|

Bicentenary of the birth of Ludwig van Beethoven (1770-1827), composer.

Dancer's Mask, South Seas A396

Works from Ethnological Museum, Leipzig: 20pf, Bronze head, Africa. 25pf, Tea pot, Asia. 40pf, Clay figure (jaguar), Mexico.

**1971, Jan. 12          Photo.          Perf. 13**

| 1258 | A396 10pf multicolored | .20 | .20 |
|---|---|---|---|
| 1259 | A396 20pf multicolored | .20 | .20 |
| 1260 | A396 25pf multicolored | .60 | .60 |
| 1261 | A396 40pf multicolored | .25 | .20 |
| | Nos. 1258-1261 (4) | 1.25 | 1.20 |

Venus 5, Soft-landing on Moon — A397

#1263, Model of space station. #1264, Luna 16 and Luna 10 satellites. #1265, Group flight of Sojuz 6, 7 and 8. #1266, Proton 1, radiation measuring satellite. #1267, Communications

satellite Molniya 1. #1268, Yuri A. Gagarin, first flight of Vostok 1. #1269, Alexei Leonov walking in space, Voskhod 2.

**1971, Feb. 11  Litho.  Perf. 13x12½**

| 1262 | A397 20pf dk blue & multi | .25 | .25 |
|---|---|---|---|
| 1263 | A397 20pf dk blue & multi | .25 | .25 |
| 1264 | A397 20pf dk blue & multi | .45 | .45 |
| 1265 | A397 20pf dk blue & multi | .45 | .45 |
| 1266 | A397 20pf dk blue & multi | .45 | .45 |
| 1267 | A397 20pf dk blue & multi | .45 | .45 |
| 1268 | A397 20pf dk blue & multi | .25 | .25 |
| 1269 | A397 20pf dk blue & multi | .25 | .25 |
| a. | Sheet of 8, #1262-1269 | 3.00 | 3.00 |

Soviet space research.

Johannes R. Becher
A398

Karl Liebknecht
A399

Portraits: 10pf, Heinrich Mann. 15pf, John Heartfield. 20pf, Willi Bredel. 25pf, Franz Mehring. 40pf, Rudolf Virchow. 50pf, Johannes Kepler.

**1971          Engr.          Perf. 14**

| 1270 | A398 5pf brown | .20 | .20 |
|---|---|---|---|
| 1271 | A398 10pf vio blue | .20 | .20 |
| 1272 | A398 15pf black | .20 | .20 |
| 1273 | A398 20pf rose lake | .20 | .20 |
| 1274 | A398 25pf green | .45 | .50 |
| 1274A | A398 40pf pale purple | .40 | .20 |
| 1275 | A398 50pf dp black | .25 | .20 |
| | Nos. 1270-1275 (7) | 1.90 | 1.70 |

Honoring prominent Germans. See Nos. 1349-1353.

**1971, Feb. 23          Photo.**

Design: 25pf, Rosa Luxemburg.

| 1276 | A399 20pf gold, mag & blk | .35 | .35 |
|---|---|---|---|
| 1277 | A399 25pf gold, mag & blk | .35 | .35 |
| a. | Pair, #1276-1277 | 1.00 | 1.00 |

Karl Liebknecht (1871-1919) and Rosa Luxemburg (1871-1919), leaders of Spartacist Movement.

Soldier and Army Emblem — A400

**1971, Mar. 1          Perf. 13½x14**

| 1278 | A400 20pf gray & multi | .30 | .20 |
|---|---|---|---|

15th anniv. of the National People's Army.

Crushing and Conveyor Plant, Magdeburg — A401

Leipzig Spring Fair: 15pf, Dredger for low temperature work.

**1971, Mar. 9  Litho.  Perf. 13x12½**

| 1279 | A401 10pf green & multi | .20 | .20 |
|---|---|---|---|
| 1280 | A401 15pf multicolored | .20 | .20 |

Proclamation of the Commune, Town Hall, Paris — A402

Designs: 20pf, Barricade at Place Blanche, defended by women. 25pf, Illustration by Theophile A. Steinlen for The International. 30pf, Title page for "The Civil War in France," by Karl Marx.

**1971, Mar. 9**      **Perf. 13**
1281 A402 10pf red, bis & blk   .25   .20
1282 A402 20pf red, bis & blk   .25   .20
1283 A402 25pf red, buff & blk   .45   .45
1284 A402 30pf red, gray & blk   .25   .20
    Nos. 1281-1284 (4)   1.20 1.05

Centenary of the Paris Commune.

Lunokhod 1 on Moon — A403

**1971, Mar. 30**   **Photo.**   **Perf. 14**
1285 A403 20pf multicolored   .55   .30

Luna 17 unmanned, automated moon mission, Nov. 10-17, and the 24th Communist Party Congress of the Soviet Union.

Discobolus — A404

**1971, Apr. 6**   **Litho.**   **Perf. 13½x13**
1286 A404 20pf dull bl, lt bl & buff   .65   .25

20th anniversary of the Olympic Committee of German Democratic Republic.

Köpenick Castle — A405

Clasped Hands — A406

Berlin Buildings: 10pf, St. Mary's Church, vert. 20pf, Old Library. 25pf, Ermeler House, vert. 50pf, New Guard Memorial. 70pf, Natl. Gallery of Art.

**Perf. 13½x14, 14x13½**
**1971, Apr. 6**       **Photo.**
1287 A405 10pf multicolored   .20   .20
1288 A405 15pf multicolored   .20   .20
1289 A405 20pf multicolored   .20   .20
1290 A405 25pf multicolored   2.40 2.25
1291 A405 50pf multicolored   .25   .20
1292 A405 70pf multicolored   .30   .20
    Nos. 1287-1292 (6)   3.55 3.25

**Lithographed and Embossed**
**1971, Apr. 20**     **Perf. 13x13½**
1293 A406 20pf red, blk & gold   .30   .20

25th anniversary of Socialist Unity Party of Germany (SED).

Dance Costume, Schleife — A407    Self-Portrait, by Dürer — A408

Sorbian Dance Costumes from: 20pf, Hoyerswerda. 25pf, Cottbus. 40pf, Kamenz.

**1971, May 4**   **Litho.**   **Perf. 13½x13**
       **Size: 33x42mm**
1294 A407 10pf multicolored   .20   .20
1295 A407 20pf green & multi   .20   .20
1296 A407 25pf blue & multi   .55   .55
1297 A407 40pf multicolored   .25   .20
    Nos. 1294-1297 (4)   1.20 1.15

**1971, Nov. 23**     **Perf. 13½x13**
       **Booklet Stamps**
       **Size: 23x28mm**
1297A A407 10pf multicolored   .25   .20
  c.   Booklet pane of 4   1.40 1.10
  d.   Booklet pane, 2 #1297A, 2    #1297B   3.00 2.50
1297B A407 20pf multicolored   .50   .30

**1971, May 18**      **Perf. 12½x13**

Art Works by Dürer: 40pf, Three Peasants. 70pf, Portrait of Philipp Melanchthon.

1298 A408 10pf multicolored   .25   .20
1299 A408 40pf brown & multi   .25   .20
1300 A408 70pf gray & multi   1.50   .75
    Nos. 1298-1300 (3)   2.00 1.15

500th anniversary of the birth of Albrecht Dürer (1471-1528), painter and engraver.

Building Industry — A409    Congress Emblem — A410

Designs: 10pf, Science and technology. No. 1303, Farming. 25pf, Civilian defense.

**1971, June 9**   **Photo.**   **Perf. 14**
1301 A409 5pf cream, red & blk   .20   .20
1302 A409 10pf cream, red & blk   .20   .20
1303 A409 20pf cream, red, bl &    blk   .20   .20
1304 A410 20pf gold, dp car &    red   .25   .20
1305 A409 25pf cream, red & blk   .30   .35
    Nos. 1301-1305 (5)   1.15 1.15

8th Congress of Socialist Unity Party of Germany (SED).

Golden Fleece, 1730 A411

Treasures from the Green Vault, Dresden: 5pf, Cherry stone with 180 heads carved on it, 1590. 15pf, Tankard, Nuremberg, 1530. 20pf, Moor with drums on horseback, 1720. 25pf, Decorated writing box, 1562. 30pf, St. George pendant, 1570.

**1971, June 22**      **Perf. 13**
1306 A411 5pf dp car & multi   .20   .20
1307 A411 10pf green & multi   .20   .20
1308 A411 15pf violet & multi   .20   .20
1309 A411 20pf multicolored   .20   .20
1310 A411 25pf multicolored   .55   .75
1311 A411 30pf multicolored   .20   .20
    Nos. 1306-1311 (6)   1.55 1.75

Prisoners, by Fritz Cremer A412

Design: 25pf, Brutality in Buchenwald Concentration Camp, by Fritz Cremer.

**1971, June 22**   **Litho.**   **Perf. 13**
1312 A412 20pf bister & blk   .45   .45
1313 A412 25pf lt blue & blk   .45   .45
  a.   Pair, #1312-1313 with label between   1.40 1.60

Intl. Federation of Resistance Fighters (FIR), 20th anniv.

Coat of Arms of Mongolia — A413

**1971, July 6**   **Litho.**   **Perf. 13**
1314 A413 20pf dk red, yel & blk   .30   .25

50th anniv. of the Mongolian People's Revolution.

Child's Head, UNICEF Emblem A414

**1971, July 13**      **Photo.**
1315 A414 20pf multicolored   .30   .20

25th anniv. of UNICEF.

Militiaman, Soldier and Brandenburg Gate — A415

Design: 35pf, Brandenburg Gate and new buildings in East Berlin.

**1971, Aug. 12**
1316 A415 20pf red & multi   .60   .25
1317 A415 35pf yel & multi   1.50   .75

10 years of Berlin Wall.

Passenger Ship Iwan Franko — A416

Ships: 15pf, Freighter, type 17. 20pf, Freighter Rostock, type XD. 25pf, Fish processing ship "Junge Welt." 40pf, Container cargo ship. 50pf, Explorer ship Akademik Kurtschatow.

**1971, Aug. 24**       **Engr.**
1318 A416 10pf pale purple   .20   .20
1319 A416 15pf pale brn & ind   .20   .20
1320 A416 20pf gray green   .20   .20
1321 A416 25pf slate   1.00   .90
1322 A416 40pf maroon   .20   .20
1323 A416 50pf grysh blue   .25   .20
    Nos. 1318-1323 (6)   2.05 1.90

Shipbuilding industry.

Butadiene Plant — A417

Leipzig Fall Fair: 25pf, Refinery.

**1971, Sept. 2**   **Photo.**   **Perf. 13**
1324 A417 10pf olive, vio & mag   .20   .20
1325 A417 25pf blue, vio & ol   .25   .20

Raised Fists, Photo Montage by John Heartfield, 1937 A418

**1971, Sept. 23**
1326 A418 35pf grnsh bl, blk & sil   .30   .20

Intl. Year Against Racial Discrimination.

Karl Marx Monument A419

**1971, Oct. 5**   **Photo.**   **Perf. 14x13½**
1327 A419 35pf vio brn, pink & buff   .35   .20

Unveiling of Karl Marx memorial at Karl-Marx-Stadt (Chemnitz).

Wiltz Memorial, Flag of Luxembourg A420

**1971, Oct. 5**
1328 A420 25pf multicolored   .25   .20

Memorial for Nazi victims, Wiltz, Luxembourg.

Postal Milestones, Saxony, and
Zürner's Surveyor Carriage — A421

**Photo. & Engr.**
**1971, Oct. 5**                    *Perf. 14*
1329  A421  25pf blue, olive & lilac   .35  .35
Philatelists' Day 1971. See No. B162.

Darbuka, North
Africa — A422

Geodetic
Apparatus — A423

Musical Instruments: 15pf, Two morin chuur,
Mongolia. 20pf, Violin, Germany. 25pf, Mandolin, Italy. 40pf, Bagpipes, Bohemia. 50pf,
Kasso, Sudan.

**1971, Oct. 26  Photo.   Perf. 14x13½**
1330  A422  10pf multicolored    .20   .20
1331  A422  15pf multicolored    .20   .20
1332  A422  20pf ocher & multi   .20   .20
1333  A422  25pf blue & multi    .20   .20
1334  A422  40pf gray & multi    .20   .20
1335  A422  50pf multicolored    .85   .85
       Nos. 1330-1335 (6)       1.85  1.85
Instruments from the Music Museum in
Markneukirchen.

**1971, Nov. 9  Photo.   Perf. 13½x14**
20pf, Ergaval microscope. 25pf,
Planetarium.
**Size: 23½x28½mm**
1336  A423  10pf blue, blk & red  .35  .35
1337  A423  20pf blue, blk & red  .35  .35
**Size: 50½x28½mm**
1338  A423  25pf blue, vio bl & yel .35  .35
  a.   Strip of 3, #1336-1338   3.00 3.00
Carl Zeiss optical works in Jena, 125th
anniv.

**Fairy Tale Type of 1966**
Designs: Various Scenes from Fairy Tale
"The Bremen Town Musicians."

**1971, Nov. 23  Litho.   Perf. 13½x13**
1339  A290  5pf multicolored     .20   .20
1340  A290  10pf ocher & multi   .20   .20
1341  A290  15pf gray & multi    .55   .65
1342  A290  20pf ver & multi     .55   .65
1343  A290  25pf violet & multi  .20   .20
1344  A290  30pf yellow & multi  .20   .20
  a.   Sheet of 6, #1339-1344   3.00 7.50

Olympic Rings and Sledding — A424

Olympic Rings and: 20pf, Long-distance skiing. 25pf, Biathlon. 70pf, Ski jump.

---

**1971, Dec. 7  Photo.   Perf. 13½x14**
1345  A424  5pf green, car & blk  .20   .20
1346  A424  20pf car rose, vio &
             blk                  .20   .20
1347  A424  25pf vio, car & blk  1.25  1.00
1348  A424  70pf vio bl, vio & blk .25  .20
     Nos. 1345-1348,B163-B164 (6) 2.30 2.00
11th Winter Olympic Games, Sapporo,
Japan, Feb. 3-13, 1972.

**Portrait Type of 1971**
Portraits: 10pf, Johannes Tralow (1882-
1968), playwright. 20pf, Leonhard Frank
(1882-1961), writer. 25pf, K. A. Kocor (1822-
1904), composer. 35pf, Heinrich Schliemann
(1822-1890), archaeologist. 50pf, F. Caroline
Neuber (1697-1760), actress.

**1972, Jan. 25  Engr.   Perf. 14**
1349  A398  10pf green           .20   .20
1350  A398  20pf rose claret     .20   .20
1351  A398  25pf dk blue         .20   .20
1352  A398  35pf brown           .20   .20
1353  A398  50pf rose violet     .75  1.00
      Nos. 1349-1353 (5)        1.55  1.80
Honoring famous personalities.

Gypsum,
Eisleben
A425

Minerals found in East Germany: 10pf,
Zinnwaldite, Zinnwald. 20pf, Malachite, Ullersreuth. 25pf, Amethyst, Wiesenbad. 35pf,
Halite, Merkers. 50pf, Proustite, Schneeberg.

**1972, Feb. 22  Photo.   Perf. 13**
1354  A425  5pf grnsh bl & brn
             blk                 .20   .20
1355  A425  10pf citron, brn & blk .20  .20
1356  A425  20pf multicolored    .20   .20
1357  A425  25pf multicolored    .20   .20
1358  A425  35pf lt green, ind &
             blk                 .20   .20
1359  A425  50pf gray & multi    .90  1.00
      Nos. 1354-1359 (6)        1.90  2.00

Russian
Pavilion
and Fair
Emblem
A426

Design: 25pf, Flags of East Germany and
Russia, and Fair emblem.

**1972, Mar. 3  Photo.   Perf. 14**
1360  A426  10pf vio blue & multi .20  .20
1361  A426  25pf claret & multi  .25   .20
50 years of Russian participation in the
Leipzig Fair.

**Miniature Sheets**

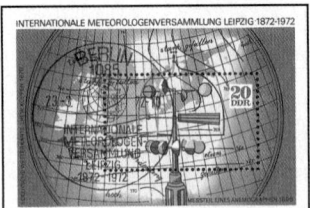

Anemometer, 1896, and
Meteorological Chart, 1876 — A427

Designs: 35pf, Dipole and cloud photograph
taken by satellite. 70pf, Meteor weather satellite and weather map.

**1972, Mar. 23  Litho.   Perf. 13x12½**
1362  A427  20pf multicolored    .70   .80
1363  A427  35pf multicolored    .70   .80
1364  A427  70pf green & multi   .70   .80
      Nos. 1362-1364 (3)        2.10  2.40
Intl. Meteorologists' Cent. Meeting, Leipzig.

---

World Health Organization
Emblem — A428

**1972, Apr. 4  Photo.   Perf. 13**
1365  A428  35pf lt bl, vio bl & sil  .30  .20
World Health Day.

Kamov
Helicopter
A429

Aircraft: 10pf, Agricultural spray plane. 35pf,
Ilyushin jet. 1m, Jet and tail with Interflug
emblem.

**1972, Apr. 25  Perf. 14**
1366  A429  5pf blue & multi     .20   .20
1367  A429  10pf multicolored    .20   .20
1368  A429  35pf blue grn & multi .20  .20
1369  A429  1m multicolored     1.00  1.10
      Nos. 1366-1369 (4)        1.65  1.70

Wrestling and Olympic Rings — A430

Sport and Olympic Rings: 20pf, Pole vault.
35pf, Volleyball. 70pf, Women's gymnastics.

**1972, May 16  Photo.   Perf. 13½x14**
1370  A430  5pf blue, gold & blk  .20   .20
1371  A430  20pf mag, gold & blk  .20   .20
1372  A430  35pf ol bis, gold & blk .20  .20
1373  A430  70pf yel grn, gold &
             blk                 2.50  1.50
     Nos. 1370-1373,B166-B167 (6) 3.50 2.50
20th Olympic Games, Munich, 8/26-9/11.

Flags of USSR and German
Democratic Republic — A431

20pf, Flags, Leonid Brezhnev & Erich
Honecker.

**1972, May 24  Engr. & Photo.**
1374  A431  10pf red, yel & blk  1.00   .60
1375  A431  20pf red, yel & blk  1.00   .60
Soc. for German-Soviet Friendship, 25th
anniv.

Workers — A432

Design: 35pf, Students.

---

**1972, May 24  Litho.   Perf. 13**
1376  A432  10pf dull yel, org &
             mag                  .25   .25
1377  A432  35pf dull yel & ultra .25   .25
  a.   Strip of 2, #1376-1377 + label 1.00 1.00
8th Congress of Free German Trade
Unions, Berlin.

Karneol
Rose
A433

**1972, June 13  Photo.   Perf. 13**
**Size: 36x36mm**
1378  A433  5pf shown            .20   .20
1379  A433  10pf Berger's Erfurt
             Rose                 .20   .20
1380  A433  15pf Charme         1.25  1.25
1381  A433  20pf Izetka Spree-
             Athens               .20   .20
1382  A433  25pf Kopenick sum-
             mer                  .20   .20
1383  A433  35pf Prof. Knoll     .25   .20
      Nos. 1378-1383 (6)        2.30  2.25
International Rose Exhibition.

**Redrawn**
**1972, Aug. 22  Perf. 13½x13**
**Booklet Stamps**
**Size: 23x28mm**
1383A  A433  10pf multicolored   .20   .20
  d.    Booklet pane of 4       1.00   .75
1383B  A433  25pf multicolored  1.00   .35
  e.    Booklet pane of 4 (2
         #1383B, 2 #1383C)      4.50  3.75
1383C  A433  35pf multicolored  1.00   .35
      Nos. 1383A-1383C (3)      2.20   .90

Young Mother
and Child, by
Cranach
A434

Paintings by Lucas Cranach: 5pf, Young
man. 35pf, Margarete Luther (Martin's
mother). 70pf, Reclining nymph, horiz.

**1972, July 4  Perf. 14x13½, 13½x14**
1384  A434  5pf gold & multi     .20   .20
1385  A434  20pf gold & multi    .20   .20
1386  A434  35pf gold & multi    .25   .25
1387  A434  70pf gold & multi   1.80  2.25
      Nos. 1384-1387 (4)        2.45  2.90
Lucas Cranach (1472-1553), painter.

Compass and Motorcyclist — A435

Designs: 10pf, Parachute and light plane.
20pf, Target and military obstacle race. 25pf,
Amateur radio transmitter, Morse key and
tape. 35pf, Propeller and sailing ship.

**1972, Aug. 8  Photo.   Perf. 14**
1388  A435  5pf multicolored     .20   .20
1389  A435  10pf multicolored    .20   .20
1390  A435  20pf multicolored    .20   .20
1391  A435  25pf multicolored    .55   .65
1392  A435  35pf multicolored    .20   .20
      Nos. 1388-1392 (5)        1.35  1.45
Society for Sport and Technology.

Young Worker Reading, by Jutta
Damme — A436

**1972, Aug. 22 Photo. Perf. 13½x14**
1393 A436 50pf multicolored .55 .30
International Book Year 1972.

Polylux Writing
Projector — A437

George
Dimitrov — A438

25pf, Pentacon-audiovision projector, horiz.

**Perf. 12½x13, 13x12½**
**1972, Aug. 29 Litho.**
1394 A437 10pf crimson & blk .20 .20
1395 A437 25pf brt green & blk .25 .25

Leipzig Fall Fair, 1972.

**1972, Sept. 19 Perf. 13x13½**
1396 A438 20pf rose red & blk .35 .25
George Dimitrov (1882-1949), Bulgarian
Communist party leader.

Bird Catchers,
Egypt, c. 2400
B.C. — A439

Design: 20pf, Tapestry with animal design,
Anatolia, c. 1400 A.D.

**1972, Sept. 19 Photo. Perf. 14**
1397 A439 10pf multicolored .20 .20
1398 A439 20pf multicolored .20 .20
Nos. 1397-1398,B168-B169 (4) 1.35 1.35

Interartes Philatelic Exhib., Berlin, Oct. 4-
Nov. 11.

Red Cross Trainees
and Red
Cross — A440

**1972, Oct. 3 Litho. Perf. 13**
Designs: 15pf, Red Cross rescue launch in
the Baltic. 35pf, Red Cross with world map,
ship, plane and vehicles.

**Size: 23x28mm**
1399 A440 10pf grnsh bl, dk bl &
red .25 .25

1400 A440 15pf grnsh bl, dk bl &
red .25 .25
**Size: 50x28mm**
1401 A440 35pf grnsh bl, dk bl &
red .25 .25
a. Strip of 3, #1399-1401 1.40 1.40

Red Cross at work in the DDR.

Arab Celestial
Globe,
1279 — A441

Anti-Fascists
Monument — A442

10pf, Globe, by Joachim R. Praetorius,
1568. 15pf, Globe clock, by Reinhold & Roll,
1586. 20pf, Globe clock, by J. Bürgi, c. 1590.
25pf, Armillary sphere, by J. Moeller, 1687.
35pf, Heraldic celestial globe, 1690.

**1972, Oct. 17 Photo. Perf. 14x13½**
1402 A441 5pf gray & multi .20 .20
1403 A441 10pf gray & multi .20 .20
1404 A441 15pf gray & multi 1.90 2.00
1405 A441 20pf gray & multi .20 .20
1406 A441 25pf gray & multi .20 .20
1407 A441 35pf gray & multi .25 .20
Nos. 1402-1407 (6) 2.95 3.00

Celestial and terrestrial globes from the
National Mathematical and Physics Collection,
Dresden.

**1972, Oct. 24 Litho. Perf. 12½x13**
1408 A442 25pf multicolored .35 .20
Monument for Polish soldiers and German
anti-Fascists, unveiled in Berlin, May 14, 1972.

Young Workers Receiving Technical
Education — A443

25pf, Workers with modern welding
machine.

**1972, Nov. 2 Photo. Perf. 13½x14**
1409 A443 10pf blue & multi .20 .20
1410 A443 25pf blue & multi .20 .20
a. Strip of 2, #1409-1410 + label .75 .90

15th Central Fair of Masters of Tomorrow.

Mauz and
Hoppel
A444

Designs: Children's television characters.

**1972, Nov. 28 Litho. Perf. 13½x13**
1411 A444 5pf shown .20 .20
1412 A444 10pf Fox and magpie .20 .20
1413 A444 15pf Mr. Owl .70 .70
1414 A444 20pf Mrs. Hedgehog
and Borstel .70 .70

1415 A444 25pf Schnuffel and
Peips .20 .20
1416 A444 35pf Paul from the Library .20 .20
a. Sheet of 6, #1411-1416 2.75 2.75

Grandmother,
Children, Magic
Mirror — A445

Scenes from Hans Christian Andersen's
"Snow Queen": 10pf, Kay and Snow Queen.
15pf, Gerda in magic garden. 20pf, Gerda and
crows at palace. 25pf, Gerda and reindeer in
Lapland. 35pf, Gerda and Kay at Snow
Queen's palace.

**1972, Nov. 28 Perf. 13x13½**
1417 A445 5pf multicolored .25 .25
1418 A445 10pf multicolored .55 .75
1419 A445 15pf multicolored .25 .25
1420 A445 20pf multicolored .25 .25
1421 A445 25pf multicolored .55 .75
1422 A445 35pf multicolored .25 .25
a. Sheet of 6, #1417-1422 4.00 8.00

See designs A469, A490.

**Souvenir Sheet**

Heinrich Heine — A446

**1972, Dec. 5 Perf. 12½x13**
1423 A446 1m brn ol, blk & red 1.50 1.50
150th anniversary of the birth of Heinrich
Heine (1797-1856), poet.

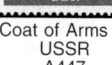

Coat of Arms of
USSR
A447

Michelangelo da
Caravaggio
A448

**1972, Dec. 5 Photo. Perf. 13½x14**
1424 A447 20pf red & multi .35 .20
50th anniversary of the Soviet Union.

**1973 Litho. Perf. 13½x13**
1425 A448 5pf brown .60 .70
1426 A448 10pf dull green .20 .20
1427 A448 20pf rose lilac .20 .20
1428 A448 25pf blue .20 .20
1429 A448 35pf brown red .20 .20
1429A A448 40pf rose claret .35 .25
Nos. 1425-1429A (6) 1.75 1.75

Michelangelo da Caravaggio (1565(?)-
1609), Italian painter (5pf). Friedrich Wolf
(1888-1953), writer (10pf). Max Reger (1873-
1916), composer (20pf). Max Reinhardt (1873-
1943), Austrian theatrical director (25pf).
Johannes Dieckmann (1893-1969), member
and president of People's Chamber (35pf).
Hermann Matern (1893-1971), vice-president
of DDR (40pf).

Lenin Square,
Berlin — A449

Coat of Arms of
DDR — A449a

Designs: 5pf, Pelican, Berlin Zoo. 10pf,
Neptune Fountain, City Hall Street. 15pf, Fisherman's Island, Berlin. 25pf, World clock, Alexander Square, Berlin. 30pf, Workers' Memorial, Halle. 35pf, Marx monument, Karl-Marx-
Stadt. 40pf, Brandenburg Gate, Berlin. 50pf,
New Guardhouse, Berlin. 60pf, Zwinger, Dresden. 70pf, Old Town Hall, Office Building, Leipzig. 80pf, Old and new buildings, Rostock-
Warnemunde. 1m, Soviet War Memorial,
Treptow.

**1973-74 Engr. Perf. 14x14**
**Size: 29x23½mm**
1430 A449 5pf blue green .20 .20
1431 A449 10pf emerald .45 .20
1432 A449 15pf rose lilac .35 .20
1433 A449 20pf rose ma-
genta .75 .25
1434 A449 25pf grnsh blue .90 .20
1435 A449 30pf orange .20 .20
1436 A449 35pf grnsh blue .75 .25
1437 A449 40pf dull violet .30 .25
1438 A449 50pf blue, bluish .35 .25
1439 A449 60pf lilac ('74) .75 .30
1440 A449 70pf redsh
brown .65 .35
1441 A449 80pf vio blue
('74) .75 .30
1442 A449 1m olive 1.10 .25
1443 A449a 2m lake 1.80 .20
1443A A449a 3m rose lilac
('74) 2.25 .50
Nos. 1430-1443A (15) 11.55 3.90

See Nos. 1610-1617, 2071-2085.

Lebachia
Speciosa
(Oldest
Conifer)
A450

Fossils from Natural History Museum, Berlin: 15pf, Sphenopteris hollandica (carbon
fern). 20pf, Pterodactylus kochi (flying reptile).
25pf, Botryopteris (permian fern). 35pf,
Archaeopteryx lithographica (primitive reptile-
like bird). 70pf, Odontopieura ovata (trilobite).

**1973, Feb. 6 Photo. Perf. 13**
1444 A450 10pf multicolored .20 .20
1445 A450 15pf ultra, gray & blk .20 .20
1446 A450 20pf yellow & multi .20 .20
1447 A450 25pf emerald, blk &
brn .20 .20
1448 A450 35pf ocher & multi .20 .20
1449 A450 70pf ind, blk & yel 1.40 1.50
Nos. 1444-1449 (6) 2.40 2.50

Bobsled Track,
Oberhof — A451

**1973, Feb. 13   Litho.   Perf. 12½x13**
1450 A451 35pf dk bl, bl & org   .35 .30

15th Bobsledding Championships, Oberhof.

Combines
A452

Leipzig Spring Fair: 25pf, Computerized
threshing and silage producing machine.

**1973, Mar. 6   Litho.   Perf. 13x12½**
1451 A452 10pf olive & multi   .20 .20
1452 A452 25pf blue & multi   .30 .30

Firecrests
A453

Songbirds: 10pf, White-winged crossbill.
15pf, Waxwing. 20pf, White-spotted and redspotted bluethroats. 25pf, Goldfinch. 35pf,
Golden oriole. 40pf, Gray wagtail. 50pf, Wall
creeper.

**1973, Mar. 20   Photo.   Perf. 14x13½**
1453 A453  5pf multicolored   .20 .20
1454 A453 10pf multicolored   .20 .20
1455 A453 15pf multicolored   .20 .20
1456 A453 20pf multicolored   .20 .20
1457 A453 25pf multicolored   .20 .20
1458 A453 35pf multicolored   .20 .20
1459 A453 40pf multicolored   .25 .25
1460 A453 50pf ocher & multi   2.25 2.25
     Nos. 1453-1460 (8)   3.70 3.70

Copernicus and Title Page — A454

**1973, Feb. 13   Litho.   Perf. 13½x13**
1461 A454 70pf multicolored   .75 .35

500th anniversary of the birth of Nicolaus
Copernicus (1473-1543), astronomer.

Electric Locomotive — A455

Railroad Cars Manufactured in DDR: 10pf,
Refrigerator car. 20pf, Long-distance coach.
25pf, Multiple tank car with pneumatic filling
device. 35pf, Two-story coach. 85pf, International coaches.

**1973, May 22   Litho.   Perf. 13x12½**
1462 A455  5pf gray & multi   .20 .20
1463 A455 10pf brt blue & multi   .20 .20
1464 A455 20pf dk blue & multi   .20 .20
1465 A455 25pf gray & multi   .20 .20
1466 A455 35pf multicolored   .20 .20
1467 A455 85pf green & multi   1.90 2.00
     Nos. 1462-1467 (6)   2.90 3.00

King Lear,
Staged by
Wolfgang
Langhoff
A456

Great Theatrical Productions: 25pf, Midsummer Marriage, staged by Walter Felsen-
stein. 35pf, Mother Courage, staged by Bertolt
Brecht.

**1973, May 29   Photo.   Perf. 13**
1468 A456 10pf maroon, rose &
            yel   .20 .20
1469 A456 25pf vio bl, lt bl &
            rose   .20 .20
1470 A456 35pf dk gray, bis & bl   .70 .75
     Nos. 1468-1470 (3)   1.10 1.15

Goethe and his     Fireworks, TV
Home in         Tower, World
Weimar — A457    Clock — A458

Designs (Portraits and Houses): 15pf, Christoph Martin Wieland. 20pf, Friedrich von Schiller. 25pf, Johann Gottfried Herder. 35pf, Lucas
Cranach, the Elder. 50pf, Franz Liszt.

**1973, June 26   Litho.   Perf. 12½x13**
1471 A457 10pf blue & multi   .20 .20
1472 A457 15pf multicolored   .20 .20
1473 A457 20pf multicolored   .20 .20
1474 A457 25pf multicolored   .20 .20
1475 A457 35pf green & multi   .20 .20
1476 A457 50pf multicolored   1.90 1.10
     Nos. 1471-1476 (6)   2.90 2.10

Famous men and their homes in Weimar.

**1973**

Designs (Festival Emblem and): 15pf,
Vietnamese and European men, book and
girder. 20pf, Construction workers and valve.
30pf, Negro and European students, dam and
retort. 35pf, Emblems of World Federation of
Democratic Youth and International Students
Union. 50pf, Brandenburg Gate.

1477 A458  5pf vio blue & multi   .20 .20
  *a.*    Booklet pane of 4   1.50 1.50
1478 A458 15pf olive & multi   .20 .20
1479 A458 20pf multicolored   .20 .20
  *a.*    Booklet pane of 4   1.50 1.50
1480 A458 30pf blue & multi   .80 .60
1481 A458 35pf green & multi   .20 .20
     Nos. 1477-1481 (5)   1.60 1.40

**Souvenir Sheet**
1482 A458 50pf aqua & multi   1.00 .75

10th Festival of Youths and Students, Berlin,
July 1973.
   Issued: #1477-1481, July 3; #1482, July 26.

**Ulbricht Type of 1961-67**
**1973, Aug. 8   Engr.   Perf. 14**
         **Size: 24x28½mm**
1483 A189 20pf black   .55 .30

In memory of Walter Ulbricht (1893-1973),
chairman of Council of State.

Pylon, Map of
Electric Power
System — A459

**1973, Aug. 14   Photo.   Perf. 14**
1484 A459 35pf magenta, org & lt
            bl   .35 .30

10th anniversary of the united East European electric power system "Peace."

Sports Equipment — A460

Design: 25pf, Sailboat, guitar, electric drill.

**1973, Aug. 28   Photo.   Perf. 14**
1485 A460 10pf multicolored   .20 .20
1486 A460 25pf multicolored   .30 .20

Leipzig Fall Fair and EXPOVITA exhibition
for leisure time equipment.

Militiaman
and
Emblem
A461

Designs: 20pf, Militia guarding border at
Brandenburg Gate. 50pf, Representatives of
Red Veterans' League, International Brigade
in Spain and Workers' Militia in DDR, vert.

**1973, Sept. 11   Litho.   Perf. 13x12½**
1487 A461 10pf multicolored   .20 .20
1488 A461 20pf tan, red & blk   .30 .20

**Souvenir Sheet**
     **Perf. 12½x13**
1489 A461 50pf multicolored   .65 .75

20th anniversary of Workers' Militia of the
German Democratic Republic.

Globe and Red
Flag Emblem
A462

**1973, Sept. 11   Photo.   Perf. 13½x14**
1490 A462 20pf gold & red   .45 .25

15th anniversary of the review "Problems of
Peace and Socialism," published in Prague in
28 languages.

Memorial, Langenstein-
Zwieberge — A463

**1973, Sept. 18      Perf. 14x13½**
1491 A463 25pf multicolored   .45 .25

In memory of the workers who perished in
the subterranean munitions works at Langen-
stein-Zwieberge.

UN Headquarters, NY, UN and DDR
Emblems — A464

**1973, Sept. 21      Perf. 13**
1492 A464 35pf multicolored   .45 .25

Admission of the DDR to the UN.

Union Emblem
A465

**1973, Oct. 11   Photo.   Perf. 14x13½**
1493 A465 35pf silver & multi   .35 .30

8th Congress of the World Federation of
Trade Unions, Varna, Bulgaria.

Rocket
Launching — A466

**1973, Oct. 23      Perf. 14**

20pf, Emblem with map of Russia & hammer & sickle, horiz. 25pf, Oil refinery, Ryazan.

1494 A466 10pf violet bl & multi   .20 .20
1495 A466 20pf vio bl, red & sil   .20 .20
1496 A466 25pf multicolored   .75 .75
     Nos. 1494-1496 (3)   1.15 1.15

Soviet Science & Technology Days in DDR.

Madonna with
the Rose, by
Parmigianino
A467

Paintings: 10pf Child with Doll, by Christian
L. Vogel. 20pf, Woman with Plaited Blond Hair,
by Rubens. 25pf, Lady in White, by Titian.
35pf, Archimedes, by Domenico Fetti. 70pf,
Bouquet with Blue Iris, by Jan D. de Heem.

**1973, Nov. 13   Photo.   Perf. 14**
1497 A467 10pf gold & multi   .20 .20
1498 A467 15pf gold & multi   .20 .20
1499 A467 20pf gold & multi   .20 .20
1500 A467 25pf gold & multi   .20 .20
1501 A467 35pf gold & multi   .20 .20
1502 A467 70pf gold & multi   2.10 1.40
     Nos. 1497-1502 (6)   3.10 2.40

Human
Rights
Flame
A468

**1973, Nov. 20**   *Perf. 13*
1503 A468 35pf dp rose, dk car & sil   .45 .30
25th anniv. of the Universal Declaration of Human Rights.

Boy Holding Pike — A469

Designs: Various scenes from Russian Folktale "At the Bidding of the Pike."

**1973, Dec. 4**   *Litho.*   *Perf. 13x13½*
1504 A469 5pf multicolored   .25 .25
1505 A469 10pf multicolored   .75 1.00
1506 A469 15pf multicolored   .25 .25
1507 A469 20pf multicolored   .25 .25
1508 A469 25pf multicolored   .75 1.00
1509 A469 35pf multicolored   .25 .25
a.   Sheet of 6, #1504-1509   2.75 6.50

Edwin Hoernle — A470

**1974**   *Litho.*   *Perf. 13½x13*
#1511, Etkar Andre. #1512, Paul Merker. #1513, Hermann Duncker. #1514, Fritz Heckert. #1515, Otto Grotewohl. #1516, Wilhelm Florin. #1517, Georg Handke. #1518, Rudolf Breitscheid. #1519, Kurt Bürger. #1519A Carl Moltmann.

1510 A470 10pf gray green   .20 .20
1511 A470 10pf rose violet   .20 .20
1512 A470 10pf dark blue   .20 .20
1513 A470 10pf brown   .20 .20
1514 A470 10pf dull green   .20 .20
1515 A470 10pf red brown   .20 .20
1516 A470 10pf vio blue   .20 .20
1517 A470 10pf olive brown   .20 .20
1518 A470 10pf slate green   .20 .20
1519 A470 10pf dull violet   .20 .20
1519A A470 10pf brown   .20 .20
Nos. 1510-1519A (11)   2.20 2.20

Leaders of German labor movement.
Issued: #1510-1517, Jan. 8; others July 9.

Flags of Comecon Members A471

**1974, Jan. 22**   *Photo.*   *Perf. 13*
1520 A471 20pf red & multi   .35 .20
25th anniversary of the Council of Mutual Economic Assistance (Comecon).

Pablo Neruda and Chilean Flag A472

**1974, Jan. 22**   *Perf. 14*
1521 A472 20pf multicolored   .35 .25
Pablo Neruda (Neftali Ricardo Reyes, 1904-1973), Chilean poet.

Echinopsis Multiplex A473   Fieldball A474

Various Flowering Cacti: 10pf, Lobivia haageana. 15pf, Parodia sanguiniflora. 20pf, Gymnocal. monvillei. 25pf, Neoporteria rapifera. 35pf, Notocactus concinnus.

**1974, Feb. 12**   *Photo.*   *Perf. 14*
1522 A473 5pf multicolored   .20 .20
1523 A473 10pf tan & multi   .20 .20
1524 A473 15pf green & multi   1.90 1.90
1525 A473 20pf multicolored   .20 .20
1526 A473 25pf violet & multi   .20 .20
1527 A473 35pf multicolored   .25 .25
Nos. 1522-1527 (6)   2.95 2.95

**1974, Feb. 26**   *Litho.*   *Perf. 13*
Design: Various fieldball scenes.
1528 A474 5pf green & multi   .30 .30
1529 A474 10pf green & multi   .30 .30
1530 A474 35pf green & multi   1.10 1.10
a.   Strip of 3, #1528-1530   .90 .90
8th World Fieldball Championships for Men.

Power Testing Station — A475

Leipzig Spring Fair: 25pf, Robotron EC 2040 data processer, horiz.

**1974, Mar. 5**   *Photo.*   *Perf. 14*
1531 A475 10pf multicolored   .20 .20
1532 A475 25pf multicolored   .30 .20

Poisonous European Mushrooms A476

**1974, Mar. 19**   *Litho.*   *Perf. 13x13½*
Designs: 5pf, Rhodophyllus Sinuatus. 10pf, Boletus satanas. 15pf, Amanita pantherina. 20pf, Amanita muscaria. 25pf, Gyromitra esculenta. 30pf, Inocybe patouillardii. 35pf, Amanita phalloides. 40pf, Clitocybe dealbata.
1533 A476 5pf buff & multi   .20 .20
1534 A476 10pf buff & multi   .20 .20
1535 A476 15pf buff & multi   .20 .20
1536 A476 20pf buff & multi   .20 .20
1537 A476 25pf buff & multi   .20 .20
1538 A476 30pf buff & multi   .25 .20
1539 A476 35pf buff & multi   .25 .20
1540 A476 40pf buff & multi   1.25 1.25
Nos. 1533-1540 (8)   2.75 2.65

Gustav Robert Kirchhoff — A477

Portraits: 10pf, Immanuel Kant. 20pf, Ehm Welk. 25pf, Johann Gottfried Herder. 35pf, Lion Feuchtwanger.

**1974, Mar. 26**   *Litho.*   *Perf. 13½x13*
1541 A477 5pf black & gray   .20 .20
1542 A477 10pf vio bl & dull bl   .20 .20
1543 A477 20pf maroon & rose   .20 .20
1544 A477 25pf slate grn & grn   .20 .20
1545 A477 35pf brn & lt brn   .60 .50
Nos. 1541-1545 (5)   1.40 1.30

"Peace" A477a

**1974, Apr. 16**   *Perf. 13*
1548 A477a 35pf silver & multi   .35 .30
1st World Peace Congress, 25th anniv.

Oil Pipeline Operator and Arms of DDR A477b

**1974, Apr. 30**   *Photo.*   *Perf. 13*
1549 A477b 10pf shown   .20 .20
1550 A477b 20pf Students   .20 .20
1551 A477b 25pf Woman worker   .20 .20
1552 A477b 35pf Family   .85 .85
Nos. 1549-1552 (4)   1.45 1.45
25th anniv. of the DDR.

Buk Lighthouse, 1878, and Map — A478

Lighthouses, Maps and Nautical Charts: 15pf, Warnemünde, 1898. 20pf, Darsser Ort, 1848. 35pf, Arkona, 1827 and 1902. 40pf, Greifswalder Oie, 1855.

**1974, May 7**   *Litho.*   *Perf. 14*
1553 A478 10pf multicolored   .20 .20
1554 A478 15pf multicolored   .20 .20
1555 A478 20pf multicolored   .20 .20
1556 A478 35pf multicolored   .20 .20
1557 A478 40pf multicolored   1.00 .80
Nos. 1553-1557 (5)   1.80 1.60

Hydrographic Service of German Democratic Republic. See Nos. 1645-1649.

The Ages of Man, by C. D. Friedrich — A479

C. D. Friedrich, Self-portrait — A480

Paintings by Friedrich: 10pf, Two Men Observing Moon. 25pf, The Heath near Dresden. 35pf, View of Elbe Valley.

**1974, May 21**   *Photo.*   *Perf. 13½*
1558 A479 10pf gold & multi   .20 .20
1559 A479 20pf gold & multi   .20 .20
1560 A479 25pf gold & multi   1.50 1.50
1561 A479 35pf gold & multi   .25 .20
Nos. 1558-1561 (4)   2.15 2.10

**Souvenir Sheet**
**Engr.**
*Perf. 14x13½*
1562 A480 70pf sepia   1.20 1.60
Caspar David Friedrich (1774-1840), German Romantic painter.

Plauen Lace — A481

Designs: Various Plauen lace patterns.

**1974, June 11**   *Litho.*   *Perf. 13*
1563 A481 10pf violet, lil & blk   .20 .20
1564 A481 20pf brown ol & blk   .20 .20
1565 A481 25pf bl, lt bl & blk   1.10 1.10
1566 A481 35pf lil rose, rose & blk   .20 .20
Nos. 1563-1566 (4)   1.70 1.70

Trotter — A482

Designs: 10pf, Thoroughbred hurdling, vert. 25pf, Haflinger breed horses. 35pf, British thoroughbred race horse.

*Perf. 14x13½, 13½x14*
**1974, Aug. 13**   *Photo.*
1570 A482 10pf olive & multi   .20 .20
1571 A482 20pf multicolored   .20 .20
1572 A482 25pf lt blue & multi   1.25 1.40
1573 A482 35pf ocher & multi   .20 .20
Nos. 1570-1573 (4)   1.85 2.00

International Horse Breeders' of Socialist Countries Congress, Berlin.

Crane Lifting Diesel Locomotive — A483

Leipzig Fall Fair: 25pf, Sugar beet harvester, type KS6.

**1974, Aug. 27**   *Litho.*   *Perf. 13x12½*
1574 A483 10pf multicolored   .20 .20
1575 A483 25pf orange & multi   .30 .25

Miniature China and Mirror Exhibits — A484

Designs: Scenes from 18th century Thuringia, Dolls' Village, Arnstadt Castle Museum.

**1974, Sept. 10**   *Photo.*   *Perf. 14x13½*
1576 A484 10pf shown   .20 .20
1577 A484 10pf Harlequin barker at Fair   .20 .20

| | | | | |
|---|---|---|---|---|
| 1578 | A484 | 15pf | Wine tasters | .20 .20 |
| 1579 | A484 | 20pf | Cooper and apprentice | .20 .20 |
| 1580 | A484 | 25pf | Bagpiper | 1.10 1.25 |
| 1581 | A484 | 35pf | Butcher and beggar, women | .20 .20 |
| | | | Nos. 1576-1581 (6) | 2.10 2.25 |

Bound Guerrillas, Ardeatine Caves,
Rome — A485

Design: No. 1583, Resistance Fighters,
monument near Chateaubriant, France.

**1974, Sept. 24　　　Perf. 13½x14**

| | | | | |
|---|---|---|---|---|
| 1582 | A485 | 35pf green, blk & red | | .30 .30 |
| 1583 | A485 | 35pf blue, blk & red | | .30 .30 |

International war memorials.

Souvenir Sheet

Family and Flag — A486

**1974, Oct. 3　　Photo.　　Perf. 13**

| | | | |
|---|---|---|---|
| 1584 | A486 | 1m multicolored | 1.25 1.25 |

25th anniv. of the DDR.

Freighter and Paddle
Steamer — A487

Cent. of the UPU: 20pf, Old steam locomotive and modern Diesel. 25pf, Bi-plane and jet. 35pf, Mail coach and truck.

**1974, Oct. 9　　　　　　Perf. 14**

| | | | |
|---|---|---|---|
| 1585 | A487 | 10pf green & multi | .20 .20 |
| 1586 | A487 | 20pf multicolored | .20 .20 |
| 1587 | A487 | 25pf blue & multi | .20 .20 |
| 1588 | A487 | 35pf multicolored | .90 .75 |
| | | Nos. 1585-1588 (4) | 1.50 1.35 |

"In Praise of
Dialectics"
A488

**1974, Oct. 24　Litho.　Perf. 13x13½**

Designs: 10pf+5pf, "Praise to the Revolutionaries." 25pf, "Praise to the Party." Designs

are from bas-reliefs by Rossdeutscher, Jastram and Wetzel, illustrating poems by Bertholt Brecht.

| | | | |
|---|---|---|---|
| 1589 | A488 | 10pf + 5pf multi | .20 .20 |
| 1590 | A488 | 20pf multicolored | .20 .20 |
| 1591 | A488 | 25pf multicolored | .20 .20 |
| a. | | Strip of 3, #1589-1591 | 1.10 1.10 |

DDR '74 Natl. Stamp Exhib., Karl-Marx-Stadt.

Souvenir Sheet

Drawings by Young Pioneers — A489

**1974, Nov. 26　Litho.　　Perf. 14**

| | | | |
|---|---|---|---|
| 1592 | A489 | Sheet of 4 | 1.50 1.50 |
| a. | | 20pf Sun shines on everybody | .30 .30 |
| b. | | 20pf My Friend Sascha | .30 .30 |
| c. | | 20pf Carsten, the Best Swimmer | .30 .30 |
| d. | | 20pf Me at the Blackboard | .30 .30 |

Young Pioneers' drawings (7-10 years old).

Man Cutting Tree,
and Bird — A490

Designs: Various scenes from Russian folktale "Twittering To and Fro."

**1974, Dec. 3　　　　　Perf. 13x13½**

| | | | |
|---|---|---|---|
| 1593 | A490 | 10pf multicolored | .20 .20 |
| 1594 | A490 | 15pf multicolored | .85 .85 |
| 1595 | A490 | 20pf multicolored | .20 .20 |
| 1596 | A490 | 30pf multicolored | .20 .20 |
| 1597 | A490 | 35pf multicolored | .85 .85 |
| 1598 | A490 | 40pf multicolored | .20 .20 |
| a. | | Sheet of 6, #1593-1598 | 2.50 3.00 |

Meditating Girl,
by Wilhelm
Lachnit — A491

**1974, Dec. 10　Perf. 13½x14, 14x13½**

Paintings: 10pf, Still Life, by Ronald Paris, horiz. 20pf, Fisherman's House, Vitte, by Harald Hakenbeck. 35pf, Girl in Red, by Rudolf Bergander, horiz. 70pf, The Artist's Parents, by Willi Sitte.

| | | | |
|---|---|---|---|
| 1599 | A491 | 10pf multicolored | .20 .20 |
| 1600 | A491 | 15pf multicolored | .20 .20 |
| 1601 | A491 | 20pf multicolored | .20 .20 |
| 1602 | A491 | 35pf multicolored | .25 .20 |
| 1603 | A491 | 70pf multicolored | 1.50 1.50 |
| | | Nos. 1599-1603 (5) | 2.35 2.30 |

Paintings in Berlin Museums.

Banded
Jasper — A492

Minerals from the collection of the Mining Academy in Freiberg: 15pf, Smoky quartz. 20pf, Topaz. 25pf, Amethyst. 35pf, Aquamarine. 70pf, Agate.

**1974, Dec. 17　　Photo.　　Perf. 14**

| | | | |
|---|---|---|---|
| 1604 | A492 | 10pf lt yellow & multi | .20 .20 |
| 1605 | A492 | 15pf lt yellow & multi | .20 .20 |
| 1606 | A492 | 20pf lt yellow & multi | .20 .20 |
| 1607 | A492 | 25pf lt yellow & multi | .20 .20 |
| 1608 | A492 | 35pf lt yellow & multi | .25 .20 |
| 1609 | A492 | 70pf lt yellow & multi | 1.50 1.50 |
| | | Nos. 1604-1609 (6) | 2.55 2.50 |

**Type of 1973**
**Coil Stamps**

**1974-75　　　Photo.　　　Perf. 14**
**Size: 21x17½mm**

| | | | |
|---|---|---|---|
| 1610 | A449 | 5pf blue grn ('74) | .20 .20 |
| 1611 | A449 | 10pf emerald | .35 .35 |
| 1612 | A449 | 20pf rose magenta | .35 .35 |
| 1613 | A449 | 25pf green ('75) | .35 .25 |
| 1615 | A449 | 50pf blue ('74) | .65 .50 |
| 1617 | A449 | 1m olive ('74) | .90 .90 |
| | | Nos. 1610-1617 (6) | 2.80 2.55 |

Black control number on back of every fifth stamp.
The 20pf was issued in sheets of 100 in 1975.

Martha Arendsee
(1885-1953),
Communist
Politician — A493

**1975, Jan. 14　Litho.　Perf. 13½x13**

| | | | |
|---|---|---|---|
| 1618 | A493 | 10pf dull red | .30 .20 |

Souvenir Sheet

Peasants' War, Contemporary
Woodcuts — A494

**1975, Feb. 11　　　　Perf. 12½x13**

| | | | |
|---|---|---|---|
| 1619 | A494 | Sheet of 6 + label | 3.00 3.00 |
| a. | | 5pf Forced labor | .30 .30 |
| b. | | 10pf Peasant paying tithe | .30 .30 |
| c. | | 20pf Thomas Munzer | .30 .30 |
| d. | | 25pf Armed peasants | .55 .55 |
| e. | | 35pf Peasant, "Liberty" flag | .55 .55 |
| f. | | 50pf Peasant on trial | .30 .30 |

Peasants' War, 450th anniversary.

Black
Women — A495

Designs: 20pf, Caucasian women. 25pf, Indian woman and child.

**1975, Feb. 25　　Litho.　　Perf. 13**

| | | | |
|---|---|---|---|
| 1620 | A495 | 10pf red & multi | .25 .25 |
| 1621 | A495 | 20pf red & multi | .25 .25 |
| 1622 | A495 | 25pf red & multi | .25 .25 |
| a. | | Strip of 3, Nos. 1620-1622 | 1.00 .95 |

International Women's Year 1975.

Microfilm
Pentakta
Camera
A496

Leipzig Spring Fair: 25pf, Sket cement plant.

**1975, Mar. 4　　Photo.　　Perf. 14**

| | | | |
|---|---|---|---|
| 1623 | A496 | 10pf ultra & multi | .25 .20 |
| 1624 | A496 | 25pf orange & multi | .25 .25 |

A497

Portraits: 5pf, Hans Otto (1900-33), actor. 10pf, Thomas Mann (1875-1955), writer. 20pf, Albert Schweitzer (1875-1965), medical missionary. 25pf, Michelangelo (1475-1564), painter and sculptor. 35pf, André Marie Ampère (1775-1836), scientist.

**1975, Mar. 18　Litho.　Perf. 13½x13**

| | | | |
|---|---|---|---|
| 1625 | A497 | 5pf dk blue | .20 .20 |
| 1626 | A497 | 10pf dk car rose | .20 .20 |
| 1627 | A497 | 20pf dk green | .20 .20 |
| 1628 | A497 | 25pf sepia | .20 .20 |
| 1629 | A497 | 35pf vio blue | .75 .65 |
| | | Nos. 1625-1629 (5) | 1.55 1.45 |

Famous men, birth anniversaries.

A498

German Zoological Gardens: 5pf, Blue and yellow macaws, Magdeburg Zoo. 10pf, Orangutan family, Dresden. 15pf, Siberian chamois, Halle. 20pf, Rhinoceros, Berlin. 25pf, Dwarf hippopotamus, Erfurt. 30pf, Baltic seal and pup, Rostock. 35pf, Siberian tiger, Leipzig. 50pf, Boehm's zebra, Cottbus. 20pf, 25pf, 30pf, 35pf are horiz.

**1975, Mar. 25　Perf. 13½x13, 13x13½**

| | | | |
|---|---|---|---|
| 1630 | A498 | 5pf multicolored | .20 .20 |
| 1631 | A498 | 10pf multicolored | .20 .20 |
| 1632 | A498 | 15pf multicolored | .20 .20 |
| 1633 | A498 | 20pf multicolored | .20 .20 |
| 1634 | A498 | 25pf multicolored | .20 .20 |
| 1635 | A498 | 30pf multicolored | .20 .20 |
| 1636 | A498 | 35pf multicolored | .20 .20 |
| 1637 | A498 | 50pf multicolored | 1.40 1.40 |
| | | Nos. 1630-1637 (8) | 2.80 2.80 |

Soldiers, Industry and
Agriculture — A499

**1975, May 6　Photo.　Perf. 13½x14**

| | | | |
|---|---|---|---|
| 1638 | A499 | 20pf multicolored | 1.00 .30 |

20th anniv. of the signing of the Warsaw Treaty (Bulgaria, Czechoslovakia, DDR, Hungary, Poland, Romania, USSR).

Soviet War
Memorial,
Berlin-Treptow
A500

Designs (Arms of German Democratic Rep. and): 20pf, Buchenwald Memorial (detail). 25pf, Woman reconstruction worker. 35pf, Skyscraper and statue at Orenburg (economic integration). 50pf, Soldier raising Red Flag on Reichstag Building, Berlin.

**1975, May 6**  **Perf. 14x13½**
**1639** A500 10pf red & multi  .20  .20
**1640** A500 20pf red & multi  .20  .20
**1641** A500 25pf red & multi  .20  .20
**1642** A500 35pf red & multi  .60  .60
Nos. 1639-1642 (4)  1.20 1.20

**Souvenir Sheet**
*Imperf*
**1643** A500 50pf red & multi  .70  .70

30th anniversary of liberation from fascism.

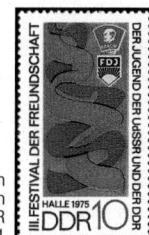

Ribbons, Youth Organization Emblems of DDR and USSR — A501

**1975, May 13**  **Perf. 14**
**1644** A501 10pf multicolored  .35  .20

Third Friendship Festival of Russian and German Youths, Halle, 1975.

**Lighthouse Type of 1974**
Lighthouses, Maps and Nautical Charts: 5pf, Timmendorf, 1872. 10pf, Gellen, 1905. 20pf, Sassnitz, 1904. 25pf, Dornbush, 1888. 35pf, Peenemünde, 1954.

**1975, May 13**  **Litho.**  **Perf. 14**
**1645** A478  5pf multicolored  .20  .20
**1646** A478 10pf multicolored  .20  .20
**1647** A478 20pf multicolored  .20  .20
**1648** A478 25pf multicolored  .20  .20
**1649** A478 35pf multicolored  .75  .75
Nos. 1645-1649 (5)  1.55 1.55

Hydrographic Service of the DDR.

Wilhelm Liebknecht, August Bebel — A502

20pf, Tivoli House & front page of Protocol of Gotha. 25pf, Karl Marx & Friedrich Engels.

**1975, May 21**  **Photo.**
**1650** A502 10pf buff, brn & red  .20  .20
**1651** A502 20pf salmon, brn & red  .20  .20
**1652** A502 25pf buff, brn & red  .20  .20
*a.* Strip of 3, #1650-1652  1.00 1.00

Centenary of the Congress of Gotha, the beginning of German Socialist Workers' Party.

Construction Workers, Union Emblem — A503

**1975, June 10**  **Photo.**  **Perf. 14**
**1653** A503 20pf red & multi  .30  .20

Free German Association of Trade Unions (FDGB), 30th anniversary.

"Socialist Scientific Cooperation" Mosaic by Walter Womacka A504

**1975, June 10**  **Litho.**  **Perf. 13**
**1654** A504 20pf multicolored  .30  .20

Eisenhüttenstadt, first socialist city of DDR, 25th anniversary.

Automatic Clock by Paulus Schuster, 1585 — A505

Clocks, Dresden Museums: 10pf, Astronomical table clock, Augsburg, c. 1560. 15pf, Automatic clock, Hans Schlottheim, c. 1600. 20pf, Table clock, Johann Heinrich Köhler, c. 1720. 25pf, Table clock, Köhler, c. 1700. 35pf, Astronomical clock, Johannes Klein, 1738.

**1975, June 24**  **Photo.**  **Perf. 14**
**1655** A505  5pf multicolored  .20  .20
**1656** A505 10pf ultra & multi  .20  .20
**1657** A505 15pf red & multi  1.10 1.10
**1658** A505 20pf olive & multi  .20  .20
**1659** A505 25pf multicolored  .20  .20
**1660** A505 35pf ocher & multi  .20  .20
Nos. 1655-1660 (6)  2.10 2.10

Dictionary, Compiled by Jacob and Wilhelm Grimm — A506

20pf, Karl-Schwarzschild Observatory, Tautenburg near Jena. 25pf, Electron microscope & chemical plant (scientific & practical cooperation). 35pf, Intercosmos 10 satellite.

**1975, July 2**  **Litho.**  **Perf. 13½x13**
**1661** A506 10pf plum, ol & blk  .20  .20
**1662** A506 20pf vio bl & blk  .20  .20
**1663** A506 25pf green, yel & blk  .20  .20
**1664** A506 35pf blue & multi  .75  .75
Nos. 1661-1664 (4)  1.35 1.35

German Academy of Sciences, 275th anniv.

Torch Bearer — A507

**1975, July 15**  **Perf. 13½x13**
**1665** A507 10pf shown  .20  .20
**1666** A507 20pf Hurdling  .20  .20
**1667** A507 25pf Diving  .20  .20
**1668** A507 35pf Gymnast on bar  .75  .75
Nos. 1665-1668 (4)  1.35 1.35

5th Children and Youths Spartakiad.

Map of Europe A508

**1975, July 30**  **Photo.**  **Perf. 13**
**1669** A508 20pf multicolored  .35  .25

European Security and Cooperation Conference, Helsinki, July 30-Aug. 1.

China Aster — A509

Medimorph Anesthesia Unit — A510

**1975, Aug. 19**  **Photo.**  **Perf. 13½x14**
**1670** A509  5pf shown  .20  .20
**1671** A509 10pf Geranium  .20  .20
**1672** A509 20pf Transvaal daisies  .20  .20
**1673** A509 25pf Carnation  .20  .20
**1674** A509 35pf Chrysanthemum  .25  .20
**1675** A509 70pf Pansies  2.10 1.90
Nos. 1670-1675 (6)  3.15 2.90

**1975, Aug. 28**  **Perf. 14**
Leipzig Fall Fair: 25pf, Motorcycle, type MZ TS 250, horiz.
**1676** A510 10pf multicolored  .20  .20
**1677** A510 25pf yellow & multi  .35  .25

Children and Child Crossing Guard A511

Designs: 15pf, Traffic policewoman. 20pf, Policeman helping, motorist. 25pf, Motor vehicle inspection. 35pf, Volunteer instructor.

**1975, Sept. 9**  **Litho.**  **Perf. 13x12½**
**1678** A511 10pf multicolored  .20  .20
**1679** A511 15pf green & multi  1.20  .75
**1680** A511 20pf brown & multi  .20  .20
**1681** A511 25pf violet & multi  .20  .20
**1682** A511 35pf multicolored  .20  .20
Nos. 1678-1682 (5)  2.00 1.55

Traffic police serving and instructing the public.

Soyuz Take-off — A512

Designs: 20pf, Soyuz and Apollo in space. 70pf, Spacecraft after link-up, horiz., 79x28mm.

**Perf. 14x13½, 13½x14**
**1975, Sept. 15**  **Photo.**
**1683** A512 10pf multicolored  .20  .20
**1684** A512 20pf multicolored  .20  .20
**1685** A512 70pf multicolored  1.50 1.50
Nos. 1683-1685 (3)  1.90 1.90

Apollo Soyuz space test project (Russo-American space cooperation), launching July 15; link-up, July 17.

Weimar, 1630, after Merian — A513

Designs: 20pf, Buchenwald Liberation Monument, vert. 35pf, Composite view of old and new buildings in Weimar.

**1975, Sept. 23**  **Litho.**  **Perf. 13½x13**
**1686** A513 10pf green, gray & blk  .20  .20
**1687** A513 20pf red & multi  .20  .20
**1688** A513 35pf ultra & multi  .45  .45
Nos. 1686-1688 (3)  .85  .85

Millennium of Weimar.

Monument, Vienna — A514

**1975, Oct. 14**  **Photo.**  **Perf. 14x13½**
**1689** A514 35pf red & multi  .35  .20

Memorial for the victims of the struggle for a free Austria, 1934-1945.

Louis Braille and Dots — A515

Designs: 35pf, Hands reading Braille. 50pf, Eyeball and protective glasses.

**1975, Oct. 14**
**1690** A515 20pf gray & multi  .20  .20
**1691** A515 35pf multicolored  .20  .20
**1692** A515 50pf multicolored  1.20 1.20
Nos. 1690-1692 (3)  1.60 1.60

World Braille Year 1975. Sesquicentennial of the invention of Braille system of writing for the blind, by Louis Braille (1809-1852).

Post Office Bärenfels A516

**1975, Oct. 21**  **Photo.**  **Perf. 14**
**1693** A516 20pf multicolored  .20  .20

Philatelists' Day 1975. See No. B177.

Emperor Ordering Clothes — A517

Designs: Scenes from "The Emperor's New Clothes," by Hans Christian Andersen and Andersen portrait.

**1975, Nov. 18    Litho.    Perf. 14x13**
1694 A517 20pf ocher & multi        .35    .35
1695 A517 35pf ocher & multi        .60    .60
1696 A517 50pf ocher & multi        .35    .35
a.      Sheet of 3, #1694-1696      1.90   1.90

Tobogganing and Olympic Rings — A518

Olympic Rings and: 20pf, Speed-skating Rink, Berlin. 35pf, Figure-skating Hall, Karl-Marx Stadt. 70pf, Mass skiing at Schmiedefeld. 1m, Innsbruck & surrounding mountains.

**1975, Dec. 2    Photo.    Perf. 14**
1697 A518 5pf multicolored          .20    .20
1698 A518 20pf olive & multi        .20    .20
1699 A518 35pf multicolored         .25    .20
1700 A518 70pf multicolored        1.60   1.50
    Nos. 1697-1700,B178-B179 (6)    2.70   2.50

**Souvenir Sheet**
1701 A518 1m ultra & multi          1.90   1.50
12th Winter Olympic Games, Innsbruck, Austria, Feb. 4-15, 1976.
No. 1701 contains one 32x27mm stamp.

Pres. Wilhelm Pieck (1876-1960) A519

**1975, Dec. 30    Litho.    Perf. 13½x13**
1702 A519 10pf lt ultra & blk       .25    .20

Ernst Thälmann (1886-1944) A520

Labor Leaders: No. 1704, Georg Schumann (1886-1945). No. 1705, Wilhelm Koenen (1886-1963). No. 1706, John Schehr (1896-1934).

**1976, Jan. 13    Perf. 13½x13**
1703 A520 10pf rose & blk           .20    .20
1704 A520 10pf emerald & blk        .20    .20
1705 A520 10pf ocher & blk          .20    .20
1706 A520 10pf violet & blk         .20    .20
    Nos. 1703-1706 (4)              .80    .80

See Nos. 1852-1854.

Silbermann Organ, Rötha — A521

Silbermann Organs: 20pf, Freiberg. 35pf, Fraureuth. 50pf, Dresden.

**1976, Jan. 27    Photo.    Perf. 14**
1707 A521 10pf green & multi        .20    .20
1708 A521 20pf red & multi          .20    .20
1709 A521 35pf multicolored         .20    .20
1710 A521 50pf brown & multi       1.10    .90
    Nos. 1707-1710 (4)             1.70   1.50
Organs built by Gottfried Silbermann (1683-1753).

**Souvenir Sheet**

Richard Sorge — A522

**1976, Feb. 3    Litho.    Imperf.**
1711 A522 1m multicolored          1.60   1.60
Dr. Richard Sorge (1895-1944), Soviet intelligence agent. No. 1711 contains one stamp with simulated perforations.

Military Flag, Sailor, Soldier, Aviator — A523

20pf, Military flag, ships, tanks, missile & planes.

**1976, Feb. 24    Litho.    Perf. 13½x14**
1712 A523 10pf multicolored         .20    .20
1713 A523 20pf multicolored         .30    .25

National People's Army, 20th anniversary.

Telephone A524        Apartment House, Leipzig A525

**1976, Mar. 2    Perf. 13**
1714 A524 20pf light blue           .30    .20
Centenary of first telephone call by Alexander Graham Bell, March 10, 1876.

**1976, Mar. 9    Photo.    Perf. 14**
Design: 25pf, Ocean super trawler, horiz.
1715 A525 10pf green & multi        .20    .20
1716 A525 25pf vio blue, blk & grn  .35    .25

Leipzig Spring Fair.

Palace of the Republic — A526

**1976, Apr. 22    Photo.    Perf. 14**
1717 A526 10pf vio blue & multi     .70    .20
Inauguration of Palace of the Republic, Berlin. See No. 1721.

Post Office Radar Station — A527

**1976, Apr. 27    Photo.    Perf. 13½x14**
1718 A527 20pf multicolored         .30    .20

Intersputnik 1976.

Marx, Engels, Lenin and Party Flag — A528

20pf, New factories & apartment houses, party flag, horiz. 1m, Palace of the Republic.

**1976, May 11    Perf. 14x13½, 13½x14**
1719 A528 10pf dp mag, gold & red   .25    .20
1720 A528 20pf multicolored         .25    .20

**Souvenir Sheet**
**Perf. 14**
1721 A526 1m multicolored          1.25   1.25
9th Congress of Unity Party (SED).

Peace Bicycle Race and Olympic Rings — A529

Designs: 20pf, Town and sport halls, Suhl. 25pf, Regatta course, Brandenburg. 70pf, 1500-meter race. 1m, Central Stadium, Leipzig.

**1976, May 18    Photo.    Perf. 13½x14**
1722 A529 5pf green & multi         .20    .20
1723 A529 20pf blue & multi         .20    .20
1724 A529 25pf multicolored         .20    .20
1725 A529 70pf ultra & multi       1.90   1.75
    Nos. 1722-1725,B180-B181 (6)    2.95   2.75

**Souvenir Sheet**
**Perf. 14**
1726 A529 1m multicolored          1.40   1.40
21st Olympic Games, Montreal, Canada, July 17-Aug. 1. No. 1726 contains one stamp (32x27mm).

Ribbons and Emblem A530

Design: 20pf, Young man and woman, industrial installations.

**1976, May 25    Perf. 14**
1727 A530 10pf blue & multi         .20    .20
1728 A530 20pf multicolored         .25    .20
10th Parliamentary Meeting of the Free German Youth Organization.

Himantoglossum Hircinum — A531

Designs: European orchids.

**1976, June 15    Litho.    Perf. 12½x13**
1729 A531 10pf shown                .20    .20
1730 A531 20pf Dactylorhiza incarnata   .20    .20
1731 A531 25pf Anacamptis pyramidalis    .20    .20
1732 A531 35pf Dactylorhiza sambucina    .25    .20
1733 A531 40pf Orchis coriophora         .25    .20
1734 A531 50pf Cypripedium calceolus    2.10   1.75
    Nos. 1729-1734 (6)             3.20   2.75

Dancer at Rest, by Walter Arnold — A532

Small Sculptures: 10pf, Shetland Pony, by Heinrich Drake, horiz. 25pf, "At the Beach," by Ludwig Engelhardt. 35pf, Hermann Duncker, by Walter Howard. 50pf, "The Conversation," by Gustav Weidanz.

**1976, June 22    Photo.    Perf. 14**
1735 A532 10pf blk & bl grn         .20    .20
1736 A532 20pf ocher & blk          .20    .20
1737 A532 25pf ocher & blk          .20    .20
1738 A532 35pf yel grn & blk        .20    .20
1739 A532 50pf brick red & blk     1.50   1.50
    Nos. 1735-1739 (5)             2.30   2.30

Marx, Engels, Lenin, Red Flags, Berlin Buildings A533

**1976, June 29    Photo.    Perf. 14**
1740 A533 20pf blue, red & dk red   .35    .20
European Communist Workers' Congress, Berlin.

Coronation Coach, 1790 — A534

Historic Coaches: 20pf, Open carriage, Russia, 1800. 25pf, Court landau, Saxony, 1840. 35pf, State carriage, Saxony, 1860. 40pf, Mail coach, 1850. 50pf, Town carriage, Saxony, 1889.

**1976, July 27**
1741 A534 10pf multicolored         .20    .20
1742 A534 20pf multicolored         .20    .20
1743 A534 25pf multicolored         .20    .20
1744 A534 35pf multicolored         .20    .20

| | | | | |
|---|---|---|---|---|
| 1745 | A534 | 40pf multicolored | .25 | .20 |
| 1746 | A534 | 50pf multicolored | 2.25 | 2.00 |
| | | *Nos. 1741-1746 (6)* | 3.30 | 3.00 |

View of Gera
A535

Design: 10pf+5pf, View of Gera, c. 1652.

**1976, Aug. 5    Litho.    *Perf. 13***

| | | | | |
|---|---|---|---|---|
| 1747 | A535 | 10pf + 5pf multi | .20 | .20 |
| 1748 | A535 | 20pf multicolored | .20 | .20 |
| a. | | Pair, #1747-1748 + label | .90 | .75 |

4th German Youth Philatelic Exhib., Gera.

Boxer — A536

Dogs: 10pf, Airedale terrier. 20pf, German shepherd. 25pf, Collie. 35pf, Giant schnauzer. 70pf, Great Dane.

**1976, Aug. 17    *Perf. 14***

| | | | | |
|---|---|---|---|---|
| 1749 | A536 | 5pf multicolored | .20 | .20 |
| 1750 | A536 | 10pf multicolored | .20 | .20 |
| 1751 | A536 | 20pf multicolored | .20 | .20 |
| 1752 | A536 | 25pf multicolored | .20 | .20 |
| 1753 | A536 | 35pf multicolored | .20 | .20 |
| 1754 | A536 | 70pf multicolored | 2.00 | 2.10 |
| | | *Nos. 1749-1754 (6)* | 3.00 | 3.10 |

Oil Distillery
A537

Design: 25pf, German Library, Leipzig.

**1976, Sept. 1    *Perf. 13x12½***

| | | | | |
|---|---|---|---|---|
| 1755 | A537 | 10pf multicolored | .20 | .20 |
| 1756 | A537 | 25pf multicolored | .30 | .20 |

Leipzig Fall Fair.

Templin Lake Bridge — A538

Designs: 15pf, Overpass, Berlin-Adlergestell. 20pf, Elbe River Bridge, Rosslau. 25pf, Göltzschtal Viaduct. 35pf, Elbe River Bridge, Magdeburg. 50pf, Grosser Dreesch Overpass, Schwerin.

**1976, Sept. 21    Photo.    *Perf. 14***

| | | | | |
|---|---|---|---|---|
| 1757 | A538 | 10pf multicolored | .20 | .20 |
| 1758 | A538 | 15pf multicolored | .20 | .20 |
| 1759 | A538 | 20pf multicolored | .20 | .20 |
| 1760 | A538 | 25pf multicolored | .20 | .20 |
| 1761 | A538 | 35pf multicolored | .20 | .20 |
| 1762 | A538 | 50pf multicolored | 1.50 | 1.60 |
| | | *Nos. 1757-1762 (6)* | 2.50 | 2.60 |

Memorial Monument (detail), Budapest — A539

**1976, Oct. 5    Photo.    *Perf. 14***

| | | | | |
|---|---|---|---|---|
| 1763 | A539 | 35pf tan & multi | .35 | .30 |

Memorial to World War II victims.

Brass Jug, c. 1500 — A540

Artistic Handicraft Works: 20pf, Faience vase with lid, c. 1710. 25pf, Porcelain centerpiece (woman carrying bowl), c. 1768. 35pf, Porter, gilded silver, c. 1700. 70pf, Art Nouveau glass vase, c. 1900.

**1976, Oct. 19**

| | | | | |
|---|---|---|---|---|
| 1764 | A540 | 10pf dk car & multi | .20 | .20 |
| 1765 | A540 | 20pf ultra & multi | .20 | .20 |
| 1766 | A540 | 25pf green & multi | .20 | .20 |
| 1767 | A540 | 35pf vio blue & multi | .20 | .20 |
| 1768 | A540 | 70pf red brn & multi | 1.60 | 1.60 |
| | | *Nos. 1764-1768 (5)* | 2.40 | 2.40 |

Guppy A541

Designs: Various guppies.

**1976, Nov. 9    Litho.    *Perf. 13½x13***

| | | | | |
|---|---|---|---|---|
| 1769 | A541 | 10pf multicolored | .20 | .20 |
| 1770 | A541 | 15pf multicolored | .20 | .20 |
| 1771 | A541 | 20pf multicolored | .20 | .20 |
| 1772 | A541 | 25pf multicolored | .20 | .20 |
| 1773 | A541 | 35pf multicolored | .20 | .20 |
| 1774 | A541 | 70pf multicolored | 1.80 | 1.80 |
| | | *Nos. 1769-1774 (6)* | 2.80 | 2.80 |

Vessels, c. 3000 B.C. — A542

20pf, Cult cart, c. 1300 B.C. 25pf, Roman gold coin, 270-273 A.D. 35pf, Gold pendant, 950 A.D. 70pf, Glass cup, 3rd cent. A.D.

**1976, Nov. 23    Photo.    *Perf. 13***

| | | | | |
|---|---|---|---|---|
| 1775 | A542 | 10pf multicolored | .20 | .20 |
| 1776 | A542 | 20pf multicolored | .20 | .20 |
| 1777 | A542 | 25pf multicolored | .20 | .20 |
| 1778 | A542 | 35pf multicolored | .20 | .20 |
| 1779 | A542 | 70pf multicolored | 1.60 | 1.60 |
| | | *Nos. 1775-1779 (5)* | 2.40 | 2.40 |

Archaeological finds in DDR.

"Air," by Rosalba Carriera — A543

Paintings, Dresden Museum: 15pf, Virgin and Child, by Murillo. 20pf, Woman Viola da Gamba Player, by Bernardo Strozzi. 25pf, Ariadne Forsaken, by Angelica Kauffmann. 35pf, Old Man with Black Cap, by Bartolomeo Nazzari. 70pf, Officer Reading a Letter, by Gerard Terborch.

**1976, Dec. 14    Photo.    *Perf. 13½x14***

| | | | | |
|---|---|---|---|---|
| 1780 | A543 | 10pf multicolored | .20 | .20 |
| 1781 | A543 | 15pf multicolored | .20 | .20 |
| 1782 | A543 | 20pf multicolored | .20 | .20 |
| 1783 | A543 | 25pf multicolored | .20 | .20 |

| | | | | |
|---|---|---|---|---|
| 1784 | A543 | 35pf multicolored | .20 | .20 |
| 1785 | A543 | 70pf multicolored | 1.90 | 1.75 |
| | | *Nos. 1780-1785 (6)* | 2.90 | 2.75 |

Rumpelstiltskin and King — A544

Scenes from fairy tale "Rumpel-stiltskin."

**1976, Dec. 14    Litho.    *Perf. 13***

| | | | | |
|---|---|---|---|---|
| 1786 | A544 | 5pf multicolored | .20 | .20 |
| 1787 | A544 | 10pf multicolored | .55 | .55 |
| 1788 | A544 | 15pf multicolored | .20 | .20 |
| 1789 | A544 | 20pf multicolored | .20 | .20 |
| 1790 | A544 | 25pf multicolored | .55 | .55 |
| 1791 | A544 | 30pf multicolored | .20 | .20 |
| a. | | Sheet of 6, #1786-1791 | 2.40 | 2.40 |

Arnold Zweig and Quotation A545

Designs: 20pf, Otto von Guericke and Magdeburg hemispheres. 35pf, Albrecht D. Thaer, wheat, plow and sheep. 40pf, Gustav Hertz and diagram of separation of isotopes.

**1977, Feb. 8    Litho.    *Perf. 13x12½***

| | | | | |
|---|---|---|---|---|
| 1792 | A545 | 10pf rose & blk | .20 | .20 |
| 1793 | A545 | 20pf gray & blk | .20 | .20 |
| 1794 | A545 | 35pf lt green & blk | .20 | .20 |
| 1795 | A545 | 40pf blue & blk | .75 | .75 |
| | | *Nos. 1792-1795 (4)* | 1.35 | 1.35 |

Zweig (1887-1968), novelist; von Guericke (1602-86), physicist; Thaer (1752-1828), agronomist & physician; Hertz (1887-1975), physicist.

Spring near Plaue — A546

Natural Monuments: 20pf, Small Organ, Johnsdorf. 25pf, Ivenacker Oaks, Reuterstadt. 35pf, Stone Rose, Saalburg. 50pf, Rauenscher Stein (boulder), Furstenwalde.

**1977, Feb. 24    Litho.    *Perf. 12½x13***

| | | | | |
|---|---|---|---|---|
| 1796 | A546 | 10pf multicolored | .20 | .20 |
| 1797 | A546 | 20pf multicolored | .20 | .20 |
| 1798 | A546 | 25pf multicolored | .20 | .20 |
| 1799 | A546 | 35pf multicolored | .20 | .20 |
| 1800 | A546 | 50pf multicolored | 1.20 | 1.20 |
| | | *Nos. 1796-1800 (5)* | 2.00 | 2.00 |

Fair Building, Book Fair A547

Leipzig Spring Fair: 25pf, Wide aluminum roll casting machine, Nachterstedt factory.

**1977, Mar. 8    Photo.    *Perf. 14***

| | | | | |
|---|---|---|---|---|
| 1801 | A547 | 10pf multicolored | .20 | .20 |
| 1802 | A547 | 25pf multicolored | .25 | .20 |

Costume Senftenberg A548

Start after Wheel Change A549

Sorbian Costumes from: 20pf, Bautzen. 25pf, Klitten. 35pf, Nochten. 70pf, Muskau.

**1977, Mar. 22**

| | | | | |
|---|---|---|---|---|
| 1803 | A548 | 10pf multicolored | .20 | .20 |
| 1804 | A548 | 20pf multicolored | .20 | .20 |
| 1805 | A548 | 25pf multicolored | .20 | .20 |
| 1806 | A548 | 35pf multicolored | .20 | .20 |
| 1807 | A548 | 70pf multicolored | 2.00 | 1.75 |
| | | *Nos. 1803-1807 (5)* | 2.80 | 2.55 |

**1977, Apr. 19    Photo.    *Perf. 14***

Designs: 20pf, Sprint. 35pf, At finish line.

| | | | | |
|---|---|---|---|---|
| 1808 | A549 | 10pf multicolored | .25 | .25 |
| 1809 | A549 | 20pf multicolored | .25 | .25 |
| 1810 | A549 | 35pf multicolored | .25 | .25 |
| a. | | Strip of 3, #1808-1810 | 1.20 | 1.20 |

30th International Peace Bicycling Race.

Carl Friedrich Gauss A550

**1977, Apr. 19    Litho.    *Perf. 13x12½***

| | | | | |
|---|---|---|---|---|
| 1811 | A550 | 20pf lt ultra & blk | .55 | .25 |

Carl Friedrich Gauss (1777-1855), mathematician, 200th birth anniversary.

Flags and Handshake A551

**1977, May 3    Photo.    *Perf. 13***

| | | | | |
|---|---|---|---|---|
| 1812 | A551 | 20pf vio bl & multi | .30 | .20 |

9th German Trade Union Congress, Berlin.

VKM Channel Converter, Filter and ITU Emblem — A552

**1977, May 17    Litho.    *Perf. 14***

| | | | | |
|---|---|---|---|---|
| 1813 | A552 | 20pf multicolored | .30 | .20 |

International Telecommunications Day.

Pistol Shooting A553

Designs: 20pf, Deep-sea diver. 35pf, Radio controlled model boat.

**1977, May 17              Photo.**
1814 A553 10pf lt green & multi        .20   .20
1815 A553 20pf lt blue & multi         .20   .20
1816 A553 35pf salmon & multi          .70   .70
    Nos. 1814-1816 (3)                 1.10  1.10
Organization for Physical and Technical Training.

Accordion, c. 1900 — A554

Designs: 20pf, Treble viola da gamba, 1747. 25pf, Oboe, 1785, Clarinet, 1830 and flute, 1817. 35pf, Concert zither, 1891. 70pf, Trumpet, 1860.

**1977, June 14**
1817 A554 10pf multicolored           .20   .20
1818 A554 20pf multicolored           .20   .20
1819 A554 25pf multicolored           .20   .20
1820 A554 35pf multicolored           .20   .20
1821 A554 70pf multicolored          2.00  2.00
    Nos. 1817-1821 (5)                2.80  2.80
Vogtland musical instruments from Markneukirchen Museum.

Mercury and Argus, by Rubens — A555

Rubens Paintings in Dresden Gallery: 10pf, Bath of Bathsheba, vert. 20pf, The Drunk Hercules, vert. 25pf, Diana Returning from the Hunt. 35pf, Old Woman with Brazier, vert. 50pf, Leda and the Swan.

**1977, June 28         Photo.    Perf. 14**
1822 A555 10pf multicolored           .20   .20
1823 A555 15pf multicolored           .20   .20
1824 A555 20pf multicolored           .20   .20
1825 A555 25pf multicolored           .20   .20
1826 A555 35pf multicolored           .25   .20
1827 A555 50pf multicolored          3.00  2.25
    Nos. 1822-1827 (6)                4.05  3.25
Peter Paul Rubens (1577-1640), Flemish painter, 400th birth anniversary.

Souvenir Sheet

Wreath, Flags of USSR and DDR — A556

**1977, June 28**
1828 A556 50pf multicolored          1.00  1.00
Soc. for German-Soviet Friendship, 30th anniv.

Tractor with Plow — A557

Designs: 20pf, Fertilizer-spreader. 25pf, Potato digger and loader. 35pf, High-pressure harvester. 50pf, Rotating milking machine.

**1977, July 12     Litho.     Perf. 13x12½**
1829 A557 10pf multicolored           .20   .20
1830 A557 20pf multicolored           .20   .20
1831 A557 25pf multicolored           .20   .20
1832 A557 35pf multicolored           .20   .20
1833 A557 50pf multicolored          1.60  1.60
    Nos. 1829-1833 (5)                2.40  2.40
Motorized modern agriculture.

High Jump A558

Designs: 20pf, Hurdles, girls. 35pf, Dancing. 40pf, Torch bearer and flags.

**1977, July 19**
1834 A558  5pf red & multi            .20   .20
1835 A558 20pf lt green & multi       .20   .20
1836 A558 35pf green & multi          .20   .20
1837 A558 40pf blue & multi          1.50  1.50
    Nos. 1834-1837,B183-B184 (6)     6.10  4.10
6th Gymnastics and Sports Festival and 6th Children's and Youth Spartacist Games.

"Bread for all" by Wolfram Schubert A559    Konsument Department Store, Leipzig A560

Design: 25pf, "When Communists Dream," by Walter Womacka (detail) and Sozphilex emblem.

**1977, Aug. 16      Photo.      Perf. 14**
1838 A559 10pf multicolored          .25   .20
  a.   Souvenir sheet of 4          1.00   .90
1839 A559 25pf multicolored          .45   .35
  a.   Souvenir sheet of 4          2.00  2.00
SOZPHILEX '77 Philatelic Exhibition, Berlin, Aug. 19-28. See No. B185.

**1977, Aug. 30**
Design: 25pf, Glasses and wooden plate.
1840 A560 10pf blue & multi          .20   .20
1841 A560 25pf multicolored          .30   .25
Leipzig Fall Fair.

Souvenir Sheet

Dzerzhinski and Quotation from Mayakovsky — A561

**1977, Sept. 6     Litho.     Perf. 12½x13**
1842 A561   Sheet of 2              1.40  1.40
  a.   20pf multicolored            .30   .30
  b.   35pf multicolored            .45   .45
Feliks E. Dzerzhinski (1877-1926), organizer and head of Russian Secret Police (Cheka), birth centenary.

Muldenthal Locomotive, 1861 — A562

Designs: 10pf, Trolley car, Dresden, 1896. 20pf, First successful German plane, 1909. 25pf, 3-wheel car "Phäno-mobile," 1924. 35pf, Passenger steamship on the Elbe, 1837.

**1977, Sept. 13     Photo.     Perf. 14**
1843 A562  5pf green & multi         .25   .20
1844 A562 10pf green & multi         .25   .20
1845 A562 20pf green & multi         .25   .20
1846 A562 25pf green & multi         .25   .20
1847 A562 35pf green & multi        2.25  1.75
    Nos. 1843-1847 (5)              3.25  2.55
Transportation Museum, Dresden.

Cruiser "Aurora" A563

Designs: 25pf, Storming of the Winter Palace. 1m, Lenin, vert.

**1977, Sept. 20**
1848 A563 10pf multicolored          .25   .20
1849 A563 25pf multicolored          .45   .35

**Souvenir Sheet**
**Perf. 12½x13**
1850 A563   1m carmine & blk        2.00  2.00
60th anniversary of the Russian Revolution.

Mother Russia and Obelisk — A564

**1977, Sept. 20     Litho.     Perf. 14**
1851 A564 35pf multicolored          .35   .20
Soviet soldiers' memorial, Berlin-Schönholz.

Labor Leaders Type of 1976
Portraits: No. 1852, Ernst Meyer (1887-1930). No. 1853, August Fröhlich (1877-1966). No. 1854, Gerhart Eisler (1897-1968).

**1977, Oct. 18     Litho.     Perf. 14**
1852 A520 10pf olive & brown         .20   .20
1853 A520 10pf rose & brown          .20   .20
1854 A520 10pf lt blue & blk brn     .20   .20
    Nos. 1852-1854 (3)               .60   .60

Souvenir Sheet

Heinrich von Kleist, by Peter Friedl, 1801 — A565

**1977, Oct. 18**
1855 A565   1m multicolored         2.40  2.00
Heinrich von Kleist (1777-1811), poet and playwright, birth bicentenary.

Rocket A566

Design: 20pf, as 10pf, design reversed.

**1977, Nov. 8      Photo.     Perf. 14**
1856 A566 10pf red, blk & sil        .20   .20
1857 A566 20pf ultra, blk & gold     .20   .20
  a.   Pair, #1856-1857 + label      .85   .85
20th Central Young Craftsmen's Exhibition (Masters of Tomorrow).

A567          A568

Hunting in East Germany: 10pf, Mouflons. 15pf, Red deer. 20pf, Retriever with pheasant, hunter. 25pf, Red fox, wild duck. 35pf, Tractor driver saving fawn. 70pf, Wild boars.

**1977, Nov. 15**
1858 A567 10pf multicolored          .20   .20
1859 A567 15pf multicolored         1.90  1.90
1860 A567 20pf multicolored          .20   .20
1861 A567 25pf multicolored          .25   .20
1862 A567 35pf multicolored          .25   .20
1863 A567 70pf multicolored          .30   .20
    Nos. 1858-1863 (6)              3.10  2.90

**1977, Nov. 22     Litho.     Perf. 14**
Firemen's Activities: 10pf, Firemen racing with ladders. 20pf, Children Visiting Firehouse. 25pf, Fire engines fighting forest and brush fires. 35pf, Artificial respiration. 50pf, Fireboat alongside freighter.

1864 A568 10pf multi, horiz.         .20   .20
1865 A568 20pf multi                 .20   .20
1866 A568 25pf multi, horiz.         .20   .20
1867 A568 35pf multi                 .20   .20
1868 A568 50pf multi, horiz.        1.80  1.80
    Nos. 1864-1868 (5)              2.60  2.60

Knight and King — A569

Designs: Various scenes from fairytale: "Six Men Around the World."

**1977, Nov. 22              Perf. 13x13½**
1869 A569  5pf black & multi         .20   .20
1870 A569 10pf black & multi         .70   .70
1871 A569 20pf black & multi         .20   .20
1872 A569 25pf black & multi         .20   .20
1873 A569 35pf black & multi         .70   .70
1874 A569 60pf black & multi         .20   .20
  a.   Sheet of 6, #1869-1874       3.50  3.25

Hips and Dog Rose A570

Medicinal Plants: 15pf, Birch. 20pf, Chamomile. 25pf, Coltsfoot. 35pf, Linden. 50pf, Elder.

**1978, Jan. 10     Photo.     Perf. 14**
1875 A570 10pf multicolored          .20   .20
1876 A570 15pf multicolored          .20   .20
1877 A570 20pf multicolored          .20   .20
1878 A570 25pf multicolored          .20   .20
1879 A570 35pf multicolored          .25   .20
1880 A570 50pf multicolored         2.00  2.00
    Nos. 1875-1880 (6)              3.05  3.00

Amilcar Cabral — A571

**1978, Jan. 17    Litho.    Perf. 14**
1881 A571 20pf multicolored          .35   .30
Amilcar Cabral (1924-1973), freedom movement leader from Guinea-Bissau.

Town Hall, Suhl-Heinrichs A572

Half-timbered Buildings, 17th-18th Centuries: 20pf, Farmhouse, Niederoderwitz. 25pf, Farmhouse, Strassen. 35pf, Townhouse, Quedlinburg. 40pf, Townhouse, Eisenach.

**1978, Jan. 24    Photo.    Perf. 14**
1882 A572 10pf multicolored          .20   .20
1883 A572 20pf multicolored          .20   .20
1884 A572 25pf multicolored          .20   .20
1885 A572 30pf multicolored          .20   .20
1886 A572 40pf multicolored         1.80  1.80
    Nos. 1882-1886 (5)              2.60  2.60

Mail Truck, 1921 A573

Past and Present Mail Transport: 20pf, Mail truck, 1978. 25pf, Railroad mail car, 1896. 35pf, Railroad mail car, 1978.

**1978, Feb. 9    Litho.    Perf. 13x12½**
1887 A573 10pf brown & multi         .20   .20
1888 A573 20pf brown & multi         .35   .35
1889 A573 25pf brown & multi         .45   .45
1890 A573 35pf brown & multi         .60   .60
    a. Block of 4, #1887-1890       2.25  2.25

Earring, 11th Century — A574

Archaeological Artifacts: 20pf, Earring, 10th century. 25pf, Bronze sheath, 10th century. 35pf, Bronze horse, 12th century. 70pf, Arabian coin, 8th century.

**1978, Feb. 21    Photo.    Perf. 14**
1891 A574 10pf multicolored          .20   .20
1892 A574 20pf multicolored          .20   .20
1893 A574 25pf multicolored          .20   .20
1894 A574 35pf multicolored          .25   .20
1895 A574 70pf multicolored         1.50  1.50
    Nos. 1891-1895 (5)              2.35  2.30
Treasures found on Slavic sites.

Royal House, Leipzig — A575

Leipzig Spring Fair: 25pf, Universal measuring instrument by Carl Zeiss.

**1978, Mar. 7**
1896 A575 10pf multicolored          .20   .20
1897 A575 25pf multicolored          .35   .30

M-100 Meteorological Rocket — A576

Designs: 20pf, Intercosmos I satellite. 35pf, Meteor satellite with spectometric complex. 1m, MFK-6 multi-spectral camera over city.

**1978, Mar. 21    Photo.    Perf. 14x13½**
1898 A576 10pf multicolored          .20   .20
1899 A576 20pf multicolored          .20   .20
1900 A576 35pf multicolored          .90   .90
    Nos. 1898-1900 (3)              1.30  1.30
        **Souvenir Sheet**
1901 A576  1m multicolored          2.25  1.75
Achievements in atmospheric and space research.

Samuel Heinicke, Leipzig, c. 1800 A577

25pf, Deaf child learning sign language.

**1978, Apr. 4    Litho.    Perf. 13x12½**
1902 A577 20pf multicolored          .20   .20
1903 A577 25pf multicolored          .60   .60
National Institute for the Education of the Deaf, established by Samuel Heinicke, 200th anniversary.

Radio Tower, Dequede, TV Truck — A578

Design: 20pf, TV equipment and tower, vert.

**1978, Apr. 25    Perf. 13½x14, 14x13½**
1904 A578 10pf multicolored          .25   .20
1905 A578 20pf multicolored          .25   .25
World Telecommunications Day.

Saxon Miner, 19th Century — A579

Dress Uniforms, 19th Century: 20pf, Foundry worker, Freiberg. 25pf, Mining Academy student. 35pf, Chief Inspector of Mines.

**1978, May 9    Perf. 12½x13**
1906 A579 10pf silver & multi        .20   .20
1907 A579 20pf silver & multi        .20   .20
1908 A579 25pf silver & multi        .20   .20
1909 A579 35pf silver & multi       1.10  1.00
    Nos. 1906-1909 (4)              1.70  1.60

Lion Cub — A580

Young Animals: 20pf, Leopard. 35pf, Tiger. 50pf, Snow leopard.

**1978, May 23    Photo.    Perf. 14**
1910 A580 10pf multicolored          .20   .20
1911 A580 20pf multicolored          .20   .20
1912 A580 35pf multicolored          .20   .20
1913 A580 50pf multicolored         1.10  1.10
    Nos. 1910-1913 (4)              1.70  1.70
Centenary of Leipzig Zoo.

Loading Container — A581

Designs: 20pf, Loading container on flatbed truck. 35pf, Container trains in terminal. 70pf, Loading container on ship.

**1978, June 13    Litho.    Perf. 12½x13**
1914 A581 10pf multicolored          .20   .20
1915 A581 20pf multicolored          .20   .20
1916 A581 35pf multicolored          .20   .20
1917 A581 70pf multicolored         1.60  1.50
    Nos. 1914-1917 (4)              2.20  2.10

Ceramic Bull — A582

Designs: 10pf, Woman's head, ceramic. 20pf, Gold armband, horiz. 25pf, Animal head, gold ring. 35pf, Seated family from signet ring. 40pf, Necklace, horiz.

**Perf. 14x13½, 13½x14**
**1978, June 20    Photo.**
1918 A582  5pf multicolored          .20   .20
1919 A582 10pf multicolored          .20   .20
1920 A582 20pf multicolored          .20   .20
1921 A582 25pf multicolored          .20   .20
1922 A582 35pf multicolored          .20   .20
1923 A582 40pf multicolored         1.10  1.10
    Nos. 1918-1923 (6)              2.10  2.10
African art from 1st and 2nd centuries in Berlin and Leipzig Egyptian museums.

Old and New Buildings, Cottbus — A583

Design: 10pf + 5pf, View of Cottbus, 1730.

**1978, July 18    Litho.    Perf. 13x12½**
1924    10pf + 5pf multi             .25   .25
1925 A583 20pf multicolored          .25   .25
    a. A583 Pair, #1924-1925 + label .60   .60
5th Youth Philatelic Exhibition, Cottbus.

Justus von Liebig, Wheat and Retort A584

Famous Germans: 10pf, Joseph Dietzgen (1828-1888) and title page. 15pf, Alfred Döblin (1878-1957) and title page. 20pf, Hans Loch (1898-1960) and signature, president of Liberal Democratic Party. 25pf, Dr. Theodor Brugsch (1878-1963), and blood circulation. 35pf, Friedrich Ludwig Jahn (1778-1852) and gymnast. 70pf, Dr. Albrecht von Graefe (1828-1870) and ophthalmological instruments.

**1978, July 18**
1926 A584  5pf yellow & blk          .20   .20
1927 A584 10pf gray & blk            .20   .20
1928 A584 15pf yel grn & blk         .20   .20
1929 A584 20pf ultra & blk           .20   .20
1930 A584 25pf salmon & blk          .20   .20
1931 A584 35pf lt green & blk        .20   .20
1932 A584 70pf ol & blk             1.25  1.25
    Nos. 1926-1932 (7)              2.45  2.45

Festival Emblem and New Buildings, Havana A585

35pf, Balloons and new buildings, Berlin.

**1978, July 25    Litho.    Perf. 13x12½**
1933 A585 20pf multicolored          .30   .30
1934 A585 35pf multicolored          .30   .30
    a. Strip of 2, #1933-1934 + label 1.00  1.00
11th World Youth Festival, Havana, 7/28-8/5.

Foot Soldier, by Hans Schäufelein — A586

Etchings: 20pf, Woman Reading Letter, by Jean Antoine Watteau. 25pf, Seated Boy, by Gabriel Metsu. 30pf, Seated Young Man, by Cornelis Saftleven. 35pf, St. Anthony, by Matthias Grunewald. 50pf, Seated Man, by Abraham van Diepenbeeck.

**1978, July 25    Perf. 13½x14**
1935 A586 10pf lemon & black         .20   .20
1936 A586 20pf lemon & black         .75   .75
1937 A586 25pf lemon & black         .20   .20
1938 A586 30pf lemon & black         .20   .20
1939 A586 35pf lemon & black         .75   .75
1940 A586 50pf lemon & black         .20   .20
    a. Sheet of 6, #1935-1940       2.75  2.75
Etchings from Berlin Museums.

Fair Building "Three Kings," Leipzig — A587

Leipzig Fall Fair: 10pf, IFA Multicar 25 truck, horiz.

**1978, Aug. 29    Photo.    Perf. 14**
1941 A587 10pf multicolored          .20   .20
1942 A587 25pf multicolored          .35   .30

Mauthausen Memorial — A588

**1978, Sept. 5    Perf. 13½x14**
1943 A588 35pf multicolored          .35   .25
International war memorials.

Soyuz, Intercosmos and German-Soviet Space Flight Emblems — A589

Soyuz, Camera and Space Complex A590

Designs: 10pf, Soyuz and Albert Einstein. 20pf, Sigmund Jähn, 1st German cosmonaut, vert. 35pf, Salyut-Soyuz space station, Otto Lilienthal and his glider. 1m, Cosmonauts Bykovsky and Jähn and space ships.

**1978, Sept.**   Photo.   *Perf. 14*
| | | | | |
|---|---|---|---|---|
| 1944 | A589 | 20pf multicolored | .35 | .25 |

**Litho.**   *Perf. 13½x13*
| | | | | |
|---|---|---|---|---|
| 1945 | A590 | 5pf multicolored | .20 | .20 |
| 1946 | A590 | 10pf multicolored | .20 | .20 |
| 1947 | A590 | 20pf multicolored | .20 | .20 |
| 1948 | A590 | 35pf multicolored | .75 | .75 |
| | *Nos. 1944-1948 (5)* | | 1.70 | 1.60 |

**Souvenir Sheet**   *Perf. 13½x14*
| | | | | |
|---|---|---|---|---|
| 1949 | A590 | 1m multicolored | 1.80 | 1.80 |

1st German cosmonaut on Russian space mission. #1949 contains 1 54x33mm stamp. Issued: #1944, Sept. 4; others, Sept. 21.

Marching Soldiers, Tractor, Factory A591

Design: 35pf, Russian and German Soldiers, Communist war veteran, 1933.

**1978, Sept. 19**   Photo.   *Perf. 14*
| | | | | |
|---|---|---|---|---|
| 1950 | A591 | 20pf multicolored | .30 | .30 |
| 1951 | A591 | 35pf multicolored | .30 | .30 |
| *a.* | Strip of 2, #1950-1951 + label | | 1.20 | 1.20 |

Workers' military units, 25th anniv.

Seven-person Pyramid — A592

10pf, Elephant on tricycle. 20pf, Dressage. 35pf, Polar bear kissing woman trainer.

**1978, Sept. 26**   Photo.   *Perf. 14*
| | | | | |
|---|---|---|---|---|
| 1952 | A592 | 5pf black & multi | .30 | .50 |
| 1953 | A592 | 10pf black & multi | .55 | .75 |
| 1954 | A592 | 20pf black & multi | .90 | 1.25 |
| 1955 | A592 | 35pf black & multi | 1.50 | 2.50 |
| *a.* | Block of 4, #1952-1955 | | 6.00 | 13.50 |

Circus in German Democratic Republic.

Construction of Gas Pipe Line, Drushba Section — A593

**1978, Oct. 3**   Litho.   *Perf. 13x12½*
| | | | | |
|---|---|---|---|---|
| 1956 | A593 | 20pf multicolored | .35 | .20 |

German youth helping to build gas pipe line from Orenburg to Russian border.

African Behind Barbed Wire — A594

Papilio Hahneli — A595

**1978, Oct. 3**   Litho.   *Perf. 12½x13*
| | | | | |
|---|---|---|---|---|
| 1957 | A594 | 20pf multicolored | .35 | .20 |

Anti-Apartheid Year.

**1978, Oct. 24**   Photo.   *Perf. 14*

20pf, Agama lehmanni (lizards). 25pf, Agate from Wiederau. 35pf, Paleobatrachus diluvianus. 40pf, Clock, 1720. 50pf, Table telescope, 1750.
| | | | | |
|---|---|---|---|---|
| 1958 | A595 | 10pf multicolored | .20 | .20 |
| 1959 | A595 | 20pf multicolored | .20 | .20 |
| 1960 | A595 | 25pf multicolored | .20 | .20 |
| 1961 | A595 | 35pf multicolored | .20 | .20 |
| 1962 | A595 | 40pf multicolored | .20 | .20 |
| 1963 | A595 | 50pf multicolored | 1.90 | 1.90 |
| | *Nos. 1958-1963 (6)* | | 2.90 | 2.90 |

Dresden Museum of Natural History, 250th anniversary.

Wheel Lock Gun, 1630 — A596

Hunting Guns: 10pf, Double-barreled gun, 1978. 20pf, Spring-cock gun, 1780. 25pf, Superimposed double-barreled gun, 1978. 35pf, Percussion gun, 1850. 70pf, Three-barreled gun, 1978.

**1978, Nov. 21**   Photo.   *Perf. 14*
| | | | | |
|---|---|---|---|---|
| 1964 | A596 | 5pf silver & multi | .20 | .20 |
| 1965 | A596 | 10pf silver & multi | .20 | .20 |
| 1966 | A596 | 20pf silver & multi | .25 | .25 |
| 1967 | A596 | 25pf silver & multi | .30 | .30 |
| 1968 | A596 | 35pf silver & multi | .45 | .45 |
| *a.* | Vert. strip of 3, 5, 20, 35pf | | 1.40 | 1.25 |
| 1969 | A596 | 70pf silver & multi | .90 | .90 |
| *a.* | Vert. strip of 3, 10, 25, 70pf | | 2.40 | 2.25 |
| | *Nos. 1964-1969 (6)* | | 2.30 | 2.30 |

Printed in sheets of 9.

Rapunzel's Father and Witch — A597

Designs: Scenes from fairy tale "Rapunzel."

**1978, Nov. 21**   Litho.   *Perf. 13*
| | | | | |
|---|---|---|---|---|
| 1970 | A597 | 10pf multicolored | .20 | .20 |
| 1971 | A597 | 15pf multicolored | .85 | .85 |
| 1972 | A597 | 20pf multicolored | .20 | .20 |
| 1973 | A597 | 25pf multicolored | .20 | .20 |
| 1974 | A597 | 35pf multicolored | .85 | .85 |
| 1975 | A597 | 50pf multicolored | .20 | .20 |
| *a.* | Sheet of 6, #1970-1975 | | 2.90 | 2.90 |

Chaffinches A598

Song Birds: 10pf, Nuthatch. 20pf, Robin. 25pf, Bullfinches. 35pf, Blue tit. 50pf, Red linnets.

**1979, Jan. 9**   Photo.   *Perf. 13½x14*
| | | | | |
|---|---|---|---|---|
| 1976 | A598 | 5pf multicolored | .20 | .20 |
| 1977 | A598 | 10pf multicolored | .20 | .20 |
| 1978 | A598 | 20pf multicolored | .20 | .20 |
| 1979 | A598 | 25pf multicolored | .20 | .20 |
| 1980 | A598 | 35pf multicolored | .20 | .20 |
| 1981 | A598 | 50pf multicolored | 2.25 | 1.50 |
| | *Nos. 1976-1981 (6)* | | 3.25 | 2.50 |

Chabo Cock — A599

German Cocks: 15pf, Kraienkopp. 20pf, Porcelain-colored bantam. 25pf, Saxonian. 35pf, Phoenix. 50pf, Striped Italian.

**1979, Jan. 23**   *Perf. 14x13½*
| | | | | |
|---|---|---|---|---|
| 1982 | A599 | 10pf multicolored | .20 | .20 |
| 1983 | A599 | 15pf multicolored | .20 | .20 |
| 1984 | A599 | 20pf multicolored | .20 | .20 |
| 1985 | A599 | 25pf multicolored | .20 | .20 |
| 1986 | A599 | 35pf multicolored | .20 | .20 |
| 1987 | A599 | 50pf multicolored | 1.90 | 1.90 |
| | *Nos. 1982-1987 (6)* | | 2.90 | 2.90 |

Telephone Operators, 1900 and 1979 — A600

35pf, Telegraph operators, 1880 and 1979.

**1979, Feb. 6**   Photo.   *Perf. 13½x14*
| | | | | |
|---|---|---|---|---|
| 1988 | A600 | 20pf multicolored | .20 | .20 |
| 1989 | A600 | 35pf multicolored | .65 | .65 |

Development of German postal telephone and telegraph service.

**Souvenir Sheet**

Albert Einstein (1879-1955), Theoretical Physicist — A601

**1979, Feb. 20**   Litho.   *Perf. 14*
| | | | | |
|---|---|---|---|---|
| 1990 | A601 | 1m multicolored | 2.00 | 1.90 |

Max Klinger House, Leipzig — A602

Leipzig Spring Fair: 25pf, Horizontal drilling and milling machine, horiz.

**1979, Mar. 6**   Litho.   *Perf. 14*
| | | | | |
|---|---|---|---|---|
| 1991 | A602 | 10pf multicolored | .20 | .20 |
| 1992 | A602 | 25pf multicolored | .30 | .25 |

Container Ship, Tug, World Map and IMCO Emblem — A603

**1979, Mar. 20**     Photo.
| | | | | |
|---|---|---|---|---|
| 1993 | A603 | 20pf multicolored | .35 | .25 |

World Navigation Day.

Otto Hahn and Equation of Nuclear Fission A604

Famous Germans: 10pf, Max von Laue (1879-1969) and diagram of sulphide zinc. 20pf, Arthur Scheunert (1879-1957), symbol of nutrition and health. 25pf, Friedrich August Kekulé (1829-1896), and benzene ring. 35pf, George Forster (1754-1794) and Capt. Cook's ship Resolution. 70pf, Gotthold Ephraim Lessing (1729-1781) and title page for Nathan the Wise.

**1979, Mar. 20**   Litho.   *Perf. 13x12½*
| | | | | |
|---|---|---|---|---|
| 1994 | A604 | 5pf pale salmon & blk | .20 | .20 |
| 1995 | A604 | 10pf blue gray & blk | .20 | .20 |
| 1996 | A604 | 20pf lemon & blk | .20 | .20 |
| 1997 | A604 | 25pf lt green & blk | .20 | .20 |
| 1998 | A604 | 35pf lt blue & blk | .20 | .20 |
| 1999 | A604 | 70pf pink & blk | 1.90 | 1.50 |
| | *Nos. 1994-1999 (6)* | | 2.90 | 2.50 |

See Nos. 2088-2093.

**Miniature Sheet**

Horch 8, 1911 — A605

Design: 35pf, Trabant 601S de luxe, 1978.

**1979, Apr. 3**   Litho.   *Perf. 14*
| | | | | |
|---|---|---|---|---|
| 2000 | | Sheet of 2 + label | 1.50 | 1.50 |
| *a.* | A605 20pf multicolored | | .30 | .30 |
| *b.* | A605 35pf multicolored | | .65 | .65 |

Sachsenring automobile plant, Zwickau.

Self-Propelled Car — A606

DDR Railroad Cars: 10pf, Self-unloading freight car Us-y. 20pf, Diesel locomotive BR 110. 35pf, Laaes automobile carrier.

**1979, Apr. 17**   Litho.   *Perf. 13*
| | | | | |
|---|---|---|---|---|
| 2001 | A606 | 5pf multicolored | .20 | .20 |
| 2002 | A606 | 10pf multicolored | .20 | .20 |
| 2003 | A606 | 20pf multicolored | .20 | .20 |
| 2004 | A606 | 35pf multicolored | .75 | .75 |
| | *Nos. 2001-2004 (4)* | | 1.35 | 1.35 |

Durga, 18th Century — A607

Indian Miniatures in Berlin Museums: 35pf, Mahavira, 15th-16th cents. 50pf, Todi Ragini, 17th cent. 70pf, Asavari Ragini, 17th cent.

**1979, May 8  Photo.  Perf. 14x13½**
| | | | |
|---|---|---|---|
| **2005** | A607 | 20pf multicolored | .20 .20 |
| **2006** | A607 | 35pf multicolored | .20 .20 |
| **2007** | A607 | 50pf multicolored | .25 .25 |
| **2008** | A607 | 70pf multicolored | 2.10 2.00 |
| | | *Nos. 2005-2008 (4)* | 2.75 2.60 |

Youth Gathering A608

Design: 10pf+5pf, Torchlight parade of German youth, Oct. 7, 1949.

**1979, May 22  Photo.  Perf. 14**
| | | | |
|---|---|---|---|
| **2009** | A608 | 10pf + 5pf multi | .20 .20 |
| **2010** | A608 | 20pf multicolored | .25 .25 |
| *a.* | | Strip of 2, #2009-2010 + label | .60 .60 |

National Youth Festival, Berlin.

Housing Project, Berlin A609

20pf, Berlin-Marzahn building site & surveyors.

**1979, May 22  Litho.  Perf. 13x12½**
| | | | |
|---|---|---|---|
| **2011** | A609 | 10pf multicolored | .20 .20 |
| **2012** | A609 | 20pf multicolored | .30 .30 |

Berlin Project of Free German Youth.

Children Playing and Reading — A610

Exhibition Emblem — A611

20pf, Doctor with black & white children.

**1979, May 22  Photo.  Perf. 14**
| | | | |
|---|---|---|---|
| **2013** | A610 | 10pf multicolored | .20 .20 |
| **2014** | A610 | 20pf multicolored | .35 .40 |

International Year of the Child.

**1979, June 5**
| | | | |
|---|---|---|---|
| **2015** | A611 | 10pf multicolored | .35 .20 |

Agra '79 Agricultural Exhib., Markkleeberg.

Ferry Boats A612

**1979, June 26  Photo.  Perf. 14**
| | | | |
|---|---|---|---|
| **2016** | A612 | 20pf Rostock | .30 .30 |
| **2017** | A612 | 35pf Rugen | .30 .30 |
| *a.* | | Strip of 2, #2016-2017 + label | 1.10 1.10 |

Railroad ferry from Sassnitz, DDR, to Trelleborg, Sweden, 70th anniversary.

Hospital Classroom — A613

Design: 35pf, Handicapped workers.

**1979, June 26  Litho.  Perf. 13x12½**
| | | | |
|---|---|---|---|
| **2018** | A163 | 10pf multicolored | .20 .20 |
| **2019** | A163 | 35pf multicolored | .45 .35 |

Rehabilitation in DDR.

Bicyclists A614

Design: 20pf, Roller skating.

**1979, July 3**
| | | | |
|---|---|---|---|
| **2020** | A614 | 10pf multicolored | .20 .20 |
| **2021** | A614 | 20pf multicolored | .45 .35 |

7th Children's and Youth Spartakiad, Berlin.

Dahlia "Rubens" A615

Dahlias: 20pf, Rosalie. 25pf, Corinna. 35pf, Enzett-Dolli. 50pf, Enzett-Carola. 70pf, Don Lorenzo.

**1979, July 17  Photo.  Perf. 13**
| | | | |
|---|---|---|---|
| **2022** | A615 | 10pf multicolored | .20 .20 |
| **2023** | A615 | 20pf multicolored | .20 .20 |
| **2024** | A615 | 25pf multicolored | .20 .20 |
| **2025** | A615 | 35pf multicolored | .20 .20 |
| **2026** | A615 | 50pf multicolored | .25 .20 |
| **2027** | A615 | 70pf multicolored | 2.25 2.25 |
| | | *Nos. 2022-2027 (6)* | 3.30 3.25 |

Dahlias shown at International Garden Exhibition, Erfurt.

Russian Alphabet Around Congress Emblem A616

**1979, Aug. 7  Photo.  Perf. 13**
| | | | |
|---|---|---|---|
| **2028** | A616 | 20pf multicolored | .30 .20 |

4th International Congress of Teachers of Russian Language and Literature, Berlin.

Dandelion Fountain, Dresden — A617

Composite of Dresden Buildings — A618

The A618 illustration is reduced.

**1979, Aug. 7  Perf. 14**
| | | | |
|---|---|---|---|
| **2029** | A617 | multicolored | .20 .20 |

Souvenir Sheet
**Litho.  Perf. 13x12½**
| | | | |
|---|---|---|---|
| **2030** | A618 | 1m multicolored | 1.90 1.75 |

DDR '79, Natl. Stamp Exhib., Dresden. See No. B187.

Italian Lira da Gamba, 1592 — A619

Musical Instruments, Leipzig Museum: 25pf, French "serpent," 17th-18th centuries. 40pf, French barrel lyre, 18th century. 85pf, German tenor trumpet, 19th century.

**1979, Aug. 21  Perf. 14**
| | | | |
|---|---|---|---|
| **2031** | A619 | 20pf multicolored | .20 .20 |
| **2032** | A619 | 25pf multicolored | .20 .20 |
| **2033** | A619 | 40pf multicolored | .25 .20 |
| **2034** | A619 | 85pf multicolored | 2.10 1.60 |
| | | *Nos. 2031-2034 (4)* | 2.75 2.20 |

Galloping — A620

**1979, Aug. 21**
| | | | |
|---|---|---|---|
| **2035** | A620 | 10pf shown | .20 .20 |
| **2036** | A620 | 25pf Dressage | .75 .65 |

30th International Horse-breeding Congress of Socialist Countries, Berlin.

Memorial Monument, Nordhausen A621

**1979, Aug. 28  Photo.  Perf. 14**
| | | | |
|---|---|---|---|
| **2037** | A621 | 35pf dull vio & blk | .45 .30 |

Memorial to World War II victims.

Teddy Bear — A622

Leipzig Autumn Fair: 25pf, Grosser Blumenberg (building), Leipzig, horiz.

**1979, Aug. 28**
| | | | |
|---|---|---|---|
| **2038** | A622 | 10pf multicolored | .20 .20 |
| **2039** | A622 | 25pf multicolored | .25 .20 |

Philipp Dengel (1888-1948) A623

Working-Class Movement Leaders: No. 2041, Heinrich Rau (1899-1961). No. 2042, Otto Buchwitz (1879-1964). No. 2043, Bernard Koenen (1889-1964).

**1979, Sept. 11  Litho.**
| | | | |
|---|---|---|---|
| **2040** | A623 | 10pf multicolored | .20 .20 |
| **2041** | A623 | 10pf multicolored | .20 .20 |
| **2042** | A623 | 10pf multicolored | .20 .20 |
| **2043** | A623 | 10pf multicolored | .20 .20 |
| | | *Nos. 2040-2043 (4)* | .80 .80 |

See Nos. 2166-2169, 2249-2253, 2314-2318, 2390-2392, 2452-2454.

DDR Arms and Flag, Worker A624

DDR Arms, Flag and: 10pf, Young man and woman. 15pf, Soldiers. 20pf, Workers.

**1979, Oct. 2  Photo.  Perf. 13**
| | | | |
|---|---|---|---|
| **2044** | A624 | 5pf multicolored | .20 .20 |
| **2045** | A624 | 10pf multicolored | .20 .20 |
| **2046** | A624 | 15pf multicolored | .35 .35 |
| **2047** | A624 | 20pf multicolored | .20 .20 |
| | | *Nos. 2044-2047 (4)* | .95 .95 |

**Souvenir Sheet**
| | | | |
|---|---|---|---|
| **2048** | A624 | 1m multicolored | 1.50 1.40 |

DDR, 30th anniv. No. 2048 contains one stamp (33x55mm).

Altozier Porcelain Coffee Pot — A625

Meissen Porcelain and Hallmark, 18th-20th Centuries: 5pf, Woman applying make-up, 1967. 15pf, "Grosser Ausschnitt" coffee pot, 1974. 20pf, Covered vase. 25pf, Parrot. 35pf, Harlequin drinking. 50pf, Woman selling flowers. 70pf, Sake bottle.

**1979, Nov. 6  Photo.  Perf. 14**
| | | | |
|---|---|---|---|
| **2049** | A625 | 5pf multicolored | .20 .20 |
| **2050** | A625 | 10pf multicolored | .20 .20 |
| **2051** | A625 | 15pf multicolored | .25 .25 |
| **2052** | A625 | 20pf multicolored | .30 .30 |
| *a.* | | Block of 4, #2049-2052 | 3.00 2.25 |

| | | | |
|---|---|---|---|
| 2053 | A625 25pf multicolored | .35 | .35 |
| 2054 | A625 35pf multicolored | .60 | .60 |
| 2055 | A625 50pf multicolored | .85 | .85 |
| 2056 | A625 70pf multicolored | 1.10 | 1.10 |
| a. | Block of 4, #2053-2056 | 6.00 | 5.50 |

Rag Doll, 1800 — A626

Historic Dolls: 15pf, Ceramic, 1960. 20pf, Wooden, 1780. 35pf, Straw, 1900. 50pf, Jointed, 1800. 70pf, Tumbler, 1820.

**1979, Nov. 20                    Litho.**

| | | | |
|---|---|---|---|
| 2057 | A626 10pf multicolored | .20 | .20 |
| 2058 | A626 15pf multicolored | .90 | .90 |
| 2059 | A626 20pf multicolored | .20 | .20 |
| 2060 | A626 35pf multicolored | .20 | .20 |
| 2061 | A626 50pf multicolored | .90 | .90 |
| 2062 | A626 70pf multicolored | .20 | .20 |
| a. | Sheet of 6, #2057-2062 | 3.25 | 3.25 |

Bobsledding, by Gunter Rechn, Olympic Rings — A627

Olympic Rings and: 20pf, Figure Skating, by Johanna Stake, vert. 35pf, Speed Skating, by Axel Wunsch, vert. 1m, Cross-country Skiing, by Lothar Zitzmann.

**1980, Jan. 15      Photo.      Perf. 14**

| | | | |
|---|---|---|---|
| 2063 | A627 10pf multicolored | .20 | .20 |
| 2064 | A627 20pf multicolored | .20 | .20 |
| 2065 | A627 35pf multicolored | 1.10 | 1.00 |
| | Nos. 2063-2065,B189 (4) | 1.70 | 1.60 |

**Souvenir Sheet**

| | | | |
|---|---|---|---|
| 2066 | A627 1m multicolored | 1.90 | 1.90 |

13th Winter Olympic Games, Lake Placid, NY, Feb. 12-24. No. 2066 contains one 29x23½mm stamp. See Nos. 2098-2099, 2119-2121, B190, B192.

"Quiet Music," Grossedlitz — A628

Baroque Gardens: 20pf, Orange grove, Belvedere, Weimar. 50pf, Flower garden, Dornburg Castle. 70pf, Park, Rheinsberg Castle.

**1980, Jan. 29**

| | | | |
|---|---|---|---|
| 2067 | A628 10pf multicolored | .20 | .20 |
| 2068 | A628 20pf multicolored | .20 | .20 |
| 2069 | A628 50pf multicolored | .25 | .20 |
| 2070 | A628 70pf multicolored | 1.40 | 1.40 |
| | Nos. 2067-2070 (4) | 2.05 | 2.00 |

**Type of 1973**

Designs as before and: 10pf, Palace of the Republic, Berlin.

**1980-81      Engr.      Perf. 14**
**Size: 22x17mm**

| | | | |
|---|---|---|---|
| 2071 | A449 5pf blue green | .20 | .20 |
| 2072 | A449 10pf emerald | .25 | .20 |
| 2073 | A449 15pf rose lilac | .35 | .20 |
| 2074 | A449 20pf rose mag | .45 | .20 |
| 2075 | A449 25pf grnsh bl | .35 | .25 |
| 2076 | A449 30pf org ('81) | .45 | .25 |
| 2077 | A449 35pf blue | .45 | .25 |
| 2078 | A449 40pf dull vio | .90 | .50 |
| 2079 | A449 50pf blue | .55 | .25 |
| 2080 | A449 60pf lilac ('81) | .55 | .25 |
| 2081 | A449 70pf redsh brn ('81) | .70 | .50 |
| 2082 | A449 80pf vio bl ('81) | .85 | .50 |
| 2083 | A449 1m olive | .90 | .80 |
| 2084 | A449 2m red | 1.60 | .90 |
| 2085 | A449a 3m rose lil ('81) | 2.60 | 1.25 |
| | Nos. 2071-2085 (15) | 11.15 | 6.55 |

Cable-Laying Vehicle, Dish Antenna — A629

20pf, Radio tower, television screen.

**1980, Feb. 5                    Photo.**

| | | | |
|---|---|---|---|
| 2086 | A629 10pf multicolored | .20 | .20 |
| 2087 | A629 20pf multicolored | .25 | .20 |

**Famous Germans Type of 1979**

Designs: 5pf, Johann Wolfgang Dobereiner (1780-1849), chemist. 10pf, Frederic Joliot-Curie (1900-1958), French physicist. 20pf, Johann Friedrich Naumann (1780-1857), ornithologist. 25pf, Alfred Wegener (1880-1930), geophysicist and meteorologist. 35pf, Carl von Clausewitz (1780-1831), Prussian major general. 70pf, Helene Weigel (1900-1971), actress.

**1980, Feb. 26      Litho.      Perf. 13x12½**

| | | | |
|---|---|---|---|
| 2088 | A604 5pf pale yel & blk | .20 | .20 |
| 2089 | A604 10pf multicolored | .20 | .20 |
| 2090 | A604 20pf lt yel grn & blk | .20 | .20 |
| 2091 | A604 25pf multicolored | .20 | .20 |
| 2092 | A604 35pf lt blue & blk | .20 | .20 |
| 2093 | A604 70pf lt red brn & blk | 1.20 | 1.10 |
| | Nos. 2088-2093 (6) | 2.20 | 2.10 |

Type A17-303 Tractor A630

1980 Leipzig Spring Fair: 10pf, Karl Marx University, Leipzig, vert.

**1980, Mar. 4      Photo.      Perf. 14**

| | | | |
|---|---|---|---|
| 2094 | A630 10pf multicolored | .20 | .20 |
| 2095 | A630 25pf multicolored | .30 | .25 |

Werner Eggerath (1900-1977), Labor Leader — A631

**1980, Mar. 18                    Litho.**

| | | | |
|---|---|---|---|
| 2096 | A631 10pf brick red & blk | .45 | .30 |

**Souvenir Sheet**

Cosmonauts, Salyut 6 and Soyuz — A632

**1980, Apr. 11      Litho.      Perf. 14**

| | | | |
|---|---|---|---|
| 2097 | A632 1m multicolored | 1.80 | 1.60 |

Intercosmos cooperative space program.

**Olympic Type of 1980**

Designs: 10pf, On the Bars, by Erich Wurzer. 50pf, Scull's Crew, by Wilfried Falkenthal.

**1980, Apr. 22      Photo.      Perf. 14**

| | | | |
|---|---|---|---|
| 2098 | A627 10pf multicolored | .25 | .20 |
| 2099 | A627 50pf multicolored | 1.20 | 1.00 |
| | Nos. 2098-2099,B190 (3) | 1.70 | 1.40 |

22nd Summer Olympic Games, Moscow, July 19-Aug. 3. See No. B190.

Flags of Member Countries A633

Bauhaus Cooperative Society Building, 1928, Gropius A634

**1980, May 13                    Photo.**

| | | | |
|---|---|---|---|
| 2100 | A633 20pf multicolored | .45 | .20 |

Signing of Warsaw Pact (Bulgaria, Czechoslovakia, DDR, Hungary, Poland, Romania, USSR), 25th anniv.

**1980, May 27**

Bauhaus Architecture: 10pf, Socialists' Memorial, 1926, by Mies van der Rohe, horiz. 15pf, Monument, 1922, by William Gropius. 20pf, Steel building, 1926, by Muche and Paulick, horiz. 50pf, Trade-Union School, 1928, by Meyer. 70pf, Bauhaus Building, 1926, by Gropius, horiz.

| | | | |
|---|---|---|---|
| 2101 | A634 5pf multicolored | .25 | .20 |
| 2102 | A634 10pf multicolored | .25 | .20 |
| 2103 | A634 15pf multicolored | .25 | .20 |
| 2104 | A634 20pf multicolored | .25 | .20 |
| 2105 | A634 50pf multicolored | .30 | .20 |
| 2106 | A634 70pf multicolored | 1.80 | 1.60 |
| | Nos. 2101-2106 (6) | 3.10 | 2.60 |

Rostock View A635

**1980, June 10      Photo.      Perf. 14**

| | | | |
|---|---|---|---|
| 2107 | A635 10pf shown | .20 | .20 |
| 2108 | A635 20pf Dancers | .30 | .25 |

18th Workers' Festival, Rostock, June 27-29.

Dish Antenna, Interflug Airlines A636

**1980, June 10      Litho.      Perf. 13x12½**

| | | | |
|---|---|---|---|
| 2109 | A636 20pf shown | .30 | .30 |
| 2110 | A636 25pf Jet | .30 | .30 |
| 2111 | A636 35pf Agricultural plane | .45 | .45 |
| 2112 | A636 70pf Aerial photography | .90 | .90 |
| a. | Block of 4, #2109-2112 | 2.60 | 2.60 |

Interflug Airlines. See No. B191.

Okapi — A637

**1980, June 24                    Perf. 14**

| | | | |
|---|---|---|---|
| 2113 | A637 5pf shown | .20 | .20 |
| 2114 | A637 10pf Wild cats | .20 | .20 |
| 2115 | A637 15pf Prairie wolf | .20 | .20 |
| 2116 | A637 20pf Arabian oryx | .20 | .20 |
| 2117 | A637 25pf White-eared pheasant | .20 | .20 |
| 2118 | A637 35pf Musk oxen | 1.60 | 1.60 |
| | Nos. 2113-2118 (6) | 2.60 | 2.60 |

**Olympic Type of 1980**

Designs: 10pf, Judo, by Erhard Schmidt. 50pf, Final Spurt, by Siegfried Schreiber. 1m, Spinnaker Yachts, by Karl Raetsch.

**1980, July 8      Photo.      Perf. 14**

| | | | |
|---|---|---|---|
| 2119 | A627 10pf multicolored | .20 | .20 |
| 2120 | A627 50pf multicolored | 1.25 | 1.25 |
| | Nos. 2119-2120,B192 (3) | 1.65 | 1.65 |

**Souvenir Sheet**

| | | | |
|---|---|---|---|
| 2121 | A627 1m multicolored | 2.10 | 1.75 |

22nd Summer Olympic Games, Moscow, 7/19-8/3. #2121 contains one 29x24mm stamp.

Old and New Buildings, Suhl A638

Design: 10pf + 5pf, View of Suhl, 1700.

**1980, July 22      Litho.      Perf. 13x12½**

| | | | |
|---|---|---|---|
| 2122 | A638 10pf + 5pf multi | .30 | .30 |
| 2123 | A638 20pf multicolored | .30 | .30 |
| a. | Pair, #2122-2123 + label | 1.10 | 1.10 |

6th National Youth Philatelic Exhibition, Suhl. Surtax for East German Association of Philatelists.

Huntley Microscope, London, 1740 — A639

Optical Museum, Karl Zeiss Foundation, Jena: 25pf, Magny microscope, Paris, 1751. 35pf, Amici microscope, Modena, 1845. 70pf, Zeiss microscope, Jena, 1873.

**1980, Aug. 12      Photo.      Perf. 14**

| | | | |
|---|---|---|---|
| 2124 | A639 20pf multicolored | .30 | .30 |
| 2125 | A639 25pf multicolored | .30 | .30 |
| 2126 | A639 35pf multicolored | .55 | .55 |
| 2127 | A639 70pf multicolored | .75 | .75 |
| a. | Block of 4, #2124-2127 | 2.75 | 2.40 |

Maidenek Memorial — A640

**1980, Aug. 26**

| | | | |
|---|---|---|---|
| 2128 | A640 35pf multicolored | .45 | .30 |

Leipzig 1980 Autumn Fair, Information Center — A641

**1980, Aug. 26**

| | | | |
|---|---|---|---|
| 2129 | A641 10pf shown | .20 | .20 |
| 2130 | A641 25pf Carpet loom | .45 | .25 |

67th Interparliamentary Conference, Berlin — A642

**1980, Sept. 9      Photo.      Perf. 14**

| | | | |
|---|---|---|---|
| 2131 | A642 20pf Republic Palace, Berlin | .70 | .25 |

Paintings by
Frans Hals
(1580-1666)
A643

**1980, Sept. 23**
2132 A643 10pf *Laughing Boy
with Flute* .20 .20
2133 A643 20pf *Man in Gray
Coat* .20 .20
2134 A643 25pf *The Mulatto* .20 .20
2135 A643 35pf *Man in Black
Coat* .90 .90
*Nos. 2132-2135 (4)* 1.50 1.50
**Souvenir Sheet**
2136 A643 1m *Self-portrait,
horiz.* 1.90 1.50

A644

Edible Mushrooms: 5pf, Leccinum Testaceo
Scabrum. 10pf, Boletus erythropus. 15pf,
Agaricus campester. 20pf, Xerocomus badius.
35pf, Boletus edulis. 70pf, Cantharellus
cibarius.

**1980, Oct. 28 Litho. Perf. 13x13½**
2137 A644 5pf multicolored .20 .20
2138 A644 10pf multicolored .20 .20
2139 A644 15pf multicolored .20 .20
2140 A644 20pf multicolored .20 .20
2141 A644 35pf multicolored .25 .20
2142 A644 70pf multicolored 1.60 1.60
*Nos. 2137-2142 (6)* 2.65 2.60

Exploration of Lignite Deposits
(Gravimetry) — A645

Geophysical Exploration: 25pf, Bore-hole
measuring (water). 35pf, Seismic geology.
(mineral oil, natural gas). 50pf, Seismology.

**1980, Nov. 11 Litho. Perf. 13**
2143 A645 20pf multicolored .30 .20
2144 A645 25pf multicolored .35 .30
2145 A645 35pf multicolored .45 .45
2146 A645 50pf multicolored .75 .75
a. Block of 4, #2143-2146 2.25 3.00

Radebeul-Radeburg Railroad
Locomotive — A646

**1980, Nov. 25 Perf. 13x12½**
2147 Strip of 2 + label 1.40 1.00
a. A646 20pf shown .30 .30
b. A646 25pf Passenger car .30 .30
2148 Strip of 2 + label 1.40 1.00
a. A646 20pf Bad Doberan-Osteebad
Kuhlungsborn Locomotive .30 .30
b. A646 35pf Passenger car .30 .30

Labels show maps of routes and Moritzburg
Castle (No. 2147), Bad Doberan Street (No.
2148).
See Nos. 2205-2206.

Toy Locomotive,
1850 — A647

**1980, Dec. 9 Perf. 14**
2149 Sheet of 6 3.00 3.00
a. A647 10pf shown .25 .25
b. A647 20pf Airplane, 1914 .90 .90
c. A647 25pf Steam roller, 1920 .25 .25
d. A647 35pf Ship, 1825 .25 .25
e. A647 40pf Car, 1900 .90 .90
f. A647 50pf Balloon, 1920 .25 .25

**Souvenir Sheet**

Wolfgang Amadeus Mozart, 225th
Birth Anniv. — A648

**1981, Jan. 13 Litho.**
2150 A648 1m multicolored 2.25 1.80

St. John's
Apple — A649

**1981, Jan. 13 Photo.**
2151 A649 5pf shown .20 .20
2152 A649 10pf Snow drop,
horiz. .20 .20
2153 A649 20pf Bladder bush .20 .20
2154 A649 25pf Paulownia to-
mentose .20 .20
2155 A649 35pf German honeysuckle, horiz. .25 .20
2156 A649 50pf Genuine spice
bush 1.90 1.90
*Nos. 2151-2156 (6)* 2.95 2.90

Heinrich von
Stephan (1831-
97), Founder of
UPU — A650

**1981, Jan. 20 Litho. Perf. 13x13½**
2157 A650 10pf lt lemon & blk .35 .25

Dedication of National Commemorative
Plaza, Sachsenhausen — A651

**1981, Jan. 27 Photo. Perf. 14**
2158 A651 10pf shown .25 .20
2159 A651 20pf Changing of guard .30 .20
National People's Forces, 25th anniversary.

Socialist Union Party, 10th
Congress — A652

**1981, Feb. 10**
2160 A652 10pf multicolored .35 .20

Postal and Newspaper Apprentice
Training — A653

**1981, Feb. 10 Litho.**
2161 A653 5pf shown .20 .20
2162 A653 10pf Telephone and
telex service .20 .20
2163 A653 15pf Radio communications .20 .20
2164 A653 20pf School of Engineering, Leipzig .25 .20
2165 A653 25pf Communications
Academy, Dres-
den 1.00 .90
*Nos. 2161-2165 (5)* 1.85 1.70

**Working-class Leader Type of 1979**
Designs: No. 2166, Erich Baron (1881-
1933). No. 2167, Conrad Blenkle (1901-1943).
No. 2168, Arthur Ewert (1890-1959). No.
2169, Walter Stoecker (1891-1939).

**1981, Feb. 24 Litho. Perf. 14**
2166 A623 10pf gray grn & blk .20 .20
2167 A623 10pf lemon & blk .20 .20
2168 A623 10pf bl vio & blk .20 .20
2169 A623 10pf lt red brn & blk .20 .20
*Nos. 2166-2169 (4)* .80 .80

Merkur Hotel,
Leipzig — A654

1981 Leipzig Spring Fair: 25pf, Takraf mining conveyor system, horiz.

**1981, Mar. 10 Photo. Perf. 14**
2170 A654 10pf multicolored .20 .20
2171 A654 25pf multicolored .35 .25

Ernst Thälmann,
by Willi
Sitte — A655

10th Communist Party Congress (Paint-
ings): 20pf, Worker, by Bernhard Heising,
25pf, Festivities, by Rudolf Bergander. 35pf,
Brotherhood in Arms, by Paul Michaelis. 1m,
When Communists Dream, by Walter
Womacka.

**1981, Mar. 24**
2172 A655 10pf multicolored .20 .20
2173 A655 20pf multicolored .20 .20
2174 A655 25pf multicolored .75 .75
2175 A655 35pf multicolored .20 .20
*Nos. 2172-2175 (4)* 1.35 1.35
**Souvenir Sheet**
2176 A655 1m multicolored 1.50 1.50

**Souvenir Sheet**

Opening of Sport and Recreation
Center, Berlin — A656

**1981, Mar. 24 Litho.**
2177 A656 1m multicolored 2.10 1.90

Energy Conservation
A657

**1981, Apr. 21 Litho. Perf. 12½x13**
2178 A657 10pf orange & blk .25 .20

Heinrich Barkhausen (1881-1956),
Physicist — A658

Famous Men: 20pf, Johannes R. Becher
(1891-1958), poet. 25pf, Richard Dedekind
(1831-1916), mathematician. 35pf, Georg Philipp Telemann (1681-1767), composer. 50pf,
Adelbert V. Chamisso (1781-1838), botanist.
70pf, Wilhelm Raabe (1831-1910), writer.

**1981, May 5 Perf. 13x12½**
2179 A658 10pf dull bl & blk .20 .20
2180 A658 20pf brick red & blk .20 .20
2181 A658 25pf dull brn & blk 2.10 1.50
2182 A658 35pf lt vio & blk .25 .20
2183 A658 50pf yel grn & blk .30 .20
2184 A658 70pf ol bis & blk .45 .25
*Nos. 2179-2184 (6)* 3.50 2.55

Free
German
Youth
Members
A659

**1981, May 19**
2185 A659 10pf shown .25 .25
2186 A659 20pf Youths, diff. .25 .25
a. Pair, #2185-2186 + label .85 .80
Free German Youth, 11th Parliament, Berlin.

View and Map of
Worlitz Park — A660

**1981, June 9    Litho.    *Perf. 12½x13***
2187  A660  5pf shown            .20   .20
2188  A660  10pf Tiefurt          .20   .20
2189  A660  15pf Marxwalde        .20   .20
2190  A660  20pf Branitz          .20   .20
2191  A660  25pf Treptow         1.50  1.50
2192  A660  35pf Wiesenburg       .25   .20
        *Nos. 2187-2192 (6)*      2.55  2.50

Artistic Gymnastics — A661

8th Children's and Youth Spartacist Games:
No. 2193, children and youths.

**1981, June 23    Photo.    *Perf. 14***
2193  A661  10pf + 5pf multi      .55   .35
2194  A661  20pf multicolored     .25   .20

Javelin
Throwers
A662

**1981, June 23    Litho.    *Perf. 13x12½***
2195  A662  5pf shown            .25   .20
2196  A662  15pf Men at museum    .25   .20
   a.    Pair, #2195-2196 + label  .60   .55

Intl. Year of the Disabled.

Schinkel's Berlin Playhouse — A663

Karl Friedrich Schinkel, (1781-1841), Architect: 25pf, Old Museum, Berlin.

**1981, June 23         Litho. & Engr.**
2197  A663  10pf tan & blk        .85   .20
2198  A663  25pf tan & blk       1.90   .85

Sugar Loaf
House, Gross
Zicker — A664

Frame Houses: 10pf, Zaulsdorf, 19th cent.,
vert. 25pf, Farmhouse, stable, Weckersdorf,
vert. 35pf, Restaurant (former farmhouse),
Pillgram. 50pf, Eschenbach, vert. 70pf, Farmhouse, Lüdersdorf.

**1981, July 7                    Photo.**
2199  A664  10pf multicolored     .20   .20
2200  A664  20pf multicolored     .20   .20
2201  A664  25pf multicolored     .20   .20
2202  A664  35pf multicolored     .25   .20
2203  A664  50pf multicolored     .30   .20
2204  A664  70pf multicolored    2.50  2.10
        *Nos. 2199-2204 (6)*      3.65  3.10

**Railroad Type of 1980**

**1981, July 21    Litho.    *Perf. 13x12½***
2205      Strip of 2 + label      .75   .60
   a.    A646 5pf Locomotive, Freital-Kurort-
            Kipsdorf line          .20   .20
   b.    A646 15pf Luggage car     .20   .20
2206      Strip of 2 + label      .75   .60
   a.    A646 5pf Locomotive, Putbus-
            Gohren line           .20   .20
   b.    A646 20pf Passenger car   .20   .20

Labels show maps of train routes.

Ebers Papyrus
(Egyptian
Medical Text,
1600 B.C.),
Leipzig — A665

Literary Treasures in DDR Libraries: 35pf,
Maya manuscript, 12th cent., Dresden. 50pf,
Petrarch sonnet illustration, 16th century
French manuscript, Berlin.

**1981, Aug. 18    Photo.    *Perf. 14***
2207  A665  20pf multicolored     .20   .20
2208  A665  35pf multicolored     .20   .20
2209  A665  50pf multicolored    1.40  1.40
        *Nos. 2207-2209 (3)*      1.80  1.80

**1981, Aug. 18**

Leipzig 1981 Autumn Fair: 25pf, Concert
Hall, Leipzig, horiz.

2210  A666  10pf multicolored     .20   .20
2211  A666  25pf multicolored     .35   .30

Chemical
Plant — A666

Anti-Fascist
Resistance
Monument,
Sassnitz
A667

**1981, Sept. 8    Photo.    *Perf. 14***
2212  A667  35pf multicolored     .45   .30

Forceps, 18th
Cent., Speculum,
17th Cent. — A668

Historic Medical Instruments, Karl Sudhoff
Institute, Leipzig: 10pf, Henbana, censer, 16th
cent. 20pf, Pelican, dental elevator and extrac-
tors, 17th cent. 25pf, Seton forceps, 17th cent.
35pf, Lithotomy knife, 18th cent., hernia scissors, 17th cent. 85pf, Elevators, 17th cent.
10pf, 20pf, 25pf, 35pf horiz.

**1981, Sept. 22**
2213  A668  10pf multicolored     .20   .20
2214  A668  20pf multicolored     .20   .20
2215  A668  25pf multicolored     .20   .20
2216  A668  35pf multicolored     .25   .20
2217  A668  50pf multicolored    2.75  2.25
2218  A668  85pf multicolored     .45   .30
        *Nos. 2213-2218 (6)*      4.05  3.35

Philatelists' Day — A669

**1981, Oct. 6    Photo.    *Perf. 14***
2219  A669  10pf + 5pf Letter by En-
              gels, 1840           .75   .50
2220  A669  20pf Postcard by Marx,
              1878                 .25   .20

River
Boat
A670

**1981, Oct. 20**
2221  A670  10pf Tugboat          .20   .20
2222  A670  20pf Tugboat, diff.   .20   .20
2223  A670  25pf Diesel paddle
              liner               .20   .20
2224  A670  35pf Ice breaker      .25   .20
2225  A670  50pf Motor freighter  .30   .20
2226  A670  85pf Bucket dredger  2.40  2.40
        *Nos. 2221-2226 (6)*      3.55  3.40

Windmill,
Dabel — A671

**1981, Nov. 10    Photo.    *Perf. 14***
2227  A671  10pf shown            .20   .20
2228  A671  20pf Pahrenz          .20   .20
2229  A671  25pf Dresden-Gohlis   .20   .20
2230  A671  70pf Ballstadt       1.50  1.50
        *Nos. 2227-2230 (4)*      2.10  2.10

Toys — A672

**1981, Nov. 24    Litho.    *Perf. 13½***
2231      Sheet of 6             3.25  3.25
   a.    A672 10pf Jointed snake, 1850  .25  .25
   b.    A672 20pf Teddy bear, 1910     .25  .25
   c.    A672 25pf Fish, 1935           .90  .90
   d.    A672 35pf Hobby horse, 1850    .90  .90
   e.    A672 40pf Cuckoo, 1800         .25  .25
   f.    A672 70pf Frog, 1930           .25  .25

Meissen Porcelain
Teapot,
1715 — A673

**1982, Jan. 26    Photo.    *Perf. 14***
2232  A673  10pf shown            .20   .20
2233  A673  20pf Vase, 1715       .30   .30
2234  A673  25pf Oberon figurine,
              1969                .45   .45
2235  A673  35pf Day and Night
              vase, 1979          .60   .60
   a.    Block of 4, #2232-2235  2.10  1.80

**Souvenir Sheet**
2236      Sheet of 2            2.40  1.90
   a.    A673 50pf Portrait       .75   .75
   b.    A673 50pf Emblem         .75   .75

Johann Friedrich Bottger (1682-1719),
inventor of Dresden china. No. 2236 contains
two 24x29mm stamps.

Post Offices — A674

**1982, Feb. 9**
2237  A674  20pf Liebenstein     .20   .20
2238  A674  25pf Berlin          .20   .20
2239  A674  35pf Erfurt          .25   .20
2240  A674  50pf Dresden        1.50  1.50
        *Nos. 2237-2240 (4)*     2.15  2.10

Intl. Fur
Auction,
Leipzig
A675

**1982, Feb. 23    Photo.    *Perf. 14***
2241  A675  10pf Marmot, vert.   .20   .20
2242  A675  20pf Polecat         .20   .20
2243  A675  25pf Mink            .25   .20
2244  A675  35pf Stone marten   1.10  1.10
        *Nos. 2241-2244 (4)*     1.75  1.70

**Souvenir Sheet**

Goethe-Schiller Awards, 1980-
1984 — A676

**1982, Mar. 9                    Litho.**
2245      Sheet of 2            2.60  2.10
   a.    50pf Goethe            1.00  1.00
   b.    50pf Schiller          1.00  1.00

1982
Leipzig
Spring
Fair
A677

**1982, Mar. 9             *Perf. 13x12½***
2246  A677  10pf Entrance        .20   .20
2247  A677  25pf Exhibit         .30   .20

**Souvenir Sheet**

TB Bacillus Centenary — A678

**1982, Mar. 23             *Perf. 14***
2248  A678  1m multi            2.00  1.60

**Working-class Leader Type of 1979**

#2249, Max Fechner (1892-1973). #2250,
Ottomar Greschke (1882-1957). #2251,
Helmut Lehmann (1882-1959). #2252, Herbert
Warnke (1902-75). #2253, Otto Winzer (1902-
75).

**1982, Mar. 23                    Engr.**
2249  A623  10pf dk red brn      .20   .20
2250  A623  10pf green           .20   .20
2251  A623  10pf violet          .20   .20
2252  A623  10pf dull blue       .20   .20
2253  A623  10pf gray olive      .20   .20
        *Nos. 2249-2253 (5)*     1.00  1.00

Poisonous
Plants — A679

**1982, Apr. 6    Litho.    *Perf. 14***
2254  A679  10pf Meadow saffron  .20   .20
2255  A679  15pf Water arum      .20   .20
2256  A679  20pf Marsh tea       .20   .20
2257  A679  25pf White bryony    .20   .20

| | | | |
|---|---|---|---|
| 2258 | A679 | 35pf Common monkshood | .25 .20 |
| 2259 | A679 | 50pf Henbane | 1.20 1.25 |
| | | Nos. 2254-2259 (6) | 2.25 2.25 |

Free Federation
of German
Trade Unions,
10th Congress
A680

Paintings: 10pf, Mother and Child, by Walter Womacka. 20pf, Discussion at the Innovator Collective, by Willi Neubert, horiz. 25pf, Young Couple, by Karl-Heinz Jacob.

**1982, Apr. 20**                    **Photo.**
| | | | |
|---|---|---|---|
| 2260 | A680 | 10pf multi | .20 .20 |
| 2261 | A680 | 20pf multi | .20 .20 |
| 2262 | A680 | 25pf multi | .55 .55 |
| | | Nos. 2260-2262 (3) | .95 .95 |

Intl. Book Art
Exhibition,
Leipzig — A681

**1982, Apr. 20**
| | | | |
|---|---|---|---|
| 2263 | A681 | 15pf "I" | .35 .35 |
| 2264 | A681 | 35pf Emblem | .35 .35 |
| a. | | Pair, #2263-2264 + label | 1.25 1.10 |

A682

Protected species. 10pf, 25pf, 35pf vert.

**Perf. 13½x14, 14x13½**
**1982, May 18**                    **Photo.**
| | | | |
|---|---|---|---|
| 2265 | A682 | 10pf Fish hawk | .25 .20 |
| 2266 | A682 | 20pf Sea eagle | .25 .20 |
| 2267 | A682 | 25pf Tawny eagle | .25 .20 |
| 2268 | A682 | 35pf Eagle owl | 1.25 1.25 |
| | | Nos. 2265-2268 (4) | 2.00 1.85 |

19th Workers' Festival,
Neubrandenburg — A683

**1982, June 8**              **Photo.**              **Perf. 14**
| | | | |
|---|---|---|---|
| 2269 | A683 | 10pf View of Neubrandenburg | .20 .20 |
| 2270 | A683 | 20pf Traditional costumes | .35 .30 |

Souvenir Sheet

Dimitrov Memorial Medal — A684

**1982, June 8**
| | | | |
|---|---|---|---|
| 2271 | A684 | 1m multi | 2.25 2.25 |

George Dimitrov (1882-1947), first prime minister of Bulgaria.

Cargo Ship Frieden — A685

**1982, June 22**
| | | | |
|---|---|---|---|
| 2272 | A685 | 5pf shown | .20 .20 |
| 2273 | A685 | 10pf Fichtelberg | .20 .20 |
| 2274 | A685 | 15pf Brocken | .20 .20 |
| 2275 | A685 | 20pf Weimar | .20 .20 |
| 2276 | A685 | 25pf Vorwarts | .25 .20 |
| 2277 | A685 | 35pf Berlin | 1.20 1.20 |
| | | Nos. 2272-2277 (6) | 2.25 2.20 |

Society for Sport &
Technology — A686

**1982, June 22**      **Litho.**      **Perf. 13x12½**
| | | | |
|---|---|---|---|
| 2278 | A686 | 20pf multi | .35 .20 |

Bird Wedding — A687

Sorbian Folklore: 20pf, Zampern masqueraders. 25pf, Easter egg game. 35pf, Painting Easter eggs. 40pf, St. John's Day parade. 50pf, Christmas celebration.

**1982, July 6**      **Litho.**      **Perf. 13x12½**
| | | | |
|---|---|---|---|
| 2279 | A687 | Block of 6 | 3.75 3.25 |
| a. | | 10pf multi | .20 .20 |
| b. | | 20pf multi | .25 .20 |
| c. | | 25pf multi | .30 .30 |
| d. | | 35pf multi | .55 .55 |
| e. | | 40pf multi | .60 .60 |
| f. | | 50pf multi | .75 .75 |

View of
Schwerin
A688

7th Youth Stamp Exhibition, Schwerin: 10pf + 5pf, View, 1640.

**1982, July 6**
| | | | |
|---|---|---|---|
| 2280 | A688 | 10pf + 5pf multi | .30 .30 |
| 2281 | A688 | 20pf multi | .30 .30 |
| a. | | Pair, #2280-2281 + label | 1.25 1.00 |

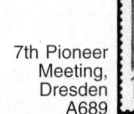

7th Pioneer
Meeting,
Dresden
A689

**1982, July 20**      **Photo.**      **Perf. 14x13½**
| | | | |
|---|---|---|---|
| 2282 | A689 | 10pf + 5pf Pioneers, banner | .45 .45 |
| 2283 | A689 | 20pf Bugle, pennant | .20 .20 |

Seascape, by Ludolf Backhuysen
(1631-1708) — A690

17th Cent. Paintings in Natl. Museum, Schwerin: 10pf, Music Making at Home, by Frans van Mieris (1635-1681), vert. 20pf, The Gate Guard, by Carel Fabritius (1622-1654), vert. 25pf, Farmers Company, by Adriaen Brouwer (1606-1638). 35pf, Breakfast Table with Ham, by Willem Claesz Heda (1593-1680). 70pf, River Landscape, by Jan van Goyen (1596-1656).

**1982, Aug. 10**                    **Perf. 14**
| | | | |
|---|---|---|---|
| 2284 | A690 | 5pf multi | .20 .20 |
| 2285 | A690 | 10pf multi | .20 .20 |
| 2286 | A690 | 20pf multi | .20 .20 |
| 2287 | A690 | 25pf multi | .25 .20 |
| 2288 | A690 | 35pf multi | .25 .20 |
| 2289 | A690 | 70pf multi | 1.80 1.50 |
| | | Nos. 2284-2289 (6) | 2.90 2.50 |

1982
Leipzig
Autumn
Fair
A691

**1982, Aug. 24**      **Litho.**      **Perf. 13x12½**
| | | | |
|---|---|---|---|
| 2290 | A691 | 10pf Exhibition Hall | .20 .20 |
| 2291 | A691 | 25pf Decorative box, ring | .25 .20 |

Karl-Marx-Stadt Buildings and
Monument — A692

**1982, Aug. 24**      **Photo.**      **Perf. 14**
| | | | |
|---|---|---|---|
| 2292 | A692 | 10pf multi + label | .20 .20 |

Org. for the Cooperation of Socialist Countries and Posts and Telecommunications Dept., 13th Conference, Karl-Marx-Stadt, Sept. 6-11.

Intl. Federation of
Resistance
Fighters, 9th
Congress,
Berlin — A693

**1982, Sept. 7**      **Litho.**      **Perf. 14**
| | | | |
|---|---|---|---|
| 2293 | A693 | 10pf Emblem | .35 .25 |

Auschwitz-
Birkenau Intl.
Memorial
A694

**1982, Sept. 7**                    **Photo.**
| | | | |
|---|---|---|---|
| 2294 | A694 | 35pf multi | .35 .30 |

Autumn
Flowers — A695

**1982, Sept. 21**
| | | | |
|---|---|---|---|
| 2295 | A695 | 5pf Autumn anemones | .20 .20 |
| 2296 | A695 | 10pf Student flowers | .20 .20 |
| 2297 | A695 | 15pf Hybrid gazanias | .20 .20 |
| 2298 | A695 | 20pf Sunflowers | .20 .20 |
| 2299 | A695 | 25pf Chrysanthemums | .25 .20 |
| 2300 | A695 | 35pf Cosmos bipinnatus | 1.80 1.50 |
| | | Nos. 2295-2300 (6) | 2.85 2.50 |

Ambulance — A696

**1982, Oct. 5**      **Litho.**      **Perf. 13x12½**
| | | | |
|---|---|---|---|
| 2301 | A696 | 5pf shown | .20 .20 |
| 2302 | A696 | 10pf Street cleaner | .20 .20 |
| 2303 | A696 | 20pf Bus | .20 .20 |
| 2304 | A696 | 25pf Platform truck | .25 .20 |
| 2305 | A696 | 35pf Platform truck, diff. | .25 .20 |
| 2306 | A696 | 85pf Milk truck | 2.10 1.80 |
| | | Nos. 2301-2306 (6) | 3.20 2.80 |

25th Masters of
Tomorrow Central
Fair — A697

**1982, Oct. 19**                    **Perf. 14**
| | | | |
|---|---|---|---|
| 2307 | A697 | 20pf multicolored | .30 .20 |

Martin Luther
(1483-1546)
A698

Designs: 10pf, Seal of Eisleben (town of birth and death). 20pf, Portrait, Eisenach, 1521. 35pf, Wittenberg seal, 1500. 85pf, Portrait, after Cranach, 1528.

**1982, Nov. 23**      **Photo.**      **Perf. 14x13½**
| | | | |
|---|---|---|---|
| 2308 | A698 | 10pf multi | .25 .20 |
| 2309 | A698 | 20pf multi | .25 .20 |
| a. | | Miniature sheet of 10 | 7.50 7.50 |
| 2310 | A698 | 35pf multi | .35 .20 |
| 2311 | A698 | 85pf multi | 3.00 1.90 |
| | | Nos. 2308-2311 (4) | 3.85 2.50 |

Toy Carpenter,
1830 — A699

**1982, Nov. 23**      **Litho.**      **Perf. 14**
| | | | |
|---|---|---|---|
| 2312 | | Sheet of 6 | 3.25 3.25 |
| a. | A699 | 10pf shown | .20 .20 |
| b. | A699 | 20pf Cobbler | 1.00 1.00 |
| c. | A699 | 25pf Baker | .20 .20 |
| d. | A699 | 35pf Cooper | .20 .20 |
| e. | A699 | 40pf Tanner | 1.00 1.00 |
| f. | A699 | 70pf Carter | .20 .20 |

Souvenir Sheet

Johannes Brahms (1833-1897),
Composer — A700

**1983, Jan. 11    Litho.    Perf. 14**
2313  A700  1.15m multi                2.60 2.10

**Working-class Leader Type of 1979**

#2314, Franz Dahlem (1892-1981). #2315,
Karl Maron (1903-75). #2316, Josef Miller
(1883-1964). #2317, Fred Oelssner (1903-77).
#2318, Siegfried Radel (1893-1943).

**1983, Jan. 25                     Photo.**
2314  A623  10pf dark brown            .20   .20
2315  A623  10pf dark green            .20   .20
2316  A623  10pf dark olive grn        .20   .20
2317  A623  10pf deep plum             .20   .20
2318  A623  10pf dark blue             .20   .20
      Nos. 2314-2318 (5)              1.00  1.00

World Communications Year — A701

**1983, Feb. 8      Photo.      Perf. 14**
2319  A701   5pf Telephone re-
                 ceiver, buttons      .20   .20
2320  A701  10pf Rugen radio          .20   .20
2321  A701  20pf Surface and air
                 mail                 .20   .20
2322  A701  35pf Optical conduc-
                 tors                1.10  1.10
      Nos. 2319-2322 (4)             1.70  1.70

Otto Nuschke
(1883-1957),
Statesman
A702

**1983, Feb. 8**
2323  A702  20pf red brn, bl & blk    .30   .20

Town Hall, Gera,
1576 — A703

**1983, Feb. 22     Photo.      Perf. 14**
2324  A703  10pf Stolberg, 1482,
                 horiz.               .20   .20
2325  A703  20pf shown                .20   .20
2326  A703  25pf Possneck, 1486       .20   .20
2327  A703  35pf Berlin, 1869,
                 horiz.              1.20  1.20
      Nos. 2324-2327 (4)             1.80  1.80

1983 Leipzig
Spring
Fair — A704

**1983, Mar. 8**
2328  A704  10pf Fair building        .20   .20
2329  A704  25pf Robotron
                 microcomputer        .30   .25

Paul Robeson (1898-1976),
Singer — A705

**1983, Mar. 22    Litho.    Perf. 13x12½**
2330  A705  20pf multicolored         .30   .25

Souvenir Sheet

Schulze-Boysen/Harnack Resistance
Org. — A706

Arvid Harnack (1901-42), Harro Schulze-
Boysen (1909-42), John Sieg (1903-42).

**1983, Mar. 22**
2331  A706  85pf multicolored        1.40  1.40

Karl Marx (1818-1883), and
Newspaper Mastheads — A707

Portraits and: 20pf, Lyons silk weavers'
revolt, 1831, French-German Yearbook. 35pf,
Engels, Communist Manifesto. 50pf, Das
Kapital titlepage. 70pf, Program of German
Workers' Movement text. 85pf, Engels, Lenin,
globe. 1.15m Portrait (24x29mm).

**1983, Apr. 11   Photo.   Perf. 13x12½**
2332  A707  10pf multicolored         .20   .20
2333  A707  20pf multicolored         .20   .20
2334  A707  35pf multicolored         .25   .20
2335  A707  50pf multicolored         .25   .20
2336  A707  70pf multicolored         .35   .25
2337  A707  85pf multicolored        2.25  2.25
      Nos. 2332-2337 (6)             3.50  3.30

Souvenir Sheet

**            Litho.      Perf. 14**
2338  A707  1.15m multi              2.25  1.80

Works of Art from
Berlin State
Museums — A708

**1983, Apr. 19     Photo.      Perf. 14**
2339  A708  10pf Athena               .20   .20
2340  A708  20pf Amazon, bronze,
                 430 BC               .35   .25

Narrow-Gauge Railroads — A709

**1983, May 17   Litho.   Perf. 13x12½**
2341      Pair, Wernigerode-Nord-
              hausen line            1.50  1.10
  a.  A709 15pf Locomotive           .35   .35
  b.  A709 20pf Passenger car        .35   .35
2342      Pair, Zittau-
              Oybin/Johnsdorf line   1.50  1.10
  a.  A709 20pf Locomotive           .35   .35
  b.  A709 50pf Freight car          .35   .35

    Nos. 2341 and 2342 se-tenant with labels
showing maps. See Nos. 2405-2406.

Sand Glasses          Cacti
and Sundials          A711
A710

**1983, June 7      Photo.      Perf. 14**
2343  A710   5pf Sand glass,
                 16/4                 .20   .20
2344  A710  10pf Sand glass,
                 1700                 .20   .20
2345  A710  20pf Sundial, 1611        .20   .20
  a.       Sheet of 6                2.25  2.25
2346  A710  30pf Sundial, 1750        .25   .20
2347  A710  50pf Sundial, 1760        .35   .20
2348  A710  85pf Sundial, 1800       2.10  1.90
      Nos. 2343-2348 (6)             3.30  2.90

**1983, June 21**
2349  A711   5pf Coryphantha ele-
                 phantidens          .20   .20
2350  A711  10pf Thelocactus
                 schwarzii           .20   .20
2351  A711  20pf Leuchtenbergia
                 principis           .20   .20
2352  A711  25pf Submatucana
                 madisoniorum        .25   .20
2353  A711  35pf Oroya peruviana     .25   .20
2354  A711  50pf Copiapoa ciner-
                 ea                  1.50  1.50
      Nos. 2349-2354 (6)             2.60  2.50

Naumberg
Cathedral
Statues,
15th Cent.
A712

**1983, July 5      Photo.      Perf. 13**
2355  A712  20pf Thimo and Wil-
                 helm                 .35   .35
2356  A712  25pf Gepa and
                 Gerburg             .45   .45
2357  A712  35pf Hermann and
                 Reglindis           .55   .55
2358  A712  85pf Eckehard and
                 Uta                 1.25  1.25
  a.       Block of 4, #2355-2358    3.00  2.90

Technical
Training,
by Harald
Metzkes
(b. 1929)
A713

SOZPHILEX '83 Junior Stamp Exhibition,
Berlin:  10pf+5pf, Glasewaldt and Zinna
Defending the Barricade-18th March, 1848, by
Theodor Hosemann, vert.  Surtax was for
exhibition.

**1983, July 5      Litho.      Perf. 13x12½**
2359  A713  10pf + 5pf multi          .60   .55
2360  A713  20pf multi                .25   .20

Volleyball
A714

**1983, July 19    Photo.    Perf. 14**
2361  A714  10pf + 5pf Passing
                 beach balls         .55   .35
2362  A714  20pf shown                .20   .20

    7th Gymnastic and Sports Meeting; 9th Chil-
dren's and Youth Spartikiade, Leipzig.

Simon Bolivar (1783-1830) — A715

**1983, July 19**
2363  A715  35pf Bolivar, Alexander
                 von Humboldt         .55   .30

A715A                 A716

City Arms

**1983, Aug. 9**
2364  A715A 50pf Berlin               .70   .60
2365  A716  50pf Cottbus              .70   .60
2366  A716  50pf Dresden              .70   .60
2367  A716  50pf Erfurt               .70   .60
2368  A716  50pf Frankfurt            .70   .60
      Nos. 2364-2368 (5)             3.50  3.00

    See Nos. 2398-2402, 2464-2468.

1983 Leipzig
Autumn
Fair — A717

**1983, Aug. 30**
2369  A717  10pf Central Palace       .20   .20
2370  A717  25pf Microelectronic pat-
                 tern                 .45   .25

Leonhard Euler (1707-1783),
Mathematician — A718

**1983, Sept. 6**
2371  A718  20pf multi                .45   .25

## Souvenir Sheet

30th Anniv. of Working-Class Brigade Groups — A719

**1983, Sept. 6   Litho.   Perf. 12½x13**
2372  A719  1m multicolored   2.10 1.50

Governmental Palaces, Potsdam Gardens — A720

**1983, Sept. 20   Perf. 13x12½**
2373  A720  10pf Sanssouci Palace   .20 .20
2374  A720  20pf Chinese teahouse   .25 .25
2375  A720  40pf Charlottenhof Palace   .35 .25
2376  A720  50pf Royal Stables, Film Museum   2.25 2.25
   Nos. 2373-2376 (4)   3.05 2.90

Monument, Mamajew-Kurgan Hill — A721

**1983, Oct. 4   Perf. 14**
2377  A721  35pf Mother Home   .45 .25

## Souvenir Sheet

Martin Luther — A722

**1983, Oct. 18   Litho.   Perf. 14**
2378  A722  1m multi   2.60 2.25
   Margin shows title page from Luther Bible, 1541.

Thuringian Glass — A723

**1983, Nov. 8   Photo.   Perf. 13½x14**
2379  A723  10pf Cock   .25 .20
2380  A723  20pf Cup   .25 .20
2381  A723  25pf Vase   .25 .20
2382  A723  70pf Ornamental Glass   1.60 1.50
   Nos. 2379-2382 (4)   2.35 2.10

## Souvenir Sheet

New Year 1984 — A724

**1983, Nov. 22   Litho.   Perf. 14**
2383  Sheet of 4   1.60 1.50
a.  A724 10pf multi   .20 .20
b.  A724 20pf multi   .25 .20
c.  A724 25pf multi   .35 .30
d.  A724 35pf multi   .55 .45

Winter Olympics 1984, Sarajevo A725

**1983, Nov. 22   Photo.   Perf. 14**
2384  A725  10pf + 5pf 2-man luge   .20 .20
2385  A725  20pf + 10pf Ski jump   .20 .20
2386  A725  25pf Skiing   .20 .20
2387  A725  35pf Biathlon   1.50 1.10
   Nos. 2384-2387 (4)   2.10 1.70

**Souvenir Sheet**
2388  A725  85pf Olympic Center   1.60 1.50

Jena Glass Centenary — A726

**1984, Jan. 10   Litho.   Perf. 12½x13**
2389  A726  20pf Otto Schott   .35 .25

**Working-class Leader Type of 1979**
   Designs: No. 2390, Friedrich Ebert (1894-1979). No. 2391, Fritz Grosse (1904-1957). No. 2392, Albert Norden (1904-1982).

**1984, Jan. 24   Engr.   Perf. 14**
2390  A623  10pf black   .20 .20
2391  A623  10pf dark green   .20 .20
2392  A623  10pf dark blue   .20 .20
   Nos. 2390-2392 (3)   .60 .60

## Souvenir Sheet

Felix Mendelssohn (1809-1847), Composer — A727

**1984, Jan. 24   Litho.**
2393  A727  85pf multi   1.00 1.00
   Margin shows Song Without Words score.

Postal Milestones — A728

   Designs: 10pf, Muhlau, 1725; Oederan, 1722. 20pf, Johanngeorgenstadt, 1723; Schonbrunn, 1724. 35pf, Freiberg, 1723. 85pf, Pegau, 1723.

**1984, Feb. 7   Photo.   Perf. 14**
2394  A728  10pf multi   .20 .20
2395  A728  20pf multi   .30 .25
2396  A728  35pf multi   .35 .30
2397  A728  85pf multi   .75 .75
   Nos. 2394-2397 (4)   1.60 1.50

**City Arms Type of 1983**
**1984, Feb. 21**
2398  A716  50pf Gera   .45 .35
2399  A716  50pf Halle   .45 .35
2400  A716  50pf Karl-Marx-Stadt   .45 .35
2401  A716  50pf Leipzig   .45 .35
2402  A716  50pf Magdeburg   .45 .35
   Nos. 2398-2402 (5)   2.25 1.75

1984 Leipzig Spring Fair A729

**1984, Mar. 6   Perf. 14**
2403  A729  10pf Old Town Hall   .20 .20
2404  A729  25pf Factory   .30 .25

**Railroad Type of 1983**
**1984, Mar. 20   Litho.   Perf. 13x12½**
2405  Pair, Cranzahl Oberwiesenthal line   1.40 1.20
a.  A709 30pf Locomotive   .25 .25
b.  A709 80pf Passenger car   .60 .60
2406  Pair, Selke Valley line   1.30 1.05
a.  A709 40pf Locomotive   .30 .30
b.  A709 60pf Passenger car   .35 .35
   Labels show maps of routes.

Stone Door, Rostock — A730     Council Building — A731

   Intl. Society of Monument Preservation 7th General Meeting: 10pf, Town Hall, Rostock. 15pf, Albrecht Castle, Meissen. 85pf, Stable Courtyard, Dresden. 10pf, 15pf, 85pf horiz.

**1984, Apr. 24   Photo.   Perf. 14**
2407  A730  10pf multi   .20 .20
2408  A730  15pf multi   .20 .20
2409  A730  40pf multi   .45 .35
2410  A730  85pf multi   1.10 1.00
   Nos. 2407-2410 (4)   1.95 1.75

**1984, May 8**
2411  A731  70pf multi   .70 .30
   Standing Commission of Posts and Telecommunications of Council of Mutual Economic Aid, 25th meeting.

Cast-iron Bowl, 19th Cent. A732     Marionette A733

   Cast-Iron, Lauchhammer: 85pf, Ascending Man, by Fritz Cremer, 1967.

**1984, May 22**
2412  A732  20pf multi   .25 .20
2413  A732  85pf multi   .85 .85

**1984, June 5**
2414  A733  50pf shown   .55 .55
2415  A733  80pf Puppet   .90 .90

Natl. Youth Festival A734

**1984, June 5   Litho.   Perf. 13x12½**
2416  A734  10pf + 5pf Demonstration   .20 .20
2417  A734  20pf Construction workers   .25 .25
a.  Pair, #2416-2417 + label   1.10 .60

20th Workers' Festival A735

**1984, June 19**
2418  A735  10pf View of Gera   .20 .20
2419  A735  20pf Traditional costumes   .25 .25
a.  Pair, #2418-2419 + label   .85 .55

Natl. Stamp Exhib., Halle — A736

**1984, July 3   Perf. 13½x14**
2420  A736  10pf + 5pf Salt carrier   .20 .20
2421  A736  20pf Wedding couple   .30 .25

Historic Seals, 1442 — A737

**1984, Aug. 7   Litho.   Perf. 14**
2422  A737  5pf Baker, Berlin   .30 .20
2423  A737  10pf Wool weaver, Berlin   .55 .30
2424  A737  20pf Wool weaver, Cologne   1.00 .35
2425  A737  35pf Shoemaker, Cologne   1.60 1.50
a.  Block of 4, #2422-2425   4.25 2.50

Building Renovation and Construction A738

Ironwork Collective Combine East — A739

Litho., Photo. (#2427, 2429, 25pf)

1984 ***Perf. 14x13½***

2426 A738 10pf shown .20 .20
2427 A739 10pf shown .20 .20
2428 A738 20pf Surface mining .30 .30
2429 A739 20pf Armed forces .25 .25
2430 A739 25pf Petro-chemical Collective Combine, Schwedt .30 .30
Nos. 2426-2430 (5) 1.25 1.25

Souvenir Sheets

2431 A738 1m Privy Council Building 1.00 1.00
2432 A739 1m Family 1.00 1.00

DDR, 35th anniv. Issued: A738, 8/21; A739, 9/11.

1984 Leipzig Autumn Fair — A740

1984, Aug. 28 **Photo.** ***Perf. 14***

2433 A740 10pf Frege House, Katharine St. .20 .20
2434 A740 25pf Crystal bowl, Olbernhau .30 .25

Members of the Resistance, Sculpture by Arno Wittig — A741

1984, Sept. 18 **Photo.** ***Perf. 14***

2435 A741 35pf multi .70 .30

View of Magdeburg — A742

1984, Oct. 4 **Litho.** ***Perf. 13x12½***

2436 A742 10pf + 5pf shown .20 .20
2437 A742 20pf Old & modern buildings .20 .20
a. Pair, #2436-2437 + label 1.00 .75

8th Youth Stamp Exhibition, Magdeburg.

35th Anniv. of Republic — A743

1984, Oct. 4 **Photo.** ***Perf. 14***

2438 A743 10pf Construction .20 .20
2439 A743 20pf Military .25 .20
2440 A743 25pf Heavy industry .30 .30
2441 A743 35pf Agriculture .35 .35
Nos. 2438-2441 (4) 1.10 1.05

Souvenir Sheet

2442 A743 1m Arms, dove, vert. 1.00 1.00

Figurines, Green Vault of Dresden — A744

1984, Oct. 23

2443 A744 10pf Spring .20 .20
2444 A744 20pf Summer .25 .20
a. Miniature sheet of 8, litho., perf. 12½x13 2.40 2.40
2445 A744 35pf Autumn .30 .30
2446 A744 70pf Winter .75 .75
Nos. 2443-2446 (4) 1.50 1.45

Falkenstein Castle — A745

1984, Nov. 6 **Litho.** ***Perf. 14***

2447 A745 10pf shown .20 .20
2448 A745 20pf Kriebstein .25 .25
2449 A745 35pf Ranis .45 .45
2450 A745 80pf Neuenburg .75 .75
Nos. 2447-2450 (4) 1.65 1.65

See Nos. 2504-2507.

Dead Tsar's Daughter and the Seven Warriors — A746

Various scenes from the fairytale.

1984, Nov. 27 **Litho.** ***Perf. 13***

2451 Sheet of 6 *10.00* 4.50
a. A746 5pf multi *.25* .25
b. A746 10pf multi *.25* .25
c. A746 15pf multi *2.60* 1.50
d. A746 20pf multi *2.60* 1.50
e. A746 35pf multi *.25* .25
f. A746 50pf multi *.25* .25

Working-class Leader Type of 1979

Designs: No. 2452, Anton Ackermann (1905-1973). No. 2453, Alfred Kurella (1895-1975). No. 2454, Otto Schon (1905-1968).

1985, Jan. 8 **Engr.** ***Perf. 14***

2452 A623 10pf blk brn .20 .20
2453 A623 10pf red brn .20 .20
2454 A623 10pf gray vio .20 .20
Nos. 2452-2454 (3) .60 .60

24th World Luge Championship — A747

1985, Jan. 22 **Photo.**

2455 A747 10pf Single seat luge .30 .20

Antique Mailboxes — A748

1985, Feb. 5 **Litho.** ***Perf. 14***

2456 A748 10pf 1850 .20 .20
2457 A748 20pf 1860 .20 .20
2458 A748 35pf 1900 .30 .30
2459 A748 50pf 1920 .45 .45
a. Block of 4, Nos. 2456-2459 1.40 1.40

Souvenir Sheet

Dresden Opera House Reopening — A749

Litho. & Engr.

1985, Feb. 12 ***Perf. 13***

2460 A749 85pf multicolored 1.00 1.00

1985 Leipzig Spring Fair A750

Bach, Handel and Schutz Tribute A751

1985, Mar. 5 **Photo.** ***Perf. 14***

2461 A750 10pf Statue of Bach, Leipzig .20 .20
2462 A750 25pf Porcelain pot, Meissen .30 .25

Souvenir Sheet

1985, Mar. 19 **Litho.**

2463 Sheet of 3 1.80 1.80
a. A751 10pf Bach .25 .25
b. A751 20pf Handel .25 .25
c. A751 85pf Heinrich Schutz (1585-1672) .75 .75

City Arms Type of 1983

1985, Apr. 9 **Photo.** ***Perf. 14***

2464 A716 50pf Neubrandenburg .45 .35
2465 A716 50pf Potsdam .45 .35
2466 A716 50pf Rostock .45 .35
2467 A716 50pf Schwerin .45 .35
2468 A716 50pf Suhl .75 .75
Nos. 2464-2468 (5) 2.55 2.15

Seelow Heights Memorial — A752

1985, Apr. 16 **Photo.** ***Perf. 14***

2469 A752 35pf multi .45 .30

Egon Erwin Kisch, Journalist (1885-1948) — A753

1985, Apr. 23 **Photo.** ***Perf. 14***

2470 A753 35pf multi .30 .20

No. 2470 was printed se-tenant with label showing the house where Kisch was born. Value, single with attached label: unused 45c; used 35c.

Liberation from Fascism, 40th Anniv. — A754

Designs: 10pf, German and Soviet astronauts. 20pf, Coal miner Adolf Hennecke, symbols of industry and energy. 25pf, farm workers, symbols of socialist agriculture. 50pf, Technicians manufacturing microchips, science and technology.

1985, May 7 **Photo.** ***Perf. 14x13½***

2471 A754 10pf multi .20 .20
2472 A754 20pf multi .25 .25
2473 A754 25pf multi .25 .25
2474 A754 50pf multi .45 .45
Nos. 2471-2474 (4) 1.15 1.15

Souvenir Sheet

Perf. 12½x13

2475 A754 1m Berlin-Treptow Soviet Heroes Monument 1.10 1.10

Warsaw Treaty, 30th Anniv. — A755

1985, May 14 **Litho.** ***Perf. 13x12½***

2476 A755 20pf Flags of pact nations .35 .25

Historical and Modern Buildings A756

12th Youth Parliament, Berlin: 20pf, Ernst Thalmann, flags.

1985, May 21 **Litho.**

2477 A756 10pf + 5pf multi .20 .20
2478 A756 20pf multi .20 .20
a. Pair, #2477-2478 + label .60 .60

Intl. Olympic Committee 90th Meeting — A757

1985, May 28 **Litho.** ***Perf. 14***

2479 A757 35pf Flag .30 .25

No. 2479 was printed setenant with label depicting Olympic Torches. Value of single with attached label: unused 85c; used 60c.

Free German Trade Unions, 40th Anniv. — A758

1985, June 11 **Photo.**

2480 A758 20pf Red flags .30 .20

Wildlife Preservation A759

**1985, June 25**     Photo.
2481 A759 5pf Harpy eagle, vert. .20 .20
2482 A759 10pf Red-necked goose .20 .20
2483 A759 20pf Spectacled bear .25 .20
2484 A759 50pf Banteng (Javanese) buffalo .45 .45
2485 A759 85pf Sunda Straits crocodile .90 .90
Nos. 2481-2485 (5) 2.00 1.95

19th Century Steam Engines A760

**1985, July 9**     Photo.
2486 A760 10pf Bock engine, vert. .20 .20
2487 A760 85pf Beam engine .85 .75

12th World Youth and Student Festival, Moscow A761

**1985, July 23**    Litho.   Perf. 13x12½
2488 A761 20pf + 5pf Students reading .25 .25
2489 A761 50pf Student demonstration .35 .35
a. Pair, #2488-2489 + label 1.00 .90

2nd World Orienteering and Deep-sea Diving Championship — A762

**1985, Aug. 13**   Photo.   Perf. 14
2490 A762 10pf Diver at turning buoy .20 .20
2491 A762 70pf Long-distance divers .75 .75

Bose House Fair Building, St. Thomas Churchyard — A763

**1985, Apr. 27**     Photo.
2492 A763 10pf shown .20 .20
2493 A763 25pf Bach trumpet .35 .25

Leipzig Autumn Fair.

A764

SOZPHILEX '85: 19th century coach and team, 1878, bas-relief by Hermann Steinemann, in the court of the former Berlin Post Office.

**1985, Sept. 10**   Litho.   Perf. 13x12½
2494 5pf multi .20 .20
2495 20pf + 5pf multi .25 .25
a. Miniature sheet of 4 #2495b .75 .75
b. A764 Pair, #2494-2495 .45 .45

No. 2495b has a continuous design.

German Railways 150th Anniv. — A765

Socialist Railway Org.: 20pf, GS II signal box, track diagram. 25pf, 1838 Saxonia, first German locomotive, designer Johann Andreas Schubert (1808-1870), Model 250 electric locomotive. 50pf, Helicopter lifting cable drum, section electrification. 85pf, Leipzig Central Station.

**Litho.**   Perf. 12½x13
**1985, Sept. 24**
2496 A765 20pf multi .25 .20
2497 A765 25pf multi .30 .25
2498 A765 50pf multi .60 .55
2499 A765 85pf multi .90 .90
Nos. 2496-2499 (4) 2.05 1.90

Bridges in East Berlin A766

**Photo.; Litho. (#2501a)**
**1985, Oct. 8**     Perf. 14
2500 A766 10pf Gertrauden .20 .20
2501 A766 20pf Jungfern .25 .25
a. Min. sheet of 8, perf. 13x12½ 3.00 3.00
2502 A766 35pf Weidendammer .35 .35
2503 A766 70pf Marx-Engels .60 .60
Nos. 2500-2503 (4) 1.40 1.40

**Castles Type of 1984**
**1985, Oct. 15**     Litho.
2504 A745 10pf Hohnstein .20 .20
2505 A745 20pf Rochsburg .20 .20
2506 A745 35pf Schwarzenberg .30 .30
2507 A745 80pf Stein .90 .90
Nos. 2504-2507 (4) 1.60 1.60

Humboldt University, 175th Anniv. — A767

85pf, Charity Hospital, Berlin, 275th anniv.

**1985, Oct. 22**     Perf. 14
2508 A767 20pf Administration bldg. .25 .20
2509 A767 85pf Buildings, 1897, 1982 .90 .90

Castle Cacilienhof, UN Emblem A768

**1985, Oct. 22**   Photo.   Perf. 13
2510 A768 85pf multi .90 .45

UN, 40th Anniv.

Circus Art — A769

**1985, Nov. 12**     Perf. 14
2511 A769 10pf Elephant training .25 .25
2512 A769 20pf Trapeze artist .45 .45
2513 A769 35pf Acrobats on unicycles .90 .90
2514 A769 50pf Tiger training 1.40 1.40
a. Block of 4, #2511-2514 5.50 12.50

**Souvenir Sheet**

Brothers Grimm, Fabulists & Philologists A770

Fairy tales compiled by Wilhelm (1786-1859) and Jacob (1785-1863) Grimm.

**1985, Nov. 26**   Litho.   Perf. 13½x13
2515 Sheet of 6 2.75 6.75
a. A770 5pf multi .20 .20
b. A770 10pf Valiant Tailor .20 .20
c. A770 20pf Lucky John .55 1.25
d. A770 25pf Puss-in-Boots .55 1.25
e. A770 35pf Seven Ravens .20 .20
f. A770 85pf Sweet Porridge .20 .20

Monuments to Water Power — A772

Designs: 10pf, Cast iron hand pump, c. 1900. 35pf, Berlin-Altglienicke water tower, c. 1900. 50pf, Berlin-Friedrichshagen waterworks, 1893. 70pf, Rapphoden Hydro-electric Dam, 1959.

**Engr., Photo. & Engr. (35pf)**
**1986, Jan. 21**     Perf. 14
2516 A772 10pf dk grn & lake .20 .20
2517 A772 35pf buff, blk & dk grn .30 .30
2518 A772 50pf dk red brn & lt ol grn .55 .55
2519 A772 70pf dk bl & brn .70 .70
Nos. 2516-2519 (4) 1.75 1.75

Postal Uniforms, c. 1850 — A773

**1986, Feb. 4**   Photo.   Perf. 14½x14
2520 A773 10pf Saxon postillion .20 .20
a. Litho., perf. 12½x13 .20 .20
2521 A773 20pf Prussian postman .30 .25
a. Litho., perf. 12½x13 .30 .30
2522 A773 85pf Prussian P.O. clerk 1.05 1.00
a. Litho., perf. 12½x13 1.05 1.00
2523 A773 1m Mecklenburg clerk 1.40 1.40
a. Litho., perf. 12½x13 1.40 1.40
b. Block of 4, #2520a-2523a 3.25 3.00

Natl. People's Army, 30th Anniv. A774

**1986, Feb. 18**     Perf. 14
2524 A774 20pf multi .35 .20

No. 2524 printed se-tenant with gold and red inscribed label. Value of single with attached label: unused 60c; used 45c.

Free German Youth Org., 40th Anniv. — A775

**1986, Feb. 18**
2525 A775 20pf multi .35 .30

Leipzig Spring Fair A776

**1986, Mar. 11**   Litho.   Perf. 13x12½
2526 A776 35pf Fair grounds entrance, 1946 .30 .25
2527 A776 50pf Trawler Atlantik 488 .45 .35

Manned Space Flight, 25th Anniv. — A777

Designs: 40pf, Yuri Gagarin, Soviet cosmonaut, Vostok rocket, 1961. 50pf, Cosmonauts V. Bykowski, USSR, and S. Jahn, DDR, Vega probe, 1986, Intercosmos emblem. 70pf, Venera probe, Venus, spectrometer. 85pf, MKF-6 multi-spectral reconnaissance camera.

**1986, Mar. 25**     Perf. 14
2528 A777 40pf multi .30 .30
2529 A777 50pf multi .35 .35
2530 A777 70pf multi .55 .55
2531 A777 85pf multi .70 .70
a. Block of 4, #2528-2531 3.00 3.25

Socialist Unity 11th Party Day — A778

10pf, Marx, Engels & Lenin. 20pf, Ernst Thalmann. 50pf, Wilhelm Pieck & Otto Grotewohl, Uniting Party Day, 1946. 85pf,Family, motto. 1m, Construction worker, key to economic progress.

**1986, Apr. 8**     Perf. 13½x13
2532 A778 10pf multi .20 .20
2533 A778 20pf multi .25 .25
2534 A778 50pf multi .45 .45
2535 A778 85pf multi .90 .90
Nos. 2532-2535 (4) 1.80 1.80

**Souvenir Sheet**   Perf. 13x14
2536 A778 1m multi 1.05 1.05

Ernst Thalmann Park Opening, Berlin — A779

**1986, Apr. 15    Photo.    Perf. 14**
2537 A779 20pf Memorial statue    .35   .30

Trams and Streetcars — A780

Designs: 10pf, Dresden horse-drawn tram, 1886. 20pf, Leipzig streetcar, 1896. 40pf, Berlin streetcar, 1919. 70pf, Halle streetcar, 1928.

**1986, May 20    Photo.    Perf. 14**
2538 A780 10pf multicolored    .20   .20
2539 A780 20pf multicolored    .25   .25
2540 A780 40pf multicolored    .55   .55
2541 A780 70pf multicolored    .75   .75
     Nos. 2538-2541 (4)    1.75 1.75

Dresden Zoo, 125th Anniv. — A781    Berlin, 750th Anniv. — A782

**1986, May 27    Litho.    Perf. 14**
2542 A781 10pf Orangutan    .25   .25
2543 A781 20pf Colobus monkey    .35   .30
2544 A781 50pf Mandrill    .75   .75
2545 A781 70pf Lemur    .90   .90
     Nos. 2542-2545 (4)    2.25 2.15

**Litho. & Engr., Engr. (70pf, 1m)**
**1986, June 3    Perf. 12½x13, 13x12½**

20pf, 50pf are horiz.

2546 A782 10pf City seal, 1253    .25   .20
2547 A782 20pf Map, 1648    .45   .25
2548 A782 50pf City arms, 1253    .90   .60
2549 A782 70pf Nicholas Church, 1832    1.50 1.00
     Nos. 2546-2549 (4)    3.10 2.05
**Souvenir Sheet**
2550 A782 1m Royal Palace, 1986    1.25 1.25

21st Workers' Games, Magdeburg — A783

20pf, Couple in folk dress, house construction. 50pf, Magdeburg Port, River Elbe.

**1986, June 17   Litho.   Perf. 13x12½**
2551 A783 20pf multi    .20   .20
2552 A783 50pf multi    .30   .30
    a.   Pair, #2551-2552 + label    1.00 1.00

9th Youth Stamp Exhibition, Berlin — A784

**1986, July 22   Litho.   Perf. 13x12½**
2553 A784 10pf + 5pf Berlin, c. 1652    .20   .20
2554 A784 20pf Art, architecture, 1986    .20   .20
    a.   Pair, #2553-2554 + label    .45   .60

Castles A785

**1986, July 29     Perf. 13x12½**
2555 A785 10pf Schwerin    .20   .20
    a.   Miniature sheet of 4    .80   .80
2556 A785 20pf Gustrow    .25   .20
    a.   Miniature sheet of 4    1.10 1.10
2557 A785 85pf Rheinsberg    .85   .85
2558 A785 1m Ludwigslust    1.10 1.10
     Nos. 2555-2558 (4)    2.40 2.35

Intl. Peace Year A786

**1986, Aug. 5    Photo.    Perf. 13**
2559 A786 35pf multi    .55   .35

Berlin Wall, 25th Anniv. — A787

**1986, Aug. 5    Litho.    Perf. 14**
2560 A787 20pf Soldiers, Brandenburg Gate    .60   .35

**Souvenir Sheet**

Leipzig Autumn Fair — A788

**1986, Aug. 19**
2561 A788 Sheet of 2    1.20 1.20
    a.   25pf Fair building    .25   .25
    b.   85pf Cloth merchants, 15th cent.    .75   .75

City Coins A789

**1986, Sept. 2    Photo.    Perf. 13**
2562 A789 10pf Rostock, 1637    .20   .20
2563 A789 35pf Nordhausen, 1660    .30   .30
2564 A789 50pf Erfurt, 1633    .45   .35
2565 A789 85pf Magdeburg, 1638    .75   .75
2566 A789 1m Stralsund, 1622    1.10 1.10
     Nos. 2562-2566 (5)    2.80 2.70

44th World Sports Shooting Championships, Suhl — A790

**1986, Sept. 2      Perf. 14**
2567 A790 20pf Rifle shooting    .25   .20
2568 A790 70pf Woman firing handgun    .75   .70
2569 A790 85pf Skeet-shooting    .90   .85
     Nos. 2567-2569 (3)    1.90 1.75

11th World Trade Unions Congress, Berlin — A791

**1986, Sept. 9**
2570 A791 70pf multi+label    .90   .75

Border Guards, 40th Anniv. — A792

**1986, Sept. 9**
2571 A792 20pf multi    .35   .30

Intl. Brigades in Spain, 50th Anniv. — A793

**1986, Sept. 11**
2572 A793 20pf Memorial, Friedrichshain    .35   .25

Natl. Memorial for Concentration Camp Victims, Sachsenhausem, 25th Anniv. — A794

**1986, Sept. 23**
2573 A794 35pf multi    .45   .30

Mukran-Klaipeda Train-Ferry, Inauguration — A795

**1986, Sept. 23**
2574 A795 50pf Pier, Mukran    .35   .35
2575 A795 50pf Ferry    .35   .35
    a.   Pair, #2574-2575    1.25 1.25

**Souvenir Sheet**

Carl Maria von Weber (1786-1826), Composer — A796

**1986, Nov. 4    Litho.    Perf. 14**
2576 A796 85pf multi    1.10 1.10

Indira Gandhi (1917-1984), Prime Minister of India — A797

**1986, Nov. 18      Photo.**
2577 A797 10pf multi    .30   .20

**Miniature Sheet**

Chandeliers from the Ore Mountains A798

Wrought iron candle-carrying chandeliers presented to Johann Georgenstadt miners annually by the mine blacksmith.

**1986, Nov. 18    Photo.    Perf. 14**
2578    Sheet of 6    2.25 2.25
    a.   A798 10pf 1778    .20   .20
    b.   A798 20pf 1796    .20   .20
    c.   A798 25pf 1810    .55   .55
    d.   A798 35pf 1821    .55   .55
    e.   A798 40pf 1830    .20   .20
    f.   A798 85pf 1925    .20   .20

Statues of Roland, Medieval Hero — A799

**1987, Jan. 20   Photo.   Perf. 14½x14**
2579 A799 10pf Stendal, 1525    .20   .20
2580 A799 20pf Halle, 1719    .25   .20
2581 A799 35pf Brandenburg, 1474    .30   .30
2582 A799 50pf Quedlinburg, 1460    .55   .55
     Nos. 2579-2582 (4)    1.30 1.25

See Nos. 2782-2785.

Historic Post Offices A800

**1987, Feb. 3   Photo.   Perf. 14x14½**
2583 A800 10pf Freiberg, 1889    .20   .20
2584 A800 20pf Perleberg, 1897    .25   .25
2585 A800 70pf Weimar, 1889    .55   .55
2586 A800 1.20m Kirschau, 1926    1.10 1.10
    a.   Block of 4, #2583-2586    2.25 2.25

Nos. 2583-2586 printed in sheets of fifty and se-tenant in sheets of 40.

Berlin, 750th Anniv. A801

Architecture: 20pf, Reconstructed Palais Ephraim, Nikolai Quarter, demolished 1936, reopened 1987, vert. 35pf, Old Marzahn Village, modern housing. 70pf, Marx-Engels Forum, Central Berlin. 85pf, Reconstructed Friedrichstadt Palace Theater, reopened 1984.

**Perf. 12½x13, 13x12½**

**1987, Feb. 17**                    **Engr.**
2587 A801 20pf vio brn & bluish
grn                              .20   .20
2588 A801 35pf sage grn & dk
rose brn                        .30   .25
2589 A801 70pf org & dk bl          .70   .70
2590 A801 85pf dk ol grn & yel
grn                            1.00  1.00
   Nos. 2587-2590 (4)             2.20  2.15
      See Nos. 2628-2631.

Democratic Women's Federation, 40th Anniv. — A802

**1987, Mar. 3   Litho.   Perf. 13½**
2591 A802 10pf sil, dk bl & brt red  .30  .25

Leipzig Spring Fair A803

**1987, Mar. 10          Perf. 13x12½**
2592 A803 35pf New Fair Hall No.
20                               .30  .25
2593 A803 50pf Traders at market,
c. 1804                         .60  .60

Leaders of the German Workers' Movement — A804

#2594, Fritz Gabler (1897-1974). #2595, Robert Siewert (1887-1973). #2596, Walter Vesper (1897-1978). #2597, Clara Zetkin (1857-1933).

**1987, Mar. 24   Engr.   Perf. 14**
2594 A804 10pf dark gray           .20  .20
2595 A804 10pf dark green          .20  .20
2596 A804 10pf black               .20  .20
2597 A804 10pf vio black           .20  .20
   Nos. 2594-2597 (4)              .80  .80
      See Nos. 2721-2724.

K.A. Lingner (1861-1916), Museum A805

**1987, Apr. 7   Photo.   Perf. 14**
2598 A805 85pf multi               .85  .75
German Hygiene Museum, Dresden, 75th anniv.

Free German Trade Unions 11th Congress A806

**1987, Apr. 7   Litho.   Perf. 13x12½**
2599 A806 20pf Construction        .20  .20
2600 A806 50pf Computer, ship      .45  .45
   a.   Pair, #2599-2600 + label   .90  .90

German Red Cross 10th Congress A807

**1987, Apr. 7   Photo.   Perf. 14**
2601 A807 35pf multi               .45  .25

Agricultural Cooperative, 35th Anniv. — A808

**1987, Apr. 21   Litho.   Perf. 13x12½**
2602 A808 20pf multi               .35  .30

Famous Men A809

Designs: 10pf, Ludwig Uhland (1787-1862), poet, philologist. 20pf, Arnold Zweig (1887-1968), novelist. 35pf, Gerhart Hauptmann (1862-1946), 1912 Nobel laureate for literature, and scene from The Weavers. 50pf, Gustav Hertz (1887-1975), physicist, and atomic energy transmission diagram.

**1987, May 5**
2603 A809 10pf multi               .20  .20
2604 A809 20pf multi               .25  .25
2605 A809 35pf multi               .35  .35
2606 A809 50pf multi               .60  .60
   Nos. 2603-2606 (4)             1.40  1.40

Freshwater Fish — A810

**1987, May 19   Litho.   Perf. 13x12½**
2607 A810  5pf Abramis brama       .20  .20
2608 A810 10pf Salmo trutta fario  .25  .25
2609 A810 20pf Silurus glanis      .25  .25
2610 A810 35pf Thymallus
thymallus                        .35  .35
2611 A810 50pf Barbus barbus       .55  .55
2612 A810 70pf Esox lucius         .75  .75
   Nos. 2607-2612 (6)             2.35  2.15
Nos. 2608-2609 exist in sheets of 4.

Fire Engines A811

**1987, June 16**
2613 A811 10pf Hand-operated,
1756                             .20  .20
2614 A811 25pf Steam, 1903         .25  .25
2615 A811 40pf LF 15, 1919         .45  .45
2616 A811 70pf LF 16-TS 8,
1971                             .75  .75
   a.   Block of 4, Nos. 2613-2616 2.10 1.90

Souvenir Sheet

Esperanto Movement, Cent. — A812

**1987, July 7   Litho.   Perf. 14**
2617 A812 85pf L.L. Zamenhof,
globe                            .90  1.20

World Wildlife Fund A813

**1987, July 7          Photo.**
2618 A813 10pf Two otters          .20  .20
2619 A813 25pf Otter swimming      .55  .20
2620 A813 35pf Otter              1.00  .30
2621 A813 60pf Close-up of head   2.25  .70
   Nos. 2618-2621 (4)             4.00  1.40

8th Sports Festival and 11th Youth Sports Championships, Leipzig — A814

**1987, July 21**
2622 A814  5pf Tug-of-war          .20  .20
2623 A814 10pf Handball            .20  .20
2624 A814 20pf + 5pf Girls' long
jump                            .25  .20
2625 A814 30pf Table tennis        .30  .30
2626 A814 40pf Bowling             .45  .45
2627 A814 70pf Running             .70  .70
   Nos. 2622-2627 (6)             2.10  2.05

**Berlin Anniversary Type of 1987**
**Perf. 12½x13, 13x12½**
**1987, Feb. 17                    Engr.**
2628 A801 10pf like No. 2587       .25  .25
   a.   Miniature sheet of 4      1.00  1.10
2629 A801 10pf like No. 2588       .25  .25
   a.   Miniature sheet of 4      1.00  1.10
2630 A801 20pf like No. 2589       .25  .25
   a.   Miniature sheet of 4      1.10  1.40
2631 A801 20pf like No. 2590       .25  .25
   a.   Miniature sheet of 4      1.00  1.40
   Nos. 2628-2631 (4)             1.00  1.00

Assoc. of Sports and Science, 35th Anniv. A815

**1987, Aug. 4   Litho.   Perf. 13x12½**
2632 A815 10pf multi               .30  .20

Stamp Day A816

Designs: 10pf+5pf, Court Post Office, Berlin, 1760. 20pf, Wartenberg Palace, former Prussian General Post Office, 1770.

**1987, Aug. 11   Photo.   Perf. 14**
2633 A816 10pf +5pf multi          .20  .20
2634 A816 20pf multi               .20  .20
   a.   Pair, #2633-2634 + label   .55  .75

Souvenir Sheet

Leipzig Autumn Fair — A817

Illustration reduced.

**1987, Aug. 25   Litho.   Perf. 13½**
2635 A817   Sheet of 2            1.20  1.40
   a.   40pf multi                 .35  .35
   b.   50pf multi                 .55  .55

Intl. War Victims' Memorial, Budapest A818

**1987, Sept. 8   Photo.   Perf. 14**
2636 A818 35pf Statue by Jozsef
Somogyi                         .35  .25

Souvenir Sheet

Thalmann Memorial — A819

Illustration reduced.

**Litho. & Engr.**
**1987, Sept. 8          Perf. 14**
2637 A819 1.35m buff, ver & blk   1.50  1.50
City of Berlin, 750th anniv.

10th Natl. Art Exhibition, Berlin — A820

Designs: 10pf, Weidendamm Bridge, Berlin, 1986, by Arno Mohr. 50pf, They Only Wanted to Learn How to Read and Write, Nicaragua, 1985-86, by Willi Sitte. 70pf, Large Figure of a Man in Mourning, 1983, scupture by Wieland Forster. 1m, Ceramic bowl, 1986, by Gerd Lucke. Nos. 2638-2640, vert.

**1987, Sept. 28          Litho.**
2638 A820 10pf multi               .20  .20
2639 A820 50pf multi               .45  .45
2640 A820 70pf multi               .60  .60
2641 A820  1m multi                .90  .90
   Nos. 2638-2641 (4)             2.15  2.15

Lenin, Flag, Smolny Institute, Cruiser Aurora A821

**1987, Oct. 27**    **Photo.**    *Perf. 14*
2642 A821 10pf shown    .20 .20
2643 A821 20pf Spasski Tower    .25 .20
October Revolution, Russia, 70th anniv.

Robot ZIM 10-S Welding A822

**1987, Nov. 3**    **Litho.**    *Perf. 13x12½*
2644 A822 10pf Personal comput-
er    .20 .20
2645 A822 20pf shown    .25 .20
30th MMM Science Fair and 10th Central Industrial Fair for Students and Youth Scientists, Leipzig.

**Miniature Sheet**

Christmas Candle Carousels from the Ore Mountains — A823

Designs: 10pf, Annaberg, c. 1810. 20pf, Freiberg, c. 1830. 25pf, Neustadtel, c. 1870. 35pf, Schneeberg, c. 1870. 40pf, Lossnitz, c. 1880. 85pf, Seiffen, c. 1910.

**1987, Nov. 3**    **Litho.**    *Perf. 12½x13*
2646    Sheet of 6    2.25 2.40
   *a.* A823 10pf multi    .25 .25
   *b.* A823 20pf multi    .55 .55
   *c.* A823 25pf multi    .25 .25
   *d.* A823 35pf multi    .25 .25
   *e.* A823 40pf multi    .55 .55
   *f.* A823 85pf multi    .25 .25

1988 Winter Olympics, Calgary — A824

**1988, Jan. 19**    **Photo.**    *Perf. 14½x14*
2647 A824 5pf Ski jumping    .25 .20
2648 A824 10pf Speed skating    .25 .20
2649 A824 20pf +10pf 4-Man
bobsled    .35 .30
2650 A824 35pf Biathlon    .45 .35
   *Nos. 2647-2650 (4)*    1.30 1.05
**Souvenir Sheet**
*Perf. 13x12½*
2651 A824 1.20m Single and
double luge    1.50 1.30
No. 2649 surtaxed for the Olympic Promotion Society.

Postal Buildings, East Berlin A825

**1988, Feb. 2**    *Perf. 14*
2652 A825 15pf Berlin-Buch post
office    .25 .20
2653 A825 20pf Natl. Postal Museum    .35 .20

2654 A825 50pf General post of-
fice, Berlin-
Marzahn    .75 .60
   *Nos. 2652-2654 (3)*    1.35 1.00

**Souvenir Sheet**

Bertolt Brecht (1898-1956), Playwright — A826

**1988, Feb. 2**    **Litho.**    *Perf. 13x12½*
2655 A826 70pf multi    1.00 .90

Flowering Plants — A827      Leipzig Spring Fair — A828

**1988, Feb. 16**    **Photo.**    *Perf. 14*
2656 A827 10pf Tillandsia
macrochlamys    .20 .20
2657 A827 25pf Tillandsia
bulbosa    .25 .25
2658 A827 40pf Tillandsia
kalmbacheri    .35 .35
2659 A827 70pf Guzmania blassii    .65 .65
   *Nos. 2656-2659 (4)*    1.45 1.45

**1988, Mar. 8**    **Litho.**    *Perf. 12½x13*
20pf, Entrance #8. 70pf, Faust & Mephistopheles, bronze statue by Matthieu Molitor.
2660 A828 20pf multi    .20 .20
2661 A828 70pf multi    .75 .60
Madler Passage (arcade), 75th anniv.

A829

**Souvenir Sheet**
**1988, Mar. 8**    *Perf. 14*
2662 A829 70pf multi    1.10 1.10
Joseph von Eichendorff (1788-1857), poet.

Seals — A830

**1988, Mar. 22**    **Photo.**    *Perf. 14*
2663 A830 10pf Muhlhausen sad-
dler, 1565    .20 .20
2664 A830 25pf Dresden butcher,
1564    .25 .25
2665 A830 35pf Nauen smith,
16th cent.    .30 .30
2666 A830 50pf Frankfurt-Oder
clothier, 16th
cent.    .35 .35
   *a.* Block of 4, #2663-2666    1.50 1.50

Georg Forster Antarctic Research Station A831

**1988, Mar. 22**    **Litho.**    *Perf. 13x12½*
2667 A831 35pf multi    .45 .25

District Capitals A832

**1988, Apr. 5**    **Photo.**    *Perf. 14*
2668 A832 5pf Wismar    .20 .20
2669 A832 10pf Anklam    .20 .20
2670 A832 25pf Ribnitz-Dam-
garten    .25 .20
2671 A832 60pf Stralsund    .55 .55
2672 A832 90pf Bergen    .75 .75
2673 A832 1.20m Greifswald    1.00 1.00
   *Nos. 2668-2673 (6)*    2.95 2.90

**Souvenir Sheet**

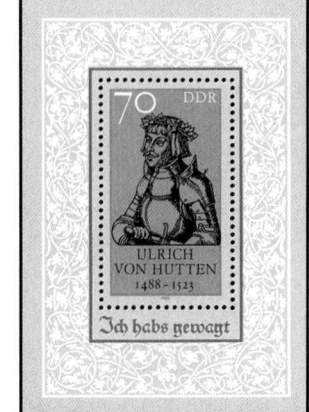

Ulrich von Hutten (1488-1523), Promulgator of the Lutheran Movement — A833

**1988, Apr. 5**    **Litho.**    *Perf. 12½x13*
2674 A833 70pf multi    1.10 .90

USSR-DDR Manned Space Flight, 10th Anniv. — A834

Designs: 5pf, Cosmonauts S. Jahn and Valery Bykowski, Soyuz-29 landing, Sept. 3, 1978. 10pf, MKS-M multi-channel spectrometer. 20pf, MIR space station.

**1988, June 21**    **Litho.**    *Perf. 14*
2675 A834 5pf multi    .20 .20
2676 A834 10pf multi    .20 .20
2677 A834 20pf multi    .25 .25
   *Nos. 2675-2677 (3)*    .65 .65
See Nos. 2698-2700.

10th Youth Stamp Exhibitions in Erfurt and Karl-Marx-Stadt — A835

Designs: 10pf+5pf, Erfurt. c. 1520. 20+5pf, Chemnitz, c. 1620. 25pf, Historic and modern buildings of Erfurt. 50pf, Historic and modern buildings of Karl-Marx-Stadt.

**1988, June 21**    **Photo.**
2678 A835 10pf +5pf multi    .20 .20
2679 A835 20pf +5pf multi    .25 .25
2680 A835 25pf multi    .25 .25
   *a.* Pair, #2678, 2680 + label    .60 .60
2681 A835 35pf multi    .55 .55
   *a.* Pair, #2679, 2681 + label    .90 .90
Nos. 2678-2679 surtaxed to benefit the Philatelists' League of the DDR Cultural Union.

22nd Workers' Games, Frankfurt-on-Oder — A836

**1988, June 7**    **Litho.**    *Perf. 13x12½*
2682    20pf multi    .20 .20
2683    50pf multi, diff.    .45 .45
   *a.* A836 Pair, #2682-2683 + label    .85 .85

Workers' Militia, 35th Anniv. — A837

**1988, July 5**    **Photo.**    *Perf. 14*
2684 A837 5pf Oath    .20 .20
2685 A837 10pf Ernst Thalmann
tribute    .20 .20
2686 A837 15pf Roll call    .20 .20
2687 A837 20pf Weapons exchange    .20 .20
   *Nos. 2684-2687 (4)*    .80 .80

8th Young Pioneers' Congress, Karl-Marx-Stadt — A838

**1988, July 19**    **Litho.**    *Perf. 13x12½*
2688 A838 10pf shown    .20 .20
2689 A838 10pf +5pf Youths
playing musical
instruments    .20 .20
   *a.* Pair, #2688-2689 + label    .45 .40
Surtax financed the congress.

1988 Summer Olympics, Seoul A839

**1988, Aug. 9**    **Photo.**    *Perf. 14*
2690 A839 5pf Swimming    .20 .20
2691 A839 10pf Handball    .20 .20
2692 A839 20pf +10pf Hurdles    .35 .35
2693 A839 25pf Rowing    .35 .35
2694 A839 35pf Boxing    .35 .35
2695 A839 50pf +20pf Cycling    .70 .70
   *Nos. 2690-2695 (6)*    2.15 2.15
**Souvenir Sheet**
**Litho.**
*Perf. 13x12½*
2696 A839 85pf Relay race    1.80 1.60

## Souvenir Sheet

Leipzig Autumn Fair — A840

**1988, Aug. 30**    **Litho.**    *Perf. 14*
| | | | | |
|---|---|---|---|---|
| 2697 | A840 | Sheet of 3 | 1.40 | 1.20 |
| *a.* | | 5pf Fair, c. 1810 | .20 | .20 |
| *b.* | | 15pf Battle of Leipzig Memorial | .25 | .20 |
| *c.* | | 1m Fair, c. 1820 | .75 | .75 |

### DDR-USSR Manned Space Flight Type

**1988, Aug. 30**    **Litho.**    *Perf. 14*
| | | | | |
|---|---|---|---|---|
| 2698 | A834 | 10pf like No. 2675 | .25 | .25 |
| *a.* | | Sheet of 4 | 1.00 | 1.00 |
| 2699 | A834 | 20pf like No. 2676 | .25 | .25 |
| *a.* | | Sheet of 4 | 1.00 | 1.00 |
| 2700 | A834 | 35pf like No. 2677 | .45 | .45 |
| *a.* | | Sheet of 4 | 1.90 | 1.90 |
| | | Nos. 2698-2700 (3) | .95 | .95 |

Fascism Resistance Memorial, Como, Italy — A841

**1988, Sept. 13**       **Photo.**
| | | | | |
|---|---|---|---|---|
| 2701 | A841 | 35pf multi | .35 | .30 |

Memorial at Buchenwald, 30th Anniv. — A842

**1988, Sept. 13**       *Perf. 14*
| | | | | |
|---|---|---|---|---|
| 2702 | A842 | 10pf multi | .25 | .20 |

Mariner's Soc., Stralsund, 500th Anniv. — A843

Paintings: 5pf, *Adolph Friedrich* at Stralsund, by C. Leplow. 10pf, *Die Gartenlaube* (built in 1872) at Stralsund, by J.F. Kruger. 70pf, Brigantine *Auguste Mathilde* (built in 1830) at Stralsund, by I.C. Grunwaldt. 1.20m, Brig *Hoffnung* at Cologne, by G.A. Luther.

**1988, Sept. 20**    **Litho.**    *Perf. 13½x13*
| | | | | |
|---|---|---|---|---|
| 2703 | A843 | 5pf multi | .20 | .20 |
| 2704 | A843 | 10pf multi | .20 | .20 |
| 2705 | A843 | 70pf multi | .75 | .70 |
| 2706 | A843 | 1.20m multi | 1.10 | 1.10 |
| | | Nos. 2703-2706 (4) | 2.25 | 2.20 |

Ship Lifts and Bridges A844

---

**1988, Oct. 18**    **Photo.**    *Perf. 14x14½*
| | | | | |
|---|---|---|---|---|
| 2707 | A844 | 5pf Magdeburg | .20 | .20 |
| 2708 | A844 | 10pf Magdeburg-Rothensee | .20 | .20 |
| 2709 | A844 | 35pf Niederfinow | .30 | .25 |
| 2710 | A844 | 70pf Altfriesack | .60 | .60 |
| 2711 | A844 | 90pf Rugendamm | .75 | .75 |
| | | Nos. 2707-2711 (5) | 2.05 | 2.00 |

1st Nazi Pogrom (Kristallnacht), Nov. 9, 1938 — A845

**1988, Nov. 8**       *Perf. 14*
| | | | | |
|---|---|---|---|---|
| 2712 | A845 | 35pf Menorah | .45 | .25 |

Paintings by Max Lingner (1888-1959) A846

**1988, Nov. 8**
| | | | | |
|---|---|---|---|---|
| 2713 | A846 | 5pf *In the Boat,* 1931 | .20 | .20 |
| 2714 | A846 | 10pf *Yvonne,* 1939 | .20 | .20 |
| 2715 | A846 | 20pf *Free, Strong and Happy,* 1944 | .25 | .20 |
| 2716 | A846 | 85pf *New Harvest,* 1951 | .75 | .75 |
| | | Nos. 2713-2716 (4) | 1.40 | 1.35 |

### Souvenir Sheet

Friedrich Wolf (1888-1953), Playwright — A847

**1988, Nov. 22**       **Litho.**
| | | | | |
|---|---|---|---|---|
| 2717 | A847 | 1.10m multi | 1.10 | 1.10 |

WHO, 40th Anniv. A848      Bone Lace from Erzgebirge A849

**1988, Nov. 22**       **Photo.**
| | | | | |
|---|---|---|---|---|
| 2718 | A848 | 85pf multi | .90 | .45 |

### Miniature Sheet

Various lace designs.

**1988, Nov. 22**    **Litho.**    *Perf. 12½x13*
| | | | | |
|---|---|---|---|---|
| 2719 | | Sheet of 6 | 2.25 | 2.25 |
| *a.* | A849 | 20pf multi | .25 | .25 |
| *b.* | A849 | 25pf multi | .55 | .55 |
| *c.* | A849 | 35pf multi | .25 | .25 |
| *d.* | A849 | 40pf multi | .25 | .25 |
| *e.* | A849 | 50pf multi | .55 | .55 |
| *f.* | A849 | 85pf multi | .25 | .25 |

---

Council for Mutual Economic Aid, 40th Anniv. A850

**1989, Jan. 10**    **Photo.**    *Perf. 13*
| | | | | |
|---|---|---|---|---|
| 2720 | A850 | 20pf multi | .30 | .25 |

### Labor Leaders Type of 1987

Portraits: No. 2721, Edith Baumann (1909-1973). No. 2722, Otto Meier (1889-1962). No. 2723, Fritz Selbmann (1899-1975). No. 2724, Alfred Oelssner (1879-1962).

**1989, Jan. 24**    **Engr.**    *Perf. 14*
| | | | | |
|---|---|---|---|---|
| 2721 | A804 | 10pf dark vio brn | .20 | .20 |
| 2722 | A804 | 10pf dark grn | .20 | .20 |
| 2723 | A804 | 10pf dark blue | .20 | .20 |
| 2724 | A804 | 10pf brn blk | .20 | .20 |
| | | Nos. 2721-2724 (4) | .80 | .80 |

Telephones A851

Designs: 10pf, Philipp Reis, 1861. 20pf, Siemens & Halske wall model, 1882. 50pf, Wall model OB 03, 1903. 85pf, Table model OB 05, 1905.

**1989, Feb. 7**       **Litho.**
| | | | | |
|---|---|---|---|---|
| 2725 | A851 | 10pf shown | .20 | .20 |
| 2726 | A851 | 20pf multi | .25 | .25 |
| 2727 | A851 | 50pf multi | .45 | .45 |
| 2728 | A851 | 85pf multi | .75 | .75 |
| *a.* | | Block of 4, #2725-2728 | 1.90 | 1.90 |

Famous Men A852

**1989, Feb. 28**       **Photo.**
| | | | | |
|---|---|---|---|---|
| 2729 | A852 | 10pf Ludwig Renn (1889-1979) | .20 | .20 |
| 2730 | A852 | 10pf Carl von Ossietzky (1889-1938) | .20 | .20 |
| 2731 | A852 | 10pf Adam Scharrer (1889-1948) | .20 | .20 |
| 2732 | A852 | 10pf Rudolf Mauersberger (1889-1971) | .20 | .20 |
| 2733 | A852 | 10pf Johann Beckmann (1739-1811) | .20 | .20 |
| | | Nos. 2729-2733 (5) | 1.00 | 1.00 |

Leipzig Spring Fair — A853

**1989, Mar. 7**       **Litho.**
| | | | | |
|---|---|---|---|---|
| 2734 | A853 | 70pf shown | .70 | .60 |
| 2735 | A853 | 85pf Buildings, 1690 | .85 | .85 |

Handelshof, 80th anniv. (70pf).

---

### Souvenir Sheet

Thomas Muntzer (c. 1468-1525), Religious Reformer — A854

**1989, Mar. 21**       *Perf. 13x12½*
| | | | | |
|---|---|---|---|---|
| 2736 | A854 | 1.10m multi | 1.10 | 1.40 |

1st Long-distance German Railway, Leipzig-Dresden, Sesquicentennial — A855

15pf, Georg Friedrich List (1789-1846), industrialist, economist. 20pf, Dresden Station in Leipzig, 1839. 50pf, Leipzig Station in Dresden, 1839.

**1989, Apr. 4**       *Perf. 14*
| | | | | |
|---|---|---|---|---|
| 2737 | A855 | 15pf multi | .30 | .25 |
| 2738 | A855 | 20pf multi | .30 | .20 |
| 2739 | A855 | 50pf multi | .55 | .55 |
| | | Nos. 2737-2739 (3) | 1.15 | 1.00 |

A856      A857

Designs: Meissen Onion-pattern Porcelain, 250th anniv., and sword emblem.

**1989, Apr. 18**    **Litho.**    *Perf. 12½x13*
| | | | | |
|---|---|---|---|---|
| 2740 | A856 | 10pf Tea caddy | .20 | .20 |
| 2741 | A856 | 25pf Vase | .25 | .20 |
| 2742 | A856 | 35pf Breadboard | .35 | .30 |
| 2743 | A856 | 70pf Teapot | .75 | .75 |
| | | Nos. 2740-2743 (4) | 1.55 | 1.45 |

**Size: 33x56mm**

*Perf. 14*
| | | | | |
|---|---|---|---|---|
| 2744 | | Block of 4 | 2.10 | 2.10 |
| *a.* | A856 | 10pf like No. 2740 | .20 | .20 |
| *b.* | A856 | 20pf like No. 2741 | .25 | .25 |
| *c.* | A856 | 35pf like No. 2742 | .35 | .35 |
| *d.* | A856 | 70pf like No. 2743 | .75 | .75 |

**1989, May 2**    **Photo.**    *Perf. 14½x14*
| | | | | |
|---|---|---|---|---|
| 2745 | A857 | 20pf "I" | .25 | .20 |
| 2746 | A857 | 50pf "B" | .45 | .35 |
| 2747 | A857 | 1.35m "A" | 1.25 | 1.25 |
| | | Nos. 2745-2747 (3) | 1.95 | 1.80 |

Intl. Book Fair (IBA), Leipzig.

Student Government — A858

**1989, May 9**    **Litho.**    *Perf. 13½x12½*
| | | | | |
|---|---|---|---|---|
| 2748 | A858 | 20pf 8th World Youth Festival, Pyongyang | .25 | .25 |
| 2749 | A858 | 20pf +5pf Whitsun meeting of Free German Youth | .25 | .25 |
| *a.* | | Pair, #2748-2749 + label | .55 | .55 |

Princess
Luise — A859

Carl Zeiss
Foundation,
Jena,
Cent. — A860

Sculptures by Johann Gottfried Schadow (1764-1850), Prussian Court Sculptor.

**1989, May 16    Photo.    Perf. 14½x14**
2750  A859  50pf shown                    .60    .45
2751  A859  85pf Princess Friede-
            rike                          1.10   .90

**1989, May 16**

Modern medical technology: 50pf, Interference microscope Jenaval. 85pf, Bicoordinate measuring instrument ZKM 01-250C.

2752  A860  50pf multi                    .35    .35
2753  A860  85pf multi                    .75    .75
  a.   Pair, #2752-2753 + label           1.40   1.40

Label pictures founder Ernst Abbe (1840-1905).

Jena University
Inaugural Address,
Bicent. — A861

**1989, May 23    Photo.    Perf. 14**
2754  A861  25pf Frontispiece             .25    .25
2755  A861  85pf Excerpt                  .70    .70
  a.   Pair, #2754-2755 + label           1.10   1.10

Label pictures bust of Friedrich Schiller, author of the address.

**Souvenir Sheet**

Zoologists — A862

**1989, June 13                 Litho.**
2756  A862  Sheet of 2                    1.50   9.00
  a.   50pf Alfred Brehm (1829-1884)      .45    2.25
  b.   85pf Christian Brehm (1787-
       1864)                              .90    3.50

French
Revolution,
Bicent.
A863

5pf, Storming of the Bastille, July 14, 1789. 20pf, Revolutionaries, flag bearer. 90pf, Storming Tuileries Palace, Aug. 10, 1792.

**1989, July 4       Photo.    Perf. 13**
2757  A863  5pf multi                     .20    .20
2758  A863  20pf multi                    .25    .20
2759  A863  90pf multi                    .75    .75
      Nos. 2757-2759 (3)                  1.20   1.15

Intl. Congress of Horse Breeders from
Socialist States — A864

**1989, July 18     Litho.    Perf. 13½**
2760  A864  10pf Haflinger                .20    .20
2761  A864  20pf English thor-
            oughbred                      .20    .20
2762  A864  70pf Cold blood               .60    .60
2763  A864  110pf Noble warm
             blood                        1.00   1.00
      Nos. 2760-2763 (4)                  2.00   2.00

Natl. Stamp Exhibition,
Magdeburg — A865

**1989, Aug. 8      Litho.    Perf. 13x12½**
2764  A865  20pf Owlglass Foun-
            tain                          .20    .20
2765  A865  70pf +5pf Demons
            Fountain                      .75    .70

No. 2765 surtaxed for the philatelic unit of the Kulturbund.

**Souvenir Sheet**

Leipzig Autumn Fair — A866

**1989, Aug. 22                 Perf. 14**
2766  A866  Sheet of 2                    1.40   1.40
  a.   50pf Fairground                    .45    .45
  b.   85pf Fairground, diff.             .75    .75

Thomas
Muntzer (1489-
1525), Religious
Reformer
A867

Various details of the painting *Early Bourgeois Revolution in Germany in 1525,* by W. Tubke.

**1989, Aug. 22**
2767  A867  5pf Globe                     .20    .20
2768  A867  10pf Fountain                 .20    .20
2769  A867  20pf Battle scene             .25    .20
  a.   Souvenir sheet of 4                1.10   1.00
2770  A867  50pf Ark                      .45    .45
2771  A867  85pf Rainbow, battle          1.00   1.00
      Nos. 2767-2771 (5)                  2.10   2.05

Muttergruppe,
1965, Bronze
Statue in the
Natl. Memorial,
Ravensbruck
A868

**1989, Sept. 5     Photo.    Perf. 14**
2772  A868  35pf multi                    .35    .30

Natl. Memorial, Ravensbruck, 30th anniv.

Flowering
Cacti
(Epiphyllum)
A869

**1989, Sept. 19    Litho.    Perf. 13**
2773  A869  10m Adriana                   .20    .20
2774  A869  35m Feuerzauber               .35    .30
2775  A869  50m Franzisko                 .60    .60
      Nos. 2773-2775 (3)                  1.15   1.10

DDR, 40th Anniv. — A870

**1989, Oct. 3                  Perf. 14**
2776  A870  5pf Education                 .20    .20
2777  A870  10pf Agriculture              .20    .20
2778  A870  20pf Construction             .30    .25
2779  A870  25pf Machinist, com-
            puter user                    .30    .30
      Nos. 2776-2779 (4)                  1.00   .95

**Souvenir Sheet**
2780  A870  135pf Two workers             3.50   1.50

Jawaharlal
Nehru, 1st
Prime Minister
of Independent
India — A871

**1989, Nov. 7      Photo.    Perf. 14**
2781  A871  35pf multicolored             .35    .30

**Statues of Roland Type of 1987**
**1989, Nov. 7                 Perf. 14½x14**
2782  A799  5pf Zerbst, 1445              .20    .20
2783  A799  10pf Halberstadt,
            1433                          .20    .20
2784  A799  20pf Buch-Altmark,
            1611                          .25    .25
2785  A799  50pf Perleberg, 1546          .45    .45
      Nos. 2782-2785 (4)                  1.10   1.10

**Miniature Sheet**

Chandeliers from
Erzgebirge — A872

Designs: a, Schneeburg, circa 1860. b, Schwarzenberg, circa 1850. c, Annaberg, circa 1880. d, Seiffen, circa 1900. e, Seiffen, circa 1930. f, Annaberg, circa 1925.

**Litho. & Engr.**
**1989, Nov. 28                 Perf. 14**
2786        Sheet of 6                    2.25   2.25
  a.   A872 10pf multicolored             .25    .25
  b.   A872 20pf multicolored             .55    .55
  c.   A872 25pf multicolored             .25    .25
  d.   A872 35pf multicolored             .25    .25
  e.   A872 50pf multicolored             .55    .55
  f.   A872 70pf multicolored             .25    .25

Bees Collecting
Nectar — A873

**1990, Jan. 9                  Litho.**
2787  A873  5pf Apple blossom             .20    .20
2788  A873  10pf Blooming heath-
            er                            .20    .20
2789  A873  20pf Rape blossom             .25    .25
2790  A873  50pf Red clover               .60    .60
      Nos. 2787-2790 (4)                  1.25   1.25

The Young Post
Rider, an
Engraving by
Albrecht
Durer — A874

**1990, Jan. 12     Litho.    Perf. 13**
2791  A874  35pf multi                    .45    .35

Postal communications in Europe, 500th anniv.
See Austria No. 1486, Belgium No. 1332, Germany No. 1592 and Berlin No. 9N584.

Labor
Leaders — A875

Portraits: #2792, Bruno Leuschner (1910-65). #2793, Erich Weinert (1890-1953).

**1990, Jan. 16                 Perf. 14**
2792  A875  10pf gray brown               .25    .25
2793  A875  10pf deep blue                .25    .25

Coats of
Arms — A876

Early postal agency insignia: 10pf, Schwarzburg-Rudolstadt and Thurn & Taxis. 20pf, Royal Saxon letter collection. 50pf, Imperial Postal Agency. 1.10pf, Auxiliary post office.

**1990, Feb. 6      Photo.    Perf. 14**
2794  A876  10pf multicolored             .20    .20
2795  A876  20pf multicolored             .25    .20
2796  A876  50pf multicolored             .60    .60
2797  A876  110pf multicolored            1.40   1.40
      Nos. 2794-2797 (4)                  2.45   2.40

**Size: 32x42mm**
**Perf. 13½**
**Litho.**
2798        Block of 4                    2.60   3.00
  a.   A876 10pf like No. 2794            .20    .20
  b.   A876 20pf like No. 2795            .25    .25
  c.   A876 50pf like No. 2796            .60    .60
  d.   A876 110pf like No. 2797           1.40   1.40

Posts & Telecommunications Workers' Day.

August Bebel
(1840-1913),
Co-founder of
the Social
Democratic
Party — A877

**1990, Feb. 20**      **Photo.**
2799 A877 20pf multicolored .35 .35

Flying Machine
Designed by
Leonardo da
Vinci — A878

**1990, Feb. 20**   **Litho.**   **Perf. 13½x13**
2800 A878 20pf shown .20 .20
2801 A878 35pf +5pf Melchior
     Bauer .45 .45
2802 A878 50pf Albrecht
     Berblinger .60 .55
2803 A878 90pf Otto Lilienthal 1.00 1.00
    Nos. 2800-2803 (4) 2.25 2.20

LILIENTHAL '91 airmail exhibition. No. 2801
surtaxed for philatelic promotion.

Leipzig Spring
Fair
Seals — A879

Dying
Warriors — A880

**1990, Mar. 6**      **Perf. 12½x13**
2804 A879 70pf Seal, 1268 1.25 .70
2805 A879 85pf Seal, 1497 1.40 .85

City of Leipzig and the Leipzig Spring Fair,
825th annivs.

**1990, Mar. 6**   **Photo.**   **Perf. 13½x14**

Sculptures by Andreas Schluter.

2806 A880 40pf shown .55 .55
2807 A880 70pf multi, diff. .75 .75

Museum of German History in the
Zeughaus of Berlin.

Famous
Men
A881

Portraits: No. 2808, Friedrich Diesterweg
(1790-1866), educator. No. 2809, Kurt Tucholsky (1890-1935), novelist, journalist.

**1990, Mar. 20**    **Photo.**    **Perf. 14**
2808 A881 10pf multicolored .30 .30
2809 A881 10pf multicolored .30 .30

Labor Day,
Cent. — A882

**1990, Apr. 3**
2810 A882 10pf shown .30 .25
2811 A882 20pf Flower,
     "1890/1990" .70 .45

Dicraeosaurus — A883

**Perf. 13x12½, 12½x13**
**1990, Apr. 17**      **Litho.**
2812 A883 10pf shown .20 .20
2813 A883 25pf Kentrurosaurus .25 .20
  a.    Miniature sheet of 4 1.40 1.40
2814 A883 35pf Dysalotosaurus .30 .30
2815 A883 50pf Brachiosaurus .45 .45
2816 A883 85pf Brachiosaurus
     skull 1.00 1.00
    Nos. 2812-2816 (5) 2.20 2.15

Natural History Museum of Berlin, cent.
Nos. 2815-2816 vert.

Penny Black, 150th
Anniv. — A884

**1990, May 8**      **Perf. 14**
2817 A884 20pf shown .35 .35
2818 A884 35pf +15pf Saxony
     #1 .70 .70
2819 A884 110pf No. 48 1.80 1.80
    Nos. 2817-2819 (3) 2.85 2.85

A885

Intl. Telecommunications Union, 125th
Anniv.: 10pf, David Edward Hughes (1831-
1900), type-printing telegraph, 1855. 20pf,
Distribution linkage, Berlin-Kopenick post
office. 25pf, TV and microwave tower. 50pf,
Molniya news satellite, globe. 70pf, Philipp
Reis (1834-1874), physicist, designed sound
transmission equipment.

**1990, May 15**
2820 A885 10pf multicolored .20 .20
2821 A885 20pf multicolored .30 .30
2822 A885 25pf multicolored .30 .30
2823 A885 50pf multicolored .75 .75
    Nos. 2820-2823 (4) 1.55 1.55

**Souvenir Sheet**
2824 A885 70pf multicolored 2.00 1.90

Pope John Paul II,
70th
Birthday — A886

**1990, May 15**
2825 A886 35pf multicolored .55 .35

11th
Youth
Stamp
Exhibition,
Halle
A887

**1990, June 5**      **Perf. 13x12½**
2826 A887 10pf +5pf 18th cent.
     Halle .25 .25
2827 A887 20pf 20th cent. Halle .30 .25
  a.    Pair, #2826-2827 + label .60 .60

Treasures
in the
German
State
Library,
Berlin
A888

Designs: 20pf, Rules of an order, 1264.
25pf, Rudimentum novitiorum, 1475. 50pf,
Chosrou wa Schirin, 18th cent. 110pf, Book-
cover of Amalienbibliothek, 18th cent.

**1990, June 19**
2828 A888 20pf multicolored .35 .25
2829 A888 25pf multicolored .35 .25
2830 A888 50pf multicolored 1.10 .70
2831 A888 110pf multicolored 2.00 1.60
    Nos. 2828-2831 (4) 3.80 2.80

Castle Albrechtsburg
and Cathedral,
Meissen — A889

30pf, Goethe-Schiller Monument, Weimar.
50pf, Brandenburg Gate, Berlin. 60pf, Kyf-
hauser Monument. 70pf, Semper Opera,
Dresden. 80pf, Castle Sanssouci, Potsdam.
100pf, Wartburg, Eisenach. 200pf, Magdeburg
Cathedral. 500pf, Schwerin Castle.

**1990, July 2**    **Photo.**    **Perf. 14**
2832 A889 10pf ultramarine .20 .20
2833 A889 30pf olive green .30 .25
2834 A889 50pf bluish green .45 .35
2835 A889 60pf violet brown .45 .55
2836 A889 70pf dark brown .60 .70
2837 A889 80pf red brown .75 1.00
2838 A889 100pf dark carmine .75 .60
2839 A889 200pf dark violet 1.50 1.50
2840 A889 500pf green 3.50 3.50
    Nos. 2832-2840 (9) 8.50 8.65

Nos. 2832-2852 have face values based on
the Federal Republic's Deutsche mark and
were valid for postage in both countries.

Postal
System,
500th
Anniv.
A890

30pf, 15th cent. postman. 50pf, 16th cent.
postrider. 70pf, Post carriages c. 1595, 1750.
100pf, Railway mail carriages 1842, 1900.

**1990, Aug. 28**   **Litho.**   **Perf. 13x13½**
2841 A890 30pf multicolored .35 .35
2842 A890 50pf multicolored .55 .55
2843 A890 70pf multicolored .70 1.00
2844 A890 100pf multicolored 1.10 1.10
    Nos. 2841-2844 (4) 2.70 3.00

Louis Lewandowski
(1821-94),
Composer — A891

50pf+15pf, New Synagogue, Berlin.

**1990, Sept. 18**      **Perf. 14**
2845 A891 30pf multicolored .30 .30
2846 A891 50pf +15pf multi .60 .60

Heinrich
Schliemann (1822-
1890),
Archaeologist
A892

**1990, Oct. 2**      **Photo.**

Design: 30pf, shown. 50pf, Schliemann,
double pot c. 2600-1900 B.C., horiz.

2847 A892 30pf multicolored .30 .30
2848 A892 50pf multicolored .60 .60

Intl. Astronautics
Federation, 41st
Congress,
Dresden
A893

**1990, Oct. 2**
2849 A893 30pf Dresden skyline .25 .25
2850 A893 50pf Globe .45 .45
2851 A893 70pf Moon .75 1.00
2852 A893 100pf Mars 1.10 1.10
    Nos. 2849-2852 (4) 2.55 2.80

Stamps of the German Democratic Republic
were replaced starting Oct. 3, 1990 by those
of the Federal Republic of Germany. #2832-
2852 remained valid until Dec. 31, 1991.

**FOR USE IN ALL PROVINCES IN
THE RUSSIAN ZONES**

**SEMI-POSTALS**
**Leipzig Fair Issue**
Type of German Semi-Postal Stamps

16pf+9pf, 1st New Year's Fair, 1459.
50pf+25pf, Arrival of clothmakers from abroad,
1469.

**Wmk. 292**
**1948, Aug. 29**   **Litho.**   **Perf. 13½**
10NB1 SP252 16 + 9pf dk vio .20 .60
10NB2 SP252 50 + 25pf dl vio
     bl .20 .60
    Set, never hinged .75

The 1948 Leipzig Autumn Fair.

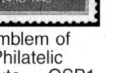

Emblem of
Philatelic
Institute — OSP1

Goethe — OSP2

**1948, Oct. 23**      **Perf. 13x13½**
10NB3 OSP1 12 + 3pf red .20 .55
    Never hinged .35

Stamp Day, Oct. 24, 1948.

**Type of German Semi-Postal
Stamps of 1947**

30pf+15pf, First fair in newly built Town Hall,
1556. 50pf+25pf, Italians at the Fair, 1536.

**1949, Mar. 6**   **Litho.**   **Perf. 13½**
10NB4 SP252 30 + 15pf red 1.10 4.00
10NB5 SP252 50 + 25pf blue 1.50 4.50
    Set, never hinged 6.00

1949 Leipzig Spring Fair.

**1949, July 20**   **Wmk. 292**   **Perf. 13**

Designs: Different Goethe portraits.

10NB6 OSP2 6 + 4pf dl vio .90 2.60
10NB7 OSP2 12 + 8pf dl brn .90 2.60
10NB8 OSP2 24 + 16pf red
     brn .75 2.25
10NB9 OSP2 50 + 25pf dk bl .75 2.25
10NB10 OSP2 84 + 36pf ol
     gray 1.10 4.50
    Nos. 10NB6-10NB10 (5) 4.40 14.20
    Set, never hinged 10.50

Johann Wolfgang von Goethe, birth bicent.

Souvenir Sheet

Profile of Goethe — OSP3

**1949, Aug. 22     Engr.     Perf. 14**
10NB11 OSP3 50pf + 4.50m
                        blue        110.00 450.00
          Never hinged               175.00

The sheet measures 106x105mm. The surtax was for the reconstruction of Weimar.

### Type of German Semi-Postal Stamps

12pf+8pf, Russian merchants at the Fair, 1650. 24pf+16pf, Young Goethe at the Fair, 1765.

**1949, Aug. 30     Litho.     Perf. 13½**
10NB12 SP252 12 + 8pf gray          1.50  6.50
10NB13 SP252 24 + 16pf lake
                        brn          1.90  7.75
          Set, never hinged          7.50

1949 Leipzig Autumn Fair.

---

### GERMAN DEMOCRATIC REPUBLIC SEMI-POSTAL STAMPS

Catalogue values for unused stamps in this section, from this point to the end of the section, are for Never Hinged items.

---

#### Canceled to Order
Used values are for CTO's from No. B14 to No. B203.

Some se-tenants include a semi-postal stamp. To avoid splitting the se-tenant piece the semi-postal is listed with the regular issue.

Bavaria No. 1 and
Magnifier — SP4

**Wmk. 292**
**1949, Oct. 30     Litho.     Perf. 14**
B14 SP4  12pf + 3pf gray blk        6.75  6.50

Stamp Day, 1949. See No. B21a.

### Leipzig Fair Issue.
German Type of 1947
Inscribed: "Deutsche Demokratische Republik"

Leipzig Spring Fair: 24pf+12pf, First porcelain at Fair, 1710. 30pf+14pf, First Fair at Municipal Store, 1894.

**1950, Mar. 5                    Perf. 13**
B15 SP252 24 + 12pf red vio        9.00  9.00
B16 SP252 30 + 14pf rose car      10.50  15.00

Shepherd Boy
with Double
Flute — SP5

"Bach Year": 24pf+6pf, Girl with hand organ. 30pf+8pf, Johann Sebastian Bach. 50pf+16pf, Chorus.

---

**1950, June 14                   Perf. 14**
B17 SP5  12pf + 4pf bl grn         6.00  5.00
B18 SP5  24pf + 6pf olive          6.00  5.00
B19 SP5  30pf + 8pf dk red        11.50  11.50
B20 SP5  50pf + 16pf blue         18.00  16.50
          Nos. B17-B20 (4)        41.50  38.00

Saxony No. 1,
Globe and
Dove — SP6

**1950, July 1     Photo.     Wmk. 292**
B21 SP6  84 + 41pf brn red        45.00  12.00
   a.  Souv. sheet of 2, #B14,
       B21, imperf.              150.00 150.00
       No. B21a hinged            52.50

German Stamp Exhib. (DEBRIA) held at Leipzig for the cent. of Saxony's 1st postage stamp.

Clearing
Land — SP7

Reconstruction program: 24pf+6pf, Bricklaying. 30pf+10pf, Carpentry. 50pf+10pf, Inspecting plans.

**1952, May 1                     Litho.**
B22 SP7  12pf + 3pf brt vio        1.60  .45
B23 SP7  24pf + 6pf henna brn      1.50  .60
B24 SP7  30pf + 10pf dp grn        1.75  .75
B25 SP7  50pf + 10pf vio bl        2.25  1.50
          Nos. B22-B25 (4)         7.10  3.30

Dam — SP8

**1954, Aug. 16                   Unwmk.**
B26 SP8  24pf + 6pf green           .60  .75

The surtax was for flood victims.

#### Surcharged with New Value and "X"
**1955, Feb. 25**
B27 SP8  20 +5pf on 24+6pf          .75  .55

The surtax was for flood victims.

Buchenwald Memorial — SP9

**Perf. 13½x13**
**1956, Sept. 8               Wmk. 297**
B28 SP9  20pf + 80pf rose red      1.10  3.50

The surtax was for the erection of national memorials at the concentration camps of Buchenwald, Ravensbruck and Sachsenhausen. See No. B43.

#### Type of 1955 Surcharged "HELFT ÄGYPTEN +10" (#B29) or "HELFT DEM SOZIALISTISCHEN UNGARN +10" (#B30)
**Perf. 13½x13**
**1956, Dec. 20               Wmk. 313**
B29 A75  20pf + 10pf carmine        .45  .35
B30 A75  20pf + 10pf carmine        .45  .35

---

Monument to
Ravensbrück
SP10

Memorial Park and Lake — SP11

**Perf. 13x13½, 13½x13**
**1957, Apr. 25                    Litho.**
B31 SP10 5pf + 5pf grn             .20  .25
B32 SP11 20pf + 10pf rose red      .30  .35

Intl. Day of Liberation. See Nos. B54, B70.

Ernst Thälmann          Bugler, Flag and
SP12                    Camp SP13

Portraits: 25pf+15pf, Rudolf Breitscheid. 40pf+20pf, Rev. Paul Schneider.

**1957, Dec. 3     Photo.     Perf. 13**
**Portraits in Gray**
B33 SP12 20pf + 10pf dp plum       .20  .20
B34 SP12 25pf + 15pf dk blue       .20  .20
B35 SP12 40pf + 20pf violet        .30  .35
   a.  Souv. sheet of 3, #B33-B35,
       imperf.                    57.50 125.00
       Nos. B33-B35 (3)            .70  .75

No. B35a issued Sept. 15, 1958.

**1958, July 11   Wmk. 313   Perf. 13**
Portraits: 5pf+5pf, Albert Kuntz. 10pf+5pf, Rudi Arndt. 15pf+10pf, Kurt Adams. 20pf+10pf, Rudolf Renner. 25pf+15pf, Walter Stoecker.

**Portraits in Gray**
B36 SP12 5pf + 5pf brn blk         .20  .75
B37 SP12 10pf + 5pf dk sl grn      .20  .75
B38 SP12 15pf + 10pf dp vio        .20  4.50
B39 SP12 20pf + 10pf dk red
                        brn         .20  .75
B40 SP12 25pf + 15pf bl blk        .55  11.50
          Nos. B36-B40 (5)        1.35  18.25

Issued to honor the murdered victims of the Nazis at Buchenwald. The surtax was for the erection of national memorials.
See Nos. B49-B53, B55-B57, B60-B64, B71-B75, B79-B81.

**1958, Aug. 7     Litho.     Perf. 12½**
Design: 20pf+10pf, Pioneers and flag.
B41 SP13 10pf + 5pf green          .25  .25
B42 SP13 20pf + 10pf red           .35  .25

Pioneer organization, 10th anniversary.

#### Type of 1956 Overprinted in Black "14. September 1958"
**Perf. 13½x13**
**1958, Sept. 15                  Unwmk.**
B43 SP9  20pf + 20pf rose red      .50  .50

Dedication of the memorial at Buchenwald concentration camp, Sept. 14, 1958.

---

Exercises with
Hoops — SP14

Designs: 10pf+5pf, High jump. 20pf+10pf Vaulting. 25pf+10pf, Girl gymnasts. 40pf+20pf, Leipzig stadium and fireworks.

**Perf. 13x13½**
**1959, Aug. 10     Litho.     Wmk. 313**
B44 SP14 5pf + 5pf org             .20  .20
B45 SP14 10pf + 5pf grn            .20  .20
B46 SP14 15pf + 10pf brt car       .20  .20
B47 SP14 25pf + 10pf brt bl        .20  .20
B48 SP14 40pf + 20pf red vio      2.00  .70
          Nos. B44-B48 (5)        2.80  1.50

3rd German Sports Festival, Leipzig.

#### Portrait Type of 1957-58
Portraits: 5pf+5pf, Tilde Klose. 10pf+5pf, Kathe Niederkirchner. 15pf+10pf, Charlotte Eisenblatter. 20pf+10pf, Olga Benario-Prestes. 25pf+15pf, Maria Grollmuss.

**1959, Sept. 3     Photo.     Perf. 13**
**Portraits in Gray**
B49 SP12 5pf + 5pf sep             .20  .20
B50 SP12 10pf + 5pf dp grn         .20  .20
B51 SP12 15pf + 10pf dp vio        .20  .20
B52 SP12 20pf + 10pf mag           .20  .20
B53 SP12 25pf + 15pf dk bl         .35  .90
          Nos. B49-B53 (5)        1.15  1.70

Issued to honor women murdered by the Nazis at Buchenwald.

#### Ravensbrück Type of 1957 Dated: "12. September 1959"
**Perf. 13½x13**
**1959, Sept. 11     Litho.     Wmk. 313**
B54 SP11 20pf + 10pf dp car &
                        blk         .55  .30

#### Portrait Type of 1957-58
5pf+5pf, Lothar Erdmann. 10pf+5pf, Ernst Schneller. 20pf+10pf, Lambert Horn.

**1960, Feb. 25   Photo.   Perf. 13½x13**
**Portraits in Gray**
B55 SP12 5pf + 5pf ol bis          .25  .20
B56 SP12 10pf + 5pf dk grn         .25  .20
B57 SP12 20pf + 10pf dl mag        .25  .20
          Nos. B55-B57 (3)         .75  .60

Issued to honor murdered victims of the Nazis at Sachsenhausen.

#### Type of Regular Issue, 1960
Designs: 10pf+5pf, Vacation ship under construction, Wismar. 20pf+10pf, Ship before Stubbenkammer and sailboat.

**Wmk. 313**
**1960, June 23     Litho.     Perf. 13**
B58 A162 10pf + 5pf blk, yel &
                        red         .20  .20
B59 A162 20pf + 10pf blk, red &
                        bl          .25  .20

#### Portrait Type of 1957-58
Portraits: 10pf+5pf, Max Lademann. 15pf+5pf, Lorenz Breunig. 20pf+10pf, Mathias Thesen. 25pf+10pf, Gustl Sandtner. 40pf+20pf, Hans Rothbarth.

**1960     Wmk. 313     Perf. 13½x13**
**Portraits in Gray**
B60 SP12 10pf + 5pf grn            .20  .20
B61 SP12 15pf + 5pf dp vio        1.00  .70
B62 SP12 20pf + 10pf maroon        .20  .20
B63 SP12 25pf + 10pf dk bl         .25  .25
B64 SP12 40pf + 20pf lt red brn   2.00  1.40
          Nos. B60-B64 (5)        3.65  2.75

Issued to honor the murdered victims of the Nazis at Sachsenhausen.

Bicyclist — SP15

25pf+10pf, Bicyclists and spectators.

**1960, Aug. 3**  *Perf. 13x13½, 13x12½*
**Size: 28x23mm**

B65 SP15 20pf + 10pf multi .25 .25
**Size: 38½x21mm**

B66 SP15 25pf + 10pf bl, gray
& brn 1.50 2.50

Bicycling World Championships, Aug. 3-14.

Rook and
Congress
Emblem
SP16

20pf+10pf, Knight. 25pf+10pf, Bishop.

*Perf. 14x13½*
**1960, Sept. 19  Engr.  Wmk. 313**
B67 SP16 10pf + 5pf blue green .20 .20
B68 SP16 20pf + 10pf rose claret .20 .20
B69 SP16 25pf + 10pf blue 1.10 2.75
Nos. B67-B69 (3) 1.50 3.15

14th Chess Championships, Leipzig.

**Type of 1957**

Design: Monument and memorial wall of
Sachsenhausen National Memorial.

**1960, Sept. 8  Litho.  Perf. 13x13½**
B70 SP10 20pf + 10pf dp car .35 .30

No. B70 was re-issued Apr. 20, 1961, with
gray label adjoining each stamp in sheet, to
commemorate the dedication of Sachsenhausen National Memorial.

**Type of 1957**

Portraits: 5pf+5pf, Werner Kube. 10pf+5pf,
Hanno Gunther. 15pf+5pf, Elvira
Eisenschneider. 20pf+10pf, Hertha Lindner.
25pf+10pf, Herbert Tschäpe.

**1961, Feb. 6  Perf. 13½x13**
**Portraits in Black**
B71 SP12 5pf + 5pf brt brn .20 .20
B72 SP12 10pf + 5pf bl grn .20 .20
B73 SP12 15pf + 5pf brt lilac 1.00 2.10
B74 SP12 20pf + 10pf dp rose .20 .20
B75 SP12 25pf + 10pf brt bl .20 .20
Nos. B71-B75 (5) 1.80 2.90

Surtax for the erection of natl. memorials.

Pioneers
Playing
Volleyball
SP17

Designs: 20pf+10pf, Folk dancing.
25pf+10pf, Building model airplanes.

**1961, May 25  Perf. 13x12½**
B76 SP17 10pf + 5pf multi .20 .20
B77 SP17 20pf + 10pf multi .20 .20
B78 SP17 25pf + 10pf multi 3.00 2.40
Nos. B76-B78 (3) 3.40 2.80

Young Pioneers' meeting, Erfurt.

**Type of 1957 and**

Sophie
and
Hans
Scholl
SP18

Portraits: 5pf+5pf, Carlo Schönhaar.
10pf+5pf, Herbert Baum. 20pf+10pf, Liselotte
Herrmann. 40pf+20pf, Hilde and Hans Coppi.

*Perf. 13½x13, 13x13½*
**1961, Sept. 7  Litho.  Wmk. 313**
**Portraits in Black**
B79 SP12 5pf + 5pf green .20 .20
B80 SP12 10pf + 5pf bl grn .20 .20
B81 SP12 20pf + 10pf rose car .20 .20

B82 SP18 25pf + 10pf blue .20 .20
B83 SP18 40pf + 20pf rose brn 2.10 5.00
Nos. B79-B83 (5) 2.90 5.80

Surtax was the support of natl. memorials at
Buchenwald, Ravensbrück & Sachsenhausen.

Danielle Casanova
of France — SP19

Portraits: 10pf+5pf, Julius Fucik, Czechoslovakia. 20pf+10pf, Johanna Jannetje Schaft,
Netherlands. 25pf+10pf, Pawel Finder,
Poland. 40pf+20pf, Soya Anatolyevna Kos-
modemyanskaya, Russia.

**1962, Mar. 22  Engr.  Perf. 13½**
B84 SP19 5pf + 5pf gray .20 .20
B85 SP19 10pf + 5pf green .20 .20
B86 SP19 20pf + 10pf maroon .20 .20
B87 SP19 25pf + 10pf deep blue .25 .20
B88 SP19 40pf + 20pf sepia 1.60 2.25
Nos. B84-B88 (5) 2.45 3.05

Issued in memory of foreign victims of the
Nazis.

**Type of Regular Issue, 1962**

Design: 20pf+10pf, Three cyclists and Warsaw Palace of Culture and Science.

*Perf. 13x12½*
**1962, Apr. 26  Litho.  Wmk. 313**
B89 A192 20pf + 10pf ver, bl, blk &
yel .20 .20

Folk
Dance — SP20

15pf+5pf, Youths of three nations parading.

**1962, July 17  Wmk. 313  Perf. 14**
B90 SP20 10pf + 5pf multi .30 .20
B91 SP20 15pf + 5pf multi .30 .20
a. Pair, #B90-B91 1.10 1.00

Issued to publicize the 8th Youth Festival for
Peace and Friendship, Helsinki, July 28-Aug.
6, 1962.
No. B91a forms the festival emblem.

**Type of Regular Issue, 1962**

Design: 20pf+10pf, Springboard diving.

**1962, Aug. 7  Wmk. 313  Perf. 13**
B92 A199 20pf + 10pf lil rose &
grnsh bl .20 .20

René Blieck of
Belgium — SP21

Seven
Cervi
Brothers
of Italy
SP22

Portraits: 10pf+5pf, Dr. Alfred Klahr, Austria.
15pf+5pf, José Diaz, Spain. 20pf+10pf, Julius
Alpari, Hungary.

**1962, Oct. 4  Engr.  Perf. 14**
B93 SP21 5pf + 5pf dk bl gray .20 .20
B94 SP21 10pf + 5pf green .20 .20
B95 SP21 15pf + 5pf brt vio .20 .20
B96 SP21 20pf + 10pf dl red brn .20 .20
B97 SP22 70pf + 30pf sepia 1.90 2.50
Nos. B93-B97 (5) 2.70 3.30

Issued to commemorate foreign victims of
the Nazis.

Walter Bohne,
Runner
SP23

Gymnasts
SP24

Portraits: 10pf+5pf, Werner Seelenbinder,
wrestler. 15pf+5pf, Albert Richter, bicyclist.
20pf+10pf, Heinz Steyer, soccer player.
25pf+10pf, Kurt Schlosser, mountaineer.

**Engr. & Photo.**
**1963, May 27  Wmk. 313  Perf. 14**
B98 SP23 5pf + 5pf yel & blk .20 .20
B99 SP23 10pf + 5pf pale yel
grn & blk .20 .20
B100 SP23 15pf + 5pf rose lil &
blk .20 .20
B101 SP23 20pf + 10pf pink &
blk .20 .20
B102 SP23 25pf + 10pf pale bl &
blk 1.90 4.50
Nos. B98-B102 (5) 2.70 5.30

Issued to commemorate sportsmen victims
of the Nazis. Each stamp printed with alternating label showing sporting events connected
with each person honored. The surtax went for
the maintenance of national memorials. See
Nos. B106-B110.

**1963, June 13  Litho.  Perf. 12½x13**

Designs: 20pf+10pf, Women gymnasts.
25pf+10pf, Relay race.

B103 SP24 10pf + 5pf blk, yel
grn & lem .20 .20
B104 SP24 20pf + 10pf blk, red
& vio .25 .20
B105 SP24 25pf + 10pf blk, bl, &
gray 3.00 3.00
Nos. B103-B105 (3) 3.45 3.40

4th German Gymnastic and Sports Festival,
Leipzig. The surtax went to the festival
committee.

**Type of 1963**

Portraits: 5pf+5pf, Hermann Tops, gymnastics instructor. 10pf+5pf, Käte Tucholla, field
hockey players. 15pf+5pf, Rudolph Seiffert,
long-distance swimmers. 20pf+10pf, Ernst
Grube, sportsmen demonstrating for peace.
40pf+20pf, Kurt Biedermann, kayak in rapids.

**Engraved and Photogravure**
**1963, Sept. 24  Wmk. 313  Perf. 14**
B106 SP23 5pf + 5pf bl & blk .20 .20
B107 SP23 10pf + 5pf grn & blk .20 .20
B108 SP23 15pf + 5pf lil & blk .20 .20
B109 SP23 20pf + 10pf pale pink
& blk .20 .20
B110 SP23 40pf + 20pf lt bl & blk 2.50 2.75
Nos. B106-B110 (5) 3.30 3.55

See note after No. B102.

**Type of Regular Issue, 1963**

Design: 20pf+10pf, Ski jumper in mid-air.

*Perf. 13½x13*
**1963, Dec. 16  Litho.  Wmk. 313**
B111 A224 20pf + 10pf multi .20 .20

Surtax for the Natl. Olympic Committee.

Anton
Saefkow
SP25

Designs: 10pf+5pf, Franz Jacob. 15pf+5pf,
Bernhard Bästlein. 20pf+5pf, Harro Schulze-
Boysen. 25pf+10pf, Adam Kuckhoff.
40pf+10pf, Mildred and Arvid Harnack. Nos.
B112-B114 show group posting anti-Hitler and
pacifist posters. Nos. B115-B117 show production of anti-fascist pamphlets.

**1964, Mar. 24  Wmk. 313  Perf. 13**
**Size: 41x32mm**
B112 SP25 5pf + 5pf .25 .20
B113 SP25 10pf + 5pf .25 .20
B114 SP25 15pf + 5pf .25 .20
B115 SP25 20pf + 5pf .25 .20
B116 SP25 25pf + 5pf .35 .25
**Size: 48½x28mm**
B117 SP25 40pf + 10pf 1.25 1.50
Nos. B112-B117 (6) 2.60 2.55

The surtax was for the support of national
memorials for victims of the Nazis.

**Olympic Types of Regular Issues**

Designs: 40pf+20pf, Two runners. #B119,
Equestrian. #B120, Three runners.

**Lithographed and Engraved**
**1964, July 15  Wmk. 313  Perf. 14**
B118 A232 40pf + 20pf multi .30 .20

**Litho.**
*Perf. 13*
B119 A233 10pf + 5pf multi 2.25 2.75
B120 A233 10pf + 5pf multi 2.25 2.75
Nos. B118-B120 (3) 4.80 5.70

See note after No. 714.

Pioneers Studying — SP26

Designs: 20pf+10pf, Pioneers planting tree.
25pf+10pf, Pioneers playing.

**1964, July 29**
B121 SP26 10pf + 5pf multi 1.90 .35
B122 SP26 20pf + 10pf multi 1.90 .35
B123 SP26 25pf + 10pf multi 3.50 3.50
Nos. B121-B123 (3) 7.30 4.20

Fifth Young Pioneers Meeting, Karl-Marx-
Stadt.

**Stamp Exhibition Type of 1964**

Designs: 10pf+5pf, Stamp of 1958 (No.
390). 20pf+10pf, Stamp of 1950 (No. 73).

*Perf. 13x13½*
**1964, Sept. 23  Wmk. 313**
B124 A238 10pf + 5pf org & emer .25 .20
B125 A238 20pf + 10pf brt pink &
bl .30 .25

**Boxing Type of Regular Issue**

10pf+5pf, Two boxing gloves and laurel.

*Perf. 13½x14*
**1965, Apr. 27  Photo.  Wmk. 313**
B126 A247 10pf + 5pf blk, gold,
red & blue .20 .20

The surtax went to the German Turner and
Sport Organization.

**Type of Regular Issue, 1965**

5pf+5pf, George Dimitrov at Leipzig trial &
communist newspaper. 10pf+5pf, Anti-fascists
clandestinely distributing leaflets. 15pf+5pf,
Fighting in Spanish Civil War. 20pf+10pf,
Ernst Thalman behind bars & demonstration
for his release. 25pf+10pf, Founding of Natl.
Committee for Free Germany & signatures.

**Wmk. 313**
**1965, May 5  Photo.  Perf. 14**
**Flags in Red, Black and Yellow**
B127 A248 5pf + 5pf blk, org
& red .25 .20
B128 A248 10pf + 5pf grn & red .25 .20
B129 A248 15pf + 5pf lil, red &
yel .25 .20
B130 A248 20pf + 10pf blk &
red .25 .20
B131 A248 25pf + 10pf ol grn,
yel & blk .25 .20
Nos. B127-B131 (5) 1.25 1.00

The surtax went for the maintenance of
national memorials.

Doves, Globe and Finnish Flag — SP27

**1965, July 5　Litho.　Perf. 13x13½**
B132 SP27 10pf + 5pf vio bl & emer　.20　.20
B133 SP27 20pf + 5pf red & vio bl　.45　.30
World Peace Congress, Helsinki, July 10-17. The surtax went to the peace council of the DDR.

No. 725 Surcharged

**Perf. 13½x13**
**1965, Aug. 23　　　Wmk. 313**
B134 A239 10pf + 10pf multi　.35　.20
Surtax was for North Viet Nam.

**Sports Type of Regular Issue**
**Perf. 13½x13**
**1965, Sept. 15　Litho.　Unwmk.**
B135 A257 10pf + 5pf Fencer　.25　.20
B136 A257 10pf + 5pf Pistol shooter　.25　.20
International Modern Pentathlon Championships, Leipzig.

**Type of Regular Issue**
Designs: 10pf+5pf, Willi Bredel and instruction of International Brigade. 20pf+10pf, Heinrich Rau and parade after battle of Brunete. 25pf+10pf, Hans Marchwitza, international fighters and globe. 40pf+10pf, Artur Becker and battle on the Ebro.

**1966, July 15　Photo.　Perf. 14**
B137 A277 10pf + 10pf multi　.25　.20
B138 A277 20pf + 10pf multi　.25　.20
B139 A277 25pf + 10pf multi　.25　.20
B140 A277 40pf + 10pf multi　1.10　.90
　Nos. B137-B140 (4)　1.85　1.50
The surtax was for the maintenance of national memorials.

**Canoe Type of Regular Issue**
Design: 10pf+5pf, Men's single canoe race.

**Perf. 13x12½**
**1966, Aug. 16　Litho.　Unwmk.**
B141 A279 10pf + 5pf multi　.25　.20

**Red Cross Type of Regular Issue**
Design: ICY Red Crescent, Red Cross, and Red Lion and Sun emblems, horiz.

**1966, Sept. 13　Wmk. 313　Perf. 14**
B142 A281 20pf + 10pf vio & red　.35　.20
International health cooperation. Surtax for German Red Cross.

**Sports Type of Regular Issue**
Design: 20pf+5pf, Weight lifter.

**Perf. 13½x13**
**1966, Sept. 22　Litho.　Unwmk.**
B143 A282 20pf + 5pf ultra & blk　.35　.20

Armed Woman Planting Flower — SP28

**1966, Oct. 25　　　Perf. 13½x13**
B144 SP28 20pf + 5pf blk & pink　.35　.25
Surtax was for North Viet Nam.

**Wartburg Type of Regular Issue**
Design: Wartburg, view from the East.

**1966, Nov. 23　　　Perf. 13x13½**
B145 A288 10pf + 5pf slate　.20　.20
See note after No. 878.

**Olympic Type of Regular Issue**
Design: 10pf+5pf, Tobogganing.

**1968, Jan. 17　Litho.　Perf. 13½x13**
B146 A314 10pf + 5pf grnsh bl, vio bl & red　.20　.20
The surtax was for the Olympic Committee of the German Democratic Republic.

Armed Mother and Child — SP29　　Armed Vietnamese Couple — SP30

**1968, May 8　　　Perf. 13½x13**
B147 SP29 10pf + 5pf yel & multi　.25　.20
Surtax was for North Viet Nam.

**Festival Type of Regular Issue**
**1968, June 20　Litho.　Perf. 13½x13**
B148 A327 20pf + 5pf multi　.30　.20

**Olympic Games Type of Regular Issue, 1968**
Designs: 10pf+5pf, Pole vault, vert. 20pf+10pf, Soccer, vert.

**1968, Sept. 18　Photo.　Perf. 14**
B149 A336 10pf + 5pf multi　.20　.20
B150 A336 20pf + 10pf multi　.20　.20
The surtax was for the Olympic Committee.

**1969, June 4**
B151 SP30 10pf + 5pf multi　.30　.20
Surtax was for North Viet Nam.

**Sports Type of Regular Issue, 1969**
Designs: 10pf+5pf, Gymnastics. 20pf+5pf, Art Exhibition with sports motifs.

**Photo. & Engr.**
**1969, June 18　　　Perf. 14**
B152 A353 10pf + 5pf multi　.20　.20
B153 A353 20pf + 5pf multi　.20　.20
The surtax was for the German Gymnastic and Sports League.

Otto von Guericke's Vacuum Test with Magdeburg Hemispheres — SP31

**1969, Oct. 28　Litho.　Perf. 13x12½**
B154 SP31 40pf + 10pf multi　.95　.45
See note after No. 1146.

**Folk Art Type of Regular Issue**
Design: 20pf+5pf, Decorative plate.

**1969, Nov. 25　Litho.　Perf. 13½x13**
B155 A365 20pf + 5pf yel blk & ultra　.30　.30

**Sports Type of Regular Issue**
Design: 20pf+5pf, Children hurdling.

**1970, July 1　Photo.　Perf. 14x13½**
B156 A382 20pf + 5pf multi　.35　.20

Pioneer Waving Kerchief, and Pioneer Activities — SP32

Design: 25pf+5pf, Girl Pioneer holding kerchief, and Pioneer activities.

**1970, July 28　Litho.　Perf. 13x12½**
B157 SP32 10pf + 5pf multi　.25　.25
B158 SP32 25pf + 5pf multi　.25　.25
　a.　Pair, #B157-B158　1.10　2.25
6th Youth Pioneer Meeting, Cottbus. No. B158a has continuous design.

Ho Chi Minh — SP33

**1970, Sept. 2　　　Perf. 13x13½**
B159 SP33 20pf + 5pf rose, blk & red　.40　.20
Surtax was for North Viet Nam.

German Democratic Republic No. 460 — SP34

**1970, Oct. 1　Photo.　Perf. 14x13½**
B160 SP34 15pf + 5pf multi　.20　.30
2nd National Youth Philatelic Exhibition, Karl-Marx-Stadt, Oct. 4-11.

Mother and Child — SP35　　Vietnamese Farm Woman — SP36

**Photo. & Engr.**
**1971, Sept. 2　　　Perf. 14**
B161 SP35 10pf + 5pf multi　.30　.20
Surtax was for North Viet Nam.

**Type of Regular Issue**
10pf+5pf, Loading & unloading mail at airport.

**Photo. & Engr.**
**1971, Oct. 5　　　Perf. 14**
B162 A421 5pf + 5pf multi　.20　.20

**Olympic Games Type of Regular Issue**
Olympic Rings and: 10pf+5pf, Figure skating, pairs. 15pf+5pf, Speed skating.

**1971, Dec. 7　Photo.　Perf. 13½x14**
B163 A424 10pf + 5pf bl, car & blk　.20　.20
B164 A424 15pf + 5pf grn, blk & bl　.20　.20

**1972, Feb. 22　Litho.　Perf. 13½x13**
B165 SP36 10pf + 5pf multi　.30　.20
Surtax was for North Viet Nam.

**Olympic Games Type of Regular Issue**
Sport and Olympic Rings: 10pf+5pf, Diving. 25pf+10pf, Rowing.

**1972, May 16　Photo.　Perf. 13½x14**
B166 A430 10pf + 5pf grnsh bl, gold & blk　.20　.20
B167 A430 25pf + 10pf multi　.20　.20

**Interartes Type of Regular Issue**
Designs: 15pf+5pf, Spear carrier, Persia, 500 B.C. 35pf+5pf, Grapes Sellers, by Max Lingner, 1949, horiz.

**1972, Sept. 19　Photo.　Perf. 14**
B168 A439 15pf + 5pf multi　.75　.75
B169 A439 35pf + 5pf multi　.20　.20

Flags and World Time Clock SP37　　Young Couple, by Günter Glombitza SP38

25pf+5pf, Youth group with guitar and dove.

**1973, Feb. 13　Litho.　Perf. 12½x13**
B170 SP37 10pf + 5pf multi　.20　.20
B171 SP37 25pf + 5pf multi　.30　.25
10th World Youth Festival, Berlin.

**1973, Oct. 4　Photo.　Perf. 13½x14**
B172 SP38 20pf + 5pf multi　.30　.20
Philatelists' Day and for the 3rd National Youth Philatelic Exhibition, Halle.

Child, Symbols of Reconstruction SP39

Luis Corvalan, Red Flag — SP40

**1973, Oct. 11　　　Perf. 14x13½**
B173 SP39 10pf + 5pf multi　.30　.20
Surtax was for North Viet Nam.

**1973, Nov. 5　　　Perf. 13½x14**
25pf+5pf, Salvador Allende, Chilean flag.
B174 SP40 10pf + 5pf multi　.20　.20
B175 SP40 25pf + 5pf multi　.50　.50
Solidarity with the people of Chile.

Raised Fist and Star — SP41

**1975, Sept. 23　Litho.　Perf. 13x13½**
B176 SP41 10pf + 5pf multi　.30　.20
Surtax was for the Solidarity Committee of the German Democratic Republic.

**Restored Post Gate, Wurzen, 1734 — SP42**

**1975, Oct. 21   Photo.   Perf. 14**
B177 SP42 10pf + 5pf multi         .35 .35
Philatelists' Day 1975.

**Olympic Games Type of 1975**
Designs: 10pf+5pf, Luge run, Oberhof. 25pf+5pf, Ski jump, Rennsteig at Oberhof.

**1975, Dec. 2   Photo.   Perf. 14**
B178 A518 10pf + 5pf multi         .20 .20
B179 A518 25pf + 5pf multi         .25 .20

**Olympic Games Type of 1976**
Designs: 10pf+5pf, Swimming pool, High School for Physical Education, Leipzig. 35pf+10pf, Rifle range, Suhl.

**1976, May 18   Photo.   Perf. 13½x14**
B180 A529 10pf + 5pf multi         .20 .20
B181 A529 35pf + 10pf multi        .25 .20

**TV Tower, Berlin, and Perforations SP43**

**1976, Oct. 19   Litho.   Perf. 13**
B182 SP43 10pf + 5pf org & bl      .30 .20
Surtax was for Sozphilex 77, Philatelic Exhibition of Socialist Countries, in connection with 60th anniversary of October Revolution.

**Sports Type of 1977**
10pf+5pf, Young milers.  25pf+5pf, Girls artistic gymnastic performance.

**1977, July 19   Litho.   Perf. 13x12½**
B183 A558 10pf + 5pf multi         .20 .20
B184 A558 25pf + 5pf multi         .20 .20

**Sozphilex Type of 1977**
**Souvenir Sheet**
Design: 50pf+20pf, World Youth Song, by Lothar Zitzmann, horiz.

**1977, Aug. 16   Photo.   Perf. 13**
B185 A559 50pf + 20pf multi       1.50 1.10

**Hand Holding Torch — SP44**

**1977, Oct. 18   Litho.   Perf. 14**
B186 SP44 10pf + 5pf multi         .30 .20
Surtax was for East German Solidarity Committee.

**Fountain Type of 1979**
Design: 10pf+5pf, Goose Boy Fountain.

**1979, Aug. 7   Photo.   Perf. 14**
B187 A617 10pf + 5pf multi         .45 .35

**Vietnamese Soldier, Mother and Child — SP45**

**1979, Nov. 6   Litho.   Perf. 14**
B188 SP45 10pf + 5pf red org & blk .35 .25
Surtax was for Vietnam.

**Olympic Type of 1980**
Ski Jump, sculpture by Gunther Schutz.

**1980, Jan. 15   Photo.**
B189 A627 25pf + 10pf multi        .20 .20

**1980, Apr. 22   Photo.   Perf. 14**
Design: 20pf+5pf, Runners at the Finish, by Lothar Zitzmann.
B190 A627 20 + 5pf multi           .25 .20

**Interflug Type of 1980**
**Souvenir Sheet**
**1980, June 10   Litho.   Perf. 13x12½**
B191 A636 1m + 10pf Jet, globe    2.50 1.90
AEROSOZPHILEX 1980 International Airpost Exhibition, Berlin, Aug. 1-10.

**Olympic Type of 1980**
Design: Swimmer, by Willi Sitte, vert.

**1980, July 8   Photo.   Perf. 14**
B192 A627 20pf + 10pf multi        .20 .20
22nd Summer Olympic Games, Moscow, July 19-Aug. 3.

**International Solidarity**
**SP46              SP47**
**1980, Oct. 14   Photo.   Perf. 14**
B193 SP46 10pf + 5pf multi         .35 .20

**1981, Oct. 6   Photo.   Perf. 14**
B194 SP47 10pf + 5pf multi         .30 .20

**Palestinian Solidarity — SP48**

Palestinian family, Tree of Life.

**1982, Sept. 21   Litho.   Perf. 14**
B195 SP48 10pf + 5pf multi         .35 .25

**Nicaraguan Solidarity SP49**

**1983, Nov. 8   Litho.   Perf. 14x13½**
Literacy, home defense.
B196 SP49 10pf + 5pf multi         .30 .20

**Solidarity — SP50**

**1984, Oct. 23   Photo.   Perf. 14**
B197 SP50 10pf + 5pf Knot          .35 .25

**Solidarity SP51**

**1985, May 28   Photo.**
B198 SP51 10pf + 5pf Globe, peace dove        .30 .20
Surtax for the Solidarity Committee.

**Technical Assistance to Developing Nations — SP52**

**1986, Nov. 4   Photo.**
B199 SP52 10pf + 5pf multi         .30 .25
Surtax for the Solidarity Committee.

**Solidarity with South Africans Opposing Apartheid SP53**

**1987, June 16   Litho.   Perf. 14**
B200 SP53 10pf + 5pf multi         .30 .25

**Solidarity SP54**

**1988, Oct. 4   Photo.   Perf. 14**
B201 SP54 10pf + 5pf multi         .40 .40
Surtax for the Solidarity Committee. No. B201 printed se-tenant with label containing a Wilhelm Pieck quote.

**UNICEF Emblem and Children of Africa — SP55**

**1989, Sept. 5   Photo.   Perf. 14½x14**
B202 SP55 10pf + 5pf multi         .30 .20
Surtax for the Solidarity Committee.

**Leipzig Church, Municipal Arms SP56**

**1990, Feb. 28   Photo.   Perf. 13**
B203 SP56 35pf + 15pf multi        .75 .50
We are the People.

**Intl. Literacy Year — SP57**

**1990, July 24   Photo.   Perf. 14**
B204 SP57 30pf+5pf on 10pf+5pf    1.50 1.00
Not issued without surcharge.

---

**AIR POST STAMPS**

Catalogue values for unused stamps in this section, from this point to the end of the section, are for Never Hinged items.

Canceled to Order
Used values are for CTO's.

**Stylized Plane**
**AP1              AP2**
**Perf. 13x12½, 13x13½ (AP2)**
**1957, Dec. 13   Litho.   Wmk. 313**
C1 AP1 5pf gray & blk             3.50 .20
C2 AP1 20pf brt car & blk          .20 .20
C3 AP1 35pf violet & blk           .20 .20
C4 AP1 50pf maroon & blk           .30 .20
C5 AP2 1m olive & yel             1.00 .20
C6 AP2 3m choc & yel              1.60 .45
C7 AP2 5m dk bl & yel             3.75 .70
Nos. C1-C7 (7)                   10.55 2.15

**Plane and Envelope — AP3**

**1982-87   Photo.   Perf. 14**
C8 AP3 5pf lt bl & blk             .20 .20
C9 AP3 15pf brt rose lil & blk     .20 .30
C10 AP3 20pf ocher & blk           .25 .20
C11 AP3 25pf ol bis & blk          .35 .25
C12 AP3 30pf brt grn & blk         .25 .20
C13 AP3 40pf ol grn & blk          .35 .20
C14 AP3 1m blue & blk             1.00 .45
C15 AP3 3m brown & blk            3.00 1.75
C16 AP3 5m dk red & blk           4.50 1.50
Nos. C8-C16 (9)                  10.10 5.15

Issued: 30, 40pf, 1m, 10/26; 5, 20pf, 10/4/83; 3m, 4/10/84; 5m, 9/10/85; 15, 25pf, 10/6/87.

---

**OFFICIAL STAMPS**

While valid, these Official stamps were not sold to the public unused. After their period of use, some sets were sold abroad by the government stamp sales agency. Used values of Official stamps are for canceled-to-order copies. Reprints of type O1 stamps have printed cancellations.

Catalogue values for unused stamps in this section, from this point to the end of the section, are for Never Hinged items.

Arms of
Republic — O1

### Perf. 13x12½

| 1954 | | Wmk. 297 | Litho. | |
|------|---|----------|--------|---|
| O1 | O1 | 5pf emerald | 13.50 | .20 |
| O2 | O1 | 6pf violet | 7.50 | .20 |
| O3 | O1 | 8pf org brown | 13.50 | .20 |
| O4 | O1 | 10pf lt bl grn | 13.50 | .20 |
| O5 | O1 | 12pf blue | 45.00 | .20 |
| O6 | O1 | 15pf dark violet | 13.50 | .20 |
| O7 | O1 | 16pf dark violet | 7.50 | .20 |
| O8 | O1 | 20pf olive | 9.00 | .20 |
| O9 | O1 | 24pf brown red | 9.00 | .20 |
| O10 | O1 | 25pf sage green | 9.00 | .20 |
| O11 | O1 | 30pf brown red | 6.00 | .20 |
| O12 | O1 | 40pf red | 9.75 | .20 |
| O13 | O1 | 48pf rose lilac | 5.25 | 1.10 |
| O14 | O1 | 50pf rose lilac | 4.50 | .20 |
| O15 | O1 | 60pf bright blue | 4.50 | .20 |
| O16 | O1 | 70pf brown | 4.50 | .20 |
| O17 | O1 | 84pf brown | 7.50 | 3.00 |
| | | Nos. O1-O17 (17) | 183.00 | 7.10 |

#### Type of 1954 Redrawn

Arc of compass projects at right except on No. O22.

| 1954-56 | | | Typo. | |
|---------|---|---|-------|---|
| O18 | O1 | 5pf emer ('54) | 3.75 | .25 |
| O19 | O1 | 10pf bl grn | 2.25 | .25 |
| O20 | O1 | 12pf dk bl ('54) | 2.25 | .25 |
| O21 | O1 | 15pf dk vio | 2.75 | .25 |
| O22 | O1 | 20pf ol, arc at left | | |
| | | ('55) | 52.50 | .25 |
| a. | | Arc of compass projects at right ('56) | 525.00 | .25 |
| O23 | O1 | 25pf dark green | 2.25 | .25 |
| O24 | O1 | 30pf brown red | 4.50 | .25 |
| O25 | O1 | 40pf red | 4.50 | .25 |
| O26 | O1 | 50pf rose lilac | 2.25 | .25 |
| O27 | O1 | 70pf brown | 2.25 | .25 |
| | | Nos. O18-O27 (10) | 79.25 | 2.50 |

Shaded background of emblem consists of vertical lines; on Nos. O1-O17 it consists of dots.

Granite paper was used for a 1956 printing of the 5pf, 10pf, 15pf, 20pf and 40pf. Value for set unused $300, used 30 cents.

See Nos. O37-O43.

O2

O3

| 1956 | | Wmk. 297 | Perf. 13x12½ | |
|------|---|----------|--------------|---|
| O28 | O2 | 5pf black | .25 | .20 |
| O29 | O2 | 10pf black | .25 | .20 |
| O30 | O2 | 20pf black | .30 | .20 |
| O31 | O2 | 40pf black | .40 | .20 |
| O32 | O2 | 70pf black | .45 | .20 |
| | | Nos. O28-O32 (5) | 1.65 | 1.00 |

| 1956 | | Litho. | Wmk. 297 | |
|------|---|--------|----------|---|
| O33 | O3 | 10pf lilac & black | .90 | .75 |
| O34 | O3 | 20pf lilac & black | 140.00 | 1.10 |
| O35 | O3 | 40pf lilac & black | 1.50 | .70 |
| O36 | O3 | 70pf lilac & black | 2.25 | 2.50 |
| | | Nos. O33-O36 (4) | 144.65 | 5.10 |

Nos. O33-O36 exist also with black or violet overprint of 4-digit control number.
See Nos. O44-O45.

No. O34 was reprinted with watermark sideways ("DDR" vertical). Value $4.

#### Redrawn Type of 1954-56
#### Perf. 13x12½, 14

| 1957-60 | | Typo. | Wmk. 313 | |
|---------|---|-------|----------|---|
| | | **Granite Paper** | | |
| O37 | O1 | 5pf emerald | .25 | .25 |
| O38 | O1 | 10pf blue green | .25 | .25 |
| O39 | O1 | 15pf dark vio | .35 | .25 |
| O40 | O1 | 20pf olive | .35 | .25 |
| O41 | O1 | 30pf dark red ('58) | .75 | .25 |
| O42 | O1 | 40pf red | .55 | .25 |
| O42A | O1 | 50pf rose lilac ('60) | 1.60 | .35 |
| O43 | O1 | 70pf brown ('58) | 1.60 | .35 |
| | | Nos. O37-O43 (8) | 5.70 | 2.20 |

Nos. O37-O43 were all issued in perf. 13x12½. Nos. O37-O40 were also issued perf. 14. Values are the same.

---

#### Type of 1956

| 1957 | | Litho. | Perf. 13x12½ | |
|------|---|--------|--------------|---|
| O44 | O3 | 10pf lilac & black | .65 | .35 |
| O45 | O3 | 20pf lilac & black | .65 | .35 |

Nos. O44-O45 have black or violet overprint of four-digit control number.
Stamps similar to type O3 were issued later, with denomination expressed in dashes: one for 10pf, two for 20pf.

---

### ISSUED UNDER RUSSIAN OCCUPATION

---

### BERLIN-BRANDENBURG

Berlin Bear — OS1

| 1945 | | Litho. | Perf. 14 | |
|------|---|--------|----------|---|
| 11N1 | OS1 | 5pf shown | .20 | .55 |
| 11N2 | OS1 | 6pf Bear holding spade | .20 | .35 |
| 11N3 | OS1 | 8pf Bear on shield | .20 | .35 |
| 11N4 | OS1 | 10pf Bear holding brick | .20 | .55 |
| 11N5 | OS1 | 12pf Bear carrying board | .20 | .35 |
| 11N6 | OS1 | 20pf Bear on small shield | .20 | .35 |
| 11N7 | OS1 | 30pf Oak sapling, ruins | .20 | .55 |
| | | Nos. 11N1-11N7 (7) | | 3.05 |
| Set, never hinged | | | | 1.40 |

Issued: 5pf, 8pf, 6/9; 12pf, 7/5; others, 7/18.

| 1945, Dec. 6 | | Serrate Roulette 13½ | |
|--------------|---|----------------------|---|
| 11N1a | OS1 | 5pf | .20 | .55 |
| 11N2a | OS1 | 6pf | 3.75 | 90.00 |
| 11N3a | OS1 | 8pf | 2.25 | 90.00 |
| 11N4a | OS1 | 10pf | 3.75 | 90.00 |
| 11N5a | OS1 | 12pf | 4.50 | 125.00 |
| 11N6a | OS1 | 20pf | 3.00 | 97.50 |
| 11N7a | OS1 | 30pf | 4.50 | 125.00 |
| | | Nos. 11N1a-11N7a (7) | 21.95 | 618.05 |
| Set, never hinged | | | 70.00 | |

No. 11N1a comes with two different roulettes. The roulette that matches Nos. 11N2-11N7a is valued at $2. No. 11N5a in the second roulette is rare.

---

### MECKLENBURG-VORPOMMERN

OS1

Plowman — OS2

Design: 12pf, Wheat.

| 1945-46 | | Typo. | Perf. 10½ | |
|---------|---|-------|-----------|---|
| 12N1 | OS1 | 6pf black, green | .20 | 1.90 |
| 12N2 | OS1 | 6pf purple | 1.10 | 3.00 |
| 12N3 | OS1 | 6pf purple, green | 1.10 | 3.00 |
| 12N4 | OS2 | 8pf red, rose | .30 | 2.25 |
| a. | | 8pf red lilac, rose | .75 | 19.00 |
| 12N5 | OS2 | 8pf black, rose | 1.90 | 9.75 |
| 12N6 | OS2 | 8pf red lilac, green | .55 | 4.50 |
| 12N7 | OS2 | 8pf black, green | 3.00 | 12.00 |
| 12N8 | OS2 | 8pf brown | .45 | 4.50 |
| 12N9 | OS2 | 8pf black, rose | .25 | 1.60 |
| 12N10 | OS2 | 12pf brown lilac | .30 | 1.90 |
| 12N11 | OS2 | 12pf red | 1.90 | 12.00 |
| 12N12 | OS2 | 12pf red, rose | .30 | 2.40 |
| | | Nos. 12N1-12N12 (12) | 11.35 | 58.80 |
| Set, never hinged | | | 30.00 | |

Many shades.
Issued: #12N1, 12N9, 8/28; #12N4, 10/6; #12N5, 10/19; #12N7, 11/2; #12N6, 11/3; #12N10, 11/9; #12N2, 11/16; #12N11, 12/20; #12N8, 1/7/46; #12N3, 1/11/46; #12N12, 1/30/46.

Buildings — OS3

Designs: 4pf, Deer. 5pf, Fishing boats. 6pf, Harvesting grain. 8pf, Windmill. 10pf, Two-horse plow. 12pf, Bricklayer on scaffolding. 15pf, Tractor plowing field. 20pf, Ship, warehouse. 30pf, Factory. 40pf, Woman spinning.

| 1946 | | Typo. | Imperf. | |
|------|---|-------|---------|---|
| 12N13 | OS3 | 3pf brown | 1.10 | 35.00 |
| 12N14 | OS3 | 4pf blue | 13.50 | 52.50 |
| 12N15 | OS3 | 4pf red brown | 1.10 | 45.00 |
| 12N16 | OS3 | 5pf green | 1.10 | 35.00 |
| 12N17 | OS3 | 8pf orange | 1.10 | 35.00 |
| 12N18 | OS3 | 10pf brown | .90 | 35.00 |
| | | **Perf. 10½** | | |
| 12N19 | OS3 | 6pf purple | .75 | 6.00 |
| 12N20 | OS3 | 6pf blue | 3.75 | 18.00 |
| 12N21 | OS3 | 12pf red | .60 | 3.25 |
| 12N22 | OS3 | 12pf brown | .60 | 5.75 |
| 12N23 | OS3 | 20pf blue | .90 | 9.75 |
| 12N24 | OS3 | 30pf blue green | .75 | 7.50 |
| 12N25 | OS3 | 40pf red violet | .75 | 8.25 |
| | | Nos. 12N13-12N25 (13) | 26.90 | 296.00 |
| Set, never hinged | | | 52.50 | |

Issued: 3pf, #12N14, 5pf, 6pf, 8pf, 1/17; 10pf, 12pf, 40pf, 1/22; 15pf, 1/24; 30pf, 1/26; 20pf, 1/29; #12N15, 2/25.
Nos. 12N13-12N21 exist on both white and toned paper.

### MECKLENBURG-VORPOMMERN SEMI-POSTAL STAMPS

Rudolf Breitscheid (1874-1944), Politician OSP1

Designs: 8pf+22pf, Dr. Erich Klausener (1885-1934), theologian. 12pf+28pf, Ernst Thalmann (1886-1944), politician.

| 1945, Oct. 21 | | Typo. | Perf. 10½x11 | |
|---------------|---|-------|--------------|---|
| 12NB1 | OSP1 | 6 +14pf green | 10.50 | 45.00 |
| 12NB2 | OSP1 | 8 +22pf purple | 10.50 | 45.00 |
| 12NB3 | OSP1 | 12 +28pf red | 10.50 | 45.00 |
| | | Nos. 12NB1-12NB3 (3) | 31.50 | 135.00 |
| Set, never hinged | | | 75.00 | |

Sower
OSP2

Child Welfare
OSP3

6pf+14pf, Horsedrawn Plow. 12pf+28pf, Reaper.

| 1945 | | | | |
|------|---|---|---|---|
| 12NB4 | OSP2 | 6 +14pf bl grn | 2.25 | 22.50 |
| 12NB5 | OSP2 | 6 +14pf grn | 2.25 | 22.50 |
| 12NB6 | OSP2 | 8 +22pf brn | 2.25 | 22.50 |
| 12NB7 | OSP2 | 8 +22pf yel brn | 2.25 | 22.50 |
| 12NB8 | OSP2 | 12 +28pf red | 2.25 | 22.50 |
| 12NB9 | OSP2 | 12 +28pf org | 2.25 | 22.50 |
| | | Nos. 12NB4-12NB9 (6) | 13.50 | 135.00 |
| Set, never hinged | | | 37.50 | |

Issued: #12NB4, 12NB6, 12NB8, Dec. 8; others Dec. 31.

| 1945, Dec. 31 | | | Perf. 11 | |
|---------------|---|---|----------|---|
| 12NB10 | OSP3 | 6 +14pf Child in hand | 2.75 | 30.00 |

| 12NB11 | OSP3 | 8 +22pf Girl in winter | .95 | 30.00 |
|--------|------|------------------------|-----|-------|
| 12NB12 | OSP3 | 12 +28pf Boy | .95 | 30.00 |
| | | Nos. 12NB10-12NB12 (3) | 4.65 | 90.00 |
| | | Set, never hinged | 11.00 | |

---

### SAXONY PROVINCE

Coat of
Arms — OS1

Land
Reform — OS2

#### Perf. 13x12½

| 1945-46 | | Typo. | Wmk. 48 | |
|---------|---|-------|---------|---|
| 13N1 | OS1 | 1pf slate | .20 | 1.90 |
| a. | | Imperf. | .20 | 4.50 |
| | | Never hinged | .60 | |
| 13N2 | OS1 | 3pf yellow brown | .20 | 2.25 |
| a. | | Imperf. | .20 | 3.00 |
| | | Never hinged | .60 | |
| 13N3 | OS1 | 5pf green | .20 | 2.00 |
| a. | | Imperf. | .55 | 11.00 |
| | | Never hinged | 1.50 | |
| 13N4 | OS1 | 6pf purple | .20 | 2.25 |
| a. | | Imperf. | .35 | 1.90 |
| | | Never hinged | 1.00 | |
| 13N5 | OS1 | 8pf orange | .20 | 2.50 |
| a. | | Imperf. | .20 | 3.00 |
| | | Never hinged | .60 | |
| 13N6 | OS1 | 10pf brown | .20 | 2.50 |
| a. | | Imperf. | 2.75 | 110.00 |
| | | Never hinged | 6.00 | |
| 13N7 | OS1 | 12pf red | .20 | 1.90 |
| a. | | Imperf. | .20 | 1.90 |
| | | Never hinged | .60 | |
| 13N8 | OS1 | 15pf red brown | .20 | 19.00 |
| 13N9 | OS1 | 20pf blue | .20 | 3.00 |
| 13N10 | OS1 | 24pf orange brown | .20 | 3.00 |
| 13N11 | OS1 | 30pf olive green | .20 | 3.00 |
| 13N12 | OS1 | 40pf lake | .60 | 6.75 |
| | | Nos. 13N1-13N12 (12) | 2.80 | 50.05 |
| Set, never hinged | | | 3.50 | |

Issued: #13N1-13N12, 12/1945; #13N1a-13N5a, 13N7a, 10/10/45; #13N6a, 1/1946.

| 1945-46 | | Unwmk. | Imperf. | |
|---------|---|--------|---------|---|
| 13N13 | OS2 | 6pf green | .20 | 1.80 |
| 13N14 | OS2 | 12pf red | .20 | 1.80 |

#### On Thin Transparent Paper
#### Wmk. 397
#### Perf. 13x13½

| 13N15 | OS2 | 6pf green | .20 | 1.80 |
|-------|-----|-----------|-----|------|
| 13N16 | OS2 | 12pf red | .20 | 1.80 |
| | | Nos. 13N13-13N16 (4) | | 7.20 |
| Set, never hinged | | | 1.20 | |

Issued: #13N13-13N14, 12/17/45; others 2/21/46.

---

### SAXONY PROVINCE SEMI-POSTAL STAMPS

Reconstruction
OSP1

Designs: 6+4pf, Housing construction. 12+8pf, Bridge repair. 42+28pf, Locomotives.

| 1946, Jan. 19 | | Typo. | Perf. 13 | |
|---------------|---|-------|----------|---|
| 13NB1 | OSP1 | 6pf +4pf green | .20 | 1.80 |
| a. | | Imperf. | .20 | 15.00 |
| 13NB2 | OSP1 | 12pf +8pf red | .20 | 1.80 |
| a. | | Imperf. | .20 | 15.00 |
| 13NB3 | OSP1 | 42pf +28pf violet | .20 | 1.80 |
| a. | | Imperf. | .20 | 15.00 |
| | | Nos. 13NB1-13NB3 (3) | | 5.40 |
| Set, never hinged | | | .70 | |
| Set, 13NB1a-13NB3a, never hinged | | | 1.60 | |

Nos. 13NB1a-13NB3a issued Feb. 21.

## WEST SAXONY

OS1

Leipzig
Fair — OS2

| 1945 | | Typo. | Wmk. 48 | Perf. 13x12½ | |
|---|---|---|---|---|---|
| 14N1 | OS1 | 3pf brown | | .20 | 1.90 |
| 14N2 | OS1 | 4pf slate | | .20 | 3.75 |
| 14N3 | OS1 | 5pf green | | .20 | 1.90 |
| a. | | Imperf. | | .20 | 1.90 |
| | | Never hinged | | .25 | |
| 14N4 | OS1 | 6pf violet | | .20 | 1.90 |
| a. | | Imperf. | | .20 | 1.90 |
| | | Never hinged | | .25 | |
| 14N5 | OS1 | 8pf orange | | .20 | 4.50 |
| a. | | Imperf. | | .20 | 1.90 |
| | | Never hinged | | .25 | |
| 14N6 | OS1 | 10pf gray | | .20 | 4.00 |
| 14N7 | OS1 | 12pf red | | .20 | 1.90 |
| a. | | Imperf. | | .20 | 1.90 |
| | | Never hinged | | .25 | |
| 14N8 | OS1 | 15pf red brown | | .30 | 4.25 |
| 14N9 | OS1 | 20pf blue | | .30 | 3.75 |
| 14N10 | OS1 | 30pf olive green | | .30 | 2.25 |
| 14N11 | OS1 | 40pf red lilac | | .30 | 4.50 |
| 14N12 | OS1 | 60pf maroon | | .30 | 15.00 |
| | Nos. 14N1-14N12 (12) | | | 2.80 | 49.60 |
| | Set, never hinged | | | 12.00 | |

Issued: 3-4, 20-30pf, 11/9; 5-8, 12pf, 11/12; 10, 15, 40-60pf, 11/15; imperfs., 9/28.

| 1945, Oct. 18 | | | | | |
|---|---|---|---|---|---|
| 14N13 | OS2 | 6pf green | | .25 | 2.90 |
| 14N14 | OS2 | 12pf red | | .25 | 2.90 |
| | Set, never hinged | | | 1.00 | |

Leipzig Arms — OS3

Designs: 5pf, 6pf, St. Nicholas Church. 8pf, 12pf, Leipzig Town Hall.

| 1946, Feb. 12 | | | | | |
|---|---|---|---|---|---|
| 14N15 | OS3 | 3pf brown | | .20 | 6.00 |
| a. | | Unwatermarked | | .20 | 9.00 |
| 14N16 | OS3 | 4pf slate | | .20 | 6.00 |
| a. | | Unwatermarked | | .20 | 9.00 |
| 14N17 | OS3 | 5pf green | | .20 | 6.00 |
| a. | | Unwatermarked | | .20 | 9.00 |
| 14N18 | OS3 | 6pf violet | | .20 | 6.00 |
| a. | | Unwatermarked | | .20 | 9.00 |
| 14N19 | OS3 | 8pf orange | | .20 | 6.00 |
| a. | | Unwatermarked | | .20 | 9.00 |
| 14N20 | OS3 | 12pf red | | .20 | 6.00 |
| a. | | Unwatermarked | | .20 | 9.00 |
| | Nos. 14N15-14N20 (6) | | | | 36.00 |
| | Set, never hinged | | | 1.40 | |
| | Set, 14N15a-14N20a, never hinged | | | 1.50 | |

Nos. 14N15a-14N20a issued Mar. 15.

## WEST SAXONY SEMI-POSTAL STAMPS

OSP1

Market, Old Town Hall — OSP2

| 1946 | | Typo. | Wmk. 48 | Perf. 13x12½ | |
|---|---|---|---|---|---|
| 14NB1 | OSP1 | 3 +2pf yel brn | | .20 | 2.10 |
| 14NB2 | OSP1 | 4 +3pf slate | | .20 | 2.10 |
| 14NB3 | OSP1 | 5 +3pf green | | .20 | 2.10 |
| 14NB4 | OSP1 | 6 +4pf violet | | .20 | 2.10 |
| 14NB5 | OSP1 | 8 +4pf orange | | .20 | 2.10 |
| 14NB6 | OSP1 | 10 +5pf gray | | .20 | 2.10 |
| 14NB7 | OSP1 | 12 +6pf red | | .20 | 2.10 |
| 14NB8 | OSP1 | 15 +10pf red brn | | .20 | 2.10 |
| 14NB9 | OSP1 | 20 +10pf blue | | .20 | 2.10 |

| 14NB10 | OSP1 | 30 +20pf olive grn | | .20 | 2.10 |
|---|---|---|---|---|---|
| 14NB11 | OSP1 | 40 +30pf red lilac | | .20 | 2.10 |
| 14NB12 | OSP1 | 60 +40pf lake | | .20 | 3.00 |
| | Nos. 14NB1-14NB12 (12) | | | 2.40 | 26.10 |
| | Set, never hinged | | | 4.50 | |

Issue dates: Nos. 14NB1, 14NB4, 14NB7, 14NB11, Jan. 7; others, Jan. 28.

| 1946, May 8 | | | Perf. 13 | | |
|---|---|---|---|---|---|
| 14NB13 | OSP2 | 6 +14pf violet | | .20 | 2.50 |
| a. | | Imperf. | | .35 | 9.00 |
| b. | | Unwatermarked | | .35 | 3.75 |
| 14NB14 | OSP2 | 12 +18pf bl gray | | .20 | 4.50 |
| a. | | Imperf. | | .35 | 9.00 |
| b. | | Unwatermarked | | .25 | 6.00 |
| 14NB15 | OSP2 | 24 +26pf org brn | | .20 | 2.50 |
| a. | | Imperf. | | .35 | 9.00 |
| b. | | Unwatermarked | | .25 | 2.25 |
| 14NB16 | OSP2 | 84 +66pf green | | .20 | 6.00 |
| a. | | Imperf. | | .35 | 22.50 |
| c. | | Sheet of 4, #14NB13a-14NB16a | | 75.00 | 240.00 |
| | | Never hinged | | 150.00 | |
| | Nos. 14NB13-14NB16 (4) | | | .80 | 15.50 |
| | Set, never hinged | | | 1.50 | |
| | Set, 14NB13a-14NB16a, never hinged | | | 3.50 | |
| | Set, 14NB13b-14NB16b, never hinged | | | 2.10 | |

Issue date: Imperf., May 20.

## EAST SAXONY

OS1

OS2

| 1945, June 23 | | Photo. | Imperf. | | |
|---|---|---|---|---|---|
| 15N1 | OS1 | 12pf red | | 190.00 | 600.00 |
| | | Never hinged | | 410.00 | |

Withdrawn on day of issue.

### Litho. (3pf, #15N9), Photo.
### 1945-46

| 15N2 | OS2 | 3pf sepia | | .30 | 2.25 |
|---|---|---|---|---|---|
| 15N3 | OS2 | 4pf blue gray | | .20 | 1.90 |
| a. | | 4pf gray | | .20 | .90 |
| 15N4 | OS2 | 5pf brown | | .30 | 2.00 |
| 15N5 | OS2 | 6pf green | | 2.50 | 6.00 |
| 15N6 | OS2 | 6pf violet | | .20 | .90 |
| 15N7 | OS2 | 8pf dark violet | | .35 | 2.00 |
| 15N8 | OS2 | 10pf dark brown | | .45 | 4.00 |
| 15N9 | OS2 | 10pf gray | | .30 | 2.25 |
| 15N10 | OS2 | 12pf red | | .30 | 2.00 |
| 15N11 | OS2 | 15pf lemon | | .45 | 2.60 |
| 15N12 | OS2 | 20pf blue | | .20 | 1.90 |
| a. | | 20pf gray blue | | .60 | 2.60 |
| | | Never hinged | | 1.20 | |
| 15N13 | OS2 | 25pf blue | | .45 | 2.75 |
| 15N14 | OS2 | 30pf yellow | | .20 | 1.90 |
| 15N15 | OS2 | 40pf lilac | | .45 | 2.75 |

### Typo.
### Perf. 13x12½

| 15N16 | OS2 | 3pf brown | | .20 | 1.90 |
|---|---|---|---|---|---|
| 15N17 | OS2 | 5pf green | | .20 | 1.90 |
| 15N18 | OS2 | 6pf violet | | .20 | 1.90 |
| 15N19 | OS2 | 8pf orange | | .20 | 1.90 |
| 15N20 | OS2 | 12pf vermilion | | .20 | 1.90 |
| | Nos. 15N2-15N20 (19) | | | 7.65 | 44.70 |
| | Set, never hinged | | | 17.50 | |

Issued: 12pf, 6/28; #15N5, 6/30; 8pf, #15N8, 7/3; 25pf, 7/5; 5pf, 6/6; 40pf, 7/7; 15pf, 7/10; #15N12a, 7/26; #15N9, 15N12, 15N17-15N20, 11/3; #15N3, 30pf, 11/5; 3pf, 12/5; #15N15, 12/21; #15N6, 1/22/46.

## EAST SAXONY SEMI-POSTAL STAMPS

Zwinger, Dresden — OSP1

---

Design: 12pf+88pf, Rathaus, Dresden.

| 1946, Feb. 6 | | Photo. | Perf. 11 | | |
|---|---|---|---|---|---|
| 15NB1 | OSP1 | 6pf +44pf green | | .20 | 4.50 |
| 15NB2 | OSP1 | 12pf +88pf red | | .20 | 4.50 |
| | Set, never hinged | | | .70 | |

## THURINGIA

Fir Trees — OS1

Designs: 6pf, 8pf, Posthorn. 12pf, Schiller. 20pf, 30pf, Goethe.

| 1945-46 | | Typo. | Perf. 11 | | |
|---|---|---|---|---|---|
| 16N1 | OS1 | 3pf brown | | .20 | 3.00 |
| 16N2 | OS1 | 4pf black | | .20 | 3.00 |
| 16N3 | OS1 | 5pf green | | .20 | 3.00 |
| a. | | Souvenir sheet of 3, #16N1-16N3 | | 150.00 | 825.00 |
| | | Never hinged | | 300.00 | |
| 16N4 | OS1 | 6pf dark green | | .20 | 1.90 |
| 16N5 | OS1 | 8pf orange | | .20 | 2.60 |
| 16N6 | OS1 | 12pf red | | .20 | 2.50 |
| 16N7 | OS1 | 20pf blue | | .20 | 2.25 |
| a. | | Imperf. | | .20 | 3.00 |
| | | Never hinged | | .35 | |
| b. | | Souv. sheet of 4, #16N2, 16N4, 16N6-16N7, rouletted x imperf. btwn. | | 575.00 | 2,250. |
| | | | | 1,150. | |
| 16N8 | OS1 | 30pf gray | | .55 | 3.00 |
| a. | | Imperf. | | 1.50 | 15.00 |
| | | Never hinged | | 3.00 | |
| | Nos. 16N1-16N8 (8) | | | 1.95 | 21.25 |
| | Set, never hinged | | | 3.50 | |

#16N3a sold for 2m, #16N7b for 10m.
Issued: 6pf, 10/1; 12pf, 10/19; 5pf, 10/20; 8pf, 11/3; 20pf, 11/24; #16N3a, 16N7b, 12/18; 30pf, 12/22; 3pf, 4pf, 1/4/46.

### Souvenir Sheet

Rebuilding of German Natl. Theater, Weimar — OS2

a, 6pf, Schiller. b, 10pf, Goethe. c, 12pf, Liszt. d, 16pf, Wieland. e, 40pf, Natl. Theater.

| 1946, Mar. 27 | | Wmk. 48 | Imperf. | | |
|---|---|---|---|---|---|
| 16N9 | OS2 | Sheet of 5, #a.-e. | | 15.00 | 60.00 |
| f. | | Sheet, unwatermarked, rouletted | | 26.00 | 150.00 |
| | | Never hinged | | 52.50 | |

No. 16N9 was issued without gum. Sold for 7.50 marks.

---

## THURINGIA SEMI-POSTAL STAMPS

Bridge Reconstruction OSP1

Designs: 10pf+60pf, Saalburg Bridge. 12pf+68pf, Camsdorf Bridge, Jena. 16pf+74pf, Goschwitz Bridge. 24pf+76pf, Ilm Bridge, Mellingen.

---

| 1946, Mar. 30 | | Typo. | Imperf. | | |
|---|---|---|---|---|---|
| 16NB1 | OSP1 | 10 +60pf red brn | | .20 | 9.00 |
| 16NB2 | OSP1 | 12 +68pf red | | .20 | 9.00 |
| 16NB3 | OSP1 | 16 +74pf dark grn | | .20 | 9.00 |
| 16NB4 | OSP1 | 24 +76pf brown | | .20 | 9.00 |
| a. | | Souv. sheet of 4, #16NB1-16NB4 | | 150.00 | 1,250. |
| | | Never hinged | | 300.00 | |
| | Nos. 16NB1-16NB4 (4) | | | | 36.00 |
| | Set, never hinged | | | 1.10 | |

# GHANA

'gä-nə

LOCATION — West Africa between Benin and Ivory Coast
GOVT. — Republic
AREA — 92,010 sq. mi.
POP. — 18,101,000 (1997 est.)
CAPITAL — Accra

Ghana is the former British colony of Gold Coast, which achieved independence March 6, 1957. It includes the former trusteeship territory of British Togoland.

12 Pence = 1 Shilling
20 Shillings = 1 Pound
100 Pesewas = 1 Cedi (1965, 1972)
100 New Pesewas = 1 New Cedi (1967)

**Used Values in Italics**
In 1961 the government canceled all remainder stocks, using cancellations which closely resemble genuine postmarks. Catalogue values in italics (in Ghana) are for canceled-to-order stamps. Postally used stamps are worth more.

Catalogue values for all unused stamps in this country are for Never Hinged items.

**Watermark**

Wmk. 325 — Stars and G Multiple

Kwame Nkrumah, Map and Palm-nut Vulture — A1

**Perf. 14x14½**
**1957, Mar. 6     Wmk. 4     Photo.**
| | | | | |
|---|---|---|---|---|
| 1 | A1 | 2p rose red | .20 | .20 |
| 2 | A1 | 2½p green | .20 | .20 |
| 3 | A1 | 4p brown | .20 | .20 |
| 4 | A1 | 1sh3p dark blue | .20 | .20 |
| | | Nos. 1-4 (4) | .80 | .80 |

Independence, Mar. 6, 1957.
For overprints see Nos. 28-31.

Stamps of Gold Coast, 1952-54, Overprinted in Black or Red

**Perf. 11½x12, 12x11½**
**1957, Mar. 6     Engr.**
| | | | | |
|---|---|---|---|---|
| 5 | A14 | ½p yel brown & car | .30 | .20 |
| 6 | A14 | 1p deep blue (R) | .30 | .20 |
| 7 | A14 | 1½p green | .30 | .20 |
| 8 | A14 | 3p rose | .50 | .20 |
| 9 | A15 | 6p org & black (R) | .30 | .20 |
| 10 | A14 | 1sh red org & black | .30 | .20 |
| 11 | A14 | 2sh rose car & ol brn | .70 | .20 |
| 12 | A14 | 5sh gray & red vio | 1.10 | .25 |
| 13 | A15 | 10sh olive grn & black | 1.25 | .50 |
| | | Nos. 5-13 (9) | 5.05 | 2.15 |

Nos. 5-6 exist in vertical coils.
See Nos. 25-27.

Viking Ship and Angelfish A2

1sh3p, Medieval galleon and swordfish. 5sh, Modern cargo ship and flyingfish.

**Perf. 12x11½**
**1957, Dec. 27     Engr.     Unwmk.**
| | | | | |
|---|---|---|---|---|
| 14 | A2 | 2½p emerald | .20 | .20 |
| 15 | A2 | 1sh3p dark blue | .35 | .35 |
| 16 | A2 | 5sh red lilac | 1.25 | 1.25 |
| | | Nos. 14-16 (3) | 1.80 | 1.80 |

Black Star Line inauguration.

Ambassador Hotel — A3

Coat of Arms — A4

Design: 2½p, Opening of Parliament. 1sh3p, National monument.

**Perf. 14x14½, 14½x14**
**1958, Mar. 6     Photo.     Wmk. 4**
**Flags in Original Colors**
| | | | | |
|---|---|---|---|---|
| 17 | A3 | ½p car rose & black | .20 | .20 |
| 18 | A3 | 2½p org yel, red & blk | .20 | .20 |
| 19 | A3 | 1sh3p blue & black | .20 | .20 |
| 20 | A4 | 2sh multicolored | .20 | .20 |
| | | Nos. 17-20 (4) | .80 | .80 |

First anniversary of Independence.

Map of Africa — A5

Map and Torch — A6

**1958, Apr. 15     Perf. 13½x14½**
| | | | | |
|---|---|---|---|---|
| 21 | A5 | 2½p multicolored | .20 | .20 |
| 22 | A5 | 3p multicolored | .20 | .20 |
| 23 | A6 | 1sh multicolored | .20 | .20 |
| 24 | A6 | 2sh6p multicolored | .20 | .20 |
| | | Nos. 21-24 (4) | .80 | .80 |

1st conf. of Independent African States, Accra, Apr. 15-22.

Gold Coast Nos. 151-152 and 154 Overprinted Like Nos. 5-13
**Perf. 11½x12, 12x11½**
**1958, May 26     Engr.     Wmk. 4**
| | | | | |
|---|---|---|---|---|
| 25 | A15 | 2p chocolate | .50 | .35 |
| 26 | A15 | 2½p red | 1.40 | 1.40 |
| 27 | A14 | 4p deep blue | 5.50 | 5.00 |
| | | Nos. 25-27 (3) | 7.40 | 6.75 |

Nos. 25-27 were prepared in 1957 and some were sold without authorization. The set was officially released in 1958.

Nos. 1-4 Overprinted: "Prime Minister's Visit U. S. A. and Canada"
**1958, July 18     Photo.     Perf. 14x14½**
| | | | | |
|---|---|---|---|---|
| 28 | A1 | 2p rose red | .20 | .20 |
| 29 | A1 | 2½p green | .20 | .20 |
| 30 | A1 | 4p brown | .20 | .20 |
| 31 | A1 | 1sh3p dark blue | .20 | .20 |
| | | Nos. 28-31 (4) | .80 | .80 |

Prime Minister Kwame Nkrumah's visit to the US and Canada, July, 1958.

Palm-nut Vulture over Globe — A7

"Britannia" Plane — A8

Designs: 2sh, Stratocruiser and albatross. 2sh6p, Palm-nut vulture and jet plane, horiz.

**1958, July 15     Perf. 14x14½, 14½x14**
| | | | | |
|---|---|---|---|---|
| 32 | A7 | 2½p multicolored | .20 | .20 |
| 33 | A8 | 1sh3p multicolored | .25 | .25 |
| 34 | A8 | 2sh multicolored | .35 | .35 |
| 35 | A7 | 2sh6p olive bister & blk | .75 | .75 |
| | | Nos. 32-35 (4) | 1.55 | 1.55 |

Inauguration of Ghana Airways.

A9

**Perf. 14x14½**
**1958, Oct. 24     Wmk. 4     Litho.**
| | | | | |
|---|---|---|---|---|
| 36 | A9 | 2½p multicolored | .20 | .20 |
| 37 | A9 | 1sh3p multicolored | .20 | .20 |
| 38 | A9 | 2sh6p multicolored | .20 | .20 |
| | | Nos. 36-38 (3) | .60 | .60 |

United Nations Day, Oct. 24.

A10

**Perf. 14x14½**
**1959, Feb. 12     Photo.     Wmk. 325**

Lincoln Memorial and Kwame Nkrumah.
| | | | | |
|---|---|---|---|---|
| 39 | A10 | 2½p dp plum & brt pink | .20 | .20 |
| 40 | A10 | 1sh3p dp blue & lt bl | .20 | .20 |
| 41 | A10 | 2sh6p ol gray & org yel | .20 | .20 |
| a. | | Souv. sheet of 3, #39-41, imperf. | .80 | .80 |
| | | Nos. 39-41 (3) | .60 | .60 |

Lincoln's birth sesquicentennial.

Kente Cloth with Traditional Symbols A11

Symbol of Greeting — A12

2½p, Talking drums and elephant horn-blower. 2sh, Map of Africa, flag and palm tree.

**Perf. 14½x14, 14x14½**
**1959, Mar. 6     Photo.     Wmk. 325**
| | | | | |
|---|---|---|---|---|
| 42 | A11 | ½p multicolored | .20 | .20 |
| 43 | A11 | 2½p multicolored | .20 | .20 |
| 44 | A12 | 1sh3p multicolored | .20 | .20 |
| 45 | A11 | 2sh multicolored | .30 | .25 |
| | | Nos. 42-45 (4) | .90 | .85 |

Independence, 2nd anniversary.

Flags of Independent States of Africa and Globe — A13

**1959, Apr. 15     Perf. 14½x14**
| | | | | |
|---|---|---|---|---|
| 46 | A13 | 2½p multicolored | .20 | .20 |
| 47 | A13 | 8½p multicolored | .20 | .20 |

Africa Freedom Day, Apr. 15.

Kente Cloth and "God's Omnipotence" Symbol — A13a

Nkrumah Statue, Accra — A14

Shell Ginger — A15

Cacao A16

"God's Omnipotence" Symbol — A16a

Blackwinged Red Bishop — A17

1½p, Ghana timber. 2p, Volta river. 4p, Diamond and mine. 11p, Golden spider lily. 2sh6p, Great blue turaco. 5sh, Tiger orchid. 10sh, Jewelfish (tropical African cichlid).

### Perf. 11½x12, 12x11½, 14x14½, 14½x14

**1959, Oct. 5  Photo.  Wmk. 325**
**Size: 30½x21mm, 21x30½mm**

| 48 | A13a | ½p multi (God's Omnipotence) | .25 | .20 |
|---|---|---|---|---|
| 49 | A14 | 1p multicolored | .25 | .20 |

**Size: 26½x37mm, 37x26½mm**

| 50 | A15 | 1½p multicolored | .25 | .20 |
| 51 | A16 | 2p multicolored | .25 | .20 |
| 52 | A16a | 2½p multicolored | .25 | .20 |
| 53 | A16a | 3p multi (God's Omnipotence) | .25 | .20 |
| 54 | A16 | 4p multicolored | .25 | .20 |
| 55 | A17 | 6p multicolored | .25 | .20 |
| a. | | Booklet pane of 4 | 1.10 | |
| 56 | A15 | 11p multicolored | .40 | .20 |
| 57 | A15 | 1sh multicolored | .30 | .20 |
| 58 | A17 | 2sh6p multicolored | .75 | .30 |
| 59 | A15 | 5sh multicolored | 1.60 | .60 |

**Size: 45x26mm**

| 60 | A16 | 10sh multicolored | 3.00 | 1.50 |
| | | Nos. 48-60,C1-C2 (15) | 9.25 | 5.05 |

Nos. 48 and 53 inscribed "God's Omnipotence." Nos. 95-96 inscribed "Gye Nyame."
For surcharges see Nos. 216-217, 219-225, 277-283.

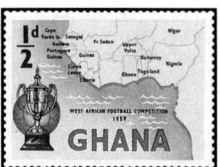

Map and Gold Cup — A18

1p, Soccer players, vert. 3p, Flags and goalkeeper in stadium. 8p, Soccer player at goal. 2sh6p, Kwame Nkrumah Gold Cup, vert.

**1959, Oct. 15  Perf. 14½x14, 14x14½**

| 61 | A18 | ½p multicolored | .20 | .20 |
| 62 | A18 | 1p multicolored | .20 | .20 |
| 63 | A18 | 3p multicolored | .20 | .20 |
| 64 | A18 | 8p multicolored | .20 | .20 |
| 65 | A18 | 2sh6p multicolored | .30 | .30 |
| | | Nos. 61-65 (5) | 1.10 | 1.10 |

West African Soccer Competitions.

Prince Philip A19

**Perf. 14½x14**
**1959, Nov. 24  Photo.  Wmk. 325**

| 66 | A19 | 3p brt pink & black | .30 | .25 |

Visit of Prince Philip.

Talking Drums A20

Designs: 6p, 1sh3p, Ghana flag and UN emblem, vert. 2sh6p, Pile of Ceremonial Stools and "UNTC," vert.

**1959, Dec. 10  Perf. 14½x14, 14x14½**
**Flag in Original Colors**

| 67 | A20 | 3p violet & org yel | .20 | .20 |
| 68 | A20 | 6p Prus green & blk | .20 | .20 |
| 69 | A20 | 1sh3p grnsh bl, blk & vio | .20 | .20 |
| 70 | A20 | 2sh6p dark blue & black | .25 | .20 |
| | | Nos. 67-70 (4) | .85 | .80 |

United Nations Trusteeship Council.

Three Flying Eagles — A21

Designs: 3p, Three clusters of fireworks. 1sh3p, Ghana flag forming "3" and dove. 2sh, Ghana flag forming triple sail of symbolic ship.

**Perf. 13½x14½**
**1960, Mar. 6  Wmk. 325**

| 71 | A21 | ½p multicolored | .20 | .20 |
| 72 | A21 | 3p multicolored | .20 | .20 |
| 73 | A21 | 1sh3p multicolored | .25 | .20 |
| 74 | A21 | 2sh multicolored | .25 | .20 |
| | | Nos. 71-74 (4) | .90 | .80 |

Independence, 3rd anniversary.

Flags Forming "A" and Map A22

Designs: 6p, Letter "F." 1sh, "D."

**1960, Apr. 15  Photo.  Wmk. 325**
**Flags in Original Colors**

| 75 | A22 | 3p green, red & black | .20 | .20 |
| 76 | A22 | 6p rose & black | .20 | .20 |
| 77 | A22 | 1sh blue, black & red | .20 | .20 |
| | | Nos. 75-77 (3) | .60 | .60 |

Africa Freedom Day, Apr. 15.

President Kwame Nkrumah — A23

Olympic Rings and Hand Holding Torch — A24

Designs: 1sh3p, Flag and star. 2sh, Hand holding torch. 10sh, Coat of Arms and flag of Ghana, horiz.

**Perf. 14x14½, 14½x14**
**1960, July 1  Litho.**

| 78 | A23 | 3p multicolored | .20 | .20 |
| 79 | A23 | 1sh3p multicolored | .25 | .20 |
| 80 | A23 | 2sh multicolored | .35 | .35 |
| 81 | A23 | 10sh multicolored | .75 | .75 |
| a. | | Souv. sheet of 4, #78-81, imperf. | .50 | .50 |
| | | Nos. 78-81 (4) | 1.55 | 1.55 |

Declaration of the Republic, July 1, 1960.

**1960, Aug. 15  Photo.  Wmk. 325**

Design: 1sh3p, 2sh6p, Runner, Map of Africa and Olympic Rings, horiz.

| 82 | A24 | 3p multicolored | .20 | .20 |
| 83 | A24 | 6p multicolored | .20 | .20 |
| 84 | A24 | 1sh3p multicolored | .20 | .20 |
| 85 | A24 | 2sh6p multicolored | .35 | .25 |
| | | Nos. 82-85 (4) | .95 | .85 |

17th Olympic Games, Rome, Aug. 25-Sept. 11.

Map and Arch — A25

UN Emblem and Ghana Flag — A26

Designs: 3p, Flag and Kwame Nkrumah, horiz. 6p, Star and Nkrumah.

**1960, Sept. 21  Photo.**

| 86 | A25 | 3p multicolored | .20 | .20 |
| 87 | A25 | 6p multicolored | .20 | .20 |
| 88 | A25 | 1sh3p multicolored | .20 | .20 |
| | | Nos. 86-88 (3) | .60 | .60 |

Founder's Day, Sept. 21, birthday of Dr. Kwame Nkrumah.

**1960, Dec. 10  Perf. 14x14½**

6p, Flame & emblem. 1sh3p, UN Emblem.

| 89 | A26 | 3p multicolored | .20 | .20 |
| 90 | A26 | 6p multicolored | .20 | .20 |
| 91 | A26 | 1sh3p multicolored | .20 | .20 |
| | | Nos. 89-91 (3) | .60 | .60 |

Human Rights Day, Dec. 10, 1960.

Talking Drums and Map — A27

Designs: 6p, Map of Africa showing 25 independent states. 2sh, Map of Africa and flags of independent nations in 1958, horiz.

**Perf. 14x14½, 14½x14**
**1961, Apr. 15  Wmk. 325**

| 92 | A27 | 3p multicolored | .20 | .20 |
| 93 | A27 | 6p multicolored | .20 | .20 |
| 94 | A27 | 2sh multicolored | .25 | .20 |
| | | Nos. 92-94 (3) | .65 | .65 |

Africa Freedom Day, Apr. 15, 1961.

Types of 1959 Redrawn and

Red-fronted Gazelle — A28

**Perf. 11½x12, 14½x14**
**1961, Apr. 29  Photo.  Wmk. 325**

| 95 | A13a | ½p "Gye Nyame" | .25 | .20 |
| 96 | A16a | 3p "Gye Nyame" | .25 | .20 |
| a. | | Booklet pane of 4 | 1.00 | |

**Perf. 14x14½**

| 97 | A28 | £1 multicolored | 8.00 | 8.00 |
| | | Nos. 95-97 (3) | 8.50 | 8.40 |

Nos. 95-96 are the same sizes as Nos. 48 and 53 which are inscribed "God's Omnipotence."
For surcharges see Nos. 218, 226, 284.

Column, Eagle and Star — A29

Dove with Olive Branch — A30

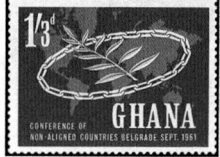

World Map, Chain and Olive Branch A31

Designs: 1sh3p, Symbolic flower and star. 2sh, Star and 3 Ghana flags.

**1961, July 1  Perf. 14x14½**

| 98 | A29 | 3p multicolored | .20 | .20 |
| 99 | A29 | 1sh3p multicolored | .20 | .20 |
| 100 | A29 | 2sh multicolored | .25 | .20 |
| | | Nos. 98-100 (3) | .65 | .60 |

First anniversary of the Republic.

**1961, Sept. 1  Perf. 14x14½, 14½x14**

Design: 5sh, Rostrum and olive branch.

| 101 | A30 | 3p green | .20 | .20 |
| 102 | A31 | 1sh3p dark blue | .25 | .20 |
| 103 | A31 | 5sh rose carmine | .25 | .25 |
| | | Nos. 101-103 (3) | .70 | .65 |

Conference of Non-aligned Nations, Belgrade, Sept. 1961.

Kwame Nkrumah and Globe A32

Designs: 1sh3p, Kente cloth and Nkrumah, vert. 5sh, Kwame Nkrumah, vert.

**Perf. 14½x14, 14½x14½**
**1961, Sept. 21  Wmk. 325**

| 104 | A32 | 3p multicolored | .20 | .20 |
| a. | | Souvenir sheet of 4, imperf. | 1.25 | 1.25 |
| 105 | A32 | 1sh3p multicolored | .25 | .20 |
| a. | | Souvenir sheet of 4, imperf. | 1.75 | 1.75 |
| 106 | A32 | 5sh multicolored | .50 | .50 |
| a. | | Souvenir sheet of 4, imperf. | 4.50 | 4.50 |
| | | Nos. 104-106 (3) | .95 | .95 |

Founder's Day.
The souvenir sheets contain four imperf. stamps each with simulated perforations.

Elizabeth II and Map of Africa A33

**1961, Nov. 10  Perf. 14½x14**
**Gold Inscriptions: Design in Black, Red, Yellow & Green**

| 107 | A33 | 3p claret | .20 | .20 |
| 108 | A33 | 1sh3p Prussian blue | .25 | .20 |
| 109 | A33 | 5sh violet blue | 1.10 | .90 |
| a. | | Souvenir sheet of 3 | 4.75 | 4.75 |
| | | Nos. 107-109 (3) | 1.55 | 1.30 |

Visit of Queen Elizabeth II to Ghana, Nov. 10-22.
No. 109a contains four imperf. copies of No. 109 with simulated perforations.

Map of Tema Harbor and Ships A34

## Perf. 14x13
**1962, Feb. 10**   **Litho.**   **Unwmk.**
110 A34 3p multicolored .20 .20
   *Nos. 110,C3-C4 (3)* 1.60 1.60

Opening of Tema Harbor, as part of Volta River Project.

Dove Flying over Map of Africa — A35

**1962, Mar. 6**   **Perf. 13x14**
111 A35 3p multicolored .20 .20
   *Nos. 111,C5-C6 (3)* 1.25 1.25

Conference of African heads of state at Casablanca, 1st anniv.

"Freedom" Illuminating Africa — A36

"Five Continents at Peace" — A37

## Perf. 14x14½
**1962, Apr. 15**   **Photo.**   **Wmk. 325**
112 A36 3p multicolored .20 .20
113 A36 6p multicolored .20 .20
114 A36 1sh3p multicolored .20 .20
   *Nos. 112-114 (3)* .60 .60

Africa Freedom Day, Apr. 15.

**1962, June 21**   **Wmk. 325**

Designs: 6p, Atom bomb blast in shape of skull. 1sh3p, Peace dove and globe.

115 A37 3p deep rose & black .20 .20
116 A37 6p black & dk red .20 .20
117 A37 1sh3p greenish blue .40 .30
   *Nos. 115-117 (3)* .80 .70

Accra Assembly of Africans for a "World Without Bomb," June 21-28.

Patrice Lumumba A38

**1962, June 30**   **Perf. 14½x14**
118 A38 3p black & orange .20 .20
119 A38 6p mar, grn & blk .20 .20
120 A38 1sh3p dk grn, pink & blk .20 .20
   *Nos. 118-120 (3)* .60 .60

1st anniv. (on Feb. 12) of the death of Patrice Lumumba, premier of Congo.

---

Arch and Star — A39

Designs: 6p, Torch in flag colors and globe. 1sh3p, Palm-nut vulture trailing flag, horiz.

## Perf. 13x13½, 13½x13
**1962, July 1**   **Unwmk.**
121 A39 3p multicolored .20 .20
122 A39 6p multicolored .20 .20
123 A39 1sh3p multicolored .25 .25
   *Nos. 121-123 (3)* .65 .65

Second anniversary of the republic.

Kwame Nkrumah — A40

**1962, Sept. 21**   **Litho.**   **Perf. 13x14**

3p, Nkrumah medal. 1sh3p, Nkrumah's head & stars. 2sh, Hands with trowel & building block.

124 A40 1p multicolored .20 .20
125 A40 3p multicolored .20 .20
126 A40 1sh3p ultra & black .20 .20
127 A40 2sh multicolored .25 .25
   *Nos. 124-127 (4)* .85 .85

Founder's Day, Nkrumah's 53rd birthday.

Malaria Eradication Emblem — A41

## Perf. 14x14½
**1962, Dec. 1**   **Photo.**   **Wmk. 325**
128 A41 1p carmine rose .20 .20
129 A41 4p yellow green .20 .20
130 A41 6p olive bister .20 .20
131 A41 1sh3p violet .30 .25
   *a.* Souvenir sheet of 4, imperf. 1.10 1.10
   *Nos. 128-131 (4)* .90 .85

WHO drive to eradicate malaria. No. 131a contains one each of Nos. 128-131, with simulated perforation.

Wheat Emblem and Globe — A42

## Perf. 14x14½, 14½x14
**1963, Mar. 21**   **Wmk. 325**

Designs: 4p, Hands holding Wheat Emblem, horiz. 1sh3p, Globe, horiz.

132 A42 1p multicolored .30 .20
133 A42 4p multicolored .40 .30
134 A42 1sh3p multicolored 2.00 1.50
   *Nos. 132-134 (3)* 2.70 2.00

FAO "Freedom from Hunger" campaign.

---

Map of Africa in Sun — A43

Cross, Flag and Centenary Emblem — A44

Designs: 4p, Symbolic wood carving, horiz. 1sh3p, Map of Africa and ceremonial fire. 2sh6p, Gazelle and flag.

**1963, Apr. 15**   **Photo.**
135 A43 1p crimson & gold .20 .20
136 A43 4p orange, blk & red .20 .20
137 A43 1sh3p multicolored .20 .20
138 A43 2sh6p multicolored .25 .20
   *Nos. 135-138 (4)* .85 .80

Africa Freedom Day, Apr. 15.

## Perf. 14x14½, 14½x14
**1963, May 28**   **Wmk. 325**

1½p, Centenary emblem, horiz. 4p, Family & emblem, horiz. 1sh3p, Emblem & globe.

139 A44 1p multicolored .50 .20
140 A44 1½p multicolored .80 .75
141 A44 4p multicolored 1.25 .20
142 A44 1sh3p multicolored 2.40 1.75
   *a.* Souvenir sheet of 4, imperf. 5.00 5.00
   *Nos. 139-142 (4)* 4.95 2.90

Cent. of the founding of the Intl. Red Cross. No. 142a contains one each of Nos. 139-142, with simulated perforation.

A45

Designs: 4p, Three flags. 1sh3p, Map of Africa with Ghana, vert. 2sh6p, Torch, vert.

## Perf. 14½x14, 14x14½
**1963, July 1**   **Photo.**
143 A45 1p multicolored .20 .20
144 A45 4p multicolored .20 .20
145 A45 1sh3p multicolored .20 .20
146 A45 2sh6p multicolored .25 .25
   *Nos. 143-146 (4)* .85 .85

The 3rd anniversary of the republic.

Dancers, Fireworks and Nkrumah A46

1p, Nkrumah & streamer. 4p, Nkrumah & flag. 5sh, Wisdom symbol.

## Perf. 14x14½, 14½x14
**1963, Sept. 21**
147 A46 1p multi, vert. .20 .20
148 A46 4p multi, vert. .20 .20
149 A46 1sh3p multi .20 .20
150 A46 5sh multi .25 .25
   *Nos. 147-150 (4)* .85 .85

Founder's Day, Nkrumah's 54th birthday.

---

Ramses II at Abu Simbel — A47

Designs: 1½p, Rock painting, bird and fish, horiz. 2p, Queen Nefertari, horiz. 4p, Sphinx of Wadi es-Sebua. 1sh3p, Statues of Ramses II at Abu Simbel, horiz.

**1963, Nov. 1**   **Unwmk.**   **Perf. 11½x11**
151 A47 1p multicolored .20 .20
152 A47 1½p multicolored .20 .20
153 A47 2p multicolored .20 .20
154 A47 4p multicolored .50 .20
155 A47 1sh3p multicolored 1.50 1.00
   *Nos. 151-155 (5)* 2.60 1.80

UNESCO world campaign to save historic monuments in Nubia.

Steam and Diesel Engines A48

**1963, Nov. 1**   **Wmk. 325**
## Perf. 14½x14
156 A48 1p multicolored .20 .20
157 A48 6p multicolored .75 .20
158 A48 1sh3p multicolored 1.25 .50
159 A48 2sh6p multicolored 1.75 1.75
   *Nos. 156-159 (4)* 3.95 2.65

The 60th anniversary of Ghana's railroads.

Eleanor Roosevelt and Flame — A49

6p, Mrs. Roosevelt & flag. 1sh3p, Mrs. Roosevelt, flag, flame & Ghanaian symbols, horiz.

## Perf. 11½x11, 11x11½
**1963, Dec. 10**   **Unwmk.**
160 A49 1p multicolored .20 .20
161 A49 4p multicolored .20 .20
162 A49 6p multicolored .20 .20
163 A49 1sh3p multicolored .30 .25
   *Nos. 160-163 (4)* .90 .85

Eleanor Roosevelt; 15th anniv. of the Universal Declaration of Human Rights.

### Imperforates
Starting in 1964, certain sets of Ghana exist imperf.

IQSY Emblem and Satellites — A50

**1964, June 1**   **Photo.**   **Perf. 14**
164 A50 3p multicolored .20 .20
165 A50 6p multicolored .20 .20
166 A50 1sh3p multicolored .35 .25
   *a.* Souvenir sheet of 4 1.00 1.00
   *Nos. 164-166 (3)* .75 .65

Intl. Quiet Sun Year, 1964-65. No. 166a contains 4 imperf. stamps similar to No. 166 with simulated perforations.
See Nos. 186-188.

Harvest on State Farm A51

Designs: 6p, Oil refinery, Tema. 1sh3p, Communal labor. 5sh, Ghana flag and people.

**1964, July 1**      *Perf. 13x14*
| | | | | |
|---|---|---|---|---|
| 167 | A51 | 3p multicolored | .20 | .20 |
| 168 | A51 | 6p multicolored | .20 | .20 |
| 169 | A51 | 1sh3p multicolored | .20 | .20 |
| 170 | A51 | 5sh multicolored | .30 | .30 |
| a. | | Souvenir sheet of 4 | .80 | .80 |
| | | Nos. 167-170 (4) | .90 | .90 |

4th anniv. of the Republic. No. 170a contains four stamps similar to Nos. 167-170 with simulated perforations.

Dove, Globe, Olive Branch and Flag — A52

Designs: 6p, Map of Africa and quill pen, vert. 1sh3p, Knotted rope and map of Africa. 5sh, Hands planting symbolic tree, vert.

**1964, July 6**      *Perf. 14*
| | | | | |
|---|---|---|---|---|
| 171 | A52 | 3p multicolored | .20 | .20 |
| 172 | A52 | 6p black & red | .20 | .20 |
| 173 | A52 | 1sh3p blue & multi | .20 | .20 |
| 174 | A52 | 5sh yel & multi | .25 | .25 |
| | | Nos. 171-174 (4) | .85 | .85 |

Signing of the African Unity Charter, 1st anniv.

Nkrumah and Hibiscus — A53

Boxing — A54

**Perf. 14x14½**
**1964, Sept. 21**   **Photo.**   **Wmk. 325**
**Design in Brown, Green and Rose Red**
| | | | | |
|---|---|---|---|---|
| 175 | A53 | 3p light blue | .20 | .20 |
| 176 | A53 | 6p yellow | .20 | .20 |
| 177 | A53 | 1sh3p gray | .20 | .20 |
| 178 | A53 | 2sh6p emerald | .30 | .30 |
| a. | | Souvenir sheet of 4 | 1.00 | 1.00 |
| | | Nos. 175-178 (4) | .90 | .90 |

Founder's Day, Nkrumah's 55th birthday. No. 178a contains four of No. 178 with simulated perforation.

**1964, Oct. 25**      *Perf. 14½x14*

Sport: 1p, Hurdling, horiz. 2½p, Running, horiz. 4p, Broad jump. 6p, Soccer. 1sh3p, Athlete with Olympic torch. 5sh, Banners and Tokyo Olympic emblem, horiz.

| | | | | |
|---|---|---|---|---|
| 179 | A54 | 1p yellow & multi | .20 | .20 |
| 180 | A54 | 2½p multicolored | .20 | .20 |
| 181 | A54 | 3p red & multi | .20 | .20 |
| 182 | A54 | 4p blue & multi | .20 | .20 |
| 183 | A54 | 6p multicolored | .20 | .20 |
| 184 | A54 | 1sh3p blue & multi | .25 | .25 |
| 185 | A54 | 5sh gray & multi | .30 | .25 |
| a. | | Souvenir sheet of 3 | 1.25 | 1.25 |
| | | Nos. 179-185 (7) | 1.55 | 1.45 |

18th Olympic Games, Tokyo, Oct. 10-25. No. 185a contains stamps similar to Nos. 183-185 with simulated perforation.

**Quiet Sun Year Type of 1964**
**Unwmk.**
**1964, Oct.**   **Photo.**      *Perf. 14*
| | | | | |
|---|---|---|---|---|
| 186 | A50 | 3p gray, bl, grn, yel & red | 1.25 | 1.25 |
| 187 | A50 | 6p pink, bl, grn, yel & red | 2.50 | 2.50 |
| 188 | A50 | 1sh3p tan, bl, grn, yel, & red | 4.00 | 4.00 |
| | | Nos. 186-188 (3) | 7.75 | 7.75 |

Each issued in sheets of 12, with star-strewn blue border inscribed "Ghana International Quiet Sun Year." Stamps arranged in square surrounding vignette of New York World's Fair Unisphere in blue.

G. W. Carver and Sweet Potato A55

Design: 1sh3p, Albert Einstein, theory of relativity formula and atom symbol.

**1964, Dec. 7**   **Wmk. 325**   *Perf. 14½*
| | | | | |
|---|---|---|---|---|
| 189 | A55 | 6p grn & dk blue | .20 | .20 |
| 190 | A55 | 1sh3p Prus bl & claret | .30 | .25 |
| 191 | A55 | 5sh org ver & brn blk | 1.25 | 1.25 |
| a. | | Souvenir sheet of 3 | 1.25 | 1.25 |
| | | Nos. 189-191 (3) | 1.75 | 1.70 |

Human Rights Day; Albert Einstein (1878-1955) and George Washington Carver (1864-1943), scientists.
No. 191a commemorates UNESCO Week and contains one each of Nos. 189-191 with simulated perforations.

Secretary Bird — A56

Designs: 1p, Elephant, vert. 2½p, Purple wreath, vert. 3p, Gray parrot, vert. 4p, Blue-naped mousebird. 6p, African tulip tree flowers. 1sh3p, Amethyst starling. 2sh6p, Hippopotamuses.

**Perf. 11½x11, 11x11½**
**1964, Dec. 14**   **Photo.**     **Unwmk.**
| | | | | |
|---|---|---|---|---|
| 192 | A56 | 1p blue & multi | .30 | .30 |
| 193 | A56 | 1½p org & multi | .50 | .50 |
| 194 | A56 | 2½p lt green & multi | .35 | .35 |
| a. | | Souv. sheet of 3, #192-194, imperf. | 2.00 | 2.00 |
| 195 | A56 | 3p lt green & multi | .85 | .30 |
| 196 | A56 | 4p multicolored | .85 | .40 |
| 197 | A56 | 6p multicolored | .35 | .20 |
| 198 | A56 | 1sh3p multicolored | 1.00 | .60 |
| 199 | A56 | 2sh6p multicolored | 1.00 | 1.00 |
| a. | | Souv. sheet of 5, #195-199, imperf. | 4.00 | 4.00 |
| | | Nos. 192-199 (8) | 5.20 | 3.65 |

ICY Emblem A57

**1965, Feb. 15**   **Litho.**   *Perf. 14x13*
**Design in Black, Red and Green**
| | | | | |
|---|---|---|---|---|
| 200 | A57 | 1p gray | .40 | .35 |
| 201 | A57 | 4p bister | 1.50 | 1.25 |
| 202 | A57 | 6p tan | 1.50 | .35 |
| 203 | A57 | 1sh3p light green | 2.00 | 1.75 |
| a. | | Souvenir sheet of 4 | 6.50 | 6.50 |
| | | Nos. 200-203 (4) | 5.40 | 3.70 |

Intl. Cooperation Year. No. 203a contains 4 imperf. stamps similar to No. 203.

ITU Emblem, Old and New Communication Equipment — A58

**1965, Apr. 12**      *Perf. 13½*
| | | | | |
|---|---|---|---|---|
| 204 | A58 | 1p multicolored | .20 | .20 |
| 205 | A58 | 6p multicolored | .20 | .20 |
| 206 | A58 | 1sh3p multicolored | 1.00 | .25 |
| 207 | A58 | 5sh multicolored | 2.50 | 2.00 |
| a. | | Souvenir sheet of 4 | 13.00 | 13.00 |
| | | Nos. 204-207 (4) | 3.90 | 2.65 |

Cent. of the ITU. No. 207a contains 4 imperf. stamps similar to Nos. 204-207 with simulated perforations.

Lincoln's Home, Springfield, Ill. — A59

1sh3p, Inaugural Address and Lincoln. 2sh, Lincoln and his signature. 5sh, Adaptation of 1869 US Lincoln stamp (No. 122).

**Wmk. 325**
**1965, Apr.**   **Photo.**    *Perf. 12½*
| | | | | |
|---|---|---|---|---|
| 208 | A59 | 6p multicolored | .20 | .20 |
| 209 | A59 | 1sh3p multicolored | .25 | .20 |
| 210 | A59 | 2sh multicolored | .30 | .35 |
| 211 | A59 | 5sh red & black | .65 | .50 |
| a. | | Souvenir sheet of 4 | 1.75 | 1.75 |
| | | Nos. 208-211 (4) | 1.40 | 1.25 |

Centenary of death of Abraham Lincoln. No. 211a contains one each of Nos. 208-211 with simulated perforation.

5-Pesewa Coin, Nkrumah's Head — A60

Coins: 10pa, 10 pesewas. 25pa, 25 pesewas. 50pa, 50 pesewas.

**Perf. 11x13**
**1965, July 19**   **Unwmk.**   **Litho.**
**Coin in Silver and Black**
**Size: 45x32mm**
| | | | | |
|---|---|---|---|---|
| 212 | A60 | 5pa red, grn & lt grn | .20 | .20 |
| 213 | A60 | 10pa red, grn, & pink | .25 | .20 |

**Size: 62x39mm**
| | | | | |
|---|---|---|---|---|
| 214 | A60 | 25pa red, grn, & pink | .75 | .75 |

**Size: 71x43½mm**
| | | | | |
|---|---|---|---|---|
| 215 | A60 | 50pa red, grn & lt grn | 2.00 | 2.00 |
| | | Nos. 212-215 (4) | 3.20 | 3.15 |

Introduction of decimal currency.

Regular Issue of 1959-61 Surcharged in Red, Blue, Brown, Black or White with New Value and: "Ghana New Currency / 19th July, 1965"
**Perf. 12x11½, 14½x14, 14x14½**
**1965, July 19**   **Photo.**   **Wmk. 325**
| | | | | |
|---|---|---|---|---|
| 216 | A14 | 1pa on 1p (R) | .20 | .20 |
| 217 | A16 | 2pa on 2p (Bl) | .20 | .20 |
| 218 | A16a | 3pa on 3p (#96, Br) | 1.00 | 1.00 |
| 219 | A16 | 4pa on 4p (Bl) | 4.00 | .50 |
| 220 | A17 | 6pa on 6p (Bk) | .50 | .25 |
| 221 | A15 | 11pa on 11p (W) | .25 | .20 |
| 222 | A15 | 12pa on 1sh (Bl) | .25 | .20 |
| 223 | A17 | 30pa on 2sh6p (Bl) | 3.00 | 3.00 |
| 224 | A15 | 60pa on 5sh (Bl) | 4.00 | .70 |
| 225 | A16 | 1.20c on 10s (Bl) | .75 | .75 |
| 226 | A28 | 2.40c on £1 (Bl) | 1.00 | 5.75 |
| | | Nos. 216-226, C7-C8 (13) | 19.15 | 13.75 |

The two lines of the overprint are diagonal on the 1pa, 11pa, 12pa, 60pa, 1.20c and 2.40c.
The surcharge exists double or inverted on six or seven denominations.

Summit Conference, Accra — A61

Map of Africa and Flags A62

Designs: 2pa, "OAU" and three heads (triangle pointing up). 5pa, Symbol of African Unity. 15pa, Sunburst and map of Africa. 24pa, Map of Africa.

**Perf. 14, 14½x14**
**1965, Oct. 21**      **Photo.**
**Ghana Flag in Red, Black & Green**
| | | | | |
|---|---|---|---|---|
| 227 | A61 | 1pa multicolored | .20 | .20 |
| 228 | A61 | 2pa multicolored | .20 | .20 |
| 229 | A61 | 5pa multicolored | .20 | .20 |
| 230 | A62 | 6pa orange & black | .20 | .20 |
| 231 | A62 | 15pa light blue & blk | .25 | .25 |
| 232 | A62 | 24pa lt ultra & green | .45 | .40 |
| | | Nos. 227-232 (6) | 1.50 | 1.45 |

Summit Conference of the Organization for African Unity, Accra, Oct. 1965.

Soccer Goalkeeper — A63

Designs: 15pa, Soccer player and cup, vert. 24pa, Two soccer players and cup.

**Perf. 14x13, 13x14**
**1965, Nov. 15**      **Unwmk.**
| | | | | |
|---|---|---|---|---|
| 233 | A63 | 6pa ocher & multi | .20 | .20 |
| 234 | A63 | 15pa multicolored | .40 | .20 |
| 235 | A63 | 24pa lt blue & multi | .45 | .45 |
| | | Nos. 233-235 (3) | 1.05 | .85 |

African Soccer Cup competition. For overprints see Nos. 244-246.

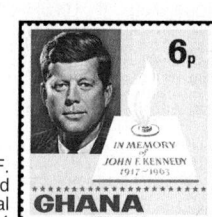

John F. Kennedy and Eternal Flame — A64

Various Kennedy portraits.

**1965, Dec. 15**   **Wmk. 325**   *Perf. 12½*
| | | | | |
|---|---|---|---|---|
| 236 | A64 | 6pa blk, yel, gold & grn | .20 | .20 |
| 237 | A64 | 15pa vio, crim & brt grn | .25 | .25 |
| 238 | A64 | 24pa dp pur & blk | .30 | .30 |
| 239 | A64 | 30pa vio brn & blk | .40 | .40 |
| a. | | Souvenir sheet of 4 ('66) | 4.50 | 4.50 |
| | | Nos. 236-239 (4) | 1.15 | 1.15 |

President John F. Kennedy (1917-1963). No. 239a contains four imperf. stamps similar to Nos. 236-239.

Generators, Volta River Project A65

Designs: 15pa, Dam and Lake Volta. 24pa, "Ghana" forming dam. 30pa, Grain.

**1966, Jan. 22                              Unwmk.**
240 A65  6pa sepia & multi            .20   .20
241 A65  15pa multicolored            .20   .20
242 A65  24pa multicolored            .25   .25
243 A65  30pa brt blue & blk          .40   .40
   *Nos. 240-243 (4)*            1.05  1.05

Opening of the Volta River dam and electric power station at Akosombo.

Nos. 233-235 Overprinted Diagonally:
"Black Stars Retain Africa Cup / 21st Nov. 1965"

**1966, Feb. 7        Perf. 14x13, 13x14**
244 A63  6pa ocher & multi            .20   .20
245 A63  15pa multicolored            .30   .30
246 A63  24pa lt bl & multi           .55   .55
   *Nos. 244-246 (3)*            1.05  1.05

Ghana's soccer victory, Nov. 21, 1965.

Inauguration of WHO Headquarters, Geneva — A66

Designs: 24pa, 30pa, WHO Headquarters from the west and WHO emblem.

**Perf. 14x14½**
**1966, July 1      Photo.      Wmk. 325**
247 A66  6pa multicolored             .50   .20
248 A66  15pa multicolored            1.00   .40
249 A66  24pa multicolored            1.25  1.00
250 A66  30pa multicolored            1.50  1.50
  a.  Souvenir sheet of 4          32.50 32.50
   *Nos. 247-250 (4)*            4.25  3.10

No. 250a contains 4 imperf. stamps similar to Nos. 247-250 with simulated perforations.

Herring, Fishermen and Flag A67

Designs: 15pa, Flatfish and canoes. 24pa, Spadefish and schooner. 30pa, Red snapper and fishing trawler "Shama". 60pa, Mackerel and steamer.

**1966, Aug. 10   Unwmk.    Perf. 14x13**
251 A67  6pa ocher & multi            .20   .20
252 A67  15pa yel grn & multi         .40   .25
253 A67  24pa ver & multi             .70   .30
254 A67  30pa blue & multi            1.10   .40
  a.  Souvenir sheet of 4          14.00 14.00
255 A67  60pa green & multi           1.50   .85
   *Nos. 251-255 (5)*            3.90  2.00

1966 Freedom from Hunger campaign "Young World Against Hunger."
No. 254a contains 4 imperf. stamps similar to No. 254.

Flags of African Unity Charter Signers, Map and Diamond A68

Designs: 6p, Ghana flag and links enclosing map of Africa, vert. 24p, Ship's wheel enclosing map of Africa, and cacao pod.

**1966, Sept.   Unwmk.    Perf. 13x13½**
256 A68  6pa brt blue & multi         .20   .20
257 A68  15pa blue & multi            .25   .25
258 A68  24pa dp green & multi        .30   .30
   *Nos. 256-258 (3)*             .75   .75

Signing of the African Unity Charter, 3rd anniv.

Soccer Player and Rimet Cup — A69

Various Soccer Scenes.

**Perf. 14½x14**
**1966, Nov. 14     Photo.    Wmk. 325**
259 A69  5pa brown & multi            .25   .20
260 A69  15pa blue & multi            .70   .25
261 A69  24pa green & multi           1.00   .40
262 A69  30pa brt rose & multi        1.25  1.00
263 A69  60pa lilac & multi           1.75  1.50
  a.  Souvenir sheet of 4          34.00 34.00
   *Nos. 259-263 (5)*            4.95  3.35

World Cup Soccer Championship, Wembley, England, July 11-30.
No. 263a contains 4 imperf. stamps similar to No. 263 with simulated perforations.

UNESCO Emblem A70

**1966, Dec. 23   Wmk. 325   Perf. 14½**
264 A70  5pa multicolored             .25   .20
265 A70  15pa multicolored            .75   .30
266 A70  24pa multicolored            1.00   .75
267 A70  30pa multicolored            1.50  1.25
268 A70  60pa multicolored            2.25  2.00
  a.  Souvenir sheet of 5          35.00 35.00
   *Nos. 264-268 (5)*            5.75  4.50

UNESCO, 20th anniv. No. 268a contains 5 imperf. stamps similar to Nos. 264-268 with simulated perforations.

Packing Cases and Fair Emblem A71

Fair Emblem and: 15pa, World map and trade routes to Accra. 24pa, Freighters and loading crane, vert. 36pa, Hand holding cargo net.

**1967, Feb. 1      Perf. 14½x14, 14x14½**
269 A71  5pa multicolored             .20   .20
270 A71  15pa multicolored            .20   .20
271 A71  24pa multicolored            .30   .30
272 A71  36pa multicolored            .40   .40
   *Nos. 269-272 (4)*            1.10  1.10

International Trade Fair, Accra, Feb. 1-19.

Eagle and Flag — A72

**1967, Feb. 24    Photo.    Perf. 14x14½**
**Flag in Red, Yellow, Black and Green**
273 A72  1np gray bl & dk brn         .20   .20
274 A72  4np ocher & dk brn           .20   .20
275 A72  12½np ol grn & dk brn        .40   .40
276 A72  25np dl cl & dk brn          .85   .85
  a.  Souvenir sheet of 4, #273-276  8.00  8.00
   *Nos. 273-276 (4)*            1.65  1.65

1st anniv. of the revolution which overthrew the regime of Kwame Nkrumah.
No. 276a has dull claret marginal inscriptions. An imperf. sheet similar to No. 276a has solid margins of dull claret, colorless inscriptions. Value $9.

Nos. 51, 54-58, 60 and 97 Surcharged in Black, Red or White
**1967, Feb. 27   Perf. 14½x14, 14x14½**
**Size: 30½x21mm, 21x30½mm**
277 A16  1½np on 2p (B)               3.50  5.00
278 A16  3½np on 4p (R)               4.50  1.75
279 A17  5np on 6p (R)                1.25  1.00
280 A15  9np on 11p (W)               .30   .20
281 A15  10np on 1sh (W)              .35   .35
282 A17  25np on 2sh6p (R)            3.50  7.00
**Size: 45x26mm**
283 A16  1nc on 10sh (R)              3.00 20.00
284 A28  2nc on £1 (R)                6.00 30.00
   *Nos. 277-284,C9-C10 (10)*   31.40 72.30

Corn — A73

Forest Kingfisher — A74

African Lungfish A75

Designs: 2np, Ghana Mace (golden staff). 2½np, Commelina flower. 4np, Rufous-crowned roller, vert. 6np, Akosombo Dam, Volta River. 8np, Adomi Bridge, Volta River. 9np, Chameleon. 10np, Quay No. 2, Tema Harbor. 20np, Cape hare. 50np, Black-winged stilt. 1nc, Chief's ceremonial stool. 2nc, Frangipani. 2.50nc, State Chair.

**Perf. 11½x12, 12x11½ (A73), 14x14½, 14½x14 (A74-A75)**
**1967            Photo.        Wmk. 325**
286 A73  1np multicolored             .20   .20
287 A74  1½np multicolored            1.10  2.25
288 A74  2np multicolored             .20   .20
289 A74  2½np multicolored            .40   .20
290 A75  3np multicolored             .25   .45
291 A73  4np multicolored             1.90   .20
292 A75  6np multicolored             .20   .90
293 A73  8np multicolored             .20   .20
294 A75  9np multicolored             .90   .20
295 A75  10np multicolored            .20   .20
296 A74  20np blue                    .20   .20
297 A74  50np multicolored            6.50  2.00
298 A74  1nc multicolored             3.00   .90
299 A74  2nc multicolored             2.50  4.00
300 A74  2.50nc multicolored          3.75  9.00
   *Nos. 286-300 (15)*          21.55 21.10

For overprints & surcharges see #356-370, 858, 1091, 1092A-1092C, 1092E-1093, 1095, 1096B.

Kumasi Fort, 1896 A76

Castles on Ghana Coast: 12½np, Christiansborg Castle, 1659, and British galleon. 20np, Elmina Castle, 1482, and Portuguese galleon. 25np, Cape Coast Castle, 1664, and Spanish galleon.

**1967, June 12                  Perf. 14½**
301 A76  4np grnsh bl & multi         .20   .20
302 A76  12½np red org & multi        .90   .90
303 A76  20np brt grn & multi         1.90  1.90
304 A76  25np lt red brn & multi      2.40  2.40
   *Nos. 301-304 (4)*            5.40  5.40

Orbiter 1 Landing on Moon — A77

Designs: 4np, Luna 10 on the moon, and globe. 12½np, Astronaut walking in space.

**1967, Aug. 16    Unwmk.    Perf. 13½**
305 A77  4np multicolored             .20   .20
306 A77  10np multicolored            .20   .20
307 A77  12½np multicolored           .20   .20
  a.  Souvenir sheet of 3          2.50  2.50
   *Nos. 305-307 (3)*             .60   .60

Achievements in space. Issued in Ghana in sheets of 30. Sheets of 12 with ornamented, inscribed border also exist; these were sold in Ghana in 1968.
No. 307a contains 3 imperf. stamps similar to Nos. 305-307.

Boy Scouts at Campfire A78

Designs: 10np, Hiking Boy Scout. 12½np, Lord Baden-Powell.

**1967, Sept. 18    Photo.    Perf. 14x13½**
308 A78  4np multicolored             .20   .20
309 A78  10np multicolored            .40   .30
310 A78  12½np multicolored           .50   .40
  a.  Souvenir sheet of 3          8.00  8.00
   *Nos. 308-310 (3)*            1.10   .90

50th anniv. of the Ghana (Gold Coast) Boy Scouts. Issued in Ghana in sheets of 30. Sheets of 12 with ornamented, inscribed border also exist; these were sold in Ghana in 1968.
No. 310a contains 3 imperf. stamps similar to Nos. 308-310 with simulated perforations.

UN Secretariat Building — A79

Design: 50np, 2.50nc, UN Headquarters.

**1967, Oct. 24    Litho.    Perf. 13½x13**
311 A79  4np multicolored             .20   .20
312 A79  10np multicolored            .20   .20
313 A79  50np multicolored            .30   .30
314 A79  2.50nc multicolored          1.00  1.00
  a.  Souvenir sheet               6.50  6.50
   *Nos. 311-314 (4)*            1.70  1.70

United Nations Day. No. 314a contains one imperf. stamp similar to No. 314 with simulated perforations.

Leopard — A80

Designs: 12½np, Christmas butterfly. 20np, Nubian carmine bee-eaters. 50np, Waterbuck.

**Wmk. 325**
**1967, Dec. 28    Photo.    Perf. 12½**
315 A80  4np multicolored             1.50   .20
316 A80  12½np multicolored           3.00  1.75
317 A80  20np multicolored            3.75  3.25

318 A80 50np multicolored 3.75 3.50
a. Souvenir sheet of 3 25.00 25.00
*Nos. 315-318 (4)* 12.00 8.70

Intl. Tourist Year. No. 318a contains 3 imperf. stamps similar to Nos. 316-318 with simulated perforations.

Convoy Entering Accra A81

12½np, Victory parade. 20np, Waving crowd. 40np, Singing and dancing crowd.

**Unwmk.**

**1968, Feb. 24 Litho. Perf. 14**
319 A81 4np sal & multi .20 .20
320 A81 12½np multicolored .25 .25
321 A81 20np multicolored .30 .30
322 A81 40np yel & multi .60 .60
*Nos. 319-322 (4)* 1.35 1.35

2nd anniversary of Feb. 24th Revolution.

Cacao Beans and Microscope A82

4np, 25np, Cacao tree & beans, microscope.

**Perf. 14½x14**
**1968, Mar. 18 Photo. Wmk. 325**
323 A82 2½np grn & multi .20 .20
324 A82 4np gray & multi .20 .20
325 A82 10np scar & multi .20 .20
326 A82 25np multicolored .50 .50
a. Souvenir sheet of 4 3.00 3.00
*Nos. 323-326 (4)* 1.10 1.10

Issued to publicize Ghana's cocoa production. Sheets of 30.
No. 326a contains four imperf. stamps similar to Nos. 323-326 with simulated perforations.
Nos. 323-326 also exist in sheets of 12 believed not to have been on sale in Ghana.

Lt. Gen. E. K. Kotoka A83

Various portraits of Lt. Gen. Kotoka. 40np vert.

**1968, Apr. 17 Unwmk. Perf. 14**
327 A83 4np pur & multi .20 .20
328 A83 12½np grn & multi .25 .25
329 A83 20np multicolored .45 .45
330 A83 40np gray & multi .75 .75
*Nos. 327-330 (4)* 1.65 1.65

Lt. Gen. Emmanuel Kwasi Kotoka (1926-967), leader of the Revolution of 1966 against Nkrumah.

Tobacco — A84

Designs: 5np, Crested porcupine. 12½np, Tapped rubber tree. 20np, Cymothoe sangaris butterfly. 40np, Charaxes ameliae butterfly.

**1968, Aug. Photo. Perf. 14x14½**
331 A84 4np multicolored .20 .20
332 A84 5np multicolored .20 .20
333 A84 12½np multicolored .75 .75
334 A84 20np multicolored 2.75 2.75
335 A84 40np multicolored 3.00 3.00
a. Souvenir sheet of 4 8.00 8.00
*Nos. 331-335 (5)* 6.90 6.90

No. 335a contains 4 stamps similar to Nos. 331, 332-335 with simulated perforations.

Surgical Team A85

**1968, Nov. 11 Perf. 14x13**
336 A85 4np grn & multi .25 .20
337 A85 12½np multicolored .60 .30
338 A85 20np pur & multi 1.00 1.00
339 A85 40np bl & multi 1.75 1.75
a. Souvenir sheet of 4 5.25 5.25
*Nos. 336-339 (4)* 3.60 3.25

WHO, 20th anniv. No. 339a contains 4 imperf. stamps similar to Nos. 336-339.

Hurdling — A86

12½np, Boxing. 20np, Torch bearer, flags & Olympic rings. 40np, Soccer.

**1968, Dec. Unwmk. Perf. 14x14½**
340 A86 4np gray & multi .20 .20
341 A86 12½np gray & multi .25 .25
342 A86 20np ultra & multi .50 .50
343 A86 40np gray & multi .80 .80
a. Souvenir sheet of 4 5.25 5.25
*Nos. 340-343 (4)* 1.75 1.75

19th Olympic Games, Mexico City, Oct. 12-27, 1968. No. 343a contains 4 imperf. stamps with simulated perforations similar to Nos. 340-343.

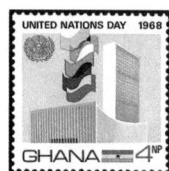

UN Headquarters and Flags — A87

UN Day, 1968: 12np, UN emblem and Ghanaian staff and stool. 20np, UN Headquarters, New York, UN emblem and Ghana flag. 40np, UN emblem surrounded by flags.

**1969, Feb. 1 Litho. Perf. 13x13½**
344 A87 4np multicolored .20 .20
345 A87 12½np pink & multi .20 .20
346 A87 20np blk & multi .25 .25
347 A87 40np lt bl & multi .50 .50
a. Souvenir sheet of 4 1.40 1.40
*Nos. 344-347 (4)* 1.15 1.15

No. 347a contains 4 imperf. stamps with simulated perforations similar to #344-347.

Joseph Boakye Danquah A88

12½np, 20np, Dr. Martin Luther King, Jr., Human Rights flame & flag of Ghana.

**1969, Mar. 7 Photo. Perf. 14½x14½**
348 A88 4np gray & multi .20 .20
349 A88 12½np multicolored .20 .20
350 A88 20np blue & multi .60 .60

351 A88 40np grn & multi .75 .75
a. Souvenir sheet of 4 2.25 2.25
*Nos. 348-351 (4)* 1.75 1.75

Intl. Human Rights Year, Rev. Martin Luther King, Jr. (1929-1968), American civil rights leader, and Joseph Boakye Danquah (1895-1965), lawyer, writer and Ghanaian political leader.
No. 351a contains 4 imperf. stamps with simulated perforations similar to #348-351.

Parliament A89

Design: 12½np, 40np, Coat of Arms.

**Perf. 14½x14**
**1969, Sept. Wmk. 325**
352 A89 4np multicolored .20 .20
353 A89 12½p multicolored .20 .20
354 A89 20np multicolored .20 .20
355 A89 40np multicolored .20 .20
a. Souvenir sheet of 4 1.25 1.25
*Nos. 352-355 (4)* .80 .80

3rd anniv. of the revolution. No. 355a contains 4 imperf. stamps with simulated perforations similar to Nos. 352-355.

Nos. 286-300 Overprinted in Black, Yellow or Red

**Perf. 11½x12, 12x11½ (A73), 14x14½, 14½x14 (A74-A75)**
**1969, Oct. 1 Photo. Wmk. 325**
356 A73 1np multicolored .20 1.75
357 A74 1½np multicolored 1.00 3.00
358 A73 2np multicolored .20 2.75
359 A73 2½np multicolored .20 2.00
360 A75 3np multicolored .60 2.50
361 A73 4np multi (Y) 2.50 .50
362 A75 6np multicolored .20 2.50
363 A75 8np multicolored .20 2.50
364 A75 9np multicolored .20 2.50
365 A75 10np multicolored .20 2.00
366 A74 20np blue .45 2.00
367 A74 50np multicolored 5.50 8.50
368 A74 1nc multicolored 2.25 11.00
369 A74 2nc multi (R) 3.00 12.00
370 A74 2.50nc multicolored 3.00 13.00
*Nos. 356-370 (15)* 19.70 68.25

Overprint vertical on vertical stamps. The 4np also exists with overprint in black and in red.

Map of Africa, Two Ghana Flags Rising from Ghana — A90

Designs: 12½np, "2" with laurel and star. 20np, Three hands and egg (symbol of rebirth) and Kente cloth. 40np, like 4np.

**Unwmk.**
**1969, Dec. 4 Litho. Perf. 14**
371 A90 4np multicolored .20 .20
372 A90 12½np bl & multi .35 .35
373 A90 20np multicolored .50 .50
374 A90 40np bl & multi 1.00 1.00
*Nos. 371-374 (4)* 2.05 2.05

Inauguration of the 2nd Republic, Oct. 1969.

Cogwheels and ILO Emblem A91

**Perf. 14½x14**
**1970, Jan. 5 Photo. Wmk. 325**
375 A91 4np rose red & multi .20 .20
376 A91 12½np multicolored .30 .30
377 A91 20np multicolored .40 .40
a. Souvenir sheet of 3 1.75 1.75
*Nos. 375-377 (3)* .90 .90

ILO, 50th anniv. No. 377a contains 3 imperf. stamps similar to Nos. 375-377 with simulated perforations.
Nos. 375-377 printed in sheets of 12.

Red Cross Helping Wounded A92

4np, Red Cross & globe, vert. 12½np, Henri Dunant, Red Cross, Red Crescent, Lion & Sun emblems. 40np, Red Cross and first aid.

**1970, Feb. 2 Perf. 14x14½, 14½x14**
378 A92 4np gold & multi .50 .50
379 A92 12½np gold & multi .60 .60
380 A92 20np blue & multi .70 .70
381 A92 40np multicolored 1.00 1.00
a. Souvenir sheet of 4 5.00 5.00
*Nos. 378-381 (4)* 2.80 2.80

League of Red Cross Societies, 50th anniv. No. 381a contains 4 imperf. stamps similar to Nos. 378-381 with simulated perforations.

Kotoka Airport, Gen. Kotoka and VC10 — A93

12½np, Control tower & tail section of VC10. 20np, Bird's eye view of airport and runway. 40np, Flags in front of Kotoka Airport.

**Perf. 13x14**
**1970, Apr. Unwmk. Litho.**
382 A93 4np multicolored .20 .20
383 A93 12½np multicolored .30 .20
384 A93 20np multicolored .50 .50
385 A93 40np multicolored 1.00 1.00
*Nos. 382-385 (4)* 2.00 1.90

Inauguration of Kotoka Airport.

Lunar Landing Module and Spacecraft — A94

Designs: 12½np, Neil A. Armstrong stepping onto the moon. 20np, Scientific experiments on the moon, horiz. 40np, Neil A. Armstrong, Michael Collins and Edwin E. Aldrin, Jr., after return to earth, horiz.

**1970, June 15 Litho. Perf. 12½**
386 A94 4np multicolored .25 .25
387 A94 12½np multicolored 1.10 1.10
388 A94 20np multicolored 1.40 1.40
389 A94 40np multicolored 4.25 4.25
a. Souvenir sheet of 4 7.50 7.50
*Nos. 386-389 (4)* 7.00 7.00

See note after US No. C76. No. 389a contains 4 imperf. stamps similar to Nos. 386-389. Exists with and without simulated perfs.
Nos. 386-389 and 389a were overprinted "PHILYMPIA/LONDON 1970" in black or silver in Sept. 1970. They are believed not to have been regularly issued.

Adult Education A95

Education Year Emblem and: 12½np, Children of various races studying together. 20np, "Ntesie" symbol of wisdom and knowledge. 40np, Nursery school children.

**1970, Aug. 10   Litho.   Perf. 13x12½**

| | | | | |
|---|---|---|---|---|
| 390 | A95 | 4np blue & multi | .20 | .20 |
| 391 | A95 | 12½np blue & multi | .30 | .30 |
| 392 | A95 | 20np blue & multi | .45 | .45 |
| 393 | A95 | 40np blue & multi | .65 | .65 |
| | | Nos. 390-393 (4) | 1.60 | 1.60 |

Issued for International Education Year.

Inauguration of Second Republic A96

Designs: 12½np, Mace and words of proclamation by K. A. Busia. 20np, Mace and globe with doves. 40np, Opening of Parliament of Second Republic.

**1970, Oct. 1   Litho.   Perf. 13**

| | | | | |
|---|---|---|---|---|
| 398 | A96 | 4np multicolored | .20 | .20 |
| 399 | A96 | 12½np multicolored | .35 | .35 |
| 400 | A96 | 20np multicolored | .55 | .55 |
| 401 | A96 | 40np lt bl & multi | .65 | .65 |
| | | Nos. 398-401 (4) | 1.75 | 1.75 |

First anniversary of the Second Republic.

Amaryllis A97

**Perf. 14½x14**

**1970   Photo.   Wmk. 325**

| | | | | |
|---|---|---|---|---|
| 402 | A97 | 4np shown | 1.75 | .20 |
| 403 | A97 | 12½np Lioness | 1.75 | 1.00 |
| 404 | A97 | 20np African orchid | 2.00 | 1.60 |
| 405 | A97 | 40np Elephant | 6.00 | 6.00 |
| | | Nos. 402-405 (4) | 11.50 | 8.80 |

Kuduo Brass Casket A98

Designs: 12½np, Akan traditional house, Danmum. 20np, Larabanga Mosque. 40np, Akan funerary clay head.

**1970, Dec. 7   Litho.   Perf. 14½x14**

| | | | | |
|---|---|---|---|---|
| 406 | A98 | 4np gray & multi | .20 | .20 |
| 407 | A98 | 12½np blue & multi | .45 | .30 |
| 408 | A98 | 20np multicolored | .75 | .55 |
| a. | | Souvenir sheet of 4 | 8.00 | 8.00 |
| 409 | A98 | 40np blue & multi | 1.60 | 1.60 |
| | | Nos. 406-409 (4) | 3.00 | 2.65 |

No. 408a contains stamps similar to Nos. 406 and 408, a 12½np (Pompeii Basilica) and a 40np (Pompeii scene). Simulated perforation.

Fair Building and Emblem A99

Fair Emblem and: 12½np, Drugstore merchandise. 20np, Automotives and tools. 40np, Cranes and trucks. 50np, Cargo, ship and plane, vert.

**Perf. 14½x14, 14x14½**

**1971, Feb. 5   Photo.   Wmk. 325**

| | | | | |
|---|---|---|---|---|
| 410 | A99 | 4np multicolored | .20 | .20 |
| 411 | A99 | 12½np lilac & multi | .45 | .45 |
| 412 | A99 | 20np blue & multi | .80 | .80 |
| 413 | A99 | 40np multicolored | 1.60 | 1.60 |
| 414 | A99 | 50np multicolored | 2.00 | 2.00 |
| | | Nos. 410-414 (5) | 5.05 | 5.05 |

2nd Ghana International Trade Fair, Accra, Feb. 1-14, 1971.

Crucifixion A100

Easter: 12½np, Jesus and disciples. 20np, Resurrection.

**Perf. 13½**

**1971, May 19   Litho.   Unwmk.**

| | | | | |
|---|---|---|---|---|
| 415 | A100 | 4np multicolored | .20 | .20 |
| 416 | A100 | 12½np multicolored | .50 | .50 |
| 417 | A100 | 20np multicolored | .90 | .90 |
| | | Nos. 415-417 (3) | 1.60 | 1.60 |

Corn and FAO Emblem — A101

**Perf. 14x14½**

**1971, June   Wmk. 325   Photo.**

| | | | | |
|---|---|---|---|---|
| 418 | A101 | 4np lilac & multi | .20 | .20 |
| 419 | A101 | 12½np lt bl & multi | .45 | .45 |
| 420 | A101 | 20np multicolored | .75 | .75 |
| | | Nos. 418-420 (3) | 1.40 | 1.40 |

Freedom from Hunger, second development decade, 1970-1980.

The overprint "In Memoriam / Lord Boyd ORR / 1880-1971" was applied to Nos. 418-420 in October, 1971. The 4np was also surcharged "60NP."

Girl Guide Emblem on Flag of Ghana A102

12½np, Mrs. Elsie Ofuatey-Kodjoe, national founder. 20np, Girl Guides at play. 40np, Campfire and tent. 50np, Girl Guides signalling.

**Unwmk.**

**1971, July 22   Litho.   Perf. 14**

| | | | | |
|---|---|---|---|---|
| 421 | A102 | 4np multicolored | .20 | .20 |
| 422 | A102 | 12½np yel & multi | .90 | .80 |
| 423 | A102 | 20np sal & multi | 1.75 | 1.60 |
| 424 | A102 | 40np multicolored | 3.00 | 2.50 |
| 425 | A102 | 50np lilac & multi | 3.25 | 2.75 |
| a. | | Souvenir sheet of 5 | 16.00 | 16.00 |
| | | Nos. 421-425 (5) | 9.10 | 7.85 |

50th anniversary of the Girl Guides of Ghana. No. 425a contains 5 imperf. stamps similar to Nos. 421-425.

Child Care Center — A103

YWCA Emblem and: 12½np, World Council Meeting and map of Ghana. 20np, Typing class. 40np, Building fund day.

**1971, Aug. 5   Perf. 13**

| | | | | |
|---|---|---|---|---|
| 426 | A103 | 4np multicolored | .20 | .20 |
| 427 | A103 | 12½np ultra & multi | .20 | .20 |
| 428 | A103 | 20np blue & multi | .20 | .20 |
| 429 | A103 | 40np yel & multi | .30 | .30 |
| a. | | Souvenir sheet of 4 | .90 | .90 |
| | | Nos. 426-429 (4) | .90 | .90 |

World Council Meeting of Young Women's Christian Association, Accra, Aug. 5. No. 429a contains 4 stamps similar to Nos. 426-429 with simulated perforations.

African Nativity Scene A104

Christmas: 1np, Fireworks, vert. 6np, Flight into Egypt.

**Perf. 14x14½, 14½x14**

**1971, Nov.   Photo.   Wmk. 325**

| | | | | |
|---|---|---|---|---|
| 433 | A104 | 1np multicolored | .20 | .20 |
| 434 | A104 | 3np orange & multi | .20 | .20 |
| 435 | A104 | 6np blue & multi | .20 | .20 |
| | | Nos. 433-435 (3) | .60 | .60 |

UNICEF Emblem, and Child A105

UNICEF Emblem and: 5np, Infant weighed in net scale, vert. 30np, Student midwife, vert. 50np, Boy in day care center.

**Perf. 13½x13, 13x13½**

**1971, Dec. 20   Litho.   Unwmk.**

| | | | | |
|---|---|---|---|---|
| 436 | A105 | 5np grn & multi | .20 | .20 |
| 437 | A105 | 15np yel & multi | .20 | .20 |
| 438 | A105 | 30np pink & multi | .45 | .45 |
| 439 | A105 | 50np blue & multi | .80 | .80 |
| a. | | Souvenir sheet of 4 | 6.50 | 6.50 |
| | | Nos. 436-439 (4) | 1.65 | 1.65 |

25th anniv. of UNICEF. No. 439a contains 4 stamps with simulated perforations similar to Nos. 436-439.

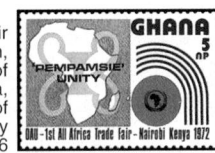

Fair Emblem, Map of Africa, Symbol of Unity A106

Fair Emblem and: 15np, Horn of Plenty. 30np, Fireworks over Africa. 60np, 1nc, Names of participating nations over map of Africa.

**1972, Feb. 23   Litho.   Perf. 14**

| | | | | |
|---|---|---|---|---|
| 440 | A106 | 5np lt brn & multi | .20 | .20 |
| 441 | A106 | 15np lt bl & multi | .20 | .20 |
| 442 | A106 | 30np green & multi | .30 | .30 |
| 443 | A106 | 60np yel & multi | .35 | .35 |
| 444 | A106 | 1nc lt bl & multi | .60 | .60 |
| | | Nos. 440-444 (5) | 1.65 | 1.65 |

First All-Africa Trade Fair, Nairobi, Kenya, Feb. 23-Mar. 5.

Nos. 440-444 were overprinted "BELGICA 72" in red for release June 24, 1972. The regularity of this issue has been questioned. Value $8.

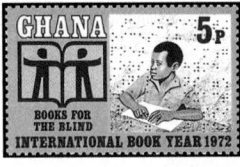

Books for the Blind A107

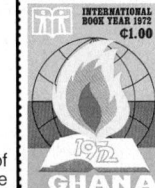

Book and Flame of Knowledge A108

Book Year Emblem and: 15p, Books for Children ("Anansi and Snake the Postman"). 30p, Books for Recreation (Accra Central Library). 50p, Books for Students (2 students).

**1972, Apr. 21   Perf. 13½**

| | | | | |
|---|---|---|---|---|
| 445 | A107 | 5p blue & multi | .30 | .20 |
| 446 | A107 | 15p yel & multi | .75 | .50 |
| 447 | A107 | 30p lilac & multi | 1.25 | 1.00 |
| 448 | A107 | 50p green & multi | 2.25 | 1.90 |

| | | | | |
|---|---|---|---|---|
| 449 | A108 | 1ce blue & multi | 3.25 | 2.75 |
| a. | | Souvenir sheet of 5 | 12.00 | 12.00 |
| | | Nos. 445-449 (5) | 7.80 | 6.35 |

Intl. Book Year. No. 449a contains one each of Nos. 445-449 with simulated perforations.

Star Grass A109

**1972, July 3   Litho.   Perf. 13½**

| | | | | |
|---|---|---|---|---|
| 450 | A109 | 5p shown | .30 | .30 |
| 451 | A109 | 15p Mona monkey | .90 | .90 |
| 452 | A109 | 30p Amaryllis | 5.50 | 5.50 |
| 453 | A109 | 1ce Side-striped squirrel | 6.25 | 6.25 |
| | | Nos. 450-453 (4) | 12.95 | 12.95 |

Olympic Emblems, Soccer A110

**1972, Sept. 5   Litho.   Perf. 13½x13**

| | | | | |
|---|---|---|---|---|
| 454 | A110 | 5p shown | .20 | .20 |
| 455 | A110 | 15p Running | .30 | .20 |
| 456 | A110 | 30p Boxing | .55 | .55 |
| 457 | A110 | 50p Long jump | .90 | .90 |
| 458 | A110 | 1ce High jump | 2.00 | 2.00 |
| | | Nos. 454-458 (5) | 3.95 | 3.85 |

**Souvenir Sheet**

| | | | | |
|---|---|---|---|---|
| 459 | | Sheet of 2 | 4.00 | 4.00 |
| a. | A110 | 40p like 30p | 1.50 | 1.50 |
| b. | A110 | 60p like 5p | 2.00 | 2.00 |

20th Olympic Games, Munich, 8/26-9/11.

Senior and Cub Scouts, Badge A111

Designs: 15p, Scout in front of tent. 30p, 40p, Sea Scouts in canoe. 50p, Cub Scouts with den mother. 60p, 1ce, Scouts studying.

**1972, Oct.   Litho.   Perf. 14**

| | | | | |
|---|---|---|---|---|
| 460 | A111 | 5p blue grn & multi | .20 | .20 |
| 461 | A111 | 15p ocher & multi | .55 | .55 |
| 462 | A111 | 30p lilac & multi | 1.10 | 1.10 |
| 463 | A111 | 50p multicolored | 2.00 | 2.00 |
| 464 | A111 | 1ce blue & multi | 4.25 | 4.25 |
| | | Nos. 460-464 (5) | 8.10 | 8.00 |

**Souvenir Sheet**

**Perf. 13½**

| | | | | |
|---|---|---|---|---|
| 465 | | Sheet of 2 | 5.00 | 5.00 |
| a. | A111 | 40p brown & multi | 1.75 | 1.75 |
| b. | A111 | 60p green & multi | 2.75 | 2.75 |

Boy Scout Movement, 65th anniversary. For overprints see Nos. 484-489.

Virgin and Child, by Holbein the Younger — A112

Paintings: 1p, Holy Night, by Correggio. 15p, Virgin and Child, by Andrea Rico. 30p, Melchior. 60p, Virgin and Child with Caspar. 1ce, Balthasar. 30p, 60p, 1ce, are from early 16th century stained glass windows.

## 1972, Dec. 2 — Perf. 14x13½

| | | | | |
|---|---|---|---|---|
| 466 | A112 | 1p black & multi | .20 | .20 |
| 467 | A112 | 3p black & multi | .20 | .20 |
| 468 | A112 | 15p black & multi | .40 | .35 |
| 469 | A112 | 30p black & multi | .80 | .80 |
| 470 | A112 | 60p black & multi | 1.75 | 1.75 |
| 471 | A112 | 1ce black & multi | 3.00 | 3.00 |
| a. | | Souvenir sheet of 3 | 9.50 | 9.50 |
| | | Nos. 466-471 (6) | 6.35 | 6.30 |

Christmas. No. 471a contains one each of Nos. 469-471 with simulated perforations.

Market A113

Designs: 1p, Unity Declaration at Kumasi Durbar. 5p, Woman with child selling bananas, vert. 15p, Farmer at rest and produce, vert. 30p, Market. 40p, 1ce, Farmer cutting palm nuts with cutlass. 60p, Miners.

## Perf. 14x13½, 13½x14

### 1973, Apr. — Litho.

| | | | | |
|---|---|---|---|---|
| 472 | A113 | 1p multicolored | .20 | .20 |
| 473 | A113 | 3p multicolored | .20 | .20 |
| 474 | A113 | 5p multicolored | .20 | .20 |
| 475 | A113 | 15p multicolored | .30 | .30 |
| 476 | A113 | 30p multicolored | .30 | .30 |
| 477 | A113 | 1ce multicolored | .75 | .75 |
| | | Nos. 472-477 (6) | 1.95 | 1.85 |

### Souvenir Sheet

| | | | | |
|---|---|---|---|---|
| 478 | | Sheet of 2 | 2.75 | 2.75 |
| a. | A113 | 40p multicolored | 1.00 | 1.00 |
| b. | A113 | 60p multicolored | 1.50 | 1.50 |

Operation "Feed Yourself" and for 1st anniv. of the Oct. 13 Revolution.

Children's Clinic — A114

WHO Emblem and: 15p, Radiology. 30p, Immunization. 50p, Fight against malnutrition (starving child). 1ce, WHO Headquarters, Geneva.

### 1973, July — Perf. 14x13½

| | | | | |
|---|---|---|---|---|
| 479 | A114 | 5p rose red & multi | .20 | .20 |
| 480 | A114 | 15p blue & multi | .20 | .20 |
| 481 | A114 | 30p bister & multi | .40 | .35 |
| 482 | A114 | 50p green & multi | .65 | .60 |
| 483 | A114 | 1ce multicolored | 1.25 | 1.10 |
| | | Nos. 479-483 (5) | 2.70 | 2.45 |

WHO, 25th anniversary.

### Nos. 460-465 Overprinted: "1st WORLD SCOUTING CONFERENCE IN AFRICA"

### 1973, July — Litho. — Perf. 14

| | | | | |
|---|---|---|---|---|
| 484 | A111 | 5p green & multi | .20 | .20 |
| 485 | A111 | 15p ocher & multi | .30 | .25 |
| 486 | A111 | 30p lilac & multi | .60 | .50 |
| 487 | A111 | 50p multicolored | 1.00 | .80 |
| 488 | A111 | 1ce blue & multi | 2.10 | 1.60 |
| | | Nos. 484-488 (5) | 4.20 | 3.35 |

### Souvenir Sheet — Perf. 13½

| | | | | |
|---|---|---|---|---|
| 489 | | Sheet of 2 | 4.25 | 10.00 |
| a. | A111 | 40p brown & multi | 1.50 | 3.00 |
| b. | A111 | 60p green & multi | 2.25 | 6.00 |

24th Boy Scout World Conference (1st in Africa), Nairobi, Kenya, July 16-21.

Poultry Farming A115

FAO/UN Emblem and: 15p, 40p, Tractor. 50p, Cacao harvest. 60p, 1ce, FAO Headquarters, Rome.

## 1973 — Litho. — Perf. 14½x14

| | | | | |
|---|---|---|---|---|
| 490 | A115 | 5p blue & multi | .20 | .20 |
| 491 | A115 | 15p blue & multi | .20 | .20 |
| 492 | A115 | 50p blue & multi | .40 | .40 |
| 493 | A115 | 1ce blue & multi | .60 | .60 |
| | | Nos. 490-493 (4) | 1.40 | 1.40 |

### Souvenir Sheet

| | | | | |
|---|---|---|---|---|
| 494 | | Sheet of 2 | 1.25 | 2.00 |
| a. | A115 | 40p blue & multi | .40 | .75 |
| b. | A115 | 60p blue & multi | .60 | 1.00 |

World Food Program, 10th anniversary.

INTERPOL Emblem, Observer A116

INTERPOL Emblem and: 30p, Judge's wig, poison bottle, handcuffs. 50p, photograph and fingerprint. 1ce, Corpse and question mark.

### 1973 — Perf. 13x13½

| | | | | |
|---|---|---|---|---|
| 495 | A116 | 5p emerald & multi | .20 | .20 |
| 496 | A116 | 30p rose red & multi | .80 | .80 |
| 497 | A116 | 50p ultra & multi | 1.90 | 1.90 |
| 498 | A116 | 1ce gray & multi | 3.50 | 3.50 |
| | | Nos. 495-498 (4) | 6.40 | 6.40 |

50th anniv. the Intl. Criminal Police Org. (INTERPOL).

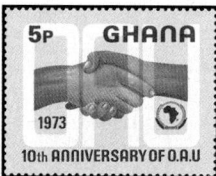

Handclasp and "OAU" A117

"OAU" and: 30p, Africa Hall, Addis Ababa. 50p, OAU emblem (map of Africa). 1ce, "X" in Ghana flag colors.

### 1973, Oct. 22 — Litho. — Perf. 14x14½

| | | | | |
|---|---|---|---|---|
| 499 | A117 | 5p lt bl, blk & brn | .20 | .20 |
| 500 | A117 | 30p bluish grn, blk & brn | .20 | .20 |
| 501 | A117 | 50p pink, black & ol | .30 | .30 |
| 502 | A117 | 1ce multicolored | .45 | .45 |
| | | Nos. 499-502 (4) | 1.15 | 1.15 |

Org. for African Unity, 10th anniv.

Weather Balloon, WMO Emblem A118

WMO Emblem and: 15p, 40p, Tiros weather satellite. 30p, 60p, Computer weather map. 1ce, Radar cloud scanner.

### 1973, Nov. 16

| | | | | |
|---|---|---|---|---|
| 503 | A118 | 5p multicolored | .20 | .20 |
| 504 | A118 | 15p multicolored | .20 | .20 |
| 505 | A118 | 30p multicolored | .40 | .40 |
| 506 | A118 | 1ce multicolored | .75 | .75 |
| | | Nos. 503-506 (4) | 1.55 | 1.55 |

### Souvenir Sheet

| | | | | |
|---|---|---|---|---|
| 507 | | Sheet of 2 | 1.75 | 1.75 |
| a. | A118 | 40p multicolored | .50 | .50 |
| b. | A118 | 60p multicolored | .90 | .90 |

Intl. meteorological cooperation, cent. #507 exists imperf.

Adoration of the Kings — A119

Christmas: 3p, 40p, Madonna and Child (contemporary). Nos. 510, 511d, Madonna and Child, by Murillo. No. 511, 60p, Adoration of the Kings, by Tiepolo. No. 511b as 1p.

### 1973, Dec. 10 — Perf. 14

| | | | | |
|---|---|---|---|---|
| 508 | A119 | 1p black & multi | .20 | .20 |
| 509 | A119 | 3p gray & multi | .20 | .20 |
| 510 | A119 | 30p multicolored | .55 | .55 |
| 511 | A119 | 50p multicolored | 1.10 | 1.10 |
| | | Nos. 508-511 (4) | 2.05 | 2.05 |

### Souvenir Sheet — Imperf

| | | | | |
|---|---|---|---|---|
| 511A | | Sheet of 4 | 2.50 | 2.50 |
| b. | A119 | 30p black & multi | .35 | .35 |
| c. | A119 | 40p gray & multi | .45 | .45 |
| d. | A119 | 50p multicolored | .55 | .55 |
| e. | A119 | 60p multicolored | .65 | .65 |

No. 511A has simulated perforations.

Various Envelopes A120

UPU Emblem and: 9p, 30p, UPU Headquarters, Bern. 40p, 50p, Airmail envelope with Ghana No. 296. 60p, 1ce, Ghana No. 296.

### 1974, May — Litho. — Perf. 14½

| | | | | |
|---|---|---|---|---|
| 512 | A120 | 5p blue, blk & org | .20 | .20 |
| 513 | A120 | 9p blue, blk & org | .20 | .20 |
| 514 | A120 | 50p blue, blk & org | .40 | .40 |
| 515 | A120 | 1ce blue, blk & org | .65 | .65 |
| | | Nos. 512-515 (4) | 1.45 | 1.45 |

### Souvenir Sheet

| | | | | |
|---|---|---|---|---|
| 515A | | Sheet of 4 | .90 | .90 |
| b. | A120 | 20p blue, blk & org | .20 | .20 |
| c. | A120 | 30p blue, blk & org | .20 | .20 |
| d. | A120 | 40p blue, blk & org | .20 | .20 |
| e. | A120 | 50p blue, blk & org | .20 | .20 |

Centenary of Universal Postal Union. For overprints see Nos. 521-524A.

The Betrayal — A121

Designs: 5p, 15p, Jesus Carrying Cross, painting by Thomas de Coloswar, 1427. 20p, 30p, The Betrayal. 25p, 50p, The Deposition. 40p, 1ce, Risen Christ and Mary Magdalene. The designs (except 5p, 15p) are from 15th century English ivory carvings.

### 1974, Apr. — Litho. — Perf. 14

| | | | | |
|---|---|---|---|---|
| 516 | A121 | 5p black & multi | .20 | .20 |
| 517 | A121 | 30p sil, ultra & brn | .20 | .20 |
| 518 | A121 | 50p sil, red & brn | .35 | .35 |
| 519 | A121 | 1ce silver, ol & brn | .55 | .55 |
| | | Nos. 516-519 (4) | 1.30 | 1.30 |

### Souvenir Sheet — Imperf

| | | | | |
|---|---|---|---|---|
| 520 | | Sheet of 4 | 1.10 | 1.10 |
| a. | A121 | 15p black & multi | .20 | |
| b. | A121 | 20p silver, ultra & brn | .20 | |
| c. | A121 | 25p silver, red & brn | .20 | |
| d. | A121 | 50p silver, olive & brn | .20 | |

Easter. No. 520 contains 4 stamps with simulated perforations.

### Nos. 512-515A Overprinted "INTERNABA 1974"

### 1974, June 7 — Perf. 14½

| | | | | |
|---|---|---|---|---|
| 521 | A120 | 5p blue, blk & org | .20 | .20 |
| 522 | A120 | 9p blue, blk & org | .20 | .20 |
| 523 | A120 | 50p blue, blk & org | .35 | .35 |
| 524 | A120 | 1ce blue, blk & org | .55 | .55 |
| | | Nos. 521-524 (4) | 1.30 | 1.30 |

### Souvenir Sheet

| | | | | |
|---|---|---|---|---|
| 524A | | Sheet of 4 | 2.10 | 2.10 |
| b. | A120 | 20p blue, blk & org | .20 | .20 |
| c. | A120 | 30p blue, blk & org | .20 | .20 |
| d. | A120 | 40p blue, blk & org | .30 | .30 |
| e. | A120 | 60p blue, blk & org | .35 | .35 |

INTERNABA 1974 International Philatelic Exhibition, Basel, June 7-16. Overprint is applied to individual stamps of No. 524A.

Soccer and World Cup Emblem A122

Designs: Various soccer scenes and world cup emblem.

### 1974, June 17 — Litho. — Perf. 14½, 13

| | | | | |
|---|---|---|---|---|
| 525 | A122 | 5p multicolored | .20 | .20 |
| 526 | A122 | 30p multicolored | .20 | .20 |
| 527 | A122 | 50p multicolored | .30 | .30 |
| 528 | A122 | 1ce multicolored | .35 | .35 |
| | | Nos. 525-528 (4) | 1.05 | 1.05 |

### Souvenir Sheet — Perf. 14½

| | | | | |
|---|---|---|---|---|
| 529 | | Sheet of 4 | 2.00 | 2.00 |
| a. | A122 | 25p multicolored | .20 | |
| b. | A122 | 40p multicolored | .25 | .25 |
| c. | A122 | 55p multicolored | .30 | .30 |
| d. | A122 | 60p multicolored | .35 | .35 |

World Cup Soccer Championship, June 13-July 7.

Nos. 525-528 were issued in sheets of 30, perf. 14½, and in sheets of 5 plus label, perf. 13.

For overprints, see Nos. 535-539, 549-553.

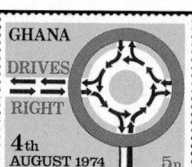

Traffic Diagram at Traffic Circle A123

Designs: 15p, Traffic sign "Two-way traffic." 30p, "Change to right hand drive!," vert. 50p, Warning hands sign, vert. 1ce, 2 hands and car symbolizing traffic change, vert.

### 1974, July 16 — Perf. 13½

### Size: 35x28½mm

| | | | | |
|---|---|---|---|---|
| 530 | A123 | 5p yel grn, red & blk | .20 | .20 |
| 531 | A123 | 15p lilac, red & blk | .20 | .20 |

### Size: 28½x41mm — Perf. 14½

| | | | | |
|---|---|---|---|---|
| 532 | A123 | 30p multicolored | .35 | .35 |
| 533 | A123 | 50p multicolored | .80 | .80 |
| 534 | A123 | 1ce red, green & blk | 1.75 | 1.75 |
| | | Nos. 530-534 (5) | 3.30 | 3.30 |

Publicity for change to right-hand driving, Aug. 4, 1974.

### Nos. 525-529 Overprinted: "WEST GERMANY WINNERS"

### 1974, Aug. 30 — Litho. — Perf. 14½, 13

| | | | | |
|---|---|---|---|---|
| 535 | A122 | 5p multicolored | .20 | .20 |
| 536 | A122 | 30p multicolored | .45 | .45 |
| 537 | A122 | 50p multicolored | .65 | .65 |
| 538 | A122 | 1ce multicolored | 1.10 | 1.10 |
| | | Nos. 535-538 (4) | 2.40 | 2.40 |

### Souvenir Sheet

| | | | | |
|---|---|---|---|---|
| 539 | | Sheet of 4 | 2.00 | 2.00 |
| a. | A122 | 25p multicolored | .25 | .25 |
| b. | A122 | 40p multicolored | .40 | .40 |
| c. | A122 | 55p multicolored | .45 | .45 |
| d. | A122 | 60p multicolored | .50 | .50 |

World Cup Soccer Championship, 1974, victory of German Federal Republic. Overprint is applied to individual stamps of No. 539.

Family and WPY Emblem A124

### 1974, Sept. 27 — Perf. 12½

| | | | | |
|---|---|---|---|---|
| 540 | A124 | 5p shown | .20 | .20 |
| 541 | A124 | 30p Clinic | .30 | .30 |
| 542 | A124 | 50p Immunization of children | .35 | .35 |
| 543 | A124 | 1ce Census | .65 | .65 |
| | | Nos. 540-543 (4) | 1.50 | 1.50 |

World Population Year.

Angel — A125

Nativity — A127

Three Kings, Candles — A126

Design: 60p. 1ce, Annunciation.

**Perf. 13½, 14 (7p)**

| 1974, Dec. 19 | | Litho. | | |
|---|---|---|---|---|
| 544 | A125 | 5p red & multi | .20 | .20 |
| 545 | A126 | 7p blue & multi | .20 | .20 |
| 546 | A127 | 9p orange & multi | .20 | .20 |
| 547 | A127 | 1ce orange & multi | .85 | .85 |
| | *Nos. 544-547 (4)* | | 1.45 | 1.45 |

**Souvenir Sheet**

*Imperf*

| 548 | | Sheet of 4 | 1.25 | 1.25 |
|---|---|---|---|---|
| a. | A125 15p red & multi | | .20 | |
| b. | A126 30p blue & multi | | .20 | |
| c. | A127 45p orange & multi | | .20 | |
| d. | A127 60p orange & multi | | .20 | |

Christmas. No. 548 contains 4 stamps with simulated perforations.

Nos. 525-529 Overprinted "APOLLO / SOYUZ / JULY 15, 1975"

| 1975, Aug. 15 | | Litho. | Perf. 14½, 13 | |
|---|---|---|---|---|
| 549 | A122 | 5p multicolored | .20 | .20 |
| 550 | A122 | 30p multicolored | .25 | .25 |
| 551 | A122 | 50p multicolored | .65 | .55 |
| 552 | A122 | 1ce multicolored | 1.00 | 1.00 |
| | *Nos. 549-552 (4)* | | 2.00 | 2.00 |

**Souvenir Sheet**

*Perf. 14½*

| 553 | | Sheet of 4 | 2.75 | 2.75 |
|---|---|---|---|---|
| a. | A122 25p multicolored | | .25 | .25 |
| b. | A122 40p multicolored | | .40 | .40 |
| c. | A122 55p multicolored | | .60 | .60 |
| d. | A122 60p multicolored | | .65 | .65 |

Apollo Soyuz space test project (Russo-American cooperation), launching July 15, link-up, July 17.
Overprint is applied to individual stamps of No. 553.
Nos. 549-552 with perf. 13 are from the sheets of 5 plus label.

IWY Emblem, Woman Tractor Driver — A128

Intl. Women's Year Emblem and: 15p, like 7p. 30p, 40p, Automobile mechanic. 60p, 65p, Factory workers. 80p, 1ce, Cocoa research.

| 1975, Sept. 3 | | Litho. | Perf. 14 | |
|---|---|---|---|---|
| 554 | A128 | 7p multicolored | .20 | .20 |
| 555 | A128 | 30p lt violet & multi | .55 | .55 |
| 556 | A128 | 60p multicolored | 1.40 | 1.40 |
| 557 | A128 | 1ce lilac & multi | 2.25 | 2.25 |
| | *Nos. 554-557 (4)* | | 4.40 | 4.40 |

**Souvenir Sheet**

*Imperf*

| 558 | | Sheet of 4 | 4.00 | 4.00 |
|---|---|---|---|---|
| a. | A128 15p Prus green & multi | | .30 | .30 |
| b. | A128 40p light violet & multi | | .75 | .75 |
| c. | A128 65p dull green & multi | | 1.00 | 1.00 |
| d. | A128 80p lilac & multi | | 1.25 | 1.25 |

Intl. Women's Year. No. 558 contains 4 stamps with simulated perforations.

Angel over Child in Crib A129

Angel with Harp A130

Designs: 7p, 40p, Angels with lute and bell. 30p, 65p, Angel with viol. 1ce, 80p, Angels with trumpets. 15p, like 5p.

| 1975, Dec. 31 | | Litho. | Perf. 14x13½ | |
|---|---|---|---|---|
| 559 | A129 | 2p org & multi | .20 | .20 |
| 560 | A130 | 5p yel, brown & grn | .20 | .20 |
| 561 | A130 | 7p yel, brown & grn | .20 | .20 |
| 562 | A130 | 30p yel, brown & grn | .35 | .20 |
| 563 | A130 | 1ce yel, brown & grn | .75 | .75 |
| | *Nos. 559-563 (5)* | | 1.70 | 1.55 |

**Souvenir Sheet**

*Imperf*

| 564 | | Sheet of 4 | 2.00 | 2.00 |
|---|---|---|---|---|
| a. | A130 15p yellow, green & brown | | .20 | .20 |
| b. | A130 40p yellow, green & brown | | .20 | .20 |
| c. | A130 65p yellow, green & brown | | .50 | .50 |
| d. | A130 80p yellow, green & brown | | .60 | .60 |

Christmas. No. 564 has simulated perforations.

Boy Scouts Reading Map — A131

30p, 40p, Sailing. 60p, 65p, Hiking. 80p, 1ce, Life saving (swimmers). 15p, like 7p.

| 1976, Jan. 5 | | | Perf. 13½x14 | |
|---|---|---|---|---|
| 565 | A131 | 7p ocher & multi | .20 | .20 |
| 566 | A131 | 30p blue & multi | .75 | .75 |
| 567 | A131 | 60p green & multi | 1.75 | 1.75 |
| 568 | A131 | 1ce multicolored | 2.75 | 2.75 |
| | *Nos. 565-568 (4)* | | 5.45 | 5.45 |

**Souvenir Sheet**

| 569 | | Sheet of 4 | 5.00 | 5.00 |
|---|---|---|---|---|
| a. | A131 15p ocher & multi | | .40 | .40 |
| b. | A131 40p blue & multi | | .90 | .90 |
| c. | A131 65p green & multi | | 1.25 | 1.25 |
| d. | A131 80p rose claret & multi | | 1.50 | 1.50 |

Nordjamb 75, 14th World Boy Scout Jamboree, Lillehammer, Norway, July 29-Aug. 7.
For overprints, see Nos. 578-582.

Map of Ghana and: 30p, "2¼ lbs of jam a little more than a kilogram." 60p, "A meter of cloth will be a little more than 3 foot 3." 1ce, Thermometer, ice and boiling tea kettle.

1 ¾ Pints Equal 1 Liter A132

| 1976, Jan. 5 | | Litho. | Perf. 14x13½ | |
|---|---|---|---|---|
| 570 | A132 | 7p bluish gray & blk | .20 | .20 |
| 571 | A132 | 30p vio blue & multi | .50 | .25 |
| 572 | A132 | 60p ocher & multi | .90 | .45 |
| 573 | A132 | 1ce multicolored | 1.60 | .90 |
| | *Nos. 570-573 (4)* | | 3.20 | 1.80 |

Introduction of metric system, Sept. 1975.

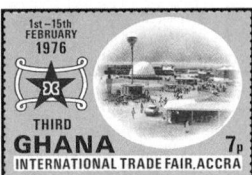
Fair Grounds — A133

Designs: Various exhibition halls.

| 1976, Apr. 6 | | Litho. | Perf. 14 | |
|---|---|---|---|---|
| 574 | A133 | 7p multicolored | .20 | .20 |
| 575 | A133 | 30p yellow & multi | .20 | .20 |
| 576 | A133 | 60p multicolored | .40 | .40 |
| 577 | A133 | 1ce salmon & multi | .65 | .65 |
| | *Nos. 574-577 (4)* | | 1.45 | 1.45 |

International Trade Fair, Accra, Feb. 1-15.

Nos. 565-569 Overprinted in Violet Blue

'INTERPHIL' 76 BICENTENNIAL EXHIBITION

| 1976, May 29 | | Litho. | Perf. 13½x14 | |
|---|---|---|---|---|
| 578 | A131 | 7p ocher & multi | .20 | .20 |
| 579 | A131 | 30p blue & multi | .55 | .20 |
| 580 | A131 | 60p green & multi | 1.10 | .40 |
| 581 | A131 | 1ce multicolored | 1.60 | .80 |
| | *Nos. 578-581 (4)* | | 3.45 | 1.60 |

**Souvenir Sheet**

| 582 | | Sheet of 4 | 2.25 | 2.25 |
|---|---|---|---|---|
| a. | A131 15p ocher & multi | | .20 | .20 |
| b. | A131 40p blue & multi | | .40 | .40 |
| c. | A131 65p green & multi | | .50 | .50 |
| d. | A131 80p rose claret & multi | | .50 | .50 |

Interphil 76 International Philatelic Exhibition, Philadelphia, Pa., May 29-June 6. Overprint applied to individual stamps of No. 582.

Shot Put — A134

Olympic Rings, Map of Ghana and: 15p, like 7p. 30p, 40p, Soccer. 60p, 65p, Women's 1500 meters. 80p, 1ce, Boxing.

| 1976, Aug. 9 | | Litho. | Perf. 14x13½ | |
|---|---|---|---|---|
| 583 | A134 | 7p lt blue & multi | .20 | .20 |
| 584 | A134 | 30p yellow & multi | .30 | .30 |
| 585 | A134 | 60p multicolored | .65 | .65 |
| 586 | A134 | 1ce yellow & multi | 1.00 | 1.00 |
| | *Nos. 583-586 (4)* | | 2.15 | 2.15 |

**Souvenir Sheet**

| 587 | | Sheet of 4 | 1.75 | 1.75 |
|---|---|---|---|---|
| a. | A134 15p light blue & multi | | .20 | .20 |
| b. | A134 40p yellow & multi | | .20 | .20 |
| c. | A134 65p emerald & multi | | .30 | .30 |
| d. | A134 80p yellow & multi | | .40 | .40 |

21st Olympic Games, Montreal, Canada, July 17-Aug. 1.
For overprints see Nos. 606-610.

Supreme Court, Accra A135

Designs: Various views of Supreme Court Building, Scales of Justice, law book.

| 1976, Sept. 7 | | Litho. | Perf. 14 | |
|---|---|---|---|---|
| 588 | A135 | 8p lilac & multi | .20 | .20 |
| 589 | A135 | 30p blue & multi | .25 | .25 |
| 590 | A135 | 60p ver & multi | .40 | .40 |
| 591 | A135 | 1ce multicolored | .85 | .85 |
| | *Nos. 588-591 (4)* | | 1.70 | 1.70 |

Ghana Supreme Court, centenary.

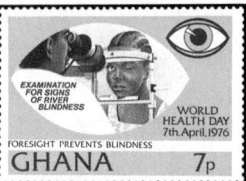
Examination for River Blindness — A136

Designs: 30p, Ghanaian entomologist with microscope. 60p, Flowers. 1ce, Boatmen checking effectiveness of black fly larvae insecticide.

| 1976, Oct. 28 | | Litho. | Perf. 14½x14 | |
|---|---|---|---|---|
| 592 | A136 | 7p multicolored | .85 | .85 |
| 593 | A136 | 30p multicolored | 2.25 | 1.75 |
| 594 | A136 | 60p multicolored | 3.50 | 3.50 |
| 595 | A136 | 1ce multicolored | 5.75 | 5.75 |
| | *Nos. 592-595 (4)* | | 12.35 | 11.20 |

World Health Day. Prevention of blindness.

Children with Gifts and Christmas Tree — A137

Designs: 6p, 15p, Children with firecrackers. 30p, 65p, Family at Christmas dinner. 40p, 80p, 1ce, like 8p.

| 1976, Dec. 15 | | Litho. | Perf. 13½ | |
|---|---|---|---|---|
| 596 | A137 | 6p multicolored | .20 | .20 |
| 597 | A137 | 8p multicolored | .20 | .20 |
| 598 | A137 | 30p multicolored | .65 | .65 |
| 599 | A137 | 1ce multicolored | 1.75 | 1.75 |
| | *Nos. 596-599 (4)* | | 2.80 | 2.80 |

**Souvenir Sheet**

*Imperf*

| 600 | | Sheet of 4 | 3.25 | 3.25 |
|---|---|---|---|---|
| a. | A137 15p multicolored | | .20 | |
| b. | A137 40p multicolored | | .55 | .55 |
| c. | A137 65p multicolored | | .90 | .90 |
| d. | A137 80p multicolored | | 1.10 | 1.10 |

Christmas. No. 600 has simulated perfs.

1876 Gallows Frame Telephone and A. G. Bell — A138

A. G. Bell and: 15p, like 8p. 30p, 40p, 1895 telephone. 60p, 65p, 1929 telephone. 80p, 1ce, 1976 telephone.

| 1976, Dec. 17 | | | Perf. 14½ | |
|---|---|---|---|---|
| 601 | A138 | 8p multicolored | .20 | .20 |
| 602 | A138 | 30p multicolored | .50 | .50 |
| 603 | A138 | 60p multicolored | 1.40 | 1.40 |
| 604 | A138 | 1ce multicolored | 2.00 | 2.00 |
| | *Nos. 601-604 (4)* | | 4.10 | 4.10 |

**Souvenir Sheet**

*Perf. 13*

| 605 | | Sheet of 4 | 3.00 | 3.00 |
|---|---|---|---|---|
| a. | A138 15p multicolored | | .20 | |
| b. | A138 40p multicolored | | .50 | |
| c. | A138 65p multicolored | | .85 | |
| d. | A138 80p multicolored | | 1.10 | |

Centenary of first telephone call by Alexander Graham Bell, Mar. 10, 1876.
For overprints, see Nos. 616-620.

Nos. 583-587 Overprinted:
a. EAST GERMANY / WINNERS
b. U.S.S.R. WINNERS
c. U.S.A. WINNERS

| 1977, Feb. 22 | | Litho. | Perf. 14x13½ | |
|---|---|---|---|---|
| 606 | A134(a) | 7p multicolored | .20 | .20 |
| 607 | A134(a) | 30p multicolored | .35 | .20 |
| 608 | A134(b) | 60p multicolored | .75 | .30 |
| 609 | A134(c) | 1ce multicolored | 1.60 | .55 |
| | *Nos. 606-609 (4)* | | 2.90 | 1.25 |

## Souvenir Sheet

| 610 | Sheet of 4 | 3.50 | 2.50 |
|---|---|---|---|
| a. | A134(a) 15p multicolored | .30 | .30 |
| b. | A134(a) 40p multicolored | .70 | .70 |
| c. | A134(b) 65p multicolored | 1.00 | 1.00 |
| d. | A134(c) 80p multicolored | 1.10 | 1.10 |

1976 Montreal Olympic Games' winners.

Klama Dance, Dipo Tribe — A139

Festival Emblem and: 15p, like 8p. 30p, 40p, African artifacts. 60p, 65p, Acon dance. 80p, 1ce, Mud, straw and wooden huts.

**1977, Mar. 24    Litho.    Perf. 14x13½**

| 611 | A139 8p multicolored | .20 | .20 |
|---|---|---|---|
| 612 | A139 30p multicolored | .50 | .50 |
| 613 | A139 60p multicolored | .80 | .80 |
| 614 | A139 1ce multicolored | 1.25 | 1.25 |
| | Nos. 611-614 (4) | 2.75 | 2.75 |

### Souvenir Sheet

| 615 | Sheet of 4 | 3.50 | 3.50 |
|---|---|---|---|
| a. | A139 15p multicolored | .35 | .35 |
| b. | A139 40p multicolored | .75 | .75 |
| c. | A139 65p multicolored | 1.00 | 1.10 |
| d. | A139 80p multicolored | 1.25 | 1.25 |

2nd World Black and African Festival of Arts and Culture, Lagos, Nigeria, Jan. 15-Feb. 12.

Nos. 601-605 Overprinted: "PRINCE CHARLES / VISITS GHANA / 17th TO 25th / MARCH, 1977"

**1977, June 2    Litho.    Perf. 14½**

| 616 | A138 8p multicolored | .75 | .75 |
|---|---|---|---|
| 617 | A138 30p multicolored | 2.00 | 2.00 |
| 618 | A138 60p multicolored | 3.00 | 3.00 |
| 619 | A138 1ce multicolored | 4.00 | 4.00 |
| | Nos. 616-619 (4) | 9.75 | 9.75 |

### Souvenir Sheet
#### Perf. 13

| 620 | Sheet of 4 | 14.00 | 14.00 |
|---|---|---|---|
| a. | A138 15p multicolored | 1.50 | 1.25 |
| b. | A138 40p multicolored | 2.75 | 2.25 |
| c. | A138 65p multicolored | 4.00 | 3.50 |
| d. | A138 80p multicolored | 4.50 | 4.00 |

Visit of Prince Charles, Mar. 17-25. Overprint applied to individual stamps of No. 620.

Olive Colobus — A140

Wildlife Fund Emblem and: 15p, like 8p. 20p, 40p, Ebien palm squirrel. 30p, 65p, African wild dog. 60p, 80p, West African manatee.

**1977, June 22    Litho.    Perf. 13½x14**

| 621 | A140 8p multicolored | 4.00 | 1.50 |
|---|---|---|---|
| 622 | A140 20p multicolored | 9.00 | 2.00 |
| 623 | A140 30p multicolored | 12.00 | 5.00 |
| 624 | A140 60p multicolored | 16.00 | 7.00 |
| | Nos. 621-624 (4) | 41.00 | 15.50 |

### Souvenir Sheet

| 625 | Sheet of 4 | 22.50 | 22.50 |
|---|---|---|---|
| a. | A140 15p multicolored | 3.00 | |
| b. | A140 40p multicolored | 5.00 | |
| c. | A140 65p multicolored | 6.00 | |
| d. | A140 80p multicolored | 7.00 | |

Wildlife protection.

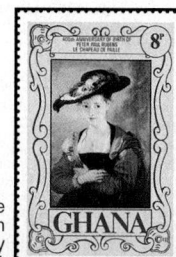

Suzanne Fourment in Velvet Hat, by Rubens — A141

Paintings: 15p, like 8p. 30p, 40p, Isabella of Portugal, by Titian. 60p, 65p, Duke and Duchess of Cumberland, by Gainsborough. 80p, 1ce, Rubens and his wife Isabella, by Rubens.

**1977, Sept.    Litho.    Perf. 14x13½**

| 626 | A141 8p lt blue & multi | .20 | .20 |
|---|---|---|---|
| 627 | A141 30p lt blue & multi | .65 | .65 |
| 628 | A141 60p lt blue & multi | 1.40 | 1.40 |
| 629 | A141 1ce lt blue & multi | 2.50 | 2.50 |
| | Nos. 626-629 (4) | 4.75 | 4.75 |

### Souvenir Sheet

| 630 | Sheet of 4 | 4.25 | 4.25 |
|---|---|---|---|
| a. | A141 15p light blue & multi | .25 | .25 |
| b. | A141 40p light blue & multi | .75 | .75 |
| c. | A141 65p light blue & multi | 1.25 | 1.25 |
| d. | A141 80p light blue & multi | 1.50 | 1.50 |

Painters, birth annivs.: Peter Paul Rubens (1577-1640); Titian (1477-1576); Thomas Gainsborough (1727-1788).

Adoration of the Kings — A142

Guild of the Good Shepherd, Abossey Okai — A143

Designs: 6p, 40p, Methodist Church, Wesley, Accra. 8p, Virgin and Child, and Star. 15p, like 2p. 30p, 65p, Holy Spirit Cathedral, Accra. 80p, 1ce, Ebenezer Presbyterian Church, Osu, Accra. Type A143 designs include score of "Hark the Herald Angels Sing."

**Perf. 14x14½, 14**

| 1977, Dec. 30 | | Litho. | |
|---|---|---|---|
| 631 | A142 1p multicolored | .20 | .20 |
| 632 | A143 2p multicolored | .20 | .20 |
| 633 | A143 6p multicolored | .20 | .20 |
| 634 | A142 8p multicolored | .20 | .20 |
| 635 | A143 30p multicolored | .60 | .60 |
| 636 | A143 1ce multicolored | 2.00 | 2.00 |
| | Nos. 631-636 (6) | 3.40 | 3.40 |

### Souvenir Sheet
#### Imperf

| 637 | Sheet of 4 | 4.75 | 4.75 |
|---|---|---|---|
| a. | A143 15p multicolored | .25 | .25 |
| b. | A143 40p multicolored | .75 | .75 |
| c. | A143 65p multicolored | 1.25 | 1.25 |
| d. | A143 80p multicolored | 1.50 | 1.50 |

Christmas. No. 637 has simulated perfs.

No. 631-637 Overprinted: "REFERENDUM 1978 VOTE EARLY"

**Perf. 14x14½, 14**

| 1978, Mar. 28 | | Litho. | |
|---|---|---|---|
| 638 | A142 1p multicolored | .20 | .20 |
| 639 | A143 2p multicolored | .20 | .20 |
| 640 | A143 6p multicolored | .20 | .20 |
| 641 | A142 8p multicolored | .20 | .20 |
| 642 | A143 30p multicolored | .70 | .70 |
| 643 | A143 1ce multicolored | 2.50 | 2.50 |
| | Nos. 638-643 (6) | 4.00 | 4.00 |

### Souvenir Sheet
#### Imperf

| 644 | Sheet of 4 | 40.00 | |
|---|---|---|---|
| a. | A143 15p multicolored | 3.00 | |
| b. | A143 40p multicolored | 7.50 | |
| c. | A143 65p multicolored | 13.00 | |
| d. | A143 80p multicolored | 15.00 | |

Banana Harvest — A144

Designs: 8p, Vegetable garden. 30p, Produce market. 60p, Fishing. 1ce, Tractor.

**1978, May 15    Perf. 14**

| 645 | A144 2p multicolored | .20 | .20 |
|---|---|---|---|
| 646 | A144 8p multicolored | .20 | .20 |
| 647 | A144 30p multicolored | .50 | .50 |
| 648 | A144 60p multicolored | 1.10 | 1.10 |
| 649 | A144 1ce multicolored | 1.90 | 1.90 |
| | Nos. 645-649 (5) | 3.90 | 3.90 |

Operation feed yourself.

Wright Biplane and Crowd — A145

Planes and Crowd: 15p, like 8p. 30p, 40p, Heracles, 1st practical airliner. 60p, 65p, D. H. Comet, 1st jet airliner. 80p, 1ce, Concorde, 1st supersonic airliner.

**1978, June 6    Litho.    Perf. 14x13½**

| 650 | A145 8p multicolored | .20 | .20 |
|---|---|---|---|
| 651 | A145 30p multicolored | .55 | .50 |
| 652 | A145 60p multicolored | 1.10 | 1.00 |
| 653 | A145 1ce multicolored | 1.75 | 1.00 |
| | Nos. 650-653 (4) | 3.60 | 2.70 |

### Souvenir Sheet

| 654 | Sheet of 4 | 3.25 | 3.25 |
|---|---|---|---|
| a. | A145 15p multicolored | .20 | .20 |
| b. | A145 40p multicolored | .60 | .60 |
| c. | A145 65p multicolored | 1.00 | 1.00 |
| d. | A145 80p multicolored | 1.10 | 1.10 |

75th anniversary of first powered flight. The cheering crowd forms a continuing design on Nos. 650-654.

Nos. 650-653, 654a-654d Overprinted: "CAPEX 78 / JUNE 9-18 1978"

**1978, June 9**

| 655 | A145 8p multicolored | .20 | .20 |
|---|---|---|---|
| 656 | A145 30p multicolored | .30 | .25 |
| 657 | A145 60p multicolored | .55 | .50 |
| 658 | A145 1ce multicolored | 1.40 | .80 |
| | Nos. 655-658 (4) | 2.45 | 1.75 |

### Souvenir Sheet

| 659 | Sheet of 4 | 2.25 | 2.25 |
|---|---|---|---|
| a. | A145 15p multicolored | .20 | .20 |
| b. | A145 40p multicolored | .40 | .40 |
| c. | A145 65p multicolored | .65 | .65 |
| d. | A145 80p multicolored | .80 | .80 |

CAPEX, Canadian International Philatelic Exhibition, Toronto, Ont., June 9-18.

Soccer, Africa Cup Emblem and Ghana Flag — A146

15p, like 8p. 30p, 40p, Three soccer players, Africa Cup emblem, Ghana flag. 60p, 65p, Two soccer players. Argentine '78 emblem, Argentine flag. 80p, 1ce, Goalkeeper, Argentina '78 emblem and Argentine flag.

**1978, July 1    Litho.    Perf. 13½x14**

| 660 | A146 8p multicolored | .20 | .20 |
|---|---|---|---|
| 661 | A146 30p multicolored | .35 | .35 |
| 662 | A146 60p multicolored | .85 | .85 |
| 663 | A146 1ce multicolored | 1.60 | 1.60 |
| | Nos. 660-663 (4) | 3.00 | 3.00 |

### Souvenir Sheet

| 664 | Sheet of 4 | 2.10 | 2.10 |
|---|---|---|---|
| a. | A146 15p multicolored | .20 | .20 |
| b. | A146 40p multicolored | .40 | .40 |
| c. | A146 65p multicolored | .65 | .65 |
| d. | A146 80p multicolored | .80 | .80 |

11th African Cup of Nations, Ghana, Mar. 5-19, and 11th World Cup Soccer Championship, Argentina, June 1-25.

Nos. 660-661, 664a-664b Overprinted: "GHANA WINNERS"
Nos. 662-663, 664c-664d Overprinted: "ARGENTINA WINS"

**1978, Aug. 21    Litho.    Perf. 13½x14**

| 665 | A146 8p multicolored | .20 | .20 |
|---|---|---|---|
| 666 | A146 30p multicolored | .45 | .45 |
| 667 | A146 60p multicolored | .90 | .90 |
| 668 | A146 1ce multicolored | 1.60 | 1.60 |
| | Nos. 665-668 (4) | 3.15 | 3.15 |

### Souvenir Sheet

| 669 | Sheet of 4 | 1.75 | 1.75 |
|---|---|---|---|
| a. | A146 15p multicolored | .20 | .20 |
| b. | A146 40p multicolored | .30 | .30 |
| c. | A146 65p multicolored | .45 | .45 |
| d. | A146 80p multicolored | .65 | .65 |

Winners, 11th African Cup and 11th World Cup Soccer Championships.
Overprint on 60p and 65p is in two lines.

The Betrayal, by Dürer — A147

Etchings by Albrecht Dürer: 39p, The Crucifixion. 60p, The Deposition. 1ce, The Resurrection.

**1978, Sept. 1    Litho.    Perf. 14x13½**

| 670 | A147 11p lilac & black | .20 | .20 |
|---|---|---|---|
| 671 | A147 39p salmon & black | .35 | .35 |
| 672 | A147 60p orange & black | .55 | .55 |
| 673 | A147 1ce yel green & black | .85 | .85 |
| | Nos. 670-673 (4) | 1.95 | 1.95 |

Easter.

Bauhinia Purpurea A148

Flowers: 39p, Cassia fistula. 60p, Frangipani. 1ce, Jacaranda mimosifolia.

**1978, Nov. 20    Litho.    Perf. 14x13½**

| 674 | A148 11p multicolored | .20 | .20 |
|---|---|---|---|
| 675 | A148 39p multicolored | .25 | .25 |
| 676 | A148 60p multicolored | .55 | .55 |
| 677 | A148 1ce multicolored | .80 | .80 |
| | Nos. 674-677 (4) | 1.80 | 1.80 |

Mail Railroad Car — A149

Ghana railroad, 75th Anniv.: 39p, Pay and bank car. 60p, Locomotive, 1922. 1ce, Diesel locomotive, 1960.

**1978, Dec. 4    Litho.    Perf. 13½**

| 678 | A149 11p multicolored | .20 | .20 |
|---|---|---|---|
| 679 | A149 39p multicolored | .25 | .25 |
| 680 | A149 60p multicolored | .50 | .50 |
| 681 | A149 1ce multicolored | .75 | .75 |
| | Nos. 678-681 (4) | 1.70 | 1.70 |

Orbiter Spacecraft — A150

15p, like 11p. 39p, 40p, Multiprobe spacecraft. 60p, 65p, Orbiter and Multiprobe circling
Venus. 2ce, 3ce, Radar chart of Venus.

**1979, July 5    Litho.        Perf. 14x13½**
| | | | |
|---|---|---|---|
| 682 | A150 | 11p multicolored | .20 | .20 |
| 683 | A150 | 39p multicolored | .25 | .25 |
| 684 | A150 | 60p multicolored | .45 | .45 |
| 685 | A150 | 3ce multicolored | .70 | .70 |
| | | Nos. 682-685 (4) | 1.60 | 1.60 |

**Souvenir Sheet**
*Imperf*
| | | | |
|---|---|---|---|
| 686 | | Sheet of 4 | 2.25 | 2.25 |
| a. | A150 | 15p multicolored | .20 | .20 |
| b. | A150 | 40p multicolored | .25 | .25 |
| c. | A150 | 65p multicolored | .45 | .45 |
| d. | A150 | 2ce multicolored | 1.10 | 1.10 |

Pioneer Venus Space Project.

O Come
All Ye
Faithful
A152

Christmas Carols: 10p, O Little Town of
Bethlehem. 15p, 65p, We Three Kings of Ori-
ent Are. 20p, I Saw Three Ships Come Sailing
By. 25p, like 8p. No. 696, 1ce, Away in a Man-
ger. 4ce, No. 698d, Ding Dong Merrily on
High.

**1979, Dec. 20                Perf. 14½**
| | | | |
|---|---|---|---|
| 692 | A152 | 8p multicolored | .20 | .20 |
| 693 | A152 | 10p multicolored | .20 | .20 |
| 694 | A152 | 15p multicolored | .20 | .20 |
| 695 | A152 | 20p multicolored | .20 | .20 |
| 696 | A152 | 2ce multicolored | .35 | .35 |
| 697 | A152 | 4ce multicolored | .50 | .50 |
| | | Nos. 692-697 (6) | 1.65 | 1.65 |

**Souvenir Sheet**
| | | | |
|---|---|---|---|
| 698 | | Sheet of 4 | 1.25 | 1.25 |
| a. | A152 | 25p multicolored | .20 | .20 |
| b. | A152 | 65p multicolored | .20 | .20 |
| c. | A152 | 1ce multicolored | .30 | .30 |
| d. | A152 | 2ce multicolored | .60 | .60 |

Christmas.

J.B. Danquah
(1895-1965)
A153

National Leaders: 65p, John Mensah
Sarbah (1864-1910). 80p, J.E.K. Aggrey
(1875-1925). 2ce, Kwame Nkrumah (1909-
1972). 4ce, G.E. Grant (1878-1956).

**1980, Jan. 21    Litho.       Perf. 13½x14**
| | | | |
|---|---|---|---|
| 699 | A153 | 20p multicolored | .20 | .20 |
| 700 | A153 | 65p multicolored | .20 | .20 |
| 701 | A153 | 80p multicolored | .20 | .20 |
| 702 | A153 | 2ce multicolored | .50 | .50 |
| 703 | A153 | 4ce multicolored | .90 | .90 |
| | | Nos. 699-703 (5) | 2.00 | 2.00 |

Man with
Clack
Bells, Hill
A154

Hill and: 25p, Man with clack bells. 50p, 65p,
Chief, elephant staff. 1ce, 2ce, Drummer. 4ce,
5ce, Chief, ivory staff.

**1980, Mar. 12    Litho.      Perf. 14½**
| | | | |
|---|---|---|---|
| 704 | A154 | 20p multicolored | .20 | .20 |
| 705 | A154 | 65p multicolored | .20 | .20 |
| 706 | A154 | 2ce multicolored | .55 | .55 |
| 707 | A154 | 4ce multicolored | 1.00 | 1.00 |
| | | Nos. 704-707 (4) | 1.95 | 1.95 |

**Souvenir Sheet**
| | | | |
|---|---|---|---|
| 708 | | Sheet of 4 | 2.00 | 2.00 |
| a. | A154 | 25p multicolored | .20 | .20 |
| b. | A154 | 50p multicolored | .20 | .20 |
| c. | A154 | 1ce multicolored | .40 | .40 |
| d. | A154 | 5ce multicolored | 1.00 | 1.00 |

Sir Rowland Hill (1795-1879), originator of
penny postage.
Nos. 708a-708d also exist perf 13½, issued
in small individual sheetlets. Values slightly
more than perf 14½.
For overprints see Nos. 714-718.

Students, IYC
Emblem — A155

IYC Emblem and: 25p like 20p. 50p, 65p,
Boys playing soccer. 1ce, 2ce, Boys in canoe.
3ce, 4ce, Mother and child.

**1980, Apr. 2    Litho.        Perf. 15**
| | | | |
|---|---|---|---|
| 709 | A155 | 20p multicolored | .20 | .20 |
| 710 | A155 | 65p multicolored | .20 | .20 |
| 711 | A155 | 2ce multicolored | .60 | .60 |
| 712 | A155 | 4ce multicolored | 1.25 | 1.25 |
| | | Nos. 709-712 (4) | 2.25 | 2.25 |

**Souvenir Sheet**
| | | | |
|---|---|---|---|
| 713 | | Sheet of 4 | 2.75 | 2.75 |
| a. | A155 | 25p multicolored | .20 | .20 |
| b. | A155 | 50p multicolored | .30 | .30 |
| c. | A155 | 1ce multicolored | .40 | .40 |
| d. | A155 | 3ce multicolored | 1.10 | 1.10 |

Intl. Year of the Child (in 1979).
For overprints see Nos. 719-723.

Nos. 704-708 Overprinted: "LONDON
1980" / 6th-14th May 1980

**1980, May 6    Litho.        Perf. 14½**
| | | | |
|---|---|---|---|
| 714 | A154 | 20p multicolored | .20 | .20 |
| 715 | A154 | 65p multicolored | .35 | .35 |
| 716 | A154 | 2ce multicolored | .85 | .85 |
| 717 | A154 | 4ce multicolored | 1.40 | 1.40 |
| | | Nos. 714-717 (4) | 2.80 | 2.80 |

**Souvenir Sheet**
| | | | |
|---|---|---|---|
| 718 | | Sheet of 4 | 3.50 | 3.50 |
| a. | A154 | 25p multicolored | .20 | .20 |
| b. | A154 | 50p multicolored | .30 | .30 |
| c. | A154 | 1ce multicolored | .55 | .55 |
| d. | A154 | 5ce multicolored | 2.25 | 2.25 |

London 1980 Intl. Stamp Exhib., May 6-14.
#718a-718d also exist perf 13½, issued in
small individual sheetlets. Value, unused or
used, $15.

Nos. 709-713 Overprinted: "PAPAL
VISIT" / 8th-9th May / 1980

**1980, May 8                    Perf. 15**
| | | | |
|---|---|---|---|
| 719 | A155 | 20p multicolored | .75 | .20 |
| 720 | A155 | 65p multicolored | 1.40 | .70 |
| 721 | A155 | 2ce multicolored | 2.25 | 1.40 |
| 722 | A155 | 4ce multicolored | 3.50 | 2.25 |
| | | Nos. 719-722 (4) | 7.90 | 4.55 |

**Souvenir Sheet**
| | | | |
|---|---|---|---|
| 723 | | Sheet of 4 | 14.00 | 14.00 |
| a. | A155 | 25p multicolored | 1.00 | 1.00 |
| b. | A155 | 50p multicolored | 2.00 | 2.00 |
| c. | A155 | 1ce multicolored | 3.00 | 3.00 |
| d. | A155 | 3ce multicolored | 7.25 | 7.25 |

Visit of Pope John Paul II to Ghana, 5/8-9.

Parliament
House
A156

**1980, Aug. 4    Litho.        Perf. 14**
| | | | |
|---|---|---|---|
| 724 | A156 | 20p shown | .20 | .20 |
| 725 | A156 | 65p Supreme Court | .20 | .20 |
| 726 | A156 | 2ce The Castle | .40 | .40 |
| | | Nos. 724-726 (3) | .80 | .80 |

**Souvenir Sheet**
| | | | |
|---|---|---|---|
| 727 | | Sheet of 3 | .75 | .75 |
| a. | A156 | 25p like #724 | .20 | .20 |
| b. | A156 | 1ce like #725 | .25 | .25 |
| c. | A156 | 3ce like #726 | .30 | .30 |

Third Republic.

Map of West
African
Member
Countries,
Flag of
Ghana,
Jet — A157

**1980, Nov. 5    Litho.        Perf. 14½**
| | | | |
|---|---|---|---|
| 728 | A157 | 20p shown | .20 | .20 |
| 729 | A157 | 65p Dish antenna | .20 | .20 |
| 730 | A157 | 80p Cogwheels | .20 | .20 |
| 731 | A157 | 2ce Corn | .25 | .25 |
| | | Nos. 728-731 (4) | .85 | .85 |

5th Anniversary of ECOWAS (Economic
Community of West African States).

A158

A159

**1980, Nov. 26**
| | | | |
|---|---|---|---|
| 732 | A158 | 20p "OAU" | .20 | .20 |
| 733 | A158 | 65p OAU Banner, Maps | .20 | .20 |
| 734 | A158 | 80p Waves on map of Africa | .20 | .20 |
| 735 | A158 | 2ce Flag, banner, map | .25 | .25 |
| | | Nos. 732-735 (4) | .85 | .85 |

Org. for African Unity summit conference,
Lagos, Nigeria, Apr. 28-29.

**1980, Dec. 10                 Perf. 14**

Christmas (Fra Angelico Paintings): 15p,
25p, Adoration of the Magi. 20p, 50p, Virgin
and Child Enthroned with Four Angels. 1ce,
2ce, Virgin and Child Enthroned with Eight
Angels. 3ce, 4ce, Annunciation.
| | | | |
|---|---|---|---|
| 736 | A159 | 15p multicolored | .20 | .20 |
| 737 | A159 | 20p multicolored | .20 | .20 |
| 738 | A159 | 2ce multicolored | .40 | .40 |
| 739 | A159 | 4ce multicolored | .90 | .90 |
| | | Nos. 736-739 (4) | 1.70 | 1.70 |

**Souvenir Sheet**
| | | | |
|---|---|---|---|
| 740 | | Sheet of 4 | 1.10 | 1.10 |
| a. | A159 | 25p multicolored | .20 | .20 |
| b. | A159 | 50p multicolored | .20 | .20 |
| c. | A159 | 1ce multicolored | .25 | .25 |
| d. | A159 | 3ce multicolored | .40 | .40 |

Nurse
Weighing
Newborn,
Rotary
Emblem
A160

**1980, Dec. 18**
| | | | |
|---|---|---|---|
| 741 | A160 | 20p shown | .20 | .20 |
| 742 | A160 | 65p Map of Ghana and world | .20 | .20 |
| 743 | A160 | 2ce Helping hands, world map | .55 | .55 |
| 744 | A160 | 4ce Food distribution | 1.10 | 1.10 |
| | | Nos. 741-744 (4) | 2.05 | 2.05 |

**Souvenir Sheet**
| | | | |
|---|---|---|---|
| 745 | | Sheet of 4 | 2.25 | 2.25 |
| a. | A160 | 25p like #741 | .25 | .20 |
| b. | A160 | 50p like #742 | .25 | .20 |
| c. | A160 | 1ce like #743 | .30 | .30 |
| d. | A160 | 3ce like #744 | 1.00 | 1.00 |

Rotary International, 75th anniv.

Narina
Trogon — A161

**1981, Jan. 12    Litho.       Perf. 14**
| | | | |
|---|---|---|---|
| 746 | A161 | 20p shown | 1.40 | .20 |
| 747 | A161 | 65p White-crowned robin-chat | 2.25 | .50 |
| 748 | A161 | 2ce Swallow-tailed bee-eater | 2.75 | 1.50 |
| 749 | A161 | 4ce Long-tailed para-keet | 4.50 | 2.75 |
| | | Nos. 746-749 (4) | 10.90 | 4.95 |

**Souvenir Sheet**
| | | | |
|---|---|---|---|
| 750 | | Sheet of 4 | 7.50 | 7.50 |
| a. | A161 | 25p like #746 | .30 | .30 |
| b. | A161 | 50p like #747 | .75 | .30 |
| c. | A161 | 1ce like #748 | 1.25 | .55 |
| d. | A161 | 3ce like #749 | 3.50 | 1.60 |

Pope John Paul II, Pres. Limann,
Archbishop of Canterbury — A162

**1981, Mar. 3    Litho.        Perf. 14**
| | | | |
|---|---|---|---|
| 751 | A162 | 20p multicolored | .20 | .20 |
| 752 | A162 | 65p multicolored | .55 | .55 |
| 753 | A162 | 80p multicolored | .70 | .70 |
| 754 | A162 | 2ce multicolored | 2.00 | 2.00 |
| | | Nos. 751-754 (4) | 3.45 | 3.45 |

Visit of Pope John Paul II, May 8-10, 1980.

Earth Satellite
Station — A163

**1981, Sept. 28    Litho.      Perf. 14**
| | | | |
|---|---|---|---|
| 755 | A163 | 20p shown | .20 | .20 |
| 756 | A163 | 65p Satellites orbiting earth | .20 | .20 |
| 757 | A163 | 80p Satellite | .20 | .20 |
| 758 | A163 | 4ce Satellite, earth | 1.40 | 1.40 |
| | | Nos. 755-758 (4) | 2.00 | 2.00 |

**Souvenir Sheet**
| | | | |
|---|---|---|---|
| 758A | | Sheet of 4 | 1.75 | 1.75 |
| b. | A163 | 25p like #755 | .20 | .20 |
| c. | A163 | 50p like #756 | .20 | .20 |
| d. | A163 | 1ce like #757 | .20 | .20 |
| e. | A163 | 3ce like #758 | .75 | .75 |

Earth Satellite Station commission.

Common Design Types
pictured following the introduction.

**Royal Wedding Issue**
Common Design Type
**1981                Litho.       Perf. 14**
| | | | |
|---|---|---|---|
| 759 | CD331a | 20p Couple | .20 | .20 |
| 759A | CD331a | 65p like 20p | .20 | .20 |
| 760 | CD331a | 80p Charles | .20 | .20 |
| 760A | CD331a | 1ce like 80p | .20 | .20 |
| 760B | CD331a | 3ce like 4ce | .50 | .50 |
| 761 | CD331a | 4ce Royal yacht Britannia | .60 | .60 |
| | | Nos. 759-761 (6) | 1.90 | 1.90 |

## Souvenir Sheet

**762**  CD331  7ce St. Paul's Cathedral                    1.00  1.00

Nos. 759-761 each printed se-tenant with
label showing heraldic design.
Issued: 20p, 80p, 4ce, 7ce, 7/8; 65p, 1ce,
3ce, 9/16.
For surcharges see Nos. 859, 866, 871,
880, 1168-1169, 1195-1197.

**1981, Sept. 16   Litho.   Perf. 14**
**763**  CD331  2ce like 4ce       .50   .50
**764**  CD331  5ce like 20p      1.25  1.25
*a.*  Bklt. pane, 2 each #763-764   3.50  3.50

Nos. 763-764 issued only in booklets.

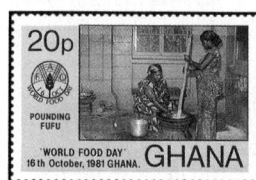

World
Food
Day
A164

**1981, Oct. 16   Litho.   Perf. 14**
**765**  A164  20p Women pounding
fufu                      .20   .20
**766**  A164  65p Plucking cocoa    .30   .30
**767**  A164  80p Preparing banku   .45   .45
**768**  A164  2ce Processing garri  .90   .90
*Nos. 765-768 (4)*        1.85  1.85

## Souvenir Sheet

**769**           Sheet of 4        1.75  1.75
*a.*  A164 25p like #765     .20   .20
*b.*  A164 50p like #766     .20   .20
*c.*  A164 1ce like #767     .35   .35
*d.*  A164 3ce like #768    1.00  1.00

Angelic Musicians
Play for Mary and
Child, by Aachener
Altares (1480-
1520)
A165

Christmas (Paintings): 15p, The Betrothal of
St. Catherine of Alexandria, by Lucas Cranach
(1472-1553). 65p, Child Jesus Embracing His
Mother, by Gabriel Metsu (1629-1667). 80p,
Virgin and Child, by Fra Filippo Lippi (1406-
1469). $2, The Virgin with Infant Jesus, by
Barnaba da Modena (1361-1383). $4, The
Immaculate Conception, by Bartolome Murillo
(1618-1682). $6, Virgin and Child, by Hans
Memling (1430-1494).

**1981, Nov. 26              Perf. 14**
**770**  A165  15p multicolored    .20   .20
**771**  A165  20p multicolored    .20   .20
**772**  A165  65p multicolored    .20   .20
**773**  A165  80p multicolored    .20   .20
**774**  A165  $2 multicolored     .65   .65
**775**  A165  $4 multicolored     .95   .95
*Nos. 770-775 (6)*        2.40  2.40

## Souvenir Sheet

**776**  A165  $6 multicolored    1.75  1.75

Intl. Year
of the
Disabled
A166

**1982, Feb. 8   Litho.   Perf. 14**
**777**  A166  20p Blind man       .20   .20
**778**  A166  65p Woman, crutch   .35   .35
**779**  A166  80p Girl reading Braille  .45   .45
**780**  A166  4ce Couple         1.80  1.80
*Nos. 777-780 (4)*        2.80  2.80

## Souvenir Sheet

**781**  A166  6ce Group          2.50  2.50

Clawless
Otter — A167

**1982, Feb. 22**
**782**  A167  20p shown          .20   .20
**783**  A167  65p Bushbuck       .55   .55
**784**  A167  80p Aardvark       .65   .65
**785**  A167  1ce Scarlet bell tree  .95   .95
**786**  A167  2ce Glory lilies   1.75  1.75
**787**  A167  4ce Blue peas      3.50  3.50
*Nos. 782-787 (6)*        7.60  7.60

## Souvenir Sheet

**788**  A167  5ce Chimpanzees    3.50  3.50

Blue-spot
Commodore
A168

**1982, Apr. 27   Litho.   Perf. 14**
**789**  A168  20p shown          .90   .90
**790**  A168  65p Emperor swallowtail                  1.50  1.50
**791**  A168  2ce Orange admiral 2.75  2.75
**792**  A168  4ce Giant charaxes 4.50  4.50
*Nos. 789-792 (4)*        9.65  9.65

## Souvenir Sheet

**Perf. 14½**
**793**           Sheet of 4       10.00 10.00
*a.*  A168 25p like #789    .75   .75
*b.*  A168 50p like #790   1.25  1.25
*c.*  A168 1ce like #791   2.00  2.00
*d.*  A168 3ce like #792   5.00  5.00

Scouting
Year
A169

**1982, June 1   Litho.   Perf. 15**
**794**  A169  20p Tree planting   .20   .20
**795**  A169  65p Camping         .85   .85
**796**  A169  80p Sailing        1.10  1.10
**797**  A169  3ce Watching elephant 2.75  2.75
*Nos. 794-797 (4)*        4.90  4.90

## Souvenir Sheet

**798**  A169  5ce Baden-Powell,
vert.                    5.00  5.00

For surcharges see Nos. 867, 870, 875, 877.

Kpong Hydroelectric Dam
Opening — A170

**1982, June 28   Litho.   Perf. 14**
**799**  A170  20p Cranes, lifts   .55   .20
**800**  A170  65p Construction   1.10   .55
**801**  A170  80p Turbines       1.50  1.50
**802**  A170  2ce Aerial view    3.25  3.25
*Nos. 799-802 (4)*        6.40  5.50

1982
World
Cup
A171

**Perf. 15, 14½x15 (30p, No. 807, 1ce,
3ce)**
**1982, July 19              Litho.**
**803**  A171  20p multi          .20   .20
**804**  A171  30p multi, like 20p  .30   .30
**805**  A171  65p multi          .90   .90
**806**  A171  80p multi, like 65p  1.10  1.10
**807**  A171  80p multi, diff.   .65   .65
**808**  A171  1ce multi, like #807  .80   .80
**809**  A171  3ce multi         1.90  1.90
**810**  A171  4ce multi, like 3ce  2.75  2.75
*Nos. 803-810 (8)*        8.60  8.60

## Souvenir Sheet

**811**  A171  6ce multi          2.25  2.25

Nos. 804, 806, 808-809 in sheets of 5 plus
label.
For overprints & surcharges see #826-834,
861-862, 864-865, 868-869, 872-873, 878-
879, 912-917.

TB
Bacillus
Centenary
A172

**1982, Aug. 9              Perf. 14**
**812**  A172  20p Child immunization  .55   .55
**813**  A172  65p Koch, Berlin   1.50  1.50
**814**  A172  80p Koch, Africa   1.90  1.90
**815**  A172  1ce Looking through
microscope               2.25  2.25
**816**  A172  2ce Koch, 1905 Nobel
medal                    3.75  3.75
*Nos. 812-816 (5)*        9.95  9.95

Christmas — A173

**1982, Dec.   Litho.   Perf. 15**
**817**  A173  15p Nativity       .20   .20
**818**  A173  20p Holy Family    .20   .20
**819**  A173  65p Three Kings    .35   .35
**820**  A173  4ce Angel with banner  1.25  1.25
*Nos. 817-820 (4)*        2.00  2.00

## Souvenir Sheet

**821**  A173  6ce Nativity, diff.  2.25  2.25

A173a

**1983, Mar. 10   Litho.   Perf. 15**
**822**  A173a  20p Flags         .30   .30
**823**  A173a  55p Aerial view   .55   .55
**824**  A173a  80p Minerals     1.25  1.25
**825**  A173a  3ce Eagle        1.90  1.90
*Nos. 822-825 (4)*        4.00  4.00

Commonwealth Day. For surcharges see
Nos. 860, 863, 874, 876.

### Nos. 803-811 Overprinted in Gold:
"WINNER ITALY / 3-1"

**1983, June                 Litho.**
**826**  A171  20p multicolored    .20   .20
**827**  A171  30p multicolored    .20   .20
**828**  A171  65p multicolored    .40   .40
**829**  A171  80p multi, on #806  .40   .40
**830**  A171  80p multi, on #807 1.25  1.25
**831**  A171  1ce multicolored   1.40  1.40
**832**  A171  3ce multicolored   3.00  3.00
**833**  A171  4ce multicolored   2.75  2.75
*Nos. 826-833 (8)*        9.60  9.60

## Souvenir Sheet

**834**  A171  6ce multicolored   4.00  4.00

Italy's victory in 1982 World Cup.
For surcharges see Nos. 862, 865, 869,
873, 879, 913, 915, 917.

World
Communications
Year — A173b

**1983, Dec. 13   Litho.   Perf. 14**
**835**  A173b  1ce shown         .20   .20
**836**  A173b  1.40ce Dish antenna                       .20   .20
**837**  A173b  2.30ce Cable ship  .40   .40
**838**  A173b  3ce Switchboard   .55   .55
**839**  A173b  5ce Control tow-
er                       .85   .85
*Nos. 835-839 (5)*        2.20  2.20

## Souvenir Sheet

**840**  A173b  6ce Satellite     .90   .90

For surcharges see Nos. 1107-1111.

Coastal
Marine
Mammals
A173c

**1983, Nov. 15   Litho.   Perf. 15**
**841**  A173c  1ce Short fin pilot whale                1.50  1.50
**842**  A173c  1.40ce Gray
dolphin                  1.60  1.60
**843**  A173c  2.30ce False killer
whale                    2.00  2.00
**844**  A173c  3ce Spinner
dolphin                  2.50  2.50
**845**  A173c  5ce Atlantic
humpback
dolphin                  3.00  3.00
*Nos. 841-845 (5)*        10.60 10.60

## Souvenir Sheet

**846**  A173c  6ce White Alan-
tic humpback
dolphin                  3.00  3.00

For surcharges see Nos. 918-920.

A174

Christmas
A175

**1983, Dec. 28   Perf. 14x13½, 14½x14**
**852**  A174  70p Children receiving gifts                .20   .20
**853**  A175  1ce Nativity       .20   .20
**854**  A175  1.40ce Children playing  .45   .45
**855**  A175  2.30ce Family praying  .55   .55
**856**  A174  3ce Bongo drums,
festivities              .65   .65
*Nos. 852-856 (5)*        2.05  2.05

## Souvenir Sheet

**857**  A175  6ce like #855      .55   .55

### Surcharges
Many inverts, doubles, etc., exist on
the surcharged stamps that follow.

### Previous Issues Surcharged
**1984, Feb. 8**
**858**  A74  1ce on 20np
#296                 .20   .20
**859**  CD331  1ce on 20p #759  3.00  3.75
**860**  A173a  1ce on 20p #822   .20   .20
**861**  A171  1ce on 20p #803    .35   .35

| | | | | |
|---|---|---|---|---|
| 862 | A171 | 1ce on 20p #826 | .20 | .20 |
| 863 | A173a | 9ce on 55p #823 | .50 | .55 |
| 864 | A171 | 9ce on 65p #805 | .90 | .90 |
| 865 | A171 | 9ce on 65p #828 | .50 | .55 |
| 866 | CD331 | 9ce on 80p #760 | 3.75 | 5.00 |
| 867 | A169 | 10ce on 20p #794 | .50 | .55 |
| 868 | A171 | 10ce on 80p #806 | .90 | .90 |
| 869 | A171 | 10ce on 80p #830 | .50 | .55 |
| 870 | A169 | 19ce on 65p #795 | 1.00 | 1.10 |
| 871 | CD331 | 20ce on 4ce #761 | 4.50 | 7.50 |
| 872 | A171 | 20ce on 4ce #810 | 2.00 | 2.00 |
| 873 | A171 | 20ce on 4ce #833 | 1.00 | 1.10 |
| 874 | A173a | 30ce on 80p #824 | 2.00 | 2.00 |
| 875 | A169 | 30ce on 3ce #797 | 2.00 | 2.00 |
| 876 | A173a | 50ce on 3ce #825 | 3.50 | 3.50 |
| | | Nos. 858-876 (19) | 27.50 | 32.90 |

**Souvenir Sheets**

| | | | | |
|---|---|---|---|---|
| 877 | A169 | 60ce on 5ce #798 | 1.25 | 4.00 |
| 878 | A171 | 60ce on 6ce #811 | 1.25 | 2.75 |
| 879 | A171 | 60ce on 6ce #834 | 1.25 | 4.00 |
| 880 | CD331 | 60ce on 7ce #762 | 1.25 | 2.00 |

For surcharges on this issue see #1092A-1092C.

Namibia Day
A176

Scorpion Weight
A177

**1984, Jan. 26**     *Perf. 14*

| | | | | |
|---|---|---|---|---|
| 881 | A176 | 50p Soldiers raising rifles | .20 | .20 |
| 882 | A176 | 1ce Soldiers, tank | .20 | .20 |
| 883 | A176 | 1.40ce Machete cutting chains | .20 | .20 |
| 884 | A176 | 2.30ce Namibian woman | .20 | .20 |
| 885 | A176 | 3ce Soldiers in combat | .20 | .20 |
| | | Nos. 881-885 (5) | 1.00 | 1.00 |

**1983, Dec. 12**    **Litho.**    *Perf. 14*

| | | | | |
|---|---|---|---|---|
| 886 | A177 | 5p Hemichramis fasciatus, horiz. | .20 | .20 |
| 887 | A177 | 10p Hemichramis fasciatus, map, horiz. | .40 | .20 |
| 888 | A177 | 20p Haemanthus rupestris | .50 | .20 |
| 889 | A177 | 50p Mounted warrior (gold statuette) | .50 | .20 |
| 890 | A177 | 1ce shown | .60 | .20 |
| 891 | A177 | 2ce Jet, horiz. | .60 | .30 |
| 892 | A177 | 3ce Cercocebus torquatus | 1.90 | .30 |
| 893 | A177 | 4ce Galagoides demidovii | .50 | .30 |
| 894 | A177 | 5ce Kaempheria nigerica | .60 | .45 |
| 895 | A177 | 10ce Camaroptera brevicaudata | .75 | .90 |
| | | Nos. 886-895 (10) | 6.55 | 3.25 |

For surcharges see Nos. 1089A-1090, 1092, 1092D, 1093A-1094A, 1096-1096A.

Easter — A178

Local Flowers — A179

**1984, Apr.**    **Litho.**    *Perf. 14½*

| | | | | |
|---|---|---|---|---|
| 906 | A178 | 1ce Cross, crown of thorns | .20 | .20 |
| 907 | A178 | 1.40ce Jesus praying | .20 | .20 |
| 908 | A178 | 2.30ce Jesus going to Jerusalem | .20 | .20 |
| 909 | A178 | 3ce Jesus entering Jerusalem | .20 | .20 |
| 910 | A178 | 50ce Jesus with Disciples | 1.25 | 2.50 |
| | | Nos. 906-910 (5) | 2.05 | 3.30 |

**Souvenir Sheet**

| | | | | |
|---|---|---|---|---|
| 911 | A178 | 60ce Cross, crown of thorns | 4.00 | 4.00 |

---

Nos. 804, 806, 809, 827, 829, 832 Surcharged

**1984, Feb. 8**       **Litho.**

| | | | | |
|---|---|---|---|---|
| 912 | A171 | 9ce on 3ce #809 | .85 | .85 |
| 913 | A171 | 9ce on 3ce #832 | .55 | .55 |
| 914 | A171 | 10ce on 30p #804 | .85 | .85 |
| 915 | A171 | 10ce on 30p #827 | .55 | .55 |
| 916 | A171 | 20ce on 80p #806 | 2.00 | 2.00 |
| 917 | A171 | 20ce on 80p #829 | 1.00 | 1.00 |
| | | Nos. 912-917 (6) | 5.80 | 5.80 |

Nos. 844-846 Surcharged and Overprinted in Red with UPU Emblem and: "19th U.P.U. CONGRESS-HAMBURG"

**1984**    **Litho.**    *Perf. 14½*

| | | | | |
|---|---|---|---|---|
| 918 | A173c | 10ce on 3ce multi | .55 | .55 |
| 919 | A173c | 50ce on 5ce multi | 2.75 | 2.75 |

**Souvenir Sheet**

| | | | | |
|---|---|---|---|---|
| 920 | A173c | 60ce on 6ce multi | 3.25 | 3.25 |

**1984, July**    **Litho.**    *Perf. 14*

| | | | | |
|---|---|---|---|---|
| 921 | A179 | 1ce Amorphophallus johnsonii | .20 | .20 |
| 922 | A179 | 1.40ce Pancratium trianthum | .20 | .20 |
| 923 | A179 | 2.30ce Eulophia cucullata | .20 | .20 |
| 924 | A179 | 3ce Amorphophallus abyssinicus | .20 | .20 |
| 925 | A179 | 50ce Chlorophytum togoense | 3.25 | 4.00 |
| | | Nos. 921-925 (5) | 4.05 | 4.80 |

**Souvenir Sheet**

| | | | | |
|---|---|---|---|---|
| 926 | A179 | 60ce like 1ce | 3.25 | 3.25 |

Endangered Species — A180

**1984, Aug.**      *Perf. 14*

| | | | | |
|---|---|---|---|---|
| 927 | A180 | 1ce Bongo | .70 | .70 |
| 928 | A180 | 2.30ce Males locking horns | 1.50 | 1.50 |
| 929 | A180 | 3ce Family | 1.75 | 1.75 |
| 930 | A180 | 20ce Herd | 5.00 | 5.00 |
| | | Nos. 927-930 (4) | 8.95 | 8.95 |

**Souvenir Sheets**

| | | | | |
|---|---|---|---|---|
| 931 | A180 | 70ce Kob | 7.00 | 7.00 |
| 932 | A180 | 70ce Bushbuck | 7.00 | 7.00 |

1984 Summer Olympics — A181 / Native Dancers — A182

**1984, Aug.**      *Perf. 15*

| | | | | |
|---|---|---|---|---|
| 933 | A181 | 1ce Running | .20 | .20 |
| 934 | A181 | 1.40ce Boxing | .20 | .20 |
| 935 | A181 | 2.30ce Field hockey | .20 | .20 |
| 936 | A181 | 3ce Hurdles | .20 | .20 |
| 937 | A181 | 50ce Rhythmic gymnastics | 3.50 | 4.00 |
| | | Nos. 933-937 (5) | 4.30 | 4.80 |

**Souvenir Sheet**

| | | | | |
|---|---|---|---|---|
| 938 | A181 | 70ce Soccer | 2.75 | 2.75 |

For surcharges see #945-950, 1112-1116.

**1984, Sept.**      *Perf. 14*

| | | | | |
|---|---|---|---|---|
| 939 | A182 | 1ce Dipo | .20 | .20 |
| 940 | A182 | 1.40ce Adowa | .20 | .20 |
| 941 | A182 | 2.30ce Agbadza | .20 | .20 |
| 942 | A182 | 3ce Damba | .20 | .20 |
| 943 | A182 | 50ce Dipo, diff. | 1.50 | 3.00 |
| | | Nos. 939-943 (5) | 2.30 | 3.80 |

**Souvenir Sheet**

| | | | | |
|---|---|---|---|---|
| 944 | A182 | 70ce Mandolin player | 2.25 | 2.25 |

Nos. 933-938 Ovptd. in Gold with Winner and Country

**1984, Dec. 3**    **Litho.**    *Perf. 15*

| | | | | |
|---|---|---|---|---|
| 945 | A181 | 1ce Valerie Brisco-Hooks, US | .20 | .20 |
| 946 | A181 | 1.40ce US winners | .20 | .20 |

---

| | | | | |
|---|---|---|---|---|
| 947 | A181 | 2.30ce Pakistan, (field hockey) | .20 | .20 |
| 948 | A181 | 3ce Edwin Moses, US | .20 | .20 |
| 949 | A181 | 50ce Lauri Fung, Canada | 2.25 | 2.25 |
| | | Nos. 945-949 (5) | 3.05 | 3.05 |

**Souvenir Sheet**

| | | | | |
|---|---|---|---|---|
| 950 | A181 | 70ce France | 2.75 | 2.75 |

Christmas A183

Queen Mother, 85th Birthday A184

**1984, Nov. 19**     *Perf. 12x12½*

| | | | | |
|---|---|---|---|---|
| 951 | A183 | 70p Adoration of the Magi | .20 | .20 |
| 952 | A183 | 1ce Chorus of angels | .20 | .20 |
| 953 | A183 | 1.40ce Adoration of the shepherds | .20 | .20 |
| 954 | A183 | 2.30ce Flight into Egypt | .20 | .20 |
| 955 | A183 | 3ce King holding Christ | .20 | .20 |
| 956 | A183 | 50ce Adoration of the angels | 2.00 | 2.00 |
| | | Nos. 951-956 (6) | 3.00 | 3.00 |

**Souvenir Sheet**

| | | | | |
|---|---|---|---|---|
| 957 | A183 | 70ce like 70p | 3.00 | 3.00 |

**1985**      *Perf. 14*

Portraits.

| | | | | |
|---|---|---|---|---|
| 958 | A184 | 5ce multicolored | .20 | .20 |
| 959 | A184 | 8ce like 5ce | .20 | .20 |
| 960 | A184 | 12ce multicolored | .25 | .25 |
| 961 | A184 | 20ce like 12ce | .35 | .35 |
| 962 | A184 | 70ce multicolored | 1.10 | 1.10 |
| 963 | A184 | 100ce like 70ce | 1.40 | 1.40 |
| | | Nos. 958-963 (6) | 3.50 | 3.50 |

**Souvenir Sheet**

| | | | | |
|---|---|---|---|---|
| 964 | A184 | 110ce multicolored | 3.50 | 3.50 |

Issue dates: 5ce, 12ce, 100ce, 110ce, July 29. 8ce, 20ce, 70ce, Dec.
Nos. 959, 961-962 issued in sheets of 5 + label.
For surcharges see Nos. 1117-1119A, 1198-1200, 1311-1317.

Id-El-Fitr Islamic Festival — A185

**1985, Aug. 1**

| | | | | |
|---|---|---|---|---|
| 965 | A185 | 5ce Entering mosque | .20 | .20 |
| 966 | A185 | 8ce Prayer rug | .40 | .40 |
| 967 | A185 | 12ce Mosque | .65 | .65 |
| 968 | A185 | 18ce Public Koran reading | 1.00 | 1.00 |
| 969 | A185 | 50ce Map, Banda Nkwanta Mosque | 2.75 | 2.75 |
| | | Nos. 965-969 (5) | 5.00 | 5.00 |

Intl. Youth Year — A186

---

**1985, Aug. 9**

| | | | | |
|---|---|---|---|---|
| 970 | A186 | 5ce Street clean-up | .20 | .20 |
| 971 | A186 | 8ce Tree planting | .20 | .20 |
| 972 | A186 | 12ce Food production | .30 | .30 |
| 973 | A186 | 100ce Education | 1.50 | 2.50 |
| | | Nos. 970-973 (4) | 2.20 | 3.20 |

**Souvenir Sheet**

| | | | | |
|---|---|---|---|---|
| 974 | A186 | 110ce like 8ce | 2.25 | 2.25 |

Motorcycle Centenary — A187

**1985, Sept. 9**

| | | | | |
|---|---|---|---|---|
| 975 | A187 | 5ce 1984 Honda Interceptor | .60 | .30 |
| 976 | A187 | 8ce 1938 DKW | .80 | .40 |
| 977 | A187 | 12ce 1923 BMW R 32 | 1.25 | .85 |
| 978 | A187 | 100ce 1900 NSU | 7.00 | 7.00 |
| | | Nos. 975-978 (4) | 9.65 | 8.55 |

**Souvenir Sheet**

| | | | | |
|---|---|---|---|---|
| 979 | A187 | 110ce 1973 Zundapp | 6.00 | 6.00 |

Audubon Birth Bicent. — A188

**1985, Oct. 16**

| | | | | |
|---|---|---|---|---|
| 980 | A188 | 5ce York-tailed flycatcher | 1.50 | 1.50 |
| 981 | A188 | 8ce Barred owl | 2.50 | 2.50 |
| 982 | A188 | 12ce Black-throated mango | 2.50 | 2.50 |
| 983 | A188 | 100ce White-crowned pigeon | 6.00 | 6.00 |
| | | Nos. 980-983 (4) | 12.50 | 12.50 |

**Souvenir Sheet**

| | | | | |
|---|---|---|---|---|
| 984 | A188 | 110ce Downy woodpecker | 8.50 | 8.50 |

For surcharges see Nos. 1124-1127.

UN, 40th Anniv. A189

**1985, Oct. 24**     *Perf. 14½x14*

| | | | | |
|---|---|---|---|---|
| 985 | A189 | 5ce UN building | .20 | .20 |
| 986 | A189 | 8ce UN building, diff. | .20 | .20 |
| 987 | A189 | 12ce Dove | .20 | .30 |
| 988 | A189 | 18ce General Assembly | .30 | .40 |
| 989 | A189 | 100ce Flags | 2.00 | 2.25 |
| | | Nos. 985-989 (5) | 2.90 | 3.35 |

**Souvenir Sheet**

| | | | | |
|---|---|---|---|---|
| 990 | A189 | 110ce UN No. 36 | 2.00 | 2.00 |

UNCTAD, 20th Anniv. A190

**1985, Nov. 4**     *Perf. 14*

| | | | | |
|---|---|---|---|---|
| 991 | A190 | 5ce Coffee | .20 | .20 |
| 992 | A190 | 8ce Cocoa | .20 | .20 |
| 993 | A190 | 12ce Lumber | .30 | .30 |
| 994 | A190 | 18ce Bauxite mining | 1.25 | 1.25 |
| 995 | A190 | 100ce Gold mining | 7.00 | 7.00 |
| | | Nos. 991-995 (5) | 8.95 | 8.95 |

**Souvenir Sheet**    *Perf. 15x14*

| | | | | |
|---|---|---|---|---|
| 996 | A190 | 110ce Produce | 3.00 | 3.00 |

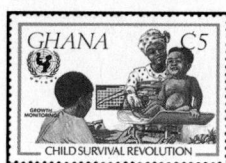

UN Child Survival Campaign A191

**1985, Dec. 16**     **Perf. 14**
997 A191 5ce Weighing .20 .20
998 A191 8ce Oral rehydration therapy .35 .35
999 A191 12ce Breast-feeding .60 .60
1000 A191 100ce Immunization 4.25 4.25
    Nos. 997-1000 (4) 5.40 5.40

**Souvenir Sheet**
**Perf. 15x14**
1001 A191 110ce Emblem, pinwheel 2.25 2.25

AMERIPEX '86 — A192

**Perf. 14½x14, 14x14½**
**1986, Oct. 27**     **Litho.**
1002 A192 5ce Young collectors .30 .30
1003 A192 25ce Earth, jet .85 .85
1004 A192 100ce Stewardess, vert. 2.75 2.75
    Nos. 1002-1004 (3) 3.90 3.90

**Souvenir Sheet**
1005 A192 150ce Young collectors, diff. 4.00 4.00

INTER-TOURISM '86, Nov. 8-17 — A193

Designs: 5ce, Kejetia Roundabout, Kumasi. 15ce, Fort St. Jago, Elmina. 25ce, Warriors. 100ce, Chief, retinue. 150ce, Elephants.

**1986, Nov. 10**     **Perf. 14**
1006 A193 5ce multi .20 .20
1007 A193 15ce multi .40 .40
1008 A193 25ce multi .65 .65
1009 A193 100ce multi 2.75 2.75
    Nos. 1006-1009 (4) 4.00 4.00

**Souvenir Sheet**
**Perf. 15x14**
1010 A193 150ce multi 5.50 5.50

1986 World Cup Soccer Championships, Mexico — A194

Fertility Dolls — A195

Various soccer plays.

**1987, Jan. 16**   **Litho.**   **Perf. 14x14½**
1011 A194 5ce multi .35 .35
1012 A194 15ce multi .45 .45
1013 A194 25ce multi .65 .65
1014 A194 100ce multi 2.25 2.25
    Nos. 1011-1014 (4) 3.70 3.70

**Souvenir Sheet**
1015 A194 150ce multi 2.75 2.75

For surcharges see Nos. 1120-1123D.

**1987, Jan. 22**
Various dolls.
1016 A195 5ce multi .20 .20
1017 A195 15ce multi .20 .20
1018 A195 25ce multi .35 .35
1019 A195 100ce multi 1.50 1.50
    Nos. 1016-1019 (4) 2.25 2.25

**Souvenir Sheet**
1020 A195 150ce like #1016 2.25 2.25

Intl. Peace Year A196

**Perf. 14½x14, 14x14½**
**1987, Mar. 2**     **Litho.**
1021 A196 5ce Children playing .30 .30
1022 A196 25ce Plow .85 .85
1023 A196 100ce Earth, doves, vert. 3.25 3.25
    Nos. 1021-1023 (3) 4.40 4.40

**Souvenir Sheet**
1024 A196 150ce Dove, plow, vert. 3.00 3.00

GIFEX '87 A197

**1987, Mar. 10**     **Perf. 14**
1025 A197 5ce Lumber, house construction .20 .20
1026 A197 15ce Furniture .20 .20
1027 A197 25ce Tree stumps .40 .40
1028 A197 200ce Logs, art objects 2.50 2.50
    Nos. 1025-1028 (4) 3.30 3.30

Ghana Intl. Forestry Exposition, Accra.

A198

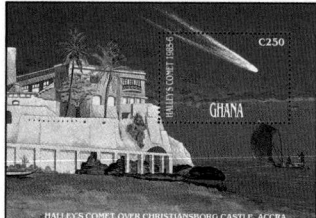

Halley's Comet — A199

Designs: 5ce, Mikhail Vasilyevich Lomonosov (1711-1765), Russian scientist, and the Chamber of Curiosities. 25ce, Landing of the US probe Surveyor on the Moon's surface, 1966. 200ce, Wedgwood memorial to Sir Isaac Newton, the appearance of Halley's Comet in 1790 and US astronauts Armstrong and Aldrin landing Eagle on the Moon in 1969. 250ce, Comet over Fishermen near Christianborg Castle.

**1987, Apr. 8**     **Perf. 14½x14**
1029 A198 5ce multi .30 .20
1030 A198 25ce multi .90 .90
1031 A198 200ce multi 4.75 4.75
    Nos. 1029-1031 (3) 5.95 5.85

**Souvenir Sheet**
1032 A199 250ce multi 5.50 5.50

For surcharges see Nos. 1128-1131,

Solidarity with South Africans for Abolition of Apartheid — A200

**1987, May 18**     **Perf. 14x14½**
1033 A200 5ce Liberated prisoner .20 .20
1034 A200 15ce Miner, gold ingots .35 .35
1035 A200 25ce Zulu warrior .35 .35
1036 A200 100ce Nelson Mandela, shackles 1.90 1.90
    Nos. 1033-1036 (4) 2.80 2.80

**Souvenir Sheet**
1037 A200 150ce Mandela, map, star 2.75 2.75

Traditional Musical Instruments — A201

**1987, July 13**     **Perf. 14½x14**
1038 A201 5ce Horns .20 .20
1039 A201 15ce Xylophone .30 .30
1040 A201 25ce String instruments .55 .55
1041 A201 100ce Drums 1.40 1.40
    Nos. 1038-1041 (4) 2.45 2.45

**Souvenir Sheet**
1042 A201 200ce Percussion instruments 3.25 3.25

Intl. Year of Shelter for the Homeless A202

**1987, Sept. 21**   **Litho.**   **Perf. 14**
1043 A202 5ce Public well .20 .20
1044 A202 15ce Home construction .30 .30
1045 A202 25ce Village, bridge, car .45 .45
1046 A202 100ce Village, electric power lines 1.50 1.50
    Nos. 1043-1046 (4) 2.45 2.45

Festivals — A203

Designs: Preparation of Kpokpoi, Homowo Festival. 15ce, Hunters with catch, Aboakyir Festival. 25ce, Chief dancing, Odwira Festival. 100ce, Chief held aloft in a palanquin, Yam Festival.

**1988, Jan. 6**   **Litho.**   **Perf. 15**
1047 A203 5ce multi .20 .20
1048 A203 15ce multi .25 .25
1049 A203 25ce multi .40 .40
1050 A203 100ce multi 1.40 1.40
    Nos. 1047-1050 (4) 2.25 2.25

December 31, 1981 Revolution — A203a

**1988, Jan. 26**   **Litho.**   **Perf. 13**
1050A A203a 5ce Ports 1.75 .50
1050B A203a 15ce Railways 15.00 3.00
1050C A203a 25ce Cocoa industry 3.00 .75
1050D A203a 100ce Mining industry 17.50 17.50
    Nos. 1050A-1050D (4) 37.25 21.75

UN Universal Immunization Campaign — A204

Child Survival Campaign emblem and: 5ce, Nurse immunizing woman. 15ce, Child receiving intramuscular vaccine. 25ce, Youth crippled by polio. 100ce, Nurse handing infant to mother.

**1988, Feb. 1**     **Perf. 15**
1051 A204 5ce multi .20 .20
1052 A204 15ce multi .25 .25
1053 A204 25ce multi .45 .45
1054 A204 100ce multi 1.10 1.10
    Nos. 1051-1054 (4) 2.00 2.00

Intl. Fund for Agricultural Development — A204a

**1988, Apr. 14**     **Perf. 13**
1054A A204a 5ce Fishing .65 .65
1054B A204a 15ce Harvesting 1.10 1.10
1054C A204a 25ce Cattle 1.75 1.75
1054D A204a 100ce Granary 4.00 4.00
    Nos. 1054A-1054D (4) 7.50 7.50

Tribal Costumes — A205

**1988, May 9**   **Litho.**   **Perf. 14**
1055 A205 5ce Akwadjan .20 .20
1056 A205 25ce Banaa .60 .60
1057 A205 250ce Agwasen 2.75 2.75
    Nos. 1055-1057 (3) 3.55 3.55

1988 Summer Olympics, Seoul A206

**1988, Oct. 10**
1058 A206 20ce Boxing .20 .20
1059 A206 60ce Running .65 .65
1060 A206 80ce Discus .90 .90

| | | | | |
|---|---|---|---|---|
| **1061** | A206 | 100ce Javelin | 1.10 | 1.10 |
| **1062** | A206 | 350ce Weight lifting | 3.75 | 3.75 |
| | | *Nos. 1058-1062 (5)* | 6.60 | 6.60 |

**Souvenir Sheet**

| | | | | |
|---|---|---|---|---|
| **1063** | A206 | 500ce like 80ce | 6.00 | 6.00 |

For overprints see Nos. 1084-1089.

Intl. Red Cross, 125th Anniv. — A207

**1988, Dec. 14**    Litho.    *Perf. 14*

| | | | | |
|---|---|---|---|---|
| **1064** | A207 | 20ce Nutrition | .60 | .60 |
| **1065** | A207 | 50ce Voluntary service | 1.25 | 1.25 |
| **1066** | A207 | 60ce Disaster relief (flood) | 1.50 | 1.50 |
| **1067** | A207 | 200ce Medical assistance | 4.00 | 4.00 |
| | | *Nos. 1064-1067 (4)* | 7.35 | 7.35 |

Christmas Symbolism — A208

**1988, Dec. 19**    Litho.    *Perf. 14*

| | | | | |
|---|---|---|---|---|
| **1068** | A208 | 20ce shown | .20 | .20 |
| **1069** | A208 | 60ce Mother and child, vert. | .55 | .55 |
| **1070** | A208 | 80ce Mother, child, tree, vert. | .65 | .65 |
| **1071** | A208 | 100ce Magi follow star | .85 | .85 |
| **1072** | A208 | 350ce Abstract, diff., vert. | 3.25 | 3.25 |
| | | *Nos. 1068-1072 (5)* | 5.50 | 5.50 |

**Souvenir Sheet**

| | | | | |
|---|---|---|---|---|
| **1073** | A208 | 500ce Mother and child, diff., vert. | 4.00 | 4.00 |

Organization of African Unity, 25th Anniv. — A209

Titian, 500th Birth Anniv. (in 1988) — A210

**1989, Jan. 3**

| | | | | |
|---|---|---|---|---|
| **1074** | A209 | 20ce Solidarity | .20 | .20 |
| **1075** | A209 | 50ce OAU, Addis Ababa | .20 | .20 |
| **1076** | A209 | 60ce Haile Selassie, Ethiopia | .45 | .45 |
| **1077** | A209 | 200ce Kwame Nkrumah, Ghana | .70 | .70 |
| | | *Nos. 1074-1077 (4)* | 1.55 | 1.55 |

"Selassie" is spelled incorrectly on No. 1076. Nos. 1076-1077 horiz.

**1989, Jan. 16**

| | | | | |
|---|---|---|---|---|
| **1078** | A210 | 20ce Amor, 1515 | .50 | .20 |
| **1079** | A210 | 60ce The Appeal | .85 | .85 |
| **1080** | A210 | 80ce Bacchus and Ariadne, c. 1523 | 1.25 | 1.25 |
| **1081** | A210 | 100ce Portrait of a Musician, c. 1518 | 1.50 | 1.50 |
| **1082** | A210 | 350ce Philip II Seated | 4.00 | 4.00 |
| | | *Nos. 1078-1082 (5)* | 8.10 | 7.80 |

**Souvenir Sheet**

| | | | | |
|---|---|---|---|---|
| **1083** | A210 | 500ce Portrait of a Gentleman, c. 1550 | 4.00 | 4.00 |

**Nos. 1058-1063 Ovptd. with Winners' Names**

**1989, Jan. 23**

| | | | | |
|---|---|---|---|---|
| **1084** | A206 | 20ce "A. ZUELOW / DDR / 60 KG" | .45 | .45 |
| **1085** | A206 | 60ce "G. BORDIN / ITALY / MARATHON" | .55 | .55 |
| **1086** | A206 | 80ce "J. SCHULT / DDR" | .65 | .65 |
| **1087** | A206 | 100ce "T. KORJUS / FINLAND" | .80 | .80 |
| **1088** | A206 | 350ce "B. GUIDIKOV / BULGARIA / 75 KG" | 2.00 | 2.00 |
| | | *Nos. 1084-1088 (5)* | 4.45 | 4.45 |

**Souvenir Sheet**

| | | | | |
|---|---|---|---|---|
| **1089** | A206 | 500ce multi | 4.25 | 4.25 |

1988 Summer Olympics, Seoul. Margin of No. 1089 ovptd. "GOLD / J. SCHULT DDR / SILVER / R. OUBARTAS USSR / BRONZE / R. DANNEBERG W. GERMANY."

**Stamps of 1967-1984 Surcharged**

**1988-91**

| | | | | |
|---|---|---|---|---|
| **1089A** | A177 | 20ce on 50p #889 | .35 | .20 |
| **1090** | A177 | 20ce on 1ce #890 | .35 | .20 |
| **1091** | A75 | 50ce on 10np #295 | .35 | .30 |
| **1092** | A177 | 50ce on 10p #887 | .35 | .20 |
|   **f.** | | 50ce' on 10p Denomination below obliterator | | |
| **1092A** | A74 | 50ce on 1ce #858 | 5.00 | .50 |
| **1092B** | A74 | 50ce on 1ce #858 | 5.00 | .50 |
| **1092C** | A74 | 50ce on 1ce #858 | 5.00 | .50 |
| **1092D** | A177 | 50ce on 1ce #890 | 5.00 | .50 |
| **1092E** | A73 | 60ce on 10np #286 | 5.00 | .50 |
| **1093** | A73 | 60ce on 4np #291 | 5.00 | .50 |
| **1093A** | A177 | 60ce on 3ce #892 | .50 | .25 |
|   **b.** | | Decimal point omitted | | |
| **1094** | A177 | 80ce on 5p #886 | .80 | .80 |
| **1094A** | A177 | 80ce on 5ce #894 | 5.00 | 5.00 |
| **1095** | A74 | 100ce on 20np #296 | .50 | .50 |
| **1096** | A177 | 100ce on 20p #888 | .50 | .50 |
| **1096A** | A177 | 100ce on 3ce #892 | .50 | .50 |
| **1096B** | A75 | 200ce on 6np #292 | .60 | .60 |

Surcharge has no decimal on No. 1092A, is vertical on No. 1092B and horizontal on No. 1092C.

No. 1090 also exists with 5mm spacing between block and $20.00.

Surcharge on No. 1093A has decimal point. Unauthorized surcharges exist.

Issued: #1089A, 1096B, 7/1/88; #1092A, 1092B, 1092D, 1092E, 1094A, 1096A, 1990; #1092C, 1991; others, 1989.

Minamoto-no-Yoritomo, by Fujiwara-no-Takanobu (1142-1205) — A211

Paintings: 50ce, Takami Senseki, by Watanabe Kazan (1793-1841). 60ce, Ikkyu Sojum, by Bokusai, Muromachi period. 75ce, Nakamura Kuranosuke, by Ogata Korin (1658-1716). 125ce, Portrait of a Lady, Kyoto branch of Kano school, Momoyama period. 150ce, Portrait of Zemmui, anonymous, 12th cent. 200ce, Ono no Komachi, the Poetess, by Hokusai. No. 1104, Kobo Daisi as a Child, anonymous, Kamakura period. No. 1105, Portrait of Kodai-no-Kimi, attributed to Fujiwara-no-Nobuzane, 12th cent. No. 1106, Portrait of Emperor Hanazono, by Fujiwara-no-Goshin, 14th cent.

**1989, Aug. 21**    Litho.    *Perf. 13½x14*

| | | | | |
|---|---|---|---|---|
| **1097** | A211 | 20ce shown | .20 | .20 |
| **1098** | A211 | 50ce multi | .45 | .45 |
| **1099** | A211 | 60ce multi | .50 | .50 |
| **1100** | A211 | 75ce multi | .70 | .70 |
| **1101** | A211 | 125ce multi | 1.10 | 1.10 |
| **1102** | A211 | 150ce multi | 1.50 | 1.50 |
| **1103** | A211 | 200ce multi | 1.90 | 1.90 |
| **1104** | A211 | 500ce multi | 2.75 | 2.75 |
| | | *Nos. 1097-1104 (8)* | 9.10 | 9.10 |

**Souvenir Sheets**

| | | | | |
|---|---|---|---|---|
| **1105** | A211 | 500ce multi | 6.50 | 6.50 |
| **1106** | A211 | 500ce multi | 6.50 | 6.50 |

Hirohito (1901-1989) and enthronement of Akihito as emperor of Japan.

**Nos. 835-838 and 840 Surcharged**

**1989, July 3**    Litho.    *Perf. 14*

| | | | | |
|---|---|---|---|---|
| **1107** | A173b | 60ce on 1ce | 1.00 | .60 |
| **1108** | A173b | 80ce on 1.40ce | 1.25 | .75 |
| **1109** | A173b | 200ce on 2.30ce | 3.25 | 3.25 |
| **1110** | A173b | 300ce on 3ce | 4.00 | 4.00 |
| | | *Nos. 1107-1110 (4)* | 9.50 | 8.60 |

**Souvenir Sheet**

| | | | | |
|---|---|---|---|---|
| **1111** | A173b | 500ce on 6ce | 7.50 | 7.50 |

**Nos. 933-936 and 938 Surcharged**

**1989, July 3**    *Perf. 15*

| | | | | |
|---|---|---|---|---|
| **1112** | A181 | 60ce on 1ce | .45 | .45 |
| **1113** | A181 | 80ce on 1.40ce | .65 | .65 |
| **1114** | A181 | 200ce on 2.30ce | 1.60 | 1.60 |
| **1115** | A181 | 300ce on 3ce | 2.25 | 2.25 |
| | | *Nos. 1112-1115 (4)* | 4.95 | 4.95 |

**Souvenir Sheet**

| | | | | |
|---|---|---|---|---|
| **1116** | A181 | 600ce on 70ce | 4.50 | 4.50 |

**Nos. 958, 960 and 963-964 Surcharged**

**1989, Nov. 20**    Litho.    *Perf. 14*

| | | | | |
|---|---|---|---|---|
| **1117** | A184 | 80ce on 5ce #958 | .65 | .65 |
| **1118** | A184 | 250ce on 12ce #960 | 2.10 | 2.10 |
| **1119** | A184 | 300ce on 100ce #963 | 2.50 | 2.50 |
| | | *Nos. 1117-1119 (3)* | 5.25 | 5.25 |

**Souvenir Sheet**

| | | | | |
|---|---|---|---|---|
| **1119A** | A184 | 500ce on 110ce #964 | 5.50 | 5.50 |

**Nos. 1011-1013 and 1015 Surcharged**

**1989**    Litho.    *Perf. 14x14½*

| | | | | |
|---|---|---|---|---|
| **1120** | A194 | 60ce on 5ce #1011 | .60 | .60 |
| **1121** | A194 | 200ce on 15ce #1012 | 2.00 | 2.00 |
| **1122** | A194 | 300ce on 25ce #1013 | 2.75 | 2.75 |
| | | *Nos. 1120-1122 (3)* | 5.35 | 5.35 |

**Souvenir Sheet**

| | | | | |
|---|---|---|---|---|
| **1123** | A194 | 600ce on 110ce #1015 | 8.00 | 8.00 |

Nos. 1120-1123 Surcharged

**1989**    Litho.    *Perf. 14x14½*

| | | | | |
|---|---|---|---|---|
| **1123A** | A194 | 60ce on 5ce | .55 | .55 |
| **1123B** | A194 | 200ce on 15ce | 1.75 | 1.75 |
| **1123C** | A194 | 300ce on 25ce | 2.75 | 2.75 |
| | | *Nos. 1123A-1123C (3)* | 5.05 | 5.05 |

**Souvenir Sheet**

| | | | | |
|---|---|---|---|---|
| **1123D** | A194 | 600ce on 150ce | 6.50 | 6.50 |

**Nos. 980-982 and 984 Surcharged**

**1989, Nov. 20**    Litho.    *Perf. 14*

| | | | | |
|---|---|---|---|---|
| **1124** | A188 | 80ce on 5ce #980 | 2.00 | 2.00 |
| **1125** | A188 | 100ce on 8ce #981 | 3.50 | 3.50 |
| **1126** | A188 | 300ce on 12ce #982 | 4.00 | 4.00 |
| | | *Nos. 1124-1126 (3)* | 9.50 | 9.50 |

**Souvenir Sheet**

| | | | | |
|---|---|---|---|---|
| **1127** | A188 | 500ce on 110ce #984 | 10.50 | 10.50 |

**Nos. 1029-1032 Surcharged**

**1989, Nov. 20**    *Perf. 14½x14*

| | | | | |
|---|---|---|---|---|
| **1128** | A198 | 60ce on 5ce #1029 | 1.00 | 1.00 |
|   **a.** | | With comet logo | | |
| **1129** | A198 | 80ce on 25ce #1030 | 1.25 | 1.25 |
|   **a.** | | With comet logo | .55 | .55 |
| **1130** | A198 | 500ce on 200ce #1031 | 4.75 | 4.75 |
|   **a.** | | With comet logo | 3.50 | 3.50 |
| | | *Nos. 1128-1130 (3)* | 7.00 | 7.00 |
| | | *Nos. 1128a-1130a (3)* | 4.45 | 4.45 |

**Souvenir Sheet**

| | | | | |
|---|---|---|---|---|
| **1131** | A199 | 750ce on 250ce #1032 | 6.50 | 6.50 |
|   **a.** | | With comet logo | 5.50 | 5.50 |

PHILEXFRANCE '89, French Revolution Bicent. — A212

Emblems, French arms and flags: 20ce, Tube-mounted field carriage, flag of 1643 to 1790. 60ce, Infantryman, flag of 1789. 80ce, Handgun, flag of 1789, diff. 350ce, Musket, flag of 1794 to 1814 and 1848 to present. 600ce, Map of Paris.

**1989, Sept. 22**    Litho.    *Perf. 14*

| | | | | |
|---|---|---|---|---|
| **1132** | A212 | 20ce shown | .75 | .75 |
| **1133** | A212 | 60ce multi | 1.40 | 1.40 |
| **1134** | A212 | 80ce multi | 1.75 | 1.75 |
| **1135** | A212 | 350ce multi | 4.50 | 4.50 |
| | | *Nos. 1132-1135 (4)* | 8.40 | 8.40 |

**Souvenir Sheet**

| | | | | |
|---|---|---|---|---|
| **1136** | A212 | 600ce multi | 5.00 | 5.00 |

Mushrooms

A213      A214

**1989, Oct. 2**    Litho.    *Perf. 14*

| | | | | |
|---|---|---|---|---|
| **1137** | A213 | 20ce Collybia | .20 | .20 |
| **1138** | A213 | 50ce Lawyer's wig | .40 | .40 |
| **1139** | A214 | 60ce *Xerocomus subtomentosus* | .50 | .50 |
| **1140** | A213 | 80ce Wood belwits | .70 | .70 |
| **1141** | A214 | 150ce *Suillus placidus* | 1.40 | 1.40 |
| **1142** | A214 | 200ce *Lepista nuda* | 1.75 | 1.75 |
| **1143** | A214 | 300ce Fairy rings | 2.50 | 2.50 |
| **1144** | A213 | 500ce Field mushroom | 4.25 | 4.25 |
| | | *Nos. 1137-1144 (8)* | 11.70 | 11.70 |

**Souvenir Sheets**

| | | | | |
|---|---|---|---|---|
| **1145** | A213 | 600ce Three *Amanita* species | 5.00 | 5.00 |
| **1146** | A214 | 600ce Three *Boletus* species | 5.00 | 5.00 |

**Souvenir Sheet**

A Midsummer Night's Dream, by Shakespeare — A215

Designs: a, "The course of true love never did run smooth." b, "Love looks not with the eye but with the mind." c, "Nature here shows art." d, "Things growing are not ripe till their season." e, "He is defiled that draws a sword on thee." f, "It is not enough to speak but to speak true." g, "Thou art wise as thou art beautiful." h, Leopard behind trees. i, Theseus. j, Boy holding flower, trees. k, Oberon and Titania among trees. l, Bottom wearing head of a jackass. m, Bottom's leg, leopard behind trees. n, Hippolyta. o, Leopard, tree trunk. p, Tree trunk, foliage, lower portion of Theseus's robe. q, Wisps of fragrance, clouds, hills, foliage. r, Wisps of fragrance, flowering plants. s, Flowering plants. t, Lion, foliage. u, Lion's mane, foliage.

**1989, Oct. 9**    *Perf. 13½x13*

| | | | | |
|---|---|---|---|---|
| **1147** | A215 | Sheet of 21 | 16.00 | 16.00 |
|   **a.-u.** | | 40ce any single | .70 | .70 |

425th Birth anniv. of William Shakespeare, playwright.

Birds
A216

**1989, Oct. 16** — Perf. 14

| 1148 | A216 | 20ce | Spermestes cuculatus | .40 | .20 |
|---|---|---|---|---|---|
| 1149 | A216 | 50ce | Motacilla aguimp | .60 | .35 |
| 1150 | A216 | 60ce | Halcyon malimbicus | 1.90 | 1.90 |
| 1151 | A216 | 80ce | Ispidina picta | 3.25 | 3.25 |
| 1152 | A216 | 150ce | Striped kingfisher | 2.50 | 2.50 |
| 1153 | A216 | 200ce | Shikra | 2.25 | 2.25 |
| 1154 | A216 | 300ce | Gray parrot | 3.25 | 3.25 |
| 1155 | A216 | 500ce | Black kite | 4.50 | 4.50 |
| | | | Nos. 1148-1155 (8) | 18.65 | 18.20 |

**Souvenir Sheets**

| 1156 | A216 | 600ce | Four birds | 9.50 | 9.50 |
|---|---|---|---|---|---|
| 1157 | A216 | 600ce | Three birds | 9.50 | 9.50 |

Nos. 1152-1156 vert.

1st Moon Landing, 20th Anniv. A217

Highlights of the Apollo 11 mission.

**1989, Nov. 6** — Perf. 14

| 1158 | A217 | 20ce | Columbia | .20 | .20 |
|---|---|---|---|---|---|
| 1159 | A217 | 80ce | Footprint | .75 | .75 |
| 1160 | A217 | 200ce | Aldrin on Moon | 1.75 | 1.75 |
| 1161 | A217 | 300ce | Splashdown | 2.75 | 2.75 |
| | | | Nos. 1158-1161 (4) | 5.45 | 5.45 |

**Souvenir Sheets**

| 1162 | A217 | 500ce | Liftoff, vert. | 4.50 | 4.50 |
|---|---|---|---|---|---|
| 1163 | A217 | 500ce | Earth, vert. | 4.50 | 4.50 |

World Environment Day — A218

**1989, Nov. 20** — Litho. — Perf. 14

| 1164 | A218 | 20ce | Desertification | .20 | .20 |
|---|---|---|---|---|---|
| 1165 | A218 | 60ce | Bush fires | .60 | .60 |
| 1166 | A218 | 400ce | Industrial pollution | 3.50 | 3.50 |
| 1167 | A218 | 500ce | Soil erosion | 5.00 | 5.00 |
| | | | Nos. 1164-1167 (4) | 9.30 | 9.30 |

Nos. 760 and 761 Surcharged

**1989, Nov. 20** — Litho. — Perf. 14

| 1168 | CD331 | 100ce on 80p | 1.00 | 1.00 |
|---|---|---|---|---|
| 1169 | CD331 | 500ce on 4ce | 5.00 | 5.00 |

French Revolution, Bicent. — A219

Designs: 20ce, Storming of the Bastille, vert. 60ce, Declaration of Human Rights and Citizenship, vert. 80ce, Storming of the Bastille, diff. 200ce, Departure of the Volunteers in 1792, high relief on the Arc de Triomphe, 1833-35, by Francis Rude. 350ce, Planting the Liberty Tree.

Perf. 14x13½, 13½x14

**1989, Sept. 22**

| 1170 | A219 | 20ce | multicolored | .55 | .55 |
|---|---|---|---|---|---|
| 1171 | A219 | 60ce | multicolored | 1.25 | 1.25 |
| 1172 | A219 | 80ce | multicolored | 1.50 | 1.50 |
| 1173 | A219 | 200ce | multicolored | 2.75 | 2.75 |
| 1174 | A219 | 350ce | multicolored | 4.00 | 4.00 |
| | | | Nos. 1170-1174 (5) | 10.05 | 10.05 |

Butterflies
A220

**1990, Feb. 15** — Litho. — Perf. 14

| 1175 | A220 | 20ce | Bebearia arcadius | .60 | .60 |
|---|---|---|---|---|---|
| 1176 | A220 | 60ce | Charaxes laodice | .80 | .80 |
| 1177 | A220 | 80ce | Euryphura porphyrion | 1.00 | 1.00 |
| 1178 | A220 | 100ce | Neptis nicomedes | 1.10 | 1.10 |
| 1179 | A220 | 150ce | Citrinophila erastus | 1.40 | 1.40 |
| 1180 | A220 | 200ce | Epitola honorius | 2.00 | 2.00 |
| 1181 | A220 | 300ce | Precis westermanni | 2.50 | 2.50 |
| 1182 | A220 | 500ce | Cymothoe hypatha | 3.25 | 3.25 |
| | | | Nos. 1175-1182 (8) | 12.65 | 12.65 |

**Souvenir Sheets**

| 1183 | A220 | 600ce | Telipna bimacula | 7.00 | 7.00 |
|---|---|---|---|---|---|
| 1184 | A220 | 600ce | Pentila phidia | 7.00 | 7.00 |

Seashells — A221

**1990, Feb. 20** — Perf. 14x14½

| 1185 | A221 | 20ce | Cymbium glans | 1.00 | 1.00 |
|---|---|---|---|---|---|
| 1186 | A221 | 60ce | Cardium costatum | 1.75 | 1.75 |
| 1187 | A221 | 80ce | Conus genuanus | 2.25 | 2.25 |
| 1188 | A221 | 200ce | Ancilla tankervillei | 4.00 | 4.00 |
| 1189 | A221 | 350ce | Tectarius coronatus | 5.75 | 5.75 |
| | | | Nos. 1185-1189 (5) | 14.75 | 14.75 |

Jawaharlal Nehru, 1st Prime Minister of Independent India — A222

Designs: 20ce, Greeting Pres. Kwame Nkrumah of Ghana. 60ce, Addressing Afro-Asian conference. 80ce, Return from tour of China, vert. 200ce, Releasing dove during a children's celebration in New Delhi, vert. 350ce, Portrait, vert.

Perf. 14½x14, 14x14½

**1990, Mar. 27** — Litho.

| 1190 | A222 | 20ce | shown | .75 | .75 |
|---|---|---|---|---|---|
| 1191 | A222 | 60ce | multicolored | .90 | .90 |
| 1192 | A222 | 80ce | multicolored | 1.25 | 1.25 |
| 1193 | A222 | 200ce | multicolored | 1.75 | 1.75 |
| 1194 | A222 | 350ce | multicolored | 2.75 | 2.75 |
| | | | Nos. 1190-1194 (5) | 7.40 | 7.40 |

Nos. 759A and 760A-760B Surcharged

**1990** — Perf. 14

| 1195 | CD331 | 80ce on 65p | .80 | .80 |
|---|---|---|---|---|
| 1196 | CD331 | 100ce on 1ce | 1.00 | 1.00 |
| 1197 | CD331 | 300ce on 3ce | 3.00 | 3.00 |
| | | Nos. 1195-1197 (3) | 4.80 | 4.80 |

Nos. 961, 959 and 962 Surcharged

**1990**

| 1198 | A184 | 80ce on 20ce | .80 | .80 |
|---|---|---|---|---|
| 1199 | A184 | 200ce on 8ce | 2.00 | 2.00 |
| 1200 | A184 | 250ce on 70ce | 2.50 | 2.50 |
| | | Nos. 1198-1200 (3) | 5.30 | 5.30 |

Penny Black, 150th Anniv. A223

Great Britain No. 1 and: 20ce, City Medal containing portrait of Victoria by William Wyon adapted for use on the Penny Black. 60ce, No. 1208, Bath mail coach. 80ce, Leeds Mail coach. 200ce, Heath's engraving, based on the Wyon portrait. 350ce, Penny Black master die. 400ce, London mail coach. No. 1207, Printers and flat-bed presses of Perkins, Bacon & Petch, 1840.

**1990, May 3** — Perf. 13½x14

| 1201 | A223 | 20ce | shown | .35 | .35 |
|---|---|---|---|---|---|
| 1202 | A223 | 60ce | multicolored | .65 | .65 |
| 1203 | A223 | 80ce | multicolored | .90 | .90 |
| 1204 | A223 | 200ce | multicolored | 1.90 | 1.90 |
| 1205 | A223 | 350ce | multicolored | 2.50 | 2.50 |
| 1206 | A223 | 400ce | multicolored | 2.50 | 2.50 |
| | | | Nos. 1201-1206 (6) | 8.80 | 8.80 |

**Souvenir Sheets**

| 1207 | A223 | 600ce | multicolored | 6.25 | 6.25 |
|---|---|---|---|---|---|
| 1208 | A223 | 600ce | multicolored | 6.25 | 6.25 |

June 4, Revolution, 10th Anniv. (in 1989) — A224

**1990, June 5** — Litho. — Perf. 14½x14

| 1209 | A224 | 20ce | shown | .20 | .20 |
|---|---|---|---|---|---|
| 1210 | A224 | 60ce | Pineapple, lobsters | .50 | .50 |
| 1211 | A224 | 80ce | Corn, cacao beans | .65 | .65 |
| 1212 | A224 | 200ce | Mining | 1.75 | 1.75 |
| 1213 | A224 | 350ce | Scales, sword | 3.00 | 3.00 |
| | | | Nos. 1209-1213 (5) | 6.10 | 6.10 |

Intelsat, 25th Anniv. A225

Satellites over: 60ce, Pacific Ocean. 80ce, Pacific, diff. 200ce, South Atlantic. 350ce, Pacific, Indian Oceans.

**1990, July 12** — Perf. 14x14½

| 1214 | A225 | 20ce | multicolored | .20 | .20 |
|---|---|---|---|---|---|
| 1215 | A225 | 60ce | multicolored | .55 | .55 |
| 1216 | A225 | 80ce | multicolored | .65 | .65 |
| 1217 | A225 | 200ce | multicolored | 1.60 | 1.60 |
| 1218 | A225 | 350ce | multicolored | 2.50 | 2.50 |
| | | | Nos. 1214-1218 (5) | 5.50 | 5.50 |

Introduction of Intl. Direct Dialing Service (in 1988) — A226

**1990, July 16**

| 1219 | A226 | 20ce | shown | .20 | .20 |
|---|---|---|---|---|---|
| 1220 | A226 | 60ce | Man using telephone | .55 | .55 |
| 1221 | A226 | 80ce | Man using pay telephone | .65 | .65 |
| 1222 | A226 | 200ce | Telephone booths | 1.60 | 1.60 |
| 1223 | A226 | 350ce | Satellite dish | 2.50 | 2.50 |
| | | | Nos. 1219-1223 (5) | 5.50 | 5.50 |

Miniature Sheet

African Tropical Rain Forest A227

Designs: No. 1224a, Blue fairy flycatcher. b, Boomslang. c, Superb sunbird. d, Bateleur eagle. e, Yellow-casqued hornbill. f, Salamis temora. g, Potto. h, Leopard. i, Bongo. j, Gray parrot. k, Okapi. l, Gorilla. m, Flap-necked chameleon. n, West African dwarf crocodile. o, Python. p, Giant pangolin. q, Pseudacraea boisduvali. r, African crested porcupine. s, Rosy-columned aerangis. t, Cymothoe sangaris.

No. 1225, Leopard, vert.

**1990, Oct. 25** — Litho. — Perf. 14x14½

| 1224 | | Sheet of 20 | 18.00 | 18.00 |
|---|---|---|---|---|
| a.-t. | A227 | 40ce any single | .80 | .80 |

**Souvenir Sheet**

| 1225 | A227 | 600ce | multicolored | 8.50 | 8.50 |
|---|---|---|---|---|---|

Miniature Sheet

Voyager 2 — A228

Photographs from Voyager 2: No. 1226a, Jupiter. b, Neptune, Triton. c, Ariel, moon of Uranus. d, Saturn, Mimas. e, Saturn. f, Rings of Saturn. g, Neptune. h, Uranus, Miranda. i, Volcano on Io.

**1990, Dec. 13** — Litho. — Perf. 14

| 1226 | A228 | 100ce | Sheet of 9, #1226a-1226i | 10.00 | 10.00 |
|---|---|---|---|---|---|

**Souvenir Sheets**

| 1227 | A228 | 600ce | Voyager 2 liftoff, vert. | 4.25 | 4.25 |
|---|---|---|---|---|---|
| 1228 | A228 | 600ce | Voyager 2, vert. | 4.25 | 4.25 |

Orchids — A229

Designs: 20ce, Eulophia guineensis. 40ce, Eurychone rothschildiana. 60ce, Bulbophyllum barbigerum. 80ce, Polystachya galeata. 200ce, Diaphananthe kamerunensis. 300ce, Podangis dactyloceras. 400ce, Ancistrochilus rothschildianus. 500ce, Rangaeris muscicola. No. 1237, Bolusiella imbricata. No. 1238, Diaphananthe rutila.

**1990, Dec. 17**

| 1229 | A229 | 20ce | multicolored | .20 | .20 |
|---|---|---|---|---|---|
| 1230 | A229 | 40ce | multicolored | .30 | .30 |
| 1231 | A229 | 60ce | multicolored | .55 | .55 |
| 1232 | A229 | 80ce | multicolored | .70 | .70 |
| 1233 | A229 | 200ce | multicolored | 1.75 | 1.75 |
| 1234 | A229 | 300ce | multicolored | 2.75 | 2.75 |
| 1235 | A229 | 400ce | multicolored | 3.75 | 3.75 |
| 1236 | A229 | 500ce | multicolored | 4.50 | 4.50 |
| | | | Nos. 1229-1236 (8) | 14.50 | 14.50 |

**Souvenir Sheets**

| 1237 | A229 | 600ce | multicolored | 7.25 | 7.25 |
|---|---|---|---|---|---|
| 1238 | A229 | 600ce | multicolored | 7.25 | 7.25 |

Mushrooms — A230

Designs: 20ce, Coprinus atramentarius. 50ce, Marasmius oreades. 60ce, Oudamansiella radicata. 80ce, Cep. 150ce, Hebeloma crustuliniforme. 200ce, Coprinus micaceus. 300ce, Lepiota procera. 500ce, Amanita phalloides.

**1990, Dec. 18**
| | | | | |
|---|---|---|---|---|
| 1239 | A230 | 50ce multicolored | .85 | .55 |
| 1240 | A230 | 50ce multicolored | 1.10 | .85 |
| 1241 | A230 | 60ce multicolored | 1.40 | .85 |
| 1242 | A230 | 80ce multicolored | 1.75 | 1.25 |
| 1243 | A230 | 150ce multicolored | 2.50 | 1.75 |
| 1244 | A230 | 200ce multicolored | 3.50 | 2.50 |
| 1245 | A230 | 300ce multicolored | 3.50 | 3.50 |
| a. | | Min. sheet of 4, #1240, 1243-1245 | 7.25 | 7.25 |
| 1246 | A230 | 100ce multicolored | 4.50 | 4.50 |
| a. | | Min. sheet of 4, #1239, 1241-1242, 1246 | 7.25 | 7.25 |
| | | Nos. 1239-1246 (8) | 19.10 | 15.75 |

World Cup Soccer Championships, Italy — A231

Players from participating countries.

**1990, Dec. 18**    Litho.    Perf. 14
| | | | | |
|---|---|---|---|---|
| 1247 | A231 | 20ce Italy | .50 | .50 |
| 1248 | A231 | 50ce Egypt | .65 | .65 |
| 1249 | A231 | 60ce Cameroun | .70 | .70 |
| 1250 | A231 | 80ce Romania | .85 | .85 |
| 1251 | A231 | 100ce Yugoslavia | 1.00 | 1.00 |
| 1252 | A231 | 150ce Cameroun, vert. | 1.75 | 1.75 |
| 1253 | A231 | 400ce South Korea | 2.75 | 2.75 |
| 1254 | A231 | 600ce West Germany | 3.25 | 3.25 |
| | | Nos. 1247-1254 (8) | 11.45 | 11.45 |

**Souvenir Sheets**
| | | | | |
|---|---|---|---|---|
| 1255 | A231 | 800ce UAE | 5.50 | 5.50 |
| 1256 | A231 | 800ce Colombia | 5.50 | 5.50 |

Peter Paul Rubens (1577-1640), Painter A232

Portraits by Rubens: 20ce, Duke of Mantua. 50ce, Jan Brant. 60ce, Young man. 80ce, Michel Ophovius. 100ce, Caspar Gevaerts. 200ce, Head of a warrior (detail). 300ce, Bearded man. 400ce, Paracelsus. No. 1265, Archduke Ferdinand. No. 1266, Warrior with Two Pages.

**1990, Dec. 24**    Litho.    Perf. 14
| | | | | |
|---|---|---|---|---|
| 1257 | A232 | 20ce multicolored | .20 | .20 |
| 1258 | A232 | 50ce multicolored | .40 | .40 |
| 1259 | A232 | 60ce multicolored | .50 | .50 |
| 1260 | A232 | 80ce multicolored | .65 | .65 |
| 1261 | A232 | 100ce multicolored | .80 | .80 |
| 1262 | A232 | 200ce multicolored | 1.90 | 1.90 |
| 1263 | A232 | 300ce multicolored | 2.75 | 2.75 |
| 1264 | A232 | 400ce multicolored | 3.75 | 3.75 |
| | | Nos. 1257-1264 (8) | 10.95 | 10.95 |

**Souvenir Sheets**
| | | | | |
|---|---|---|---|---|
| 1265 | A232 | 600ce multicolored | 5.75 | 5.75 |
| 1266 | A232 | 600ce multicolored | 5.75 | 5.75 |

Minerals — A233

**1991, May 2**    Litho.    Perf. 14½x14
| | | | | |
|---|---|---|---|---|
| 1267 | A233 | 20ce Manganese ore | .55 | .55 |
| 1268 | A233 | 60ce Iron ore | .70 | .70 |
| 1269 | A233 | 80ce Bauxite ore | 1.25 | 1.25 |

---

| | | | | |
|---|---|---|---|---|
| 1270 | A233 | 200ce Gold ore | 3.00 | 3.00 |
| 1271 | A233 | 350ce Diamond | 4.50 | 4.50 |
| | | Nos. 1267-1271 (5) | 10.00 | 10.00 |

**Souvenir Sheet**
| | | | | |
|---|---|---|---|---|
| 1272 | A233 | 600ce Diamonds | 10.00 | 10.00 |

Tribal Drums — A234

**1991, May 9**
| | | | | |
|---|---|---|---|---|
| 1273 | A234 | 20ce Damba | .45 | .20 |
| 1274 | A234 | 60ce Atumpan | .85 | .55 |
| 1275 | A234 | 80ce Kroboto | 1.10 | .70 |
| 1276 | A234 | 200ce Asafo | 1.90 | 1.90 |
| 1277 | A234 | 350ce Obonu | 3.00 | 3.00 |
| | | Nos. 1273-1277 (5) | 7.30 | 6.35 |

**Souvenir Sheet**
| | | | | |
|---|---|---|---|---|
| 1278 | A234 | 600ce Single drum | 7.50 | 7.50 |

Flowers — A235     A236

**1991, May 15**
| | | | | |
|---|---|---|---|---|
| 1279 | A235 | 20ce Amorphophallus dracontioides | .75 | .35 |
| 1280 | A235 | 60ce Anchomanes difformis | 1.10 | .55 |
| 1281 | A235 | 80ce Kaemferia nigerica | 1.40 | .70 |
| 1282 | A235 | 200ce Aframomum sceptrum | 2.75 | 2.75 |
| 1283 | A235 | 350ce Amorphophallus flavovirens | 3.00 | 3.00 |
| | | Nos. 1279-1283 (5) | 9.00 | 7.35 |

**Souvenir Sheet**
| | | | | |
|---|---|---|---|---|
| 1284 | A235 | 600ce White flowers | 7.00 | 7.00 |

**1991, May 17**    Litho.    Perf. 14½x14
| | | | | |
|---|---|---|---|---|
| 1285 | A235 | 20ce Urginea indica | .55 | .35 |
| 1286 | A235 | 60ce Hymenocallis littoralis | 1.00 | .55 |
| 1287 | A235 | 80ce Crinum jagus | 1.60 | .80 |
| 1288 | A235 | 200ce Dipcadi tacazzeanum | 2.25 | 2.25 |
| 1289 | A235 | 350ce Haemanthus rupestris | 2.75 | 2.75 |
| | | Nos. 1285-1289 (5) | 8.15 | 6.70 |

**Souvenir Sheet**
| | | | | |
|---|---|---|---|---|
| 1290 | A235 | 600ce Red flowers | 7.50 | 7.50 |

**1991, June 21**    Litho.    Perf. 13½x14

Designs: 20ce, Satellite transmissions, airplane. 60ce, Scientific research, honey bee. 80ce, Literacy instruction. 200ce, Agricultural development. 350ce, Industry.

| | | | | |
|---|---|---|---|---|
| 1291 | A236 | 20ce multicolored | .20 | .20 |
| 1292 | A236 | 60ce multicolored | 1.00 | .55 |
| 1293 | A236 | 80ce multicolored | 1.10 | .70 |
| 1294 | A236 | 200ce multicolored | 1.75 | 1.75 |
| 1295 | A236 | 350ce multicolored | 3.00 | 3.00 |
| | | Nos. 1291-1295 (5) | 7.05 | 6.20 |

UN Development Program, 40th anniv.

Lord Robert Baden-Powell (1857-1941), Founder of Boy Scouts — A237

---

Designs: 20ce, Sketch by Baden-Powell used in first scouting handbook, vert. 50ce, Portrait, vert. 80ce, Scout handbook illustration by Norman Rockwell. 100ce, Native runner, Cape of Good Hope #178. 200ce, Scouts aiding victims after V-1 attack, London, 1944. 500ce, Scout praying, vert. 600ce, Emblem, Cape of Good Hope #178 used. No. 1304, Cover with Cape of Good Hope #178 from Mafeking, 1900. No. 1305, Campsites, 17th World Scout Jamboree, Korea, 1991.

**1991, July 16**    Litho.    Perf. 14
| | | | | |
|---|---|---|---|---|
| 1296 | A237 | 20ce buff & black | .60 | .20 |
| 1297 | A237 | 50ce multicolored | .75 | .40 |
| 1298 | A237 | 60ce multicolored | .75 | .50 |
| 1299 | A237 | 80ce black & buff | 1.25 | .65 |
| 1300 | A237 | 100ce multicolored | 1.60 | 1.00 |
| 1301 | A237 | 200ce multicolored | 2.00 | 2.00 |
| 1302 | A237 | 500ce multicolored | 4.25 | 4.25 |
| 1303 | A237 | 600ce multicolored | 5.00 | 5.00 |
| | | Nos. 1296-1303 (8) | 16.20 | 14.00 |

**Souvenir Sheets**
| | | | | |
|---|---|---|---|---|
| 1304 | A237 | 800ce multicolored | 5.50 | 5.50 |
| 1305 | A237 | 800ce multicolored | 5.50 | 5.50 |

For overprints see Nos. 1567-1572.

Chorkor Smoker A238

Designs: 20ce, Placing fish on racks. 60ce, Preparing smokers. 80ce, Preparing fish. 200ce, Preparing racks for smoker. 350ce, Placing racks in smoker.

**1991, July 22**    Litho.    Perf. 14x14½
| | | | | |
|---|---|---|---|---|
| 1306 | A238 | 20ce multicolored | .40 | .20 |
| 1307 | A238 | 60ce multicolored | .70 | .45 |
| 1308 | A238 | 80ce multicolored | .80 | .65 |
| 1309 | A238 | 200ce multicolored | 1.90 | 1.90 |
| 1310 | A238 | 350ce multicolored | 2.50 | 2.50 |
| | | Nos. 1306-1310 (5) | 6.30 | 5.70 |

Nos. 958-964 Overprinted "90th Birthday / 4th August 1990" and Surcharged

**Perf. 14, 12½x12 (#1312-1313, 1315)**

**1991, July 22**
| | | | | |
|---|---|---|---|---|
| 1311 | A184 | 20ce on 5ce #958 | .20 | .20 |
| 1312 | A184 | 20ce on 8ce #959 | .20 | .20 |
| 1313 | A184 | 40ce on 20ce #961 | .35 | .35 |
| 1314 | A184 | 60ce on 12ce #960 | .60 | .60 |
| 1315 | A184 | 80ce on 70ce #962 | .75 | .75 |
| 1316 | A184 | 150ce on 100ce #963 | 1.50 | 1.50 |
| | | Nos. 1311-1316 (6) | 3.60 | 3.60 |

**Souvenir Sheet**
| | | | | |
|---|---|---|---|---|
| 1317 | A184 | 200ce on 110ce #964 | 2.00 | 2.00 |

Nos. 1312-1313, 1315 issued in sheets of 5 + label. Overprint is vertical on stamp in No. 1317, horizontal on sheet margin.
The status of this issue is uncertain.

Fish A239

**1991, July 29**    Litho.    Perf. 14
| | | | | |
|---|---|---|---|---|
| 1318 | A239 | 20ce Cephalopholis taeniops | .20 | .20 |
| 1319 | A239 | 50ce Synodontis sorex | .40 | .40 |
| 1320 | A239 | 80ce Balistes forcipatus | .40 | .40 |
| 1321 | A239 | 100ce Petrocephalus bane | .50 | .50 |
| 1322 | A239 | 200ce Syngnathus rastellatus | 1.00 | 1.00 |
| 1323 | A239 | 300ce Gymnarchus niloticus | 2.50 | 2.50 |
| 1324 | A239 | 400ce Hemichromis bimaculatus | 3.50 | 3.50 |
| 1325 | A239 | 500ce Sphyrna zygaena | 2.75 | 2.75 |
| | | Nos. 1318-1325 (8) | 11.25 | 11.25 |

**Souvenir Sheets**
| | | | | |
|---|---|---|---|---|
| 1326 | A239 | 800ce Bagrus bayad | 5.25 | 5.25 |
| 1327 | A239 | 800ce Dactyloptena orientalis | 3.75 | 3.75 |

While Nos. 1320-1322, 1325, 1327 have the same issue date as Nos. 1318-1319, 1323-1324, 1326, the value of Nos. 1320-1322, 1325, 1327 was lower when they were released.
For overprints see Nos. 1573-1578.

---

Paintings by Vincent Van Gogh A240

Designs: 20ce, Reaper with Sickle. 50ce, The Thresher. 60ce, The Sheaf Binder. 80ce, The Sheep Shearers. 100ce, Peasant Woman Cutting Straw. 200ce, The Sower. 500ce, The Plow and the Harrow, horiz. 600ce, The Woodcutter. No. 1336, Evening: The Watch. No. 1337, Evening: The End of the Day.

**Perf. 13x13½, 13½x13**

**1991, Aug. 12**       Litho.
| | | | | |
|---|---|---|---|---|
| 1328 | A240 | 20ce multicolored | .20 | .20 |
| 1329 | A240 | 50ce multicolored | .40 | .40 |
| 1330 | A240 | 60ce multicolored | .50 | .50 |
| 1331 | A240 | 80ce multicolored | .65 | .65 |
| 1332 | A240 | 100ce multicolored | .80 | .80 |
| 1333 | A240 | 200ce multicolored | 1.60 | 1.60 |
| 1334 | A240 | 500ce multicolored | 4.00 | 4.00 |
| 1335 | A240 | 600ce multicolored | 4.75 | 4.75 |
| | | Nos. 1328-1335 (8) | 12.90 | 12.90 |

**Size: 106x80mm**
**Imperf**
| | | | | |
|---|---|---|---|---|
| 1336 | A240 | 800ce multicolored | 6.50 | 6.50 |
| 1337 | A240 | 800ce multicolored | 6.50 | 6.50 |

10th Non-aligned Ministers Conference, Accra — A241

Natl. Leaders: 20ce, Nasser, Egypt (1952-1970). 60ce, Tito, Yugoslavia (1945-1980). 80ce, Nehru, India (1947-1964). 200ce, Nkrumah, Ghana (1957-1966). 350ce, Sukarno, Indonesia (1945-1967).

**1991, Sept. 2**    Perf. 13½x14
| | | | | |
|---|---|---|---|---|
| 1338 | A241 | 20ce multicolored | .50 | .35 |
| 1339 | A241 | 60ce multicolored | .60 | .50 |
| 1340 | A241 | 80ce multicolored | 4.25 | 1.50 |
| 1341 | A241 | 200ce multicolored | 2.25 | 2.25 |
| 1342 | A241 | 350ce multicolored | 3.00 | 3.00 |
| | | Nos. 1338-1342 (5) | 10.60 | 7.60 |

Birds of Ghana — A242

Designs: No. 1343a, Melba finch. b, Orange-cheeked waxbill. c, Paradise flycatcher. d, Blue plantain-eater. e, Red bishop. f, Splendid glossy starling. g, Red-headed lovebird. h, Palm swift. i, Narina trogon. j, Tawny eagle. k, Bateleur eagle. l, Hoopoe. m, Secretary bird. n, White-backed vulture. o, Bare-headed rockfowl. p, Ground hornbill.
No. 1344a, Openbilled stork. b, African spoonbill. c, Pink-backed pelican. d, Little bittern. e, King reed-hen. f, Saddlebill stork. g, Glossy ibis. h, White-faced tree duck. i, Black-headed heron. j, Hammerkop. k, African darter. l, Woolly-necked stork. m, Yellow-billed stork. n, Black-winged stilt. o, Goliath heron. p, Lily trotter.
No. 1345a, Shikra. b, Abyssinian roller (c, g). c, Carmine bee-eater (g). d, Pintailed whydah (h). e, Purple glossy starling. f, Yellow-backed whydah (j). g, Pel's fishing owl. h, Verreaux's touraco (l). i, Red-cheeked cordon-bleu. j, Olive-bellied sunbird. k, Red-billed hornbill. l, Red-billed quelea. m, Crowned crane (i). n, Blue quail. o, Egyptian vulture. p, Helmeted guineafowl.
No. 1346, Marabou stork. No. 1347, Saddlebill stork, diff. No. 1348, African river eagle.

## 1991, Oct. 14   Litho.   Perf. 14½x14
### Sheets of 16
| | | | | |
|---|---|---|---|---|
| **1343** | A242 | 80ce #a.-p. | 9.00 | 9.00 |
| **1344** | A242 | 100ce #a.-p. | 13.50 | 13.50 |
| **1345** | A242 | 100ce #a.-p. | 16.00 | 16.00 |
| | *Nos. 1343-1345 (3)* | | 38.50 | 38.50 |

### Souvenir Sheets
| | | | | |
|---|---|---|---|---|
| **1346** | A242 | 800ce multicolored | 6.00 | 6.00 |
| **1347** | A242 | 800ce multicolored | 6.00 | 6.00 |
| **1348** | A242 | 800ce multicolored | 6.00 | 6.00 |

While No. 1344 has the same issue date as No. 1345, the value of No. 1344 was lower when it was released.

Insects
A243

## 1991, Oct. 25   Perf. 14x13½
| | | | | |
|---|---|---|---|---|
| **1349** | A243 | 20ce Nularda | .65 | .25 |
| **1350** | A243 | 50ce Zonocrus | .80 | .40 |
| **1351** | A243 | 60ce Gryllotalpa africana | 1.00 | .50 |
| **1352** | A243 | 80ce Weevil | 1.40 | 1.25 |
| **1353** | A243 | 100ce Coenagrion | 1.75 | 2.00 |
| **1354** | A243 | 150ce Sahlbergella | 2.00 | 2.25 |
| **1355** | A243 | 200ce Anthia | 2.25 | 3.00 |
| **1356** | A243 | 350ce Megacephala | 3.00 | 3.00 |
| | *Nos. 1349-1356 (8)* | | 12.85 | 12.65 |

### Souvenir Sheet
### Perf. 13x12
| | | | | |
|---|---|---|---|---|
| **1357** | A243 | 600ce Lacetus | 12.00 | 12.00 |

Landmarks and Shells — A243a

Designs: 50ce, Boti Falls, vert. 60ce, Larabanga Mosque. 80ce, Fort Sebastian, Shama. 100ce, Cape Coast Castle. 200ce, Leucodon cowrie. 400ce, Achatina achatina.

100ce exists in four types:

Type I, "G" has angled curve, bars in "A"s slope down to left, "c" has straight line, bottom inscription 10mm.

Type II, "G" is rounded, bars in "A"s slope down to right, "c" has slanted line, bottom inscription 13mm.

Type III, "G" is rounded, bars in "A"s slope down to right, "c" has straight line, bottom inscription 10mm.

Type IV, "G" rounded, but cut off at top, bars in "A"s slope to right, "C" with slanted line, bottom inscription 10mm.

200ce, 400ce

Nos. 1357E, 1357Ej, 1357F, Type I: "G" has angled curve, bar in "A's" slope down to left.

Nos. 1357Ek, 1357Fl, Type II: "G" is rounded, bars in "A's" slope down to right.

### Perf. 13¾x13½, 13½x13¾
| 1991 | | | Litho. |
|---|---|---|---|
| **1357A** | A243a | 50ce multi | — |
| **1357B** | A243a | 60ce multi | — |
| **1357C** | A243a | 80ce multi | — |
| **1357D** | A243a | 100ce multi (I) | — |
| *g.* | | Type II | |
| *h.* | | Type I, perf 14¼x13¾ | |
| *i.* | | Type III, perf 14¼x13¾ | |
| *m.* | | Type IV | — |
| **1357E** | A243a | 200ce multi (I) | — |
| *j.* | | Type I, perf. 14¼x13¾ | |
| *k.* | | Type II, perf. 14¼x13¾ | |
| **1357F** | A243a | 400ce multi (I) | — |
| *l.* | | Type II, perf. 14¼x13¾ | |

This set was printed locally. Shades exist.
Issue dates: 50ce, Nov. 21; others, Dec. 12.
#1357Dm, 2004(?).

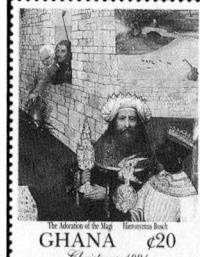

Adoration of the Magi by Hieronymus Bosch
A244

Details or entire paintings: 50ce, The Annunciation by Robert Campin. 60ce, Virgin and Child by Dirk Bouts. 80ce, Presentation in the Temple by Hans Memling. 100ce, The Virgin and Child Enthroned with an Angel and a Donor by Memling. 200ce, The Virgin and Child with Saints and a Donor by Jan van Eyck. 400ce, St. Luke Painting the Virgin by Rogier van der Weyden. 700ce, Virgin and Child by Bouts, diff. No. 1366. The Annunciation by Memling. No. 1367, The Virgin and Child Standing in a Niche by van der Weyden.

## 1991, Dec. 23   Perf. 12
| | | | | |
|---|---|---|---|---|
| **1358** | A244 | 20ce multicolored | .20 | .20 |
| **1359** | A244 | 50ce multicolored | .45 | .45 |
| **1360** | A244 | 60ce multicolored | .55 | .55 |
| **1361** | A244 | 80ce multicolored | .70 | .70 |
| **1362** | A244 | 100ce multicolored | .90 | .90 |
| **1363** | A244 | 200ce multicolored | 1.75 | 1.75 |
| **1364** | A244 | 400ce multicolored | 3.50 | 3.50 |
| **1365** | A244 | 700ce multicolored | 6.00 | 6.00 |
| | *Nos. 1358-1365 (8)* | | 14.05 | 14.05 |

### Souvenir Sheets
### Perf. 14½
| | | | | |
|---|---|---|---|---|
| **1366** | A244 | 800ce multicolored | 5.50 | 5.50 |
| **1367** | A244 | 800ce multicolored | 5.50 | 5.50 |

Christmas.

Reunification of Germany — A245

Designs: 20ce, Opening of German border, Nov. 9, 1989. 60ce, Signing of Two Plus Four Treaty, Sept. 12, 1990. 80ce, Opening of Brandenburg Gate, Dec. 22, 1989. 800ce, German leaders, Unity Day, Oct. 3, 1990. 1000ce, Currency union, July 1, 1990.

No. 1371Ab, USSR Pres. Mikhail Gorbachev, vert. c, Chancellor Helmut Kohl, vert. d, Map of West Germany, vert. e, Map of East Germany, vert.

No. 1371g, Doves. h, German Chancellor Helmut Kohl, Foreign Minister Hans-Dietrich Genscher.

## 1992, Feb. 17   Litho.   Perf. 14
| | | | | |
|---|---|---|---|---|
| **1368** | A245 | 20ce multi | .30 | .20 |
| **1369** | A245 | 60ce multi | .55 | .55 |
| **1370** | A245 | 80ce multi | .75 | .75 |
| **1371** | A245 | 1000ce multi | 9.00 | 9.00 |
| | *Nos. 1368-1371 (4)* | | 10.60 | 10.50 |

### Souvenir Sheets
| | | | | |
|---|---|---|---|---|
| **1371A** | A245 | 300ce Sheet of 4, #b.-e. | 7.50 | 7.50 |
| **1371F** | A245 | 400ce Sheet of 2, #g.-h. | 2.50 | 2.50 |
| **1372** | A245 | 800ce multicolored | 5.50 | 5.50 |

While No. 1371F has the same issue date as No. 1371A, the dollar value of No. 1371F was lower when it was released.

1992 Summer Olympics, Barcelona
A246

Map and: 20ce, Eddie Blay, boxing, Ghana, 1964. 60ce, Mike Ahey, track, Ghana, 1964-1972. 80ce, T. Wilson, ski jumping, US, 1988. 100ce, East German 4-Man bobsled, 1988. 200ce, Greg Louganis, diving, US, 1984. 300ce, L. Visser, speed skating, Netherlands, 1988. 350ce, J. Passler, biathlon, Italy, 1988. 400ce, Mary Lou Retton, gymnastics, US, 1984. 500ce, Jurgen Hingsen, decathlon, Germany, 1984. 600ce, R. Neubert, heptathlon, West Germany, 1984. No. 1380, Jai alai player, vert. No. 1381, Windmill.

## 1992, Mar. 3   Litho.   Perf. 14
| | | | | |
|---|---|---|---|---|
| **1373** | A246 | 20ce multi | .50 | .20 |
| **1373A** | A246 | 60ce multi | .60 | .45 |
| **1374** | A246 | 80ce multi | .90 | .55 |
| **1375** | A246 | 100ce multi | 1.25 | .90 |
| **1376** | A246 | 200ce multi | 2.25 | 1.60 |
| **1377** | A246 | 300ce multi | 2.25 | 2.10 |
| **1378** | A246 | 350ce multi | 2.25 | 2.10 |
| **1378A** | A246 | 400ce multi | 3.00 | 2.75 |
| **1378B** | A246 | 500ce multi | 3.00 | 2.75 |
| **1379** | A246 | 600ce multi | 3.00 | 2.75 |
| | *Nos. 1373-1379 (10)* | | 19.00 | 16.15 |

### Souvenir Sheets
| | | | | |
|---|---|---|---|---|
| **1380** | A246 | 800ce multi | 7.00 | 7.00 |
| **1381** | A246 | 800ce multi | 7.00 | 7.00 |

While Nos. 1373A, 1378A-1378B have the same issue date as rest of the set the dollar value of Nos. 1373A, 1378A-1378B were lower when they were released.

Phila Nippon '91
A247

## 1992, Feb. 16   Litho.   Perf. 14
| | | | | |
|---|---|---|---|---|
| **1382** | A247 | 20ce shown | .20 | .20 |
| **1383** | A247 | 60ce Torii of Itsukushima Jingu shrine | .40 | .40 |
| **1384** | A247 | 80ce Geisha | .50 | .50 |
| **1385** | A247 | 100ce Samurai residence | .65 | .65 |
| **1386** | A247 | 200ce Bonsai tree | 1.50 | 1.50 |
| **1387** | A247 | 400ce Olympic sports hall | 3.00 | 3.00 |
| **1388** | A247 | 500ce Great Buddha | 3.50 | 3.50 |
| **1389** | A247 | 600ce Nagoya castle | 4.75 | 4.75 |
| | *Nos. 1382-1389 (8)* | | 14.50 | 14.50 |

### Souvenir Sheets
| | | | | |
|---|---|---|---|---|
| **1390** | A247 | 800ce Takamatsu castle | 6.50 | 6.50 |
| **1391** | A247 | 800ce Heian shrine | 6.50 | 6.50 |

Ghana Natl. Railways
A248

Designs: 20c, Engine, 1903, Gold Coast Railway. 50c, Diesel passenger locomotive, Ghana Railways Corp. 60ce, First class coach, 1931 Gold Coast Railway. 80ce, Official inspection coach, Gold Coast Railway. 100ce, Engine No. 401 on turntable. 200c, Twin-bogie cocoa wagon, 1921, Gold Coast Railway. 500ce, Engine No. 223, "Prince of Wales." 600c, Twin-bogie cattle wagon, Gold Coast Railway. No. 1400, German-made locomotive, Gold Coast Railway. No. 1401, Beyer-Garratt #301, 1943, Gold Coast Railway.

## 1992, Mar. 2
| | | | | |
|---|---|---|---|---|
| **1392** | A248 | 20ce multicolored | .20 | .20 |
| **1393** | A248 | 50ce multicolored | .35 | .35 |
| **1394** | A248 | 60ce multicolored | .45 | .45 |
| **1395** | A248 | 80ce multicolored | .55 | .55 |
| **1396** | A248 | 100ce multicolored | .65 | .65 |
| **1397** | A248 | 200ce multicolored | 1.40 | 1.40 |
| **1398** | A248 | 500ce multicolored | 3.50 | 3.50 |
| **1399** | A248 | 600ce multicolored | 4.75 | 4.75 |
| | *Nos. 1392-1399 (8)* | | 11.85 | 11.85 |

### Souvenir Sheets
| | | | | |
|---|---|---|---|---|
| **1400** | A248 | 800ce multicolored | 5.50 | 5.50 |
| **1401** | A248 | 800ce multicolored | 5.50 | 5.50 |

Decade of Revolutionary Progress
A249

## 1992, Feb. 2   Litho.   Perf. 14x13½
| | | | | |
|---|---|---|---|---|
| **1402** | A249 | 20ce Bore hole water | .30 | .30 |
| **1403** | A249 | 50ce Mining industry | .35 | .35 |
| **1404** | A249 | 60ce Small scale industry | .45 | .45 |
| **1405** | A249 | 80ce Timber industry | .50 | .50 |
| **1406** | A249 | 200ce Cocoa rehabilitation | 1.00 | 1.00 |
| **1407** | A249 | 350ce Rural electrification | 1.25 | 1.25 |
| | *Nos. 1402-1407 (6)* | | 3.85 | 3.85 |

Reptiles
A251

## 1992, Mar. 30   Litho.   Perf. 14
| | | | | |
|---|---|---|---|---|
| **1414** | A251 | 20ce Angides lugubris | .20 | .20 |
| **1415** | A251 | 50ce Kinixys erosa | .35 | .35 |
| **1416** | A251 | 60ce Agama agama | .35 | .35 |
| **1417** | A251 | 80ce Chameleo gracilis | .45 | .45 |
| **1418** | A251 | 100ce Naja melanleuca | .65 | .65 |
| **1419** | A251 | 200ce Crocodylus niloticus | 1.10 | 1.10 |
| **1420** | A251 | 400ce Chelonia mydas | 2.25 | 2.25 |
| **1421** | A251 | 500ce Varanus exanthematicus | 2.75 | 2.75 |
| | *Nos. 1414-1421 (8)* | | 8.10 | 8.10 |

### Souvenir Sheet
| | | | | |
|---|---|---|---|---|
| **1422** | A251 | 600ce Snake & tortoise | 5.25 | 5.25 |

Numbers have been reserved for additional values in this set.

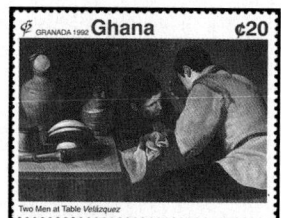

Easter
A252

Details from paintings: 20ce, The Four Apostles: Sts. John, Peter, Paul & Mark, by Durer. 50ce, The Last Judgment, by Rubens. 60ce, The Four Apostles: Sts. John, Peter, Paul and Mark, diff. by Durer. 80ce, The Last Judgment, diff. by Rubens. 100ce, Crucifixion, by Rubens. 200ce, The Last Judgment, diff. by Rubens. 500ce, Christum Videre, by Rubens. 600ce, The Last Judgment, diff. by Rubens. No. 1432, Last Communion of St. Francis of Assisi, by Rubens. No. 1432A, Scourging the Money Changers from the Temple, by El Greco, horiz.

## 1992, Mar. 13   Perf. 13½x14
| | | | | |
|---|---|---|---|---|
| **1424** | A252 | 20ce multi | .20 | .20 |
| **1425** | A252 | 50ce multi | .35 | .35 |
| **1426** | A252 | 60ce multi | .45 | .45 |
| **1427** | A252 | 80ce multi | .55 | .55 |
| **1428** | A252 | 100ce multi | .65 | .65 |
| **1429** | A252 | 200ce multi | 1.10 | 1.10 |
| **1430** | A252 | 500ce multi | 3.00 | 3.00 |
| **1431** | A252 | 600ce multi | 3.25 | 3.25 |
| | *Nos. 1424-1431 (8)* | | 9.55 | 9.55 |

### Souvenir Sheets
| | | | | |
|---|---|---|---|---|
| **1432** | A252 | 800ce multi | 5.50 | 5.50 |

### Perf. 14x13½
| | | | | |
|---|---|---|---|---|
| **1432A** | A252 | 800ce multi | 5.50 | 5.50 |

Spanish Art — A253

Paintings by Velazquez: 20ce, Two Men at Table. 60ce, Christ in the House of Mary and Martha (detail). 80ce, The Supper at Emmaus. 100ce, Three Muscians. 200ce, Old Woman Cooking Eggs, vert. 400ce, Old Woman Cooking Eggs (detail), vert. 500ce, The Surrender of Breda (detail) diff., vert. 700ce, The Surrender of Breda (detail), vert.

No. 1441, They Still Say that Fish is Expensive, by Joaquin Sorolla y Bastida. No. 1442, The Waterseller of Seville.

## 1992, May 4   Perf. 13½
| | | | | |
|---|---|---|---|---|
| **1433** | A253 | 20ce multicolored | .20 | .20 |
| **1434** | A253 | 60ce multicolored | .30 | .30 |
| **1435** | A253 | 80ce multicolored | .40 | .40 |
| **1436** | A253 | 100ce multicolored | .60 | .60 |
| **1437** | A253 | 200ce multicolored | 1.25 | 1.25 |
| **1438** | A253 | 400ce multicolored | 2.00 | 2.00 |
| **1439** | A253 | 500ce multicolored | 2.50 | 2.50 |
| **1440** | A253 | 700ce multicolored | 4.25 | 4.25 |

## Size: 120x95mm
### *Imperf*

| | | | | | |
|---|---|---|---|---|---|
| **1441** | A253 | 900ce multicolored | | 5.75 | 5.75 |
| **1442** | A253 | 900ce multicolored | | 5.25 | 5.25 |
| | | *Nos. 1433-1442 (10)* | | 22.50 | 22.50 |

Granada '92. While Nos. 1434-1435, 1438-1439, 1442 have the same issue date as Nos. 1433, 1436-1437, 1440-1441, the value in relation to the dollar of Nos. 1434-1435, 1438-1439, 1442 was lower when they were released.

Butterflies — A254      Dinosaurs — A255

### 1992, May 25      Litho.      *Perf. 14*

| | | | | |
|---|---|---|---|---|
| **1443** | A254 | 20ce African monarch | .20 | .20 |
| **1444** | A254 | 60ce Mocker swallowtail | .40 | .40 |
| **1445** | A254 | 80ce Painted lady | .55 | .55 |
| **1446** | A254 | 100ce Mountain beauty | .65 | .65 |
| **1447** | A254 | 200ce Blue temora | 1.50 | 1.50 |
| **1448** | A254 | 400ce Foxy charaxes | 3.00 | 3.00 |
| **1449** | A254 | 500ce Blue pansy | 3.50 | 3.50 |
| **1450** | A254 | 700ce Golden pansy | 5.00 | 5.00 |
| | | *Nos. 1443-1450 (8)* | 14.80 | 14.80 |

### Souvenir Sheets

| | | | | |
|---|---|---|---|---|
| **1451** | A254 | 900ce Gaudy commodore | 5.50 | 5.50 |
| **1452** | A254 | 900ce Christmas butterfly | 5.50 | 5.50 |

Genoa '92. For overprints see Nos. 1471-1480.

### 1992, June 1      Litho.      *Perf. 14*

| | | | | |
|---|---|---|---|---|
| **1453** | A255 | 20ce Iguanodon | .45 | .35 |
| **1454** | A255 | 50ce Anchisaurus | .65 | .45 |
| **1455** | A255 | 60ce Heterodontosaurus | .70 | .45 |
| **1456** | A255 | 80ce Ouranosaurus | .75 | .55 |
| **1457** | A255 | 100ce Anatosaurus | 1.00 | .65 |
| **1458** | A255 | 200ce Elaphrosaurus | 1.60 | 1.60 |
| **1459** | A255 | 500ce Coelophysis | 3.00 | 3.00 |
| **1460** | A255 | 600ce Rhamphorynchus | 3.50 | 3.50 |
| | | *Nos. 1453-1460 (8)* | 11.65 | 10.55 |

### Souvenir Sheets

| | | | | |
|---|---|---|---|---|
| **1461** | A255 | 1500ce like #1459 | 6.75 | 6.75 |
| **1462** | A255 | 1500ce like #1458 | 6.75 | 6.75 |

While Nos. 1453, 1456, 1458-1459 and 1462 have the same issue date as Nos. 1454-1455, 1457, 1460-1461, their value in relation to the dollar was lower when they were released.

Discovery of America, 500th Anniv. — A256

No. 1463: a, Capt. Martin Alonzo Pinzon, Pinta. b, Capt. Vicente Yanez Pinzon, Nina. c, Columbus, Fr. Marchena in La Rabida, 1485. d, Columbus in cabin. e, Land sighted, Oct. 12, 1492. f, Columbus lands on Samana Cay. g, Shipwreck of Santa Maria. h, Columbus returns to Spanish Court, 1493.
No. 1464, Columbus, ship.

### 1992, July      Litho.      *Perf. 14*

| | | | | |
|---|---|---|---|---|
| **1463** | A256 | 200ce Sheet of 8, #a.-h. | 10.00 | 10.00 |

### Souvenir Sheet

| | | | | |
|---|---|---|---|---|
| **1464** | A256 | 500ce multicolored | 4.00 | 4.00 |

World Columbian Stamp Expo '92, Chicago.

---

Shells — A257

### 1992, Oct. 5      Litho.      *Perf. 14*

| | | | | |
|---|---|---|---|---|
| **1465** | A257 | 20ce Olivancillaria hiatula | .20 | .20 |
| **1465A** | A257 | 20ce Tympanotonus fuscatus | .20 | .20 |
| **1466** | A257 | 60ce Donax rugosus | .35 | .35 |
| **1466A** | A257 | 60ce Murex cornutus | .35 | .35 |
| **1467** | A257 | 80ce Sigaretus concavus | .45 | .45 |
| **1467A** | A257 | 80ce Tivela tripla | .45 | .45 |
| **1468** | A257 | 200ce Pila africana | 1.25 | 1.25 |
| **1468A** | A257 | 200ce Cypraea stercoraria | 1.25 | 1.25 |
| **1469** | A257 | 350ce Thais hiatula | 2.00 | 2.00 |
| **1469A** | A257 | 350ce Cassis tessellata | 2.00 | 2.00 |
| | | *Nos. 1465-1469A (10)* | 8.50 | 8.50 |

### Souvenir Sheet

| | | | | |
|---|---|---|---|---|
| **1470** | A257 | 600ce Natica favel | 5.00 | 5.00 |
| **1470A** | A257 | 600ce Semifusos morio | 5.00 | 5.00 |

Nos. 1443-1452 Ovptd. "40th / Anniversary / of the / Accession / of / HM Queen / Elizabeth II / 1952-1992" in Silver

### 1992, Aug. 10      Litho.      *Perf. 14*

| | | | | |
|---|---|---|---|---|
| **1471** | A254 | 20ce on #1443 | .20 | .20 |
| **1472** | A254 | 60ce on #1444 | .35 | .35 |
| **1473** | A254 | 80ce on #1445 | .50 | .50 |
| **1474** | A254 | 100ce on #1446 | .60 | .60 |
| **1475** | A254 | 200ce on #1447 | 1.25 | 1.25 |
| **1476** | A254 | 400ce on #1448 | 2.25 | 2.25 |
| **1477** | A254 | 500ce on #1449 | 3.00 | 3.00 |
| **1478** | A254 | 700ce on #1450 | 4.00 | 4.00 |
| | | *Nos. 1471-1478 (8)* | 12.15 | 12.15 |

### Souvenir Sheets

| | | | | |
|---|---|---|---|---|
| **1479** | A254 | 900ce on #1451 | 6.00 | 6.00 |
| **1480** | A254 | 900ce on #1452 | 6.00 | 6.00 |

Christmas — A259

Details or entire paintings: 20ce, Presentation in the Temple, by Master of Brunswick. 50ce, Presentation in the Temple, by Master of St. Severin. 60ce, The Visitation, by Sebastiano del Piombo. 80ce, The Visitation, by Giotto. 100ce, The Circumcision, by Studio of Giovanni Bellini. 200ce, The Circumcision, by Workshop of Benvenuto Garofalo. 500ce, The Visitation, by Workshop of Rogier van der Weyden. 800ce, The Visitation, by Workshop of Rogier Van der Weyden. No. 1491, The Visitation, by Giotto. No. 1492, The Presentation in the Temple, by Bartolo di Fredi.

### 1992      Litho.      *Perf. 13½x14*

| | | | | |
|---|---|---|---|---|
| **1483** | A259 | 20ce multicolored | .20 | .20 |
| **1484** | A259 | 50ce multicolored | .30 | .30 |
| **1485** | A259 | 60ce multicolored | .35 | .35 |
| **1486** | A259 | 80ce multicolored | .40 | .40 |
| **1487** | A259 | 100ce multicolored | .50 | .50 |
| **1488** | A259 | 200ce multicolored | 1.00 | 1.00 |
| **1489** | A259 | 500ce multicolored | 2.75 | 2.75 |
| **1490** | A259 | 800ce multicolored | 4.25 | 4.25 |
| | | *Nos. 1483-1490 (8)* | 9.75 | 9.75 |

### Souvenir Sheet

| | | | | |
|---|---|---|---|---|
| **1491** | A259 | 900ce multicolored | 5.50 | 5.50 |
| **1492** | A259 | 900ce multicolored | 5.50 | 5.50 |

No. 1492 exists imperf.

---

Anniversaries and Events
A260          A261

Designs: 20ce, LZ3, floating hangar at Lake Constance, horiz. 100ce, Lift-off of Ariane 4 rocket, horiz. 200ce, Leopard in tree, horiz. 300ce, Roman Colosseum, fruits and vegetables, horiz. 400ce, Wolfgang Amadeus Mozart. 600ce, Lift-off of H-1 rocket, Japan. 800ce, LZ10, Schwaben, horiz. No. 1501, Scene from "The Marriage of Figaro." No. 1502, Space shuttle, US. No. 1503, Count Ferdinand von Zeppelin. No. 1504, Bongo, horiz.

### 1992, Dec.      Litho.      *Perf. 14*

| | | | | |
|---|---|---|---|---|
| **1493** | A260 | 20ce multicolored | .20 | .20 |
| **1494** | A260 | 100ce multicolored | .55 | .55 |
| **1495** | A260 | 200ce multicolored | 1.10 | 1.10 |
| **1496** | A260 | 300ce multicolored | 1.75 | 1.75 |
| **1497** | A261 | 400ce multicolored | 2.50 | 2.50 |
| **1499** | A260 | 600ce multicolored | 3.75 | 3.75 |
| **1500** | A260 | 800ce multicolored | 5.00 | 5.00 |
| | | *Nos. 1493-1500 (7)* | 14.85 | 14.85 |

### Souvenir Sheets

| | | | | |
|---|---|---|---|---|
| **1501** | A261 | 900ce multicolored | 5.50 | 5.50 |
| **1502** | A260 | 900ce multicolored | 5.50 | 5.50 |
| **1503** | A260 | 900ce multicolored | 5.50 | 5.50 |
| **1504** | A260 | 900ce multicolored | 5.50 | 5.50 |

Count Ferdinand von Zeppelin, 75th anniv. of death (#1493, 1500, 1503). Intl. Space Year (#1494, 1499, 1502). UN Earth Summit, Rio de Janeiro (#1495, 1504). WHO, Intl. Conference on Nutrition, Rome (1496). Mozart, bicent. of death (in 1991) (#1497, 1501).

Flowers — A262

Designs: Nos. 1505, 1514d (100ce), Lagerstroemia flos-reginae. No. 1506, Clerodendrum thomsoniae. Nos. 1507, 1514c (50ce), Spathodea campanulata. No. 1508, Cassia fistula. Nos. 1509, 1514e (150ce), Mellitea ferrugenea. Nos. 1510, 1514j (300ce), Hildegardia barteri. Nos. 1511, 1514i (150ce), Ipomoea asarifolia. No. 1512, Petrea volubilis. Nos. 1513, 1514f (300ce), Ritchiea reflexa. Nos. 1514, 1514h (100ce), Bryphyllum pinnatum.

### 1993, Mar. 1      Litho.      *Perf. 14*

| | | | | |
|---|---|---|---|---|
| **1505** | A262 | 20ce multicolored | .20 | .20 |
| **1506** | A262 | 20ce multicolored | .20 | .20 |
| **1507** | A262 | 60ce multicolored | .30 | .30 |
| **1508** | A262 | 60ce multicolored | .30 | .30 |
| **1509** | A262 | 80ce multicolored | .40 | .40 |
| **1510** | A262 | 80ce multicolored | .40 | .40 |
| **1511** | A262 | 200ce multicolored | 1.00 | 1.00 |
| **1512** | A262 | 200ce multicolored | 1.00 | 1.00 |
| **1513** | A262 | 350ce multicolored | 1.75 | 1.75 |
| **1514** | A262 | 350ce multicolored | 1.75 | 1.75 |
| | | *Nos. 1505-1514 (10)* | 7.30 | 7.30 |

### Souvenir Sheets

| | | | | |
|---|---|---|---|---|
| **1514A** | A262 | Sheet of 4, #c.-f. | 3.75 | 3.75 |
| **1514B** | A262 | Sheet of 4, #g.-j. | 3.75 | 3.75 |

Intl. Conference on Nutrition, Rome — A263

### 1993, Jan.      Litho.      *Perf. 14*

| | | | | |
|---|---|---|---|---|
| **1515** | A263 | 20ce Energy foods | .20 | .20 |
| **1516** | A263 | 60ce Body-building foods | .30 | .30 |
| **1517** | A263 | 80ce Protective foods | .40 | .40 |

---

| | | | | |
|---|---|---|---|---|
| **1518** | A263 | 200ce Disease prevention | 1.00 | 1.00 |
| **1519** | A263 | 400ce Food quality control, preservation | 2.00 | 2.00 |
| | | *Nos. 1515-1519 (5)* | 3.90 | 3.90 |

Crabs — A264

Designs: 20ce, Clappa rubroguttata. 60ce, Cardisoma amatum. 80ce, Maia squinado. 400ce, Ocypoda cursor. 800ce, Grapus grapus.

### 1993, Feb.      *Perf. 14x13½*

| | | | | |
|---|---|---|---|---|
| **1520** | A264 | 20ce multicolored | .20 | .20 |
| **1521** | A264 | 60ce multicolored | .35 | .35 |
| **1522** | A264 | 80ce multicolored | .45 | .45 |
| **1523** | A264 | 400ce multicolored | 2.25 | 2.25 |
| *a.* | | Souv. sheet of 4, #1520-1523 | 7.50 | 7.50 |
| **1524** | A264 | 800ce multicolored | 4.50 | 4.50 |
| | | *Nos. 1520-1524 (5)* | 7.75 | 7.75 |

### Miniature Sheet of 8

Louvre Museum, Bicent. A265

No. 1525 — Details or entire paintings, by Giovanni Domenico Tiepolo (1727-1804) (a-e) and Giovanni Battista Tiepolo (1696-1770) (f-h): a-c, Carnival Scene, (left, center, right). d-e, Tooth Puller, (left, right). f, Rebecca at the Well. g-h, Presenting Christ to the People, (left, right).
700ce, Chancellor Seguier, by Le Brun, horiz.

### 1993, Mar. 1      Litho.      *Perf. 12*

| | | | | |
|---|---|---|---|---|
| **1525** | A265 | 200ce Sheet of 8, #a.-h. + label | 10.00 | 10.00 |

### Souvenir Sheet
### *Perf. 14½*

| | | | | |
|---|---|---|---|---|
| **1526** | A265 | 700ce multicolored | 4.25 | 4.25 |

No. 1526 contains one 55x88mm stamp.

Oil Palm Fruit — A265a

### 1993, Apr.      Litho.      *Perf. 13½*

| | | | | |
|---|---|---|---|---|
| **1526A** | A265a | 20ce multi | — | — |

Faberge Eggs — A266      4th Republic — A268

Wild Animals — A267

Easter: 50ce, Resurrection Egg. 80ce, Imperial Red Cross Egg with Resurrection Triptych. 100ce, Imperial Uspensky Cathedral Egg. 150ce, Imperial Red Cross Egg with portraits. 200ce, Orange Tree Egg. 250ce, Rabbit Egg. 400ce, Imperial Coronation Egg. 900ce, Silver-gilt enamel Easter Egg. No. 1535, Spring Flower Egg. No. 1536, Egg charms, horiz.

**1993, Apr. 26**      **Perf. 14**

| | | | | |
|---|---|---|---|---|
| 1527 | A266 | 50ce multi | .30 | .30 |
| 1528 | A266 | 80ce multi | .50 | .50 |
| 1529 | A266 | 100ce multi | .60 | .60 |
| 1530 | A266 | 150ce multi | .90 | .90 |
| 1531 | A266 | 200ce multi | 1.25 | 1.25 |
| 1532 | A266 | 250ce multi | 1.75 | 1.75 |
| 1533 | A266 | 400ce multi | 3.50 | 3.50 |
| 1534 | A266 | 900ce multi | 7.50 | 7.50 |
| | | Nos. 1527-1534 (8) | 16.30 | 16.30 |

**Souvenir Sheets**

| | | | | |
|---|---|---|---|---|
| 1535 | A266 | 1000ce multi | 6.50 | 6.50 |
| 1536 | A266 | 1000ce multi | 6.50 | 6.50 |

**1993, May 24**   **Litho.**   **Perf. 14**

| | | | | |
|---|---|---|---|---|
| 1537 | A267 | 20ce African buffalo | .20 | .20 |
| 1538 | A267 | 50ce Giant forest hog | .50 | .50 |
| 1539 | A267 | 60ce Potto | .60 | .60 |
| 1540 | A267 | 80ce Bay duiker | .80 | .80 |
| 1541 | A267 | 100ce Royal antelope | 1.00 | 1.00 |
| 1542 | A267 | 200ce Serval | 2.00 | 2.00 |
| 1543 | A267 | 500ce Golden cat | 5.00 | 5.00 |
| 1544 | A267 | 800ce Megaloglossus woermanni | 8.50 | 8.50 |
| | | Nos. 1537-1544 (8) | 18.60 | 18.60 |

**Souvenir Sheets**

| | | | | |
|---|---|---|---|---|
| 1545 | A267 | 900ce Dormouse | 6.50 | 6.50 |
| 1546 | A267 | 900ce White collared mangabey | 6.50 | 6.50 |

**1993, May**   **Litho.**   **Perf. 14**

50ce, Kwame Nkrumah Mausoleum, horiz. 100ce, Kwame Nkrumah Conference Center, horiz. 200ce, Constitution book. 350ce, Independence Square. 400ce, Christiansborg Castle.

| | | | | |
|---|---|---|---|---|
| 1547 | A268 | 50ce multicolored | .30 | .30 |
| 1548 | A268 | 100ce multicolored | .60 | .60 |
| 1549 | A268 | 200ce multicolored | 1.25 | 1.25 |
| 1550 | A268 | 350ce multicolored | 2.25 | 2.25 |
| 1551 | A268 | 400ce multicolored | 2.75 | 2.75 |
| | | Nos. 1547-1551 (5) | 7.15 | 7.15 |

A269

Aviation and Automotive Anniversaries — A270

Designs: 50ce, Graf Zeppelin over Alps, vert. No. 1552, Mercedes Benz 300 SLR in 1955 Mille Miglia. No. 1553, LZ7 Deutschland. No. 1554, Vulcan bomber. No. 1555, Ford Trimotor. No. 1556, 1920 Ford Depot Wagon. No. 1557, Nieuport 27, vert. No. 1558, Graf Zeppelin taking aboard letters, vert. No. 1559, 1970 Ford Mach 1 Mustang.
No. 1560, LZ10 Schwaben. No. 1561, Mercedes wins 1937 Monaco Grand Prix. No. 1562, Graf Zeppelin over Rome. No. 1563, 1955 Mercedes Benz Type 196. No. 1564, Early US air mail flight. No. 1565, S.E.5A, 1918. No. 1566, 1910 Ford Super T, 999.

**1993**   **Litho.**   **Perf. 14**

| | | | | |
|---|---|---|---|---|
| 1551A | A269 | 50ce multi | .40 | .40 |
| 1552 | A270 | 150ce multi | 1.00 | 1.00 |
| 1553 | A269 | 150ce multi | 1.00 | 1.00 |
| 1554 | A269 | 400ce multi | 3.00 | 3.00 |
| 1555 | A269 | 400ce multi | 3.00 | 3.00 |
| 1556 | A270 | 400ce multi | 3.00 | 3.00 |
| 1557 | A269 | 600ce multi | 4.25 | 4.25 |
| 1558 | A269 | 600ce multi | 4.25 | 4.25 |
| 1559 | A269 | 600ce multi | 4.25 | 4.25 |
| 1560 | A269 | 800ce multi | 5.50 | 5.50 |
| 1561 | A270 | 800ce multi | 5.50 | 5.50 |
| | | Nos. 1551A-1561 (11) | 35.15 | 35.15 |

---

**Souvenir Sheets**

| | | | | |
|---|---|---|---|---|
| 1562 | A269 | 1000ce multi | 5.50 | 5.50 |
| 1563 | A270 | 1000ce multi | 5.50 | 5.50 |
| 1564 | A269 | 1000ce multi | 5.50 | 5.50 |
| 1565 | A269 | 1000ce multi | 5.50 | 5.50 |
| 1566 | A270 | 1000ce multi | 5.50 | 5.50 |

Capt. Hugo Eckener, 125th birth anniv. (#1551A, 1553-1554, 1562). Benz's first four-wheeled vehicle, cent. (#1552, 1561, 1563). Royal Air Force, 75th anniv. (#1554, 1557, 1564). Henry Ford's first gasoline powered engine, cent. (#1556, 1559, 1566).
No. 1564 contains one 57x42mm stamp. Nos. 1563, 1566 contains one 85x28mm stamp.
Issued: #1555-1556, 1558-1559, 1565-1566, May. #1551A-1554, 1557, 1560-1564, June.

Nos. 1300-1305 Ovptd.

**1993**   **Litho.**   **Perf. 14**

| | | | | |
|---|---|---|---|---|
| 1567 | A237 | 100ce multicolored | .75 | .75 |
| 1568 | A237 | 200ce multicolored | 1.75 | 1.75 |
| 1569 | A237 | 500ce multicolored | 3.50 | 3.50 |
| 1570 | A237 | 600ce multicolored | 5.00 | 5.00 |
| | | Nos. 1567-1570 (4) | 11.00 | 11.00 |

**Souvenir Sheet**

| | | | | |
|---|---|---|---|---|
| 1571 | A237 | 800ce on #1304 | 6.00 | 6.00 |
| 1572 | A237 | 800ce on #1305 | 6.00 | 6.00 |

Nos. 1321, 1323-1327 Ovptd. a. in Black "35 YEARS OF / ROTARY INTERNATIONAL / GHANA 1958" or b. in Red "GHANA / RED CROSS SOCIETY / FOUNDED 1932"

**1993**

| | | | | |
|---|---|---|---|---|
| 1573 | A239(a) | 100ce multi | .75 | .75 |
| 1574 | A239(b) | 300ce multi | 2.00 | 2.00 |
| 1575 | A239(b) | 400ce multi | 3.25 | 3.25 |
| 1576 | A239(a) | 500ce multi | 4.00 | 4.00 |
| | | Nos. 1573-1576 (4) | 10.00 | 10.00 |

**Souvenir Sheets**

| | | | | |
|---|---|---|---|---|
| 1577 | A239(a) | 800ce on #1326 | 6.50 | 6.50 |
| 1578 | A239(b) | 800ce on #1327 | 6.50 | 6.50 |

A271

Mushrooms A272

Designs: 20ce, Cantharellus cibarius. 50ce, Russula cyanoxantha. 60ce, Clitocybe rivulosa. No. 1581, Boletus chrysenteron. No. 1582, Cortinarius elatior. No. 1583, Mycena galericulata. No. 1584, Boletus edulis. No. 1585, Tricholoma gambosum. No. 1586, Lepista saeva. 250ce, Gyroporus castaneus. No. 1589, Nolanea sericea. No. 1590, Hygrophorus puiceus. 500ce, Gomphidius glutinosus. No. 1592, Russula olivacea. 1000ce, Russula aurata.
No. 1594a, 100ce, Cantharellus cibarius. b, 150ce, Cortinarius elatior. c, 300ce, Tricholoma gambosum. d, 600ce, Hygrophorus puiceus.
No. 1595: a, 50ce, like #1581. b, 100ce, like #1583. c, 150ce, like #1584. d, 1000ce, like #1589.

**1993, July 30**   **Litho.**   **Perf. 14**

| | | | | |
|---|---|---|---|---|
| 1579 | A271 | 20ce multi | .20 | .20 |
| 1580 | A271 | 50ce multi | .25 | .25 |
| 1581 | A271 | 60ce multi | .30 | .30 |
| 1582 | A271 | 80ce multi | .40 | .40 |

---

| | | | | |
|---|---|---|---|---|
| 1583 | A271 | 80ce multi | .40 | .40 |
| 1584 | A271 | 200ce multi | 1.00 | 1.00 |
| 1585 | A271 | 200ce multi | 1.00 | 1.00 |
| 1586 | A272 | 200ce multi | 1.00 | 1.00 |
| 1587 | A272 | 250ce multi | 1.25 | 1.25 |
| 1588 | A271 | 300ce multi | 1.50 | 1.50 |
| 1589 | A271 | 350ce multi | 2.00 | 2.00 |
| 1590 | A271 | 350ce multi | 2.00 | 2.00 |
| 1591 | A272 | 500ce multi | 3.00 | 3.00 |
| 1592 | A272 | 600ce multi | 3.50 | 3.50 |
| 1593 | A272 | 1000ce multi | 6.00 | 6.00 |
| | | Nos. 1579-1593 (15) | 23.80 | 23.80 |

**Souvenir Sheets**

| | | | | |
|---|---|---|---|---|
| 1594 | A271 | Sheet of 4, #a.-d. | 8.00 | 8.00 |
| 1595 | A271 | Sheet of 4, #a.-d. | 8.00 | 8.00 |

Copernicus (1473-1543) A273

Designs: 20ce, Early astronomical instrument. 200ce, Telescope. No. 1598, Copernicus, long hair. No. 1599, Copernicus, shorter hair.

**1993, Oct. 19**   **Litho.**   **Perf. 13½x14**

| | | | | |
|---|---|---|---|---|
| 1596 | A273 | 20ce multicolored | .20 | .20 |
| 1597 | A273 | 200ce multicolored | 1.10 | 1.10 |

**Souvenir Sheets**

**Perf. 12x13**

| | | | | |
|---|---|---|---|---|
| 1598 | A273 | 1000ce multicolored | 6.25 | 6.25 |
| 1599 | A273 | 1000ce multicolored | 6.25 | 6.25 |

Picasso (1881-1973) A274

Paintings: 20ce, The Actor, 1905. 80ce, Portrait of Allen Stein, 1906. 800ce, Seated Male Nude, 1908-09.

**1993, Oct. 19**      **Perf. 14**

| | | | | |
|---|---|---|---|---|
| 1600-1602 | A274 | Set of 3 | 6.25 | 6.25 |

**Souvenir Sheet**

| | | | | |
|---|---|---|---|---|
| 1603 | A274 | 900ce Man with a Javelin, 1958 | 6.25 | 6.25 |

Polska '93 — A275     1994 World Cup Soccer, US — A276

Paintings: 200ce, Tattoo, by Sobocki, 1978. 600ce, Prison, by Blonder, 1934. 1000ce, Fable of the Fortunate Man, by Michalak, 1925, horiz.

**1993, Oct. 19**

| | | | | |
|---|---|---|---|---|
| 1604-1605 | A275 | Set of 2 | 5.25 | 5.25 |

**Souvenir Sheet**

| | | | | |
|---|---|---|---|---|
| 1606 | A275 | 1000ce multicolored | 5.25 | 5.25 |

**1993, Dec. 1**      **Perf. 13½x14**

Designs: 50ce, Abedi Pele, Ghana. 80ce, Pedro Troglio, Argentina. 100ce, Fernando Alvez, Uruguay. 200ce, Franco Baresi, Italy. 250ce, Gomez, Colombia; Katanec. 250ce, Gomez, Colombia; Katanec, Yugoslavia. 600ce, Diego Maradona, Argentina. 800ce, Hasek, Czech Republic; Wynalda, US. 1000ce, Lothar Mattheaus, Germany.

---

No. 1615, Giuseppe Giannini, Italy. No. 1616, Rabie Yassein, Egypt; Ruud Gullit, Holland.

| | | | | |
|---|---|---|---|---|
| 1607 | A276 | 50ce multi | .30 | .30 |
| 1608 | A276 | 80ce multi | .50 | .50 |
| 1609 | A276 | 100ce multi | .60 | .60 |
| 1610 | A276 | 200ce multi | 1.25 | 1.25 |
| 1611 | A276 | 250ce multi | 1.75 | 1.75 |
| 1612 | A276 | 600ce multi | 3.75 | 3.75 |
| 1613 | A276 | 800ce multi | 4.75 | 4.75 |
| 1614 | A276 | 1000ce multi | 5.75 | 5.75 |
| | | Nos. 1607-1614 (8) | 18.65 | 18.65 |

**Souvenir Sheets**

**Perf. 13**

| | | | | |
|---|---|---|---|---|
| 1615 | A276 | 1200ce multi | 7.00 | 7.00 |
| 1616 | A276 | 1200ce multi | 7.00 | 7.00 |

Domestic Animals A277

Designs: 50ce, Meleagris gallopvo. 100ce, Capra hircus. 150ce, Carina moschata. 200ce, Eguus asinus. 250ce, Male gallus gallus. 300ce, Sus vittatus. 400ce, Numida meleagris. 600ce, Canis domesticus. 800ce, Female gallus gallus. 1000ce, Ovis aries.
No. 1627: a, 100ce, Like #1618. b, 250ce, Like #1624. c, 350ce, Like #1622. d, 500ce, Like #1626.
No. 1628: a, 100ce, Like #1623. b, 250ce, Like #1621. c, 350ce, Like #1625. d, 500ce, Like #1617.

**1993, Dec. 8**      **Perf. 14**

| | | | | |
|---|---|---|---|---|
| 1617-1626 | A277 | Set of 10 | 18.50 | 18.50 |

**Souvenir Sheets**

| | | | | |
|---|---|---|---|---|
| 1627 | A277 | Sheet of 4, #a-d | 7.50 | 7.50 |
| 1628 | A277 | Sheet of 4, #a-d | 7.50 | 7.50 |

Arts and Crafts — A278

Designs: No. 1629, 50ce, Doll. No. 1630, 50ce, Pot and lid. No. 1631, 200ce, Beads. No. 1632, 200ce, Snake charmers. No. 1633, 250ce, Hoe. No. 1634, 250ce, Scabbard. No. 1635, 600ce, Pipe. No. 1636, 600ce, Deer. No. 1637, 1000ce, Mask. No. 1638, 1000ce, Doll with baby.
No. 1639: a, 100ce, Like #1629. b, 250ce, Like #1631. c, 350ce, Like #1633. d, 500ce, Like #1635.
No. 1640: a, 100ce, Like #1630. b, 250ce, Like #1632. c, 350ce, Like #1634. d, 500ce, Like #1636.

**1994, Jan. 24**   **Litho.**   **Perf. 14**

| | | | | |
|---|---|---|---|---|
| 1629-1638 | A278 | Set of 10 | 15.00 | 15.00 |

**Souvenir Sheets**

| | | | | |
|---|---|---|---|---|
| 1639 | A278 | Sheet of 4, #a-d | 4.25 | 4.25 |
| 1640 | A278 | Sheet of 4, #a-d | 4.25 | 4.25 |

Christmas A279

Paintings and Woodcuts: 50ce, Adoration of the Magi. 100ce, The Virgin and Child with Saint John and an Angel, by Botticelli. 150ce, Mary as Queen of Heaven. 200ce, Saint Anne. 250ce, The Madonna of the Magnificat, by Botticelli. 400ce, The Madonna of the Goldfinch, by Tiepolo. 600ce, The Virgin and Child with the Young St. John the Baptist, by Correggio. 1000ce, Adoration of the Shepherds.

No. 1649, Mystic Nativity (detail), by Botticelli, horiz. No. 1650, Madonna in a Circle, by Durer.

Woodcuts (50ce, 150ce, 200ce, 1000ce) are from Nuremberg Prayer Books, by Durer.

**Perf. 13½x14, 14x13½**
**1993, Dec. 20** **Litho.**
1641-1648 A279 Set of 8 15.00 15.00

**Souvenir Sheets**
1649 A279 1000ce multicolored 6.50 6.50
1650 A279 1000ce multicolored 6.50 6.50

A280    Hong Kong '94 — A281

Stamps, tram from Kennedy Town to Shau Kei: No. 1651, Hong Kong #470, back of tram. No. 1652, Front of tram, #1392.

No. 1653 — Imperial Palace clocks: a, Windmill. b, Horse. c, Balloon. d, Zodiac. e, Shar-Pei dog. f, Cat.

**1994, Feb. 18** **Litho.** **Perf. 14**
1651 A280 200ce multicolored 1.00 1.00
1652 A280 200ce multicolored 1.00 1.00
  a. Pair, #1651-1652 2.00 2.00

**Miniature Sheet**
1653 A281 100ce Sheet of 6, #a.-f. 6.50 6.50

Nos. 1651-1652 issued in sheets of 5 pairs. No. 1652a is a continuous design.
New Year 1994 (Year of the Dog) (#1653e).

Mickey Mouse, 65th Birthday A282

Mickey's films: 50ce, Steamboat Willie, 1928. 100ce, The Band Concert, 1937. 150ce, Moose Hunters, 1937. 200ce, Brave Little Taylor, 1938. 250ce, Fantasia, 1940. 400ce, The Nifty Nineties, 1941. 600ce, Canne Caddy, 1944. 1000ce, Mickey's Christmas Carol, 1983.
No. 1662, 1200ce, Mickey's Elephant, 1936. No. 1663, 1200ce, Mickey's Amateurs, 1937.

**1994, Mar. 1** **Litho.** **Perf. 13½x14**
1654-1661 A282 Set of 8 12.50 12.50

**Souvenir Sheets**
1662-1663 A282 Set of 2 11.00 11.00

A283

Hummel Figurines: 50ce, Boy with backpack, walking stick. 100ce, Girl holding basket behind back. 150ce, Boy with rabbits. 200ce, Boy carrying chicks in basket. 250ce, Girl with chicks. 400ce, Girl petting lamb. 600ce, Lamb, girl waving handkerchief. 1000ce, Girl with basket, flowers.
No. 1672: a, 500ce, Like #1665; b, 150ce, Like #1671; c, 1200ce, Like #1667.
No. 1673: a, 300ce, Like #1668; b, 200ce, Like #1669; c, 500ce, Like #1670; d, 1000ce, Like #1666.

**1994, Apr. 6** **Perf. 14**
1664-1671 A283 Set of 8 11.00 11.00

**Souvenir Sheets**
1672 A283 Sheet of 4, #a.-c., #1664 5.75 5.75
1673 A283 Sheet of 4, #a.-d. 6.00 6.00

World Wildlife Fund — A284

Diana Monkeys: 50ce, Adult, young. 200ce, Sitting in tree. 500ce, Holding food. 800ce, Close-up of face.

**1994, May 16** **Litho.** **Perf. 14**
1674-1677 A284 Set of 4 8.50 8.50
1677a Sheet, 3 each #1674-1677 26.00 26.00

Wild Animals A285

Designs: 100ce, Bushbuck. 150ce, Spotted hyena. 1000ce, Aardvark. No. 1681, 2000ce, Leopard, vert. No. 1682, 2000ce, Waterbuck, vert.

**1994, May 16**
1678-1680 A285 Set of 3 7.00 7.00

**Souvenir Sheets**
1681-1682 A285 Set of 2 14.00 14.00

Cats A286

No. 1683, 200ce: a, Sorrel Abyssinian. b, Silver classic tabby. c, Chocolate-point Siamese. d, Brown tortie Burmese. e, Exotic shorthair. f, Havana brown. g, Devon rex. h, Black manx. i, British blue shorthair. j, Calico American wirehair. k, Spotted oriental Siamese. l, Red classic tabby.
No. 1684, 200ce: a, Norwegian forest cat. b, Blue longhair. c, Red self longhair. d, Black longhair. e, Chinchilla. f, Dilut calico longhair. g, Blue tabby-&-white longhair. h, Ruby somali. i, Blue smoke longhair. j, Calico longhair. k, Brown tabby longhair. l, Balinese.
No. 1685, 2000ce, Brown mackeral tabby Scottish fold. No. 1686, 2000ce, Seal-point colorpoint.

**1994, June 6** **Litho.** **Perf. 14**
Sheets of 12, #a-l
1683-1684 A286 Set of 2 18.00 18.00

**Souvenir Sheets**
1685-1686 A286 Set of 2 13.00 13.00

Birds A287

No. 1687, 200ce: a, Red-bellied paradise flycatcher (b, e). b, Many-colored bush-shrike. c, Broad-tailed paradise whydah (b, e). d, White-crowned robin-chat. e, Violet plantain-eater. f, Village weaver. g, Fire-crowned bishop. h, Shoveler. i, Spur-winged goose (l). j, African crake. k, King reed-hen. l, Tiger bittern.
No. 1688, 200ce: a, Moho. b, Superb sunbird. c, Blue-breasted kingfisher. d, Blue cuckoo-shrike. e, Blue plantain-eater (d, g). f, Greater flamingo (i). g, Lily-trotter (j). h, Night heron. i, Black-winged stilt (l). j, White-spotted pigmy rail. k, Pigmy goose. k, Angola pitta.

No. 1689, 2000ce, Goliath heron. No. 1690, 2000ce, African spoonbill.

**1994, June 13**
Sheets of 12, #a-l
1687-1688 A287 Set of 2 21.00 21.00

**Souvenir Sheets**
1689-1690 A287 Set of 2 14.50 14.50

4th Republic, 1st Anniv. A288

Designs: 50ce, Rural water projects. 100ce, Honoring farmers. 200ce, Rural electrification. 600ce, Rural bridge construction. 800ce, Natl. Theater. 1000ce, Lighting Perpetual Flame.

**1994, July 11** **Litho.** **Perf. 14**
1691-1696 A288 Set of 6 7.50 7.50

D-Day, 50th Anniv. A289

Designs: 60ce, 15-inch Monitor HMS Roberts fires on Houlgate Battery. 100ce, HMS Warspite hits Villerville. 200ce, Flagship USS Augusta.
1500ce, USS Nevada bombards Utah Beach.

**1994, July 4** **Litho.** **Perf. 14**
1697-1699 A289 Set of 3 4.00 4.00

**Souvenir Sheet**
1700 A289 1500ce multicolored 7.50 7.50

First Manned Moon Landing, 25th Anniv. A290

No. 1701 — German, Japanese, scientist-astronauts: a, Sigmund Jahn. b, Ulf Merbold. c, Hans Wilhelm Schlegal. d, Ulrich Walter. e, Reinhard Furrer. f, Ernst Messerschmid. g, Mamoru Mohri. h, Klaus-Dietrich Flade. i, Chaiki Naito-Mukai.
2000ce, "Frau im Mond."

**1994, July 4**
1701 A290 300ce Sheet of 9, #a.-i. 9.50 9.50

**Souvenir Sheet**
1702 A290 2000ce multicolored 8.75 8.75

Duiker Antelopes A291

Designs: 50ce, Crowned. 100ce, Red-flanked. 200ce, Yellow-backed. 400ce, Ogilby's. 600ce, Bay. 800ce, Jentink's.
No. 1709, 2000ce, Cephalophus natalensis. No. 1710, 2000ce, Cephalophus niger.

**1994, May 16** **Litho.** **Perf. 14**
1703-1708 A291 Set of 6 7.50 7.50

**Souvenir Sheets**
1709-1710 A291 Set of 2 11.00 11.00

A292

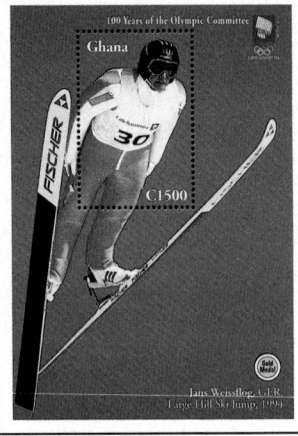

Intl. Olympic Committee, Cent. — A293

Designs: 300ce, Dieter Modenburg, Germany, high jump, 1984. 400ce, Ruth Fuchs, German Democratic Republic, javelin, 1972, 1976.
1500ce, Jans Weissflog, Germany, large hill ski jump, 1994.

**1994, July 4** **Litho.** **Perf. 14**
1711 A292 300ce multicolored .90 .90
1712 A292 400ce multicolored 1.10 1.10

**Souvenir Sheet**
1713 A293 1500ce multicolored 5.50 5.50

A294

PHILAKOREA '94 — A295

Designs: 20ce, Ch'unghak-dong village elder in traditional clothes. 150ce, Stone pagoda, Punhwangsa, Korea. 300ce, Traditional country house, Andong region.
No. 1717 — Letter pictures, eight-panel screen, Choson Dynasty, 20th cent: a, Shown. b, f, Birds. c, Rooster. d, Animal with antennae. e, g, Flowers. h, Fish.
1500ce, Temple judges determine final afterlife judgments, horiz.

**1994, July 4** **Perf. 14, 13 (#1717)**
1714-1716 A294 Set of 3 1.25 1.25
1717 A295 250ce Sheet of 8, #a.-h. 7.25 7.25

**Souvenir Sheet**
1718 A294 1500ce multicolored 6.00 6.00

Miniature Sheet of 6

1994 World Cup Soccer
Championships, US — A296

No. 1719: a, Dennis Bergkamp, Netherlands. b, Lothar Matthaus, Germany. c, Giuseppe Signori, Italy. d, Carlos Valderrama, Colombia. e, Jorge Campos, Mexico. f, Tony Meola, US.
No. 1720, 1200ce, Citrus Bowl, Orlando, FL, vert. No. 1721, 1200ce, Giants Stadium, Meadowlands, NJ, vert.

**1994, July 25**     **Perf. 14**
1719 A296 200ce Sheet of 6,
    #a.-f.     4.50 4.50
**Souvenir Sheets**
1720-1721 A296   Set of 2    8.00 .800

Christmas
A297

Italian art: 100ce, Madonna of the Annunciation, by Simone Martini. 200ce, Madonna and Child, by Niccolo di Pietro Gerini. 250ce, Virgin and Child on the Throne with Angels and Saints, by Raffaello Botticelli. 300ce, Madonna and Child with Saints, by Antonio Fiorentino. 400ce, Adoration of the Magi, by Bartolo di Fredi. 500ce, The Annunciation, by Cima da Congeliano. 600ce, Virgin and Child with the Young St. John the Baptist, by Workshop of Botticelli. 1000ce, The Holy Family, by Giorgione.
Details from Adoration of the Kings, by Giorgione: No. 1730, 2000ce, Presenting gifts. No. 1731, 20000ce, Madonna & Child.

**1994, Dec. 5 Litho. Perf. 13½x14**
1722-1729 A297   Set of 8    10.00 10.00
**Souvenir Sheets**
1730-1731 A297   Set of 2    12.00 12.00

Intl. Year of the
Family — A298

Designs: 50ce, Family. 100ce, Technical training. 200ce, Child care. 400ce, Care for the aged. 600ce, Vocational training. 1000ce, Adult education.

**1994, Dec. 20**     **Perf. 14**
1732-1737 A298   Set of 6    6.00 6.00

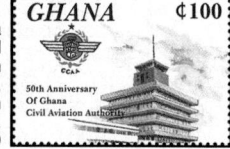

Ghana Civil Aviation Authority, 50th Anniv. A299

Designs: 100ce, Control tower. 400ce, Insignia, marker light. 1000ce, Airplane leaving runway.

**1994, Dec. 20**
1738-1740 A299   Set of 3    5.00 5.00
See Nos. 1766-1768.

Red Cross & Red Crescent Societies
in Ghana, 75th Anniv.
A300

Designs: 50ce, Transporting victim. 200ce, Aiding mother, children. 600ce, Erecting tents.

**1994, Dec. 20 Litho. Perf. 14**
1741-1743 A300   Set of 3    4.00 4.00
**Souvenir Sheet**
1744   Sheet of 3, #1741-1742,
    1744a     7.25 7.25
   a. A300 1000ce like #1743   6.00 6.00

Fertility
Dolls — A301

Various carvings with background colors of: 50ce, Green. 100ce, Yellow (red frame). 150ce, Blue (black doll). 200ce, Rose. 400ce, Dull orange. 600ce, Yellow green. 800ce, Yellow (green frame). 1000ce, Blue (white doll).

**1994, Dec. 20**
1745-1752 A301   Set of 8    9.00 9.00
**Souvenir Sheet**
1753   Sheet of 4, #1745, 1748-
    1749, 1753a     7.25 7.25
   a. A301 250ce like #1752   1.75 1.75

Donald Duck, 60th Birthday (in
1994) — A302

Designs: 40ce, Pluto, Donald, Chip 'n Dale. 50ce, Mickey, pup. 60ce, Daisy. 100ce, Goofy. 150ce, Goofy, diff. 250ce, Donald, Goofy. 400ce, Ludwig Von Drake, Pluto. 500ce, Gramdma Duck, pups. 1000ce, Mickey, Minnie. 1500ce, Pluto.
No. 1764, 2000ce, Daisy, Donald, cake, Mickey, vert. No. 1765, 2000ce, Donald holding fork, spoon, vert.

**1995, Feb. 2 Litho. Perf. 14x13½**
1754-1763 A302   Set of 10   11.50 11.50
**Souvenir Sheets**
**Perf. 13½x14**
1764-1765 A302   Set of 2    10.00 10.00

Civil Aviation Authority Type of 1994
with
ICAO Emblem and New Inscription

Designs: 100ce, Like #1738. 400ce, Like #1739. 1000ce, Like #1740.

**1994, Dec. 20 Litho. Perf. 14**
1766-1768 A299   Set of 3    10.00 10.00
Nos. 1766-1768 are inscribed "50th Anniversary of The International Civil Aviation Organization (ICAO)."

Panafest
'94 — A303

Designs: 50ce, Northern region dancer. 100ce, Relics with landmark. 200ce, Chief sitting in state. 400ce, Royalist ceremonial dress. 600ce, Cape Coast Castle. 800ce, Clay figurines of West Africa.

**1994, Dec. 9 Litho. Perf. 13½**
1769-1774 A303   Set of 6    9.50 9.50
Pan African Historical Theatre Festival, Dec. 1994.

Forts
A304

Castles
A305

Forts: 50ce, Apolonia, Beyin. 200ce, Patience, Apam. 250ce, Amsterdam, Kormantin. 300ce, St. Jago, Elmina. 400ce, William, Anomabo. 600ce, Kumasi.
Castles: 150ce, Cochem, Germany. 600ce, Hohenzollern, Germany. 800ce, Uwajima, Japan. 100ce, Hohenschwangau, Germany.
Castles: No. 1785a, Windsor, England. b, Osaka, Japan. c, Vaj Dahunyad, Hungary. d, Karlstejn, Czech Republic. e, Kronborg, Denmark. f, Alcazar of Segovia, Spain. g, Chambourd, France. h, Linderhof, Bavaria. i, Red Fort, India.
No. 1786, 800ce, Elmira Castle. No. 1787, 1000ce, Fort St. Antonio, Axim. No. 1788, 2500ce, Himeji Castle, Japan. No. 1789, 2500ce, Neuschwanstein Castle, Germany.

**1995, Apr. 3**     **Perf. 14**
1775-1780 A304   Set of 6    6.00 6.00
1781-1784 A305   Set of 4    8.50 8.50
1785 A305   500ce Sheet of 9,
    #a.-i.     14.50 14.50
**Souvenir Sheets**
1786-1787 A304   Set of 2    6.00 6.00
1788-1789 A305   Set of 2   10.00 10.00

Water
Birds
A306

Designs: 200ce, Eurasian pochard. 500ce, Maccoa duck. 800ce, Cape shoveler. 1000ce, Red-crested pochard.
No. 1794: a, African pygmy goose. b, Southern pochard. c, Cape teal. d, Ruddy shelduck. e, Fulvous whistling duck. f, White-faced whistling geese. g, Ferruginous white-eye. h, Hottentot teal. i, African black duck. j, Yellow-billed duck. k, White-checked pintail duck. l, Hartlaub's duck.
No. 1795, 2500ce, Roseate tern. No. 1796, 2500ce, Northern shoveler.

**1995, Apr. 28**
1790-1793 A306   Set of 4    7.00 7.00
1794 A306   400ce Sheet of 12,
    #a.-l.     10.50 10.50
**Souvenir Sheets**
1795-1796 A306   Set of 2   11.00 11.00
Nos. 1794-1796 have a continuous design. Nos. 1790-1793 have a white border.

1996 Summer Olympics, Atlanta
A307      A308

Athletes: 500ce, Carl Lewis. 800ce, Eric Liddell. 900ce, Runner. 1000ce, Jim Thorpe.
No. 1801: a, Cycling. b, Archery. c, Diving. d, Swimming. e, Gymnastics-Floor Exercise. f, Fencing. g, Boxing. h, Gymnastics-Rings. i, Javelin. j, Tennis. k, Soccer. l, Equestrian.
No. 1802, 1200ce, John Akii Bua. No. 1803, 1200ce, Pierre de Cobertin.

**1995, May 2**
1797-1800 A307   Set of 4    7.00 7.00
1801 A308   300ce Sheet of 12,
    #a.-l.     8.00 8.00
**Souvenir Sheets**
1802-1803 A308   Set of 2    5.50 5.50

UN, 50th
Anniv. — A309

No. 1804 — Secretaries General: a, 200ce, Trygve Lie, Norway, 1946-52. b, 300ce, Dag Hammarskjold, Sweden, 1953-61. c, 400ce, U Thant, Burma, 1961-71. d, 500ce, Kurt Waldheim, Austria, 1972-81. e, 600ce, Javier Perez de Cuellar, Peru, 1982-91. f, 800ce, Boutros Boutros-Ghali, Egypt, 1992-.
No. 1805, UN flag, horiz.

**1995, July 6 Litho. Perf. 14**
1804 A309   Sheet of 6, #a.-f.   6.00 6.00
**Souvenir Sheet**
1805 A309   1200ce multicolored   3.00 3.00

Miniature Sheets of 6 or 8

A310

End of
World
War II,
50th
Anniv.
A311

No. 1806 — Military decorations: a, US Navy Cross, US Purple Heart. b, UK Air Force Cross, UK Distinguished Flying Cross. c, US Navy and Marine Corps Medal, US Distinguished Service Cross. d, UK Distinguished Service Medal, UK Distinguished Conduct Medal. e, UK Military Medal, UK Military Cross. f, UK Distinguished Service Cross, UK Distinguished Service Order.
No. 1807: a, Churchill. b, Eisenhower. c, Air Chief Marshall Sir Arthur Tedder. d, Montgomery. e, Bradley. f, de Gaulle. g, French Resistance Organization. h, Patton.
No. 1808, 1200ce, U.S. Medal of Honor. No. 1809, 1200ce, Fuhrer's promise.

**1995, July 6 Litho. Perf. 14**
1806 A310   500ce Sheet of 6,
    #a.-f. + label   8.00 8.00
1807 A311   400ce Sheet of 8,
    #a.-h. + label     8.00 8.00
**Souvenir Sheets**
1808-1809 A310   Set of 2    7.00 7.00
No. 1809 contains one 42x56mm stamp.

FAO, 50th
Anniv.
A312

Designs: 200ce, Fish preservation. 300ce,
Fishing. 400ce, Ox-drawn plow. 600ce, Harvesting. 800ce, Aforestation.
2000ce, Boat, shoreline, oxen, fruit.

**1995, July 6      Litho.      Perf. 14**
1810-1814  A312  Set of 5          5.00  5.00
**Souvenir Sheet**
1815  A312  2000ce multicolored    4.50  4.50

Rotary
Intl., 90th
Anniv.
A313

Designs: 600ce, Natl. flag, Rotary emblem.
1200ce, Rotary emblem on banner, vert.

**1995, July 6**
1816  A313  600ce multicolored     1.25  1.25
**Souvenir Sheet**
1817  A313  1200ce multicolored    3.00  3.00

1995 Boy Scout
Jamboree,
Holland — A314

No. 1818: a, 400ce, Two boys. 800ce, Two
boys, one wearing glasses. c, 1000ce, Two
boys facing left.
1200ce, Boy with bamboo poles.

**1995, July 6**
1818  A314  Strip of 3, #a.-c.     4.75  4.75
**Souvenir Sheet**
1819  A314  1200ce multicolored    4.00  4.00
No. 1818 is a continuous design.

Queen
Mother, 95th
Birthday
A315

No. 1820: a, Drawing. b, Bright green blue
hat. c, Formal portrait. d, Coral outfit.
2500ce, Pale blue outfit.

**1995, July 6          Perf. 13½x14**
1820  A315  600ce Strip or block
                 of 4, #a.-d.      5.50  5.50
**Souvenir Sheet**
1821  A315  2500ce multicolored    4.50  4.50
No. 1820 was issued in sheets of 8 stamps.

Singapore
'95 — A316

No. 1822, 400ce: a, Seismosaurus (d-f). b,
Supersaurus (a, d). c, Ultrasaurus (f). d,
Saurolophus (e). e, Lambeosaurus (d, g-h). f,
Parasaurolophus (e, i). g, Triceratops (h). h,
Styracosaurus (e, g i). i, Pachyrhinosaurus (h).
No. 1823, 400ce: a, Peteinosaurus (b, d-e).
b, Quetzalcoatlus (a, c, e). c, Eudimorphodon
(b). d, Allosaurus (e-f, h-i). e, Daspletosaurus
(f). f, Tarbosaurus (i). g, Velociraptor (h-i). h,
Herrerasaurus (i). i, Coelophysis.
No. 1824, 2500ce, Albertosaur. No. 1825,
2500ce, Tyrannosaurus rex.

**1995, Aug. 8      Litho.      Perf. 14**
**Sheets of 9, #a-i**
1822-1823  A316  Set of 2        16.00 16.00
**Souvenir Sheets**
1824-1825  A316  Set of 2        11.00 11.00

Nobel Prize
Recipients — A317

No. 1826: a, Nelson Mandela, peace, 1993.
b, Albert Schweitzer, peace, 1952. c, Wole
Soyinka, literature, 1986. d, Emil Fischer,
chemistry, 1902. e, Rudolf Mossbauer, physics, 1961. f, Archbishop Desmond Tutu, peace,
1984. g, Max Born, physics, 1954. h, Max
Planck, physics, 1918. i, Hermann Hesse,
literature, 1946.
1200ce, Paul Ehrlich, medicine, 1908.

**1995, Oct. 2      Litho.      Perf. 14**
1826  A317  400ce Sheet of 9,
                 #a.-i.           8.00  8.00
**Souvenir Sheet**
1827  A317  1200ce multicolored   2.75  2.75

Asantehene, 25th
Anniv. — A318

Designs: 50ce, Emblem. 100ce, Silver casket. 200ce, Golden stool. 400ce, Busummuru
sword bearer. 600ce, 800ce, Diff. portraits of
Otumfuo Opoku Ware II. 1000ce, Mponpon-
suo sword bearer.

**1995                Perf. 13½x13**
1828-1834  A318  Set of 7        6.25  6.25

Fauna — A319

Designs: 400ce, Cymothoe beckeri. 500ce,
Graphium policene. 1000ce, Urotriorchis
macrourus, vert. 2000ce, Xiphias gladius.
3000ce, Monodoctylus sabee. 5000ce, Ardea
purpurea, vert.

**Perf. 14¼x13¾, 13¾x14¼**
**1995, June 19                  Litho.**
1835  A319  400ce multi         .80   .80
1836  A319  500ce multi        1.00  1.00
1837  A319  1000ce multi       2.00  2.00
   a.    Perf. 11½

1838  A319  2000ce multi       4.25  4.25
1839  A319  3000ce multi       6.25  6.25
1840  A319  5000ce multi      10.50 10.50
   Nos. 1835-1840 (6)         24.80 24.80

Christmas
A320

Details or entire paintings: 50ce, The Infant
Jesus and the Young St. John, by Murillo.
80ce, Rest on Flight to Egypt, by Memling.
300ce, Sacred Family, by Van Dyck. 600ce,
The Virgin and the Infant, by Uccello. 800ce,
The Virgin and the Infant, by Van Eyck.
1000ce, Head of Christ, by Rembrandt.
No. 1847, 2500ce, Madonna, by Montagna.
No. 1848, 2500ce, The Holy Family, by
Pulzone.

**1995, Dec. 1      Litho.      Perf. 13½x14**
1841-1846  A320  Set of 6        6.00  6.00
**Souvenir Sheets**
1847-1848  A320  Set of 2       20.00 20.00

Motion
Pictures,
Cent.
A321

No. 1849: a, 1903 H. Ernmann camera. b,
Charles Chaplin. c, Rudolph Valentino. d, Will
Rogers. e, Greta Garbo. f, Jackie Cooper. g,
Bette Davis. h, John Barrymore. i, Shirley
Temple.
No. 1850, Laurel and Hardy.

**1995, Dec. 8**
1849  A321  400ce Sheet of 9,
                 #a.-i.          11.00 11.00
**Souvenir Sheet**
1850  A321  2500ce multi         7.25  7.25

A322

John
Lennon
(1940-80)
A323

No. 1852: a-g, i, Various portraits. h, Like
No. 1851.
2000ce, Lennon playing guitar, water in
background.

**1995, Dec. 8              Perf. 14**
1851  A322  400ce shown         .65   .65

**Miniature Sheet**
**Perf. 13½x14**
1852  A323  400ce Sheet of 9,
                 #a.-i.         12.50 12.50
**Souvenir Sheet**
1853  A323  2000ce multi         9.00  9.00
No. 1851 was issued in sheets of 16.

Louis Pasteur
(1822-95) — A324

No. 1854: a, In laboratory. b, Discovery of
rabies virus and vaccine. c, Pneumococcus
discovery, 1880. d, Development of first vaccine with birds. e, Perfection of brewer's yeast
culture.

**1995, Dec. 13                Perf. 14**
1854  A324  600ce Sheet of 5,
                 #a.-e.          7.25  7.25

Paintings
from the
Metropolitan
Museum of
Art — A325

No. 1855, 400ce: a, Portrait of a Man, by
Van Der Goes. b, Paradise, by Giovanni di
Paolo. c, Portrait of a Young Man, by Antonello
da Messina. d, Tommaso Portinari, by Mem-
ling. e, Wife Maria Portinari, by Memling. f,
Portrait of a Lady, by Ghirlandaio. g, St. Chris-
topher & Infant Christ, by Ghirlandaio. h, Fran-
cesco D'Este, by van der Weyden.
No. 1856, 400ce: a, The Interrupted Sleep,
by Boucher. b, Diana and Cupid, by Batoni. c,
Boy Blowing Bubbles, by Chardin. d, Ancient
Rome, by Pannini. e, Modern Rome, by Pan-
nini. f, The Calmady Children, by Lawrence. g,
The Triumph of Marius, by G.B. Tiepolo. h,
Garden at Vaucresson, by E. Vuillard.
No. 1857, 2500ce, The Epiphany, by Giotto.
No. 1858, 2500ce, The Calling of Matthew, by
Hemessen.

**1996, Feb. 12  Litho.  Perf. 13½x14**
**Sheets of 8, #a-h, + Label**
1855-1856  A325  Set of 2       15.00 15.00
**Souvenir Sheets**
**Perf. 14**
1857-1858  A325  Set of 2       15.00 15.00
Nos. 1857-1858 each contain one
85x57mm stamp.

New Year 1996
(Year of the
Rat) — A326

Nos. 1859-1860 — Stylized rats: a, With
musical instruments, on horseback. b, Holding
banners. c, Carrying rat in palanquin. d, Carrying box, holding fish.
1000ce, Four rats transporting rat in palanquin, horiz.

**1996, Jan. 28  Litho.  Perf. 14**
**Country Name in White**
1859  A326  250ce Strip of 4,
                 #a.-d.          2.50  2.50

**Country Name in Red**
1860 A325   250ce Sheet of 4,
                    #a.-d.                          2.50 2.50
**Souvenir Sheet**
1861 A325   1000ce red, pink &
                    yellow                          2.50 2.50
No. 1859 was issued in sheets of 12 stamps.

Fauna of the
Rainforest — A327

No. 1862, 400ce: a, Ramphastos toco. b,
Choloepus didactylus. c, Pongo pygmaeus. d,
Spiaetus cirrhatus. e, Panthera tigris. f, Ibis
leucocephallus. g, Ara chloroptera. h, Saimiri
sciureus. i, Macaca fascicularis. j, Cithaerias
menander, ithomiidae. k, Coryptophanes cristatus, gekkonidae. l, Boa caninus.
   No. 1863, 400ce: a, Opisthoccomus hoazin.
b, Tarsius bancanus. c, Leontopithecus rosalia. d, Pteropus gouldii. e, Rupicola rupicola. f,
Pharomachrus mocino. g, Hyla boans, den-
drobates leucomeles. h, Lemur catta. i, Iguana
iguana. j, Heliconius burneyi. k, Mellisuga min-
ima. l, Propithecus verreauxi.
   No. 1864, 3000ce, Sarcoramphus papa. No.
1865, 3000ce, Pteridophora alberti.

**1996, Apr. 15**
               **Sheets of 12, #a-l**
1862-1863 A327   Set of 2          20.00 20.00
               **Souvenir Sheets**
1864-1865 A327   Set of 2          15.00 15.00

China '96 — A328

No. 1866: a, Kaiyuan Si Temple, Fujian. b,
Kaiyuan Si Temple, Hebei. c, Fogong Si Tem-
ple, Shanxi. d, Xiangshan, Beijing.
   No. 1867, Baima Si Temple, Henan.

**1996, May 13   Litho.      Perf. 14**
1866 A328   400ce Strip of 4,
                    #a.-d.               4.75 4.75
               **Souvenir Sheet**
1867 A328   1000ce multicolored      2.75 2.75
No. 1866 was issued in sheets of 8 stamps.
See No. 1913.

Queen
Elizabeth II,
70th
Birthday
A329

No. 1868: a, Portrait. b, Wearing blue hat,
coat. c, Wearing printed dress, wide-brim hat.
2500ce, Riding in horse-drawn carriage,
horiz.

**1996, June 10   Litho.   Perf. 13½x14**
1868 A329   1000ce Strip of 3,
                    #a.-c.               7.25 7.25
               **Souvenir Sheet**
                    **Perf. 14x13½**
1869 A329   2500ce multicolored      6.50 6.50
No. 1868 was issued in sheets of 9 stamps.

1996
Summer
Olympics,
Atlanta
A330

Designs: 300ce, Two wrestlers, javelin
thrower, Bas Relief, 500BC. 500ce, Wilma
Rudolph, gold medalist in track and field,
Rome, 1960, Olympic torch. 600ce, The
Forum, St. Peter's Basilica, Colosseum,
Olympic Stadium, Rome, 1960. 800ce, Soviet
flag, ladies' kayak pairs gold medal winners,
Rome, 1960.
   No. 1874, 400ce — Medalists in swimming,
diving: a, Aileen Riggin, springboard, 1920. b,
Pat McCormick, platform, 1952. c, Dawn Fra-
ser, 100m freestyle, 1956. d, Chris Von Saltza,
400m freestyle, 1960. e, Anita Lonsbrough,
200m breaststroke, 1960. f, Debbie Meyer,
400m freestyle, 1968. g, Shane Gould, 400m
freestyle, 1972. h, Petra Thuemer, 800m
freestyle, 1976. i, Marjorie Gestring, springboard, 1936.
   No. 1875, 400ce, vert. — Soccer players: a,
Abedi Pele, Ghana. b, Quico Navarez, Spain.
c, Heino Hanson, Denmark. d, Mostafa Ismail,
Egypt. e, Anthony Yeboah, Ghana. f, Jurgen
Klinsmann, Germany. g, Cobi Jones, US. h,
Franco Baresi, Italy. i, Igor Dobrovolski,
Russia.
   No. 1876, 2000ce, Kornella Ender, 200m
freestyle gold medalist, 1976. No. 1877,
2000ce, Tracy Caulkins, 200m individual
medlay gold medalist, 1984.

**1996, June 27                Perf. 14**
1870-1873 A330   Set of 4          4.50 4.50
               **Sheets of 9, #a-i**
1874-1875 A330   Set of 2          27.50 27.50
               **Souvenir Sheets**
1876-1877 A330   Set of 2          13.00 13.00

Intl. Amateur
Boxing Assoc.,
50th
Anniv. — A331

Boxers: 300ce, Serafim Todorow, Bulgaria.
400ce, Oscar de La Hoya, US. 800ce, Ariel
Hernandez, Cuba. 1500ce, Arnaldo Mesa,
Cuba.
   3000ce, Tadahiro Sasaki, Japan.

**1996, July 31**
1878-1881 A331   Set of 4          7.50 7.50
               **Souvenir Sheet**
1882 A331   3000ce multicolored      7.50 7.50

UNESCO, 50th Anniv. — A332

Designs: 400ce, The Citadel, Haiti, vert.
800ce, Ait-Ben-Haddou (Fortified Village),
Morocco, vert. 1000ce, Spissky Hrad (exterior
of castle), Slovakia.
   2000ce, Cape Coast, Ghana.

**1996, July 31   Litho.      Perf. 14**
1883-1885 A332   Set of 3          3.75 3.75
               **Souvenir Sheet**
1886 A332   2000ce multicolored      3.50 3.50

UNICEF, 50th
Anniv. — A333

Designs: 400ce, Baby. 500ce, Mother, baby.
600ce, Mother, child drinking from glass.
1000ce, Child, diff.

**1996, July 31**
1887-1889 A333   Set of 3          2.00 2.00
               **Souvenir Sheet**
1890 A333   1000ce multicolored      1.75 1.75

Jerusalem,
3000th
Anniv. — A334

Landmark, flower: 400ce, St. Stephen's
(Lion) Gate, Jasminum mesnyi. 600ce, Citadel
and Tower of David, nerium oleander. 800ce,
Chapel of the Ascension, romulea
bulbocodium.
   2000ce, Russian Church of St. Mary
Magdalene.

**1996, July 31**
1891-1893 A334   Set of 3          2.25 2.25
               **Souvenir Sheet**
1894 A334   2000ce multicolored      3.50 3.50
   For overprints see Nos. 2032-2035.

Musical
Instruments
A335

No. 1895: a, Fiddles. b, Proverbial drum. c,
Double clapless bell & castanet. d, Gourd rattle. e, Horns.

**1996, Aug. 5**
1895 A335   500ce Sheet of 5,
                    #a.-e.           5.25 5.25

Disney's Best Friends — A336

No. 1896, 60ce, Ariel, Flounder, Sebastian.
No. 1897, 60ce, Pinocchio, Jiminy Cricket. No.
1898, 60ce, Cogsworth, Lumiere. No. 1899,
60ce, Copper, Tod. No. 1900, 60ce, Pocahon-
tas, Meeko, Flit. No. 1901, 60ce, Bambi,
Flower, Thumper.
   No. 1902: a, 450ce, Pocahontas, Meeko,
Flit. b, 150ce, Pinocchio, Jiminy Cricket. c,
200ce, Copper, Tod. d, 600ce, Aladdin, Abu.
e, 700ce, Penny, Rufus. f, 350ce, Cogsworth,
Lumiere. g, 800ce, Mowgli, Baloo. h, 200ce,
Ariel, Flounder, Sebastian, i, 300ce, Bambi,
Flower, Thumper.
   No. 1903, Winnie the Pooh, vert. No. 1904,
Simba, Pumbaa.

     **Perf. 14x13½, 13½x14**
**1996, Aug. 25**
1896-1901 A336   Set of 6          2.25 2.25

1902   A336   Sheet of 9, #a.-
                    i.               6.50 6.50
               **Souvenir Sheets**
1903 A336   3000ce multicolored      5.00 5.00
1904 A336   3000ce multicolored      5.00 5.00
   Stampshow '96 (#1902).

E.W. Agyare
(1937-72), Ghana
Broadcasting
Corp.
Technician — A337

**1996, July 31                Perf. 14**
1905 A337   100ce multicolored      .25  .25

Radio, Cent.
A338

Entertainers: 500ce, Frank Sinatra. No.
1907, 600ce, Judy Garland. No. 1908, 600ce,
Bing Crosby. 800ce, Dean Martin, Jerry Lewis.
2000ce, Edgar Bergen, Charlie McCarthy.

**1996, July 31             Perf. 13½x14**
1906-1909 A338   Set of 4          3.50 3.50
               **Souvenir Sheet**
1910 A338   2000ce multicolored      3.50 3.50

Sylvester
Stallone in
Movie, "Rocky
II" — A339

**1996, Nov. 21   Litho.      Perf. 14**
1911 A339   2000ce multi            2.40 2.40
   Issued in sheets of 3.

New Year
1997 (Year
of the
Ox) — A340

Various scenes from Chinese story, "Herd
Boy and Girl Weaver."

**1997, Jan. 22   Litho.      Perf. 14**
1912 A340   500ce Sheet of 9,
                    #a.-i.           7.00 7.00

## Souvenir Sheet

China '96 — A341

Statue of the Devil.

**1996, May 13    Litho.    Perf. 14**
1913 A341 1000ce multicolored    1.75 1.75

No. 1913 was not available until March 1997.

African Hair
Styles — A342

No. 1914, 1000ce: a, Dipo. b, Oduku. c, Dansinkran. d, Mbobom. e, Oduku 2.
No. 1915, 1000ce: a, African corn row. b, Chinese raster. c, Chinese raster 2. d, Corn row. e, Mbakaa.

**1997, Mar. 3**
**Sheets of 5, #a-e**
1914-1915 A342    Set of 2    10.00 10.00

Dr. Hideyo
Noguchi (1876-
1928), Pathologist
A343

No. 1916: a, Tomb. b, Portrait. c, Birth place. d, Noguchi Institute, Legon. e, Noguchi Gardens, Accra.
No. 1917, 3000ce, Dr. Noguchi in laboratory. No. 1918, 3000ce, Statue.

**1997, Mar. 3**
1916 A343 1000ce Sheet of 5,
#a.-e.    7.00 7.00
**Souvenir Sheets**
1917-1918 A343    Set of 2    8.50 8.50

Independence, 40th Anniv. — A344

Designs: 200ce, Emblem. 550ce, Dr. Kwame Nkrumah, first president of Ghana, vert. 800ce, Achievement in education. 1100ce, Akosombo Dam.
2000ce, Declaration of independence, Old Polo Grounds, vert. 3000ce, Kofi Annan, UN Secretary General, vert.

**1997, Mar. 6    Litho.    Perf. 14**
1919-1922 A344    Set of 4    8.00 8.00
**Souvenir Sheets**
1923 A344 2000ce multicolored    3.00 3.00
1924 A344 3000ce multicolored    5.00 5.00

Deng Xiaoping
(1904-97),
Chinese
Leader — A345

No. 1925: a, 300ce, Smiling. b, 600ce, Wearing glasses. c, 800ce, Like #1925b. d, 1000ce, Like #1925a.
No. 1926: a, 500ce, Lips pursed. b, 600ce, Teeth showing. c, 800ce, Like #1926b. d, 1000ce, Like #1926a.
No. 1927, Reading. No. 1928, Hand in air.

**1997, Apr. 28    Perf. 14x13½**
1925 A345    Sheet of 4, #a.-d.    3.75 3.75
1926 A345    Sheet of 4, #a.-d.    4.00 4.00
**Souvenir Sheets**
**Perf. 13½**
1927 A345 3000ce multicolored    3.75 3.75
1928 A345 4000ce multicolored    5.00 5.00

Nos. 1927-1928 each contain one 51x38mm stamp.

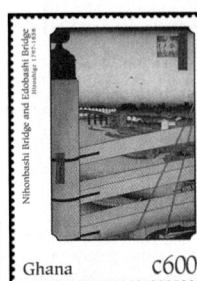

Paintings by
Hiroshige
(1797-1858)
A346

No. 1929: a, Nihonbashi Bridge and Edobashi Bridge. b, View of Nihonbashi Tori 1-chome. c, Open Garden at Fukagawa Hachiman Shrine. d, Inari Bridge and Minato Shrine, Teppozu. e, Bamboo Yards, Kyobashi Bridge. f, Hall of Thirty-Three Bays, Fukagawa.
No. 1930, 3000ce, Teppozu and Tsukiji Honganji Temple. No. 1931, 3000ce, Sumiyoshi Festival, Tsukudajima.

**1997, May 29    Litho.    Perf. 13½x14**
1929 A346    600ce Sheet of 6,
#a.-f.    5.00 5.00
**Souvenir Sheets**
1930-1931 A346    Set of 2    7.50 7.50

Queen
Elizabeth
II, Prince
Philip,
50th
Wedding
Anniv.
A347

No. 1932: a, Queen. b, Royal Arms. c, Queen, Prince waving. d, Queen, Prince. e, Royal carriage. f, Portrait of Prince Philip.
3000ce, Portrait of Queen Elizabeth II.

**1997, May 29    Perf. 14**
1932 A347    800ce Sheet of 6,
#a.-f.    5.75 5.75
**Souvenir Sheet**
1933 A347 3000ce multicolored    2.00 2.00

Heinrich
von
Stephan
(1831-97),
Founder
of UPU
A348

No. 1934 — Portrait of Von Stephan and: a, Automobile used for postal delivery. b, UPU emblem. c, First airmail flight, Pierre Blanchard, 1784.
3000ce, African messenger with cleft stick.

**1997, May 29    Litho.    Perf. 14**
1934 A348 1000ce Sheet of 3,
#a.-c.    3.50 3.50
**Souvenir Sheet**
1935 A348 3000ce multicolored    3.50 3.50
PACIFIC 97.

Paul P. Harris (1868-1947), Founder
of Rotary Intl. — A349

Portrait of Harris, Rotary emblem and: 2000ce, PolioPlus oral vaccine administration, Egypt. 3000ce, Emblem for PolioPlus vaccine, "A world free of disease."

**1997, May 29**
1936 A349 2000ce multicolored    3.50 3.50
**Souvenir Sheet**
1937 A349 3000ce multicolored    3.50 3.50

Chernobyl,
10th Anniv.
A350

Designs: 800ce, UNESCO. 1000ce, Chabad's Children of Chernobyl.

**1997, May 29    Perf. 13½x14**
1938 A350    800ce multicolored    1.25 1.25
1939 A350 1000ce multicolored    1.50 1.50

Cyrestes Camillus —
A350a

Designs: 550ce, Ajumpan drums. 1100ce Kente cloth.

**1997    Litho.    Perf. 13½x14¼**
1939A A350a    550ce multi    — —
1939B A350a    800ce multi    — —
1939C A350a 1100ce multi    — —

Issued: 550ce, 5/30; 800ce, 6/4. 1100ce, 6/7.
For surcharge see No. 2360.

A351

## Entertainers — A352

No. 1940: a, Jackie Gleason. b, Danny Kaye. c, John Cleese. d, Lucille Ball. e, Jerry Lewis. f, Sidney James. g, Louis de Fuenes. h, Mae West. i, Bob Hope.
No. 1941: a, Professor Ajax Bukana with fingers making "V." b, Bukana with arms spread.
3000ce, Groucho Marx.

**1997, July 1    Perf. 13½x14**
1940 A351    600ce Sheet of 9,
#a.-i.    7.00 7.50
**Souvenir Sheets**
**Perf. 14**
1941 A352 2000ce Sheet of 2,
#a-b    3.50 3.50
**Perf. 13½x14**
1942 A351 3000ce multicolored    2.25 2.25

Mushrooms
A353

Designs: 200ce, Galerina calyptrata. 300ce, Lepiota ignivolvata. 400ce, Omphalotus olearius. 550ce, Amanita phalloides. 600ce, Entoloma conferendum. 800ce, Entoloma nitidum.
No. 1949: a, Coprinus picaceus. b, Stropharia aurantiaca. c, Cortinarius splendens. d, Gomphidius roseus. e, Russula sardonia. f, Geastrum schmidelia.
No. 1950, 3000ce, Mycena crocata. No. 1951, 3000ce, Craterellus cornucopioides.

**1997, July 9    Perf. 14**
1943-1948 A353    Set of 6    3.50 3.50
1949 A353    800ce Sheet of 6,
#a.-f.    5.75 5.75
**Souvenir Sheets**
1950-1951 A353    Set of 2    7.00 7.00

Fish
A354

Designs: 400ce, African pygmy angelfish. 600ce, Angelfish. 800ce, Broomtail wrasse. 1000ce, Indian butterfly fish.
No. 1956: a, Violet crested turaco. b, Pied avocet. c, Bottle-nosed dolphin. d, Bottle-nosed dolphin, long-toed lapwing. e, Longfined spadefish (i). f, Imperial angelfish,

Seabirds,
Marine
Life
A355

manta ray. g, Raccoon butterfly fish, African pompano (h, k). h, Silvertip shark (g, l). i, Longfin banner fish (e, j). j, Longfin banner fish, manta ray (f, i). k, Rusty parrot fish (j). l, Coral trout.
No. 1957, 3000ce, Crown butterfly fish. No. 1958, 3000ce, King angelfish.

**1997, July 15**
1952-1955 A354 Set of 4 ........ 3.50 3.50
1956 A355 500ce Sheet of 12, #a.-l. ........ 7.25 7.25

**Souvenir Sheets**
1957-1958 A355 Set of 2 ........ 8.00 8.00

Flowers A356

Designs: 200ce, Eurychone rothschildiana. 550ce, Bulbophyllum lepidum. No. 1961, 800ce, Ansellia africana. 1100ce, Combretum grandiflorum.
No. 1963, vert: a, Strophanthus preusii. b, Ancistrochilus rothschildianus. c, Mussaendra arcuata. d, Microcoelia guyoniana. e, Gloriosa simplex. f, Brachycorythis kalbreyeri. g, Aframomum sceptrum. h, Thunbergia alata. i, Clerodendrum thomsoniae.
No. 1964, 3000ce, Kigelia africana. No. 1965, 3000ce, Spathodea campanulata.

**1997, Aug. 1    Litho.    Perf. 14½**
1959-1962 A356 Set of 4 ........ 4.00 4.00
1963 A356 800ce Sheet of 9, #a.-i. ........ 10.00 10.00

**Souvenir Sheets**
1964-1965 A356 Set of 2 ........ 8.00 8.00

1998 World Cup Soccer Championships, France — A357

Stadiums: 200ce, Azteca, Mexico, 1970, 1986. 300ce, Rose Bowl, US, 1994. 400ce, Giuseppe Meazza, Italy, 1990. 500ce, Olympic, Germany, 1974. 1000ce, Maracana, Brazil, 1950. 2000ce, Bernabeu, Spain, 1982.
No. 1972 — Soccer players: a, Patrick Kluivert, Holland. b, Roy Deane, Ireland. c, Abedi Pele Ayew, Ghana. d, Peter Schmeichel, Denmark. e, Roberto di Matteo, Italy. f, Bebeto, Brazil. g, Steve McManaman, England. h, George Appong Weah, Liberia.
No. 1973, 3000ce, Juninho, Brazil. No. 1974, 3000ce, Seaman, England.

**1997, July 12    Perf. 14x13½**
1966-1971 A357 Set of 6 ........ 5.00 5.00
1972 A357 600ce Sheet of 8, #a.-h. + label ........ 5.00 5.00

**Souvenir Sheets**
1973-1974 A357 Set of 2 ........ 7.50 7.50
Nos. 1966-1971 were issued in sheets of 10 each.

Birds — A358

Designs: 200ce, Eurasian goldfinch. 300ce, Cape batis. 400ce, Bearded barbet. 500ce, White-necked raven. 600ce, Purple grenadier. 1000ce, Zebra waxbill.
No. 1981: a, Black bustard. b, Northern lapwing. c, Sandgrouse. d, Red-crested turaco. e, White-browed coucal. f, Lilac-breasted roller. g, Golden pipet. h, Crimson-breasted gonolek. i, Blackcap.

No. 1982, 3000ce, Nectarina famosa. No. 1983, 3000ce, Vidua regia.

**1997, Oct. 20    Litho.    Perf. 14**
1975-1980 A358 Set of 6 ........ 3.50 3.50
1981 A358 800ce Sheet of 9, #a.-i. ........ 8.50 8.50

**Souvenir Sheets**
1982-1983 A358 Set of 2 ........ 8.00 8.00

Cats and Dogs A359

Cats, #1984-1989: 20ce, Havana. 50ce, Singapura. 100ce, Sphinx. 150ce, British white. 300ce, Snowshoe. 600ce, Persian.
Dogs, #1989A-1989F: 80ce, Papillon. 200ce, Bulldog. 400ce, Shetland sheepdog. 500ce, Schnauzer. 800ce, Shih tzu. 2000ce, Chow chow.
No. 1990, 1000ce — Dogs and cats: a, Russian wolfhound. b, Birman. c, Basset hound. d, Silver tabby. e, Afghan. f, Burmilla.
No. 1991, 1000ce: a, Abyssinian. b, Border terrier. c, Scottish fold. d, Boston terrier. e, Oriental. f, Keeshond.
No. 1992, 3000ce, Ragdoll. No. 1992A, 3000ce, Alaskan malamute.

**1997, Oct. 20**
1984-1989 A359 Set of 6 ........ 2.00 2.00
1989A- A359 Set of 6
1989F ........ 4.00 4.00

**Sheets of 6, #a-f**
1990-1991 A359 Set of 2 ........ 16.50 16.50

**Souvenir Sheets**
1992-1992A A359 Set of 2 ........ 9.00 9.00

Return of Hong Kong to China — A360

No. 1993: a, Lin Tsi-Hsu (1785-1850). b, Gwan Tian-Pei. Illustration reduced.

**1997, Nov. 10**
1993 A360 1000ce Sheet of 4, 2 each #a.-b. ........ 4.00 4.00

Huang Binhong (1865-1955) — A361

No. 1994 — Various details of "Color Landscape": a, 200ce. b, 300ce. c, 400ce. d, 500ce. e, 600ce. f, 800ce. g, 1000ce. h, 2000ce.
No. 1995: a, Detail with Chinese inscription. b, Detail without inscription.

**1997, Nov. 10**
1994 A361 Sheet of 8, #a.-h. ........ 5.75 5.75

**Souvenir Sheet**
1995 A361 2000ce Sheet of 2, #a.-b. ........ 4.00 4.00
Nos. 1994a-1994h are each 28x90mm.

Christmas A362

Entire paintings or details: 200ce, Cupid by Botticelli. 550ce, Zephyr and Chloris, by Botticelli. 800ce, Trumphant Cupid, by Caravaggio. 1100ce, The Seven Works of Mercy, by Caravaggio. 1500ce, The Toilet of Venus, by Diego Velazquez. 2000ce, Freeing of Saint Peter, by Raphael.
Sculptures: No. 2002, 5000ce, The Cavalcant Annunciation, by Donatello. No. 2003, 5000ce, Isis and Nepthys Protecting the Cartouches of Tutankhamen with their Wings.

**1997, Dec. 8    Litho.    Perf. 14**
1996-2001 A362 Set of 6 ........ 7.00 7.00

**Souvenir Sheets**
2002-2003 A362 Set of 2 ........ 10.50 10.50

Diana, Princess of Wales (1961-97) — A363

Various portraits, background color of sheet margin: No. 2004, 1200ce, Pink. No. 2005, 1200ce, Blue.
Portraits with (in margin): No. 2006, 3000ce, Elizabeth Taylor. No. 2007, 3000ce, Henry Kissinger.

**1997, Dec. 22**

**Sheets of 6, #a-f**
2004-2005 A363 Set of 2 ........ 12.00 12.00

**Souvenir Sheets**
2006-2007 A363 Set of 2 ........ 7.00 7.00

Mickey and Friends A364

No. 2008, 1000ce — Characters, month: a, Mortie and Ferdie, Jan. b, Minnie, Feb. c, Goofy, Mar. d, Mickey, Minnie, & Pluto, Apr. e, Minnie, May. f, Daisy, June.
No. 2009, 1000ce: a, Donald, July. b, Donald and Daisy, Aug. c, Morty and Ferdie, Sept. d, Huey, Dewey, & Louie, Oct. e, Mickey, Nov. f, Mickey & Minnie, Dec.
Characters, season: No. 2010, 5000ce, Daisy, nephews, winter, horiz. No. 2011, 5000ce, Goofy, fall. No. 2012, 5000ce, Mickey, spring, horiz. No. 2013, 5000ce, Minnie, summer.

**Perf. 13½x14, 14x13½**
**1998, Jan. 29    Litho.**

**Sheets of 6, #a-f**
2008-2009 A364 Set of 2 ........ 24.00 24.00

**Sheets of 6 With Added Marginal Inscription**
*2008g-2009g* Set of 2 ........ 24.00 24.00

**Souvenir Sheets**
2010-2013 A364 Set of 4 ........ 32.50 32.50

**Souvenir Sheets With Added Marginal Inscriptions**
*2012a-2013a* Set of 2 ........ 55.00 55.00
Nos. 2008g, 2009g, 2012a, 2013a have added inscription in sheet margin showing "Happy Birthday," Mickey Mouse, and "1998" in emblem.
Issued: #2008g, 2009g, 2012a, 2013a, 8/4/98.

Trains A365

Designs: 300ce, Union Pacific SD60M, US. 500ce, ETR 450, Italy. No. 2018, 800ce, X200 Sweden. 1000ce, TGV Duplex, France. 2000ce, El Class Co-Co, Australia. 3000ce, Eurostar, Britain.
No. 2020, 800ce: a, SPS 4-4-0, Pakistan. b, Class WP 4-6-2, India. c, Class QI 2-10-2, China. d, Class 12 4-4-2, Belgium. e, Class P8 4-6-0, Germany. f, Castle Class 4-6-0, Britain. g, Tank engine 2-6-0, Austria. h, Class P36 4-8-4, Russia. i, William Mason 4-4-0, US.
No. 2021, 800ce: a, AVE, Spain. b, Class 1600, Luxembourg. c, Bullet train, Japan. d, GM F7 Warbonnet, US. e, Class E1500, Morocco. f, Deltic, Great Britain. g, XPT, Australia. h, Le Shuttle, France/Britain. i, Class 201, Ireland.
No. 2022, 5500ce, Duchess Class 4-6-2, Britain. No. 2023, 5500ce, TGV, France.

**1998, Feb. 26    Litho.    Perf. 14**
2014-2019 A365 Set of 6 ........ 7.75 7.75

**Sheets of 9, #a-i**
2020-2021 A365 Set of 2 ........ 14.50 14.50

**Souvenir Sheets**
2022-2023 A365 Set of 2 ........ 11.00 11.00
Nos. 2022-2023 each contain one 57x42mm stamp.

Lunar New Year — A366

No. 2025 — Signs of Chinese zodiac: a, Horse. b, Monkey. c, Ram. d, Rooster. e, Dog. f, Ox. g, Rabbit. h, Boar. i, Snake. j, Dragon. k, Tiger. l, Rat.

**1998    Litho.    Perf. 13½**
2025 A366 400ce Sheet of 12, #a.-l. ........ 6.00 6.00
Numbers have been reserved for additional values in this set.

Great Black Writers of the 20th Century — A368

No. 2027: a, Maya Angelou. b, Alex Haley. c, Charles Johnson. d, Richard Wright. e, Toni Cade Bambara. f, Henry Louis Gates, Jr.

**1998, Mar. 25    Litho.    Perf. 14**
2027 A368 350ce Sheet of 6, #a.-f. ........ 2.75 2.75

Aircraft
A369

No. 2028, 800ce: a, Messerschmitt Bf 109 E-7. b, Lockheed PV-2 Harpoon. c, Airspeed Oxford MK1. d, Junkers Ju87D-1. e, Yakovlev Yak-9D. f, North American P-51D Mustang. g, Douglas A-20 Havoc. h, Supermarine Attacker F1. i, Mikoyan-Gurevich MIG-15.

No. 2029, 800ce: a, Breguet 14 B2. b, Curtiss BF2C-1 Goshawk. c, Supermarine Spitfire MK IX. d, Fiat G.50. e, Douglas B-18A. f, Boeing FB-5. g, Bristol F.2B. h, Hawker Fury 1. i, Fiat CR42.

No. 2030, 3000ce, Mitsubishi AGM8 Reisen. No. 2031, 3000ce, Supermarine Spitfire MK XIV, Supermarine Spitfire MK 1.

**1998, May 5       Sheets of 9, #a-i**
2028-2029  A369  Set of 2      14.50  14.50
**Souvenir Sheets**
2030-2031  A369  Set of 2       6.00  63.00
#2030-2031 each contain one 57x42mm stamp.

Nos. 1891-1894
Overprinted

**1998, May 13**
2032  A334  400ce  multi       .45   .45
2033  A334  600ce  multi       .65   .65
2034  A334  800ce  multi       .90   .90
**Souvenir Sheet**
2035  A334  2000ce  multi      2.50  2.50
No. 2035 contains additional inscription in sheet margin: "ISRAEL 98 — WORLD STAMP EXHIBITION / TEL-AVIV 13-21 MAY 1998."

Ships
A370

No. 2036, 800ce — Ocean liners: a, Empress of Ireland. b, Transylvania. c, Mauritania. d, Reliance. e, Aquitania. f, Lapland. g, Cap Polonio. h, France. i, Imperator.

No. 2037, 800ce — Warships: a, HMS Rodney. b, USS Alabama. c, HMS Nelson. d, SS Ormonde. e, USS Radford. f, SS Empress of Russia. g, Type XIV, Germany. h, Type A Midget, Japan. i, Brin, Italy.

No. 2038, 5500ce, Titanic. No. 2039, 5500ce, Amistad.

**1998, May 5       Litho.       Perf. 14**
**Sheets of 9, #a-i**
2036-2037  A370  Set of 2      14.50  14.50
**Souvenir Sheets**
2038-2039  A370  Set of 2      11.00  11.00
#2038-2039 each contain one 42x56mm stamp.

Orchids — A371

No. 2040, 800ce: a, Renanthera imschootiana. b, Arachnis flosaeris. c, Restrepia lansbergi. d, Paphiopedilum tonsum. e, Phalaenopsis ebauche. f, Pleione limprichti.

No. 2041, 800ce: a, Phragmipedium schroderae. b, Zygopetalum clayii. c, Vanda coerulea. d, Odontonia boussole. e, Disa uniflora. f, Dendrobium bigibbum.

No. 2042, 5500ce, Cypripedium calceolus. No. 2043, 5500ce, Sobralia candida.

**1998, June 2**
**Sheets of 6, #a-f**
2040-2041  A371  Set of 2      11.00  11.00
**Souvenir Sheets**
2042-2043  A371  Set of 2      12.00  12.00

Elvis Presley (1935-77), Television Comeback Special, 30th Anniv. A372

Various portraits during performance.

**1998, June 16    Litho.      Perf. 13½**
2044  A372  800ce  Sheet of 6, #a.-f.      5.50  5.50

Japanese Flowers — A373

No. 2045, 2000ce — Predominant color of flowers, location of denomination : a, Green (bamboo), UR. b, Red, LR. c, Yellow, LR. d, Pale green & pink, UR.

No. 2046, 2000ce: a, Pale green, yellow & pink, LR. b, Red, UR. c, Pink, LR. d, White, LR.

No. 2047, 5500ce, Small pink & yellow, LR. No. 2048, 5500ce, Pink, UL.

**1998, June 2      Litho.      Perf. 14**
**Sheets of 4, #a-d**
2045-2046  A373  Set of 2      14.00  14.00
**Souvenir Sheets**
2047-2048  A373  Set of 2      11.00  11.00

Ghana Cocoa Board, 50th Anniv. A374

Designs: 200ce, Tetteh Quarshie, pioneer of Ghana Cocoa industry. 550ce, Ripe hybrid cocoa pods. 800ce, Opening of cocoa pods. 1100ce, Fermenting cocoa beans. 1500ce, Shipment of cocoa.

**1998, July 8       Perf. 13x13½**
2049-2053  A374  Set of 5      5.00  5.00

Metropolitan Assembly, Cent. — A375

Designs: 200ce, AMA Centennial emblem. 550ce, King Tackie Tawiah I (1862-1902). 800ce, Achimota School, Accra. 1100ce, Korle Bu Hospital, Accra. 1500ce, Christianborg Castle, Accra.

**1998, July 8**
2054-2058  A375  Set of 5      5.00  5.00

Intl. Year of the Ocean A376

No. 2059: a, Dolphins. b, Dolphin (f). c, Seagull. d, Least tern, seagulls. e, Emperor angelfish (i). f, Whit ear. g, Blue shark, diver (k). h, Parrotfish. i, Dottyback. j, Blue-spotted stingray (m, n). k, Masked butterfly fish. l, Jack knife fish (h). m, Octopus (i). n, Turkeyfish (lionfish) (j, k, o). o, Seadragon. p, Rock cod.

No. 2060, 3000ce, Devil ray. No. 2061, 3000ce, Great white shark.

**1998, Aug. 18                    Perf. 14**
2059  A376  500ce  Sheet of 16, #a.-p.     10.50  10.50
**Souvenir Sheets**
2060-2061  A376  Set of 2      10.00  10.00

Inventors and Inventions — A377

No. 2062, 1000ce: a, Edison, light bulb. b, Peephole kinetoscope, Edison. c, Tesla coil, Tesla. d, Nikola Tesla (1856-1943). e, Gottlieb Wilhelm Daimler (1834-1900). f, Motorcycle, Daimler. g, Transmitter circuit for telescope, Marconi. h, Guglielmo Marconi.

#2063, 1000ce: a, Orville & Wright. b, 1st Flyer, Wright Brothers. c, Neon lighting and signs, Claude. d, Georges Claude (1870-1960). e, Alexander Graham Bell. f, The telephone, transmitter, Bell. g, Various uses of lasers, Townes. h, Charles Townes (b. 1915).

No. 2064, 5500ce, Robert Goddard (1882-1945), physicist. No. 2065, 5500ce, Paul Ehrlich (1854-1915), chemist, bacteriologist.

**1998, Sept. 1                   Perf. 14**
**Sheets of 8, #a-h**
2062-2063  A377  Set of 2      16.00  16.00
**Souenir Sheets**
2064-2065  A377  Set of 2      11.00  11.00
Nos. 2062b-2062c, 2062f-2062g, 2063b-2063c, 2063f-2063g are each 53x38mm.

Christmas — A378

Cats and dogs in Christmas scenes: 500ce, British colorpoint. 600ce, American shorthair-Dilute calico. 800ce, Peke-faced Persian. 1000ce, Small German spitz. 2000ce, British shorthair blue. 3000ce, Persian Dilute calico.

No. 2072, 5500ce, English pointer. No. 2073, 5500ce, Rumpy max.

**1998, Dec. 1       Litho.      Perf. 14**
2066-2071  A378  Set of 6      7.50  7.50
**Souvenir Sheets**
2072-2073  A378  Set of 2      14.00  14.00

Ferrari Automobiles — A378a

No. 2073A: c, : Lampredi. d, 250 GT Cabriolet. e, 121 LM.
3000ce, 365 GTS/4 Spyder.
Illustration reduced.

**1998, Dec. 24     Litho.      Perf. 14**
2073A  A378a  2000ce  Sheet of 3, #c-e       5.25  5.25
**Souvenir Sheet**
**Perf. 13¾x14¼**
2073B  A378a  3000ce  multi      4.00  4.00
No. 2073A contains three 39x25mm stamps.

Diana, Princess of Wales (1961-97) — A379

**1998, Dec. 24     Litho.      Perf. 14½**
2074  A379  1000ce  multicolored   1.00  1.00
No. 2074 was issued in sheets of 6.

Gandhi — A380

No. 2075: a, After 8 month prison term in Poona, 1931. b, On Salt March, 1930. c, Picking up natural salt at end of Salt March, 1930. d, After graduating from high school in Rajkot, 1887.
5500ce, At age 61, 1931.

**1998, Dec. 24**
2075  A380  2000ce  Sheet of 4, #a.-d.      6.00  6.00
**Souvenir Sheet**
2076  A380  5500ce  multicolored   5.50  5.50
Nos. 2075b-2075c are each 53x38mm.

Pablo Picasso A381

Designs : No. 2077, 1000ce, Collage, Composition with Butterfly, 1932. No. 2078, 1000ce, Sculpture, Mandolin and Clarinet, 1913, vert. 2000ce, Painting, Ballplayers on the Beach, 1931.
5500ce, Tomato Plant, 1944, vert.

**1998, Dec. 24                   Perf. 14x14½**
2077-2079  A381  Set of 3      4.00  4.00
**Souenir Sheet**
2080  A381  5500ce  multicolored   5.50  5.50

19th World Scouting Jamboree, Chile — A382

No. 2081: a, Scout sign. b, Camping. c, Tying a bowline.
5000ce, Robert Baden-Powell.

## 1998, Dec. 24 — Perf. 14
2081 A382 2000ce Sheet of 3,
#a.-c.                                        6.00 6.00
### Souvenir Sheet
2082 A382 5000ce multicolored       5.00 5.00

Royal Air Force, 80th Anniv. A383

No. 2083: a, C130 Hercules. b, Chinook HC2. c, C130 Hercules W2. d, Panavia Tornado F3ADV.
No. 2084, 5500ce, Eurofighter 2000, Chipmunk. No. 2085, 5500ce, Hawk's head, biplane.

## 1998, Dec. 24
2083 A383 2000ce Sheet of 4,
#a.-d.                                        8.00 8.00
### Souvenir Sheets
2084-2085 A383 Set of 2              11.00 11.00

New Year 1999 (Year of the Rabbit) A384

No. 2086 — Scenes showing farmer from "Farmer and Rabbit," by Han Fei Tzu: a, Working in field. b, Watching rabbit run into tree. c, Holding rabbit. d, Dreaming of rabbit.

## 1999, Jan. 4
2086 A384 1400ce Sheet of 4,
#a.-d.                                        5.50 5.50

Dinosaurs A385

Designs: 400ce, Corythosaurus. 600ce, Struthiomimus. 1000ce, Lambeosaurus. No. 2089A, 2000ce, Hesperosuchus.
No. 2090, 800ce: a, Ankylosaurus. b, Anatosaurus. c, Diplodocus. d, Monoclonius. e, Tyrannosaurus. f, Camptosaurus. g, Ornitholestes. h, Archaeopteryx. i, Allosaurus.
No. 2091, 800ce: a, Pterodactylus. b, Scelidosaurus. c, Pteranodon. d, Plateosaurus. e, Ornithosuchus. f, Kentrosaurus. g, Hypsognathus. h, Erythrosuchus. i, Stegoceros.
No. 2092, 5000ce, Dimorphodon, vert. No. 2093, 5000ce, Apatosaurus.

## 1999, Mar. 1 — Perf. 13½
2087- A385 Set of 4
2089A                                        4.00 4.00
### Sheets of 9, #a-i
2090-2091 A385 800ce Set of 2       14.50 14.50
### Souvenir Sheets
2092-2093 A385 5000ce Set of 2       10.00 10.00

Australia '99, World Stamp Expo A386

Butterflies: 300ce, California sister. 500ce, Red-splashed sulphur. 600ce, Checked white. 800ce, Blue emperor.
No. 2098, 1000ce, vert: a, Red admiral. b, Buckeye. c, Desert checkered skipper. d, Orange sulphur. e, Tiger swallowtail. f,

---

Orange-bordered blue. g, Agraulis vanillae. h, Monarch.
No. 2099, 1000ce, vert: a, Small tortoiseshell. b, Brimstone. c, Camberwell beauty. d, Marbled white. e, Purple emperor. f, Clouded yellow. g, Ladoga camilla. h, Marsh fritillary.
No. 2100, 5000ce, Papilio homerus, vert.
No. 2101, 5000ce, Blue copper.

## 1999, Apr. 26 — Litho. — Perf. 14
2094-2097 A386 Set of 4              2.25 2.25
### Sheets of 8, #a-h
2098-2099 A386 Set of 2              16.00 16.00
### Souvenir Sheets
2100-2101 A386 Set of 2              10.00 10.00

Shirley Temple as "Curly Top" — A387

No. 2102, vert.: a, Saying prayers. b, Actor John Boles looking at portrait. c, Taking Boles' hand. d, Dressed as old woman.
No. 2103: a, Hugging older sister. b, Dressed as a man. c, Looking at stuffed animals. d, Pulling Boles' tie. e, With family. f, Looking at sister and Boles together.
5000ce, In pink dress, vert.

### Perf. 13½x14, 14x13½
## 1999, Mar. 1 — Litho.
2102 A387 1000ce Sheet of 4,
#a.-d.                                        3.50 3.50
2103 A387 1000ce Sheet of 6,
#a.-f.                                        5.50 5.50
### Souvenir Sheet
2104 A387 5000ce multicolored       5.50 5.50

Amorphophallus Flavovirens — A387a

## 1999, May 6 — Litho. — Perf. 14x14¼
2104A A387a 200ce multi

Trains A388

Designs: 400ce, ICE 2, Germany, 1966. 500ce, M41, Hungary, 1982. 600ce, DVR, Finland, 1963. 1000ce, AVE 100 class, Spain, 1982.
No. 2109, 1300ce: a, EMD GP7 Illinois Terminal RR, 1949-54. b, EMD SD 38-2, 1972-79. c, EMD SD 60M Soo Line, 1989-96. d, GE U25C, 1963-65. e, EMD GP 28, 1961-63. f, EMD SD 9, 1954-59.
No. 2110, 1300ce: a, Conrail EMD SD80, 1993-99. b, Columbus & Greenville RR EMD SDP35, 1964-66. c, Providence & Worcester RR, MLW M420 Loc. Works, 1973-77. d, Missouri Pacific C36-7, 1978-85. e, Alco C-420 Virginia & Maryland RR, 1963-68. f, Reading RR EMD GP30, 1961-63.
No. 2111, 5000ce, Swiss Federal RR Class RE 6/6 Co-Co, 1972. No. 2112, 5000ce, AGP44, ABB Traction, Inc. 1990-91.

## 1999, May 10 — Perf. 14
2105-2108 A388 Set of 4              2.50 2.50
### Sheets of 6, #a-f
2109-2110 A388 Set of 2              15.00 15.00
### Souvenir Sheets
2111-2112 A388 Set of 2              10.00 10.00

---

Paintings by Hokusai (1760-1849) — A389

No. 2113: a, Girl Picking Plum Blossoms. b, Surveying a Region. c, Sumo Wrestlers (rear view). d, Sumo Wrestlers (front view). e, Landscape with Seaside Village. f, Courtiers Crossing a Bridge.
No. 2114: a, Climbing the Mountain. b, Nakahara in Sagami Province. c, Sumo Wrestlers (2 fighting). d, An Oiran and Maid by a Fence. e. Fujiwara Yoshitaka.
No. 2115, 5000ce, Palanquin Bearers on a Steep Hill, vert. No. 2116, 5000ce, Three Ladies by a Well, vert.

## 1999, Aug. 3 — Litho. — Perf. 13¾
2113 A389 1300ce Sheet of 6,
#a.-f.                                        7.00 7.00
2114 A389 1300ce Sheet of 6,
#a.-e., 2113c 7.00 7.00
### Souvenir Sheets
2115-2116 A389 Set of 2              9.00 9.00

IBRA '99, World Philatelic Exhibition, Nuremberg — A390

Exhibition emblem, sailing ship Schomberg and: No. 2117, 500ce, Hanover #1. No. 2119, 1000ce, Lubeck #1.
Emblem, Class P8 4-6-0 locomotive and: No. 2118, 800ce, Hamburg #1. No. 2120, 2000ce, Heligoland #1A.
5000ce, Germany #66 tied to airmail label on cover, vert.
Illustration reduced.

## 1999, Aug. 3 — Perf. 14x14½
2117-2120 A390 Set of 4             4.25 4.25
### Souvenir Sheet
### Perf. 14½x14
2121 A390 5000ce multicolored       4.50 4.50

First Manned Moon Landing, 30th Anniv. — A391

No. 2122: a, Command Module. b, Lunar Module ascension. c, Giant moon rock. d, Lunar module signals home. e, Neil Armstrong. f, One small step.
5000ce, Earth rise, horiz.

## 1999, Aug. 3 — Perf. 14
2122 A391 1300ce Sheet of 6,
#a.-f.                                        8.50 8.50
### Souvenir Sheet
2123 A391 5000ce multicolored       5.00 5.00

---

Queen Mother, 100th Birthday (in 2000) A392

Queen Mother, 100th Birthday (in 2000) — No. 2124: a, Lady Elizabeth Bowles-Lyon with brother David, 1904. b, Queen Elizabeth, 1957. c, Queen Mother, 1970. d, Queen Mother, 1992.
5000ce, Queen Mother, 1970, diff.

## 1999, Aug. 4
### Gold Frames
2124 A392 2000ce Sheet of 4,
#a.-d. + label                                7.75 7.75
### Souvenir Sheet
2125 A392 5000ce multicolored       6.50 6.50

No. 2125 contains one 38x50mm stamp. Margins of sheets are embossed.
See Nos. 2273-2274.

Fauna A393

Designs: 200ce, Meles meles. 800ce, Vulpes vulpes.
No. 2128: a, Martes martes. b, Strix aluco. c, Sus scrofa. d, Accipiter gentilis. e, Eliomys quercinus. f, Lucanus cervus.
No. 2129: a, Merops apiaster. b, Upupa epops. c, Cervus elaphus. d, Circaetus gallicus. e, Lacerta ocellata. f, Lynx pardellus.
5000ce, Canis lupus, vert.

## 1999, Mar. 29 — Litho. — Perf. 14
2126-2127 A393 Set of 2             .90 .90
2128 A393 1000ce Sheet of 6,
#a.-f.                                        5.50 5.50
2129 A393 1000ce Sheet of 6,
#a.-f.                                        5.50 5.50
### Souvenir Sheet
2130 A393 5000ce multicolored       5.00 5.00

## 1999
Birds: 400ce, Cyanopica cyana. 600ce, Ciconia ciconia. 2000ce, Aegypius monachus, vert. 3000ce, Garrulus glandarius, vert. 5000ce, Aquila heliaca adalberti.
2131-2134 A393 Set of 4             5.50 5.50
### Souvenir Sheet
2135 A393 5000ce multicolored       4.75 4.75

Rights of the Child — A394

No. 2136: a, Child, UN building. b, Dove, earth. c, Mother, child.
5000ce, Child.

## 1999, Aug. 3 — Litho. — Perf. 14
2136 A394 3000ce Sheet of 3,
#a.-c.                                        8.50 8.50
### Souvenir Sheet
2137 A394 5000ce multicolored       5.50 5.50

Souvenir Sheets

PhilexFrance 99 — A395

Locomotives: No. 2138, 5000ce, 232-U1 Four cylinder compound 4-6-4. No. 2139, 5000ce, 0-6-0 Suburban tank engine.

**1999, Aug. 3          Perf. 14x13¾**
2138-2139  A395  Set of 2        17.00 17.00

Johann Wolfgang von Goethe (1749-1832), German Poet — A396

No. 2140: a, Wagner entreats Faust in his study. b, Goethe and Friedrich von Schiller. c, Mephistopheles disguised as the fool. 5000ce, Faust attended by spirits.

**1999, Aug. 3     Litho.     Perf. 14**
2140  A396  2000ce Sheet of 3,
        #a.-c.                    6.00 6.00
        **Souvenir Sheet**
2141  A396  5000ce multicolored   5.50 5.50

Return of Macao to People's Republic of China — A397

**1999, Aug. 20   Litho.   Perf. 14x13¾**
2142  A397  1000ce multicolored   1.50 1.50
        Issued in sheets of 4.

Save the Ozone Layer — A398

Designs: 200ce, Fish. 550ce, Earth surrounded by ozone layer, man. 800ce, Crying Earth. 1100ce, People holding up shield against sunlight. 1500ce, Objects with ozone-depleting and non-harmful chemicals.

**1999          Litho.       Perf. 13½x13**
2143-2147  A398  Set of 5        5.50 5.50

SOS Children's Villages, 50th Anniv. A399

Designs: 200ce, Grandma Alice. 550ce, Kindergarten. 800ce, SOS Children's Village founder Herrmann Gmeiner (1919-86),

---

Asikawa SOS building. 1100ce, Food preparation.

**1999                    Perf. 13x13½**
2148-2151  A399  Set of 4        3.00 3.00

Dr. Ephraim Apu, Musician, Birth Cent. — A400

Designs: 200ce, Apu, clef, note. 800ce, Apu playing Odurugya flute. 1100ce, Apu, indiginous flutes.

**1999                    Perf. 13½x13**
2152-2154  A400  Set of 3        2.00 2.00

Millennium — A401

Designs: 300ce, Millennium emblem, vert. 700ce, Emblem, Kwame Nkrumah. 1200ce, Emblem, University of Ghana, vert.

**1999, Dec. 28    Litho.    Perf. 13¼**
2155-2157  A401  Set of 3        3.75 3.75

New Year 2000 — A402

Various scenes from Chinese story, "Daughter of the Dragon King." Stamps from the two sheets are numbered 1-12 in Chinese numeral characters. The numerals are at the bottom of the top group of Chinese characters. See Chinese numerals in Illustrated Identifier.

**2000, Feb. 5          Perf. 14½x14¼**
2158  A402  1600ce Sheet of 6,
        #a.-f.                    5.75 5.75
2159  A402  1700ce Sheet of 6,
        #a.-f.                    6.25 6.25

Wildlife A403

Designs: 300ce, Black-faced impala. 500ce, Cheetah. 1000ce, Wildebeest. 3000ce, Hippopotamus.
No. 2164, vert.: a, Chimpanzee. b, Boomslang. c, Vulture. d, Leopard. e, Rhinoceros. f, Zebra. g, Crowned crane. h, Lesser kudu.
No. 2165, vert.: a, Purple roller. b, Pelicans. c, Egrets. d, Orange-breasted waxbill. e, Giraffe. f, African buffalo. g, African elephant. h, African lion.
No. 2166, 7000ce, Waterbuck. No. 2167, 7000ce, Ostrich.

**2000, Feb. 28    Litho.    Perf. 14**
2160-2163  A403  Set of 4        3.00 3.00
2164  A403  1100ce Sheet of 8,
        #a.-h.                    7.25 7.25
2165  A403  1200ce Sheet of 8,
        #a.-h.                    7.50 7.50
        **Souvenir Sheets**
2166-2167  A403  each            9.00 9.00

---

Tourism A404

No. 2168: a, 300ce, Building, palm trees. b, 300ce, Mud building, natives. c, 300ce, Elephants. d, 1100ce, Natives. e, 1200ce, Natives carrying animal. f, 1800ce, Natives, diff.

**2000          Litho.       Perf. 13x13¼**
2168  A404  Booklet pane of 6,
        #a.-h.                    2.25 2.25
        Complete booklet, 4 #2168   9.00
There are 2 types of #2168, which differ only by the arrangement of the stamps on the pane. The booklet contains 2 of each type.

Wildlife A405

Designs: 500ce, Zebra duiker. 600ce, Leopard. 2000ce, Bush buck. 3000ce, African wood owl.
No. 2173, 1600ce: a, Blotted genet. b, Tree pangolin. c, Bongo. d, Elephant. e, Flap-necked chameleon. f, West African dwarf crocodile.
No. 2174, 1600ce: a, Lowe's monkey. b, Diana monkey. c, Potto. d, Moustached monkey. e, Thomas's galago. f, Chimpanzee.
No. 2175, 1600ce: a, Gray parrot. b, Hoopoe. c, European roller. d, European beeeater. e, Blue-breasted kingfisher. f, White-throated bee-eater.
No. 2176, 6000ce, Hippopotamus, vert. No. 2177, 6000ce, Great blue turaco, vert.

**2000, May 1      Litho.      Perf. 14**
2169-2172  A405  Set of 4        3.50 3.50
        **Sheets of 6, #a.-f.**
2173-2175  A405  Set of 3       18.00 18.00
        **Souvenir Sheets**
2176-2177  A405  Set of 2       10.00 10.00

Mushrooms — A406

No. 2178, horiz.: a, Slippery jack. b, Violet deceiver. c, Fairy stool. d, Honey fungus. e, Shaggy parasol. f, Russula sp.
No. 2179, horiz.: a, Grisette. b, Common puffball. c, Fan. d, Gray chanterelle. e, Fairies' bonnets. f, Russula sp., diff.
5000ce, Great orange elf-cup. 8000ce, Bitter boletus.

**2000, May 15**
2178  A406  1500ce Sheet of 6,
        #a.-f.                    7.50 7.50
2179  A406  2000ce Sheet of 6,
        #a.-f.                    9.50 9.50
        **Souvenir Sheets**
2180  A406  5000ce multi         4.50 4.50
2181  A406  8000ce multi         5.50 5.50
        The Stamp Show 2000, London.

---

Eurasian Goldfinch — A406a

**2000, June 1  Litho.  Perf. 13¾x13¼**
2181A  A406a  300ce multi          —  —

Prince William, 18th Birthday — A407

No. 2182: a, In ski gear. b, With ribbons wrapped around fingers. c, With jacket, no tie. d, Close-up.
8000ce, In sweater.
Illustration reduced.

**2000, June 26    Litho.    Perf. 14**
2182  A407  2000ce Sheet of 4,
        #a-d                      6.00 6.00
        **Souvenir Sheet**
        **Perf. 13¾**
2183  A407  8000ce multi         6.00 6.00
No. 2182 contains four 28x42mm stamps.

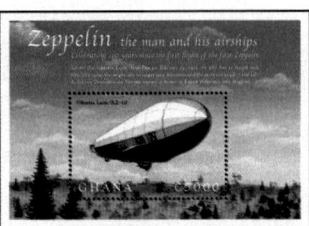

First Zeppelin Flight, Cent. — A408

No. 2184: a, LZ-129. b, LZ-9. c, LZ-4. 5000ce, LZ-11.
Illustration reduced.

**2000, June 26              Perf. 13¾**
2184  A408  1600ce Sheet of 3,
        #a-c                      5.50 5.50
        **Souvenir Sheet**
2185  A408  5000ce multi         5.75 5.75

Berlin Film Festival, 50th Anniv. — A409

No. 2186: a, Wetherby. b, Die Frau und der Fremde. c, Hong Gao Liang (Red Sorghum). d, Skrivánci na Niti. e, Music Box. f, Tema. 6000ce, Justice Est Faite.
Illustration reduced.

**2000, June 26              Perf. 14**
2186  A409  2000ce Sheet of 6,
        #a-f                      9.25 9.25
        **Souvenir Sheet**
2187  A409  6000ce multi         7.00 7.00

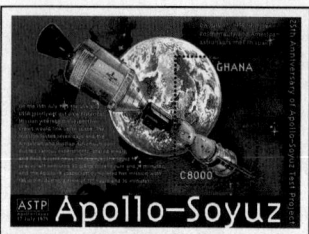

Apollo-Soyuz Mission, 25th
Anniv. — A410

No. 2188: a, Apollo 18. b, Docked spacecraft. c, Soyuz 19.
8000ce, Soyuz, Earth.
Illustration reduced.

**2000, June 26**
2188 A410 4000ce Sheet of 3,
#a-c                         8.50  8.50
**Souvenir Sheet**
2189 A410 8000ce multi         6.50  6.50

Souvenir Sheets

2000 Summer Olympics,
Sydney — A411

No. 2190: a, Gymnastics. b, Long jump. c,
Los Angeles Coliseum, and US flag. d,
Ancient Greek chariot racer.
Illustration reduced.

**2000, June 26**
2190 A411 1300ce Sheet of 4,
#a-d                         5.50  5.50

Public Railways, 175th Anniv. — A412

No. 2191: a, Marc Seguin. b, Blenkinsop
locomotive. c, Pumping station, Dawlish.
Illustration reduced.

**2000, June 26**
2191 A412 4000ce Sheet of 3,
#a-c                         8.75  8.75

Albert Einstein (1879-1955) — A413

Illustration reduced.

**2000, June 26**          **Perf. 13¾**
2192 A413 8000ce multi        6.50  6.50

Ghana Home Economics
Assoc. — A414

Designs: 300ce, Women, cooking pots.
700ce, Woman with home economics text-
book, vert. 1200ce, Emblem, Alberta Ollennu,
Patience A. Adow. 1800ce, Emblems, vert.

**2000**          **Perf. 13x13¼, 13¼x13**
2193-2196 A414  Set of 4      5.25  5.25

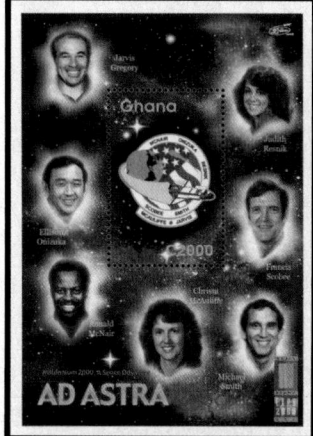

Space — A415

No. 2197, horiz.: a, Mercury. b, Gemini. c,
Apollo. d, Vostok. e, Voskhod 2. f, Soyuz.
Illustration reduced.

**2000, June 26    Litho.    Perf. 14**
2197 A415 2000ce Sheet of 6,
#a-f                         8.50  8.50
**Souvenir Sheet**
2198 A415 2000ce Challenger
51-L patch      5.00  5.00
World Stamp Expo 2000, Anaheim.

Cats and
Dogs — A416

Designs:   1100ce,  African  shorthair.
1200ce, Russian Blue. 1800ce, Basenji.
2000ce, Basset hound.
No. 2203, horiz. a, 1600ce, Weimaraner. b,
1800ce, Keeshond. c, 1800ce, Fox terrier. d,
1800ce, Saluki. e, 1800ce, Dalmatian. f,
1800ce, English setter.
No. 2204, 1800ce, horiz.: a, Silver Persian.
b, Creampoint Himalayan. c, British tortoiseshell shorthair. d, American shorthair tabby. e,
Black Persian. f, Turkish Van.
No. 2205, 8000ce, Cocker spaniels. No.
2206, 8000ce, Lilac Persian.

**2000, Aug. 21**
2199-2202 A416  Set of 4      3.25  3.25
**Sheets of 6, #a-f**
2203-2204 A416  Set of 2     13.50 13.50
**Souvenir Sheets**
2205-2206 A416  Set of 2     11.00 11.00

Scenes from Tale of the White
Snake — A417

No. 2207, 2500ce: a, Xu Xian offers
umbrella to White Lady and maid. b, White
Lady (with basket) helps husband Xu Xian
with business. c, Monk Fa Hai (with necklace)
talks to Xu Xian. d, Xu Xian gives wine to wife.
e, White Lady becomes snake, Xu Xian has
heart attack. f, White Lady (with swords) trying
to get medicinal herbs.
No. 2208, 2500ce: a, White Lady and maid
at Fa Hai's temple. b, Maid threatens to kill Xu
Xian. c, Fa Hai captures White Lady in bowl. d,
Maid, Xu Xian at pagoda. e, Maid with sword
attacks Fa Hai. f, Maid turns Fa Hai into crab.
Illustration reduced.

**2001, Jan. 2      Litho.      Perf. 14**
**Sheets of 6, #a-f**
2207-2208 A417  Set of 2      8.75  8.75
New Year 2001 (Year of the snake).

Edward G. Robinson — A418

Color of photograph: a, Gray green. b, Lilac.
c, Red violet (with hat). d, Brown (with cigar).
e, Orange brown (with pipe). f, Blue green.

**2001, Apr. 16      Litho.      Perf. 14**
2209 A418 4000ce Sheet of 6,
#a-f                         6.50  6.50

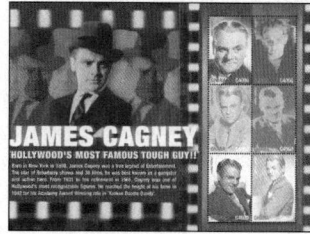

James Cagney — A419

Color of photograph: a, Olive green. b,
Emerald. c, Blue. d, Brown. e, Red violet. f,
Orange.

**2001, Apr. 16**
2210 A419 4000ce Sheet of 6,
#a-f                         6.50  6.50

Millennium — A420

No. 2211, 2500ce — Architects: a, Walter
Gropius. b, Aldo Rossi. c, Le Corbusier. d,
Antonio Gaudi. e, Paolo Soleri. f, Ludwig Mies
van de Rohe.
No. 2212, 2500ce — Artists: a, Wassily
Kandinsky. b, Henry Moore. c, Marc Chagall.
d, Norman Rockwell. e, Antonio López García.
f, Frida Kahlo.
No. 2213, 14,000ce, Frank Lloyd Wright.
No. 2214, 14,000ce, Pablo Picasso. No. 2215,
14,000ce, Human Genome Project.

**2001, Apr. 16**
**Sheets of 6, #a-f**
2211-2212 A420  Set of 2      8.25  8.25
**Souvenir Sheets**
2213-2215 A420  Set of 3     11.50 11.50

Jazz Musicians — A421

No. 2216, 4000ce: a, Scott Joplin. b, Clar-
ence Williams. c, Sidney Bechet. d, Willie "The
Lion" Smith. e, Ferdinand "Jelly Roll" Morton. f,
Coleman "Bean" Hawkins.
No. 2217, 4000ce: a, Kid Ory. b, Earl
"Fatha" Hines. c, Lil Hardin Armstrong. d, John
Philip Sousa. e, James P. Johnson. f, Johnny
St. Cyr.
No. 2218, 14,000ce, Joe "King" Oliver. No.
2219, 14,000ce, Louis "Satchmo" Armstrong.

**2001, Apr. 16**
**Sheets of 6, #a-f**
2216-2217 A421  Set of 2     13.00 13.00
**Souvenir Sheets**
2218-2219 A421  Set of 2      7.75  7.75

Oriental
Art
A422

Designs: 500ce, Cranes, by Kano Eisenin
Michinobu. 800ce, Flowers and Trees in Chen
Chun's Style, by Tsubaki Chinzan. 1200ce, A
Poetry Contest of 42 Matches, by unknown
artist. 2000ce, Cranes, by Kano, diff. 5000ce,
A Poetry Contest of 42 Matches, diff.
12,000ce, Plum Trees, by Tani Buncho.
No. 2226, 3000ce, vert. — The Tales of Ise,
by Sumiyoshi Jokei: a, Chapter 1. b, Chapter
4. c, Chapter 6. d, Chapter 9 (Eastboud Trip,
Mt. Utsu). e, Chapter 9, (Eastbound Trip, Mt.
Fuji). f, Chapter 9, (Eastbound Trip, Black-
headed Gulls). g, Chapter 23, (Crossing
Kawachi). h, Chapter 23, (By the Well Wall).
No. 2227, 4000ce, vert. — The Story of
Sakyamuni, by unknown artist: a, Siddhartha's
Excursion Through the South Gate. b, Sid-
dhartha's Excursion Through the East Gate. c,
Siddhartha's Excursion Through the North
Gate. d, Siddhartha's Excursion Through the
West Gate. e, Sakyamuni Entering Nirvana. f,
Untitled.

No. 2228, 14,000ce, Cranes, by Kano (red denomination), diff. No. 2229, 14,000ce, Cranes, by Kano (yellow denomination), diff. No. 2230, 14,000ce, Chapter 1, by Sumiyoshi. No. 2231, Chapter 12, by Sumiyoshi.

**2001, Apr. 30**
2220-2225 A422   Set of 6        6.00  6.00
2226 A422  3000ce Sheet of 8,
                    #a-h         6.50  6.50
2227 A422  4000ce Sheet of 6,
                    #a-f         6.50  6.50
**Souvenir Sheets**
2228-2231 A422   Set of 4       15.00 15.00
Phila Nippon '01, Japan.

Automobiles — A423

Designs: 2000ce, 1950 Bentley S Series convertible. 3000ce, 1948 Chrysler Town and Country. 5000ce, 1957 Lotus Elite. 6000ce, 1966 Chevrolet Corvette Sting Ray.
No. 2236, 4000ce: a, 1956-59 BMW 507. b, 1934 Bentley English Tourer. c, 1948 Morris Minor MM. d, 1954 Daimler SP-250 Dart. e, 1950 DeSoto custom convertible. f, 1955-60, Ford Thunderbird.
No. 2237, 4000ce: a,1959-63 Porshe 356B. b, 1962 Rolls-Royce Silver Cloud. c, 1958 Austin Healey Sprite MK-1. d, 1954-57 Mercedes 300SL. e, 1949 Citroen 2CV. f, 1949 Cadillac Series 62.
No. 2238, 14,000ce: a, 1933 Mercedes-Benz. No. 2239, 1953-55 Triumph TR-2.

**2001, June 18**
2232-2235 A423   Set of 4        4.50  4.50
**Sheets of 6, #a-f**
2236-2237 A423   Set of 2       13.00 13.00
**Souvenir Sheets**
2238-2239 A423   Set of 2        7.75  7.75
Belgica 2001 Intl. Stamp Exhibition, Brussels. No. 2238-2239 each contain one 85x28mm stamp.

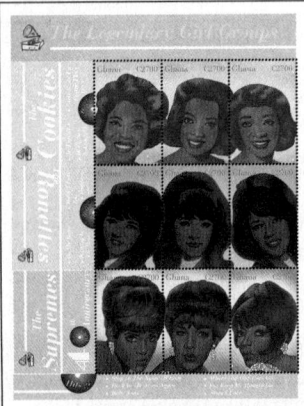
Female Recording Groups of the 1960s — A424

No. 2240 — Various members of: a-c, The Cookies. d-f, The Ronettes. g-i, The Supremes.

**2001, Apr. 16   Litho.      Perf. 14**
2240 A424  2700ce Sheet of 9,
                    #a-i        6.75  6.75

Mao Zedong (1893-1976) — A425

No. 2241: a, With arm raised, orange and light orange background. b, Portrait. c, With arm raised, tan gray and blue background. 12,000ce, With flag.

**2001, Aug. 27**
2241 A425  7000ce Sheet of 3,
                    #a-c        6.00  6.00
**Souvenir Sheet**
2242 A425  12,000ce multi       3.50  3.50

Giuseppe Verdi (1813-1901), Opera Composer — A426

No. 2243: a, Verdi. b, Scores for Aida and Rigoletto. c, Verdi's birthplace. d, Map of Italy. 13,000ce, Verdi and score.

**2001, Aug. 27**
2243 A426  5000ce Sheet of 4,
                    #a-d        5.75  5.75
**Souvenir Sheet**
2244 A426  13,000ce multi       3.75  3.75

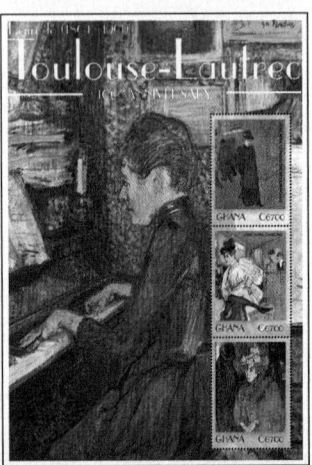
Toulouse-Lautrec Paintings — A427

No. 2245: a, Jane Avril Leaving the Moulin Rouge. b, Jane Avril Dancing. c, Jane Avril Entering the Moulin Rouge.

**2001, Aug. 27          Perf. 13¾**
2245 A427  6700ce Sheet of 3,
                    #a-c        5.75  5.75

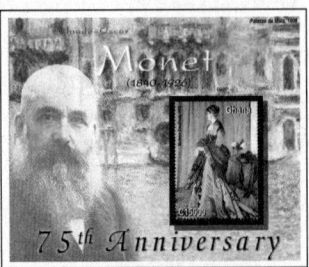
Monet Paintings — A428

No. 2246, horiz.: a, Zaandam. b, On the Seine at Bennecourt. c, The Studio Boat. d, Houses on the Waterfront, Zaandam. 15,000ce, Madame Gaudibert.

**2001, Aug. 27**
2246 A428  5000ce Sheet of 4,
                    #a-d        5.75  5.75
**Souvenir Sheet**
2247 A428  15,000ce multi       4.25  4.25

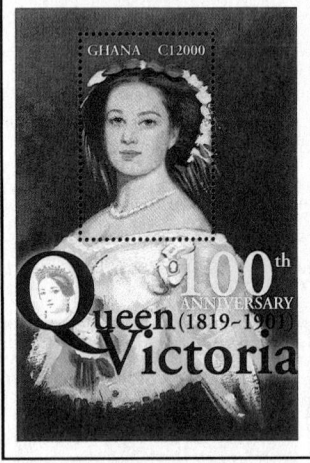
Queen Victoria (1819-1901) — A429

No. 2248: a, Victoria. b, Prince Albert. c, Albert and Victoria. d, Victoria and Albert on wedding day.
12,000ce, Victoria with green and white headpiece.

**2001, Aug. 27          Perf. 14**
2248 A429  5000ce Sheet of 4,
                    #a-d        5.75  5.75
**Souvenir Sheet**
2249 A429  12,000ce multi       4.00  4.00

Queen Elizabeth II, 75th Birthday — A430

No. 2250, vert.: a, Bright pink hat. b, White hat. c, Peach hat. d, Crown. e, Blue and pink hat. f, In uniform.
15,000ce, with Prince Philip.

**2001, Aug. 27**
2250 A430  4000ce Sheet of 6,
                    #a-f        6.75  6.75
**Souvenir Sheet**
2251 A430  15,000ce multi       4.25  4.25

Whales
A431

Designs: 1000ce, Killer whale. 3000ce, Narwhal. 5000ce, Beluga. 6000ce, Bowhead whale.
No. 2256, 4000ce: a, Blue whale. b, Killer whale, diff. c, Northern bottlenose whale. d,

Sperm whale. e, Southern right whale. f, Pygmy right whale.
No. 2257, 4000ce: a, Humpback whale. b, Fin whale. c, Bowhead whale, diff. d, Gray whale. e, Narwhal, diff. f, Beluga, diff.
No. 2258, 14,000ce, Sperm whale. No. 2259, 14,000ce, Blue whales.

**2001, Oct. 1**
2252-2255 A431   Set of 4        6.00  6.00
**Sheets of 6, #a-f**
2256-2257 A431   Set of 2       17.50 17.50
**Souvenir Sheets**
2258-2259 A431   Set of 2       11.00 11.00

Rotary Intl. In Ghana, 40th Anniv. (in 1998) A432

Rotary Intl. emblem and: 300ce, Polio victim. 1100ce, Clean water. 1200ce, Founder Paul Harris. 1800ce, Blood donation.

**2001 ?                 Perf. 13¼**
2260-2263 A432   Set of 4        1.25  1.25

Orchids — A433

Designs: 1100ce, Paphiopedilum hennisianum. 1200ce, Vuylstekeara cambria Plush. 1800ce, Cymbidium ormoulu. 2000ce, Phalaenopsis Barbara Moler.
No. 2268, 4500ce: a, Cattleya capra. b, Odontoglossum rossii. c, Epidendrum pseudepidendrum. d, Encyclia cochleata. e, Cymbidium baldoyle Melbury. f, Phalaenopsis asean.
No. 2269, 4500ce: a, Odontocidium Tigersun. b, Miltonia Emotion. c, Odontonia sappho Excul. d, Cymbidium Bulbarrow. e, Dendrobium nobile. f, Paphiopedilum insigne.
No. 2270, 15,000ce, Calanthe vestita. No. 2271, 15,000ce, Angraecum eburneum.

**2001, Oct. 30   Litho.      Perf. 14**
2264-2267 A433   Set of 4        3.00  3.00
**Sheets of 6, #a-f**
2268-2269 A433   Set of 2       17.50 17.50
**Souvenir Sheets**
2270-2271 A433   Set of 2       10.00 10.00

Musical Instruments — A434

No. 2272: a, Bamboo orchestra. b, Mmensuon. c, Fontomfrom. d, Pati.

**2001, Dec. 3           Perf. 14¼**
2272 A434  4000ce Sheet of 4,
                    #a-d        4.50  4.50

**Queen Mother Type of 1999 Redrawn**

No. 2273: a, Lady Elizabeth Bowles-Lyon with brother David, 1904. b, In Rhodesia, 1957. c, In 1970. d, In 1992.
5000ce, In 1970, diff.

**2001, Dec.             Perf. 14**
**Yellow Orange Frames**
2273 A392  2000ce Sheet of 4,
                 #a-d, + label  2.25  2.25

## Souvenir Sheet
**Perf. 13¾**

**2274** A392 5000ce multi    1.40 1.40

Queen Mother's 101st birthday. No. 2274 contains one 38x50mm stamp with a darker background than on No. 2125. Sheet margins of Nos. 2273-2274 lack embossing and gold arms and frames found on Nos. 2124-2125.

Kwame Nkrumah University of Science and Technology, Kumasi, 50th Anniv. — A435

Designs: 300ce, Emblem. No. 2276, 700ce, No. 2280a, 4000ce, Main gate. No. 2277, 1100ce, No. 2280b, 4000ce, Dairy production. No. 2278, 1200ce, No. 2280c, 4000ce, Pharmacy Department. No. 2279, 1800ce, No. 2280d, 4000ce, Residence hall.

**2001**    **Perf. 13x13¼**

**2275-2279** A435   Set of 5   1.40 1.40

### Souvenir Sheet
**2280** A435 4000ce Sheet of 4, #a-d   4.50 4.50

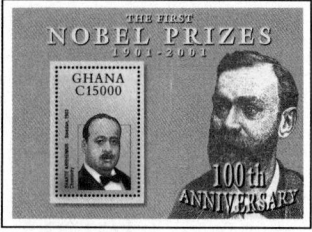

Nobel Prizes, Cent. (In 2001) — A436

No. 2281, 4000ce — Chemistry laureates: a, George A. Olah, 1994. b, Kary Mullis, 1993. c, Sir Harold W. Kroto, 1996. d, Richard R. Ernst, 1991. e, Ahmed H. Zewail, 1999. f, Paul Crutzen, 1995.

No. 2282, 4000ce — Chemistry laureates: a, John E. Walker, 1997. b, Jens C. Skou, 1997. c, Alan G. MacDiarmid, 2000. d, Thomas Robert Cech, 1989. e, John Pole, 1998. f, Rudolph A. Marcus, 1992.

No. 2283, 4000ce — Chemistry laureates: a, Walter Kohn, 1998. b, F. Sherwood Rowland, 1995. c, Mario Molina, 1995. d, Hideki Shirakawa, 2000. e, Paul D. Boyer, 1997. f, Richard Smalley, 1996.

No. 2284, 15,000ce, Svante Arrhenius, Chemistry, 1903. No. 2285, 15,000ce, Alfred Werner, Chemistry, 1913. No. 2286, 15,000ce, Peter Debye, Chemistry, 1936. No. 2287, 15,000ce, Wole Soyinka, Literature, 1986. No. 2288, 15,000ce, Nelson Mandela, Peace, 1993.

**2002, Jan. 9**    **Perf. 14**
**Sheets of 6, #a-f**

**2281-2283** A436   Set of 3   20.00 20.00

### Souvenir Sheets
**2284-2288** A436   Set of 5   21.00 21.00

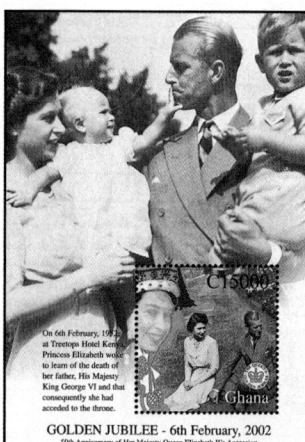

GOLDEN JUBILEE - 6th February, 2002
50th Anniversary of Her Majesty Queen Elizabeth II's Accession

Reign of Queen Elizabeth II, 50th Anniv. — A437

No. 2289: a, Wearing pink dress. b, Sitting on horse. c, Looking at horses. d, In carriage with Prince Philip.

15,000ce, Sitting with Prince Philip (black and white photograph).

**2002, Feb. 6**   **Litho.**   **Perf. 14¼**
**2289** A437   6500ce Sheet of 4, #a-d   7.25 7.25

### Souvenir Sheet
**2290** A437 15,000ce multi   4.75 4.75

Intl. Copyright Conference, Accra — A438

Designs: 300ce, Conference emblem, vert. 700ce, Person reading. 1100ce, Spider, web, map of Ghana. 1200ce, Map of Ghana, Kente cloth. 1800ce, Drummer.

**2002, Feb. 20**   **Perf. 14¼x14, 14x14¼**
**2291-2295** A438   Set of 5   1.40 1.40

2002 World Cup Soccer Championships, Japan and Korea — A439

World Cup trophy and: 100ce, Jay Jay Okacha, flag of Nigeria. 150ce, South African player and flag. 300ce, Pele, flag of Brazil. 400ce, Roger Milla, flag of Cameroun. 500ce, Bobby Charlton, flag of England. 800ce, Michel Platini, flag of France. 1000ce, Franz Beckenbauer, flag of West Germany. 1500ce, Ulsan Munsu Stadium, Korea, horiz. 2000ce, German player and flag. 3000ce, Brazilian player and flag. 5000ce, Yokohama Intl. Sports Stadium, Japan, horiz. 6000ce, Italian player and flag. 11,000ce, 1950 World Cup poster. 12,000ce, 1934 World Cup poster.

No. 2311, 15,000ce, Geoff Hurst's hat trick for England, 1966. No. 2312, 15,000ce, Gordon Banks making save on Pele, 1970.

**2002, Mar. 4**    **Perf. 14**
**2296-2310** A439   Set of 15   13.00 13.00

### Souvenir Sheets
**2311-2312** A439   Set of 2   9.00 9.00

### Souvenir Sheet

New Year 2002 (Year of the Horse) — A440

No. 2313: a, Brown panel at L, country name at LR. b, Brown panel at R, country name at UR. c, Brown panel at L, country name at LL. d, Brown panel at R, country name at LR.

**2002, Mar. 4**    **Perf. 13¾**
**2313** A440 4000ce Sheet of 4, #a-d   5.00 5.00

Visit of Netherlands Prince Willem-Alexander and Princess Máxima to Ghana — A441

Couple: a, With Prince wearing sash. b, Holding hands, Prince wearing hat. c, With windmills and flags. d, At wedding ceremony, with another man. e, In crowd. f, Kissing.

**2002**    **Perf. 14**
**2314** A441 6000ce Sheet of 6, #a-f   8.75 8.75

Amphilex 2002 Intl. Stamp Show, Amsterdam.

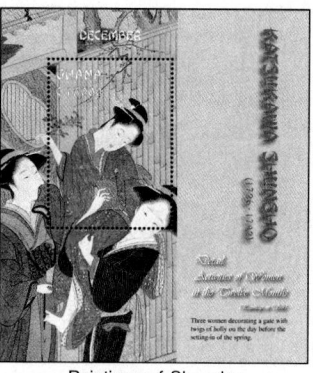

Paintings of Shunsho Katsukawa — A442

No. 2315, 9000ce — Activities of Women in the Twelve Months: a, Trying to retrieve a ball caught in a tree (March). b, Listening to a cuckoo in the bedroom (April). c, Holding a cage filled with fireflies for a woman to read a book (May).

No. 2316, 9000ce — Activities of Women in the Twelve Months: a, Mother and child taking a tub bath while woman holds a revolving lantern (June). b, Strips of paper with wishes and poems are tied on bamboo (July). c, Women enjoying the cool air on a boat (August).

No. 2317, 9000ce — Activities of Women in the Twelve Months: a, Celebrating Feast of the Chrysanthemum (September). b, Looking out for colored leaves (October). c, Mother reading picture book while sitting at a foot warmer (November).

No. 2318, 15,000ce, Three women decorating a gate (woman in blue kimono), from Activities of Women in the Twelve Months. No. 2319, 15,000ce, Part 1 (woman in red kimono) from Snow, Moonlight and Flowers. No. 2320, 15,000ce, Part 2 (woman in black kimono) from Snow, Moonlight and Flowers. No. 2321, 15,000ce, Part 3 (woman in gray kimono) from Snow, Moonlight and Flowers.

**2002, July 29**   **Litho.**   **Perf. 14¼**
**Sheets of 3, #a-c**
**2315-2317** A442   Set of 3   20.00 20.00

### Souvenir Sheets
**2318-2321** A442   Set of 4   14.50 14.50

United We Stand — A443

**2002, Aug. 15**    **Perf. 14**
**2322** A443 7000ce multi   1.75 1.75

Printed in sheets of 4.

2002 Winter Olympics, Salt Lake City — A444

Designs: No. 2323, 7000ce, Figure skaters. No. 2324, 7000ce, Freestyle skier.

**2002, Aug. 15**
**2323-2324** A444   Set of 2   4.00 4.00
*2324a*   Souvenir sheet, #2323-2324   4.25 4.25

Intl. Year of Mountains — A445

No. 2325: a, Tateyama, Japan. b, Mt. Shivling, India. c, Wong Leng, Hong Kong. d, Mt. Blanc, France.

15,000ce, Mt. Fuji, Japan.

**2002, Aug. 15**
**2325** A445   6000ce Sheet of 4, #a-d   6.00 6.00

### Souvenir Sheet
**2326** A445 15,000ce multi   3.75 3.75

20th World Scout Jamboree, Thailand — A446

No. 2327, horiz.: a, Scout with walking stick. b, Scout with backpack. c, Tent and campfire. d, Tent and scout tying knots.

15,000ce, Scout with red neckerchief.

**2002, Aug. 15**
**2327** A446   6500ce Sheet of 4, #a-d   6.25 6.25

### Souvenir Sheet
**2328** A446 15,000ce multi   5.25 5.25

First Solo Transatlantic Flight, 75th
Anniv. — A447

No. 2329, 8500ce, horiz.: a, Charles
Lindbergh and Spirit of St. Louis. b, Charles
and Anne Morrow Lindbergh in airplane.
15,000ce, Lindbergh wearing flying gear.

**2002, Aug. 15**
2329 A447 8500ce Sheet of 2,
#a-b    4.25 4.25
**Souvenir Sheet**
2330 A447 15,000ce multi    3.75 3.75

Intl. Year of Ecotourism — A448

No. 2331: a, Nectarinia venusta. b, Panthera
pardus. c, Kobus kob. d, Syncerus caffer. e,
Pan troglodytes. f, Galago.
12,000ce, Loxodonta africana.

**2002, Aug. 15**
2331 A448 4000ce Sheet of 6,
#a-f    6.00 6.00
**Souvenir Sheet**
2332 A448 12,000ce multi    3.00 3.00

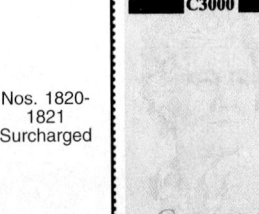

Nos. 1820-
1821
Surcharged

**2002, Aug. 15**    *Perf. 13½x14*
2333   Strip or block of 4   3.00 3.00
   *a.* A315 3000ce on 600ce #1820a   .75 .75
   *b.* A315 3000ce on 600ce #1820b   .75 .75
   *c.* A315 3000ce on 600ce #1820c   .75 .75
   *d.* A315 3000ce on 600ce #1820d   .75 .75
**Souvenir Sheet**
2334 A315 20,000ce on 2500ce
#1821    5.00 5.00

No. 2334 and sheets of No. 2333 are additionally overprinted in margin with black border
and inscription "In Memoriam / 1900-2002."

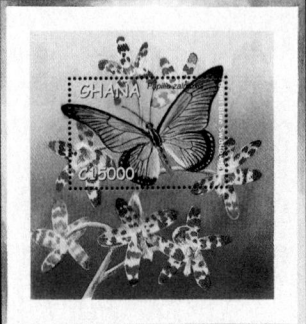

Butterflies, Moths, Insects and
Birds — A449

No. 2335, 4500ce — Butterflies: a, Iolaus
menas. b, Neptis melicerta. c, Cymothoe
lucasi. d, Euphaedra francina. e, Lilac nymph.
f, Mocker swallowtail.
No. 2336, 4500ce — Moths: a, Phiala
cunina. b, Mazuca strigicincta. c,
Steindachner's emperor. d, Amphicallia
pactolicus. e, Verdant sphinx. f, Oleander
hawkmoth.
No. 2337, 4500ce — Insects: a, Bush hop-
per. b, Ant lion. c, Digger bee. d, Stag beetle.
e, Mantis. f, Longhorn beetle.
No. 2338, 4500ce — Birds: a, Malachite
kingfisher. b, Brown harrier eagle. c, Heuglin's
masked weaver. d, Egyptian plover. e, Swallow-tailed bee-eater. f, Black-faced fire finch.
No. 2339, 15,000ce, Giant blue swallowtail
butterfly. No. 2340, 15,000ce, African moon
moth. No. 2341, 15,000ce, Mantis nymph. No.
2342, 15,000ce, Rufous fishing owl.

**2002, Aug. 26**    *Perf. 14*
**Sheets of 6, #a-f**
2335-2338 A449 Set of 4   26.00 26.00
**Souvenir Sheets**
2339-2342 A449 Set of 4   14.50 14.50

Edina
Bakatue
Festival
A450

Designs: No. 2343, 1000ce, No. 2349e,
4000ce, Casting of net. No. 2344, 2000ce, No.
2349b, 4000ce, Chief in palanquin. No. 2345,
2500ce, No. 2349c, 4000ce, Regatta. No.
2346, 3000ce, No. 2349d, 4000ce, Festival
boat. No. 2347, 4000ce, Opening ritual. No.
2348, 5000ce, No. 2349a, 4000ce,
Priestesses.

**2002, Oct. 21**    *Perf. 14x13½*
2343-2348 A450 Set of 6   4.25 4.25
2349 A450 Sheet of 6, #2347,
2349a-e    6.00 6.00

Japan Overseas
Cooperation
Volunteers, 25th
Anniv. in
Ghana — A451

Designs: No. 2350, 1000ce, Health. No.
2351, 1000ce, Education (Home economics).
2000ce, Education (Science and math).
2500ce, Education (Computer technology).
3000ce, Sports.
No. 2355 (without white inscriptions): a, Like
2000ce. b, Like No. 2350. c, Like 3000ce. d,
Like 2500ce. e, Like No. 2351.

**2002, Oct. 23**    *Perf. 14*
2350-2354 A451 Set of 5   2.40 2.40
2355 A451 4000ce Sheet of 5,
#a-e    5.00 5.00

Awarding of Nobel
Peace Prize to UN
Secretary General
Kofi Annan — A452

Designs: 1000ce, With Ghana Pres. J. A.
Kufuor at award ceremony. 2000ce, With
Nobel medal and citation. 2500ce, Portrait.
3000ce, In academic procession at Kwame
Nkrumah University.

**2002, Oct. 28**
2356-2359 A452 Set of 4   2.10 2.10

Nos. 1939C, 1939B
Surcharged

**2002, Mar. 7**
2360 A350b 1000ce on 1100ce
multi    — —
2360A A350a 2500ce on 800ce
multi    — —

Charlie Chaplin (1889-1977) — A453

No. 2361: a, In suit and tie. b, As "Little
Tramp," wearing hat. c, Wearing overalls. d,
Holding Academy Award.

**2003, Jan. 14**   Litho.   *Perf. 14*
2361 A453 6500ce Sheet of 4,
#a-d    6.25 6.25

Marlene Dietrich (1901-92) — A454

No. 2362 — Background colors: a, Violet
black (hair parted in middle, name at left). b,
Gray (wearing scarf, name at right). c, Brown
(name at left). d, Dark brown (wearing hat). e,
Blue gray (name at left). f, Brown black (name
at right).
15,000ce, Holding cigarette.

**2003, Jan. 14**
2362 A454 4500ce Sheet of 6,
#a-f    6.50 6.50
**Souvenir Sheet**
2363 A454 15,000ce multi    3.75 3.75

Popeye in Amsterdam — A455

No. 2364: a, Along the canal. b, Anne Frank
House. c, Restaurant Row. d, Downtown. e,
Central Station. f, Windmills.

**2003, Jan. 14**    *Perf. 13¾*
2364 A455 4500ce Sheet of 6,
#a-f    6.50 6.50
**Souvenir Sheet**
2365 A455 15,000ce shown   3.75 3.75

No. 2364 contains six 38x51mm stamps.

New Year 2003 (Year
of the Ram) — A456

**2003, Feb. 24**    *Perf. 14*
2366 A456 5000ce multi   1.25 1.25
Issued in sheets of 4.

Famous
Women — A457

Designs: 1000ce, Nana Yaa Asantewaa
(1822-1923), Asante warrior. 2000ce, Justice
Annie Jiagge (1918-96). 2500ce, Dr. Esther
Ocloo (1919-2002), industrialist. 3000ce, Dr.
Efua T. Sutherland (1924-96), playwright.
5000ce, Rebecca Dedei Aryeetey (1924-60),
activist.

**2003, Apr. 23**    *Perf. 13½x14*
2367-2371 A457 Set of 5   3.25 3.25

British Council,
60th
Anniv. — A458

Designs: 1000ce, Tomorrow's leaders.
2000ce, Women reading Africawoman Newspaper. 2500ce, Partners in culture. 3000ce,
Window on the world. 5000ce, Leadership
through sport.

**2003, June 12**
2372-2376 A458 Set of 5   3.25 3.25

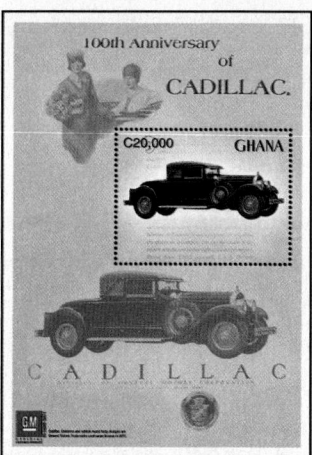

General Motors Automobiles — A459

No. 2377, 7000ce — Cadillacs: a, 1941 Sixty Special. b, 1953 Eldorado. c, 1957 Eldorado Brougham. d, 1959 Eldorado Convertible.
No. 2378, 7000ce — Corvettes: a, 1962. b, 1963 Sting Ray. c, 1964 Sting Ray. d, 1968.
No. 2379, 20,000ce, Cadillac. No. 2380, 20,000ce, 1966 Corvette Sting Ray.

**2003, July 2**                        *Perf. 13¾*
**Sheets of 4, #a-d**
2377-2378  A459  Set of 2      17.00 17.00
**Souvenir Sheets**
2379-2380  A459  Set of 2      11.00 11.00

Coronation of Queen Elizabeth II, 50th Anniv. — A460

No. 2381: a, Wearing tiara. b, Wearing blue hat. c, Wearing black hat.
20,000ce, Wearing black hat, diff.

**2003, July 2**                        *Perf. 14*
2381  A460  10,000ce Sheet of 3,
              #a-c                         7.00 7.00
**Souvenir Sheet**
2382  A460  20,000ce multi               4.75 4.75

Tour de France Bicycle Race, Cent. — A461

No. 2383: a, Romain Maes, 1935. b, Sylvére Maes, 1936. c, Roger Lapebie, 1937. d, Gino Bartali, 1938.
20,000ce, Henri Pelissier, 1923.

---

**2003, July 2**                        *Perf. 13½x13¼*
2383  A461  7000ce Sheet of 4,
              #a-d                         6.50 6.50
**Souvenir Sheet**
2384  A461  20,000ce multi               4.75 4.75

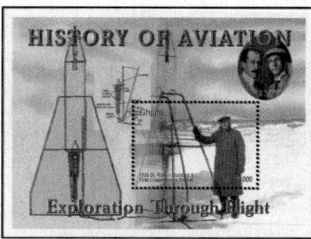

History of Aviation — A462

No. 2385: a, Charles Lindbergh makes first non-stop solo Atlantic crossing, 1927. b, Wiley Post makes first round-the-world solo flight, 1933. c, Heinkel He178, first turbojet powered aircraft, 1939. d, Chuck Yeager flies Bell X-1 to break sound barrier, 1947.
20,000ce, Dr. Robert Goddard and first liquid-fueled rocket, 1926.

**2003, July 2**                        *Perf. 14*
2385  A462  7000ce Sheet of 4,
              #a-d                         6.50 6.50
**Souvenir Sheet**
2386  A462  20,000ce multi               4.75 4.75

Christmas A463

Children's art: 2000ce, Preparation for Christmas, by Kwame Owusu Aduomi. 4000ce, Typical Christmas Present, by Thomas Kyeremateng, vert. 4500ce, Making Merry at Christmas, by Samuel Baffoe Maison. 5000ce, Christmas is Here, by Patrick Annan-Noonoo.

**Perf. 14x13¼, 13¼x14**
**2003, Dec. 1**                            *Litho.*
2387-2390  A463  Set of 4                3.75 3.75

Boletus Edulis — A463a

**2003**               *Litho.*       *Perf. 14x13½*
2390A A463a 1000ce multi                 — —

New Year 2004 (Year of the Monkey) — A464

No. 2391: a, Dark gray monkey. b, Light gray monkey. c, Buff monkey.

**2004, Jan. 29**        *Litho.*      *Perf. 14*
2391  A464  5000ce Sheet of 3,
              #a-c                         3.50 3.50

---

Chinese Actors — A465

No. 2392, 5000ce — Richie Jen: a, With hair below ears, wearing black shirt. b, With hair above ears, wearing black shirt. c, Wearing helmet. d, With mustache. e, Wearing head covering. f, Wearing red jacket.
No. 2393, 5000ce — Ray Lui: a, Wearing suit and tie. b, With shaved head. c, Wearing black hood. d, Wearing polka dot shirt. e, Wearing costume. f, Wearing costume with red headpiece. g, Wearing costume with wound on forehead.
No. 2394, 5000ce — Jiang Wen: a, Wearing glasses, fingers showing at LR. b, Wearing costume with headpiece. c, Sepia photograph, wearing glasses. d, Wearing suit and tie. e, Sepia photograph, without glasses. f, Wearing striped shirt.

**2004, Feb. 1**                        *Perf. 13¾*
**Sheets of 6, #a-f**
2392-2394  A465  Set of 3      21.00 21.00

Kente Cloth Patterns A466

Designs: 2000ce, Edwene Asa. 4000ce, Fatia Fata Nkruma. 4500ce, Asam Takra. 5000ce, Toku Akra Ntoma. 6000ce, Sika Futuro.

**2004, Feb. 27**                      *Perf. 14x13¼*
2395-2399  A466  Set of 5      5.00 5.00

Hogbetsotso Festival — A467

Designs: 2000ce, Exodus from Notsie. 4000ce, Misego Dance. 4500ce, Royal stools. 5000ce, Pouring libation. 6000ce, King aloft.
No. 2405: a, Pouring libation, diff. b, Togbe Adeladza II, Awomefia of Anlo. c, Display of traditional symbols of wealth. d, Exodus from Notsie, diff. e, Procession of the royalty. f, Royalty at Durbar. g, Ewe cultural dance. h, Bountiful harvest. i, Royal stools, diff.

**2004, Mar. 1**
2400-2404  A467  Set of 5      5.00 5.00
2405  A467  3000ce Sheet of 9,
              #a-i                         6.25 6.25

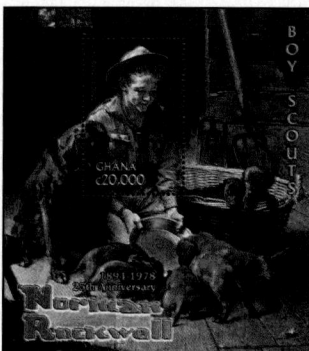

Paintings of Scouts by Norman Rockwell (1894-1978) — A468

No. 2406 — Paintings from 1974 Boy Scout Calendar: a, Female scout leader. b, Webelo

---

(plaid neckerchief). c, Boy scout (green cap). d, Cub scout (blue and yellow neckerchief).
20,000ce, Good Friends.

**2004, Mar. 18**                      *Perf. 14*
2406  A468  7000ce Sheet of 4,
              #a-d                         6.50 6.50
**Souvenir Sheet**
2407  A468  20,000ce multi               4.50 4.50

Paintings by Pablo Picasso (1881-1973) — A469

No. 2408: a, Jacqueline in a Black Scarf. b, Portrait of Olga. c, Woman in White (Sara Murphy). d, Portrait of Dora Maar.
16,000ce, Portrait of the Artist's Sister, Lola.

**2004, Mar. 18**                      *Perf. 14¼*
2408  A469  6500ce Sheet of 4,
              #a-d                         6.00 6.00
*Imperf*
2409  A469  16,000ce multi               3.75 3.75
No. 22408 contains four 37x50mm stamps.

Paintings of James Abbott McNeill Whistler (1834-1903) A470

Designs: 2000ce, Head of a Peasant Woman. 4000ce, The Master Smith of Lyme Regis. 5000ce, The Little Rose of Lyme Regis. 6000ce, Arrangement in Gray: Portrait of a Painter (self-portrait).
No. 2414: a, Rose and Siver: La Princesse du Pays de la Porcelaine. b, Variations in Flesh Color and Green: The Balcony. c, Caprice in Purple and Gold: The Golden Screen. d, Purple and Rose: The Lange Lijzen of the Six Marks.
20,000ce, Harmony in Green and Rose: The Music Room, horiz.

**2004, Mar. 18**                      *Perf. 14¼*
2410-2413  A470  Set of 4      4.00 4.00
2414  A470  7500ce Sheet of 4,
              #a-d                         6.75 6.75
**Souvenir Sheet**
2415  A470  20,000ce multi               4.50 4.50

Paintings in the Hermitage, St. Petersburg, Russia A471

Designs: 2000ce, Portrait of Anne of Austria as Minerva, by Simon Vouet. 3000ce, Lasciviousness, by Pompeo Giroloamo Batoni. 10,000ce, Allegory of Faith, by Moretto da Brescia.

282

# GHANA

No. 2419: a, Allegory of the Arts, by Bernardo Strozzi. b, Vulcan's Forge, by Luca Giordano. c, Daedalus and Icarus, by Charles Lebrun. d, The Infant Hercules Strangling Serpents in His Cradle, by Sir Joshua Reynolds.
No. 2420, Cupid Undoing Venus's Belt, by Reynolds. No. 2421, Perseus Liberating Andromeda, by Peter Paul Rubens, horiz.

**2004, Mar. 18**     **Perf. 14¼**
2416-2418 A471   Set of 3   3.50   3.50
2419 A471   6500ce Sheet of 4,
     #a-d   6.00   6.00
*Imperf*
**Size: 55x78mm**
2420 A471   20,000ce multi   4.50   4.50
**Size: 78x55mm**
2421 A471   20,000ce multi   4.50   4.50

Rotary International, Cent. (in 2005) — A471a

Rotary International emblem and: 2000ce, Polio Plus emblem. 4000ce, Anopheles mosquito, flag of Ghana, vert. 4500ce, Paul P. Harris, flag of Ghana, vert. 5000ce, 2003-04 Rotary International President Jonathan B. Majiyagbe, flag of Ghana, vert. 6000ce, "100 Years," flag of Ghana, vert.
No. 2421F, vert.: g, Women filling water containers. h, Men building shelters. i, Women planting tree.

**Perf. 13x13¼, 13¼x13**
**2004, Sept. 14**     **Litho.**
2421A-2421E A471a   Set of 5   4.75   4.75
**Souvenir Sheet**
2421F A471a 10,000ce Sheet of
     3, #g-i   6.75   6.75

No. 2421F contains three 28x42mm stamps.

Souvenir Sheet

Deng Xiaoping (1904-97), Chinese Leader — A472

**2004, Nov. 29**   **Litho.**   **Perf. 14**
2422 A472 20,000ce multi   4.50   4.50

Souvenir Sheet

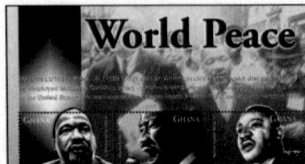

World Peace — A473

No. 2423 — Dr. Martin Luther King, Jr. with: a, Country name at UL. b, Microphone. c, Hands at tie.

**2004, Nov. 29**
2423 A473 10,000ce Sheet of 3,
     #a-c   6.75   6.75

---

Miniature Sheet

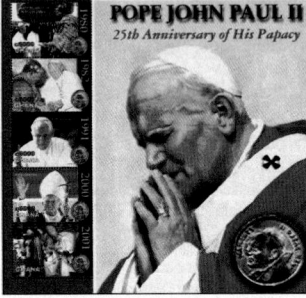

Election of Pope John Paul II, 25th Anniv. (in 2003) — A474

No. 2424 — Photos from: a, 1980. b, 1982. c, 1991. d, 2000. e, 2001.

**2004, Nov. 29**
2424 A474 6000ce Sheet of 5,
     #a-e   6.75   6.75

2004 Summer Olympics, Athens A475

Designs: 500ce, Intl. Olympic Committee President Jacques Rogge. 800ce, Soccer player Abedi Ayew Pele. 7000ce, Athlete Margaret Simpson. 10,000ce, Art depicting athletes of ancient Greece, horiz.

**2004, Nov. 29**     **Perf. 14¼**
2425-2428 A475   Set of 4   4.25   4.25

D-Day, 60th Anniv. — A476

No. 2429, vert.: a, Fleet Admiral Ernest J. King. b, Gen. William C. Lee. c, Lt. Commander John D. Bulkeley. d, Admiral Sir Bertram H. Ramsey.
20,000ce, Rear Admiral Alan G. Kirk.

**2004, Nov. 29**
2429 A476   8000ce Sheet of 4,
     #a-d   7.25   7.25
**Souvenir Sheet**
2430 A476 20,000ce multi   4.50   4.50

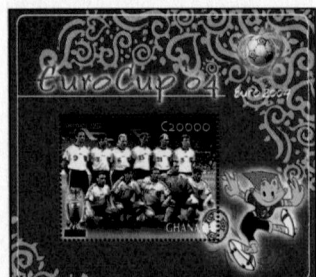

European Soccer Championships, Portugal — A477

No. 2431, vert.: a, Gerd Müller. b, Presentation of European Cup. c, Franz Beckenbauer. d, Heysel Stadium, Brussels.
20,000ce, 1972 German team.

---

**2004, Nov. 29**     **Perf. 14**
2431 A477   7500ce Sheet of 4,
     #a-d   6.75   6.75
**Souvenir Sheet**
**Perf. 14¼**
2432 A477 20,000ce multi   4.50   4.50
No. 2431 contains four 28x42mm stamps.

Worldwide Fund for Nature (WWF) — A478

No. 2433 — African lions: a, Three cubs. b, Lions in water. c, Male lion. d, Female and cubs.

**2004, Dec. 27**     **Perf. 14**
2433 A478 5000ce Block or
     strip of 4,
     #a-d   5.00   5.00
  e.   Miniature sheet, 2 each
     #2433a-2433d   10.00   10.00

Mushrooms — A479

Designs: 500ce, Boletus badius. 3000ce, Clitocybe nebularis. 5000ce, Amanita muscaria. 8000ce, Russula vesca.
No. 2438, vert.: a, Boletus parasiticus. b, Cortinarius armillatus. c, Gymnopilus spectabilis. d, Cortinarius flexipes.
20,000ce, Chlorosplenium aeruginosum, vert.

**2004, Dec. 27**
2434-2437 A479   Set of 4   3.75   3.75
2438 A479   7500ce Sheet of 4,
     #a-d   6.75   6.75
**Souvenir Sheet**
2439 A479 20,000ce multi   4.50   4.50

Orchids A480

Designs: 800ce, Oncidium desertorum. 3500ce, Oncidium variegatum. 4000ce, Anguloa uniflora, vert. 10,000ce, Oncidium gardneri, vert.
No. 2444: a, Vanda rothschildiana. b, Laelia cattleya. c, Laelia anceps. d, Odontioda dalmar.
20,000ce, Renanthera bella, vert.

**2004, Dec. 27**
2440-2443 A480   Set of 4   4.25   4.25
2444 A480   7500ce Sheet of 4,
     #a-d   6.75   6.75
**Souvenir Sheet**
2445 A480 20,000ce multi   4.50   4.50

Mammals — A481

---

Designs: 1000ce, Serval. 1200ce, Sable antelope. 2000ce, Cheetah. 3000ce, Bohor reedbuck.
No. 2450, horiz.: a, White rhinoceros. b, Leopard. c, Burchell's zebra. d, Red river hog.
20,000ce, Hippopotamus, horiz.

**2004, Dec. 27**
2446-2449 A481   Set of 4   1.60   1.60
2450 A481   7500ce Sheet of 4,
     #a-d   6.75   6.75
**Souvenir Sheet**
2451 A481 20,000ce multi   4.50   4.50

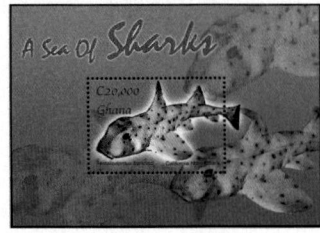

Sharks — A482

No. 2452: a, Zebra bullhead shark. b, Swellshark. c, Port Jackson shark. d, Leopard shark.
20,000ce, California horn shark.

**2004, Dec. 27**
2452 A482   7500ce Sheet of 4,
     #a-d   6.75   6.75
**Souvenir Sheet**
2453 A482 20,000ce multi   4.50   4.50

New Juaben Akwantukese Afahye Festival — A483

Designs: 2000ce, State emblem Yiadom and Hwedie. No. 2455, 4000ce, Migrating to freedom. 4500ce, Crossing Suhyien River. 5000ce, Chief at State Durbar. 6000ce, Sacrificing at the cave.
No. 2459: a, Like 4500ce. b, Palace guards. c, Like 2000ce. d, Like 5000ce. e, Libation pouring. f, Parading the royal treasury.

**2005, Mar. 1**     **Perf. 13¼x13**
2454-2458 A483   Set of 5   4.75   4.75
2459 A483   4000ce Sheet of 6,
     #a-f   5.50   5.50

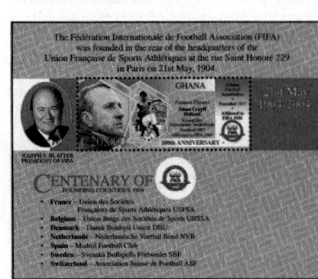

FIFA (Fédération Internationale de Football Association), Cent. — A484

No. 2460: a, Roberto Di Matteo. b, Marcel Desailly. c, Osei Kufuor. d, Eusebio.
20,000ce, Johan Cruyff.

**2005, Mar. 14**     **Perf. 13¼**
2460 A484   7500ce Sheet of 4,
     #a-d   6.75   6.75
**Souvenir Sheet**
2461 A484 20,000ce multi   4.50   4.50

Ipomoea
Asarifolia — A485

**2005 ?    Litho.    Perf. 13¾x13½**
2462 A485 2000ce multi                — —

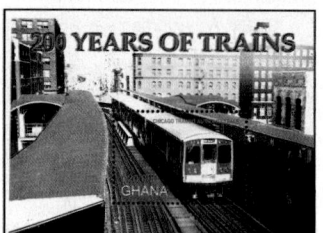

Trains — A486

No. 2463, 5000ce: a, Stanier Class 5-4-6-0. b, Central Pacific Jupiter. c, Robe River RSC3 Class 9401. d, Bangkok BTS train. e, Streamlined tank locomotive. f, ETR450.

No. 2464, 5000ce: a, Talgo train, Spain. b, VIA Turbotrain, Canada. c, Southern Pacific 4-8-4 #4449. d, Union Pacific "City of Portland." e, Shinkansen, Japan (white denomination). f, Deltic Diesel-electric engine, Great Britain.

No. 2465, 5000ce: a, Mogul 2-6-0. b, Milwaukee Railroad 4-6-2. c, Shinkansen (red denomination). d, Former Reading #2101 4-8-4. e, HST Inter-city 125. f, Daylight train.

No. 2466: a, Baldwin 4-6-0 steam train. b, Atchison, Topeka & Santa Fe 4-4-0 "American" steam train. c, Baldwin 4-6-0 Engine #44. d, Baldwin 2-6-0 #3 Three-spot.

No. 2467, 20,000ce, Chicago Transit Authority train. No. 2468, 20,000ce, Santa Fe train. No. 2469, 20,000ce, Empire Builder. No. 2470, 20,000ce, LMS 5305 steam train.

**2005, June 1    Litho.    Perf. 12¾**
**Sheets of 6, #a-f**
2463-2465 A486    Set of 3    20.00 20.00
2466 A486 8000ce Sheet of 4,
              #a-d             7.25  7.25
**Souvenir Sheets**
2467-2470 A486    Set of 4    18.00 18.00

Motor
Vehicles
A487

Designs: 2000ce, Setra State Transport bus. 4000ce, Albium double-decker bus. 4500ce, Bedford Mummy truck and trailer. 5000ce, 1925 Mail carrier. 6000ce, Morris truck.

**2005, June 21   Litho.    Perf. 13x13¼**
2471-2475 A487    Set of 5    4.75  4.75

Friedrich von Schiller (1759-1805),
Writer — A488

No. 2476: a, Schiller, with hand touching head. b, Schiller and birthplace. c, Schiller with beard.

20,000ce, Portraits of old and young Schiller and Johannes Brahms.

**2005    Litho.    Perf. 13¼**
2476 A488  11,000ce Sheet of 3,
              #a-c             7.25  7.25
**Imperf**
2477 A488  20,000ce shown     4.50  4.50
No. 2476 contains three 42x28mm stamps.

World Cup Soccer Championships,
75th Anniv. — A489

No. 2478: a, 1938 Italian team. b, Scene from 1938 Italy vs. Hungary match. c, Olympic Stadium. d, Silvio Piola.
20,000ce, Italian team with World Cup.

**2005    Perf. 13¼**
2478 A489  8000ce Sheet of 4,
              #a-d             7.00  7.00
**Souvenir Sheet**
2479 A489  20,000ce multi     4.50  4.50

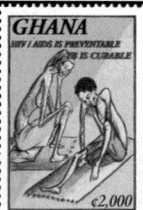

Disease Treatment
and Prevention
A490

Designs: No. 2480, 2000ce, Emaciated people on rugs. No. 2481, 2000ce, Map of Ghana, symbols of medicine, red ribbon. No. 2482, 2000ce, People holding signs, horiz. 3000ce, Red ribbon, head. 4000ce, Maps of Africa and Ghana, arms, stylized people. No. 2485, 4500ce, Diseases on ladder destroying human body of bricks. No. 2486, 4500ce, Hand holding egg depicting health care workers. No. 2487, 5000ce, Emaciated man carrying bags of diseases. No. 2488, 5000ce, Heart, man lifting stylized globe. 6000ce, Whistle, hands holding cards with slogans.

**2006, Jan. 26   Perf. 13¼x13, 13x13¼**
2480-2489 A490    Set of 10   8.50  8.50

National Basketball Association
Players and Team Emblems — A491

No. 2490, 3500ce: a, Carlos Boozer. b, Utah Jazz emblem

No. 2491, 3500ce: a, Carlos Arroyo. b, Detroit Pistons emblem.

No. 2492, 3500ce: a, Corey Magette. b, Los Angeles Clippers emblem.

No. 2493, 3500ce: a, David Wesley. b, Houston Rockets emblem.

No. 2494, 3500ce: a, Manu Ginobili. b, San Antonio Spurs emblem.

No. 2495, 3500ce: a, Al Harrington. b, Atlanta Hawks emblem.

**2006, Mar. 15    Perf. 13¼**
**Sheets of 12, 10 each #a, 2 each #b**
2490-2495 A491    Set of 6    55.00 55.00

A492

A493

Elvis Presley (1935-77) — A494

No. 2496 — Background color: a, Lilac. b, Green. c, Yellow green. d, Blue.

No. 2497 — Face color: a, Lilac. b, Green. c, Yellow green. d, Blue.

No. 2498: a, Blue background. b, Green background with dark red halo, ghost image at right. c, Yellow background with orange halo. d, Green background with orange red halo, ghost image above head. e, Yellow background, ghost image showing teeth at left. f, Yellow background, gray area at right. g, Green background, blue halo.

**2006, Mar. 15    Perf. 14**
2496 A492  8000ce Sheet of 4,
              #a-d             7.00  7.00
2497 A493  8000ce Sheet of 4,
              #a-d             7.00  7.00
2498 A494  3500ce Sheet of 9,
              #a-f, 3 #g       7.00  7.00

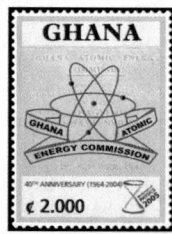

Intl. Year of
Physics (in
2005) — A495

Designs: 2000ce, Emblem of Ghana Atomic Energy Commission. 4000ce, Ghana research reactor. 4500ce, Albert Einstein. 5000ce, Prof. Francis K. Allotey, physicist. 6000ce, Electricity experiment in physics laboratory.

**2006. Mar. 29    Perf. 13¼x14**
2499-2503 A495    Set of 5    4.75  4.75

Pope John Paul II
(1920-2005)
A496

**2006, Apr. 7    Perf. 13¼**
2504 A496  12,000ce multi    2.75  2.75
Printed in sheets of 4.

Battle of
Trafalgar,
Bicent. (in
2005)
A497

Designs: 2000ce, Sir John Jervis. 3000ce, Chase and Race. 5000ce, Goliath fires at Guerrier, horiz. 10,000ce, Death of Adm. Horatio Nelson, horiz.

20,000ce, Napoleon's flagships, Agamemnon. Vanguard, Elephant and Captain, horiz.

**2006, Apr. 7    Perf. 13x13¼, 13¼x13**
2505-2508 A497    Set of 4    4.50  4.50
**Souvenir Sheet**
**Perf. 12**
2509 A497  20,000ce multi    4.50  4.50

Jules Verne (1828-1905),
Writer — A498

No. 2510: a, Verne. b, Original book illustrations of balloons in flight. c, Montgolfier hot air balloon. d, Modern hot air balloon.
20,000ce, The Hindenburg.

**2006, Apr. 7    Perf. 12¾**
2510 A498  8000ce Sheet of 4,
              #a-d             7.00  7.00
**Souvenir Sheet**
2511 A498  20,000ce multi    4.50  4.50

2006 World Cup Soccer
Championships, Germany — A499

Designs: No. 2512, 2000ce, Line of Ghana Black Stars players. No. 2513, 2000ce, Captain Stephen Appiah and opposing player, vert. No. 2514, 4000ce, Exchange of pennants. No. 2515, 4000ce, Joy of success. No. 2516, 4500ce, Michael Essien. No. 2517, 4500ce, Franz Beckenbauer, FIFA World Cup Stadium, Hanover. No. 2518, 5000ce, Scene from Ghana vs. Burkina Faso match. No. 2519, 5000ce, Black Stars team photo. No. 2520, 6000ce, Scene from Ghana vs. South Africa match. No. 2521, 6000ce, Fans celebrating Black Stars victory.

No. 2522, 4000ce: a, Appiah. b, Issah Ahmed. c, John Paintsil. d, Laryea Kingston.

e, Essien, diff. f, Sule Ali Muntari. g, Joe Tex Frimpong. h, Coach Ratomir Dujkovic.
No. 2523, 4000ce: a, Asamoah Gyan. b, Sammy Adjei. c, Matthew Amoah. d, John Mensah. e, Emmanuel Pappoe. f, Mark Caniel Edusei. g, Abubakari Yakubu. h, Godwin Attram.

**2006, May 18**      *Perf. 13½*
2512-2521 A499   Set of 10    9.50   9.50
**Sheets of 8, #a-h**
*Perf. 13¼*
2522-2523 A499   Set of 2    14.00   14.00

Nos. 2522-2523 each contain eight 42x28mm stamps.

Musa Sapientum A501      Bebearia Arcadius A502

Euphaedra Francina — A504

**2006?**    **Litho.**    *Perf. 13½*
2525 A501   800ce multi    —   —
2526 A502   1500ce multi    —   —
2528 A504   2000ce multi    —   —

Two additional stamps exist in this set. The editors would like to examine any examples.

Nos. 1674-1677 Surcharged

**2006, Aug. 28**    **Litho.**    *Perf. 14*
2530 A284   2000ce on 50ce
     #1674    29.00   10.00
2531 A284   2000ce on 200ce
     #1675    29.00   10.00
2532 A284   2000ce on 500ce
     #1676    29.00   10.00
2533 A284   2000ce on 800ce
     #1677    29.00   10.00
  Nos. 2530-2533 (4)    116.00   40.00

Nos. 1810-1814 Surcharged

**2006, Aug. 28**    **Litho.**    *Perf. 14*
2534 A312   2000ce on 200ce
     #1810    .45   .45
2535 A312   2000ce on 300ce
     #1811    .45   .45
2536 A312   2000ce on 400ce
     #1812    .45   .45
2537 A312   2000ce on 600ce
     #1813    .45   .45
2538 A312   2000ce on 800ce
     #1814    .45   .45
  Nos. 2534-2538 (5)    2.25   2.25

Nos. 1703-1708 Surcharged

---

**2006, Aug. 28**    **Litho.**    *Perf. 14*
2539 A291   3000ce on 50ce
     #1703    .65   .65
2540 A291   3000ce on 100ce
     #1704    .65   .65
2541 A291   3000ce on 200ce
     #1705    .65   .65
2542 A291   3000ce on 400ce
     #1706    .65   .65
2543 A291   3000ce on 600ce
     #1707    .65   .65
2544 A291   3000ce on 800ce
     #1708    .65   .65
  Nos. 2539-2544 (6)    3.90   3.90

Nos. 1741-1743 Surcharged

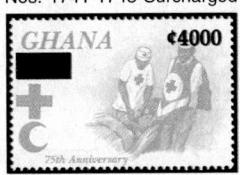

**2006, Aug. 28**    **Litho.**    *Perf. 14*
2545 A300   4000ce on 50ce
     #1741    .90   .90
2546 A300   4000ce on 200ce
     #1742    .90   .90
2547 A300   4000ce on 600ce
     #1743    .90   .90
  Nos. 2545-2547 (3)    2.70   2.70

Nos. 1738-1740 Surcharged

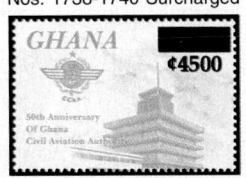

**2006, Aug. 28**    **Litho.**    *Perf. 14*
2548 A299   4500ce on 100ce
     #1738    1.00   1.00
2549 A299   4500ce on 400ce
     #1739    1.00   1.00
2550 A299   4500ce on 1000ce
     #1740    1.00   1.00
  Nos. 2548-2550 (3)    3.00   3.00

Nos. 1745-1752 Surcharged

**2006, Aug. 28**    **Litho.**    *Perf. 14*
2551 A301   5000ce on 50ce
     #1745    1.10   1.10
2552 A301   5000ce on 100ce
     #1746    1.10   1.10
2553 A301   5000ce on 150ce
     #1747    1.10   1.10
2554 A301   5000ce on 200ce
     #1748    1.10   1.10
2555 A301   5000ce on 400ce
     #1749    1.10   1.10
2556 A301   5000ce on 600ce
     #1750    1.10   1.10
2557 A301   5000ce on 800ce
     #1751    1.10   1.10
2558 A301   5000ce on 1000ce
     #1752    1.10   1.10
  Nos. 2551-2558 (8)    8.80   8.80

Nos. 1766-1768 Surcharged

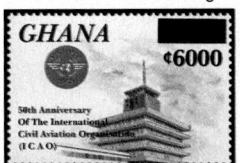

---

**2006, Aug. 28**    **Litho.**    *Perf. 14*
2559 A299   6000ce on 100ce
     #1766    1.25   1.25
2560 A299   6000ce on 400ce
     #1767    1.25   1.25
2561 A299   6000ce on 1000ce
     #1768    1.25   1.25
  Nos. 2559-2561 (3)    3.75   3.75

**Miniature Sheets**

Ghana Soccer Players — A506

No. 2562, 4000ce: a, Asamoah Gyan. b, Sammy Adjei. c, Matthew Amoah. d, John Mensah. e, Emmanuel Pappoe. f, Mark Daniel Edusei. g, Abubakari Yakubu. h, Godwin Attram.
No. 2563, 4000ce: a, Stephen Appiah. b, Issah Ahmed. c, John Paintsil. d, Laryea Kingston. e, Michael Essien. f, Sule Ali Muntari. g, Joe Tex Frimpong. h, Ghana Team Coach Ratomir Dujkovic.

**2007, Jan. 22**    **Litho.**    *Perf. 13½*
**Sheets of 8, #a-h**
2562-2563 A506   Set of 2    14.00   14.00

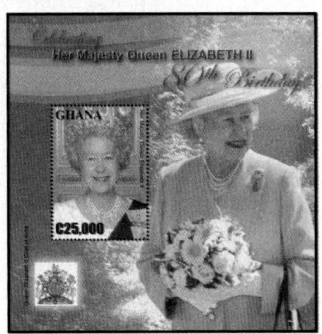

Queen Elizabeth II, 80th Birthday — A507

No. 2564: a, Holding flowers. b, Wearing purple hat. c, Wearing light green hat, denomination in purple. d, Wearing light green hat, denomination in white.
25,000ce, Wearing tiara.

**2007, Jan. 22**
2564 A507   6000ce Sheet of 4,
     #a-d    5.25   5.25
**Souvenir Sheet**
2565 A507   25,000ce multi    5.50   5.50

Marilyn Monroe (1926-62), Actress — A508

No. 2566: a, Wearing glasses. b, Wearing bathrobe. c, Looking left. d, Wearing red dress and earrings.
20,000ce, With eyes closed.

**2007, Jan. 22**
2566 A508   9000ce Sheet of 4,
     #a-d    8.00   8.00
**Souvenir Sheet**
2567 A508   20,000ce multi    4.50   4.50

---

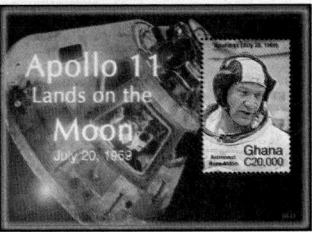

Space Achievements — A509

No. 2568, horiz. — Luna 9: a, Distant view of spacecraft and moon, denomination in black. b, Spacecraft, denomination in white. c, Close-up view of spacecraft and moon, denomination in black. d, Spacecraft in frame, denomination in white.
No. 2569, 6500ce, horiz. — Apollo-Soyuz Test Project: a, Apollo and Soyuz spacecraft docked. b, Mission emblem. c, Astronaut Tom Stafford. d, Cosmonaut Aleksei Leonov. e, Astronaut Deke Slayton. f, Astronaut Vance Brand and Cosmonaut Valeri Kubasov.
No. 2570, 6500ce — Giotto Comet Probe: a, Probe in space, black background. b, Comet, probe in space, red text at bottom. c, Top of probe, white background. d, Comet, probe in space, purple background. e, Probe and schematic diagram. f, Bottom of probe.
No. 2571, 20,000ce, Astronaut Buzz Aldrin. No. 2572, 20,000ce, Apollo-Soyuz crew members shaking hands in space, horiz. No. 2573, 20,000ce, Viking 1, horiz.

**2007, Jan. 22**
2568 A509   10,000ce Sheet of
     4, #a-d    8.75   8.75
**Sheets of 6, #a-f**
2569-2570 A509   Set of 2    17.00   17.00
**Souvenir Sheets**
2571-2573 A509   Set of 3    13.00   13.00

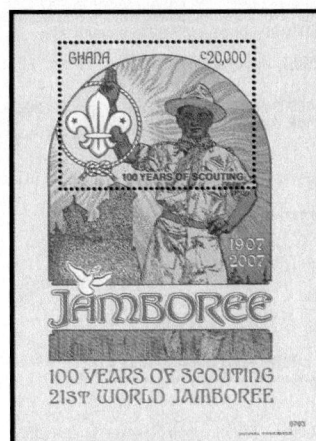

Scouting, Cent. — A510

No. 2574, vert. — Dove, Scout emblem and Scout: a, Giving Scout sign. b, Blowing bugle. c, Carrying injured boy.
20,000ce, Scout emblem, Scout giving Scout sign.

**2007**      *Perf. 13¼*
2574 A510   12,000ce Sheet of 3,
     #a-c    8.00   8.00
**Souvenir Sheet**
2575 A510   20,000ce multi    4.50   4.50

Independence, 50th Anniv. — A511

**2007, Sept. 15**    **Litho.**    *Perf. 13¼*
2576 A511   4000ce multi    .90   .90

Kente Cloth Designs — A512

Designs: 4000ce, Sika ne Barima. 7300ce, Edwene Si So. 7500ce, Dakoro Yesere. No. 2580, 9000ce, Agyenegyne Nsu. No. 2581, 9000ce, Nkatoa Sa. 10,000ce, Edwene Asa.

2007, Sept. 15        Perf. 13½x13¼
2577-2582 A512   Set of 6      10.00 10.00

Aburi Botanical Gardens — A513

Designs: 4000ce, Bamboo groves. 7300ce, School of Horticulture. 7500ce, Silk cotton tree, vert. 9000ce, Royal Palm Walkway. 10,000ce, Famous ficus tree, vert.
No. 2588: a, Like 9000ce. b, Like 7300ce. c, Silk cotton tree. d, Famous ficus tree. e, Like 4000ce. f, Sanatorium.

Perf. 13¼x13½, 13½x13¼
2007, Sept. 15
2583-2587 A513   Set of 5      8.25 8.25
2588 A513 6000ce Sheet of 6,
            #a-f              7.75 7.75

Cocoa — A514

Designs: 4000ce, Cocoa beverages and spread. 7300ce, Cocoa Pebbles. 7500ce, Assorted chocolates. 9000ce, Man at cocoa processing plant. 10,000ce, Finished cocoa products.
No. 2594: a, Like 10,000ce. b, Cacao pods. c, Like 7500ce. d, Like 9000ce. e, Like 7300ce. f, Workers packaging cocoa products.

2007, Sept. 15        Perf. 13¼x13½
2589-2593 A514   Set of 5      8.25 8.25
2594 A514 6000ce Sheet of 6,
            #a-f              7.75 7.75

Cats and Dogs — A515

Designs: 6000ce, Chartreux cat. 7000ce, Blue-mitted ragdoll cat. 8000ce, Blue lynx point Birman cat, horiz. 9000ce, Norwegian Forest cat.
No. 2599, horiz.: a, American bulldog. b, Old English sheepdog. c, Shar-pei. d, Boston terrier.
No. 2600, 20,000ce, Cinnamon point Siamese cat. No. 2601, 20,000ce, Greyhound.

2007, Sept. 15        Perf. 14
2595-2598 A515   Set of 4      6.50 6.50

2599 A515 7500ce Sheet of 4,
            #a-d              6.50 6.50
    Souvenir Sheets
2600-2601 A515   Set of 2      8.75 8.75

Orchids — A516

No. 2602: a, Epipactis atrorubens. b, Galeandra bicarinata. c, Platanthera tipuloides. d, Platanthera ciliaris.
20,000ce, Spathoglottis plicata.

2007, Sept. 15
2602 A516   7500ce Sheet of 4,
            #a-d              6.50 6.50
    Souvenir Sheet
2603 A516 20,000ce multi       4.50 4.50

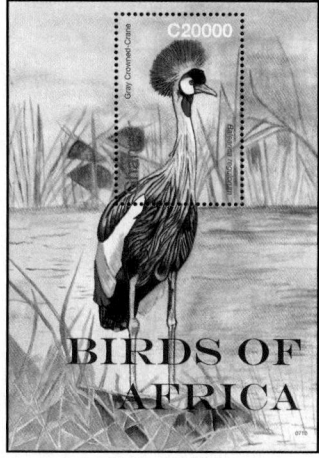

Birds — A517

No. 2604, horiz.: a, Red-billed hornbill. b, Bearded barbet. c, Hoopoe. d, Pygmy kingfisher.
20,000ce, Gray-crowned crane.

2007, Sept. 15
2604 A517   7500ce Sheet of 4,
            #a-d              6.50 6.50
    Souvenir Sheet
2605 A517 20,000ce multi       4.50 4.50

Traditional Costumes A518

Designs: 4000ce, War dress, Northern Ghana. 7300ce, Woman. 7500ce, Mourning wear. 9000ce, Smock. 10,000ce, Wulomo costume.

Perf. 13½x13¼
2007, Sept. 15        Litho.
2606-2610 A518   Set of 5      8.25 8.25

Famous People — A519

Designs: No. 2611, 4000ce, Sir Arko Korsah, first Chief Justice. No. 2612, 4000ce, Amon Kotei, designer of national coat of arms. No. 2613, 4000ce, Philip Gbeho, composer of national anthem. 4500ce, F. K. Buah, historian. 6000ce, Prof. Albert Adu Boahene, historian and politician. 7300ce, Leticia Obeng, aquatic biologist. 7500ce, Peter Cardinal Appiah Turkson, first Ghanaian cardinal. 9000ce, Susanna Alhassan, first femal government minister.

2007, Sept. 15        Perf. 13¼
2611-2618 A519   Set of 8      10.00 10.00

On July 3, 2007, Ghana's currency was revalued at a rate of 10,000 old cedis to 1 new cedi. Old cedis continued to be valid until Dec. 31, 2007. Nos. 2576-2618 and 2641-2646 were issued after July 3, but have denominations expressed in old cedis.

Antrak Air A520

Airplane: 40p, On ground. 73p, In flight.

2007, Sept. 15        Perf. 13¼
2619-2620 A520   Set of 2      2.25 2.25

Accra Tourist Attractions — A521

Designs: 20p, Independence Arch. 40p, Independence Square. 73p, Supreme Court. 75p, National Theater. 90p, Intl. Conference Center.

2007, Sept. 15
2621-2625 A521   Set of 5      6.50 6.50

Agricultural Development Bank — A522

Designs: 40p, Emblem. 75p, Home Link Account, vert. 90p, Young Farmers Program, vert. 1ce, Gold Drive Motor Loan, vert.

2007, Sept. 15
2626-2629 A522   Set of 4      6.75 6.75

Ghana Commercial Bank — A523

Designs: 40p, Emblem. 73p, Eagle, world map. 75p, Ghana Commercial Bank Tower, vert. 90p, Xpress Money Transfer, vert.

2007, Sept. 15
2630-2633 A523   Set of 4      6.00 6.00

State Insurance Company A524

Designs: 40p, Emblem. 73p, Executives. 75p, New office building. 90p, Child pointing. 1ce, Three CIMG Awards, vert.

2007, Sept. 15
2634-2638 A524   Set of 5      8.25 8.25

Ghanaian Heads of State — A525

Dr. Kwame Nkrumah and Pres. J. A. Kufuor With State Sword — A526

No. 2639: a, Dr. Kwame Nkrumah. b, Lieutenant General J. A. Ankrah. c, General A. A. Afrifa. d, Dr. Kofi Abrefa Busia. e, General I. K. Acheampong. f, Lieutenant General W. A. Akuffo. g, Dr. Hilla Limann. h, Flight Lieutenant J. J. Rawlings. i, Pres. J. A. Kufuor.

2007, Sept. 15        Perf. 13½x13¼
2639 A525 60p Sheet of 9, #a-
            i                11.00 11.00
    Souvenir Sheet
2640 A526 1ce multi           1.10 1.10

Pope Benedict XVI — A527

2007, Nov. 15        Perf. 13¼
2641 A527 4000ce multi         .90 .90
    Printed in sheets of 8.

Gold
A528

Designs: 4000ce, Gold ore. 7300ce, Melting gold ore. 7500ce, Woman holding gold bar. 9000ce, Entrance of Obuasi Gold Mines, horiz. 10,000ce, Gold-plated chair.

**2007**          *Perf. 13½x13¼, 13¼x13½*
2642-2646  A528    Set of 5        8.25  8.25

 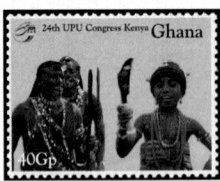

24th UPU
Congress,
Nairobi
A529

Designs: 40p, Dancers. 73p, Flags of Ghana and Kenya, warrior with shield, vert. 75p, UPU emblem in opened box. 90p, UPU emblem on map of Africa, vert.
No. 2651: a, Part of UPU emblem, folded map of world, denomination at LL. b, Part of UPU emblem, folded map of world, denomination at UR. c, Folded map of world, map and flag of Kenya.

**2007, Dec. 3**                  *Perf. 12½*
2647-2650  A529    Set of 4        6.00  6.00
**Souvenir Sheet**
2651  A529  1ce Sheet of 3, #a-c    6.50  6.50

Miniature Sheet

Wedding of Queen Elizabeth II and Prince Philip, 60th Anniv. (in 2007) — A530

No. 2652: a, Queen, denomination in green. b, Couple, denomination in green. c, Couple, denomination in orange. d, Queen, denomination in orange. e, Queen, denomination in blue. f, Couple, denomination in blue.

**2008, Jan. 31  Litho.  Perf. 13¼x13½**
2652  A530  60p Sheet of 6, #a-f    7.75  7.75

Paintings by Qi Baishi (1864-1957) — A531

No. 2653: a, Top half of Lotus and Mandarin Ducks (lotus). b, Top half of River Landscape with Boats (boats). c, Bottom half of Lotus and Mandarin Ducks (ducks). d, Bottom half of River Landscape with Boats (trees).
3ce, Peony in a Dragon Vase.

**2008, Jan. 31**               *Perf. 12x11½*
2653  A531  90p Sheet of 4, #a-d   7.75  7.75
**Souvenir Sheet**
*Perf. 11½*
2654  A531  3ce multi            6.50  6.50
No. 2653 contains four 30x40mm stamps.

Miniature Sheet

2008 Summer Olympics, Beijing — A532

No. 2655: a, Boxing. b, Relay race. c, Long jump. d, Soccer.

**2008, May 8**                  *Perf. 12¾*
2655  A532  40p Sheet of 4, #a-d   3.25  3.25

Souvenir Sheet

Visit of US Pres. George W. Bush to Ghana — A533

No. 2656: a, US Pres. George W. Bush. b, Ghana Pres. John Agyekum Kufuor.

**2008, Sept. 17**               *Perf. 13½*
2656  A533  1.25ce Sheet of 2, #a-b   4.50  4.50

---

## SEMI-POSTAL STAMPS

Starlets, 1995 Under-17 World Soccer Champions — SP1

200ce+50ce, Holding gold cup won at Ecuador, vert. 550ce+50ce, Starlets '95 team photo. 800ce+50ce, Abu Idorisu, vert. 1100ce+50ce, Emmanuel Bentil, vert. 1500ce+50ce, Bashiru Gambo, vert.

*Perf. 13½x13, 13x13½*
**1997, Aug. 12**               Litho.
B1-B5  SP1  Set of 5           6.25  6.25

---

## AIR POST STAMPS

Type of Regular Issue
Designs: 1sh3p, Pennant-winged nightjar. 2sh, Crowned cranes, vert.

*Perf. 14½x14, 14x14½*
**1959, Oct. 5    Photo.    Wmk. 325**
C1   A17  1sh3p multicolored     .50  .20
  a.   Booklet pane of 4         2.25
C2   A17  2sh multicolored       .70  .45
For surcharges see Nos. C7-C10.

Ships, Tema Harbor and Jet — AP1

*Perf. 14x13*
**1962, Feb. 10  Litho.     Unwmk.**
C3   AP1  1sh3p multicolored    .40   .40
C4   AP1  2sh6p multicolored   1.00  1.00
  Nos. C3-C4,110 (3)           1.60  1.60

Opening of Tema Harbor, as part of the Volta River Project.

Type of Regular Issue, 1962
**1962, Mar. 6**             *Perf. 13x14*
C5   A35  1sh3p multicolored    .30   .30
C6   A35  2sh6p multicolored    .75   .75

Nos. C1-C2 Surcharged in White or Green with New Value and: "Ghana New Currency / 19th July, 1965"
*Perf. 14½x14, 14x14½*
**1965, July 19    Photo.    Wmk. 325**
C7   A17  15pa on 1sh3p multi (W)  2.00  .70
C8   A17  24pa on 2sh multi (G)    2.00  .35

The two lines of the overprint are diagonal on No. C8.

Nos. C1, C8 Surcharged in White or Red
**1967, Feb. 27   Photo.   Wmk. 325**
C9   A17  12½np on 1sh3p (W)    4.00  3.00
C10  A17  20np on 24pa on 2sh   5.00  4.00

---

## POSTAGE DUE STAMPS

Gold Coast Nos. J2-J6 Overprinted "GHANA" and Bar in Red
*Perf. 14*
**1958, June 25    Wmk. 4    Typo.**
J1   D1  1p black       .20  .45
J2   D1  2p black       .20  .45
J3   D1  3p black       .20  .45
J4   D1  6p black       .20  1.00
J5   D1  1sh black      .20  2.00
  Nos. J1-J5 (5)       1.00  4.35

Type of Gold Coast Inscribed "Ghana"
**1958, Dec. 1**              *Perf. 14*
J6   D1  1p carmine rose  .20  .45
J7   D1  2p green         .20  .45
J8   D1  3p orange        .20  .45

---

J9   D1  6p ultramarine    .20  1.00
J10  D1  1sh purple        .20  2.00
  Nos. J6-J10 (5)         1.00  4.35

Nos. J6-J10 Surcharged in Black, Blue or Red with New Value and "Ghana New Currency / 19th July, 1965."
**1965, July 19**
J11  D1  1pa on 1p car rose    .20  .60
J12  D1  2pa on 2p grn (Bl)    .20  .75
J13  D1  3pa on 3p org (Bl)    .20  .75
J14  D1  6pa on 6p ultra (R)   .30  2.00
J15  D1  12pa on 1sh pur (Bl)  .50  2.50
  Nos. J11-J15 (5)            1.40  6.60

Surcharge diagonal on Nos. J11 and J15.
No. J12 with additional surcharge, "1½Np" in red, was reported to have been used at one branch post office (Burma Camp) despite official intention. Four similar added surcharges were prepared: 1np on 1pa, 2½np on 3pa, 5np on 6pa, and 10np on 12pa.

D2

**1970  Unwmk.  Litho.  Perf. 14½x14**
J16  D2  1np carmine rose    .75   5.00
J17  D2  1½np green          .90   6.00
J18  D2  2½np orange        1.50   8.00
J19  D2  5np ultramarine    2.00   8.50
J20  D2  10np dull purple   3.00   9.50
  Nos. J16-J20 (5)          8.15  37.00

**1981         Litho.    Perf. 14½x14**
J21  D2  2p red orange      1.35   5.25
J22  D2  3p brown           1.35   5.25

# GIBRALTAR

jə-'brol-tər

LOCATION — A fortified promontory, including the Rock, extending from Spain's southeast coast at the entrance to the Mediterranean Sea
GOVT. — British Crown Colony
AREA — 2.5 sq. mi.
POP. — 29,165 (1999 est.)
CAPITAL — Gibraltar

12 Pence = 1 Shilling
20 Shillings = 1 Pound
100 Centimos = 1 Peseta (1889-95)
100 Pence = 1 Pound (1971)

**Catalogue values for unused stamps in this country are for Never Hinged items, beginning with Scott 119 in the regular postage section and Scott J1 in the postage due section.**

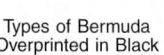

Types of Bermuda
Overprinted in Black

**1886, Jan. 1    Wmk. 2    Perf. 14**

| 1 | A6 | ½p green | 16.00 | 9.00 |
|---|----|----------|-------|------|
| 2 | A1 | 1p rose | 72.50 | 5.50 |
| 3 | A2 | 2p violet brown | 132.50 | 92.50 |
| 4 | A8 | 2½p ultra | 175.00 | 4.25 |
| 5 | A7 | 4p orange brn | 175.00 | 100.00 |
| 6 | A4 | 6p violet | 300.00 | 225.00 |
| 7 | A5 | 1sh bister brn | 500.00 | 400.00 |
| | | Nos. 1-7 (7) | 1,371. | 836.25 |

Forged overprints of No. 7 are plentiful.

Victoria
A6        A7

A8        A9

**1886-98    Typo.**

| 8 | A6 | ½p dull green ('87) | 11.00 | 4.50 |
|---|----|---------------------|-------|------|
| 9 | A6 | ½p gray grn ('98) | 9.00 | 2.00 |
| 10 | A7 | 1p rose ('87) | 50.00 | 5.00 |
| 11 | A7 | 1p car rose ('98) | 9.00 | .55 |
| 12 | A8 | 2p brn violet | 35.00 | 25.00 |
| 13 | A8 | 2p brn vio & ultra ('98) | 27.50 | 2.00 |
| 14 | A9 | 2½p brt ultra ('98) | 36.00 | .80 |
| a. | | 2½p violet gray | 95.00 | 3.25 |
| 16 | A8 | 4p orange brn | 90.00 | 90.00 |
| 17 | A8 | 4p org brn & grn ('98) | 21.00 | 7.50 |
| 18 | A8 | 6p violet | 130.00 | 130.00 |
| 19 | A8 | 6p vio & car rose ('98) | 47.50 | 25.00 |
| 20 | A8 | 1sh bister | 275.00 | 225.00 |
| 21 | A8 | 1sh bis & car rose ('98) | 47.50 | 18.00 |
| | | Nos. 8-14,16-21 (13) | 788.50 | 535.35 |

Stamps of 1886 Issue
Surcharged in Black

**1889, July**

| 22 | A6 | 5c on ½p green | 8.75 | 24.00 |
|----|----|----------------|------|-------|
| 23 | A7 | 10c on 1p rose | 14.50 | 13.00 |
| 24 | A8 | 25c on 2p brn vio | 6.00 | 8.50 |
| a. | | Small "I" in "CENTIMOS" | 140.00 | 190.00 |
| b. | | Broken "N" | 140.00 | 190.00 |

---

| 25 | A9 | 25c on 2½p ultra | 25.00 | 2.75 |
|----|----|------------------|-------|------|
| a. | | Small "I" in "CENTIMOS" | 400.00 | 125.00 |
| b. | | Broken "N" | 400.00 | 125.00 |
| 26 | A8 | 40c on 4p org brn | 62.50 | 87.50 |
| 27 | A8 | 50c on 6p violet | 67.50 | 87.50 |
| 28 | A8 | 75c on 1sh bister | 67.50 | 82.50 |
| | | Nos. 22-28 (7) | 251.75 | 305.75 |

There are two varieties of the figure "5" in the 5c, 25c, 50c and 75c.

A11

**1889-95**

| 29 | A11 | 5c green | 5.50 | 1.00 |
|----|-----|----------|------|------|
| 30 | A11 | 10c rose | 5.50 | .60 |
| a. | | Value omitted | 6,200. | |
| 31 | A11 | 20c ol green ('95) | 14.00 | 82.50 |
| 31A | A11 | 20c grn & brn ('95) | 50.00 | 22.50 |
| 32 | A11 | 25c ultra | 22.50 | .90 |
| 33 | A11 | 40c orange brn | 4.75 | 3.25 |
| 34 | A11 | 50c violet | 4.25 | 2.50 |
| 35 | A11 | 75c olive green | 42.50 | 42.50 |
| 36 | A11 | 1p bister | 92.50 | 25.00 |
| 36A | A11 | 1p bis & bl ('95) | 6.00 | 6.00 |
| 37 | A11 | 2p blk & car rose | 13.00 | 37.50 |
| 38 | A11 | 5p steel blue | 52.50 | 125.00 |
| | | Nos. 29-38 (12) | 313.00 | 349.25 |

King Edward VII
A12        A13

**1903, May 1**

| 39 | A12 | ½p grn & bl grn | 12.00 | 11.00 |
|----|-----|-----------------|-------|-------|
| 40 | A12 | 1p violet, red | 37.50 | .70 |
| 41 | A12 | 2p grn & car rose | 22.50 | 30.00 |
| 42 | A12 | 2½p vio & blk, bl | 6.00 | .70 |
| 43 | A12 | 6p violet & pur | 20.00 | 26.00 |
| 44 | A12 | 1sh blk & car rose | 32.50 | 42.50 |
| 45 | A13 | 2sh green & ultra | 175.00 | 210.00 |
| 46 | A13 | 4sh vio & green | 110.00 | 160.00 |
| 47 | A13 | 8sh vio & blk, bl | 150.00 | 160.00 |
| 48 | A13 | £1 vio & blk, red | 600.00 | 700.00 |
| | | Nos. 39-48 (10) | 1,165. | 1,340. |

**1904-12    Wmk. 3**
**Ordinary or Chalky Paper**

| 49 | A12 | ½p blue green ('07) | 5.75 | 2.00 |
|----|-----|---------------------|------|------|
| 49A | A12 | ½p dull grn & br grn | 15.00 | 3.00 |
| 50b | A12 | 1p violet, red ('05) | 5.75 | 1.00 |
| a. | | Bisected, used as ½p on card | | 1,600. |
| 51 | A12 | 1p car ('07) | 6.50 | .70 |
| 52a | A12 | 2p grn & car rose ('07) | 9.50 | 8.00 |
| 53 | A12 | 2p gray ('10) | 10.00 | 13.00 |
| 54 | A12 | 2½p vio & blk, bl ('07) | 45.00 | 110.00 |
| 55 | A12 | 2½p ultra ('07) | 6.25 | 1.90 |
| 56b | A12 | 6p vio & pur ('08) | 35.00 | 10.00 |
| a. | | 6p vio & red violet ('12) | 160.00 | 450.00 |
| 57 | A12 | 1sh blk & car rose ('08) | 62.50 | 17.50 |
| 58 | A12 | 1sh blk, grn ('10) | 27.50 | 25.00 |
| 59a | A13 | 2sh grn & ultra ('10) | 95.00 | 110.00 |
| 60 | A13 | 2sh vio & bl, bl ('10) | 60.00 | 57.50 |
| 61 | A13 | 4sh vio & grn ('10) | 275.00 | 350.00 |
| 62 | A13 | 4sh blk & red ('10) | 125.00 | 160.00 |
| 63 | A13 | 8sh vio & grn ('11) | 225.00 | 225.00 |
| 64 | A12 | £1 vio & blk, red ('11) | 600.00 | 625.00 |
| | | Nos. 49-64 (17) | 1,608. | 1,719. |

Nos. 51, 53, 55 are on ordinary paper. Nos. 54, 58, 60-64 are on chalky paper. Others come on both papers. The least expensive varieties are listed above. For detailed listing, see the *Scott Specialized Catalogue of Stamps and Covers*.

No. 56a, used, must have a 1912 cancellation. Stamps used later sell for about the same as unused.

---

A14        King George V — A15

**1912, July 17    Ordinary Paper**

| 66 | A14 | ½p green | 4.00 | .80 |
|----|-----|----------|------|-----|
| 67 | A14 | 1p carmine | 4.00 | .90 |
| a. | | 1p scarlet ('16) | 4.25 | 1.60 |
| 68 | A14 | 2p gray | 12.00 | 1.75 |
| 69 | A14 | 2½p ultra | 8.25 | 2.50 |

**Chalky Paper**

| 70 | A14 | 6p dl vio & red vio | 11.00 | 19.00 |
|----|-----|---------------------|-------|-------|
| 71 | A14 | 1sh black, green | 11.00 | 4.25 |
| a. | | 1sh black, emerald ('24) | 22.50 | 100.00 |
| b. | | 1sh blk, bl grn, ol back ('19) | 15.00 | 30.00 |
| c. | | 1sh blk, emer, ol back ('23) | 20.00 | 82.50 |
| 72 | A15 | 2sh vio & ultra, bl | 30.00 | 4.00 |
| 73 | A15 | 4sh black & scar | 37.50 | 65.00 |
| 74 | A15 | 8sh vio & green | 90.00 | 110.00 |
| 75 | A15 | £1 vio & blk, red | 160.00 | 230.00 |
| | | Nos. 66-75 (10) | 367.75 | 438.20 |

**1921-32    Ordinary Paper    Wmk. 4**

| 76 | A14 | ½p green ('26) | 1.60 | 1.90 |
|----|-----|----------------|------|------|
| 77 | A14 | 1p rose red | 2.25 | 1.40 |
| 78a | A14 | 1½p pale red brown | 2.25 | .40 |
| 79 | A14 | 2p gray | 1.60 | 1.60 |
| 80 | A14 | 2½p ultra | 22.50 | 35.00 |
| 81 | A14 | 3p ultra | 2.75 | 1.75 |

**Chalky Paper**

| 82 | A14 | 6p dl vio & red vio ('26) | 1.75 | 4.00 |
|----|-----|---------------------------|------|------|
| a. | | 6p gray lilac & red violet ('23) | 7.00 | 4.25 |
| 83 | A14 | 1sh black, emer ('24) | 12.00 | 19.00 |
| 84 | A14 | 1sh ol grn & blk ('29) | 17.50 | 27.50 |
| a. | | 1sh brn olive & black ('32) | 17.50 | 14.00 |
| 85a | A15 | 2sh red vio & ultra, blue ('25) | 8.25 | 47.50 |
| 86 | A15 | 2sh red brn & black ('29) | 11.00 | 35.00 |
| 87 | A15 | 2sh6p green & blk | 11.00 | 21.00 |
| 88 | A15 | 4sh black & scar | 75.00 | 125.00 |
| 89 | A15 | 5sh car & black | 17.50 | 57.50 |
| 90 | A15 | 8sh vio & green | 250.00 | 425.00 |
| 91 | A15 | 10sh ultra & black | 37.50 | 80.00 |
| 92 | A15 | £1 org & black | 175.00 | 225.00 |
| 93 | A15 | £5 dl vio & blk | 1,750. | 4,750. |
| | | Nos. 76-92 (17) | 649.45 | 1,108. |

Years issued: 1½p, 1922. 6p, 1923. Nos. 83, 85, 4sh, 8sh, 1924. 2sh6p, 5sh, 10sh, £5, 1925. ½p, £1, 1927. Nos. 84, 86, 1929.

Type of 1912 Issue
Inscribed: "THREE PENCE"

**1930, Apr. 12    Ordinary Paper**

| 94 | A14 | 3p ultramarine | 9.50 | 2.25 |
|----|-----|----------------|------|------|

Rock of Gibraltar
A16

**1931-33    Engr.    Perf. 14**

| 96 | A16 | 1p red | 3.25 | 3.50 |
|----|-----|--------|------|------|
| a. | | Perf. 13½x14 | 17.50 | 6.50 |
| 97 | A16 | 1½p red brown | 2.75 | 3.25 |
| a. | | Perf. 13½x14 | 14.50 | 5.00 |
| 98 | A16 | 2p gray ('32) | 8.75 | 2.25 |
| a. | | Perf. 13½x14 | 17.50 | 2.75 |
| 99 | A16 | 3p dk blue ('33) | 7.75 | 4.25 |
| a. | | Perf. 13½x14 | 30.00 | 32.50 |
| | | Nos. 96-99 (4) | 22.50 | 13.25 |
| | | Set, never hinged | 45.00 | |
| | | Nos. 96a-99a (4) | 79.50 | 46.75 |
| | | Set, never hinged | 150.00 | |

---

Common Design Types
pictured following the introduction.

Silver Jubilee Issue
Common Design Type

**1935, May 6    Perf. 11x12**

| 100 | CD301 | 2p black & ultra | 1.40 | 2.50 |
|-----|-------|------------------|------|------|
| 101 | CD301 | 3p ultra & brown | 3.50 | 4.00 |
| 102 | CD301 | 6p indigo & green | 11.50 | 15.00 |
| 103 | CD301 | 1sh brown vio & ind | 11.50 | 12.00 |
| | | Nos. 100-103 (4) | 27.90 | 33.50 |
| | | Set, never hinged | 57.50 | |

Coronation Issue
Common Design Type

**1937, May 12    Perf. 11x11½**

| 104 | CD302 | ½p deep green | .20 | .20 |
|-----|-------|---------------|-----|-----|
| 105 | CD302 | 2p gray black | .70 | 2.10 |
| 106 | CD302 | 3p deep ultra | 1.50 | 2.10 |
| | | Nos. 104-106 (3) | 2.40 | 4.40 |
| | | Set, never hinged | 5.00 | |

George VI — A17

Rock of Gibraltar
A18

Designs: 2p, Rock from north side. 3p, 5p, Europa Point. 6p, Moorish Castle. 1sh, Southport Gate. 2sh, Eliott Memorial. 5sh, Government House. 10sh, Catalan Bay.

**Perf. 13, 13½x14 (½p, No. 118), 14 (1½p)**

**1938-49    Engr.    Wmk. 4**

| 107 | A17 | ½p gray green | .20 | .35 |
|-----|-----|---------------|-----|-----|
| 108 | A18 | 1p red brn ('42) | .35 | .55 |
| a. | | 1p chestnut, perf. 14 | 27.50 | 2.75 |
| b. | | 1p chestnut, perf. 13½ | 27.50 | 2.50 |
| c. | | Perf. 13½, wmk. sideways ('41) | 6.75 | 8.25 |
| 109 | A18 | 1½p carmine rose | 30.00 | .90 |
| b. | | Perf. 13½ | 275.00 | 45.00 |
| 109A | A18 | 1½p gray vio ('43) | .25 | 1.60 |
| 110 | A18 | 2p dk gray ('42) | .35 | 1.40 |
| a. | | Perf. 14 | 27.50 | .55 |
| c. | | Perf. 13½ | 1.75 | .45 |
| d. | | Perf. 13½, wmk. sideways ('41) | 650.00 | 52.50 |
| 110B | A18 | 2p car rose ('44) | .30 | .55 |
| 111 | A18 | 3p blue ('42) | .35 | .35 |
| a. | | Perf. 14 | 140.00 | 6.00 |
| b. | | Perf. 13½ | 22.50 | 1.10 |
| 112 | A18 | 5p red org ('47) | 1.00 | 1.25 |
| 113 | A18 | 6p dl vio & car rose | 3.75 | 1.90 |
| a. | | Perf. 14 | 125.00 | 1.60 |
| b. | | Perf. 13½ | 50.00 | 4.00 |
| 114 | A18 | 1sh grn & blk ('42) | 3.00 | 4.50 |
| a. | | Perf. 14 | 45.00 | 27.50 |
| b. | | Perf. 13½ | 70.00 | 8.25 |
| 115 | A18 | 2sh org brn & blk ('42) | 4.00 | 6.50 |
| a. | | Perf. 14 | 70.00 | 30.00 |
| b. | | Perf. 13½ | 100.00 | 42.50 |
| 116 | A18 | 5sh dk car & blk ('44) | 12.50 | 21.00 |
| a. | | Perf 14 ('38) | 100.00 | 175.00 |
| b. | | Perf. 13½ | 40.00 | 22.50 |
| 117 | A18 | 10sh bl & blk ('43) | 27.50 | 27.50 |
| a. | | Perf. 14 | 70.00 | 150.00 |
| 118 | A17 | £1 orange | 37.50 | 37.50 |
| | | Nos. 107-118 (14) | 121.05 | 105.85 |
| | | Set, never hinged | 175.00 | |

Nos. 108c and 110d were issued in coils.
No. 108 (1p, perf. 13) exists with watermark both normal and sideways. Nos. 110 and 110B (both 2p, perf. 13) have watermark sideways.
For overprints see Nos. 127-130.

**Catalogue values for unused stamps in this section, from this point to the end of the section, are for Never Hinged items.**

## Peace Issue
### Common Design Type
**1946, Oct. 12**          **Perf. 13½x14**
| | | | | |
|---|---|---|---|---|
| 119 | CD303 | ½p bright green | .30 | .20 |
| 120 | CD303 | 3p bright ultra | .35 | .20 |

## Silver Wedding Issue
### Common Design Types
**1948, Dec. 1   Photo.   Perf. 14x14½**
| | | | | |
|---|---|---|---|---|
| 121 | CD304 | ½p dark green | .80 | .70 |

### Engr.; Name Typo.
### Perf. 11½x11
| | | | | |
|---|---|---|---|---|
| 122 | CD305 | £1 brown orange | 70.00 | 87.50 |
| | *Set, hinged* | | 55.00 | |

## UPU Issue
### Common Design Types
### Engr.; Name Typo. on 3p, 6p
### Perf. 13½, 11x11½
**1949, Oct. 10**          **Wmk. 4**
| | | | | |
|---|---|---|---|---|
| 123 | CD306 | 2p rose carmine | 1.00 | 1.25 |
| 124 | CD307 | 3p indigo | 2.50 | 1.50 |
| 125 | CD308 | 6p rose violet | 2.00 | 2.50 |
| 126 | CD309 | 1sh blue green | 1.25 | 4.25 |
| | *Nos. 123-126 (4)* | | 6.75 | 9.50 |

Nos. 110B, 111, 113-114 overprinted in Black or Carmine

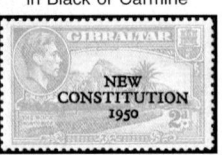

**1950, Aug. 1**          **Perf. 13x12½**
| | | | | |
|---|---|---|---|---|
| 127 | A18 | 2p carmine rose | .40 | 1.25 |
| 128 | A18 | 3p blue | 1.00 | 1.25 |
| 129 | A18 | 6p dl vio & car rose | 1.25 | 1.75 |
| a. | Double overprint | | 950.00 | 1,100. |
| 130 | A18 | 1sh grn & blk (C) | 1.25 | 1.75 |
| | *Nos. 127-130 (4)* | | 3.90 | 6.00 |

Adoption of Constitution of 1950.

## Coronation Issue
### Common Design Type
**1953, June 2   Engr.   Perf. 13½x13**
| | | | | |
|---|---|---|---|---|
| 131 | CD312 | ½p olive green & black | .40 | .50 |

Wharves A26

Moorish Castle — A27

Designs: 1p, South view. 1½p, Tunny fishing industry. 2p, Southport Gate. 2½p, Sailing in the bay. 3p, Ocean liner. 4p, Coaling wharf. 5p, Airport. 6p, Europa Point. 1sh, Strait from Buena Vista. 2sh, Rosia Bay. 5sh, Government House. £1, Arms of Gibraltar.

**1953, Oct. 19**          **Perf. 12½**
| | | | | |
|---|---|---|---|---|
| 132 | A26 | ½p dk grn & ind | .20 | .25 |
| 133 | A26 | 1p blue green | 1.60 | .25 |
| 134 | A26 | 1½p dark gray | .95 | .80 |
| 135 | A26 | 2p sepia | 1.60 | .80 |
| 136 | A26 | 2½p car lake | 2.75 | .55 |
| 137 | A26 | 3p grnsh blue | 4.00 | .20 |
| 138 | A26 | 4p ultra | 2.75 | 1.40 |
| 139 | A26 | 5p deep plum | .70 | .70 |
| 140 | A26 | 6p blue & black | .65 | .45 |
| 141 | A26 | 1sh red brn & bl | .35 | .55 |
| 142 | A26 | 2sh vio & org | 22.50 | 3.25 |
| 143 | A26 | 5sh dark brown | 30.00 | 11.00 |
| 144 | A27 | 10sh ultra & brn | 57.50 | 30.00 |
| 145 | A27 | £1 yellow & red | 57.50 | 37.50 |
| | *Nos. 132-145 (14)* | | 183.05 | 87.70 |
| | *Set, hinged* | | 100.00 | |

---

Inscribed: "ROYAL VISIT 1954"
**1954, May 10**
| | | | | |
|---|---|---|---|---|
| 146 | A26 | 3p greenish blue | .35 | .35 |

Candytuft — A28        Rock and Badge of Gibraltar Regiment — A30

Moorish Castle A29

Designs: 2p, St. George's Hall and cannons. 2½p, The keys. 3p, Rock by moonlight. 4p, Catalan Bay. 6p, Map. 7p, Air terminal. 9p, American war memorial. 1sh, Barbary ape. 2sh, Barbary partridge. 5sh, Blue rock thrush. 10sh, Narcissus.

### Wmk. 314
**1960, Oct. 29   Photo.   Perf. 12½**
| | | | | |
|---|---|---|---|---|
| 147 | A28 | ½p brt green & lil | .20 | .50 |
| 148 | A29 | 1p black & yel grn | .20 | .20 |
| 149 | A29 | 2p org brn & sl | .50 | .20 |
| 150 | A28 | 2½p blue & black | .60 | .55 |
| 151 | A29 | 3p dk blue & ver | .20 | .20 |
| 152 | A29 | 4p choc & grnsh bl | 3.00 | .90 |
| a. | Wmkd. sideways ('66) | | .25 | .30 |
| 153 | A28 | 6p brown & emer | .90 | .70 |
| 154 | A28 | 7p gray & car | .90 | 1.75 |
| 155 | A28 | 9p grnsh blue & bluish gray | 1.00 | .80 |
| 156 | A29 | 1sh brown & green | 1.10 | .60 |
| 157 | A29 | 2sh dark red brn & ultra | 15.00 | 2.50 |
| 158 | A29 | 5sh ol & Prus grn | 9.00 | 6.00 |
| 159 | A28 | 10sh blue, yel & grn | 16.00 | 14.00 |

### Perf. 14
### Engr.
| | | | | |
|---|---|---|---|---|
| 160 | A30 | £1 org red & slate | 19.00 | 13.00 |
| | *Nos. 147-160 (14)* | | 67.60 | 41.90 |

For overprints see Nos. 165-166.

## Freedom from Hunger Issue
### Common Design Type
**1963, June 4**          **Perf. 14x14½**
| | | | | |
|---|---|---|---|---|
| 161 | CD314 | 9p sepia | 10.00 | 3.25 |

## Red Cross Centenary Issue
### Common Design Type
**1963, Sept. 2   Litho.   Perf. 13**
| | | | | |
|---|---|---|---|---|
| 162 | CD315 | 1p black & red | .55 | 1.40 |
| 163 | CD315 | 9p ultra & red | 13.00 | 5.50 |

## Shakespeare Issue
### Common Design Type
**1964, Apr. 23   Photo.   Perf. 14x14½**
| | | | | |
|---|---|---|---|---|
| 164 | CD316 | 7p brown | .65 | .55 |

Nos. 151 and 153 Overprinted: "NEW / CONSTITUTION / 1964."

**1964, Oct. 16**          **Perf. 12½**
| | | | | |
|---|---|---|---|---|
| 165 | A29 | 3p dk blue & ver | .20 | .20 |
| 166 | A28 | 6p brown & emer | .35 | .45 |
| a. | No period in overprint | | 17.00 | 19.00 |

## ITU Issue
### Common Design Type
### Perf. 11x11½
**1965, May 17   Litho.   Wmk. 314**
| | | | | |
|---|---|---|---|---|
| 167 | CD317 | 4p emerald & yel | 2.75 | .45 |
| 168 | CD317 | 2sh ap grn & dk bl | 17.00 | 5.50 |

## Intl. Cooperation Year Issue
### Common Design Type
**1965, Oct. 25**          **Perf. 14½**
| | | | | |
|---|---|---|---|---|
| 169 | CD318 | ½p lt violet & grn | .20 | .80 |
| 170 | CD318 | 4p blue green & cl | 1.50 | .95 |

---

## Churchill Memorial Issue
### Common Design Type
**1966, Jan. 24   Photo.   Perf. 14**
### Design in Black, Gold and Carmine Rose
| | | | | |
|---|---|---|---|---|
| 171 | CD319 | ½p bright blue | .20 | .80 |
| 172 | CD319 | 1p green | .20 | .20 |
| 173 | CD319 | 4p brown | .90 | .45 |
| 174 | CD319 | 9p violet | 2.10 | 1.90 |
| | *Nos. 171-174 (4)* | | 3.40 | 3.35 |

## World Cup Soccer Issue
### Common Design Type
**1966, July 1   Litho.   Perf. 14**
| | | | | |
|---|---|---|---|---|
| 175 | CD321 | 2½p multicolored | .75 | .35 |
| 176 | CD321 | 6p multicolored | 1.40 | .80 |

Sea Bream A30a

7p, Orange scorpionfish. 1sh, Stone bass, vert.

### Perf. 14x13½, 13½x14
**1966, Aug. 27   Photo.   Wmk. 314**
| | | | | |
|---|---|---|---|---|
| 177 | A30a | 4p ultra, rose red & black | .20 | .20 |
| 178 | A30a | 7p ol, rose red & blk | .35 | .20 |
| a. | Value omitted | | 1,300. | |
| 179 | A30a | 1sh brt grn, brn & blk | .45 | .35 |
| | *Nos. 177-179 (3)* | | 1.00 | .75 |

European Sea Angling Championships, Gibraltar, Aug. 28-Sept. 3.

## WHO Headquarters Issue
### Common Design Type
**1966, Sept. 20   Litho.   Perf. 14**
| | | | | |
|---|---|---|---|---|
| 180 | CD322 | 6p multicolored | 2.75 | 1.10 |
| 181 | CD322 | 9p multicolored | 4.25 | 1.90 |

"Our Lady of Europa" A31

### Perf. 14x14½
**1966, Nov. 15   Photo.   Wmk. 314**
| | | | | |
|---|---|---|---|---|
| 182 | A31 | 2sh ultra & black | .60 | 1.00 |

Enthronement of the recovered statue of the Madonna in its new shrine, cent.

## UNESCO Anniversary Issue
### Common Design Type
**1966, Dec. 1   Litho.   Perf. 14**
| | | | | |
|---|---|---|---|---|
| 183 | CD323 | 2p "Education" | .20 | .20 |
| 184 | CD323 | 7p "Science" | .80 | .20 |
| 185 | CD323 | 5sh "Culture" | 5.75 | 3.25 |
| | *Nos. 183-185 (3)* | | 6.75 | 3.65 |

Cable Ship Mirror — A32

Ships and Arms of Gibraltar: ½p Victory, Nelson's flagship. 1p, S.S. Arab. 2p, H.M.S. Carmania. 2½p, M.V. Mons Calpe. 3p, S.S. Canberra. 4p, H.M.S. Hood. 6p, Xebec, Moorish vessel. 7p, Amerigo Vespucci, Italian training ship (sails). 9p, Raffaello, Italian liner. 1sh, H.M.S. Royal Katherine, 17th century British warship. 2sh, H.M.S. Ark Royal, aircraft carrier. 5sh, H.M.S. Dreadnought, atomic submarine. 10sh, S.S. Neuralia, troopship. £1, Mary Celeste, 19th century mystery ship (sails).

### Perf. 14x14½
**1967-69   Photo.   Wmk. 314**
### Design in Black, Red and Gold; Background as Indicated
| | | | | |
|---|---|---|---|---|
| 186 | A32 | ½p deep rose | .20 | .20 |
| 187 | A32 | 1p yellow | .20 | .20 |
| 188 | A32 | 2p ultra | .20 | .20 |

---

| | | | | |
|---|---|---|---|---|
| 189 | A32 | 2½p orange | .35 | .25 |
| 190 | A32 | 3p violet | .20 | .20 |
| 191 | A32 | 4p rose | .35 | .20 |
| 191A | A32 | 5p brn & multi ('69) | 3.50 | .65 |
| 192 | A32 | 6p gray | .35 | .50 |
| 193 | A32 | 7p yellow grn | .35 | .45 |
| 194 | A32 | 9p green | .35 | .60 |
| 195 | A32 | 1sh rose brown | .35 | .25 |
| 196 | A32 | 2sh brt yellow | 4.00 | 2.40 |
| 197 | A32 | 5sh brick red | 4.00 | 5.75 |
| 198 | A32 | 10sh emerald | 17.00 | 20.00 |
| 199 | A32 | £1 lt ultra | 17.00 | 20.00 |
| | *Nos. 186-199 (15)* | | 48.40 | 51.85 |

Cable Car and ITY Emblem — A33

ITY emblem and: 9p, Bull shark, horiz. 1sh, Skin diver, horiz.

### Perf. 14½x14, 14x14½
**1967, June 15   Photo.   Wmk. 314**
| | | | | |
|---|---|---|---|---|
| 200 | A33 | 7p red brn, red & blk | .20 | .20 |
| 201 | A33 | 9p brt blue, blk & slate | .20 | .20 |
| 202 | A33 | 1sh emer, blk & org brn | .35 | .25 |
| | *Nos. 200-202 (3)* | | .75 | .65 |

International Tourist Year.

Holy Family A34

Christmas: 6p, Church window, vert.

**1967, Nov. 1**          **Perf. 14½**
| | | | | |
|---|---|---|---|---|
| 203 | A34 | 2p dark red & multi | .20 | .20 |
| 204 | A34 | 6p dark green & multi | .20 | .20 |

General Eliott and Map of Europe and Great Britain A35

Designs: 9p, Eliott Memorial and tower. 1sh, Gen. Eliott and map of Gibraltar, vert. 2sh, Gen. Eliott directing rescue operations for enemy sailors during Great Siege 1779-83.

### Perf. 14½x14, 14x14½
**1967, Dec. 11   Photo.   Wmk. 314**
### Size: 37x21mm, 21x37mm
| | | | | |
|---|---|---|---|---|
| 205 | A35 | 4p multicolored | .20 | .20 |
| 206 | A35 | 9p multicolored | .20 | .20 |
| 207 | A35 | 1sh multicolored | .20 | .20 |

### Size: 58x21½mm
| | | | | |
|---|---|---|---|---|
| 208 | A35 | 2sh multicolored | .45 | .25 |
| | *Nos. 205-208 (4)* | | 1.05 | .85 |

250th anniv. of the birth of General George Augustus Eliott (1717-1790), Governor of Gibraltar during Great Siege.

Lord Baden-Powell — A36

Designs: 7p, Scout flag, Rock of Gibraltar and globe with map of Europe. 9p, Symbolic tents, heads and Scout salute. 1sh, Three Scout badges.

### Perf. 14x14½
**1968, Mar. 27   Photo.   Wmk. 314**
| | | | | |
|---|---|---|---|---|
| 209 | A36 | 4p dull yellow & pur | .20 | .20 |
| 210 | A36 | 7p brown org, brn & grn | .20 | .20 |

211 A36 9p ultra, black & org .20 .25
212 A36 1sh yellow & emerald .20 .25
Nos. 209-212 (4) .80 .90
60th anniv. of the Gibraltar Scout Assoc.

Nurse and WHO Emblem A37

20th anniv. of WHO: 4p, Physician with microscope and WHO emblem.

**1968, July 1 Photo. Wmk. 314**
213 A37 2p yellow, ultra & blk .20 .20
214 A37 4p pink, black & slate .20 .20

King John Signing Magna Carta — A38

Shepherd, Lamb and Star — A39

Design: 2sh, Rock of Gibraltar, "Freedom" and Human Rights flame.

**1968, Aug. 26 Perf. 13½x14½**
215 A38 1sh org, gold & dk brn .25 .25
216 A38 2sh brt green & gold .35 .35

International Human Rights Year.

**1968, Nov. 1 Perf. 14x13½**
Christmas: 9p, Mary, Jesus and lamb.
217 A39 4p lt brown & multi .20 .20
218 A39 9p rose & multi .20 .20

Government House, Gibraltar — A40

9p, Rock of Gibraltar, Commonwealth Parliamentary Association emblem. 2sh, Big Ben, London, arms of Gibraltar.

**Perf. 14½x14, 14x14½**
**1969, May 26 Photo. Wmk. 314**
219 A40 4p green & gold .20 .20
220 A40 9p brt violet & gold .20 .20
221 A40 2sh lt ultra, gold & red .35 .20
Nos. 219-221 (3) .75 .60

Meeting of the Executive Committee of the General Council of the Commonwealth Parliamentary Assoc., Gibraltar, May 1969.

Rock of Gibraltar A41

**1969, July 30 Perf. 14½x13½**
222 A41 ½p orange & gold .20 .20
223 A41 5p emerald & silver .20 .20
224 A41 7p brt rose lil & silver .20 .20
225 A41 5sh ultra & gold 1.40 1.25
Nos. 222-225 (4) 2.00 1.85
Gibraltar's new constitution.
Nos. 222-225 are valued with surrounding selvage.

Royal Artillery Officer, 1758 — A42

Madonna della Seggiola, by Raphael — A43

Uniforms: 6p, Contemporary soldier of the Royal Anglian Regiment. 9p, Soldier, Royal Engineers, 1786. 2sh, Private of Fox's Marines, 1704.

**1969, Nov. 6 Photo. Perf. 14**
226 A42 1p gold & multi .20 .20
227 A42 6p silver, gold & multi .50 .30
228 A42 9p silver, gold & multi .65 .40
229 A42 2sh gold & multi 2.50 1.75
Nos. 226-229 (4) 3.85 2.65
Descriptions are printed on back on top of gum.
See Nos. 234-237, 276-279, 286-289, 299-302, 310-313, 318-321, 330-333.

**1969, Dec. 1 Perf. 13½x Roulette 9**
Christmas (Paintings): 7p, Madonna and Child, by Luis Morales. 1sh, Virgin of the Rocks, by Leonardo da Vinci.
230 A43 5p gold & multi .20 .20
231 A43 7p gold & multi .35 .35
232 A43 1sh gold & multi .55 .55
a. Triptych, Nos. 230, 232, 231 1.00 1.00

**Europa Issue**

Europa Point — A44

**1970, June 8 Perf. 13½**
233 A44 2sh multicolored .45 .40

Uniform Type of 1969
Uniforms: 2p, Royal Scots officer, 1839. 5p, Private of South Wales Borderers. 7p, Private of Queen's Royal Regiment, 1742. 2sh, Piper of Royal Irish Rangers, 1969.

**1970, Aug. 28 Photo. Perf. 14**
234 A42 2p gold & multi .40 .20
235 A42 5p gold & multi .75 .45
236 A42 7p gold & multi .75 .55
237 A42 2sh gold & multi 2.75 1.60
Nos. 234-237 (4) 4.65 2.80
Descriptions are printed on back on top of gum.

No. 178a and Rock of Gibraltar A45

Design: 2sh, No. 30a and Moorish Castle.
**1970, Sept. 18 Perf. 13**
238 A45 1sh red & olive .20 .20
239 A45 2sh ultra & rose .40 .55
Philympia, London Phil. Exhib., Sept. 18-26.

Virgin Mary by Gabriel Loire A46

**1970, Dec. 1 Photo. Perf. 13x14**
240 A46 2sh multicolored .35 .35
Christmas. The design is after a stained glass window in the Church of Our Lady of Perpetual Succour, Glasgow.

**Decimal Currency Issue**

Prince George of Cambridge Quarters, and Trinity Church — A47

Designs show for each denomination a 19th century print and a contemporary photograph of the same view: ½p Battery Rosia. 1½p, Wellington Monument, Alameda Gardens. 2p, View from North Bastion. 2½p, Catalan Bay. 3p, Convent, seen from garden. 4p, The Exchange and Spanish Chapel. 5p, Commercial Square, Library and Main Guard. 7p, South Barracks and Rosia Magazine. 8p, Moorish Mosque and Castle. 9p, Europa Pass. 10p, South Barracks, from Rosia Bay. 12½p, Southport Gates. 25p, Guards on Alameda. 50p, Europa Pass Gorge, vert. £1 Prince Edward Gate, vert.
In the listing the 1st number is for the 19th cent. design, the 2nd for the 20th cent. design.

**Wmk. 314 Sideways**
**1971, Feb. 15 Litho. Perf. 14**
**Multicolored and:**
241 ½p brown red .20 .20
242 ½p brown red .20 .20
a. A47 Pair, Nos. 241-242 .35 .40
243 1p light blue .85 .25
244 1p light blue .85 .25
b. A47 Pair, Nos. 243-244 1.75 .60
245 1½p emerald .25 .30
246 1½p emerald .25 .30
a. A47 Pair, Nos. 245-246 .50 .90
247 2p dark brown 1.50 1.75
248 2p dark brown 1.50 1.75
b. A47 Pair, Nos. 247-248 3.00 4.75
249 2½p vermilion .20 .35
250 2½p vermilion .20 .35
a. A47 Pair, Nos. 249-250 .35 .65
251 3p pale green .20 .20
252 3p pale green .20 .20
a. A47 Pair, Nos. 251-252 .35 .35
253 4p gray 2.00 2.25
254 4p gray 2.00 2.25
b. A47 Pair, Nos. 253-254 4.00 6.00
255 5p dark green .30 .25
256 5p dark green .30 .25
a. A47 Pair, Nos. 255-256 .60 .60
257 7p orange .70 .40
258 7p orange .70 .40
a. A47 Pair, Nos. 257-258 1.40 .95
259 8p dark blue .75 .50
260 8p dark blue .75 .50
a. A47 Pair, Nos. 259-260 1.50 1.10
261 9p brick red .75 .45
262 9p brick red .75 .45
a. A47 Pair, Nos. 261-262 1.50 1.00
263 10p black .85 .60
264 10p black .85 .60
a. A47 Pair, Nos. 263-264 1.75 1.50
265 12½p bister 1.10 1.75
266 12½p bister 1.10 1.75
a. A47 Pair, Nos. 265-266 2.25 4.75
267 25p deep purple 1.10 1.75
268 25p deep purple 1.10 1.75
a. A47 Pair, Nos. 267-268 2.25 4.75
269 50p blue 1.35 2.75
270 50p blue 1.35 2.75
a. A47 Pair, Nos. 269-270 2.75 7.25
271 £1 sepia 2.00 4.25
272 £1 sepia 2.00 4.25
a. A47 Pair, Nos. 271-272 4.00 10.50
Nos. 241-272 (32) 28.20 36.00
Se-tenant both horizontally and vertically.

**1973, Sept. 12 Wmk. 314 Upright**
247a A47 2p dark brown & multi 1.80 2.75
248a A47 2p dark brown & multi 1.80 2.75
c. Pair, Nos. 247a-248a 3.75 5.50
253a A47 4p gray & multi 2.30 2.50
254a A47 4p gray & multi 2.30 2.50
c. Pair, Nos. 253a-254a 4.75 5.50
Nos. 247a-254a (4) 8.20 10.50

**1975, July 9 Wmk. 373**
243a A47 1p blue & multi 3.00 3.25
244a A47 1p blue & multi 3.00 3.25
c. Pair, Nos. 243a-244a 6.00 6.50

Elizabeth II — A48

Regimental Coat of Arms — A49

Coil Stamps
**Perf. 14½x14**
**1971, Feb. 15 Photo. Wmk. 314**
273 A48 ½p red orange .20 .25
274 A48 1p bright blue .35 .25
275 A48 2p lt yellow green .55 .80
a. Strip of 5 (½p, ½p, 1p, 1p, 2p) 1.60 26.00
Nos. 273-275 (3) 1.10 1.30

Uniform Type of 1969
Uniforms: 1p, Soldier, Black Watch, 1845. 2p, Drum Major with antelope mascot, Royal Fusiliers, 1971. 4p, Soldier, Kings Own Royal Border Regiment, 1704. 10p, Soldier, Devonshire and Dorset Regiment, 1801.

**1971, Sept. 6 Litho. Perf. 14**
276 A42 1p silver & multi .40 .30
277 A42 2p gold & multi .85 .30
278 A42 4p gold & multi 1.50 .50
279 A42 10p sil, gold & multi 4.75 2.50
Nos. 276-279 (4) 7.50 3.60
Descriptions are printed on back on top of gum.

**1971, Sept. 25 Perf. 13x12**
280 A49 3p red, bister & black .45 .40
Presentation of colors to Gibraltar Regiment, Sept. 25, 1971.

Nativity — A50
Christmas: 5p, Journey to Bethlehem.

**1971, Dec. 1 Photo. Perf. 13x13½**
281 A50 3p silver & multi .50 .50
282 A50 5p gold & multi .70 .70

Artificer, 1773 — A51

"Our Lady of Europa" — A52

3p, Tunneler with drill, 1969. 5p, Royal Engineers, 1772 and 1972, and regimental crest, horiz.

**1972, Mar. 6 Perf. 14x13½, 13½x14**
283 A51 1p dk blue & multi .55 .55
284 A51 3p red & multi .65 .65
285 A51 5p green & multi .95 1.00
Nos. 283-285 (3) 2.15 2.20
Bicent. of the Royal Engineers in Gibraltar.

## Uniform Type of 1969

Uniforms: 1p, Soldier, Duke of Cornwall's Light Infantry, 1704. 3p, Officer, King's Royal Rifle Corps, 1830. 7p, Officer, 37th North Hampshire Regiment, 1825. 10p, Sailor, Royal Navy, 1972.

**1972, July 19      Litho.      *Perf. 14***
| | | | | |
|---|---|---|---|---|
| 286 | A42 | 1p silver & multi | .60 | .20 |
| 287 | A42 | 3p slate & multi | 1.90 | .40 |
| 288 | A42 | 7p silver & multi | 2.75 | .80 |
| 289 | A42 | 10p gold & multi | 3.25 | 1.60 |
| | | *Nos. 286-289 (4)* | 8.50 | 3.00 |

Design descriptions printed on back on top of gum.

**1972, Oct. 1                    *Perf. 14½x14***
| | | | | |
|---|---|---|---|---|
| 290 | A52 | 3p brown & multi | .20 | .20 |
| 291 | A52 | 5p green & multi | .20 | .40 |

Christmas. Design description printed on back.

### Silver Wedding Issue, 1972
Common Design Type

Design: Queen Elizabeth II, Prince Philip, keys of Gibraltar and white narcissus.

**1972, Nov. 20   Photo.   *Perf. 14x14½***
| | | | | |
|---|---|---|---|---|
| 292 | CD324 | 5p car rose & multi | .25 | .20 |
| 293 | CD324 | 7p slate green & multi | .25 | .20 |

Flags of EEC Members and EEC Emblem — A53

***Perf. 14½x14***
**1973, Feb. 22   Litho.   Unwmk.**
| | | | | |
|---|---|---|---|---|
| 294 | A53 | 5p red & multi | .50 | .40 |
| 295 | A53 | 10p ultra & multi | .80 | .80 |

Entry into European Economic Community.

Gibraltar Skull — A54

Designs: 6p, Head of Neanderthal man. 10p, Neanderthal family.

**1973, May 22   Wmk. 314   *Perf. 13½***
| | | | | |
|---|---|---|---|---|
| 296 | A54 | 4p lilac rose & multi | 1.50 | .50 |
| 297 | A54 | 6p lt ultra & multi | 1.50 | .70 |
| 298 | A54 | 10p yel green & multi | 2.25 | 1.25 |
| | | *Nos. 296-298 (3)* | 5.25 | 2.45 |

125th anniv. of the discovery of the Gibraltar skull.

## Uniform Type of 1969

Uniforms: 1p, Fifer, King's Own Scottish Borderers, 1770. 4p, Officer, Royal Welsh Fusiliers, 1800. 6p, Soldier, Royal Northumberland Fusiliers, 1736. 10p, Private, Grenadier Guards, 1898.

**1973, Aug. 22   Litho.   *Perf. 14***
| | | | | |
|---|---|---|---|---|
| 299 | A42 | 1p multicolored | .50 | .35 |
| 300 | A42 | 4p multicolored | 1.75 | .95 |
| 301 | A42 | 6p multicolored | 2.75 | 1.90 |
| 302 | A42 | 10p multicolored | 3.50 | 4.00 |
| | | *Nos. 299-302 (4)* | 8.50 | 7.20 |

Descriptions printed on back on top of gum.

Nativity, by Justus Danckerts — A55

**1973, Oct. 17   Litho.   *Perf. 12½x12***
| | | | | |
|---|---|---|---|---|
| 303 | A55 | 4p brown org & blue | .40 | .20 |
| 304 | A55 | 6p green & claret | .60 | .80 |
| | | Christmas. | | |

### Princess Anne's Wedding Issue
Common Design Type

**1973, Nov. 14                    *Perf. 14***
| | | | | |
|---|---|---|---|---|
| 305 | CD325 | 6p bl grn & multi | .20 | .20 |
| 306 | CD325 | 14p brt grn & multi | .45 | .45 |

Wedding of Princess Anne and Capt. Mark Phillips, Nov. 14, 1973.

V.R. (Queen Victoria) Pillar Box — A56

Virgin with Green Cushion, Andrea Solario — A57

Pillar Boxes: 6p, G.R. (King George). 14p, E.R. (Queen Elizabeth).

**1974, May 2      Litho.      *Perf. 14***
| | | | | |
|---|---|---|---|---|
| 307 | A56 | 2p yel green & multi | .20 | .25 |
| 308 | A56 | 6p gray & multi | .35 | .35 |
| 309 | A56 | 14p dull yel & multi | .65 | .65 |
| a. | | Souvenir booklet | 11.00 | |
| | | *Nos. 307-309 (3)* | 1.20 | 1.25 |
| | | UPU, cent. | | |

No. 309a contains 2 self-adhesive panes printed on peelable paper backing with multicolored advertising on back. One pane of 6 contains 3 each similar to Nos. 307-308; the other pane of 3 contains one each similar to Nos. 307-309. Stamps are imperf. x roulette.

## Uniform Type of 1969

Uniforms: 4p, Officer, East Lancashire Regiment, 1742. 6p, Sergeant, Somerset Light Infantry, 1833. 10p, Company man, Royal Sussex Regiment, 1790. 16p, Officer, Royal Air Force, 1974.

**1974, Aug. 21                    *Perf. 14***
| | | | | |
|---|---|---|---|---|
| 310 | A42 | 4p silver & multi | .55 | .50 |
| 311 | A42 | 6p silver & multi | .95 | .85 |
| 312 | A42 | 10p silver & multi | 1.50 | 1.50 |
| 313 | A42 | 16p silver & multi | 2.75 | 3.50 |
| | | *Nos. 310-313 (4)* | 5.75 | 6.35 |

Descriptions are printed on back on top of gum.

**1974, Nov. 5                    Litho.**

Christmas (Painting): 6p, Madonna of the Meadow, by Giovanni Bellini.
| | | | | |
|---|---|---|---|---|
| 314 | A57 | 4p gold & multi | .35 | .35 |
| 315 | A57 | 6p gold & multi | .75 | 1.00 |

Churchill, Parliament and Big Ben A58

20p, Churchill & George V-class battleship.

**1974, Nov. 30                    *Perf. 14x14½***
| | | | | |
|---|---|---|---|---|
| 316 | A58 | 6p violet & multi | .20 | .20 |
| 317 | A58 | 20p multicolored | .60 | .60 |
| a. | | Souvenir sheet of 2, #316-317 | 5.25 | 6.00 |

Sir Winston Churchill (1874-1965).

## Uniform Type of 1969

Uniforms: 4p, Officer, East Surrey Regiment, 1846. 6p, Private, Highland Light Infantry, 1777. 10p, Officer, Coldstream Guards, 1704. 20p, Sergeant, Gibraltar Regiment, 1974.

**1975, Mar. 14   Wmk. 373   *Perf. 14***
| | | | | |
|---|---|---|---|---|
| 318 | A42 | 4p multicolored | .25 | .25 |
| 319 | A42 | 6p multicolored | .55 | .50 |
| 320 | A42 | 10p multicolored | 1.00 | .90 |
| 321 | A42 | 20p multicolored | 2.10 | 2.25 |
| | | *Nos. 318-321 (4)* | 3.90 | 3.90 |

Descriptions are printed on back on top of gum.

Girl Guides Emblem A59

**1975, Oct. 10               *Perf. 13½x13***
| | | | | |
|---|---|---|---|---|
| 322 | A59 | 5p violet, gold & blue | .35 | .45 |
| 323 | A59 | 7p red brn, gold & blk | .50 | .50 |
| 324 | A59 | 15p ocher, silver & blk | .80 | 1.00 |
| | | *Nos. 322-324 (3)* | 1.65 | 1.95 |

Girl Guides, 50th anniversary.

Child and Bird — A60

Bruges Madonna, by Michelangelo A61

b, Angel playing lute. c, Singing boy. d, Mother & children. e, Praying child. f, Child & lamb.

**1975, Nov. 25                    *Perf. 14x14½***
| | | | | |
|---|---|---|---|---|
| 325 | | Block of 6 | 2.75 | 3.25 |
| a.-f. | | A60 6p any single | .45 | .55 |

Christmas. No. 325 printed in sheets of 60 containing 10 blocks of 6 (3x2) stamps with horizontal and vertical gutters between blocks.

**1975, Dec. 17   Litho.   *Perf. 14x13½***

Sculptures by Michelangelo: 9p, Traddei Madonna. 15p, Pietà.
| | | | | |
|---|---|---|---|---|
| 326 | A61 | 6p violet blk & multi | .25 | .25 |
| 327 | A61 | 9p black brn & multi | .35 | .45 |
| 328 | A61 | 15p dk purple & multi | .40 | .75 |
| a. | | Souvenir booklet | 5.00 | |
| | | *Nos. 326-328 (3)* | 1.00 | 1.45 |

500th birth anniv. of Michelangelo Buonarroti (1475-1564), Italian sculptor, painter and architect.

No. 328a contains 2 self-adhesive panes printed on peelable paper backing with stamp dealer's advertisements on back. One pane of 6 contains 2 each similar to Nos. 326-328; the other pane of 3 contains one each similar to Nos. 326-328. Stamps are imperf. x roulette.

American Bicentennial Emblem, Arms of Gibraltar — A62

Holy Family — A63

**1976, May 28                    *Perf. 14x14½***
| | | | | |
|---|---|---|---|---|
| 329 | A62 | 25p multicolored | .80 | .70 |
| a. | | Souvenir sheet of 4 | 4.50 | 6.50 |

American Bicentennial. No. 329a is rouletted all around.

## Uniform Type of 1969

Uniforms: 1p, Suffolk Regiment, 1795. 6p, Northamptonshire Regiment, 1779. 12p, Lancashire Fusiliers, 1793. 25p, Royal Army Ordnance Corps. 1896.

**1976, July 21                    *Perf. 14***
| | | | | |
|---|---|---|---|---|
| 330 | A42 | 1p multicolored | .25 | .20 |
| 331 | A42 | 6p multicolored | .55 | .25 |
| 332 | A42 | 12p multicolored | .80 | .45 |
| 333 | A42 | 25p multicolored | 1.10 | 1.00 |
| | | *Nos. 330-333 (4)* | 2.70 | 1.90 |

Descriptions printed on back on top of gum.

**1976, Nov. 3      Litho.      Wmk. 373**

Stained Glass Windows: 9p, St. Bernard of Clairvaux. 12p, St. John the Evangelist. 20p, Archangel Michael.
| | | | | |
|---|---|---|---|---|
| 334 | A63 | 6p ultra & multi | .25 | .20 |
| 335 | A63 | 9p brt green & multi | .35 | .20 |
| 336 | A63 | 12p orange & multi | .50 | .55 |
| 337 | A63 | 20p dk carmine & multi | .95 | 1.25 |
| | | *Nos. 334-337 (4)* | 2.05 | 2.20 |
| | | Christmas. | | |

Elizabeth II and Royal Crest — A64

**1977, Feb. 7      Litho.      *Perf. 14x13½***
| | | | | |
|---|---|---|---|---|
| 338 | A64 | 6p multicolored | .20 | .20 |
| 339 | A64 | £1 multicolored | 1.25 | 1.75 |
| a. | | Souv. sheet of 2, #338-339, perf. 13 | 2.00 | 2.50 |

25th anniv. of the reign of Queen Elizabeth II. Nos. 338-339 issued in sheets of 9.

Red Mullet A65

Designs: ½p, 3p, 9p, 15p, 25p, Flowers. 1p, 4p, 10p, 50p, Fish. 2p, 5p, 12p, £1, Butterflies. 2½p, 6p, 20p, £2, Birds. ½p, 2½p, 3p, 6p, 9p, 15p, 20p, 25p, £2, £5, vertical.

**1977-80                    *Perf. 14½x14, 14x14½***
| | | | | |
|---|---|---|---|---|
| 340 | A65 | ½p Toothed orchid | .45 | 1.40 |
| 341 | A65 | 1p shown | .20 | .45 |
| 342 | A65 | 2p Large blue | .20 | .80 |
| 343 | A65 | 2½p Sardinian warbler | .75 | 1.40 |
| 344 | A65 | 3p Giant squill | .20 | .20 |
| 345 | A65 | 4p Gray wrasse | .20 | .20 |
| 346 | A65 | 5p Red admiral | .40 | .80 |
| 347 | A65 | 6p Black kite | 1.40 | .45 |
| 348 | A65 | 9p Scorpion vetch | .55 | .55 |
| 349 | A65 | 10p John Dory | .35 | .20 |
| 350 | A65 | 12p Clouded yellow | .75 | .35 |
| 350A | A65 | 15p Winged asparagus pea | 1.25 | .45 |
| 351 | A65 | 20p Andouin's gull | 1.25 | 2.10 |
| 352 | A65 | 25p Barbary nut | 1.00 | 1.60 |
| 353 | A65 | 50p Swordfish | 1.50 | .80 |
| 354 | A65 | £1 Swallowtail | 3.25 | 4.00 |
| 355 | A65 | £2 Hoopoe | 7.00 | 8.25 |
| 355A | A65 | £5 Coat of Arms | 7.75 | 9.00 |
| | | *Nos. 340-355A (18)* | 28.45 | 33.00 |

½p also comes inscribed 1982, the 4p, 10p, 12p, 25p & 50p inscribed 1981, 9p inscribed 1978.

Issued: £5, 5/16/79; 15p, 11/12/80; others, 4/1/77.

Gibraltar No. 182 — A66

12p, Gibraltar #233. 25p, Gibraltar #294.

**1977, May 27    Litho.    Perf. 14**
356 A66  6p multi          .25  .20
357 A66  12p multi, vert.  .30  .45
358 A66  25p multi, vert.  .30  .55
    Nos. 356-358 (3)        .85 1.20

Amphilex 77 Intl. Phil. Exhib., Amsterdam, May 26-June 5. Issued in sheets of 6.

Annunciation, by Rubens — A67

Rubens Paintings: 9p, Nativity. 12p, Adoration of the Kings. 15p, Holy Family under Apple Tree.

**Perf. 14x13½, 13½x14**
**1977, Nov. 2          Litho.**
359 A67  3p multi          .20  .20
360 A67  9p multi          .20  .20
361 A67  12p multi, horiz. .35  .35
362 A67  15p multi         .35  .35
  a.  Souvenir sheet of 4, #359-362  4.00 4.00
    Nos. 359-362 (4)       1.10 1.10

Christmas and 400th birth anniv. of Peter Paul Rubens.

Gibraltar from Space A68

Design: 25p, Strait of Gibraltar, aerial view.

**1978, May 3          Litho.    Perf. 13½**
363 A68  12p multicolored  .35  .50

**Souvenir Sheet**
364 A68  25p multicolored  .90  .90

No. 363 issued in sheets of 10. No. 364 contains one stamp.

Holyroodhouse — A69

Royal Houses: 9p, St. James Palace. 12p, Sandringham House. 18p, Balmoral.

**1978, June 12         Litho.    Perf. 13½**
365 A69  6p multicolored   .20  .20
366 A69  9p multicolored   .25  .20
367 A69  12p multicolored  .40  .35
368 A69  18p multicolored  .50  .50
  a.  Souvenir booklet      3.00
    Nos. 365-368 (4)       1.35 1.25

25th anniv. of coronation of Queen Elizabeth II. No. 368a contains 2 panes printed on peelable paper backing with pictures of castles. One pane contains 6 rouletted stamps, 3 each similar to Nos. 367-368; the other pane contains one 25p (Windsor Castle) rouletted stamp.

Sunderland Seaplane Landing — A70

Gibraltar and: 9p, Two-tiered Caudron taking off, 1918. 12p, Shackleton, 1953-1966. 16p, Hunter warplane, 1954-1966. 18p, Nimrod, 1969-1978.

**1978, Sept. 6         Litho.    Perf. 14**
369 A70  3p multicolored   .20  .20
370 A70  9p multicolored   .25  .35
371 A70  12p multicolored  .40  .45
372 A70  16p multicolored  .55  .65
373 A70  18p multicolored  .75  .80
    Nos. 369-373 (5)       2.15 2.45

Royal Air Force, 60th anniversary.

Madonna with Goldfinch, by Dürer — A71

Christmas (Paintings by Albrecht Dürer): 5p, Madonna with Animals. 9p, Nativity. 15p, Adoration of the Kings.

**1978, Nov. 1          Litho.    Perf. 14**
374 A71  5p multicolored   .20  .20
375 A71  9p multicolored   .25  .25
376 A71  12p multicolored  .35  .40
377 A71  15p multicolored  .40  .45
    Nos. 374-377 (4)       1.20 1.30

Rowland Hill and Gibraltar No. 10 — A72

Sir Rowland Hill (1795-1879), originator of penny postage and: 9p, Gibraltar No. 274. 12p, Parchment scroll with early postal regulations. 25p, "Barred G" cancellation used on British stamps.

**1979, Feb. 7          Litho.    Perf. 13½**
378 A72  3p multicolored   .20  .20
379 A72  9p multicolored   .20  .20
380 A72  12p yellow grn & black .20 .20
381 A72  25p yellow & black .35  .55
    Nos. 378-381 (4)        .95 1.15

Satellite Earth Station, Post Horn, Telephone — A73

**1979, May 16          Perf. 13½x14**
382 A73  3p lt green & green .20 .20
383 A73  9p lt brown & brown .25 .65
384 A73  12p gray & ultra   .40 1.10
    Nos. 382-384 (3)        .85 1.95

European telecommunications system.

Children, IYC Emblem, Nativity — A74

a, African girl. b, Chinese girl. c, Pacific islands girl. d, American Indian girl. e, Shown. f, Scandinavian boy.

**Litho.; Silver Embossed**
**1979, Nov. 14         Perf. 14**
385    Block of 6         1.60 1.60
  a.-f. A74 12p any single  .25  .25

Christmas; IYC. No. 385 printed in sheets of 12 containing 2 No. 385 with vertical rouletted gutter between.

Officers, Exchange and Commercial Library, 1830 — A75

Gibraltar Police Force, 150th anniv.: 6p, Early and modern uniforms, Rock of Gibraltar. 12p, Traffic Officer, ambulance. 37p, Policeman and woman, Police Station, Irish Town.

**Perf. 14x14½**
**1980, Feb. 5          Litho.    Wmk. 373**
386 A75  3p multicolored   .20  .20
387 A75  6p multicolored   .20  .20
388 A75  12p multicolored  .35  .35
389 A75  37p multicolored  .55  .80
    Nos. 386-389 (4)       1.30 1.55

Archbishop Peter Amigo (1864-1949) — A76

Europa: No. 391, Gustavo Charles Bacarisas (1872-1971), artist. No. 392, John Mackintosh (1865-1940), philanthropist.

**1980, May 6    Wmk. 373    Perf. 14½**
390 A76  12p multicolored  .20  .25
391 A76  12p multicolored  .20  .25
392 A76  12p multicolored  .20  .25
    Nos. 390-392 (3)        .60  .75

**Queen Mother Elizabeth Birthday Issue**
**Common Design Type**
**1980, Aug. 4          Litho.    Perf. 14**
393 CD330  15p multicolored .35  .35

"Victory" and Rock of Gibraltar, by Monamy Swaine A77

Paintings: 3p, Lord Nelson, by John Francis Rigaud, 1781, vert. 15p, Lord Nelson, by William Beechey, vert. 40p, Victory Towed into Gibraltar by Clarkson Stanfield.

**1980, Aug. 20         Litho.    Perf. 14**
394 A77  3p multicolored   .20  .20
395 A77  9p multicolored   .25  .25
396 A77  15p multicolored  .35  .35
  a.  Souvenir sheet       1.00 1.10
397 A77  40p multicolored  .80  .80
    Nos. 394-397 (4)       1.60 1.60

Horatio Nelson (1758-1805).

Holy Family A78

**1980, Nov. 12**
398 A78  15p shown         .25  .40
399 A78  15p Three kings   .25  .40
  a.  Pair, #398-399        .50  .70

Christmas. No. 399a has continuous design.

Hercules Separating Africa and Europe — A79

Dining Room, The Convent — A80

Europa: 15p, Hercules standing on Rock of Gibraltar and Morocco.

**Perf. 14x13½**
**1981, Feb. 24          Wmk. 373**
400 A79  9p multicolored   .20  .20
401 A79  15p multicolored  .35  .40

**1981, May 22   Litho.   Perf. 14½x14**
402 A80  4p shown          .20  .20
403 A80  14p King's Chapel .25  .20
404 A80  15p Aerial view   .40  .20
405 A80  55p Cloister      .80  .80
    Nos. 402-405 (4)       1.65 1.40

450th anniv. of The Convent (Governor's residence, originally Franciscan monastery).

Prince Charles and Lady Diana A81

**1981, July 27         Litho.    Perf. 14½**
406 A81  £1 multicolored   2.00 2.00

Royal wedding. Se-tenant with decorative label.

Queen Elizabeth II — A82

**1981, Sept. 29         Perf. 14½**
**Booklet Stamps**
407 A82  1p black          .45  .45
  a. Bklt. pane of 10 + 2 labels (2 #407, 2 #408, 6 #409)  2.25
  b. Bklt. pane of 5 + label (#407, #408, 3 #409)  1.60
408 A82  4p dark blue      .45  .45
409 A82  15p green         .45  .45
    Nos. 407-409 (3)       1.35 1.35

Airmail Service, 50th Anniv. A83

**1981, Sept. 29**          *Perf. 14½*
410 A83 14p Paper plane                    .35    .35
411 A83 15p Envelopes, aero-
               gram                        .35    .35
412 A83 55p Airplane circling
               globe                      1.00   1.00
       *Nos. 410-412 (3)*                 1.70   1.70

               Intl. Year of
               the Disabled
               A84

**1981, Nov. 19    Litho.    Wmk. 373**
413 A84 14p multicolored                   .35    .35

Christmas
A85

**1981, Nov. 19**                *Perf. 14*
414 A85 15p Children singing
               carols                      .35    .20
415 A85 55p Decorated mailbox,
               vert.                      1.25    .80

Douglas
DC-3 — A86

**1982, Feb. 10    Litho.    Perf. 14**
416 A86     1p shown                       .20    .20
417 A86     2p Vickers Viking              .20    .20
   a.   Wmk. 384, dated 1986 ('87)        3.25   4.00
418 A86     3p Airspeed Am-
               bassador                    .20    .20
419 A86     4p Vickers Viscount            .20    .20
420 A86     5p Boeing 727                  .20    .20
   a.   Wmk. 384, dated 1986 ('87)        3.25   4.00
421 A86    10p Vickers Van-
               guard                       .50    .55
422 A86    14p Short Solent                .60    .65
423 A86    15p Fokker F-27
               Friendship                 1.25    .85
424 A86    17p Boeing 737                  .75    .90
425 A86    20p BAC One-eleven             1.00   1.10
426 A86    25p Lockheed Con-
               stellation                 2.50   1.60
427 A86    50p De Havilland
               Comet 4B                   3.50   2.75
428 A86    £1 Saro Windhover              5.50   3.50
429 A86    £2 Hawker Sid-
               deley Trident 2            8.00   8.50
430 A86    £5 DH-89A Dragon
               Rapide                    11.00  18.00
       *Nos. 416-430 (15)*               35.60  39.40

No. 425 exists with 1985 imprint.

Royal Navy Ship
Crests — A87

**1982, Apr. 14    Litho.    Perf. 14**
431 A87    ½p Opossum                      .20    .20
432 A87  15½p Norfolk                      .50    .50
433 A87    17p Fearless                    .65    .65
434 A87    60p Rooke                      1.75   2.50
       *Nos. 431-434 (4)*                 3.10   3.85

See Nos. 449-452, 465-468, 474-477, 492-
495, 501-504, 528-531, 552-555, 574-577,
587-590.

Europa
A88

**1982, June 11    Litho.    Perf. 14**
435 A88 14p Planes preparing for
               takeoff                     .25    .65
436 A88 17p Generals Eisenhow-
               er and Giraud               .40    .75
       Operation Torch, 1943.

Chamber of
Commerce
Centenary — A89

Anniversaries: 15½p, British Forces Postal
Service centenary. 60p, Scouting year.

**1982, Sept. 22**
437 A89   ½p multicolored                  .20    .20
438 A89 15½p multicolored                  .45    .45
439 A89  60p multicolored                 1.60   1.60
       *Nos. 437-439 (3)*                 2.25   2.25

Intl. Direct Telephone Dialing System
Inauguration — A90

**1982, Oct. 1**                 *Perf. 14½*
440 A90 17p Map                            .45    .45

Christmas
A91

**Perf. 14x14½**
**1982, Nov. 18    Litho.    Wmk. 373**
441 A91 14p Holly                          .40    .35
442 A91 17p Mistletoe                      .55    .40

A92

**1983, Mar. 14    Litho.    Perf. 14**
443 A92  4p Local street                   .20    .20
444 A92 14p Scouts on parade               .35    .35
445 A92 17p Flag, vert.                    .45    .45
446 A92 60p Queen Elizabeth II,
               vert.                      1.10   1.40
       *Nos. 443-446 (4)*                 2.10   2.40

Commonwealth Day.

Europa
A93

**1983, May 21**                *Perf. 14x13½*
447 A93 16p St. George's Hall              .35    .35
448 A93 19p Water catchments              .45    .45

Royal Navy Crest Type of 1982
**1983, July 1    Litho.    Perf. 14**
449 A87  4p Faulknor                       .20    .20
450 A87 14p Renown                        1.10    .40
451 A87 17p Ark Royal                     1.25    .50
452 A87 60p Sheffield                     1.90   1.75
       *Nos. 449-452 (4)*                 4.45   2.85

Fortresses — A94

**1983, Sept. 13**              *Perf. 13½x14*
453 A94  4p Landport Gate,
               1729                        .20    .20
454 A94 17p Koehler gun, 1782              .45    .45
455 A94 77p King's Bastion,
               1799                       1.50   1.50
   a.   Souvenir sheet of 3, #453-455     3.00   3.00
       *Nos. 453-455 (3)*                 2.15   2.15

Christmas
A95

Raphael Paintings.

**1983, Nov. 17    Litho.    Perf. 14**
456 A95  4p Adoration of the
               Magi                        .20    .20
457 A95 17p Madonna of
               Foligno, vert.             .55    .50
458 A95 60p Sistine Madonna,
               vert.                      1.90   1.90
       *Nos. 456-458 (3)*                 2.65   2.60

Europa (1959-
1984)
A96

Intl. Postal and Telecommunication Links.

**1984, Mar. 6    Litho.    Perf. 14½**
459 A96 17p No. 98                         .40    .50
460 A96 23p Communications cir-
               cuit                        .50    .80

Field Hockey
A97

**1984, May 25    Litho.    Perf. 14**
461 A97 20p shown                          .55    .70
462 A97 21p Basketball                     .65    .75
463 A97 26p Rowing                         .70    .90
464 A97 29p Soccer                         .80   1.00
       *Nos. 461-464 (4)*                 2.70   3.35

Royal Navy Crest Type of 1982
**1984, Sept. 21    Litho.    Perf. 13½x13**
465 A87 20p Active                        1.90   1.60
466 A87 21p Foxhound                      1.90   1.90
467 A87 26p Valiant                       2.10   1.90
468 A87 29p Hood                          2.25   2.25
       *Nos. 465-468 (4)*                 8.15   7.65

Christmas
A98

**Perf. 14x14½**
**1984, Nov. 7    Litho.    Wmk. 373**
469 A98 20p Parade float                   .55    .55
470 A98 80p Float, diff.                  2.25   2.25

**Europa Issue**

Musical
Symbols — A99

**1985, Feb. 26    Photo.    Perf. 12½**
**Granite Paper**
471 A99 20p multi, diff.                   .45    .40
472 A99 29p shown                          .65   1.60

Save the
Children
Fund
A100

Globe and legend in various positions.

**1985, May 3    Litho.    Perf. 13x13½**
473     Strip of 4                        5.00   4.50
   a.-d.  A100 26p any single            1.10   1.10

Royal Navy Crests Type of 1982
**1985, July 3    Litho.    Perf. 14**
474 A87  4p Duncan                        2.00    .70
475 A87  9p Fury                          2.50   1.40
476 A87 21p Firedrake                     2.75   2.75
477 A87 80p Malaya                        3.25   3.75
       *Nos. 474-477 (4)*                10.50   8.60

Intl. Youth
Year — A101

**1985, Sept. 6**                *Perf. 14½*
478 A101  4p Emblem                        .55    .20
479 A101 20p Hands, diamond               1.90   1.50
480 A101 80p Girl Guides anniv.
               emblem                     4.25   4.00
       *Nos. 478-480 (3)*                 6.70   5.70

St. Joseph's
Parish Church,
Cent. — A102

Creche,
Detail — A103

**Perf. 13½xRoulette 7 Between, 13½**

**1985, Oct. 25    Wmk. 373    Litho.**
481 A102      Pair                     1.75   1.40
  a.     4p Centenary seal            .85    .60
  b.     4p Church                     .85    .60
  c.     No. 481a, perf. 13½ on 4 sides  .80    .60
482 A103 80p multicolored              5.75   4.75

Christmas. Nos. 481a-481b rouletted between. Printed in sheets of 10 pairs with the bottom row containing 5 No. 481c. Strips of 3, Nos. 481a-481c exist.

Europa
A104

**1986, Feb. 10    Litho.    Perf. 13x13½**
483 A104 22p Butterfly, house           .80    .55
484 A104 29p Seagull, hotel            1.40   2.75

Postage Stamp
Cent. — A105

Elizabeth II, 60th
Birthday — A106

**1986, Mar. 25              Perf. 13½x13**
485 A105  4p No. 18                     .35    .20
486 A105 22p No. 42                    1.40   1.25
487 A105 32p No. 67                    2.25   2.40
488 A105 36p No. 118                   2.25   2.75

**Size: 32x48mm**
**Perf. 14**
489 A105 44p No. 131                   3.25   3.75
   Nos. 485-489 (5)                9.50  10.35

**Souvenir Sheet**
490 A105 29p No. 2                     4.00   4.00

**1986, May 22    Litho.    Perf. 14**
491 A106 £1 multicolored               2.50   3.25

Royal Naval Crests Type of 1982
**1986, Aug. 28    Litho.    Perf. 14**
492 A87 22p Lightning                  2.50   1.00
493 A87 29p Hermione                   2.75   1.60
494 A87 32p Laforey                    3.00   3.00
495 A87 44p Nelson                     3.50   3.75
   Nos. 492-495 (4)               11.75   9.35

Christmas, Intl. Peace
Year — A107

**1986, Oct. 14    Litho.    Perf. 14½x14**
496 A107 18p St. Mary the
     Crowned Cathe-
     dral                          1.25    .50
497 A107 32p St. Andrew's
     Church                        1.75   2.50

Souvenir Sheet

Wedding of Prince Andrew and Sarah
Ferguson — A108

**1986, Aug. 28    Litho.    Perf. 15**
498 A108 44p multicolored              1.25   1.75

Europa — A109

**1987, Feb. 17    Wmk. 384    Perf. 15**
499 A109 22p Neptune House             1.60    .50
500 A109 29p Ocean Heights             2.10   3.50

Royal Navy Crests Type of 1982
**1987, Apr. 2              Perf. 13½x13**
501 A87 18p Wishart                    1.90    .70
502 A87 22p Charybdis                  2.25   1.10
503 A87 32p Antelope                   3.00   2.75
504 A87 44p Eagle                      4.00   3.50
   Nos. 501-504 (4)               11.15   8.05

Warrant Granted to
the Royal
Engineers, 200th
Anniv. — A110

**1987, Apr. 25    Wmk. 373    Perf. 14½**
505 A110 18p Victoria Stadium          1.50    .55
506 A110 32p Casket, Freedom
     Scroll                        2.75   3.25
507 A110 44p Monogram                  4.00   4.00
   Nos. 505-507 (3)                8.25   7.80

Guns and
Artillery
A111

Designs: 1p, 13-inch mortar, 1783. 2p, 6-inch Coast, 1909. 3p, 8-inch Howitzer, 1783. 4p, Bofors L40/70, 1951. 5p, 100-ton RML, 1882. 10p, 5.25 HAA, 1953. 18p, 25-pounder Gun-howitzer, 1943. 19p, 64-pounder RML, 1873. 22p, 12-pounder, 1758. 50p, 10-inch RML, 1870. £1, Russian 24-pounder, 1854. £3, 9.2-inch Coast Mk. 10, 1935. £5, 24-pounder, 1779.

**1987, June 1    Wmk. 373    Perf. 12½**
508 A111   1p multicolored             .20    .40
509 A111   2p multicolored             .35    .40
510 A111   3p multicolored             .35    .40
511 A111   4p multicolored             .45    .20
512 A111   5p multicolored             .45    .40
513 A111  10p multicolored             .45    .45
514 A111  18p multicolored             .70    .75
515 A111  19p multicolored             .70    .80
516 A111  22p multicolored             .70    .40
517 A111  50p multicolored            1.40   2.75
518 A111  £1 multicolored             3.00   3.50
519 A111  £3 multicolored             7.75   4.50
520 A111  £5 multicolored            12.50  17.00
   Nos. 508-520 (13)              29.00  31.95

For surcharge see No. 595.

Christmas — A112

**1987, Nov. 12    Wmk. 384    Perf. 14½**
521 A112  4p Three Wise Men            .20    .20
522 A112 22p Holy Family              1.25    .95
523 A112 44p Shepherds                2.25   3.00
   Nos. 521-523 (3)                3.70   4.15

Europa — A113

Transport and communication: No. 524, Rock of Gibraltar, Cruise Ship. No. 525, Passenger jet, yacht, dish aerial. No. 526, Bus, buggy. No. 527, Rock of Gibraltar, automobile, telephone.

**Perf. 14½x14 on 3 Sides; Rouletted
Between**
**1988, Feb. 16    Litho.    Wmk. 373**
524       22p multicolored            1.50   1.60
525       22p multicolored            1.50   1.60
  a.    A113 Pair, #524-525           3.25   3.25
526       32p multicolored            2.10   2.25
527       32p multicolored            2.10   2.25
  a.    A113 Pair, #526-527           4.75   4.75
   Nos. 524-527 (4)                7.20   7.70

Nos. 525a, 527a have continuous design.

Royal Navy Crests Type of 1982
**Perf. 13½x13**
**1988, Apr. 7              Wmk. 384**
528 A87 18p Clyde                     2.25    .65
529 A87 22p Foresight                 2.75   1.25
530 A87 32p Severn                    3.00   3.00
531 A87 44p Rodney                    4.25   4.75
   Nos. 528-531 (4)               12.25   9.65

Birds
A114

**1988, June 15    Wmk. 373    Perf. 14**
532 A114  4p Bee eater                 .75    .20
533 A114 22p Common puffin            2.25   1.00
534 A114 32p Honey buzzard            3.25   3.25
535 A114 44p Blue rock thrush         4.00   4.25
   Nos. 532-535 (4)               10.25   8.70

Operation
Raleigh,
1984-88
A115

Designs: 19p, Square-rigger. 22p, Sir Walter Raleigh and expedition emblem. 32p, Maps and modern transport ship Sir Walter Raleigh. 44p, Ship Sir Walter Raleigh.

**Perf. 13x13½**
**1988, Sept. 14    Litho.    Wmk. 373**
536 A115 19p multicolored              .85    .85
537 A115 22p multicolored             1.00   1.00
538 A115 32p multicolored             1.40   1.40
   Nos. 536-538 (3)                3.25   3.25

**Souvenir Sheet**
539       Sheet of 2, #537, 539a      5.75   5.75
  a.    A115 44p multicolored         2.25   2.25

400th anniv. of Sir Walter Raleigh's voyage to the New World to establish the 1st English-speaking colony, in what is now North Carolina.

Christmas
A116

Children's drawings: 4p, Snowman, by Rebecca Falero. 22p, Nativity, by Dennis Penalver. 44p, Santa Claus, by Gavin Key.

**1988, Nov. 2    Wmk. 384    Perf. 14**
540 A116  4p multicolored              .20    .20
541 A116 22p multicolored              .60    .75

**Size: 25x33mm**
542 A116 44p multicolored             1.40   1.90
   Nos. 540-542 (3)                2.20   2.85

Europa
A117

Toys: 32p, Doll, doll house, puppy, ball, boat.

**Perf. 13x13½**
**1989, Feb. 15              Wmk. 384**
543 A117 25p shown                    1.75    .80
544 A117 32p multicolored             2.00   2.50

Gibraltar Regiment,
50th Anniv. — A118

**Perf. 13½x13**
**1989, Apr. 28              Wmk. 373**
545 A118  4p The Port Sergeant         .50    .20
546 A118 22p Regimental colors,
     Queen's colors                1.75    .90
547 A118 32p Drum Major               2.50   2.10
   Nos. 545-547 (3)                4.75   3.20

**Souvenir Sheet**
548       Sheet of 2, Nos. 546, 548a  5.75   5.75
  a.    A118 44p Regimental arms      2.25   2.25

Intl. Red Cross,
125th
Anniv. — A119

**Perf. 15x14½**
**1989, July 7              Wmk. 384**
549 A119 25p Mother and child         1.10    .60
550 A119 32p Malnourished chil-
     dren                          1.50   1.50
551 A119 44p Accident victims         2.10   2.50
   Nos. 549-551 (3)                4.70   4.60

Royal Navy Crests Type of 1982
**1989, Sept. 7    Litho.    Perf. 14**
552 A87 22p Blankney                  2.10    .70
553 A87 25p Deptford                  2.10   1.50
554 A87 32p Exmoor                    3.00   2.10
555 A87 44p Stork                     4.50   3.50
   Nos. 552-555 (4)               11.70   7.80

## Souvenir Sheets

Coins — A120

No. 556: a, 1p Barbary Partridge. b, 2p Lighthouse at Europa Point. c, 10p Tower of Homage. d, 5p Barbary Ape.

No. 557: a, 50p Gibraltar Candytuft. b, £5 Pillars of Hercules. c, £2 Cannon from the Great Siege Period, 1779-1783. d, £1 Natl. coat of arms. e, Common obverse side of coins picturing Maklouf head of Queen Elizabeth II. f, 20p Our Lady of Europa.

| | | **1989, Oct. 10** | **Perf. 14½x15** | |
|---|---|---|---|---|
| 556 | | Sheet of 4 | 2.25 | 2.25 |
| a.-d. | A120 4p any single | | .55 | .55 |
| 557 | | Sheet of 6 | 7.75 | 7.75 |
| a.-f. | A120 22p any single | | 1.25 | 1.25 |

Christmas A121

**Wmk. 384**

| | | | **1989, Oct. 11** | **Litho.** | **Perf. 14½** | |
|---|---|---|---|---|---|---|
| 558 | A121 | 4p | Santa's sleigh | | .20 | .20 |
| 559 | A121 | 22p | Shepherds see star | | 1.40 | .85 |
| 560 | A121 | 32p | Holy family | | 2.10 | 2.10 |
| 561 | A121 | 44p | Adoration of the Magi | | 3.25 | 3.50 |
| | | | Nos. 558-561 (4) | | 6.95 | 6.65 |

Europa 1990 — A122

Post offices: No. 562, G.P.O. exterior. No. 563, Carved crown and "VR" from p.o. archway and G.P.O. interior. No. 564, South District P.O. interior. No. 565, South District P.O. exterior.

**Perf. 14½, Rouletted 9½ Between**

| | | **1990, Mar. 6** | **Litho.** | **Unwmk.** | |
|---|---|---|---|---|---|
| 562 | | 22p multicolored | | 1.75 | 1.50 |
| 563 | | 22p multicolored | | 1.75 | 1.50 |
| a. | A122 Pair, #562-563 | | | 3.50 | 3.00 |
| 564 | | 32p multicolored | | 2.25 | 2.25 |
| 565 | | 32p multicolored | | 2.25 | 2.25 |
| a. | A122 Pair, #564-565 | | | 4.50 | 4.50 |
| | | Nos. 562-565 (4) | | 8.00 | 7.50 |

Pairs are rouletted between.

Early Fire Truck A123

| | | **1990, Apr. 2** | | **Perf. 14½x14** | |
|---|---|---|---|---|---|
| 566 | A123 | 4p | Early firemen, hose, vert. | 1.50 | .20 |
| 567 | A123 | 20p | shown | 3.00 | 1.00 |
| 568 | A123 | 42p | Modern truck | 3.25 | 3.00 |
| 569 | A123 | 44p | Modern fireman, vert. | 3.50 | 3.00 |
| | | | Nos. 566-569 (4) | 11.25 | 7.20 |

Fire Service, 125th anniv.

Penny Black, 150th Anniv. — A124

19p, Henry Corbould, Great Britain No. 1. 22p, 1st Royal Mail coach, Bristol-London. 32p, Sir Rowland Hill, Great Britain No. 1. 44p, Great Britain No. 1, Maltese Cross cancel.

| | | **1990, May 3** | | **Perf. 13½x14** | |
|---|---|---|---|---|---|
| 570 | A124 | 19p | multicolored | 1.25 | .90 |
| 571 | A124 | 22p | multicolored | 1.75 | .95 |
| 572 | A124 | 32p | multicolored | 3.50 | 3.25 |
| | | | Nos. 570-572 (3) | 6.50 | 5.10 |

### Souvenir Sheet

| | | | | | |
|---|---|---|---|---|---|
| 573 | A124 | 44p | multicolored | 7.00 | 7.00 |

### Royal Navy Crest Type of 1982

| | | **1990, July 10** | **Litho.** | **Perf. 14** | |
|---|---|---|---|---|---|
| 574 | A87 | 22p Calpe | | 2.25 | .80 |
| 575 | A87 | 25p Gallant | | 2.50 | 1.90 |
| 576 | A87 | 32p Wrestler | | 3.25 | 3.00 |
| 577 | A87 | 44p Greyhound | | 4.00 | 4.00 |
| | | Nos. 574-577 (4) | | 12.00 | 9.70 |

Europort Model A125

| | | **1990, Oct. 10** | **Litho.** | **Perf. 14½** | |
|---|---|---|---|---|---|
| 578 | A125 | 22p shown | | 1.10 | .95 |
| 579 | A125 | 23p Building components | | 1.10 | 1.40 |
| 580 | A125 | 25p Land reclamation | | 1.25 | 1.40 |
| | | Nos. 578-580 (3) | | 3.45 | 3.75 |

Christmas — A126

Europa A127

| | | **1990, Oct. 10** | | **Perf. 13½** | |
|---|---|---|---|---|---|
| 581 | A126 | 4p shown | | .20 | .20 |
| 582 | A126 | 22p Santa Claus | | .90 | .55 |
| 583 | A126 | 42p Christmas tree | | 2.25 | 2.40 |
| 584 | A126 | 44p Creche | | 2.25 | 2.40 |
| | | Nos. 581-584 (4) | | 5.60 | 5.55 |

| | | **1991, Feb. 26** | **Litho.** | **Perf. 13½** | |
|---|---|---|---|---|---|
| 585 | A127 | 25p Spaceplane, satellite | | 1.00 | .80 |
| 586 | A127 | 32p ERS-1 satellite | | 1.50 | 1.75 |

### Royal Navy Crest Type of 1982

| | | **1991, Apr. 9** | **Litho.** | **Perf. 13½x13** | |
|---|---|---|---|---|---|
| 587 | A87 | 4p Hesperus | | .50 | .20 |
| 588 | A87 | 21p Forester | | 2.00 | 1.50 |
| 589 | A87 | 22p Furious | | 2.00 | 1.50 |
| 590 | A87 | 62p Scylla | | 5.25 | 5.50 |
| | | Nos. 587-590 (4) | | 9.75 | 8.70 |

Birds A128

| | | **1991, May 30** | **Litho.** | **Perf. 13½** | |
|---|---|---|---|---|---|
| 591 | A128 | 13p Black stork | | 1.60 | 1.25 |
| 592 | A128 | 13p Egyptian vulture | | 1.60 | 1.25 |
| 593 | A128 | 13p Barbary partridge | | 1.60 | 1.25 |
| 594 | A128 | 13p Shag | | 1.60 | 1.25 |
| a. | | Block of 4, #591-594 | | 7.00 | 7.50 |

World Wildlife Fund.

### No. 519 Surcharged

**Wmk. 373**

| | | **1991, May 30** | **Litho.** | **Perf. 12½** | |
|---|---|---|---|---|---|
| 595 | A111 | £1.05 on £3 multi | | 6.50 | 3.25 |

Views of Gibraltar A129

Paintings: 22p, North View of Gibraltar, by Gustavo Bacarisas (1873-1971). 26p, Parson's Lodge, by Elena Mifsud (1906-1989). 32p, Governor's Parade, by Jacobo Azabury, OBE (1890-1980). 42p, Waterport Wharf, by Rudesindo Mannia (1899-1982), vert.

| | | **1991, Sept. 10** | **Litho.** | **Perf. 15x14** | |
|---|---|---|---|---|---|
| 596 | A129 | 22p multicolored | | 1.25 | .90 |
| 597 | A129 | 26p multicolored | | 1.40 | .90 |
| 598 | A129 | 32p multicolored | | 2.10 | 2.10 |

| | | | | **Perf. 14x15** | |
|---|---|---|---|---|---|
| 599 | A129 | 42p multicolored | | 3.00 | 3.00 |
| | | Nos. 596-599 (4) | | 7.75 | 6.50 |

Christmas A130

Christmas carols: 4p, Once in Royal David's City. 24p, Silent Night. 25p, Angels We Have Heard on High. 49p, O Come All Ye Faithful.

| | | **1991, Oct. 15** | **Litho.** | **Perf. 14½** | |
|---|---|---|---|---|---|
| 600 | A130 | 4p multicolored | | .25 | .20 |
| 601 | A130 | 24p multicolored | | 2.00 | .75 |
| 602 | A130 | 25p multicolored | | 2.00 | 1.50 |
| 603 | A130 | 49p multicolored | | 3.50 | 3.50 |
| | | Nos. 600-603 (4) | | 7.75 | 5.95 |

### Souvenir Sheet

Phila Nippon '91 — A131

**1991, Nov. 15**

| | | | | | |
|---|---|---|---|---|---|
| 604 | A131 | £1.05 Plain tiger | | 5.75 | 5.75 |

### Queen Elizabeth II's Accession to the Throne, 40th Anniv.
### Common Design Type
**Wmk. 373**

| | | **1992, Feb. 6** | | **Perf. 14** | |
|---|---|---|---|---|---|
| 605 | CD349 | 4p multicolored | | .20 | .20 |
| 606 | CD349 | 20p multicolored | | .80 | .80 |
| 607 | CD349 | 24p multicolored | | 1.00 | 1.10 |
| 608 | CD349 | 44p multicolored | | 2.00 | 2.10 |
| 609 | CD349 | 54p multicolored | | 2.50 | 2.75 |
| | | Nos. 605-609 (5) | | 6.50 | 6.95 |

Discovery of America, 500th Anniv. — A132

| | | **1992, Feb. 6** | **Unwmk.** | **Perf. 14½** | |
|---|---|---|---|---|---|
| 610 | A132 | 24p Columbus, Santa Maria | | 2.10 | 1.75 |
| 611 | A132 | 24p Map, Nina | | 2.10 | 1.75 |
| a. | | Pair, #610-611 | | 4.25 | 3.50 |
| 612 | A132 | 34p Map, Pinta | | 2.30 | 1.90 |
| 613 | A132 | 34p Map, sailor | | 2.30 | 1.90 |
| a. | | Pair, #612-613 | | 4.75 | 3.75 |
| | | Nos. 610-613 (4) | | 8.80 | 7.30 |

Europa. Printed in sheets containing 4 pairs.

Around the World Yacht Rally, 1991-92 A133

Compass rose, sail and maps of routes through: 21p, Atlantic Ocean, vert. 24p, Malay Archipelago. 25p, Indian Ocean. 49p, Mediterranean and Red Seas, vert.

| | | **1992, Apr. 15** | **Litho.** | **Perf. 13½** | |
|---|---|---|---|---|---|
| 614 | A133 | 21p multicolored | | 1.10 | .90 |
| 615 | A133 | 24p multicolored | | 1.40 | 1.50 |
| 616 | A133 | 25p multicolored | | 1.40 | 1.60 |
| | | Nos. 614-616 (3) | | 3.90 | 4.00 |

### Souvenir Sheet

| | | | | | |
|---|---|---|---|---|---|
| 617 | A133 | Sheet of 2, #614 & 617a | | 3.25 | 3.25 |
| a. | A133 | 49p multicolored | | 2.10 | 2.10 |

Anglican Diocese of Gibraltar, 150th Anniv. A134

4p, Holy Trinity Cathedral, vert. 24p, Crest and map. 44p, Construction work on Cathedral during 1800's. 54p, Bishop Tomlinson, first Bishop of Diocese (1842-1863), vert.

| | | **1992, Aug. 21** | **Litho.** | **Perf. 14** | |
|---|---|---|---|---|---|
| 618 | A134 | 4p multicolored | | .50 | .20 |
| 619 | A134 | 24p multicolored | | 1.50 | .60 |
| 620 | A134 | 44p multicolored | | 2.75 | 2.75 |
| 621 | A134 | 54p multicolored | | 3.00 | 3.00 |
| | | Nos. 618-621 (4) | | 7.75 | 6.55 |

Christmas A135

Designs: 4p, Church of the Sacred Heart of Jesus. 24p, Cathedral of St. Mary the Crowned. 34p, St. Andrew's Church. 49p, St. Joseph's Church.

| | | **1992, Nov. 10** | **Litho.** | **Perf. 14** | |
|---|---|---|---|---|---|
| 622 | A135 | 4p multicolored | | .20 | .20 |
| 623 | A135 | 24p multicolored | | 1.50 | .50 |
| 624 | A135 | 34p multicolored | | 3.00 | 2.25 |
| 625 | A135 | 49p multicolored | | 4.25 | 4.00 |
| | | Nos. 622-625 (4) | | 8.95 | 6.95 |

Contemporary Art — A136

Europa: No. 626, Masks of Comedy and Tragedy, record. No. 627, Painting, dancer, pottery. No. 628, Architecture, sculpture. No. 629, Video camera, 35mm film.

**1993, Mar. 2    Litho.    Perf. 14½**
| 626 | A136 24p multicolored | 2.30 | 1.50 |
| 627 | A136 24p multicolored | 2.30 | 1.50 |
| a. | Pair, #626-627 | 4.75 | 3.00 |
| 628 | A136 34p multicolored | 2.60 | 2.25 |
| 629 | A136 34p multicolored | 2.60 | 2.25 |
| a. | Pair, #628-629 | 5.25 | 4.75 |
| | Nos. 626-629 (4) | 9.80 | 7.50 |

**Souvenir Sheet**

World War II Warships A137

Designs: a, HMS Hood. b, HMS Ark Royal c, HMAS Waterhen. d, USS Gleaves.

**1993, Apr. 27    Litho.    Perf. 14**
630 A137 24p Sheet of 4, #a.-d.    12.00 12.00

See Nos. 660, 684, 714, 732.

Architectural Heritage A138

**1993-94    Litho.    Perf. 13**
| 631 | A138 1p Landport Gate | .20 | .20 |
| 632 | A138 2p St. Mary the Crowned | .20 | .20 |
| 633 | A138 3p Parsons Lodge Battery | .20 | .20 |
| 634 | A138 4p Moorish Castle | .20 | .20 |
| 635 | A138 5p General Post Office | .20 | .20 |
| 636 | A138 10p South Barracks | .25 | .25 |
| 637 | A138 21p American War Memorial | .85 | .85 |
| 638 | A138 24p Garrison Library | .95 | .95 |
| 639 | A138 25p Southport Gates | .95 | .95 |
| 640 | A138 26p Casemates Gate | 1.00 | 1.00 |
| 641 | A138 50p Central Police Station | 1.75 | 1.75 |
| 642 | A138 £1 Prince Edward's Gate | 3.25 | 3.25 |
| 643 | A138 £3 Lighthouse | 10.00 | 10.00 |
| 644 | A138 £5 Coat of arms, keys to fortress, vert. | 15.00 | 15.00 |
| | Nos. 631-644 (14) | 35.00 | 35.00 |

Nos. 631, 635, 637, 639, 642-643 are vert. Portions of the design on No. 644 were applied by a thermographic process producing a shiny, raised effect.
Issued: £5, 6/6/94; others, 6/28/93.
See Nos. 686-693.

Anniversaries — A139

**1993, Sept. 21    Litho.    Perf. 13**
| 645 | A139 21p Coins | 1.25 | .75 |
| 646 | A139 24p Jet, biplane fighters | 2.00 | 1.00 |
| 647 | A139 34p Garrison Library | 2.50 | 2.25 |
| 648 | A139 49p Churchill, searchlights | 4.25 | 3.50 |
| | Nos. 645-648 (4) | 10.00 | 7.50 |

First decimal coins, 25th anniv. Royal Air Force, 75th anniv. Garrison Library, bicent. Churchill's visit to Gibraltar, 50th anniv.

Christmas A140

Mice and: 5p, Christmas tree. 24p, Christmas cracker. 44p, Singing carols. 49p, Snowman.

**1993, Nov. 16    Litho.    Perf. 13½**
| 649 | A140 5p multicolored | .20 | .20 |
| 650 | A140 24p multicolored | 1.25 | .70 |
| 651 | A140 44p multicolored | 3.00 | 2.10 |
| 652 | A140 49p multicolored | 3.25 | 2.75 |
| | Nos. 649-652 (4) | 7.70 | 5.75 |

European Discoveries — A141

Europa: No. 653, Atoms exploding, Lord Penney (1909-91). No. 654, Chemistry flasks, polonium, radium, Marie Curie. No. 655, Diesel engine, Rudolf Diesel. No. 656, Telescope, Galileo.

**1994, Mar. 1    Litho.    Perf. 13½**
| 653 | A141 24p multicolored | 1.60 | 1.25 |
| 654 | A141 24p multicolored | 1.60 | 1.25 |
| a. | Pair, #653-654 | 3.25 | 2.50 |
| 655 | A141 34p multicolored | 1.80 | 1.60 |
| 656 | A141 34p multicolored | 1.80 | 1.60 |
| a. | Pair, #655-656 | 3.75 | 3.50 |
| | Nos. 653-656 (4) | 6.80 | 5.70 |

1994 World Cup Soccer Championships, US — A142

26p, FIFA cup, US map, flag. 39p, Players, US map as playing field. 49p, Leg action.

**1994, Apr. 19    Litho.    Perf. 13½**
| 657 | A142 26p multi | 1.25 | .65 |
| 658 | A142 39p multi | 2.00 | 1.75 |
| 659 | A142 49p multi, vert. | 2.75 | 2.50 |
| | Nos. 657-659 (3) | 6.00 | 4.90 |

**Souvenir Sheet**
World War II Warships Type of 1993

Designs: a, 5p, HMS Penelope. b, 25p, HMS Warspite. c, 44p, USS McLanahan. d, 49p, HNLMS Isaac Sweers.

**1994, June 6    Litho.    Perf. 13½x13**
660 A137 Sheet of 4, #a.-d.    11.50 11.50

**Souvenir Sheet**

PHILAKOREA '94 — A143

**1994, Aug. 16    Litho.    Perf. 13**
661 A143 £1.05 multicolored    5.25 5.25

Marine Life — A144

**1994, Sept. 27    Litho.    Perf. 14**
| 662 | A144 21p Golden star coral | 1.40 | 1.40 |
| 663 | A144 24p Star fish | 1.60 | 1.60 |
| 664 | A144 34p Gorgonian sea fan | 2.25 | 2.25 |
| 665 | A144 49p Turkish wrasse | 3.25 | 3.25 |
| | Nos. 662-665 (4) | 8.50 | 8.50 |

Intl. Olympic Committee, Cent. — A145

**1994, Nov. 22    Litho.    Perf. 14**
| 666 | A145 49p Discus | 3.00 | 2.25 |
| 667 | A145 54p Javelin | 3.50 | 2.50 |

Christmas Songbirds A146

**1994, Nov. 22    Litho.    Perf. 13½**
| 668 | A146 5p Great tit, vert. | .20 | .20 |
| 669 | A146 24p Robin | 2.50 | 1.40 |
| 670 | A146 34p Blue tit | 3.00 | 2.10 |
| 671 | A146 54p Goldfinch, vert. | 5.25 | 3.25 |
| | Nos. 668-671 (4) | 10.95 | 6.95 |

New Members in European Union A147

Flags: 24p, Austria. 26p, Finland. 34p, Sweden. 49p, Sweden, Finland, Austria, emblem of European Union.

**1995, Jan. 3    Litho.    Perf. 14**
| 672 | A147 24p multicolored | 1.00 | .90 |
| 673 | A147 26p multicolored | 1.25 | 1.00 |
| 674 | A147 34p multicolored | 1.40 | 1.40 |
| 675 | A147 49p multicolored | 2.10 | 1.90 |
| | Nos. 672-675 (4) | 5.75 | 5.20 |

Peace & Freedom — A148

Europa: No. 676, Cross, barbed wire, text. No. 677, Rainbow, dove, hands. No. 678, Shackles, text. No. 679, Doves, hands.

**1995, Feb. 28    Litho.    Perf. 13½**
| 676 | 24p multicolored | 1.60 | 1.25 |
| 677 | 24p multicolored | 1.60 | 1.25 |
| a. | A148 Pair, #676-677 | 3.25 | 2.75 |
| 678 | 34p multicolored | 2.25 | 1.75 |
| 679 | 34p multicolored | 2.25 | 1.75 |
| a. | A148 Pair, #678-679 | 4.75 | 4.25 |
| | Nos. 676-679 (4) | 7.70 | 6.00 |

Island Games — A149

**1995, May 8    Litho.    Perf. 14x13½**
| 680 | A149 24p Sailing | 1.25 | .90 |
| 681 | A149 44p Running | 2.25 | .90 |
| 682 | A149 49p Swimming | 2.75 | 2.10 |
| | Nos. 680-682 (3) | 6.25 | 3.90 |
| 680a | Booklet pane of 3 | | 3.75 |
| 681a | Booklet pane of 3 | | 6.75 |
| 682a | Booklet pane of 3 | | 8.25 |
| 682b | Bklt. pane, 1 ea. #680-682 | | 6.25 |
| | Commemorative booklet, 1 each #680a-682b | | 26.00 |

**Souvenir Sheet**

VE Day, 50th Anniv. — A150

Illustration reduced.

**1995, May 8**
683 A150 £1.05 multicolored    6.00 6.00

World War II Warships Type of 1993 Souvenir Sheet

Designs: a, 5p, HMS Calpe. b, 24p, HMS Victorious. c, 44p, USS Weehawken. d, 49p, FFS Savorgnan de Brazza.

**1995, June 6    Litho.    Perf. 13½x14**
684 A137 Sheet of 4, #a.-d.    11.50 11.50

Singapore '95 — A151

Orchids: a, 22p, Bee. b, 23p, Brown bee. c, 24p, Pyramidal. d, 25p, Mirror. e, 26p, Sawfly.

**1995, Sept. 1    Litho.    Perf. 14x14½**
685 A151 Strip of 5, #a.-e.    9.00 6.25

Architectural Heritage Type of 1993

**1995, Sept. 1    Litho.    Perf. 13**
| 686 | A138 6p House of Assembly | .20 | .20 |
| 687 | A138 7p Bleak House | .20 | .20 |
| 688 | A138 8p Bust of Gen. Eliott | .25 | .25 |
| 689 | A138 9p Supreme Court Bldg. | .40 | .40 |
| 690 | A138 20p Convent | .75 | .75 |
| 691 | A138 30p St. Bernard's Hospital | 1.10 | 1.10 |
| 692 | A138 40p City Hall | 1.60 | 1.60 |
| 693 | A138 £2 Church of Sacred Heart of Jesus | 8.50 | 8.50 |
| | Nos. 686-693 (8) | 13.00 | 13.00 |

Nos. 686, 688, 691, 693 are vert.

UN, 50th Anniv. A152

**1995, Oct. 24    Litho.    Perf. 13½**
| 694 | A152 34p shown | 2.00 | 2.00 |
| 695 | A152 49p Peace dove | 2.75 | 2.75 |

**Miniature Sheets of 4 + 4 Labels**

Motion Pictures, Cent. — A153

Designs: No. 696: a, Ingrid Bergman. b, Vittorio De Sica. c, Marlene Dietrich. d, Laurence Olivier.
No. 697: a, 38p, Audrey Hepburn. b, 25p, Romy Schneider. c, 28p, Yves Montand. d, 5p, Marilyn Monroe.

**1995, Nov. 13    Litho.    *Perf. 14½x14***
696   A153   24p #a.-d.       4.25   4.25
697   A153       #a.-d.       4.25   4.25

Christmas
A154

Designs: 5p, Santa Claus. 24p, Sack of toys. 34p, Reindeer. 54p, Santa with sleigh, reindeer flying over rooftops.

**1995, Nov. 27           *Perf. 14***
698   A154   5p multicolored     .25   .25
699   A154   24p multicolored   1.75   1.75
700   A154   34p multicolored   2.50   2.50
701   A154   54p multicolored   4.00   4.00
     *Nos. 698-701 (4)*    8.50   8.50

Miniature Sheet

Puppies
A155

#702: a, 5p, Shih tzu. b, 21p, Dalmatian. c, Cocker spaniel. d, 25p, West Highland white terrier. e, 34p, Labrador. f, 35p, Boxer.

**1996, Jan. 24    Litho.       *Perf. 14***
702   A155   Sheet of 6, #a.-f.    7.00   7.00

No. 702 is a continuous design.

Women of the British Royal Family
A156

**1996, Feb. 9    Litho.       *Perf. 13½***
703   A156   24p Princess Anne    1.60   1.60
704   A156   24p Princess Diana   1.60   1.60
705   A156   34p Queen Mother    2.40   2.40
706   A156   34p Queen Elizabeth II   2.40   2.40
     *Nos. 703-706 (4)*    8.00   8.00

Europa.

European Soccer — A157

Team members in action scenes: 21p, West Germany, 1980. 24p, France, 1964. 34p, Holland, 1988. £1.20, Denmark, 1992.

**1996, Apr. 2           *Perf. 13***
707   A157   21p multicolored    .70   .70
708   A157   24p multicolored    .90   .90
709   A157   34p multicolored   1.40   1.40
710   A157   £1.20 multicolored   5.00   5.00
  *a.*    Souvenir sheet, Nos. 707-710   12.00   12.00
     *Nos. 707-710 (4)*    8.00   8.00

Modern Olympic Games, Cent.
A158

**1996, May 2    Litho.      *Perf. 13½***
711   A158   34p Ancient athletes   1.40   1.40
712   A158   49p Athletes, 1896   2.10   2.10
713   A158   £1.05 Athletes, 1990s   4.75   4.75
     *Nos. 711-713 (3)*    8.25   8.25

World War II Type of 1993
Souvenir Sheet

a, 5p, HMS Starling. b, 25p, HMS Royalist. c, 49p, USS Philadelphia. d, 54p, HMCS Prescott.

**1996, June 8    Litho.    *Perf. 13½x14***
714   A137   Sheet of 4, #a.-d.    8.00   8.00

UNICEF, 50th Anniv.
A159

a, 21p, Girl, boy. b, 24p, Three children. c, 49p, Three children, diff. d, 54p, Girl, boy, diff.

**1996, June 8         *Perf. 13½x13***
715   A159   Strip of 4, #a.-d.    6.25   6.25

World Wildlife Fund
A160

Red kite: a, In flight. b, One adult. c, One on rock, one in flight. d, Adults, young in nest.

**1996, July 12        *Perf. 14½***
716   A160   34p Block or strip of 4,    9.00   9.00
           #a.-d.

Christmas Images Formed with "Lego" Blocks — A161

**1996, Nov. 27    Litho.       *Perf. 14***
717   A161   5p Pudding       .20   .20
718   A161   21p Snowman    1.00   1.00
719   A161   24p Present      1.10   1.10
720   A161   34p Santa Claus   1.50   1.50
721   A161   54p Candle       2.50   2.50
     *Nos. 717-721 (5)*    6.30   6.30

Sailing Ship "Mary Celeste" — A162

Europa: No. 722, "Mary Celeste" in rough seas. No. 723, Men on board ship. No. 724, Boat approaching "Mary Celeste." No. 725, In full sail.

**1997, Feb. 12    Litho.       *Perf. 14***
722   A162   28p multicolored   1.10   1.10
723   A162   28p multicolored   1.10   1.10
724   A162   30p multicolored   1.50   1.50
725   A162   30p multicolored   1.50   1.50
     *Nos. 722-725 (4)*    5.20   5.20

Kittens
A163

Designs: a, 5p, Silver tabby American shorthair. b, 24p, "Rumpy" Manx red tabby. c, 26p, Blue point Birmans. d, 28p, Red self longhair. e, 30p, British shorthair, tortoiseshell & white. f, 35p, British bicolor shorthairs.

**1997, Feb. 12**
726   A163   Sheet of 6, #a.-f.    7.75   7.75
  *g.*   Bklt. pane of 3, #726a, 726c,          3.00   3.00
      726e
  *h.*   Bklt. pane of 3, #726b, 726c,          4.25
      726d
  *i.*   Bklt. pane of 4, #726a, 726b,          5.00
      726e, 726f
  *j.*   Bklt. pane of 4, #726c, 726d,          6.00
      726e, 726f
  *k.*   Booklet pane, #726          8.25
      Complete booklet, #726g-726k   26.00

Hong Kong '97. No. 726k is rouletted at left and does not have Hong Kong '97 emblem and inscription in bottom selvage.

Butterflies — A164

Designs: 23p, Anthocharis belia euphenoides. 26p, Charaxes jasius. 30p, Vanessa cardui. £1.20, Iphiclides podalirius.

**1997, Apr. 7    Litho.    *Perf. 14x13½***
728   A164   23p multicolored   1.00   1.00
729   A164   26p multicolored   1.25   1.25
730   A164   30p multicolored   1.50   1.50
731   A164   £1.20 multicolored   5.50   5.50
  *a.*   Souvenir sheet of 4, #728-      9.00   9.00
      731
     *Nos. 728-731 (4)*    9.25   9.25

Warships Type of 1993

a, 24p, HMS Enterprise. b, 26p, HMS Cleopatra. c, 38p, USS Iowa. d, 50p, Polish Warship Orkan.

**1997, June 9    Litho.       *Perf. 13½***
732   A137   Sheet of 4, #a.-d.    6.25   6.25

Queen Elizabeth II and Prince Philip, 50th Wedding Anniv. — A165

Designs: £1.20, Prince Philip driving a four-in-hand, Queen beside him. £1.40, Queen, Prince Philip at Royal Ascot, Queen "Trooping the Color."

**1997, July 10    Litho.    *Perf. 14x13½***
733   A165   £1.20 multicolored   4.75   4.75
734   A165   £1.40 multicolored   5.75   5.75
  *a.*   Pair, #733-734    10.50   10.50

1997 Dior Fashion Designs, by John Galliano — A166

30p, Long black dress, hat. 35p, Mini skirt, lace top. 50p, Formal gown. 62p, Suit, hat. £1.20, Formal gown, diff.

**1997, Sept. 9    Litho.    *Perf. 13½x13***
735   A166   30p multicolored   1.25   1.25
736   A166   35p multicolored   1.50   1.50
737   A166   50p multicolored   2.00   2.00
  *a.*   Pair, #735, 737    3.25   3.25
738   A166   62p multicolored   2.75   2.75
  *a.*   Pair, #736, 738    4.25   4.25
     *Nos. 735-738 (4)*    7.50   7.50

**Souvenir Sheet**
739   A166   £1.20 multicolored   4.50   4.50

Christmas
A167

Stained glass windows: 5p, Our Lady and St. Bernard. 26p, The Epiphany of the Lord. 38p, St. Joseph holding Jesus. 50p, The Holy Family. 62p, The Miraculous Medal Madonna.

**1997, Nov. 18    Litho.      *Perf. 13½***
740   A167   5p multicolored    .20   .20
741   A167   26p multicolored   1.00   1.00
742   A167   38p multicolored   1.75   1.75
743   A167   50p multicolored   2.50   2.50
744   A167   62p multicolored   3.00   3.00
     *Nos. 740-744 (5)*    8.45   8.45

A168

A169

**1997, Dec. 15    Litho.      *Perf. 13***
745   A168   26p multicolored    .90   .90

Sir Joshua Hassan (1915-97), government leader.

**1998, Jan. 23**

Scenes from previous World Cup Championships: 5p, Wales v. Brazil, 1958. 26p, N. Ireland v. France, 1958. 38p, Scotland v. Holland, 1978. £1.20, England v. W. Germany, 1966.

746   A169   5p multicolored    .35   .35
747   A169   26p multicolored   1.20   1.20
748   A169   38p multicolored   1.60   1.60
749   A169   £1.20 multicolored   4.75   4.75
  *a.*   Souvenir sheet, #746-749   8.00   8.00
     *Nos. 746-749 (4)*    7.90   7.90

1998 World Cup Soccer Championships, France.

**Diana, Princess of Wales (1961-97)**
Common Design Type

Various portraits: a, 26p, Wearing black & white outfit. b, 26p, Wearing pink & white outfit. c, 38p, In black dress. d, 38p, In blue & gold jacket.

**1998, Mar. 31    Litho.    *Perf. 14½x14***
754   CD355   Sheet of 4, #a.-d.    5.50   5.50

The 20p surtax from international sales was donated to the Princess Diana Memorial Fund and the surtax from national sales was donated to a designated local charity.

**Royal Air Force, 80th Anniv.**
Common Design Type of 1993 Re-inscribed

Designs: 24p, Saro London. 26p, Fairey Fox. 38p, Handley Page Halifax GR.VI. 50p, Hawker Siddeley Buccaneer S.2B.
No. 759: a, 24p, Sopwith 1½ Strutter. b, 26p, Bristol M.1B. c, 38p, Supermarine Spitfire XII. d, 50p, Avro York.

**1998, Apr. 1**      *Perf. 14*
755 CD350 24p multicolored   1.00   1.00
756 CD350 26p multicolored   1.10   1.10
757 CD350 38p multicolored   1.75   1.75
758 CD350 50p multicolored   2.10   2.10
    Nos. 755-758 (4)   5.95   5.95

**Souvenir Sheet of 4**
759 CD350   #a.-d.   6.25   6.25

Europa — A170

Costumes worn by Miss Gibraltar for National Day: No. 760, Military style. No. 761, Long skirt, long-sleeved top. No. 762, Short skirt, long cape. No. 763, Black lace scarf, ruffled petticoat.

**1998, May 22**   **Litho.**   *Perf. 13*
760 A170 26p multicolored   .95   .95
761 A170 26p multicolored   .95   .95
762 A170 38p multicolored   1.40   1.40
763 A170 38p multicolored   1.40   1.40
    Nos. 760-763 (4)   4.70   4.70

UNESCO 1998 Intl. Year of the Ocean A171

Marine life: a, 5p, Striped dolphin. b, 26p, Killer whale. c, £1.20, Blue whale. d, 5p, Common dolphin, vert.

**1998, May 22**      *Perf. 14*
764 A171 Sheet of 4, #a.-d.   8.00   8.00

Italia '98 and Portugal '98.

Battle of the Nile — A172

**1998, Aug. 1**   **Litho.**   *Perf. 13½*
765 A172 12p Nileus   .60   .60
766 A172 26p Lord Nelson   1.25   1.25
   a.   Booklet pane of 1   1.50
767 A172 28p Frances Nisbet   1.40   1.40
   a.   Bklt. pane, #765-767   3.50
768 A172 35p HMS Vanguard   1.75   1.75

**Size: 45x27mm**
769 A172 50p Battle of the Nile   2.50   2.50
   a.   Bklt. pane, #768-769, 2 #766   7.00
   b.   Bklt. pane, #766, 768-769   5.75
   c.   Bklt. pane, #765-769   8.00
     Complete booklet, #766a, 767a, 769a-769c   26.00
    Nos. 765-769 (5)   7.50   7.50

Quotations From Famous People A173

#770, "Love comforts like sunshine after rain," Shakespeare. #771, "The price of greatness is responsibility," Churchill. #772, "Hate the sin, love the sinner," Gandhi. #773, "Imagination is more important than knowledge," Einstein.

**1998, Oct. 6**   **Litho.**   *Perf. 14½*
770 A173 26p multicolored   1.00   1.00
771 A173 26p multicolored   1.00   1.00
772 A173 38p multicolored   1.75   1.75
773 A173 38p multicolored   1.75   1.75
    Nos. 770-773 (4)   5.50   5.50

Nos. 770-773 were each printed in sheets of 6 with se-tenant labels.

A174        A175

**1998, Nov. 10**   **Litho.**   *Perf. 13*
774 A174 5p Nativity   .45   .45
775 A174 26p Star over manger   1.10   1.10
776 A174 30p Balthasar   1.25   1.25
777 A174 35p Melchoir   1.60   1.60
778 A174 50p Caspar   2.10   2.10
    Nos. 774-778 (5)   6.50   6.50

Christmas.

**1999, Mar. 4**   **Litho.**   *Perf. 13½*
779 A175 1p claret   .20   .20
780 A175 2p brown   .20   .20
781 A175 4p blue   .20   .20
782 A175 5p green   .20   .20
783 A175 10p brown orange   .40   .40
784 A175 12p red   .45   .45
785 A175 20p blue green   .75   .75
786 A175 28p lilac rose   1.00   1.00
787 A175 30p vermilion   1.10   1.10
788 A175 40p gray olive   1.50   1.50
789 A175 42p slate   1.60   1.60

**Size: 22½x28mm**
**Perf. 14½**
790 A175 50p olive bister   1.90   1.90
791 A175 £1 black   4.00   4.00
792 A175 £3 ultramarine   10.00   10.00

**Self-Adhesive**
**Die Cut Perf. 9x9½**
793 A175 1st vermilion   1.00   1.00
    Nos. 779-793 (15)   24.50   24.50

No. 793 was valued at 26p on day of issue.

Nature Reserves — A176

**1999, Mar. 4**      *Perf. 13½x13*
794 A176 30p Barbary macaque   1.75   1.75
795 A176 30p Dartford warbler   1.75   1.75
796 A176 42p Kingfisher   2.25   2.25
797 A176 42p Dusky perch   2.25   2.25
    Nos. 794-797 (4)   8.00   8.00

Europa.

Maritime Heritage — A177

Designs: 5p, Roman Anchorage. 30p, Medieval galley house. 42p, British relief ships. £1.20, HMS Berwick.

**1999, Mar. 19**      *Perf. 12½*
798 A177 5p multicolored   .25   .25
799 A177 30p multicolored   1.50   1.50
800 A177 42p multicolored   2.25   2.25
801 A177 £1.20 multicolored   5.75   5.75
   a.   Souvenir sheet, #798-801   10.00   10.00
    Nos. 798-801 (4)   9.75   9.75

John Lennon (1940-80) A178

Portraits: 20p, With flower over one eye. 30p, Black and white photo. 40p, Wearing glasses.
No. 805, Holding marriage license in front of Rock of Gibraltar. No. 806, Standing in front of airplane.

**1999, Mar. 20**      *Perf. 13*
802 A178 20p multicolored   .90   .90
803 A178 30p multicolored   1.50   1.50
804 A178 40p multicolored   2.10   2.10
    Nos. 802-804 (3)   4.50   4.50

**Souvenir Sheets**
805 A178 £1 multicolored   7.00   7.00
806 A178 £1 multicolored   7.00   7.00

UPU, 125th Anniv. — A179

**1999, June 7**   **Litho.**   *Perf. 12½*
807 A179 5p Postal van   .25   .25
808 A179 30p Space station   1.50   1.50

Fighter Planes and Raptors A180

Designs: No. 809, RAF Eurofighter 2000 Typhoon. No. 810, RAF F3 Tornado. No. 811, RAF GR7 Harrier II. No. 812, Lesser kestrel. No. 813, Peregrine falcon. No. 814, Kestrel.

**1999, June 7**      *Perf. 13x13¼*
809 A180 30p multicolored   1.10   1.10
810 A180 30p multicolored   1.10   1.10
811 A180 30p multicolored   1.10   1.10
   a.   Sheet of 3, #809-811   3.50   3.50
812 A180 42p multicolored   2.00   2.00
   a.   Pair, #809, 812   3.25   3.25
813 A180 42p multicolored   2.00   2.00
   a.   Pair, #810, 813   3.25   3.25
814 A180 42p multicolored   2.00   2.00
   a.   Pair, #811, 814   3.25   3.25
   b.   Sheet of 3, #812-814   6.50   6.50

See Nos. 851-853.

Wedding of Prince Edward and Sophie Rhys-Jones A181

**Perf. 13x13¼, 13¼x13**
**1999, June 19**      **Litho.**
815 A181 30p shown   1.50   1.50
816 A181 42p Couple, vert.   2.25   2.25

Sports in Gibraltar, Cent. — A182

**1999, July 2**      *Perf. 13*
817 A182 30p Soccer   1.25   1.25
818 A182 42p Rowing   1.75   1.75
819 A182 £1.20 Cricket   5.00   5.00
    Nos. 817-819 (3)   8.00   8.00

Wedding of Prince Edward to Sophie Rhys-Jones A183

**Perf. 13x13¼, 13¼x13**
**1999, Oct. 11**      **Litho.**
820 A183 54p shown   2.25   2.25
821 A183 66p Couple standing, vert.   2.75   2.75

Christmas and New Year's Greetings A184

Designs: No. 822, "Happy Christmas," Santa, sleigh. No. 823, "Season's Greetings." No. 824, "Happy Millennium." No. 825, "Happy Christmas," Santa, reindeer. 42p, "Yo ho ho." 54p, Santa, tree, fireplace.

**1999, Nov. 11**   **Litho.**   *Perf. 14*
822 A184 5p multicolored   .20   .20
823 A184 5p multicolored   .20   .20
824 A184 30p multicolored   1.40   1.40
825 A184 30p multicolored   1.40   1.40
826 A184 42p multicolored   2.00   2.00
827 A184 54p multicolored   2.25   2.25
    Nos. 822-827 (6)   7.45   7.45

Stampin' the Future Children's Stamp Design Contest Winners A185

Artwork by: 30p, Colin Grech. 42p, Kim Barea. 54p, Stephan Williamson-Fa. 66p, Michael Podesta.

**2000. Jan. 28**   **Litho.**   *Perf. 14½x14*
828 A185 30p multi   1.25   1.25
829 A185 42p multi   1.75   1.75
830 A185 54p multi   2.25   2.25
831 A185 66p multi   2.75   2.75
   a.   Block or strip of 4, #828-831   8.00   8.00

European Soccer — A186

**2000, Apr. 17**   **Litho.**   *Perf. 12½*
832 A186 30p France   1.00   1.00
833 A186 30p Holland   1.00   1.00
834 A186 42p Denmark   1.40   1.40
835 A186 42p Germany   1.40   1.40
   a.   Souvenir sheet, #832-835   5.00   5.00
836 A186 54p England   1.75   1.75
   a.   Souvenir sheet of 2   7.25   7.25
    Nos. 832-836 (5)   6.55   6.55

The Stamp Show 2000, London (#836a).

Europa — A187

**2000, Apr. 17**      *Perf. 13¼x13*
837 A187 30p Fountain   1.25   1.25
838 A187 40p Hands   1.50   1.50
839 A187 42p Airplane   1.75   1.75
840 A187 54p Rainbow   2.50   2.50
    Nos. 837-840 (4)   7.00   7.00

Millennium — A188

History of Gibraltar: a, 3000-meter waterfall. b, The sandy plains. c, The Neanderthals. d, The Phoenicians. e, The Romans. f, The Arabs. g, Coat of arms, 1502. h, British Gibraltar. i, The great siege. j, Trafalgar. k, The city. l, Fortifications. m, The evacuation. n, The fortress. o, Queen Elizabeth II. p, European finance center.
Illustration reduced.

| **2000, May 9** | | | **Perf. 14** |
|---|---|---|---|
| **841** | A188 | Sheet of 16 | 14.00 14.00 |
| *a.-h.* | | 5p any single | .30 .30 |
| *i.-p.* | | 30p Any single | 1.40 1.40 |
| *q.* | | Souvenir booklet | 30.00 |

No. 841q contains a pane of 2 of each of Nos. 841a-841j and a pane of 3 of each of Nos. 841k-841p.

Prince William, 18th Birthday — A189

Designs: 30p, With Princess Diana. 42p, As child. 54p, With Prince Charles. 66p, In suit.

| **2000, June 21** | | **Litho.** | **Perf. 12½** |
|---|---|---|---|
| **842** | A189 | 30p multi | 1.00 1.00 |
| **843** | A189 | 42p multi | 1.75 1.40 |
| **844** | A189 | 54p multi | 2.00 2.00 |
| **845** | A189 | 66p multi | 2.75 2.75 |
| *a.* | | Souvenir sheet, #842-845 | 9.00 9.00 |
| | | *Nos. 842-845 (4)* | 7.50 7.15 |

Queen Mother, 100th Birthday — A190

Designs: 30p, As young woman. 42p, With King George VI. 54p, With blue hat. 66p, With orange hat.

| **2000, Aug. 4** | | | |
|---|---|---|---|
| **846** | A190 | 30p multi | 1.00 1.00 |
| **847** | A190 | 42p multi | 1.75 1.75 |
| **848** | A190 | 54p multi | 2.25 2.25 |
| **849** | A190 | 66p multi | 3.00 3.00 |
| *a.* | | Souvenir sheet, #846-849 | 8.25 8.25 |
| | | *Nos. 846-849 (4)* | 8.00 8.00 |

Moorish Castle A191

| | | **Photo. & Engr.** | |
|---|---|---|---|
| **2000, Sept. 15** | | | **Perf. 11½x11¾** |
| **850** | A191 | £5 multi | 20.00 20.00 |

**Fighter Planes and Raptors Type**

No. 851: a, RAF "Gibraltar" Supermarine Spitfire. b, Male merlin.
No. 852: a, RAF "City of Lincoln" Avro Lancaster B1-3. b, Bonelli's eagle.
No. 853: a, RAF Hawker Hurricane MK IIC. b, Female merlin.

| **2000, Sept. 15** | **Litho.** | | **Perf. 14½x14** |
|---|---|---|---|
| **851** | | Pair | 4.00 4.00 |
| *a.* | A180 | 30p multi | 1.50 1.50 |
| *b.* | A180 | 42p multi | 2.50 2.50 |
| **852** | | Pair | 4.00 4.00 |
| *a.* | A180 | 30p multi | 1.50 1.50 |
| *b.* | A180 | 42p multi | 2.50 2.50 |
| **853** | | Pair | 4.00 4.00 |
| *a.* | A180 | 30p multi | 1.50 1.50 |
| *b.* | A180 | 42p multi | 2.50 2.50 |
| *c.* | | Souvenir sheet, #851a, 852a, 853a | 5.00 5.00 |
| *d.* | | Souvenir sheet, #851b, 852b, 853b | 7.50 7.50 |
| | | *Nos. 851-853 (3)* | 12.00 12.00 |

Christmas A192

5p, Baby Jesus. No. 855, 30p, Joseph, Mary, donkey. No. 856, 30p, Mary, Jesus. 40p, Joseph, Mary, innkeeper. 42p, Holy Family, donkey. 54p, Holy Family, Magi.

| **2000, Nov. 13** | | | **Perf. 14** |
|---|---|---|---|
| **854-859** | A192 | Set of 6 | 9.00 9.00 |

Queen Victoria (1819-1901) — A193

Designs: 30p, On wedding day. 42p, Portrait. 54p, In carriage. 66p, Jubilee portrait.

| **2001, Jan. 22** | | | **Perf. 12¾** |
|---|---|---|---|
| **860-863** | A193 | Set of 4 | 9.00 9.00 |

New Year 2001 (Year of the Snake) — A194

Snakes: No. 864, 5p, Grass. No. 865, 5p, Ladder. No. 866, 5p, Montpelier. No. 867, 30p, Viperine. No. 868, 30p, Southern smooth. No. 869, 30p, False smooth. 66p, Horseshoe whip.

| **2001, Feb. 1** | **Litho.** | | **Perf. 13¾** |
|---|---|---|---|
| **864-870** | A194 | Set of 7 | 8.50 8.50 |
| *870a* | | Souvenir sheet, #864-870 | 10.00 10.00 |

Size of No. 870: 31x62mm. Hong Kong 2001 Stamp Exhibition (No. 870a).

Europa — A195

Designs: 30p, Long-snouted seahorse. 40p, Snapdragon. 42p, Yellow-legged gull. 54p, Goldfish.

| **2001, Feb. 1** | | | **Perf. 13¼x13** |
|---|---|---|---|
| **871-874** | A195 | Set of 4 | 10.00 10.00 |

Queen Elizabeth II, 75th Birthday A196

Designs: No. 875, 30p, As child. No. 876, 30p, As young woman. No. 877, 42p, In wedding dress. No. 878, 42p, At coronation. 54p, Wearing hat. £2, In blue dress.

| **2001, Apr. 21** | **Litho.** | | **Perf. 14** |
|---|---|---|---|
| **875-879** | A196 | Set of 5 | 9.25 9.25 |

**Souvenir Sheet**

**Perf. 13¾**

| **880** | A196 | £2 multi | 8.50 8.50 |
|---|---|---|---|

No. 880 contains one 35x48mm stamp.

Gibraltar Chronicle, Bicent. — A197

Designs: 30p, Battle of Trafalgar. 42p, Invention of the telephone. 54p, The end of World War II. 66p, First man on the Moon.

| **2001, May 21** | | | **Perf. 14x14½** |
|---|---|---|---|
| **881-884** | A197 | Set of 4 | 9.00 9.00 |

**Queen Type of 1999**

| **2001, June 1** | **Litho.** | **Perf. 14x14¼** |
|---|---|---|
| | **Size: 22x28mm** | |
| **885** | A175 | £1.20 carmine | 6.00 6.00 |
| **886** | A175 | £1.40 blue | 6.50 6.50 |

**Fighter Planes and Raptors Type of 1999**

No. 887: a, 40p, RAF Jaguar GR1B. b, 40p, Hobby.
No. 888: a, 40p, Royal Navy Sea Harrier FA MK 2. b, 40p, Marsh harrier.
No. 889: a, 40p, RAF Hawk T MK 1. b, 40p, Sparrowhawk.

| **2001, Sept. 3** | **Litho.** | | **Perf. 14½x14** |
|---|---|---|---|
| | | **Pairs, #a-b** | |
| **887-889** | A180 | Set of 3 | 10.00 10.00 |
| *889c* | | Souvenir sheet, #887a, 888a, 889a | 5.00 5.00 |
| *889d* | | Souvenir sheet, #887b, 888b, 889b | 5.00 5.00 |

Christmas A198

Snoopy, from Peanuts comic strip: 5p, In Santa Claus suit ringing bell, Woodstock. 30p, Charlie Brown, Christmas tree. 40p, Wreath. 42p, In Santa Claus suit carrying cookies, Woodstock. 54p, On dog house.

| **2001, Nov. 12** | | | **Perf. 14** |
|---|---|---|---|
| **890-894** | A198 | Set of 5 | 7.25 7.25 |
| *894a* | | Souvenir sheet, #890-894 | 7.50 7.50 |

**Souvenir Sheet**

Introduction of Euro Coinage to Europe — A199

Coins in denominations of: a, 5p, 1 cent. b, 12p, 2 cents. c, 30p, 5 cents. d, 35p, 10 cents. e, 40p, 20 cents. f, 42p, 50 cents. g, 54p, 1 euro. h, 66p, 2 euro.

| **2002, Jan. 1** | **Litho.** | | **Perf. 13¼x13** |
|---|---|---|---|
| **895** | A199 | Sheet of 8, #a-h | 12.00 12.00 |

A clear varnish was applied by a thermographic process producing a shiny, raised effect.

**Reign Of Queen Elizabeth II, 50th Anniv. Issue**
Common Design Type

Designs: No. 896, 30p, Princess Elizabeth in field, 1942. No. 897, 30p, Wearing tiara, 1961. No. 898, 30p, With Princess Margaret, microphones. No. 899, 30p, Wearing hat, 1993. 75p, 1955 portrait by Annigoni (38x50mm).

| | **Perf. 14¼x14½, 13¾ (75p)** | | |
|---|---|---|---|
| **2002, Feb. 6** | **Litho.** | | **Wmk. 373** |
| **896-900** | CD360 | Set of 5 | 8.00 8.00 |
| *a.* | | Souvenir sheet, #896-900 | 10.00 10.00 |

Europa — A200

Famous clowns: 30p, Joseph Grimaldi (1778-1831). 40p, Karl Adrien Wettach (1880-1959). 42p, Nicholai Polakovs (1900-74). 54p, Hubert Jean Charles Cairoli (1910-80).

| | **Perf. 13¼x13** | | |
|---|---|---|---|
| **2002, Mar. 4** | **Litho.** | | **Unwmk.** |
| **901-904** | A200 | Set of 4 | 6.25 6.25 |

Bobby Moore, English Soccer Player — A201

Moore in 1966: 30p, Holding up World Cup. 42p, Kissing World Cup. 54p, With Queen Elizabeth II. 66p, In action.

| | **Perf. 13¼x13** | | |
|---|---|---|---|
| **2002, May 1** | **Litho.** | | **Unwmk.** |
| **905-908** | A201 | Set of 4 | 8.50 8.50 |
| *a.* | | Souvenir sheet, #905-908 | 8.50 8.50 |

Wildlife A202

Designs: No. 909, 30p, Red fox. No. 910, 30p, Barbary macaque, vert. 40p, White tooth shrew. £1, Rabbit, vert.

| | **Perf. 14¼x14, 14x14¼** | | |
|---|---|---|---|
| **2002, June 6** | **Litho.** | | **Unwmk.** |
| **909-912** | A202 | Set of 4 | 8.50 8.50 |
| *a.* | | Souvenir sheet, #909-912 | 9.00 9.00 |

Prince Harry, 18th Birthday — A203

Designs: 30p, As child in Princess Diana's arms. 42p, Waving. 54p, Wearing baseball cap. 66p, In suit and tie.

| **2002, Sept. 15** | **Litho.** | | **Perf. 12½** |
|---|---|---|---|
| **913-916** | A203 | Set of 4 | 8.25 8.25 |
| *a.* | | Souvenir sheet, #913-916 | 9.00 9.00 |

Rock of Gibraltar — A204

View of Rock from: a, North. b, South. c, East (46x38mm). d, West (46x38mm).

**2002, Sept. 15   Litho.   Perf. 13¼x13**
| | | | |
|---|---|---|---|
| 917 | Horiz. strip of 4 | 11.00 | 11.00 |
| a.-b. | A204 30p Either single | 1.25 | 1.25 |
| c.-d. | A204 £1 Either single | 3.75 | 3.75 |

Particles of the Rock of Gibraltar were applied to portions of the designs by a thermographic process.

Christmas — A205

Creche scenes from: 5p, Cathedral of St. Mary the Crowned. 30p, St. Joseph's Parish Church. 40p, St. Theresa's Parish Church. 42p, Our Lady of Sorrows Church, Catalan Bay. 52p, St. Bernard's Church. 54p, Cathedral of the Holy Trinity.

**2002, Nov. 13   Perf. 13**
918-923  A205   Set of 6   10.00   10.00

Coronation of Queen Elizabeth II, 50th Anniv. — A206

Designs: No. 924, 30p, Queen receiving crown. No. 925, 30p, Queen on throne. 40p, Queen holding orb. £1, Queen in profile.

**Perf. 12½**
**2003, Feb. 20   Litho.   Unwmk.**
924-927  A206   Set of 4   8.50   8.50
927a     Souvenir sheet, #924-927   9.00   9.00

Europa — A207

Poster art for: 30p, Drama Festival. 40p, Spring Festival. 42p, Art Festival. 54p, Dance Festival.

**2003, Mar. 3   Perf. 14x14½**
928-931  A207   Set of 4   7.00   7.00

Powered Flight, Cent. A208

Designs: 30p, Wright Flyer, 1903. No. 933, 40p, Charles Lindbergh and Spirit of St. Louis, 1927. No. 934, 40p, Boeing 314 Yankee Clipper, 1939. 42p, Saunders Roe SARO-21 Windhover Amphibian, 1931 (77x27mm). 44p, Concorde, 1976 (77x27mm). 66p, Space Shuttle Columbia, 1981, vert. (37x57mm).

**2003, Mar. 31   Litho.   Perf. 13x13¼**
| | | | |
|---|---|---|---|
| 932-937 | A208   Set of 6 | 13.00 | 13.00 |
| 937a | Souvenir sheet, #932-937, perf. 12½ | 14.00 | 14.00 |

Martyrdom of St. George, 1700th Anniv. — A209

Designs: 30p, Cross of St. George. 40p, Constantinian Order of St. George. £1.20, Stained glass window depiction of St. George, vert. (31x63mm).

**2003, Apr. 23   Perf. 13¾**
| | | | |
|---|---|---|---|
| 938-940 | A209   Set of 3 | 8.00 | 8.00 |
| 940a | Souvenir sheet, #938-940 | 8.50 | 8.50 |

Big Ben, Swift and Rock of Gibraltar A210

**Photo. & Engr.**
**2003, June 21   Perf. 11½**
941  A210   (£3) multi   11.50   11.50

Prince William, 21st Birthday — A211

Prince William: No. 942, 30p, As a child, with Princess Diana. No. 943, 30p, With hands in pockets. 40p, Close-up, wearing suit. £1, Wearing sweatshirt.

**2003, June 21   Litho.   Perf. 12½**
| | | | |
|---|---|---|---|
| 942-945 | A211   Set of 4 | 11.50 | 11.50 |
| 945a | Souvenir sheet, #942-945 | 11.50 | 11.50 |

Enlargement of European Union — A212

National flowers of newly-added countries: 30p, Daisy (Latvia), Cornflower (Estonia), Rue (Lithuania). 40p, Rose (Cyprus), Maltese centaury (Malta). 42p, Tulip (Hungary), Carnation (Slovenia), Dog rose (Slovakia). 54p, Corn poppy (Poland), Scented thyme (Czech Republic).

**2003, Sept. 15   Litho.   Perf. 13¾**
946-949  A212   Set of 4   7.75   7.75

Mushrooms A213

Designs: No. 950, 30p, Lepista nuda. No. 951, 30p, Clitocybe odora. No. 952, 30p, Hypholoma fasciculare. £1.20, Agaricus campestris.

**2003, Sept. 15   Perf. 14¼**
| | | | |
|---|---|---|---|
| 950-953 | A213   Set of 4 | 9.50 | 9.50 |
| 953a | Souvenir sheet, #950-953 | 10.00 | 10.00 |

A214

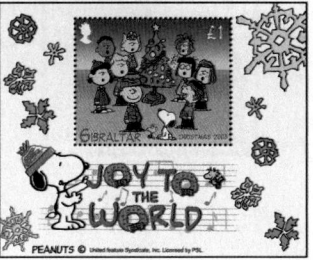

Christmas — A215

Designs: 5p, Baby Jesus crib, Our Lady of Sorrows Church. 30p, Building a traditional creche at home. 40p, Three Kings Cavalcade on January 5. 42p, Children's provisions for Santa and reindeer on Christmas Eve. 54p, Christmas Eve midnight mass at the Cathedral of St. Mary the Crowned.

**2003, Nov. 17   Litho.   Perf. 14**
954-958  A214   Set of 5   7.00   7.00
**Souvenir Sheet**
**Perf. 12¼x12**
959  A215   £1 multi   5.00   5.00

Europa — A216

Designs: No. 960, 40p, Outdoor cafe. No. 961, 40p, St. Michael's Cave. No. 962, 54p, Seaside cafe. No. 963, 54p, Dolphin.

**2004, Feb. 20   Litho.   Perf. 14x14½**
960-963  A216   Set of 4   7.00   7.00

British Gibraltar, 300th Anniv. A217

Designs: 8p, British flag, Gibraltar coat of arms.
No. 965: a, Ship with large flag. b, Ship, rowboat, cannons. c, Soldiers. d, Military uniform. e, Telephone booth, police hat. f, Mail box. g, Neckties, university documents, graduates in caps and gowns. h, Crowd waving flags. i, British flag.

**2004   Litho.   Perf. 13x13¼**
| | | | |
|---|---|---|---|
| 964 | A217 8p multi | .75 | .75 |
| 965 | Sheet of 9 | 17.00 | 17.00 |
| a.-h. | A217 30p Any single | 1.50 | 1.50 |
| i. | A217 £1.20 multi | 4.50 | 4.50 |
| j. | Souvenir sheet, #965i | 4.75 | 4.75 |

Issued: Nos. 964-965i, 4/26. No. 965j, 9/10. Sir Elton John's Tercentenary Concert (No. 965j).
A perforated "black print" sheet of No. 965 exists with cancels.

Visit of Queen Elizabeth II to Gibraltar, 50th Anniv. — A218

Queen: 38p, Holding flowers. 40p, With arm extended. 47p, In limousine. £1, With children and soldiers.
£1.50, Standing in limousine with Prince Philip.

**2004, May 4   Perf. 12½**
966-969  A218   Set of 4   9.25   9.25
**Souvenir Sheet**
970  A218   £1.50 multi   6.75   6.75

European Soccer — A219

Designs: 30p, Goalie defending shot. No. 972, 40p, Players near side of goal. No. 973, 40p, Player making scissor kick. £1, Goalie playing ball near goal post.
£1.50, Player with arms extended, horiz.

**2004, June 6**
| | | | |
|---|---|---|---|
| 971-974 | A219   Set of 4 | 7.75 | 7.75 |
| 974a | Souvenir sheet, #971-974 | 7.75 | 7.75 |
**Souvenir Sheet**
975  A219   £1.50 multi   5.50   5.50

No. 975 contains one 48x37mm stamp.

D-Day, 60th Anniv. A220

Designs: 38p, Soldiers leaving landing craft. 40p, Tank approaching beach. 47p, Airplane. £1, Ships.

**2004, June 6   Perf. 13x13¼**
| | | | |
|---|---|---|---|
| 976-979 | A220   Set of 4 | 9.25 | 9.25 |
| 979a | Souvenir sheet, #976-979 | 9.25 | 9.25 |

Flowers — A221

Designs: 1p, Mallow-leaved bindweed. 2p, Gibraltar sea lavender. 5p, Gibraltar chickweed. G, Romulea. 10p, Common centaury. G1, Pyramidal orchid. S, Friar's cowl. UK, Corn poppy. E, Giant Tangier fennel. U, Snapdragon. 50p, Common gladiolus. £1, Yellow horned poppy. £3, Gibraltar candytuft.

**2004, Sept. 10   Litho.   Perf. 13¼**
| | | | | |
|---|---|---|---|---|
| 980 | A221 | 1p multi | .20 | .20 |
| a. | | Booklet pane of 1 | .20 | — |
| 981 | A221 | 2p multi | .20 | .20 |
| a. | | Booklet pane of 1 | .20 | — |
| 982 | A221 | 5p multi | .20 | .20 |
| a. | | Booklet pane of 1 | .20 | — |
| 983 | A221 | G multi | .25 | .25 |
| a. | | Booklet pane of 1 | .25 | — |
| 984 | A221 | 10p multi | .35 | .35 |
| a. | | Booklet pane of 1 | .35 | — |
| 985 | A221 | G1 multi | .45 | .45 |
| a. | | Booklet pane of 1 | .45 | — |
| 986 | A221 | S multi | 1.00 | 1.00 |
| a. | | Booklet pane of 1 | 1.00 | — |
| 987 | A221 | UK multi | 1.40 | 1.40 |
| a. | | Booklet pane of 1 | 1.40 | — |
| 988 | A221 | E multi | 1.50 | 1.50 |
| a. | | Booklet pane of 1 | 1.50 | — |
| 989 | A221 | U multi | 1.60 | 1.60 |
| a. | | Booklet pane of 1 | 1.60 | — |
| 990 | A221 | 50p multi | 1.75 | 1.75 |
| a. | | Booklet pane of 1 | 1.75 | — |
| 991 | A221 | £1 multi | 3.50 | 3.50 |
| a. | | Booklet pane of 1 | 3.50 | — |
| 992 | A221 | £3 multi | 11.00 | 11.00 |
| a. | | Booklet pane of 1 | 11.00 | — |
| | | Complete booklet, #980a-992a | 23.50 | |
| | | Nos. 980-992 (13) | 23.40 | 23.40 |

Nos. 983, 985, 986, 987, 988 and 989 sold for 7p, 12p, 28p, 38p, 40p and 47p respectively on day of issue.

Ferrari
Race Cars
A222

Designs: No. 993, 5p, F2003GA. No. 994,
5p, F2004. No. 995, 30p, F2001. No. 996,
30p, F2002. No. 997, 75p, F399. No. 998,
75p, F1-2000.

**2004, Nov. 12**                      **Perf. 14¾x14¼**
993-998   A222   Set of 6            8.25  8.25
*998a*         Souvenir sheet, #993-998   8.25  8.25

Christmas
A223

Christmas tree ornaments: 7p, Santa Claus.
28p, Angel. 38p, Red star. 40p, Gold bell. 47p,
Red ball. 53p, White star.

**2004, Nov. 12**                      **Perf. 12½**
999-1004   A223   Set of 6            8.00  8.00

Battle of Trafalgar, Bicent. — A224

Designs: 38p, Soldier guarding wine cask
containing Admiral Horatio Nelson's body.
40p, HMS Entrepenante. 47p, Admiral Nelson,
vert. £1.60, HMS Victory.
£2, HMS Vctory being towed to Gibraltar.

**2005, Jan. 29   Litho.   Perf. 13¼**
1005-1008   A224   Set of 4         11.00 11.00
**Souvenir Sheet**
**Perf. 13¾**
1009   A224   £2 multi               7.50  7.50

No. 1008 has particles of wood from the
HMS Victory embedded in the areas covered
by a thermographic process that produces a
raised, shiny effect. No. 1009 contains one
44x44mm stamp.
See Nos. 1027-1028.

Europa — A225

Designs: No. 1010, 47p, Sherry trifle. No.
1011, 47p, Spinach pie. No. 1012, 47p, Veal
birds. No. 1013, 47p, Grilled sea bass.

**Perf. 14¼x14¾**
**2005, Mar. 31**                          **Litho.**
1010-1013   A225   Set of 4           7.25  7.25

V-E Day, 60th
Anniv. — A226

Designs: 38p, Winston Churchill. 40p,
Woman, children, British flags. 47p, Servicewomen in car waving flags. £1, People at
dock.

**2005, May 8**
1014-1017   A226   Set of 4           8.25  8.25
*1017a*         Souvenir sheet, #1014-
                1017                  8.25  8.25

Anniversaries — A227

Designs: 38p, Royal Gibraltar Police, 175th
anniv. 47p, Gibraltar Museum, 75th anniv. £1,
Grant of Charter of Justice, 175th anniv.

**2005, June 17**              **Perf. 14¾x14¼**
1018-1020   A227   Set of 3           6.75  6.75

Cruise
Ships
A228

Designs: 38p, Circassia. 40p, Nevassa. 47p,
Black Prince. £1, Arcadia.

**2005, June 17**               **Perf. 13x13¼**
1021-1024   A228   Set of 4           8.00  8.00
*1024a*         Souvenir sheet, #1021-1024   8.00  8.00

Pope John Paul II
(1920-2005)
A229

**2005, July 15**               **Perf. 14¼x14¾**
1025   A229   75p multi               2.75  2.75
Printed in sheets of 6.

Europa Stamps, 50th Anniv. (in
2006) — A230

**Litho. With Foil Application**
**2005, Sept. 30**                  **Perf. 14¼**
1026   A230   £5 multi                17.50 17.50

**Battle of Trafalgar Type of 2005**
**Souvenir Sheets**
Designs: Nos. 1027, 1028a, Admiral Nelson
mortally wounded.

**2005, Oct. 21   Litho.   Perf. 13¼**
1027   A224   £1 multi                3.50  3.50
1028         Sheet, #1028a, Isle of
             Man #1127a                7.25  7.25
   *a.*  A224 £1 multi, 47x30mm        3.50  3.50
No. 1028 has a Gibraltar Post emblem in
sheet margin. See Isle of Man No. 1127.

Christmas
A231

Various angels: 7p, 28p, 40p, 47p, 53p.

**2005, Oct. 21**               **Perf. 13¼x13**
1029-1033   A231   Set of 5           6.25  6.25
*1033a*         Souvenir sheet, #1029-1033   6.25  6.25

**Flowers Type of 2004**
Designs: 3p, Gibraltar restharrow. 15p,
Paper-white narcissus. 53p, Gibraltar cam-
pion. £1.60, Sea daffodil.

**2006, Jan. 31   Litho.   Perf. 13¼**
1033B   A221   3p multi          .20   .20
1034    A221   15p multi         .55   .55
1035    A221   53p multi        1.90  1.90
1036    A221   £1.60 multi       5.75  5.75
        *Nos. 1033B-1036 (4)*     8.40  8.40

Worldwide
Fund for
Nature
(WWF)
A232

Various depictions of Giant devil ray.

**2006, Feb. 20**               **Perf. 13x13¼**
1037   Strip of 4                     8.00  8.00
   *a.*  A232 38p multi               1.25  1.25
   *b.*  A232 40p multi               1.50  1.50
   *c.*  A232 47p multi               1.75  1.75
   *d.*  A232 £1 multi                3.50  3.50

Queen
Elizabeth
II, 80th
Birthday
A233

Various photographs.

**2006, Mar. 31**               **Perf. 14¾x14**
1038   Block of 4                     8.00  8.00
   *a.*  A233 38p multi               1.25  1.25
   *b.*  A233 40p multi               1.50  1.50
   *c.*  A233 47p multi               1.75  1.75
   *d.*  A233 £1 multi                3.50  3.50
   *e.*  Souvenir sheet, #1038b, 1038c  3.25  3.25
   *f.*  Souvenir sheet, #1038a, 1038d  4.75  4.75

**Miniature Sheet**

2006 World Cup Soccer
Championships, Germany — A234

No. 1039 — Children with faces painted as
flags of World Cup champions: a, Uruguay. b,
Italy. c, Germany. d, Brazil. e, England. f,
Argentina. g, France.

**2006, May 4**                       **Perf. 15**
1039   A234   Sheet of 7             10.00 10.00
   *a.-g.*   38p Any single           1.40  1.40

Europa
A235

Children: No. 1040, 47p, Holding books and
notebook paper. No. 1041, 47p, Playing musical instruments. No. 1042, 47p, Building birdhouse. No. 1043, 47p, Playing soccer.

**2006, June 30**               **Perf. 13x13¼**
1040-1043   A235   Set of 4           7.00  7.00

Gibraltar
Packet
Agency,
Bicent:
A236

Ships: 8p, Cornwallis. 40p, Meteor. 42p,
Carteret. 68p, Prince Regent.

**Perf. 14¾x14¼**
**2006, Sept. 15**                      **Litho.**
1044-1047   A236   Set of 4           6.00  6.00

Airmail
Service,
75th
Anniv.
A237

Airplanes: 8p, Saro A21 Windhover. 40p,
Vickers Vanguard. 49p, Vickers Viscount.
£1.60, Boeing 737.

**2006, Sept. 15**
1048-1051   A237   Set of 4           9.75  9.75

Cruise
Ships
A238

Designs: 40p, Coral. 42p, Legend of the
Seas. 66p, Saga Ruby. 78p, Costa Concordia.

**2006, Sept. 15**                      **Perf. 13**
1052-1055   A238   Set of 4           8.50  8.50
*1055a*         Souvenir sheet, #1052-1055  8.50  8.50

Christopher Columbus (1451-1506),
Explorer — A239

Designs: 40p, Navigational equipment. 42p,
Columbus on ship. 66p, Santa Maria. 78p,
Columbus and Indian.
£1.60, Nina, Pinta and Santa Maria

**2006, Nov. 1   Litho.   Perf. 13x13¼**
1056-1059   A239   Set of 4           8.75  8.75
**Souvenir Sheet**
**Perf. 13¼**
1060   A239   £1.60 multi             6.25  6.25
No. 1060 contains one 48x48mm stamp.

Christmas
A240

Various depictions of Santa Claus with
panel colors of: 8p, Red brown. 40p, Prussian
blue. 42p, Olive bister. 49p, Green. 55p, Gray
blue.

**2006, Nov. 1**        **Perf. 13¼x13**
1061-1065 A240    Set of 5    7.50 7.50
1065a    Souvenir sheet, #1061-1065,
      perf. 13¼x12½      7.50 7.50

Miniature Sheet

Treaty of Rome, 50th Anniv. — A241

No. 1066 — European Union flag and flag
of: a, Belgium. b, Germany. c, France. d, Italy.
e, Luxembourg. f, Netherlands.

**Perf. 14½x14¼**
**2007, Feb. 28**        **Litho.**
1066 A241 40p Sheet of 6, #a-f   9.50 9.50

Wedding of Queen
Elizabeth II and
Prince Philip, 60th
Anniv. — A242

Designs: 40p, Royal engagement, 1947.
42p, Royal wedding, 1947. 66p, Silver anniversary, 1972. 78p, Ruby anniversary, 1987.
£1.60, Wedding party.

**2007, Feb. 28**        **Perf. 13½**
1067-1070 A242   Set of 4    8.75 8.75
**Souvenir Sheet**
**Perf. 13½x13**
1071 A242 £1.60 multi      6.25 6.25

No. 1071 contains one 85x85mm diamond-
shaped stamp.

Princess
Diana (1961-
97)
A243

Various photographs: 8p, 40p, 42p, £1.60.

**2007, Mar. 31**        **Perf. 13½**
1072-1075 A243   Set of 4   10.00 10.00
1075a    Souvenir sheet, #1072-
      1075          10.00 10.00

**Cruise Ships Type of 2006**
Designs: 40p, Oriana. 42p, Oceana. 66p,
Queen Elizabeth 2.78p, Queen Mary 2.

**2007, May 15**    **Litho.**    **Perf. 14¾x14**
1076-1079 A258   Set of 4    9.00 9.00
1079a    Souvenir sheet, #1076-1079   9.00 9.00

Europa — A244

Designs: 8p, Scout from 1908. 40p, Scout
from 1950s, 42p, Sea Scout from 1980s. £1,
Scout from 2007.

**2007, June 30**    **Litho.**    **Perf. 13**
1080-1083 A244   Set of 4    7.75 7.75

Gibraltar Postal Anniversaries — A245

Designs: 8p, Last-day-of-validity postcard
from Fez, Morocco (cessation of Gibraltar's
responsibility for the British postal service in
Morocco in 1907). 40p, Stampless cover with
last Gibraltar datestamp of the Packet Agency
(creation of Gibraltar Post Office in 1857). 42p,
Cover franked with stamps of Great Britain
(sale of British stamps in Gibraltar in 1857).
£1, Cover to London from Morocco via Gibraltar (placement of British postal service in
Morocco under control of Gibraltar in 1857).

**2007, Sept. 26**        **Perf. 14¾x14**
1084-1087 A245   Set of 4    7.75 7.75

Stork Carrying Baby, Baby Bottle,
Pacifier, Rubber Duck — A246

Diamond Ring and Heart — A247

Sheep, Lion, Dog at Party — A248

Lamb, Dolphins, Rock of
Gibraltar — A249

Shell, Crab and Heart — A250

Illustrations reduced.

**2007, Sept. 26**        **Perf. 12½x13**
1088 A246 G multi + label    .35   .35
1089 A247 G multi + label    .35   .35
1090 A248 G multi + label    .35   .35
1091 A249 G multi + label    .35   .35
1092 A250 G multi + label    .35   .35
1093 A246 E multi + label   1.75 1.75
1094 A247 E multi + label   1.75 1.75
1095 A248 E multi + label   1.75 1.75
1096 A249 E multi + label   1.75 1.75
1097 A250 E multi + label   1.75 1.75
   Nos. 1088-1097 (10)    10.50 10.50

On day of issue Nos. 1088-1092 each sold
for 8p, and Nos. 1093-1097 each sold for 42p.
Labels shown with each stamp are the generic
labels for that stamp type. Labels could be
personalized for an additional fee.

Prehistoric
Wildlife of
Gibraltar
A251

Designs: 8p, Bears and dolphins. 40p,
Eagle owl. 42p, Great auk and eagle. 55p,
Red deer and bear. 78p, Wolf and vulture eating horse.
£2, Ibex.

**2007, Sept. 26**        **Perf. 13**
1098-1102 A251   Set of 5   9.25 9.25
1098a    Booklet pane of 1    .35   —
1099a    Booklet pane of 1   1.60   —
1100a    Booklet pane of 1   1.75   —
1101a    Booklet pane of 1   2.25   —
1102a    Booklet pane of 1   3.00   —
   Complete booklet, #1098a-
     1103a, 1103b     18.00
**Souvenir Sheet**
1103 A251 £2 multi     8.25 8.25
  a.    Booklet pane of 1    8.25  —
  b.    Booklet pane of 6, #1098-
     1102

No. 1103a has text in margin not found on
the margin of No. 1103.

Views of Gibraltar — A252

Trinity Lighthouse — A253

Various views: 40p, 42p, 55p, 78p.

**2007, Nov. 2**    **Litho.**    **Perf. 13¼**
1104-1107 A252   Set of 4   9.00 9.00
**Souvenir Sheet**
**Perf. 13¼x13**
1108 A253 £1.70 multi    7.25 7.25

Christmas
A254

Porcelain Nativity figurines: No. 1109, 8p,
Joseph. No. 1110, 8p, Baby Jesus. 40p, Mary.
42p, King Melchior. 49p, King Balthasar. 55p,
King Gaspar.

**2007, Nov. 2**        **Perf. 13¼x13**
1109-1114 A254   Set of 6   8.50 8.50
1109a    Perf. 12½x13, + label    .35   .35
1111a    Perf. 12½x13, + label   1.75 1.75
1114a    Miniature sheet, #1109-1114   8.50 8.50

Nos. 1109a and 1111a were available with
generic labels. Labels could be personalized
for an additional fee.

Birds — A255

Designs: 1p, Woodchat shrike. 2p, Balearic
shearwater. 5p, Eagle owl. G, European bee-
eater. 10p, Razorbill. S, Egyptian vulture. UK,
Blue rock thrush. E, Hoopoe. U, Bonelli's
eagle. 50p, Greater flamingo. 55p, Mediterranean shag. £1, Honey buzzard. £5, Lesser
kestrel.

**2008, Feb. 15**    **Litho.**    **Perf. 13x12½**
1115 A255 1p multi     .20   .20
1116 A255 2p multi     .20   .20
1117 A255 5p multi     .20   .20
1118 A255 G multi     .35   .35
1119 A255 10p multi    .40   .40
1120 A255 S multi    1.25 1.25
1121 A255 UK multi   1.60 1.60
1122 A255 E multi    1.75 1.75
1123 A255 U multi    1.90 1.90
1124 A255 50p multi   2.00 2.00
1125 A255 55p multi   2.25 2.25
**Size: 32x45mm**
**Perf. 13x13¼**
1126 A255 £1 multi    4.00 4.00
1127 A255 £5 multi   20.00 20.00
   Nos. 1115-1127 (13)   36.10 36.10

On day of issue Nos. 1118, 1120, 1121,
1122 and 1123 sold for 8p, 30p, 40p, 42p and
49p, respectively.

Admiral Horatio
Nelson (1758-
1805)
A256

Designs: No. 1128, 40p, HMS Agamemnon.
No. 1129, 40p, HMS La Minerve. No. 1130,
42p, HMS Captain. No. 1131, 42p, HMS Vanguard. No. 1132, 49p, HMS Amphion. No.
1133, 49p, HMS Victory.
£2, Nelson's Birthplace, Burnham Thorpe,
England, horiz.

**Perf. 14¼x14¾**
**2008, Mar. 15**        **Litho.**
1128-1133 A256   Set of 6   10.50 10.50
**Souvenir Sheet**
**Perf. 14¾x14¼**
1134 A256 £2 multi    8.00 8.00

Royal Air Force,
90th
Anniv. — A257

Rock of Gibraltar and airplanes: No. 1135,
40p, Short 184, Saro London. No. 1136, 40p,
Spitfire IV, Hurricane IIc. No. 1137, 42p,
Beaufighter II, Lancaster TS III. No. 1138, 42p,
Hunter Mk. 6, Shackleton MR2. No. 1139,
49p, Vulcan, Mosquito. No. 1140, 49p, Tornado GR4, Jaguar GR3.
£2, Felixstowe F3.

**2008, Mar. 15**　　*Perf. 14¼x14¾*
1135-1140　A257　Set of 6　　10.50 10.50
**Souvenir Sheet**
1141　A257　£2 multi　　8.00　8.00

Europa — A258

Famous letter writers: 10p, Sir Winston Churchill. 42p, Admiral Horatio Nelson. 44p, Pres. John F. Kennedy. £1, Mohandas K. Gandhi.

**2008, June 1**　*Litho.*　*Perf. 14x14¾*
1142-1145　A258　Set of 4　　7.75 7.75

New Seven
Wonders of the
World — A259

Designs: No. 1146, 8p, Roman Colosseum. No. 1147, 8p, Christ the Redeemer Statue, Rio de Janeiro. No. 1148, 38p, Great Wall of China. No. 1149, 38p, Petra, Jordan. No. 1150, 40p, Chichen Itza Pyramid, Mexico. No. 1151, 40p, Machu Picchu, Peru. 66p, Taj Mahal, India.

**2008, June 1**
1146-1152　A259　Set of 7　　9.50 9.50

**Cruise Ships Type of 2006**
Designs: 40p, Century. 42p, Grand Princess. 66p, Queen Victoria. 78p, Costa Mediterranea.

**2008, Sept. 15**　*Litho.*　*Perf. 13x13¼*
1153-1156　A238　Set of 4　　8.00 8.00
1156a　　Souvenir sheet, #1153-
　　　　　1156　　　　　8.00 8.00
Miniature Sheet

National Aeronautics and Space
Administration, 50th Anniv. — A260

No. 1157: a, Liftoff of Apollo 11. b, Earthrise from Moon. c, Lunar Module leaving Moon. d, US flag on Moon.

**2008, Sept. 15**　　　*Perf. 13¼*
1157　A260　Sheet of 4　　9.75 9.75
　a.　10p multi　　　　.35　.35
　b.　17p multi　　　　.60　.60
　c.　42p multi　　　1.50 1.50
　d.　£2 multi　　　　7.25 7.25

Royal Gibraltar
Regiment — A261

Designs: No. 1158, 10p, Gibraltar Volunteer Corps in World War I. No. 1159, 10p, Gibraltar Defense Force in World War II. No. 1160, 10p, National Service recruits at Buena Vista Barracks. No. 1161, 42p, Soldiers and large guns, Thomson's Battery of Gibraltar Regiment, 1958-91. No. 1162, 42p, Soldier from Infantry Company of Gibraltar Regiment, 1958-99. No. 1163, 44p, Soldier from Air Defense Troop of Gibraltar Regiment, 1958-91. No. 1164, 44p, Royal Gibraltar Regiment soldier guarding the rock. No. 1165, 51p, Royal Gibraltar Regiment soldier training African Peacekeepers. No. 1166, 51p, Royal Gibraltar Regiment soldier serving in operations in Iraq. £2, Royal Gibraltar Regiment soldier serving in operations in Afghanistan.

**2008, Nov. 11**　*Litho.*　*Perf. 15x14*
1158-1167　A261　Set of 10　　15.00 15.00

Christmas
A262

Songs: 10p, When Santa Got Stuck in a Chimney. 42p, Rudolph, the Red-nosed Reindeer. 44p, Oh, Christmas Tree. 51p, Away in a Manger. 59p, Jingle Bells.

**2008, Nov. 11**　　　*Perf. 12½*
1168-1172　A262　Set of 5　　6.25 6.25

---

### POSTAGE DUE STAMPS

**Catalogue values for unused stamps in this section are for Never Hinged items.**

D1　　　　　　D2

**Perf. 14**
**1956, Dec. 1**　　*Wmk. 4*　　*Typo.*
**Chalky Paper**
J1　D1　1p green　　　1.75　2.00
J2　D1　2p brown　　　2.60　3.25
J3　D1　4p ultramarine　　3.25　3.75
　　　Nos. J1-J3 (3)　　7.60　9.00

**"p" instead of "d"**
**Perf. 17½x18**
**1971, Feb. 15**　*Typo.*　*Wmk. 314*
**Chalky Paper**
J4　D1　½p green　　　.50　.60
J5　D1　1p dark brown　　.50　.55
J6　D1　2p dark blue　　.60　.60
　　　Nos. J4-J6 (3)　　1.60 1.75

**Perf. 14x13½**
**1976, Oct. 13**　*Litho.*　*Wmk. 373*
J7　D2　1p orange　　　.20　.20
J8　D2　3p bright ultra　　.20　.20
J9　D2　5p vermilion　　.20　.20
J10　D2　7p bright red lilac　.25　.35
J11　D2　10p gray　　　.45　.50
J12　D2　20p green　　　.80　.90
　　　Nos. J7-J12 (6)　　2.10 2.35

D3　　　　　　D4

**1984, July 2**　　　*Perf. 14½x14*
J13　D3　1p black　　　.20　.20
J14　D3　3p red　　　.20　.20
J15　D3　5p blue　　　.20　.20
J16　D3　5p sky blue　　.40　.40
J17　D3　25p lilac　　　1.25 1.25
J18　D3　50p orange　　2.25 2.25
J19　D3　£1 green　　　4.50 4.50
　　　Nos. J13-J19 (7)　9.00 9.00

**1996, Sept. 30**　*Litho.*　*Perf. 14½x14*
Landmarks: 1p, Water Port Gates. 10p, HM Dockyard. 25p, Military Hospital. 50p, Governor's Cottage. £1, Laguna. £2, Catalan Bay.
J20　D4　1p multicolored　　.20　.20
J21　D4　10p multicolored　.35　.35
J22　D4　25p multicolored　.80　.80
J23　D4　50p multicolored　1.60 1.60
J24　D4　£1 multicolored　3.25 3.25
J25　D4　£2 multicolored　7.00 7.00
　　　Nos. J20-J25 (6)　13.20 13.20

Finches — D5

Designs: 5p, Greenfinch. 10p, Serin. 20p, Siskin. 50p, Linnet. £1, Chaffinch. £2, Goldfinch.

**Perf. 13x13¼**
**2002, June 6**　*Litho.*　*Unwmk.*
J26-J31　D5　Set of 6　　12.50 12.50

---

### WAR TAX STAMP

No. 66 Overprinted

**1918, Apr.**　　*Wmk. 3*　　*Perf. 14*
MR1　A14　½p green　　1.75　2.40
　a.　Double overprint　　900.00

---

## GILBERT AND ELLICE ISLANDS

ˈgil-bərt əndˌ 'e-ləs 'ī-lənds

LOCATION — Groups of islands in the Pacific Ocean northeast of Australia
GOVT. — British Crown Colony
AREA — 375 sq. mi.
POP. — 57,816 (est. 1973)
CAPITAL — Tarawa

The Gilbert group of which Butaritari, Tarawa and Tamana are the more important, is on the Equator. Ellice Islands, Phoenix Islands, Line Islands (Fanning, Washington and Christmas), and Ocean Island are included in the Colony. The islands were annexed by Great Britain in 1892 and formed into the Gilbert and Ellice Islands Colony in 1915 on request of the native governments.

The colony divided into the Gilbert Islands and Tuvalu, Jan. 1, 1976.

12 Pence = 1 Shilling
20 Shillings = 1 Pound
100 Cents = 1 Dollar (1966)

**Catalogue values for unused stamps in this country are for Never Hinged items, beginning with Scott 52.**

Stamps and Type of Fiji Overprinted
in Black or Red

**1911, Jan. 1**　　*Wmk. 3*　　*Perf. 14*
**Ordinary Paper**
1　A22　½p green　　　10.00　60.00
2　A22　1p carmine　　45.00　37.50
　a.　Pair, one without overprint
3　A22　2p gray　　　10.00　20.00
4　A22　2½p ultramarine　20.00　37.50
**Chalky Paper**
5　A22　5p violet & ol grn　45.00　90.00
6　A22　6p violet　　　27.50　55.00
7　A22　1sh black, green　25.00　75.00
　　　Nos. 1-7 (7)　　182.50 370.00

Pandanus — A2

**1911, Mar.**　　　　*Engr.*
**Ordinary Paper**
8　A2　½p green　　　6.00　17.50
9　A2　1p carmine　　2.25　9.00
10　A2　2p gray　　　1.75　9.00
11　A2　2½p ultramarine　6.00　16.00
　　　Nos. 8-11 (4)　　16.00　51.50

King George V — A3

For description of Dies I and II, see back of this section of the Catalogue.

**Die I**
**1912-24**　　　　　*Typo.*
14　A3　½p deep green　.90　5.00
15　A3　1p carmine　　2.75　12.00
　a.　1p scarlet　　　4.75　30.00
16　A3　2p gray ('16)　17.50　12.00
17　A3　2½p ultra ('16)　2.00　10.00
**Chalky Paper**
18　A3　3p vio, yel ('19)　2.75　8.50
19　A3　4p blk & red,
　　　　yel　　　　.90　7.00
20　A3　5p vio & ol grn　2.00　6.25
21　A3　6p vio & red vio　1.50　6.75
22　A3　1sh black, green　1.50　5.25
23　A3　2sh vio & ultra,
　　　　bl　　　　16.50　27.50
24　A3　2sh6p blk & red, bl　18.00　22.50
25　A3　5sh grn & red,
　　　　yel　　　37.50　60.00
**Die II**
26　A3　£1 vio & blk,
　　　　red ('24)　700.00　1,600.
　　　Nos. 14-25 (12)　103.80 182.75

**Die II**
**1921-27**　*Ordinary Paper*　*Wmk. 4*
27　A3　½p green　　　2.50　3.00
28　A3　1p deep vio ('27)　5.50　4.50
29　A3　1½p scarlet ('24)　5.50　2.50
30　A3　2p gray　　　8.00　35.00
**Chalky Paper**
31　A3　10sh green & red,
　　　　emer ('24)　190.00 375.00
　　　Nos. 27-31 (5)　211.50 420.00

---

Common Design Types
pictured following the introduction.

**Silver Jubilee Issue**
Common Design Type
**1935, May 6**　*Engr.*　*Perf. 11x12*
33　CD301　1p black & ultra　2.25　10.00
34　CD301　1½p car & blue　1.75　3.75
35　CD301　3p ultra & brn　5.00　14.00
36　CD301　1sh brn vio & indi-
　　　　　go　　　30.00　27.50
　　　Nos. 33-36 (4)　39.00　55.25
　　　Set, never hinged　65.00

**Coronation Issue**
Common Design Type
**1937, May 12**　　*Perf. 13½x14*
37　CD302　1p dark purple　.20　.20
38　CD302　1½p carmine　.25　.25
39　CD302　3p bright ultra　.45　.45
　　　Nos. 37-39 (3)　　.90　.90
　　　Set, never hinged　1.25

Great Frigate Bird — A4

Pandanus — A5

Designs: 1½p, Canoe crossing reef. 2p, Canoe and boat house. 2½p, Islander's house. 3p, Seascape. 5p, Ellice Islands canoe. 6p, Coconut trees. 1sh, Phosphate loading jetty, Ocean Island. 2sh, Cutter "Nimanoa." 2sh6p, Gilbert Islands canoe. 5sh, Coat of arms of colony.

**Perf. 11½x11 (Nos. 40, 43, 50), 12½ (Type A5), 13½ (Nos. 42, 44, 45, 48)**

| | | | 1939, Jan. 14 Engr. Wmk. 4 | | |
|---|---|---|---|---|---|
| 40 | A4 | ½p dk grn & sl bl | .50 | .80 |
| 41 | A5 | 1p dk vio & brt bl green | .25 | 1.40 |
| 42 | A4 | 1½p car & black | .25 | 1.00 |
| 43 | A4 | 2p black & brn | .50 | .95 |
| 44 | A4 | 2½p dp olive & blk | .40 | .65 |
| 45 | A4 | 3p ultra & black | .40 | .95 |
| a. | | Perf. 12 ('55) | .50 | 2.10 |
| 46 | A5 | 5p dk brn & dp ultra | 4.50 | 2.25 |
| 47 | A5 | 6p dl vio & olive | .55 | .55 |
| 48 | A4 | 1sh gray bl & blk | 8.00 | 2.75 |
| b. | | Perf. 12 ('51) | 2.75 | 15.00 |
| 49 | A5 | 2sh red org & ultra | 9.50 | 10.00 |
| 50 | A4 | 2sh6p brt bl grn & bl | 10.00 | 17.50 |
| 51 | A5 | 5sh dp blue & red | 12.50 | 20.00 |
| | | Nos. 40-51 (12) | 47.35 | 58.80 |
| | | Set, never hinged | 80.00 | |

**Catalogue values for unused stamps in this section, from this point to the end of the section, are for Never Hinged items.**

### Peace Issue
Common Design Type

| | | | 1946, Dec. 16 Perf. 13½x14 | | |
|---|---|---|---|---|
| 52 | CD303 | 1p deep magenta | .20 | .20 |
| 53 | CD303 | 3p deep blue | .25 | .25 |

### Silver Wedding Issue
Common Design Types

1949, Aug. 29 Photo. Perf. 14x14½
| 54 | CD304 | 1p violet | .20 | .20 |
|---|---|---|---|---|

Engraved; Name Typographed
Perf. 11½x11
| 55 | CD305 | £1 red | 22.50 | 25.00 |
|---|---|---|---|---|

### UPU Issue
Common Design Types

Engr.; Name Typo. on 2p, 3p
1949, Oct. 1 Perf. 13½, 11x11½
| 56 | CD306 | 1p rose violet | .75 | 1.10 |
|---|---|---|---|---|
| 57 | CD307 | 2p gray black | 2.75 | 2.25 |
| 58 | CD308 | 3p indigo | 1.00 | 2.40 |
| 59 | CD309 | 1sh blue | 1.00 | 2.00 |
| | | Nos. 56-59 (4) | 5.50 | 7.75 |

### Coronation Issue
Common Design Type

1953, June 2 Engr. Perf. 13½x13
| 60 | CD312 | 2p gray & black | .80 | 2.25 |
|---|---|---|---|---|

Types of 1939-42 with Portrait of Queen Elizabeth II, and

Canoe Crossing Reef — A6

**Perf. 11½x11 (Nos. 61, 63, 70), 12½ (Type A5), 12 (Nos. 64-65, 68, 72)**

1956, Aug. 1
| 61 | A4 | ½p brt ultra & blk | .55 | 1.00 |
|---|---|---|---|---|
| 62 | A5 | 1p violet & olive | .50 | .75 |
| 63 | A4 | 2p dull pur & brt green | .80 | 2.00 |
| 64 | A4 | 2½p green & black | .40 | .50 |
| 65 | A4 | 3p dk car & black | .45 | .45 |
| 66 | A5 | 5p red orange & brt ultra | 8.00 | 1.75 |

---

| 67 | A5 | 6p dk gray & red brown | 1.10 | 2.00 |
|---|---|---|---|---|
| 68 | A4 | 1sh ol green & blk | 2.25 | .55 |
| 69 | A5 | 2sh dk brown & brt ultra | 8.00 | 5.00 |
| 70 | A4 | 2sh6p dp ultra & rose red | 12.00 | 6.00 |
| 71 | A5 | 5sh green & blue | 17.50 | 12.50 |
| 72 | A6 | 10sh turq blue & blk | 35.00 | 27.50 |
| | | Nos. 61-72 (12) | 86.55 | 60.00 |

See Nos. 84-85.

Loading Phosphate on Freighter A7

2½p, Original lump of phosphate. 1sh, Loading phosphate on truck, Ocean Island.

**Wmk. 314**
1960, May 1 Photo. Perf. 12
| 73 | A7 | 2p rose lilac & green | .90 | 1.10 |
|---|---|---|---|---|
| 74 | A7 | 2½p olive & black | .90 | 1.10 |
| 75 | A7 | 1sh grnsh blue & blk | .90 | 1.10 |
| | | Nos. 73-75 (3) | 2.70 | 3.30 |

60th anniversary of the discovery of phosphate deposits at Ocean Island.

### Freedom from Hunger Issue
Common Design Type

1963, June 4 Perf. 14x14½
| 76 | CD314 | 10p ultramarine | 2.25 | .55 |
|---|---|---|---|---|

### Red Cross Centenary Issue
Common Design Type

1963, Sept. 2 Litho. Perf. 13
| 77 | CD315 | 2p black & red | 1.00 | .45 |
|---|---|---|---|---|
| 78 | CD315 | 10p ultra & red | 2.00 | 3.00 |

Plane and Fiji-Ellice-Gilbert Route — A8

Designs: 1sh, Eastern reef heron in flight, horiz. 3sh7p, Plane and Tarawa sailboat.

1964, July 20 Perf. 11½x11, 11x11½
| 79 | A8 | 3p lt blue, bl & blk | .75 | .35 |
|---|---|---|---|---|
| 80 | A8 | 1sh dk blue, bl & blk | .95 | .35 |
| 81 | A8 | 3sh7p lt green, grn & blk | 1.50 | 1.40 |
| | | Nos. 79-81 (3) | 3.20 | 2.10 |

Inauguration of air service between Fiji and Gilbert and Ellice Islands.

Queen Types of 1956
**Perf. 11½x11, 12½**
1964-65 Engr. Wmk. 314
| 84 | A4 | 2p dull pur & brt green | 1.10 | 1.75 |
|---|---|---|---|---|
| 85 | A5 | 6p dk gray & red brown | 2.25 | 2.75 |

Issue dates: 2p, Oct. 30. 6p, Apr. 1965.

### ITU Issue
Common Design Type

1965, June 4 Litho. Perf. 11x11½
| 87 | CD317 | 3p dp org & turq blue | .20 | .20 |
|---|---|---|---|---|
| 88 | CD317 | 2sh6p grnsh bl & red lilac | 1.40 | 1.40 |

Village Elder Blowing Conch and Meeting House (Maneaba) — A9

Designs: 1p, Ellice Islanders torch fishing. 2p, Gilbertese girl weaving frangipani garland. 3p, Gilbertese woman dancing The Ruoia. 4p, Gilbertese man dancing. 5p, Gilbertese

---

woman drawing water. 6p, Ellice kosu dance. 7p, Fatele taua dance, Ellice men. 1sh, Gilbertese woman harvesting taro roots (babai). 1sh6p, Ellice man and woman dancing fatele toka. 2sh, Ellice Islanders pounding taro roots. 3sh7p, Gilbertese sitting dance, ruoia, horiz. 5sh, Gilbertese boys playing stick game, horiz. 10sh, Ellice men beating box-drum, horiz. £1, Coat of arms, horiz.

**Perf. 12x11, 11x12**
1965, Aug. 16 Litho. Wmk. 314
| 89 | A9 | ½p blue grn & multi | .20 | .20 |
|---|---|---|---|---|
| 90 | A9 | 1p vio bl & multi | .20 | .20 |
| 91 | A9 | 2p lt olive & multi | .20 | .20 |
| 92 | A9 | 3p red & multi | .20 | .20 |
| 93 | A9 | 4p purple & multi | .20 | .20 |
| 94 | A9 | 5p car rose & multi | .25 | .20 |
| 95 | A9 | 6p multicolored | .25 | .20 |
| 96 | A9 | 7p brown & multi | .40 | .20 |
| 97 | A9 | 1sh bl vio & multi | .70 | .20 |
| 98 | A9 | 1sh6p yel & multi | 1.40 | .65 |
| 99 | A9 | 2sh multicolored | 1.40 | 1.25 |
| 100 | A9 | 3sh7p ultra & multi | 2.50 | .70 |
| 101 | A9 | 5sh multicolored | 2.50 | .90 |
| 102 | A9 | 10sh green & multi | 3.25 | 1.40 |
| 103 | A9 | £1 blue & multi | 4.00 | 2.75 |
| | | Nos. 89-103 (15) | 17.65 | 9.45 |

See #135-149. For surcharges see #110-124.

### Intl. Cooperation Year Issue
Common Design Type

1965, Oct. 25 Litho. Perf. 14½
| 104 | CD318 | ½p blue grn & cl | .20 | .20 |
|---|---|---|---|---|
| 105 | CD318 | 3sh7p lt violet & grn | .90 | .35 |

### Churchill Memorial Issue
Common Design Type

1966, Jan. 24 Photo. Perf. 14
Design in Black, Gold and Carmine Rose
| 106 | CD319 | ½p brt blue | .20 | .20 |
|---|---|---|---|---|
| 107 | CD319 | 3p green | .35 | .20 |
| 108 | CD319 | 3sh brown | .65 | .45 |
| 109 | CD319 | 3sh7p violet | .75 | .45 |
| | | Nos. 106-109 (4) | 1.95 | 1.30 |

Nos. 89-103 Surcharged with New Value and Three Bars
**Perf. 12x11, 11x12**
1966, Feb. 14 Litho.
| 110 | A9 | 1c on 1p multi | .20 | .20 |
|---|---|---|---|---|
| 111 | A9 | 2c on 2p multi | .20 | .20 |
| 112 | A9 | 3c on 3p multi | .20 | .20 |
| 113 | A9 | 4c on ½p multi | .20 | .20 |
| 114 | A9 | 5c on 5p multi | .20 | .20 |
| 115 | A9 | 6c on 4p multi | .20 | .20 |
| 116 | A9 | 8c on 5p multi | .20 | .20 |
| 117 | A9 | 10c on 1sh multi | .20 | .20 |
| 118 | A9 | 15c on 7p multi | .90 | .70 |
| 119 | A9 | 20c on 1sh6p multi | .75 | .45 |
| 120 | A9 | 25c on 2sh multi | .75 | .40 |
| 121 | A9 | 35c on 3sh7p multi | 1.75 | .35 |
| 122 | A9 | 50c on 5sh multi | 1.00 | .60 |
| 123 | A9 | $1 on 10sh multi | 1.00 | .70 |
| 124 | A9 | $2 on £1 multi | 2.25 | 3.00 |
| | | Nos. 110-124 (15) | 10.00 | 7.80 |

### World Cup Soccer Issue
Common Design Type

1966, July 1 Litho. Perf. 14
| 125 | CD321 | 3c multicolored | .20 | .20 |
|---|---|---|---|---|
| 126 | CD321 | 35c multicolored | .65 | .35 |

### WHO Headquarters Issue
Common Design Type

1966, Sept. 20 Litho. Perf. 14
| 127 | CD322 | 3c multicolored | .20 | .20 |
|---|---|---|---|---|
| 128 | CD322 | 12c multicolored | .55 | .45 |

### UNESCO Anniversary Issue
Common Design Type

1966, Dec. 1 Litho. Perf. 14
| 129 | CD323 | 5c "Education" | .65 | .90 |
|---|---|---|---|---|
| 130 | CD323 | 10c "Science" | 1.00 | .20 |
| 131 | CD323 | 20c "Culture" | 1.60 | 1.10 |
| | | Nos. 129-131 (3) | 3.25 | 2.20 |

H.M.S. Royalist, 1892, and Union Jack A10

10c, Cutter & canoe at trading post. 35c, Family.

---

**Perf. 14½x14**
1967, Sept. 1 Photo. Wmk. 314
| 132 | A10 | 3c green, blue & red | .25 | .35 |
|---|---|---|---|---|
| 133 | A10 | 10c multicolored | .20 | .20 |
| 134 | A10 | 35c multicolored | .50 | .45 |
| | | Nos. 132-134 (3) | .95 | 1.00 |

75th anniv. as a British Protectorate.

Type of 1965
**Perf. 12x11, 11x12**
1968, Jan. 1 Litho. Wmk. 314
| 135 | A9 | 1c like 1p | .20 | .20 |
|---|---|---|---|---|
| 136 | A9 | 2c like 2p | .20 | .20 |
| 137 | A9 | 3c like 3p | .20 | .20 |
| 138 | A9 | 4c like ½p | .20 | .20 |
| 139 | A9 | 5c like 6p | .20 | .20 |
| 140 | A9 | 6c like 4p | .20 | .20 |
| 141 | A9 | 8c like 5p | .20 | .20 |
| 142 | A9 | 10c like 1sh | .20 | .20 |
| 143 | A9 | 15c like 7p | .70 | .20 |
| 144 | A9 | 20c like 1sh6p | 1.00 | .20 |
| 145 | A9 | 25c like 2sh | 1.90 | .30 |
| 146 | A9 | 35c like 3sh7p | 2.40 | .30 |
| 147 | A9 | 50c like 5sh | 2.40 | 2.50 |
| 148 | A9 | $1 like 10sh | 2.40 | 3.50 |
| 149 | A9 | $2 like £1 | 6.00 | 3.75 |
| | | Nos. 135-149 (15) | 18.40 | 12.35 |

Map of Tarawa Atoll — A11

Designs: 10c, US Marines wading ashore at Betio. 15c, Battle scene on Betio. 35c, Raising US and British flags on Betio.

1968, Nov. 21 Photo. Perf. 14
| 150 | A11 | 3c multicolored | .20 | .20 |
|---|---|---|---|---|
| 151 | A11 | 10c multicolored | .20 | .20 |
| 152 | A11 | 15c multicolored | .35 | .35 |
| 153 | A11 | 35c multicolored | .55 | .55 |
| | | Nos. 150-153 (4) | 1.30 | 1.30 |

Battle of Tarawa against Japan, 25th anniv.

School Boy and Map of Abemama Atoll A12

Designs: 10c, Secondary school boy and girl on map of Tarawa, with rest of Gilbert and Ellice Islands. 35c, Student in cap and gown on main Fiji island (Viti Levu) and map of South Pacific Islands.

1969, June 2 Litho. Perf. 12½
| 154 | A12 | 3c dull org & multi | .20 | .20 |
|---|---|---|---|---|
| 155 | A12 | 10c black & multi | .20 | .20 |
| 156 | A12 | 35c dull grn & multi | .45 | .45 |
| | | Nos. 154-156 (3) | .85 | .85 |

1st anniv. of the University of the South Pacific in Fiji, and to show the progress of education in the area it serves.

Polynesian Madonna A13

1969, Oct. 20 Perf. 11½
| 157 | A13 | 2c multicolored | .20 | .20 |
|---|---|---|---|---|
| 158 | A13 | 10c multicolored | .45 | .25 |

Christmas.

**Canceled to Order**

The Philatelic Bureau of Gilbert and Ellice Islands began in 1970 to sell canceled sets of new issues. Values in the second ("used") column are for these canceled-to-order stamps.

Mouth-to-Mouth Resuscitation — A14

**1970, Mar. 9    Litho.    Perf. 14½**
159 A14 10c multi            .20  .20
160 A14 15c multi, diff.     .40  .35
161 A14 35c multi, diff.     .80  .80
    Nos. 159-161 (3)        1.40 1.35

Centenary of the British Red Cross.

Mother and Child Care A15

Designs: 10c, Woman physician and laboratory equipment. 15c, Chest X-ray and technician. 35c, Map of Gilbert and Ellice Islands and UN emblem.

**Perf. 12½x13**
**1970, June 26    Litho.    Wmk. 314**
162 A15 5c lilac & multi      .20  .20
163 A15 10c black, gray & red .20  .20
164 A15 15c yellow & multi    .40  .40
165 A15 35c blue grn, bl & blk .55  .55
    Nos. 162-165 (4)        1.35 1.35

25th anniv. of the United Nations.

Map of Onotoa, Beru, Tamana and Arorae Islands A16

Designs: 10c, Sailing ship "John Williams III," vert. 25c, Rev. Samuel James Whitmee, vert. 35c, Map of Islands and steamship "John Williams VII."

**Perf. 14x14½, 14½x14**
**1970, Sept. 1    Litho.    Wmk. 314**
166 A16 2c blue & multi       .20  .20
167 A16 10c brt green & black .35  .35
168 A16 25c lt ultra & red brn .55  .55
169 A16 35c ver, blk & lt gray .80  .80
    Nos. 166-169 (4)        1.90 1.90

Centenary of the landing in the Southern Gilbert Islands by the first missionaries of the London Missionary Society.

Island Child with Halo on Pandanus Mat — A17

Christmas: 10c, Sanctuary of New Tarawa Cathedral. 35c, Three Gilbertese sailing canoes within Star of Bethlehem.

**1970, Oct. 3    Perf. 14½**
170 A17 2c ocher & multi      .20  .20
171 A17 10c ocher & multi     .20  .20
172 A17 35c pink & multi      .45  .45
    Nos. 170-172 (3)          .85  .85

Harvesting Copra — A18

Lagoon Fishing A19

3c, Women cleaning pandanus leaves. 4c, Fishermen casting nets. 5c, Gilbertese canoes. 6c, Dehusking coconuts. 8c, Woman weaving pandanus fronds. 10c, Basket weaving. 15c, Tiger shark. 20c, Beating rolled pandanus leaf. 25c, Loading copra. 35c, Night fishing. 50c, Local handicraft. $1, Woman weaving coconut screen. $2, Coat of arms.

**Wmk. 314 Upright (A18), Sideways (A19)**
**1971, May 31    Litho.    Perf. 14**
173 A18 1c multicolored       .20  .20
174 A19 2c multicolored       .20  .20
175 A19 3c multicolored       .20  .20
176 A19 4c multicolored       .35  .20
177 A19 5c multicolored       .70  .25
178 A18 6c multicolored       .45  .35
179 A18 8c multicolored       .55  .35
180 A18 10c multicolored      .60  .45
181 A18 15c multicolored     4.00  .90
182 A19 20c multicolored     2.40 1.75
183 A19 25c multicolored     3.00 1.40
184 A19 35c multicolored     3.50 1.00
185 A18 50c multicolored     1.90 2.40
186 A18 $1 multicolored      2.75 4.75
187 A18 $2 multicolored      7.75 9.25
    Nos. 173-187 (15)       28.55 23.65

**Wmk. 314 Upright (A19), Sideways (A18)**
**1972-73**
174a A19 2c multicolored     12.00 16.50
177a A19 5c multicolored      4.75 7.75
178a A18 6c multicolored     12.00 17.50
181a A18 15c multicolored     5.00 8.00
182a A19 20c multicolored     5.25 8.50
    Nos. 174a-182a (5)       39.00 58.25

Issue dates: Sept. 7, 1972, June 13, 1973.

Legislative Council, 1971 (former House of Representatives) — A20

New Constitution: 10c, Meeting House.

**1971, Aug. 1    Wmk. 314    Perf. 14**
188 A20 3c orange & multi     .20  .20
189 A20 10c green & multi     .40  .40

Nativity Scene — A21

Christmas: 10c, Star of Bethlehem and palm fronds. 35c, Fishermen in outrigger canoe looking at Star.

**1971, Oct. 1**
190 A21 3c vio blue, blk & yel .20  .55
191 A21 10c grnsh bl, blk & gold .35 .35
192 A21 35c car rose, blk & rose .55 .55
    Nos. 190-192 (3)         1.10 1.45

Children and UNICEF Emblem A22

25th Anniv. of UNICEF: 10c, Seated child. 35c, Child's head.

**1971, Dec. 11**
193 A22 3c brt pink & multi   .20  .45
194 A22 10c black & multi     .20  .20
195 A22 35c blue & multi      .65  .80
    Nos. 193-195 (3)         1.05 1.45

Commission Flag, Map of South Pacific — A23

South Pacific Commission, 25th Anniv.: 10c, Island boats. 35c, Flags of 8 member nations plus Tonga, a non-member.

**1972, Feb. 21    Perf. 13½x14**
196 A23 3c gray & multi       .20  .55
197 A23 10c tan, ultra & brown .35  .25
198 A23 35c ultra & multi     .35  .80
    Nos. 196-198 (3)          .90 1.60

Corals A24

**1972, May 26    Perf. 14x14½**
199 A24 3c Alveopora          .20  .35
200 A24 10c Euphyllia         .50  .20
201 A24 15c Melithea          .65  .35
202 A24 35c Spongodes        1.90 1.10
    Nos. 199-202 (4)         3.25 2.00

"Peace" on Star of Bethlehem A25

Christmas: 10c, Holy Family, made of shells. 35c, Christ child sleeping in giant clam and covered with dawn cowrie, horiz.

**1972, Sept. 15    Perf. 13½**
203 A25 3c gold & multi       .20  .20
204 A25 10c gold & multi      .20  .20
205 A25 35c gold & multi      .50  .50
    Nos. 203-205 (3)          .90  .90

**Silver Wedding Issue, 1972**
Common Design Type

Design: Queen Elizabeth II, Prince Philip and kaue floral headdress.

**1972, Nov. 20    Photo.    Perf. 14x14½**
206 CD324 3c olive & multi    .20  .20
207 CD324 35c rose brown & multi .40 .25

Funafuti, Land of Bananas A26

Designs: 10c, Butaritari, the smell of the sea. 25c, Tarawa, the center of the world. 35c, Abemama, the land of the moon.

**1973, Mar. 5    Litho.    Perf. 14½x14**
208 A26 3c yellow & multi     .20  .45
209 A26 10c brt green & multi .35  .35
210 A26 25c dull blue & multi .50  .65
211 A26 35c orange & multi    .55  .75
    Nos. 208-211 (4)         1.60 2.20

Legends of island names.

Ellice Dancer — A27

Christmas (Within Outline of Nautilus Shell): 10c, Outrigger canoe in lagoon. 35c, Evening on the lagoon. 50c, Map of Christmas Island, Pacific Ocean.

**1973, Sept. 24    Perf. 14**
212 A27 3c vio blue & multi   .20  .20
213 A27 10c multicolored      .20  .20
214 A27 35c multicolored      .45  .20
215 A27 50c vio blue & multi  .55 1.00
    Nos. 212-215 (4)         1.40 1.60

**Princess Anne's Wedding Issue**
Common Design Type

**1973, Nov. 14    Perf. 14**
216 CD325 3c brt green & multi .20  .20
217 CD325 35c slate & multi   .45  .35

Meteorological Observation — A28

WMO Emblem and: 10c, Island observation station. 35c, Wind finding radar. 50c, Map of Gilbert and Ellice Islands world weather watch stations.

**1973, Nov. 26    Litho.    Perf. 14½**
218 A28 3c orange & multi     .95  .55
219 A28 10c dp bister & multi 1.00 .40
220 A28 35c gray & multi     1.40  .55
221 A28 50c dk blue & multi  2.25 2.25
    Nos. 218-221 (4)         5.60 3.75

Cent. of intl. meteorological cooperation.

Te-Mataaua Crest and Canoe — A29

Designs: Various family crests and canoes.

**1974, Mar. 4    Litho.    Perf. 13½**
222 A29 3c tan & multi        .20  .20
223 A29 10c lt blue & multi   .20  .20
224 A29 35c yellow & multi    .35  .20
225 A29 50c pink & multi      .35  .65
a.  Souvenir sheet of 4, #222-225 8.50 9.50
    Nos. 222-225 (4)         1.10 1.25

UPU Emblem, "Te Koroba" and No. 26 — A30

UPU cent.: 10c, Sailing ship "Kiakia" and No. 51. 25c, BAC 111 jet and No. 187. 35c, UPU emblem.

**1974, June 10**     **Perf. 14**
226 A30 4c blue green & multi .20 .20
227 A30 10c orange & multi .20 .20
228 A30 25c dp blue & multi .40 .35
229 A30 35c red orange & black .55 .45
    Nos. 226-229 (4) 1.35 1.20

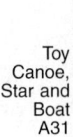

Toy Canoe, Star and Boat A31

Star of Bethlehem and: 10c, Pinwheel and boat. 25c, Coconut ball (crate) and boat. 35c, Three boats (Wise Men) and stars.

**1974, Sept. 23**
230 A31 4c yel green & multi .20 .25
231 A31 10c red brown & multi .20 .20
232 A31 25c multicolored .25 .45
233 A31 35c red brown & multi .40 .50
    Nos. 230-233 (4) 1.05 1.40

Christmas.

Blenheim Palace, Entrance — A32    Churchill Painting — A33

Design: 35c, Churchill Statue, London.

**1974, Nov. 30**    **Litho.**    **Perf. 14**
234 A32 4c multicolored .20 .20
235 A33 10c ultra & black .20 .20
236 A33 35c blue, ocher & blk .35 .35
    Nos. 234-236 (3) .75 .75

Sir Winston Churchill (1874-1965).

Carpilius Maculatus — A34

Crabs: 10c, Ranina ranina. 25c, Portunus pelagicus. 35c, Ocypode ceratophthalma.

**1975, Jan. 27**    **Litho.**    **Perf. 14**
237 A34 4c violet & multi .25 .25
238 A34 10c green & multi .60 .60
239 A34 25c buff & multi 1.50 1.50
240 A34 35c lt blue & multi 2.00 2.00
    Nos. 237-240 (4) 4.35 4.35

Living Cowries and Empty Shells — A35

**1975, May 26**    **Wmk. 314**    **Perf. 14**
241 A35 4c Cypraea argus .60 .60
242 A35 10c Cypraea cribraria .85 .85
243 A35 25c Cypraea talpa 2.00 2.00
244 A35 35c Cypraea mappa 3.00 3.00
    a. Souvenir sheet of 4, #241-244 22.50 22.50
    Nos. 241-244 (4) 6.45 6.45

Map of Beru (The Bud) A36

Designs: 10c, Map of Onotoa (Six Giants). 25c, Map of Abaiang (Land to the North). 35c, Map of Marakei (Floating fish trap).

**Wmk. 314**
**1975, Aug. 1**    **Litho.**    **Perf. 14**
245 A36 4c brt green & multi .20 .20
246 A36 10c brown & multi .20 .20
247 A36 25c vio blue & multi .45 .45
248 A36 35c org red & multi .65 .65
    Nos. 245-248 (4) 1.50 1.50

Legends of island names.

Christ Child Within Coconut — A37

Christmas: 10c, Sadd Memorial Chapel (Protestant), Tarawa. 25c, R.C. Church, Ocean Island. 35c, Fishermen in outrigger canoes seeing star.

**1975, Sept. 22**     **Perf. 14**
249 A37 4c brown & multi .20 .40
250 A37 10c brt blue & multi .20 .20
251 A37 25c violet & multi .45 .55
252 A37 35c green & multi .55 .80
    Nos. 249-252 (4) 1.40 1.95

## POSTAGE DUE STAMPS

D1

**1940, Aug.**   **Typo.**   **Wmk. 4**   **Perf. 12**
J1 D1 1p emerald 5.50 20.00
J2 D1 2p dark red 6.00 22.00
J3 D1 3p chocolate 8.25 24.00
J4 D1 4p deep blue 10.00 25.00
J5 D1 5p deep green 13.00 25.00
J6 D1 6p brt red vio 13.00 40.00
J7 D1 1sh dull violet 22.50 70.00
J8 D1 1sh6p turq green 32.50 100.00
    Nos. J1-J8 (8) 110.75 326.00
    Set, never hinged 165.00

## WAR TAX STAMP

No. 15a Overprinted

**1918**    **Wmk. 3**    **Perf. 14**
MR1 A3 1p scarlet .70 6.50

## GILBERT ISLANDS

ˈgil-bərt ˈī-ləndz

LOCATION — A group of islands in the Pacific Ocean northeast of Australia.
GOVT. — British Crown Colony
AREA — 270 sq. mi.
POP. — 52,000 (1973)
CAPITAL — Tarawa

The Gilbert Islands Colony consists of the Gilbert Islands, Phoenix, Ocean and Line Islands. They were part of the Gilbert and Ellice Islands colony until 1976. See Tuvalu.

**Catalogue values for all unused stamps in this country are for Never Hinged items.**

Stamps and Types of Gilbert and Ellice Islands 1971 Overprinted in Red, Black or Gold

**Wmk. 373; 314 (2c, 4c)**
**1976, Jan. 2**    **Litho.**    **Perf. 14**
253 A18 1c multi (R) .20 .75
   a. Watermark 314 .25 .30
254 A19 2c multi (R) .40 .25
   a. Watermark upright .50 2.25
255 A19 3c multi (R) .35 1.50
   a. Watermark 314 19.00 15.00
256 A19 4c multi (R) .30 1.00
257 A19 5c multi (R) .40 1.00
258 A18 6c multi (B) .40 1.00
259 A18 8c multi (B) .40 1.00
260 A18 10c multi (B) .50 1.00
261 A18 15c multi (R) 2.25 1.25
262 A19 20c multi (R) 1.60 1.75
   a. Watermark 314 sideways 2.25 1.90
   b. Watermark 314 upright 77.50 77.50
263 A19 25c multi (B) 1.90 1.40
   a. Watermark 314 47.50 47.50
264 A19 35c multi (G) 2.00 1.75
   a. Watermark 314 950.00 1,000.
265 A18 50c multi (B) 3.50 2.25
   a. Watermark 314 950.00 1,000.
266 A18 $1 multi (B) 17.00 9.00
    Nos. 253-266 (14) 31.20 24.90

Location of overprint varies.

Maps of Tarawa and Funafuti A38

4c, Charts of Gilbert and Tuvalu Islands.

**1976, Jan. 2**    **Wmk. 373**
267 A38 4c multicolored .20 .55
268 A38 35c multicolored 1.40 1.60

Separation of the Gilbert and Ellice Islands.

M.V. Teraaka A39

3c, M.V. Tautunu. 4c, Moorish idol. 5c, Hibiscus. 6c, Reef egret. 7c, Roman Catholic Cathedral, Tarawa. 8c, Frangipani. 10c, Maneaba meeting house. 12c, Betio Harbor. 15c, Sunset. 20c, Marakei Atoll. 35c, Chapel, Tangintebu. 40c, Flamboyant tree. 50c, Hypolimnas bolina elliciana (butterfly). $1, Landing craft, Tabakea. $2, Gilbert Islands flag.

**1976, July 1**    **Litho.**    **Perf. 14**
269 A39 1c multicolored .45 .60
270 A39 3c multicolored .65 .70
271 A39 4c multicolored .35 .60
272 A39 5c multicolored .40 .25
273 A39 6c multicolored 1.75 .90
274 A39 7c multicolored .20 .25
275 A39 8c multicolored .20 .25
276 A39 10c multicolored .20 .25
277 A39 12c multicolored .50 .45
278 A39 15c multicolored .55 .45
279 A39 20c multicolored .50 .35
280 A39 35c multicolored .50 .35
281 A39 40c multicolored .55 .50
282 A39 50c multicolored 2.25 1.75
283 A39 $1 multicolored 1.50 3.00
284 A39 $2 multicolored 1.75 3.00
    Nos. 269-284 (16) 12.30 13.65

Church A40

Children's Drawings: 15c, Feasting (vegetables, fish, pig, chicken), vert. 20c, Communal meeting house, vert. 35c, Children watching dancer.

**1976, Sept. 15**    **Litho.**    **Perf. 14**
285 A40 5c blue & multi .50 .20
286 A40 15c green & multi .70 .20
287 A40 20c rose & multi .70 .70
288 A40 35c salmon & multi .70 .70
    Nos. 285-288 (4) 2.60 1.80

Christmas.

Porcupine Fish Helmet — A41

Artifacts: 15c, Shark's teeth dagger. 20c, Fighting gauntlet. 35c, Coconut body armor.

**1976, Dec. 6**    **Litho.**    **Perf. 13½x13**
289 A41 5c multicolored .25 .20
290 A41 15c multicolored .55 .35
291 A41 20c multicolored .55 .45
292 A41 35c multicolored .80 .90
    a. Souvenir sheet of 4, #289-292 11.00 11.00
    Nos. 289-292 (4) 2.15 1.90

Prince Charles, 1970 Visit — A42

**1977, Feb. 7**     **Perf. 14**

Designs: 20c, Prince Philip, 1959 visit. 40c, Queen in coronation robes.

293 A42 8c multicolored .25 .20
294 A42 20c multicolored .50 .20
295 A42 40c multicolored .60 .40
    Nos. 293-295 (3) 1.35 .80

Reign of Queen Elizabeth II, 25th anniv.

John Byron and Dolphin, 1765 A43

Explorers: 15c, Edmund Fanning, 1798, and "Betsey." 20c, Fabian Gottlieb von Bellingshausen, 1820, and "Vostok." 35c, Charles Wilkes, 1838-42, and "Vincennes."

**1977, June 1**    **Wmk. 373**    **Perf. 14**
296 A43 5c multicolored 1.25 1.40
297 A43 15c multicolored 1.50 2.75
298 A43 20c multicolored 1.50 2.75
299 A43 35c multicolored 1.75 4.25
    Nos. 296-299 (4) 6.00 11.15

Resolution and Discovery off Christmas Island — A44

15c, Capt. Cook's logbook entry, 1777. 20c, Capt. Cook on board ship. 40c, Capt. Cook landing on Christmas Island.

| | | 1977, Sept. 12 | Litho. | Perf. 14 | |
|---|---|---|---|---|---|
| 300 | A44 | 8c multi | | .60 | .20 |
| 301 | A44 | 15c multi, horiz. | | .60 | .20 |
| 302 | A44 | 20c multi | | .80 | .45 |
| 303 | A44 | 40c multi, horiz. | | .80 | .45 |
| a. | | Souvenir sheet of 4, #300-303 | | 13.50 | 13.50 |
| | | Nos. 300-303 (4) | | 2.80 | 1.65 |

Christmas; bicentenary of Capt. Cook's discovery of Christmas Island.

Scout Emblem, Beach Scene — A45

. 15c, Patrol meeting. 20c, Scout weaving mat. 40c, Canoeing.

| | | 1977, Dec. 5 | Litho. | Perf. 13 | |
|---|---|---|---|---|---|
| 304 | A45 | 8c gold & multi | | .20 | .20 |
| 305 | A45 | 15c gold & multi, horiz. | | .25 | .25 |
| 306 | A45 | 20c gold & multi, horiz. | | .50 | .45 |
| 307 | A45 | 40c gold & multi | | 1.10 | .90 |
| | | Nos. 304-307 (4) | | 2.05 | 1.80 |

50th anniversary of Gilbert Islands Scouting.

Taurus with Aldebaran — A46

| | | 1978, Feb. 20 | Litho. | Perf. 14 | |
|---|---|---|---|---|---|
| | | | | | |

Night Sky over Gilbert Islands: 20c, Canis Major with Sirius. 25c, Scorpio with Antares. 45c, Orion with Betelgeuse and Rigel.

| | | | | | |
|---|---|---|---|---|---|
| 308 | A46 | 10c blue & black | | .20 | .20 |
| 309 | A46 | 20c dp rose & black | | .55 | .25 |
| 310 | A46 | 25c olive grn & black | | .55 | .55 |
| 311 | A46 | 45c orange & black | | 1.00 | 1.00 |
| | | Nos. 308-311 (4) | | 2.30 | 2.00 |

Common Design Types pictured following the introduction.

**Elizabeth II Coronation Anniversary**
Common Design Types
Souvenir Sheet

| | 1978, Apr. 21 | | Unwmk. | |
|---|---|---|---|---|
| 312 | | Sheet of 6 | 1.50 | 1.50 |
| a. | CD326 45c Unicorn of Scotland | | .25 | .25 |
| b. | CD327 45c Elizabeth II | | .25 | .25 |
| c. | CD328 45c Great frigate bird | | .25 | .25 |

Arrows, Tarawa and Abemama Islands, School Insignia — A47

 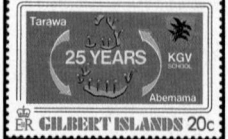

10c, Birds inscribed Bikenibeu, Abemama, Bairiki (school locations). 25c, Children greeting each other from maps of Islands. 45c, Abemama & Tarawa school buildings.

---

*Perf. 14x13½*

| 1978, June 5 | | | Wmk. 373 | |
|---|---|---|---|---|
| 313 | A47 | 10c multicolored | .20 | .20 |
| 314 | A47 | 20c multicolored | .25 | .25 |
| 315 | A47 | 25c multicolored | .25 | .25 |
| 316 | A47 | 45c multicolored | .45 | .45 |
| | | Nos. 313-316 (4) | 1.15 | 1.15 |

King George V School, 25th anniversary of return from Abemama to Tarawa.

Garland A48

Christmas: Various garlands.

| 1978, Sept. 4 | | Litho. | Perf. 14 | |
|---|---|---|---|---|
| 317 | A48 | 10c multicolored | .25 | .20 |
| 318 | A48 | 20c multicolored | .25 | .20 |
| 319 | A48 | 25c multicolored | .25 | .20 |
| 320 | A48 | 45c multicolored | .50 | .35 |
| a. | | Souvenir sheet of 4, #317-320, perf. 13x13½ | 3.25 | 3.50 |
| | | Nos. 317-320 (4) | 1.25 | .95 |

Endeavour A49

Designs: 20c, Green turtle. 25c, Quadrant. 45c, Capt. Cook after Flaxman/Wedgwood medallion.

| 1979, Jan. 15 | | Litho. | Perf. 11 | |
|---|---|---|---|---|
| 321 | A49 | 10c multicolored | .30 | .35 |
| 322 | A49 | 20c multicolored | .55 | .40 |
| 323 | A49 | 25c multicolored | .55 | .55 |

| | | **Litho.; Embossed** | | |
|---|---|---|---|---|
| 324 | A49 | 45c multicolored | .55 | .80 |
| | | Nos. 321-324 (4) | 1.95 | 2.10 |

Capt. Cook's voyages.
Gilbert Islands stamps were replaced in 1979 by those of Kiribati.

---

# GOLD COAST

'gōld 'kōst

LOCATION — West Africa between Dahomey and Ivory Coast
GOVT. — Former British Crown Colony
AREA — 91,843 sq. mi.
POP. — 3,089,000 (1952)
CAPITAL — Accra

Attached to the colony were Ashanti and Northern Territories (protectorate). Togoland, under British mandate, was also included for administrative purposes.
Gold Coast became the independent state of Ghana in 1957.
See Ghana.

12 Pence = 1 Shilling
20 Shillings = 1 Pound

Catalogue values for unused stamps in this country are for Never Hinged items, beginning with Scott 128.

---

Queen Victoria
A1      A3

*Perf. 12½*

| 1875, July | | Typo. | Wmk. 1 | |
|---|---|---|---|---|
| 1 | A1 | 1p blue | 550.00 | 95.00 |
| 2 | A1 | 4p red violet | 525.00 | 140.00 |
| 3 | A1 | 6p orange | 825.00 | 75.00 |
| | | Nos. 1-3 (3) | 1,900. | 310.00 |

| 1876-79 | | | Perf. 14 | |
|---|---|---|---|---|
| 4 | A1 | ½p bister ('79) | 90.00 | 32.50 |
| 5 | A1 | 1p blue | 30.00 | 8.00 |
| a. | | Half used as ½p on cover | | 3,900. |
| 6 | A1 | 2p green ('79) | 105.00 | 11.50 |
| a. | | Half used as 1p on cover | | 3,250. |
| b. | | Quarter used as ½p on cover | | 6,000. |
| 7 | A1 | 4p red violet | 250.00 | 7.25 |
| a. | | Quarter used as 1p on cover | | 9,500. |
| b. | | Half used as 2p on cover | | 7,250. |
| 8 | A1 | 6p orange | 200.00 | 22.50 |
| a. | | One sixth used as 1p on cover | | 10,500. |
| b. | | Half used as 3p on cover | | 9,000. |
| | | Nos. 4-8 (5) | 675.00 | 81.75 |

**Handstamp Surcharged "1D" in Black**

| 1883, May | | | | |
|---|---|---|---|---|
| 9 | A1 | 1p on 4p red violet | | |

Some experts question the status of No. 9. One canceled copy is in the British Museum. Another copy is supposed to exist (Ferrari).

| 1883-91 | | | Wmk. 2 | |
|---|---|---|---|---|
| 10 | A1 | ½p bister ('83) | 210.00 | 75.00 |
| 11 | A1 | ½p green ('84) | 4.25 | 1.50 |
| 12 | A1 | 1p blue ('83) | 1,000. | 85.00 |
| 13 | A1 | 1p rose ('84) | 4.75 | .60 |
| a. | | Half used as ½p on cover | | 4,500. |
| 14a | A1 | 2p slate ('84) | 7.25 | .60 |
| b. | | Half used as 1p on cover | | 5,000. |
| 15 | A1 | 2½p bl & grn ('91) | 7.25 | .85 |
| 16 | A1 | 3p ol green ('89) | 15.00 | 6.50 |
| a. | | 3p olive bister | 15.00 | 6.00 |
| 17 | A1 | 4p dull vio ('84) | 15.00 | 2.75 |
| a. | | 4p claret | 19.00 | 4.50 |
| b. | | Half used as 2p on cover | | — |
| 18 | A1 | 6p orange ('89) | 15.00 | 6.00 |
| a. | | One sixth used as 1p on cover | | — |
| 19 | A1 | 1sh purple ('88) | 9.00 | 1.50 |
| a. | | 1sh violet | 37.50 | 15.00 |
| 20 | A1 | 2sh brown ('84) | 60.00 | 17.50 |
| a. | | 2sh yellow brown ('88) | 95.00 | 42.50 |

No. 18 Surcharged in Black

| 1889, Mar. | | | | |
|---|---|---|---|---|
| 21 | A1 | 1p on 6p orange | 140.00 | 60.00 |
| a. | | Double surcharge | | 4,500. |

The surcharge exists in two spacings between "PENNY" and bar: 7mm (normal) and 8mm.
No. 21a does not exist unused.

| 1889 | | | | |
|---|---|---|---|---|
| 22 | A3 | 5sh lilac & ultra | 75.00 | 20.00 |
| 23 | A3 | 10sh lilac & red | 95.00 | 17.50 |
| 24 | A3 | 20sh green & red | 325.00 | |

| 1894 | | | | |
|---|---|---|---|---|
| 25 | A3 | 20sh vio & blk, red | 190.00 | 40.00 |

| 1898-1902 | | | | |
|---|---|---|---|---|
| 26 | A3 | ½p lilac & green | 3.75 | 1.25 |
| 27 | A3 | 1p lil & car rose | 4.50 | .60 |
| 28 | A3 | 2p lil & red ('02) | 60.00 | 175.00 |
| 29 | A3 | 2½p lilac & ultra | 7.25 | 7.25 |
| 30 | A3 | 3p lilac & yel | 7.25 | 2.25 |
| 31 | A3 | 6p lilac & purple | 8.50 | 2.25 |
| 32 | A3 | 1sh gray grn & blk | 12.00 | 24.00 |
| 33 | A3 | 2sh gray grn & car rose | 19.00 | 25.00 |
| 34 | A3 | 5sh grn & lil ('00) | 65.00 | 42.50 |
| 35 | A3 | 10sh grn & brn ('00) | 175.00 | 65.00 |
| | | Nos. 26-35 (10) | 362.25 | 345.10 |

Numerals of 2p, 3p and 6p of type A3 are in color on colorless tablet.

---

Nos. 29 and 31 Surcharged in Black

| 1901, Oct. 6 | | | | |
|---|---|---|---|---|
| 36 | A3 | 1p on 2½p lil & ultra | 5.00 | 5.00 |
| a. | | "ONE" omitted | 1,200. | |
| 37 | A3 | 1p on 6p lilac & pur | 5.00 | 4.25 |
| a. | | "ONE" omitted | 325.00 | 650.00 |

Beware of copies offered as No. 37a that have part of "ONE" showing.

King Edward VII
A5      A6

| 1902 | | | Wmk. 2 | |
|---|---|---|---|---|
| 38 | A5 | ½p violet & green | 1.75 | .50 |
| 39 | A5 | 1p vio & car rose | 1.75 | .25 |
| 40 | A5 | 2p vio & red org | 27.50 | 8.50 |
| 41 | A5 | 2½p vio & ultra | 5.50 | 11.00 |
| 42 | A5 | 3p vio & orange | 3.50 | 1.75 |
| 43 | A5 | 6p violet & pur | 4.50 | 1.75 |
| 44 | A5 | 1sh green & blk | 17.00 | 4.00 |
| 45 | A5 | 2sh grn & car rose | 17.50 | 25.00 |
| 46 | A5 | 5sh green & violet | 57.50 | 110.00 |
| 47 | A5 | 10sh green & brn | 72.50 | 150.00 |
| 48 | A5 | 20sh vio & blk, red | 160.00 | 210.00 |
| | | Nos. 38-48 (11) | 369.00 | 522.75 |

Numerals of 2p, 3p, 6p and 2sh6p of type A5 are in color on colorless tablet.

| 1904-07 | | | Wmk. 3 | |
|---|---|---|---|---|
| 49 | A5 | ½p vio & grn ('07) | 3.00 | 8.50 |
| 50 | A5 | 1p vio & car rose | 11.00 | .40 |
| 51 | A5 | 2p vio & red org | 6.50 | .60 |
| 52 | A5 | 2½p vio & ultra ('06) | 57.50 | 57.50 |
| 53a | A5 | 3p vio & org ('06) | 19.00 | .70 |
| 54 | A5 | 6p vio & pur ('06) | 50.00 | 2.00 |
| 55 | A5 | 2sh6p grn & yel ('06) | 32.50 | 130.00 |
| | | Nos. 49-55 (7) | 179.50 | 199.70 |

Nos. 49 and 52 are on ordinary paper. Nos. 50, 51, 53 and 54 are on both ordinary and chalky paper. No. 55 is on chalky paper. For detailed listings, see the *Scott Specialized Catalogue of Stamps and Covers.*

| 1907-13 | | | Ordinary Paper | |
|---|---|---|---|---|
| 56 | A5 | ½p green | 7.25 | .40 |
| 57 | A5 | 1p carmine | 12.00 | .50 |
| 58 | A5 | 2p gray | 2.75 | .55 |
| 59 | A5 | 2½p ultramarine | 13.00 | 3.00 |

| | | | **Chalky Paper** | |
|---|---|---|---|---|
| 60 | A5 | 3p violet, yel ('09) | 9.50 | .65 |
| 61 | A5 | 6p dull violet ('08) | 21.00 | .65 |
| a. | | 6p dull violet & red violet | 4.50 | 4.25 |
| 62 | A5 | 1sh blk, grn ('09) | 17.50 | .65 |
| 63 | A5 | 2sh violet & bl, bl ('10) | 9.50 | 19.00 |
| 64 | A5 | 2sh6p blk & red, blue ('11) | 35.00 | 105.00 |
| 65 | A5 | 5sh grn & red, yel ('13) | 65.00 | 225.00 |
| | | Nos. 56-65 (10) | 192.50 | 355.40 |

#63 is on both ordinary and chalky paper.

| 1908, Nov. | | | Ordinary Paper | |
|---|---|---|---|---|
| 66 | A6 | 1p carmine | 5.25 | .20 |

King George V
A7      A8

For description of Dies I and II, see front of this section of the Catalogue.

Die I

| 1913-21 | | | Ordinary Paper | |
|---|---|---|---|---|
| 69 | A7 | ½p green | 3.00 | 1.25 |
| 70 | A8 | 1p carmine | 1.50 | .20 |
| a. | | 1p scarlet | 1.75 | .60 |

| | | | | |
|---|---|---|---|---|
| 71 | A7 | 2p gray | 5.25 | 3.00 |
| 72 | A7 | 2½p ultramarine | 9.00 | 1.25 |

**Chalky Paper**

| | | | | |
|---|---|---|---|---|
| 73 | A7 | 3p vio, yel ('15) | 2.50 | 1.00 |
| a. | | Die II ('19) | 57.50 | 6.00 |
| 74 | A7 | 6p dull vio & red vio | 5.00 | 2.75 |
| 75 | A7 | 1sh black, green | 4.50 | 1.50 |
| a. | | 1sh black, emerald | 2.50 | 2.50 |
| b. | | 1sh black, bl grn, ol back | 10.00 | .95 |
| c. | | Die II ('21) | 1.75 | .60 |
| 76 | A7 | 2sh vio & bl, bl | 10.50 | 3.50 |
| a. | | Die II ('21) | 190.00 | 77.50 |
| 77 | A7 | 2sh6p blk & red, bl | 8.50 | 16.00 |
| a. | | Die II ('21) | 27.50 | 50.00 |
| 78 | A7 | 5sh grn & red, yel | 20.00 | 60.00 |
| a. | | Die II ('21) | 35.00 | 160.00 |
| 79 | A7 | 10sh grn & red, grn ('16) | 60.00 | 110.00 |
| a. | | 10sh grn & red, emer | 37.50 | 175.00 |
| b. | | 10sh grn & red, bl grn, ol back | 24.00 | 85.00 |
| 80 | A7 | 20sh vio & blk, red ('16) | 140.00 | 95.00 |

**Surface-colored Paper**

| | | | | |
|---|---|---|---|---|
| 81 | A7 | 3p violet, yel | 2.10 | 1.00 |
| 82 | A7 | 5sh grn & red, yel | 16.00 | 72.50 |
| | | Nos. 69-82 (14) | 287.85 | 368.95 |

Numerals of 2p, 3p, 6p and 2sh6p of type A7 are in color on plain tablet.

**Die II**

**1921-25    Ordinary Paper    Wmk. 4**

| | | | | |
|---|---|---|---|---|
| 83 | A7 | ½p green ('22) | 1.00 | .60 |
| 84 | A8 | 1p brown ('22) | .90 | .20 |
| 85 | A7 | 1½p carmine ('22) | 2.10 | .20 |
| 86 | A7 | 2p gray | 2.10 | .40 |
| 87 | A7 | 2½p orange ('23) | 1.50 | 11.00 |
| 88 | A7 | 3p ultra ('22) | 2.10 | .70 |

**Chalky Paper**

| | | | | |
|---|---|---|---|---|
| 89 | A7 | 6p dl vio & red vio ('22) | 2.75 | 3.50 |
| 90 | A7 | 1sh blk, emer ('25) | 4.25 | 4.00 |
| 91 | A7 | 2sh vio & bl, bl ('24) | 4.00 | 4.00 |
| 92 | A7 | 2sh6p blk & red, bl ('25) | 8.50 | 32.50 |
| 93 | A7 | 5sh grn & red, yel ('25) | 16.00 | 77.50 |

**Die I**

| | | | | |
|---|---|---|---|---|
| 94 | A7 | 15sh dl vio & grn ('21) | 175.00 | 475.00 |
| a. | | Die II ('25) | 140.00 | 475.00 |
| 95 | A7 | £2 grn & org | 500.00 | 1,300. |
| | | Nos. 83-95 (13) | 720.20 | 1,909. |

Christiansborg Castle — A9

**1928, Aug. 1    Photo.    Perf. 13½x14½**

| | | | | |
|---|---|---|---|---|
| 98 | A9 | ½p green | 1.20 | .50 |
| 99 | A9 | 1p red brown | 1.00 | .20 |
| 100 | A9 | 1½p scarlet | 2.10 | 1.75 |
| 101 | A9 | 2p slate | 2.10 | .20 |
| 102 | A9 | 2½p yellow | 2.40 | 4.25 |
| 103 | A9 | 3p ultramarine | 2.10 | .50 |
| 104 | A9 | 6p dull vio & blk | 2.10 | .50 |
| 105 | A9 | 1sh red org & blk | 3.75 | .95 |
| 106 | A9 | 2sh purple & black | 30.00 | 6.00 |
| 107 | A9 | 5sh ol green & car | 72.50 | 52.50 |
| | | Nos. 98-107 (10) | 119.25 | 67.35 |

Common Design Types pictured following the introduction.

**Silver Jubilee Issue**
Common Design Type

**1935, May 6    Engr.    Perf. 11x12**

| | | | | |
|---|---|---|---|---|
| 108 | CD301 | 1p black & ultra | 1.00 | .60 |
| 109 | CD301 | 3p ultra & brown | 3.25 | 7.25 |
| 110 | CD301 | 6p indigo & green | 11.50 | 17.00 |
| 111 | CD301 | 1sh brn vio & indigo | 5.50 | 22.50 |
| | | Nos. 108-111 (4) | 21.25 | 47.35 |
| | | Set, never hinged | 35.00 | |

**Coronation Issue**
Common Design Type

**1937, May 12    Perf. 11x11½**

| | | | | |
|---|---|---|---|---|
| 112 | CD302 | 1p brown | .55 | 2.50 |
| 113 | CD302 | 2p dark gray | .75 | 4.50 |
| 114 | CD302 | 3p deep ultra | 1.00 | 2.75 |
| | | Nos. 112-114 (3) | 2.30 | 9.75 |
| | | Set, never hinged | 5.00 | |

A10

George VI and Christiansborg Castle — A11

**1938-41    Wmk. 4    Perf. 12**

| | | | | |
|---|---|---|---|---|
| 115 | A10 | ½p green | .35 | .50 |
| 116 | A10 | 1p red brown | .35 | .20 |
| 117 | A10 | 1½p rose red | .35 | .50 |
| 118 | A10 | 2p gray black | .35 | .20 |
| 119 | A10 | 3p ultramarine | .35 | .35 |
| 120 | A10 | 4p rose lilac | .70 | 1.10 |
| 121 | A10 | 6p rose violet | .70 | .20 |
| 122 | A10 | 9p red orange | 1.10 | .55 |
| 123 | A11 | 1sh gray grn & blk | 1.40 | .55 |
| 124 | A11 | 1sh3p turq grn & red brown | 1.75 | .45 |
| 125 | A11 | 2sh dk vio & dp bl | 4.75 | 14.00 |
| 126 | A11 | 5sh rose car & ol green | 9.25 | 17.50 |
| 127 | A11 | 10sh purple & black | 6.50 | 26.00 |
| | | Nos. 115-127 (13) | 27.90 | 62.10 |
| | | Set, never hinged | 40.00 | |

Issued: 10sh, July, 1940; 1sh3p, Apr. 12, 1941; others, Apr. 1.

> Catalogue values for unused stamps in this section, from this point to the end of the section, are for Never Hinged items.

**Peace Issue**
Common Design Type

**1946, Oct. 14    Perf. 13½**

| | | | | |
|---|---|---|---|---|
| 128 | CD303 | 2p purple | .25 | .20 |
| a. | | Perf. 13½x14 | 18.00 | 3.00 |
| 129 | CD303 | 4p deep red violet | 1.60 | 3.50 |
| a. | | Perf. 13½x14 | 2.25 | 3.50 |

A12

A13

½p, Mounted Constable. 1p, Christiansborg Castle. 1½p, Emblem of Joint Provincial Council. 2p, Talking Drums. 2½p, Map. 3p, Manganese mine. 4p, Lake Bosumtwi. 6p, Cacao farmer. 1sh, Breaking cacao pods. 2sh, Trooping the colors. 5sh, Surfboats. 10sh, Forest.

**1948, July 1    Engr.    Perf. 12**

| | | | | |
|---|---|---|---|---|
| 130 | A12 | ½p emerald | .20 | .35 |
| 131 | A13 | 1p deep blue | .20 | .20 |
| 132 | A13 | 1½p red | 1.50 | .90 |
| 133 | A12 | 2p chocolate | .65 | .20 |
| 134 | A13 | 2½p lt brown & red | 2.50 | 4.25 |
| 135 | A13 | 3p blue | 5.00 | .60 |
| 136 | A13 | 4p dk car rose | 4.25 | 2.50 |
| 137 | A12 | 6p org & black | .40 | .40 |
| 138 | A13 | 1sh red org & blk | .70 | .40 |
| 139 | A13 | 2sh rose car & ol brn | 4.00 | 2.50 |
| 140 | A13 | 5sh gray & red vio | 30.00 | 7.25 |
| 141 | A12 | 10sh ol grn & black | 10.50 | 7.25 |
| | | Nos. 130-141 (12) | 59.90 | 26.80 |

**Silver Wedding Issue**
Common Design Types

**1948, Dec. 20    Photo.    Perf. 14x14½**

| | | | | |
|---|---|---|---|---|
| 142 | CD304 | 1½p scarlet | .20 | .20 |

**Engraved; Name Typographed**
**Perf. 11½x11**

| | | | | |
|---|---|---|---|---|
| 143 | CD305 | 10sh dk brn olive | 22.50 | 22.50 |

**UPU Issue**
Common Design Types

**Engr.; Name Typo. on 2½p and 3p**
**1949, Oct. 10    Perf. 13½, 11x11½**

| | | | | |
|---|---|---|---|---|
| 144 | CD306 | 2p red brown | .25 | .25 |
| 145 | CD307 | 2½p deep orange | 1.90 | 4.25 |
| 146 | CD308 | 3p indigo | .45 | 1.75 |
| 147 | CD309 | 1sh blue green | .45 | .45 |
| | | Nos. 144-147 (4) | 3.05 | 6.70 |

Map of West Africa — A14

Mounted Constable — A15

Designs: 1p, Christiansborg Castle. 1½p, Emblem of Joint Provincial Council. 2p, Talking drums. 3p, Manganese mine. 4p, Lake Bosumtwi. 6p, Cacao farmer. 1sh, Breaking cacao pods. 2sh, Trooping the colors. 5sh, Surfboats. 10sh, Forest.

**Perf. 11½x12, 12x11½**

**1952-54    Engr.**

| | | | | |
|---|---|---|---|---|
| 148 | A14 | ½p yel brn & car | .20 | .20 |
| 149 | A14 | 1p deep blue | .40 | .20 |
| 150 | A14 | 1½p green | .40 | 1.50 |
| 151 | A15 | 2p chocolate | .40 | .20 |
| 152 | A15 | 2½p red | .45 | .45 |
| 153 | A14 | 3p rose | .95 | .20 |
| 154 | A14 | 4p deep blue | .45 | 1.25 |
| 155 | A15 | 6p orange & black | .45 | .20 |
| 156 | A14 | 1sh red org & black | .50 | .20 |
| 157 | A14 | 2sh rose car & ol brn | 13.00 | 1.00 |
| 158 | A14 | 5sh gray & red vio | 21.00 | 6.00 |
| 159 | A15 | 10sh olive grn & blk | 19.00 | 15.00 |
| | | Nos. 148-159 (12) | 57.25 | 26.40 |

Nos. 148-149 exist in vertical coils.
Issued: 2½p, 12/19/52; ½p, 1½p, 3p, 4p, 4/1/53; 1p, 2p, 6p, 1sh-10sh, 3/1/54.
For overprints see Ghana #5-13, 25-27.

**Coronation Issue**
Common Design Type

**1953, June 2    Perf. 13½x13**

| | | | | |
|---|---|---|---|---|
| 160 | CD312 | 2p dk brown & black | .80 | .20 |

**POSTAGE DUE STAMPS**

D1

**1923    Typo.    Wmk. 4    Perf. 14**
**Yellowish Toned Paper**

| | | | | |
|---|---|---|---|---|
| J1 | D1 | ½p black | 19.00 | 125.00 |
| J2 | D1 | 1p black | .95 | 1.50 |
| J3 | D1 | 2p black | 12.00 | 3.50 |
| J4 | D1 | 3p black | 20.00 | 3.00 |
| | | Nos. J1-J4 (4) | 51.95 | 133.00 |

**1951-52    Typo.    Wmk. 4    Perf. 14**
**Chalk-Surfaced Paper**

| | | | | |
|---|---|---|---|---|
| J5 | D1 | 2p black | 3.75 | 22.50 |
| a. | | Wmk. 4a (error) | 425.00 | |
| J6 | D1 | 3p black | 3.00 | 21.00 |
| a. | | Wmk. 4a (error) | 425.00 | |
| J7 | D1 | 6p black ('52) | 2.10 | 10.00 |
| a. | | Wmk. 4a (error) | 1,200. | |
| J8 | D1 | 1sh black ('52) | 2.10 | 80.00 |
| a. | | Wmk. 4a (error) | 900.00 | |
| | | Nos. J5-J8 (4) | 10.95 | 133.50 |

Issued: #J7-J8, 10/1.

**WAR TAX STAMP**

Regular Issue of 1913 Surcharged

**1918, June    Wmk. 3    Perf. 14**

| | | | | |
|---|---|---|---|---|
| MR1 | A8 | 1p on 1p scarlet | 3.00 | .90 |

# GRAND COMORO

'grand 'kä-mə-ˌrō

LOCATION — One of the Comoro Islands in the Mozambique Channel between Madagascar and Mozambique.
GOVT. — French Colony
AREA — 385 sq. mi. (approx.)
POP. — 50,000 (approx.)
CAPITAL — Moroni

100 Centimes = 1 Franc

See Comoro Islands.

Navigation and Commerce — A1

**Perf. 14x13½**

**1897-1907　　Typo.　　Unwmk.**
Name of Colony in Blue or Carmine

| | | | | |
|---|---|---|---|---|
| 1 | A1 | 1c blk, *lil bl* | 1.25 | 1.25 |
| 2 | A1 | 2c brn, *buff* | 1.75 | 1.75 |
| 3 | A1 | 4c claret, *lav* | 2.25 | 2.25 |
| 4 | A1 | 5c grn, *grnsh* | 4.50 | 4.50 |
| 5 | A1 | 10c blk, *lavender* | 9.50 | 6.50 |
| 6 | A1 | 10c red ('00) | 11.00 | 11.00 |
| 7 | A1 | 15c blue, quadrille paper | 20.00 | 14.50 |
| 8 | A1 | 15c gray, *lt gray* ('00) | 11.00 | 11.00 |
| 9 | A1 | 20c red, *grn* | 12.50 | 12.50 |
| 10 | A1 | 25c blk, *rose* | 18.50 | 17.00 |
| 11 | A1 | 25c blue ('00) | 21.50 | 21.50 |
| 12 | A1 | 30c brn, *bister* | 22.50 | 20.00 |
| 13 | A1 | 35c blk, *yel* ('06) | 20.00 | 20.00 |
| 14 | A1 | 40c red, *straw* | 22.50 | 20.00 |
| 15 | A1 | 45c blk, *gray grn* ('07) | 80.00 | 67.50 |
| 16 | A1 | 50c car, *rose* | 45.00 | 24.00 |
| 17 | A1 | 50c brn, *bluish* ('00) | 47.50 | 45.00 |
| 18 | A1 | 75c dp vio, *org* | 60.00 | 40.00 |
| 19 | A1 | 1fr brnz grn, *straw* | 40.00 | 36.00 |
| | | *Nos. 1-19 (19)* | 451.25 | 376.25 |

Perf. 13½x14 stamps are counterfeits.

Issues of 1897-1907 Surcharged in Black or Carmine

**1912**

| | | | | |
|---|---|---|---|---|
| 20 | A1 | 5c on 2c brn, *buff* | 1.40 | 1.40 |
| a. | | Inverted surcharge | 240.00 | |
| 21 | A1 | 5c on 4c cl, *lav* (C) | 1.50 | 1.50 |
| 22 | A1 | 5c on 15c blue (C) | 1.40 | 1.40 |
| 23 | A1 | 5c on 20c red, *grn* | 1.60 | 1.60 |
| 24 | A1 | 5c on 25c blk, *rose* (C) | 1.50 | 1.50 |
| 25 | A1 | 5c on 30c brn, *bis* (C) | 1.60 | 1.60 |
| 26 | A1 | 10c on 40c red, *straw* | 1.60 | 1.60 |
| 27 | A1 | 10c on 45c blk, *gray grn* (C) | 2.40 | 2.40 |
| 28 | A1 | 10c on 50c car, *rose* | 2.10 | 2.10 |
| 29 | A1 | 10c on 75c dp vio, *org* | 2.50 | 2.50 |
| | | *Nos. 20-29 (10)* | 17.60 | 17.60 |

Two spacings between the surcharged numerals are found on Nos. 20-29. For detailed listings, see the *Scott Classic Specialized Catalogue of Stamps and Covers.*

---

Nos. 20-29 were available for use in Madagascar and the entire Comoro archipelago.
Stamps of Grand Comoro were superseded by those of Madagascar, and in 1950 by those of Comoro Islands.

---

# GREAT BRITAIN

'grāt 'bri-tən

(United Kingdom)

LOCATION — Northwest of the continent of Europe and separated from it by the English Channel
GOVT. — Constitutional monarchy
AREA — 94,511 sq. mi.
POP. — 59,128,000 (1998 est.)
CAPITAL — London

12 Pence = 1 Shilling
20 Shillings = 1 Pound
100 Pence = 1 Pound (1970)

**Catalogue values for unused stamps in this country are for Never Hinged items, beginning with Scott 264 in the regular postage section, Scott B1 in the semipostal section. Scott J34 in the postage due section, and Scott 93, Scott 246 and Scott 521 in British Offices in Morocco. All of the listings in British Offices — Middle East Forces, for Use in Eritrea, for Use in Somalia and for Use in Tripolitania are valued as never-hinged.**

The letters in the corners of the early postage issues indicate position in the horizontal and vertical rows in which that particular specimen was placed.

In the case of illustration A1, this stamp came from the 15th horizontal row (O) and was the second stamp (B) from the left in that row. The left corner refers to the horizontal row and the right corner to the vertical row. Thus no two stamps on the plate bore the same combination of letters.

When four corner letters are used (starting in 1858), the lower ones indicate the stamp's position in the sheet and the top ones are the same letters reversed.

**Watermarks**

Wmk. 18 — Small Crown　　Wmk. 19 — V R

Wmk. 20 — Large Crown

Wmk. 21 — Small Garter

Wmk. 22 — Medium Garter

Wmk. 23 — Large Garter

Wmk. 24 — Heraldic Emblems

Wmk. 25 — Spray of Rose

Wmk. 26 — Maltese Cross

Wmk. 27 — "Half Penny" in Script

Wmk. 28 — Anchor

Wmk. 29 — Orb

Wmk. 30 — Imperial Crown

Wmk. 31 — Anchor

Wmk. 32 — Crown and GvR Multiple

Wmk. 33 — Crown and GvR

Wmk. 33 — In the normal watermark (sometimes termed the "repeated" watermark) the letters "GvR" are extended. The royal cyphers are placed one above the other and usually two appear on each stamp. In the multiple watermark the letters "GvR" are condensed, the cyphers are smaller and are so placed that those in each succeeding row are below the spaces between the cyphers in the row above.

Wmk. 34 — Large Crown and GvR

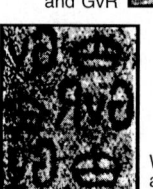

Wmk. 35 — Crown and Block GvR Multiple

Wmk. 219 — Large Crown and GvR

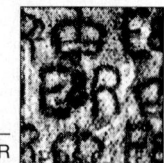

Wmk. 250 — Crown and E8R Multiple

Wmk. 251 — Crown and GviR Multiple

---

Wmk. 259 —
Crown and
Large G VI R

Wmk. 298 —
Tudor Crown and
E 2 R Multiple

Wmk. 308 — St.
Edward's Crown
and E 2 R
Multiple

Wmk. 322 — St.
Edward's Crown
Multiple

Wmk. 401

Values for unused stamps are for examples with original gum as defined in the catalogue introduction. Very fine stamps will be sound and have fresh color, but expect Nos. 8-56, 58-73, 78-89, 94-95, and the Official overprints on these designs, to have perforations touching the design on at least one side due to the narrow spacing of the stamps on the plates. Stamps with perfs clear of the design on all four sides range from scarce to very rare and command substantially higher prices.

Cancellations on stamps from the 1847 issue to the 1884 issues, and in many cases beyond, are usually heavy. Values quoted are for stamps with better than average cancellations. Stamps with circular date stamps (especially those with a steel cds) range from scarce to very rare and command much higher prices.

Queen Victoria — A1

**1840, May  Wmk. 18  Engr.  Imperf.**
**White Paper**
1  A1  1p black              7,500.  300.00
2  A1  2p blue             24,000.  800.00

No. 1 was printed from 11 plates; No. 2 from 2 plates. The 1p plates 1, 2, 5, 6, 8 and 9 can be found in two or more states. Stamp values are for the most common plates.
Issue dates: 1p, May 6; 2p, May 7.
See Nos. 3, 8-9, 11-12, 14, 16, 18, 20, O1.
Compare designs A1-A2 with A8, A10.
For shades, see the *Scott Classic Catalogue.*

A2

**1841                      Bluish Paper**
3  A1  1p red brown          450.00   21.50
  c.   Rouletted 12          10,000.
  d.   "A" missing in lower right
       corner (position BA,
       P77)                       —   11,000.
4  A2  2p blue             3,900.    80.00
  c.   2p violet blue       18,000.  1,300.

No. 3 exists on silk thread paper, but was not regularly issued.
No. 4 was printed from two plates.
See Nos. 10, 13, 15, 17, 19, 21.
For shades, see the *Scott Classic Catalogue.*

During the reigns of Victoria and Edward VII, many color trials were produced on perfed, gummed and watermarked papers.

A3

A4

**With Vertical Silk Threads**
**1847      Embossed      Unwmk.**
5  A3  1sh pale green     11,000.  800.00
  a.   1sh green          11,000.  850.00
       Cut to shape                 20.00

Die numbers (on base of bust): 1 and 2.

Nos. 5-7 were printed one stamp at a time on the sheet. Space between the stamps usually is very small. Impressions that touch, or even overlap, are numerous.
Values for Nos. 5-6 are for examples with complete frames and clear white margins on all four sides. Values for No. 7 are for examples with complete design but not necessarily clear margins around the design.

**1848**
6  A3  10p red brown     7,250.  1,100.
       Cut to shape                30.00

Die numbers (on base of bust): 1, 2, 3, 4; also without die number.

**1854                      Wmk. 19**
7  A4  6p red violet     9,000.  850.00
  a.   6p dull violet    9,000.  850.00
  b.   6p deep violet   16,000.  3,000.
       Cut to shape                16.00

**1854-55  Wmk. 18  Engr.  Perf. 16**
**Bluish Paper**
8  A1  1p red brown       300.00   24.00
  a.   1p yellow brown     350.00   47.50
9  A1  1p red brown, re-en-
       graved ('55)        350.00   65.00
  a.   Imperf.
10  A2  2p blue          3,250.    95.00
  a.   2p pale blue      3,500.   105.00

In the re-engraved 1p stamps, the lines of the features are deeper and stronger, the fillet behind the ear more distinct, the shading about the eye heavier, the line of the nostril is turned downward at right and an indentation of color appears between lower lip and chin.

**Perf. 14**
11  A1  1p red brown ('55)  525.00   75.00
  a.   Imperf.
12  A1  1p red brown, re-en-
        graved ('55)        475.00   52.50
  a.   1p org brn, re-engraved  1,500.  150.00
13  A2  2p blue ('55)     6,750.  220.00
  a.   Imperf. (P5)

Wmk. 20 exists in two types. The first includes two vertical prongs, rising from the top of the crown's headband and extending into each of the two balancing midsections. The second type (illustrated), introduced in 1861, omits these prongs.

**1855          Wmk. 20          Perf. 16**
**Bluish Paper**
14  A1  1p red brown, re-
        engraved            850.00  160.00
15  A2  2p blue          9,000.   400.00
  a.   Imperf. (P5)                6,000.

**1855      Bluish Paper      Perf. 14**
16  A1  1p red brown, re-
        engraved            250.00   19.00
  a.   1p orange brn, re-en-
       graved               600.00   60.00

---

  b.   1p brown rose, re-en-
       graved               300.00   42.50
  c.   Imperf.             3,400.   2,750.
17  A2  2p blue          2,000.    60.00

**1856-58      White Paper      Perf. 16**
18  A1  1p rose red, re-
        engraved ('57)    1,800.    70.00
19  A2  2p blue, thin lines
        ('58)             8,500.   350.00

**Perf. 14**
20  A1  1p rose red, re-
        engraved ('57)     47.50    11.00
  a.   Imperf.            3,200.   2,500.
  b.   1p red brown, re-en-
       graved              925.00  275.00
21  A2  2p blue, thin lines
        ('57)             2,400.    60.00
  a.   Imperf.                —    6,000.
  b.   Vertical pair, imperf horiz.

Queen Victoria — A5

**1855         Typo.         Wmk. 21**
22  A5  4p rose, *bluish*  6,000.  400.00
23  A5  4p rose, *white*        —  850.00

Compare design A5 with A11, A16, A31.

**1856                       Wmk. 22**
24  A5  4p rose, *bluish*  7,200.  450.00
25  A5  4p rose, *white*   5,750.  375.00

**1857                       Wmk. 23**
26  A5  4p rose, *white*   1,300.  105.00

A6

A7

**1856                       Wmk. 24**
27  A6  6p lilac         1,100.   100.00
  a.   6p deep lilac     1,350.   130.00
  b.   Wmk. 3 roses and sham-
       rock
28  A7  1sh green        1,600.   275.00
  a.   1sh pale green    1,600.   275.00
  b.   1sh deep green    3,250.   450.00
  e.   Imperf                        —

Compare design A6 with A13, A18, A22.
Compare A7 with A15, A21, A29.

A8

A9

**1858-69  Engr.  Wmk. 20  Perf. 14**
29  A8  2p blue (P9)       325.00   12.50
        Plate 7           1,300.    52.50
        Plate 8           1,200.    37.50
        Plate 12          1,900.   125.00
  b.   Imperf. (P9)                6,000.

Plate numbers are contained in the scroll work at the sides of the stamp.

### Lines Above and Below Head Thinner

| | | | |
|---|---|---|---|
| **30** | A8 | 2p blue ('69) (P13) | 350.00 | 32.50 |
| | | Plate 14 | 450.00 | 32.50 |
| | | Plate 15 | 425.00 | 32.50 |
| a. | | Imperf. (P13) | 7,000. | |

### 1860-70

| | | | | |
|---|---|---|---|---|
| **31** | A9 | 1½p lilac rose, *bluish* (P1) ('60) | 6,500. | |
| **32** | A9 | 1½p dull rose (P3) ('70) | 425.00 | 52.50 |
| a. | | 1½p lake red | 425.00 | 52.50 |
| | | Plate 1 | 600.00 | 75.00 |
| c. | | Imperf (P1, 3) | 5,500. | |

The 1½p stamps from Plate 1 carry no plate number. The Plate 3 number is in the border at each side above the lower corner letters.
No. 31 was prepared but not issued.
The "OP-PC" variety is a broken letter.

Queen Victoria — A10

### 1864

| | | | | |
|---|---|---|---|---|
| **33** | A10 | 1p rose red | 19.00 | 2.50 |
| a. | | 1p brick red | 19.00 | 2.50 |
| b. | | 1p lake red | 19.00 | 2.50 |
| c. | | Imperf. (P116, see footnote) | 1,800. | 1,000. |
| | | Plate 71 | 42.50 | 3.75 |
| | | Plate 72 | 47.50 | 4.75 |
| | | Plate 73 | 47.50 | 3.75 |
| | | Plate 74 | 47.50 | 2.50 |
| | | Plate 76 | 42.50 | 2.50 |
| | | Plate 77 | — | 175,000. |
| | | Plate 78 | 105.00 | 2.50 |
| | | Plate 79 | 37.50 | 2.50 |
| | | Plate 80 | 52.50 | 2.50 |
| | | Plate 81 | 52.50 | 3.00 |
| | | Plate 82 | 105.00 | 4.75 |
| | | Plate 83 | 135.00 | 8.50 |
| | | Plate 84 | 70.00 | 3.00 |
| | | Plate 85 | 47.50 | 4.00 |
| | | Plate 86 | 60.00 | 4.75 |
| | | Plate 87 | 37.50 | 2.50 |
| | | Plate 88 | 160.00 | 9.00 |
| | | Plate 89 | 47.50 | 2.50 |
| | | Plate 90 | 47.50 | 2.50 |
| | | Plate 91 | 65.00 | 7.00 |
| | | Plate 92 | 42.50 | 2.50 |
| | | Plate 93 | 60.00 | 2.50 |
| | | Plate 94 | 52.50 | 6.00 |
| | | Plate 95 | 47.50 | 2.50 |
| | | Plate 96 | 52.50 | 2.50 |
| | | Plate 97 | 47.50 | 4.25 |
| | | Plate 98 | 60.00 | 7.00 |
| | | Plate 99 | 65.00 | 6.00 |
| | | Plate 100 | 70.00 | 3.00 |
| | | Plate 101 | 70.00 | 10.50 |
| | | Plate 102 | 52.50 | 2.50 |
| | | Plate 103 | 60.00 | 4.25 |
| | | Plate 104 | 85.00 | 6.00 |
| | | Plate 105 | 105.00 | 8.50 |
| | | Plate 106 | 65.00 | 2.50 |
| | | Plate 107 | 70.00 | 8.50 |
| | | Plate 108 | 90.00 | 3.00 |
| | | Plate 109 | 95.00 | 4.25 |
| | | Plate 110 | 70.00 | 10.75 |
| | | Plate 111 | 60.00 | 3.00 |
| | | Plate 112 | 80.00 | 3.00 |
| | | Plate 113 | 60.00 | 15.00 |
| | | Plate 114 | 300.00 | 15.00 |
| | | Plate 115 | 105.00 | 3.00 |
| | | Plate 116 | 85.00 | 10.75 |
| | | Plate 117 | 52.50 | 2.50 |
| | | Plate 118 | 60.00 | 2.50 |
| | | Plate 119 | 52.50 | 2.50 |
| | | Plate 120 | 29.00 | 2.50 |
| | | Plate 121 | 47.50 | 10.75 |
| | | Plate 122 | 19.00 | 2.50 |
| | | Plate 123 | 47.50 | 2.50 |
| | | Plate 124 | 35.00 | 2.50 |
| | | Plate 125 | 47.50 | 2.50 |
| | | Plate 127 | 65.00 | 3.00 |
| | | Plate 129 | 47.50 | 9.50 |
| | | Plate 130 | 65.00 | 3.00 |
| | | Plate 131 | 75.00 | 20.00 |
| | | Plate 132 | 160.00 | 27.50 |
| | | Plate 133 | 135.00 | 10.75 |
| | | Plate 134 | 19.00 | 2.50 |
| | | Plate 135 | 105.00 | 30.00 |
| | | Plate 136 | 105.00 | 24.00 |
| | | Plate 137 | 35.00 | 3.00 |
| | | Plate 138 | 24.00 | 2.50 |
| | | Plate 139 | 70.00 | 20.00 |
| | | Plate 140 | 24.00 | 2.50 |
| | | Plate 141 | 135.00 | 10.75 |
| | | Plate 142 | 80.00 | 30.00 |
| | | Plate 143 | 70.00 | 17.00 |
| | | Plate 144 | 105.00 | 24.00 |
| | | Plate 145 | 37.50 | 2.50 |
| | | Plate 146 | 47.50 | 7.00 |
| | | Plate 147 | 60.00 | 3.75 |
| | | Plate 148 | 47.50 | 3.75 |
| | | Plate 149 | 47.50 | 7.00 |
| | | Plate 150 | 19.00 | 2.50 |
| | | Plate 151 | 70.00 | 10.75 |
| | | Plate 152 | 70.00 | 6.50 |
| | | Plate 153 | 115.00 | 10.75 |
| | | Plate 154 | 60.00 | 2.50 |
| | | Plate 155 | 60.00 | 2.50 |
| | | Plate 156 | 52.50 | 2.50 |
| | | Plate 157 | 60.00 | 2.50 |
| | | Plate 158 | 37.50 | 2.50 |
| | | Plate 159 | 37.50 | 2.50 |
| | | Plate 160 | 37.50 | 2.50 |
| | | Plate 161 | 70.00 | 8.50 |
| | | Plate 162 | 60.00 | 8.50 |
| | | Plate 163 | 60.00 | 3.75 |
| | | Plate 164 | 60.00 | 3.75 |
| | | Plate 165 | 52.50 | 2.50 |
| | | Plate 166 | 52.50 | 7.00 |
| | | Plate 167 | 52.50 | 2.50 |
| | | Plate 168 | 60.00 | 9.50 |
| | | Plate 169 | 70.00 | 8.50 |
| | | Plate 170 | 42.50 | 2.50 |
| | | Plate 171 | 19.00 | 2.50 |
| | | Plate 172 | 37.50 | 2.50 |
| | | Plate 173 | 80.00 | 10.75 |
| | | Plate 174 | 37.50 | 2.50 |
| | | Plate 175 | 70.00 | 4.25 |
| | | Plate 176 | 70.00 | 3.00 |
| | | Plate 177 | 47.50 | 2.50 |
| | | Plate 178 | 70.00 | 4.25 |
| | | Plate 179 | 60.00 | 2.50 |
| | | Plate 180 | 70.00 | 6.00 |
| | | Plate 181 | 52.50 | 2.50 |
| | | Plate 182 | 105.00 | 6.00 |
| | | Plate 183 | 65.00 | 3.75 |
| | | Plate 184 | 37.50 | 2.50 |
| | | Plate 185 | 60.00 | 3.75 |
| | | Plate 186 | 75.00 | 3.00 |
| | | Plate 187 | 60.00 | 2.50 |
| | | Plate 188 | 80.00 | 12.00 |
| | | Plate 189 | 80.00 | 8.00 |
| | | Plate 190 | 60.00 | 7.00 |
| | | Plate 191 | 37.50 | 8.50 |
| | | Plate 192 | 60.00 | 2.50 |
| | | Plate 193 | 37.50 | 2.50 |
| | | Plate 194 | 60.00 | 9.50 |
| | | Plate 195 | 60.00 | 9.50 |
| | | Plate 196 | 60.00 | 6.00 |
| | | Plate 197 | 65.00 | 10.75 |
| | | Plate 198 | 47.50 | 7.00 |
| | | Plate 199 | 65.00 | 7.00 |
| | | Plate 200 | 70.00 | 2.50 |
| | | Plate 201 | 37.50 | 6.00 |
| | | Plate 202 | 70.00 | 9.50 |
| | | Plate 203 | 37.50 | 20.00 |
| | | Plate 204 | 65.00 | 2.50 |
| | | Plate 205 | 65.00 | 3.75 |
| | | Plate 206 | 65.00 | 8.25 |
| | | Plate 207 | 70.00 | 10.75 |
| | | Plate 208 | 65.00 | 20.00 |
| | | Plate 209 | 60.00 | 10.75 |
| | | Plate 210 | 75.00 | 14.00 |
| | | Plate 211 | 80.00 | 24.00 |
| | | Plate 212 | 70.00 | 13.00 |
| | | Plate 213 | 70.00 | 13.00 |
| | | Plate 214 | 75.00 | 21.50 |
| | | Plate 215 | 75.00 | 21.50 |
| | | Plate 216 | 80.00 | 21.50 |
| | | Plate 217 | 80.00 | 8.50 |
| | | Plate 218 | 75.00 | 9.50 |
| | | Plate 219 | 105.00 | 80.00 |
| | | Plate 220 | 47.50 | 8.50 |
| | | Plate 221 | 80.00 | 20.00 |
| | | Plate 222 | 90.00 | 47.50 |
| | | Plate 223 | 105.00 | 70.00 |
| | | Plate 224 | 135.00 | 60.00 |
| | | Plate 225 | 2,750. | 750.00 |

Plate numbers are contained in the scroll work at the sides of the stamp.
No. 33 was printed from 1864 to 1879.
Thirty-nine plate numbers besides Plate 116 (No. 33c) are also known imperforate. Values for used copies start at $450.
Stamps from plate 177 have been altered and offered as plate 77.

A11

### 1862    Typo.    Wmk. 23

| | | | | |
|---|---|---|---|---|
| **34** | A11 | 4p vermilion (P3) | 1,400. | 95.00 |
| b. | | Hair lines (P4) | 1,700. | 110.00 |
| d. | | Imperf. (P4) | 3,500. | |

Hair lines on No. 34a are fine colorless lines drawn diagonally across the corners of the stamp.

A12      A13

A14      A15

### 1862      Wmk. 24

| | | | | |
|---|---|---|---|---|
| **37** | A12 | 3p pale rose | 1,800. | 260.00 |
| a. | | 3p deep rose | 3,750. | 450.00 |
| b. | | With white dots under side ornaments | 27,000. | 10,000. |
| **39** | A13 | 6p lilac | 1,650. | 95.00 |
| c. | | Wmk. 3 roses & thistle | — | 8,000. |
| d. | | Hair lines (P4) | 2,150. | 190.00 |
| e. | | As "d," imperf | 3,600. | |
| h. | | 6p deep lilac | 1,800. | 115.00 |
| **40** | A14 | 9p straw | 3,250. | 375.00 |
| c. | | Wmk. 3 roses & thistle | — | |
| d. | | 9p bister | 4,000. | 425.00 |
| e. | | Hair lines (P3) | 18,000. | 9,000. |

| | | | | |
|---|---|---|---|---|
| **42** | A15 | 1sh green | 2,000. | 210.00 |
| a. | | 1sh deep green (P1) | 3,200. | 375.00 |
| b. | | As "c," imperf. | 4,500. | |
| c. | | 1sh deep green, with hair lines (P2) | 24,000. | |

Hair lines on Nos. 39b, 40b, 42c are fine colorless lines drawn diagonally across the corners of the stamp.
Compare design A14 with A19.

A16

### 1865      Wmk. 23

| | | | | |
|---|---|---|---|---|
| **43** | A16 | 4p vermilion (P12) | 475.00 | 60.00 |
| | | Plate 10 | 700.00 | 140.00 |
| | | Plate 11 | 525.00 | 65.00 |
| | | Plate 14 | 575.00 | 90.00 |
| a. | | 4p dull vermilion (P8) | 550.00 | 90.00 |
| | | Plate 7 | 600.00 | 105.00 |
| | | Plate 9 | 525.00 | 65.00 |
| | | Plate 13 | 525.00 | 60.00 |
| b. | | Imperf. (P11, 12) | 2,000. | |

A17      (Hyphen after SIX) — A18

A19      A20

A21

### 1865      Wmk. 24

| | | | | |
|---|---|---|---|---|
| **44** | A17 | 3p rose (P4) | 1,600. | 190.00 |
| a. | | Wmk. 3 roses & shamrock | 3,750. | 950.00 |
| **45** | A18 | 6p lilac (P5) | 825.00 | 85.00 |
| a. | | 6p deep lilac | 1,350. | 135.00 |
| | | Plate 6 | 2,700. | 160.00 |
| b. | | Double impression | 13,000. | |
| c. | | Wmk. 3 roses & shamrock (P5) | | 800.00 |
| | | As "c," plate 6 | | 1,000. |
| **46** | A19 | 9p straw (P4) | 3,600. | 525.00 |
| | | Plate 5 | 20,000. | |
| a. | | Wmk. 3 roses & shamrock (P4) | — | 1,500. |
| **47** | A20 | 10p red brn (P1) | | 36,000. |
| **48** | A21 | 1sh green (P4) | 1,800. | 210.00 |
| b. | | Wmk. 3 roses & shamrock | | 1,175. |
| c. | | Vert. pair, imperf. btwn. | | 11,000. |

No. 46, plate 5, is from a proof sheet.
See Nos. 49-50, 52-54. Compare design A17 with A27.

 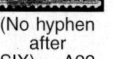

(No hyphen after SIX) — A22      A23

### 1867-80      Wmk. 25

| | | | | |
|---|---|---|---|---|
| **49** | A17 | 3p rose (P5) | 475.00 | 60.00 |
| a. | | 3p deep rose | 850.00 | 90.00 |
| | | Plate 6 | 1,000. | 240.00 |
| | | Plate 7 | 475.00 | 60.00 |
| | | Plate 8 | 600.00 | 65.00 |
| | | Plate 9 | 575.00 | 65.00 |
| | | Plate 10 | 725.00 | 115.00 |
| b. | | Imperf. (P5,6,8,9) | 3,500. | |
| **50** | A18 | 6p dull violet (P6) | 1,350. | 85.00 |
| a. | | bright violet (P6) | 1,250. | 95.00 |
| **51** | A22 | 6p red violet (P8, 9) ('69) | 575.00 | 85.00 |
| | | Plate 10 | | 27,500. |
| a. | | 6p violet (P8) | 600.00 | 115.00 |
| b. | | Imperf. (P8, 9) | 5,500. | 3,750. |

| | | | | |
|---|---|---|---|---|
| **52** | A19 | 9p bister (P4) ('67) | 2,000. | 300.00 |
| a. | | Imperf. (P4) | 7,200. | |
| **53** | A20 | 10p red brown (P1) | 2,650. | 325.00 |
| | | Plate 2 | 32,000. | 11,000. |
| a. | | 10p deep red brown | 3,750. | 500.00 |
| b. | | Imperf. (P1) | 7,200. | |
| **54** | A21 | 1sh green (P4) | 1,000. | 52.50 |
| | | Plate 5 | 700.00 | 37.50 |
| | | Plate 6 | 1,100. | 37.50 |
| | | Plate 7 | 1,100. | 65.00 |
| a. | | 1sh deep green | 775.00 | 42.50 |
| b. | | Imperf. (P4) | 5,500. | 2,700. |
| **55** | A23 | 2sh blue (P1) | 2,600. | 180.00 |
| | | Plate 3 | 3,100. | 210.00 |
| | | Plate 3 | | 9,000. |
| b. | | Imperf. (P1) | 10,000. | |
| **56** | A23 | 2sh pale brn (P1) ('80) | 18,500. | 3,500. |
| a. | | Imperf. (P1) | 20,000. | |

No. 51, plate 10 and No. 53, plate 2, are from proof sheets.

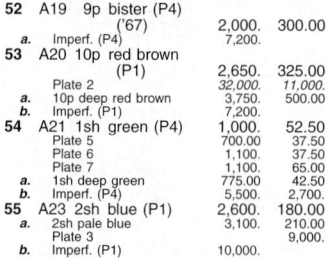

A24

### 1867    Wmk. 26    Perf. 15½x15

| | | | | |
|---|---|---|---|---|
| **57** | A24 | 5sh rose (P1) | 7,400. | 650.00 |
| | | Plate 2 | 11,000. | 1,100. |
| a. | | 5sh pale rose | 7,400. | 650.00 |
| b. | | Imperf. (P1) | 12,500. | |

See No. 90. Compare design A24 with A51.

A25

### 1870    Engr.    Wmk. 27    Perf. 14

| | | | | |
|---|---|---|---|---|
| **58** | A25 | ½p rose (P5) | 95.00 | 19.00 |
| | | Plate 1 | 240.00 | 80.00 |
| | | Plate 3 | 160.00 | 42.50 |
| | | Plate 4 | 140.00 | 32.50 |
| | | Plate 6 | 105.00 | 19.00 |
| | | Plate 8 | 350.00 | 100.00 |
| | | Plate 9 | 5,000. | 750.00 |
| | | Plate 10 | 115.00 | 19.00 |
| | | Plate 11-14 | 105.00 | 19.00 |
| | | Plate 15 | 160.00 | 42.50 |
| | | Plate 19 | 180.00 | 60.00 |
| | | Plate 20 | 275.00 | 80.00 |
| a. | | Imperf (see footnote) | — | |

Plates 1, 3-6, 8, 10, 14 are known imperf. Values: from $3,250 unused, $2,100 used.

A26      A27

A28      A29

Type A28 has a lined background.

### 1872-73    Wmk. 25    Typo.

| | | | | |
|---|---|---|---|---|
| **59** | A26 | 6p brown (P11) | 725.00 | 52.50 |
| | | Plate 12 | | 3,500. |
| a. | | 6p deep brown (P11) | 1,000. | 95.00 |
| | | Plate 12 | | 3,250. |
| b. | | 6p pale buff (P11) | 725.00 | 90.00 |
| | | Plate 12 | 2,400. | 265.00 |
| **60** | A26 | 6p gray (P12) ('73) | 1,600. | 240.00 |
| a. | | Imperf. | 5,000. | |

### 1873-80

| | | | | |
|---|---|---|---|---|
| **61** | A27 | 3p rose (shades) (P11, 17-18) | 425.00 | 47.50 |
| | | Plates 12, 15-16, 19 | 375.00 | 47.50 |
| | | Plate 14 | 450.00 | 47.50 |
| | | Plate 20 | 600.00 | 100.00 |
| **62** | A28 | 6p gray (P13-16) | 425.00 | 65.00 |
| | | Plate 17 | 725.00 | 150.00 |
| **63** | A28 | 6p buff (P13) | | 21,000. |
| **64** | A29 | 1sh pale green (P12, 13) | 525.00 | 105.00 |
| | | Plate 10 | 625.00 | 150.00 |
| | | Plate 11 | 625.00 | 130.00 |

| | | | |
|---|---|---|---|
| Plate 14 | | | 16,500. |
| *a.* | 1sh deep green (P8, 9) | 625.00 | 130.00 |
| **65** | A29 1sh salmon (P13) ('80) | 4,000. | 625.00 |

No. 64, plate 14, is from a proof sheet.
See Nos. 83, 86-87. For surcharges see Nos. 94-95. For overprints see Nos. O6, O30.

A30

**1875** **Wmk. 28**

| | | | |
|---|---|---|---|
| **66** | A30 2½p claret (P1, 2) | 550.00 | 85.00 |
| | Plate 3 | 850.00 | 130.00 |
| *a.* | Bluish paper (P1) | 800.00 | 130.00 |
| | As "a," P2 | 6,500. | 1,450. |
| | As "a," P3 | | 4,500. |
| *b.* | Lettered "LH-FL" | 17,500. | 2,150. |

**1876-80** **Wmk. 29**

| | | | |
|---|---|---|---|
| **67** | A30 2½p claret (P4-9, 11-16) | 450.00 | 52.50 |
| | Plate 3 | 1,000. | 115.00 |
| | Plate 10 | 500.00 | 70.00 |
| | Plate 17 | 1,350. | 250.00 |
| **68** | A30 2½p ultra (P18-20) ('80) | 500.00 | 42.50 |
| | Plate 17 | 500.00 | 60.00 |

A31   A32

**1876-80** **Wmk. 23**

| | | | |
|---|---|---|---|
| **69** | A31 4p vermilion (P15) | 2,200. | 450.00 |
| | Plate 16 | | 27,500. |
| **70** | A31 4p pale ol grn ('77) (P16) | 950.00 | 260.00 |
| | Plate 15 | 1,050. | 300.00 |
| | Plate 17 | | 17,500. |
| *a.* | Imperf (P15) | 675.00 | |
| **71** | A31 4p gray brn (P17) ('80) | 1,950. | 475.00 |
| **72** | A32 8p brn lilac (P1) ('76) | 11,750. | |
| **73** | A32 8p org (P1) ('76) | 1,300. | 325.00 |

No. 72 was never placed in use.
No. 69, plate 16, is from proof sheets.

A33   A34

**1878** **Wmk. 26** **Perf. 15½x15**

| | | | |
|---|---|---|---|
| **74** | A33 10sh slate (P1) | 45,000. | 2,900. |
| **75** | A34 £1 brn lil (P1) | 72,000. | 4,000. |

See Nos. 91-92. Compare design A34 with A52.

A35   A36

A37   A38

A39   A40

**1880-81** **Wmk. 30** **Perf. 14**

| | | | |
|---|---|---|---|
| **78** | A35 ½p green | 47.50 | 13.00 |
| *a.* | Imperf. | 2,250. | |
| *b.* | No watermark | 6,500. | |
| **79** | A36 1p red brown | 24.00 | 13.00 |
| *a.* | Imperf. | 2,250. | |
| *b.* | Wmk. 29, error | | |
| **80** | A37 1½p red brown | 185.00 | 47.50 |
| **81** | A38 2p lilac rose | 250.00 | 95.00 |
| **82** | A30 2½p ultra (P23) ('81) | 375.00 | 30.00 |
| | Plate 21 | 400.00 | 37.50 |
| | Plate 22 | 375.00 | 37.50 |
| *a.* | Imperf. (P23) | 600.00 | |
| **83** | A27 3p rose (P21) ('81) | 425.00 | 85.00 |
| | Plate 20 | 750.00 | 150.00 |
| **84** | A31 4p gray brown (P17, 18) | 375.00 | 65.00 |
| **85** | A39 5p dp indigo ('81) | 675.00 | 115.00 |
| *a.* | Imperf. | 3,800. | 3,250. |
| **86** | A28 6p gray (P18) | 375.00 | 65.00 |
| | Plate 17 | 375.00 | 65.00 |
| **87** | A29 1sh sal (P14) | 525.00 | 150.00 |
| | Plate 13 | 675.00 | 150.00 |

The 1sh in purple was not issued. Value, unused, $8,750.
See No. 98. For overprints see Nos. O2-O3, O37, O45, O55.
Compare design A35 with A54.

**1881**

| | | | |
|---|---|---|---|
| **88** | A40 1p lilac (14 dots in each angle) | 220.00 | 32.50 |
| **89** | A40 1p lilac (16 dots in each angle) | 2.75 | 2.00 |
| *a.* | Printed on both sides | 800.00 | |
| *b.* | Imperf., pair | 5,500. | |
| *c.* | No watermark | 5,000. | |
| *d.* | Bluish paper | 4,500. | |
| *e.* | Printed on the gummed side | 800.00 | |

For overprint see No. O4.

**1882-83** **Wmk. 31**

| | | | |
|---|---|---|---|
| **90** | A24 5sh rose, *bluish* (P4) | 25,000. | 4,250. |
| *a.* | White paper | 22,500. | 3,250. |
| **91** | A33 10sh slate, *bluish* (P1) | 100,000. | 5,250. |
| *a.* | White paper | 110,000. | 4,000. |
| **92** | A34 £1 brown lilac, *bluish* (P1) | 112,500. | 9,250. |
| *a.* | White paper | 135,000. | 7,750. |

A41

**1882** **Wmk. Two Anchors (31)**

| | | | |
|---|---|---|---|
| **93** | A41 £5 brt orange (P1) | 12,750. | 5,000. |
| *a.* | £5 pale dull orange, *bluish* | 55,000. | 13,000. |
| *b.* | £5 bright orange, *bluish* | 56,000. | 13,000. |

The paper of No. 93b is less bluish than that of No. 93a, and it is a later printing.

Types of 1873-80
Surcharged in Carmine

**1883** **Wmk. 30**

| | | | |
|---|---|---|---|
| **94** | A27 3p on 3p violet | 475.00 | 140.00 |
| **95** | A28 6p on 6p violet | 525.00 | 140.00 |
| *a.* | Double surcharge | | 10,000. |

A44

**1883** **Wmk. 31**

| | | | |
|---|---|---|---|
| **96** | A44 2sh6p lilac | 475.00 | 150.00 |
| *a.* | Bluish paper | 7,500. | 3,250. |

**See British Offices Abroad for overprints on types A44-A133.** These overprints include "M.E.F.," "B.A.," "B.M.A.," "E.A.F.," "CHINA," "Morocco Agencies," "TANGIER," "LEVANT," "PARAS," and "PIASTRE(S)."

A45   A46

A47   A48

A49   A50

**1883-84** **Wmk. 30**

| | | | |
|---|---|---|---|
| **98** | A35 ½p slate blue ('84) | 27.50 | 8.50 |
| **99** | A45 1½p lilac ('84) | 100.00 | 40.00 |
| **100** | A46 2p lilac ('84) | 185.00 | 75.00 |
| **101** | A47 2½p lilac ('84) | 80.00 | 16.00 |
| **102** | A48 3p lilac ('84) | 200.00 | 95.00 |
| **103** | A45 4p green ('84) | 450.00 | 200.00 |
| **104** | A45 5p green ('84) | 450.00 | 200.00 |
| **105** | A46 6p green ('84) | 475.00 | 225.00 |
| **106** | A50 9p green ('84) | 950.00 | 425.00 |
| **107** | A48 1sh green ('84) | 1,000. | 250.00 |
| | Nos. 98-107 (10) | 3,917. | 1,534. |

Nos. 99-107 were printed by De La Rue in a newly invented doubly fugitive ink that was only available in lilac and green. The stamps were unpopular with the public and postal clerks because they were unattractive and the different denominations were difficult to distinguish from one another.
Values are for stamps of good color. Faded stamps sell for much less. Soaking stamps will cause the color to run.
No. 104 with line instead of period under "d" was not regularly issued. Value, $27,500.
Nos. 98-105 and 107 exist imperf. Values from $2,150 to $3,000 each for Nos. 98-105, $4,500 for No. 107.
For overprints see Nos. O5, O7, O27-O29.

A51   A52

**1884** **Wmk. 31**

| | | | |
|---|---|---|---|
| **108** | A51 5sh carmine rose | 950.00 | 220.00 |
| *a.* | Bluish paper | 12,500. | 3,750. |
| **109** | A52 10sh ultra | 1,900. | 500.00 |
| *a.* | 10sh cobalt | 30,000. | 7,250. |
| *b.* | Bluish paper | 37,500. | 8,000. |
| *c.* | As "a," bluish paper | 50,000. | 14,000. |

For overprints see Nos. O8-O9.

A53

**1884** **Wmk. 30**

| | | | |
|---|---|---|---|
| **110** | A53 £1 brown violet | 26,000. | 3,250. |

See Nos. 123-124. For overprints see Nos. O10, O13, O15.

### Queen Victoria Jubilee Issue

A54   A55

A56   A57

A58   A59

A60   A61

A62   A63

A64   A65

Two types of 5p:
I — Squarish dots beside "d."
II — Tiny vertical dashes beside "d."

**1887-92** **Wmk. 30**

| | | | |
|---|---|---|---|
| **111** | A54 ½p vermilion | 1.60 | 1.00 |
| *a.* | Printed on both sides | | |
| *b.* | Double impression | 15,000. | |
| **112** | A55 1½p violet & grn | 16.00 | 7.50 |
| **113** | A56 2p grn & car rose | 30.00 | 13.00 |
| *a.* | 2p green & vermilion | 375.00 | 240.00 |
| **114** | A57 2½p violet, *blue* | 24.00 | 3.25 |
| **115** | A58 3p violet, *yellow* | 24.00 | 3.50 |
| *a.* | 3p violet, *orange* | 575.00 | 175.00 |
| **116** | A59 4p brown & grn | 32.50 | 14.00 |
| **117** | A60 4½p car rose & grn ('92) | 10.50 | 42.50 |
| **118** | A61 5p lilac & bl, II | 37.50 | 11.50 |
| *a.* | Type I | 550.00 | 90.00 |
| **119** | A62 6p violet, *rose* | 32.50 | 10.50 |
| **120** | A63 9p blue & lilac | 65.00 | 42.50 |
| **121** | A64 10p car rose & lilac ('90) | 47.50 | 40.00 |
| **122** | A65 1sh green | 220.00 | 65.00 |
| | Nos. 111-122 (12) | 541.10 | 254.25 |

The unpopular green and lilac issue (Nos. 98-107) were replaced by these stamps in brightly colored inks and papers that made it easier to distinguish the different denominations.

See Nos. 125-126. For overprints see Nos. O11-O12, O14, O16-O18, O31-O36, O38, O44, O46-O48, O54, O56-O58, O65-O66.

**1888       Wmk. Three Orbs (29)**

| | | | | |
|---|---|---|---|---|
| 123 | A53 | £1 brown violet | 60,000. | 4,250. |

**1891       Wmk. 30**

| | | | | |
|---|---|---|---|---|
| 124 | A53 | £1 green | 3,500. | 700.00 |

**1900       Wmk. 30**

| | | | | |
|---|---|---|---|---|
| 125 | A54 | ½p blue green | 1.90 | 2.10 |
| *a.* | | Imperf | 5,000. | |
| 126 | A65 | 1sh car rose & green | 52.50 | 135.00 |

No. 125 in bright blue is a color changeling.

King Edward VII — A66      A67

A68      A69

A70      A71

A72      A73

A74      A75

A76      A77

A78

**1902-11    Wmk. 30    Perf. 14**
**Ordinary Paper**

| | | | | |
|---|---|---|---|---|
| 127 | A66 | ½p gray green | 2.25 | 1.75 |
| 128 | A66 | 1p scarlet | 2.25 | 1.75 |
| *c.* | | 1p aniline rose ('11) | 225.00 | 160.00 |
| *e.* | | Booklet pane of 6 | 50.00 | |
| *f.* | | No watermark | 45.00 | 45.00 |
| *g.* | | Imperf., pair | 20,000. | |
| 129 | A67 | 1½p vio & green | 45.00 | 22.50 |
| 130 | A68 | 2p yel grn & car | 52.50 | 22.50 |
| *b.* | | 2p deep grn & red | 60.00 | 32.50 |
| 131 | A66 | 2½p ultra | 22.50 | 11.50 |
| 132 | A69 | 3p dull pur, org yel | 45.00 | 19.00 |
| 133 | A70 | 4p gray brn & grn | 57.50 | 35.00 |

| | | | | |
|---|---|---|---|---|
| 134 | A71 | 5p dull pur & ultra | 67.50 | 22.50 |
| 135 | A66 | 6p pale dull vio | 45.00 | 22.50 |
| *a.* | | 6p slate purple | 45.00 | 22.50 |
| *b.* | | 6p red violet | 45.00 | 22.50 |
| *c.* | | 6p dark violet | 45.00 | 40.00 |
| 136 | A72 | 9p ultra & dull vio | 100.00 | 70.00 |
| 137 | A73 | 10p car & dull pur | 100.00 | 70.00 |
| *a.* | | 10p scarlet & dull purple | 92.50 | 85.00 |
| 138 | A74 | 1sh car & dull grn | 92.50 | 40.00 |
| *a.* | | 1sh scarlet & dark green | 92.50 | 60.00 |

**Wmk. 31**

| | | | | |
|---|---|---|---|---|
| 139 | A75 | 2sh6p lilac | 260.00 | 150.00 |
| *a.* | | 2sh6p dark violet | 260.00 | 175.00 |
| 140 | A76 | 5sh car rose | 400.00 | 225.00 |
| *b.* | | 5sh carmine | 400.00 | 225.00 |
| 141 | A77 | 10sh ultra | 775.00 | 525.00 |

**Wmk. Three Imperial Crowns (30)**

| | | | | |
|---|---|---|---|---|
| 142 | A78 | £1 blue green | 2,000. | 750.00 |
| | | Nos. 127-138 (12) | 632.00 | 339.00 |

Nos. 129, 130 and 132 to 139 inclusive exist on both ordinary and chalky paper.

See Nos. 143, 144, 146-150. For overprints see Nos. O19-O26, O39-O43, O49-O53, O59-O64, O67-O83.

**See British Offices Abroad for overprints on types A44-A133.**
These overprints include "M.E.F.," "B.A.," "B.M.A.," "E.A.F.," "CHINA," "Morocco Agencies," "TANGIER," "LEVANT," "PARAS," and "PIASTRE(S)."

**1904       Wmk. 30**

| | | | | |
|---|---|---|---|---|
| 143 | A66 | ½p pale yellow green | 2.25 | 1.75 |
| *b.* | | Booklet pane of 5 + label | 450.00 | |
| *c.* | | Booklet pane of 6 | 37.50 | |
| *d.* | | Double impression | 29,000. | |
| *e.* | | Imperf., pair | 27,500. | |

Edward VII — A79

**1909-10**

| | | | | |
|---|---|---|---|---|
| 144 | A70 | 4p pale orange ('10) | 22.50 | 17.50 |
| 145 | A79 | 7p gray ('10) | 13.50 | 22.50 |

**1911       Perf. 15x14**

| | | | | |
|---|---|---|---|---|
| 146 | A66 | ½p dull yel green | 45.00 | 50.00 |
| 147 | A66 | 1p carmine rose | 17.50 | 17.50 |
| 148 | A66 | 2½p brt ultra | 25.00 | 17.50 |
| 149 | A69 | 3p violet, *yellow* | 52.50 | 17.50 |
| *a.* | | 3p gray, *lemon* | 3,000. | |
| 150 | A70 | 4p orange | 35.00 | 17.50 |
| | | Nos. 146-150 (5) | 175.00 | 120.00 |

A80      A81

**King George V**

**1911     Wmk. 30    Perf. 15x14**

| | | | | |
|---|---|---|---|---|
| 151 | A80 | ½p yellow green | 5.75 | 4.50 |
| *a.* | | Booklet pane of 6 | 62.50 | |
| *b.* | | Perf. 14 (error) | 17,500. | 700.00 |
| 152 | A81 | 1p carmine | 5.25 | 3.00 |
| *a.* | | Booklet pane of 6 | 62.50 | |
| *b.* | | Perf. 14 (error) | — | — |
| *c.* | | 1p pale carmine | 16.00 | 3.50 |
| *d.* | | As "c," booklet pane of 6 | 125.00 | |

**1912, Jan. 1     Re-engraved**

| | | | | |
|---|---|---|---|---|
| 153 | A80 | ½p yellow green | 10.00 | 4.50 |
| 154 | A81 | 1p scarlet | 7.50 | 3.50 |
| *a.* | | 1p aniline scarlet | 225.00 | 125.00 |

In the re-engraved stamps the lines of the hair and beard are clearer. The re-engraved ½p has 3 lines of shading instead of 4 between the point of neck and frame; in the 1p the body of the lion is nearly covered by lines of shading.

**1912, Aug.   Wmk. 33   Perf. 15x14**
**Die I (Before Re-engraving)**

| | | | | |
|---|---|---|---|---|
| 155 | A80 | ½p yellow green | 45.00 | 45.00 |
| *a.* | | Booklet pane of 6 | 270.00 | |

| | | | | |
|---|---|---|---|---|
| 156 | A81 | 1p scarlet | 35.00 | 35.00 |
| *a.* | | Booklet pane of 6 | 210.00 | |

**Die II (Re-engraved)**

| | | | | |
|---|---|---|---|---|
| 157 | A80 | ½p yellow green | 8.00 | 3.50 |
| 158 | A81 | 1p scarlet | 9.25 | 3.50 |

**1912, Oct.       Wmk. 32**

| | | | | |
|---|---|---|---|---|
| 158A | A80 | ½p yellow green | 14.00 | 9.25 |
| *e.* | | Imperf., pair | 300.00 | |
| 158B | A81 | 1p scarlet | 20.00 | 11.50 |
| *g.* | | Imperf., pair | 300.00 | |

A82      A83

A84      A85

A86      A87

A88      A89

King George V — A90

"Britannia Rule the Waves" A91

TWO PENCE:
Die I — Four horizontal lines above the head. Heavy colored lines above and below the bottom tablet. The inner frame line is closer to the central design than it is to the outer frame line.
Die II — Three lines above the head. Thinner lines above and below the bottom tablet. The inner frame line is midway between the central design and the outer frame line.

**1912-13    Wmk. 33    Perf. 15x14**

| | | | | |
|---|---|---|---|---|
| 159 | A82 | ½p green | 1.10 | 1.10 |
| *a.* | | Double impression | 22,500. | |
| *b.* | | Booklet pane of 6 | 15.00 | |
| 160 | A83 | 1p scarlet | 1.10 | 1.10 |
| *a.* | | Booklet pane of 6 | 15.00 | |
| *b.* | | Tete beche pair | 67,500. | |
| 161 | A84 | 1½p red brown | 4.50 | 1.75 |
| *a.* | | 1½p orange brown | 22.50 | 18.00 |
| *b.* | | "PENCF" | 220.00 | 175.00 |
| *c.* | | Unwmkd. | 200.00 | 140.00 |
| *d.* | | Booklet pane of 6 | 30.00 | |
| *e.* | | Booklet pane of 4 + 2 labels | 525.00 | |
| 162 | A85 | 2p deep orange (I) | 5.00 | 3.50 |
| *a.* | | 2p deep orange (II) | 5.75 | 4.25 |
| *b.* | | Booklet pane of 6 (I) | 67.50 | |
| *c.* | | Booklet pane of 6 (II) | 110.00 | |
| 163 | A86 | 2½p ultra | 14.00 | 4.50 |
| 164 | A87 | 3p bluish violet | 8.00 | 2.25 |
| 165 | A88 | 4p slate green | 17.50 | 2.25 |
| 166 | A89 | 5p yellow brown | 17.50 | 5.75 |
| *a.* | | Unwmkd. | 950.00 | |
| 167 | A89 | 6p rose lilac | 17.50 | 8.00 |
| *a.* | | 6p dull violet | 30.00 | 11.50 |
| *b.* | | Perf. 14 | 105.00 | 125.00 |
| 168 | A89 | 7p olive green | 22.50 | 11.50 |
| 169 | A89 | 8p black, *yellow* | 37.50 | 12.50 |
| 170 | A90 | 9p black brown | 22.50 | 6.75 |

| | | | | |
|---|---|---|---|---|
| 171 | A90 | 10p light blue | 25.00 | 22.50 |
| 172 | A90 | 1sh bister | 24.00 | 4.50 |
| | | Nos. 159-172 (14) | 217.70 | 87.95 |

No. 167 is on chalky paper.
Nos. 159-172 were printed in a variety of shades.
See #177-178, 183, 187-200, 210, 212-220. Compare design A83 with A97.

**See British Offices Abroad for overprints on types A44-A133.**
These overprints include "M.E.F.," "B.A.," "B.M.A.," "E.A.F.," "CHINA," "Morocco Agencies," "TANGIER," "LEVANT," "PARAS," and "PIASTRE(S)."

**Perf. 11x12**

**1913-18    Engr.      Wmk. 34**

| | | | | |
|---|---|---|---|---|
| 173 | A91 | 2sh6p dark brown | 275.00 | 190.00 |
| *a.* | | 2sh6p light brown | 260.00 | 220.00 |
| 174 | A91 | 5sh rose car | 450.00 | 310.00 |
| *a.* | | 5sh carmine | 475.00 | 375.00 |
| 175 | A91 | 10sh indigo blue | 900.00 | 475.00 |
| *a.* | | 10sh blue | 2,250. | 800.00 |
| 176 | A91 | £1 green | 2,450. | 1,550. |
| | | Nos. 173-176 (4) | 4,075. | 2,525. |

Nos. 173-176 were printed in 1913 by Waterlow Bros. & Layton; Nos. 173a-175a were printed in 1915-18 by Thomas De La Rue & Co.
See Nos. 179-181, 222-224.

**1913   Wmk. 32   Typo.   Perf. 15x14**
**Coil Stamps**

| | | | | |
|---|---|---|---|---|
| 177 | A82 | ½p green | 175.00 | 210.00 |
| 178 | A83 | 1p scarlet | 260.00 | 260.00 |

**Type of 1913-18 Retouched**

**1919   Engr.    Wmk. 34    Perf. 11x12**

| | | | | |
|---|---|---|---|---|
| 179 | A91 | 2sh6p olive brown | 115.00 | 75.00 |
| 180 | A91 | 5sh car rose | 290.00 | 125.00 |
| 181 | A91 | 10sh blue | 425.00 | 180.00 |
| | | Nos. 179-181 (3) | 830.00 | 380.00 |

The retouched stamps usually have a dot above the middle of the top frame. They are 22¾mm high, whereas Nos. 173-176 are 22mm high.
Nos. 179-181 were printed by Bradbury, Wilkinson & Co.

**Type of 1912-13**

**1922    Typo.   Wmk. 33    Perf. 15x14**

| | | | | |
|---|---|---|---|---|
| 183 | A90 | 9p olive green | 120.00 | 35.00 |

**British Empire Exhibition Issue**

British Lion and George V A92

**Wmk. 35**

**1924, Apr. 23    Engr.    Perf. 14**

| | | | | |
|---|---|---|---|---|
| 185 | A92 | 1p vermilion | 11.50 | 12.50 |
| | | Never hinged | 17.50 | |
| 186 | A92 | 1½p dark brown | 17.50 | 17.50 |
| | | Never hinged | 26.00 | |

See Nos. 203-204.

**Types of 1912-13 Issue**

**1924      Typo.      Perf. 15x14**

| | | | | |
|---|---|---|---|---|
| 187 | A82 | ½p green | 1.10 | 1.10 |
| | | Never hinged | 1.50 | |
| *a.* | | Wmk. sideways | 10.00 | 3.75 |
| | | Never hinged | 18.00 | |
| *b.* | | Booklet pane of 6 | 12.00 | |
| | | Never hinged | 18.00 | |
| *c.* | | Double impression | 9,250. | |
| 188 | A83 | 1p scarlet | 1.10 | 1.10 |
| | | Never hinged | 1.40 | |
| *a.* | | Wmk. sideways | 22.50 | 17.50 |
| | | Never hinged | 45.00 | |
| *b.* | | Booklet pane of 6 | 12.50 | |
| | | Never hinged | 18.50 | |
| 189 | A84 | 1½p red brown | 1.10 | 1.10 |
| | | Never hinged | 1.40 | |
| *a.* | | Tête bêche pair | 550.00 | 875.00 |
| | | Never hinged | 775.00 | |
| *b.* | | Wmk. sideways | 20.00 | 4.00 |
| | | Never hinged | 40.00 | |
| *c.* | | Booklet pane of 6 | 12.50 | |
| | | Never hinged | 18.50 | |
| *d.* | | Bklt. pane of 4 + 2 labels | 160.00 | |
| | | Never hinged | 260.00 | |
| *e.* | | Double impression | 16,500. | |
| 190 | A85 | 2p dp orange (II) | 2.90 | 2.90 |
| | | Never hinged | 3.75 | |
| *a.* | | Wmk. sideways | 110.00 | 110.00 |
| | | Never hinged | 200.00 | |
| *b.* | | Unwatermarked | 925.00 | |
| | | Never hinged | 1,400. | |

| 191 | A86 | 2½p ultra | 5.75 | 3.50 |
|---|---|---|---|---|
| | | Never hinged | 10.00 | |
| a. | | Unwatermarked | 1,750. | |
| | | Never hinged | 2,250. | |
| 192 | A87 | 3p violet | 11.50 | 2.75 |
| | | Never hinged | 19.00 | |
| 193 | A88 | 4p slate green | 14.00 | 2.75 |
| | | Never hinged | 29.00 | |
| 194 | A89 | 5p yel brown | 22.50 | 3.50 |
| | | Never hinged | 45.00 | |
| 195 | A89 | 6p dull violet | 3.50 | 1.75 |
| | | Never hinged | 5.00 | |
| 198 | A90 | 9p olive green | 13.50 | 4.00 |
| | | Never hinged | 21.50 | |
| 199 | A90 | 10p dull blue | 45.00 | 45.00 |
| | | Never hinged | 110.00 | |
| 200 | A90 | 1sh bister | 25.00 | 3.50 |
| | | Never hinged | 50.00 | |
| | | Nos. 187-200 (12) | 146.95 | 72.95 |

Nos. 187a, 188a, 189b, 190a issued in coils. Inverted watermarks on the three lowest values are usually from booklet panes.

Nos. 188-189 were issued also on experimental paper with variety of Wmk. 35: closer spacing; letters shorter, rounder.

### British Empire Exhibition Issue
Type of 1924, Dated "1925"

| **1925, May 9** | | **Engr.** | **Perf. 14** | |
|---|---|---|---|---|
| 203 | A92 | 1p vermilion | 17.00 | 35.00 |
| | | Never hinged | 25.00 | |
| 204 | A92 | 1½p brown | 45.00 | 80.00 |
| | | Never hinged | 67.50 | |

A93       A94

A95

St. George Slaying the Dragon A96

| **1929, May 10** | | **Typo.** | **Perf. 15x14** | |
|---|---|---|---|---|
| 205 | A93 | ½p green | 2.50 | 2.50 |
| | | Never hinged | 3.75 | |
| a. | | Wmk. sideways | 45.00 | 45.00 |
| | | Never hinged | 120.00 | |
| b. | | Booklet pane of 6 | 27.50 | |
| 206 | A94 | 1p scarlet | 2.50 | 2.50 |
| | | Never hinged | 3.75 | |
| a. | | Wmk. sideways | 82.50 | 82.50 |
| | | Never hinged | 120.00 | |
| b. | | Booklet pane of 6 | 27.50 | |
| 207 | A94 | 1½p dark brown | 2.60 | 2.00 |
| | | Never hinged | 4.00 | |
| a. | | Wmk. sideways | 90.00 | 45.00 |
| | | Never hinged | 90.00 | |
| b. | | Booklet pane of 6 | 20.00 | |
| c. | | Booklet pane of 4 + 2 labels | 250.00 | |
| 208 | A95 | 2½p deep blue | 11.50 | 11.50 |
| | | Never hinged | 24.00 | |
| | | Nos. 205-208 (4) | 19.10 | 18.50 |

Nos. 205a, 206a and 207a were issued in coils.

### Wmk. 219
| | | **Engr.** | **Perf. 12** | |
|---|---|---|---|---|
| 209 | A96 | £1 black | 850.00 | 625.00 |
| | | Never hinged | 1,400. | |

Universal Postal Union, 9th Congress.

A97

Type A97 designs are re-engraved versions of the types of the 1912-13 issue, with the most obvious difference being the solid appearance of the central field. The backgrounds appear to be solid, although the photoengraving screen can be seen under magnification.

| **Perf. 14½x14** | | | | |
|---|---|---|---|---|
| **1934-36** | | **Photo.** | **Wmk. 35** | |
| 210 | A97 | ½p dark green | .60 | .60 |
| | | Never hinged | 1.10 | |
| a. | | Wmk. sideways | 8.00 | 4.00 |
| | | Never hinged | 17.50 | |
| b. | | Booklet pane of 6 | 11.00 | |
| 211 | A83 | 1p carmine | .60 | .60 |
| | | Never hinged | 1.00 | |
| a. | | Wmk. sideways | 22.50 | 9.00 |
| | | Never hinged | 45.00 | |
| b. | | Booklet pane of 6 | 11.00 | |
| c. | | Imperf., pair | 2,500. | |
| d. | | Pair, imperf. btwn. | 3,850. | |
| 212 | A97 | 1½p red brown | .60 | .60 |
| | | Never hinged | 1.00 | |
| a. | | Imperf., pair | 750.00 | |
| b. | | Wmk. sideways | 9.00 | 4.50 |
| | | Never hinged | 13.00 | |
| c. | | Booklet pane of 6 | 5.50 | |
| d. | | Booklet pane of 4 + 2 labels | 110.00 | |
| 213 | A97 | 2p red org ('35) | .85 | .85 |
| | | Never hinged | 1.25 | |
| a. | | Imperf., pair | 4,500. | |
| b. | | Wmk. sideways | 140.00 | 100.00 |
| | | Never hinged | 250.00 | |
| 214 | A97 | 2½p ultra ('35) | 1.75 | 1.40 |
| | | Never hinged | 2.50 | |
| 215 | A97 | 3p dk violet ('35) | 1.75 | 1.40 |
| | | Never hinged | 2.50 | |
| 216 | A97 | 4p dk sl grn ('35) | 2.25 | 1.40 |
| | | Never hinged | 3.50 | |
| 217 | A97 | 5p yel brown ('36) | 7.00 | 3.00 |
| | | Never hinged | 11.00 | |
| 218 | A97 | 9p dk ol grn ('35) | 14.00 | 2.75 |
| | | Never hinged | 20.00 | |
| 219 | A97 | 10p Prus blue ('36) | 17.50 | 11.50 |
| | | Never hinged | 30.00 | |
| 220 | A97 | 1sh bister brn ('36) | 17.50 | 1.40 |
| | | Never hinged | 30.00 | |
| | | Nos. 210-220 (11) | 64.40 | 25.50 |

The designs in this set are slightly smaller than the 1912-13 issue.
Nos. 210a, 211a, 212b and 213b were issued in coils.

### Britannia Type of 1913-18
| **1934** | **Engr.** | **Wmk. 34** | **Perf. 11x12** | |
|---|---|---|---|---|
| 222 | A91 | 2sh6p brown | 90.00 | 45.00 |
| | | Never hinged | 150.00 | |
| 223 | A91 | 5sh carmine | 190.00 | 100.00 |
| | | Never hinged | 340.00 | |
| 224 | A91 | 10sh dark blue | 400.00 | 92.50 |
| | | Never hinged | 650.00 | |
| | | Nos. 222-224 (3) | 680.00 | 237.50 |

Waterlow & Sons. Can be distinguished by the crossed lines in background of portrait. Previous issues have horizontal lines only.

### Silver Jubilee Issue

A98

| **Perf. 14½x14** | | | | |
|---|---|---|---|---|
| **1935, May 7** | | **Photo.** | **Wmk. 35** | |
| 226 | A98 | ½p dark green | 1.05 | .60 |
| | | Never hinged | 1.55 | |
| a. | | Booklet pane of 4 | 18.50 | |
| 227 | A98 | 1p carmine | 1.60 | 1.90 |
| | | Never hinged | 2.30 | |
| | | Booklet pane of 4 | 18.50 | |
| 228 | A98 | 1½p red brown | 1.05 | .60 |
| | | Never hinged | 1.55 | |
| a. | | Booklet pane of 4 | 9.50 | |
| 229 | A98 | 2½p ultramarine | 5.50 | 6.25 |
| | | Never hinged | 7.75 | |
| a. | | 2½p Prussian blue | 8,250. | 10,000. |
| | | Never hinged | 9,500. | |
| | | Nos. 226-229 (4) | 9.20 | 9.35 |

25th anniv. of the reign of George V. Device at right differs on 1½p and 2½p.

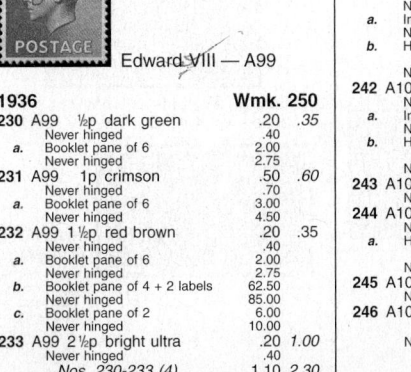

Edward VIII — A99

| **1936** | | | **Wmk. 250** | |
|---|---|---|---|---|
| 230 | A99 | ½p dark green | .20 | .35 |
| | | Never hinged | .40 | |
| a. | | Booklet pane of 6 | 2.00 | |
| | | Never hinged | 2.75 | |
| 231 | A99 | 1p crimson | .50 | .60 |
| | | Never hinged | .70 | |
| a. | | Booklet pane of 6 | 3.00 | |
| | | Never hinged | 4.50 | |
| 232 | A99 | 1½p red brown | .20 | .35 |
| | | Never hinged | .40 | |
| a. | | Booklet pane of 6 | 2.00 | |
| | | Never hinged | 2.75 | |
| b. | | Booklet pane of 4 + 2 labels | 62.50 | |
| | | Never hinged | 85.00 | |
| c. | | Booklet pane of 2 | 6.00 | |
| | | Never hinged | 10.00 | |
| 233 | A99 | 2½p bright ultra | .20 | 1.00 |
| | | Never hinged | .40 | |
| | | Nos. 230-233 (4) | 1.10 | 2.30 |

King George VI and Queen Elizabeth A100

| **Perf. 14½x14** | | | | |
|---|---|---|---|---|
| **1937, May 13** | | | **Wmk. 251** | |
| 234 | A100 | 1½p purple brown | .25 | .25 |
| | | | .35 | |

Coronation of George VI and Elizabeth.

**See British Offices Abroad for overprints on types A44-A133.**

**These overprints include "M.E.F.," "B.A.," "B.M.A.," "E.A.F.," "CHINA," "Morocco Agencies," "TANGIER," "LEVANT," "PARAS," and "PIASTRE(S)."**

A101      A102

 King George VI — A103

Nos. 235-240 show face and neck highlighted, background solid.

| **1937-39** | | | | |
|---|---|---|---|---|
| 235 | A101 | ½p deep green | .20 | .25 |
| | | Never hinged | .25 | |
| a. | | Wmk. sideways | .40 | .45 |
| | | Never hinged | .55 | |
| b. | | Booklet pane of 6 | 5.50 | |
| | | Never hinged | 7.50 | |
| c. | | Booklet pane of 4 | 25.00 | 32.50 |
| | | Never hinged | 50.00 | |
| d. | | Booklet pane of 2 | 8.50 | |
| | | Never hinged | 12.50 | |
| 236 | A101 | 1p scarlet | .20 | .20 |
| | | Never hinged | .25 | |
| a. | | Wmk. sideways | 8.50 | 9.50 |
| | | Never hinged | 22.50 | |
| b. | | Booklet pane of 6 | 8.50 | |
| | | Never hinged | 12.50 | |
| c. | | Booklet pane of 4 | 55.00 | 55.00 |
| | | Never hinged | 110.00 | |
| d. | | Booklet pane of 2 | 8.50 | |
| | | Never hinged | 12.50 | |
| 237 | A101 | 1½p red brown | .20 | .20 |
| | | Never hinged | .25 | |
| a. | | Wmk. sideways | .80 | 1.25 |
| | | Never hinged | 1.10 | |
| b. | | Booklet pane of 6 | 8.50 | |
| | | Never hinged | 12.50 | |
| c. | | Booklet pane of 4 + 2 labels | 57.50 | |
| | | Never hinged | 80.00 | |
| d. | | Booklet pane of 2 | 6.25 | |
| | | Never hinged | 9.00 | |
| 238 | A101 | 2p orange ('38) | .60 | .50 |
| | | Never hinged | 1.00 | |
| a. | | Wmk. sideways | 50.00 | 45.00 |
| | | Never hinged | 85.00 | |
| b. | | Booklet pane of 6 | 25.00 | |
| | | Never hinged | 37.50 | |
| 239 | A101 | 2½p bright ultra | .20 | .20 |
| | | Never hinged | .35 | |
| a. | | Wmk. sideways | 45.00 | 25.00 |
| | | Never hinged | 80.00 | |
| b. | | Booklet pane of 6 | 25.00 | |
| | | Never hinged | 37.50 | |
| c. | | Tête bêche pair | 24,000. | |
| 240 | A101 | 3p dk purple ('38) | 3.00 | 1.10 |
| | | Never hinged | 5.25 | |
| 241 | A102 | 4p gray green ('38) | .45 | .80 |
| | | Never hinged | .70 | |
| a. | | Imperf., pair | 4,750. | |
| | | Never hinged | 6,000. | |
| b. | | Horiz. pair, imperf. on 3 sides | 4,500. | |
| | | Never hinged | 6,000. | |
| 242 | A102 | 5p lt brown ('38) | 1.70 | .90 |
| | | Never hinged | 3.00 | |
| a. | | Imperf., pair | 5,500. | |
| | | Never hinged | 7,000. | |
| b. | | Horiz. pair, imperf. on 3 sides | 4,500. | |
| | | Never hinged | 6,000. | |
| 243 | A102 | 6p rose lilac ('39) | 1.10 | .65 |
| | | Never hinged | 1.50 | |
| 244 | A103 | 7p emerald ('39) | 2.75 | .65 |
| | | Never hinged | 5.50 | |
| a. | | Horiz. pair, imperf. on 3 sides | 4,400. | |
| | | Never hinged | 5,750. | |
| 245 | A103 | 8p brt rose ('39) | 3.75 | .90 |
| | | Never hinged | 6.00 | |
| 246 | A103 | 9p dp ol green ('39) | 3.50 | .90 |
| | | Never hinged | 6.50 | |

| 247 | A103 | 10p royal bl ('39) | 4.00 | .85 |
|---|---|---|---|---|
| | | Never hinged | 7.50 | |
| a. | | Imperf., pair | 5,700. | |
| | | Never hinged | 7,000. | |
| 248 | A103 | 1sh brown ('39) | 4.75 | 1.00 |
| | | Never hinged | 9.00 | |
| | | Nos. 235-248 (14) | 26.40 | 9.10 |
| | | Set, never hinged | 47.00 | |

Nos. 235a, 236a, 237a, 238a and 239a were issued in coils.
Nos. 235c and 236c are watermarked sideways.
The 1½p, 1p, 1½p, 2p and 2½p with watermark inverted are from booklet panes.
No. 238 bisects were used in Guernsey from 12/27/40 to 2/24/41.
See Nos. 258-263, 266, 280-285.

### Oman Surcharges
Various definitive and commemorative stamps between Nos. 243 and 372 were surcharged in annas (a), new paisa (np) and rupees (r) for use in Oman. The surcharges do not indicate where the stamps were used.

King George VI and Royal Arms — A104

King George VI — A105

| **1939-42** | **Engr.** | **Wmk. 259** | **Perf. 14** | |
|---|---|---|---|---|
| 249 | A104 | 2sh6p chestnut | 19.00 | 8.50 |
| | | Never hinged | 52.50 | |
| 249A | A104 | 2sh6p yel green ('42) | 6.00 | 1.75 |
| | | Never hinged | 16.00 | |
| 250 | A104 | 5sh dull red | 8.50 | 2.25 |
| | | Never hinged | 25.00 | |
| 251 | A105 | 10sh indigo | 150.00 | 24.00 |
| | | Never hinged | 325.00 | |
| 251A | A105 | 10sh ultra ('42) | 17.50 | 5.75 |
| | | Never hinged | 35.00 | |
| | | Nos. 249-251A (5) | 201.00 | 42.25 |

See No. 275.

Victoria and George VI A106

| **Perf. 14½x14** | | | | |
|---|---|---|---|---|
| **1940, May 6** | | **Photo.** | **Wmk. 251** | |
| 252 | A106 | ½p deep green | .20 | .25 |
| | | Never hinged | .30 | |
| 253 | A106 | 1p scarlet | .55 | .40 |
| | | Never hinged | 1.10 | |
| 254 | A106 | 1½p red brown | .25 | .85 |
| | | Never hinged | .55 | |
| 255 | A106 | 2p orange | .60 | .85 |
| | | Never hinged | 1.10 | |
| 256 | A106 | 2½p brt ultra | 1.25 | .55 |
| | | Never hinged | 2.50 | |
| 257 | A106 | 3p dark purple | 1.90 | 4.50 |
| | | Never hinged | 3.50 | |
| | | Nos. 252-257 (6) | 4.75 | 7.40 |

Centenary of the postage stamp.
No. 255 bisects were used in Guernsey from 12/27/40 to 2/24/41.

### Type of 1937-39, with Background Lightened

| **1941-42** | | | | |
|---|---|---|---|---|
| 258 | A101 | ½p green | .20 | .20 |
| | | Never hinged | .25 | |
| a. | | Booklet pane of 6 | 3.00 | |
| | | Never hinged | 4.25 | |
| b. | | Booklet pane of 2 | 1.20 | |
| | | Never hinged | 1.50 | |
| c. | | Imperf., pair | 5,000. | |
| | | Never hinged | 7,000. | |
| d. | | Tete beche pair | 8,000. | |
| | | Never hinged | 17,500. | |
| e. | | Booklet pane of 4 | | |
| 259 | A101 | 1p vermilion | .20 | .25 |
| | | Never hinged | .25 | |
| a. | | Wmk. sideways ('42) | 3.00 | 5.75 |
| | | Never hinged | 5.00 | |
| b. | | Booklet pane of 2 | 1.25 | |

| | | | | |
|---|---|---|---|---|
| *c.* | Never hinged | 1.60 | | |
| *c.* | Imperf., pair | 5,000. | | |
| *d.* | Booklet pane of 4 | 7,000. | | |
| *e.* | Horiz. pair, imperf on 3 sides | 5,000. | | |
| | Never hinged | 7,000. | | |
| **260** | A101 1½p lt red brn ('42) | .30 | .85 | |
| | Never hinged | .60 | | |
| *a.* | Booklet pane of 2 | 2.75 | | |
| | Never hinged | 4.00 | | |
| **261** | A101 2p light orange | .25 | .50 | |
| | Never hinged | .50 | | |
| *a.* | Wmk. sideways ('42) | 16.50 | 21.00 | |
| | Never hinged | 32.50 | | |
| *b.* | Booklet pane of 6 | 6.75 | | |
| | Never hinged | 10.00 | | |
| *c.* | Imperf., pair | 4,350. | | |
| | Never hinged | 6,000. | | |
| *d.* | Tete beche pair | 11,500. | | |
| | Never hinged | 17,500. | | |
| **262** | A101 2½p ultra | .25 | .40 | |
| | Never hinged | .35 | | |
| *a.* | Wmk. sideways ('42) | 9.00 | 11.00 | |
| | Never hinged | 17.50 | | |
| *b.* | Booklet pane of 6 | 3.75 | | |
| | Never hinged | 5.00 | | |
| *c.* | Imperf., pair | 3,350. | | |
| | Never hinged | 4,750. | | |
| *d.* | Tete beche pair | 11,500. | | |
| | Never hinged | 17,500. | | |
| **263** | A101 3p violet | 1.40 | 1.10 | |
| | Never hinged | 2.75 | | |
| | *Nos. 258-263 (6)* | 2.60 | 3.30 | |

Nos. 259a, 261a and 262a were issued in coils.

Nos. 258b, 258e, 259b, 259d, 260a-260b are made from sheets.

> **Catalogue values for unused stamps in this section, from this point to the end of the section, are for Never Hinged items.**

### Peace Issue

A107

King George VI and Symbols of Peace and Industry A108

**Perf. 14½x14**

| | | | |
|---|---|---|---|
| **1946, June 11** | **Photo.** | **Wmk. 251** | |
| **264** | A107 2½p bright ultra | .20 | .20 |
| **265** | A108 3p violet | .20 | .45 |

Return to peace at the close of WW II.

### George VI Type of 1939

| | | | |
|---|---|---|---|
| **1947, Dec. 29** | | | |
| **266** | A103 11p violet brown | 3.50 | *4.00* |

A109

King George VI and Queen Elizabeth A110

| | | | |
|---|---|---|---|
| **1948, Apr. 26** | **Perf. 14½x14, 14x14½** | | |
| **267** | A109 2½p brt ultra | .40 | .20 |
| **268** | A110 £1 dp chalky blue | 50.00 | 50.00 |

25th anniv. of the marriage of King George VI and Queen Elizabeth.

A111

Vraicking (Gathering Seaweed) A112

| | | | |
|---|---|---|---|
| **1948, May 10** | **Perf. 14½x14** | | |
| **269** | A111 1p red | .20 | .20 |
| **270** | A112 2½p bright ultra | .20 | .20 |

3rd anniversary of the liberation of the Channel Islands from German occupation.
Sold at post offices in the Channel Islands, but valid for postage throughout Great Britain.

A113

A114

A115

A116

| | | | |
|---|---|---|---|
| **1948, July 29** | | | |
| **271** | A113 2½p bright ultra | .35 | .20 |
| **272** | A114 3p deep violet | .60 | .65 |
| **273** | A115 6p red violet | 1.40 | .45 |
| **274** | A116 1sh dark brown | 2.75 | 1.75 |
| | *Nos. 271-274 (4)* | 5.10 | 3.05 |

1948 Olympic Games held at Wembley during July and August.

### George VI Type of 1939
### Wmk. 259

| | | | |
|---|---|---|---|
| **1948, Oct. 1** | **Engr.** | **Perf. 14** | |
| **275** | A105 £1 red brown | 20.00 | 25.00 |

A117

A118

A119

A120

| | | | |
|---|---|---|---|
| | **Perf. 14½x14** | | |
| **1949, Oct. 10** | **Photo.** | **Wmk. 251** | |
| **276** | A117 2½p bright ultra | .20 | .20 |
| **277** | A118 3p brt violet | .20 | .55 |
| **278** | A119 6p red violet | .50 | .55 |
| **279** | A120 1sh brown | 1.10 | 1.40 |
| | *Nos. 276-279 (4)* | 2.00 | 2.70 |

UPU, 75th anniversary.

### Types of 1937

| | | | |
|---|---|---|---|
| **1950-51** | **Wmk. 251** | **Perf. 14½x14** | |
| **280** | A101 ½p light orange | .20 | .20 |
| *a.* | Booklet pane of 2 | 1.20 | |
| *b.* | Booklet pane of 4 | 2.00 | |
| *c.* | Booklet pane of 6 | 3.00 | |
| *d.* | Imperf., pair | 5,000. | |
| *e.* | Tete beche pair | 17,500. | |
| **281** | A101 1p ultramarine | .20 | .20 |
| *a.* | Wmk. sideways | 1.25 | 1.40 |
| *b.* | Booklet pane of 2 | 1.40 | |
| *c.* | Booklet pane of 4 | 2.10 | |
| *d.* | Booklet pane of 6 | 3.00 | |
| *e.* | Booklet pane of 3 + 3 labels | 20.00 | |
| *f.* | Imperf., pair | 5,000. | |
| *g.* | Horiz. pair, imperf on 3 sides | 6,000. | |
| **282** | A101 1½p green | .75 | .70 |
| *a.* | Wmk. sideways | 3.75 | *5.75* |
| *b.* | Booklet pane of 2 | 2.00 | |
| *c.* | Booklet pane of 4 | 3.75 | |
| *d.* | Booklet pane of 6 | 5.50 | |
| **283** | A101 2p lt red brown | .85 | .45 |
| *a.* | Wmk. sideways | 2.00 | *2.25* |
| *b.* | Booklet pane of 6 | 9.00 | |
| *c.* | Tete beche pair | 17,500. | |
| *d.* | Horiz. pair, imperf on 3 sides | 6,000. | |
| **284** | A101 2½p vermilion | .70 | .45 |
| *a.* | Wmk. sideways | 2.00 | 2.00 |
| *b.* | Booklet pane of 6 | 4.75 | |
| *c.* | Tete beche pair | | |
| **285** | A102 4p ultra ('50) | 2.25 | 2.00 |
| *a.* | Double impression | | *8,250.* |
| | *Nos. 280-285 (6)* | 4.95 | 4.00 |

Nos. 281a, 282a, 283a and 284a were issued in coils.

H.M.S. Victory A121

St. George Slaying the Dragon A122

Royal Arms A123

Design: 5sh, White Cliffs, Dover.

| | | | |
|---|---|---|---|
| | **Perf. 11x12** | | |
| **1951, May 3** | **Engr.** | **Wmk. 259** | |
| **286** | A121 2sh6p green | 6.50 | 1.10 |
| **287** | A121 5sh dull red | 45.00 | 1.75 |
| **288** | A122 10sh ultra | 16.00 | 9.75 |
| **289** | A123 £1 lt red brown | 55.00 | 22.50 |
| | *Nos. 286-289 (4)* | 122.50 | 35.10 |

Britannia, Symbols of Commerce and Prosperity, King George VI — A124

Festival Symbol A125

| | | | |
|---|---|---|---|
| | **Perf. 14½x14** | | |
| **1951, May 3** | **Photo.** | **Wmk. 251** | |
| **290** | A124 2½p scarlet | .25 | .25 |
| **291** | A125 4p bright ultra | .35 | .75 |

Festival of Britain, 1951.

Queen Elizabeth
A126      A127

A128      A129

A130      A131

A132

The 2½d exists in two types: Type I, in the front cross of the diadem, the top line extends half the width of the cross; Type II, the top line extends across the full width of the top of the cross.

| | | | |
|---|---|---|---|
| | **Perf. 14½x14** | | |
| **1952-54** | **Photo.** | **Wmk. 298** | |
| **292** | A126 ½p red orange ('53) | .20 | .20 |
| *a.* | Booklet pane of 2 | .70 | |
| *b.* | Booklet pane of 4 | 1.25 | |
| *c.* | Booklet pane of 6 | 1.50 | |
| **293** | A126 1p ultra ('53) | .20 | .20 |
| *a.* | Booklet pane of 2 | .90 | |
| *b.* | Booklet pane of 4 | 1.75 | |
| *c.* | Booklet pane of 6 | 2.25 | |
| *d.* | Booklet pane 3 + 3 labels | 32.50 | |
| **294** | A126 1½p green ('52) | .20 | .20 |
| *a.* | Booklet pane of 2 | .70 | |
| *b.* | Booklet pane of 4 | 1.25 | |
| *c.* | Booklet pane of 6 ('53) | 1.50 | |
| *d.* | Wmk. sideways | .55 | *.80* |
| *e.* | As "c," imperf. (error) | 750.00 | |
| **295** | A126 2p red brn ('53) | .20 | .20 |
| *a.* | Booklet pane of 6 | 2.50 | |
| *b.* | Wmk. sideways | 1.10 | *2.25* |
| **296** | A127 2½p scarlet, Type I ('52) | .20 | .20 |
| *a.* | Booklet pane of 6, Type II ('53) | 7.00 | |
| *b.* | Wmk. sideways, Type I ('54) | 8.00 | *9.25* |
| *c.* | Type II | 1.40 | 1.40 |
| **297** | A127 3p dk purple | .85 | .65 |
| **298** | A128 4p ultra ('53) | 3.75 | 1.40 |
| **299** | A129 5p lt brn ('53) | .85 | 4.00 |
| **300** | A129 6p lilac rose | 4.50 | 1.10 |
| **301** | A129 7p emerald | 11.00 | 6.25 |
| **302** | A130 8p brt rose ('53) | .80 | 1.00 |
| **303** | A130 9p dp ol grn | 26.00 | 5.50 |
| **304** | A130 10p royal blue | 21.00 | 5.50 |
| **305** | A130 11p vio brown | 35.00 | 17.50 |
| **306** | A131 1sh brown ('53) | .90 | .55 |
| **307** | A132 1sh3p dk grn ('53) | 5.25 | 3.75 |
| **308** | A131 1sh6p dk bl ('53) | 16.00 | 4.25 |
| | *Nos. 292-308 (17)* | 126.90 | 52.45 |

Nos. 294d, 295b, 296b issued in coils.
Nos. 292-296 with watermark inverted are from booklets.
Type II stamps of No. 296 come only from booklet panes.
See Nos. 317-333, 353-369, 1801-1803, 2022-2023, 2086, 2125.
Compare design A128 with A139.
See regional issues, Guernsey, Jersey and Isle of Man for other stamps showing this portrait of the Queen, which have different frames or devices added to the design.

---

**See British Offices Abroad for overprints on types A44-A133.**
    These overprints include "M.E.F.," "B.A.," "B.M.A.," "E.A.F.," "CHINA," "Morocco Agencies," "TANGIER," "LEVANT," "PARAS," and "PIASTRE(S)."

Caernarfon Castle, Wales — A133

Castles: 2sh6p, Carrickfergus, Ireland. 10sh, Edinburgh, Scotland. £1, Windsor, England.

**1955 Engr. Wmk. 308 Perf. 11x12**
309 A133 2sh6p dark brown 12.50 2.25
310 A133 5sh crimson 40.00 4.50
311 A133 10sh brt ultra 100.00 16.00
312 A133 £1 intense blk 150.00 40.00
Nos. 309-312 (4) 302.50 62.75
See Nos. 371-374, 525-528.

A134

A135

A136

A137

**Perf. 14½x14**
**1953, June 3 Photo. Wmk. 298**
313 A134 2½p scarlet .30 .25
314 A135 4p ultra 1.40 2.25
315 A136 1sh3p dark green 5.50 3.50
316 A137 1sh6p dark blue 11.00 5.50
Nos. 313-316 (4) 18.20 11.50
See No. 1942.

**Types of 1952-54**
**1955-57 Wmk. 308 Perf. 14½x14**
317 A126 ½p red orange ('56) .20 .20
a. Booklet pane of 6 1.75
b. Booklet pane of 4 1.50
d. Booklet pane of 2 .70
318 A126 1p ultra ('56) .20 .20
a. Bklt. pane of 3 + 3 labels 19.00
b. Booklet pane of 6 2.00
c. Booklet pane of 4 1.50
e. Tete Beche pair —
f. Booklet pane of 2 .80
319 A126 1½p green ('56) .25 .25
a. Booklet pane of 6 8.50
b. Booklet pane of 4 6.50
c. Wmk. sideways ('56) .40 .80
e. Tete beche pair 3,000.
f. Booklet pane of 2 1.50
320 A126 2p red brown ('56) .20 .25
a. Wmk. sideways ('56) 7.50 6.00
b. Booklet pane of 6 3.00
d. Tete beche pair 2,000.
e. Vert. pair, imperf. between 3,000.
f. As "a," horiz. pair, imperf. between 3,000.
h. Imperf., pair 350.00
321 A127 2½p scar, Type I ('56) .20 .25
a. Booklet pane of 6, Type II 4.50
b. Wmk. sideways, Type I ('56) 1.75 2.00
d. Type II .50 .50
e. Tete beche pair 2,100.
f. Imperf., pair
322 A127 3p dk purple ('56) .20 .25
a. Booklet pane of 6 4.50
b. Booklet pane of 4 6.00
c. Wmk. sideways 22.50 20.00
e. Tete beche pair 2,100.
323 A128 4p ultra 1.40 .50
324 A129 5p lt brn ('56) 6.75 6.75
325 A129 6p lilac rose ('56) 5.00 1.40
326 A129 7p emerald 60.00 12.50
327 A130 8p brt rose ('56) 8.00 1.40

328 A130 9p dp ol grn ('56) 22.50 3.25
329 A130 10p royal bl ('56) 22.50 3.25
330 A130 11p vio brown .55 1.40
331 A131 1sh brown 25.00 .75
332 A132 1sh3p dk grn ('56) 35.00 1.90
333 A131 1sh6p dark blue 26.00 1.90
Nos. 317-333 (17) 213.95 36.40

Nos. 319c, 320a, 321b, 322c issued in coils.
Nos. 317-322 with watermark inverted are from booklets. See Nos. 353-369.

**Black Graphite Lines on Back**
**1957-59 Wmk. 308**
317c A126 ½p red orange ('56) .25 .20
p. Phosphor. ('59) 4.50 4.50
318d A126 1p ultra .25 .25
p. Phosphor. ('59) 12.50 12.50
319d A126 1½p green 1.30 1.60
p. Phosphor. ('59) 4.50 4.50
320c A126 2p red brown 1.75 2.50
p. Phosphor. ('59) 210.00 175.00
321c A127 2½p scarlet (II) 10.00 8.25
322d A127 3p dark purple .95 .60
Nos. 317c-322d (6) 14.50 13.40

The vertical black graphite lines were applied to facilitate mail sorting by an electronic machine. The 2p has one line (at right, seen from back), the others two.

Phosphorescent bands were overprinted vertically in Nov. 1959 on the face of the preceding ½p, 1p, 1½p and 2p graphite-lined stamps, plus the 2p, 2½p, 3p, 4p and 4½p graphite-lined stamps with Wmk. 322, in a letter-sorting experiment. These faint bands can be seen best with an ultraviolet lamp; without it they can be seen best on unused stamps.

Scout Emblem and Rolling Hitch Knot A138

4p, Swallows. 1sh3p, Globe encircled by compass.

**Perf. 14½x14**
**1957, Aug. 1 Wmk. 308**
334 A138 2½p scarlet .25 .20
335 A138 4p ultra .60 1.00
336 A138 1sh3p dk green 5.50 4.00
Nos. 334-336 (3) 6.35 5.20

50th anniv. of the Boy Scout movement and the World Scout Jubilee Jamboree, Sutton Coldfield, Aug. 1-12.

A139

**1957, Sept. 12 Photo.**
337 A139 4p ultra 1.10 1.10
46th Conf. of the Inter-Parliamentary Union, London, Sept. 12-19.

Welsh Dragon A140

Designs: 6p, Flag with British Empire and Commonwealth Games Emblem. 1sh3p, Welsh dragon holding laurel.

**1958, July 18 Perf. 14½x14**
338 A140 3p dk purple .20 .20
339 A140 6p red lilac .45 .50
340 A140 1sh3p green 2.50 2.75
Nos. 338-340 (3) 3.15 3.45

6th British Empire and Commonwealth Games, Cardiff, July 18-26.

Regional Issues of Great Britain for Guernsey, Jersey, Isle of Man, Northern Ireland, Scotland and Wales-Monmouthshire are listed in separate sections following Great Britain Envelopes.

**Types of 1952-55**
**Perf. 14½x14**
**1958-65 Wmk. 322**
353 A126 ½p red orange .20 .20
a. Booklet pane of 6 .70
b. Booklet pane of 4 4.00
e. Booklet pane of 4 (3 No. 353 + No. 357) ('63) 10.50 10.50
f. Tete beche pair 850.00
g. Booklet pane of 4 (2 Nos. 353 + 2 No. 357) ('64) 2.50 2.50
354 A126 1p ultra ('59) .20 .20
a. Booklet pane of 6 ('59) 1.00
b. Booklet pane of 4 5.25
e. Imperf., pair
f. Bklt. pane, #2 #354, 2 #358 ('65) 11.50 11.50
355 A126 1½p green .20 .20
a. Booklet pane of 6 1.00
b. Booklet pane of 4 40.00
356 A126 2p red brown .20 .20
a. Wmk. sideways .55 1.10
b. Booklet pane of 6 6.00
357 A127 2½p scarlet, type II ('59) .20 .20
a. Type I ('61) .80 .80
b. Wmk. sideways, type I .30 .50
c. Booklet pane of 6, Type II ('59) 1.00
f. Tete beche pair, type II 5,000.
g. Booklet pane of 4, type II ('64) 2.50
h. Imperf., pair
358 A127 3p dark purple .20 .20
a. Booklet pane of 6 1.75
b. Booklet pane of 4 3.75
e. Imperf., pair 250.00
g. Wmk. sideways .30 .40
359 A128 4p ultra .50 .40
a. Booklet pane of 6 ('65) 6.00
c. Booklet pane of 4 ('65) 3.75
d. Wmk. sideways .80 .65
360 A128 4½p henna brn .20 .20
361 A129 5p light brown .30 .40
362 A129 6p lil rose ('59) .35 .25
363 A129 7p emerald .60 .50
364 A130 8p brt rose ('60) .70 .45
365 A130 9p dp ol grn ('59) .70 .45
366 A130 10p royal blue 1.00 .55
367 A131 1sh brown .50 .35
368 A132 1sh3p dk grn ('59) .50 .35
369 A131 1sh6p dark blue 4.50 .70
Nos. 353-369 (17) 11.05 5.80

Nos. 356a and 357b were issued in coils. The 3p and 4p watermarked sideways may be from a coil or booklet pane of 4.
Booklet panes of this issue have watermarks normal, inverted or sideways.
Part perf. booklet panes exist of No. 353a and No. 354a.

**Black Graphite Lines on Back**
**1958-59 Wmk. 322**
353c A126 ½p red orange ('59) 10.50 10.50
d. Booklet pane of 6 27.50
354c A126 1p ultra 1.50 1.75
d. Booklet pane of 6 17.50
355c A126 1½p green ('59) 100.00 92.50
d. Booklet pane of 6 600.00
356c A126 2p red brown 8.75 4.00
cp. Phosphor. ('59) 5.50 5.00
357d A127 2½p scarlet (II) ('59) 10.50 11.50
dp. Phosphor. ('59) 25.00 20.00
e. Booklet pane of 6 100.00
358c A127 3p dark purple .75 .75
cp. Phosphor. ('59) 10.00 8.00
d. Booklet pane of 6 5.50
359a A128 4p ultra ('59) 5.25 5.75
ap. Phosphor. ('59) 22.50 20.00
360a A128 4½p henna brn ('59) 7.50 5.75
ap. Phosphor. ('59) 35.00 25.00
Nos. 353c-360a (8) 144.75 132.50

The vertical black graphite lines were applied to facilitate mail sorting by an electronic machine. The 2p has one line; the others two. Missing or misplaced lines occur on 1p, 3p and 4p.
Nos. 353c and 354c were issued only in booklets or coils; No. 355c only in booklets.

**Phosphorescent Stamps of 1958-65**
**1960-67 Wmk. 322**
353p A126 ½p red orange .20 .20
ap. Booklet pane of 6 4.00
bp. Booklet pane of 4 50.00
354p A126 1p ultra .20 .20
ap. Booklet pane of 6 5.00
bp. Booklet pane of 4 12.00
fp. Booklet pane of 2 each #354p, 358p 40.00
355p A126 1½p green .20 .20
ap. Booklet pane of 6 5.00
bp. Booklet pane of 4 50.00
356p A126 2p red brown .20 .20
ap. Watermark sideways .20
357p A127 2½p scarlet (II) .20 .40
ap. Type I ('61) 47.50 37.50
cp. Booklet pane of 6 60.00
358p A127 3p dark purple .70 .65
ap. Booklet pane of 6 7.50
bp. Booklet pane of 4 12.50
gp. Watermark sideways 1.25 .50
359p A128 4p ultramarine .25 .25
bp. Booklet pane of 6 6.25
cp. Booklet pane of 4 5.00
dp. Watermark sideways .40 .60
360p A128 4½p henna brown ('61) .25 .25
361p A129 5p lt brown ('67) .25 .25
362p A129 6p lilac rose .40 .25
363p A129 7p emerald ('67) .65 .60
364p A130 8p brt rose ('67) .45 .50
365p A130 9p dp ol grn ('67) .65 .65
366p A130 10p royal blue ('67) .80 .70
367p A131 1sh brown ('67) .40 .40
368p A132 1sh3p dark green 2.25 2.75
369p A131 1sh6p dark blue ('66) 2.40 1.75
Nos. 353p-369p (17) 10.45 10.30

The 2p, 2½p (II) and 3p were issued with both one and two phosphorescent bands. The less expensive is valued here.
Watermarked sideways, the 2p is from a coil; the 3p and 4p from booklet pane or coil; the ½p, 1p and 1½p from booklet panes (hence unlisted in this state).
Booklet panes of 4 with phosphorescent bands; ½p, 1p, 1½p, 3p (2 bands), 4p, and 1p se-tenant with 3p (1 or 2 bands). Booklet panes of 6 with phosphorescent bands: ½p, 1p, 1½p, 2½p (II) (1 or 2 bands), 3p (1 or 2 bands), 4p.

**1959 Engr. Wmk. 322 Perf. 11x12**
371 A133 2sh6p dark brown .40 .45
372 A133 5sh crimson 1.00 .60
373 A133 10sh bright ultra 4.50 5.25
374 A133 £1 intense blk 12.50 8.00
Nos. 371-374 (4) 18.40 14.30

Postboy on Horseback A147

Queen Elizabeth II, Oak Leaves and 1660 Post Horn — A148

**Perf. 14½x14, 14x14½**
**1960, July 7 Photo. Wmk. 322**
375 A147 3p bright violet .50 .50
376 A148 1sh3p dark green 3.50 4.25

Tercentenary of the act establishing the General Letter Office (General Post Office).

Symbolic Wheel CD3

**Perf. 14½x14**
**1960, Sept. 19 Wmk. 322**
377 CD3 6p red lilac & grn 1.75 .60
378 CD3 1sh6p dk bl & red brn 13.50 6.25
1st anniv. of the establishment of CEPT.

Symbolic Thrift Plant — A150

Nut Tree, Nest, Squirrel, Owl A151

Thrift Plant A152

**Perf. 14x14½, 14½x14**
**1961, Aug. 28 Photo. Wmk. 322**
379 A150 2½p scar & blk .20 .20
a. Black omitted 18,500.

**380** A151    3p pur &
               org                         .20    .20
  **a.**    Orange omitted              190.00  90.00
**381** A152  1sh6p dk bl &
               ver                        2.50   2.50
        Nos. 379-381 (3)                  2.90   2.90
Centenary of Post Office Savings Bank.

CEPT
Emblem
A153

Nineteen
Doves
Flying as
One
CD4

Design: 10p, Queen at right.

**1961, Sept. 18**    *Perf. 14½x14*
**382** A153    2p red brn, yel &
               rose                        .20    .20
**383** CD4     4p ultra, pink &
               buff                        .20    .20
**384** CD4    10p dk bl, yel grn
               & Prus blue                 .20    .90
  **a.**    Yellow green omitted       13,500.
  **b.**    Dark blue omitted          4,500.
        Nos. 382-384 (3)                   .60   1.30

Hammer Beam Roof of Westminster
Hall — A155

Parliament — A156

*Perf. 14½x14, 14x14½*
**1961, Sept. 25**              **Wmk. 322**
**385** A155    6p red lil &
               gold                        .30    .20
  **a.**    Gold omitted               1,600.
**386** A156  1sh3p green &
               slate                      3.00   3.25
  **a.**    Slate (Queen's head) omit-
               ted                       16,500.
7th Commonwealth Parliamentary Conf.

National Productivity Symbol — A157

Designs: 3p, Two arrows and map of the
British Isles. 1sh3p, Five arrows pointing up.

*Perf. 14½x14*
**1962, Nov. 14   Photo.      Wmk. 322**
**387** A157   2½p car rose &
               dk grn                      .20    .20
**388** A157    3p violet & blue           .30    .20
  **a.**    Queen's head omitted       2,250.
**389** A157  1sh3p dk grn, car
               rose & bl                  2.00   2.00
  **a.**    Queen's head omitted      10,000.
        Nos. 387-389 (3)                  2.50   2.40

**Phosphorescent**
**387p** A157   2½p car rose & dk
               grn                         .70    .60
**388p** A157    3p violet & blue         1.75    .95
**389p** A157  1sh3p dk grn, car
               rose & bl                 40.00  25.00
        Nos. 387p-389p (3)               42.45  26.55
National Productivity Year. The watermark
on Nos. 387-388 is inverted.

---

Phosphorescent Commemorative
stamps between Nos. 387-493 were
issued both with and without phosphorescence on the front unless otherwise
noted with the issue.
  Starting with No. 514, commemorative stamps were issued only with phosphorescence on the front unless otherwise noted.
  Phosphorescent Regulars: Starting in
1967, all small stamps (lower values) of
the regular series were issued only with
phosphorescence.

Wheat
Emblem
and People
A158

1sh3p, Children of different races.

**1963, Mar. 21**             **Wmk. 322**
**390** A158   2½p pink & dp car           .25    .20
  **p.**    Phosphor.                     3.50   1.40
**391** A158  1sh3p yellow & brn          2.25   2.25
  **p.**    Phosphor.                    35.00  26.00
FAO "Freedom from Hunger" campaign.

Paris
Postal
Conference
A159

**1963, May 7**              **Wmk. 322**
**392** A159    6p purple & green          .35    .45
  **a.**    Green omitted               4,000.
  **p.**    Phosphor.                     7.25   7.25
Cent. of the 1st Intl. Postal Conf., Paris,
1863, and Paris Postal Conf., May 7-9, 1963.

Buttercups,
Daisies
and Bee
A160

Design: 4½p, Badger, Fawn, woodpecker,
lark, titmouse, butterfly, mouse and wild
plants.

**1963, May 16**          *Perf. 14½x14*
**393** A160    3p multicolored            .20    .20
  **p.**    Phosphor.                      .70    .70
**394** A160   4½p multicolored            .20    .40
  **p.**    Phosphor.                     3.50   3.50
Natl. Nature Week, May 18-25, and the
importance of wildlife conservation.

Helicopter
Lifting Man
from
Lifeboat
A161

Lifeboat
Men
A162

Design: 4p, 19th cent. lifeboat under sail.

**1963, May 31**              **Photo.**
**395** A161   2½p multicolored            .20    .20
**396** A161    4p multicolored            .45    .45
**397** A162  1sh6p multicolored          2.75   3.00
        Nos. 395-397 (3)                  3.40   3.65

**Phosphorescent**
**395p** A161   2½p multicolored           .60    .70
**396p** A161    4p multicolored           .60    .70
**397p** A162  1sh6p multicolored        55.00  32.50
        Nos. 395p-397p (3)               56.20  33.90
9th Intl. Life-Boat Conf., Edinburgh, 6/3-5.

---

Red Cross
and
Elizabeth
II — A163

1sh3p, Cross at UL. 1sh6p, Cross in center.

**1963, Aug. 15**            **Wmk. 322**
**Cross in Red**
**398** A163    3p purple                  .20    .20
  **a.**    Red cross omitted          5,750.
**399** A163  1sh3p gray & blue           2.75   2.75
**400** A163  1sh6p dl bl & ol
               bister                     2.75   2.75
        Nos. 398-400 (3)                  5.70   5.70

**Phosphorescent**
**398p** A163    3p purple                1.25   1.00
**399p** A163  1sh3p gray & blue         42.50  35.00
**400p** A163  1sh6p dull blue & ol
               bister                    40.00  32.50
        Nos. 398p-400p (3)               83.75  68.50
Red Cross Cent. Cong., Geneva, Sept. 2.

Cable
Around
World and
Under Sea
A164

**1963, Dec. 3**          *Perf. 14½x14*
**401** A164  1sh6p blue & blk            3.25   2.75
  **a.**    Black omitted              4,000.
  **p.**    Phosphor.                    19.00  18.00
Opening of the Commonwealth Pacific (telephone) cable service, COMPAC.

Puck and Bottom from "A Midsummer
Night's Dream," Shakespeare — A165

Hamlet
Holding
Yorick's
Skull
A166

First Folio Portrait of Shakespeare and: 6p,
Feste the Clown, from "Twelfth Night." 1sh3p,
Romeo and Juliet. 1sh6p, Henry V praying at
Agincourt.

*Perf. 14½x14*
**1964, Apr. 23    Photo.     Wmk. 322**
**402** A165    3p multicolored            .20    .20
**403** A165    6p multicolored            .45    .35
**404** A165  1sh3p multicolored          1.00   1.00
**405** A165  1sh6p multicolored          1.60   1.25

*Perf. 11x12*
**Engr.**
**406** A166  2sh6p dark gray             2.00   1.50
        Nos. 402-406 (5)                  5.25   4.30

**Phosphorescent**
**402p** A165    3p multicolored           .30    .35
**403p** A165    6p multicolored           .90   1.10
**404p** A165  1sh3p multicolored         4.75   7.50
**405p** A165  1sh6p multicolored         9.25   5.25
        Nos. 402p-405p (4)               15.20  14.20
  400th anniv. of the birth of William Shakespeare. No. 406 was not issued with
phosphorescence.

Apartment
Buildings,
London
A170

Designs: 4p, Shipyards, Belfast. 8p, Beddgelert Forest Park, Snowdonia. 1sh6p,
Dounreay nuclear reactor and sheaves of
wheat.

---

**1964, July 1    Photo.    *Perf. 14½x14***
**410** A170   2½p multicolored            .20    .20
**411** A170    4p multicolored            .40    .35
  **a.**    Violet ("4d") omitted       225.00
  **b.**    Ocher omitted              475.00
  **c.**    Violet & ocher omitted     475.00
**412** A170    8p multicolored            .85    .85
  **a.**    Green omitted            13,500.
**413** A170  1sh6p multicolored          3.75   3.50
        Nos. 410-413 (4)                  5.20   4.90

**Phosphorescent**
**410p** A170   2½p multicolored           .45    .60
**411p** A170    4p multicolored          1.40   1.40
**412p** A170    8p multicolored          3.00   3.99
**413p** A170  1sh6p multicolored        32.50  25.00
        Nos. 410p-413p (4)               37.35  30.25
20th Intl. Geographical Cong., London, July
20-28.

Spring
Gentian
A171

**1964, Aug. 5**             **Wmk. 322**
**414** A171    3p shown                   .20    .20
  **a.**    Blue omitted             8,000.
  **b.**    Sage green omitted      13,500.
**415** A171    6p Dog rose                .35    .40
**416** A171    9p Honeysuck-
               le                         2.00   2.50
  **a.**    Light green omitted      13,500.
**417** A171  1sh3p Fringed
               water lily                 2.75   2.75
        Nos. 414-417 (4)                  5.30   5.85

**Phosphorescent**
**414p** A171    3p shown                  .45    .45
**415p** A171    6p Dog rose              2.75   3.25
**416p** A171    9p Honeysuckle          5.25   4.50
**417p** A171  1sh3p Fringed water
               lily                      27.50  22.50
        Nos. 414p-417p (4)               35.95  30.70
10th Intl. Botanical Cong., Edinburgh, Aug.
3-12.

Forth
Road
Bridge
A172

Design: 6p, Bridge and railroad bridge.

**1964, Sept. 4**        *Perf. 14½x14*
**418** A172    3p blk, lil & blue         .20    .20
  **p.**    Phosphor.                      .75    .75
**419** A172    6p vio blk,
               grnsh bl &
               car lake                    .45    .45
  **a.**    Greenish blue omitted     4,250.  1,500.
  **p.**    Phosphor.                     5.50   5.25
Opening of Forth Road Bridge, Scotland.

Winston
Churchill
A173

Design: 1sh3p, Large portrait.

**1965, July 8    Photo.     Wmk. 322**
**420** A173    4p dk brown & blk          .20    .20
  **p.**    Phosphor.                      .30    .30
**421** A173  1sh3p gray & black           .35    .45
  **p.**    Phosphor.                     3.00   3.50
Sir Winston Spencer Churchill (1874-1965),
statesman and WWII leader.

Seal of
Simon de
Montfort
A174

St. Stephen's Hall, Westminster Hall
and Abbey, Engraving by Wenceslaus
Hollar, 1647 — A175

**1965, July 19**     **Perf. 14½x14**
422 A174   6p dark olive    .20   .20
423 A175   2sh6p brown black   .90   1.10

700th anniv. of Parliament. No. 423 was not issued with phosphorescence; size: 58x21mm.

Salvation Army Band and "Blood and Fire" Flag A176

1sh6p, Salvation Army officers and flag.

**1965, Aug. 9**
424 A176   3p dk bl, yel & brt car    .25   .25
   p.   Phosphor.    .35   .45
425 A176   1sh6p red, yel & brt bl   1.00   1.50
   p.   Phosphor.    3.00   3.50

Centenary of the Salvation Army.

Lister's Carbolic Spray A177

1sh, Joseph Lister & carbolic acid formula.

**1965, Sept. 1**
426 A177   4p gray, bluish blk & red brn   .20   .20
   a.   Red brown (tubing) omitted   425.00
   b.   Bluish black omitted   5,750.
   p.   Phosphor.    .25   .25
427 A177   1sh blk, blue & pur   .80   1.25
   p.   Phosphor.    2.25   2.60

Introduction of antiseptic surgery by Joseph Lister, cent.

Trinidad Folk Dancers, Shrove Monday Carnival A178

Design: 1sh6p, French Canadian folk dancers, Les Feux Follets.

**Perf. 14½x14**
**1965, Sept. 1**    **Photo.**    **Wmk. 322**
428 A178   6p orange & blk   .20   .20
   p.   Phosphor.    .35   .45
429 A178   1sh6p brt vio & blk   .90   1.25
   p.   Phosphor.    3.00   3.50

1st Commonwealth Arts Festival, 9/16-10/2.

Supermarine Spitfire Fighters — A179

Anti-Aircraft Gun Battery in Action A180

Designs: No. 431, Pilot in cockpit of Hawker Hurricane fighter. No. 432, Wing tips of Messerschmitt ME-109 and Spitfire. No. 433, Two Spitfires attacking Heinkel HE-111 bomber. No. 434, Spitfire attacking Junkers JU-187B Stuka dive bomber. No. 435, Hurricanes returning over wreckage of Dornier DO-17 Z bomber. 1sh3p, Vapor trails over St. Paul's Cathedral, London.

**Perf. 14½x14**
**1965, Sept. 13**    **Photo.**    **Wmk. 322**
430 A179   4p slate & dk ol   .60   .80
431 A179   4p slate & dk ol   .60   .80
432 A179   4p sl, dk ol, brt bl & red   .60   .80
433 A179   4p slate & dk ol   .60   .80
434 A179   4p slate & dk ol   .60   .80

---

435 A179   4p sl, dk ol & brt blue   .60   .80
   a.   Bright blue omitted    5,500.
   b.   Block of 6, #430-435   5.00   5.00
436 A180   9p vio bl, org & vio black   2.25   1.75
437 A180   1sh3p brt bl, sl & grnsh gray   2.25   1.75
   Nos. 430-437 (8)   8.10   8.30

**Phosphorescent**
430p A179   4p slate & dark ol   1.10   1.10
431p A179   4p slate & dark ol   1.10   1.10
432p A179   4p sl, dk ol, brt bl & red   1.10   1.10
433p A179   4p slate & dark ol   1.10   1.10
434p A179   4p slate & dark ol   1.10   1.10
435p A179   4p sl, dk ol & brt bl   1.10   1.10
   a.   Block of 6, #430p-435p   11.00   11.00
436p A180   9p vio bl, org & vio black   2.50   2.50
437p A180   1sh3p brt bl, slate & grnsh gray   2.50   2.50
   Nos. 430p-437p (8)   11.60   11.60

25th anniv. of the Battle of Britain. Nos. 430-435 printed in blocks of 6 (3x2) in sheets of 120.

Post Office Tower and Georgian Buildings — A181

Design: 1sh3p, Post Office Tower and Nash Terrace, Regents Park, horiz.

**1965, Oct. 8**    **Perf. 14x14½, 14½x14**
438 A181   3p brt bl, lem & ol green   .20   .20
   p.   Phosphor.    .20   .20
439 A181   1sh3p grn, ol grn & bl   .35   .50
   p.   Phosphor.    .35   .60

Opening of the Post Office Tower, London.

UN Emblem A182

ICY Emblem A183

**1965, Oct. 25**    **Perf. 14½x14x14**
440 A182   3p multicolored   .20   .20
   p.   Phosphor.    .35   .35
441 A183   1sh6p multicolored   .85   .85
   p.   Phosphor.    3.25   3.50

20th anniv. of the UN and Intl. Cooperation Year, 1965.

"World Telecommunication Stations" — A184

ITU Cent.: 1sh6p, "Radio waves & switchboard."

**1965, Nov. 15**    **Photo.**    **Wmk. 322**
442 A184   9p multicolored   .35   .45
   p.   Phosphor.    1.00   .85
443 A184   1sh6p bl, red, blk, ind & pink   1.10   1.40
   a.   Pink omitted    3,000.
   p.   Phosphor.    5.50   6.00

Robert Burns and Saltier Cross of St. Andrew A185

---

Design: 1sh3p, Alexander Nasmyth portrait of Burns, his signature and symbols of his life. Portrait of Burns on 4p stamp is adaptation of Archibald Skirvings', chalk drawing, 1798.

**1966, Jan. 25**    **Perf. 14½x14**
444 A185   4p blue, blk & dk sl   .20   .20
   p.   Phosphor.    .25   .45
445 A185   1sh3p org, blk & Prus blue   .45   .80
   p.   Phosphor.    2.50   2.50

Robert Burns (1759-1796), Scottish national poet.

Westminster Abbey — A186

Fan Vaulting, Chapel of Henry VII A187

**1966, Feb. 28**    **Photo.**    **Perf. 14½x14**
452 A186   3p blue, blk, & red brn   .20   .20
   p.   Phosphor.    .20   .20

**Perf. 11x12**
**Engr.**
453 A187   2sh6p black   .65   .90

900th anniv. of Westminster Abbey. No. 453 issued only without phosphor.

Landscape near Hassock, Sussex A188

Views: 6p, Antrim, Northern Ireland. 1sh3p, Harlech Castle, Wales. 1sh6p, The Cairngorms (mountains), Scotland.

**Perf. 14½x14**
**1966, May 2**    **Photo.**    **Wmk. 322**
454 A188   4p multicolored   .20   .20
455 A188   6p multicolored   .20   .20
456 A188   1sh3p multicolored   .25   .40
457 A188   1sh6p multicolored   .45   .40
   Nos. 454-457 (4)   1.10   1.20

**Phosphorescent**
454p A188   4p multicolored   .20   .20
455p A188   6p multicolored   .20   .20
456p A188   1sh3p multicolored   .25   .40
457p A188   1sh6p multicolored   .45   .45
   Nos. 454p-457p (4)   1.10   1.25

Soccer Players — A189

Players and Crowd A190

1sh3p, Goalkeeper and two players.

**Perf. 14x14½, 14½x14**
**1966, June 1**    **Photo.**    **Wmk. 322**
458 A189   4p multicolored   .20   .20
459 A190   6p multicolored   .20   .20
   a.   Black omitted    175.00
   b.   Yellow green omitted    4,500.
   c.   Red omitted    7,250.

---

460 A190   1sh3p multicolored   .60   .80
   a.   Blue omitted    300.00
   Nos. 458-460 (3)   1.00   1.20

**Phosphorescent**
458p A189   4p multicolored   .20   .20
459p A190   6p multicolored   .20   .20
   d.   Black omitted    1,900.
460p A190   1sh3p multicolored   .50   .75
   Nos. 458p-460p (3)   .90   1.15

Final games of the 1965-66 World Soccer Championship for the Jules Rimet Cup, Wembley, July 11-30.
See No. 465.

Blackheaded Gull — A191

**Perf. 14½x14**
**1966, Aug. 8**    **Photo.**    **Wmk. 322**
**Birds in Natural Colors**
461 A191   4p shown   .20   .20
   p.   Phosphor.    .20   .20
462 A191   4p Blue tit   .20   .20
   p.   Phosphor.    .20   .20
463 A191   4p European robin   .20   .20
   p.   Phosphor.    .20   .20
464 A191   4p European blackbird   .20   .20
   p.   Phosphor.    .20   .20
   a.   Block of 4, #461-464   .90   .90
   a.   Block of 4, #461p-464p   .90   .80

Seven colors have been found omitted (singly or in combinations) on Nos. 461-464; green, red, ultramarine, brown, red brown, yellow and black.

**No. 458 Inscribed: "ENGLAND WINNERS"**
**1966, Aug. 18**    **Perf. 14x14½**
465 A189   4p multicolored   .25   .25

England's victory in the World Soccer Cup Championship.

Jodrell Bank Radio Telescope A192

Designs: 6p, Automobiles (Jaguar and 3 Mini-Minors). 1sh3p, SR N6 Hovercraft. 1sh6p, Windscale atomic reactor.

**1966, Sept. 19**    **Perf. 14½x14**
466 A192   4p yellow & blk   .20   .20
467 A192   6p org, red & dk bl   .20   .20
   a.   Red (Mini-Minors) omitted   11,500.
   b.   Dark blue (Jaguar & imprint) omitted   8,000.
468 A192   1sh3p sl, blk, org & bl   .30   .45
469 A192   1sh6p multicolored   .40   .45
   Nos. 466-469 (4)   1.10   1.30

**Phosphorescent**
466p A192   4p yellow & black   .20   .20
467p A192   6p org, red & dk bl   .20   .20
468p A192   1sh3p slate, blk, org & bl   .40   .45
469p A192   1sh6p multicolored   .60   .70
   Nos. 466p-469p (4)   1.40   1.55

British technology.

Battle of Hastings A193

Battle of Hastings from Bayeux Tapestry: No. 471, Two knights on horseback, one killed, one attacking. No. 472, Slain Harold on horseback and knight with shield. No. 473, Knight with shield and axe fighting horseman. No. 474, Knight on foot killing man, and horseman attacking with lance. No. 475, Four knights and two horses in battle scene. 6p, Norman ship. 1sh3p, King Harold's housecarls (body guard) battling Normans.

## Photo.; Gold Impressed on 6p, 1sh3p
### Perf. 14½x14
**1966, Oct. 14**      **Wmk. 322**
#### Size: 38½x22mm

| | | | | |
|---|---|---|---|---|
| 470 | A193 | 4p multicolored | .20 | .20 |
| 471 | A193 | 4p multicolored | .20 | .20 |
| 472 | A193 | 4p multicolored | .20 | .20 |
| 473 | A193 | 4p multicolored | .20 | .20 |
| 474 | A193 | 4p multicolored | .20 | .20 |
| 475 | A193 | 4p multicolored | .20 | .20 |
| a. | | Strip of 6, #470-475 | 2.25 | |
| 476 | A193 | 6p multi & gold | .30 | .30 |

#### Size: 58x22mm

| | | | | |
|---|---|---|---|---|
| 477 | A193 | 1sh3p multi & gold | .75 | .65 |
| | | Nos. 470-477 (8) | 2.25 | 2.15 |

#### Phosphorescent

| | | | | |
|---|---|---|---|---|
| 470p | A193 | 4p multicolored | .20 | .20 |
| 471p | A193 | 4p multicolored | .20 | .20 |
| 472p | A193 | 4p multicolored | .20 | .20 |
| 473p | A193 | 4p multicolored | .20 | .20 |
| 474p | A193 | 4p multicolored | .20 | .20 |
| 475p | A193 | 4p multicolored | .20 | .20 |
| b. | | Strip of 6, #470p-475p | 2.25 | |
| 476p | A193 | 6p multi & gold | .30 | .30 |
| 477p | A193 | 1sh3p multi & gold | .85 | .85 |
| | | Nos. 470p-477p (8) | 2.35 | 2.35 |

900th anniv. of the Battle of Hastings. Eight colors have been found omitted (singly or in pair) on Nos. 470-475 and 470p-477p: gray, orange, blue, dark blue, bright green, olive green, brown and magenta. Also violet on 1sh3p.

### Gold Omitted
The variety "Gold (Queen's head) omitted" can be counterfeited by chemically removing the gold.

Christmas — A194

### Photo.; Gold Impressed
**1966, Dec. 1**      **Perf. 14x14½**

| | | | | |
|---|---|---|---|---|
| 478 | A194 | 3p King | .20 | .20 |
| b. | | Green omitted | | |
| p. | | Phosphor. | .20 | .20 |
| 479 | A194 | 1sh6p Snowman | .35 | .35 |
| b. | | Pink omitted | 2,500. | |
| p. | | Phosphor. | .35 | .40 |

Loading Ship at Dock and Train A195

Design: 1sh6p, Loading plane from trucks and flags of EFTA members.

### Perf. 14½x14
**1967, Feb. 20**    **Photo.**    **Wmk. 322**

| | | | | |
|---|---|---|---|---|
| 480 | A195 | 9p blue & multi | .20 | .20 |
| p. | | Phosphor. | .20 | .20 |
| 481 | A195 | 1sh6p violet & multi | .35 | .50 |
| p. | | Phosphor. | .30 | .45 |

European Free Trade Assoc. Tariffs were abolished Dec. 31, 1966, among EFTA members (Austria, Denmark, Finland, Great Britain, Norway, Portugal, Sweden, Switzerland).
Colors include: 9p — yellow, brown, light blue, light violet and green singly; black, brown, light blue and yellow simultaneously. 1sh6p — dark blue, bister, yellow, red, ultramarine and gray. 9p, value range for one-color omissions, $75 to $200. 1sh6p, value for red omitted $5,000 (used), dark blue omitted $500, value for other color-omitted errors $75 to $125 each.

Hawthorn and Wild Blackberry A196

Flowers: No. 489, Morning-glory and viper's bugloss. No. 490, Ox-eye daisy, coltsfoot and buttercup. No. 491, Bluebell, red campion and wood anemone. 9p, Dog violet. 1sh9p, Primrose.

### Perf. 14½x14
**1967, Apr. 24**    **Photo.**    **Wmk. 322**

| | | | | |
|---|---|---|---|---|
| 488 | A196 | 4p multicolored | .20 | .20 |
| 489 | A196 | 4p multicolored | .20 | .20 |
| 490 | A196 | 4p multicolored | .20 | .20 |
| 491 | A196 | 4p multicolored | .20 | .20 |
| a. | | Block of 4, #488-491 | .45 | |
| 492 | A196 | 9p multicolored | .30 | .40 |
| 493 | A196 | 1sh9p multicolored | .40 | .35 |
| | | Nos. 488-493 (6) | 1.50 | 1.55 |

#### Phosphorescent

| | | | | |
|---|---|---|---|---|
| 488p | A196 | 4p multicolored | .20 | .20 |
| 489p | A196 | 4p multicolored | .20 | .20 |
| 490p | A196 | 4p multicolored | .20 | .20 |
| 491p | A196 | 4p multicolored | .20 | .20 |
| a. | | Block of 4, #488p-491p | .45 | |
| 492p | A196 | 9p multicolored | .25 | .40 |
| 493p | A196 | 1sh9p multicolored | .35 | .35 |
| | | Nos. 488p-493p (6) | 1.40 | 1.55 |

Four colors have been found omitted on Nos. 488-491 and three on 488p-491p: dark brown, red, violet and dull purple.

For QEII Machin definitives, see listings following Regional Issues and preceding Booklets.

Master Lambton, by Thomas Lawrence — A198

Mares and Foals, by George Stubbs A199

Design: 1sh6p, Children Coming out of School, by Laurence Stephen Lowry.

### Photo.; Gold Impressed on 4p, 1sh6p
### Perf. 14x14½, 14½x14
**1967, July 10**      **Unwmk.**

| | | | | |
|---|---|---|---|---|
| 514 | A198 | 4p multicolored | .20 | .20 |
| a. | | Gold (Queen's head & value) omitted | 325.00 | |
| 515 | A199 | 9p multicolored | .20 | .20 |
| a. | | Black (Queen's head & value) omitted | 750.00 | |
| b. | | Black (Queen's head only) omitted | 1,750. | |
| 516 | A199 | 1sh6p multicolored | .20 | .20 |
| a. | | Blue omitted | 250.00 | |
| b. | | Gray omitted | 150.00 | |
| c. | | Gold (Queen's head) omitted | 13,500. | |
| | | Nos. 514-516 (3) | .60 | .60 |

See Nos. 568-571.

Gipsy Moth IV — A200

**1967, July 24**    **Photo.**    **Perf. 14½x14**

| | | | | |
|---|---|---|---|---|
| 517 | A200 | 1sh9p multicolored | .20 | .20 |

Sir Francis Chichester's one-man voyage around the world, Aug. 27, 1966-May 28, 1967.

Radar Screen A201

British Discoveries: 1sh, Penicillin mold. 1sh6p, Vickers 10 twin jet engines. 1sh9p, Television camera, vert.

### Perf. 14½x14, 14x14½
**1967, Sept. 19**    **Photo.**    **Wmk. 322**

| | | | | |
|---|---|---|---|---|
| 518 | A201 | 4p multicolored | .20 | .20 |
| 519 | A201 | 1sh multicolored | .20 | .20 |
| 520 | A201 | 1sh6p multicolored | .20 | .20 |
| 521 | A201 | 1sh9p multicolored | .20 | .20 |
| a. | | Gray omitted | 4,500. | |
| | | Nos. 518-521 (4) | .80 | .80 |

Adoration of the Shepherds, Ascribed to School of Seville — A202

Adoration of the Shepherds, by Le Nain A203

Christmas 1967: 4p, Madonna and Child, by Murillo.

### Photo.; Gold Impressed
### Perf. 14x14½, 14½x14
**1967**      **Unwmk.**

| | | | | |
|---|---|---|---|---|
| 522 | A202 | 3p multicolored | .20 | .20 |
| a. | | Gold (Queen's head & value) omitted | 100.00 | |
| b. | | Pink omitted | 3,250. | |
| 523 | A202 | 4p multicolored | .20 | .20 |
| a. | | Gold (Queen's head & value) omitted | 90.00 | |
| b. | | Gold ("4d" only) omitted | 2,750. | |
| c. | | Yellow omitted | 7,000. | |
| d. | | Greenish yellow & gold omitted | 11,500. | |
| 524 | A203 | 1sh6p multicolored | .20 | .20 |
| a. | | Gold (Queen's head & value) omitted | 7,000. | |
| b. | | Blue omitted | 500.00 | |
| c. | | Yellow omitted | 13,500. | |
| d. | | Gold (Queen's head only) omitted | 2,250. | |
| | | Nos. 522-524 (3) | .60 | .60 |

Issue dates: 4p, Oct. 18; 3p, 1sh6p, Nov. 27.

### Castle Type of 1955
### Perf. 11x12
**1967-68**    **Engr.**    **Unwmk.**

| | | | | |
|---|---|---|---|---|
| 525 | A133 | 2sh6p dk brown ('68) | .35 | .50 |
| 526 | A133 | 5sh crimson ('68) | .80 | .85 |
| 527 | A133 | 10sh brt ultra ('68) | 5.50 | 7.25 |
| 528 | A133 | £1 intense black | 5.25 | 7.00 |
| | | Nos. 525-528 (4) | 11.90 | 15.60 |

Aberfeldy Bridge, Perthshire A204

Designs: 4p, Prehistoric Tarr Steps, Exmoor. 1sh6p, Menai Bridge, North Wales, 1826. 1sh9p, Viaduct, Highway M4.

### Perf. 14½x14
**1968, Apr. 29**      **Unwmk.**

| | | | | |
|---|---|---|---|---|
| 560 | A204 | 4p gold & multi | .20 | .20 |
| 561 | A204 | 9p gold & multi | .20 | .20 |
| a. | | Blue omitted | 6,500. | |
| b. | | Gold (Queen's head) omitted | 190.00 | |
| 562 | A204 | 1sh6p gold & multi | .20 | .30 |
| a. | | Gold (Queen's head) omitted | 250.00 | |
| b. | | Red omitted | 350.00 | |
| 563 | A204 | 1sh9p gold & multi | .20 | .35 |
| a. | | Gold (Queen's head) omitted | 250.00 | |
| | | Nos. 560-563 (4) | .80 | 1.05 |

Emmeline Pankhurst Statue A205

Designs: 4p, Letters "TUC" and faces. 1sh, Sopwith Camel 1914-1918 fighter plane and formation of Lightning jets. 1sh9p, Capt. Cook's "Endeavour" and signature.

**1968, May 29**

| | | | | |
|---|---|---|---|---|
| 564 | A205 | 4p brt grn, blk, ol & bl | .20 | .20 |
| 565 | A205 | 9p gray, violet & blk | .20 | .20 |
| 566 | A205 | 1sh gray, ol, red, bl & blk | .20 | .20 |
| 567 | A205 | 1sh9p blk & bister | .40 | .45 |
| | | Nos. 564-567 (4) | 1.00 | 1.05 |

Cent. of Trades Union Congress (4p); 50th anniv. of women's suffrage (9p); 50th anniv. of the Royal Air Force (1sh); bicent. of Captain Cook's first discovery voyage (1sh9p).

### Paintings Types of 1967
Paintings: 4p, Elizabeth I, c. 1575, artist unknown. 1sh, Pinkie (Miss Sarah Moulton-Barrett) by Sir Thomas Lawrence. 1sh6p, St. Mary le Port, by John Piper. 1sh9p, The Hay Wain (landscape), by John Constable.

### Photo.; Gold Impressed
### Perf. 14x14½, 14½x14
**1968, Aug. 12**

| | | | | |
|---|---|---|---|---|
| 568 | A198 | 4p multi | .20 | .20 |
| a. | | Gold (Queen's head & value) omitted | 250.00 | |
| b. | | Vermilion omitted | 525.00 | |
| 569 | A198 | 1sh multi | .20 | .25 |
| a. | | Gold (Queen's head & value) omitted | 5,750. | |
| 570 | A198 | 1sh6p multi | .20 | .30 |
| a. | | Gold (Queen's head & value) omitted | 200.00 | |
| 571 | A199 | 1sh9p multi | .25 | .45 |
| a. | | Gold (Queen's head & value) omitted | 825.00 | |
| b. | | Red omitted | 13,500. | |
| | | Nos. 568-571 (4) | .85 | 1.20 |

Sizes: 4p, 27x37½mm; 1sh, 25½x37½mm; 1sh6p, 31x37½mm; 1sh9p, 38x28mm.

Boy and Girl with Rocking Horse A206

Girl Playing with Dolls and Dollhouse — A207

Christmas: 1sh6p, Boy with toy train and building blocks.

### Perf. 14½x14, 14x14½
**1968, Nov. 25**      **Photo.**

| | | | | |
|---|---|---|---|---|
| 572 | A206 | 4p gold & multi | .20 | .20 |
| a. | | Gold omitted | 8,000. | |
| b. | | Vermilion omitted | 500.00 | |
| c. | | Ultramarine omitted | 375.00 | |
| 573 | A207 | 9p gold & multi | .20 | .20 |
| a. | | Yellow omitted | 100.00 | |
| 574 | A207 | 1sh6p gold & multi | .20 | .35 |
| | | Nos. 572-574 (3) | .60 | .75 |

British Ships — A208

Designs: 5p, R.M.S. Queen Elizabeth 2. No. 576, Elizabethan Galleon. No. 577, East Indiaman. No. 578, Cutty Sark. No. 579, S.S. Great Britain. No. 580, R.M.S. Mauretania.

**1969, Jan. 15**      **Perf. 14½x14**
#### Size: 58x22mm

| | | | | |
|---|---|---|---|---|
| 575 | A208 | 5p multicolored | .20 | .20 |
| a. | | Black omitted | 1,600. | |
| b. | | Gray omitted | 200.00 | |

| | | | |
|---|---|---|---|
| c. | Red omitted | | 110.00 |

**Size: 38½x22mm**

| 576 | A208 | 9p multicolored | .20 | .20 |
|---|---|---|---|---|
| a. | | Red & blue omitted | | 2,400. |
| b. | | Blue omitted | | 2,750. |
| 577 | A208 | 9p multicolored | .20 | .30 |
| 578 | A208 | 9p multicolored | .20 | .30 |
| a. | | Strip of 3, #576-578 | | .60 |

**Size: 58x22mm**

| 579 | A208 | 1sh multicolored | .45 | .40 |
|---|---|---|---|---|
| a. | | Greenish yellow omitted | | 3,500. |
| 580 | A208 | 1sh multicolored | .45 | .40 |
| a. | | Pair, #579-580 | | 1.40 |
| b. | | Carmine (hull overlay) omitted | | 20,000. |
| c. | | Red (funnels) omitted | | 18,000. |
| d. | | Carmine and red omitted | | 18,000. |
| | | Nos. 575-580 (6) | 1.70 | 1.80 |

British seamen and shipbuilders.

Concorde over Great Britain and France A209

Designs: 9p, Concorde seen from above and from side, flags of France and Great Britain. 1sh6p, Outlines of plane's nose and tail superimposed.

**1969, Mar. 3  Photo.  Perf. 14½x14**

| 581 | A209 | 4p multicolored | .30 | .30 |
|---|---|---|---|---|
| a. | | Violet omitted | | 500.00 |
| b. | | Orange omitted | | 500.00 |
| 582 | A209 | 9p multicolored | .65 | .90 |
| 583 | A209 | 1sh6p multicolored | 1.00 | 1.25 |
| a. | | Silver omitted | | 500.00 |
| | | Nos. 581-583 (3) | 1.95 | 2.45 |

First flight of the prototype Concorde plane at Toulouse, France, Mar. 1, 1969.

Alcock, Brown, Daily Mail and Vickers Vimy Plane A210

"EUROPA" and "CEPT" CD12

Hand Holding Wrench A212

Flags of NATO Nations Forming one Flag A213

Vickers-Vimy Plane and Globe — A214

**1969, Apr. 2**

| 584 | A210 | 5p multicolored | .25 | .20 |
|---|---|---|---|---|
| 585 | CD12 | 9p multicolored | .25 | .25 |
| 586 | A212 | 1sh multicolored | .25 | .25 |
| 587 | A213 | 1sh6p multicolored | .25 | .30 |
| a. | | Black omitted | | 110.00 |
| b. | | Green omitted | | 90.00 |
| c. | | Yellow omitted | | 4,000. |
| 588 | A214 | 1sh9p multicolored | .25 | .40 |
| | | Nos. 584-588 (5) | 1.25 | 1.40 |

50th anniv. of the 1st non-stop Atlantic flight from Newfoundland to Ireland of Capt. John Alcock and Lt. Arthur Whitten Brown; 10th anniv. of the Conference of European Postal and Telecommunications Administrations; 50th anniv. of the ILO (1sh); 20th anniv. of NATO; 50th anniv. of the first England to Australia flight (1sh9p).

Durham Cathedral A215

British Cathedrals: No. 590, York Minster. No. 591, St. Giles', Edinburgh. No. 592, Canterbury. 9p, St. Paul's. 1sh6p, Liverpool Metropolitan.

**Perf. 14½x14**

**1969, May 28  Photo.  Unwmk.**

| 589 | A215 | 5p multicolored | .20 | .20 |
|---|---|---|---|---|
| a. | | Bluish violet omitted | | 6,500. |
| 590 | A215 | 5p multicolored | .20 | .20 |
| a. | | Bluish violet omitted | | 6,500. |
| 591 | A215 | 5p multicolored | .20 | .20 |
| a. | | Green omitted | | 90.00 |
| 592 | A215 | 5p multicolored | .20 | .20 |
| a. | | Block of 4, #589-592 | | .25 | .25 |
| 593 | A215 | 5p multicolored | .25 | .30 |
| a. | | Black (denomination) omitted | | 160.00 |
| 594 | A215 | 1sh6p multicolored | .40 | .40 |
| a. | | Black (denomination) omitted | | 4,500. |
| | | Nos. 589-594 (6) | 1.45 | 1.50 |

King's Gate, Caernarvon Castle, Wales — A216

Celtic Cross, Margam Abbey, Glamorgan A217

Prince of Wales — A218

Designs: No. 596, Eagle Tower, Caernarvon Castle (2 flags). No. 597, Queen Eleanor's Gate, Caernarvon Castle.

**Perf. 14x14½**

**1969, July 1  Photo.  Unwmk.**

| 595 | A216 | 5p silver & multi | .20 | .20 |
|---|---|---|---|---|
| 596 | A216 | 5p silver & multi | .20 | .20 |
| 597 | A216 | 5p silver & multi | .20 | .20 |
| a. | | Strip of 3, #595-597 | | .25 | .25 |
| 598 | A217 | 9p gold, gray & black | .20 | .20 |
| 599 | A218 | 1sh black & gold | .20 | .20 |
| | | Nos. 595-599 (5) | 1.00 | 1.00 |

Investiture of Prince Charles as Prince of Wales, July 1.

Mahatma Gandhi and Flag of India A219

**1969, Aug. 13  Perf. 14½x14**

| 600 | A219 | 1sh6p orange, blk & grn | .20 | .20 |
|---|---|---|---|---|

Mohandas K. Gandhi (1869-1948), leader in India's fight for independence.

Emblem of Post Office Bank A220

International Subscriber Dialing — A221

Automatic Letter Sorting A222

Design: 1sh, Telecommunications (pulse code modulation graph).

**Perf. 13½x14**

**1969, Oct. 1  Litho.  Unwmk.**

| 601 | A220 | 5p blue & multi | .20 | .20 |
|---|---|---|---|---|
| 602 | A221 | 9p ultra & multi | .20 | .20 |
| 603 | A221 | 1sh green & multi | .20 | .20 |
| 604 | A222 | 1sh6p multicolored | .20 | .40 |
| | | Nos. 601-604 (4) | .80 | 1.00 |

Technological advancements of the British Post Office, transfer of responsibility from the government to the Post Office Corporation.

Angel A223

Christmas: 5p, Three shepherds. 1sh6p, The Three Kings.

**Photo.; Gold Embossed**

**1969, Nov. 26  Perf. 14x15**

| 605 | A223 | 4p multicolored | .20 | .20 |
|---|---|---|---|---|
| 606 | A223 | 5p multicolored | .20 | .20 |
| 607 | A223 | 1sh6p multicolored | .20 | .20 |
| | | Nos. 605-607 (3) | .60 | .60 |

Fife Harling House, Scotland A224

British Rural Architecture: 9p, Cotswold limestone house, Gloucestershire, England. 1sh, Aberaeron town house, Wales. 1sh6p, Irish cottage with Ulster thatching.

**Perf. 14x15**

**1970, Feb. 11  Photo.  Unwmk.**

**Size: 38½x22mm**

| 608 | A224 | 5p multicolored | .20 | .20 |
|---|---|---|---|---|
| 609 | A224 | 9p multicolored | .20 | .20 |

**Size: 38½x27mm**

| 610 | A224 | 1sh multicolored | .20 | .20 |
|---|---|---|---|---|
| 611 | A224 | 1sh6p multicolored | .25 | .25 |
| | | Nos. 608-611 (4) | .85 | .85 |

Mayflower Leaving Plymouth, England A225

Designs: 5p, Signing of the Declaration of Arbroath. 9p, Florence Nightingale and soldiers in Scutari Hospital. 1sh, Earl Grey, Great Britain; Charles Robert, France; Victor Bohmert, Germany; De Keussler, Russia, and document in 4 languages. 1sh9p, Sir William Herschel, Francis Bailey, Sir John Herschel and telescope.

**Photo.; Gold Embossed**

**1970, Apr. 1  Perf. 14x15**

| 612 | A225 | 5p red & multi | .20 | .20 |
|---|---|---|---|---|
| 613 | A225 | 9p blue & multi | .20 | .20 |
| 614 | A225 | 1sh lt blue & multi | .25 | .25 |
| 615 | A225 | 1sh6p olive & multi | .30 | .35 |
| 616 | A225 | 1sh9p brt pink & multi | .30 | .35 |
| | | Nos. 612-616 (5) | 1.25 | 1.35 |

650th anniv. of the Declaration of Arbroath (5p); Florence Nightingale (1820-1910), nurse and hospital reformer (9p); Intl.Cooperative Alliance, 75th anniv. (1sh); 350th anniv. of Mayflower sailing (1sh6p); sesquicentennial of the Royal Astronomical Soc. (1sh9p).

Missing colors or embossing occur on each denomination.

"The Pickwick Papers," by Dickens A226

Wordsworth's Grasmere, Lake District A227

Designs: No. 618, Mr. and Mrs. Micawber ("David Copperfield"). No. 619, David Copperfield and Betsy Trotwood ("David Copperfield"). No. 620, "Oliver Twist."

**Perf. 14x14½**

**1970, June 3  Photo.  Unwmk.**

| 617 | A226 | 5p orange & multi | .20 | .20 |
|---|---|---|---|---|
| 618 | A226 | 5p lil rose & multi | .20 | .20 |
| 619 | A226 | 5p grnsh blue & multi | .20 | .20 |
| 620 | A226 | 5p lemon & multi | .20 | .20 |
| a. | | Block of 4, #617-620 | | .40 | .30 |
| 621 | A227 | 1sh6p citron & multi | .30 | .40 |
| | | Nos. 617-621 (5) | 1.10 | 1.20 |

Charles Dickens (1812-70), novelist. William Wordsworth (1770-1850), poet, No. 621.

Athletics A228

**1970, July 15  Litho.  Perf. 14x14½**

| 639 | A228 | 5p shown | .20 | .20 |
|---|---|---|---|---|
| 640 | A228 | 1sh6p Swimming | .30 | .40 |
| 641 | A228 | 1sh9p Bicycling | .35 | .40 |
| | | Nos. 639-641 (3) | .85 | 1.00 |

9th British Commonwealth Games, Edinburgh, July 16-25.

Philympia, London Phil. Exhib., Sept. 18-26 — A229

5p, Penny black. 9p, 1847 1-shilling stamp, #5. 1sh6p, 1855 4-pence stamp, #22.

**1970, Sept. 18  Photo.  Perf. 14x14½**

| 642 | A229 | 5p multicolored | .20 | .20 |
|---|---|---|---|---|
| 643 | A229 | 9p multicolored | .20 | .35 |
| 644 | A229 | 1sh6p multicolored | .20 | .50 |
| | | Nos. 642-644 (3) | .60 | 1.05 |

Christmas (Illuminations from 14th Century de Lisle Psalter) — A230

Designs: 4p, Angel and Shepherds. 5p, Nativity. 1sh6p. Adoration of the Kings.

**1970, Nov. 25   Photo.   Perf. 14x14½**

| | | | | |
|---|---|---|---|---|
| 645 | A230 | 4p red & multi | .20 | .20 |
| 646 | A230 | 5p violet & multi | .20 | .20 |
| a. | | Imperf., pair | 400.00 | |
| 647 | A230 | 1sh6p olive & multi | .25 | .35 |
| | | *Nos. 645-647 (3)* | .65 | .75 |

### Decimal Currency Issue
### "P" instead of "D"

Mountain
Road, by
T.P.
Flanagan
A231

Paintings from Northern Ireland: 7½p, Deer's Meadow, by Thomas Carr. 9p, Tollymore Forest Park, by Colin Middleton.

**1971, June 16   Photo.   Perf. 14½x14**

| | | | | |
|---|---|---|---|---|
| 648 | A231 | 3p multicolored | .20 | .20 |
| 649 | A231 | 7½p multicolored | .35 | .35 |
| 650 | A231 | 9p multicolored | .45 | .45 |
| | | *Nos. 648-650 (3)* | 1.00 | 1.00 |

Ulster '71 Festival, Belfast, May-Oct.

John Keats (1795-1821) — A232

Writers and their signatures: 5p, Thomas Gray (1716-71). 7½p, Sir Walter Scott (1771-1832).

**1971, July 28   Photo.   Perf. 14½x14**

| | | | | |
|---|---|---|---|---|
| 651 | A232 | 3p dull bl, blk & gold | .20 | .20 |
| 652 | A232 | 5p olive, blk & gold | .35 | .35 |
| 653 | A232 | 7½p yel brn, blk & gold | .45 | .45 |
| | | *Nos. 651-653 (3)* | 1.00 | 1.00 |

Soldier,
Sailor,
Airman,
Nurse,
1921, and
Poppy
A233

Designs: 7½p, Roman centurion on horseback, York Castle and coat of arms. 9p, Rugby players 100 years ago, and rose.

**1971, Aug. 25**

| | | | | |
|---|---|---|---|---|
| 654 | A233 | 3p ultra & multi | .20 | .20 |
| 655 | A233 | 7½p ocher & multi | .40 | .40 |
| 656 | A233 | 9p olive & multi | .40 | .40 |
| | | *Nos. 654-656 (3)* | 1.00 | 1.00 |

50th anniv. of the British Legion (3p); 1900th anniv. of the founding of York (7½p); cent. of the Rugby Football Union (9p).

Physical Sciences Building, University
College of Wales,
Aberystwyth — A234

Modern University Buildings: 5p, Faraday Building, Engineering Faculty, University of Southampton. 7½p, Engineering Building, University of Leicester. 9p, Hexagon Restaurant, University of Essex.

**1971, Sept. 22  Photo.   Perf. 14½x14**

| | | | | |
|---|---|---|---|---|
| 657 | A234 | 3p citron & multi | .20 | .20 |
| 658 | A234 | 5p rose vio & multi | .20 | .20 |
| 659 | A234 | 7½p dp brn & multi | .45 | .45 |
| 660 | A234 | 9p dk blue & multi | .75 | .75 |
| | | *Nos. 657-660 (4)* | 1.60 | 1.60 |

No. 658 exists with large "p" in "5p." These are from plate combination 1A1B1C1D and were not officially issued.

Dream of
the Kings
A235

Christmas (from Stained Glass Windows, Canterbury Cathedral): 3p, Adoration of the Kings. 7½p, Journey of the Kings.

**1971, Oct. 13**

| | | | | |
|---|---|---|---|---|
| 661 | A235 | 2½p scarlet & multi | .20 | .20 |
| 662 | A235 | 3p ultra & multi | .20 | .20 |
| 663 | A235 | 7½p green & multi | .75 | .75 |
| | | *Nos. 661-663 (3)* | 1.15 | 1.15 |

James Clark Ross
(1800-1862) and
Map of South
Polar Sea — A236

British Polar Explorers: 5p, Martin Frobisher (1535-1594), and Desceliers map, 1550. 7½p, Henry Hudson (c. 1560-1611) and Petrus Plancius map, 1592. 9p, Robert Falcon Scott (1868-1912) and map of Antarctica.

**1972, Feb. 16                Perf. 14x14½**

| | | | | |
|---|---|---|---|---|
| 664 | A236 | 3p dp bister & multi | .20 | .20 |
| 665 | A236 | 5p brick red & multi | .20 | .20 |
| 666 | A236 | 7½p violet & multi | .40 | .40 |
| 667 | A236 | 9p blue & multi | .60 | .60 |
| | | *Nos. 664-667 (4)* | 1.40 | 1.40 |

See Nos. 689-693.

Head of Tutankhamen as
Fisherman — A237

Coast
Guard
A238

Ralph
Vaughan
Williams
and "Sea
Symphony"
A239

**1972, Apr. 26   Photo.   Perf. 14½x14**

| | | | | |
|---|---|---|---|---|
| 668 | A237 | 3p gold & multi | | .20 |

**Photo.; Queen's Head Gold
Embossed**

| | | | | |
|---|---|---|---|---|
| 669 | A238 | 7½p blue & multi | .35 | .35 |
| 670 | A239 | 9p multicolored | .70 | .70 |
| | | *Nos. 668-670 (3)* | 1.25 | 1.25 |

50th anniv. of the discovery of the tomb of Tutankhamen by Howard Carter and Lord Carnarvon; sesquicentennial of the British Coast guard; Ralph Vaughan Williams (1872-1958), composer.

St. Andrew's, Greensted-Juxta-
Ongar — A240

Old Village Churches: 4p, All Saints, Earls Barton. 5p, St. Andrew's, Letheringsett. 7½p, St. Andrew's, Helpringham. 9p, St. Mary the Virgin, Huish Episcopi.

**Photo.; Queen's Head Gold
Embossed**

**1972, June 21                Perf. 14x14½**

| | | | | |
|---|---|---|---|---|
| 671 | A240 | 3p dull blue & multi | .20 | .20 |
| 672 | A240 | 4p olive & multi | .20 | .20 |
| 673 | A240 | 5p dp grn & multi | .20 | .20 |
| 674 | A240 | 7½p red & multi | .70 | .70 |
| 675 | A240 | 9p blue & multi | .70 | .70 |
| | | *Nos. 671-675 (5)* | 2.00 | 2.00 |

Various BBC Microphones — A241

Designs: 5p, Wooden horn loudspeaker 1925. 7½p, Color TV camera, 1972. 9p, Marconi's oscillator and spark transmitter, 1897.

**1972, Sept. 13  Photo.   Perf. 14½x14**

| | | | | |
|---|---|---|---|---|
| 676 | A241 | 3p black, brn & yel | .20 | .20 |
| 677 | A241 | 5p henna brn & blk | .20 | .20 |
| 678 | A241 | 7½p black & magenta | .45 | .45 |
| 679 | A241 | 9p black & yel | .50 | .50 |
| | | *Nos. 676-679 (4)* | 1.35 | 1.35 |

Daily broadcasting in the United Kingdom, 50th anniv. (British Broadcasting Corp., #676-678), Marconi-Kemp experiments resulting in the 1st radio transmission across water, 75th anniv. (#679).

Angel with
Trumpet — A242

**Photo.; Gold Embossed**

**1972, Oct. 18                Perf. 14½x14**

| | | | | |
|---|---|---|---|---|
| 680 | A242 | 2½p shown | .20 | .20 |
| 681 | A242 | 3p Angel with lute | .20 | .20 |
| 682 | A242 | 7½p Angel with harp | .30 | .30 |
| | | *Nos. 680-682 (3)* | .70 | .70 |

Christmas.

Queen Elizabeth
II, Prince
Philip — A243

**1972, Nov. 20  Photo.   Perf. 14x14½**

| | | | | |
|---|---|---|---|---|
| 683 | A243 | 3p dk bl, sep & sil | .25 | .25 |
| 684 | A243 | 20p dk pur, sepia & sil | .75 | .75 |

25th anniv. of the marriage of Queen Elizabeth II and Prince Philip. No. 684 is without phosphor.

Britain as Part of
European
Community
A244

**1973, Jan. 3**

| | | | | |
|---|---|---|---|---|
| 685 | A244 | 3p brown org & multi | .20 | .20 |
| 686 | A244 | 5p blue & multi | .45 | .45 |
| 687 | A244 | 5p emerald & multi | .45 | .45 |
| a. | | Pair, #686-687 | .90 | 1.10 |
| | | *Nos. 685-687 (3)* | 1.10 | 1.10 |

Britain's entry into the European Community.

Oak
A245

**1973, Feb. 28   Photo.   Perf. 14½x14**

| | | | | |
|---|---|---|---|---|
| 688 | A245 | 9p multicolored | .40 | .40 |

Tree Planting Year.

### Explorer Type of 1972

British Explorers: No. 689, David Livingstone and map of Africa. No. 690, Henry Stanley and map of Africa. 5p, Sir Francis Drake and world map. 7½p, Sir Walter Raleigh and world map. 9p, Charles Sturt and map of Australia.

**1973, Apr. 8    Photo.   Perf. 14x14½**

| | | | | |
|---|---|---|---|---|
| 689 | A236 | 3p multicolored | .20 | .20 |
| 690 | A236 | 3p multicolored | .20 | .20 |
| a. | | Pair, #689-690 | .75 | 1.00 |
| 691 | A236 | 5p multicolored | .30 | .30 |
| 692 | A236 | 7½p multicolored | .35 | .35 |
| 693 | A236 | 9p multicolored | 1.00 | .90 |
| | | *Nos. 689-693 (5)* | 2.05 | 1.95 |

William Gilbert
Grace — A246

Designs: Caricatures of William Gilbert Grace, the Great Cricketer, by Harry Furniss.

**1973, May 16   Photo.   Perf. 14½x14**

| | | | | |
|---|---|---|---|---|
| 694 | A246 | 3p brown & black | .20 | .20 |
| 695 | A246 | 7½p green & black | .60 | .60 |
| 696 | A246 | 9p blue & black | .80 | .80 |
| | | *Nos. 694-696 (3)* | 1.60 | 1.60 |

Centenary of British County Cricket.

Sir Joshua
Reynolds, Self-
portrait
A247

**1973, July 4    Photo.   Perf. 14x14½**

Paintings: 5p, Sir Henry Raeburn (1756-1823), self-portrait. 7½p, Nelly O'Brien, by Reynolds (1723-92). 9p, Rev. R. Walker (The Skater), by Raeburn.

| | | | | |
|---|---|---|---|---|
| 697 | A247 | 3p multicolored | .20 | .20 |
| 698 | A247 | 5p multicolored | .20 | .20 |
| 699 | A247 | 7½p multicolored | .40 | .40 |
| 700 | A247 | 9p gray & multi | .45 | .45 |
| | | *Nos. 697-700 (4)* | 1.25 | 1.25 |

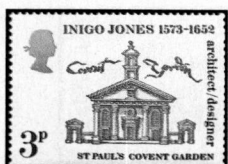

Tuscan Portico, St. Paul's Church, Covent Garden
A248

Designs: No. 701, Costumes for Oberon and Titania. No. 703, Prince's Lodging, Newmarket. No. 704, Stage scenery for Oberon.

**1973, Aug. 15     Litho. and Typo.**
701 A248 3p black, pur & gold        .20   .20
702 A248 3p gold, brn & blk          .20   .20
  a.  Pair, #701-702                .45   .30
703 A248 5p black, blue & gold       .50   .50
704 A248 5p gold, olive & blk        .50   .50
  a.  Pair, #703-704               1.25  1.25
    Nos. 701-704 (4)             1.40  1.40

400th birth anniv. of Inigo Jones (1573-1652), architect and designer.

Parliament, from Millbank
A249

Design: 8p, Parliament, from Whitehall.

**1973, Sept. 12     Engr. and Typo.**
705 A249 8p buff, gray & blk         .35   .35
706 A249 10p black & gold            .45   .45

Opening by the Queen of the 19th Commonwealth Parliamentary Assoc. Conf., Westminster Hall.

Princess Anne and Mark Phillips
A250

**1973, Nov. 14   Photo.   Perf. 14½x14**
707 A250 3½p violet & silver         .20   .20
708 A250 20p brown & silver          .75   .75

Wedding of Princess Anne and Captain Mark Phillips, Nov. 14, 1973.

Good King Wenceslas
A251

Christmas: Illustrations for Christmas carol "Good King Wenceslas" showing king and page.

**1973, Nov. 28**
709 A251 3p shown                    .40   .35
710 A251 3p Page looking out
        of window                .40   .35
711 A251 3p Page leaving cas-
        tle                      .40   .35
712 A251 3p Page in storm            .40   .35
713 A251 3p Page bringing
        gifts                    .40   .35
  a.  Strip of 5, #709-713        2.50  2.50
714 A251 3½p Page and peasant        .40   .35
    Nos. 709-714 (6)             2.40  2.10

Horse Chestnut
A252

**1974, Feb. 27   Photo.   Perf. 14½x14**
715 A252 10p green & multi           .40   .40

Fire Engine, 1766
A253

Designs: 3½p, First motorized fire engine, 1904. 5½p, Prize winning Sutherland fire engine, 1863. 8p, First steam engine, 1830.

**1974, Apr. 24**
716 A253 3½p multicolored            .20   .20
717 A253 5½p multicolored            .30   .30
718 A253 8p multicolored             .35   .35
719 A253 10p multicolored            .45   .45
    Nos. 716-719 (4)             1.30  1.30

Fire Prevention (Metropolis) Act, bicent.

Packet "Peninsular," 1888, and "Southampton Packet Letter" Postmark — A254

Development of Overseas Mail Transport: 5½p, Farnham Biplane and "Aerial Post" postmark. 8p, Truck and pillar box for airmail and "London F.S. Air Mail" postmark. 10p, Imperial Airways flying boat and "Southampton Airport" postmark.

**1974, June 12     Perf. 14½x14**
720 A254 3½p multicolored            .20   .20
721 A254 5½p multicolored            .20   .20
722 A254 8p multicolored             .30   .30
723 A254 10p multicolored            .40   .40
    Nos. 720-723 (4)             1.10  1.10

UPU, Cent.

Robert the Bruce
A255

"Great Britons" on caparisoned chargers.

**1974, July 10     Perf. 14½x14**
724 A255 4½p shown                   .20   .20
725 A255 5½p Owain Glyndwr           .20   .20
726 A255 8p King Henry V             .35   .35
727 A255 10p Black Prince            .45   .45
    Nos. 724-727 (4)             1.20  1.20

Churchill, Lord Warden of the Cinque Ports, 1942 — A256

Designs (Churchill): 5½p, with bowler and cigar, 1940. 8p, with top hat, as Secretary of War and Air, 1919. 10p, in uniform of South African Light Horse Regiment, 1899.

**1974, Oct. 9   Photo.   Perf. 14x14½**
728 A256 4½p silver & multi          .20   .20
729 A256 5½p silver & multi          .30   .30
730 A256 8p silver & multi           .40   .40
731 A256 10p silver & multi          .55   .55
    Nos. 728-731 (4)             1.45  1.45

Sir Winston Spencer Churchill (1874-1965).

Adoration of the Kings, York Minster, c. 1355
A257

Christmas (Roof Bosses): 4½p, Nativity, St. Helen's, Norwich, c. 1480. 8p, Virgin and Child, Church of Ottery St. Mary, Devonshire, c. 1350. 10p, Virgin and Child, Lady Chapel, Worcester Cathedral, c. 1224.

**1974, Nov. 27     Perf. 14½x14**
732 A257 3½p gold & multi            .20   .20
733 A257 4½p gold & multi            .20   .20
734 A257 8p gold & multi             .30   .30
735 A257 10p gold & multi            .40   .40
    Nos. 732-735 (4)             1.10  1.10

"Peace-Burial at Sea," by Turner — A258

Paintings: 5½p, "Snowstorm-Steamer off a Harbour's Mouth." 8p, "Arsenal, Venice." 10p, "View of St. Laurent."

**1975, Feb. 19   Photo.   Perf. 14½x14**
736 A258 4½p multicolored            .20   .20
737 A258 5½p multicolored            .20   .20
738 A258 8p multicolored             .30   .30
739 A258 10p multicolored            .40   .40
    Nos. 736-739 (4)             1.10  1.10

Birth bicent. of Joseph Mallord William Turner (1775-1851), painter.

Charlotte Square, Edinburgh
A259

National Theater, London
A260

Designs: No. 740, The Rows, Chester (double-storied medieval shopping streets). 8p, Sir Christopher Wren's Flamsteed House, Royal Observatory, Greenwich. 10p, St. George's Chapel, Windsor.

**1975, Apr. 23     Perf. 14½x14**
740 A259 7p multicolored             .25   .25
741 A259 7p multicolored             .25   .25
  a.  Pair, #740-741              .50   .50
742 A259 8p multicolored             .30   .30
743 A259 10p multicolored            .40   .40
744 A260 12p multicolored            .45   .45
    Nos. 740-744 (5)             1.65  1.65

European Architectural Heritage Year 1975. Nos. 740-741 printed se-tenant in sheets of 100. 300th anniv. of Royal Observatory, (No. 742) and 500th anniv. of St. George's Chapel (No. 743).

Dinghies
A261

**1975, June 11     Photo. & Engr.**
745 A261 7p shown                    .25   .25
746 A261 8p Racing keelboats         .30   .30
747 A261 10p Cruising yachts         .40   .40
748 A261 12p Multihulls              .50   .50
    Nos. 745-748 (4)             1.45  1.45

Royal Thames Yacht Club bicent. and other sailing club anniversaries.

Stephenson's Locomotion, 1825 — A262

Locomotives: 8p, Abbotsford, Waverley Class, 1876. 10p, Caerphilly Castle, 1923. 12p, High-speed train, 1975.

**1975, Aug. 13   Photo.   Perf. 14½x14**
749 A262 7p multicolored             .25   .20
750 A262 8p multicolored             .30   .30
751 A262 10p multicolored            .40   .40
752 A262 12p multicolored            .50   .50
    Nos. 749-752 (4)             1.45  1.40

Sesquicentennial of public railroads in Great Britain.

Parliament
A263

**1975, Sept. 3**
753 A263 12p multicolored            .50   .50

62nd Inter-Parliamentary Conference, London, Sept. 1975.

Emma and Mr. Woodhouse from "Emma" — A264

Designs (Illustrations by Barbara Brown of Characters from Jane Austen's Novels): 10p, Catherine Morland from "Northanger Abbey." 11p, Mr. Darcy from "Pride and Prejudice." 13p, Mary and Henry Crawford from "Mansfield Park."

**1975, Oct. 22   Photo.   Perf. 14x14½**
754 A264 8½p multicolored            .30   .30
755 A264 10p multicolored            .40   .40
756 A264 11p multicolored            .45   .45
757 A264 13p multicolored            .50   .50
    Nos. 754-757 (4)             1.65  1.65

Jane Austen (1775-1817), novelist.

Angels with Lute and Harp
A265

Christmas: 8½p, Angel with mandolin. 11p, Angel with horn. 13p, Angel with trumpet.

**1975, Nov. 26   Photo.   Perf. 14½x14**
758 A265 6½p violet & multi          .25   .25
759 A265 8½p multicolored            .30   .30
760 A265 11p multicolored            .45   .45
761 A265 13p ocher & multi           .50   .50
    Nos. 758-761 (4)             1.50  1.50

Woman
Making
Social Call
A266

Designs: 10p, Policeman making emergency call. 11p, District nurse making social welfare call. 13p, Refinery worker making field call.

**1976, Mar. 10   Photo.   Perf. 14½x14**
777  A266  8½p multicolored          .30    .30
778  A266  10p multicolored          .40    .40
779  A266  11p multicolored          .45    .45
780  A266  13p multicolored          .50    .50
       Nos. 777-780 (4)              1.65   1.65

1st telephone call by Alexander Graham Bell, Mar. 10, 1876.

Coal
Miner's
Hands
(Thomas
Hepburn)
A267

Designs: 10p, Child's hands, textile mill (Robert Owen). 11p, Boy's hand sweeping chimney (Lord Shaftesbury). 13p, Woman's hands holding prison bars (Elizabeth Frey).

**1976, Apr. 28   Photo.   Perf. 14½x14**
781  A267  8½p gray & black          .30    .30
782  A267  10p multicolored          .40    .40
783  A267  11p multicolored          .45    .45
784  A267  13p multicolored          .50    .50
       Nos. 781-784 (4)              1.65   1.65

19th cent. industrial & social reformers: Hepburn formed 1st miners' union in 1831; Owen, improved working conditions in his mill and established schools; Lord Shaftesbury, philanthropist and sponsor of reform work laws; Frey, pioneer of women's prison reforms.

Benjamin Franklin,
by Jean-Jacques
Caffieri — A268

**1976, June 2           Perf. 14x14½**
785  A268  11p multicolored          .45    .45
       American Bicentennial.

Royal National
Rose Society,
Centenary
A269

Roses Painted by Kristin Rosenberg.

**1976, June 30   Photo.   Perf. 14x14½**
786  A269  8½p Elizabeth of
                Glamis Rose          .30    .30
787  A269  10p Grandpa Dickson       .40    .40
788  A269  11p Rosa Mundi            .45    .45
789  A269  13p Sweet Briar           .50    .50
       Nos. 786-789 (4)              1.65   1.65

Archdruid,
Eisteddfod
A270

Morris
Dancing — A271

British Cultural Traditions: 11p, Piper and dancers, Highland gathering. 13p, Woman playing Welsh harp (telyn), Eisteddfod.

**1976, Aug. 4   Photo.   Perf. 14x14½**
790  A270  8½p multicolored          .30    .30
791  A271  10p multicolored          .40    .40
792  A271  11p multicolored          .45    .45
793  A270  13p multicolored          .50    .50
       Nos. 790-793 (4)              1.65   1.65

Squire, from
Canterbury
Tales — A272

Designs: 10p, Page from Tretyse of Love, c. 1493, set in Caxton typeface. 11p, Philosopher, from The Game and Playe of Chesse, c. 1483. 13p, Printing press and printers, early 16th century woodcut.

**Photo.; Queen's Head Gold
Embossed**
**1976, Sept. 29           Perf. 14x14½**
794  A272  8½p blue & indigo         .30    .30
795  A272  9p olive & dk grn         .40    .40
796  A272  11p gray & black          .40    .40
797  A272  13p ocher & red brn       .50    .50
       Nos. 794-797 (4)              1.60   1.60

500 years of British printing, introduced by William Caxton (1422-1491).

Virgin and
Child, Clare
Chasuble
A273

Christmas (English medieval embroideries): 8½p, Angel with crown. 11p, Angel appearing to the shepherds. 13p, Three Kings bringing gifts, Butler-Bowden cope.

**1976, Nov. 24   Photo.   Perf. 14½x14**
798  A273  6½p multicolored          .30    .30
799  A273  8½p multicolored          .35    .35
800  A273  11p multicolored          .45    .45
801  A273  13p multicolored          .50    .50
       Nos. 798-801 (4)              1.60   1.60

Racket
Sports
A274

**1977, Jan. 12   Photo.   Perf. 14½x14**
802  A274  8½p Tennis                .30    .30
803  A274  10p Table tennis          .40    .40
804  A274  11p Squash                .45    .45
805  A274  13p Badminton             .50    .50
       Nos. 802-805 (4)              1.65   1.65

Wimbledon Tennis Championships, cent. and 1977 World Table Tennis Championships, Birmingham.

Steroids Conformational
Analysis — A275

Designs: 10p, Vitamin C synthesis (formula and orange). 11p, Starch chromatography. 13p, Salt crystallography.

**1977, Mar. 2   Photo.   Perf. 14½x14**
806  A275  8½p multicolored          .30    .30
807  A275  10p multicolored          .40    .40
808  A275  11p multicolored          .45    .45
809  A275  13p multicolored          .50    .50
       Nos. 806-809 (4)              1.65   1.65

British chemists who won Nobel prize. Derek Barton, 1969 (8½p); Walter Norman Haworth, 1937 (10p); Archer J. P. Martin and Richard L. P. Synge, 1952 (11p); William and Lawrence Bragg, 1915 (13p).

Queen
Elizabeth
II — A276

**1977           Photo.   Perf. 14½x14**
810  A276  8½p silver & multi        .30    .30
811  A276  9p silver & multi         .35    .35
812  A276  10p silver & multi        .40    .40
813  A276  11p silver & multi        .45    .45
814  A276  13p silver & multi        .50    .50
       Nos. 810-814 (5)              2.00   2.00

25th anniv. of the reign of Elizabeth II. Issue dates: 9p, June 15; others, May 11.

Pentagons,
Symbolic of
Continents and
Nations — A277

**1977, June 8   Photo.   Perf. 14x14½**
815  A277  13p multicolored          .50    .50

Summit Conference of Commonwealth Heads of Government, London, June 1977.

Wildlife
Protection — A278

**1977, Oct. 5   Photo.   Perf. 14x14½**
816  A278  9p Hedgehog               .35    .25
817  A278  9p Brown hare             .35    .25
818  A278  9p Red squirrel           .35    .25
819  A278  9p Otter                  .35    .25
820  A278  9p Badger                 .35    .25
    a.   Strip of 5, #816-820        2.00

"Two Turtle Doves, Three French
Hens. . ." — A279

The Twelve Days of Christmas: No. 822, 4 colly birds, 5 gold rings, 6 geese a-laying. No. 823, 7 swans a-swimming, 8 maids a-milking. No. 824, 9 drummers drumming, 10 pipers piping. No. 825, 11 ladies dancing, 12 lords a-leaping. 9p, A partridge in a pear tree.

**1977, Nov. 23   Photo.   Perf. 14½x14**
821  A279  7p multicolored           .25    .20
822  A279  7p multicolored           .25    .20
823  A279  7p multicolored           .25    .20
824  A279  7p multicolored           .25    .20
825  A279  7p multicolored           .25    .20
    a.   Strip of 5, #821-825        1.00
826  A279  9p multicolored           .35    .20
       Nos. 821-826 (6)              1.60   1.20

Oil Production
Platform, North
Sea — A280

Designs: 10½p, Coal, pithead. 11p, Natural gas, flame. 13p, Electricity-producing nuclear power plant and uranium atom diagram.

**1978, Jan. 25   Photo.   Perf. 14x14½**
827  A280  9p multicolored           .35    .20
828  A280  10½p multicolored         .35    .20
829  A280  11p multicolored          .45    .20
830  A280  13p multicolored          .50    .25
       Nos. 827-830 (4)              1.65    .85

Great Britain's wealth of energy resources.

Tower of
London
A281

British Architecture: 10½p, Abbey and Palace, Holyrood House, Edinburgh. 11p, Caernarvon Castle, Wales. 13p, Hampton Court Palace, London.

**1978, Mar. 1   Photo.   Perf. 14½x14½**
831  A281  9p multicolored           .35    .20
832  A281  10½p multicolored         .40    .25
833  A281  11p multicolored          .40    .25
834  A281  13p multicolored          .50    .25
    a.   Souv. sheet of 4, #831-834  1.75   1.75
       Nos. 831-834 (4)              1.65    .95

No. 834a issued to publicize London 1980 Intl. Stamp Exhib. and sold for 53½p. The surtax went to exhibition fund.

Gold State
Coach — A282

Designs: 10½p, St. Edward's crown. 11p, Orb. 13p, Imperial State crown.

**1978, May 31   Photo.   Perf. 14x14½**
835  A282  9p vio blue & gold        .35    .25
836  A282  10½p car lake & gold      .40    .25
837  A282  11p dp green & gold       .45    .30
838  A282  13p purple & gold         .50    .35
       Nos. 835-838 (4)              1.70   1.15

25th anniv. of coronation of Elizabeth II.

Shire Horse A283

British Horses: 10½p, Shetland pony. 11p, Merlyn Cymreig Welsh pony. 13p, Thoroughbred.

**1978, July 5  Photo.  Perf. 14½x14**
839 A283 9p multicolored .35 .25
840 A283 10½p multicolored .40 .25
841 A283 11p multicolored .45 .25
842 A283 13p multicolored .50 .35
Nos. 839-842 (4) 1.70 1.10

"Penny-farthing," 19th Century — A284

British bicycles: 10½p, 1920 touring bicycles. 11p, Modern small-wheel bicycles. 13p, Road racers.

**1978, Aug. 2  Photo.  Perf. 14½x14**
843 A284 9p multicolored .35 .25
844 A284 10½p multicolored .40 .25
845 A284 11p multicolored .45 .25
846 A284 13p multicolored .50 .35
Nos. 843-846 (4) 1.70 1.10

Cent. of 1st natl. cycling organizations: British Cycling Fed. and Cyclists Touring Club.

Carolers Around Christmas Tree A285

Christmas: 9p, Christmas waits (watchmen). 11p, 18th century carolers. 13p, Boar's head carol.

**1978, Nov. 22  Photo.  Perf. 14½x14**
847 A285 7p multicolored .25 .25
848 A285 9p multicolored .35 .25
849 A285 11p multicolored .45 .25
850 A285 13p multicolored .50 .35
Nos. 847-850 (4) 1.55 1.10

Old English Sheepdog A286

British dogs: 10½p, Welsh springer spaniel. 11p, West Highland white terrier. 13p, Irish setter.

**1979, Feb. 7  Photo.  Perf. 14½x14**
851 A286 9p multicolored .35 .25
852 A286 10½p multicolored .40 .25
853 A286 11p multicolored .45 .25
854 A286 13p multicolored .50 .35
Nos. 851-854 (4) 1.70 1.10

British Wild Flowers — A287

**1979, Mar. 21  Photo.  Perf. 14x14½**
855 A287 9p Primroses .35 .25
856 A287 10½p Daffodils .40 .25
857 A287 11p Bluebells .45 .25
858 A287 13p Snowdrops .50 .35
Nos. 855-858 (4) 1.70 1.10

Flags of Member Nations as Ballots A288

Flags of European Community Members: United Kingdom, Italy, Denmark, Belgium, Fed. Rep. of Germany, France, Netherlands, Ireland, Luxembourg. Positions of hands and flags different on each denomination.

**1979, May 9  Photo.  Perf. 14½x14**
859 A288 9p multicolored .35 .25
860 A288 10½p multicolored .40 .25
861 A288 11p multicolored .45 .25
862 A288 13p multicolored .50 .35
Nos. 859-862 (4) 1.70 1.10

European Parliament, 1st direct elections, 6/7-10.

Saddling of Mahmoud, 1936 Derby, by Alfred Munnings A289

200th Anniv. of the Derby: 10½p, Liverpool Great National Steeple Chase, 1839, aquatint by F. C. Turner. 11p, First Spring Meeting, Newmarket, 1793, by J. N. Sartorius. 13p, Charles II watching racing at Dorsett Ferry, Windsor, 1684, by Francis Barlow.

**1979, June 6  Photo.  Perf. 14½x14**
863 A289 9p multicolored .35 .25
864 A289 10½p multicolored .40 .25
865 A289 11p multicolored .45 .25
866 A289 13p multicolored .50 .35
Nos. 863-866 (4) 1.70 1.10

Peter Rabbit — A290

Children's books: 10½p, The Wind in the Willows. 11p, Winnie the Pooh. 13p, Alice's Adventures in Wonderland.

**1979, July 11  Photo.  Perf. 14x14½**
867 A290 9p multicolored .40 .20
868 A290 10½p multicolored .45 .20
869 A290 11p multicolored .45 .25
870 A290 13p multicolored .55 .25
Nos. 867-870 (4) 1.85 .90

International Year of the Child.

Rowland Hill — A291

Designs: 11½p, Bellman, early 19th cent. 13p, London post office and mailman, early 19th cent. 15p, Victorian woman and child mailing letter.

**1979, Aug. 22  Photo.  Perf. 14x14½**
871 A291 10p multicolored .40 .25
872 A291 11½p multicolored .45 .25
873 A291 13p multicolored .50 .25

874 A291 15p multicolored .60 .30
a. Souvenir sheet of 4, #871-874 2.00 1.75
Nos. 871-874 (4) 1.95 1.05

Sir Rowland Hill (1795-1879), originator of penny postage.
No. 874a issued 10/24/79 to publicize London 1980 Intl. Stamp Exhib. and sold for 59½p. The surtax went to exhibition fund.

Police Constable and Children A292

Designs: 11½p, Police constable directing traffic. 13p, Police woman on horseback. 15p, River patrol boat.

**1979, Sept. 26  Photo.  Perf. 14½x14**
875 A292 10p multicolored .40 .25
876 A292 11½p multicolored .45 .25
877 A292 13p multicolored .50 .25
878 A292 15p multicolored .60 .35
Nos. 875-878 (4) 1.95 1.10

London Metropolitan Police, 150th anniv.

Three Kings Following Star A293

Christmas: 10p, Angel appearing before the shepherds. 11½p, Nativity. 13p, Joseph and Mary traveling to Bethlehem. 15p, Annunciation.

**1979, Nov. 21  Photo.  Perf. 14½x14**
879 A293 8p multicolored .30 .25
880 A293 10p multicolored .40 .25
881 A293 11½p multicolored .45 .30
882 A293 13p multicolored .50 .35
883 A293 15p multicolored .60 .35
Nos. 879-883 (5) 2.25 1.50

Kingfisher — A294

**1980, Jan. 16  Photo.  Perf. 14x14½**
884 A294 10p shown .40 .25
885 A294 11½p Dipper .45 .25
886 A294 13p Moorhen .50 .25
887 A294 15p Yellow wagtail .60 .35
Nos. 884-887 (4) 1.95 1.10

"Rocket" Locomotive A295

**1980, Mar. 12  Photo.  Perf. 14½x14**
904 A295 12p shown .50 .30
905 A295 12p 1st, 2nd class cars .50 .30
906 A295 12p 3rd class and
               sheep cars .50 .30
907 A295 12p Flat cars .50 .30
908 A295 12p Flat car, mail
               coach .50 .30
a. Strip of 5, #904-908 2.50 2.50

Liverpool-Manchester Railroad, 150th anniv. No. 908a has a continuous design.

London View A296

**1980, Apr. 9  Engr.  Perf. 14½**
909 A296 50p multicolored 2.00 1.25
a. Souvenir sheet 2.00 2.00

London 1980, Intl. Stamp Exhib., May 6-14. No. 909a, issued May 7, sold for 75p.

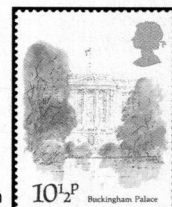

Buckingham Palace — A297

**1980, May 7  Photo.  Perf. 14x14½**
910 A297 10½p shown .40 .25
911 A297 12p Albert Memorial .50 .25
912 A297 13½p Royal Opera
               House .50 .25
913 A297 15p Hampton Court .60 .25
914 A297 17½p Kensington Pal-
               ace .70 .35
Nos. 910-914 (5) 2.70 1.35

Emily Bronte and "Wuthering Heights" A298

Victorian novelists and scenes from their novels: 12p, Charlotte Bronte, "Jane Eyre." 13½p, George Eliot, "The Mill on the Floss." 17½p, Mrs. Gaskell, "North and South." 12p and 13½p show CEPT (Europa) emblem.

**1980, July 9  Photo.  Perf. 15x14**
915 A298 12p multicolored .50 .30
916 A298 13½p multicolored .55 .35
917 A298 15p multicolored .60 .40
918 A298 17½p multicolored .70 .55
Nos. 915-918 (4) 2.35 1.60

Queen Mother Elizabeth, 80th Birthday — A299

**1980, Aug. 4  Photo.  Perf. 14x14½**
919 A299 12p multicolored .45 .20

English Conductors A300

Designs: 12p, Henry Wood, (1869-1944) Conductor. 13½p, Thomas Beecham (1879-

1961). 15p, Malcolm Sargent (1895-1967). 17½p, John Barbirolli (1899-1970).

**1980, Sept. 10**
| | | | | |
|---|---|---|---|---|
| 920 | A300 | 12p multicolored | .50 | .30 |
| 921 | A300 | 13½p multicolored | .55 | .30 |
| 922 | A300 | 15p multicolored | .60 | .40 |
| 923 | A300 | 17½p multicolored | .70 | .45 |
| | | *Nos. 920-923 (4)* | 2.35 | 1.45 |

Running — A301

**1980, Oct. 10    Litho.    Perf. 14x14½**
| | | | | |
|---|---|---|---|---|
| 924 | A301 | 12p shown | .50 | .30 |
| 925 | A301 | 13½p Rugby | .55 | .30 |
| 926 | A301 | 15p Boxing | .60 | .40 |
| 927 | A301 | 17½p Cricket | .70 | .45 |
| | | *Nos. 924-927 (4)* | 2.35 | 1.45 |

Centenaries: Amateur Athletics Assoc.; Welsh Rugby Union; Amateur Boxing Assoc.; 1st cricket test match against Australia.

Christmas Tree with Candles A302

Christmas (Traditional Decorations): 12p, Candles, ivy, ribbons. 13½p, Mistletoe, apples. 15p, Paper chain and bell. 17½p, Holly wreath.

**1980, Nov. 19    Photo.    Perf. 14½x14**
| | | | | |
|---|---|---|---|---|
| 928 | A302 | 10p multicolored | .40 | .25 |
| 929 | A302 | 12p multicolored | .50 | .30 |
| 930 | A302 | 13½p multicolored | .55 | .35 |
| 931 | A302 | 15p multicolored | .60 | .40 |
| 932 | A302 | 17½ multicolored | .70 | .50 |
| | | *Nos. 928-932 (5)* | 2.75 | 1.80 |

Lovebirds, Angels and Heart (Valentine's Day) A303

Folklore: 18p, Morris Dancers, 16th century window, Shropshire. 22p, Wheat, fruit, farm couple dancing (Lammastide). 25p, Medieval mummers, 14th century manuscript illustration. 14p and 18p show CEPT (Europa) emblem.

**1981, Feb. 6    Photo.    Perf. 14½x14**
| | | | | |
|---|---|---|---|---|
| 933 | A303 | 14p multicolored | .50 | .30 |
| 934 | A303 | 18p multicolored | .65 | .65 |
| 935 | A303 | 22p multicolored | .90 | .75 |
| 936 | A303 | 25p multicolored | 1.00 | .85 |
| | | *Nos. 933-936 (4)* | 3.05 | 2.55 |

Guide Dog Leading Blind Man A304

**1981, Mar. 25    Photo.**
| | | | | |
|---|---|---|---|---|
| 937 | A304 | 14p shown | .50 | .30 |
| 938 | A304 | 18p Sign language | .70 | .45 |
| 939 | A304 | 22p Man in wheelchair | .90 | .65 |
| 940 | A304 | 25p Foot painting | 1.00 | .75 |
| | | *Nos. 937-940 (4)* | 3.10 | 2.15 |

International Year of the Disabled.

Small Tortoiseshell A305

**1981, May 13    Perf. 14x14½**
| | | | | |
|---|---|---|---|---|
| 941 | A305 | 14p shown | .55 | .30 |
| 942 | A305 | 18p Large blue | .70 | .40 |
| 943 | A305 | 22p Peacock | .90 | .70 |
| 944 | A305 | 25p Checkered skipper | 1.00 | .80 |
| | | *Nos. 941-944 (4)* | 3.15 | 2.25 |

Glenfinnan, Highlands, Scotland A306

50th anniv. of National Trust for Scotland: 18p, Derwentwater, Lake District, England. 20p, Stackpole Head, Dyfed, Wales. 22p, Giant's Causeway, County Antrim, Northern Ireland. 25p, St. Kilda, Scotland.

**1981, June 24    Photo.    Perf. 14½x14**
| | | | | |
|---|---|---|---|---|
| 945 | A306 | 14p multicolored | .55 | .25 |
| 946 | A306 | 18p multicolored | .70 | .35 |
| 947 | A306 | 20p multicolored | .80 | .45 |
| 948 | A306 | 22p multicolored | .90 | .65 |
| 949 | A306 | 25p multicolored | 1.00 | .75 |
| | | *Nos. 945-949 (5)* | 3.95 | 2.45 |

Prince Charles and Lady Diana A307

**1981, July 22    Photo.    Perf. 14x14½**
| | | | | |
|---|---|---|---|---|
| 950 | A307 | 14p multicolored | .90 | .40 |
| 951 | A307 | 25p multicolored | 1.60 | .75 |

Wedding of Charles, Prince of Wales, and Lady Diana Spencer, St. Paul's Cathedral, July 29.

Hikers Reading Map A308

**1981, Aug. 12    Litho.    Perf. 14**
| | | | | |
|---|---|---|---|---|
| 952 | A308 | 14p shown | .55 | .25 |
| 953 | A308 | 18p Girl at potter's wheel | .70 | .50 |
| 954 | A308 | 22p Woman administering artificial respiration | .90 | .65 |
| 955 | A308 | 25p Hurdler | 1.00 | .75 |
| | | *Nos. 952-955 (4)* | 3.15 | 2.15 |

The Duke of Edinburgh's Awards (expeditions, skills, service, recreation), 25th anniv.

Cockle Dredging A309

**1981, Sept. 23    Photo.    Perf. 14½x14**
| | | | | |
|---|---|---|---|---|
| 956 | A309 | 14p shown | .55 | .25 |
| 957 | A309 | 18p Hauling trawl net | .70 | .50 |
| 958 | A309 | 22p Lobster potting | .90 | .65 |
| 959 | A309 | 25p Hauling seine net | 1.00 | .75 |
| | | *Nos. 956-959 (4)* | 3.15 | 2.15 |

Fishermen's Year and Royal Natl. Mission to Deep Sea Fishermen centenary.

Joseph and Mary Arriving at Bethlehem A310

Christmas: Children's Drawings.

**1981, Nov. 18    Photo.**
| | | | | |
|---|---|---|---|---|
| 960 | A310 | 11½p Santa Claus | .45 | .25 |
| 961 | A310 | 14p Jesus | .55 | .30 |
| 962 | A310 | 18p Angel | .70 | .40 |
| 963 | A310 | 22p shown | .90 | .50 |
| 964 | A310 | 25p Three Kings | 1.00 | .60 |
| | | *Nos. 960-964 (5)* | 3.60 | 2.05 |

Death Centenary of Charles Darwin (1809-1882) — A311

**1982, Feb. 10    Photo.**
| | | | | |
|---|---|---|---|---|
| 965 | A311 | 15½p Giant tortoises | .60 | .35 |
| 966 | A311 | 19½p Iguanas | .80 | .50 |
| 967 | A311 | 26p Darwin's finches | 1.05 | .80 |
| 968 | A311 | 29p Skulls | 1.15 | .95 |
| | | *Nos. 965-968 (4)* | 3.60 | 2.60 |

Youth Organizations A312

**1982, Mar. 24    Photo.    Perf. 14x14½**
| | | | | |
|---|---|---|---|---|
| 983 | A312 | 15½p Boy's Brigade | .60 | .35 |
| 984 | A312 | 19½p Girl's Brigade | .80 | .50 |
| 985 | A312 | 26p Boy Scouts | 1.05 | .80 |
| 986 | A312 | 29p Girl Guides | 1.15 | .95 |
| | | *Nos. 983-986 (4)* | 3.60 | 2.60 |

75th anniv. of scouting and 125th birth anniv. of founder Robert Baden-Powell (26p).

Performing Arts — A313

**1982, Apr. 28    Photo.    Perf. 14x14½**
| | | | | |
|---|---|---|---|---|
| 987 | A313 | 15½p Ballet | .65 | .25 |
| 988 | A313 | 19½p Pantomime | .85 | .50 |
| 989 | A313 | 26p Shakespearean drama | 1.15 | .90 |
| 990 | A313 | 29p Opera | 1.25 | 1.00 |
| | | *Nos. 987-990 (4)* | 3.90 | 2.65 |

Nos. 987-990 show CEPT (Europa) emblem.

King Henry VIII and the Mary Rose A314

**1982, June 16    Perf. 14½x14**
| | | | | |
|---|---|---|---|---|
| 991 | A314 | 15½p shown | .60 | .25 |
| 992 | A314 | 19½p Admiral Blake, Triumph | .75 | .50 |
| 993 | A314 | 24p Lord Nelson, Victory | .90 | .65 |
| 994 | A314 | 26p Lord Fisher, Dreadnought | 1.05 | .75 |
| 995 | A314 | 29p Viscount Cunningham, Warspite | 1.15 | .90 |
| | | *Nos. 991-995 (5)* | 4.45 | 3.05 |

Textile Designs — A315

**1982, July 23    Photo.    Perf. 14x14½**
| | | | | |
|---|---|---|---|---|
| 996 | A315 | 15½p Strawberry Thief, 1883 | .60 | .20 |
| 997 | A315 | 19½p Tulips, 1906 | .80 | .50 |
| 998 | A315 | 26p Cherry Orchard, 1930 | 1.05 | .75 |
| 999 | A315 | 29p Chevron, 1973 | 1.15 | .85 |
| | | *Nos. 996-999 (4)* | 3.60 | 2.30 |

Information Technology — A316

15½p, Hieroglyphics, library, word processor. 26p, Viewdata set, satellite, laser pen.

**1982, Sept. 8    Photo.**
| | | | | |
|---|---|---|---|---|
| 1000 | A316 | 15½p multicolored | .60 | .25 |
| 1001 | A316 | 26p multicolored | 1.05 | .70 |

Austin's Seven (1922) and Metro A317

Cars: 19½p, Ford Model T (1913) and Escort. 26p, Jaguar SS (1931) and XJ6 (1967). 29p, Rolls-Royce Silver Ghost (1907) and Silver Spirit (1982).

**1982, Oct. 13    Litho.    Perf. 14½x14**
| | | | | |
|---|---|---|---|---|
| 1002 | A317 | 15½p multicolored | .60 | .45 |
| 1003 | A317 | 19½p multicolored | .80 | .60 |
| 1004 | A317 | 26p multicolored | 1.05 | .75 |
| 1005 | A317 | 29p multicolored | 1.15 | .85 |
| | | *Nos. 1002-1005 (4)* | 3.60 | 2.65 |

Christmas 1982 A318

Designs: Christmas carols.

**1982, Nov. 17    Photo.**
| | | | | |
|---|---|---|---|---|
| 1006 | A318 | 12½p While Shepherds Watched | .50 | .20 |
| 1007 | A318 | 15½p The Holly and the Ivy | .60 | .35 |
| 1008 | A318 | 19½p I Saw Three Ships | .80 | .60 |
| 1009 | A318 | 26p We Three Kings | 1.05 | .70 |
| 1010 | A318 | 29p Good King Wenceslas | 1.15 | .80 |
| | | *Nos. 1006-1010 (5)* | 4.10 | 2.65 |

River Fish
A319

**1983, Jan. 26    Photo.    Perf. 15x14**

| | | | | |
|---|---|---|---|---|
| 1011 | A319 | 15½p Salmon | .60 | .25 |
| 1012 | A319 | 19½p Pike | .80 | .55 |
| 1013 | A319 | 26p Trout | 1.05 | .65 |
| 1014 | A319 | 29p Perch | 1.15 | .75 |
| | | *Nos. 1011-1014 (4)* | 3.60 | 2.20 |

Commonwealth
Day — A320

Landscapes by Donald Hamilton Fraser.

**1983, Mar. 9    Photo.    Perf. 14x14½**

| | | | | |
|---|---|---|---|---|
| 1015 | A320 | 15½p Tropical island | .60 | .35 |
| 1016 | A320 | 19½p Desert | .80 | .55 |
| 1017 | A320 | 26p Farmland | 1.05 | .65 |
| 1018 | A320 | 29p Mountains | 1.15 | .75 |
| | | *Nos. 1015-1018 (4)* | 3.60 | 2.30 |

Engineering Achievements
(Europa) — A321

**1983, May 25    Photo.    Perf. 15x14**

| | | | | |
|---|---|---|---|---|
| 1019 | A321 | 16p Humber Bridge | .60 | .20 |
| 1020 | A321 | 20½p Thames Flood Barrier | 1.25 | 1.10 |
| 1021 | A321 | 28p Emergency oil rig support vessel Iolair | 1.75 | 1.40 |
| | | *Nos. 1019-1021 (3)* | 3.60 | 2.70 |

A322

Designs: 16p, The Royal Scots (Royal Regiment). 20½p, Royal Welsh Fusiliers. 26p, Royal Green Jackets. 28p, Irish Guards. 31p, Parachute Regiment.

**1983, July 6    Perf. 14x14½**

| | | | | |
|---|---|---|---|---|
| 1022 | A322 | 16p multicolored | .65 | .35 |
| 1023 | A322 | 20½p multicolored | .80 | .55 |
| 1024 | A322 | 26p multicolored | 1.05 | .65 |
| 1025 | A322 | 28p multicolored | 1.10 | .70 |
| 1026 | A322 | 31p multicolored | 1.20 | .75 |
| | | *Nos. 1022-1026 (5)* | 4.80 | 3.00 |

A323

Designs: 16p, 20th cent. garden, Sissinghurst. 20½p, Biddulph Grange, 19th cent. 28p, Blenheim, 18th cent. 31p, Pitmeeden, 17th cent.

---

**1983, Aug. 24    Litho.    Perf. 14**

| | | | | |
|---|---|---|---|---|
| 1027 | A323 | 16p multicolored | .65 | .35 |
| 1028 | A323 | 20½p multicolored | .80 | .55 |
| 1029 | A323 | 28p multicolored | 1.10 | .70 |
| 1030 | A323 | 31p multicolored | 1.20 | .75 |
| | | *Nos. 1027-1030 (4)* | 3.75 | 2.35 |

British
Fairs
A324

**1983, Oct. 5    Photo.    Perf. 14½x14**

| | | | | |
|---|---|---|---|---|
| 1031 | A324 | 16p Merry-go-round | .65 | .40 |
| 1032 | A324 | 20½p Animals, rides | .80 | .50 |
| 1033 | A324 | 28p Games | 1.10 | .75 |
| 1034 | A324 | 31p Ancient market fair | 1.20 | .75 |
| | | *Nos. 1031-1034 (4)* | 3.75 | 2.40 |

850th anniv. of St. Bartholomew's Fair.

Christmas
A325

**1983, Nov. 16    Photo.**

| | | | | |
|---|---|---|---|---|
| 1035 | A325 | 12½p Birds mailing cards | .50 | .30 |
| 1036 | A325 | 16p Three Kings chimney pots | .65 | .40 |
| 1037 | A325 | 20½p Birds under umbrella | .80 | .55 |
| 1038 | A325 | 28p Birds under street lamp | 1.10 | .75 |
| 1039 | A325 | 31p Topiary dove | 1.20 | .80 |
| | | *Nos. 1035-1039 (5)* | 4.25 | 2.80 |

Heraldry
A326

Designs: 16p, Arms of The College of Arms. 20½p, Arms of Richard III, founder. 28p, Arms of The Earl Marshal. 31p, Arms of The City of London.

**1984, Jan. 17    Photo.    Perf. 14½**

| | | | | |
|---|---|---|---|---|
| 1040 | A326 | 16p multicolored | .65 | .40 |
| 1041 | A326 | 20½p multicolored | .80 | .50 |
| 1042 | A326 | 28p multicolored | 1.10 | .75 |
| 1043 | A326 | 31p multicolored | 1.20 | .80 |
| | | *Nos. 1040-1043 (4)* | 3.75 | 2.45 |

National
Cattle
Breeders'
Association
A327

**1984, Mar. 6    Litho.    Perf. 15x14½**

| | | | | |
|---|---|---|---|---|
| 1044 | A327 | 16p Highland Cow | .65 | .40 |
| 1045 | A327 | 20½p Chillingham Wild Bull | .80 | .55 |
| 1046 | A327 | 26p Hereford Bull | 1.05 | .65 |
| 1047 | A327 | 28p Welsh Black Bull | 1.10 | .70 |
| 1048 | A327 | 31p Irish Moiled Cow | 1.20 | .75 |
| | | *Nos. 1044-1048 (5)* | 4.80 | 3.05 |

Royal Institute of British Architects
Sesquicentennial — A328

---

Urban renewal projects and plans.

**1984, Apr. 3    Photo.**

| | | | | |
|---|---|---|---|---|
| 1049 | A328 | 16p Liverpool | .65 | .40 |
| 1050 | A328 | 20½p Durham | .80 | .55 |
| 1051 | A328 | 28p Bristol | 1.10 | .70 |
| 1052 | A328 | 31p Perth | 1.20 | .75 |
| | | *Nos. 1049-1052 (4)* | 3.75 | 2.40 |

Europa (1959-1984) — A329

**1984, May 9    Photo.    Perf. 14½x14**

| | | | | |
|---|---|---|---|---|
| 1053 | A329 | 16p Bridge | .75 | .25 |
| 1054 | A329 | 16p Abduction of Europa | .75 | .25 |
| a, | | Pair, #1053-1054 | 1.50 | .75 |
| 1055 | A329 | 20½p like No. 1053 | 1.75 | 1.25 |
| 1056 | A329 | 20½p like No. 1054 | 1.75 | 1.25 |
| a, | | Pair, #1055-1056 | 3.50 | 3.00 |
| | | *Nos. 1053-1056 (4)* | 5.00 | 3.00 |

Nos. 1054, 1056 also for 2nd Election of the European Parliament.

London Economic
Summit, June 7-
9 — A330

**1984, June 5    Photo.    Perf. 14x15**

| | | | | |
|---|---|---|---|---|
| 1057 | A330 | 31p Lancaster House | 1.20 | .80 |

Greenwich
Meridian,
Cent. — A331

**1984, June 26    Litho.    Perf. 14x14½**

| | | | | |
|---|---|---|---|---|
| 1058 | A331 | 16p View from Apollo 11 | .65 | .40 |
| 1059 | A331 | 20½p English Channel map | .80 | .50 |
| 1060 | A331 | 28p Greenwich Observatory | 1.10 | .70 |
| 1061 | A331 | 31p Airy's transit telescope, 1850 | 1.20 | .75 |
| | | *Nos. 1058-1061 (4)* | 3.75 | 2.35 |

Bath-Bristol-London Mail Coach
Bicentenary — A332

18th century drawings by James Pollard.

**Photo. & Engr.**

**1984, July 31    Perf. 14½x14**

| | | | | |
|---|---|---|---|---|
| 1062 | A332 | 16p Bath, 1784 | .65 | .40 |
| 1063 | A332 | 16p Exeter, 1816 | .65 | .40 |
| 1064 | A332 | 16p Norwich, 1827 | .65 | .40 |
| 1065 | A332 | 16p Holyhead & Liverpool | .65 | .40 |
| 1066 | A332 | 16p Edinburgh, 1831 | .65 | .40 |
| a, | | Strip of 5, #1062-1066 | 3.25 | 2.75 |

---

50th Anniv.
of British
Council
A333

**1984, Sept. 25    Photo.**

| | | | | |
|---|---|---|---|---|
| 1067 | A333 | 17p Education for development | .65 | .35 |
| 1068 | A333 | 22p Promoting the arts | .85 | .45 |
| 1069 | A333 | 31p Technical training | 1.20 | .65 |
| 1070 | A333 | 34p Language & libraries | 1.35 | .80 |
| | | *Nos. 1067-1070 (4)* | 4.05 | 2.25 |

Christmas
1984
A334

Crayon Sketches by Yvonne Gilbert.

**1984, Nov. 20    Photo.    Perf. 15x14**

| | | | | |
|---|---|---|---|---|
| 1088 | A334 | 13p Holy Family | .50 | .30 |
| a. | | Booklet pane of 20 (BK770) | 10.50 | |
| 1089 | A334 | 17p Arrival in Bethlehem | .70 | .35 |
| 1090 | A334 | 22p Shephard and Lamb | .90 | .50 |
| 1091 | A334 | 31p Virgin and child | 1.20 | .75 |
| 1092 | A334 | 34p Offering Frankincense | 1.35 | .90 |
| | | *Nos. 1088-1092 (5)* | 4.65 | 2.80 |

Bklt. of 20 13p sold at 30p discount. Stamps have blue stars printed on the back.

Great Western Railway
Sesquicentennial — A335

**1985, Jan. 22    Photo.    Perf. 15x14**

| | | | | |
|---|---|---|---|---|
| 1093 | A335 | 17p Flying Scotsman | .65 | .45 |
| 1094 | A335 | 22p Golden Arrow | .85 | .60 |
| 1095 | A335 | 29p Cheltenham Flyer | 1.20 | .85 |
| 1096 | A335 | 31p Royal Scot | 1.25 | 1.00 |
| 1097 | A335 | 34p Cornish Riviera | 1.25 | 1.05 |
| | | *Nos. 1093-1097 (5)* | 5.20 | 3.95 |

Insects — A336

**1985, Mar. 12    Photo.    Perf. 15x14½**

| | | | | |
|---|---|---|---|---|
| 1098 | A336 | 17p Buff tailed bumble bee | .70 | .40 |
| 1099 | A336 | 22p Seven spotted ladybird | .90 | .60 |
| 1100 | A336 | 29p Wart-biter bush-cricket | 1.20 | .80 |
| 1101 | A336 | 31p Stag beetle | 1.25 | .85 |
| 1102 | A336 | 34p Emperor dragonfly | 1.35 | .90 |
| | | *Nos. 1098-1102 (5)* | 5.40 | 3.55 |

Music Year
(Europa)
A337

British Composers: 17p, Water Music, by George Frideric Handel. 22p, The Planets

Suite, by Gustav Holst. 31p, The First Cockoo, by Frederick Delius. 34p, Sea Pictures, by Edward Elgar.

**1985, May 14**                    **Perf. 14½**
1103  A337  17p  Reflections in
                 pool                .75  .20
1104  A337  22p  View of planets    1.10  1.25
1105  A337  31p  Roosting cuckoo    1.75  1.50
1106  A337  34p  Waves, wing        2.00  1.75
      Nos. 1103-1106 (4)            5.60  4.70

Safety at
Sea
A338

**1985, June 18    Litho.    Perf. 14**
1107  A338  17p  Lifeboat           .70  .40
1108  A338  22p  Beachy Head
                 Lighthouse,
                 chart              .90  .55
1109  A338  31p  Marecs-A satellite 1.25  .80
1110  A338  34p  Signal buoy,
                 yacht             1.35  .85
      Nos. 1107-1110 (4)           4.20  2.60

Royal Mail
Service, 350th
Anniv. — A339

Designs: 17p, Royal Mail Datapost motorcyclist and plane. 22p, Postbus on country road. 31p, Parcel service delivery. 34p, Postman delivering mail.

**1985, July 30    Photo.    Perf. 14x14½**
1111  A339  17p  multicolored      .70  .45
1112  A339  22p  multicolored      .90  .55
1113  A339  31p  multicolored     1.25  .80
1114  A339  34p  multicolored     1.35  .85
      Nos. 1111-1114 (4)          4.20  2.65

Arthurian
Legends
A340

Designs: 17p, Arthur consulting with Merlin. 22p, The Lady of the Lake with the sword "Excalibur." 31p, Guinevere and Lancelot fleeing from Camelot. 34p, Sir Galahad praying during his quest for the Holy Grail.

**1985, Sept. 3    Photo.    Perf. 15x14**
1115  A340  17p  multicolored      .70  .45
1116  A340  22p  multicolored      .90  .55
1117  A340  31p  multicolored     1.25  .80
1118  A340  34p  multicolored     1.35  .85
      Nos. 1115-1118 (4)          4.20  2.65

500th anniv. of William Caxton's edition of Le Morte D'Arthur, by Sir Thomas Mallory.

20th Cent.
Stars and
Directors of
Film — A341

Photographs: 17p, Peter Sellers (1925-80). 22p, David Niven (1910-83). 29p, Charlie Chaplin (1889-1977). 31p, Vivien Leigh (1913-67). 34p, Sir Alfred Hitchcock (1899-1980), director.

**1985, Oct. 8    Photo.    Perf. 14½**
1119  A341  17p  multicolored      .70  .45
1120  A341  22p  multicolored      .90  .60
1121  A341  29p  multicolored     1.15  .80
1122  A341  31p  multicolored     1.25  .90
1123  A341  34p  multicolored     1.35  1.00
      Nos. 1119-1123 (5)          5.35  3.75

Christmas
Pantomime
A342

**1985, Nov. 19    Photo.    Perf. 15x14½**
1124  A342  12p  Principal boy     .50  .30
   a.   Booklet pane of 20 (BK 780) 10.00
1125  A342  17p  Genie             .70  .50
1126  A342  22p  Grande dame       .90  .60
1127  A342  31p  Good fairy       1.25  .75
1128  A342  34p  Cat              1.35  .85
      Nos. 1124-1128 (5)          4.70  3.00

No. 1124a has random star design printed on back.

Industry
Year
A343

**1986, Jan. 14    Litho.    Perf. 15x14**
1129  A343  17p  North Sea oil rig,
                 light bulb       .70  .40
1130  A343  22p  Medical research
                 lab, thermome-
                 ter              .90  .60
1131  A343  31p  Steel mill, garden
                 hoe             1.25  .75
1132  A343  34p  Cornfield, bread 1.35  .85
      Nos. 1129-1132 (4)         4.20  2.60

Halley's
Comet
A344

Designs: 17p, Caricature, Edmond Halley (1656-1742), astronomer. 22p, European Space Agency Giotto spacecraft pursuing comet. 31p, Comet and legend, Maybe Twice in a Lifetime. 34p, Comet orbiting sun.

**1986, Feb. 18                    Photo.**
1133  A344  17p  multicolored      .70  .40
1134  A344  22p  multicolored      .90  .60
1135  A344  31p  multicolored     1.25  .75
1136  A344  34p  multicolored     1.35  .85
      Nos. 1133-1136 (4)          4.20  2.60

A345

Queen
Elizabeth
II, 60th
Birthday
A346

**1986, Apr. 21                    Photo.**
1137  A345  17p  multicolored      .75  .50
1138  A346  17p  multicolored      .75  .50
   a.   Pair, #1137-1138          1.50  1.25
1139  A345  34p  multicolored     1.40  .90
1140  A346  34p  multicolored     1.40  .90
   a.   Pair, #1139-1140          2.80  2.50

Europa
A347

**1986, May 20    Photo.    Perf. 14½**
1141  A347  17p  Barn owl          .70  .55
1142  A347  22p  Pine marten       .90  .85
1143  A347  31p  Wild cat         1.25  1.00
1144  A347  34p  Natterjack toad  1.40  1.25
      Nos. 1141-1144 (4)          4.25  3.65

Domesday
Book,
900th
Anniv.
A348

**1986, June 17                    Photo.**
1145  A348  17p  Peasant           .70  .50
1146  A348  22p  Freeman           .90  .60
1147  A348  31p  Knight           1.25  .80
1148  A348  34p  Lord             1.40  .90
      Nos. 1145-1148 (4)          4.25  2.80

Domesday Book, first nationwide survey in British history.

Sports
A349

**1986, July 15    Photo.    Perf. 15x14**
1149  A349  17p  Track and field   .70  .45
1150  A349  22p  Rowing            .90  .65
1151  A349  29p  Weight lifting   1.20  .80
1152  A349  31p  Shooting         1.25  .85
1153  A349  34p  Field hockey     1.35  .90
      Nos. 1149-1153 (5)          5.40  3.65

1986 Commonwealth Games, Edinburgh. World Hockey Cup, London.

*ANNUAL\gb\REG\REG7.TXT*

Wedding of
Prince Andrew
and Sarah
Ferguson — A350

**1986, July 22                    Perf. 14x15**
1154  A350  12p  multicolored      .60  .40
1155  A350  17p  multicolored      .80  .50

Commonwealth
Parliamentary
Assoc. Conf.,
London — A351

**1986, Aug. 19    Litho.    Perf. 14x14½**
1156  A351  34p  multicolored     1.35  .85

Royal Air
Force
Commanders
and Aircraft
A352

Designs: 17p, Lord Dowding (1882-1970), Hurricane. 22p, Lord Tedder (1890-1967), Hawker Typhoon. 29p, Lord Trenchard (1873-1956), De Havilland 9A World War I bomber. 31p, Sir Arthur Harris (1892-1984), Avro Lancaster. 34p, Lord Portal (1893-1971), De Havilland Mosquito.

**1986, Sept. 16    Photo.    Perf. 14½**
1157  A352  17p  multicolored      .70  .45
1158  A352  22p  multicolored      .90  .65
1159  A352  29p  multicolored     1.15  .75
1160  A352  31p  multicolored     1.25  .80
1161  A352  34p  multicolored     1.35  .90
      Nos. 1157-1161 (5)          5.35  3.55

Christmas
A353

Customs: 12p, 13p, Glastonbury Thorn. 18p, Tanad Valley Plygain. 22p, Hebrides Tribute. 31p, Dewsbury Church Knell. 34p, Hereford Boy Bishop.

**1986, Nov. 18    Photo.    Perf. 15x14½**
1162  A353  12p  multicolored      .50  .30
1163  A353  13p  multicolored      .50  .35
   a.   Pane of 36                18.00
1164  A353  18p  multicolored      .70  .45
1165  A353  22p  multicolored      .90  .70
1166  A353  31p  multicolored     1.25  .80
1167  A353  34p  multicolored     1.35  .90
      Nos. 1162-1167 (6)          5.20  3.50

No. 1163a printed in two panes of 18 with gutter between, stars on back; folded and sold in discount booklet for £4.30.

Flora — A354

Photographs by Alfred Lammer.

**1987, Jan. 20    Photo.    Perf. 14½**
1168  A354  18p  Gaillardia        .70  .40
1169  A354  22p  Echinops          .90  .65
1170  A354  31p  Echeveria        1.25  .80
1171  A354  34p  Colchicum        1.35  .90
      Nos. 1168-1171 (4)          4.20  2.75

Sir Isaac Newton
(1642-1727),
Physicist,
Mathematician
A355

Manuscripts and principles: 18p, Philosophiae Naturalis Principia Mathematica, 1687. 22p, Motion of bodies in ellipses. 31p, Optics Treatise of the Refraction, Reflections and Colors of Light. 34p, The System of the World.

**1987, Mar. 24    Photo.    Perf. 14**
1172  A355  18p  multicolored      .70  .40
1173  A355  22p  multicolored      .90  .65
1174  A355  31p  multicolored     1.25  .80
1175  A355  34p  multicolored     1.35  .90
      Nos. 1172-1175 (4)          4.20  2.75

Europa
A356

Modern architecture: 18p, Willis Faber & Dumas Building, Ipswich, designed by Norman Foster. 22p, Pompidou Centre, Paris, designed by Richard Rogers and Renzo Piano. 31p, Staatsgalerie, Stuttgart, designed by James Stirling and Michael Wilford. 34p, European Investment Bank, Luxembourg, designed by Sir Denys Lasdun.

**1987, May 12   Photo.   Perf. 15x14**

| | | | | |
|---|---|---|---|---|
| 1176 | A356 | 18p multicolored | .70 | .30 |
| 1177 | A356 | 22p multicolored | 1.00 | .80 |
| 1178 | A356 | 31p multicolored | 1.40 | 1.25 |
| 1179 | A356 | 34p multicolored | 1.75 | 1.25 |
| | *Nos. 1176-1179 (4)* | | 4.85 | 3.60 |

St. John Ambulance, Cent. — A357

First aid.

**1987, June 16   Litho.   Perf. 14x14½**

| | | | | |
|---|---|---|---|---|
| 1180 | A357 | 18p Ambulance, 1887 | .70 | .50 |
| 1181 | A357 | 22p War victims, 1940 | .90 | .60 |
| 1182 | A357 | 31p Public event, 1965 | 1.25 | .80 |
| 1183 | A357 | 34p Transplant organ flight, 1987 | 1.35 | .90 |
| | *Nos. 1180-1183 (4)* | | 4.20 | 2.80 |

Order of the Thistle, Scotland, 300th Anniv. of Revival A358

Coats of arms: 18p, Lord Lyon, King of Arms, 1687. 22p, Duke of Rothesay, bestowed on Prince Charles in 1974. 31p, Royal Scottish Academy of Painting, Sculpture & Architecture, 1826. 34p, The Royal Society of Edinburgh, 1783.

**1987, July 21   Photo.   Perf. 14½**

| | | | | |
|---|---|---|---|---|
| 1184 | A358 | 18p multicolored | .70 | .50 |
| 1185 | A358 | 22p multicolored | .90 | .60 |
| 1186 | A358 | 31p multicolored | 1.25 | .80 |
| 1187 | A358 | 34p multicolored | 1.35 | .90 |
| | *Nos. 1184-1187 (4)* | | 4.20 | 2.80 |

Accession of Queen Victoria, 150th Anniv. A359

Portraits of Victoria and: 18p, Great Exhibition (1851) at the Crystal Palace, Grace Darling's rescue (1838) of the Forfashire's survivors, and Monarch of the Glen, by Sir Edwin Henry Landseer. 22p, Launching of Brunel's ship Great Eastern, portrait of Prince Consort Albert, Mrs. Beeton's Book of Household Management (1889). 31p, The Albert Memorial, Prime Minister Disraeli and 1st ballot box. 34p, The Boer War, Guglielmo Marconi's wireless telegraph communications linking Paris and London (1898), and diamond jubilee emblem.

**Photo. & Engr.**

**1987, Sept. 8   Perf. 15x14**

| | | | | |
|---|---|---|---|---|
| 1188 | A359 | 18p multicolored | .70 | .45 |
| 1189 | A359 | 22p multicolored | .90 | .60 |
| 1190 | A359 | 31p multicolored | 1.25 | .80 |
| 1191 | A359 | 34p multicolored | 1.35 | .90 |
| | *Nos. 1188-1191 (4)* | | 4.20 | 2.75 |

Studio Pottery A360

**1987, Oct. 13   Photo.   Perf. 14½**

| | | | | |
|---|---|---|---|---|
| 1192 | A360 | 18p Bernard Leach | .70 | .45 |
| 1193 | A360 | 26p Elizabeth Fritsch | 1.05 | .60 |
| 1194 | A360 | 31p Lucie Rie | 1.25 | .80 |
| 1195 | A360 | 34p Hans Coper | 1.35 | .90 |
| | *Nos. 1192-1195 (4)* | | 4.35 | 2.75 |

Christmas A361

Childhood memories: 13p, Decorating tree. 18p, Looking out window, Christmas eve. 26p, Sweet dreams. 31p, Reading new book to toys, Christmas morning. 34p, Playing horn, snowman.

**1987, Nov. 17   Photo.   Perf. 15x14**

| | | | | |
|---|---|---|---|---|
| 1196 | A361 | 13p multicolored | .50 | .30 |
| a. | | Pane of 36 | 18.00 | |
| 1197 | A361 | 18p multicolored | .70 | .45 |
| 1198 | A361 | 26p multicolored | 1.05 | .60 |
| 1199 | A361 | 31p multicolored | 1.25 | .80 |
| 1200 | A361 | 34p multicolored | 1.35 | .90 |
| | *Nos. 1196-1200 (5)* | | 4.85 | 3.05 |

No. 1196a printed in two panes of 18 with gutter between, stars on back; folded and sold in discount booklets for £4.30.

Linnean Society of London, 200th Anniv. A362

**1988, Jan. 19   Perf. 15x14½**

| | | | | |
|---|---|---|---|---|
| 1201 | A362 | 18p Bull-rout fish | .70 | .45 |
| 1202 | A362 | 26p Yellow waterlily | 1.05 | .60 |
| 1203 | A362 | 31p Bewick's swan | 1.25 | .80 |
| 1204 | A362 | 34p Morel | 1.35 | .90 |
| | *Nos. 1201-1204 (4)* | | 4.35 | 2.75 |

Linnaeus (Carl von Linne, 1707-78), inventor of system of taxonomic nomenclature.

Welsh Bible, 400th Anniv. — A363

**1988, Mar. 1   Photo.   Perf. 14½**

| | | | | |
|---|---|---|---|---|
| 1205 | A363 | 18p William Morgan | .70 | .50 |
| 1206 | A363 | 26p William Salesbury | 1.05 | .70 |
| 1207 | A363 | 31p Richard Davies | 1.25 | .80 |
| 1208 | A363 | 34p Richard Parry | 1.35 | .90 |
| | *Nos. 1205-1208 (4)* | | 4.35 | 2.90 |

Sports — A364

**1988, Mar. 22   Photo.   Perf. 14½**

| | | | | |
|---|---|---|---|---|
| 1209 | A364 | 18p Balance beam | .70 | .50 |
| 1210 | A364 | 26p Downhill skiing | 1.05 | .70 |
| 1211 | A364 | 31p Tennis | 1.25 | .80 |
| 1212 | A364 | 34p Soccer | 1.35 | .90 |
| | *Nos. 1209-1212 (4)* | | 4.35 | 2.90 |

Ski Club of Great Britain and centenaries of the British Amateur Gymnastics Assoc., Lawn Tennis Assoc. and the Soccer League.

Europa 1988 A365

Transportation and communication, 1938.

**1988, May 10   Perf. 15x14**

| | | | | |
|---|---|---|---|---|
| 1213 | A365 | 18p Mallard locomotive | .75 | .50 |
| 1214 | A365 | 26p Queen Elizabeth ocean liner | 1.10 | .70 |
| 1215 | A365 | 31p Tram No. 1173, Glasgow | 1.25 | .85 |
| 1216 | A365 | 34p Handley Page aircraft, Croydon Airport | 1.40 | 1.00 |
| | *Nos. 1213-1216 (4)* | | 4.50 | 3.05 |

Defeat of the Spanish Armada by the Royal Navy, 400th Anniv. A366

Designs: No. 1217, Armada approaching The Lizard, July 19, 1588. No. 1218, Royal Navy vessels sailing from Plymouth to engage Spaniards in battle, July 21. No. 1219, Battle scene off the Isle of Wight, July 25. No. 1220, Battle scene off Calais, France, July 28-29. No. 1221, Spanish ships foundering in the North Sea storms, July 30-Aug. 2. Printed in a continuous design.

**1988, July 19**

| | | | | |
|---|---|---|---|---|
| 1217 | A366 | 18p multicolored | .70 | .45 |
| 1218 | A366 | 18p multicolored | .70 | .45 |
| 1219 | A366 | 18p multicolored | .70 | .45 |
| 1220 | A366 | 18p multicolored | .70 | .45 |
| 1221 | A366 | 18p multicolored | .70 | .45 |
| a. | | Strip of 5, Nos. 1217-1221 | 3.50 | 2.50 |

Australia Bicentennial A367

Designs: No. 1222, Colonist, First Fleet vessel. No. 1223, British and Australian parliaments, Queen Elizabeth II. No. 1224, Cricketer W.G. Grace. No. 1225, John Lennon (1940-1980), William Shakespeare (1564-1616) and Sydney Opera House. Flag of Australia appears on #1223a, 1225a.

**1988, June 21   Litho.   Perf. 14½**

| | | | | |
|---|---|---|---|---|
| 1222 | A367 | 18p multicolored | .70 | .50 |
| 1223 | A367 | 18p multicolored | .70 | .50 |
| a. | | Pair, #1222-1223 | 1.40 | 1.00 |
| 1224 | A367 | 34p multicolored | 1.35 | .90 |
| 1225 | A367 | 34p multicolored | 1.35 | .90 |
| a. | | Pair, #1224-1225 | 2.70 | 1.80 |
| | *Nos. 1222-1225 (4)* | | 4.10 | 2.80 |

See Australia Nos. 1082-1085.

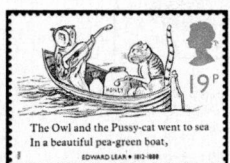

Nonsensical Drawings by Edward Lear (1812-1888) — A368

Illustrations and text: 19p, *The Owl and the Pussycat*, 1867. 27p, Self-portrait as a bird, pen-and-ink sketch from a letter. 32p, "C" is for Cat, alphabet book character. 35p, Girl, birds and part of a limerick.

**1988, Sept. 6   Photo.   Perf. 15x14**

| | | | | |
|---|---|---|---|---|
| 1226 | A368 | 19p multicolored | .75 | .45 |
| 1227 | A368 | 27p multicolored | 1.10 | .70 |
| 1228 | A368 | 32p multicolored | 1.30 | .90 |
| 1229 | A368 | 35p multicolored | 1.30 | .90 |
| a. | | Souv. sheet of 4, #1226-1229 | 10.00 | 10.00 |
| | *Nos. 1226-1229 (4)* | | 4.45 | 2.95 |

No. 1229a sold for £1.35. The surtax benefited Stamp World London '90.

CARRICKFERGUS CASTLE

Photographs of Castles by Prince Andrew — A369

**1988, Oct. 18   Engr.**

| | | | | |
|---|---|---|---|---|
| 1230 | A369 | £1 Carrickfergus | 4.00 | 1.00 |
| 1231 | A369 | £1.50 Caernarfon | 6.00 | 1.75 |
| 1232 | A369 | £2 Edinburgh | 8.00 | 2.00 |
| 1233 | A369 | £5 Windsor | 20.00 | 7.00 |
| | *Nos. 1230-1233 (4)* | | 38.00 | 11.75 |

See Nos. 1445-1448.

Christmas Cards A370

**1988, Nov. 15   Photo.   Perf. 15x14½**

| | | | | |
|---|---|---|---|---|
| 1234 | A370 | 14p Journey to Bethlehem | .55 | .25 |
| 1235 | A370 | 19p Shepherds see star | .75 | .45 |
| 1236 | A370 | 27p Magi follow star | 1.10 | .70 |
| 1237 | A370 | 32p Nativity | 1.30 | .80 |
| 1238 | A370 | 35p The Annunciation | 1.40 | .90 |
| | *Nos. 1234-1238 (5)* | | 5.10 | 3.10 |

Birds — A371

**1989, Jan. 17   Perf. 14x15**

| | | | | |
|---|---|---|---|---|
| 1239 | A371 | 19p Puffin | .75 | .55 |
| 1240 | A371 | 27p Avocet | 1.10 | .70 |
| 1241 | A371 | 32p Oystercatcher | 1.30 | .80 |
| 1242 | A371 | 35p Gannet | 1.40 | .90 |
| | *Nos. 1239-1242 (4)* | | 4.55 | 2.95 |

Special Occasions A372

**1989, Jan. 31   Photo.   Perf. 15x14**
**Booklet Stamps**

| | | | | |
|---|---|---|---|---|
| 1243 | A372 | 19p Rose | 6.50 | 4.50 |
| 1244 | A372 | 19p Cupid | 6.50 | 4.50 |
| 1245 | A372 | 19p Ships | 6.50 | 4.50 |
| 1246 | A372 | 19p Fruit bowl | 6.50 | 4.50 |
| 1247 | A372 | 19p Teddy Bear | 6.50 | 4.50 |
| a. | | Bklt. pane of 10 (2 each #1243-1247) +12 labels (BK733) | 65.00 | |
| | *Nos. 1243-1247 (5)* | | 32.50 | 22.50 |

Labels inscribed "CONGRATULATIONS," "BEST WISHES," "HAPPY BIRTHDAY," "HAPPY ANNIVERSARY," "WITH LOVE," or "THANK YOU."

No. 1247a is valued with perfs guillotined. Full perfs sell for more.

Food and Farming Year — A373

Foods and tile mosaics in agricultural motifs.

**1989, Mar. 7 Photo. Perf. 14½**
1248 A373 19p Fruit and vegetables .75 .50
1249 A373 27p Meat, fish, fruit 1.10 .75
1250 A373 32p Dairy products 1.30 .90
1251 A373 35p Breads, cake, cereal 1.40 1.00
Nos. 1248-1251 (4) 4.55 3.15

Fireworks — A374

**1989, Apr. 11 Photo. Perf. 14x14½**
1252 A374 19p Mortarboard 1.00 .75
1253 A374 19p "X" on ballot 1.00 .75
a. Pair, #1252-1253 2.00 2.00
1254 A374 35p Posthorn 1.75 1.50
1255 A374 35p Globe 1.75 1.50
a. Pair, #1254-1255 3.50 3.50
Nos. 1252-1255 (4) 5.50 4.50

Public education in England and Wales, 150th anniv. (#1252); European Parliament 3rd elections (#1253); 26th world congress of Postal Telegraph and Telephone Intl., Brighton, Sept. 18-23 (#1254); Interparliamentary Union Cent. Conf., 82nd session, Sept. 4-9 (#1255).

Europa 1989 — A375

**1989, May 16 Perf. 14x15**
Children's toys.
1256 A375 19p Airplane, locomotive .90 .50
1257 A375 27p Building-block tower 1.25 .80
1258 A375 32p Checkerboard, die, ladder, chips 1.40 .90
1259 A375 35p Doll house, boat, robot 1.50 1.00
Nos. 1256-1259 (4) 5.05 3.20

Industrial Archaeology A376

**1989, July 4 Photo. Perf. 14x15**
1280 A376 19p Ironbridge .75 .50
1281 A376 27p Tin Mine 1.10 .75
1282 A376 32p Mills 1.30 .80
1283 A376 35p Pontcysyllte Aqueduct 1.40 .90
Nos. 1280-1283 (4) 4.55 2.90

**1989, July 25 Souvenir Sheet**
1284 Sheet of 4 7.50 7.50
a. A376 19p like #1280, horiz. .85 .85
b. A376 27p like #1281, horiz. 1.25 1.25
c. A376 32p like #1282, horiz. 1.50 1.50
d. A376 35p like #1283, horiz. 1.75 1.75
No. 1284 sold for £1.40.

Microscopy A377

Specimens under magnification: 19p, Snowflake, the soc. emblem. 27p, Blue fly. 32p, Blood cells. 35p, Microchip.

**1989, Sept. 5 Litho. Perf. 14½x14**
1285 A377 19p multicolored .75 .55
1286 A377 27p multicolored 1.10 .70
1287 A377 32p multicolored 1.30 .80
1288 A377 35p multicolored 1.40 .90
Nos. 1285-1288 (4) 4.55 2.95
Royal Microscopical Soc., 150th anniv.

The Lord Mayor's Show, London — A378

Procession of the Lord Mayor's coach from Guildhall to the Law Courts in the Strand: No. 1289, Royal mail coach and The Guildhall. No. 1290, Drummer, cavalrymen and Mansion House. No. 1291, Gold coach, 1757, and The Royal Exchange. No. 1292, Coachman and St. Paul's Cathedral. No. 1293, Drummer, cavalryman and the Law Courts.

**1989, Oct. 17 Litho. Perf. 14x15**
1289 A378 20p multicolored .80 .55
1290 A378 20p multicolored .80 .55
1291 A378 20p multicolored .80 .55
1292 A378 20p multicolored .80 .55
1293 A378 20p multicolored .80 .55
a. Strip of 5, #1289-1293 4.00 3.75

Ely Cathedral, Cambridgeshire, 800th Anniv. — A379

**1989, Nov. 14 Photo. Perf. 15x14**
1294 A379 15p Gothic arches, 4 peasants .60 .30
Nos. 1294,B2-B5 (5) 4.85 3.05
Christmas.

Royal Soc. for the Prevention of Cruelty to Animals, 150th Anniv. — A381

**1990, Jan. 23 Litho. Perf. 14x15**
1300 A381 20p Kitten .80 .55
1301 A381 29p Rabbit 1.15 .85
1302 A381 34p Duckling 1.35 1.00
1303 A381 37p Puppy 1.50 1.10
Nos. 1300-1303 (4) 4.80 3.50

Miniature Sheet

Famous Smiles A382

**1990, Feb. 6 Photo. Perf. 15x14**
1304 A382 20p Teddy bear 3.25 2.50
1305 A382 20p Dennis the Menace 3.25 2.50
1306 A382 20p Mr. Punch 3.25 2.50
1307 A382 20p Cheshire Cat 3.25 2.50
1308 A382 20p Man in the Moon 3.25 2.50
1309 A382 20p The Laughing Policeman 3.25 2.50
1310 A382 20p Clown 3.25 2.50
1311 A382 20p Mona Lisa 3.25 2.50
1312 A382 20p Queen of Hearts 3.25 2.50
1313 A382 20p Stan Laurel 3.25 2.50
a. Pane of 10, #1304-1313 37.50 37.50
Nos. 1304-1313 (10) 32.50 25.00
No. 1313a sold folded and unattached in booklet cover.
See Nos. 1364-1373.

A383

Europa 1990: No. 1314, Alexandra Palace. No. 1315, School of Art, Glasgow. 29p, British Philatelic Bureau, Edinburgh. 37p, Templeton Carpet Factory, Glasgow.

**1990, Mar. 6 Photo. Perf. 14x15**
1314 A383 20p multicolored .80 .45
a. Bklt. pane of 4 + printed margin 5.00
1315 A383 20p multicolored .80 .45
1316 A383 29p multicolored 1.15 .65
1317 A383 37p multicolored 1.50 .85
Nos. 1314-1317 (4) 4.25 2.40

Stamp World '90, London (No. 1314); Glasgow, European City of Culture (Nos. 1315, 1317).
For Prestige booklet containing pane #1314a, see listings in the Booklets section.

Queen's Awards for Export and Technological Achievement, 25th Anniv. — A384

**1990, Apr. 10 Litho.**
1318 A384 20p Export .80 .45
1319 A384 20p Technology .80 .45
a. Pair, #1318-1319 1.60 1.50
1320 A384 37p like No. 1318 1.50 1.00
1321 A384 37p like No. 1319 1.50 1.00
a. Pair, #1320-1321 3.00 2.80
Nos. 1318-1321 (4) 4.60 2.90
Se-tenant pairs have continuous designs.

Kew Gardens, 150th Anniv. — A385

**1990, June 5 Photo.**
1322 A385 20p Cycad .80 .50
1323 A385 29p Stone pine 1.15 .70
1324 A385 34p Willow tree 1.35 .80
1325 A385 37p Cedar 1.50 .90
Nos. 1322-1325 (4) 4.80 2.90

Thomas Hardy (1840-1928), Writer and Clyffe Clump, Dorset — A386

**1990, July 10 Photo. Perf. 14x15**
1326 A386 20p multicolored .80 .50

Queen Mother, 90th Birthday — A387

Designs: Portraits of Queen Elizabeth, The Queen Mother.

**1990, Aug. 2 Perf. 14x15, 14½**
1327 A387 20p Recent portrait .80 .35
1328 A387 29p As Queen Consort, 1937 1.25 1.25
1329 A387 34p As Duchess of York 1.70 1.70
1330 A387 37p As Lady Elizabeth Bowes-Lyon 1.80 1.80
Nos. 1327-1330 (4) 5.55 5.10

Gallantry Awards — A388

Designs: No. 1331, Victoria Cross. No. 1332, George Cross. No. 1333, Military Cross, Military Medal. No. 1334, Distinguished Flying Cross, Distinguished Flying Medal. No. 1335, Distinguished Service Cross, Distinguished Service Medal. Nos. 1333-1335 horiz.

**1990, Sept. 11 Perf. 14x15, 15x14**
1331 A388 20p multicolored .80 .55
a. Litho., perf. 14x14¼, black denomination ('06) .80 .35
b. Booklet pane of 4 #1331a (BK180) 3.25 —
1332 A388 20p multicolored .80 .55
1333 A388 20p multicolored .80 .55
1334 A388 20p multicolored .80 .55
1335 A388 20p multicolored .80 .55
Nos. 1331-1335 (5) 4.00 2.75
Denomination on No. 1331 is gray.
Nos. 1331a, 1331b issued 9/21/2006.

Astronomy A389

Designs: 22p, Armagh Observatory, Jodrell Bank and La Palma telescopes. 26p, Early telescope, celestial diagram. 31p, Greenwich Old Observatory, sextant, chronometer. 37p, Stonehenge, celestial navigation.

**1990, Oct. 16 Perf. 14**
1336 A389 22p multicolored .90 .60
1337 A389 26p multicolored 1.05 .70
1338 A389 31p multicolored 1.25 .80
1339 A389 37p multicolored 1.50 .90
Nos. 1336-1339 (4) 4.70 3.00

Christmas A390

**1990, Nov. 13 Litho. Perf. 15x14**
1340 A390 17p Building snowman .70 .25
a. Booklet pane of 20 15.00
1341 A390 22p Carrying Christmas tree .90 .30
1342 A390 26p Caroling 1.05 .70
1343 A390 31p Sledding 1.25 .80
1344 A390 37p Ice skating 1.50 .90
Nos. 1340-1344 (5) 5.40 2.95

Dogs — A391

Paintings by George Stubbs: 22p, King Charles Spaniel. 26p, A Pointer. 31p, Two Hounds in a Landscape. 33p, A Rough Dog. 37p, Fino and Tiny.

**1991, Jan. 8    Photo.    Perf. 14x14½**
| 1345 | A391 | 22p multicolored | .90 | .55 |
|---|---|---|---|---|
| 1346 | A391 | 26p multicolored | 1.05 | .70 |
| 1347 | A391 | 31p multicolored | 1.25 | .80 |
| 1348 | A391 | 33p multicolored | 1.30 | .90 |
| 1349 | A391 | 37p multicolored | 1.50 | 1.00 |
| | | Nos. 1345-1349 (5) | 6.00 | 3.95 |

Royal Veterinary College bicentennial, National Canine Defense League and Cruft's Dog Show, centennial.

Symbols of Good Luck A392

**1991, Feb. 5    Photo.    Perf. 15x14**
**Booklet Stamps**
| 1350 | A392 | 1st shown | 1.50 | 1.00 |
|---|---|---|---|---|
| 1351 | A392 | 1st Shooting star, rainbow | 1.50 | 1.00 |
| 1352 | A392 | 1st Bird, charm bracelet | 1.50 | 1.00 |
| 1353 | A392 | 1st Black cat | 1.50 | 1.00 |
| 1354 | A392 | 1st Bluebird, key | 1.50 | 1.00 |
| 1355 | A392 | 1st Duck, frog | 1.50 | 1.00 |
| 1356 | A392 | 1st Black boot, shamrocks | 1.50 | 1.00 |
| 1357 | A392 | 1st Rainbow, pot of gold | 1.50 | 1.00 |
| 1358 | A392 | 1st Peacock moths | 1.50 | 1.00 |
| 1359 | A392 | 1st Wishing well, sixpence | 1.50 | 1.00 |
| a. | | Bklt. pane of 10, #1350-1359 (BK1160) | 16.00 | |

No. 1359a printed se-tenant with 12 greetings labels. No. 1359a sold for £2.20 at date of issue.

Scientists & Their Technology A393

Designs: No. 1360, Michael Faraday, electricity. No. 1361, Charles Babbage, computers. 31p, Radar, developed by Robert Watson-Watt. 37p, Jet engine developed by Frank Whittle.

**1991, Mar. 5    Perf. 14x15**
| 1360 | A393 | 22p multicolored | .90 | .60 |
|---|---|---|---|---|
| 1361 | A393 | 22p multicolored | .90 | .60 |
| 1362 | A393 | 31p multicolored | 1.25 | .80 |
| 1363 | A393 | 37p multicolored | 1.50 | .90 |
| | | Nos. 1360-1363 (4) | 4.55 | 2.90 |

**Famous Smiles Type of 1990**
**1991, Mar. 26    Photo.    Perf. 15x14**
**Booklet Stamps**
| 1364 | A382 | 1st Teddy bear | 1.10 | 1.10 |
|---|---|---|---|---|
| a. | | Sheet of 20 + 20 labels, litho., perf. 14¼x14 | 37.50 | — |
| 1365 | A382 | 1st Dennis the Menace | 1.10 | 1.10 |
| a. | | Sheet, 10 each #1364-1365 + 20 labels | 14.00 | |
| b. | | Sheet of 20 + 20 labels, litho., perf. 14½x14 | 37.50 | — |
| 1366 | A382 | 1st Mr. Punch | 1.10 | 1.10 |
| 1367 | A382 | 1st Cheshire Cat | 1.10 | 1.10 |
| 1368 | A382 | 1st Man in the Moon | 1.10 | 1.10 |
| 1369 | A382 | 1st The Laughing Policeman | 1.10 | 1.10 |
| 1370 | A382 | 1st Clown | 1.10 | 1.10 |
| 1371 | A382 | 1st Mona Lisa | 1.10 | 1.10 |
| 1372 | A382 | 1st Queen of Hearts | 1.10 | 1.10 |

| 1373 | A382 | 1st Stan Laurel | 1.10 | 1.10 |
|---|---|---|---|---|
| a. | | Booklet pane of 10 | 12.00 | |
| b. | | Sheet, #1364-1373 + 10 labels | 11.50 | |

No. 1373a sold for £2.20 at date of issue. No. 1373a was affixed to booklet cover and was printed se-tenant with 12 greetings labels.

No. 1373b issued 5/22/00. Labels depict ribbons and are inscribed "The Stamp Show / 2000". The sheet with ribbon labels sold for £2.95, while the sheet with personalized labels sold for £5.95.

A sheet similar to No. 1373b with labels inscribed "Collect British Stamps" was specially produced for stamp dealers.

No. 1365a issued 2002. It sold for £5.95 and had labels that could be personalized.

Nos. 1364a, 1365b issued 2002. Each sold for £14.95 and has labels that can be personalized.

A394

Europa — A395

Illustrations reduced.

**1991, Apr. 23    Photo.    Perf. 14x15**
| 1374 | A394 | 22p Planets | .90 | .55 |
|---|---|---|---|---|
| 1375 | A394 | 22p Stars | .90 | .55 |
| a. | | Pair, #1374-1375 | 1.80 | 1.50 |
| 1376 | A395 | 37p shown | 2.00 | 1.40 |
| 1377 | A395 | 37p Crescent eye | 2.00 | 1.40 |
| a. | | Pair, #1376-1377 | 4.50 | 3.25 |
| | | Nos. 1374-1377 (4) | 5.80 | 3.90 |

Sports — A396

**1991, June 11    Photo.    Perf. 14½x14**
| 1378 | A396 | 22p Fencing | .80 | .60 |
|---|---|---|---|---|
| 1379 | A396 | 26p Hurdling | 1.05 | .70 |
| 1380 | A396 | 31p Diving | 1.25 | .90 |
| 1381 | A396 | 37p Rugby | 1.50 | .90 |
| | | Nos. 1378-1381 (4) | 4.60 | 3.00 |

World Student Games, Nos. 1378-1380. Rugby World Cup, No. 1381.

Roses — A397

**1991, July 16    Litho.    Perf. 14½x14**
| 1382 | A397 | 22p Silver Jubilee | .90 | .50 |
|---|---|---|---|---|
| 1383 | A397 | 26p Mme. Alfred Carriere | 1.05 | .60 |
| 1384 | A397 | 31p Rosa moyesii | 1.25 | .70 |
| 1385 | A397 | 33p Harvest Fayre | 1.30 | .80 |
| 1386 | A397 | 37p Mutabilis | 1.50 | .90 |
| | | Nos. 1382-1386 (5) | 6.00 | 3.50 |

Dinosaurs A398

**1991, Aug. 20    Photo.    Perf. 14½x14**
| 1387 | A398 | 22p Iguanodon | .90 | .65 |
|---|---|---|---|---|
| 1388 | A398 | 26p Stegosaurus | 1.05 | .70 |
| 1389 | A398 | 31p Tyrannosaurus | 1.25 | .75 |
| 1390 | A398 | 33p Protoceratops | 1.30 | .80 |
| 1391 | A398 | 37p Triceratops | 1.50 | .90 |
| | | Nos. 1387-1391 (5) | 6.00 | 3.80 |

First use of word "dinosaur" by Sir Richard Owen, 150th anniv.

Ordnance Survey Maps, Bicent. — A399

Maps of village of Hamstreet, Kent.

**1991, Sept. 17    Litho. & Engr.**
| 1392 | A399 | 24p 1816 | .90 | .50 |
|---|---|---|---|---|

**Litho.**
| 1393 | A399 | 28p 1906 | 1.10 | .70 |
|---|---|---|---|---|
| 1394 | A399 | 33p 1959 | 1.30 | .80 |
| 1395 | A399 | 39p 1991 | 1.55 | .90 |
| | | Nos. 1392-1395 (4) | 4.85 | 2.90 |

Christmas A400

Illuminated leters from Venetian manuscript "Acts of Mary and Jesus": 18p, "P," Adoration of the Magi. 24p, "M," Mary placing Jesus in manger. 28p, "A," Angel warning Joseph. 33p, "Q," The Annunciation. 39p, "N," Flight into Egypt.

**1991, Nov. 12    Photo.    Perf. 15x14**
| 1416 | A400 | 18p multicolored | .70 | .25 |
|---|---|---|---|---|
| a. | | Booklet pane of 20 | 14.00 | |
| 1417 | A400 | 24p multicolored | .95 | .30 |
| 1418 | A400 | 28p multicolored | 1.10 | .80 |
| 1419 | A400 | 33p multicolored | 1.25 | .85 |
| 1420 | A400 | 39p multicolored | 1.55 | 1.10 |
| | | Nos. 1416-1420 (5) | 5.55 | 3.30 |

Animals in Winter A401

**1992, Jan. 14    Photo.    Perf. 15x14**
| 1421 | A401 | 18p Fallow deer | .70 | .45 |
|---|---|---|---|---|
| 1422 | A401 | 24p Brown hare | .95 | .60 |
| 1423 | A401 | 28p Fox | 1.10 | .75 |
| 1424 | A401 | 33p Redwing | 1.25 | .90 |
| 1425 | A401 | 39p Welsh mountain sheep | 1.55 | 1.00 |
| a. | | Booklet pane of 4 | 6.00 | |
| | | Nos. 1421-1425 (5) | 5.55 | 3.70 |

For Prestige booklet containing pane #1425a, see BK156.
Issue date: No. 1425a, Mar. 1.

Memories A402

**1992, Jan. 28    Litho.    Perf. 15x14**
**Booklet Stamps**
| 1426 | A402 | 1st Flowers | 1.30 | 1.00 |
|---|---|---|---|---|
| 1427 | A402 | 1st Locket | 1.30 | 1.00 |
| 1428 | A402 | 1st Key | 1.30 | 1.00 |
| 1429 | A402 | 1st Model car | 1.30 | 1.00 |
| 1430 | A402 | 1st Compass, 4-leaf clover | 1.30 | 1.00 |
| 1431 | A402 | 1st Pocket watch | 1.30 | 1.00 |
| 1432 | A402 | 1st Envelope, fountain pen | 1.30 | 1.00 |
| 1433 | A402 | 1st Buttons, pearls | 1.30 | 1.00 |
| 1434 | A402 | 1st Marbles | 1.30 | 1.00 |
| 1435 | A402 | 1st Starfish, shovel and bucket | 1.30 | 1.00 |
| a. | | Bklt. pane of 10, #1426-1435 (BK1171) | 13.00 | |

No. 1435a printed se-tenant with 12 greeting labels and sold for £2.40 at date of issue.

Queen Elizabeth II's Accession to the Throne, 40th Anniv. A403

Queen Elizabeth II: No. 1436, In coronation regalia. No. 1437, Facing right, wearing garter robes as head of Church of England. No. 1438, Holding infant Prince Andrew. No. 1439, Wearing military uniform at Trooping of the Color. No. 1440, Wearing purple hat.

**1992, Feb. 6    Litho.    Perf. 14½x14**
| 1436 | A403 | 24p multicolored | 1.20 | .90 |
|---|---|---|---|---|
| 1437 | A403 | 24p multicolored | 1.20 | .90 |
| 1438 | A403 | 24p multicolored | 1.20 | .90 |
| 1439 | A403 | 24p multicolored | 1.20 | .90 |
| 1440 | A403 | 24p multicolored | 1.20 | .90 |
| a. | | Strip of 5, #1436-1440 | 6.00 | 6.00 |

Alfred, Lord Tennyson, Death Cent. — A404

Portraits and illustrations for poems: 24p, The Beguiling of Merlin by Sir Edward Burne-Jones. 28p, April Love by Arthur Hughes. 33p, The Lady of Shalott by John William Waterhouse. 39p, Mariana by Dante Gabriel Rossetti.

**1992, Mar. 10    Photo.**
| 1441 | A404 | 24p multicolored | .95 | .65 |
|---|---|---|---|---|
| 1442 | A404 | 28p multicolored | 1.10 | .80 |
| 1443 | A404 | 33p multicolored | 1.25 | .90 |
| 1444 | A404 | 39p multicolored | 1.55 | 1.00 |
| | | Nos. 1441-1444 (4) | 4.85 | 3.35 |

**Castle Type of 1988**

Nos. 1445-1448 have been re-engraved to show greater detail than on Nos. 1230-1233. The silhouette of the Queen's head on Nos. 1445-1448 is printed in a special ink that changes color from green to gold.

**Perf. 15x14 Syncopated**
**1992-95    Engr.**
| 1445 | A369 | £1 like #1230 | 4.00 | 1.00 |
|---|---|---|---|---|
| 1446 | A369 | £1.50 like #1231 | 6.00 | 1.10 |
| 1447 | A369 | £2 like #1232 | 8.00 | 1.10 |
| 1447A | A369 | £3 like #1230 | 17.50 | 3.00 |
| 1448 | A369 | £5 like #1233 | 20.00 | 4.00 |
| | | Nos. 1445-1448 (5) | 55.50 | 10.20 |

Nos. 1445-1447, 1448 were re-issued 12/6/94 with lines strengthened. Castles appear darker than on original issue.
Issued: £3, 8/22/95; others, 3/24/92.

## Castle Type Re-engraved

**1997, July 29**

| | | | | |
|---|---|---|---|---|
| 1446a | A369 | £1.50 Caernarfon | 10.00 | 3.00 |
| 1447b | A369 | £2 Edinburgh | 12.00 | 1.50 |
| 1447Ac | A369 | £3 Carrickfergus | 30.00 | 2.50 |
| 1448a | A369 | £5 Windsor | 35.00 | 6.00 |

Queen's head is silkscreened and feels smooth on Nos. 1446a, 1447b, 1447Ac, 1448a. Letters "C" and "S" in Castle do not have serifs. Letters in castle names also differ from the 1992 and 1995 printings. The elliptical perforation begins one perf hole higher than on the earlier printings.

Discovery of America, 500th Anniv. A405

Design: 39p, Sailing ship, Operation Raleigh Grand Regatta.

### Litho. & Engr.

**1992, Apr. 7**      **Perf. 14½**

| | | | | |
|---|---|---|---|---|
| 1449 | A405 | 24p multicolored | 1.50 | .40 |
| 1450 | A405 | 39p multicolored | 2.25 | .90 |

Europa.

Events A406

Designs: No. 1451, British Olympic Assoc. flag. No. 1452, Flying torch flag of British Paralympic Assoc. No. 1453, British pavilion.

**1992, Apr. 7**      **Litho.**

| | | | | |
|---|---|---|---|---|
| 1451 | A406 | 24p multicolored | .95 | .60 |
| 1452 | A406 | 24p multicolored | .95 | .60 |
| a. | | Pair, #1451-1452 | 1.80 | 1.50 |
| 1453 | A406 | 39p multicolored | 1.75 | 1.00 |
| | | Nos. 1451-1453 (3) | 3.65 | 2.20 |

1992 Summer Olympics (No. 1451) and Paralympics (No. 1452), Barcelona. Expo '92, Seville (No. 1453).

English Civil War, 350th Anniv. — A407

**1992, June 16**      **Photo.**    **Perf. 14½**

| | | | | |
|---|---|---|---|---|
| 1454 | A407 | 24p Pikeman | .95 | .65 |
| 1455 | A407 | 28p Drummer | 1.10 | .80 |
| 1456 | A407 | 33p Musketeer | 1.25 | .90 |
| 1457 | A407 | 39p Standard bearer | 1.55 | 1.00 |
| | | Nos. 1454-1457 (4) | 4.85 | 3.35 |

Yeoman of the Guard, by Gilbert & Sullivan A408

Scenes from comic operas: 24p, The Gondoliers. 28p, The Mikado. 33p, The Pirates of Penzance. 39p, Iolanthe.

**1992, July 21**      **Photo.**    **Perf. 14½x14**

| | | | | |
|---|---|---|---|---|
| 1458 | A408 | 18p multicolored | .70 | .50 |
| 1459 | A408 | 24p multicolored | .95 | .65 |
| 1460 | A408 | 28p multicolored | 1.10 | .80 |
| 1461 | A408 | 33p multicolored | 1.25 | .90 |
| 1462 | A408 | 39p multicolored | 1.55 | 1.00 |
| | | Nos. 1458-1462 (5) | 5.55 | 3.85 |

Sir Arthur Sullivan, 150th anniv. of birth.

Protect the Environment A409

Children's drawings: 24p, Acid rain kills. 28p, Ozone layer. 33p, Greenhouse effect. 39p, Bird of hope.

**1992, Sept. 15**     **Photo.**    **Perf. 14½**

| | | | | |
|---|---|---|---|---|
| 1463 | A409 | 24p multicolored | .95 | .60 |
| 1464 | A409 | 28p multicolored | 1.10 | .80 |
| 1465 | A409 | 33p multicolored | 1.25 | .90 |
| 1466 | A409 | 39p multicolored | 1.55 | 1.00 |
| | | Nos. 1463-1466 (4) | 4.85 | 3.30 |

Single European Market A410

**1992, Oct. 13**     **Photo.**    **Perf. 15x14**

| | | | | |
|---|---|---|---|---|
| 1467 | A410 | 24p multicolored | .95 | .80 |

Christmas A411

Stained glass windows: 18p, Angel Gabriel. 24p, Madonna and Child. 28p, King offering gold crown. 33p, Shepherds. 39p, Kings offering frankincense and myrrh.

**1992, Nov. 10**    **Photo.**    **Perf. 15x14**

| | | | | |
|---|---|---|---|---|
| 1468 | A411 | 18p multicolored | .70 | .25 |
| a. | | Booklet pane of 20 | 14.00 | |
| 1469 | A411 | 24p multicolored | .95 | .25 |
| 1470 | A411 | 28p multicolored | 1.10 | .80 |
| 1471 | A411 | 33p multicolored | 1.25 | .90 |
| 1472 | A411 | 39p multicolored | 1.55 | 1.00 |
| | | Nos. 1468-1472 (5) | 5.55 | 3.20 |

Mute Swans — A412

Designs: 18p, Male, St. Catherine's Chapel, Abbotsbury. 24p, Cygnet, reed bed, Abbotsbury Swannery. 28p, Pair, cygnet. 33p, Eggs in nest, Tithe Barn. 39p, Head of young swan.

**1993, Jan. 19**    **Photo.**    **Perf. 14x15**

| | | | | |
|---|---|---|---|---|
| 1473 | A412 | 18p multicolored | 1.10 | .40 |
| 1474 | A412 | 24p multicolored | 1.10 | .50 |
| 1475 | A412 | 28p multicolored | 1.40 | 1.00 |
| 1476 | A412 | 33p multicolored | 1.80 | 1.75 |
| 1477 | A412 | 39p multicolored | 2.00 | 1.75 |
| | | Nos. 1473-1477 (5) | 7.40 | 5.40 |

Abbotsbury Swannery, 600th anniv.

Britannia — A413

### Litho., Typo. and Embossed
*Perf. 14x14½ Syncopated*

**1993, Mar. 2**

**Granite Paper**

| | | | | |
|---|---|---|---|---|
| 1478 | A413 | £10 multicolored | 37.50 | 12.50 |
| a. | | Silver (Queen's head, security crosses) omitted | 1,750. | |

Soaking may damage these stamps.

Greetings Stamps A414

Children's Characters: No. 1479, Long John Silver, parrot. No. 1480, Tweedledum, Tweedledee. No. 1481, Just William, Violet Elizabeth. No. 1482, Toad, Mole. No. 1483, Bash Street Kids, teacher. No. 1484, Peter Rabbit, Mrs. Rabbit. No. 1485, Father Christmas, Snowman. No. 1486, Big Friendly Giant, Sophie. No. 1487, Rupert Bear, Bill Badger. No. 1488, Aladdin, Genie.

*Perf. 15x14 Syncopated*

**1993, Feb. 2**

| | | | | |
|---|---|---|---|---|
| 1479 | A414 | (1st) multicolored | 1.30 | 1.00 |
| 1480 | A414 | (1st) multicolored | 1.30 | 1.00 |
| 1481 | A414 | (1st) multicolored | 1.30 | 1.00 |
| 1482 | A414 | (1st) multicolored | 1.30 | 1.00 |
| 1483 | A414 | (1st) multicolored | 1.30 | 1.00 |
| 1484 | A414 | (1st) multicolored | 1.30 | 1.00 |
| a. | | Booklet pane of 4 (BK1172) | 5.00 | |
| 1485 | A414 | (1st) multicolored | 1.30 | 1.00 |
| 1486 | A414 | (1st) multicolored | 1.30 | 1.00 |
| 1487 | A414 | (1st) multicolored | 1.30 | 1.00 |
| 1488 | A414 | (1st) multicolored | 1.30 | 1.00 |
| a. | | Bklt. pane of 10, #1479-1488 | 12.50 | |

No. 1479-1488 sold for 24p on day of issue. No. 1488a printed se-tenant with 20 greetings labels. See note above No. 1445.

Issue date: No. 1484a, Aug. 10.

For booklets containing panes of #1484a and #1488a, see BK158 and BK1172, respectively.

Marine Chronometer No. 4 — A415

Designs: 24p, Face. 28p, Escapement, remontoire and fusee. 33p, Balance spring, temperature compensator. 39p, Back of movement.

**1993, Feb. 16**    **Litho.**    **Perf. 14½**

| | | | | |
|---|---|---|---|---|
| 1489 | A415 | 24p multicolored | .95 | .45 |
| 1490 | A415 | 28p multicolored | 1.10 | .70 |
| 1491 | A415 | 33p multicolored | 1.25 | .65 |
| 1492 | A415 | 39p multicolored | 1.55 | .90 |
| | | Nos. 1489-1492 (4) | 4.85 | 2.70 |

John Harrison (1693-1776), inventor of marine chronometer.

Orchids A416

14th World Orchid Conf., Glasgow: 18p, Dendrobium hellwigianum. 24p, Paphiopedilum Maudiae "Magnificum." 28p, Cymbidium lowianum. 33p, Vanda Rothschildiana. 39p, Dendrobium vexillarius.

**1993, Mar. 16**    **Litho.**    **Perf. 15x14**

| | | | | |
|---|---|---|---|---|
| 1493 | A416 | 18p multicolored | .70 | .40 |
| 1494 | A416 | 24p multicolored | .95 | .55 |
| 1495 | A416 | 28p multicolored | 1.10 | .70 |
| 1496 | A416 | 33p multicolored | 1.25 | .80 |
| 1497 | A416 | 39p multicolored | 1.55 | .90 |
| | | Nos. 1493-1497 (5) | 5.55 | 3.35 |

Contemporary Art — A417

Europa: 24p, Sculpture, Family Group, by Henry Moore. 28p, Print, Kew Gardens, by Edward Bawden. 33p, Painting, St. Francis and the Birds, by Stanley Spencer. 39p, Painting, Still Life, Odyssey 1, by Ben Nicholson.

**1993, May 11**    **Photo.**    **Perf. 14x14½**

| | | | | |
|---|---|---|---|---|
| 1498 | A417 | 24p multicolored | .95 | .20 |
| 1499 | A417 | 28p multicolored | 1.10 | .85 |
| 1500 | A417 | 33p multicolored | 1.25 | .90 |
| 1501 | A417 | 39p multicolored | 1.55 | .90 |
| | | Nos. 1498-1501 (4) | 4.85 | 2.85 |

Roman Artifacts A418

24p, Gold aureus of Claudius. 28p, Bronze bust of Hadrian. 33p, Gemstone carved with head of Roma. 39p, Mosaic of Christ.

**1993, June 15**    **Photo.**    **Perf. 14½x14**

| | | | | |
|---|---|---|---|---|
| 1502 | A418 | 24p multicolored | .95 | .60 |
| 1503 | A418 | 28p multicolored | 1.10 | .90 |
| 1504 | A418 | 33p multicolored | 1.25 | .90 |
| 1505 | A418 | 39p multicolored | 1.55 | 1.00 |
| | | Nos. 1502-1505 (4) | 4.85 | 3.40 |

British Canals, Bicent. A419

Designs: 24p, Grand Junction Canal boats. 28p, Stainforth and Keadby Canal. 33p, Brecknock and Abergavenny Canal boats, horse. 39p, Crinan Canal, steamers and fishing boats.

**1993, July 20**    **Litho.**    **Perf. 14½x14**

| | | | | |
|---|---|---|---|---|
| 1506 | A419 | 24p multicolored | .95 | .60 |
| 1507 | A419 | 28p multicolored | 1.10 | .90 |
| 1508 | A419 | 33p multicolored | 1.25 | .90 |
| 1509 | A419 | 39p multicolored | 1.55 | 1.00 |
| | | Nos. 1506-1509 (4) | 4.85 | 3.40 |

Autumn Fruits A420

**1993, Sept. 14**    **Photo.**    **Perf. 15x14**

| | | | | |
|---|---|---|---|---|
| 1510 | A420 | 18p Horse chestnut | .70 | .35 |
| 1511 | A420 | 24p Blackberries | .95 | .55 |
| 1512 | A420 | 28p Filbert | 1.10 | .90 |
| 1513 | A420 | 33p Rowanberries | 1.25 | .90 |
| 1514 | A420 | 39p Pears | 1.55 | 1.00 |
| | | Nos. 1510-1514 (5) | 5.55 | 3.70 |

Sherlock Holmes — A421

Holmes and: No. 1515, Dr. Watson, The Reigate Squire. No. 1516, Sir Henry, The

Hound of the Baskervilles. No. 1517, Lestrade, The Six Napoleons. No. 1518, Mycroft, The Greek Interpreter. No. 1519, Moriarty, The Final Problem.

**1993, Oct. 12    Litho.    Perf. 14x14½**
| | | | | |
|---|---|---|---|---|
| 1515 | A421 | 24p multicolored | 1.00 | .75 |
| 1516 | A421 | 24p multicolored | 1.00 | .75 |
| 1517 | A421 | 24p multicolored | 1.00 | .75 |
| 1518 | A421 | 24p multicolored | 1.00 | .75 |
| 1519 | A421 | 24p multicolored | 1.00 | .75 |
| a. | | Strip of 5, #1515-1519 | 5.00 | 4.50 |

"A Christmas Carol," by Charles Dickens, 150th Anniv. A423

Designs: 19p, Tiny Tim, Bob Cratchit. 25p, Mr. & Mrs. Fezziwig. 30p, Scrooge. 35p, Prize Turkey. 41p, Mr. Scrooge's Nephew.

**1993, Nov. 9    Photo.    Perf. 15x14**
| | | | | |
|---|---|---|---|---|
| 1528 | A423 | 19p multicolored | .75 | .25 |
| a. | | Booklet pane of 20 | 15.00 | |
| 1529 | A423 | 25p multicolored | 1.00 | .25 |
| 1530 | A423 | 30p multicolored | 1.20 | .90 |
| 1531 | A423 | 35p multicolored | 1.40 | .90 |
| 1532 | A423 | 41p multicolored | 1.65 | 1.00 |
| | | Nos. 1528-1532 (5) | 6.00 | 3.30 |

For booklet containing #1528a, see BK857.

Age of Steam — A424

Designs: 19p, Tandem locomotives, West Highland Line, North British Railway. 25p, Locomotive #60149, Kings Cross Station, London. 30p, Locomotive #43000 on turntable, Blyth North engine shed. 35p, Locomotive entering station. 41p, Locomotive on bridge over Worcester & Birmingham Canal.

**1994, Jan. 18    Photo.    Perf. 14½**
| | | | | |
|---|---|---|---|---|
| 1533 | A424 | 19p black & green | .75 | .35 |
| 1534 | A424 | 25p black & purple | 1.00 | .55 |
| 1535 | A424 | 30p black & red brn | 1.20 | .90 |
| 1536 | A424 | 35p black & red violet | 1.40 | .90 |
| 1537 | A424 | 41p black & dark blue | 1.65 | 1.00 |
| | | Nos. 1533-1537 (5) | 6.00 | 3.70 |

Dan Dare A425

The Three Bears A426

Rupert the Bear A427

Alice in Wonderland — A428

Noggin the Nog A429

Peter Rabbit A430

Little Red Riding Hood A431

Orlando, the Marmalade Cat A432

Biggles A433

Paddington A434

**Perf. 15x14 Syncopated**
**1994, Feb. 1    Photo.**
**Booklet Stamps**
| | | | | |
|---|---|---|---|---|
| 1538 | A425 | (1st) multicolored | 1.35 | 1.00 |
| 1539 | A426 | (1st) multicolored | 1.35 | 1.00 |
| 1540 | A427 | (1st) multicolored | 1.35 | 1.00 |
| 1541 | A428 | (1st) multicolored | 1.35 | 1.00 |
| 1542 | A429 | (1st) multicolored | 1.35 | 1.00 |
| 1543 | A430 | (1st) multicolored | 1.35 | 1.00 |
| 1544 | A431 | (1st) multicolored | 1.35 | 1.00 |
| 1545 | A432 | (1st) multicolored | 1.35 | 1.00 |
| 1546 | A433 | (1st) multicolored | 1.35 | 1.00 |
| 1547 | A434 | (1st) multicolored | 1.35 | 1.00 |
| a. | | Bklt. pane of 10, #1538-1547 | 13.50 | |

Nos. 1538-1547 sold for 25p on day of issue. No. 1547a was printed se-tenant with 20 greetings labels.
For booklet containing #1547a, see BK1182.

Investiture of Prince of Wales, 25th Anniv. A435

Watercolor landscapes, by Prince Charles: 19p, Chirk Castle, Clwyd, Wales. 25p, Ben Arkle, Sutherland, Scotland. 30p, Mourne Mountains, County Down, Northern Ireland. 35p, Dersingham, Norfolk, England. 41p, Dolwyddelan, Gwynedd, Wales.

**1994, Mar. 1    Photo.    Perf. 15x14**
| | | | | |
|---|---|---|---|---|
| 1548 | A435 | 19p multicolored | .75 | .35 |
| 1549 | A435 | 25p multicolored | 1.00 | .55 |
| 1550 | A435 | 30p multicolored | 1.20 | .90 |
| a. | | Booklet pane of 4 | 4.80 | |
| 1551 | A435 | 35p multicolored | 1.40 | .90 |
| 1552 | A435 | 41p multicolored | 1.65 | 1.00 |
| | | Nos. 1548-1552 (5) | 6.00 | 3.70 |

For booklet containing pane #1550a, see No. BK159.

British Picture Postcards, Cent. — A436

Seaside characters: 19p, "Bather at Blackpool." 25p, "Where's my Little Lad." 30p, "Wish You Were Here." 35p, "Punch and Judy Show." 41p, "The Tower Crane."

**1994, Apr. 12    Litho.    Perf. 14x14½**
| | | | | |
|---|---|---|---|---|
| 1553 | A436 | 19p multicolored | .75 | .35 |
| 1554 | A436 | 25p multicolored | 1.00 | .55 |
| 1555 | A436 | 30p multicolored | 1.20 | .90 |
| 1556 | A436 | 35p multicolored | 1.40 | .90 |
| 1557 | A436 | 41p multicolored | 1.65 | 1.00 |
| | | Nos. 1553-1557 (5) | 6.00 | 3.70 |

Blackpool Tower, cent. (#1553). Tower Bridge, cent. (#1557).

Opening of Channel Tunnel — A437

Nos. 1558, 1560, British lion, French rooster, meeting over Channel. Nos. 1559, 1561, Joined hands above speeding train.

**1994, May 3    Photo.    Perf. 14x14½**
| | | | | |
|---|---|---|---|---|
| 1558 | A437 | 25p dk blue & multi | 1.00 | .60 |
| 1559 | A437 | 25p dk blue & multi | 1.00 | .60 |
| a. | | Pair, #1558-1559 | 2.00 | 1.25 |
| 1560 | A437 | 41p lt blue & multi | 1.65 | 1.00 |
| 1561 | A437 | 41p multicolored | 1.65 | 1.00 |
| a. | | Pair, #1560-1561 | 3.30 | 2.75 |
| | | Nos. 1558-1561 (4) | 5.30 | 3.20 |

See France Nos. 2421-2424.

D-Day, 50th Anniv. — A438

Photographs from Imperial War Museum's archives: No. 1562, Ground crew reloading FAF Bostons. No. 1563, Coastal bombardment by HMS Warspite. No. 1564, Commandos landing on Gold Beach. No. 1565, Infantry regrouping on Sword Beach. No. 1566, Advancing inland from Ouistreham.

**1994, June 6    Litho.    Perf. 14**
| | | | | |
|---|---|---|---|---|
| 1562 | A438 | 25p multicolored | 1.00 | .65 |
| 1563 | A438 | 25p multicolored | 1.00 | .65 |
| 1564 | A438 | 25p multicolored | 1.00 | .65 |
| 1565 | A438 | 25p multicolored | 1.00 | .65 |
| 1566 | A438 | 25p multicolored | 1.00 | .65 |
| a. | | Strip of 5, #1562-1566 | 5.00 | 3.50 |

Honorable Company of Edinburgh Golfers, 250th Anniv. — A439

Golf courses: 19p, St. Andrews, old course. 25p, Muirfield, 18th hole. 30p, Carnoustie, 15th hole. 35p, Royal Troon, "postage stamp" 8th hole. 41p, Turnberry, 9th hole.

**1994, July 5    Photo.    Perf. 14**
| | | | | |
|---|---|---|---|---|
| 1567 | A439 | 19p multicolored | .75 | .35 |
| 1568 | A439 | 25p multicolored | 1.00 | .55 |
| 1569 | A439 | 30p multicolored | 1.20 | .90 |
| 1570 | A439 | 35p multicolored | 1.40 | .90 |
| 1571 | A439 | 41p multicolored | 1.65 | 1.00 |
| | | Nos. 1567-1571 (5) | 6.00 | 3.70 |

Summertime Events — A440

Designs: 19p, Royal Welsh Agricultural Show, Llanelwedd. 25p, Wimbledon. 30p, Yachts on Solent during Cowes Week. 35p, Cricket at Lord's. 41p, Scottish Highland Games, Braemar.

**1994, Aug. 2    Perf. 14½x14**
| | | | | |
|---|---|---|---|---|
| 1572 | A440 | 19p multicolored | .75 | .35 |
| 1573 | A440 | 25p multicolored | 1.00 | .55 |
| 1574 | A440 | 30p multicolored | 1.20 | .90 |
| 1575 | A440 | 35p multicolored | 1.40 | .90 |
| 1576 | A440 | 41p multicolored | 1.65 | 1.00 |
| | | Nos. 1572-1576 (5) | 6.00 | 3.70 |

Medical Discoveries — A441

Europa: 25p, Ultrasonic imaging. 30p, Scanning electron microscope. 35p, Magnetic resonance imaging. 41p, Computed tomography.

**1994, Sept. 27    Photo.    Perf. 14x14½**
| | | | | |
|---|---|---|---|---|
| 1577 | A441 | 25p multicolored | 1.00 | .20 |
| 1578 | A441 | 30p multicolored | 1.20 | .80 |
| 1579 | A441 | 35p multicolored | 1.40 | .90 |
| 1580 | A441 | 41p multicolored | 1.65 | 1.00 |
| | | Nos. 1577-1580 (4) | 5.25 | 2.90 |

Christmas A442

School children portraying: 19p, Mary, Joseph, with infant Jesus. 25p, Magi. 30p, Mary holding Jesus. 35p, Shepherds. 41p, Angels.

**1994, Nov. 1    Photo.    Perf. 15x14**
| | | | | |
|---|---|---|---|---|
| 1581 | A442 | 19p multicolored | .75 | .25 |
| a. | | Booklet pane of 20 | 15.00 | |
| 1582 | A442 | 25p multicolored | 1.00 | .25 |
| 1583 | A442 | 30p multicolored | 1.20 | .90 |
| 1584 | A442 | 35p multicolored | 1.40 | .90 |
| 1585 | A442 | 41p multicolored | 1.65 | 1.00 |
| | | Nos. 1581-1585 (5) | 6.00 | 3.30 |

For booklet containing #1581a, see #BK858.

Cats A443

Designs: 19p, Black cat. 25p, Siamese, tabby cats. 30p, Yellow cat. 35p, Calico, Abyssinian cats. 41p, Black & white cat.

**1995, Jan. 17    Litho.    Perf. 15x14**
| | | | | |
|---|---|---|---|---|
| 1586 | A443 | 19p multicolored | .75 | .35 |
| 1587 | A443 | 25p multicolored | 1.00 | .55 |
| 1588 | A443 | 30p multicolored | 1.20 | .90 |
| 1589 | A443 | 35p multicolored | 1.40 | .90 |
| 1590 | A443 | 41p multicolored | 1.65 | 1.00 |
| | | Nos. 1586-1590 (5) | 6.00 | 3.70 |

Springtime
A444

Sculptures from natural materials, by Andy Goldsworthy: 19p, Dandelions. 25p, Chestnut leaves. 30p, Garlic leaves. 35p, Hazel leaves. 41p, Spring grass.

**1995, Mar. 14　Photo.　Perf. 15x14**

| | | | | |
|---|---|---|---|---|
| 1591 | A444 | 19p multicolored | .75 | .35 |
| 1592 | A444 | 25p multicolored | 1.00 | .55 |
| 1593 | A444 | 30p multicolored | 1.20 | .90 |
| 1594 | A444 | 35p multicolored | 1.40 | .90 |
| 1595 | A444 | 41p multicolored | 1.65 | 1.00 |
| | | Nos. 1591-1595 (5) | 6.00 | 3.70 |

'La Danse a la Campagne,' by Renoir — A445

'Troilus and Criseyde,' by Peter Brookes
A446

'The Kiss,' by Rodin
A447

'Girls on the Town,' by Beryl Cook
A448

'Jazz,' by Andrew Mockett
A449

'Girls Performing aKathal Dance' (Aurangzeb Period)
A450

'Alice Keppel with her Daughter,' by Alice Hughes
A451

'Children Playing,' by L.S. Lowry
A452

'Circus Clowns,' by Emily Firmin and Justin Mitchell
A453

Decoration from 'All the Love Poems of Shakespeare,' by Eric Gill — A454

**Perf. 14 Syncopated**

**1995, Mar. 21　　　　　Litho.**

| | | | | |
|---|---|---|---|---|
| 1596 | A445 | 1st multicolored | 1.35 | 1.00 |
| 1597 | A446 | 1st multicolored | 1.35 | 1.00 |
| 1598 | A447 | 1st multicolored | 1.35 | 1.00 |
| 1599 | A448 | 1st multicolored | 1.35 | 1.00 |
| 1600 | A449 | 1st multicolored | 1.35 | 1.00 |
| 1601 | A450 | 1st multicolored | 1.35 | 1.00 |
| 1602 | A451 | 1st multicolored | 1.35 | 1.00 |
| 1603 | A452 | 1st multicolored | 1.35 | 1.00 |
| 1604 | A453 | 1st multicolored | 1.35 | 1.00 |
| 1605 | A454 | 1st multicolored | 1.35 | 1.00 |
| a. | | Bklt. pane of 10, #1596-1605 | 13.50 | |

Complete booklet sold for £2.50 on day of issue.
For booklet containing #1605a, see #BK1183.

The National Trust, Celebrating 100 Years　19　National Trust, Cent. — A455

Designs: 19p, Celebrating 100 years. 25p, Protecting land. 30p, Conserving art. 35p, Saving coast. 41p, Repairing buildings.

**1995, Apr. 11　Photo.　Perf. 14x15**

| | | | | |
|---|---|---|---|---|
| 1606 | A455 | 19p multicolored | .75 | .35 |
| 1607 | A455 | 25p multicolored | 1.00 | .55 |
| a. | | Booklet pane of 6 | 6.00 | |
| 1608 | A455 | 30p multicolored | 1.20 | .90 |
| 1609 | A455 | 35p multicolored | 1.40 | .90 |
| 1610 | A455 | 41p multicolored | 1.65 | 1.00 |
| | | Nos. 1606-1610 (5) | 6.00 | 3.70 |

For booklet containing panes #1607a, see #BK160.
Issued: #1607a, 4/25/95.

Peace & Freedom
A456

Designs: No. 1611, Hands, British Red Cross 1870-1995. No. 1612, British troops, people celebrating liberation of Paris. No. 1613, Dove, outstretched hand, UN, 1945-95. No. 1614, St. Paul's Cathedral, floodlights forming Victory V. 30p, Hands above earth, UN 1945-95.

**1995, May 2　Photo.　Perf. 14½x14**

| | | | | |
|---|---|---|---|---|
| 1611 | A456 | 19p multicolored | .75 | .40 |
| 1612 | A456 | 19p multicolored | .75 | .40 |
| 1613 | A456 | 25p multicolored | 1.00 | .55 |
| 1614 | A456 | 25p multicolored | 1.00 | .55 |
| 1615 | A456 | 30p multicolored | 1.20 | .80 |
| | | Nos. 1611-1615 (5) | 4.70 | 2.70 |

End of World War II, 50th anniv. (#1612, 1614), Europa (#1613, 1615).

H. G. Wells (1866-1946), Science Fiction Writer — A457

Novels: 25p, The Time Machine. 30p, The First Men on the Moon. 35p, The War of the Worlds. 41p, The Shape of Things to Come.

**1995, June 6　Litho.　Perf. 14½x14**

| | | | | |
|---|---|---|---|---|
| 1616 | A457 | 25p multicolored | 1.00 | .55 |
| 1617 | A457 | 30p multicolored | 1.20 | .90 |
| 1618 | A457 | 35p multicolored | 1.40 | .90 |
| 1619 | A457 | 41p multicolored | 1.65 | 1.00 |
| | | Nos. 1616-1619 (4) | 5.25 | 3.35 |

Opening of Shakespeare's New Globe Theatre
A458

Bankside theatres: No. 1620, Swan, 1595. No. 1621, The Rose, 1595. No. 1622, The Globe, 1599. No. 1623, The Hope, 1613. No. 1624, The Globe, 1614.

**1995, Aug. 8　Litho.　Perf. 14½x14**

| | | | | |
|---|---|---|---|---|
| 1620 | A458 | 25p multicolored | 1.00 | .60 |
| 1621 | A458 | 25p multicolored | 1.00 | .60 |
| 1622 | A458 | 25p multicolored | 1.00 | .60 |
| 1623 | A458 | 25p multicolored | 1.00 | .60 |
| 1624 | A458 | 25p multicolored | 1.00 | .60 |
| a. | | Strip of 5, #1620-1624 | 5.00 | 4.50 |

Pioneers of Communication — A459

Designs: 19p, Sir Rowland Hill, introduction of uniform penny postage. 25p, Hill as older man, design A1. 41p, Guglielmo Marconi, early wireless equipment. 60p, Marconi as older man using radiophone, sinking *Titanic*.

**Litho. & Engr.**

**1995, Sept. 5　　　　　Perf. 14½**

| | | | | |
|---|---|---|---|---|
| 1625 | A459 | 19p multicolored | .75 | .35 |
| 1626 | A459 | 25p multicolored | 1.00 | .50 |
| 1627 | A459 | 41p multicolored | 1.65 | 1.00 |
| 1628 | A459 | 60p multicolored | 2.40 | 1.25 |
| | | Nos. 1625-1628 (4) | 5.80 | 3.10 |

Rugby League, Cent. — A460

**1995, Oct. 3　Photo.　Perf. 14x14½**

| | | | | |
|---|---|---|---|---|
| 1629 | A460 | 19p Harold Wagstaff | .75 | .35 |
| 1630 | A460 | 25p Gus Risman | 1.00 | .55 |
| 1631 | A460 | 30p Jim Sullivan | 1.20 | .90 |
| 1632 | A460 | 35p Billy Batten | 1.40 | .90 |
| 1633 | A460 | 41p Brian Bevan | 1.65 | 1.00 |
| | | Nos. 1629-1633 (5) | 6.00 | 3.70 |

Christmas — A461

Designs showing robin in winter scene: 19p, In pillar box. 25p, On fence rail, holly bush. 30p, Standing on snow covered milk bottle. 41p, Sitting on snow covered road sign, blue fence. 60p, Sitting on door knob, Chistmas decoration on door.

**1995, Oct. 30　Photo.　Perf. 14¾x14**

| | | | | |
|---|---|---|---|---|
| 1634 | A461 | 19p multicolored | .75 | .25 |
| a. | | Booklet pane of 20 | 15.00 | |
| b. | | Sheet of 20 + 20 labels | 25.00 | |
| 1635 | A461 | 25p multicolored | 1.00 | .25 |
| 1636 | A461 | 30p multicolored | 1.20 | .90 |
| 1637 | A461 | 41p multicolored | 1.65 | 1.00 |
| 1638 | A461 | 60p multicolored | 2.40 | 1.40 |
| a. | | Booklet pane of 4 | 9.75 | |
| | | Nos. 1634-1638 (5) | 7.00 | 3.80 |

No. 1634b was issued 10/3/00. It sold for £3.99 and has labels that read "Seasons Greetings" and "Glad Tidings." Sheets with personalized labels were made available only to select Royal Post customers via mail order purchases, and sold for more.
For booklets containing Nos. 1634a and 1638a, see Nos. BK859 and BK792, respectively.

Robert Burns (1759-1796), Poet — A462

Lines from poems: 19p, "Wee sleeket, cowran, tim'rous beastie." 25p, "O my luve's like a red, red rose." 41p, "Scots, wha hae wi Wallace bled." 60p, "Should auld acquaintance be forgot."

**1996, Jan. 25　Litho.　Perf. 14½**

| | | | | |
|---|---|---|---|---|
| 1639 | A462 | 19p multicolored | .75 | .35 |
| 1640 | A462 | 25p multicolored | 1.00 | .55 |
| 1641 | A462 | 41p multicolored | 1.65 | 1.00 |
| 1642 | A462 | 60p multicolored | 2.40 | 1.40 |
| | | Nos. 1639-1642 (4) | 5.80 | 3.30 |

Greetings Cartoons
A463

#1643, More Love. #1644, Sincerely. #1645, Human condition. #1646, Mental Floss. #1647, Don't ring. #1648, Dear lottery prize winner. #1649, I'm writing to you... #1650, Fetch this... #1651, My day starts... #1652, The check in the post.

**Perf. 14½ Syncopated**

**1996-2001　　　　　　　Litho.**

| | | | | |
|---|---|---|---|---|
| 1643 | A463 | 1st black & lilac | 1.35 | .85 |
| 1644 | A463 | 1st black & green | 1.35 | .85 |
| 1645 | A463 | 1st black & blue | 1.35 | .85 |
| 1646 | A463 | 1st black & purple | 1.35 | .85 |
| 1647 | A463 | 1st black & red | 1.35 | .85 |
| 1648 | A463 | 1st black & blue | 1.35 | .85 |
| 1649 | A463 | 1st black & red | 1.35 | .85 |
| 1650 | A463 | 1st black & purple | 1.35 | .85 |
| 1651 | A463 | 1st black & green | 1.35 | .85 |
| 1652 | A463 | 1st black & lilac | 1.35 | .85 |
| a. | | Booklet pane, #1643-1652+20 labels | 13.50 | |
| b. | | Sheet of 10, #1643-1652, + 10 labels, perf. 14½x14 | 13.50 | |
| c. | | Sheet of 20, 2 each #1643-1652, + 20 labels, perf. 14¼ | — | — |

Issued: No. 1652b, 12/18/01. 1652a, 2/26/96. 1652c, 7/29/03.
No. 1652b lacks perforation syncopation. Labels could be personalized for an additional amount.
Nos. 1643-1652 sold for 25p on day of issue.
No. 1652c sold for £6.15.
For booklet containing #1652a, see #BK1184.

Wildfowl and Wetlands Trust, 50th Anniv.
A464

Paintings by Charles Tunnicliffe RA (1901-79): 19p, Muscovy duck. 25p, Lapwing. 30p, White-fronted goose. 35p, Bittern. 41p, Whooper swan.

**1996, Mar. 12   Photo.   Perf. 14x14½**
| | | | | |
|---|---|---|---|---|
| 1653 | A464 | 19p multicolored | .75 | .35 |
| 1654 | A464 | 25p multicolored | 1.00 | .55 |
| 1655 | A464 | 30p multicolored | 1.20 | .90 |
| 1656 | A464 | 35p multicolored | 1.40 | .90 |
| 1657 | A464 | 41p multicolored | 1.65 | 1.00 |
| | | Nos. 1653-1657 (5) | 6.00 | 3.70 |

Motion Pictures, Cent. — A465

Designs: 19p, Exterior of Odeon at Harrogate, 1930s theater. 25p, Laurance Olivier, Vivien Leigh in scene from "That Hamilton Woman." 30p, Cinema ticket from "The Picture House." 35p, Rooster emblem of Pathe News, motion picture newsreels. 41p, Theater marquee.

**1996, Apr. 16   Photo.   Perf. 14x14½**
| | | | | |
|---|---|---|---|---|
| 1658 | A465 | 19p multicolored | .75 | .35 |
| 1659 | A465 | 25p multicolored | 1.00 | .55 |
| 1660 | A465 | 30p multicolored | 1.20 | .90 |
| 1661 | A465 | 35p multicolored | 1.40 | .90 |
| 1662 | A465 | 41p multicolored | 1.65 | 1.00 |
| | | Nos. 1658-1662 (5) | 6.00 | 3.70 |

1996 European Soccer Championships — A466

Lengendary players: 19p, Dixie Dean (1907-80). 25p, Bobby Moore (1941-93). 35p, Duncan Edwards (1936-58). 41p, Billy Wright (1924-94). 60p, Danny Blanchflower (1926-93).

**1996, May 14   Litho.   Perf. 15x14**
| | | | | |
|---|---|---|---|---|
| 1663 | A466 | 19p gray, red & blk | .75 | .35 |
| a. | | Bklt. pane of 4 + printed margin (BK161) | 3.00 | |
| 1664 | A466 | 25p gray, grn & blk | 1.00 | .55 |
| a. | | Bklt. pane of 4 + printed margin (BK161) | 4.00 | |
| 1665 | A466 | 35p gray, yel & blk | 1.40 | .90 |
| 1666 | A466 | 41p blk, blue & gray | 1.65 | 1.00 |
| 1667 | A466 | 60p gray, org & blk | 2.40 | 1.40 |
| a. | | Bklt. pane, 2 ea #1665-1667 (BK161) | 9.75 | |
| | | Nos. 1663-1667 (5) | 7.20 | 4.20 |

1996 Summer Olympic, Paralympic Games, Atlanta A467

**1996, July 9   Litho.   Perf. 15x14**
| | | | | |
|---|---|---|---|---|
| 1688 | A467 | 26p Sprinting | 1.05 | .60 |
| 1689 | A467 | 26p Javelin | 1.05 | .60 |
| 1690 | A467 | 26p Basketball | 1.05 | .60 |
| 1691 | A467 | 26p Swimming | 1.05 | .60 |
| 1692 | A467 | 26p Victorious athlete | 1.05 | .60 |
| a. | | Strip of 5, #1688-1692 | 5.25 | 4.00 |

Issued: No. 1652b, 12/18/01. 1652a, 2/26/96. 1652c, 7/29/03. Compare with Type A588.

20th Century Women of Achievement A468

Designs: 20p, Dorothy Hodgkin (1910-94), chemist. 26p, Margot Fonteyn (1919-91), ballerina. 31p, Elisabeth Frink (1930-93), sculptor. 37p, Daphne du Maurier (1907-89), novelist. 43p, Marea Hartman (1920-94), sports administrator.

**1996, Aug. 6   Photo.   Perf. 14½**
| | | | | |
|---|---|---|---|---|
| 1693 | A468 | 20p multicolored | .80 | .35 |
| 1694 | A468 | 26p multicolored | 1.05 | .55 |
| 1695 | A468 | 31p multicolored | 1.25 | .90 |
| 1696 | A468 | 37p multicolored | 1.50 | .90 |
| 1697 | A468 | 43p multicolored | 1.70 | 1.10 |
| | | Nos. 1693-1697 (5) | 6.30 | 3.80 |

Europa, Nos. 1694-1695.

British Television Programs for Children, 50th Anniv. A469

Designs: 20p, Annette Mills, "Muffin the Mule." 26p, Sooty. 31p, String puppets Troy Tempest and Lord Titan. 37p, The Clangers. 43p, Dangermouse.

**1996, Sept. 3   Perf. 14½x14**
| | | | | |
|---|---|---|---|---|
| 1698 | A469 | 20p multicolored | .80 | .30 |
| a. | | Pane of 4 #1698b + printed margin | 8.00 | |
| b. | | Perf. 15x14 | 2.00 | 1.50 |
| 1699 | A469 | 26p multicolored | 1.05 | .40 |
| 1700 | A469 | 31p multicolored | 1.25 | 1.00 |
| 1701 | A469 | 37p multicolored | 1.50 | 1.10 |
| 1702 | A469 | 43p multicolored | 1.70 | 1.50 |
| | | Nos. 1698-1702 (5) | 6.30 | 4.30 |

For Prestige booklet containing pane #1698a, see BK162.
Issued: #1698a, 9/23/97.

Classic British Sports Cars — A470

Designs: 20p, 1955 Triumph TR3. 26p, MG TD. 37p, Austin-Healy 100. 43p, 1948 Jaguar XK 120. 63p, Morgan Plus Four.

**1996, Oct. 1   Photo.   Perf. 14½**
| | | | | |
|---|---|---|---|---|
| 1703 | A470 | 20p multicolored | .80 | .35 |
| 1704 | A470 | 26p multicolored | 1.05 | .55 |
| 1705 | A470 | 37p multicolored | 1.50 | 1.10 |
| 1706 | A470 | 43p multicolored | 1.70 | 1.25 |
| 1707 | A470 | 63p multicolored | 2.50 | 1.60 |
| | | Nos. 1703-1707 (5) | 7.55 | 4.85 |

Christmas A471

Designs: 2nd, Three kings, star. 1st, The Annunciation. 31p, Mary, Joseph on journey to Bethlehem. 43p, Madonna and Child. 63p, Angel telling shepherds of Christ's birth.

**1996, Oct. 28   Photo.   Perf. 14½x14**
| | | | | |
|---|---|---|---|---|
| 1708 | A471 | 2nd multicolored | .95 | .25 |
| a. | | Booklet pane of 20 | 19.00 | |
| 1709 | A471 | 1st multicolored | 1.35 | .25 |
| 1710 | A471 | 31p multicolored | 1.25 | 1.10 |
| 1711 | A471 | 43p multicolored | 1.70 | 1.25 |
| 1712 | A471 | 63p multicolored | 2.50 | 1.50 |
| | | Nos. 1708-1712 (5) | 7.75 | 4.35 |

Nos. 1708-1709 sold for 20p and 26p respectively on day of issue.
For booklet containing #1708a, see #BK1220.

Gentiana Acaulis A472

Magnolia Altissima A473

Camellia Japonica A474

Tulip A475

Fuchsia "Princess of Wales" A476

Le Perroquet Rouge A477

Gazania Splendens A478

Iris Latifolia A479

Amaryllis Bresiliensis A480

Granadilla A481

**Perf. 14½x14 Syncopated**
**1997, Jan. 6   Litho.**
**Booklet Stamps**
| | | | | |
|---|---|---|---|---|
| 1713 | A472 | 1st multicolored | 1.35 | .85 |
| a. | | Perf 15x14 | 3.25 | 3.25 |
| 1714 | A473 | 1st multicolored | 1.35 | .85 |
| 1715 | A474 | 1st multicolored | 1.35 | .85 |
| 1716 | A475 | 1st multicolored | 1.35 | .85 |
| a. | | Perf 15x14 | 2.00 | 2.00 |
| 1717 | A476 | 1st multicolored | 1.35 | .85 |
| 1718 | A477 | 1st multicolored | 1.35 | .85 |
| 1719 | A478 | 1st multicolored | 1.35 | .85 |
| 1720 | A479 | 1st multicolored | 1.35 | .85 |
| a. | | Perf 15x14 | 3.25 | 3.25 |
| b. | | Booklet pane, #1713a, 1720a, 2 #1716a (BK176) | 8.50 | |

| | | | | |
|---|---|---|---|---|
| 1721 | A480 | 1st multicolored | 1.35 | .85 |
| 1722 | A481 | 1st multicolored | 1.35 | .85 |
| a. | | Bklt. pane of 10, #1713-1722 | 13.50 | |
| b. | | Sheet, 2 each #1713-1722, + 20 labels, perf. 14¼ | 45.00 | |

Nos. 1713-1722, 1722a issued 1/9/97. 1722a sold for £2.50 on day of issue, but stamps each had 26p of franking value.
No. 1722b issued 2003. It sold for £14.95 and had labels that could be personalized.
No. 1720a issued 5/25/04. 1720a sold for £1.12 on day of issue.
For booklet containing #1722a, see #BK1195.

King Henry VIII and His Six Wives A482

**1997, Jan. 21   Photo.   Perf. 15**
| | | | | |
|---|---|---|---|---|
| 1723 | A482 | 26p shown | 1.05 | .60 |

**Size: 27x38mm**
**Perf. 14x15**
| | | | | |
|---|---|---|---|---|
| 1724 | A482 | 26p Catherine of Aragon | 1.05 | .65 |
| 1725 | A482 | 26p Anne Boleyn | 1.05 | .65 |
| 1726 | A482 | 26p Jane Seymour | 1.05 | .65 |
| 1727 | A482 | 26p Anne of Cleves | 1.05 | .65 |
| 1728 | A482 | 26p Catherine Howard | 1.05 | .65 |
| 1729 | A482 | 26p Catherine Parr | 1.05 | .65 |
| a. | | Strip of 6, #1724-1729 | 6.25 | 5.25 |
| | | Nos. 1723-1729 (7) | 7.35 | 4.50 |

St. Augustine of Canterbury & St. Columba of Iona — A483

Designs: 26p, St. Columba's journey across Irish Sea to Iona. 37p, St. Columba at work, Ionian Sea. 43p, St. Augustine baptizing King Ethelbert. 63p, St. Augustine outside Cathedral at Canterbury, Kent coastline.

**1997, Mar. 11   Photo.   Perf. 14½x14**
| | | | | |
|---|---|---|---|---|
| 1730 | A483 | 26p multicolored | 1.05 | .50 |
| 1731 | A483 | 37p multicolored | 1.50 | 1.10 |
| 1732 | A483 | 43p multicolored | 1.70 | 1.25 |
| 1733 | A483 | 63p multicolored | 2.50 | 1.60 |
| | | Nos. 1730-1733 (4) | 6.75 | 4.45 |

Stories and Legends — A484

Europa: 26p, Dracula. 31p, Frankenstein. 37p, Dr. Jekyll and Mr. Hyde. 43p, The Hound of the Baskervilles.

**1997, May 13   Photo.   Perf. 14x15**
| | | | | |
|---|---|---|---|---|
| 1754 | A484 | 26p multicolored | 1.05 | .45 |
| 1755 | A484 | 31p multicolored | 1.25 | 1.10 |
| 1756 | A484 | 37p multicolored | 1.50 | 1.25 |
| 1757 | A484 | 43p multicolored | 1.70 | 1.40 |
| | | Nos. 1754-1757 (4) | 5.50 | 4.20 |

Aircraft, Designers A485

20p, Supermarine Spitfire, R.J. Mitchell. 26p, Avro Lancaster, Roy Chadwick. 37p, DeHavilland Mosquito, R.E. Bishop. 43p,

Gloster Meteor, George Carter. 63p, Hawker Hunter, Sidney Camm.

**1997, June 10    Photo.    Perf. 15x14**
| | | | | |
|---|---|---|---|---|
| 1758 | A485 | 20p multicolored | .80 | .45 |
| a. | | Litho., perf. 14¼x14 (#2587b) ('08) | .75 | .35 |
| 1759 | A485 | 26p multicolored | 1.05 | .80 |
| 1760 | A485 | 37p multicolored | 1.50 | 1.10 |
| 1761 | A485 | 43p multicolored | 1.70 | 1.25 |
| 1762 | A485 | 63p multicolored | 2.50 | 1.60 |
| | | *Nos. 1758-1762 (5)* | 7.55 | 5.20 |

Issued: No. 1758a, 9/18/08.

All the Queen's Horses
A486

20p, 43p, Carriage horses from Royal Mews. 26p, 63p, Mount horses from Household Cavalry.

**1997, July 9    Litho.    Perf. 14x14½**
| | | | | |
|---|---|---|---|---|
| 1763 | A486 | 20p multicolored | .80 | .35 |
| 1764 | A486 | 26p multicolored | 1.05 | .80 |
| 1765 | A486 | 43p multicolored | 1.70 | 1.40 |
| 1766 | A486 | 63p multicolored | 2.50 | 1.75 |
| | | *Nos. 1763-1766 (4)* | 6.05 | 4.30 |

British Horse Society, 50th anniv.

Post Offices
A487

Designs: 20p, Haroldswick, Shetland Islands, Scotland. 26p, Painswick, Gloucestershire, England. 43p, Beddgelert, Gwynedd, Wales. 63p, Ballyroney, County Down, Northern Ireland.

**1997, Aug. 12    Litho.    Perf. 14½x14**
| | | | | |
|---|---|---|---|---|
| 1767 | A487 | 20p multicolored | .80 | .35 |
| 1768 | A487 | 26p multicolored | 1.05 | .80 |
| 1769 | A487 | 43p multicolored | 1.70 | 1.40 |
| 1770 | A487 | 63p multicolored | 2.50 | 1.75 |
| | | *Nos. 1767-1770 (4)* | 6.05 | 4.30 |

Enid Blyton, Author of Children's Stories, Birth Cent. — A488

Characters from books: 20p, "Noddy." 26p, "Famous Five." 37p, "Secret Seven." 43p, "Faraway Tree." 63p, "Malory Towers."

**1997, Sept. 9    Litho.    Perf. 14x14½**
| | | | | |
|---|---|---|---|---|
| 1771 | A488 | 20p multicolored | .80 | .25 |
| 1772 | A488 | 26p multicolored | 1.05 | .25 |
| 1773 | A488 | 37p multicolored | 1.50 | .85 |
| 1774 | A488 | 43p multicolored | 1.70 | 1.40 |
| 1775 | A488 | 63p multicolored | 2.50 | 1.75 |
| | | *Nos. 1771-1775 (5)* | 7.55 | 4.50 |

Christmas Crackers
A489

Designs: 2nd, Santa as Man in Moon sharing cracker with two children. 1st, Santa bursting through wrapping paper with cracker. 31p, Santa riding across sky on giant cracker. 43p, Santa on giant snowball holding cracker. 63p, Santa climbing into chimney with sack full of crackers.

**1997, Oct. 27    Photo.    Perf. 15x14**
| | | | | |
|---|---|---|---|---|
| 1776 | A489 | 2nd multicolored | .95 | .30 |
| a. | | Booklet pane of 20 | 19.00 | |
| 1777 | A489 | 1st multicolored | 1.35 | .35 |
| b. | | Sheet of 10 + 10 labels | 17.50 | |
| c. | | Sheet of 20 + 20 labels, litho., perf 14½x14 | 27.50 | |
| 1778 | A489 | 31p multicolored | 1.35 | .80 |
| 1779 | A489 | 43p multicolored | 1.70 | 1.25 |
| 1780 | A489 | 63p multicolored | 2.50 | 1.60 |
| | | *Nos. 1776-1780 (5)* | 7.85 | 4.30 |

Nos. 1776-1777 were sold for 20p and 26p, respectively, on day of issue.

No. 1777b issued 10/3/00. It sold for £2.95 and has labels that read "Seasons Greetings" and "Ho Ho Ho." Sheets with personalized labels were made available only to select Royal Post customers via mail order purchases, and sold for more.

No. 1777c issued 2003. It sold for £5.95 and had labels that could be personalized.

For booklet containing #1776a, see #BK1221.

Queen Elizabeth II, Prince Philip, 50th Wedding Anniv. A490

Designs: 20p, 43p, Wedding portrait, 1947. 26p, 63p, Anniversary portrait, 1997.

**1997, Nov. 13    Photo.    Perf. 15**
| | | | | |
|---|---|---|---|---|
| 1781 | A490 | 20p multicolored | .80 | .30 |
| 1782 | A490 | 26p multicolored | 1.05 | .55 |
| 1783 | A490 | 43p multicolored | 1.70 | 1.25 |
| 1784 | A490 | 63p multicolored | 2.50 | 1.60 |
| | | *Nos. 1781-1784 (4)* | 6.05 | 3.70 |

Endangered Species — A491

Designs: 20p, Common dormouse. 26p, Lady's slipper orchid. 31p, Song thrush. 37p, Shining ram's horn snail. 43p, Mole cricket. 63p, Devil's bolete.

**1998, Jan. 20    Litho.    Perf. 14x14½**
| | | | | |
|---|---|---|---|---|
| 1785 | A491 | 20p multicolored | .80 | .35 |
| 1786 | A491 | 26p multicolored | 1.05 | .45 |
| 1787 | A491 | 31p multicolored | 1.35 | .80 |
| 1788 | A491 | 37p multicolored | 1.50 | 1.10 |
| 1789 | A491 | 43p multicolored | 1.70 | 1.40 |
| 1790 | A491 | 63p multicolored | 2.50 | 1.75 |
| | | *Nos. 1785-1790 (6)* | 8.90 | 5.85 |

Diana, Princess of Wales (1961-97) — A492

Portraits of Diana wearing: No. 1791, Choker. No. 1792, Blue dress. No. 1793, Tiara. No. 1794, Checked dress. No. 1795, Black dress.

**1998, Feb. 3    Photo.    Perf. 14x15**
| | | | | |
|---|---|---|---|---|
| 1791 | A492 | 26p multicolored | 1.25 | .65 |
| 1792 | A492 | 26p multicolored | 1.25 | .65 |
| 1793 | A492 | 26p multicolored | 1.25 | .65 |
| 1794 | A492 | 26p multicolored | 1.25 | .65 |
| 1795 | A492 | 26p multicolored | 1.25 | .65 |
| a. | | Strip of 5, #1791-1795 | 6.25 | 6.00 |
| b. | | As "a," imperf. | | |

Order of the Garter, 650th Anniv.
A493

Queen's Beasts (supporters of Royal Arms created for Queen Elizabeth II's coronation in 1953): No. 1796, Lion of England, Griffin of Edward III. No. 1797, Falcon of Plantagenet, Bull of Clarence. No. 1798, Lion of Mortimer, Yale of Beaufort. No. 1799, Greyhound of Richmond, Dragon of Wales. No. 1800, Unicorn of Scotland, Horse of Hanover.

**Litho. & Engr.**
**1998, Feb. 24    Perf. 15x14**
| | | | | |
|---|---|---|---|---|
| 1796 | A493 | 26p multicolored | 1.05 | .65 |
| 1797 | A493 | 26p multicolored | 1.05 | .65 |
| 1798 | A493 | 26p multicolored | 1.05 | .65 |
| 1799 | A493 | 26p multicolored | 1.05 | .65 |
| 1800 | A493 | 26p multicolored | 1.05 | .65 |
| a. | | Strip of 5, #1796-1800 | 5.25 | 4.75 |

**Queen Type of 1952 with Face Values in Decimal Currency**
**Perf. 14 Syncopated**
**1998, Mar. 10    Litho.**
| | | | | |
|---|---|---|---|---|
| 1801 | A129 | 20p dk grn & lt grn | .80 | .50 |
| a. | | Booklet pane of 6 + printed margin (BK163) | 4.75 | |
| 1802 | A129 | 26p dk brn & lt brn | 1.05 | .80 |
| a. | | Booklet pane of 9 + printed margin (BK163) | 10.50 | |
| 1803 | A129 | 37p dk red lil & lt lil | 2.50 | 2.00 |
| a. | | Booklet pane 3 each #1802-1803 + printed margin (BK163) | 11.00 | |
| b. | | Booklet pane, 4 #1801, 2 ea #1802-1803 + printed margin (BK163) | 11.00 | |

Lighthouses
A494

**1998, Mar. 24    Perf. 14x14½**
| | | | | |
|---|---|---|---|---|
| 1804 | A494 | 20p St. John's Point | .80 | .30 |
| 1805 | A494 | 26p The Smalls | 1.05 | .55 |
| 1806 | A494 | 37p Needles Rocks | 1.50 | 1.10 |
| 1807 | A494 | 43p Bell Rock | 1.70 | 1.40 |
| 1808 | A494 | 63p Eddystone | 2.50 | 1.75 |
| | | *Nos. 1804-1808 (5)* | 7.55 | 5.10 |

Comedians
A495

20p, Tommy Cooper (1922-84). 26p, Eric Morecambe (1926-84). 37p, Joyce Grenfell (1910-79). 43p, Les Dawson (1933-93). 63p, Peter Cook (1937-95).

**1998, Apr. 23    Litho.    Perf. 14½x14**
| | | | | |
|---|---|---|---|---|
| 1809 | A495 | 20p multicolored | .80 | .35 |
| 1810 | A495 | 26p multicolored | 1.05 | .60 |
| 1811 | A495 | 37p multicolored | 1.50 | .80 |
| 1812 | A495 | 43p multicolored | 1.70 | 1.20 |
| 1813 | A495 | 63p multicolored | 2.50 | 1.60 |
| | | *Nos. 1809-1813 (5)* | 7.55 | 4.55 |

National Health Service, 50th Anniv. — A496

Designs: 20p, Hands forming heart, "10,000 donors give blood every day." 26p, Adult hand clasping child's, "1,700,000 prescriptions dispensed every day." 43p, Hands forming cradle, "2,000 babies delivered every day." 63p, Taking pulse, "130,000 hospital outpatients seen every day."

**1998, June 23    Litho.    Perf. 14x14½**
| | | | | |
|---|---|---|---|---|
| 1814 | A496 | 20p multicolored | .80 | .35 |
| 1815 | A496 | 26p multicolored | 1.05 | .60 |
| 1816 | A496 | 43p multicolored | 1.70 | 1.40 |
| 1817 | A496 | 63p multicolored | 2.50 | 1.75 |
| | | *Nos. 1814-1817 (4)* | 6.05 | 4.10 |

Magical World of Children's Literature
A496a

Stories depicted: 20p, "The Hobbit," by J.R.R. Tolkien. 26p, "The Lion, The Witch and the Wardrobe," by C.S. Lewis. 37p, "The Phoenix and the Carpet," by E. Nesbit. 43p, "The Borrowers," by Mary Norton. 63p, "Through the Looking Glass," by Lewis Carroll.

**1998, July 21    Photo.    Perf. 15x14**
| | | | | |
|---|---|---|---|---|
| 1820 | A496a | 20p multicolored | .80 | .35 |
| 1821 | A496a | 26p multicolored | 1.05 | .55 |
| 1822 | A496a | 37p multicolored | 1.50 | .80 |
| 1823 | A496a | 43p multicolored | 1.70 | 1.40 |
| 1824 | A496a | 63p multicolored | 2.50 | 1.75 |
| | | *Nos. 1820-1824 (5)* | 7.55 | 4.85 |

Notting Hill Carnival
A497

Expressionist photographic images of dancers, color of costumes: 20p, Yellow. 26p, Blue. 43p, Gold and white. 63p, Green.

**1998, Aug. 25    Perf. 14x14½**
| | | | | |
|---|---|---|---|---|
| 1825 | A497 | 20p multicolored | .80 | .35 |
| 1826 | A497 | 26p multicolored | 1.05 | .50 |
| 1827 | A497 | 43p multicolored | 1.70 | 1.20 |
| 1828 | A497 | 63p multicolored | 2.50 | 1.60 |
| | | *Nos. 1825-1828 (4)* | 6.05 | 3.65 |

Europa (#1825-1826).

Land Speed Records
A498

Car, driver, year, record speed: 20p, Bluebird, Sir Malcolm Campbell, 1925, 151 mph. 26p, Red Sunbeam, Sir Henry Segrave, 1926, 152 mph. 30p, Babs, John G. Parry Thomas, 1926, 171 mph. 43p, Railton Mobil Special, John R. Cobb, 1947, 394 mph. 63p, Bluebird CN7, Donald Campbell, 1964, 403 mph.

**1998, Sept. 29    Photo.    Perf. 15x14**
| | | | | |
|---|---|---|---|---|
| 1829 | A498 | 20p multicolored | .80 | .35 |
| a. | | Perf. 14½x13½ | 2.25 | 1.25 |
| b. | | As "a," booklet pane of 4 + printed margin (BK164) | 9.00 | |
| 1830 | A498 | 26p multicolored | 1.05 | .55 |
| 1831 | A498 | 30p multicolored | 1.20 | .80 |
| 1832 | A498 | 43p multicolored | 1.70 | 1.40 |
| 1833 | A498 | 63p multicolored | 2.50 | 1.75 |
| | | *Nos. 1829-1833 (5)* | 7.25 | 4.85 |

Christmas Angels
A499

**1998, Nov. 2    Photo.    Perf. 15x14**
| | | | | |
|---|---|---|---|---|
| 1834 | A499 | 20p shown | .80 | .25 |
| a. | | Booklet pane of 20 | 16.00 | |
| 1835 | A499 | 26p Praying | 1.05 | .25 |
| 1836 | A499 | 30p Playing flute | 1.20 | .80 |
| 1837 | A499 | 43p Playing lute | 1.70 | 1.40 |
| 1838 | A499 | 63p Praying, diff. | 2.50 | 1.75 |
| | | *Nos. 1834-1838 (5)* | 7.25 | 4.45 |

British Achievements During Past 1000 Years — A500

Inventions: 20p, Timekeeping, John Harrison's chronometer. 26p, Development of steam power. 43p, William Henry Fox Talbot's use of negatives to create photographs. 63p, Development of computers.

Transportation: 20p, Jet travel. 26p, Development of bicycle. 43p, Isambard Kingdom Brunel's Clifton Suspension Bridge, Great Western Railway. 63p, Capt. Cook's expeditions.

Health care: 20p, First smallpox vaccination, by Edward Jenner. 26p, Development of nursing care. 43p, Discovery of penicillin, by Alexander Fleming. 63p, First "test tube" baby (invitro fertilization), pioneered by Patrick Steptoe and Robert Edwards.

Emigration: 20p, Migration to Scotland. 26p, Pilgrim fathers. 43p, Destination Australia. 63p, Migration to UK.

Workers: 19p, Weavers. 26p, Mill towns. 44p, Ship building. 64p, City finance.

Entertainment and sports: 19p, Freddie Mercury, lead singer of Queen. 26p, Bobby Moore, 1966 World Cup Soccer Champions. 44p, Dalek from "Dr. Who" television series. 64p, Charlie Chaplin.

Citizens' Rights: 19p, Equal rights. 26p, Right to health. 44p, Right to learn. 64p, First rights.

Scientists: 19p, Decoding DNA. 26p, Darwin's theory. 44p, Faraday's electricity. 64p, Newton, Hubble Telescope.

Farmers: 19p, Strip farming (Europa). 26p, Mechanical farming. 44p, Food from afar. 64p, Satellite agriculture.

Soldiers: 19p, Battle of Bannockburn. 26p, Civil War. 44p, World Wars, cemetery. 64p, Peace keeping.

Christians: 19p, John Wesley (1703-91), founder of Methodism, and "Hark, The Herald Angels Sing," hymn by brother Charles (1707-88). 26p, King James Bible. 44p, St. Andrews Pilgrimage. 64p, First Christmas.

Artists: 19p, World of the stage. 26p, World of music. 44p, World of literature. 64p, New worlds.

**1999     Photo.     Perf. 14¼x14½**

**Inventions**

| | | | |
|---|---|---|---|
| 1839 | A500 20p multi (48) | .80 | .40 |
| 1840 | A500 26p multi (47) | 1.05 | .80 |
| 1841 | A500 43p multi (46) | 1.70 | 1.40 |
| 1842 | A500 63p multi (45) | 2.50 | 1.75 |
| a. | Perf. 13¾ | 4.25 | |
| b. | Booklet pane, 4 #1842a (BK165) | 17.00 | |

**Transportation**

| | | | |
|---|---|---|---|
| 1843 | A500 20p multi (44) | .80 | .40 |
| 1844 | A500 26p multi (43) | 1.05 | .80 |
| 1845 | A500 43p multi (42) | 1.70 | 1.40 |
| 1846 | A500 63p multi (41) | 2.50 | |

**Health Care**

*Perf. 13¾x14*

| | | | |
|---|---|---|---|
| 1847 | A500 20p multi (40) | .80 | .40 |
| a. | Booklet pane of 4 (BK165) | 3.25 | |
| 1848 | A500 26p multi (39) | 1.05 | .80 |
| 1849 | A500 43p multi (38) | 1.70 | 1.40 |
| 1850 | A500 63p multi (37) | 2.25 | 1.75 |

**Emigration**

*Perf. 14¼x14½*

| | | | |
|---|---|---|---|
| 1851 | A500 20p multi (36) | .80 | .40 |
| 1852 | A500 26p multi (35) | 1.05 | .80 |
| 1853 | A500 43p multi (34) | 1.70 | 1.40 |
| 1854 | A500 63p multi (33) | 2.50 | 1.75 |

**Workers**

*Perf. 14¼x14½*

| | | | |
|---|---|---|---|
| 1855 | A500 19p multi (32) | .75 | .40 |
| 1856 | A500 26p multi (31) | 1.05 | .80 |
| a. | Booklet pane, #1852, 1856 (BK1141) | 2.10 | |
| 1857 | A500 44p multi (30) | 1.75 | 1.40 |
| 1858 | A500 64p multi (29) | 2.60 | 1.75 |

**Entertainment & Sports**

*Perf. 14¼x14½*

| | | | |
|---|---|---|---|
| 1859 | A500 19p multi (28) | .75 | .40 |
| 1860 | A500 26p multi (27) | 1.05 | .80 |
| 1861 | A500 44p multi (26) | 1.75 | 1.40 |
| 1862 | A500 64p multi (25) | 2.60 | 1.75 |

**Citizen's Rights**

*Perf. 14¼x14½*

| | | | |
|---|---|---|---|
| 1863 | A500 19p multi (24) | .80 | .40 |
| 1864 | A500 26p multi (23) | 1.05 | .80 |
| 1865 | A500 44p multi (22) | 1.75 | 1.40 |
| 1866 | A500 64p multi (21) | 2.60 | 1.75 |

**Scientists**

*Perf. 14¼ (#1868-1869), 13¾ (#1867, 1870)*

| | | | |
|---|---|---|---|
| 1867 | A500 19p multi (20) | .75 | .40 |
| 1868 | A500 26p multi (19) | 1.05 | .80 |
| a. | Perf. 14¼x14 | 3.00 | 3.00 |
| b. | Booklet pane, 4 #1868a (BK165) | 12.00 | |
| 1869 | A500 44p multi (18) | 1.75 | 1.40 |
| a. | Perf. 14¼x14 | 4.00 | 4.00 |
| b. | Booklet pane, 4 #1869a (BK165) | 12.00 | |
| 1870 | A500 64p multi (17) | 2.60 | 1.75 |
| a. | Perf. 14¼ | 6.50 | 6.50 |
| b. | Souvenir sheet, 4 #1870a | 30.00 | 25.00 |

**Farmers**

*Perf. 14¼x14½*

| | | | |
|---|---|---|---|
| 1871 | A500 19p multi (16) | .75 | .40 |
| 1872 | A500 26p multi (15) | 1.05 | .80 |
| a. | Booklet pane of 2 (BK1142) | 2.10 | |
| 1873 | A500 44p multi (14) | 1.75 | 1.40 |
| 1874 | A500 64p multi (13) | 2.60 | 1.75 |

Europa, No. 1871.

**Soldiers**

*Perf. 14¼x14½*

| | | | |
|---|---|---|---|
| 1875 | A500 19p multi (12) | .75 | .40 |
| 1876 | A500 26p multi (11) | 1.05 | .80 |
| 1877 | A500 44p multi (10) | 1.75 | 1.40 |
| 1878 | A500 64p multi (9) | 2.60 | 1.75 |

**Christians**

| | | | |
|---|---|---|---|
| 1879 | A500 19p multi (8) | .75 | .40 |
| a. | Booklet pane of 20 | 15.00 | |
| 1880 | A500 26p multi (7) | 1.05 | .80 |
| 1881 | A500 44p multi (6) | 1.75 | 1.40 |
| 1882 | A500 64p multi (5) | 2.60 | 1.75 |

**Artists**

*Perf. 14¼x14½*

| | | | |
|---|---|---|---|
| 1883 | A500 19p multi (4) | .75 | .40 |
| 1884 | A500 26p multi (3) | 1.05 | .80 |
| 1885 | A500 44p multi (2) | 1.75 | 1.40 |
| 1886 | A500 64p multi (1) | 2.60 | 1.75 |
| | Nos. 1839-1886 (48) | 73.20 | 52.20 |

Issued: #1839-1842, 1/12; #1843-1846, 2/2; #1847-1850, 3/2; #1851-1854, 4/6; #1855-1858, 5/4; #1859-1862, 6/1; #1863-1866, 7/6; #1867-1870, 8/3; #1871-1874, 9/7; #1870b, 8/11; #1875-1878, 10/5; #1879-1882, 11/2; #1883-1886, 12/7.

See #1889, 1890-1929, 1938, 1942-1943.

Marriage of Prince Edward and Sophie Rhys-Jones — A501

**1999, June 15    Photo.    Perf. 15x14**

| | | | |
|---|---|---|---|
| 1887 | A501 26p shown | 1.05 | .80 |
| 1888 | A501 64p Profile portrait | 2.60 | 1.75 |

**Souvenir Sheet**

Millennium A502

Clock and globe showing: a, North America. b, Southeast Asia. c, Middle East. d, Europe.

*Perf. 14¼x14½*

**1999, Dec. 14     Photo.**

| | | | |
|---|---|---|---|
| 1889 | Sheet of 4 | 32.50 | 27.50 |
| a.-d. | A502 64p any single | 8.00 | 4.00 |

Millennium Projects A503

Above and Beyond: 19p, Barn owl's head, 3rd Millennium conservation projects, Muncaster. 26p, Night sky, National Space Center, Leicester. 44p, Buildings and waterfall, Torrs Walkway project, Derbyshire. 64p, Sea birds, Scottish Sea Bird Center.

Fire & Light: 19p, Beacon, Beacon Millennium project. 26p, Rheilffordd Eryri / Snowdonia, Welsh Highland Railway rebuilding project. 44p, Lightning bolt, Dynamic Earth project. 64p, Lights, Croydon Skyline project.

Water & Coast: 19p, Stones, Durham Coast restoration project. 26p, Frog, flowers, National Pondlife Center, conservation project. 44p, Parc Arfordirol project. 64p, Portsmouth Harbor project.

Life & Earth: 2nd, Wetlands, ECOS/Ballymena Project. 1st, Ants, Web of Life Exhibition at London Zoo. 44p, Solar cells, Earth Center, Doncaster. 64p, Plant leaves in water, Project SUZY, Teeside.

Art & Craft: 2nd, Ceramica project, Stoke-on-Trent. 1st, Tate Gallery of Modern Art, London. 45p, Cycle Network Artworks Project. 65p, The Lowry Arts Complex, Balford.

People & Place: 2nd, Millennium Greens project. 1st, Gateshead Millennium Bridge, Newcastle. 45p, Mile End Park, London. 65p, On the Line project.

Stone & Soil: 2nd, Raising of Strangford Stone, Killyleagh, Northern Ireland. 1st, Trans Pennine Trail project. 45p, Kingdom of Fife Cycle Ways project, Scotland. 65p, Changing Places project of Groundwork Foundation.

Tree & Leaf: 2nd, Yews for the Millennium project. 1st, Eden Project, St. Austell. 45p, Millennium Seed Bank project, Ardingly. 65p, Forest for Scotland project.

Mind & Matter: 2nd, Ant's head, Wildscreen at Bristol Project. 1st, People in rowboat, Norfolk and Norwich Project, Newport. 45p, X-ray image of hand and computer mouse, Millennium Point Project, Birmingham. 65p, Plaid globe, Scottish Cultural Resources Access Network.

Body & Bone: 2nd, Dancers, Millennium Dome project, Greenwich. 1st, Soccer players, Hampden Park project, Glasgow. 45p, Bath Spa project. 65p, Center for Life, Newcastle.

Spirit & Faith: 2nd, Stained glass window, St. Edmundsbury Cathedral project. 1st, Church floodlighting project. 45p, St. Patrick Center project, Downpatrick. 65p, York mystery plays.

Sound & Vision: 2nd, Bells, Ringing in the Millennium project. 1st, Eye, Year of the Artist. 45p, Harp, Camofym Millennium Center, Cardiff. 65p, TS2K Talent and Skills project.

**Photo., Litho. (#1892, 1900, 1911, 1913)**

**2000**

**Above & Beyond**

*Perf. 13¾x14, 14¼x14½ (#1892)*

| | | | |
|---|---|---|---|
| 1890 | A503 19p multi (1) | .75 | .40 |
| 1891 | A503 26p multi (2) | 1.05 | .80 |
| 1892 | A503 44p multi (3) | 1.75 | 1.40 |
| 1893 | A503 64p multi (4) | 2.60 | 1.75 |

*Perf. 14¼x14½*

**Fire & Light**

| | | | |
|---|---|---|---|
| 1894 | A503 19p multi (5) | .75 | .40 |
| 1895 | A503 26p multi (6) | 1.05 | .80 |
| 1896 | A503 44p multi (7) | 1.75 | 1.40 |
| 1897 | A503 64p multi (8) | 2.60 | 1.75 |

**Water & Coast**

| | | | |
|---|---|---|---|
| 1898 | A503 19p multi (9) | .75 | .40 |
| 1899 | A503 26p multi (10) | 1.05 | .80 |
| 1900 | A503 44p multi (11) | 1.75 | 1.40 |
| 1901 | A503 64p multi (12) | 2.60 | 1.75 |

**Life & Earth**

| | | | |
|---|---|---|---|
| 1902 | A503 2nd multi (13) | .95 | .40 |
| 1903 | A503 1st multi (14) | 1.35 | .80 |
| 1904 | A503 44p multi (15) | 1.75 | 1.40 |
| 1905 | A503 64p multi (16) | 2.60 | 1.75 |

**Art & Craft**

| | | | |
|---|---|---|---|
| 1906 | A503 2nd multi (17) | .95 | .40 |
| 1907 | A503 1st multi (18) | 1.35 | .80 |
| 1908 | A503 45p multi (19) | 1.80 | 1.40 |
| 1909 | A503 65p multi (20) | 2.60 | 1.75 |

**People & Place**

| | | | |
|---|---|---|---|
| 1910 | A503 2nd multi (21) | .95 | .40 |
| 1911 | A503 1st multi (22) | 1.35 | .80 |
| 1912 | A503 45p multi (23) | 1.80 | 1.40 |
| 1913 | A503 65p multi (24) | 2.60 | 1.75 |

**Stone & Soil**

| | | | |
|---|---|---|---|
| 1914 | A503 2nd multi (25) | .95 | .40 |
| 1915 | A503 1st multi (26) | 1.35 | .80 |
| 1916 | A503 45p multi (27) | 1.80 | 1.40 |
| 1917 | A503 65p multi (28) | 2.60 | 1.75 |
| a. | Booklet pane of 2 (BK169) | 5.25 | |

**Tree & Leaf**

| | | | |
|---|---|---|---|
| 1918 | A503 2nd multi (29) | .95 | .40 |
| a. | Bklt. pane of 4 (BK169) | 3.75 | |
| 1919 | A503 1st multi (30) | 1.35 | .80 |
| a. | Bklt. pane, #1915, 1919 (BK1202) | 2.70 | |
| 1920 | A503 45p multi (31) | 1.80 | 1.40 |
| a. | Bklt. pane of 4 (BK169) | 8.00 | |
| 1921 | A503 65p multi (32) | 2.60 | 1.75 |
| a. | Bklt. pane of 2 (BK169) | 5.25 | |

**Mind & Matter**

**Litho.**

| | | | |
|---|---|---|---|
| 1922 | A503 2nd multi (33) | .95 | .40 |
| 1923 | A503 1st multi (34) | 1.35 | .80 |
| 1924 | A503 45p multi (35) | 1.80 | 1.40 |
| 1925 | A503 65p multi (36) | 2.60 | 1.75 |

**Body & Bone**

| | | | |
|---|---|---|---|
| 1926 | A503 2nd multi (37) | .95 | .40 |

**Photo.**

*Perf. 13¾*

| | | | |
|---|---|---|---|
| 1927 | A503 1st multi (38) | 1.35 | .80 |
| 1928 | A503 45p multi (39) | 1.80 | 1.40 |
| 1929 | A503 65p multi (40) | 2.60 | 1.75 |

*Perf. 14¼*

**Spirit & Faith**

| | | | |
|---|---|---|---|
| 1930 | A503 2nd multi (41) | .95 | .40 |
| a. | Bklt. pane of 20 (BK1211) | 19.00 | |
| 1931 | A503 1st multi (42) | 1.35 | .80 |
| 1932 | A503 45p multi (43) | 1.80 | 1.40 |
| 1933 | A503 65p multi (44) | 2.60 | 1.75 |

**Sound & Vision**

| | | | |
|---|---|---|---|
| 1934 | A503 2nd multi (45) | .95 | .40 |
| 1935 | A503 1st multi (46) | 1.35 | .80 |
| 1936 | A503 45p multi (47) | 1.80 | 1.40 |
| 1937 | A503 65p multi (48) | 2.60 | 1.75 |
| | Nos. 1890-1937 (48) | 78.70 | 52.20 |

#1902, 1906, 1910, 1914, 1918, 1922, 1926, 1930, 1934 sold for 19p; #1903, sold for 26p; #1907, 1911, 1915, 1919, 1923, 1927, 1931, 1935 sold for 27p on day of issue.

Issued: #1890-1893, 1/18; #1894-1897, 2/1; #1898-1901, 3/7; #1902-1905, 4/4; #1906-1909, 5/2; #1910-1913, 6/6; #1914-1917, 7/4; #1918-1921, 8/1; #1917a-1921a, 9/18; #1922-1925, 9/5; #1926-1929, 10/3; #1930-1933, 11/7; #1934-1937, 12/5.

**2000-02    Photo.    Perf. 14¼x14½**

| | | | |
|---|---|---|---|
| 1938 | A503 (1st) Like #1891 | 7.50 | 5.00 |
| a. | Booklet pane, #1903, 1938 (BK1201) | 9.00 | |
| b. | Booklet pane of 4 (BK172) | 30.00 | |

Issued: No. 1938, 5/26. No. 1938b, 9/24/02.

Nos. 1938 sold for 27p on day of issue, and was issued only in booklets.

**Types of 1953 and 2000**

Stamp Show 2000, London — A503a

**Souvenir Sheet**

**2000, May 23    Photo.    Perf. 14¾x14**

| | | | |
|---|---|---|---|
| 1942 | Sheet, #1942a, 4 #MH335 | 25.00 | 25.00 |
| a. | A136 £1 dark green | 20.00 | 17.50 |

**Souvenir Sheet**

Queen Mother's 100th Birthday — A504

Designs: a, Queen Elizabeth II. b, Prince William. c, Queen Mother. d, Prince Charles. Illustration reduced.

**2000, Aug. 4    Photo.    Perf. 14½**

| | | | |
|---|---|---|---|
| 1943 | A504 Sheet of 4 | 11.00 | 11.00 |
| a.-d. | 27p Any single | 1.10 | .50 |
| e. | Booklet pane, #1943 with silver border (BK168) | 11.00 | 11.00 |
| f. | Booklet pane, 4 #1943c (BK168) | 5.00 | |

Millennium 2001 A505

Painted faces of children: 2nd, Flower. 1st, Tiger. 45p, Owl. 65p, Butterfly.

**Perf. 14¼x14½**

| | | | Photo. | |
|---|---|---|---|---|
| **2001, Jan. 16** | | | | |
| 1944 | A505 | 2nd multi | .95 | .50 |
| 1945 | A505 | 1st multi | 1.35 | .90 |
| 1946 | A505 | 45p multi | 1.80 | 1.40 |
| 1947 | A505 | 65p multi | 2.60 | 1.75 |
| | | *Nos. 1944-1947 (4)* | 6.70 | 4.55 |

Stamps inscribed "2nd" and "1st" sold for 19p and 27p respectively on day of issue.

Greetings
A506

| | | | Photo. | Perf. 14¼ |
|---|---|---|---|---|
| **2001, Feb. 6** | | | | |
| 1948 | A506 | 1st shown | 1.35 | .70 |
| 1949 | A506 | 1st Cheers | 1.35 | .70 |
| 1950 | A506 | 1st Love | 1.35 | .70 |
| 1951 | A506 | 1st Thanks | 1.35 | .70 |
| 1952 | A506 | 1st Welcome | 1.35 | .70 |
| *a.* | | Sheet, 4 vert. strips #1948-1952 + 20 labels, litho. | 27.50 | 25.00 |
| | | *Nos. 1948-1952 (5)* | 6.75 | 3.50 |

Nos. 1948-1952 each sold for 27p on day of issue.

No. 1952a issued 6/5/01. No. 1952a sold for £5.95.

A sheet containing 7 #1949 and 3 #1951 + 10 labels depicting Spiderman was specially produced for stamp dealers.

Dogs and Cats
A507

Designs: No. 1953, Dog and man on park bench. No. 1954, Dog in bathtub. No. 1955, Dog looking over carrel. No. 1956, Cat in handbag. No. 1957, Cat on fence. No. 1958, Dog in automobile. No. 1959, Cat in curtained window. No. 1960, Dog looking over fence. No. 1961, Cat looking at bird through window. No. 1962, Cat in sink.

**2001, Feb. 13    Die Cut Perf. 14½x14**
**Self- Adhesive**
**Booklet Stamps**

| 1953 | A507 | 1st blk & sil | 1.50 | 1.00 |
|---|---|---|---|---|
| 1954 | A507 | 1st blk & sil | 1.50 | 1.00 |
| 1955 | A507 | 1st blk & sil | 1.50 | 1.00 |
| 1956 | A507 | 1st blk & sil | 1.50 | 1.00 |
| 1957 | A507 | 1st blk & sil | 1.50 | 1.00 |
| 1958 | A507 | 1st blk & sil | 1.50 | 1.00 |
| 1959 | A507 | 1st blk & sil | 1.50 | 1.00 |
| 1960 | A507 | 1st blk & sil | 1.50 | 1.00 |
| 1961 | A507 | 1st blk & sil | 1.50 | 1.00 |
| 1962 | A507 | 1st blk & sil | 1.50 | 1.00 |
| *a.* | | Booklet, #1953-1962 | 15.00 | |
| *b.* | | Booklet, #1953-1962, 2 #MH297 | 32.50 | |
| | | *Nos. 1953-1962 (10)* | 15.00 | 10.00 |

Nos. 1953-1962 each sold for 27p on day of issue.

The Weather
A508

Designs: 19p, Rain. 27p, Fair. 45p, Much rain, storms. 65p, Very dry, set fair.

**Perf. 14¼x14½**

| | | | Photo. | |
|---|---|---|---|---|
| **2001, Mar. 13** | | | | |
| 1963 | A508 | 19p multi | .75 | .40 |
| 1964 | A508 | 27p multi | 1.10 | .80 |
| 1965 | A508 | 45p multi | 1.80 | 1.40 |
| 1966 | A508 | 65p multi | 2.60 | 1.75 |
| *a.* | | Souvenir sheet, #1963-1966 | 20.00 | 14.00 |
| | | *Nos. 1963-1966 (4)* | 6.25 | 4.35 |

Purple cloud at bottom of No. 1964 is printed with thermochromic ink and changes color when warmed.

Submarines — A509

Designs: 2nd, Vanguard Class, 1992. 1st, Swiftsure Class, 1973. 45p, Unity Class, 1939. 65p, Holland Class, 1901.

| **2001** | | | Photo. | Perf. 14¾x14 |
|---|---|---|---|---|
| 1967 | A509 | 2nd multi | .95 | .40 |
| *a.* | | Perf. 15¼x14¾ | 5.00 | 5.00 |
| 1968 | A509 | 1st multi | 1.35 | .80 |
| *a.* | | Perf. 15¼x14¾ | 5.00 | 4.00 |
| 1969 | A509 | 45p multi | 1.80 | 1.25 |
| *a.* | | Perf. 15¼x14¾ | 5.00 | 4.00 |
| *b.* | | Booklet pane, 2 each #1967a, 1969a (BK170) | 12.00 | |
| 1970 | A509 | 65p multi | 2.60 | 1.60 |
| *a.* | | Perf. 15¼x14¾ | 5.00 | 4.00 |
| *b.* | | Booklet pane, 2 each #1968a, 1970a (BK170) | 20.00 | |
| | | *Nos. 1967-1970 (4)* | 6.70 | 4.05 |

**Self-Adhesive**
**Die Cut Perf. 15½x14¼**

| 1971 | A509 | 1st multi | 60.00 | 30.00 |
|---|---|---|---|---|
| *a.* | | Booklet, 2 #1971, 4 #MH298 | 125.00 | |

Issued: Nos. 1967-1970, 4/10; No. 1971, 4/17; No. 1967a, 1968a, 1969a, 1970a, 10/22/01.

On day of issue No. 1967 sold for 19p and Nos. 1968 and 1971 sold for 27p.

Buses
A510

Designs: No. 1972, Blue and red Leyland X-type (half), London General (#11), yellow green and orange Leyland Titan, dark green and yellow AEC Regent I (half). No. 1973, AEC Regent I (half), Daimler COG5 (#8), Guy Arab Mk II (#51), green and yellow AEC Regent (half). No. 1974, AEC Regent (half), Bristol KSW 5G (#68), AEC Routemaster (#21), red and yellow Bristol Lodekka (half). No. 1975, Bristol Lodekka (half), Leyland Titan (#12B), Leyland Atlantean (#53X), red and yellow Daimler Fleetline (half). No. 1976, Daimler Fleetline (half), MCW Metrobus (#770), Leyland Olympian (#12), red and blue Dennis Trident (half).

| **2001, May 15** | | | Photo. | Perf. 14¼x14 |
|---|---|---|---|---|
| 1972 | A510 | 1st multi | 1.35 | .90 |
| 1973 | A510 | 1st multi | 1.35 | .90 |
| 1974 | A510 | 1st multi | 1.35 | .90 |
| 1975 | A510 | 1st multi | 1.35 | .90 |
| 1976 | A510 | 1st multi | 1.35 | .90 |
| *a.* | | Horiz. strip, #1972-1976 | 6.75 | 5.75 |
| *b.* | | Souvenir sheet, #1972-1976 | 12.50 | 10.00 |

Nos. 1972-1976 each sold for 27p on day of issue.

Women's Hats — A511

Hats designed by: 1st, Pip Hackett. E, Dai Rees. 45p, Stephen Jones. 65p, Philip Treacy.

**Perf. 14½x14¼**

| **2001, June 19** | | | Litho. | |
|---|---|---|---|---|
| 1977 | A511 | 1st multi | 1.35 | .60 |
| 1978 | A511 | E multi | 1.90 | 1.20 |
| 1979 | A511 | 45p multi | 1.80 | 1.40 |
| 1980 | A511 | 65p multi | 2.60 | 1.75 |
| | | *Nos. 1977-1980 (4)* | 7.65 | 4.95 |

Nos. 1977 and 1978 sold for 27p and 36p respectively on day of issue.

Europa
A512

| **2001, July 10** | | Photo. | Perf. 14¾x14 | |
|---|---|---|---|---|
| 1981 | A512 | 1st Frog | 1.35 | .60 |
| 1982 | A512 | E Great diving beetle | 1.90 | 1.20 |
| 1983 | A512 | 45p Stickleback | 1.80 | 1.40 |
| 1984 | A512 | 65p Dragonfly | 2.60 | 1.75 |
| | | *Nos. 1981-1984 (4)* | 7.65 | 4.95 |

Nos. 1981 and 1982 sold for 27p and 36p respectively on day of issue.

Puppets — A513

| **2001, Sept. 4** | | Photo. | Perf. 14x15 | |
|---|---|---|---|---|
| 1985 | A513 | 1st Policeman | 1.35 | .80 |
| 1986 | A513 | 1st Clown | 1.35 | .80 |
| 1987 | A513 | 1st Punch | 1.35 | .80 |
| 1988 | A513 | 1st Judy | 1.35 | .80 |
| 1989 | A513 | 1st Beadle | 1.35 | .80 |
| 1990 | A513 | 1st Crocodile | 1.35 | .80 |
| *a.* | | Horiz. strip of 6, #1985-1990 | 8.00 | 6.00 |
| | | *Nos. 1985-1990 (6)* | 8.10 | 4.80 |

**Booklet Stamps**
**Self-Adhesive**
**Die Cut Perf. 14x15½**

| 1991 | A513 | 1st Punch | 12.50 | 10.00 |
|---|---|---|---|---|
| 1992 | A513 | 1st Judy | 12.50 | 10.00 |
| *a.* | | Booklet, Nos. 1991-1992, 4 #MH298 | 30.00 | |

Nos. 1985-1992 sold for 27p on day of issue.

Nobel Prizes, Cent. — A514

Items symbolic of prize categories: 2nd, Carbon 60 molecule (Chemistry). 1st, Globe (Economics). E, Dove (Peace). 40p, Crosses (Physiology or Medicine). 45p, The Addressing of Cats, by T.S. Eliot (Literature). 65p, Boron atom (Physics).

| **2001, Oct. 2** | | Photo. | Perf. 14½x14¼ | |
|---|---|---|---|---|
| 1993 | A514 | 2nd multi | .95 | .50 |

**Photo. & Engr.**

| 1994 | A514 | 1st multi | 1.35 | .65 |
|---|---|---|---|---|

**Photo. & Embossed**

| 1995 | A514 | E multi | 1.90 | .90 |
|---|---|---|---|---|

**Photo.**

| 1996 | A514 | 40p multi | 1.60 | .65 |
|---|---|---|---|---|
| 1997 | A514 | 45p multi | 1.80 | 1.40 |

**Photo. With Hologram Affixed**

| 1998 | A514 | 65p multi | 2.60 | 1.75 |
|---|---|---|---|---|
| | | *Nos. 1993-1998 (6)* | 10.20 | 5.85 |

Nos. 1993-1995 each sold for 19p, 27p and 37p respectively on day of issue. Molecule on No. 1993 is covered with a thermochromic film that changes color when warmed. No. 1996 has a scrach and sniff coating with a eucalyptus odor. Soaking in water may affect holographic images.

Flags — A515

Designs: Nos. 1999a, 2001, White ensign. No. 1999b, Union flag. Nos. 1999c, 2000, Jolly Roger. No. 1999d, Flag of the Chief of the Defense Staff.

| **2001, Oct. 22** | | Photo. | Perf. 14¾ | |
|---|---|---|---|---|
| **Miniature Sheet** | | | | |
| 1999 | A515 | Sheet of 4 | 12.00 | 10.00 |
| *a.-d.* | | 1st Any single | 3.00 | 1.50 |
| *e.* | | Booklet pane, #1999 + selvage at L (BK170) | 12.00 | |
| *f.* | | Sheet of 20 #1999b + 20 labels, litho. | 60.00 | — |
| *g.* | | Sheet of 20 #1999a + 20 labels, litho. | 30.00 | — |
| *h.* | | Booklet pane of 3 #1999a, litho. (BK178) | 4.75 | |
| *i.* | | Booklet pane of 4, 2 each #1999a, 1999b, litho. (BK184) | 5.50 | |

**Booklet Stamps**
**Self-Adhesive**
**Die Cut Perf. 14¾**

| 2000 | A515 | 1st multi | 12.50 | 9.00 |
|---|---|---|---|---|
| 2001 | A515 | 1st multi | 12.50 | 9.00 |
| *a.* | | Booklet, #2000-2001, 4 #MH298 | 32.50 | |

Nos. 1999a-1999d, 2000-2001 each sold for 27p on day of issue. The left edge of No. 1999 is straight while rouletting separates the selvage from the sheet on No. 1999e.

No. 1999f issued 2004. It sold for £14.95 and has labels that can be personalized.
No. 1999h issued 10/18/2005. No. 1999i issued 1/8/08.

Christmas
A516

Robins and: 2nd, Snowman. 1st, Birdhouse. E, Birdbath. 45p, Suet ball. 65p, Nest.

**Die Cut Perf. 14¼x14½**

| **2001, Nov. 6** | | | Photo. | |
|---|---|---|---|---|
| **Self-Adhesive** | | | | |
| 2002 | A516 | 2nd multi | .95 | .25 |
| *a.* | | Booklet of 24 | 23.00 | |
| *b.* | | Sheet of 20 + 20 labels, litho. | 35.00 | — |
| 2003 | A516 | 1st multi | 1.35 | .25 |
| *a.* | | Booklet of 12 | 16.50 | |
| *b.* | | Sheet of 20 + 20 labels, litho. | 27.50 | |
| *c.* | | Sheet, 10 each #2002-2003 +20 labels, litho. | 27.50 | — |
| 2004 | A516 | E multi | 1.90 | 1.00 |
| 2005 | A516 | 45p multi | 1.80 | 1.40 |
| 2006 | A516 | 65p multi | 2.60 | 1.75 |
| | | *Nos. 2002-2006 (5)* | 8.60 | 4.65 |

Nos. 2002-2004 each sold for 19p, 27p, and 37p respectively on day of issue.
Issued: No. 2003b, 9/30/03. No. 2003b sold for £6.15 and had labels that could be personalized.
Issued: No. 2202b, 2203c, 2005. No. 2002b sold for £9.95 and had labels that could be personalized. No. 2003c sold for £5.60.

Just So Stories, by Rudyard Kipling, Cent. A517

Designs: No. 2007, How the Whale Got His Throat (whale in bed). No. 2008, How the Camel Got His Hump (genie, camel). No. 2009, How the Rhinoceros Got His Skin (man in palm tree, rhinoceros). No. 2010, How the Leopard Got His Spots (man putting spots on leopard). No. 2011, The Elephant's Child (crocodile, elephant, snake). No. 2012, The Sing-song of Old Man Kangaroo (dog chasing kangaroo). No. 2013, The Beginning of the Armadilloes (jaguar, armadillo). No. 2014, The Crab That Played With the Sea (people in boat, giant crab). No. 2015, The Cat That Walked by Himself (people, dog, cat and shadow in cave). No. 2016, The Butterfly That Stamped (castle, giant butterfly).

### Serpentine Die Cut 14½x14

**2002, Jan. 15**        **Photo.**

#### Booklet Stamps
#### Self-Adhesive

| | | | | |
|---|---|---|---|---|
| 2007 | A517 | 1st multi | 1.35 | .85 |
| 2008 | A517 | 1st multi | 1.35 | .85 |
| 2009 | A517 | 1st multi | 1.35 | .85 |
| 2010 | A517 | 1st multi | 1.35 | .85 |
| 2011 | A517 | 1st multi | 1.35 | .85 |
| 2012 | A517 | 1st multi | 1.35 | .85 |
| 2013 | A517 | 1st multi | 1.35 | .85 |
| 2014 | A517 | 1st multi | 1.35 | .85 |
| 2015 | A517 | 1st multi | 1.35 | .85 |
| 2016 | A517 | 1st multi | 1.35 | .85 |
| a. | | Booklet, #2007-2016 | 13.50 | |

Nos. 2007-2016 each sold for 27p on day of issue. Titles of stories are not on stamps, but in margin.

Reign of Queen Elizabeth II, 50th Anniv. — A518

Photographs of Queen by: 2nd, Dorothy Wilding, 1952. 1st, Cecil Beaton, 1968. E, Lord Snowdon, 1978, 45p, Yousef Karsh, 1984. 65p, Tim Graham, 1996.

### Perf. 14½x14¼

**2002, Feb. 6**    **Photo.**    **Wmk. 401**

| | | | | |
|---|---|---|---|---|
| 2017 | A518 | 2nd blk & sil | .95 | .50 |
| 2018 | A518 | 1st blk & sil | 1.35 | .85 |
| 2019 | A518 | E blk & sil | 1.90 | .90 |
| 2020 | A518 | 45p blk & sil | 1.80 | 1.40 |
| a. | | Booklet pane, #2017-2020 (BK171) | 6.00 | — |
| 2021 | A518 | 65p blk & sil | 2.60 | 1.75 |
| a. | | Booklet pane, #2018-2021 (BK171) | 7.75 | — |
| | | Nos. 2017-2021 (5) | 8.60 | 5.40 |

Nos. 2017-2019 each sold for 19p, 27p, and 37p respectively on day of issue.

### Queen Types of 1952
### Tan Surface-colored Paper

### Perf. 14¾x14 Syncopated

**2002, Feb. 6**    **Photo.**    **Wmk. 401**

| | | | | |
|---|---|---|---|---|
| 2022 | A127 | 2nd red | 1.50 | 1.00 |
| 2023 | A126 | 1st green | 1.75 | 1.50 |
| a. | | Booklet pane, 5 #2022, 4 #2023, + label (BK171) | 14.50 | — |

Nos. 2022 and 2023 sold for 19p and 27p respectively on day of issue.

A New Baby A519

Hello A520

Moving A521

Best Wishes A522

Love A523

### Perf. 14¾x14

**2002-3**    **Litho.**    **Unwmk.**

| | | | | |
|---|---|---|---|---|
| 2024 | A519 | 1st multi | 1.35 | .60 |
| a. | | Perf. 14¼ + label | 2.50 | 2.50 |
| 2025 | A520 | 1st multi | 1.35 | .60 |
| a. | | Perf. 14¼ + label | 2.50 | 2.50 |
| 2026 | A521 | 1st multi | 1.35 | .60 |
| a. | | Perf. 14¼ + label | 2.50 | 2.50 |
| 2027 | A522 | 1st multi | 1.35 | .60 |
| a. | | Perf. 14¼ + label | 2.50 | 2.50 |
| 2028 | A523 | 1st multi | 1.35 | .65 |
| a. | | Perf. 14¼ + label | 2.50 | 2.50 |
| c. | | Sheet of 20, 4 each #2024-2028, + 20 labels, perf. 14¼ | — | — |
| | | Nos. 2024-2028 (5) | 6.75 | 3.05 |

#### Self-Adhesive
#### Booklet Stamp
#### Die Cut Perf. 14¾x14

| | | | | |
|---|---|---|---|---|
| 2028A | A520 | 1st multi | 6.00 | .65 |
| b. | | Booklet pane, 2 #2028A, 4 #MH300 | 15.00 | |

Nos. 2024-2028A each sold for 27p on day of issue.

Nos. 2024a-2028a each sold for £14.95 and have labels that can be personalized. No. 2028c sold for £5.95.

Sheets of No. 2025a with a Washington 2006 World Philatelic Exhibition margin and labels sold for £6.95. Value $27.50.

Issued, Nos. 2024-2028, 3/5/02; No. 2028c, 4/23/02; Nos. 2024a-2028a, 2002; No. 2028A, 3/4/03.

Aerial Photographs of Coastline A524

**2002, Mar. 19**     **Perf. 14¼x14½**

| | | | | |
|---|---|---|---|---|
| 2029 | A524 | 27p Studland Bay | 1.10 | .80 |
| 2030 | A524 | 27p Luskentyre | 1.10 | .80 |
| 2031 | A524 | 27p Dover | 1.10 | .80 |
| 2032 | A524 | 27p Padstow | 1.10 | .80 |
| 2033 | A524 | 27p Broadstairs | 1.10 | .80 |
| 2034 | A524 | 27p St. Abb's Head | 1.10 | .80 |
| 2035 | A524 | 27p Dunster Beach | 1.10 | .80 |
| 2036 | A524 | 27p Newquay | 1.10 | .80 |
| 2037 | A524 | 27p Portrush | 1.10 | .80 |
| 2038 | A524 | 27p Conwy | 1.10 | .80 |
| a. | | Block of 10, #2029-2038 | 11.00 | 10.00 |

Circus — A525

Designs: 2nd, High wire performer. 1st, Lion tamer. E, Trick tricyclists. 45p, Krazy kar. 65p, Equestrienne.

**2002, Apr. 9**    **Photo.**    **Perf. 14¼x14½**

| | | | | |
|---|---|---|---|---|
| 2039 | A525 | 2nd multi | .95 | .50 |
| 2040 | A525 | 1st multi | 1.35 | .80 |
| 2041 | A525 | E multi | 1.90 | 1.00 |
| 2042 | A525 | 45p multi | 1.80 | 1.40 |
| 2043 | A525 | 65p multi | 2.60 | 1.75 |
| | | Nos. 2039-2043 (5) | 8.60 | 5.45 |

Europa (Nos. 2040-2041). Nos. 2039-2041 sold for 19p, 27p and 37p respectively on day of issue.

First day covers of Nos. 2039-2043 bear an April 9, 2001, date, but the issue of the stamps was delayed until April 10 due to the funeral of the Queen Mother.

Queen Mother (1900-2002) A526

**2002, Apr. 25**     **Perf. 14x14¾**

| | | | | |
|---|---|---|---|---|
| 2044 | A526 | 1st 1990 photo | 1.35 | .80 |
| 2045 | A526 | E 1948 photo | 1.90 | 1.00 |
| 2046 | A526 | 45p 1930 photo | 1.80 | 1.40 |
| 2047 | A526 | 65p 1907 photo | 2.60 | 1.75 |
| | | Nos. 2044-2047 (4) | 7.65 | 4.95 |

Nos. 2044-2045 sold for 27p and 37p respectively on day of issue. Compare with Type A387.

Jet Aircraft — A527

Designs: 2nd, Airbus A340-600, 2002. 1st, Concorde, 1976. E, Trident, 1964. 45p, VC10, 1964. 65p, Comet, 1952.

**2002, May 2**     **Perf. 14½**

| | | | | |
|---|---|---|---|---|
| 2048 | A527 | 2nd multi | .95 | .50 |
| 2049 | A527 | 1st multi | 1.35 | .80 |
| a. | | Litho. (#2619a) ('09) | 1.10 | .55 |
| 2050 | A527 | E multi | 1.90 | 1.00 |
| 2051 | A527 | 45p multi | 1.80 | 1.40 |
| 2052 | A527 | 65p multi | 2.60 | 1.75 |
| a. | | Souvenir sheet, #2048-2052 | 12.00 | 9.00 |
| | | Nos. 2048-2052 (5) | 8.60 | 5.45 |

#### Booklet Stamp
#### Self-Adhesive
#### Die Cut Perf. 14½

| | | | | |
|---|---|---|---|---|
| 2053 | A527 | 1st multi | 6.00 | 5.00 |
| a. | | Booklet, 2 #2053, 4 #MH297 | 16.00 | |

Nos. 2048-2052 sold for 19p, 27p and 37p respectively on day of issue.

No. 2049a issued 1/13/09. No. 2049a sold for 36p on day of issue.

A528

2002 World Cup Soccer Championships, Japan and Korea — A529

Soccer ball and: Nos. 2056a, 2057, Upper left portion of English flag. Nos. 2056b, 2058, Upper right portion of English flag. No. 2056c, Lower left portion of English flag. Nos. 2055, 2056d, Lower right portion of English flag.

#### Photo., Litho. (#2055)

**2002, May 21**     **Perf. 14¼**

| | | | | |
|---|---|---|---|---|
| 2054 | A528 | 1st multi | 1.80 | 1.50 |
| 2055 | A529 | 1st dull blue & multi | 1.80 | 1.50 |

#### Souvenir Sheet

| | | | | |
|---|---|---|---|---|
| 2056 | | Sheet, #2054, #2056a-2056d | 9.00 | 9.00 |
| a.-d. | A529 | 1st deep blue & multi, perf. 14¾x14, any single | 1.80 | 1.50 |

### Booklet Stamps
### Die Cut Perf. 14¾x14
### Self-Adhesive

| | | | | |
|---|---|---|---|---|
| 2057 | A529 | 1st deep blue & multi | 7.00 | 3.50 |
| 2058 | A529 | 1st deep blue & multi | 7.00 | 3.50 |
| a. | | Booklet, #2057, 2058, 4 #MH298 | 17.50 | |

Nos. 2054, 2056a-2056d, 2057-2058 sold for 27p on day of sale. No. 2055 was issued only in sheets of 20 stamps + 16 labels that sold for £5.95, and which could have the labels personalized for an additional fee.

17th Commonwealth Games, Manchester — A530

Designs: 2nd, Swimming. 1st, Running. E, Cycling. 47p, Long jump. 68p, Wheelchair racing.

### Perf. 14¾x14¼

**2002, July 16**     **Photo.**

| | | | | |
|---|---|---|---|---|
| 2059 | A530 | 2nd multi | .95 | .35 |
| 2060 | A530 | 1st multi | 1.35 | .55 |
| 2061 | A530 | E multi | 1.90 | 1.00 |
| 2062 | A530 | 47p multi | 1.90 | 1.00 |
| 2063 | A530 | 68p multi | 2.70 | 1.40 |
| | | Nos. 2059-2063 (5) | 8.80 | 4.30 |

Nos. 2059-2061 each sold for 19p, 27p and 37p respectively on day of issue.

Peter Pan, by J. M. Barrie, 150th Anniv. A531

Designs: 2nd, Tinkerbell. 1st, Darling children. E, Crocodile and clock. 47p, Captain Hook. 68p, Peter Pan.

### Perf. 14¾x14¼

**2002, Aug. 20**     **Photo.**

| | | | | |
|---|---|---|---|---|
| 2064 | A531 | 2nd multi | .95 | .35 |
| 2065 | A531 | 1st multi | 1.35 | .55 |
| 2066 | A531 | E multi | 1.90 | 1.00 |
| 2067 | A531 | 47p multi | 1.90 | 1.00 |
| 2068 | A531 | 68p multi | 2.70 | 1.40 |
| | | Nos. 2064-2068 (5) | 8.80 | 4.30 |

Nos. 2064-2066 each sold for 19p, 27p and 37p respectively on day of issue.

Thames River Bridges in London A532

**2002, Sept. 10**    **Litho.**    **Perf. 14¾x14**

| | | | | |
|---|---|---|---|---|
| 2069 | A532 | 2nd Millennium | 1.25 | .35 |
| 2070 | A532 | 1st Tower | 1.50 | .55 |
| 2071 | A532 | E Westminster | 2.25 | 1.00 |
| 2072 | A532 | 47p Blackfriars | 2.25 | 1.00 |
| 2073 | A532 | 68p London | 3.00 | 1.40 |
| | | Nos. 2069-2073 (5) | 10.25 | 4.30 |

#### Booklet Stamp
#### Serpentine Die Cut 14¾x14

| | | | | |
|---|---|---|---|---|
| 2074 | A532 | 1st Tower | 7.50 | 6.00 |
| a. | | Booklet, 2 #2074, 4 #MH300 | 19.00 | |

Nos. 2070 and 2074 sold for 27p; Nos. 2069, 2071 sold for 19p and 37p respectively on day of sale.

## Souvenir Sheet

Astronomy — A533

No. 2075: a, Planetary nebula in Aquila. b, Seyfert 2 galaxy in Pegasus. c, Planetary nebula in Norma. d, Seyfert 2 galaxy in Circinus.

**Perf. 14¾x14¼**

| | | | | |
|---|---|---|---|---|
| 2002, Sept. 24 | | | **Photo.** | |
| 2075 | A533 | Sheet of 4 | 6.00 | 5.00 |
| a.-d. | | (1st) Any single | 1.50 | .75 |
| e. | | Booklet pane, #2075, rouletted at left (BK172) | 5.50 | |

Nos. 2075a-2075d each sold for 27p on day of issue.

Pillar Boxes, 150th Anniv. — A534

Designs: 2nd, Decorative box, 1857. 1st, Mainland box, 1874. E, Airmail box, 1934. 47p, Oval dual-aperture box, 1939. 68p, Modern box, 1980.

**Litho. & Engr.**

| | | | Perf. 14x14¼ | |
|---|---|---|---|---|
| 2002, Oct. 8 | | | | |
| 2076 | A534 | 2nd multi | .95 | .35 |
| 2077 | A534 | 1st multi | 1.35 | .55 |
| 2078 | A534 | E multi | 1.90 | 1.00 |
| 2079 | A534 | 47p multi | 1.90 | 1.00 |
| 2080 | A534 | 68p multi | 2.70 | 1.40 |
| | | Nos. 2076-2080 (5) | 8.80 | 4.30 |

Nos. 2076-2078 each sold for 19p, 27p and 37p on day of issue.

Christmas A535

**Die Cut Perf. 14½x14**

| | | | | |
|---|---|---|---|---|
| 2002, Nov. 5 | | | **Photo.** | |
| **Self-Adhesive** | | | | |
| 2081 | A535 | 2nd Spruce branches | .95 | .25 |
| a. | | Booklet pane of 24 | 23.00 | |
| 2082 | A535 | 1st Holly | 1.35 | .25 |
| a. | | Booklet pane of 12 | 16.50 | |
| 2083 | A535 | E Ivy | 1.90 | .80 |
| 2084 | A535 | 47p Mistletoe | 1.90 | .95 |
| 2085 | A535 | 68p Pine cone | 2.70 | 1.40 |
| | | Nos. 2081-2085 (5) | 8.80 | 3.65 |

Nos. 2081-2085 each sold for 19p, 27p and 37p on day of issue.

**Types of 1952-54**
Souvenir Sheet
**Tan Surface-colored Paper**

**Perf. 14¾x14 Syncopated**

| | | | Wmk. 401 | |
|---|---|---|---|---|
| 2002, Dec. 5 | **Photo.** | | | |
| 2086 | | Sheet of 9, #2022-2023, 2086a-2086g + label | 12.50 | 8.50 |
| a. | A126 | 1p red orange | .30 | .25 |
| b. | A126 | 2p ultramarine | .30 | .25 |
| c. | A126 | 5p brown | .30 | .25 |
| d. | A129 | 33p light brown | 2.00 | .90 |
| e. | A130 | 37p bright rose | 2.50 | 1.00 |
| f. | A131 | 47p brown | 3.00 | 1.10 |
| g. | A132 | 50p dark green | 3.50 | 1.25 |

Barn Owl in Flight — A536

Barn Owl in Flight — A537

Barn Owl in Flight — A538

Barn Owl in Flight — A539

Barn Owl in Flight — A540

Kestrel in Flight — A541

Kestrel in Flight — A542

Kestrel in Flight — A543

Kestrel in Flight — A544

Kestrel in Flight — A545

**2003, Jan. 14 Litho. Perf. 14¼x14½**

| | | | | |
|---|---|---|---|---|
| 2087 | A536 | 1st multi | 1.35 | .80 |
| 2088 | A537 | 1st multi | 1.35 | .80 |
| 2089 | A538 | 1st multi | 1.35 | .80 |
| 2090 | A539 | 1st multi | 1.35 | .80 |
| 2091 | A540 | 1st multi | 1.35 | .80 |
| 2092 | A541 | 1st multi | 1.35 | .80 |
| 2093 | A542 | 1st multi | 1.35 | .80 |
| 2094 | A543 | 1st multi | 1.35 | .80 |
| 2095 | A544 | 1st multi | 1.35 | .80 |
| 2096 | A545 | 1st multi | 1.35 | .80 |
| a. | | Block of 10, #2087-2096 | 13.50 | 11.50 |

Nos. 2087-2096 each sold for 27p on day of issue.

Check-off Slogans A546

Designs: No. 2097, Gold star, See me, Playtime. No. 2098, I love you, XXXX, S.W.A.L.K. No. 2099, Angel, Poppet, Little terror. No. 2100, Yes, No, Maybe. No. 2101, Oops!, Sorry, Will try harder. No. 2102, I did it!, You did it!, We did it!

**2003, Feb. 4 Litho. Perf. 14¼x14**

| | | | | |
|---|---|---|---|---|
| 2097 | A546 | 1st multi | 1.35 | .80 |
| 2098 | A546 | 1st multi | 1.35 | .80 |
| 2099 | A546 | 1st multi | 1.35 | .80 |
| 2100 | A546 | 1st multi | 1.35 | .80 |
| 2101 | A546 | 1st multi | 1.35 | .80 |
| 2102 | A546 | 1st multi | 1.35 | .80 |
| a. | | Block of 6, #2097-2102 | 8.25 | 6.25 |
| b. | | Sheet, 3 each #2097, 2099, 2101-2102, 4 each #2098, 2100 + 20 labels | 27.50 | |

No. 2102b sold for £5.95 and had labels that could be personalized.

Genetics A548

Designs: 2nd, Scientists with jigsaw puzzle. 1st, Chimpanzee and scientist. E, Scientist, DNA double helix, snake. 47p, Scientists with animals. 68p, Scientist with doctor's satchel, crystal ball.

**Perf. 14¼x14½**

| | | | Litho. | |
|---|---|---|---|---|
| 2003, Feb. 25 | | | | |
| 2103 | A548 | 2nd multi | .95 | .35 |
| 2104 | A548 | 1st multi | 1.35 | .45 |
| a. | | Booklet pane, 2 each #2103-2104 (BK173) | 4.50 | |
| 2105 | A548 | E multi | 1.90 | .90 |
| a. | | Booklet pane of 4 (BK173) | 7.50 | |
| 2106 | A548 | 47p multi | 1.90 | .90 |
| 2107 | A548 | 68p multi | 2.70 | 1.40 |
| | | Nos. 2103-2107 (5) | 8.80 | 4.00 |

Nos. 2103-2105 sold for 19p, 27p and 37p respectively on day of issue.

Fruit and Vegetables A549

**Die Cut Perf. 14¼x14**

| | | | | |
|---|---|---|---|---|
| 2003, Mar. 25 | | | **Photo.** | |
| **Self-Adhesive** | | | | |
| **Booklet Stamps** | | | | |
| 2108 | A549 | 1st Strawberry | 1.35 | .75 |
| 2109 | A549 | 1st Potato | 1.35 | .75 |
| 2110 | A549 | 1st Apple | 1.35 | .75 |
| 2111 | A549 | 1st Pepper | 1.35 | .75 |
| 2112 | A549 | 1st Pear | 1.35 | .75 |
| 2113 | A549 | 1st Orange | 1.35 | .75 |
| 2114 | A549 | 1st Tomato | 1.35 | .75 |
| 2115 | A549 | 1st Lemon | 1.35 | .75 |
| 2116 | A549 | 1st Brussels sprout | 1.35 | .75 |
| 2117 | A549 | 1st Eggplant | 1.35 | .75 |
| a. | | Pane, #2108-2117 + 76 stickers | 13.50 | |
| b. | | Sheet, 2 each #2108-2117, litho., + 20 labels +93 stickers ('06) | 26.00 | |

Nos. 2108-2117 each sold for 27p on day of issue.

No. 2117b issued 3/7/06. No. 2117b sold for £6.55.

Adventurers — A550

Designs: 2nd, Amy Johnson (1903-41), first woman to fly to Australia. 1st, British Mount Everest expedition of 1953. E, Freya Stark (1893-1993), Middle East traveler and writer. 42p, Ernest Shackleton (1874-1922), Antarctic explorer. 47p, Francis Chichester (1901-72), sailor. 68p, Robert Falcon Scott (1868-1912), Antarctic explorer.

**Perf. 14¾x14¼**

| | | | Unwmk. | |
|---|---|---|---|---|
| 2003, Apr. 29 | **Photo.** | | | |
| 2118 | A550 | 2nd multi | .95 | .35 |
| 2119 | A550 | 1st multi | 1.35 | .50 |
| 2120 | A550 | E multi | 1.90 | .85 |
| 2121 | A550 | 42p multi | 1.70 | .85 |
| 2122 | A550 | 47p multi | 1.90 | 1.00 |
| 2123 | A550 | 68p multi | 2.70 | 1.40 |
| | | Nos. 2118-2123 (6) | 10.50 | 4.95 |

**Booklet Stamp**
**Self-Adhesive**
**Die Cut Perf. 14¾x14¼**

| | | | | |
|---|---|---|---|---|
| 2124 | A550 | 1st multi | 5.00 | 1.00 |
| a. | | Booklet pane, 2 #2124, 4 #MH300 | 14.00 | |

Nos. 2118-2120 each sold for 19p, 27p and 38p respectively on day of issue.

**Types of 1952-54**

A550a

**Perf. 14¾x14 Syncopated**
**Tan Surface-colored Paper**
**Souvenir Sheet**

| | | | Wmk. 401 | |
|---|---|---|---|---|
| 2003, May 20 | **Photo.** | | | |
| 2125 | | Sheet of 9 + label | 13.00 | 13.00 |
| a. | A127 | 4p orange | .20 | .20 |
| b. | A128 | 8p ultramarine | .30 | .20 |
| c. | A129 | 10p lilac rose | .40 | .20 |
| d. | A129 | 20p emerald | .80 | .40 |
| e. | A130 | 28p deep olive green | 1.10 | .50 |
| f. | A130 | 34p violet brown | 1.35 | .65 |
| g. | A128 | E henna brown | 1.90 | .80 |
| h. | A130 | 42p royal blue | 1.75 | .75 |
| i. | A131 | 68p dark blue | 3.00 | 1.25 |

**Booklet Stamp**
**Perf. 14¾x14**

| | | | | |
|---|---|---|---|---|
| 2126 | A136 | £1 dark green | 65.00 | 55.00 |
| a. | | Booklet pane, #2126, 2 each #2086f, 2125i (BK174) | 72.50 | |

No. 2125g sold for 38p on day of issue.

Coronation of Queen Elizabeth II, 50th Anniv. — A551

Designs: No. 2127, Aerial view of parade entering circle. No. 2128, Children reading coronation party sign. No. 2129, Queen at coronation. No. 2130, Children at wall of pictures. No. 2131, Queen holding orb and scepter. No. 2132, Children running in street. No. 2133, Royal carriage under arch. No. 2134, Children standing in front of house. No. 2135, Royal carriage. No. 2136, Children at party.

**Perf. 14½x14¼**

**2003, June 2    Photo.    Wmk. 401**

| | | | | |
|---|---|---|---|---|
| 2127 | A551 | 1st multi | 1.35 | .80 |
| 2128 | A551 | 1st multi | 1.35 | .80 |
| 2129 | A551 | 1st multi | 1.35 | .80 |
| 2130 | A551 | 1st multi | 1.35 | .80 |
| 2131 | A551 | 1st multi | 1.35 | .80 |
| 2132 | A551 | 1st multi | 1.35 | .80 |
| 2133 | A551 | 1st multi | 1.35 | .80 |
| 2134 | A551 | 1st multi | 1.35 | .80 |
| a. | | Booklet pane, #2127, 2129, 2132, 2134 (BK174) | 5.50 | |
| 2135 | A551 | 1st multi | 1.35 | .80 |
| 2136 | A551 | 1st multi | 1.35 | .80 |
| a. | | Block of 10, #2127-2136 | 13.50 | 12.00 |
| b. | | Booklet pane, #2128, 2131, 2133, 2136 (BK174) | 5.50 | |

Nos. 2127-2136 each sold for 28p on day of issue.

Prince William, 21st Birthday A552

Various portraits.

**2003, June 17    Photo.    Perf. 14¼**
**Background Color**

| | | | | |
|---|---|---|---|---|
| 2137 | A552 | 28p silver | 1.10 | .50 |
| 2138 | A552 | E brown | 1.90 | .90 |
| 2139 | A552 | 47p green | 1.90 | 1.00 |
| 2140 | A552 | 68p olive green | 2.70 | 1.40 |
| | | Nos. 2137-2140 (4) | 7.60 | 3.80 |

No. 2138 sold for 38p on day of issue. Background colors are printed with Iriodin ink, giving the stamp a three dimensional appearance.

Scottish Scenery A553

Designs: 2nd: Loch Assynt, Sutherland. 1st, Ben More, Isle of Mull. E, Rothiemurchus, Cairngorms. 42p, Dalveen Pass, Lowther Hills. 47p, Glenfinnan Viaduct, Lochaber. 68p, Papa Little, Shetland Islands.

**2003, July 15    Photo.    Perf. 14½**

| | | | | |
|---|---|---|---|---|
| 2141 | A553 | 2nd multi | .95 | .35 |
| 2142 | A553 | 1st multi | 1.35 | .50 |
| 2143 | A553 | E multi | 1.90 | .75 |
| 2144 | A553 | 42p multi | 1.70 | .90 |
| 2145 | A553 | 47p multi | 1.90 | 1.00 |
| 2146 | A553 | 68p multi | 2.70 | 1.40 |
| | | Nos. 2141-2146 (6) | 10.50 | 4.90 |

**Booklet Stamp**
**Self-Adhesive**
**Die Cut Perf. 14½**

| | | | | |
|---|---|---|---|---|
| 2147 | A553 | 1st multi | 6.00 | 1.00 |
| a. | | Booklet pane, 2 #2147, 4 #MH300 | 16.00 | |

Nos. 2141 and 2143 each sold for 20p and 38p respectively on day of issue, while Nos. 2142 and 2147 sold for 28p on day of issue.

Pub Signs — A554

Designs: 1st, The Station, Thurnscoe. E, Black Swan, Lincoln. 42p, The Cross Keys, London. 47p, The Mayflower, Southsea. 68p, The Barley Sheaf, Bodmin.

**2003, Aug. 12    Photo.    Perf. 14x14¼**

| | | | | |
|---|---|---|---|---|
| 2148 | A554 | 1st multi | 1.35 | .50 |
| a. | | Booklet pane of 4 (BK175) | 5.50 | |
| 2149 | A554 | E multi | 1.90 | .75 |
| 2150 | A554 | 42p multi | 1.70 | .90 |
| 2151 | A554 | 47p multi | 1.90 | 1.00 |
| 2152 | A554 | 68p multi | 2.70 | 1.40 |
| | | Nos. 2148-2152 (5) | 9.55 | 4.55 |

Europa (#2148-2149).

Nos. 2148 and 2149 each sold for 28p and 38p, respectively, on day of issue.

Toys A555

Designs: 1st, Meccano Constructor Biplane, c. 1931. E, Wells-Brimtoy Clockwork Double-decker Omnibus, c. 1938. 42p, Hornby M1 Clockwork Locomotive and Tender, c. 1948. 47p, Dinky Toys Ford Zephyr, c. 1956. 68p, Mettoy Friction drive Space Ship Eagle c. 1960.

**2003, Sept. 18    Photo.    Perf. 14¼x14**

| | | | | |
|---|---|---|---|---|
| 2153 | A555 | 1st multi | 1.35 | .50 |
| 2154 | A555 | E multi | 1.90 | .75 |
| 2155 | A555 | 42p multi | 1.70 | .90 |
| 2156 | A555 | 47p multi | 1.90 | 1.00 |
| 2157 | A555 | 68p multi | 2.70 | 1.40 |
| a. | | Souvenir sheet, #2153-2157 | 10.00 | 10.00 |
| | | Nos. 2153-2157 (5) | 9.55 | 4.55 |

**Booklet Stamp**
**Self-Adhesive**
**Die Cut Perf. 14¼x14**

| | | | | |
|---|---|---|---|---|
| 2158 | A555 | 1st multi | 6.00 | 1.00 |
| a. | | Booklet, 2 #2158, 4 #MH300 | 16.00 | |

Nos. 2153 and 2158 each sold for 28p on day of issue. No. 2154 sold for 38p on day of issue.

British Museum, 250th Anniv. — A556

Museum Exhibits: 2nd, Coffin of Denytenamun, c. 900 B.C. 1st, Bust of Alexander the Great, c. 200 B.C. E, Sutton Hoo Helmet, c. 600. 42p, Sculpture of Indian Goddess Parvati, c. 1500. 47p, Mask of Xiuhtecuhtli, c. 1500. 68p, Hoa Hakananai'a Easter Island moai, c. 1000.

**2003, Oct. 7                Perf. 14x14¼**

| | | | | |
|---|---|---|---|---|
| 2159 | A556 | 2nd multi | .95 | .40 |
| 2160 | A556 | 1st multi | 1.35 | .50 |
| 2161 | A556 | E multi | 1.90 | .75 |
| 2162 | A556 | 42p multi | 1.70 | .90 |
| 2163 | A556 | 47p multi | 1.90 | 1.00 |
| 2164 | A556 | 68p multi | 2.70 | 1.40 |
| | | Nos. 2159-2164 (6) | 10.50 | 4.95 |

Nos. 2159-2161 each sold for 20p, 28p and 38p respectively on day of issue.

Christmas A557

Ice and snow sculptures by Andy Goldsworthy: 2nd, Ice Spiral. 1st, Icicle Star. E, Wall of Frozen Snow. 53p, Ice Ball. 68p, Ice Hole. £1.12, Snow Pyramids.

**Die Cut Perf. 14¼x14**

**2003, Nov. 4                        Photo.**
**Self-Adhesive**

| | | | | |
|---|---|---|---|---|
| 2165 | A557 | 2nd multi | .95 | .25 |
| a. | | Booklet pane of 24 | 23.00 | |
| b. | | Sheet of 20 + 20 labels, litho. | 19.00 | |
| 2166 | A557 | 1st multi | 1.35 | .25 |
| a. | | Booklet pane of 12 | 16.00 | |
| b. | | Sheet of 20 + 20 labels, litho. | 30.00 | |
| 2167 | A557 | E multi | 1.90 | .85 |
| 2168 | A557 | 53p multi | 2.10 | 1.00 |
| 2169 | A557 | 68p multi | 2.70 | 1.40 |
| 2170 | A557 | £1.12 multi | 4.50 | 2.00 |
| | | Nos. 2165-2170 (6) | 13.50 | 5.75 |

Nos. 2165-2167 sold for 20p, 28p and 38p respectively on day of issue.

Nos. 2165b and 2166b sold for £4.20 and £6.15 respectively and had labels that could be personalized.

**Souvenir Sheet**

England, Winners of 2003 Rugby World Cup Championships — A558

No. 2171: a, English flags. b, Players with red shirts in huddle. c, World Cup. d, Players in white jerseys, celebrating.

**2003, Dec. 19    Litho.    Perf. 13¾x14**

| | | | | |
|---|---|---|---|---|
| 2171 | A558 | Sheet of 4 | 19.50 | 19.50 |
| a.-b. | | 1st Either single | 2.00 | .75 |
| c.-d. | | 68p Either single | 4.00 | 1.75 |

Nos. 2171a-2171b sold for 28p on day of issue.

Locomotives — A559

Designs: 20p, Dolgoch 0-4-0T. 28p, CR 439 0-4-4T. E, GCR 8K 2-8-0. 42p, GWR Manor 4-6-0. 47p, SR West Country 4-6-2. 68p, BR Standard 4 2-6-4T.

**2004, Jan. 13    Litho.    Perf. 14¾x14¼**

| | | | | |
|---|---|---|---|---|
| 2172 | A559 | 20p multi | .80 | .35 |
| 2173 | A559 | 28p multi | 1.10 | .55 |
| 2174 | A559 | E multi | 1.90 | .80 |
| 2175 | A559 | 42p multi | 1.70 | .90 |
| a. | | Booklet pane, #2173-2175 (BK175) | 4.50 | — |
| 2176 | A559 | 47p multi | 1.90 | 1.00 |
| 2177 | A559 | 68p multi | 2.70 | 1.40 |
| a. | | Souvenir sheet, #2172-2177 | 45.00 | 45.00 |
| | | Nos. 2172-2177 (6) | 10.10 | 5.00 |

First steam locomotive, bicent. No. 2174 sold for 38p on day of issue.

Special Occasions A560

**2004, Feb. 3    Litho.    Perf. 14¼x14**

| | | | | |
|---|---|---|---|---|
| 2178 | A560 | 1st Postman | 1.35 | .55 |
| 2179 | A560 | 1st Face | 1.35 | .55 |
| 2180 | A560 | 1st Duck | 1.35 | .55 |
| 2181 | A560 | 1st Baby | 1.35 | .55 |

| | | | | |
|---|---|---|---|---|
| 2182 | A560 | 1st Airplane | 1.35 | .55 |
| a. | | Horiz. strip of 5, #2178-2182 | 6.75 | 3.25 |
| c. | | Sheet, 4 each #2178-2182, + 20 labels | 27.50 | — |

Nos. 2178-2182 each sold for 28p on day of issue. No. 2182c sold for £6.15 and had labels that could not be personalized.

Map — A561

Forest of Lothlórien A562

The Fellowship of the Ring — A563

Rivendell A564

Hall at Bag-End A565

Orthanc A566

Doors of Durin — A567

Barad-Dur A568

Minas
Tirith — A569

Fangorn
Forest
A570

**2004, Feb. 26**     *Perf. 14½x14¼*

| | | | | |
|---|---|---|---|---|
| 2183 | A561 | 1st multi | 1.35 | .55 |
| 2184 | A562 | 1st multi | 1.35 | .55 |
| 2185 | A563 | 1st multi | 1.35 | .55 |
| 2186 | A564 | 1st multi | 1.35 | .55 |
| 2187 | A565 | 1st multi | 1.35 | .55 |
| 2188 | A566 | 1st multi | 1.35 | .55 |
| 2189 | A567 | 1st multi | 1.35 | .55 |
| 2190 | A568 | 1st multi | 1.35 | .55 |
| 2191 | A569 | 1st multi | 1.35 | .55 |
| 2192 | A570 | 1st multi | 1.35 | .55 |
| *a.* | | Block of 10, #2183-2192 | 13.50 | 5.50 |

Publication of *The Lord of the Rings*, by
J.R.R. Tolkein, 50th anniv. Nos. 2183-2192
each sold for 28p on day of issue.

Northern
Ireland
Scenery
A571

Designs: 2nd, Ely, Island, Lower Lough
Erne. 1st, Giant's Causeway, Antrim Coast. E,
Slemish, Antrim Mountains. 42p, Banns Road,
Mourne Mountain. 47p, Glenelly Valley, Sper-
rins. 68p, Islandmore, Strangford Lough.

**2004, Mar. 16**    Photo.    *Perf. 14½*

| | | | | |
|---|---|---|---|---|
| 2193 | A571 | 2nd multi | .95 | .35 |
| 2194 | A571 | 1st multi | 1.35 | .50 |
| 2195 | A571 | E multi | 1.90 | .70 |
| 2196 | A571 | 42p multi | 1.70 | .75 |
| 2197 | A571 | 47p multi | 1.90 | .85 |
| 2198 | A571 | 68p multi | 2.70 | 1.25 |
| | | *Nos. 2193-2198 (6)* | 10.50 | 4.40 |

**Booklet Stamp**
**Self-Adhesive**
*Die Cut Perf. 14½*

| | | | | |
|---|---|---|---|---|
| 2199 | A571 | 1st multi | 3.25 | .50 |
| *a.* | | Booklet, 2 #2199, 4 #MH301 | 11.00 | |

Nos. 2193-2195 each sold for 20p, 28p and
38p respectively on day of issue.

Entente
Cordiale,
Cent. — A572

Designs: 28p, Lace 1 (trial proof) 1968, by
Sir Terry Frost. 57p, Coccinelle, by Sonia
Delaunay.

**2004, Apr. 6**    Photo.    *Perf. 14x14¼*

| | | | | |
|---|---|---|---|---|
| 2200 | A572 | 28p multi | 1.10 | .50 |
| 2201 | A572 | 57p multi | 2.25 | 1.10 |

See France Nos. 3009-3010.

---

Ocean
Liners
A573

Designs: 1st, RMS Queen Mary 2, 2004. E,
SS Canberra, 1961. 42p, RMS Queen Mary,
1936. 47p, RMS Mauretania, 1907. 57p, SS
City of New York, 1888. 68p, PS Great Western, 1838.

**2004, Apr. 13**     *Perf. 14¼x14*

| | | | | |
|---|---|---|---|---|
| 2202 | A573 | 1st multi | 1.35 | .50 |
| 2203 | A573 | E multi | 1.90 | .80 |
| 2204 | A573 | 42p multi | 1.70 | .85 |
| 2205 | A573 | 47p multi | 1.90 | .90 |
| 2206 | A573 | 57p multi | 2.30 | 1.40 |
| 2207 | A573 | 68p multi | 2.70 | 1.40 |
| *a.* | | Souvenir sheet, #2202-2207 | 22.50 | 12.50 |
| *b.* | | Litho. (from #2356a) | 2.70 | 1.40 |
| | | *Nos. 2202-2207 (6)* | 11.85 | 5.85 |

**Booklet Stamp**
**Self-Adhesive**
*Serpentine Die Cut 14¼x14*

| | | | | |
|---|---|---|---|---|
| 2208 | A573 | 1st multi | 3.50 | 1.00 |
| *a.* | | Booklet pane, 2 #2208, 4 #MH300 | 11.00 | |

Nos. 2202 and 2203 sold for 28p and 40p
respectively on day of issue.
No. 2207b is contained in the booklet pane
No. 2356a, issued 2/23/06.

Royal
Horticultural
Society,
Bicent.
A574

Designs: 2nd, Dianthus Allwoodii Group.
1st, Dahlia "Garden Princess." E, Clematis
"Arabella." 42p, Miltonia "French Lake." 47p,
Lilium "Lemon Pixie." 68p, Delphinium "Clifford
Sky."

**2004, May 25**    Photo.    *Perf. 14½*

| | | | | |
|---|---|---|---|---|
| 2209 | A574 | 2nd multi | .95 | .35 |
| 2210 | A574 | 1st multi | 1.35 | .50 |
| *a.* | | Perf. 14¼ + label, litho. | 1.40 | 1.10 |
| 2211 | A574 | E multi | 1.90 | .85 |
| 2212 | A574 | 42p multi | 1.70 | .85 |
| 2213 | A574 | 47p multi | 1.90 | 1.00 |
| *a.* | | Booklet pane, 2 each #2210, 2213 (BK176) | 6.50 | — |
| 2214 | A574 | 68p multi | 2.70 | 1.40 |
| *a.* | | Souvenir sheet, #2209-2214 | 15.00 | 9.00 |
| *b.* | | Booklet pane, #2209, 2211, 2212, 2214 (BK176) | 7.25 | — |
| | | *Nos. 2209-2214 (6)* | 10.50 | 4.95 |

Nos. 2209-2211 each sold for 21p, 28p and
40p respectively on day of issue.
No. 2210a was printed in sheets of 20
stamps + 20 labels that sold for £6.15.

Wales Scenery
A575

Designs: 2nd, Barmouth Bridge. 1st,
Hyddgen, Plynlimon. 40p, Brecon Beacons
National Park. 43p, Pen-pych, Rhondda Val-
ley. 47p, Rhewl, Dee Valley. 68p, Marloes
Sands.

**2004, June 15**    Photo.    *Perf. 14½*

| | | | | |
|---|---|---|---|---|
| 2215 | A575 | 2nd multi | .95 | .40 |
| 2216 | A575 | 1st multi | 1.35 | .50 |
| 2217 | A575 | 40p multi | 1.60 | .80 |
| 2218 | A575 | 43p multi | 1.70 | .90 |
| 2219 | A575 | 47p multi | 1.90 | 1.00 |
| 2220 | A575 | 68p multi | 2.70 | 1.40 |
| | | *Nos. 2215-2220 (6)* | 10.20 | 5.00 |

---

**Booklet Stamp**
**Self-Adhesive**
*Die Cut Perf. 14½*

| | | | | |
|---|---|---|---|---|
| 2221 | A575 | 1st multi | 6.00 | .50 |
| *a.* | | Booklet pane, 2 #2221, 4 #MH300 | 16.00 | |

Europa (#2216, 2217, 2221). Nos. 2215-
2216 each sold for 21p and 28p respectively
on day of issue.

Royal
Society of
Arts, 250th
Anniv.
A576

Designs: 1st, Great Britain #1. 40p, William
Shipley, Society founder. 43p, Stylized typewriter keys, shorthand. 47p, Apparatus for
sweeping chimneys invented by George
Smart. 57p, Typeface designed by Eric Gill.
68p, Zero waste.

**Perf. 13¾x14¼**

**2004, Aug. 10**    Litho.

| | | | | |
|---|---|---|---|---|
| 2222 | A576 | 1st multi | 1.35 | .50 |
| 2223 | A576 | 40p multi | 1.60 | .80 |
| 2224 | A576 | 43p multi | 1.70 | .90 |
| 2225 | A576 | 47p multi | 1.90 | 1.00 |
| 2226 | A576 | 57p multi | 2.30 | 1.25 |
| 2227 | A576 | 68p multi | 2.70 | 1.40 |
| | | *Nos. 2222-2227 (6)* | 11.55 | 5.85 |

No. 2222 sold for 28p on day of issue.

Mammals
A577

**Perf. 14½x14¼**

**2004, Sept. 16**    Photo.

| | | | | |
|---|---|---|---|---|
| 2228 | A577 | 1st Pine marten | 1.35 | .50 |
| 2229 | A577 | 1st Roe deer | 1.35 | .50 |
| 2230 | A577 | 1st Badger | 1.35 | .50 |
| 2231 | A577 | 1st Yellow-necked mouse | 1.35 | .50 |
| 2232 | A577 | 1st Wild cat | 1.35 | .50 |
| 2233 | A577 | 1st Red squirrel | 1.35 | .50 |
| 2234 | A577 | 1st Stoat | 1.35 | .50 |
| 2235 | A577 | 1st Natterer's bat | 1.35 | .50 |
| 2236 | A577 | 1st Mole | 1.35 | .50 |
| 2237 | A577 | 1st Fox | 1.35 | .50 |
| *a.* | | Block of 10, #2228-2237 | 13.50 | 7.50 |

Nos. 2228-2237 each sold for 28p on day of
issue.

Crimean War,
150th
Anniv. — A578

Photographs of Crimean War heroes: 2nd,
Private Michael MacNamara. 1st, Piper David
Muir. 40p, Sergeant Major Edward Edwards.
57p, Sergeant William Powell. 68p, Sergeant
Major John Poole. £1.12, Sergeant Robert
Glasgow.

**2004, Oct. 12**    Litho.    *Perf. 14x13¾*

| | | | | |
|---|---|---|---|---|
| 2238 | A578 | 2nd multi | .95 | .40 |
| 2239 | A578 | 1st multi | 1.35 | .50 |
| 2240 | A578 | 40p multi | 1.60 | .85 |
| 2241 | A578 | 57p multi | 2.30 | 1.25 |
| 2242 | A578 | 68p multi | 2.70 | 1.40 |
| 2243 | A578 | £1.12 multi | 4.50 | 2.00 |
| | | *Nos. 2238-2243 (6)* | 13.40 | 6.40 |

Nos. 2238-2239 each sold for 21p and 28p
respectively on day of issue.

---

Christmas
A579

Santa Claus: Nos. 2244a, 2245, Walking
toward chimney in snow. Nos. 2244b, 2246,
Looking at rising sun. Nos. 2244c, 2247, In
wind. Nos. 2244d, 2248, With umbrella in rain
storm. Nos. 2244e, 2249, With flashlight in
fog. Nos. 2244f, 2250, Taking protection from
hail storm.

**2004, Nov. 2**    Photo.    *Perf. 14½x14*

| | | | | |
|---|---|---|---|---|
| 2244 | | Sheet of 6 | 13.50 | 7.00 |
| *a.* | A579 | (2nd) multi | .95 | .40 |
| *b.* | A579 | (1st) multi | 1.35 | .55 |
| *c.* | A579 | 40p multi | 1.60 | .85 |
| *d.* | A579 | 57p multi | 2.30 | 1.25 |
| *e.* | A579 | 68p multi | 2.70 | 1.40 |
| *f.* | A579 | £1.12 multi | 4.50 | 2.10 |

**Self-Adhesive**
*Die Cut Perf. 14½x14*

| | | | | |
|---|---|---|---|---|
| 2245 | A579 | (2nd) multi | .95 | .25 |
| *a.* | | Booklet pane of 24 | 23.00 | |
| *b.* | | Sheet of 20 + 20 personalized labels, litho. | 40.00 | |
| 2246 | A579 | (1st) multi | 1.35 | .25 |
| *a.* | | Booklet pane of 12 | 16.00 | |
| *b.* | | Sheet, 10 each #2245-2246, + 20 labels, litho. | 21.00 | |
| *c.* | | Sheet of 20 + 20 personalized labels, litho. | 57.50 | |
| 2247 | A579 | 40p multi | 1.60 | .85 |
| 2248 | A579 | 57p multi | 2.30 | 1.25 |
| 2249 | A579 | 68p multi | 2.70 | 1.40 |
| 2250 | A579 | £1.12 multi | 4.50 | 2.10 |
| | | *Nos. 2245-2250 (6)* | 13.00 | 6.40 |

Nos. 2244a and 2245 each sold for 21p and
Nos. 2244b and 2246 each sold for 28p on day
of issue.
No. 2245b sold for £9.95; No. 2246b sold for
£5.40; No. 2246c sold for £14.95.

Farm Animals
A580

Designs: No. 2251, British Saddleback pigs.
No. 2252, Two Khaki Campbell ducks. No.
2253, Clydesdale horses. No. 2254, Shorthorn
cattle. No. 2255, Border collie. No. 2256,
Chicks. No. 2257, Suffolk sheep. No. 2258,
Bagot goat. No. 2259, Norfolk Black turkeys.
No. 2260, Three Embden geese.

**2005, Jan. 11**    Photo.    *Perf. 14½*

| | | | | |
|---|---|---|---|---|
| 2251 | A580 | 1st multi | 1.35 | .55 |
| 2252 | A580 | 1st multi | 1.35 | .55 |
| 2253 | A580 | 1st multi | 1.35 | .55 |
| 2254 | A580 | 1st multi | 1.35 | .55 |
| 2255 | A580 | 1st multi | 1.35 | .55 |
| 2256 | A580 | 1st multi | 1.35 | .55 |
| 2257 | A580 | 1st multi | 1.35 | .55 |
| 2258 | A580 | 1st multi | 1.35 | .55 |
| 2259 | A580 | 1st multi | 1.35 | .55 |
| 2260 | A580 | 1st multi | 1.35 | .55 |
| *a.* | | Block of 10, #2251-2260 | 13.50 | 5.50 |
| *b.* | | Sheet, 2 each #2251-2260 + 20 labels, litho. | 27.50 | — |

Nos. 2251-2260 each sold for 28p on day of
issue. No. 2260b sold for £6.15.

Southwestern
England
Scenery
A581

Designs: 2nd, Old Harry Rocks, Studland
Bay. 1st, Wheal Coates mine, St. Agnes. 40p,
Start Point and Start Bay. 43p, Norton Down,
Wiltshire. 57p, Chiselcombe, Exmoor. 68p, St.
James Stone, Lundy.

**2005, Feb. 8**    Photo.    *Perf. 14½*

| | | | | |
|---|---|---|---|---|
| 2261 | A581 | 2nd multi | .95 | .40 |
| 2262 | A581 | 1st multi | 1.35 | .50 |
| 2263 | A581 | 40p multi | 1.60 | .80 |
| 2264 | A581 | 43p multi | 1.70 | .90 |

| 2265 | A581 | 57p multi | 2.30 | 1.25 |
|---|---|---|---|---|
| 2266 | A581 | 68p multi | 2.70 | 1.40 |
| | | Nos. 2261-2266 (6) | 10.60 | 5.25 |

Nos. 2261 and 2262 sold for 21p and 28p respectively on day of issue.

Jane Eyre, by Charlotte Bronte (1816-55) — A582

Various characters.

| 2005, Feb. 24 | | Litho. | Perf. 14¼ | |
|---|---|---|---|---|
| 2267 | A582 | 2nd multi | .95 | .40 |
| 2268 | A582 | 1st multi | 1.35 | .50 |
| a. | | Booklet pane, 2 each #2267-2268 (BK177) | 5.50 | |
| 2269 | A582 | 40p multi | 1.60 | .85 |
| 2270 | A582 | 57p multi | 2.30 | 1.25 |
| 2271 | A582 | 68p multi | 2.70 | 1.40 |
| 2272 | A582 | £1.12 multi | 4.50 | 2.10 |
| a. | | Souvenir sheet, #2267-2272 | 14.00 | 7.00 |
| b. | | Booklet pane, #2269-2272 (BK177) | 11.00 | |
| | | Nos. 2267-2272 (6) | 13.40 | 6.50 |

Nos. 2267 and 2268 sold for 21p and 28p respectively on day of issue.

Magic Tricks A583

Designs: 1st, Magician, "heads or tails" coin. 40p, Rabbit and hat. 47p, Popper. 68p, Ace of Hearts. £1.12, Pyramids and fezzes.

| 2005, Mar. 15 | | Photo. | Perf. 14¼x14 | |
|---|---|---|---|---|
| 2273 | A583 | 1st multi, un-scratched coin | 1.35 | .55 |
| a. | | Scratched coin, heads | 1.35 | .55 |
| b. | | Scratched coin, tails | 1.35 | .55 |
| c. | | Vert. pair, unscratched | 2.70 | 1.10 |
| d. | | Sheet of 20 + 20 labels, un-scratched, litho. | 27.00 | — |
| 2274 | A583 | 40p multi | 1.60 | .95 |
| 2275 | A583 | 47p multi | 1.90 | .95 |
| 2276 | A583 | 68p multi | 2.70 | 1.40 |
| 2277 | A583 | £1.12 multi | 4.50 | 2.10 |
| | | Nos. 2273-2277 (5) | 12.05 | 5.80 |

No. 2273 sold for 28p on day of issue. No. 2273 has a chalky covering over the coin that can be scratched away with a coin or other metal object to reveal a "heads" picture, showing a face composed of a planet, star and a crescent, or a "tails" picture, showing a shooting star. The chalky covering may, like earlier British chalky paper stamps, dissolve in any fluid.

No. 2273c will have both versions of the stamp. Vertical or horizontal pairs from No. 2273d will have both versions of the stamp. No. 2273d sold for £6.15.

Portions of the designs of Nos. 2275 and 2277 are printed with a thermochromic ink that changes color when warmed.

**Castles Type of 1955**
**Miniature Sheet**
**Litho. & Engr.**

| 2005, Mar. 22 | | | Perf. 11x11¾ | |
|---|---|---|---|---|
| | | On Cream-Colored Paper | | |
| 2278 | | Sheet of 4 | 12.00 | 12.00 |
| a. | A133 | 50p Carrickfergus (brown) | 2.00 | 1.00 |
| b. | A133 | 50p Windsor (black) | 2.00 | 1.00 |
| c. | A133 | £1 Caernarfon (red) | 4.00 | 2.00 |
| d. | A133 | £1 Edinburgh (blue) | 4.00 | 2.00 |

Trooping the Color Ceremony A586

Designs: 2nd, Soldier holding regimental flag. 1st, Queen Elizabeth II saluting. 42p, Bugler on horseback. 60p, Soldier holding scabbard. 68p, Queen on horseback. £1.12, Queen and soldier in phaeton.

| 2005, June 7 | | Litho. | Perf. 14½ | |
|---|---|---|---|---|
| 2288 | A586 | 2nd multi | .95 | .40 |
| 2289 | A586 | 1st multi | 1.35 | .55 |
| 2290 | A586 | 42p multi | 1.70 | .85 |
| 2291 | A586 | 60p multi | 2.40 | 1.25 |

**Miniature Sheet**

Wedding of Prince Charles and Camilla Parker Bowles — A584

No. 2279 — Couple: a, 30p, Prince wearing blue, red and green tie. b, 68p, Prince wearing vest.

| 2005, Apr. 8 | | Litho. | Perf. 13½x14 | |
|---|---|---|---|---|
| 2279 | A584 | Sheet, 2 each #a-b | 8.50 | 8.50 |
| a. | | 30p multi | 1.75 | .60 |
| b. | | 68p multi | 2.75 | 1.40 |

The marginal inscription states that the wedding took place on Apr. 8, but it was delayed until Apr. 9, due to Prince Charles's attendance at the Apr. 8 funeral of Pope John Paul II. Post offices were requested not to sell the stamps until Apr. 9, but first day covers have Apr. 8 cancels.

UNESCO World Heritage Sites in Great Britain and Australia A585

Designs: No. 2280, Hadrian's Wall, England. No. 2281, Ayers Rock, Uluru-Kata Tjuta National Park, Australia. No. 2282, Stonehenge, England. No. 2283, Wet Tropics of Queensland, Australia. No. 2284, Blenheim Palace, England. No. 2285, Greater Blue Mountains Area, Australia. No. 2286, Heart of Neolithic Orkney, Scotland. No. 2287, Purnululu National Park, Australia.

| 2005, Apr. 21 | | | Perf. 14½ | |
|---|---|---|---|---|
| 2280 | A585 | 2nd multi | .95 | .40 |
| 2281 | A585 | 2nd multi | .95 | .40 |
| a. | | Horiz. pair, #2280-2281 | 1.80 | 1.00 |
| 2282 | A585 | 1st multi | 1.35 | .55 |
| 2283 | A585 | 1st multi | 1.35 | .55 |
| a. | | Horiz. pair, #2282-2283 | 2.70 | 1.50 |
| 2284 | A585 | 47p multi | 1.90 | 1.00 |
| 2285 | A585 | 47p multi | 1.90 | 1.00 |
| a. | | Horiz. pair, #2284-2285 | 3.75 | 2.25 |
| 2286 | A585 | 68p multi | 2.70 | 1.40 |
| 2287 | A585 | 68p multi | 2.70 | 1.40 |
| a. | | Horiz. pair, #2286-2287 | 5.50 | 3.00 |
| | | Nos. 2280-2287 (8) | 13.80 | 6.70 |

Nos. 2280 and 2281 each sold for 21p, and Nos. 2282 and 2283 each sold for 30p on day of issue.

See Australia Nos. 2369-2376.

| 2292 | A586 | 68p multi | 2.70 | 1.25 |
|---|---|---|---|---|
| 2293 | A586 | £1.12 multi | 4.50 | 2.00 |
| a. | | Souvenir sheet, #2288-2293 | 14.00 | 14.00 |
| | | Nos. 2288-2293 (6) | 13.60 | 6.30 |

Nos. 2288 and 2289 sold for 21p and 30p respectively on day of issue.

**St. Paul's Cathedral Type of 1995**
**Souvenir Sheet**

| 2005, July 5 | | Photo. | Perf. 14½ | |
|---|---|---|---|---|
| 2294 | | Sheet of 6, #2294a, 5 #MH287 | 8.50 | 7.50 |
| a. | A456 | (1st) deep blue & silver | 1.35 | .50 |

No. 2294a issued 6/21/2005 and sold for 30p on day of issue. End of World War II, 60th anniv.

Motorcycles — A587

Designs: 1st, 1991 Norton F.1. 40p, 1969 BSA Rocket 3. 42p, 1949 Vincent Black Shadow. 47p, 1938 Triumph Speed Twin. 60p, 1930 Brough Superior. 68p, 1914 Royal Enfield.

| 2005, July 19 | | Litho. | Perf. 13¾x14 | |
|---|---|---|---|---|
| 2295 | A587 | 1st multi | 1.35 | .55 |
| 2296 | A587 | 40p multi | 1.60 | .80 |
| 2297 | A587 | 42p multi | 1.70 | .85 |
| 2298 | A587 | 47p multi | 1.90 | 1.00 |
| 2299 | A587 | 60p multi | 2.40 | 1.25 |
| 2300 | A587 | 68p multi | 2.70 | 1.40 |
| | | Nos. 2295-2300 (6) | 11.65 | 5.85 |

No. 2295 sold for 30p on day of issue.

**Miniature Sheet**

Selection of London as Host of 2012 Summer Olympics — A588

No. 2301: a, Javelin. b, Swimming. c, Sprinting. d, Basketball. e, Victorious athlete.

| 2005, Aug. 5 | | | Perf. 14¼ | |
|---|---|---|---|---|
| 2301 | A588 | Sheet of 6, #a-d, 2 #e | 8.50 | 7.50 |
| a.-e. | | 1st Any single | 1.35 | .55 |

Nos. 2301a-2301e each sold for 30p on day of issue. Compare with Type A467.

Changing Tastes in Britain — A589

Designs: 2nd, Woman with rice bowl and chopsticks. 1st, Woman with mug of tea. 42p, Man eating sushi. 47p, Woman with pasta bowl and wine glass. 60p, Woman with bag of French fries. 68p, Man with bowl of fruit.

| 2005, Aug. 23 | | Photo. | Perf. 14½ | |
|---|---|---|---|---|
| 2302 | A589 | 2nd multi | .95 | .40 |
| 2303 | A589 | 1st multi | 1.35 | .55 |
| 2304 | A589 | 42p multi | 1.70 | .90 |
| 2305 | A589 | 47p multi | 1.90 | 1.00 |
| 2306 | A589 | 60p multi | 2.40 | 1.25 |
| 2307 | A589 | 68p multi | 2.70 | 1.40 |
| | | Nos. 2302-2307 (6) | 11.00 | 5.50 |

Europa (#2303, 2304). Nos. 2302 and 2303 sold for 21p and 30p respectively on day of issue.

Television Shows A590

Designs: 2nd, Inspector Morse. 1st, Emmerdale. 42p, Rising Damp. 47p, The Avengers. 60p, The South Bank Show. 68p, Who Wants To Be a Millionaire?

| 2005, Sept. 15 | | Litho. | Perf. 14¼x14 | |
|---|---|---|---|---|
| 2308 | A590 | 2nd multi | .95 | .40 |
| 2309 | A590 | 1st multi | 1.35 | .55 |
| a. | | Sheet of 20 + 20 labels | 27.00 | |
| 2310 | A590 | 42p multi | 1.70 | .85 |
| 2311 | A590 | 47p multi | 1.90 | 1.00 |
| 2312 | A590 | 60p multi | 2.40 | 1.25 |
| 2313 | A590 | 68p multi | 2.70 | 1.40 |
| | | Nos. 2308-2313 (6) | 11.00 | 5.45 |

Independent Television, 50th anniv. Nos. 2308 and 2309 sold for 21p and 30p respectively on day of issue. No. 2309a sold for £6.65.

Labels on No. 2309a could be personalized for a fee.

Flower A591 · Hello A592

Love — A593 · Flag — A594

Teddy Bear — A595 · Bird — A596

***Serpentine Die Cut 14¾x14***

| 2005, Oct. 4 | | | Photo. | |
|---|---|---|---|---|
| | | **Self-Adhesive** | | |
| | | **Booklet Stamps** | | |
| 2314 | A591 | 1st multi | 1.35 | .55 |
| a. | | Sheet of 20 + 20 labels, litho. | 52.50 | — |
| 2315 | A592 | 1st multi | 1.35 | .55 |
| a. | | Sheet of 20 + 20 labels, litho. | 52.50 | — |
| 2316 | A593 | 1st multi | 1.35 | .55 |
| a. | | Sheet of 20 + 20 labels, litho. | 52.50 | — |
| 2317 | A594 | 1st multi | 1.35 | .55 |
| a. | | Sheet of 20 + 20 labels, litho. | 52.50 | — |
| 2318 | A595 | 1st multi | 1.35 | .55 |
| a. | | Sheet of 20 + 20 labels, litho. | 52.50 | — |
| 2319 | A596 | 1st multi | 1.35 | .55 |
| a. | | Booklet pane, #2314-2319 | 8.00 | |
| b. | | Sheet of 20 + 20 labels, litho. | 52.50 | — |
| c. | | Sheet, 4 each #2315-2316, 3 each #2314, 2317-2319, + 20 labels, litho. ('06) | 27.50 | |

Each stamp sold for 30p on day of issue. Nos. 2314a-2318a, 2319b each sold for £14.95 and had labels that could be personalized.

No. 2319 issued 7/4/06. No. 2319c sold for £6.95.

See Nos. 2427, 2545.

## Souvenir Sheet

### Great Britain's Victory Over Australia in Ashes Cricket Test Match Series — A597

No. 2320: a, Players celebrating with trophy. b, Players celebrating. c, Batsman. d, Players in action.

**2005, Oct. 6   Litho.   Perf. 14¼x14**

| | | | |
|---|---|---|---|
| 2320 | A597 | Sheet of 4 | 8.50 | 8.50 |
| a.-b. | | 1st Either single | 1.35 | .55 |
| c.-d. | | 68p Either single | 2.70 | 1.40 |

Nos. 2320a and 2320b each sold for 30p on day of issue.

### Battle of Trafalgar, Bicent. — A598

Designs: No. 2321, Ships in battle. No. 2322, Wounded Admiral Horatio Nelson on deck of HMS Victory. No. 2323, Ship on fire. No. 2324, Ships in battle, diff. No. 2325, Columns of British ships. No. 2326, French and Spanish ships.

**2005, Oct. 18   Litho.   Perf. 14¾x14¼**

| | | | | |
|---|---|---|---|---|
| 2321 | A598 | 1st multi | 1.35 | .55 |
| 2322 | A598 | 1st multi | 1.35 | .55 |
| a. | | Horiz. pair, #2321-2322 | 2.70 | 1.25 |
| 2323 | A598 | 42p multi | 1.70 | .85 |
| 2324 | A598 | 42p multi | 1.70 | .85 |
| a. | | Horiz. pair, #2323-2324 | 3.50 | 1.75 |
| 2325 | A598 | 68p multi | 2.70 | 1.40 |
| a. | | Booklet pane, #2321, 2323, 2325 (BK178) | 5.25 | — |
| 2326 | A598 | 68p multi | 2.70 | 1.40 |
| a. | | Horiz. pair, #2325-2326 | 5.50 | 3.50 |
| b. | | Booklet pane, #2322, 2324, 2326 (BK178) | 5.75 | — |
| c. | | Souvenir sheet, #2321-2326 | 12.00 | 12.00 |

Nos. 2321-2322 each sold for 30p on day of issue.

### Christmas A599

Madonna and Child in artistic style of: 2nd, Haiti. 1st, Europe. 42p, Europe. 60p, Native Americans. 68p, India. £1.12, Australian Aborigines.

**2005, Nov. 1   Photo.   Perf. 14½x14**

| | | | | |
|---|---|---|---|---|
| 2327 | | Sheet of 6 | 14.00 | 14.00 |
| a. | A599 | 2nd multi | .95 | .40 |
| b. | A599 | 1st multi | 1.35 | .55 |
| c. | A599 | 42p multi | 1.70 | .90 |
| d. | A599 | 60p multi | 2.40 | 1.25 |
| e. | A599 | 68p multi | 2.70 | 1.40 |
| f. | A599 | £1.12 multi | 4.50 | 2.00 |

### Self-Adhesive
### Die Cut Perf. 14½x14

| | | | | |
|---|---|---|---|---|
| 2328 | A599 | 2nd multi | .95 | .25 |
| a. | | Booklet pane of 24 | 23.00 | |
| 2329 | A599 | 1st multi | 1.35 | .25 |
| a. | | Booklet pane of 12 | 16.50 | |
| 2330 | A599 | 42p multi | 1.70 | .90 |
| 2331 | A599 | 60p multi | 2.40 | 1.25 |
| 2332 | A599 | 68p multi | 2.70 | 1.40 |
| 2333 | A599 | £1.12 multi | 4.50 | 2.00 |
| | | Nos. 2328-2333 (6) | 13.60 | 6.05 |

Nos. 2327a and 2328 each sold for 21p and Nos. 2327b and 2329 each sold for 30p on day of issue.

---

### Animals From Children's Books — A600

Designs: No. 2334, Jeremy Fisher, from *The Tale of Mr. Jeremy Fisher*, by Beatrix Potter. No. 2335, Kipper, from *Kipper*, by Mick Inkpen. No. 2336, The Enormous Crocodile, from *The Enormous Crocodile*, by Roald Dahl. No. 2337, Paddington Bear, from *More About Paddington*, by Michael Bond. No. 2338, Boots, from *The Comic Adventures of Boots*, by Satoshi Kitamura. No. 2339, White Rabbit, from *Alice's Adventures in Wonderland*, by Lewis Carroll. No. 2340, The Very Hungry Caterpillar, from *The Very Hungry Caterpillar*, by Eric Carle. No. 2341, Maisy, from *Maisy's ABC*, by Lucy Cousins. No. 2342, Like #2337.

**2006, Jan. 10   Litho.   Perf. 14½**

| | | | | |
|---|---|---|---|---|
| 2334 | A600 | 2nd multi | .95 | .40 |
| 2335 | A600 | 2nd multi | .95 | .40 |
| a. | | Horiz. pair, #2334-2335 | 1.90 | .95 |
| 2336 | A600 | 1st multi | 1.35 | .55 |
| 2337 | A600 | 1st multi | 1.35 | .55 |
| a. | | Horiz. pair, #2336-2337 | 2.70 | 1.40 |
| 2338 | A600 | 42p multi | 1.70 | .75 |
| 2339 | A600 | 42p multi | 1.70 | .75 |
| a. | | Horiz. pair, #2338-2339 | 3.50 | 1.75 |
| 2340 | A600 | 68p multi | 2.70 | 1.40 |
| 2341 | A600 | 68p multi | 2.70 | 1.40 |
| a. | | Horiz. pair, #2340-2341 | 5.50 | 3.00 |
| | | Nos. 2334-2341 (8) | 13.40 | 6.20 |

### Self-Adhesive
### Serpentine Die Cut 14½

| | | | | |
|---|---|---|---|---|
| 2342 | A600 | 1st multi + label | 1.25 | .60 |

Nos. 2334-2335 each sold for 21p, and Nos. 2336-2337 each sold for 30p on day of issue. No. 2340 has two die cut holes repesenting holes eaten by the caterpillar.
See United States Nos. 3987, 3990.
No. 2342 had a franking value of 30p on the day of issue, and was issued in sheets of 20 stamps + 20 different labels that sold for £6.55.

### English Scenery A601

Designs: No. 2343, Carding Mill Valley, Shropshire. No. 2344, Beachy Head, Sussex coast. No. 2345, St. Paul's Cathedral, London. No. 2346, Brancastle, Norfolk coast. No. 2347, Derwent Edge, Peak District. No. 2348, Robin Hood's Bay, Yorkshire coast. No. 2349, Buttermere, Lake District. No. 2350, Chipping Campden, Cotswolds. No. 2351, St. Boniface Down, Isle of Wight. No. 2352, Chamberlain Square, Birmingham.

**2006, Feb. 7   Photo.   Perf. 14½**

| | | | | |
|---|---|---|---|---|
| 2343 | A601 | 1st multi | 1.35 | .55 |
| 2344 | A601 | 1st multi | 1.35 | .55 |
| 2345 | A601 | 1st multi | 1.35 | .55 |
| 2346 | A601 | 1st multi | 1.35 | .55 |
| 2347 | A601 | 1st multi | 1.35 | .55 |
| 2348 | A601 | 1st multi | 1.35 | .55 |
| 2349 | A601 | 1st multi | 1.35 | .55 |
| 2350 | A601 | 1st multi | 1.35 | .55 |
| 2351 | A601 | 1st multi | 1.35 | .55 |
| 2352 | A601 | 1st multi | 1.35 | .55 |
| a. | | Block of 10, #2343-2352 | 13.50 | 7.50 |

Nos. 2343-2352 each sold for 30p on day of issue.

### Isambard Kingdom Brunel (1806-1859), Engineer — A602

Engineering projects of Brunel: 1st, Royal Albert Bridge. 40p, Box Tunnel. 42p, Paddington Station. 47p, PSS Great Eastern. 60p, Clifton Suspension Bridge design. 68p, Maidenhead Bridge.

---

**2006, Feb. 23   Litho.   Perf. 14x13¼**

| | | | | |
|---|---|---|---|---|
| 2353 | A602 | 1st multi | 1.35 | .55 |
| 2354 | A602 | 40p multi | 1.60 | .80 |
| 2355 | A602 | 42p multi | 1.70 | .90 |
| 2356 | A602 | 47p multi | 1.90 | 1.00 |
| a. | | Booklet pane, #2356, 2 #2207b (BK179) | 7.25 | — |
| 2357 | A602 | 60p multi | 2.40 | 1.25 |
| a. | | Booklet pane, #2354, 2356, 2357 (BK179) | 6.00 | — |
| 2358 | A602 | 68p multi | 2.70 | 1.40 |
| a. | | Souvenir sheet, #2353-2358 | 12.00 | 7.50 |
| b. | | Booklet pane, #2353, 2355, 2358 (BK179) | 5.75 | — |
| | | Nos. 2353-2358 (6) | 11.65 | 5.90 |

No. 2353 sold for 30p on day of issue.

### Ice Age Animals A603

Designs: 1st, Saber-tooth cat. 42p, Giant deer. 47p, Woolly rhinoceros. 68p, Woolly mammoth. £1.12, Cave bear.

### Perf. 14¼x14½

**2006, Mar. 21                    Litho.**

| | | | | |
|---|---|---|---|---|
| 2359 | A603 | 1st gray & blk | 1.35 | .55 |
| 2360 | A603 | 42p gray & blk | 1.70 | .90 |
| 2361 | A603 | 47p gray & blk | 1.90 | 1.00 |
| 2362 | A603 | 68p gray & blk | 2.70 | 1.40 |
| 2363 | A603 | £1.12 gray & blk | 4.50 | 2.00 |
| | | Nos. 2359-2363 (5) | 12.15 | 5.85 |

No. 2359 sold for 30p on day of issue.

### Queen Elizabeth II, 80th Birthday A604

Queen: No. 2364, Wearing sunglasses, 1972. No. 2365, With horse, 1985. No. 2366, Wearing hat, 2001. No. 2367, As child, with mother, 1931. No. 2368, Wearing tiara, 1951. No. 2369, Wearing hat, 1960. No. 2370, As teenager, 1940. No. 2371, With Prince Philip, 1950.

**2006, Apr. 18   Photo.   Perf. 14¼x14**

| | | | | |
|---|---|---|---|---|
| 2364 | A604 | 2nd gray & blk | .95 | .40 |
| 2365 | A604 | 2nd gray & blk | .95 | .40 |
| a. | | Horiz. pair, #2364-2365 | 1.90 | 1.00 |
| 2366 | A604 | 1st gray & blk | 1.35 | .55 |
| 2367 | A604 | 1st gray & blk | 1.35 | .55 |
| a. | | Horiz. pair, #2366-2367 | 2.70 | 1.50 |
| 2368 | A604 | 44p gray & blk | 1.75 | .90 |
| 2369 | A604 | 44p gray & blk | 1.75 | .90 |
| a. | | Horiz. pair, #2368-2369 | 3.50 | 2.25 |
| 2370 | A604 | 72p gray & blk | 2.90 | 1.40 |
| 2371 | A604 | 72p gray & blk | 2.90 | 1.40 |
| a. | | Horiz. pair, #2370-2371 | 5.75 | 3.00 |
| | | Nos. 2364-2371 (8) | 13.90 | 6.50 |

On day of issue, Nos. 2364-2365 each sold for 23p; Nos. 2366-2367 each sold for 32p.

### 2006 World Cup Soccer Championships, Germany — A605

Globe, soccer player and flag from: 1st, England. 42p, Italy. 44p, Argentina. 50p, Germany. 64p, France. 72p, Brazil.

**2006, June 6   Litho.   Perf. 14½**

| | | | | |
|---|---|---|---|---|
| 2372 | A605 | 1st multi | 1.35 | .60 |
| a. | | Sheet of 20 + 20 labels | 27.00 | |
| 2373 | A605 | 42p multi | 1.70 | .85 |
| 2374 | A605 | 44p multi | 1.75 | .90 |
| 2375 | A605 | 50p multi | 2.00 | 1.00 |
| 2376 | A605 | 64p multi | 2.50 | 1.25 |
| 2377 | A605 | 72p multi | 2.90 | 1.40 |
| | | Nos. 2372-2377 (6) | 12.20 | 6.00 |

No. 2372 sold for 32p on day of issue.
No. 2372a sold for £6.95.

---

### Modern Architecture A606

Designs: 1st, 30 St. Mary Axe, London, designed by Sir Norman Foster. 42p, Maggie's Center, Dundee, designed by Frank Gehry. 44p, Selfridges, Birmingham, designed by Future Systems. 50p, Downland Gridshell, Chichester, by Edward Cullinan. 64p, An Turas, Isle of Tiree, by Sutherland Hussey Architects. 72p, The Deep Hull, by Terry Farrell and Partners.

**2006, June 20                    Photo.**

| | | | | |
|---|---|---|---|---|
| 2378 | A606 | 1st multi | 1.35 | .60 |
| 2379 | A606 | 42p multi | 1.70 | .85 |
| 2380 | A606 | 44p multi | 1.75 | .90 |
| 2381 | A606 | 50p multi | 2.00 | 1.00 |
| 2382 | A606 | 64p multi | 2.50 | 1.40 |
| 2383 | A606 | 72p multi | 2.90 | 1.50 |
| | | Nos. 2378-2383 (6) | 12.20 | 6.25 |

No. 2378 sold for 32p on day of issue.

### National Portrait Gallery, 150th Anniv. — A607

Famous Britons in art from National Portrait Gallery: No. 2384, Sir Winston Churchill, by Walter Sickert. No. 2385, Self-portrait of Sir Joshua Reynolds. No. 2386, T. S. Eliot, by Patrick Heron. No. 2387, Emmeline Pankhurst, by Georgina Brakenbury. No. 2388, Virginia Woolf, photograph by George Beresford. No. 2389, Sir Walter Scott, bust by Sir Francis Chantry. No. 2390, Mary Seacole, by Albert Challen. No. 2391, William Shakespeare, by John Taylor. No. 2392, Dame Cicely Saunders, by Catherine Goodman. No. 2393, Charles Darwin, by John Collier.

**2006, July 18                    Perf. 14¼**

| | | | | |
|---|---|---|---|---|
| 2384 | A607 | 1st multi | 1.35 | .60 |
| 2385 | A607 | 1st multi | 1.35 | .60 |
| 2386 | A607 | 1st multi | 1.35 | .60 |
| 2387 | A607 | 1st multi | 1.35 | .60 |
| 2388 | A607 | 1st multi | 1.35 | .60 |
| 2389 | A607 | 1st multi | 1.35 | .60 |
| 2390 | A607 | 1st multi | 1.35 | .60 |
| 2391 | A607 | 1st multi | 1.35 | .60 |
| 2392 | A607 | 1st multi | 1.35 | .60 |
| 2393 | A607 | 1st multi | 1.35 | .60 |
| a. | | Block of 10, #2384-2393 | 13.50 | 7.50 |
| | | Nos. 2384-2393 (10) | 13.50 | 6.00 |

Nos. 2384-2393 each sold for 32p on day of issue.

### Recipients of Victoria Cross A608

Designs: No. 2394, Corporal Agansing Rai. No. 2395, Boy Seaman First Class Jack Cornwell. No. 2396, Midshipman Charles Lucas. No. 2397, Captain Noel Chavasse. No. 2398, Captain Albert Ball. No. 2399, Captain Charles Upham.

**2006, Sept. 21   Litho.   Perf. 14¼x14**

| | | | | |
|---|---|---|---|---|
| 2394 | A608 | 1st multi | 1.35 | .60 |
| 2395 | A608 | 1st multi | 1.35 | .60 |
| a. | | Horiz. pair, #2394-2395 | 2.70 | 1.50 |
| 2396 | A608 | 64p multi | 2.50 | 1.40 |
| 2397 | A608 | 64p multi | 2.50 | 1.40 |
| a. | | Horiz. pair, #2396-2397 | 5.00 | 3.25 |
| 2398 | A608 | 72p multi | 2.90 | 1.00 |
| a. | | Booklet pane, #2394, 2396, 2398 (BK180) | 6.75 | — |
| 2399 | A608 | 72p multi | 2.90 | 1.50 |
| a. | | Horiz. pair, #2398-2399 | 5.75 | 3.75 |
| b. | | Booklet pane #2395, 2397, 2399 (BK180) | 6.75 | — |
| c. | | Souvenir sheet, #1331a, 2394-2399 | 14.00 | 8.00 |
| | | Nos. 2394-2399 (6) | 13.50 | 6.50 |

Nos. 2394-2395 each sold for 32p on day of issue.

Musicians and Dancers A609

Designs: 1st, Sitar player and dancer. 42p, Guitarist and drummer. 50p, Violinist and harpist. 72p, Saxophone player and guitarist. £1.19, Maracas player and dancers.

**2006, Oct. 3**      *Perf. 14¼x14½*

| | | | | |
|---|---|---|---|---|
| 2400 | A609 | 1st multi | 1.35 | .60 |
| 2401 | A609 | 42p multi | 1.70 | .90 |
| 2402 | A609 | 50p multi | 2.00 | 1.05 |
| 2403 | A609 | 72p multi | 2.90 | 1.50 |
| 2404 | A609 | £1.19 multi | 4.75 | 2.25 |
| | | *Nos. 2400-2404 (5)* | 12.70 | 6.30 |

Europa (#2402).

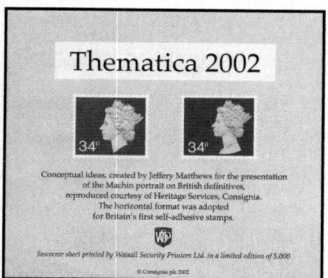

The gummed souvenir sheets shown above, created for the 2002 and 2006 Thematica stamp shows, contain invalid imperforate stamps with simulated perforations that were never issued by Royal Mail. The stamps on these sheets have no obliterators.

The gummed 2005 Thematica sheet reproduces reduced versions of Nos. 440, 441, 683, 1040 and 1796. These reproduced images lack obliterators, and are also invalid for postage.

Gummed Thematica sheets for other years exist, each showing reproductions of other stamps with obliterators to invalidate the images.

"New Baby" A610

"Best Wishes" A611

"Thank You" A612

Balloons A613

Fireworks A614

Flowers, Butterflies and Champagne Bottle A615

**Die Cut Perf. 14¾x14¼**

**2006, Oct. 17**     **Photo.**

**Self-Adhesive**

| | | | | |
|---|---|---|---|---|
| 2405 | A610 | 1st multi | 1.35 | .60 |
| 2406 | A611 | 1st multi | 1.35 | .60 |
| 2407 | A612 | 1st multi | 1.35 | .60 |
| 2408 | A613 | 1st multi | 1.35 | .60 |
| 2409 | A614 | 1st multi | 1.35 | .60 |
| 2410 | A615 | 1st multi | 1.35 | .60 |
| a. | | Booklet pane, #2405-2410 | 8.00 | |
| b. | | Sheet, 3 each #2406-2409, 4 each #2405, 2410 + 20 labels, litho. | 29.00 | |
| | | *Nos. 2405-2410 (6)* | 8.10 | 3.60 |

Nos. 2405-2410 each sold for 32p on day of issue. No. 2410b sold for £6.95.
See Nos. 2546-2548.

Christmas
A616      A617

Designs: Nos. 2411a, 2411c, 2412, 2414, Snowman. Nos. 2411b, 2411d, 2413, 2415, Santa Claus. Nos. 2411e, 2416, Reindeer. Nos. 2411f, 2417, Christmas tree.

**2006, Nov. 7**   **Photo.**   *Perf. 14¾x14*

| | | | | |
|---|---|---|---|---|
| 2411 | | Sheet of 6 | 13.00 | 6.50 |
| a. | A616 | 2nd multi | .95 | .45 |
| b. | A616 | 1st multi | 1.35 | .60 |
| c. | A617 | 2nd Large multi | 1.50 | .80 |
| d. | A617 | 1st Large multi | 1.75 | .90 |
| e. | A616 | 72p multi | 2.90 | 1.50 |
| f. | A616 | £1.19 multi | 4.75 | 2.40 |

**Self-Adhesive**
**Die Cut Perf. 14¾x14**

| | | | | |
|---|---|---|---|---|
| 2412 | A616 | 2nd multi | .95 | .25 |
| a. | | Booklet pane of 12 | 11.50 | |
| 2413 | A616 | 1st multi | 1.35 | .25 |
| a. | | Booklet pane of 12 | 16.00 | |
| b. | | Sheet, 10 each #2412-2413, + 20 labels, litho. | 24.00 | |
| 2414 | A617 | 2nd Large multi | 1.50 | .80 |
| 2415 | A617 | 1st Large multi | 1.75 | .90 |
| 2416 | A616 | 72p multi | 2.90 | 1.50 |
| 2417 | A616 | £1.19 multi | 4.75 | 2.40 |
| | | *Nos. 2412-2417 (6)* | 13.20 | 6.10 |

On day of issue, Nos. 2411a and 2412 each sold for 23p, Nos. 2411b and 2413 each sold for 32p, Nos. 2411c and 2414 each sold for 37p, and Nos. 2411d and 2415 each sold for 44p. No. 2413b sold for £6.

Souvenir Sheet

Battle of the Somme, 90th Anniv. — A618

*Perf. 14½x14¼ (#2418a), 14¾x14 Syncopated*

**2006, Nov. 9**      **Photo.**

| | | | | |
|---|---|---|---|---|
| 2418 | A618 | Sheet of 5 | 13.00 | 6.50 |
| a. | | 1st Poppies | 1.35 | .60 |
| b. | | Sheet of 20 #2418a + 20 labels, litho. | 27.50 | |
| c. | | Single stamp, litho. (#2614b) ('08) | 1.10 | .55 |

No. 2418 contains #2418a, England #13, Northern Ireland #24, Scotland #27 and Wales & Monmouthshire #27. No. 2418a sold for 32p on day of issue. No. 2418b sold for £6.95.
No. 2418c issued 11/6/08. It sold for 36p on day of issue.

Souvenir Sheet

Heritage of Scotland — A619

No. 2419: a, National flag (Scotland type A4). b, St. Andrew (58x22mm). c, Edinburgh Castle (58x22mm).

*Perf. 14¾x14 Syncopated, 14¾x14 (#2419b, 2419c)*

**2006, Nov. 30**      **Photo.**

| | | | | |
|---|---|---|---|---|
| 2419 | A619 | Sheet of 4, #2419a-2419c, Scotland #21 | 8.50 | 5.00 |
| a. | | 1st multi | 1.35 | .60 |
| b.-c. | | 72p Either single | 2.90 | 1.50 |

No. 2419a sold for 32p on day of issue.

Beatles Memorabilia — A620

Beatles Album Covers A621

No. 2420: a, Toy guitar, button. b, Lunch box, buttons. c, 45RPM record of "Love Me Do." d, Tray picturing the Beatles, buttons.
No. 2421, "With The Beatles." No. 2422, "Sgt. Pepper's Lonely Hearts Club Band." No. 2423, "Help!" No. 2424, "Abbey Road." No. 2425, "Let It Be." No. 2426, "Revolver."

**2007, Jan. 9**   **Litho.**   *Perf. 14*

| | | | | |
|---|---|---|---|---|
| 2420 | A620 | Sheet of 4 | 5.50 | 3.00 |
| a.-d. | | 1st Any single | 1.35 | .60 |

**Self-Adhesive**
**Photo.**
*Die Cut Perf. 13x13¾*

| | | | | |
|---|---|---|---|---|
| 2421 | A621 | 1st multi | 1.35 | .60 |
| 2422 | A621 | 1st multi | 1.35 | .60 |
| 2423 | A621 | 64p multi | 2.50 | 1.25 |
| 2424 | A621 | 64p multi | 2.50 | 1.25 |
| 2425 | A621 | 72p multi | 3.00 | 1.50 |
| 2426 | A621 | 72p multi | 3.00 | 1.50 |
| | | *Nos. 2421-2426 (6)* | 13.70 | 6.70 |

Nos. 2420a-2420d, 2421-2422 each sold for 32p on day of issue.

**Love Type of 2005**
*Serpentine Die Cut 14¾x14 Syncopated*

**2007-08**      **Photo.**

**Self-Adhesive**
**Booklet Stamp**

| | | | | |
|---|---|---|---|---|
| 2427 | A593 | 1st multi | 10.00 | .65 |
| a. | | Booklet pane, #2427, 5 #MH380 | 15.00 | |
| b. | | Booklet pane, 2 #2427, 4 #MH300 + 3 labels | 8.25 | |
| c. | | As #2427, litho. (from 2538a) | 1.50 | 1.50 |

No. 2427 sold for 32p on day of issue. Compare with No. 2316 which is not syncopated.
Issued: Nos. 2427, 2427a, 1/16/07. Nos. 2427b, 2427c, 1/15/08.
No. 2427c had a franking value of 34p on day of issue.

Marine Life — A622

Designs: No. 2428, Moon jellyfish. No. 2429, Common starfish. No. 2430, Beadlet anemone. No. 2431, Bass. No. 2432, Thornback ray. No. 2433, Lesser octopus. No. 2434, Common mussels. No. 2435, Gray seal. No. 2436, Shore crab. No. 2437, Common sun star.

**2007, Feb. 1**   **Litho.**   *Perf. 14½*

| | | | | |
|---|---|---|---|---|
| 2428 | A622 | 1st multi | 1.35 | .65 |
| 2429 | A622 | 1st multi | 1.35 | .65 |
| 2430 | A622 | 1st multi | 1.35 | .65 |
| 2431 | A622 | 1st multi | 1.35 | .65 |
| 2432 | A622 | 1st multi | 1.35 | .65 |
| 2433 | A622 | 1st multi | 1.35 | .65 |
| 2434 | A622 | 1st multi | 1.35 | .65 |
| 2435 | A622 | 1st multi | 1.35 | .65 |
| 2436 | A622 | 1st multi | 1.35 | .65 |
| 2437 | A622 | 1st multi | 1.35 | .65 |
| a. | | Block of 10, #2428-2437 | 13.50 | 6.50 |

Nos. 2428-2437 each sold for 32p on day of issue.

Astronomical Objects — A623

Designs: No. 2438, Saturn Nebula (C55). No. 2439, Eskimo Nebula (C39). No. 2440, Cat's Eye Nebula (C6). No. 2441, Helix Nebula (C63). No. 2442, Flaming Star Nebula (C31). No. 2443, Spindle Galaxy (C53).

*Serpentine Die Cut 14¼x14*

**2007, Feb. 13**      **Photo.**

| | | | | |
|---|---|---|---|---|
| 2438 | A623 | 1st multi | 1.35 | .65 |
| 2439 | A623 | 1st multi | 1.35 | .65 |
| 2440 | A623 | 50p multi | 2.00 | 1.00 |
| 2441 | A623 | 50p multi | 2.00 | 1.00 |
| 2442 | A623 | 72p multi | 3.00 | 1.50 |
| 2443 | A623 | 72p multi | 3.00 | 1.50 |
| | | *Nos. 2438-2443 (6)* | 12.70 | 6.30 |

Nos. 2438-2439 each sold for 32p on day of issue.

World of Invention A624

Designs: Nos. 2444, 2450, Man thinking about bridge. Nos. 2445, 2451, Locomotive and tracks. Nos. 2446, 2452, People using telephones, maps of Great Britain, Ireland and Australia. Nos. 2447, 2453, Television camera, man with microphone, man watching television. Nos. 2448, 2454, Man at computer with cord in large ball. Nos. 2449, 2455, Man and woman travelers on cratered planet.

**2007, Mar. 1**   **Photo.**   *Perf. 14½x14*

| | | | | |
|---|---|---|---|---|
| 2444 | A624 | 1st multi | 1.35 | .60 |
| 2445 | A624 | 1st multi | 1.35 | .60 |
| 2446 | A624 | 64p multi | 2.50 | 1.25 |
| 2447 | A624 | 64p multi | 2.50 | 1.25 |
| a. | | Booklet pane, #2444-2447 (BK181) | 7.75 | — |
| 2448 | A624 | 72p multi | 3.00 | 1.50 |
| 2449 | A624 | 72p multi | 3.00 | 1.50 |
| a. | | Souvenir sheet, #2444-2449 | 13.75 | 7.00 |
| b. | | Booklet pane, #2444-2445, 2448-2449 | 8.75 | — |
| | | *Nos. 2444-2449 (6)* | 13.70 | 6.70 |

**Self-Adhesive**
**Die Cut Perf. 14½x14**

| | | | | |
|---|---|---|---|---|
| 2450 | A624 | 1st multi | 1.35 | .60 |
| 2451 | A624 | 1st multi | 1.35 | .60 |
| 2452 | A624 | 64p multi | 2.50 | 1.25 |
| 2453 | A624 | 64p multi | 2.50 | 1.25 |
| 2454 | A624 | 72p multi | 3.00 | 1.50 |
| 2455 | A624 | 72p multi | 3.00 | 1.50 |
| | | *Nos. 2450-2455 (6)* | 13.70 | 6.70 |

Nos. 2444-2445, 2450-2451 each sold for 32p on day of issue.

Abolition of the
Slave Trade,
Bicent. — A625

Designs: No. 2456, William Wilberforce (1759-1833), abolitionist leader in Parliament, and poster. No. 2457, Olaudah Equiano (c. 1750-97), freed slave and abolitionist writer, and map. No. 2458, Granville Sharp (1735-1813), abolitionist, and ship. No. 2459, Thomas Clarkson (1760-1846), abolitionist and diagram of slaves in slave ship. No. 2460, Hannah More (1745-1833), religious writer, and illustration from Cheap Repository Tracts. No. 2461, Ignatius Sancho (c. 1729-80), abolitionist and actor, poster for performance by Sancho.

**2007, Mar. 22     Litho.     Perf. 14¼**
| | | | | |
|---|---|---|---|---|
| 2456 | A625 | 1st multi | 1.25 | .60 |
| 2457 | A625 | 1st multi | 1.25 | .60 |
| a. | | Horiz. pair, #2456-2457 | 2.50 | 1.20 |
| 2458 | A625 | 50p multi | 2.00 | 1.00 |
| 2459 | A625 | 50p multi | 2.00 | 1.00 |
| a. | | Horiz. pair, #2458-2459 | 4.00 | 2.00 |
| 2460 | A625 | 72p multi | 3.00 | 1.50 |
| 2461 | A625 | 72p multi | 3.00 | 1.50 |
| a. | | Horiz. pair, #2460-2461 | 6.00 | 3.00 |
| | | Nos. 2456-2461 (6) | 12.50 | 6.20 |

Nos. 2456-2457 each sold for 32p on day of issue.

**Souvenir Sheet**

Heritage of England — A626

No. 2462: a, English flag (18x22mm). b, St. George slaying dragon (59x22mm). c, Parliament (59x22mm).

**Perf. 14 Syncopated, 14¾x14 (#2462b, 2642c)**
**2007, Apr. 23     Photo.**
| | | | | |
|---|---|---|---|---|
| 2462 | A626 | Sheet of 4, #2462a-2462c, England #7 | 9.00 | 4.50 |
| a. | | 1st multi | 1.40 | .70 |
| b.-c. | | 78p Either single | 3.00 | 1.50 |

On day of issue, No. 2462a and England #7 sold for 34p.

Seaside
Resort Scenes
A627

Designs: 1st, Giant ice cream cone. 46p, Sand castle. 48p, Carousel horses. 54p, Beach cabins. 69p, Beach chairs. 78p, Hitched donkeys.

**2007, May 15     Photo.     Perf. 14½**
| | | | | |
|---|---|---|---|---|
| 2463 | A627 | 1st multi | 1.40 | .70 |
| 2464 | A627 | 46p multi | 1.90 | .95 |
| 2465 | A627 | 48p multi | 2.00 | 1.00 |
| 2466 | A627 | 54p multi | 2.10 | 1.10 |
| 2467 | A627 | 69p multi | 2.75 | 1.40 |
| 2468 | A627 | 78p multi | 3.25 | 1.60 |
| | | Nos. 2463-2468 (6) | 13.40 | 6.75 |

No. 2463 sold for 34p on day of issue. See No. 2573.

Crowned Lion of England — A628

**2007, May 17     Litho.     Perf. 14½x14¼**
| | | | | |
|---|---|---|---|---|
| 2469 | A628 | 1st gray bl & dk red + label | 1.50 | 1.50 |

**Souvenir Sheet**
**Photo.**
| | | | | |
|---|---|---|---|---|
| 2470 | | Sheet, #2470a, 2 each England #6, 15 + label | 9.50 | 9.50 |
| a. | | A628 1st bl grn & brt red | 1.40 | .70 |

No. 2469 was issued in sheets of 20 stamps + 20 labels that sold for £7.35. No. 2470 sold for £2.38 on day of issue. Nos. 2469 and 2470 each had a franking value of 34p on day of issue.

**Souvenir Sheet**

Definitive Stamps Designed by Arnold Machin, 40th Anniv. — A629

**Photo. & Embossed (#2471a-2471b)**
**Perf. 14½x14¼(#2471a-2471b)**
**2007, June 5**
| | | | | |
|---|---|---|---|---|
| 2471 | A629 | Sheet, #2471a, 2471b, MH237, MH373 | 11.50 | 11.50 |
| a. | | 1st Arnold Machin | 1.40 | .70 |
| b. | | 1st #MH6 | 1.40 | .70 |
| c. | | Booklet pane, 2 each #2471a, 2471b (BK182) | 5.75 | |

Nos. 2471a and 2471b each sold for 34p on day of issue and were only issued in the souvenir sheet and the booklet pane.

**Machin Anniversary Type of 2007**

Design: Arnold Machin.

**Perf. 14½x14¼**
**2007, June 5     Photo.**
| | | | | |
|---|---|---|---|---|
| 2472 | A629 | 1st multi + label | 1.50 | .75 |

No. 2472, having a franking value of 34p on day of issue, was issued only in sheets of 20 stamps + 20 labels. The sheets sold for £7.35.

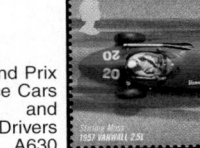

Grand Prix
Race Cars
and
Drivers
A630

Designs: No. 2473, 1957 Vanwall 2.5-liter, Stirling Moss. No. 2474, 1962 BRM P57, Graham Hill. No. 2475, 1963 Lotus 25 Climax, Jim Clark. No. 2476, 1973 Tyrrell 006/2, Jackie Stewart. No. 2477, 1976 McLaren M23, James Hunt. No. 2478, 1986 Williams FW11, Nigel Mansell.

**2007, July 3     Litho.     Perf. 14¼x14**
| | | | | |
|---|---|---|---|---|
| 2473 | A630 | 1st multi | 1.40 | .70 |
| 2474 | A630 | 1st multi | 1.40 | .70 |
| 2475 | A630 | 54p multi | 2.25 | 1.10 |
| 2476 | A630 | 54p multi | 2.25 | 1.10 |
| 2477 | A630 | 78p multi | 3.25 | 1.60 |
| 2478 | A630 | 78p multi | 3.25 | 1.60 |
| | | Nos. 2473-2478 (6) | 13.80 | 6.80 |

Nos. 2473 and 2474 each sold for 34p on day of issue.

Publication of
Last Harry Potter
Novel by J. K.
Rowling
A631

Coats of
Arms From
Harry Potter
Novels
A632

Novels: No. 2479, Harry Potter and the Philosopher's Stone. No. 2480, Harry Potter and the Chamber of Secrets. No. 2481, Harry Potter and the Prisoner of Azkaban. No. 2482, Harry Potter and the Goblet of Fire. No. 2483, Harry Potter and the Order of the Phoenix. No. 2484, Harry Potter and the Half-Blood Prince. No. 2485, Harry Potter and the Deathly Hallows.

Arms of: Nos. 2486a, 2487, Gryffindor. Nos. 2486b, 2488, Hufflepuff. Nos. 2486c, 2489, Hogwarts. Nos. 2486d, 2490, Ravenclaw. Nos. 2486e, 2491, Slytherin.

**2007, July 17     Perf. 14x14¼**
| | | | | |
|---|---|---|---|---|
| 2479 | A631 | 1st multi | 1.40 | .70 |
| 2480 | A631 | 1st multi | 1.40 | .70 |
| 2481 | A631 | 1st multi | 1.40 | .70 |
| 2482 | A631 | 1st multi | 1.40 | .70 |
| 2483 | A631 | 1st multi | 1.40 | .70 |
| 2484 | A631 | 1st multi | 1.40 | .70 |
| 2485 | A631 | 1st multi | 1.40 | .70 |
| a. | | Horiz. strip of 7, #2479-2485 | 9.80 | 4.90 |

**Souvenir Sheet**
**Perf. 14¾x14**
| | | | | |
|---|---|---|---|---|
| 2486 | | Sheet of 5 | 7.00 | 7.00 |
| a.-e. | | A632 1st Any single | 1.40 | .70 |

**Self-Adhesive**
**Die Cut Perf. 14¾x14**
| | | | | |
|---|---|---|---|---|
| 2487 | A632 | 1st multi + label | 1.50 | 1.50 |
| 2488 | A632 | 1st multi + label | 1.50 | 1.50 |
| 2489 | A632 | 1st multi + label | 1.50 | 1.50 |
| 2490 | A632 | 1st multi + label | 1.50 | 1.50 |
| 2491 | A632 | 1st multi + label | 1.50 | 1.50 |
| a. | | Vert. strip of 5, #2487-2491, + 5 labels | 7.50 | |
| | | Nos. 2487-2491 (5) | 7.50 | 7.50 |

Nos. 2479-2485, 2486a-2486e, each sold for 34p on day of issue. Nos. 2487-2491, having a franking value of 34p on day of issue, were sold in a sheet of 20 stamps + 20 labels that sold for £7.35. Labels could be personalized for an extra fee.

Scouting,
Cent.
A633

Designs: 1st, Scouts around campfire, Scout looking at sky. 46p, Scouts climbing rocks. 48p, Scout planting tree. 54p, Scout learning archery from volunteer. 69p, Scouts and glider. 78p, Nine Scouts.

**2007, July 26     Perf. 14¼x14**
| | | | | |
|---|---|---|---|---|
| 2492 | A633 | 1st multi | 1.40 | .70 |
| 2493 | A633 | 46p multi | 1.90 | .95 |
| 2494 | A633 | 48p multi | 2.00 | 1.00 |
| 2495 | A633 | 54p multi | 2.25 | 1.10 |
| 2496 | A633 | 69p multi | 2.75 | 1.40 |
| 2497 | A633 | 78p multi | 3.25 | 1.60 |
| | | Nos. 2492-2497 (6) | 13.55 | 6.75 |

Europa (#2492, 2494). No. 2492 sold for 34p on day of issue.

Endangered
Birds — A634

**2007, Sept. 4     Litho.     Perf. 14½**
| | | | | |
|---|---|---|---|---|
| 2498 | A634 | 1st White-tailed eagle | 1.40 | .70 |
| 2499 | A634 | 1st Bearded tit | 1.40 | .70 |
| 2500 | A634 | 1st Red kite | 1.40 | .70 |
| 2501 | A634 | 1st Cirl bunting | 1.40 | .70 |
| 2502 | A634 | 1st Marsh harrier | 1.40 | .70 |
| 2503 | A634 | 1st Avocet | 1.40 | .70 |
| 2504 | A634 | 1st Bittern | 1.40 | .70 |
| 2505 | A634 | 1st Dartford warbler | 1.40 | .70 |
| 2506 | A634 | 1st Corncrake | 1.40 | .70 |
| 2507 | A634 | 1st Peregrine falcon | 1.40 | .70 |
| a. | | Block of 10, #2498-2507 | 14.00 | 7.00 |

Nos. 2498-2507 each sold for 34p on day of issue.

British Army
Uniforms — A635

Designs: No. 2508, Non-commissioned officer, Royal Military Police, 1999. No. 2509, Tank commander, 5th Royal Tank Regiment, 1944. No. 2510, Observer, Royal Field Artillery, 1917. No. 2511, Rifleman, 95th Rifles, 1813. No. 2512, Grenadier, Royal Regiment of Foot of Ireland, 1704. No. 2513, Trooper, Earl of Oxford's Horse, 1661.

**2007, Sept. 20     Litho.     Perf. 14¼**
| | | | | |
|---|---|---|---|---|
| 2508 | A635 | 1st multi | 1.40 | .70 |
| 2509 | A635 | 1st multi | 1.40 | .70 |
| 2510 | A635 | 1st multi | 1.40 | .70 |
| a. | | Horiz. strip of 3, #2508-2510 | 4.20 | 2.10 |
| b. | | Booklet pane of 3, #2508-2510 (BK183) | 4.20 | |
| 2511 | A635 | 78p multi | 3.25 | 1.60 |
| 2512 | A635 | 78p multi | 3.25 | 1.60 |
| 2513 | A635 | 78p multi | 3.25 | 1.60 |
| a. | | Horiz. strip of 3, #2511-2513 | 9.75 | 4.80 |
| b. | | Booklet pane of 3, #2511-2513 (BK183) | 9.75 | |
| | | Nos. 2508-2513 (6) | 13.95 | 6.90 |

Nos. 2508-2510 each sold for 34p on day of sale.

Wedding
of Queen
Elizabeth II
and Prince
Philip, 60th
Anniv.
A636

Royal Family — A637

Various photographs of couple from: No. 2514, 2006. No. 2515, 1997. No. 2516, 1980. No. 2517, 1969. No. 2518, 1961. No. 2519, 1947.

No. 2520: a, Royal family, log and flowers (35x35mm). b, Queen Elizabeth II and Prince Philip (40x30mm). c, Royal family, baby carriage (41x30mm). d, Queen Elizabeth II, Prince Philip, Princess Anne and Prince Charles (27x38mm).

**2007, Oct. 26     Litho.     Perf. 14¼x14**
| | | | | |
|---|---|---|---|---|
| 2514 | A636 | 1st black | 1.40 | .70 |
| 2515 | A636 | 1st black | 1.40 | .70 |
| a. | | Horiz. pair, #2514-2515 | 2.80 | 1.40 |
| 2516 | A636 | 54p black | 2.25 | 1.10 |
| 2517 | A636 | 54p black | 2.25 | 1.10 |
| a. | | Horiz. pair, #2516-2517 | 4.50 | 2.10 |
| 2518 | A636 | 78p black | 3.25 | 1.60 |
| 2519 | A636 | 78p black | 3.25 | 1.60 |
| a. | | Horiz. pair, #2518-2519 | 6.50 | 3.20 |
| | | Nos. 2514-2519 (6) | 13.80 | 6.80 |

**Souvenir Sheet**
**Self-Adhesive**
| | | | | |
|---|---|---|---|---|
| 2520 | A637 | Sheet of 4 | 9.00 | |
| a. | | 1st multi, die cut perf. 14½ | 1.40 | .70 |
| b. | | 1st multi, die cut perf. 14½x14¼ | 1.40 | .70 |
| c. | | 69p multi, die cut perf. 14¼x14 | 2.75 | 1.40 |
| d. | | 78p multi, die cut perf. 14¼ | 3.25 | 1.60 |

Nos. 2514-2515, 2520a and 2520b each sold for 34p on day of sale.

Madonna and Child, by William Dyce A638

Madonna of Humility, by Lippo di Dalmasio A639

**Die Cut Perf. 14¾x14 Syncopated**
**2007, Nov. 6**     Photo.
**Self-Adhesive**

| | | | |
|---|---|---|---|
| 2521 | A638 | 2nd multi | 1.00 | .50 |
| 2522 | A639 | 1st multi | 1.50 | .75 |

On day of issue, No. 2521 sold for 24p; No. 2522 for 34p.

Christmas
A640       A641

Angels with banners inscribed: Nos. 2523a, 2523c, 2524, 2526, Peace. Nos. 2523b, 2523d, 2525, 2527, Goodwill. Nos. 2523e, 2528, Joy. Nos. 2523f, 2529, Glory.

**2007, Nov. 6**   Photo.   **Perf. 14¾x14**

| | | | |
|---|---|---|---|
| 2523 | | Sheet of 6 | 15.00 | 15.00 |
| a. | A640 | 2nd multi | 1.00 | .50 |
| b. | A640 | 1st multi | 1.50 | .75 |
| c. | A641 | 2nd Large multi | 1.75 | .85 |
| d. | A641 | 1st Large multi | 2.00 | 1.00 |
| e. | A640 | 78p multi | 3.25 | 1.60 |
| f. | A640 | £1.24 multi | 5.25 | 2.60 |

**Self-Adhesive**
**Die Cut Perf. 14¾x14**

| | | | |
|---|---|---|---|
| 2524 | A640 | 2nd multi | 1.00 | .50 |
| a. | | Booklet pane of 12 | 12.00 | |
| b. | | Sheet of 20 + 20 labels, litho. | 35.00 | |
| 2525 | A640 | 1st multi | 1.50 | .75 |
| a. | | Booklet pane of 12 | 18.00 | |
| b. | | Sheet of 20 + 20 labels, litho. | 57.50 | |
| 2526 | A641 | 2nd Large multi | 1.75 | .85 |
| 2527 | A641 | 1st Large multi | 2.00 | 1.00 |
| 2528 | A640 | 78p multi | 3.25 | 1.60 |
| a. | | Sheet, 8 each #2524-2525, 4 #2528, + 20 labels, litho. | 35.00 | |
| b. | | Sheet of 10 + 10 labels, litho. | 57.50 | |
| 2529 | A640 | £1.24 multi | 5.25 | 2.60 |
| | | Nos. 2524-2529 (6) | 14.75 | 7.30 |

On day of issue, Nos. 2523a and 2524 sold for 24p, Nos. 2523b and 2425 sold for 34p, Nos. 2523c and 2426 sold for 40p, and Nos. 2523d and 2427 sold for 48p. No. 2528a sold for £8.30. No. 2524b sold for £8.50, Nos. 2525b and 2528b each sold for £13.50. Labels on Nos. 2524b, 2525b, and 2528b were personalizable.

Poppy and Soldiers A642

**2007, Nov. 8**   Litho.   **Perf. 14½x14¼**

| | | | |
|---|---|---|---|
| 2530 | A642 | 1st multi | 1.50 | .75 |
| a. | | Souvenir sheet of 5 | 14.50 | 14.50 |

Battle of Passchendaele, 90th anniv. No. 2530a contains #2530, England #15, Northern Ireland #26, Scotland #29, and Wales & Monmouthshire #30. No. 2530 was also printed in a sheet of 20 + 5 labels that sold for £7.35, and a limited-quantity privately-contracted sheet of 10 + 10 labels, that sold for £28.50.

Book Covers of James Bond Novels by Ian Fleming — A643

Designs: No. 2531, Casino Royale. No. 2532, Doctor No. No. 2533, Goldfinger. No. 2534, Diamonds Are Forever. No. 2535, For Your Eyes Only. No. 2536, From Russia, with Love.
Illustration reduced.

**2008, Jan. 8**   Litho.   **Perf. 14¾x14¼**

| | | | |
|---|---|---|---|
| 2531 | A643 | 1st multi | 1.40 | .70 |
| 2532 | A643 | 1st multi | 1.40 | .70 |
| 2533 | A643 | 54p multi | 2.10 | 1.10 |
| 2534 | A643 | 54p multi | 2.10 | 1.10 |
| 2535 | A643 | 78p multi | 3.25 | 1.60 |
| a. | | Booklet pane of 3, #2531, 2533, 2535 (BK184) | 6.75 | |
| 2536 | A643 | 78p multi | 3.25 | 1.60 |
| a. | | Miniature sheet of 6, #2531-2536 | 13.50 | 13.50 |
| b. | | Booklet pane of 3, #2532, 2534, 2536 (BK184) | 6.75 | — |
| | | Nos. 2531-2536 (6) | 13.50 | 6.80 |

On day of issue, Nos. 2531-2532 each sold for 34p.

**Hello and Flag Types of 2005**
**Die Cut Perf 14¾x14 Syncopated**
**2008, Jan. 15**     Litho.
**Self-Adhesive**

| | | | |
|---|---|---|---|
| 2537 | A592 | 1st Hello | 1.50 | 1.50 |
| 2538 | A594 | 1st Flag | 1.50 | 1.50 |
| a. | | Sheet, 8 #2427c, 6 each #2537-2538, + 20 labels | 30.00 | |

No. 2538a sold for £7.35. Nos. 2537-2538 each had a franking value of 34p on day of issue.

Working Dogs — A644

Designs: 1st, Assistance dog. 46p, Mountain rescue dog. 48p, Police dog. 54p, Customs dog. 69p, Sheepdog. 78p, Guide dog.

**2008, Feb. 5**   Litho.   **Perf. 14¼x14½**

| | | | |
|---|---|---|---|
| 2539 | A644 | 1st multi | 1.40 | .70 |
| 2540 | A644 | 46p multi | 1.75 | .90 |
| 2541 | A644 | 48p multi | 1.90 | .95 |
| 2542 | A644 | 54p multi | 2.10 | 1.10 |
| 2543 | A644 | 69p multi | 2.75 | 1.40 |
| 2544 | A644 | 78p multi | 3.25 | 1.60 |
| | | Nos. 2539-2544 (6) | 13.15 | 6.65 |

No. 2539 sold for 34p on day of issue. Europa (#2539).

**Types of 2005-06**
**Die Cut Perf. 14¾x14 Syncopated**
**2008, Feb. 28**     Litho.
**Booklet Stamps**
**Self-Adhesive**

| | | | |
|---|---|---|---|
| 2545 | A591 | 1st multi | 1.40 | .70 |
| 2546 | A613 | 1st multi | 1.40 | .70 |
| 2547 | A614 | 1st multi | 1.40 | .70 |
| 2548 | A615 | 1st multi | 1.40 | .70 |
| a. | | Booklet pane of 6, #2537-2538, 2545-2548 | 8.50 | |

On day of issue, Nos. 2545-2548 each sold for 34p.

British Royalty and History — A645

Designs: No. 2549, King Henry IV. No. 2550, King Henry V. No. 2551, King Henry VI. No. 2552, King Edward IV. No. 2553, King Edward V. No. 2554, King Richard III.
No. 2555: a, Owen Glendower (Owain Glyn Dwr), Welsh rebel. b, Battle of Agincourt. c, Battle of Tewkesbury. d, William Caxton, first English printer.

**2008, Feb. 28**     Litho.   **Perf. 14¼**

| | | | |
|---|---|---|---|
| 2549 | A645 | 1st multi | 1.40 | .70 |
| 2550 | A645 | 1st multi | 1.40 | .70 |
| 2551 | A645 | 54p multi | 2.25 | 1.10 |
| 2552 | A645 | 54p multi | 2.25 | 1.10 |
| 2553 | A645 | 69p multi | 2.75 | 1.40 |
| 2554 | A645 | 69p multi | 2.75 | 1.40 |
| | | Nos. 2549-2554 (6) | 12.80 | 6.40 |

**Souvenir Sheet**

| | | | |
|---|---|---|---|
| 2555 | | Sheet of 4 | 9.50 | 9.50 |
| a.-b. | A645 | 1st Either single | 1.40 | .70 |
| c.-d. | A645 | 78p Either single | 3.25 | 1.60 |

On day of issue, Nos. 2549, 2550, 2555a and 2555b each sold for 34p.

**Souvenir Sheet**

Heritage of Northern Ireland — A646

No. 2556: a, Carrickfergus Castle (18x21mm). b, Giant's Causeway, ocean and sky (18x21mm). c, St. Patrick (57x21mm). d, Queen's Bridge and Friendship Beacon, Belfast (57x21mm).

**Perf. 14¾x14¼ Syncopated, 14¾x14¼ (78p)**
**2008, Mar. 11**     Litho.

| | | | |
|---|---|---|---|
| 2556 | A646 | Sheet of 4 | 9.50 | 9.50 |
| a.-b. | | 1st Either single | 1.40 | .70 |
| c.-d. | | 78p Either single | 3.25 | 1.60 |

On day of issue Nos. 2556a-2556b each sold for 34p.

Rescue at Sea A647

Sea rescuers in action near: 1st, Barra. 46p, Appledore. 48p, Portland. 54p, St. Ives. 69p, Lee-on-Solent. 78p, Tenby.

**Perf. 14¼x14¼ Syncopated**
**2008, Mar. 13**

| | | | |
|---|---|---|---|
| 2557 | A647 | 1st multi | 1.40 | .70 |
| 2558 | A647 | 46p multi | 1.90 | .95 |
| 2559 | A647 | 48p multi | 2.00 | 1.00 |
| 2560 | A647 | 54p multi | 2.25 | 1.10 |
| 2561 | A647 | 69p multi | 2.75 | 1.40 |
| 2562 | A647 | 78p multi | 3.25 | 1.60 |
| | | Nos. 2557-2562 (6) | 13.55 | 6.75 |

No. 2557 sold for 34p on day of issue.

Endangered Insects A648

Designs: No. 2563, Adonis blue butterfly. No. 2564, Southern damselfly. No. 2565, Red-barbed ant. No. 2566, Barberry carpet moth. No. 2567, Stag beetle. No. 2568, Hazel pot beetle. No. 2569, Field cricket. No. 2570, Silver-spotted skipper. No. 2571, Purbeck mason wasp. No. 2572, Noble chafer.

**2008, Apr. 15**     Litho.   **Perf. 14½**

| | | | |
|---|---|---|---|
| 2563 | A648 | 1st multi | 1.50 | .75 |
| 2564 | A648 | 1st multi | 1.50 | .75 |
| 2565 | A648 | 1st multi | 1.50 | .75 |
| 2566 | A648 | 1st multi | 1.50 | .75 |
| 2567 | A648 | 1st multi | 1.50 | .75 |
| 2568 | A648 | 1st multi | 1.50 | .75 |
| 2569 | A648 | 1st multi | 1.50 | .75 |
| 2570 | A648 | 1st multi | 1.50 | .75 |
| 2571 | A648 | 1st multi | 1.50 | .75 |
| 2572 | A648 | 1st multi | 1.50 | .75 |
| a. | | Block of 10, #2563-2572 | 15.00 | 7.50 |

Nos. 2563-2572 each sold for 36p on day of issue.

**Seaside Resorts Type of 2007**
**Die Cut Perf. 14½**
**2008, May 13**     Photo.
**Booklet Stamp**
**Self-Adhesive**

| | | | |
|---|---|---|---|
| 2573 | A627 | 1st Like #2463 | 1.40 | .70 |
| a. | | Booklet pane, 2 #2573, 4 #MH300 | 8.50 | |

No. 2573 sold for 36p on day of issue.

A649

Cathedrals — A650

Designs: No. 2574, Lichfield Cathedral. 48p, Belfast Cathedral. 50p, Gloucester Cathedral. 56p, St. David's Cathedral, Wales. 72p, Westminster Cathedral. 81p, St. Magnus Cathedral, Orkney.
No. 2580 — St. Paul's Cathedral: a, Ceiling, denomination at UL. b, Ceiling, denomination at UR. c, Floor, denomination at UL. d, Floor, denomination at UR.

**2008, May 13**     Litho.   **Perf. 14¼**

| | | | |
|---|---|---|---|
| 2574 | A649 | 1st black | 1.40 | .70 |
| 2575 | A649 | 48p black | 1.90 | .95 |
| 2576 | A649 | 50p black | 2.00 | 1.00 |
| 2577 | A649 | 56p black | 2.25 | 1.10 |
| 2578 | A649 | 72p black | 3.00 | 1.50 |
| 2579 | A649 | 81p black | 3.25 | 1.60 |
| | | Nos. 2574-2579 (6) | 13.80 | 6.85 |

**Souvenir Sheet**

| | | | |
|---|---|---|---|
| 2580 | A650 | Sheet of 4 | 9.50 | 9.50 |
| a.-b. | | 1st Either single | 1.40 | .70 |
| c.-d. | | 81p Either single | 3.25 | 1.60 |

Nos. 2574, 2580a-2580b each sold for 36p on day of issue.

Posters of British Comedy and Horror Films A651

Poster for: 1st, Carry On Sergeant. 48p, Dracula. 50p, Carry On Cleo. 56p, The Curse of Frankenstein. 72p, Carry On Screaming. 81p, The Mummy.

**2008, June 10**   Litho.   **Perf. 13¾x14**

| | | | |
|---|---|---|---|
| 2581 | A651 | 1st multi | 1.40 | .70 |
| 2582 | A651 | 48p multi | 1.90 | .95 |
| 2583 | A651 | 50p multi | 2.00 | 1.00 |
| 2584 | A651 | 56p multi | 2.25 | 1.10 |
| 2585 | A651 | 72p multi | 3.00 | 1.50 |
| 2586 | A651 | 81p multi | 3.25 | 1.60 |
| | | Nos. 2581-2586 (6) | 13.80 | 6.85 |

No. 2581 sold for 36p on day of issue.

First Powered Flight in Great Britain, Cent. A652

Air displays: 1st, Red Arrow aerobatic team. 48p, Royal Air Force Falcons parachuting squad. 50p, Boy watching airplanes in formation. 56p, Avro Vulcans and Avro 707s in flight. 72p, Parachutist Robert Wyndham on wing of Avro 504 biplane. 81p, Blériot airplane and air race tower.

**2008, July 17  Photo.  *Perf. 14¼x14***

| | | | | |
|---|---|---|---|---|
| 2587 | A652 | 1st multi | 1.50 | .75 |
| a. | | Sheet of 20 + 17 labels, litho. | 31.00 | |
| b. | | Litho. | 1.25 | .65 |
| c. | | Booklet pane of 4, 2 each #1758a, 2587b (BK185) | 4.00 | |
| 2588 | A652 | 48p multi | 1.90 | .95 |
| 2589 | A652 | 50p multi | 2.00 | 1.00 |
| 2590 | A652 | 56p multi | 2.25 | 1.10 |
| 2591 | A652 | 72p multi | 3.00 | 1.50 |
| 2592 | A652 | 81p multi | 3.25 | 1.60 |
| | | *Nos. 2587-2592 (6)* | 13.90 | 6.90 |

No. 2587 sold for 36p on day of issue. No. 2587a sold for £7.75. Labels could not be personalized.
No. 2587c issued 9/18.

### Souvenir Sheet

**2008 Olympic Games, Beijing and 2012 Olympic Games, London — A653**

No. 2593: a, National Stadium, Beijing. b, London Eye. c, Tower of London. d, Corner Tower, Forbidden City, Beijing.

### Litho. & Silk Screened

**2008, Aug. 22  *Perf. 14½***

| | | | | |
|---|---|---|---|---|
| 2593 | A653 | Sheet of 4 | 5.75 | 5.75 |
| a.-d. | | 1st Any single | 1.40 | .70 |

On day of issue Nos. 2593a-2593d each sold for 36p.

**Royal Air Force Uniforms — A654**

Designs: No. 2594, Drum major, Royal Air Force Central Band, 2007. No. 2595, Helicopter rescue winchman, 1984. No. 2596, Hawker Hunter pilot, 1951. No. 2597, Lancaster air gunner, 1944. No. 2598, Plotter, Women's Army Air Force, 1940. No. 2599, Pilot, 1918.

**2008, Sept. 18  Litho.  *Perf. 14¼***

| | | | | |
|---|---|---|---|---|
| 2594 | A654 | 1st multi | 1.25 | .65 |
| 2595 | A654 | 1st multi | 1.25 | .65 |
| 2596 | A654 | 1st multi | 1.25 | .65 |
| a. | | Horiz. strip of 3, #2594-2596 | 3.75 | 2.00 |
| b. | | Booklet pane of 3, #2594-2596 (BK185) | 3.75 | — |
| 2597 | A654 | 81p multi | 3.00 | 1.50 |
| 2598 | A654 | 81p multi | 3.00 | 1.50 |
| 2599 | A654 | 81p multi | 3.00 | 1.50 |
| a. | | Horiz. strip of 3, #2597-2599 | 9.00 | 4.50 |
| b. | | Booklet pane of 3, #2597-2599 (BK185) | 9.00 | — |
| | | *Nos. 2594-2599 (6)* | 12.75 | 6.45 |

Nos. 2594-2596 each sold for 36p on day of issue.

### Miniature Sheet

**Country Definitive Stamps, 50th Anniv. — A655**

**Perf. 14¾x14 Syncopated**

**2008, Sept. 29  Photo.**

**Buff Paper**

| | | | | |
|---|---|---|---|---|
| 2600 | A655 | Sheet of 9 + label | 11.50 | 6.00 |
| a. | | 1st Wales & Monmouthshire Type A1 | 1.25 | .65 |
| b. | | 1st Scotland Type A1 | 1.25 | .65 |
| c. | | 1st Wales & Monmouthshire Type A3 | 1.25 | .65 |
| d. | | 1st Scotland Type A3 | 1.25 | .65 |
| e. | | 1st Northern Ireland Type A1 | 1.25 | .65 |
| f. | | 1st Wales & Monmouthshire Type A2 | 1.25 | .65 |
| g. | | 1st Scotland Type A2 | 1.25 | .65 |

| | | | | |
|---|---|---|---|---|
| h. | | 1st Northern Ireland Type A2 | 1.25 | .65 |
| i. | | 1st Northern Ireland Type A3 | 1.25 | .65 |
| j. | | As #2600e, litho., white paper | 1.25 | .65 |
| k. | | As #2600i, litho., white paper | 1.25 | .65 |
| l. | | As #2600h, litho., white paper | 1.25 | .65 |
| m. | | As #2600a, litho., white paper | 1.25 | .65 |
| n. | | As #2600b, litho., white paper | 1.25 | .65 |
| o. | | As #2600f, litho., white paper | 1.25 | .65 |
| p. | | As #2600d, litho., white paper | 1.25 | .65 |
| q. | | As #2600c, litho., white paper | 1.25 | .65 |
| r. | | As #2600g, litho., white paper | 1.25 | .65 |
| s. | | Booklet pane of 9, #2600j-2600r (BK186) | 11.50 | |
| t. | | Booklet pane of 6, #2600p-2600r, 3 Scotland #21a (BK186) | 7.50 | |
| u. | | Booklet pane of 6, #2600j-2600l, 3 Northern Ireland #18a (BK186) | 7.50 | |
| v. | | Booklet pane of 6, #2600m-2600o, 3 Wales & Monmouthshire #21b (BK186) | 7.50 | |

Nos. 2600a-2600r each sold for 36p on day of issue.

**Famous Women A656**

Designs: 1st, Millicent Garrett Fawcett (1847-1929), suffragist. 48p, Elizabeth Garrett Anderson (1836-1917), first female physician in Britain. 50p, Marie Stopes (1880-1958), birth control advocate. 56p, Eleanor Rathbone (1872-1946), politician and advocate for family allowance. 72p, Claudia Jones (1915-64), civil rights activist. 81p, Barbara Castle (1910-2002), politician and advocate for equal pay for women.

**Perf. 14¼x14½**

**2008, Oct. 14  Photo.**

| | | | | |
|---|---|---|---|---|
| 2601 | A656 | 1st multi | 1.25 | .60 |
| 2602 | A656 | 48p multi | 1.60 | .80 |
| 2603 | A656 | 50p multi | 1.60 | .80 |
| 2604 | A656 | 56p multi | 1.90 | .95 |
| 2605 | A656 | 72p multi | 2.40 | 1.25 |
| 2606 | A656 | 81p multi | 2.60 | 1.40 |
| | | *Nos. 2601-2606 (6)* | 11.35 | 5.80 |

On day of issue, No. 2601 sold for 36p.

**Christmas**

**A657            A658**

Pantomime actors: Nos. 2607a, 2607c, 2608, 2610, Ugly sisters from Cinderella. Nos. 2607b, 2607e, 2609, 2612, Genie from Aladdin. 50p, Captain Hook from Peter Pan. 81p, Wicked queen from Snow White.

**2008, Nov. 4  Photo.  *Perf. 14¾x14***

| | | | | |
|---|---|---|---|---|
| 2607 | | Sheet of 6 | 9.25 | 9.25 |
| a. | | A657 2nd multi | .85 | .40 |
| b. | | A657 1st multi | 1.10 | .55 |
| c. | | A658 2nd Large multi | 1.40 | .70 |
| d. | | A658 50p multi | 1.60 | .80 |
| e. | | A658 1st Large multi | 1.60 | .80 |
| f. | | A657 81p multi | 2.60 | 1.40 |

**Self-Adhesive**

| | | | | |
|---|---|---|---|---|
| 2608 | A657 | 2nd multi | .85 | .40 |
| a. | | Booklet pane of 12 | 10.50 | |
| b. | | Litho., die cut perf. 14¾x14 syncopated + label | .90 | .90 |
| 2609 | A657 | 1st multi | 1.10 | .55 |
| a. | | Booklet pane of 12 | 13.50 | |
| b. | | Litho., die cut perf. 14¾x14 syncopated + label | 1.25 | 1.25 |
| 2610 | A658 | 2nd Large multi | 1.40 | .70 |
| 2611 | A657 | 50p multi | 1.60 | .80 |
| 2612 | A658 | 1st Large multi | 1.60 | .80 |
| 2613 | A657 | 81p multi | 2.60 | 1.40 |
| a. | | Litho., die cut perf. 14¾x14 syncopated + label | 2.75 | 2.75 |
| b. | | Sheet of 20, 8 each #2608, 2609b, 4 #2613a + 20 labels | 28.50 | — |
| | | *Nos. 2608-2613 (6)* | 9.15 | 4.65 |

On day of issue, the franking value of Nos. 2607a, 2608, and 2608b was 27p, and that of Nos. 2607b, 2609 and 2609b was 36p. On day of issue, Nos. 2607c and 2610 sold for 42p, and Nos. 2607e and 2612 sold for 52p. No. 2613b sold for £8.85. Labels could not be personalized.
No. 2608 was also printed in sheets of 20 stamps + 20 labels that could be personalized. No. 2609b was also printed in sheets of 10 stamps + 10 labels and 20 stamps + 20 labels that could be personalized. No. 2613a was also available in a sheet of 10 stamps + 10 labels that could be personalized.

**Poppy With Soldier's Face — A659**

**2008, Nov. 6  Litho.  *Perf. 14½x14¼***

| | | | | |
|---|---|---|---|---|
| 2614 | A659 | 1st multi | 1.10 | .55 |
| a. | | Souvenir sheet of 5 | 11.50 | 11.50 |
| b. | | Horiz. strip, #2418c, 2530, 2614 | 3.50 | 1.75 |

End of World War I, 90th anniv. On day of issue, No. 2614 sold for 36p. No. 2614a contains #2614, England #18, Northern Ireland #29, Scotland #32, and Wales and Monmouthshire #32. No. 2614 also was printed in a sheet of 20 + 5 labels that sold for £7.75, and in a series of limited-quantity privately contracted sheets of 10 + 10 labels that sold for various prices.

**British Design A660**

Designs: No. 2615, Supermarine Spitfire, designed by R. J. Mitchell. No. 2616, Miniskirt, designed by Mary Quant. No. 2617, Mini Cooper, designed by Sir Alec Issigonis. No. 2618, Anglepoise lamp, designed by George Carwardine. No. 2619, Concorde, designed by Aérospatiale-BAC. No. 2620, K2 telephone kiosk, designed by Sir Giles Gilbert Scott. No. 2621, Polypropylene chair, designed by Robin Day. No. 2622, Penguin books, designed by Edward Young. No. 2623, London Underground map, designed by Harry Beck. No. 2624, Routemaster Bus, designed by AAM Durrant.

**2009, Jan. 13  Litho.  *Perf. 14½***

| | | | | |
|---|---|---|---|---|
| 2615 | A660 | 1st multi | 1.10 | .55 |
| 2616 | A660 | 1st multi | 1.10 | .55 |
| 2617 | A660 | 1st multi | 1.10 | .55 |
| a. | | Sheet of 20 + 20 labels | 24.00 | — |
| 2618 | A660 | 1st multi | 1.10 | .55 |
| 2619 | A660 | 1st multi | 1.10 | .55 |
| a. | | Booklet pane of 4, 2 each #2049a, 2619 (BK187) | 4.50 | — |
| 2620 | A660 | 1st multi | 1.10 | .55 |
| 2621 | A660 | 1st multi | 1.10 | .55 |
| 2622 | A660 | 1st multi | 1.10 | .55 |
| 2623 | A660 | 1st multi | 1.10 | .55 |
| a. | | Booklet pane of 6, #2616, 2618, 2620-2623 (BK187) | 6.75 | — |
| 2624 | A660 | 1st multi | 1.10 | .55 |
| a. | | Block of 10, #2615-2624 | 11.00 | 5.50 |
| b. | | Booklet pane of 4, #2615, 2617, 2 #2624 (BK187) | 4.50 | — |

On day of issue, Nos. 2615-2624 each sold for 36p. No. 2617a sold for £7.74. Labels on No. 2617a could not be personalized.

---

## SEMI-POSTAL STAMPS

**Catalogue values for unused stamps in this section are for Never Hinged items.**

**Handicapped Person — SP1**

**Perf. 14½x14**

**1975, Jan. 22  Photo.  Unwmk.**

| | | | | |
|---|---|---|---|---|
| B1 | SP1 | 4½p +1½p blue & lt blue | .25 | .25 |

For the benefit of health and handicap charities. No. B1 is phosphorescent.

### Christmas Type of 1989

Ely Cathedral, Cambridgeshire: No. B2, Romanesque arches, west front. No. B3, Central tower. No. B4, Interlocking arches, Romanesque arcades, west transept. No. B5, Peasant, stained-glass window in triple arch, west front.

**1989, Nov. 14  Photo.  *Perf. 15x14***

| | | | | |
|---|---|---|---|---|
| B2 | A379 | 15p +1p multicolored | .60 | .40 |
| B3 | A379 | 20p +1p multicolored | .80 | .55 |
| B4 | A379 | 34p +1p multicolored | 1.35 | .85 |
| B5 | A379 | 37p +1p multicolored | 1.50 | .95 |
| | | *Nos. B2-B5 (4)* | 4.25 | 2.75 |

### AIR POST STAMPS

**Queen Elizabeth II**
**AP1          AP2**

***Serpentine Die Cut 14¾x14 Syncopated***

**2003, Mar. 27  Photo.**

**Self-Adhesive**

**Booklet Stamps**

| | | | | |
|---|---|---|---|---|
| C1 | AP1 | (69p) blue & red | 2.75 | .85 |
| a. | | Booklet pane of 4 | 11.00 | |
| C2 | AP2 | (£1.24) red & blue | 5.00 | 1.90 |
| a. | | Booklet pane of 4 | 20.00 | |

**Queen Elizabeth II — AP3**

***Die Cut Perf. 14¾x14 Syncopated***

**2004, Apr. 1  Photo.**

**Self-Adhesive**

| | | | | |
|---|---|---|---|---|
| C3 | AP3 | (54p) blk, red & blue | 1.70 | .80 |
| a. | | Booklet of 4 + 4 etiquettes | 6.75 | |

Nos. C1-C3 were sold for 52p, £1.12 and 43p, respectively, when issued. Current face values are shown in listings.

---

### POSTAGE DUE STAMPS

**D1                D2**

**Perf. 14x14½**

| | | | Wmk. 33 | |
|---|---|---|---|---|
| **1914-22** | | **Typo.** | | |
| J1 | D1 | ½p emerald | .60 | .30 |
| | | Never hinged | 1.25 | |
| J2 | D1 | 1p rose | .60 | .30 |
| | | Never hinged | 1.75 | |
| J3 | D1 | 1½p red brown ('22) | 55.00 | 22.50 |
| | | Never hinged | 160.00 | |
| J4 | D1 | 2p brown black | .60 | .30 |
| | | Never hinged | 1.75 | |
| J5 | D1 | 3p violet ('18) | 5.75 | .85 |
| | | Never hinged | 27.50 | |
| J6 | D1 | 4p gray green ('21) | 35.00 | 5.75 |
| | | Never hinged | 140.00 | |
| J7 | D1 | 5p org brown | 7.00 | 4.00 |
| | | Never hinged | 16.00 | |
| J8 | D1 | 1sh blue | 45.00 | 5.50 |
| | | Never hinged | 150.00 | |
| | | *Nos. J1-J8 (8)* | 149.55 | 39.50 |

| | | | Wmk. 35 | |
|---|---|---|---|---|
| **1924-30** | | | | |
| J9 | D1 | ½p emerald | 1.10 | .85 |
| | | Never hinged | 3.00 | |
| J10 | D1 | 1p car rose | .65 | .30 |
| | | Never hinged | 3.00 | |
| J11 | D1 | 1½p red brown | 52.50 | 20.00 |
| | | Never hinged | 150.00 | |
| J12 | D1 | 2p black brown | 1.40 | .30 |
| | | Never hinged | 10.50 | |
| J13 | D1 | 3p violet | 1.75 | .30 |
| | | Never hinged | 11.50 | |
| a. | | Experimental wmk. | 45.00 | 40.00 |
| | | Never hinged | 92.50 | |
| b. | | Printed on the gummed side | 87.50 | |
| | | Never hinged | 140.00 | |
| J14 | D1 | 4p deep green | 17.50 | 3.50 |
| | | Never hinged | 57.50 | |
| J15 | D1 | 5p org brown ('30) | 40.00 | 32.50 |
| | | Never hinged | 110.00 | |

| J16 | D1 | 1sh blue | 11.50 | 1.10 |
|---|---|---|---|---|
| | | Never hinged | 35.00 | |
| J17 | D2 | 2sh6p brown, *yellow* | 60.00 | 2.25 |
| | | Never hinged | 250.00 | |
| | | *Nos. J9-J17 (9)* | 186.40 | 61.10 |

The experimental watermark of No. J13a resembles Wmk. 35 but is spaced more closely, with letters short and rounded, crown with flat arch and sides high, lines thicker.

**1936-37**       **Wmk. 250**

| J18 | D1 | ½p emerald ('37) | 4.25 | 9.25 |
|---|---|---|---|---|
| | | Never hinged | 8.50 | |
| J19 | D1 | 1p car rose ('37) | 1.25 | 2.25 |
| | | Never hinged | 2.50 | |
| J20 | D1 | 2p blk brown ('37) | 5.25 | 12.50 |
| | | Never hinged | 12.00 | |
| J21 | D1 | 3p violet ('37) | 1.50 | 2.50 |
| | | Never hinged | 2.75 | |
| J22 | D1 | 4p slate green | 19.00 | 40.00 |
| | | Never hinged | 40.00 | |
| J23 | D1 | 5p bister ('37) | 9.00 | 26.00 |
| | | Never hinged | 18.00 | |
| a. | | 5p orange brown | 32.50 | 29.00 |
| | | Never hinged | 62.50 | |
| J24 | D1 | 1sh blue ('36) | 6.50 | 10.50 |
| | | Never hinged | 12.50 | |
| J25 | D2 | 2sh6p brn, *yel* ('37) | 190.00 | 10.50 |
| | | Never hinged | 350.00 | |
| | | *Nos. J18-J25 (8)* | 236.75 | 113.50 |

**1938-39**       **Wmk. 251**

| J26 | D1 | ½p emerald | 5.25 | 5.75 |
|---|---|---|---|---|
| | | Never hinged | 10.50 | |
| J27 | D1 | 1p carmine rose | 1.75 | .85 |
| | | Never hinged | 3.50 | |
| J28 | D1 | 2p black brown | 1.50 | .85 |
| | | Never hinged | 3.00 | |
| J29 | D1 | 3p violet | 7.00 | 1.10 |
| | | Never hinged | 14.00 | |
| J30 | D1 | 4p slate green | 40.00 | 15.00 |
| | | Never hinged | 87.50 | |
| J31 | D1 | 5p bister ('39) | 6.00 | .85 |
| | | Never hinged | 16.00 | |
| J32 | D1 | 1sh blue | 35.00 | 2.25 |
| | | Never hinged | 80.00 | |
| J33 | D2 | 2sh6p brown, *yel* ('39) | 40.00 | 3.00 |
| | | Never hinged | 87.50 | |
| | | *Nos. J26-J33 (8)* | 136.50 | 29.65 |

> Catalogue values for unused stamps in this section, from this point to the end of the section, are for Never Hinged items.

**1951-52**

| J34 | D1 | ½p orange | 1.10 | *3.50* |
|---|---|---|---|---|
| J35 | D1 | 1p violet blue | 1.50 | 1.75 |
| J36 | D1 | 1½p green ('52) | 2.00 | 3.50 |
| J37 | D1 | 4p bright blue | 45.00 | 14.00 |
| J38 | D1 | 1sh olive bister | 40.00 | 16.00 |
| | | *Nos. J34-J38 (5)* | 89.60 | 38.75 |

**1954-55**       **Wmk. 298**

| J39 | D1 | ½p orange ('55) | 5.25 | *9.25* |
|---|---|---|---|---|
| J40 | D1 | 2p brn black ('55) | 11.50 | 14.00 |
| J41 | D1 | 3p purple ('55) | 62.50 | 42.50 |
| J42 | D1 | 4p brt blue ('55) | 22.50 | 26.00 |
| a. | | Imperf., pair | 300.00 | |
| J43 | D1 | 5p bister brn ('55) | 29.00 | 14.00 |
| J44 | D2 | 2sh6p dk pur brn, *yel* | 125.00 | 9.00 |
| | | *Nos. J39-J44 (6)* | 255.75 | 114.75 |

**1955-57**   **Wmk. 308**   **Perf. 14x14½**

| J45 | D1 | ½p orange ('56) | 2.25 | 4.50 |
|---|---|---|---|---|
| J46 | D1 | 1p ultra ('56) | 6.25 | 2.00 |
| J47 | D1 | 1½p green ('56) | 7.00 | 5.75 |
| J48 | D1 | 2p brown blk ('56) | 52.50 | 4.50 |
| J49 | D1 | 3p purple ('56) | 8.00 | 2.25 |
| J50 | D1 | 4p brt blue ('56) | 22.50 | 4.75 |
| J51 | D1 | 5p bister brn ('56) | 37.50 | 2.75 |
| J52 | D1 | 1sh dp olive bister | 80.00 | 2.75 |
| J53 | D2 | 2sh6p dk red brn, *yel* ('57) | 175.00 | 12.50 |
| J54 | D2 | 5sh red, *yellow* | 95.00 | 30.00 |
| | | *Nos. J45-J54 (10)* | 486.00 | 71.75 |

**1959-63**   **Wmk. 322**   **Perf. 14x14½**

| J55 | D1 | ½p orange ('61) | .20 | 1.40 |
|---|---|---|---|---|
| J56 | D1 | 1p ultra ('60) | .20 | .60 |
| J57 | D1 | 1½p green ('60) | 1.00 | *4.00* |
| J58 | D1 | 2p brown black | 1.25 | .60 |
| J59 | D1 | 3p purple | .40 | .35 |
| J60 | D1 | 4p brt blue ('60) | .40 | .35 |
| J61 | D1 | 5p bister brn ('62) | .50 | .70 |
| J62 | D1 | 6p dp mag ('62) | .60 | .35 |
| J63 | D1 | 1sh dp ol bis ('60) | 1.00 | .35 |
| J64 | D2 | 2sh6p dark red brown, *yellow* ('61) | 5.50 | .85 |
| J65 | D2 | 5sh red, *yellow* ('61) | 7.50 | 1.10 |
| J66 | D2 | 10sh ultra, *yel* ('63) | 11.50 | 6.25 |
| J67 | D2 | £1 blk, *yellow* ('63) | 47.50 | 8.75 |
| | | *Nos. J55-J67 (13)* | 77.55 | 25.65 |

Nos. J1-J67 are watermarked sideways.

**1968-69**   **Unwmk.**   **Typo.**

| J68 | D1 | 2p greenish black | .50 | .85 |
|---|---|---|---|---|
| J69 | D1 | 3p purple | .50 | .85 |
| J70 | D1 | 4p bright blue | .60 | .25 |
| J71 | D1 | 5p brown org ('69) | 6.00 | 11.50 |
| J72 | D1 | 6p deep magenta | 1.00 | 1.10 |
| J73 | D1 | 1sh bister ('69) | 2.25 | 1.10 |
| | | *Nos. J68-J73 (6)* | 10.85 | 15.65 |

**1968-69**      **Photo.**

| J74 | D1 | 4p bright blue ('69) | 6.00 | 5.00 |
|---|---|---|---|---|
| J75 | D1 | 8p bright red | 1.25 | .90 |

D3          D4

**Perf. 14x14½**

**1970-75**    **Photo.**    **Unwmk.**

| J79 | D3 | ½p grnsh blue ('71) | .20 | .60 |
|---|---|---|---|---|
| J80 | D3 | 1p magenta ('71) | .20 | .20 |
| J81 | D3 | 2p green ('71) | .20 | .20 |
| J82 | D3 | 3p ultra ('71) | .20 | .20 |
| J83 | D3 | 4p olive bister ('71) | .25 | .20 |
| J84 | D3 | 5p bluish lilac ('71) | .25 | .20 |
| J85 | D3 | 7p brown red ('74) | .40 | .90 |
| J86 | D4 | 10p carmine rose | .40 | .25 |
| J87 | D4 | 11p slate ('75) | .60 | 1.10 |
| J88 | D4 | 20p olive | .75 | .50 |
| J89 | D4 | 50p ultramarine | 2.00 | 1.00 |
| J90 | D4 | £1 black | 4.00 | 2.25 |
| J91 | D4 | £5 org & black ('73) | 40.00 | 3.50 |
| | | *Nos. J79-J91 (13)* | 49.45 | 11.10 |

D5          D6

**1982, June 9**   **Photo.**   **Perf. 14x14½**

| J92 | D5 | 1p rose carmine | .20 | .35 |
|---|---|---|---|---|
| J93 | D5 | 2p ultramarine | .35 | .35 |
| J94 | D5 | 3p deep rose lilac | .20 | .35 |
| J95 | D5 | 4p dark blue | .20 | .30 |
| J96 | D5 | 5p sepia | .20 | .30 |
| J97 | D5 | 10p brown | .35 | .45 |
| J98 | D5 | 20p dark ol green | .60 | .70 |
| J99 | D5 | 25p slate blue | .90 | 1.00 |
| J100 | D5 | 50p black | 1.75 | 1.25 |
| J101 | D5 | £1 vermilion | 3.50 | 1.40 |
| J102 | D5 | £2 greenish blue | 7.00 | 2.75 |
| J103 | D5 | £5 yellow bister | 16.00 | 2.25 |
| | | *Nos. J92-J103 (12)* | 31.25 | 11.45 |

**Perf. 15x14 Syncopated, Type C (2 Sides)**

**1994, Feb. 15**   **Photo. & Embossed**

| J104 | D6 | 1p vermilion & org | .20 | .60 |
|---|---|---|---|---|
| J105 | D6 | 2p red lilac & red | .20 | .60 |
| J106 | D6 | 5p yel & brn | .20 | .40 |
| J107 | D6 | 10p yel & grn | .50 | .50 |
| J108 | D6 | 20p green & blue | 1.00 | .80 |
| J109 | D6 | 25p red | 1.50 | .85 |
| J110 | D6 | £1 vio & red lilac | 7.50 | 3.00 |
| J111 | D6 | £1.20 blue & green | 10.00 | 4.00 |
| J112 | D6 | £5 green & black | 25.00 | 14.00 |
| | | *Nos. J104-J112 (9)* | 46.10 | 24.75 |

## OFFICIAL STAMPS

**Type of Regular Issue of 1840 "V R" in Upper Corners**

O1

**1840**     **Wmk. 18**     *Imperf.*

| O1 | O1 | 1p black | 20,000. | 27,500. |
|---|---|---|---|---|

No. O1 was never placed in use. Postage stamps perforated with a crown and initials "H.M.O.W.," "O.W.," "B.T." or "S.O.," or with only the initials "H.M.S.O." or "D.S.I.R.," were used for official purposes.

Counterfeits exist of Nos. O2-O83.

### Inland Revenue
Regular Issues Overprinted in Black:

a          b

Type "a" is overprinted on the stamps of ½ penny to 1 shilling, type "b" on the higher values.

**1882-85**    **Wmk. 30**    **Perf. 14**

| O2 | A35 | ½p green | 100.00 | 35.00 |
|---|---|---|---|---|
| O3 | A35 | ½p slate bl ('85) | 75.00 | 26.00 |
| O4 | A40 | 1p lilac | 4.75 | 2.50 |
| a. | | "OFFICIAL" omitted | | 8,250. |
| b. | | Ovpt. lines transposed | | |
| O5 | A47 | 2½p lilac ('85) | 350.00 | 120.00 |
| O6 | A28 | 6p gray | 475.00 | 100.00 |
| O7 | A48 | 1sh green ('85) | 4,750. | 1,400. |

     **Wmk. 31**

| O8 | A51 | 5sh car rose ('85) | 4,000. | 1,400. |
|---|---|---|---|---|
| a. | | Bluish paper ('85) | 8,750. | 3,500. |
| O9 | A52 | 10sh ultramarine | 6,000. | 2,150. |
| a. | | 10sh cobalt | 18,500. | 5,500. |
| b. | | Bluish paper | 14,000. | 4,250. |

**Wmk. Three Imperial Crowns (30)**

| O10 | A53 | £1 brown vio | 42,500. | 22,500. |
|---|---|---|---|---|

**1888-89**        **Wmk. 30**

| O11 | A54 | ½p vermilion | 9.50 | 3.50 |
|---|---|---|---|---|
| a. | | "I.R." omitted | | 4,250. |
| O12 | A65 | 1sh green ('89) | 650.00 | 220.00 |

**1890**      **Wmk. Three Orbs (29)**

| O13 | A53 | £1 brown vio | 65,000. | 30,000. |
|---|---|---|---|---|

**1891**         **Wmk. 30**

| O14 | A57 | 2½p violet, *blue* | 130.00 | 16.00 |
|---|---|---|---|---|

**Wmk. Three Imperial Crowns (30)**

**1892**

| O15 | A53 | £1 green | 8,750. | 2,250. |
|---|---|---|---|---|
| a. | | No period after "R" | — | 3,000. |

**1901**         **Wmk. 30**

| O16 | A54 | ½p blue green | 16.00 | 11.00 |
|---|---|---|---|---|
| O17 | A62 | 6p violet, *rose* | 350.00 | 100.00 |
| O18 | A65 | 1sh car rose & green | 3,000. | 1,000. |

**1902-04**

| O19 | A66 | ½p gray green | 26.00 | 2.75 |
|---|---|---|---|---|
| O20 | A66 | 1p carmine | 19.00 | 1.90 |
| O21 | A66 | 2½p ultra | 825.00 | 100.00 |
| O22 | A66 | 6p dull vio ('04) | 165,000. | 75,000. |
| O23 | A74 | 1sh car rose & green | 2,750. | 140.00 |

     **Wmk. 31**

| O24 | A76 | 5sh car rose | 12,000. | 7,000. |
|---|---|---|---|---|
| O25 | A77 | 10sh car ultra | 65,000. | 30,000. |

**Wmk. Three Imperial Crowns (30)**

| O26 | A78 | £1 green | 45,000. | 22,500. |
|---|---|---|---|---|

Nos. O4, O8, O9 and O15 also exist with overprint in blue black.

### Government Parcels

Overprinted

**1883-86**        **Wmk. 30**

| O27 | A45 | 1½p lilac ('86) | 350.00 | 70.00 |
|---|---|---|---|---|
| O28 | A46 | 6p green ('86) | 2,100. | 875.00 |
| O29 | A50 | 9p green | 1,750. | 700.00 |
| O30 | A29 | 1sh salmon (P13) | 1,050. | 250.00 |
| | | Plate 14 | 2,500. | 350.00 |
| | | *Nos. O27-O30 (4)* | 5,250. | 1,895. |

**1887-92**

| O31 | A55 | 1½p violet & green | 100.00 | 8.50 |
|---|---|---|---|---|
| O32 | A56 | 2p green & car rose ('91) | 175.00 | 24.00 |
| O33 | A60 | 4½p car rose & grn ('92) | 300.00 | 220.00 |
| O34 | A62 | 6p violet, *rose* | 175.00 | 37.50 |

| O35 | A63 | 9p blue & lil ('88) | 275.00 | 55.00 |
|---|---|---|---|---|
| O36 | A65 | 1sh green | 500.00 | 200.00 |
| | | *Nos. O31-O36 (6)* | 1,525. | 545.00 |

**1897**

| O37 | A40 | 1p lilac | 82.50 | 17.50 |
|---|---|---|---|---|
| a. | | Inverted overprint | 4,500. | 2,100. |

**1900**

| O38 | A65 | 1sh car rose & grn | 525.00 | 200.00 |
|---|---|---|---|---|
| a. | | Inverted overprint | | 11,000. |

**1902**

| O39 | A66 | 1p carmine | 35.00 | 14.00 |
|---|---|---|---|---|
| O40 | A68 | 2p green & car | 160.00 | 40.00 |
| O41 | A66 | 6p dull violet | 275.00 | 40.00 |
| O42 | A72 | 9p ultra & violet | 550.00 | 175.00 |
| O43 | A74 | 1sh car rose & grn | 1,000. | 275.00 |
| | | *Nos. O39-O43 (5)* | 2,020. | 544.00 |

### Office of Works

Overprinted

| O44 | A54 | ½p vermilion | 250.00 | 120.00 |
|---|---|---|---|---|
| O45 | A40 | 1p lilac | 400.00 | 120.00 |

Overprinted

**1901-02**

| O46 | A54 | ½p blue green | 350.00 | 175.00 |
|---|---|---|---|---|
| O47 | A61 | 5p lilac & ultra | 2,500. | 875.00 |
| O48 | A64 | 10p car rose & lil | 4,000. | 1,200. |

**1902**

| O49 | A66 | ½p gray green | 600.00 | 175.00 |
|---|---|---|---|---|
| O50 | A66 | 1p carmine | 600.00 | 175.00 |
| O51 | A68 | 2p green & car | 1,750. | 425.00 |
| O52 | A66 | 2½p ultramarine | 2,400. | 650.00 |
| O53 | A73 | 10p car rose & vio | 25,000. | 5,500. |

### Army
Overprinted:

a          b

**1896**

| O54 | A54(a) | ½p vermilion | 5.25 | 2.75 |
|---|---|---|---|---|
| a. | | "OFFICIAI" | 240.00 | 110.00 |
| O55 | A40(a) | 1p lilac | 4.25 | 3.00 |
| a. | | "OFFICIAI" | 175.00 | 105.00 |
| O56 | A57(b) | 2½p violet, *blue* | 35.00 | 24.00 |
| | | *Nos. O54-O56 (3)* | 44.50 | 29.75 |

**1900**

| O57 | A54(a) | ½p blue green | 5.00 | 8.25 |
|---|---|---|---|---|

**1901**

| O58 | A62(b) | 6p violet, *rose* | 87.50 | 47.50 |
|---|---|---|---|---|

**1902**

| O59 | A66(a) | ½p gray green | 6.00 | 2.40 |
|---|---|---|---|---|
| O60 | A66(a) | 1p carmine | 6.00 | 2.40 |
| a. | | "ARMY" omitted | | — |
| O61 | A66(a) | 6p dull violet | 175.00 | 80.00 |
| | | *Nos. O59-O61 (3)* | 187.00 | 84.80 |

Overprinted

**1903**

| O62 | A66 | 6p dull violet | 2,200. | 875.00 |
|---|---|---|---|---|

## Royal Household

Overprinted

**1902**
| | | | | |
|---|---|---|---|---|
| O63 | A66 | ½p gray green | 400.00 | 220.00 |
| O64 | A66 | 1p carmine | 350.00 | 190.00 |

## Board of Education

Overprinted

**1902**
| | | | | |
|---|---|---|---|---|
| O65 | A61 | 5p lilac & ultra | 2,500. | 650.00 |
| O66 | A65 | 1sh car rose & grn | 6,500. | 4,000. |

**1902-04**
| | | | | |
|---|---|---|---|---|
| O67 | A66 | ½p gray green | 175.00 | 40.00 |
| O68 | A66 | 1p carmine | 175.00 | 40.00 |
| O69 | A66 | 2½p ultramarine | 3,500. | 300.00 |
| O70 | A71 | 5p lilac & ultra ('04) | 17,500. | 5,000. |
| O71 | A74 | 1sh car rose & grn | 82,500. | — |

## Admiralty

Overprinted

**1903**
| | | | | |
|---|---|---|---|---|
| O72 | A66 | ½p gray green | 30.00 | 14.00 |
| O73 | A66 | 1p carmine | 17.50 | 7.00 |
| O74 | A67 | 1½p vio & green | 275.00 | 130.00 |
| O75 | A68 | 2p green & car | 300.00 | 140.00 |
| O76 | A66 | 2½p ultra | 425.00 | 130.00 |
| O77 | A69 | 3p violet, yel | 350.00 | 140.00 |
| | | Nos. O72-O77 (6) | 1,397. | 561.00 |

Overprinted

**1903**
| | | | | |
|---|---|---|---|---|
| O78 | A66 | ½p gray green | 60.00 | 24.00 |
| O79 | A66 | 1p carmine | 60.00 | 24.00 |
| O80 | A67 | 1½p vio & green | 800.00 | 550.00 |
| O81 | A68 | 2p green & car | 1,300. | 600.00 |
| O82 | A66 | 2½p ultramarine | 1,400. | 800.00 |
| O83 | A69 | 3p violet, yel | 1,200. | 300.00 |

The two types of the "Admiralty Official" overprint differ principally in the shape of the letter "M."

## ENVELOPES

Britannia Sending Letters to World
(William Mulready, Designer) — E1

Illustration reduced.

**1840**
| | | | | |
|---|---|---|---|---|
| U1 | E1 | 1p black | 350.00 | 450.00 |
| U2 | E1 | 2p blue | 450.00 | 1,650. |

---

### LETTER SHEETS
| | | | | |
|---|---|---|---|---|
| U3 | E1 | 1p black | 325.00 | 425.00 |
| U4 | E1 | 2p blue | 400.00 | 1,650. |

### REGIONAL ISSUES

Sold only at post offices within the respective regions, but valid for postage throughout Great Britain. Issues for Guernsey, Jersey and Isle of Man are listed with the Bailiwick issues that follow.

Starting in 1967, all Regional stamps were issued only with phosphorescence.

> Catalogue values for unused stamps in this section are for Never Hinged items.

---

## ENGLAND

Three Lions — A1

***Perf. 15x14 Syncopated***
**2001-02** — Photo.
| | | | | |
|---|---|---|---|---|
| 1 | A1 | 2nd shown | .95 | .40 |
| 2 | A1 | 1st Crowned Lion | 1.35 | .55 |
| 3 | A1 | E Oak tree | 1.90 | 1.00 |
| 4 | A1 | 65p Tudor rose | 2.60 | 2.00 |
| 5 | A1 | 68p Tudor rose | 2.90 | 1.50 |
| | | Nos. 1-5 (5) | 9.70 | 5.45 |

Issued: Nos. 1-4, 4/23/01. No. 5, 7/4/02.
Nos. 1-3 sold for 19p, 27p and 36p respectively on day of issue.

### Type of 2001 With White Frames
***Perf. 14¾x14 Syncopated***
**2003, Oct. 14** — Photo.
| | | | | |
|---|---|---|---|---|
| 6 | A1 | 2nd Three lions | .95 | .40 |
| 7 | A1 | 1st Crowned lion | 1.35 | .60 |
| 8 | A1 | E Oak tree | 1.90 | 1.00 |
| 9 | A1 | 68p Tudor rose | 2.90 | 1.50 |
| | | Nos. 6-9 (4) | 7.10 | 3.50 |

Nos. 6-8 each sold for 20p, 28p and 38p respectively on day of issue.

### Type of 2001 With White Frames
***Perf. 14¾x14 Syncopated***
**2004, May 11** — Photo.
| | | | | |
|---|---|---|---|---|
| 10 | A1 | 40p Oak tree | 1.60 | .80 |
| a. | | Booklet pane, 2 each #6, 10 + label (BK177) | 5.00 | — |

No. 10a issued 2/24/05.

### Type of 2001 With White Frames
***Perf. 14¾x14 Syncopated***
**2005, Apr. 5** — Photo.
| | | | | |
|---|---|---|---|---|
| 11 | A1 | 42p Oak tree | 1.70 | .85 |

### Type of 2001 With White Frames
***Perf. 14¾x14 Syncopated***
**2006, Mar. 28** — Photo.
| | | | | |
|---|---|---|---|---|
| 12 | A1 | 44p Oak tree | 1.75 | .90 |
| 13 | A1 | 72p Tudor rose | 2.90 | 1.50 |

### Type of 2001 With White Frames
***Perf. 14¾x14 Syncopated***
**2007** — Photo.
| | | | | |
|---|---|---|---|---|
| 14 | A1 | 48p Oak tree | 1.90 | .95 |
| 15 | A1 | 78p Tudor rose | 3.25 | 1.60 |

**Litho.**
**Self-Adhesive**
***Die Cut Perf. 14¾x14***
**Stamp + Label**
| | | | | |
|---|---|---|---|---|
| 16 | A1 | 1st Crowned lion | 1.50 | 1.50 |

Issued: Nos. 14, 15, 3/27; No. 16, 4/23. No. 16 was issued in sheets of 20 stamps + 20 labels that sold for £7.35 and had a franking value of 34p on day of issue.

---

### Types of 2001 With White Frames
***Perf. 14¾x14 Syncopated***
**2008, Apr. 1** — Photo.
| | | | | |
|---|---|---|---|---|
| 17 | A1 | 50p Oak tree | 2.00 | 1.00 |
| 18 | A1 | 81p Tudor rose | 3.25 | 1.60 |

## NORTHERN IRELAND

A1　　　　　　　　A2

Flax and Red Hand of Ulster — A3

***Perf. 15x14***
**1958-67** — Photo. — Wmk. 322
| | | | | |
|---|---|---|---|---|
| 1 | A1 | 3p dark purple | .20 | .20 |
| p. | | Phosphor. ('67) | .20 | .20 |
| 2 | A1 | 4p ultra ('66) | .20 | .20 |
| p. | | Phosphor. ('67) | .20 | .20 |
| 3 | A2 | 6p rose lilac | .30 | .20 |
| 4 | A2 | 9p dk green ('67) | .35 | .80 |
| 5 | A3 | 1sh3p dark green | .35 | .80 |
| 6 | A3 | 1sh6p dark blue ('67) | .35 | .80 |
| | | Nos. 1-6 (6) | 1.75 | 3.00 |

Nos. 4, 6 and following are phosphorescent. For stamps with denomination of "1st" see No. 2600.

**1968-69** — Unwmk.

Design: 1sh6p, Flax plant, Red Right Hand of Ulster and Ulster field gate.
| | | | | |
|---|---|---|---|---|
| 7 | A1 | 4p ultramarine | .20 | .20 |
| 8 | A1 | 4p olive brown | .20 | .20 |
| 9 | A1 | 4p bright red ('69) | .30 | .20 |
| 10 | A1 | 5p dark blue | .20 | .20 |
| 11 | A3 | 1sh6p dark blue ('69) | 3.00 | 3.00 |
| | | Nos. 7-11 (5) | 3.90 | 3.80 |

Giants Causeway — A4

***Perf. 14¾x14 Syncopated***
**2001-02** — Litho.
| | | | | |
|---|---|---|---|---|
| 12 | A4 | 2nd shown | .95 | .25 |
| 13 | A4 | 1st Farm fields | 1.35 | .60 |
| a. | | Booklet pane, 5 #12, 4 #13 (BK173) | 10.00 | |
| 14 | A4 | E Linen | 1.90 | .90 |
| 15 | A4 | 65p Parian China | 2.60 | 1.35 |
| 16 | A4 | 68p Parian China | 2.70 | 1.40 |
| | | Nos. 12-16 (5) | 9.50 | 4.50 |

Issued: Nos. 12-15, 3/6/01; No. 16, 7/4/02; No. 13a, 2/25/03.
Nos. 12-14 sold for 19p, 27p and 36p respectively on day of issue.

### Type of 2001 With White Frames
***Perf. 14¾x14 Syncopated***
**2003, Oct. 14** — Photo.
| | | | | |
|---|---|---|---|---|
| 17 | A4 | 2nd Giant's Causeway | .95 | .40 |
| 18 | A4 | 1st Farm fields | 1.35 | .50 |
| a. | | Litho. (#2600u) ('08) | 1.25 | .65 |
| 19 | A4 | E Linen | 1.90 | .90 |
| 20 | A4 | 68p Parian China | 2.70 | 1.40 |
| | | Nos. 17-20 (4) | 6.90 | 3.20 |

Nos. 17-19 each sold for 20p, 28p and 38p respectively on day of issue.
No. 21a issued 9/28/08.

### Type of 2001 With White Frames
***Perf. 14¾x14 Syncopated***
**2004, May 11** — Photo.
| | | | | |
|---|---|---|---|---|
| 21 | A4 | 40p Linen | 1.60 | .80 |

### Type of 2001 With White Frames
***Perf. 14¾x14 Syncopated***
**2005, Apr. 5** — Photo.
| | | | | |
|---|---|---|---|---|
| 22 | A4 | 42p Linen | 1.70 | .90 |

---

### Type of 2001 With White Frames
***Perf. 14¾x14 Syncopated***
**2006, Mar. 28** — Photo.
| | | | | |
|---|---|---|---|---|
| 23 | A4 | 44p Linen | 1.75 | .90 |
| 24 | A4 | 72p Parian China | 2.90 | 1.50 |

### Type of 2001 With White Frames
***Perf. 14¾x14 Syncopated***
**2007, Mar. 27** — Photo.
| | | | | |
|---|---|---|---|---|
| 25 | A4 | 48p Linen | 1.90 | .95 |
| 26 | A4 | 78p Parian China | 3.25 | 1.60 |

### Type of 2001 With White Frames
***Die Cut Perf. 14¾x14***
**2008, Mar. 11** — Litho.
**Self-Adhesive**
**Stamp + Label**
| | | | | |
|---|---|---|---|---|
| 27 | A4 | 1st Farm fields | 1.50 | 1.50 |

No. 27 was issued in sheets of 20 stamps + 20 labels that sold for £7.35, and had a franking value of 34p on day of issue.

### Types of 2001 With White Frames
***Perf. 14¾x14 Syncopated***
**2008, Apr. 1** — Photo.
| | | | | |
|---|---|---|---|---|
| 28 | A4 | 50p Linen | 2.00 | 1.00 |
| 29 | A4 | 81p Parian China | 3.25 | 1.60 |

## SCOTLAND

St. Andrew's Cross and Thistle — A1　　　A2

A3

***Perf. 15x14***
**1958-67** — Photo. — Wmk. 322
| | | | | |
|---|---|---|---|---|
| 1 | A1 | 3p dark purple | .20 | .20 |
| p. | | Phosphor. | .20 | .20 |
| 2 | A1 | 4p ultra ('66) | .20 | .20 |
| p. | | Phosphor. ('67) | .20 | .20 |
| 3 | A2 | 6p rose lilac | .25 | .20 |
| p. | | Phosphor. ('63) | .25 | .20 |
| 4 | A2 | 9p dark green ('67) | .40 | .45 |
| 5 | A3 | 1sh3p dark green | .45 | .45 |
| p. | | Phosphor. ('63) | .45 | .45 |
| 6 | A3 | 1sh6p dark blue ('67) | .50 | .55 |
| | | Nos. 1-6 (6) | 2.00 | 2.05 |

The 3p with two phosphorescent bands was issued in 1963; with one side band in 1965, and one center band in 1967. The value of No. 1p is for one center band. Nos. 4, 6 and following are phosphorescent. For stamps with denomination of "1st" see No. 2600.

**1967-70** — Unwmk.
| | | | | |
|---|---|---|---|---|
| 7 | A1 | 3p purple ('68) | .20 | .20 |
| 8 | A1 | 4p ultramarine | .20 | .20 |
| 9 | A1 | 4p olive brown ('68) | .20 | .20 |
| 10 | A1 | 4p brt red ('69) | .20 | .20 |
| 11 | A1 | 5p dark blue ('68) | .25 | .20 |
| 12 | A2 | 9p dark green ('70) | 6.50 | 5.75 |
| 13 | A3 | 1sh6p dark blue ('68) | 1.60 | 1.60 |
| | | Nos. 7-13 (7) | 9.15 | 8.35 |

Natl. Flag (St. Andrew's Cross) — A4

***Perf. 14¾x14 Syncopated***
**1999-2002** — Photo.
| | | | | |
|---|---|---|---|---|
| 14 | A4 | (2nd) shown | .95 | .30 |
| 15 | A4 | (1st) Lion Rampant | 1.35 | .45 |
| a. | | Booklet pane, #15, 4 England #1, 4 England #2 (BK172) | 10.50 | |
| 16 | A4 | (E) Thistle | 1.10 | .50 |
| a. | | Booklet pane, 4 each #15-16, + label (BK170) | 8.25 | |

| 17 | A4 | 64p Tartan | 10.00 | 2.50 |
| 18 | A4 | 65p As #17 | 2.40 | 1.25 |
| a. | | Booklet pane, 6 #14, 2 #18 + label (BK168) | 9.00 | |
| 19 | A4 | 68p Tartan | 2.50 | 1.40 |
| | | *Nos. 14-19 (6)* | 18.30 | 6.40 |

#14-16 sold for 19p, 26p, & 30p, respectively, on day of issue.
Issued: #14-17, 6/8; #18, 4/25/00; #18a, 8/4/00; #16a, 10/22/01. #19, 7/4/02. #15a, 9/24/02.

### Type of 1999 With White Frames
*Perf. 14¾x14 Syncopated*

| 2003, Oct. 14 | | | Photo. | |
|---|---|---|---|---|
| 20 | A4 | 2nd National flag | .95 | .40 |
| a. | | Booklet pane, 3 each England #9, Scotland #20 (BK175) | 11.50 | — |
| 21 | A4 | 1st Lion rampant | 1.35 | .50 |
| 21a | | Litho. (#2600t) | 1.25 | .65 |
| 22 | A4 | E Thistle | 1.90 | .90 |
| 23 | A4 | 68p Tartan | 2.70 | 1.30 |
| | | *Nos. 20-23 (5)* | 8.15 | 3.75 |

Nos. 20-22 each sold for 20p, 28p and 38p respectively on day of issue.
No. 20a issued 3/16/04. No. 21a issued 9/28/08.
See Great Britain No. 2419a for National Flag stamp inscribed "1st."

### Type of 1999 With White Frames
*Perf. 14¾x14 Syncopated*

| 2004, May 11 | | | Photo. | |
|---|---|---|---|---|
| 24 | A4 | 40p Thistle | 1.60 | .80 |
| a. | | Souvenir sheet, #20, 2 each #21, 24 | 6.75 | 4.50 |

No. 24a issued 10/5/04.

### Type of 1999 With White Frames
*Perf. 14¾x14 Syncopated*

| 2005, Apr. 5 | | | Photo. | |
|---|---|---|---|---|
| 25 | A4 | 42p Thistle | 1.70 | .85 |

### Type of 1999 With White Frames
*Perf. 14¾x14 Syncopated*

| 2006, Mar. 28 | | | Photo. | |
|---|---|---|---|---|
| 26 | A4 | 44p Thistle | 1.75 | .90 |
| 27 | A4 | 72p Tartan | 2.90 | 1.50 |

### Type of 1999 With White Frames
*Perf. 14¾x14 Syncopated*

| 2007, Mar. 27 | | | Photo. | |
|---|---|---|---|---|
| 28 | A4 | 48p Thistle | 1.90 | .95 |
| 29 | A4 | 78p Tartan | 3.25 | 1.60 |

### Type of 1999 With White Frames
*Die Cut Perf. 14¾x14*

| 2007, Nov. 30 | | | Litho. | |
|---|---|---|---|---|

**Self-Adhesive**
**Stamp + Label**

| 30 | A4 | 1st Lion rampant | 1.75 | 1.75 |

No. 30 was issued in sheets of 20 stamps + 20 labels that sold for £8.50, and had a franking value of 34p on day of issue.

### Types of 1999 With White Frames
*Perf. 14¾x14 Syncopated*

| 2008, Apr. 1 | | | Photo. | |
|---|---|---|---|---|
| 31 | A4 | 50p Thistle | 2.00 | 1.00 |
| 32 | A4 | 81p Tartan | 3.25 | 1.60 |

## WALES & MONMOUTHSHIRE

A1

A2

Welsh Dragon — A3

Designs: 6p, 9p, Dragon in rectangular panel at bottom. 1sh3p, 1sh6p, Dragon and leek.

---

### Perf. 15x14

| 1958-67 | | | Photo. | Wmk. 322 |
|---|---|---|---|---|
| 1 | A1 | 3p dark purple | .20 | .20 |
| p. | | Phosphor. band ('67) | .20 | .20 |
| 2 | A1 | 4p ultra ('66) | .20 | .20 |
| p. | | Phosphor. bands ('67) | .20 | .20 |
| 3 | A2 | 6p rose lilac | .40 | .35 |
| 4 | A2 | 9p dark green ('67) | .45 | .40 |
| 5 | A3 | 1sh3p dark green | .45 | .45 |
| 6 | A3 | 1sh6p dark blue ('67) | .45 | .45 |
| | | *Nos. 1-6 (6)* | 2.15 | 2.05 |

Nos. 4, 6 and following are phosphorescent. For stamps with denomination of "1st" see No. 2600.

| 1967-69 | | | | Unwmk. |
|---|---|---|---|---|
| 7 | A1 | 3p dark purple | .20 | .20 |
| 8 | A1 | 4p ultra ('68) | .20 | .20 |
| 9 | A1 | 4p olive brown ('68) | .20 | .20 |
| 10 | A1 | 4p brt red ('69) | .20 | .20 |
| 11 | A1 | 5p dark blue ('68) | .20 | .20 |
| 12 | A3 | 1sh6p dark blue ('69) | 4.00 | 4.00 |
| | | *Nos. 7-12 (6)* | 5.00 | 5.00 |

Leek — A4

### Perf. 15x14 Syncopated

| 1999-2002 | | | Photo. | |
|---|---|---|---|---|
| 13 | A4 | 2nd shown | .95 | .30 |
| 14 | A4 | 1st Dragon | 1.35 | .45 |
| 15 | A4 | E Daffodil | 1.90 | .75 |
| 16 | A4 | 64p Prince of Wales feathers | 10.00 | 3.50 |
| 17 | A4 | 65p Prince of Wales feathers | 2.60 | 1.30 |
| | | *Nos. 13-17 (5)* | 16.80 | 6.30 |
| 18 | A2 | 2nd Leek, perf 13¾x14¼ | 5.50 | .30 |
| a. | | Booklet pane, 4 each #18, MH336 + label (BK169) | 27.50 | |
| 19 | A4 | 68p Prince of Wales Feathers | 3.00 | 1.50 |

#13, 18 sold for 19p; #14, 26p; & #15, 30p, on day of issue.
Issued: #13-16, 6/8; #17, 4/25/00. #19, 7/4/02.
No. 18 is a booklet stamp.

### Type of 1999 With White Frames
*Perf. 14¾x14 Syncopated*

| 2003, Oct. 14 | | | Photo. | |
|---|---|---|---|---|
| 20 | A4 | 2nd Leek | .95 | .40 |
| 21 | A4 | 1st Dragon | 1.35 | .50 |
| a. | | Booklet pane, England #7, Northern Ireland #18, Scotland, #21, Wales & Monmouthshire #21, + 5 labels (BK183) | 5.75 | |
| b. | | Litho. (#2600v) ('08) | 1.25 | .65 |
| 22 | A4 | E Daffodil | 1.90 | .70 |
| 23 | A4 | 68p Prince of Wales feathers | 2.70 | 1.40 |
| a. | | Souvenir sheet, #20, 2 each #21, 23 ('06) | 9.00 | 5.00 |
| | | *Nos. 20-23 (4)* | 6.90 | 3.00 |

Nos. 20-22 each sold for 20p, 28p and 38p respectively on day of issue.
No. 23a issued 3/1/06. No. 21b issued 9/28/08

### Type of 1999 With White Frames
*Perf. 14¾x14 Syncopated*

| 2004, May 11 | | | Photo. | |
|---|---|---|---|---|
| 24 | A4 | 40p Daffodil | 1.60 | .80 |

### Type of 1999 With White Frames
*Perf. 14¾x14 Syncopated*

| 2005, Apr. 5 | | | Photo. | |
|---|---|---|---|---|
| 25 | A4 | 42p Daffodil | 1.70 | .85 |

### Type of 1999 With White Frames
*Perf. 14¾x14 Syncopated*

| 2006-07 | | | Photo. | |
|---|---|---|---|---|
| 26 | A4 | 44p Daffodil | 1.75 | .90 |
| a. | | Booklet pane, 3 each Scotland #20, Wales & Monmouthshire #26 (BK181) ('07) | 8.00 | — |
| 27 | A4 | 72p Prince of Wales feathers | 2.90 | 1.50 |

**Self-Adhesive**
**Litho.**
**Stamp + Label**
*Die Cut Perf. 14¾x14*

| 28 | A4 | 1st Dragon | 1.40 | 1.40 |
| a. | | Sheet, 5 each #28, England #16, Northern Ireland #27, Scotland #30 + 20 labels ('08) | 27.50 | — |

No. 28 was issued in a sheet of 20 stamps + 20 different se-tenant labels that sold for

---

£6.95. The franking value of No. 28 was 32p on day of issue.
No. 28a issued 9/29/08. No. 28a sold for £7.74. Labels could not be personalized.
Issued: Nos. 26, 27, 3/28; Nos. 26a, 28 issued 3/1/07.

### Type of 1999 With White Frames
*Perf. 14¾x14 Syncopated*

| 2007, Mar. 27 | | | Photo. | |
|---|---|---|---|---|
| 29 | A4 | 48p Daffodil | 1.90 | .95 |
| 30 | A4 | 78p Prince of Wales feathers | 3.25 | 1.60 |

### Types of 1999 With White Frames
*Perf. 14¾x14 Syncopated*

| 2008, Apr. 1 | | | Photo. | |
|---|---|---|---|---|
| 31 | A4 | 50p Daffodil | 2.00 | 1.00 |
| 32 | A4 | 81p Prince of Wales feathers | 3.25 | 1.60 |

---

# MACHINS

## MACHIN DEFINITIVE STAMPS

### Sterling Currency Issue

MA1

Type I          Type II

Two types of 2p:
Type I — Head off-center to right. Foot of "2" 1mm from left margin.
Type II — Head centered. Foot of "2" ½mm from left margin.

£1          £1
MH21          MH168

Two types of "£" symbol:
No. MH21 has a loop at the bottom and the numeral is a figure "1."
No. MH168 has no loop and numeral is like a capital "I."

### Perf. 15x14

| 1967-69 | | | Photo. | Unwmk. |
|---|---|---|---|---|
| | | Size: 17½x21½mm | | |
| MH1 | | ½ brown orange | .20 | .20 |
| MH2 | | 1p olive | .20 | .20 |
| a. | | Booklet pane of 6 (BK101-BK104, BK121) | 1.00 | |
| MH3 | | 2p maroon (I) | .20 | .20 |
| MH4 | | 2p maroon (II) | .20 | .20 |
| MH5 | | 3p dark violet | .20 | .20 |
| a. | | Booklet pane of 6 (BK121) | 12.00 | |
| b. | | Booklet pane, 2 ea #MH2, MH5 (BK83) | 3.50 | |
| c. | | imperf, pair | 800.00 | |
| MH6 | | 4p brown black | .20 | .20 |
| a. | | Bklt. pane of 2 + 2 labels (BK84) | 1.10 | |
| b. | | Bklt. pane of 4 (BK83-BK84) | 1.10 | |
| c. | | Booklet pane of 6 (BK101-BK102, BK114-BK115, BK121-BK122) | 1.50 | |
| d. | | Booklet pane, 4 #MH2, 2 #MH6 (BK122) | 4.50 | |
| MH7 | | 4p bright red | .20 | .20 |
| a. | | Bklt. pane of 2 + 2 labels (BK85) | 1.10 | |
| b. | | Booklet pane of 4 (BK85) | 1.10 | |
| c. | | Booklet pane of 6 (BK103-BK104, BK116-BK117, BK123-BK124) | 1.10 | |
| d. | | Booklet pane of 15 + recipe (BK125-BK126) | 5.00 | |
| e. | | Booklet pane, 4 #MH2, 2 #MH7 (BK123-BK124) | 4.00 | |
| f. | | Coil strip of 5, #MH2, #MH5, #MH7, 2 #MH4 | 3.00 | |
| MH8 | | 5p dark blue | .20 | .20 |
| a. | | Booklet pane of 6 (BK110-BK112, BK122-BK124) | 1.50 | |
| b. | | Booklet pane, 6 each #MH2, #MH7, 3 #MH8 + recipe (BK125-BK126) | 16.00 | |
| c. | | Booklet pane of 15 + recipe (BK125-BK126) | 6.00 | |
| MH9 | | 6p magenta | .30 | .30 |
| MH10 | | 7p bright green | .45 | .40 |

---

| MH11 | | 8p scarlet | .20 | .50 |
|---|---|---|---|---|
| MH12 | | 8p lt greenish blue | .60 | .70 |
| MH13 | | 9p dark green | .45 | .30 |
| MH14 | | 10p gray | .60 | .60 |
| MH15 | | 1sh light violet | .50 | .30 |
| MH16 | | 1sh6p indigo & greenish bl | .60 | .60 |
| a. | | Greenish blue omitted | 110.00 | |
| MH17 | | 1sh9p black & orange | .60 | .50 |

### Perf. 12
**Engr.**
**Size: 27x31mm**

| MH18 | | 2sh6p brown | .90 | .20 |
|---|---|---|---|---|
| MH19 | | 5sh dark carmine | 2.25 | .70 |
| MH20 | | 10sh ultramarine | 7.00 | 7.00 |
| MH21 | | £1 bluish black | 3.75 | 1.75 |
| | | *Nos. MH1-MH21 (21)* | 19.80 | 15.45 |

Nos. MH10-MH13 have denomination at right. Many of Nos. MH1-MH17 exist with phosphor bands omitted in error.
Issued: ½p, 1p, #MH3, 6p, 2/5/68; #MH4, 8/27/69; 3p, 4/6/68; #MH6, 1sh, 1sh9p, 6/5/67; #MH7, #MH12, 1/6/69; 5p, 7p, #MH11, 10p, 7/1/68; 9p, 1sh6p, 8/8/67; #MH18-MH21, 3/5/69.

### Decimal Currency Issues
(P Instead of D)

MA2

Nos. MH22-MH189, MH199-MH243 are Type MA2. Specialized illustrations are shown for identification purposes.
Two types of 1p: Type I: Thick numeral and "p," which are 2½mm from bottom of design. Type II: Thinner numeral and "p," which are 3mm from bottom of design.

### Perf. 15x14

| 1970-95 | | | Photo. | Unwmk. |
|---|---|---|---|---|
| | | Size: 17½x21½mm | | |
| MH22 | | ½p greenish blue | .20 | .20 |
| a. | | Booklet pane of 5 + label (BK129-BK130, BK132, BK138, BK143) | 4.50 | |
| MH23 | | 1p magenta, Type I | .20 | .20 |
| MH23A | | 1p magenta, Type II | .60 | .60 |
| MH24 | | 1½p black | .20 | .20 |
| a. | | Booklet pane, 2 each #MH23-MH24 (BK127-BK128) | 2.00 | |

Issued: ½p, #MH23, 1½p, 2/15/71. #MH23A, 8/4/80.

2p   2p   2p
a    b    c

Three types of 2p:
a, Wide "2," thick at bottom of curve.
b, Wide "2," thin at bottom of curve.
c, Narrow "2."

| MH25 | | 2p light green (a) | .20 | .20 |
|---|---|---|---|---|
| a. | | Coil strip, 2 ea #MH22-MH23, 1 #MH25 | .60 | |
| MH26 | | 2p light green (b) | .20 | .20 |
| a. | | Booklet pane, 2 each #MH22, MH26(BK127-BK128) | 4.00 | |
| b. | | Booklet pane of 6 + printed margin (BK145) | .60 | |
| MH27 | | 2p dark green (c) | .20 | .20 |
| MH28 | | 2p light green (c) | 4.00 | 3.00 |

**Litho.**

| MH29 | | 2p dk grn, perf 14 (a) | .20 | .20 |
|---|---|---|---|---|
| MH30 | | 2p dark green (a) | .30 | .20 |
| MH31 | | 2p dark green (c) | 1.00 | .80 |
| MH31A | | 2p dk grn, perf 14 (c) | 2.00 | 1.00 |

Nos. MH24a, MH26a exist with with stamps se-tenant vertically or horizontally.
Issued: #MH25, 12/12/79; #MH26, 2/15/71; #MH27, 9/5/88; #MH28, 7/26/88; #MH29, 5/21/80; #MH30, 7/10/84; #MH31, 2/23/88; MH31A, 2/9/93.
No. MH31A comes from #MH128a (BK420) only.

2½p   2½p   2½p
a      b      c

Three types of 2½p:
a, Thick numerals & "P," end of curve of small "2" is thick.

b, Thinner numerals & "P," end of curve of small "2" is thin.
c, Very thin numerals & "P," end of curve of small "2" is pointy.

| | | | |
|---|---|---|---|
| **MH32** | 2½p pink (a) | .20 | .20 |
| *a.* | Booklet pane of 4 + 2 labels (BK129-BK130, BK132) | 5.75 | |
| *b.* | Booklet pane of 5 + label (BK129-BK130, BK132, BK138, BK143) | 5.50 | |
| **MH33** | 2½p pink (b) | .30 | .60 |
| **MH34** | 2½p pink (c) | 2.00 | 3.00 |
| *a.* | Booklet pane, 3 #MH22, 9 #MH34 + printed margin (BK144) | 25.00 | |
| *b.* | Booklet pane, 4 #MH22, 2 #MH34 + printed margin (BK144) | 75.00 | |

#MH34a, MH34b valued in F-VF condition.

| | | | |
|---|---|---|---|
| **MH35** | 2½p vermilion (b) | .45 | .70 |

Issued: #MH32 2/15/71; MH33, 5/21/75; #MH34, 5/24/72; MH35, 1/14/81.
#MH34 issued only in booklets.

a     b

Two types of 3p:
a, Thick numeral with top serif.
b, Thin numeral without serif.

| | | | |
|---|---|---|---|
| **MH36** | 3p ultramarine (a) | .20 | .20 |
| *a.* | Booklet pane, 2 #MH32, 4 #MH36 (BK138, BK143) | 8.00 | |
| *b.* | Booklet pane, 5 + label (BK131, BK133-BK136, BK139) | 5.00 | |
| *c.* | Bklt. pane of 6 (BK138, BK143) | 5.00 | |
| *d.* | Booklet pane of 12, 6 each #MH34, #MH36 + printed margin (BK144) | 18.00 | |
| *e.* | Booklet pane of 12 + printed margin (BK144) | 10.00 | |
| **MH37** | 3p deep lilac rose (a) | .20 | .20 |
| *a.* | Coil strip, #MH35, 3 #MH37 | .75 | .35 |
| **MH38** | 3p deep lilac rose (b) | 1.50 | .75 |

Issued: #MH36, 9/10/73; #MH37, 10/22/80; #MH38, 1/21/92.

a     b

Two types of 3½p:
a, Numerals in fraction aligned diagonally.
b, Numerals in fraction aligned vertically.

| | | | |
|---|---|---|---|
| **MH39** | 3½p gray green (a) | .40 | .40 |
| *a.* | Booklet pane of 5 + label (BK137, BK139-BK141) | 6.00 | |
| **MH40** | 3½p violet brown (b) | 1.25 | 1.40 |

Issued: #MH39, 6/24/74; #MH40, 3/30/83.

a    b    c

Three types of 4p:
a, Wide "4" with large serif and thick crossbar.
b, Wide "4" with small serif and thin crossbar.
c, Narrow "4."

| | | | |
|---|---|---|---|
| **MH41** | 4p olive bister (a) | .30 | .20 |
| *a.* | Imperf., pair | | |
| **MH42** | 4p greenish blue (a) | .40 | .75 |
| *a.* | Coil strip, #MH22, 3 MH42 | 1.50 | 2.50 |
| **MH43** | 4p brt greenish bl (a) | .20 | .20 |
| *a.* | Coil strip, #MH23, 3 MH43 | 3.25 | |
| *b.* | Coil strip, #MH28, 3 MH43 | 4.25 | |
| **MH44** | 4p greenish blue (b) | 2.25 | 2.25 |
| **MH45** | 4p brt greenish bl (c) | 1.75 | 2.25 |
| **MH46** | 4p bright blue (c) | 1.25 | .20 |
| *a.* | Coil strip, #MH38, 3 MH46 | 5.25 | |
| **MH47** | 4p Prussian blue, litho., perf 13½x14 (b) | .30 | .40 |
| **MH48** | 4p Prus blue, litho. (c) | .80 | .85 |
| **MH49** | 4½p grayish blue | .50 | .20 |
| *a.* | Booklet pane of 5 + label (BK140, BK142) | 6.00 | |

Issued: #MH41, 2/15/71; #MH42-MH42a, 12/30/81; #MH43-MH43a, 8/14/84; #MH43b, 9/5/88. #MH44, 8/26/81; #MH45, 9/3/84; #MH46, 7/26/88; #MH46a, 9/19/89. #MH47, 1/30/80; #MH48, 5/13/86; 4 1/2p, 10/24/73.
#MH43 issued only in strips.

a     b

---

Two types of 5p:
a, 5p is 3.25mm wide.
b, 5p is 2.75mm wide.

| | | | |
|---|---|---|---|
| **MH50** | 5p bluish lilac (a) | .30 | .20 |
| **MH51** | 5p lilac, litho., perf 13½x14 (a) | .45 | .45 |
| **MH52** | 5p red brown, litho., perf 13½x14 (a) | .60 | .60 |
| **MH53** | 5p red brown, litho. (a) | .70 | .20 |
| **MH54** | 5p red brown (b) | 2.50 | 1.25 |
| **MH55** | 5p brown (b) | .20 | .35 |
| *a.* | Coil strip, #MH55, 3 #MH46 | 4.00 | |
| *b.* | Coil strip, 2 ea #MH46, #MH55 | 2.75 | |
| *c.* | Coil strip, #MH46, 3 #MH55 | 1.75 | |
| **MH56** | 5½p dark violet | .35 | .35 |

Issued: #MH50, 2/15/71; #MH51, 5/21/80; #MH52, 1/27/82; #MH53, 2/21/84; #MH54, 10/20/86; #MH55, 7/26/88; #MH55b, 11/27/90; #MH55b, 10/1/91. #MH55c, 1/31/95. 5 1/2p, 10/24/73.

a    b    c

Three types of 6p:
a, Thick numeral and "P."
b, Thinner numeral and "P," numeral is pointed at top and very thin where loop joins.
c, Narrow numeral.

| | | | |
|---|---|---|---|
| **MH57** | 6p light emerald (a) | .30 | .20 |
| **MH58** | 6p light emerald (b) | .65 | .20 |
| *a.* | Booklet pane, #MH58, 2 #MH22, 3 #MH23 (BK225) | 1.50 | |
| *b.* | Coil strip, #MH23, MH26, MH58, 2 #MH22 | 1.10 | |
| **MH59** | 6p brt olive green (c) | .25 | .20 |
| **MH60** | 6½p Prussian blue | .35 | .40 |

Issued: #MH57, 2/15/71; #MH58, 6/9/76; #MH58b, 12/3/75. #MH59, 9/10/91; 6 1/2p, 9/4/74.
#MH58 issued only in booklets and strips.

a     b

Two types of 7p:
a, Wide numeral.
b, Narrow numeral.

| | | | |
|---|---|---|---|
| **MH61** | 7p dark red brown (a) | .35 | .40 |
| *a.* | Coil strip, #MH61, 2 ea MH22-MH23 | | .60 |
| *b.* | Booklet pane, #MH61, 2 ea MH22-MH23 + label (BK226) | .75 | |
| **MH62** | 7p henna brown (b) | 1.25 | *1.50* |
| **MH63** | 7½p lt red brown | .40 | .40 |
| **MH64** | 8p red | .35 | .20 |
| *a.* | Coil strip, #MH64, 2 #MH23 + 2 labels | .60 | |
| *b.* | Booklet pane, #MH64, 2 MH23 + label (BK227) | .75 | |
| **MH65** | 8½p yellow green | .35 | .20 |
| *a.* | Bklt. pane, 2 ea #MH22-MH23, MH60, 4 MH65 (BK228) | 5.25 | |

No. MH65a exists with the four 8 1/2p stamps se-tenant on either the left or right side of the pane.

| | | | |
|---|---|---|---|
| **MH66** | 9p black & ocher | .65 | .25 |
| **MH67** | 9p violet blue | .45 | .20 |
| *a.* | Booklet pane, 2 #MH23, 3 ea MH61, MH67 (BK229-BK230) | 3.50 | |
| *b.* | Booklet pane, 10 ea #MH61, MH67 (BK672) | 6.50 | |

No. MH67a exists with the three 9p stamps se-tenant on either the left or right side of the pane.

| | | | |
|---|---|---|---|
| **MH68** | 9½p bright lilac | .40 | .50 |

Issued: #MH61, 1/15/75; #MH61a, 12/14/77. #MH62, 10/29/85; 7 1/2p, 2/15/71; 8p, 10/24/73; #MH64a, 1/16/80. 8 1/2p, 9/24/75; #MH66, 2/15/71; #MH67 9 1/2p, 2/25/76.

a    b    c

Three types of 10p:
a, Round "0."
b, Thin part of "0" at upper left, lower right.
c, Thin part of "0" at top, bottom.

| | | | |
|---|---|---|---|
| **MH69** | 10p org brn & lt org (a) | .65 | .35 |
| **MH70** | 10p light org brn (b) | .45 | .30 |
| *a.* | Bklt. pane of 9 + printed margin (BK145) | 2.50 | |
| *b.* | Booklet pane, 2 ea #MH26, MH64, 3 #MH70 + label (BK231-BK232) | 2.50 | |

---

| | | | |
|---|---|---|---|
| *c.* | Booklet pane, 10 ea #MH64, MH70 (BK709) | 6.25 | |
| **MH70D** | 10p light org brn (c) | 35.00 | 20.00 |

No. MH70b exists with the three 10p stamps se-tenant on either the left or right side of the pane.

| | | | |
|---|---|---|---|
| **MH71** | 10p brn orange (c) | .60 | .50 |
| **MH72** | 10½p yellow | .50 | .50 |
| **MH73** | 10½p steel blue | .80 | .60 |
| **MH74** | 11p pink | .50 | .20 |

Issued: #MH69, 8/11/71; #MH70, MH72, 11p, 2/25/76; #MH71, 9/4/90; #MH73, 4/26/78; #MH70D, 9/4/84.

a     b

Two types of 11½p:
a, Thin numerals in fraction.
b, Thick numerals in fraction.

| | | | |
|---|---|---|---|
| **MH75** | 11½p olive bister (a) | .65 | .65 |
| **MH76** | 11½p gray brown (a) | .50 | .40 |
| *a.* | Booklet pane, 2 #MH42, 3 each MH35, MH76 (BK236) | 4.50 | |
| **MH77** | 11½p gray brown (b) | .60 | .20 |

#MH77 comes from #MH86c (BK826), only.
Issued: #MH75, 8/15/79; #MH76, 1/14/81; #MH77, 11/11/81;

a     b

Two types of 12p:
a, Wide numerals.
b, Narrow, thin numerals.

| | | | |
|---|---|---|---|
| **MH78** | 12p yellow green (a) | .55 | .50 |
| *a.* | Booklet pane of 9 + printed margin (BK145) | 3.00 | |
| *b.* | Booklet pane of 9 (#MH26, 4 each #MH70, MH78) + printed margin (BK145) | 13.50 | |
| *c.* | Booklet pane of 10 each #MH70, MH78 (BK759) | 9.00 | |
| *d.* | Booklet pane, 3 #MH26, 2 each MH70, MH78 + label (BK233) | 2.25 | |
| **MH79** | 12p bright green (b) | .60 | .35 |
| *a.* | Booklet pane of 9 + printed margin (BK140) | 6.00 | |
| *b.* | Booklet pane, 2 #MH23, 4 MH79 (BK245) | 8.00 | |

Issued: #MH78, 1/30/80; #MH79, 10/29/85.

 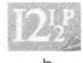

a     b

Two types of 12½p:
a, Thin, narrow numerals.
b, Thick, wider numerals.

| | | | |
|---|---|---|---|
| **MH80** | 12½p light emerald (a) | .50 | .25 |
| *a.* | Booklet pane of 6 + printed margin (BK146-BK147) | 5.00 | |
| *b.* | Booklet pane of 9, #MH25, MH37, 7 MH80 + printed margin (BK146) | 6.00 | |
| *c.* | Booklet pane, #MH22, 4 MH37, 3 MH80 (BK237-BK238) | 3.00 | |
| *d.* | Booklet pane, 2 #MH23, 3 each MH40, MH80 (BK239) | 7.50 | |
| *e.* | Booklet pane of 20 (BK760) | 8.00 | |

No. MH80c exists with the three 12½p stamps se-tenant on either the left or right side of the pane. Booklets with 20 #MH80 were sold at a discount. Stamps in these booklets had 5-point double-lined stars printed on the reverse.

| | | | |
|---|---|---|---|
| **MH81** | 12½p green (b) | .80 | .25 |

No. MH81 comes from #MH93d (BK572).
Issued: #MH80, 1/27/82; #MH81, 2/1/82.

a     b

Two types of 13p:
a, "3" with serif.
b, "3" without serif.

| | | | |
|---|---|---|---|
| **MH82** | 13p gray green (a) | .60 | .55 |
| **MH83** | 13p lt red brown (b) | .50 | .20 |
| *a.* | Booklet pane of 6 + printed margin (BK148, BK151) | 3.50 | |
| *b.* | Booklet pane of 9 + printed margin (BK149, BK151) | 5.00 | |
| *c.* | Booklet pane, 2 #MH45, 3 each MH23, MH83 (BK240) | 4.75 | |

---

| | | | |
|---|---|---|---|
| *d.* | Booklet pane, #MH23, 2 MH54, 3 #MH83 (BK244, BK248) | 5.00 | |
| *e.* | Booklet pane of 4, margins all around (BK285) | 3.00 | |
| *f.* | Booklet pane of 10, margins all around (BK534) | 6.00 | |
| *g.* | As "d," imperf edges (BK248A, BK250-BK251) | 5.00 | |

Panes of #MH83 with stars printed on the reverse were sold at a discount.

| | | | |
|---|---|---|---|
| **MH84** | 13p lt red brn, litho. (b) | 1.00 | .85 |
| *a.* | Booklet pane of 6 + printed margin (BK152) | 6.00 | |
| **MH85** | 13½p brown purple | .70 | .70 |

Issued: #MH82, 8/15/79; #MH83, 8/28/84; #MH84, 2/9/88; 13½p, 1/30/80.

a     b

Two types of 14p:
a, Wide "4."
b, Narrow "4."

| | | | |
|---|---|---|---|
| **MH86** | 14p gray blue (a) | .70 | .60 |
| *a.* | Bklt. pane, #MH22-MH23, MH86, 3 #MH76 (BK234-BK235) | 2.25 | |
| *b.* | Booklet pane, 4 #MH76, 6 MH86 (BK524) | 5.25 | |
| *c.* | Booklet pane, 10 each #MH77, MH86 (BK826) | 12.50 | |
| **MH87** | 14p dark blue (b) | .60 | .40 |
| *a.* | Booklet pane of 4, margins all around (BK295) | 5.00 | |
| *b.* | Booklet pane of 4, imperf on B (BK296) | 5.00 | |
| *c.* | Booklet pane of 4, imperf on T, B, R (BK297) | 19.00 | |
| *d.* | Booklet pane of 10, margins all around (BK558) | 5.50 | |
| *e.* | Booklet pane of 10, imperf on T, B (BK560) | 8.00 | |
| **MH88** | 14p dark blue, litho. (b) | 2.00 | 2.00 |
| **MH89** | 14p dark blue, litho., perf 14 (b) | 5.00 | .90 |

No. MH89 comes from #MH108a (BK412), only.

| | | | |
|---|---|---|---|
| **MH90** | 15p deep ultramarine | .70 | .70 |
| **MH91** | 15p bright blue | .75 | .25 |

Issued: #MH86, 1/14/81; #MH87, 9/5/88; #MH88, 10/11/88; #MH89, 4/25/89; #MH90, 8/15/79; #MH91, 9/26/89.

a     b

Two types of 15½p:
a, Thin numerals in fraction, top bar of "5" thin.
b, Thick numerals in fraction, top bar of "5" thick.

| | | | |
|---|---|---|---|
| **MH92** | 15½p light violet (a) | .70 | .60 |
| *a.* | Booklet pane of 6 + printed margin (BK146) | 4.25 | |
| *b.* | Booklet pane of 9 + printed margin (BK146) | 6.50 | |
| **MH93** | 15½p light violet (b) | .70 | .35 |
| *c.* | Booklet pane, 4 #MH80, 6 MH93 (BK573-BK574) | 6.75 | |
| *d.* | Booklet pane, 4 #MH81, 6 MH93 (BK572) | 8.25 | |
| *e.* | Booklet pane, 10 each #MH80, MH93 (BK802) | 11.00 | |

No. MH93e was printed with 10-point single-line blue stars on the reverse over the gum.

| | | | |
|---|---|---|---|
| **MH94** | 16p brownish gray | .65 | .65 |
| *a.* | Booklet pane, #MH37, 2 MH40, 6 MH94 + printed margin (BK147) | 4.50 | |
| *b.* | Booklet pane of 9 + printed margin (BK147) | 5.50 | |
| *c.* | Booklet pane, 4 #MH80, 6 MH94 (BK594) | 12.00 | |

Panes of #MH94 with double-line D printed on reverse were sold at a discount in BK584.

| | | | |
|---|---|---|---|
| **MH95** | 16½p fawn | 1.00 | .85 |

Issued: #MH92, 1/14/81; #MH93, 2/1/82; 16p, 3/30/83; 16 1/2p, 1/27/82.
#MH93 issued only in booklets.

a     b

Two types of 17p:
a, Wide "7."
b, Narrow "7."

| | | | |
|---|---|---|---|
| **MH96** | 17p light green (a) | .85 | .70 |
| **MH97** | 17p blue gray (b) | .70 | .70 |
| *a.* | Booklet pane of 3 + label (star printed on reverse-BK241-BK242) | 2.50 | |

|   |   |   |   |
|---|---|---|---|
| b. | Booklet pane of 9 + printed margin (BK149-BK150) | 7.00 | |
| c. | Booklet pane of 6 + printed margin (BK148-BK150) | 20.00 | |
| d. | Booklet pane of, #MH70D, MH83, 7 MH97 + printed margin (BK148) | 45.00 | |
| e. | Booklet pane, 4 #MH79, 6 MH97 (BK616-BK618) | 7.00 | |
| f. | Booklet pane, 4 #MH83, 6 MH97 (BK641) | 6.00 | |
| g. | Booklet pane of 10 (double-lined "D" printed on reverse-BK652) | 6.00 | |
| MH98 | 17p dark blue (b) | 1.25 | .35 |
| a. | Bklt. pane of 3 + label (BK256) | 3.00 | |
| MH99 | 17p dk bl, litho. (b) | 1.00 | .35 |
| a. | Booklet pane of 6 + printed margin (BK155) | 6.50 | |
| MH100 | 17½p lt red brown | .90 | .85 |
| MH101 | 18p violet blue | .80 | .80 |
| MH102 | 18p olive green | .85 | .70 |
| a. | Booklet pane of 9 + printed margin (BK151) | 7.00 | |
| b. | Booklet pane, #MH23, MH83, 2 MH102 (BK246-BK247, BK249) | 3.00 | |
| c. | Booklet pane of 4, margins all around (BK328) | 4.00 | |
| d. | Booklet pane, #MH83, 5 MH102 (BK406-BK407) | 6.00 | |
| e. | Booklet pane of 10, margins all around (BK714) | 8.75 | |
| f. | As "d," imperf edges (BK408-BK410) | 6.00 | |
| MH103 | 18p ol grn, litho. | 1.00 | 1.10 |
| a. | Booklet pane of 6 + printed margin (BK152) | 5.75 | |
| b. | Booklet pane of 9 + printed margin (BK157) | 7.75 | |
| MH104 | 18p brt yel grn | .75 | .40 |
| MH105 | 18p brt yel grn, litho. | 1.40 | 1.60 |
| a. | Booklet pane of 6 + printed margin (BK157) | 7.75 | |
| MH106 | 19p brt orange | 1.25 | .35 |
| a. | Bklt. pane, #MH87, 2 MH106 + label (BK252-BK253) | 3.75 | |
| b. | Booklet pane, 2 #MH87, 4 MH106 (BK411, BK413) | 8.00 | |
| c. | Booklet pane of 4, margins all around (BK348) | 8.00 | |
| d. | Booklet pane of 4, imperf on T, B (BK349) | 9.75 | |
| e. | Booklet pane of 4, imperf on T, B, R (BK350) | 19.00 | |
| f. | Booklet pane of 4, margins all around (BK729) | 14.00 | |
| g. | Booklet pane of 10, imperf on T, B (BK730) | 10.00 | |
| MH107 | 19p red org, litho. | 2.25 | 2.25 |
| MH108 | 19p red org, litho., perf 14 | 2.50 | 1.00 |
| a. | Booklet pane, 2#MH89, 4 MH108 (BK412) | 17.00 | |
| MH110 | 19½p olive gray | 1.75 | 1.50 |

Issued: #MH96, 1/30/80; #MH97, 3/30/80; #MH98, 9/4/90; #MH99, 3/19/91; 17½p, 1/30/80; #MH101, 1/14/81; #MH102, 8/28/84; #MH103, 2/9/88; #MH104, 9/10/91; #MH105, 10/27/92; #MH106, 8/3/88; #MH107, 10/11/88; #MH108, 4/25/89; 19½p, 1/27/82.

#MH99, MH103, MH105, MH108 issued only in booklets.

 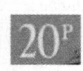

a      b

Two types of 20p:
a, Thin part of "0" at upper left, lower right.
b, Thin part of "0" at top, bottom.

|   |   |   |   |
|---|---|---|---|
| MH111 | 20p dp pur brn (a) | 1.25 | .20 |
| MH112 | 20p dp pur brn, litho., perf 13¾x14 (a) | 1.40 | 1.10 |
| MH113 | 20p dp pur brn, litho., perf 15x14 (b) | 2.00 | 1.25 |
| MH114 | 20p greenish bl (b) | 1.00 | .80 |
| MH115 | 20p brown black | 1.10 | 1.10 |
| a. | Booklet pane, 2 #MH91, MH115 + label (BK254) | 5.00 | |
| b. | Booklet pane of 5 + label (BK414) | 8.00 | |
| MH116 | 20½p ultramarine | 1.50 | 1.10 |
| MH117 | 22p dark blue | 1.00 | .85 |
| MH118 | 22p yellow green | 1.00 | .90 |
| MH119 | 22p yel grn, litho. (MH150a) | 14.00 | 3.00 |
| MH120 | 22p orange red | 1.00 | .90 |
| a. | Booklet pane, 2 #MH98, 3 MH120 + 3 labels (BK417) | 3.75 | |
| MH121 | 22p org red, litho. | 1.40 | 1.00 |
| a. | Booklet pane of 9 + printed margin (BK155) | 10.00 | |
| MH122 | 23p rose pink | 1.50 | .50 |
| MH123 | 23p brt yel grn | 1.00 | 1.00 |
| MH124 | 24p violet | 1.75 | 1.75 |
| MH125 | 24p brown red | 2.25 | 1.90 |
| MH126 | 24p brown | 1.00 | .90 |
| a. | Booklet pane, 2 each #MH23, MH126 (BK257-BK259) | 1.75 | |
| b. | Booklet pane, 2 #MH27, 4 MH126 + 2 labels (BK418-BK419) | 3.50 | |
| MH127 | 24p brown, litho. | 1.25 | 1.25 |
| a. | Booklet pane of 6 + printed margin (BK157) | 8.00 | |

|   |   |   |   |
|---|---|---|---|
| MH128 | 24p brn, litho. perf 14 | 1.50 | .35 |
| a. | Booklet pane, 2 #MH31A, 4 MH128 + 2 labels (BK420) | 9.50 | |
| MH129 | 25p lilac | 1.00 | 1.10 |
| MH129A | 25p salmon | 12.50 | 12.50 |

Issued: #MH111, 2/25/76; #MH112, 5/21/80; #MH113, 5/13/86; #MH114, 8/23/88; #MH115, 9/26/89; 20½p, 3/30/83; #MH117, 10/22/80; #MH118, 8/28/84; #MH119, 2/9/88; #MH120, 9/4/90; #MH121, 3/19/91; #MH122, 3/30/83; #MH123, 8/3/88; #MH124, 8/28/84; MH125, 9/26/89; #MH126, 9/10/91; #MH127, 10/27/92; #MH128, 2/9/93; 25p, 1/14/81.

#MH119, MH121, MH127 issued only in booklets.

No. MH129A was issued 2/6/96 only in coils.

a      b

Two types of 26p:
a, Wide numerals.
b, Narrow numerals.

|   |   |   |   |
|---|---|---|---|
| MH130 | 26p red (a) | 1.25 | .70 |
| a. | Booklet pane, #MH23, MH130, 2 MH83, 5 MH102 + printed margin (BK151) | 20.00 | |
| MH131 | 26p red (b) | 6.00 | 6.00 |
| a. | Booklet pane of 4, margins all around (BK446) | 24.00 | |
| MH132 | 26p olive gray (b) | 1.75 | 1.40 |
| MH133 | 27p brown | 1.50 | 1.50 |
| a. | Booklet pane of 4, margins all around (BK456) | 14.50 | |
| b. | Booklet pane of 4, horiz. edges imperf (BK457) | 35.00 | |
| MH134 | 27p violet | 1.75 | 1.40 |
| MH135 | 28p deep violet blue | 1.40 | 1.40 |
| MH136 | 28p dk violet bister | 1.60 | 1.40 |
| MH137 | 28p dull blue green | 1.60 | 1.40 |

Issued: #MH130, 1/27/82; #MH131, 8/4/87; #MH132, 9/4/90; #MH133, 8/3/88; #MH134, 9/4/90; #MH135, 3/30/83; #MH136, 8/23/88; #MH137, 9/10/91.

#MH131 issued only in booklets.

a      b

Two types of 29p:
a, Wide numerals.
b, Narrow numerals.

|   |   |   |   |
|---|---|---|---|
| MH138 | 29p brown olive (a) | 2.25 | 2.00 |
| MH139 | 29p dp rose lilac (b) | 2.50 | 2.00 |
| MH140 | 29p dp rose lilac, litho., perf 14 (b) | 4.75 | 3.00 |
| a. | Booklet pane of 4, imperf edges (BK478) | 20.00 | |
| MH141 | 30p dk olive green | 1.40 | 1.40 |
| MH142 | 31p brt rose lilac | 1.40 | 1.40 |
| a. | Bklt. pane, #MH142, 6 MH79, 2 MH97 + printed margin (BK150) | 17.00 | |
| MH143 | 31p ultramarine | 1.90 | 1.75 |
| MH144 | 31p ultra, litho., perf 14 | 2.75 | 1.60 |
| a. | Booklet pane of 4, imperf on T, B (BK503) | 11.00 | |
| MH145 | 32p Prussian blue | 2.25 | 2.00 |
| MH146 | 33p emerald | 2.00 | 1.90 |
| MH147 | 33p emerald, litho. | 3.00 | 3.00 |
| a. | Bklt. pane, 6 #MH121, 2 MH147 + label, printed margin (BK155) | 15.00 | |
| MH148 | 33p emer., litho. perf 14 | 2.75 | .45 |
| a. | Booklet pane of 4 margins all around (BK544) | 11.00 | |
| MH149 | 34p dark brown | 2.00 | 2.00 |
| a. | Bklt. pane, #MN149, 2 MH45, 4 MH83, 2 MH97 + printed margin (BK149) | 17.00 | |
| MH150 | 34p dark brn, litho. | 9.50 | 2.00 |
| a. | Bklt. pane, 4 #MH84, 1 ea MH103, MH119, MH150 + printed margin (BK152) | 27.50 | |
| MH151 | 34p dull blue green | 2.25 | 2.10 |
| MH152 | 34p brt rose lilac | 2.00 | 2.00 |
| MH153 | 35p dark brown | 1.90 | 1.90 |
| MH154 | 35p orange yellow | 2.00 | 1.90 |
| MH155 | 37p scarlet | 2.25 | 2.00 |
| MH156 | 39p brt rose lilac | 1.90 | 1.75 |
| MH157 | 39p brt rose lil, litho., perf 14 | 2.25 | .80 |
| a. | Booklet pane of 4, imperf on T, B (BK662) | 9.00 | |
| MH158 | 39p brt rose lil, litho. (MH178a, MH187b) | 2.50 | .80 |

Issued: #MH138, 1/27/82; #MH139, 9/26/89; #MH140, 10/2/89; #MH141, 9/26/89; #MH142, 3/30/83; #MH143, 9/4/90; #MH144, 9/17/90; #MH145, 8/23/88; #MH146, 9/4/90; #MH147, 3/19/91; #MN148, 9/16/91; #MH149, 8/28/84; #MH150, 2/9/88; #MH151, 9/26/89; #MH152, 9/10/91; #MH153, 8/23/88; #MH154, 9/10/91; #MH155, 9/26/89; #MH156, 9/10/91; #MH157, 9/16/91; #MH158, 10/27/92.

#MH144, MH147-MH148, MH150 issued only in booklets.

 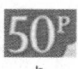

a      b

Two types of 50p:
a, Wide numerals.
b, Narrow numerals.

|   |   |   |   |
|---|---|---|---|
| MH159 | 50p bister brown (a) | 2.25 | .35 |
| MH160 | 50p ocher (b) | 2.00 | .80 |

Issued: #MH159, 2/2/77; #MH160, 5/21/80.

a      b

Two types of 75p:
a, Wide numerals.
b, Narrow numerals.

|   |   |   |   |
|---|---|---|---|
| MH161 | 75p black, litho., perf 13½x14 (a) | 4.00 | 1.50 |
| MH162 | 75p black, litho. (a) | 4.00 | 1.50 |
| MH163 | 75p black, litho. (b) | 12.00 | 9.75 |
| MH164 | 75p black (b) | 4.00 | 2.00 |

Issued: #MH161, 3/1/80; #MH162, 2/21/84; #MH163, 2/23/88; #MH164, 7/26/88.

### Engr.
### Perf. 12
### Size: 27x31mm

|   |   |   |   |   |
|---|---|---|---|---|
| MH165 | 10p carmine rose | | .60 | .85 |
| MH166 | 20p olive | | 1.00 | .20 |
| MH167 | 50p ultramarine | | 2.00 | .60 |
| p. | Phosphor | | 2.50 | .60 |
| MH168 | £1 bluish black | | 4.25 | 1.25 |

For illustration of £1, see above #MH1.
No. MH168, imperf, are from printers' waste.
Issued: #MH165-MH167, 6/17/70; £1, 12/6/72.

### Photo.
### Perf. 14x15
### Size: 27x38mm

|   |   |   |   |
|---|---|---|---|
| MH169 | £1 olive grn & yel | 4.00 | .60 |
| MH170 | £1.30 slate bl & buff | 6.25 | 7.00 |
| MH171 | £1.33 black & pale rose lilac | 8.75 | 8.00 |
| MH172 | £1.41 indigo & buff | 9.25 | 9.75 |
| MH173 | £1.50 blk & lt pink | 5.75 | 5.75 |
| MH174 | £1.60 indigo & buff | 7.50 | 8.00 |
| MH175 | £2 mar & lt grn | 14.00 | 1.50 |
| MH176 | £5 dk bl & pink | 32.50 | 4.00 |

Issued: £1, 2/2/77; £1.30, 8/3/83; £1.33, 8/28/84; £1.41, 9/17/85; £1.50, 9/2/86; £1.60, 9/15/87; £2, £5, 2/2/77.

### 2nd or 1st Class (Non-Denominated)

2nd and 1st class stamps sell for the current rates and remain valid indefinitely for the indicated service

#### Perf. 15x14

|   |   |   |   |
|---|---|---|---|
| MH177 | 2nd bright blue | 1.25 | 1.10 |
| a. | Booklet pane of 4, imperf on T, B, R (BK961) | 25.00 | |
| b. | Booklet pane of 10, imperf on T, B (BK1028, BK1078) | 15.00 | |
| MH178 | 2nd bright blue, litho. | 1.25 | 1.00 |
| a. | Booklet pane, 2 each #MH105, MH147, MH158, MH178 + label, printed margin (BK158) | 15.00 | |
| MH179 | 2nd bright blue, litho., perf 14 | 1.25 | 1.10 |
| a. | Booklet pane of 4, imperf on T, B, R (BK960) | 5.00 | |
| b. | Booklet pane of 4, imperf on T, B (BK963-BK964) | 5.00 | |
| c. | Booklet pane of 10, imperf on T, B (BK1034-BK1035) | 12.50 | |

Nos. MH177-MH179 each sold for 14p on day of issue.

|   |   |   |   |
|---|---|---|---|
| MH180 | 2nd dark blue | 1.40 | .30 |
| a. | Booklet pane of 10, imperf on T, B (BK1030) | 8.50 | |
| MH181 | 2nd dark blue, litho. | 2.00 | .30 |
| MH182 | 2nd dark blue, litho., perf 14 | .95 | .30 |
| a. | Booklet pane of 4, imperf on T, B (BK962) | 3.75 | |
| b. | Booklet pane of 10, imperf on T, B (BK1032) | 20.00 | |

Nos. MH180-MH182 each sold for 15p on day of issue.

|   |   |   |   |
|---|---|---|---|
| MH183 | 1st brown black | 2.00 | .65 |
| a. | Booklet pane of 4, imperf on T, B, R (BK995) | 25.00 | |
| b. | Booklet pane of 10, imperf on T, B (BK1041) | 20.00 | |

|   |   |   |   |
|---|---|---|---|
| MH184 | 1st brown black, litho., perf 14 | 2.25 | .65 |
| a. | Booklet pane of 4, imperf on T, B, R (BK994) | 9.50 | |
| MH185 | 1st brown black, litho. | 2.50 | .65 |

Nos. MH183-MH185 each sold for 19p on day of issue.

|   |   |   |   |
|---|---|---|---|
| MH186 | 1st orange red | 1.35 | .40 |
| a. | Booklet pane of 10, imperf on T, B (BK1068, BK1091) | 13.50 | |
| MH187 | 1st orange red, litho. | 1.35 | .40 |
| a. | Booklet pane, 3 each #MH178, MH187 + printed margin (BK158) | 7.75 | |
| b. | Booklet pane, #MH178, MH187, 2 ea MH105, MH127, MH158 + label, printed margin (BK157) | 15.00 | |
| c. | Booklet pane of 8+ label, printed margin (BK156) | 10.50 | |
| d. | Booklet pane of 10, imperf on T, B (BK1092-BK1093) | 13.50 | |

No. MH187c contains #MH178, MH187, 2 each MH147, WMMH34, WMMH45.

|   |   |   |   |
|---|---|---|---|
| MH188 | 1st orange red, litho., perf 14 | 1.35 | .40 |
| a. | Booklet pane of 4, imperf on T, B (BK996-BK997) | 5.50 | |
| b. | Booklet pane of 10, imperf on T, B (BK1070) | 13.50 | |
| MH189 | 1st orange red, litho., perf 13x13½ | 2.50 | 1.50 |

Nos. MH186-MH189 each sold for 20p on day of issue.
Distance of denomination to the margin and bust may vary on different printings of the same stamp.
Issued: #MH177, 8/22/89; #MH178, 9/18/89; #MH179, 8/22/89; #MH180-MH182, 8/7/90; #MH183-MH184, 8/22/89; #MH185, 9/19/89; #MH186-MH188, 8/7/90; #MH189, 10/90.

#MH177-MH189 issued only in booklets.

Victoria and Elizabeth II — MA3

### 1990-2000   Photo.   Perf. 15x14

|   |   |   |   |
|---|---|---|---|
| MH190 | 15p bright blue | .90 | .90 |
| a. | Booklet pane of 10, imperf on T, B (BK619) | 11.50 | |
| MH191 | 15p brt bl, litho., perf 14 | 1.75 | 2.00 |
| a. | Booklet pane of 4 with imperf on T, B, R (BK307) | 8.00 | |
| b. | Booklet pane of 10 with imperf on T, B, R (BK620) | 14.00 | |
| MH192 | 15p bright blue, litho. | 2.50 | 2.50 |
| a. | Booklet pane of 10 (BK621) | 22.50 | |
| MH193 | 20p black & brown black | .90 | .90 |
| a. | Booklet pane, #MH193, 2 MH190 + label (BK255) | 3.00 | |
| b. | Booklet pane of 4 with imperf on T, B (BK371) | 6.00 | |
| c. | Bklt. pane of 5 + label (BK415) | 4.00 | |
| d. | Booklet pane of 6 + printed margin (BK154) | 4.00 | |
| e. | Booklet pane of 10 with imperf on T, B (BK743) | 12.00 | |
| f. | Souvenir sheet of 1 | 7.00 | 7.00 |
| MH194 | 20p black & brn blk, litho., perf 14 | 1.90 | 1.90 |
| a. | Booklet pane of 4 with imperf on T, B, R (BK372) | 11.50 | |
| b. | Bklt. pane of 5 + label (BK416) | 11.50 | |
| c. | Booklet pane of 10 with imperf on T, B, R (BK744) | 17.50 | |
| MH195 | 20p black & brn blk, litho. | 2.25 | 2.25 |
| a. | Booklet pane of 10 (BK745) | 22.50 | |
| MH196 | 29p deep rose lilac | 2.00 | 2.00 |
| a. | Booklet pane, 3 #MH91, MH115, MH160, MH177, MH183, MH193, MH196 + label, printed margin (BK159) | 22.50 | |
| MH197 | 34p dull blue green | 2.25 | 2.25 |
| MH198 | 37p scarlet | 2.50 | 2.50 |

#### Perf. 13¾x14¼ Syncopated

|   |   |   |   |
|---|---|---|---|
| MH198A | 1st blk & yel | 2.25 | 1.40 |
| b. | Booklet pane of 6 (BK167) | 13.50 | |

Nos. MH191-MH192, MH194-MH195, MH198A were issued only in booklets.
No. MH198A sold for 26p on day of issue.
Issued: #MH190, MH193, MH196-MH198, 1/10; #MH191, MH194, 1/30; #MH192, MH195, 4/17; #MH198A, 2/15/00.

## Syncopated Perf. 15x14

| 1993-97 | | | Type MA2 |
|---|---|---|---|
| MH199 | 1p magenta | .20 | .20 |
| MH200 | 1p mag, litho. | | |
| | (MH216b) | .75 | .45 |
| MH201 | 2p dark green | .20 | .20 |
| MH202 | 4p Prussian blue | .20 | .20 |
| MH203 | 5p rose brown | .20 | .20 |
| MH204 | 6p bright olive green | .25 | .35 |
| MH205 | 6p bright olive green, litho. (MH214a) | 15.00 | 15.00 |
| MH206 | 10p brown orange | .35 | .35 |
| MH207 | 10p brown orange, litho. (MH231a) | 6.00 | 5.50 |
| MH208 | 19p olive green | .75 | .70 |
| MH209 | 19p ol grn, litho. (MH214a, MH231a) | 2.25 | 2.00 |
| a. | Booklet pane of 6 + printed margin (BK160) | 13.50 | |
| MH210 | 20p greenish blue | 1.00 | 1.00 |
| MH211 | 20p bright yel grn | .80 | .80 |
| MH212 | 20p brt yel grn, litho. (MH216a-MH216b) | 2.75 | 2.25 |
| MH213 | 25p salmon | 1.00 | .40 |
| MH214 | 25p sal, litho. (MH231a) | 1.25 | 1.25 |
| a. | Bkt. pane, #MH205, MH209, 4 MH214 + printed margin (BK159) | 22.50 | |
| b. | Booklet pane of 8 + label, printed margin (see footnote) (BK161) | 11.00 | |

No. MH214b contains 2 each #MH214, NIMH59, SMH65, WMMH60.

| MH215 | 26p brown | 1.25 | 1.25 |
|---|---|---|---|
| MH216 | 26p brown, litho. | 1.10 | 1.10 |
| a. | Bkt. pane, #MH212, 7 MH216 (BK749) | 10.00 | |
| b. | Bkt. pane, #MH212, 2 MH200, 3 MH216 + 2 labels (BK426) | 4.00 | |
| MH218 | 29p gray | 1.40 | 1.40 |
| MH219 | 30p olive green | 1.25 | 1.25 |
| MH220 | 30p olive green, litho. (MH231a) | 6.00 | 4.50 |
| MH221 | 31p deep rose lilac | 1.25 | 1.25 |
| MH222 | 35p orange yellow | 1.60 | 1.75 |
| MH223 | 35p org yel, litho. | 1.90 | 1.90 |
| a. | Booklet pane of 4 (BK562-BK563) | 10.00 | |

| MH224 | 36p blue | 1.75 | 1.75 |
|---|---|---|---|
| MH225 | 37p bright rose lilac | 1.60 | 1.60 |
| MH226 | 37p brt rose lilac, litho. | 3.50 | 2.75 |
| a. | Booklet pane of 4 (BK605) | 14.00 | |
| MH227 | 38p red | 1.75 | 1.75 |
| MH228 | 39p bright pink | 1.55 | 1.60 |
| MH230 | 41p drab | 1.75 | 1.60 |
| MH231 | 41p drab, litho. | 3.50 | 2.00 |
| a. | Booklet pane, #MH207, MH220, MH223, MH231, 2 each MH209, MH214 + label, printed margin (BK160) | 17.50 | |
| b. | Booklet pane of 4 (BK685-BK686) | 15.00 | |
| MH232 | 43p dark brown | 2.00 | 2.00 |
| MH233 | 50p ocher | 2.00 | 1.10 |
| MH234 | 60p slate blue, litho. | 2.75 | 2.75 |
| a. | Booklet pane of 4 (BK790-BK791) | 11.00 | |
| MH235 | 63p bright green | 2.50 | 2.25 |
| MH236 | 63p brt grn, litho. | 4.50 | 3.50 |
| a. | Bkt. pane of 4 (BK815-BK816) | 18.00 | |
| MH237 | £1 violet | 4.50 | 3.25 |

No. MH237 is printed with Iriodin ink, giving stamp design a three dimensional appearance.

| MH238 | 2nd bright blue | 1.00 | 1.00 |
|---|---|---|---|
| MH239 | 2nd bright blue, litho. | .90 | .90 |
| MH240 | 1st orange red | 1.75 | 1.40 |
| MH241 | 1st orange red, litho. | 1.35 | 1.00 |
| a. | Miniature sheet of 1 | 6.50 | 6.50 |
| b. | Booklet pane of 4 + label (BK1000, BK1002, BK1004) | 6.50 | |
| c. | Booklet pane of 9 + printed margin (BK165) | 12.00 | |

No. MH241a was sold for £1 on day of issue in pre-packaged greeting cards at Boots pharmacy. Unfolded examples were later sold by British Philatelic Bureau. Value indicated is for unfolded example.

### Size: 21½x17½mm
### Self-Adhesive

MH243            MH309

### Die Cut 14x15 Syncopated Litho.

| MH243 | 1st orange red | 1.35 | .35 |
|---|---|---|---|
| a. | Booklet pane of 20 | 27.00 | |

#MH238-MH239 each sold for 18p on day of issue; #MH240-MH241, MH243 each for 24p.
Issued: #MH201, 4/11/95; #MH204, 4/27/93; #MH219, 7/27/93; #MH222, 8/17/93; #MH234, 8/9/94; #MH237, 8/22/95; #MH238, 9/7/93; #MH241, 9/6/93. #MH241c, 2/16/99.
Nos. MH239, MH240, 4/6/93.
Nos. MH199, MH203, MH212, MH206, 6/8/93.
No. MH243, 10/19/93.
Nos. MH208, MH213, MH218, MH224, MH227, MH230, 10/26/93.
Nos. MH214, MH223, MH222, 11/1/93.
Nos. MH202, MH210, MH233, 12/14/93.
Nos. MH205, MH209, 7/26/94.
Nos. MH207, MH220, 4/25/95.
Nos. MH215, MH221, MH225, MH228, MH232, MH235, 6/25/96.
Nos. MH200, MH203, MH216, MH226, MH236, 7/8/96.
Nos. MH200, MH205, MH207, MH209, MH212, MH216, MH219, MH226, MH231, MH236 issued only in booklets.
No. MH243a is a complete booklet.

### Queen Type of 1970 with Redrawn Portrait

Type MA2: Upper lip not defined by sharp line, nostril is incomplete, hairlines not sharply defined, upper corners of cross formeé are widely separated.
Redrawn portrait: Upper lip sharply outlined, nostril is complete and defined by two lines, hairlines are sharply defined, upper corners of cross formeé are close together so they nearly complete a square.

### Perf. 15x14 Syncopated, 13¾x14¼ Syncopated (#MH251, MH254A, MH264B, MH269, MH285, MH289)

| 1997-2004 | | | Photo. |
|---|---|---|---|
| MH245 | 1p magenta | .20 | .20 |
| MH246 | 2p dark green | .20 | .20 |
| MH247 | 4p Prussian blue | .20 | .20 |
| MH248 | 5p rose brown | .20 | .20 |
| MH249 | 6p bright olive green | .35 | .20 |
| MH249A | 7p gray | 5.00 | 1.00 |
| MH249B | 8p dk olive bister | .40 | .40 |
| MH250 | 10p brown orange | .40 | .20 |
| MH251 | 10p brn org, perf 13¾x14¼ | 3.50 | .20 |
| MH254 | 19p bister | .75 | .30 |
| MH254A | 19p bister (MH264c), perf 13¾x14¼ | 2.25 | 2.25 |
| MH255 | 20p bright yellow green | 1.60 | 1.60 |
| MH256 | 26p gold | 1.25 | 1.10 |
| MH257 | 26p brown | 1.05 | .40 |
| a. | Booklet pane, 3 each #MH255, MH257 + printed margin (BK162) | 8.00 | |
| b. | Bkt. pane, #MH255, 2 MH245, 3 MH257 + 2 labels (BK427) | 15.00 | |
| c. | Booklet pane, #MH255, 7 MH257 (BK751) | 17.50 | |
| d. | Booklet pane, #MH245-MH246, MH254, 3 #MH257 + 2 labels (BK428) | 7.50 | |
| e. | Booklet pane, #MH254, 7 #MH257 (BK752) | 9.00 | |
| f. | Booklet pane, 2 each #MH245, 3 #MH254, 1 #MH257 + label | 4.00 | |
| MH259 | 30p olive green | 1.20 | .45 |
| MH260 | 31p deep rose lil | 1.25 | .50 |
| MH261 | 33p dk blue green | 1.30 | 1.20 |
| MH261A | 34p olive green | 3.75 | 1.00 |
| MH262 | 37p brt rose lilac | 1.60 | 1.60 |
| MH263 | 37p black | 1.50 | 1.25 |
| MH264 | 38p dark blue | 2.10 | 1.75 |
| MH264B | 38p dk blue, perf 13¾x14¼ | 7.50 | 1.00 |
| c. | Booklet pane, 4 #MH254A, 2 #MH264B (BK167) | 20.00 | |
| MH265 | 39p brt pink | 1.70 | .30 |
| MH266 | 40p chalky blue | 1.60 | 1.40 |
| a. | Booklet pane of 4 (BK676) | 6.50 | |
| MH267 | 41p carmine rose | 1.65 | 1.40 |
| MH267A | 42p olive | 1.70 | 1.40 |
| MH268 | 43p dark brown | 1.80 | .70 |
| MH269 | 43p dk brn, perf 13¾x14¼ | 2.25 | 2.25 |
| a. | Booklet pane, #NIMH70, SMH76, WMMH71, 3 MH269 + printed margin (BK164) | 12.00 | |
| MH270 | 44p brown | 6.25 | 2.25 |
| MH270A | 45p brt rose lilac | 1.80 | 1.40 |
| MH270B | 47p blue green | 1.90 | 1.60 |
| MH271 | 50p ocher | 2.00 | 1.10 |
| MH275 | 63p bright green | 2.50 | 1.25 |
| MH276 | 64p greenish blue | 2.60 | 2.40 |
| MH277 | 65p Prussian blue | 2.60 | 2.10 |
| a. | Booklet pane of 4 (BK830) | 10.50 | |
| MH278 | 68p drab | 2.70 | 2.10 |
| MH279 | £1 violet | 4.50 | 3.00 |
| a. | Souv. sheet, see footnote | 32.50 | 12.00 |

No. MH279 is printed with Iriodin ink, giving stamp design a three dimensional appearance.
No. MH279a contains #MH247-MH249, MH250, MH260, MH265, MH276, MH279 + 2 labels.

| MH280 | £1.50 red, engr. | 6.00 | 2.25 |
|---|---|---|---|
| MH281 | £2 slate blue, engr. | 8.00 | 3.25 |
| MH282 | £3 purple, engr. | 12.00 | 4.75 |
| MH283 | £5 brown, engr. | 20.00 | 8.00 |
| MH284 | 2nd bright blue | .95 | .30 |
| a. | Litho. (#MH287h) ('08) | .95 | .50 |
| MH285 | 2nd bright blue, perf 13¾x14¼ | .95 | .30 |
| a. | Booklet pane, #NIMH74, SMH80, WMMH75, 3 MH285 + printed margin (BK164) | 11.00 | |
| b. | Booklet pane, 2 #MH251, 3 each MH269, MH285 + label, printed margin (BK164) | 16.50 | |
| MH287 | 1st gold | 1.35 | .30 |
| a. | Bkt. pane, 4 ea #MH256, MH287 + label, printed margin (BK162) | 10.50 | |
| b. | Booklet pane, 4 each #MH284, MH287 + label (BK174) | 9.25 | |
| c. | Booklet pane, 4 each #MH263, MH287 + label | 11.50 | — |
| d. | Booklet pane, 2 each #MH267A, MH270B, 4 #MH287, + label (BK176) | 11.00 | |
| e. | Booklet pane, 2 each #MH271, MH278, 4 #MH287 + label (BK178) | 15.00 | — |
| f. | Booklet pane, 8 + central label, litho. (BK184) | 11.00 | — |
| g. | Litho. (#MH287f) ('08) | 1.25 | .65 |
| h. | Booklet pane of 8, 4 #MH284a, MH287g + label (BK185) ('08) | 9.00 | |
| MH288 | 1st orange red (BK1005, BK1140) | 1.35 | .30 |
| a. | Booklet pane of 8, label + printed margin (BK165) | 11.00 | |
| b. | Booklet pane of 8 (BK1141-BK1144) | 11.00 | |
| c. | Booklet pane of 4 + label (BK1006) | 5.50 | |

| d. | Booklet pane, #MH284, 3 #MH288 + 4 labels (BK429) | 6.25 | |
|---|---|---|---|
| e. | Bkt. pane, 2 #MH284, 4 #MH288 (BK753) | 7.25 | |
| MH289 | 1st org red, perf 13¾x14¼ | 2.00 | .40 |
| a. | Booklet pane of 10 (BK1139A) | 20.00 | |
| MH290 | E dark blue | 1.90 | .40 |
| a. | Booklet pane of 4 (BK1010) | 7.50 | |
| b. | Booklet pane, 4 each #MH284, MH290, + label (BK171) | 11.50 | — |
| c. | Booklet pane, 4 #MH287, 4 #MH290 + label (BK172, BK173) | 13.00 | |

#MH284-MH285 sold for 20p on day of issue; #MH287-MH289 for 26p; #MH298 for 30p. #MH284-MH285 were later sold for 19p. Selling prices for booklets containing these stamps will be considered to have 20p stamps.

### Queen Type of 1970 with Redrawn Portrait

MH292         MH294

MH297         MH299

MH300         MH301

On Nos. MH292 and MH297, the numeral and letters are thinner, and perf tips are flat with distinct corners, while on MH294 and MH299, numeral and letters are thicker and bolder, and perf tips have a slight arc and are rounded at the corners.
On No. MH300 the numeral and letters are thick and bold and perf tips have a slight arc and are rounded at the corners, while on No. MH301, the numeral and letters are distinctly serpentine with little flatness on the peaks or valleys.

### Die Cut Perf. 14¾x14 Sync., Die Cut Perf. 15x14¼ Sync. (MH 293, MH298)
### Self-Adhesive Stamps
### Booklet Stamps (MH293, MH298)

| MH292 | 2nd bright blue | 1.25 | .35 |
|---|---|---|---|
| a. | Booklet pane of 6 | 7.50 | |
| MH293 | 2nd bright blue | 1.00 | .30 |
| a. | Booklet pane of 10 | 10.00 | |
| b. | Booklet pane of 12 | 12.00 | |
| c. | Booklet of 6 | 6.00 | |
| MH294 | 2nd bright blue | .95 | .30 |
| a. | Booklet pane of 12 | 11.50 | |
| MH297 | 1st vermilion | 1.50 | .45 |
| a. | Booklet pane of 6 | 9.00 | |
| b. | Booklet pane of 12 | 18.00 | |
| MH298 | 1st vermilion | 1.35 | .40 |
| a. | Booklet pane of 10 | 13.50 | |
| b. | Booklet pane of 12 | 16.00 | |
| c. | Booklet of 6 | 8.00 | |
| MH299 | 1st vermilion | 1.35 | .40 |
| a. | Booklet pane of 6 | 8.00 | |
| MH300 | 1st gold | 1.35 | .40 |
| a. | Booklet pane of 6 | 8.00 | |
| MH301 | 1st gold | 1.35 | .40 |
| a. | Booklet pane of 6 | 8.00 | |
| b. | Booklet pane of 12 | 16.00 | |
| MH302 | E dark blue | 2.25 | .55 |
| a. | Booklet of 6 | 13.50 | |
| MH304 | 42p olive | 6.50 | 1.00 |
| a. | Booklet pane of 6 | 40.00 | |
| MH306 | 68p drab | 4.75 | 1.10 |
| a. | Booklet pane of 6 | 28.50 | |

Nos. MH292, MH293, MH297 and MH298 were also issued as coils, which have no selvage surrounding stamps.
No. MH293 & single stamps from No. MH292a sold for 19p on day of issue; #MH292, 20p; #MH297, 26p; and single stamps from #MH297a, MH297b, 27p.
Nos. MH292a, MH293a, MH293b, MH297a, MH297b, MH298a, and MH298b are complete booklets.
No. MH297a exists with self-adhesive label depicting Queen Victoria.

### Die Cut Perf. 14x15 Syncopated
### Self-Adhesive Coil Stamps
### Size: 21x17mm

| MH308 | 2nd bright blue | 7.00 | 3.00 |
|---|---|---|---|

| MH309 | 1st orange red | 3.00 | 3.00 |
|---|---|---|---|

**Size: 30x40mm**
**Perf. 14x14½**

| MH310 | 1st black, engr. | 2.50 | 2.50 |
|---|---|---|---|
| a. | Booklet pane of 4 + printed margin (BK165) | 10.00 | |
| MH311 | 1st black, typo. | 2.50 | 2.50 |
| a. | Booklet pane of 4 + printed margin (BK165) | 10.00 | |

**Self-Adhesive**
**Die Cut Perf. 14x14½**

| MH312 | 1st gray, litho. & embossed | 2.50 | .40 |
|---|---|---|---|
| a. | Booklet pane of 4 + printed margin (BK165) | 10.00 | |

#MH312 is valued in used condition on piece. Soaking and pressing #MH312 removes the embossed image of the Queen.

No. MH300 sold for 20p on day of issue. Nos. MH305, MH310-MH312 sold for 26p on day of issue.

Issued: #MH245, MH249, MH268, MH271, MH279, 4/1/97; #MH256, MH287, 4/21/97; #MH255, MH284, MH308, MH309, 4/29/97; #MH246-MH248, MH250, MH259, MH265, 5/27/97; #MH260, MH262, MH275, MH288, 8/26/97; #MH257, 11/18/97; #MH292, MH297, 4/6/98; #MH251, MH269, MH285, 10/13/98; #MH289, 12/1/98; #MH290, 1/12/99; #MH288c, 5/12/99; #MH280-MH283, 3/9/99; #MH310-MH312, 2/16/99; #MH289, 3/16/99; #MH249A, MH254, MH264, MH270, MH276, 4/20/99; #MH254A, MH264B, 2/15/00; 8p, 33p, 40p, 41p, 45p, 65p #MH288d, MH288e, 4/25/00; #MH279a, 5/22/00; #MH292a, MH293, MH297a, MH297b, MH298, 1/29/01.

Nos. MH293c, MH298c issued 1/29/01.

Nos. MH251, MH254A, MH264B, MH269, MH285 (BK164), MH289 (BK1139A), MH290 (BK1010) issued only in booklets.

No. MH290b issued 2/6/02. E stamps from MH 290b issued on day of issue.

No. MH290c issued 9/24/02.

Issued: Nos. MH263, MH267A, MH278, MH270B, MH294, MH299, MH302, MH304, MH306, 7/4/02; Nos. MH300-MH301, 6/5/02. No. MH294 sold for 19p, Nos. MH299, MH300 and MH301 sold for 27p, and No. MH302 sold for 37p on day of issue.

Issued: No. MH261A, 5/6/03; No. MH287b, 6/2/03. Nos. MH284a, MH287h, 9/18/08; No. MH287g, 1/8/08.

This is an expanding set. Nos. MH245-MH312 may change.

### Queen Type of 1970 With Redrawn Portraits
**Perf. 14¾x14 Syncopated**

| 2003, July 1 | | Photo. |
|---|---|---|

**Printed in Iriodin Ink**

| MH321 | £1.50 rose | 6.00 | 5.00 |
|---|---|---|---|
| MH322 | £2 greenish blue | 8.00 | 7.00 |
| a. | Pound symbol missing in denomination | 200.00 | — |
| MH323 | £3 violet | 12.00 | 11.00 |
| a. | Souvenir sheet of 1 ('06) | 12.00 | 11.00 |
| MH324 | £5 light blue | 20.00 | 17.50 |
| | Nos. MH321-MH324 (4) | 46.00 | 40.50 |

Issued: £1.50, £2, £3, £5, 7/1. No. MH323a, 8/31/06.

No. MH323a has margin depicting invalid imperforate examples of Nos. 211, 231, and 236.

Queen Elizabeth II (No Frame, Perforations Touch Vignette) — MA4

**Perf. 14¾x14 Syncopated**

| 2000 | | Photo. | Design MA4 |
|---|---|---|---|
| MH335 | 1st olive green | 1.35 | .45 |
| a. | Bklt. pane of 8 (BK1201) | 11.00 | |
| b. | Bklt. pane of 9 (BK168) | 12.25 | |
| c. | Bklt. pane of 4 + label (BK1007) | 5.50 | |

**Perf. 13¾x14¼ Syncopated**

| MH336 | 1st olive green | 1.35 | .45 |
|---|---|---|---|
| a. | Booklet pane of 10 (BK1144) | 13.50 | |
| b. | Booklet pane of 8 + label (BK167) | 11.00 | |

Issued: #MH335, MH336, 1/6; #MH336b, 2/15; #MH335a, 5/26; #MH335b, 8/4.

No. MH335c comes in two versions (as does No. MH1007): with Postman Pat on label and with Botanical Garden of Wales on label.

No. MH336 issued only in booklets. Perforations are Syncopated.

No. MH335 and MH336 sold for 26p on day of issue.

### Queen Type of 1970 With Redrawn Portraits
**Perf. 14¾x14 Syncopated**

| 2004-08 | | | Photo. |
|---|---|---|---|

**Type MA2**

| MH344 | 7p bright pink | .25 | .20 |
|---|---|---|---|
| MH346 | 9p brt orange | .35 | .20 |
| MH347 | 12p blue green | .50 | .25 |
| MH348 | 14p vermilion | .55 | .25 |
| MH348A | 15p brt pink | .60 | .30 |
| MH349 | 16p lilac rose | .65 | .30 |
| a. | Litho. (MH365b) ('09) | .50 | .25 |
| MH351 | 35p brown | 1.40 | .65 |
| MH352 | 35p olive green | 1.40 | .70 |
| MH353 | 37p olive green | 1.45 | .70 |
| MH354 | 39p gray | 1.55 | .70 |
| a. | Booklet pane, 4 #MH284, 2 each #MH267A, MH354 + label (BK177) | 10.25 | — |
| MH355 | 40p Prussian blue | 1.60 | .75 |
| a. | Booklet pane, 4 #MH287, 2 each #MH352, MH355 + central label (BK179) | 11.50 | — |
| MH358 | 43p emerald | 1.70 | .80 |
| MH359 | 44p bright blue | 1.75 | .80 |
| MH361 | 46p dk ol bister | 1.85 | .85 |
| MH363 | 48p brt rose lil | 1.90 | .95 |
| a. | Booklet pane, 4 #MH246, 2 each #MH361, MH363, + label (BK182) | 7.75 | — |
| MH364 | 49p brown | 1.95 | .85 |
| MH365 | 50p gray | 2.00 | 1.00 |
| a. | Litho. (MH365b) ('09) | 1.50 | .75 |
| b. | Booklet pane, 4 each #MH349a, MH365a, + central label (BK187) ('09) | 8.00 | — |
| MH366 | 54p brown | 2.10 | 1.10 |
| a. | Booklet pane, 2 each #MH245, MH366, 4 #MH361, + label (BK183) | 12.00 | |
| MH367 | 56p lt olive grn | 2.25 | 1.10 |
| MH370 | 72p carmine rose | 2.90 | 1.25 |
| MH371 | 78p emerald | 3.25 | 1.60 |
| MH372 | 81p greenish blue | 3.25 | 1.60 |
| MH373 | £1 cerise | 4.00 | 2.00 |
| a. | Booklet pane of 2 + label (BK182) | 8.00 | — |
| | Nos. MH344-MH373 (23) | 39.20 | 18.90 |

Issued: 7p, 35p, 39p, 40p, 43p, 4/1. MH354a, 2/24/05. 9p, No. MH352, 46p, 4/5/05. No. MH355a, 2/23/05. 37p, 44p, 49p, 72p, 3/28/06. 12p, 14p, 8/1/06. 16p, 48p, 50p, 54p, 78p, 3/27/07. No. MH363a, MH373, 6/5/07. MH366a, 9/20/07. 15p, 56p, 81p, 4/1/08. Nos. MH349a, MH365a, MH365b, 1/13/09.

A silver 1st class stamp of type MA2 was included in a product commemorating the 40th anniversary of Machin definitive stamps that sold for £48. This silver stamp was not available separately.

This is an expanding set, numbers may change.

| Queen Elizabeth II | |
|---|---|
| MA5 | MA6 |

**Perf. 14¾x14 Syncopated**

| 2006 | | | Photo. |
|---|---|---|---|
| MH375 | MA5 | 2nd bright blue | .95 .45 |
| MH376 | MA5 | 1st gold | 1.35 .60 |
| a. | | Booklet pane, 4 each #MH271, MH376 + central label (BK180) | 13.50 — |
| b. | | Booklet pane, 4 each #MH248, MH376, + central label (BK181) | 6.00 |

**Inscribed "Large"**

| MH377 | MA6 | 2nd bright blue | 1.40 | .70 |
|---|---|---|---|---|
| MH378 | MA6 | 1st gold | 1.75 | .85 |
| a. | | Booklet pane, #MH375, MH376, 2 each #MH377-MH378, + label (BK182) | 9.25 | — |
| | | Nos. MH375-MH378 (4) | 5.45 | 2.60 |

**Booklet Stamps**
**Self-Adhesive**
**Serpentine Die Cut 14¾x14 Syncopated**

| MH379 | MA5 | 2nd bright blue | .95 | .45 |
|---|---|---|---|---|
| a. | | Booklet pane of 12 | 11.50 | |
| MH380 | MA5 | 1st gold | 1.35 | .60 |
| a. | | Booklet pane of 6 | 8.00 | |
| b. | | Booklet pane of 12 | 16.00 | |

**Inscribed "Large"**

| MH381 | MA6 | 2nd bright blue | 1.40 | .70 |
|---|---|---|---|---|
| a. | | Booklet pane of 4 | 5.75 | |
| MH382 | MA6 | 1st gold | 1.75 | .85 |
| a. | | Booklet pane of 4 | 7.00 | |
| | | Nos. MH379-MH382 (4) | 5.45 | 2.60 |

Issued: Nos. MH375-MH378, 8/1; Nos. MH379-MH380, 9/12; Nos. MH381-MH382, 8/15. No. MH376a, 9/21. No. MH376b, 3/1/07. No. MH378a, 6/5/07.

On day of issue, Nos. MH375 and MH379 each sold for 23p, Nos. MH376 and MH380 each sold for 32p, Nos. MH377 and MH381

each sold for 37p, and Nos. MH378 and MH382 each sold for 44p.

---

# MACHINS REGIONAL ISSUES

## NORTHERN IRELAND

All stamps are Design MA2 unless noted.

| Type I | Type II |
|---|---|

Two types of crown:
Type I: All pearls individually drawn, screened background.
Type II: Large pearls with strong white line below them.
First three pearls at left joined together. Solid background.

| 1971-93 | | Photo. | Perf. 15x14 |
|---|---|---|---|
| NIMH1 | 2½p bright pink | .75 | .50 |
| NIMH2 | 3p ultramarine | .40 | .30 |
| NIMH3 | 3½p slate | .30 | .30 |
| NIMH4 | 4½p dark blue | .30 | .30 |
| NIMH5 | 5p bright violet | 1.40 | 1.40 |
| NIMH6 | 5½p dark violet | .30 | .20 |
| NIMH7 | 6½p Prussian blue | .30 | .20 |
| NIMH8 | 7p dark red brn | .40 | .30 |
| NIMH9 | 7½p chestnut | 2.25 | 2.00 |
| NIMH10 | 8p red | .40 | .40 |
| NIMH11 | 8½p yellow green | .40 | .45 |
| NIMH12 | 9p violet blue | .45 | .45 |
| NIMH13 | 10p orange brown | .45 | .55 |
| NIMH14 | 10½p steel blue | .55 | .55 |
| NIMH15 | 11p red | .55 | .55 |
| NIMH16 | 11½p gray brn, litho., perf 13½x14 | 1.00 | 1.00 |
| NIMH17 | 12p yellow green | .70 | .60 |
| NIMH18 | 12p brt grn, litho. | .95 | .90 |
| NIMH19 | 12½p lt emer., litho., perf 13½x14 | .70 | .70 |
| NIMH20 | 12½p lt emer., litho. | 6.00 | 4.50 |
| NIMH21 | 13p brt red brown, litho., type II | 1.00 | .55 |
| a. | Type I | 1.25 | .50 |
| NIMH22 | 13½p brown purple | .80 | .80 |
| NIMH23 | 14p gray bl, litho., perf 13½x14 | .90 | .85 |
| NIMH24 | 14p dark bl, litho. | 1.00 | .70 |
| NIMH25 | 15p deep ultra | 1.00 | .70 |

**Litho.**

| NIMH26 | 15p bright blue | 1.00 | .70 |
|---|---|---|---|
| NIMH27 | 15½p light violet, perf 13½x14 | .90 | .90 |
| NIMH28 | 16p brownish gray, perf 13½x14 | 1.10 | 1.25 |
| NIMH29 | 16p brownish gray | 8.00 | 6.00 |
| NIMH30 | 17p blue gray, type I | .95 | 1.10 |
| a. | Type II | 160.00 | |
| NIMH31 | 17p dark blue | 1.10 | .90 |
| NIMH32 | 18p violet blue, perf 13½x14 | 1.10 | 1.10 |
| NIMH33 | 18p olive green | 1.10 | 1.00 |
| NIMH34 | 18p bright yel grn | 1.10 | 1.00 |
| NIMH35 | 18p bright yel grn, perf 13½x14 | 2.75 | 1.90 |
| NIMH36 | 19p red orange | 1.10 | 1.10 |
| NIMH37 | 19½p olive gray, perf 13½x14 | 2.25 | 2.50 |
| NIMH38 | 20p brown black | 1.10 | .90 |
| NIMH39 | 20½p ultramarine, perf 13½x14 | 4.75 | 4.00 |
| NIMH40 | 22p dark blue, perf 13½x14 | 1.25 | 1.25 |
| NIMH41 | 22p yellow green | 1.25 | 1.25 |
| NIMH42 | 22p red orange | 1.40 | 1.00 |
| NIMH43 | 23p bright yel grn | 1.40 | 1.25 |
| NIMH44 | 24p brown red | 1.75 | 1.10 |
| NIMH45 | 24p brown | 1.25 | 1.00 |
| a. | Bklt. pane, see footnote (BK158) | 4.25 | |

#NIMH45a contains NIMH34, NIMH45, SMH35, SMH47, WMMH34, WMMH45.

| NIMH46 | 26p red, perf 13½x14, type I | 1.40 | 1.40 |
|---|---|---|---|
| NIMH47 | 26p red, type II | 4.50 | 4.00 |
| NIMH48 | 26p olive gray | 1.75 | 1.50 |
| NIMH49 | 28p deep viol bl, perf 13½x14, type I | 1.60 | 1.40 |

| NIMH50 | 28p deep viol bl, type II | 1.75 | 1.40 |
|---|---|---|---|
| NIMH51 | 28p dull blue green | 1.90 | 1.60 |
| NIMH52 | 31p brt rose lil, type I | 1.75 | 1.75 |
| a. | Type II | 2.25 | 2.00 |
| NIMH53 | 32p Prussian blue | 2.00 | 2.00 |
| NIMH54 | 34p dull blue green | 2.25 | 2.25 |
| NIMH55 | 37p scarlet | 2.25 | 2.25 |
| NIMH56 | 39p brt rose lilac | 2.25 | 2.25 |

Issued: #NIMH1, 3p, 5p, NIMH9, 7/7/71; #NIMH3, NIMH6, 8p, 1/23/74; #NIMH4, 11/6/74;

#NIMH7, NIMH11, 1/14/76; 10p, 11p, 10/20/76; 7p, 9p, NIMH14, 1/18/78.

#NIMH17, NIMH22, #NIMH25, 7/23/80; #NIMH16, #NIMH23, NIMH32, NIMH40, 4/8/81; #NIMH19, 1/24/82; #NIMH27, #NIMH28, NIMH37, NIMH46, 2/24/82; #NIMH49, 4/27/83;

#NIMH20, NIMH29, 2/28/84; 13p, #NIMH30, NIMH41, 31p, 10/23/84; #NIMH18, 1/7/86; #NIMH33, 1/6/87; #NIMH50, 1/27/87; #NIMH24, 19p, 23p, 32p, 11/8/88; #NIMH26, 30p, NIMH44, 34p, 11/28/89; #NIMH31, NIMH42, NIMH48, 37p, 12/4/90; #NIMH34, NIMH45, NIMH51, 39p, 12/3/91; #NIMH35, NIMH45a, 8/10/93; #NIMH47, 12/7/93.

### Perf. 15x14 Syncopated

| 1993-96 | | Litho. |
|---|---|---|
| NIMH57 | 19p olive green | 1.00 | .90 |
| NIMH58 | 20p brt yel green | 1.75 | 1.40 |
| NIMH59 | 25p salmon | 1.00 | .90 |
| a. | Bklt. pane, see footnote (BK160) | 5.00 | |

No. NIMH59a contains #NIMH57, NIMH59, SMH63, SMH65, WMMH58, WMMH60 + label, printed margin.

| NIMH60 | 26p brown | 1.60 | 1.60 |
|---|---|---|---|
| NIMH61 | 30p olive green | 1.75 | 1.60 |
| NIMH62 | 37p bright rose lilac | 2.50 | 2.50 |
| NIMH63 | 41p drab | 2.00 | 1.75 |
| a. | Bklt. pane, #NIMH61, NIMH63, 2 #NIMH57, 4 #NIMH59 + label, printed margin (BK159) | 6.25 | |
| b. | Bklt. pane, #NIMH57, NIMH59, NIMH61, NIMH63 + printed margin (BK159) | 3.50 | |
| NIMH64 | 63p bright green | 4.00 | 4.00 |

Issued: 19p, 25p, 30p, 41p, 12/7/93; #NIMH59a, 4/25/95; 20p, 26, 37p, 63p, 7/23/96.

### Queen Design of 1970 with Redrawn Portrait
**Perf. 15x14 Syncopated**

| 1997-2000 | | Photo. |
|---|---|---|
| NIMH68 | 19p olive green | 1.50 | .80 |
| NIMH69 | 20p brt yel grn | 1.00 | .80 |
| NIMH70 | 20p brt yel grn, perf 14 | 2.25 | 2.10 |
| NIMH73 | 26p brown | 1.50 | 1.10 |
| NIMH74 | 26p brown, perf 14 | 2.75 | 2.00 |
| NIMH81 | 37p bright rose lilac | 2.50 | 1.40 |
| a. | Bklt. pane, see footnote (BK162) | 7.50 | |

No. NIMH81a contains #NIMH73, NIMH81, SMH79, SMH87, WMMH74, WMMH82 + printed margin.

| NIMH82 | 38p dark blue | 9.00 | 7.50 |
|---|---|---|---|
| NIMH83 | 40p chalky blue | 3.00 | 2.50 |
| NIMH91 | 63p bright green | 6.00 | 5.00 |
| NIMH92 | 64p greenish blue | 11.00 | 8.00 |
| NIMH93 | 65p Prussian blue | 3.50 | 3.00 |

Issued: #NIMH69, NIMH73, 37p, 63p, 7/1/97; #NIMH81a, 9/24/97; #NIMH70, NIMH74, 10/13/98; #NIMH68, NIMH82, NIMH92, 6/8/99; 40p, 65p, 4/25/00. Nos. NIMH70, NIMH74 issued only in booklets (BK164).

### Perf. 13¾x14¼ Syncopated

| 2000 | | Photo. |
|---|---|---|
| NIMH96 | 1st orange red (WM-MH96a) | 3.00 | 2.75 |

### Perf. 15x14 Syncopated

| NIMH99 | 1st org red | 10.00 | 7.50 |
|---|---|---|---|

#NIMH96, NIMH99 sold for 26p on day of issue. #NIMH96 issued only in booklets.
Issued: NIMH96, 2/15/00; #NIMH99, 4/25/00.

---

## SCOTLAND

All stamps are Design MA2 unless noted.

Type I      Type II

Two types of lion:
Type I: Thin tongue, no line across bridge of nose, three "feathers" on left of tail are widely separated.
Type II: Thick tongue where it enters mouth, eye connected to background by solid line, three "feathers" on left of tail are close together.

### 1971-93    Photo.    Perf. 15x14

| | | | |
|---|---|---|---|
| SMH1 | 2½p bright pink | .30 | .20 |
| SMH2 | 3p ultramarine | .40 | .20 |
| SMH3 | 3½p slate | .30 | .20 |
| SMH4 | 4½p dark blue | .35 | .30 |
| SMH5 | 5p brt violet | 1.50 | 1.25 |
| SMH6 | 5½p dark violet | .30 | .20 |
| SMH7 | 6½p Prussian blue | .30 | .20 |
| SMH8 | 7p dark red brn | .35 | .35 |
| SMH9 | 7½p chestnut | 1.50 | 1.50 |
| SMH10 | 8p red | .50 | .40 |
| SMH11 | 8½p yellow green | .50 | .45 |
| SMH12 | 9p violet blue | .50 | .45 |
| SMH13 | 10p orange brown | .50 | .60 |
| SMH14 | 10½p steel blue | .50 | .55 |
| SMH15 | 11p red | .55 | .55 |
| SMH16 | 11½p gray brn, litho., perf 13½x14 | 1.00 | .90 |
| SMH17 | 12p yellow green | .55 | .55 |
| SMH18 | 12p brt green, litho., perf 13½x14 | 2.25 | 1.90 |
| SMH19 | 12p green, litho. | 2.10 | 2.10 |
| SMH20 | 12½p lt emer, litho., perf 13½x14 | .70 | .80 |
| SMH21 | 13p lt red brown, litho., perf 13½x14, type I | .85 | .85 |
| a. | Type II | 9.25 | 4.75 |
| SMH22 | 13p lt red brn, litho. | .85 | .85 |
| SMH23 | 13½p brown purple | .80 | .90 |
| SMH24 | 14p gray blue, litho., perf 13½x14 | .85 | .85 |
| SMH25 | 14p dk bl, litho. | .55 | .35 |
| a. | Booklet pane of 6 + printed margin (BK153) | 3.50 | |
| SMH26 | 15p deep ultra | .70 | .80 |

### Litho.

| | | | |
|---|---|---|---|
| SMH27 | 15p bright blue | .80 | .80 |

### Perf. 13½x14

| | | | |
|---|---|---|---|
| SMH28 | 15½p light violet | .90 | .90 |
| SMH29 | 16p brownish gray | .90 | .95 |
| SMH30 | 17p blue gray, type II | 1.50 | 1.10 |
| a. | Type I | 3.50 | 2.50 |

### Perf. 15x14

| | | | |
|---|---|---|---|
| SMH31 | 17p blue gray | 4.50 | 4.50 |
| SMH32 | 17p dark blue | 1.10 | 1.25 |
| SMH33 | 18p violet blue, perf 13½x14 | 1.00 | .75 |
| SMH34 | 18p olive green | 1.25 | 1.00 |
| SMH35 | 18p bright yel grn | .70 | .30 |
| SMH36 | 18p brt yel grn, perf 13½x14 | 1.40 | 1.00 |
| SMH37 | 19p red orange | .80 | .80 |
| a. | Booklet pane of 6 + printed margin (BK153) | 5.25 | |
| b. | Booklet pane of 9 + printed margin (BK153) | 6.50 | |
| SMH38 | 19½p green, perf 13½x14 | 2.00 | 2.00 |
| SMH39 | 20p brown black | 1.10 | 1.10 |

### Perf. 13½x14

| | | | |
|---|---|---|---|
| SMH40 | 20½p ultra | 4.75 | .75 |
| SMH41 | 22p dk blue | 1.10 | 1.00 |
| SMH42 | 22p yel grn, type I | 2.75 | 2.00 |
| a. | Type II | 50.00 | 40.00 |

### Perf. 15x14

| | | | |
|---|---|---|---|
| SMH43 | 22p yellow green | 1.60 | 1.75 |
| SMH44 | 22p red orange | 1.40 | 1.00 |
| SMH45 | 23p bright yel grn | 1.50 | 1.25 |
| a. | Booklet pane #SMH45, 2 #SMH37, 5 #SMH25 + printed margin (BK153) | 5.25 | |
| SMH46 | 24p brown red | 1.75 | 1.10 |
| SMH47 | 24p brown | 1.60 | 1.40 |
| SMH48 | 24p chestnut, perf 13½x14 | 3.25 | 3.25 |
| SMH49 | 26p red, perf 13½x14, type I | 1.10 | .90 |
| SMH50 | 26p red | 3.75 | 3.50 |
| SMH51 | 26p olive gray | 1.40 | 1.40 |
| SMH52 | 28p dp vio bl, perf 13½x14 | 1.40 | 1.40 |
| SMH53 | 28p deep violet blue | 1.25 | 1.25 |
| SMH54 | 28p dull bl grn | 1.75 | 1.60 |
| SMH55 | 28p dull bl grn, perf 13½x14 | 5.50 | 4.00 |
| SMH56 | 31p brt rose lilac, perf 13½x14 | 2.25 | 2.10 |
| a. | Type II | 110.00 | 90.00 |

| | | | |
|---|---|---|---|
| SMH57 | 31p brt rose lilac | 2.50 | .90 |
| SMH58 | 32p Prussian blue | 2.00 | 1.75 |
| SMH59 | 34p dull bl grn | 2.25 | 2.25 |
| SMH60 | 37p scarlet | 2.25 | 2.25 |
| SMH61 | 39p brt rose lilac | 2.25 | 2.25 |
| SMH62 | 39p brt rose lilac, perf 13½x14 | 3.25 | 2.00 |

Issued: #SMH1, 3p, 5p, #SMH9, 7/7/71; #SMH3, SMH6, 8p, 1/23/74; #SMH4, #SMH7, SMH11, 1/14/76; 10p, 11p, 10/20/76; 7p, 9p, #SMH14, 1/18/78; #SMH17, SMH23, #SMH26, 7/23/80. #SMH16, #SMH24, SMH33, SMH41, 4/8/81; #SMH20, SMH28, SMH38, #SMH49, 2/24/82; 16p, #SMH40, #SMH52, 4/27/83; #SMH21, SMH30, SMH42, SMH56, 10/23/84; #SMH18, 1/7/86; #SMH19, 7/23/86; SMH31, SMH57, 4/29/86; #SMH22, 11/4/86; #SMH34, 1/6/87; #SMH43, SMH50, SMH53, 1/27/87; #SMH25, 19p, 23p, 32p, 11/8/88; #SMH27, 20p, SMH46, 34p, 1/28/89; #SMH32, SMH44, SMH51, 37p, 12/4/90; #SMH35, SMH47, SMH54, SMH61, 12/3/91; #SMH36, 9/26/92; #SMH48, 10/92; #SMH62, 11/92; #SMH55, 2/18/93.

### Perf. 15x14 Syncopated
### 1993-96     Litho.

| | | | |
|---|---|---|---|
| SMH63 | 19p olive green | .90 | .80 |
| SMH64 | 20p brt yel green | 1.40 | 1.10 |
| SMH65 | 25p salmon | 1.25 | 1.10 |
| SMH66 | 26p brown | 1.75 | 1.75 |
| SMH67 | 30p olive green | 2.00 | 1.40 |
| SMH68 | 37p bright rose lilac | 3.00 | 2.50 |
| SMH69 | 41p drab | 2.25 | 2.25 |
| SMH70 | 63p bright green | 4.00 | 3.75 |

Issued: 19p, 20p, 30p, 41p, 12/7/93; 20p, 26p, 37p, 63p, 7/23/96.

### Queen Design of 1970 with Redrawn Portrait
### Perf. 15x14 Syncopated
### 1997-98     Photo.

| | | | |
|---|---|---|---|
| SMH75 | 20p brt yel green | 1.50 | .70 |
| SMH76 | 20p brt yel grn, perf 14 | 3.75 | 2.50 |
| SMH79 | 26p brown | 1.50 | 1.25 |
| SMH80 | 26p brown, perf 14 | 3.50 | 3.00 |
| SMH87 | 37p bright rose lilac | 2.00 | 1.50 |
| SMH97 | 63p bright green | 5.00 | 3.75 |

Issued: #SMH75, SMH79, 37p, 63p, 7/1/97; #SMH76, SMH80, 10/13/98.
Nos. SMH76, SMH80 issued only in booklets (BK164).
This is an expanding set, numbers may change.

### Perf. 13¾x14¼ Syncopated
### 2000     Photo.

| | | | |
|---|---|---|---|
| SMH101 | 1st org red (WM-MH96a) | 3.50 | 3.00 |

Issued: No. SMH96, 2/15/00. No. SMH96 sold for 26p on day of issue and was issued only in booklets.

## WALES & MONMOUTHSHIRE

All stamps are Design MA2 unless noted.

Type I      Type II

Two types of dragon:
Type I: Eye is complete with white dot in center. Wing tips, tail and tongue are thin.
Type II: Eye is joined to nose by solid line. Wing tips, tail and tongue are thick.

### 1971-93    Photo.    Perf. 15x14

| | | | |
|---|---|---|---|
| WMMH1 | 2½p bright pink | .20 | .20 |
| WMMH2 | 3p ultra | .30 | .20 |
| WMMH3 | 3½p slate | .30 | .35 |
| WMMH4 | 4½p dark blue | .35 | .35 |
| WMMH5 | 5p brt violet | 1.25 | 1.25 |
| WMMH6 | 5½p dark violet | .30 | .35 |
| WMMH7 | 6½p Prussian blue | .30 | .20 |
| WMMH8 | 7p dark red brn | .30 | .20 |
| WMMH9 | 7½p chestnut | 1.75 | 2.00 |
| WMMH10 | 8p red | .40 | .40 |
| WMMH11 | 8½p yel grn | .40 | .40 |
| WMMH12 | 9p violet blue | .45 | .45 |
| WMMH13 | 10p orange brn | .45 | .45 |
| WMMH14 | 10½p steel blue | .55 | .50 |
| WMMH15 | 11p red | .55 | .50 |
| WMMH16 | 11½p gray brn, litho., perf 13½x14 | 1.00 | .90 |
| WMMH17 | 12p yel grn | .60 | .55 |

### Litho.

| | | | |
|---|---|---|---|
| WMMH18 | 12p brt grn | 1.75 | 1.40 |
| WMMH19 | 12½p lt emer, perf 13½x14 | .80 | .80 |
| WMMH20 | 12½p lt emer | 6.00 | 5.75 |
| WMMH21 | 13p lt red brn, type I | .70 | .70 |
| a. | Type II | 2.25 | |

### Photo.

| | | | |
|---|---|---|---|
| WMMH22 | 13½p brown pur | .85 | .75 |
| WMMH23 | 14p gray blue, litho., perf 13½x14 | .85 | .85 |
| WMMH24 | 14p dark blue | .85 | .85 |
| WMMH25 | 15p deep ultra | .70 | .80 |

### Litho.

| | | | |
|---|---|---|---|
| WMMH26 | 15p bright blue | .90 | .85 |
| WMMH27 | 15½p light violet | .95 | .85 |
| WMMH28 | 16p brownish gray, perf 13½x14 | 1.75 | 1.90 |
| WMMH29 | 16p brownish gray | 2.00 | 2.25 |
| WMMH30 | 17p blue gray, type I | .95 | .90 |
| a. | Type II | 45.00 | 22.50 |
| WMMH31 | 17p dark blue | 1.00 | .90 |
| WMMH32 | 18p vio bl, perf 13½x14 | 1.10 | 1.10 |
| WMMH33 | 18p olive green | 1.10 | 1.00 |
| WMMH34 | 18p brt yel grn | .85 | .85 |
| a. | Booklet pane of 6 + printed margin (BK156) | 3.90 | |
| WMMH35 | 18p brt yel grn, perf 13½x14 | 5.00 | 4.00 |
| WMMH36 | 19p red or- | 1.10 | .90 |
| WMMH37 | 19½p ol gray, perf 13½x14 | 2.00 | 2.00 |
| WMMH38 | 20p brown black | 1.00 | 1.00 |
| WMMH39 | 20½p ultra | 3.75 | 3.75 |
| WMMH40 | 22p dk bl, perf 13½x14 | 1.25 | 1.25 |
| WMMH41 | 22p yel grn | 1.10 | 1.25 |
| WMMH42 | 22p orange red | 1.25 | 1.25 |
| WMMH43 | 23p brt yel grn | 1.10 | 1.25 |
| WMMH44 | 24p brown red | 1.10 | 1.25 |
| WMMH45 | 24p brown | .95 | .85 |
| a. | Booklet pane of 6 + printed margin (BK156) | 5.75 | |
| WMMH46 | 24p brown, perf 13½x14 | 3.50 | 3.25 |
| WMMH47 | 26p red, type I, perf 13½x14 | 1.25 | 1.25 |
| WMMH48 | 26p red, type II | 6.25 | 5.75 |
| WMMH49 | 26p olive gray | 1.60 | 1.60 |
| WMMH50 | 28p dp vio bl, type I, perf 13½x14 | 1.40 | 1.40 |
| WMMH51 | 28p dp vio bl, type II | 1.60 | 1.60 |
| WMMH52 | 28p dull bl grn | 1.75 | 1.60 |
| WMMH53 | 31p brt rose lil | 1.60 | 1.60 |
| WMMH54 | 32p Prus blue | 1.75 | 1.75 |
| WMMH55 | 34p dull bl grn | 1.75 | 1.75 |
| WMMH56 | 37p scarlet | 2.25 | 2.25 |
| WMMH57 | 39p brt rose lil | 2.25 | 2.25 |

Issued: #WMMH1, 3p, 5p, WMMH9, 7/7/71; #WMMH3, WMMH6, 8p, 1/23/74; #WMMH4, 11/6/74; #WMMH7, WMMH11, 1/14/76; 10p, 11p, 10/20/76.

7p, 9p, #WMMH14, 1/18/78; #WMMH17, WMMH22, WMMH25, 7/23/80; #WMMH16, #WMMH23, WMMH32, WMMH40, 4/8/81;

#WMMH19, WMMH27, WMMH37, WMMH47, 2/24/82; #WMMH28, WMMH39, WMMH50, 4/27/83; #WMMH20, WMMH29, 1/10/84.

139, #WMMH30, WMMH41, 31p, 10/23/84; #WMMH18, 1/7/86; #WMMH33, 1/6/87;

#WMMH48, WMMH51, 1/27/87; #WMMH24, 19p, 23p, 8/11/88; #WMMH26, 20p, WMMH44, 34p, 11/28/89; #WMMH31, WMMH42, WMMH49, 37p, 12/4/90; #WMMH34, WMMH45, WMMH52,

39p, 12/3/91; #WMMH46, 9/14/92; #WMMH35, 1/12/93.

### Perf. 15x14 Syncopated
### 1993-96     Litho.

| | | | |
|---|---|---|---|
| WMMH58 | 19p olive green | .90 | .80 |
| WMMH59 | 20p brt yel grn | 2.00 | 1.75 |
| WMMH60 | 25p salmon | 1.40 | 1.10 |
| WMMH61 | 26p brown | 2.25 | 2.00 |
| WMMH62 | 30p olive green | 1.40 | 1.40 |
| WMMH63 | 37p bright rose lilac | 3.00 | 2.75 |
| WMMH64 | 41p drab | 2.25 | 2.25 |
| WMMH65 | 63p bright green | 5.00 | 4.50 |

Issued: 19p, 25p, 30p, 41p, 12/7/93. 20p, 26p, 37p, 63p, 7/23/96.

### Queen Design of 1970 with Redrawn Portrait
### "P" Removed
### Perf. 15x14 Syncopated
### 1997-98     Photo.

| | | | |
|---|---|---|---|
| WMMH70 | 20p brt yel grn | 1.00 | .90 |
| WMMH71 | 20p brt yel grn, perf 14 | 2.75 | 2.25 |
| WMMH74 | 26p brown | 1.25 | 1.10 |
| WMMH75 | 26p brown, perf 14 | 2.50 | 2.25 |
| WMMH82 | 37p bright rose lilac | 3.00 | 2.50 |
| WMMH92 | 63p bright green | 5.00 | 4.00 |

Issued: #WMMH70, WMMH74, 37p, 63p, 7/1/97; #WMMH71, WMMH75, 10/13/98.
Nos. WMMH71, WMMH75 issued only in booklets (BK164).
This is an expanding set, numbers may change.

### Perf. 13¾x14¼ Syncopated
### 2000     Photo.

| | | | |
|---|---|---|---|
| WMMH96 | 1st orange red | 3.50 | 2.50 |
| a. | Bklt. pane, 3 ea #NIMH96, SMH101, WMMH96 (BK167) | 30.00 | |

Issued: No. WMMH96, 2/15/00. No. WMMH96 sold for 26p on day of issue and was issued only in booklets.

See Isle of Man #8-11 for additional Machin Head definitives.

## BOOKLETS

Booklets are listed in denomination sequence by reign. Numbers in parenthesis following each listing reflect the number of cover varieties or edition numbers that apply to each cover style.

Values shown for complete booklets are for examples containing most panes having full perforations on two edges of the pane only. Booklets containing most or all panes with very fine, full perforations on all sides are scarce and will sell for more. Also, in booklets where most of the value is contained in only one pane of several, it is assumed that this pane has full perforations on two sides only. If this pane is very fine, the booklet will be worth a considerable premium over the value given.

This section does not contain complete booklets consisting solely of self-adhesive stamps. These are catalogued as minors under stamp listings.

### Sterling Currency

BC1

### 1904

| | | | |
|---|---|---|---|
| BK1 | BC1 | 2sh½p red, 4 #128e | 350.00 |

### 1906-11

| | | | |
|---|---|---|---|
| BK2 | BC1 | 2sh red, 2 #128e, 3 #143c, #143b | 950.00 |

**BK3** BC1 2sh *red*, 3 #128e,
1 each
#143b-143c
(4)                    1,150.

Cover inscription on Nos. BK2-BK3 revised to reflect changed contents.

**1911**
**BK4** BC1 2sh *red*, 2#151a, 3
#152a                  750.00

BC2

**1912-13**
**BK5** BC2 2sh *red*, 2 #151a,
3 #152a              1,050.
**BK6** BC2 2sh *red*, 2 #155a,
3 #156a (4)          1,000.

Cover inscription on Nos. BK5-BK6 shows only Inland Postage Rates.

**1913**
**BK7** BC2 2sh *red*, 2
#159b, 3
#160a (35)           500.00
**BK8** BC2 2sh *org*, 2
#159b,3
#160a (20)           525.00

BC3

**1917**
**BK9** BC3 2sh *org*, 2 #159b,
3 #160a (17)         500.00

BC4

**1924-34**
**BK10** BC4 2sh *blue*, #159b,
160a, 161d-
161e (2)            -1,250.
**BK11** BC4 2sh *blue*,
#187b,
188b, 189c-
189d (277)           475.00

BC5

**1929**
**BK12** BC5 2sh *blue, buff,*
#205b-207b,
207c                 550.00

**1935**
**BK13** BC4 2sh *blue*, #210b-
211b, 212c-
212d (58)            550.00

BC6

**1935**
**BK14** BC6 2sh *blue, buff,*
#226a-227a,
3 #228a              100.00

**1918-19**
**BK15** BC4 3sh *org*, 2 each #159b,
160a, 161d (11)      650.00
**BK16** BC4 3sh *org*, #159b, 160a, 3
#161d (15)           650.00

Cover used for Nos. BK15-BK16 does not have inscription above top line.

**1921**
**BK17** BC4 3sh *blue*, 3 #162b (3)    850.00
**BK18** BC4 3sh *blue*, 3 #162c (3)    900.00

**1922**
**BK19** BC4 3sh *scar*, #159b,
160a, 3 #161d
(33)                 850.00
**BK20** BC4 3sh *blue*, 4 #161d
(2)                  900.00

**1924-34**
**BK21** BC4 3sh *scar*, #187b-
188b, 3
#189c (237)          375.00

**1929**
**BK22** BC5 3sh *blue, buff,*
#205b-206b,
3 #207b (5)          450.00

**1935**
**BK23** BC4 3sh *scar*, #210b-
211b, 3 #212c
(27)                 375.00
**BK24** BC6 3sh *red, buff,*
#226a-227a, 5
#228a (4)            100.00

**1920**
**BK25** BC4 3sh6p *org*, #160a, 3
#162b (6)            850.00

Cover used for No. BK25 does not have inscription above top line.

**1921**
**BK26** BC4 3sh6p *org red*, #159b,
160a, 161d, 2
#162b (7)            900.00
**BK27** BC4 3sh6p *org red*, #159b,
160a, 161d, 2
#162c (13)           900.00

**1931-35**
**BK28** BC4 5sh *grn*, #187b-188b,
189d, 5 #189c        4,000.
**BK29** BC4 5sh *buff*, #187b-188b,
189d, 5 #189c (7)    1,250.
**BK30** BC4 5sh *buff*, #210b-211b,
212d, 5 #212c (7)    450.00

BC7

**1936**
**BK31** BC7 6p *buff*, 2 #232c    70.00

BC8

**BK32** BC8 2sh *blue*, #230a-231a,
#232a-232b (31)      140.00
**BK33** BC8 3sh *scar*, #230a-231a, 3
#232a (12)           110.00
**BK34** BC8 5sh *buff*, #230a-231a, 6
#232a (2)            250.00

**1938-40**
**BK35** BC7 6p *buff*, 2 #237d    70.00
**BK36** BC7 6p *pink*, #235d-237d  325.00
**BK37** BC7 6p *pale grn*, #235c-236c  150.00

No. BK37 is 53x41mm.

**1947-51**
**BK38** BC7 1sh *buff*, 2 ea #258b-
259b, 260a           27.50
**BK39** BC7 1sh *buff*, 2 ea #280a,
281b-282b            27.50
**BK40** BC7 1sh *buff*, #258e, 259d,
260b                 6,000.
**BK41** BC7 1sh *buff*, #280b-282b   32.50

Nos. BK40-BK41 are 53x41mm.

Round GPO Emblem — BC9

**1952-53**
**BK42** BC9 1sh *buff*, #280b, 281c-
282c                 22.50
**a.** Inland postage rate corrected in
ink on inside booklet cover    25.00

Oval GPO Emblem — BC10

**1954**
**BK43** BC10 1sh *buff*, #280b,
281c-282c            32.50

**1937**
**BK44** BC8 2sh *blue*, #235b-
236b, #237b-
237c (26)            450.00

BC11

BC12

**1938**
**BK45** BC11 2sh *blue*, #235b-
236b, #237b-
237c (95)            450.00

**1940-42**
                     **2sh6p Booklets**
**BK46** BC11 *scar*, #235b, #238b-
239b (7)             1,050.
**BK47** BC11 *blue*, #235b, #238b-
239b (6)             1,050.

Denomination part of cover of Nos. BK46-BK47 is printed in white on black background.

**BK48** BC11 *grn*, #235b, #238b-
239b (80)            550.00
**BK49** BC11 *grn*, #258a, #261b-
262b (120)           550.00

**1943**
**BK50** BC12 *grn*, #258a, #261b-
262b (90)            65.00

With booklets issued in August and September 1943, commercial advertising on British booklets was discontinued. Covers and interleaving were used for Post Office slogans. Booklets were no longer numbered, but carried the month and year of issue.

**1951-52**
**BK51** BC12 *grn*, #280c, #283b-
284b (10)            42.50
**BK52** BC12 *grn*, #280c, 281e,
#282d, 284b (15)     40.00

**1937-38**
                     **3sh Booklets**
**BK53** BC8 *scar*, #235a-236a, 3
#237b (10)           850.00
**BK54** BC11 *scar*, #235a-236a, 3
#237b (34)           850.00

**1937-43**
                     **5sh Booklets**
**BK55** BC8 *buff*, #235b-236b,
237c, 5 #237b (3)    1,000.
**BK56** BC11 *buff*, #235b-236b,
237c, 5 #237b (9)    950.00
**BK57** BC11 *buff*, #235b, 238b, 3
#239b (16)           975.00
**BK58** BC11 *buff*, #258a, 261b, 3
#262b (20)           950.00

**1943-53**
**BK59** BC12 *tan*, #258a, 261b, 3
#262b (49)           110.00
**BK60** BC12 *tan*, #258a, 261b, 3
#262b (20)           1,250.

Cover on No. BK60 has thick horizontal lines separating the GPO emblem and the various inscriptions.

**BK61** BC12 *tan*, #280a, 283b, 3
#284b (5)            62.50
**BK62** BC12 *tan*, #280c, 281e, 282d,
3 #284b (5)          62.50
**BK63** BC12 *tan*, #280c, 281d-282d,
283b, 2 #284b (2)    62.50

BC13

**1953-54**
                     **2sh6p Booklets**
**BK64** BC12 *grn*, #280c, 281e,
294c, #296a (6)      29.00
**BK65** BC13 *grn*, #280c, 281e,
294c, 296a (7)       32.50

**BK66** BC13  *grn*, #281e, 292c, 294c, 296a        500.00

**5sh Booklets**

**BK67** BC12  *brn*, #280c, 281d, 283b, 294c, 2 #296a (3)        40.00

**BK68** BC13  *brn*, #280c, 281d, 283b, 294c, 2 #296a (2)        45.00

**BK69** BC13  *brn*, #281d, 283b, 292c, 294c, 2 #296a        300.00

**BK70** BC13  *brn*, #283b, 292c-294c, 2 #296a        160.00

**1953-57**

**1sh Booklets**

**BK71** BC7  *buff*, 2 each #292a-294a        8.50

**BK72** BC7  *buff*, 2 each #317d, 318f, 319f        25.00

**1954-59**

**BK73** BC10  *buff*, #292b-294b (2)        8.00

**BK74** BC10  *buff*, #317b, 318c, 319b (3)        8.00

**BK75** BC10  *buff*, #353b-355b (2)        10.00

**1959**

**2sh Booklets**

**BK76** BC10  *salmon*, #317b, 318c, 319b, 322b        6.50

BC14

**1960-65**

**2sh Booklets**

**BK77** BC14  *sal*, #353b-355b, 358b        10.00

**BK77A** BC14  *pale yel*, 353b-355b, 358b        10.00

**BK78** BC14  *red, pale yel*, #353e, 2 #357g        4.00
   *a.* White stiching        4.00

**BK79** BC14  *pale yel*, #353b-355b, 358b (17)        30.00
   *a.* #353bp-355bp, 358bp (13)        100.00

**BK80** BC14  *red, pale yel*, 4 #353g        5.00

**BK81** BC14  *org yel*, #354f, 359c (7)        3.50
   *a.* #354fp, 359cp (12)        17.50

**BK82** BC14  *red, org yel*, 2 #358b        .80

**1968-69**

**BK83** BC14  *org yel*, #MH5b, MH6b (3)        1.40

**BK84** BC14  *gray*, #MH6a-MH6b (5)        1.00

**BK85** BC14  *gray*, #MH7a-MH7b (12)        1.25

**1954, Mar.**

**2sh6p Booklets**

**BK86** BC13  *grn*, #292c, 293d, 294c, 296a (19)        37.50

No. BK86 inscribed Apr. 1954 through Aug. 1955 are valued. Booklet inscribed Mar. 1954 is valued at $325.

No. BK86 inscribed Aug. 1955 through Nov. 1955, may contain one or more panes watermarked 308 substituted for those listed. Value $50.

**1955, Dec.**

**BK87** BC13  *grn*, #317b, 318b, 319a, 321a (16)        40.00

No. BK87 inscribed Dec. 1955 through June 1956 may contain one or more panes watermarked 298 substituted for those listed. Value $15.

**1957**

**BK88** BC13  *grn*, #317a, 320b, 321a (9)        40.00

**3sh Booklets**

**1958, Jan.**

**BK89** BC13  *red*, #317a, 318b, 319a, 322a (9)        25.00

No. BK89 inscribed Nov. 1958, may contain one or more panes watermarked 322 substituted for those listed. Value $13.

**1958, Dec.-59**

**BK90** BC13  *red*, #353a-355a, 358a (5)        29.00
   *a.* #353d, 354d, 355d, 358d (2)        300.00

No. BK90 dated Dec. 1958, may contain one or more panes watermarked 308 substituted for those listed. Value $14.

**BK91** BC13  *brick red*, #353a-355a, 358a (14)        32.50
   *a.* #353d, 354d, 355d, 358d (4)        325.00
   *b.* #353ap, 354ap, 355ap, 358ap (2)        65.00

BC15

**1960**

**BK92** BC15  *brick red*, #353a-355a, 358a (46)        32.50
   *a.* #353ap-355ap, 358ap (35)        75.00

**3sh9p Booklets**

**1953, Nov.**

**BK93** BC13  *red*, 3 #296a (10)        35.00

No. BK93 inscribed Oct. or Dec. 1955 may contain one or more panes watermarked 308 substituted for those listed. Value $16.

**1956, Feb.**

**BK94** BC13  *red*, 3 #321a (10)        25.00

**1957, Oct.-Dec. 1960**

**4sh6p Booklets**

**BK95** BC13  *dull mauve*, 3 #322a (5)        25.00

**BK96** BC13  *dull mauve*, 3 #358a        90.00

**BK97** BC13  *dull mauve*, 3 #358a (4)        26.00
   *a.* 3 #358d        37.50

**BK98** BC14  *pale reddish lil*, 3 #358a (9)        37.50
   *a.* 3 #358d (4)        25.00
   *b.* 3 #358ap        30.00

**BK99** BC15  *pale reddish lil*, 3 #358a (36)        45.00
   *a.* 3 #358ap (31)        35.00

**1965**

**BK100** BC15  *slate bl*, #354a, 2 #359b (7)        25.00
   *a.* #354ap, 2 #359bp (13)        32.50

**1968**

**BK101** BC15  *slate bl*, #MH2a, 2 #MH6c        7.50

Ship with GPO Emblem — BC16

**1968-70**

**4sh6p Booklets**

**BK102** BC16  *blue*, #MH2a, 2 #MH6c (3)        2.00

**BK103** BC16  *blue*, #MH2a, 2 #MH7c (9)        3.75

**Ship Type with St. Edward's Crown instead of GPO emblem**

**BK104** BC16  *blue*, #MH2a, 2 #MH7c (2)        4.50

**5sh Booklets**

**1954, Mar.**

**BK105** BC13  *brn*, #292c-294c, 295a-296a (10)        45.00

No. BK105 inscribed Sept. 1955 may contain one or more panes watermarked 308 substituted for those listed. Value $16.

**1955, Nov.**

**BK106** BC13  *brn*, #317a, 318b, 319a, 320b, 321a (14)        40.00

No. BK106 inscribed Nov. 1955, Jan. 1956 or May 1956 may contain one or more panes watermarked 298 substituted for those listed. Value $17.

**1958**

**BK107** BC13  *brn*, #317a, 318b, 321a, 9 #322a (5)        40.00

No. BK107 inscribed July or Nov. 1958 may contain one or more panes watermarked 322 substituted for those listed. Value $15.

**1959, Jan.**

**BK108** BC14  *bl*, #353a-354a, 357c, 2 #358a (11)        32.50
   *a.* #353a-354d, 357e, 2 #358d (3)        150.00
   *b.* #353ap-354ap, 357cp, 2 #358ap        125.00

No. BK108 inscribed Jan. 1959 may contain one or more panes watermarked 308 substituted for those listed. Value $15.

**1961, Jan.**

**BK109** BC15  *bl*, #353a-354a, 357c, 2 #358a (27)        50.00
   *a.* #353ap-354ap, 357cp, 2 #358ap (24)        150.00

House with GPO Emblem — BC17

**1968-70**

**BK110** BC17  *org brn*, 2 #MH8a (5)        3.00

**House Type with St. Edward's Crown instead of GPO Emblem**

**BK111** BC17  *5sh org brn*, 2 #MH8a (7)        3.25

BC18

**1970**

**BK112** BC18  *org brn*, 2 #MH8a        3.50

**6sh Booklets**

**1965**

**BK113** BC15  *claret*, 3 #359b (23)        30.00
   *a.* 3 #359bp (27)        37.50

**1967**

**BK114** BC15  *claret*, 3 #MH6c (10)        50.00

Bird with GPO Emblem — BC19

**1968-70**

**BK115** BC19  *org*, 3 #MH6c (8)        2.25
**BK116** BC19  *org*, 3 #MH7c (5)        2.25

**Bird Type with St. Edward's Crown instead of GPO Emblem**

**BK117** BC19  *org*, 3 #MH7c (5)        4.25

**1961-67**

**10sh Booklets**

**BK118** BC15  *grn*, #353a-355a, 356b, 5 #358a (2)        140.00

**BK119** BC15  *gray grn*, #354a-355a, 357c, 5 #358a (7)        115.00

**BK120** BC15  *tan*, #354a, 358a, 4 #359b (2)        30.00
   *a.* #354ap, 358ap, 4 #359bp (3)        9.25

Explorers with GPO Emblem — BC20

**1968-70**

**BK121** BC20  *pur*, #MH2a, MH5a, 4 #MH6c (2)        6.75

**Explorer Type with clear GPO Emblem**

**BK122** BC20  *yel grn*, #MH6d, 2 ea #MH6c, #MH8a        6.75

**BK123** BC20  *yel grn*, #MH7c, MH7e, MH8a (4)        4.00

**Explorer Type with St. Edward's Crown instead of GPO Emblem**

**BK124** BC20  *yel grn*, #MH7e, 2 ea #MH7c, MH8a (2)        8.00

BC21

**£1 Booklets**

**1969**

**BK125** BC21  *multi*, 2 #MH7d, MH8b-MH8c        17.50

**BK126** BC21  2 #MH7d, MH8b-MH8c, stapled        400.00

**Decimal Currency Booklets (Stitched)**

BC22

## 1971-74
**BK127** BC22 10p *org yel,*
#MH24a,
MH26a (21) 2.50

BC23

## 1974-76
**BK128** BC23 10p *org yel,*
#MH24a,
MH26a (9) 2.75

BC24

## 1971-73
**BK129** BC24 25p *dull purple*
(12) 5.00
Contents: #MH22a, MH32a-MH32b.

BC25

## 1971
**BK130** BC25 25p *dull purple* 8.25
Contents: #MH22a, MH32a-MH32b.

**BK131** BC25 30p *bright pur,*
#MH36b 5.75

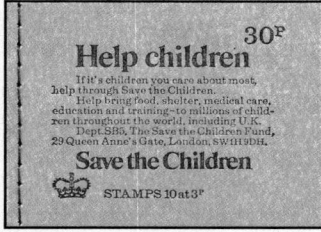

BC26

## 1973-74
**BK132** BC26 25p *dull mauve* 10.50
Contents: #MH22a, MH32a-MH32b.

**BK133** BC26 30p *vermilion, 2*
#MH36b 6.50

## Bird Type with St. Edward's Crown instead of GPO Emblem

## 1971-73
**BK134** BC19 30p *pur, 2*
#MH36b (16) 5.50
**BK135** BC19 30p *buff, 2*
#MH36b 8.25

BC27

## 1973-74
**BK136** BC27 30p *red, 2*
#MH36b 6.00
**BK137** BC27 35p *blue, 2*
#MH39a 4.00
**BK138** BC27 50p *pale bluish*
*grn* 12.00
Contents: #MH22a, MH32b, MH36a, MH36c (4).

**BK139** BC27 50p *pale grn,*
MH36b, 2
#MH39a (2) 10.50
**BK140** BC27 85p *purple,*
#MH39a, 3
#MH49a 10.50

BC28

## 1973-74
**BK141** BC28 35p *bl, 2* #MH39a
(3) 4.25
**BK142** BC28 45p *yel brn, 2*
#MH49a (3) 7.00

BC29

## 1971-72
**BK143** BC29 50p *pale bluish*
*green* 11.50
Contents: #MH22a, MH32b, MH36a, MH36c (8).

---

## Prestige Booklets

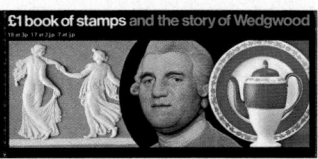

BC30

## 1972, May 24
**BK144** BC30 £1 *Wedg-*
*wood* 150.00
Contents: #MH34a-MH34b, #MH36d-MH36e. Valued with a F-VF 1/2p stamp.

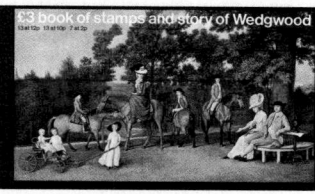

BC31

## 1980, Apr. 16
**BK145** BC31 £3 *Wedgwood* 20.00
Contents: #MH26b, MH70a, MH78a-MH78b.

## 1982, May 19
**BK146** £4 *Stanley Gibbons* 20.00
Contents: #MH80a-MH80b, MH92a-MH92b.

## 1983, Sept. 14
**BK147** £4 *Royal Mint* 19.00
Contents: #MH94a-MH94b, 2 #MH80a.

## 1984, Sept. 4
**BK148** £4 *Christian Heritage* 55.00
Contents: #MH97c-MH97d, 2 #MH83a.

## 1985, Jan. 8
**BK149** £5 *The Times* 50.00
Contents: #MH83b, MH97b-MH97c, MH149a.

## 1986, Mar. 18
**BK150** £5 *British Rail* 50.00
Contents: #MH79a, MH97b-MH97c, MH142a.

## 1987, Mar. 3
**BK151** £5 *P & O* 32.50
Contents: #MH83a-MH83b, MH102a, MH130a.

## 1988, Feb. 9
**BK152** £5 *The Financial*
*Times* 47.50
Contents: #MH84a, MH103a-MH103b, MH150a.

## 1989, Mar. 21
**BK153** £5 *Scots Connection* 27.50
Contents: #SMH25a,SMH37a-SMH37b, SMH45a.

## 1990, Mar. 20
**BK154** £5 *London Life* 37.50
Contents: #1314a, MH196a, 2 #MH193d.

## 1991, Mar. 19
**BK155** £6 *Agatha Christie* 37.50
Contents: #MH121a, MH147a, 2 #MH99a.

## 1992, Feb. 25
**BK156** £6 *Cymru-Wales* 30.00
Contents: #1425a, MH187c, WMMH34a, WMMH45a.

## 1992, Oct. 27
**BK157** £6 *J.R.R. Tolkien* 32.50
Contents: #MH105a, MH187b, 2 #MH127a.

## 1993, Aug. 10
**BK158** £5.64 *Beatrix Potter* 30.00
Although inscribed £6 on the cover, No. BK158 was sold for £5.64, the face value of its contents, which were #1484a, MH178a, MH187a, NIMH45a.

## 1994, July 26
**BK159** £6.04 *N. Ireland* 32.50
Contents: #1550a, MH214a, NIMH63a-NIMH63b, 2 postal cards.

## 1995, Apr. 25
**BK160** £6 *National Trust* 32.50
Contents: #1607a, MH209a, MH231a, NIMH59a.

## 1996, May 14
**BK161** £6.48 *European Soc-*
*cer Champi-*
*onships* 21.00
Contents: #1663a, 1664a, 1667a, MH214b.

## 1997, Sept. 23
**BK162** £6.15 *75th Anniv. of*
*BBC* 30.00
Contents: #1698a, MH287a, MH257a, NIMH81a.

## 1998, Mar. 10
**BK163** £7.49 *Definitive Por-*
*trait* 30.00
Contents: #1801a, 1802a, 1803a-1803b.

## 1998, Oct. 13
**BK164** £6.16 *Breaking Barri-*
*ers* 35.00
Contents: #1829b, MH269a, MH285a-MH285b.

## 1999, Feb. 16
**BK165** (£7.54) *Profile on*
*Print* 45.00
Contents: #MH241c, MH288a, MH310a-MH312a.

## 1999, Sept. 21
**BK166** (£6.99) *World*
*Changers* 37.50
Contents: #1842b, 1847a, 1868b, 1869b, MH257f.

## 2000, Feb. 15
**BK167** (£7.50) *Special by Design* 50.00
Contents: #MH198Ab, MH264Bc, MH336b, WMMH96a.

## 2000, Aug. 4
**BK168** (£7.03) *The Life of the*
*Century* 35.00
Contents: #1943e, 1943f, Scotland 18a, MH335b.

## 2000, Sept. 18
**BK169** (£7) *A Treasury of Trees* 35.00
Contents: #1917a, 1918a, 1920a, 1921a, Wales and Monmouthshire 18a.

## 2001, Oct. 22
**BK170** (£6.76) *Unseen and*
*Unheard* 45.00
Contents: #1969b, 1970b, 1999e, Scotland 16a.

## 2002, Feb. 6
**BK171** (£7.23) *A Gracious*
*Accession* 35.00
Contents: #2020a, 2021a, 2023a, MH290b.

## 2002, Sept. 24
**BK172** (£6.83) *Across the*
*Universe* 30.00
Contents: 1938b, 2075e, Scotland 15a, MH290c.

## 2003, Feb. 25
**BK173** (£6.99) *Microcosmos* 24.00
Contents: #2104a, 2105a, Northern Ireland 13a, MH290c.

## 2003, June 2
**BK174** (£7.46) *A Perfect Cor-*
*onation* 85.00
Contents: #2126a, 2134a, 2136b, MH287b.

## 2004, Mar. 16
**BK175** (£7.44) *Letters by*
*Night* 27.00
Contents: #2148a, 2175a, Scotland 20a, MH287c.

## 2004, May 25
**BK176** (£7.23) *The Glory of*
*the Garden* 32.50
Contents: #1720b, 2213a, 2214b, MH287d.

**2005, Feb. 24**
BK177    (£7.43)   *The Bronte Sisters*    28.00

Contents: #2268a, 2272b, England 10a, MH354a.

**2005, Oct. 18**
BK178    (£7.26)   *Battle of Trafalgar*    27.00

Contents: #1999h, 2325a, 2326b, MH287e.

**2006, Feb. 23**
BK179    (£7.40)   *Isambard Kingdom Brunel*    27.00

Contents: #2356a, 2357a, 2358b, MH355a.

**2006, Sept. 21**
BK180    (£7.44)   *Victoria Cross*    28.50

Contents: #1331b, 2398a, 2399b, MH376a.

**2007, Mar. 1**
BK181    (£7.49)   *World of Invention*    30.00

Contents: #2447a, 2449b, Wales & Monmouthshire 26a, MH376b.

**2007, June 5**
BK182    (£7.66)   *The Machin*    31.00

Contents: #2471c, MH363a, MH373a, MH378a.

**2007, Sept. 20**
BK183    (£7.66)   *British Army Uniforms*    32.00

Contents: #2510b, 2513b, MH366a, Wales & Monmouthshire #21a.

**2008, Jan. 8**
BK184    (£7.40)   *Ian Fleming's James Bond*    30.00

Contents: #1999i, 2535a, 2536b, MH287f.

**2008, Sept. 18**
BK185    (£7.15)   *RAF Uniforms*    26.00

Contents: #2587c, 2596b, 2599b, MH287h.

**2008, Sept. 29**
BK186    (£9.72)   *The Regional Definitives: Heraldry and Symbol*    34.00

Contents: #2600s, 2600t, 2600u, 2600v.

**2009, Jan. 13**
BK187    (£7.68)   *British Design Classics*    24.00

Contents: #2619a, 2623a, 2624b, MH365b.

Numbers have been reserved for future prestige booklets.

---

### Decimal Currency Booklets (Folded)

Booklets are listed in denomination sequence in chronological order in this section.

BC32

**1976-77**
BK225   BC32   10p red, *gray*, #MH58a (3)    1.25

---

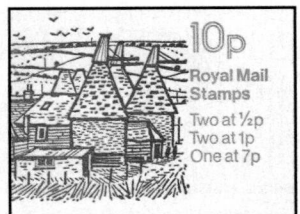

BC33

**1978**
BK226   BC33   10p brn, *bl*, #MH61b (6)    1.25

**1979-80**
BK227   BC33   10p *London '80*, #MH64b (2)    .75

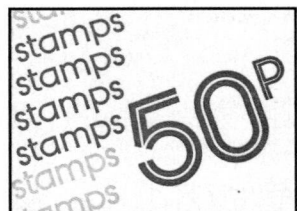

BC34

**1977**
BK228   BC34   50p #MH65a    5.25
BK229   BC34   50p #MH67a    3.50

Nos. BK228-BK229, BK230-BK231, BK237-BK238 exist with either version of #MH65a, MH67a, MH70b, MH80c. See the notes following the listings for these panes.

---

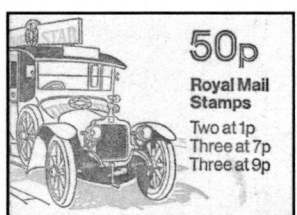

Commercial Vehicles — BC35

**1978-95**
**50p Booklets, Cover BC35**
| | | |
|---|---|---|
| BK230 | *Commercial Vehicles*, #MH67a (6) | 5.75 |
| BK231 | *Commercial Vehicles*, #MH70b | 3.75 |
| BK232 | *Veteran Cars*, #MH70b | 3.00 |
| BK233 | *Veteran Cars*, #MH78d (3) | 3.00 |
| BK234 | *Veteran Cars*, #MH86a (2) | 3.00 |
| BK235 | *Follies*, #MH86a | 3.00 |
| BK236 | *Follies*, #MH76a (2) | 8.25 |
| BK237 | *Follies*, #MH80c (4) | 3.50 |
| BK238 | *Rare Farm Animals*, #MH80c | 3.75 |
| BK239 | *Rare Farm Animals*, #MH80d (4) | 7.50 |
| BK240 | *Orchids*, #MH83c (4) | 4.75 |
| BK241 | *Pillar Box*, #MH97a | 5.50 |
| BK242 | *Pond Life*, #MH97a (2) | 3.50 |

Nos. BK241-BK242 sold for a 1p discount. Some panes have stars on reverse.

| | | |
|---|---|---|
| BK244 | *Pond Life*, #MH83d (2) | 5.00 |
| BK245 | *Roman Britain*, #MH79b | 11.50 |
| BK246 | *Roman Britain*, #MH102b (2) | 5.25 |
| BK247 | *Marylebone Cricket Club*, #MH102b (4) | 3.50 |
| BK248 | *Botanical Gardens*, #MH83d (2) | 6.00 |
| BK248A | *Botanical Gardens*, #MH83g (2) | 5.75 |
| BK249 | *London Zoo*, #MH102b (2) | 4.00 |
| BK250 | *London Zoo*, #MH83g | 5.00 |
| BK251 | *Marine Life*, #MH83g | 5.00 |
| BK252 | *Marine Life*, #MH106a | 4.00 |
| BK253 | *Gilbert & Sullivan Operas*, #MH106a (3) | 6.00 |
| BK254 | *Aircraft*, #MH115a | 14.00 |

---

| | | |
|---|---|---|
| BK255 | *Aircraft*, #MH193a | 10.50 |
| BK256 | *Aircraft*, #MH98a (2) | 6.25 |
| BK257 | *Archaeology*, #MH126a (4) | 3.50 |
| BK258 | *Sheriff's Millennium*, #MH126a | 2.50 |
| BK259 | *Postal History*, #MH126a (3) | 3.00 |
| BK260 | *Postal History*, #MH213a | 3.00 |
| BK261 | *Coaching Inns*, #MH213a (4) | 3.00 |
| BK262 | *Sea Charts*, #MH213a (4) | 3.00 |

With Window — BC36

Without Window — BC37

**1987**
BK285   BC36   52p #MH83e    4.50

**1988-89**
BK295   BC36   56p #MH87a (2)    7.00
BK296   BC37   56p #MH87b    11.00
BK297   BC37   56p #MH87c    45.00

**1990**
BK307   BC37   60p #MH191a    7.50

**1976-77**
BK317   BC34   65p 10 #MH60    10.50
BK325   BC34   70p 10 #MH61    7.00

Nos. BK317, BK325-BK327, BK370, BK394, BK404-BK405, BK467-BK468, BK488-BK492, BK513-BK514, BK524-BK533, BK554-BK557, BK573-BK574, BK584, BK594, BK616-BK618, BK631, BK641, BK651-BK652, BK673-BK675, BK696-BK699, BK709-BK713, BK715-BK718, BK728, BK732-BK733 exist with stamps affixed to cover by selvage at either right or left edges of block or pane of stamps.

BC38

**1978-79**
**70p Booklets**
BK326   BC38   *Country Crafts*, 10 #MH61 (6)    5.75
BK327   BC38   *Derby Mechanized Letter Office*, 10 #MH61    10.50

**1987**
BK338   BC36   72p red, yel & blk, #MH102c    4.50

**1988-89**
BK348   BC36   76p #MH106c (2)    9.00
BK349   BC37   76p #MH106d    9.00
BK350   BC37   76p #MH106e    45.00

---

BC39

**1992**
BK360   BC39   78p 2 #MH157    4.00

Cover of #BK360 does not show the numeral four. Contents of #BK360 is 1/2 of #MH157a, the right hand vertical pair of stamps being removed.

**1979**
BK370   BC38   80p *Military Aircraft*, 10 #MH64    3.00

**1990**
BK371   BC37   80p red, yel & blk, #MH193b    10.00
BK372   BC37   80p red, yel & blk, #MH194a    7.50

**1976-79**
BK382   BC34   85p gray & ol grn, 10 #MH65    10.50
BK392   BC34   90p lt & dk bl, 10 #MH67    7.00
BK393   BC38   90p *British Canals*, 10 #MH67 (6)    8.00
BK394   BC38   90p *Derby Letter Office*, 10 #MH67    12.50

**1979-95**
**£1 Booklets**
| | | |
|---|---|---|
| BK403 | BC38 | *Industrial Archaeology*, 10 #MH70   5.25 |
| BK404 | BC38 | *Military Aircraft*, 10 #MH70 (3)   5.25 |
| BK405 | BC35 | *Violin*, 6 #MH97   5.75 |
| BK406 | BC35 | *Musical Instruments*, #MH102d (2)   6.00 |
| BK407 | BC35 | *Sherlock Holmes*, #MH102d (2)   6.00 |
| BK408 | BC35 | *Sherlock Holmes*, #MH102f (2)   6.00 |
| BK409 | BC35 | *London Zoo*, #MH102f   6.00 |
| BK410 | BC35 | *Oliver Twist*, #MH102f   8.00 |
| BK411 | BC35 | *Nicholas Nickleby*, #MH106b (2)   8.00 |
| BK412 | BC35 | *Great Expectations*, #MH108a   15.00 |
| BK413 | BC35 | *Marine Life*, #MH106b   8.00 |
| BK414 | BC35 | *Wicken Fen*, #MH115b   11.00 |
| BK415 | BC35 | *Click Mill*, #MH193c   8.50 |
| BK416 | BC35 | *Wicken Fen*, #MH194b   8.00 |
| BK417 | BC35 | *Jack & Jill Mills*, #MH120a (2)   5.00 |
| BK418 | BC35 | *Punch Magazine*, #MH126b (4)   4.00 |
| BK419 | BC35 | *Sheriff's Millennium*, #MH126b   4.25 |
| BK420 | BC35 | *Educational Institutions*, #MH128a (3)   8.25 |
| BK421 | BC35 | *Educational Institutions*, 4 #MH214   8.25 |
| BK422 | BC35 | *Prime Ministers*, 4 #MH214   3.75 |
| BK423 | BC35 | *Prime Ministers*, 4 #MH213 (3)   4.00 |
| BK424 | BC35 | *End of World War II*, 4 #MH213 (4)   4.00 |

BC40

## 1996-2000

| BK425 BC40 | £1 multi, 4 #MH214 | 8.00 |
|---|---|---|
| BK426 BC40 | £1 multi, #MH216b | 8.00 |
| BK427 BC40 | £1 multi, #MH257b | 12.50 |
| BK428 BC40 | £1 multi, #MH257d | 7.00 |
| BK429 BC40 | £1 #MH288d | 6.00 |

## 1987-88
### £1.04 Booklet
| BK446 BC36 | #MH131a | 24.00 |
|---|---|---|

### £1.08 Booklets
| BK456 BC36 | #MH133a | 16.00 |
|---|---|---|
| BK457 BC37 | #MH133b | 40.00 |

## 1981
### £1.15 Booklets
| BK467 BC38 | Military Aircraft, 10 #MH76 (2) | 5.75 |
|---|---|---|
| BK468 BC38 | Museums, 10 #MH76 (2) | 5.75 |

## 1989
### £1.16 Booklet
| BK478 BC37 | multi, #MH140a | 25.00 |
|---|---|---|

## 1980-86
### £1.20 Booklets
| BK488 BC38 | Industrial Archaeology, 10 #MH78 (3) | 5.75 |
|---|---|---|
| BK489 BC38 | Pillar Box, 10 #MH79 | 8.00 |
| BK490 BC38 | National Gallery, 10 #MH79 | 7.50 |
| BK491 BC38 | Handwriting, 10 #MH79 | 7.50 |
| BK492 BC38 | Christmas, 10 #MH83 | 10.00 |

No. BK492 was sold at a discount. Each stamp has a blue double-line star printed on reverse.

BC41

## 1998
### £1.20 Booklet
| BK493 BC41 | multi, 4 #MH259 | 4.75 |
|---|---|---|

## 1990
### £1.24 Booklet
| BK503 BC39 | multi, #MH144a | 8.00 |
|---|---|---|

## 1982-83
### £1.25 Booklets
| BK513 BC38 | Museums, 10 #MH81 (4) | 6.25 |
|---|---|---|
| BK514 BC38 | Railway Engines, 10 #MH81 (5) | 8.00 |

## 1981-88
### £1.30 Booklets
| BK524 BC38 | Postal History, #MH86b (2) | 8.00 |
|---|---|---|
| BK525 BC38 | Trams, 10 #MH83 (4) | 6.25 |
| BK526 BC38 | Books for Children, 10 #MH83 | 6.25 |
| BK527 BC38 | Keep in Touch, 10 #MH83 | 6.25 |
| BK528 BC38 | Ideas for your Garden, 10 #MH83 | 6.25 |
| BK529 BC38 | Brighter Writer, 10 #MH83 | 6.25 |
| BK530 BC38 | Jolly Postman, 10 #MH83 | 6.50 |
| BK531 BC38 | Linnean Society, 10 #MH83 | 7.75 |
| BK532 BC38 | Recipe Cards, 10 #MH83 | 6.25 |
| BK533 BC38 | Party Pack, 10 #MH83 | 6.25 |
| BK534 BC36 | red, yel & blk, #MH83f | 7.00 |

## 1991
### £1.32 Booklet
| BK544 BC39 | multi, #MH148a | 8.50 |
|---|---|---|

## 1981-89
### £1.40 Booklets
| BK554 BC38 | Industrial Archaeology, 10 #MH86 (2) | 6.25 |
|---|---|---|
| BK555 BC38 | Women's Costumes, 10 #MH86 | 6.25 |
| BK556 BC38 | Pocket Planner, 10 #MH87 | 6.25 |
| BK557 BC38 | William Henry Fox Talbot, 10 #MH87 | 6.50 |

## 1988-95
### £1.40 Booklets
| BK558 BC36 | #MH87d | 9.50 |
|---|---|---|
| BK559 BC36 | 10 #MH88 | 20.00 |
| BK560 BC37 | #MH87e | 11.50 |
| BK561 BC37 | 10 #MH88 | 20.00 |
| BK562 BC39 | 4 #MH223 | 8.00 |
| BK563 BC41 | 4 #MH223 (2) | 8.00 |

## 1982
### £1.43 Booklets
| BK572 BC38 | James Chalmers, #MH93d | 7.00 |
|---|---|---|
| BK573 BC38 | Postal History, #MH93c (4) | 7.00 |
| BK574 BC38 | Holiday Postcard Stamp Book, #MH93c | 7.00 |

## 1983
### £1.45 Booklet
| BK584 BC38 | Britain's Countryside, 10 #MH94 | 5.50 |
|---|---|---|

Stamps in #BK584 have double-lined D printed on reverse.

## 1983
### £1.46 Booklet
| BK594 BC38 | Postal History, #MH94c (4) | 12.50 |
|---|---|---|

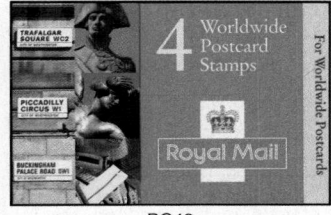

BC42

## 1996-97
### £1.48 Booklets
| BK605 BC41 | #MH226a (2) | 11.50 |
|---|---|---|
| BK606 BC42 | 4 #MH264 | 11.50 |

## 1986-90
### £1.50 Booklets
| BK616 BC38 | Pillar Box, #MH97e | 8.00 |
|---|---|---|
| BK617 BC38 | National Gallery, #MH97e | 8.00 |
| BK618 BC38 | Handwriting, #MH97e | 8.00 |
| BK619 BC37 | #MH190a | 7.50 |
| BK620 BC37 | #MH191b | 12.00 |
| BK621 BC37 | #MH192a | 11.00 |

## 1999
### £1.52 Booklet
| BK630 BC41 | 4 #MH264 | 8.00 |
|---|---|---|

## 1985
### £1.53 Booklet
| BK631 BC38 | Royal Mail, 350th Anniv., 10 #1111 | 7.00 |
|---|---|---|

## 1984
### £1.54 Booklet
| BK641 BC38 | Postal History, #MH97f (4) | 7.00 |
|---|---|---|

## 1982-85
### £1.55 Booklets
| BK651 BC38 | Women's Costumes, 10 #MH93 (4) | 6.50 |
|---|---|---|
| BK652 BC38 | Social Letter Writing, 10 #MH97 | 6.50 |

No. BK652 sold for a 15p discount. Panes have double-lined "D" printed on reverse.

## 1991
### £1.56 Booklet
| BK662 BC39 | #MH157a | 12.50 |
|---|---|---|

## 1978-2000
### £1.60 Booklets
| BK672 BC38 | Christmas, #MH67b | 8.00 |
|---|---|---|
| BK673 BC38 | Birthday Box, 10 #MH97 (2) | 8.00 |
| BK674 BC38 | Britain's Countryside, 10 #MH97 | 7.00 |
| BK675 BC38 | Write It, 10 #MH97 | 8.00 |
| BK676 BC41 | #MH266a | 8.75 |

## 1993-96
### £1.64 Booklets
| BK685 BC39 | #MH231a | 10.00 |
|---|---|---|
| BK686 BC41 | #MH231b (2) | 10.00 |

## 1984-86
### £1.70 Booklets
| BK696 BC38 | Love Letters, 10 #MH97 (2) | 8.00 |
|---|---|---|
| BK697 BC38 | Pillar Box, 10 #MH97 (2) | 8.00 |
| BK698 BC38 | National Gallery, 10 #MH97 | 8.00 |
| BK699 BC38 | Handwriting, 10 #MH97 | 8.00 |

## 1979-88
### £1.80 Booklets
| BK709 BC38 | Christmas, #MH70c | 10.50 |
|---|---|---|
| BK710 BC38 | Books for Children, 10 #MH102 | 8.00 |
| BK711 BC38 | Keep in Touch, 10 #MH102 | 8.00 |
| BK712 BC38 | Ideas for your Garden, 10 #MH102 | 8.00 |
| BK713 BC38 | Brighter Writer, 10 #MH102 | 8.00 |
| BK714 BC36 | red, yel & blk, #MH102e | 10.50 |
| BK715 BC38 | Jolly Postman, 10 #MH102 | 8.00 |
| BK716 BC38 | Linnean Society, 10 #MH102 | 8.00 |
| BK717 BC38 | Recipe Cards, 10 #MH102 | 8.00 |
| BK718 BC38 | Party Pack, 10 #MH102 | 8.00 |

## 1988-89
### £1.90 Booklets
| BK728 BC38 | Pocket Planner, 10 #MH106 | 10.00 |
|---|---|---|
| BK729 BC36 | red, yel & blk, #MH106f | 14.00 |
| BK730 BC37 | #MH106g | 14.00 |
| BK731 BC37 | 10 #MH107 | 27.50 |
| BK732 BC38 | William Henry Fox Talbot, 10 #MH106 | 10.00 |

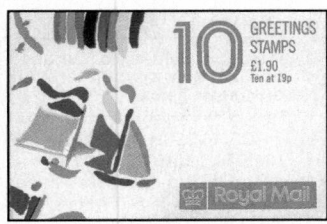

BC43

## 1989
### £1.90 Booklet
| BK733 BC43 | Greetings, #1247a | 65.00 |
|---|---|---|

Artwork for #BC43 spanned six booklet covers. Only portions of the design appear on each cover.

Value is for pane with perfs guillotined. Value for booklet with pane having full perfs is approximately 60% more.

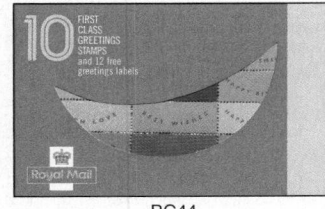

BC44

## 1990
### £2 Booklets
| BK742 BC44 | #1313a | 40.00 |
|---|---|---|
| BK743 BC37 | #MH193e | 12.00 |
| BK744 BC37 | #MH194c | 12.00 |
| BK745 BC37 | #MH195a | 20.00 |
| BK746 BC35 | Postal Vehicles, 8 #MH213 (3) | 8.50 |
| BK747 BC35 | Rowland Hill, 8 #MH213 (4) | 8.50 |
| BK748 BC40 | 8 #MH214 | 8.00 |
| BK749 BC40 | #MH216a | 9.00 |

## 1998-2000
| BK751 BC40 | #MH257c | 15.00 |
|---|---|---|
| BK752 BC40 | #MH257e | 8.50 |
| BK753 BC40 | #MH288e | 8.00 |

## 1980-93
### £2.20 Booklets
| BK759 BC38 | Christmas, #MH78c | 9.00 |
|---|---|---|
| BK760 BC38 | Christmas, 20 #MH80 | 8.00 |

### £2.30 Booklet
| BK770 BC38 | Christmas, 20 #1088 | 11.00 |
|---|---|---|

### £2.40 Booklet
| BK780 BC38 | Christmas, 20 #1124 | 10.50 |
|---|---|---|

Stamps in #BK760, BK770, BK780 have double-line star printed on reverse over gum.

BC45

## 1994-95
### £2.40 Booklets
| BK790 BC39 | #MH234a (2) | 9.25 |
|---|---|---|
| BK791 BC41 | #MH234a (2) | 9.25 |
| BK792 BC45 | #1638a | 9.50 |

## 1981-94
### £2.50 Booklets
| BK802 BC38 | Christmas, #MH93e | 10.50 |
|---|---|---|

No. BK802 was sold for a 30p discount. Stamps in #BK802 have a 10-point single-line blue star printed on reverse over gum.

| BK803 BC45 | Santa, Reindeer, 10 #1529 | 11.50 |
|---|---|---|
| BK804 BC45 | Christmas Play Props, 10 #1582 | 9.00 |
| BK805 BC45 | Christmas Robin, 10 #1635 | 9.00 |

## 1996-97
### £2.52 Booklet
| BK815 BC41 | #MH236a (3) | 15.00 |
|---|---|---|

## 1981
### £2.55 Booklet
| BK826 BC38 | Christmas, #MH86c | 11.00 |
|---|---|---|

## 1999
### £2.56 Booklet
| BK827 BC41 | 4 #MH276 | 10.50 |
|---|---|---|

## 2000
### £2.60 Booklet
| BK830 BC41 | #MH277a | 11.50 |
|---|---|---|

## 1990-95
### £3.40 Booklet
| BK836 BC45 | Snowman, #1340a | 14.00 |
|---|---|---|

### £3.60 Booklets
| BK846 BC45 | Holly, #1416a | 14.00 |
|---|---|---|
| BK847 BC45 | Santa, Reindeer, #1468a | 14.00 |

### £3.80 Booklets
| BK857 BC45 | Santa, Reindeer, #1528a | 15.00 |
|---|---|---|
| BK858 BC45 | Christmas Play Props, #1581a | 15.00 |
| BK859 BC45 | Christmas Robin, #1634a | 15.00 |

## No-Value Indicated Booklets

BC46

### 1989-2000

| | | | |
|---|---|---|---|
| BK960 | BC37 | (56p) #MH179a | 10.00 |
| BK961 | BC37 | (60p) #MH177a | 30.00 |
| BK962 | BC39 | (60p) #MH182a | 4.50 |
| BK963 | BC39 | (68p) #MH179b | 5.00 |
| BK964 | BC46 | (72p) #MH179b | 8.00 |
| BK965 | BC39 | (72p) 4 #MH238 | 4.50 |
| BK966 | BC39 | (72p) 4 #MH239 | 4.50 |
| BK967 | BC41 | (76p) 4 #MH238 | 4.50 |
| BK968 | BC41 | (76p) 4 #MH239 (2) | 4.50 |
| BK969 | BC41 | (80p) 4 #MH284 (2) | 5.00 |
| BK994 | BC37 | (76p) #MH184a | 10.00 |
| BK995 | BC37 | (80p) #MH183a | 40.00 |
| BK996 | BC39 | (80p) #MH188a (2) | 4.50 |
| BK997 | BC46 | (96p) #MH188a | 4.00 |
| BK998 | BC39 | (96p) 4 #MH240 | 4.50 |
| BK999 | BC39 | (96p) 4 #MH241 | 5.00 |
| BK1000 | BC39 | (£1) #MH241b | 11.00 |
| BK1001 | BC41 | (£1) 4 #MH241 (4) | 5.00 |
| BK1002 | BC41 | (£1) 4 #MH241b (4) | 7.00 |

### (£1.04) Booklets

| | | | |
|---|---|---|---|
| BK1003 | BC41 | 4 #MH288 | 5.75 |
| BK1004 | BC41 | 4 #MH241b | 7.00 |
| BK1005 | BC41 | 4 #MH288 | 8.50 |
| BK1006 | BC41 | 4 #MH288+label | 9.75 |

### (£1.20) Booklet

| | | | |
|---|---|---|---|
| BK1007 | BC41 | #MH335c | 5.50 |
| BK1010 | BC41 | #MH290a | 6.50 |

### (£1.40) Booklets

| | | | |
|---|---|---|---|
| BK1028 | BC37 | #MH177b | 15.00 |
| BK1029 | BC37 | 10 #MH178 | 12.50 |

### (£1.50) Booklets

| | | | |
|---|---|---|---|
| BK1030 | BC39 | #MH180a | 8.50 |
| BK1031 | BC39 | 10 #MH181 | 20.00 |
| BK1032 | BC39 | #MH182b | 9.50 |

### (£1.70) Booklets

| | | | |
|---|---|---|---|
| BK1033 | BC39 | 10 #MH178 | 12.50 |
| BK1034 | BC39 | 10 #MH179c | 12.50 |

### (£1.80) Booklets

| | | | |
|---|---|---|---|
| BK1035 | BC46 | #MH179c | 12.50 |
| BK1036 | BC46 | 10 #MH178 | 12.50 |
| BK1037 | BC39 | #MH177b | 15.00 |
| BK1038 | BC39 | 10 #MH239 (3) | 10.00 |

### (£1.90) Booklets

| | | | |
|---|---|---|---|
| BK1039 | BC41 | 10 #MH239 (5) | 10.00 |
| BK1040 | BC41 | 10 #MH238 (4) | 10.00 |
| BK1041 | BC37 | #MH183b | 20.00 |

### (£2) Booklets

| | | | |
|---|---|---|---|
| BK1068 | BC39 | #MH186a (2) | 13.50 |
| BK1069 | BC39 | 10 #MH187 (3) | 13.50 |
| BK1070 | BC39 | #MH188b (3) | 13.50 |
| BK1071 | BC41 | 10 #MH284 | 9.50 |
| BK1072 | BC41 | 10 #MH285 | 9.50 |

### (£2.40) Booklets

| | | | |
|---|---|---|---|
| BK1091 | BC46 | #MH186a | 13.50 |
| BK1092 | BC46 | #MH187d | 13.50 |
| BK1093 | BC39 | #MH187d | 13.50 |
| BK1094 | BC39 | 10 #MH240 | 14.00 |
| BK1095 | BC39 | 10 #MH241 (11) | 14.00 |

### (£2.50) Booklets

| | | | |
|---|---|---|---|
| BK1116 | BC41 | 10 #MH240 (11) | 12.50 |
| BK1117 | BC41 | 10 #MH241 (12) | 11.00 |

### (£2.60) Booklets

| | | | |
|---|---|---|---|
| BK1137 | BC41 | 10 #MH287 | 12.50 |
| BK1139 | BC41 | 10 #MH288 | 12.50 |
| BK1139A | BC41 | #MH289a | 20.00 |
| BK1140 | BC41 | 10 #MH288 | 12.50 |
| BK1141 | BC41 | #1856a, MH288b | 11.00 |
| BK1142 | BC41 | #1872a, MH288b | 11.00 |
| BK1143 | BC41 | 10 #MH335 | 12.50 |
| BK1144 | BC41 | #MH336a | 12.50 |

---

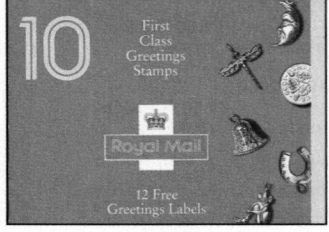

BC47

### 1991-2000

#### (£2.20) Booklets

| | | | |
|---|---|---|---|
| BK1160 | BC47 | #1359a | 16.00 |
| BK1161 | BC47 | Laughing Pillar Box, #1373a | 12.00 |

#### (£2.40) Booklets

| | | | |
|---|---|---|---|
| BK1171 | BC47 | Memories, #1435a | 11.00 |
| BK1172 | BC47 | Rupert Bear, #1488a (3) | 12.00 |

#### (£2.50) Booklets

| | | | |
|---|---|---|---|
| BK1182 | BC47 | Rupert Bear, Paddington Bear, #1547a | 13.50 |
| BK1183 | BC47 | Clown, #1605a | 13.50 |
| BK1184 | BC47 | More Love, #1652a | 13.50 |

#### (£2.60) Booklets

| | | | |
|---|---|---|---|
| BK1194 | BC47 | Christmas, 10 #1709 | 15.00 |
| BK1195 | BC47 | Flower, #1722a (4) | 12.50 |
| BK1196 | BC47 | Chocolates, #1722a | 14.00 |
| BK1197 | BC47 | Memorable Post, #1722a | 14.00 |
| BK1198 | BC47 | Santa Claus, 10 #1777 | 11.50 |
| BK1199 | BC47 | Christmas, 10 #1835 | 10.50 |
| BK1200 | BC47 | 10 #1880 | 10.50 |

#### (£2.70) Booklets

| | | | |
|---|---|---|---|
| BK1201 | BC41 | #1938a, MH335a | 11.00 |
| BK1202 | BC47 | #1919a, MH335a | 11.00 |
| BK1203 | BC47 | 10 #1931 | 13.50 |

#### (£3.80) Booklet

| | | | |
|---|---|---|---|
| BK1210 | BC47 | #1879a | 15.00 |
| BK1211 | BC47 | #1930a | 19.00 |

#### (£4) Booklets

| | | | |
|---|---|---|---|
| BK1220 | BC47 | Magi, #1708a | 19.00 |
| BK1221 | BC47 | Santa Claus, Children, #1776a | 19.00 |
| BK1222 | BC47 | Christmas, #1834a | 16.00 |

---

## BRITISH OFFICES ABROAD

Catalogue values for unused stamps in this section are for Never Hinged items.

### OFFICES IN AFRICA
### MIDDLE EAST FORCES

For use in Ethiopia, Cyrenaica, Eritrea, the Dodecanese and Somalia Stamps of Great Britain, 1937-42 Overprinted in Black or Blue Black

| | | | | |
|---|---|---|---|---|
| **1942-43** | | **Wmk. 251** | **Perf. 14½x14** | |
| 1 | A101 | 1p scarlet | 2.00 | 3.00 |
| 2 | A101 | 2p orange | 1.50 | 4.50 |
| 3 | A101 | 2½p bright ultra | 1.10 | 1.40 |
| 4 | A101 | 3p dark purple | .90 | .20 |
| 5 | A102 | 5p lt brn (Blk) | .80 | .35 |
| a. | | Blue black overprint ('43) | 4.25 | .20 |
| 6 | A102 | 6p rose lilac ('43) | .45 | .20 |
| 7 | A102 | 9p dp olive grn ('43) | 1.00 | .20 |
| 8 | A103 | 1sh brown ('43) | .55 | .20 |
| | | **Wmk. 259** | **Perf. 14** | |
| 9 | A104 | 2sh6p yel green ('43) | 8.00 | 1.10 |
| | | Nos. 1-9 (9) | 16.30 | 11.30 |

---

### Same Overprint in Blue Black on Nos. 259, 261, 262 and 263

| | | | | |
|---|---|---|---|---|
| **1943, Jan. 1** | | **Wmk. 251** | | |
| 10 | A101 | 1p vermilion | 1.75 | .20 |
| 11 | A101 | 2p light orange | 1.75 | 1.40 |
| 12 | A101 | 2½p ultramarine | .55 | .20 |
| 13 | A101 | 3p violet | 1.75 | .20 |
| | | Nos. 10-13 (4) | 5.80 | 2.00 |

There were two printings of Nos. 1-5, both issued Mar. 2, 1942, and both black. The Cairo printing measures 13½mm, the London printing 14mm.

Nos. 5a and 6-13 compose a third printing, also made in London. On these stamps, issued Jan. 1, 1943, the overprint is 13½mm wide. The 2sh6p overprint is black, the others blue black.

### Same Ovpt. in Black on #250, 251A

| | | | | |
|---|---|---|---|---|
| **1947** | | **Wmk. 259** | **Perf. 14** | |
| 14 | A104 | 5sh dull red | 17.50 | 20.00 |
| 15 | A105 | 10sh ultramarine | 22.50 | 11.50 |

In 1950 Nos. 1-15 were declared valid for use in Great Britain. Used values are for stamps postmarked in territory of issue. Others sell for about 25 percent less.

---

## POSTAGE DUE STAMPS

Postage Due Stamps of Great Britain Overprinted in Blue

| | | | | |
|---|---|---|---|---|
| **1942** | | **Wmk. 251** | **Perf. 14x14½** | |
| J1 | D1 | ½p emerald | .35 | 14.00 |
| J2 | D1 | 1p carmine rose | .35 | 2.00 |
| J3 | D1 | 2p black brown | 1.40 | 1.40 |
| J4 | D1 | 3p violet | .55 | 4.75 |
| J5 | D1 | 1sh blue | 4.25 | 14.00 |
| | | Nos. J1-J5 (5) | 6.90 | 36.15 |

No. J1-J5 were used in Eritrea.

---

## FOR USE IN ERITREA

Catalogue values for unused stamps in this section are for Never Hinged items.

100 Cents = 1 Shilling
Stamps of Great Britain 1937-42 Surcharged

a

| | | | | |
|---|---|---|---|---|
| **1948, June** | | **Wmk. 251** | **Perf. 14½x14** | |
| 1 | A101 | 5c on ½p green (II) | 1.60 | .75 |
| 2 | A101 | 10c on 1p vermilion (II) | 1.60 | 2.75 |
| 3 | A101 | 20c on 2p light org (II) | 1.10 | 2.50 |
| 4 | A101 | 25c on 2½p ultra (II) | 1.35 | .70 |
| 5 | A101 | 30c on 3p violet (II) | 1.60 | 5.00 |
| 6 | A101 | 40c on 5p light brown | 1.10 | 4.75 |
| 7 | A101 | 50c on 6p rose lilac | .70 | 1.10 |
| 8 | A103 | 75c on 9p deep ol grn | 1.35 | .85 |
| 9 | A103 | 1sh on 1sh brown | 1.35 | .55 |

"B. M. A." stands for British Military Administration.

Great Britain Nos. 249A, 250 and 251A Surcharged

| | | | | |
|---|---|---|---|---|
| **1948, June** | | **Wmk. 259** | **Perf. 14** | |
| 10 | A104 | 2sh50c on 2sh6p yel grn | 9.25 | 11.50 |
| 11 | A104 | 5sh on 5sh dl red | 9.25 | 18.00 |
| 12 | A105 | 10sh on 10sh ultra | 25.00 | 25.00 |

---

### Great Britain No. 245 Surcharged
### Type "a"

| | | | | |
|---|---|---|---|---|
| **1949** | | **Wmk. 251** | **Perf. 14½x14** | |
| 13 | A103 | 65c on 8p brt rose | 8.00 | 2.25 |
| | | Nos. 1-13 (13) | 63.25 | 75.70 |

Stamps of Great Britain 1937-42 Surcharged

c

| | | | | |
|---|---|---|---|---|
| **1950, Feb. 6** | | | | |
| 14 | A101 | 5c on ½p green (II) | 1.60 | 9.25 |
| 15 | A101 | 10c on 1p ver (II) | .45 | 3.50 |
| 16 | A101 | 25c on 2½p ultra (II) | .55 | .90 |
| 17 | A101 | 25c on 2½p ultra (II) | .55 | .70 |
| 18 | A101 | 30c on 3p violet (II) | .45 | 2.50 |
| 19 | A102 | 40c on 5p light brown | .80 | 2.00 |
| 20 | A102 | 50c on 6p rose lilac | .45 | .25 |
| 21 | A103 | 65c on 8p bright rose | 3.25 | 1.75 |
| 22 | A103 | 75c on 9p dp ol grn | .65 | .30 |
| 23 | A103 | 1sh on 1sh brown | .45 | .20 |

Great Britain Nos. 249A, 250, 251A Surcharged

| | | | | |
|---|---|---|---|---|
| | | **Wmk. 259** | **Perf. 14** | |
| 24 | A104 | 2sh50c on 2sh6p yel grn | 8.00 | 5.50 |
| 25 | A104 | 5sh on 5sh dl red | 8.00 | 14.00 |
| 26 | A105 | 10sh on 10sh ultra | 70.00 | 62.50 |
| | | Nos. 14-26 (13) | 95.20 | 103.35 |

### Great Britain Nos. 280, 281, 283 and 284 Surcharged Type "c"

| | | | | |
|---|---|---|---|---|
| **1951, May 3** | | | **Perf. 14½x14** | |
| | | | **Wmk. 251** | |
| 27 | A101 | 5c on ½p lt orange | .55 | .85 |
| 28 | A101 | 10c on 1p ultra | .55 | .85 |
| 29 | A101 | 20c on 2p lt red brown | .55 | .35 |
| 30 | A101 | 25c on 2½p vermilion | .55 | .35 |

Great Britain Nos. 286-288 Surcharged

| | | | | |
|---|---|---|---|---|
| | | **Perf. 11x12** | | |
| **1951, May 31** | | | **Wmk. 259** | |
| 31 | A121 | 2sh50c on 2sh6p grn | 11.50 | 26.00 |
| 32 | A121 | 5sh on 5sh dl red | 24.00 | 26.00 |
| 33 | A122 | 10sh on 10sh ultra | 25.00 | 26.00 |
| | | Nos. 27-33 (7) | 62.70 | 80.40 |

Surcharge arranged to fit the design on #33.

---

## POSTAGE DUE STAMPS

Catalogue values for unused stamps in this section are for Never Hinged items.

Great Britain Nos. J26-J29, J32 Surcharged

| | | | | |
|---|---|---|---|---|
| **1948** | | **Wmk. 251** | **Perf. 14x14½** | |
| J1 | D1 | 5c on ½p emer | 11.00 | 25.00 |
| J2 | D1 | 10c on 1p car rose | 11.00 | 27.50 |
| J3 | D1 | 20c on 2p blk brn | 12.00 | 18.00 |
| J4 | D1 | 30c on 3p violet | 11.00 | 18.00 |
| J5 | D1 | 1sh on 1sh blue | 20.00 | 35.00 |
| | | Nos. J1-J5 (5) | 65.00 | 123.50 |

Great Britain Nos. J26 to J29 and J32 Surcharged

**1950, Feb. 6**

| | | | | |
|---|---|---|---|---|
| J6 | D1 | 5c on ½p emer | 13.00 | 55.00 |
| J7 | D1 | 10c on 1p car rose | 13.00 | 18.50 |
| a. | | "C" of CENTS omitted | | 2,750. |
| J8 | D1 | 20c on 2p blk brn | 14.00 | 20.00 |
| J9 | D1 | 30c on 3p violet | 17.50 | 28.00 |
| J10 | D1 | 1sh on 1sh blue | 17.50 | 28.00 |
| | | Nos. J6-J10 (5) | 74.00 | 149.50 |

# EAST AFRICAN FORCES

### FOR USE IN SOMALIA (ITALIAN SOMALILAND)

12 Pence = 1 Shilling
100 Cents = 1 Shilling

Catalogue values for unused stamps in this section, from this point to the end of the section, are for Never Hinged items.

Stamps of Great Britain 1938-42 Overprinted in Blue

**Perf. 14½x14**

**1943, Jan. 15**      **Wmk. 251**

| | | | | |
|---|---|---|---|---|
| 1 | A101 | 1p vermilion | .80 | .65 |
| 2 | A101 | 2p light orange | 1.75 | 1.35 |
| 3 | A101 | 2½p ultramarine | .80 | 3.75 |
| 4 | A101 | 3p violet | 1.10 | .20 |
| 5 | A101 | 5p light brown | 1.90 | .45 |
| 6 | A101 | 6p rose lilac | 1.10 | 1.35 |
| 7 | A103 | 9p dp olive green | 1.60 | 2.40 |
| 8 | A103 | 1sh brown | 3.00 | .20 |

On Great Britain No. 249A

**1946**      **Wmk. 259**      **Perf. 14**

| | | | | |
|---|---|---|---|---|
| 9 | A104 | 2sh6p yellow green | 16.00 | 8.00 |
| | | Nos. 1-9 (9) | 28.05 | 18.35 |

Stamps of Great Britain, 1937-42 Surcharged

**Perf. 14½x14**

**1948, May 27**      **Wmk. 251**

| | | | | |
|---|---|---|---|---|
| 10 | A101 | 5c on ½p grn (II) | 1.40 | 2.10 |
| 11 | A101 | 15c on 1½p lt red brn (II) | 2.00 | 17.50 |
| 12 | A101 | 20c on 2p lt org (II) | 3.50 | 5.00 |
| 13 | A101 | 25c on 2½p ultra (II) | 2.50 | 5.00 |
| 14 | A101 | 30c on 3p vio (II) | 2.50 | 10.50 |
| 15 | A102 | 40c on 5p lt brown | 1.40 | .20 |
| 16 | A102 | 50c on 6p rose lilac | .55 | 2.25 |
| 17 | A103 | 75c on 9p dp ol grn | 2.25 | 21.00 |
| 18 | A103 | 1sh on 1sh brown | 1.40 | .20 |

Great Britain Nos. 249A and 250 Surcharged

**Wmk. 259**      **Perf. 14**

| | | | | |
|---|---|---|---|---|
| 19 | A104 | 2sh50c on 2sh6p yel grn | 5.00 | 29.00 |
| 20 | A104 | 5sh on 5sh dl red | 11.00 | 45.00 |
| | | Nos. 10-20 (11) | 33.50 | 137.75 |

Stamps of Great Britain 1937-42 Surcharged

**Perf. 14½x14**

**1950, Jan. 2**      **Wmk. 251**

| | | | | |
|---|---|---|---|---|
| 21 | A101 | 5c on ½p grn (II) | .20 | 3.50 |
| 22 | A101 | 15c on 1½p lt red brn (II) | .85 | 19.00 |
| 23 | A101 | 20c on 2p lt org (II) | .85 | 8.50 |
| 24 | A101 | 25c on 2½p ultra (II) | .55 | 8.50 |
| 25 | A101 | 30c on 3p violet (II) | 1.40 | 5.00 |
| 26 | A102 | 40c on 5p light brn | .65 | 1.10 |
| 27 | A102 | 50c on 6p rose lilac | .55 | 1.10 |
| 28 | A103 | 75c on 9p deep ol grn | 2.25 | 8.00 |
| 29 | A103 | 1sh on 1sh brown | .70 | 1.75 |

Great Britain Nos. 249A and 250 Surcharged

**Wmk. 259**      **Perf. 14**

| | | | | |
|---|---|---|---|---|
| 30 | A104 | 2sh50c on 2sh 6p yel grn | 4.50 | 27.50 |
| 31 | A104 | 5sh on 5sh dull red | 12.50 | 37.50 |
| | | Nos. 21-31 (11) | 25.00 | 121.45 |

### FOR USE IN TRIPOLITANIA

Catalogue values for unused stamps in this section are for Never Hinged items.

Stamps of Great Britain, 1937-42, Surcharged

**M.A.L. = Military Authority Lire**

**Perf. 14½x14**

**1948, July 1**      **Wmk. 251**

| | | | | |
|---|---|---|---|---|
| 1 | A101 | 1 l on ½p green (II) | 1.00 | 1.75 |
| 2 | A101 | 2 l on 1p ver (II) | .35 | .20 |
| 3 | A101 | 3 l on 1½p lt red brn (II) | .35 | .55 |
| 4 | A101 | 4 l on 2p lt org (II) | .35 | .80 |
| 5 | A101 | 5 l on 2½p ultra (II) | .35 | .20 |
| 6 | A101 | 6 l on 3p violet (II) | .35 | .45 |
| 7 | A102 | 10 l on 5p lt brown | .35 | .20 |
| 8 | A102 | 12 l on 6p rose lilac | .35 | .20 |
| 9 | A103 | 18 l on 9p dp ol grn | .90 | .75 |
| 10 | A103 | 24 l on 1sh brown | .80 | 1.75 |

Great Britain Nos. 249A, 250 and 251A Surcharged

**Wmk. 259**      **Perf. 14**

| | | | | |
|---|---|---|---|---|
| 11 | A104 | 60 l on 2sh6p yel grn | 4.00 | 9.75 |
| 12 | A104 | 120 l on 5sh dl red | 17.50 | 21.00 |
| 13 | A105 | 240 l on 10sh ultra | 27.50 | 110.00 |
| | | Nos. 1-13 (13) | 54.15 | 147.60 |

Stamps of Great Britain 1937-42 Surcharged

**Perf. 14½x14**

**1950, Feb. 6**      **Wmk. 251**

| | | | | |
|---|---|---|---|---|
| 14 | A101 | 1 l on ½p green (II) | 3.50 | 14.00 |
| 15 | A101 | 2 l on 1p ver (II) | 3.00 | .45 |
| 16 | A101 | 3 l on 1½p lt red brn (II) | 1.75 | 14.00 |
| 17 | A101 | 4 l on 2p lt org (II) | 1.75 | 5.00 |
| 18 | A101 | 5 l on 2½p ultra (II) | .90 | .80 |
| 19 | A101 | 6 l on 3p violet (II) | 2.00 | 3.75 |
| 20 | A102 | 10 l on 5p lt brown | .70 | 4.50 |

| | | | | |
|---|---|---|---|---|
| 21 | A102 | 12 l on 6p rose lilac | 2.75 | .55 |
| 22 | A103 | 18 l on 9p dp ol grn | 3.00 | 3.00 |
| 23 | A103 | 24 l on 1sh brown | 3.50 | 4.25 |

Great Britain Nos. 249A, 250 and 251A Surcharged

**Wmk. 259**      **Perf. 14**

| | | | | |
|---|---|---|---|---|
| 24 | A104 | 60 l on 2sh6p yel grn | 9.00 | 14.00 |
| 25 | A104 | 120 l on 5sh dl red | 24.00 | 25.00 |
| 26 | A105 | 240 l on 10sh ultra | 42.50 | 57.50 |
| | | Nos. 14-26 (13) | 98.35 | 146.80 |

Great Britain Nos. 280-284 Surcharged like Nos. 14-23

**Perf. 14½x14**

**1951, May 3**      **Wmk. 251**

| | | | | |
|---|---|---|---|---|
| 27 | A101 | 1 l on ½p lt org | .20 | 7.00 |
| 28 | A101 | 2 l on 1p ultra | .20 | 1.10 |
| 29 | A101 | 3 l on 1½p green | .35 | 9.25 |
| 30 | A101 | 4 l on 2p lt red brown | .20 | 1.40 |
| 31 | A101 | 5 l on 2½p ver | .30 | 8.50 |

Great Britain Nos. 286-288 Surcharged

**1951, May 3**      **Wmk. 259**      **Perf. 11x12**

| | | | | |
|---|---|---|---|---|
| 32 | A121 | 60 l on 2sh6p grn | 7.00 | 25.00 |
| 33 | A121 | 120 l on 5sh dl red | 10.00 | 30.00 |
| 34 | A122 | 240 l on 10sh ultra | 42.50 | 60.00 |
| | | Nos. 27-34 (8) | 60.75 | 142.25 |

Surcharge arranged to fit the design on #34.

### POSTAGE DUE STAMPS

Catalogue values for unused stamps in this section are for Never Hinged items.

Great Britain Nos. J26-J29, J32 Surcharged

**1948**      **Wmk. 251**      **Perf. 14x14½**

| | | | | |
|---|---|---|---|---|
| J1 | D1 | 1 l on ½p emer | 6.25 | 60.00 |
| J2 | D1 | 2 l on 1p car rose | 2.75 | 40.00 |
| J3 | D1 | 4 l on 2p blk brn | 8.50 | 40.00 |
| J4 | D1 | 6 l on 3p violet | 8.50 | 24.00 |
| J5 | D1 | 24 l on 1sh blue | 32.50 | 110.00 |
| | | Nos. J1-J5 (5) | 58.50 | 274.00 |

Great Britain Nos. J26-J29, J32 Surcharged

**1950, Feb. 6**

| | | | | |
|---|---|---|---|---|
| J6 | D1 | 1 l on ½p emer | 14.00 | 92.50 |
| J7 | D1 | 2 l on 1p car rose | 4.25 | 30.00 |
| J8 | D1 | 4 l on 2p blk brn | 6.00 | 40.00 |
| J9 | D1 | 6 l on 3p violet | 21.00 | 70.00 |
| J10 | D1 | 24 l on 1sh blue | 55.00 | 160.00 |
| | | Nos. J6-J10 (5) | 100.25 | 392.50 |

# CHINA

100 Cents = 1 Dollar

Stamps of Hong Kong, 1912-14, Overprinted

**1917**      **Wmk. 3**      **Perf. 14**

**Ordinary Paper**

| | | | | |
|---|---|---|---|---|
| 1 | A11 | 1c brown | 5.50 | 3.00 |
| 2 | A11 | 2c deep green | 10.00 | .35 |
| 3 | A12 | 4c scarlet | 7.00 | .35 |
| 4 | A13 | 6c orange | 7.00 | .70 |
| 5 | A12 | 8c gray | 15.00 | 1.40 |
| 6 | A11 | 10c ultramarine | 15.00 | .35 |

**Chalky Paper**

| | | | | |
|---|---|---|---|---|
| 7 | A14 | 12c violet, yel | 15.00 | 6.25 |
| 8 | A14 | 20c olive grn & vio | 15.00 | .70 |
| 9 | A15 | 25c red vio & dl vio (on #117) | 9.25 | 17.50 |
| 10 | A13 | 30c orange & violet | 45.00 | 6.25 |
| 11 | A14 | 50c black, emerald | 45.00 | 6.50 |
| a. | | 50c blk, blue green, ol back | 77.50 | 1.75 |
| b. | | 50c blk, emerald, ol back | 55.00 | 9.75 |
| 12 | A11 | $1 blue & vio, bl | 80.00 | 2.90 |
| 13 | A14 | $2 black & red | 260.00 | 70.00 |
| 14 | A13 | $3 violet & grn | 725.00 | 210.00 |
| 15 | A14 | $5 red & grn, bl grn, ol back | 400.00 | 290.00 |
| 16 | A13 | $10 blk & vio, red | 1,050. | 600.00 |
| | | Nos. 1-16 (16) | 2,703. | 1,216. |

Stamps of Hong Kong, 1921-26, Overprinted

**1922-27**      **Wmk. 4**

**Ordinary Paper**

| | | | | |
|---|---|---|---|---|
| 17 | A11 | 1c brown | 2.75 | 4.50 |
| 18 | A11 | 2c green | 5.00 | 2.60 |
| 19 | A12 | 4c scarlet | 9.00 | 2.60 |
| 20 | A13 | 6c orange | 5.25 | 4.75 |
| 21 | A12 | 8c gray | 10.50 | 17.50 |
| 22 | A11 | 10c ultramarine | 12.50 | 4.50 |

**Chalky Paper**

| | | | | |
|---|---|---|---|---|
| 23 | A14 | 20c ol grn & vio | 17.50 | 5.75 |
| 24 | A15 | 25c red violet & dull vio | 26.00 | 80.00 |
| 25 | A14 | 50c blk, emerald ('27) | 70.00 | 210.00 |
| 26 | A11 | $1 ultra & vio, bl | 85.00 | 75.00 |
| 27 | A14 | $2 black & red | 225.00 | 290.00 |
| | | Nos. 17-27 (11) | 468.50 | 697.20 |

# MOROCCO

100 Centimos = 1 Peseta
12 Pence = 1 Shilling
20 Shillings = 1 Pound
100 Centimes = 1 Franc

These stamps were issued for various purposes:

a — For general use at the British Post Offices throughout Morocco.

b — For use in the Spanish Zone of Northern Morocco.

c — For use in the French Zone of Southern Morocco.

d — For use in the International Zone of Tangier.

For convenience these stamps are listed in four groups according to the coinage expressed or surcharged on the stamps, namely:

#1-108: Value expressed in Spanish currency.

#201-280: Value in British currency.

#401-440: Value in French currency.

#501-611: Stamps overprinted "Tangier."

## Spanish Currency

Gibraltar Stamps of
1889-95 Overprinted

**1898** **Wmk. 2** **Perf. 14**
**Black Overprint**

| | | | | |
|---|---|---|---|---|
| 1 | A11 | 5c green | 3.75 | 3.50 |
| 2 | A11 | 10c carmine rose | 6.00 | .85 |
| b. | | Double overprint | 675.00 | |
| 3 | A11 | 20c olive green | 12.50 | 6.75 |
| 4 | A11 | 25c ultramarine | 5.50 | .70 |
| 5 | A11 | 40c orange brown | 7.00 | 3.75 |
| 6 | A11 | 50c violet | 20.00 | 26.00 |
| 7 | A11 | 1pe bister & blue | 20.00 | 30.00 |
| 8 | A11 | 2pe blk & car rose | 27.50 | 30.00 |
| | | Nos. 1-8 (8) | 102.25 | 101.55 |

**Dark Blue Overprint**

| | | | | |
|---|---|---|---|---|
| 9 | A11 | 40c orange brown | 50.00 | 35.00 |
| 10 | A11 | 50c violet | 14.00 | 14.00 |
| 11 | A11 | 1pe bister & blue | 175.00 | 225.00 |

**Inverted "V" for "A"**

| | | | | |
|---|---|---|---|---|
| 1a | A11 | 5c | 42.50 | 50.00 |
| 2a | A11 | 10c | 260.00 | 310.00 |
| 3a | A11 | 20c | 85.00 | 95.00 |
| 4a | A11 | 25c | 140.00 | 150.00 |
| 5a | A11 | 40c | 190.00 | 210.00 |
| 6a | A11 | 50c | 290.00 | 375.00 |
| 7a | A11 | 1pe | 275.00 | 400.00 |
| 8a | A11 | 2pe | 350.00 | 400.00 |

**Overprinted in Black**

(Narrower "M," ear of
"g" horiz.)

**1899**

| | | | | |
|---|---|---|---|---|
| 12 | A11 | 5c green | .55 | 1.10 |
| 13 | A11 | 10c carmine rose | 3.25 | .35 |
| 14 | A11 | 20c olive green | 9.00 | 1.35 |
| 15 | A11 | 25c ultramarine | 12.50 | 1.00 |
| 16 | A11 | 40c orange brown | 52.50 | 40.00 |
| 17 | A11 | 50c violet | 11.00 | 4.00 |
| 18 | A11 | 1pe bister & blue | 32.50 | 50.00 |
| 19 | A11 | 2pe blk & car rose | 67.50 | 55.00 |
| | | Nos. 12-19 (8) | 188.80 | 152.80 |

**"M" with long serif**

| | | | | |
|---|---|---|---|---|
| 12a | A11 | 5c | 10.00 | 15.00 |
| 13a | A11 | 10c | 13.00 | 15.00 |
| 14a | A11 | 20c | 45.00 | 50.00 |
| 15a | A11 | 25c | 52.50 | 55.00 |
| 16a | A11 | 40c | 260.00 | 290.00 |
| 17a | A11 | 50c | 130.00 | 140.00 |
| 18a | A11 | 1pe | 175.00 | 290.00 |
| 19a | A11 | 2pe | 375.00 | 400.00 |

**Type of Gibraltar, 1903, with Value
in Spanish Currency, Overprinted**
**1903-05**

| | | | | |
|---|---|---|---|---|
| 20 | A12 | 5c gray grn & bl grn | 11.00 | 4.00 |
| 21 | A12 | 10c violet, *red* | 9.75 | .45 |
| 22 | A12 | 20c gray grn & car rose ('04) | 20.00 | 52.50 |
| 23 | A12 | 25c vio & blk, *bl* | 9.25 | .35 |
| 24 | A12 | 50c violet | 100.00 | 190.00 |
| 25 | A12 | 1pe blk & car rose | 47.50 | 175.00 |
| 26 | A12 | 2pe black & ultra | 57.50 | 140.00 |
| | | Nos. 20-26 (7) | 255.00 | 562.30 |

**"M" with long serif**

| | | | | |
|---|---|---|---|---|
| 20a | A12 | 5c | 60.00 | 65.00 |
| 21a | A12 | 10c | 60.00 | 47.50 |
| 22a | A12 | 20c | 125.00 | 225.00 |
| 23a | A12 | 25c | 60.00 | 52.50 |
| 24a | A12 | 50c | 400.00 | 700.00 |
| 25a | A12 | 1pe | 260.00 | 600.00 |
| 26a | A12 | 2pe | 300.00 | 550.00 |

**1905-06** **Wmk. 3** **Chalky Paper**

| | | | | |
|---|---|---|---|---|
| 27 | A12 | 5c gray grn & bl grn | 13.50 | 4.25 |
| 28 | A12 | 10c violet, *red* | 14.00 | 2.25 |
| 29 | A12 | 20c gray grn & car rose ('06) | 6.50 | 35.00 |
| 30 | A12 | 25c violet & blk, *bl* ('06) | 50.00 | 9.75 |
| 31 | A12 | 50c violet | 8.50 | 55.00 |
| 32 | A12 | 1pe blk & car rose | 37.50 | 92.50 |
| 33 | A12 | 2pe black & ultra | 20.00 | 40.00 |
| | | Nos. 27-33 (7) | 150.00 | 238.75 |

No. 29 is on ordinary paper. Nos. 27 and 28
are on both ordinary and chalky paper.

**"M" with long serif**

| | | | | |
|---|---|---|---|---|
| 27a | A12 | 5c | 75.00 | 50.00 |
| 28a | A12 | 10c | 75.00 | 45.00 |
| 29a | A12 | 20c | 65.00 | 190.00 |
| 30a | A12 | 25c | 350.00 | 175.00 |

---

| | | | | |
|---|---|---|---|---|
| 31a | A12 | 50c | 175.00 | 325.00 |
| 32a | A12 | 1pe | 250.00 | 375.00 |
| 33a | A12 | 2pe | 210.00 | 290.00 |

Numerous other minor overprint varieties
exist of Nos. 1-33.

British Stamps of 1902-10 Surcharged
in Spanish Currency:

a: #34-42,　　　　b: #43-45
46-48, 49,
63, 71

**1907-10** **Wmk. 30**

| | | | | |
|---|---|---|---|---|
| 34 | A66 | 5c on ½p pale grn | 12.50 | .20 |
| 35 | A66 | 10c on 1p car | 15.00 | .20 |
| 36 | A67 | 15c on 1½p vio & grn | 4.00 | .25 |
| a. | | "1" of "15" omitted | 6,000. | |
| 37 | A68 | 20c on 2p grn & car | 3.50 | .30 |
| 38 | A66 | 25c on 2½p ultra | 2.00 | .25 |
| 39 | A70 | 40c on 4p brn & grn | 1.40 | 3.50 |
| 40 | A70 | 40c on 4p org ('10) | 1.10 | .70 |
| 41 | A71 | 50c on 5p lil & ultra | 2.25 | 3.75 |
| 42 | A73 | 1pe on 10p car rose & vio | 25.00 | 14.00 |

**Wmk. 31**

| | | | | |
|---|---|---|---|---|
| 43 | A75 | 3pe on 2sh6p vio | 24.00 | 29.00 |
| 44 | A76 | 6pe on 5sh car rose | 40.00 | 52.50 |
| 45 | A77 | 12pe on 10sh ultra | 90.00 | 85.00 |
| | | Nos. 34-45 (12) | 220.75 | 189.65 |

Nos. 36-37, 39-43 are on chalky paper.

Great Britain Nos. 153, 154 and 148
Surcharged

**1912** **Wmk. 30** **Perf. 15x14**

| | | | | |
|---|---|---|---|---|
| 46 | A80 | 5c on ½p yel grn | 3.50 | .20 |
| 47 | A81 | 10c on 1p scarlet | 1.10 | .20 |
| 48 | A66 | 25c on 2½p ultra | 47.50 | 30.00 |
| | | Nos. 46-48 (3) | 52.10 | 30.40 |

British Stamps of 1912-18 Surcharged
in Black or Carmine:

c　　　　　　　　d

e

**1914-18** **Wmk. 33**

| | | | | |
|---|---|---|---|---|
| 49 | A82(a) | 5c on ½p grn | .85 | .20 |
| 50 | A83(a) | 10c on 1p scar | 1.75 | .20 |
| 51 | A84(c) | 15c on 1½p red brn ('15) | 1.10 | .25 |
| 52 | A85(d) | 20c on 2p org (I) | 1.10 | .25 |
| 53 | A86(d) | 25c on 2½p ultra | 2.00 | .25 |
| 54 | A90(d) | 1pe on 10p lt bl | 4.50 | 9.00 |

**Wmk. 34**
**Perf. 11x12**

| | | | | |
|---|---|---|---|---|
| 55 | A91(e) | 3pe on 2sh6p lt brn | 40.00 | 160.00 |
| a. | | 3pe on 2sh6p dark brown | 45.00 | 130.00 |
| 56 | A91(e) | 6pe on 5sh car | 32.50 | 55.00 |
| a. | | 6pe on 5sh light carmine | 150.00 | 210.00 |
| 57 | A91(e) | 12pe on 10sh dk bl (C) | 110.00 | 190.00 |
| a. | | 12pe on 10sh blue | 100.00 | 190.00 |
| | | Nos. 49-57 (9) | 193.80 | 415.15 |

---

Great Britain Nos. 159, 165
Surcharged in Spanish Currency

f　　　　　　　　g

**1917-23** **Wmk. 33** **Perf. 15x14**

| | | | | |
|---|---|---|---|---|
| 58 | A82(f) | 3c on ½p green | 1.40 | 5.00 |
| 59 | A88(g) | 40c on 4p sl green | 4.00 | 4.50 |

**Great Britain Nos. 189, 191, 179
Surcharged in Spanish Currency**

**1926** **Wmk. 35**

| | | | | |
|---|---|---|---|---|
| 60 | A84(c) | 15c on 1½p red brn | 8.50 | 26.00 |
| 61 | A86(d) | 25c on 2½p ultra | 2.90 | 2.90 |

**Wmk. 34**
**Perf. 11x12**

| | | | | |
|---|---|---|---|---|
| 62 | A91(e) | 3pe on 2sh6p brn | 26.00 | 85.00 |
| | | Nos. 60-62 (3) | 37.40 | 113.90 |

**British Stamps of 1924 Surcharged
in Spanish Currency**

**1929-31** **Wmk. 35** **Perf. 15x14**

| | | | | |
|---|---|---|---|---|
| 63 | A82(a) | 5c on ½p grn ('31) | 3.50 | 19.00 |
| 64 | A83(d) | 10c on 1p scar | 22.50 | 30.00 |
| 65 | A85(d) | 20c on 2p org (II) ('31) | 3.50 | 10.00 |
| 66 | A88(g) | 40c on 4p sl grn ('30) | 2.90 | 2.90 |
| | | Nos. 63-66 (4) | 32.40 | 61.90 |

**Silver Jubilee Issue**
Great Britain Nos. 226-229
Surcharged in Blue or Red

**1935, May 8** **Perf. 14½x14**

| | | | | |
|---|---|---|---|---|
| 67 | A98 | 5c on ½p dk grn | 1.10 | 1.10 |
| 68 | A98 | 10c on 1p car | 3.00 | 2.50 |
| a. | | Pair, one reading "CEN-TIMES" | 1,600. | 2,100. |
| 69 | A98 | 15c on 1½p red brn | 6.25 | 20.00 |
| 70 | A98 | 25c on 2½p ultra (R) | 4.00 | 2.50 |
| | | Nos. 67-70 (4) | 14.35 | 26.10 |

25th anniv. of the reign of King George V.

> Catalogue values for unused
> stamps in this section, from this
> point to the end of the section, are
> for Never Hinged items.

**Great Britain Nos. 210-214, 216, 219
Surcharged in Spanish Currency**

**1935-37** **Photo.**

| | | | | |
|---|---|---|---|---|
| 71 | A82(a) | 5c on ½p dk grn ('36) | 1.25 | 21.00 |
| 72 | A97(d) | 10c on 1p car | 3.25 | 11.00 |
| 73 | A84(c) | 15c on 1½p red brn | 7.00 | 3.75 |
| 74 | A85(d) | 20c on 2p red org ('36) | .75 | .30 |
| 75 | A97(d) | 25c on 2½p ultra ('36) | 1.75 | 5.00 |
| 76 | A88(d) | 40c on 4p dk sl grn ('37) | .75 | 3.50 |
| 77 | A90(d) | 1pe on 10p Prus bl ('37) | 7.00 | .35 |
| | | Nos. 71-77 (7) | 21.75 | 44.90 |

Great Britain Nos. 230-
233 Surcharged

**"MOROCCO" 14mm**

**1936** **Wmk. 250**

| | | | | |
|---|---|---|---|---|
| 78 | A99 | 5c on ½p dk green | .20 | .20 |
| 79 | A99 | 10c on 1p crimson | .55 | 2.25 |
| a. | | "Morocco" 15mm long | 4.00 | 16.00 |

---

| | | | | |
|---|---|---|---|---|
| 80 | A99 | 15c on 1½p red brown | .20 | .20 |
| 81 | A99 | 25c on 2½p brt ultra | .20 | .20 |
| | | Nos. 78-81 (4) | 1.15 | 2.85 |

Great Britain #234 Surcharged in Blue

**Perf. 14½x14**
**1937, May 13** **Wmk. 251**

| | | | | |
|---|---|---|---|---|
| 82 | A100 | 15c on 1½p purple brn | .80 | .80 |

Coronation of George VI and Elizabeth.

Great Britain Nos. 235-237, 239, 241,
244 Surcharged in Blue or Black

h

**1937-40**

| | | | | |
|---|---|---|---|---|
| 83 | A101 | 5c on ½p dp grn (Bl) | 1.40 | .35 |
| 84 | A101 | 10c on 1p scarlet | 1.10 | .20 |
| 85 | A101 | 15c on 1½p red brown (Bl) | 1.40 | .30 |
| 86 | A101 | 25c on 2½p brt ultra | 2.25 | 1.40 |
| 87 | A102 | 40c on 4p gray green ('40) | 35.00 | 15.00 |
| 88 | A103 | 70c on 7p emer ('40) | 2.00 | 16.00 |
| | | Nos. 83-88 (6) | 43.15 | 33.25 |

Great Britain
Nos. 252-254,
256 Surcharged
in Blue or Black

**1940, May 6**

| | | | | |
|---|---|---|---|---|
| 89 | A106 | 5c on ½p deep grn (Bl) | .35 | 3.00 |
| 90 | A106 | 10c on 1p scarlet | 4.25 | 2.90 |
| 91 | A106 | 15c on 1½p red brn (Bl) | .80 | 2.90 |
| 92 | A106 | 25c on 2½p brt ultra | .90 | 1.10 |
| | | Nos. 89-92 (4) | 6.30 | 9.90 |

Centenary of the postage stamp.

Great Britain Nos. 267 and 268
Surcharged in Black:

i

j

**Perf. 14½x14, 14x14½**
**1948, Apr. 26** **Wmk. 251**

| | | | | |
|---|---|---|---|---|
| 93 | A109(i) | 25c on 2½p | 1.10 | .35 |
| 94 | A110(j) | 45pe on £1 | 19.00 | 25.00 |

25th anniv. of the marriage of King George
VI and Queen Elizabeth.

## Great Britain Nos. 271-274 Surcharged "MOROCCO AGENCIES" and New Value

| | | | 1948, July 29 | Perf. 14½x14 |
|---|---|---|---|---|
| 95 | A113 | 25c on 2½p brt ultra | .55 | 1.40 |
| 96 | A114 | 30c on 3p dp vio | .55 | 1.40 |
| 97 | A115 | 60c on 6p red vio | .55 | 1.40 |
| 98 | A116 | 1.20pe on 1sh dk brn | .70 | 1.40 |
| a. | | Double surcharge | 925.00 | |
| | | Nos. 95-98 (4) | 2.35 | 5.60 |

1948 Olympic Games, Wembley, July-Aug.
A square of dots obliterates the original denomination on No. 98.

## Great Britain Nos. 280-282, 284-285, 247 Surcharged Type "h"

| | | | 1951-52 Wmk. 251 | Perf. 14½x14 |
|---|---|---|---|---|
| 99 | A101 | 5c on ½p lt orange | 2.25 | 5.00 |
| 100 | A101 | 10c on 1p ultra | 3.75 | 8.50 |
| 101 | A101 | 15c on 1½p green | 2.00 | 19.00 |
| 102 | A101 | 25c on 2½p ver | 2.00 | 11.00 |
| 103 | A102 | 40c on 4p ultra ('52) | .70 | 11.50 |
| 104 | A103 | 1pe on 10p ryl bl ('52) | 2.50 | 4.00 |
| | | Nos. 99-104 (6) | 13.20 | 59.00 |

## Great Britain Nos. 292-293 Surcharged Type "h"

| | | | 1954-55 | Wmk. 298 |
|---|---|---|---|---|
| 105 | A126 | 5c on ½p red org | .25 | 2.00 |
| 106 | A126 | 10c on 1p ultra ('55) | .50 | 3.00 |

## Great Britain Nos. 317 and 323 Surcharged Type "h"

| | | | 1956 Wmk. 308 | Perf. 14x14½ |
|---|---|---|---|---|
| 107 | A126 | 5c on ½p red org | .25 | 2.00 |
| 108 | A128 | 40c on 4p ultra | 1.10 | 3.00 |

## BRITISH CURRENCY

Stamps of Morocco Agencies were accepted for postage in Great Britain, starting in mid-1950. Copies with contemporaneous Morocco cancellations sell for more.

British Stamps of 1902-11 Overprinted

a        b

Overprint "a" 14½mm long

| | | | 1907-12 Wmk. 30 | Perf. 14 |
|---|---|---|---|---|
| | | **Ordinary Paper** | | |
| 201 | A66 | ½p pale yel grn | 2.50 | 9.75 |
| 202 | A66 | 1p carmine | 11.00 | 6.25 |
| | | **Chalky Paper** | | |
| 203 | A68 | 2p green & car | 11.50 | 6.25 |
| 204 | A70 | 4p brown & grn | 4.25 | 4.50 |
| 205 | A70 | 4p orange ('12) | 11.50 | 12.50 |
| a. | | Perf. 15x14 | 25.00 | 27.50 |
| 206 | A66 | 6p dull vio | 17.00 | 21.00 |
| 207 | A74 | 1sh car rose & grn | 30.00 | 19.00 |
| | | **Overprinted Type "b"** | | |
| | | Wmk. 31 | | |
| 208 | A75 | 2sh6p violet | 100.00 | 140.00 |
| | | Nos. 201-208 (8) | 187.75 | 219.25 |

## British Stamps of 1912-18 Overprinted Type "a"

| | | | Perf. 14½x14, 15x14 | |
|---|---|---|---|---|
| | | | 1914-21 | Wmk. 33 |
| 209 | A82 | ½p green ('18) | 4.00 | .55 |
| 210 | A83 | 1p scarlet ('17) | 1.25 | .20 |
| 211 | A84 | 1½p red brn ('21) | 4.00 | 14.00 |
| 212 | A85 | 2p orange ('18) | 4.50 | .70 |
| 213 | A87 | 3p violet ('21) | 1.40 | .40 |
| 214 | A88 | 4p slate grn ('21) | 3.75 | 1.40 |
| 215 | A89 | 6p dull vio ('21) | 5.50 | 17.50 |
| 216 | A90 | 1sh bister ('17) | 7.25 | 1.40 |

---

c

| | | | Wmk. 34 | Perf. 11x12 |
|---|---|---|---|---|
| 217 | A91 | 2sh6p lt brown | 42.50 | 57.50 |
| a. | | 2sh6p brown | 55.00 | 35.00 |
| b. | | 2sh6p black brown | 52.50 | 62.50 |
| c. | | Double overprint | 1,900. | 1,350. |
| | | Nos. 209-217 (9) | 74.15 | 93.65 |

### Same Overprint on Great Britain Nos. 179-180

| | | | 1925-31 | |
|---|---|---|---|---|
| 218 | A91 | 2sh6p gray brown | 42.50 | 29.00 |
| 219 | A91 | 5sh car rose ('31) | 62.50 | 100.00 |

### British Stamps of 1924 Overprinted Type "a" (14½mm long)

| | | | 1925-31 Wmk. 35 | Perf. 15x14 |
|---|---|---|---|---|
| 220 | A82 | ½p green | 2.25 | .55 |
| 221 | A84 | 1½p red brn ('31) | 13.50 | 15.00 |
| 222 | A85 | 2p dp org (Die I) | 2.50 | 1.10 |
| 223 | A86 | 2½p ultra | 3.00 | 5.75 |
| 224 | A89 | 6p red vio ('31) | 2.25 | 9.50 |
| 225 | A90 | 1sh bister | 19.00 | 5.75 |
| | | Nos. 220-225 (6) | 42.50 | 37.65 |

### Silver Jubilee Issue
Great Britain Nos. 226-229 Overprinted in Blue or Red

| | | | 1935, May 8 | Perf. 14½x14 |
|---|---|---|---|---|
| 226 | A98 | ½p dark green (Bl) | 1.60 | 7.50 |
| 227 | A98 | 1p carmine (Bl) | 1.60 | 7.50 |
| 228 | A98 | 1½p red brown (Bl) | 3.00 | 11.00 |
| 229 | A98 | 2½p ultramarine (R) | 2.90 | 2.90 |
| | | Nos. 226-229 (4) | 9.10 | 28.90 |

25th anniversary of the reign of King George V.

### British Stamps of 1924 Overprinted Type "a" (15½mm long)

| | | | 1935-36 | |
|---|---|---|---|---|
| 230 | A82 | ½p green | 11.00 | 45.00 |
| 231 | A86 | 2½p ultra | 110.00 | 35.00 |
| 232 | A88 | 4p slate grn | 8.00 | 40.00 |
| 233 | A89 | 6p red violet | 1.10 | .70 |
| 234 | A90 | 1sh bister | 62.50 | 57.50 |
| | | Nos. 230-234 (5) | 192.60 | 178.20 |

### British Stamps of 1934-36 Overprinted "MOROCCO AGENCIES"

| | | | 1935-36 | |
|---|---|---|---|---|
| 235 | A97 | 1p carmine | 3.50 | 16.00 |
| 236 | A84 | 1½p red brn ('36) | 3.50 | 19.00 |
| 237 | A85 | 2p red org ('36) | 1.40 | 9.00 |
| 238 | A97 | 2½p ultra ('36) | 2.00 | 4.75 |
| 239 | A87 | 3p dk violet ('36) | .55 | .35 |
| 240 | A88 | 4p dk slate grn ('36) | .55 | .35 |
| 241 | A90 | 1sh bis brn ('36) | .90 | 4.50 |
| | | **Overprinted Type "c"** | | |
| | | Wmk. 34 | | |
| | | Perf. 11x12 | | |
| 242 | A91 | 2sh6p brown | 47.50 | 70.00 |
| 243 | A91 | 5sh carmine ('37) | 27.50 | 110.00 |
| | | Nos. 235-243 (9) | 87.40 | 233.95 |

> Catalogue values for unused stamps in this section, from this point to the end of the section, are for Never Hinged items.

Great Britain Nos. 231, 233 Overprinted

---

"MOROCCO" 14mm

| | | | 1936 Wmk. 250 | Perf. 14½x14 |
|---|---|---|---|---|
| 244 | A99 | 1p crimson | .20 | .20 |
| a. | | "Morocco" 15mm long | 7.00 | 19.00 |
| 245 | A99 | 2½p bright ultra | .20 | .20 |
| a. | | "Morocco" 15mm long | 1.10 | 4.75 |

### Great Britain Nos. 258-263, 241-248, 266, 249A-250 Overprinted "MOROCCO AGENCIES" (14½mm long)

| | | | 1949, Aug. 16 | Wmk. 251 |
|---|---|---|---|---|
| 246 | A101 | ½p green | 2.00 | 8.00 |
| 247 | A101 | 1p vermilion | 3.00 | 10.00 |
| 248 | A101 | 1½p lt red brown | 3.00 | 9.50 |
| 249 | A101 | 2p lt orange | 3.50 | 10.00 |
| 250 | A101 | 2½p ultra | 3.75 | 11.50 |
| 251 | A101 | 3p violet | 1.75 | 2.00 |
| 252 | A102 | 4p gray green | .55 | 1.40 |
| 253 | A102 | 5p lt brown | 3.50 | 17.00 |
| 254 | A102 | 6p rose lilac | 1.75 | 1.75 |
| 255 | A103 | 7p emerald | .55 | 18.00 |
| 256 | A103 | 8p brt rose | 3.50 | 7.50 |
| 257 | A103 | 9p dp olive grn | .55 | 12.50 |
| 258 | A103 | 10p royal blue | .55 | 7.50 |
| 259 | A103 | 11p violet brn | .80 | 8.50 |
| 260 | A103 | 1sh brown | 3.00 | 7.00 |

### "MOROCCO AGENCIES" 17½mm long
### Wmk. 259
### Perf. 14

| | | | | |
|---|---|---|---|---|
| 261 | A104 | 2sh6p yellow grn | 20.00 | 40.00 |
| 262 | A104 | 5sh dull red | 35.00 | 70.00 |
| | | Nos. 246-262 (17) | 86.75 | 242.15 |

### Great Britain Nos. 280-284, 286-287 Overprinted "MOROCCO AGENCIES" (14½mm long)
### Perf. 14½x14

| | | | 1951, May 3 | Wmk. 251 |
|---|---|---|---|---|
| 263 | A101 | ½p lt orange | 2.25 | 1.10 |
| 264 | A101 | 1p ultra | 2.25 | 1.60 |
| 265 | A101 | 1½p green | 2.25 | 3.00 |
| 266 | A101 | 2p lt red brown | 2.50 | 4.50 |
| 267 | A101 | 2½p vermilion | 2.25 | 4.75 |

### "MOROCCO AGENCIES" 17½mm long
### Wmk. 259
### Perf. 11x12

| | | | | |
|---|---|---|---|---|
| 268 | A121 | 2sh6p green | 15.00 | 24.00 |
| 269 | A121 | 5sh dull red | 15.00 | 26.00 |
| | | Nos. 263-269 (7) | 41.50 | 64.95 |

### Great Britain Nos. 292-296, 298-300 302 and 306 Overprinted "MOROCCO AGENCIES" (14½mm long)

| | | | 1952-55 Wmk. 298 | Perf. 14½x14 |
|---|---|---|---|---|
| 270 | A126 | ½p red orange | .20 | .20 |
| 271 | A126 | 1p ultramarine | .55 | 2.00 |
| 272 | A126 | 1½p green ('52) | .20 | .20 |
| 273 | A126 | 2p red brown | .30 | 2.25 |
| 274 | A127 | 2½p scarlet ('52) | .20 | 1.40 |
| 275 | A128 | 4p ultra ('55) | 1.75 | 4.00 |
| 276 | A129 | 5p light brown | .75 | .70 |
| 277 | A129 | 6p lilac rose ('55) | 1.00 | 4.00 |
| 278 | A130 | 8p bright rose | .80 | .80 |
| 279 | A131 | 1sh brown | .80 | .70 |
| | | Nos. 270-279 (10) | 6.20 | 16.25 |

### Same Ovpt. on Great Britain No. 321

| | | | 1956 Wmk. 308 | Perf. 14½x14 |
|---|---|---|---|---|
| 280 | A127 | 2½p scarlet | 1.00 | 3.75 |

### French Currency
British Stamps of 1912-22 Surcharged in French Currency in Red or Black:

h              i

| | | | Perf. 14½x14, 15x14 | |
|---|---|---|---|---|
| | | | 1917-24 | Wmk. 33 |
| 401 | A82(h) | 3c on ½p green (R) | 1.10 | 2.90 |
| 402 | A82(h) | 5c on ½p green | .45 | .20 |
| 403 | A83(h) | 10c on 1p scarlet | 3.75 | .45 |
| 404 | A84(h) | 15c on 1½p red brn | 2.90 | .20 |
| 405 | A86(h) | 25c on 2½p ultra | 2.25 | .20 |
| 406 | A88(h) | 40c on 4p slate green | 2.90 | 1.75 |
| 407 | A89(h) | 50c on 5p yel brn ('23) | .90 | 3.00 |

---

| | | | | |
|---|---|---|---|---|
| 408 | A90(h) | 75c on 9p ol grn ('24) | 1.10 | .85 |
| 409 | A90(i) | 1fr on 10p lt blue | 8.50 | 3.50 |
| | | Nos. 401-409 (9) | 23.85 | 13.05 |

### Great Britain No. 179 Surcharged:

k

| | | | 1924 Wmk. 34 | Perf. 11x12 |
|---|---|---|---|---|
| 410 | A91(k) | 3fr on 2sh6p brn | 8.50 | 1.75 |

### British Stamps of 1924 Surcharged in French Currency as in 1917-24

| | | | 1925-26 Wmk. 35 | Perf. 15x14 |
|---|---|---|---|---|
| 411 | A82(h) | 5c on ½p green | .35 | 7.50 |
| 412 | A83(h) | 10c on 1p scarlet | .35 | 2.25 |
| 413 | A84(h) | 15c on 1½p red brn | 1.10 | 2.00 |
| 414 | A86(h) | 25c on 2½p ultra | 1.75 | .55 |
| 415 | A88(h) | 40c on 4p sl green | .70 | .90 |
| 416 | A89(h) | 50c on 5p yel brown | 1.75 | .20 |
| 417 | A90(h) | 75c on 9p ol grn | 4.00 | .20 |
| 418 | A90(i) | 1fr on 10p dl blue | 1.40 | .20 |
| | | Nos. 411-418 (8) | 11.40 | 13.80 |

### Great Britain Nos. 180, 198 and 200 Surcharged type "k"

| | | | 1932 Wmk. 34 | Perf. 11x12 |
|---|---|---|---|---|
| 419 | A91 | 6fr on 5sh car rose | 42.50 | 47.50 |

| | | | 1934 Wmk. 35 | Perf. 14½x14 |
|---|---|---|---|---|
| 420 | A90 | 90c on 9p ol green | 18.00 | 8.50 |
| 421 | A90 | 1.50fr on 1sh bister | 11.50 | 2.50 |

### Silver Jubilee Issue
Great Britain Nos. 226-229 Surcharged in Blue or Red

| | | | 1935, May 8 | Perf. 14½x14 |
|---|---|---|---|---|
| 422 | A98 | 5c on ½p dk green | .20 | .20 |
| 423 | A98 | 10c on 1p carmine | 3.50 | .85 |
| 424 | A98 | 15c on 1½p red brn | .40 | .55 |
| 425 | A98 | 25c on 2½p ultra (R) | .25 | .35 |
| | | Nos. 422-425 (4) | 4.35 | 1.95 |

25th anniv. of the reign of King George V.

### British Stamps of 1934-36 Surcharged Types "h" or "k"
### Perf. 14½x14

| | | | 1935-37 Photo. | Wmk. 35 |
|---|---|---|---|---|
| 426 | A82(h) | 5c on ½p dk grn | .55 | 5.75 |
| 427 | A97(h) | 10c on 1p car ('36) | .40 | .35 |
| 428 | A84(h) | 15c on 1½p red brn | 5.50 | 6.25 |
| 429 | A97(h) | 25c on 2½p ultra | .35 | .20 |
| 430 | A88(h) | 40c on 4p dk sl grn | .35 | .20 |
| 431 | A89(h) | 50c on 5p yel brn | .35 | .20 |
| 432 | A90(h) | 90c on 9p dk ol grn | .40 | 2.00 |
| 433 | A90(k) | 1fr on 10p Prus bl | .35 | .35 |
| 434 | A90(h) | 1.50fr on 1sh bister brn ('37) | .85 | 3.75 |

### Waterlow Printing
### Wmk. 34    Perf. 11x12

| | | | | |
|---|---|---|---|---|
| 435 | A91(k) | 3fr on 2sh6p brn | 5.50 | 14.00 |
| 436 | A91(k) | 6fr on 5sh car ('36) | 7.00 | 24.00 |
| | | Nos. 426-436 (11) | 21.60 | 57.05 |

Great Britain Nos. 230, 232 Surcharged

| | | | 1936 Wmk. 250 | Perf. 14½x14 |
|---|---|---|---|---|
| 437 | A99 | 5c on ½p dark green | .20 | .20 |
| 438 | A99 | 15c on 1½p red brown | .20 | .20 |

## Great Britain No. 234 Surcharged in Blue

**1937, May 13**       **Wmk. 251**
439 A100   15c on 1½p purple brn   .35   .20
*Coronation of George VI and Elizabeth.*

## Great Britain No. 235 Surcharged in Blue

**1937**
440 A101   5c on ½p deep green   2.50   2.90

### For Use in the International Zone of Tangier
Great Britain Nos. 187-190
Overprinted in Black

a

**1927**     **Wmk. 35**     **Perf. 15x14**
501 A82   ½p green     3.50   .20
502 A83   1p scarlet     3.50   .30
503 A84   1½p red brown     7.00   4.25
504 A85   2p orange (II)     3.75   4.25
     *Nos. 501-504 (4)*     17.75   4.95

### Same Overprint on Great Britain Nos. 210-212

**1934-35**    **Photo.**    **Perf. 14½x14**
505 A82   ½p dark green    1.40   1.75
506 A97   1p carmine    5.50   2.75
507 A84   1½p red brown    .55   .20
     *Nos. 505-507 (3)*    7.45   4.70

### Silver Jubilee Issue
Great Britain Nos. 226-228
Overprinted in Blue

b

**1935, May 8**
508 A98   ½p dark green    1.40   5.75
509 A98   1p carmine    17.50   17.50
510 A98   1½p red brown    1.40   1.10
     *Nos. 508-510 (3)*    20.30   24.35
*25th anniv. of the reign of King George V.*

> Catalogue values for unused stamps in this section, from this point to the end of the section, are for Never Hinged items.

### Great Britain Nos. 230-232 Overprinted Type "a"

**1936**       **Wmk. 250**
511 A99   ½p dark green    .20   .20
512 A99   1p crimson    .20   .20
513 A99   1½p red brown    .20   .20
     *Nos. 511-513 (3)*    .60   .60

### Great Britain No. 234 Overprinted Type "b" in Blue

**1937, May 13**       **Wmk. 251**
514 A100   1½p purple brown    .55   .55
*Coronation of George VI and Elizabeth.*

---

### Great Britain Nos. 235-237 Overprinted in Blue or Black

c

**1937**       **Perf. 14½x14**
515 A101   ½p deep green (Bl)    2.75   1.75
516 A101   1p scarlet (Bk)    10.00   1.75
517 A101   1½p red brown (Bl)    2.75   .30
     *Nos. 515-517 (3)*    15.50   3.80

### Great Britain Nos. 252-254 Ovptd. Type "a" in Blue or Black

**1940, May 6**
518 A106   ½p deep green (Bl)    .35   5.50
519 A106   1p scarlet (Bk)    .50   .60
520 A106   1½p red brown (Bl)    2.25   5.75
     *Nos. 518-520 (3)*    3.10   11.85
*Centenary of the postage stamp.*

### Great Britain Nos. 258 and 259 Overprinted Type "c" in Blue or Black

**1944-45**
521 A101   ½p green (Bl)    15.00   6.00
522 A101   1p ver (Bk) ('45)    15.00   3.75

### Great Britain Nos. 264-265 Overprinted:

d

e

**1946, June 11**
523 A107(d)   2½p bright ultra    .75   .75
524 A108(e)   3p violet    .75   2.25
*Return to peace at close of World War II.*

### Great Britain Nos. 267 and 268 Overprinted Type "a"

**1948, Apr. 26**   **Perf. 14½x14, 14x14½**
525 A109   2½p bright ultra    .60   .20
   a.   Pair, one without overprint    6,000.
526 A110   £1 dp chalky bl    22.50   29.00
*25th anniv. of the marriage of King George VI and Queen Elizabeth.*

### Great Britain Nos. 271 to 274 Overprinted Type "a"

**1948, July 29**      **Perf. 14½x14**
527 A113   2½p bright ultra    1.10   2.25
528 A114   3p deep violet    1.10   2.25
529 A115   6p red violet    1.10   2.25
530 A116   1sh dark brown    1.10   1.40
     *Nos. 527-530 (4)*    4.40   8.15
*1948 Olympic Games, Wembley, July-Aug.*

### Stamps of Great Britain, 1937-47, and Nos. 249A, 250 and 251A Overprinted Type "c"

**1949, Jan. 1**
531 A101   2p lt org (II)    5.75   7.00
532 A101   2½p ultra (II)    2.00   7.00
533 A101   3p violet (II)    .80   1.40
534 A102   4p gray green    12.50   11.50
535 A102   5p light brown    4.25   22.50
536 A102   6p rose lilac    .80   .35
537 A103   7p emerald    1.40   15.00
538 A103   8p bright rose    4.25   12.00
539 A103   9p deep ol grn    1.40   13.50
540 A103   10p royal blue    1.40   15.00
541 A103   11p violet brn    1.75   12.50
542 A103   1sh brown    1.40   3.00

**Wmk. 259**
               **Perf. 14**
543 A104   2sh6p yellow grn    5.00   13.50
544 A104   5sh dull red    15.00   42.50
545 A105   10sh ultra    55.00   110.00
     *Nos. 531-545 (15)*    112.70   287.25

---

### Great Britain Nos. 276 to 279 Overprinted Type "a"

**Perf. 14½x14**
**1949, Oct. 10**      **Wmk. 251**
546 A117   2½p bright ultra    .80   3.00
547 A118   3p bright violet    .80   2.00
548 A119   6p red violet    .80   1.40
549 A120   1sh brown    .80   3.75
     *Nos. 546-549 (4)*    3.20   10.15

### Great Britain Nos. 280-288 Overprinted Type "c" or "a" (Shilling Values)

**1950-51**
550 A101   ½p lt orange    1.00   1.75
551 A101   1p ultra    1.10   3.50
552 A101   1½p green    1.10   16.00
553 A101   2p lt red brn    1.10   2.90
554 A101   2½p vermilion    1.10   5.75
555 A102   4p ultra ('50)    3.50   3.50

**Wmk. 259**
               **Perf. 11x12**
556 A121   2sh6p green    11.00   5.75
557 A121   5sh dull red    17.50   19.00
558 A122   10sh ultra    22.50   19.00
     *Nos. 550-558 (9)*    59.90   77.15

### Great Britain Nos. 292-308 Overprinted Type "c"

**1952-54**   **Wmk. 298**   **Perf. 14½x14**
559 A126   ½p red org ('53)    .20   .35
560 A126   1p ultra ('53)    .20   .45
561 A126   1½p green ('52)    .20   .35
562 A126   2p red brn ('53)    .20   .90
563 A127   2½p scarlet ('52)    .20   1.10
564 A127   3p dk pur (Dk Bl)    .25   1.40
565 A128   4p ultra ('53)    .70   2.25
566 A129   5p lt brown ('53)    .70   2.25
567 A129   6p lilac rose    .50   .20
568 A129   7p emerald    .90   3.00
569 A130   8p brt rose ('53)    .70   1.75
570 A130   9p dp olive grn    1.60   .85
571 A130   10p royal blue    1.60   3.00
572 A130   11p violet brn    1.60   3.75
573 A131   1sh brown ('53)    .55   .80
574 A132   1sh3p dk grn ('53)    .75   4.75
575 A131   1sh6p dk blue ('53)    1.10   2.00
     *Nos. 559-575 (17)*    11.95   29.15

### Stamp and Type of Great Britain 1955 Overprinted Type "a"

**Perf. 11x12**
**1955, Sept. 23**   **Engr.**   **Wmk. 308**
576 A133   2sh6p dark brown    4.00   10.00
577 A133   5sh crimson    5.00   18.00
578 A133   10sh brt ultra    18.00   24.00
     *Nos. 576-578 (3)*    27.00   52.00

### Coronation Issue
Great Britain Nos. 313-316
Overprinted Type "a"

**1953, June 3**    **Photo.**    **Wmk. 298**
579 A134   2½p scarlet    .50   .40
580 A135   4p brt ultra    .90   .65
581 A136   1sh3p dark green    2.75   1.90
582 A137   1sh6p dark blue    3.25   2.25
     *Nos. 579-582 (4)*    7.40   5.20

### Great Britain Nos. 317-323, 325 and 332 Overprinted Type "c"

**1956**    **Wmk. 308**    **Perf. 14½x14**
583 A126   ½p red orange    .20   .55
584 A126   1p ultramarine    .35   .55
585 A126   1½p green    .65   1.40
586 A126   2p red brown    1.10   .55
587 A127   2½p scarlet    .75   .55
588 A127   3p dark purple    .85   1.00
589 A128   4p ultra    1.75   4.00
590 A129   6p lilac rose    1.10   1.00
591 A132   1sh3p dark green    1.25   15.00
     *Nos. 583-591 (9)*    8.00   24.60

### Great Britain Nos. 317-333 and 309-311 Overprinted "1857-1957 TANGIER"

**1957, Apr. 1**    **Photo.**    **Wmk. 308**
592 A126   ½p red orange    .20   .20
593 A126   1p ultramarine    .20   .20
594 A126   1½p green    .20   .20
595 A126   2p red brown    .20   .20
596 A127   2½p scarlet    .20   1.40
597 A127   3p dark purple    .20   .45
598 A128   4p ultramarine    .35   .20
599 A129   5p lt brown    .35   .40
600 A129   6p lilac rose    .35   .40
601 A129   7p emerald    .35   .40
602 A130   8p brt rose    .35   1.10
603 A130   9p dp olive grn    .35   .35
   a.   "TANGIER" omitted    5,500.
604 A130   10p royal blue    .35   .35
605 A130   11p violet brown    .35   .35
606 A131   1sh brown    .35   .35
607 A132   1sh3p dark green    .50   5.50
608 A131   1sh6p dark blue    .55   1.75

---

**Engr.**
**Perf. 11x12**
609 A133   2sh6p dark brown    2.25   4.25
610 A133   5sh crimson    3.00   7.00
611 A133   10sh ultramarine    4.25   8.50
     *Nos. 592-611 (20)*    14.90   33.55
*Centenary of British P.O. in Tangier.*
*Nos. 609-611 are found with hyphen omitted (one stamp in sheet of 40).*
*British stamps overprinted "Tangier" were discontinued Apr. 30, 1957.*

## TURKISH EMPIRE

40 Paras = 1 Piaster
12 Pence = 1 Shilling (1905)

a

b

c          d

Surcharged on Great Britain Nos. 101, 104, 96

**1885, Apr. 1**    **Wmk. 30**    **Perf. 14**
1   A47(a)   40pa on 2½p lil    110.00   1.50
2   A45(b)   80pa on 5p grn    210.00   12.50

**Wmk. 31**
3   A44(c)   12pi on 2sh6p
           lilac    52.50   27.50
   a.   Bluish paper    450.00   260.00
     *Nos. 1-3 (3)*    372.50   41.50

### Great Britain Nos. 114, 118 Surcharged

**1887**               **Wmk. 30**
4   A57(a)   40pa on 2½p vio,
           bl    4.75   .20
   a.   Double surcharge    2,250.   2,900.
5   A61(b)   80pa on 5p lil & bl    17.50   .35
   a.   Small "0" in "80"    275.00   100.00

### Great Britain No. 111 Handstamp Surcharged

**1893, Feb. 25**
6   A54(d)   40pa on ½p ver    500.00   125.00
*No. 6 was a provisional, made and used at Constantinople for five days. Excellent forgeries are known.*

### Great Britain No. 121 Surcharged

e

**1896**
7   A64(e)   4pi on 10p car rose
           & lil    47.50   9.25

### British Stamps of 1902 Surcharged

**1902-05**             **Wmk. 30**
8   A66(a)   40pa on 2½p ultra    17.50   .20
9   A71(b)   80pa on 5p lil & bl    9.00   2.90
   a.   Small "0" in "80"    300.00   210.00
10   A73(e)   4pi on 10p car
           rose & vio    13.50   4.50

**Wmk. 31**
11   A75(c)   12pi on 2sh6p
           vio ('03)    40.00   40.00
12   A76(c)   24pi on 2sh6p
           rose ('05)    35.00   47.50
     *Nos. 8-12 (5)*    115.00   95.10

Great Britain Nos. 131, 134
Surcharged

f

**1906**                          **Wmk. 30**
| 13 | A66(f) | 1pi on 2½p ultra | 20.00 | .20 |
| 14 | A71(f) | 2pi on 5p lil & ultra | 35.00 | 2.75 |

Nos. 10, 11, 14 are on both ordinary and chalky paper.

Great Britain Nos. 127-135, 138
Overprinted

g

**1905**
| 15 | A66 | ½p pale green | 10.00 | .20 |
| 16 | A66 | 1p carmine | 9.50 | .20 |
| 17 | A67 | 1½p violet & grn | 6.25 | 2.00 |
| 18 | A68 | 2p green & car | 3.50 | 8.00 |
| 19 | A66 | 2½p ultra | 10.00 | 22.50 |
| 20 | A69 | 3p violet, yel | 7.25 | 13.50 |
| 21 | A70 | 4p brown & grn | 10.00 | 50.00 |
| 22 | A71 | 5p lilac & ultra | 19.00 | 32.50 |
| 23 | A66 | 6p dull violet | 15.00 | 29.00 |
| 24 | A74 | 1sh car rose & grn | 42.50 | 57.50 |
| | | Nos. 15-24 (10) | 133.00 | 215.40 |

Nos. 17, 18 and 24 are on both ordinary and chalky paper.

No. 18 Surcharged

**1906, July 2**
| 25 | A68 | 1pi on 2p grn & car | 1,500. | 700.00 |

British Stamps of 1902-09 Surcharged:

j                              k

**1909**
| 26 | A67 | 30pa on 1½p vio & grn | 13.50 | 1.40 |
| 27 | A69 | 1pi10pa on 3p vio, yel | 13.50 | 40.00 |
| 28 | A70 | 1pi30pa on 4p brn & grn | 5.75 | 19.00 |
| 29 | A70 | 1pi30pa on 4p org | 20.00 | 70.00 |
| 30 | A66 | 2pi20pa on 6p dl violet | 22.50 | 70.00 |
| 31 | A74 | 5pi on 1sh car rose & grn | 5.00 | 11.00 |
| | | Nos. 26-31 (6) | 80.25 | 211.40 |

No. 29 is on ordinary paper, the others are on chalky paper.

Great Britain Nos. 132, 144, 135
Surcharged:

m                              n

**1910**
| 32 | A69(m) | 1¼pi on 3p vio, yel | .60 | 1.25 |
| 33 | A70(m) | 1¾pi on 4p orange | .60 | .75 |
| 34 | A66(n) | 2½pi on 6p dl vio | 1.60 | .80 |
| | | Nos. 32-34 (3) | 2.80 | 2.80 |

There are three different varieties of "4" in the fraction of the 1¾ piastre.

Great Britain Nos. 151-154
Overprinted Type "g"

**1911-12**                        **Perf. 15x14**
| 35 | A80 | ½p yellow green | 2.25 | 1.75 |
| 36 | A81 | 1p carmine | .55 | 7.00 |
| | | **Re-engraved** | | |
| 37 | A80 | ½p yel grn ('12) | .90 | .20 |
| 38 | A81 | 1p scarlet ('12) | .90 | 1.75 |

Great Britain No. 148 Surcharged

o

| 39 | A66(o) | 1pi on 2½p ultra | 17.50 | 3.00 |
| | | Nos. 35-39 (5) | 22.10 | 13.70 |

The surcharge on No. 39 exists in two types with the letters 2½ and 3mm high respectively. The stamp also differs from No. 13 in the perforation.

British Stamps of 1912-13 Surcharged with New Values

**1913-14**                        **Wmk. 33**
| 40 | A84(j) | 30pa on 1½p red brown | 4.00 | 16.00 |
| 41 | A86(o) | 1pi on 2½p ultra | 8.50 | .20 |
| 42 | A87(m) | 1¼pi on 3p vio | 5.50 | 4.75 |
| 43 | A88(m) | 1¾pi on 4p sl grn | 3.50 | 7.00 |
| 44 | A90(o) | 4pi on 10p lt bl | 9.00 | 22.50 |
| 45 | A90(o) | 5pi on 1sh bis | 45.00 | 70.00 |
| | | Nos. 40-45 (6) | 75.50 | 120.45 |

British Stamps of 1912-19 Overprinted Type "g"

**1913-21**
| 46 | A82 | ½p green | .45 | 1.40 |
| 47 | A83 | 1p scarlet | .35 | 5.75 |
| 48 | A85 | 2p orange ('21) | 1.40 | 32.50 |
| 49 | A87 | 3p violet ('21) | 8.50 | 11.50 |
| 50 | A88 | 4p sl grn ('21) | 5.75 | 16.00 |
| 51 | A89 | 5p yel brn ('21) | 13.50 | 32.50 |
| 52 | A89 | 6p dl vio ('21) | 30.00 | 10.00 |
| 53 | A90 | 1sh bister ('21) | 15.00 | 10.00 |
| | | **Wmk. 34** | | |
| | | **Perf. 11x12** | | |
| 54 | A91 | 2sh6p brn ('21) | 42.50 | 100.00 |
| | | Nos. 46-54 (9) | 117.45 | 219.65 |

British Stamps of 1912-19 Surcharged as in 1909-10 and

p

q

**1921**                **Wmk. 33**    **Perf. 14½x14**
| 55 | A82(j) | 30pa on ½p grn | .90 | 13.50 |
| a. | | Inverted surcharge | 100.00 | |
| 56 | A83(p) | 1½pi on 1p scar | 1.75 | 1.40 |
| 57 | A86(p) | 3¾pi on 2½p ultra | 1.50 | .35 |
| 58 | A87(p) | 4½pi on 3p vio | 2.25 | 4.25 |
| 59 | A89(p) | 7½pi on 5p yel brn | .60 | .20 |
| 60 | A90(p) | 15pi on 10p lt bl | .85 | .20 |
| 61 | A90(p) | 18¾pi on 1sh bis | 5.00 | 5.00 |
| | | **Wmk. 34** | | |
| | | **Perf. 11x12** | | |
| 62 | A91(q) | 45pi on 2sh6p brown | 22.50 | 52.50 |
| 63 | A91(q) | 90pi on 5sh car rose | 30.00 | 35.00 |
| 64 | A91(q) | 180pi on 10sh blue | 52.50 | 45.00 |
| | | Nos. 55-64 (10) | 117.85 | 157.40 |

# GUERNSEY

ˈgərn-zē

LOCATION — A group of islands in the English Channel
GOVT. — Dependent territory (bailiwick) of the British Crown
AREA — 30 sq. mi.
POP. — 58,681 (1996)
CAPITAL — St. Peter Port

The bailiwick includes the islands of Guernsey, Alderney, Sark, Herm, Jethou and Lithou.
Following the establishment of the British General Post Office as a public corporation on October 1, 1969, the post office of the Bailiwick of Guernsey became a separate entity and British postage stamps ceased to be valid.

> Catalogue values for unused stamps in this country are for Never Hinged items.

Watermark

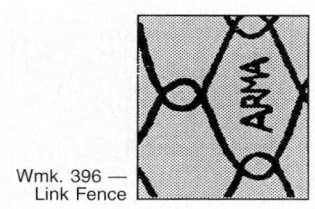

Wmk. 396 —
Link Fence

**British Regional Issue**

Guernsey Lily and Crown
of William the Conqueror
A1          A2

**Perf. 15x14**
**1958-69**         **Photo.**      **Wmk. 322**
| 1 | A1 | 2½p rose red ('64) | .35 | .35 |
| 2 | A2 | 3p light purple | .30 | .20 |
| p. | | Phosphor. ('67) | .20 | .20 |
| 3 | A2 | 4p ultra ('66) | .30 | .20 |
| p. | | Phosphor. ('67) | .20 | .20 |
| | | **Unwmk.** | | |
| 4 | A2 | 4p ultra ('68) | .20 | .20 |
| 5 | A2 | 4p olive brown ('68) | .20 | .20 |
| 6 | A2 | 4p bright red ('69) | .20 | .20 |
| 7 | A2 | 5p dark blue ('68) | .20 | .20 |
| | | Nos. 1-7 (7) | 1.75 | 1.55 |

Nos. 4-7 are phosphorescent.
Sold to the general public only at post offices within Guernsey, but valid for postage throughout Great Britain.
See also Great Britain Nos. 269-270, which were sold only in the Channel Islands and at a few philatelic windows in Great Britain, and may be considered to be precursors to the regional issues.

**Bailiwick Issues**

William the Conqueror, Queen
Elizabeth II and Map of Bailiwick — A3

Creux Harbor, Sark — A4

Designs (Queen Elizabeth II and): ½p, Castle Cornet and Edward the Confessor. 1½p, Martello Tower and Henry II. 2p, Arms of Sark and King John. 3p, Arms of Alderney and Edward III. 4p, Guernsey lily and Henry V. 5p, Arms of Guernsey and Queen Elizabeth I. 6p, Arms of Alderney and Charles II. 9p, Arms of Sark and George III. 1sh, Arms of Guernsey and Queen Victoria. 1sh6p, Map of Bailiwick and William I. 1sh9p, Guernsey lily and Queen Elizabeth I. 2sh6p, Martello Tower and King John. 10sh, Braye Harbor, Alderney. £1, St. Peter Port, Guernsey.

**Perf. 14½x14**
**1969-70**         **Photo.**      **Unwmk.**
| 8 | A3 | ½p magenta & blk | .25 | .20 |
| 9 | A3 | 1p ultra & black | .25 | .20 |
| 10 | A3 | 1½p bister & blk | .25 | .20 |
| 11 | A3 | 2p dk blue & multi | .25 | .20 |
| 12 | A3 | 3p deep org & multi | .30 | .20 |
| 13 | A3 | 4p yel green & multi | .40 | .40 |
| a. | | Booklet pane of 1 | 1.00 | 1.00 |
| 14 | A3 | 5p vio blue & multi | .35 | .20 |
| a. | | Booklet pane of 1 | 1.50 | 1.50 |
| 15 | A3 | 6p ol green & multi | .40 | .50 |
| 16 | A3 | 9p plum & multi | .50 | .60 |
| 17 | A3 | 1sh dk olive & multi | .40 | .50 |
| 18 | A3 | 1sh6p blue grn & blk | .40 | .50 |
| 19 | A3 | 1sh9p magenta & multi | 1.50 | 1.40 |
| 20 | A3 | 2sh6p purple & blk | 7.00 | 6.00 |
| | | **Perf. 12½** | | |
| 21 | A4 | 5sh multicolored | 4.00 | 3.00 |
| 22 | A4 | 10sh multicolored | 27.50 | 25.00 |
| a. | | Perf. 13½x13 | 57.50 | 50.00 |
| | | **Perf. 13½x13** | | |
| 23 | A4 | £1 multicolored | 3.75 | 3.50 |
| a. | | Perf. 12½ | 4.50 | 4.50 |
| | | Nos. 8-23 (16) | 47.50 | 42.60 |

Issued: #22a, 23, 3/4/70; others, 10/1/69. Nos. 9 and 18 are inscribed "40o 30' N." See Nos. 28-29, 41-55. See also No. 749.

Col. Isaac
Brock — A5

Designs: 5p, Sir Isaac Brock as major general. 1sh9p, as ensign, flags of 1789 and 1969. 2sh6p, Regimental coat of arms and flags, horiz.

**Perf. 14x13½, 13½x14**
**1969, Dec. 1**      **Litho.**      **Unwmk.**
| 24 | A5 | 4p multicolored | .25 | .20 |
| 25 | A5 | 5p black & multi | .25 | .20 |
| 26 | A5 | 1sh9p dp blue & multi | 1.25 | 1.10 |
| 27 | A5 | 2sh6p purple & multi | 1.25 | 1.10 |
| | | Nos. 24-27 (4) | 3.00 | 2.60 |

Sir Isaac Brock (1769-1812), born on Guernsey, commander of Quebec garrison.

**Map Type of 1969 Redrawn**
**1969-70**    **Photo.**    **Perf. 14½x14**
| 28 | A3 | 1p "49o 30'N" | .25 | .25 |
| a. | | Booklet pane of 1 | .45 | .45 |
| 29 | A3 | 1sh9p "49o 30'N" | 3.00 | 2.00 |

No. 28a was issued Dec. 12, 1969, in booklets containing Nos. 13a, 14a, 28a. Nos. 28-29 issued 2/4/70.
Nos. 9 and 18 are inscribed "40o 30' N."

Destroyer "Bulldog" near Castle
Cornet — A6

Designs: 5p, Liberation fleet in roadsteads between Guernsey, Herm and Jethou. 1sh6p, Brigadier A. E. Snow reading proclamation of King George VI on steps of Elizabeth College in Guernsey, vert.

| 1970, May 9 | Photo. | Perf. 11½ | | |
|---|---|---|---|---|
| 30 | A6 | 4p vio blue & lt blue | .25 | .20 |
| 31 | A6 | 5p dp plum & gray | .25 | .20 |
| 32 | A6 | 1sh6p dk brown & bis | 1.75 | 1.75 |
| | | Nos. 30-32 (3) | 2.25 | 2.15 |

25th anniv. of Guernsey's liberation from the Germans.

Guernsey Cow — A7

| 1970, Aug. 12 | Photo. | Perf. 11½ | | |
|---|---|---|---|---|
| 33 | A7 | 4p Tomatoes | 1.10 | .45 |
| 34 | A7 | 5p shown | 1.10 | .45 |
| 35 | A7 | 9p Guernsey bull | 5.50 | 2.25 |
| 36 | A7 | 1sh6p Freesias | 6.00 | 4.50 |
| | | Nos. 33-36 (4) | 13.70 | 7.65 |

For similar design see No. 68.

St. Anne, Alderney A8

Christmas (Churches): 5p, St. Peter, Town Church, Guernsey. 9p, St. Peter, Sark, vert. 1sh6p, St. Tugual Chapel, Herm, vert.

| 1970, Nov. 11 | Photo. | Perf. 11½ | | |
|---|---|---|---|---|
| 37 | A8 | 4p blue, gold & brn | .30 | .20 |
| 38 | A8 | 5p brt grn, gold & brn | .40 | .20 |
| 39 | A8 | 9p rose red, gold & brown | 1.10 | 1.00 |
| 40 | A8 | 1sh6p brt purple, gold & brown | 2.10 | 1.60 |
| | | Nos. 37-40 (4) | 3.90 | 3.00 |

### Decimal Currency Issue
### Types of 1969
### "p" instead of "d"

Designs: ½p, Castle Cornet and Edward the Confessor. 1p, 5p, Map of Bailiwick and William the Conqueror. 1½p, Martello Tower and Henry II. 2p, Guernsey lily and Henry V. 2½p, Arms of Guernsey and Elizabeth I. 3p, Arms of Alderney and Edward III. 3½p, Guernsey lily and Elizabeth I. 4p, Arms of Sark and King John. 6p, Arms of Alderney and Charles II. 7½p, Arms of Guernsey and Queen Victoria. 9p, Arms of Sark and George III. 10p, Martello Tower and King John. 20p, Creux Harbor. 50p, Braye Harbor.

| 1971 | Photo. | Perf. 14½x14 | | |
|---|---|---|---|---|
| 41 | A3 | ½p magenta & blk | .20 | .20 |
| a. | | Booklet pane of 1 | .20 | |
| 42 | A3 | 1p ultra & black | .20 | .20 |
| 43 | A3 | 1½p bister & blk | .25 | .25 |
| 44 | A3 | 2p yel green & multi | .25 | .25 |
| a. | | Booklet pane of 1 | .35 | |
| 45 | A3 | 2½p vio blue & multi | .25 | .25 |
| a. | | Booklet pane of 1 | .35 | |
| 46 | A3 | 3p dp orange & multi | .30 | .30 |
| 47 | A3 | 3½p magenta & multi | .30 | .30 |
| 48 | A3 | 4p dk blue & multi | .30 | .30 |
| 49 | A3 | 5p brt green & multi | .30 | .30 |
| 50 | A3 | 6p dk green & multi | .30 | .30 |
| 51 | A3 | 7½p brn olive & multi | .40 | .40 |
| 52 | A3 | 9p plum & multi | .80 | .80 |
| 53 | A3 | 10p purple & black | 1.60 | 1.60 |
| | | Perf. 13 | | |
| 54 | A4 | 20p dk red & multi | 1.00 | 1.00 |
| 55 | A4 | 50p multicolored | 2.40 | 2.40 |
| | | Nos. 41-55 (15) | 8.85 | 8.85 |

Issue dates: #53-55, Jan. 6; others Feb. 15.

Thomas de la Rue, Hong Kong No. 1 — A9

Thomas de la Rue and: 2½p, GB No. 22. 4p, Italy No. 26. 7½p, US Confederate States No. 6.

| 1971, June 2 | Engr. | Perf. 14x13½ | | |
|---|---|---|---|---|
| 56 | A9 | 2p brown | .60 | .60 |
| 57 | A9 | 2½p carmine | .60 | .60 |
| 58 | A9 | 4p dark green | 1.90 | 1.60 |
| 59 | A9 | 7½p violet blue | 2.25 | 1.60 |
| | | Nos. 56-59 (4) | 5.35 | 3.60 |

Thomas de la Rue (1793-1866), founder of Thomas de la Rue & Co., Ltd., security printers.

Ebenezer Methodist Church — A10

Historic Churches of Guernsey: 2½p, St. Pierre du Bois. 5p, St. Joseph's, vert. 7½p, St. Philippe de Torteval, vert.

| 1971, Oct. 27 | Photo. | Perf. 11½ | | |
|---|---|---|---|---|
| 60 | A10 | 2p green, sil & blk | .35 | .35 |
| 61 | A10 | 2½p blue, sil & blk | .40 | .35 |
| 62 | A10 | 5p pur, silver & blk | 1.75 | 1.40 |
| 63 | A10 | 7½p red, silver & blk | 2.50 | 2.25 |
| | | Nos. 60-63 (4) | 5.00 | 4.35 |

Christmas 1971.

Mail Boat, Earl of Chesterfield, 1794 — A11

| 1972, Feb. 10 | Photo. | Perf. 11½ | | |
|---|---|---|---|---|
| 64 | A11 | 2p shown | .20 | .20 |
| 65 | A11 | 2½p Dasher, 1827 | .20 | .20 |
| 66 | A11 | 7½p Ibex, 1891 | .35 | .35 |
| 67 | A11 | 9p Alberta, 1900 | .55 | .55 |
| | | Nos. 64-67 (4) | 1.30 | 1.30 |

See Nos. 77-80.

Guernsey Bull — A12

| 1972, May 22 | Photo. | Perf. 11½ | | |
|---|---|---|---|---|
| 68 | A12 | 5p brown & multi | .65 | .55 |

Guernsey Breeders, 2nd World Conf. For similar designs see Nos. 33-36.

Wild Flowers A13

| 1972, May 24 | | | | |
|---|---|---|---|---|
| 69 | A13 | 2p Sorrel | .20 | .20 |
| 70 | A13 | 2½p Orchis maculata, vert. | .20 | .20 |
| 71 | A13 | 7½p Carpobrotus edulis | .40 | .40 |
| 72 | A13 | 9p Pimpernel, vert. | .50 | .50 |
| | | Nos. 69-72 (4) | 1.30 | 1.30 |

Angels, St. Martin's Church — A14

Stained Glass Windows from Guernsey Churches: 2½p, Virgin and Child, St. André's.

7½p, Virgin Mary, St. Sampson's. 9p, Christ Victorious, St. Pierre's.

| 1972, Nov. 20 | Photo. | Perf. 11½ | | |
|---|---|---|---|---|
| 73 | A14 | 2p brick red & multi | .20 | .20 |
| 74 | A14 | 2½p lt violet & multi | .20 | .20 |
| 75 | A14 | 7½p yellow & multi | .30 | .30 |
| 76 | A14 | 9p lt green & multi | .30 | .30 |
| | | Nos. 73-76 (4) | 1.00 | 1.00 |

Christmas 1972 and for the 25th anniv. of the marriage of Queen Elizabeth II and Prince Philip.

### Mail Boat Type of 1972

| 1973, Mar. 9 | Photo. | Perf. 11½ | | |
|---|---|---|---|---|
| 77 | A11 | 2½p St. Julien, 1925 | .20 | .20 |
| 78 | A11 | 3p Isle of Sark, 1932 | .25 | .25 |
| 79 | A11 | 7½p St. Patrick, 1947 | .40 | .40 |
| 80 | A11 | 9p Sarnia, 1961 | .40 | .40 |
| | | Nos. 77-80 (4) | 1.25 | 1.25 |

No. 78 is incorrectly inscribed "Isle of Guernsey 1930."

Supermarine Sea Eagle — A15

Airplanes: 3p, Westland Wessex. 5p, De Havilland Rapide. 7½p, Douglas Dakota. 9p, Vickers Viscount.

| 1973, July 4 | Photo. | Perf. 11½ | | |
|---|---|---|---|---|
| 81 | A15 | 2½p multicolored | .20 | .20 |
| 82 | A15 | 3p multicolored | .20 | .20 |
| 83 | A15 | 5p multicolored | .20 | .20 |
| 84 | A15 | 7½p multicolored | .40 | .40 |
| 85 | A15 | 9p multicolored | .50 | .50 |
| | | Nos. 81-85 (5) | 1.50 | 1.50 |

50th anniversary of air service to Guernsey.

The Good Shepherd, St. Michel du Valle — A16

Stained-glass Windows from Guernsey Churches: 3p, Jesus preaching, St. Marie du Castel. 7½p, St. Dominic, Notre Dame du Rosaire. 20p, Virgin and Child, St. Sauveur.

| 1973, Oct. 24 | Photo. | Perf. 11½ | | |
|---|---|---|---|---|
| 86 | A16 | 2½p salmon & multi | .20 | .20 |
| 87 | A16 | 3p blue & multi | .20 | .20 |
| 88 | A16 | 7½p yellow & multi | .20 | .20 |
| 89 | A16 | 20p multicolored | .50 | .50 |
| | | Nos. 86-89 (4) | 1.10 | 1.10 |

Christmas 1973.

Princess Anne and Mark Phillips — A17

**1973, Nov. 14**

| 90 | A17 | 25p blue & multi | .70 | .70 |
|---|---|---|---|---|

Wedding of Princess Anne and Capt. Mark Phillips, Nov. 14, 1973.

"John Lockett," 1875 — A18

Guernsey Lifeboats: 3p, "Arthur Lionel," 1875. 8p, "Euphrosyne Kendal," 1954. 10p, "Arun," 1972.

| 1974, Jan. 15 | Photo. | Perf. 11½ | | |
|---|---|---|---|---|
| | | Granite Paper | | |
| 91 | A18 | 2½p multicolored | .20 | .20 |
| 92 | A18 | 3p multicolored | .20 | .20 |
| 93 | A18 | 8p multicolored | .20 | .20 |
| 94 | A18 | 10p multicolored | .20 | .20 |
| | | Nos. 91-94 (4) | .80 | .80 |

Sesqui. of Royal Natl. Lifeboat Institution.

A19

Militia — A20

| 1974-78 | Photo. | Perf. 11½ | | |
|---|---|---|---|---|
| | | Granite Paper (Nos. 95-107) | | |
| 95 | A19 | ½p 1815 | .20 | .20 |
| 96 | A19 | 1p 1825 | .20 | .20 |
| 97 | A19 | 1½p 1787 | .20 | .20 |
| 98 | A19 | 2p 1815 | .20 | .20 |
| 99 | A19 | 2½p Royal, 1868 | .20 | .20 |
| | | Complete booklet, pane of 8 (5 #95, 3 #99) | .35 | |
| 100 | A19 | 3p Royal, 1895 | .20 | .20 |
| | | Complete booklet, pane of 16 (4 #95, 6 #99 and 6 #100) | 1.10 | |
| 101 | A19 | 3½p Royal, 1867 | .20 | .20 |
| 102 | A19 | 4p 1822 | .20 | .20 |
| 102A | A19 | 5p Royal, 1895 | .25 | .25 |
| | | Complete booklet, pane of 8 (4 #96, #100, 2 #102, #102A) ('77) | .85 | |
| | | Complete booklet, pane of 4 (#96, 2 #98, #102A) ('78) | .55 | |
| 103 | A19 | 5½p Royal, 1833 | .20 | .20 |
| 104 | A19 | 6p Royal, 1832 | .20 | .20 |
| 104A | A19 | 7p 1822 | .35 | .35 |
| 105 | A19 | 8p Royal, 1868 | .20 | .20 |
| 106 | A19 | 9p 1785 | .20 | .20 |
| 107 | A19 | 10p 1824 | .20 | .20 |
| | | Perf. 13x13½, 13½x13 | | |
| 108 | A20 | 20p Royal, 1848, vert. | .70 | .50 |
| 109 | A20 | 50p Royal, 1868, vert. | 1.50 | 1.40 |
| 110 | A20 | £1 1814 | 3.00 | 2.50 |
| | | Nos. 95-110 (18) | 8.40 | 7.60 |

Issued: #95-107, 4/2/74; #108-110, 4/1/75; #102A, 104A, 5/2976; #96a, 2/8/77; #96b, 2/7/78.

Stamps in booklet panes are from special sheets of 80 (two 8x5 panes) which were sold separately.

Bailiwick Seal and UPU Emblem — A21

UPU Cent.: 3p, Map of Guernsey. 8p, UPU Headquarters, Bern, flag of Guernsey. 10p, Legislative Chamber, Parliament.

| 1974, June 11 | Photo. | Perf. 11½ | | |
|---|---|---|---|---|
| | | Granite Paper | | |
| 111 | A21 | 2½p multicolored | .20 | .20 |
| 112 | A21 | 3p ultra & multi | .20 | .20 |
| 113 | A21 | 8p multicolored | .20 | .20 |
| 114 | A21 | 10p multicolored | .20 | .20 |
| | | Nos. 111-114 (4) | .80 | .80 |

Cradle Rock, by Renoir A22

Paintings by Renoir: 5½p, Moulin-Huet Bay. 8p, Woman at the Shore, vert. 10p, Self-portrait, vert.

**1974, Sept. 21    Photo.    Perf. 13¼**

| | | | | |
|---|---|---|---|---|
| 115 | A22 | 3p multicolored | .20 | .20 |
| 116 | A22 | 5½p multicolored | .20 | .20 |
| 117 | A22 | 8p multicolored | .20 | .20 |
| 118 | A22 | 10p multicolored | .20 | .20 |
| | | Nos. 115-118 (4) | .80 | .80 |

Pierre Auguste Renoir (1841-1919), who painted pictures shown on Nos. 115-117 while visiting Guernsey.

Guernsey Spleenwort — A23

Designs: Guernsey ferns.

**1975, Jan. 7    Photo.    Perf. 11½**

| | | | | |
|---|---|---|---|---|
| 119 | A23 | 3½p shown | .20 | .20 |
| 120 | A23 | 4p Sand quillwort | .20 | .20 |
| 121 | A23 | 8p Guernsey fern | .20 | .20 |
| 122 | A23 | 10p Least adder's tongue | .20 | .20 |
| | | Nos. 119-122 (4) | .80 | .80 |

Hauteville, Hugo's House A24

Victor Hugo Statue, Candie Gardens — A25

Designs: 8p, United Europe Oak, Hauteville (planted by Hugo). 10p, Departure for the Hunt, Aubusson tapestry, Hauteville.

**1975, June 6    Photo.    Granite Paper**

| | | | | |
|---|---|---|---|---|
| 123 | A24 | 3½p dull yel & multi | .20 | .20 |
| 124 | A25 | 4p lt blue & multi | .20 | .20 |
| 125 | A25 | 8p yel green & multi | .20 | .20 |
| 126 | A24 | 10p multicolored | .20 | .20 |
| a. | | Souvenir sheet of 4, #123-126 | .80 | .80 |
| | | Nos. 123-126 (4) | .80 | .80 |

Victor Hugo (1802-85), French writer, political exile in Guernsey (1855-70).

Arms and Map of Guernsey — A26

Designs (Globe with Map of Bailiwick): 6p, Flag of Guernsey. 10p, Flag of Guernsey and arms of Alderney, horiz. 12p, Flag of Guernsey and arms of Sark, horiz.

---

**1975, Oct. 7    Photo.    Perf. 13½**

| | | | | |
|---|---|---|---|---|
| 127 | A26 | 4p olive green & multi | .20 | .20 |
| 128 | A26 | 6p rose lilac & multi | .20 | .20 |
| 129 | A26 | 10p brt green & multi | .20 | .20 |
| 130 | A26 | 12p orange & multi | .20 | .20 |
| | | Nos. 127-130 (4) | .80 | .80 |

Christmas 1975.

Lighthouses — A27

**1976, Feb. 10    Photo.    Perf. 11½**
**Granite Paper**

| | | | | |
|---|---|---|---|---|
| 131 | A27 | 4p Les Hanois | .20 | .20 |
| 132 | A27 | 6p Les Casquets | .20 | .20 |
| 133 | A27 | 11p Quesnard, Alderney | .20 | .20 |
| 134 | A27 | 13p Point Robert, Sark | .30 | .30 |
| | | Nos. 131-134 (4) | .90 | .90 |

Guernsey Milk Can — A28

Europa: 25p, Silver christening cup.

**1976, May 29    Photo.    Perf. 11½**
**Granite Paper**

| | | | | |
|---|---|---|---|---|
| 135 | A28 | 10p multicolored | .35 | .30 |
| 136 | A28 | 25p multicolored | .70 | .50 |
| | | Sheets of 9. | | |

Pine Forest, Guernsey — A29

Guernsey Views: 7p, Herm Harbor and Jethou. 11p, Grande Grave Bay, Sark Cliffs, vert. 13p, Trois Vaux Bay, Alderney Cliffs, vert.

**1976, Aug. 3    Photo.    Perf. 11½**
**Granite Paper**

| | | | | |
|---|---|---|---|---|
| 137 | A29 | 5p multicolored | .20 | .20 |
| 138 | A29 | 7p multicolored | .20 | .20 |
| 139 | A29 | 11p multicolored | .25 | .25 |
| 140 | A29 | 13p multicolored | .25 | .25 |
| | | Nos. 137-140 (4) | .90 | .90 |

Royal Court House, Guernsey — A30

Christmas (Buildings in the Bailiwick): 7p, Elizabeth College, Guernsey. 11p, La Seigneurie, Sark. 13p, Island Hall, Alderney.

**1976, Oct. 14    Photo.    Perf. 11½**
**Granite Paper**

| | | | | |
|---|---|---|---|---|
| 141 | A30 | 5p multicolored | .20 | .20 |
| 142 | A30 | 7p multicolored | .20 | .20 |
| 143 | A30 | 11p multicolored | .25 | .25 |
| 144 | A30 | 13p multicolored | .25 | .25 |
| | | Nos. 141-144 (4) | .90 | .90 |

---

Elizabeth II with Order of the Garter — A31

Design: 7p, Queen Elizabeth II.

**1977, Feb. 8    Photo.    Perf. 12x11½**

| | | | | |
|---|---|---|---|---|
| 145 | A31 | 7p blue & multi | .20 | .20 |
| 146 | A31 | 35p purple & multi | .70 | .70 |

25th anniv. of the reign of Elizabeth II.

Talbots Valley — A32

Europa: 25p, Fields and hedges, Talbots Valley.

**1977, May 17    Photo.    Perf. 11½**
**Granite Paper**

| | | | | |
|---|---|---|---|---|
| 147 | A32 | 7p multicolored | .20 | .20 |
| 148 | A32 | 25p multicolored | .70 | .70 |

Megalithic Tomb, Le Catioroc — A33

Prehistoric monuments: 5p, Menhir (statue), Castel, vert. 11p, Cist (tomb), Alderney. 13p, Menhir, St. Martin, vert.

**1977, Aug. 2    Photo.    Perf. 11½**

| | | | | |
|---|---|---|---|---|
| 149 | A33 | 5p multicolored | .20 | .20 |
| 150 | A33 | 7p multicolored | .20 | .20 |
| 151 | A33 | 11p multicolored | .30 | .30 |
| 152 | A33 | 13p multicolored | .30 | .30 |
| | | Nos. 149-152 (4) | 1.00 | 1.00 |

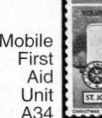

Mobile First Aid Unit A34

7p, Mobile radar & rescue coordination unit, for ships in distress. 11p, Marine ambulance "Flying Christine II," vert. 13p, Cliff rescue, vert.

**1977, Oct. 25    Photo.    Perf. 11½**

| | | | | |
|---|---|---|---|---|
| 153 | A34 | 5p multicolored | .20 | .20 |
| 154 | A34 | 7p multicolored | .20 | .20 |
| 155 | A34 | 11p multicolored | .30 | .30 |
| 156 | A34 | 13p multicolored | .30 | .30 |
| | | Nos. 153-156 (4) | 1.00 | 1.00 |

St. John Ambulance Assoc. cent. (in GB).

View from Clifton, c. 1830 A35

19th Century Prints, Guernsey: 7p, Market Square, c. 1838. 11p, Petit-Bo Bay, c. 1839. 13p, The Quay, c. 1830.

---

**1978, Feb. 7    Litho.    Perf. 14x13½**

| | | | | |
|---|---|---|---|---|
| 157 | A35 | 5p pale green & black | .20 | .20 |
| 158 | A35 | 7p buff & black | .20 | .20 |
| 159 | A35 | 11p pink & black | .30 | .30 |
| 160 | A35 | 13p lt violet & black | .30 | .30 |
| | | Nos. 157-160 (4) | 1.00 | 1.00 |

See Nos. 236-239.

Memorial to Seamen of Ship Prosperity; Sank 1974 — A36

Europa: 7p, Victoria monument, vert.

**1978, May 2    Litho.    Perf. 14½**

| | | | | |
|---|---|---|---|---|
| 161 | A36 | 5p multicolored | .20 | .20 |
| 162 | A36 | 7p multicolored | .25 | .25 |

Elizabeth II — A37

**1978, May 2    Photo.    Perf. 11½**

| | | | | |
|---|---|---|---|---|
| 163 | A37 | 20p ultra & black | .70 | .70 |

25th anniv. of coronation of Elizabeth II.

Inscribed: "VISIT OF/H.M. THE QUEEN AND/H.R.H. THE DUKE OF EDINBURGH/JUNE 28-29, 1978"

**1978, June 28**

| | | | | |
|---|---|---|---|---|
| 164 | A37 | 7p emerald & black | .30 | .30 |

Gannet A38

Birds: 7p, Firecrest. 11p, Dartford warbler. 13p, Spotted redshank.

**1978, Aug. 29    Photo.    Perf. 11½**

| | | | | |
|---|---|---|---|---|
| 165 | A38 | 5p multicolored | .20 | .20 |
| 166 | A38 | 7p multicolored | .20 | .20 |
| 167 | A38 | 11p multicolored | .30 | .30 |
| 168 | A38 | 13p multicolored | .30 | .30 |
| | | Nos. 165-168 (4) | 1.00 | 1.00 |

Solanum — A39

Christmas: 7p, Christmas rose. 11p, Holly, vert. 13p, Mistletoe, vert.

**1978, Oct. 31    Photo.    Perf. 11½**

| | | | | |
|---|---|---|---|---|
| 169 | A39 | 5p multicolored | .20 | .20 |
| 170 | A39 | 7p multicolored | .20 | .20 |
| 171 | A39 | 11p multicolored | .30 | .30 |
| 172 | A39 | 13p multicolored | .30 | .30 |
| | | Nos. 169-172 (4) | 1.00 | 1.00 |

1 Double, 1930 — A40

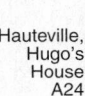

## 1979, Feb. 13

**Granite Paper**

| | | | | |
|---|---|---|---|---|
| 173 | A40 | ½p 1 double, 1930 | .20 | .20 |
| 174 | A40 | 1p 2 doubles, 1899 | .20 | .20 |
| 175 | A40 | 2p 4 doubles, 1902 | .20 | .20 |
| 176 | A40 | 4p 8 doubles, 1959 | .20 | .20 |
| 177 | A40 | 5p 3 pence, 1956 | .20 | .20 |
| 178 | A40 | 6p 5 new pence, 1968 | .20 | .20 |
| 179 | A40 | 7p 50 new pence, 1969 | .20 | .20 |
| 180 | A40 | 8p 10 new pence, 1970 | .20 | .20 |
| a. | | Horiz. strip of 5, #175, 2 each #178, 180 | 1.25 | |
| b. | | Horiz. strip of 4, #175, 178, 2 #174 | 1.00 | |
| | | Complete booklet of 10, 5 each #176, 180 | 2.25 | |
| 181 | A40 | 9p ½ new penny, 1971 | .20 | .20 |
| 182 | A40 | 10p 1 new penny, 1971 | .30 | .20 |
| 183 | A40 | 11p 2 new pence, 1971 | .30 | .20 |
| 184 | A40 | 12p 1 penny, 1977 | .30 | .20 |
| | | Complete booklet of 15, 5 each #176, 180, 184 | 3.50 | |
| 185 | A40 | 13p 2 pence, 1977 | .30 | .20 |
| | | Complete booklet of 10, 2 #176, 3 #181, 5 #185 | 2.25 | |
| | | Complete booklet of 15, 5 each #176, 181, 185 | 3.50 | |
| 186 | A40 | 14p 5 pence, 1977 | .35 | .20 |
| 187 | A40 | 15p 10 pence, 1977 | .35 | .20 |
| 188 | A40 | 20p 25 pence, 1977 | .45 | .20 |
| | | *Nos. 173-188 (16)* | 4.15 | 3.20 |

No. 177 is dark brown, No. 182, green & bronze. See Nos. 198B-203A.

Booklets were produced from sheets of 40, 30 and 20. These sheets were sold both as complete sheets and as strips, folded and affixed by the sheet selvage or inserted unattached into booklet covers.

Oldest Pillar Box, 1853 Cancel, Truck — A41

Europa: 8p, Telephone, 1897, telex machine.

## 1979, May 8　Photo.　Perf. 11½

| | | | | |
|---|---|---|---|---|
| 189 | A41 | 6p multicolored | .20 | .20 |
| 190 | A41 | 8p multicolored | .20 | .20 |

Steam Tram, 1879 A42

Public Transportation: 8p, Electric tram, 1896. 11p, Autobus, 1911. 13p, Autobus, 1979.

## 1979, Aug. 7　Photo.　Perf. 11½

| | | | | |
|---|---|---|---|---|
| 191 | A42 | 6p multicolored | .20 | .20 |
| 192 | A42 | 8p multicolored | .20 | .20 |
| 193 | A42 | 11p multicolored | .30 | .30 |
| 194 | A42 | 13p multicolored | .30 | .30 |
| | | *Nos. 191-194 (4)* | 1.00 | 1.00 |

Centenary of public transportation.

Postal Bureau and Headquarters — A43

Designs: 8p, Mail and telegram deliverymen. 13p, Parcel trucks. 15p, Post Office philatelic room.

## 1979, Oct. 1　Photo.　Perf. 11½

| | | | | |
|---|---|---|---|---|
| 195 | A43 | 6p multicolored | .20 | .20 |
| 196 | A43 | 8p multicolored | .20 | .20 |
| 197 | A43 | 13p multicolored | .30 | .30 |

| | | | | |
|---|---|---|---|---|
| 198 | A43 | 15p multicolored | .40 | .40 |
| a. | | Souvenir sheet of 4, Nos. 195-198 | 1.25 | 1.25 |
| | | *Nos. 195-198 (4)* | 1.10 | 1.10 |

Guernsey PO, 10th anniv.; Christmas 1979.

### Coin Type of 1979

Designs: 10p, like No. 182. 11½p, ½ pence, 1979. 50p, Battle of Hastings coin, 1966. £1, Queen Elizabeth II 25th anniv., 1977, horiz. £2, Queen Elizabeth II 25th wedding anniv., 1972, horiz. £5, Official seal.

## 1980-81　Photo.　Perf. 11½

| | | | | |
|---|---|---|---|---|
| 198B | A40 | 5p orange brown & multi | .45 | .45 |
| | | Complete booklet of 15, 5 each #180, 185, 198B | 2.00 | |
| | | Complete booklet of 10, #185, 4 #180, 5 #198B | 3.50 | |
| 199 | A40 | 10p orange & bronze | .25 | .20 |
| | | Complete booklet of 10, #177, 199, 2 each #173, 175, 3 each #174 | 2.00 | |
| | | Complete booklet of 10, #174, 2 each #173, 175, 179, 3 #199 | 2.50 | |
| 200 | A40 | 11½p red & bronze | .30 | .20 |

**Size: 26x45, 45x26mm**

| | | | | |
|---|---|---|---|---|
| 201 | A40 | 50p red org & sil | 1.50 | 1.25 |
| 202 | A40 | £1 green & sil | 2.75 | 2.25 |
| 203 | A40 | £2 blue & silver | 5.25 | 3.50 |
| 203A | A40 | £5 multi ('81) | 12.00 | 12.00 |
| | | *Nos. 198B-203A (7)* | 22.50 | 19.85 |

No. 177 is dark brown.
For booklets, see note following No. 188.
Issue dates: £5, May 22, others, Feb. 5.

Policewoman Helping Child — A44

Guernsey Police Force, 60th Anniv.: 15p, Policeman on motorcycle. 17½p, Police dog and officer.

## 1980, May 6　Litho.　Perf. 14

| | | | | |
|---|---|---|---|---|
| 204 | A44 | 7p multicolored | .20 | .20 |
| 205 | A44 | 15p multicolored | .40 | .40 |
| 206 | A44 | 17½p multicolored | .45 | .45 |
| | | *Nos. 204-206 (3)* | 1.05 | 1.05 |

Major Gen. John Gaspard Le Marchant — A45

Europa: 13½p, Admiral James Lord de Saumarez (1757-1836).

## 1980, May 6　Photo.　Perf. 11½

**Granite Paper**

| | | | | |
|---|---|---|---|---|
| 207 | A45 | 10p multicolored | .25 | .25 |
| 208 | A45 | 13½p multicolored | .40 | .40 |

Guernsey Golden Goat — A46

Designs: Various Guernsey golden goats.

## 1980, Aug. 5　Photo.　Perf. 13

| | | | | |
|---|---|---|---|---|
| 209 | A46 | 7p multicolored | .20 | .20 |
| 210 | A46 | 10p multicolored | .20 | .20 |
| 211 | A46 | 15p multicolored | .40 | .40 |
| 212 | A46 | 17½p multicolored | .50 | .50 |
| | | *Nos. 209-212 (4)* | 1.30 | 1.30 |

Sark Cottage, by Peter Le Lievre, 1847 — A47

Christmas 1980 (Le Lievre Paintings): 10p, Moulin Huet, 1850. 13½p, Boats at Sea, 1850. 15p, Cow Lane, 1852, vert. 17½p, Portrait, by Le Lievre's sister, vert.

## 1980, Nov. 15　Photo.　Perf. 12

**Granite Paper**

| | | | | |
|---|---|---|---|---|
| 213 | A47 | 7p multicolored | .20 | .20 |
| 214 | A47 | 10p multicolored | .25 | .25 |
| 215 | A47 | 13½p multicolored | .40 | .40 |
| 216 | A47 | 15p multicolored | .45 | .45 |
| 217 | A47 | 17½p multicolored | .50 | .50 |
| | | *Nos. 213-217 (5)* | 1.80 | 1.80 |

Common Blue A48

## 1981, Feb. 24　Photo.　Perf. 14½

| | | | | |
|---|---|---|---|---|
| 218 | A48 | 8p shown | .20 | .20 |
| 219 | A48 | 12p Red Admiral | .20 | .20 |
| 220 | A48 | 22p Small Tortoiseshell | .60 | .60 |
| 221 | A48 | 25p Wall Brown | .70 | .70 |
| | | *Nos. 218-221 (4)* | 1.70 | 1.70 |

Le Petit Bonhomme Andriou (Head-shaped Rock) — A49

## 1981, May 22　Litho.　Perf. 14½

| | | | | |
|---|---|---|---|---|
| 222 | A49 | 12p shown | .35 | .35 |
| 223 | A49 | 18p Guernsey lily | .55 | .55 |

Europa.

Prince Charles and Lady Diana — A50

Royal Wedding: a, Charles. c, Diana.

## 1981, July 29　Litho.　Perf. 14½x15

| | | | | |
|---|---|---|---|---|
| 224 | | Strip of 3 | .90 | .90 |
| a.-c. | A50 | 8p any single | .30 | .30 |
| 225 | | Strip of 3 | 1.25 | 1.25 |
| a.-c. | A50 | 12p any single | .40 | .40 |

**Size: 49x32mm**

| | | | | |
|---|---|---|---|---|
| 226 | A50 | 25p Royal family | .90 | .90 |
| a. | | Souv. sheet, #224-226, perf. 14x14½ | 3.25 | 3.25 |
| | | *Nos. 224-226 (3)* | 3.05 | 3.05 |

Sark Launch — A51

Designs: Interisland transportation.

## 1981, Aug. 25　Photo.　Perf. 11½

**Granite Paper**

| | | | | |
|---|---|---|---|---|
| 227 | A51 | 8p shown | .20 | .20 |
| 228 | A51 | 12p Trislander plane | .35 | .35 |
| 229 | A51 | 18p Hydrofoil | .55 | .55 |

| | | | | |
|---|---|---|---|---|
| 230 | A51 | 22p Herm catamaran | .75 | .75 |
| 231 | A51 | 25p Alderney coaster | .80 | .80 |
| | | *Nos. 227-231 (5)* | 2.65 | 2.65 |

Rifle-shooting Competition A52

## 1981, Nov. 17　Litho.　Perf. 14¾

| | | | | |
|---|---|---|---|---|
| 232 | A52 | 8p shown | .20 | .20 |
| 233 | A52 | 12p Riding | .35 | .35 |
| 234 | A52 | 22p Swimming | .70 | .70 |
| 235 | A52 | 25p Electronics workers | .80 | .80 |
| | | *Nos. 232-235 (4)* | 2.05 | 2.05 |

Intl. Year of the Disabled.

### Print Type of 1978

## 1982, Feb. 2　Litho. & Engr.

| | | | | |
|---|---|---|---|---|
| 236 | A35 | 8p Jethou | .20 | .20 |
| 237 | A35 | 12p Fermain Bay | .35 | .35 |
| 238 | A35 | 22p The Terres | .70 | .70 |
| 239 | A35 | 25p St. Pierre Port | .80 | .80 |
| | | *Nos. 236-239 (4)* | 2.05 | 2.05 |

La Societe Guernesiaise Centenary A53

Society Emblem and Activities: 8p, Sir Edgar MacCulloch, founding president. 13p, William the Conqueror's fleet, Battle of Hastings (history). 20p, Sir James Saumarez's Crescent rescued from French fleet (history). 24p, Dragonfly (entomology). 26p, Vale Parish Church bird sanctuary (ornithology). 29p, Samian bowl, King's Road excavation (archaeology). 13p and 20p show CEPT (Europa) emblem.

## 1982, Apr. 28　Photo.　Perf. 11½

**Granite Paper**

| | | | | |
|---|---|---|---|---|
| 240 | A53 | 8p multicolored | .30 | .30 |
| 241 | A53 | 13p multicolored | .40 | .40 |
| 242 | A53 | 20p multicolored | .65 | .65 |
| 243 | A53 | 24p multicolored | .80 | .80 |
| 244 | A53 | 26p multicolored | .80 | .80 |
| 245 | A53 | 29p multicolored | .85 | .85 |
| | | *Nos. 240-245 (6)* | 3.80 | 3.80 |

Scouting Year — A54

## 1982, July 13　Litho.　Perf. 14½

| | | | | |
|---|---|---|---|---|
| 246 | A54 | 8p Sea scouts, Castle Cornet, St. Peter Port | .25 | .25 |
| 247 | A54 | 13p Boy scouts building bridge | .35 | .35 |
| 248 | A54 | 26p Cub scouts parading | .80 | .80 |
| 249 | A54 | 29p Air scouts reading chart | .85 | .85 |
| | | *Nos. 246-249 (4)* | 2.25 | 2.25 |

Christmas 1982 — A55

## 1982, Oct. 12　Photo.　Perf. 14½

| | | | | |
|---|---|---|---|---|
| 250 | A55 | 8p Midnight mass, St. Peter Port Church | .20 | .20 |
| 251 | A55 | 13p Exchanging presents | .35 | .35 |
| 252 | A55 | 24p Dinner | .70 | .70 |
| 253 | A55 | 26p Exchanging cards | .75 | .75 |
| 254 | A55 | 29p Watching Queen's TV greeting | .90 | .90 |
| | | *Nos. 250-254 (5)* | 2.90 | 2.90 |

Centenary of Boys' Brigade — A56

Designs: Various brigade activities.

**1983, Jan. 18          Perf. 14**
255 A56  8p multicolored          .25   .25
256 A56  13p multicolored         .40   .40
257 A56  24p multicolored         .75   .75
258 A56  28p multicolored         .80   .80
259 A56  29p multicolored        1.00  1.00
    Nos. 255-259 (5)             3.20  3.20

Europa 1983 — A57

Views of the development of St. Peter Port Harbor.

**1983, Mar. 14    Photo.    Perf. 11½**
**Granite Paper**
260 A57  13p multicolored         .40   .40
261 A57  13p multicolored         .40   .40
  a.   Pair, #260-261             .90   .90
262 A57  20p multicolored         .65   .65
263 A57  20p multicolored         .65   .65
  a.   Pair, #262-263            1.40  1.40

View at Guernsey, by Renoir — A58

Centenary of Renoir's Visit: 13p, Children at the Seashore (26x39mm). 26p, Marine Guernsey. 28p, Moulin Huet Bay through the Trees. 31p, Fog in Guernsey.

**Perf. 12, 11½x12 (13p)**
**1983, Sept. 6               Photo.**
**Granite Paper**
264 A58  9p multicolored          .30   .30
265 A58  13p multicolored         .40   .40
266 A58  26p multicolored         .85   .85
267 A58  28p multicolored         .90   .90
268 A58  31p multicolored        1.00  1.00
    Nos. 264-268 (5)             3.45  3.45

Star of the West, 1869 Merchant Ship, Capt. J.G. Lenfestey — A59

**1983, Nov. 15    Photo.    Perf. 14½**
269 A59  9p Launching             .30   .30
270 A59  13p Leaving St. Peter
             Port                 .40   .40
271 A59  26p Rio Grande Bar       .85   .85
272 A59  28p St. Lucia            .90   .90
273 A59  31p Voyage Map          1.00  1.00
    Nos. 269-273 (5)             3.45  3.45

Dame of Sark (Sibyl Hathaway, 1884-1974) — A60

Biographical Scenes: 9p, Portrait, La Seigneurie (residence). 13p, German occupation, 1940-45. 26p, Royal visit, 1957. 28p, Chief Pleas (parliament). 31p, Dame of Sark rose.

---

**1984, Feb. 7     Litho.    Perf. 14½**
274 A60  9p multicolored          .30   .30
275 A60  13p multicolored         .40   .40
276 A60  26p multicolored         .85   .85
277 A60  28p multicolored         .90   .90
278 A60  31p multicolored        1.00  1.00
    Nos. 274-278 (5)             3.45  3.45

Links with the Commonwealth — A61

Designs: 9p, Flag of Guernsey, Royal Court. 31p, Union Jack, Castle Cornet.

**1984, Apr. 10    Litho.    Perf. 14½**
279 A61  9p multicolored          .30   .30
280 A61  31p multicolored        1.25  1.25

Europa (1959-84) — A62

**1984, Apr. 10              Perf. 15**
281 A62  13p multicolored         .50   .50
282 A62  20½p multicolored        .75   .75

Petit Port — A63

**Perf. 15x14½, 14½x15**
**1984-85                          Litho.**
283 A63  1p Little Chapel,
             vert. ('85)          .20   .20
284 A63  2p Ft. Grey ('85)        .20   .20
285 A63  3p St. Apolline
             Chapel, vert.        .20   .20
286 A63  4p shown                 .20   .20
287 A63  5p Little Russel ('85)   .20   .20
288 A63  6p The Harbour,
             Herm ('85)           .20   .20
289 A63  7p Saints ('85)          .20   .20
290 A63  8p St. Saviour, vert.
             ('85)                .20   .20
291 A63  9p Cambridge Berth       .20   .20
292 A63  10p Belvoir, Herm        .35   .20
  a.   Min. sheet, 2 2p, 4 4p, 2 5p, 2
       10p                       2.50
293 A63  11p La Seigneurie,
             Sark ('85)           .20   .20
294 A63  13p St. Saviour's
             Reservoir            .35   .35
  a.   Min. sheet, 4 9p, 6 14p    4.50
  b.   Min. sheet, 5 each 4p, 9p, 13p  5.00
295 A63  14p St. Peter Port,
             vert.                .20   .20
  a.   Min. sheet, 4 9p, 6 14p    4.50
  b.   Min. sheet, 2 9p, 8 14p    4.75
  c.   Min. sheet, 5 10p, 5 14p   4.50
296 A63  15p Havelet, vert.
             ('85)                .35   .20
  a.   Min. sheet, 3p, 2 4p, 4 11p, 3
       15p                       3.75
  b.   Min. sheet, 5 each 11p, 15p  4.50
297 A63  20p La Coupee, Sark      .60   .20
  a.   Booklet pane, 4 6p, 4 14p, 2
       20p                       3.00
  b.   Booklet pane, 5 14p, 5 20p  3.50
298 A63  30p Grandes Roc-
             ques ('85)          1.00  1.00
299 A63  40p St. Torteval
             Church, vert.       1.25  1.25
300 A63  50p Bordeaux            1.60  1.60
301 A63  £1 Albecq               3.50  3.50
302 A63  £2 L'Ancresse ('85)     7.00  7.00
    Nos. 283-302 (20)           18.20 17.50

Issued: 1p, 2p, 5p, 6p, 7p, 8p, 11p, 15p, 30p, £2, 7/23/84; 3p, 4p, 9p, 10p, 13p, 14p, 20p, 40p, 50p, £1, 9/18/84; #292a, 12/2/85; #294a-294b, 9/18/84; #295a-295b, 3/19/85; #295c, 4/1/86; #296a-296b, 3/30/87; #297a-297b, 12/27/89.
Miniature sheets have surrounding selvage and were sold folded and unattached in booklet covers. Nos. 297a, 297b with straight edges around stamps and attached to booklet covers by tabs.
See Nos. 372-378, 453-454.

---

Lieutenant-General John Doyle (1756-1834) — A64

Designs: 13p, Portrait by James Ramsey, 1817. 29p, American War of Independence battle. 31p, Land fill, Grand Havre Bay. 34p, Ship approaching Casquets Reef, 1811. 29p, 31p, horiz.

**1984, Nov. 20    Photo.    Perf. 11½**
303 A64  13p multicolored         .40   .40
304 A64  29p multicolored         .95   .95
305 A64  31p multicolored        1.00  1.00
306 A64  34p multicolored        1.10  1.00
    Nos. 303-306 (4)             3.45  3.35

Christmas 1984 — A65

Twelve Days of Christmas: a, Partridge in a Pear Tree. b, 2 Turtle Doves. c, 3 French Hens. d, 4 Colly Birds. e, 5 Golden Rings. f, 6 Geese-a-Laying. g, 7 Swans a-Swimming. h, 8 Maids a-Milking. i, 9 Drummers Drumming. j, 10 Pipers Piping. k, 11 Ladies Dancing. l, 12 Lords a-Leaping. Illustration reduced.

**1984, Nov. 20    Litho.    Perf. 14½**
307 A65  Sheet of 12            2.50  2.50
  a.-l.   5p any single          .20   .20

Indigenous Fish — A66

**1985, Jan. 22    Photo.    Perf. 12**
308 A66  9p Cockoo Wrasse         .40   .40
309 A66  13p Red Gurnard          .65   .65
310 A66  29p Red Mullet          1.25  1.25
311 A66  31p Mackerel            1.60  1.60
312 A66  34p Sunfish             1.75  1.75
    Nos. 308-312 (5)             5.65  5.65

Liberation from German Forces, 40th Anniv. — A67

**1985, May 9    Litho.    Perf. 14x14½**
313 A67  22p Peace dove          1.00  1.00

Celebrating the end of the war in Europe (VE-Day).

Europa 1985 — A68

Designs: 14p, Musical staff, flags of Great Britain, Netherlands, Germany, Italy, Cross of St. George. 22p, Music, cello, French horn.

---

**1985, May 14    Litho.    Perf. 14½**
314 A68  14p multicolored         .55   .55
315 A68  22p multicolored         .90   .90

Intl. Youth Year — A69

**1985, May 14    Litho.    Perf. 14**
316 A69  9p IYY emblem, circle
             of children          .35   .35
317 A69  31p Girl Guides in camp 1.25  1.25

Children's drawings.

Girl Guides, 75th Anniv. — A70

**1985, May 14    Litho.    Perf. 14**
318 A70  34p Leader, guide and
             brownie             1.40  1.40

Child's drawing.

Christmas 1985 — A71

Religious and folk figures: a, Santa Claus. b, Lussibruden. c, Balthasar. d, St. Nicholas. e, La Befana. f, Julenisse. g, Christkind. h, King Wenceslas. i, Shepherd of Les Baux. j, Caspar. k, Baboushka. l, Melchior.

**1985, Nov. 19    Litho.    Perf. 12½**
**Granite Paper**
319 A71  Sheet of 12            5.00  5.00
  a.-l.   5p any single          .40   .40

Watercolors by Paul Jacob Naftel — A72

**1985, Nov. 19              Perf. 15x14½**
320 A72  9p Vraicing             .35   .35
321 A72  14p Castle Cornet       .55   .55
322 A72  22p Rocquaine Bay       .90   .90
323 A72  31p Little Russel      1.25  1.25
324 A72  34p Seaweed Gatherers  1.40  1.40
    Nos. 320-324 (5)            4.45  4.45

Adm. Lord De Saumarez, 150th Death Anniv. — A73

Designs: 9p, Squadron off Nargue Is., 1809. 14p, Battle of the Nile, 1798. 29p, Battle of St. Vincent, 1797. 31p, HMS Crescent off Cherbourg, 1793. 34p, Battle of the Saints, 1782.

**1986, Feb. 4    Litho.    Perf. 12x11½**
**Granite Paper**

| | | | | |
|---|---|---|---|---|
| 325 | A73 | 9p multicolored | .35 | .35 |
| 326 | A73 | 14p multicolored | .55 | .55 |
| 327 | A73 | 29p multicolored | 1.10 | 1.10 |
| 328 | A73 | 31p multicolored | 1.25 | 1.25 |
| 329 | A73 | 34p multicolored | 1.40 | 1.40 |
| | | *Nos. 325-329 (5)* | 4.65 | 4.65 |

Queen Elizabeth
II, 60th
Birthday — A74

**1986, Apr. 21                    Perf. 14**
330   A74   60p multicolored         2.40  2.40

Europa
1986 — A75

**1986, May 22                    Perf. 11½**
**Granite Paper**

| | | | | |
|---|---|---|---|---|
| 331 | A75 | 10p Operation Gannet | .40 | .40 |
| 332 | A75 | 14p Whitsun orchid | .55 | .55 |
| 333 | A75 | 22p Guernsey elm | .90 | .90 |
| | | *Nos. 331-333 (3)* | 1.85 | 1.85 |

Wedding of
Prince Andrew
and Sarah
Ferguson — A76

**1986, July 23    Litho.    Perf. 14**
334   A76   14p Couple               .60   .60
**Size: 48x32mm**
335   A76   34p Couple, diff.        1.50  1.50

Sports
A77

**1986, July 24                    Perf. 14½**

| | | | | |
|---|---|---|---|---|
| 336 | A77 | 10p Lawn bowling, vert. | .40 | .40 |
| 337 | A77 | 14p Cricket, vert. | .55 | .55 |
| 338 | A77 | 22p Badminton, vert. | .90 | .90 |
| 339 | A77 | 29p Field hockey, vert. | 1.10 | 1.10 |
| 340 | A77 | 31p Swimming | 1.25 | 1.25 |
| 341 | A77 | 34p Rifle shooting | 1.40 | 1.40 |
| | | *Nos. 336-341 (6)* | 5.60 | 5.60 |

Museums
A78

**1986, Nov. 18    Litho.    Perf. 14½**

| | | | | |
|---|---|---|---|---|
| 342 | A78 | 14p Guernsey Museum and Art Gallery | .55 | .55 |
| 343 | A78 | 29p Ft. Grey Maritime Museum | 1.10 | 1.10 |
| 344 | A78 | 31p Castle Cornet | 1.25 | 1.25 |
| 345 | A78 | 34p Natl. Trust of Guernsey Folk Museum | 1.40 | 1.40 |
| | | *Nos. 342-345 (4)* | 4.30 | 4.30 |

---

Miniature Sheet

Christmas — A79

Carols: a, "While Shepherds Watched Their Flocks by Night." b, "In the Bleak Mid-Winter." c, "O Little Town of Bethlehem." d, "The Holly and the Ivy." e, "O Little Christmas Tree." f, "Away in a Manger." g, "Good King Wenceslas." h, "We Three Kings of Orient Are." i, "Hark the Herald Angels Sing." j, "I Saw Three Ships." k, "Little Donkey." l, "Jingle Bells."

**1986, Nov. 18                    Perf. 12½**
346   A79   Sheet of 12              2.75  2.75
  a.-l.    6p any single             .20   .20

Souvenir Sheet

Duke of Richmond, 18th Century Map
Detail — A80

**1987, Feb. 10    Litho.    Perf. 14½**
347          Sheet of 4              4.50  4.50
  a.   A80   14p shown               .55   .55
  b.   A80   29p North               1.10  1.10
  c.   A80   31p Southwest           1.25  1.25
  d.   A80   34p Southeast           1.40  1.40

Duke of Richmond's survey of Guernsey, bicent.

Europa
1987 — A81

Modern architecture.

**1987, May 5    Litho.    Perf. 13x13½**

| | | | | |
|---|---|---|---|---|
| 348 | A81 | 15p Postal headquarters | .60 | .60 |
| 349 | A81 | 15p Headquarters, schematic view | .60 | .60 |
| a. | | Pair, #348-349 | 1.25 | 1.25 |
| 350 | A81 | 22p Grammar school entrance | .90 | .90 |
| 351 | A81 | 22p School, schematic view | .90 | .90 |
| a. | | Pair, #350-351 | 1.90 | 1.90 |

Andros and
La Plaiderie
Court
House,
Guernsey
A82

Andros and: 29p, Governor's Palace, Virginia. 31p, "Governor Andros and the Boston People," print from Harper's New Monthly Magazine. 34p, Map of New Amsterdam (New York City).

---

**1987, July 7                    Perf. 12**
**Granite Paper**

| | | | | |
|---|---|---|---|---|
| 352 | A82 | 15p multicolored | .60 | .60 |
| 353 | A82 | 29p multicolored | 1.10 | 1.10 |
| 354 | A82 | 31p multicolored | 1.25 | 1.25 |
| 355 | A82 | 34p multicolored | 1.40 | 1.40 |
| | | *Nos. 352-355 (4)* | 4.35 | 4.35 |

Sir Edmund Andros (1637-1714), lieutenant-governor of Guernsey (1704-1706) and statesman of Colonial America (1672-1710).

William the
Conqueror (c.
1028-1087), King
of England (1066-
1087) — A83

11p, Jester warning young William of a plot to murder him. #357, Battle of Hastings. #358, King William, his banner at the Battle of Hastings. #359, William the Conqueror. #360, Abbey at Caen & Queen Matilda of Flanders (d. 1083). 34p, Halley's Comet & regalia of William I.

**1987, Sept. 9                    Perf. 13½x14**

| | | | | |
|---|---|---|---|---|
| 356 | A83 | 11p multicolored | .45 | .50 |
| 357 | A83 | 15p multicolored | .60 | .65 |
| 358 | A83 | 15p multicolored | .60 | .65 |
| a. | | Pair, #357-358 | 1.25 | 1.40 |
| 359 | A83 | 22p multicolored | .90 | .95 |
| 360 | A83 | 22p multicolored | .90 | .95 |
| a. | | Pair, #359-360 | 1.90 | 2.00 |
| 361 | A83 | 34p multicolored | 1.40 | 1.50 |
| | | *Nos. 356-361 (6)* | 4.85 | 5.20 |

Visit of John Wesley (1703-1791),
Religious Reformer, Bicent. — A84

Designs: 7p, Preaching at the quay, Alderney. 15p, Preaching at Mon Plaisir. 29p, Preaching at Assembly Rooms, St. Peter Port. 31p, Wesley and La Ville Baudu, an early Methodist meeting place, Vale Parish. 34p, Wesley and Ebenezer Methodist Church, first Methodist chapel, Union Street, 1816.

**1987, Nov. 17    Litho.    Perf. 14½**

| | | | | |
|---|---|---|---|---|
| 362 | A84 | 7p multicolored | .30 | .30 |
| 363 | A84 | 15p multicolored | .60 | .60 |
| 364 | A84 | 29p multicolored | 1.10 | 1.10 |
| 365 | A84 | 31p multicolored | 1.25 | 1.25 |
| 366 | A84 | 34p multicolored | 1.40 | 1.40 |
| | | *Nos. 362-366 (5)* | 4.65 | 4.65 |

Voyage of the Golden Spur, Apr. 12,
1872-Jan. 4, 1874 — A85

Designs: 11p, Off St. Sampson's Harbor. 15p, Entering Hong Kong Harbor. 29p, Anchored off Macao. 31p, In China Tea Race. 34p, Golden Spur, map of voyage.

**1988, Feb. 9    Litho.    Perf. 13½x14**

| | | | | |
|---|---|---|---|---|
| 367 | A85 | 11p multicolored | .45 | .45 |
| 368 | A85 | 15p multicolored | .60 | .60 |
| 369 | A85 | 29p multicolored | 1.10 | 1.10 |
| 370 | A85 | 31p multicolored | 1.25 | 1.25 |
| 371 | A85 | 34p multicolored | 1.40 | 1.40 |
| | | *Nos. 367-371 (5)* | 4.80 | 4.80 |

Guernsey's Golden Age of Shipping: largest vessel built on Guernsey, the Golden Spur, launched Oct. 15, 1864, wrecked at Haiphong on Feb. 27, 1879.

---

**Landscape Type of 1984**
**Perf. 14½x15, 15x14½**
**1988-89                             Litho.**

| | | | | |
|---|---|---|---|---|
| 372 | A63 | 12p Petit Bot beach, vert. | .50 | .50 |
| 373 | A63 | 16p St. John's Hostel for the Aged | .65 | .65 |
| a. | | Min. sheet, 5 each 12p, 16p | 6.50 | |
| b. | | Min. sheet, 4 4p, 3 12p, 3 16p | 5.00 | |
| 374 | A63 | 18p Le Variouf, vert. | .70 | .70 |
| a. | | Booklet pane, 4p, 6p, 3 12p, 3 18p | 4.00 | |
| b. | | Booklet pane, 4 12p, 4 18p | 3.50 | |
| | | *Nos. 372-374 (3)* | 1.85 | 1.85 |

Nos. 373a-373b have surrounding selvage and were sold unattached in booklet covers. Nos. 374a, 374b with straight edges around stamps and attached to booklet covers by tabs.
Issued: Nos. 372-373b, 3/28/88; Nos. 374-374b, 2/28/89.

**Coil Stamps**
**Sizes: 21½x17½mm, 17½x21½mm**
**Perf. 14x14½, 14½x14**

| | | | | |
|---|---|---|---|---|
| 375 | A63 | 11p La Seigneurie, Sark | .45 | .45 |
| 376 | A63 | 12p Petit Bot beach | .50 | .50 |
| 377 | A63 | 15p Havelet, vert. | .60 | .60 |
| 378 | A63 | 16p St. John's Hostel for the Aged | .65 | .65 |
| | | *Nos. 375-378 (4)* | 2.20 | 2.20 |

Issued: 11p, 15p, 5/15/87; 12p, 16p, 3/28/88.

Waves, Map — A85a

**Perf. 14½x14**
**1989, Apr. 3    Photo.    Coil Stamp**
380   A85a   (18p) green              1.00  1.00

Inscribed "MINIMUM FIRST CLASS POSTAGE TO UK PAID." See No. 431.

Europa
1988
A86

Communication and transportation: No. 381, Bedford Rascal postal van, Lihou Is. rowboat. No. 382, Rowboat, Viscount plane. No. 383, Horse and buggy, front wheel of bicycle. No. 384, Back wheel of bicycle, No. 4 coach.

**1988, May 10    Litho.    Perf. 14½**

| | | | | |
|---|---|---|---|---|
| 381 | A86 | 16p multicolored | .65 | .65 |
| 382 | A86 | 16p multicolored | .65 | .65 |
| a. | | Pair, #381-382 | 1.40 | 1.40 |
| 383 | A86 | 22p multicolored | .90 | .90 |
| 384 | A86 | 22p multicolored | .90 | .90 |
| a. | | Pair, #383-384 | 1.90 | 1.90 |
| | | *Nos. 381-384 (4)* | 3.10 | 3.10 |

#382a, 384a have continuous designs.

Frederick
Corbin Lukis
(1788-1871),
Archaeologist
A87

Designs: 12p, Entrance to Lukis House, St. Peter Port, and portrait. 16p, Bound manuscript containing illustrations painted by Lukis's daughter Mary Anne (born 1822). 29p, Lukis supervising excavation of Le Creux es Faies dolmen at L'Eree, Guernsey. 31p, Rear of Lukis House and garden. 34p, Artifacts recovered by Lukis and preserved as part of the museum collection.

**1988, July 12    Photo.    Perf. 12½**
**Granite Paper**

| | | | | |
|---|---|---|---|---|
| 385 | A87 | 12p multicolored | .50 | .50 |
| 386 | A87 | 16p multicolored | .65 | .65 |
| 387 | A87 | 29p multicolored | 1.10 | 1.10 |
| 388 | A87 | 31p multicolored | 1.25 | 1.25 |
| 389 | A87 | 34p multicolored | 1.40 | 1.40 |
| | | *Nos. 385-389 (5)* | 4.90 | 4.90 |

1988 World Offshore Powerboat Championships — A88

Designs: 16p, Racing boats, Royal Navy helicopter. 30p, Boats racing through Gouliot Passage (separating Sark from Brecqhou). 32p, Boats, helicopter, St. John's Ambulance rescue ship, vert. 35p, Race course marked in red on Admiralty Chart, vert.

1988, Sept. 6 *Perf. 12*

Granite Paper

390 A88 16p multicolored .65 .65
391 A88 30p multicolored 1.25 1.25
392 A88 32p multicolored 1.25 1.25
393 A88 35p multicolored 1.40 1.40
Nos. 390-393 (4) 4.55 4.55

Publication of *Flora Sarniensis,* Bicent. — A89

Designs: 12p, Joshua Gosselin (1739-1813), botanist, and herbarium made by Rollo Sherwill in 1976. No. 395, *Lagurus ovatus* (pressed specimen). No. 396, *Lagurus ovatus,* diff. No. 397, *Silene gallica quinquevulnera* (pressed specimen). No. 398, *Silene gallica quinquevulnera,* diff. 35p, *Limonium binervosum sarniense serquense.*

1988, Nov. 15 **Litho.** *Perf. 14*

394 A89 12p shown .50 .50
395 A89 16p multicolored .65 .65
396 A89 16p multicolored .65 .65
a. Pair, #395-396 1.40 1.40
397 A89 23p multicolored .90 .90
398 A89 23p multicolored .90 .90
a. Pair, #397-398 1.90 1.90
399 A89 35p multicolored 1.40 1.40
Nos. 394-399 (6) 5.00 5.00

Miniature Sheet

Ecclesiastical Links to France and Great Britain — A90

Church interiors, exteriors and artifacts: a, Coutances Cathedral, France. b, Notre Dame du Rosaire Church interior, Guernsey. c, Stained-glass window, St. Sampson's Church, Guernsey. d, Dol-de-Bretagne Cathedral, France. e, Bishop's Throne, Town Church, Guernsey. f, Winchester Cathedral, England. g, St. John's Cathedral, Portsmouth, England. h, High Altar, St. Joseph's Church, Guernsey. i, Mont Saint-Michel, France. j, Chancel, Vale Church, Guernsey. k, The Lychgate, Forest Church, Guernsey. l, Marmoutier Abbey, France.

1988, Nov. 15 *Perf. 14½x15*

400 A90 Sheet of 12 4.00 4.00
a.-l. 8p any single .30 .30

Christmas 1988.

Europa 1989 — A91

Traditional children's toys and games.

1989, Feb. 28 **Litho.** *Perf. 13½*

401 A91 12p Tip cat (Le Cat) *.50 .50*
402 A91 16p Girl, Cobo Alice doll *.65 .65*
403 A91 23p Hopscotch (Le Colimachaon) *.90 .90*
Nos. 401-403 (3) 2.05 2.05

Aircraft A92

1989, May 5

404 A92 12p DH86 Express .50 .50
a. Booklet pane of 6 3.25
405 A92 12p Southampton .50 .50
406 A92 18p DH89 Rapide .70 .70
a. Booklet pane of 6 4.75
407 A92 18p Sunderland .70 .70
408 A92 35p BAe 146 1.40 1.40
a. Booklet pane of 6 9.50
Complete booklet, #404a, 406a, 408a 17.50
409 A92 35p Shackleton 1.40 1.40
Nos. 404-409 (6) 5.20 5.20

Guernsey Airport, 50th anniv. (Nos. 404, 406, 408); others, 201st Squadron Affiliation, 50th anniv.

Visit of Queen Elizabeth II, May 23-24 — A93

1989, May 23 *Perf. 15x14*

410 A93 30p Portrait by June Mendoza 1.25 1.25

Great Western Railway Steamer Service Between Weymouth and the Channel Isls., Cent. — A94

1989, Sept. 5 **Litho.** *Perf. 13½*

411 A94 12p S.S. *Ibex,* 1891 .50 .50
412 A94 18p P.S. *Great Western,* 1872 .70 .70
413 A94 29p S.S. *St. Julien,* 1925 1.10 1.10
414 A94 34p S.S. *Roebuck,* 1925 1.40 1.40
415 A94 37p S.S. *Antelope,* 1889 1.50 1.50
a. Souvenir sheet of 5, #411-415 5.50 5.50
Nos. 411-415 (5) 5.20 5.20

Zoological Trust of Guernsey — A95

1989, Nov. 17 **Litho.** *Perf. 14x13½*

416 A95 18p Two-toed sloth .70 .70
417 A95 29p Capuchin monkey 1.10 1.10
418 A95 32p White-lipped tamarin 1.25 1.25
419 A95 34p Squirrel monkey 1.40 1.40
420 A95 37p Lar gibbon 1.50 1.50
a. Strip of 5, #416-420 6.00 6.00

Animals of the rainforest.

Miniature Sheet

Christmas — A96

Ornaments on tree: a, Star. b, Angel. c, Candles. d, Robin red breast. e, Presents on sled. f, Caroler. g, Santa Claus pictured on Christmas cracker. h, Herald and stars pictured on glass ball. i, Presents in stocking. j, Bell. k, Reindeer. l, Chapel.

1989, Nov. 17 *Perf. 13*

421 A96 Sheet of 12 5.00 5.00
a.-l. 10p any single .40 .40

Europa 1990 — A97

Post offices.

1990, Feb. 27 **Litho.** *Perf. 13½x14*

422 A97 20p Sark, c. 1890 *.80 .80*
423 A97 20p Sark, 1990 *.80 .80*
424 A97 24p Arcade, c. 1840 *.95 .95*
425 A97 24p Arcade, 1990 *.95 .95*
Nos. 422-425 (4) 3.50 3.50

Penny Black, 150th Anniv. A98

Designs: 14p, Great Britain No. 1, Maltese Cross cancellation in red, mail steamer in St. Peter Port Harbor. 20p, Great Britain No. 3, Maltese Cross cancellation in black, pedestrians, mailbox at Elm Grove and Union Street in 1852. 32p, Great Britain No. 255 bisected, 1940, and military band. 34p, Guernsey No. 2, crown of William the Conqueror, Guernsey lily. 37p, Guernsey No. 10, crowd in line outside Guernsey P.O.

1990, May 3 *Perf. 14*

426 A98 14p multicolored .55 .55
427 A98 20p multicolored .80 .80
428 A98 32p multicolored 1.25 1.25
429 A98 34p multicolored 1.40 1.40
430 A98 37p multicolored 1.50 1.50
a. Souvenir sheet of 5, #426-430 6.00 6.00
b. No. 430a ovptd. "NZ 1990" emblem, "FROM LONDON 90 TO NEW ZEALAND 90" 16.00 16.00
Nos. 426-430 (5) 5.50 5.50

Map and Waves Type of 1989

1989, Dec. 27 **Photo.** *Perf. 14½x14*

Coil Stamp

431 A85a (14p) ultra & lt ultra .85 .85

Inscribed "MINIMUM BAILIWICK POSTAGE PAID."

Lord Anson's Circumnavigation of the World, 250th Anniv. — A99

Designs: 14p, Philip Saumarez writing ship's log. 20p, *Centurion, Gloucester, Severn, Pearle, Wager* and *Tryal* departing from Portsmouth. 29p, Landfall at St. Catherine's Is. off Brazil, 1740. 34p, *Tryal* rounding Cape Horn, 1741. 37p, Camp at Juan Fernandez, 1741.

1990, July 24 **Litho.** *Perf. 13½x14*

436 A99 14p multicolored .55 .55
437 A99 20p multicolored .80 .80
438 A99 29p multicolored 1.10 1.10
439 A99 34p multicolored 1.40 1.40
440 A99 37p multicolored 1.50 1.50
Nos. 436-440 (5) 5.35 5.35

Gray Seal A100

1990, Oct. 16 **Litho.** *Perf. 14½*

441 A100 20p shown *1.00* .60
442 A100 26p Bottlenose dolphin *2.00* 1.00
443 A100 31p Basking shark *2.25* 1.25
444 A100 37p Harbor porpoise *2.50* 1.50
Nos. 441-444 (4) 7.75 4.35

World Wildlife Fund.

Miniature Sheet

Christmas — A101

Winter birds: a, Blue and Great Tits. b, Snow Bunting. c, Kestrel. d, Starling. e, Greenfinch. f, Robin. g, Wren. h, Barn owl. i, Mistle Thrush. j, Heron. k, Chaffinch. l, Kingfisher.

1990, Oct. 16 *Perf. 13½*

445 A101 Sheet of 12 5.00 5.00
a.-l. 10p any single .40 .40

Occupation Stamp No. N1, 50th Anniv. A102

1991, Feb. 18 **Litho.** *Perf. 13½*

446 A102 37p shown 1.50 1.50
447 A102 53p No. N2 2.10 2.10
448 A102 57p No. N3 2.25 2.25
a. Booklet pane of 3, #446-448 6.00
Complete booklet, 3 #448a 18.00

No. 448a printed in three formats with Nos. 446-448 in different order.

Europa — A103

Designs: No. 449, Royal Visit to Guernsey, discovery of Neptune, 1846. No. 450, Royal Visit to Sark, launch of Sputnik, 1957. No. 451, Maiden voyage of ferry Sarnia, first manned space flight, 1961. No. 452, Independence of Guernsey Post Office, first man on moon, 1969.

**1991, Apr. 1    Litho.    Perf. 13½x14**
449 A103 21p multicolored .85 .85
450 A103 21p multicolored .85 .85
451 A103 26p multicolored 1.00 1.00
452 A103 26p multicolored 1.00 1.00
    Nos. 449-452 (4) 3.70 3.70

**Landscape Type of 1984**
**1991    Litho.    Perf. 15x14½, 14½x15**
453 A63 21p King's Mills, St. Saviours .85 .85
  a. Booklet pane, 3 each #453, #296, 2 each #287, #288) 3.50
  b. Booklet pane, 5 each #453, #296) 6.00
454 A63 26p Town Church, St. Peter Port, vert. 1.00 1.00

Issued: 21p, 26p, 4/1; #453a, 453b, 4/2. #453a, 453b with straight edges around stamps and attached to booklet covers by tabs.

Guernsey Yacht Club, Cent. — A104

**1991, July 2    Litho.    Perf. 14**
459 A104 15p Guernsey Sailing Trust .60 .60
460 A104 21p Guernsey Regatta .80 .80
461 A104 26p Channel Islands Challenge 1.00 1.00
462 A104 31p Rolex Swan Regatta 1.25 1.25
463 A104 37p Old Gaffers Assoc. 1.50 1.50
  a. Souvenir sheet of 5, #459-463 5.50 5.50
    Nos. 459-463 (5) 5.15 5.15

"Guernsey" and denomination in white on sheet stamps, yellow on souvenir sheet stamps.

Miniature Sheet

Christmas — A105

Children's Paintings: a, Reindeer by Melanie Sharpe. b, Christmas pudding by James Quinn. c, Snowman by Lisa Marie Guille. d, Snowman by Jessica Ede-Golightly. e, Birds by Sharon Le Page. f, Shepherds, sheep, angels by Anna Coquelin. g, Manger scene by Claudine Lihou. h, Three kings by Jonathan Le Noury. i, Children, angels, Star of Bethlehem by Marcia Mahy. j, Christmas tree, presents by Laurel Garfield. k, Santa Claus by Rebecca Driscoll. l, Snowman by Ian Lowe.

**1991, Oct. 15    Litho.    Perf. 13**
464 A105 Sheet of 12 5.75 5.75
  a.-l. 12p any single .45 .45

Nature Conservation A106

Birds and plants: No. 465: a, Two oyster catchers. b, Three turnstones. c, Two dunlins, two turnstones. d, Curlew, two turnstones. e, Ringed plover, chicks.
No. 466: a, Violet and white flowers. b, Yellow flowers. c, Small yellow flowers. d, Violet, yellow and white flowers. e, Long-stemmed yellow flowers.

**1991, Oct. 15    Perf. 14½**
465 Strip of 5 3.00 3.00
  a.-e. A106 15p any single .60 .60
466 Strip of 5 4.25 4.25
  a.-e. A106 21p any single .85 .85

Discovery of America, 500th Anniv. — A107

**1992, Feb. 6    Litho.    Perf. 13½x14**
467 A107 23p Columbus .90 .90
468 A107 23p Columbus' signatures .90 .90
469 A107 28p Map of 1st voyage 1.10 1.10
470 A107 28p Santa Maria 1.10 1.10
  a. Souvenir sheet, #467-470 7.00 7.00
  b. No. 470a overprinted in brown in sheet margin 8.00 8.00
    Nos. 467-470 (4) 4.00 4.00

Europa. No. 470b overprint shows emblem of World Columbian Stamp Expo '92. Issue date: No. 470b, May 22.

Queen Elizabeth II's Accession to Throne, 40th Anniv. — A108

Various portraits of Queen Elizabeth II from 1952, 1977, 1986 and 1992.

**1992, Feb. 6    Litho.    Perf. 14**
471 A108 23p multicolored .90 .90
472 A108 28p multicolored 1.10 1.10
473 A108 33p multicolored 1.25 1.25
474 A108 39p multicolored 1.60 1.60
    Nos. 471-474 (4) 4.85 4.85

Souvenir Sheet

Guernsey Cows — A109

**1992, May 22    Litho.    Perf. 14**
475 A109 75p multicolored 3.00 3.00
Royal Guernsey Agricultural and Horticultural Society, 150th anniv.

Flowers — A110

**1992-96    Perf. 13**
476 A110 1p Stephanotis floribunda .20 .20
477 A110 2p Potted hydrangea .20 .20
478 A110 3p Stock .20 .20
479 A110 4p Anemones .20 .20
480 A110 5p Gladiolus .20 .20
481 A110 6p Gypsophila paniculata, asparagus plumosus .25 .25
482 A110 7p Guernsey lily .25 .25
483 A110 8p Enchantment lily .30 .30
484 A110 9p Clematis freckles .35 .35
485 A110 10p Alstroemeria .40 .40
486 A110 16p Standard carnation, horiz. .65 .55
  a. Perf. 14 on 3 sides .65 .55
  b. Booklet pane of 8 #486a 5.00
    Complete booklet, 1 #486b 5.00
487 A110 20p Spray rose .80 .75
488 A110 23p Mixed freesia, horiz. .90 .85
  a. Perf. 14 on 3 sides .90 .85
  b. Bklt. pane of 5 #486a, 3 #488a 6.50 6.50
    Complete booklet, 1 #488b 6.50
  c. Booklet pane of 8, #488a 8.00 8.00
    Complete booklet, 1 #488c 8.00
489 A110 24p Standard rose, horiz. .95 .80
  a. Perf. 14 on 3 sides 1.00 .80
  b. Booklet pane of 8 #489a 8.00
    Complete booklet, 1 #489b 8.00
490 A110 25p Iris ideal 1.00 .80
  a. Perf. 14½ on 3 sides 1.10 .80
  b. As "a," booklet pane of 4 4.50
    Complete booklet, 1 #490b 4.50
491 A110 28p Lisianthus, horiz. 1.10 .75
  a. Perf. 14 on 3 sides 1.25 .80
  b. Booklet pane of 4 #491a 5.00
    Complete booklet, 1 #491b 5.00
492 A110 30p Spray chrysanthemum, horiz. 1.25 1.10
493 A110 40p Spray carnation 1.60 1.25
494 A110 50p Single freesia, horiz. 2.00 1.50
**Size: 39x30mm**
**Perf. 13¾**
495 A110 £1 Bouquet, horiz. 4.00 3.00
  a. Souv. sheet of 1 + label, perf. 13 4.50 4.50
  b. Souv. sheet of 1 + label, perf. 13 4.50 4.50
496 A110 £2 Chelsea flower show, horiz. 8.00 8.00
**Size: 39x31mm**
**Perf. 13¼**
497 A110 £3 Floral fantasia, horiz. 12.00 10.00
    Nos. 476-497 (21) 35.85 31.10

PHILAKOREA '94 (#495a). Singapore '95 (#495b).
Issued: 3p, 4p, 5p, 10p, 16p, 20p, 23p, 40p, 50p, £1, 5/22/92; 1p, 2p, 6p, 7p, 8p, 9p, 24p, 28p, 30p, £2, #486a, 3/2/93; #486b, 489b, 491b, 3/3/93: #488a, 488b, 5/22/92; 25p, 2/18/94; #489a, 2/18/94; #495a, 8/94; #495b, 9/1/95; £3, 1/24/96.
#495 dated "1992," #495a, 495b "1994, 1995."
Perf 14 or 14½ stamps issued only in booklets. No. 486a exists dated "1992" from booklet pane 488a, and "1993" from booklet pane 486b.
See Nos. 584-585.

Operation Asterix A111

**1992, Sept. 18    Litho.    Perf. 13**
498 A111 16p Ship construction .65 .65
499 A111 23p Loading cargo .90 .90
500 A111 28p Ship at sea 1.10 1.10
501 A111 33p Ship on fire 1.25 1.25
502 A111 39p Ship sinking 1.50 1.50
  a. Bklt. pane of #498-502 + label 5.50
    Complete booklet, 4 #502a 22.50
    Nos. 498-502 (5) 5.40 5.40

No. 502a exists with four different labels: Great Britain, France, Italy, Germany. Booklet contains one of each type.

Historic Trams A112

Designs: 16p, Tram No. 10 decorated for Battle of Flowers. 23p, No. 10 passing Hougue a la Perre. 28p, Tram No. 1 at St. Sampsons. 33p, First steam tram, St. Peter Port, 1879. 39p, Last electric tram, 1934.

**1992, Nov. 17    Litho.    Perf. 13½x14**
503 A112 16p multicolored .65 .65
504 A112 23p multicolored .90 .90
505 A112 28p multicolored 1.10 1.10
506 A112 33p multicolored 1.25 1.25
507 A112 39p multicolored 1.50 1.50
    Nos. 503-507 (5) 5.40 5.40

Christmas — A113

a, Father dressed as Santa. b, Girl pulling end of cracker. c, Mother. d, Champagne, mince pies. e, Turkey. f, Plum pudding. g, Cake. h, Cookies. i, Wine, blue cheese. j, Nuts. k, Ham. l, Cake roll.

**1992, Nov. 17    Perf. 13½**
508 A113 Sheet of 12 6.25 6.25
  a.-l. 13p any single .50 .50

A114

Rupert Bear and friends, created by Mary Tourtel: No. 509: Rupert Bear, Bingo, and dog. No. 510a, 24p, Bill Badger, Willie Mouse, Reggie Rabbit, and Podgy Pig with snowman. No. 510b, 16p, Airplane above castle tower. No. 510c, 24p, Balloonist leaping away from Gregory on sled. No. 510d, 16p, Professor's servant and Autumn Elf. No. 510e, 16p, Algy Pug. No. 510f, 16p, Baby Badger on sled. No. 510g, 24p, Tiger Lily and Edward Trunk.

**1993, Feb. 2    Litho.    Perf. 13½x13**
509 A114 24p multicolored .95 .95
510 A114 Sheet of 8, #a.-g. 
    & #509 7.00 7.00

No. 510 printed in continuous design. Nos. 510b, 510d-510f are 25x26mm.

Contemporary Art — A115

Europa: No. 511, Tapestry, by Kelly Fletcher. No. 512, The Fish Market, by Sally Reed. No. 513, Dress Shop, King's Road, by

Damon Bell. No. 514, Red Abstract, by Molly Harris.

**1993, May 7    Litho.    Perf. 13½x14**
Size: 45x30mm (#512, 513)

| | | | | |
|---|---|---|---|---|
| 511 | A115 | 24p multicolored | .95 | .95 |
| 512 | A115 | 24p multicolored | .95 | .95 |
| 513 | A115 | 28p multicolored | 1.10 | 1.10 |
| 514 | A115 | 28p multicolored | 1.10 | 1.10 |
| | | Nos. 511-514 (4) | 4.10 | 4.10 |

Siege of Castle Cornet, 1643-51 — A116

16p, Shipboard arrest of Parliamentarian officials. 24p, Parliamentarian warships firing on castle. 28p, Captured officials fleeing from castle. 33p, Cannon firing from castle into St. Peter Port. 39p, Surrender of castle.

**1993, May 7    Perf. 15x14**

| | | | | |
|---|---|---|---|---|
| 515 | A116 | 16p multicolored | .65 | .65 |
| 516 | A116 | 24p multicolored | .95 | .95 |
| 517 | A116 | 28p multicolored | 1.10 | 1.10 |
| 518 | A116 | 33p multicolored | 1.25 | 1.25 |
| 519 | A116 | 39p multicolored | 1.50 | 1.50 |
| a. | | Souvenir sheet of 5, #515-519 | 5.50 | 5.50 |
| | | Nos. 515-519 (5) | 5.45 | 5.45 |

Thomas de la Rue, Printer, Birth Bicent. — A117

Designs: 16p, Playing card king, queen and jack. 24p, Swift reservoir fountain pens. 28p, Envelope folding machine. 33p, Great Britain type A5. 39p, £1 Mauritius bank note, portrait of de la Rue.

**1993, July 27    Litho.    Perf. 13½**

| | | | | |
|---|---|---|---|---|
| 520 | A117 | 16p multicolored | .65 | .65 |
| 521 | A117 | 24p multicolored | .95 | .95 |
| 522 | A117 | 28p multicolored | 1.10 | 1.10 |

**Engr.**

| | | | | |
|---|---|---|---|---|
| 523 | A117 | 33p rose carmine | 1.25 | 1.25 |
| 524 | A117 | 39p green | 1.50 | 1.50 |
| | | Nos. 520-524 (5) | 5.45 | 5.45 |

| | | | |
|---|---|---|---|
| 520a | | Booklet pane of 4 | 3.00 |
| 521a | | Booklet pane of 4 | 4.25 |
| 522a | | Booklet pane of 4 | 4.75 |
| 523a | | Booklet pane of 4 | 5.50 |
| 524a | | Booklet pane of 4 | 6.50 |
| | | Complete booklet, #520a-524a | 24.00 |

**Miniature Sheet**

Christmas — A118

Stained glass windows, Chapel of Christ the Healer: a, Sunburst. b, Light from sun. c, Hand of God. d, Doves descending left. e, Christ raising hand. f, Doves descending right. g, Christ Child sitting in temple. h, Christ raising daughter of Jairus from dead. i, "Suffer little children to come unto me." j, Scene from Pilgrim's Progress. k, The Light of the World. l, Archangel of Healing.

**1993, Nov. 2    Litho.    Perf. 13x13½**

| | | | | |
|---|---|---|---|---|
| 525 | A118 | Sheet of 12 | 6.25 | 6.25 |
| a.-l. | | 13p any single | .50 | .45 |

Archaeological Discoveries — A119

Europa: No. 526, Warrior on horseback. No. 527, Burial site, Les Fouaillages. No. 528, Sword, scabbard, spear. No. 529, Cerny-style pots, arrowheads, axe.

**1994, Feb. 18    Litho.    Perf. 13½**

| | | | | |
|---|---|---|---|---|
| 526 | A119 | 24p multicolored | .95 | .95 |
| a. | | Sheet of 10 with added inscription | 12.00 | 12.00 |
| 527 | A119 | 24p multicolored | .95 | .95 |
| 528 | A119 | 30p multicolored | 1.25 | 1.25 |
| 529 | A119 | 30p multicolored | 1.25 | 1.25 |
| | | Nos. 526-529 (4) | 4.40 | 4.40 |

No. 526a inscribed in sheet margin with Hong Kong '94 emblem and "PHILATELIC EXHIBITION / 18-21 FEBRUARY 1994" in English and Chinese.

**Souvenir Sheet**

D-Day, 50th Anniv. — A120

£2, Canadian Wing Spitfires flying over Normandy coastline.

**1994, June 6    Litho.    Perf. 14**

| | | | | |
|---|---|---|---|---|
| 530 | A120 | £2 multicolored | 8.00 | 5.00 |

Classic Cars A121

Designs: 16p, 1894 Peugeot Type 3. 24p, 1903 Mercedes Simplex. 35p, 1906 Humber 14.4hp. 41p, 1936 Bentley 4¼ L. 60p, 1948 MG TC.

**1994, July 19    Litho.    Perf. 15x14**

| | | | | |
|---|---|---|---|---|
| 531 | A121 | 16p multicolored | .65 | .65 |
| 532 | A121 | 24p multicolored | .95 | .95 |
| 533 | A121 | 35p multicolored | 1.40 | 1.40 |
| 534 | A121 | 41p multicolored | 1.60 | 1.60 |
| 535 | A121 | 60p multicolored | 2.40 | 2.40 |
| | | Nos. 531-535 (5) | 7.00 | 7.00 |

| | | | |
|---|---|---|---|
| 531a | | Booklet pane of 4 | 3.00 |
| 532a | | Booklet pane of 4 | 4.25 |
| 533a | | Booklet pane of 4 | 6.00 |
| 534a | | Booklet pane of 4 | 6.50 |
| 535a | | Booklet pane or 4 | 9.75 |
| | | Complete booklet, #531a-535a | 29.50 |

Guernsey Post Office, 25th Anniv. A122

Designs: 16p, Trident ferry. 24p, Handley Page Super Dart Herald of Channel Express. 35p, Aurigny Air Services' JOEY. 41p, Bon Marin de Serk ferry. 60p, Map of Guernsey, Herm, Alderney, Sark.

**1994, Oct. 1    Litho.    Perf. 14**

| | | | | |
|---|---|---|---|---|
| 536 | A122 | 16p multicolored | .65 | .65 |
| 537 | A122 | 24p multicolored | .95 | .95 |
| 538 | A122 | 35p multicolored | 1.40 | 1.40 |
| 539 | A122 | 41p multicolored | 1.60 | 1.60 |
| 540 | A122 | 60p multicolored | 2.40 | 2.40 |
| a. | | Souvenir sheet, #536-540 | 7.50 | 7.50 |
| | | Nos. 536-540 (5) | 7.00 | 7.00 |

See Jersey Nos. 685-689a.

**Miniature Sheets**

Christmas — A123

Antique toys — #541: a, Doll house. b, Doll. c, Small teddy bear in carriage. d, Cards, post boxes with candy. e, Top. f, Picture puzzle blocks.
#542: a, Rocking horse. b, Large teddy bear. c, Tricycle. d, Wooden pull duck. e, Tin plate locomotive. f, Ludo game.

**1994, Oct. 1    Perf. 13**

| | | | | |
|---|---|---|---|---|
| 541 | A123 | Sheet of 6 | 3.25 | 3.25 |
| a.-f. | | 13p any single | .50 | .50 |
| 542 | A123 | Sheet of 6 | 5.75 | 5.75 |
| a.-f. | | 24p any single | .90 | .90 |

Greetings — A124

Faces formed by: No. 543, Shrimp, oyster, lobster, fish. No. 544, Sand buckets, shovel, sand. No. 545, Flowers. No. 546, Lettuce, tomatoes, mushroom, squash. No. 547, Seaweed, shells. No. 548, Anchor, life preservers. No. 549, Wine, cork, knife, fork. No. 550, Butterflies, caterpillars.

**1995, Feb. 2    Litho.    Perf. 14**

| | | | | |
|---|---|---|---|---|
| 543 | A124 | 24p multicolored | .95 | .95 |
| 544 | A124 | 24p multicolored | .95 | .95 |
| 545 | A124 | 24p multicolored | .95 | .95 |
| 546 | A124 | 24p multicolored | .95 | .95 |
| 547 | A124 | 24p multicolored | .95 | .95 |
| 548 | A124 | 24p multicolored | .95 | .95 |
| 549 | A124 | 24p multicolored | .95 | .95 |
| 550 | A124 | 24p multicolored | .95 | .95 |
| a. | | Miniature sheet of 8, #543-550 | 8.00 | 7.25 |
| | | Complete booklet, #550a | 8.00 | |
| | | Nos. 543-550 (8) | 7.60 | 7.60 |

Doves — A125

Europa: 25p, Doves standing. 30p, Doves in flight. Illustration reduced.

**1995, May 9    Litho.    Perf. 14**

| | | | | |
|---|---|---|---|---|
| 551 | A125 | 25p green | 1.00 | 1.00 |
| 552 | A125 | 30p blue | 1.25 | 1.25 |

Nos. 551-552 contain a three-dimensional image hidden in the patterns composed of doves.

Visit by Prince of Wales A127

**1995, May 9    Perf. 13½x14**

| | | | | |
|---|---|---|---|---|
| 553 | A126 | 16p multicolored | .65 | .65 |
| 554 | A126 | 24p multicolored | .95 | .95 |
| 555 | A126 | 35p multicolored | 1.40 | 1.40 |
| 556 | A126 | 41p multicolored | 1.60 | 1.60 |
| 557 | A126 | 60p multicolored | 2.40 | 2.40 |
| a. | | Souvenir sheet of 5, #553-557 | 7.50 | 7.50 |
| | | Nos. 553-557 (5) | 7.00 | 7.00 |

**1995, May 9    Perf. 14**

| | | | | |
|---|---|---|---|---|
| 558 | A127 | £1.50 multicolored | 6.00 | 6.00 |

UN, 50th Anniv. — A128

Portion of UN emblem, denomination: a, UL. b, UR. c, LL. d, LR.

**Litho. & Embossed**

**1995, Oct. 24    Perf. 14x13½**

| | | | | |
|---|---|---|---|---|
| 559 | A128 | Block of 4 | 8.00 | 8.00 |
| a.-d. | | 50p any single | 2.00 | 2.00 |

Christmas — A129

Designs, with denomination at:
Shops in the city, children playing in snow — #560: a, LL. b, LR.
Homes in winter, children playing in snow — #561: a, LL. b, LR.
Children playing instruments, singing — #562: a, LL. b, LR.
Children of many nations — #563: a, LL. b, LR.

**1995, Nov. 16    Litho.    Perf. 13½x13**

| | | | | |
|---|---|---|---|---|
| 560 | A129 | Pair | 1.00 | 1.00 |
| a.-b. | | 13p any single | .50 | .50 |
| 561 | A129 | Pair | 1.00 | 1.00 |
| a.-b. | | 13p +1p, any single | .50 | .50 |
| 562 | A129 | Pair | 1.90 | 1.90 |
| a.-b. | | 24p any single | .95 | .95 |
| 563 | A129 | Pair | 1.90 | 1.90 |
| a.-b. | | 24p +2p, any single | .95 | .95 |
| | | Nos. 560-563 (4) | 5.80 | 5.80 |

Nos. 560-563 are each continuous designs. UNICEF, 50th anniv.

Women of Achievement — A130

Europa: 25p, Princess Anne, children of different nations. 30p, Queen Elizabeth II, people of different nations.

**1996, Apr. 21    Litho.    Perf. 14**

| | | | | |
|---|---|---|---|---|
| 564 | A130 | 25p multicolored | 1.00 | 1.00 |
| 565 | A130 | 30p multicolored | 1.25 | 1.25 |

Queen Elizabeth II, 70th birthday (#565). See Isle of Man Nos. 679-680.

**1996 European Soccer Championships — A131**

Various flags from participating countries and: No. 566a, USSR player kicking ball. No. 566b, English players in white shirts, 1968. No. 567a, Italian player in blue shirt with ball. No. 567b, Belgium player in red, Italian players, 1972. No. 568a, Irish player in green kicking. No. 568b, Dutch player in blue, 1988. No. 569a, German player in white with ball. No. 569b, Danish player in red, 1992.

| 1996, Apr. 25 | | Perf. 14x13½ | |
|---|---|---|---|
| 566 | A131 Pair | 1.25 | 1.25 |
| a.-b. | 16p any single | .60 | .60 |
| 567 | A131 Pair | 1.90 | 1.90 |
| a.-b. | 24p any single | .95 | .95 |
| 568 | A131 Pair | 3.00 | 3.00 |
| a.-b. | 35p any single | 1.40 | 1.40 |
| 569 | A131 Pair | 3.25 | 3.25 |
| a.-b. | 41p any single | 1.60 | 1.60 |
| | Nos. 566-569 (4) | 9.40 | 9.40 |

**Souvenir Sheet**

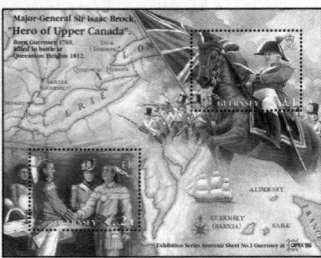

**Sir Isaac Brock (1769-1812), British Commander in Upper Canada — A132**

Designs: a, 24p, Brock shaking hands with Tecumseh. b, £1, Brock on horse.

| 1996, June 8 | Litho. | Perf. 14x13½ | |
|---|---|---|---|
| 570 | A132 Sheet of 2, #a.-b. | 5.00 | 5.00 |

CAPEX '96.

Modern Olympic Games, Cent. — A133

The original pentathlon.

| 1996, July 19 | Litho. | Perf. 14 | |
|---|---|---|---|
| 571 | A133 16p Running | .65 | .65 |
| 572 | A133 24p Javelin | .95 | .95 |
| 573 | A133 41p Discus | 1.60 | 1.60 |
| 574 | A133 55p Wrestling | 2.25 | 2.25 |
| 575 | A133 60p Jumping | 2.40 | 2.40 |
| a. | Souvenir sheet, #571-575 | 8.00 | 8.00 |
| | Nos. 571-575 (5) | 7.85 | 7.85 |

No. 574 is 53x31mm. Olymphilex'96 (#574).

Motion Pictures, Cent. A134

Classic Movie Detectives: 16p, Humphrey Bogart as Philip Marlowe. 24p, Peter Sellers as Inspector Clouseau. 35p, Basil Rathbone as Sherlock Holmes. 41p, Margaret Rutherford as Miss Marple. 60p, Warner Oland as Charlie Chan.

| 1996, Nov. 6 | Litho. | Perf. 15x14 | |
|---|---|---|---|
| 576 | A134 16p multicolored | .65 | .65 |
| 577 | A134 24p multicolored | .95 | .95 |
| 578 | A134 35p multicolored | 1.40 | 1.40 |

| 579 | A134 41p multicolored | 1.60 | 1.60 |
|---|---|---|---|
| 580 | A134 60p multicolored | 2.40 | 2.40 |
| | Nos. 576-580 (5) | 7.00 | 7.00 |
| 576a | Booklet pane of 3 | 2.00 | |
| 577a | Booklet pane of 3 | 3.00 | |
| 578a | Booklet pane of 3 | 4.25 | |
| 579a | Booklet pane of 3 | 5.00 | |
| 580a | Booklet pane of 3 | 7.25 | |
| 580b | Bkt. pane of 5, #576-580 | 7.50 | |
| | Complete booklet, #576a-580b | 30.00 | |

Christmas A135

Scenes depicting the Christmas story: 24p, Madonna and Child. 25p, Nativity.

No. 583, vert: a, Annunciation by Angel Gabriel. b, Mary, Joseph on way to Bethlehem. c, Inn keeper turning them away. d, Angel appearing before shepherds. e, Holy Family in stable. f, Adoration of the shepherds. g, Magi following star. h, Magi presenting gifts. i, Prophet's warning to Mary, Joseph. j, Madonna and Child. k, Angel appearing in Joseph's dream. l, Flight into Egypt.

| 1996, Nov. 6 | | Perf. 13 | |
|---|---|---|---|
| 581 | A135 24p multicolored | .95 | .95 |
| 582 | A135 25p multicolored | 1.00 | 1.00 |

**Miniature Sheet**

| 583 | Sheet of 12 | 6.25 | 6.25 |
|---|---|---|---|
| a.-l. | A135 13p Any single | .50 | .50 |

**Flower Type of 1992**

| 1997 | Litho. | Perf. 13 | |
|---|---|---|---|
| 584 | A110 18p Standard rose | .70 | .60 |
| a. | Perf. 14 on 3 Sides | .75 | .65 |
| b. | As "a," booklet pane of 8 | 7.50 | |
| | Complete booklet, #584b | 7.50 | |
| 585 | A110 26p Freesia pink glow, horiz. | 1.00 | .80 |
| a. | Perf. 14 on 3 Sides | 1.10 | .80 |
| b. | As "a," booklet pane of 4 | 5.25 | |
| | Complete booklet, #585b | 5.25 | |

Butterflies and Moths A136

Designs: 18p, Holly blue. 25p, Hummingbird hawk-moth. 26p, Emperor moth. 37p, Brimstone. £1, Painted lady.

| 1997, Feb. 12 | Litho. | Perf. 14 | |
|---|---|---|---|
| 586 | A136 18p multicolored | 1.00 | 1.00 |
| 587 | A136 25p multicolored | 1.25 | 1.25 |
| 588 | A136 26p multicolored | 1.50 | 1.50 |
| 589 | A136 37p multicolored | 2.00 | 2.00 |
| | Nos. 586-589 (4) | 5.75 | 5.75 |

**Souvenir Sheet**
**Perf. 13½**

| 590 | A136 £1 multicolored | 4.00 | 4.00 |
|---|---|---|---|

World Wildlife Fund (#586-589), Hong Kong '97 (#590).

Stories and Legends — A137

The Toilers of the Sea, by Victor Hugo: 26p, Man fighting sea monster, face in sea, ship. 31p, Ship, man seated on rock visualizing woman.

| 1997, Apr. 24 | Litho. | Perf. 13½ | |
|---|---|---|---|
| 591 | A137 26p multicolored | 1.00 | 1.00 |
| 592 | A137 31p multicolored | 1.25 | 1.25 |

Nos. 591-592 each issued in sheets of 10. Europa.

Island Scenes — A138

18p, Shell Beach, Herm. 25p, La Seigneurie, Sark, vert. 26p, Castle Comet, Guernsey.

**Die Cut Perf. 9½x9, 9x9½**
**1997, Apr. 24**
**Self-Adhesive**

| 593 | A138 18p multicolored | .70 | .70 |
|---|---|---|---|
| a. | Booklet pane of 8 | 6.50 | |
| | Complete booklet, #593a | 6.50 | |
| 594 | A138 25p multicolored | 1.00 | 1.00 |
| a. | Booklet pane of 8 | 9.00 | |
| | Complete booklet, #594a | 9.00 | |
| 595 | A138 26p multicolored | 1.00 | 1.00 |
| a. | Booklet pane of 4 | 4.50 | |
| | Complete booklet, #595a | 4.50 | |
| | Nos. 593-595 (3) | 2.70 | 2.70 |

See Nos. 625-628.

**Souvenir Sheet**

**PACIFIC 97 — A139**

a, 30p, St. Peter Port, 1868. b, £1, Sailing ships.

| 1997, May 29 | Litho. | Perf. 14 | |
|---|---|---|---|
| 596 | A139 Sheet of 2, #a.-b. | 5.25 | 5.25 |

Communications — A140

| 1997, Aug. 21 | Litho. | Perf. 13½x13 | |
|---|---|---|---|
| 597 | A140 18p Radio | .70 | .70 |
| 598 | A140 25p Television | 1.00 | 1.00 |
| 599 | A140 26p Telephone | 1.00 | 1.00 |
| 600 | A140 37p Newspaper | 1.50 | 1.50 |
| 601 | A140 43p Post system | 1.60 | 1.60 |
| 602 | A140 63p Computer network | 2.50 | 2.50 |
| | Nos. 597-602 (6) | 8.30 | 8.30 |

Queen Elizabeth II and Prince Philip, 50th Wedding Anniv. — A141

Designs: 18p, At St. George's Hall, Guernsey, 1957. 25p, Queen being saluted by guardsman, 1953. 26p, Queen, family on horseback, 1957. 37p, Prince, Queen in casual attire, 1972. 43p, Queen saluting, at Trooping of the Color, 1987. 63p, Portrait, 1997.

| 1997, Nov. 20 | Litho. | Perf. 14 | |
|---|---|---|---|
| 603 | A141 18p multicolored | .70 | .70 |
| 604 | A141 25p multicolored | 1.00 | 1.00 |
| a. | Bkt. pane, 3 each #603-604 | 5.75 | |
| 605 | A141 26p multicolored | 1.00 | 1.00 |
| 606 | A141 37p multicolored | 1.50 | 1.50 |
| a. | Bkt. pane, 3 each #605-606 | 8.50 | |
| 607 | A141 43p multicolored | 1.60 | 1.60 |
| 608 | A141 63p multicolored | 2.50 | 2.50 |
| a. | Bkt. pane, 3 each #607-608 | 13.50 | |
| b. | Booklet pane, #603-608 | 9.00 | |
| | Complete booklet, #604a, 606a, 608a, 608b | 37.50 | |
| | Nos. 603-608 (6) | 8.30 | 8.30 |

A142

Teddy Bears celebrating Christmas: 15p, Baking in kitchen. 25p, Beside Christmas tree. 26p, Seated in chair reading story. 37p, As Santa Claus. 43p, With presents. 63p, Seated at Christmas dinner.

| 1997, Nov. 6 | | | |
|---|---|---|---|
| 609 | A142 15p multicolored | .60 | .60 |
| 610 | A142 25p multicolored | 1.00 | 1.00 |
| 611 | A142 26p multicolored | 1.00 | 1.00 |
| 612 | A142 37p multicolored | 1.50 | 1.50 |
| 613 | A142 43p multicolored | 1.60 | 1.60 |
| 614 | A142 63p multicolored | 2.50 | 2.50 |
| a. | Souvenir sheet, #609-614 | 8.25 | 7.50 |
| | Nos. 609-614 (6) | 8.20 | 8.20 |

A143

| 1998, Feb. 10 | Litho. | Perf. 14½ | |
|---|---|---|---|

Millennium Tapestries: Embroidered panels showing images of Guernsey during last ten centuries, Guernsey-French inscriptions.

| 615 | A143 25p 11th century | 1.00 | 1.00 |
|---|---|---|---|
| 616 | A143 25p 12th century | 1.00 | 1.00 |
| 617 | A143 25p 13th century | 1.00 | 1.00 |
| 618 | A143 25p 14th century | 1.00 | 1.00 |
| a. | Bkt. pane, 2 each #615-616, 1 each #617-618 | 6.50 | |
| 619 | A143 25p 15th century | 1.00 | 1.00 |
| 620 | A143 25p 16th century | 1.00 | 1.00 |
| a. | Bkt. pane, 2 each #617-618, 1 each #619-620 | 6.50 | |
| 621 | A143 25p 17th century | 1.00 | 1.00 |
| 622 | A143 25p 18th century | 1.00 | 1.00 |
| a. | Bkt. pane, 2 each #619-620, 1 each #621-622 | 6.50 | |
| 623 | A143 25p 19th century | 1.00 | 1.00 |
| 624 | A143 25p 20th century | 1.00 | 1.00 |
| a. | Bkt. pane, 2 each #621-622, 1 each #623-624 | 6.50 | |
| b. | Bkt. pane, 2 each #623-624, 1 each #615-616 | 6.50 | |
| | Complete booklet, #618a, 620a, 622a, 624a-624b | 35.00 | |
| c. | Strip of 10, #615-624 | 10.00 | 10.00 |

**Island Scenes Type of 1997**
**Die Cut Perf. 9½x9**

| 1998, Mar. 25 | | Litho. | |
|---|---|---|---|
| **Self-Adhesive** | | | |
| 625 | A138 (20p) Fort Grey | .80 | .80 |
| 626 | A138 (20p) Grand Havre | .80 | .80 |
| a. | Booklet pane, 4 each #625-626 | 7.50 | |
| | Complete booklet, #626a | 7.50 | |
| 627 | A138 (25p) Little Chapel | 1.00 | 1.00 |
| 628 | A138 (25p) Guernsey cow | 1.00 | 1.00 |
| a. | Booklet pane, 4 each #627-628 | 8.75 | |
| | Complete booklet, #628a | 8.75 | |
| | Nos. 625-628 (4) | 3.60 | 3.60 |

Nos. 625-626 are inscribed "Bailwick Minimum Postage Paid" and were valued at 20p on day of issue. Nos. 627-628 are inscribed "UK Minimum Postage Paid" and were valued at 25p on day of issue.

Aircraft A144

Designs: 20p, Fairey IIIC, Balloon, Sopwith Camel, Avro 504. 25p, Fairey Swordfish, Tiger Moth, Supermarine Walrus, Gloster Gladiator. 30p, Hawker Hurricane, Supermarine Spitfire, Vickers Wellington, Short Sunderland, Westland Lysander, Bristol Blenheim. 37p, De Havilland Mosquito, Avro Lancaster, Auster III, Gloster Meteor, Horsa glider. 43p, Canberra, Hawker Sea Fury, Bristol Sycamore, Hawker Hunter, Handley Page Victor, BAe Lightning. 63p, Pavania Tornado GRI, BAe Hawk, BAe

Sea Harrier, Westland Lynx, Hawker Siddeley Nimrod.

| 1998, May 7 | | | Perf. 13½x13 | |
|---|---|---|---|---|
| 629 | A144 | 20p multicolored | .80 | .80 |
| 630 | A144 | 25p multicolored | 1.00 | 1.00 |
| 631 | A144 | 30p multicolored | 1.25 | 1.25 |
| 632 | A144 | 37p multicolored | 1.50 | 1.50 |
| 633 | A144 | 43p multicolored | 1.60 | 1.60 |
| 634 | A144 | 63p multicolored | 2.50 | 2.50 |
| | | Nos. 629-634 (6) | 8.65 | 8.65 |

Royal Air Force, 80th anniv.

### Souvenir Sheet

Cambridge Rules for Soccer, 150th Anniv. — A145

a, 30p, Jules Rimet, first president of FIFA. b, £1.75, Bobby Moore, Queen Elizabeth II.

| 1998, May 7 | | | Perf. 13½x14 | |
|---|---|---|---|---|
| 635 | A145 | Sheet of 2, #a.-b. | 8.25 | 8.25 |

Natl. Holidays and Festivals — A146

Europa: 20p, People in traditional costumes watching animals, West Show. 25p, Band in parade, Battle of Flowers, North Show. 30p, Prince Charles, Liberation Monument under Guernsey flag, tank, Liberation Day. 37p, Goat, equestrian event, flowers, South Show.

| 1998, Aug. 11 | | Litho. | Perf. 13½ | |
|---|---|---|---|---|
| 636 | A146 | 20p multicolored | .80 | .80 |
| 637 | A146 | 25p multicolored | 1.00 | 1.00 |
| 638 | A146 | 30p multicolored | 1.25 | 1.25 |
| 639 | A146 | 37p multicolored | 1.50 | 1.50 |
| | | Nos. 636-639 (4) | 4.55 | 4.55 |

A147

Royal Yacht Britannia — A148

Designs: 1p, Small fishing boat. 2p, St. John Ambulance Inshore Rescue inflatable dinghy. 3p, Pilot boat. 4p, St. John Ambulance boat, Flying Christine III. 5p, Crab boat. 6p, Ferry. 7p, Workboat, Sarnia. 8p, Fisheries Protecton vessel, Leopardess. 9p, Large fishing boat. 10p, Powerboat. 20p, Dart 18 racing catamaran. 30p, Bermudan rigged sloop. 40p, Motor cruiser. 50p, Ocean-going yacht. 75p, Motor cruiser anchored. £1, Cruise ship, Queen Elizabeth II. £3, Cruise ship Oriana.

| 1998-2000 | | Litho. | Perf. 14 | |
|---|---|---|---|---|
| 640 | A147 | 1p multicolored | .20 | .20 |
| 641 | A147 | 2p multicolored | .20 | .20 |
| 642 | A147 | 3p multicolored | .20 | .20 |
| 643 | A147 | 4p multicolored | .20 | .20 |
| 644 | A147 | 5p multicolored | .20 | .20 |
| 645 | A147 | 6p multicolored | .25 | .25 |
| 646 | A147 | 7p multicolored | .25 | .25 |
| 647 | A147 | 8p multicolored | .30 | .30 |
| 648 | A147 | 9p multicolored | .35 | .35 |

**Size: 27x27mm**
**Perf. 14½x14¼**

| 649 | A147 | 10p multicolored | .40 | .40 |
|---|---|---|---|---|
| 650 | A147 | 20p multicolored | .80 | .80 |
| 651 | A147 | 30p multicolored | 1.25 | 1.25 |
| 652 | A147 | 40p multicolored | 1.60 | 1.60 |
| 654 | A147 | 50p multicolored | 2.00 | 2.00 |
| 656 | A147 | 75p multicolored | 3.00 | 3.00 |

**Size: 34x26mm**
**Litho. & Embossed**
**Perf. 14¼x14½**

| 658 | A148 | £1 multicolored | 4.00 | 4.00 |
|---|---|---|---|---|
| 660 | A148 | £3 multicolored | 12.00 | 12.00 |

**Size: 48x36mm**
**Perf. 14¾x14½**

| 663 | A148 | £5 gold & multi | 20.00 | 20.00 |
|---|---|---|---|---|
| | | Nos. 640-663 (18) | 47.20 | 47.20 |

Issued: £5, 8/11; 1p, 2p, 3p, 4p, 5p, 6p, 7p, 8p, 10p, 40p, 50p, 75p, £1, 7/27/99; 20p, 30p, £3, 8/4/00.
See also No. 867.

Introduction of Christmas Tree to Britain, 150th Anniv. — A149

Christmas tree and toys from past 150 years: 17p, Teletubby "Po," video game machine, 1998. 25p, Doll, double decker bus, c. 1968. 30p, Stuffed panda, toy army tank, c. 1938. 37p, Model of Bluebird race car, doll, c. 1928. 43p, Teddy bear, train pull toy, c. 1908. 63p, Spinning top, wooden doll, c. 1850.

| 1998, Nov. 10 | | Litho. | Perf. 13½ | |
|---|---|---|---|---|
| 664 | A149 | 17p multicolored | .65 | .65 |
| 665 | A149 | 25p multicolored | 1.00 | 1.00 |
| 666 | A149 | 30p multicolored | 1.25 | 1.25 |
| 667 | A149 | 37p multicolored | 1.50 | 1.50 |
| 668 | A149 | 43p multicolored | 1.60 | 1.60 |
| 669 | A149 | 63p multicolored | 2.50 | 2.50 |
| a. | | Souvenir sheet, #664-669 | 8.50 | 8.50 |
| | | Nos. 664-669 (6) | 8.50 | 8.50 |

Queen Elizabeth, the Queen Mother — A150

Three strings of pearls and photographs: No. 670, As a child, 1907. No. 671, At wedding, 1923. No. 672, Holding newly-born Princess Elizabeth, 1926. No. 673, Wearing crown at coronation of King George VI, 1937. No. 674, In green hat, 1940. No. 675, Holding fishing pole, 1966. No. 676, Wearing tiara, 1963. No. 677, Holding flowers, 1992. No. 678, Presenting trophy, 1989. No. 679, In blue hat, 1990.

| 1999, Feb. 4 | | Litho. | Perf. 13 | |
|---|---|---|---|---|
| | | **Color of LL Corner** | | |
| 670 | A150 | 25p pink | 1.00 | 1.00 |
| 671 | A150 | 25p blue | 1.00 | 1.00 |
| 672 | A150 | 25p red brown | 1.00 | 1.00 |
| 673 | A150 | 25p purple | 1.00 | 1.00 |
| a. | | Bklt. pane, 2 each #670-671, 1 each #672-673 | 6.50 | |
| 674 | A150 | 25p green | 1.00 | 1.00 |
| 675 | A150 | 25p green | 1.00 | 1.00 |
| a. | | Bklt. pane, 2 each #672-673, 1 each #673-674 | 6.50 | |
| 676 | A150 | 25p purple | 1.00 | 1.00 |
| 677 | A150 | 25p red brown | 1.00 | 1.00 |
| 678 | A150 | 25p blue | 1.00 | 1.00 |
| a. | | Bklt. pane, 2 each #674-675, 1 each #676-677 | 6.50 | |
| 679 | A150 | 25p pink | 1.00 | 1.00 |
| a. | | Bklt. pane, 2 each #676-677, 1 each #678-679 | 6.50 | |
| b. | | Bklt. pane, 2 each #678-679, 1 each #670-671 | 6.50 | |
| | | Complete booklet, #673a, 675a, 678a, 679a, 679b | 35.00 | |
| c. | | Strip of 10, #670-679 | 10.00 | 10.00 |

Herm Island — A151

Local Carriage Labels and: 20p, Burnet roses, Shell Beach. 25p, Puffins, Belvoir Bay. 30p, Small Heath butterfly. 38p, Various shells, Shell Beach.

| 1999, Apr. 27 | | Litho. | Perf. 13½x13 | |
|---|---|---|---|---|
| 680 | A151 | 20p multicolored | .80 | .80 |
| 681 | A151 | 25p multicolored | 1.00 | 1.00 |
| 682 | A151 | 30p multicolored | 1.25 | 1.25 |
| 683 | A151 | 38p multicolored | 1.50 | 1.50 |
| | | Nos. 680-683 (4) | 4.55 | 4.55 |

Europa.

Royal Lifeboat Assoc., 175th Anniv. A152

20p, Spirit of Guernsey, 1995. 25p, Sir William Arnold, 1973. 30p, Euphrosyne Kendal, 1954. 38p, Queen Victoria, 1929. 44p, Arthur Lionel, 1912. 64p, Vincent Kirk Ella, 1888.

| 1999, Apr. 27 | | | | |
|---|---|---|---|---|
| 684 | A152 | 20p multicolored | .80 | .80 |
| 685 | A152 | 25p multicolored | 1.00 | 1.00 |
| 686 | A152 | 30p multicolored | 1.25 | 1.25 |
| 687 | A152 | 38p multicolored | 1.50 | 1.50 |
| 688 | A152 | 44p multicolored | 1.75 | 1.75 |
| 689 | A152 | 64p multicolored | 2.50 | 2.50 |
| | | Nos. 684-689 (6) | 8.80 | 8.80 |

### Souvenir Sheet

Wedding of Prince Edward and Sophie Rhys-Jones — A153

Illustration reduced.

| 1999, June 19 | | Litho. | Perf. 13½ | |
|---|---|---|---|---|
| 690 | A153 | £1 multicolored | 4.00 | 4.00 |

Royal Military Academy, Sandhurst, Bicent. — A154

20p, Major General Le Marchant, founder, 1799. 25p, Duke of York, sponsor, 1802. 30p, Field Marshal Earl Haig, 1884-85. 38p, Field Marshal Montgomery, 1907-08. 44p, Major David Niven, actor, 1928-30. 64p, Sir Winston Churchill, 1893-95.

| 1999, July 27 | | Litho. | Perf. 14 | |
|---|---|---|---|---|
| 691 | A154 | 20p multicolored | .80 | .80 |
| 692 | A154 | 25p multicolored | 1.00 | 1.00 |
| 693 | A154 | 30p multicolored | 1.25 | 1.25 |
| 694 | A154 | 38p multicolored | 1.50 | 1.50 |
| 695 | A154 | 44p multicolored | 1.75 | 1.75 |
| 696 | A154 | 64p multicolored | 2.50 | 2.50 |
| | | Nos. 691-696 (6) | 8.80 | 8.80 |

Christmas A155

Creche figures around manger: 17p, Magus, shepherd, Mary, Joseph, donkey. 25p, Mary. 30p, Joseph, Mary. 38p, Donkey, Mary, cow. 44p, Mary, two shepherds. 64p, Three Magi.

| 1999, Oct. 19 | | Litho. | Perf. 13¾x14¼ | |
|---|---|---|---|---|
| 697 | A155 | 17p multicolored | .65 | .65 |
| 698 | A155 | 25p multicolored | 1.00 | 1.00 |
| 699 | A155 | 30p multicolored | 1.25 | 1.25 |
| 700 | A155 | 38p multicolored | 1.50 | 1.50 |
| 701 | A155 | 44p multicolored | 1.75 | 1.75 |
| 702 | A155 | 64p multicolored | 2.50 | 2.50 |
| a. | | Souvenir sheet, #697-702 | 11.00 | 11.00 |
| | | Nos. 697-702 (6) | 8.65 | 8.65 |

Millennium A156

Children's drawings by: 20p, Fallon Ephgrave. 25p, Abigail Downing. 30p, Laura Martin. 38p, Sarah Haddow. 44p, Sophie Medland. 64p, Danielle McIver.

| 2000, Jan. 1 | | Litho. | Perf. 14¼x14½ | |
|---|---|---|---|---|
| 703 | A156 | 20p multi | .80 | .80 |
| 704 | A156 | 25p multi | 1.00 | 1.00 |
| 705 | A156 | 30p multi | 1.25 | 1.25 |
| 706 | A156 | 38p multi | 1.50 | 1.50 |
| 707 | A156 | 44p multi | 1.75 | 1.75 |
| 708 | A156 | 64p multi | 2.50 | 2.50 |
| | | Nos. 703-708 (6) | 8.80 | 8.80 |

Nos. 703-708 depict the winning designs in the Future Children's Stamp Design Contest.

### Europa, 2000
### Common Design Type and

A157

Designs: 21p, Kite. 26p, Yacht sails. 65p, Rainbow and doves.

| 2000, May 9 | | Litho. | Perf. 13¼ | |
|---|---|---|---|---|
| 709 | A157 | 21p multi | .85 | .85 |
| 710 | A157 | 26p multi | 1.00 | 1.00 |
| 711 | CD17 | 36p multi | 1.40 | 1.40 |
| 712 | A157 | 65p multi | 2.50 | 2.50 |
| | | Nos. 709-712 (4) | 5.75 | 5.75 |

Battle of Britain, 60th Anniv. A158

Designs: 21p, Bristol Blenheim. 26p, Hawker Hurricane. 36p, Boulton Paul Defiant II. 40p, Gloster Gladiator. 45p, Bristol Beaufighter IF. 65p, Supermarine Spitfire IIc.

| 2000, April 28 | | Litho. | Perf. 13¼x13 | |
|---|---|---|---|---|
| 713 | A158 | 21p multi | .85 | .85 |
| 714 | A158 | 26p multi | 1.00 | 1.00 |
| 715 | A158 | 36p multi | 1.40 | 1.40 |
| 716 | A158 | 40p multi | 1.60 | 1.60 |
| 717 | A158 | 45p multi | 1.75 | 1.75 |
| a. | | Booklet pane, #713-715, 717 | 5.75 | |
| b. | | Booklet pane, #713, 715-717 | 6.25 | |
| c. | | Booklet pane, #714-717 | 6.25 | |
| 718 | A158 | 65p multi | 2.50 | 2.50 |
| a. | | Booklet pane of 2 | 5.75 | |
| b. | | Bklt. pane, #713-714, 716, 718 | 6.50 | |
| | | Complete booklet, #717a-717c, 718a-718b | 32.50 | |
| | | Nos. 713-718 (6) | 9.10 | 9.10 |

The Stamp Show 2000, London (Nos. 717a-717c, 718a-718b).

Flowers in Candie Gardens — A159

No. 719: a, Long styled iris. b, Watsonia. c, Arum lily. d, Hoop petticoat daffodil. e, Triteleia laxa. f, Peacock flower. g, African blue lily. h, Corn lily. i, Sea lily. j, Guernsey lily.

| | | | |
|---|---|---|---|
| **2000, Aug. 4** | **Litho.** | **Perf. 13½x13** | |
| 719 | Horiz. strip of 10 | 10.50 | 10.50 |
| *a.-j.* | A159 26p Any single | 1.00 | 1.00 |

Christmas A160

Snow-covered churches: 18p, Town Church, St. Peter's Port. 26p, St. Sampson's Church. 36p, Vale Church. 40p, St. Pierre du Bois Church. 45p, St. Martin's Church. 65p, St. John's Church, St. Peter's Port.

| | | | | |
|---|---|---|---|---|
| **2000, Oct. 19** | | **Litho.** | **Perf. 14¼x13¾** | |
| 720 | A160 | 18p multi | .70 | .70 |
| 721 | A160 | 26p multi | 1.00 | 1.00 |
| 722 | A160 | 36p multi | 1.40 | 1.40 |
| 723 | A160 | 40p multi | 1.60 | 1.60 |
| 724 | A160 | 45p multi | 1.75 | 1.75 |
| 725 | A160 | 65p multi | 2.50 | 2.50 |
| *a.* | Souvenir sheet, #720-725 | | 9.25 | 9.25 |
| | *Nos. 720-725 (6)* | | 8.95 | 8.95 |

Queen Victoria (1819-1901) — A161

Various portraits and: 21p, Statue of Victoria. 26p, Document. 36p, Statues of Victoria and Prince Albert. 40p, Commemoration stone, St. Peter's Port. 45p, Statue of Prince Albert. 65p, Victoria Tower.

| | | | | |
|---|---|---|---|---|
| **2001, Jan. 22** | | | **Perf. 14¾** | |
| 726 | A161 | 21p multi | .85 | .85 |
| 727 | A161 | 26p multi | 1.00 | 1.00 |
| 728 | A161 | 36p multi | 1.40 | 1.40 |
| 729 | A161 | 40p multi | 1.60 | 1.60 |
| 730 | A161 | 45p multi | 1.75 | 1.75 |
| 731 | A161 | 65p multi | 2.50 | 2.50 |
| *a.* | Souvenir sheet, #726-731 | | 9.25 | 9.25 |
| | *Nos. 726-731 (6)* | | 9.10 | 9.10 |

Hong Kong 2001 Stamp Exhibition (No. 731a).

Birds A162

| | | | | |
|---|---|---|---|---|
| **2001, Feb. 1** | | **Litho.** | **Perf. 14x14¾** | |
| 732 | A162 | 21p Kingfisher | .85 | .85 |
| 733 | A162 | 26p Garganey | 1.00 | 1.00 |
| 734 | A162 | 36p Little egret | 1.40 | 1.40 |
| 735 | A162 | 65p Little ringed plover | 2.50 | 2.50 |
| | *Nos. 732-735 (4)* | | 5.75 | 5.75 |

Europa (26p, 36p).

Guernsey Dog Club, Cent. — A163

Island Views — A164

Designs: 22p, Cavalier King Charles spaniel. 27p, Miniature schnauzer. 36p, German shepherd. 40p, Cocker spaniel. 45p, West Highland terrier. 65p, Dachshund.

| | | | | |
|---|---|---|---|---|
| **2001, Apr. 26** | | **Litho.** | **Perf. 13x13¼** | |
| 736 | A163 | 22p multi | .85 | .85 |
| 737 | A163 | 27p multi | 1.00 | 1.00 |
| 738 | A163 | 36p multi | 1.40 | 1.40 |
| 739 | A163 | 40p multi | 1.60 | 1.60 |
| 740 | A163 | 45p multi | 1.75 | 1.75 |
| 741 | A163 | 65p multi | 2.50 | 2.50 |
| | *Nos. 736-741 (6)* | | 9.10 | 9.10 |

***Serpentine Die Cut 14¼x14***

| | | |
|---|---|---|
| **2001, Apr. 26** | | **Litho.** |

No. 742: a, La Corbière sunset. b, Rue des Hougues. c, St. Saviour's Reservoir. d, Shell Beach, Herm. e, Telegraph Bay, Alderney. f, Alderney Railway. g, Vazon Bay. h, La Coupée, Sark. i, Les Hanois. j, Albecq,

**Self-Adhesive**

| | | | |
|---|---|---|---|
| **742** | Sheet of 10 | | 9.50 |
| *a.-e.* | A164 GY Any single | .85 | .85 |
| *f.-j.* | A164 UK Any single | 1.00 | 1.00 |
| *k.* | Booklet, 2 each #742a-742e | | 9.50 |
| *l.* | Booklet, 2 each #742f-742j | | 11.00 |
| *m.-q.* | As "a-e," photo., any single | .85 | .85 |
| *r.* | Strip, #742m-742q | | 4.25 |
| *s.-w.* | As "f-j," photo., any single | 1.00 | 1.00 |
| *x.* | Strip, #742s-742w | | 5.00 |

The photogravure stamps have a fuzzier appearance overall than the lithographed stamps. This is most noticeable in the crown where under magnification the bumps on the crown's outline are clearly distinct and well-defined as semicircles on the lithographed stamps, while ragged and ill-defined with a pointy appearance, on the photogravure stamps.

Nos. 742a-742e each sold for 22p, and Nos. 742f-742j each sold for 27p on day of issue.

No. 742 itself was available only from the Philatelic Bureau.

**Type of 1969 and**

Change of Guernsey Post Office to Guernsey Post Ltd., Oct. 1, 2001 — A165

Designs: 22p, Vision (water droplet on leaf). 27p, Understanding (hummingbird and flower). 36p, Individuality (butterfly's wing). 40p, Strength (nautilus shell cross-section). 45p, Community (honeycomb). 65p, Maturity (Dandelion gone to seed). £1, Like No. 23.

| | | | | |
|---|---|---|---|---|
| **2001, Aug. 1** | | **Litho.** | **Perf. 13¼x13** | |
| 743 | A165 | 22p multi | .85 | .85 |
| *a.* | Booklet pane of 3 | | 3.00 | — |
| 744 | A165 | 27p multi | 1.00 | 1.00 |
| *a.* | Booklet pane of 3 | | 3.25 | — |
| 745 | A165 | 36p multi | 1.40 | 1.40 |
| *a.* | Booklet pane of 3 | | 4.50 | — |
| 746 | A165 | 40p multi | 1.60 | 1.60 |
| *a.* | Booklet pane of 3 | | 5.50 | — |
| 747 | A165 | 45p multi | 1.75 | 1.75 |
| *a.* | Booklet pane of 3 | | 6.00 | — |
| 748 | A165 | 65p multi | 2.50 | 2.50 |
| *a.* | Booklet pane of 3 | | 8.25 | — |

***Perf. 14x14¼***

| | | | | |
|---|---|---|---|---|
| 749 | A4 | £1 Booklet pane of 1 | 8.50 | 8.50 |
| | Booklet, #743a, 744a, 745a, 746a, 747a, 748a, 749 | | 40.00 | |
| | *Nos. 743-749 (7)* | | 17.60 | 17.60 |

Panels on the at top and bottom of No. 749 are dark blue and clouds in silver margin are distinct. Never-bound examples of No. 749 with Prussian blue panels and less distinct clouds in the silver margin were given to standing order subscribers at no charge.

Christmas A166

Decorations: 19p, Tree of Joy, St. Peter Port. 27p, Cross, Les Cotils Christian Center. 36p, Les Ruettes Cottage, St. Saviour's. 40p, 17th cent. farmhouse. 45p, Sark Post Office. 65p, High Street, St. Peter Port.

| | | | | |
|---|---|---|---|---|
| **2001, Oct. 16** | | | **Perf. 14¼x14½** | |
| 750 | A166 | 19p multi | .75 | .75 |
| 751 | A166 | 27p multi | 1.00 | 1.00 |
| 752 | A166 | 36p multi | 1.40 | 1.40 |
| 753 | A166 | 40p multi | 1.60 | 1.60 |
| 754 | A166 | 45p multi | 1.75 | 1.75 |
| 755 | A166 | 65p multi | 2.50 | 2.50 |
| *a.* | Souvenir sheet, #750-755 | | 9.00 | 9.00 |
| | *Nos. 750-755 (6)* | | 9.00 | 9.00 |

Hafnia 01 Philatelic Exhibition, Copenhagen (#755a).

Circus — A167

Designs: 22p, Juggler. 27p, Clowns. 36p, Trapeze artists. 40p, Knife thrower. 45p, Acrobat. 65p, High-wire cyclist.

| | | | | |
|---|---|---|---|---|
| **2002, Feb. 6** | | **Litho.** | **Perf. 14¾x14½** | |
| 756 | A167 | 22p multi | .85 | .85 |
| 757 | A167 | 27p multi | 1.00 | 1.00 |
| 758 | A167 | 36p multi | 1.40 | 1.40 |
| 759 | A167 | 40p multi | 1.60 | 1.60 |
| 760 | A167 | 45p multi | 1.75 | 1.75 |
| 761 | A167 | 65p multi | 2.50 | 2.50 |
| | *Nos. 756-761 (6)* | | 9.10 | 9.10 |

Europa (27p, 36p).

Victor Hugo (1802-85), Writer — A168

Designs: 22p, Hugo and St. Peter Port. 27p, Cosette from Les Misérables. 36p, Valjean from Les Misérables. 40p, Javert from Les Misérables. 45p, Cosette and Marius from Les Misérables. 65p, Les Misérables, score from play based on book.

| | | | | |
|---|---|---|---|---|
| **2002, Feb. 6** | | | **Perf. 13¼x13** | |
| 762 | A168 | 22p multi | .85 | .85 |
| 763 | A168 | 27p multi | 1.00 | 1.00 |
| 764 | A168 | 36p multi | 1.40 | 1.40 |
| 765 | A168 | 40p multi | 1.60 | 1.60 |
| 766 | A168 | 45p multi | 1.75 | 1.75 |
| 767 | A168 | 65p multi | 2.50 | 2.50 |
| *a.* | Souvenir sheet of 6, #762-767 | | 9.25 | 9.25 |
| | *Nos. 762-767 (6)* | | 9.10 | 9.10 |

Souvenir Sheet

Pillar Boxes, 150th Anniv. — A169

| | | | |
|---|---|---|---|
| **2002, Apr. 30** | | **Perf. 14½x14¼** | |
| 768 | A169 | £1.75 multi | 5.25 5.25 |

Reign of Queen Elizabeth II, 50th Anniv. — A170

Various views of Queen.

| | | | | |
|---|---|---|---|---|
| **2002, Apr. 30** | | | **Perf. 13½** | |
| 769 | A170 | 22p multi | .85 | .85 |
| 770 | A170 | 27p multi | 1.00 | 1.00 |
| 771 | A170 | 36p multi | 1.40 | 1.40 |
| 772 | A170 | 40p multi | 1.60 | 1.60 |
| 773 | A170 | 45p multi | 1.75 | 1.75 |
| *a.* | Booklet pane, #770-773 | | 6.00 | |
| 774 | A170 | 65p multi | 2.50 | 2.50 |
| *a.* | Booklet pane, #769, 772-774 | | 6.50 | |
| *b.* | Booklet pane, #769-771, 774 | | 5.75 | |
| *c.* | Booklet pane, #769-774 | | 9.00 | |
| | *Nos. 769-774 (6)* | | 9.10 | 9.10 |

For complete booklet, see Alderney No. 184a.

Vacations in Sark — A171

No. 775: a, Family on dock, boat near dock. b, Family disembarking tractor-pulled transport. c, Family at campground. d, Family with bicycles at La Coupée. e, Swimming at Venus Pool. f, Family at La Seigneurie Gardens. g, Family at village pillar box. h, Family in horse-drawn cart. i, Family dining outdoors. j, Family at beach.

| | | | |
|---|---|---|---|
| **2002, July 30** | | **Perf. 13¼** | |
| 775 | Block of 10 | 10.00 | 10.00 |
| *a.-j.* | A171 27p Any single | 1.00 | 1.00 |

Awarding of Victoria Cross to Major Herbert Wallace Le Patourel, 60th Anniv. A172

Designs: 22p, Parade of Elizabeth College Combined Cadet Corps, 1934. 27p, In battle, Tunisia, 1942. 36p, As repatriated prisoner of war, 1943. 40p, Presentation of Victoria Cross ribbon, 1943. 45p, Return to Guernsey, 1948. 65p, Carrying King's Colors, 1968.

**2002, July 30**     **Perf. 13¼x13**
| | | | |
|---|---|---|---|
| 777 | A172 22p multi | .85 | .85 |
| 778 | A172 27p multi | 1.00 | 1.00 |
| 779 | A172 36p multi | 1.40 | 1.40 |
| 780 | A172 40p multi | 1.60 | 1.60 |
| 781 | A172 45p multi | 1.75 | 1.75 |
| 782 | A172 65p multi | 2.50 | 2.50 |
| | *Nos. 777-782 (6)* | 9.10 | 9.10 |

**Souvenir Sheet**

Queen Mother Elizabeth (1900-2002) — A173

**Litho. With Foil Application**
**2002, Aug. 4**     **Perf. 13¼**
| | | | |
|---|---|---|---|
| 783 | A173 £2 multi | 8.00 | 8.00 |

Christmas A174

Designs: 22p, Madonna and Child. 27p, Holy Family. 36p, Angel announcing birth to shepherds. 40p, Adoration of the shepherds. 45p, Three Kings. 65p, Star of Bethlehem.

**2002, Oct. 17**    **Litho.**    **Perf. 13¼x13**
| | | | |
|---|---|---|---|
| 784 | A174 22p multi | .85 | .85 |
| 785 | A174 27p multi | 1.00 | 1.00 |
| 786 | A174 36p multi | 1.40 | 1.40 |
| 787 | A174 40p multi | 1.60 | 1.60 |
| 788 | A174 45p multi | 1.75 | 1.75 |
| 789 | A174 65p multi | 2.50 | 2.50 |
| a. | Souvenir sheet, #784-789 | 9.25 | 9.25 |
| | *Nos. 784-789 (6)* | 9.10 | 9.10 |

World War II — A175

Designs: 22p, Pilots and airplanes. 27p, Airplanes over shoreline. 36p, Airplanes and searchlights. 40p, Airplanes dropping bombs. £1.50, HMS Charybdis and HMS Limbourne.

**2003, Jan. 30**     **Perf. 14**
| | | | |
|---|---|---|---|
| 790 | A175 | 22p multi | .85 | .85 |
| 791 | A175 | 27p multi | 1.00 | 1.00 |
| 792 | A175 | 36p multi | 1.40 | 1.40 |
| 793 | A175 | 40p multi | 1.60 | 1.60 |

**Size: 40x31mm**
**Perf. 14¼x14½**
| | | | |
|---|---|---|---|
| 794 | A175 £1.50 multi | 6.00 | 6.00 |
| | *Nos. 790-794 (5)* | 10.85 | 10.85 |

Dambusters Raid (#790-793), Operation Tunnel (#794), 60th anniv.

Island Games — A176

Designs: 22c, Hurdles. 27p, Cycling. 36p, Gymnastics. 40p, Windsurfing. 45p, Golf. 65p, Triathlon.

**2003, Jan. 30**     **Perf. 12½**
| | | | |
|---|---|---|---|
| 795 | A176 22p multi | .85 | .85 |
| 796 | A176 27p multi | 1.00 | 1.00 |
| 797 | A176 36p multi | 1.40 | 1.40 |
| 798 | A176 40p multi | 1.60 | 1.60 |
| 799 | A176 45p multi | 1.75 | 1.75 |
| 800 | A176 65p multi | 2.50 | 2.50 |
| a. | Souvenir sheet, #795-800 | 9.25 | 9.25 |
| | *Nos. 795-800 (6)* | 9.10 | 9.10 |

Poster Art — A177

Poster art from: 22p, 2003. 27p, 1995. 36p, 1988. 40p, 1978. 45p, 1968. 65p, 1956.

**2003, Apr. 10**     **Perf. 14¾x14½**
| | | | |
|---|---|---|---|
| 801 | A177 22p multi | .85 | .85 |
| 802 | A177 27p multi | 1.00 | 1.00 |
| 803 | A177 36p multi | 1.40 | 1.40 |
| 804 | A177 40p multi | 1.60 | 1.60 |
| 805 | A177 45p multi | 1.75 | 1.75 |
| 806 | A177 65p multi | 2.50 | 2.50 |
| | *Nos. 801-806 (6)* | 9.10 | 9.10 |

Europa (#802, 803).

**Souvenir Sheet**

Decommissioning of HMS Guernsey — A178

**2003, Apr. 10**     **Perf. 13¾x14¼**
| | | | |
|---|---|---|---|
| 807 | A178 £1.50 multi | 6.00 | 6.00 |

Prince William, 21st Birthday — A179

No. 808: a, With Princess Diana, 1983. b, With Princes Charles and Harry, 1985. c, At play in military uniform, 1986. d, In school uniform, with Prince Harry, 1989. e, Holding hand of Prince Charles, 1990. f, In ski jacket, with Princess Diana, 1991. g, In suit, 1995. h, With Princes Charles and Harry, 1997. i, Wearing helmet, 2000. j, Playing polo, 2002.

**2003, June 21**     **Perf. 13½x13**
| | | | |
|---|---|---|---|
| 808 | Horiz. strip of 10 | 10.00 | 10.00 |
| a.-j. | A179 27p Any single | 1.00 | 1.00 |
| k. | As #808a, perf. 13½x14 | 1.00 | 1.00 |
| l. | As #808b, perf. 13½x14 | 1.00 | 1.00 |
| m. | As #808c, perf. 13½x14 | 1.00 | 1.00 |
| n. | As #808d, perf. 13½x14 | 1.00 | 1.00 |
| o. | As #808e, perf. 13½x14 | 1.00 | 1.00 |
| p. | As #808f, perf. 13½x14 | 1.00 | 1.00 |
| q. | As #808g, perf. 13½x14 | 1.00 | 1.00 |
| r. | As #808h, perf. 13½x14 | 1.00 | 1.00 |
| s. | As #808i, perf. 13½x14 | 1.00 | 1.00 |
| t. | As #808j, perf. 13½x14 | 1.00 | 1.00 |
| u. | Booklet pane, #808k, 808m, 808p, 808q, 808s, 808t | 6.00 | — |
| v. | Booklet pane, #808l, 808m, 808np, 808o, 808r, 808s | 6.00 | — |
| w. | Booklet pane, #808k, 808n, 808p, 808q, 808r, 808t | 6.00 | — |
| x. | Booklet pane, #808k, 808l, 808m, 808o, 808r, 808t | 6.00 | — |
| y. | Booklet pane, #808l, 808n, 808o, 808p, 808q, 808s | 6.00 | — |
| | Complete booklet, #808u-808y | 30.00 | |

Letters A180

**Litho. With Foil Application**
**2003, July 3**     **Perf. 13¼**
| | | | |
|---|---|---|---|
| 809 | A180 £5 multi | 20.00 | 20.00 |

No. 809 is printed with thermochromatic ink that changes color when warmed.

Christmas A181

Scenes from *'Twas the Night Before Christmas*: 10p, Boy in bed, Christmas tree. 27p, Arrival of St. Nicholas. 36p, St. Nicholas near chimney. 40p, St. Nicholas carrying gifts. 45p, St. Nicholas placing gifts near tree. 65p, Departure of St. Nicholas.

**2003, Oct. 16**    **Litho.**    **Perf. 14¼**
| | | | |
|---|---|---|---|
| 810 | A181 10p multi | .40 | .40 |
| 811 | A181 27p multi | 1.00 | 1.00 |
| 812 | A181 36p multi | 1.40 | 1.40 |
| 813 | A181 40p multi | 1.60 | 1.60 |
| 814 | A181 45p multi | 1.75 | 1.75 |
| 815 | A181 65p multi | 2.50 | 2.50 |
| a. | Souvenir sheet, #810-815 | 8.75 | 8.75 |
| | *Nos. 810-815 (6)* | 8.65 | 8.65 |

**Souvenir Sheet**

Golden Snub-nosed Monkey — A182

**2004, Jan. 29**    **Litho.**    **Perf. 13¾x14¼**
| | | | |
|---|---|---|---|
| 816 | A182 £2 multi | 8.25 | 8.25 |

Clematis Flower Varieties — A183

**Serpentine Die Cut 12½**
**2004, Jan. 29**     **Litho.**
**Self-Adhesive**
**Inscribed "GY"**
| | | | |
|---|---|---|---|
| 817 | A183 (22p) Rosemoor | .85 | .85 |
| 818 | A183 (22p) Arctic Queen | .85 | .85 |
| 819 | A183 (22p) Harlow Carr | .85 | .85 |
| 820 | A183 (22p) Guernsey Cream | .85 | .85 |
| 821 | A183 (22p) Josephine | .85 | .85 |
| a. | Booklet pane, 2 each #817-821 | 8.50 | |
| | Complete booklet, No. 821a | 8.50 | |
| b. | Booklet pane 2 each #817-821 (see note) | 8.50 | |
| | Complete booklet, 10 No. 821b | 85.00 | |

**Inscribed "UK"**
| | | | |
|---|---|---|---|
| 822 | A183 (27p) Blue Moon | 1.10 | 1.10 |
| 823 | A183 (27p) Wisley | 1.10 | 1.10 |
| 824 | A183 (27p) Liberation | 1.10 | 1.10 |
| 825 | A183 (27p) Royal Velvet | 1.10 | 1.10 |
| 826 | A183 (27p) Hyde Hall | 1.10 | 1.10 |
| a. | Sheetlet, #817-826 | 10.00 | |
| b. | Booklet pane, 2 each #822-826 | 11.00 | |
| | Complete booklet, #826b | 11.00 | |
| c. | Booklet pane, 2 each #822-826 (see note) | 11.00 | |
| | Complete booklet, 10 #826c | 110.00 | |
| | *Nos. 817-826 (10)* | 9.75 | 9.75 |

Booklet panes Nos. 821a and 826b have blocks of 6 and 4 separated by a space with text. Nos. 821b and 826c do not have a space between stamps.

**World War II Type of 2003**
Scenes of D-Day: 26p, Royal Air Force Spitfire. 32p, Arrival of landing craft. 36p, Soldiers approaching Gold Beach, open door of landing craft. 40p, Soldiers seeking shelter behind obstacles. £1.50, SS Vega.

**2004, May 12**     **Perf. 14¼**
| | | | |
|---|---|---|---|
| 827 | A175 | 26p multi | 1.00 | 1.00 |
| 828 | A175 | 32p multi | 1.25 | 1.25 |
| 829 | A175 | 36p multi | 1.40 | 1.40 |
| 830 | A175 | 40p multi | 1.60 | 1.60 |

**Perf. 14¾x14¼**
**Size: 40x30mm**
| | | | |
|---|---|---|---|
| 831 | A175 £1.50 multi | 6.00 | 6.00 |
| | *Nos. 827-831 (5)* | 11.25 | 11.25 |

Vacations — A184

Inscriptions: 26p, Sand, Beaches, Sunshine. 32p, Views, Walking, Cliff top trails. 36p, Marina, Yachts, Cruisers. 40p, Dining, Seafood, A la carte. 45p, Churches, History, Monuments. 65p, Fauna, Flora, Colors.

**2004, May 12**     **Perf. 13½**
| | | | |
|---|---|---|---|
| 832 | A184 26p multi | 1.00 | 1.00 |
| 833 | A184 32p multi | 1.25 | 1.25 |
| 834 | A184 36p multi | 1.40 | 1.40 |
| 835 | A184 40p multi | 1.60 | 1.60 |
| 836 | A184 45p multi | 1.75 | 1.75 |
| 837 | A184 65p multi | 2.50 | 2.50 |
| | *Nos. 832-837 (6)* | 9.50 | 9.50 |

Europa (32p, 36p).

Loyalty to the British Crown, 800th Anniv. — A185

**2004, June 24**     **Perf. 13¼x14**
| | | | |
|---|---|---|---|
| 838 | A185 26p Loyalty | 1.00 | 1.00 |
| 839 | A185 32p Trade | 1.25 | 1.25 |
| 840 | A185 36p Unity | 1.40 | 1.40 |
| 841 | A185 40p Protection | 1.60 | 1.60 |
| 842 | A185 45p Justice | 1.75 | 1.75 |
| 843 | A185 65p Industry | 2.50 | 2.50 |
| a. | Souvenir sheet, #838-843, perf. 14x13¼ | 10.00 | 10.00 |
| | *Nos. 838-843 (6)* | 9.50 | 9.50 |

2004 Summer Olympics, Athens — A186

**2004, July 29**     **Perf. 13½**
| | | | |
|---|---|---|---|
| 844 | A186 32p Discus | 1.25 | 1.25 |
| 845 | A186 36p Javelin | 1.40 | 1.40 |
| 846 | A186 45p Runners | 1.75 | 1.75 |
| a. | Booklet pane, #845, 846, 2 #844 | 5.75 | — |
| 847 | A186 65p Wrestlers | 2.50 | 2.50 |
| a. | Booklet pane, #846, 847, 2 #845 | 7.25 | — |
| b. | Booklet pane, #844, 847, 2 #846 | 7.25 | — |
| c. | Booklet pane, #844, 845, 2 #847 | 7.75 | — |
| d. | Booklet pane, #844-847 | 7.00 | — |
| | *Nos. 844-847 (4)* | 6.90 | 6.90 |

Nos. 846a, 847a-847d are perf 14¾x14.

**Souvenir Sheet**
**Perf. 14¾x14**
| | | | |
|---|---|---|---|
| 848 | A186 £1 Athletes, horiz. | 4.00 | 4.00 |
| a. | Booklet pane, #848 | 4.00 | — |
| | Complete booklet, Nos. 846a, 847a-847d, 848a | 40.00 | |

No. 848 contains one 40x30mm stamp. No. 848a has binding stub at left.

Christmas A187

Designs: No. 849a, Little Donkey. No. 849b, While Shepherds Watched. No. 849c, Away in a Manger. No. 849d, Unto Us a Child is Born. No. 849e, We Three Kings.

32p, Angel wings. 36p, Christmas tree ornament. 40p, Holly leaf and berries. 45p, Snowman's scarf and buttons. 65p, Christmas tree star.

**2004, Oct. 28**    Litho.    *Perf. 13*

| | | | | |
|---|---|---|---|---|
| 849 | | Horiz. strip of 5 | 4.00 | 4.00 |
| *a.-e.* | A187 | 20p Any single | .80 | .80 |
| 850 | A187 | 32p multi | 1.25 | 1.25 |
| 851 | A187 | 36p multi | 1.40 | 1.40 |
| 852 | A187 | 40p multi | 1.60 | 1.60 |
| 853 | A187 | 45p multi | 1.75 | 1.75 |
| 854 | A187 | 65p multi | 2.50 | 2.50 |
| | | *Nos. 849-854 (6)* | 12.50 | 12.50 |

**World War II Type of 2003**

Designs: 26p, Soldiers on Army Landrover greet Guernsey residents. 32p, Woman celebrating liberation from German rule. 36p, Parents reunite with children. 40p, Soldiers return home. £1.50, Winston Churchill.

**2005, Feb. 3**    Litho.    *Perf. 14¼*

| | | | | |
|---|---|---|---|---|
| 855 | A175 | 26p multi | 1.00 | 1.00 |
| 856 | A175 | 32p multi | 1.25 | 1.25 |
| 857 | A175 | 36p multi | 1.40 | 1.40 |
| 858 | A175 | 40p multi | 1.60 | 1.60 |

**Size: 40x30mm**
**Perf. 14¾x14¼**

| | | | | |
|---|---|---|---|---|
| 859 | A175 | £1.50 multi | 6.00 | 6.00 |
| | | *Nos. 855-859 (5)* | 11.25 | 11.25 |

Paintings of Flowers by William John Caparne — A188

Designs: 26p, Iris "Dorothea" and "Royal." 32p, Nerine fothergilli "Major." 36p, Iris "Garnet." 40p, Narcissus "Sir Watkin." 45p, Narcissus "Rip Van Winkle." 65p, Narcissus "Sulphur Phoenix."

**2005, Feb. 3**    *Perf. 13¼*

| | | | | |
|---|---|---|---|---|
| 860 | A188 | 26p multi | 1.00 | 1.00 |
| 861 | A188 | 32p multi | 1.25 | 1.25 |
| 862 | A188 | 36p multi | 1.40 | 1.40 |
| 863 | A188 | 40p multi | 1.60 | 1.60 |
| 864 | A188 | 45p multi | 1.75 | 1.75 |
| 865 | A188 | 65p multi | 2.50 | 2.50 |
| *a.* | | Souvenir sheet, #860-865 | 10.00 | 10.00 |
| | | *Nos. 860-865 (6)* | 9.50 | 9.50 |

Liberation of Guernsey, 60th Anniv. A189

No. 866: a, King George VI. b, Queen Elizabeth II.

**Litho. With Foil Application**

**2005, May 9**    *Perf. 14¾x14*

| | | | | |
|---|---|---|---|---|
| 866 | | Horiz. pair | 8.50 | 8.50 |
| *a.-b.* | A189 | £1 Either single | 4.00 | 4.00 |

Queen Mary 2 Ocean Liner — A190

**Litho. & Embossed With Foil Application**

**2005, May 9**    *Perf. 13¼*

| | | | | |
|---|---|---|---|---|
| 867 | A190 | £4 multi | 16.00 | 16.00 |

Gastronomy A191

Dishes: 26p, Spider crab. 32p, Red mullet and crab cake. 36p, Lobster salad. 40p, Brill on spinach with mussels. 45p, Prawn salad.

---

65p, Salmon wrapped in spinach with mussels.

**2005, May 9**    Litho.    *Perf. 14x13¼*

| | | | | |
|---|---|---|---|---|
| 868 | A191 | 26p multi | 1.00 | 1.00 |
| 869 | A191 | 32p multi | 1.25 | 1.25 |
| 870 | A191 | 36p multi | 1.40 | 1.40 |
| 871 | A191 | 40p multi | 1.60 | 1.60 |
| 872 | A191 | 45p multi | 1.75 | 1.75 |
| 873 | A191 | 65p multi | 2.50 | 2.50 |
| | | *Nos. 868-873 (6)* | 9.50 | 9.50 |

Europa (32p, 36p).

**Souvenir Sheet**

Basking Shark — A192

**2005, July 21**    *Perf. 13¼*

| | | | | |
|---|---|---|---|---|
| 874 | A192 | £2 multi | 8.50 | 8.50 |

SeaGuernsey 2005 — A193

Designs: 26p, Fishing boat and gulls. 32p, Sailboat. 36p, Windsurfer. 40p, Fisherman. 65p, Horse and rider on beach.

**2005, July 21**    *Perf. 13¼x13¾*

| | | | | |
|---|---|---|---|---|
| 875 | A193 | 26p multi | 1.00 | 1.00 |
| 876 | A193 | 32p multi | 1.25 | 1.25 |
| *a.* | | Booklet pane, 2 each #875-876 | 4.75 | |
| 877 | A193 | 36p multi | 1.40 | 1.40 |
| *a.* | | Booklet pane, 2 each #876-877 | 5.50 | |
| 878 | A193 | 40p multi | 1.60 | 1.60 |
| *a.* | | Booklet pane, 2 each #877-878 | 6.25 | |
| 879 | A193 | 65p multi | 2.50 | 2.50 |
| *a.* | | Booklet pane, 2 each #878-879 | 8.50 | |
| *b.* | | Booklet pane, 2 each #875, 879 | 7.50 | — |
| *c.* | | Booklet pane, #876-879 | 7.00 | — |
| | | Complete booklet, #876a, 877a, 878a, 879a, 879b, 879c | 40.00 | |
| | | *Nos. 875-879 (5)* | 7.75 | 7.75 |

Christmas — A194

No. 880 — Stained glass windows from: a, St. Pierre du Bois Church. b, St. Saviour's Church. c, St. Martin's Church. d, Torteval Church. e, St. Sampson's Church.

32p, Vale Church. 36p, Castel Church. 40p, St. Anne's Church, Alderney. 45p, St. Andrew's Church. 65p, Forest Church.

**2005, Oct. 27**    *Perf. 14x14¼*

| | | | | |
|---|---|---|---|---|
| 880 | | Horiz. strip of 5 | 4.00 | 4.00 |
| *a.-e.* | A194 | 20p Any single | .80 | .80 |
| 881 | A194 | 32p multi | 1.25 | 1.25 |
| 882 | A194 | 36p multi | 1.40 | 1.40 |
| 883 | A194 | 40p multi | 1.60 | 1.60 |
| 884 | A194 | 45p multi | 1.75 | 1.75 |
| 885 | A194 | 65p multi | 2.50 | 2.50 |
| | | *Nos. 880-885 (6)* | 12.50 | 12.50 |

Victoria Cross, 150th Anniv. A195

Battle scenes and medals from: 29p, Iraq Conflict, 2004. 34p, Falklands Conflict, 1982. 38p, Battle of El Alamein, World War II, 1942. 42p, Battle of Gallipoli, World War I, 1915. 47p, Battle of Rorke's Drift, Zulu War, 1879. 68p, Charge of the Light Brigade, Crimean War, 1854.

---

**Perf. 13¾x13½**

**2006, Feb. 16**    Litho.

| | | | | |
|---|---|---|---|---|
| 886 | A195 | 29p multi | 1.10 | 1.10 |
| 887 | A195 | 34p multi | 1.40 | 1.40 |
| 888 | A195 | 38p multi | 1.50 | 1.50 |
| 889 | A195 | 42p multi | 1.60 | 1.60 |
| 890 | A195 | 47p multi | 1.90 | 1.90 |
| 891 | A195 | 68p multi | 2.75 | 2.75 |
| | | *Nos. 886-891 (6)* | 10.25 | 10.25 |

**Souvenir Sheet**

Endangered Species of the Florida Everglades — A196

No. 892: a, £1, Leatherback turtle. b, £1.50, Wood stork.

**2006, Feb. 16**    *Perf. 14x14¾*

| | | | | |
|---|---|---|---|---|
| 892 | A196 | Sheet of 2, #a-b | 10.00 | 10.00 |

International Tourist Attractions — A197

Designs: 29p, Eiffel Tower, Paris. 34p, Sphinx, Egypt. 42p, Great Wall of China. 45p, Uluru (Ayers Rock), Australia. 47p, Statue of Liberty, New York. 68p, Taj Mahal, India.

**2006, May 20**    *Perf. 13¼x13½*

| | | | | |
|---|---|---|---|---|
| 893 | A197 | 29p multi | 1.10 | 1.10 |
| 894 | A197 | 34p multi | 1.40 | 1.40 |
| 895 | A197 | 42p multi | 1.60 | 1.60 |
| 896 | A197 | 45p multi | 1.75 | 1.75 |
| 897 | A197 | 47p multi | 1.90 | 1.90 |
| 898 | A197 | 68p multi | 2.75 | 2.75 |
| | | *Nos. 893-898 (6)* | 10.50 | 10.50 |

Europa (34p, 42p).

Isambard Kingdom Brunel (1806-59) — A198

Designs: 29p, Brunel, mailbags for Guernsey at Paddington Station, London. 34p, Mail train leaving Paddington Station. 42p, Train on Wharncliffe Viaduct. 45p, Mail train and ship at harbor, Weymouth. 47p, Mailboat Ibex in English Channel. 68p, Ibex at St. Peter Port.

**2006, May 20**    *Perf. 13¼x13*

| | | | | |
|---|---|---|---|---|
| 899 | A198 | 29p multi | 1.10 | 1.10 |
| 900 | A198 | 34p multi | 1.40 | 1.40 |
| 901 | A198 | 42p multi | 1.60 | 1.60 |
| 902 | A198 | 45p multi | 1.75 | 1.75 |
| *a.* | | Booklet pane, #899-902 | 6.00 | |
| 903 | A198 | 47p multi | 1.90 | 1.90 |
| *a.* | | Booklet pane, #900-903 | 6.75 | |
| 904 | A198 | 68p multi | 2.75 | 2.75 |
| *a.* | | Booklet pane, #901-904 | 8.00 | — |
| *b.* | | Booklet pane, #899, 902-904 | 7.50 | — |
| *c.* | | Booklet pane, #899-900, 903-904 | 7.00 | — |
| *d.* | | Booklet pane, #899-901, 904 | 7.00 | — |
| | | Complete booklet, #902a, 903a, 904a-904d | 42.50 | |
| | | *Nos. 899-904 (6)* | 10.50 | 10.50 |

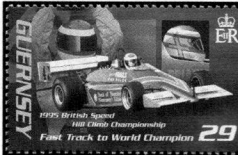

Andy Priaulx, Race Car Driver A199

---

Priaulx, car and events: 29p, British Speed Hill Climb Championship, 1995. 34p, Renault Spider Cup, 1999. 42p, British Formula 3, 2001. 45p, FIA European Touring Car Championship, 2004. 47p, Nürburgring, Germany, 2005. 68p, FIA World Touring Car Championship, 2005.

**2006, May 20**    *Perf. 13½*

| | | | | |
|---|---|---|---|---|
| 905 | A199 | 29p multi | 1.10 | 1.10 |
| 906 | A199 | 34p multi | 1.40 | 1.40 |
| 907 | A199 | 42p multi | 1.60 | 1.60 |
| 908 | A199 | 45p multi | 1.75 | 1.75 |
| 909 | A199 | 47p multi | 1.90 | 1.90 |
| 910 | A199 | 68p multi | 2.75 | 2.75 |
| *a.* | | Souvenir sheet, #905-910 | 11.00 | 11.00 |
| | | *Nos. 905-910 (6)* | 10.50 | 10.50 |

Queen Elizabeth II, 80th Birthday A200

**Litho. & Embossed with Foil Application**

**2006, June 17**    *Perf. 14¾x14¼*

| | | | | |
|---|---|---|---|---|
| 911 | A200 | £10 multi | 40.00 | 40.00 |

L'Erée Wetlands A201

Designs: 29p, Gray seal. 34p, Ormer. 42p, Common blenny. 45p, Le Creux ès Faies. 47p, Yellow-horned poppy. 68p, Oyster catchers.

**2006, July 27**    Litho.    *Perf. 14x13¼*

| | | | | |
|---|---|---|---|---|
| 912 | A201 | 29p multi | 1.10 | 1.10 |
| 913 | A201 | 34p multi | 1.40 | 1.40 |
| 914 | A201 | 42p multi | 1.60 | 1.60 |
| 915 | A201 | 45p multi | 1.75 | 1.75 |
| 916 | A201 | 47p multi | 1.90 | 1.90 |
| 917 | A201 | 68p multi | 2.75 | 2.75 |
| *a.* | | Souvenir sheet, #912-917 | 11.00 | 11.00 |
| | | *Nos. 912-917 (6)* | 10.50 | 10.50 |

Addition of L'Erée Wetlands to Ramsar Convention Protected Wetlands List. See Nos. 972-977.

The Twelve Days of Christmas A202

No. 918: a, A partridge in a pear tree. b, Two turtle doves. c, Three French hens. d, Four calling birds. e, Five gold rings. f, Six geese a-laying.

29p, Seven swans a-swimming. 34p, Eight maids a-milking. 42p, Nine ladies dancing. 45p, Ten lords a-leaping. 47p, Eleven pipers piping. 68p, Twelve drummers drumming.

**2006, Nov. 2**    Litho.    *Perf. 14¾x15*

| | | | | |
|---|---|---|---|---|
| 918 | | Horiz. strip of 6 | 5.00 | 5.00 |
| *a.-f.* | A202 | 22p Any single | .80 | .80 |
| 919 | A202 | 29p multi | 1.10 | 1.10 |
| 920 | A202 | 34p multi | 1.40 | 1.40 |
| 921 | A202 | 42p multi | 1.60 | 1.60 |
| 922 | A202 | 45p multi | 1.75 | 1.75 |
| 923 | A202 | 47p multi | 1.90 | 1.90 |
| 924 | A202 | 68p multi | 2.60 | 2.60 |
| | | *Nos. 918-924 (7)* | 15.35 | 15.35 |

La Société Guernesiaise, 125th Anniv. — A203

No. 925: a, Rocks, Albecq. b, Ivy bee. c, Vale Church. d, Common frog. e, Parasol mushroom. f, Southern marsh orchid. g, Shore crab. h, Alderney blonde hedgehog. i, Barn owl. j, Le Trépied dolmen.

## Serpentine Die Cut 12½
**2007, Mar. 8**
### Self-Adhesive

| | | | |
|---|---|---|---|
| 925 | Sheet of 10 | 13.50 | |
| a.-e. | A203 (32p) Any single | 1.25 | 1.25 |
| f.-j. | A203 (37p) Any single | 1.40 | 1.40 |
| k. | Booklet pane of 10, 2 each #925a-925e | 12.50 | |
| | Complete booklet, 1 #925k | 12.50 | |
| l. | Booklet pane of 10, 2 each #925f-925j | 14.00 | |
| | Complete booklet, 1 #925l | 14.00 | |
| m. | Booklet pane of 10, 2 each #925m (see note) | 14.00 | |
| | Complete booklet, 10 #925m | 125.00 | |
| n. | Booklet pane of 10, 2 each #925n (see note) | 14.00 | |
| | Complete booklet, 1 #925n | 140.00 | |

Nos. 925a-925e are inscribed "GY"; Nos. 925f-925j, "UK."

Booklet panes Nos. 925k and 925l have blocks of 6 and 4 separated by a space between stamps. Booklet panes Nos. 925m and 925n do not have a space between stamps.

Falkland Islands War, 25th Anniv. A204

Designs: 32p, Troops leaving for war. 37p, Landing at San Carlos Bay. 45p, Harriers flying over SS Canberra. 48p, Lieutenant Colonel H. Jones firing gun. 50p, Helicopter evacuating men from ship. 71p, Troops marching toward Port Stanley.

**2007, Mar. 8**      **Perf. 13½**

| | | | | |
|---|---|---|---|---|
| 926 | A204 | 32p multi | 1.25 | 1.25 |
| 927 | A204 | 37p multi | 1.40 | 1.40 |
| 928 | A204 | 45p multi | 1.75 | 1.75 |
| 929 | A204 | 48p multi | 1.90 | 1.90 |
| 930 | A204 | 50p multi | 1.90 | 1.90 |
| 931 | A204 | 71p multi | 2.75 | 2.75 |
| a. | Souvenir sheet, #926-931 | | 11.00 | 11.00 |

Scouting, Cent. — A205

Designs: 32p, 1907 Scout camping. 37p, 1924 Scout sailing. 45p, 1947 Scouts fishing. 48p, 1968 Scouts making model airplanes. 50p, 1990 Scouts exploring cave. 71p, 2007 Scouts on rollerblades.

**2007, May 24**   **Litho.**   **Perf. 13¼x13**

| | | | | |
|---|---|---|---|---|
| 932 | A205 | 32p multi | 1.25 | 1.25 |
| 933 | A205 | 37p multi | 1.50 | 1.50 |
| 934 | A205 | 45p multi | 1.75 | 1.75 |
| 935 | A205 | 48p multi | 1.90 | 1.90 |
| 936 | A205 | 50p multi | 2.00 | 2.00 |
| 937 | A205 | 71p multi | 3.00 | 3.00 |
| | Nos. 932-937 (6) | | 11.40 | 11.40 |

Europa (37p, 45p).

British Formula 1 World Championship Cars and Drivers — A206

Driver and championship year: No. 938, Mike Hawthorn, 1958. No. 939, Jackie Stewart, 1971. No. 940, Graham Hill, 1962. No. 941, James Hunt, 1976. 45p, Jim Clark, 1963. 48p, Nigel Mansell, 1992. 50p, John Surtees, 1964. 71p, Damon Hill, 1996.

**2007, May 24**      **Perf. 14x13¾**

| | | | | |
|---|---|---|---|---|
| 938 | A206 | 32p multi | 1.25 | 1.25 |
| 939 | A206 | 32p multi | 1.25 | 1.25 |
| 940 | A206 | 37p multi | 1.50 | 1.50 |
| 941 | A206 | 37p multi | 1.50 | 1.50 |
| 942 | A206 | 45p multi | 1.75 | 1.75 |
| 943 | A206 | 48p multi | 1.90 | 1.90 |
| 944 | A206 | 50p multi | 2.00 | 2.00 |
| 945 | A206 | 71p multi | 3.00 | 3.00 |
| | Nos. 938-945 (8) | | 14.15 | 14.15 |

Wedding of Queen Elizabeth II and Prince Philip, 60th Anniv. — A207

Designs: 32p, Princess Elizabeth and Prince Philip, c. 1967. 37p, With baby Princess Anne. 45p, Off duty, wearing casual clothes. 48p, On tour, Queen in jacket and hat. 50p, With grandchildren Princes William and Henry. 71p, Recent photo.

**2007, Aug. 2**      **Perf. 13¼x13¾**
### Background Color

| | | | | |
|---|---|---|---|---|
| 946 | A207 | 32p red brown | 1.40 | 1.40 |
| 947 | A207 | 37p tan | 1.50 | 1.50 |
| a. | Booklet pane, 2 each #946-947 | | 6.00 | — |
| 948 | A207 | 45p light blue | 1.90 | 1.90 |
| a. | Booklet pane, 2 each #947-948 | | 7.00 | — |
| 949 | A207 | 48p light green | 2.00 | 2.00 |
| a. | Booklet pane, 2 each #948-949 | | 8.00 | — |
| 950 | A207 | 50p orange | 2.10 | 2.10 |
| a. | Booklet pane, 2 each #949-950 | | 8.25 | — |
| 951 | A207 | 71p lilac | 3.00 | 3.00 |
| a. | Booklet pane, 2 each #950-951 | | 10.50 | — |
| b. | Booklet pane, 2 each #946, 951 | | 9.00 | — |
| | Complete booklet, #947a, 948a, 949a, 950a, 951a, 951b | | 49.00 | |
| | Nos. 946-951 (6) | | 11.90 | 11.90 |

### Souvenir Sheet

Mountain Gorilla — A208

**2007, Aug. 2**      **Perf. 14**

| | | | | |
|---|---|---|---|---|
| 952 | A208 | £2.50 multi | 10.50 | 10.50 |

Seaside Views A209

Designs: 32p, St. Peter Port Harbor. 37p, Fort Grey, Rocquaine. 45p, Point Robert Lighthouse, Sark. 48p, Brecqhou Island as seen from Sark. 50p, Vazon Bay. 71p, Fontenelle Bay.

**2007, Oct. 1**   **Litho.**   **Perf. 13¾x13½**

| | | | | |
|---|---|---|---|---|
| 953 | A209 | 32p multi | 1.40 | 1.40 |
| 954 | A209 | 37p multi | 1.50 | 1.50 |
| 955 | A209 | 45p multi | 1.90 | 1.90 |
| 956 | A209 | 48p multi | 2.00 | 2.00 |
| 957 | A209 | 50p multi | 2.10 | 2.10 |
| 958 | A209 | 71p multi | 3.00 | 3.00 |
| | Nos. 953-958 (6) | | 11.90 | 11.90 |

Christmas — A210

Decorations: No. 959, Crystal snowflake in snow. No. 960, Crystal snowflake pendant. No. 961, Angel candle accent. No. 962, Crystal angel pendant. No. 963, Pine cone in snow. No. 964, Spherical ornament with leaf pattern. 32p, Spherical ornament with spiral pattern. 37p, Candles. 45p, Bell. 48p, Ribbon bow. 50p, Christmas tree star. 71p, Porcelain angel.

**2007, Oct. 25**      **Perf. 14½x15**

| | | | | |
|---|---|---|---|---|
| 959 | A210 | 27p multi | 1.10 | 1.10 |
| 960 | A210 | 27p multi | 1.10 | 1.10 |
| 961 | A210 | 27p multi | 1.10 | 1.10 |
| 962 | A210 | 27p multi | 1.10 | 1.10 |
| 963 | A210 | 27p multi | 1.10 | 1.10 |
| 964 | A210 | 27p multi | 1.10 | 1.10 |
| 965 | A210 | 32p multi | 1.40 | 1.40 |
| 966 | A210 | 37p multi | 1.50 | 1.50 |
| 967 | A210 | 45p multi | 1.90 | 1.90 |
| 968 | A210 | 48p multi | 2.00 | 2.00 |
| 969 | A210 | 50p multi | 2.10 | 2.10 |
| 970 | A210 | 71p multi | 3.00 | 3.00 |
| | Nos. 959-970 (12) | | 18.50 | 18.50 |

### Souvenir Sheet

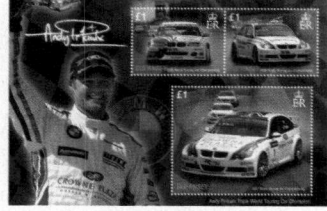

Race Cars Used by World Touring Car Champion Andy Priaulx — A211

Race cars used by Priaulx in: a, 2005 (40x30mm). b, 2006 (40x30mm). c, 2007 (60x48mm).

**2008, Jan. 18 Litho.**   **Perf. 13¾x14¼**

| | | | | |
|---|---|---|---|---|
| 971 | A211 | Sheet of 3 | 12.00 | 12.00 |
| a.-c. | £1 Any single | | 4.00 | 4.00 |

### Wetlands Type of 2006

Designs: 34p, Beadlet anemones. 40p, Sand crocus. 48p, Fulmars. 51p, Sheep's bit. 53p, Thick-lipped gray mullets. 74p, Light bulb sea squirts.

**2008, Feb. 28**      **Perf. 13x13¼**

| | | | | |
|---|---|---|---|---|
| 972 | A201 | 34p multi | 1.40 | 1.40 |
| 973 | A201 | 40p multi | 1.60 | 1.60 |
| 974 | A201 | 48p multi | 1.90 | 1.90 |
| 975 | A201 | 51p multi | 2.00 | 2.00 |
| 976 | A201 | 53p multi | 2.10 | 2.10 |
| 977 | A201 | 74p multi | 3.00 | 3.00 |
| a. | Miniature sheet, #972-977 | | 12.00 | 12.00 |
| | Nos. 972-977 (6) | | 12.00 | 12.00 |

Addition of Sark to Ramsar Convention Protected Wetlands List.

Flowers — A212

Designs: 10p, Red campion. 20p, Great bindweed. 30p, Spear thistle. 40p, Greater bird's foot trefoil. 50p, Sheep's bit. £1, Marguerite, vert. £2, Sea campion, vert.

**2008, Feb. 28**    **Litho.**    **Perf. 14**

| | | | | |
|---|---|---|---|---|
| 978 | A212 | 10p multi | .40 | .40 |
| 979 | A212 | 20p multi | .80 | .80 |
| 980 | A212 | 30p multi | 1.25 | 1.25 |
| 981 | A212 | 40p multi | 1.60 | 1.60 |
| 982 | A212 | 50p multi | 2.00 | 2.00 |

### Litho. & Embossed

| | | | | |
|---|---|---|---|---|
| 983 | A212 | £1 multi | 4.00 | 4.00 |
| 984 | A212 | £2 multi | 8.00 | 8.00 |
| | Nos. 978-984 (7) | | 18.05 | 18.05 |

Mr. Men and Little Miss Children's Book Characters A213

Designs: 34p, Mr. Happy. 40p, Mr. Bump. 48p, Little Miss Naughty. 51p, Mr. Greedy. 53p, Mr. Strong. 74p, Mr. Tickle.

**2008, May 15**   **Litho.**   **Perf. 14x13½**

| | | | | |
|---|---|---|---|---|
| 985 | A213 | 34p multi | 1.40 | 1.40 |
| 986 | A213 | 40p multi | 1.60 | 1.60 |
| 987 | A213 | 48p multi | 1.90 | 1.90 |
| 988 | A213 | 51p multi | 2.00 | 2.00 |
| 989 | A213 | 53p multi | 2.10 | 2.10 |
| 990 | A213 | 74p multi | 3.00 | 3.00 |
| | Nos. 985-990 (6) | | 12.00 | 12.00 |

Guernesiais Phrases — A214

Guernesias phrases for: 34p, Till the next time. 40p, Hello. 48p, Oh! There you are. 51p, Good gracious. 53p, Cor blimey. 74p, How are things?

**2008, May 15**      **Perf. 13¼x13**

| | | | | |
|---|---|---|---|---|
| 991 | A214 | 34p multi | 1.40 | 1.40 |
| 992 | A214 | 40p multi | 1.60 | 1.60 |
| 993 | A214 | 48p multi | 1.90 | 1.90 |
| 994 | A214 | 51p multi | 2.00 | 2.00 |
| 995 | A214 | 53p multi | 2.10 | 2.10 |
| 996 | A214 | 74p multi | 3.00 | 3.00 |
| | Nos. 991-996 (6) | | 12.00 | 12.00 |

Europa (40p, 48p).

### La Société Guernsiaise Type of 2007

No. 997 — Photographs of Guernsey: a, Pleimont Point. b, Saint's Harbor. c, Rocks at Albecq. d, Groins at Vazon Bay. e, La Bette Bay. f, Bordeaux Harbor. g, St. Saviour's Reservoir. h, Vazon Bay. i, St. Peter Port Lighthouse. j, Petit Port.

### Serpentine Die Cut 12½
**2008, June 9**      **Litho.**
### Self-Adhesive

| | | | | |
|---|---|---|---|---|
| 997 | | Sheet of 10 | 15.00 | |
| a.-e. | A203 (34p) Any single | | 1.40 | 1.40 |
| f.-j. | A203 (40p) Any single | | 1.60 | 1.60 |
| k. | Booklet pane of 10, 2 each #997a-997e | | 14.00 | |
| l. | Booklet pane of 10, 2 each #997f-997j | | 16.00 | |

Nos. 997a-997e are inscribed "GY"; Nos. 997f-997j, "UK."

Ford Model T, Cent. A215

Model T: 34p, And house. 40p, Converted to truck. 48p, Converted to pickup truck. 51p, On tree-lined street. 53p, Converted to World War I army ambulance. 74p, Red 1912 Roadster.

**2008, July 31**      **Perf. 13¼**

| | | | | |
|---|---|---|---|---|
| 998 | A215 | 34p multi | 1.40 | 1.40 |
| 999 | A215 | 40p multi | 1.60 | 1.60 |
| 1000 | A215 | 48p multi | 1.90 | 1.90 |
| 1001 | A215 | 51p multi | 2.00 | 2.00 |
| a. | Booklet pane of 4, #998-1001 | | 7.00 | |
| 1002 | A215 | 53p multi | 2.10 | 2.10 |
| a. | Booklet pane of 4, #998-999, 1001-1002 | | 7.25 | — |
| 1003 | A215 | 74p multi | 3.00 | 3.00 |
| a. | Booklet pane of 4, #1000-1003 | | 9.00 | |
| b. | Booklet pane of 4, #998-999, 1002-1003 | | 8.25 | — |
| c. | Booklet pane of 4, #999-1000, 1002-1003 | | 8.75 | — |
| d. | Booklet pane of 4, #998, 1000-1001, 1003 | | 8.50 | — |
| | Complete booklet, #1001a, 1002a, 1003a, 1003b, 1003c, 1003d | | 49.00 | |
| | Nos. 998-1003 (6) | | 12.00 | 12.00 |

St. Paul's Cathedral, London, 300th Anniv. — A216

Blocks of granite from Guernsey and various depictions of cathedral.

## 2008, Oct. 30                    Perf. 13¼

| | | | | |
|---|---|---|---|---|
| 1004 | A216 | 34p multi | 1.10 | 1.10 |
| 1005 | A216 | 40p multi | 1.40 | 1.40 |
| 1006 | A216 | 48p multi | 1.60 | 1.60 |
| 1007 | A216 | 51p multi | 1.75 | 1.75 |
| 1008 | A216 | 53p multi | 1.75 | 1.75 |
| 1009 | A216 | 74p multi | 2.40 | 2.40 |
| | Nos. 1004-1009 (6) | | 10.00 | 10.00 |

Particles of granite were applied to parts of the designs by a thermographic process.

Christmas — A217

## 2008, Oct. 30                    Perf. 13¾x13¼

| | | | | |
|---|---|---|---|---|
| 1010 | A217 | 29p Spruce | .95 | .95 |
| 1011 | A217 | 29p Butchers broom | .95 | .95 |
| 1012 | A217 | 29p Mistletoe | .95 | .95 |
| 1013 | A217 | 29p Ivy | .95 | .95 |
| 1014 | A217 | 29p Cactus | .95 | .95 |
| 1015 | A217 | 29p Cyclamen | .95 | .95 |
| 1016 | A217 | 34p Holly | 1.10 | 1.10 |
| 1017 | A217 | 40p Poinsettia | 1.40 | 1.40 |
| 1018 | A217 | 48p Bracken | 1.60 | 1.60 |
| 1019 | A217 | 51p Hawthorn | 1.75 | 1.75 |
| 1020 | A217 | 53p Peppermint clematis | 1.75 | 1.75 |
| 1021 | A217 | 74p Pyracantha | 2.40 | 2.40 |
| | Nos. 1010-1021 (12) | | 15.70 | 15.70 |

## POSTAGE DUE STAMPS

Castle Cornet and St. Peter Port — D1

### Perf. 12½x12

## 1969, Oct. 1    Photo.    Unwmk.

### Black Numeral

| | | | | |
|---|---|---|---|---|
| J1 | D1 | 1p deep magenta | 1.75 | 1.00 |
| J2 | D1 | 2p yellow green | 2.25 | 1.75 |
| J3 | D1 | 3p red | 3.00 | 3.00 |
| J4 | D1 | 4p ultra | 4.00 | 4.00 |
| J5 | D1 | 5p yellow bister | 7.00 | 4.00 |
| J6 | D1 | 6p greenish blue | 8.00 | 4.50 |
| J7 | D1 | 1sh red brown | 21.00 | 13.00 |
| | Nos. J1-J7 (7) | | 47.00 | 31.25 |

### Type of 1969
### "p" instead of "d"

## 1971-76

### Black Numeral

| | | | | |
|---|---|---|---|---|
| J8 | D1 | ½p deep magenta | .20 | .20 |
| J9 | D1 | 1p yellow green | .20 | .20 |
| J10 | D1 | 2p red | .20 | .20 |
| J11 | D1 | 3p ultra | .20 | .20 |
| J12 | D1 | 4p yellow bister | .20 | .20 |
| J13 | D1 | 5p greenish blue | .25 | .25 |
| J14 | D1 | 6p purple ('76) | .25 | .25 |
| J15 | D1 | 8p orange ('75) | .25 | .25 |
| J16 | D1 | 10p red brown | .50 | .50 |
| J17 | D1 | 15p gray ('76) | .50 | .50 |
| | Nos. J8-J17 (10) | | 2.75 | 2.75 |

Town Church, St. Peter Port — D2

## 1977-80    Photo.    Perf. 13½x13
### Arms and Denomination in Black

| | | | | |
|---|---|---|---|---|
| J18 | D2 | ½p red brown | .20 | .20 |
| J19 | D2 | 1p lilac rose | .20 | .20 |
| J20 | D2 | 2p orange | .20 | .20 |
| J21 | D2 | 3p red | .20 | .20 |
| J22 | D2 | 4p greenish blue | .20 | .20 |
| J23 | D2 | 5p olive green | .20 | .20 |
| J24 | D2 | 6p greenish blue | .20 | .20 |
| J25 | D2 | 8p ocher | .25 | .25 |
| J26 | D2 | 10p dark blue | .30 | .30 |
| J27 | D2 | 14p green ('80) | .40 | .40 |
| J28 | D2 | 15p purple | .40 | .40 |
| J29 | D2 | 16p salmon rose ('80) | .50 | .50 |
| | Nos. J18-J29 (12) | | 3.25 | 3.25 |

Woman Milking Cow — D3

## 1982, July 13    Litho.    Perf. 14½

| | | | | |
|---|---|---|---|---|
| J30 | D3 | 1p shown | .20 | .20 |
| J31 | D3 | 2p Vale Mill | .20 | .20 |
| J32 | D3 | 3p Sark cottage | .20 | .20 |
| J33 | D3 | 4p St. Peter Port | .20 | .20 |
| J34 | D3 | 5p Well, Moulin Huet | .20 | .20 |
| J35 | D3 | 16p Seaweed gathering | .40 | .40 |
| J36 | D3 | 18p Upper Walk, White Rock | .45 | .45 |
| J37 | D3 | 20p Cobo Bay | .50 | .50 |
| J38 | D3 | 25p Saints' Bay | .55 | .55 |
| J39 | D3 | 30p La Coupee, Sark | .75 | .75 |
| J40 | D3 | 50p Old Harbor, St. Peter Port | 1.10 | 1.10 |
| J41 | D3 | £1 Greenhouses, Victoria Tower | 2.50 | 2.50 |
| | Nos. J30-J41 (12) | | 7.25 | 7.25 |

## OCCUPATION STAMPS

### Issued Under German Occupation

Bisects of Great Britain Nos. 238 and 255 were used in Guernsey from 12/27/40 to 2./24/41. Values, on cover or postcard: No. 238, $45; No. 255, $40.

OS1

### Rouletted 14x7
## 1941-44    Typo.    Unwmk.

| | | | | |
|---|---|---|---|---|
| N1 | OS1 | ½p light green | 5.50 | 3.25 |
| N2 | OS1 | 1p red | 3.00 | 2.00 |
| N3 | OS1 | 2½p ultramarine | 12.00 | 11.00 |
| | Nos. N1-N3 (3) | | 20.50 | 16.25 |

Issued: ½p, 4/7; 1p, 2/18; 2½p, 4/4/44. Numerous shades and papers exist. The rouletting is very crude and may not be measurable. This is not a defect.
See *Scott Classic Specialized Catalogue* for detailed listings.

### Wmk. 396 Chain Link Fence
## 1942    Rouletted 14x7
### Bluish French Bank Note Paper

| | | | | |
|---|---|---|---|---|
| N4 | OS1 | ½p green | 27.50 | 27.50 |
| N5 | OS1 | 1p red | 14.50 | 21.00 |

Issue dates: ½p, Mar. 11; 1p, Apr. 9.

Nos. N1-N5 remained valid until 4/13/46.

## ALDERNEY
'ol-dər-nē

LOCATION — Northernmost of the Channel Islands in the Guernsey Bailiwick
GOVT. — Dependent territory under Bailiwick of Guernsey.
AREA — 3 sq. mi.
POP. — 2, 373 (1994 est.)
CAPITAL — St. Anne's

Part of the Bailiwick of Guernsey, this island began issuing its own stamps.

Catalogue values for unused stamps in this section are for Never Hinged items.

Map of Alderney, Arms — A1

## 1983, June 14    Litho.    Perf. 12

| | | | | |
|---|---|---|---|---|
| 1 | A1 | 1p shown | .40 | .40 |
| 2 | A1 | 4p Hanging Rock | .40 | .40 |
| 3 | A1 | 9p States Building | .45 | .45 |
| 4 | A1 | 10p St. Anne's Church | .45 | .45 |
| 5 | A1 | 11p Yachts, Braye Bay | .50 | .50 |
| 6 | A1 | 12p Victoria St., St. Anne | .50 | .50 |
| 7 | A1 | 13p Map, arms | .50 | .50 |
| 8 | A1 | 14p Ft. Clonque | .55 | .55 |
| 9 | A1 | 15p Corblets Bay Port | .55 | .55 |
| 10 | A1 | 16p Old Tower, St. Anne | .65 | .65 |
| 11 | A1 | 17p Essex Castle Golf Course | .70 | .70 |
| 12 | A1 | 18p Ships in Old Harbor | .70 | .70 |
| | Nos. 1-12 (12) | | 6.35 | 6.35 |

See Nos. 42-46, which is considered to be the higher-denomination continuation of this definitive set.

Oystercatcher, Telegraph Bay — A2

## 1984, June 12    Perf. 14½

| | | | | |
|---|---|---|---|---|
| 13 | A2 | 9p shown | 1.50 | 1.10 |
| 14 | A2 | 13p Turnstone, Corblets Bay | 1.50 | 1.00 |
| 15 | A2 | 26p Ringed plover, Corblets Bay | 4.00 | 3.00 |
| 16 | A2 | 28p Dunlin, Arch Bay | 4.00 | 3.25 |
| 17 | A2 | 31p Curlew, Old Harbor | 4.00 | 3.25 |
| | Nos. 13-17 (5) | | 15.00 | 11.60 |

Alderney Airport, 50th Anniv. A3

Aircraft: 9p, Wessex helicopter of the Queen's Flight, 1984. 13p, Aurigny Air Joey Britten-Norman Trislander, 1981. 29p, Morton Air Services DeHavilland Heron, 1946. 31p, DeHavilland Dragon Rapide, c. 1930. 34p, Saunders-Roe Saro Windhover, 1935.

## 1985, Mar. 19    Perf. 12x11½

| | | | | |
|---|---|---|---|---|
| 18 | A3 | 9p multicolored | 1.75 | 1.50 |
| 19 | A3 | 13p multicolored | 2.50 | 1.50 |
| 20 | A3 | 29p multicolored | 4.25 | 3.50 |
| 21 | A3 | 31p multicolored | 5.25 | 3.75 |
| 22 | A3 | 34p multicolored | 5.25 | 3.75 |
| | Nos. 18-22 (5) | | 19.00 | 14.00 |

Regimental Uniforms, Alderney Garrison — A4

## 1985, Sept. 24    Perf. 14½

| | | | | |
|---|---|---|---|---|
| 23 | A4 | 9p Royal Engineers, 1890 | .30 | .30 |
| 24 | A4 | 14p Duke of Albany's Own Highlanders, 1856 | 1.10 | .55 |
| 25 | A4 | 29p Royal Artillery, 1855 | 1.10 | 1.10 |
| 26 | A4 | 31p South Hampshire Regiment, 1810 | 1.50 | 1.25 |
| 27 | A4 | 34p Royal Irish Regiment, 1782 | 1.75 | 1.40 |
| | Nos. 23-27 (5) | | 5.75 | 4.60 |

Forts — A5

## 1986, Sept. 23    Litho.    Perf. 13x13½

| | | | | |
|---|---|---|---|---|
| 28 | A5 | 10p Grosnez | 1.25 | 1.25 |
| 29 | A5 | 14p Tourgis | 1.50 | 1.50 |
| 30 | A5 | 31p Clonque | 3.50 | 3.50 |
| 31 | A5 | 34p Albert | 3.75 | 3.75 |
| | Nos. 28-31 (4) | | 10.00 | 10.00 |

Shipwrecks A6

## 1987, May 5    Litho.    Perf. 14½

| | | | | |
|---|---|---|---|---|
| 32 | A6 | 11p Liverpool, 1902 | 2.00 | .80 |
| 33 | A6 | 15p Petit Raymond, 1906 | 2.50 | .80 |
| 34 | A6 | 29p Maina, 1910 | 5.00 | 5.00 |
| 35 | A6 | 31p Burton, 1911 | 5.25 | 5.00 |
| 36 | A6 | 34p Point Law, 1975 | 5.25 | 5.25 |
| | Nos. 32-36 (5) | | 20.00 | 16.85 |

18th-20th Cent. Maps — A7

Designs: 12p, Herman Moll map, 1724. 18p, Survey by J.H. Bastide, 1739. 27p, Land survey by M.P. Goodwin, 1830. 32p, Wartime occupation map, 1943. 35p, Ordnance survey, 1988.

## 1989, July 7    Litho.    Perf. 13½x14

| | | | | |
|---|---|---|---|---|
| 37 | A7 | 12p multicolored | .50 | .50 |
| 38 | A7 | 18p multicolored | .75 | .75 |
| 39 | A7 | 27p multicolored | 1.10 | 1.10 |
| 40 | A7 | 32p multicolored | 1.25 | 1.25 |
| 41 | A7 | 35p multicolored | 1.40 | 1.40 |
| | Nos. 37-41 (5) | | 5.00 | 5.00 |

Quesnard Lighthouse A8

Designs: 21p, Inner Harbor, Braye. 23p, The Island Hall, Alderney. 24p, Alderney Railway locomotive, J. T. Daly. 28p, Lifeboat, Louis Marchesi of Round Table.

## 1989-93    Litho.    Perf. 15x14

| | | | | |
|---|---|---|---|---|
| 42 | A8 | 20p multicolored | 1.25 | 1.00 |
| 43 | A8 | 21p multicolored | 1.25 | 1.00 |
| 44 | A8 | 23p multicolored | .85 | .75 |
| 45 | A8 | 24p multicolored | 2.25 | 2.00 |
| 46 | A8 | 28p multicolored | 2.40 | 2.00 |
| | Nos. 42-46 (5) | | 8.00 | 6.75 |

Issued: 20p, 12/27; 21p, 4/2/91; 23p, 2/6/92; 24p, 28p, 3/3/93.

Ships Called HMS *Alderney* A9

## 1990, May 3   Litho.   Perf. 13½

| | | | | |
|---|---|---|---|---|
| 55 | A9 | 14p Bomb ketch, 1738 | .55 | .55 |
| 56 | A9 | 20p Sixth-rate, 1742 | .70 | .70 |
| 57 | A9 | 29p Sloop, 1755 | 1.00 | 1.00 |
| 58 | A9 | 34p A-Class submarine, 1945 | 1.25 | 1.25 |
| 59 | A9 | 37p Fishery protection vessel, 1979 | 1.50 | 1.50 |
| | | Nos. 55-59 (5) | 5.00 | 5.00 |

Automation of Casquets
Lighthouse — A10

## 1991, Apr. 20   Litho.   Perf. 14x13½

| | | | | |
|---|---|---|---|---|
| 60 | A10 | 21p Wreck of HMS Victory, 1744 | 1.90 | 1.90 |
| 61 | A10 | 26p Returning by row-boat | 2.10 | 2.10 |
| 62 | A10 | 31p Helicopter relief | 2.50 | 2.50 |
| 63 | A10 | 37p Lighthouse, birds | 3.00 | 3.00 |
| 64 | A10 | 50p MV Patricia | 4.00 | 4.00 |
| | | Nos. 60-64 (5) | 13.50 | 13.50 |

Battle of La Hogue,
300th Anniv. — A11

23p, 28p, and 33p, Various details from painting by unknown artist. 50p, Entire painting.

## 1992, Sept. 18   Litho.   Perf. 13½

| | | | | |
|---|---|---|---|---|
| 65 | A11 | 23p multicolored | 2.00 | 2.00 |
| 66 | A11 | 28p multicolored | 2.50 | 2.50 |
| 67 | A11 | 33p multicolored | 3.00 | 3.00 |

### Size: 45x30mm
### Perf. 14x14½

| | | | | |
|---|---|---|---|---|
| 68 | A11 | 50p multicolored | 3.75 | 3.75 |
| | | Nos. 65-68 (4) | 11.25 | 11.25 |

Marine
Life — A12

Designs: a, 24p, Palinurus elephas. b, 28p, Metridium senile. c, 33p, Luidia ciliaris. d, 39p, Psammechinus miliaris.

## 1993, Nov. 2   Litho.   Perf. 15x14½

| | | | | |
|---|---|---|---|---|
| 69 | A12 | Strip of 4, #a.-d. | 9.50 | 9.50 |

Flora and
Fauna — A13

Designs: 1p, Ischnura elegans, ranunculus trichophyllus, sparganium erectum. 2p, Crocidura russula, hypericum linarifolium. 3p, Fulmarus glacialis, carpobrotus edulis. 4p, Colias croceus, trifolium pratense. 5p, Bombus lucorum, orobanche rapum-genistae, cytisus scoparius. 6p, Sylvia undata, cuscuta epithymum, ulex europaeus. 7p, Inachis io, sium acaule. 8p, Talpa europaea, endymion non-scripta. 9p, Tettigonia viridissima, ulex europaeus. 10p, Zygaena filipendulae, echium vulgare. 16p, Polyommatus icarus, anacamptis pyramidalis. 20p, Oryctolagus cuniculus, rannunculus repens, pteridium aquilinum. 24p, Larus marinus, romulea columnae. 30p, Fratercula arctica, sedum anglicum. 40p, Saturnia pavonia, rubus fruticosus. 50p, Erinaceus europaeus, oxalis articulata. £1,

Sterna hirundo, cynodon dactylon, horiz. £2, Morus bassanus, fucus vesiculosus.

## 1994-95   Litho.   Perf. 14

| | | | | |
|---|---|---|---|---|
| 70 | A13 | 1p multicolored | .20 | .20 |
| 71 | A13 | 2p multicolored | .20 | .20 |
| 72 | A13 | 3p multicolored | .20 | .20 |
| 73 | A13 | 4p multicolored | .20 | .20 |
| 74 | A13 | 5p multicolored | .20 | .20 |
| 75 | A13 | 6p multicolored | .25 | .25 |
| 76 | A13 | 7p multicolored | .25 | .25 |
| 77 | A13 | 8p multicolored | .30 | .30 |
| 78 | A13 | 9p multicolored | .35 | .35 |
| 79 | A13 | 10p multicolored | .40 | .40 |
| 80 | A13 | 16p multicolored | .60 | .60 |
| a. | | Perf. 14x15 on three sides | .65 | .65 |
| b. | | As "a," booklet pane of 8 | 5.75 | |
| 81 | A13 | 20p multicolored | .80 | .80 |
| a. | | Perf. 14x15 on three sides | .85 | .85 |
| b. | | As "a," booklet pane of 8 | 7.25 | |
| 82 | A13 | 24p multicolored | .95 | .95 |
| a. | | Perf. 14x15 on three sides | 1.00 | 1.00 |
| b. | | As "a," booklet pane of 8 | 9.00 | |
| 83 | A13 | 30p multicolored | 1.10 | 1.10 |
| 84 | A13 | 40p multicolored | 1.60 | 1.60 |
| 85 | A13 | 50p multicolored | 2.00 | 2.00 |
| 86 | A13 | £1 multicolored | 4.00 | 4.00 |

### Perf. 14x15

| | | | | |
|---|---|---|---|---|
| 87 | A13 | £2 multicolored | 8.00 | 8.00 |
| | | Nos. 70-87 (18) | 21.60 | 21.60 |

No. 81 is dated "1994." Nos. 81a-81b are dated "1998."
Issued: £2, 2/28/95; others, 5/5/94.
See Nos. 98-100.

Career of Flt. Lt. Tommy Rose DFC
(1895-1968) — A14

No. 88: a, 1917-18 Royal Flying Corps. b, 1939-45 Chief Test Pilot. c, Phillips & Powis (Miles) Aircraft.
No. 89: a, Winner, 1935 King's Cup Air Race. b, Winner, 1947 Manx Air Derby. c, UK-Cape-UK Speed Record, 1936.

## 1995, Sept. 1   Litho.   Perf. 14x15

| | | | | |
|---|---|---|---|---|
| 88 | A14 | 35p Strip of 3, #a.-c. | 4.25 | 4.25 |
| 89 | A14 | 41p Strip of 3, #a.-c. | 5.00 | 5.00 |

Nos. 88-89 printed in sheets of 12 stamps + 3 labels.

### Souvenir Sheet

Return of Islanders, 50th
Anniv. — A15

Illustration reduced.

## 1995, Nov. 16   Litho.   Perf. 13½

| | | | | |
|---|---|---|---|---|
| 90 | A15 | £1.65 multicolored | 6.50 | 6.50 |

30th Signal Regiment Activities in
Alderney, 25th Anniv.
A16

a, 24p, Training. b, 41p, Natl. contingencies overseas. c, 60p, Strategic communications. d, 75p, UN operations.

## 1996, Jan. 24   Litho.   Perf. 14

| | | | | |
|---|---|---|---|---|
| 91 | A16 | Strip of 4, #a.-d. | 8.00 | 8.00 |

Domestic
Cats — A17

16p, Butterfly, brown & white cat. 24p, Gray cat on table. 25p, Two cats on chair. 35p, Cat pulling on table cloth. 41p, Calico cat in toy cart, white cat. 60p, Siamese cat with yarn.

## 1996, July 19   Litho.   Perf. 13½

| | | | | |
|---|---|---|---|---|
| 92 | A17 | 16p multicolored | .60 | .60 |
| 93 | A17 | 24p multicolored | .95 | .95 |
| 94 | A17 | 25p multicolored | 1.00 | 1.00 |
| 95 | A17 | 35p multicolored | 1.40 | 1.40 |
| 96 | A17 | 41p multicolored | 1.60 | 1.60 |
| 97 | A17 | 60p multicolored | 2.40 | 2.40 |
| a. | | Souvenir sheet, #92-97 | 8.00 | 8.00 |
| | | Nos. 92-97 (6) | 7.95 | 7.95 |

No. 97a is a continuous design.

### Fauna and Flora Type of 1994

Designs: 18p, Aglais urticae, Buddleja davidii. 25p, Anthus petrosus, matthiola incana. 26p, Ammophila sabulosa, calystegia soldanella, horiz.

## 1997, Jan. 2   Litho.   Perf. 14½

| | | | | |
|---|---|---|---|---|
| 98 | A13 | 18p multicolored | .70 | .70 |
| a. | | Perf. 14x15 on 3 sides | 1.00 | |
| b. | | As "a," booklet pane of 8 | 8.75 | |
| | | Complete booklet, #98b | 8.75 | |
| 99 | A13 | 25p multicolored | 1.00 | 1.00 |
| a. | | Perf. 14x15 on 3 sides | 1.00 | |
| b. | | As "a," booklet pane of 8 | 8.75 | |
| | | Complete booklet, #99b | 8.75 | |
| 100 | A13 | 26p multicolored | 1.00 | 1.00 |
| | | Nos. 98-100 (3) | 2.70 | 2.70 |

Alderney Cricket
Club, 150th
Anniv. — A18

## 1997, Aug. 21   Litho.   Perf. 13½

| | | | | |
|---|---|---|---|---|
| 101 | A18 | 18p Harold Larwood | .70 | .70 |
| 102 | A18 | 25p John Arlott | 1.00 | 1.00 |
| 103 | A18 | 37p Pelham J. Warner | 1.40 | 1.40 |
| 104 | A18 | 43p W.G. Grace | 1.60 | 1.60 |
| 105 | A18 | 63p John Wisden | 2.50 | 2.50 |
| a. | | Souvenir sheet, #101-105 + label | 8.00 | 8.00 |
| | | Nos. 101-105 (5) | 7.20 | 7.20 |

Garrison
Island — A19

#106, Founding of the harbor. #107, Ariadne at anchor. #108, Quarrying at Mannez. #109, Earliest train ferrying stone. #110, Queen Victoria arrives ashore. #111, Royal yacht at anchor. #112, Railway and quarry workers greet the Queen. #113, Queen Victoria tours the island.

## 1997, Nov. 20   Litho.   Perf. 14½x14

| | | | | |
|---|---|---|---|---|
| 106 | A19 | 18p multicolored | .70 | .70 |
| 107 | A19 | 18p multicolored | .70 | .70 |
| a. | | Pair, #106-107 | 1.40 | 1.40 |
| 108 | A19 | 25p multicolored | 1.00 | 1.00 |
| 109 | A19 | 25p multicolored | 1.00 | 1.00 |
| a. | | Pair, #108-109 | 2.00 | 2.00 |
| b. | | Booklet pane, #107a, 109a | 3.75 | |
| 110 | A19 | 26p multicolored | 1.00 | 1.00 |
| 111 | A19 | 26p multicolored | 1.00 | 1.00 |
| a. | | Pair, #110-111 | 2.00 | 2.00 |
| b. | | Booklet pane, #107a, 111a | 3.75 | |
| 112 | A19 | 31p multicolored | 1.25 | 1.25 |
| 113 | A19 | 31p multicolored | 1.25 | 1.25 |
| a. | | Pair, #112-113 | 2.50 | 2.50 |
| b. | | Booklet pane, #111a, 113a | 4.75 | |
| c. | | Booklet pane, #109a, 113a | 4.75 | |
| | | Nos. 106-113 (8) | 7.90 | 7.90 |

Nos. 109b, 111b, 113b, 113c issued 11/10/98.
See Nos. 119-126, 134-141, 155-162, 176-183.

Alderney Diving
Club, 21st
Anniv. — A20

20p, Modern superlite helmet. 30p, Cousteau-Gagnan demand valve, 1943. 37p, Heinke closed helmet, 1845. 43p, Siebe closed helmet, 1840. 63p, Deane open helmet, 1829.

## 1998, Feb. 10   Litho.   Perf. 13

| | | | | |
|---|---|---|---|---|
| 114 | A20 | 20p multicolored | .80 | .80 |
| 115 | A20 | 30p multicolored | 1.10 | 1.10 |
| 116 | A20 | 37p multicolored | 1.40 | 1.40 |
| 117 | A20 | 43p multicolored | 1.60 | 1.60 |
| 118 | A20 | 63p multicolored | 2.50 | 2.50 |
| a. | | Souvenir sheet, #114-118 + label | 7.50 | 7.50 |
| | | Nos. 114-118 (5) | 7.40 | 7.40 |

### Garrison Island Type of 1997

#119, Alderney Post Office. #120, Traders in Victoria Street. #121, Court House. #122, Police Station and Fire Service. #123, St. Anne's Church. #124, Wedding Party at The Albert Gate. #125, SS Courier unloading. #126, Fishermen at quay.

## 1998, Nov. 10   Litho.   Perf. 14½x14

| | | | | |
|---|---|---|---|---|
| 119 | A19 | 20p multicolored | .80 | .80 |
| 120 | A19 | 20p multicolored | .80 | .80 |
| a. | | Pair, #119-120 | 1.60 | 1.60 |
| 121 | A19 | 25p multicolored | 1.00 | 1.00 |
| 122 | A19 | 25p multicolored | 1.00 | 1.00 |
| a. | | Pair, #121-122 | 2.00 | 2.00 |
| b. | | Booklet pane, #120a, 122a | 3.75 | |
| 123 | A19 | 30p multicolored | 1.25 | 1.25 |
| 124 | A19 | 30p multicolored | 1.25 | 1.25 |
| a. | | Pair, #123-124 | 2.50 | 2.50 |
| b. | | Booklet pane, #120a, 124a | 4.25 | |
| 125 | A19 | 37p multicolored | 1.60 | 1.60 |
| 126 | A19 | 37p multicolored | 1.60 | 1.60 |
| a. | | Pair, #125-126 | 3.25 | 3.25 |
| b. | | Booklet pane, #124a, 126a | 6.00 | |
| c. | | Booklet pane, #122a, 126a | 5.75 | |
| | | Complete booklet, #109b, 111b, 113b, 113c, 122b, 124b, 126b, 126c | 37.50 | |
| | | Nos. 119-126 (8) | 9.30 | 9.30 |

### Souvenir Sheet

The Wreck of the SS Stella,
Cent. — A21

a, 25p, Stained glass window, Anglican Cathedral, Liverpool, dedicated to Mary Rogers, chief stewardess. b, £1.75, Ship leaving Southampton.

## 1999, Feb. 4   Litho.   Perf. 14

| | | | | |
|---|---|---|---|---|
| 127 | A21 | Sheet of 2, #a.-b. | 8.00 | 8.00 |

Total Solar
Eclipse — A22

Stages of eclipse on 8/11/99: 20p, 10:15. 25p, 10:51. 30p, 11:14. 38p, 11:16. 44p, 11:17. 64p, 11:36.

## 1999, Apr. 27   Litho.   Perf. 13½x13

| | | | | |
|---|---|---|---|---|
| 128 | A22 | 20p multicolored | .80 | .80 |
| 129 | A22 | 25p multicolored | 1.00 | 1.00 |
| 130 | A22 | 30p multicolored | 1.25 | 1.25 |
| 131 | A22 | 38p multicolored | 1.50 | 1.50 |
| 132 | A22 | 44p multicolored | 1.75 | 1.75 |

**133** A22 64p multicolored          2.50  2.50
  *a.*   Souvenir sheet, #128-133 + label  8.75  8.75
    *Nos. 128-133 (6)*       8.80  8.80

### Garrison Island Type of 1997

Designs: No. 134, Fort Grosnez, c. 1855. No. 135, Ninth Battalion, Royal Garrison Artillery. No. 136, Arsenal, Fort Albert. No. 137, Royal Engineer Unit. No. 138, Fort Tourgis, c. 1865. No. 139, Second Battalion, Royal Scots Regiment. No. 140, Fort Houmet Herbé, c. 1870. No. 141, Royal Alderney Artillery Militia.

**1999, Oct. 19   Litho.   Perf. 14¼x13¾**

| | | | |
|---|---|---|---|
| **134** A19 20p multicolored | .80 | .80 |
| **135** A19 20p multicolored | .80 | .80 |
|  *a.*  Pair, #134-135 | 1.60 | 1.60 |
| **136** A19 25p multicolored | 1.00 | 1.00 |
| **137** A19 25p multicolored | 1.00 | 1.00 |
|  *a.*  Pair, #136-137 | 2.00 | 2.00 |
|  *b.*  Booklet pane, #135a, 137a | 3.75 | |
| **138** A19 30p multicolored | 1.25 | 1.25 |
| **139** A19 30p multicolored | 1.25 | 1.25 |
|  *a.*  Pair, #138-139 | 2.50 | 2.50 |
|  *b.*  Booklet pane, #135a, 139a | 4.50 | |
|  *c.*  Booklet pane, #137a, 139a | 4.75 | |
| **140** A19 38p multicolored | 1.50 | 1.50 |
| **141** A19 38p multicolored | 1.50 | 1.50 |
|  *a.*  Pair, #140-141 | 3.25 | 3.25 |
|  *b.*  Booklet pane, #135a, 141a | 5.25 | |
|  *c.*  Booklet pane, #137a, 141a | 5.50 | |
|  *d.*  Booklet pane, #139a, 141a | 6.00 | |
|    Complete booklet, #137b, 139b, 139c, 141b, 141c, 141d | 32.50 | |
|    *Nos. 134-141 (8)* | 9.10 | 9.10 |

Peregrine Falcon — A23

Falcons: 21p, Attacking turnstone near lighthouse. 26p, With prey. 34p, With eggs. 38p, With chicks. 44p, With young near Fort Clonque. 64p, Preparing to fly.

**2000, Feb. 4   Litho.   Perf. 14½x14**

| | | | |
|---|---|---|---|
| **142** A23 21p multi | 1.10 | 1.10 |
|  *a.*  Booklet pane of 10 | 11.00 | |
|    Complete booklet | 11.00 | |
| **143** A23 26p multi | 1.25 | 1.25 |
|  *a.*  Booklet pane of 10 | 12.00 | |
|    Complete booklet | 12.00 | |
| **144** A23 34p multi | 1.50 | 1.50 |
| **145** A23 38p multi | 1.60 | 1.60 |
| **146** A23 44p multi | 2.00 | 2.00 |
| **147** A23 64p multi | 2.75 | 2.75 |
|    *Nos. 142-147 (6)* | 10.20 | 10.20 |

Worldwide Fund for Nature, Nos. 144-147.

The Wombles on Vacation A24

Wombles: 21p, With map. 26p, On beach. 36p, At lighthouse. 40p, Picnicking. 45p, On golf course. 65p, At airport.

**2000, Apr. 28   Litho.   Perf. 14¼x13¾**

| | | | |
|---|---|---|---|
| **148** A24 21p multi | .85 | .85 |
| **149** A24 26p multi | 1.00 | 1.00 |
| **150** A24 36p multi | 1.40 | 1.40 |
| **151** A24 40p multi | 1.60 | 1.60 |
| **152** A24 45p multi | 1.75 | 1.75 |
| **153** A24 65p multi | 2.50 | 2.50 |
|  *a.*  Souvenir sheet, #148-153 | 9.25 | 9.25 |
|    *Nos. 148-153 (6)* | 9.10 | 9.10 |

The Stamp Show 2000, London (No. 153a).

### Souvenir Sheet

Queen Mother, 100th Birthday — A25

Illustration reduced.

---

### Litho. with Foil Application
**2000, Aug. 4                     Perf. 13¼**

**154** A25  £1.50 multi            6.00  6.00

### Garrison Island Type of 1997

#155, Regimental boxing tournament. #156, Sports Day of Alderney Gala Week, 1924. #157, Regimental Band of 15th entertains. #158, Garrison Ball, 1873, Fort Albert mess room. #159, Garrison assembly for Queen's birthday celebrations, 1859. #160, Demonstration of field guns on the Butes. #161, Inspection of honor guard, 1863. #162, Arrival of Lt. Gov. Major Gen. Marcus Slade.

**2000, Oct. 19   Litho.   Perf. 13¼x13**

| | | | |
|---|---|---|---|
| **155** A19 21p multi | .85 | .85 |
| **156** A19 21p multi | .85 | .85 |
|  *a.*  Pair, #155-156 | 1.75 | 1.75 |
| **157** A19 26p multi | 1.00 | 1.00 |
| **158** A19 26p multi | 1.00 | 1.00 |
|  *a.*  Pair, #157-158 | 2.00 | 2.00 |
|  *b.*  Booklet pane, #156a, 158a | 4.00 | |
| **159** A19 36p multi | 1.40 | 1.40 |
| **160** A19 36p multi | 1.40 | 1.40 |
|  *a.*  Pair, #159-160 | 3.00 | 3.00 |
|  *b.*  Booklet pane, #158a, 160a | 5.50 | |
| **161** A19 40p multi | 1.60 | 1.60 |
| **162** A19 40p multi | 1.60 | 1.60 |
|  *a.*  Pair, #161-162 | 3.25 | 3.25 |
|  *b.*  Booklet pane, #156a, 162a | 5.00 | |
|  *c.*  Booklet pane, #160a, 162a | 6.25 | |
|    Booklet, #158b, 162c, 2 each #160b, 162b | 30.00 | |
|    *Nos. 155-162 (8)* | 9.70 | 9.70 |

Each of the two panes of Nos. 160b and 162b in the booklet have different selvages.

### Souvenir Sheet

Queen Elizabeth, 75th Birthday — A26

**2001, Feb. 1      Litho.      Perf. 14¼**

**163** A26  £1.75 multi           7.00  7.00

Community Health Services A27

Health care workers and: 22p, Hospital x-ray department. 27p, Mignot Memorial Hospital in 1980s. 36p, Princess Anne visiting hospital, 1972. 40p, Nurse with infant, 1960s. 45p, Queen Elizabeth II laying hospital cornerstone, 1957. 65p, Opening of original hospital, 1920s.

**2001-02      Litho.      Perf. 14¼x14½**

| | | | |
|---|---|---|---|
| **164** A27 22p multi | .85 | .85 |
|  *a.*  Perf. 13¼x13 | .90 | .90 |
| **165** A27 27p multi | 1.00 | 1.00 |
|  *a.*  Perf. 13¼x13 | 1.40 | 1.40 |
| **166** A27 36p multi | 1.40 | 1.40 |
|  *a.*  Perf. 13¼x13 | 1.40 | 1.40 |
| **167** A27 40p multi | 1.60 | 1.60 |
|  *a.*  Perf. 13¼x13 | 1.60 | 1.60 |
|  *b.*  Booklet pane, #164a, 165a, 166a, 167a | 5.50 | — |
| **168** A27 45p multi | 1.75 | 1.75 |
|  *a.*  Perf. 13¼x13 | 1.75 | 1.75 |
| **169** A27 65p multi | 2.50 | 2.50 |
|  *a.*  Perf. 13¼x13 | 2.40 | 2.40 |
|  *b.*  Booklet pane, #166a, 167a, 168a, 169a | 7.25 | — |
|  *c.*  Booklet pane, #164a, 165a, 168a, 169a | 6.50 | — |
|    *Nos. 164-169 (6)* | 9.10 | 9.10 |

Issued: Nos. 164-169, 4/26/01; Nos. 164a-169a, 10/17/02.

---

Alderney Golf Club — A28

Designs: 22p, Golf ball with core of feathers, 1901. 27p, Golfing fashions, 1920s. 36p, Player and ball on Alderney Golf Club green, 1970s. 40p, Modern putter. 45p, Golf accessories. 65p, Modern lofted wood.

**2001, Aug. 1      Litho.      Perf. 14¾**

| | | | |
|---|---|---|---|
| **170** A28 22p multi | .85 | .85 |
| **171** A28 27p multi | 1.00 | 1.00 |
| **172** A28 36p multi | 1.40 | 1.40 |
| **173** A28 40p multi | 1.60 | 1.60 |
| **174** A28 45p multi | 1.75 | 1.75 |
| **175** A28 65p multi | 2.50 | 2.50 |
|  *a.*  Souvenir sheet, #170-175 | 9.25 | 9.25 |
|    *Nos. 170-175 (6)* | 9.10 | 9.10 |

Phila Nippon '01 (#175a).

### Garrison Island Type of 1997

Designs: No. 176, Work continues at the breakwater. No. 177, Officials observe work in progress. No. 178, Steam frigate Emerald grounded. No. 179, Soldiers disembarking Emerald. No. 180, Torpedo boats moored at breakwater. No. 181, Railway provides mobile artillery. No. 182, HMS Majestic at anchor, 1901. No. 183, Torpedo boats maneuver at speed.

**2001, Oct. 16   Litho.   Perf. 13¼x13**

| | | | |
|---|---|---|---|
| **176** A19 22p multi | .85 | .85 |
| **177** A19 22p multi | .85 | .85 |
|  *a.*  Pair, #176-177 | 1.75 | 1.75 |
| **178** A19 27p multi | 1.00 | 1.00 |
| **179** A19 27p multi | 1.00 | 1.00 |
|  *a.*  Pair, #178-179 | 2.00 | 2.00 |
|  *b.*  Booklet pane, #177a, 179a | 4.00 | — |
| **180** A19 36p multi | 1.40 | 1.40 |
| **181** A19 36p multi | 1.40 | 1.40 |
|  *a.*  Pair, #180-181 | 3.00 | 3.00 |
|  *b.*  Booklet pane, #179a, 181a | 5.25 | — |
| **182** A19 40p multi | 1.60 | 1.60 |
| **183** A19 40p multi | 1.60 | 1.60 |
|  *a.*  Pair, #182-183 | 3.25 | 3.25 |
|  *b.*  Booklet pane, #177a, 183a | 4.75 | — |
|  *c.*  Booklet pane, #179a, 183a | 5.25 | — |
|  *d.*  Booklet pane, #181a, 183a | 5.25 | — |
|    Booklet, #179b, 181b, 183c, 183d, 2 #183b | 32.50 | |
|    *Nos. 176-183 (8)* | 9.70 | 9.70 |

Booklet sold for £7.50. Each of the two panes of No. 183b in the booklet have different selvages.

### Souvenir Sheet

Reign of Queen Elizabeth II, 50th Anniv. — A29

**2002, Feb. 6   Litho.   Perf. 13¾x13½**

**184** A29  £2 multi               8.00  8.00
 *a.*  Booklet pane of 1         8.00
   Complete booklet, #184a, Guernsey #773a, 774a, 774b, 774c         37.50

No. 184a is sewn into booklets, but is otherwise identical to No. 184.
Issued: #184: 2/6; #184a, 4/30.

Alderney

Birds — A30

**2002, Apr. 30                     Perf. 13¾**

| | | | |
|---|---|---|---|
| **185** A30 22p Hobby | .85 | .85 |
| **186** A30 27p Black kite | 1.00 | 1.00 |
| **187** A30 36p Merlin | 1.40 | 1.40 |
| **188** A30 40p Honey buzzard | 1.60 | 1.60 |
| **189** A30 45p Osprey | 1.75 | 1.75 |

---

**190** A30 65p Marsh harrier       2.50  2.50
 *a.*  Souvenir sheet, #185-190  9.25  9.25
   *Nos. 185-190 (6)*        9.10  9.10

Lighting at Les Casquets Lighthouse — A31

Designs: 22p, Coal fire, 1725. 27p, Oil lantern, 1779. 36p, Argand lamp, 1790. 45p, Revolving apparatus, 1818. 65p, Electrification, 1952.

**2002, July 30                 Perf. 12¾x13¼**

| | | | |
|---|---|---|---|
| **191** A31 22p multi | .85 | .85 |
| **192** A31 27p multi | 1.00 | 1.00 |
| **193** A31 36p multi | 1.40 | 1.40 |
| **194** A31 45p multi | 1.75 | 1.75 |
| **195** A31 65p multi | 2.50 | 2.50 |
|    *Nos. 191-195 (5)* | 7.50 | 7.50 |

Emergency Medical Services A32

Designs: 22p, Ambulance technician, crew running to ambulance. 27p, Emergency medical technician on radio, ambulance on road. 36p, Doctor, transfer of patient to airplane. 40p, Pilot, Aurigny Trislander airplane. 45p, Emergency dispatch operator, transfer of patient to lifeboat. 65p, Lifeboat crewman, speeding lifeboat.

**2002, Oct. 17   Litho.   Perf. 14x14½**

| | | | |
|---|---|---|---|
| **196** A32 22p multi | .85 | .85 |
|  *a.*  Perf. 13¼x13 | .85 | .85 |
| **197** A32 27p multi | 1.00 | 1.00 |
|  *a.*  Perf. 13¼x13 | 1.00 | 1.00 |
| **198** A32 36p multi | 1.40 | 1.40 |
|  *a.*  Perf. 13¼x13 | 1.40 | 1.40 |
| **199** A32 40p multi | 1.60 | 1.60 |
|  *a.*  Perf. 13¼x13 | 1.60 | 1.60 |
|  *b.*  Booklet pane, #196a, 197a, 198a, 199a | 5.00 | — |
| **200** A32 45p multi | 1.75 | 1.75 |
|  *a.*  Perf. 13¼x13 | 1.75 | 1.75 |
| **201** A32 65p multi | 2.50 | 2.50 |
|  *b.*  Booklet pane, #198a, 199a, 200a, 201a | 6.25 | — |
|  *c.*  Booklet pane, #196a, 197a, 200a, 201a | 5.50 | — |
|    Complete booklet, #167b, 169b, 169c, 199b, 201b, 201c | 35.00 | |
|    *Nos. 196-201 (6)* | 9.10 | 9.10 |

### Souvenir Sheet

Coronation of Queen Elizabeth II, 50th Anniv. — A33

### Litho. & Embossed
**2003, Jan. 30                     Perf. 13½**

**202** A33  £2 multi               8.00  8.00

Powered Flight, Cent. A34

Designs: 22p, Wright Flyer, 1903. 27p, Vickers Vimy, 1919. 36p, Douglas DC-3, 1936. 40p, Comet, 1946. 45p, Concorde, 1969. 65p, Airbus A380.

**2003, Apr. 10                     Litho.**

| | | | |
|---|---|---|---|
| **203** A34 22p multi | .85 | .85 |
| **204** A34 27p multi | 1.00 | 1.00 |
| **205** A34 36p multi | 1.40 | 1.40 |
| **206** A34 40p multi | 1.60 | 1.60 |

| | | | | |
|---|---|---|---|---|
| 207 | A34 | 45p multi | 1.75 | 1.75 |
| 208 | A34 | 65p multi | 2.50 | 2.50 |
| | | *Nos. 203-208 (6)* | 9.10 | 9.10 |

### Bird Type of 2002

**2003, July 3**      *Perf. 13¾*

| | | | | |
|---|---|---|---|---|
| 209 | A30 | 22p Arctic tern | .85 | .85 |
| 210 | A30 | 27p Great skua | 1.00 | 1.00 |
| 211 | A30 | 36p Sandwich tern | 1.40 | 1.40 |
| 212 | A30 | 40p Sooty shearwater | 1.60 | 1.60 |
| 213 | A30 | 45p Arctic skua | 1.75 | 1.75 |
| 214 | A30 | 65p Manx shearwater | 2.50 | 2.50 |
| *a.* | | Souvenir sheet, #209-214 | 9.25 | 9.25 |
| | | *Nos. 209-214 (6)* | 9.10 | 9.10 |

Island
Police — A35

Police officer and: 22p, Policemen patrolling streets. 27p, Police vehicle. 36p, Member of forensics team. 40p, Policeman assisting child on bicycle. 45p, Police at car accident. 65p, Policeman working with customs officer.

**2003, Oct. 16**    **Litho.**    *Perf. 13¼x13*

| | | | | |
|---|---|---|---|---|
| 215 | A35 | 22p multi | .85 | .85 |
| 216 | A35 | 27p multi | 1.00 | 1.00 |
| 217 | A35 | 36p multi | 1.40 | 1.40 |
| 218 | A35 | 40p multi | 1.60 | 1.60 |
| *a.* | | Booklet pane, #215-218 | 5.00 | — |
| 219 | A35 | 45p multi | 1.75 | 1.75 |
| *a.* | | Booklet pane, #215-217, 219 | 5.25 | — |
| 220 | A35 | 65p multi | 2.50 | 2.50 |
| *a.* | | Booklet pane, #215-216, 219-220 | 6.25 | — |
| *b.* | | Booklet pane, #217-220 | 7.25 | — |
| *c.* | | Booklet pane, #215-216, 218, 220 | 6.00 | — |
| | | Complete booklet, #218a, 219a, 220a, 220c, 2 #220b | 37.50 | |
| | | *Nos. 215-220 (6)* | 9.10 | 9.10 |

The two examples of No. 220b in the booklet have different margins.

Fungi — A36

Designs: 22p, Sulphur tuft. 27p, Orange peel fungus. 36p, Shining ink-cap. 40p, Giant puffball. 45p, Parasol. 65p, Candle snuff fungus.

**2004, Jan. 29**    **Litho.**    *Perf. 13¼*

| | | | | |
|---|---|---|---|---|
| 221 | A36 | 22p multi | .85 | .85 |
| 222 | A36 | 27p multi | 1.00 | 1.00 |
| 223 | A36 | 36p multi | 1.40 | 1.40 |
| 224 | A36 | 40p multi | 1.60 | 1.60 |
| 225 | A36 | 45p multi | 1.75 | 1.75 |
| 226 | A36 | 65p multi | 2.50 | 2.50 |
| | | *Nos. 221-226 (6)* | 9.10 | 9.10 |

FIFA (Fédération Internationale de Football Association), Cent. — A37

Designs: 26p, Challenge on Tourgis Close. 32p, Soccer on the beach. 36p, Playground school soccer. 40p, Friendly kickabout. 45p, Turning the defender. 65p, Tackling Dad at Arch Bay.

**2004, May 12**    **Litho.**    *Perf. 13¼*

| | | | | |
|---|---|---|---|---|
| 227 | A37 | 26p multi | 1.00 | 1.00 |
| 228 | A37 | 32p multi | 1.25 | 1.25 |
| 229 | A37 | 36p multi | 1.40 | 1.40 |
| 230 | A37 | 40p multi | 1.60 | 1.60 |
| 231 | A37 | 45p multi | 1.75 | 1.75 |
| 232 | A37 | 65p multi | 2.50 | 2.50 |
| | | *Nos. 227-232 (6)* | 9.50 | 9.50 |

Values are for stamps with surrounding selvage.

### Birds Type of 2002

**2004, July 29**    **Litho.**    *Perf. 13¼*

| | | | | |
|---|---|---|---|---|
| 233 | A30 | 26p Wheatear | 1.00 | 1.00 |
| 234 | A30 | 32p Redstart | 1.25 | 1.25 |
| 235 | A30 | 36p Yellow wagtail | 1.40 | 1.40 |
| 236 | A30 | 40p Hoopoe | 1.60 | 1.60 |
| 237 | A30 | 45p Ring ouzel | 1.75 | 1.75 |
| 238 | A30 | 65p Sand martin | 2.50 | 2.50 |
| *a.* | | Souvenir sheet, #233-238 | 9.50 | 9.50 |
| | | *Nos. 233-238 (6)* | 9.50 | 9.50 |

Fire Services
A38

Designs: 26p, Fireman and fire truck. 32p, Firemen and fire truck. 36p, Fireman and airport fire truck. 40p, Fire chief, fire truck at station. 45p, Training grounds at airport. 65p, Road accicent training exercise.

**2004, Oct. 28**    **Litho.**    *Perf. 13¼x13*

| | | | | |
|---|---|---|---|---|
| 239 | A38 | 26p multi | 1.00 | 1.00 |
| 240 | A38 | 32p multi | 1.25 | 1.25 |
| 241 | A38 | 36p multi | 1.40 | 1.40 |
| 242 | A38 | 40p multi | 1.60 | 1.60 |
| *a.* | | Booklet pane, #239-242 | 5.50 | — |
| 243 | A38 | 45p multi | 1.75 | 1.75 |
| *a.* | | Booklet pane, #239-241, 243 | 5.75 | — |
| 244 | A38 | 65p multi | 2.50 | 2.50 |
| *a.* | | Booklet pane, #239-240, 243-244 | 6.75 | — |
| *b.* | | Booklet pane, #241-244 | 7.50 | — |
| *c.* | | Booklet pane, #239-240, 242, 244 | 6.50 | — |
| | | Complete booklet, #242a, 243a, 244a, 244c, 2 #244b | 42.50 | |
| | | *Nos. 239-244 (6)* | 9.50 | 9.50 |

The two examples of No. 244b in the complete booklet have different margins.

Hans Christian Andersen (1805-75),
Author — A39

Scenes from "The Little Mermaid": 26p, Mermaid, fish, castle. 32p, Mermaid rescues prince. 36p, Mermaid and sea witch. 40p, Mermaid and prince on land. 65p, Dead mermaid and angels.

**2005, Feb. 3**    **Litho.**    *Perf. 13½*

| | | | | |
|---|---|---|---|---|
| 245 | A39 | 26p multi | 1.00 | 1.00 |
| 246 | A39 | 32p multi | 1.25 | 1.25 |
| 247 | A39 | 36p multi | 1.40 | 1.40 |
| 248 | A39 | 40p multi | 1.60 | 1.60 |
| 249 | A39 | 65p multi | 2.50 | 2.50 |
| | | *Nos. 245-249 (5)* | 7.75 | 7.75 |

Battle of
Trafalgar,
Bicent. — A40

Designs: 26p, Admiral Horatio Nelson. 32p, HMS Victory. 36p, Enemy in sight. 40p, Fall of Nelson. 45p, Breaking the line. 65p, Admiral James de Saumarez.

**2005, May 9**    **Litho.**    *Perf. 14x13¼*

| | | | | |
|---|---|---|---|---|
| 250 | A40 | 26p multi | 1.00 | 1.00 |
| 251 | A40 | 32p multi | 1.25 | 1.25 |
| 252 | A40 | 36p multi | 1.40 | 1.40 |
| 253 | A40 | 40p multi | 1.60 | 1.60 |
| *a.* | | Booklet pane, #250-253 | 5.50 | — |
| 254 | A40 | 45p multi | 1.75 | 1.75 |
| 255 | A40 | 65p multi | 2.50 | 2.50 |
| *a.* | | Booklet pane, #250-251, 254-255 | 6.50 | — |
| *b.* | | Booklet pane, #252-255 | 7.25 | |
| *c.* | | Booklet pane, #251-252, 254-255 | 7.00 | — |
| *d.* | | Booklet pane, #250, 253-255 | 6.75 | — |
| | | Complete booklet, #255a, 255b, 255c, 255d, 2 #253a | 42.50 | |
| | | *Nos. 250-255 (6)* | 9.50 | 9.50 |

The two examples of No. 253a in the complete booklet have different pane margins.

### Bird Type of 2002

**2005, July 21**      *Perf. 13¼*

| | | | | |
|---|---|---|---|---|
| 256 | A30 | 26p Little stint | 1.00 | 1.00 |
| 257 | A30 | 32p Greenshank | 1.25 | 1.25 |
| 258 | A30 | 36p Golden plover | 1.40 | 1.40 |
| 259 | A30 | 40p Bar-tailed godwit | 1.60 | 1.60 |
| 260 | A30 | 45p Green sandpiper | 1.75 | 1.75 |
| 261 | A30 | 65p Sanderling | 2.50 | 2.50 |
| *a.* | | Souvenir sheet, #256-261 | 11.00 | 11.00 |
| | | *Nos. 256-261 (6)* | 9.50 | 9.50 |

### Souvenir Sheet

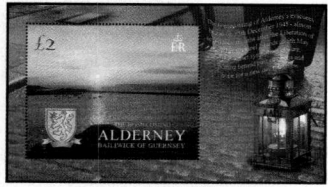

Homecoming of World War II
Evacuees, 60th Anniv. — A41

**2005, Oct. 27**      *Perf. 13¾*

| | | | | |
|---|---|---|---|---|
| 262 | A41 | £2 multi | 8.00 | 8.00 |

Legend of King
Arthur — A42

Designs: 29p, King Arthur. 34p, Merlyn. 38p, Morgause. 42p, Queen Guenever. 47p, Lancelot. 68p, Mordred.

**2006, Feb. 16**    **Litho.**    *Perf. 13½x14*

| | | | | |
|---|---|---|---|---|
| 263 | A42 | 29p multi | 1.10 | 1.10 |
| 264 | A42 | 34p multi | 1.40 | 1.40 |
| 265 | A42 | 38p multi | 1.50 | 1.50 |
| 266 | A42 | 42p multi | 1.60 | 1.60 |
| 267 | A42 | 47p multi | 1.90 | 1.90 |
| 268 | A42 | 68p multi | 2.75 | 2.75 |
| *a.* | | Souvenir sheet, #263-268 | 10.50 | 10.50 |
| | | *Nos. 263-268 (6)* | 10.25 | 10.25 |

Queen Elizabeth II, 80th
Birthday — A43

Various photographs of Queen with predominant background colors of:
No. 269: a, Blue violet. b, Red violet.
No. 270: a, Green. b, Orange brown.
No. 271: a, Yellow brown. b, Bright red.
No. 272: a, Red. b, Violet.
Illustration reduced.

**2006, Apr. 21**      *Perf. 13¾*

| | | | | |
|---|---|---|---|---|
| 269 | A43 | Horiz. pair | 2.25 | 2.25 |
| *a.-b.* | | 29p Either single | 1.10 | 1.10 |
| 270 | A43 | Horiz. pair | 3.00 | 3.00 |
| *a.-b.* | | 34p Either single | 1.50 | 1.50 |
| 271 | A43 | Horiz. pair | 3.25 | 3.25 |
| *a.-b.* | | 42p Either single | 1.60 | 1.60 |
| 272 | A43 | Horiz. pair | 3.50 | 3.50 |
| *a.-b.* | | 45p Either single | 1.75 | 1.75 |
| | | *Nos. 269-272 (4)* | 12.00 | 12.00 |

Birds — A44

Designs: 29p, Fulmar. 34p, Gannet. 42p, Lesser black-backed gull. 45p, Storm petrel. 47p, Kittiwake. 68p, Puffin.

**2006, July 27**    **Litho.**    *Perf. 13¾*

| | | | | |
|---|---|---|---|---|
| 273 | A44 | 29p multi | 1.10 | 1.10 |
| *a.* | | Booklet pane of 4 | 4.50 | |
| 274 | A44 | 34p multi | 1.50 | 1.50 |
| *a.* | | Booklet pane of 4 | 6.00 | |
| 275 | A44 | 42p multi | 1.60 | 1.60 |
| *a.* | | Booklet pane of 4 | 6.50 | |
| 276 | A44 | 45p multi | 1.75 | 1.75 |
| *a.* | | Booklet pane of 4 | 7.00 | |
| 277 | A44 | 47p multi | 2.00 | 2.00 |
| *a.* | | Booklet pane of 4 | 8.00 | |

| | | | | |
|---|---|---|---|---|
| 278 | A44 | 68p multi | 2.75 | 2.75 |
| *a.* | | Booklet pane of 4 | 11.00 | — |
| | | Complete booklet, #273a, 274a, 275a, 276a, 277a, 278a | 45.00 | |
| | | *Nos. 273-278 (6)* | 10.70 | 10.70 |

See Nos. 297-302, 319-324.

Corals and
Anemones — A45

Designs: 1p, Burrowing anemone. 2p, Colonial anemone. 3p, Jewel anemone. 4p, Sagartia elegans. 5p, Red fingers. 6p, Plumose anemone. 7p, Fan coral. 8p, Jewel anemone, diff. 9p, Actinothoe sphyrodeta. 10p, Snakelocks anemone. £1, Beadlet anemone. £2, Sunset cup coral.

**2006, Nov. 2**    **Litho.**    *Perf. 13x13½*

| | | | | |
|---|---|---|---|---|
| 279 | A45 | 1p multi | .20 | .20 |
| 280 | A45 | 2p multi | .20 | .20 |
| 281 | A45 | 3p multi | .20 | .20 |
| 282 | A45 | 4p multi | .20 | .20 |
| 283 | A45 | 5p multi | .20 | .20 |
| 284 | A45 | 6p multi | .20 | .20 |
| 285 | A45 | 7p multi | .25 | .25 |
| 286 | A45 | 8p multi | .30 | .30 |
| 287 | A45 | 9p multi | .35 | .35 |
| 288 | A45 | 10p multi | .40 | .40 |

**Litho. & Embossed**
**Size: 22x27mm**
*Perf. 12¾x13¼*

| | | | | |
|---|---|---|---|---|
| 289 | A45 | £1 multi | 3.75 | 3.75 |
| 290 | A45 | £2 multi | 7.75 | 7.75 |
| | | *Nos. 279-290 (12)* | 14.00 | 14.00 |

See Nos. 303-306.

Alderney
Wetlands
A46

Designs: 32p, Cushion starfish. 37p, Gannet. 45p, Squat lobster. 48p, Gray seal. 50p, Golden samphire. 71p, Little egret.

**2007, Mar. 8**    **Litho.**    *Perf. 13¼*

| | | | | |
|---|---|---|---|---|
| 291 | A46 | 32p multi | 1.25 | 1.25 |
| 292 | A46 | 37p multi | 1.50 | 1.50 |
| 293 | A46 | 45p multi | 1.75 | 1.75 |
| 294 | A46 | 48p multi | 1.90 | 1.90 |
| 295 | A46 | 50p multi | 2.00 | 2.00 |
| 296 | A46 | 71p multi | 2.75 | 2.75 |
| *a.* | | Souvenir sheet, #291-296 | 11.50 | 11.50 |
| | | *Nos. 291-296 (6)* | 11.15 | 11.15 |

Addition of Alderney Wetlands and Burhou Islands to Ramsar Convention Protected Wetlands List.

### Birds Type of 2006

Designs: 32p, Blackbird. 37p, Dartford warbler. 45p, Blue tit. 48p, Wren. 50p, House sparrow. 71p, Jackdaw.

**2007, May 24**    **Litho.**    *Perf. 13¾*

| | | | | |
|---|---|---|---|---|
| 297 | A44 | 32p multi | 1.25 | 1.25 |
| *a.* | | Booklet pane of 4 | 5.00 | — |
| 298 | A44 | 37p multi | 1.50 | 1.50 |
| *a.* | | Booklet pane of 4 | 6.00 | — |
| 299 | A44 | 45p multi | 1.75 | 1.75 |
| *a.* | | Booklet pane of 4 | 7.00 | — |
| 300 | A44 | 48p multi | 1.90 | 1.90 |
| *a.* | | Booklet pane of 4 | 7.75 | — |
| 301 | A44 | 50p multi | 2.00 | 2.00 |
| *a.* | | Booklet pane of 4 | 8.00 | — |
| 302 | A44 | 71p multi | 3.00 | 3.00 |
| *a.* | | Booklet pane of 4 | 12.00 | — |
| | | Complete booklet, #297a-302a | 46.00 | |
| | | *Nos. 297-302 (6)* | 11.40 | 11.40 |

### Corals and Anemones Type of 2006

Designs: 20p. Devonshire cup coral. 40p, Fried egg anemone. 50p, Parasitic anemone. £4, Strawberry anemone.

**2007, Aug. 2**    **Litho.**    *Perf. 14*
**Size: 27x23mm**

| | | | | |
|---|---|---|---|---|
| 303 | A45 | 20p multi | .80 | .80 |
| 304 | A45 | 40p multi | 1.60 | 1.60 |
| 305 | A45 | 50p multi | 2.10 | 2.10 |

**Litho. & Embossed**
**Size: 27x28mm**

| | | | | |
|---|---|---|---|---|
| 306 | A45 | £4 multi | 16.00 | 16.00 |
| | | *Nos. 303-306 (4)* | 20.50 | 20.50 |

Just So Stories, by
Rudyard
Kipling — A47

Designs: 32p, How the Camel Got His
Hump. 37p, How the Whale Got His Throat.
45p, The Elephant's Child. 48p, How the
Leopard Got His Spots. 50p, The Cat That
Walked by Himself. 71p, How the Rhinoceros
Got His Skin.

| 2007, Oct. 25 | Litho. | Perf. 13x13¼ | |
|---|---|---|---|
| 307 A47 | 32p multi | 1.40 | 1.40 |
| 308 A47 | 37p multi | 1.50 | 1.50 |
| 309 A47 | 45p multi | 1.90 | 1.90 |
| 310 A47 | 48p multi | 2.00 | 2.00 |
| 311 A47 | 50p multi | 2.10 | 2.10 |
| 312 A47 | 71p multi | 3.00 | 3.00 |
| a. | Miniature sheet, #307-312 | 12.00 | 12.00 |
| | Nos. 307-312 (6) | 11.90 | 11.90 |

Butterflies
A48

Butterflies: 34p, Painted lady. 40p, Grayling.
48p, Green hairstreak. 51p, Speckled wood.
53c, Common blue. 74p, Glanville fritillary.

| 2008, Feb. 28 | Litho. | Perf. 13¾ | |
|---|---|---|---|
| 313 A48 | 34p multi | 1.40 | 1.40 |
| 314 A48 | 40p multi | 1.60 | 1.60 |
| 315 A48 | 48p multi | 1.90 | 1.90 |
| 316 A48 | 51p multi | 2.00 | 2.00 |
| 317 A48 | 53p multi | 2.10 | 2.10 |
| 318 A48 | 74p multi | 3.00 | 3.00 |
| a. | Miniature sheet, #313-318 | 12.00 | 12.00 |
| | Nos. 313-318 (6) | 12.00 | 12.00 |

### Birds Type of 2006

Designs: 34p, Common buzzard. 40p, Peregrine falcon. 48p, Kestrel. 51p, Barn owl. 53p,
Long-eared owl. 74p, Sparrowhawk.

| 2008, May 15 | Litho. | Perf. 13¾ | |
|---|---|---|---|
| 319 A44 | 34p multi | 1.40 | 1.40 |
| a. | Booklet pane of 4 | 5.75 | |
| 320 A44 | 40p multi | 1.60 | 1.60 |
| a. | Booklet pane of 4 | 6.50 | |
| 321 A44 | 48p multi | 1.90 | 1.90 |
| a. | Booklet pane of 4 | 7.75 | |
| 322 A44 | 51p multi | 2.00 | 2.00 |
| a. | Booklet pane of 4 | 8.00 | |
| 323 A44 | 53p multi | 2.10 | 2.10 |
| a. | Booklet pane of 4 | 8.50 | |
| 324 A44 | 74p multi | 3.00 | 3.00 |
| a. | Booklet pane of 4 | 12.00 | |
| | Complete booklet, #319a-324a | 49.00 | |
| | Nos. 319-324 (6) | 12.00 | 12.00 |

Alderney Postage Stamps, 25th
Anniv. — A49

Flag and tourist sites: 34p, Old Harbor. 40p,
Breakwater. 48p, Fort Clonque Causeway.
51p, Golf course. 53p, Hanging Rock. 74p,
Fort Clonque.

| 2008, June 14 | Litho. | Perf. 14x13¾ | |
|---|---|---|---|
| 325 A49 | 34p multi | 1.40 | 1.40 |
| 326 A49 | 40p multi | 1.60 | 1.60 |
| 327 A49 | 48p multi | 1.90 | 1.90 |
| 328 A49 | 51p multi | 2.00 | 2.00 |
| 329 A49 | 53p multi | 2.10 | 2.10 |
| 330 A49 | 74p multi | 3.00 | 3.00 |
| | Nos. 325-330 (6) | 12.00 | 12.00 |

Heraldic
Lion — A50

### Litho. & Embossed With Foil Application

| 2008, June 14 | | Perf. 14¼x13½ | |
|---|---|---|---|
| 331 A50 | £5 multi | 20.00 | 20.00 |

Aurigny Air Services, 40th
Anniv. — A51

Various airplanes.

| 2008, Oct. 30 | Litho. | Perf. 13½ | |
|---|---|---|---|
| 332 A51 | 34p multi | 1.10 | 1.10 |
| 333 A51 | 40p multi | 1.25 | 1.25 |
| 334 A51 | 48p multi | 1.60 | 1.60 |
| 335 A51 | 51p multi | 1.75 | 1.75 |
| 336 A51 | 53p multi | 1.75 | 1.75 |
| 337 A51 | 74p multi | 2.40 | 2.40 |
| a. | Souvenir sheet, #332-337 | 10.00 | 10.00 |
| | Nos. 332-337 (6) | 9.85 | 9.85 |

# JERSEY

jәr-zē

LOCATION — Island in the English
Channel
GOVT. — Dependent territory (baili-
wick) of the British Crown
AREA — 45 sq. mi.
POP. — 89,721 (1999 est.)
CAPITAL — St. Helier

Following the establishment of the
British General Post Office as a public
corporation on October 1, 1969, the
post office of the Bailiwick of Jersey
became a separate entity and British
postage stamps ceased to be valid.

> **Catalogue values for unused
> stamps in this country are for
> Never Hinged items.**

### British Regional Issue

A1

Royal Mace
and Arms of
Jersey — A2

| | | Perf. 15x14 | | |
|---|---|---|---|---|
| 1958-69 | | Photo. | Wmk. 322 | |
| 1 A1 | 2½p rose red ('64) | | .35 | .25 |
| 2 A2 | 3p light purple | | .35 | .20 |
| p. | Phosphor. ('67) | | .20 | .20 |
| p. | Phosphor. ('67) | | .20 | .20 |
| 3 A2 | 4p ultra ('66) | | .35 | .20 |
| p. | Phosphor. ('67) | | .20 | .20 |
| | | Unwmk. | | |
| 4 A2 | 4p olive brown ('68) | | .20 | .20 |
| 5 A2 | 4p brt red ('69) | | .20 | .20 |
| 6 A2 | 5p dark blue ('68) | | .20 | .20 |
| | Nos. 1-6 (6) | | 1.65 | 1.25 |

Nos. 4-6 are phosphorescent.
Sold to the general public only at post
offices within Jersey, but valid for postage
throughout Great Britain.
See also Great Britain Nos. 269-270, which
were sold only in the Channel Islands and at a
few philatelic windows in Great Britain, and
may be considered to be precursors to the
regional issues.

### Bailiwick Issues

Elizabeth Castle and Queen Elizabeth
II — A3

Queen Elizabeth
II — A4

Designs (Queen Elizabeth II and): 1p, La
Hougue Bie (prehistoric tomb). 2p, Portelet
Bay. 3p, La Corbière Lighthouse. 4p, Mont
Orgueil by night. 5p, Arms of Jersey and Royal
Mace. 6p, Jersey cow. 9p, 1sh6p, Map of
English Channel with Jersey. 1sh, Mont
Orgueil. 2sh6p, Airport. 5sh, Legislative
Chamber. 10sh, Royal Court. £1, Queen Eliza-
beth II, photograph by Cecil Beaton.

| | | Perf. 14½ | | |
|---|---|---|---|---|
| 1969, Oct. 1 | | Photo. | Unwmk. | |
| 7 A3 | ½p ocher & multi | | .20 | .20 |
| 8 A3 | 1p brown & multi | | .20 | .20 |
| a. | Booklet pane of 1 | | .35 | |
| b. | Booklet pane of 2 | | .90 | |
| 9 A3 | 2p multicolored | | .20 | .20 |
| 10 A3 | 3p dp blue & multi | | .20 | .20 |
| 11 A3 | 4p multicolored | | .20 | .20 |
| a. | Booklet pane of 1 | | .60 | |
| b. | Booklet pane of 2 | | 1.10 | |
| 12 A3 | 5p multicolored | | .20 | .20 |
| a. | Booklet pane of 2 | | 1.75 | |
| 13 A3 | 6p multicolored | | .40 | .20 |
| 14 A3 | 9p multicolored | | .60 | .30 |
| 15 A3 | 1sh lilac & multi | | .80 | .70 |
| 16 A3 | 1sh6p green & multi | | 1.40 | 1.40 |
| 17 A4 | 1sh9p multicolored | | 2.00 | 2.00 |
| | | Perf. 12 | | |
| 18 A3 | 2sh6p multicolored | | 3.25 | 2.75 |
| 19 A3 | 5sh multicolored | | 12.00 | 10.00 |
| 20 A3 | 10sh gray & multi | | 27.50 | 20.00 |
| a. | 10sh green & multi (error) | | 4,000. | |
| 21 A4 | £1 tan & multi | | 3.50 | 3.75 |
| | Nos. 7-21 (15) | | 52.65 | 42.05 |

A second post-1971 printing of No. 21
shows the background drapery less purple
and more blue.
See Nos. 34-48, 107-109.

Jersey
Post
Office
First Day
Cover
A5

| 1969, Oct. 1 | | | Perf. 14½ | |
|---|---|---|---|---|
| 22 A5 | 4p multicolored | | .35 | .20 |
| 23 A5 | 5p blue & multi | | .40 | .20 |
| 24 A5 | 1sh6p brown & multi | | 1.10 | 1.25 |
| 25 A5 | 1sh9p emerald & multi | | 1.75 | 2.10 |
| | Nos. 22-25 (4) | | 3.60 | 3.75 |

Inauguration of independent postal service.

Jersey Woman Reaching for Royal
Mace, Flags of USSR, US and Great
Britain — A6

4p, Lord Coutanche, Bailiff of Jersey, by
James Gunn, vert. 5p, Sir Winston Churchill,
by D. Van Praag, vert. 1sh9p, Swedish Red
Cross ship "Vega."

| 1970, May 9 | | Photo. | Perf. 11½ | |
|---|---|---|---|---|
| 26 A6 | 4p gold & multi | | .50 | .20 |
| 27 A6 | 5p gold & multi | | .50 | .20 |
| 28 A6 | 1sh6p gold & multi | | 2.00 | 2.00 |
| 29 A6 | 1sh9p gold & multi | | 2.00 | 2.00 |
| | Nos. 26-29 (4) | | 5.00 | 4.40 |

25th anniv. of Jersey's liberation from the
Germans.

"Rags to Riches" Cinderella — A7

Designs (Parade Floats Made of Flowers):
4p, "A Tribute to Enid Blyton," author of children's books. 1sh6p, "Gourmet's Delight."
1sh9p, "We're the Greatest" (ostriches and
trees).

| 1970, July 28 | | Photo. | Perf. 11½ | |
|---|---|---|---|---|
| 30 A7 | 4p gold & multi | | .60 | .20 |
| 31 A7 | 5p gold & multi | | .60 | .60 |
| 32 A7 | 1sh6p gold & multi | | 8.00 | 5.00 |
| 33 A7 | 1sh9p gold & multi | | 8.00 | 6.50 |
| | Nos. 30-33 (4) | | 17.20 | 12.30 |

"Battle of Flowers" annual parade.

### Decimal Currency Issue
### Types of 1969
### "p" instead of "d"

Designs: ½p, Elizabeth Castle. 1p, La
Corbière Lighthouse. 1½p, Jersey cow. 2p,
Mont Orgueil by night. 2½p, Arms of Jersey
and Royal Mace. 3p, La Hougue Bie. 3½p,
Portelet Bay. 4p, 7½p, Map of English Chan-
nel and Jersey. 5p, Mont Orgueil by day. 6p,
Martello Tower at Archirondel. 9p, Queen Eliz-
abeth II, by Cecil Beaton. 10p, Airport. 20p,
Legislative Chamber. 50p, Royal Court.

| 1970-75 | | Photo. | Perf. 14½ | |
|---|---|---|---|---|
| 34 A3 | ½p ocher & multi ('71) | | .20 | .20 |
| a. | Booklet pane of 1 | | .20 | |
| 35 A3 | 1p multicolored ('71) | | .20 | .20 |
| a. | Booklet pane of 2 ('75) | | .20 | |
| b. | Booklet pane of 4 ('75) | | .35 | |
| 36 A3 | 1½p multicolored ('71) | | .20 | .20 |
| 37 A3 | 2p multicolored ('71) | | .20 | .20 |
| a. | Booklet pane of 2 | | .20 | |
| b. | Booklet pane of 4 | | .35 | |
| 38 A3 | 2½p multicolored ('71) | | .20 | .20 |
| a. | Booklet pane of 1 | | .35 | |
| b. | Booklet pane of 2 | | .45 | |
| 39 A3 | 3p brn & multicolored ('71) | | .20 | .20 |
| a. | Booklet pane of 1 ('72) | | .35 | |
| b. | Booklet pane of 2 ('72) | | .45 | |
| 40 A3 | 3½p multicolored ('71) | | .20 | .20 |
| a. | Booklet pane of 1 ('74) | | .35 | |
| b. | Booklet pane of 2 ('74) | | .50 | |
| 41 A3 | 4p multicolored ('71) | | .20 | .20 |
| a. | Booklet pane of 2 ('75) | | .50 | |
| b. | Booklet pane of 4 ('75) | | .75 | |
| 42 A3 | 5p lilac & multi ('71) | | .20 | .20 |
| a. | Booklet pane of 2 ('75) | | .55 | |
| b. | Booklet pane of 4 ('75) | | .95 | |
| 43 A3 | 6p green & multi ('71) | | .20 | .20 |
| 44 A3 | 7½p multicolored ('71) | | .25 | .25 |
| 45 A4 | 9p multicolored ('71) | | .35 | .35 |
| | | Perf. 12 | | |
| 46 A3 | 10p multicolored | | .40 | .40 |
| 47 A3 | 20p multicolored | | .75 | .75 |
| 48 A3 | 50p multicolored | | 1.90 | 1.90 |
| | Nos. 34-48 (15) | | 5.65 | 5.65 |

See also Nos. 107-109.

White-eared Pheasant — A8

2½p, Thick-billed parrots, vert. 7½p, Ursine
colobus monkeys, vert. 9p, Ring-tailed lemurs.

| 1971, Mar. 9 | | Photo. | Perf. 11½ | |
|---|---|---|---|---|
| 49 A8 | 2p deep plum & multi | | .70 | .20 |
| 50 A8 | 2½p dark gray & multi | | .80 | .20 |
| 51 A8 | 7½p olive & multi | | 6.00 | 5.00 |
| 52 A8 | 9p vio blue & multi | | 8.00 | 8.00 |
| | Nos. 49-52 (4) | | 15.50 | 13.40 |

Jersey Wildlife Preservation Trust.
See Nos. 65-68.

British Legion Emblem
A9

2½p, Poppy field & poppy emblem. 7½p, Jack Counter (1899-1970) & Victoria Cross. 9p, Flags of France & Great Britain.

**1971, June 15      Litho.      Perf. 14½**

| | | | |
|---|---|---|---|
| 53 | A9 | 2p multicolored | .35 | .20 |
| 54 | A9 | 2½p multicolored | .35 | .20 |
| 55 | A9 | 7½p multicolored | 2.25 | 2.00 |
| 56 | A9 | 9p multicolored | 2.25 | 2.25 |
| | | Nos. 53-56 (4) | 5.20 | 4.65 |

50th anniversary of the British Legion.

English Fleet in Channel, by Peter Monamy
A10

Paintings by Jersey Artists: 2p, Tante Elizabeth (women in farm kitchen), by Edmund Blampied, vert. 7½p, Boyhood of Raleigh (man and boys at seashore), by Sir John Millais. 9p, The Blind Beggar (old man and girl), by W. W. Ouless, vert.

**1971, Oct. 5      Photo.      Perf. 11½**

| | | | |
|---|---|---|---|
| 57 | A10 | 2p gold & multi | .30 | .20 |
| 58 | A10 | 2½p gold & multi | .40 | .20 |
| 59 | A10 | 7½p gold & multi | 3.00 | 2.50 |
| 60 | A10 | 9p gold & multi | 3.00 | 2.50 |
| | | Nos. 57-60 (4) | 6.70 | 5.40 |

Jersey Fern — A11      Jersey Royal Artillery Shako — A12

Jersey Wild Flowers: 5p, Thrift. 7½p, Orchid (laxiflora). 9p, Viper's bugloss.

**1972, Jan. 18**
**Flowers in Natural Colors**

| | | | |
|---|---|---|---|
| 61 | A11 | 3p brown & blk | .35 | .20 |
| 62 | A11 | 5p lt blue & blk | .75 | .35 |
| 63 | A11 | 7½p lilac & blk | 2.25 | 1.90 |
| 64 | A11 | 9p green & blk | 2.25 | 2.00 |
| | | Nos. 61-64 (4) | 5.60 | 4.45 |

**Wildlife Type of 1971**

2½p, Cheetahs. 3p, Rothschild's mynahs, vert. 7½p, Spectacled bear. 9p, Tuatara reptiles.

**1972, Mar. 17      Photo.      Perf. 11½**
**Queen's Head in Gold**

| | | | |
|---|---|---|---|
| 65 | A8 | 2½p Prus blue & multi | .85 | .20 |
| 66 | A8 | 3p dk pur & multi | .60 | .20 |
| 67 | A8 | 7½p yel bis & multi | 1.25 | 1.25 |
| 68 | A8 | 9p multicolored | 1.75 | 1.75 |
| | | Nos. 65-68 (4) | 4.45 | 3.40 |

Jersey Wildlife Preservation Trust.

**1972, June 27**

| | | | |
|---|---|---|---|
| 69 | A12 | 2½p shown | .25 | .20 |
| 70 | A12 | 3p 2nd North Regiment | .25 | .20 |
| 71 | A12 | 7½p South West Regiment | .60 | .30 |
| 72 | A12 | 9p 3rd (South) Light Infantry | .85 | .65 |
| | | Nos. 69-72 (4) | 1.95 | 1.35 |

Royal Jersey Militia shakos of 19th century.

Princess Anne — A13

Designs: 3p, Queen Elizabeth II and Prince Philip, horiz. 7½p, Prince Charles. 20p, Queen Elizabeth II and family, horiz.

**1972, Nov. 1      Photo.      Perf. 11½**

| | | | |
|---|---|---|---|
| 73 | A13 | 2½p citron & multi | .20 | .20 |
| 74 | A13 | 3p rose & multi | .20 | .20 |
| 75 | A13 | 7½p blue & multi | .25 | .20 |
| 76 | A13 | 20p gray & multi | .75 | .50 |
| | | Nos. 73-76 (4) | 1.40 | 1.10 |

25th anniversary of the marriage of Queen Elizabeth II and Prince Philip.

Silver Wine and Christening Cups, 18th Century
A14

Designs: 3p, Gold torque, Bronze Age, vert. 7½p, Seal of Charles II, 1659, vert. 9p, Armorican (Brittany) coins, c. 55 B.C.

**1973, Jan. 23      Photo.      Perf. 11½**

| | | | |
|---|---|---|---|
| 77 | A14 | 2½p ultra & multi | .20 | .20 |
| 78 | A14 | 3p dp car & multi | .20 | .20 |
| 79 | A14 | 7½p org & multi | .25 | .25 |
| 80 | A14 | 9p blue & multi | .35 | .25 |
| | | Nos. 77-80 (4) | 1.00 | .90 |

Cent. of the Jersey Soc. Designs are from exhibits in the Soc. museum in St. Helier.

Balloon, Letter to Jersey from Siege of Paris, 1870 — A15

5p, Astra seaplane, 1912. 7½p, Supermarine Sea Eagle, 1923. 9p, De Havilland DH86, 1933.

**1973, May 16      Photo.      Perf. 11½**

| | | | |
|---|---|---|---|
| 81 | A15 | 3p brt blue & multi | .20 | .20 |
| 82 | A15 | 5p blue grn & multi | .20 | .20 |
| 83 | A15 | 7½p ultra & multi | .25 | .25 |
| 84 | A15 | 9p vio blue & multi | .35 | .35 |
| | | Nos. 81-84 (4) | 1.00 | 1.00 |

Aviation history connected with Jersey before 1939.

19th Century Locomotives
A16

**1973, Aug. 6      Photo.      Perf. 11½**

| | | | |
|---|---|---|---|
| 85 | A16 | 2½p North Western | .20 | .20 |
| 86 | A16 | 3p Calvados | .20 | .20 |
| 87 | A16 | 7½p Carteret | .30 | .20 |
| 88 | A16 | 9p Caesarea | .45 | .30 |
| | | Nos. 85-88 (4) | 1.15 | .90 |

Centenary of Jersey Eastern Railroad.

Princess Anne and Mark Phillips
A17

**1973, Nov. 14      Photo.      Perf. 11½**

| | | | |
|---|---|---|---|
| 89 | A17 | 3p lt blue & multi | .20 | .20 |
| 90 | A17 | 20p pink & multi | .60 | .80 |

Wedding of Princess Anne and Capt. Mark Phillips, Nov. 14, 1973.

Spider Crab
A18

**1973, Nov. 15      Photo.      Perf. 11½**

| | | | |
|---|---|---|---|
| 91 | A18 | 2½p shown | .20 | .20 |
| 92 | A18 | 3p Conger eel | .20 | .20 |
| 93 | A18 | 7½p Lobster | .30 | .25 |
| 94 | A18 | 20p Ormer | .60 | .30 |
| | | Nos. 91-94 (4) | 1.30 | .95 |

Jersey Spring Flowers — A19

**1974, Feb. 13      Photo.      Perf. 12x11½**

| | | | |
|---|---|---|---|
| 95 | A19 | 3p Freesias | .20 | .20 |
| 96 | A19 | 5½p Anemones | .20 | .20 |
| 97 | A19 | 8p Carnations & gladioli | .25 | .25 |
| 98 | A19 | 10p Daffodils & iris | .35 | .35 |
| | | Nos. 95-98 (4) | 1.00 | 1.00 |

First Letter Box, Letter with 1852 Cancel
A20

UPU Cent.: 3p, Postmen, 1862 and 1969. 5½p, Contemporary pillar box and first day cover of No. 101. 20p, BAC 111 and paddle steamer "Aquila," 1874.

**1974, June 7      Photo.      Perf. 11½**

| | | | |
|---|---|---|---|
| 99 | A20 | 2½p multicolored | .20 | .20 |
| 100 | A20 | 3p ultra & multi | .20 | .20 |
| 101 | A20 | 5½p olive & multi | .20 | .20 |
| 102 | A20 | 20p gray & multi | .75 | .40 |
| | | Nos. 99-102 (4) | 1.35 | 1.00 |

John Wesley — A21

**Lithographed and Engraved**

**1974, July 31      Perf. 13½x14**

| | | | |
|---|---|---|---|
| 103 | A21 | 3p shown | .20 | .20 |
| 104 | A21 | 3½p Hillary | .20 | .20 |
| 105 | A21 | 8p Wace | .25 | .25 |
| 106 | A21 | 20p Churchill | .75 | .50 |
| | | Nos. 103-106 (4) | 1.40 | 1.15 |

Anniversaries: Methodism in Jersey, bicen.; John Wesley, theologian, founder of Methodism. Sesquicentennial of Royal Natl. Lifeboat Institution, Lt. Col. Sir William Hillary, founder. 800th death anniv. of Canon Wace, poet and chronicler. Sir Winston Churchill, birth centenary.

**Type of 1969**

4½p, Arms of Jersey and Royal Mace. 5½p, Jersey cow. 8p, Mont Orgueil by night.

**1974, Oct. 31      Photo.      Perf. 14½**

| | | | |
|---|---|---|---|
| 107 | A3 | 4½p olive & multi | .20 | .20 |
| 108 | A3 | 5½p magenta & multi | .20 | .20 |
| 109 | A3 | 8p yellow & multi | .30 | .30 |
| | | Nos. 107-109 (3) | .70 | .70 |

English Yacht, 1660, by Peter Monamy
A22

Marine paintings by Peter Monamy (d. 1749): 5½p, French ship. 8p, Dutch ship, horiz. 25p, Naval battle, 1662.

**1974, Nov. 22      Photo.      Perf. 11½**
**Size: 31x38, 38x31mm**

| | | | |
|---|---|---|---|
| 116 | A22 | 3½p gold & multi | .20 | .20 |
| 117 | A22 | 5½p gold & multi | .20 | .20 |
| 118 | A22 | 8p gold & multi | .25 | .25 |

**Size: 54x25mm**

| | | | |
|---|---|---|---|
| 119 | A22 | 25p gold & multi | .65 | .65 |
| | | Nos. 116-119 (4) | 1.30 | 1.30 |

Potato Digger — A23

19th cent. farming tools: 3½p, Cider apple crusher. 8p, Six-horse plow. 10p, Hay cart.

**1975, Feb. 25      Photo.      Perf. 11½**

| | | | |
|---|---|---|---|
| 120 | A23 | 3p multicolored | .20 | .20 |
| 121 | A23 | 3½p multicolored | .20 | .20 |
| 122 | A23 | 8p multicolored | .30 | .30 |
| 123 | A23 | 10p multicolored | .35 | .35 |
| | | Nos. 120-123 (4) | 1.05 | 1.05 |

Shell Design as Letter "J" — A24

Posters: 8p, Beach umbrella. 10p, Beach chair. 12p, Sand castle with Union Jacks & Jersey flag.

**1975, June 8      Photo.      Perf. 11½**

| | | | |
|---|---|---|---|
| 124 | A24 | 5p multicolored | .20 | .20 |
| 125 | A24 | 8p multicolored | .20 | .20 |
| 126 | A24 | 10p multicolored | .30 | .30 |
| 127 | A24 | 12p multicolored | .40 | .40 |
| a. | | Souvenir sheet of 4 | 1.25 | 1.25 |
| | | Nos. 124-127 (4) | 1.10 | 1.10 |

Tourist publicity. No. 127a contains Nos. 124-127 in continuous design extending into margin.

Queen Mother Elizabeth
A25

**1975, May 30      Photo.      Perf. 11½**

| | | | |
|---|---|---|---|
| 128 | A25 | 20p multicolored | .75 | .50 |

Visit of Queen Mother Elizabeth to Jersey.

Common Tern — A26

## 1975, July 28    Photo.    *Perf. 11½*

| | | | | |
|---|---|---|---|---|
| 129 | A26 | 4p shown | .20 | .20 |
| 130 | A26 | 5p Storm petrel | .20 | .20 |
| 131 | A26 | 8p Brent geese | .40 | .40 |
| 132 | A26 | 25p Shag | .80 | .35 |
| | | *Nos. 129-132 (4)* | 1.60 | .95 |

Siskin 3A, 1925 — A27

R.A.F. Planes: 5p, Southampton 1, 1925. 10p, Spitfire 1, 1931. 25p, Gnat T.1, 1962.

## 1975, Oct. 30    Photo.    *Perf. 11½*

| | | | | |
|---|---|---|---|---|
| 133 | A27 | 4p blue & multi | .20 | .20 |
| 134 | A27 | 5p lt green & multi | .20 | .20 |
| 135 | A27 | 10p yellow & multi | .35 | .35 |
| 136 | A27 | 25p ultra & multi | .70 | .70 |
| | | *Nos. 133-136 (4)* | 1.45 | 1.45 |

Royal Air Force Assoc., Jersey Branch, 50th anniv.

Map of Jersey with 12 Parishes A28

Arms of Trinity and Zoo — A29

Queen Elizabeth II — A30

Arms and scene: 5p, Church of St. Mary. 6p, Grouville, Seymour Tower. 7p, St. Brelade, La Corbière Lighthouse. 8p, Church of St. Saviour. 9p, St. Helier, Elizabeth Castle. 10p, St. Martin, Gorey Harbor. 11p, St. Peter, Jersey Airport. 12p, St. Ouen, Grosnez Castle. 13p, St. John, Bonne Nuit Harbor. 14p, St. Clement and Le Hocq Tower. 15p, St. Lawrence, Morel Farm. 20p, 12 Parishes, view of harbor. 30p, Jersey flag, map of Island. 40p, Postal Administration emblem, PO Headquarters. 50p, Jersey, Parliament and Royal Court. £1, Flag of Lt.-Governor, Government House.

## 1976-77    Litho.    *Perf. 14½*
### Size: 33x23mm

| | | | | |
|---|---|---|---|---|
| 137 | A28 | ½p lt blue & multi | .20 | .20 |
| 138 | A29 | 1p bister & multi | .20 | .20 |
| a. | | Bklt. pane of 2 + 2 labels | .80 | |
| b. | | Booklet pane of 4 | .80 | |
| 139 | A29 | 5p rose & multi | .20 | .20 |
| a. | | Booklet pane of 4 | .80 | |
| 140 | A29 | 6p vio blue & multi | .25 | .25 |
| a. | | Booklet pane of 4 ('78) | 1.00 | |
| 141 | A29 | 7p fawn & multi | .25 | .25 |
| a. | | Booklet pane of 4 | 1.10 | |
| 142 | A29 | 8p yel grn & multi | .25 | .25 |
| a. | | Booklet pane of 4 ('78) | 1.10 | |
| 143 | A29 | 9p lil rose & multi | .25 | .25 |
| a. | | Booklet pane of 4 ('80) | 1.25 | |
| 144 | A29 | 10p ol bis & multi | .30 | .30 |
| 145 | A29 | 11p bl grn & multi | .35 | .35 |
| 146 | A29 | 12p org & multi | .35 | .35 |
| 147 | A29 | 13p blue & multi | .35 | .35 |
| 148 | A29 | 14p yel org & multi | .50 | .50 |
| 149 | A29 | 15p vio & multi | .50 | .50 |

### Photo.
*Perf. 12*
### Size: 41x26mm, 26x41mm

| | | | | |
|---|---|---|---|---|
| 150 | A29 | 20p gold & multi | .55 | .55 |
| 151 | A28 | 30p gold & multi | .70 | .70 |
| 152 | A29 | 40p gold & multi | 1.00 | 1.00 |
| 153 | A29 | 50p gold & multi | 1.25 | 1.25 |
| 154 | A29 | £1 gold & multi | 3.50 | 3.50 |

| | | | | |
|---|---|---|---|---|
| 155 | A30 | £2 multicolored | | |
| | |    ('77) | 5.00 | 5.00 |
| | | *Nos. 137-155 (19)* | 15.95 | 15.95 |

Issue dates: Nos. 137-149, Jan. 29; Nos. 150-154, Aug. 20. No. 155, Nov. 16.

Sir Walter Raleigh and Old Map of Virginia — A31

US Bicentennial: 7p, Sir George Carteret and old map of New Jersey. 11p, Philippe Dauvergne and ships landing on Long Island. 13p, John Singleton Copley and his "Death of Major Pierson."

## 1976, May 29    Photo.    *Perf. 11½*

| | | | | |
|---|---|---|---|---|
| 160 | A31 | 5p multicolored | .20 | .20 |
| 161 | A31 | 7p multicolored | .25 | .25 |
| 162 | A31 | 11p multicolored | .35 | .35 |
| 163 | A31 | 13p multicolored | .45 | .45 |
| | | *Nos. 160-163 (4)* | 1.25 | 1.25 |

Dr. Grandin, Central and Southern China Map A32

7p, Yangtze River journey. 11p, On horseback to Chaotung. 13p, Dr. Grandin holding infant.

## 1976, Nov. 25    Photo.    *Perf. 11½*

| | | | | |
|---|---|---|---|---|
| 164 | A32 | 5p multicolored | .20 | .20 |
| 165 | A32 | 7p multicolored | .25 | .25 |
| 166 | A32 | 11p multicolored | .35 | .35 |
| 167 | A32 | 13p multicolored | .45 | .45 |
| | | *Nos. 164-167 (4)* | 1.25 | 1.25 |

Lilian Mary Grandin (1876-1924), Jersey-born missionary doctor in China.

Queen Wearing St. Edward's Crown — A33

7p, Queen with Jersey Bailiff Sir Alexander Coutanche, 1957. 25p, Portrait, 1976.

## 1977, Feb. 7    Photo.    *Perf. 11½*

| | | | | |
|---|---|---|---|---|
| 168 | A33 | 5p multicolored | .20 | .20 |
| 169 | A33 | 7p multicolored | .30 | .30 |
| 170 | A33 | 25p multicolored | .70 | .70 |
| | | *Nos. 168-170 (3)* | 1.20 | 1.20 |

25th anniv. of the reign of Elizabeth II.

1/13th sh, 1871 and 1/12th sh, 1877 A34

Coins: 7p, 1/12th sh, 1949. 11p, Silver crown, 1966. 13p, Silver £2, 1972.

## 1977, Mar. 25    Litho.    *Perf. 14*

| | | | | |
|---|---|---|---|---|
| 171 | A34 | 5p multicolored | .20 | .20 |
| 172 | A34 | 7p multicolored | .25 | .25 |
| 173 | A34 | 11p multicolored | .40 | .40 |
| 174 | A34 | 13p multicolored | .45 | .45 |
| | | *Nos. 171-174 (4)* | 1.30 | 1.30 |

Centenary of Jersey's currency reform.

Sir William Weston and Santa Anna, 1530 A35

Designs: 7p, Sir William Drogo and horse-drawn ambulance, 1877. 11p, Duke of Connaught and Jersey ambulance, 1917. 13p, Richard, Duke of Gloucester and ambulance team, 1977.

## 1977, June 24    Litho.    *Perf. 14x13½*

| | | | | |
|---|---|---|---|---|
| 175 | A35 | 5p multicolored | .20 | .20 |
| 176 | A35 | 7p multicolored | .25 | .25 |
| 177 | A35 | 11p multicolored | .35 | .35 |
| 178 | A35 | 13p multicolored | .45 | .45 |
| | | *Nos. 175-178 (4)* | 1.25 | 1.25 |

St. John Ambulance Assoc. cent. (in GB).

Victoria and Albert Arriving in Jersey, 1846 A36

Designs: 10½p, Victoria College, 1852. 11p, Statue of Sir Galahad near college gate, vert. 13p, College Hall, interior, vert.

## 1977, Sept. 29    Litho.    *Perf. 14½*

| | | | | |
|---|---|---|---|---|
| 179 | A36 | 7p multicolored | .20 | .20 |
| 180 | A36 | 10½p multicolored | .25 | .25 |
| 181 | A36 | 11p multicolored | .35 | .35 |
| 182 | A36 | 13p multicolored | .45 | .45 |
| | | *Nos. 179-182 (4)* | 1.25 | 1.25 |

Jersey Victoria College, 125th anniv.

Harry Vardon Statuette, Layout of Golf Course A37

Designs: 8p, Golf grip and swing perfected by Vardon. 11p, Vardon's putting grip and stance. 13p, Vardon's British and US Open Golf trophies, his book "The Complete Golfer" and biography.

## 1978, Feb. 28    Litho.    *Perf. 14*

| | | | | |
|---|---|---|---|---|
| 183 | A37 | 6p multicolored | .20 | .20 |
| 184 | A37 | 8p multicolored | .30 | .30 |
| 185 | A37 | 11p multicolored | .35 | .35 |
| 186 | A37 | 13p multicolored | .40 | .40 |
| | | *Nos. 183-186 (4)* | 1.25 | 1.25 |

Cent. of Royal Jersey Golf Club and to honor Vardon (1870-1937), Jersey-born golfer.

Mont Orgueil — A38

Europa: 8p, St. Aubin's Fort. 10½p, Elizabeth Castle.

## 1978, May 1    Photo.    *Perf. 11½*

| | | | | |
|---|---|---|---|---|
| 187 | A38 | 6p multicolored | .20 | .20 |
| 188 | A38 | 8p multicolored | .25 | .25 |
| 189 | A38 | 10½p multicolored | .35 | .35 |
| | | *Nos. 187-189 (3)* | .80 | .80 |

Gaspe Basin, by P. J. Ouless — A39

8p, Early map of Gaspe Peninsula, after Capt. Cook. 10½p, Sailing ship Century. 11p, Early map of Jersey. 13p, St. Aubin's Bay Town & Harbor.

## 1978, June 9    Litho.    *Perf. 14x15*

| | | | | |
|---|---|---|---|---|
| 190 | A39 | 6p multicolored | .20 | .20 |
| 191 | A39 | 8p multicolored | .25 | .25 |
| 192 | A39 | 10½p multicolored | .30 | .25 |
| 193 | A39 | 11p multicolored | .35 | .25 |
| 194 | A39 | 13p multicolored | .45 | .30 |
| | | *Nos. 190-194 (5)* | 1.55 | 1.25 |

Jersey's links with Canada and for CAPEX, Canadian Intl. Phil. Exhib., Toronto, Ont., June 9-18.

Elizabeth II, Portraits 1953 and 1977 — A40

Design: 8p, Elizabeth II and Prince Philip.

## 1978, June 27    Photo.    *Perf. 11½*

| | | | | |
|---|---|---|---|---|
| 195 | A40 | 8p car, sil & black | .25 | .25 |
| 196 | A40 | 25p blue, sil & black | .75 | .70 |

25th anniv. of coronation of Queen Elizabeth II and for Royal visit, June 27.

Mail Cutter — A41

Packets: 8p, Flamer, paddle vessel. 10½p, Diana, screw steamer. 11p, Ibex, steamer. 13p, Caesarea, mini-liner.

## 1978, Oct. 18    Photo.    *Perf. 14½x14*

| | | | | |
|---|---|---|---|---|
| 197 | A41 | 6p multicolored | .20 | .20 |
| 198 | A41 | 8p multicolored | .25 | .25 |
| 199 | A41 | 10½p multicolored | .30 | .25 |
| 200 | A41 | 11p multicolored | .35 | .25 |
| 201 | A41 | 13p multicolored | .45 | .30 |
| | | *Nos. 197-201 (5)* | 1.55 | 1.25 |

First Government packet between Britain and Jersey, bicentenary.

Jersey Pillar Box, 1860 — A42

Europa: No. 203, Mailman emptying 1979 mailbox. No. 204, Telephone switchboard, c. 1900. No. 205, Technician working on contemporary telecommunications system.

### *Perf. 14, 14½x15*

## 1979, Mar. 1    Litho.

| | | | | |
|---|---|---|---|---|
| 202 | A42 | 8p yellow & blk | .25 | .25 |
| 203 | A42 | 8p carmine & blk | .25 | .25 |
| a. | | Pair, #202-203 | .50 | .50 |
| 204 | A42 | 10½p violet & blk | .45 | .45 |
| 205 | A42 | 10½p blue & blk | .45 | .45 |
| a. | | Pair, #204-205 | .90 | .90 |
| | | *Nos. 202-205 (4)* | 1.40 | 1.40 |

Nos. 203a, 205a have continuous design. Both exist perf. 14 and 14½x15.

Soft-colored Jersey Heifer — A43

25p, Milk-laden Jersey cow with 1st Prize ribbon.

## Perf. 14 (#206), 13¾ (#207)
**1979, Mar. 1**
206 A43  6p multicolored      .30  .30
### Size: 48x31mm
207 A43  25p multicolored      .95  .95

30th anniv. of 1st Intl. Conf. of Jersey Breed Societies and 9th Conf. of the World Jersey Cattle Bureau.

Percival Mew Gull — A44

Planes: 8p, De Havilland Chipmunk. 10½p, Druine D-31 Turbulent. 11p, De Havilland Tiger Moth. 13p, North American Harvard Mk. 4.

**1979, Apr. 24    Photo.    Perf. 11½**
208 A44  6p multicolored      .20  .20
209 A44  8p multicolored      .25  .25
210 A44  10½p multicolored      .25  .25
211 A44  11p multicolored      .40  .40
212 A44  13p multicolored      .50  .50
   Nos. 208-212 (5)      1.60  1.60

25th International Air Rally.

My First Sermon, by Millais — A45

Paintings by Millais: 10½p, Orphan. 11p, The Princes in the Tower. 25p, Jesus in the Home of His Parents, horiz.

**1979, Aug. 13    Photo.    Perf. 11½**
### Size: 25x35mm
213 A45  8p multicolored      .30  .30
214 A45  10½p multicolored      .35  .35
215 A45  11p multicolored      .35  .35
### Size: 49x30mm
#### Perf. 12x12½
216 A45  25p multicolored      .75  .75
   Nos. 213-216 (4)      1.75  1.75

IYC and for John Everett Millais (1829-96).

Waldrapp Ibis — A46

**1979, Nov. 8    Photo.    Perf. 11½**
217 A46  6p Pink pigeons      .20  .20
218 A46  8p Orangutans      .25  .25
219 A46  11½p shown      .25  .25
220 A46  13p Lowland gorillas      .40  .40
221 A46  15p Rodrigues fruit bats      .60  .60
   Nos. 217-221 (5)      1.70  1.70

Nos. 217-218, 220-221 vertical.

Mont Orgueil Fortress A47

Fortresses, 300th Anniversary: 11½p, St. Aubin Tower. 13p, Elizabeth. 25p, Map of Jersey showing fortress locations.

**1980, Feb. 5    Litho.    Perf. 14½x13½**
222 A47  8p multicolored      .25  .25
223 A47  11½p multicolored      .30  .30
224 A47  13p multicolored      .35  .35
#### Perf. 13½x14
### Size: 37½x26mm
225 A47  25p multicolored      .70  .70
   Nos. 222-225 (4)      1.60  1.60

Potato Harvest — A48

Royal Jersey Potato Cent.: 7p, Planting potatoes. 17½p, Loading dock, Weighbridge.

**1980, May 6    Litho.    Perf. 14**
226 A48  7p multicolored      .25  .25
227 A48  15p multicolored      .40  .40
228 A48  17½p multicolored      .55  .55
   Nos. 226-228 (3)      1.20  1.20

A49

Europa (Wax Figures from Mont Orgueil and Elizabeth Castles): No. 229a, Sir Walter Raleigh; 229b, Paul Ivy. No. 230a, Charles II and Sir George Carteret; 230b, Lady Carteret. Pairs in continuous design.

**1980, May 6**
229 A49  Pair      .60  .60
   a.-b.  9p any single      .30  .30
230 A49  Pair      .70  .70
   a.-b.  13½p any single      .35  .35

Three-lap Motorcycle Race — A51

**1980, July 24    Litho.    Perf. 12**
#### Granite Paper
231 A51  7p shown      .25  .25
232 A51  9p Intl. road race      .25  .25
233 A51  13½p Motorcycle scrambling      .45  .45
234 A51  15p Sand racing, saloon cars      .50  .50
235 A51  17½p Natl. Hill climb      .55  .55
   Nos. 231-235 (5)      2.00  2.00

Jersey Motorcycle and Light Car Club, 60th anniv.

"Eye of the Wind" Leaving St. Helier — A52

Designs: 9p, Medical research, Cuna Indians, Panama. 13½p, Exploration, Papua New Guinea. 14p, Capt. Scott's ship, Antarctica. 15p, Conservation, Sulawesi. 17½p, Marine studies.

**1980, Oct. 1    Litho.    Perf. 14½**
236 A52  7p multicolored      .25  .25
237 A52  9p multicolored      .25  .25
238 A52  13½ multicolored      .30  .30
239 A52  14p multicolored      .30  .30
240 A52  15p multicolored      .45  .45
241 A52  17½p multicolored      .55  .55
   Nos. 236-241 (6)      2.10  2.10

Operation Drake, a two-year, round-the-world scientific expedition in tribute to Royal Geographic Society sesquicentennial.

Armed Soldiers and Wounded Drummer A53

Designs: Details from The Death of Major Peirson, by John Singleton Copley.

**1981, Jan. 6    Photo.    Perf. 12½**
#### Granite Paper
242 A53  7p multicolored      .25  .25
243 A53  10p multicolored      .30  .30
244 A53  15p multicolored      .45  .45
245 A53  17½p multicolored      .60  .60
   a.  Souvenir sheet of 4, #242-245      2.00  2.00
   Nos. 242-245 (4)      1.60  1.60

Battle of Jersey bicentenary. No. 245a has continuous design.

De Bagot Family Arms — A54

Jersey, Channel Map A54a

Queen Elizabeth II, by Norman Hepple — A54b

**1981-83    Litho.    Perf. 14**
246 A54  ½p shown      .20  .20
247 A54  1p De Carteret      .20  .20
   a.  Booklet pane of 6      .35
248 A54  2p La Cloche      .20  .20
   a.  Booklet pane of 6      .55
249 A54  3p Dumaresq      .20  .20
   a.  Booklet pane of 6      .65
250 A54  4p Payn      .20  .20
251 A54  5p Janvrin      .20  .20
252 A54  6p Poingdestre      .20  .20
253 A54  7p Pipon      .30  .25
   a.  Booklet pane of 6      1.90
254 A54  8p Marett      .35  .30
   a.  Booklet pane of 6 ('83)      2.40
255 A54  9p Le Breton      .35  .25
256 A54  10p Le Maistre      .40  .25
   a.  Booklet pane of 6      2.75
257 A54  11p Bisson      .45  .25
   b.  Booklet pane of 6 ('83)      3.25
258 A54  12p Robin      .45  .30
259 A54  13p Herault      .50  .30
260 A54  14p Messervy      .55  .30
261 A54  15p Fiott      .60  .35
262 A54  20p Badier      .80  .35
263 A54  25p L'Arbalestier      1.00  .35
264 A54  30p Journeaulx      1.25  .60
265 A54  40p Lempriere      1.40  .60
266 A54  50p D'Auvergne      1.60  .75
267 A54a  £1 shown      2.25  1.50
#### Photo.
#### Perf. 12½x12
268 A54b  £5 multi      11.00  9.25
   Nos. 246-268 (23)      24.65  17.20

Issued: #246-256, 2/24; #248a, 12/1; #257-262, 7/28; #263-267, 2/23/82; #254a, 257a, 4/19/83; £5, 11/17/83.

**1984-88    Perf. 15x14**
247b A54  1p ('88)      .35  .25
248b A54  2p Bklt. pane of 6 ('86)      .65
248c A54  2p ('84)      .25  .20
249b A54  3p Bklt. pane of 6 ('84)      .75
249c A54  3p ('84)      .30  .20

250a A54  4p Bklt. pane of 6 ('87)      1.25
250b A54  4p ('86)      .30  .25
251a A54  5p ('86)      .30  .35
252a A54  6p ('86)      .30  .20
255a A54  9p Bklt. pane of 6 ('84)      1.75
255b A54  9p ('84)      .60  .50
256b A54  10p Bklt. pane of 6 ('86)      2.50
256c A54  10p ('86)      .50  .35
257a A54  11p Bklt. pane of 6 ('87)      3.00
257c A54  11p ('87)      .55  .45
258a A54  12p Bklt. pane of 6 ('84)      3.00
258b A54  12p ('84)      .80  .60
259a A54  13p ('84)      .50  .25
260a A54  14p Bklt. pane of 6 ('86)      3.25
260b A54  14p ('84)      .45  .25
261a A54  15p ('87)      .60  .45
261b A54  15p Bklt. pane of 6 ('87)      3.50
262a A54  20p ('86)      .85  .60
264a A54  30p ('86)      1.50  1.25
265a A54  40p ('87)      2.00  1.50
266a A54  50p ('87)      2.75  2.25

Issued: #251a, 252a, 262a, 264a, Mar. 4. No. 247a dated "February 1981," "December 1981" or "April 1983"; No. 248a dated "December 1981" or "April 1983"; Nos. 253a, 256a dated "February 1981" or "December 1981;" No. 250a dated "April 1987" or "May 1988." No. 258a dated "April 1984" or "May 1988."

See Nos. 381-388.

Knight of Hamby Killing the Dragon A55

Europa (Legends): 10p, La Hougue Bie. 18p, Easter Voyage of St. Brelade. No. 272, Servant killing Knight of Hamby. No. 273, Shipwreck of St. Brelade. No. 274, Fish, ships' departure.

**1981, Apr. 7    Perf. 14½**
271 A55  10p multicolored      .35  .35
272 A55  10p multicolored      .35  .35
   a.  Pair, #271-272      .70  .70
273 A55  18p multicolored      .55  .55
274 A55  18p multicolored      .55  .55
   a.  Pair, #273-274      1.10  1.10
   Nos. 271-274 (4)      1.80  1.80

Royal Square by Gaslight A56

**1981, May 22    Photo.    Perf. 12**
#### Granite Paper
275 A56  7p The Harbor      .25  .25
276 A56  10p The Quay      .30  .30
277 A56  18p shown      .45  .45
278 A56  22p Halkett Place      .55  .55
279 A56  25p Central Market      .65  .65
   Nos. 275-279 (5)      2.20  2.20

Gas light sesquicentennial.

Prince Charles and Lady Diana A57

**1981, July 28    Photo.    Perf. 12**
#### Granite Paper
280 A57  10p multicolored      .30  .30
281 A57  25p multicolored      1.40  1.40

Royal Wedding.

Christmas Tree, Royal Square, St. Helier — A58

**1981, Sept. 29    Litho.    Perf. 14½**
| | | | | |
|---|---|---|---|---|
| 282 | A58 | 7p shown | .25 | .25 |
| 283 | A58 | 10p East window, St. Helier's Church, choir | .35 | .35 |
| 284 | A58 | 18p Boxing Day, Jersey Drag Hunt | .60 | .60 |
| | | *Nos. 282-284 (3)* | 1.20 | 1.20 |

Christmas 1981.

Europa
1982 — A59

Designs: Maps showing formation of Channel Islands resulting from rise in sea level.

**1982, Apr. 20    Litho.    Perf. 14½**
| | | | | |
|---|---|---|---|---|
| 285 | A59 | 11p 16,000 BC | .35 | .35 |
| 286 | A59 | 11p 10,000 BC, vert. | .35 | .35 |
| 287 | A59 | 19½p 7,000 BC, vert. | .55 | .55 |
| 288 | A59 | 19½p 4,000 BC | .55 | .55 |
| | | *Nos. 285-288 (4)* | 1.80 | 1.80 |

Rollon Duke of Normandy, William the Conqueror, Clameur de Haro (Plea of Injunction) — A60

Links with France: No. 290, Kings John and Philippe Auguste, Siege of Rouen. No. 291, Jean Martxell (1694-1753), brandy merchant. No. 292, Victor Hugo. No. 293, Pierre Teilhard de Chardin (1881-1955), theologian. No. 294, Charles Rey (1897-1981), meteorologist.

**1982, June 11    Litho.    Perf. 14**
| | | | | |
|---|---|---|---|---|
| 289 | A60 | 8p multicolored | .25 | .25 |
| 290 | A60 | 8p multicolored | .25 | .25 |
| a. | | Bklt. pane of 4+label, 2 each #289-290 | 1.00 | 1.00 |
| b. | | Pair, #289-290 | .50 | .50 |
| 291 | A60 | 11p multicolored | .35 | .35 |
| 292 | A60 | 11p multicolored | .35 | .35 |
| a. | | Bklt. pane of 4+label, 2 each #291-292 | 1.50 | 1.50 |
| b. | | Pair, #291-292 | .70 | .70 |
| 293 | A60 | 19½p multicolored | .60 | .60 |
| 294 | A60 | 19½p multicolored | .60 | .60 |
| a. | | Bklt. pane of 4+label, 2 each #293-294 | 2.75 | 2.75 |
| b. | | Pair, #293-294 | 1.25 | 1.25 |
| | | Complete booklet, 2 each #290a, 292a, 294a | 11.00 | |
| | | *Nos. 289-294 (6)* | 2.40 | 2.40 |

Issue date: Nos. 290a-294a, Sept. 7. Two versions of Nos. 290a, 292a and 294a exist: the label is inscribed in English or French.

Scouting
Year
A61

Designs: 8p, Sir William Smith (Boys Brigade founder). 11p, Liberation parade, 1945, vert. 24p, Boys Brigade annual display, 1903. 26p, The Baden-Powells, 1924, vert. 29p, Scouts.

**1982, Nov. 18    Photo.    Perf. 12**
**Granite Paper**
| | | | | |
|---|---|---|---|---|
| 295 | A61 | 8p multicolored | .30 | .30 |
| 296 | A61 | 11p multicolored | .40 | .40 |
| 297 | A61 | 24p multicolored | .75 | .75 |
| 298 | A61 | 26p multicolored | .80 | .80 |
| 299 | A61 | 29p multicolored | .95 | .85 |
| | | *Nos. 295-299 (5)* | 3.20 | 3.10 |

Port Egmont
A62

250th Birth Anniv. of Capt. Philippe de Carteret (1733-97): 18th cent. engravings.

**1983, Feb. 15    Litho.    Perf. 14¼**
| | | | | |
|---|---|---|---|---|
| 300 | A62 | 8p shown | .30 | .30 |
| 301 | A62 | 11p Dolphin, Swallow | .40 | .40 |
| 302 | A62 | 19½p Discovering Pitcairn Is. | .65 | .65 |
| 303 | A62 | 24p English Cove, New Ireland | .80 | .80 |
| 304 | A62 | 26p Sinking pirate ship | .85 | .85 |
| 305 | A62 | 29p Endymion | 1.00 | 1.00 |
| | | *Nos. 300-305 (6)* | 4.00 | 4.00 |

No.
19
A63

Royal Mace — A64

**1983, Apr. 19    Litho.**
| | | | | |
|---|---|---|---|---|
| 306 | A63 | 11p shown | .45 | .45 |
| 307 | A64 | 11p shown | .45 | .45 |
| a. | | Pair, #306-307 | .90 | .90 |
| 308 | A63 | 19½p No. 20a | .65 | .65 |
| 309 | A64 | 19½p Bailiff's seal | .65 | .65 |
| a. | | Pair, #308-309 | 1.40 | 1.40 |
| | | *Nos. 306-309 (4)* | 2.20 | 2.20 |

Europa.

World Communications Year — A65

1st Postmaster Charles William LeGeyt (1733-1827): 8p, Commanding Grenadier Co., 25th Foot, Battle of Minden, 1759. 11p, London-Weymouth mail coach. 24p, PO Mail Packet attacked by French privateer. 26p, Hue St. PO. 29p, St. Helier Harbor.

**1983, June 21    Litho.    Perf. 14**
| | | | | |
|---|---|---|---|---|
| 310 | A65 | 8p multicolored | .35 | .35 |
| 311 | A65 | 11p multicolored | .45 | .45 |
| 312 | A65 | 24p multicolored | .85 | .85 |
| 313 | A65 | 26p multicolored | .90 | .90 |
| 314 | A65 | 29p multicolored | 1.10 | 1.10 |
| | | *Nos. 310-314 (5)* | 3.65 | 3.65 |

Intl. Assoc. of French-Speaking Parliamentarians 1983 General Assembly — A66

**1983, June 21    Perf. 15**
| | | | | |
|---|---|---|---|---|
| 315 | A66 | 19½p multicolored | .80 | .80 |

Cardinal Newman, by Walter William Ouless (1848-1933) A67

**1983, Sept. 20    Photo.    Perf. 11½**
| | | | | |
|---|---|---|---|---|
| 316 | A67 | 8p shown | .35 | .35 |
| 317 | A67 | 11p M. De Cazotte and his Daughter | .55 | .55 |
| 318 | A67 | 20½p Thomas Hardy | .85 | .85 |
| | | **Size: 41x34mm** | | |
| 319 | A67 | 31p David with the Head of Goliath | 1.25 | 1.25 |
| | | *Nos. 316-319 (4)* | 3.00 | 3.00 |

Jersey Wildlife Preservation Trust — A68

**1984, Jan. 17    Litho.    Perf. 14**
| | | | | |
|---|---|---|---|---|
| 320 | A68 | 9p Golden Lion Tamarin | .40 | .40 |
| 321 | A68 | 12p Snow Leopard | .45 | .45 |
| 322 | A68 | 20½p Jamaican Boa | .75 | .75 |
| 323 | A68 | 26p Round Island Gecko | 1.00 | 1.00 |
| 324 | A68 | 28p Coscoroba Swan | 1.00 | 1.00 |
| 325 | A68 | 31p St. Lucia Parrot | 1.10 | 1.10 |
| | | *Nos. 320-325 (6)* | 4.70 | 4.70 |

Europa 1984 (25th Anniv.) — A69

**1984, Mar. 12    Perf. 14½x15**
| | | | | |
|---|---|---|---|---|
| 326 | A69 | 9p multicolored | .35 | .35 |
| 327 | A69 | 12p multicolored | .40 | .40 |
| 328 | A69 | 20½p multicolored | .70 | .70 |
| | | *Nos. 326-328 (3)* | 1.45 | 1.45 |

**Souvenir Sheet**

Jersey Links with the Commonwealth — A70

**1984, Mar. 12    Perf. 15x14½**
| | | | | |
|---|---|---|---|---|
| 329 | A70 | 75p multicolored | 3.00 | 3.00 |

Commonwealth Postal Administrations Conf.

Royal Natl. Lifeboat Institution Centenary A71

Rescue Scenes (Lifeboats and Ships).

**1984, June 1    Litho.    Perf. 14½**
| | | | | |
|---|---|---|---|---|
| 330 | A71 | 9p Sarah Brooshoft, Demie de Pas Light | .35 | .35 |
| 331 | A71 | 9p Hearts of Oak, Maurice Georges | .35 | .35 |
| 332 | A71 | 12p Elizabeth Rippon, Hanna | .45 | .45 |
| 333 | A71 | 12p Elizabeth Rippon, Santa Maria | .45 | .45 |
| 334 | A71 | 20½p Elizabeth Rippon, Bacchus | .75 | .75 |
| 335 | A71 | 20½p Thomas James King, Cythara | .75 | .75 |
| | | *Nos. 330-335 (6)* | 3.10 | 3.10 |

40th Anniv. of Intl. Civil Aviation Org. A72

**1984, July 24    Litho.    Perf. 14**
**Granite Paper**
| | | | | |
|---|---|---|---|---|
| 336 | A72 | 9p Bristol Type 170 | .35 | .35 |
| 337 | A72 | 12p Airspeed AS-57 Ambassador 2 | .50 | .50 |
| 338 | A72 | 26p De Havilland Heron 1B | .90 | .90 |
| 339 | A72 | 31p DH-89A Dragon Rapide | 1.25 | 1.25 |
| | | *Nos. 336-339 (4)* | 3.00 | 3.00 |

Robinson Crusoe, by John Alexander Gilfillan (1793-1864) — A73

Gilfillan Paintings.

**1984, Sept. 21    Photo.    Perf. 11½**
| | | | | |
|---|---|---|---|---|
| 340 | A73 | 9p shown | .35 | .35 |
| 341 | A73 | 12p Edinburgh Castle | .45 | .45 |
| 342 | A73 | 20½p Maori Village | .70 | .70 |
| 343 | A73 | 26p Australian Landscape | .95 | .95 |
| 344 | A73 | 28p Waterhouse's Corner, Adelaide | 1.00 | 1.00 |
| 345 | A73 | 31p Capt. Cook at Botany Bay | 1.10 | 1.10 |
| | | *Nos. 340-345 (6)* | 4.55 | 4.55 |

Christmas
1984 — A74

**1984, Nov. 15    Photo.    Perf. 12x11½**
| | | | | |
|---|---|---|---|---|
| 346 | A74 | 9p St. Helier orchid | .60 | .60 |
| 347 | A74 | 12p Mt. Bingham orchid | .80 | .80 |

Ship Paintings by Philip John Ouless (1817-85) — A75

**1985, Feb. 26    Photo.    Perf. 14x14½**
| | | | | |
|---|---|---|---|---|
| 348 | A75 | 9p Hebe, 1874 | .30 | .30 |
| 349 | A75 | 12p Gaspe | .35 | .35 |
| 350 | A75 | 22p London, 1856 | .75 | .75 |
| 351 | A75 | 31p Rambler | 1.25 | 1.25 |
| 352 | A75 | 34p Elizabeth Castle | 1.40 | 1.40 |
| | | *Nos. 348-352 (5)* | 4.05 | 4.05 |

Europa
1985
A76

Performing Arts: 10p, John Ireland, composer (1879-1962). 13p, Ivy St. Helier, actress (1886-1971). 22p, Claude Debussy, composer.

**1985, Apr. 23    Litho.    Perf. 14**
| | | | | |
|---|---|---|---|---|
| 353 | A76 | 10p multicolored | .35 | .35 |
| 354 | A76 | 13p multicolored | .45 | .45 |
| 355 | A76 | 22p multicolored | .80 | .80 |
| | | *Nos. 353-355 (3)* | 1.60 | 1.60 |

Intl. Youth Year — A77

**1985, May 30    Litho.    Perf. 14½**
356 A77 10p Girls' Brigade          .35   .35
357 A77 13p Girl Guides             .45   .45
358 A77 29p Jersey Youth Service    .95   .95
359 A77 31p Sea Cadet Corps        1.00  1.00
360 A77 34p Air Training Corps     1.25  1.25
    Nos. 356-360 (5)               4.00  4.00

Railway History A78

**1985, July 16    Photo.    Perf. 12x11½**
361 A78 10p Duke of Normandy,
            Cheapside               .45   .45
362 A78 13p Saddletank, First
            Tower                    .50   .50
363 A78 22p La Moye, Millbrook      .90   .90
364 A78 29p St. Helier's, St.
            Aubin                   1.10  1.10
365 A78 34p St. Aubyns,
            Corbiere                1.40  1.40
    Nos. 361-365 (5)               4.35  4.35
Centenary of Jersey's first train from St. Helier to Corbiere.

Huguenot Heritage A79

300th anniv. of revocation of the Edict of Nantes (religious tolerance) by King Louis XIV of France: No. 366, James Hemery (1814-1849), Dean of Jersey, Rector of St. Helier. No. 367, Francis Henry Jeune, Baron St. Helier, law lord and junior counsel in the Tichbourne case. No. 368, Francois Voisin, merchant. No. 369, Pierre Amiraux, silversmith. No. 370, George Henry Ingouville, Victoria Cross recipient. No. 371, Robert Brohier, co-founder of Schweppes soft-drink company.

**1985, Sept. 10    Litho.    Perf. 14**
366 A79 10p Memorial window,
            St. Helier Town
            Church                   .40   .40
  a.     Booklet pane of 4          1.60
367 A79 10p Houses of Parliament, Westminster .40   .40
  a.     Booklet pane of 4          1.60
368 A79 13p Great Fair, Nijni-
            Novgorod, Russia         .45   .45
  a.     Booklet pane of 4          1.90
369 A79 13p Silver coffee pot,
            pitcher                  .45   .45
  a.     Booklet pane of 4          1.90
370 A79 22p Naval Battle of
            Viborg                   .70   .70
  a.     Booklet pane of 4          3.25
371 A79 22p Glass bottles, carbonated water commercial patent .70   .70
  a.     Booklet pane of 4          3.25
         Complete booklet, #366a-371a  14.00
    Nos. 366-371 (6)               3.10  3.10

Thomas Benjamin Frederick Davis (1867-1942), Shipping Magnate, Philanthropist — A80

Portrait and endowments: 10p, Howard Davis Hall, Victoria College. 13p, Yacht, racing schooner Westward. 31p, Howard Davis Park,

St. Helier. 34p, Howard Davis Agricultural Development Farm, Trinity.

**1985, Oct. 25    Perf. 13½**
372 A80 10p multicolored           .40   .40
373 A80 13p multicolored           .45   .45
374 A80 31p multicolored          1.10  1.10
375 A80 34p multicolored          1.25  1.25
    Nos. 372-375 (4)               3.20  3.20
50th anniv. of Howard Davis Hall, Victoria College, donated by Davis in memory of his son.

**Arms Type of 1981-82 and**

Elizabeth II, 60th Birthday — A80a

**1985-91    Litho.    Perf. 15x14**
381 A54 16p Malet                  .55   .35
  a.     Booklet pane of 6 ('88)  3.50
382 A54 17p Mabon                  .55   .45
383 A54 18p De St. Martin
            ('88)                   .80   .75
384 A54 19p Hamptonne
            ('88)                   .95   .80
386 A54 26p De Bagot ('88)         .80   .65
388 A54 75p Remon ('87)           2.40  1.75
        **Perf. 11½x12**
389 A80a £1 multicolored          3.50  3.25
        **Photo.**
        **Granite Paper**
390 A80a £2 multicolored          6.50  4.00
    Nos. 381-390 (8)              16.05 12.00
Issued: 16, 17p, 10/25; £1, 75p, 4/23/87; 18, 19, 26p, 4/26/88; £2, 3/19/91. No. 381a inscribed "May 1988."

Jersey Lily — A81

Lillie Langtry, by Sir John Millais — A82

**1986, Jan. 28    Litho.    Perf. 15x14½**
391 A81 13p multicolored           .60   .60
392 A82 34p multicolored          1.40  1.40
  a.     Souvenir sheet of 5 (4 13p, 34p)  4.25  4.25
Intl. Flower Gala, June 10-14.

Halley's Comet Sightings A83

Comet and coinciding historic events: 10p, Conquest of England, Bayeux Tapestry, A.D. 912 and 1066 sightings. 22p, Lady Carteret signing New Jersey over to William Penn, Edmond Halley observing comet, comets of 1301 & 1682. 31p, Giotto spacecraft and technology developed in 1910, 1986. Caesarea maiden voyage.

**1986, Mar. 4    Perf. 13½x13**
393 A83 10p multicolored           .35   .35
394 A83 22p multicolored           .90   .90
395 A83 31p multicolored          1.25  1.25
    Nos. 393-395 (3)               2.50  2.50

Europa 1986 — A84

**1986, Apr. 21    Perf. 14½**
396 A84 10p Viola kitaibeliana     .35   .35
397 A84 14p Matthiola sinuata      .60   .60
398 A84 22p Romulea columnae       .95   .95
    Nos. 396-398 (3)               1.90  1.90
Environmental conservation.

Jersey Natl. Trust, 50th Anniv. A85

**1986, June 17    Litho.    Perf. 13½x13**
399 A85 10p Le Rat cottage         .40   .40
400 A85 14p The Elms, head-
            quarters                .45   .45
401 A85 22p Morel Farm entrance    .70   .70
402 A85 29p Quetivel Mill         1.10  1.10
403 A85 31p La Vallette           1.25  1.25
    Nos. 399-403 (5)               3.90  3.90

Wedding of Prince Andrew and Sarah Ferguson — A86

**1986, July 23    Perf. 13½**
404 A86 14p multicolored           .55   .55
405 A86 40p multicolored          1.75  1.75

Paintings by Edmund Blampied (1886-1966), Artist — A87

**1986, Aug. 28    Litho.    Perf. 14**
406 A87 10p Gathering Vraic        .40   .40
407 A87 14p Driving Home in the
            Rain                    .55   .55
408 A87 29p The Miller            1.10  1.10
409 A87 31p The Joy Ride          1.25  1.25
410 A87 34p Tante Elizabeth       1.40  1.40
    Nos. 406-410 (5)               4.70  4.70

Christmas, Intl. Peace Year — A88

**1986, Nov. 4    Perf. 14½**
411 A88 10p Dove, map, flower      .40   .40
412 A88 14p Lovebirds              .55   .55
413 A88 34p Dove, noise-maker     1.40  1.40
    Nos. 411-413 (3)               2.35  2.35

Racing Schooner Westward A89

**1987, Jan. 15    Litho.    Perf. 13½**
414 A89 10p Under full sail        .40   .40
415 A89 14p T.B. Davis, owner      .55   .55
416 A89 31p Overhauling Britannia 1.25  1.25
417 A89 34p Dry dock, St. Helier  1.50  1.50
    Nos. 414-417 (4)               3.70  3.70

Jersey Airport, 50th Anniv. A90

**1987, Mar. 3    Litho.    Perf. 14**
418 A90 10p DH86 Belcroute Bay     .40   .40
419 A90 14p Boeing 757, Douglas DC-9  .55   .55
420 A90 22p Britten Norman Trislander, Islander  .85   .85
421 A90 29p Short SD330, Vickers Viscount  1.10  1.10
422 A90 31p BAC1-11, HPR.7
            Dart Herald           1.25  1.25
    Nos. 418-422 (5)               4.15  4.15

Europa 1987 A91

Modern architecture.

**1987, Apr. 23    Perf. 15x14**
423 A91 11p St. Mary and St.
            Peter's Church         .45   .45
424 A91 15p Villa Devereux         .60   .60
        **Size: 61x31mm**
425 A91 22p Fort Regent, St.
            Helier                  .85   .85
    Nos. 423-425 (3)               1.90  1.90

Adm. Philippe D'Auvergne (1754-1816) — A92

Ships: 11p, Racehorse trapped in the Arctic. 15p, Alarm burned at Rhode Island. 29p, Arethusa wrecked off Ushant, France. 31p, Rattlesnake stranded on Trinidad. 34p, Mont Orgueil Castle.

**1987, July 9    Perf. 14**
426 A92 11p multicolored           .40   .40
427 A92 15p multicolored           .50   .50
428 A92 29p multicolored          1.00  1.00
429 A92 31p multicolored          1.00  1.00
430 A92 34p multicolored          1.10  1.10
    Nos. 426-430 (5)               4.00  4.00

William the Conqueror (c. 1028-87), King of England (1066-87) — A93

Designs in the style of the Bayeux Tapestry: 11p, King Charles negotiating peace with the Vikings, 911, and cession of Jersey to Rollo's son William, 933. 15p, Duke Robert I and King Edward ashore Jersey after storm, 1030; Edward's succession to the throne of England,

1042. 22p, William the Conqueror's coronation, 1066, and succession of William II, 1087. 29p, Death of King William Rufus, and Henry defeating Duke Robert to unite England and Normandy, 1106. 31p, Death of Henry, battle for the throne and succession of King Stephen, 1135. 34p, Successions of Henry II, 1154, and John Lackland, 1189.

| | | | Perf. 13½ |
|---|---|---|---|
| **1987** | | | |
| 431 | A93 | 11p multicolored | .45 .45 |
| a. | | Booklet pane of 4 + label | 2.00 |
| 432 | A93 | 15p multicolored | .60 .60 |
| a. | | Booklet pane of 4 + label | 2.50 |
| 433 | A93 | 22p multicolored | .85 .85 |
| a. | | Booklet pane of 4 + label | 3.75 |
| 434 | A93 | 29p multicolored | 1.10 1.10 |
| a. | | Booklet pane of 4 + label | 4.75 4.75 |
| 435 | A93 | 31p multicolored | 1.25 1.25 |
| a. | | Booklet pane of 4 + label | 5.50 |
| 436 | A93 | 34p multicolored | 1.40 1.40 |
| a. | | Booklet pane of 4 + label | 6.50 |
| | | Complete booklet, #431a-436a | 26.00 |
| | | *Nos. 431-436 (6)* | 5.65 5.65 |

Paintings by John Le Capelain (1812-1848) — A94

| | | | |
|---|---|---|---|
| **1987, Nov. 3** | **Photo.** | | **Perf. 12x11½** |
| 437 | A94 | 11p Grosnez Castle | .45 .45 |
| 438 | A94 | 15p St. Aubin's Bay | .60 .60 |
| 439 | A94 | 22p Mt. Orgueil Castle | .85 .85 |
| 440 | A94 | 31p Town Fort and Harbor, St. Helier | 1.25 1.25 |
| 441 | A94 | 34p The Hermitage | 1.40 1.40 |
| | | *Nos. 437-441 (5)* | 4.55 4.55 |

Christmas.

Hybrids, Eric Young Orchid Foundation, Trinity — A95

Nos. 443, 445 are vertical.

| | | | |
|---|---|---|---|
| **1988, Jan. 12** | **Litho.** | | **Perf. 14** |
| 442 | A95 | 11p Cymbidium pontac | .45 .45 |
| 443 | A95 | 15p Odontioda Eric Young | .60 .60 |
| 444 | A95 | 29p Lycaste auburn Seaford and Ditchling | 1.10 1.10 |
| 445 | A95 | 31p Odontoglossum St. Brelade | 1.25 1.25 |
| 446 | A95 | 34p Cymbidium mavourneen Jester | 1.40 1.40 |
| | | *Nos. 442-446 (5)* | 4.80 4.80 |

Jersey Dog Club, Cent. A96

| | | | |
|---|---|---|---|
| **1988, Mar. 2** | | | |
| 447 | A96 | 11p Labrador retriever | .45 .45 |
| 448 | A96 | 15p Wire-haired dachshund | .60 .60 |
| 449 | A96 | 22p Pekingese | .85 .85 |
| 450 | A96 | 31p Cavalier King Charles spaniel | 1.25 1.25 |
| 451 | A96 | 34p Dalmatian | 1.40 1.40 |
| | | *Nos. 447-451 (5)* | 4.55 4.55 |

Europa 1988 A97

Nos. 453 and 455 vert.

| | | | |
|---|---|---|---|
| | | *Perf. 14x13½, 13½x14* | |
| **1988, Apr. 26** | | | **Litho.** |
| 452 | A97 | 16p Air transport | .65 .65 |
| 453 | A97 | 16p Air communication | .65 .65 |
| 454 | A97 | 22p Sea transport | .85 .85 |
| 455 | A97 | 22p Sea communication | .85 .85 |
| | | *Nos. 452-455 (4)* | 3.00 3.00 |

Wildlife Preservation Trust, 25th Anniv. — A98

| | | | |
|---|---|---|---|
| **1988, July 6** | | | **Litho.** |
| 456 | A98 | 12p Rodrigues fody, vert. | .45 .45 |
| 457 | A98 | 16p Volcano rabbit | .65 .65 |
| 458 | A98 | 29p White-faced marmoset, vert. | 1.10 1.10 |
| 459 | A98 | 31p Ploughshare tortoise | 1.25 1.25 |
| 460 | A98 | 34p Mauritius kestrel, vert. | 1.40 1.40 |
| | | *Nos. 456-460 (5)* | 4.85 4.85 |

Operation Raleigh A99

Activities: 12p, Rain Forest Leaf Frog, Costa Rica. 16p, Archaeological Survey, Peru. 22p, Glacier Climbing, Chile. 29p, Medical Assistance, Solomon Isls. 31p, Underwater Exploration, Australia. 34p, *Zebu* returns to St. Helier, Jersey.

| | | | |
|---|---|---|---|
| **1988, Sept. 27** | **Photo.** | | **Perf. 12** |
| 461 | A99 | 12p multicolored | .45 .45 |
| 462 | A99 | 16p multicolored | .65 .65 |
| 463 | A99 | 22p multicolored | .85 .85 |
| 464 | A99 | 29p multicolored | 1.10 1.10 |
| 465 | A99 | 31p multicolored | 1.25 1.25 |
| 466 | A99 | 34p multicolored | 1.40 1.40 |
| | | *Nos. 461-466 (6)* | 5.70 5.70 |

Operation Raleigh: voyage of the *Zebu*, on which youths were trained with the aim of remotivating them and helping them to earn new self-respect.

WHO 40th anniv. (29p).

Parish Churches A100

| | | | |
|---|---|---|---|
| **1988, Nov. 15** | **Litho.** | | **Perf. 14** |
| 467 | A100 | 12p St. Clement | .45 .45 |
| 468 | A100 | 16p St. Ouen | .55 .55 |
| 469 | A100 | 31p St. Brelade | 1.10 1.10 |
| 470 | A100 | 34p St. Lawrence | 1.25 1.25 |
| | | *Nos. 467-470 (4)* | 3.35 3.35 |

Christmas. See Nos. 549-552, 610-613.

Classic Cars A101

Designs: 12p, 1912 Talbot Tourer, seaweed harvest at Le Hocq. 16p, 1920 De Dion Bouton, Grosnez Castle ruins. 23p, 1926 Austin Chummy, brick kiln at Mont a l'Abbe. 30p, 1926 Ford Model T, harvest of the Jersey royal potato crop. 32p, 1930 Bentley 8-Litre, Guard House and Gate at Government House. 35p, 1931 Cadillac V16 Fleetwood Sports Phaeton, St. Ouen's Manor.

| | | | |
|---|---|---|---|
| **1989, Jan. 31** | | | |
| 471 | A101 | 12p multicolored | .45 .45 |
| 472 | A101 | 16p multicolored | .60 .60 |
| 473 | A101 | 23p multicolored | .80 .80 |
| 474 | A101 | 30p multicolored | 1.00 1.00 |
| 475 | A101 | 32p multicolored | 1.10 1.10 |
| 476 | A101 | 35p multicolored | 1.25 1.25 |
| | | *Nos. 471-476 (6)* | 5.20 5.20 |

See Nos. 604-609, 903-908.

Scenic Views — A102

Coronation of Queen Elizabeth II, 40th Anniv. — A102a

Royal Arms A102b

| | | | |
|---|---|---|---|
| **1989-95** | **Litho.** | | **Perf. 13½** |
| 477 | A102 | 1p Belcroute Bay | .20 .20 |
| 478 | A102 | 2p High St., St. Aubin | .20 .20 |
| 480 | A102 | 4p Royal Jersey Golf Course | .20 .20 |
| a. | | Booklet pane of 6 | .80 .80 |
| 481 | A102 | 5p Portelet Bay | .20 .20 |
| a. | | Booklet pane of 6 | 1.40 1.40 |
| 485 | A102 | 10p Les Charrieres D'Anneport | .30 .30 |
| 486 | A102 | 13p St. Helier Marina | .45 .45 |
| 487 | A102 | 14p St. Ouen's Bay | .45 .45 |
| a. | | Booklet pane of 6 | 3.00 3.00 |
| b. | | Booklet pane of 8 | 4.25 4.25 |
| 488 | A102 | 15p Rozel Harbor | .50 .50 |
| a. | | Booklet pane of 6 | 3.25 3.25 |
| 489 | A102 | 16p St. Aubin's Harbor | .55 .55 |
| a. | | Booklet pane of 8 | 5.00 5.00 |
| 490 | A102 | 17p Jersey Airport | .55 .55 |
| 491 | A102 | 18p Corbiere Lighthouse | .60 .60 |
| a. | | Booklet pane of 6 | 4.25 4.25 |
| 492 | A102 | 19p Val de la Mare | .60 .60 |
| 493 | A102 | 20p Elizabeth Castle | .50 .50 |
| a. | | Booklet pane of 8 | 3.25 3.25 |
| 494 | A102 | 21p Greve de Lecq | .55 .55 |
| 495 | A102 | 22p Samares Manor | .50 .50 |
| a. | | Booklet pane of 8 | 4.50 4.50 |
| 496 | A102 | 23p Bonne Nuit Harbor | .85 .85 |
| 497 | A102 | 24p Grosnez Castle | .70 .70 |
| 498 | A102 | 25p Augres Manor | .80 .80 |
| 499 | A102 | 26p Central Market | .90 .90 |
| 500 | A102 | 27p St. Brelade's Bay | 1.00 1.00 |
| 501 | A102 | 30p St. Ouen's Manor | 1.10 1.10 |
| 502 | A102 | 40p La Hougue Bie | 1.40 1.40 |
| 503 | A102 | 50p Mont Orgueil Castle | 1.60 1.60 |
| 504 | A102 | 75p Royal Square | 2.50 2.50 |
| | | **Perf. 14½** | |
| 505 | A102a | £1 multicolored | 3.50 3.50 |
| | | **Perf. 15x14** | |
| 506 | A102b | £4 multicolored | 13.00 13.00 |
| | | *Nos. 477-506 (26)* | 33.70 33.70 |

Pane Nos. 480a, 487a and 491a issued for Stamp World London '90 and are inscribed "May 1990."

Issued: 1p-20p, 3/21/89; 21p-27p, 1/16/90; 30p-75p, 3/13/90; #481a, 488a, 493a, 2/12/91; £1, 6/2/93; £4, 1/2/95. Nos. 487b, 489a, 495a were released on May 22, but were not readily available until September 1992. Other booklet panes, 1990.

World Wildlife Fund — A103

| | | | |
|---|---|---|---|
| **1989, Apr. 25** | **Litho.** | | **Perf. 13x13¼** |
| 507 | A103 | 13p Large checkered skipper | 2.00 2.00 |
| | | **Perf. 13¼x13** | |
| 508 | A103 | 13p Agile frog, horiz. | 2.00 2.00 |
| 509 | A103 | 17p Green lizard, horiz. | 2.00 2.00 |
| | | **Perf. 13½x13¾** | |
| 510 | A103 | 17p Barn owl | 2.00 2.00 |
| | | *Nos. 507-510 (4)* | 8.00 8.00 |

Europa 1989 — A104

Children's games.

| | | | |
|---|---|---|---|
| **1989, Apr. 25** | | | **Perf. 14** |
| 511 | A104 | 17p Playpen | .65 .65 |
| 512 | A104 | 17p Playground | .65 .65 |
| 513 | A104 | 23p Magician, games | .90 .90 |
| 514 | A104 | 23p Cricket, rugby, tennis | .90 .90 |
| | | *Nos. 511-514 (4)* | 3.10 3.10 |

Visit of Queen Elizabeth II — A105

| | | | |
|---|---|---|---|
| **1989, May 24** | **Litho.** | | **Perf. 14½** |
| 515 | A105 | £1 Ferry Terminal, St. Helier | 4.00 4.00 |

French Revolution, Bicent. A106

Designs: 13p, D'Auvergne meets Louis XVI, 1786. 17p, Storming the Bastille, 1789. 23p, Marie de Bouillon at the Chateau de Navarre, 1790. 30p, Mission from Mont Orgueil, 1795. 32p, Support for the Chouans, 1796. 35p, The last Chouannerie, 1799.

| | | | |
|---|---|---|---|
| **1989, July 7** | | | **Perf. 13½** |
| 516 | A106 | 13p multicolored | .45 .45 |
| 517 | A106 | 17p multicolored | .55 .55 |
| 518 | A106 | 23p multicolored | .75 .75 |
| 519 | A106 | 30p multicolored | 1.00 1.00 |
| 520 | A106 | 32p multicolored | 1.10 1.10 |
| 521 | A106 | 35p multicolored | 1.25 1.25 |
| | | *Nos. 516-521 (6)* | 5.10 5.10 |

| | | | |
|---|---|---|---|
| 516a | | Booklet pane of 4 | 1.90 |
| 517a | | Booklet pane of 4 | 2.50 |
| 518a | | Booklet pane of 4 | 3.50 |
| 519a | | Booklet pane of 4 | 4.25 |
| 520a | | Booklet pane of 4 | 5.50 |
| 521a | | Booklet pane of 4 | 5.00 |
| | | Complete booklet, #516a-521a | 23.00 |

Great Western Railway Steamer Service Between Weymouth and the Channel Isls., Cent. — A107

**1989, Sept. 5    Litho.    Perf. 13½x14**

| | | | | |
|---|---|---|---|---|
| 522 | A107 | 13p St. Helier, 1925 | .45 | .45 |
| 523 | A107 | 17p Caesarea II, 1910 | .55 | .55 |
| 524 | A107 | 27p Reindeer, 1897 | .95 | .95 |
| 525 | A107 | 32p Ibex and Frederica, 1891 | 1.25 | 1.10 |
| 526 | A107 | 35p Lynx, 1889 | 1.40 | 1.40 |
| | | Nos. 522-526 (5) | 4.60 | 4.45 |

Paintings by Sarah Louisa Kilpack (1839-1909) — A108

**1989, Oct. 24    Litho.    Perf. 13x12½**

| | | | | |
|---|---|---|---|---|
| 527 | A108 | 13p Gorey Harbour | .50 | .50 |
| 528 | A108 | 17p La Corbiere | .65 | .65 |
| 529 | A108 | 23p Greve de Lecq | .90 | .90 |
| 530 | A108 | 32p Bouley Bay | 1.25 | 1.25 |
| 531 | A108 | 35p Mont Orgueil | 1.40 | 1.40 |
| | | Nos. 527-531 (5) | 4.70 | 4.70 |

Europa 1990
A109

Post offices.

**Perf. 13½x14, 14x13½**

**1990, Mar. 13    Litho.**

| | | | | |
|---|---|---|---|---|
| 532 | A109 | 18p Broad Street, 1969 | .70 | .70 |
| 533 | A109 | 18p Mont Millais, 1990 | .70 | .70 |
| 534 | A109 | 24p Hue Street, 1815 | .95 | .95 |
| 535 | A109 | 24p Halkett Place, 1890 | .95 | .95 |
| | | Nos. 532-535 (4) | 3.30 | 3.30 |

Nos. 532-533 vert.

Festival of Tourism — A110

**1990, May 3    Litho.    Perf. 14x13½**

| | | | | |
|---|---|---|---|---|
| 536 | A110 | 18p Battle of Flowers | .70 | .70 |
| 537 | A110 | 24p Recreation | .95 | .95 |
| 538 | A110 | 29p History | 1.10 | 1.10 |
| 539 | A110 | 32p Salon Culinaire | 1.25 | 1.25 |
| a. | | Souvenir sheet of 4, #536-539 | 4.50 | 4.50 |
| | | Nos. 536-539 (4) | 4.00 | 4.00 |

News Media
A111

**1990, June 26    Litho.    Perf. 13½**

| | | | | |
|---|---|---|---|---|
| 540 | A111 | 14p Print (newspapers), 1784-1889 | .55 | .55 |
| 541 | A111 | 18p The Evening Post, 1890 | .70 | .70 |
| 542 | A111 | 34p BBC Radio Jersey, 1982 | 1.40 | 1.40 |
| 543 | A111 | 37p Channel Television, 1962 | 1.50 | 1.50 |
| | | Nos. 540-543 (4) | 4.15 | 4.15 |

UNESCO World Literacy Year.

Battle of Britain, 50th Anniv.
A112

**1990, Sept. 4    Perf. 14**

| | | | | |
|---|---|---|---|---|
| 544 | A112 | 14p Hawk | .65 | .65 |
| 545 | A112 | 18p Spitfire | .75 | .75 |
| 546 | A112 | 24p Hurricane | 1.00 | 1.00 |
| 547 | A112 | 34p Wellington | 1.50 | 1.50 |
| 548 | A112 | 37p Lancaster | 1.60 | 1.60 |
| | | Nos. 544-548 (5) | 5.50 | 5.50 |

**Parish Churches Type of 1988**

**1990, Nov. 13    Litho.    Perf. 13½x14**

| | | | | |
|---|---|---|---|---|
| 549 | A100 | 14p St. Helier | .55 | .55 |
| 550 | A100 | 18p Grouville | .70 | .70 |
| 551 | A100 | 34p St. Saviour | 1.40 | 1.40 |
| 552 | A100 | 37p St. John | 1.50 | 1.50 |
| | | Nos. 549-552 (4) | 4.15 | 4.15 |

Prince's Tower, La Hougue Bie, 1801
A113

Philippe d'Auvergne: 20p, Arrested in Paris, 1802. 26p, Plotting against Napoleon, 1803. 31p, Execution of Cadoudal, 1804. 37p, H.M. Cutter Surly, 1809. 44p, Prince de Bouillon, 1816.

**1991, Jan. 22    Litho.    Perf. 13½**

| | | | | |
|---|---|---|---|---|
| 553 | A113 | 15p multicolored | .60 | .60 |
| 554 | A113 | 20p multicolored | .80 | .80 |
| 555 | A113 | 26p multicolored | 1.00 | 1.00 |
| 556 | A113 | 31p multicolored | 1.25 | 1.25 |
| 557 | A113 | 37p multicolored | 1.50 | 1.50 |
| 558 | A113 | 44p multicolored | 1.75 | 1.75 |
| | | Nos. 553-558 (6) | 6.90 | 6.90 |

A114

Europa (Satellites and their functions): No. 559, ERS-1, oceanography. No. 560, Landsat, Earth resources. No. 561, Meteosat, meteorology. No. 562, Olympus, communications.

**1991, Mar. 19    Litho.    Perf. 14½x13**

| | | | | |
|---|---|---|---|---|
| 559 | A114 | 20p multicolored | .80 | .80 |
| 560 | A114 | 20p multicolored | .80 | .80 |
| 561 | A114 | 26p multicolored | 1.00 | 1.00 |
| 562 | A114 | 26p multicolored | 1.00 | 1.00 |
| | | Nos. 559-562 (4) | 3.60 | 3.60 |

A115

15p, German Occupation Stamps for Jersey, 50th anniv. 20p, Eastern Railway extension to Gorey Pier, 100th anniv. 26p, Jersey Herd Book, 125th anniv. 31p, Victoria Harbor, 150th anniv. 53p, Hospital bequest of Marie Bartlett, 250th anniv.

**1991, May 16    Litho.    Perf. 13½**

| | | | | |
|---|---|---|---|---|
| 563 | A115 | 15p multicolored | .60 | .60 |
| 564 | A115 | 20p multicolored | .80 | .80 |
| 565 | A115 | 26p multicolored | 1.00 | 1.00 |
| 566 | A115 | 31p multicolored | 1.25 | 1.25 |
| 567 | A115 | 53p multicolored | 2.10 | 2.10 |
| | | Nos. 563-567 (5) | 5.75 | 5.75 |

Butterflies & Moths
A116

**1991, July 9    Litho.    Perf. 13x12½**

| | | | | |
|---|---|---|---|---|
| 568 | A116 | 15p Glanville fritillary | .60 | .60 |
| 569 | A116 | 20p Jersey tiger | .80 | .80 |
| 570 | A116 | 37p Small elephant hawk-moth | 1.50 | 1.50 |
| 571 | A116 | 57p Peacock | 2.25 | 2.25 |
| | | Nos. 568-571 (4) | 5.15 | 5.15 |

See Nos. 727-731.

Overseas Aid — A117

Designs: 15p, Water drilling rig, Ethiopia. 20p, Construction work, Rwanda. 26p, Technical school, Kenya. 31p, Leprosy and eye care, Tanzania. 37p, Agriculture and cultivation aid, Zambia. 44p, Health care and immunization, Lesotho.

**1991, Sept. 3    Litho.    Perf. 13½**

| | | | | |
|---|---|---|---|---|
| 572 | A117 | 15p multicolored | .60 | .60 |
| 573 | A117 | 20p multicolored | .80 | .80 |
| 574 | A117 | 26p multicolored | 1.00 | 1.00 |
| 575 | A117 | 31p multicolored | 1.25 | 1.25 |
| 576 | A117 | 37p multicolored | 1.50 | 1.50 |
| 577 | A117 | 44p multicolored | 1.75 | 1.75 |
| | | Nos. 572-577 (6) | 6.90 | 6.90 |

Christmas — A118

Illustrations by Edmund Blampied from Peter Pan: 15p, This is the place for me. 20p, The Island Come True. 37p, The Never Bird. 53p, The Great White Father.

**1991, Nov. 5    Litho.    Perf. 14**

| | | | | |
|---|---|---|---|---|
| 578 | A118 | 15p multicolored | .60 | .60 |
| 579 | A118 | 20p multicolored | .80 | .80 |
| 580 | A118 | 37p multicolored | 1.50 | 1.50 |
| 581 | A118 | 53p multicolored | 2.10 | 2.10 |
| | | Nos. 578-581 (4) | 5.00 | 5.00 |

Winter Birds — A119

**1992, Jan. 7    Litho.    Perf. 13½x14**

| | | | | |
|---|---|---|---|---|
| 582 | A119 | 16p Pied wagtail | .55 | .55 |
| 583 | A119 | 22p Firecrest | .75 | .75 |
| 584 | A119 | 28p Snipe | 1.00 | 1.00 |
| 585 | A119 | 39p Lapwing | 1.50 | 1.50 |
| 586 | A119 | 57p Fieldfare | 2.10 | 2.10 |
| | | Nos. 582-586 (5) | 5.90 | 5.90 |

Shanghai Harbor, 1860
A120

William Mesny, 150th birth anniv: No. 588, Running the Taiping blockade, 1862. No. 589, General Mesny, River Gate, 1874. No. 590, Mesny accompanying Gill to Burma, 1877. No. 591, Mesny advises Governor Chang, 1882. No. 592, Mesny, Mandarin First Class, 1886.

**1992, Feb. 25    Litho.    Perf. 13½**

| | | | | |
|---|---|---|---|---|
| 587 | A120 | 16p multicolored | .55 | .55 |
| 588 | A120 | 16p multicolored | .55 | .55 |
| 589 | A120 | 22p multicolored | .80 | .80 |
| 590 | A120 | 22p multicolored | .80 | .80 |
| 591 | A120 | 33p multicolored | 1.10 | 1.10 |
| 592 | A120 | 33p multicolored | 1.10 | 1.10 |
| | | Nos. 587-592 (6) | 4.90 | 4.90 |

| | | | | |
|---|---|---|---|---|
| 587a | | Booklet pane of 4 | 2.25 | 2.25 |
| 588a | | Booklet pane of 4 | 2.25 | 2.25 |
| 589a | | Booklet pane of 4 | 3.50 | 3.50 |
| 590a | | Booklet pane of 4 | 3.50 | 3.50 |
| 591a | | Booklet pane of 4 | 5.00 | 5.00 |
| 592a | | Booklet pane of 4 | 5.00 | 5.00 |
| | | Complete booklet, #587a-592a | 22.00 | |

Discovery of America, 500th Anniv.
A121

Columbus, ship and: 22p, John Bertram (1796-1882). 28p, Sir George Carteret (1610-1680). 39p, Sir Walter Raleigh (1554-1618).

**1992, Apr. 14    Litho.    Perf. 14½**

| | | | | |
|---|---|---|---|---|
| 593 | A121 | 22p multicolored | .85 | .85 |
| 594 | A121 | 28p multicolored | 1.10 | 1.10 |
| 595 | A121 | 39p multicolored | 1.60 | 1.60 |
| | | Nos. 593-595 (3) | 3.55 | 3.55 |

Europa.

Jersey-Built Sailing Ships — A122

**1992, Apr. 14    Litho.    Perf. 14**

| | | | | |
|---|---|---|---|---|
| 596 | A122 | 16p Tickler | .55 | .55 |
| 597 | A122 | 22p Hebe | .75 | .75 |
| 598 | A122 | 50p Gemini | 1.75 | 1.75 |
| 599 | A122 | 57p Percy Douglas | 1.90 | 1.90 |
| a. | | Souvenir sheet of 4, #596-599 | 5.25 | 5.25 |
| | | Nos. 596-599 (4) | 4.95 | 4.95 |

Batik — A123

16p, Snow leopards. 22p, Three elements. 39p, Three men in a tub. 57p, Cockatoos.

**1992, June 23    Litho.    Perf. 14½**

| | | | | |
|---|---|---|---|---|
| 600 | A123 | 16p multicolored | .65 | .65 |
| 601 | A123 | 22p multicolored | .90 | .90 |
| 602 | A123 | 39p multicolored | 1.50 | 1.50 |
| 603 | A123 | 57p multicolored | 2.10 | 2.10 |
| | | Nos. 600-603 (4) | 5.15 | 5.15 |

**Classic Car Type of 1989**

Designs: 16p, 1925 Morris Cowley "Bull-nose." 22p, 1932 Rolls Royce 20/25. 28p, 1924 Chenard & Walcker T5. 33p, 1932 Packard 900 Series Light Eight. 39p, 1927 Lanchester 21. 50p, 1913 Buick 30 Roadster.

**1992, Sept. 8    Litho.    Perf. 13x12½**

| | | | | |
|---|---|---|---|---|
| 604 | A101 | 16p multicolored | .50 | .50 |
| 605 | A101 | 22p multicolored | .70 | .70 |
| 606 | A101 | 28p multicolored | .90 | .90 |
| 607 | A101 | 33p multicolored | 1.10 | 1.10 |
| 608 | A101 | 39p multicolored | 1.25 | 1.25 |
| 609 | A101 | 50p multicolored | 1.60 | 1.60 |
| | | Nos. 604-609 (6) | 6.05 | 6.05 |

**Parish Church Type of 1988**

**1992, Nov. 3    Litho.    Perf. 13½x14**

| | | | | |
|---|---|---|---|---|
| 610 | A100 | 16p Trinity | .50 | .50 |
| 611 | A100 | 22p St. Mary | .70 | .65 |
| 612 | A100 | 39p St. Martin | 1.25 | 1.25 |
| 613 | A100 | 57p St. Peter | 1.75 | 1.75 |
| | | Nos. 610-613 (4) | 4.20 | 4.15 |

Non-Value Indicator Stamps — A124

Scenic views: No. 614, Building with arches. No. 615, Cemetery, Trinity Church. No. 616, Daffodils, cattle. No. 617, Cattle in pasture.

Beach scenes: No. 618, People lying on beach with umbrella. No. 619, Man with windsurfer. No. 620, Crab facing right. No. 621, Crab, facing left.

Parade floats: No. 622, Smiling face, rainbow. No. 623, Dragon head, Oriental theme. No. 624, Umbrellas, Asian theme. No. 625, Elephant's tusks, African theme.

**1993, Jan. 26    Litho.    Perf. 13½**
| | | | |
|---|---|---|---|
| 614 A124 | (17p) Bailiwick | .55 | .55 |
| 615 A124 | (17p) Bailiwick | .55 | .55 |
| 616 A124 | (17p) Bailiwick | .55 | .55 |
| 617 A124 | (17p) Bailiwick | .55 | .55 |
| a. | Block of 4, #614-617 | 2.25 | 2.25 |
| b. | Booklet pane of 8, 2 each #614-617 | 4.50 | |
| 618 A124 | (23p) UK | .70 | .70 |
| 619 A124 | (23p) UK | .70 | .70 |
| 620 A124 | (23p) UK | .70 | .70 |
| 621 A124 | (23p) UK | .70 | .70 |
| a. | Block of 4, #618-621 | 3.00 | 3.00 |
| b. | Booklet pane of 8, 2 each #618-621 | 6.00 | |
| 622 A124 | (28p) European | .80 | .80 |
| 623 A124 | (28p) European | .80 | .80 |
| 624 A124 | (28p) European | .80 | .80 |
| 625 A124 | (28p) European | .80 | .80 |
| a. | Block of 4, #622-625 | 3.25 | 3.25 |
| b. | Booklet pane of 8, 2 each #622-625 | 6.50 | 6.50 |
| | Nos. 614-625 (12) | 8.20 | 8.20 |

The minimum postage rate is represented for each area where mail is delivered.

Orchids — A125

17p, Phragmipedium Eric Young "Jersey." 23p, Odontoglossum Augres "Trinity." 28p, Miltonia Saint Helier "Colomberie." 39p, Phragmipedium pearcei. 57p, Calanthe Grouville "Gorey."

**1993, Jan. 26    Litho.    Perf. 14½x13**
| | | | |
|---|---|---|---|
| 626 A125 | 17p multicolored | .60 | .60 |
| 627 A125 | 23p multicolored | .80 | .80 |
| 628 A125 | 28p multicolored | 1.00 | 1.00 |
| 629 A125 | 39p multicolored | 1.40 | 1.40 |
| 630 A125 | 57p multicolored | 1.90 | 1.90 |
| | Nos. 626-630 (5) | 5.70 | 5.70 |

Europa — A126

Contemporary Art: 23p, Jersey Opera House, by Ian Rolls. 28p, The Ham and Tomato Bap, by Jonathan Hubbard. 39p, Vase of Flowers, by Neil MacKenzie.

**1993, Apr. 1    Litho.    Perf. 13½x14**
| | | | |
|---|---|---|---|
| 631 A126 | 23p multicolored | .90 | .90 |
| 632 A126 | 28p multicolored | 1.10 | 1.10 |
| 633 A126 | 39p multicolored | 1.50 | 1.50 |
| | Nos. 631-633 (3) | 3.50 | 3.50 |

Royal Air Force, 75th Anniv. A127

Designs: 17p, Douglas Dakota. 23p, Wight Seaplane. 28p, Avro Shackleton AEW2. 33p, Gloster Meteor, DeHavilland Vampire. 39p, BAe Harrier GR1A. 57p, Panavia Tornado F3.

**1993, Apr. 1    Perf. 14**
| | | | |
|---|---|---|---|
| 634 A127 | 17p multicolored | .65 | .65 |
| 635 A127 | 23p multicolored | .90 | .90 |
| 636 A127 | 28p multicolored | 1.10 | 1.10 |
| 637 A127 | 33p multicolored | 1.25 | 1.25 |
| 638 A127 | 39p multicolored | 1.50 | 1.50 |

| | | | |
|---|---|---|---|
| 639 A127 | 57p multicolored | 2.25 | 2.25 |
| a. | Souvenir sheet of 2, #635, 639 | 7.75 | 7.75 |
| | Nos. 634-639 (6) | 7.65 | 7.65 |

Stamps from No. 639a do not have white border.

German Occupation Stamps by Edmund Blampied, 50th Anniv. A128

**1993, June 2    Litho.    Perf. 13½**
| | | | |
|---|---|---|---|
| 640 A128 | 17p No. N3 | .65 | .65 |
| 641 A128 | 23p No. N4 | .90 | .90 |
| 642 A128 | 28p No. N5 | 1.10 | 1.10 |
| 643 A128 | 33p No. N6 | 1.25 | 1.25 |
| 644 A128 | 39p No. N7 | 1.50 | 1.50 |
| 645 A128 | 50p No. N8 | 2.00 | 2.00 |
| | Nos. 640-645 (6) | 7.40 | 7.40 |

Birds — A129

**1993, Sept. 7    Litho.    Perf. 13½x14**
| | | | |
|---|---|---|---|
| 646 A129 | 17p Short-toed treecreeper | .65 | .65 |
| 647 A129 | 23p Dartford warbler | .90 | .90 |
| 648 A129 | 28p Wheatear | 1.10 | 1.10 |
| 649 A129 | 39p Cirl bunting | 1.50 | 1.50 |
| 650 A129 | 57p Jay | 2.25 | 2.25 |
| | Nos. 646-650 (5) | 6.40 | 6.40 |

Christmas — A130

Stained glass windows by Henry Bosdet, from St. Aubin on the Hill.

**1993, Nov. 2    Litho.    Perf. 14½x13**
| | | | |
|---|---|---|---|
| 651 A130 | 17p multicolored | .65 | .65 |
| 652 A130 | 23p multicolored | .90 | .90 |
| 653 A130 | 39p multicolored | 1.50 | 1.50 |
| 654 A130 | 57p multicolored | 2.25 | 2.25 |
| | Nos. 651-654 (4) | 5.30 | 5.30 |

Mushrooms A131

**1994, Jan. 11    Litho.    Perf. 14½**
| | | | |
|---|---|---|---|
| 655 A131 | 18p Shaggy ink cap | .70 | .70 |
| 656 A131 | 23p Fly agaric | .90 | .90 |
| 657 A131 | 30p Chanterelle | 1.25 | 1.25 |
| 658 A131 | 41p Parasol mushroom | 1.60 | 1.60 |
| 659 A131 | 60p Latticed stinkhorn | 2.40 | 2.40 |
| | Nos. 655-659 (5) | 6.85 | 6.85 |

Souvenir Sheet

New Year 1994 (Year of the Dog) — A132

**1994, Feb. 18    Litho.    Perf. 15x14½**
| | | | |
|---|---|---|---|
| 660 A132 | £1 multicolored | 4.00 | 4.00 |

Hong Kong '94.

Cats — A133

**1994, Apr. 5    Litho.    Perf. 13½**
| | | | |
|---|---|---|---|
| 661 A133 | 18p Maine coon, vert. | .70 | .70 |
| 662 A133 | 23p British shorthair | .90 | .90 |
| 663 A133 | 35p Persian, vert. | 1.40 | 1.40 |
| 664 A133 | 41p Siamese | 1.60 | 1.60 |
| 665 A133 | 60p Non-pedigree, vert. | 2.40 | 2.40 |
| | Nos. 661-665 (5) | 7.00 | 7.00 |

Jersey Cat Club, 21st anniv., and 4th Championship Show.

Europa A134

Designs: No. 666, Mammoths on cliff, c. 250,000 B.C. No. 667, Paleolithic hunters dragging mammoth by tusks. No. 668, Neolithic dolmen, "La Hougue Bie," c. 4,000 B.C. No. 669, Exterior of "La Hougue Bie," during construction.

**1994, Apr. 5    Litho.    Perf. 13½x14**
| | | | |
|---|---|---|---|
| 666 A134 | 23p multicolored | .90 | .90 |
| 667 A134 | 23p multicolored | .90 | .90 |
| a. | Pair, #666-667 | 1.90 | 1.90 |
| 668 A134 | 30p multicolored | 1.25 | 1.25 |
| 669 A134 | 30p multicolored | 1.25 | 1.25 |
| a. | Pair, #668-669 | 2.50 | 2.50 |
| | Nos. 666-669 (4) | 4.30 | 4.30 |

D-Day, 50th Anniv. A135

#670, Airborne Forces enroute to drop zones. #671, Allied Fleet of Normandy Coast. #672, Coming ashore, Gold Beach. #673, Coming ashore, Sword Beach. #674, Spitfires on beachead patrol. #675, Normandy invasion map.

**1994, June 6    Litho.    Perf. 13½**
| | | | |
|---|---|---|---|
| 670 A135 | 18p multicolored | .70 | .70 |
| 671 A135 | 18p multicolored | .70 | .70 |
| a. | Bklt. pane, 3 each #670-671 | 4.50 | |
| 672 A135 | 23p multicolored | .90 | .90 |
| 673 A135 | 23p multicolored | .90 | .90 |
| a. | Bklt. pane, 3 each #672-673 | 6.00 | |
| 674 A135 | 30p multicolored | 1.25 | 1.25 |
| 675 A135 | 30p multicolored | 1.25 | 1.25 |
| a. | Bklt. pane, 3 each #674-675 | 8.00 | |
| b. | Bklt. pane of 6, #670-675 | 6.50 | |
| | Complete booklet, #671a, 673a, 675a, 675b | 25.00 | |
| | Nos. 670-675 (6) | 5.70 | 5.70 |

No. 675b also sold by the Philatelic Bureau separate from the booklet. without stitching, as a souvenir sheet.

Intl. Olympic Committee, Cent. — A136

**1994, June 6    Perf. 14**
| | | | |
|---|---|---|---|
| 676 A136 | 18p Sailing | .70 | .70 |
| 677 A136 | 23p Rifle shooting | .90 | .90 |
| 678 A136 | 30p Hurdles | 1.25 | 1.25 |
| 679 A136 | 41p Swimming | 1.60 | 1.60 |
| 680 A136 | 60p Field hockey | 2.40 | 2.40 |
| | Nos. 676-680 (5) | 6.85 | 6.85 |

Marine Life A137

Designs: 18p, Strawberry anemone. 23p, Hermit crab, parasitic anemone. 41p, Velvet swimming crab. 60p, Common jellyfish.

**1994, Aug. 2    Litho.    Perf. 13½x13**
| | | | |
|---|---|---|---|
| 681 A137 | 18p multicolored | .70 | .70 |
| 682 A137 | 23p multicolored | .90 | .90 |
| 683 A137 | 41p multicolored | 1.60 | 1.60 |
| 684 A137 | 60p multicolored | 2.40 | 2.40 |
| | Nos. 681-684 (4) | 5.60 | 5.60 |

Postal Independence, 25th Anniv. — A138

Designs: 18p, Condor 10 Wavepiercer. 23p, Map of Jersey, postbox. 35p, BEA "Vanguard" aircraft. 41p, Aurigny "Short 360" aircraft. 60p, Sealink vessel "Caesarea."

**1994, Oct. 1    Litho.    Perf. 14**
| | | | |
|---|---|---|---|
| 685 A138 | 18p multicolored | .70 | .70 |
| 686 A138 | 23p multicolored | .90 | .90 |
| 687 A138 | 35p multicolored | 1.40 | 1.40 |
| 688 A138 | 41p multicolored | 1.60 | 1.60 |
| 689 A138 | 60p multicolored | 2.40 | 2.40 |
| a. | Souvenir sheet, #685-689 + label | 7.25 | 7.25 |
| | Nos. 685-689 (5) | 7.00 | 7.00 |

See Guernsey Nos. 536-540a.

Christmas A139

Christmas carols: 18p, "Away in the manger..." 23p, "Hark! the herald angels sing..." 41p, "While shepherds watched..." 60p, "We three kings of Orient are..."

**1994, Nov. 8**
| | | | |
|---|---|---|---|
| 690 A139 | 18p multicolored | .70 | .70 |
| 691 A139 | 23p multicolored | .90 | .90 |
| 692 A139 | 41p multicolored | 1.60 | 1.60 |
| 693 A139 | 60p multicolored | 2.40 | 2.40 |
| | Nos. 690-693 (4) | 5.60 | 5.60 |

Greetings Stamps — A140

Designs: No. 694, Dog, "Good Luck." No. 695, Rose, "With Love." No. 696, Chick, "Congratulations." No. 697, Bouquet of flowers, "Thank You."

No. 698, Dove, "With love." No. 699, Cat, "Good Luck." No. 700, Carnations, "Thank You." No. 701, Parrot, "Congratulations." 60p, Boar, "Happy New Year."

**1995, Jan. 24    Litho.    Perf. 13½x13**
| | | | | |
|---|---|---|---|---|
| 694 | A140 | 18p multicolored | .70 | .70 |
| 695 | A140 | 18p multicolored | .70 | .70 |
| 696 | A140 | 18p multicolored | .70 | .70 |
| 697 | A140 | 18p multicolored | .70 | .70 |
| a. | | Strip of 4, #694-697 | 3.00 | 3.00 |
| 698 | A140 | 23p multicolored | .90 | .90 |
| 699 | A140 | 23p multicolored | .90 | .90 |
| 700 | A140 | 23p multicolored | .90 | .90 |
| 701 | A140 | 23p multicolored | .90 | .90 |
| a. | | Strip of 4, #698-701 | 3.75 | 3.75 |

**Size: 25x64mm**
| | | | | |
|---|---|---|---|---|
| 702 | A140 | 60p multicolored | 2.40 | 2.40 |
| a. | | Booklet pane, #697a, #701a, #702 | 10.00 | |
| | | Complete booklet, #702a | 10.00 | |
| | | Nos. 694-702 (9) | 8.80 | 8.80 |

New Year 1995 (Year of the Boar) (#702).

Camellias A141

**1995, Mar. 21    Litho.    Perf. 14**
| | | | | |
|---|---|---|---|---|
| 703 | A141 | 18p Captain Rawes | .70 | .70 |
| 704 | A141 | 23p Brigadoon | .90 | .90 |
| 705 | A141 | 30p Elsie Jury | 1.25 | 1.25 |
| 706 | A141 | 35p Augusto L'Gouveia Pinto | 1.40 | 1.40 |
| 707 | A141 | 41p Bella Romana | 1.60 | 1.60 |
| | | Nos. 703-707 (5) | 5.85 | 5.85 |

International Camellia Society conference, Jersey, Mar. 30-Apr. 4, 1995.

Liberation, by Philip Jackson A142

**1995, May 9    Litho.    Perf. 13½**
| | | | | |
|---|---|---|---|---|
| 708 | A142 | 23p gray & black | .90 | .90 |
| 709 | A142 | 30p pink & black | 1.25 | 1.25 |

Europa.

Liberation, 50th Anniv. A143

#710, Bailiff, Crown Officers taken to HMS Beagle. #711, Red Cross ship SS Vega. #712, Germans surrender on board HMS Beagle. #713, First troops of task force 135, Ordinance Yard, St. Helier. #714, Royal visitors, June 1945. #715, Supplies come ashore from LSTs, Operation Nestegg.
£1, Princess Elizabeth, Queen Elizabeth, Winston Churchill, King George VI, Princess Margaret at Buckingham Palace, VE Day.

**1995, May 9    Litho.    Perf. 14½x14**
| | | | | |
|---|---|---|---|---|
| 710 | A143 | 18p multicolored | .70 | .70 |
| 711 | A143 | 18p multicolored | .70 | .70 |
| a. | | Bklt. pane, 3 each #710-711 | 4.75 | |
| 712 | A143 | 23p multicolored | .90 | .90 |
| 713 | A143 | 23p multicolored | .90 | .90 |
| a. | | Bklt. pane, 3 each #712-713 | 6.25 | |
| 714 | A143 | 60p multicolored | 2.40 | 2.40 |
| 715 | A143 | 60p multicolored | 2.40 | 2.40 |
| a. | | Bklt. pane, 3 each #714-715 | 16.00 | |
| | | Nos. 711-715 (5) | 7.30 | 7.30 |

**Souvenir Sheet**
| | | | | |
|---|---|---|---|---|
| 716 | A143 | £1 multicolored | 4.00 | 4.00 |
| a. | | Booklet pane, #716 | 4.50 | |
| | | Complete booklet, #711a, #713a, #715a, #716a | 32.50 | |

No. 716 contains one 81x29mm stamp.

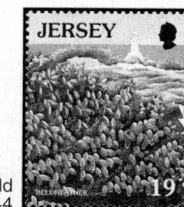

Wild Flowers — A144

**1995, July 4    Litho.    Perf. 13½**
| | | | | |
|---|---|---|---|---|
| 717 | A144 | 19p Bell heather | .75 | .75 |
| 718 | A144 | 19p Sea campion | .75 | .75 |
| 719 | A144 | 19p Spotted rock-rose | .75 | .75 |
| 720 | A144 | 19p Thrift | .75 | .75 |
| 721 | A144 | 19p Sheep's-bit scabious | .75 | .75 |
| a. | | Strip of 5, #717-721 | 3.75 | 3.75 |
| 722 | A144 | 23p Field bind-weed | .90 | .90 |
| 723 | A144 | 23p Common bird's-foot trefoil | .90 | .90 |
| 724 | A144 | 23p Sea holly | .90 | .90 |
| 725 | A144 | 23p Common centaury | .90 | .90 |
| 726 | A144 | 23p Dwarf pansy | .90 | .90 |
| a. | | Strip of 5, #722-726 | 4.75 | 4.75 |
| | | Nos. 717-726 (10) | 8.25 | 8.25 |

**Butterfly & Moth Type of 1991**
**1995, Sept. 1    Litho.    Perf. 14**
| | | | | |
|---|---|---|---|---|
| 727 | A116 | 19p Peacock pansy | .75 | .75 |
| 728 | A116 | 23p Green-barred swallowtail | .90 | .90 |
| 729 | A116 | 30p Orange emigrant | 1.25 | 1.25 |
| 730 | A116 | 41p Scarlet mormon | 1.60 | 1.60 |
| 731 | A116 | 60p Common birdwing | 2.40 | 2.40 |
| a. | | Souvenir sheet of 2, #730-731 | 4.00 | 4.00 |
| | | Nos. 727-731 (5) | 6.90 | 6.90 |

Singapore '95 (#731a).
Stamps from No. 731a do not have border around the designs or inscriptions at bottom.

Christmas Pantomimes — A145

Childrens' stories: 19p, Puss in Boots. 23p, Cinderella. 41p, Sleeping Beauty. 60p, Aladdin.

**1995, Oct. 24    Litho.    Perf. 13½**
| | | | | |
|---|---|---|---|---|
| 732 | A145 | 19p multicolored | .75 | .75 |
| 733 | A145 | 23p multicolored | .90 | .90 |
| 734 | A145 | 41p multicolored | 1.60 | 1.60 |
| 735 | A145 | 60p multicolored | 2.40 | 2.40 |
| | | Nos. 732-735 (4) | 5.65 | 5.65 |

UN, 50th Anniv. A146

**1995, Oct. 24    Litho.    Perf. 13x14**
| | | | | |
|---|---|---|---|---|
| 736 | A146 | 19p Doves, emblem | .75 | .75 |
| 737 | A146 | 23p Wheat ear, emblem | .90 | .90 |
| 738 | A146 | 41p As 23p | 1.60 | 1.60 |
| 739 | A146 | 60p As 19p | 2.40 | 2.40 |
| | | Nos. 736-739 (4) | 5.65 | 5.65 |

UNICEF, 50th Anniv. A147

Children, map areas of UNICEF activities: 19p, Africa. 23p, Globe. 30p, Europe, Balkans. 35p, South America, Caribbean. 41p, South Asia. 60p, Australasia, South Pacific.

**1996, Feb. 19    Litho.    Perf. 14½**
| | | | | |
|---|---|---|---|---|
| 740 | A147 | 19p multicolored | .75 | .75 |
| 741 | A147 | 23p multicolored | .90 | .90 |
| 742 | A147 | 30p multicolored | 1.25 | 1.25 |
| 743 | A147 | 35p multicolored | 1.40 | 1.40 |
| 744 | A147 | 41p multicolored | 1.60 | 1.60 |
| 745 | A147 | 60p multicolored | 2.40 | 2.40 |
| | | Nos. 740-745 (6) | 8.30 | 8.30 |

**Souvenir Sheet**

New Year 1996 (Year of the Rat) — A148

Illustration reduced.

**1996, Feb. 19    Perf. 14**
| | | | | |
|---|---|---|---|---|
| 746 | A148 | £1 multicolored | 4.00 | 4.00 |

Queen Elizabeth II, 70th Birthday — A149

**1996, Apr. 21    Litho.    Perf. 14x15**
| | | | | |
|---|---|---|---|---|
| 747 | A149 | £5 multicolored | 20.00 | 20.00 |

Women of Achievement A150

Europa: 23p, Elizabeth Garrett, first British woman physician. 30p, Emmeline Pankhurst (1858-1928), suffragist.

**1996, Apr. 25    Perf. 14**
| | | | | |
|---|---|---|---|---|
| 748 | A150 | 23p multicolored | .90 | .90 |
| 749 | A150 | 30p multicolored | 1.25 | 1.25 |

1996 European Soccer Chamionships — A151

Various soccer plays.

**1996, Apr. 25**
| | | | | |
|---|---|---|---|---|
| 750 | A151 | 19p multicolored | .75 | .75 |
| 751 | A151 | 23p multicolored | .90 | .90 |
| 752 | A151 | 35p multicolored | 1.40 | 1.40 |
| 753 | A151 | 41p multicolored | 1.60 | 1.60 |
| 754 | A151 | 60p multicolored | 2.40 | 2.40 |
| | | Nos. 750-754 (5) | 7.05 | 7.05 |

Modern Olympic Games, Cent. A152

**1996, June 8    Litho.    Perf. 14**
| | | | | |
|---|---|---|---|---|
| 755 | A152 | 19p Rowing | .75 | .75 |
| 756 | A152 | 23p Judo | .90 | .90 |
| 757 | A152 | 35p Fencing | 1.40 | 1.40 |
| 758 | A152 | 41p Boxing | 1.60 | 1.60 |
| 759 | A152 | 60p Basketball | 2.40 | 2.40 |
| | | Nos. 755-759 (5) | 7.05 | 7.05 |

**Souvenir Sheet**
| | | | | |
|---|---|---|---|---|
| 760 | A152 | £1 Olympic torch, flame | 4.00 | 4.00 |

Intl. Amateur Boxing Assoc., 50th anniv. (#758). CAPEX '96 (#760). No. 760 contains one 50x38mm stamp.

Tourism A153

**1996, June 8    Litho.    Perf. 14**
| | | | | |
|---|---|---|---|---|
| 761 | A153 | 19p North Coast | .75 | .75 |
| 762 | A153 | 23p Portelet Bay | .90 | .90 |
| a. | | Bklt. pane, 3 each #761-762 | 5.75 | |
| 763 | A153 | 30p Greve de Lecq Bay | 1.25 | 1.25 |
| 764 | A153 | 35p Beauport Beach | 1.25 | 1.25 |
| a. | | Bklt. pane, 3 each #763-764 | 8.50 | |
| 765 | A153 | 41p Plemont Bay | 1.60 | 1.60 |
| 766 | A153 | 60p St. Brelade's Bay | 2.40 | 2.40 |
| a. | | Bklt. pane, 3 each #765-766 | 8.75 | |
| b. | | Bklt. pane, 3 each #765-766 | 13.00 | |
| | | Complete booklet, #762a, 764a, 766a, 766b | 37.50 | |
| | | Nos. 761-766 (6) | 8.15 | 8.15 |

Horses A154

**1996, Sept. 13    Litho.    Perf. 13½x14**
| | | | | |
|---|---|---|---|---|
| 767 | A154 | 19p Drag hunt | .75 | .75 |
| 768 | A154 | 23p Horse driving | .90 | .90 |
| 769 | A154 | 30p Race training | 1.25 | 1.25 |
| 770 | A154 | 35p Show jumping | 1.40 | 1.40 |
| 771 | A154 | 41p Pony club | 1.60 | 1.60 |
| 772 | A154 | 60p Shire horses | 2.40 | 2.40 |
| | | Nos. 767-772 (6) | 8.30 | 8.30 |

Christmas A155

19p, Journey to Bethlehem. 23p, Archangel Gabriel visits shepherds. 30p, Nativity. 60p, Magi.

**1996, Nov. 12    Perf. 13x13½**
| | | | | |
|---|---|---|---|---|
| 773 | A155 | 19p multicolored | .75 | .75 |
| 774 | A155 | 23p multicolored | .90 | .90 |
| 775 | A155 | 30p multicolored | 1.25 | 1.25 |
| 776 | A155 | 60p multicolored | 2.40 | 2.40 |
| | | Nos. 773-776 (4) | 5.30 | 5.30 |

**Souvenir Sheet**

New Year 1997 (Year of the Ox) — A156

Illustration reduced.

**1997, Feb. 7    Litho.    Perf. 13½**
| | | | | |
|---|---|---|---|---|
| 777 | A156 | £1 multicolored | 4.00 | 4.00 |
| a. | | With added inscription in sheet margin | 4.00 | 4.00 |

No. 777a inscribed in sheet margin with "JERSEY AT HONG KONG '97" in red and Hong Kong '97 emblem in black.

Birds — A157

**1997, Feb. 12    Perf. 14½**
| | | | | |
|---|---|---|---|---|
| 778 | A157 | 1p Red-breasted merganser | .20 | .20 |
| 779 | A157 | 10p Common tern | .40 | .40 |
| 780 | A157 | 15p Black-headed gull | .60 | .60 |

| | | | | |
|---|---|---|---|---|
| 781 | A157 | 20p Dunlin | .80 | .80 |
| 782 | A157 | 24p Puffin | .95 | .95 |
| 783 | A157 | 37p Oystercatcher | 1.50 | 1.50 |
| 784 | A157 | 75p Redshank | 3.00 | 3.00 |
| 785 | A157 | £2p Shag | 8.00 | 8.00 |
| a. | | Souv. sheet of 8, #778-785 | 16.00 | 16.00 |
| b. | | As "a," with added inscription in sheet margin | 16.00 | 16.00 |

No. 785b contains PACIFIC '97 World Philatelic Exhibition emblem in sheet margin. Issued: 5/29.
Nos. 781-782 exist dated "1998."
See Nos. 825-832, 864-871, 909-916.

Lillie the Cow — A158

Designs: No. 786, Building sand castle. No. 787, Taking photographs. No. 788, Lying on beach. No. 789, In restaurant.

**1997, Feb. 12** — *Die Cut Perf 9½x9*
**Self-Adhesive**

| | | | | |
|---|---|---|---|---|
| 786 | A158 | (23p) multicolored | .90 | .90 |
| 787 | A158 | (23p) multicolored | .90 | .90 |
| 788 | A158 | (23p) multicolored | .90 | .90 |
| 789 | A158 | (23p) multicolored | .90 | .90 |
| a. | | Strip of 4, #786-789 | 3.75 | 3.75 |

Peelable backing is rouletted 9 between stamps.

**Coil Stamps**

| | | | | |
|---|---|---|---|---|
| 786a | | Die cut perf. 8-¾x9, dated "2000" | 6.00 | 6.00 |
| 787a | | Die cut perf. 8-¾x9, dated "2000" | 6.00 | 6.00 |
| 788a | | Die cut perf. 8-¾x9, dated "2000" | 6.00 | 6.00 |
| 789b | | Die cut perf. 8-¾x9, dated "2000" | 6.00 | 6.00 |
| c. | | Strip of 4, #786a-789b | 25.00 | |

Nos. 786-789 are inscribed "U.K. MINIMUM POSTAGE PAID." Stamps dated "1999" were originally sold for 25p. Stamps dated "2000" were originally sold for 26p.

Jersey Airport, 60th Anniv. A159

**1997, Mar. 10 Litho. Perf. 13½x14**

| | | | | |
|---|---|---|---|---|
| 790 | A159 | 20p DH95 Flamingo | .80 | .80 |
| 791 | A159 | 24p HPR1 Marathon | .95 | .95 |
| 792 | A159 | 31p DH114 Heron | 1.25 | 1.25 |
| 793 | A159 | 37p Boeing 737-236 | 1.40 | 1.40 |
| 794 | A159 | 43p BN Trislander | 1.75 | 1.75 |
| 795 | A159 | 63p BAe 146-200 | 2.50 | 2.50 |
| | | Nos. 790-795 (6) | 8.65 | 8.65 |

Stories and Legends A160

Europa: 20p, Bull of St. Clement. 24p, Black Horse of St. Ouen. 31p, Black Dog of Bouley Bay. 63p, Les Fontaines des Mittes.

**1997, Apr. 15 Litho. Perf. 14½x14**

| | | | | |
|---|---|---|---|---|
| 796 | A160 | 20p multicolored | .75 | .75 |
| 797 | A160 | 24p multicolored | .85 | .85 |
| 798 | A160 | 31p multicolored | 1.10 | 1.10 |
| 799 | A160 | 63p multicolored | 2.10 | 2.10 |
| | | Nos. 796-799 (4) | 4.80 | 4.80 |

1997 Jersey Island Games A161

**1997, June 28 Litho. Perf. 13½x14**

| | | | | |
|---|---|---|---|---|
| 800 | A161 | 20p Cycling | .75 | .75 |
| 801 | A161 | 24p Archery | .85 | .85 |
| a. | | Booklet pane, 3 each #800-801 | 4.75 | |
| 802 | A161 | 31p Windsurfing | 1.10 | 1.10 |
| 803 | A161 | 37p Gymnastics | 1.40 | 1.40 |
| a. | | Booklet pane, 3 each #802-803 | 7.50 | |

| | | | | |
|---|---|---|---|---|
| 804 | A161 | 43p Volleyball | 1.60 | 1.60 |
| 805 | A161 | 63p Running | 2.50 | 2.50 |
| a. | | Booklet pane, 3 each #804-805 | 12.00 | |
| b. | | Booklet pane, #800-805 | 8.25 | — |
| | | Complete booklet, #801a, 803a, 805a-805b | 32.50 | |
| | | Nos. 800-805 (6) | 8.20 | 8.20 |

Jersey Wildlife Preservation Trust A162

Endangered species: 20p, Mallorcan midwife toad. 24p, Aye-aye. 31p, Echo parakeet. 37p, Pigmy hog. 43p, St. Lucia whip-tail. 63p, Madagascar teal.

**1997, Sept. 2 Litho. Perf. 13**

| | | | | |
|---|---|---|---|---|
| 806 | A162 | 20p multicolored | .80 | .80 |
| 807 | A162 | 24p multicolored | .95 | .95 |
| 808 | A162 | 31p multicolored | 1.25 | 1.25 |
| 809 | A162 | 37p multicolored | 1.50 | 1.50 |
| 810 | A162 | 43p multicolored | 1.75 | 1.75 |
| 811 | A162 | 63p multicolored | 2.50 | 2.50 |
| | | Nos. 806-811 (6) | 8.75 | 8.75 |

Trees — A163

**1997, Sept. 2 Perf. 14½**

| | | | | |
|---|---|---|---|---|
| 812 | A163 | 20p Ash | .80 | .80 |
| 813 | A163 | 24p Elder | .95 | .95 |
| 814 | A163 | 31p Beech | 1.25 | 1.25 |
| 815 | A163 | 37p Sweet chestnut | 1.50 | 1.50 |
| 816 | A163 | 43p Hawthorn | 1.75 | 1.75 |
| 817 | A163 | 63p Common oak | 2.50 | 2.50 |
| | | Nos. 812-817 (6) | 8.75 | 8.75 |

Christmas A164

Santa Claus at various Jersey landmarks: 20p, Jersey Airport. 24p, St. Aubin's Harbor. 31p, Mont Orgueil Castle. 63p, Royal Square, St. Helier.

**1997, Nov. 11 Litho. Perf. 14**

| | | | | |
|---|---|---|---|---|
| 818 | A164 | 20p multicolored | .80 | .80 |
| 819 | A164 | 24p multicolored | .95 | .95 |
| 820 | A164 | 31p multicolored | 1.25 | 1.25 |
| 821 | A164 | 63p multicolored | 2.50 | 2.50 |
| | | Nos. 818-821 (4) | 5.50 | 5.50 |

Queen Elizabeth II and Prince Philip, 50th Wedding Anniv. A165

Designs: No. 822, Wedding portrait. No. 823, Anniversary portrait. £1.50, Full length wedding portrait, vert.

**1997, Nov. 20 Litho. Perf. 14½**

| | | | | |
|---|---|---|---|---|
| 822 | A165 | 50p multicolored | 2.00 | 2.00 |
| 823 | A165 | 50p multicolored | 2.00 | 2.00 |
| a. | | Pair, #822-823 | 4.00 | 4.00 |

**Souvenir Sheet**
**Perf. 13½x14**

| | | | | |
|---|---|---|---|---|
| 824 | A165 | £1.50 multicolored | 4.75 | 4.75 |

No. 824 contains one 38x51mm stamp.

**Bird Type of 1997**

**1998, Jan. 28 Litho. Perf. 14½**

| | | | | |
|---|---|---|---|---|
| 825 | A157 | 2p Sanderling | .20 | .20 |
| 826 | A157 | 5p Great crested grebe | .20 | .20 |
| 827 | A157 | 21p Sandwich tern | .80 | .80 |

| | | | | |
|---|---|---|---|---|
| 828 | A157 | 25p Brent goose | 1.00 | 1.00 |
| 829 | A157 | 30p Fulmar | 1.25 | 1.25 |
| 830 | A157 | 40p Turnstone | 1.60 | 1.60 |
| 831 | A157 | 60p Avocet | 2.50 | 2.50 |
| 832 | A157 | £1 Razorbill | 4.00 | 4.00 |
| a. | | Souvenir sheet of 8, #825-832 | 12.00 | 12.00 |
| | | Nos. 825-832 (8) | 11.55 | 11.55 |

**Souvenir Sheet**

New Year 1998 (Year of the Tiger) — A166

Illustration reduced.

**1998, Jan. 28 Perf. 14**

| | | | | |
|---|---|---|---|---|
| 833 | A166 | £1 multicolored | 4.00 | 4.00 |

Buses A167

Designs: 20p, JMT Bristol 4 Tonner, 1923. 24p, SCS Regent Double Decker, 1934. 31p, Slade's Dennis Lancet, 1936. 37p, Tantivy Leyland PLSC Lion, 1947. 43p, JBS Morris Bus, 1958. 63p, JMT Leyland Titan TD4 Double Decker, 1961.

**1998, Apr. 2 Litho. Perf. 14**

| | | | | |
|---|---|---|---|---|
| 834 | A167 | 20p multicolored | .80 | .80 |
| 835 | A167 | 24p multicolored | .95 | .95 |
| a. | | Bklt. pane, 3 each #834-835 | 5.75 | |
| 836 | A167 | 31p multicolored | 1.25 | 1.25 |
| 837 | A167 | 37p multicolored | 1.50 | 1.50 |
| a. | | Bklt. pane, 3 each #836-837 | 8.50 | |
| 838 | A167 | 43p multicolored | 1.75 | 1.75 |
| 839 | A167 | 63p multicolored | 2.50 | 2.50 |
| a. | | Bklt. pane, 3 each #838-839 | 13.50 | |
| b. | | Bklt. pane, 1 each, #834-839 | 9.00 | |
| | | Complete booklet, #835a, 837a, 839a, 839b | 37.50 | |
| | | Nos. 834-839 (6) | 8.75 | 8.75 |

National Festivals — A168

Europa: 20p, Creative Arts Festival. 24p, Jazz Festival. 31p, Good Food Festival. 63p, Floral Festival.

**1998, Apr. 2 Perf. 14x13½**

| | | | | |
|---|---|---|---|---|
| 840 | A168 | 20p multicolored | .80 | .80 |
| 841 | A168 | 24p multicolored | .95 | .95 |
| 842 | A168 | 31p multicolored | 1.25 | 1.25 |
| 843 | A168 | 63p multicolored | 2.50 | 2.50 |
| | | Nos. 840-843 (4) | 5.50 | 5.50 |

Yachting — A169

Nos. 844-848: Various Hobie Cats sailing in St. Aubin's Bay.
Nos. 849-853: Various yachts racing in annual "Lombard Challenge."

**1998, May 18 Litho. Perf. 13**

| | | | | |
|---|---|---|---|---|
| 844 | A169 | 20p multicolored | .80 | .80 |
| 845 | A169 | 20p multicolored | .80 | .80 |
| 846 | A169 | 20p multicolored | .80 | .80 |

| | | | | |
|---|---|---|---|---|
| 847 | A169 | 20p multicolored | .80 | .80 |
| 848 | A169 | 20p multicolored | .80 | .80 |
| a. | | Strip of 5, #844-848 | 4.25 | 4.25 |
| 849 | A169 | 24p multicolored | .95 | .95 |
| 850 | A169 | 24p multicolored | .95 | .95 |
| 851 | A169 | 24p multicolored | .95 | .95 |
| 852 | A169 | 24p multicolored | .95 | .95 |
| 853 | A169 | 24p multicolored | .95 | .95 |
| a. | | Strip of 5, #849-853 | 5.00 | 5.00 |

"Days Gone By" — A170

Jersey lily and: No. 854, Cider making. No. 855, Potato barrels transported by horse and cart. No. 856, Gathering seaweed for fertilizer. No. 857, Milking Jersey cows by hand.

*Serpentine Die Cut Perf. 11¼*
**1998, Aug. 11 Litho.**
**Self-Adhesive**

| | | | | |
|---|---|---|---|---|
| 854 | A170 | (20p) multicolored | .80 | .80 |
| 855 | A170 | (20p) multicolored | .80 | .80 |
| 856 | A170 | (20p) multicolored | .80 | .80 |
| 857 | A170 | (20p) multicolored | .80 | .80 |
| a. | | Strip of 4, #854-857 | 3.25 | 3.25 |

Nos. 854-857 are inscribed "Bailiwick / Minimum Postage Paid." They were sold for 22p. Stamps from the first printing are dated "1998." Stamps from subsequent printings are dated "1999", "2000", "2001" and "2003."

Marine Life A171

**1998, Aug. 11 Litho. Perf. 15x14½**

| | | | | |
|---|---|---|---|---|
| 858 | A171 | 20p Bass | .80 | .80 |
| 859 | A171 | 24p Red gurnard | .95 | .95 |
| 860 | A171 | 31p Skate | 1.25 | 1.25 |
| 861 | A171 | 37p Mackerel | 1.50 | 1.50 |
| 862 | A171 | 43p Tope | 1.75 | 1.75 |
| 863 | A171 | 63p Cuckoo wrasse | 2.50 | 2.50 |
| | | Nos. 858-863 (6) | 8.75 | 8.75 |

Intl. Year of the Ocean.

**Bird Type of 1997**

**1998, Aug. 11 Perf. 14½**

| | | | | |
|---|---|---|---|---|
| 864 | A157 | 4p Gannet | .20 | .20 |
| 865 | A157 | 22p Ringed plover | .85 | .85 |
| 866 | A157 | 26p Grey plover | 1.00 | 1.00 |
| 867 | A157 | 31p Golden plover | 1.25 | 1.25 |
| 868 | A157 | 32p Greenshank | 1.25 | 1.25 |
| 869 | A157 | 35p Curlew | 1.40 | 1.40 |
| 870 | A157 | 44p Herring gull | 1.75 | 1.75 |
| 871 | A157 | 50p Great black-backed gull | 2.00 | 2.00 |
| a. | | Souvenir sheet of 8, #864-871 | 9.75 | 9.75 |
| | | Nos. 864-871 (8) | 9.70 | 9.70 |

Jersey Autumn Flowers A172

**1998, Oct. 23 Litho. Perf. 14½**

| | | | | |
|---|---|---|---|---|
| 872 | A172 | 20p Iris | .80 | .80 |
| 873 | A172 | 24p Carnations | .95 | .95 |
| 874 | A172 | 31p Chrysanthemums | 1.25 | 1.25 |
| 875 | A172 | 37p Pinks | 1.50 | 1.50 |
| 876 | A172 | 43p Roses | 1.75 | 1.75 |
| 877 | A172 | 63p Lilies | 2.50 | 2.50 |
| | | Nos. 872-877 (6) | 8.75 | 8.75 |

**Souvenir Sheet**
**Perf. 14**

| | | | | |
|---|---|---|---|---|
| 878 | A172 | £1.50 Lilium star gazer | 6.00 | 6.00 |

No. 878 contains one 50x38mm stamp. Italia '98 (#878).

Christmas
A173

Island manger (crib), service club sponsor: 20p, Central Market, Jersey Round Table. 24p, St. Thomas' Church, Soroptimist Intl. of Jersey. 31p, Trinity Parish Church, Rotary Club of Jersey. 63p, Royal Square, Lions Club of Jersey.

**1998, Nov. 10**     **Perf. 13x13½**
| | | | | |
|---|---|---|---|---|
| 879 | A173 | 20p multicolored | .80 | .80 |
| 880 | A173 | 24p multicolored | .95 | .95 |
| 881 | A173 | 31p multicolored | 1.25 | 1.25 |
| 882 | A173 | 63p multicolored | 2.50 | 2.50 |
| | | Nos. 879-882 (4) | 5.50 | 5.50 |

Souvenir Sheet

New Year 1999 (Year of the Rabbit) — A174

Illustration reduced.

**1999, Feb. 16**   **Litho.**   **Perf. 13½**
| | | | | |
|---|---|---|---|---|
| 883 | A174 | £1 multicolored | 4.00 | 4.00 |

UPU, 125th Anniv. A175

Jersey mail transport: 20p, Eastern Railway train. 24p, Mail steamer, "Brighton." 43p, DH 86A, first airmail arrival. 63p, Morris Minor P.O. van.

**1999, Feb. 16**     **Perf. 14**
| | | | | |
|---|---|---|---|---|
| 884 | A175 | 20p multicolored | .80 | .80 |
| 885 | A175 | 24p multicolored | .95 | .95 |
| 886 | A175 | 43p multicolored | 1.75 | 1.75 |
| 887 | A175 | 63p multicolored | 2.50 | 2.50 |
| | | Nos. 884-887 (4) | 6.00 | 6.00 |

Royal Natl. Lifeboat Institution, 175th Anniv. A176

**1999, Feb. 16**     **Perf. 14½**
| | | | | |
|---|---|---|---|---|
| 888 | A176 | 75p Jessica Eliza, St. Catherine | 3.00 | 3.00 |
| 889 | A176 | £1 Alexander Coutanche, St. Helier | 4.00 | 4.00 |
| a. | | Pair, #888-889 | 7.00 | 7.00 |

Orchids — A177

Designs: 21p, Cymbidium Maufant "Jersey." 25p, Miltonia Millbrook "Jersey." 31p, Paphiopedilum Transvaal. 37p, Paphiopedilum Elizabeth Castle. 43p, Calanthe Five Oaks. 63p, Cymbidium Icho Tower "Trinity." £1.50, Miltonia Portelet.

**Perf. 14¼x13¼**
**1999, Mar. 19**     **Litho.**
| | | | | |
|---|---|---|---|---|
| 890 | A177 | 21p multicolored | .80 | .80 |
| 891 | A177 | 25p multicolored | 1.00 | 1.00 |
| 892 | A177 | 31p multicolored | 1.25 | 1.25 |
| 893 | A177 | 37p multicolored | 1.50 | 1.50 |
| 894 | A177 | 43p multicolored | 1.75 | 1.75 |
| 895 | A177 | 63p multicolored | 2.50 | 2.50 |
| | | Nos. 890-895 (6) | 8.80 | 8.80 |

Souvenir Sheet
**Perf. 13½**
| | | | | |
|---|---|---|---|---|
| 896 | A177 | £1.50 multicolored | 6.00 | 6.00 |

Australia '99 World Stamp Expo (#896).

IBRA'99 Intl. Philatelic Exhibition, Nuremberg A178

National Parks: 21p, Howard Davis Park. 25p, Sir Winston Churchill Memorial Park. 31p, Coronation Park. 63p, La Collette Gardens.

**1999, Apr. 27**     **Perf. 13x13½**
| | | | | |
|---|---|---|---|---|
| 897 | A178 | 21p multicolored | .80 | .80 |
| 898 | A178 | 25p multicolored | 1.00 | 1.00 |
| 899 | A178 | 31p multicolored | 1.25 | 1.25 |
| 900 | A178 | 63p multicolored | 2.25 | 2.25 |
| | | Nos. 897-900 (4) | 5.30 | 5.30 |

Europa (#898-899).

Wedding of Prince Edward and Sophie Rhys-Jones — A179

**1999, June 19**   **Litho.**   **Perf. 14½**
| | | | | |
|---|---|---|---|---|
| 901 | A179 | 35p yellow & multi | 1.40 | 1.40 |
| 902 | A179 | 35p blue & multi | 1.40 | 1.40 |
| a. | | Pair, #901-902 | 3.00 | 3.00 |

Classic Car Type of 1989

Designs: 21p, 1899 Jersey-built Benz. 25p, 1910 Star Tourer. 31p, 1938 Citroen "Traction Avant." 37p, 1937 Talbot BG110 Tourer. 43p, 1934 Morris Cowley Six Special Coupé. 63p, 1946 Ford Anglia E04A Saloon.

**1999, July 2**   **Litho.**   **Perf. 14**
| | | | | |
|---|---|---|---|---|
| 903 | A101 | 21p multicolored | .80 | .80 |
| 904 | A101 | 25p multicolored | 1.00 | 1.00 |
| a. | | Bklt. pane, 3 each #903-904 | 5.75 | |
| 905 | A101 | 31p multicolored | 1.25 | 1.25 |
| 906 | A101 | 37p multicolored | 1.50 | 1.50 |
| a. | | Bklt. pane, 3 each #905-906 | 8.75 | |
| 907 | A101 | 43p multicolored | 1.75 | 1.75 |
| 908 | A101 | 63p multicolored | 2.50 | 2.50 |
| a. | | Bklt. pane, 3 each #907-908 | 13.50 | |
| b. | | Booklet pane, #903-908 | 9.25 | |
| | | Complete booklet, #904a, 906a, 908a, 908b | 40.00 | |
| | | Nos. 903-908 (6) | 8.80 | 8.80 |

PhilexFrance '99 (#904a, 906a, 908a-908b).

Bird Type of 1997

**1999, Aug. 21**   **Litho.**   **Perf. 14¾**
| | | | | |
|---|---|---|---|---|
| 909 | A157 | 23p Bar-tailed godwit | .90 | .90 |
| 910 | A157 | 27p Common scoter | 1.10 | 1.10 |
| 911 | A157 | 28p Lesser black-backed gull | 1.10 | 1.10 |
| 912 | A157 | 29p Little egret | 1.10 | 1.10 |
| 913 | A157 | 33p Little grebe | 1.25 | 1.25 |
| 914 | A157 | 34p Cormorant | 1.25 | 1.25 |
| 915 | A157 | 45p Rock pipit | 1.75 | 1.75 |
| 916 | A157 | 65p Gray heron | 2.50 | 2.50 |
| a. | | Souvenir sheet of 8, #909-916 | 11.00 | 11.00 |
| | | Nos. 909-916 (8) | 10.95 | 10.95 |

Small Mammals A180

Designs: 21p, Hedgehog. 25p, Red squirrel. 31p, Nathusius pipestrelle. 37p, Jersey bank vole. 43p, Lesser white-toothed shrew. 63p, Common mole.

**1999, Aug. 21**   **Litho.**   **Perf. 13¼x13**
| | | | | |
|---|---|---|---|---|
| 917 | A180 | 21p multicolored | .80 | .80 |
| 918 | A180 | 25p multicolored | 1.00 | 1.00 |
| 919 | A180 | 31p multicolored | 1.25 | 1.25 |
| 920 | A180 | 37p multicolored | 1.50 | 1.50 |
| 921 | A180 | 43p multicolored | 1.75 | 1.75 |
| 922 | A180 | 63p multicolored | 2.50 | 2.50 |
| | | Nos. 917-922 (6) | 8.80 | 8.80 |

Lighthouses A181

**1999, Oct. 5**   **Litho.**   **Perf. 14**
| | | | | |
|---|---|---|---|---|
| 923 | A181 | 21p Gorey Pierhead | .80 | .80 |
| 924 | A181 | 25p La Corbiere | 1.00 | 1.00 |
| 925 | A181 | 34p Noirmont Point | 1.40 | 1.40 |
| 926 | A181 | 38p Demie de Pas | 1.50 | 1.50 |
| 927 | A181 | 44p Greve d'Azette | 1.75 | 1.75 |
| 928 | A181 | 64p Sorel Point | 2.50 | 2.50 |
| | | Nos. 923-928 (6) | 8.95 | 8.95 |

Christmas A182

Poinsettias and: 21p, Mistletoe. 25p, Holly. 34p, Ivy. 64p, Christmas rose.

**1999, Nov. 9**   **Litho.**   **Perf. 13¾**
| | | | | |
|---|---|---|---|---|
| 929 | A182 | 21p multi | .80 | .80 |
| 930 | A182 | 25p multi | 1.00 | 1.00 |
| 931 | A182 | 34p multi | 1.40 | 1.40 |
| 932 | A182 | 64p multi | 2.50 | 2.50 |
| | | Nos. 929-932 (4) | 5.70 | 5.70 |

Coat of Arms A183

Litho. & Embossed with Foil Application
**2000, Jan. 1**     **Perf. 13¼**
| | | | | |
|---|---|---|---|---|
| 933 | A183 | £10 gold & multi | 40.00 | 40.00 |

Millennium.

Souvenir Sheet

New Year 2000 (Year of the Dragon) — A184

Illustration reduced.

**2000, Feb. 5**   **Litho.**   **Perf. 13¾**
| | | | | |
|---|---|---|---|---|
| 934 | A184 | £1 multi | 4.00 | 4.00 |

Europa, 2000
Common Design Type and

A185

**2000, May 9**     **Perf. 13¼x13**
| | | | | |
|---|---|---|---|---|
| 935 | A185 | 26p multi | 1.00 | 1.00 |
| 936 | CD17 | 34p multi | 1.40 | 1.40 |

Stampin' the Future — A186

Children's Stamp Design Contest Winners: No. 937, Ocean Adventure, by Gemma Carré. No. 938, Solar Power, by Chantal Varley-Best. No. 939, Floating City and Space Cars, by Nicola Singleton. No. 940, Conservation, by Carly Logan.

**2000, May 9**   **Litho.**   **Perf. 14**
| | | | | |
|---|---|---|---|---|
| 937 | A186 | 22p multi | .85 | .85 |
| 938 | A186 | 22p multi | .85 | .85 |
| 939 | A186 | 22p multi | .85 | .85 |
| 940 | A186 | 22p multi | .85 | .85 |
| a. | | Souvenir sheet, #937-940 | 3.50 | 3.50 |
| | | Nos. 937-940 (4) | 3.40 | 3.40 |

Ships — A187

#941, Roman merchant ship. #942, Viking long boat. #943, Warship, 13th cent. #944, Merchant ship, 14th-15th cent. #945, Tudor warship, 16th cent.
#946, Warship, 17th cent. #947, Navy cutter, 18th cent. #948, Barque, 19th cent. #949, Oyster cutter, 19th cent. #950, Ketch, 20th cent.

**2000, May 22**     **Perf. 13¾**
| | | | | |
|---|---|---|---|---|
| 941 | A187 | 22p multi | .85 | .85 |
| 942 | A187 | 22p multi | .85 | .85 |
| 943 | A187 | 22p multi | .85 | .85 |
| 944 | A187 | 22p multi | .85 | .85 |
| 945 | A187 | 22p multi | .85 | .85 |
| a. | | Strip of 5, #941-945 | 4.25 | 4.25 |
| 946 | A187 | 26p multi | 1.00 | 1.00 |
| 947 | A187 | 26p multi | 1.00 | 1.00 |
| 948 | A187 | 26p multi | 1.00 | 1.00 |
| 949 | A187 | 26p multi | 1.00 | 1.00 |
| a. | | Booklet pane, #941-944, 946-949 | 7.50 | 7.50 |
| 950 | A187 | 26p multi | 1.00 | 1.00 |
| a. | | Strip of 5, #946-950 | 5.00 | 5.00 |
| b. | | Souvenir sheet, #941-950 | 9.25 | 9.25 |
| c. | | Booklet pane, #941-942, 944-946, 948-950 | 7.50 | |
| d. | | Booklet pane, #941, 943-947, 949-950 | 7.50 | |
| e. | | Booklet pane, #941-943, 945-948, 950 | 7.50 | |
| f. | | Bklt. pane, #942-945, 947-950 | 7.50 | |
| | | Booklet, #949a, 950c-950f | 37.50 | |
| g. | | As "b," with Stamp Show 2000 emblem added in sheet margin | 9.25 | 9.25 |

Marine Mammals A188

Designs: 22p, Bottle-nosed dolphin. 26p, Long-finned pilot whale. 34p, Harbor porpoise.

38p, Atlantic gray seal. 44p, Risso's dolphin.
64p, White-beaked dolphin.
£1.50, Common dolphin.

| **2000, June 5** | | **Perf. 14¾x14** | |
|---|---|---|---|
| **951** | A188 | 22p multi | .85 | .85 |
| **952** | A188 | 26p multi | 1.00 | 1.00 |
| **953** | A188 | 34p multi | 1.25 | 1.25 |
| **954** | A188 | 38p multi | 1.50 | 1.50 |
| **955** | A188 | 44p multi | 1.75 | 1.75 |
| **956** | A188 | 64p multi | 2.50 | 2.50 |
| | *Nos. 951-956 (6)* | | 8.85 | 8.85 |

**Souvenir Sheet**

| **957** | A188 | £1.50 multi | 6.00 | 6.00 |
|---|---|---|---|---|
| a. | As #957, with World Stamp Expo 2000 emblem in margin | | 6.00 | 6.00 |

No. 957 contains one 81x29mm stamp.
Issued: No. 957a, 7/7/00.

Prince
William,
18th
Birthday
A189

William &: #958, Mountain. #959, Polo
player. #960, Fireworks. #961, Castle.

| **2000, June 21** | | **Perf. 14¼x14½** | |
|---|---|---|---|
| **958** | A189 | 75p multi | 3.00 | 3.00 |
| **959** | A189 | 75p multi | 3.00 | 3.00 |
| **960** | A189 | 75p multi | 3.00 | 3.00 |
| **961** | A189 | 75p multi | 3.00 | 3.00 |
| | *Nos. 958-961 (4)* | | 12.00 | 12.00 |

Queen Mother,
100th Birthday
A190

**Litho. with Foil Application**

| **2000, Aug. 4** | | **Perf. 14½x14¼** | |
|---|---|---|---|
| **962** | A190 | 50p Purple hat | 2.00 | 2.00 |
| **963** | A190 | 50p Pink hat | 2.00 | 2.00 |
| a. | Souvenir sheet, #962-963 | | 4.00 | 4.00 |

Battle of
Britain,
60th
Anniv.
A191

Designs: 22p, Supermarine Spitfire Mk. Ia.
26p, Hawker Hurricane Mk. I. 36p, Bristol
Blenheim Mk. IV. 40p, Vickers Wellington Mk.
Ic. 45p, Boulton Paul Defiant Mk. I. 65p, Short
Sunderland Mk. I.

| **2000, Sept. 15** | | **Litho.** | **Perf. 14¼x14** | |
|---|---|---|---|---|
| **964** | A191 | 22p multi | .85 | .85 |
| **965** | A191 | 26p multi | 1.00 | 1.00 |
| **966** | A191 | 36p multi | 1.40 | 1.40 |
| **967** | A191 | 40p multi | 1.60 | 1.60 |
| **968** | A191 | 45p multi | 1.75 | 1.75 |
| **969** | A191 | 65p multi | 2.50 | 2.50 |
| | *Nos. 964-969 (6)* | | 9.10 | 9.10 |

Christmas
A192

| **2000, Nov. 7** | | **Perf. 13** | |
|---|---|---|---|
| **970** | A192 | 22p Virgin Mary | .85 | .85 |
| **971** | A192 | 26p Shepherd | 1.00 | 1.00 |
| **972** | A192 | 36p Angel | 1.40 | 1.40 |
| **973** | A192 | 65p Magus | 2.50 | 2.50 |
| | *Nos. 970-973 (4)* | | 5.75 | 5.75 |

Souvenir Sheet

New Year 2001 (Year of the
Snake) — A193

| **2001, Jan. 24** | | **Litho.** | **Perf. 13¾** | |
|---|---|---|---|---|
| **974** | A193 | £1 multi | | 4.00 | 4.00 |

Steamships on Jersey-France
Route — A194

| **2001, Jan. 24** | | **Perf. 13x13¼** | |
|---|---|---|---|
| **975** | A194 | 22p Rose | .85 | .85 |
| **976** | A194 | 26p Comete | 1.00 | 1.00 |
| **977** | A194 | 36p Cygne | 1.40 | 1.40 |
| **978** | A194 | 40p Victoria | 1.60 | 1.60 |
| **979** | A194 | 45p Attala | 1.75 | 1.75 |
| **980** | A194 | 65p Brittany | 2.50 | 2.50 |
| | *Nos. 975-980 (6)* | | 9.10 | 9.10 |

Agricultural
Products — A195

No. 981: a, Jersey cows. b, Royal potatoes.
c, Tomatoes. d, Cauliflower and purple broccoli. e, Zucchini and peppers.

***Serpentine Die Cut 11¼***

**2001, Apr. 1**

**Self-Adhesive**

| **981** | | Strip of 5 | 5.25 | 5.25 |
|---|---|---|---|---|
| a.-e. | A195 (26p) Any single | | 1.00 | 1.00 |

No. 981 exists dated "2002," "2003" and
"2005."

Navy
Ships
Named
Jersey
A196

Ships in service from: 23p, 1654-91. 26p,
1694-98. 37p, 1698-1731. 41p, 1736-83. 46p,
1860-73. 66p, 1938-41.

| **2001, Apr. 3** | | **Perf. 14** | |
|---|---|---|---|
| **982** | A196 | 23p multi | .90 | .90 |
| **983** | A196 | 26p multi | 1.00 | 1.00 |
| **984** | A196 | 37p multi | 1.50 | 1.50 |
| **985** | A196 | 41p multi | 1.60 | 1.60 |
| **986** | A196 | 46p multi | 1.75 | 1.75 |
| **987** | A196 | 66p multi | 2.50 | 2.50 |
| | *Nos. 982-987 (6)* | | 9.25 | 9.25 |

Queen Elizabeth II, 75th
Birthday — A197

| **2001, Apr. 21** | | **Perf. 14x14¾** | |
|---|---|---|---|
| **988** | A197 | £3 multi | | 12.00 | 12.00 |

Pond Life
A198

Designs: 23p, Agile frog. 26p, Trout. 37p,
White water lily. 41p, Common blue damselfly.
46p, Palmate newt. 66p, Tufted duck.

| **2001, May 22** | | **Perf. 14¾x14** | |
|---|---|---|---|
| **989** | A198 | 23p multi | .90 | .90 |
| **990** | A198 | 26p multi | 1.00 | 1.00 |
| **991** | A198 | 37p multi | 1.40 | 1.40 |
| **992** | A198 | 41p multi | 1.50 | 1.50 |
| **993** | A198 | 46p multi | 1.60 | 1.60 |
| **994** | A198 | 66p multi | 2.40 | 2.40 |
| | *Nos. 989-994 (6)* | | 8.80 | 8.80 |

**Souvenir Sheet**

**Perf. 14¼**

| **995** | A198 | £1.50 Kingfisher | 6.00 | 6.00 |
|---|---|---|---|---|
| a. | As #995, with Belgica 2001 emblem in margin | | 6.50 | 6.50 |

Europa (#990-991). No. 995 contains one
38x50mm stamp.
Issued: No. 995a, 6/9/01.

Birds of
Prey — A199

Designs: 23p, Long-eared owl. 26p, Peregrine falcon. 37p, Short-eared owl. 41p, Marsh
harrier. 46p, Sparrowhawk. 66p, Tawny owl.
£1.50, Barn owl.

| **2001, July 3** | | **Litho.** | **Perf. 13½** | |
|---|---|---|---|---|
| **996** | A199 | 23p multi | .90 | .90 |
| **997** | A199 | 26p multi | 1.00 | 1.00 |
| **998** | A199 | 37p multi | 1.50 | 1.50 |
| **999** | A199 | 41p multi | 1.60 | 1.60 |
| **1000** | A199 | 46p multi | 1.75 | 1.75 |
| a. | Booklet pane, #997, 998, 2 each #996, 1000 | | 8.00 | |
| **1001** | A199 | 66p multi | 2.50 | 2.50 |
| a. | Booklet pane, #996-1001 | | 9.25 | |
| b. | Booklet pane, 2 each #996, 998, 1001 | | 9.75 | |
| c. | Booklet pane, #996-998, 1001, 2 #999 | | 8.75 | |
| | *Nos. 996-1001 (6)* | | 9.25 | 9.25 |
| **1002** | A199 | £1.50 Booklet pane of 1 | 17.50 | 12.50 |
| | Booklet, #1000a, 1001a, 1001b, 1001c, 1002 | | 55.00 | |

**Souvenir Sheet**

| **1003** | A199 | £1.50 multi | 6.00 | 6.00 |
|---|---|---|---|---|
| a. | Like #1003, with Hafnia 01 emblem | | 6.00 | 6.00 |

Issued: No. 1003a, 10/16/01.
On No. 1002, "Tyto" is 4mm from the owl's
head (owl is in center of stamp), while on No.
1003, it is 9mm from the head (owl is at right of
stamp). The size of No. 1002 is 154x100mm,
while the size of No. 1003 is 110x75.

Souvenir Sheet

Racing Yacht Jersey Clipper — A200

| **2001, Sept. 17** | | **Perf. 13¾** | |
|---|---|---|---|
| **1004** | A200 | £1.50 multi | 6.00 | 6.00 |

Fire
Engines
A201

Designs: 23p, Tilley 26 manual, c. 1845.
26p, Albion Merryweather, c. 1935. 37p, Dennis Ace, c. 1940. 41p, Dennis F8 pump
escape, c. 1952. 46p, Land Rover Merryweather, c. 1968. 66p, Dennis Carmichael,
c. 1989.

| **2001, Sept. 25** | | **Perf. 13x13¼** | |
|---|---|---|---|
| **1005** | A201 | 23p multi | .90 | .90 |
| **1006** | A201 | 26p multi | 1.00 | 1.00 |
| **1007** | A201 | 37p multi | 1.50 | 1.50 |
| **1008** | A201 | 41p multi | 1.60 | 1.60 |
| **1009** | A201 | 46p multi | 1.75 | 1.75 |
| **1010** | A201 | 66p multi | 2.50 | 2.50 |
| | *Nos. 1005-1010 (6)* | | 9.25 | 9.25 |

Christmas
A202

No. 1011: a, Nativity. b, Street decorations.
c, Carolers. d, Santa Claus. e, Bells and other
ornaments on Christmas tree.
No. 1012: a, Adoration of the Shepherds. b,
Carolers, Santa Claus, reindeer. c, Bell ornament, Christmas tree with candles. d, Church
bells. e, Cracker with bells on wrapper.

***Serpentine Die Cut 11x11¼***

**2001, Nov. 6**

**Coil Stamps**

**Self-Adhesive**

| **1011** | | Horiz. strip of 5 | 4.75 | — |
|---|---|---|---|---|
| a.-e. | A202 (23p) green & multi, any single | | .90 | .90 |
| **1012** | | Horiz. strip of 5 | 5.75 | — |
| a.-e. | A202 (29p) red & multi, any single | | 1.10 | 1.10 |
| f. | Booklet pane of 16, 2 each #1011a, 1011c-1011e, 1012a-1012b, 1012d-1012e | | 16.00 | |

Nos. 1011 and 1012 exist dated "2002." No.
1011 also exists dated "2003."

Jersey State
Vessels
A203

Designs: 23p, Launch "Duchess of Normandy." 29p, Tugboat "Duke of Normandy."
38p, Customs patrol boat "Challenger." 47p,
Pilot boat "Le Fret." 68p, Sea fisheries protection boat "Norman Le Brocq."

| **2002, Jan. 22** | | **Litho.** | **Perf. 13x13¼** | |
|---|---|---|---|---|
| **1013** | A203 | 23p multi | .90 | .90 |
| **1014** | A203 | 29p multi | 1.10 | 1.10 |
| **1015** | A203 | 38p multi | 1.50 | 1.50 |
| **1016** | A203 | 47p multi | 1.75 | 1.75 |
| **1017** | A203 | 68p multi | 2.75 | 2.75 |
| | *Nos. 1013-1017 (5)* | | 8.00 | 8.00 |

Reign of
Queen
Elizabeth II,
50th
Anniv. — A204

**Litho. & Embossed With Foil
Application**

| **2002, Feb. 6** | | **Perf. 13¼** | |
|---|---|---|---|
| **1018** | A204 | £3 multi | | 12.00 | 12.00 |

Souvenir Sheet

New Year 2002 (Year of the Horse) — A205

**2002, Feb. 12     Litho.     Perf. 13¾**
1019  A205  £1 multi          4.00  4.00

Battle of Flowers Depictions of Circus Figures — A206

**2002, Mar. 12     Litho.     Perf. 13¾**
1020  A206  23p Elephant, cats   .90   .90
1021  A206  29p Clown          1.10  1.10
1022  A206  38p Clown, diff.   1.50  1.50
1023  A206  68p Seal           2.75  2.75
      Nos. 1020-1023 (4)       6.25  6.25
         Europa (#1021-1022).

La Moye Golf Club, Cent. A207

Designs: 23p, Aubrey Boomer. 29p, Harry Vardon. 38p, Sir Henry Cotton. 47p, Golfer's swing. 68p, Golfer addressing ball.

**2002, Apr. 16     Perf. 14**
1024  A207  23p multi          .90   .90
1025  A207  29p multi         1.10  1.10
1026  A207  38p multi         1.50  1.50
1027  A207  47p multi         1.75  1.75
1028  A207  68p multi         2.75  2.75
      Nos. 1024-1028 (5)      8.00  8.00

Police Vehicles A208

Designs: 23p, Vauxhall 12, c. 1952. 29p, 1959-60 Jaguar 2.4 MkII. 38p, 1972-73 Austin 1800. 40p, Ford Cortina MkIV, c. 1978. 47p, 1995-2000 Honda motorcycle. 68p, 1998-2000 Vauxhall Vectra.

**2002, May 24     Litho.     Perf. 13x13¼**
1029  A208  23p multi          .90   .90
1030  A208  29p multi         1.10  1.10
1031  A208  38p multi         1.50  1.50
1032  A208  40p multi         1.60  1.60
1033  A208  47p multi         1.75  1.75
1034  A208  68p multi         2.75  2.75
      Nos. 1029-1034 (6)      9.60  9.60

Insects A209

Designs: 23p, Honeybee. 29p, Seven-spot ladybug. 38p, Great green bush cricket. 40p, Greater horntail. 47p, Emperor dragonfly. 68p, Hawthorn shield bug.

**2002, June 18     Perf. 14¾x14**
1035  A209  23p multi          .90   .90
1036  A209  29p multi         1.10  1.10
1037  A209  38p multi         1.50  1.50
1038  A209  40p multi         1.60  1.60
1039  A209  47p multi         1.75  1.75
1040  A209  68p multi         2.75  2.75
      Nos. 1035-1040 (6)      9.60  9.60

Queen Mother Elizabeth (1900-2002) — A210

**Litho. with Foil Application**
**2002, Aug. 4     Perf. 14x14¾**
1041  A210  £2 multi          8.00  8.00

Battle of Flowers, Cent. A211

Designs: 23p, Hydrangeas. 29p, Chrysanthemums. 38p, Hare's tails, pampas grass. 40p, Asters. 47p, Carnations. 68p, Gladioli. £2, Float "Zanzibar."

**2002, Aug. 8     Litho.     Perf. 13x13¼**
1042  A211  23p multi          .90   .90
1043  A211  29p multi         1.10  1.10
1044  A211  38p multi         1.50  1.50
1045  A211  40p multi         1.60  1.60
1046  A211  47p multi         1.75  1.75
1047  A211  68p multi         2.75  2.75
   a.   Booklet pane, #1042-1047    9.75
      Nos. 1042-1047 (6)      9.60  9.60

**Souvenir Sheet**
**Perf. 13**
1048  A211  £2 multi          8.00  8.00
   a.   Booklet pane of 1          8.00
         Booklet, #1048a, 3 #1047a  37.50

No. 1047a has three different layouts of stamps on pane. No. 1048 contains one 76x39mm stamp. No. 1048a is larger than No. 1048, having extra selvage at left, with rouletting separating the selvage from the rest of the sheet.

Cats A212

Designs: 23p, British dilute tortoiseshell. 29p, Cream Persian. 38p, Blue exotic shorthair. 40p, Black smoke Devon Rex. 47p, British silver tabby. 68p, Usual Abyssinian. £2, British cream and white bi-color, vert.

**2002, Oct. 12     Perf. 14¾x14¼**
1049  A212  23p multi          .90   .90
1050  A212  29p multi         1.10  1.10
1051  A212  38p multi         1.50  1.50
1052  A212  40p multi         1.60  1.60
1053  A212  47p multi         1.75  1.75
1054  A212  68p multi         2.75  2.75
      Nos. 1049-1054 (6)      9.60  9.60

**Souvenir Sheet**
**Perf. 14¼**
1055  A212  £2 multi          8.00  8.00

No. 1055 contains one 38x50mm stamp.

Letter Boxes, 150th Anniv. — A213

Designs: 23p, Pillar box, Central Market. 29p, Wall box, Colomberie. 38p, Wall box, St. Clement's Inner Road. 40p, Ship box. 47p, Pillar box, Parade, 1952. 68p, Pillar box, La Collette, 2000. £2, First letter box, David Place, 1852.

**2002, Nov. 23     Perf. 14½x14¼**
1056  A213  23p multi          .90   .90
1057  A213  29p multi         1.10  1.10
1058  A213  38p multi         1.50  1.50
1059  A213  40p multi         1.60  1.60
1060  A213  47p multi         1.75  1.75
1061  A213  68p multi         2.75  2.75
      Nos. 1056-1061 (6)      9.60  9.60

**Souvenir Sheet**
**Perf. 14¾**
1062  A213  £2 multi          8.00  8.00

No. 1062 contains one 39x76mm stamp.

Airplanes A214

Designs: 23p, Sanchez-Besa Hydroplane. 29p, Supermarine S.6B. 38p, De Havilland DH84 Dragon. 40p, De Havilland DH89a Rapide. 47p, Vickers 701 Viscount. 68p, BAC One-Eleven. £2, 1906 Biplane of Jacob Christian Hansen Ellehammer.

**2003, Jan. 21     Litho.     Perf. 13x13¼**
1063  A214  23p multi          .90   .90
1064  A214  29p multi         1.10  1.10
1065  A214  38p multi         1.50  1.50
1066  A214  40p multi         1.60  1.60
1067  A214  47p multi         1.75  1.75
1068  A214  68p multi         2.75  2.75
   a.   Booklet pane, #1063-1068    9.75
      Nos. 1063-1068 (6)      9.60  9.60

**Souvenir Sheet**
**Perf. 13¼x13**
1069  A214  £2 multi          8.00  8.00
   a.   Booklet pane, #1069        8.00
         Complete booklet, #1069a,
         3 #1068a                  37.50

No. 1069 contains one 60x40mm stamp.
The booklet contains three examples of No. 1068a, each with different margins. No. 1069a has a larger margin than No. 1069, which contains additional text and illustrations. The £2 stamp from the booklet pane No. 1069a has the date under the second "e" of "Ellehammer," while the date on the stamp from the souvenir sheet No. 1069 has the date under the first "m" of "Ellehammer."

Souvenir Sheet

New Year 2003 (Year of the Ram) — A215

**2003, Feb. 1     Perf. 13¾**
1070  A215  £1 multi          4.00  4.00

Poster Art A216

Designs: 23p, Portelet, c. 1935. 29p, Southern British Railways, c. 1952, vert. 38p, Chemins de Fer de l'Ouest, c. 1910, vert. 68p, Jersey, the Sunny Channel Island, c. 1947.

**2003, Mar. 11     Perf. 13½**
1071  A216  23p multi          .90   .90
1072  A216  29p multi         1.10  1.10
1073  A216  38p multi         1.50  1.50
1074  A216  68p multi         2.75  2.75
      Nos. 1071-1074 (4)      6.25  6.25
         Europa (29p, 38p).

Lighthouses and Buoys — A217

No. 1075: a, St. Catherine's Breakwater Light. b, Violet Channel Buoy.
No. 1076: a, Mont Ubé Lighthouse. b, Frouquie Aubert Buoy.
No. 1077: a, Gronez Point Lighthouse. b, Banc des Ormes Buoy.

**2003, Apr. 15     Perf. 13¾**
1075  A217  Horiz. pair       2.25  2.25
   a.-b.   29p Either single  1.10  1.10
1076  A217  Horiz. pair       2.50  2.50
   a.-b.   30p Either single  1.25  1.25
1077  A217  Horiz. pair       4.00  4.00
   a.-b.   48p Either single  1.90  1.90
      Nos. 1075-1077 (3)      8.75  8.75

Wild Orchids — A218

Designs: 29p, Southern-marsh orchid. 30p, Loose-flowered orchid. 39p, Spotted orchid. 50p, Autumn Ladies Tresses. 53p, Greenwinged orchid. 69p, Pyramidal orchid. £2, Loose-flowered orchid, diff.

**2003, May 13     Perf. 13¼x13**
1078  A218  29p multi         1.10  1.10
1079  A218  30p multi         1.25  1.25
1080  A218  39p multi         1.60  1.60
1081  A218  50p multi         2.00  2.00
1082  A218  53p multi         2.10  2.10
1083  A218  69p multi         2.75  2.75
      Nos. 1078-1083 (6)     10.80 10.80

**Souvenir Sheet**
1084  A218  £2 multi          8.00  8.00
   a.   As #1084, with added marginal inscription  8.25  8.25

No. 1084a has Bangkok 2003 Philatelic Exhibition emblem and text, "Jersey at Bangkok 2003," added in margin. Issued, 10/4.

Coronation of Queen Elizabeth II, 50th Anniv. A219

Designs: 29p, Sovereign's orb. 30p, St. Edward's Crown. 39p, Scepter with Cross. 50p, Ampulla and Spoon. 53p, Sovereign's Ring. 69p, Armills.

**Litho. With Foil Application**
**2003, June 2     Perf. 14¾x14**
1085  A219  29p multi         1.10  1.10
1086  A219  30p multi         1.25  1.25
1087  A219  39p multi         1.60  1.60
1088  A219  50p multi         2.00  2.00
1089  A219  53p multi         2.10  2.10
1090  A219  69p multi         2.75  2.75
   a.   Souvenir sheet, #1085-1090  11.00 11.00
      Nos. 1085-1090 (6)     10.80 10.80

## Souvenir Sheet

Prince William, Prince Charles and
Queen Elizabeth II — A220

**2003, June 21　Litho.　Perf. 13¾**
1091 A220 £2 multi　　　　　　8.00 8.00
Prince William, 21st birthday.

Offshore Reefs
and
Flowers — A221

No. 1092: a, Les Ecrehous Reef, tree mallow. b, Les Minquiers Reef, smooth sow-this-
tle. c, Les Minquiers Reef, thrift. d, Paternos-
ters Reef, rock samphire. e, Les Ecrehous
Reef, bluebells.
No. 1092g, Like No. 1092a. No. 1092h, Like
No. 1092b. No. 1092i, Like No. 1092c. No.
1092j, Like No. 1092d. No. 1092k, Like No.
1092e.

*Serpentine Die Cut 11*
**2003, Aug. 5　　　　　　　　Photo.**
**Coil Stamps**
**Self-Adhesive**
1092　　Horiz. strip of 5　　5.50 5.50
*a.-e.* A221 (29p) Any single　　1.10 1.10
*f.* Like #1092, serpentine die cut
　　　11¼　　　　　　　　7.00
*g.-k.* A221 (32p) Any single, serpen-
　　tine die cut 11¼　　　　1.40 1.40
Nos. 1092g-1092k are dated "2004." Also
exists dated "2006."
Nos. 1092f-k issued 11/3/04.

Pets — A222

Designs: 29p, Albino Rex rabbit. 30p, Labrador retriever. 38p, Canary and budgerigar.
53p, Hamster. 69p, Guinea pig.
£2, Border collie.

**2003, Sept. 9　Litho.　Perf. 13¾**
1093 A222 29p multi　　　　1.10 1.10
1094 A222 30p multi　　　　1.25 1.25
1095 A222 38p multi　　　　1.50 1.50
1096 A222 53p multi　　　　2.10 2.10
1097 A222 69p multi　　　　2.75 2.75
Nos. 1093-1097 (5)　　　　8.70 8.70
**Souvenir Sheet**
**Perf. 13¼**
1098 A222 £2 multi　　　　8.00 8.00
No. 1098 contains one 39x51mm stamp.

Winter Flowers
A223

Designs: 29p, Japanese quince. 30p, Winter
jasmine. 39p, Snowdrop. 48p, Winter heath.
53p, Chinese witch hazel. 69p, Winter daphne.

**2003, Nov. 10　　　　　Perf. 14¼**
1099 A223 29p multi　　　　1.10 1.10
1100 A223 30p multi　　　　1.25 1.25
1101 A223 39p multi　　　　1.60 1.60
1102 A223 48p multi　　　　1.90 1.90

1103 A223 53p multi　　　　2.10 2.10
1104 A223 69p multi　　　　2.75 2.75
Nos. 1099-1104 (6)　　　10.70 10.70

## Souvenir Sheet

New Year 2004 (Year of the
Monkey) — A224

**2004, Jan. 22　Litho.　Perf. 13¾**
1105 A224 £1 multi　　　　4.00 4.00

British Chess
Federation,
Cent. — A225

**2004, Jan. 22**
1106 A225 29p Rook　　　1.10 1.10
1107 A225 30p Knight　　　1.25 1.25
1108 A225 39p Bishop　　　1.60 1.60
1109 A225 48p Pawn　　　1.90 1.90
1110 A225 53p Queen　　　2.10 2.10
1111 A225 69p King　　　2.75 2.75
Nos. 1106-1111 (6)　　　10.70 10.70

Tourist
Attractions
A226

Designs: 29p, St. Aubin's Harbor. 30p, Mont
Orgueil Castle. 39p, Corbiere Lighthouse. 69p,
Rozel Harbor.

**2004, Mar. 9　　　　Perf. 13x13¼**
1112 A226 29p multi　　　　1.10 1.10
1113 A226 30p multi　　　　1.25 1.25
1114 A226 39p multi　　　　1.60 1.60
1115 A226 69p multi　　　　2.75 2.75
Nos. 1112-1115 (4)　　　　6.70 6.70
Europa (#1113, 1114).

Waterfowl
A227

Designs: 32p, Eurasian teal. 33p, Mute
swan. 40p, Northern shoveler. 49p, Common
pochard. 62p, Black swan. 70p, Eurasian
wigeon.
£2, Mallard, vert.

**2004, Apr. 6　　　　Perf. 14¾x14**
1116 A227 32p multi　　　　1.25 1.25
1117 A227 33p multi　　　　1.25 1.25
1118 A227 40p multi　　　　1.60 1.60
1119 A227 49p multi　　　　2.00 2.00
1120 A227 62p multi　　　　2.50 2.50
1121 A227 70p multi　　　　2.75 2.75
Nos. 1116-1121 (6)　　　11.35 11.35
**Souvenir Sheet**
**Perf. 14¼**
1122 A227 £2 multi　　　　8.00 8.00
No. 1122 contains one 38x50mm stamp.

Orchids
A228

Designs: 32p, Cymbidium lowianum "Concolor." 33p, Phragmipedium besseae var.
flavum. 40p, Peristeria elata. 54p, Cymbidium
tracyanum. 62p, Paphiopedilum "Victoria Village Isle of Jersey." 70p, Paphiopedilum
hirsutissimum.
£2, Phragmipedium "Jason Fischer."

**2004, May 25　　　　Perf. 13x13¼**
1123 A228 32p multi　　　　1.25 1.25
1124 A228 33p multi　　　　1.25 1.25
1125 A228 40p multi　　　　1.60 1.60
1126 A228 54p multi　　　　2.10 2.10
1127 A228 62p multi　　　　2.50 2.50
1128 A228 70p multi　　　　2.75 2.75
*a.* Booklet pane, #1123-1128　11.50
Nos. 1123-1128 (6)　　　11.45 11.45
**Souvenir Sheet**
1129 A228 £2 multi　　　　8.00 8.00
*a.* Booklet pane #1129　　8.00
　　Complete booklet, #1129a,
　　3 #1128a　　　　　　42.50
*b.* Like #1129, with added mar-
　　ginal inscription　　　8.25 8.25
The booklet contains three examples of No.
1128a each with different arrangements of the
stamps. No. 1129a has a larger margin than
No. 1129.
No. 1129b issued 6/26. It is inscribed
"Jersey at / Le Salon du Timbre 2004" in
margin.

## Souvenir Sheet

D-Day, 60th Anniv. — A229

**2004, June 4　　　　　Perf. 13**
1130 A229 £2 multi　　　　8.00 8.00

Mont Orgueil Castle and
Monarchs — A230

No. 1131: a, Castle in 13th century
(49x32mm). b, King John, vert. (29x32mm).
No. 1132: a, Castle in 17th century
(49x32mm). b, King Charles II, vert.
(29x32mm).
No. 1133: a, Castle in 21st century
(49x32mm). b, Queen Elizabeth II, vert.
(29x32mm).
Illustration reduced.

**2004, June 25　　　　Perf. 14¾**
1131 A230 Horiz. pair　　　2.50 2.50
*a.-b.* 32p Either single　　1.25 1.25
1132 A230 Horiz. pair　　　2.50 2.50
*a.-b.* 33p Either single　　1.25 1.25
1133 A230 Horiz. pair　　　3.25 3.25
*a.-b.* 40p Either single　　1.60 1.60
Nos. 1131-1133 (3)　　　　8.25 8.25

Worldwide
Fund for
Nature
(WWF)
A231

Designs: 32p, Wall lizard. 33p, Ant lion. 49p,
Field cricket. 70p, Dartford warbler.

**2004, July 27　　　　Perf. 14¾x14**
1134 A231 32p multi　　　　1.25 1.25
1135 A231 33p multi　　　　1.25 1.25
1136 A231 49p multi　　　　2.00 2.00
1137 A231 70p multi　　　　2.75 2.75
*a.* Miniature sheet, 2 each
　　#1134-1137　　　　14.50 14.50
Nos. 1134-1137 (4)　　　　7.25 7.25

Corals
A232

Designs: 32p, Dead man's fingers. 33p,
Devonshire cup. 40p, White sea fan. 54p, Pink
sea fan. 62p, Sunset cup. 70p, Red fingers.

**2004, Sept. 28　Litho.　Perf. 13x13¼**
1138 A232 32p multi　　　　1.25 1.25
1139 A232 33p multi　　　　1.25 1.25
1140 A232 40p multi　　　　1.60 1.60
1141 A232 54p multi　　　　2.10 2.10
1142 A232 62p multi　　　　2.50 2.50
1143 A232 70p multi　　　　2.75 2.75
*a.* Souvenir sheet, #1141-1143　7.50 7.50
Nos. 1138-1143 (6)　　　11.45 11.45

Christmas
A233

No. 1144: a, Nativity. b, Street with Christmas decorations. c, Santa Claus, children,
Christmas tree. d, Church interior. e, Candles
and holly. Each inscribed "Jersey Minimum
Postage Paid."
No. 1145: a, Madonna and Child, lilies. b,
Christmas stocking on mantle. c, Candles and
flowers. d, Angel and candle. e, Candles in
window. Each inscribed "U.K. Minimum Postage Paid."

*Serpentine Die Cut 11¼x11½*
**2004, Nov. 2　　　　　　　　Litho.**
**Self-Adhesive**
**Coil Stamps**
1144　　Horiz. strip of 5　　6.00
*a.-e.* A233 (32p) Any single　1.25 1.25
1145　　Horiz. strip of 5　　6.25
*a.-e.* A233 (33p) Any single　1.25 1.25
Nos. 1144 and 1145 exist dated "2005" and
"2006." Values the same.

Rescue
Craft
A234

Designs: 32p, Channel Islands Air Search
airplane. 33p, Burby helicopter. 40p, Beach
Lifeguard Service Surf Rescue boat. 49p, Fire
Rescue inflatable boat. 70p, Royal Air Force
Sea King helicopter.

**2005, Jan. 18　Litho.　Perf. 13x13¼**
1146 A234 32p multi　　　　1.25 1.25
1147 A234 33p multi　　　　1.25 1.25
1148 A234 40p multi　　　　1.60 1.60
1149 A234 49p multi　　　　2.00 2.00
1150 A234 70p multi　　　　2.75 2.75
Nos. 1146-1150 (5)　　　　8.85 8.85

## Souvenir Sheet

New Year 2005 (Year of the Rooster) — A235

| 2005, Feb. 9 | | | Perf. 14¼ | |
|---|---|---|---|---|
| 1151 | A235 | £1 multi | 4.00 | 4.00 |

Gastronomy A236

Designs: 32p, Conger eel soup. 33p, Oysters. 40p, Bean crock. 70p, Bourdélots with black butter.

| 2005, Mar. 8 | | | Litho. | Perf. 13¾ | |
|---|---|---|---|---|---|
| 1152 | A236 | 32p multi | | 1.25 | 1.25 |
| 1153 | A236 | 33p multi | | 1.25 | 1.25 |
| 1154 | A236 | 40p multi | | 1.60 | 1.60 |
| 1155 | A236 | 70p multi | | 2.75 | 2.75 |
| | | Nos. 1152-1155 (4) | | 6.85 | 6.85 |

Europa (33p, 40p).

Fairy Tales A237

Designs: 33p, Little Red Riding Hood. 34p, The Little Mermaid. 41p, Beauty and the Beast. 50p, Rumpelstiltskin. 73p, The Goose That Laid the Golden Egg. £2, The Ugly Duckling.

| 2005, Apr. 2 | | | Perf. 13x13¼ | |
|---|---|---|---|---|
| 1156 | A237 | 33p multi | 1.25 | 1.25 |
| 1157 | A237 | 34p multi | 1.40 | 1.40 |
| 1158 | A237 | 41p multi | 1.60 | 1.60 |
| 1159 | A237 | 50p multi | 2.00 | 2.00 |
| 1160 | A237 | 73p multi | 3.00 | 3.00 |
| | | Nos. 1156-1160 (5) | 9.25 | 9.25 |

### Souvenir Sheet
#### Perf. 13¼

| 1161 | A237 | £2 multi | 8.00 | 8.00 |
|---|---|---|---|---|
| a. | | As No. 1161, with Nordia 2005 emblem in sheet margin | 7.75 | 7.75 |

No. 1161 contains one 49x35mm stamp, and has a hologram applied in the sheet margin.
No. 1161a issued 5/26.

## Souvenir Sheet

Jersey Soccer Association and Muratti Vase Soccer Competition, Cent. — A238

| 2005, Apr. 27 | | | Perf. | |
|---|---|---|---|---|
| 1162 | A238 | £2 multi | 8.00 | 8.00 |

## Souvenir Sheet

End of World War II, 60th Anniv. — A239

| 2005, May 9 | | | Litho. | Perf. 14¼ | |
|---|---|---|---|---|---|
| 1163 | A239 | £2 multi | | 8.00 | 8.00 |

Jersey Motor Festival A240

Automobiles: 33p, MGB GT. 34p, Mini Cooper. 41p, Citroen DS. 50p, Jaguar E Type. 56p, Volkswagen Beetle. 73p, Aston Martin DB5.

| 2005, June 6 | | | Perf. 13x13¼ | |
|---|---|---|---|---|
| 1164 | A240 | 33p multi | 1.25 | 1.25 |
| 1165 | A240 | 34p multi | 1.40 | 1.40 |
| 1166 | A240 | 41p multi | 1.60 | 1.60 |
| 1167 | A240 | 50p multi | 2.00 | 2.00 |
| 1168 | A240 | 56p multi | 2.25 | 2.25 |
| 1169 | A240 | 73p multi | 3.00 | 3.00 |
| a. | | Booklet pane, #1164-1169 | 11.50 | — |
| | | Complete booklet, 3 #1169a | 35.00 | |
| | | Nos. 1164-1169 (6) | 11.50 | 11.50 |

Complete booklet contains three examples of No. 1169a, each with a different margin and layout of the stamps.

Flowers — A241

Designs: 2p, Scarlet pimpernel. 4p, Common knapweed. 20p, Greater stitchwort. 30p, Common mallow. 40p, White campion. 50p, Common dog-violet. 65p, Herb Robert. £1, Three-cornered garlic.

| 2005, July 19 | | | Perf. 13¼ | |
|---|---|---|---|---|
| 1170 | A241 | 2p multi | .20 | .20 |
| 1171 | A241 | 4p multi | .20 | .20 |
| 1172 | A241 | 20p multi | .80 | .80 |
| 1173 | A241 | 30p multi | 1.25 | 1.25 |
| 1174 | A241 | 40p multi | 1.60 | 1.60 |
| 1175 | A241 | 50p multi | 2.00 | 2.00 |
| 1176 | A241 | 65p multi | 2.50 | 2.50 |
| 1177 | A241 | £1 multi | 4.00 | 4.00 |
| a. | | Souvenir sheet, #1170-1177 | 12.50 | 12.50 |
| | | Nos. 1170-1177 (8) | 12.55 | 12.55 |

See Nos. 1228-1235a, 1267-1274a.

Martello Towers — A242

| 2005, Aug. 9 | | | Perf. 13¾ | |
|---|---|---|---|---|
| 1178 | A242 | 33p Le Hocq | 1.25 | 1.25 |
| 1179 | A242 | 34p Seymour | 1.40 | 1.40 |
| 1180 | A242 | 41p Archirondel | 1.60 | 1.60 |
| 1181 | A242 | 56p Kempt | 2.25 | 2.25 |
| 1182 | A242 | 73p Le Rocco | 3.00 | 3.00 |
| | | Nos. 1178-1182 (5) | 9.50 | 9.50 |

Mushrooms A243

Designs: 33p, Pink waxcap. 34p, Boletus erythropus. 41p, Inocybe godeyi. 50p, Pepperpot earthstar. 56p, White elfin saddle. 73p, Red waxy cap.
£2, Fairy ring mushrooms, horiz.

| 2005, Sept. 13 | | | Perf. 13¾ | |
|---|---|---|---|---|
| 1183 | A243 | 33p multi | 1.25 | 1.25 |
| 1184 | A243 | 34p multi | 1.40 | 1.40 |
| 1185 | A243 | 41p multi | 1.60 | 1.60 |
| 1186 | A243 | 50p multi | 2.00 | 2.00 |
| 1187 | A243 | 56p multi | 2.25 | 2.25 |
| 1188 | A243 | 73p multi | 3.00 | 3.00 |
| | | Nos. 1183-1188 (6) | 11.50 | 11.50 |

### Souvenir Sheet
#### Perf. 14¼

| 1189 | A243 | £2 multi | 8.00 | 8.00 |
|---|---|---|---|---|

No. 1189 contains one 50x38mm stamp.

Battle of Trafalgar, Bicent. A244

Designs: 33p, HMS Belleisle. 34p, HMS Royal Sovereign. 41p, HMS Neptune. 50p, HMS Euryalus. 73p, HMS Mars.
£2, HMS Victory.

| 2005, Oct. 21 | | | Perf. 14 | |
|---|---|---|---|---|
| 1190 | A244 | 33p multi | 1.25 | 1.25 |
| 1191 | A244 | 34p multi | 1.40 | 1.40 |
| 1192 | A244 | 41p multi | 1.60 | 1.60 |
| 1193 | A244 | 50p multi | 2.00 | 2.00 |
| 1194 | A244 | 73p multi | 3.00 | 3.00 |
| | | Nos. 1190-1194 (5) | 9.25 | 9.25 |

### Souvenir Sheet
#### Perf. 14¼

| 1195 | A244 | £2 multi | 8.00 | 8.00 |
|---|---|---|---|---|

No. 1195 contains one 50x38mm stamp.

Royal Jersey Militia Uniforms and Badges A245

Uniforms and badges from: 33p, Royal Jersey Regiment, ca. 1830. 34p, Royal Jersey Regiment, ca. 1844. 41p, Royal Jersey Artillery, ca. 1881. 50p, Royal Jersey Light Infantry ca. 1890. 73p, Royal Engineers, present day.

| 2006, Jan. 6 | | | Litho. | Perf. 13¼ | |
|---|---|---|---|---|---|
| 1196 | A245 | 33p multi | | 1.25 | 1.25 |
| 1197 | A245 | 34p multi | | 1.40 | 1.40 |
| 1198 | A245 | 41p multi | | 1.60 | 1.60 |
| 1199 | A245 | 50p multi | | 2.00 | 2.00 |
| 1200 | A245 | 73p multi | | 3.00 | 3.00 |
| | | Nos. 1196-1200 (5) | | 9.25 | 9.25 |

## Souvenir Sheet

New Year 2006 (Year of the Dog) — A246

| 2006, Jan. 29 | | | Litho. | Perf. 14¼ | |
|---|---|---|---|---|---|
| 1201 | A246 | £1 multi | | 4.00 | 4.00 |

## Souvenir Sheet

Victoria Cross, 150th Anniv. — A247

| 2006, Jan. 29 | | | Perf. 13¼x14 | |
|---|---|---|---|---|
| 1202 | A247 | £2 multi | 8.00 | 8.00 |

Multiculturalism — A248

Designs: 33p, Chinese costumes. 34p, Portuguese Fado Music Festival. 41p, Polish Pisanki Easter egg tradition. 73p, Indian costumes.

| 2006, Mar. 7 | | | Perf. 14 | |
|---|---|---|---|---|
| 1203 | A248 | 33p multi | 1.25 | 1.25 |
| 1204 | A248 | 34p multi | 1.40 | 1.40 |
| 1205 | A248 | 41p multi | 1.60 | 1.60 |
| 1206 | A248 | 73p multi | 3.00 | 3.00 |
| | | Nos. 1203-1206 (4) | 7.25 | 7.25 |

Europa (34p, 41p).

Shells A249

Designs: 34p, Flat periwinkle. 37p, Painted top shell. 42p, Dog cockle. 51p, Variegated scallop. 57p, Blue-rayed limpet. 74p, European cowrie.
£2, Ormer shell.

| 2006, Apr. 4 | | | Litho. | Perf. 13x13¼ | |
|---|---|---|---|---|---|
| 1207 | A249 | 34p multi | | 1.40 | 1.40 |
| 1208 | A249 | 37p multi | | 1.50 | 1.50 |
| 1209 | A249 | 42p multi | | 1.60 | 1.60 |
| 1210 | A249 | 51p multi | | 2.00 | 2.00 |
| 1211 | A249 | 57p multi | | 2.25 | 2.25 |
| 1212 | A249 | 74p multi | | 3.00 | 3.00 |
| | | Nos. 1207-1212 (6) | | 11.75 | 11.75 |

### Souvenir Sheet
#### Litho. & Embossed With Hologram Affixed
#### Perf.

| 1213 | A249 | £2 multi | 8.00 | 8.00 |
|---|---|---|---|---|
| a. | | Like #1213, with Belgica '06 emblem added in sheet margin | 9.00 | 9.00 |

Portions of the designs of Nos. 1207-1212 were applied by a thermographic process producing a shiny, raised effect. No. 1213 contains one 46x30 oval stamp.
Issued: No. 1213a, 11/16.

Wedding of Prince Charles and Camilla Parker-Bowles, 1st Anniv. — A250

| 2006, Apr. 9 | | | Litho. | Perf. 13¼ | |
|---|---|---|---|---|---|
| 1214 | A250 | £2 multi | | 8.00 | 8.00 |

Queen
Elizabeth II,
80th
Birthday
A251

**Litho. & Embossed With Foil
Application**

| 2006, Apr. 21 | | | Perf. 13½ | |
|---|---|---|---|---|
| 1215 | A251 | £5 dk bl & multi | 20.00 | 20.00 |
| a. | | Prussian blue & multi | 20.00 | 20.00 |
| b. | | Souvenir sheet, #1215a, New Zealand #2068a | 27.50 | 27.50 |

See New Zealand No. 2068. No. 1215b sold
for £7.

**Souvenir Sheet**

2006 World Cup Soccer
Championships, Germany — A252

| 2006, June 9 | | Litho. | Perf. 14¼ | |
|---|---|---|---|---|
| 1216 | A252 | £2 multi | 8.00 | 8.00 |

Island
Views — A253

*Serpentine Die Cut 11¼*

**2006, July 11**
**Self-Adhesive**
**Coil Stamps**

| 1217 | A253 | (37p) | Greve de Lecq | 1.50 | 1.50 |
|---|---|---|---|---|---|
| 1218 | A253 | (37p) | La Rocque | 1.50 | 1.50 |
| 1219 | A253 | (37p) | Portelet | 1.50 | 1.50 |
| 1220 | A253 | (37p) | St. Brelade's Bay | 1.50 | 1.50 |
| a. | | | Horiz. strip of 4, #1217-1220 | 6.00 | 6.00 |

Butterflies
& Moths
A254

Designs: 34p, Red underwing moth. 37p,
Comma butterfly. 42p, Black arches moth.
51p, Small copper butterfly. 57p, Holly blue
butterfly. 74p, Orange-tip butterfly.

| 2006, Aug. 1 | | | Perf. 14¾x14 | |
|---|---|---|---|---|
| **Stamps With White Margin** | | | | |
| 1221 | A254 | 34p multi | 1.40 | 1.40 |
| 1222 | A254 | 37p multi | 1.50 | 1.50 |
| 1223 | A254 | 42p multi | 1.60 | 1.60 |
| 1224 | A254 | 51p multi | 2.00 | 2.00 |
| 1225 | A254 | 57p multi | 2.25 | 2.25 |
| 1226 | A254 | 74p multi | 3.00 | 3.00 |
| | | Nos. 1221-1226 (6) | 11.75 | 11.75 |
| **Souvenir Sheet** | | | | |
| **Stamps Without White Margin** | | | | |
| 1227 | | Sheet of 3 | 7.50 | 7.50 |
| a. | A254 | 51p multi | 2.00 | 2.00 |
| b. | A254 | 57p multi | 2.25 | 2.25 |
| c. | A254 | 74p multi | 3.00 | 3.00 |

**Flowers Type of 2005**

Designs: 1p, Yellow bartsia. 3p, Wild angelica. 5p, Marsh St. John's wort. 15p, Bog pimpernel. 70p, Ragged robin. 75p, Brooklime.
85p, Cuckoo flower. 90p, Yellow iris.

| 2006, Sept. 26 | | Litho. | Perf. 13¼ | |
|---|---|---|---|---|
| 1228 | A241 | 1p multi | .20 | .20 |
| 1229 | A241 | 3p multi | .20 | .20 |
| 1230 | A241 | 5p multi | .20 | .20 |
| 1231 | A241 | 15p multi | .60 | .60 |
| 1232 | A241 | 70p multi | 2.75 | 2.75 |
| 1233 | A241 | 75p multi | 3.00 | 3.00 |
| 1234 | A241 | 85p multi | 3.50 | 3.50 |
| 1235 | A241 | 90p multi | 3.50 | 3.50 |
| a. | | Souvenir sheet, #1228-1235 | 14.00 | 14.00 |
| | | Nos. 1228-1235 (8) | 13.95 | 13.95 |

Jersey
Post
Vehicles
A255

Designs: 34p, 2004 LDV Luton Van. 37p,
1999-2004 Renault Kangaroo. 42p, 1994-
2004 LDV Pilot. 51p, 1988-96 Ford Transit
Luton Body. 57p, Morris Marina 440/575, c.
1978. 74p, Morris Minor, c. 1969.

| 2006, Oct. 31 | | | Perf. 13x13¼ | |
|---|---|---|---|---|
| 1236 | A255 | 34p multi | 1.40 | 1.40 |
| 1237 | A255 | 37p multi | 1.50 | 1.50 |
| 1238 | A255 | 42p multi | 1.60 | 1.60 |
| 1239 | A255 | 51p multi | 2.00 | 2.00 |
| 1240 | A255 | 57p multi | 2.25 | 2.25 |
| 1241 | A255 | 74p multi | 3.00 | 3.00 |
| a. | | Booklet pane, #1236-1241 | 12.00 | — |
| b. | | Booklet pane, #1239-1241 + binding stub | 7.50 | — |
| | | Complete booklet, #1241b, 3 #1241a | 45.00 | |
| c. | | Souvenir sheet, #1239-1241 | 7.50 | 7.50 |

No. 1241a has three different layouts of
stamps on pane and three different margins.
No. 1241c has a straight edge at left, while No.
1241b is separated from binding stub by a row
of rouletting.

Minerals
A256

Designs: 34p, Molybdenite. 37p, Muscovite
in pegmatite vein, feldspar and quartz. 42p,
Orthoclase and plagioclase. 51p, Quartz
coated with manganese oxide. 74p, Smoky
quartz.

| 2007, Jan. 23 | | Litho. | Perf. 13x13¼ | |
|---|---|---|---|---|
| 1242 | A256 | 34p multi | 1.40 | 1.40 |
| 1243 | A256 | 37p multi | 1.50 | 1.50 |
| 1244 | A256 | 42p multi | 1.60 | 1.60 |
| 1245 | A256 | 51p multi | 2.00 | 2.00 |
| 1246 | A256 | 74p multi | 3.00 | 3.00 |
| | | Nos. 1242-1246 (5) | 9.50 | 9.50 |

**Souvenir Sheet**

New Year 2007 (Year of the
Pig) — A257

| 2007, Feb. 18 | | | Perf. 14¼ | |
|---|---|---|---|---|
| 1247 | A257 | £1 multi | 4.00 | 4.00 |

Scouting,
Cent.
A258

Lord Robert Baden-Powell and Scouts: 34p,
With kayak, sailboard and kite-propelled vehicle. 37p, With musical instruments and flags.
42p, In go-carts and wagons, scouts climbing.
74p, With uniform patches.

| 2007, Mar. 6 | | | Perf. 14 | |
|---|---|---|---|---|
| 1248 | A258 | 34p multi | 1.40 | 1.40 |
| 1249 | A258 | 37p multi | 1.50 | 1.50 |
| 1250 | A258 | 42p multi | 1.60 | 1.60 |
| 1251 | A258 | 74p multi | 3.00 | 3.00 |
| | | Nos. 1248-1251 (4) | 7.50 | 7.50 |

Europa (37p, 42p).

Mammals
A259

Designs: 34p, Long-tailed field mouse. 37p,
Rabbits. 42p, Polecat. 51p, Common shrew.
57p, Stoat. 74p, Brown rat.

| 2007, Apr. 10 | | | Perf. 14¾x14 | |
|---|---|---|---|---|
| **Stamps With White Frames** | | | | |
| 1252 | A259 | 34p multi | 1.40 | 1.40 |
| 1253 | A259 | 37p multi | 1.50 | 1.50 |
| 1254 | A259 | 42p multi | 1.75 | 1.75 |
| 1255 | A259 | 51p multi | 2.00 | 2.00 |
| 1256 | A259 | 57p multi | 2.25 | 2.25 |
| 1257 | A259 | 74p multi | 3.00 | 3.00 |
| | | Nos. 1252-1257 (6) | 11.90 | 11.90 |
| **Souvenir Sheet** | | | | |
| **Stamps Without White Frames** | | | | |
| 1258 | | Sheet of 3 | 7.25 | 7.25 |
| a. | A259 | 51p multi | 2.00 | 2.00 |
| b. | A259 | 57p multi | 2.25 | 2.25 |
| c. | A259 | 74p multi | 3.00 | 3.00 |

Birds
A260

Designs: 34p, House sparrow. 37p, Chaffinch. 42p, Blue tit. 51p, Blackbird. 57p, Magpie. 74p, Great tit.

| 2007, June 19 | | Litho. | Perf. 13x13½ | |
|---|---|---|---|---|
| **Stamps With White Frames** | | | | |
| 1259 | A260 | 34p multi | 1.40 | 1.40 |
| 1260 | A260 | 37p multi | 1.50 | 1.50 |
| 1261 | A260 | 42p multi | 1.75 | 1.75 |
| 1262 | A260 | 51p multi | 2.10 | 2.10 |
| 1263 | A260 | 57p multi | 2.25 | 2.25 |
| 1264 | A260 | 74p multi | 3.00 | 3.00 |
| a. | | Miniature sheet, #1259-1264 | 12.00 | 12.00 |
| | | Nos. 1259-1264 (6) | 12.00 | 12.00 |
| **Souvenir Sheet** | | | | |
| **Stamps Without White Frames** | | | | |
| 1265 | | Sheet of 3 | 7.50 | 7.50 |
| a. | A260 | 51p multi | 2.10 | 2.10 |
| b. | A260 | 57p multi | 2.25 | 2.25 |
| c. | A260 | 74p multi | 3.00 | 3.00 |

**Souvenir Sheet**

Gorey Regatta — A261

| 2007, June 22 | | | Perf. 12¾x13½ | |
|---|---|---|---|---|
| 1266 | A261 | £2 multi | 8.00 | 8.00 |

**Flowers Type of 2005**

Designs: 10p, Black bryony. 25p, Horse-
shoe vetch. 35p, English stonecrop. 45p, Tut-
san. 55p, Ox-eye daisy. 60p, Rock sea-spur-
rey. 80p, Mouse-ear hawkweed. £1.50,
Devil's-bit scabious.

| 2007, July 25 | | | Perf. 13¼ | |
|---|---|---|---|---|
| 1267 | A241 | 10p multi | .40 | .40 |
| 1268 | A241 | 25p multi | 1.00 | 1.00 |
| 1269 | A241 | 35p multi | 1.40 | 1.40 |
| 1270 | A241 | 45p multi | 1.90 | 1.90 |
| 1271 | A241 | 55p multi | 2.25 | 2.25 |
| 1272 | A241 | 60p multi | 2.50 | 2.50 |
| 1273 | A241 | 80p multi | 3.25 | 3.25 |
| 1274 | A241 | £1.50 multi | 6.25 | 6.25 |
| a. | | Miniature sheet, #1267-1274 | 19.00 | 19.00 |
| | | Nos. 1267-1274 (8) | 18.95 | 18.95 |

Summer
Flowers
A262

Designs: 34p, Clematis. 37p, Roses. 42p,
Honeysuckles. 51p, Fuchsias. 57p, Sweet
peas. 74p, Lilacs.

| 2007, July 25 | | | Perf. 13½ | |
|---|---|---|---|---|
| 1275 | A262 | 34p multi | 1.40 | 1.40 |
| 1276 | A262 | 37p multi | 1.50 | 1.50 |
| 1277 | A262 | 42p multi | 1.75 | 1.75 |
| 1278 | A262 | 51p multi | 2.10 | 2.10 |
| 1279 | A262 | 57p multi | 2.40 | 2.40 |
| 1280 | A262 | 74p multi | 3.00 | 3.00 |
| | | Nos. 1275-1280 (6) | 12.15 | 12.15 |

Airplanes
A263

Designs: 34p, Dornier Do 24 ATT. 37p, Avro
Vulcan B-2. 42p, Junkers Ju-52. 51p, Sukhoi
Su-27 Flanker. 57p, Boeing B-52 Stratofor-
tress. 74p, Concorde.
£2.50, Red Arrows in formation.

| 2007, Sept. 13 | | | Perf. 13x13¼ | |
|---|---|---|---|---|
| 1281 | A263 | 34p multi | 1.40 | 1.40 |
| 1282 | A263 | 37p multi | 1.50 | 1.50 |
| 1283 | A263 | 42p multi | 1.75 | 1.75 |
| 1284 | A263 | 51p multi | 2.10 | 2.10 |
| 1285 | A263 | 57p multi | 2.40 | 2.40 |
| 1286 | A263 | 74p multi | 3.00 | 3.00 |
| a. | | Booklet pane, #1281-1286 | 12.50 | — |
| | | Complete booklet, #1287a, 3 #1286a | 48.00 | |
| | | Nos. 1281-1286 (6) | 12.15 | 12.15 |
| **Souvenir Sheet** | | | | |
| | | | Perf. 13¼x13 | |
| 1287 | A263 | £2.50 multi | 10.50 | 10.50 |
| a. | | Booklet pane, #1287 | 10.50 | — |

No. 1287 contains one 60x40mm stamp.
Size of No. 1287a: 150x100mm. The complete
booklet contains three examples of No. 1286a,
each of which has a different arrangement of
the stamps.

Jersey Attractions — A264

Designs: 34p, Queen's Valley Reservoir.
37p, Mont Orgueil Castle. 42p, Bonne Nuit
Harbor. 51, La Hougue Bie. 57p, Bouley Bay.
74p, Le Corbiere Lighthouse.

| 2007, Oct. 1 | | | Perf. 14x13½ | |
|---|---|---|---|---|
| 1288 | A264 | 34p multi | 1.40 | 1.40 |
| 1289 | A264 | 37p multi | 1.50 | 1.50 |
| 1290 | A264 | 42p multi | 1.75 | 1.75 |
| 1291 | A264 | 51p multi | 2.10 | 2.10 |
| 1292 | A264 | 57p multi | 2.40 | 2.40 |
| 1293 | A264 | 74p multi | 3.00 | 3.00 |
| | | Nos. 1288-1293 (6) | 12.15 | 12.15 |

Christmas
Songs
A265

No. 1294: a, Minuit Chrétiens. b, While
Shepherds Watched. c, O Come, All Ye Faith-
ful. d, O Christmas Tree. e, Jingle Bells.
No. 1295: a, Hark! The Herald Angels Sing.
b, We Three Kings. c, Ding Dong! Merrily On
High. d, Holly and the Ivy. e, Good King
Wenceslas.

## Serpentine Die Cut 11¼

**2007, Nov. 7**       **Litho.**

### Self-Adhesive
### Coil Stamps

| | | | |
|---|---|---|---|
| 1294 | Horiz. strip of 5 | 7.25 | |
| a.-e. | A265 (35c) Any single | 1.40 | 1.40 |
| 1295 | Horiz. strip of 5 | 8.00 | |
| a.-e. | A265 (39c) Any single | 1.60 | 1.60 |

Wedding of Queen Elizabeth II and
Prince Philip, 60th Anniv. — A266

**2007, Nov. 20**       **Perf. 13¼**

| | | | | |
|---|---|---|---|---|
| 1296 | A266 | £3 multi | 12.50 | 12.50 |

Jersey
Signal
Station,
300th
Anniv.
A267

Designs: 35p, Sun, sunshine recorder, clouds. 39p, Clouds, weather symbols for wind speed, weather vane. 43p, Clouds, raindrops, weather symbols and barometer. 58p, Sun, thermometer and weather station. 76p, Tide measuring device, French flag, Moon.

**2008, Jan. 15**    **Litho.**    **Perf. 14**

| | | | | |
|---|---|---|---|---|
| 1297 | A267 | 35p multi | 1.40 | 1.40 |
| 1298 | A267 | 39p multi | 1.60 | 1.60 |
| 1299 | A267 | 43p multi | 1.75 | 1.75 |
| 1300 | A267 | 58p multi | 2.40 | 2.40 |
| 1301 | A267 | 76p multi | 3.00 | 3.00 |
| | Nos. 1297-1301 (5) | | 10.15 | 10.15 |

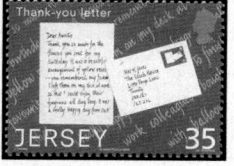

Letters
A268

Designs: 35p, Thank-you letter. 39p, Love letter. 43p, Letter to Santa Claus. 76p, Family letter.

**2008, Feb. 14**      **Perf. 13½x14**

| | | | | |
|---|---|---|---|---|
| 1302 | A268 | 35p multi | 1.40 | 1.40 |
| 1303 | A268 | 39p multi | 1.60 | 1.60 |
| 1304 | A268 | 43p multi | 1.75 | 1.75 |
| 1305 | A268 | 76p multi | 3.00 | 3.00 |
| | Nos. 1302-1305 (4) | | 7.75 | 7.75 |

Europa (39p, 43p).

Jersey
Eisteddfod,
Cent.
A269

Designs: 35p, Arts and crafts. 39p, Dance and drama. 43p, Speech. 58p, Films and photography. 76p, Music.

**2008, Mar. 3**      **Perf. 14**

| | | | | |
|---|---|---|---|---|
| 1306 | A269 | 35p multi | 1.40 | 1.40 |
| 1307 | A269 | 39p multi | 1.60 | 1.60 |
| 1308 | A269 | 43p multi | 1.75 | 1.75 |
| 1309 | A269 | 58p multi | 2.40 | 2.40 |
| 1310 | A269 | 76p multi | 3.25 | 3.25 |
| | Nos. 1306-1310 (5) | | 10.40 | 10.40 |

Buses
A270

Designs: 35p, Grey Bus Services Daimler CB bus. 39p, Safety Coach Service Ex LGOC K single decker bus. 43p, Jersey Motor Transport horse-drawn town bus. 52p, Jersey Motor Transport Leyland Lion Charcoal Burner bus. 58p, Jersey Bus Service Bedford WLB bus. 76p, Jersey Motor Transport Commer Commando bus. £2.50, Jersey Motor Transport Ford Willowbrook bus.

**2008, Apr. 8**      **Perf. 14¼x14**

| | | | | |
|---|---|---|---|---|
| 1311 | A270 | 35p multi | 1.40 | 1.40 |
| 1312 | A270 | 39p multi | 1.60 | 1.60 |
| 1313 | A270 | 43p multi | 1.75 | 1.75 |
| 1314 | A270 | 52p multi | 2.10 | 2.10 |
| 1315 | A270 | 58p multi | 2.40 | 2.40 |
| 1316 | A270 | 76p multi | 3.00 | 3.00 |
| | Nos. 1311-1316 (6) | | 12.25 | 12.25 |

### Souvenir Sheet
### Perf. 13½x13¾

| | | | | |
|---|---|---|---|---|
| 1317 | A270 | £2.50 multi | 1.40 | 1.40 |
| a. | As #1317, with WIPA 08 emblem in sheet margin | | 9.00 | 9.00 |

No. 1317 contains one 75x30mm stamp. No. 1317a issued 9/18.

### Souvenir Sheet

World Jersey Cattle Bureau
Conference — A271

**2008, May 18**      **Perf. 13**

| | | | | |
|---|---|---|---|---|
| 1318 | A271 | £2 multi | 8.00 | 8.00 |

Orchids
A272

Designs: 35p, Cymbidium Avranches "Victoria Village." 39p, Miltonia "Tesson Mill." 43p, Anguloa Victoire "Trinity." 52p, Phragmipedium La Hougette. 58p, Phragmipedium Havre des Pas "Jersey." 76p, Paphiopedilum Rolfei "Trinity." £2.50, Paphiopedilum Rocco Tower.

**2008, May 20**      **Perf. 13x13¼**

| | | | | |
|---|---|---|---|---|
| 1319 | A272 | 35p multi | 1.40 | 1.40 |
| 1320 | A272 | 39p multi | 1.60 | 1.60 |
| 1321 | A272 | 43p multi | 1.75 | 1.75 |
| 1322 | A272 | 52p multi | 2.10 | 2.10 |
| 1323 | A272 | 58p multi | 2.40 | 2.40 |
| 1324 | A272 | 76p multi | 3.00 | 3.00 |
| | Nos. 1319-1324 (6) | | 12.25 | 12.25 |

### Souvenir Sheet

| | | | | |
|---|---|---|---|---|
| 1325 | A272 | £2.50 multi | 10.00 | 10.00 |

### Souvenir Sheet

2008 World Cricket League Division 5
Tournament, Jersey — A273

**2008, May 23**    **Litho.**    **Perf. 12¾x13¼**

| | | | | |
|---|---|---|---|---|
| 1326 | A273 | £2 multi | 8.00 | 8.00 |

Royal
Navy
Vessels
A274

Designs: 35p, HMS Roebuck. 39p, HMS Monmouth. 43p, HMS Edinburgh. 52p, HMS Express. 58p, HMS Severn. 76p, HMS Cottesmore. £2.50, HMY Britannia.

**2008, June 24**    **Litho.**    **Perf. 13x13¼**

| | | | | |
|---|---|---|---|---|
| 1327 | A274 | 35p multi | 1.40 | 1.40 |
| 1328 | A274 | 39p multi | 1.60 | 1.60 |
| 1329 | A274 | 43p multi | 1.75 | 1.75 |
| 1330 | A274 | 52p multi | 2.10 | 2.10 |
| 1331 | A274 | 58p multi | 2.40 | 2.40 |
| 1332 | A274 | 76p multi | 3.00 | 3.00 |
| a. | Booklet pane, #1327-1332 | | 12.50 | — |
| | Nos. 1327-1332 (6) | | 12.25 | 12.25 |

### Souvenir Sheet
### Perf. 13¼x13

| | | | | |
|---|---|---|---|---|
| 1333 | A274 | £2.50 multi | 10.00 | 10.00 |
| a. | Booklet pane of 1 #1333 | 10.00 | |
| | Complete booklet, #1333a, 3 #1332a | 47.50 | |

No. 1333 contains one 60x40mm stamp. No. 1333a has a binding stub at left. Complete booklet contains 3 examples of No. 1332a, each with a different margin and different arrangement of the stamps.

### Souvenir Sheet

Jersey Festival of Speed — A275

**2008, Aug. 23**    **Litho.**    **Perf. 13x13¼**

| | | | | |
|---|---|---|---|---|
| 1334 | A275 | £2.50 multi | 9.25 | 9.25 |

Farm Animals
and Their
Young — A276

No. 1335: a, Rooster, hen and chicks. b, Sheep and lambs. c, Sow and piglets. d, Ducks and ducklings. e, Cows and calf.

### Serpentine Die Cut 11¼
**2008, Aug. 26**
### Coil Stamps
### Self-Adhesive

| | | | |
|---|---|---|---|
| 1335 | Horiz. strip of 5 | 6.50 | |
| a.-e. | A276 (35p) Any single | 1.25 | 1.25 |

Insects
A277

Designs: 35p, Carpenter bee. 39p, Buff-tailed bumblebee. 43p, Clown-faced bug. 52p, Large migrant hoverfly. 58p, Ruby-tailed wasp. 76p, 22-spot ladybug.

**2008, Sept. 8**      **Perf. 13x13¼**

| | | | | |
|---|---|---|---|---|
| 1336 | A277 | 35p multi | 1.25 | 1.25 |
| 1337 | A277 | 39p multi | 1.40 | 1.40 |
| 1338 | A277 | 43p multi | 1.60 | 1.60 |
| 1339 | A277 | 52p multi | 1.90 | 1.90 |
| 1340 | A277 | 58p multi | 2.10 | 2.10 |
| 1341 | A277 | 76p multi | 2.75 | 2.75 |
| | Nos. 1336-1341 (6) | | 11.00 | 11.00 |

### Birds Type of 2007

Designs: 35p, Northern wheatear. 39p, Whinchat. 43p, Pied flycatcher. 52p, Yellow wagtail. 58p, Ring ouzel. 76p, Common redstart.

**2008, Oct. 21**      **Litho.**

### Stamps With White Frames

| | | | | |
|---|---|---|---|---|
| 1342 | A260 | 35p multi | 1.10 | 1.10 |
| 1343 | A260 | 39p multi | 1.25 | 1.25 |
| 1344 | A260 | 43p multi | 1.40 | 1.40 |
| 1345 | A260 | 52p multi | 1.75 | 1.75 |
| 1346 | A260 | 58p multi | 1.90 | 1.90 |
| 1347 | A260 | 76p multi | 2.50 | 2.50 |
| a. | Souvenir sheet, #1342-1347 | | 10.00 | 10.00 |
| | Nos. 1342-1347 (6) | | 9.90 | 9.90 |

### Souvenir Sheet
### Stamps Without White Frames

| | | | | |
|---|---|---|---|---|
| 1348 | | Sheet of 3 | 6.25 | 6.25 |
| a. | A260 | 52p multi | 1.75 | 1.75 |
| b. | A260 | 58p multi | 1.90 | 1.90 |
| c. | A260 | 76p multi | 2.50 | 2.50 |

Prince
Charles,
60th
Birthday
A278

**2008, Nov. 14**      **Perf. 13¼**

| | | | | |
|---|---|---|---|---|
| 1349 | A278 | £4 multi | 12.00 | 12.00 |
| a. | Souvenir sheet of 1 | | 12.00 | 12.00 |

## POSTAGE DUE STAMPS

Numeral — D1      Map of Jersey — D2

### Unwmk.

**1969, Oct. 1**    **Litho.**    **Perf. 14**

| | | | | |
|---|---|---|---|---|
| J1 | D1 | 1p violet blue | 2.75 | 2.50 |
| J2 | D1 | 2p sepia | 4.00 | 3.75 |
| J3 | D1 | 3p brt carmine | 5.50 | 5.25 |
| J4 | D2 | 1sh emerald | 15.00 | 14.50 |
| J5 | D2 | 2sh6p gray green | 25.00 | 27.50 |
| J6 | D2 | 5sh red orange | 42.50 | 42.50 |
| | Nos. J1-J6 (6) | | 94.75 | 96.00 |

### Type of 1969
### Decimal Currency

**1971-75**    **Litho.**    **Perf. 14**

| | | | | |
|---|---|---|---|---|
| J7 | D2 | ½p black | .20 | .20 |
| J8 | D2 | 1p pale violet | .20 | .20 |
| J9 | D2 | 2p brown | .20 | .20 |
| J10 | D2 | 3p bright pink | .20 | .20 |
| J11 | D2 | 4p orange | .20 | .20 |
| J12 | D2 | 5p emerald | .20 | .20 |
| J13 | D2 | 6p orange ('74) | .20 | .20 |
| J14 | D2 | 7p brt yellow ('74) | .25 | .25 |
| J15 | D2 | 8p grnsh blue ('75) | .30 | .30 |
| J16 | D2 | 10p gray | .35 | .35 |
| J17 | D2 | 11p bister ('75) | .40 | .40 |
| J18 | D2 | 14p lilac | .50 | .50 |
| J19 | D2 | 25p dull green ('74) | .90 | .90 |
| J20 | D2 | 50p plum ('75) | 1.90 | 1.90 |
| | Nos. J7-J20 (14) | | 6.00 | 6.00 |

St. Clement Arms,
Dovecote,
Samares — D3

Arms and Scenes from Jersey Parishes: 2p, St. Lawrence and Handois Reservoir. 3p, St. John and Sorel Point. 4p, St. Ouen and Pinnacle Rock. 5p, St. Peter and Quetivel Mill. 10p, St. Martin and St. Catherine's Breakwater. 12p, St. Helier and St. Helier Harbor. 14p, St. Saviour and Highlands College. 15p, St. Brelade and Beauport Bay. 20p, Grouville and La Hougue Bie. 50p, St. Mary and Perry Farm. £1, Trinity and Bouley Bay.

**1978, Jan. 17**    **Litho.**    **Perf. 14**

| | | | | |
|---|---|---|---|---|
| J21 | D3 | 1p brt green & blk | .20 | .20 |
| J22 | D3 | 2p orange & blk | .20 | .20 |
| J23 | D3 | 3p maroon & blk | .20 | .20 |
| J24 | D3 | 4p vermilion & blk | .20 | .20 |
| J25 | D3 | 5p dp ultra & blk | .20 | .20 |
| J26 | D3 | 10p olive & blk | .25 | .25 |

| | | | |
|---|---|---|---|
| J27 | D3 | 12p blue & blk | .30 | .30 |
| J28 | D3 | 14p red org & blk | .35 | .35 |
| J29 | D3 | 15p lilac rose & blk | .40 | .40 |
| J30 | D3 | 20p yel green & blk | .45 | .45 |
| J31 | D3 | 50p brown & blk | 1.10 | 1.10 |
| J32 | D3 | £1 violet & blk | 2.40 | 2.40 |
| | | *Nos. J21-J32 (12)* | 6.25 | 6.25 |

St. Brelade — D4

| | | | | |
|---|---|---|---|---|
| **1982, Sept. 4** | | **Litho.** | **Perf. 13½x14** | |
| J33 | D4 | 1p shown | .20 | .20 |
| J34 | D4 | 2p St. Aubin | .20 | .20 |
| J35 | D4 | 3p Rozel | .20 | .20 |
| J36 | D4 | 4p Greve de Lecq | .20 | .20 |
| J37 | D4 | 5p Bouley Bay | .20 | .20 |
| J38 | D4 | 6p St. Catherine | .25 | .25 |
| J39 | D4 | 7p Gorey | .25 | .25 |
| J40 | D4 | 8p Bonne Nuit | .25 | .25 |
| J41 | D4 | 9p La Rocque | .30 | .30 |
| J42 | D4 | 10p St. Helier | .35 | .35 |
| J43 | D4 | 20p Ronez | .60 | .60 |
| J44 | D4 | 30p La Collette | 1.00 | 1.00 |
| J45 | D4 | 40p Elizabeth Castle | 1.25 | 1.25 |
| J46 | D4 | £1 Upper Harbor Marina | 2.75 | 2.75 |
| | | *Nos. J33-J46 (14)* | 8.00 | 8.00 |

## OCCUPATION STAMPS

### Issued Under German Occupation

OS1

| | | | | |
|---|---|---|---|---|
| **1941-42** | | **Typo.** | **Unwmk.** | **Perf. 11** |
| N1 | OS1 | ½p bright green | 7.25 | 5.50 |
| N2 | OS1 | 1p vermilion | 7.25 | 5.00 |

Numerous shades and papers exist.
Issue dates: 1p, Apr. 1; ½p, Jan. 29, 1942.
See *Scott Classic Specialized Catalogue* for detailed listings.

Jersey Views — OS2

Designs: ½p, Old Jersey farm; 1p, Portelet Bay; 1½p, Corbiere Lighthouse; 2p, Elizabeth Castle; 2½p, Mont Orgueil Castle; 3p, Gathering seaweed.

| | | | | |
|---|---|---|---|---|
| **1943-44** | | | **Perf. 13½** | |
| N3 | OS2 | ½p dark green | 11.00 | 11.00 |
| a. | | On rough, gray paper | 13.50 | 12.50 |
| N4 | OS2 | 1p scarlet | 2.75 | .80 |
| a. | | On newsprint | 3.00 | 1.50 |
| N5 | OS2 | 1½p brown | 7.25 | 5.25 |
| N6 | OS2 | 2p orange | 6.75 | 3.25 |
| N7 | OS2 | 2½p blue | 2.75 | 1.40 |
| a. | | On newsprint | .90 | 1.50 |
| N8 | OS2 | 3p red violet | 2.75 | 3.25 |
| | | *Nos. N3-N8 (6)* | 33.25 | 24.95 |

Issued: ½p, 1p, 6/1/43; 1½p, 2p, 6/8/43; 2½p, 3p, 6/29/43; #N4a, 2/28/44; #N7a, 2/25/44.

Nos. N1-N8 remained valid until 4/13/46.

## ISLE OF MAN

ˈīˌel əv ˈman

**LOCATION** — In the Irish Sea, off Northwest coast of England
**GOVT.** — Semi-autonomous within the British Commonwealth
**AREA** — 221 sq. mi.
**POP.** — 75,686 (1999 est.)

---

CAPITAL — Douglas

> Catalogue values for unused stamps in this section are for Never Hinged items, beginning with Scott 1 in the regular postage section and Scott J1 in the postage due section.

### British Regional Issues

A1

A2

Manx Emblem — A3

| | | | |
|---|---|---|---|
| | | **Perf. 15x14** | |
| **1958-69** | | **Photo.** | **Wmk. 322** |
| 1 | A1 | 2½p rose red ('64) | .60 | .50 |
| 2 | A2 | 3p purple | .20 | .20 |
| p. | | Phosphor. ('68) | .20 | .20 |
| 3 | A2 | 4p ultra ('66) | 1.50 | .20 |
| p. | | Phosphor. ('67) | .20 | .20 |
| | | **Unwmk.** | | |
| 4 | A2 | 4p ultra ('68) | .20 | .20 |
| 5 | A2 | 4p olive brown ('68) | .20 | .20 |
| 6 | A2 | 4p bright red ('69) | .65 | .30 |
| 7 | A2 | 5p dark blue ('68) | .65 | .30 |
| | | *Nos. 1-7 (7)* | 4.00 | 1.90 |

Nos. 4-7 are phosphorescent.
A 1963 printing of No. 2 is on chalky paper.

| | | | |
|---|---|---|---|
| **1971, July 7** | | **Photo.** | **Unwmk.** |
| 8 | A3 | 2½p bright pink | .35 | .20 |
| 9 | A3 | 3p ultramarine | .35 | .20 |
| 10 | A3 | 5p bluish lilac | .65 | .60 |
| 11 | A3 | 7½p light red brown | .65 | .70 |
| | | *Nos. 8-11 (4)* | 2.00 | 1.70 |

Sold to the general public only at post offices within the Isle of Man, but valid for postage throughout Great Britain.

### Bailiwick Issues

Castletown and Manx Emblem A4

Manx Cat — A5

| | | | |
|---|---|---|---|
| | | **Perf. 11½** | |
| **1973, July 5** | | **Photo.** | **Unwmk.** |
| 12 | A4 | ½p shown | .20 | .20 |
| a. | | Booklet pane of 2 | 2.75 | |
| b. | | Booklet pane of 4 ('74) | .90 | |
| 13 | A4 | 1p Port Erin | .20 | .20 |
| 14 | A4 | 1½p Mt. Snaefell | .20 | .20 |
| 15 | A4 | 2p Laxey Village | .20 | .20 |
| a. | | Booklet pane of 2 | 2.75 | |
| 16 | A4 | 2½p Tynwald Hill | .20 | .20 |
| a. | | Booklet pane of 2 | .75 | |
| 17 | A4 | 3p Douglas Promenade | .20 | .20 |
| a. | | Booklet pane of 2 | .70 | |
| b. | | Booklet pane of 4 ('74) | .90 | |
| 18 | A4 | 3½p Port St. Mary | .20 | .20 |
| a. | | Booklet pane of 4 ('74) | 1.40 | |
| 19 | A4 | 4p Fairy Bridge | .20 | .20 |
| 20 | A4 | 5p Peel, Castle and shore | .20 | .20 |
| 21 | A4 | 6p Cregneish Village | .35 | .35 |
| 22 | A4 | 7½p Ramsey Bay | .35 | .35 |
| 23 | A4 | 9p Douglas Bay | .35 | .35 |
| 24 | A5 | 10p shown | .45 | .45 |
| 25 | A5 | 20p Manx ram | .75 | .75 |
| 26 | A5 | 50p Manx shearwaters | 2.00 | 2.00 |
| 27 | A5 | £1 Viking longship | 4.00 | 4.00 |
| | | *Nos. 12-27 (16)* | 10.05 | 10.05 |

See Nos. 52-59.

---

Vikings Landing on Man, 938 — A6

| | | |
|---|---|---|
| **1973, July 5** | | **Perf. 14** |
| 28 | A6 | 15p multicolored | .60 | .60 |

Inauguration of postal independence.
Compare with No. 251. Inscription under "Isle of Man" reads "Post Office Decennium" on No. 251.

Engine No. 1, Sutherland, 1873 — A7

| | | |
|---|---|---|
| **1973, Aug. 4** | | **Perf. 14½x14** |
| 29 | A7 | 2½p shown | .20 | .20 |
| 30 | A7 | 3p Caledonia, 1885 | .20 | .20 |
| 31 | A7 | 7½p Kissack, 1910 | .50 | .50 |
| 32 | A7 | 9p Pender, 1873 | .60 | .60 |
| | | *Nos. 29-32 (4)* | 1.50 | 1.50 |

Centenary of Manx steam railroad.

Leslie Randles, 1923 Winner A8

3½p, Alan Holmes, 1957 double winner.

| | | | |
|---|---|---|---|
| **1973, Sept. 4** | | **Litho.** | **Perf. 14** |
| 33 | A8 | 3p multicolored | .20 | .20 |
| 34 | A8 | 3½p multicolored | .20 | .20 |

Manx Grand Prix Motorcycle Race, 50th anniversary.

Princess Anne and Mark Phillips — A9

| | | | |
|---|---|---|---|
| | **Litho. & Engr.** | | |
| **1973 Nov. 14** | | | **Perf. 14x13½** |
| 35 | A9 | 25p lt blue & multi | .95 | .95 |

Wedding of Princess Anne and Capt. Mark Phillips, Nov. 14, 1973.

William Hillary, R.N.L.I. Badge A10

Wreck of "St. George" A11

Designs: 8p, Tower of Refuge and lifeboat "Manchester & Salford." 10p, "Osman Gabriel" at Port Erin. 3½p and 8p are from paintings.

---

| | | | |
|---|---|---|---|
| **1974, Mar. 4** | | **Photo.** | **Perf. 11½** |
| 36 | A10 | 3p black & multi | .20 | .20 |
| 37 | A11 | 3½p black & multi | .20 | .20 |
| 38 | A11 | 8p black & multi | .45 | .45 |
| 39 | A11 | 10p black & multi | .55 | .55 |
| | | *Nos. 36-39 (4)* | 1.40 | 1.40 |

Sesqui. of the founding of the Royal Natl. Lifeboat Institution by Sir William Hillary.

Stanley Woods on Moto Guzzi Motorcycle — A12

Designs: 3½p, Freddie Frith on Norton. 8p, Max Deubel on BMW with sidecar. 10p, Mike Hailwood on Honda.

| | | | |
|---|---|---|---|
| **1974, May 29** | | **Litho.** | **Perf. 13** |
| 40 | A12 | 3p yellow grn & multi | .20 | .20 |
| 41 | A12 | 3½p crimson & multi | .20 | .20 |
| 42 | A12 | 8p yellow & multi | .30 | .25 |
| 43 | A12 | 10p ultra & multi | .40 | .35 |
| | | *Nos. 40-43 (4)* | 1.10 | 1.00 |

Tourist Trophy Motorcycle Races on the Isle of Man.

Arms and Ruins of Rushen Abbey A13

Designs: 4½p, King Edgar of England visiting Chester in boat rowed by 8 kings including King Magnus Haraldson. 8p, Fleet under King Magnus' command and arms he gave to Isle of Man. 10p, Bridge at Avignon, Bishop's mitre and Three Legs of Man.

| | | | |
|---|---|---|---|
| **1974, Sept. 18** | | **Litho.** | **Perf. 14** |
| 44 | A13 | 3½p multicolored | .20 | .20 |
| 45 | A13 | 4½p multicolored | .20 | .20 |
| 46 | A13 | 8p multicolored | .30 | .30 |
| 47 | A13 | 10p multicolored | .40 | .40 |
| | | *Nos. 44-47 (4)* | 1.10 | 1.10 |

1,000th death anniv. of Magnus Haraldson, King of Many Islands (Nos. 45-46), and 600th death anniv. of William Russell, Bishop of Sodor and Mann (Nos. 44, 47).

Churchill and "Bugler Dunne at Colenso, 1899" — A14

Sir Winston Churchill: 4½p, Government Buildings, Douglas, and Warrant of Appointment. 8p, Manx A.A. Regiment in action. 20p, Freedom of Douglas Scroll, and casket.

| | | | |
|---|---|---|---|
| **1974, Nov. 22** | | **Photo.** | **Perf. 11½** |
| 48 | A14 | 3½p multicolored | .20 | .20 |
| 49 | A14 | 4½p multicolored | .20 | .20 |
| 50 | A14 | 8p multicolored | .25 | .25 |
| 51 | A14 | 20p multicolored | .65 | .65 |
| a. | | Souvenir sheet of 4, #48-51 | 1.40 | 1.40 |
| | | *Nos. 48-51 (4)* | 1.30 | 1.30 |

| | | | |
|---|---|---|---|
| | **Type of 1973** | | |
| **1975** | | **Unwmk.** | **Perf. 11½** |
| 52 | A4 | 4½p Tynwald Hill | .20 | .20 |
| 53 | A4 | 5½p Douglas Promenade | .20 | .20 |
| 54 | A4 | 7p Laxey Village | .40 | .40 |
| 55 | A4 | 8p Ramsey Bay | .40 | .40 |
| 58 | A4 | 11p Monk's Bridge | .45 | .45 |
| 59 | A4 | 13p Derbyhaven | .60 | .60 |
| | | *Nos. 52-59 (6)* | 2.25 | 2.25 |

Issued: #52, 55, 1/8; #53-54, 5/28; #58-59, 10/29.

Log Cabin School, Cleveland Medal, Names of Settlers A15

Designs: 5 1/2p, Terminal Tower Building, Cleveland, John Gill and Robert Carran. 8p, Clague House Museum, Margaret and Robert Clague. 10p, Thomas Quayle and S. S. William T. Graves.

**1975, Mar. 14    Photo.    Perf. 11 1/2**
| 62 | A15 | 4 1/2p multicolored | .20 | .20 |
| 63 | A15 | 5 1/2p multicolored | .20 | .20 |
| 64 | A15 | 8p multicolored | .30 | .30 |
| 65 | A15 | 10p multicolored | .35 | .35 |
| | | Nos. 62-65 (4) | 1.05 | 1.05 |

Sesquicentennial of arrival of Manx settlers in Cleveland, Ohio area.

Tom Sheard and "Douglas" — A16

Designs: 7p, Walter L. Handley and "Rex-Acme." 10p, Geoffrey Duke and "Gilera." 12p, Peter Williams and "Norton."

**1975, May 28    Litho.    Perf. 13 1/2**
| 66 | A16 | 5 1/2p bister & multi | .20 | .20 |
| 67 | A16 | 7p salmon & multi | .25 | .25 |
| 68 | A16 | 10p lt green & multi | .35 | .35 |
| 69 | A16 | 12p ultra & multi | .40 | .40 |
| | | Nos. 66-69 (4) | 1.20 | 1.20 |

Tourist Trophy Motorcycle races on Isle of Man.

Sir George Goldie and his Birthplace A17

Designs (Sir George Goldie and): 7p, Map of Africa with Niger River basin, vert. 10p, Goldie as president of Royal Geographical Society and Society emblem, vert. 12p, River boats: trading hulk, native canoe, sternwheeler.

**1975, Sept. 9    Photo.    Perf. 11 1/2**
| 70 | A17 | 5 1/2p multicolored | .20 | .20 |
| 71 | A17 | 7p multicolored | .25 | .25 |
| 72 | A17 | 10p multicolored | .35 | .35 |
| 73 | A17 | 12p multicolored | .40 | .40 |
| | | Nos. 70-73 (4) | 1.20 | 1.20 |

Sir George Dashwood Goldie-Taubman (1846-1925), founder of Royal Niger Company.

Manx Bible — A18

Bicentenary of Manx Bible and Christmas 1975: 7p, Rev. Philip Moore and Old Ballaugh Church. 11p, Bishop Mark Hildesley and Bishops Court. 13p, Shipwreck off Cumberland Coast with John Kelly holding manuscript above water.

**1975, Oct. 29    Litho.    Perf. 14**
| 74 | A18 | 5 1/2p multicolored | .20 | .20 |
| 75 | A18 | 7p multicolored | .25 | .25 |
| 76 | A18 | 11p multicolored | .35 | .35 |
| 77 | A18 | 13p multicolored | .40 | .40 |
| | | Nos. 74-77 (4) | 1.20 | 1.20 |

William Christian Listening to Patrick Henry — A19

Designs: 7p, Christian carrying Fincastle Resolutions to Williamsburg. 13p, Col. Patrick Henry and Lt. Col. William Christian of 1st Virginia Regiment. 20p, Christian as frontiersman and Indians.

**1976, Mar. 12    Litho.    Perf. 13 1/2**
| 78 | A19 | 5 1/2p multicolored | .20 | .20 |
| 79 | A19 | 7p multicolored | .25 | .25 |
| 80 | A19 | 13p multicolored | .40 | .40 |
| 81 | A19 | 20p multicolored | .45 | .45 |
| a. | | Souv. sheet of 4, #78-81, perf. 14 | 1.75 | 1.75 |
| | | Nos. 78-81 (4) | 1.30 | 1.30 |

American Bicentennial. William Christian (1743-1786), patriot, son of a Manx-man and Patrick Henry's brother-in-law.

First Double-decker Tram Car — A20

Designs: 7p, Toast-rack tram, 1890. 11p, Horse bus, 1895. 13p, Decorated tram with Queen Elizabeth II and Prince Philip.

**1976, May 26    Litho.    Perf. 11 1/2**
| 82 | A20 | 5 1/2p multicolored | .20 | .20 |
| 83 | A20 | 7p multicolored | .25 | .25 |
| 84 | A20 | 11p multicolored | .40 | .40 |
| 85 | A20 | 13p multicolored | .40 | .40 |
| | | Nos. 82-85 (4) | 1.25 | 1.25 |

Douglas horse trams, centenary.

Barroose Beaker, Bronze Age — A21

Virgin and Child, on Sodor and Man Banner — A22

Europa (Manx Ceramic Art): No. 87, Souvenir teapot (3-legged man), 19th cent. No. 88, Laxey jug, 1854. No. 89, Cronk Aust food vessel, early Bronze Age. No. 90, Sansbury bowl, 1851. No. 91, Knox urn, 20th cent. Nos. 89-91, horiz.

**1976, July 28    Photo.    Perf. 11 1/2**
| 86 | A21 | 5p multicolored | .25 | .25 |
| 87 | A21 | 5p multicolored | .25 | .25 |
| 88 | A21 | 5p multicolored | .25 | .25 |
| a. | | Strip of 3, #86-88 | .80 | .80 |
| 89 | A21 | 10p multicolored | .25 | .25 |
| 90 | A21 | 10p multicolored | .25 | .25 |
| 91 | A21 | 10p multicolored | .25 | .25 |
| a. | | Strip of 3, #89-91 | .80 | .80 |
| | | Nos. 86-91 (6) | 1.50 | 1.50 |

Printed in sheets of 9 (3x3).

**1976, Oct. 14    Litho.    Perf. 14 3/4x14 1/2**
Virgin and Child on Embroidered Church Banners: 7p, St. Peter's, Onchan, Mothers' Union. 11p, Castletown. 13p, St. Olav's, Ramsey.
| 92 | A22 | 6p multicolored | .25 | .25 |
| 93 | A22 | 7p multicolored | .25 | .25 |
| 94 | A22 | 11p multicolored | .35 | .35 |
| 95 | A22 | 13p multicolored | .45 | .45 |
| | | Nos. 92-95 (4) | 1.30 | 1.30 |

Christmas 1976 & cent. of Mothers' Union.

Elizabeth II and Arms of Man A23

Designs: 7p, Queen Elizabeth II and Prince Philip, vert. 25p, Queen, 1976 portrait.

**Perf. 13 1/2x14, 14x13 1/2**
**1977, Mar. 1    Litho. & Engr.**
| 96 | A23 | 6p multicolored | .25 | .25 |
| 97 | A23 | 7p multicolored | .25 | .25 |
| 98 | A23 | 25p multicolored | .75 | .75 |
| | | Nos. 96-98 (3) | 1.25 | 1.25 |

25th anniv. of the reign of Elizabeth II.

Carrick Bay from Tom-the-Dipper's — A24

Europa: 10p, Looking south from Mooragh Park, Ramsey.

**1977, May 25    Litho.    Perf. 14**
| 99 | A24 | 6p multicolored | .25 | .25 |
| 100 | A24 | 10p multicolored | .35 | .35 |

"Pa" Applebee at Ballig Bridge, 1912 — A25

Designs: 7p, Hairpin curve at Governor's Bridge and ambulance attendants. 11p, Boy Scouts tending scoreboards. 13p, John Williams at Windy Corner on Snaefell Mountain, winner of 1976 Open Classic Race.

**1977, May 25    Perf. 13 1/2**
| 101 | A25 | 6p multicolored | .20 | .20 |
| 102 | A25 | 7p multicolored | .30 | .30 |
| 103 | A25 | 11p multicolored | .40 | .40 |
| 104 | A25 | 13p multicolored | .45 | .45 |
| | | Nos. 101-104 (4) | 1.35 | 1.35 |

Tourist Trophy Motorcycle Races, and Boy Scouts, 70th anniv.; St. John Ambulance Assoc. cent. (in GB).

Meeting House, Mt. Morrison — A26

Designs: 7p, John Wesley preaching at Castletown, 1777. 11p, Wesley preaching outside Braddan Church. 13p, Methodist Church on Douglas Promenade, 1976.

**1977, Oct. 19    Photo.    Perf. 11 1/2**
**Size: 30x24mm**
| 105 | A26 | 6p multicolored | .20 | .20 |
**Size: 37 1/2x24mm**
| 106 | A26 | 7p multicolored | .30 | .30 |
| 107 | A26 | 11p multicolored | .40 | .40 |
**Size: 30x24mm**
| 108 | A26 | 13p multicolored | .45 | .45 |
| | | Nos. 105-108 (4) | 1.35 | 1.35 |

Bicentenary of John Wesley's first visit to the Isle of Man.

Seaplane and Carrier Ben My Chree — A27

Royal Air Force, 60th Anniv.: 7p, Bristol Scout and carrier Vindex, 1915. 11p, Boulton Paul Defiant over Douglas Bay, 1941. 13p, RAF Jaguar over Ramsey, 1977.

**1978, Feb. 28    Litho.    Perf. 13 1/2x14**
| 109 | A27 | 6p multicolored | .20 | .20 |
| 110 | A27 | 7p multicolored | .30 | .30 |
| 111 | A27 | 11p multicolored | .40 | .40 |
| 112 | A27 | 13p multicolored | .45 | .45 |
| | | Nos. 109-112 (4) | 1.35 | 1.35 |

Watch Tower, Langness — A28

Jurby Church — A29

Fuchsia — A30

Landmarks: 6p, Government buildings. 7p, Tynwald Hill. 8p, Milner's Tower. 9p, Laxey Wheel. 10p, Castle Rushen. 11p, St. Ninian's Church. 12p, Tower of Refuge. 13p, St. German's Cathedral. 14p, Point of Ayre Lighthouse. 15p, Corrin's Tower. 16p, Douglas Head Lighthouse. 25p, Manx cat. 50p, Chough (crows). £1, Viking warrior.

**1978    Litho.    Perf. 14**
| 113 | A28 | 1/2p multicolored | .20 | .20 |
| 114 | A29 | 1p multicolored | .20 | .20 |
| 115 | A29 | 6p multicolored | .20 | .20 |
| 116 | A29 | 7p multicolored | .20 | .20 |
| 117 | A28 | 8p multicolored | .25 | .25 |
| 118 | A29 | 9p multicolored | .30 | .30 |
| 119 | A29 | 10p multicolored | .45 | .45 |
| 120 | A28 | 11p multicolored | .45 | .45 |
| 121 | A29 | 12p multicolored | .50 | .50 |
| 122 | A29 | 13p multicolored | .70 | .70 |
| 123 | A29 | 14p multicolored | .70 | .70 |
| 124 | A29 | 15p multicolored | .85 | .85 |
| 125 | A29 | 16p multicolored | .60 | .60 |

**Photo.**
**Perf. 11 1/2**
| 126 | A30 | 20p multicolored | .60 | .60 |
| 127 | A30 | 25p multicolored | .90 | .90 |
| 128 | A30 | 50p multicolored | 1.60 | 1.60 |
| 129 | A30 | £1 multicolored | 3.50 | 3.50 |
| | | Nos. 113-129 (17) | 12.20 | 12.20 |

Issued: #113-125, 2/28; #126-129, 10/18.

**Perf. 14 1/2**
| 113a | A28 | 1/2p multicolored | .25 | .20 |
| 114a | A29 | 1p multicolored | .25 | .20 |
| 116a | A29 | 7p multicolored | 9.00 | 7.00 |
| 117a | A28 | 8p multicolored | .40 | .40 |
| 118a | A29 | 9p multicolored | .30 | .30 |
| 119a | A29 | 10p multicolored | .40 | .40 |
| 120a | A28 | 11p multicolored | .45 | .45 |
| 121a | A29 | 12p multicolored | .60 | .60 |
| 122a | A29 | 13p multicolored | .35 | .35 |
| 123a | A29 | 14p multicolored | .35 | .35 |
| 124a | A29 | 15p multicolored | .35 | .35 |
| 125a | A29 | 16p multicolored | 30.00 | 25.00 |
| | | Nos. 113a-125a (12) | 42.70 | 35.60 |

# ISLE OF MAN

404

Elizabeth II — A31

**1978, May 24  Litho.  Perf. 14½x14¼**
130  A31  25p blue & multi  .80  .80
25th anniv. of coronation of Elizabeth II.

Keeil Chiggyrt Stone — A32

Europa (Carved Gravestones): No. 132, Wheel-headed cross slab. No. 133, Celtic Wheel cross. No. 134, Thor cross. No. 135, Olaf Liotulfson cross. No. 136, Odd's and Thorleif's crosses.

**1978, May 24  Perf. 11½**
131  A32  6p multicolored  .20  .20
132  A32  6p multicolored  .20  .20
133  A32  6p multicolored  .20  .20
a.  Strip of 3, #131-133  .50  .50
134  A32  11p multicolored  .35  .35
135  A32  11p multicolored  .35  .35
136  A32  11p multicolored  .35  .35
a.  Strip of 3, #134-136  1.10  1.10
Nos. 131-136 (6)  1.65  1.65
Printed se-tenant in sheets of 9 (3x3).

J. K. Ward, Ward Library, Peel — A33

13p, Lumber camp at Three Rivers & J. K. Ward.

**1978, June 10  Litho.  Perf. 13½**
137  A33  6p multicolored  .20  .20
138  A33  13p multicolored  .35  .35
James K. Ward (1819-1910), Manx pioneer in Canada.

Athletes, Games' Emblem and Manx Arms A34

Eagle, Manx Arms, Maple Leaf A35

**1978, June 10**
139  A34  7p multicolored  .25  .25
140  A35  11p multicolored  .35  .35
11th Commonwealth Games, Edmonton, Aug. 3-12 (7p); North American Manx Soc., 50th anniv. (11p).

"Hunt the Wren" — A36

**1978, Oct. 18  Litho.  Perf. 13**
141  A36  5p multicolored  .35  .25
Christmas 1978.

Philip M. C. Kermode and Nassa Kermodei A37

7p, Peregrine falcons. 11p, Fulmars. 13p, Asilid fly.

**1979, Feb. 27  Litho.  Perf. 14**
142  A37  6p multicolored  .20  .20
143  A37  7p multicolored  .30  .30
144  A37  11p multicolored  .35  .35
145  A37  13p multicolored  .45  .45
Nos. 142-145 (4)  1.30  1.30
Isle of Man Natural History and Antiquarian Society.

Viking Ship — A38          A39

Viking Raid at Garwick A40

Designs (Tynwald Emblem and): 7p, 10th century meeting at Tynwald. 11p, Tynwald Hill and St. John's Church. 13p, Contemporary Tynwald Day parade.

***Perf. 14½x14 (#146-147), 13¼ (#148-151)***

**1979, May 16  Litho.**
146  A38  3p Insularem  .20  .20
a.  Bklt. pane, 4 #146, 2 #147  .60
b.  Insularum ("1980")  .25  .20
c.  Bklt. pane, 4 #146b, 2 #147  1.25
147  A39  4p multicolored  .20  .20
148  A40  6p multicolored  .20  .20
149  A40  7p multicolored  .25  .25
150  A40  11p multicolored  .30  .30
151  A40  13p multicolored  .35  .35
Nos. 146-151 (6)  1.50  1.50
Millennium of Tynwald, Legislative Council. #146-147 printed se-tenant in sheets of 80. No. 146a comes in two arrangements. The Nos. 147 in Nos. 146c and 190a are dated "1980."

19th Century Mailman — A41

Europa: 11p, Contemporary mailman.

**1979, May 16  Perf. 14½**
152  A41  6p multicolored  .20  .20
153  A41  11p multicolored  .40  .40

Ceremony on Tynwald Hill — A42

Design: 13p, Procession from St. John's Church to Tynwald Hill.

**1979, July 5  Litho.  Perf. 14½**
154  A42  7p multicolored  .25  .25
155  A42  13p multicolored  .45  .45
Visit of Queen Elizabeth II for the celebration of millennium of Tynwald.

Girl Holding Teddy Bear — A43

Christmas and IYC: 7p, Children with Santa.

**1979, Oct. 19  Litho.  Perf. 13¼x13½**
156  A43  5p multicolored  .20  .20
157  A43  7p multicolored  .30  .30

Capt. John Quilliam and Spencer A44

Capt. Quilliam: 6p, Seized by press gang. 8p, Battle of Trafalgar. 15p, Castle Rushen.

**1979, Oct. 19  Perf. 14**
158  A44  6p multicolored  .25  .25
159  A44  8p multicolored  .25  .25
160  A44  13p multicolored  .35  .35
161  A44  15p multicolored  .45  .45
Nos. 158-161 (4)  1.30  1.30
Capt. John Quilliam (1771-1829), British naval hero and member of House of Keys.

"Odin's Raven" A45

**1979, Oct. 19  Perf. 14x14½**
162  A45  15p multicolored  .65  .65
Voyage of replica Viking longboat across North Sea (Trondheim to Peel), May 27-July 4. See No. 176a.

Conglomerate Arch, Langness, and Emblem — A46

Royal Geographical Society Emblem and: 8p, Braaid Circle. 12p, Cashtal yn Ard (Neolithic burial ground). 13p, Volcanic rocks, Scarlett. 15p, Sugar-loaf Rock.

**1980, Feb. 5  Litho.  Perf. 14½**
163  A46  7p multicolored  .25  .25
164  A46  8p multicolored  .30  .30
165  A46  12p multicolored  .40  .40
166  A46  13p multicolored  .40  .40
167  A46  15p multicolored  .40  .40
Nos. 163-167 (5)  1.75  1.75
Royal Geographical Society, 150th anniv.

"Mona's Isle I" A47

**1980, May 6  Photo.  Perf. 11½**
**Granite Paper**
168  A47  7p shown  .25  .25
169  A47  8p Douglas I  .25  .25
170  A47  11½p Mona's Queen II, sinking U-boat  .30  .30
171  A47  12p King Orry III  .35  .35
172  A47  13p Ben-My-Chree IV  .40  .40
173  A47  15p Lady of Mann II  .50  .50
a.  Souvenir sheet of 6, #168-173  2.25  2.25
Nos. 168-173 (6)  2.05  2.05
Isle of Man Steam Packet Co. sesqui.; London 80 Intl. Stamp Exhib., May 6-14.

Thomas Edward Brown and Characters from his Poems — A48

Europa (Brown (1830-1897), Poet and Scholar): 13½p, Cricket game, Clifton College Bristol.

**1980, May 6**
174  A48  7p multicolored  .30  .30
175  A48  13½p multicolored  .40  .40

Visit of King Olav V of Norway A49

**1980, June 13  Litho.  Perf. 14½**
176  A49  12p multicolored  .75  .75
a.  Souv. sheet of 2, #162, 176  1.25  1.25
Visit of King Olav V of Norway, Aug. 2-7, 1979, and NORWEX 80 stamp exhibition, Oslo, June 13-22.

William Kermode and "Robert Quayle" A50

Kermode Family (First Manx Pioneers in Tasmania): 9p, First homestead, Mona Vale, Merino sheep, 1834. 13½p, Ross Bridge, W. Kermode. 15p, Calendar House, 1868. 17½p, Parliament Buildings, Hobart, Robert Quayle Kermode.

**1980, Sept. 29  Litho.**
177  A50  7p multicolored  .25  .25
178  A50  9p multicolored  .30  .30
179  A50  13½p multicolored  .45  .45
180  A50  15p multicolored  .50  .50
181  A50  17½p multicolored  .55  .55
Nos. 177-181 (5)  2.05  2.05

Wren A51

**1980, Sept. 29  Litho.  Perf. 13½x14**
182  A51  6p shown  .20  .20
183  A51  8p Robin  .20  .20
Wildlife conservation and Christmas 1980.

Luggers, Red Pier, Douglas A52

**1981, Feb. 24     Litho.     Perf. 14**

| | | | | |
|---|---|---|---|---|
| 184 | A52 | 8p shown | .25 | .25 |
| 185 | A52 | 9p Wanderer saving Lusitania Survivors | .25 | .25 |
| 186 | A52 | 18p Nickey, Port St. Mary | .50 | .50 |
| 187 | A52 | 20p Nobby, Ramsey Harbor | .60 | .60 |
| 188 | A52 | 22p Sunbeam and Zebra, Port Erin | .65 | .65 |
| | | Nos. 184-188 (5) | 2.25 | 2.25 |

Royal National Mission to Deep Sea Fishermen centenary.

Peregrine Falcon — A53

**1980, Sept. 29     Litho.     Perf. 14½x14**
**Booklet Stamps**

| | | | | |
|---|---|---|---|---|
| 189 | A53 | 1p shown | .35 | .35 |
| 190 | A53 | 5p Loaghtyn ram | .35 | .35 |
| a. | | Bklt. pane, 2 each #147, 189, 190 | 1.25 | |

Crosh Cuirn (Cross of Mountain Ash Twigs, Harvest Charm) — A54

Europa: 18p, Bollan fish cross-bone (fishermen's charm).

**1981, May 22     Litho.     Perf. 14½**

| | | | | |
|---|---|---|---|---|
| 191 | A54 | 8p multicolored | .25 | .25 |
| 192 | A54 | 18p multicolored | .65 | .65 |

Col. Mark Wilks, Peel Castle A55

**1981, May 22     Perf. 14**

| | | | | |
|---|---|---|---|---|
| 193 | A55 | 8p shown | .30 | .30 |
| 194 | A55 | 20p Wilks, Fort. St. George, Madras | .50 | .50 |
| 195 | A55 | 22p Wilks, Napoleon | .65 | .65 |
| 196 | A55 | 25p Wilks at Kirby estate | .75 | .75 |
| | | Nos. 193-196 (4) | 2.20 | 2.20 |

Wilks (d. 1831), governor of St. Helena.

Suffragettes Emmeline Goulden Pankhurst and Sophia Jane Goulden — A56

**1981, May 22     Perf. 14**

| | | | | |
|---|---|---|---|---|
| 197 | A56 | 9p multicolored | .40 | .40 |

Centenary of women's suffrage and of House of Keys Election Act (granting widows and unmarried women voting rights).

Prince Charles and Lady Diana A57

**1981, July 29     Litho.     Perf. 14**

| | | | | |
|---|---|---|---|---|
| 198 | A57 | 9p multicolored | .25 | .25 |
| 199 | A57 | 25p multicolored | 1.00 | 1.00 |
| a. | | Souv. sheet, 2 each #198-199 | 2.75 | 2.75 |

Royal Wedding.

Queen Elizabeth II — A58

**1981, Sept. 29     Photo.     Perf. 11½**
**Granite paper**

| | | | | |
|---|---|---|---|---|
| 200 | A58 | £2 multicolored | 6.00 | 6.00 |

Douglas War Memorial, Poppies, Quote from Laurence Binyon's For the Fallen — A59

**1981, Sept. 29**
**Granite Paper**

| | | | | |
|---|---|---|---|---|
| 201 | A59 | 8p shown | .25 | .25 |
| 202 | A59 | 10p Maj. R.H. Cain, Battle of Arnhem, 1944 | .30 | .30 |
| 203 | A59 | 18p Festival of Remembrance | .60 | .60 |
| 204 | A59 | 20p Tynwald and Spitfire, Dunkirk, 1940 | .70 | .70 |
| | | Nos. 201-204 (4) | 1.85 | 1.85 |

Royal British Legion, 60th anniv.

Nativity Stained-glass Window, 1865, St. George's Church, Douglas — A60

9p: Christmas pageant, Glencrutchery Special School, Douglas.

**1981, Sept. 29     Litho.     Perf. 14½x14**

| | | | | |
|---|---|---|---|---|
| 205 | A60 | 7p multicolored | .25 | .25 |

**Size: 47x28mm**

| | | | | |
|---|---|---|---|---|
| 206 | A60 | 9p multicolored | .35 | .35 |

Christmas and St. George's Church bicen. (7p), IYD (9p).

Scouting Year — A61

Designs: 9p, Cunningham House (Man Scout Headquarters). 10p, Baden-Powell's

visit, 1911. 19½p, Portrait (32x41mm., Perf. 14½). 24p, Baden-Powell with scouts, message. 29p, Sign, handshake, globe, emblem.

**1982, Feb. 23     Litho.     Perf. 13½x14**

| | | | | |
|---|---|---|---|---|
| 207 | A61 | 9p multicolored | .25 | .25 |
| 208 | A61 | 10p multicolored | .25 | .25 |
| 209 | A61 | 19½p multicolored | .65 | .65 |
| 210 | A61 | 24p multicolored | .80 | .80 |
| 211 | A61 | 29p multicolored | 1.00 | 1.00 |
| | | Nos. 207-211 (5) | 2.95 | 2.95 |

Europa 1982 — A62

Designs: 9p, Bishop Thomas Wilson (1663-1755) and his "The Principles and Duties of Christianity," first book printed in Manx, 1707. 19½p, Visit of Thomas, 2nd Earl of Derby, 1507.

**1982, June 1     Photo.     Perf. 12½**
**Granite Paper**

| | | | | |
|---|---|---|---|---|
| 212 | A62 | 9p multicolored | .30 | .30 |
| 213 | A62 | 19½p multicolored | .60 | .60 |

75th Anniv. of Tourist Trophy Motorcycle Races — A63

Designs: Winners on their bikes.

**1982, June 1     Litho.     Perf. 14**

| | | | | |
|---|---|---|---|---|
| 214 | A63 | 9p Charlie Collier, 431 Matchless, 1907 | .25 | .25 |
| 215 | A63 | 10p Freddie Dixon, Douglas, 1923 | .25 | .25 |
| 216 | A63 | 24p Jimmie Simpson, Norton, 1932 | .90 | .90 |
| 217 | A63 | 26p Mike Hailwood, Norton, 1961 | .90 | .90 |
| 218 | A63 | 29p Jock Taylor, 700 Fowler Yamaha, '80 | .90 | .90 |
| | | Nos. 214-218 (5) | 3.20 | 3.20 |

Isle of Man Steam Packet Co. Mail Contract Sesquicentennial — A64

**1982, Oct. 5     Litho.     Perf. 13½x14**

| | | | | |
|---|---|---|---|---|
| 219 | A64 | 12p Mona I | .55 | .55 |
| 220 | A64 | 19½p Manx Maid II | .80 | .80 |

Christmas 1982 A65

**Perf. 13¼x13½, 13½x13¼**
**1982, Oct. 5**

| | | | | |
|---|---|---|---|---|
| 221 | A65 | 8p Three Kings | .30 | .30 |
| 222 | A65 | 11p Robin, Christmas tree, vert. | .55 | .55 |

Souvenir Sheet

Princess Diana and Prince William — A66

**1982, Oct. 12     Perf. 14½x14¼**

| | | | | |
|---|---|---|---|---|
| 223 | A66 | 50p multicolored | 2.75 | 2.75 |

Birth of Prince William of Wales (June 21) and 21st birthday of Princess Diana (July 1).

Marine Birds A67

**1983, Feb. 15     Litho.     Perf. 14½**

| | | | | |
|---|---|---|---|---|
| 224 | A67 | 1p Puffins, Cranstal | .20 | .20 |
| 225 | A67 | 2p Gannets, Point of Ayre | .20 | .20 |
| 226 | A67 | 5p Lesser black-backed gulls, Santon | .20 | .20 |
| 227 | A67 | 8p Cormorants, Maughold Head | .35 | .35 |
| 228 | A67 | 10p Kittiwakes, White Strand | .45 | .45 |
| 229 | A67 | 11p Shags, Calf of Man | .50 | .50 |
| 230 | A67 | 12p Herons, Douglas Foreshore | .55 | .55 |
| 231 | A67 | 13p Herring gulls, Peel | .60 | .60 |
| 232 | A67 | 14p Razorbills, Calf of Man | .60 | .60 |
| 233 | A67 | 15p Great black-backed gulls, Calf of Man | .70 | .70 |
| 234 | A67 | 16p Shelducks, Poyll Vaaish | .75 | .75 |
| 235 | A67 | 18p Oystercatchers, Langness | .80 | .80 |

**1983, Sept. 14     Perf. 14**
**Size: 39x25mm**

| | | | | |
|---|---|---|---|---|
| 236 | A67 | 20p Arctic terns, Blue Point | .90 | .90 |
| 237 | A67 | 25p Guillemots, Calf of Man | 1.10 | 1.10 |
| 238 | A67 | 50p Redshanks, Langness | 2.00 | 2.00 |
| 239 | A67 | £1 Mute swans, Port St. Mary Bay | 4.00 | 4.00 |
| | | Nos. 224-239 (16) | 13.90 | 13.90 |

Centenary of Salvation Army in Isle of Man — A68

Designs: 10p, Citadel opening ceremony, 1932, T.H. Cannell. 12p, Founder William Booth, early meeting place (former Unitarian Church, Douglas). 19½p, Band, Bandmaster Gordon Cowley, 1981. 26p, Lt.-Col. Thomas Bridson, treating lepers in Dutch East Indies.

**1983, Feb. 15     Photo.     Perf. 11½**
**Granite Paper**

| | | | | |
|---|---|---|---|---|
| 240 | A68 | 10p multicolored | .35 | .35 |
| 241 | A68 | 12p multicolored | .45 | .45 |
| 242 | A68 | 19½p multicolored | .75 | .75 |
| 243 | A68 | 26p multicolored | .95 | .95 |
| | | Nos. 240-243 (4) | 2.50 | 2.50 |

Europa 1983 — A69

**1983, May 18**     *Perf. 14*
244 A69 10p Laxey Wheel   .45   .45
245 A69 20½p Designer Robert
     Casement   .80   .80

King William's College
Sesquicentennial — A70

Graduates: 10p, Nick Keig, Yachtsman. 12p, College, arms. 28p, William Bragg, 1915 Nobel Prize winner in physics, ionization spectrometer. 31p, Gen. George Stuart White, Defense of Ladysmith, Boer War.

**1983, May 18**   **Photo.**   *Perf. 11½*
**Granite Paper**
246 A70 10p multicolored   .30   .30
247 A70 12p multicolored   .40   .40
248 A70 28p multicolored   1.10   1.10
249 A70 31p multicolored   1.25   1.25
    *Nos. 246-249 (4)*   3.05   3.05

World Communications Year and 10th
Anniv. of Post Office — A71

**1983, July 5**   **Litho.**   *Perf. 15*
250 A71 10p New P.O. Head-
     quarters   .45   .45
251 A6 15p Viking landing, 938   .75   .75
    Compare No. 251 with No. 28.

Christmas
1983
A72

**1983, Sept. 14**   **Litho.**   *Perf. 13x13½*
252 A72 9p Shepherds   .40   .40
253 A72 12p Three Kings   .50   .50

Karran
Fleet
A73

Links with Falkland Islands — A74

**1984, Feb. 14**   **Litho.**   *Perf. 14*
254 A73 10p Manx King, 1884   .30   .30
255 A73 13p Hope, 1858   .45   .45
256 A73 20½p Rio Grande, 1868   .65   .65
257 A73 28p Lady Elizabeth,
     1879   1.10   1.10
258 A73 31p Sumatra, 1858   1.25   1.25
    *Nos. 254-258 (5)*   3.75   3.75

---

**1984, Feb. 14**
259   Sheet of 2, #257, 259a   3.50   3.50
  a. A74 31p multicolored   1.50   1.50

Europa
(1959-1984)
A75

**1984, Apr. 27**   **Photo.**   *Perf. 11½*
260 A75 10p dk yel org, dk brn
     & buff   .40   .40
261 A75 20½p blue, dk bl & lt bl   .75   .75

DH-48, Ronaldsway Airport — A76

**1984, Apr. 27**   **Litho.**   *Perf. 14*
262 A76 11p shown   .50   .50
263 A76 13p DH-86, Calf of Man   .55   .55
264 A76 26p DC-3, Ronaldsway
     Airport   1.00   1.00
265 A76 28p Vickers Viscount,
     Douglas   1.00   1.00
266 A76 31p Islander, Ronald-
     sway Airport   1.00   1.00
    *Nos. 262-266 (5)*   4.05   4.05
50th Anniv. of official airmail service and 40th anniv. of Intl. Civil Aviation Org.

William Cain as Mayor of Melbourne,
1886-87 — A77

**1984, Sept. 21**   **Litho.**   *Perf. 14½*
267 A77 11p Ballasalla (birth-
     place)   .45   .45
268 A77 22p Voyage to Australia   .80   .80
269 A77 28p Railway, Victoria   1.00   1.00
270 A77 30p shown   1.10   1.10
271 A77 33p Royal Exhibition
     Buildings, Mel-
     bourne   1.10   1.10
    *Nos. 267-271 (5)*   4.45   4.45
William Cain (1831-1914), building contractor and public servant in Australia.

Queen
Elizabeth
II, CPA
Emblem
A78

**1984, Sept. 21**   *Perf. 14*
272 A78 14p shown   .50   .50
273 A78 33p Arms, Elizabeth II   1.25   1.25
30th Conference of Commonwealth Parliamentary Assoc., Sept. 28-Oct. 5.

Christmas — A79

Stained-glass windows.

---

**1984, Sept. 21**
274 A79 10p Birds, Glencrutch-
     ery House   .50   .50
275 A79 13p Arms, Lonan Old
     Church   .60   .60

75th Anniv. of Girl Guides — A80

Designs: 11p, Cunningham House (headquarters), Mrs. W. and J. Cunningham (early Island Commissioners). 14p, Princess Margaret (president), color guard. 29p, Lady Olave Baden-Powell, headquarters opening. 31p, Uniforms, 1910-85. 34p, Sign, handclasp, trefoil.

**1985, Jan. 31**   **Photo.**   *Perf. 12*
276 A80 11p multicolored   .45   .45
277 A80 14p multicolored   .55   .55
278 A80 29p multicolored   1.10   1.10
279 A80 31p multicolored   1.25   1.25
280 A80 34p multicolored   1.40   1.40
    *Nos. 276-280 (5)*   4.75   4.75

Elizabeth II
A81

**1985, Jan. 31**   **Litho.**   *Perf. 14*
281 A81 £5 multicolored   15.00   15.00

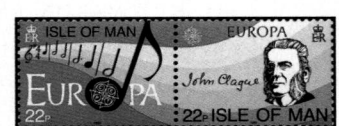

Europa 1985 — A82

Manx composers and excerpts from their works: No. 282a, "O'Land of our Birth." No. 282b, William H. Gill (1839-1922). No. 283a, Hymn "Crofton;" No. 283b, Dr. John Clague (1842-1908).

**1985, Apr. 24**   **Photo.**   *Perf. 12*
282 A82 Pair   1.25   1.25
  a.-b.   12p any single   .65   .65
283 A82 Pair   1.50   1.50
  a.-b.   22p any single   .75   .75

Motoring — A83

Motor races and winning vehicles: No. 284a, 1906 Tourist Trophy Race. No. 284b, 1922 Tourist Trophy Race. No. 285a, 1950 British Empire Trophy Race. No. 285b, 1934 Manin Moar Race. No. 286a, 1984 Tourist Trophy Motorcycle Race (official car). No. 286b, 1981 Rothmans Manx Intl. Rally.

**1985, May 25**   **Litho.**   *Perf. 14*
284 A83 Pair   .90   .90
  a.-b.   12p any single   .45   .45
285 A83 Pair   1.25   1.25
  a.-b.   14p any single   .60   .60
286 A83 Pair   2.50   2.50
  a.-b.   31p any single   1.25   1.25
    *Nos. 284-286 (3)*   4.65   4.65

---

H.R.H. Alexandra (1885-1925),
Princess of Wales — A84

SSA presidents: 15p, Queen Mary (1925-1953). 29p, Earl Mountbatten of Burma (1953-1979). 34p, Prince Michael of Kent (1982- ).

**1985, Sept. 4**   **Litho.**   *Perf. 14*
287 A84 12p multicolored   .45   .45
288 A84 15p multicolored   .60   .60
289 A84 29p multicolored   1.10   1.10
290 A84 34p multicolored   1.40   1.40
    *Nos. 287-290 (4)*   3.55   3.55
Soldier's, Sailors' & Airmen's Families Assoc., cent.

Lt.-Gen. Sir Mark Cubbon, K.C.B.
(1785-1861), Commissioner of
Mysore — A85

**1985, Oct. 2**   **Litho.**   *Perf. 14*
291 A85 12p Kirk Maughold Par-
     ish Church, 14th
     century   .50   .50
292 A85 22p Portrait, vert.   .90   .90
293 A85 45p Equestrian monu-
     ment, 1866 Ban-
     galore, India, vert.   1.75   1.75
    *Nos. 291-293 (3)*   3.15   3.15

Christmas
1985
A86

**1985, Oct. 2**   **Litho.**   *Perf. 13½*
294 A86 11p Onchan Parish
     Church, 1833   .40   .40
295 A86 14p St. John's Church   .65   .65
296 A86 31p Bride Parish
     Church, 1876   1.50   1.50
    *Nos. 294-296 (3)*   2.55   2.55

1986 Commonwealth Games,
Edinburgh — A87

**1986, Feb. 5**   **Litho.**   *Perf. 14*
297 A87 12p Women's swimming   .50   .50
298 A87 15p Walking   .65   .65
299 A87 31p Rifle shooting   1.10   1.10
300 A87 34p Bicycling   1.50   1.50
    *Nos. 297-300 (4)*   3.75   3.75

Viking
Necklace,
Peel
Castle
A88

Artifacts, architecture: 15p, Meayll Circle burial ground, Rushen. 22p, Prehistoric Cervus giganteus skeleton, Glose-y-Garey, vert. 26p, Norwegian viking longship, vert. 29p, Open-air Museum, Cregneash.

**1986, Feb. 5**   *Perf. 14½x14, 14x14½*
301 A88 12p multicolored   .50   .50
302 A88 15p multicolored   .60   .60
303 A88 22p multicolored   .90   .90

| 304 | A88 | 26p multicolored | 1.00 | 1.00 |
| 305 | A88 | 29p multicolored | 1.25 | 1.25 |
| | | Nos. 301-305 (5) | 4.25 | 4.25 |

Centenaries of Manx Museum and Ancient Monuments Act.

Europa 1986, Manx National Trust — A89

Designs: No. 306a, Bride hills and the Ayres. No. 306b, Calf of Man. No. 307a, Eary Cushlin. No. 307b, St. Michael's Isle.

**1986, Apr. 10**    **Litho.**    **Perf. 12**
| 306 | A89 | Pair | 1.00 | 1.00 |
| a.-b. | | 12p any single | .50 | .50 |
| 307 | A89 | Pair | 2.00 | 2.00 |
| a.-b. | | 22p any single | 1.00 | 1.00 |

Settling of Plymouth — A90

Designs: 12p, Ellanbane, Isle of Man, Myles Standish's home. 15p, The Mayflower. 31p, Pilgrims landing, 1620. 34p, Capt. Myles Standish (c. 1584-1656).

**1986, May 22**    **Perf. 13½**
| 308 | A90 | 12p multicolored | .50 | .50 |
| 309 | A90 | 15p multicolored | .60 | .60 |
| 310 | A90 | 31p multicolored | 1.25 | 1.25 |
| 311 | A90 | 34p multicolored | 1.40 | 1.40 |
| a. | | Souvenir sheet of 2, #310-311, perf. 13x12½ | 3.00 | 3.00 |
| | | Nos. 308-311 (4) | 3.75 | 3.75 |

AMERIPEX '86, Chicago, May 22-June 1.

Heritage Year — A91

**1986, Apr. 10**    **Litho.**    **Perf. 15x14**
| 312 | A91 | 2p Viking longship bow | .20 | .20 |
| a. | | Bklt. pane of 6, 2 #312, 4 #313 | 4.50 | |
| 313 | A91 | 10p Celtic cross | .90 | .90 |
| a. | | Bklt. pane of 3 + 3 labels | 2.75 | |

Issued in booklets only.

Wedding of Prince Andrew and Sarah Ferguson A92

**1986, July 23**
| 314 | A92 | 15p Wedding date | .80 | .80 |
| 315 | A92 | 40p Engagement date | 1.75 | 1.75 |

Royal Birthdays — A93

No. 316: a, Prince Philip, 65. #b, Elizabeth II, 60. No. 317 is the same size as No. 316.

**1986, Aug. 28**    **Perf. 11½**
| 316 | A93 | Pair | 1.40 | 1.40 |
| a.-b. | | 15p any single | .70 | .70 |
| 317 | A93 | 34p Royal couple | 1.40 | 1.40 |

STOCKHOLMIA '86, Swedish Post Office 350th anniv. Stamps issued in sheets of 6.

Intl. Peace Year — A94

**1986, Sept. 25**    **Litho.**    **Perf. 14**
| 318 | A94 | 11p Robins, globe, Braille | .45 | .45 |
| 319 | A94 | 14p Hands, dove | .55 | .55 |
| 320 | A94 | 31p Hand-holding, sign language | 1.25 | 1.25 |
| | | Nos. 318-320 (3) | 2.25 | 2.25 |

Accession of Queen Victoria to the British Throne, 150th Anniv. A95

Photographs of Victorian Douglas, by John Miller Nicholson.

**1987, Jan. 21**    **Litho.**    **Perf. 14½**
| 321 | A95 | 2p North Quay | .20 | .20 |
| 322 | A95 | 3p The Old Fish Market | .20 | .20 |
| 323 | A95 | 10p Breakwater | .40 | .40 |
| a. | | Bklt. pane of 8 (2 2p, 2 3p, 4 10p) ('87) | 2.10 | |
| | | Complete booklet, #323a | 2.10 | |
| 324 | A95 | 15p Jubilee Clock | .60 | .60 |
| a. | | Bklt. pane of 8 (2 2p, 2 3p, 2 10p, 2 15p) ('87) | 2.40 | |
| | | Complete booklet, #323a, #324a | 4.50 | |
| 325 | A95 | 31p Loch Promenade | 1.40 | 1.40 |
| 326 | A95 | 34p Beach | 1.50 | 1.50 |
| | | Nos. 321-326 (6) | 4.30 | 4.30 |

No. 323a comes in two arrangements.

19th Century Paintings by John Miller Nicholson (1840-1913) — A96

Harbor scenes: 12p, The Old Fish Market and Harbor, Douglas. 26p, Red Sails at Douglas. 29p, The Double Corner. 34p, Peel Harbor.

**1987, Feb. 18**    **Perf. 13½**
| 327 | A96 | 12p multicolored | .50 | .50 |
| 328 | A96 | 26p multicolored | 1.00 | 1.00 |
| 329 | A96 | 29p multicolored | 1.10 | 1.10 |
| 330 | A96 | 34p multicolored | 1.40 | 1.40 |
| | | Nos. 327-330 (4) | 4.00 | 4.00 |

Promenade, Douglas — A97

**1987, Apr. 29**    **Litho.**    **Perf. 13½**
| 331 | A97 | 12p Sea Terminal, 1965 | .65 | .65 |
| 332 | A97 | 12p Tower of Refuge, 1832 | .65 | .65 |
| a. | | Pair, #331-332 | 1.25 | 1.25 |
| 333 | A97 | 22p Gaiety Theater, c. 1900 | 1.00 | 1.00 |
| 334 | A97 | 22p Villa Marina | 1.00 | 1.00 |
| a. | | Pair, #333-334 | 2.00 | 2.00 |
| | | Nos. 331-334 (4) | 3.30 | 3.30 |

Europa 1987.

Tourist Trophy Motorcycle Races, 80th Anniv. — A98

**1987, May 27**    **Perf. 13½x13**
| 335 | A98 | 12p 1939 Supercharged BMW 500CC | .45 | .45 |
| 336 | A98 | 15p 1953 Manx "Kneeler" Norton 350CC | .60 | .60 |
| 337 | A98 | 29p 1956 MV Agusta 500CC 4 | 1.10 | 1.10 |
| 338 | A98 | 31p 1957 Guzzi 500CC V8 | 1.25 | 1.25 |
| 339 | A98 | 34p 1967 Honda 250CC 6 | 1.40 | 1.40 |
| a. | | Souv. sheet of 5, #335-339 + 7 labels, perf 14x13½ | 5.00 | 5.00 |
| | | Nos. 335-339 (5) | 4.80 | 4.80 |

Wildflowers — A99

**1987, Sept. 9**    **Litho.**    **Perf. 14½x13½**
| 340 | A99 | 16p Fuchsia, wild roses | .60 | .60 |
| 341 | A99 | 29p Field scabius, ragwort | 1.10 | 1.10 |
| 342 | A99 | 31p Wood anemone, celandine | 1.25 | 1.25 |
| 343 | A99 | 34p Violets, primroses | 1.40 | 1.40 |
| | | Nos. 340-343 (4) | 4.35 | 4.35 |

Christmas — A100

Victorian family scenes based on drawings by Alfred Hunt for The Illustrated London News, c. 1870-1890.

**1987, Oct. 16**    **Perf. 14**
| 344 | A100 | 12p Stirring the pudding | .50 | .50 |
| 345 | A100 | 15p Christmas tree selection | .60 | .60 |
| 346 | A100 | 31p Decorating tree | 1.40 | 1.40 |
| | | Nos. 344-346 (3) | 2.50 | 2.50 |

Railways & Tramways A101

Designs: 1p, Horse-drawn "Toast Rack" tram, Douglas Bay, 1884. 2p, No. 5 electric tram, Snaefell Mountain Railway, 1895. 3p, No. 3 open-top double-deck electric tram, Marine Drive-Port Soderick line, Douglas Southern Electric Tramway, 1896. 5p, Tower of Refuge and open tram, Douglas Head Incline Railway. 10p, Electric tram at Maughold Head, 1893, Douglas and Laxey Coast Electric Tramway. 13p, Douglas Cable Car No. 72, 1896. 14p, Manx Northern Railway No. 4 Caledonia, a Dubs 0-6-0T, 1885, at Gob-y-Deigan. 15p, Great Laxey Mine Railway Lewin steam engine Ant pulling coal cars. 16p, Henry B. Loch, first locomotive on the island, Port Erin Breakwater Railway, 1864. 17p, Locomotive No. 1, Ramsey Harbor Tramway. 18p, Engine No. 7 Tynwald, 1880, Foxdale Railway. 19p, Douglas Corp. engine, Baldwin Reservoir Railway. 20p, "Kissack" leaving St. John's for Peel. 25p, "Hutchinson" leaving Douglas Station. 50p, "Polar Bear" of Groudle Glen Railway. £1, The Royal Train.

**1988**    **Litho.**    **Perf. 13½**
| 347 | A101 | 1p multicolored | .20 | .20 |
| 348 | A101 | 2p multicolored | .20 | .20 |
| 349 | A101 | 3p multicolored | .20 | .20 |
| 350 | A101 | 5p multicolored | .20 | .20 |
| 351 | A101 | 10p multicolored | .40 | .40 |
| 352 | A101 | 13p multicolored | .50 | .50 |
| 353 | A101 | 14p multicolored | .55 | .55 |
| 354 | A101 | 15p multicolored | .60 | .60 |
| 355 | A101 | 16p multicolored | .65 | .65 |
| a. | | Bklt. pane, 2 3p, 13p, 2 16p | 2.25 | |
| b. | | Bklt. pane, 4 13p, 6 16p | 6.00 | |
| 356 | A101 | 17p multicolored | .70 | .70 |
| a. | | Bklt. pane, 2 3p, 2 14p, 17p | 2.25 | |
| b. | | Booklet pane, 4 14p, 6 17p | 6.50 | |
| 357 | A101 | 18p multicolored | .70 | .70 |
| 358 | A101 | 19p multicolored | .75 | .75 |
| e. | | Bklt. pane, 4 15p, 6 19p | 7.00 | |
| f. | | Bklt. pane, 2 15p, 2 19p | 2.10 | |

   **Perf. 15**
| 358A | A101 | 20p multicolored | .80 | .80 |
| 358B | A101 | 25p multicolored | 1.00 | 1.00 |
| 358C | A101 | 50p multicolored | 2.00 | 2.00 |
| 358D | A101 | £1 multicolored | 4.00 | 4.00 |
| | | Nos. 347-358D (16) | 13.45 | 13.45 |

Stamps in Nos. 356a, 356b inscribed 1989, No. 358e inscribed 1990. Nos. 358C-358D exist inscribed "1992;" Nos. 349, 353, 356 "1989;" No. 356 "1991."

Nos. 356a and 356b also exist in special booklet sheets of 50 stamps containing either 10 #356a or 5 #356b.

Issued: 1p-19p, 2/10; #355a-355b, 3/16; 20p-£1, 9/21; #356a, 356b, 10/16/89; #358e, 2/14/90.

See Nos. 448-459.

Car Racing — A102

Winning automobiles, drivers: 13p, Vauxhall Opel, Russell Brookes, 1985. 26p, Ford Escort, Ari Vatanen of Finland, 1976. 31p, Repco March 761, Terry Smith, 1980. 34p, Williams/Honda Nigel Mansell, 1986-87.

**1988, Feb. 10**    **Perf. 13½x14½**
| 359 | A102 | 13p multicolored | .60 | .60 |
| 360 | A102 | 26p multicolored | 1.25 | 1.25 |
| 361 | A102 | 31p multicolored | 1.40 | 1.40 |
| 362 | A102 | 34p multicolored | 1.50 | 1.50 |
| | | Nos. 359-362 (4) | 4.75 | 4.75 |

Europa 1988 A103

Telecommunications: No. 363, IOM-UK optical fiber cable-laying plow. No. 364, Cable-laying ship. No. 365, 1st IOM Earth station, Braddan, established by Manx Telecom. No. 366, Intelsat V satellite.

**1988, Apr. 14**    **Litho.**    **Perf. 14x13½**
| 363 | A103 | 13p multicolored | .60 | .60 |
| 364 | A103 | 13p multicolored | .60 | .60 |
| a. | | Pair, #363-364 | 1.25 | 1.25 |
| 365 | A103 | 22p multicolored | 1.00 | 1.00 |
| 366 | A103 | 22p multicolored | 1.00 | 1.00 |
| a. | | Pair, #365-366 | 2.00 | 2.00 |
| | | Nos. 363-366 (4) | 3.20 | 3.20 |

Submarine cable linking the Isle of Man and Silecroft in Cumbria, 1987 (13p). Nos. 364a, 366a have continuous designs.

Historic Ships Built on the Isle A104

Isle of Man flag, Australia bicen. emblem or US flag and: 16p, Euterpe, 1863, built in Ramsey. 29p, Vixen leaving Peel for Australia, 1853. 31p, Ramsey, an immigrant ship in Brisbane, 1870. 34p, Star of India (renamed in 1906, was the Euterpe), restored 1960-1976, Maritime Museum at San Diego.

**1988, May 11**    **Litho.**    **Perf. 14**
| 367 | A104 | 16p multicolored | .60 | .60 |
| 368 | A104 | 29p multicolored | 1.10 | 1.10 |
| 369 | A104 | 31p multicolored | 1.10 | 1.10 |

| | | | |
|---|---|---|---|
| 370 | A104 34p multicolored | 1.25 | 1.25 |
| a. | Souvenir sheet of 2 (16p, 34p) | 2.75 | 2.75 |
| | Nos. 367-370 (4) | 4.05 | 4.05 |

Fuchsia Blossoms — A105

**1988, Sept. 21    Litho.    Perf. 13½x14**

| | | | |
|---|---|---|---|
| 371 | A105 13p Magellanica | .45 | .45 |
| 372 | A105 16p Pink cloud | .55 | .55 |
| 373 | A105 22p Leonora | .80 | .80 |
| 374 | A105 29p Satellite | 1.10 | 1.10 |
| 375 | A105 31p Preston Guild | 1.25 | 1.25 |
| 376 | A105 34p Thalia | 1.40 | 1.40 |
| | Nos. 371-376 (6) | 5.55 | 5.55 |

British Fuchsia Society, 50th anniv.

Christmas A106

**1988, Oct. 12    Perf. 14**

| | | | |
|---|---|---|---|
| 377 | A106 12p Long-eared owl | .75 | .75 |
| 378 | A106 15p Robin | .90 | .90 |
| 379 | A106 31p Partridge | 1.75 | 1.75 |
| | Nos. 377-379 (3) | 3.40 | 3.40 |

Manx Cats A107

Designs: 16p, Ginger. 27p, Black and white. 30p, Tortoiseshell and white. 40p, Tortoiseshell.

**1989, Feb. 8**

| | | | |
|---|---|---|---|
| 380 | A107 16p multicolored | .65 | .65 |
| 381 | A107 27p multicolored | 1.10 | 1.10 |
| 382 | A107 30p multicolored | 1.40 | 1.40 |
| 383 | A107 40p multicolored | 1.60 | 1.60 |
| | Nos. 380-383 (4) | 4.75 | 4.75 |

Celtic Works of Art by Archibald Knox (1864-1933) — A108

Designs: 13p, Tudric pewter and enamel clock, 1903, vert. 16p, Cross, a watercolor, vert. 23p, Silver tankard, 1902, vert. 32p, Liberty silver and Cymric gold brooches. 35p, Silver jewel box with inlaid turquoise, mother-of-pearl and enamel, 1900.

**1989, Feb. 8    Litho.    Perf. 13**

| | | | |
|---|---|---|---|
| 384 | A108 13p multicolored | .50 | .50 |
| 385 | A108 16p multicolored | .60 | .60 |
| 386 | A108 23p multicolored | .85 | .85 |
| 387 | A108 32p multicolored | 1.10 | 1.10 |
| 388 | A108 35p multicolored | 1.25 | 1.25 |
| | Nos. 384-388 (5) | 4.30 | 4.30 |

Mutiny on the Bounty A109

Designs: 13p, William Bligh, Old Onchan Church. 16p, Bligh and crewmen cast adrift. 30p, Peter Heywood on Tahiti, 1770. 32p, Bounty off Pitcairn. 35p, Fletcher Christian on Pitcairn.

**1989, Apr. 28    Litho.    Perf. 14**

| | | | |
|---|---|---|---|
| 389 | A109 13p multicolored | .45 | .45 |
| 390 | A109 16p multicolored | .60 | .60 |
| 391 | A109 30p multicolored | 1.00 | 1.00 |
| 392 | A109 32p multicolored | 1.10 | 1.10 |
| 393 | A109 35p multicolored | 1.25 | 1.25 |
| | Nos. 389-393 (5) | 4.40 | 4.40 |

**Souvenir Sheet**

| | | | |
|---|---|---|---|
| 394 | Sheet of 3 + label | 4.50 | 4.50 |
| a. | A109 23p Pitcairn Isls. No. 321d | .80 | .80 |
| b. | A109 27p Norfolk Is. No. 453 | .95 | .95 |
| c. | Booklet pane, #394 | 4.50 | |
| d. | Booklet pane, 1 each #389-393, 394a | | 5.50 |
| e. | Bklt. pane of 6, #389-393, 394a | | 5.50 |
| f. | Booklet pane, 3 each #394a, #394b | | 5.25 |
| | Complete booklet, #394c, 394d, 394e, 394f | | 22.00 |

See Norfolk Is. Nos. 452-456 and Pitcairn Isls. Nos. 320-322.
No. 394 contains Nos. 393, 394a-394b.
No. 394c is 145x101mm and is rouletted at left.

Europa 1989 A110

Children's games: No. 395, Jumping rope, hopscotch, London Bridge is falling down. No. 396, Running, wheelbarrow race, leap frog, piggyback ride. No. 397, Boy building fort, girl blowing soap bubbles, puzzle. No. 398, Doll house, blocks, girl playing with rag doll and puzzle.

**1989, May 17    Perf. 13½**

| | | | |
|---|---|---|---|
| 395 | A110 13p multicolored | .50 | .50 |
| 396 | A110 13p multicolored | .50 | .50 |
| a. | Pair, #395-396 | 1.00 | 1.00 |
| 397 | A110 23p multicolored | 1.00 | 1.00 |
| 398 | A110 23p multicolored | 1.00 | 1.00 |
| a. | Pair, #397-398 | 2.00 | 2.00 |
| | Nos. 395-398 (4) | 3.00 | 3.00 |

Nos. 396a, 398a have continuous designs.

World Wildlife Fund — A111

**1989, Sept. 20    Litho.    Perf. 14**

| | | | |
|---|---|---|---|
| 399 | A111 13p Puffin | 1.50 | 1.50 |
| 400 | A111 13p Black guillemot | 1.50 | 1.50 |
| 401 | A111 13p Cormorant | 1.50 | 1.50 |
| 402 | A111 13p Kittiwake | 1.50 | 1.50 |
| a. | Block or strip of 4, #399-402 | 7.50 | 7.50 |
| | Nos. 399-402 (4) | 6.00 | 6.00 |

Exists as sheetlet of 16 with "World Stamp Expo '89" printed in selvage.

Intl. Red Cross, 125th Anniv. A112

**1989, Oct. 16    Litho.    Perf. 14**

| | | | |
|---|---|---|---|
| 403 | A112 14p Training youths | .55 | .55 |
| 404 | A112 17p Emblems | .65 | .65 |
| 405 | A112 23p Signing 1st Geneva convention, 1864 | .90 | .90 |
| 406 | A112 30p Ambulance services | 1.25 | 1.25 |
| 407 | A112 35p Henri Dunant, founder | 1.40 | 1.40 |
| | Nos. 403-407 (5) | 4.75 | 4.75 |

Noble's Hospital, Douglas, cent.

Christmas — A113

**1989, Oct. 16    Perf. 14½x15**

| | | | |
|---|---|---|---|
| 408 | A113 13p Maternity home | .45 | .45 |
| 409 | A113 16p Mother and child | .55 | .55 |
| 410 | A113 34p Madonna and child, scripture | 1.25 | 1.25 |
| 411 | A113 37p Church, baptismal ceremony | 1.40 | 1.40 |
| | Nos. 408-411 (4) | 3.65 | 3.65 |

Jane Crookall Maternity Home 50th anniv. (13p) and 75th anniv. of the consecration of St. Ninian's Church (37p).

Queen Elizabeth II, Lord of Man, Trooping the Colors — A114

**1990, Feb. 14    Litho.    Perf. 14½**

| | | | |
|---|---|---|---|
| 412 | A114 £2 multicolored | 6.50 | 6.50 |

Humorous Edwardian Postcards — A115

15p, The Isle of Man Express Going Up a Gradient. 19p, A Way We Have in the Isle of Man. 32p, Douglas — Waiting for the Male Boat. 34p, The Last Toast Rack Home Douglas Parade. 37p, The Last Isle of Man Boat.

**1990, Feb. 14    Perf. 14**

| | | | |
|---|---|---|---|
| 413 | A115 15p multicolored | .55 | .55 |
| 414 | A115 19p multicolored | .75 | .75 |
| 415 | A115 32p multicolored | 1.25 | 1.25 |
| 416 | A115 34p multicolored | 1.40 | 1.40 |
| 417 | A115 37p multicolored | 1.60 | 1.60 |
| | Nos. 413-417 (5) | 5.55 | 5.55 |

Europa 1990 — A116

Mailmen and post offices.

**1990, Apr. 18    Litho.    Perf. 13½**
Size of Nos. 419, 421: 42x28mm

| | | | |
|---|---|---|---|
| 418 | A116 15p Mailman, 1990 | .75 | .75 |
| 419 | A116 15p Ramsey P.O., 1990 | .75 | .75 |
| a. | Pair, #418-419 | 1.50 | 1.50 |
| 420 | A116 24p Mailman, c. 1890 | 1.25 | 1.25 |
| 421 | A116 24p Douglas P.O., c. 1890 | 1.25 | 1.25 |
| a. | Pair, #420-421 | 2.50 | 2.50 |
| | Nos. 418-421 (4) | 4.00 | 4.00 |

Great Britain No. 1 — A117

Designs: 19p, Wyon Medal. 32p, William Wyon's essay. 34p, Perkins Bacon engraved-turned essay of 1839. 37p, Great Britain No. 2.

No. 423 (various Penny Blacks and text): a.-e. Positions AA-AE. f.-j. Positions BA-BE. k.-n. Positions CA-CE. p.-t. Positions DA-DE. u.-y. Positions EA-EE.
**Note** that A-A top of square on No. 423a, centered on No. 422a.

**1990, May 3    Litho.    Perf. 14x13½**

| | | | |
|---|---|---|---|
| 422 | Pane of 5 | 5.25 | 5.25 |
| a. | A117 1p shown | .20 | .20 |
| b. | A117 19p multicolored | .75 | .75 |
| c. | A117 32p multicolored | 1.25 | 1.25 |
| d. | A117 34p multicolored | 1.40 | 1.40 |
| e. | A117 37p multicolored | 1.50 | 1.50 |
| g. | Bklt. pane, 2 each #422b-422e | 10.00 | |
| h. | No. 422 ovptd. "From STAMP WORLD LONDON '90 / To NEW ZEALAND '90" | 16.00 | 16.00 |

**Miniature Sheet**

| | | | |
|---|---|---|---|
| 423 | Sheet of 25 | 2.50 | 2.50 |
| a.-y. | A117 1p like #422a, any single | .20 | .20 |
| z. | Pane of 8, #a.-d., f.-i. | | .55 |

**Souvenir Sheet**
**Litho. & Engr.**

| | | | |
|---|---|---|---|
| 424 | A117 £1 4 Great Britain #1 | 4.50 | 4.50 |
| a. | Booklet pane of 1 | 4.50 | 4.50 |
| | Complete booklet, #422g, 423z, 424a | 15.00 | |

Left margin of #422g, 423z and 424a rouletted.

Queen Mother, 90th Birthday — A118

**1990, Aug. 4    Litho.    Perf. 13x13½**

| | | | |
|---|---|---|---|
| 425 | A118 90p multicolored | 3.50 | 3.50 |

Sheets of 10 alternating with 10 labels.

Battle of Britain, 50th Anniv. A119

**1990, Sept. 5    Litho.    Perf. 14**

| | | | |
|---|---|---|---|
| 426 | A119 15p Home defense | .70 | .70 |
| 427 | A119 15p Air sea rescue | .70 | .70 |
| a. | Pair, #426-427 | 1.40 | 1.40 |
| 428 | A119 24p Rearming fighters | 1.00 | 1.00 |
| 429 | A119 24p Height of battle | 1.00 | 1.00 |
| a. | Pair, #428-429 | 2.00 | 2.00 |
| 430 | A119 29p Civil defense | 1.25 | 1.25 |
| 431 | A119 29p Anti-aircraft defense | 1.25 | 1.25 |
| a. | Pair, #430-431 | 2.50 | 2.50 |
| | Nos. 426-431 (6) | 5.90 | 5.90 |

Sir Winston Churchill (1874-1965) — A120

**1990, Sept. 5    Perf. 13½**

| | | | |
|---|---|---|---|
| 432 | A120 19p multicolored | .75 | .75 |
| 433 | A120 32p multicolored | 1.25 | 1.25 |
| 434 | A120 34p multicolored | 1.40 | 1.40 |
| 435 | A120 37p multicolored | 1.50 | 1.50 |
| | Nos. 432-435 (4) | 4.90 | 4.90 |

Christmas — A121

**1990, Oct. 10    Perf. 13x13½**

| | | | |
|---|---|---|---|
| 436 | A121 14p Mailing letters | .55 | .55 |
| 437 | A121 18p Sledding, skating | .70 | .70 |
| 438 | A121 34p Snowman | 1.25 | 1.25 |

439 A121 37p Throwing snowball 1.40 1.40
  *a.* Souvenir sheet of 4, #436-439 4.25 4.25
  *Nos. 436-439 (4)* 3.90 3.90

Denominations on stamps in No. 439a are black.

Manx Photographers A122

Designs: 17p, Henry Bloom Noble, by Marshall Wane. 21p, Douglas, by Frederic Frith & Co. 26p, Studio Portrait, by Hilda Newby. 31p, Cashtal yn Ard, by Christopher Killip. 40p, Peel, by Colleen Corlett.

**1991, Jan. 6**   Litho.   *Perf. 14x14½*
440 A122 17p multicolored .60 .60
441 A122 21p multicolored .70 .70
442 A122 26p multicolored .90 .90
443 A122 31p multicolored 1.25 1.25
444 A122 40p multicolored 1.60 1.60
  *Nos. 440-444 (5)* 5.05 5.05

**Railways and Tramways Type of 1988 with Queen's Head in White (#448, 458-459)**

Designs: 18p, TPO Special leaving Douglas Station, 1991. 23p, Double decker horse tram.

**1991-92**   Litho.   *Perf. 13½*
448 A101 4p like No. 352 .20 .20
456 A101 18p multicolored .70 .70
458 A101 21p like No. 353 .85 .85
  *a.* Souv. sheet, 2 each #448, #458 2.75 2.75
  *b.* Bklt. pane, #458, 3 #448, 4 #356 3.75
  *c.* Bklt. pane, 3 #448, 1 each #356, #458 1.90
459 A101 23p multicolored .90 .90
  *a.* Bklt. pane, 6 #456, 4 #459 8.00
  *b.* Bklt. pane, 2 #456, 2 #459 4.00
  *Nos. 448-459 (4)* 2.65 2.65

No. 458a for Ninth Conf. of Commonwealth Postal Administrations, Douglas, Isle of Man.
Issued: 4p, 21p, #458b, 458c, 1/9; #458a, 7/1; 18p, 23p, #459a, 1/8/92.
No. 458b exists in special booklet sheets containing 5 #458b and 5 each #448, #458.
No. 458b dated 1991.

Manx Lifeboats A123

**1991, Feb. 13**   *Perf. 14*
463 A123 17p Sir William Hillary .65 .65
464 A123 21p Osman Gabriel .85 .85
465 A123 26p James & Ann Ritchie 1.00 1.00
466 A123 31p The Gough Ritchie 1.25 1.25
467 A123 37p John Batstone 1.40 1.40
  *Nos. 463-467 (5)* 5.15 5.15

Europa — A124

**1991, Apr. 24**   Litho.   *Perf. 14*
468 A124 17p Satellites .80 .80
469 A124 17p Boats, Ariane rocket .80 .80
  *a.* Vert. pair, #468-469 1.60 1.60
470 A124 26p Satellites, diff. 1.25 1.25
471 A124 26p Space shuttle, jet 1.25 1.25
  *a.* Vert. pair, #470-471 2.50 2.50
  *Nos. 468-471 (4)* 4.10 4.10

Tourist Trophy Mountain Course, 80th Anniv. A125

Designs: 17p, Oliver Godfrey, Indian 500cc, Bray Hill, 1911. 21p, Freddie Dixon, Douglas banking sidecar, Ballacraine, 1923. 26p, Bill Ivy, Yamaha 125cc, Waterworks, 1968. 31p, Giacomo Agostini, MV Agusta 500cc, Cregny-Baa, 1972. 37p, Joey Dunlop, RVF Honda 750cc, Ballaugh Bridge, 1985.

**1991, May 30**   Litho.   *Perf. 14½x13*
472 A125 17p multicolored .70 .70
473 A125 21p multicolored .85 .85
474 A125 26p multicolored 1.00 1.00
475 A125 31p multicolored 1.25 1.25
476 A125 37p multicolored 1.50 1.50
  *a.* Souv. sheet of 5, #472-476 + 7 labels 5.50 5.50
  *b.* As "a," ovptd. in black & red in sheet margin 15.00 15.00
  *Nos. 472-476 (5)* 5.30 5.30

No. 476b overprint includes show emblem and "PHILA / NIPPON '91."
Issue date: No. 476b, Nov. 16.

Fire Engines A126

Designs: 17p, Laxey hand cart. 21p, Douglas horse drawn steamer. 30p, Merryweather Hatfield pump. 33p, Dennis F8 pumping appliance. 37p, Volvo turntable ladder.

**1991, Sept. 18**   Litho.   *Perf. 14½*
477 A126 17p multicolored .60 .60
478 A126 21p multicolored .80 .80
479 A126 30p multicolored 1.10 1.10
480 A126 33p multicolored 1.25 1.25
481 A126 37p multicolored 1.40 1.40
  *Nos. 477-481 (5)* 5.15 5.15

Swans A127

Designs: No. 482, Mute swans, Douglas Harbor. No. 483, Black swans, Curraghs Wildlife Park. No. 484, Whooper swans, Bishops Dub, Ballaugh. No. 485, Bewick's swans, Eairy Dam, Foxdale. No. 486, Coscaroba swans, Curraghs Wildlife Park. No. 487, Trumpeter swans.

**1991, Sept. 18**   *Perf. 13*
482 A127 17p multicolored .75 .75
483 A127 17p multicolored .75 .75
  *a.* Pair, #482-483 1.50 1.50
484 A127 26p multicolored 1.10 1.10
485 A127 26p multicolored 1.10 1.10
  *a.* Pair, #484-485 2.25 2.25
486 A127 37p multicolored 1.60 1.60
487 A127 37p multicolored 1.60 1.60
  *a.* Pair, #486-487 3.25 3.25
  *Nos. 482-487 (6)* 6.90 6.90

Pairs have continuous designs.

Christmas — A128

**1991, Oct. 14**   *Perf. 14x14½*
488 A128 16p Three kings .55 .55
489 A128 20p Jesus in manger, Mary .70 .70
490 A128 26p Shepherds .90 .90
491 A128 37p Angels 1.25 1.25
  *Nos. 488-491 (4)* 3.40 3.40

**Litho.**
**Die Cut**
**Self-Adhesive Booklet Stamps**
492 A128 16p like #488 1.00 1.00
493 A128 20p like #489 1.25 1.25
  *a.* Bklt. pane, 8 #492, 4 #493 13.50 13.50
  Complete booklet, 2 #493a 27.00

Queen Elizabeth II's Accession to the Throne, 40th Anniv. — A129

Various portraits of Queen Elizabeth II.

**1992, Feb. 6**   Litho.   *Perf. 14*
494 A129 18p multicolored .60 .60
495 A129 23p multicolored .80 .80
496 A129 28p multicolored 1.00 1.00
497 A129 33p multicolored 1.10 1.10
498 A129 39p multicolored 1.50 1.50
  *Nos. 494-498 (5)* 5.00 5.00

Parachute Regiment, 50th Anniv. A130

Designs: No. 499, North Africa & Italy, 1942-43. No. 500, Operation Overlord, Normandy, 1944. No. 501, Operation Market Garden, Arnhem, 1944. No. 502, Operation Varsity, Rhine, 1945. No. 503, Near, Middle and Far East, 1945-68. No. 504, Operation Corporate, Falkland Islands, 1982, and Utrinque Paratus, 1992.

**1992, Feb. 6**   *Perf. 14*
499 A130 23p multicolored .80 .80
500 A130 23p multicolored .80 .80
  *a.* Pair, #499-500 1.60 1.60
501 A130 28p multicolored 1.00 1.00
502 A130 28p multicolored 1.00 1.00
  *a.* Pair, #501-502 2.00 2.00
503 A130 39p multicolored 1.50 1.50
504 A130 39p multicolored 1.50 1.50
  *a.* Pair, #503-504 3.00 3.00
  *Nos. 499-504 (6)* 6.60 6.60

Printed in sheets of 8.

Pilgrims' Voyage to America, 1620 — A131

Europa: No. 505, Pilgrims in longboats. No. 506, Speedwell, Delfshaven, Holland. No. 507, Mayflower. No. 508, Speedwell, Dartmouth, England.

**1992, Apr. 16**   Litho.   *Perf. 14x13½*
505 A131 18p multicolored .80 .80
506 A131 18p multicolored .80 .80
  *a.* Pair, #505-506 1.60 1.60
507 A131 28p multicolored 1.75 1.75
508 A131 28p multicolored 1.75 1.75
  *a.* Pair, #507-508 3.50 3.50
  *Nos. 505-508 (4)* 5.10 5.10

Nos. 506a, 508a have continuous design.

Port Erin Marine Laboratory, Cent. A132

**1992, Apr. 16**   *Perf. 14½*
509 A132 18p Brittle stars .65 .65
510 A132 23p Phytoplankton .85 .85
511 A132 28p Herring 1.00 1.00
512 A132 33p Great scallop 1.10 1.10
513 A132 39p Dahlia anemone, delesseria 1.40 1.40
  *Nos. 509-513 (5)* 5.00 5.00

Union Pacific, First Transcontinental Railroad — A133

#514, "Jupiter," 1869. #515, "#119," 1869. #516, "#844," 1992. #517, "#3985," 1992. £1.50, Golden Spike Ceremony, Union Pacific and Central Pacific Railroads, 1869.

**1992, May 22**   Litho.   *Perf. 13½x14*
514 A133 33p multicolored 1.10 1.10
515 A133 33p multicolored 1.10 1.10
  *a.* Pair, #514-515 + label 2.25 2.25
516 A133 39p multicolored 1.40 1.40
517 A133 39p multicolored 1.40 1.40
  *a.* Pair, #516-517 + label 3.00 3.00
  *b.* Bklt. pane, 1 ea #515a, 517a 5.25

**Souvenir Sheet**
518 A133 £1.50 multicolored 6.00 6.00
  *a.* Booklet pane, #518 6.00
  *b.* Bklt. pane, #518a, 2 #517b 17.00
  Complete booklet, #518b 17.00

World Columbian Stamp Expo '92. No. 518 contains one 60x50mm stamp.
Nos. 514-515 and 516-517 issued in sheets of 10.
Nos. 515a, 517a have 3 different labels. No. 517b exists with two different pairs of labels. No. 518a has a rouletted white border at left and right.

Manx Harbors — A134

#519, King Orry V, Douglas Harbor. 23p, Castletown Harbor. 37p, Port St. Mary Harbor. 40p, Ramsey Harbor. a, King Orry. b, St. Eloi. Illustration reduced.

**1992, Sept. 18**   Litho.   *Perf. 14½x14*
519 A134 18p multicolored .60 .60
520 A134 23p multicolored .75 .75
521 A134 37p multicolored 1.25 1.25
522 A134 40p multicolored 1.40 1.40
  *Nos. 519-522 (4)* 4.00 4.00

**Souvenir Sheet**
523 Sheet of 2 4.75 4.75
  *a.* A134 18p multicolored .75 .75
  *b.* A134 £1 multicolored 4.00 4.00

Genoa '92. #523 contains 30x24mm stamps.

Christmas — A135

Designs: 17p, Nativity window, St. German's Cathedral, Peel. 22p, Adoration of the Magi panel, St. Matthew's Church, Douglas. 28p, Nativity window, St. George's Church, Douglas. 37p, Reredos of The Annunciation, St. Mary of the Isle, Douglas. 40p, Good Shepherd window, Trinity Methodist Church, Douglas.

**1992, Oct. 13**   Litho.   *Perf. 14½*
524 A135 17p multicolored .55 .55
525 A135 22p multicolored .75 .75
526 A135 28p multicolored 1.00 1.00
527 A135 37p multicolored 1.25 1.25
528 A135 40p multicolored 1.40 1.40
  *Nos. 524-528 (5)* 4.95 4.95

Nigel Mansell, Formula I World Champion, 1992 A136

Williams Renault FW 14B at: 20p, British Grand Prix, 1992. 24p, French Grand Prix, 1992.

| 1992, Nov. 8 | | | *Perf. 13½* | |
|---|---|---|---|---|
| 529 | A136 | 20p multicolored | .85 | .85 |
| 530 | A136 | 24p multicolored | 1.00 | 1.00 |

Ships
A137

British Red
Ensign
A137a

Queen Elizabeth
II — A137b

| 1993-96 | | | *Litho.* | *Perf. 13½* | |
|---|---|---|---|---|---|
| 531 | A137 | 1p HMS Amazon | | .20 | .20 |
| 532 | A137 | 2p Fingal | | .20 | .20 |
| 533 | A137 | 4p Sir Winston Churchill | | .20 | .20 |
| 534 | A137 | 5p Dar Mlodziezy | | .20 | .20 |
| 543 | A137 | 20p Tynwald I | | .45 | .45 |
| 544 | A137 | 21p Ben Veg | | .55 | .55 |
| 545 | A137 | 22p Waverley | | .55 | .55 |
| 546 | A137 | 23p HMY Britannia | | .60 | .60 |
| *a.* | | Souv. sheet of 1, Perf. 13 | | 1.00 | 1.00 |
| 547 | A137 | 24p Francis Drake | | .55 | .55 |
| *a.* | | Bklt. pane, 4 #543, 6 #547 | | 5.50 | |
| | | Complete booklet, #547a | | 5.50 | |
| *b.* | | Bklt. pane, 2 #543, 3 #547 | | 2.75 | |
| | | Complete booklet, #547b | | 2.75 | |
| 548 | A137 | 25p Royal Viking Sky | | .65 | .65 |
| *a.* | | Booklet pane, 2 #533, 2 #544, 2 #548 | | 4.25 | |
| | | Complete booklet, #548a | | 4.25 | |
| 549 | A137 | 26p Lord Nelson | | .70 | .70 |
| 550 | A137 | 27p Europa | | .70 | .70 |
| 551 | A137 | 30p Snaefell V | | .80 | .80 |
| 551A | A137 | 35p Sea Cat | | .95 | .95 |
| 552 | A137 | 40p Lady of Mann I | | 1.10 | 1.10 |
| 553 | A137 | 50p Mona's Queen II | | 1.40 | 1.40 |
| 553A | A137 | £1 QE2, Mona's Queen V | | 3.50 | 3.50 |

| | | | *Perf. 14½* | |
|---|---|---|---|---|
| 553B | A137a | £2 multicolored | 6.00 | 6.00 |
| 553C | A137b | £5 multicolored | 17.00 | 17.00 |
| | | *Nos. 531-553C (19)* | 36.30 | 36.30 |

#546a, for return of Hong Kong to China, is wmk. 373.

No. 553C has a holographic image. Soaking in water may affect the hologram.

Issued: 1p-5p, 20p-27p, 1/4/93; 30p, 40p-£1, 9/15/93; £2, 1/24/94; £5, 7/5/94; 35p, 1/11/96; #546a, 7/1/97; #548a, 1997.

Nos. 543, 547 exist dated "1995;" Nos. 533, 544, 546a, 548, 548a, 553A dated "1997."

See Nos. 683-697.

Manx Electric Railway, Cent. — A138

20p, #13 trailer, #1 motor car. 24p, #19 trailer, #9 tunnel car. 28p, #59 Royal trailer special saloon car. #19 motor car. 39p, #33 motor car, #45 trailer, #13 small van.
Illustration reduced.

| 1993, Feb. 3 | | | *Perf. 14* | |
|---|---|---|---|---|
| 554 | A138 | 20p multicolored | .75 | .75 |
| 555 | A138 | 24p multicolored | .85 | .85 |
| 556 | A138 | 28p multicolored | 1.10 | 1.10 |
| 557 | A138 | 39p multicolored | 1.25 | 1.25 |
| *a.* | | Booklet pane of #554-557 | 4.25 | 4.25 |
| | | Complete booklet, 4 #557a | 17.00 | |
| | | *Nos. 554-557 (4)* | 3.95 | 3.95 |

No. 557a exists with four different marginal inscriptions and in four different arrangements.

Contemporary
Art by Bryan
Kneale — A139

Europa: No. 558, Statue of Sir Hall Caine. No. 559, Painting, The Brass Bedstead. No. 560, Abstract bronze. No. 561, Drawing of polar bear skeleton.

| 1993, Apr. 14 | | | *Litho.* | *Perf. 14* | |
|---|---|---|---|---|---|
| 558 | A139 | 20p multicolored | | .80 | .80 |
| 559 | A139 | 20p multicolored | | .80 | .80 |
| *a.* | | Pair, #558-559 | | 1.60 | 1.60 |
| 560 | A139 | 28p multicolored | | 1.00 | 1.00 |
| 561 | A139 | 28p multicolored | | 1.00 | 1.00 |
| *a.* | | Pair, #560-561 | | 2.00 | 2.00 |
| | | *Nos. 558-561 (4)* | | 3.60 | 3.60 |

Motorcycling Events — A140

Riders and events: 20p, Gold Medalists Graham Oates, Bill Marshall, Intl. Six-Day Trial, 1933, Ariel Square Four. 24p, Geoff Duke, Team Sergeant, Royal Signals Display Team, 1947, Triumph Twin. 28p, Denis Parkinson, winner of Senior Manx Grand Prix, 1953, Manx Norton. 33p, Richard Swallow, winner of Junior Classic Manx Grand Prix, 1991, Aermacchi. 39p, Steve Colley, winner of Scottish Six-Day Trial, 1992, Beta Zero.

| 1993, June 3 | | | *Litho.* | *Perf. 13½x14* | |
|---|---|---|---|---|---|
| 562 | A140 | 20p multicolored | | .80 | .80 |
| 563 | A140 | 24p multicolored | | .85 | .85 |
| 564 | A140 | 28p multicolored | | 1.00 | 1.00 |
| 565 | A140 | 33p multicolored | | 1.25 | 1.25 |
| 566 | A140 | 39p multicolored | | 1.40 | 1.40 |
| *a.* | | Souv. sheet of 5, #562-566 + 4 labels | | 5.50 | 5.50 |
| | | *Nos. 562-566 (5)* | | 5.30 | 5.30 |

Butterflies
A141

| 1993, Sept. 15 | | | *Litho.* | *Perf. 14½* | |
|---|---|---|---|---|---|
| 567 | A141 | 24p Dark green fritillary | | .85 | .85 |
| 568 | A141 | 24p Painted lady | | .85 | .85 |
| 569 | A141 | 24p Holly blue | | .85 | .85 |
| 570 | A141 | 24p Red admiral | | .85 | .85 |
| 571 | A141 | 24p Peacock | | .85 | .85 |
| *a.* | | Strip of 5, #567-571 | | 4.50 | 4.50 |

Christmas — A142

Designs: 19p, Children decorating Christmas tree. 23p, Snowman, girl. 28p, Boy unwrapping presents. 39p, Girl, teddy bear. 40p, Girl with holly basket, boy on sled.

| 1993, Oct. 12 | | | *Perf. 14* | |
|---|---|---|---|---|
| 572 | A142 | 19p multicolored | .70 | .70 |
| | | Complete booklet, 10 #572 | 7.00 | |
| 573 | A142 | 23p multicolored | .80 | .80 |
| | | Complete booklet, 10 #573 | 8.00 | |
| 574 | A142 | 28p multicolored | 1.00 | 1.00 |
| 575 | A142 | 39p multicolored | 1.40 | 1.40 |
| 576 | A142 | 40p multicolored | 1.40 | 1.40 |
| | | *Nos. 572-576 (5)* | 5.30 | 5.30 |

Tourism
A143

No. 577, Gaiety Theatre, Douglas. No. 578, Field hockey, golf, soccer (#577). No. 579, Yacht racing, artist's hand painting picture of castle (#580). No. 580, TT Motorcycle Races, Red Arrows demonstration squadron. (#581). No. 581, Musical instruments. No. 582, Laxey Wheel, Manx cat. No. 583, Tower of Refuge, beach, sand bucket (#584). No. 584, Cyclist. No. 585, Tynwald Day, classic racing car (#579, 580, 584, 586). No. 586, Santa Claus riding Mince Pie Train, Groudle Glen.

| 1994, Feb, 18 | | | *Litho.* | *Perf. 13½* | |
|---|---|---|---|---|---|
| | | **Booklet Stamps** | | | |
| 577 | A143 | 24p multicolored | | .80 | .80 |
| 578 | A143 | 24p multicolored | | .80 | .80 |
| 579 | A143 | 24p multicolored | | .80 | .80 |
| 580 | A143 | 24p multicolored | | .80 | .80 |
| 581 | A143 | 24p multicolored | | .80 | .80 |
| 582 | A143 | 24p multicolored | | .80 | .80 |
| 583 | A143 | 24p multicolored | | .80 | .80 |
| 584 | A143 | 24p multicolored | | .80 | .80 |
| 585 | A143 | 24p multicolored | | .80 | .80 |
| 586 | A143 | 24p multicolored | | .80 | .80 |
| *a.* | | Booklet pane of 10, #577-586 | | 8.25 | |
| | | Complete booklet, #586a | | 8.25 | |

Birds
A144

Magpie, Calf of Man Bird
Observatory — A145

| 1994, Feb. 18 | | | *Perf. 14* | |
|---|---|---|---|---|
| 587 | A144 | 20p White-throated robin | .80 | .80 |
| 588 | A144 | 20p Black-eared wheatear | .80 | .80 |
| *a.* | | Pair, #587-588 | 1.60 | 1.60 |
| 589 | A144 | 24p Goldcrest | .95 | .95 |
| 590 | A144 | 24p Northern oriole | .95 | .95 |
| *a.* | | Pair, #589-590 | 1.90 | 1.90 |
| 591 | A144 | 30p Kingfisher | 1.25 | 1.25 |
| 592 | A144 | 30p Hoopoe | 1.25 | 1.25 |
| *a.* | | Pair, #591-592 | 2.50 | 2.50 |
| | | *Nos. 587-592 (6)* | 6.00 | 6.00 |

| | | **Souvenir Sheet** | | |
|---|---|---|---|---|
| | | | *Perf. 13½x13* | |
| 593 | A145 | £1 shown | 4.00 | 4.00 |

Hong Kong '94 (#593).

Europa
A146

Designs, Forbes and Discoveries: No. 594, Eubranchus tricolor. No. 595, Loligo forbesii. No. 596, Edward Forbes (1815-54), naturalist. No. 597, Solaster moretonis. No. 598, Adamsia carciniopados on hermit crab. No. 599, Solaster endeca.

| 1994, May 5 | | | *Litho.* | *Perf. 13¼x14½* | |
|---|---|---|---|---|---|
| 594 | A146 | 20p multicolored | | .80 | .80 |
| 595 | A146 | 20p multicolored | | .80 | .80 |
| 596 | A146 | 20p multicolored | | .80 | .80 |
| *a.* | | Strip of 3, #594-596 | | 2.40 | 2.40 |
| 597 | A146 | 30p multicolored | | 1.25 | 1.25 |
| 598 | A146 | 30p multicolored | | 1.25 | 1.25 |
| 599 | A146 | 30p multicolored | | 1.25 | 1.25 |
| *a.* | | Strip of 3, #597-599 | | 3.75 | 3.75 |

D-Day,
50th
Anniv.
A147

Designs: No. 600, Transport Ben-My-Chree IV, landing ships, US Maj. Gen. Walter Bedell Smith. No. 601, Transports Victoria, Lady of Mann I, Adm. Sir Bertram Ramsay, RN, Naval Commander. No. 602, Infantry, tanks on Gold, Juno, Sword Beaches, Gen. Montgomery, Commander, 21st Army Group. No. 603, Tanks, landing craft on Gold, Juno, Sword Beaches, Lt. Gen. Sir Miles C. Dempsey, Commander, British 2nd Army. No. 604, US 8th, 9th Air Forces, Air Chief Marshal Sir Trafford Leigh-Mallory, RAF, Air Force Commander. No. 605, Air Chief Marshall Sir Arthur Tedder, RAF, Deputy Supreme Allied Commander, RAF 2nd Tactical Air Force & Bomber Command. No. 606, Landing craft, Omaha, Utah Beaches, Lt. Gen. Omar N. Bradley, Commander, US 1st Army. No. 607, Infantry, tanks on Omaha, Utah Beaches, Gen. Eisenhower, Supreme Allied Commander.

| 1994, June 6 | | | *Litho.* | *Perf. 14* | |
|---|---|---|---|---|---|
| 600 | A147 | 4p multicolored | | .20 | .20 |
| 601 | A147 | 4p multicolored | | .20 | .20 |
| *a.* | | Pair, #600-601 | | .25 | .25 |
| 602 | A147 | 20p multicolored | | .75 | .75 |
| 603 | A147 | 20p multicolored | | .75 | .75 |
| *a.* | | Pair, #602-603 | | 1.50 | 1.50 |
| 604 | A147 | 30p multicolored | | 1.10 | 1.10 |
| 605 | A147 | 30p multicolored | | 1.10 | 1.10 |
| *a.* | | Pair, #604-605 | | 2.25 | 2.25 |
| 606 | A147 | 41p multicolored | | 1.60 | 1.60 |
| 607 | A147 | 41p multicolored | | 1.60 | 1.60 |
| *a.* | | Pair, #606-607 | | 3.25 | 3.25 |
| | | *Nos. 600-607 (8)* | | 7.30 | 7.30 |

Nos. 601a, 603a, 605a, 607a are continuous designs.

Postman
Pat
A148

Postman Pat at: 1p, Sea Terminal, Douglas. 20p, Laxey Wheel. 24p, Cregneash. 30p, Manx Electric Railway. 36p, Peel Harbor. 41p, Tourist office, Douglas Promenade. £1, Postman Pat.

| 1994, Sept. 14 | | | *Litho.* | *Perf. 14½x14* | |
|---|---|---|---|---|---|
| 608 | A148 | 1p multicolored | | .20 | .20 |
| *a.* | | Booklet pane of 2 | | .20 | |
| 609 | A148 | 20p multicolored | | .65 | .65 |
| *a.* | | Booklet pane of 2 | | 1.40 | |
| 610 | A148 | 24p multicolored | | .80 | .80 |
| *a.* | | Booklet pane of 2 | | 1.60 | |
| 611 | A148 | 30p multicolored | | 1.00 | 1.00 |
| *a.* | | Booklet pane of 2 | | 2.10 | |
| 612 | A148 | 36p multicolored | | 1.25 | 1.25 |
| *a.* | | Booklet pane of 2 | | 2.50 | |
| 613 | A148 | 41p multicolored | | 1.40 | 1.40 |
| *a.* | | Booklet pane of 2 | | 3.00 | |
| | | *Nos. 608-613 (6)* | | 5.30 | 5.30 |

| | | **Souvenir Sheet** | | |
|---|---|---|---|---|
| 614 | A148 | £1 multicolored | 4.00 | 4.00 |
| *a.* | | Booklet pane of 1 | 4.00 | 4.00 |
| | | Complete booklet, #608a-614a | 16.00 | |

No. 614a is rouletted 9 at left.

Intl. Olympic
Committee,
Cent. — A149

| 1994, Oct. 11 | | | *Perf. 14* | |
|---|---|---|---|---|
| 615 | A149 | 10p Cycling | .40 | .40 |
| 616 | A149 | 20p Alpine skiing | .75 | .75 |
| 617 | A149 | 24p Swimming | .90 | .90 |

| 618 | A149 | 35p Steeplechase | 1.40 | 1.40 |
|---|---|---|---|---|
| 619 | A149 | 48p Emblem | 1.60 | 1.60 |
| | | *Nos. 615-619 (5)* | 5.05 | 5.05 |

A150

### 1994, Oct. 11

Christmas: 19p, Santa, Mrs. Claus greeting children on Santa Train to Santon, horiz. 23p, Santa Claus on tractor, Postman Pat. 60p, Santa Claus arriving by boat, Port St. Mary, horiz.

| 620 | A150 | 19p multicolored | .75 | .75 |
|---|---|---|---|---|
| 621 | A150 | 23p multicolored | 1.00 | 1.00 |
| 622 | A150 | 60p multicolored | 2.00 | 2.00 |
| | | *Nos. 620-622 (3)* | 3.75 | 3.75 |

Snaefell Mountain Electric Railway, Cent. — A151

Designs: 20p, Opening day, Car No. 2. 24p, Car 3 ascending Laxey Valley, Car 4 in green livery. 35p, Car 5, Car 6. 42p, Caledonia on construction duty, Goods Car 7.
£1, Bungalow Hotel & Station, Snaefell.
Illustration reduced.

### 1995, Feb. 8    Litho.    *Perf. 14*

| 623 | A151 | 20p multicolored | .75 | .75 |
|---|---|---|---|---|
| 624 | A151 | 24p multicolored | .95 | .95 |
| 625 | A151 | 35p multicolored | 1.40 | 1.40 |
| 626 | A151 | 42p multicolored | 1.60 | 1.60 |
| a. | | Bklt. pane, #623-626 | 4.75 | |
| | | *Nos. 623-626 (4)* | 4.70 | 4.70 |

### Souvenir Sheet
### *Perf. 14x13½*

| 627 | A151 | £1 multicolored | 4.00 | 4.00 |
|---|---|---|---|---|
| a. | | Sheet from souvenir booklet | 4.00 | 4.00 |
| | | Complete booklet, 3 #626a, #627a | 18.50 | |

No. 627 contains one 61x38mm stamp.
No. 626a comes with three different arrangements of the stamps. Value the same for each.
No. 627a is rouletted in margin at left with additional vertical sheet margin inscriptions. At left is a description of the design. At right is "1895-Centenary Snaefell Mountain Railway-1995."

Steam-Powered Vehicles — A152

Designs: 20p, Foden Wagon, 5 ton. 24p, Clayton & Shuttleworth, 7hp, Fowler, 6hp. 30p, Wallis & Steevens, 6hp. 35p, Marshall, 6hp. 41p, Marshall Convertible, 5hp.

### 1995, Feb. 8    *Perf. 13½*

| 628 | A152 | 20p multicolored | .70 | .70 |
|---|---|---|---|---|
| 629 | A152 | 24p multicolored | .90 | .90 |
| 630 | A152 | 30p multicolored | 1.10 | 1.10 |
| 631 | A152 | 35p multicolored | 1.40 | 1.40 |
| 632 | A152 | 41p multicolored | 1.50 | 1.50 |
| | | *Nos. 628-632 (5)* | 5.60 | 5.60 |

Peace & Freedom — A153

Europa: 20p, Flight of doves forming tidal wave, Tower of Refuge, Douglas Bay. 30p, Dove with olive branch breaking barbed wire.

### 1995, Apr. 28    Litho.    *Perf. 13½*

| 633 | A153 | 20p multicolored | .80 | .80 |
|---|---|---|---|---|
| 634 | A153 | 30p multicolored | 1.25 | 1.25 |

VE Day, 50th Anniv. A154

Designs: No. 635, Spitfire, tank, 1939-45 Star, African Star. No. 636, France and Germany Star, Italy Star, Hawker Typhoon, artillery. No. 637, Lancaster bomber, aircraft carrier, Air Crew Europe Star, Atlantic Star. No. 638, Pacific Star, Burma Star, Avenger torpedo bomber, soldiers. No. 639, Parliament, Manx flag. No. 640, British flag, crowd celebrating. No. 641, Children celebrating at street party, Manx flag. No. 642, British flag, visit of Queen Elizabeth, King George VI, 1945.

### 1995, May 8    *Perf. 14*

| 635 | A154 | 10p multicolored | .40 | .40 |
|---|---|---|---|---|
| 636 | A154 | 10p multicolored | .40 | .40 |
| a. | | Pair, #635-636 | .80 | .80 |
| 637 | A154 | 24p multicolored | .75 | .75 |
| 638 | A154 | 24p multicolored | .75 | .75 |
| a. | | Pair, #637-638 | 1.50 | 1.50 |
| 639 | A154 | 24p multicolored | .85 | .85 |
| 640 | A154 | 24p multicolored | .85 | .85 |
| a. | | Pair, #639-640 | 1.75 | 1.75 |
| 641 | A154 | 40p multicolored | 1.50 | 1.50 |
| 642 | A154 | 40p multicolored | 1.50 | 1.50 |
| a. | | Pair, #641-642 | 3.25 | 3.25 |
| | | *Nos. 635-642 (8)* | 7.00 | 7.00 |

British Motor Car Racing, 90th Anniv. A155

Tourist Trophy Race drivers, cars: 20p, R. Parnell, 1951 Maserati 4 CLT. 24p, S. Moss, 1951 Frazer Nash. 30p, R.J.B. Seaman, 1936 Delage. 36p, Prince Bira, 1937 ERA R2B Romulus. 41p, K. Lee Guinness, 1914 Sunbeam 1. 42p, F. Dixon, 1934 Riley.
£1, John S. Napier, 1905 Arrol Johnston.

### 1995, May 8

| 643 | A155 | 20p multicolored | .75 | .75 |
|---|---|---|---|---|
| 644 | A155 | 24p multicolored | .90 | .90 |
| 645 | A155 | 30p multicolored | 1.10 | 1.10 |
| 646 | A155 | 36p multicolored | 1.40 | 1.40 |
| 647 | A155 | 41p multicolored | 1.50 | 1.50 |
| 648 | A155 | 42p multicolored | 1.60 | 1.60 |
| | | *Nos. 643-648 (6)* | 7.25 | 7.25 |

### Souvenir Sheet

| 649 | A155 | £1 multicolored | 4.00 | 4.00 |
|---|---|---|---|---|

No. 649 contains one 47x58mm stamp.

Mushrooms A156

Designs: 20p, Amanita muscaria. 24p, Boletus edulis. 30p, Coprinus disseminatus. 35p, Pleurotus ostreatus. 45p, Geastrum triplex. £1, Shaggy ink cap, bee orchid.

### 1995, Sept. 1    Litho.    *Perf. 13½x14*

| 650 | A156 | 20p multicolored | .80 | .80 |
|---|---|---|---|---|
| 651 | A156 | 24p multicolored | .95 | .95 |
| 652 | A156 | 30p multicolored | 1.25 | 1.25 |

| 653 | A156 | 35p multicolored | 1.40 | 1.40 |
|---|---|---|---|---|
| 654 | A156 | 45p multicolored | 1.75 | 1.75 |
| | | *Nos. 650-654 (5)* | 6.15 | 6.15 |

### Souvenir Sheet
### *Perf. 14x13½*

| 655 | A156 | £1 multicolored | 4.00 | 4.00 |
|---|---|---|---|---|

No. 655 contains one 51x60mm stamp. Singapore '95 (#655).

Thomas the Tank Engine A157

Designs: 20p, Bertie arrives on the quayside. 24p, Mail train and Thomas. 30p, Bertie and trains at Ballasalla. 36p, Viking and Thomas at Port Erin. 41p, The mail gets through. 45p, Race at Laxey Wheel.

### 1995, Sept. 1    *Perf. 14*

| 656 | A157 | 20p multicolored | .75 | .75 |
|---|---|---|---|---|
| 657 | A157 | 24p multicolored | .85 | .85 |
| a. | | Booklet pane of 2, #656-657 | 1.60 | |
| 658 | A157 | 30p multicolored | 1.10 | 1.10 |
| a. | | Booklet pane of 2, #657-658 | 2.00 | |
| 659 | A157 | 36p multicolored | 1.40 | 1.40 |
| a. | | Booklet pane of 2, #658-659 | 2.50 | |
| 660 | A157 | 41p multicolored | 1.50 | 1.50 |
| a. | | Booklet pane of 2, #659-660 | 3.00 | |
| 661 | A157 | 45p multicolored | 1.60 | 1.60 |
| a. | | Booklet pane of 2, #656, 661 | 2.50 | |
| b. | | Booklet pane of 2, #660-661 | 3.25 | |
| | | Complete booklet, #657a, 658a, 659a, 660a, 661a-661b | 16.00 | |
| | | *Nos. 656-661 (6)* | 7.20 | 7.20 |

Christmas A158

Designs: 19p, Church, holly. 23p, Bird on holly branch. 42p, Snow crocuses, church. 50p, Antique farming equipment in snow.

### 1995, Oct. 10    Litho.    *Perf. 14x14½*

| 662 | A158 | 19p multicolored | .70 | .70 |
|---|---|---|---|---|
| 663 | A158 | 23p multicolored | .80 | .80 |
| 664 | A158 | 42p multicolored | 1.50 | 1.50 |
| 665 | A158 | 50p multicolored | 1.75 | 1.75 |
| | | *Nos. 662-665 (4)* | 4.75 | 4.75 |

Lighthouses — A159

Location, year opened: 20p, Langness, 1880, vert. 24p, Point of Ayre, 1818. 30p, Chicken Rock, 1873, vert. 36p, Calf of Man, 1818. 41p, Douglas Head, 1832. vert. 42p, Maughold Head, 1914.

### 1996, Feb. 27    Litho.    *Perf. 14*

| 666 | A159 | 20p multicolored | .70 | .70 |
|---|---|---|---|---|
| a. | | Booklet pane of 4 + 4 labels | 3.00 | |
| 667 | A159 | 24p multicolored | .80 | .80 |
| a. | | Booklet pane of 4 | 3.25 | |
| 668 | A159 | 30p multicolored | 1.10 | 1.10 |
| 669 | A159 | 36p multicolored | 1.25 | 1.25 |
| 670 | A159 | 41p multicolored | 1.50 | 1.50 |
| a. | | Booklet pane, 2 each #668, 670 + 4 labels | 5.25 | |
| 671 | A159 | 42p multicolored | 1.50 | 1.50 |
| a. | | Bklt. pane, 2 ea #669, 671 | 5.50 | |
| | | Complete booklet, #666a, 667a, 670a, 671a | 17.50 | |
| | | *Nos. 666-671 (6)* | 6.85 | 6.85 |

Manx Cats A160

Various cats and: 20p, Arms of Man. 24p, British Union Flag as of ball yarn. 36p, Brandenburg Gate. 42p, US flag, Statue of Liberty. 48p, Australian flag, map.
£1.50, Gray adult cat, gray and yellow kittens.

### 1996, Mar. 14

| 672 | A160 | 20p multicolored | .70 | .70 |
|---|---|---|---|---|
| 673 | A160 | 24p multicolored | .80 | .80 |
| 674 | A160 | 36p multicolored | 1.25 | 1.25 |
| 675 | A160 | 42p multicolored | 1.50 | 1.50 |
| 676 | A160 | 48p multicolored | 1.75 | 1.75 |
| | | *Nos. 672-676 (5)* | 6.00 | 6.00 |

### Souvenir Sheet

| 677 | A160 | £1.50 multicolored | 6.00 | 6.00 |
|---|---|---|---|---|
| a. | | With additional inscription | 9.50 | 9.50 |

No. 677 contains one 51x60mm stamp. No. 677a contains CAPEX '96 exhibition emblem in sheet margin. Issued 6/8/96.

Douglas Borough, Cent. — A161

### *Die Cut Perf. 9x9½*
### 1996, Mar. 14    Litho.
### Self-Adhesive

| 678 | A161 | (40p) multicolored | 1.50 | 1.50 |
|---|---|---|---|---|

The backing of No. 678 is rouletted 13.

Women of Achievement — A162

Europa: 24p, Princess Anne, children of different nations. 30p, Queen Elizabeth II, people of different nations.

### 1996    *Perf. 14*

| 679 | A162 | 24p multicolored | .90 | .90 |
|---|---|---|---|---|
| 680 | A162 | 30p multicolored | 1.25 | 1.25 |

Queen Elizabeth II, 70th birthday (#680). See Guernsey Nos. 564-565.

### Ship Type of 1993

### 1996    Litho.    *Perf. 14*
### Size: 21x19mm

| 683 | A137 | 4p like #533 | .20 | .20 |
|---|---|---|---|---|
| 693 | A137 | 20p like #543 | .80 | .80 |
| 697 | A137 | 24p like #547 | .90 | .90 |
| | | *Nos. 683-697 (3)* | 1.90 | 1.90 |
| a. | | Bklt. pane, 2 ea 4p, 20p, 24p | 4.00 | |
| | | Complete booklet, No. 697a | 4.00 | |

Irish Winners of Tourist Trophy Motorcycle Races — A163

20p, Alec Bennett. 24p, Stanley Woods. 45p, Artie Bell. 60p, Robert & Joey Dunlop. £1, Demonstration squadron Hawks flying over motorcycles, vert.

### 1996, May 30    Litho.    *Perf. 14*

| 701 | A163 | 20p multicolored | .75 | .75 |
|---|---|---|---|---|
| 702 | A163 | 24p multicolored | .85 | .85 |
| 703 | A163 | 45p multicolored | 1.60 | 1.60 |
| 704 | A163 | 60p multicolored | 2.10 | 2.10 |
| | | *Nos. 701-704 (4)* | 5.30 | 5.30 |

### Souvenir Sheet

| 705 | A163 | £1 multicolored | 3.75 | 3.75 |
|---|---|---|---|---|

See Ireland Nos. 1010-1014.

Royal British Legion, 75th Anniv. — A164

Poppies and: 20p, National poppy appeal trophy. 24p, Manx war memorial. 42p, Poppy appeal. 75p, Crest.

**1996, June 8**
| | | | | |
|---|---|---|---|---|
| 706 | A164 | 20p multicolored | .75 | .75 |
| 707 | A164 | 24p multicolored | .85 | .85 |
| 708 | A164 | 42p multicolored | 1.60 | 1.60 |
| 709 | A164 | 75p multicolored | 2.75 | 2.75 |
| | | *Nos. 706-709 (4)* | 5.95 | 5.95 |

UNICEF, 50th Anniv. A165

Children receiving aid, map of country: #710, Mexico. #711, Sri Lanka. #712, Colombia. #713, Zambia. #714, Afghanistan. #715, Viet Nam.

**1996, Sept. 18    Litho.    Perf. 13½x14**
| | | | | |
|---|---|---|---|---|
| 710 | A165 | 24p multicolored | .85 | .85 |
| 711 | A165 | 24p multicolored | .85 | .85 |
| *a.* | | *Pair, #710-711* | 1.75 | 1.75 |
| 712 | A165 | 30p multicolored | 1.10 | 1.10 |
| 713 | A165 | 30p multicolored | 1.10 | 1.10 |
| *a.* | | *Pair, #712-713* | 2.25 | 2.25 |
| 714 | A165 | 42p multicolored | 1.60 | 1.60 |
| 715 | A165 | 42p multicolored | 1.60 | 1.60 |
| *a.* | | *Pair, #714-715* | 3.25 | 3.25 |
| | | *Nos. 710-715 (6)* | 7.10 | 7.10 |

Dogs — A166

**1996, Sept. 18    Perf. 14½**
| | | | | |
|---|---|---|---|---|
| 716 | A166 | 20p Labrador | .75 | .75 |
| *a.* | | *Booklet pane of 4* | 3.00 | |
| 717 | A166 | 24p Border collie | .80 | .80 |
| *a.* | | *Booklet pane of 4* | 3.25 | |
| 718 | A166 | 31p Dalmatian | 1.10 | 1.10 |
| 719 | A166 | 38p Mongrel | 1.40 | 1.40 |
| 720 | A166 | 43p English setter | 1.60 | 1.60 |
| 721 | A166 | 63p Alsatian | 2.40 | 2.40 |
| *a.* | | *Booklet pane, 1 each #718-721* | 6.50 | |
| | | *Nos. 716-721 (6)* | 8.05 | 8.05 |

**Souvenir Sheet**
**Perf. 13½x14**
| | | | | |
|---|---|---|---|---|
| 722 | A166 | £1.20 Border collie, labrador | 4.75 | 4.75 |
| *a.* | | *Booklet pane of 1* | 4.75 | |
| | | *Complete booklet, #716a, 717a, 721a, 722a* | 19.00 | |

Nos. 716-721 are each printed with se-tenant label. No. 722 contains one 38x50mm stamp. No. 722a is rouletted around margin of sheet.

Christmas A167

Children's drawings: 19p, Snowman. 23p, Santa, "Happy Christmas" in Manx. 50p, Family, Christmas tree, presents. 75p, Santa in sleigh flying over rooftops.

**1996, Nov. 2    Litho.    Perf. 14x14½**
| | | | | |
|---|---|---|---|---|
| 723 | A167 | 19p multicolored | .70 | .70 |
| 724 | A167 | 23p multicolored | .80 | .80 |
| 725 | A167 | 50p multicolored | 1.60 | 1.60 |
| 726 | A167 | 75p multicolored | 2.75 | 2.75 |
| | | *Nos. 723-726 (4)* | 5.85 | 5.85 |

Owls — A168

**1997, Feb. 12    Litho.    Perf. 14**
| | | | | |
|---|---|---|---|---|
| 727 | A168 | 20p Barn owl | .75 | .75 |
| *a.* | | *Booklet pane of 4* | 3.00 | |
| 728 | A168 | 24p Short-eared owl | .85 | .85 |
| *a.* | | *Booklet pane of 4* | 3.50 | |
| 729 | A168 | 31p Long-eared owl | 1.10 | 1.10 |
| 730 | A168 | 36p Little owl | 1.25 | 1.25 |
| 731 | A168 | 43p Snowy owl | 1.60 | 1.60 |
| 732 | A168 | 56p Tawny owl | 2.00 | 2.00 |
| *a.* | | *Booklet pane of 4, #729-732* | 6.00 | |
| | | *Nos. 727-732 (6)* | 7.55 | 7.55 |

**Souvenir Sheet**
**Perf. 13**
| | | | | |
|---|---|---|---|---|
| 733 | A168 | £1.20 Long-eared owl | 4.00 | 4.00 |
| *a.* | | *Booklet pane of 1* | 4.00 | |
| | | *Complete booklet, #727a, 728a, 732a, 733a* | 16.50 | |

No. 733, 733a each contain one 56x60mm stamp. No. 733a is rouletted at left. Hong Kong '97 (#733, 733a).

Springtime A169

**1997, Feb. 12    Perf. 14**
| | | | | |
|---|---|---|---|---|
| 734 | A169 | 20p Spring flowers | .70 | .70 |
| 735 | A169 | 24p Sheep | .80 | .80 |
| 736 | A169 | 43p Waterfowl | 1.60 | 1.60 |
| 737 | A169 | 63p Frog, ducks | 2.40 | 2.40 |
| | | *Nos. 734-737 (4)* | 5.50 | 5.50 |

Stories and Legends A170

21p, Moddey Dhoo. 25p, The Trammen Tree. 31p, Fairy Bridge. 36p, Fin Macooil. 37p, The Buggane of St. Trinian's. 43p, Fynoderee.

**1997, Apr. 24    Litho.    Perf. 13½x14**
| | | | | |
|---|---|---|---|---|
| 738 | A170 | 21p multicolored | .70 | .70 |
| 739 | A170 | 25p multicolored | .85 | .85 |
| 740 | A170 | 31p multicolored | 1.10 | 1.10 |
| 741 | A170 | 36p multicolored | 1.25 | 1.25 |
| 742 | A170 | 37p multicolored | 1.25 | 1.25 |
| 743 | A170 | 43p multicolored | 1.60 | 1.60 |
| | | *Nos. 738-743 (6)* | 6.75 | 6.75 |

Europa (#739-740).

Aircraft A171

Designs: No. 744, Sopwith Tabloid. No. 745, Grumman Tiger. No. 746, Manx Airlines BAe ATP. No. 747, Manx Airlines BAe 146-200. No. 748 Boeing 757-200. No. 749, Farman biplane. No. 750, Spitfire. No. 751, Hurricane.

**1997, Apr. 24    Perf. 14**
| | | | | |
|---|---|---|---|---|
| 744 | A171 | 21p multicolored | .70 | .70 |
| 745 | A171 | 21p multicolored | .70 | .70 |
| *a.* | | *Pair, #744-745* | 1.40 | 1.40 |
| 746 | A171 | 25p multicolored | .85 | .85 |
| 747 | A171 | 25p multicolored | .85 | .85 |
| *a.* | | *Pair, #746-747* | 1.75 | 1.75 |
| 748 | A171 | 31p multicolored | 1.10 | 1.10 |
| 749 | A171 | 31p multicolored | 1.10 | 1.10 |
| *a.* | | *Pair, #748-749* | 2.25 | 2.25 |
| 750 | A171 | 36p multicolored | 1.25 | 1.25 |
| 751 | A171 | 36p multicolored | 1.25 | 1.25 |
| *a.* | | *Pair, #750-751* | 2.50 | 2.50 |
| | | *Nos. 744-751 (8)* | 7.80 | 7.80 |

Golf Courses A172

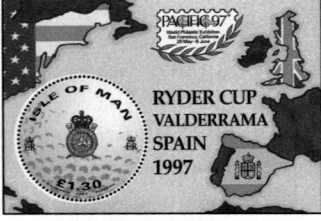

1997 Ryder Cup, Valderrama, Spain — A173

21p, 14th Hole, Ramsey Golf Club. 25p, 15th Hole, King Edward Bay Golf and Country Club. 43p, 17th Hole, Rowany Golf Club. 50p, 8th Hole, Castletown Golf Links.

**1997, May 29    Litho.    Perf. 14**
| | | | | |
|---|---|---|---|---|
| 752 | A172 | 21p multicolored | .70 | .70 |
| *a.* | | *Booklet pane of 3* | 2.10 | |
| 753 | A172 | 25p multicolored | .90 | .90 |
| *a.* | | *Booklet pane of 3* | 2.75 | |
| 754 | A172 | 43p multicolored | 1.60 | 1.60 |
| 755 | A172 | 50p multicolored | 1.75 | 1.75 |
| *a.* | | *Bklt. pane, 2 ea #754-755* | 6.75 | |
| | | *Nos. 752-755 (4)* | 4.95 | 4.95 |

**Souvenir Sheet**
| | | | | |
|---|---|---|---|---|
| 756 | A173 | £1.30 multicolored | 5.25 | 5.25 |
| *a.* | | *Complete booklet, #752a, 753a, 755a, 756a* | 17.00 | |

PACIFIC 97 (#756). No. 756 contains one 40mm diameter stamp.
No. 756a has a large white border, is 155x96mm and is sewn into booklet.

Trial of Nations Motorcycle Competition — A174

Various motorcyclists: 21p, Steve Colley. 25p, Steve Saunders. 37p, Sammy Miller. 44p, Don Smith..

**1997, Sept. 29    Litho.    Perf. 13½**
| | | | | |
|---|---|---|---|---|
| 757 | A174 | 21p multicolored | .70 | .70 |
| 758 | A174 | 25p multi, vert. | .85 | .85 |
| 759 | A174 | 37p multi, vert. | 1.40 | 1.40 |
| 760 | A174 | 44p multicolored | 1.60 | 1.60 |
| | | *Nos. 757-760 (4)* | 4.55 | 4.55 |

Queen Elizabeth II and Prince Philip, 50th Wedding Anniv. — A175

Designs: a, Early drawing of couple. b, Wedding portrait. c, Drawing of Queen waving, Prince in top hat. d, Portrait, 1997.
£1, Queen, Prince touring Isle of Man, 1989.

**1997, Nov. 3    Perf. 14x14½**
| | | | | |
|---|---|---|---|---|
| 761 | A175 | 50p Strip of 4, #a.-d. | 7.00 | 7.00 |

**Souvenir Sheet**
**Perf. 14**
| | | | | |
|---|---|---|---|---|
| 762 | A175 | £1 multicolored | 3.75 | 3.75 |

No. 761 was issued in sheets of 16 stamps. No. 762 contains one 48x58mm stamp.

Christmas — A176

**1997, Nov. 3    Perf. 14**
| | | | | |
|---|---|---|---|---|
| 763 | A176 | 20p Angel, shepherd | .75 | .75 |
| 764 | A176 | 24p Wise man, angel | .85 | .85 |
| | | **Size: 54x39mm** | | |
| 765 | A176 | 63p Angel and one of the Three Kings | 2.40 | 2.40 |
| | | *Nos. 763-765 (3)* | 4.00 | 4.00 |

Flowers — A177

**1998, Feb. 12    Litho.    Perf. 13x13½**
| | | | | |
|---|---|---|---|---|
| 766 | A177 | 4p Shamrocks | .20 | .20 |
| 767 | A177 | 21p Cushag | .80 | .80 |
| 768 | A177 | 25p Princess of Wales Rose | 1.00 | 1.00 |
| | | *Complete booklet, 2 each #766-768* | 4.00 | |
| 769 | A177 | 50p Daffodil | 2.00 | 2.00 |
| 770 | A177 | £1 Spear thistle | 4.00 | 4.00 |
| | | *Nos. 766-770 (5)* | 8.00 | 8.00 |

Nos. 766-768 also exist in special booklet sheets containing 10 of each denomination. Booklet panes made from these sheets contain 2 each #766-768.
No. 766 exists dated "1999."
See Nos. 794-801.

A178

Viking Longships: 21p, Dragon's head figurehead. 25p, Ship under full sail. 31p, Ship with sail furled. 75p Ship's stern.
£1, Man on ship pointing, fortress.

**1998, Feb. 14    Perf. 14**
| | | | | |
|---|---|---|---|---|
| 771 | A178 | 21p multicolored | .80 | .80 |
| 772 | A178 | 25p multicolored | 1.00 | 1.00 |
| 773 | A178 | 31p multicolored | 1.25 | 1.25 |
| 774 | A178 | 75p multicolored | 3.00 | 3.00 |
| | | *Nos. 771-774 (4)* | 6.05 | 6.05 |

**Souvenir Sheet**
| | | | | |
|---|---|---|---|---|
| 775 | A178 | £1 multicolored | 4.00 | 4.00 |

Marine Life A179

Designs: 10p, Bottle-nosed dolphin. 21p, Basking shark swimming right. 25p, Basking shark swimming forward. 31p, Minke whale. 63p, Killer whale.

**1998, Mar. 14    Litho.    Perf. 14**
| | | | | |
|---|---|---|---|---|
| 776 | A179 | 10p multicolored | .40 | .40 |
| 777 | A179 | 21p multicolored | .80 | .80 |
| *a.* | | *Booklet pane of 6, 3 each #776-777 + 3 labels* | 3.75 | |
| 778 | A179 | 25p multicolored | 1.00 | 1.00 |
| 779 | A179 | 31p multicolored | 1.25 | 1.25 |
| 780 | A179 | 63p multicolored | 2.40 | 2.40 |
| *a.* | | *Bklt. pane of 8, 2 ea #778-780 + label* | 11.00 | |
| | | *Souvenir booklet, #777a, 780a* | 15.00 | |
| | | *Nos. 776-780 (5)* | 5.85 | 5.85 |

Trains
A180

Designs: 21p, Hutchinson 2-4-0. 25p, G.H. Wood 2-4-0. 31p, Maitland 2-4-0. 63p, Loch 2-4-0.

**1998, May 2    Litho.    Perf. 14½x14**

| | | | | |
|---|---|---|---|---|
| 781 | A180 | 21p multicolored | .80 | .80 |
| 782 | A180 | 25p multicolored | 1.00 | 1.00 |
| 783 | A180 | 31p multicolored | 1.25 | 1.25 |
| 784 | A180 | 63p multicolored | 2.40 | 2.40 |
| a. | | Bklt. pane of 4, #781-784 | 5.50 | 5.50 |
| | | Nos. 781-784 (4) | 5.45 | 5.45 |

**Souvenir Sheet**

| | | | | |
|---|---|---|---|---|
| 785 | A180 | Sheet of 2 | 5.50 | 5.50 |
| a. | | £1 Engine | 4.50 | 4.50 |
| b. | | 25p Passenger cars | 1.00 | 1.00 |
| c. | | Booklet pane of 1 | 5.50 | 5.50 |
| | | Complete bklt., #785c, 2 #784a | 17.00 | |
| d. | | As #785, inscribed in sheet margin | 5.50 | 5.50 |

No. 784a exists with two different backgrounds and stamps in different order. Complete booklets contain one of each pane.
No. 785d is inscribed in sheet margin with PhilexFrance '99, World Philatelic Exhibition emblem and was issued 7/2/99.

Europa
A181

National Days celebration: 25p, People under tent, seated in stand, watching ceremony. 30p, Women dancing in traditional costumes.

**1998, July 2    Perf. 13x13½**

| | | | | |
|---|---|---|---|---|
| 786 | A181 | 25p multicolored | 1.00 | 1.00 |
| 787 | A181 | 30p multicolored | 1.25 | 1.25 |

1998 Tourist Trophy Motorcycle Races — A182

Designs: 21p, Eight-man pyramid. 25p, Joey Dunlop rounding curve. 31p, Dave Molyneux with side car. 43p, Naomi Taniguchi racing. 63p, Mike Hailwood racing.

**1998, June 1    Litho.    Perf. 14**

| | | | | |
|---|---|---|---|---|
| 788 | A182 | 21p multicolored | .80 | .80 |
| 789 | A182 | 25p multicolored | 1.00 | 1.00 |
| 790 | A182 | 31p multicolored | 1.25 | 1.25 |
| 791 | A182 | 43p multicolored | 1.60 | 1.60 |
| 792 | A182 | 63p multicolored | 2.50 | 2.50 |
| | | Nos. 788-792 (5) | 7.15 | 7.15 |

A183

Diana, Princess of Wales (1961-97): a, In black evening dress. b, Accepting flowers. c, Holding hand to face. d, In protective clothing.

**1998, June 19    Perf. 13**

| | | | | |
|---|---|---|---|---|
| 793 | A183 | 25p Strip of 4, #a.-d. | 4.00 | 4.00 |

**Flower Type**
**Perf. 13, 13x13½ (5p, 22p, 26p)**
**1998-99    Litho.**

Flowers: 1p, Bearded iris. 2p, Daisy. 5p, Silver jubilee rose. 10p, Oriental poppy. 20p,

Heath spotted orchid. 22p, Gorse. 26p, Dog rose. 30p, Fuchsia - lady thumb.

| | | | | |
|---|---|---|---|---|
| 794 | A177 | 1p multicolored | .20 | .20 |
| 795 | A177 | 2p multicolored | .20 | .20 |
| 796 | A177 | 5p multicolored | .20 | .20 |
| 797 | A177 | 10p multicolored | .40 | .40 |
| 798 | A177 | 20p multicolored | .80 | .80 |
| 799 | A177 | 22p multicolored | .85 | .85 |
| 800 | A177 | 26p multicolored | 1.00 | 1.00 |
| a. | | Bklt. pane, #800, 2 #766, 3 #799 | 4.00 | |
| | | Complete booklet, #800a | 4.00 | |
| 801 | A177 | 30p multicolored | 1.25 | 1.25 |
| | | Nos. 794-801 (8) | 4.90 | 4.90 |

Issued: 5p, 22p, 26p, 4/26/99; others, 7/2/98.

Queen Mother and Queen Elizabeth II
A185

**1998, July 2    Litho.    Perf. 13**

| | | | | |
|---|---|---|---|---|
| 802 | A185 | £2.50 multicolored | 10.00 | 10.00 |

Christmas
A186

Santa Claus: 20p, Loading sleigh at North Pole. 24p, With list, reindeer standing in clouds, Isle of Man below. 30p, Going over Spring Valley Sorting Office. 43p, Passing through Baldrine. 63p, Leaving presents, children inside house.

**1998, Sept. 25    Litho.    Perf. 14½x14**

| | | | | |
|---|---|---|---|---|
| 803 | A186 | 20p multicolored | .70 | .70 |
| 804 | A186 | 24p multicolored | .85 | .85 |
| 805 | A186 | 30p multicolored | 1.25 | 1.25 |
| 806 | A186 | 43p multicolored | 1.60 | 1.60 |
| 807 | A186 | 63p multicolored | 2.50 | 2.50 |
| | | Nos. 803-807 (5) | 6.90 | 6.90 |

Manx Nature Reserve and Parks (Europa) — A187

Designs: 25p, Cottage, Ballaglass Glen. 30p, Glen Maye Waterfall.

**1999, Mar. 4    Litho.    Perf. 14**

| | | | | |
|---|---|---|---|---|
| 808 | A187 | 25p multicolored | 1.00 | 1.00 |
| 809 | A187 | 30p multicolored | 1.25 | 1.25 |

Post Boxes — A188

10p, Oval box, Kirk Onchan Post Office. 20p, Wall box, Ballaterson, Ballaugh. 21p, Cylindrical box, Laxey Station. 25p, Wall box, Spaldrick, Port Erin. 44p, Oval box, Derby Road, Douglas. 63p, Wall box, Baldrine Station.

**1999, Mar. 4**

| | | | | |
|---|---|---|---|---|
| 810 | A188 | 10p multicolored | .40 | .40 |
| 811 | A188 | 20p multicolored | .80 | .80 |
| 812 | A188 | 21p multicolored | .80 | .80 |
| 813 | A188 | 25p multicolored | .95 | .95 |
| 814 | A188 | 44p multicolored | 1.60 | 1.60 |
| 815 | A188 | 63p multicolored | 2.40 | 2.40 |
| | | Nos. 810-815 (6) | 6.95 | 6.95 |

Royal Natl. Lifeboat Institution, 175th Anniv. — A189

**1999, Mar. 4**

| | | | | |
|---|---|---|---|---|
| 816 | A189 | 21p Ramsey lifeboat | .80 | .80 |
| 817 | A189 | 25p Douglas lifeboat | 1.00 | 1.00 |
| 818 | A189 | 37p Peel lifeboat | 1.50 | 1.50 |
| 819 | A189 | 43p Port Erin lifeboat | 1.60 | 1.60 |
| 820 | A189 | 56p Port St. Mary lifeboat | 2.25 | 2.25 |
| a. | | Bklt. pane, #816-820 + 4 labels | 7.25 | |
| | | Nos. 816-820 (5) | 7.15 | 7.15 |

**Booklet Stamps**

| | | | | |
|---|---|---|---|---|
| 821 | A189 | 43p #38 | 1.60 | 1.60 |
| 822 | A189 | 56p #464 | 2.25 | 2.25 |
| a. | | Booklet pane, #816-818, #821-822 + 4 labels | 7.25 | |

**Souvenir Sheet**

| | | | | |
|---|---|---|---|---|
| 823 | A189 | £1 William Hillary (1771-1847) | 4.00 | 4.00 |
| a. | | Booklet pane of 1 | 4.00 | |
| | | Complete booklet, #820a, #822a, #823a | 19.00 | |

IBRA '99 (#822a), Australia '99, World Stamp Expo. (#823). No. 823 contains one 38x50mm stamp.

Celtic Jewelry Depicting Seasons — A190

**1999, May 14    Perf. 14½x14**

| | | | | |
|---|---|---|---|---|
| 824 | A190 | 22p Winter | .85 | .85 |
| 825 | A190 | 26p Spring | 1.00 | 1.00 |
| 826 | A190 | 50p Summer | 1.90 | 1.90 |
| 827 | A190 | 63p Autumn | 2.50 | 2.50 |
| | | Nos. 824-827 (4) | 6.25 | 6.25 |

20th Century British Monarchs
A191

Monarch: a, Victoria. b, Edward VII. c, George V. d, Edward VIII. e, George VI. f, Elizabeth II.

**1999, June 2    Litho.    Perf. 14**

| | | | | |
|---|---|---|---|---|
| 828 | A191 | 26p Sheet of 6, #a.-f. | 6.00 | 6.00 |

Manx Buses
A192

22p, 1922 Tilling Stevens 46 double-decker. 26p, 1928 Thornycroft BC 28-seat. 28p, 1927 ADC 416 28-seat. 37p, 1914 Staker Squire 25-seat. 38p, 1927 Thornycroft A2 20-seat. 40p, 1938 Leyland Lion LT9 34-seat.

**1999, June 18**

| | | | | |
|---|---|---|---|---|
| 829 | A192 | 22p multicolored | .85 | .85 |
| 830 | A192 | 26p multicolored | 1.00 | 1.00 |
| 831 | A192 | 28p multicolored | 1.10 | 1.10 |
| 832 | A192 | 37p multicolored | 1.50 | 1.50 |
| 833 | A192 | 38p multicolored | 1.50 | 1.50 |
| 834 | A192 | 40p multicolored | 1.60 | 1.60 |
| | | Nos. 829-834 (6) | 7.55 | 7.55 |

| | | | |
|---|---|---|---|
| 831a | Bklt. pane, #829-830, 2 #831 | 4.25 | |
| 832a | Bklt. pane, #829-830, 2 #832 | 5.00 | |
| 833a | Bklt. pane, #829-830, 2 #833 | 5.00 | |
| 834a | Bklt. pane, #829-830, 2 #834 | 5.25 | |
| | Complete booklet, #831a-834a | 19.50 | |

Wedding of Prince Edward and Sophie Rhys-Jones — A193

**1999, June 19**

| | | | | |
|---|---|---|---|---|
| 835 | A193 | 22p Sophie, vert. | .85 | .85 |
| 836 | A193 | 39p Prince Edward, vert. | 1.40 | 1.40 |
| 837 | A193 | 44p Couple | 1.60 | 1.60 |
| | | Nos. 835-837 (3) | 3.85 | 3.85 |

Royal Wedding Photos — A193a

Designs: 26p, Couple standing, vert. 53p, Couple seated in carriage.

**1999, Sept. 1    Litho.    Perf. 14¼**

| | | | | |
|---|---|---|---|---|
| 837A | A193a | 26p multi | 1.00 | 1.00 |
| 837B | A193a | 53p multi | 2.00 | 2.00 |

Churches — A194

Illustration reduced.

**Perf. 13¼x13½**
**1999, Sept. 22    Litho.**

| | | | | |
|---|---|---|---|---|
| 838 | A194 | 21p St. Luke's | .80 | .80 |
| 839 | A194 | 25p St. Mark's, Malew | .95 | .95 |
| 840 | A194 | 30p Cathedral Peel | 1.10 | 1.10 |
| 841 | A194 | 64p Kirk Christ Church, Rushan | 2.50 | 2.50 |
| | | Nos. 838-841 (4) | 5.35 | 5.35 |

Bee Gees Songs
A195

Designs: 22p, "Massachusetts." 26p, "Words." 29p, "I've Gotta Get a Message to You." 37p, "Ellan Vannin." 38p, "You Win Again." 66p, "Night Fever." 60p, "Immortality." 90p, "Stayin' Alive."

**1999, Oct. 12    Litho.    Perf. 13¼x13½**

| | | | | |
|---|---|---|---|---|
| 842 | A195 | 22p multicolored | .85 | .85 |
| 843 | A195 | 26p multicolored | 1.00 | 1.00 |
| 844 | A195 | 29p multicolored | 1.10 | 1.10 |
| 845 | A195 | 37p multicolored | 1.40 | 1.40 |
| 846 | A195 | 38p multicolored | 1.40 | 1.40 |
| 847 | A195 | 60p multicolored | 2.50 | 2.50 |
| | | Nos. 842-847 (6) | 8.25 | 8.25 |

**Souvenir Sheets**

| | | | | |
|---|---|---|---|---|
| 848 | A195 | 60p multicolored | 4.00 | 4.00 |
| 849 | A195 | 90p multicolored | 6.00 | 6.00 |

Nos. 848-849 each contain one 40mm diameter stamp. Nos. 842-847 each issued in sheets of 9 stamps and 3 labels.

Souvenir Sheet

Millennium A196

Objects in the night sky: a, 50p, Mars, stars Deneb, Altair, Vega. b, £2, Constellations Lynx, Draco, Ursa Minor, Ursa Major. c, 50p, Mercury, Venus, Deneb, Vega, Altair, orbit of International Space Station (ISS).

Perf. 14¼x14½

1999, Dec. 31 Litho.

850	A196	Sheet of 3, #a.-c.	13.00	13.00

History of Time — A197

Clock escapements of: 22p, 1735 by John Harrison. 26p, 2000 by George Daniels. 29p, 1767 by Harrison. 34p, 1769 by Thomas Mudge. 38p, 1779 by John Arnold. 44p, 1780 by Thomas Earnshaw.

2000, Jan. 24 Litho. *Perf. 13x13½*

851	A197	22p multi	.90	.90
852	A197	26p multi	1.00	1.00
853	A197	29p multi	1.10	1.10
854	A197	34p multi	1.40	1.40
855	A197	38p multi	1.50	1.50
856	A197	44p multi	1.75	1.75
		Nos. 851-856 (6)	7.65	7.65

Queen Mother (b. 1900) — A198

Pictures of Queen Mother from — No. 857: a, 1923. b, 1940. c, 1944.
No. 858: a, 1954. b, 1985. c, 1988.
No. 859, 1984.
£1, Queen Mother on Isle of Man.
Illustration reduced.

2000, Feb. 29 Litho. *Perf. 14*

857		Strip of 3	3.00	3.00
a.		A198 22p multi	.80	.80
b.		A198 26p multi	1.00	1.00
c.		A198 30p multi	1.10	1.10
858		Strip of 3	6.00	6.00
a.		A198 44p multi	1.60	1.60
b.		A198 52p multi	1.90	1.90
c.		A198 64p multi	2.40	2.40

Souvenir Sheet

Perf. 14¼

859	A198	£1 multi	3.75	3.75
a.		With emblem of The Stamp Show 2000 in margin	7.00	7.00

Size of Nos. 857a-857c, 858a-858c, 42x28mm.
Issued: No. 859a, 5/22/00.

Song Birds — A199

2000, May 5 *Perf. 14½x14¼*

860		Strip of 4	8.50	8.50
a.		A199 22p Swallow	1.00	1.00
b.		A199 26p Spotted flycatcher	1.10	1.10
c.		A199 64p Skylark	2.75	2.75
d.		A199 77p Yellowhammer	3.25	3.25

Military Leaders and Isle of Man Military Personnel A200

Battle of Britain, 60th Anniv. — A201

#861: a, John Quilliam (1771-1829), Admiral Lord Nelson (1758-1805). b, Caesar Bacon (1791-1876), Duke of Wellington (1769-1852).
#862: a, Thomas Leigh Goldie (1807-54), Earl of Cardigan (1797-1868). b, John Dunne (1884-1950), Sir Robert Baden-Powell (1857-1941).
#863: a, George Kneale (1896-1917), Viscount Kitchener (1850-1916). b, Alan Watterson (1910-42), Sir Winston Churchill (1874-1965).
#864: a, Planes in air. b, Plane on ground.
Illustration A201 reduced.

2000, May 22 Litho. *Perf. 13¼*

861		Pair, #a-b, + central label	1.90	1.90
a.		A200 22p multi	.80	.80
b.		A200 26p multi	1.00	1.00
862		Pair, #a-b, + central label	3.25	3.25
a.		A200 36p multi	1.40	1.40
b.		A200 48p multi	1.75	1.75
863		Pair, #a-b, + central label	4.75	4.75
a.		A200 50p multi	1.90	1.90
b.		A200 77p multi	2.75	2.75
c.		Booklet pane, #861a, 861b, 862a, 862b, 863a	7.00	
d.		Booklet pane, #861a, 862b, 863a, 863b	6.75	
		Nos. 861-863 (3)	9.90	9.90

Souvenir Sheet

Perf. 14¾x14¼

864	A201	60p Sheet of 2, #a-b	5.25	5.25
c.		Booklet pane, #864	5.25	
		Booklet, #863c, 863d, 864c	21.00	

No. 864c has stitched margin at left.

Souvenir Sheet

Prince William, 18th Birthday — A202

2000, June 21 Litho. *Perf. 14*

865		Sheet of 5	6.50	6.50
a.		A202 22p As toddler	.80	.80
b.		A202 26p With Queen Mother	1.00	1.00
c.		A202 45p In checked shirt	1.75	1.75
d.		A202 52p With Princes Charles, Harry	1.90	1.90
e.		A202 56p In ski gear	2.00	2.00

Gaiety Theater, Cent. A203

2000, July 16

866	A203	22p Ballet	.80	.80
867	A203	26p Comedy	1.00	1.00
868	A203	36p Drama	1.40	1.40
869	A203	45p Pantomime	1.75	1.75
870	A203	52p Opera	1.90	1.90
871	A203	65p Musicals	2.40	2.40
		Nos. 866-871 (6)	9.25	9.25

Global Challenge Yacht Race — A204

Sail from yacht "Isle of Man," and ports of call: 22p, Southampton. 26p, Sydney. 36p, Wellington. 40p, Buenos Aires. 44p, Boston. 65p, Cape Town.

Perf. 13¼x13¾

2000, Sept. 10 Litho.

872	A204	22p multi	.80	.80
873	A204	26p multi	1.00	1.00
874	A204	36p multi	1.40	1.40
875	A204	40p multi	1.50	1.50
876	A204	44p multi	1.60	1.60
877	A204	65p multi	2.40	2.40
		Nos. 872-877 (6)	8.70	8.70

Travel Poster Art of Isle of Man Steam Packet Co. — A205

Designs: 22p, Three legs of Man, ship. 26p, Cliffs and sailboats. 36p, Woman and Isle of Man. 45p, Woman, ship, flag. 65p, Ship.

2000, Oct. 16 *Perf. 13½x13¼*

878	A205	22p multi	.80	.80
879	A205	26p multi	1.00	1.00
880	A205	36p multi	1.40	1.40
881	A205	45p multi	1.75	1.75
882	A205	65p multi	2.40	2.40
		Nos. 878-882 (5)	7.35	7.35

Europa, 2000

Common Design Type

2000, Nov. 7 *Perf. 14*

883	CD17	36p multi	1.50	1.50

Christmas A206

2000, Nov. 7

884	A206	21p Peace	.80	.80
885	A206	25p Hope	.90	.90
886	A206	45p Love	1.75	1.75
887	A206	65p Faith	2.40	2.40
		Nos. 884-887 (4)	5.85	5.85

Souvenir Sheet

New Year 2001 (Year of the Snake) — A207

Litho. with Foil Application

2001, Jan. 22 *Perf. 13¾*

888	A207	£1 St. Patrick	4.00	4.00

Hong Kong 2001 Stamp Exhibition.

Queen Victoria (1819-1901) — A208

Designs: 22p, Wyon medal, Queen Victoria, Great Britain Type A1. 26p, Great Exhibition medal, Albert Tower. 34p, Coin, Steamship Great Britain. 39p, Coin, scene from Oliver Twist, St. Thomas' Church, Douglas. 40p, Coin, first train to arrive in Vancouver, Canada and Jubilee streetlamp standard. 52p, Coin, Foxdale Clock Tower, family of diamond magnate Joe Mylchreest.

2001, Jan. 22 Litho. *Perf. 13½*

889	A208	22p multi	.85	.85
890	A208	26p multi	1.00	1.00
891	A208	34p multi	1.40	1.40
892	A208	39p multi	1.50	1.50
893	A208	40p multi	1.60	1.60
894	A208	52p multi	2.00	2.00
		Nos. 889-894 (6)	8.35	8.35

Insects A209

Designs: 22p, White-tailed bumblebee. 26p, Seven-spot ladybug. 29p, Lesser mottled grasshopper. 58p, Manx robber fly. 66p, Elephant hawkmoth.

2001, Feb. 1 *Perf. 14½*

895	A209	22p multi	.85	.85
896	A209	26p multi	1.00	1.00
897	A209	29p multi	1.10	1.10
898	A209	58p multi	2.25	2.25
899	A209	66p multi	2.50	2.50
		Nos. 895-899 (5)	7.70	7.70

Souvenir Sheet

Queen Elizabeth II, 75th Birthday — A210

Stamps: 29p, Great Britain #MH1. 34p, Great Britain #300. 37p, Isle of Man #8. 50p, Isle of Man #3.

2001, Apr. 18 Litho. *Perf. 14*

900	A210	Sheet of 4, #a-d	6.00	6.00
e.		As #900, with Hafnia 01 emblem added in sheet margin	7.50	7.50

No. 900e issued 10/29.

Manx Postmen and Cancels — A211

2001, Apr. 18

901	A211	22p 1805	.85	.85
902	A211	26p 1859	1.00	1.00
903	A211	36p 1910	1.40	1.40
904	A211	39p 1933	1.50	1.50
905	A211	40p 1983	1.60	1.60
906	A211	66p 2001	2.50	2.50
		Nos. 901-906 (6)	8.85	8.85

William Joseph Dunlop (1952-2000),
Motorcycle Racer — A212

Various photographs.

**2001, May 17**
| | | | | |
|---|---|---|---|---|
| 907 | A212 | 22p multi | .85 | .85 |
| 908 | A212 | 26p multi | 1.00 | 1.00 |
| 909 | A212 | 36p multi | 1.40 | 1.40 |
| 910 | A212 | 45p multi | 1.75 | 1.75 |
| 911 | A212 | 65p multi | 2.50 | 2.50 |
| 912 | A212 | 77p multi | 2.75 | 2.75 |
| | Nos. 907-912 (6) | | 10.25 | 10.25 |

Horse
Racing
A213

Designs: 22p, Manx Derby. 26p, Post Haste. 36p, Red Rum. 52p, Hyperion. 63p, Isle of Man.

**2001, May 18**     **Perf. 13¼x13½**
| | | | | |
|---|---|---|---|---|
| 913 | A213 | 22p multi | .85 | .85 |
| 914 | A213 | 26p multi | 1.00 | 1.00 |
| 915 | A213 | 36p multi | 1.40 | 1.40 |
| 916 | A213 | 52p multi | 1.90 | 1.90 |
| 917 | A213 | 63p multi | 2.40 | 2.40 |
| | Nos. 913-917 (5) | | 7.55 | 7.55 |

Gourmet
Food — A214

**2001, Aug. 10**     **Litho.**     **Perf. 14¼**
| | | | | |
|---|---|---|---|---|
| 918 | A214 | 22p Beef | .80 | .80 |
| 919 | A214 | 26p Queenies | .90 | .90 |
| a. | | Sheet of 10 | 9.00 | |
| 920 | A214 | 36p Seafood | 1.25 | 1.25 |
| a. | | Sheet of 10 | 12.50 | |
| 921 | A214 | 45p Lamb | 1.60 | 1.60 |
| 922 | A214 | 50p Kippers | 1.90 | 1.90 |
| 923 | A214 | 66p Lemon tart | 2.40 | 2.40 |
| | Nos. 918-923 (6) | | 8.85 | 8.85 |

Europa (#919, 920).

Architecture of Mackay Hugh Baillie
Scott — A215

Designs: 22p, Castletown Police Station, 1901. 26p, Leafield/Braeside, 1897. 37p, Red House, 1893. 40p, Ivydene, 1893. 80p, Onchan Village Hall, 1898.

**2001, Sept. 3**     **Perf. 13¼x13½**
| | | | | |
|---|---|---|---|---|
| 924 | A215 | 22p multi | .85 | .85 |
| 925 | A215 | 26p multi | 1.00 | 1.00 |
| 926 | A215 | 37p multi | 1.40 | 1.40 |
| 927 | A215 | 40p multi | 1.60 | 1.60 |
| 928 | A215 | 80p multi | 3.00 | 3.00 |
| | Nos. 924-928 (5) | | 7.85 | 7.85 |

Reign of Queen
Elizabeth II, 50th
Anniv. (in
2002) — A216

Drawings of Queen: 22p, At dining table. 26p, With crowd, holding flower bouquet. 39p, With dogs. 40p, With men wearing hats. 45p, With correspondence. 65p, Alone, holding flower bouquet.

**Litho. With Foil Application**
**2001-02**     **Perf. 14¼**
| | | | | |
|---|---|---|---|---|
| 929 | A216 | 22p multi | .85 | .85 |
| 930 | A216 | 26p multi | 1.00 | 1.00 |
| 931 | A216 | 39p multi | 1.60 | 1.60 |
| a. | | Booklet pane of 3, #929-931 | 3.50 | — |
| 932 | A216 | 40p multi | 1.60 | 1.60 |
| 933 | A216 | 45p multi | 1.75 | 1.75 |
| 934 | A216 | 65p multi | 2.50 | 2.50 |
| a. | | Booklet pane of 3, #932-934 | 6.00 | — |
| | Nos. 929-934 (6) | | 9.30 | 9.30 |

Issued: Nos. 929-934, 10/29/01. Nos. 931a, 934a, 2/6/02.

Christmas
A217

Floral arrangements: 21p, Holly on Christmas tree-shaped frame. 25p, Wreath. 37p, Table decoration with candles. 45p, Topiary tree. 65p, Wreath, diff.

**2001, Nov. 5**     **Litho.**     **Perf. 14x14½**
**Stamp + Label**
**Background Color**
| | | | | |
|---|---|---|---|---|
| 935 | A217 | 21p green | .80 | .80 |
| 936 | A217 | 25p red | 1.00 | 1.00 |
| 937 | A217 | 37p gold | 1.40 | 1.40 |
| 938 | A217 | 45p silver | 1.75 | 1.75 |
| 939 | A217 | 65p violet | 2.40 | 2.40 |
| | Nos. 935-939 (5) | | 7.35 | 7.35 |

Reign of Queen
Elizabeth II, 50th
Anniv. — A218

No. 940 — Paintings: a, The Coronation, by Terence Cuneo. b, Her Majesty the Queen as Colonel in Chief, Grenadier Guards on Imperial, by Cuneo (Queen on horse). c, Her Majesty in Evening Dress, by June Mendoza. d, Her Majesty the Queen, by Chen Yan Ning. e, The Royal Family, by John Wonnacott.
£1, Her Majesty Queen Elizabeth II Lord of Mann, sculpture by David Cregeen.

**Litho. with Foil Application**
**2002, Feb. 6**     **Perf. 14**
| | | | | |
|---|---|---|---|---|
| 940 | | Vert. strip of 5 | 10.00 | 10.00 |
| a.-e. | | A218 50p Any single | 2.00 | 2.00 |
| f. | | Booklet pane of 3, #940a-940c | 6.25 | — |
| g. | | Booklet pane of 2, #940d-940e | 4.25 | — |

**Souvenir Sheet**
**Perf. 14½x14**
| | | | | |
|---|---|---|---|---|
| 941 | A218 | £1 multi | 4.00 | 4.00 |
| a. | | Booklet pane of 1 with larger margin | 4.00 | |
| | | Booklet, #931a, 934a, 940f, 940g, 941a | 24.00 | |

No. 941 contains one 60x40mm stamp.

No. 941 exists with purple inscription in sheet margin, "The Isle of Man Celebrates The Jubilee / 4th June 2002."

17th Commonwealth Games,
Manchester, England — A219

Designs: 22p, Cycling. 26p, Running. 29p, Javelin, women's high jump. 34p, Swimming. 40p, Hurdles, pole vault. 45p, Wheelchair racing.

**2002, Mar. 11**     **Litho.**     **Perf. 14**
| | | | | |
|---|---|---|---|---|
| 942 | A219 | 22p multi | .80 | .80 |
| 943 | A219 | 26p multi | .90 | .90 |
| 944 | A219 | 29p multi | 1.10 | 1.10 |
| 945 | A219 | 34p multi | 1.25 | 1.25 |
| 946 | A219 | 40p multi | 1.50 | 1.50 |
| 947 | A219 | 45p multi | 1.60 | 1.60 |
| | Nos. 942-947 (6) | | 7.15 | 7.15 |

Queen Mother
Elizabeth (1900-
2002)
A220

**2002, Apr. 23**     **Perf. 13x13¼**
| | | | | |
|---|---|---|---|---|
| 948 | A220 | £3 multi | 12.00 | 12.00 |

Paintings
by Toni
Onley
A221

Designs: 22p, Monks' Bridge, Ballasalla. 26p, Laxey. 37p, Langness Lighthouse. 45p, King William's College. 65p, The Mull Circle & Bradda Head.

**2002, May 1**     **Perf. 13¼x13½**
| | | | | |
|---|---|---|---|---|
| 949 | A221 | 22p multi | .85 | .85 |
| 950 | A221 | 26p multi | 1.00 | 1.00 |
| 951 | A221 | 37p multi | 1.50 | 1.50 |
| 952 | A221 | 45p multi | 1.75 | 1.75 |
| 953 | A221 | 65p multi | 2.50 | 2.50 |
| | Nos. 949-953 (5) | | 7.60 | 7.60 |

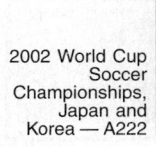

2002 World Cup
Soccer
Championships,
Japan and
Korea — A222

Various players.

**2002, May 1**     **Perf. 13½**
| | | | | |
|---|---|---|---|---|
| 954 | A222 | 22p multi | .85 | .85 |
| 955 | A222 | 26p multi | 1.00 | 1.00 |
| 956 | A222 | 39p multi | 1.60 | 1.60 |
| 957 | A222 | 40p multi | 1.60 | 1.60 |
| 958 | A222 | 66p multi | 2.50 | 2.50 |
| 959 | A222 | 68p multi | 2.75 | 2.75 |
| | Nos. 954-959 (6) | | 10.30 | 10.30 |

Flower
Sketches by
Sir Paul
McCartney
A223

Various sketches.

**2002, July 1**     **Litho.**     **Perf. 13¼x12¾**
| | | | | |
|---|---|---|---|---|
| 960 | A223 | 22p multi | .85 | .85 |
| 961 | A223 | 26p multi | 1.00 | 1.00 |
| 962 | A223 | 29p multi | 1.10 | 1.10 |
| 963 | A223 | 52p multi | 2.00 | 2.00 |
| 964 | A223 | 63p multi | 2.50 | 2.50 |
| 965 | A223 | 77p multi | 3.00 | 3.00 |
| | Nos. 960-965 (6) | | 10.45 | 10.45 |

Photographs of
Local
Scenes — A224

Designs: a, Laxey Wheel, by Kathy Brown. b, Sheep at Druidale, by John Hall. c, Carousel at Silverdale, by Colin Edwards. d, Grandma, by Stephanie Corkill. e, Manx Rock, by Ruth Nicholls. f, TT Riders at Signpost, by Neil Brew. g, Groudle Railway, by Albert Lowe. h, Royal Cascade, by Brian Speedie. i, St. Johns, by John Hall. j, Niarbyl Cottages with Poppies, by Cathy Galbraith.

**2002, Aug. 30**     **Litho.**     **Perf. 14**
| | | | | |
|---|---|---|---|---|
| 966 | | Block of 10 | 11.00 | 11.00 |
| a.-j. | | A224 27p Any single | 1.10 | 1.10 |

**Photography Type of 2002**
Designs like No. 966.

**Serpentine Die Cut 6¼**
**2002, Aug. 30**     **Litho.**
**Self-Adhesive**
| | | | | |
|---|---|---|---|---|
| 967 | | Booklet of 10 | 11.00 | 11.00 |
| a.-j. | | A224 27p Any single | 1.10 | 1.10 |

**Photography Type of 2002**
Designs: a, Manx Milestone, by Mrs. B. J. Trimble. b, Plow Horses, by Miss D. Flint. c, Manx Emblem, by Ruth Nicholls. d, Loaghtan Sheep, by Diana Buford. e, Fishing Fleet at Port St. Mary, by Phil Thomas. f, Peel, by Michael Thompson. g, Daffodils, by Michael Thompson. h, Millennium Sword, by Mr. F. K. Smith. i, Peel Castle, by Kathy Brown. j, Snaefell Railway, by Joan Burgess.

**2002, Oct. 1**     **Litho.**     **Perf. 14**
| | | | | |
|---|---|---|---|---|
| 968 | | Block of 10 | 9.00 | 9.00 |
| a.-j. | | A224 23p Any single | .90 | .90 |

**Self-Adhesive**
**Serpentine Die Cut 6¼**
| | | | | |
|---|---|---|---|---|
| 969 | | Booklet of 10 | 9.00 | 9.00 |
| a.-j. | | A224 23p Any single | .90 | .90 |

Christmas and
Europa — A225

Designs: 22p, Santa Claus. 26p, Madonna and Child. 37p, Clown. 47p, Cymbal player. 68p, Fairy. £1.30, "Christmas."

**2002, Nov. 5**     **Perf. 14x14½**
| | | | | |
|---|---|---|---|---|
| 970 | A225 | 22p multi | .80 | .80 |
| 971 | A225 | 26p multi | .95 | .95 |
| 972 | A225 | 37p multi | 1.50 | 1.50 |
| a. | | Sheet of 10 + 10 labels | 15.00 | 15.00 |
| 973 | A225 | 47p multi | 1.75 | 1.75 |
| 974 | A225 | 68p multi | 2.75 | 2.75 |
| | Nos. 970-974 (5) | | 7.75 | 7.75 |

**Miniature Sheet**
**Perf. 14¾**
| | | | | |
|---|---|---|---|---|
| 975 | A225 | £1.30 multi | 5.25 | 5.25 |

Europa (#972). No. 975 contains one 99x38mm stamp.

Post Office
Vehicles
A226

Designs: 23p, Handcart. 27p, Morris Z van. 37p, Morris LD van. 42p, DI BSA Bantam motorcycle. 89p, Ford Escort 55 delivery van.

**2003, Feb. 14**                         *Perf. 14¼*
| | | | | |
|---|---|---|---|---|
| **976** | A226 | 23p multi | .90 | .90 |
| **977** | A226 | 27p multi | 1.10 | 1.10 |
| **978** | A226 | 37p multi | 1.50 | 1.50 |
| **979** | A226 | 42p multi | 1.60 | 1.60 |
| **980** | A226 | 89p multi | 3.50 | 3.50 |
| | | *Nos. 976-980 (5)* | 8.60 | 8.60 |

Space Exploration — A227

No. 981: a, Tromode Teleport. b, Satellite earth station.
No. 982: a, Pioneering the space frontier (denomination at left). b, Pioneering the space frontier (denomination at right).
No. 983: a, Sea Launch Odyssey launch platform. b, Sea Launch Commander.
No. 984: a, Loral Skynet Telstar 1. b, Loral Skynet Telstar 8.
No. 985: a, Space station, Phobos. b, Astronauts, Mars.
Illustration reduced.

**2003, Feb. 14**                     *Perf. 13¼x13½*
| | | | | |
|---|---|---|---|---|
| **981** | A227 | Horiz. pair | 1.90 | 1.90 |
| *a.-b.* | | 23p Either single | .90 | .90 |
| **982** | A227 | Horiz. pair | 2.25 | 2.25 |
| *a.-b.* | | 27p Either single | 1.10 | 1.10 |
| **983** | A227 | Horiz. pair | 3.00 | 3.00 |
| *a.-b.* | | 37p Either single | 1.50 | 1.50 |
| **984** | A227 | Horiz. pair | 3.25 | 3.25 |
| *a.-b.* | | 42p Either single | 1.60 | 1.60 |
| | | *Nos. 981-984 (4)* | 10.40 | 10.40 |

**Souvenir Sheet**
*Perf. 13¼x13*
| | | | | |
|---|---|---|---|---|
| **985** | A227 | Horiz. pair | 6.00 | 6.00 |
| *a.-b.* | | 75p Either single | 3.00 | 3.00 |

No. 985 contains two 29x38mm stamps.

Coronation of Queen Elizabeth II, 50th Anniv. — A228

No. 986: a, Queen wearing St. Edward's Crown (brown background, 29x59mm). b, Queen wearing Sovereign's ring and armills (29x29mm). c, Sovereign's orb (29x29mm). d, Scepter with Cross, Rod with Dove (29x29mm). e, Queen wearing Imperial State Crown (blue green background, 29x59mm) f, Queen in State Coach (89x29mm).
Illustration reduced.

**Litho. With Foil Application**
**2003, Apr. 12**                        *Perf. 13¼*
| | | | | |
|---|---|---|---|---|
| **986** | A228 | Block of 6 | 12.00 | 12.00 |
| *a.-f.* | | 50p Any single | 2.00 | 2.00 |

Powered Flight, Cent. — A229

No. 987: a, DH 83 Fox Moth, Saro Cloud. b, DH 61 Giant Moth, DH Puss Moth. c, Avro Anson, B-17 Flying Fortress.
No. 988: a, Eurofighter Typhoon, Avro Vulcan. b, Handley Page Herald, Bristol Wayfarer. c, Concorde, A380 Airbus.

**2003, May 9**        Litho.       *Perf. 13¼*
| | | | | |
|---|---|---|---|---|
| **987** | | Strip of 3 | 3.50 | 3.50 |
| *a.* | A229 | 23p multi | .90 | .90 |
| *b.* | A229 | 27p multi | 1.10 | 1.10 |
| *c.* | A229 | 37p multi | 1.50 | 1.50 |
| **988** | | Strip of 3 | 8.00 | 8.00 |
| *a.* | A229 | 40p multi | 1.60 | 1.60 |
| *b.* | A229 | 67p multi | 2.75 | 2.75 |
| *c.* | A229 | 89p multi | 3.50 | 3.50 |

Souvenir Sheet

Dambuster's Raid, 60th Anniv. — A230

**2003**
| | | | | |
|---|---|---|---|---|
| **989** | A230 | £2 multi | 8.00 | 8.00 |
| *a.* | | With "Ticino 2003" emblem in margin | 8.50 | 8.50 |

Issued: No. 989, 5/9; No. 989a, 6/18.

Prince William, 21st Birthday A231

Various photographs.

**2003, June 9**                   *Perf. 13¼x13½*
| | | | | |
|---|---|---|---|---|
| **990** | A231 | 42p black | 1.60 | 1.60 |
| **991** | A231 | 47p black | 1.90 | 1.90 |
| **992** | A231 | 52p black | 2.00 | 2.00 |
| **993** | A231 | 68p black | 2.50 | 2.50 |
| | | *Nos. 990-993 (4)* | 8.00 | 8.00 |

Literature With Manx Connections — A232

Designs: 23p, Manx Gold, by Agatha Christie. 27p, Quartermass and the Pit, by Nigel Kneale. 30p, Flashman at the Charge, by George MacDonald Fraser. 38p, The Eternal City, by Hall Caine. 40p, Islanders, by Mona Douglas. 53p, Emma's Secret, by Barbara Taylor Bradford.

**2003, July 9**                          *Perf. 13¼*
**Stamp + Label**
| | | | | |
|---|---|---|---|---|
| **994** | A232 | 23p multi | .90 | .90 |
| **995** | A232 | 27p multi | 1.10 | 1.10 |
| **996** | A232 | 30p multi | 1.25 | 1.25 |
| **997** | A232 | 38p multi | 1.50 | 1.50 |
| *a.* | | Sheet of 10 + 10 labels | 15.00 | 15.00 |
| **998** | A232 | 40p multi | 1.60 | 1.60 |
| **999** | A232 | 53p multi | 2.00 | 2.00 |
| | | *Nos. 994-999 (6)* | 8.35 | 8.35 |

Europa (#997).

End of Tudor Reign, 400th Anniv. A233

Designs: 23p, Crowning of King Henry VII at Bosworth. 27p, King Henry VIII, Dissolution of the Monasteries. 38p, Queen Elizabeth I, Sir Francis Drake circumnavigates the globe. 40p, King Henry VIII, Hampton Court. 47p, Queen Mary I, Tudor rose. 67p, Queen Elizabeth I, Spanish Armada.

**2003, Sept. 15**                        *Perf. 14*
| | | | | |
|---|---|---|---|---|
| **1000** | A233 | 23p multi | .90 | .90 |
| **1001** | A233 | 27p multi | 1.10 | 1.10 |
| **1002** | A233 | 38p multi | 1.50 | 1.50 |
| **1003** | A233 | 40p multi | 1.60 | 1.60 |
| **1004** | A233 | 47p multi | 1.90 | 1.90 |
| **1005** | A233 | 67p multi | 2.50 | 2.50 |
| | | *Nos. 1000-1005 (6)* | 9.50 | 9.50 |

Henry Bloom Noble Trust, Cent. — A234

No. 1006: a, Boys' Orphanage. b, Ramsey Cottage Hospital. c, Children's Home. d, Noble's Baths. e, Scout Headquarters.
No. 1007: a, Noble's Hospital. b, Villa Marina. c, Noble's Park. d, St. Ninian's Church. e, Noble's Library.

**2003, Oct. 1**
| | | | | |
|---|---|---|---|---|
| **1006** | | Horiz. strip of 5 | 4.50 | 4.50 |
| *a.-e.* | | A234 23p Any single | .90 | .90 |
| **1007** | | Horiz. strip of 5 | 5.50 | 5.50 |
| *a.-e.* | | A234 27p Any single | 1.10 | 1.10 |

**Booklet Stamps**
**Self-Adhesive**
*Serpentine Die Cut 6¼*
| | | | | |
|---|---|---|---|---|
| **1007F** | A234 | 23p Like #1006a | .90 | .90 |
| **1007G** | A234 | 23p Like #1006b | .90 | .90 |
| **1007H** | A234 | 23p Like #1006c | .90 | .90 |
| **1007I** | A234 | 23p Like #1006d | .90 | .90 |
| **1007J** | A234 | 23p Like #1006e | .90 | .90 |
| *p.* | | Booklet pane, 2 each #1007F-1007J | 9.00 | |
| **1007K** | A234 | 27p Like #1007a | 1.10 | 1.10 |
| **1007L** | A234 | 27p Like #1007b | 1.10 | 1.10 |
| **1007M** | A234 | 27p Like #1007c | 1.10 | 1.10 |
| **1007N** | A234 | 27p Like #1007d | 1.10 | 1.10 |
| **1007O** | A234 | 27p Like #1007e | 1.10 | 1.10 |
| *q.* | | Booklet pane, 2 each #1007K-1007O | 11.00 | |
| | | *Nos. 1007F-1007O (10)* | 10.00 | 10.00 |

Nos. 1007Jp and 1007Oq are complete booklets, the backing serving as the booklet covers.

Christmas A235

Various snowmen, based on Raymond Briggs' children's story *The Snowman*.

**Litho. With Foil Application**
**2003, Nov. 5**                          *Perf. 14¼*
**Background Color**
| | | | | |
|---|---|---|---|---|
| **1008** | A235 | 22p red | .90 | .90 |
| **1009** | A235 | 26p deep blue | 1.00 | 1.00 |
| **1010** | A235 | 38p blue green | 1.50 | 1.50 |
| **1011** | A235 | 47p orange | 1.90 | 1.90 |
| **1012** | A235 | 68p yellow | 2.50 | 2.50 |
| | | *Nos. 1008-1012 (5)* | 7.80 | 7.80 |

Debut of Movie *The Lord of the Rings: The Return of the King* — A236

Designs: 23p, Aragorn. 27p, Gimli. 30p, Gandalf the White. 38p, Legolas on horseback. 42p, Gollum. 47p, Frodo Baggins and Samwise Gamgee. 68p, Legolas with bow and arrow. 85p, Aragorn on horseback. £2, Ring.

**2003, Dec. 17**      Litho.      *Perf. 13¼*
| | | | | |
|---|---|---|---|---|
| **1013** | A236 | 23p multi | .90 | .90 |
| **1014** | A236 | 27p multi | 1.10 | 1.10 |
| **1015** | A236 | 30p multi | 1.25 | 1.25 |
| **1016** | A236 | 38p multi | 1.50 | 1.50 |
| **1017** | A236 | 42p multi | 1.60 | 1.60 |
| **1018** | A236 | 47p multi | 1.90 | 1.90 |
| **1019** | A236 | 68p multi | 2.75 | 2.75 |
| **1020** | A236 | 85p multi | 3.50 | 3.50 |
| | | *Nos. 1013-1020 (8)* | 14.50 | 14.50 |

**Souvenir Sheet**
*Perf. 13½*
| | | | | |
|---|---|---|---|---|
| **1021** | A236 | £2 multi | 8.00 | 8.00 |

No. 1021 contains one 44x39mm stamp. Nos. 1013-1020 were each printed in sheets of six.

Steam Locomotives — A237

Designs: 23p, Maitland. 27p, Evening Star. 40p, Penydarren Tramroad locomotive. 57p, Duchess of Hamilton. 61p, City of Truro. 90p, Mallard.

**2004, Feb. 21**      Litho.      *Perf. 13x13½*
| | | | | |
|---|---|---|---|---|
| **1022** | A237 | 23p multi | .90 | .90 |
| **1023** | A237 | 27p multi | 1.10 | 1.10 |
| **1024** | A237 | 40p multi | 1.60 | 1.60 |
| **1025** | A237 | 57p multi | 2.25 | 2.25 |
| **1026** | A237 | 61p multi | 2.40 | 2.40 |
| **1027** | A237 | 90p multi | 3.50 | 3.50 |
| | | *Nos. 1022-1027 (6)* | 11.75 | 11.75 |

D-Day, 60th Anniv. — A238

No. 1028: a, Two soldiers near walkways, tanks on beach. b, Soldiers in water, tanks on beach.
No. 1029: a, Soldiers in water between two boats. b, Soldiers in water, landing craft with gangway open.
No. 1030: a, Lady of Mann, two blimps. b, Ben-my-Chree, three landing craft, five blimps.
No. 1031: a, Two US B-24 Liberators, RAF Horsa glider. b, Three RAF Horsa gliders.
No. 1032: a, Sir Winston Churchill. b, Soldiers near airplane propeller. c, Military vehicles on street in residential area. d, Soldiers reading book.
Illustration reduced.

**2004, Apr. 6**                          *Perf. 14*
| | | | | |
|---|---|---|---|---|
| **1028** | A238 | Horiz. pair | 1.90 | 1.90 |
| *a.-b.* | | 23p Either single | .90 | .90 |
| **1029** | A238 | Horiz. pair | 2.25 | 2.25 |
| *a.-b.* | | 27p Either single | 1.10 | 1.10 |
| **1030** | A238 | Horiz. pair | 4.00 | 4.00 |
| *a.-b.* | | 47p Either single | 1.90 | 1.90 |
| **1031** | A238 | Horiz. pair | 5.50 | 5.50 |
| *a.-b.* | | 68p Either single | 2.75 | 2.75 |
| | | *Nos. 1028-1031 (4)* | 13.65 | 13.65 |

**Souvenir Sheet**
*Perf. 13¼x13¾*
| | | | | |
|---|---|---|---|---|
| **1032** | A238 | Sheet of 4 | 8.00 | 8.00 |
| *a.-d.* | | 50p Any single | 2.00 | 2.00 |

Flowers A239

Designs: 25p, Lesser celandine. 28p, Red campion. 37p, Devil's bit scabious. 40p, Northern harebell. 68p, Wood anemone. 85p, Common spotted orchid.

**2004, May 3**                           *Perf. 13½*
| | | | | |
|---|---|---|---|---|
| **1033** | A239 | 25p multi | 1.00 | 1.00 |
| **1034** | A239 | 28p multi | 1.10 | 1.10 |
| **1035** | A239 | 37p multi | 1.50 | 1.50 |
| **1036** | A239 | 40p multi | 1.60 | 1.60 |
| **1037** | A239 | 68p multi | 2.75 | 2.75 |
| **1038** | A239 | 85p multi | 3.50 | 3.50 |
| | | *Nos. 1033-1038 (6)* | 11.45 | 11.45 |

George Formby (1904-61), Movie Actor — A240

Various scenes from film *No Limit* and text: 25p, No Limit. 28p, George. 40p, Speed Demon. 43p, Florence. 50p, Shuttleworth. 74p, Formby.

**2004, May 26**                          *Perf. 13¼*
| | | | | |
|---|---|---|---|---|
| **1039** | A240 | 25p multi | 1.00 | 1.00 |
| **1040** | A240 | 28p multi | 1.10 | 1.10 |
| **1041** | A240 | 40p multi | 1.60 | 1.60 |

| | | | | |
|---|---|---|---|---|
| 1042 | A240 | 43p multi | 1.75 | 1.75 |
| 1043 | A240 | 50p multi | 2.00 | 2.00 |
| 1044 | A240 | 74p multi | 3.00 | 3.00 |
| | | Nos. 1039-1044 (6) | 10.45 | 10.45 |

2004 Summer Olympics, Athens — A241

Designs: 25p, Johnny Weismuller, Paris Olympics, 1924. 28p, Jesse Owens, runners, Berlin Olympics, 1936. 43p, John Mark, torch bearer, London Olympics, 1948. 55p, Fanny Blankers-Koen, runners, London Olympics, 1948. 91p, Sir Steve Redgrave, rowers, Sydney Olympics, 2000.

**2004, July 1    Litho.    Perf. 14**

| | | | | |
|---|---|---|---|---|
| 1045 | A241 | 25p multi | 1.00 | 1.00 |
| 1046 | A241 | 28p multi | 1.10 | 1.10 |
| 1047 | A241 | 43p multi | 1.75 | 1.75 |
| 1048 | A241 | 55p multi | 2.25 | 2.25 |
| 1049 | A241 | 91p multi | 3.50 | 3.50 |
| | | Nos. 1045-1049 (5) | 9.60 | 9.60 |

Manx History — A242

Designs: Nos. 1050a, 1052, Celtic islander and Viking invaders. Nos. 1050b, 1053, Ships and the sea. Nos. 1050c, 1054, Laxey miners. Nos. 1050d, 1055, Kings and Lords of Mann. Nos. 1050e, 1056, Farmers and crofters. Nos. 1051a, 1057, Calf of Man. Nos. 1051b, 1058, Peel Castle. Nos. 1051c, 1059, Laxey Wheel. Nos. 1051d, 1060, Castle Rushen. Nos. 1051e, 1061, Cregneash.

**2004, Aug. 3    Perf. 14¼**

| | | | | |
|---|---|---|---|---|
| 1050 | | Horiz. strip of 5 | 5.00 | 5.00 |
| a.-e. | A242 | (25p) Any single | 1.00 | 1.00 |
| 1051 | | Horiz. strip of 5 | 5.50 | 5.50 |
| a.-e. | A242 | (28p) Any single | 1.10 | 1.10 |

**Booklet Stamps**
**Self-Adhesive**
**Serpentine Die Cut 12½**

| | | | | |
|---|---|---|---|---|
| 1052 | A242 | (25p) multi | 1.00 | 1.00 |
| 1053 | A242 | (25p) multi | 1.00 | 1.00 |
| 1054 | A242 | (25p) multi | 1.00 | 1.00 |
| 1055 | A242 | (25p) multi | 1.00 | 1.00 |
| 1056 | A242 | (25p) multi | 1.00 | 1.00 |
| a. | | Booklet pane, 2 each #1052-1056 | 10.00 | |
| 1057 | A242 | (28p) multi | 1.10 | 1.10 |
| 1058 | A242 | (28p) multi | 1.10 | 1.10 |
| 1059 | A242 | (28p) multi | 1.10 | 1.10 |
| 1060 | A242 | (28p) multi | 1.10 | 1.10 |
| 1061 | A242 | (28p) multi | 1.10 | 1.10 |
| a. | | Booklet pane, 2 each #1057-1061 | 11.00 | |
| | | Nos. 1050-1061 (12) | 21.00 | 21.00 |

Nos. 1056a and 1061a are complete booklets, the backing serving as the booklet covers.

**Souvenir Sheet**

Laxey Wheel, 150th Anniv. — A243

**2004, Aug. 3    Perf. 14¼**

| | | | | |
|---|---|---|---|---|
| 1062 | A243 | £2 multi | 8.00 | 8.00 |
| a. | | With Sindelfingen 2004 emblem added in sheet margin | 8.50 | 8.50 |

No. 1062a issued 10/29.

Watercolors by Alfred Heaton Cooper (1864-1929) A244

Designs: 25p, Maughold Church. 28p, Port St. Mary. 40p, Ballaugh Old Church. 41p, Douglas Bay (A Midsummer's Night). 43p, Point of Ayre. 74p, Peel Harbor and Castle.

**2004, Oct. 21    Litho.    Perf. 13¼x12¾**

| | | | | |
|---|---|---|---|---|
| 1063 | A244 | 25p multi | 1.00 | 1.00 |
| 1064 | A244 | 28p multi | 1.10 | 1.10 |
| a. | | Sheet of 10 + 10 labels | 11.00 | 11.00 |
| 1065 | A244 | 40p multi | 1.60 | 1.60 |
| a. | | Sheet of 10 + 10 labels | 16.00 | 16.00 |
| 1066 | A244 | 41p multi | 1.60 | 1.60 |
| 1067 | A244 | 43p multi | 1.75 | 1.75 |
| 1068 | A244 | 74p multi | 3.00 | 3.00 |
| | | Nos. 1063-1068 (6) | 10.05 | 10.05 |

Europa (#1064-1065).

Robins A245

Robin on: 25p, Flowerpot. 28p, Rock. 40p, Branch. 47p, Window sill. 68p, Log.

**2004, Nov. 9    Perf. 12½x13**

| | | | | |
|---|---|---|---|---|
| 1069 | A245 | 25p multi | 1.00 | 1.00 |
| 1070 | A245 | 28p multi | 1.10 | 1.10 |
| 1071 | A245 | 40p multi | 1.60 | 1.60 |
| 1072 | A245 | 47p multi | 1.90 | 1.90 |
| 1073 | A245 | 68p multi | 2.75 | 2.75 |
| a. | | Miniature sheet, 2 each #1069-1073 | 19.00 | 19.00 |
| | | Nos. 1069-1073 (5) | 8.35 | 8.35 |

Scenes from Harry Potter and the Prisoner of Azkaban A246

Designs: 25p, Harry Potter, Ron Weasley and Hermione Granger. 28p, Owl Post. 39p, Harry and Petronus. 40p, Hogwarts Express. 49p, Hagrid. 55p, Knight Bus. 57p, Harry and Dementor. 68p, Harry and Buckbeak.

**2004, Dec. 7    Perf. 13¼**

| | | | | |
|---|---|---|---|---|
| 1074 | A246 | 25p multi | 1.00 | 1.00 |
| 1075 | A246 | 28p multi | 1.10 | 1.10 |
| 1076 | A246 | 39p multi | 1.60 | 1.60 |
| 1077 | A246 | 40p multi | 1.60 | 1.60 |
| 1078 | A246 | 49p multi | 2.00 | 2.00 |
| 1079 | A246 | 55p multi | 2.25 | 2.25 |
| 1080 | A246 | 57p multi | 2.25 | 2.25 |
| 1081 | A246 | 68p multi | 2.75 | 2.75 |
| | | Nos. 1074-1081 (8) | 14.55 | 14.55 |

Each printed in sheets of 5.

Battle of Trafalgar, Bicent. — A247

No. 1082: a, Nile Campaign. b, Battle of Copenhagen.
No. 1083: a, Emma Horatia Nelson. b, Band of brothers.
No. 1084: a, Prepare for battle. b, Victory in sight.
No. 1085: a, Fall of Nelson. b, Death of Nelson.
No. 1086: a, #861a. b, #159.
Illustration reduced.

**2005    Perf. 12½x13**

| | | | | |
|---|---|---|---|---|
| 1082 | A247 | Horiz. pair | 2.00 | 2.00 |
| a.-b. | | 25p Either single | 1.00 | 1.00 |
| 1083 | A247 | Horiz. pair | 2.25 | 2.25 |
| a.-b. | | 28p Either single | 1.10 | 1.10 |
| 1084 | A247 | Horiz. pair | 4.00 | 4.00 |
| a.-b. | | 50p Either single | 2.00 | 2.00 |
| 1085 | A247 | Horiz. pair | 5.00 | 5.00 |
| a.-b. | | 65p Either single | 2.50 | 2.50 |
| | | Nos. 1082-1085 (4) | 13.25 | 13.25 |

**Souvenir Sheet**

| | | | | |
|---|---|---|---|---|
| 1086 | A247 | Sheet of 2 | 8.00 | 8.00 |
| a.-b. | | £1 Either single | 4.00 | 4.00 |

Issued: Nos. 1082-1085, 1/9; No. 1086, 2/1.

Victory in World War II, 60th Anniv. — A248

No. 1087: a, Women and sailors. b, Soldiers and women marching together.
No. 1088: a, Soldier trying on hat. b, Servicewomen.
No. 1089: a, Winston Churchill and Royal family waving. b, Royal family in carriage.
No. 1090: a, Servicemen without shirts. b, Cemetery.
No. 1091: a, Manx Regiment. b, Royal visit, 1945.
Illustration reduced.

**2005, Apr. 15    Litho.    Perf. 13¼x13¾**

| | | | | |
|---|---|---|---|---|
| 1087 | A248 | Horiz. pair | 2.25 | 2.25 |
| a.-b. | | 26p Either single | 1.10 | 1.10 |
| 1088 | A248 | Horiz. pair | 2.50 | 2.50 |
| a.-b. | | 29p Either single | 1.25 | 1.25 |
| 1089 | A248 | Horiz. pair | 5.00 | 5.00 |
| a.-b. | | 60p Either single | 2.50 | 2.50 |
| 1090 | A248 | Horiz. pair | 5.50 | 5.50 |
| a.-b. | | 65p Either single | 2.75 | 2.75 |
| | | Nos. 1087-1090 (4) | 15.25 | 15.25 |

**Souvenir Sheet**

| | | | | |
|---|---|---|---|---|
| 1091 | A248 | Sheet of 2 | 9.00 | 9.00 |
| a.-b. | | £1 Either single | 4.50 | 4.50 |

Paintings of Isle of Man Steam Packet Company Ships — A249

No. 1092: a, Mona's Isle, by Samuel Walters. b, Viking, by Norman Wilkinson.
No. 1093: a, King Orry, by Robert Lloyd. b, Mona's Queen, by Arthur Burgess.
No. 1094: a, Ben-my-Chree, by John Nicholson. b, King Orry, by Robert Lloyd, diff.
No. 1095: a, Ben-my-Chree, by Robert Lloyd. b, Lady of Mann, by Robert Lloyd.
Illustration reduced.

**2005, May 6    Perf. 14**

| | | | | |
|---|---|---|---|---|
| 1092 | A249 | Horiz. pair | 2.25 | 2.25 |
| a.-b. | | 26p Either single | 1.10 | 1.10 |
| 1093 | A249 | Horiz. pair | 2.50 | 2.50 |
| a.-b. | | 29p Either single | 1.25 | 1.25 |
| c. | | Booklet pane, #1092, 1093 | 4.75 | — |
| 1094 | A249 | Horiz. pair | 3.50 | 3.50 |
| a.-b. | | 40p Either single | 1.75 | 1.75 |
| c. | | Booklet pane, #1092, 1094 | 5.75 | — |
| 1095 | A249 | Horiz. pair | 5.50 | 5.50 |
| a.-b. | | 66p Either single | 2.75 | 2.75 |
| c. | | Booklet pane, #1093, 1095 | 8.00 | — |
| d. | | Booklet pane, #1094, 1095 | 9.00 | — |
| e. | | Booklet pane, #1095 | 5.50 | — |
| | | Complete booklet, #1093c, 1094c, 1095c, 1095d, 1095e | 35.00 | |
| | | Nos. 1092-1095 (4) | 13.75 | 13.75 |

Complete booklet sold for £7.80.

Motorcycle Racers — A250

Designs: 26p, Bill Ivy, Phil Read. 29p, Joey Dunlop, Ray McCullough. 40p, Steve Hislop. 42p, Carl Fogarty. 68p, David Jefferies. 78p, John McGuinness.

**2005, May 17**

| | | | | |
|---|---|---|---|---|
| 1096 | A250 | 26p multi | 1.00 | 1.00 |
| 1097 | A250 | 29p multi | 1.10 | 1.10 |
| 1098 | A250 | 40p multi | 1.60 | 1.60 |
| 1099 | A250 | 42p multi | 1.75 | 1.75 |
| 1100 | A250 | 68p multi | 2.75 | 2.75 |
| 1101 | A250 | 78p multi | 3.00 | 3.00 |
| a. | | Miniature sheet, 2 each #1096-1101 | 22.50 | 22.50 |
| | | Nos. 1096-1101 (6) | 11.20 | 11.20 |

Yamaha motorcycles, 50th anniv.

Rotary International, Cent. — A251

Rotary International emblem, various photos and inscription: 26p, Paul Harris, The Man Behind The Movement. 29p, Rotary's Dreams For The Future. 40p, Polioplus: Rotary's Finest Hour. 42p, Youth Programme: Junior Masterchef. 64p, A Day In The Life of Rotary International. 68p, Serving The World Community.

**Perf. 13¼x13½**
**2005, June 15    Litho.**

| | | | | |
|---|---|---|---|---|
| 1102 | A251 | 26p multi | 1.00 | 1.00 |
| 1103 | A251 | 29p multi | 1.10 | 1.10 |
| 1104 | A251 | 40p multi | 1.60 | 1.60 |
| 1105 | A251 | 42p multi | 1.75 | 1.75 |
| a. | | Sheet of 10 + 10 labels | 17.50 | 17.50 |
| 1106 | A251 | 64p multi | 2.50 | 2.50 |
| 1107 | A251 | 68p multi | 2.75 | 2.75 |
| | | Nos. 1102-1107 (6) | 10.70 | 10.70 |

No. 1105 is inscribed "Europa 2005."

Photographs of Everyday Life — A252

Inscriptions: Nos. 1108a, 1110, Guttin' Herrin'. Nos. 1108b, 1111, Pickin' Spuds. Nos. 1108c, 1112, Master Butcher. Nos. 1108d, 1113, Winckles: Foxdale. Nos. 1108e, 1114, Palace Ballroom. Nos. 1109a, 1115, Land Army. Nos. 1109b, 1116, Farmyard Glen Maye. Nos. 1109c, 1117, Summer Season Stars. Nos. 1109d, 1118, Donkey Rides. Nos. 1109e, 1119, Give us a go Mister!

**2005, Aug. 12    Perf. 12½x13**

| | | | | |
|---|---|---|---|---|
| 1108 | | Horiz. strip of 5 | 5.00 | 5.00 |
| a.-e. | A252 | 26p Any single | 1.00 | 1.00 |
| 1109 | | Horiz. strip of 5 | 5.50 | 5.50 |
| a.-e. | A252 | 29p Any single | 1.10 | 1.10 |

**Booklet Stamps**
**Self-Adhesive**
**Serpentine Die Cut 10½x10¼**

| | | | | |
|---|---|---|---|---|
| 1110 | A252 | 26p multi | 1.00 | 1.00 |
| a. | | Die cut perf 12½x13 | 1.00 | 1.00 |
| 1111 | A252 | 26p multi | 1.00 | 1.00 |
| a. | | Die cut perf 12½x13 | 1.00 | 1.00 |
| 1112 | A252 | 26p multi | 1.00 | 1.00 |
| a. | | Die cut perf 12½x13 | 1.00 | 1.00 |
| 1113 | A252 | 26p multi | 1.00 | 1.00 |
| a. | | Die cut perf 12½x13 | 1.00 | 1.00 |
| 1114 | A252 | 26p multi | 1.00 | 1.00 |
| a. | | Booklet pane, 2 each #1110-1114 | 10.00 | |
| | | Complete booklet, #1114a | 10.00 | |
| b. | | Die cut perf 12½x13 | 1.00 | 1.00 |
| c. | | Strip of 5, #1110a-1113a, 1114b | 5.00 | |
| 1115 | A252 | 29p multi | 1.10 | 1.10 |
| a. | | Die cut perf 12½x13 | 1.10 | 1.10 |
| 1116 | A252 | 29p multi | 1.10 | 1.10 |
| a. | | Die cut perf 12½x13 | 1.10 | 1.10 |
| 1117 | A252 | 29p multi | 1.10 | 1.10 |
| a. | | Die cut perf 12½x13 | 1.10 | 1.10 |
| 1118 | A252 | 29p multi | 1.10 | 1.10 |
| a. | | Die cut perf 12½x13 | 1.10 | 1.10 |
| 1119 | A252 | 29p multi | 1.10 | 1.10 |
| a. | | Booklet pane, 2 each #1115-1119 | 11.00 | |
| | | Complete booklet, #1119a | 11.00 | |
| b. | | Die cut perf 12½x13 | 1.10 | 1.10 |
| c. | | Strip of 5, #1115a-1118a, 1119b | 5.50 | |
| | | Nos. 1110-1119 (10) | 10.50 | 10.50 |

Nos. 1114a and 1119a are complete booklets, the backing serving as booklet covers.

Souvenir Sheet

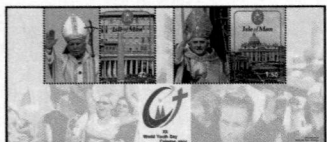

20th World Youth Day, Cologne, Germany — A253

**Perf. 14x14¾ on 3 Sides**
**2005, Aug. 15**
| | | | | |
|---|---|---|---|---|
| 1120 | A253 | Sheet of 2 + 2 labels | 8.00 | 8.00 |
| a. | | 42p Apostolic Palace | 1.75 | 1.75 |
| b. | | £1.50 St. Peter's Basilica | 6.00 | 6.00 |

Scenes From *Harry Potter and the Goblet of Fire* — A254

Designs: 26p, Harry Potter. 29p, Harry, Ron Weasley, Hermione Granger, Goblet of Fire. 33p, Triwizard Cup. 64p, Hungarian Horntail. 68p, Hogwarts coat of arms. 75p, Murcus.

**2005, Oct. 21** — **Perf. 13¼**
| | | | | |
|---|---|---|---|---|
| 1121 | A254 | 26p multi | 1.00 | 1.00 |
| 1122 | A254 | 29p multi | 1.10 | 1.10 |
| 1123 | A254 | 33p multi | 1.40 | 1.40 |
| 1124 | A254 | 64p multi | 2.50 | 2.50 |
| 1125 | A254 | 68p multi | 2.75 | 2.75 |
| 1126 | A254 | 75p multi | 3.00 | 3.00 |
| | | Nos. 1121-1126 (6) | 11.75 | 11.75 |

Souvenir Sheet

Battle of Trafalgar, Bicent. — A255

**2005, Oct. 21 Litho. Perf. 13¼**
| | | | | |
|---|---|---|---|---|
| 1127 | A255 | Sheet, #1127a, Gibraltar #1028a | 8.00 | 8.00 |
| a. | | £1 Funeral of Admiral Nelson | 4.00 | 4.00 |

See Gibraltar No. 1028. No. 1127 has an Isle of Man Post emblem in the margin.

Christmas — A256

Stained glass windows: 26p, Madonna and Child, St. German's Cathedral, Peel. 29p, Angel with Crown of Glory, St. German's Cathedral. 42p, Adoration of the Shepherds, St. German's Cathedral. 60p, Nativity, Kirk Church, Rushen. 68p, Adoration of the Magi, Kirk Church.

**2005, Nov. 7 Litho. Perf. 13½x13**
| | | | | |
|---|---|---|---|---|
| 1128 | A256 | 26p multi | 1.00 | 1.00 |
| 1129 | A256 | 29p multi | 1.10 | 1.10 |
| 1130 | A256 | 42p multi | 1.75 | 1.75 |
| 1131 | A256 | 60p multi | 2.40 | 2.40 |
| 1132 | A256 | 68p multi | 2.75 | 2.75 |
| | | Nos. 1128-1132 (5) | 9.00 | 9.00 |

Queen Elizabeth II, 80th Birthday A257

No. 1133: a, At age 5 with family, 1931. b, In uniform, 1944. c, Wearing tiara, 1952. d, With husband and children, 1972.
No. 1134: a, With Prince Philip, 1972. b, Seated in Throne Room, 2001. c, With Prince William. d, With crowd, 2002.

**2006, Jan. 16 Perf. 13¾**
| | | | | |
|---|---|---|---|---|
| 1133 | | Horiz. strip of 4 | 3.25 | 3.25 |
| a.-d. | A257 20p Any single | | .80 | .80 |
| 1134 | | Horiz. strip of 4 | 13.00 | 13.00 |
| a.-d. | A257 80p Any single | | 3.25 | 3.25 |

Isle of Man Natural History and Antiquarian Society — A258

Designs: 26p, Jurby Church, chalice. 29p, Peel Castle, Viking pinhead. 64p, Meayll Hill, Neolithic potsherd. 68p, Cronk Sumark, Manx stoat. 78p, South Barrule Hill, hen harrier. 97p, Scarlett Point, ammonite fossil.

**2006, Feb. 15 Litho. Perf. 14**
| | | | | |
|---|---|---|---|---|
| 1135 | A258 | 26p multi | 1.00 | 1.00 |
| 1136 | A258 | 29p multi | 1.10 | 1.10 |
| 1137 | A258 | 64p multi | 2.50 | 2.50 |
| 1138 | A258 | 68p multi | 2.75 | 2.75 |
| 1139 | A258 | 78p multi | 3.00 | 3.00 |
| 1140 | A258 | 97p multi | 3.75 | 3.75 |
| | | Nos. 1135-1140 (6) | 14.10 | 14.10 |

Birds — A259

No. 1141: a, Peregrine falcon. b, Puffin. c, Manx shearwater. d, Chough. e, Guillemot.
No. 1142: a, Whinchat. b, Hen harrier. c, Goldcrest. d, Gray wagtail. e, Wren.
No. 1142G: i, Peregrine falcon. j, Puffin. k, Manx shearwater. l, Chough. m, Guillemot.
No. 1142H: n, Whinchat. o, Hen harrier. p, Goldcrest. q, Gray wagtail. r, Wren.

**2006, Apr. 17 Perf. 12½**
| | | | | |
|---|---|---|---|---|
| 1141 | | Horiz. strip of 5 | 5.50 | 5.50 |
| a.-e. | A259 28p multi | | 1.10 | 1.10 |
| 1142 | | Horiz. strip of 5 | 6.25 | 6.25 |
| a.-e. | A259 31p multi | | 1.25 | 1.25 |
| f. | | Miniature sheet, #1141a-1141e, 1142a-1142e | 12.00 | 12.00 |

**Self-Adhesive**
| | | | | |
|---|---|---|---|---|
| 1142G | | Horiz. strip of 5 | 5.25 | 5.25 |
| i.-m. | A259 28p Any single | | 1.00 | 1.00 |
| 1142H | | Horiz. strip of 5 | 5.75 | 5.75 |
| n.-r. | A259 31p Any single | | 1.10 | 1.10 |

No. 1142f issued 10/11, for Belgica '06 Intl. Philatelic Exhibition.

Souvenir Sheet

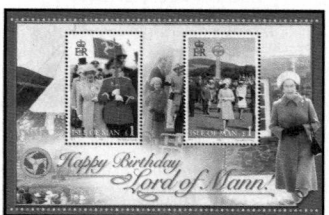

Queen Elizabeth II, 80th Birthday — A260

No. 1143: a, Queen, swordbearer, Manx flag, 2003. b, Queen, crowd, cross, 1972.

**2006, Apr. 21 Perf. 14**
| | | | | |
|---|---|---|---|---|
| 1143 | A260 | Sheet of 2 | 8.00 | 8.00 |
| a.-b. | | £1 Either single | 4.00 | 4.00 |

Souvenir Sheet

Europa Stamps, 50th Anniv. — A261

No. 1144: a, #100. b, #419a.

**2006, May 2 Perf. 13¼x13¾**
| | | | | |
|---|---|---|---|---|
| 1144 | A261 | Sheet of 2 | 5.25 | 5.25 |
| a. | | 42p multi | 1.75 | 1.75 |
| b. | | 83p multi | 3.50 | 3.50 |

2006 World Cup Soccer Championships, Germany — A262

Various photographs of English team's 1966 World Cup championship match and celebrations.

**2006, May 2 Perf. 12½**
| | | | | |
|---|---|---|---|---|
| 1145 | A262 | 28p multi | 1.10 | 1.10 |
| 1146 | A262 | 31p multi | 1.25 | 1.25 |
| 1147 | A262 | 44p multi | 1.75 | 1.75 |
| 1148 | A262 | 72p multi | 2.75 | 2.75 |
| 1149 | A262 | 83p multi | 3.25 | 3.25 |
| 1150 | A262 | 94p multi | 3.75 | 3.75 |
| | | Nos. 1145-1150 (6) | 13.85 | 13.85 |

Manx Ties to Washington, D.C. A263

Designs: 28p, Letitia Tyler, wife of Pres. John Tyler, White House. 31p, Speaker of the House Joseph G. Cannon, Cannon House Office Building. 45p, Matthew Quay, Medal of Honor recipient, battle scene. 50p, Mary Clemmer, journalist, inkwell and U.S. Constitution. 76p, Ewan Clague, economist, Castletown. 83p, Henry "Marse" Watterson, newspaper publisher, Pres. Theodore Roosevelt.

**2006, May 23 Perf. 13¾**
| | | | | |
|---|---|---|---|---|
| 1151 | A263 | 28p multi | 1.10 | 1.10 |
| 1152 | A263 | 31p multi | 1.25 | 1.25 |
| 1153 | A263 | 45p multi | 1.75 | 1.75 |
| 1154 | A263 | 50p multi | 2.00 | 2.00 |
| 1155 | A263 | 76p multi | 3.00 | 3.00 |
| 1156 | A263 | 83p multi | 3.25 | 3.25 |
| | | Nos. 1151-1156 (6) | 12.35 | 12.35 |

Peel Cars — A264

Designs: 28p, Peel P50. 31p, Trident. 38p, Viking Sport. 41p, BMC GRP Mini. 54p, Manxcar. 94p, P1000.

**2006, July 23 Perf. 13¼**
| | | | | |
|---|---|---|---|---|
| 1157 | A264 | 28p multi | 1.10 | 1.10 |
| 1158 | A264 | 31p multi | 1.25 | 1.25 |
| 1159 | A264 | 38p multi | 1.50 | 1.50 |
| 1160 | A264 | 41p multi | 1.60 | 1.60 |
| 1161 | A264 | 54p multi | 2.10 | 2.10 |
| 1162 | A264 | 94p multi | 3.75 | 3.75 |
| | | Nos. 1157-1162 (6) | 11.30 | 11.30 |

National Portrait Gallery, 150th Anniv. A265

Portraits: 28p, Ewan Christian, by unknown artist. 31p, Dame Agatha Christie, by John Gay. 38p, Sir Hall Caine, by Harry Furniss. 41p, William Bligh, by John Condé. 44p, Lady Maria Callcott, by Sir Thomas Lawrence. 54p, John Martin, by Henry Warren. 64p, Sir John Betjeman, by Stephen Hyde. 96p, Sir Edward Elgar, by Herbert Lambert.

**2006, Aug. 25 Litho. Perf. 13½**
| | | | | |
|---|---|---|---|---|
| 1163 | A265 | 28p multi | 1.10 | 1.10 |
| 1164 | A265 | 31p multi | 1.25 | 1.25 |
| 1165 | A265 | 38p multi | 1.50 | 1.50 |
| 1166 | A265 | 41p multi | 1.60 | 1.60 |
| 1167 | A265 | 44p multi | 1.75 | 1.75 |
| 1168 | A265 | 54p multi | 2.10 | 2.10 |
| 1169 | A265 | 64p multi | 2.50 | 2.50 |
| 1170 | A265 | 96p multi | 3.75 | 3.75 |
| | | Nos. 1163-1170 (8) | 15.55 | 15.55 |

Souvenir Sheet

Tales of Beatrix Potter — A266

No. 1171: a, Benjamin Bunny. b, Jemima Puddle-duck, horiz. c, Peter Rabbit, horiz. d, Jeremy Fisher.

**2006, Oct. 11 Perf. 13**
| | | | | |
|---|---|---|---|---|
| 1171 | A266 | Sheet of 4 | 9.00 | 9.00 |
| a. | | 28p multi | 1.10 | 1.10 |
| b. | | 50p multi | 2.00 | 2.00 |
| c. | | 72p multi | 2.75 | 2.75 |
| d. | | 75p multi | 3.00 | 3.00 |

Christmas — A267

Various Christmas trees with panel colors of: 28p, Red. 31p, Dark violet. 41p, Green. 44p, Light blue. 72p, Purple. 94p, Orange.

**Litho. with Foil Application**
**2006, Oct. 11 Perf. 14¼**
| | | | | |
|---|---|---|---|---|
| 1172 | A267 | 28p multi | 1.10 | 1.10 |
| 1173 | A267 | 31p multi | 1.25 | 1.25 |
| a. | | Sheet of 10 | 12.50 | |
| 1174 | A267 | 41p multi | 1.60 | 1.60 |
| 1175 | A267 | 44p multi | 1.75 | 1.75 |
| a. | | Sheet of 10 | 17.50 | |
| 1176 | A267 | 72p multi | 2.75 | 2.75 |
| 1177 | A267 | 94p multi | 3.75 | 3.75 |
| | | Nos. 1172-1177 (6) | 12.20 | 12.20 |

**Self-Adhesive**
**Booklet Stamps**
**Die Cut Perf. 9x9½**
| | | | | |
|---|---|---|---|---|
| 1178 | A267 | 28p multi | 1.10 | 1.10 |
| a. | | Booklet pane of 10 | 11.00 | |
| 1179 | A267 | 31p multi | 1.25 | 1.25 |
| a. | | Booklet pane of 10 | 12.50 | |

Europa (31p, 44p).
Nos. 1178a and 1179a are complete booklets, the backing serving as the booklet covers.

TT Motorcycle Races, Cent. — A268

No. 1180 — Various racers with panel color of: a, Pink. b, Light blue. c, Purple. d, Indigo. e, Orange.

No. 1181: a, Red violet. b, Green. c, Gray blue. d, Red. e, Red brown.

2007, Jan. 1 Litho. *Perf. 14¼*

1180	Horiz. strip of 5	6.25	6.25
a.-e.	A268 UK Any single	1.25	1.25
1181	Horiz. strip of 5	8.75	8.75
a.-e.	A268 E Any single	1.75	1.75

On day of issue Nos. 1180a-1180e each sold for 31p, Nos. 1181a-1181e each sold for 44p.

A269

Scouting, Cent. — A270

Designs: 28p, Hiking expedition near South Barrule. 31p, Scout investiture on Douglas Beach. 44p, Backpacking below Cronk-ny-Arrey-Laa. 72p, Manx Scouts on parade at St. Johns. 83p, Sea kayaking off Laxey Beach. £1, Manx Scouts operating the TT scoreboard.

No. 1188: a, Scouts and table (43x29mm). b, Scouts, tent and campfire (43x57mm).

2007, Feb. 22 Litho. *Perf. 14*

1182	A269 28p multi	1.10	1.10
1183	A269 31p multi	1.25	1.25
a.	Sheet of 10	12.50	
1184	A269 44p multi	1.75	1.75
a.	Booklet pane, #1182-1184	4.25	—
a.	Sheet of 10	17.50	
1185	A269 72p multi	2.75	2.75
1186	A269 83p multi	3.25	3.25
a.	Booklet pane, #1182, 1184, 1186	6.25	—
1187	A269 £1 multi	4.00	4.00
a.	Booklet pane, #1185-1187	10.00	—
b.	Booklet pane, #1183, 1185, 1187	8.00	—
	Nos. 1182-1187 (6)	14.10	14.10

Souvenir Sheet

1188	A270 Sheet of 2	7.75	7.75
a.	50p multi	2.00	2.00
b.	£1.50 multi	5.75	5.75
c.	Booklet pane, #1188 (154x96mm)	7.75	—
	Complete booklet, #1184a, 1186a, 1187a, 1187b, 1188c	36.50	
d.	As No. 1188, with 2007 Intl. Scout Jamboree emblem in margin	8.25	8.25

Europa (31p, 44p). No. 1188d issued 7/26.

Wedding of Queen Elizabeth II and Prince Philip, 60th Anniv. — A271

Various photos of Queen and Prince with denomination colors of: a, Dark blue. b, Lilac. c, Rose pink. d, Light blue. e, Dark green. f, Yellow bister.

2007, Feb. 22 *Perf. 14*

1189	Horiz. strip of 6	14.00	14.00
a.-f.	A271 60p Any single	2.25	2.25

Paintings by Norman Sayle A272

Designs: Nos. 1190, 1198, Headland, Cornaa. Nos. 1191, 1199, Headland, Sound. Nos. 1192, 1200, St. Mark's Church. Nos. 1193, 1201, Castletown Harbour Moonlight. 42p, Bridge House, Castletown. 44p, Winter Sun. 65p, In Ancient Times. 75p, Bracken Mountain.

2007, Apr. 12 *Perf. 12½x13*

1190	A272 28p multi	1.10	1.10
1191	A272 28p multi	1.10	1.10
1192	A272 31p multi	1.25	1.25
1193	A272 31p multi	1.25	1.25
1194	A272 42p multi	1.75	1.75
1195	A272 44p multi	1.75	1.75
1196	A272 65p multi	2.60	2.60
1197	A272 75p multi	3.00	3.00
	Nos. 1190-1197 (8)	13.80	13.80

Booklet Stamps

Self-Adhesive

Serpentine Die Cut 10x9½

1198	A272 28p multi	1.10	1.10
1199	A272 28p multi	1.10	1.10
a.	Booklet pane, 5 each #1198-1199	11.00	
1200	A272 31p multi	1.25	1.25
1201	A272 31p multi	1.25	1.25
a.	Booklet pane, 5 each #1200-1201	12.50	
	Nos. 1198-1201 (4)	4.70	4.70

Nos. 1199a and 1201a are complete booklets, the backing serving as the booklet covers.

Settlement of Jamestown, Virginia, 400th Anniv. — A273

Designs: 28p, Map. 31p, Capt. John Smith and ships. 44p, Aerial view of settlement. 54p, Indians and colonists. 78p, Settlement buildings. 90p, Indian village.

2007, Apr. 26 *Perf. 13½*

1202	A273 28p multi	1.10	1.10
1203	A273 31p multi	1.25	1.25
1204	A273 44p multi	1.75	1.75
1205	A273 54p multi	2.25	2.25
1206	A273 78p multi	3.25	3.25
1207	A273 90p multi	3.75	3.75
	Nos. 1202-1207 (6)	13.35	13.35

Royal Charter of Liverpool, 800th Anniv. A274

Designs: 31p, King John and Royal Charter. 48p, The spiritual heart of Liverpool. 54p, Liverpool war heroes. 74p, Liverpool heritage. 80p, Port of Liverpool. £1, Wall of Fame.

No. 1214: a, James Brown, Manx election pioneer. b, Joseph Cunningham, philantropist. c, William Gill, ship captain. d, Dalrymple Maitland, industrialist.

2007, May 10 *Perf. 14*

1208	A274 31p multi	1.25	1.25
1209	A274 48p multi	1.90	1.90
1210	A274 54p multi	2.25	2.25
1211	A274 74p multi	3.00	3.00
1212	A274 80p multi	3.25	3.25
1213	A274 £1 multi	4.00	4.00
	Nos. 1208-1213 (6)	15.65	15.65

Souvenir Sheet

1214	Sheet of 4	9.00	9.00
a.	A274 25p multi	1.00	1.00
b.	A274 40p multi	1.50	1.50
c.-d.	A274 80p Either single	3.25	3.25

Historical Maps of Isle of Man A275

Designs: 28p, Map by John Speed, 1605. 31p, Map by Capt. Greenville Collins, 1693. 44p, Map by John Drinkwater, 1826. 48p, Ordnance Survey County Series map, 1870. 75p, Six-inch Series map, 1975. 88p, 1:100,000 map by Isle of Man Government Mapping Office, 2006.

2007, Aug. 1 Litho. *Perf. 12½x13*

1215	A275 28p multi	1.10	1.10
1216	A275 31p multi	1.25	1.25
1217	A275 44p multi	1.75	1.75
1218	A275 48p multi	2.00	2.00
1219	A275 75p multi	3.00	3.00
1220	A275 88p multi	3.75	3.75
	Nos. 1215-1220 (6)	12.85	12.85

Intl. Polar Year A276

Designs: 28p, Capt. John Ross, ship Victory trapped in ice. 31p, Flares shot from Victory. 55p, Victory crewmen hunting with Inuit. 75p, Musk ox hunted by Victory crewmen. 90p, Victory crewmen pulling sled after abandoning ship. 117p, Whaler Isabella rescuing Victory crewmen.

2007, Aug. 20

1221	A276 28p multi	1.10	1.10
1222	A276 31p multi	1.25	1.25
1223	A276 55p multi	2.25	2.25
1224	A276 75p multi	3.00	3.00
1225	A276 90p multi	3.75	3.75
1226	A276 117p multi	4.75	4.75
	Nos. 1221-1226 (6)	16.10	16.10

Souvenir Sheet

Manx Connections With Northern Canada — A277

No. 1227: a, Ben-My-Chree Cabin, British Columbia. b, Graham "Jimmy" Oates, first man to reach Hudson Bay on rubber-tired vehicle, vert. c, Kermode bear, vert. d, Hudson Bay Post Office and dog team.

2007, Aug. 20 *Perf. 13*

1227	A277 Sheet of 4	10.00	10.00
a.-b.	50p Either single	2.00	2.00
c.-d.	75p Either single	3.00	3.00

Intl. Polar Year.

Europen Vintage Plowing Championships — A278

Designs: 28p, Manx-style plowing. 31p, Vintage plowing. 48p, Horse and digger plow. 71p, Swing plow. 90p, World-style plowing. £1.27, Jean Burns, first woman to compete in Manx plowing contest, on tractor.

2007, Sept. 1 *Perf. 13¼*

1228	A278 28p multi	1.10	1.10
1229	A278 31p multi	1.25	1.25
1230	A278 48p multi	2.00	2.00
1231	A278 71p multi	3.00	3.00
1232	A278 90p multi	3.75	3.75
1233	A278 £1.27 multi	5.25	5.25
	Nos. 1228-1233 (6)	16.35	16.35

Christmas — A279

Various angels with panel color of: 28p, Blue. 31p, Pink. 69p, Orange. 78p, Green. £1.24, Dark blue.

Serpentine Die Cut 13x13¼

2007, Oct. 19

Self-Adhesive

1234	A279 28p multi	1.25	1.25
1235	A279 31p multi	1.40	1.40
1236	A279 69p multi	3.00	3.00
1237	A279 78p multi	3.25	3.25
1238	A279 £1.24 multi	5.25	5.25
	Nos. 1234-1238 (5)	14.15	14.15

Souvenir Sheet

Cunard Ocean Liners — A280

No. 1239: a, Queen Elizabeth 2. b, Queen Mary 2. c, Queen Victoria.

2008, Jan. 13 Litho. *Perf. 14x13¼*

1239	A280 Sheet of 3	12.00	12.00
a.-c.	£1 Any single	4.00	4.00

Royal Air Force, 90th Anniv. A281

Aircraft: No. 1240, H.P. 0/400, Bristol F2B fighter. No. 1241, Avro 504N, Westland Wapiti. No. 1242, Hawker Hurricane, Short Sunderland. No. 1243, Gloster Meteor, Westland Whirlwind. No. 1244, Hawker Hunter, E.E. Canberra. No. 1245, BAE Harrier, Lockheed Hercules.

2008, Jan. 15 *Perf. 13¼*

1240	A281 31p multi	1.25	1.25
1241	A281 31p multi	1.25	1.25
1242	A281 31p multi	1.25	1.25
a.	Horiz. strip, #1240-1242	3.75	3.75
1243	A281 90p multi	3.75	3.75
a.	Booklet pane, #1240-1243	7.50	—
1244	A281 90p multi	3.75	3.75
a.	Booklet pane, #1240-1241, 1243-1244	10.00	—
1245	A281 90p multi	3.75	3.75
a.	Horiz. strip, #1243-1245	11.25	11.25
b.	Booklet pane, #1242-1245	12.50	—
c.	Booklet pane, #1240-1241, 1244-1245	10.00	—
	Complete booklet, #1243a, 1244a, 1245b, 1245c	40.00	
	Nos. 1240-1245 (6)	15.00	15.00

Vikings on Isle of Man — A282

Designs: 28p, Pagan Lady of Peel. 31p, Ship burial. 44p, Godred Crovan (King Orry). 54p, Gautr the Sculptor. 69p, Sigurd the Dragon Slayer. £1.24, Coming of Christianity.

2008, Feb. 18 Litho. *Perf. 13¼*

1246	A282 28p multi	1.10	1.10
1247	A282 31p multi	1.25	1.25
1248	A282 44p multi	1.75	1.75
1249	A282 54p multi	2.25	2.25

| 1250 | A282 | 69p multi | 2.75 | 2.750 |
| 1251 | A282 | £1.24 multi | 5.00 | 5.00 |
| | | *Nos. 1246-1251 (6)* | 14.10 | 20.85 |

Manx Bank Notes A283

Designs: 30p, 1956 Isle of Man Bank one-pound note. 31p, 1972 Isle of Man Government ten-pound note. 44p, 1882 Manx Bank one-pound note. 56p, 1969 Isle of Man Government fifty-pence note. 85p, 1983 Isle of Man Government fifty-pound note. 114p, 1918 Parr's Bank one-pound note.

**2008, Apr. 7**     **Perf. 14**
| 1252 | A283 | 30p multi | 1.25 | 1.25 |
| 1253 | A283 | 31p multi | 1.25 | 1.25 |
| 1254 | A283 | 44p multi | 1.75 | 1.75 |
| 1255 | A283 | 56p multi | 2.25 | 2.25 |
| 1256 | A283 | 85p multi | 3.50 | 3.50 |
| 1257 | A283 | 114p multi | 4.50 | 4.50 |
| | | *Nos. 1252-1257 (6)* | 14.50 | 14.50 |

**Booklet Stamp**
**Self-Adhesive**
*Die Cut Perf. 12x12¼*
| 1258 | A283 | 30p multi | 1.25 | 1.25 |
| a. | | Booklet pane of 10 | 12.50 | |

**Miniature Sheet**

2008 Summer Olympics, Beijing — A284

**2008, Apr. 21**     **Perf. 13¼**
| 1259 | A284 | Sheet of 4 | 4.00 | 4.00 |
| a. | | 1p Archery | .20 | .20 |
| b. | | 2p Equestrian | .20 | .20 |
| c. | | 3p Cycling | .20 | .20 |
| d. | | 94p Olympic torch | 3.75 | 3.75 |

Interceltic Music Festival, Loreint, France A285

Flags of regions with Celtic language heritage: 20p, Cornwall. 30p, Isle of Man. 31p, Scotland. 48p, Brittany. 50p, Ireland. 56p, Asturias. 72p, Wales. £1.13, Galicia.

**2008, May 12**     **Perf. 13¼**
| 1260 | A285 | 20p multi | .80 | .80 |
| 1261 | A285 | 30p multi | 1.25 | 1.25 |
| 1262 | A285 | 31p multi | 1.25 | 1.25 |
| 1263 | A285 | 48p multi | 1.90 | 1.90 |
| 1264 | A285 | 50p multi | 2.00 | 2.00 |
| 1265 | A285 | 56p multi | 2.25 | 2.25 |
| 1266 | A285 | 72p multi | 3.00 | 3.00 |
| 1267 | A285 | £1.13 multi | 4.50 | 4.50 |
| | | *Nos. 1260-1267 (8)* | 16.95 | 16.95 |

Europa (31p, 50p).

Famous Race Drivers and Their Cars A286

Designs: 20p, Reg Parnell. 30p, Mike Hawthorn. 70p, Tony Brooks. 81p, Roy Salvadori. 94p, Stirling Moss. £1.22, Jim Clark.

**2008, July 10**    **Litho.**    **Perf. 14**
| 1268 | A286 | 20p multi | .80 | .80 |
| 1269 | A286 | 30p multi | 1.25 | 1.25 |
| 1270 | A286 | 70p multi | 2.75 | 2.75 |
| 1271 | A286 | 81p multi | 3.25 | 3.25 |
| 1272 | A286 | 94p multi | 3.75 | 3.75 |
| 1273 | A286 | £1.22 multi | 5.00 | 5.00 |
| | | *Nos. 1268-1273 (6)* | 16.80 | 16.80 |

**Miniature Sheet**

Race Cars — A287

No. 1274: a, 1961 Aston Martin DB4 GT Zagato. b, 1965 Ferrari 250 LM. c, 1962 Ferrari 250 GTO. d, 1965 Ford GT40. e, 1955 Mercedes-Benz 300 SLR. f, 1964 Shelby Cobra.

**2008, July 10**     **Perf. 14¾x14**
| 1274 | A287 | Sheet of 6 | 12.00 | 12.00 |
| a.-f. | | 50p Any single | 2.00 | 2.00 |

Famous People — A288

No. 1275: a, Mary Louisa Wood (1839-1925), founder of Isle of Man Fine Arts and Industrial Guild. b, Harry Kelly (1852-1935), last native Manx speaker. c, Sir Frank Gill (1866-1950), telephone and communications engineer. d, Ramsey Gelling Johnson (1889-1972), judge, president of Royal Manx Agricultural Society. e, John Nicholson (1911-88), stamp designer.

No. 1276: a, Dr. Dorothy Pantin (1896-1985), first female doctor. b, Richard Costain (1839-1902), construction business entrepreneur. c, Sir William Percy Cowley (1886-1958), judge. d, Rev. Fred Cubbon (1902-80), philanthropist. e, William Henry Gill (1839-1922), author, musician.

**2008, Aug. 1**     **Perf. 13¼**
| 1275 | | Horiz. strip of 5 | 6.25 | 6.25 |
| a.-e. | A288 31p Any single | | 1.25 | 1.25 |
| 1276 | | Horiz. strip of 5 | 10.00 | 10.00 |
| a.-e. | A288 50p Any single | | 2.00 | 2.00 |

End of World War I, 90th Anniv. — A289

Poppy and letter from soldier: 30p, Second Lieutenant Roy F. Corlett. 31p, Second Lieutenant John W. Lewis. 44p, Private Joseph Killey. 56p, Lieutenant Colonel W. A. W. Crellin. 81p, Lance Corporal Tom Quilliam. 94p, Private Robert Oates. £2, National War Memorial, St. John's.

**2008, Oct. 1**    **Litho.**    **Perf. 14**
| 1277 | A289 | 30p multi | 1.10 | 1.10 |
| 1278 | A289 | 31p multi | 1.10 | 1.10 |
| 1279 | A289 | 44p multi | 1.60 | 1.60 |
| 1280 | A289 | 56p multi | 2.00 | 2.00 |
| 1281 | A289 | 81p multi | 3.00 | 3.00 |
| 1282 | A289 | 94p multi | 3.50 | 3.50 |
| | | *Nos. 1277-1282 (6)* | 12.30 | 12.30 |

**Souvenir Sheet**
| 1283 | A289 | £2 multi | 7.25 | 7.25 |

Flora and Fauna of Ballaugh Curragh A290

Designs: 30p, Orange-tip butterfly. 31p, Curlew. 50p, Birch bracket fungus. 70p, Large red damsel. 82p, Marsh cinquefoil. £1.38, Royal fern.

**2008, Oct. 1**     **Perf. 13¼**
| 1284 | A290 | 30p multi | 1.10 | 1.10 |
| 1285 | A290 | 31p multi | 1.10 | 1.10 |
| 1286 | A290 | 50p multi | 1.75 | 1.75 |
| 1287 | A290 | 70p multi | 2.50 | 2.50 |
| 1288 | A290 | 82p multi | 3.00 | 3.00 |
| 1289 | A290 | £1.38 multi | 5.00 | 5.00 |
| | | *Nos. 1284-1289 (6)* | 14.45 | 14.45 |

Christmas A291

Postman from *The Jolly Christmas Postman*, by Janet and Allen Ahlberg: 28p, On bicycle, letters. 31p, And mouse in cracker box. 48p, And bear family. 50p, And Toy Town. 56p, On bicycle, with truck and horsecart on winding road. £1.56, At home.

**2008, Oct. 20**     **Perf. 14x14¼**
| 1290 | A291 | 28p multi | .90 | .90 |
| 1291 | A291 | 31p multi | 1.00 | 1.00 |
| 1292 | A291 | 48p multi | 1.60 | 1.60 |
| 1293 | A291 | 50p multi | 1.60 | 1.60 |
| 1294 | A291 | 56p multi | 1.90 | 1.90 |
| 1295 | A291 | £1.56 multi | 5.00 | 5.00 |
| | | *Nos. 1290-1295 (6)* | 12.00 | 12.00 |

## POSTAGE DUE STAMPS

> Catalogue values for unused stamps in this section are for Never Hinged items.

D1             D2

Imprint: "1973 Questa"
*Perf. 13½*
**1973, July 5**    **Litho.**    **Unwmk.**
**Inscriptions and Coat of Arms in Black and Red**
| J1 | D1 | ½p yellow | .20 | .20 |
| J2 | D1 | 1p buff | .30 | .30 |
| J3 | D1 | 2p lt yellow grn | 1.10 | 1.10 |
| J4 | D1 | 3p gray | 2.00 | 2.00 |
| J5 | D1 | 4p dull rose | 3.00 | 3.00 |
| J6 | D1 | 5p light blue | 3.25 | 3.25 |
| J7 | D1 | 10p light violet | 7.50 | 7.50 |
| J8 | D1 | 20p lt grnsh blue | 18.00 | 18.00 |
| | | *Nos. J1-J8 (8)* | 35.35 | 35.35 |

Imprint: "1973 A Questa"
**1973, Sept.**
| J1a | D1 | ½p | 1.75 | 1.50 |
| J2a | D1 | 1p | .90 | .45 |
| J3a | D1 | 2p | .25 | .20 |
| J4a | D1 | 3p | .20 | .20 |
| J5a | D1 | 4p | .25 | .20 |
| J6a | D1 | 5p | .25 | .20 |
| J7a | D1 | 10p | .45 | .40 |
| J8a | D1 | 20p | .90 | .65 |
| | | *Nos. J1a-J8a (8)* | 4.95 | 3.80 |

**1975, Jan. 8**    **Litho.**    **Perf. 14**
**Inscriptions and Coat of Arms in Black and Red**
| J9 | D2 | ½p yellow | .20 | .20 |
| J10 | D2 | 1p buff | .20 | .20 |
| J11 | D2 | 4p lilac rose | .20 | .20 |
| J12 | D2 | 7p blue | .30 | .30 |
| J13 | D2 | 9p sepia | .35 | .35 |
| J14 | D2 | 10p lilac | .40 | .40 |
| J15 | D2 | 50p orange | 1.25 | 1.25 |
| J16 | D2 | £1 bright green | 2.50 | 2.50 |
| | | *Nos. J9-J16 (8)* | 5.40 | 5.40 |

D3             D4

**1982-92**    **Litho.**    **Perf. 15x14**
| J17 | D3 | 1p light green | .20 | .20 |
| J18 | D3 | 2p bright pink | .20 | .20 |
| J19 | D3 | 5p grnsh blue | .20 | .20 |
| J20 | D3 | 10p bright lilac | .40 | .40 |
| J21 | D3 | 20p gray | .75 | .75 |
| J22 | D3 | 50p dull yellow | 2.00 | 2.00 |
| J23 | D3 | £1 brick red | 3.00 | 3.00 |
| J24 | D3 | £2 blue | 6.00 | 6.00 |

**Litho.**
*Perf. 13x13½*
| J25 | D4 | £5 multicolored | 15.00 | 15.00 |
| | | *Nos. J17-J25 (9)* | 27.75 | 27.75 |

Issued: £5, 9/16/92; others, 10/5/82.

# GREECE

'grēs

(Hellas)

LOCATION — Southern part of the Balkan Peninsula in southeastern Europe, bordering on the Ionian, Aegean and Mediterranean Seas
GOVT. — Republic
AREA — 50,949 sq. mi.
POP. — 10,511,000 (1997 est.)
CAPITAL — Athens

In 1923 the reigning king was forced to abdicate and the following year Greece was declared a republic. In 1935, the king was recalled by a "plebiscite" of the people. Greece became a republic in June 1973. The country today includes the Aegean Islands of Chios, Mytilene (Lesbos), Samos, Icaria (Nicaria) and Lemnos, the Ionian Islands (Corfu, etc.) Crete, Macedonia, Western Thrace and part of Eastern Thrace, the Mount Athos District, Epirus and the Dodecanese Islands.

100 Lepta = 1 Drachma
100 Cents = 1 Euro (2002)

> Catalogue values for unused stamps in this country are for Never Hinged items, beginning with Scott 472 in the regular postage section, Scott B1 in the semipostal section, Scott C48 in the airpost section, Scott CB1 in the airpost semi-postal section, Scott RA69 in the postal tax section, and Scott N239 in the occupation and annexation section.

Values for unused stamps are for examples with original gum as defined in the catalogue introduction. Any exceptions will be noted.
Values for Large Hermes Head stamps with double control numbers on the back, Nos. 20e, 21c, 27a, et al, are for examples with two distinct and separate impressions, not for blurred or "slide doubles" caused by paper slippage on the press.

### Watermarks

Wmk. 129 —
Crown and ET

Wmk. 252 —
Crowns

### Paris Print

Hermes (Mercury) — A1

Paris Print, Fine Impression

The enlarged illustrations show the head in various states of the plates. The differences are best seen in the shading lines on the cheek and neck.

**1861    Unwmk.    Typo.    Imperf.**
**Without Figures on Back**

| | | | | |
|---|---|---|---|---|
| 1 | A1 | 1 l choc, *brnish* | 500.00 | 475.00 |
| a. | | 1 l red brown, *brnish* | 675.00 | 600.00 |
| 2 | A1 | 2 l ol bis, *straw* | 45.00 | 45.00 |
| a. | | 2 l brown buff, *buff* | 45.00 | 45.00 |
| 3 | A1 | 5 l yel grn, *grnsh* | 650.00 | 125.00 |
| 4 | A1 | 20 l bl, *bluish* | 850.00 | 75.00 |
| a. | | 20 l deep blue, *bluish* | 1,200. | 240.00 |
| b. | | On pelure paper | 1,750. | 275.00 |
| 5 | A1 | 40 l vio, *bl* | 325.00 | 100.00 |
| 6 | A1 | 80 l rose, *pink* | 225.00 | 100.00 |
| a. | | 80 l carmine, *pink* | 225.00 | 100.00 |

**Large Figures, 8mm high, on Back**

| | | | | |
|---|---|---|---|---|
| 7 | A1 | 10 l red org, *bl* | 750.00 | 475.00 |
| a. | | "10" on back inverted | | |
| c. | | "0" of "10" invtd. on back | — | 2,400. |
| d. | | "1" of "10" invtd. on back | — | 2,750. |

No. 7 without "10" on back is a proof.
Trial impressions of Paris prints exist in many shades, some being close to those of the issued stamps. The gum used was thin and smooth instead of thick, brownish and crackly as on the issued stamps.
See #8-58. For surcharges see #130, 132-133, 137-139, 141-143, 147-149, 153-154, 157-158.

Faint quadrille, horizontal or vertical lines are visible in the background of some Athens print large Hermes head stamps.
Nos. 16, 16a, 16b are the only 1 l stamps that have these lines.

### Athens Prints

Athens Print, Typical Clear Impression

Athens Print, Typical Coarse Impression

**Figures on Back**
5 l:

#11

5
#18-45

**Fine Printing (F)**
**Fine Printing (F, '62) see footnote**
**Coarse Printing (C)**

**1861-62**
**Without Figures on Back**

| | | | | |
|---|---|---|---|---|
| 8 | A1 | 1 l choc, *brnish* (F, '62) | 45.00 | 67.50 |
| a. | | 1 l dk chocolate, *brnish* (F) | 1,300. | 1,300. |
| b. | | 1 l chocolate, *brnish* (F) | 575.00 | 575.00 |
| 9 | A1 | 2 l bis brn, *bister* (F) | 67.50 | 110.00 |
| a. | | 2 l dark brown, *straw*, (C) | 6,000. | |
| b. | | 2 l bister brown, *bister* (C) | 80.00 | 90.00 |
| c. | | 2 l bis brn, *bister* (F, '62) | 82.50 | 90.00 |
| 10 | A1 | 20 l dk bl, *bluish* (C) | | 15,000. |

**With Figures on Back**

| | | | | |
|---|---|---|---|---|
| 11 | A1 | 5 l grn, *grnsh* (F, '62) | 300.00 | 110.00 |
| a. | | 5 l green, *greenish* (C) | 325.00 | 125.00 |
| b. | | As "a," double "5" on back (F, C) | | 2,000. |
| c. | | 5 l green, *greenish*, bl grn figures on back (F, '62) | 350.00 | 72.50 |
| 12 | A1 | 10 l org, *grnsh* (F, '62) | 350.00 | 40.00 |
| a. | | 10 l orange, *greenish* (C) | 750.00 | 110.00 |
| c. | | 10 l orange, *greenish* (C) | 550.00 | 100.00 |
| 13 | A1 | 20 l blue, *bluish* (F, '62) | 475.00 | 57.50 |
| a. | | 20 l dull blue, *bluish* (C) | 6,750. | 190.00 |
| b. | | 20 l dark blue, *bluish*, (F) | 3,500. | 87.50 |
| 14 | A1 | 40 l red vio, *pale bl* (F, '62) | 2,500. | 125.00 |
| a. | | 40 l red violet, *blue* (C) | 6,750. | 450.00 |
| b. | | 40 l red violet, *blue*, (F) | 4,000. | 300.00 |
| 15 | A1 | 80 l carmine, *pink* (F, '62) | 90.00 | 72.50 |
| a. | | 80 l carmine, *pink* (F) | 850.00 | 140.00 |
| b. | | 80 l dl rose, *pink* (F) | 775.00 | 110.00 |

Nos. 8-15 are known as the "Athens Provisionals." The first printings were not very successful, producing the "coarse printings." Later printings used an altered printing method that gave better results (the "fine printings"). All these were issued in the normal manner by the Post Office.
Nos. 8, 9c, 11c, 12, 13, 14, 15 have uninterrupted and even shading lines that do not taper off at the ends. They were produced in May 1862 (F, '62). Other fine printing stamps were produced in Feb.-Apr. 1862 (F).
The numerals on the back are strongly shaded in the right lines with the corresponding left lines being quite thin. The colors of the numerals are generally strong and often show clumps of ink.
Nos. 15a and 15b have vermilion figures on the back, while those of all later printings are carmine.

**1862-67**
**With Figures on Back, Except 1 l and 2 l**

| | | | | |
|---|---|---|---|---|
| 16 | A1 | 1 l brn, *brnish* (poor print) | 47.50 | 47.50 |
| a. | | 1 l red brn, *brnish* (poor print) | 110.00 | 110.00 |
| b. | | 1 l choc, *brnish* | 67.50 | 67.50 |
| 17 | A1 | 2 l bister, *bister* | 7.50 | 12.00 |
| a. | | 2 l brnsh bis, *bister* | 12.00 | 15.00 |
| 18 | A1 | 5 l grn, *grnsh* | 250.00 | 12.00 |
| a. | | 5 l yellowish green, *grnsh* | 250.00 | 12.00 |
| 19 | A1 | 10 l org, *blue* ('64) | 300.00 | 25.00 |
| a. | | 10 l yel org, *bluish* | 350.00 | 60.00 |
| b. | | As "b," "10" inverted on front of stamp | | 15,000. |
| c. | | 10 l red org, *bl* (Dec. '65) | 300.00 | 25.00 |
| d. | | "01" on back | 7,000. | 110.00 |
| 20 | A1 | 20 l bl, *bluish* | 250.00 | 7.50 |
| a. | | 20 l lt bl, *bluish* (fine print) | 300.00 | 15.00 |
| b. | | 20 l dark blue, *bluish* | 375.00 | 26.00 |
| c. | | 20 l blue, *greenish* | 1,000. | 15.00 |
| d. | | "80" on back | | 2,000. |
| e. | | Double "20" on back | | 1,100. |
| f. | | Without "20" on back | | 5,500. |
| 21 | A1 | 40 l lilac, *bl* | 450.00 | 22.50 |
| a. | | 40 l grayish lilac, *blue* | 1,750. | 35.00 |
| b. | | 40 l lilac brown, *lil gray* | 1,000. | 47.50 |
| c. | | Double "40" on back | | 1,600. |
| 22 | A1 | 80 l car, *pale rose* | 77.50 | 12.00 |
| a. | | 80 l rose, *pale rose* | 77.50 | 12.00 |
| b. | | "8" on back inverted | — | 400.00 |
| c. | | "80" on back inverted | | |
| d. | | "8" only on back | | 700.00 |
| e. | | "0" only on back | | 700.00 |

Nos. 16-22 represent a series of printings for each value, from 1862 through 1867, until a major cleaning of the plates was done in 1868. Impressions range from very fine and clear to coarse and blotchy.
Some printings of Nos. 16, 16a, 16b show faint vertical, horizontal or quadrilled lines in the background. Later 1 l stamps do not show these lines.
Many stamps of this and succeeding issues which are normally imperforate are known privately rouletted, pin-perforated, percé en scie, etc.

**1868**
**From Cleaned Plates**
**With Figures on Back, Except 1 l and 2 l**

| | | | | |
|---|---|---|---|---|
| 23 | A1 | 1 l gray brn, *brnish* | 55.00 | 55.00 |
| a. | | 1 l brown, *brownish* | 60.00 | 60.00 |
| 24 | A1 | 2 l gray bis, *bister* | 22.50 | 27.00 |
| 25 | A1 | 5 l grn, *grnsh* | 3,000. | 100.00 |
| 26 | A1 | 10 l pale org, *bluish* | 1,200. | 19.00 |
| a. | | "01" on back | | |
| 27 | A1 | 20 l pale bl, *bluish* | 1,400. | 8.00 |
| a. | | Double "20" on back | | 1,200. |
| 28 | A1 | 40 l rose vio, *bl* | 275.00 | 22.50 |
| a. | | "20" on back, corrected to "40" | 2,100. | 1,600. |
| 29 | A1 | 80 l rose car, *pale rose* | 175.00 | 175.00 |

The "0" on the back of No. 29 is printed more heavily than the "8."

**1870**
**With Figures on Back, Except 1 l**

| | | | | |
|---|---|---|---|---|
| 30 | A1 | 1 l deep reddish brn, *brnish* | 100.00 | 160.00 |
| a. | | 1 l redsh brn, *brnish* | 160.00 | 175.00 |
| 31 | A1 | 20 l lt bl, *bluish* | 1,350. | 18.00 |
| a. | | 20 l blue, *bluish* | 1,600. | 35.00 |
| b. | | "02" on back | | 525.00 |
| c. | | "20" on back inverted | | 525.00 |

Nos. 30 and 30a have short lines of shading on cheek. The spandrels of No. 31 are very pale with the lines often broken or missing.
This was an Athens Printing made under supervision of German workmen.

**1870**

### Medium to Thin Paper
### Without Mesh
### With Figures on Back, Except 1 l and 2 l

| | | | | |
|---|---|---|---|---|
| 32 | A1 | 1 l brn, *brnish* | 150.00 | 150.00 |
| a. | | 1 l purple brown, *brnish* | 150.00 | 150.00 |
| 33 | A1 | 2 l sal bis, *bister* | 12.00 | 20.00 |
| 34 | A1 | 5 l grn, *grnsh* | 3,000. | 67.50 |
| 35 | A1 | 10 l lt red org, *grnsh* | 1,200. | 52.50 |
| a. | | "01" on back | | 650.00 |
| b. | | "10" on back inverted | — | 650.00 |
| 36 | A1 | 20 l bl, *bluish* | 900.00 | 8.50 |
| a. | | "02" on back | | 375.00 |
| b. | | Double "20" on back | | 850.00 |
| 37 | A1 | 40 l sal, *grnsh* | 475.00 | 60.00 |
| a. | | 40 l lilac, *greenish* | | 75,000. |

The stamps of this issue have rather coarse figures on back.

No. 37a is printed in the exact shade of the numerals on the back of No. 37.

**1872**

### Thin Transparent Paper
### Showing Mesh
### With Figures on Back, Except 1 l

| | | | | |
|---|---|---|---|---|
| 38 | A1 | 1 l grayish brown, *straw* | 55.00 | 65.00 |
| a. | | 1 l red brn, *yelsh* | 60.00 | 75.00 |
| 39 | A1 | 5 l grn, *greenish* | 500.00 | 21.00 |
| a. | | 5 l dark green, *grnsh* | 700.00 | 40.00 |
| b. | | Double "5" on back | | 125.00 |
| 40 | A1 | 10 l red org, *grnsh* | 725.00 | 9.50 |
| a. | | 10 l red orange, *pale lilac* | 3,250. | 110.00 |
| b. | | As #40, "10" on back inverted | — | 60.00 |
| c. | | Double "10" on back | | 800.00 |
| d. | | "0" on back | | 400.00 |
| e. | | "01" on back | — | 1,600. |
| 41 | A1 | 20 l dp bl, *bluish* | 950.00 | 9.50 |
| a. | | 20 l blue, *bluish* | 950.00 | 32.50 |
| b. | | 20 l dark blue, *blue* | 1,200. | 27.50 |
| 42 | A1 | 40 l brn, *bl* | 32.50 | 40.00 |
| a. | | 40 l olive brown, *blue* | 40.00 | 70.00 |
| b. | | 40 l red violet, *blue* | 600.00 | 65.00 |
| c. | | 40 l gray violet, *blue* | 650.00 | 65.00 |
| d. | | Figures on back bister (#42b, 42c) | — | 70.00 |

The mesh is not apparent on Nos. 38, 38a.

**1875**

### On Cream Paper Unless Otherwise Stated
### With Figures on Back, Except 1 l and 2 l

| | | | | |
|---|---|---|---|---|
| 43 | A1 | 1 l gray brn | 7.00 | 5.25 |
| a. | | 1 l dark gray brown | 40.00 | 40.00 |
| b. | | 1 l black brown | 52.50 | 60.00 |
| c. | | 1 l red brown | 27.50 | 32.50 |
| d. | | 1 l dark red brown | 27.50 | 40.00 |
| e. | | 1 l purple brown | 42.50 | 52.50 |
| 44 | A1 | 2 l bister | 12.50 | 32.50 |
| 45 | A1 | 5 l pale yel grn | 160.00 | 17.50 |
| a. | | 5 l dk yel grn | 275.00 | 40.00 |
| 46 | A1 | 10 l orange | 175.00 | 15.00 |
| a. | | 10 l orange, *yellow* | 175.00 | 15.00 |
| c. | | "00" on back | 925.00 | 90.00 |
| d. | | "1" on back | — | 160.00 |
| e. | | "0" on back | — | 125.00 |
| f. | | "01" on back | — | 275.00 |
| g. | | Double "10" on back | — | 375.00 |
| 47 | A1 | 20 l ultra | 110.00 | 6.50 |
| a. | | 20 l blue | 200.00 | 16.00 |
| b. | | 20 l deep Prussian blue | 1,600. | 42.50 |
| c. | | "02" on back | — | 300.00 |
| d. | | "20" on back inverted | — | 6,250. |
| e. | | "2" in "20" inverted and broken | | 90.00 |
| f. | | Double "20" on back | — | 400.00 |
| 48 | A1 | 40 l salmon | 25.00 | 60.00 |

The back figures are found in many varieties, including "1" and "0" inverted in "10."

Value for No. 47e is for example with "2" of "02" broken (deformed). Also known with unbroken "2"; value used about $600.

**1876**

### Without Figures on Back
### Paris Print, Clear Impression

| | | | | |
|---|---|---|---|---|
| 49 | A1 | 30 l ol brn, *yelsh* | 175.00 | 37.50 |
| a. | | 30 l brown, *yellowish* | 275.00 | 72.50 |
| 50 | A1 | 60 l grn, *grnsh* | 30.00 | 80.00 |

### Athens Print, Coarse Impression, Yellowish Paper

| | | | | |
|---|---|---|---|---|
| 51 | A1 | 30 l dark brown | 50.00 | 9.00 |
| a. | | 30 l black brown | 50.00 | 9.00 |
| 52 | A1 | 60 l green | 425.00 | 55.00 |

**1880-82**   Cream Paper

### Without Figures on Back

| | | | | |
|---|---|---|---|---|
| 53 | A1 | 5 l green | 25.00 | 6.50 |
| 54 | A1 | 10 l orange | 21.00 | 4.00 |
| a. | | 10 l yellow | 21.00 | 4.00 |
| b. | | 10 l red orange | 2,500. | 47.50 |
| 55 | A1 | 20 l ultra | 300.00 | 125.00 |
| 56 | A1 | 20 l pale rose (aniline ink) ('82) | 8.00 | 2.50 |
| a. | | 20 l rose (aniline ink) ('82) | 8.00 | 3.25 |
| b. | | 20 l deep carmine | 200.00 | 10.00 |

| | | | | |
|---|---|---|---|---|
| 57 | A1 | 30 l ultra ('82) | 175.00 | 16.00 |
| a. | | 30 l slate blue | 175.00 | 12.00 |
| 58 | A1 | 40 l lilac | 60.00 | 12.00 |
| a. | | 40 l violet | 67.50 | 24.00 |

Stamps of type A1 were not regularly issued with perf. 11½ but were freely used on mail.

Hermes — A2

Lepta denominations have white numeral tablets.

### Belgian Print, Clear Impression

**1886-88**   Imperf.

| | | | | |
|---|---|---|---|---|
| 64 | A2 | 1 l brown ('88) | 2.75 | 1.60 |
| 65 | A2 | 2 l bister ('88) | 9.50 | 125.00 |
| 66 | A2 | 5 l yel grn ('88) | 12.00 | 2.40 |
| 67 | A2 | 10 l yellow ('88) | 16.00 | 2.40 |
| 68 | A2 | 20 l car rose ('88) | 25.00 | 1.25 |
| 69 | A2 | 25 l blue | 80.00 | 2.75 |
| 70 | A2 | 40 l violet ('88) | 75.00 | 24.00 |
| 71 | A2 | 50 l gray grn | 4.75 | 2.75 |
| 72 | A2 | 1d gray | 110.00 | 3.50 |
| | | Nos. 64-72 (9) | 335.00 | 165.65 |

See Nos. 81-116. For surcharges see Nos. 129, 134, 140, 144, 150, 151-152, 155-156.

**1891**   Perf. 11½

| | | | | |
|---|---|---|---|---|
| 81 | A2 | 1 l brown | 4.00 | 3.50 |
| 82 | A2 | 2 l bister | 8.25 | |
| 83 | A2 | 5 l yel grn | 18.00 | 13.00 |
| 84 | A2 | 10 l yellow | 26.00 | 13.00 |
| 85 | A2 | 20 l car rose | 47.50 | 18.00 |
| 86 | A2 | 25 l blue | 140.00 | 25.00 |
| 87 | A2 | 40 l violet | 125.00 | 77.50 |
| 88 | A2 | 50 l gray grn | 22.50 | 6.50 |
| 89 | A2 | 1d gray | 140.00 | 7.00 |
| | | Nos. 81-89 (9) | 531.25 | |

The Belgian Printings perf. 13½ and most of the values perf. 11½ (Nos. 82-86) were perforated on request of philatelists at the main post office in Athens. While not regularly issued they were freely used for postage.

### Athens Print, Poor Impression
### Wmk. Greek Words in Some Sheets

**1889-95**   Imperf.

| | | | | |
|---|---|---|---|---|
| 90 | A2 | 1 l black brn | 3.50 | 1.10 |
| a. | | 1 l brown | 2.50 | 1.10 |
| 91 | A2 | 2 l pale bister | 1.75 | 1.60 |
| a. | | 2 l buff | | 2.50 |
| 92 | A2 | 5 l green | 10.00 | 1.60 |
| a. | | Double impression | 150.00 | 300.00 |
| b. | | 5 l deep green | 10.50 | 2.10 |
| 93 | A2 | 10 l yellow | 13.00 | 1.25 |
| a. | | 10 l orange | 25.00 | 4.00 |
| b. | | 10 l dull yellow | 35.00 | 3.00 |
| 94 | A2 | 20 l carmine | 6.00 | 1.25 |
| a. | | 20 l rose | 20.00 | 1.60 |
| 95 | A2 | 25 l dull blue | 52.50 | 1.75 |
| a. | | 25 l indigo | 97.50 | 5.00 |
| b. | | 25 l ultra | 95.00 | 3.50 |
| c. | | 25 l brt blue | 50.00 | 2.50 |
| 96 | A2 | 25 l lilac | 4.75 | 1.75 |
| a. | | 25 l red vio ('93) | 10.00 | 2.50 |
| 97 | A2 | 40 l red vio ('91) | 65.00 | 32.50 |
| 98 | A2 | 40 l blue ('93) | 9.50 | 2.50 |
| 99 | A2 | 1d gray ('95) | 250.00 | 7.00 |

### Perf. 13½

| | | | | |
|---|---|---|---|---|
| 100 | A2 | 1 l brown | 22.50 | 22.50 |
| 101 | A2 | 2 l buff | 2.00 | 1.60 |
| 104 | A2 | 20 l carmine | 18.00 | 5.25 |
| a. | | 20 l rose | 25.00 | 6.25 |
| 105 | A2 | 40 l red violet | 80.00 | 47.50 |

Other denominations of type A2 were not officially issued with perf. 13½.

### Perf. 11½

| | | | | |
|---|---|---|---|---|
| 107 | A2 | 1 l brown | 3.00 | 1.60 |
| a. | | 1 l black brown | 7.25 | 5.75 |
| 108 | A2 | 2 l pale bister | 2.50 | 2.00 |
| a. | | 2 l buff | 2.75 | 2.75 |
| 109 | A2 | 5 l pale green | 8.75 | 2.00 |
| a. | | 5 l deep green | 14.00 | 3.00 |
| 110 | A2 | 10 l yellow | 13.00 | 1.25 |
| a. | | 10 l dull yellow | 35.00 | 2.50 |
| b. | | 10 l orange | 50.00 | 5.75 |
| 111 | A2 | 20 l carmine | 5.25 | .75 |
| a. | | 20 l rose | 25.00 | 1.60 |
| 112 | A2 | 25 l dull blue | 77.50 | 3.75 |
| a. | | 25 l indigo | 110.00 | 21.00 |
| b. | | 25 l ultra | 77.50 | 52.50 |
| c. | | 25 l bright blue | 57.50 | 9.00 |
| 113 | A2 | 25 l lilac | 5.25 | 1.60 |
| a. | | 25 l red violet | 12.00 | 2.75 |
| 114 | A2 | 40 l red violet | 65.00 | 37.50 |
| 115 | A2 | 40 l blue | 14.00 | 2.75 |
| 116 | A2 | 1d gray | 275.00 | 10.00 |

Partly-perforated varieties sell for about twice as much as normal stamps.

The watermark on Nos. 90-116 consists of three Greek words meaning Paper for Public Service. It is in double-lined capitals, measures 270x35mm, and extends across three panes.

Boxers — A3          Discobolus by Myron — A4

Vase Depicting Pallas Athene (Minerva) — A5

Chariot Driving A6

Stadium and Acropolis A7

Statue of Hermes by Praxiteles — A8      Statue of Victory by Paeonius — A9

Acropolis and Parthenon A10

### Perf. 14x13½, 13½x14

**1896**   Unwmk.

| | | | | |
|---|---|---|---|---|
| 117 | A3 | 1 l ocher | 1.00 | .50 |
| 118 | A3 | 2 l rose | 1.50 | .50 |
| a. | | Without engraver's name | 13.50 | 11.50 |
| 119 | A4 | 5 l lilac | 2.75 | 1.00 |
| 120 | A4 | 10 l slate gray | 3.50 | 1.50 |
| 121 | A5 | 20 l red brn | 14.00 | 2.50 |
| 122 | A6 | 25 l red | 27.50 | 2.50 |
| 123 | A5 | 40 l violet | 14.00 | 6.25 |
| 124 | A6 | 60 l black | 30.00 | 16.00 |
| 125 | A7 | 1d blue | 70.00 | 13.50 |
| 126 | A8 | 2d bister | 200.00 | 60.00 |
| a. | | Horiz. pair, imperf. btwn. | | |
| 127 | A9 | 5d green | 400.00 | 275.00 |
| 128 | A10 | 10d brown | 500.00 | 325.00 |
| | | Nos. 117-128 (12) | 1,264. | 704.25 |

1st intl. Olympic Games of the modern era, held at Athens. Counterfeits of Nos. 123-124 and 126-128 exist.

For surcharges see Nos. 159-164.

Preceding Issues Surcharged

**1900**   Imperf.

| | | | | |
|---|---|---|---|---|
| 129 | A2 | 20 l on 25 l dl bl, #95c | 2.75 | 1.60 |
| a. | | 20 l on 25 l indigo, #95a | 40.00 | 35.00 |
| b. | | 20 l on 25 l ultra, #95b | 70.00 | 55.00 |
| c. | | Double surcharge | 50.00 | |
| d. | | Triple surcharge | 65.00 | |
| e. | | Inverted surcharge | 50.00 | |
| f. | | "20" above word | 110.00 | |
| g. | | Pair, one without surcharge | 175.00 | |
| h. | | "20" without word | 110.00 | |

| | | | | |
|---|---|---|---|---|
| 130 | A1 | 30 l on 40 l vio, cr, #58a | 6.50 | 4.75 |
| a. | | 30 l on 40 l lilac, #58 | 7.00 | 6.00 |
| b. | | Broad "0" in "30" | 10.50 | 6.50 |
| c. | | First letter of word is "A" | 75.00 | 47.50 |
| d. | | Double surcharge | 300.00 | 250.00 |
| 132 | A1 | 40 l on 2 l bis, cr, #44 | 6.00 | 4.75 |
| a. | | Broad "0" in "40" | 10.00 | 7.25 |
| b. | | First letter of word is "A" | 75.00 | 55.00 |
| 133 | A1 | 50 l on 40 l sal, cr, #48 | 6.00 | 6.00 |
| a. | | Broad "0" in "50" | 10.00 | 7.00 |
| b. | | First letter of word is "A" | 75.00 | 55.00 |
| c. | | "50" without word | 200.00 | 150.00 |
| d. | | "50" above word | 200.00 | 150.00 |
| 134 | A2 | 1d on 40 l red vio (No. 97) | 12.00 | 5.25 |
| 137 | A1 | 3d on 10 l org, cr, #54 | 47.50 | 47.50 |
| a. | | 3d on 10 l org, cr, #54a | 47.50 | 47.50 |
| 138 | A1 | 5d on 40 l red vio, bl, #21 | 95.00 | 95.00 |
| a. | | 5d on 40 l red vio, bl, #28 | 125.00 | 140.00 |
| b. | | "20" on back corrected to "40" | 1,400. | |
| 139 | A1 | 5d on 40 l red vio, bl, #42b | 350.00 | |

### Perf. 11½

| | | | | |
|---|---|---|---|---|
| 140 | A2 | 20 l on 25 l dl bl, #112 | 3.25 | 3.25 |
| a. | | 20 l on 25 l indigo, #112a | 92.50 | 60.00 |
| b. | | 20 l on 25 l ultra, #112b | 75.00 | 55.00 |
| c. | | Double surcharge | 47.50 | |
| d. | | Triple surcharge | 65.00 | — |
| e. | | Inverted surcharge | 47.50 | — |
| f. | | "20" above word | 110.00 | |
| 141 | A1 | 30 l on 40 l vio, cr, #58a | 8.00 | 4.75 |
| a. | | 30 l on 40 l lilac, #58 | 9.25 | 8.75 |
| b. | | Broad "0" in "30" | 8.75 | 8.75 |
| c. | | First letter of word "A" | 85.00 | 72.50 |
| d. | | Double surcharge | | |
| 142 | A1 | 40 l on 2 l bis, cr, #44 | 8.00 | 4.75 |
| a. | | Broad "0" in "40" | 9.25 | 9.25 |
| b. | | First letter of word "A" | 95.00 | 95.00 |
| 143 | A1 | 50 l on 40 l sal, cr, #48 | 8.00 | 6.50 |
| a. | | Broad "0" in "50" | 12.00 | 9.25 |
| b. | | First letter of word "A" | 95.00 | 95.00 |
| c. | | "50" without word | 200.00 | |
| 144 | A2 | 1d on 40 l red vio, #114 | 24.00 | 16.00 |
| 147 | A1 | 3d on 10 l yel, cream, #54a | 47.50 | 47.50 |
| a. | | 3d on 10 l org, cr, #54 | 60.00 | 65.00 |
| 148 | A1 | 5d on 40 l red vio, bl, #21 | 125.00 | 125.00 |
| a. | | 5d on 40 l red vio, bl, #28 | 140.00 | 150.00 |
| 149 | A1 | 5d on 40 l red vio, bl, #42 | 350.00 | |

### Perf. 13½

| | | | | |
|---|---|---|---|---|
| 150 | A2 | 2d on 40 l red vio, #105 | 12.00 | 12.00 |

The 1d on 40 l perf. 13½ and the 2d on 40 l, both imperf. and perf. 13½, were not officially issued.

### Surcharge Including "A M"

"A M" = "Axia Metalliki" or "Value in Metal (gold)."

**1900**   Imperf.

| | | | | |
|---|---|---|---|---|
| 151 | A2 | 25 l on 40 l vio, #70 | 6.00 | 6.00 |
| 152 | A2 | 50 l on 25 l bl, #69 | 24.00 | 24.00 |
| 153 | A1 | 1d on 40 l brn, bl, #42b | 125.00 | 140.00 |
| 154 | A1 | 2d on 5 l grn, cr, #53 | 16.00 | 20.00 |

### Perf. 11½

| | | | | |
|---|---|---|---|---|
| 155 | A2 | 25 l on 40 l vio, #87 | 12.00 | 9.50 |
| 156 | A2 | 50 l on 25 l bl, #86 | 40.00 | 40.00 |
| 157 | A1 | 1d on 40 l brn, bl, #42b | 160.00 | 160.00 |
| 158 | A1 | 2d on 5 l grn, cr, #53 | 20.00 | 20.00 |
| | | Nos. 151-158 (8) | 403.00 | 419.50 |

Partly-perforated varieties of Nos. 129-158 sell for about two to three times as much as normal stamps.

### Surcharge Including "A M" on Olympic Issue in Red

**1900-01**   Perf. 14x13½

| | | | | |
|---|---|---|---|---|
| 159 | A7 | 5 l on 1d blue | 15.00 | 9.50 |
| a. | | Wrong font "M" with serifs | 70.00 | 80.00 |
| b. | | Double surcharge | 200.00 | 200.00 |
| 160 | A5 | 25 l on 40 l vio | 70.00 | 67.50 |
| a. | | Double surcharge | 875.00 | |
| 161 | A8 | 50 l on 2d bister | 80.00 | 62.50 |
| a. | | Broad "0" in "50" | 80.00 | 62.50 |
| 162 | A9 | 1d on 5d grn ('01) | 250.00 | 200.00 |
| a. | | Greek "D" instead of "A" as 3rd letter | 650.00 | 550.00 |
| 163 | A10 | 2d on 10d brn ('01) | 70.00 | 100.00 |
| a. | | Greek "D" instead of "A" as 3rd letter | 275.00 | 250.00 |
| | | Nos. 159-163 (5) | 485.00 | 439.50 |

### Black Surcharge on No. 160

| | | | | |
|---|---|---|---|---|
| 164 | A5 | 50 l on 25 l on 40 l vio (R + Bk) | 500.00 | 475.00 |
| a. | | Broad "0" in "50" | 475.00 | 575.00 |

Nos. 151-164 and 179-183, gold currency stamps, were generally used for parcel post and foreign money orders. They were also available for use on letters, but cost about 20 per cent more than the regular stamps of the same denomination.

Counterfeit surcharges exist of #159-164.

Giovanni da Bologna's Hermes
A11        A12

A13

**FIVE LEPTA.**
Type I — Letters of "ELLAS" not outlined at top and left. Only a few faint horizontal lines between the outer vertical lines at sides.
Type II — Letters of "ELLAS" fully outlined. Heavy horizontal lines between the vertical frame lines.

### Perf. 11½, 12½, 13½

| 1901 | | Engr. | | Wmk. 129 | |
|---|---|---|---|---|---|
| **165** | A11 | 1 l yellow brn | | .40 | .20 |
| **166** | A11 | 2 l gray | | .60 | .20 |
| **167** | A11 | 3 l orange | | .65 | .30 |
| **168** | A12 | 5 l grn, type I | | .80 | .20 |
| a. | | 5 l yellow green, type I | | .60 | .20 |
| b. | | 5 l yellow green, type II | | .60 | .20 |
| **169** | A12 | 10 l rose | | 3.25 | .20 |
| **170** | A11 | 20 l red lilac | | 6.50 | .20 |
| **171** | A12 | 25 l ultra | | 6.50 | .20 |
| **172** | A11 | 30 l dl vio | | 12.00 | 2.00 |
| **173** | A11 | 40 l dk brn | | 20.00 | 3.00 |
| **174** | A11 | 50 l brn lake | | 17.00 | 1.50 |

### Perf. 12½, 14 and Compound

| | | | | | |
|---|---|---|---|---|---|
| **175** | A13 | 1d black | | 47.50 | 3.00 |
| a. | Horiz. pair, imperf. btwn. | | | 325.00 | |
| c. | Horiz. pair, imperf. vert. | | | 300.00 | |
| d. | Vert. pair, imperf. horiz. | | | 300.00 | |

### Litho.
### Perf. 12½

| | | | | | |
|---|---|---|---|---|---|
| **176** | A13 | 2d bronze | | 11.00 | 8.00 |
| **177** | A13 | 3d silver | | 11.00 | 12.00 |
| a. | Horiz. pair, imperf. btwn. | | | 900.00 | |
| **178** | A13 | 5d gold | | 13.00 | 15.00 |
| | *Nos. 165-178 (14)* | | | 150.20 | 46.00 |
| | Set, never hinged | | | 325.00 | |

All values 1 l through 1d issued on both thick and thin paper. Nos. 173-174 are values for thin paper — values for thick paper are higher.

For overprints and surcharges see Nos. RA3-RA13, N16, N109.

### Imperf., Pairs

| | | | | |
|---|---|---|---|---|
| 165a | A11 | 1 l | | 12.00 |
| 166a | A11 | 2 l | | 15.00 |
| 167a | A11 | 3 l | | 15.00 |
| 168c | A12 | 5 l | | 12.00 |
| 169a | A12 | 10 l | | 19.00 |
| 170a | A11 | 20 l | | 15.00 |
| 171a | A12 | 25 l | | 15.00 |
| 172a | A11 | 30 l | | 250.00 |
| 173a | A11 | 40 l | | 300.00 |
| 174a | A11 | 50 l | | 70.00 |
| 175b | A13 | 1d | | 250.00 |

Nos. 165a-175a were issued on both thick and thin paper. Values are for the less expensive thin paper.

Hermes — A14

| 1902, Jan. 1 | | Engr. | | Perf. 13½ | |
|---|---|---|---|---|---|
| **179** | A14 | 5 l deep orange | | 2.00 | 1.10 |
| a. | Imperf., pair | | | 82.50 | |
| **180** | A14 | 25 l emerald | | 30.00 | 3.00 |
| **181** | A14 | 50 l ultra | | 30.00 | 3.75 |
| a. | Imperf., pair | | | 550.00 | |
| **182** | A14 | 1d rose red | | 30.00 | 8.25 |
| **183** | A14 | 2d orange brn | | 52.50 | 50.00 |
| | *Nos. 179-183 (5)* | | | 144.50 | 66.10 |
| | Set, never hinged | | | 375.00 | |

See note after No. 164. In 1913 remainders of Nos. 179-183 were used as postage dues.

Apollo Throwing Discus
A15

Jumper, with Jumping Weights
A16

Victory — A17

Atlas and Hercules
A18

Struggle of Hercules and Antaeus
A19

Wrestlers
A20

Daemon of the Games
A21

Foot Race
A22

Nike, Priest and Athletes in Pre-Games Offering to Zeus
A23

### Wmk. Crown and ET (129)

| 1906, Mar. | | Engr. | | Perf. 13½, 14 | |
|---|---|---|---|---|---|
| **184** | A15 | 1 l brown | | .55 | .40 |
| a. | Imperf., pair | | | 300.00 | |
| **185** | A15 | 2 l gray | | .55 | .40 |
| a. | Imperf., pair | | | 300.00 | |
| **186** | A16 | 3 l orange | | .55 | .40 |
| a. | Imperf., pair | | | 300.00 | |
| **187** | A16 | 5 l green | | 1.25 | .40 |
| a. | Imperf., pair | | | 110.00 | |
| **188** | A17 | 10 l rose red | | 2.40 | .60 |
| a. | Imperf., pair | | | 300.00 | |
| **189** | A18 | 20 l magenta | | 4.00 | .60 |
| a. | Imperf., pair | | | 575.00 | |
| **190** | A19 | 25 l ultra | | 5.25 | .85 |
| a. | Imperf., pair | | | 575.00 | |
| **191** | A20 | 30 l dl pur | | 4.00 | 2.75 |
| a. | Double impression | | | 1,100. | |
| **192** | A21 | 40 l dk brown | | 4.00 | 2.75 |
| **193** | A18 | 50 l brn lake | | 8.00 | 3.25 |
| **194** | A22 | 1d gray blk | | 65.00 | 13.00 |
| a. | Imperf., pair | | | 1,100. | |
| **195** | A22 | 2d rose | | 95.00 | 35.00 |
| **196** | A22 | 3d olive yel | | 155.00 | 125.00 |
| **197** | A23 | 5d dull blue | | 160.00 | 140.00 |
| | *Nos. 184-197 (14)* | | | 505.55 | 325.40 |
| | Set, never hinged | | | 1,200. | |

Greek Special Olympic Games of 1906 at Athens, celebrating the 10th anniv. of the modern Olympic Games.

Surcharged stamps of this issue are revenues.

A24

Iris Holding Caduceus
A25

Hermes Donning Sandals
A26

Hermes Carrying Infant Arcas — A27

Hermes, from Old Cretan Coin — A28

Designs A24 to A28 are from Cretan and Arcadian coins of the 4th Century, B.C.

### Serrate Roulette 13½

| 1911-21 | | Engr. | | Unwmk. | |
|---|---|---|---|---|---|
| **198** | A24 | 1 l green | | .65 | .30 |
| **199** | A25 | 2 l car rose | | .65 | .30 |
| **200** | A24 | 3 l vermilion | | .95 | .30 |
| **201** | A26 | 5 l green | | 2.00 | .30 |
| **202** | A24 | 10 l car rose | | 9.50 | .30 |
| **203** | A25 | 20 l gray lilac | | 2.75 | .80 |
| **204** | A25 | 25 l ultra | | 13.50 | .80 |
| a. | Rouletted in black | | | 190.00 | 140.00 |
| **205** | A26 | 30 l car rose | | 3.50 | 1.60 |
| **206** | A25 | 40 l deep blue | | 8.00 | 4.00 |
| **207** | A26 | 50 l dl vio | | 13.50 | 3.00 |
| **208** | A27 | 1d ultra | | 16.00 | .80 |
| **209** | A27 | 2d vermilion | | 22.50 | .95 |
| **210** | A27 | 3d car rose | | 22.50 | 1.40 |
| a. | Size 20¼x25½mm ('21) | | | 80.00 | 35.00 |
| **211** | A27 | 5d ultra | | 35.00 | 4.00 |
| a. | Size 20x26½mm ('21) | | | 200.00 | 25.00 |
| **212** | A27 | 10d dp bl ('21) | | 140.00 | 70.00 |
| a. | Size 20x26½mm ('11) | | | 300.00 | 125.00 |
| **213** | A28 | 25d deep blue | | 87.50 | 55.00 |
| | *Nos. 198-213 (16)* | | | 378.50 | 143.85 |
| | Set, never hinged | | | 750.00 | |

The 1921 reissues of the 3d, 5d and 10d measure 20¼x25½mm instead of 20x26½mm.

See Nos. 214-231. For overprints see Nos. 233-248B, N1, N10-N15, N17-N52A, N110-N148, Thrace 22-30, N26-N75.

### Imperf., Pairs

| | | | | |
|---|---|---|---|---|
| 198a | A24 | 1 l | 90.00 | 90.00 |
| 200a | A24 | 3 l | 240.00 | 240.00 |
| 201a | A26 | 5 l | 30.00 | 30.00 |
| 202a | A24 | 10 l | 52.50 | 52.50 |
| 203a | A25 | 20 l | 225.00 | 225.00 |
| 204b | A25 | 25 l | 300.00 | 300.00 |
| 206a | A25 | 40 l | 350.00 | |
| 207a | A26 | 50 l | 350.00 | |
| 208a | A27 | 1d | 350.00 | |
| 209a | A27 | 2d | 350.00 | |
| 210b | A27 | 3d | 350.00 | |
| 211b | A27 | 5d | 240.00 | |
| 212b | A27 | 10d As "a" | 1,600. | |
| 213a | A28 | 25d | 2,250. | |

### Serrate Roulette 10½x13½, 13½

| 1913-23 | | | | Litho. | |
|---|---|---|---|---|---|
| **214** | A24 | 1 l green | | .20 | .20 |
| a. | Without period after "El-las" | | | 77.50 | — |
| **215** | A25 | 2 l rose | | .20 | .20 |
| **216** | A24 | 3 l vermilion | | .20 | .20 |
| **217** | A24 | 5 l green | | .20 | .20 |
| **218** | A24 | 10 l carmine | | .20 | .20 |
| **219** | A25 | 15 l dl bl ('18) | | .35 | .20 |
| **220** | A25 | 20 l slate | | .35 | .20 |
| **221** | A25 | 25 l ultra | | 4.00 | .50 |
| a. | 25 l blue | | | .20 | |
| b. | Double impression | | | | |
| **222** | A26 | 30 l rose ('14) | | .95 | .40 |
| **223** | A25 | 40 l indigo ('14) | | 2.10 | .70 |
| **224** | A26 | 50 l vio brn ('14) | | 4.25 | .35 |
| **225** | A27 | 80 l vio brn ('23) | | 5.25 | 1.40 |
| **226** | A27 | 1d ultra ('19) | | 7.00 | .70 |
| **227** | A27 | 2d ver ('19) | | 6.50 | .70 |
| **228** | A27 | 3d car rose ('20) | | 8.50 | .80 |
| **229** | A27 | 5d car ('22) | | 12.00 | 1.00 |

| **230** | A27 | 10d dp bl ('22) | | 12.00 | 1.25 |
|---|---|---|---|---|---|
| **231** | A28 | 25d indigo ('22) | | 16.00 | 4.75 |
| | *Nos. 214-231 (18)* | | | 80.25 | 13.95 |
| | Set, never hinged | | | 225.00 | |

Nos. 221, 223 and 226 were re-issued in 1926, printed in Vienna from new plates. There are slight differences in minor details.

The 10 lepta brown, on thick paper, type A28, is not a postage stamp. It was issued in 1922 to replace coins of this denomination during a shortage of copper.

### Imperf., Pairs

| | | | | |
|---|---|---|---|---|
| 214b | A24 | 1 l | 65.00 | |
| 215a | A25 | 2 l | 110.00 | |
| 216a | A24 | 3 l | 175.00 | |
| 217a | A26 | 5 l | 65.00 | |
| 218a | A24 | 10 l | 82.50 | |
| 220a | A25 | 20 l | 82.50 | |
| 221b | A25 | 25 l | 175.00 | |
| 222a | A26 | 30 l | 175.00 | |
| 223a | A25 | 40 l | 175.00 | |
| 224a | A26 | 50 l | 300.00 | |
| 225b | A26 | 80 l | 92.50 | |
| 226a | A27 | 1d | 100.00 | 250.00 |
| 227a | A27 | 2d | 300.00 | |
| 228b | A27 | 3d | 300.00 | |
| 229a | A27 | 5d | 360.00 | |

Raising Greek Flag at Suda Bay, Crete
A29

| 1913, Dec. 1 | | Engr. | | Perf. 14½ | |
|---|---|---|---|---|---|
| **232** | A29 | 25 l blue & black | | 6.75 | 5.00 |
| | Never hinged | | | 13.00 | |
| a. | Imperf., pair | | | 1,100. | |

Union of Crete with Greece. Used only in Crete.

Stamps of 1911-14 Overprinted in Red or Black

### Serrate Roulette 13½

| 1916, Nov. 1 | | | | Litho. | |
|---|---|---|---|---|---|
| **233** | A24 | 1 l green (R) | | .20 | .20 |
| **234** | A25 | 2 l rose | | .20 | .20 |
| **235** | A24 | 3 l vermilion | | .20 | .20 |
| **236** | A26 | 5 l green (R) | | .50 | .40 |
| **237** | A24 | 10 l carmine | | .75 | .40 |
| **238** | A25 | 20 l slate (R) | | 1.25 | .40 |
| **239** | A25 | 25 l blue (R) | | 1.25 | .40 |
| a. | 25 l ultra | | | 140.00 | 26.00 |
| **240** | A26 | 30 l rose | | 1.25 | .90 |
| a. | Pair, one without ovpt. | | | | |
| **241** | A25 | 40 l indigo (R) | | 11.00 | 3.00 |
| **242** | A26 | 50 l vio brn (R) | | 37.50 | 2.50 |

### Engr.

| | | | | | |
|---|---|---|---|---|---|
| **243** | A24 | 3 l vermilion | | .50 | .50 |
| **244** | A26 | 30 l car rose | | 1.25 | 1.25 |
| **245** | A27 | 1d ultra (R) | | 40.00 | .80 |
| a. | Rouletted in black | | | 325.00 | 225.00 |
| **246** | A27 | 2d vermilion | | 24.00 | 3.50 |
| **247** | A27 | 3d car rose | | 14.00 | 3.50 |
| **248** | A27 | 5d ultra (R) | | 95.00 | 15.00 |
| **248B** | A27 | 10d dp bl (R) | | 24.00 | 22.50 |
| | *Nos. 233-248B (17)* | | | 252.85 | 55.65 |
| | Set, never hinged | | | 500.00 | |

Most of Nos. 233-248B exist with overprint double, inverted, etc. Minimum value of errors $18. Excellent counterfeits of the overprint varieties exist.

### Issued by the Venizelist Provisional Government

Iris — A32

| 1917, Feb. 5 | | | | Litho. | Perf. 14 | |
|---|---|---|---|---|---|---|
| **249** | A32 | 1 l dp green | | .40 | .20 |
| **250** | A32 | 5 l yel grn | | .40 | .20 |
| **251** | A32 | 10 l rose | | .80 | .35 |
| **252** | A32 | 25 l lt blue | | 1.10 | .35 |
| **253** | A32 | 50 l gray vio | | 9.00 | 2.50 |
| **254** | A32 | 1d ultra | | 2.25 | .75 |
| **255** | A32 | 2d lt red | | 4.50 | 1.50 |
| **256** | A32 | 3d claret | | 25.00 | 7.75 |
| **257** | A32 | 5d gray bl | | 5.75 | 3.00 |

| | | | | |
|---|---|---|---|---|
| 258 | A32 | 10d dk blue | 70.00 | 20.00 |
| 259 | A32 | 25d slate | 125.00 | 160.00 |
| | | Nos. 249-259 (11) | 244.20 | 196.60 |
| | | Set, never hinged | 400.00 | |

The 4d was used only as a revenue stamp.

**Imperf., Pairs**

| | | | |
|---|---|---|---|
| 249a | A32 | 1 l | 9.50 |
| 250a | A32 | 5 l | 9.50 |
| 251a | A32 | 10 l | 9.50 |
| 252a | A32 | 25 l | 17.50 |
| 253a | A32 | 50 l | 25.00 |
| 254a | A32 | 1d | 22.50 |
| 255a | A32 | 2d | 30.00 |
| 256a | A32 | 3d | 65.00 |
| 257a | A32 | 5d | 65.00 |
| 258a | A32 | 10d | 110.00 |
| 259a | A32 | 25d | 125.00 |

Stamps of 1917
Surcharged

**1923**

| | | | | |
|---|---|---|---|---|
| 260 | A32 | 5 l on 10 l rose | .25 | .25 |
| a. | | Inverted surcharge | 24.00 | 35.00 |
| 261 | A32 | 50 l on 50 l gray vio | .25 | .25 |
| 262 | A32 | 1d on 1d ultra | .25 | .25 |
| a. | | 1d on 1d gray | .25 | .25 |
| 263 | A32 | 2d on 2d lt red | .55 | .55 |
| 264 | A32 | 3d on 3d claret | 1.60 | 1.60 |
| 265 | A32 | 5d on 5d dk bl | 2.00 | 2.00 |
| 266 | A32 | 25d on 25d slate | 27.50 | 27.50 |
| | | Nos. 260-266 (7) | 32.40 | 32.40 |
| | | Set, never hinged | 25.00 | |

**Same Surcharge on Occupation of Turkey Stamps, 1913**

**Perf. 13½**

| | | | | |
|---|---|---|---|---|
| 267 | O2 | 5 l on 3 l org | .25 | .25 |
| a. | | Inverted surcharge | 19.00 | |
| 268 | O1 | 10 l on 20 l vio | 1.50 | 1.50 |
| a. | | Inverted surcharge | 82.50 | |
| 269 | O2 | 10 l on 25 l pale bl | .25 | .25 |
| a. | | Inverted surcharge | 60.00 | 35.00 |
| 270 | O1 | 10 l on 30 l gray grn | .25 | .25 |
| 271 | O2 | 10 l on 40 l ind | 1.25 | 1.25 |
| 272 | O1 | 50 l on 50 l dk bl | .25 | .25 |
| a. | | Inverted surcharge | 72.50 | 37.50 |
| 273 | O1 | 2d on 2d gray brn | 60.00 | 60.00 |
| 274 | O2 | 3d on 3d dl bl | 4.50 | 6.00 |
| a. | | Imperf., pair | 500.00 | |
| 275 | O1 | 5d on 5d gray | 4.00 | 7.00 |
| 276 | O2 | 10d on 1d vio brn | 15.00 | 22.50 |
| 276A | O2 | on 10d on 10d car | 800.00 | |
| | | Never hinged | 1,200. | |
| | | Nos. 267-276 (10) | 87.25 | 99.25 |
| | | Set, never hinged | 150.00 | |

Dangerous counterfeits of No. 276A exist.

**Same Surcharge on Stamps of Crete**

**Perf. 14**

**On Crete #50, 52, 59**

| | | | | |
|---|---|---|---|---|
| 276B | A6 | 5 l on 1 l red brn | 27.50 | 27.50 |
| 277 | A8 | 10 l on 10 l red | .25 | .25 |
| 277B | A8 | 10 l on 25 l bl | 110.00 | 110.00 |

**On Crete #66-69, 71**

| | | | | |
|---|---|---|---|---|
| 278 | A8 | 10 l on 25 l blue | .25 | .25 |
| 279 | A6 | 50 l on 50 l lilac | .45 | .70 |
| 279A | A6 | 50 l on 50 l ultra | 8.50 | 14.00 |
| 280 | A9 | 50 l on 1d gray vio | 3.00 | 4.00 |
| 280A | A11 | 50 l on 5d grn & blk | 27.50 | 27.50 |

**On Crete #77-82**

| | | | | |
|---|---|---|---|---|
| 281 | A15 | 10 l on 20 l bl grn | 125.00 | 125.00 |
| 282 | A16 | 10 l on 25 l ultra | .45 | .45 |
| a. | | Double surcharge | 50.00 | 50.00 |
| 283 | A17 | 50 l on 50 l yel brn | .25 | .35 |
| 284 | A18 | 50 l on 1d rose car & brn | 2.00 | 1.75 |
| a. | | Imperf., pair | 425.00 | |
| 285 | A19 | 3d on 3d org & blk | 14.00 | 14.00 |
| 286 | A20 | 5d on 5d ol grn & blk | 9.00 | 9.00 |

**On Crete #83-84**

| | | | | |
|---|---|---|---|---|
| 287 | A21 | 10 l on 25 l bl & blk | 3.25 | 1.75 |
| a. | | Imperf., pair | | |
| 287B | A22 | 50 l on 1d grn & blk | 8.00 | 4.50 |

**On Crete #96**

| | | | | |
|---|---|---|---|---|
| 288 | A23 | 10 l on 10 l brn red | .25 | .25 |
| a. | | Inverted surcharge | 45.00 | 40.00 |

**On Crete #91**

| | | | | |
|---|---|---|---|---|
| 288B | A17 | 50 l on 50 l yel brn | | 800.00 |

Dangerous counterfeits of the overprint on No. 288B are plentiful.

**On Crete #109**

| | | | | |
|---|---|---|---|---|
| 289 | A19 | 3d on 3d org & blk | 17.50 | 17.50 |

**On Crete #111, 113-120**

| | | | | |
|---|---|---|---|---|
| 290 | A6 | 5 l on 1 l vio brn | .25 | .25 |
| a. | | Inverted surcharge | 25.00 | |
| 291 | A13 | 5 l on 5 l grn | .25 | .25 |
| a. | | Inverted surcharge | 47.50 | |
| 292 | A23 | 10 l on 10 l brn red | .25 | .25 |
| a. | | Inverted surcharge | 47.50 | |
| 293 | A15 | 10 l on 20 l bl grn | .30 | .30 |
| a. | | Inverted surcharge | 47.50 | |
| 294 | A16 | 10 l on 25 l ultra | .35 | .35 |
| a. | | Inverted surcharge | 47.50 | |
| 295 | A17 | 50 l on 50 l yel brn | .40 | .40 |
| 296 | A18 | 50 l on 1d rose car & brn | 5.25 | 5.25 |
| a. | | Inverted surcharge | | |
| b. | | Double surcharge | 225.00 | |
| c. | | Double surch., one invtd. | | |
| d. | | Imperf., pair | | |
| 297 | A19 | 3d on 3d org & blk | 16.00 | 16.00 |
| 298 | A20 | 5d on 5d ol grn & blk | 200.00 | 200.00 |

Dangerous counterfeits of No. 298 exist.

**Crete #J2-J9**

| | | | | |
|---|---|---|---|---|
| 299 | D1 | 5 l on 5 l red | .25 | .25 |
| 300 | D1 | 5 l on 10 l red | .30 | 6.75 |
| a. | | Inverted surcharge | 45.00 | .30 |
| 301 | D1 | 5 l on 10 l red | 12.00 | 12.00 |
| a. | | Inverted surcharge | | |
| 302 | D1 | 10 l on 40 l red | .30 | .30 |
| 303 | D1 | 50 l on 50 l red | .30 | .55 |
| 304 | D1 | 50 l on 1d red | .30 | .50 |
| a. | | Double surcharge | | |
| 305 | D1 | 50 l on 1d on 1d red | 9.50 | 9.50 |
| 306 | D1 | 2d on 2d red | 1.25 | 1.25 |

**On Crete #J11-J13**

| | | | | |
|---|---|---|---|---|
| 307 | D1 | 5 l on 5 l red | 6.00 | 6.00 |
| 308 | D1 | 5 l on 10 l red | 1.50 | 1.50 |
| a. | | "Ellas" inverted | 6.50 | |
| 309 | D1 | 10 l on 20 l red | 55.00 | 55.00 |

**On Crete #J20-J22, J24-J26**

| | | | | |
|---|---|---|---|---|
| 310 | D1 | 5 l on 5 l red | .25 | .25 |
| 311 | D1 | 5 l on 10 l red | .25 | .25 |
| a. | | Inverted surcharge | 12.00 | |
| 312 | D1 | 10 l on 20 l red | .25 | .25 |
| 313 | D1 | 50 l on 50 l red | .55 | .55 |
| 314 | D1 | 50 l on 1d red | 4.00 | 4.00 |
| 315 | D1 | 2d on 2d red | 7.00 | 7.00 |

These surcharged Postage Due stamps were intended for the payment of ordinary postage.

Nos. 260 to 315 were surcharged in commemoration of the revolution of 1922.

Nos. 59, 91, 109, 111, 113-120, J11-J13, J20-J22, J24-J26 are on stamps previously overprinted by Crete.

**Issues of the Republic**

Lord Byron — A33

Byron at Missolonghi — A34

**1924, Apr. 16  Engr.  Perf. 12**

| | | | | |
|---|---|---|---|---|
| 316 | A33 | 80 l dark blue | .55 | .20 |
| 317 | A34 | 2d dk vio & blk | 1.25 | .65 |
| | | Set, never hinged | 3.25 | |

Death of Lord Byron (1788-1824) at Missolonghi.

Tomb of Markos Botsaris — A35

**Serrate Roulette 13½**

**1926, Apr. 24  Litho.**

| | | | | |
|---|---|---|---|---|
| 318 | A35 | 25 l lilac | .85 | .50 |
| | | Never hinged | 1.75 | |

Centenary of the defense of Missolonghi against the Turks.

Corinth Canal A36

Dodecanese Costume A37

Macedonian Costume A38

Monastery of Simon Peter on Mt. Athos A39

White Tower of Salonika A40

Temple of Hephaestus A41

The Acropolis — A42

Cruiser "Georgios Averoff" — A43

Academy of Sciences, Athens — A44

Temple of Hephaestus A45

Acropolis A46

**Perf. 12½x13, 13, 13x12½, 13½, 13½x13**

**1927, Apr. 1  Engr.**

| | | | | |
|---|---|---|---|---|
| 321 | A36 | 5 l dark green | .20 | .20 |
| a. | | Vert. pair, imperf. horiz. | 140.00 | 92.50 |
| 322 | A37 | 10 l orange red | .30 | .20 |
| a. | | Horiz. pair, imperf. between | 140.00 | 92.50 |
| c. | | Double impression | 77.50 | |
| 323 | A38 | 20 l violet | .30 | .20 |
| 324 | A39 | 25 l slate blue | .50 | .20 |
| a. | | Imperf., pair | 140.00 | 140.00 |
| b. | | Vert. pair, imperf. between | 150.00 | 110.00 |
| 325 | A40 | 40 l slate blue | .50 | .20 |
| 326 | A36 | 50 l violet | 1.10 | .20 |

| | | | | |
|---|---|---|---|---|
| 327 | A36 | 80 l dk bl & blk | .95 | .20 |
| a. | | Imperf., pair | 825.00 | |
| 328 | A41 | 1d dk bl & bis brn (I) | 1.10 | .20 |
| a. | | Imperf., pair | 150.00 | 125.00 |
| b. | | Center inverted | | 6,500. |
| c. | | Double impression of center | 325.00 | 225.00 |
| d. | | Double impression of frame | 325.00 | 225.00 |
| 329 | A42 | 2d dk green & blk | 6.50 | .30 |
| a. | | Imperf., pair | 600.00 | 800.00 |
| 330 | A43 | 3d dp violet & blk | 6.00 | .30 |
| a. | | Double impression of center | 225.00 | 275.00 |
| b. | | Center inverted | | 8,000. |
| 331 | A44 | 5d yellow & blk | 15.00 | 2.00 |
| a. | | Imperf., pair | 925.00 | 925.00 |
| b. | | Center inverted | 10,000. | 4,500. |
| c. | | 5d yellow & green | 110.00 | 37.50 |
| 332 | A45 | 10d brn car & blk | 45.00 | 11.00 |
| 333 | A44 | 15d brt yel grn & blk | 57.50 | 16.00 |
| 334 | A46 | 25d green & blk | 110.00 | 18.00 |
| a. | | Double impression of center | | — |
| | | Nos. 321-334 (14) | 244.95 | 49.20 |
| | | Set, never hinged | 700.00 | |

See Nos. 364-371 and notes preceding No. 364. For overprints see Nos. RA55, RA57, RA60, RA66, RA70-RA71.

This series as prepared, included a 1 lepton dark brown, type A37, but that value was never issued. Most stamps were burned. Value $300.

Gen. Charles N. Fabvier and Acropolis A47

**1927, Aug. 1  Perf. 12**

| | | | | |
|---|---|---|---|---|
| 335 | A47 | 1d red | .30 | .20 |
| 336 | A47 | 3d dark blue | 2.00 | .60 |
| 337 | A47 | 6d green | 12.00 | 9.00 |
| | | Nos. 335-337 (3) | 14.30 | 9.80 |
| | | Set, never hinged | 42.50 | |

Cent. of the liberation of Athens from the Turks in 1826.

For surcharges see Nos. 376-377.

Bay of Navarino and Pylos A48

Battle of Navarino A49

"Edward" omitted — A50

"Edward" added — A51

Admiral de Rigny — A52

Admiral van der Heyden — A53

Designs: #340-341, Sir Edward Codrington.

## Perf. 13½x12½, 12½x13½, 13x12½, 12½x13

**1927-28**     Litho.
| | | | | |
|---|---|---|---|---|
| 338 | A48 | 1.50d gray green | 1.60 | .35 |
| a. | | Imperf., pair | 275.00 | |
| b. | | Horiz. pair, imperf. btwn. | 875.00 | |
| c. | | Horiz. pair, imperf. vert. | 250.00 | |
| 339 | A49 | 4d dk gray bl ('28) | 7.00 | 1.50 |
| 340 | A50 | 5d dk brn & gray | 5.50 | 4.75 |
| a. | | 5d blk brn & blk ('28) | 13.00 | 6.50 |
| 341 | A51 | 5d dk brn & blk ('28) | 35.00 | 12.00 |
| 342 | A52 | 5d vio bl & blk ('28) | 35.00 | 12.00 |
| 343 | A53 | 5d lake & blk ('28) | 20.00 | 9.50 |
| | | Nos. 338-343 (6) | 104.10 | 40.10 |
| | | Set, never hinged | 275.00 | |

Centenary of the naval battle of Navarino. For surcharges see Nos. 372-375.

Admiral Lascarina Bouboulina A54

Athanasios Diakos A55

Map of Greece in 1830 and 1930 — A56

Sortie from Missolonghi A58

Patriots Declaring Independence — A57

Portraits: 10 l, Constantine Rhigas Ferreos. 20 l, Gregorios V. 40 l, Prince Alexandros Ypsilantis. No. 345, Bouboulina. No. 355, Diakos. No. 346, Theodoros Kolokotronis. No. 356, Konstantinos Kanaris. No. 347, Georgios Karaiskakis. No. 357, Markos Botsaris. 2d, Andreas Miaoulis. 3d, Lazaros Koundouriotis. 5d, Count John Capo d'Istria (Capodistria), statesman and doctor. 10d, Petros Mavromichalis. 15d, Dionysios Solomos. 20d, Adamantios Korais.

### Various Frames
**1930, Apr. 1**   Engr.   Perf. 13½, 14
**Imprint of Perkins, Bacon & Co.**
| | | | | |
|---|---|---|---|---|
| 344 | A55 | 10 l brown | .20 | .20 |
| 345 | A54 | 50 l red | .20 | .20 |
| 346 | A54 | 1d car rose | .30 | .30 |
| 347 | A55 | 1.50d lt blue | .40 | .40 |
| 348 | A55 | 2d orange | .45 | .45 |
| 349 | A55 | 5d purple | 1.50 | 1.50 |
| 350 | A54 | 10d gray blk | 6.50 | 6.50 |
| 351 | A54 | 15d yellow grn | 12.00 | 12.00 |
| 352 | A55 | 20d blue blk | 17.50 | 17.50 |

**Imprint of Bradbury, Wilkinson & Co.**
**Perf. 12**
| | | | | |
|---|---|---|---|---|
| 353 | A55 | 20 l black | .20 | .20 |
| 354 | A55 | 40 l blue grn | .20 | .20 |
| 355 | A55 | 50 l brt blue | .20 | .20 |

| | | | | |
|---|---|---|---|---|
| 356 | A55 | 1d brown org | .30 | .30 |
| 357 | A55 | 1.50d dk red | .40 | .40 |
| 358 | A55 | 3d dk brown | .65 | .65 |
| 359 | A56 | 4d dk blue | 3.00 | 3.00 |
| 360 | A57 | 25d black | 17.50 | 17.50 |
| 361 | A58 | 50d red brn | 45.00 | 45.00 |
| | | Nos. 344-361 (18) | 106.50 | 106.50 |
| | | Set, never hinged | 275.00 | |

Greek independence, cent. Some exist imperf.

Arcadi Monastery and Abbot Gabriel (Mt. Ida in Background) A60

**1930, Nov. 8**     Perf. 12
| | | | | |
|---|---|---|---|---|
| 363 | A60 | 8d deep violet | 13.00 | 1.10 |
| | | Never hinged | 55.00 | |

### Issue of 1927 Re-engraved
50 l, Design is clearer, especially "50" and the 10 letters.

Type I

Type II

1d. Type I — Greek letters "L," "A," "D" have sharp pointed tops; numerals "1" are 1½mm wide at the foot, and have a straight slanting serif at top.

1d. Type II — Greek letters "L," "A," "D" have flat tops; numerals "1" are 2mm wide at foot and the serif at top is slightly curved. Perf. 14. There are many minor differences in the lines of the two designs.

1d. Type III — The "1" in lower left corner has no serif at left of foot. Lines of temple have been deepened, so details stand out more clearly.

2d. On 1927 stamp the Parthenon is indistinct and blurred. On 1933 stamp it is strongly outlined and clear. Between the two pillars at lower right are four blocks of marble. These blocks are clear and distinct on the 1933 stamp but run together on the 1927 issue.

3d. Design is clearer, especially vertical lines of shading in smoke stacks and reflections in the water. Two or more sides perf. 11½.

10d. Background and shading of entire stamp have been lightened. Detail of frame is clearer and more distinct.

15d. Many more lines of shading in sky and foreground. Engraving is sharp and clear, particularly in frame. Two or more sides perf. 11½.

25d. Background has been lightened and foreground reduced until base of larger upright column is removed and fallen column appears nearly submerged.
Sizes in millimeters:
50 l, 1927, 18x24¾. 1933, 18½x24½.
1d, 1927, 24¾x17¾. 1931, 24¾x17¼. 1933, 24½x18¼.
2d, 1927, 24½x17¾. 1933, 24½x18½.

### Perf. 11½, 11½x12½, 12½x10, 13, 13x12½, 14
**1931-35**
| | | | | |
|---|---|---|---|---|
| 364 | A36 | 50 l dk vio ('33) | 4.00 | 1.00 |
| 365 | A41 | 1d dk bl & org brn, type II | 10.00 | 1.00 |
| 366 | A41 | 1d dk bl & org brn, type III ('33) | 5.75 | .20 |
| 367 | A42 | 2d dk grn & blk ('33) | 2.75 | .50 |
| 368 | A43 | 3d red vio & blk ('34) | 3.25 | .25 |
| a. | | Imperf., pair | | |
| 369 | A45 | 10d brn car & blk ('35) | 47.50 | 1.50 |
| 370 | A44 | 15d pale yel grn & blk ('34) | 82.50 | 17.50 |
| a. | | Imperf., pair | 1,100. | |
| 371 | A46 | 25d grn & blk ('35) | 25.00 | 17.00 |
| | | Nos. 364-371 (8) | 180.75 | 38.95 |
| | | Set, never hinged | 600.00 | |

Nos. 336-337, 340-343 Surcharged in Red

**1932**   Perf. 12½x13½, 12½x13
| | | | | |
|---|---|---|---|---|
| 372 | A52 | 1.50d on 5d | 2.00 | .20 |
| 373 | A53 | 1.50d on 5d | 2.00 | .20 |
| a. | | Double surcharge | 110.00 | |
| 374 | A50 | 2d on 5d | 5.00 | .20 |
| 375 | A51 | 2d on 5d | 9.00 | .20 |

**Perf. 12**
| | | | | |
|---|---|---|---|---|
| 376 | A47 | 2d on 3d | 2.25 | .20 |
| a. | | Double surcharge | 125.00 | |
| 377 | A47 | 4d on 6d | 2.50 | 1.10 |
| | | Nos. 372-377 (6) | 22.75 | 2.10 |
| | | Set, never hinged | 50.00 | |

Adm. Pavlos Koundouriotis and Cruiser "Averoff" — A61

Pallas Athene — A62

Youth of Marathon — A63

**1933**   Perf. 13½x13, 13x13½
| | | | | |
|---|---|---|---|---|
| 378 | A61 | 50d black & ind | 45.00 | 1.60 |
| a. | | Imperf., pair | 2,250. | |
| 379 | A62 | 75d blk & vio brn | 100.00 | 175.00 |
| a. | | Imperf., pair | 825.00 | |
| | | Never hinged | 1,700. | |
| 380 | A63 | 100d brn & dull grn | 550.00 | 29.00 |
| a. | | Imperf., pair | 2,750. | |
| | | Nos. 378-380 (3) | 695.00 | 205.60 |
| | | Set, never hinged | 1,600. | |

The imperf pairs are without gum.
For surcharges see Nos. 386-387.

Approach to Athens Stadium A64

### Perf. 11½, 11½x10, 13½x11½
**1934, Dec. 10**
| | | | | |
|---|---|---|---|---|
| 381 | A64 | 8d blue | 57.50 | 2.25 |
| | | Never hinged | 175.00 | |

Perforations on No. 381 range from 10½ to 13, including compounds.

Church of Pantanassa, Mistra — A65

**1935, Nov. 1**     Perf. 13x12½
| | | | | |
|---|---|---|---|---|
| 382 | A65 | 4d brown | 17.00 | 1.60 |
| | | Never hinged | 47.50 | |
| a. | | Horiz. pair, imperf. between | 725.00 | |
| b. | | Imperf., pair | 725.00 | |

### Issues of the Monarchy
J71, J76, J82, 380, 379 Surcharged in Red or Blue

Nos. 383-385

Nos. 386-387

### Serrate Roulette 13½
**1935, Nov. 24**     Litho.
| | | | | |
|---|---|---|---|---|
| 383 | D3 | 50 l on 40 l indigo (R) | .20 | .20 |
| a. | | Double surcharge | | 27.50 |
| 384 | D3 | 3d on 3d car (Bl) | .55 | .40 |

**Perf. 13**
| | | | | |
|---|---|---|---|---|
| 385 | D3 | 3d on 3d rose red (Bl) | 2.75 | 2.00 |

**Perf. 13x13½**
| | | | | |
|---|---|---|---|---|
| 386 | A63 | 5d on 100d (R) | 2.25 | 2.00 |
| 387 | A62 | 15d on 75d (Bl) | 6.50 | 6.00 |
| | | Nos. 383-387 (5) | 12.25 | 10.60 |
| | | Set, never hinged | 30.00 | |

King Constantine — A66

### Center Engr., Frame Litho.
**Perf. 12x13½**
**1936, Nov. 18**     Wmk. 252
| | | | | |
|---|---|---|---|---|
| 389 | A66 | 3d black & brown | .55 | .40 |
| a. | | Pair, printer's name in Greek | 22.50 | |
| b. | | Pair, printer's name in English | 22.50 | |
| 390 | A66 | 8d black & blue | 1.10 | .90 |
| a. | | Pair, printer's name in Greek | 22.50 | |
| b. | | Pair, printer's name in English | 22.50 | |
| | | Set, never hinged | 3.25 | |

Re-burial of the remains of King Constantine and Queen Sophia.
Two printings exist, the first containing varieties "a" and "b" with gray border; second with black border.

King George II — A67

Pallas Athene — A68

**1937, Jan. 24**   Engr.   Perf. 12½x12
| | | | | |
|---|---|---|---|---|
| 391 | A67 | 1d green | .20 | .20 |
| 392 | A67 | 3d red brown | .25 | .20 |
| 393 | A67 | 8d dp blue | .90 | .40 |
| 394 | A67 | 100d carmine lake | 12.00 | 12.00 |
| | | Nos. 391-394 (4) | 13.35 | 12.80 |
| | | Set, never hinged | 30.00 | |

For surcharges see Nos. 484-487, 498-500, RA86-RA87, N241-N242.

**1937, Apr. 17**   Unwmk.   Perf. 11½
| | | | | |
|---|---|---|---|---|
| 395 | A68 | 3d yellow brown | .55 | .25 |
| | | Never hinged | 1.10 | |

Centenary of the University of Athens.

Contest with Bull — A69

Lady of Tiryns — A70

Zeus of Dodona — A71

Coin of Amphictyonic League A72

Diagoras of Rhodes, Victor at Olympics A73

Venus of Melos — A74

Battle of Salamis A75

Chariot of Panathenaic Festival A76

Alexander the Great at Battle of Issos — A77

St. Paul Preaching to Athenians A78

St. Demetrius' Church at Salonika A79

Leo III Victory over Arabs — A80

Allegorical Figure of Glory — A81

**Perf. 13½x12, 12x13½**

| 1937, Nov. 1 | | Litho. | Wmk. 252 | |
|---|---|---|---|---|
| 396 | A69 | 5 l brn red & bl | .20 | .20 |
| a. | | Double impression of frame | 60.00 | |
| 397 | A70 | 10 l bl & brn red | .20 | .20 |
| a. | | Double impression of frame | 60.00 | |
| 398 | A71 | 20 l black & grn | .20 | .20 |
| 399 | A72 | 40 l green & blk | .20 | .20 |
| a. | | Green impression doubled | 60.00 | |
| 400 | A73 | 50 l brown & blk | .20 | .20 |
| 401 | A74 | 80 l ind & yel brn | .20 | .20 |

**Engr.**

| 402 | A75 | 2d ultra | .20 | .20 |
|---|---|---|---|---|
| 403 | A76 | 5d red | .20 | .20 |
| a. | | Printer's name omitted | 5.50 | |
| 404 | A77 | 6d olive brn | .20 | .20 |
| 405 | A78 | 7d dk brown | .55 | .50 |
| 406 | A79 | 10d red brown | .20 | .20 |

| 407 | A80 | 15d green | .20 | .20 |
|---|---|---|---|---|
| 408 | A81 | 25d dk blue | .20 | .20 |
| | | Nos. 396-408 (13) | 2.95 | 2.90 |
| | | Set, never hinged | 4.00 | |

See Nos. 413, 459-466. For overprints and surcharges see Nos. 455-458, 476-477, RA75-RA78, RA83-RA85, N202-N217, N246-N247.

---

**Cerigo, Paxos, Lefkas**

Greek stamps with Italian overprints for the islands of Cerigo (Kithyra), Paxos and Lefkas (Santa Maura) are fraudulent.

---

### Royal Wedding Issue

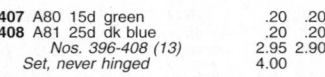

Princess Frederika-Louise and Crown Prince Paul — A82

| 1938 | | Wmk. 252 | Perf. 13½x12 | |
|---|---|---|---|---|
| 409 | A82 | 1d green | .20 | .20 |
| 410 | A82 | 3d orange brn | .30 | .20 |
| 411 | A82 | 8d dark blue | .55 | .65 |
| | | Nos. 409-411 (3) | 1.05 | 1.05 |
| | | Set, never hinged | 2.75 | |

Arms of Greece, Romania, Yugoslavia and Turkey A83

Statue of King Constantine A84

**Perf. 12x12½**

| 1938, Feb. 8 | | Litho. | Unwmk. | |
|---|---|---|---|---|
| 412 | A83 | 6d blue | 5.50 | 1.75 |
| | | Never hinged | 14.00 | |

Balkan Entente.

**Tiryns Lady Type of 1937 Corrected Inscription**

| 1938 | | Wmk. 252 | Perf. 12x13½ | |
|---|---|---|---|---|
| 413 | A70 | 10 l blue & brn red | .50 | .70 |
| | | Never hinged | .85 | |

The first four letters of the third word of the inscription read "TIPY" instead of "TYPI."

**Perf. 12x13½**

| 1938, Oct. 8 | | Engr. | Unwmk. | |
|---|---|---|---|---|
| 414 | A84 | 1.50d green | .45 | .20 |
| 415 | A84 | 30d orange brn | 2.25 | 3.25 |
| | | Set, never hinged | 5.50 | |

For overprint see No. N218.

Coats of Arms of Ionian Islands — A85

Fort at Corfu — A86

King George I of Greece and Queen Victoria of England A87

---

**Perf. 12½x12, 13½x12**

| 1939, May 21 | | Engr. | Unwmk. | |
|---|---|---|---|---|
| 416 | A85 | 1d dk blue | .85 | .25 |
| 417 | A86 | 4d green | 2.90 | 1.00 |
| 418 | A87 | 20d yellow org | 17.00 | 17.00 |
| 419 | A87 | 20d dull blue | 17.00 | 17.00 |
| 420 | A87 | 20d car lake | 17.00 | 17.00 |
| | | Nos. 416-420 (5) | 54.75 | 52.25 |
| | | Set, never hinged | 125.00 | |

75th anniv. of the union of the Ionian Islands with Greece.

Runner with Shield — A88

10th Pan-Balkan Games: 3d, Javelin thrower. 6d, Discus thrower. 8d, Jumper.

**Perf. 12x13½**

| 1939, Oct. 1 | | Litho. | Unwmk. | |
|---|---|---|---|---|
| 421 | A88 | 50 l slate grn & grn | .25 | .20 |
| 422 | A88 | 3d henna brn & dl rose | 1.25 | .55 |
| 423 | A88 | 6d cop brn & dl org | 3.00 | 2.25 |
| 424 | A88 | 8d ultra & gray | 3.00 | 2.50 |
| | | Nos. 421-424 (4) | 7.50 | 5.50 |
| | | Set, never hinged | 18.00 | |

Arms of Greece, Romania, Turkey and Yugoslavia — A92

**Perf. 13x12½**

| 1940, May 27 | | | Wmk. 252 | |
|---|---|---|---|---|
| 425 | A92 | 6d blue | 8.00 | 2.25 |
| 426 | A92 | 8d blue gray | 5.50 | 2.25 |
| | | Set, never hinged | 35.00 | |

Balkan Entente.

Emblem of Youth Organization A93

Boy Member — A94

Designs: 3d, 100d, Emblem of Greek Youth Organization. 10d, Girl member. 15d, Javelin Thrower. 20d, Column of members. 25d, Flag bearers and buglers. 30d, Three youths. 50d, Line formation. 75d, Coat of arms.

**Perf. 12½, 13½x12½**

| 1940, Aug. 3 | | Litho. | Wmk. 252 | |
|---|---|---|---|---|
| 427 | A93 | 3d sil, dp ultra & red | .85 | 1.25 |
| 428 | A94 | 5d dk bl & blk | 6.50 | 7.50 |
| 429 | A94 | 10d red org & blk | 7.50 | 10.00 |
| 430 | A94 | 15d dk grn & blk | 30.00 | 32.50 |
| 431 | A94 | 20d lake & blk | 25.00 | 25.00 |
| 432 | A94 | 25d dk bl & blk | 25.00 | 25.00 |
| 433 | A94 | 30d rose vio & blk | 25.00 | 25.00 |
| 434 | A94 | 50d lake & blk | 30.00 | 30.00 |
| 435 | A94 | 75d dk bl, brn & gold | 35.00 | 32.50 |
| 436 | A93 | 100d sil, dp ultra & red | 50.00 | 37.50 |
| | | Nos. 427-436,C38-C47 (20) | 480.50 | 451.50 |
| | | Set, never hinged | 1,000. | |

4th anniv. of the founding of the Greek Youth Organization. The stamps were good for postal duty Aug. 3-5, 1940, only. They remained on sale until Feb. 3, 1941.

For overprints see Nos. N219-N238.

---

Windmills on Mykonos A103

Bourtzi Fort — A104

Aspropotamos River — A105

Candia Harbor, Crete — A106

Houses at Hydra — A107

Meteora Monasteries A108

Edessa A109

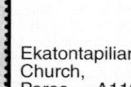

Pantokratoros Monastery and Port — A110

Bridge at Konitsa A111

Ekatontapiliani Church, Paros — A112

Ponticonissi, Corfu (Mouse Island) A113

**Perf. 12½, 13½x12½**

| 1942-44 | | Litho. | Wmk. 252 | |
|---|---|---|---|---|
| 437 | A103 | 2d red brown | .20 | .20 |
| 438 | A104 | 5d lt bl grn | .20 | .20 |
| a. | | "ΝΑΥΟ . . ." | 8.25 | 8.25 |
| 439 | A105 | 10d lt blue | .20 | .20 |
| 440 | A106 | 15d red vio | .20 | .20 |
| 441 | A107 | 25d org red | .20 | .20 |
| 442 | A108 | 50d sapphire | .20 | .20 |
| 443 | A109 | 75d dp rose | .20 | .20 |
| 444 | A110 | 100d black | .20 | .20 |

| | | | | |
|---|---|---|---|---|
| 445 | A110 | 200d ultra | .20 | .20 |
| a. | | Imprint omitted | 3.90 | 3.90 |
| 446 | A111 | 500d dk olive | .20 | .20 |
| 447 | A112 | 1000d org brn | .20 | .20 |
| 448 | A113 | 2000d dp blue | .20 | .20 |
| 449 | A111 | 5000d rose red | .20 | .20 |
| 450 | A112 | 15,000d rose lil | .20 | .20 |
| 451 | A113 | 25,000d green | .20 | .20 |
| 452 | A105 | 500,000d blue | .20 | .20 |
| 453 | A103 | 2,000,000d turq grn | .20 | .20 |
| 454 | A104 | 5,000,000d rose brn | .20 | .20 |
| | | Nos. 437-454 (18) | 3.60 | 3.60 |

Double impressions exist of 10d, 25d, 50d, 100d, 200d, 1,000d and 2,000d. Value, each $30.

Issued: #439-442, 9/1; 200d, 12/1; #446-448, 3/15/44; #449-451, 7/1/44; #452-454, 9/15/44.

For surcharges and overprint see Nos. 472C, 473B-475, 478-481, 501-505, B1-B5, B11-B15, RA72-RA74, N239-N240, N243-N245, N248.

### Imperf., Pairs

| | | | |
|---|---|---|---|
| 439a | A105 | 10d | 57.50 |
| 440a | A106 | 15d | 57.50 |
| 441a | A107 | 25d | 45.00 |
| 442a | A108 | 50d | 45.00 |
| 446a | A111 | 500d | 45.00 |
| 447a | A112 | 1000d | 45.00 |
| 448a | A113 | 2000d | 45.00 |
| 449a | A111 | 5000d | 45.00 |
| 450a | A112 | 15,000d | 45.00 |
| 451a | A113 | 25,000d | 45.00 |
| 452a | A105 | 500,000d | 45.00 |
| 454a | A104 | 5,000,000d | 45.00 |

Nos. 400, 402-404 Surcharged in Blue Black

**1944-45**    **Perf. 13½x12**

| | | | | |
|---|---|---|---|---|
| 455 | A73 | 50 l brn & blk | .20 | .20 |
| a. | | Double surcharge | 40.00 | 40.00 |
| 456 | A75 | 2d ultra | .20 | .20 |
| 457 | A76 | 5d red | .20 | .20 |
| a. | | Inverted surcharge | 47.50 | |
| b. | | Double surcharge | 47.50 | |
| c. | | Printer's name omitted (403a) | 12.00 | 12.00 |
| d. | | Pair, one without surcharge | 20.00 | |
| 458 | A77 | 6d olive brn ('45) | .25 | .25 |
| | | Nos. 455-458 (4) | .85 | .85 |

### Glory Type of 1937
**Perf. 12½x13½**

**1945**   **Litho.**   **Wmk. 252**

| | | | | |
|---|---|---|---|---|
| 459 | A81 | 1d dull rose vio | .20 | .20 |
| 460 | A81 | 3d rose brown | .20 | .20 |
| a. | | Imperf., pair | 160.00 | |
| 461 | A81 | 5d ultra | .20 | .20 |
| a. | | Imperf., pair | 160.00 | |
| 462 | A81 | 10d dull brown | .20 | .20 |
| 463 | A81 | 20d dull violet | .20 | .20 |
| 464 | A81 | 50d olive black | .20 | .20 |
| 465 | A81 | 100d pale blue | 3.50 | 3.50 |
| a. | | Imperf., pair | 190.00 | |
| 466 | A81 | 200d slate | 3.00 | 2.75 |
| | | Nos. 459-466 (8) | 7.70 | 7.50 |
| | | Set, never hinged | 16.00 | |

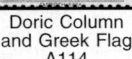

Doric Column and Greek Flag A114 | Franklin D. Roosevelt A115

**1945, Oct. 28**    **Unwmk.**

| | | | | |
|---|---|---|---|---|
| 467 | A114 | 20d orange brown | .25 | .20 |
| 468 | A114 | 40d blue | .25 | .20 |
| a. | | Double impression | 30.00 | |
| | | Set, never hinged | .45 | |

Vote of Oct. 28, 1940, refusing Italy's ultimatum. "OXI" means "No."
Exist imperf.

**1945, Dec. 21**    **Unwmk.**

| | | | | |
|---|---|---|---|---|
| 469 | A115 | 30d blk & red brn | .35 | .20 |
| a. | | Center double | 27.00 | |
| c. | | Inverted frame | 72.50 | |
| d. | | Imperf., pair | 45.00 | |
| 470 | A115 | 60d blk & sl gray | .35 | .20 |
| a. | | Center double | 27.50 | |
| b. | | 60d black & blue gray | 11.00 | 11.00 |
| c. | | Imperf., pair | 27.50 | |
| d. | | Inverted frame | 65.00 | |

| | | | | |
|---|---|---|---|---|
| 471 | A115 | 200d blk & vio brn | .35 | .20 |
| a. | | Center double | 27.50 | 77.50 |
| b. | | Imperf., pair | 45.00 | |
| | | Nos. 469-471 (3) | 1.05 | .60 |
| | | Set, never hinged | .60 | |

Death of Pres. Franklin D. Roosevelt.

> **Catalogue values for unused stamps in this section, from this point to the end of the section, are for Never Hinged items.**

Nos. C61, C63, 447-451, 453, 398, 401, 454 and 452 Surcharged in Black or Carmine

**Perf. 12½, 12x13½, 13½x12½**

**1946**     **Wmk. 252**

| | | | | |
|---|---|---|---|---|
| 472 | AP35 | 10d on 10d | .40 | .20 |
| a. | | Inverted surcharge | 100.00 | — |
| b. | | Double surcharge | 22.50 | |
| 472C | A113 | 10d on 2000d (C) | .40 | .20 |
| 473 | AP35 | 20d on 50d | .40 | .20 |
| a. | | Inverted surcharge | 125.00 | |
| 473B | A112 | 20d on 1000d | .40 | .20 |
| 474 | A113 | 50d on 25,000d (C) | .55 | .20 |
| 475 | A103 | 100d on 2,000,000d (C) | .95 | .30 |
| 476 | A71 | 130d on 20 l (C) | 1.00 | .20 |
| b. | | Double surcharge | 27.50 | |
| 476A | A71 | 250d on 20 l (C) | 1.25 | .20 |
| c. | | Double surcharge | 92.50 | |
| 477 | A74 | 300d on 80 l | 1.00 | .20 |
| a. | | Purple brown surcharge | 17.00 | 17.00 |
| b. | | Double surcharge | 90.00 | |
| 478 | A104 | 500d on 5,000,000d | 4.00 | .80 |
| a. | | Inverted surcharge | 85.00 | |
| b. | | Double surcharge | 85.00 | |
| 479 | A105 | 1000d on 500,000d (C) | 14.00 | 2.25 |
| a. | | Double surcharge | 45.00 | |
| 480 | A111 | 2000d on 5000d | 52.50 | 4.50 |
| 481 | A112 | 5000d on 15,000d | 160.00 | 35.00 |
| b. | | Blue surcharge | 160.00 | 140.00 |
| | | Nos. 472-481 (13) | 236.85 | 44.45 |

The surcharge exists in various shades on most denominations. A 150d on 20 l is fraudulent.

Eleutherios K. Venizelos A116 | Panaghiotis Tsaldaris A117

**Perf. 12x13½**

**1946, Mar. 25**   **Litho.**   **Wmk. 252**

| | | | | |
|---|---|---|---|---|
| 482 | A116 | 130d brn ol & buff | .40 | .20 |
| a. | | Double impression of brn olive | 7.25 | |
| 483 | A116 | 300d red brn & pale brn | .40 | .20 |
| a. | | Double impression of red brown | 14.00 | |

Venizelos (1864-1936), statesman.

Nos. 391 to 394 Surcharged in Blue Black

**1946, Sept. 28**    **Perf. 12½x12**

| | | | | |
|---|---|---|---|---|
| 484 | A67 | 50d on 1d | .60 | .20 |
| 485 | A67 | 250d on 3d | 1.40 | .20 |
| a. | | Date omitted | 32.50 | — |
| b. | | Inverted surcharge | 32.50 | |

| | | | | |
|---|---|---|---|---|
| 486 | A67 | 600d on 8d | 9.00 | 1.25 |
| a. | | Additional surcharge on back, inverted | 72.50 | |
| b. | | Carmine surcharge | 150.00 | |
| 487 | A67 | 3000d on 100d | 22.50 | 2.00 |
| | | Nos. 484-487 (4) | 33.50 | 3.65 |

Plebiscite of Sept. 1, 1946, which resulted in the return of King George II to Greece.

**Perf. 12½x13½**

**1946, Nov. 15**   **Litho.**   **Unwmk.**

| | | | | |
|---|---|---|---|---|
| 488 | A117 | 250d red brn & buff | 4.00 | 1.25 |
| 489 | A117 | 600d dp bl & pale bl | 4.00 | 1.25 |
| a. | | Double impression | 22.50 | |

Naval Convoy A118

Torpedoing of Cruiser Helle — A119

Women Carrying Ammunition in Pindus Mountains A120

Troops in Albania A121

Campaign of Greek Troops in Italy — A122

Allegory of Flight — A123

Greek Torpedo Boat Towing Captive Submarine A124

Design: 5000d, Memorial Tomb, El Alamein.

**1946-47**   **Unwmk.**   **Engr.**   **Perf. 13**

| | | | | |
|---|---|---|---|---|
| 490 | A118 | 50d dk bl grn | .25 | .20 |
| 491 | A119 | 100d dp ultra | .60 | .20 |
| 492 | A120 | 250d yel grn ('46) | .60 | .20 |
| 493 | A121 | 500d yel brn | .95 | .20 |
| 494 | A122 | 600d dk brown | 1.25 | .85 |
| 495 | A123 | 1000d dull lil | 6.50 | .40 |
| 496 | A124 | 2000d dp ultra | 27.50 | 2.50 |
| 497 | A119 | 5000d dk car | 35.00 | 2.50 |
| a. | | Imperf., pair | 1,500. | |
| | | Nos. 490-497 (8) | 72.65 | 7.05 |

1947 stamps issued May 1.

### King George II Memorial Issue

Nos. 391-393 Surcharged in Black

**Perf. 12½x12**

**1947, Apr. 15**    **Wmk. 252**

| | | | | |
|---|---|---|---|---|
| 498 | A67 | 50d on 1d grn | .60 | .20 |
| a. | | Double surcharge | 72.50 | |
| 499 | A67 | 250d on 3d red brn | 1.25 | .20 |
| a. | | Double surcharge | 72.50 | |
| b. | | Pair, one without surcharge | 72.50 | |
| 500 | A67 | 600d on 8d dp bl | 4.75 | .55 |
| a. | | Double surcharge | 72.50 | |
| | | Nos. 498-500 (3) | 6.60 | .95 |

Nos. 446, 438, 442, 439 and 443 Surcharged in Carmine or Black

**1947**     **Perf. 12½**

| | | | | |
|---|---|---|---|---|
| 501 | A111 | 20d on 500d | .30 | .20 |
| a. | | Double surcharge | 27.50 | |
| 502 | A104 | 30d on 5d | .95 | .40 |
| 503 | A108 | 50d on 50d | .45 | .20 |
| 504 | A105 | 100d on 10d | 1.60 | .20 |
| 505 | A109 | 450d on 75d (Bk) | 2.50 | .25 |
| | | Nos. 501-505 (5) | 5.80 | 1.25 |

Castellorizo Castle A126

Dodecanese Vase A127 | Dodecanese Costume A128

Monastery where St. John Preached, Patmos A129

Emanuel Xanthos — A130 | Sailing Vessel of 1824 — A131

Revolutionary Stamp of 1912 — A132

Statue of Hippocrates
A133

Colossus of Rhodes
A134

### Perf. 12½x13½, 13½x12½
| | | | | |
|---|---|---|---|---|
| **1947-48** | | **Litho.** | **Wmk. 252** | |
| 506 | A126 | 20d ultra | .20 | .20 |
| 507 | A127 | 30d blk brn & buff | .20 | .20 |
| 508 | A128 | 50d chlky bl | .45 | .20 |
| 509 | A129 | 100d blk grn & pale grn | .45 | .20 |
| 510 | A130 | 250d gray grn & pale grn | .85 | .20 |
| 511 | A132 | 450d dp bl ('48) | 2.25 | .20 |
| 512 | A131 | 450d dp bl & pale bl ('48) | 1.75 | .20 |
| a. | | Imperf., pair | 275.00 | |
| 513 | A132 | 500d red | 1.00 | .20 |
| 514 | A133 | 800d vio brn & pale pink | 1.00 | .20 |
| 515 | A134 | 1000d brn & cream | .85 | .20 |
| a. | | Imperf., pair | 250.00 | |
| | | Nos. 506-515 (10) | 9.00 | 2.00 |

Return of the Dodecanese to Greece. See Nos. 520-522, 525-534.

Battle of Crete — A135

**1948, Sept. 15 Engr. Perf. 13x13½**
| | | | | |
|---|---|---|---|---|
| 516 | A135 | 1000d dark green | 6.50 | .50 |

Battle of Crete, 7th anniversary.

Abduction of Children
A136

Concentration Camp — A137

Protective Mother — A138

### Perf. 13½x12½, 12½x13½
| | | | | |
|---|---|---|---|---|
| **1949, Feb. 1** | | **Litho.** | **Wmk. 252** | |
| 517 | A136 | 450d dk & lt violet | 2.50 | .65 |
| 518 | A137 | 1000d dk & lt brown | 9.00 | 4.00 |
| 519 | A138 | 1800d dk red & cream | 11.50 | .40 |
| | | Nos. 517-519 (3) | 23.00 | 5.05 |

### Types of 1947
**1950, Apr. 5 Perf. 12½x13½**
| | | | | |
|---|---|---|---|---|
| 520 | A127 | 2000d org brn & sal | 50.00 | .55 |
| a. | | Imperf., pair | 140.00 | |
| 521 | A133 | 5000d rose vio | 55.00 | .55 |
| 522 | A134 | 10,000d ultra | 95.00 | 1.25 |
| | | Nos. 520-522 (3) | 200.00 | 2.35 |

Map of Crete and Flags
A139

---

### Perf. 13½x13
**1950, Apr. 28 Engr. Wmk. 252**
| | | | | |
|---|---|---|---|---|
| 523 | A139 | 1000d deep blue | 8.00 | .40 |
| a. | | Imperf., pair | 1,500. | |

Battle of Crete, 9th anniversary.

Youth of Marathon — A140

### Engraved and Lithographed
**1950, May 21 Perf. 13x13½**
| | | | | |
|---|---|---|---|---|
| 524 | A140 | 1000d cream & dp grn | 2.00 | .60 |
| a. | | Without dates | 450.00 | |
| b. | | "1949" only | 450.00 | |
| c. | | Dates inverted | 450.00 | |
| d. | | Dates doubled | 450.00 | |

75th anniv. (in 1949) of the UPU. Exists imperf., used only.

### Types of 1947-48
### Perf. 12½x13½, 13½x12½
| | | | | |
|---|---|---|---|---|
| **1950** | | **Litho.** | **Wmk. 252** | |
| 525 | A130 | 200d orange | .50 | .20 |
| 526 | A128 | 300d orange | .65 | .20 |
| 527 | A129 | 400d blue | 1.25 | .20 |
| 528 | A133 | 700d lilac rose | 1.50 | .20 |
| 529 | A133 | 700d blue green | 20.00 | .25 |
| a. | | Imperf., pair | 290.00 | |
| 530 | A131 | 800d pur & pale grn | 1.90 | .20 |
| 531 | A132 | 1300d carmine | 8.25 | .20 |
| 532 | A126 | 1500d brn org | 57.50 | 1.10 |
| 533 | A127 | 1600d ultra & bl gray | 6.00 | .25 |
| 534 | A134 | 2600d emer & pale grn | 8.00 | .85 |
| | | Nos. 525-534 (10) | 105.55 | 3.65 |

Altar and Sword
A141

St. Paul — A142

St. Paul by El Greco — A143

**Perf. 13½x12, 12x13½**
| | | | | |
|---|---|---|---|---|
| **1951, June 15** | | **Engr.** | **Unwmk.** | |
| 535 | A141 | 700d red vio | 3.50 | 1.00 |
| 536 | A142 | 1600d lt blue | 14.50 | 8.75 |
| 537 | A143 | 2600d dk ol bis | 17.00 | 9.00 |
| 538 | A144 | 10,000d red brn | 125.00 | 80.00 |
| | | Nos. 535-538 (4) | 160.00 | 98.75 |

1900th anniv. of St. Paul's visit to Athens.

Preaching to Athenians — A144

---

Industrialization
A145

Designs: 800d, Fishing. 1300d, Rebuilding. 1600d, Farming. 2600d, Home Industries. 5000d, Electrification and map of Greece.

### Perf. 12½x13½
| | | | | |
|---|---|---|---|---|
| **1951, Sept. 20** | | | **Wmk. 252** | |
| 539 | A145 | 700d red org | 3.50 | .30 |
| 540 | A145 | 800d aqua | 7.25 | .30 |
| 541 | A145 | 1300d grnsh bl | 8.25 | .30 |
| 542 | A145 | 1600d olive grn | 25.00 | .50 |
| 543 | A145 | 2600d vio gray | 67.50 | 2.25 |
| 544 | A145 | 5000d dp plum | 87.50 | .50 |
| | | Nos. 539-544 (6) | 199.00 | 4.15 |

Issued to publicize Greek recovery under the Marshall Plan.

King Paul I — A146

Allegorical Figure and Medal — A147

**1952, Dec. 14 Engr. Perf. 12½x12**
| | | | | |
|---|---|---|---|---|
| 545 | A146 | 200d deep green | 2.00 | .20 |
| 546 | A146 | 1000d red | 5.25 | .35 |
| 547 | A147 | 1400d blue | 14.50 | 2.25 |
| 548 | A146 | 10,000d dk red lil | 50.00 | 14.00 |
| | | Nos. 545-548 (4) | 71.75 | 16.80 |

50th birthday of King Paul I.

Oranges
A148

Tobacco — A149

National Products: 1000d, Olive oil, Pallas Athene. 1300d, Wine. 2000d, Figs. 2600d, Grapes and bread. 5000d, Bacchus holding grapes.

**1953, July 1 Perf. 13½x13, 13x13½**
| | | | | |
|---|---|---|---|---|
| 549 | A148 | 500d dp car & org | 1.90 | .20 |
| 550 | A149 | 700d dk brn & org yel | 1.90 | .20 |
| 551 | A148 | 1000d bl & lt ol grn | 3.50 | .20 |
| a. | | Imperf., pair | 450.00 | |
| 552 | A149 | 1300d dp plum & org brn | 5.00 | .20 |
| 553 | A149 | 2000d dk brn & lt grn | 12.00 | .40 |
| 554 | A149 | 2600d vio & ol bis | 32.50 | 1.75 |
| 555 | A149 | 5000d dk brn & yel grn | 32.50 | .90 |
| | | Nos. 549-555 (7) | 89.30 | 3.85 |

---

Pericles
A150

Homer
A151

Hunting Wild Boar — A152

Shepherd Carrying Calf — A152a

Designs: 200d, Mycenaean oxhead vase. 500d, Zeus of Istiaea. 600d, Head of a youth. 1000d, Alexander the Great. 1200d, Charioteer of Delphi. 2000d, Vase of Dipylon. 4000d, Voyage of Dionysus. 20,000d, Pitcher bearers.

### Perf. 13½x13, 12½x12, 13x13½
| | | | | |
|---|---|---|---|---|
| **1954, Jan. 15** | | | **Litho.** | |
| 556 | A150 | 100d red brn | .40 | .20 |
| 557 | A150 | 200d black | .40 | .20 |
| 558 | A151 | 300d blue vio | .95 | .20 |
| 559 | A151 | 500d green | 1.50 | .20 |
| 560 | A151 | 600d rose pink | 1.50 | .20 |
| 561 | A151 | 1000d dl bl & blk | 2.00 | .20 |
| 562 | A150 | 1200d ol grn | 2.00 | .20 |
| 563 | A150 | 2000d red brn | 8.00 | .20 |
| 564 | A152 | 2400d grnsh bl | 8.00 | .40 |
| a. | | Double impression | 150.00 | |
| 565 | A152a | 2500d dk grn | 8.00 | .25 |
| 566 | A151 | 4000d dk car | 20.00 | .40 |
| 567 | A150 | 20,000d rose lilac | 175.00 | 1.25 |
| | | Nos. 556-567 (12) | 227.75 | 3.90 |

See Nos. 574-581, 632-638, and 689.

British Parliamentary Debate and Ink Blot — A153

**1954, Sept. Perf. 12½**
**Center in Black**
| | | | | |
|---|---|---|---|---|
| 568 | A153 | 1.20d cream | 3.00 | .45 |
| 569 | A153 | 2d orange | 14.50 | 3.75 |
| 570 | A153 | 2d lt bl | 14.50 | 9.25 |
| 571 | A153 | 2.40d lilac | 14.50 | 2.50 |
| 572 | A153 | 2.50d pink | 14.50 | 2.50 |
| 573 | A153 | 4d citron | 45.00 | 3.75 |
| | | Nos. 568-573 (6) | 106.00 | 22.20 |

Document in English on Nos. 569, 572, 573; in French on Nos. 570, 571 and in Greek on No. 568.

Issued to promote the proposed union between Cyprus and Greece.

### Types of 1954
### Perf. 13½x13, 12½x12, 13x13½
| | | | | |
|---|---|---|---|---|
| **1955** | | **Litho.** | **Wmk. 252** | |

Designs: 20 l, Mycenaean oxhead vase. 30 l, Pericles. 50 l, Zeus of Istiaea. 1d, Head of a youth. 2d, Alexander the Great. 3d, Hunting wild boar. 3.50d, Homer. 4d, Voyage of Dionysus.

| | | | | |
|---|---|---|---|---|
| 574 | A150 | 20 l dk green | .30 | .20 |
| 575 | A150 | 30 l yellow brn | .45 | .20 |
| 576 | A151 | 50 l car lake | .70 | .20 |
| 577 | A151 | 1d blue grn | 1.75 | .20 |
| 578 | A151 | 2d brown & blk | 5.50 | .20 |
| 579 | A152 | 3d red org | 8.50 | .20 |
| 580 | A151 | 3.50d rose crim | 8.50 | .70 |
| 581 | A151 | 4d violet bl | 62.50 | .45 |
| | | Nos. 574-581 (8) | 88.20 | 2.35 |

Samos Coin Picturing Pythagoras A154

Pythagorean Theorem A155

Samos Mapped in Antique Style — A156

1955, Aug. 20 *Perf. 12x13½*

No.	Type	Denomination & Color	Unused	Used
582	A154	2d green	2.75	.40
583	A155	3.50d intense blk	9.75	3.00
584	A154	5d plum	32.50	2.00
585	A156	6d blue	42.50	32.50
		Nos. 582-585 (4)	87.50	37.90

2500th anniv. of the founding of the 1st School of Philosophy by Pythagoras on Samos.

Globe and Rotary Emblem — A157

Perf. 12x13½

1956, May 15 **Litho.** **Wmk. 252**

No.	Type	Denomination & Color	Unused	Used
586	A157	2d ultra	10.00	.40

50th anniv. of Rotary Intl. (in 1955).

King Alexander A158

Crown Prince Constantine — A159

Portraits: 30 l, George I. 50 l, Queen Olga. 70 l, King Otto. 1d, Queen Amalia. 1.50d, King Constantine. 2d, 7.50d, King Paul. 3d, George II. 3.50d, Queen Sophia. 4d, Queen Frederica. 5d, King Paul and Queen Frederica. 10d, King, Queen and Crown Prince.

Perf. 13½x12, 12x13½

1956, May 21 **Engr.**

No.	Type	Denomination & Color	Unused	Used
587	A158	10 l blue vio	.20	.20
588	A159	20 l dull pur	.20	.20
589	A159	30 l sepia	.20	.20
590	A159	50 l red brn	.30	.20
591	A159	70 l lt ultra	.40	.20
592	A159	1d grnsh bl	.70	.20
593	A159	1.50d gray bl	2.40	.20
594	A159	2d black	3.25	.20
595	A159	3d brown	2.40	.20
596	A159	3.50d copper brn	8.00	.25
597	A159	4d gray green	8.00	.20
598	A158	5d rose car	8.00	.20
599	A159	7.50d ultra	8.00	2.00
600	A158	10d dk blue	40.00	.80
		Nos. 587-600 (14)	82.05	5.25

See Nos. 604-617.

Dionysios Solomos and Nicolaos Mantzaros A160

Dionysios Solomos — A161

5d, View on Zante and bust of Solomos.

Perf. 13½x12, 12x13½

1957, Mar. 26 **Litho.** **Wmk. 252**

No.	Type	Denomination & Color	Unused	Used
601	A160	2d red brn & ocher	3.50	.25
602	A161	3.50d bl & gray	5.50	2.75
603	A160	5d dk grn & ol bis	7.50	3.90
		Nos. 601-603 (3)	16.50	6.90

Centenary of the death of Dionysios Solomos (1798-1857), nationalist poet best known for the poem *Hymn to Liberty*, the first two stanzas of which were adopted as the lyrics of the Greek national anthem.

Types of 1956

Designs as before.

Perf. 13½x12

1957 **Wmk. 252** **Engr.**

No.	Type	Denomination & Color	Unused	Used
604	A158	10 l rose lake	.50	.20
605	A159	20 l orange	.50	.20
606	A159	30 l gray blk	.50	.20
607	A159	50 l grnsh blk	.50	.20
608	A159	70 l rose lil	1.50	.65
609	A159	1d rose red	1.00	.20
610	A159	1.50d lt ol grn	1.75	.20
611	A159	2d carmine	3.25	.20
612	A159	3d dk blue	4.00	.20
613	A159	3.50d blk vio	8.00	.20
a.		Imperf., pair		
614	A159	4d red brn	8.00	.20
615	A158	5d gray blue	8.00	.20
616	A159	7.50d yel org	2.50	1.25
617	A158	10d green	55.00	.80
		Nos. 604-617 (14)	95.00	4.90

Oil Tanker A162

Ships: 1d, Ocean liner. 1.50d, Sailing ship, 1820. 2d, Byzantine vessel. 3.50d, Ship from 6th century B. C. 5d, "Argo."

1958, Jan. 30 **Litho.** *Perf. 13½x12*

No.	Type	Denomination & Color	Unused	Used
618	A162	50 l multi	.40	.20
619	A162	1d ultra, blk & bis	.40	.20
620	A162	1.50d blk & car	1.25	.95
a.		Double impression of blk	160.00	
621	A162	2d vio bl, blk & red brn	.40	.30
622	A162	3.50d lt bl, blk & red	1.50	1.25
a.		Double impression of blk	160.00	125.00
623	A162	5d bl grn, blk & car	10.00	10.00
		Nos. 618-623 (6)	13.95	12.90

Issued to honor the Greek merchant marine.

Narcissus — A163

Designs: 30 l, Daphne (laurel) and Apollo. 50 l, Adonis (hibiscus) and Aphrodite. 70 l, Pitys (pine) and Pan. 1d, Crocus. 2d, Iris. 3.50d, Tulips. 5d, Cyclamen.

1958, Sept. 15 **Wmk. 252** *Perf. 13*

Size: 22½x38mm

No.	Type	Denomination & Color	Unused	Used
624	A163	20 l multi	.20	.20
625	A163	30 l multi	.20	.20
626	A163	50 l multi	.20	.20
627	A163	70 l multi	.20	.20

Perf. 12½x12

Size: 21½x26mm

No.	Type	Denomination & Color	Unused	Used
628	A163	1d multi	.45	.40

Perf. 12x13½

Size: 22x32mm

No.	Type	Denomination & Color	Unused	Used
629	A163	2d multi	.20	.20
630	A163	3.50d multi	1.75	1.75
a.		Imperf., pair	325.00	
631	A163	5d multi	2.50	2.50
		Nos. 624-631 (8)	5.70	5.65

International Congress for the Protection of Nature, held in Athens.

Types of 1954

Designs: 10 l, Pericles. 20 l, Mycenaean oxhead vase. 50 l, Zeus of Istiaea. 70 l, Charioteer of Delphi. 1d, Head of a youth. 1.50d, Pitcher bearers. 2.50d, Alexander the Great.

Two types of 2.50d:
I — 9 dots in upper half of right border.
II — 10 dots.

Perf. 13½x13, 12½x12

1959 **Litho.** **Wmk. 252**

No.	Type	Denomination & Color	Unused	Used
632	A150	10 l emerald	.40	.20
633	A150	20 l magenta	.80	.20
634	A151	50 l lt bl grn	1.50	.20
635	A150	70 l red org	.45	.20
636	A151	1d reddish brn	3.90	.20
637	A150	1.50d brt bl	20.00	.20
638	A151	2.50d mag & blk (II)	16.00	.30
a.		Type I	60.00	.55
		Nos. 632-638 (7)	43.05	1.50

Zeus-Eagle Coin — A164

Helios-Rose Coin — A165

Ancient Greek Coins: 20 l, Athena & Owl. 50 l, Nymph Arethusa & Chariot. 70 l, Hercules & Zeus. 1.50d, Griffin & Square. 2.50d, Apollo & Lyre. 4.50d, Apollo & Labyrinth. 6d, Aphrodite & Apollo. 8.50d, Ram's Head & Incuse Squares.

1959, Mar. 24 **Wmk. 252** *Perf. 14*

Coins in Various Shades of Gray

No.	Type	Denomination & Color	Unused	Used
639	A164	10 l red brn & blk	.45	.20
640	A164	20 l dp bl & blk	.45	.20
641	A164	50 l plum & blk	.60	.20
642	A164	70 l ultra & blk	1.10	.30
643	A165	1d dk car rose & blk	1.50	.20
644	A164	1.50d ocher & blk	1.75	.20
645	A164	2.50d dp mag & blk	2.50	.20
646	A165	4.50d Prus grn & blk	5.50	.40
647	A165	6d ol grn & blk	20.00	.20
648	A165	8.50d dp car & blk	7.00	1.75
		Nos. 639-648 (10)	40.85	3.85

See Nos. 750-758.

Audience, Vase 580 B. C. — A166

Theater, Delphi A167

Designs: 50 l, Clay tragedy mask, 3rd cent. B.C. 1d, Flute, drum and lyre. 2.50d, Clay statue of an actor, 3rd cent. B.C. 4.50d, Andromeda, vase, 4th cent. B.C. 6d, Actors, bowl 410 B.C.

Perf. 13x13½, 13½x13

1959, June 20 **Litho.** **Wmk. 252**

No.	Type	Denomination & Color	Unused	Used
649	A166	20 l blk, fawn & gray	.30	.20
650	A166	50 l dk red brn & ol bis	.30	.25
651	A166	1d grn, brn & ocher	.30	.25
652	A166	2.50d brn & bl	.80	.65
653	A167	3.50d red brn, grn & sep	12.00	10.50
654	A167	4.50d blk & fawn	1.50	1.25
655	A166	6d blk, fawn & gray	1.75	1.50
		Nos. 649-655 (7)	16.95	14.60

Ancient Greek theater.

"Victory" and Soldiers — A168

Perf. 13x13½

1959, Aug. 29 **Wmk. 252**

No.	Type	Denomination & Color	Unused	Used
656	A168	2.50d red brn, ultra & blk	3.50	.40

10th anniversary of civil war.

St. Basil — A169

The Good Samaritan A170

Designs: 20 l, Plane tree of Hippocrates. 50 l, Aesculapius. 2.50d, Achilles and Patroclus. 3d, Globe and Red Cross over people receiving help. 4.50d, Henri Dunant.

Perf. 13½x12, 12x13½

1959, Sept. 21 **Litho.**

No.	Type	Denomination & Color	Unused	Used
657	A170	20 l multi	.20	.20
658	A169	50 l multi	.20	.20
659	A169	70 l multi	.20	.20
660	A169	2.50d multi	.60	.50
661	A169	3d multi	8.00	8.00
662	A169	4.50d multi	1.40	1.10
663	A170	6d multi	1.25	1.00
		Nos. 657-663 (7)	11.85	11.20

Cent. of the Red Cross idea. Sizes: Nos. 658-660, 662 24½x32mm, No. 661 32x47mm.

Imre
Nagy — A171

Costis
Palamas — A172

**Perf. 13x13½**

**1959, Dec. 8**     **Wmk. 252**
| | | | | |
|---|---|---|---|---|
| 664 | A171 | 4.50d org brn & dk brn | 1.10 | .95 |
| 665 | A171 | 6d brt bl, bl & blk | 1.10 | .95 |

3rd anniv. of the crushing of the 1956 Hungarian Revolution, and to honor Premier Imre Nagy, its leader.

**1960, Jan. 25**     **Perf. 12x13½**
| | | | | |
|---|---|---|---|---|
| 666 | A172 | 2.50d multi | 3.50 | .75 |

Centenary of the birth of Costis Palamas (1859-1943), poet.

Ship
Battling
Storm
A173

4.50d, Ship in calm sea and rainbow.

**Perf. 13½x13**

**1960, Apr. 7**     **Wmk. 252**
| | | | | |
|---|---|---|---|---|
| 667 | A173 | 2.50d multi | .50 | .40 |
| 668 | A173 | 4.50d multi | 1.50 | 1.40 |

Issued to publicize World Refugee Year, July 1, 1959-June 30, 1960.

Boy Scout on
Horseback, St.
George and
Dragon — A174

Scouts
Planting
Tree
A175

30 l, Scout taking oath & boy of ancient Athens. 40 l, Scouts helping in disaster. 70 l, Scouts reading map & tent. 1d, Boy Scout, Sea Scout & Air Scout. 2.50d, Crown Prince Constantine. 6d, Scout flag of Greece & Military Merit medal.

**Perf. 13x13½, 13½x13**

**1960, Apr. 23**     **Litho.**
| | | | | |
|---|---|---|---|---|
| 669 | A174 | 20 l multi | .20 | .20 |
| 670 | A174 | 30 l multi | .20 | .20 |
| 671 | A174 | 40 l multi | .20 | .20 |
| 672 | A175 | 50 l multi | .20 | .20 |
| 673 | A174 | 70 l multi | .20 | .20 |
| 674 | A174 | 1d multi | .40 | .40 |
| 675 | A174 | 2.50d multi | 1.25 | 1.25 |
| 676 | A175 | 6d multi | 2.50 | 1.50 |
| | | Nos. 669-676 (8) | 5.15 | 4.15 |

Greek Boy Scout Organization, 50th anniv.

Greek Holding
Sacred Disk
Proclaiming
Armistice During
Games — A176

Lighting
Olympic
Flame
A177

Designs: 70 l, Youth taking oath. 80 l, Boy cutting olive branches for Olympic prizes. 1d, Judges entering stadium. 1.50d, Long jump. 2.50d, Discus thrower. 4.50d, Sprinters. 5d, Javelin thrower. 6d, Crowning the victors. 12.50d, Victor in chariot entering home town.

**Perf. 13x13½, 13½x13**

**1960, Aug. 12**     **Wmk. 252**
| | | | | |
|---|---|---|---|---|
| 677 | A176 | 20 l multi | .25 | .20 |
| 678 | A177 | 50 l multi | .25 | .20 |
| 679 | A176 | 70 l multi | .25 | .20 |
| 680 | A177 | 80 l multi | .25 | .20 |
| a. | | Imperf., pair | 450.00 | |
| 681 | A177 | 1d multi | .40 | .30 |
| 682 | A177 | 1.50d multi | .40 | .30 |
| 683 | A176 | 2.50d multi | .80 | .50 |
| 684 | A177 | 4.50d multi | .95 | .70 |
| a. | | Dbl. impression of black | 350.00 | 200.00 |
| 685 | A177 | 5d multi | 2.40 | 1.60 |
| 686 | A177 | 6d multi | 2.40 | 1.60 |
| 687 | A177 | 12.50d multi | 12.50 | 10.00 |
| | | Nos. 677-687 (11) | 20.85 | 15.80 |

17th Olympic Games, Rome, 8/25-9/11.

Common Design Types pictured following the introduction.

**Europa Issue, 1960**
Common Design Type
**Perf. 13½x12**
**1960, Sept. 19**    **Litho.**    **Wmk. 252**
**Size: 33x23mm**
| | | | | |
|---|---|---|---|---|
| 688 | CD3 | 4.50d ultra | 5.00 | 2.00 |
| a. | | Double impression | 190.00 | |

Shepherd Type of 1954
**1960, Sept. 1**    **Wmk. 252**    **Perf. 13**
| | | | | |
|---|---|---|---|---|
| 689 | A152a | 3d ultra | 2.25 | .40 |

Crown Prince Constantine and
Yacht — A178

**1961, Jan. 18**     **Perf. 13½x13**
| | | | | |
|---|---|---|---|---|
| 690 | A178 | 2.50d multi | .75 | .25 |

Victory of Crown Prince Constantine and his crew at the 17th Olympic Games, Rome (Gold medal, Yachting, Dragon class).

Castoria
A179

Delphi — A180

Landscapes and Ancient Monuments: 20 l, Meteora. 50 l, Hydra harbor. 70 l, Acropolis, Athens. 80 l, Mykonos. 1d, St. Catherine's Church, Salonika. 1.50d, Olympia. 2.50d, Knossos. 3.50d, Rhodes. 4d, Epidauros amphitheater. 4.50d, Temple of Poseidon, Sounion. 5d, Temple of Zeus, Athens. 7.50d, Aslan's mosque, Ioannina. 8d, Mount Athos. 8.50d, Santorini. 12.50d, Marble lions, Delos.

**Perf. 13½x12½, 12½x13½**

**1961, Feb. 15**    **Engr.**    **Wmk. 252**
| | | | | |
|---|---|---|---|---|
| 691 | A179 | 10 l dk gray bl | .20 | .20 |
| 692 | A179 | 20 l dk purple | .20 | .20 |
| 693 | A179 | 50 l blue | .20 | .20 |
| 694 | A179 | 70 l dk purple | .20 | .20 |
| 695 | A179 | 80 l brt ultra | .40 | .20 |
| 696 | A179 | 1d red brn | .50 | .20 |
| 697 | A179 | 1.50d brt grn | .75 | .25 |
| 698 | A179 | 2.50d carmine | 2.50 | .20 |
| 699 | A179 | 3.50d purple | 1.00 | .20 |
| 700 | A179 | 4d sl grn | 8.00 | .20 |
| 701 | A179 | 4.50d dk blue | .90 | .20 |
| 702 | A179 | 5d claret | 8.00 | .25 |
| 703 | A180 | 6d slate grn | 1.75 | .20 |
| 704 | A179 | 7.50d black | .50 | .20 |
| 705 | A180 | 8d dk vio bl | 3.25 | .25 |
| 706 | A180 | 8.50d org ver | 5.00 | .65 |
| 707 | A179 | 12.50d dk brn | 2.00 | 1.50 |
| | | Nos. 691-707 (17) | 35.35 | 5.35 |

Issued for tourist publicity.

Lily Vase — A181

Partridge
and Fig
Pecker
A182

Minoan Art: 1d, Fruit dish. 1.50d, Rhyton bearer. 2.50d, Ladies of Knossos Palace. 4.50d, Sarcophagus of Hagia Trias. 6d, Dancer. 10d, Two vessels with spouts.

**Perf. 13x13½, 13½x13**

**1961, June 30**     **Litho.**
| | | | | |
|---|---|---|---|---|
| 708 | A181 | 20 l multi | .20 | .20 |
| 709 | A182 | 50 l multi | .30 | .20 |
| 710 | A182 | 1d multi | .40 | .20 |
| 711 | A181 | 1.50d multi | .60 | .25 |
| 712 | A182 | 2.50d multi | 6.25 | .20 |
| 713 | A181 | 4.50d multi | 2.40 | 2.00 |
| 714 | A182 | 6d multi | 7.00 | 1.60 |
| 715 | A182 | 10d multi | 9.50 | 8.00 |
| | | Nos. 708-715 (8) | 26.65 | 12.65 |

Democritus Nuclear Research
Center — A183

Democritus — A184

**1961, July 31**     **Perf. 13½x13**
| | | | | |
|---|---|---|---|---|
| 716 | A183 | 2.50d dp lil rose & rose lil | .50 | .20 |
| 717 | A184 | 4.50d vio bl & pale vio bl | .75 | .60 |

Inauguration of the Democritus Nuclear Research Center at Aghia Paraskevi.

**Europa Issue, 1961**
Common Design Type
**1961, Sept. 18**    **Perf. 13½x12**
**Size: 32½x22mm**
| | | | | |
|---|---|---|---|---|
| 718 | CD4 | 2.50d ver & pink | .40 | .20 |
| a. | | Pink omitted (inscriptions white) | 20.00 | 18.00 |
| 719 | CD4 | 4.50d ultra & lt ultra | .40 | .20 |

Nicephoros
Phocas — A185

**1961, Sept. 22**     **Wmk. 252**
| | | | | |
|---|---|---|---|---|
| 720 | A185 | 2.50d multi | .80 | .60 |

1000th anniv. of the liberation of Crete from the Saracens by the Byzantine general (later emperor) Phocas.

Hermes Head of
1861 — A186

**1961, Dec. 20**    **Litho.**    **Perf. 13x13½**

Each denomination shows a different stamp of 1861 issue.
| | | | | |
|---|---|---|---|---|
| 721 | A186 | 20 l brn, red brn & cream | .20 | .20 |
| 722 | A186 | 50 l brn, bis & straw | .20 | .20 |
| 723 | A186 | 1.50d emer & gray | .20 | .25 |
| 724 | A186 | 2.50d red org & ol bis | .20 | .20 |
| 725 | A186 | 4.50d dk bl, bl & gray | .45 | .30 |
| 726 | A186 | 6d rose lil, pale rose & bl | .75 | .50 |
| 727 | A186 | 10d car, rose & cr | 1.50 | 1.50 |
| | | Nos. 721-727 (7) | 3.50 | 3.15 |

Centenary of Greek postage stamps.

Tauropos Dam and
Lake — A187

Ptolemais
Power
Station
A188

Designs: 50 l, Ladhon river hydroelectric plant. 1.50d, Louros river dam. 2.50d, Aliverion power plant. 4.50d, Salonika hydroelectric sub-station. 6d, Agra river hydroelectric station, interior.

**Perf. 13x13½, 13½x13**

**1962, Apr. 14**     **Wmk. 252**
| | | | | |
|---|---|---|---|---|
| 728 | A187 | 20 l multi | .20 | .20 |
| 729 | A187 | 50 l multi | .20 | .20 |
| 730 | A188 | 1d multi | .20 | .20 |
| 731 | A188 | 1.50d multi | .20 | .20 |
| 732 | A188 | 2.50d multi | 1.25 | .20 |
| 733 | A188 | 4.50d multi | .95 | .70 |
| 734 | A188 | 6d multi | 2.75 | 2.75 |
| | | Nos. 728-734 (7) | 5.75 | 4.45 |

National electrification project.

Youth with Shield and Helmet from Ancient Vase — A189

Designs: 2.50d, Zappion hall, horiz. 4.50d, Kneeling soldier from Temple of Aphaea, Aegina. 6d, Standing soldier from stele of Ariston.

**Perf. 13½x12, 12x13½**
**1962, May 3     Litho.     Wmk. 252**
**Sizes: 22x33mm, 33x22mm**

| | | | | |
|---|---|---|---|---|
| 735 | A189 | 2.50d grn, bl, red & brn | .25 | .20 |
| 736 | A189 | 3d brn, buff & red brn | .25 | .20 |
| 737 | A189 | 4.50d bl & gray | .40 | .40 |
| | | **Size: 21x37mm** | | |
| 738 | A189 | 6d brn red & blk | .40 | .30 |
| | | Nos. 735-738 (4) | 1.30 | 1.10 |

Ministerial congress of NATO countries, Athens, May 3-5.

## Europa Issue, 1962
### Common Design Type
**1962, Sept. 17        Perf. 13½x12**
**Size: 33x23mm**

| | | | | |
|---|---|---|---|---|
| 739 | CD5 | 2.50d ver & blk | .75 | .40 |
| 740 | CD5 | 4.50d ultra & blk | 1.50 | .75 |

Hands and Grain — A190

Demeter — A191

**1962, Oct. 30        Perf. 13x13½**

| | | | | |
|---|---|---|---|---|
| 741 | A190 | 1.50d dp car, blk & brn | .50 | .20 |
| 742 | A190 | 2.50d brt grn, blk & brn | .75 | .25 |

Agricultural Insurance Program.

**Perf. 12x13½**
**1963, Apr. 25        Wmk. 252**

Design: 4.50d, Wheat and globe.

| | | | | |
|---|---|---|---|---|
| 743 | A191 | 2.50d brn car, gray & blk | .40 | .20 |
| 744 | A191 | 4.50d multicolored | .85 | .35 |

FAO "Freedom from Hunger" campaign.

George I, Constantine XII, Alexander I, George II and Paul I — A192

**Perf. 13½x12½**
**1963, June 29        Engr.**

| | | | | |
|---|---|---|---|---|
| 745 | A192 | 50 l rose car | .20 | .20 |
| 746 | A192 | 1.50d green | .45 | .20 |
| 747 | A192 | 2.50d redsh brn | 1.00 | .20 |
| 748 | A192 | 4.50d dk blue | 1.60 | 1.25 |
| 749 | A192 | 6d violet | 3.50 | .60 |
| | | Nos. 745-749 (5) | 6.75 | 2.45 |

Centenary of the Greek dynasty.

### Coin Types of 1959

Ancient Greek Coins: 50 l, Nymph Arethusa & Chariot. 80 l, Hercules & Zeus. 1d, Helios & Rose. 1.50d, Griffin & Square. 3d, Zeus & Eagle. 3.50d, Athena & Owl. 4.50d, Apollo & Labyrinth. 6d, Aphrodite & Apollo. 8.50d, Ram's head & Incuse Squares.

---

**Perf. 13½x13, 13x13½**
**1963, July 5      Litho.      Wmk. 252**
**Coins in Various Shades of Gray**

| | | | | |
|---|---|---|---|---|
| 750 | A164 | 50 l violet bl | .20 | .20 |
| 751 | A164 | 80 l dp magenta | .20 | .20 |
| 752 | A165 | 1d emerald | .20 | .20 |
| 753 | A164 | 1.50d lilac rose | .85 | .20 |
| 754 | A164 | 3d olive | .60 | .20 |
| 755 | A164 | 3.50d vermilion | .70 | .20 |
| 756 | A165 | 4.50d redsh brn | .85 | .50 |
| 757 | A165 | 6d blue grn | 1.10 | .50 |
| 758 | A165 | 8.50d brt blue | 2.00 | .85 |
| | | Nos. 750-758 (9) | 6.70 | 2.75 |

"Acropolis at Dawn" by Lord Baden-Powell — A193

Jamboree Badge (Boeotian Shield) — A194

Athenian Treasury, Delphi — A195

Designs: 2.50d, Crown Prince Constantine, Chief Scout. 3d, Athanassios Lefkadites (founder of Greek Scouts) and Lord Baden-Powell. 4.50d, Scout bugling with conch shell.

**1963, Aug. 1**

| | | | | |
|---|---|---|---|---|
| 759 | A193 | 1d bl, sal & ol | .20 | .20 |
| 760 | A194 | 1.50d dk bl, org brn & brn | .20 | .20 |
| 761 | A194 | 2.50d multi | 1.10 | .20 |
| 762 | A193 | 3d multi | .20 | .55 |
| 763 | A194 | 4.50d multi | 1.10 | .55 |
| | | Nos. 759-763 (5) | 2.80 | 1.70 |

11th Boy Scout Jamboree, Marathon, July 29-Aug. 16, 1963.

**1963, Sept. 16        Perf. 12x13½**

2d, Centenary emblem. 2.50d, Queen Olga, founder of Greek Red Cross. 4.50d, Henri Dunant.

| | | | | |
|---|---|---|---|---|
| 764 | A195 | 1d multi | .50 | .25 |
| 765 | A195 | 2d multi | .20 | .20 |
| 766 | A195 | 2.50d multi | .30 | .20 |
| 767 | A195 | 4.50d multi | .75 | .50 |
| | | Nos. 764-767 (4) | 1.75 | 1.15 |

International Red Cross Centenary.

## Europa Issue, 1963
### Common Design Type
**1963, Sept. 16        Perf. 13½x12**
**Size: 33x23mm**

| | | | | |
|---|---|---|---|---|
| 768 | CD6 | 2.50d green | 2.25 | .40 |
| 769 | CD6 | 4.50d brt magenta | 3.00 | 1.50 |

Vatopethion Monastery A196

King Paul I (1901-1964) A197

Designs: 80 l, St. Denys' Monastery. 1d, "Protaton" (Founder's) Church, horiz. 2d, Stavronikita Monastery. 2.50d, Jeweled cover of Nicephoros Phocas Gospel. 3.50d, Fresco of St. Athanassios, founder of community. 4.50d, Presentation of Christ, 11th century manuscript. 6d, Great Lavra Church, horiz.

---

**Perf. 13x13½, 13½x13**
**1963, Dec. 5      Litho.      Wmk. 252**

| | | | | |
|---|---|---|---|---|
| 770 | A196 | 30 l multi | .20 | .20 |
| 771 | A196 | 80 l multi | .20 | .20 |
| 772 | A196 | 1d multi | .20 | .20 |
| 773 | A196 | 2d multi | .75 | .20 |
| 774 | A196 | 2.50d multi | 2.50 | .20 |
| 775 | A196 | 3.50d multi | .75 | .85 |
| 776 | A196 | 4.50d multi | .75 | .55 |
| 777 | A196 | 6d multi | .85 | .55 |
| | | Nos. 770-777 (8) | 6.20 | 2.95 |

Millennium of the founding of the monastic community on Mt. Athos.

**1964, May 6          Perf. 12x13½**

| | | | | |
|---|---|---|---|---|
| 778 | A197 | 30 l brown | .20 | .20 |
| 779 | A197 | 50 l purple | .20 | .20 |
| 780 | A197 | 1d green | .75 | .20 |
| 781 | A197 | 1.50d orange | .40 | .20 |
| 782 | A197 | 2d blue | .75 | .20 |
| 783 | A197 | 2.50d chocolate | .75 | .20 |
| 784 | A197 | 3.50d red brn | .75 | .20 |
| 785 | A197 | 4d ultra | 1.25 | .20 |
| 786 | A197 | 4.50d bluish blk | 1.25 | .80 |
| 787 | A197 | 6d rose pink | 2.25 | 1.00 |
| | | Nos. 778-787 (10) | 8.55 | 3.40 |

Archangel Michael — A198

Designs: 1d, Bulgaroctonus coin of Emperor Basil II. 1.50d, Two armed saints from ivory triptych by Harbaville, Louvre. 2.50d, Lady, fresco by Panselinos, Protaton Church, Mt. Athos. 4.50d, Angel, mosaic, Daphni Church, Athens.

**1964, June 10        Perf. 12x13½**

| | | | | |
|---|---|---|---|---|
| 788 | A198 | 1d multi | .20 | .20 |
| 789 | A198 | 1.50d multi | .20 | .20 |
| 790 | A198 | 2d multi | .20 | .20 |
| 791 | A198 | 2.50d multi | .20 | .20 |
| 792 | A198 | 4.50d multi | .80 | .50 |
| | | Nos. 788-792 (5) | 1.60 | 1.30 |

Byzantine Art and for the Byzantine Art Exhibition, Athens, Apr.-June, 1964.
Exist imperf.

Birth of Aphrodite, Emblem of Kythera A199

Designs (emblems of islands): 20 l, Trident, Paxos. 1d, Head of Ulysses, Ithaca. 2d, St. George slaying dragon, Lefkas. 2.50d, Zakynthos, Zante. 4.50d, Cephalus, dog and spear, Cephalonia. 6d, Trireme, Corfu.

**Perf. 13½x12**
**1964, July 20      Litho.      Wmk. 252**

| | | | | |
|---|---|---|---|---|
| 793 | A199 | 20 l multi | .20 | .20 |
| 794 | A199 | 30 l multi | .20 | .20 |
| 795 | A199 | 1d multi | .20 | .20 |
| 796 | A199 | 2d multi | .20 | .20 |
| 797 | A199 | 2.50d sl grn & dl grn | .35 | .20 |
| 798 | A199 | 4.50d multi | .95 | .75 |
| 799 | A199 | 6d multi | .95 | .40 |
| | | Nos. 793-799 (7) | 3.05 | 2.15 |

Centenary of the union of the Ionian Islands with Greece.

Child and Sun — A200

**1964, Sept. 10                Wmk. 252**

| | | | | |
|---|---|---|---|---|
| 800 | A200 | 2.50d multi | .80 | .20 |

50th anniv. of the Natl. Institute of Social Welfare for the Protection of Children and Mothers (P.I.K.P.A.).

---

## Europa Issue, 1964
### Common Design Type
**1964, Sept. 14    Litho.    Perf. 13x13½**
**Size: 23x39mm**

| | | | | |
|---|---|---|---|---|
| 801 | CD7 | 2.50d lt grn & dk red | 2.25 | .40 |
| 802 | CD7 | 4.50d gray & brn | 2.75 | 1.50 |

King Constantine II and Queen Anne-Marie A201

Peleus and Atalante Fighting, 6th Cent. B.C. Vase A202

**1964, Sept. 18    Engr.    Perf. 13½x14**

| | | | | |
|---|---|---|---|---|
| 803 | A201 | 1.50d green | .20 | .20 |
| 804 | A201 | 2.50d rose car | .20 | .20 |
| 805 | A201 | 4.50d brt ultra | .50 | .25 |
| | | Nos. 803-805 (3) | .90 | .65 |

Wedding of King Constantine II and Princess Anne-Marie of Denmark, Sept. 18, 1964.

**Perf. 12x13½, 13½x12**
**1964, Oct. 24      Litho.      Wmk. 252**

Designs: 1d, Runners on amphora, horiz. 2d, Athlete on vase, horiz. 2.50d, Discus thrower and judge, pitcher. 4.50d, Charioteer, sculpture, horiz. 6d, Boxers, vase, horiz. 10d, Apollo, frieze from Zeus Temple at Olympia.

| | | | | |
|---|---|---|---|---|
| 806 | A202 | 10 l multi | .20 | .20 |
| 807 | A202 | 1d multi | .20 | .20 |
| 808 | A202 | 2d multi | .20 | .20 |
| 809 | A202 | 2.50d multi | .20 | .20 |
| 810 | A202 | 4.50d multi | .40 | .30 |
| 811 | A202 | 6d multi | .20 | .20 |
| 812 | A202 | 10d multi | .30 | .20 |
| | | Nos. 806-812 (7) | 1.70 | 1.50 |

18th Olympic Games, Tokyo, Oct. 10-25.

Detail from "Christ Stripped of His Garments" by El Greco A203

Aesculapius Theatre, Epidauros A204

Paintings by El Greco: 1d, Concert of the Angels. 1.50d, El Greco's painted signature, horiz. 2.50d, Self-portrait. 4.50d, Storm-lashed Toledo.

**Perf. 12x13½, 13½x12**
**1965, Mar. 6      Litho.      Wmk. 252**

| | | | | |
|---|---|---|---|---|
| 813 | A203 | 50 l sepia & multi | .20 | .20 |
| 814 | A203 | 1d gray & multi | .20 | .20 |
| a. | | Double impression of black | 100.00 | |
| 815 | A203 | 1.50d multi | .20 | .20 |
| 816 | A203 | 2.50d slate & multi | .20 | .20 |
| 817 | A203 | 4.50d multi | .30 | .25 |
| | | Nos. 813-817 (5) | 1.10 | 1.05 |

350th anniv. of the death of Domenico Theotocopoulos, El Greco (1541-1614).

**1965, Apr. 30    Litho.    Perf. 12x13½**

Design: 4.50d, Herod Atticus Theatre, and Acropolis, Athens.

| | | | | |
|---|---|---|---|---|
| 818 | A204 | 1.50d multi | .25 | .20 |
| 819 | A204 | 4.50d multi | .30 | .30 |

Epidauros and Athens theatrical festivals.

ITU Emblem, Old and New
Telecommunication Equipment — A205

**1965, Apr. 30**     **Perf. 13½x12**
820 A205 2.50d multi     .40 .20
Cent. of the ITU.

Swearing-in
Ceremony
A206

Flag of Philiki
Hetaeria, the
Friends'
Society
A207

**Perf. 13½x12**
**1965, May 31**    **Litho.**    **Wmk. 252**
821 A206 1.50d multi     .20 .20
822 A207 4.50d gray & multi     .20 .20
150th anniv. of the Friends' Society, a
secret organization for the liberation of Greece
from Turkey.

Emblem of
A.H.E.P.A.
A208

**1965, June 30**
823 A208 6d lt bl, blk & ol     .50 .20
Congress of the American Hellenic Educational Progressive Association, Athens.

Eleutherios
Venizelos,
Therissos,
1905 — A209

Designs: 2d, Venizelos signing Treaty of
Sevres, 1920. 2.50d, Venizelos portrait.

**1965, June 30**   **Engr.**   **Perf. 12½x13**
824 A209 1.50d green     .20 .20
825 A209 2d dark blue     .40 .30
826 A209 2.50d brown     .20 .20
    Nos. 824-826 (3)     .80 .70
Cent. of the birth of Eleutherios Venizelos
(1864-1936), statesman and prime minister.

Symbols of     Astronaut in
Planets — A210     Space — A211

Design: 6d, Two space ships over globe.

**Perf. 12½x13½**
**1965, Sept. 11**   **Litho.**   **Wmk. 252**
827 A210 50 l multi     .20 .20
828 A211 2.50d multi     .20 .20
829 A211 6d multi     .20 .20
    Nos. 827-829 (3)     .60 .60
16th Astronautical Cong., Athens, 9/12-18.

Victory
Medal — A212

Stadium,
Phaleron
A213

Design: 1d, Games' emblem and "JBA."

**Perf. 13½x13, 13x13½**
**1965, Sept. 11**
830 A213 1d multicolored     .20 .20
831 A212 2d multicolored     .20 .20
832 A213 6d multicolored     .20 .20
    Nos. 830-832 (3)     .60 .60
24th Balkan Games, Sept. 1-10.

**Europa Issue, 1965**
Common Design Type
**1965, Oct. 21**     **Perf. 13½x12**
**Size: 33x23mm**
833 CD8 2.50d bl gray, blk & dk
    bl     .75 .40
834 CD8 4.50d olive, blk & grn     1.50 .75

Hipparchus
and Astrolabe
A214

**1965, Oct. 21**   **Litho.**   **Wmk. 252**
835 A214 2.50d bl grn, blk & dk red .40 .20
Opening of the Evghenides Planetarium,
Athens.

St. Andrew's     St.
Church,     Andrew — A216
Patras — A215

**1965, Nov. 30**     **Perf. 12x13½**
836 A215 1d multicolored     .20 .20
837 A216 5d multicolored     .25 .20
Return of the head of St. Andrew from St.
Peter's, Rome to St. Andrew's, Patras. The
design of the 5d is from an 11th cent. mosaic
at St. Luke's Monastery, Boeotia.

Ants and     Savings Bank
Anthill — A217     and
    Book — A218

**1965, Nov. 30**   **Litho.**   **Wmk. 252**
838 A217 10 l grn, blk & bis     .20 .20
839 A218 2.50d multi     .30 .20
50th anniv. of the Post Office Savings Bank.

Theodore     Jean Gabriel
Brysakes     Eynard
A219     A220

Banknote of 1867 — A221

Greek Painters: 1d, Nikeforus Lytras. 2.50d,
Constantin Volonakis. 4d, Nicolas Gyses. 5d,
George Jacobides.

**Perf. 13x13½**
**1966, Feb. 28**   **Litho.**   **Wmk. 252**
840 A219 80 l multi     .20 .20
841 A219 1d multi     .20 .20
842 A219 2.50d multi     .20 .20
843 A219 4d multi     .20 .20
844 A219 5d multi     .20 .20
    Nos. 840-844 (5)     1.00 1.00

**Perf. 12x13½**
**1966, Mar. 30**   **Engr.**   **Wmk. 252**
2.50d, Georgios Stavros. 4d, Bank's 1st
headquarters, etching by Yannis Kefallinos.
845 A220 1.50d gray grn     .20 .20
846 A220 2.50d brown     .20 .20
847 A221 4d ultra     .20 .20
848 A221 6d black     .20 .20
    Nos. 845-848 (4)     .80 .80
National Bank of Greece, 125th anniv.

Symbolic Water     UNESCO
Cycle — A222     Emblem — A223

WHO Headquarters, Geneva — A224

**Perf. 12x13½, 13½x12**
**1966, Apr. 18**       **Litho.**
849 A222 1d multicolored     .20 .20
850 A223 3d multicolored     .20 .20
851 A224 5d multicolored     .20 .20
    Nos. 849-851 (3)     .60 .60
Hydrological Decade (UNESCO), 1965-74,
(1d); 20th anniv. of UNESCO (3d); inauguration of the WHO Headquarters, Geneva (5d).

Geannares Michael
(Hatzes) — A225

Explosion at
Arkadi
Monastery
A226

Map of
Crete — A227

**1966, Apr. 18**
852 A225 2d multi     .20 .20
853 A226 2.50d multi     .20 .20
854 A227 4.50d multi     .25 .20
    Nos. 852-854 (3)     .65 .60
Cent. of the Cretan revolt against the Turks.
Geannares Michael (Hatzes), the leader of the
revolt, was a member of Cretan government
and a writer.

Copper Mask, 4th
Century,
B.C. — A228

Dionysus on
a Thespian
Ship-Chariot
A229

Designs: 2.50d, Old Theater of Dionysus,
Athens, 6th Century B.C. 4.50d, Dancing Dionysus, from vase by Kleophrades, c. 500 B.C.

**Perf. 12x13½, 13½x12**
**1966, May 26**   **Litho.**   **Wmk. 252**
855 A228 1d multi     .20 .20
856 A229 1.50d multi     .20 .20
857 A229 2.50d multi     .20 .20
858 A228 4.50d multi     .20 .20
    Nos. 855-858 (4)     .80 .80
2500th anniversary of Greek theater.

Boeing 707-320 over New York
Buildings and Greek Column
A230

**1966, May 26**     **Perf. 13x12½**
859 A230 6d blue & dark blue     .40 .20
Inauguration of transatlantic flights of
Olympic Airways.

Tobacco
Worker — A231

Design: 5d, Woman sorting tobacco leaves.

Perf. 12½x13½

1966, Sept. 19 Litho. Wmk. 252

860	A231	1d multicolored	.25	.20
861	A231	5d multicolored	.45	.20

Greek tobacco industry, and 4th Intl. Scientific Tobacco Congress, Athens, Sept. 19-26.

Europa Issue, 1966

Common Design Type

1966, Sept. 19 Litho. Wmk. 252

Size: 23x33mm

862	CD9	1.50d olive	*.75*	*.35*
863	CD9	4.50d lt red brown	*1.50*	*.70*

Carved Cases for Knitting Needles — A232

Bridegroom, Embroidery from Epirus A233

Designs (Popular Art): 50 l, Lyre, Crete. 1d, Massa (stringed instrument). 1.50d, Bas-relief (cross and angels). 2d, Icon (Sts. Constantine and Helena). 2.50d, Virgin (wood carving, Church of St. Nicholas, Galaxeidon). 3d, Embroidery (sailing ship from Skyros). 4d, Embroidery (wedding parade). 4.50d, Carved wooden distaff (Sts. George and Barbara). 5d, Silver and agate necklace and earrings. 20d, Handwoven cloth, Cyprus.

Perf. 12x13½, 13½x12

1966, Nov. 21 Litho. Wmk. 252

864	A232	10 l multi	.20	.20
865	A233	30 l multi	.20	.20
866	A232	50 l multi	.20	.20
867	A232	1d multi	.20	.20
868	A232	1.50d multi	.20	.20
869	A232	2d multi	1.60	.20
870	A232	2.50d multi	.20	.20
871	A233	3d multi	.20	.20
872	A233	4d multi	.65	.20
873	A232	4.50d multi	.30	.30
874	A232	5d multi	.70	.20
875	A233	20d multi	1.50	.50
		Nos. 864-875 (12)	6.15	2.80

King Constantine II, Queen Anne-Marie and Princess Alexia — A234

Designs: 2d, Princess Alexia. 3.50d, Queen Anne-Marie and Princess Alexia.

Perf. 13½x14

1966, Dec. 19 Engr. Wmk. 252

876	A234	2d green	.20	.20
877	A234	2.50d brown	.20	.20
878	A234	3.50d ultra	.20	.20
		Nos. 876-878 (3)	.60	.60

Princess Alexia, successor to the throne of Greece.

"Night" by John Cossos (1830-73) — A235

Sculptures: 50 l, Penelope by Leonides Drosses (1836-1882). 80 l, Shepherd by George Fytales. 2d, Woman's torso by Constantine Demetriades (1881-1943). 2.50d, "Colocotrones" (equestrian statue) by Lazarus Sochos (1862-1911). 3d, Sleeping Young Lady by John Halepas (1851-1938), horiz. 10d, Woodcutter by George Filippotes (1839-1919), horiz.

Perf. 12x13½, 13½x12

1967, Feb. 28 Litho. Wmk. 252

879	A235	20 l Prus bl, gray & blk	.20	.20
880	A235	50 l brn, gray & blk	.20	.20
881	A235	80 l brn red, gray & blk	.20	.20
882	A235	2d vio bl, gray & blk	.20	.20
883	A235	2.50d ultra, blk & grn	.20	.20
884	A235	3d bl, lt bl, gray & blk	.40	.25
885	A235	10d bl & multi	.30	.25
		Nos. 879-885 (7)	1.70	1.50

Issued to honor modern Greek sculptors.

World Map and Olympic Rings A236

Discus Thrower by C. Demetriades A237

Designs: 1.50d, Runners on ancient clay vessel. 2.50d, Hurdler and map of Europe and Near East. 6d, Rising sun over Altis ruins at Olympia.

Perf. 13½x12, 12x13½

1967, Apr. 6 Litho. Wmk. 252

886	A236	1d multi	.20	.20
887	A236	1.50d multi	.20	.20
888	A236	2.50d multi	.20	.20
889	A237	5d multi	.40	.30
890	A236	6d multi	.45	.25
		Nos. 886-890 (5)	1.45	1.15

Olympic Games Day, Apr. 6 (1d); Classic Marathon Race, Apr. 6 (1.5d); athletic qualifying rounds for the Cup of Europe, June 24-25 (2.50d); 9th contest for the European Athletic Championships, 1969 (5d); founding of the Intl. Academy at Olympia and the 7th meeting of the Academy, July 29-Aug. 14, 1967 (6d).

Europa Issue, 1967

Common Design Type

Perf. 12x13½

1967, May 2 Litho. Wmk. 252

Size: 23x33½mm

891	CD10	2.50d buff, lt & dk brn	*1.00*	*.25*
892	CD10	4.50d grn, lt & dk grn	*2.75*	*.75*

Chapel, Skopelos Island A238

Plaka District, Athens — A239

Intl. Tourist Year: 4.50d, Doric Temple of Epicurean Apollo, by Itkinus, c. 430 B.C.

Perf. 13½x12, 12x13½

1967, June 26 Litho. Wmk. 252

893	A238	2.50d multi	.20	.20
894	A238	4.50d multi	.40	.30
a.		Double impression of black		
895	A239	6d multi	.40	.20
		Nos. 893-895 (3)	1.00	.70

Destroyer and Sailor A240

Training Ship, Merchant Marine Academy — A241

Maritime Week: 2.50d, Merchant Marine Academy, Aspropyrgos, Attica, and rowing crew. 3d, Cruiser Georgios Averoff and Naval School, Poros. 6d, Merchant ship and bearded figurehead.

1967, June 26

896	A240	20 l multi	.20	.20
897	A241	1d multi	.20	.20
898	A240	2.50d multi	.20	.20
899	A240	3d multi	.30	.25
900	A240	6d multi	.40	.25
		Nos. 896-900 (5)	1.30	1.10

Soldier and Rising Phoenix A242

Blast Furnaces A243

Perf. 12x13½

1967, Aug. 30 Litho. Wmk. 252

901	A242	2.50d blue & multi	.20	.20
902	A242	3d orange & multi	.20	.20
903	A242	4.50d multi	.20	.20
		Nos. 901-903 (3)	.60	.60

Revolution of Apr. 21, 1967.

1967, Nov. 29 *Perf. 13x14*

904	A243	4.50d brt bl & dk vio bl	.40	.40

1st meeting of the UN Industrial Development Organization, Athens, Nov. 29-Dec. 20.

Sailboats A244

Children's Drawings: 1.50d, Steamship and island. 3.50d, Farmhouse. 6d, Church on hill.

1967, Dec. 20 *Perf. 13½x12½*

905	A244	20 l multi	.20	.20
906	A244	1.50d grn, dk bl & blk	.20	.20
907	A244	3.50d multi	.40	.40
908	A244	6d multi	.40	.40
		Nos. 905-908 (4)	1.20	1.20

Javelin A245

Apollo, Olympic Academy Seal A246

Discus Thrower by Demetriades A247

Designs: 1d, Jumping. 2.50d, Attic vase showing lighting of Olympic torch. 4d, Olympic rings and world map, horiz. 6d, Long-distance runners, vert.

Wmk. 252

1968, Feb. 28 Litho. *Perf. 12½*

909	A245	50 l ultra & bis	.20	.20
910	A245	1d grn, yel, blk & gray	.20	.20
911	A246	1.50d blk, bl & buff	.20	.20
912	A246	2.50d ol grn, blk & org brn	.20	.20
913	A246	4d gray & multi	.35	.20
914	A247	4.50d bl, grn, yel & blk	.55	.35
915	A245	6d brn, red & bl	.30	.20
		Nos. 909-915 (7)	2.00	1.55

50 l, 1d, 6d, 27th Balkan Games, Athens, Aug. 29-Sept. 1; 1.50d, Meeting of the Intl. Olympic Academy; 2.50d, Lighting of the Olympic torch for 19th Olympic Games, Mexico City; 4d, Olympic Day, Apr. 6; 4.50d, 9th European Athletic Championships, 1969.

Europa Issue, 1968

Common Design Type

Perf. 13½x12

1968, Mar. 29 Litho. Wmk. 252

Size: 33x23mm

916	CD11	2.50d cop red, bis & blk	*1.25*	*.40*
917	CD11	4.50d vio, bister & blk	*2.50*	*1.25*

Emblems of Greek and International Automobile Clubs — A248

1968, Mar. 29 *Perf. 13x14*

918	A248	5d ultra & org brn	.60	.40

General Assembly of the International Automobile Federation, Athens, Apr. 8-14.

Athena Defeating Alkyoneus, from Pergamos Altar, 180 B.C. — A249

Athena, 2nd Century, B.C. — A250

Winged Victory of Samothrace, c. 190 B.C. — A251

Designs: 50 l, Alexander the Great on horseback, from sarcophagus, c. 310 B.C. 1.50d, Emperors Constantine and Justinian bringing offerings to Virgin Mary, Byzantine mosaic. 2.50d, Emperor Constantine Paleologos, lithograph by D. Tsokos, 1859. 3d, Greece in Missolonghi, by Delacroix. 4.50d, Greek Soldier (evzone), by G. B. Scott.

**Perf. 13½x13, 13x13½, 13½x14**
**(A249)**
**1968, Apr. 27**
| | | | | |
|---|---|---|---|---|
|919|A249|10 l gray & multi|.20|.20|
|920|A250|20 l grn & multi|.20|.20|
|921|A250|50 l pur & multi|.20|.20|
|922|A249|1.50d gray & multi|.20|.20|
|923|A250|2.50d multi|.20|.20|
|924|A251|3d multi|.20|.20|
|925|A251|4.50d multi|.25|.20|
|926|A251|6d multi|.35|.30|
| |Nos. 919-926 (8)|1.80|1.70|

"The Hellenic Fight for Civilization" exhibition

Monument to the Unknown Priest and Teacher, Rhodes A252

Map & Flag of Greece — A253

Cross and Globe — A254

**Perf. 14x13½, 13½x14**
**1968, July 11 Litho. Wmk. 252**
|927|A252|2d multicolored|.40|.25|
|---|---|---|---|---|
|928|A253|5d multicolored|.80|.80|

20th anniv. of the union of the Dodecanese Islands with Greece.

**1968, July 11 Perf. 13½x14**
|929|A254|6d multicolored|.55|.40|
|---|---|---|---|---|

19th Biennial Congress of the Greek Orthodox Archdiocese of North and South America.

Antique Lamp (GAPA Emblem) A255

**1968, July 11 Perf. 14x13½**
|930|A255|6d multicolored|.50|.30|
|---|---|---|---|---|

Regional Congress of the Greek-American Progressive Association, G.A.P.A.

Fragment of Bas-relief, Temple of Aesculapius, Athens — A256

View of Olympia, Site of Ancient Games A257

**Perf. 13½x14**
**1968, Sept. 8 Litho. Wmk. 252**
|931|A256|4.50d multicolored|1.50|.90|
|---|---|---|---|---|

Issued to publicize the 5th European Cardiology Congress, Athens, Sept. 8-14.

Pindar and Olympic Ode — A258

Hygeia and WHO Emblem — A259

Design: 2.50d, Panathenaic Stadium, site of 1896 Olympic Games.

**Perf. 14x13½, 13x13½**
**1968, Sept. 25 Litho. Wmk. 252**
|932|A257|2.50d multicolored|.30|.20|
|---|---|---|---|---|
|933|A257|5d green & multi|.45|.20|
|934|A258|10d bl, yel & brn|1.25|.80|
| |Nos. 932-934 (3)|2.00|1.20|

19th Olympic Games, Mexico City, 10/12-27. On 10d, hyphen is omitted at end of 5th line of ode on 5 of 50 stamps in each sheet.

**1968, Nov. 8 Perf. 13½x14**
|935|A259|5d gray & multi|.70|.40|
|---|---|---|---|---|

20th anniv. of WHO.

Mediterranean, Breguet 19 and Flight Route, 1928 — A260

Farman, 1912, Plane and F-104G Jet — A261

St. Zeno, The Letter Bearer — A262

Design: 2.50d, Greek air force pilot ramming enemy plane over Langada.

**1968, Nov. 8 Perf. 14x13½, 13½x14**
|936|A260|2.50d ultra, blk & yel|.20|.20|
|---|---|---|---|---|
|937|A260|3.50d multicolored|.20|.20|
|938|A261|8d multicolored|1.25|.90|
| |Nos. 936-938 (3)|1.65|1.30|

Exploits of Royal Hellenic Air Force.

**Perf. 13½x14**
**1969, Feb. 10 Litho. Wmk. 252**
|939|A262|2.50d multicolored|.50|.20|
|---|---|---|---|---|

Establishment of the feast day of St. Zeno as the day of Greek p.o. personnel.

Hephaestus and Cyclops, Bas-relief A263

Parade of Harvesters, Minoan Vase — A264

**1969, Feb. 10 Perf. 13½x12½**
|940|A263|1.50d multicolored|.35|.20|
|---|---|---|---|---|
|941|A264|10d multicolored|.90|.65|

50th anniv. of the ILO.

Yachts in Vouliagmeni Harbor — A265

Athens Festival, Chorus of Elders — A266

View of Astypalaia — A267

**Perf. 13½x12½, 12½x13½**
**1969, Mar. 3**
|942|A265|1d multicolored|.20|.20|
|---|---|---|---|---|
|943|A266|5d multicolored|.80|.70|
|944|A267|6d multicolored|.40|.20|
| |Nos. 942-944 (3)|1.40|1.10|

Issued for tourist publicity.

Attic Shield and Helmet on Greek Coin, 461-450 B.C. — A268

Hoplites and Flutist, from Proto-Corinthian Pitcher, 640-630 B.C. — A269

**Perf. 12½x13½, 13½x12½**
**1969, Apr. 4 Litho. Wmk. 252**
|945|A268|2.50d rose red, blk & sl|.35|.20|
|---|---|---|---|---|
|946|A269|4.50d multi|.85|.65|

20th anniv. of NATO.

**Europa Issue, 1969**
Common Design Type
**1969, May 5 Perf. 13½x12½**
**Size: 33x23mm**
|947|CD12|2.50d multi|1.75|.25|
|---|---|---|---|---|
|948|CD12|4.50d multi|3.25|1.25|

Victory Medal A270

Pole Vault and Pentathlon (from Panathenaic Amphora) A271

5d, Relay race and runners from amphora, 525 B.C., horiz. 8d, Modern and ancient (Panathenaic amphora, c. 480 B.C.) discus throwers.

**Perf. 12½x13½, 13½x12½**
**1969, May 5**
|949|A270|20 l red & multi|.20|.20|
|---|---|---|---|---|
|950|A271|3d gray & multi|.20|.20|
|951|A271|5d multicolored|.20|.20|
|952|A271|8d multicolored|1.40|.75|
| |Nos. 949-952 (4)|2.00|1.35|

Issued to publicize the 9th European Athletic Championships, Athens, Sept. 16-21.

**Greece and the Sea Issue**

Oil Tanker A272

Merchant Vessels and Warships, 1821 — A273

Designs: 80 l, Brig and steamship, painting by Ioannis Poulakas, vert. 4.50d, Warships on maneuvers. 6d, Battle of Salamis, 480 B.C., painting by Constantine Volonakis.

**Perf. 12½x13½, 13½x12½, 13½x13**
**1969, June 28 Litho. Wmk. 252**
|953|A272|80 l multicolored|.20|.20|
|---|---|---|---|---|
|954|A272|2d blk, bl & gray|.20|.20|
|955|A273|2.50d dk bl & multi|.20|.20|
|956|A272|4.50d brn, gray & bl|.75|.35|
|957|A273|6d multicolored|.90|.45|
| |Nos. 953-957 (5)|2.25|1.40|

Raising Greek Flag — A274

**1969, Aug. 31 Perf. 13x13½**
|958|A274|2.50d blue & multi|.70|.20|
|---|---|---|---|---|

20th anniv. of the Grammos-Vitsi victory.

Athena Promachos and Map of Greece A275

"National" Resistance" A276

Greek Participation in World War II — A277

**Perf. 13x13½, 13½x14**

**1969, Oct. 12     Litho.     Wmk. 252**

| | | | | |
|---|---|---|---|---|
| 959 | A275 | 4d multicolored | .20 | .20 |
| 960 | A276 | 5d multicolored | .90 | .70 |
| 961 | A277 | 6d multicolored | .65 | .20 |
| | | Nos. 959-961 (3) | 1.75 | 1.10 |

25th anniv. of the liberation of Greece in WW II.
No. 960 exists imperf.

Demetrius Tsames Karatasios, by G. Demetriades A278

Pavlos Melas, by P. Mathiopoulos A279

2.50d, Emmanuel Pappas, statue by Nicholas Perantinos. 4.50d, Capetan Kotas.

**Perf. 12x13½**

**1969, Nov. 12     Litho.     Wmk. 252**

| | | | | |
|---|---|---|---|---|
| 962 | A278 | 1.50d multicolored | .20 | .20 |
| 963 | A278 | 2.50d blue & multi | .20 | .20 |
| 964 | A279 | 3.50d gray & multi | .20 | .20 |
| 965 | A279 | 4.50d multicolored | .95 | .55 |
| | | Nos. 962-965 (4) | 1.55 | 1.15 |

Issued to honor Greek heroes in Macedonia's struggle for liberation.

Angel of the Annunciation, Daphni Church, 11th Century — A280

Dolphins, Delos, 110 B.C. A281

Christ's Descent into Hell, Nea Moni Church, 11th Cent. A282

Greek Mosaics: 1.50d, The Holy Ghost (dove), Hosios Loukas Monastery, 11th cent. 2d, The Hunter, Pella, 4th cent. B.C. 5d, Bird, St. George's Church, Salonica, 5th cent.

**Perf. 12x13½, 13½x12 (1d), 13x13½ (6d)**

**1970, Jan. 16     Litho.     Wmk. 252**

| | | | | |
|---|---|---|---|---|
| 966 | A280 | 20 l multicolored | .20 | .20 |
| 967 | A281 | 1d multicolored | .20 | .20 |
| 968 | A280 | 1.50d blue & multi | .20 | .20 |
| 969 | A280 | 2d gray & multi | .45 | .20 |
| 970 | A280 | 5d bister & multi | .55 | .35 |
| 971 | A282 | 6d multicolored | .75 | .75 |
| | | Nos. 966-971 (6) | 2.35 | 1.90 |

Hercules and the Cretan Bull — A283

Hercules and the Erymanthian Boar — A284

Labors of Hercules: 30 l, Capture of Cerberus. 1d, Capture of the golden apples of the Hesperides. 1.50d, Lernean Hydra. 2d, Slaying of Geryon. 3d, Centaur Nessus. 4.50d, Fight with the river god Achelos. 5d, Nemean lion. 6d, Stymphalian birds. 20d, Giant Antaeus. Designs of 20 l and 1d are from Temple of Zeus, Olympia; others from various vessels; all from 7th-5th cent. B.C.

**Perf. 13½x12, 12x13½**

**1970, Mar. 16     Litho.     Wmk. 252**

| | | | | |
|---|---|---|---|---|
| 972 | A283 | 20 l gray, blk & yel | .20 | .20 |
| 973 | A283 | 30 l ocher & multi | .20 | .20 |
| 974 | A284 | 1d bl gray, blk & bl | .20 | .20 |
| 975 | A283 | 1.50d dk brn, bis & sl grn | .30 | .20 |
| 976 | A283 | 2d ocher & multi | 2.25 | .20 |
| 977 | A284 | 2.50d ocher, dk brn & dl red | .30 | .20 |
| 978 | A284 | 3d multicolored | 2.25 | .20 |
| 979 | A283 | 4.50d dk bl & multi | .50 | .20 |
| 980 | A283 | 5d multicolored | .50 | .20 |
| 981 | A283 | 6d multicolored | .50 | .20 |
| 982 | A283 | 20d black & multi | 1.75 | .85 |
| | | Nos. 972-982 (11) | 8.95 | 2.85 |

Satellite, Earth Station and Hemispheres A285

**1970, Apr. 21     Perf. 13½x12**

| | | | | |
|---|---|---|---|---|
| 983 | A285 | 2.50d bl, gray & yel | .50 | .30 |
| 984 | A285 | 4.50d brn, ol & bl | 1.25 | 1.10 |

Opening of the Earth Satellite Telecommunications Station "Thermopylae," Apr. 21, 1970.

**Europa Issue, 1970**
Common Design Type and

Owl (Post Horns and CEPT) — A287

**1970, Apr. 21     Perf. 13½x12, 12x13½**

| | | | | |
|---|---|---|---|---|
| 985 | CD13 | 2.50d rose red & org | 2.00 | .75 |
| 986 | A287 | 3d brt bl, gray & vio bl | 2.00 | .75 |
| 987 | CD13 | 4.50d ultra & org | 5.75 | 1.25 |
| | | Nos. 985-987 (3) | 9.75 | 2.75 |

St. Demetrius with Cyril and Methodius as Children A288

Emperor Michael III with Sts. Cyril and Methodius A290

A289

**Perf. 13½x14 (50 l); 12x13½ (2d, 10d); 13x13½ (5d)**

**1970, Apr. 17     Litho.     Wmk. 252**

| | | | | |
|---|---|---|---|---|
| 988 | A288 | 50 l multi | .20 | .20 |
| 989 | | 2d St. Cyril | .60 | .45 |
| 990 | A290 | 5d multi | .50 | .50 |
| 991 | | 10d St. Methodius | .70 | .50 |
| a. | A289 | Pair, #989, 991 | 1.25 | 1.25 |
| | | Nos. 988-991 (4) | 2.00 | 1.35 |

Sts. Cyril and Methodius who translated the Bible into Slavonic.

Greek Fir A292

Jankaea Heldreichii A293

6d, Rock partridge, horiz. 8d, Wild goat.

**Perf. 13x14, 14x13, 12x13½ (2.50d)**

**1970, June 16     Litho.     Wmk. 252**

| | | | | |
|---|---|---|---|---|
| 992 | A292 | 80 l multi | .35 | .35 |
| 993 | A293 | 2.50d multi | 1.25 | .20 |
| 994 | A292 | 6d multi | 2.40 | .55 |
| 995 | A292 | 8d multi | 2.75 | 2.40 |
| | | Nos. 992-995 (4) | 6.75 | 3.50 |

European Nature Conservation Year, 1970.

Map Showing Link Between AHEPA Members and Greece A294

**1970, Aug. 1     Perf. 13½x13**

| | | | | |
|---|---|---|---|---|
| 996 | A294 | 6d blue & multi | 1.00 | .40 |

48th annual AHEPA (American Hellenic Educational Progressive Assoc.) Cong., Athens, Aug. 1970.

UPU Headquarters, Bern — A295

Education Year Emblem — A296

Mahatma Gandhi — A297

United Nations Emblem — A298

Ludwig van Beethoven — A299

**Perf. 13½x12, 13x14, 12x13½**

**1970, Oct. 7     Litho.     Wmk. 252**

| | | | | |
|---|---|---|---|---|
| 997 | A295 | 50 l bis & multi | .20 | .20 |
| 998 | A296 | 2.50d bl & multi | .40 | .20 |
| 999 | A297 | 3.50d multi | .25 | .20 |
| 1000 | A298 | 4d bl & multi | .75 | .20 |
| 1001 | A299 | 4.50d blk & multi | 1.50 | 1.10 |
| | | Nos. 997-1001 (5) | 3.10 | 1.90 |

Inauguration of the UPU Headquarters, Bern (50 l); Intl. Education Year (2.50d); cent. of the birth of Mohandas K. Gandhi (1869-1948), leader in India's struggle for independence (3.50d); 25th anniv. of the UN (4d); Ludwig van Beethoven (1770-1827), composer (4.50d).

The Shepherds (Mosaic) — A300

Christmas (from Mosaic in the Monastery of Hosios Loukas, Boetia, 11th cent.): 4.50d, The Three Kings and Angel. 6d, Nativity, horiz.

**1970, Dec. 5     Perf. 13x14, 14x13**

| | | | | |
|---|---|---|---|---|
| 1002 | A300 | 2d bister & multi | .20 | .20 |
| 1003 | A300 | 4.50d bister & multi | .40 | .30 |
| 1004 | A300 | 6d bister & multi | .80 | .80 |
| | | Nos. 1002-1004 (3) | 1.40 | 1.30 |

"Leonidas"
A301

Priest Sworn in as
Fighter, from
Commemorative
Medal — A302

Eugenius
Voùlgaris (1716-
1806)
A303

Battle of Corinth
A304

Kaltetsi Monastery, Seal of
Peloponnesian Senate — A305

Death of Bishop Isaias, Battle of
Alamana — A306

Designs: No. 1009, *Pericles.* No. 1010, Sacrifice of Kapsalis. 1.50d, *Terpsichore.* No. 1012, Patriarch Grigorius IV. No. 1013, Suliot women in battle, horiz. No. 1015, *Karteria.* No. 1016, Adamantios Korais, M.D. No. 1017, Memorial column, provincial administrative seal of Epidaurus. 3d, Naval battle, Samos, horiz. 5d, Battle of Athens. 6d, Naval battle, Yeronda. 6.50d, Battle of Maniaki. 9d, Battle of Karpenisi, death of Marcos Botsaris. 10d, Bishop Germanos blessing flag. 15d, *Secret School.* 20d, John Capodistrias' signature and seal.

| 1971 | | Litho. | Wmk. 252 | |
|---|---|---|---|---|
| 1005 | A301 | 20 l multi | .20 | .20 |
| 1006 | A302 | 50 l multi | .20 | .20 |
| 1007 | A303 | 50 l multi | .20 | .20 |
| 1008 | A304 | 50 l multi | .20 | .20 |
| 1009 | A301 | 1d multi | .20 | .20 |
| 1010 | A304 | 1d multi | .20 | .20 |
| 1011 | A301 | 1.50d multi | .20 | .20 |
| 1012 | A302 | 2d multi | .20 | .20 |
| 1013 | A304 | 2d multi | .20 | .20 |
| 1014 | A305 | 2d multi | .20 | .20 |
| 1015 | A301 | 2.50d multi | .20 | .20 |
| 1016 | A303 | 2.50d multi | .25 | .20 |
| 1017 | A305 | 2.50d multi | .25 | .20 |
| 1018 | A304 | 3d multi | .65 | .40 |
| 1019 | A306 | 4d multi | .20 | .20 |
| 1020 | A304 | 5d multi | .40 | .20 |
| 1021 | A301 | 6d multi | 1.25 | .90 |
| 1022 | A301 | 6.50d multi | .40 | .25 |
| 1023 | A301 | 9d multi | 1.00 | .90 |
| 1024 | A306 | 10d multi | 1.10 | .90 |
| 1025 | A306 | 15d multi | 1.25 | 1.10 |
| 1026 | A305 | 20d multi | 2.25 | 1.40 |
| | | *Nos. 1005-1026 (22)* | 11.20 | 8.85 |

Sesquicentennial of Greece's uprising against the Turks. Emphasize role of Navy (#1005, 1009, 1011, 1015, 1018, 1021), issued 3/15; Church (#1006, 1012, 1019,

1024), 2/8; Instructors (#1007, 1016, 1025), 6/21; Land Forces (#1008, 1010, 1013, 1020, 1022-1023), 9/21; Provincial Administrations (#1014, 1017, 1026), 10/19.
  Sizes: 37x24mm: #1005, 1009, 1011, 1015; 40x27½mm; #1021; 48x33mm, #1022, 1023. Perfs.: 14x13, #1005, 1009, 1011, 1013, 1015, 1018; 13½x14, #1006, 1012; 12x13½, #1007, 1016, 1019, 1022-1025; 13x14, #1008, 1010, 1020; 13½x13, #1014, 1017, 1021, 1026.

Spyridon Louis, Winner of 1896
Marathon Race, Arriving at Stadium
A307

Pierre de Coubertin
and Memorial
Column — A308

**Perf. 13½x13, 13x13½**
| 1971, Apr. 10 | | Litho. | Wmk. 252 | |
|---|---|---|---|---|
| 1027 | A307 | 3d multi | .50 | .20 |
| 1028 | A308 | 8d multi | 1.25 | .90 |

Olympic Games revival, 75th anniv.

**Europa Issue, 1971**
Common Design Type
1971, May 18           Perf. 13½x12
Size: 33x22½mm
| 1029 | CD14 | 2.50d grn, yel & blk | 1.50 | .30 |
| 1030 | CD14 | 5d org, yel & blk | 6.00 | 1.50 |

Hosios
Lukas
Monastery
A309

  Monasteries and Churches: 1d, Daphni Church. 2d, St. John the Divine, Patmos. 2.50d, Koumbelidiki Church, Kastoria. 4.50d, Chalkeon Church, Thessalonica. 6.50d, Paregoritissa Church, Arta. 8.50d, St. Paul's Monastery, Mt. Athos.

| 1972, Jan. 17 | | | Perf. 14x13 | |
|---|---|---|---|---|
| 1031 | A309 | 50 l multi | .20 | .20 |
| 1032 | A309 | 1d multi | .20 | .20 |
| 1033 | A309 | 2d multi | .20 | .20 |
| 1034 | A309 | 2.50d multi | .20 | .20 |
| 1035 | A309 | 4.50d multi | .25 | .20 |
| 1036 | A309 | 6.50d multi | .25 | .20 |
| 1037 | A309 | 8.50d multi | 1.00 | 1.00 |
| | | *Nos. 1031-1037 (7)* | 2.30 | 2.20 |

Cretan
Costume — A310

Designs: Greek regional costumes.

| 1972, Mar. 1 | | | Perf. 12½x13½ | |
|---|---|---|---|---|
| 1038 | A310 | 50 l shown | .20 | .20 |
| 1039 | A310 | 1d Woman, Pindus | .20 | .20 |
| 1040 | A310 | 2d Man, Missolonghi | .20 | .20 |
| 1041 | A310 | 2.50d Woman, Sarakatsan, Attica | .20 | .20 |
| *a.* | | "1972" omitted | 10.00 | 10.00 |
| 1042 | A310 | 3d Woman, Island of Nisyros | .20 | .20 |
| 1043 | A310 | 4.50d Woman, Megara | .20 | .20 |
| 1044 | A310 | 6.50d Woman, Trikeri | .30 | .25 |
| 1045 | A310 | 10d Woman, Pylaia, Macedonia | 1.75 | 1.00 |
| | | *Nos. 1038-1045 (8)* | 3.25 | 2.45 |

See Nos. 1073-1089, 1121-1135.

Memorial
Medal,
Science
and
Industry
A311

Flag and Map of
Greece — A312

Honeycomb,
Transportation
and
Industry — A313

**Perf. 13½x13, 13x13½**
| 1972, Apr. 21 | | | Wmk. 252 | |
|---|---|---|---|---|
| 1046 | A311 | 2.50d blue & multi | .20 | .20 |
| 1047 | A312 | 4.50d ocher & multi | .25 | .25 |
| 1048 | A313 | 5d multi | .40 | .40 |
| | | *Nos. 1046-1048 (3)* | .85 | .85 |

5th anniversary of the revolution.

**Europa Issue 1972**
Common Design Type
1972, May 2            Perf. 12x13½
Size: 23x33mm
| 1049 | CD15 | 3d multi | .75 | .30 |
| 1050 | CD15 | 4.50d blue & multi | 4.25 | 1.25 |

Acropolis and
Car — A314

Route of
Automobile
Rally — A315

| 1972, May 26 | | | Perf. 13½x12 | |
|---|---|---|---|---|
| 1051 | A314 | 4.50d multi | .60 | .60 |
| 1052 | A315 | 5d bl & multi | .60 | .60 |

20th Acropolis Automobile Rally, May 26-29.

Gaia
Handing
Erecthonius
to Athena,
Cecrops
A316

Designs: 2d, Uranus, from altar of Zeus at Pergamum. 2.50d, Gods defeating the Giants, Treasury of Siphnos. 5d, Zeus of Dodona.

**1972, June 26   Litho.   Perf. 14x13½**
| 1053 | A316 | 1.50d yel grn & blk | .20 | .20 |
| 1054 | A316 | 2d dk bl & blk | .20 | .20 |
| 1055 | A316 | 2.50d org brn & blk | .20 | .20 |
| 1056 | A316 | 5d dk brn & blk | .50 | .40 |
| *a.* | | Strip of 4, #1053-1056 | 2.00 | 2.00 |

  Greek mythology. No. 1056 issued only setenant with Nos. 1053-1055 in sheets of 40 (4x10). Nos. 1053-1055 issued also in sheets of 50 each.

Olympic
Rings,
Wrestlers
A317

  50 l, Young athlete, crowning himself, c. 480 B.C., vert. 3.50d, Spartan woman running, Archaic period, vert. 4.50d, Episkyros ball game, 6th century B.C. 10d, Running youths, from Panathenaic amphora.

**Perf. 13½x14, 14x13½**
| 1972, July 28 | | | Litho. | Wmk. 252 | |
|---|---|---|---|---|---|
| 1057 | A317 | 50 l mar, blk & gray | .25 | .20 |
| 1058 | A317 | 1.50d brn, gray & blk | .25 | .20 |
| 1059 | A317 | 3.50d ocher & multi | .25 | .20 |
| 1060 | A317 | 4.50d grn, buff & blk | .25 | .20 |
| 1061 | A317 | 10d blk & fawn | 1.00 | .55 |
| | | *Nos. 1057-1061 (5)* | 2.00 | 1.35 |

20th Olympic Games, Munich, 8/26-9/11.

Young Stamp
Collector — A318

Three Kings and
Angels — A319

| 1972, Nov. 15 | | | Perf. 13x14 | |
|---|---|---|---|---|
| 1062 | A318 | 2.50d multi | .25 | .20 |

Stamp Day.

| 1972, Nov. 15 | | | | |
|---|---|---|---|---|
| 1063 | A319 | 2.50d shown | .20 | .20 |
| 1064 | A319 | 4.50d Nativity | .20 | .20 |
| *a.* | | Pair, #1063-1064 | .40 | .40 |

Christmas 1972.

Technical University, 1885, by Luigi
Lanza — A320

| 1973, Mar. 30 | | | Perf. 13½x13 | |
|---|---|---|---|---|
| 1065 | A320 | 2.50d multi | .40 | .20 |

  Centenary of the Metsovion National Technical University.

"Spring,"
Fresco — A321

Breast-form
Jug — A322

"Wooing and Twittering Swallows"
Fresco — A323

Designs: 30 l, "Blue Apes" fresco. 1.50d, Jug decorated with birds. 5d, "Wild Goats" fresco. 6.50d, Wrestlers, fresco.

**1973, Mar. 30    Perf. 13x13½, 13½x13**
| 1066 | A321 | 10 l multi | .20 | .20 |
|---|---|---|---|---|
| 1067 | A322 | 20 l multi | .20 | .20 |
| 1068 | A323 | 30 l multi | .20 | .20 |
| 1069 | A322 | 1.50d grn & multi | .20 | .20 |
| 1070 | A323 | 2.50d multi | .20 | .20 |
| 1071 | A323 | 5d multi | .20 | .20 |
| 1072 | A323 | 6.50d multi | .80 | .80 |
| | Nos. 1066-1072 (7) | | 2.00 | 2.00 |

Archaeological treasures from Santorini Island (Thera).

### Costume Type of 1972
Women's costumes except 10 l, 20 l, 50 l, 5d, 15d.

**1973, Apr. 18    Perf. 12½x13½**
| 1073 | A310 | 10 l Peloponnesus | .20 | .20 |
|---|---|---|---|---|
| 1074 | A310 | 20 l Central Greece | .20 | .20 |
| 1075 | A310 | 30 l Locris | .20 | .20 |
| 1076 | A310 | 50 l Skyros | .20 | .20 |
| 1077 | A310 | 1d Spetsai | .20 | .20 |
| 1078 | A310 | 1.50d Almyros | .20 | .20 |
| 1079 | A310 | 2.50d Macedonia | .20 | .20 |
| 1080 | A310 | 3.50d Salamis | .20 | .20 |
| 1081 | A310 | 4.50d Epirus | .20 | .20 |
| 1082 | A310 | 5d Lefkas | .20 | .20 |
| 1083 | A310 | 6.50d Skyros | .20 | .20 |
| 1084 | A310 | 8.50d Corinth | .40 | .25 |
| 1085 | A310 | 10d Corfu | .40 | .20 |
| 1086 | A310 | 15d Epirus | .40 | .20 |
| 1087 | A310 | 20d Thessaly | 1.25 | .25 |
| 1088 | A310 | 30d Macedonia | 1.60 | .30 |
| 1089 | A310 | 50d Thrace | 3.25 | 1.60 |
| | Nos. 1073-1089 (17) | | 9.50 | 5.05 |

### Europa Issue 1973
Common Design Type

**1973, May 2    Perf. 13½x12½**
Size: 35x22mm
| 1090 | CD16 | 2.50d dp bl & lt bl | .40 | .25 |
|---|---|---|---|---|
| 1091 | CD16 | 3d dp car & dp org | .50 | .30 |
| 1092 | CD16 | 4.50d ol grn & yel | 2.75 | .85 |
| | Nos. 1090-1092 (3) | | 3.65 | 1.40 |

Zeus Battling Typhoeus, from Amphora A324

1d, Mount Olympus, after photograph. 2.50d, Zeus battling Giants, from Pergamum Altar. 4.50d, Punishment of Atlas and Prometheus, from vase.

**Perf. 14x13½**
**1973, June 25    Wmk. 252**
| 1093 | A324 | 1d gray & blk | .25 | .20 |
|---|---|---|---|---|
| 1094 | A324 | 2d multi | .25 | .20 |
| 1095 | A324 | 2.50d gray, blk & buff | .25 | .20 |
| 1096 | A324 | 4.50d ocher & multi | .45 | .45 |
| | a. Strip of 4, #1093-1096 | | 1.75 | 1.75 |

Greek mythology.

Dr. George Papanicolaou A325

Icon, The Annunciation A326

**Perf. 13x13½**
**1973, Aug. 10    Litho.    Wmk. 252**
| 1097 | A325 | 2.50d multi | .20 | .20 |
|---|---|---|---|---|
| 1098 | A325 | 6.50d multi | .25 | .25 |

Dr. George Papanicolaou (1883-1962), cytologist and cancer researcher.

**1973, Aug. 10**
| 1099 | A326 | 2.50d multi | .40 | .25 |
|---|---|---|---|---|

Miraculous icon of Our Lady of the Annunciation found on Tinos, 1823.

A327

A328

Triptolemus holding wheat on chariot.

**Perf. 13x14**
**1973, Oct. 22    Litho.    Wmk. 252**
| 1100 | A327 | 4.50d buff, dk brn & red | .30 | .25 |
|---|---|---|---|---|

5th Symposium of the European Conf. of Transport Ministers, Athens, Oct. 22-25.

**1973, Nov. 15    Engr.**
National Benefactors: 1d, Georgios Averoff. 2d, Apostolos Arsakis. 2.50d, Constantine Zappas. 4d, Andrea Sygros. 6.50d, John Varvakis.
| 1101 | A328 | 1.50d dk red brn | .20 | .20 |
|---|---|---|---|---|
| 1102 | A328 | 2d car rose | .20 | .20 |
| 1103 | A328 | 2.50d slate green | .20 | .20 |
| 1104 | A328 | 4d purple | .20 | .20 |
| 1105 | A328 | 6.50d black | .25 | .25 |
| | Nos. 1101-1105 (5) | | 1.05 | 1.05 |

Child Examining Stamp — A329

**1973, Nov. 15    Litho.    Perf. 14x13**
| 1106 | A329 | 2.50d multi | .25 | .20 |
|---|---|---|---|---|

Stamp Day.

Lord Byron in Souliot Costume — A330

Byron Taking Oath at Grave of Botsaris — A331

**Perf. 13x14**
**1974, Apr. 4    Wmk. 252    Litho.**
| 1107 | A330 | 2.50d multi | .20 | .20 |
|---|---|---|---|---|
| 1108 | A331 | 4.50d multi | .20 | .20 |

George Gordon, Lord Byron (1788-1824), English poet involved in Greek struggle for independence.

Harpist of Keros, c. 2800-2200 B.C. — A332

Europa: 4.50d, Statue of Young Women, c. 510 B.C. 6.50d, Charioteer of Delphi, c. 480-450 B.C.

**1974, May 10    Perf. 13x14**
| 1109 | A332 | 3d dp bl & multi | .45 | .25 |
|---|---|---|---|---|
| 1110 | A332 | 4.50d dl red & multi | .65 | .30 |
| 1111 | A332 | 6.50d yel & multi | 1.75 | .80 |
| | Nos. 1109-1111 (3) | | 2.85 | 1.35 |

Zeus and Hera Enthroned, and Iris — A333

Design from Mycenean Vase and UPU Emblem — A334

Greek mythology (from Vases, 5th Cent. B.C.): 2d, Birth of Athena, horiz. 2.50d, Artemis, Apollo, Leto, horiz. 10d, Hermes, the messenger.

**1974, June 24    Perf. 13x14, 14x13**
| 1112 | A333 | 1.50d ocher, blk & brn | .20 | .20 |
|---|---|---|---|---|
| 1113 | A333 | 2d blk, ocher & brn | .20 | .20 |
| 1114 | A333 | 2.50d blk, ocher & brn | .20 | .20 |
| 1115 | A333 | 10d blk, ocher & brn | .25 | .25 |
| | Nos. 1112-1115 (4) | | .85 | .85 |

**1974, Sept. 14    Perf. 12½x13½**
UPU cent.: 4.50d, Hermes on the Move, horiz. 6.50d, Woman reading letter.
| 1116 | A334 | 2d vio & blk | .20 | .20 |
|---|---|---|---|---|
| 1117 | A334 | 4.50d vio & blk | .20 | .20 |
| 1118 | A334 | 6.50d vio & blk | .25 | .30 |
| | Nos. 1116-1118 (3) | | .65 | .70 |

Crete No. 80 A335

**1974, Nov. 15    Litho.    Perf. 13½x13**
| 1119 | A335 | 2.50d multi | .25 | .20 |
|---|---|---|---|---|

Stamp Day.

Flight into Egypt — A336

Illustration reduced.

**1974, Nov. 15    Perf. 13½x14**
| 1120 | A336 | Strip of 3 | .80 | .80 |
|---|---|---|---|---|
| | a. 2d ocher & multi | | .20 | .20 |
| | b. 4.50d ocher & multi | | .20 | .20 |
| | c. 8.50d ocher & multi | | .20 | .20 |

Christmas 1974. Design is from 11th cent. Codex of Dionysos Monastery on Mount Athos.

### Costume Type of 1972
Designs: Women's costumes, except 1.50d.

**1974, Dec. 5    Perf. 12½x13½**
| 1121 | A310 | 20 l Megara | .20 | .20 |
|---|---|---|---|---|
| 1122 | A310 | 30 l Salamis | .20 | .20 |
| 1123 | A310 | 50 l Edipsos | .20 | .20 |
| 1124 | A310 | 1d Kyme | .20 | .20 |
| 1125 | A310 | 1.50d Sterea Hellas | .20 | .20 |
| 1126 | A310 | 2d Desfina | .20 | .20 |
| 1127 | A310 | 3d Epirus | .20 | .20 |
| 1128 | A310 | 3.50d Naousa | .20 | .20 |
| 1129 | A310 | 4d Hasia | .20 | .20 |
| 1130 | A310 | 4.50d Thasos | .20 | .20 |
| 1131 | A310 | 5d Skopelos | .20 | .20 |
| 1132 | A310 | 6.50d Epirus | .20 | .20 |
| 1133 | A310 | 10d Pelion | .20 | .20 |
| 1134 | A310 | 25d Kerkyra | .40 | .20 |
| 1135 | A310 | 30d Boeotia | .75 | .60 |
| | Nos. 1121-1135 (15) | | 3.75 | 3.40 |

Secret Vostitsa Assembly, 1821 — A337

Grigorios Dikeos-Papaflessas A338

Aghioi Apostoli Church, Kalamata A339

## Perf. 13½x12½, 12½x13½

**1975, Mar. 24**

| 1136 | A337 | 4d multi | .20 | .20 |
|---|---|---|---|---|
| 1137 | A338 | 7d multi | .20 | .20 |
| 1138 | A339 | 11d multi | .25 | .25 |
| | | Nos. 1136-1138 (3) | .65 | .65 |

Grigorios Dikeos-Papaflessas (1788-1825), priest and leader in Greece's uprising against the Turks, sesquicentennial of death.

Vase with Flowers — A340

Erotokritos and Aretussa — A341

Europa: 11d, Girl with Hat. All designs are after paintings by Theophilos Hatzimichael (d. 1934).

## Perf. 12½x13½

**1975, May 10　Litho.　Wmk. 252**

| 1139 | A340 | 4d multi | .50 | .45 |
|---|---|---|---|---|
| 1140 | A341 | 7d multi | .70 | .65 |
| 1141 | A340 | 11d multi | 3.00 | 1.25 |
| | | Nos. 1139-1141 (3) | 4.20 | 2.35 |

House, Kastoria A342

Greek Houses, 18th Cent.: 40 l, Arnea, Halkidiki. 4d, Veria. 6d, Siatista. 11d, Ambelakia, Thessaly.

**1975, June 26　Perf. 13½x12½**

| 1142 | A342 | 10 l brt bl & blk | .20 | .20 |
|---|---|---|---|---|
| 1143 | A342 | 40 l red org & blk | .20 | .20 |
| 1144 | A342 | 4d bister & blk | .25 | .20 |
| 1145 | A342 | 6d ultra & multi | .20 | .20 |
| 1146 | A342 | 11d org & blk | .25 | .25 |
| | | Nos. 1142-1146 (5) | 1.10 | 1.05 |

IWY Emblem, Neolithic Goddess — A343

"Looking to the Future" — A344

8.50d, Confrontation between Antigone & Creon.

## Perf. 12½x13½

**1975, Sept. 29　Litho.　Wmk. 252**

| 1147 | A343 | 1.50d lilac & dk brn | .20 | .20 |
|---|---|---|---|---|
| 1148 | A343 | 8.50d bis, blk & brn | .20 | .20 |
| 1149 | A344 | 11d bl & blk | .25 | .25 |
| | | Nos. 1147-1149 (3) | .65 | .65 |

International Women's Year 1975.

Papanastasiou and University Buildings — A345

First University Building A346

University City Plan A347

**1975, Sept. 29　Perf. 14x13½**

| 1150 | A345 | 1.50d tan & sepia | .20 | .20 |
|---|---|---|---|---|
| 1151 | A346 | 4d multi | .20 | .20 |
| 1152 | A347 | 11d multi | .25 | .25 |
| | | Nos. 1150-1152 (3) | .65 | .65 |

Thessaloniki University, 50th anniversary. Alexandros Papanastasiou (1876-1936), founded University while Prime Minister.

Evangelos Zappas and Zappeion Building — A348

National Benefactors: 4d, Georgios Rizaris and Rizarios Ecclesiastical School. 6d, Michael Tositsas and Metsovion Technical University. 11d, Nicolaos Zosimas and Zosimea Academy.

## Perf. 14x13

**1975, Nov. 15　Litho.　Wmk. 252**

| 1153 | A348 | 1d blk & grn | .20 | .20 |
|---|---|---|---|---|
| 1154 | A348 | 4d blk & brn | .20 | .20 |
| 1155 | A348 | 6d blk & org | .20 | .20 |
| 1156 | A348 | 11d blk & brick red | .20 | .20 |
| | | Nos. 1153-1156 (4) | .80 | .80 |

Greece No. 380 — A349

**1975, Nov. 15　Perf. 13x14**

| 1157 | A349 | 11d dull grn & brn | .40 | .35 |
|---|---|---|---|---|

Stamp Day 1975.

Pontos Lyre — A350　　Musicians, Byzantine Mural — A351

Designs: 1d, Cretan lyre. 1.50d, Tambourine. 4d, Guitarist, from amphora, horiz. 6d, Bagpipes. 7d, Lute. 10d, Barrel organ. 11d, Pipes and zournadas. 20d, Musicians and singers praising God, Byzantine mural, horiz. 25d, Drums. 30d, Kanonaki, horiz.

## Perf. 12½x13½, 13½x12½

**1975, Dec. 15　　　Wmk. 252**

| 1158 | A350 | 10 l multi | .20 | .20 |
|---|---|---|---|---|
| 1159 | A351 | 20 l multi | .20 | .20 |
| 1160 | A350 | 1d ultra & multi | .20 | .20 |
| 1161 | A350 | 1.50d multi | .20 | .20 |
| 1162 | A351 | 4d multi | .20 | .20 |
| 1163 | A350 | 6d multi | .20 | .20 |
| 1164 | A350 | 7d multi | .20 | .20 |
| 1165 | A350 | 10d multi | .20 | .20 |
| 1166 | A350 | 11d red & multi | .20 | .20 |
| 1167 | A351 | 20d multi | .25 | .20 |
| 1168 | A350 | 25d multi | .45 | .20 |
| 1169 | A350 | 30d multi | 1.00 | 1.00 |
| | | Nos. 1158-1169 (12) | 3.50 | 3.20 |

Popular musical instruments.

Early Telephone, Globe, Waves A352

11d, Globe, waves, telephone 1976.

## Perf. 13½x12½

**1976, Mar. 23　Litho.　Wmk. 252**

| 1170 | A352 | 7d blk & multi | .20 | .20 |
|---|---|---|---|---|
| 1171 | A352 | 11d blk & multi | .20 | .20 |
| a. | | Pair, Nos. 1170-1171 | .50 | .50 |

1st telephone call by Alexander Graham Bell, Mar. 10, 1876.

Sortie of Missolonghi — A353

**1976, Mar. 23　Perf. 13½x13**

| 1172 | A353 | 4d multi | .25 | .25 |
|---|---|---|---|---|

Sortie of the garrison of Missolonghi, sesquicentennial.

Florina Jugn — A354　　Avramidis Plate — A355

Europa: 11d, Egina pitcher with Greek flags.

## Perf. 13x14, 12½x12 (A355)

**1976, May 10　Litho.　Wmk. 252**

| 1173 | A354 | 7d buff & multi | .40 | .30 |
|---|---|---|---|---|
| 1174 | A355 | 8.50d blk & multi | .50 | .30 |
| 1175 | A354 | 11d gray & multi | 1.75 | .90 |
| | | Nos. 1173-1175 (3) | 2.65 | 1.50 |

Lion Attacking Bull — A356　　Head of Silenus — A357

Designs: 4.50d, Flying aquatic birds. 7d, Wounded bull. 11d, Cow feeding calf, horiz. Designs from Creto-Mycenaean engraved seals, c. 1400 B.C.

## Perf. 13x12½, 13½x14, 14x13½

**1976, May 10**

| 1176 | A356 | 2d bis & multi | .20 | .20 |
|---|---|---|---|---|
| 1177 | A356 | 4.50d multi | .20 | .20 |
| 1178 | A356 | 7d multi | .20 | .20 |
| 1179 | A357 | 8.50d pur & multi | .20 | .20 |
| 1180 | A357 | 11d brn & multi | .20 | .20 |
| | | Nos. 1176-1180 (5) | 1.00 | 1.00 |

Long Jump A358

Montreal and Athens Stadiums — A359

Designs (Classical and Modern Events): 2d, Basketball. 3.50d, Wrestling. 4d, Swimming. 25d, Lighting Olympic flame and Montreal Olympic Games torch.

## Perf. 14x13½, 12½x13½ (A359)

**1976, June 25　Litho.　Wmk. 252**

| 1181 | A358 | 50 l org & multi | .20 | .20 |
|---|---|---|---|---|
| 1182 | A358 | 2d org & multi | .20 | .20 |
| 1183 | A358 | 3.50d org & multi | .20 | .20 |
| 1184 | A358 | 4d bl & multi | .20 | .20 |
| 1185 | A359 | 11d multi | .20 | .20 |
| 1186 | A358 | 25d org & multi | .75 | .75 |
| | | Nos. 1181-1186 (6) | 1.75 | 1.75 |

21st Olympic Games, Montreal, Canada, July 17-Aug. 1.

Lesbos, View and Map A360

## Perf. 13½x14, 14x13½

**1976, July 26　Litho.　Wmk. 252**

| 1187 | A360 | 30d Lemnos, vert. | .45 | .20 |
|---|---|---|---|---|
| 1188 | A360 | 50d shown | .75 | .20 |
| 1189 | A360 | 75d Chios | .90 | .25 |
| 1190 | A360 | 100d Samos | 2.10 | 1.75 |
| | | Nos. 1187-1190 (4) | 4.20 | 2.40 |

Greek Aegean Islands.

Three Kings
Speaking to the
Jews — A361

Christmas: 7d, Nativity. Designs from manuscripts in Esfigmenou Monastery, Mount Athos.

**1976, Dec. 8**    *Perf. 13½x14*
1191 A361 4d yellow & multi .20 .20
1192 A361 7d yellow & multi .20 .20

Greek
Grammar
of 1478
A362

**1976, Dec. 8**    *Perf. 14x13*
1193 A362 4d multi .25 .20

500th anniversary of printing of first Greek book by Constantin Lascaris, Milan.

Heinrich
Schliemann
A363

Brooch with
Figure of
Goddess — A364

Designs: 4d, Gold bracelet, horiz. 7d, Gold diadem, horiz. 11d, Gold mask (Agamemnon). Treasures from Mycenaean tombs.

**1976, Dec. 8**    *Perf. 13x14, 14x13*
1194 A363 2d multi .20 .20
1195 A364 4d multi .20 .20
1196 A364 5d grn & multi .20 .20
1197 A364 7d multi .20 .20
1198 A364 11d multi .25 .25
   Nos. 1194-1198 (5) 1.05 1.05

Cent. of the discovery of the Mycenaean royal shaft graves by Heinrich Schliemann.

Aesculapius with
Patients — A365
Patient in
Clinic — A366

Designs: 1.50d, Aesculapius curing young man. 2d, Young Hercules with old nurse. 20d, Old man with votive offering of large leg.

*Perf. 12½x13½ (A365); 13x12 (A366)*
**1977, Mar. 15**   Litho.   Wmk. 252
1199 A365 50 l multi .20 .20
1200 A366 1d multi .20 .20
1201 A366 1.50d multi .20 .20
1202 A366 2d multi .20 .20
1203 A365 20d multi .20 .20
   Nos. 1199-1203 (5) 1.00 1.00

International Rheumatism Year.

Winged Wheel, Modern
Transportation — A367

**1977, May 16**   Litho.   *Perf. 14x13½*
1204 A367 7d multi .25 .20

European Conference of Ministers of Transport (E.C.M.T.), Athens, June 1-3.

Mani
Castle,
Vathia
A368

Europa: 7d, Santorini, vert. 15d, Windmills on Lasithi plateau.

*Perf. 14x13½, 13½x14*
**1977, May 16**   Litho.   Wmk. 252
1205 A368 5d multicolored .45 .25
1206 A368 7d multicolored .45 .35
1207 A368 15d multicolored 3.25 1.00
   Nos. 1205-1207 (3) 4.15 1.60

Alexandria Lighthouse, from Roman
Coin — A369

Designs: 1d, Alexander places Homer's works into Achilles' tomb, fresco by Raphael. 1.50d, Alexander descends to the bottom of the sea, Flemish miniature. 3d, Alexander searching for water of life, Hindu plate. 7d, Alexander on horseback, Coptic carpet. 11d, Alexander hearing oracle that his days are numbered, Byzantine manuscript. 30d, Death of Alexander, Persian miniature. All designs include gold coin of Lysimachus with Alexander's head.

**1977, July 23**    *Perf. 14x13*
1208 A369 50 l silver & multi .20 .20
1209 A369 1d silver & multi .20 .20
1210 A369 1.50d silver & multi .20 .20
1211 A369 3d silver & multi .20 .20
1212 A369 7d silver & multi .20 .20
1213 A369 11d silver & multi .25 .25
1214 A369 30d silver & multi .35 .35
   Nos. 1208-1214 (7) 1.60 1.60

Cultural influence of Alexander the Great (356-323 B.C.), King of Macedonia.

"Greece
Rising Again"
A370

People in Front of
University
A371
Greek Flags,
Laurel,
University
A372

*Perf. 13½x12½, 12x12½, 12½x12*
**1977, July 23**    Unwmk.
1215 A370 4d multi .20 .20
1216 A371 7d multi .20 .20
1217 A372 20d multi .25 .25
   Nos. 1215-1217 (3) .65 .65

Restoration of Democracy in Greece.

Archbishop Makarios, Map of
Cyprus — A373

Design: 4d, Archbishop Makarios, vert.

*Perf. 13x13½, 13½x13*
**1977, Sept. 10**   Litho.   Unwmk.
1218 A373 4d sepia & blk .20 .20
1219 A373 7d buff, brn & blk .20 .20

Archbishop Makarios (1913-1977), President of Cyprus.

Old
Athens
Post
Office
A374

Neo-Hellenic architecture: 1d, Institution for the Blind, Salonika. 1.50d, Townhall, Syros. 2d, National Bank of Greece, Piraeus. 5d, Byzantine Museum, Athens. 50d, Municipal Theater, Patras.

**1977, Sept. 22**    *Perf. 13½x13*
1220 A374 50 l multi .20 .20
1221 A374 1d multi .20 .20
1222 A374 1.50d multi .20 .20
1223 A374 2d multi .20 .20
1224 A374 5d multi .20 .20
1225 A374 50d multi .35 .35
   Nos. 1220-1225 (6) 1.35 1.35

Battle of Navarino, Lithograph — A375

Adm. Van Heyden, Sir Edward
Codrington, Count de Rigny — A376

**1977, Oct. 20**    *Perf. 13½x13*
1226 A375 4d brn, buff & blk .20 .20
1227 A376 7d multi .20 .20

150th anniversary of Battle of Navarino.

Parthenon and
Refinery — A377
Caryatid and
Factories — A379

Fish and
Birds
Suffering
from
Pollution
A378

Design: 7d, Birds and trees in polluted air.

**1977, Oct. 20**   *Perf. 13½x14, 14x13½*
1228 A377 3d org & blk .20 .20
1229 A378 4d multi .20 .20
1230 A378 7d multi .20 .20
1231 A379 30d blk, gray & slate .40 .40
   Nos. 1228-1231 (4) 1.00 1.00

Protection of the environment.

Map of
Greece and
Ships — A380

Globe and
Swallows
A381

Letter with
Flags,
Swallow
A382

5d, Globe with Greek flag. 13d, World map showing dispersion of Greeks abroad.

**1977, Dec. 15**    *Perf. 13½x12½*
1232 A380 4d multi .20 .20
1233 A380 5d multi .20 .20
1234 A381 7d multi .20 .20
1235 A382 11d multi .20 .20
1236 A380 13d multi .25 .25
   Nos. 1232-1236 (5) 1.05 1.05

Greeks living abroad.

Kalamata Harbor, by Constantine
Parthenis — A383

Greek Paintings: 2.50d, Boats, Arsanas, by Spyros Papaloucas, vert. 4d, Santorini, by Constantine Maleas. 7d, The Engagement, by Nicolaus Gyzis. 11d, Woman with Straw Hat, by Nicolaus Lytras, vert. 15d, "Spring" (nude), by Georgio Iacovidis.

**1977, Dec. 15**   *Perf. 13½x13, 13x13½*
1237 A383 1.50d yel & multi .20 .20
1238 A383 2.50d yel & multi .20 .20
1239 A383 4d yel & multi .20 .20
1240 A383 7d yel & multi .20 .20
1241 A383 11d yel & multi .20 .20
1242 A383 15d yel & multi .25 .25
   Nos. 1237-1242 (6) 1.25 1.25

Ebenus
Cretica — A384

Greek Flora: 2.50d, Dwarf lily. 3d, Campanula oreadum. 4d, Tiger lily. 7d, Viola delphinantha. 25d, Paeonia rhodia.

**1978, Mar. 30   Litho.   Perf. 13x13½**

| | | | | |
|---|---|---|---|---|
| 1243 | A384 | 1.50d multi | .20 | .20 |
| 1244 | A384 | 2.50d multi | .20 | .20 |
| 1245 | A384 | 3d multi | .20 | .20 |
| 1246 | A384 | 4d multi | .20 | .20 |
| 1247 | A384 | 7d multi | .25 | .20 |
| 1248 | A384 | 25d multi | .30 | .25 |
| | *Nos. 1243-1248 (6)* | | 1.35 | 1.25 |

Postrider, Cancellation A385

5d, S.S. Maximilianos & Hermes Head. 7d, 19th cent. mail train & #122. 30d, Mailmen on motorcycles & #1062.

**1978, May 15   Perf. 13½x12½**

| | | | | |
|---|---|---|---|---|
| 1249 | A385 | 4d buff & multi | .20 | .20 |
| 1250 | A385 | 5d buff & multi | .20 | .20 |
| 1251 | A385 | 7d buff & multi | .20 | .20 |
| 1252 | A385 | 30d buff & multi | .25 | .20 |
| a. | Souvenir sheet of 4 | | 1.00 | 1.00 |
| | *Nos. 1249-1252 (4)* | | .85 | .80 |

150th anniv. of Greek postal service.

No. 1252a issued Sept. 25, contains Nos. 1249-1252 in slightly changed colors. Sold for 60d.

Lighting Olympic Flame, Olympia — A386

Start of 100-meter Race — A387

**1978, May 15   Perf. 13x14**

| | | | | |
|---|---|---|---|---|
| 1253 | A386 | 7d multi | .40 | .20 |
| 1254 | A387 | 13d multi | .85 | .40 |

80th session of International Olympic Committee, Athens, May 10-21.

**Europa Issue 1978**

St. Sophia, Salonica A388

Lysicrates Monument, Athens — A389

**1978, May 15   Perf. 13x14, 14x13**

| | | | | |
|---|---|---|---|---|
| 1255 | A388 | 4d multi | .75 | .30 |
| 1256 | A389 | 7d multi | 2.25 | .70 |

Aristotle, Roman Bust — A390

School of Athens, by Raphael — A391

Map of Chalcidice, Base of Statue from Attalus Arcade A392

Aristotle the Wise, Byzantine Fresco, St. George's Church, Ioannina A393

**Perf. 13x13½, 13½x14 (20d)**

**1978, July 10   Litho.**

| | | | | |
|---|---|---|---|---|
| 1257 | A390 | 2d multi | .20 | .20 |
| 1258 | A391 | 4d multi | .20 | .20 |
| 1259 | A392 | 7d multi | .20 | .20 |
| 1260 | A393 | 20d multi | .25 | .25 |
| | *Nos. 1257-1260 (4)* | | .85 | .85 |

Aristotle (384-322 B.C.), systematic philosopher.

Rotary Emblem A394

Surgeons Operating — A395

Ugo Foscolo, View of Zante — A396

Hellenistic Bronze Head — A397

Charioteer's Hand, Delphi — A398

Wright Brothers' Plane, Daedalus and Icarus — A399

**1978, Sept. 21   Litho.   Perf. 12½**

| | | | | |
|---|---|---|---|---|
| 1261 | A394 | 1d multi | .20 | .20 |
| 1262 | A395 | 1.50d multi | .20 | .20 |
| 1263 | A396 | 2.50d multi | .20 | .20 |
| 1264 | A397 | 5d multi | .20 | .20 |
| 1265 | A398 | 7d multi | .40 | .30 |
| 1266 | A399 | 13d multi | .40 | .40 |
| | *Nos. 1261-1266 (6)* | | 1.60 | 1.50 |

Rotary in Greece, 50th anniv. (1d); 11th Greek Surgery Cong., Salonica (1.50d); Ugo Foscolo (1778-1827), Italian writer (2.50d); European Convention on Human Rights, 25th anniv. (5d); 2nd Conf. of Ministers of Culture of the Council of Europe member countries, Athens, Oct. 23-27 (7d); 75th anniv. of 1st powered flight (13d).

Poor Woman and her 5 Children A400

Scenes from Fairy Tale "The 12 Months": 3d, The poor woman and the 12 months. 4d, The poor woman and the gold coins. 20d, Punishment of the greedy woman.

**1978, Nov. 6   Litho.   Perf. 13½x13**

| | | | | |
|---|---|---|---|---|
| 1267 | A400 | 2d multi | .20 | .20 |
| 1268 | A400 | 3d multi | .20 | .20 |
| 1269 | A400 | 4d multi | .20 | .20 |
| 1270 | A400 | 20d multi | .25 | .25 |
| | *Nos. 1267-1270 (4)* | | .85 | .85 |

"Transplants" A401

The Miracle of St. Anarghiri A402

**1978, Nov. 6   Perf. 12½x13½**

| | | | | |
|---|---|---|---|---|
| 1271 | A401 | 4d multi | .20 | .20 |
| 1272 | A402 | 10d multi | .20 | .20 |

Advancements in organ transplants.

Cruiser A403

New and Old Greek Naval Ships: 1d, Torpedo boats. 2.50d, Submarine Papanicolis. 4d, Battleship Psara. 5d, Sailing ship "Madonna of Hydra." 7d, Byzantine corvette. 50d, Archaic trireme.

**1978, Dec. 15   Litho.   Perf. 13½x12**

| | | | | |
|---|---|---|---|---|
| 1273 | A403 | 50 l multi | .20 | .20 |
| 1274 | A403 | 1d multi | .20 | .20 |
| 1275 | A403 | 2.50d multi | .20 | .20 |
| 1276 | A403 | 4d multi | .20 | .20 |
| 1277 | A403 | 5d multi | .20 | .20 |
| 1278 | A403 | 7d multi | .20 | .20 |
| 1279 | A403 | 50d multi | .45 | .45 |
| | *Nos. 1273-1279 (7)* | | 1.65 | 1.65 |

Cadet Officer, Military School, Nauplia A404

Cadet Officers' School Emblem — A405

Design: 10d, Cadet Officers Military School, Athens, Cadet's uniform, 1978.

**1978, Dec. 15   Perf. 13½x12, 12x13½**

| | | | | |
|---|---|---|---|---|
| 1280 | A404 | 1.50d multi | .20 | .20 |
| 1281 | A405 | 2d multi | .20 | .20 |
| 1282 | A404 | 10d multi | .25 | .25 |
| | *Nos. 1280-1282 (3)* | | .65 | .65 |

Cadet Officers Military School, 150th anniv.

Virgin and Child — A406

Baptism of Christ — A407

Designs from 16th century icon stands in Stavronikita Monastery.

**1978, Dec. 15   Perf. 13x13½**

| | | | | |
|---|---|---|---|---|
| 1283 | A406 | 4d multi | .20 | .20 |
| 1284 | A407 | 7d multi | .20 | .20 |

Christmas 1978.

Map of Greece A408

**1978, Dec. 28   Perf. 14x13**

| | | | | |
|---|---|---|---|---|
| 1285 | A408 | 7d multi | .20 | .20 |
| 1286 | A408 | 11d multi | .20 | .20 |
| 1287 | A408 | 13d multi | .25 | .25 |
| | *Nos. 1285-1287 (3)* | | .65 | .65 |

Kitsos Tzavellas — A409

Souli Castle A410

10d, Fighting Souliots. 20d, Fight of Zalongo.

**Perf. 12½x13½, 13½x12½**

**1979, Mar. 12   Litho.**

| | | | | |
|---|---|---|---|---|
| 1288 | A409 | 1.50d buff, blk & brn | .20 | .20 |
| 1289 | A410 | 3d multi | .20 | .20 |
| 1290 | A410 | 10d multi | .20 | .20 |
| 1291 | A409 | 20d buff, blk & brn | .25 | .25 |
| | *Nos. 1288-1291 (4)* | | .85 | .85 |

Struggle of the Souliots, 18th century fighters for freedom from Turkey.

Cycladic Figure from Amorgos — A411

Mailmen from Crete — A412

**1979, Apr. 26    Litho.    Perf. 12x13½**
1292  A411  20d multi                    .35  .35

Aegean art.

**1979, May 11              Perf. 13½x14**
Europa: 7d, Rural mailman on horseback, Crete.

1293  A412  4d multi              1.00  .25
1294  A412  7d multi              1.00  .55
  a.    Pair, #1293-1294          2.25  2.25

Nicolas Scoufas A413

Basketball A415

Locomotives — A414

Mene Psarianosi Symeonidis Fossil A416

Temple of Hephaestus and Byzantine Church A417

Victory of Paeonius Statue, Flags of Balkan Countries A418

**1979, May 12        Perf. 13x14, 14x13**
1295  A413  1.50d multi            .20  .20
1296  A414  2d multi               .20  .20
1297  A415  3d multi               .20  .20
1298  A416  4d multi               .20  .20
1299  A417  10d multi              .20  .20
1300  A418  20d multi              .35  .35
  Nos. 1295-1300 (6)              1.35 1.35

Nicolas Scoufas (1779-1818), founder of (patriotic) Friendly Society; Piraeus-Athens-to-the-frontier railroad, 75th anniv.; European Basketball Championship; 7th Intl. Cong. for the Study of the Neocene Period in the Mediterranean; Balkan Tourist Year 1979; 50 years of track and field competitions in Balkan countries.

Wheat with Members' Flags, Greek Coins — A419

European Parliament, Strasbourg — A420

**Perf. 13x14, 14x13**
**1979, May 28              Litho.**
1301  A419  7d multi               .20  .20
1302  A420  30d multi              .35  .35

Greece's entry into European Economic Community and Parliament.

Statue of a Girl, IYC Emblem — A421

Intl. Year of the Child: 8d, Girl & pigeons. 20d, Mother & Children, painting by Iacovides.

**1979, June 27    Litho.    Perf. 13x14**
1303  A421  5d multi               .20  .20
1304  A421  8d multi               .20  .20
1305  A421  20d multi              .20  .20
  Nos. 1303-1305 (3)               .60  .60

Philip II, Bust — A422

Purple Heron — A423

Designs: 8d, Golden wreath. 10d, Copper vessel. 14d, Golden casket, horiz. 18d, Silver ewer. 20d, Golden quiver (detail). 30d, Gold and iron cuirass.

**Perf. 13½x14, 14x13½**
**1979, Sept. 15              Litho.**
1306  A422  6d multi               .20  .20
1307  A422  8d multi               .20  .20
1308  A422  10d multi              .20  .20
1309  A422  14d multi              .20  .20
1310  A422  18d multi              .20  .20
1311  A422  20d multi              .25  .25
1312  A422  30d multi              .40  .40
  Nos. 1306-1312 (7)              1.65 1.65

Archaeological finds from Vergina, Macedonia.

**1979, Oct. 15**
Protected Birds: 8d, Gull. 10d, Falcon, horiz. 14d, Kingfisher, horiz. 20d, Pelican. 25d, White-tailed sea eagle.

1313  A423  6d multi               .20  .20
1314  A423  8d multi               .20  .20
1315  A423  10d multi              .20  .20
1316  A423  14d multi              .20  .20
1317  A423  20d multi              .20  .20
1318  A423  25d multi              .75  .60
  Nos. 1313-1318 (6)              1.75 1.60

Council of Europe wildlife and natural habitat protection campaign.

Agricultural Bank A424

St. Cosmas — A425

Basil the Great — A426

Balkan Countries, Magnifier — A427

Aristotelis Valaoritis — A428

Golfer A429

Hippocrates A430

Parliament in Session A431

**Perf. 14x13½, 13½x14**
**1979, Nov. 24              Litho.**
1319  A424  3d multi               .20  .20
1320  A425  4d multi               .20  .20
1321  A426  6d multi               .20  .20
1322  A427  8d multi               .20  .20
1323  A427  10d multi, horiz.      .20  .20
1324  A428  12d multi              .20  .20
1325  A429  14d multi              .20  .20
1326  A430  18d multi              .30  .30
1327  A431  25d multi              .40  .40
  Nos. 1319-1327 (9)              2.10 2.10

Agricultural Bank of Greece, 50th anniv.; Cosmas the Aetolian (1714-79), Greek missionary and martyr; Basil the Great (330-379), Archbishop of Caesarea; Balkanfila, Balkan Stamp Exhibition, Athens, Nov. 24-Dec. 2; Aristotelis Valaoritis (1824-79), Greek poet; 27th World Golf Championship, Nov. 8-11; Intl. Hippocratic Foundation of Cos; Greek Parliament, 104th anniv.

Parnassus — A432

Tempe Valley A433

**Perf. 12½x13½, 13½x12½**
**1979, Dec. 15              Litho.**
1328  A432  50 l  shown           .20  .20
1329  A433  1d  shown             .20  .20
1330  A432  2d  Melos             .20  .20
1331  A432  4d  Vikos Gorge       .20  .20
1332  A433  5d  Missolonghi Salt
                    Lake          .20  .20
1333  A432  6d  Louros Aqueduct   .20  .20
1334  A432  7d  Samothrace        .20  .20
1335  A433  8d  Sithonia-Halkidiki .20 .20
1336  A433  10d  Samarias Gorge,
                    vert           .20  .20
1337  A432  12d  Siphnos          .20  .20
1338  A433  14d  Kyme             .20  .20
1339  A432  18d  Ios              .20  .20
1340  A432  20d  Thasos           .20  .20
1341  A433  30d  Paros            .30  .20
1342  A432  50d  Cephalonia       .50  .40
  Nos. 1328-1342 (15)            3.40 3.20

Byzantine Castle of Thessalonica A434

4d, Aegosthena Castle, vert. 8d, Cave of Perama Ioannina, vert. 10d, Cave of Dyros, Mani, vert. 14d, Arta Bridge. 20d, Kalogiros Bridge, Epirus.

**Perf. 12½x14, 14x12½**
**1980, Mar. 15              Litho.**
1343  A434  4d multi               .20  .20
1344  A434  6d multi               .20  .20
1345  A434  8d multi               .20  .20
1346  A434  10d multi              .20  .20
1347  A434  14d multi              .20  .20
1348  A434  20d multi              .20  .20
  Nos. 1343-1348 (6)              1.20 1.20

Gate of Galerius A435

**1980, Mar. 15**
1349  A435  8d multi               .25  .20

1st Hellenic Congress of Nephrology, Thessalonica, Mar. 20-22.

Solar System A436

Design: 10d, Temple of Hera, Aristarchus' theory and diagram.

**1980, May 5    Litho.    Perf. 13½x12½**
1350  A436  10d multi              .20  .20
1351  A436  20d multi              .40  .35

Aristarchus of Samos, first astronomer to discover heliocentric theory of universe, 2300th birth anniv.; Intl. Scientific Congress on Aristarchus, Samos, June 17-19.

Maria Callas (1923-1977), Opera Singer A437

Europa: 8d, Georges Seferis (1900-1971), writer and diplomat.

**1980, May 5**
1352  A437  8d multi               .40  .40
1353  A437  14d multi             1.60 1.20

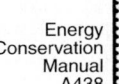

Energy Conservation Manual A438

**Perf. 13½x12½, 12½x13½**
**1980, May 5**
1354 A438 8d shown .20 .20
1355 A438 20d Candle in bulb, vert. .30 .30

Firemen
A439

St. Demetrius, Angel, Fresco — A440

Soldiers Marching through Crete — A441

Ancient Vase, Olives
A442

Federation Emblem, Newspaper
A443

Constantinos Ikonomos — A444

**1980, July 14    Litho.    Perf. 12½**
1356 A439 4d multi .20 .20
1357 A440 6d multi .20 .20
1358 A441 8d multi .20 .20
1359 A442 10d multi .20 .20
1360 A443 14d multi .20 .20
1361 A444 20d multi .40 .40
Nos. 1356-1361 (6) 1.40 1.40

Fire Brigade, 50th anniv.; St. Demetrius, 1700th birth anniv.; Therissos Revolution, 75th anniv.; 2nd Intl. Olive Oil Year; Intl. Federation of Journalists, 15th Cong., Athens, May 12-16; Constantinos Ikonomos (1780-1857), writer and revolutionary.

Olympic Stadium, Temple Coin, Olympia
A445

Olympic Rings and: 14d, Stadium and coin of Delphi 18d, Epidaurus theater, coin of Olympia 20d, Rhodes Stadium, Cos coin. 50d, Panathenean Stadium; 1st Olympic Games medal.

**1980, Aug. 11    Litho.    Perf. 13½x13**
1362 A445 8d multi .20 .20
1363 A445 14d multi .35 .30
1364 A445 18d multi .25 .20
1365 A445 20d multi .30 .20
1366 A445 50d multi .65 .55
Nos. 1362-1366 (5) 1.75 1.45

22nd Summer Olympic Games, Moscow, July 19-Aug. 3.

Asbestos
A446

**Perf. 13½x12½**
**1980, Sept. 22    Litho.**
1367 A446 6d shown .20 .20
1368 A446 8d Gypsum, vert. .20 .20
1369 A446 10d Copper ore .20 .20
1370 A446 14d Barite, vert. .35 .35
1371 A446 18d Chromite .25 .25
1372 A446 20d Mixed sulphides, vert. .25 .25
1373 A446 30d Bauxite, vert. .35 .35
Nos. 1367-1373 (7) 1.80 1.70

Tow Truck — A447

Air Force Jet — A448

Airplane and Hangar
A449

Ships in Port
A450

Students' Association Headquarters
A451

**1980, Oct. 31    Litho.    Perf. 12½**
1374 A447 6d multi .20 .20
1375 A448 8d multi .20 .20
1376 A449 12d multi .20 .20
1377 A450 20d multi .35 .30
1378 A451 25d multi .40 .40
Nos. 1374-1378 (5) 1.35 1.30

Road Assistance Service of Automobile and Touring Club of Greece, 20th anniv.; Air Force, 50th anniv.; Flyers' Club of Thessaloniki, 50th anniv.; Piraeus Port Organization, 50th anniv.; Association for Macedon ian Studies, 40th anniv.

Madonna and Child, by Theodore Poulakis — A452

Christmas 1980: He is Happy Thanks to You, by Theodore Poulakis. No. 1381a has continuous design.

**1980, Dec. 10    Perf. 13½**
1379 6d multi .20 .20
1380 14d multi .20 .20
1381 20d multi .30 .30
a. A452 Strip of 3, #1379-1381 .75 .75

Vegetables for Export — A453

**1981, Mar. 16    Litho.    Perf. 12½**
1382 A453 9d shown .20 .20
1383 A453 17d Fruits .25 .25
1384 A453 20d Cotton .25 .25
1385 A453 25d Marble .40 .40
Nos. 1382-1385 (4) 1.10 1.10

**Europa Issue 1981**

Kira Maria Folk Dance, Alexandria — A454

**1981, May 4    Litho.    Perf. 14x13**
1386 A454 12d shown .50 .20
1387 A454 17d Cretan Sousta (dance) 1.75 1.25

Runner, Olympic Stadium, Kalogreza
A455

**1981, May 4**
1388 A455 12d shown .25 .20
1389 A455 17d Runners, Europe .40 .40

13th European Athletic Championship, Athens, 1982.

Torso Showing Kidneys
A456

Sky Diver and Airplanes
A457

Views of Thessaly and Epirus — A458

Oil Rig and Map of Thassos Island — A460

Vase with Painted Eyes
A459

Globes and Ancient Coin
A461

Heart and Vessels — A462

**Perf. 13½x14, 14x13½**
**1981, May 22    Litho.**
1390 A456 2d multi .20 .20
1391 A457 3d multi .20 .20
1392 A458 6d multi .20 .20
1393 A459 9d multi .20 .20
1394 A460 12d multi .20 .20
1395 A461 21d multi .50 .45
1396 A462 40d multi .75 .75
Nos. 1390-1396 (7) 2.25 2.20

8th Intl. Nephrology Conf., Athens, June 7-12; Greek National Air Club, 50th anniv.; Intl. Historical Symposium, Volos, Sept. 27-30; Greek Ophthalmological Society, 50th anniv.; inauguration of oil production at Thassos Island; World Assoc. for Intl. Relations, Athens, 2nd anniv.; 15th Intl. Cardiovascular Surgery Conference, Athens, Sept. 6-10.

Cockles
A463

**1981, June 30    Litho.    Perf. 14x13½**
1397 A463 4d shown .20 .20
1398 A463 5d Parrot fish .20 .20
1399 A463 12d Painted comber .25 .20
1400 A463 15d Common dentex .25 .25
1401 A463 17d Parnassius apollo .50 .30
1402 A463 50d Colias hyale 1.10 .90
Nos. 1397-1402 (6) 2.50 2.05

Bell Tower, Epirus — A464

Altar Gate, St. Paraskevi's Church — A465

Bell Towers and Wood Altar Gates (Iconostases): 9d, Pelion, horiz. 12d, Church of Sts. Constantine and Helen, Epirus. 17d, St. Nicolas Church, Velvendos, horiz. 30d, St. Jacob icon, Church Museum, Alexandroupolis. 40d, St. Nicholas Church, Makrinitsa.

**1981, Sept. 30    Litho.**
1403 A464 4d multi .20 .20
1404 A465 6d multi .20 .20
1405 A465 9d multi .20 .20
1406 A465 12d multi .20 .20
1407 A465 17d multi .25 .25
1408 A465 30d multi .35 .35
1409 A465 40d multi .60 .60
Nos. 1403-1409 (7) 2.00 2.00

European Urban Renaissance Year — A466

St. Simeon, Archbishop of Thessalonica A467

Promotion of Breastfeeding A468

Gina Bachauer, Pianist, 5th Death Anniv. A469

Constantine Broumidis, Artist, Death Centenary A470

Sesquicentennial of Greek Banknotes — A471

### *Perf. 14x13½, 13½x14*

| 1981, Nov. 20 | | | Litho. | |
|---|---|---|---|---|
| 1410 | A466 | 3d multi | .20 | .20 |
| 1411 | A467 | 9d multi | .20 | .20 |
| 1412 | A468 | 12d multi | .25 | .20 |
| 1413 | A469 | 17d multi | .40 | .25 |
| 1414 | A470 | 21d multi | .45 | .25 |
| 1415 | A471 | 50d multi | .75 | .60 |
| *Nos. 1410-1415 (6)* | | | 2.25 | 1.70 |

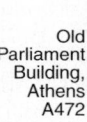

Old Parliament Building, Athens A472

Angelos Sikelianos (1884-1951), Poet A473

Harilaos Tricoupis, Politician, Birth Sesquicentennial A474

Aegean Islands Exhib., Rhodes, Athens — A475

Petralona Cave and Skull — A477

Olympic Airlines, 25th Anniv. A476

---

### *Perf. 13½x12½, 12½x13½*

| 1982, Mar. 15 | | | Litho. | |
|---|---|---|---|---|
| 1416 | A472 | 2d multi | .20 | .20 |
| 1417 | A473 | 9d multi | .20 | .20 |
| 1418 | A474 | 15d multi | .20 | .20 |
| 1419 | A475 | 21d multi | .40 | .40 |
| 1420 | A476 | 30d multi | .65 | .55 |
| 1421 | A477 | 50d multi | 1.10 | 1.00 |
| *Nos. 1416-1421 (6)* | | | 2.75 | 2.55 |

Historical and Ethnological Society centennial (2d); 3rd European Anthropology Congress, Halkidiki, Sept. (50d).

Europa 1982 — A478

| 1982, May 10 | | Litho. | *Perf. 13½x14* | |
|---|---|---|---|---|
| 1422 | A478 | 21d Battle of Marathon, 490 BC | 3.25 | 1.00 |
| 1423 | A478 | 30d 1826 Revolution | 6.50 | 2.50 |

13th European Athletic Championships, Athens — A479

| 1982, May 10 | | *Perf. 14x13½, 13½x14* | | |
|---|---|---|---|---|
| 1424 | A479 | 21d Pole vaulting, horiz. | .30 | .25 |
| 1425 | A479 | 25d Running | .40 | .25 |
| 1426 | A479 | 40d Sports, horiz. | .80 | .65 |
| *Nos. 1424-1426 (3)* | | | 1.50 | 1.15 |

Byzantine Book Illustrations A480

### *Perf. 13½x12½, 12½x13½*

| 1982, June 26 | | | Litho. | |
|---|---|---|---|---|
| 1427 | A480 | 4d Gospel book heading | .25 | .20 |
| 1428 | A480 | 6d Illuminated "E," vert. | .25 | .20 |
| 1429 | A480 | 12d Illuminated "T," vert. | .25 | .20 |
| 1430 | A480 | 15d Gospel reading canon table, vert. | .25 | .20 |
| 1431 | A480 | 80d Zoology book heading | 1.50 | 1.25 |
| *Nos. 1427-1431 (5)* | | | 2.50 | 2.05 |

Georgios Karaiskakis (1782-1827), Liberation Hero — A481

Amnesty Intl. — A482

Designs: 12d, Camp in Piraeus, by von Krazeisen. 50d, Meditating.

---

| 1982, Sept. 20 | | Litho. | *Perf. 13x13½* | |
|---|---|---|---|---|
| 1432 | A481 | 12d multi | .40 | .20 |
| 1433 | A481 | 50d multi | .80 | .50 |

| 1982, Sept. 20 | | | *Perf. 13x14* | |
|---|---|---|---|---|
| 1434 | A482 | 15d Vigil | .45 | .20 |
| 1435 | A482 | 75d Prisoners | 1.25 | 1.00 |

Natl. Resistance Movement, 1941-44 — A483

Designs: 1d, Demonstration of Mar. 24, 1942. 2d, Sacrifice of Inhabitants of Kalavrita, by S. Vasiliou. 5d, Resistance Fighters in Thrace, by A. Tassos. 9d, The Start of Resistance in Crete, by P. Gravalos. 12d, Partisan Men and Women, by P. Gravalos. 21d, Blowing Up a Bridge, by A. Tassos. 30d, Fighters at a Barricade, by G. Sikeliotis. 50d, The Fight in Northern Greece, by B. Katraki, 5d, 9d, 12d, 21d vert.

| 1982, Nov. 8 | | | Litho. | *Perf. 12½* | |
|---|---|---|---|---|
| 1436 | A483 | 1d multi | .20 | .20 |
| 1437 | A483 | 2d multi | .20 | .20 |
| 1438 | A483 | 5d multi | .20 | .20 |
| 1439 | A483 | 9d multi | .20 | .20 |
| 1440 | A483 | 12d multi | .20 | .20 |
| 1441 | A483 | 21d multi | .20 | .20 |
| *a.* | | Souv. sheet, 5d, 9d, 12d, 21d | 1.75 | 1.75 |
| 1442 | A483 | 30d multi | .40 | .35 |
| 1443 | A483 | 50d multi | .70 | .55 |
| *a.* | | Souv. sheet, 1d, 2d, 30d, 50d | 2.00 | 2.00 |
| *Nos. 1436-1443 (8)* | | | 2.30 | 2.10 |

Christmas 1982 — A484

Designs: Various Byzantine Nativity bas-reliefs, Byzantine Museum.

| 1982, Dec. 6 | | Litho. | *Perf. 13½x12½* | |
|---|---|---|---|---|
| 1444 | A484 | 9d multi | .20 | .20 |
| 1445 | A484 | 21d multi | .30 | .25 |
| *a.* | | Pair, #1444-1445 | .65 | .65 |

25th Anniv. of Intl. Maritime Org. A485

Ship Figureheads. 15d, 18d, 25d, 40d vert.

| 1983, Mar. 14 | | *Perf. 14x13½, 13½x14* | | |
|---|---|---|---|---|
| 1446 | A485 | 11d Ares, Tsamados | .20 | .30 |
| 1447 | A485 | 15d Ares, Miaoulis | .20 | .20 |
| 1448 | A485 | 18d Female figure | .25 | .20 |
| 1449 | A485 | 25d Spetses, Boubou-lina | .40 | .25 |
| 1450 | A485 | 40d Epameinondas, K. Babas | .60 | .35 |
| 1451 | A485 | 50d Carteria | 1.25 | 1.00 |
| *Nos. 1446-1451 (6)* | | | 2.90 | 2.30 |

Postal Code Inauguration A486

| 1983, Mar. 14 | | Litho. | *Perf. 12½* | |
|---|---|---|---|---|
| 1452 | A486 | 15d Cover, map | .20 | .20 |
| 1453 | A486 | 25d Hermes, post horn, vert. | .45 | .40 |

Rowing A487

---

| 1983, Apr. 28 | | | *Perf. 14x13, 13x14* | |
|---|---|---|---|---|
| 1454 | A487 | 15d shown | .25 | .20 |
| 1455 | A487 | 18d Water skiing, vert. | .35 | .20 |
| 1456 | A487 | 27d Wind surfing, vert. | .65 | .60 |
| 1457 | A487 | 50d Skiiers on chair-lift, vert. | .65 | .60 |
| 1458 | A487 | 80d Skiing | 2.00 | 1.75 |
| *Nos. 1454-1458 (5)* | | | 3.90 | 3.35 |

### Europa Issue 1983

Acropolis — A488

Archimedes and His Hydrostatic Principle — A489

### *Perf. 12½x13½, 13x13½*

| 1983, Apr. 28 | | | Litho. | |
|---|---|---|---|---|
| 1459 | A488 | 25d multi | 2.00 | 1.00 |
| 1460 | A489 | 80d multi | 9.50 | 3.00 |

Marinos Antypas (1873-1907), Farmers' Movement Leader — A490

Designs: 9d, Nicholas Plastiras (1883-1953), prime minister. 15d, George Papandreou (1888-1968), statesman. 20d, Constantine Cavafy (1863-1933), poet. 27d, Nikos Kazantzakis (1883-1957), writer. 32d, Manolis Calomiris (1883-1962), composer. 40d, George Papanicolaou (1883-1962), medical researcher. 50d, Despina Achladioti (1890-1982), nationalist.

| 1983, July 11 | | Litho. | *Perf. 13½x14* | |
|---|---|---|---|---|
| 1461 | A490 | 6d multi | .20 | .20 |
| 1462 | A490 | 9d multi | .20 | .20 |
| 1463 | A490 | 15d multi | .20 | .20 |
| 1464 | A490 | 20d multi | .30 | .20 |
| 1465 | A490 | 27d multi | .35 | .20 |
| 1466 | A490 | 32d multi | .60 | .30 |
| 1467 | A490 | 40d multi | .70 | .30 |
| 1468 | A490 | 50d multi | .85 | .60 |
| *Nos. 1461-1468 (8)* | | | 3.40 | 2.20 |

A491

| 1983, Sept. 26 | | Litho. | *Perf. 13½x13* | |
|---|---|---|---|---|
| 1469 | A491 | 50d Portrait bust | 1.00 | .50 |

1st Intl. Conf. on the Works of Democritus (Philosopher, 460-370 BC), Xanthe, Oct.

A492

**1983, Nov. 17   Litho.   Perf. 13**
1470 A492 15d Poster .25 .25
1471 A492 30d Flight from school .45 .35

Polytechnic School Uprising, 1st anniv.

The Deification of
Homer — A493

Homer Inspired Artworks: 3d, The Abduction of Helen by Paris, horiz. 4d, The Wooden Horse, horiz. 5d, Achilles Throwing Dice with Ajax, horiz. 6d, Achilles. 10d, Hector Receiving His Arms from His Parents. 14d, Single-handed Battle Between Ajax and Hector, horiz. 15d, Priam Requesting the Body of Hector, horiz. 20d, The Blinding of Polyphemus. 27d, Ulysses Escaping from Polyphemus' Cave, horiz. 30d, Ulysses Meeting with Nausica. 32d, Ulysses on the Island of the Sirens, horiz. 50d, Ulysses Slaying the Suitors, horiz. 75d, The Heroes of the Iliad, horiz. 100d, Homer.

**1983, Dec. 19   Litho.   Perf. 13**
1472 A493 2d multi .20 .20
1473 A493 3d multi .20 .20
1474 A493 4d multi .20 .20
1475 A493 5d multi .20 .20
1476 A493 6d multi .20 .20
1477 A493 10d multi .20 .20
1478 A493 14d multi .20 .20
1479 A493 15d multi .20 .20
1480 A493 20d multi .20 .20
1481 A493 27d multi .30 .20
1482 A493 30d multi .40 .20
1483 A493 32d multi .50 .20
1484 A493 50d multi .60 .20
1485 A493 75d multi 1.25 .60
1486 A493 100d multi 1.90 .80
Nos. 1472-1486 (15) 6.75 4.00

Horse's Head
from Chariot
of Seline
A494

Horsemen and
Heroes
A495

Nos. 1492a-1492b, Equestrian scene. Nos. 1492c-1492d, Athenian Elders.

**1984, Mar. 15   Litho.   Perf. 14½x14**
1487 A494 14d shown .20 .20
1488 A494 15d Dionysus .25 .20
1489 A494 20d Hestia, Dione, Aphrodite .45 .30
1490 A494 27d Ilissus .60 .30
1491 A494 32d Lapith, centaur 1.00 .75
Nos. 1487-1491 (5) 2.50 1.75

**Souvenir Sheet**
**Perf. 13x13½**
1492 Sheet of 4 4.50 4.50
a. A495 15d multi .75 .75
b. A495 21d multi .90 .90
c. A495 27d multi 1.00 1.00
d. A495 32d multi 1.25 1.25

Marble from the Parthenon. No. 1492 sold for 107d.
Nos. 1492a-1492b and 1492c-1492d have continuous designs.

Europa
(1959-84)
A496

**1984, Apr. 30   Litho.   Perf. 14x13½**
1493 A496 15d multi .75 .40
1494 A496 27d multi 1.75 1.00
a. Pair, #1493-1494 3.25 3.25

1984 Summer
Olympics — A497

Designs: 14d, Ancient Olympic stadium crypt. 15d, Athletes training. 20d, Broad jump, discus thrower. 32d, Athletes, diff. 80d, Stadium, Demetrius Bikelos, poet, organizer of 1896 Athens games.

**1984, Apr. 30   Perf. 13½x14**
1495 A497 14d multi .30 .25
1496 A497 15d multi .40 .35
1497 A497 20d multi .50 .45
1498 A497 32d multi .75 .65
1499 A497 80d multi 1.75 1.40
a. Strip of 5, #1495-1499 4.50 4.50

Also issued in booklets.

Turkish
Invasion of
Cyprus, 10th
Anniv. — A498

**1984, July 10   Litho.   Perf. 13**
1500 A498 20d Tank, map, vert. .40 .20
1501 A498 32d Map, barbed wire .60 .50

Also issued in booklets.

Greek
Railway
Centenary
A499

**Perf. 13x13½, 13½x13**
**1984, July 20   Litho.**
1502 A499 15d Pelion .45 .35
1503 A499 20d Papadia Bridge, vert. 1.40 1.40
1504 A499 30d Piraeus-Peloponnese .45 .35
1505 A499 50d Cogwheel Calavryta, vert. 1.40 1.40
Nos. 1502-1505 (4) 3.70 3.50

Sesquicentenary of Athens as Capital
City — A500

15d, 4d silver coin, 5th cent. BC, city plan, vert. 100d, Views of ancient & modern Athens.

**Perf. 13½x13, 13x13½**
**1984, Oct. 12   Litho.**
1506 A500 15d multi .40 .25
1507 A500 100d multi 1.60 1.00

10th Anniv. of
Democratic
Govt. — A501

**1984, Oct. 12   Litho.   Perf. 13x13½**
1508 A501 95d "10" on flag 1.75 .75

Christmas
1984 — A502

Scenes from 18th cent. icon by Athanasios Tountas.

**1984, Dec. 6   Litho.   Perf. 13½x13**
1509 A502 14d Annunciation .50 .30
1510 A502 20d Nativity .50 .30
1511 A502 25d Presentation in the Temple .50 .40
1512 A502 32d Baptism of Christ .50 .50
a. Block of 4, #1509-1512 2.50 2.50

Also issued in booklets.

Runner
A503

Palais des
Sports
A504

**Perf. 13, 13x13½ (#1515)**
**1985, Mar. 1   Litho.**
1513 A503 12d shown .20 .20
1514 A503 15d Shot put .35 .20
1515 A504 20d shown .35 .25
1516 A503 25d Hurdles .70 .25
1517 A503 80d Women's high jump 1.40 .80
Nos. 1513-1517 (5) 3.00 1.70

European Indoor Athletics Championships, Palais des Sports, New Phaleron.

Europa 1985 — A505

CEPT emblem and: 27d, Musical contest between Marsyas and Apollo. 80d, Dimitris Mitropoulos (1896-1960) and Nikos Skalkottas (1904-1949), composers.

**1985, Apr. 29   Perf. 14x14½**
1518 A505 27d multi 1.00 .90
1519 A505 80d multi 2.00 1.50

Exist se-tenant as strip of 3, 27d+80d+27d in booklets.

Melos
Catacombs,
A.D. 2nd
Cent., Trypete
A506

**1985, Apr. 29   Perf. 14½x14**
1520 A506 15d Niche .20 .20
1521 A506 20d Altar, Central Gallery .50 .20
1522 A506 100d Catacombs 1.60 1.10
Nos. 1520-1522 (3) 2.30 1.50

Republic of
Cyprus, 25th
Anniv. — A507

**1985, June 24   Perf. 13x13½**
1523 A507 32d Map of Cyprus, urn 1.00 .50

Coin of King Cassander (315 B.C.),
Personification of Salonika, Galerius
Era Bas-relief — A508

Sts. Demetrius and Methodius,
Mosaics — A509

Designs: 15d, Emperor sacrificing at Altar, Arch of Galerius, Roman era. 20d, Eastern walls of Salonika, Byzantine era. 32d, Houses in the Upper City. 50d, Liberation of Salonika by the Greek Army, 1912. 80d, German occupation, 1941-44, the Old Mosque. 95d, View of city, Trade Fair grounds, Aristotelian University tower.

**Perf. 14½x14 (A508), 14x14½ (A509)**
**1985, June 24**
1524 A508 1d multi .20 .20
1525 A509 5d multi .35 .20
1526 A508 15d multi .40 .20
1527 A509 20d multi .40 .20
1528 A508 32d multi .45 .20
1529 A508 50d multi .60 .20
1530 A508 80d multi 1.25 .50
1531 A508 95d multi 1.75 1.50
Nos. 1524-1531 (8) 5.40 3.20

Salonika City, 2300th anniv. Aristotelian University, Trade Fair, 60th annivs.

Athenian
Cultural
Heritage
A510

Ancient art and architecture: 15d, Democracy Crowning the City, bas-relief from a column, Ancient Agora of Athens, vert. 20d, Mosaic pavement of tritons, nereids, dolphins, etc., Roman baths at Hieratus, Isthmia, A.D. 2nd cent. 32d, Angel, fresco, Grotto of Pentheli, A.D. 13th cent., vert. 80d, Capodistrian University, Athens.

**1985, Oct. 7   Perf. 13½x13, 13x13½**
1532 A510 15d multi .25 .20
1533 A510 20d multi .25 .20
1534 A510 32d multi .65 .30
1535 A510 80d multi 1.40 1.10
Nos. 1532-1535 (4) 2.55 1.80

Intl. Youth
Year — A511

UN 40th
Anniv. — A512

#1540, Girl crowned with flowers, Stadium
of Peace and Friendship, Athens.

**1985, Oct. 7**     **Perf. 14x14½**
1536 A511 15d Children, olive
       wreath      .25 .20
1537 A511 25d Children, doves   .45 .20
1538 A512 27d UN General As-
       sembly, dove   .55 .20
1539 A512 100d UN building,
       emblem   1.60 1.50
     Nos. 1536-1539 (4)   2.85 2.10

**Souvenir Sheet**
**1985, Nov. 22**     **Perf. 14x13**
1540 A511 100d multi   2.00 2.00

No. 1540 contains one 43x47mm stamp.

Pontic
Hellenism
Cultural
Reformation
A513

**Perf. 14x12½, 12½x14**
**1985, Dec. 9**     **Litho.**
1541 A513 12d Folk dance   .20 .20
1542 A513 15d Our Lady Soume-
       la Monastery   .20 .20
1543 A513 27d Folk costumes,
       vert.   .45 .30
1544 A513 32d Trapezus High
       School   .45 .30
1545 A513 80d Sinope Castle   1.10 1.00
     Nos. 1541-1545 (5)   2.40 2.00

Greek
Gods — A514

**1986, Feb. 17**     **Litho.**     **Perf. 13**
1546 A514 5d Hestia   .20 .20
1547 A514 18d Hermes   .20 .20
1548 A514 27d Aphrodite   .30 .20
1549 A514 32d Ares   .45 .35
1550 A514 35d Athena   .60 .35
1551 A514 40d Hephaestus   .70 .20
1552 A514 50d Artemis   .95 .35
1553 A514 110d Apollo   1.10 .35
1554 A514 150d Demeter   1.75 .35
1555 A514 200d Poseidon   2.50 .45
1556 A514 300d Hera   4.25 .95
1557 A514 500d Zeus   9.50 4.50
     Nos. 1546-1557 (12)   22.50 8.45

Each denomination also sold in booklets
containing 20 panes of 5 stamps, perf 13 horizontally only. Value for set of unused booklet
stamps $25; used booklet stamps sell for
approximately half the values shown for used
sheet stamps.

Youth of
Antikythera
A515

Soccer Players
A517

---

Diadoumenos,
by Polycleitus
A516

Wrestlers,
Hellenic Era
Statue — A518

Cyclists — A520

Volleyball
Players
A519

Commemorative Design for 1st
Modern Olympic Games — A521

**1986, Mar. 3**     **Perf. 12**
1558 A515 18d multi   .40 .20
1559 A516 27d multi   .80 .40
1560 A517 32d multi   1.25 .90
1561 A518 35d multi   1.50 1.25
1562 A519 40d multi   1.25 .45
1563 A520 50d multi   1.25 .45
1564 A521 110d multi   2.50 1.60
     Nos. 1558-1564 (7)   8.95 5.25

First World Junior Athletic Championships.
Pan-European Junior Soccer Championships.
Pan-European Free-style and Greco-Roman
Wrestling Championships. Men's World Vol-
leyball Championships. Sixth International
Round-Europe Cycling Meet. Modern Olympic
Games, 90th anniv.

European Traffic
Safety Year — A522

**1986, Mar. 3**     **Perf. 12½x14**
1565 A522 18d Seat belts   .25 .20
1566 A522 27d Motorcycle   .95 .95
1567 A522 110d Speed limits   1.50 .50
     Nos. 1565-1567 (3)   2.70 1.65

Prevention
of Forest
Fires
A523

**1986, Apr. 23**     **Litho.**     **Perf. 14x13½**
1568 A523 35d shown   3.00 2.00
1569 A523 110d Prespa Lakes
       wetlands   5.00 4.00
    **a.**   Pair, 35d, 110d   9.00 9.00
    **b.**   Bklt. pane, 2 each 35d,
       110d   25.00
    **c.**   As "b," pair, 35d, 110d   12.50 12.50
     Europa.
No. 1569a is imperf horizontally.

---

New Postal
Services — A524

May Day Strike,
Chicago,
Cent. — A525

**1986, Apr. 23**     **Perf. 13½x14, 14x13½**
1570 A524 18d Intelpost   .40 .20
1571 A524 110d Express mail,
       horiz.   1.60 .80

**1986, Apr. 23**     **Perf. 12½**
1572 A525 40d Strikers, monu-
       ment   .65 .50

Eleutherios K.
Venizelos
(1864-1936),
Premier
A526

18d, Venizelos, Ministers taking oath of
office, 1917. 110d, Old Hania Harbor, Crete.

**1986, June 30**     **Litho.**     **Perf. 14x12½**
1573 A526 18d multi   .25 .20
1574 A526 110d multi   1.75 .70

6th Intl. Cretological Conference, Crete.

Intl. Peace
Year — A527

**1986, Oct. 6**     **Litho.**     **Perf. 12½**
1575 A527 18d Dove, sun, vert.   .25 .20
1576 A527 35d Flags, dove,
       vert.   .60 .40
1577 A527 110d World cage,
       dove   1.50 .70
     Nos. 1575-1577 (3)   2.35 1.30

Christmas
A528

Aesop's Fables
A529

Religious art in the Benaki Museum: 22d,
Madonna and Child Enthroned, triptych center
panel, 15th cent. 46d, Adoration of the Magi,
15th cent. 130d, Christ Enthroned with St.
John the Evangelist, triptych panel.

**1986, Dec. 1**     **Litho.**     **Perf. 13½x14**
1578 A528 22d multi   .30 .20
1579 A528 46d multi   .65 .50
1580 A528 130d multi   1.75 .40
     Nos. 1578-1580 (3)   2.70 1.10

Size of No. 1579: 27x35mm.

**1987, Mar. 5**     **Litho.**     **Perf. 12½**
1581 A529 2d Fox and the
       Grapes   .25 .20
1582 A529 5d North Wind
       and the Sun   .25 .20
1583 A529 10d Stag and the
       Lion   .30 .20
1584 A529 22d Zeus and the
       Snake   .60 .20
1585 A529 32d Crow and the
       Fox   1.10 .30
1586 A529 40d Woodcutter
       and Hermes   1.25 .40
1587 A529 46d Ass in a Lion's
       Skin   2.10 .65

---

1588 A529 130d Tortoise and
       the Hare   4.50 1.60
     Nos. 1581-1588 (8)   10.35 3.85

Each denomination also sold in booklets
containing 20 panes of 5 stamps, perf 13½
horizontally only. Value for set of unused booklet stamps $32.50; used booklet stamps sell
for approximately half the values shown for
used sheet stamps.

Europa
1987 — A530

Modern art: 40d, Composition, by Achilleas
Apergis. 130d, Delphic Light, by Gerassimos
Sklavos.

**1987, May 4**     **Litho.**     **Perf. 12½**
1589 A530 40d multi   3.00 2.00
1590 A530 130d multi   4.00 3.00
    **a.**   Pair, #1589-1590   7.50 7.50
    **b.**   Bklt. pane, 2 each #1589-
       1590   21.00
    **c.**   As "b," pair, #1589-1590   10.00 10.00
     Nos. 1590b and 1590c are imperf
horizontally.

25th European
Basketball
Championships,
Stadium of Peace
and
Friendship — A531

A532

**1987, May 4**     **Perf. 13½x14, 12½**
1591 A531 22d Jump shot, sta-
       dium, vert.   .60 .60
1592 A532 25d Emblem, spec-
       tators   .40 .20
1593 A531 130d Two players,
       vert.   1.90 1.10
     Nos. 1591-1593 (3)   2.90 1.90

Higher Education
Sesquicentenary — A533

**Perf. 14x13½, 13½x14**
**1987, May 4**     **Litho.**
1594 A533 3d Students, tapes-
       try   .20 .20
1595 A533 23d Owl, medallion   .40 .20
1596 A533 40d Institute, symbols
       of science   .70 .40
1597 A533 60d Institute, students   1.00 .75
     Nos. 1594-1597 (4)   2.30 1.55

Capodistrias University of Athens (Nos.
1594-1595); The Natl. Metsovio Polytechnic
Institute (Nos. 1596-1597). #1596-1597 vert.

**Souvenir Sheet**

25th European
Men's Basketball
Championships
A534

## 1987, June 3 Litho. Perf. 13x14
| | | | | |
|---|---|---|---|---|
| 1598 | | Sheet of 3 | 6.00 | 6.00 |
| a. | A534 | 40d Jump ball | .90 | .90 |
| b. | A534 | 60d Layup | 1.25 | 1.25 |
| c. | A534 | 100d Dunk shot | 2.25 | 2.25 |

Architecture A535

Designs: 2d, Ionic and Corinthian capitals, Archaic Era. 26d, Doric capital, the Parthenon (detail). 40d, Ionic capital and the Erechteum. 60d, Corinthian capital and the Tholos in Epidaurus.

## 1987, July 1 Litho. Perf. 13½x12½
| | | | | |
|---|---|---|---|---|
| 1599 | A535 | 2d multi | .20 | .20 |
| 1600 | A535 | 26d multi | .35 | .20 |
| 1601 | A535 | 40d multi | .55 | .35 |
| 1602 | A535 | 60d multi | 1.10 | 1.00 |
| | | Nos. 1599-1602 (4) | 2.20 | 1.75 |

Engraving by Yiannis Kephalinos — A536

Panteios School A537

## Perf. 12½x14, 14x12½
## 1987, Oct. 1 Litho.
| | | | | |
|---|---|---|---|---|
| 1603 | A536 | 26d multi | .35 | .20 |
| 1604 | A537 | 60d multi | .85 | .75 |

School of Fine Arts, 150th anniv. (26d), and Panteios School of Political Science, 60th anniv. (60d).

Greek Natl. Team, Winner, 25th European Men's Basketball Championship A538

## 1987, Oct. 1 Perf. 13x14
| | | | | |
|---|---|---|---|---|
| 1605 | A538 | 40d multi | .90 | .90 |

Traditional and Modern Greek Theater A539

Designs: 2d, Eleni Papadaki in Hecuba, by Euripides, and outdoor theater, Philippi. 4d, Christopher Nezer in The Wasps, by Aristophane, and outdoor theater, Dodona. 7d, Emilios Veakis in Oedipus Rex and theater, Delphi. 26d, Marika Cotopouli in The Shepherdess's Love, by Dimitris Koromilas. 40d, Katina Paxinou in Abraham's Sacrifice, by Vitzentzos Cornaros. 50d, Kyveli in Countess Valeraina's Secret, by Gregory Xenopoulos. 60d, Director Carolos Koun, stage setting. 100d, Dimitris Rontiris teaching ancient dance, Greek National Theater.

## 1987, Dec. 2 Litho. Perf. 14x13½
| | | | | |
|---|---|---|---|---|
| 1606 | A539 | 2d multi | .20 | .20 |
| 1607 | A539 | 4d multi | .20 | .20 |
| 1608 | A539 | 7d multi | .20 | .20 |
| 1609 | A539 | 26d multi | .35 | .20 |
| 1610 | A539 | 40d multi | .55 | .20 |
| 1611 | A539 | 50d multi | .65 | .20 |

| | | | | |
|---|---|---|---|---|
| 1612 | A539 | 60d multi | .90 | .90 |
| 1613 | A539 | 100d multi | 1.75 | .35 |
| | | Nos. 1606-1613 (8) | 4.80 | 2.50 |

Christmas — A540

## 1987, Dec. 2 Perf. 13x12½
| | | | | |
|---|---|---|---|---|
| 1614 | | 26d Angel facing right | .50 | .20 |
| 1615 | | 26d Angel facing left | .50 | .20 |
| a. | | Bklt. pane, 5 each #1614-1615 | 5.00 | |
| b. | A540 | Pair, #1614-1615 | 1.00 | 1.00 |

Marine Life — A541

## 1988, Mar. 2 Perf. 14x12½
| | | | | |
|---|---|---|---|---|
| 1616 | A541 | 30d Codonellina | .80 | .40 |
| 1617 | A541 | 40d Diaperoecia major | 1.25 | .60 |
| 1618 | A541 | 50d Artemia | 1.75 | .90 |
| 1619 | A541 | 60d Posidonia oceanica | 4.00 | 2.00 |
| 1620 | A541 | 100d Padina pavonica | 4.00 | 2.00 |
| | | Nos. 1616-1620 (5) | 11.80 | 5.90 |

Each denomination sold in booklets containing 20 panes of 5 stamps, perf 12½ vertically only. Value for set of unused booklet stamps $27.50; used booklet stamps sell for somewhat less than the values shown for sheet stamps.

Europa 1988 — A542

Communication and transport: 60d, Telecommunications satellite, telephone and facsimile machine. 150d, Passenger trains.

## 1988, May 6 Litho. Perf. 12½
| | | | | |
|---|---|---|---|---|
| 1621 | | 60d multi | 5.00 | 3.00 |
| 1622 | | 150d multi | 5.50 | 4.00 |
| a. | A542 | Pair, 60d, 150d | 11.50 | 11.50 |
| b. | | Bklt. pane of 4, 2 each #1621-1622, perf. 14 vert. | 26.00 | — |
| c. | A542 | As "b," pair, 60d, 150d | 12.00 | 12.00 |

Nos. 1622b and 1622c perf 14 vertically and imperf horizontally.

1988 Olympics A543

Designs: 4d, Ancient Olympia and Temple of Zeus. 20d, Javelin thrower and and ancient Olympians in open-air gymnasium. 30d, Centenary emblem of the modern Games (cent. in 1996). 60d, Wrestlers, runners and other ancient athletes in training. 170d, Modern torch-bearer.

## 1988, May 6 Perf. 14x12
| | | | | |
|---|---|---|---|---|
| 1623 | A543 | 4d multi | .50 | .35 |
| 1624 | A543 | 20d multi | 1.10 | .60 |
| 1625 | A543 | 30d multi | 2.00 | .90 |
| 1626 | A543 | 60d multi | 3.75 | 2.75 |
| 1627 | A543 | 170d multi | 5.25 | 3.25 |
| a. | | Strip of 5, #1623-1627 | 14.00 | 14.00 |
| b. | | Bklt. pane of 5, #1623-1627, perf. 12 ½ vert. | 19.00 | 19.00 |

Each denomination also sold in bklts. containing 20 panes of 5 stamps, perf 12 ½ vert. Value for set of unused booklet stamps $20; used booklet stamps sell for somewhat less than the values shown for sheet stamps.

See Korea No. B53.

A544      A545

Waterfalls: 10d, Cataractis village falls at the foot of the Tzoumerca Mountain Range. 60d, Edessa Waterfalls. 100d, Edessaios River cascades.

## 1988, July 4 Litho. Perf. 12½x14
| | | | | |
|---|---|---|---|---|
| 1628 | A544 | 10d multi | 1.50 | .40 |
| 1629 | A544 | 60d multi | 3.50 | 2.25 |
| 1630 | A544 | 100d multi | 5.00 | 2.25 |
| | | Nos. 1628-1630 (3) | 10.00 | 4.90 |

Each denomination also sold in booklets containing 20 panes of 5 stamps, perf. 14 vertically. Value for set of unused booklet stamps $35; used booklet stamps sell for about half the values shown for used sheet stamps.

## 1988, July 4 Perf. 13x12½
| | | | | |
|---|---|---|---|---|
| 1631 | A545 | 60d multi | 6.00 | 2.50 |

20th Pan-European Postal Trade Unions Congress. No. 1631 also sold in booklets containing 20 panes of 5 stamps, perf. 14 vertically. Value of unused booklet stamp $12; the used booklet stamp sells for about half the value shown for the used sheet stamp.

A546

A547

Designs: 30d, Premier Eleutherios Venizelos (1864-1936), natl. flag and map. 70d, Lady liberty, flag and map.

## 1988, Oct. 7 Litho. Perf. 12½x13
| | | | | |
|---|---|---|---|---|
| 1632 | A546 | 30d shown | .85 | .30 |
| 1633 | A546 | 70d multi | 1.40 | .70 |

Union of Crete with Greece and liberation of Epirus and Macedonia from Turkish rule, 75th anniv.

Each denomination also sold in booklets containing 20 panes of 5 stamps, perf. 14 horizontally. Value for set of unused booklet stamps $6; used booklet stamps sell for somewhat less than the values shown for used sheet stamps.

## 1988, Oct. 7 Perf. 13
Departmental Seats: 2d, Mytilene-Lesbos Harbor, painting by Theophilos. 3d, Alexandroupolis lighthouse. 4d, St. Nicholas bell tower, Kozane. 5d, Labor Center, Hermoupolis. 7d, Sparta Town Hall. 8d, Pegasus of Leukas. 10d, Castle of the Knights, Rhodes. 20d, The Acropolis, Athens. 25d, Kavalla aqueduct. 30d, Statue of Athanasios Diakos and castle, Lamia. 50d, Preveza cathedral bell tower and Venetian clock. 60d, Corfu promenade. 70d, Harbor view of Hagios Nicolaos. 100d, Poligiros public fountains. 200d, Church of the Apostle Paul, Corinth.

| | | | | |
|---|---|---|---|---|
| 1634 | A547 | 2d multi | .20 | .20 |
| 1635 | A547 | 3d multi | .20 | .20 |
| 1636 | A547 | 4d multi | .20 | .20 |
| 1637 | A547 | 5d multi | .20 | .20 |
| 1638 | A547 | 7d multi | .20 | .20 |
| 1639 | A547 | 8d multi | .25 | .20 |
| 1640 | A547 | 10d multi | .25 | .20 |
| 1641 | A547 | 20d multi | .30 | .20 |
| a. | | Bklt. pane, 4 each 3d, 5d, 10d, 20d | 4.25 | — |
| 1642 | A547 | 25d multi | .35 | .20 |
| 1643 | A547 | 30d multi | .40 | .20 |
| 1644 | A547 | 50d multi | .60 | .20 |
| 1645 | A547 | 60d multi | 1.25 | .60 |
| 1646 | A547 | 70d multi | 1.25 | .60 |
| 1647 | A547 | 100d multi | 2.00 | .40 |
| 1648 | A547 | 200d multi | 4.00 | .70 |
| | | Nos. 1634-1648 (15) | 11.65 | 4.50 |

Each denomination was also sold in booklets containing 20 panes of 5 stamps, perf 13 vertically or horizontally. Value for set of

unused booklet stamps $12; used booklet stamps sell for slightly less than the values shown for used sheet stamps.

Council of Europe, Rhodes, Dec. 2-3 A548     Christmas A549

Designs: 60d, Map and Castle of the Knights, Rhodes. 100d, Head of Helios, Rhodian 2nd-3rd cent. B.C. coin, and flags.

## 1988, Dec. 2 Litho. Perf. 12½
| | | | | |
|---|---|---|---|---|
| 1649 | A548 | 60d multi | 1.75 | 1.75 |
| 1650 | A548 | 100d multi | 1.75 | 1.25 |

Nos. 1649-1650 were also issued in booklets containing 20 panes of 5, perf. 14 horizontally. Value for set of unused booklet stamps $6.50; used booklet stamps sell for somewhat less than the values shown for used sheet stamps.

## 1988, Dec. 2 Perf. 12½
Paintings: 30d, Adoration of the Magi, by El Greco. 70d, The Annunciation, by Costas Parthenis, horiz.

| | | | | |
|---|---|---|---|---|
| 1651 | A549 | 30d multi | .80 | .40 |
| a. | | Bklt. pane of 10 | 24.00 | |

## Perf. 14
| | | | | |
|---|---|---|---|---|
| 1652 | A549 | 70d multi | 1.75 | .85 |

No. 1651 was issued in booklets of 10 stamps perf 12 ½ on three sides. No. 1652 was also issued in booklets containing 20 panes of 5 stamps, perf. 14 vertically. Value for booklet stamp of No. 1651 $2.50; value for booklet stamp of No. 1652 $5; used values for booklet stamps are the same as for sheet stamps.

A550      A551

Athens '96 emblem and: 30d, High jumper and ancient Olympia. 60d, Wrestlers and view of Delphi. 70d, Swimmers and The Acropolis, Athens. 170d, Sports complex.

## Perf. 13¼x13½ Vert.
## 1989, Mar. 17 Litho.
| | | | | |
|---|---|---|---|---|
| 1653 | A550 | 30d multi | .50 | .30 |
| 1654 | A550 | 60d multi | 1.00 | .90 |
| 1655 | A550 | 70d multi | 1.50 | 1.40 |
| 1656 | A550 | 170d multi | 3.00 | 2.00 |
| a. | | Strip of 4, Nos. 1653-1656 | 7.00 | 7.00 |
| b. | | Bklt. pane of 4, #1653-1656, perf 13 ¼ vert. | 10.00 | — |

## 1989, May 22 Litho. Perf. 12½x14
Europa: Children's toys.

| | | | | |
|---|---|---|---|---|
| 1657 | A551 | 60d Whistling bird | 4.50 | 2.50 |
| 1658 | A551 | 170d Butterfly | 5.00 | 2.50 |
| a. | | Pair, #1657-1658 | 10.00 | 10.00 |
| b. | | Bklt. pane, 2 each #1657-1658, perf 13 ¼ vert. | 22.00 | 22.00 |
| c. | | As "b," pair, #1657-1658 | 11.00 | 11.00 |

Printed se-tenant in sheets of 16. Nos. 1657-1658 were also issued separately in booklets containing 20 panes of 5 stamps, perf. 13 ¼ vertically.

Anniversaries — A552

**1989, May 22**    *Perf. 14x13½*
| | | | | |
|---|---|---|---|---|
| 1659 | A552 | 30d Flags | .75 | .40 |
| 1660 | A552 | 50d Flag, La Liberte | .75 | .40 |
| 1661 | A552 | 60d Flag, ballot box | 1.75 | 1.10 |
| 1662 | A552 | 70d Coin, emblem | 1.75 | 1.10 |
| 1663 | A552 | 200d Flag, "40" | 4.00 | 1.50 |
| | | *Nos. 1659-1663 (5)* | 9.00 | 4.50 |

Six-nation Initiative for Peace and Disarmament, 5th anniv. (30d); French revolution, bicent. (50d); European Parliament Elections in Greece, 10th anniv. (60d); Interparliamentary Union, cent. (70d); and Council of Europe, 40th anniv. (200d).

Nos. 1659-1663 also issued in booklets containing 20 panes of 5 stamps, perf. 13¼ horizontally. Values for unused booklet stamps: No. 1659 $1; 1660 $2.75; 1661 $7.25; 1662 $7.25; 1663 $9. Used booklet stamps sell for up to 5 times the values shown for used sheet stamps.

A553

BALKANFILA XII, Sept. 30-Oct. 8, Salonica — A554

**1989, Sept. 25**   *Litho.*   *Perf. 14x12½*
| | | | | |
|---|---|---|---|---|
| 1664 | A553 | 60d shown | .85 | .50 |
| 1665 | A553 | 70d Eye, magnifying glass | .85 | .75 |

**Souvenir Sheet**
*Perf. 14x13*
| | | | | |
|---|---|---|---|---|
| 1666 | A554 | 200d shown | 2.75 | 2.75 |

Wildflowers
A555

**1989, Dec. 8**   *Litho.*   *Perf. 14x12½*
| | | | | |
|---|---|---|---|---|
| 1667 | A555 | 8d Wild rose | .20 | .20 |
| 1668 | A555 | 10d Common myrtle | .20 | .20 |
| 1669 | A555 | 30d Field poppy | .25 | .20 |
| 1670 | A555 | 30d Anemone | .40 | .25 |
| 1671 | A555 | 60d Dandelion, chicory | .80 | .40 |
| 1672 | A555 | 70d Mallow | .90 | .50 |
| 1673 | A555 | 200d Thistle | 2.50 | 1.90 |
| | | *Nos. 1667-1673 (7)* | 5.25 | 3.65 |

*Ursus arctos*
A556

Rare and endangered species.

**1990, Mar. 16**   *Litho.*   *Perf. 14x12½*
| | | | | |
|---|---|---|---|---|
| 1674 | A556 | 40d shown | .55 | .20 |
| 1675 | A556 | 70d *Caretta caretta* | 1.00 | .45 |
| 1676 | A556 | 90d *Monachus monachus* | 1.25 | .50 |
| 1677 | A556 | 100d *Lynx lynx* | 1.40 | 1.10 |
| | | *Nos. 1674-1677 (4)* | 4.20 | 2.25 |

Europa
1990 — A557

Post offices: 70d, Old Central P.O. interior. 210d, Contemporary p.o. exterior.

**1990, May 11**   *Litho.*   *Perf. 13½x12½*
| | | | | |
|---|---|---|---|---|
| 1678 | A557 | 70d multicolored | 3.25 | 2.75 |
| 1679 | A557 | 210d multicolored | 5.75 | 4.75 |
| a. | | Pair, #1678-1679 | 9.50 | 9.50 |
| b. | | Bkt. pane, 2 each #1678-1679, perf 12½ | 20.00 | |
| c. | | As "b," pair, #1678-1679 | 10.00 | 10.00 |

Nos. 1678-1679 were printed setenant in sheets of 16 and separately in booklets. Nos. 1679b and 1679c are perf 12½ vertically and imperf horizontally.

Natl. Reconcilation    Political Reformers
A558        A559

**1990, May 11**   *Perf. 12½x13½*
| | | | | |
|---|---|---|---|---|
| 1680 | A558 | 40d Flag, handshake | .50 | .20 |
| 1681 | A558 | 70d Dove, ribbon | .85 | .35 |
| 1682 | A558 | 100d Map, gift of flowers | 1.25 | 1.25 |
| | | *Nos. 1680-1682 (3)* | 2.60 | 1.80 |

**1990, May 11**
| | | | | |
|---|---|---|---|---|
| 1683 | A559 | 40d Gregoris Lambrakis (1912-63) | .65 | .40 |
| 1684 | A559 | 40d Pavlos Bakoyiannis (1935-89) | .65 | .40 |

A560        A561

Department Seats: 2d, Karditsa, the commercial-animal fair. 5d, Trikkala fort and clock tower. 8d, Veroia, street with traditional architecture. 10d, Mesolongion, Central Monument of Fallen Heroes in the Exodus. 15d, Chios, view. 20d, Tripolis, street with neoclassical architecture. 25d, Volos, view with town hall, woodcut by A. Tassou. 40d, Kalamata, neoclassical town hall. 50d, Pyrgos, central marketplace. 70d, Ioannina, view of lake and island. 80d, Rethymnon, sculpture at the port. 90d, Argostolion, view before earthquake. 100d, Nauplia, Bourtzi with Palamidi in the background. 200d, Patras, central lighthouse. 250d, Florina, street with neoclassical architecture. Nos. 1685, 1687, 1695, 1698 vert.

**1990, June 20**   *Litho.*   *Perf. 12½*
| | | | | |
|---|---|---|---|---|
| 1685 | A560 | 2d multicolored | .20 | .20 |
| 1686 | A560 | 5d multicolored | .20 | .20 |
| 1687 | A560 | 8d multicolored | .20 | .20 |
| 1688 | A560 | 10d multicolored | .20 | .20 |
| 1689 | A560 | 15d multicolored | .20 | .20 |
| 1690 | A560 | 20d multicolored | .20 | .20 |
| 1691 | A560 | 25d multicolored | .40 | .20 |
| 1692 | A560 | 40d multicolored | .60 | .20 |
| 1693 | A560 | 50d multicolored | .75 | .20 |
| 1694 | A560 | 70d multicolored | 1.00 | .40 |
| 1695 | A560 | 80d multicolored | 1.10 | .45 |
| 1696 | A560 | 90d multicolored | 1.40 | .50 |
| 1697 | A560 | 100d multicolored | 2.25 | .60 |
| 1698 | A560 | 200d multicolored | 4.50 | 1.10 |
| 1699 | A560 | 250d multicolored | 6.00 | 1.50 |
| | | *Nos. 1685-1699 (15)* | 19.20 | 6.35 |

Each denomination was also sold in booklets containing 20 panes of 5 stamps, perf 13½ vertically or horizontally. Value for set of unused booklet stamps $10; used booklet stamps sell for about half of the value of used sheet stamps.
See Nos. 1749-1760, 1792-1801.

**1990, July 13**   *Perf. 12½x13½*
| | | | | |
|---|---|---|---|---|
| 1700 | A561 | 20d Sailing | .25 | .20 |
| 1701 | A561 | 50d Wrestling | .60 | .25 |
| 1702 | A561 | 80d Sprinting | .90 | .90 |
| 1703 | A561 | 100d Basketball | 1.25 | .90 |
| 1704 | A561 | 250d Soccer | 3.00 | 1.50 |
| a. | | Strip of 5, #1700-1704 | 7.00 | 7.00 |

1996 Summer Olympics. Athens, proposed site for centennial Summer Olympic Games. Exists perf. 13½ vert.

Heinrich Schliemann (1822-1890), Archaeologist — A562

**1990, Oct. 11**   *Litho.*   *Perf. 14x13½*
| | | | | |
|---|---|---|---|---|
| 1705 | A562 | 80d multicolored | 5.00 | 3.00 |

See Germany No. 1615.

Greco-Italian War, 50th Anniv. — A563

**1990, Oct. 11**   *Perf. 12½*
| | | | | |
|---|---|---|---|---|
| 1706 | A563 | 50d Woman knitting | .60 | .20 |
| 1707 | A563 | 80d Virgin Mary, soldier | 1.00 | .80 |
| 1708 | A563 | 100d Women volunteers | 1.40 | .80 |
| | | *Nos. 1706-1708 (3)* | 3.00 | 1.80 |

**Souvenir Sheet**

Stamp Day — A564

**1990, Dec. 14**   *Litho.*   *Perf. 14x13*
| | | | | |
|---|---|---|---|---|
| 1709 | A564 | 300d multicolored | 10.00 | 10.00 |

The Muses — A565

Designs: 50d, Calliope, Euterpe, Erato. 80d, Terpsichore, Polyhymnia, Melpomene. 250d, Thalia, Clio, Urania.

**1991, Mar. 11**   *Litho.*   *Perf. 12½*
| | | | | |
|---|---|---|---|---|
| 1710 | A565 | 50d multicolored | .60 | .20 |
| 1711 | A565 | 80d multicolored | .95 | .40 |
| 1712 | A565 | 250d multicolored | 2.75 | 1.25 |
| | | *Nos. 1710-1712 (3)* | 4.30 | 1.85 |

Battle of Crete by Ioannis Anousakis — A566

300d, Map, flags of participating allied armies.

**1991, May 20**   *Litho.*   *Perf. 12½x13½*
| | | | | |
|---|---|---|---|---|
| 1713 | A566 | 60d multicolored | 1.60 | .40 |

**Size: 32x24mm**
*Perf. 12½*
| | | | | |
|---|---|---|---|---|
| 1714 | A566 | 300d multicolored | 3.25 | 1.50 |

Battle of Crete, 50th anniv.

Europa
A567

Designs: 80d, Icarus pushing modern satellite. 300d, Chariot of the Sun.

**1991, May 20**   *Perf. 12½*
| | | | | |
|---|---|---|---|---|
| 1715 | A567 | 80d multicolored | 4.00 | 3.00 |
| 1716 | A567 | 300d multicolored | 5.50 | 4.50 |
| a. | | Pair, #1715-1716 | 10.00 | 10.00 |
| b. | | Bkt. pane, 2 ea. #1715-1716 | 22.00 | 22.00 |
| c. | | As "b," pair, 80d, 300d | 11.00 | 11.00 |

No. 1716a printed in continuous design in sheets of 16. Nos. 1715-1716 were also issued separately in booklets (#1716b), perf 12½ vertically and imperf horizontally.

A568        A569

**1991, June 25**   *Litho.*   *Perf. 13½x14*
| | | | | |
|---|---|---|---|---|
| 1717 | A568 | 10d Swimming | .20 | .20 |
| 1718 | A568 | 60d Basketball | .50 | .25 |
| 1719 | A568 | 90d Gymnastics | .90 | .30 |
| 1720 | A568 | 130d Weight lifting | 1.25 | .50 |
| 1721 | A568 | 300d Hammer throw | 3.50 | 2.00 |
| | | *Nos. 1717-1721 (5)* | 6.35 | 3.25 |

1991 Mediterranean Games, Athens.

**1991, Sept. 20**   *Litho.*   *Perf. 13½x14*
| | | | | |
|---|---|---|---|---|
| 1722 | A569 | 100d multicolored | 1.10 | .60 |

Athenian Democracy, 2500th anniv.

**Europa Souvenir Sheet**

Greek Presidency of CEPT — A570

Europe with Zeus metmorphosed into a bull, from Attic vase, c. 500 B.C.

**1991, Sept. 20**   *Perf. 14x13*
| | | | | |
|---|---|---|---|---|
| 1723 | A570 | 300d multicolored | 20.00 | 20.00 |

A571        A572

Greek Membership in EEC, 10th anniv.: 50d, Pres. Konstantin Karamanlis signing Treaty of Greek entrance into EEC. 80d, Map showing EEC members, Pres. Karamanlis.

**1991, Dec. 9**   *Litho.*   *Perf. 13x14*
| | | | | |
|---|---|---|---|---|
| 1724 | A571 | 50d multicolored | .55 | .25 |
| 1725 | A571 | 80d multicolored | .90 | .50 |

**1991, Dec. 9**   *Perf. 12½x13½*
| | | | | |
|---|---|---|---|---|
| 1726 | A572 | 80d Speed skaters | .90 | .80 |
| 1727 | A572 | 300d Slalom skier | 3.25 | 1.10 |
| a. | | Pair, #1726-1727 | 4.25 | 4.25 |

16th Winter Olympics, Albertville.

A573

1992 Summer Olympics, Barcelona A574

**Perf. 12½, 14x13½ (90d, 340d)**

| | | | | |
|---|---|---|---|---|
| **1992, Apr. 3** | | | | **Litho.** |
| 1728 | A573 | 10d Javelin | .25 | .20 |
| 1729 | A573 | 60d Equestrian | .90 | .30 |
| 1730 | A574 | 90d Runner | 1.40 | .75 |
| 1731 | A573 | 120d Gymnastics | 2.75 | .80 |
| 1732 | A574 | 340d Runners | 4.50 | 2.25 |
| | *Nos. 1728-1732 (5)* | | 9.80 | 4.30 |

Health — A575

Designs: 60d, Protection against AIDS. 80d, Diseases of digestive system. 90d, Dying flower symbolizing cancer. 120d, Hephaestus at his forge, 6th century BC. 280d, Alexandros S. Onassis Cardiosurgical Center.

| | | | | |
|---|---|---|---|---|
| **1992, May 22** | | | **Litho.** | **Perf. 12½** |
| 1733 | A575 | 60d multicolored | .60 | .30 |
| 1734 | A575 | 80d multicolored | .85 | .40 |
| 1735 | A575 | 90d multicolored | .90 | .45 |
| 1736 | A575 | 120d multicolored | 1.50 | .65 |
| 1737 | A575 | 280d multicolored | 3.25 | 1.75 |
| | *Nos. 1733-1737 (5)* | | 7.10 | 3.55 |

No. 1734, 1st United European Gastroenterology Week. No. 1736, European Year of Social Security, Hygiene and Health in the Workplace.

Discovery of America, 500th Anniv. A576

Europa: 340d, Map of 15th century Chios, Columbus.

| | | | | |
|---|---|---|---|---|
| **1992, May 22** | | | **Perf. 13½x12¼** |
| 1738 | A576 | 90d shown | 2.75 | 2.00 |
| a. | Perf. 12½ vert. | | 3.00 | 2.25 |
| 1739 | A576 | 340d multicolored | 6.50 | 4.75 |
| a. | Pair, #1738-1739 | | 10.00 | 10.00 |
| b. | Perf. 12½ vert. | | 6.75 | 5.50 |
| c. | Bklt. pane, 2 each #1738a, 1739b | | 20.00 | 20.00 |
| d. | Pair, #1738a, 1739b | | 10.00 | 10.00 |

No. 1739a was printed in continuous design in sheets of 16. Nos. 1738-1739 were also issued separately in booklets (#1739c), perf 12¼ vertically and imperf horizontally.

Souvenir Sheet

European Conference on Transportation — A577

| | | | |
|---|---|---|---|
| **1992, June 8** | | **Perf. 14x13** |
| 1740 | A577 | 300d multicolored | 8.50 8.50 |

Macedonian Treasures — A578

Designs: 10d, Head of Hercules wearing lion skin, Vergina treasures. 20d, Bust of Aristotle, map of Macedonia, horiz. 60d, Alexander the Great at Battle of Issus, horiz. 80d, Archaeologist Manolis Andronikos, tomb of King Philip II. 90d, Deer hunt mosaic, Pella. 120d, Macedonian tetradrachm. 340d, St. Paul, 4th century church near Philippi.

| | | | | |
|---|---|---|---|---|
| **1992, July 17** | | | **Litho.** | **Perf. 12½** |
| 1741 | A578 | 10d multicolored | .25 | .20 |
| 1742 | A578 | 20d multicolored | .30 | .20 |
| 1743 | A578 | 60d multicolored | .60 | .20 |
| 1744 | A578 | 80d multicolored | 1.10 | .25 |
| 1745 | A578 | 90d multicolored | 1.25 | .25 |
| 1746 | A578 | 120d multicolored | 1.60 | 1.00 |
| 1747 | A578 | 340d multicolored | 5.50 | 2.50 |
| | *Nos. 1741-1747 (7)* | | 10.60 | 4.60 |

European Unification — A579

| | | | |
|---|---|---|---|
| **1992, Oct. 12** | | **Litho.** | **Perf. 14x13** |
| 1748 | A579 | 90d multicolored | 1.00 1.00 |

**Departmental Seat Type of 1990**

Designs: 10d, Piraeus, the old clock. 20d, Amphissa, view of city with citadel. 30d, Samos (Vathy), the Heraion. 40d, Canea, city in 1800s. 50d, Zakinthos (Zante), view in 1800s. 60d, Karpenision, Velouchi and city. 70d, Kilkis, the cave, vert. 80d, Xanthe, door of Town Hall, vert. 90d, Salonika, Macedonian Struggle Museum. 120d, Komotine, Tsanakleous School. 340d, Drama, spring. 400d, Larissa, Pinios bridge.

| | | | | |
|---|---|---|---|---|
| **1992, Oct. 12** | | | **Perf. 12¾** |
| 1749 | A560 | 10d multicolored | .20 | .20 |
| 1750 | A560 | 20d multicolored | .20 | .20 |
| 1751 | A560 | 30d multicolored | .20 | .20 |
| 1752 | A560 | 40d multicolored | .35 | .20 |
| 1753 | A560 | 50d multicolored | .40 | .20 |
| 1754 | A560 | 60d multicolored | .45 | .30 |
| 1755 | A560 | 70d multicolored | .60 | .35 |
| 1756 | A560 | 80d multicolored | .60 | .35 |
| 1757 | A560 | 90d multicolored | .80 | .40 |
| 1758 | A560 | 120d multicolored | 1.10 | .65 |
| 1759 | A560 | 340d multicolored | 3.00 | 1.60 |
| 1760 | A560 | 400d multicolored | 4.50 | 2.25 |
| | *Nos. 1749-1760 (12)* | | 12.40 | 6.90 |

Each denomination was also sold in booklets containing 20 panes of 5 stamps, perf 10½ vertically or horizontally. Value for set of unused booklet stamps $14.50; used booklet stamps sell for about half the listed values for used sheet stamps.

City of Rhodes, 2400th Anniv. — A580

Designs: 60d, Headstone, 4th cent. B.C. 90d, Bathing Aphrodite, 1st cent. B.C. 120d, St. Irene, Church of St. Catherine, 14th cent. 250d, St. Paul's Gate, 15th cent.

| | | | | |
|---|---|---|---|---|
| **1993, Feb. 26** | | **Litho.** | **Perf. 13x14** |
| 1761 | A580 | 60d multicolored | .65 | .35 |
| 1762 | A580 | 90d multicolored | 1.10 | .80 |
| 1763 | A580 | 120d multicolored | 1.25 | .70 |
| 1764 | A580 | 250d multicolored | 4.00 | 1.75 |
| | *Nos. 1761-1764 (4)* | | 7.00 | 3.60 |

Remembrances of Greek Wars — A581

Designs: 10d, Death of Georgakis Olympios, 1821. 30d, Theodore Kolokotronis in battle, 1821. 60d, Pavlos Melas. 90d, Glory lays wreath over graves of dead from Balkan Wars. 120d, Greek soldiers at Battle of El Alamein, 1942, horiz. 150d, Greek troops in Aegean Islands, 1943-45, horiz. 200d, Kalavryta Massacre Memorial.

**Perf. 13x14, 14x13**

| | | | | |
|---|---|---|---|---|
| **1993, May 25** | | | **Litho.** |
| 1765 | A581 | 10d multicolored | .25 | .20 |
| 1766 | A581 | 30d multicolored | .40 | .20 |
| 1767 | A581 | 60d multicolored | .55 | .30 |
| 1768 | A581 | 90d multicolored | 1.00 | .40 |
| 1769 | A581 | 120d multicolored | 2.40 | 1.00 |
| 1770 | A581 | 150d multicolored | 2.40 | 1.60 |
| 1771 | A581 | 200d multicolored | 4.75 | 2.25 |
| | *Nos. 1765-1771 (7)* | | 11.75 | 5.95 |

The Benefits of Transportation, by K. Parthenis — A582

Europa: 90d, Tree, three people, ships. 350d, Woman and children, town.

| | | | | |
|---|---|---|---|---|
| **1993, May 25** | | | **Perf. 13x14** |
| 1772 | | 90d multicolored | 1.50 | 1.25 |
| a. | Perf. 13½ vert. | | 1.50 | 1.25 |
| 1773 | | 350d multicolored | 6.75 | 5.50 |
| a. | A582 Pair, #1772-1773 | | 9.00 | 9.00 |
| b. | Perf. 13½ vert. | | 6.75 | 5.50 |
| c. | Bklt. pane, 2 each #1772a, 1773b | | 18.00 | 18.00 |
| d. | Pair, #1772a, 1773b | | 9.00 | 9.00 |

No. 1773a was printed in continuous design in sheets of 16. Nos. 1772-1773 were also issued separately in booklets (#1773c), perf 13½ vertically and imperf horizontally.

Buildings in Athens A583

Designs: 30d, Concert Hall. 60d, Numismatic Museum (Iliou Melathron). 90d, Natl. Library of Greece. 200d, Opthalmology Hospital.

| | | | | |
|---|---|---|---|---|
| **1993, Oct. 4** | | | **Litho.** | **Perf. 14** |
| 1774 | A583 | 30d multicolored | .85 | .20 |
| 1775 | A583 | 60d multicolored | .85 | .30 |
| 1776 | A583 | 90d multicolored | 1.00 | .80 |
| 1777 | A583 | 200d multicolored | 3.25 | 1.60 |
| | *Nos. 1774-1777 (4)* | | 5.95 | 2.90 |

Souvenir Sheet

Greek Presidency of the European Community Council of Ministers — A584

| | | | |
|---|---|---|---|
| **1993, Dec. 20** | | **Litho.** | **Perf. 14** |
| 1778 | A584 | 400d multicolored | 5.00 5.00 |

Chariot of Selene Driven by Hermes A585

| | | | |
|---|---|---|---|
| **1994, Mar. 7** | | **Litho.** | **Perf. 13x13½** |
| 1779 | A585 | 200d multicolored | 2.25 1.50 |

2nd Pan-European Transportation Conference.

Passion of Christ A586

Designs: 30d, Last Supper, 16th cent. icon, St. Catherine's Church, Crete, vert. 60d, Crucifixion, detail from 1552 wall drawing, Great Meteoron, vert. 90d, Burial, 1620-45 icon, Church of the Presentation of the Lord, Patmos. 150d, Resurrection, illustrated manuscript of Mt. Athos, 11th cent.

| | | | | |
|---|---|---|---|---|
| **1994, Apr. 8** | | | **Litho.** | **Perf. 14** |
| 1780 | A586 | 30d multicolored | .40 | .25 |
| 1781 | A586 | 60d multicolored | .50 | .25 |
| 1782 | A586 | 90d multicolored | .75 | .40 |
| 1783 | A586 | 150d multicolored | 1.60 | .90 |
| | *Nos. 1780-1783 (4)* | | 3.25 | 1.80 |

European Inventors, Discoverers A587

Europa: 90d, Thales of Miletus (625?-547? B.C.), philosopher, mathematician. 350d, Konstantinos Karatheodoris (1873-1950).

| | | | | |
|---|---|---|---|---|
| **1994, May 9** | | | **Litho.** | **Perf. 14x13½** |
| 1784 | A587 | 90d multicolored | 1.75 | 1.50 |
| a. | Perf. 13¾ vert. | | 2.00 | 1.75 |
| 1785 | A587 | 350d multicolored | 3.75 | 3.25 |
| a. | Pair, #1784-1785 | | 6.00 | 6.00 |
| b. | Perf. 13¾ vert. | | 4.00 | 3.50 |
| c. | Bklt. pane, 2 each #1784a-1785b | | 13.00 | 13.00 |
| d. | Pair, #1784a, 1785b | | 6.50 | 6.50 |

Nos. 1784-1785 was issued in sheets of 16 and in booklets (#1785c), perf 13¾ vertically and imperf horizontally.

Athletic Events, Anniversaries A588

Designs: 60d, Demetrios Vikelas (1835-1908), first president Intl. Olympic Committee, vert. 90, Modern, ancient soccer players. 120d, Volleyball, net, vert. 400d, Statue of Liberty, modern, ancient soccer players.

## 1994, June 6    Litho.    *Perf. 14*

| | | | | |
|---|---|---|---|---|
| 1786 | A588 | 60d multicolored | .70 | .30 |
| 1787 | A588 | 90d multicolored | .85 | .60 |
| 1788 | A588 | 120d multicolored | 1.75 | .90 |
| | | Nos. 1786-1788 (3) | 3.30 | 1.80 |

**Souvenir Sheet**
*Perf. 14x13½*

| | | | | |
|---|---|---|---|---|
| 1789 | A588 | 400d multicolored | 4.50 | 4.50 |

Intl. Olympic Committee, cent. (#1786). 1994 World Cup Soccer Championships, US (#1787, #1789). World Volleyball Championships, Piraeus & Salonika (#1788). No. 1789 contains one 42x52mm stamp.

Greek Presidency of European Community Council of Ministers — A589

Designs: 90d, Winged chariot driven by Greece. 120d, Doric columns, European Community flag.

## 1994, June 21    *Perf. 13*

| | | | | |
|---|---|---|---|---|
| 1790 | A589 | 90d multicolored | 1.00 | .90 |
| 1791 | A589 | 120d multicolored | 1.25 | .90 |

**Departmental Seat Type of 1990**

Designs: 10d, Katerine, Tsalopoulou mansion house, vert. 20d, Arta, Byzantine Church Parigoritissas. 30d, Lebadea, medieval bridge, tower of catalanian castle, Krias springs vert. 40d, Kastoria, Church of Panagia Koumbelidkis. 50d, Grevena, outdoor theatre. 60d, Edessa, waterfall. 80d, Chalcis, red house. 90d, Serrai, government house, Merarchias road, Acropolis of Koulas. 120d, Candia (Herakleion), town hall. 150d, Egoumenitsa, Church of Evangelistria, vert.

## 1994, Oct. 5    Litho.    *Perf. 12¾*

| | | | | |
|---|---|---|---|---|
| 1792 | A560 | 10d multicolored | .20 | .20 |
| 1793 | A560 | 20d multicolored | .20 | .20 |
| 1794 | A560 | 30d multicolored | .30 | .20 |
| 1795 | A560 | 40d multicolored | .40 | .25 |
| 1796 | A560 | 50d multicolored | .50 | .25 |
| 1797 | A560 | 60d multicolored | .65 | .25 |
| 1798 | A560 | 80d multicolored | .75 | .30 |
| 1799 | A560 | 90d multicolored | .80 | .30 |
| 1800 | A560 | 120d multicolored | 1.00 | .40 |
| 1801 | A560 | 150d multicolored | 1.25 | .50 |
| | | Nos. 1792-1801 (10) | 6.05 | 2.85 |

Each denomination was also sold in booklets containing 20 panes of 5 stamps, perf 10½ vertically or horizontally. Unused booklet stamps sell for the same price as the sheet stamp values listed; used booklet stamps sell for about half the listed values for the used sheet stamps.

Constitution, 150th Anniv. — A590

Designs: 60d, People, army demonstrating, by Carl Howpt, vert. 150d, Portraits of Ioannis Makriyannis, Andreas Metaxas, Demetrios Kallergis. 200d, Painting of night of Sept. 3, 1843. 340d, Article 107, seal of Greek Parliament, signature of President.

## 1994, Nov. 21    Litho.    *Perf. 14x13*

| | | | | |
|---|---|---|---|---|
| 1802 | A590 | 60d multicolored | .65 | .40 |
| 1803 | A590 | 150d multicolored | 1.10 | .65 |
| 1804 | A590 | 200d multicolored | 2.25 | 1.00 |
| 1805 | A590 | 340d multicolored | 4.25 | 2.00 |
| | | Nos. 1802-1805 (4) | 8.25 | 4.05 |

Melina Mercouri (1925-94), Actress, Politician — A591

## 1995, Mar. 7    Litho.    *Perf. 14x13*

| | | | | |
|---|---|---|---|---|
| 1806 | A591 | 60d shown | .65 | .25 |
| 1807 | A591 | 90d Portrait, Parthenon | .80 | .40 |
| 1808 | A591 | 100d Portraits as actress | 2.00 | 1.00 |
| 1809 | A591 | 340d Portrait, vert. | 4.50 | 2.25 |
| | | Nos. 1806-1809 (4) | 7.95 | 3.90 |

Liberation of Concentration Camps, 50th Anniv. A592

Europa: 90d, Prisoners. 340d, Peace doves, broken barbed wire fence.

## 1995, May 3    Litho.    *Perf. 14*

| | | | | |
|---|---|---|---|---|
| 1810 | A592 | 90d multicolored | 2.00 | 2.00 |
| a. | | Perf. 13½ vert. | 2.00 | 2.00 |
| 1811 | A592 | 340d multicolored | 4.00 | 4.00 |
| a. | | Pair, #1810-1811 | 6.50 | 6.50 |
| b. | | Perf. 13½ vert. | 4.00 | 4.00 |
| c. | | Bklt. pane, 2 each #1810a, 1811b | 13.00 | 13.00 |
| | | Complete booklet, #1811c | 13.00 | |
| d. | | Pair, #1810a, 1811b | 6.50 | 6.50 |

Anniversaries & Events — A593

Designs: 10d, Stylized emblem, basketball, vert. 70d, University building. 90d, Architectural ruins, vert. 100d, Flag, soldier, vert. 120d, Statue of Peace, by Kifissodotos, vert. 150d, Dolphins. 200d, Early telephone, push buttons, vert. 300d, Owl, basketball, vert.

*Perf. 13½x13, 13x13½*

## 1995, June 21    Litho.

| | | | | |
|---|---|---|---|---|
| 1812 | A593 | 10d multicolored | .20 | .20 |
| 1813 | A593 | 70d multicolored | 1.00 | .30 |
| 1814 | A593 | 90d multicolored | 1.25 | .40 |
| 1815 | A593 | 100d multicolored | 1.40 | .45 |
| 1816 | A593 | 120d multicolored | 1.75 | .55 |
| 1817 | A593 | 150d multicolored | 2.00 | .65 |
| 1818 | A593 | 200d multicolored | 2.75 | .90 |
| 1819 | A593 | 300d multicolored | 4.50 | 1.25 |
| | | Nos. 1812-1819 (8) | 14.85 | 4.70 |

5th World Junior Basketball Championships (#1812). Agricultural University of Athens, 75th anniv. (#1813). UN, 50th anniv. (#1814, #1816). End of World War II, 50th anniv. (#1815). European Nature Conservation Year (#1817). Telephone in Greece, cent. (#1818). 29th European Basketball Championships (#1819).

Book of Revelation, 1900th Anniv. — A594

Visions of the Apocalypse: 80d, First vision, Angels of the Seven Churches of Asia Minor, icon by Thomas Bathas, vert. 110d, Apostle John at Cave of the Apocalypse dictating to Prochoros, miniature from manuscript of Four Gospels, vert. 300d, First Angel with trumpet from silver gilded Gospel cover.

## 1995, Sept. 18    Litho.    *Perf. 14*

| | | | | |
|---|---|---|---|---|
| 1820 | A594 | 80d multicolored | 1.50 | .35 |
| 1821 | A594 | 110d multicolored | 1.75 | .90 |
| 1822 | A594 | 300d multicolored | 2.75 | 2.00 |
| | | Nos. 1820-1822 (3) | 6.00 | 3.25 |

Jason & the Argonauts A595

Designs: 80d, Argonauts, the Argus, goddess Athena setting out for Colchis. 120d, Phineas, Hermes, one of the Voreadae, Harpy. 150d, Jason taming the bull, Medea and Nike. 200d, Jason takes Golden Fleece, kills serpent with Medea's help. 300d, Medea watches, Jason, crowned by Nike, giving Golden Fleece to Pelias.

## 1995, Nov. 6    Litho.    *Perf. 13x13½*

| | | | | |
|---|---|---|---|---|
| 1823 | A595 | 80d multicolored | .90 | .40 |
| 1824 | A595 | 120d multicolored | .90 | .75 |
| 1825 | A595 | 150d multicolored | 1.10 | .65 |
| 1826 | A595 | 200d multicolored | 1.60 | .75 |
| 1827 | A595 | 300d multicolored | 4.50 | 1.60 |
| | | Nos. 1823-1827 (5) | 9.00 | 4.15 |

Lighthouses — A596

## 1995, Dec. 18    Litho.    *Perf. 14*

| | | | | |
|---|---|---|---|---|
| 1828 | A596 | 80d Psyttaleia | .65 | .40 |
| 1829 | A596 | 120d Sapienza | .95 | .60 |
| 1830 | A596 | 150d Kastri (Othonoi) | 1.25 | 1.10 |
| 1831 | A596 | 500d Zourva (Hydra) | 4.50 | 2.40 |
| | | Nos. 1828-1831 (4) | 7.35 | 4.50 |

**Souvenir Sheets**

Modern Olympic Games, Cent. A597

*Perf. 13½x13, 13x13½*

## 1996, Mar. 25    Litho.

| | | | | |
|---|---|---|---|---|
| 1832 | | Sheet of 4 | 15.00 | 15.00 |
| a. | A597 | 80d like #117, vert. | 3.00 | 3.00 |
| b. | A597 | 120d like #118, vert. | 3.00 | 3.00 |
| c. | A597 | 150d like #119, vert. | 3.00 | 3.00 |
| d. | A597 | 650d like #120, vert. | 3.00 | 3.00 |
| 1833 | | Sheet of 4 | 15.00 | 15.00 |
| a. | A597 | 80d like #122 | 3.00 | 3.00 |
| b. | A597 | 120d like #124 | 3.00 | 3.00 |
| c. | A597 | 150d like #125 | 3.00 | 3.00 |
| d. | A597 | 650d like #128 | 3.00 | 3.00 |
| 1834 | | Sheet of 4 | 15.00 | 15.00 |
| a. | A597 | 80d like #121, vert. | 3.00 | 3.00 |
| b. | A597 | 120d like #123, vert. | 3.00 | 3.00 |
| c. | A597 | 150d like #126, vert. | 3.00 | 3.00 |
| d. | A597 | 650d like #127, vert. | 3.00 | 3.00 |

Famous Women — A598

Europa: 120d, Sappho (c.610-580BC), lyric poet. 430d, Amalia Fleming.

## 1996, Apr. 22    Litho.    *Perf. 14x14½*

| | | | | |
|---|---|---|---|---|
| 1835 | | 120d multicolored | 1.50 | 1.50 |
| a. | | Perf. 14½ vert. | 1.50 | 1.50 |
| 1836 | | 430d multicolored | 4.50 | 4.50 |
| a. | A598 | Pair, #1835-1836 | 6.25 | 6.25 |
| b. | | Perf. 14½ vert. | 4.50 | 4.50 |
| c. | | Booklet pane, 2 each #1835a, 1836b | 12.50 | 12.50 |
| | | Complete booklet, #1836c | 12.50 | |
| d. | | Pair, #1835a, 1836b | 6.25 | 6.25 |

Modern Olympic Games, Cent. A599

Stylized designs: 10d, Greek runners, vert. 80d, Discus thrower, vert. 120d, Weight lifter, vert. 200d, Wrestlers.

*Perf. 13½x14, 14x13½*

## 1996, June 4    Litho.

| | | | | |
|---|---|---|---|---|
| 1837 | A599 | 10d multicolored | .30 | .20 |
| 1838 | A599 | 80d multicolored | 1.10 | .45 |
| 1839 | A599 | 120d multicolored | 2.10 | .75 |
| 1840 | A599 | 200d multicolored | 3.25 | 2.00 |
| | | Nos. 1837-1840 (4) | 6.75 | 3.40 |

First Intl. Medical Olympiad — A600

## 1996, July 8    Litho.    *Perf. 13½*

| | | | | |
|---|---|---|---|---|
| 1841 | A600 | 80d Hippocrates | 1.25 | .80 |
| 1842 | A600 | 120d Galen | 2.00 | 1.25 |

Castles A601

## 1996, Oct. 7    Litho.    *Perf. 13x13½*

| | | | | |
|---|---|---|---|---|
| 1843 | A601 | 10d Mytilene | .20 | .20 |
| 1844 | A601 | 20d Lindos | .20 | .20 |
| 1845 | A601 | 30d Rethymnon | .30 | .25 |
| 1846 | A601 | 70d Assos Cephalonia | .65 | .35 |
| 1847 | A601 | 80d Serbs | .80 | .60 |
| 1848 | A601 | 120d Monemvasia | 1.00 | .65 |
| 1849 | A601 | 200d Didimotihon | 1.75 | 1.00 |
| 1850 | A601 | 430d Vonitsas | 4.25 | 3.00 |
| 1851 | A601 | 1000d Nikopolis | 10.00 | 6.50 |
| | | Nos. 1843-1851 (9) | 19.15 | 12.75 |

Each denomination was also sold in booklets containing 20 panes of 5 stamps, perf. 13 vertically. Unused sell for the same price as the listed sheet stamps; used booklet stamps sell for about half the values shown for used sheet stamps.

Figures from Shadow Theatre — A602

100d, Four characters, diff. 120d, Three characters. 200d, Two characters, dragon.

## 1996, Nov. 15    Litho.    *Perf. 14*

| | | | | |
|---|---|---|---|---|
| 1852 | A602 | 80d multicolored | 1.00 | .45 |
| 1853 | A602 | 100d multicolored | 1.00 | .55 |
| 1854 | A602 | 120d multicolored | 2.00 | .70 |
| 1855 | A602 | 200d multicolored | 3.00 | 1.10 |
| | | Nos. 1852-1855 (4) | 7.00 | 2.80 |

Hellenic Language A603

Designs: 80d, Oldest Hellenic inscription, wine pitcher, 720BC. 120d, Verse IX, 436-445 from Homer's Iliad, 1st-2nd cent. AD. 150d, Psalm of the Holy Apostles, 6th cent. AD. 350d, Reference to Hellenic language, Dionysios Solomos, 1824.

## 1996, Dec. 18    Litho.    *Perf. 13x13½*

| | | | | |
|---|---|---|---|---|
| 1856 | A603 | 80d multicolored | .85 | .55 |
| 1857 | A603 | 120d multicolored | 1.10 | .85 |
| 1858 | A603 | 150d multicolored | 1.75 | 1.40 |
| 1859 | A603 | 350d multicolored | 4.25 | 2.10 |
| | | Nos. 1856-1859 (4) | 7.95 | 4.90 |

Andreas G. Papandreou (1919-96), Prime Minister — A604

Papandreou at various ages and: 80d, Graduation cap, books, diploma. 120d, Leaving airplane. 150d, Building. 500d, Greek flag, dove.

**1997, Feb. 12    Litho.    *Perf. 13***
| | | | | |
|---|---|---|---|---|
|1860|A604|80d multicolored|1.10|.30|
|1861|A604|120d multicolored|1.10|.45|
|1862|A604|150d multicolored|1.75|.85|
|1863|A604|500d multicolored|4.00|.95|
| |*Nos. 1860-1863 (4)*|7.95|2.55|

Thessaloniki, European Cultural Capital A605

Designs: 80d, Frescoe of St. Dimitrios, patron saint of Thessaloniki, Church of Aghios Nikolaos Orphanos, vert. 100d, Hippocratic Hospital. 120d, Marble pedestal with inscription, medallion with woman's head, vert. 150d, Detail of mosaic from Rotunda cupola, vert. 300d, "Iaspis" chalice, 14th cent., Mt. Athos.

**1997, Mar. 26    Litho.    *Perf. 13½***
| | | | | |
|---|---|---|---|---|
|1864|A605|80d multicolored|.90|.50|
|1865|A605|100d multicolored|1.40|.65|
|1866|A605|120d multicolored|1.50|.75|
|1867|A605|150d multicolored|1.75|1.00|
|1868|A605|300d multicolored|4.50|2.00|
| |*Nos. 1864-1868 (5)*|10.05|4.90|

Bridges of Macedonia A606

**1997, Apr. 24    Litho.    *Perf. 14***
| | | | | |
|---|---|---|---|---|
|1869|A606|80d Village of Trikomo|.70|.45|
|1870|A606|120d Portitsa|1.10|.65|
|1871|A606|150d Village of Ziakas|1.40|.85|
|1872|A606|350d Village of Kastro|3.50|1.90|
| |*Nos. 1869-1872 (4)*|6.70|3.85|

Stories and Legends A607

Europa: 120d, Prometheus, the giver of fire. 430d, Digenis Akritas, Greek swordsmen on horseback.

**1997, May 19    Litho.    *Perf. 14***
| | | | | |
|---|---|---|---|---|
|1873|A607|120d multicolored|1.75|1.50|
|a.| |Perf. 13½ vert.|1.75|1.50|
|1874|A607|430d multicolored|4.00|3.50|
|a.| |Perf. 13½ vert.|4.00|3.50|
|b.| |Pair, #1873-1874|5.75|5.75|
|c.| |Booklet pane, 2 each #1873a, 1874b|11.50|11.50|
| |Complete booklet, #1874c|11.50| |
|d.| |Pair, #1873a, 1874b|5.75|5.75|

6th IAAF World Track & Field Championships, Athens — A608

Official IAAF emblem, Greek flag and: 20d, Runners. 100d, Nike. 140d, High jump. 170d, Hurdles. 500d, Olympic Stadium, Athens.

**1997, July 11    Litho.    *Perf. 13½***
| | | | | |
|---|---|---|---|---|
|1875|A608|20d multicolored|.20|.20|
|1876|A608|100d multicolored|.85|.40|
|1877|A608|140d multicolored|1.25|.80|
|1878|A608|170d multicolored|1.60|1.00|
|1879|A608|500d multicolored|5.25|2.50|
| |*Nos. 1875-1879 (5)*|9.15|4.90|

Famous People A609

Designs: 20d, Alexandros Panagoulis (1939-76), resistance leader, vert. 30d, Grigorios Xenopoulos (1867-1951), novelist, vert. 40d, Odysseus Elytis (1911-96), poet. 50d, Panayiotis Kanellopoulos (1902-86), prime minister, vert. 100d, Harilaos Trikoupis (1832-96), politician. 170d, Maria Callas (1923-77), opera singer. 200d, Rigas Vélestinlis-Feraios (1757-98), revolutionary, vert.

**Perf. 13½x13, 13x13½**
**1997, Oct. 31    Litho.**
| | | | | |
|---|---|---|---|---|
|1880|A609|20d multicolored|.20|.20|
|1881|A609|30d multicolored|.50|.20|
|1882|A609|40d multicolored|.60|.20|
|1883|A609|50d multicolored|.90|.20|
|1884|A609|100d multicolored|1.50|.75|
|1885|A609|170d multicolored|2.00|1.40|
|1886|A609|200d multicolored|2.50|1.60|
| |*Nos. 1880-1886 (7)*|8.20|4.55|

Film Comedians A610

Designs: 20d, Vassilis Avlonitis. 30d, Vassilis Argyropoulos. 50d, Georgia Vassileiadou. 70d, Lambros Constantaras. 100d, Vassilis Logothetidis. 140d, Dionysis Papagiannopoulos. 170d, Nikos Stavrides. 200d, Mimis Fotopoulos.

**1997, Dec. 17    Litho.    *Perf. 13x13½***
| | | | | |
|---|---|---|---|---|
|1887|A610|20d multicolored|.20|.20|
|1888|A610|30d multicolored|.40|.20|
|1889|A610|50d multicolored|.60|.45|
|1890|A610|70d multicolored|.85|.70|
|1891|A610|100d multicolored|1.10|.85|
|1892|A610|140d multicolored|1.60|1.60|
|1893|A610|170d multicolored|2.40|1.60|
|1894|A610|200d multicolored|2.75|1.60|
| |*Nos. 1887-1894 (8)*|9.90|7.20|

Incorporation of the Dodecanese Islands into Greece, 50th Anniv. — A611

100d, German commander signing treaty turning islands over to English and Greek military, Symi (Simi), May 8, 1945. 140d, Greece and Colossus of Rhodes, Greek flag. 170d, English general turns islands over to Greek military command, Rhodes, 3/31/47. 500d, Greek flag raised over Dodencanese, Kasos (Caso), 3/7/47.

**1998, Feb. 27    Litho.    *Perf. 13½x13***
| | | | | |
|---|---|---|---|---|
|1895|A611|100d multicolored|1.00|.65|
|1896|A611|140d multicolored|1.40|1.40|
|1897|A611|170d multicolored|1.75|1.75|
|1898|A611|500d multicolored|4.50|1.25|
| |*Nos. 1895-1898 (4)*|8.65|5.05|

Hagia Sophia General Children's Hospital, Cent. — A612

Holy Monastery of Xenon, 1000th Anniv. A613

4th World Congress of Thracians, Nea Orestiada A614

16th World Congress of Cardiology Research, Athens — A615

European Movement, 50th Anniv. — A616

**Perf. 13x13½, 13½x13**
**1998, Apr. 30    Litho.**
| | | | | |
|---|---|---|---|---|
|1899|A612|20d multicolored|.20|.20|
|1900|A613|100d multicolored|.90|.50|
|1901|A614|140d multicolored|1.25|1.25|
|1902|A615|150d Building, heart, horiz.|1.25|1.25|
|1903|A615|170d multicolored|1.75|1.60|
|1904|A616|500d multicolored|4.50|1.90|
| |*Nos. 1899-1904 (6)*|9.85|6.70|

Souvenir Sheet

1998 FIBA World Basketball Championships, Greece — A617

Illustration reduced.

**1998, June 15    Litho.    *Perf. 14***
| | | | | |
|---|---|---|---|---|
|1905|A617|300d multicolored|3.50|3.50|

Natl. Festivals A618

Europa: 140d, Culture Festival, Grecian Theatre, Epidaurus. 500d, Culture Festival, Herod Atticus Theatre, Athens.

**1998, May 29    Litho.    *Perf. 14x13½***
| | | | | |
|---|---|---|---|---|
|1906|A618|140d multicolored|1.50|1.50|
|a.| |Perf. 13 vert.|1.75|1.75|
|1907|A618|500d multicolored|4.25|4.25|
|a.| |Pair, #1906-1907|6.25|6.25|
|b.| |Perf. 13 vert.|5.00|5.00|
|c.| |Bklt. pane, 2 ea. #1906a, 1907b|14.50|14.50|
| |Complete booklet, #1907c|14.50| |
|d.| |Pair, #1906a, 1907b|7.25|7.25|

Castle Ruins in Greece A619

**1998, July 15    Litho.    *Perf. 13½***
| | | | | |
|---|---|---|---|---|
|1908|A619|30d Hierapetra|.25|.20|
|1909|A619|50d Korfu|.40|.20|
|1910|A619|70d Limnos|.55|.30|
|1911|A619|100d Argolis|.75|.40|
|1912|A619|150d Iraklion|.75|.65|
|1913|A619|170d Navpaktos, vert.|1.25|.90|
|1914|A619|200d Ioannina, vert.|1.50|1.00|
|1915|A619|400d Plataea|3.00|1.50|
|1916|A619|550d Karitainas, vert.|4.25|2.25|
|1917|A619|600d Fragkokastello, Crete|4.50|2.75|
| |*Nos. 1908-1917 (10)*|17.20|10.15|

Each denomination was also sold in booklets containing 20 panes of stamps, perf. 13⅓ horizontally or vertically. Unused booklet stamps sell for the same price as the listed sheet stamps; used booklet stamps sell for somewhat less than the values shown for used sheet stamps.

Greek Orthodox Community of Venice, 500th Anniv. — A620

Designs: 30d, Cathedral. 40d, Icon, vert. 140d, Illuminated manuscript, vert. 230d, Icon of Madonna and Child surrounded by saints.

**1998, Oct. 26    Litho.    *Perf. 14***
| | | | | |
|---|---|---|---|---|
|1918|A620|30d multicolored|.30|.25|
|1919|A620|40d multicolored|.40|.35|
|1920|A620|140d multicolored|1.10|.85|
|1921|A620|230d multicolored|2.50|2.00|
| |*Nos. 1918-1921 (4)*|4.30|3.45|

Greek Writers of Antiquity — A621

**1998    Litho.    *Perf. 13½x13***
| | | | | |
|---|---|---|---|---|
|1922|A621|20d Homer|.20|.20|
|1923|A621|100d Sophocles|1.25|1.10|
|1924|A621|140d Thucydides|1.50|1.50|
|1925|A621|200d Plato|1.90|1.60|
|1926|A621|250d Demosthenes|3.00|1.90|
| |*Nos. 1922-1926 (5)*|7.85|6.30|

Intl. Year of the Ocean A622

Designs: 40d, Ancient ship, map of Mediterranean Sea. 100d, Sailing ship, Neptune. 200d, Modern ship . 500d, Silver tetradrachm of Antigonos Doson, 229-221 B.C.

**1999, Feb. 19    Litho.    *Perf. 13x13½***
| | | | | |
|---|---|---|---|---|
|1927|A622|40d multicolored|.30|.25|
|1928|A622|100d multicolored|.90|.40|
|1929|A622|200d multicolored|1.60|1.00|
|1930|A622|500d multicolored|3.25|1.50|
| |*Nos. 1927-1930 (4)*|6.05|3.15|

Pres. Konstantin Karamanlis (1907-98) — A623

Various portraits of Karamanlis and: 100d, Representations of economic development, 1955-63. 170d, People celebrating. 200d, Emblem of European Union. 500d, National flag, vert.

**1999, Apr. 19    Litho.    *Perf. 14***
| | | | | |
|---|---|---|---|---|
|1931|A623|100d multicolored|.70|.35|
|1932|A623|170d multicolored|1.25|.75|
|1933|A623|200d multicolored|1.50|.85|
|1934|A623|500d multicolored|3.00|2.00|
| |*Nos. 1931-1934 (4)*|6.45|3.95|

Europa A624

Various views Mytikas peak (Mt. Olympus) and wildflowers.

**1999, May 24     Litho.     Perf. 14**

| | | | |
|---|---|---|---|
| **1935** | A624 | 170d multicolored | 1.75 | 1.75 |
| a. | | Perf. 13¼ vert. | 2.00 | 1.75 |
| **1936** | A624 | 550d multicolored | 4.50 | 4.00 |
| a. | | Pair, #1935-1936 | 6.75 | 6.75 |
| b. | | Perf. 13¼ vert. | 4.75 | 4.00 |
| c. | | Booklet pane, 2 each #1935a, 1936b | 14.00 | 14.00 |
| | | Complete booklet, #1936c | 14.00 | |
| d. | | Pair, #1935a, 1936b | 7.00 | 7.00 |

Greece-Japan Diplomatic Relations, Cent. — A625

**1999, June 28     Litho.     Perf. 13¾x14**

| | | | | |
|---|---|---|---|---|
| **1937** | A625 | 120d multicolored | .90 | .75 |

4000 Years of Hellenism — A626

Designs: a, Sanctuary of Apollo Hylates, Kourion. b, Mycenaean "Krater of the Warriors," Athens. c, Mycenaean amphoral krater, Cyprus Museum. d, Sanctuary of Apollo Epikourios, Delphi.

**1999, June 28     Litho.     Perf. 13½x13**

| | | | | |
|---|---|---|---|---|
| **1938** | A626 | 120d Block of 4, #a.-d. | 3.50 | 3.50 |

See Cyprus No. 936.

Community Support Framework, 5th Anniv. A627

Designs: 20d, Modernization of Greek Railway Organization. 120d, Rio-Antirrio Bridge. 140d, Modernization of Greek Post Office. 250d, Athens Metro train. 500d, Eleftherios Venizelos Airport, Athens.

**1999, Nov. 8     Litho.     Perf. 13x13¼**

| | | | | |
|---|---|---|---|---|
| **1939** | A627 | 20d multi | .20 | .20 |
| **1940** | A627 | 120d multi | .75 | .75 |
| **1941** | A627 | 140d multi | .85 | .85 |
| **1942** | A627 | 250d multi | 1.50 | 1.50 |
| **1943** | A627 | 500d multi | 3.00 | 3.00 |
| | | Nos. 1939-1943 (5) | 6.30 | 6.30 |

Armed Forces A628

20d, Exercise with helicopters, rafts. 30d, Patrol boat. 40d, F-16s in flight. 50d, CL-215 dousing forest fire. 70d, Destroyers. 120d, Distribution of goods in Bosnia. 170d, Mirage 2000 in flight. 250d, Exercise with helicopters, tanks. 600d, Submarine Okeanos.

**Perf. 13¾x13½**

**1999, Dec. 13     Litho.**

| | | | | |
|---|---|---|---|---|
| **1944** | A628 | 20d multi | .20 | .20 |
| **1945** | A628 | 30d multi | .20 | .20 |
| **1946** | A628 | 40d multi | .25 | .25 |
| **1947** | A628 | 50d multi | .30 | .30 |
| **1948** | A628 | 70d multi | .40 | .40 |
| **1949** | A628 | 120d multi | .70 | .50 |
| **1950** | A628 | 170d multi | 1.25 | 1.10 |
| **1951** | A628 | 250d multi | 1.75 | 1.50 |
| **1952** | A628 | 600d multi | 3.75 | 3.50 |
| | | Nos. 1944-1952 (9) | 8.80 | 7.95 |

Christianity, 2000th Anniv. A629

Designs: 20d, Birth of Christ, vert. 50d, Inter-religious dialogue, vert. 120d, Angels with instruments, vert. 170d, Dove. 200d, Communion. 500d, Providence, vert.

**2000, Jan. 1     Perf. 14¼x14**

| | | | | |
|---|---|---|---|---|
| **1953** | A629 | 20d multi | .20 | .20 |
| **1954** | A629 | 50d multi | .30 | .30 |
| **1955** | A629 | 120d multi | .70 | .70 |

**Perf. 14x14¼**

| | | | | |
|---|---|---|---|---|
| **1956** | A629 | 170d multi | 1.00 | 1.00 |

**Size: 35x35mm**

**Perf. 13¾**

| | | | | |
|---|---|---|---|---|
| **1957** | A629 | 200d multi | 1.25 | 1.25 |

**Size: 27x57mm**

**Perf. 13½x14**

| | | | | |
|---|---|---|---|---|
| **1958** | A629 | 500d multi | 3.00 | 3.00 |
| | | Nos. 1953-1958 (6) | 6.45 | 6.45 |

**Europa, 2000**
**Common Design Type**

**2000, May 9     Litho.     Perf. 13¼x13**

| | | | | |
|---|---|---|---|---|
| **1959** | CD17 | 170d multi | 3.00 | 3.00 |
| a. | | Perf. 13 vert. | 3.50 | 3.50 |
| b. | | Booklet pane, 4 #1959a | 14.00 | 14.00 |
| | | Complete booklet, #1959b | 14.00 | |

Ships — A630

Designs: 10d, Steamship Ilissos. 120d, Destroyer Adrias. 170d, Steamship Ia II. 400d, Destroyer Vas. Olga.

**Perf. 14¼x13¾**

**2000, June 26     Litho.**

| | | | | |
|---|---|---|---|---|
| **1960** | A630 | 10d multi | .25 | .25 |
| **1961** | A630 | 120d multi | .70 | .65 |
| **1962** | A630 | 170d multi | 1.25 | 1.10 |
| **1963** | A630 | 400d multi | 3.25 | 3.00 |
| | | Nos. 1960-1963 (4) | 5.45 | 5.00 |

Stampin' the Future Children's Stamp Design Contest Winners A631

Art by: 130d, Spyros Dalakos (rainbow). 180d, Ornella Moshovaki-Chaiger (robots). 200d, Zisis Zariotis (building, tree, vehicles). 620d, Athina Limoudi (rocket).

**2000, June 26**

| | | | | |
|---|---|---|---|---|
| **1964** | A631 | 130d multi | .70 | .70 |
| **1965** | A631 | 180d multi | .95 | .95 |
| **1966** | A631 | 200d multi | 1.40 | 1.40 |
| **1967** | A631 | 620d multi | 3.50 | 3.50 |
| | | Nos. 1964-1967 (4) | 6.55 | 6.55 |

Sydney and Athens — A632

Olympic torch, flag and: 200d, Parthenon. 650d, Sydney Opera House.

**Perf. 13¼x13¾**

**2000, Sept. 15     Litho.**

| | | | | |
|---|---|---|---|---|
| **1968-1969** | A632 | Set of 2 | 5.00 | 5.00 |

See Australia Nos. 1873-1874.

Emblem of 2004 Athens Olympic Games — A633

Various backgrounds. Denominations: 10d, 50d, 130d, 180d, 200d, 650d.

**2000, Nov. 7     Perf. 14x14¼**

| | | | | |
|---|---|---|---|---|
| **1970-1975** | A633 | Set of 6 | 8.00 | 8.00 |

**Souvenir Sheet**

Stamps of the Cretan Government, Cent. — A634

No. 1976: a, 200d, Crete #69. b, 650d, Crete #71.
Illustration reduced.

**2000, Dec. 18     Litho.     Perf. 14x14¼**

| | | | | |
|---|---|---|---|---|
| **1976** | A634 | Sheet of 2, #a-b | 12.50 | 12.50 |

Christianity, 2000th Anniv. A635

Designs: 20d, Sculpture of Christ as Orpheus, vert. 30d, Sculpture of The Good Shepherd, vert. 40d, Mosaic of Christ, vert. 100d, Mural of Christ. 130d, Icon of Christ (green frame), vert. 150d, Icon of Christ with open Bible, vert. 180d, Icon of Christ with closed Bible (dark blue frame), vert. 1000d, Byzantine coin depicting Christ.

**2000, Dec. 18     Perf. 14x14¼, 14¼x14**

| | | | | |
|---|---|---|---|---|
| **1977-1984** | A635 | Set of 8 | 10.00 | 10.00 |

Post Office Savings Bank, Cent. A636

Designs: 20d, Mother and child, vert. 130d, Emblem and 2-euro coin.

**Perf. 13¼x13¾, 13¾x13¼**

**2001, May 15     Litho.**

| | | | | |
|---|---|---|---|---|
| **1985-1986** | A636 | Set of 2 | 1.10 | 1.10 |

UN High Commissioner for Refugees, 50th Anniv. — A637

**2001, May 15     Perf. 13¾x13¼**

| | | | | |
|---|---|---|---|---|
| **1987** | A637 | 140d multi | 1.25 | 1.25 |

Thessaloniki Intl. Trade Fair, 75th Anniv. — A638

**2001, May 15     Perf. 13¼x13¾**

| | | | | |
|---|---|---|---|---|
| **1988** | A638 | 180d multi | 1.25 | 1.25 |

Aristotle University, Thessaloniki, 75th Anniv. — A639

**2001, May 15     Perf. 13¾x13¼**

| | | | | |
|---|---|---|---|---|
| **1989** | A639 | 200d multi | 1.50 | 1.50 |

Academy of Athens, 75th Anniv. A640

**2001, May 15**

| | | | | |
|---|---|---|---|---|
| **1990** | A640 | 500d multi | 3.75 | 3.75 |

Ioannis Zigdis (1913-97), Politician — A641

**2001, May 15     Perf. 13¼x13¾**

| | | | | |
|---|---|---|---|---|
| **1991** | A641 | 700d multi | 5.00 | 5.00 |

Europa — A642

Designs: Nos. 1992a, 1992c, Dry leaf, parched earth. Nos. 1992b, 1992d, Water, fresh leaves.

**2001, May 15     Perf. 14¼x13¾**

| | | | | |
|---|---|---|---|---|
| **1992** | A642 | Horiz. pair | 8.50 | 8.50 |
| a. | | 180d multi | 2.00 | 2.00 |
| b. | | 650d multi | 6.50 | 6.50 |
| c. | | Horiz. pair, perf. 13¼ vert. | 8.50 | 8.50 |
| d. | | As "a," perf. 13¼ vert. | 2.00 | 2.00 |
| e. | | As "b," perf. 13¼ vert. | 6.50 | 6.50 |
| f. | | Booklet pane, 2 # 1992c | 17.00 | |
| | | Booklet, #1992f | 17.00 | |

Birds and
Flowers
A643

Designs: 20d, Little egret. 50d, White stork.
100d, Bearded vulture. 140d, Orchid, vert.
150d, Dalmatian pelican, vert. 200d, Lily, Plas-
tira Lake. 700d, Egyptian vulture. 850d, Black
vulture.

*Perf. 13¾x13¼, 13¼x13¾*

**2001, June 27**
**1993-2000** A643     Set of 8     17.00  17.00

Symbol of Hellenic Post — A644

Illustration reduced.

**2001, Sept. 8  Litho.   Perf. 13x12¾**
**2001**                                    2.50   2.50
  Pair + 2 labels
  *a.* A644 140d blue & yellow    1.00   1.00
  *b.* A644 200d blue             1.50   1.50

Wording on label varies. No. 2001 could be
personalized by adding photos to the labels.

Souvenir Sheet

Christianity in Armenia, 1700th
Anniv. — A645

**2001, Dec. 5             Perf. 13**
**2002** A645 850d multi          6.75   6.75

Souvenir Sheet

2004 Summer Olympics,
Athens — A646

**2001, Dec. 5            Perf. 13¾**
**2003** A646 1200d multi       9.50   9.50

100 Cents = 1 Euro (€)

Dances
A647

Designs: 2c, Kamakaki. 3c, Bride's dowry.
5c, Zagorissios, vert. 10c, Balos. 15c,
Synkathistos. 20c, Tsakonikos, vert. 30c, Pyr-
richios. 35c, Fourles, vert. 40c, Apokriatikos.
45c, Kotsari. 50c, Pentozalis, vert. 55c,
Karagouna. 60c, Hassapiko. 65c, Zalistos.
85c, Pogonissios. €1, Kalamatianos. €2,
Maleviziotis. €2.15, Tsamikos. €2.60,
Zeibekikos, vert. €3, Nyfiatikos. €4,
Paschaliatikos.

*Perf. 13x13¼, 13¼x13*

**2002, Jan. 2                      Litho.**
**2004** A647      2c multi      .20     .20
**2005** A647      3c multi      .20     .20
**2006** A647      5c multi      .20     .20
**2007** A647     10c multi      .30     .30
**2008** A647     15c multi      .45     .45
**2009** A647     20c multi      .60     .60
**2010** A647     30c multi      .90     .90
**2011** A647     35c multi     1.00    1.00
**2012** A647     40c multi     1.25    1.25
**2013** A647     45c multi     1.40    1.40
**2014** A647     50c multi     1.50    1.50
**2015** A647     55c multi     1.60    1.60
**2016** A647     60c multi     1.75    1.75
**2017** A647     65c multi     1.90    1.90
**2018** A647     85c multi     2.50    2.50
**2019** A647      €1 multi     3.00    3.00
**2020** A647      €2 multi     6.00    6.00
**2021** A647   €2.15 multi     6.50    6.50
**2022** A647   €2.60 multi     7.75    7.75
**2023** A647      €3 multi     9.00    9.00
**2024** A647      €4 multi    12.00   12.00
  *Nos. 2004-2024 (21)*    60.00   60.00

Each denomination also sold in booklets
containing 20 panes of stamps, perf 13¼ vertically or horizontally. Unused booklet stamps
sell for the same prices as the sheet stamps
listed; most used booklet stamps sell for significantly less than the values shown for used
sheet stamps.

2004
Summer
Olympics,
Athens
A648

Ancient Olympics: 41c, Runners. 59c,
Sculpture of charioteer, vert. 80c, Javelin
thrower. €2.05, Doryphoros of Polycleitos,
vert. €2.35, Weight lifter.
€5, Stadium archway.

*Perf. 13¾x13¼, 13¼x13¾*

**2002, Mar. 15                   Litho.**
**2025-2029** A648     Set of 5    19.00  19.00

**Souvenir Sheet**
*Perf. 12¾*

**2030** A648   €5 multi          15.00  15.00

No. 2030 contains one 49x28mm stamp.

Europa — A649

**2002, May 9             Perf. 13¼x13¾**
**2031** A649   Horiz. pair, #a-b   8.50   8.50
  *a.* 60c Elephant         1.75   1.75
  *b.* €2.60 Equestrian act  6.75   6.75
  *c.* Horiz. pair, perf. 13¼ vert.  8.50  8.50
  *d.* As "a," perf. 13¼ vert.  1.75  1.75
  *e.* As "b," perf. 13¼ vert.  6.75  6.75
  *f.* Booklet pane, 2, #2031c  17.00  —
    Booklet, #2031f         17.00

Scouting
A650

Designs: 45c, Navy Scout, sailboats. 60c,
Scout, emblem of World Conference. 70c,
Scouts planting tree. €2.15, Scouts, map and
mountain.

**2002, June 26  Litho.   Perf. 13x13½**
**2032-2035** A650     Set of 4    11.50  11.50
*2035a*       Miniature sheet, 2 each
    #2032-2035 + 4 labels  25.00  25.00

Greek
Language
A651

Designs: 45c, Hieros Nomos, Athens Acropolis, 5th cent. B.C. 60c, Linear B script, 13th
cent. B.C., vert. 90c, The Memoirs of General
Makriyiannis. €2.15, Byzantine script, 11th
cent., vert.

*Perf. 13¾x13¼, 13¼x13¾*

**2002, Sept. 23**
**2036-2039** A651     Set of 4    12.50  12.50

Ancient Olympic
Winners With
Laurel
Wreaths — A652

Head color: 45c, Green. 60c, Dark blue.
€2.15, Pink. €2.60, Light blue.

**2002, Oct. 30  Litho.   Perf. 13¼x13¾**
**2040-2043** A652     Set of 4    17.50  17.50
*2043a*       Miniature sheet, 2 each
    #2040-2043                 35.00  35.00

Souvenir Sheet

Stadia of First Olympics — A653

**2002, Oct. 30             Perf. 12¾**
**2044** A653   €6 multi          18.00  18.00

Archbishops
of Athens
A654

Archbishop and years of reign: 10c, Chrys-
tostomos I (1923-38). 45c, Chrysanthos
(1938-41). €2.15, Damaskinos (1941-49).
€2.60, Serapheim (1974-98).

**2002, Dec. 10            Perf. 13x13½**
**2045-2048** A654     Set of 4    16.00  16.00

Olympic Sports
Equipment — A655

Designs: 2c, Discus. 5c, Hammer. 47c,
Javelin. 65c, Pole vault pole and bar. €2.17,
Hurdles. €2.85, Weights.

**2003, Feb. 11          Perf. 13¾x14¼**
**2049-2054** A655     Set of 6    19.00  19.00
*2054a*       Sheet, #2049-2054     16.00  16.00

2004 Summer Olympics, Athens.

Souvenir Sheet

Mascots for 2004 Summer Olympics,
Athens — A656

No. 2055: a, €2.50, Mascot with red shirt. b,
€2.85, Mascot with blue shirt.

**2003, Feb. 11             Perf. 13¼**
**2055** A656   Sheet of 2, #a-b   16.00  16.00

Greetings — A657

No. 2056: a, Globe. b, Athens 2004 Olympic
Games emblem and Olympic rings. c, Ancient
Greek athlete with laurel wreath. d, Roses and
wedding headband. e, Spheres and grid. f,
Child's drawing of train. g, Man and woman
holding flowers. h, Stone carving of face. i,
Acropolis.

**2003, Mar. 18  Litho.   Perf. 14x13¾**
**2056** A657   Sheet of 9        13.50  13.50
  *a.-g.* 47c Any single         1.40   1.40
  *h.-i.* 65c Either single      2.00   2.00
  *q.*   No. 2056h + label       3.75   3.75
  *r.*   #2056a + label          2.00   2.00
  *s.*   #2056b + label          2.00   2.00
  *t.*   #2056d + label          2.00   2.00
  *u.*   #2056d + label          2.00   2.00
  *v.*   #2056e + label          2.00   2.00
  *w.*   #2056f + label          2.00   2.00

No. 2056q was issued in sheets of 15
stamps and 15 labels that sold for €19.50.
Labels could be personalized. No. 2056q
exists dated "2004." Stamps dated "2004"
were issued in sheets of 5 stamps + 5
preprinted labels that sold for €4 per sheet.
Additional stamps in this set were available
with personalized labels. The editors would
like to examine any examples.

Nos. 2056r-2056w were printed in sheets of
15 + 15 labels that sold for €14.10. Labels
could be personalized. Two additional personalized stamps exist in this set. The editors
would like to examine any examples.

Dove and
Stars — A658

White Tower of
Thessaloniki in
Letters — A659

Fresco of
Birds — A660

Jigsaw Puzzle
Pieces — A661

| 2003, Apr. 16 | | | Perf. 14x13¾ | |
|---|---|---|---|---|
| 2057 | A658 | 47c multi | 1.40 | 1.40 |
| 2058 | A659 | 65c multi | 2.00 | 2.00 |
| 2059 | A660 | €2.17 multi | 6.50 | 6.50 |
| 2060 | A661 | €2.85 multi | 8.50 | 8.50 |
| 2060a | | Sheet, 2 each #2057-2060 | 37.50 | 37.50 |
| | Nos. 2057-2060 (4) | | 18.40 | 18.40 |

Greek Presidency of European Union.

Europa — A662

Poster art: a, 65c, Abstract. b, €2.85, Tourist poster.

| 2003, May 9 | | Litho. | Perf. 13¼x13¾ | |
|---|---|---|---|---|
| 2061 | A662 | Horiz. pair | 10.50 | 10.50 |
| a. | | 65c multi | 2.00 | 2.00 |
| b. | | €2.85 multi | 8.50 | 8.50 |
| c. | | Horiz. pair, perf. 13¼ | 10.50 | 10.50 |
| d. | | As "a," perf. 13¼ vert. | 2.00 | 2.00 |
| e. | | As "b," perf. 13¼ vert. | 8.50 | 8.50 |
| f. | | Booklet pane, 2 #2061c | 21.00 | |
| | | Complete booklet, #2061f | 21.00 | |

A663

No. 2062: a, Water polo. b, Diving. c, Swimming.
No. 2063, vert.: a, Table tennis. b, Basketball. c, Soccer. d, Handball.
No. 2064: a, Kayak slalom. b, Windsurfing.
No. 2065, vert.: a, Rhythmic gymnastics. b, Judo. c, Archery. d, Trampoline.
No. 2066: a, Kayak (flatwater). b, Rowing (coxswain). c, Rowing (rower).
No. 2067, vert.: a, Badminton. b, Fencing. c, Tennis. d, Taekwondo.
No. 2068: a, Cycling. b, Triathlon.
No. 2069, vert.: a, Baseball. b, Beach volleyball. c, Field hockey. d, Boxing.
No. 2070, vert.: a, Weight lifting (figure in red) b, Weight lifting (figure in blue).

| 2003, May 9 | | Litho. | Perf. 13¼ | |
|---|---|---|---|---|
| 2062 | A663 | Booklet pane of 3 + label | 4.75 | — |
| a.-c. | | 47c Any single | 1.50 | 1.40 |
| 2063 | A663 | Booklet pane of 4 | 6.00 | — |
| a.-d. | | 47c Any single | 1.50 | 1.40 |
| 2064 | A663 | Booklet pane of 2 | 3.50 | — |
| a.-b. | | 47c Either single | 1.75 | 1.40 |
| 2065 | A663 | Booklet pane of 4 | 6.00 | — |
| a. | | 30c multi | 1.25 | 1.00 |
| b.-d. | | 47c Any single | 1.50 | 1.40 |
| 2066 | A663 | Booklet pane of 3 + label | 4.75 | — |
| a.-c. | | 47c Any single | 1.50 | 1.40 |
| 2067 | A663 | Booklet pane of 4 | 6.00 | — |
| a. | | 30c multi | 1.25 | 1.00 |
| b.-d. | | 47c Any single | 1.50 | 1.40 |
| 2068 | A663 | Booklet pane of 2 | 3.50 | — |
| a.-b. | | 47c Either single | 1.75 | 1.40 |
| 2069 | A663 | Booklet pane of 4 | 6.00 | — |
| a. | | 35c multi | 1.25 | 1.10 |
| b.-d. | | 47c Any single | 1.50 | 1.40 |
| 2070 | A663 | Booklet pane of 2 | 3.50 | — |
| a.-b. | | 47c Either single | 1.75 | 1.40 |
| | | Complete booklet, #2062-2070 | 50.00 | |

Booklet containing Nos. 2062-2070 sold for €14.99.

Environmental
Protection — A664

Designs: 15c, Apple falling from tree. 47c, Apple in water. 65c, Laurel wreath over seacoast. €2.85, Moon over tree.

| 2003, June 5 | | Perf. 13¼x13¾ | |
|---|---|---|---|
| 2071-2074 | A664 | Set of 4 | 12.50 | 12.50 |

Olympic
Sports
A665

Designs: 5c, High jump. 47c, Wrestling. 65c, Running. 80c, Cycling, vert. €4, Windsurfing, vert.

| Perf. 13¾x13¼, 13¼x13¾ | | | |
|---|---|---|---|
| 2003, Sept. 9 | | | |
| 2075-2079 | A665 | Set of 5 | 18.00 | 18.00 |
| 2079a | | Miniature sheet, #2075-2079 | 18.00 | 18.00 |

Souvenir Sheet

Mascots for 2004 Summer Olympics,
Athens — A666

No. 2080: a, Figure in red. b, Figure in blue.

| 2003, Sept. 9 | | | Perf. 13¼ | |
|---|---|---|---|---|
| 2080 | A666 | Sheet of 2 | 16.00 | 16.00 |
| a. | | €2.50 multi | 7.50 | 7.50 |
| b. | | €2.85 multi | 8.50 | 8.50 |

Trades of the
Past — A667

Designs: 3c, Stair carving. 10c, Shoemaking. 50c, Blacksmithing. €1, Typesetting by hand. €1.40, Sponge fishing. €4, Weaving.

| 2003, Oct. 17 | | | Perf. 13¾x13¼ | |
|---|---|---|---|---|
| 2081-2086 | A667 | Set of 6 | 21.00 | 21.00 |
| 2086a | | Miniature sheet, #2081-2086 | 21.00 | 21.00 |

Olympic
Athletes — A668

Various athletes: 20c, 30c, 40c, 47c, €2, €2.85.

| Perf. 13¼x13¾ | | | |
|---|---|---|---|
| 2003, Nov. 28 | | | Litho. |
| 2087-2092 | A668 | Set of 6 | 19.00 | 19.00 |
| 2092a | | Miniature sheet, #2087-2092 | 19.00 | 19.00 |

Greek
Olympians
A669

Athletes: 3c, Spyridon Louis, marathon, 1896 gold medalist. 10c, Aristides Konstantinides, cycling road race, 1896 gold medalist. €2, Ioannis Fokianos, gymnastics coach. €2.17, Ioannis Mitropoulos, rings, 1896 gold medalist. €3.60, Konstantinos Tsiklitiras, standing long jump, 1912 gold medalist.

| Litho. with Foil Application | | | | |
|---|---|---|---|---|
| 2004, Jan. 15 | | | Perf. 13x13½ | |
| 2093-2097 | A669 | Set of 5 | 24.00 | 24.00 |

Cities
Hosting
Events at
2004
Olympics
A670

Designs: 1c, Volos. 2c, Patra. 5c, Iraklion. 47c, Athens. €1.40, Thessaloniki. €4, Athens, diff.

| 2004, Jan. 15 | | | Litho. | |
|---|---|---|---|---|
| 2098-2103 | A670 | Set of 6 | 18.00 | 18.00 |

Olympic
Sports
A671

Designs: 5c, Swimmer. 10c, Gymnast chalking hands. 20c, Kayak. 47c, Relay race. €2, Rhythmic gymnastics, vert. €5, Men's rings, vert.

| 2004, Mar. 24 | | Litho. | Perf. 13¼ | |
|---|---|---|---|---|
| 2104-2109 | A671 | Set of 6 | 24.00 | 24.00 |
| 2109a | | Miniature sheet, #2104-2109 | 24.00 | 24.00 |

Europa — A672

| 2004, May 4 | | | Perf. 13¼x13¾ | |
|---|---|---|---|---|
| 2110 | A672 | Horiz. pair | 10.50 | 10.50 |
| a. | | 65c Sailboat | 2.00 | 2.00 |
| b. | | €2.85 Balloon | 8.50 | 8.50 |
| c. | | Horiz. pair, perf. 13¼ vert. | 10.50 | 10.50 |
| d. | | As "a," perf. 13¼ vert. | 2.00 | 2.00 |
| e. | | As "b," perf. 13¼ vert. | 8.50 | 8.50 |
| f. | | Booklet pane, 2 #2110c | 21.00 | — |
| | | Complete booklet, #2110f | 21.00 | |

Souvenir Sheets

Olympic Flame — A673

Olympic Dove — A674

| 2004, May 4 | | | Perf. 13¾x14 | |
|---|---|---|---|---|
| 2111 | A673 | Sheet of 2 | 9.00 | 9.00 |
| a. | | 47c Torch bearer | 1.40 | 1.40 |
| b. | | €2.50 Torch bearer, city | 7.50 | 7.50 |
| c. | | #2111a + label, perf. 14x13¾ | 2.40 | 2.40 |
| | | Perf. 13¼ | | |
| 2112 | A674 | Sheet of 2 | 9.00 | 9.00 |
| a. | | 47c Dove, Olympic rings | 1.40 | 1.40 |
| b. | | €2.50 Dove, people | 7.50 | 7.50 |

No. 2111c was printed in sheets of 15 + 15 labels that sold for €15. Labels could be personalized.

Olympic
Coins — A675

Obverse and reverse of: 47c, Silver threedrachma of Cos, 480-450 BC. 65c, Gold stater of Philip II of Macedonia. €2, Silver twodrachma of Elis, 460 BC. €2.17, Silver fourdrachma of Philip II of Macedonia.

| 2004, June 15 | | | Perf. 13¼ | |
|---|---|---|---|---|
| 2113-2116 | A675 | Set of 4 | 16.00 | 16.00 |
| 2116a | | Miniature sheet, #2113-2116 | 16.00 | 16.00 |

Souvenir Sheets

Modern Art and the Olympics — A676

| 2004, July 23 | | | Perf. 13x13¼ | |
|---|---|---|---|---|
| 2117 | A676 | Sheet of 2 | 9.00 | 9.00 |
| a. | | 50c Wavy lines | 1.50 | 1.50 |
| b. | | €2.50 Stripes of color | 7.50 | 7.50 |
| | | Perf. 13¼x13 | | |
| 2118 | A676 | Sheet of 2 | 9.00 | 9.00 |
| a. | | €1 Paint brush, vert. | 3.00 | 3.00 |
| b. | | €2 Paint roller, vert. | 6.00 | 6.00 |
| c. | | Miniature sheet, #2117a-2117b, 2118a-2118b | 18.00 | 18.00 |

Greece,
2004
European
Soccer
Champions
A677

Designs: 47c, Greek flag, trophy. 65c, Greek players celebrating. €1, Greek players holding trophy. €2.88, Greek players, trophy.

| 2004, July 16 | | Litho. | Perf. 13x13¼ | |
|---|---|---|---|---|
| 2119-2122 | A677 | Set of 4 | 15.00 | 15.00 |
| a. | | Souvenir sheet, #2119-2122 | 15.00 | 15.00 |

Greek Flag and Trophy — A678

**2004, July    Litho.    Perf. 14x13¾**
2123 A678 47c multi + label    1.60   1.60
    *a.*    Sheet of 5 + 5 labels     8.25    —
    *b.*    Sheet of 10 + 10 labels    16.50    —

No. 2123 was printed in sheets of 15 + 15 labels that could be personalized. The sheet sold for €15. Nos. 2123a and 2123b have labels that depict soccer players or emblems, which cannot be personalized. Nos. 2123a and 2123b exist with two different sets of labels, and the set of 4 sheets sold for €20.

2004 Summer
Olympics,
Athens — A679

Designs: 50c, Hall of Good Harvest, Temple of Heaven, Beijing. 65c, Parthenon, Athens.

**2004, Aug. 9    Litho.    Perf. 14**
2124-2125 A679   Set of 2    4.00   4.00
    *a.*   Souvenir sheet, #2124-2125    4.00   4.00

See People's Republic of China Nos. 3376-3377.

**Souvenir Sheet**

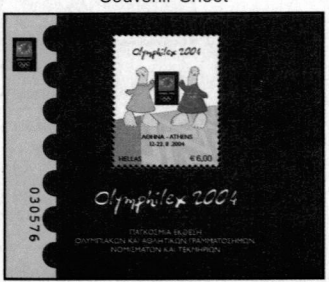

Olymphilex 2004 Philatelic
Exhibition — A680

**2004, Aug. 13     Perf. 13½x13¼**
2126 A680 €6 multi    18.00   18.00

Nikos Syranidis and Thomas Bimis, Synchronized Diving Gold Medalists A681

Leonidas Sampanis, Disqualified Bronze Medalist in 62 Kilogram Weight Lifting — A682

Ilias Iliadis, Judo Gold Medalist A683

Sofia Bekatorou and Emilia Tsoulfa, Women's 470 Sailing Gold Medalists A684

Pyrros Dimas, 85 Kilogram Weight Lifting Bronze Medalist A685

Dimosthenis Tampakos, Rings Gold Medalist A686

Anastasia Kelesidou, Women's Discus Silver Medalist A687

Vasilis Polymeros and Nikos Skiathitis, Lightweight Double Sculls Bronze Medalists A688

Athanasia Tzoumeleka, Women's 20 Kilometer Walk Gold Medalist A689

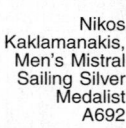

Chrysopigi Devezi, Women's Triple Jump Silver Medalist A690

Fani Chalkia, Women's 400-Meter Hurdles Gold Medalist A691

Nikos Kaklamanakis, Men's Mistral Sailing Silver Medalist A692

Artiom Kiouregian, 55 Kilogram Greco-Roman Wrestling Bronze Medalist A693

Women's Water Polo Team, Silver Medalist A694

Mirela Maniani, Women's Javelin Bronze Medalist A695

Elisavet Mystakidou, Women's 67 Kilogram Taekwondo Silver Medalist A696

Alexandros Nikolaidis, Men's 80 Kilogram Taekwondo Silver Medalist A697

**Digitally Printed**

**2004, Aug.        Perf. 13¼**
2127 A681 65c multi    1.90   1.90
2128 A682 65c multi   19.00   19.00
2129 A683 65c multi    1.90   1.90
2130 A684 65c multi    1.90   1.90
2131 A685 65c multi    1.90   1.90
2132 A686 65c multi    1.90   1.90
2133 A687 65c multi    1.90   1.90
2134 A688 65c multi    1.90   1.90
2135 A689 65c multi    1.90   1.90
2136 A690 65c multi    1.90   1.90
2137 A691 65c multi    1.90   1.90
2138 A692 65c multi    1.90   1.90
2139 A693 65c multi    1.90   1.90
2140 A694 65c multi    1.90   1.90
2141 A695 65c multi    1.90   1.90
2142 A696 65c multi    1.90   1.90
2143 A697 65c multi    1.90   1.90
    *Nos. 2127-2143 (17)*    49.40   49.40

**Litho.**
2144 A681 65c multi    1.90   1.90
2145 A682 65c multi   15.00   15.00
2146 A683 65c multi    1.90   1.90
2147 A684 65c multi    1.90   1.90
2148 A685 65c multi    1.90   1.90
2149 A686 65c multi    1.90   1.90
2150 A687 65c multi    1.90   1.90
2151 A688 65c multi    1.90   1.90
2152 A689 65c multi    1.90   1.90
2153 A690 65c multi    1.90   1.90
2154 A691 65c multi    1.90   1.90
2155 A692 65c multi    1.90   1.90
2156 A693 65c multi    1.90   1.90
2157 A694 65c multi    1.90   1.90
2158 A695 65c multi    1.90   1.90
2159 A696 65c multi    1.90   1.90
2160 A697 65c multi    1.90   1.90
    *a.*   Souvenir sheet, #2144,
       2146-2160    30.00   30.00
    *Nos. 2144-2160 (17)*    45.40   45.40

Issued: Nos. 2127-2128, 8/17; No. 2129, 8/18; Nos. 2130-2131, 8/22; Nos. 2132-2134, 8/23; Nos. 2135-2136, 8/24; Nos. 2137-2139, 8/26, No. 2140, 8/27; No. 2141, 8/28; No. 2142, 8/29; No. 2143, 8/30. Nos. 2144-2160 were to have been issued within days of the digitally printed stamp with the same design. The digitally printed stamps have almost illegible lettering above the Olympic rings at upper right, and fuzzy, indistinct details in the emblem above this lettering. These details are clearer and more readable on the lithographed stamps.

Nos. 2128 and 2145 were withdrawn from circulation after the athlete shown was stripped of his medal after failing a drug test.

2004
Paralympics,
Athens — A698

Designs: 20c, Horses and riders. 49c, Handicapped runner. €2, Wheelchair basketball. €2.24, Archer in wheelchair.

**Perf. 13¼x13¾**
**2004, Sept. 22       Litho.**
2161-2164 A698   Set of 4   12.50   12.50

Island Views — A699

**2004, Dec. 27       Perf. 14x13¾**
2165 A699    2c Santorini     .20    .20
    *a.*   Perf. 13¼ horiz.        .20    .20
2166 A699    3c Karpathos     .20    .20
    *a.*   Perf. 13¼ horiz.        .20    .20
2167 A699    5c Crete-Vai     .20    .20
    *a.*   Perf. 13¼ horiz.        .20    .20
2168 A699   10c Mykonos     .30    .30
    *a.*   Perf. 13¼ horiz.        .30    .30
2169 A699   49c Canea     1.50   1.50
2170 A699   50c Castellorizo   1.50   1.50
    *a.*   Perf. 13¼ horiz.      1.50   1.50
2171 A699   €1 Astipalaia    3.00   3.00
2172 A699   €2 Serifos     6.00   6.00
    *a.*   Perf. 13¼ horiz.      6.00   6.00
2173 A699 €2.24 Melos     6.75   6.75
    *a.*   Perf. 13¼ horiz.      6.75   6.75
2174 A699   €4 Skiathos   12.00   12.00
    *a.*   Perf. 13¼ horiz.    12.00   12.00
    *Nos. 2165-2174 (10)*   31.65   31.65

Jewelry
A700

Designs: 1c, Necklace, 730 B.C. 15c, Snake-shaped bracelet, 2nd-3rd cent. B.C., vert. 30c, Necklace, 5th cent. 49c, Crown, 2nd cent. €4, Earring, 8th cent. B.C., vert.

**Perf. 13¾x13¼, 13¼x13¾**
**2005, Feb. 25**
2175-2179 A700   Set of 5   15.00   15.00

State Laboratory,
75th
Anniv. — A701

European
Diabetes
Association, 41st
Meeting — A702

European Society for Cardiovascular
Surgery, 54th Congress — A703

I. Kondilakis, First
President of
Athens Journalists
Union — A704

Year of Economic
Competitiveness — A705

Greek Mastological
Society, 25th
Anniv. — A706

Angel, by Alekos Kontopoulos — A707

**2005, Apr. 5    Perf. 13¼x13, 13x13¼**

| | | | | |
|---|---|---|---|---|
| 2180 | A701 | 1c multi | .20 | .20 |
| 2181 | A701 | 4c multi | .20 | .20 |
| 2182 | A701 | 5c multi | .20 | .20 |
| 2183 | A701 | 40c multi | 1.25 | 1.25 |
| 2184 | A701 | 49c multi | 1.50 | 1.50 |
| 2185 | A701 | €1.40 multi | 4.25 | 4.25 |
| 2186 | A701 | €3.50 multi | 10.50 | 10.50 |
| | *Nos. 2180-2186 (7)* | | 18.10 | 18.10 |

Flowers — A708

Designs: 20c, Gladiolus illyricus. 40c, Crocus sieberi. 49c, Narcissus tazetta. €1.40, Rhododendron luteum. €3, Tulipa boeotica.

**2005, Apr. 5    Perf. 13¼x13¾**
2187-2191  A708  Set of 5  16.00 16.00

Europa — A709

**2005, May 19    Perf. 14¼x13¾**

| | | | | |
|---|---|---|---|---|
| 2192 | A709 | Horiz. pair | 9.00 | 9.00 |
| a. | | 65c Finished dish | 2.00 | 2.00 |
| b. | | €2.35 Ingredients | 7.00 | 7.00 |
| c. | | Horiz. pair, perf. 13¼ vert. | 9.00 | 9.00 |
| d. | | As "a," perf. 13¼ vert. | 2.00 | 2.00 |
| e. | | As "b," perf. 13¼ vert. | 7.00 | 7.00 |
| f. | | Booklet pane, 2 #2192c | 18.00 | — |
| | | Complete booklet, #2192f | 18.00 | |

Wine
Grapes
A710

Designs: 20c, Agiorgitiko grapes and grape pickers, Peloponnisos. 49c, Assyrtiko grapes, Santorini. 65c, Xinomavro grapes and coin, Macedonia. €2.24, Robolla grapes, Cephalonia. €2.40, Moschofilero, Peloponnisos.

**2005, May 19    Perf. 13¾x14**
2193-2197  A710  Set of 5  18.00 18.00

Blackboard
A711

Girl
Reading — A712

Envelope
A713

Stylized
People — A714

Grid — A715

Globe and
Stylized
Stamp — A716

Flowers — A717

Church — A718

**2005, July 15    Perf. 14x13¾**

| | | | | |
|---|---|---|---|---|
| 2198 | A711 | 49c multi | 1.50 | 1.50 |
| a. | | #2198 + label | 2.50 | 2.50 |
| 2199 | A712 | 49c multi | 1.50 | 1.50 |
| a. | | #2199 + label | 2.50 | 2.50 |
| 2200 | A713 | 49c multi | 1.50 | 1.50 |
| 2201 | A714 | 49c multi | 1.50 | 1.50 |
| a. | | #2201 + label | 2.50 | 2.50 |
| 2202 | A715 | 49c multi | 1.50 | 1.50 |
| a. | | #2202 + label | 2.50 | 2.50 |
| 2203 | A716 | 49c multi | 1.50 | 1.50 |
| 2204 | A717 | 49c multi | 1.50 | 1.50 |
| a. | | #2204 + label | 2.50 | 2.50 |
| 2205 | A718 | 65c multi | 1.90 | 1.90 |
| a. | | #2205 + label | 3.25 | 3.25 |
| | *Nos. 2198-2205 (8)* | | 12.40 | 12.40 |

Nos. 2198a and 2199a were printed in sheets of 10 + 10 labels that sold for €10. Nos. 2201a, 2202a and 2204a were printed in sheets of 15 + 15 labels that sold for €15. No. 2205a was printed in sheets of 10 + 10 labels that sold for €13. Labels could be personalized. Two additional personalized stamps exist in this set. The editors would like to examine any examples.

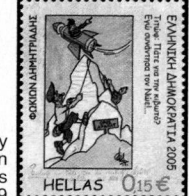

Drawing by
Fokion
Dimitriadis
A719

Drawing by
Archelaos
A720

Drawing by
Themos
Anninos — A721

Drawing by
Dimitris
Galanis — A722

Drawing by
Kostas
Mitropoulos
A723

Unattributed
Odyssey
Scene — A724

**2005, Sept. 16    Perf. 13¼x13¾**

| | | | | |
|---|---|---|---|---|
| 2206 | A719 | 15c multi | .45 | .45 |
| 2207 | A720 | 20c multi | .60 | .60 |
| 2208 | A721 | 30c multi | .90 | .90 |
| 2209 | A722 | 50c multi | 1.50 | 1.50 |

| | | | | |
|---|---|---|---|---|
| 2210 | A723 | 65c multi | 1.90 | 1.90 |
| 2211 | A724 | €4 multi | 12.00 | 12.00 |
| | *Nos. 2206-2211 (6)* | | 17.35 | 17.35 |

**Booklet Panes of 1**
**Self-Adhesive**

| | | | | |
|---|---|---|---|---|
| 2212 | A719 | 15c multi | .45 | .45 |
| 2213 | A720 | 20c multi | .60 | .60 |
| 2214 | A721 | 30c multi | .90 | .90 |
| 2215 | A722 | 50c multi | 1.50 | 1.50 |
| 2216 | A723 | 65c multi | 1.90 | 1.90 |
| 2217 | A724 | €4 multi | 12.00 | 12.00 |
| | Complete booklet, #2212-2217 | | 17.50 | |
| | *Nos. 2212-2217 (6)* | | 17.35 | 17.35 |

Greece,
2005
European
Basketball
Champions
A725

Basketball, net and: 30c, Players in game. 50c, Championship bowl. 65c, Fans. €3.55, Players celebrating.

**2005, Oct. 7    Litho.    Perf. 13x13¼**

| | | | | |
|---|---|---|---|---|
| 2218-2221 | A725 | Set of 4 | 15.00 | 15.00 |
| 2221a | | Souvenir sheet, #2218-2221 | 15.00 | 15.00 |

Automobiles — A726

Designs: 1c, Mini Cooper. 30c, Fiat 500. 50c, Citroen 2CV. €2.25, Volkswagen Beetle. €2.85, Ford Model T.

**2005, Nov. 4    Perf. 13x13¼**

| | | | | |
|---|---|---|---|---|
| 2222-2226 | A726 | Set of 5 | 17.50 | 17.50 |
| 2226a | | As #2226, without inscription "Ford Model T" | 10.00 | 10.00 |
| 2226b | | Booklet pane, #2222-2225, 2226a | 20.00 | — |
| | | Complete booklet, #2226b | 20.00 | |

Panathinaikos
Soccer Team
Emblem — A727

Panionios Soccer
Team
Emblem — A728

Iraklis Soccer
Team
Emblem — A729

PAOK Soccer
Team
Emblem — A730

Panellinios
Sports Club
Emblem — A731

Designs: 30c, Ethnikos Sports Club emblem. €4, Omilos Ereton emblem.

**2005, Nov. 30 Litho.** *Perf. 14x13¾*
| | | | | |
|---|---|---|---|---|
| 2227 | A727 | 30c multi | .90 | .90 |
| 2228 | A727 | 50c multi | 1.50 | 1.50 |
| a. | | #2228 + label | 2.40 | 2.40 |
| 2229 | A728 | 50c multi | 1.50 | 1.50 |
| a. | | #2229 + label | 2.40 | 2.40 |
| 2230 | A729 | 50c multi | 1.50 | 1.50 |
| a. | | #2230 + label | 2.40 | 2.40 |
| 2231 | A730 | 65c multi | 1.90 | 1.90 |
| a. | | #2231 + label | 3.25 | 3.25 |
| 2232 | A731 | 65c multi | 1.90 | 1.90 |
| a. | | #2232 + label | 3.25 | 3.25 |
| 2233 | A727 | €4 multi | 12.00 | 12.00 |
| | | *Nos. 2227-2233 (7)* | 21.20 | 21.20 |

Nos. 2228a, 2229a and 2230a were printed in sheets of 10 + 10 labels that sold for €10. Nos. 2231a and 2232a were printed in sheets of 10 + 10 labels that sold for €13. Labels could be personalized.

Christmas
A732

Icons: 1c, Hodeghetria Virgin. 20c, Kardiotissa Virgin. 70c, Glykophiloussa Virgin. €3.20, Virgin with Symbols of the Passion.

**Litho. With Foil Application**
**2005, Dec. 20** *Perf. 13¾*
| | | | |
|---|---|---|---|
| 2234-2237 | A732 | Set of 4 | 12.50 12.50 |

**Souvenir Sheet**

Europa Stamps, 50th Anniv. — A733

**2006, Jan. 10 Litho.** *Perf. 13x13¼*
| | | | |
|---|---|---|---|
| 2238 | A733 | Sheet of 2 | 12.00 12.00 |
| a. | €1.50 Greece #1255 | | 4.50 4.50 |
| b. | €2.50 Greece #1459 | | 7.50 7.50 |

Patras, 2006 European Cultural Capital A734

Designs: 1c, Drama masks. 15c, Buildings, sailboat, lighthouse. 20c, Child. 50c, Carnival dragon and clown. 65c, Emblem, vert. €2.25, Jars, containers and boxes. €2.30, Icon, vert.

**2006, Feb. 28** *Perf. 13x13¼, 13¼x13*
| | | | |
|---|---|---|---|
| 2239-2245 | A734 | Set of 7 | 18.00 18.00 |

Carnival Dragon and Clown — A734a

Emblem — A734b

**2006, Feb. 28 Litho.** *Perf. 14x13¾*
| | | | |
|---|---|---|---|
| 2245A | A734a 50c multi + label | 2.40 | 2.40 |
| 2245B | A734b 65c multi + label | 3.25 | 3.25 |

Patras, 2006 European Cultural Capital. Nos. 2245A and 2245B were issued in sheets of 10 stamps and 10 labels that could be personalized. Sheets of No. 2245A sold for €10; No. 2245B for €13.

Items in Greek
Museums
A735

Designs: 5c, Kouros of Anavissos, sculpture, 530 B.C., Natl. Archaeological Museum. 20c, Seated figure, 2800-2300 B.C., Museum of Cycladic Art. 50c, Spiral (28x28mm). 65c, Pediment from Parthenon, Acropolis Museum, horiz. €1.40, Greco-Roman portrait of an Egyptian, 4th cent. €2.25, Concert of the Angels, by El Greco, Natl. Art Gallery, horiz.

**Litho with Foil Application, Litho. (50c)**
**2006, Apr. 7** *Perf. 14x13¾, 13¾x14*
| | | | |
|---|---|---|---|
| 2246-2251 | A735 | Set of 6 | 15.00 15.00 |
| 2248a | | #2248 + label | 2.50 2.50 |

No. 2248a was printed in sheets of 10 + 10 labels that sold for €10. Labels could be personalized.

Pediment From Parthenon — A735a

**2006, Apr. 7 Litho.** *Perf. 14x13¾*
| | | | |
|---|---|---|---|
| 2251A | A735a 65c multi + label | 3.25 3.25 |

No. 2251A was printed in sheets of 10 + 10 labels that sold for €13. Labels could be personalized.

**Souvenir Sheets**

Stamps Issued for 1906 Interim Olympic Games — A736

No. 2252: a, 20c, #187. b, 30c, #191. c, 50c, #188. d, €2, #192.
No. 2253: a, 50c #189. b, 65c, #194. c, 85c, #197. d, €1, #190.

**2006, Apr. 7 Litho.** *Perf. 13x13¼*
**Sheets of 4, #a-d**
| | | | |
|---|---|---|---|
| 2252-2253 | A736 | Set of 2 | 18.00 18.00 |

Europa — A737

**2006, May 15** *Perf. 13¾x14¼*
| | | | |
|---|---|---|---|
| 2254 | A737 | Horiz. pair | 11.00 11.00 |
| a. | 65c Rope and moon | | 1.90 1.90 |
| b. | €3 Rope and sun | | 9.00 9.00 |
| c. | Horiz. pair, perf. 13¼ vert. | | 11.00 11.00 |
| d. | As "a," perf. 13¼ vert. | | 1.90 1.90 |
| e. | As "b," perf. 13¼ vert. | | 9.00 9.00 |
| f. | Booklet pane, 2 #2254c | | 22.50 — |
| | Complete booklet, #2254f | | 22.50 |

State General
Archives — A738

Admission to
European Union,
25th
Anniv. — A739

2006 Eurovision
Song Contest,
Athens — A740

Olive and Olive
Oil Year — A741

Tinia, Etruscan
Sky God — A742

Greek
Participation in
2005-06 UN
Security
Council — A743

**2006, May 15** *Perf. 14x13¾*
| | | | |
|---|---|---|---|
| 2255 | A738 | 15c multi | .45 | .45 |
| 2256 | A739 | 20c multi | .60 | .60 |
| 2257 | A740 | 50c multi | 1.50 | 1.50 |
| a. | | #2257 + label | 2.60 | 2.60 |
| 2258 | A741 | 65c multi | 1.90 | 1.90 |
| a. | | #2258 + label | 3.50 | 3.50 |
| 2259 | A742 | €1.40 multi | 4.25 | 4.25 |
| 2260 | A743 | €3 multi | 9.00 | 9.00 |
| | | *Nos. 2255-2260 (6)* | 17.70 | 17.70 |

No. 2257a was printed in sheets of 10 + 10 labels that sold for €10. No. 2258a was printed in sheets of 10 + 10 labels that sold for €13. Labels could be personalized.

Island
Views
A744

**2006, June 16 Litho.** *Perf. 14¼x14*
| | | | |
|---|---|---|---|
| 2261 | A744 | 1c Lesbos | .20 | .20 |
| a. | | Perf. 13¼ vert. | .20 | .20 |
| 2262 | A744 | 3c Hydra | .20 | .20 |
| a. | | Perf. 13¼ vert. | .20 | .20 |
| 2263 | A744 | 10c Sifnos | .30 | .30 |
| a. | | Perf. 13¼ vert. | .30 | .30 |
| 2264 | A744 | 20c Levkas | .60 | .60 |
| a. | | Perf. 13¼ vert. | .60 | .60 |
| 2265 | A744 | 40c Samothrace | 1.25 | 1.25 |
| a. | | Perf. 13¼ vert. | 1.25 | 1.25 |
| 2266 | A744 | 50c Syros | 1.50 | 1.50 |
| a. | | Perf. 13¼ vert. | 1.50 | 1.50 |
| 2267 | A744 | 65c Rhodes | 1.90 | 1.90 |
| a. | | Perf. 13¼ vert. | 1.90 | 1.90 |
| 2268 | A744 | 85c Cephalonia | 2.50 | 2.50 |
| a. | | Perf. 13¼ vert. | 2.50 | 2.50 |
| 2269 | A744 | €2.25 Corfu | 6.75 | 6.75 |
| a. | | Perf. 13¼ vert. | 6.75 | 6.75 |
| 2270 | A744 | €5 Naxos | 15.00 | 15.00 |
| a. | | Perf. 13¼ vert. | 15.00 | 15.00 |
| | | *Nos. 2261-2270 (10)* | 30.20 | 30.20 |

Syros — A744a

**2006, June 16 Litho.** *Perf. 14x13¾*
| | | | |
|---|---|---|---|
| 2270B | A744a 50c multi + label | 2.60 2.60 |

No. 2270B was printed in sheets of 10 + 10 labels that sold for €10. Labels could be personalized. An additional personalized stamp was issued in this set. The editors would like to examine any example.

Ancient
Greek
Technology
A745

Designs: 3c, Trireme "Olympias." 5c, Odometer, by Hero of Alexandria. 50c, Piston water pump, vert. 65c, Antikythera Mechanism, vert. €3.80, Automatic temple gates, by Hero of Alexandria, vert.

**Litho. With Foil Application**
*Perf. 13¾x13¼, 13¼x13¾*
**2006, Sept. 14**
| | | | |
|---|---|---|---|
| 2271-2275 | A745 | Set of 5 | 15.00 15.00 |

**Souvenir Sheet**

Second Place Finish of Greek Team at
2006 World Basketball
Championships — A746

**Litho. With Foil Application**
**2006, Oct. 16** *Perf. 13¼*
| | | | |
|---|---|---|---|
| 2276 | A746 | Sheet of 3 | 17.00 17.00 |
| a. | 50c Silver medal | | 1.50 1.50 |
| b. | €2 Team | | 6.00 6.00 |
| c. | €3 Team, medal ribbon | | 9.00 9.00 |

Soccer Team Emblems
A747

Designs: 2c, Apollon Kalamaria. 3c, Atromitos Athinon. 52c, Aris Thessaloniki. €2.27, Ethnikos Piraeus. €3.20, Apollon Smyrnis.

**2006, Nov. 29   Litho.   Perf. 14x13¾**
2277-2281 A747   Set of 5   18.00 18.00
2279a   #2279 + label   2.75  2.75

No. 2279a was printed in sheets of 10 + 10 labels that sold for €10. Labels could be personalized.

Items in Toys, Games and Childhood Section of Benaki Museum
A748

Designs: 5c, Doll, chest and clothing from France, c. 1905. 15c, Wooden airplanes, c. 1940. 30c, Dolls made by Skonouchi Karopoulos, c. 1925. 40c, Horses on wheels made by Anestis Romeopoulos, c. 1920. 52c, Dominos, toy cat, duck on wheels. 72c, Parachutist, c. 1950, vert. €2.27, Airplane carousel, 1950s, vert. €4, Puppet theater of the Resistance, 1941-45, vert.

**Perf. 13¾x13¼, 13¼x13¾**
**2006, Dec. 22**
2282-2289 A748   Set of 8   25.00 25.00

Faces — A749

Globe — A750

Crescents A751

Artemis — A752

Ring Around Earth — A753

Parthenon A754

Phrasikleia Kore — A755

**2007, Mar. 12   Litho.   Perf. 14x13¾**
2290 A749 52c multi   1.40 1.40
  a.   #2290 + label   2.75 2.75
2291 A750 52c multi   1.40 1.40
  a.   #2291 + label   2.75 2.75
2292 A751 52c multi   1.40 1.40
  a.   #2292 + label   2.75 2.75
2293 A752 52c multi   1.40 1.40
  a.   #2293 + label   2.75 2.75
2294 A753 52c multi   1.40 1.40
  a.   #2294 + label   2.75 2.75
2295 A754 65c multi   1.75 1.75
  a.   #2295 + label   3.50 3.50
2296 A755 65c multi   1.75 1.75
  a.   Miniature sheet, #2290-2296   10.50 10.50
  b.   #2296 + label   3.50 3.50
  Nos. 2290-2296 (7)   10.50 10.50

Nos. 2290a, 2292a amd 2293a were printed in sheets of 10 + 10 labels that sold for €10. Nos. 2291a and 2294a were printed in sheets of 15 + 15 labels that sold for €15. Nos. 2295a and 2296b were printed in sheets of 10 + 10 labels that sold for €13. Labels could be personalized.

Kostis Palamas (1859-1943), Poet — A756

Greek Cultural Year in China A757

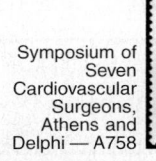

Symposium of Seven Cardiovascular Surgeons, Athens and Delphi — A758

2nd Union Network International World Postal Conference A759

Treaty of Rome, 50th Anniv. — A760

Georgios Kotzias (1918-77) A761

Rigas Velestinlis (1757-98), Poet — A762

Year of Innovation A763

State Legal Council, 125th Anniv. A764

**Perf. 13¼x13¾, 13¾x13¼**
**2007, Apr. 25**
2297 A756 2c multi   .20 .20
2298 A757 10c multi   .30 .30
2299 A758 20c multi   .55 .55
2300 A759 52c multi   1.40 1.40
2301 A760 65c multi   1.75 1.75
2302 A761 85c multi   2.40 2.40
2303 A762 €1 multi   2.75 2.75
2304 A763 €2.27 multi   6.25 6.25
2305 A764 €3 multi   8.25 8.25
  Nos. 2297-2305 (9)   23.85 23.85

Europa — A765

No. 2306: a, Scouting fleur-de-lis, dove's tail. b, Scouts, dove's head.

**2007, May 25   Perf. 14¼x14**
2306 A765   Horiz. pair   10.50 10.50
  a.   65c multi   1.75 1.75
  b.   €3.15 multi   8.75 8.75
  c.   Horiz. pair, perf. 13¾ vert.   10.50 10.50
  d.   As "a," perf. 13¾ vert.   1.75 1.75
  e.   As "b," perf. 13¾ vert.   8.75 8.75
  f.   Booklet pane, 2 #2306c   21.00
    Complete booklet, #2306f   21.00

Scouting, cent.

Signs of the Zodiac A766

**Litho. With Foil Application**
**Perf. 13¾x13¼, 13¼x13¾**
**2007, May 25**
2307 A766 2c Scorpio   .20 .20
2308 A766 3c Cancer   .20 .20
2309 A766 5c Capricorn   .20 .20
2310 A766 10c Taurus   .30 .30
2311 A766 20c Sagittarius, vert.   .55 .55
2312 A766 40c Leo, vert.   1.10 1.10
2313 A766 52c Virgo, vert.   1.40 1.40
2314 A766 65c Aries   1.75 1.75
2315 A766 85c Aquarius   2.40 2.40
2316 A766 €1 Libra   2.75 2.75
2317 A766 €2.27 Pisces   6.25 6.25
2318 A766 €2.80 Gemini   7.50 7.50
  Nos. 2307-2318 (12)   24.60 24.60

**Souvenir Sheet**

Statues of Asclepius, Greek God of Medicine — A767

No. 2319: a, Statue from Museum of Ampurias, Spain. b, Statue from National Archaeological Museum, Athens.

**2007, June 28   Litho.   Perf. 13¾**
2319 A767   Sheet of 2   13.50 13.50
  a.-b.   €2.50 Either single   6.75 6.75

See Spain No. 3521.

Discovery of the Tomb of St. Cyril, 150th Anniv. A768

University of Macedonia, 50th Anniv. — A769

Konstantinos Tsatsos (1899-1987), Politician — A770

**Litho. With Foil Application**
**2007, Sept. 28   Perf. 13¾x14**
2320 A768 2c multi   .20 .20
**Litho.**
2321 A769 3c multi   .20 .20
**Perf. 14x13¾**
2322 A770 €4 multi   11.50 11.50
  Nos. 2320-2322 (3)   11.90 11.90

Sports Team
Emblems
A771

Designs: 2c, Ergotelis Sports Club. 4c, OFI. 54c, Olympiacos C.F.P. €2.29, Doxa Dramas Sports Club. €5, Nautical Club of Mytilini.

**2007, Nov. 2    Litho.    Perf. 14x13¾**

| | | | | | |
|---|---|---|---|---|---|
| 2323-2327 | A771 | Set of 5 | | 23.00 | 23.00 |
| 2325a | | #2325 + label | | 3.00 | 3.00 |

No. 2325a was printed in sheets of 10 + 10 labels that sold for €10. Labels could be personalized.

Busts of
Goddesses — A772

Designs: 54c, Bust of Aphrodite. €2.40, Bust of Goddess Anahit, Armenia.

**2007, Dec. 14    Perf. 14x14¼**

| | | | | | |
|---|---|---|---|---|---|
| 2328-2329 | A772 | Set of 2 | | 8.75 | 8.75 |

See Armenia Nos. 774-775.

Islands
A773

**2008, Feb. 27    Litho.    Perf. 14¼x14**

| | | | | | |
|---|---|---|---|---|---|
| 2330 | A773 | 2c Chios | | .20 | .20 |
| a. | | Perf. 13¼ vert. | | .20 | .20 |
| 2331 | A773 | 5c Amorgos | | .20 | .20 |
| a. | | Perf. 13¼ vert. | | .20 | .20 |
| 2332 | A773 | 10c Nísiros | | .30 | .30 |
| a. | | Perf. 13¼ vert. | | .30 | .30 |
| 2333 | A773 | 20c Paxos | | .60 | .60 |
| a. | | Perf. 13¼ vert. | | .60 | .60 |
| 2334 | A773 | 40c Leros | | 1.25 | 1.25 |
| a. | | Perf. 13¼ vert. | | 1.25 | 1.25 |
| 2335 | A773 | 54c Kalymnos | | 1.75 | 1.75 |
| a. | | Perf. 13¼ vert. | | 1.75 | 1.75 |
| 2336 | A773 | 67c Kos | | 2.10 | 2.10 |
| a. | | Perf. 13¼ vert. | | 2.10 | 2.10 |
| 2337 | A773 | €1 Simi | | 3.00 | 3.00 |
| a. | | Perf. 13¼ vert. | | 3.00 | 3.00 |
| 2338 | A773 | €2.29 Zákinthos | | 7.00 | 7.00 |
| a. | | Perf. 13¼ vert. | | 7.00 | 7.00 |
| 2339 | A773 | €4 Inousses | | 12.50 | 12.50 |
| a. | | Perf. 13¼ vert. | | 12.50 | 12.50 |
| | | Nos. 2330-2339 (10) | | 28.90 | 28.90 |

2008 Summer
Olympics,
Beijing — A774

Designs: 3c, Discus thrower. 35c, Lighting of Olympic flame. No. 2342, 67c, Torch bearer. No. 2343, 67c, Three cyclists, horiz.

**2008, Mar. 14    Perf. 13½x13, 13x13½**

| | | | | | |
|---|---|---|---|---|---|
| 2340-2343 | A774 | Set of 4 | | 5.50 | 5.50 |

Letter — A775

Numbers — A776

Heart — A777

Kites — A778

Pillar — A779

Greek
Flag — A780

**2008, Apr. 21    Litho.    Perf. 14x13¾**

| | | | | |
|---|---|---|---|---|
| 2344 | A775 | 54c multi | 1.75 | 1.75 |
| 2345 | A776 | 54c multi | 1.75 | 1.75 |
| 2346 | A777 | 54c multi | 1.75 | 1.75 |
| 2347 | A778 | 54c multi | 1.75 | 1.75 |
| 2348 | A779 | 67c multi | 2.10 | 2.10 |
| 2349 | A780 | 67c multi | 2.10 | 2.10 |
| a. | | Miniature sheet, #2344-2349 | 11.50 | 11.50 |
| | | Nos. 2344-2349 (6) | 11.20 | 11.20 |

Europa — A781

No. 2350: a, Inkwell, pen and papers. b, Fountain pen and papers.
Illustration reduced.

**2008, May 26    Perf. 14¼x14**

| | | | | |
|---|---|---|---|---|
| 2350 | A781 | Horiz. pair | 12.50 | 12.50 |
| a. | | 67c multi | 2.25 | 2.25 |
| b. | | €3.17 multi | 10.00 | 10.00 |
| c. | | Horiz. pair, perf. 13¾ vert. | 12.50 | 12.50 |
| d. | | As "a," perf. 13¾ vert. | 2.25 | 2.25 |
| e. | | As "b," perf. 13¾ vert. | 10.00 | 10.00 |
| f. | | Booklet pane, 2 #2350c | 25.00 | — |
| | | Complete booklet, #2350f | 25.00 | |

Anniversaries
A782

Curved lines and: 3c, Emblem of Hellenic Post. 5c, Posthorn, Greek men. 10c, Ioannis Kapodistrias (1776-1831), provisional president of Greece. 57c, M. Karagatsis (1908-60), writer. 70c, Fish. €1.85, Emblem of National Hellenic Research Foundation. €3, Emblem of National Council of Women.

**2008, June 20    Perf. 13¼x13¾**

| | | | | |
|---|---|---|---|---|
| 2351-2357 | A782 | Set of 7 | 20.00 | 20.00 |

Hellenic Post, 180th anniv. (#2351-2352); Inauguration of Kapodistrias, 180th anniv. (#2353); Intl. Year of Planet Earth (#2355); National Hellenic Research Foundation, 50th anniv. (#2356), National Council of Women, cent. (#2357).

Greek
Products — A783

Designs: 3c, Feta cheese and tomatoes. 5c, Mastic. 20c, Olive, bottle of olive oil, horiz. 57c, Bottle of ouzo, marine life and boat. €1, Pistachio nuts. €4, Bees, rose, jar of honey.

**Perf. 13¼x13¾, 13¾x13¼**

**2008, Sept. 19**

| | | | | |
|---|---|---|---|---|
| 2358-2363 | A783 | Set of 6 | 16.50 | 16.50 |

Sports Team
Emblems
A784

Designs: 40c, Diagoras Rhodos Sports Club. 57c, A.E.K. soccer team. 70c, Asteras Tripolis soccer team. €2, Panserraoikos soccer team. €3, Kerkiraikos Sports Club.

**2008, Oct. 20    Perf. 14x13¾**

| | | | | |
|---|---|---|---|---|
| 2364-2368 | A784 | Set of 5 | 17.00 | 17.00 |

Fairy
Tales,
Fables
and
Children's
Literature
A785

Designs: 10c, The Mermaid and Alexander the Great. 57c, Little Red Riding Hood. €1, The Fairies. €1.85, The Little Match Girl. €3, Arion and the Lyre.

**2008, Dec. 16    Perf. 13¾x14**

| | | | | |
|---|---|---|---|---|
| 2369-2373 | A785 | Set of 5 | 18.00 | 18.00 |

## SEMI-POSTAL STAMPS

Nos. 440-444 Surcharged in Blue

ΕΛΛΑΣ
ΒΟΜΒΑΡΔΙΣΜΟΣ
ΠΕΙΡΑΙΩΣ
11-1-1944
ΔΡ. 100.000

**1944    Wmk. 252    Perf. 12½**

| | | | | |
|---|---|---|---|---|
| B1 | A106 | 100,000d on 15d | .40 | .90 |
| B2 | A107 | 100,000d on 25d | .40 | .90 |
| B3 | A108 | 100,000d on 50d | .40 | .90 |
| B4 | A109 | 100,000d on 75d | .40 | .90 |
| B5 | A110 | 100,000d on 100d | .40 | .90 |
| | | Nos. B1-B5,CB1-CB5 (10) | 4.00 | 8.75 |
| | | Set, never hinged | 6.50 | |

The proceeds aided victims of the Piraeus bombing, Jan. 11, 1944. The exceptionally high face value discouraged the use of these stamps.

Nos. 437-441
Surcharged in
Blue

**1944, July 20**
**50,000d + 450,000d**

| | | | | |
|---|---|---|---|---|
| B11 | A103 | on 2d | .30 | .65 |
| B12 | A104 | on 5d | .30 | .65 |
| B13 | A105 | on 10d | .30 | .65 |
| B14 | A106 | on 15d | .30 | .65 |
| *a.* | Pair, one without surcharge | | 65.00 | |
| B15 | A107 | on 25d | .30 | .65 |
| | *Nos. B11-B15,CB6-CB10 (10)* | | 3.00 | 6.50 |
| | Set, never hinged | | 5.50 | |

The surtax aided children's camps.

---

## AIR POST STAMPS

### Italy-Greece-Turkey-Rhodes Service

Flying Boat off Phaleron Bay — AP1

Flying Boat over Acropolis — AP2

Flying Boat over Map of Southern
Europe — AP3

Flying Boat Seen through
Colonnade — AP4

**Perf. 11½**

| | | | Unwmk. | Litho. |
|---|---|---|---|---|
| **1926, Oct. 20** | | | | |
| C1 | AP1 | 2d multicolored | 1.60 | 1.25 |
| *a.* | Horiz. pair, imperf. vert. | | 725.00 | |
| C2 | AP2 | 3d multicolored | 12.00 | 11.00 |
| C3 | AP3 | 5d multicolored | 1.60 | 1.25 |
| C4 | AP4 | 10d multicolored | 12.00 | 12.00 |
| | *Nos. C1-C4 (4)* | | 27.20 | 25.50 |
| | Set, never hinged | | 80.00 | |

### Graf Zeppelin Issue

Zeppelin
over
Acropolis
AP5

---

**1933, May 2**    **Perf. 13½x12½**

| | | | | |
|---|---|---|---|---|
| C5 | AP5 | 30d rose red | 13.00 | 13.00 |
| C6 | AP5 | 100d deep blue | 52.50 | 52.50 |
| C7 | AP5 | 120d dark brown | 52.50 | 52.50 |
| | *Nos. C5-C7 (3)* | | 118.00 | 118.00 |
| | Set, never hinged | | 325.00 | |

Propeller
and Pilot's
Head
AP6

Temple of
Apollo,
Corinth
AP7

Plane over Hermoupolis, Syros — AP8

Allegory of Flight
AP9          AP12

Map of Italy-Greece-Turkey-Rhodes
Airmail Route — AP10

Head of Hermes and
Airplane — AP11

| | | **1933, Oct. 10** | Engr. | **Perf. 12** |
|---|---|---|---|---|
| C8 | AP6 | 50 l green & org | .20 | .20 |
| C9 | AP7 | 1d bl & brn org | .30 | .25 |
| C10 | AP8 | 3d dk vio & org brn | .50 | .50 |
| C11 | AP9 | 5d brn org & dk bl | 7.25 | 4.50 |
| C12 | AP10 | 10d dp red & blk | 1.50 | 1.40 |
| C13 | AP11 | 20d black & grn | 7.25 | 4.00 |
| C14 | AP12 | 50d dp brn & dp bl | 50.00 | 55.00 |
| | *Nos. C8-C14 (7)* | | 67.00 | 65.85 |
| | Set, never hinged | | 200.00 | |

By error the 1d stamp is inscribed in the plural "Draxmai" instead of the singular "Draxmh." This stamp exists bisected, used as a 50 lepta denomination.

All values of this set exist imperforate but were not regularly issued.

---

## For General Air Post Service

Airplane over Map of       Airplane over Map
Greece — AP13               of Icarian
                            Sea — AP14

Airplane
over
Acropolis
AP15

**Perf. 13x13½, 13x12½, 13½x13,
12½x13**

**1933, Nov. 2**

| | | | | |
|---|---|---|---|---|
| C15 | AP13 | 50 l green | .20 | .25 |
| C16 | AP13 | 1d red brown | .30 | .55 |
| C17 | AP14 | 2d lt violet | .60 | .85 |
| C18 | AP15 | 5d ultra | 3.50 | 3.50 |
| *a.* | Imperf., pair | | 650.00 | 550.00 |
| *b.* | Horiz. pair, imperf. vert. | | 650.00 | |
| C19 | AP14 | 10d car rose | 6.50 | 7.75 |
| C20 | AP13 | 25d dark blue | 30.00 | 20.00 |
| C21 | AP15 | 50d dark brown | 30.00 | 42.50 |
| *a.* | Imperf., pair | | 775.00 | 650.00 |
| | *Nos. C15-C21 (7)* | | 71.10 | 75.40 |
| | Set, never hinged | | 225.00 | |

Helios
Driving the
Sun Chariot
AP16

Iris — AP17

Daedalus
Preparing Icarus
for
Flying — AP18

Hermes
AP20

Pallas Athene
Holding
Pegasus — AP19

Zeus Carrying off
Ganymede
AP21

Triptolemos,
King of
Eleusis
AP22

---

Bellerophon and
Pegasus — AP23

Phrixos and
Helle on the
Ram Flying
over the
Hellespont
AP24

**Perf. 13x12½, 12½x13**
**1935, Nov. 10**         Engr.
**Grayish Paper**
**Size: 34x23½mm, 23½x34mm**

| | | | | |
|---|---|---|---|---|
| C22 | AP16 | 1d deep red | 1.50 | 1.50 |
| C23 | AP17 | 2d dull blue | 1.50 | 1.50 |
| C24 | AP18 | 5d dk violet | 17.50 | 4.00 |
| C25 | AP19 | 7d blue violet | 25.00 | 7.25 |
| C26 | AP20 | 10d bister brown | 5.00 | 5.00 |
| C27 | AP21 | 25d rose | 6.00 | 5.75 |
| C28 | AP22 | 30d dark green | 2.00 | 2.00 |
| C29 | AP23 | 50d violet | 8.00 | 6.00 |
| C30 | AP24 | 100d brown | 2.50 | 2.25 |
| | *Nos. C22-C30 (9)* | | 69.00 | 35.25 |
| | Set, never hinged | | 150.00 | |

Re-engraved

**1937-39**

**White Paper**
**Size: 34¼x24mm, 24x34¼mm**

| | | | | |
|---|---|---|---|---|
| C31 | AP16 | 1d red | .30 | .25 |
| C32 | AP17 | 2d gray blue | .30 | .25 |
| C33 | AP18 | 5d violet | .30 | .25 |
| C34 | AP19 | 7d dp ultra | .30 | .25 |
| C35 | AP20 | 10d brn org | 2.40 | 3.50 |
| | *Nos. C31-C35 (5)* | | 3.60 | 4.50 |
| | Set, never hinged | | 7.00 | |

Issued: #C35, 3/1/39; others 8/3/37.

Postage Due Stamp,
1913, Overprinted in
Red

**Serrate Roulette 13½**
**1938, Aug. 8**    Litho.    Unwmk.

| | | | | |
|---|---|---|---|---|
| C36 | D3 | 50 l violet brown | .20 | .20 |
| | Never hinged | | .25 | |
| *a.* | "O" for "P" in word at foot | | 30.00 | 30.00 |

Same Overprint on No. J79 in Red
**1939, June 26**    **Perf. 13½x12½**

| | | | | |
|---|---|---|---|---|
| C37 | D3 | 50 l dark brown | .20 | .20 |
| | Never hinged | | .25 | |

Meteora
Monasteries, near
Trikkala — AP25

Designs: 4d, Simon Peter Monastery. 6d,
View of Santorin. 8d, Church of Pantanassa.
16d, Santorin view. 32d, Ponticonissi, Corfu.
45d, Acropolis, Athens. 55d, Erechtheum.
65d, Temple of Nike Apteros. 100d, Temple of
the Olympian Zeus, Athens.

**Wmk. Crowns (252)**
**1940, Aug. 3**    Litho.    **Perf. 12½**

| | | | | |
|---|---|---|---|---|
| C38 | AP25 | 2d red org & blk | .65 | 1.00 |
| C39 | AP25 | 4d dk grn & blk | 3.00 | 2.75 |
| C40 | AP25 | 6d lake & blk | 5.50 | 5.00 |
| C41 | AP25 | 8d dk bl & blk | 14.00 | 12.50 |
| C42 | AP25 | 16d rose vio & blk | 22.50 | 19.00 |
| C43 | AP25 | 32d red org & blk | 30.00 | 35.00 |
| C44 | AP25 | 45d dk grn & blk | 40.00 | 35.00 |
| C45 | AP25 | 55d lake & blk | 40.00 | 35.00 |
| C46 | AP25 | 65d dk bl & blk | 40.00 | 35.00 |

| | | | | |
|---|---|---|---|---|
| C47 | AP25 | 100d rose vio & blk | 50.00 | 45.00 |
| | | Nos. C38-C47 (10) | 245.65 | 225.25 |
| | | Set, never hinged | 600.00 | |

4th anniv. of the founding of the Greek Youth Organization. The stamps were good for postal duty on Aug. 3-5, 1940, only. They remained on sale until Feb. 3, 1941.

For overprints see Nos. N229-N238.

> **Catalogue values for unused stamps in this section, from this point to the end of the section, are for Never Hinged items.**

**Postage Due Stamps Nos. J81 and J75 Surcharged in Red**

| 1941-42 | | Unwmk. | Perf. 13x12½ | |
|---|---|---|---|---|
| C48 | D3 | 1d on 2d lt red | .20 | .20 |
| a. | | Inverted surcharge | 45.00 | |

| | | *Serrate Roulette 13½* | | |
|---|---|---|---|---|
| C49 | D3 | 1d on 2d ver ('42) | .20 | .20 |
| a. | | Inverted surcharge | 32.50 | |
| b. | | Double surcharge | 22.50 | |

**Nos. J83, J84, J86, J87 Overprinted in Red**

| 1941-42 | | Perf. 13, 12½x13 | | |
|---|---|---|---|---|
| C50 | D3 | 5d gray bl ('42) | .20 | .20 |
| a. | | Inverted overprint | 45.00 | |
| b. | | Double overprint | 32.50 | |
| c. | | Pair, one without ovpt. | 22.50 | |
| d. | | Surcharge on back | 22.50 | |
| e. | | On No. J78 ('42) | 140.00 | 160.00 |
| C51 | D3 | 10d gray grn | .30 | .30 |
| a. | | Inverted overprint | 16.00 | |
| b. | | Vert. pair, imperf. btwn. | 325.00 | |
| C52 | D3 | 25d lt red | .85 | .85 |
| a. | | Inverted overprint | 110.00 | |
| C53 | D3 | 50d orange | 1.50 | 1.50 |
| | | Nos. C50-C53 (4) | 2.85 | 2.85 |

**Boreas, North Wind — AP35**

Winds: 5d, Notus, South. 10d, Apeliotes, East. 20d, Lips, Southwest. 25d, Zephyrus, West. 50d, Kaikias, Northeast.

| 1942, Aug. 15 | | Wmk. 252 Litho. | Perf. 12½ | |
|---|---|---|---|---|
| C55 | AP35 | 2d emerald | .20 | .20 |
| C56 | AP35 | 5d red org | .20 | .20 |
| a. | | Imperf., pair | 325.00 | |
| b. | | Double impression | 55.00 | — |
| C57 | AP35 | 10d red brown | .25 | .25 |
| C58 | AP35 | 20d brt blue | .25 | .25 |
| C59 | AP35 | 25d dk red org | .25 | .25 |
| C60 | AP35 | 50d gray blk | 2.00 | 2.00 |
| a. | | Double impression | 110.00 | |
| | | Nos. C55-C60 (6) | 3.15 | 3.15 |

**1943, Sept. 15**

Winds: 10d, Apeliotes, East. 25d, Zephyrus, West. 50d, Kaikias, Northeast. 100d, Boreas, North. 200d, Eurus, Southeast. 400d, Skiron, Northwest.

| C61 | AP35 | 10d rose red | .20 | .20 |
|---|---|---|---|---|
| C62 | AP35 | 25d Prus green | .20 | .20 |
| C63 | AP35 | 50d violet blue | .20 | .20 |
| C64 | AP35 | 100d slate black | .20 | .20 |
| C65 | AP35 | 200d claret | .20 | .20 |
| C66 | AP35 | 400d steel blue | .20 | .20 |
| | | Nos. C61-C66 (6) | 1.20 | 1.20 |

Double impressions exist of 10d and 400d. Value, each $30.

For surcharges see #472, 473, CB1-CB10.

**Imperf., Pairs**

| C61a | AP35 | 10d | 110.00 |
|---|---|---|---|
| C62a | AP35 | 25d | 110.00 |
| C63a | AP35 | 50d | 110.00 |
| C64a | AP35 | 100d | 110.00 |
| C65a | AP35 | 200d | 110.00 |
| C66a | AP35 | 400d | 110.00 |

**Priest Blessing Troops on Summit of Mt. Grammos AP36**　　**Torchbearer AP37**

Designs: 1700d, Victory above Mt. Vitsi. 2700d, Battle Scene. 7000d, Victory leading infantry.

| 1952, Aug. 29 | | Engr. | Perf. 12x13½ | |
|---|---|---|---|---|
| C67 | AP36 | 1000d deep blue | 1.50 | .30 |
| C68 | AP36 | 1700d dp blue grn | 5.00 | 2.00 |
| C69 | AP36 | 2700d brown | 15.00 | 6.00 |
| C70 | AP36 | 7000d olive green | 45.00 | 15.00 |
| | | Nos. C67-C70 (4) | 66.50 | 23.30 |

Greek army's struggle against communism.

| 1954, May 15 | | | Perf. 13 | |
|---|---|---|---|---|

Designs: 2400dr, Coin of Amphictyonic League. 4000dr, Pallas Athene.

| C71 | AP37 | 1200d dp orange | 7.50 | .35 |
|---|---|---|---|---|
| C72 | AP37 | 2400d dk green | 37.50 | 2.50 |
| C73 | AP37 | 4000d dp ultra | 65.00 | 3.50 |
| | | Nos. C71-C73 (3) | 110.00 | 6.35 |

5th anniv. of the signing of the North Atlantic Treaty.

**Piraeus AP38**

Harbors: 15d, Salonika. 20d, Patras. 25d, Hermoupolis (Syra). 30d, Volos. 50d, Cavalla. 100d, Herakleion (Candia).

| | | Perf. 13½x13 | | |
|---|---|---|---|---|
| 1958, July 1 | | Wmk. 252 | Litho. | |
| C74 | AP38 | 10d multicolored | 12.50 | .25 |
| C75 | AP38 | 15d multicolored | 1.75 | .40 |
| C76 | AP38 | 20d multicolored | 12.50 | .25 |
| C77 | AP38 | 25d multicolored | 2.00 | .80 |
| C78 | AP38 | 30d multicolored | 2.25 | .80 |
| C79 | AP38 | 50d multicolored | 8.00 | .80 |
| C80 | AP38 | 100d multicolored | 40.00 | 4.00 |
| | | Nos. C74-C80 (7) | 79.00 | 7.30 |

### AIR POST SEMI-POSTAL STAMPS

**#C61-C65 Surcharged in Blue like #B1-B5**

| 1944, June | | Wmk. 252 | Perf. 12½ | |
|---|---|---|---|---|
| CB1 | AP35 | 100,000d on 10d | .40 | .85 |
| CB2 | AP35 | 100,000d on 25d | .40 | .85 |
| CB3 | AP35 | 100,000d on 50d | .40 | .85 |
| a. | | Inverted overprint | 32.50 | |
| CB4 | AP35 | 100,000d on 100d | .40 | .85 |
| CB5 | AP35 | 100,000d on 200d | .40 | .85 |
| | | Nos. CB1-CB5 (5) | 2.00 | 4.25 |
| | | Set, never hinged | 7.00 | |

The exceptionally high face value discouraged the use of these stamps. The proceeds aided victims of the Piraeus bombing, January 11, 1944.

**#C61-C65 Surcharged in Blue like #B11-B15**

**1944, July**

**50,000d + 450,000d**

| CB6 | AP35 | on 10d | .30 | .65 |
|---|---|---|---|---|
| CB7 | AP35 | on 25d | .30 | .65 |
| CB8 | AP35 | on 50d | .30 | .65 |
| CB9 | AP35 | on 100d | .30 | .65 |
| CB10 | AP35 | on 200d | .30 | .65 |
| | | Nos. CB6-CB10 (5) | 1.50 | 3.25 |
| | | Set, never hinged | 6.00 | |

The surtax aided children's camps. Surcharge exists inverted or double. Value, each $55.

### POSTAGE DUE STAMPS

D1　　　　　　D2

**Perf. 9, 9½, and 10, 10½ and Compound**

| 1875 | | Litho. | Unwmk. | |
|---|---|---|---|---|
| J1 | D1 | 1 l green & black | 1.25 | 1.25 |
| J2 | D1 | 2 l green & black | 1.25 | 1.25 |
| J3 | D1 | 5 l green & black | 1.50 | 1.00 |
| J4 | D1 | 10 l green & black | 1.50 | 1.00 |
| J5 | D1 | 20 l green & black | 35.00 | 25.00 |
| J6 | D1 | 40 l green & black | 7.00 | 4.50 |
| J7 | D1 | 60 l green & black | 35.00 | 25.00 |
| J8 | D1 | 70 l green & black | 7.00 | 7.00 |
| J9 | D1 | 80 l green & black | 15.00 | 12.00 |
| J10 | D1 | 90 l green & black | 9.00 | 9.00 |
| J11 | D1 | 1d green & black | 10.00 | 9.00 |
| J12 | D1 | 2d green & black | 11.00 | 9.00 |
| | | Nos. J1-J12 (12) | 134.50 | 105.00 |

Imperforate and part perforated, double and inverted center varieties of Nos. J1-J12 are believed to be printers' waste.

**Perf. 12, 13 and 10½x13**

| J13 | D1 | 1 l green & black | 1.50 | 1.50 |
|---|---|---|---|---|
| J14 | D1 | 2 l green & black | 20.00 | 20.00 |
| J15 | D1 | 5 l green & black | 2.50 | 2.50 |
| J16 | D1 | 10 l green & black | 3.00 | 3.00 |
| J17 | D1 | 20 l green & black | 35.00 | 24.00 |
| J18 | D1 | 40 l green & black | 9.00 | 7.00 |
| J19 | D1 | 60 l green & black | 37.50 | 24.00 |
| J20 | D1 | 70 l green & black | 7.00 | 7.00 |
| J21 | D1 | 80 l green & black | 11.00 | 11.00 |
| J22 | D1 | 90 l green & black | 16.00 | 11.00 |
| J23 | D1 | 1d green & black | 24.00 | 16.00 |
| J24 | D1 | 2d green & black | 21.00 | 16.00 |
| | | Nos. J13-J24 (12) | 187.50 | 143.00 |

**Redrawn**

**"Lepton" or "Lepta" in Larger Greek Letters**

| 1876 | | Perf. 9, 9½, and 10, 10½ | | |
|---|---|---|---|---|
| J25 | D2 | 1 l green & black | 3.75 | 3.75 |
| J26 | D2 | 2 l dk grn & blk | 5.00 | 4.75 |
| J27 | D2 | 5 l dk grn & blk | 300.00 | 225.00 |
| J28 | D2 | 10 l green & black | 2.50 | 1.75 |
| J29 | D2 | 20 l green & black | 3.25 | 2.50 |
| J30 | D2 | 40 l green & black | 27.50 | 21.00 |
| J31 | D2 | 60 l green & black | 22.50 | 12.50 |
| J32 | D2 | 70 l green & black | 18.00 | 21.00 |
| J33 | D2 | 80 l green & black | 15.00 | 12.50 |
| J34 | D2 | 90 l green & black | 15.00 | 13.00 |
| J35 | D2 | 100 l green & black | 18.00 | 12.50 |
| J36 | D2 | 200 l green & black | 18.00 | 12.50 |
| | | Nos. J25-J36 (12) | 448.50 | 342.75 |

**Perf. 11½ to 13**

| J37 | D2 | 1 l yel grn & blk | 1.25 | .70 |
|---|---|---|---|---|
| J38 | D2 | 2 l yel grn & blk | 1.25 | .70 |
| J39 | D2 | 5 l yel grn & blk | 3.50 | .90 |
| J40 | D2 | 10 l yel grn & blk | 2.00 | 1.50 |
| a. | | Perf. 10-10½x11½-13 | 3.00 | |
| J41 | D2 | 20 l yel grn & blk | 2.00 | 1.50 |
| J42 | D2 | 40 l yel grn & blk | 11.00 | 8.00 |
| J43 | D2 | 60 l yel grn & blk | 7.00 | 7.00 |
| J47 | D2 | 100 l yel grn & blk | 9.00 | 9.00 |
| J48 | D2 | 200 l yel grn & blk | 10.00 | 8.00 |
| | | Nos. J37-J48 (9) | 47.00 | 37.30 |

Footnote below #J12 applies to #J25-J48.

D3

| 1902 | | Engr. Wmk. 129 | Perf. 13½ | |
|---|---|---|---|---|
| J49 | D3 | 1 l chocolate | .30 | .25 |
| J50 | D3 | 2 l gray | .30 | .25 |
| J51 | D3 | 3 l orange | .30 | .25 |
| J52 | D3 | 5 l yel grn | .30 | .25 |
| J53 | D3 | 10 l scarlet | .30 | .25 |
| J54 | D3 | 20 l lilac | .45 | .25 |
| J55 | D3 | 25 l ultra | 8.00 | 4.00 |
| J56 | D3 | 30 l dp vio | .50 | .30 |
| J57 | D3 | 40 l dk brn | .60 | .50 |
| J58 | D3 | 50 l red brn | .60 | .40 |
| J59 | D3 | 1d black | 1.50 | .90 |

| | | Litho. | | |
|---|---|---|---|---|
| J60 | D3 | 2d bronze | 2.00 | 1.25 |
| J61 | D3 | 3d silver | 3.00 | 3.00 |
| J62 | D3 | 5d gold | 6.50 | 9.00 |
| | | Nos. J49-J62 (14) | 24.65 | 20.85 |

See Nos. J63-J88, J90-J93. For overprints and surcharges see Nos. 383-385, J89, RA56, RA58-RA59, NJ1-NJ31.

**Imperf., Pairs**

| J50a | D3 | 2 l | 90.00 |
|---|---|---|---|
| J51a | D3 | 3 l | 90.00 |
| J52a | D3 | 5 l | 90.00 |
| J55a | D3 | 25 l | 150.00 |
| J56a | D3 | 30 l | 150.00 |
| J58a | D3 | 50 l | 150.00 |
| J59a | D3 | 1d | 150.00 |

**Serrate Roulette 13½**

| 1913-26 | | | Unwmk. | |
|---|---|---|---|---|
| J63 | D3 | 1 l green | .20 | .20 |
| J64 | D3 | 2 l green | .20 | .20 |
| J65 | D3 | 3 l vermilion | .20 | .20 |
| J66 | D3 | 5 l green | .20 | .20 |
| a. | | Imperf., pair | 150.00 | |
| b. | | Double impression | 60.00 | |
| c. | | "o" for "p" in lowest word | 5.00 | 5.00 |
| J67 | D3 | 10 l carmine | .20 | .20 |
| J68 | D3 | 20 l slate | .20 | .20 |
| J69 | D3 | 25 l ultra | .20 | .20 |
| J70 | D3 | 30 l carmine | .20 | .20 |
| J71 | D3 | 40 l indigo | .20 | .20 |
| J72 | D3 | 50 l vio brn | .30 | .25 |
| a. | | "o" for "p" in lowest word | 25.00 | 20.00 |
| J73 | D3 | 80 l lil brn ('24) | .40 | .20 |
| J74 | D3 | 1d blue | 8.00 | 1.25 |
| a. | | 1d ultramarine | 12.00 | 5.00 |
| J75 | D3 | 2d vermilion | 8.00 | 1.50 |
| J76 | D3 | 3d carmine | 8.00 | 1.50 |
| J77 | D3 | 5d ultra | 30.00 | 12.00 |
| J78 | D3 | 5d gray bl ('26) | 8.00 | 4.00 |
| | | Nos. J63-J78 (16) | 64.50 | 22.50 |

In 1922-23 and 1941-42 some postage due stamps were used for ordinary postage.

In 1916 Nos. J52, and J63 to J75 were surcharged for the Mount Athos District (see note after No. N166) but were never issued there. By error some of them were put in use as ordinary postage due stamps in Dec., 1924. In 1932 the balance of them was burned.

**Type of 1902 Issue**

| 1930 | | Perf. 13, 13½x12½, 13½x13 | Litho. | |
|---|---|---|---|---|
| J79 | D3 | 50 l dk brown | .30 | .30 |
| J80 | D3 | 1d lt blue | .30 | .30 |
| J81 | D3 | 2d lt red | .30 | .30 |
| J82 | D3 | 3d rose red | 27.50 | 25.00 |
| J83 | D3 | 5d gray blue | .30 | .30 |
| J84 | D3 | 10d gray green | .30 | .30 |
| J85 | D3 | 15d red brown | .30 | .30 |
| J86 | D3 | 25d light red | .70 | .65 |
| | | Nos. J79-J86 (8) | 30.00 | 27.45 |

**Type of 1902 Issue**

| 1935 | | Engr. | Perf. 12½x13 | |
|---|---|---|---|---|
| J87 | D3 | 50d orange | .30 | .30 |
| J88 | D3 | 100d slate green | .30 | .30 |

**No. J70 Surcharged with New Value in Black**

**1942**

| J89 | D3 | 50 (l) on 30 l carmine | 1.50 | 1.50 |
|---|---|---|---|---|

**Type of 1902**

| 1943 | | Wmk. 252 Litho. | Perf. 12½ | |
|---|---|---|---|---|
| J90 | D3 | 10d red orange | .20 | .20 |
| J91 | D3 | 25d ultramarine | .20 | .20 |
| J92 | D3 | 100d black brown | .20 | .20 |
| J93 | D3 | 200d violet | .20 | .20 |
| | | Nos. J90-J93 (4) | .80 | .80 |

### POSTAL TAX STAMPS

**"The Tragedy of War" — PT1**

Red Cross, Nurses, Wounded and Bearers PT1a

### Serrate Roulette 13½

| | | | Unwmk. | |
|---|---|---|---|---|
| **1914** | | **Litho.** | | |
| RA1 | PT1 | 2 l red ('18) | .35 | .25 |
| a. | | 2 l carmine | .35 | .25 |
| b. | | Imperf., pair | 200.00 | |
| RA2 | PT1 | 5 l blue | .50 | .75 |
| a. | | Imperf., pair | 250.00 | |

### Serrate Roulette 13

**1915**

| RA2B | PT1a (5 l) dk bl & red | 10.00 | 2.00 |
|---|---|---|---|

The tax was for the Red Cross.

### Women's Patriotic League Badge — PT1b

**1915, Nov.**  **Perf. 11½**

| RA2C | PT1b (5 l) dk bl & car | 1.25 | 1.00 |
|---|---|---|---|
| d. | Horiz. pair, imperf. btwn. | 55.00 | |

The tax was for the Greek Women's Patriotic League.

### Nos. 165, 167, 170, 172-175 Surcharged in Black or Brown:

a      b

In type "b" the letters, especially those in the first line, are thinner than in type "a," making them appear taller.

### Perf. 11½, 12½, 13½ and Compound

| | | | Wmk. 129 | |
|---|---|---|---|---|
| **1917** | | **Engr.** | | |
| RA3 | A11(a) | 1 l on 1 l | 1.50 | 1.50 |
| a. | | Double surcharge | 7.00 | |
| RA4 | A11(a) | 1 l on 1 l (Br) | 22.50 | 22.50 |
| RA5 | A11(a) | 1 l on 3 l | .30 | .30 |
| RA6 | A11(b) | 1 l on 3 l | .30 | .30 |
| a. | | Triple surcharge | 5.00 | |
| b. | | Dbl. surch., one invtd. | 5.00 | |
| c. | | "K.M." for "K.Π." | 20.00 | |
| RA7 | A11(a) | 5 l on 1 l | 2.00 | 2.00 |
| a. | | Double surcharge | 10.00 | |
| b. | | Dbl. surch., one invtd. | 10.00 | |
| c. | | Inverted surcharge | 12.00 | |
| RA8 | A11(a) | 5 l on 20 l | .65 | .65 |
| a. | | Double surcharge | 12.00 | |
| b. | | Dbl. surch., one invtd. | 12.00 | |
| RA9 | A11(b) | 5 l on 40 l | .65 | .65 |
| a. | | Imperf. | | |
| RA10 | A11(b) | 5 l on 50 l | .65 | .65 |
| a. | | Double surcharge | 25.00 | |
| b. | | Dbl. surch., one invtd. | 25.00 | |
| RA11 | A13(b) | 5 l on 1d | 2.25 | 2.25 |
| a. | | Imperf. | | |
| b. | | Inverted surcharge | 50.00 | |
| RA12 | A11(a) | 10 l on 30 l | .80 | .80 |
| a. | | Imperf. | | |
| a. | | Double surcharge | 20.00 | |
| RA13 | A11(a) | 30 l on 30 l | .90 | .90 |
| a. | | Double surcharge | 20.00 | |
| | | *Nos. RA3-RA13 (11)* | *32.50* | *32.50* |

### Same Surcharge On Occupation Stamps of 1912

### Serrate Roulette 13½

| | | | Unwmk. | |
|---|---|---|---|---|
| **1917** | | **Litho.** | | |
| RA14 | O2 (b) | 5 l on 25 l pale bl | .45 | .45 |
| a. | | Triple surch., one invtd. | 15.00 | |
| a. | | Double surcharge | 8.00 | |
| RA15 | O2 (b) | 5 l on 40 l indigo | .45 | .45 |
| a. | | Double surch., one invtd. | 8.00 | |
| b. | | Double surcharge | 8.00 | |
| RA16 | O1 (b) | 5 l on 50 l dk bl | .45 | .45 |
| a. | | Double surcharge | 10.00 | |
| b. | | Inverted surcharge | 10.00 | |
| | | *Nos. RA14-RA16 (3)* | *1.35* | *1.35* |

There are many wrong font, omitted and misplaced letters and punctuation marks and similar varieties in the surcharges on Nos. RA3 to RA16.

### Revenue Stamps Surcharged in Brown

*K. Π.*
*λεπτοῦ*
*1*

"Victory" — R1

**1917**

| RA17 | R1 | 1 l on 10 l blue | .70 | .70 |
|---|---|---|---|---|
| RA18 | R1 | 1 l on 80 l blue | .70 | .70 |
| RA19 | R1 | 5 l on 10 l blue | 15.00 | 20.00 |
| RA20 | R1 | 5 l on 60 l blue | 4.00 | 4.00 |
| a. | | Perf. vert. through middle | 6.00 | 10.00 |
| RA21 | R1 | 5 l on 80 l blue | 3.00 | 3.00 |
| a. | | Perf. vert. through middle | 8.00 | 6.00 |
| b. | | Inverted surcharge | | |
| RA22 | R1 | 10 l on 70 l blue | 16.00 | 12.00 |
| a. | | Perf. vert. through middle | 6.00 | 8.00 |
| RA23 | R1 | 10 l on 90 l blue | 12.00 | 8.00 |
| a. | | Perf. vert. through middle | 20.00 | 25.00 |
| RA24 | R1 | 20 l on 20 l blue | 725.00 | 525.00 |
| RA25 | R1 | 20 l on 30 l blue | 4.00 | 4.00 |
| RA26 | R1 | 20 l on 40 l blue | 12.00 | 10.00 |
| RA27 | R1 | 20 l on 50 l blue | 8.00 | 6.00 |
| RA28 | R1 | 20 l on 60 l blue | 400.00 | 250.00 |
| RA29 | R1 | 20 l on 80 l blue | 40.00 | 32.50 |
| RA30 | R1 | 20 l on 90 l blue | 4.00 | 6.00 |
| a. | | Inverted surcharge | 70.00 | |
| | | *Nos. RA17-RA30 (14)* | *1,244.* | *881.90* |

No. RA19 is known only with vertical perforation through the middle.
Counterfeits exist of #RA17-RA43, used.

### Surcharged in Brown or Black

| RA31 | R1 | 1 l on 50 l vio (Bk) | .80 | 1.25 |
|---|---|---|---|---|
| RA32 | R1 | 5 l on 10 l bl (Br) | .80 | 1.25 |
| a. | | Inverted surcharge | 80.00 | |
| b. | | Left "5" invert. | 80.00 | |
| RA33 | R1 | 5 l on 10 l vio (Br) | .80 | 1.25 |
| RA34 | R1 | 5 l on 50 l vio (Br) | 5.50 | 10.00 |
| RA35 | R1 | 10 l on 50 l vio (Bk) | 22.50 | 20.00 |
| RA36 | R1 | 20 l on 2d bl (Bk) | 8.00 | 8.00 |
| a. | | Surcharged "20 lept. 30" | 65.00 | 65.00 |
| b. | | Horiz. pair, imperf. btwn. | | |
| | | *Nos. RA31-RA36 (6)* | *38.40* | *41.75* |

The "t," fourth Greek letter of the denomination in the surcharge ("Lept."), is normally omitted on Nos. RA31, RA34-RA36.

### Corfu Issue

### Surcharged in Black

**1917**

| RA37 | R1 | 1 l on 10 l blue | 1.25 | 1.25 |
|---|---|---|---|---|
| RA38 | R1 | 5 l on 50 l blue | 32.50 | 45.00 |
| RA39 | R1 | 10 l on 50 l blue | 400.00 | 350.00 |
| RA40 | R1 | 20 l on 50 l blue | 1,200. | 650.00 |

### Surcharged in Black

| RA41 | R1 | 10 l on 50 l blue | 8.00 | 6.00 |
|---|---|---|---|---|
| RA42 | R1 | 20 l on 50 l blue | 18.00 | 12.00 |
| RA43 | R1 | 30 l on 50 l blue | 12.00 | 8.00 |

### Surcharged in Black

| RA44 | R1 | 5 l on 10 l vio & red | 8.00 | 12.00 |
|---|---|---|---|---|
| a. | | "K" with serifs | 120.00 | 20.00 |

Counterfeits exist of Nos. RA17-RA44.
Similar stamps with denominations higher than 30 lepta were for revenue use.

### Wounded Soldier — PT2

**1918**  **Serrate Roulette 13½, 11½**

| RA45 | PT2 | 5 l bl, yel & red | 8.00 | 2.00 |
|---|---|---|---|---|

### Overprinted

| RA46 | PT2 | 5 l blue, yel & red | 9.50 | 2.00 |
|---|---|---|---|---|

The letters are the initials of Greek words equivalent to "Patriotic Relief Institution." The proceeds were given to the Patriotic League, for the aid of disabled soldiers.
Counterfeits exist of Nos. RA45-RA46.

PT3

### Surcharge in Red

**1922**  **Litho.**  **Perf. 11½**
### Dark Blue & Red

| RA46A | PT3 | 5 l on 10 l | *275.00* | 5.00 |
|---|---|---|---|---|
| RA46B | PT3 | 5 l on 20 l | 50.00 | 25.00 |
| RA46C | PT3 | 5 l on 50 l | 250.00 | 80.00 |
| RA46D | PT3 | 5 l on 1d | 3.25 | *35.00* |

Counterfeit surcharges exist. Examples of Nos. RA46A-RA46C without surcharge, each 50 cents.

### Red Cross Help to Soldier and Family PT3a

### St. Demetrius PT4

**1924**  **Perf. 11½, 13½ x 12½**

| RA47 | PT3a | 10 l blue, buff & red | .70 | .25 |
|---|---|---|---|---|
| a. | | Imperf., pair | 40.00 | |
| b. | | Horiz. pair, imperf. btwn. | 40.00 | |

Proceeds were given to the Red Cross.

**1934**  **Perf. 11½**

| RA48 | PT4 | 20 l brown | .40 | .20 |
|---|---|---|---|---|
| a. | | Horiz. pair, imperf. between | 10.00 | |
| b. | | Vertical pair, imperf. between | 15.00 | |
| c. | | Imperf., pair | 20.00 | |

No. RA48 was obligatory as a tax on all interior mail, including air post, mailed from Salonika.
For surcharge see No. RA69.

### "Health"

PT5      PT6

**1934, Dec. 28**  **Perf. 13, 13x13½**

| RA49 | PT5 | 10 l bl grn, org & buff | .25 | .20 |
|---|---|---|---|---|
| a. | | Vert. pair, imperf. horiz. | | |
| RA50 | PT5 | 20 l grn, org & buff | .55 | .20 |
| RA51 | PT5 | 50 l grn, org & buff | 2.00 | .50 |
| | | *Nos. RA49-RA51 (3)* | *2.80* | *.90* |

For surcharge see No. RA67.

**1935**

| RA52 | PT6 | 10 l yel grn, org & buff | .40 | .20 |
|---|---|---|---|---|
| RA53 | PT6 | 20 l ultra, org & buff | .40 | .20 |
| RA54 | PT6 | 50 l grn, org & buff | 1.25 | .65 |
| | | *Nos. RA52-RA54 (3)* | *2.05* | *1.05* |

The use of #RA49-RA54 was obligatory on all mail during 4 weeks each year including Christmas, the New Year and Easter, and on parcel post packages at all times. For the benefit of the tubercular clerks and officials of the Post, Telephone and Telegraph Service.
See No. RA64. For surcharge see No. RA68.

### No. 364 Overprinted in Red

**1937, Jan. 20**  **Engr.**  **Perf. 13x12½**

| RA55 | A36 | 50 l violet | 1.40 | .25 |
|---|---|---|---|---|
| a. | | Inverted overprint | | |

No. RA55a first appeared as an error, then was issued deliberately in quantity to avoid speculation.

### Same Overprint in Blue on No. J67
### Litho.
### Serrate Roulette 13½

| RA56 | D3 | 10 l carmine | .80 | .25 |
|---|---|---|---|---|
| a. | | Inverted overprint | 50.00 | |

No. RA56 with blue overprint double exists only with additional black overprint of Ionian Islands No. NRA1a.

### Same Overprint in Green on No. 364

**1937**  **Engr.**  **Perf. 13x12½**

| RA57 | A36 | 50 l violet | .75 | .20 |
|---|---|---|---|---|

### Same Overprint, with Surcharge of New Value, on Nos. J66, J68 and 323 in Blue or Black
### Serrate Roulette 13½

| | | | Unwmk. | |
|---|---|---|---|---|
| **1938** | | **Litho.** | | |
| RA58 | D3 | 50 l on 5 l grn | 2.40 | .80 |
| a. | | "o" for "p" in lowest word | 25.00 | 25.00 |
| b. | | Vert. pair, imperf. horiz. | 55.00 | |
| RA59 | D3 | 50 l on 20 l slate | 2.40 | .80 |

### Engr.  Perf. 13x12½

| RA60 | A38 | 50 l on 20 l vio (Bk) | .75 | .20 |
|---|---|---|---|---|
| | | *Nos. RA58-RA60 (3)* | *5.55* | *1.80* |

Surcharge on No. RA60 is 14½x16½mm.

### Queens Olga and Sophia PT7

**1939, Feb. 1**  **Litho.**  **Perf. 13½x12**

| RA61 | PT7 | 10 l brt rose, *pale rose* | .20 | .20 |
|---|---|---|---|---|
| RA62 | PT7 | 50 l gray grn, *pale grn* | .20 | .20 |
| RA63 | PT7 | 1d dl bl, *lt bl* | .20 | .20 |
| | | *Nos. RA61-RA63 (3)* | *.60* | *.60* |

For overprints and surcharges see Nos. RA65, RA79-RA81A, NRA1-NRA3.

### "Health" Type of 1935

**1939**  **Perf. 12½**

| RA64 | PT6 | 50 l brn & buff | .55 | .30 |
|---|---|---|---|---|

## No. RA62 Overprinted in Red

**1940**     *Perf. 13½x12*
RA65 PT7 50 l gray grn, *pale grn*    .25   .25
   *a.* Inverted overprint    35.00
   *b.* Pair, one without surcharge   20.00

Proceeds of #RA64-RA65 were used for the benefit of tubercular clerks and officials of the Post, Telephone and Telegraph Service. #RA65 was used in Albania during the Greek occupation, 1940-41 without additional overprint.

### No. 321 Surcharged in Carmine

**1941**   *Unwmk. Engr. Perf. 13½x13*
RA66 A36 50 l on 5 l dk grn    .20   .20
   *a.* Inverted surcharge    15.00

### No. RA49 and Type of 1935 Surcharged with New Value in Black
*Perf. 12½x13, 13x13½*
*Litho.*
RA67 PT5 50 l on 10 l    2.00   2.00
RA68 PT6 50 l on 10 l dp bl grn, dl org & buff   .20   .20
   *a.* Inverted surcharge   40.00
   *b.* Double surcharge   40.00

> Catalogue values for unused stamps in this section, from this point to the end of the section, are for Never Hinged items.

### No. RA48 Surcharged in Green

**1942**    *Perf. 11½*
RA69 PT4 1d on 20 l brn   .40   .20
   *a.* Pair, one without surcharge   25.00
   *b.* Imperf., pair   32.50
   *c.* Double surcharge   15.00

### Nos. 321, 324 Surcharged In Red or Carmine

**1942-43**   *Engr. Perf. 13½x13*
RA70 A36 10d on 5 l ('43)   .25   .20
   *a.* Double surcharge   25.00
RA71 A39 10d on 25 l (C)   .25   .20
   *a.* Inverted surcharge   25.00

### No. 444 Overprinted in Red

**1944**   *Wmk. 252 Litho. Perf. 12½*
RA72 A110 100d black   .20   .20
   *a.* Double overprint   12.00
   *b.* Inverted overprint   9.00

### No. 443 Surcharged in Blue

RA73 A109 5000d on 75d   .20   .20
   *a.* Double surcharge   25.00

### No. 437 Surcharged in Blue

RA74 A103 25000d on 2d   .20   .20
   *a.* Double surcharge   25.00
   *b.* Additional surcharge on back   17.50

### No. 399 Surcharged in Blue or Carmine

**1945**    *Perf. 13½x12*
RA75 A72 1d on 40 l   .20   .20
   *a.* Double surcharge   17.50
RA76 A72 2d on 40 l (C)   .20   .20
   *a.* Vert. pair, one without surch.   20.00
   *b.* Surcharged on back   15.00
   *c.* Inverted surcharge   22.50

Tax on Nos. RA67, RA68-RA70 to RA76 aided the postal clerks' tuberculosis fund.

### Nos. 396 and 399 Surcharged in Carmine

**1946**
RA77 A72 20d on 40 l   .50   .25
   *a.* Pair, one without surcharge   25.00
RA78 A69 20d on 5 l   1.25   .60

### Same Surcharge in Carmine on Nos. RA62 and RA63

**1946-47**   *Unwmk. Perf. 13½x12*
RA79 PT7 50d on 50 l ('47)   .50   .25
   *a.* Inverted surcharge   27.50
RA80 PT7 50d on 1d   .40   .25
   *a.* Violet black surcharge   4.75   3.00

The tax on Nos. RA77 to RA80 was for the Postal Clerks' Welfare Fund.

### Nos. RA65 and RA62 Surcharged in Carmine

**1947**
RA81 50d on 50 l (RA65)   2.00   .25
RA81A 50d on 50 l (RA62)   40.00   40.00

Tax for the postal clerks' tuberculosis fund.

St. Demetrius — PT8

**1948**   *Litho. Perf. 12x13½*
RA82 PT8 50d yellow brown   .25   .25

Obligatory on all domestic mail. The tax was for restoration of historical monuments and churches destroyed during World War II.

### Nos. 397 and 413 Surcharged in Blue

**1950**    *Wmk. 252*
RA83 A70 50d on 10 l (#397)   1.25   .30
   *a.* Stamp with double frame   125.00
   *b.* Surcharge reading down   22.50   22.50
RA84 A70 50d on 10 l (#413)   1.00   .20
   *a.* Surcharge reading down   22.50   22.50

Tax for the Postal Clerks' Welfare Fund.

### No. 396 Surcharged in Carmine

**1951**    *Perf. 13½x12*
RA85 A69 50d on 5 l   2.00   .20

Tax for the Postal Employees' Welfare Fund.

### No. 392 Surcharged in Black

**1951**   *Wmk. 252 Perf. 12½x12*
RA86 A67 50d on 3d red brn   2.00   .20
   *a.* Pair, one without surcharge   30.00
   *b.* "50" omitted   18.00

Tax for the postal clerks' tuberculosis fund.

### No. 393 Surcharged in Carmine

**1952**
RA87 A67 100d on 8d deep blue   1.00   .20

The tax was for the State Welfare Fund.

Ruins of Church of Phaneromeni, Zante — PT9    Zeus on Macedonian Coin of Philip II — PT10

500d, Map & scene of destruction, Argostoli.

**1953**   *Wmk. 252 Litho. Perf. 12½*
RA88 PT9 300d indigo & pale grn   1.25   .20
RA89 PT9 500d dk brn & buff   4.50   .70

The tax was for the reconstruction of Cephalonia, Ithaca, and Zante, Ionian Islands destroyed by earthquake.

**1956**    *Perf. 13½*
Design: 1d, Aristotle.
RA90 PT10 50 l dk car rose   1.25   .20
   *a.* Imperf., pair   125.00
RA91 PT10 1d brt blue   4.50   1.25

Tax for archaeological research in Macedonia. The coin on No. RA90 portrays Zeus despite inscription of Philip's name.

## POSTAL TAX SEMI-POSTAL STAMPS

Child — PTSP1    Mother and Child — PTSP2

Virgin and Christ Child — PTSP3

*Perf. 12x13½*
**1943**   *Wmk. 252 Litho.*
RAB1 PTSP1 25d + 25d bl grn   .20   .20
RAB2 PTSP2 100d + 50d rose vio   .20   .20
RAB3 PTSP3 200d + 100d red brn   .20   .20
Nos. RAB1-RAB3 (3)   .60   .60

Surtax aided needy children. These stamps were compulsory on domestic mail in Oct. 1943.

## OCCUPATION AND ANNEXATION STAMPS

During the Balkan wars, 1912-13, Greece occupied certain of the Aegean Islands and part of Western Turkey. She subsequently acquired these territories and they were known as the New Greece.

Most of the special issues for the Aegean Islands were made by order of the military commanders.

### For Use in the Aegean Islands Occupied by Greece

#### CHIOS

Greece No. 221 Overprinted in Red

*Serrate Roulette 13½*
**1913**   *Litho. Unwmk.*
N1 A25 25 l ultramarine   60.00   *75.00*
   *a.* Inverted overprint   225.00   175.00
   *b.* Greek "L" instead of "D"   225.00   175.00

#### ICARIA (NICARIA)

Penelope — I1

**1912 Unwmk. Litho. Perf. 11½**

| | | | | |
|---|---|---|---|---|
| N2 | I1 | 2 l orange | 1.25 | 2.40 |
| N3 | I1 | 5 l blue green | 1.25 | 2.40 |
| N4 | I1 | 10 l rose | 1.25 | 2.40 |
| N5 | I1 | 25 l ultra | 1.25 | 2.40 |
| N6 | I1 | 50 l gray lilac | 1.50 | 3.25 |
| N7 | I1 | 1d dark brown | 2.40 | 9.00 |
| N8 | I1 | 2d claret | 3.25 | 15.00 |
| N9 | I1 | 5d slate | 4.75 | 22.50 |
| | | Nos. N2-N9 (8) | 16.90 | 59.35 |

Counterfeits of Nos. N1-N15 are plentiful.

Stamps of Greece, 1911-23, Overprinted Reading Up

**1913 Engr.**

**On Issue of 1911-21**

| | | | | |
|---|---|---|---|---|
| N10 | A25 | 2 l car rose | 40.00 | 30.00 |
| N11 | A24 | 3 l vermilion | 40.00 | 30.00 |

**Litho.**

**On Issue of 1912-23**

| | | | | |
|---|---|---|---|---|
| N12 | A24 | 1 l green | 40.00 | 30.00 |
| N13 | A24 | 3 l vermilion | 40.00 | 30.00 |
| N14 | A26 | 5 l green | 40.00 | 30.00 |
| N15 | A24 | 10 l carmine | 40.00 | 30.00 |
| | | Nos. N10-N15 (6) | 240.00 | 180.00 |

**LEMNOS**

Regular Issues of Greece Overprinted in Black

**On Issue of 1901**

**1912 Wmk. 129 Engr. Perf. 13½**

| | | | | |
|---|---|---|---|---|
| N16 | A11 | 20 l red lilac | 1.60 | 1.60 |

**On Issue of 1911-21**

**Unwmk.**

**Serrate Roulette 13½**

| | | | | |
|---|---|---|---|---|
| N17 | A24 | 1 l green | .80 | .80 |
| N18 | A25 | 2 l carmine rose | .80 | .80 |
| N19 | A24 | 3 l vermilion | .80 | .80 |
| N20 | A26 | 5 l green | .80 | .80 |
| N21 | A24 | 10 l car rose | .80 | .80 |
| N22 | A25 | 20 l gray lilac | .80 | .80 |
| N23 | A25 | 25 l ultra | 1.25 | 1.25 |
| N24 | A26 | 30 l car rose | 1.25 | 1.25 |
| N25 | A26 | 40 l deep blue | 2.75 | 2.75 |
| N26 | A26 | 50 l dl violet | 2.75 | 2.75 |
| N27 | A27 | 1d ultra | 4.50 | 4.50 |
| N28 | A27 | 2d vermilion | 19.00 | 19.00 |
| N29 | A27 | 3d car rose | 22.50 | 22.50 |
| N30 | A27 | 5d ultra | 27.50 | 27.50 |
| N31 | A27 | 10d deep blue | 92.50 | 92.50 |
| N32 | A28 | 25d deep blue | 92.50 | 92.50 |

**On Issue of 1912-23**

**Litho.**

| | | | | |
|---|---|---|---|---|
| N33 | A24 | 1 l green | .40 | .40 |
| a. | | Without period after "Ellas" | 150.00 | 150.00 |
| N34 | A24 | 5 l green | .40 | .40 |
| N35 | A24 | 10 l carmine | .40 | .40 |
| N36 | A25 | 25 l ultra | 1.75 | 1.75 |
| | | Nos. N16-N36 (21) | 275.85 | 275.85 |

**Red Overprint**

**On Issue of 1911-21**

**Engr.**

| | | | | |
|---|---|---|---|---|
| N37 | A25 | 2 l car rose | .80 | .80 |
| N38 | A24 | 3 l vermilion | .80 | .80 |
| N39 | A25 | 20 l gray lilac | 6.00 | 6.00 |
| N40 | A26 | 30 l car rose | 4.25 | 4.25 |
| N41 | A26 | 40 l deep blue | 4.25 | 4.25 |
| N42 | A26 | 50 l dull violet | 4.25 | 4.25 |
| N43 | A27 | 1d ultra | 4.25 | 4.25 |
| N44 | A27 | 2d vermilion | 42.50 | 42.50 |
| N45 | A27 | 3d car rose | 25.00 | 25.00 |
| N46 | A27 | 5d ultra | 47.50 | 47.50 |
| N47 | A27 | 10d deep blue | 110.00 | 110.00 |
| N48 | A28 | 25d deep blue | 110.00 | 110.00 |

**On Issue of 1912-23**

**Litho.**

| | | | | |
|---|---|---|---|---|
| N49 | A24 | 1 l green | .80 | .80 |
| a. | | Without period after "Ellas" | 150.00 | 150.00 |

| | | | | |
|---|---|---|---|---|
| N50 | A26 | 5 l green | .40 | .40 |
| N51 | A24 | 10 l carmine | 2.00 | 2.00 |
| N52 | A25 | 25 l ultra | 2.50 | 2.50 |
| | | Nos. N37-N52 (16) | 365.30 | 365.30 |

The overprint is found inverted or double on many of Nos. N16-N52. There are several varieties in the overprint: Greek "D" for "L," large Greek "S" or "O," and small "O."

No. N49 with Added "Greek Administration" Overprint, as on Nos. N109-N148, in Black

**1913**

| | | | | |
|---|---|---|---|---|
| N52A | A24 | 1 l green | 29.00 | 29.00 |

Counterfeits of #N16-N52A are plentiful.

---

**MYTILENE (LESBOS)**

Turkey Nos. 162, 158 Overprinted in Blue

**Perf. 12, 13½ and Compound**

**1912 Typo. Unwmk.**

| | | | | |
|---|---|---|---|---|
| N53 | A21 | 20pa rose | 22.50 | 22.50 |
| N54 | A21 | 10pi dull red | 110.00 | 110.00 |

**On Turkey Nos. P68, 151-155, 137, 157-158 in Black**

| | | | | |
|---|---|---|---|---|
| N55 | A21 | 2pa olive green | 2.00 | 2.00 |
| N56 | A21 | 5pa ocher | 2.00 | 2.00 |
| N57 | A21 | 10pa blue green | 2.00 | 2.00 |
| N58 | A21 | 20pa rose | 2.00 | 2.00 |
| N59 | A21 | 1pi ultra | 4.00 | 4.00 |
| N60 | A21 | 2pi blue black | 22.50 | 22.50 |
| N61 | A19 | 2½pi dk brown | 11.00 | 11.00 |
| N62 | A21 | 5pi dk violet | 22.50 | 22.50 |
| N63 | A21 | 10pi dull red | 110.00 | 110.00 |
| | | Nos. N55-N63 (9) | 178.00 | 178.00 |

**On Turkey Nos. 161-163, 145 in Black**

| | | | | |
|---|---|---|---|---|
| N64 | A21 | 10pa blue green | 5.50 | 5.50 |
| a. | | Double overprint | 40.00 | 40.00 |
| N65 | A21 | 20pa rose | 5.50 | 5.50 |
| N66 | A21 | 1pi ultra | 5.50 | 5.50 |
| N67 | A19 | 2pi blue black | 52.50 | 52.50 |

**Nos. N55, N58, N65, N59 Surcharged in Blue or Black**

| | | | | |
|---|---|---|---|---|
| N68 | A21 | 25 l on 2pa | 8.00 | 8.00 |
| a. | | New value inverted | 40.00 | |
| N69 | A21 | 50 l on 20pa | 10.00 | 10.00 |
| b. | | New value inverted | 45.00 | |
| N70 | A21 | 1d on 20pa (N65) (Bk) | 30.00 | 30.00 |
| a. | | New value inverted | 60.00 | 60.00 |
| N71 | A21 | 2d on 1pi (Bk) | 22.50 | 22.50 |
| a. | | New value inverted | | |

**Same Overprint on Turkey No. J49**

| | | | | |
|---|---|---|---|---|
| N72 | A19 | 1pi blk, dp rose | 50.00 | 50.00 |

The overprint is found on all values reading up or down with inverted "i" in the first word and inverted "e" in the third word. No. N72 was only used for postage. Counterfeits of Nos. N53-N72 are plentiful.

---

**SAMOS**

**Issues of the Provisional Government**

Map of Samos OS1

**1912 Unwmk. Typo. Imperf.**

| | | | | |
|---|---|---|---|---|
| N73 | OS1 | 5 l gray green | 20.00 | 7.00 |
| N74 | OS1 | 10 l red | 20.00 | 7.00 |
| N75 | OS1 | 25 l blue | 40.00 | 20.00 |
| | | 25 l green (error) | 500.00 | 600.00 |
| | | Nos. N73-N75 (3) | 80.00 | 34.00 |

Nos. N73-N75 exist in tête bêche pairs. Value per set, $2,000 unused, $1,200 used. Counterfeits exist of Nos. N73 to N75.

---

Hermes — OS2

**1912 Litho. Perf. 11½**

**Without Overprint**

| | | | | |
|---|---|---|---|---|
| N76 | OS2 | 1 l gray | 3.00 | 1.50 |
| N77 | OS2 | 5 l lt green | 3.75 | 1.50 |
| N78 | OS2 | 10 l rose | 4.00 | 1.50 |
| b. | | Half used as 5 l on cover | | 200.00 |
| N79 | OS2 | 25 l lt blue | 7.00 | 1.50 |
| N80 | OS2 | 50 l violet brn | 12.50 | 10.00 |

**With Overprint**

| | | | | |
|---|---|---|---|---|
| N81 | OS2 | 1 l gray | 1.00 | 1.10 |
| N82 | OS2 | 5 l blue grn | 1.00 | 1.10 |
| N83 | OS2 | 10 l rose | 1.75 | 1.50 |
| b. | | Half used as 5 l on cover | | 200.00 |
| N84 | OS2 | 25 l blue | 2.00 | 2.00 |
| N85 | OS2 | 50 l violet brn | 11.00 | 6.50 |
| N86 | OS2 | 1d orange | 10.00 | 10.00 |
| | | Nos. N76-N86 (11) | 57.00 | 38.20 |

For overprints and surcharge see Nos. N92-N103.

**Imperf., Pairs**

**Without Overprint**

| | | | | |
|---|---|---|---|---|
| N76a | OS2 | 1 l | | 40.00 |
| N77a | OS2 | 5 l | | 40.00 |
| N78a | OS2 | 10 l | | 40.00 |
| N79a | OS2 | 25 l | | 40.00 |
| N80a | OS2 | 50 l | | 40.00 |

**With Overprint**

| | | | | |
|---|---|---|---|---|
| N81a | OS2 | 1 l | | 100.00 |
| N82a | OS2 | 5 l | | 100.00 |
| N83a | OS2 | 10 l | | 100.00 |
| N85a | OS2 | 50 l | | 100.00 | 100.00 |

Church in Savior's Name and Fort Ruins OS3

Manuscript Initials in Red or Black

**1913**

| | | | | |
|---|---|---|---|---|
| N87 | OS3 | 1d brown (R) | 16.00 | 14.00 |
| N88 | OS3 | 2d deep blue (R) | 16.00 | 14.00 |
| N89 | OS3 | 5d gray grn (R) | 30.00 | 25.00 |
| N90 | OS3 | 10d yellow grn (R) | 90.00 | 80.00 |
| N91 | OS3 | 25d red (Bk) | 80.00 | 67.50 |
| | | Nos. N87-N91 (5) | 232.00 | 200.50 |

Victory of the Greek fleet in 1824 and the union with Greece of Samos in 1912. The manuscript initials are those of Pres. Themistokles Sofulis. Values the same for stamps without initials. Exist imperf. Counterfeits of Nos. N87-N91 are plentiful. For overprints see Nos. N104-N108.

Nos. N76 to N80 Overprinted

**1914**

| | | | | |
|---|---|---|---|---|
| N92 | OS2 | 1 l gray | 4.00 | 4.00 |
| N93 | OS2 | 5 l lt green | 4.00 | 4.00 |
| N94 | OS2 | 10 l rose | 4.25 | 4.00 |
| a. | | Double overprint | 60.00 | |
| N95 | OS2 | 25 l lt blue | 12.00 | 12.00 |
| N96 | OS2 | 50 l violet brn | 8.00 | 8.00 |
| a. | | Double overprint | 100.00 | |
| | | Nos. N92-N96 (5) | 32.25 | 32.00 |

**Charity Issues of Greek Administration**

Nos. N81 to N86 Overprinted in Red or Black

---

**1915**

| | | | | |
|---|---|---|---|---|
| N97 | OS2 | 1 l gray (R) | 20.00 | 20.00 |
| a. | | Black overprint | 125.00 | |
| N98 | OS2 | 5 l blue grn (Bk) | .80 | .80 |
| a. | | Red overprint | 125.00 | |
| b. | | Double overprint | 125.00 | |
| N99 | OS2 | 10 l rose (Bk) | .90 | .90 |
| a. | | Red overprint | 125.00 | |
| b. | | Inverted overprint | 125.00 | |
| N100 | OS2 | 25 l blue (Bk) | .80 | .80 |
| a. | | Red overprint | 125.00 | |
| N101 | OS2 | 50 l violet brn (Bk) | 1.00 | 1.00 |
| a. | | Red overprint | 125.00 | |
| N102 | OS2 | 1d orange (R) | 2.00 | 2.00 |
| a. | | Inverted overprint | 125.00 | |
| b. | | Black overprint | 100.00 | |
| c. | | Double black overprint | 150.00 | |

No. N102 With Additional Surcharge in Black

| | | | | |
|---|---|---|---|---|
| N103 | OS2 | 1 l on 1d orange | 15.00 | 15.00 |
| a. | | Black surcharge double | 160.00 | |
| b. | | Black surcharge inverted | 160.00 | |
| | | Nos. N97-N103 (7) | 40.50 | 40.50 |

Issue of 1913 Overprinted in Red or Black

**1915**

| | | | | |
|---|---|---|---|---|
| N104 | OS3 | 1d brown (R) | 20.00 | 20.00 |
| N105 | OS3 | 2d dp blue (R) | 24.00 | 24.00 |
| a. | | Double overprint | | |
| N106 | OS3 | 5d gray grn (R) | 40.00 | 40.00 |
| N107 | OS3 | 10d yellow grn (Bk) | 60.00 | 60.00 |
| a. | | Inverted overprint | | |
| N108 | OS3 | 25d red (Bk) | 750.00 | 750.00 |
| | | Nos. N104-N108 (5) | 894.00 | 894.00 |

Nos. N97 to N108 inclusive have an embossed control mark, consisting of a cross encircled by a Greek inscription. Most examples of Nos. N104-N108 lack the initials. Counterfeits of Nos. N104-N108 are plentiful.

---

**FOR USE IN PARTS OF TURKEY OCCUPIED BY GREECE (NEW GREECE)**

Regular Issues of Greece Overprinted

Black Overprint Meaning "Greek Administration" On Issue of 1901

**1912 Wmk. 129 Engr. Perf. 13½**

| | | | | |
|---|---|---|---|---|
| N109 | A11 | 20 l red lilac | 3.25 | 2.40 |

**On Issue of 1911-21**

**Unwmk.**

**Serrate Roulette 13½**

| | | | | |
|---|---|---|---|---|
| N110 | A24 | 1 l green | .60 | .50 |
| N111 | A25 | 2 l car rose | .60 | .50 |
| N112 | A24 | 3 l vermilion | .60 | .50 |
| N113 | A26 | 5 l green | .80 | .70 |
| N114 | A24 | 10 l car rose | 1.25 | 1.00 |
| N115 | A25 | 20 l gray lilac | 2.00 | 1.50 |
| N116 | A25 | 25 l ultra | 2.00 | 2.00 |
| N117 | A26 | 30 l car rose | 2.50 | 2.25 |
| N118 | A26 | 40 l deep blue | 4.00 | 3.25 |
| N119 | A26 | 50 l dl violet | 4.25 | 3.25 |
| N120 | A27 | 1d ultra | 10.00 | 2.00 |
| N121 | A27 | 2d vermilion | 40.00 | 25.00 |
| N122 | A27 | 3d car rose | 90.00 | 90.00 |
| N123 | A27 | 5d ultra | 20.00 | 17.00 |
| N124 | A27 | 10d deep blue | 225.00 | 225.00 |
| N125 | A28 | 25d dp bl, ovpt. horiz. | 225.00 | 225.00 |

## On Issue of 1913-23
### Litho.

| | | | | |
|---|---|---|---|---|
| N126 | A24 | 1 l green | .60 | .60 |
| b. | | Without period after "El-las" | 100.00 | 100.00 |
| N127 | A26 | 5 l green | .60 | .50 |
| N128 | A24 | 10 l carmine | 3.25 | 2.40 |
| N129 | A25 | 25 l blue | 4.00 | 3.25 |
| | | Nos. N109-N129 (21) | 640.30 | 608.70 |

### Red Overprint
## On Issue of 1911-21
### Engr.

| | | | | |
|---|---|---|---|---|
| N130 | A24 | 1 l green | .80 | .80 |
| N131 | A25 | 2 l car rose | 9.00 | 9.00 |
| N132 | A24 | 3 l vermilion | 8.00 | 8.00 |
| N133 | A26 | 5 l green | .90 | .70 |
| N134 | A25 | 20 l gray lilac | 12.00 | 1.50 |
| N135 | A25 | 25 l ultra | 55.00 | 55.00 |
| N136 | A26 | 30 l car rose | 60.00 | 60.00 |
| N137 | A25 | 40 l deep blue | 3.00 | 3.00 |
| N138 | A26 | 50 l dl violet | 3.00 | 3.00 |
| N139 | A27 | 1d ultra | 12.00 | 12.00 |
| N140 | A27 | 2d vermilion | 60.00 | 60.00 |
| N141 | A27 | 3d car rose | 24.00 | 24.00 |
| N142 | A27 | 5d ultra | 250.00 | 225.00 |
| N143 | A27 | 10d deep blue | 35.00 | 30.00 |
| N144 | A28 | 25d dp bl, ovpt. horiz. | 55.00 | 55.00 |
| a. | | Vertical overprint | 400.00 | 400.00 |

## On Issue of 1913-23
### Litho.

| | | | | |
|---|---|---|---|---|
| N145 | A24 | 1 l green | 7.00 | 7.00 |
| a. | | Without period after "El-las" | 175.00 | |
| N146 | A26 | 5 l green | .85 | .85 |
| N147 | A24 | 10 l carmine | 60.00 | 55.00 |
| N148 | A25 | 25 l blue | 2.25 | 1.75 |
| | | Nos. N130-N148 (19) | 657.80 | 611.60 |

The normal overprint is vertical, reading upward on N109-N124, N126-N143, N145-N148. It is often double or reading downward. There are numerous broken, missing and wrong font letters with a Greek "L" instead of "D" as the first letter of the second word.

Counterfeits exist of Nos. N109-N148.

Cross of Constantine
O1

Eagle of Zeus
O2

### 1912              Litho.

| | | | | |
|---|---|---|---|---|
| N150 | O1 | 1 l brown | .25 | .25 |
| N151 | O2 | 2 l red | .25 | .25 |
| a. | | 2 l rose | .80 | .60 |
| N153 | O2 | 3 l orange | .30 | .25 |
| N154 | O1 | 5 l green | 1.25 | .25 |
| N155 | O1 | 10 l rose red | 10.00 | .25 |
| N156 | O1 | 20 l violet | 21.00 | 4.50 |
| N157 | O2 | 25 l pale blue | 4.75 | 1.25 |
| N158 | O1 | 30 l gray grn | 75.00 | 3.25 |
| N159 | O2 | 40 l indigo | 15.00 | 8.75 |
| N160 | O1 | 50 l dark blue | 8.00 | 4.50 |
| N161 | O2 | 1d violet brn | 8.75 | 4.50 |
| N162 | O1 | 2d gray brn | 60.00 | 12.00 |
| N163 | O2 | 3d dull blue | 140.00 | 27.50 |
| N164 | O1 | 5d gray | 140.00 | 32.50 |
| N165 | O2 | 10d carmine | 125.00 | 350.00 |
| N166 | O1 | 25d gray blk | 125.00 | 350.00 |
| | | Nos. N150-N166 (16) | 734.55 | 800.00 |

Occupation of Macedonia, Epirus and some of the Aegean Islands.

Sold only in New Greece.

Dangerous forgeries of #N165-N166 exist.

In 1916 some stamps of this issue were overprinted in Greek: "I (era) Koinotis Ag (iou) Orous" for the Mount Athos Monastery District. They were never placed in use and most of them were destroyed.

For surcharges and overprints see Nos. 267-276A, RA14-RA16, Thrace 31-33.

### Imperf., Pairs
### Without Overprint

| | | | |
|---|---|---|---|
| N150a | O1 | 1 l | 500.00 |
| N151b | O2 | 2 l | 500.00 |
| N153a | O2 | 3 l | 500.00 |
| N154a | O1 | 5 l | 200.00 |
| N155a | O1 | 10 l | 200.00 |
| N156a | O1 | 20 l | 1,750. |
| N157a | O2 | 25 l | 1,750. |
| N158a | O1 | 30 l | 1,750. |
| N159a | O2 | 40 l | 1,750. |
| N163a | O2 | 3d | 2,500. |

---

## CAVALLA

### ΕΛΛΗΝΙΚΗ ΔΙΟΙΚΗΣΙΣ

Bulgaria Nos. 89-97 Surcharged in Red

## 25 ΛΕΠΤΑ 25

### 1913   Unwmk.   Engr.   Perf. 12

| | | | | |
|---|---|---|---|---|
| N167 | A20 | 5 l on 1s | 22.50 | 22.50 |
| N169 | A26 | 10 l on 15s | 65.00 | 65.00 |
| N170 | A26 | 10 l on 25s | 32.50 | 32.50 |
| N171 | A21 | 15 l on 2s | 65.00 | 65.00 |
| N172 | A22 | 20 l on 3s | 65.00 | 65.00 |
| N173 | A23 | 25 l on 5s | 20.00 | 12.00 |
| N174 | A24 | 50 l on 10s | 35.00 | 22.50 |
| N175 | A25 | 1 d on 15s | 225.00 | 200.00 |
| N176 | A27 | 1 d on 30s | 95.00 | 95.00 |
| N177 | A28 | 1 d on 50s | 140.00 | 140.00 |

### Blue Surcharge

| | | | | |
|---|---|---|---|---|
| N178 | A24 | 50 l on 10s | 20.00 | 20.00 |
| | | Nos. N167-N178 (11) | 785.00 | 739.50 |

The counterfeits and reprints of Nos. N167-N178 are difficult to distinguish from originals. Many overprint varieties exist.

Some specialists question the status of Nos. N167-N178.

---

## DEDEAGATCH

### (Alexandroupolis)
### ΕΛΛΗΝΙΚΗ ΔΙΟΙΚΗΣΙΣ ΔΕΔΕΑΓΑΤΣ ΔΕΚΑ ΛΕΠΤΑ

D1-(10 lepta)

### 1913   Unwmk.   Typeset   Perf. 11½
### Control Mark in Red

| | | | | |
|---|---|---|---|---|
| N179 | D1 | 5 l black | 40.00 | 30.00 |
| N180 | D1 | 10 l black | 5.50 | 4.00 |
| N181 | D1 | 25 l black | 6.50 | 4.50 |
| a. | | Sheet of 8 | 125.00 | 125.00 |
| | | Nos. N179-N181 (3) | 52.00 | 38.50 |

Nos. N179-N181 issued without gum in sheets of 8, consisting of one 5 l, three 10 l normal, one 10 l inverted, three 25 l and one blank. The sheet yields se-tenant pairs of 5 l & 10 l, 10 l & 25 l; tete beche pairs of 5 l & 10 l, 10 l & 25 l and 10 l & 10 l.

Also issued imperf., value $200 unused, $150 canceled.

The 5 l reads "PENTE LEPTA" in Greek letters; the 10 l is illustrated; the 25 l carries the numeral "25."

Bulgaria Nos. 89-90, 92-93, 95 Surcharged

### Red Surcharge

### 1913                 Perf. 12

| | | | | |
|---|---|---|---|---|
| N182 | A20 | 5 l on 1s | 65.00 | 42.50 |
| N183 | A26 | 1d on 25s | 80.00 | 52.50 |

### Blue Surcharge

| | | | | |
|---|---|---|---|---|
| N184 | A24 | 10 l on 10s | 30.00 | 25.00 |
| N185 | A23 | 25 l on 5s | 35.00 | 25.00 |
| N187 | A21 | 50 l on 5s | 65.00 | 42.50 |
| | | Nos. N182-N185,N187 (5) | 275.00 | 187.50 |

The surcharges on Nos. N182 to N187 are printed from a setting of eight, which was used for all, with the necessary changes of value. No. 6 in the setting has a Greek "L" instead of "D" for the third letter of the third word of the surcharge.

The 25 l surcharge also exists on 8 examples of the 25s, Bulgaria No. 95.

---

D2

D3

### 1913, Sept. 15   Typeset   Perf. 11½
### Control Mark in Blue

| | | | | |
|---|---|---|---|---|
| N188 | D2 | 1 l blue | 200.00 | 65.00 |
| N189 | D2 | 2 l blue | 200.00 | 65.00 |
| N190 | D2 | 3 l blue | 200.00 | 65.00 |
| N191 | D2 | 5 l blue | 200.00 | 65.00 |
| N192 | D2 | 10 l blue | 200.00 | 65.00 |
| N193 | D2 | 25 l blue | 200.00 | 65.00 |
| N194 | D2 | 40 l blue | 200.00 | 65.00 |
| N195 | D2 | 50 l blue | 200.00 | 65.00 |
| | | Nos. N188-N195 (8) | 1,600. | |

Issued without gum in sheets of 8 containing all values.

### 1913, Sept. 25           Typeset
### Control Mark in Blue

| | | | | |
|---|---|---|---|---|
| N196 | D3 | 1 l blue, gray blue | 160.00 | 50.00 |
| N197 | D3 | 5 l blue, gray blue | 160.00 | 50.00 |
| N198 | D3 | 10 l blue, gray blue | 160.00 | 50.00 |
| N199 | D3 | 25 l blue, gray blue | 160.00 | 50.00 |
| N200 | D3 | 30 l blue, gray blue | 160.00 | 50.00 |
| N201 | D3 | 50 l blue, gray blue | 160.00 | 50.00 |
| | | Nos. N196-N201 (6) | 960.00 | |

Nos. N196 to N201 were issued without gum in sheets of six containing all values.

Counterfeits of Nos. N182-N201 are plentiful.

---

## FOR USE IN NORTH EPIRUS (ALBANIA)

Greek Stamps of 1937-38 Overprinted in Black

### Perf. 13½x12, 12x13½

| 1940 | | Litho. | Wmk. 252 | |
|---|---|---|---|---|
| N202 | A69 | 5 l brn red & bl | .25 | .25 |
| a. | | Inverted overprint | 55.00 | |
| N203 | A70 | 10 l bl & brn red (No. 413) | .25 | .25 |
| a. | | Double impression of frame | 160.00 | |
| N204 | A71 | 20 l blk & grn | .25 | .25 |
| a. | | Inverted overprint | 55.00 | |
| N205 | A72 | 40 l grn & blk | .25 | .25 |
| a. | | Inverted overprint | 55.00 | |
| N206 | A73 | 50 l brn & blk | .25 | .25 |
| N207 | A74 | 80 l ind & yel brn | .40 | .40 |
| N208 | A67 | 1d green | .40 | .40 |
| a. | | Inverted overprint | 100.00 | |
| N209 | A75 | 2d ultra | .40 | .40 |
| N210 | A67 | 3d red brn | .80 | .80 |
| N211 | A76 | 5d red | .80 | .80 |
| N212 | A77 | 6d ol brn | .80 | .80 |
| N213 | A78 | 7d dk brn | .80 | .80 |
| N214 | A67 | 8d deep blue | .80 | .80 |
| N215 | A79 | 10d red brn | 2.00 | 2.00 |
| N216 | A80 | 15d green | 2.00 | 2.00 |
| N217 | A81 | 25d dark blue | 2.75 | 4.00 |
| a. | | Inverted overprint | 90.00 | |

### Engr.
### Unwmk.

| | | | | |
|---|---|---|---|---|
| N218 | A84 | 30d org brn | 5.00 | 8.00 |
| | | Nos. N202-N218 (17) | 18.20 | 22.45 |

### Same Overprinted in Carmine on National Youth Issue

| 1941 | | Litho. | Perf. 12½, 13½x12½ | |
|---|---|---|---|---|
| N219 | A93 | 3d sil, dp ultra & red | 1.00 | 1.00 |
| N220 | A94 | 5d dk bl & blk | 3.75 | 3.75 |
| N221 | A94 | 10d red org & blk | | |
| N222 | A94 | 15d dk grn & blk | 26.00 | 26.00 |
| N223 | A94 | 20d lake & blk | 15.00 | 12.00 |
| N224 | A94 | 25d dk bl & blk | 15.00 | 12.00 |

| | | | | |
|---|---|---|---|---|
| N225 | A94 | 30d rose vio & blk | 15.00 | 12.00 |
| N226 | A94 | 50d lake & blk | 15.00 | 12.00 |
| N227 | A94 | 75d dk bl, brn & gold | 20.00 | 12.00 |
| N228 | A93 | 100d sil, dp ultra & red | 20.00 | 15.00 |
| a. | | Inverted overprint | 350.00 | |
| | | Nos. N219-N228 (10) | 136.75 | 111.75 |

### Same Overprint in Carmine on National Youth Air Post Stamps

| | | | | |
|---|---|---|---|---|
| N229 | AP25 | 2d red org & blk | 1.10 | 1.10 |
| a. | | Inverted overprint | 150.00 | |
| N230 | AP25 | 4d dk grn & blk | 4.50 | 4.50 |
| a. | | Inverted overprint | 150.00 | |
| N231 | AP25 | 6d lake & blk | 6.50 | 6.50 |
| a. | | Inverted overprint | 150.00 | |
| N232 | AP25 | 8d dk bl & blk | 6.50 | 6.50 |
| N233 | AP25 | 16d rose vio & blk | 11.00 | 6.50 |
| N234 | AP25 | 32d red org & blk | 15.00 | 12.00 |
| N235 | AP25 | 45d dk grn & blk | 15.00 | 12.00 |
| N236 | AP25 | 55d lake & blk | 15.00 | 12.00 |
| N237 | AP25 | 65d dk bl & blk | 15.00 | 12.00 |
| N238 | AP25 | 100d rose vio & blk | 20.00 | 15.00 |
| | | Nos. N229-N238 (10) | 109.60 | 88.10 |

Some specialists have questioned the status of Nos. N230a and N231a.

For other stamps issued by Greece for use in occupied parts of Epirus and Thrace, see the catalogue listings of those countries.

> **Catalogue values for unused stamps in this section, from this point to the end of the section, are for Never Hinged items.**

## FOR USE IN THE DODECANESE ISLANDS

Greece, No. 472C, with Additional Overprint in Carmine or Silver

| 1947 | | Wmk. 252 | Litho. | Perf. 12½ |
|---|---|---|---|---|
| N239 | A113 | 10d on 2,000d (C) | .80 | .80 |
| N240 | A113 | 10d on 2,000d (S) | .80 | .80 |

These stamps sold for 5 lire (100 drachmas) and paid postage for that amount.

### King George II Memorial Issue

Greece, Nos. 484 and 485, With Additional Overprint in Black

| 1947 | | Engr. | Perf. 12½x12 | |
|---|---|---|---|---|
| N241 | A67 | 50d on 1d green | 1.25 | 1.25 |
| N242 | A67 | 250d on 3d red brown | 1.25 | 1.25 |

The letters are initials of the Greek words for "Military Administration of the Dodecanese."

Greece, Nos. 501 and 502 Overprinted in Carmine

| 1947 | | Wmk. 252 | Litho. | Perf. 12½ |
|---|---|---|---|---|
| N243 | A111 | 20d on 500d dk ol | .80 | .80 |
| N244 | A104 | 30d on 5d lt bl grn | .80 | .80 |

Greece, Nos. 437, 406, 407 and 445, Surcharged in Black or Carmine

| 1947 | | | Perf. 12½, 13½x12 | |
|---|---|---|---|---|
| N245 | A103 | 50d on 2d | 1.25 | 1.25 |

**Engr.**

| | | | | |
|---|---|---|---|---|
| N246 | A79 | 250d on 10d | 1.60 | 1.60 |
| N247 | A80 | 400d on 15d (C) | 2.40 | 2.40 |
| a. | | Inverted surcharge | 150.00 | |

**Litho.**

| | | | | |
|---|---|---|---|---|
| N248 | A110 | 1000d on 200 (C) | 2.00 | 2.00 |
| a. | | Imprint omitted | 40.00 | |
| | | Nos. N245-N248 (4) | 7.25 | 7.25 |

## POSTAGE DUE STAMPS

### FOR USE IN PARTS OF TURKEY OCCUPIED BY GREECE (NEW GREECE)

Postage Due Stamps of Greece, 1902, Overprinted

**1912    Wmk. 129    Engr.    Perf. 13½**
**Black Overprint**

| | | | | |
|---|---|---|---|---|
| NJ1 | D3 | 1 l chocolate | .50 | .50 |
| NJ2 | D3 | 2 l gray | .50 | .50 |
| NJ3 | D3 | 3 l orange | .50 | .50 |
| NJ4 | D3 | 5 l yel grn | .50 | .50 |
| NJ5 | D3 | 10 l scarlet | 1.00 | 1.00 |
| NJ6 | D3 | 20 l lilac | 1.00 | 1.00 |
| NJ7 | D3 | 30 l dp vio | 3.00 | 3.00 |
| NJ8 | D3 | 40 l dk brn | 6.00 | 6.00 |
| NJ9 | D3 | 50 l red brn | 8.75 | 8.75 |
| NJ10 | D3 | 1d black | 27.50 | 27.50 |
| NJ11 | D3 | 2d bronze | 20.00 | 20.00 |
| NJ12 | D3 | 3d silver | 60.00 | 60.00 |
| NJ13 | D3 | 5d gold | 100.00 | 100.00 |
| | | Nos. NJ1-NJ13 (13) | 229.25 | 229.25 |

**Red Overprint**

| | | | | |
|---|---|---|---|---|
| NJ14 | D3 | 1 l chocolate | .60 | .60 |
| NJ15 | D3 | 2 l gray | .60 | .60 |
| NJ16 | D3 | 3 l orange | .60 | .60 |
| NJ17 | D3 | 5 l yel grn | .60 | .60 |
| NJ18 | D3 | 10 l scar, down | 6.00 | 6.00 |
| NJ19 | D3 | 20 l lilac | .60 | .60 |
| NJ20 | D3 | 30 l dp vio | 4.50 | 4.50 |
| NJ21 | D3 | 40 l dk brn | .60 | .60 |
| NJ22 | D3 | 50 l red brn | .60 | .60 |
| NJ23 | D3 | 1d black | 8.00 | 8.00 |
| NJ24 | D3 | 2d bronze | 10.00 | 10.00 |
| NJ25 | D3 | 3d silver | 17.00 | 17.00 |
| NJ26 | D3 | 5d gold | 27.50 | 27.50 |
| | | Nos. NJ14-NJ26 (13) | 77.20 | 77.20 |

The normal position of the overprint is reading upward but it is often reversed. Some of the varieties of lettering which occur on the postage stamps are also found on the postage due stamps. Double overprints exist on some denominations.

### FOR USE IN NORTH EPIRUS (ALBANIA)

Postage Due Stamps of Greece, 1930, Surcharged or Overprinted in Black:

a                          b

**Perf. 13, 13x12½**

| | | | | |
|---|---|---|---|---|
| 1940 | | Litho. | | Unwmk. |
| NJ27 | D3(a) | 50 l on 25d lt red | .80 | .80 |
| NJ28 | D3(b) | 2d light red | 1.25 | 1.40 |
| a. | | Inverted overprint | 52.50 | |
| NJ29 | D3(b) | 5d blue gray | .80 | 1.25 |
| NJ30 | D3(b) | 10d green | 1.25 | 1.40 |
| NJ31 | D3(b) | 15d red brown | 1.25 | 1.60 |
| | | Nos. NJ27-NJ31 (5) | 5.35 | 6.45 |

## POSTAL TAX STAMPS

### FOR USE IN NORTH EPIRUS (ALBANIA)

Postal Tax Stamps of Greece, Nos. RA61-RA63, Overprinted Type "b" in Black

**1940    Unwmk.    Litho.    Perf. 13½x12**

| | | | | |
|---|---|---|---|---|
| NRA1 | PT7 | 10 l | .25 | .30 |
| NRA2 | PT7 | 50 l | .40 | .65 |
| a. | | Inverted overprint | 55.00 | |
| NRA3 | PT7 | 1d | .95 | 1.40 |
| | | Nos. NRA1-NRA3 (3) | 1.60 | 2.35 |

## MOUNT ATHOS

Catalogue values for unused stamps in this section are for Never Hinged items.

All stamps also are available for postage in Greece.

Nikiforos Fokas
A1

Ioannis Tsimiskis
A2

Map of Mount Athos
A3

Church of the Protaton
A4

Staff of Protepistates — A5

**Litho. With Foil Application**
**Perf. 13¼x13**

| | | | | |
|---|---|---|---|---|
| 2008, May 16 | | | | Unwmk. |
| 1 | A1 | 40c multi + label | 1.25 | 1.25 |
| 2 | A2 | 60c multi + label | 1.90 | 1.90 |
| 3 | A3 | 70c multi + label | 2.25 | 2.25 |
| 4 | A4 | €2 multi + label | 6.50 | 6.50 |
| 5 | A5 | €4 multi + label | 13.00 | 13.00 |
| | | Nos. 1-5 (5) | 24.90 | 24.90 |

Megiste Lavra Monastery
A6

Vatopedis Monastery
A7

Koutloumousiou Monastery — A8

Iveron Monastery
A9

Chilandari Monastery
A10

**2008, June 13**

| | | | | |
|---|---|---|---|---|
| 6 | A6 | 57c multi + label | 1.75 | 1.75 |
| 7 | A7 | 70c multi + label | 2.25 | 2.25 |
| 8 | A8 | €1 multi + label | 3.25 | 3.25 |
| 9 | A9 | €1.85 multi + label | 5.75 | 5.75 |
| 10 | A10 | €3 multi + label | 9.25 | 9.25 |
| | | Nos. 6-10 (5) | 22.25 | 22.25 |

Pantokrator Monastery — A11

Xeropotamou Monastery — A12

Karakallou Monastery
A13

Zographou Monastery
A14

Docheiariou Monastery — A15

**2008, July 4**

| | | | | |
|---|---|---|---|---|
| 11 | A11 | 57c multi + label | 1.90 | 1.90 |
| 12 | A12 | 70c multi + label | 2.25 | 2.25 |
| 13 | A13 | 80c multi + label | 2.50 | 2.50 |
| 14 | A14 | €1.50 multi + label | 4.75 | 4.75 |
| 15 | A15 | €3.50 multi + label | 11.00 | 11.00 |
| | | Nos. 11-15 (5) | 22.40 | 22.40 |

Agiou Pavlou Monastery
A16

Dionysiou Monastery
A17

Stavronikita Monastery — A18

Simonos Petras Monastery
A19

Philotheou
Monastery
A20

**2008, Aug. 22**

| | | | | |
|---|---|---|---|---|
| 16 | A16 | 57c multi + label | 1.75 | 1.75 |
| 17 | A17 | 70c multi + label | 2.10 | 2.10 |
| 18 | A18 | €1.20 multi + label | 3.50 | 3.50 |
| 19 | A19 | €1.80 multi + label | 5.25 | 5.25 |
| 20 | A20 | €3 multi + label | 9.00 | 9.00 |
| | | *Nos. 16-20 (5)* | 21.60 | 21.60 |

Xenophontos Monastery — A21

Gregoriou
Monastery
A22

Esphigmenou Monastery — A23

Konstamonitou Monastery — A24

Panteleimonos-Rossikou
Monastery — A25

**2008, Nov. 7**

| | | | | |
|---|---|---|---|---|
| 21 | A21 | 57c multi + label | 1.50 | 1.50 |
| 22 | A22 | 70c multi + label | 1.90 | 1.90 |
| 23 | A23 | 85c multi + label | 2.25 | 2.25 |
| 24 | A24 | €2.42 multi + label | 6.25 | 6.25 |
| 25 | A25 | €3 multi + label | 7.75 | 7.75 |
| | | *Nos. 21-25 (5)* | 19.65 | 19.65 |

---

# GREENLAND

'grēn-lənd

LOCATION — North Atlantic Ocean
GOVT. — Danish
AREA — 840,000 sq. mi.
POP. — 56,076 (1998)
CAPITAL — Nuuk (Godthaab)

In 1953 the colony of Greenland became an integral part of Denmark.

100 Ore = 1 Krone

> Catalogue values for unused stamps in this country are for **Never Hinged items, beginning with Scott 28** in the regular postage section, **Scott B1** in the semipostal section.

Christian
X — A1

Polar Bear — A2

**Perf. 13x12½**

**1938-46　Unwmk.　　　Engr.**

| | | | | |
|---|---|---|---|---|
| 1 | A1 | 1o olive black | .30 | .30 |
| 2 | A1 | 5o rose lake | 1.75 | 1.40 |
| 3 | A1 | 7o yellow green | 2.75 | 3.25 |
| 4 | A1 | 10o purple | .85 | .65 |
| 5 | A1 | 15o red | .85 | .65 |
| 6 | A1 | 20o red ('46) | 1.25 | 1.40 |
| 7 | A2 | 30o blue | 5.00 | 7.00 |
| 8 | A2 | 40o blue ('46) | 17.50 | 7.50 |
| 9 | A2 | 1k light brown | 5.75 | 10.00 |
| | | *Nos. 1-9 (9)* | 36.00 | 32.15 |
| | | Set, never hinged | 80.00 | |

Issue dates: Nov. 1, 1938, Aug. 1, 1946.
For surcharges see Nos. 39-40.

Harp
Seal — A3

Christian
X — A4

Dog Team — A5

Designs: 1k, Polar bear. 2k, Eskimo in kayak. 5k, Eider duck.

**1945, Feb. 1　　　　　Perf. 12**

| | | | | |
|---|---|---|---|---|
| 10 | A3 | 1o ol blk & vio | 21.00 | 40.00 |
| 11 | A3 | 5o rose lake & ol bister | 21.00 | 40.00 |
| 12 | A3 | 7o green & blk | 21.00 | 40.00 |
| 13 | A4 | 10o purple & olive | 21.00 | 40.00 |
| 14 | A4 | 15o red & brt ultra | 21.00 | 40.00 |
| 15 | A5 | 30o dk blue & red brn | 21.00 | 40.00 |
| 16 | A5 | 1k brown & gray blk | 21.00 | 40.00 |
| 17 | A5 | 2k sepia & dp grn | 21.00 | 40.00 |
| 18 | A5 | 5k dk pur & dl brn | 21.00 | 40.00 |
| | | *Nos. 10-18 (9)* | 189.00 | 360.00 |
| | | Set, never hinged | 350.00 | |

Nos. 10-18 Overprinted in
Carmine or Blue

**1945**

| | | | | |
|---|---|---|---|---|
| 19 | A3 | 1o (C) | 50.00 | 60.00 |
| 20 | A3 | 5o (Bl) | 50.00 | 60.00 |
| 21 | A3 | 7o (C) | 50.00 | 60.00 |
| 22 | A4 | 10o (Bl) | 70.00 | 110.00 |
| a. | | Overprint in carmine | 375.00 | 700.00 |
| 23 | A4 | 15o (C) | 67.50 | 110.00 |
| a. | | Overprint in blue | 175.00 | 225.00 |

---

| | | | | |
|---|---|---|---|---|
| 24 | A5 | 30o (Bl) | 67.50 | 110.00 |
| a. | | Overprint in carmine | 175.00 | 225.00 |
| 25 | A5 | 1k (C) | 67.50 | 110.00 |
| a. | | Overprint in blue | 175.00 | 225.00 |
| 26 | A5 | 2k (C) | 67.50 | 110.00 |
| a. | | Overprint in blue | 175.00 | 225.00 |
| 27 | A5 | 5k (Bl) | 67.50 | 110.00 |
| a. | | Overprint in carmine | 175.00 | 225.00 |
| | | *Nos. 19-27 (9)* | 557.50 | 840.00 |
| | | Set, never hinged | 1,250. | |
| | | *Nos. 22a-27a (6)* | 1,250. | 1,825. |
| | | Set, never hinged | 2,650. | |

Liberation of Denmark from the Germans. Overprint illustrated as on Nos. 19-21. Larger type and different settings used for Types A4 and A5. Overprint often smudged. Nos. 19-27 exist with overprint inverted. Values: 1k and 30o, each $1,000; others, each $850.

> Catalogue values for unused stamps in this section, from this point to the end of the section, are for Never Hinged items.

Frederik
IX — A6

Polar Ship "Gustav
Holm" — A7

**1950-60　Unwmk.　Engr.　Perf. 13**

| | | | | |
|---|---|---|---|---|
| 28 | A6 | 1o dark olive green | .20 | .20 |
| 29 | A6 | 5o deep carmine | .20 | .20 |
| 30 | A6 | 10o green | .20 | .20 |
| 31 | A6 | 15o purple | .40 | .35 |
| a. | | 15o dull rose | 4.00 | 1.60 |
| 32 | A6 | 25o vermilion | 2.50 | 1.00 |
| 33 | A6 | 30o dark blue | 35.00 | 1.90 |
| 34 | A6 | 30o vermilion | .40 | .20 |
| 35 | A7 | 50o deep blue | 50.00 | 12.00 |
| 36 | A7 | 1k brown | 16.00 | 2.75 |
| 37 | A7 | 2k dull red | 8.00 | 2.75 |
| 38 | A7 | 5k gray | 2.25 | 1.40 |
| | | *Nos. 28-38 (11)* | 115.15 | 22.95 |

Issued: #28-30, 31a, 32, 35-37, 8/15/50; #33, 12/1/53; #38, 8/14/58; #34, 10/29/59; #31, 10/60.
For surcharges see Nos. B1-B2.

Nos. 8 and 9 Surcharged

**1956, Mar. 8**

| | | | | |
|---|---|---|---|---|
| 39 | A2 | 60o on 40o blue | 9.00 | 1.75 |
| 40 | A2 | 60o on 1k lt brown | 67.50 | 7.75 |

Drum Dancer — A8

Designs: 50o, The Boy and the Fox. 60o, The Mother of the Sea. 80o, The Girl and the Eagle. 90o, The Great Northern Diver and the Raven.

**1957-69　Engr.　　　Perf. 13**

| | | | | |
|---|---|---|---|---|
| 41 | A8 | 35o gray olive | 1.10 | .90 |
| 42 | A8 | 50o brown red | .95 | 1.25 |
| 43 | A8 | 60o blue | 3.00 | 1.25 |
| 44 | A8 | 80o light brown | 1.10 | 1.25 |
| 45 | A8 | 90o dark blue | 3.50 | 3.25 |
| | | *Nos. 41-45 (5)* | 9.65 | 7.90 |

Issued: 35o, 3/16/61; 50o, 9/22/66; 60o, 5/2/57; 80o, 9/18/69; 90o, 11/23/67.

---

Hans Egede
A9

Knud
Rasmussen
A10

**1958, Nov. 5**

| | | | | |
|---|---|---|---|---|
| 46 | A9 | 30o henna brown | 10.00 | 1.75 |

200th anniv. of death of Hans Egede, missionary to Eskimos in Greenland.

**1960, Nov. 24　　　　　Perf. 13**

| | | | | |
|---|---|---|---|---|
| 47 | A10 | 30o dull red | 1.50 | 1.10 |

50th anniv. of establishment by Rasmussen of the mission and trading station at Thule (Dundas).

Northern Lights and
Crossed
Anchors — A11

Frederik
IX — A12

Polar
Bear — A13

**1963-68　　　　　　　Engr.**

| | | | | |
|---|---|---|---|---|
| 48 | A11 | 1o gray | .20 | .35 |
| 49 | A11 | 5o rose claret | .20 | .35 |
| 50 | A11 | 10o green | .40 | .50 |
| 51 | A11 | 12o yellow grn | .30 | .40 |
| 52 | A11 | 15o rose vio | 1.00 | 1.25 |
| 53 | A12 | 20o ultra | 4.50 | 3.50 |
| 54 | A12 | 25o lt brown | .30 | .50 |
| 55 | A12 | 30o green | .30 | .50 |
| 56 | A12 | 35o dull red | .20 | .30 |
| 57 | A12 | 40o gray | .30 | .50 |
| 58 | A12 | 50o grnsh blue | 10.00 | 9.50 |
| 59 | A12 | 50o dark red | .35 | .45 |
| 60 | A12 | 60o rose claret | .35 | .45 |
| 61 | A12 | 80o orange | .80 | .85 |
| 62 | A13 | 1k brown | .60 | .35 |
| 63 | A13 | 2k dull red | 3.50 | 1.10 |
| 64 | A13 | 5k dark blue | 3.00 | 2.25 |
| 65 | A13 | 10k dull slate grn | 4.75 | 1.10 |
| | | *Nos. 48-65 (18)* | 31.05 | 24.20 |

Issued: #48-52, 3/7/63; #53, 61, 7/25/63; #62-65, 9/17/63; #54, 56-58, 3/11/64; #59, 9/9/65; #60, 2/29/68; #55, 11/21/68.

Niels Bohr (1885-
1962) and Atom
Diagram — A14

**1963, Nov. 21　　　　　Unwmk.**

| | | | | |
|---|---|---|---|---|
| 66 | A14 | 35o red brown | .25 | .25 |
| 67 | A14 | 60o dark blue | 4.75 | 4.75 |

50th anniv. of atom theory of Prof. Bohr.

A15

A16

**1964, Nov. 26**

| | | | | |
|---|---|---|---|---|
| 68 | A15 | 35o brown red | .60 | .60 |

Samuel Kleinschmidt (1814-1886), philologist.

**1967, June 10**

| | | | | |
|---|---|---|---|---|
| 69 | A16 | 50o red | 3.50 | 3.50 |

Wedding of Crown Princess Margrethe and Prince Henri de Monpezat.

Frederik IX and Map of Greenland A17

**1969, Mar. 11      Engr.      Perf. 13**
70  A17  60o dull red      1.40  1.40
70th birthday of King Frederik IX.

Musk Ox — A18

Liberation Celebration at Jakobshaven A19

Designs: 1k, Right whale diving off Disko Island. 2k, Narwhal. 5k, Polar bear. 10k, Walruses.

**1969-76      Engr.      Perf. 13**
71  A18  1k dark blue      .40  .40
72  A18  2k gray green      .85  .55
73  A18  5k blue      1.90  .70
74  A18  10k sepia      3.50  1.60
75  A18  25k greenish gray      9.25  3.25
*Nos. 71-75 (5)*      15.90  6.50

Issued: 1k, 3/5/70; 2k, 2/20/75; 5k, 2/19/76; 10k, 2/15/73; 25k, 11/27/69.

**1970, May 4**
76  A19  60o red brown      2.10  2.10

Hans Egede and Gertrude Rask on the Haabet — A20

**1971, May 6      Engr.      Perf. 13**
77  A20  60o brown red      1.75  1.75
250th anniv. of arrival of Hans Egede in Greenland and the beginning of its colonization.

 *(Mail-carrying Kayaks — A21)*

Mail-carrying Kayaks — A21

Designs: 70o, Umiak (women's rowboat). 80o, Catalina seaplane dropping mail by parachute. 90o, Dog sled. 1k, Coaster Kununguak and pilot boat. 1.30k, Schooner Sokongen. 1.50k, Longboat off Greenland coast. 2k, Helicopter over mountains.

**1971-77      Engr.      Perf. 13**
78  A21  50o green      .25  .20
79  A21  70o dull red ('72)      .35  .20
80  A21  80o black ('76)      .40  .20
81  A21  90o blue ('72)      .35  .20
82  A21  1k red ('76)      .40  .20
83  A21  1.30k dull bl ('75)      .75  .65
84  A21  1.50k gray grn ('74)      .75  .55
85  A21  2k blue ('77)      1.00  .85
*Nos. 78-85 (8)*      4.25  3.05

Issued: #78, 11/4; #81, 2/29; #79, 9/21; #84, 2/21; #83, 4/17; #80, 10/11; #85, 2/24.

Queen Margrethe — A22

**1973-79      Engr.      Perf. 13**
86  A22  5o car rose ('78)      .20  .20
87  A22  10o gray green      .20  .20
  a.  10o emerald ('89)      6.50  6.50

88  A22  60o sepia      .20  .20
89  A22  80o sepia ('79)      .40  .20
90  A22  90o red brown ('74)      .70  .70
91  A22  1k dark red ('77)      .40  .30
  a.  Bklt. pane, 4 #87a, 6 #91b      37.50
  b.  1k carmine ('89)      2.40  2.40
92  A22  1.20k dk blue ('74)      .70  .70
93  A22  1.20k maroon ('78)      .60  .50
94  A22  1.30k dk blue ('77)      .60  .60
95  A22  1.30k red ('79)      .60  .50
96  A22  1.60k blue ('79)      .70  .70
97  A22  1.80k dl green ('78)      .70  .70
*Nos. 86-97 (12)*      6.00  5.50

#86, 89, 93, 95-97 inscribed "Kalaallit Nunaat."
The background lines on Nos. 87, 91 are sharp and complete. On No. 87a, 91b they are irregular and broken.
Issue dates: Nos. 87-88, Apr. 16. Nos. 90, 92, Oct. 24. Nos. 91, 94, May 26. Nos. 86, 93, 97, Apr. 17. Nos. 89, 95-96, Mar. 29.

Trawler and Kayaks — A23

**1974, May 16      Engr.      Perf. 13**
98  A23  1k lt red brown      .60  .50
99  A23  2k sepia      .70  .60
Royal Greenland Trade Dept. Bicentennial.

**1975, Sept. 4      Engr.      Perf. 13**
100  A24  90o red      .50  .50
50th anniversary of Greenland's telecommunications system.

Sirius Sled Patrol A25

**1975, Oct. 16      Engr.      Perf. 13**
101  A25  1.20k sepia      .40  .40
Sirius sled patrol in northeast Greenland, 25th anniversary.

Inuit Cult Mask — A26      Jorgen Bronlund, Jakobshavn, Disko Bay — A27

Designs: 6k, Tupilac, a magical creature, carved whalebone. 7k, Soapstone sculpture. 8k, Eskimo with Family, driftwood sculpture, by Johannes Kreutzmann (1862-1940).

**1977-80**
102  A26  6k deep rose lilac      2.10  1.60
103  A26  7k gray olive      2.50  2.10
104  A26  8k dark blue      2.75  2.40
105  A26  9k black      3.00  3.00
*Nos. 102-105 (4)*      10.35  9.10

Issue dates: 6k, Oct. 5, 1978. 7k, Sept. 6, 1979. 8k, Feb. 29, 1980. 9k, Sept. 6, 1977.
The 6k, 7k, 8k are inscribed "Kalaallit Nunaat."

**1977, Oct. 20**
106  A27  1k red brown      .35  .25
Jorgen Bronlund, arctic explorer, birth centenary.

Meteorite — A28

**1978, Jan. 20      Engr.      Perf. 13**
107  A28  1.20k dull red      .50  .50
Scientific Research Commission, centenary.

Sun Rising over Mountains — A29

**1978, June 5      Engr.      Perf. 13**
108  A29  1.50k dark blue      .55  .55
25th anniversary of Constitution.

Hans Egede, Settlers, Troops and Drummer A30

**1978, Aug. 29      Engr.      Perf. 13**
109  A30  2.50k red brown      .90  .70
Founding of Godthaab, 250th anniversary.

A31      A32

**1979, May 1      Engr.**
110  A31  1.10k Navigator      .40  .40
Establishment of home rule, May 1, 1979.

**1979, Oct. 18      Engr.      Perf. 13**
111  A32  2k olive green      .75  .65
International Year of the Child.

The Legend of the Reindeer and the Larva, by Jens Kreutzmann, 1860 — A33

Designs: 2.70k, Harpooning a Walrus, Jakob Danielsen. No. 114, Life in Thule, c. 1900, by Aninaaq. No. 115, Landscape, Ammassalik Fjord, Eastern Greenland, Peter Rosing (1892-1965). 3k, Footrace, woodcut by Aron from Kagec (1822-1869). 3.70k, Polar Bear Killing Seal Hunter, K. Andreassen (1890-1934). 9k, Hares Hunting, Gerhard Kleist (1855-1931).

**1980-87      Engr.      Perf. 13**
112  A33  1.60k red      .60  .60
113  A33  2.70k deep violet      1.00  1.00
114  A33  2.80k lake      .90  .90
115  A33  2.80k lake      1.10  1.00
116  A33  3k black      1.25  1.10
117  A33  3.70k blue black      1.40  1.25
118  A33  9k dark green      3.50  2.50
*Nos. 112-118 (7)*      9.75  8.35

Issued: 1.60k, 3/26/81; 2.70k, 6/24/82; #114, 9/4/86; #115, 4/9/87; 3k, 9/4/80; 3.70k, 2/9/84; 9k, 9/5/85.

Queen Margrethe, Map of Greenland A34

**1980-89      Engr.      Perf. 13**
120  A34  50o purple ('81)      .30  .30
  a.  50o dull purple ('89)      7.50  7.50
121  A34  80o green      .35  .35
122  A34  1.30k red      .60  .60
123  A34  1.50k royal blue ('82)      .60  .60
124  A34  1.60k ultra      .65  .65
125  A34  1.80k dull red ('82)      1.00  .70
126  A34  2.30k dk grn ('81)      1.00  .75
127  A34  2.50k red ('83)      1.00  .75
128  A34  2.80k copper red ('85)      1.90  .80
129  A34  3k fawn ('88)      2.00  1.00
130  A34  3.20k rose ('89)      2.00  1.25
  a.  Bklt. pane of 10 (4 #120a, 6 #130)      42.50
131  A34  3.80k slate blue ('85)      1.90  1.90
132  A34  4.10k brt blue ('88)      2.25  2.25
133  A34  4.40k ultra ('89)      2.50  2.50
*Nos. 120-133 (14)*      18.05  14.40

Issued: #121-122, 124, 4/16; #120, 126, 1/29; #123, 125, 5/13; #127, 3/30; #128, 131, 2/7; #129, 132, 2/4; #130, 133, 1/30.

Rasmus Berthelsen (Teacher, Hymnist), in Training College Library, 1830 — A35

**1980, May 29      Engr.      Perf. 13**
134  A35  2k brown, *cream*      .70  .60
Greenland Public Library Service, 150th anniv.

Ejnar Mikkelsen on board Gustav Holm, 1934 — A36

**1980, Oct. 16　　Engr.　　Perf. 13**
135　A36　4k slate green　　1.40　1.25

Ejnar Mikkelsen, inspector of East Greenland, birth centenary.

Pandalus Borealis — A37

Designs: No. 137, Anarhicas minor. No. 138, Reinhardtius Hippoglossoides. No. 139, Mallotus villosus. 25k, Codfish. 50k, Salmo salar.

**1981-86　　Engr.　　Perf. 13**
136　A37　10k multicolored　　3.50　1.75
137　A37　10k dk bl & blk　　5.50　3.50
138　A37　10k multicolored　　3.75　3.50
139　A37　10k grnsh blk & blk　3.75　3.50
140　A37　25k multicolored　　8.50　3.50
141　A37　50k multicolored　　19.00　10.00
　　Nos. 136-141 (6)　　44.00　25.75

Issued: 25k, 5/21; #136, 4/1/82; 50k, 1/27/83; #137, 10/11/84; #138, 10/10/85; #139, 10/16/86.

Saqqaq Eskimo in Kayak, Reindeer — A38

5k, Tunit-Dorset hunters hauling seal.

**1981, Oct. 15　　Engr.　　Perf. 12½**
146　A38　3.50k dark blue　　1.40　1.40
147　A38　5k brown　　2.00　2.00

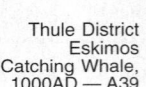

Thule District Eskimos Catching Whale, 1000AD — A39

Greenland history: No. 149, Bishop Joen Smyrill's house and staff, 12th cent. No. 150, Wooden dolls, 13th cent. No. 151, Eskimo mummy, sacrificial stones, 14th cent. No. 152, Hans Pothorst, explorer, 15th cent. No. 153, Glass pearls, 16th cent. No. 154, Apostle spoons, 17th cent. No. 155, Key, trading station, 18th cent. No. 156, Trade Ship Hvalfisken, masthead, 19th cent. No. 157, Communications satellite, Earth, 20th cent.

**1982, Sept. 30**
148　A39　2k brown red　　.70　.70
149　A39　2.70k dark blue　　1.00　1.00

**1983, Sept. 15**
150　A39　2.50k red　　.90　.90
151　A39　3.50k brown　　1.25　1.25
152　A39　4.50k blue　　1.50　1.50

**1984, Mar. 29**
153　A39　2.70k red brown　　1.50　1.40
154　A39　3.70k dark blue　　1.50　1.40
155　A39　5.50k brown　　1.90　1.90

**1985, Mar. 21**
156　A39　2.80k violet　　1.50　1.50
157　A39　6k blue black　　2.40　2.40
　　Nos. 148-157,B10 (11)　15.40　15.20

250th Anniv. of Settlement of New Herrnhut — A40

**1983, Nov. 2　　Engr.**
158　A40　2.50k brown　　1.00　1.00

Henrik Lund, Natl. Anthem Score, Lichtenau Fjord — A41

**1984, Sept. 6　　Engr.**
159　A41　5k dark green　　3.00　2.75

Henrik Lund (1875-1948), natl. anthem composer, artist, only Greenlander to win Ingenio et Arti medal.

A42　　　　A43

**1984, June 6　　Engr.　　Perf. 13**
160　A42　2.70k dull red　　1.90　1.90

Prince Henrik, 50th birthday.

**1984, July 25　　Engr.　　Perf. 13**
161　A43　3.70k Danish grenadier, 1734　　1.60　1.60

Town of Christianshab, 250th anniv.

Ingrid, Queen Mother of Denmark, Chrysanthemums — A44

**1985, May 21　　Litho. & Engr.**
162　A44　2.80k multi　　1.25　1.25

Arrival in Denmark of Princess Ingrid, 50th anniv. See Denmark No. 775.

Intl. Youth Year — A45

**1985, June 27　　Litho.**
163　A45　3.80k Emblem, birds nesting, fiord　1.25　1.25

Greenland Port Post Office, Flags — A46

**1986, Mar. 6　　Engr.　　Perf. 13**
164　A46　2.80k dark red　　1.25　1.25

Transfer of postal control under Greenland Home Rule, Jan. 1, 1986.

Artifacts — A47

**1986-88　　Engr.　　Perf. 13**
165　A47　2.80k Sewing needles, case　　1.40　.95
165A　A47　3k Buckets, bowl, scoop　　1.00　.70
166　A47　3.80k Ulos　　1.25　1.10
167　A47　3.80k Masks　　1.75　1.75
168　A47　5k Harpoon points　　1.90　1.40
169　A47　6.50k Lard lamps　　2.40　2.10
172　A47　10k Carved faces　　3.75　2.75
　　Nos. 165-172 (7)　　13.45　10.75

Issued: #166, 6.50k, May 22. 2.80k, 3.80k, June 11, 1987. 3k, 5k, 10k, Oct. 27, 1988.

**Souvenir Sheet**

HAFNIA '87 — A48

**1987, Jan. 23　　Litho.　　Perf. 13**
175　A48　Sheet of 3　　8.50　8.50
　a.　2.80k Gull in flight　　2.25　2.25
　b.　3.80k Mountain　　2.75　2.75
　c.　6.50k Gulls in water　　3.50　3.50

No. 175 sold for 19.50k. See No. 199.

Year of the Fishing, Sealing and Whaling Industries — A49

**1987, Apr. 9　　Litho.　　Perf. 13**
176　A49　3.80k multi　　1.50　1.10

Lagopus Mutus — A50　　Birds of Prey — A51

**1987-90　　Litho.　　Perf. 13**
177　A51　3k Falco rusticolus　1.75　1.60
178　A51　3.20k Clangula hyemalis　　1.40　1.25
179　A51　4k Anser caerulescens　　1.60　1.40
180　A51　4.10k Corvus corax　2.00　1.75
181　A51　4.40k Plectrophenax nivalis　　1.75　1.60
182　A50　5k shown　　2.00　1.90
183　A51　5.50k Haliaeetus albicilla　　3.00　2.50
184　A51　5.50k Cepphus grylle　2.25　2.00
185　A51　6.50k Uria lomvia　2.75　2.25
186　A51　7k Gavia immer　3.50　2.50
187　A51　7.50k Stercorarius longicaudus　　3.00　3.00
188　A50　10k Nyctea scandiaca　　4.50　3.50
　　Nos. 177-188 (12)　29.50　25.25

Issued: 5k, 10k, 9/3; 3k, 4.10k, #183, 7k, 4/14/88; 3.20k, 4.40k, #184, 6.50k, 3/16/89; 4k, 7.50k, 1/15/90.

Plants — A52

**1989-92　　Litho.　　Perf. 13**
189　A52　4k *Campanula gieseckiana*　1.75　1.50
190　A52　4k *Pedicularis hirsuta*　1.90　1.50
191　A52　5k *Eriophorum scheuchzeri*　1.90　1.75
192　A52　5.50k *Ledum groenlandicum*　2.40　2.10
193　A52　6.50k *Cassiope tetragona*　3.25　3.00
194　A52　7.25k *Saxifraga oppositifolia*　3.25　3.25
196　A52　10k *Papaver radicatum,* vert.　3.75　3.25
　　Nos. 189-196 (7)　18.20　16.35

Issued: 5k, 10k, 10/12/89; #189, 5.50k, 6.50k, 6/7/90; #190, 7.25k, 3/26/92. #189-190 vert.

**Souvenir Sheet**

Uummannaq Mountain in winter, horiz.

**1987, Oct. 16　　Litho.　　Perf. 13x12½**
199　A48　2.80k slate blue & lake　3.00　3.00

No. 199 sold for 4k.

Greenland Home Rule, 10th Anniv.
A53　　　　A54

**1989, May 1　　Litho.　　Perf. 13**
200　A53　3.20k Flag, landscape　1.40　1.25
201　A54　4.40k Coat of arms　1.90　1.75

Queen Margrethe — A55

Nos. 214, 217 Surcharged in Red or Blue

**1990-96　　Engr.　　Perf. 13**
214　A55　25o green　　.20　.20
217　A55　1k brown　　.40　.45
　a.　Bklt. pane, 4 #214, 6 #217　20.00
　b.　Bklt. pane, 4 each #214, 217　4.00
224　A55　4k carmine rose　1.75　1.75
　　Complete booklet, 217a, 10 #224　35.00
225　A55　4.25k red　　2.40　2.40
226　A55　4.25k on 25o #214　2.75　2.75
　a.　Inverted surcharge　800.00
227　A55　4.50k on 1k #217 (Bl)　3.50　3.50
228　A55　6.50k blue　　2.75　2.75
229　A55　7k violet　　3.25　3.25
　　Nos. 214-229 (8)　17.00　17.05

Issued: #217a, 5/3/90; #217b, 9/9/93; 7k, 2/10/94; #225, 1996; #226-227, 12/31/95; others, 4/5/90.

Frederik Lynge (1889-1957), Politician — A56

25k, Augo Lynge (1899-1959), politician

**1990, Oct. 18　　Engr.　　Perf. 13x12½**
231　A56　10k rose brn & dk bl　4.25　4.25
232　A56　25k vio & dk bl　10.00　10.00

See Nos. 242-243, 249.

Phoca Hispida — A57

Walrus and Seals.

**1991, Mar. 14　　Litho. & Engr.　　Perf. 13**
233　A57　4k shown　　1.50　1.50
234　A57　4k Pagophilus groenlandicus　1.50　1.50

| | | | |
|---|---|---|---|
| 235 | A57 | 7.25k Cystophora cristata | 2.75 2.75 |
| 236 | A57 | 7.25k Odobenus rosmarus | 2.75 2.75 |
| 237 | A57 | 8.50k Erignatus barbatus | 3.25 3.25 |
| 238 | A57 | 8.50k Phoca vitulina | 3.25 3.25 |
| a. | | Miniature sheet of 6, #233-238 | 17.00 16.00 |
| | | Nos. 233-238 (6) | 15.00 15.00 |

Village of
Ilulissat, 250th
Anniv. — A58

**1991, May 15     Litho.     Perf. 13**
239 A58 4k multicolored     1.75 1.50

Tourism — A59

**1991, May 15     Perf. 12½x13**
240 A59   4k Iceberg           1.50 1.50
241 A59 8.50k Skiers, sled dogs  3.50 3.50

See Nos. 259-260, 289-290.

**Famous Men Type of 1990**

10k, Jonathan Petersen (1881-1961), musician. 50k, Hans Lynge (1906-88), artist & writer. 100k, Lars Moller (1842-1926), newspaper editor.

**1991-92     Engr.     Perf. 13x12½**
242 A56  10k black & dk blue   3.75 3.50
243 A56  50k red brn & blue   19.00 17.00
249 A56 100k claret & slate   35.00 35.00
     Nos. 242-249 (3)        57.75 50.50

Issued: 10k, 50k, 9/5; 100k, 9/15/92.

Settlement
of
Paamiut,
250th
Anniv.
A60

**1992, May 14     Engr.     Perf. 13**
252 A60 7.25k dk bl & ol brn   3.25 3.00

Denmark's Queen Margrethe and
Prince Henrik, Silver Wedding
Anniv. — A61

**1992, June 10     Perf. 12½x13**
253 A61 4k multicolored     2.40 2.40

See Denmark No. 946.

A62

A63

**1992, Nov. 12     Litho.     Perf. 13**
254 A62 4k Christmas     2.75 2.10

**1993, Feb. 4     Litho.     Perf. 13**
255 A63 4k multicolored     1.50 1.50

Intl. Year of Indigenous Peoples.

Crabs — A64

4k, Neolithodes grimaldii. 7.25k, Chionoecetes oiliqo. 8.50k, Hyas coarctatus, Hyas araneus.

**Litho. & Engr.**
**1993, Mar. 25     Perf. 13**
256 A64   4k multicolored   1.50 1.50
257 A64 7.25k multicolored   4.00 4.00
  a.   Chionoecetes opilio   10.50 13.00
  b.   Booklet pane, 4 each #256, 257a   50.00
258 A64 8.50k multicolored   3.25 3.25
     Nos. 256-258 (3)       8.75 8.75

Issue date: No. 257b, Sept. 9.

**Tourism Type of 1991**

**1993, May 6     Litho.     Perf. 12½x13**
259 A57   4k Village in winter   1.50 1.50
260 A57 8.50k Ruins, coastline   3.50 3.50

AIDS
Research
A66

**1993, Sept. 9     Litho.     Perf. 13**
261 A66 4k multicolored     1.50 1.50

Native
Animals — A67

**Litho. & Engr.**
**1993, Oct. 14     Perf. 13**
262 A67   5k Canis lupus     2.00 2.00
263 A67 8.50k Alopex lagopus   3.50 3.50
264 A67  10k Rangifer tarandus   4.25 4.25
     Nos. 262-264 (3)         9.75 9.75

See Nos. 270-272, 296-298.

Christmas
A68

**1993, Nov. 11     Litho.     Perf. 13**
265 A68 4k multicolored     1.75 1.75

Buksefjord Electrical Project — A69

**Litho. & Engr.**
**1994, Mar. 24     Perf. 13**
266 A69 4k multicolored     1.50 1.50

Ammassalik,
Cent. — A70

**1994, Mar. 24**
267 A70 7.25k multicolored     3.00 3.00

Expedition
to North
East
Greenland,
1906-08
A71

Europa: 4k, Icebound Danmark. 7.25k, Danmark, expedition car, dogs.

**1994, May 5     Litho.     Perf. 13**
268 A71   4k multicolored   1.60 1.60
269 A71 7.25k multicolored   3.00 3.00

**Native Animal Type of 1993**

Designs: 5.50k, Mustela erminea. 7.25k, Dicrostonyx torquatus. 9k, Lepus arcticus.

**Litho. & Engr.**
**1994, Sept. 8     Perf. 13**
270 A67 5.50k multicolored   2.25 2.25
271 A67 7.25k multicolored   3.25 3.25
272 A67   9k multicolored   4.25 4.25
     Nos. 270-272 (3)        9.75 9.75

Ship's Figureheads — A72

**Litho. & Engr.**
**1994, Oct. 13     Perf. 13**
273 A72   4k Ceres       1.50 1.50
274 A72 8.50k Nordlyset   3.50 3.50

See Nos. 299-300, 309-310.

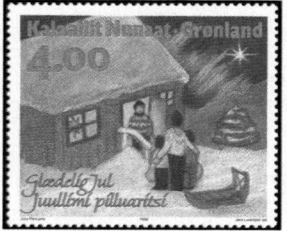

Christmas Paintings, by Julia
Pars — A73

**1994, Nov. 10     Litho.     Perf. 12½x13**
275 A73 4k shown           1.60 1.60
276 A73 5k Santa, dogs, igloo   2.25 2.25

Orchids — A74

**Litho. & Engr.**
**1995-96     Perf. 13x12½**
279 A74   4k Listera cordata   1.60 1.60
280 A74 4.25k Corallorhiza trifida   1.75 1.75
281 A74 4.50k Amerorchis rotundifolia   1.90 1.90
282 A74 7.25k Leucorchis albida   3.00 3.00

283 A74 7.50k Plantanthera hyperborea   3.25 3.25
  a.   Booklet pane, #281, 283, 2 ea   12.50
       #225, 280 + 4 labels
       Complete booklet, 2 #283a   25.00
       Nos. 279-283 (5)       11.50 11.50

No. 283a exists with different labels and stamps in different order. Complete booklet contains one of each type of No. 283a.
Issued: 4k, 7.25k, 2/9/95.

Ilinniarfissuaq Seminarium, Nuuk (The
Greenland Training College), 150th
Anniv. — A75

**Litho. & Engr.**
**1995, Mar. 23     Perf. 13**
287 A75 4k multicolored     1.60 1.60

United Nations,
50th Anniv. — A76

**1995, Mar. 23**
288 A76 7.25k multicolored     3.50 3.50

**Tourism Type of 1991**

**1995, Apr. 20     Litho.     Perf. 12½x13**
289 A59   4k Iceberg, inlet   1.75 1.75
290 A59 8.50k Mountains       4.00 4.00

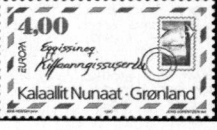

Peace &
Liberty
A77

Europa: 4k, Envelope, simulated stamp. 8.50k, Doves flying over Greenland.

**1995, May 5     Perf. 12½x13**
291 A77   4k multicolored   1.75 1.75
292 A77 8.50k multicolored   4.00 4.00

**Souvenir Sheets**
**Types A3-A5 Surcharged**

America Series — A78

Designs: No. 295a, Dog team. b, Polar bear. c, Eskimo in kayak. d, Eider duck.
Illustration reduced.

**1995, May 5     Litho.     Perf. 13**
293 A78 Sheet of 2 + 4 labels   6.50 6.50
  a.   5k on 10o pur & ol (Type A4)   3.00 3.00
  b.   5k on 15o red & vio (Type A4)   3.00 3.00
294 A78 Sheet of 3       7.75 7.75
  a.   1k on 1o dk ol & vio bl (Type A3)   .60 .60
  b.   5k on 5o rose lake & brn (Type A3)   3.00 3.00
  c.   7k on 7o dk grn & blk (Type A3)   4.25 4.25
295 A78 Sheet of 4       10.00 10.00
  a.   4k on 30o dk bl & red brn (Type A5)   2.40 2.40
  b.   4k on 1k brn & gray blk (Type A5)   2.40 2.40
  c.   4k on 2k sep & dp grn (Type A5)   2.40 2.40
  d.   4k on 5k dp pur & dl brn (Type A5)   2.40 2.40

# GREENLAND

### Native Animal Type of 1993
**1995, Sept. 7** Litho. & Engr. *Perf. 13*
| 296 | A67 | 4k Ursus maritimus | 1.60 | 1.60 |
| 297 | A67 | 7.25k Gulo gulo | 3.00 | 3.00 |
| 298 | A67 | 7.50k Ovibus moschatus | 3.25 | 3.25 |
| | | *Nos. 296-298 (3)* | 7.85 | 7.85 |

### Ship's Figureheads Type of 1994
**1995, Oct. 12** Litho. & Engr. *Perf. 13*
| 299 | A72 | 4k Hvalfisken, vert. | 1.60 | 1.60 |
| 300 | A72 | 8.50k Tjalfe | 3.75 | 3.75 |

Christmas A79

**1995, Nov. 9** Litho. *Perf. 13*
| 301 | A79 | 4k Boy running in snow | 1.60 | 1.60 |
| 302 | A79 | 5k Girl running in snow | 2.10 | 2.10 |

Whales A80

Designs: 25o, Orcinus orca. 50o, Megaptera novaeangliae. 1k, Delphinapterus leucas. 4.50k, Physeter catodon. 6.50k, Balaena mysticetus. 9.50k, Balaenoptera acutorostrata.

**1996, Apr. 25** Litho. *Perf. 13*
| 303 | A80 | 25o blue, black & red | .20 | .20 |
| 304 | A80 | 50o blue, black & red | .20 | .20 |
| 305 | A80 | 1k blue, black & red | .40 | .40 |
| 306 | A80 | 4.50k blue, black & red | 1.75 | 1.75 |
| a. | | Bkt. pane, #304, 2 ea #303, 306 | 5.00 | |
| | | Complete booklet, 2 #306a | 10.00 | |
| 307 | A80 | 6.50k blue, black & red | 3.00 | 3.00 |
| 308 | A80 | 9.50k blue, black & red | 4.00 | 4.00 |
| a. | | Souvenir sheet, Nos. 303-308 | 9.50 | 9.50 |
| | | *Nos. 303-308 (6)* | 9.55 | 9.55 |

No. 306a exists with stamps in different order. Issued: No. 306a, 1/1/97. See Nos. 319-322, 329-334.

### Ship's Figureheads Type of 1994
**1996, Sept. 5** Litho. & Engr. *Perf. 13*
| 309 | A72 | 15k Blaahejren, vert. | 6.50 | 6.50 |
| 310 | A72 | 20k Gertrud Rask | 8.50 | 8.50 |

Arnarulunnguaq (1896-1933), Member of Thule Expedition — A81

**1996, Sept. 5** Engr.
| 311 | A81 | 4.50k dark blue | 1.75 | 1.75 |

Europa.

Christmas A82

Designs: 4.25k, Girl looking through frozen window pane, angels scratched in ice. 4.50k, Paper star, children singing.

**1996, Nov. 7** Litho. *Perf. 13*
| 312 | A82 | 4.25k multicolored | 1.60 | 1.60 |
| 313 | A82 | 4.50k multicolored | 2.25 | 2.25 |
| a. | | Booklet pane, 3 each #312-313 | 12.00 | |
| | | Complete booklet, 2 #313a | 24.00 | |

No. 313a was issued in two formats, one with No. 312 at the UL, the other with No. 313 at the UL. The complete booklet contains one of each format.

A83

A84

**1997, Jan. 14** Litho. & Engr. *Perf. 13*
| 314 | A83 | 4.50k multicolored | 1.75 | 1.75 |

Coronation of Queen Margrethe II, 25th anniv.

**1997, Jan. 14**
Butterflies: 2k, Clossiana chariclea. 3k, Colias hecla. 4.75k, Plebejus franklinii. 8k, Lycaena phlaeas.
| 315 | A84 | 2k multicolored | 1.10 | 1.10 |
| 316 | A84 | 3k multicolored | 1.75 | 1.75 |
| 317 | A84 | 4.75k multicolored | 1.75 | 1.75 |
| 318 | A84 | 8k multicolored | 3.50 | 3.50 |
| a. | | Booklet pane of 6, 2 #314, 1 ea #315-318 + 2 labels | 13.00 | |
| | | Complete booklet, 2 #318a | 26.00 | |
| | | *Nos. 315-318 (4)* | 8.10 | 8.10 |

Issued: No. 318a, 5/5.
No. 318a exists with stamps in two different orders and with two different backgrounds, one of green plants, the other of red flowers. The complete booklet contains one of each type of pane.

### Whale Type of 1996
Designs: 5k, Balaenoptera musculus. 5.75k, Balaenoptera physalus. 6k, Balaenoptera borealis. 8k, Monodon monoceros.
**1997, May 5** Litho. *Perf. 13*
| 319 | A80 | 5k blue, black & red | 1.90 | 1.90 |
| 320 | A80 | 5.75k blue, black & red | 2.25 | 2.25 |
| 321 | A80 | 6k blue, black & red | 2.25 | 2.25 |
| 322 | A80 | 8k blue, black & red | 3.25 | 3.25 |
| a. | | Souvenir sheet of 4, #319-322 | 9.75 | 9.75 |
| | | *Nos. 319-322 (4)* | 9.65 | 9.65 |

Story of the "Bear of the Sea" — A85

**1997, May 5** Litho. & Engr. *Perf. 13*
| 323 | A85 | 4.75k black & blue black | *1.90* | *1.90* |

Europa.

Paintings by Aage Gitz-Johansen (1897-1977) — A87

Designs: 10k, Native dancer, Thule. 16k, Nude woman, Ammassalik.
**1997, Aug. 15** Litho. *Perf. 13x12½*
| 325 | A87 | 10k multicolored | 3.50 | 3.50 |
| 326 | A87 | 16k multicolored | 6.00 | 6.00 |

Christmas A88

Designs: 4.50k, Child with dogs in snow. 4.75k, Family in sled with Christmas presents, tree, father preparing harness.
**1997, Nov. 6** Litho. *Perf. 13x12½*
| 327 | A88 | 4.50k multicolored | 1.60 | 1.60 |
| 328 | A88 | 4.75k multicolored | 1.75 | 1.75 |
| a. | | Booklet pane, 3 each #327-328 | 11.00 | |
| | | Complete booklet, 2 #328a | 22.50 | |

No. 328a comes in two configurations. One has #327 at UL, the second has #328 at UL. Complete booklet has one of each pane.

### Whale Type of 1996
Designs: 2k, Phocoena phocoena. 3k, Lagenorhynchus albirostris. No. 331, Globicephala melaena. No. 332, Hyperoodon ampullatus. No. 333, Lagenorhynchus acutus. No. 334, Eubalaena glacialis.
**1998, Feb. 5** Litho. *Perf. 13*
| 329 | A80 | 2k multicolored | .75 | .75 |
| 330 | A80 | 3k multicolored | 1.40 | 1.40 |
| 331 | A80 | 4.50k multicolored | 1.60 | 1.60 |
| 332 | A80 | 4.50k multicolored | 1.60 | 1.60 |
| 333 | A80 | 4.75k multicolored | 1.75 | 1.75 |
| 334 | A80 | 4.75k multicolored | 1.75 | 1.75 |
| a. | | Souvenir sheet of 6, #329-334 | 9.00 | 9.00 |
| | | *Nos. 329-334 (6)* | 8.85 | 8.85 |

Intl. Year of the Ocean.

New Order of 1950 — A89

Design: Augo Lynge, Frederik Lynge, first Greenland politicians in Danish Parliament.
**1998, Feb. 5** Engr. *Perf. 13*
| 335 | A89 | 4.50k multicolored | 1.60 | 1.60 |

Europa — A90

Children's drawings of "Children's Day in Greenland:" 4.75k, Happy faces beside lake. 10k, People celebrating across Greenland.
**1998, May 29** Litho. *Perf. 13*
| 336 | A90 | 4.75k multicolored | 1.75 | 1.75 |
| 337 | A90 | 10k multicolored | 4.00 | 4.00 |

Ships — A91

**1998, Aug. 20** Litho. & Engr. *Perf. 13*
| 338 | A91 | 4.50k Gertrud Rask | 1.60 | 1.60 |
| a. | | Booklet pane of 6 | 9.75 | |
| 339 | A91 | 4.75k Hans Egede | 1.75 | 1.75 |
| a. | | Booklet pane of 6 | 10.50 | |
| | | Complete booklet, #338a, 339a | 21.00 | |

Paintings by Hans Lynge (1906-88) — A92

Designs: 11k, "Brother Gets Breast-fed." 25k, "Refuelling" (men in boat).
**1998, Aug. 20** Litho. *Perf. 13*
| 340 | A92 | 11k multicolored | 4.25 | 4.25 |
| 341 | A92 | 25k multicolored | 9.50 | 9.50 |

Christmas A93

**1998, Nov. 5** Litho. *Perf. 13*
| 342 | A93 | 4.50k Dickey, kamikker | 1.60 | 1.60 |
| a. | | Booklet pane of 6 | 12.50 | |
| 343 | A93 | 4.75k Kamikker, hat | 1.75 | 1.75 |
| a. | | Booklet pane of 6 | 12.50 | |
| | | Complete booklet, #342a, 343a | 25.00 | |

World Wildlife Fund — A94

Nyctea scandiaca (snowy owl): 1k, Nesting with young. 4.75k, In flight. 5.50k, Two adults. 5.75k, Perched on rock.
**1999, Feb. 5** Litho. & Engr. *Perf. 13*
| 344 | A94 | 1k multicolored | .50 | .50 |
| 345 | A94 | 4.75k multicolored | 1.90 | 1.90 |
| a. | | Booklet pane, 3 each #344-345 | 8.50 | |
| 346 | A94 | 5.50k multicolored | 2.25 | 2.25 |
| 347 | A94 | 5.75k multicolored | 2.50 | 2.50 |
| a. | | Booklet pane, 3 each #346-347 | 14.50 | |
| | | Complete booklet, #345a, 347a | 25.00 | |
| | | *Nos. 344-347 (4)* | 7.15 | 7.15 |

Europa A95

**1999, May 7** Litho. & Engr. *Perf. 13*
| 348 | A95 | 6k Polar bear | *2.25* | *2.25* |

Paintings, by Peter Rosing (1892-1965) — A96

Designs: 7k, The Man from Aluk, 1944. 20k, Homecoming, 1956.

**1999, May 7    Litho.    Perf. 12½x13**
349 A96  7k multicolored           2.50  2.50
350 A96  20k multicolored          7.50  7.50

Arctic Vikings A97

**1999, Aug. 13    Engr.    Perf. 13x13¼**
351 A97  4.50k Viking ship         1.60  1.60
352 A97  4.75k Man on drift-
           wood                     1.75  1.75
353 A97  5.75k Arrowhead,
           coins                    2.10  2.10
354 A97  8k Tjodhilde's
           church                   3.00  3.00
  a.  Souvenir sheet, #351-354     8.50  8.50
     Nos. 351-354 (4)              8.45  8.45
   See Nos. 358-361, 380-383.

Christmas A98

**1999, Nov. 11    Litho.    Perf. 13x13¼**
355 A98  4.50k Writing letter      1.60  1.60
  a.  Booklet pane of 6            9.75
356 A98  4.75k Handshake           1.75  1.75
  a.  Booklet pane of 6           10.50
     Complete booklet, #355a, 356a  21.00

Millennium A99

**1999, Nov. 11    Litho.    Perf. 13x13¼**
357 A99  5.75k multicolored        2.10  2.10

**Arctic Vikings Type of 1999**
Designs: 25o, Hunter, four walruses. 3k, Storyteller. 5.50k, Dog chasing reindeer. 21k, Man, gyrfalcon, polar bear, narwhal tusk, items made from animals.

**2000, Feb. 21    Engr.    Perf. 13x13¼**
358 A97  25o bl gray & brn          .20   .20
359 A97  3k bl gray & brn          1.25  1.25
360 A97  5.50k bl gray             2.10  2.10
361 A97  21k bl gray               8.25  8.25
  a.  Souvenir sheet, #358-361    12.00 12.00
     Nos. 358-361 (4)             11.80 11.80

Navy Dog Sled Patrol A100

**Litho. & Engr.**
**2000, Feb. 21    Perf. 12¾**
362 A100  10k multi                4.00  4.00

**Europa, 2000**
**Common Design Type**
**2000, May 9    Litho.    Perf. 13¼x13**
363 CD17  4.75k multi              1.90  1.90

Queen Margrethe A101

**2000-01    Engr.    Perf. 13x13¼**
364 A101  25o blk & bl gray         .20   .20
365 A101  50o red brn & bl
            gray                     .20   .20
367 A101  4.50k red & bl gray      1.75  1.75
368 A101  4.75k bl & bl gray       1.90  1.90
     Complete booklet, 4 each
       #364, #368                  8.50
372 A101  8k yel grn & bl
            gray                    3.25  3.25
374 A101  10k grn & bl gray        4.00  4.00
375 A101  12k pur & bl gray        4.75  4.75
     Nos. 364-375 (7)             16.05 16.05
   Issued: 4.50k, 4.75k, 8k, 10k, 5/9/00. 25o, 12k, 5/9/01. 50o, 10/21/02.
   This is an expanding set.

Cultural Heritage — A102

**2000, Aug. 18    Litho.    Perf. 13¼x13**
376 A102  4.50k Wooden map         1.75  1.75
  a.  Booklet pane of 6 + 2 labels 10.50
377 A102  4.75k Sealskin           1.90  1.90
  a.  Booklet pane of 6 + 2 labels 11.50
     Booklet, #376a, 377a          22.50
   See Nos. 384-385, 392-393, 414-415.

Christmas A103

**2000, Nov. 9    Litho.    Perf. 13x13¼**
378 A103  4.50k Stars, candles     1.75  1.75
  a.  Booklet pane of 6           10.50
379 A103  4.75k Star               1.90  1.90
  a.  Booklet pane of 6           11.50
     Booklet, #378a, 379a          22.50

**Arctic Vikings Type of 1999**
Designs: 1k, Hunter, dead seals. 4.50k, Mice eating food. 5k, Man and pack animals leaving. 10k, Birds on ruins.

**2001, Feb. 5    Engr.    Perf. 13x13¼**
380 A97  1k indigo & red            .40   .40
381 A97  4.50k indigo & blue       1.75  1.75
382 A97  5k indigo & blue          2.00  2.00
383 A97  10k indigo & red          4.00  4.00
  a.  Souvenir sheet, #380-383    8.25  8.25
     Nos. 380-383 (4)             8.15  8.15

**Cultural Heritage Type of 2000**
Designs: 4.50k, Smoked fish. 4.75k, Fishing spear.

**2001, May 9    Litho.    Perf. 13¼x13**
384 A102  4.50k multi              1.40  1.40
  a.  Booklet pane of 6 + 2 labels 8.00
385 A102  4.75k multi              1.40  1.40
  a.  Booklet pane of 6 + 2 labels 8.00
     Complete booklet, #384a, 385a 16.00

Europa A104

**2001, May 9    Litho. & Engr.    Perf. 13**
386 A104  15k Krill                6.00  6.00

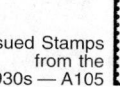

Unissued Stamps from the 1930s — A105

Designs: 5.75k, 5o Northern lights. 8k, 10o Seal. 21k, 15o Polar bear.

**Litho. & Engr.**
**2001, Oct. 16    Perf. 12¾**
387 A105  5.75k blk & brn          2.25  2.25
388 A105  8k blk & brn             3.25  3.25
389 A105  21k blk & brn            8.25  8.25
  a.  Souvenir sheet, #387-389 + 3
       labels                     14.00 14.00

Christmas A106

Grouse  and:  4.50k,  Berries.  4.75k, Mountain.

**2001, Oct. 16    Litho.    Perf. 13x13¼**
390 A106  4.50k multi              1.75  1.75
  a.  Booklet pane of 6           10.50
391 A106  4.75k multi             1.90  1.90
  a.  Booklet pane of 6           11.50
     Complete booklet, #390a, 391a 22.50

**Cultural Heritage Type of 2000**
Designs: 4.50k, Thule drum. 4.75k, Mask.

**2002, Mar. 5    Litho.    Perf. 13x13¼**
392 A102  4.50k multi              1.75  1.75
  a.  Miniature sheet of 8 + label 14.00
393 A102  4.75k multi             1.90  1.90
  a.  Miniature sheet of 8 + label 15.00

Sculptures A107

Designs: 1k, Stone and Man, by various sculptors. 31k, Nuuk Snow Festival snow sculpture.

**2002, Mar. 5    Perf. 12¾**
394 A107  1k multi                  .40   .40
395 A107  31k multi               12.00 12.00

**2002, June 24    Litho.    Perf. 12¾**
396 A108  11k multi                4.25  4.25

Ships A109

**2002, June 24    Engr.    Perf. 13x13¼**
397 A109  2k Nordlyset             .80   .80
398 A109  4k Hvidbjørnen          1.60  1.60
399 A109  6k Staerkodder           2.40  2.40
  a.  Booklet pane of 4, 2 each
        #398-399                   8.00
400 A109  16k Haabet               6.25  6.25
  a.  Booklet pane of 4, 2 each
        #397, 400                 14.00
     Complete booklet, #399a,
       400a                       22.50
     Nos. 397-400 (4)            11.05 11.05
   See Nos. 416-419, 434-437, 452-455.

Intl. Council for Exploration of the Seas, Cent. — A110

Designs: 7k, Somniosus microcephalus and iceberg. 19k, Sebastes mentella and exploration ship Paamiut.

**Litho. & Engr.**
**2002, Oct. 21    Perf. 13¼x13**
401 A110  7k multi                 2.75  2.75
402 A110  19k multi                7.50  7.50
  a.  Souvenir sheet, #401-402    10.50 10.50
   See Denmark Nos. 1237-1238, Faroe Islands No. 426.

Christmas — A111

Designs: 4.50k, Man with gifts, children on sled with tree. 4.75k, Family with gifts near fire.
Illustration reduced.

**2002, Oct. 21    Litho.    Perf. 12¾**
403 A111  4.50k multi              1.75  1.75
404 A111  4.75k multi              1.90  1.90
**Booklet Stamps**
**Self-Adhesive**
**Serpentine Die Cut 14**
405 A111  4.50k multi              1.75  1.75
406 A111  4.75k multi             1.90  1.90
  a.  Horiz. pair, #405-406        3.75
  b.  Booklet, 6 each #405-406    22.50

Danish Literary Greenland Expedition, Cent. — A112

Designs: 15k, Campsite. 21k, Knud Rasmussen.
Illustration reduced.

**2003, Mar. 12    Engr.    Perf. 12¾**
407 A112  15k multi                6.00  6.00
     **Size: 28x21mm**
408 A112  21k blue gray            8.25  8.25
  a.  Souvenir sheet, #407-408 +
       label                      14.50 14.50

Sled Dogs A113

Designs: 4.50k, Puppies playing. 4.75k, Close-up of dog. 6k, Dog in harness.

**2003, Mar. 12    Perf. 13x13¼**
409 A113  4.50k blue gray          1.75  1.75
  a.  Sheet of 8 + central label  14.00 14.00
410 A113  4.75k blue gray         1.90  1.90
  a.  Sheet of 8 + central label  15.00 15.00
411 A113  6k blue gray             2.40  2.40
  a.  Booklet pane, 2 each #409-
        411, with #411 at UL      12.00
  b.  Booklet pane, 2 each #409-
        411, with #409 at UL      12.00
     Complete booklet, #411a,
       411b                       24.00

Europa — A114

**2003, June 16    Litho.    Perf. 13¼x13**
412  A114  5.50k multi                    2.25  2.25

Town of
Qaanaaq, 50th
Anniv. — A115

**2003, June 16    Perf. 12¾**
413  A115  15k multi                      6.00  6.00

**Cultural Heritage Type of 2000**
Designs: 25o, Comb. 1k, Ice bucket.

**2003, June 16    Perf. 13¼x13**
414  A102  25o multi                       .20   .20
415  A102  1k multi                        .40   .40

**Ship Type of 2002**
**Litho. & Engr.**

**2003, Oct. 20    Perf. 13x13¼**
416  A109  6.75k Emma                     2.75  2.75
417  A109  7.75k Gamle Fox                3.00  3.00
418  A109  8.75k Godthaab                 3.50  3.50
419  A109  26k Sonja                     10.00 10.00
     Nos. 416-419 (4)                    19.25 19.25

Christmas
A116

Designs: Nos. 420, 422, Christmas tree.
Nos. 421, 423, Church.

**2003, Oct. 20    Litho.    Perf. 12¾**
420  A116  5k multi                       2.00  2.00
421  A116  5.50k multi                    2.25  2.25

**Booklet Stamps**
**Self-Adhesive**
**Serpentine Die Cut 12¼x12¾**
422  A116  5k multi                       2.00  2.00
423  A116  5.50k multi                    2.25  2.25
  a.    Horiz. pair, #422-423            4.25
  b.    Booklet pane, 6 each #423a      26.00
     Nos. 420-423 (4)                     8.50  8.50

Polar Air Route,
50th
Anniv. — A117

**2004, Mar. 26    Litho.    Perf. 13¼x13**
424  A117  8.75k multi                    3.50  3.50

Home Rule,
25th
Anniv. — A118

**2004, Mar. 26    Perf. 12¾x12½**
425  A118  11k multi                      4.25  4.25

Landing Boat
From Expedition
of Arctic Explorer
Otto Sverdrup
(1854-1930)
A119

**Litho. & Engr.**
**2004, Mar. 26    Perf. 13¼x13**
426  A119  17.50k multi                   7.00  7.00
  a.    Souvenir sheet of 1 + 2 labels   7.00  7.00
  See Canada Nos. 2026-2027, Norway Nos.
1398-1399.

Norse Mythology
A120

Designs: 5.50k, Moon Man. 6.50k, Northern
Lights.

**2004, Mar. 26    Litho.    Perf. 12¾**
427  A120  5.50k multi                    2.25  2.25
428  A120  6.50k multi                    2.50  2.50
  a.    Souvenir sheet, #427-428         4.75  4.75

Wedding of
Crown Prince
Frederik and
Mary Donaldson
A121

Designs: 5k, Couple facing right. 5.50k,
Couple facing left.

**2004, May 14    Perf. 13¼**
429  A121  5k multi                       2.00  2.00
430  A121  5.50k multi                    2.25  2.25
  a.    Souvenir sheet, #429-430 +
         central label                    4.25  4.25
  b.    Booklet pane, 3 each #429-
         430, with #429 at top           13.00   —
  c.    As "b," with #430 at top         13.00
         Complete booklet, #430b-430c    26.00

Edible
Plants
A122

Designs: 5k, Angelica archangelica. 5.50k,
Thymus praecox. 17k, Empetrum
hermaphroditum.

**2004, May 14    Perf. 13x13¼**
431  A122  5k multi                       2.00  2.00
  a.    Sheet of 8 + central label      16.00 16.00
432  A122  5.50k multi                    2.25  2.25
  a.    Sheet of 8 + central label      18.00 18.00
433  A122  17k multi                      6.75  6.75
     Nos. 431-433 (3)                    11.00 11.00
  See Nos. 459-461

**Ships Type of 2002**
**Litho. & Engr.**
**2004, Oct. 18    Perf. 13x13¼**
434  A109  6.50k Constance               2.50  2.50
435  A109  8.75k Disko                    3.50  3.50
436  A109  14k Julius Thom-
            sen                           5.50  5.50
437  A109  21.75k Misigssut               8.75  8.75
     Nos. 434-437 (4)                    20.25 20.25

Europa — A123

**2004, Oct. 18    Litho.    Perf. 13¼x13**
438  A123  6.50k multi                    2.50  2.50

Christmas
A124

Designs: 5k, Family, Christmas tree. 5.50k,
Carolers with lanterns.

**2004, Oct. 18    Perf. 12¾**
439  A124  5k multi                       2.00  2.00
440  A124  5.50k multi                    2.25  2.25

**Booklet Stamps**
**Self-Adhesive**
**Serpentine Die Cut 12¼x12¾**
441  A124  5k multi                       2.00  2.00
442  A124  5.50k multi                    2.25  2.25
  a.    Horiz. pair, #441-442            4.25
  b.    Complete booklet, 6 #442a       26.00
     Nos. 439-442 (4)                     8.50  8.50

Ilulissat Ice Fjord, UNESCO World
Heritage Site — A125

**2005, Jan. 17    Litho.    Perf. 12¾**
443  A125  6k multi                       2.40  2.40

Church and
School Systems
Law,
Cent. — A126

**2005, Jan. 17    Perf. 12¾**
444  A126  9.25k multi                    3.75  3.75

Europa — A127

**2005, Jan. 17    Perf. 13¼x13**
445  A127  11.75k multi                   4.75  4.75

Mushrooms — A128

Designs: 5.25k, Leccinum sp. 6k, Russula
subrubens. 7k, Amanita groenlandica.

**2005, Jan. 17    Perf. 13x13¼**
446  A128  5.25k multi                    2.10  2.10
  a.    Sheet of 8 + central label      17.00
447  A128  6k multi                       2.40  2.40
  a.    Sheet of 8 + central label      19.00
448  A128  7k multi                       2.75  2.75
     Nos. 446-448 (3)                     7.25  7.25

**Booklet Stamps**
**Self-Adhesive**
**Serpentine Die Cut 9¾x10¼**
449  A128  5.25k multi                    2.10  2.10
450  A128  6k multi                       2.40  2.40
451  A128  7k multi                       2.75  2.75
  a.    Booklet pane, 2 each #449-451   14.50
         Complete booklet, 2 #451a      29.00
     Nos. 449-451 (3)                     7.25  7.25
  No. 451a has two different marginal designs.

See Nos. 476-480.

**Ships Type of 2002**
**Litho. & Engr.**
**2005, June 20    Perf. 13x13¼**
452  A109  5.25k Dannebrog               2.10  2.10
453  A109  6k Kista Arctica              2.40  2.40
454  A109  18.50k Sarpik Ittuk           7.25  7.25
455  A109  23k Triton                    9.25  9.25
     Nos. 452-455 (4)                    21.00 21.00

Science In
Greenland — A129

Designs: 7.25k, Geological map. 9.25k,
Diver at limestone columns in Ikka Fjord,
horiz. 10k, Limnognathia maerski, horiz.

**Perf. 13¼x13, 13x13¼**
**2005, June 20**
456  A129  7.25k multi                    3.00  3.00
457  A129  9.25k multi                    3.75  3.75
458  A129  10k multi                      4.00  4.00
     Nos. 456-458 (3)                    10.75 10.75

**Edible Plants Type of 2004**
Designs: 75o, Ligusticum scoticum. 6.50k,
Rhodiola rosea. 8.25k, Oxyria digyna.

**2005, Oct. 31    Litho.    Perf. 13x13¼**
459  A122  75o multi                       .30   .30
460  A122  6.50k multi                    2.50  2.50
461  A122  8.25k multi                    3.25  3.25
     Nos. 459-461 (3)                     6.05  6.05

Admiral Robert E. Peary (1856-1920),
Explorer — A130

**Litho. & Engr.**
**2005, Oct. 31    Perf. 13**
462  A130  27.50k multi                  11.00 11.00
  a.    Souvenir sheet of 1            11.00 11.00

Parcel Post Stamps, Cent. — A131

**2005-07    Litho.    Perf. 14x13½**
463  A131  25k #Q3                       10.00 10.00
                          **Perf. 12¾x13**
464  A131  50k #Q4                       20.00 20.00
  a.    Perf. 14x13½, dated "2007"      18.00 18.00
  Issued: 25k, 1/16/06; No. 464, 10/3; No.
464a, 2007.
  No. 464a is found only in No. 497a, along
with an example of No. 463 dated "2007."
Issued: No. 464a, 5/21/07.
  See No. 497.

Christmas
A132

Designs: 5.25k, Boy at left. 6k, Girl at right.

**2005, Oct. 31    Perf. 12¾**
465  A132  5.25k multi                    2.10  2.10
466  A132  6k multi                       2.40  2.40

## Booklet Stamps
## Self-Adhesive
### Serpentine Die Cut 12¾x13

| | | | |
|---|---|---|---|
| 467 | A132 5.25k multi | 2.10 | 2.10 |
| 468 | A132 6k multi | 2.40 | 2.40 |
| a. | Pair, #467-468 | 4.50 | 4.50 |
| b. | Booklet pane, 6 each #467-468 | 27.50 | |

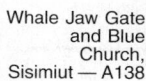

Whale Jaw Gate and Blue Church, Sisimiut — A138

**2006, Jan. 16**    *Perf. 13¾x13¼*
469 A138 9.75k multi    4.00 4.00
Sisimiut, 250th anniv.

Nordic Union "Norden" Stamps, 50th Anniv. — A139

**2006, Jan. 16**
470 A139 19.50k multi    7.75 7.75

European Philatelic Cooperation, 50th Anniv. — A140

**2006, Jan. 16**    *Perf. 14x13¼*
471 A140 26.50k #438 and stars    10.50 10.50
Europa stamps, 50th anniv.

Norse Mythology A141

Designs: 7.50k, The Mother of the Sea. 13.50k, Asiaq, Mistress of the Weather.

             *Perf. 13¾x13½*
**2006, Mar. 29**           **Litho.**

| | | | |
|---|---|---|---|
| 472 | A141 7.50k multi | 3.00 | 3.00 |
| 473 | A141 13.50k multi | 5.25 | 5.25 |
| a. | Souvenir sheet, #472-473 | 8.25 | 8.25 |

Sheep Farming in Greenland, Cent. A142

**2006, May 22**
474 A142 7.50k multi    3.00 3.00

Alfred Wegener (1880-1930), Geophysicist A143

**2006, May 22**    **Engr.**    *Perf. 13x13¼*
475 A143 20.75k red & blue    8.25 8.25
   a.    Souvenir sheet of 1    8.25 8.25

### Mushrooms Type of 2005

Designs: 5.50k, Rozites caperatus. 7k, Lactarius dryadophilus. 10k, Calvatia cretacea.

---

**2006, May 22**    **Litho.**    *Perf. 14x13¼*

| | | | |
|---|---|---|---|
| 476 | A128 5.50k multi | 2.25 | 2.25 |
| a. | Sheet of 8 + central label | 18.00 | 18.00 |
| 477 | A128 7k multi | 2.75 | 2.75 |
| a. | Sheet of 8 + central label | 22.00 | 22.00 |
| 478 | A128 10k multi | 4.00 | 4.00 |
| | Nos. 476-478 (3) | 9.00 | 9.00 |

## Self-Adhesive
## Booklet Stamps
### Serpentine Die Cut 12¼x12

| | | | |
|---|---|---|---|
| 479 | A128 5.50k multi | 2.25 | 2.25 |
| 480 | A128 7k multi | 2.75 | 2.75 |
| a. | Booklet pane, 3 each #479-480 | 15.00 | |
| | Complete booklet, 2 #480a | 30.00 | |

No. 480a has two different marginal designs.

Galathea 3 Research Expedition — A144

**2006, Sept. 9**    **Litho.**    *Perf. 13½x14*
481 A144 9.75k multi    4.00 4.00

Science — A145

Designs: 50o, Larch tree preserved in Kap Kobenhavn Formation. 8k, Geologist obtaining rock sample from mountains at Isua. 15.50k, Qeqertarsuaq Arctic Station, cent.

### Litho. & Engr.
**2006, Nov. 6**    *Perf. 13¼x13*

| | | | |
|---|---|---|---|
| 482 | A145 50o multi | .20 | .20 |
| 483 | A145 8k multi | 3.25 | 3.25 |
| 484 | A145 15.50k multi | 6.25 | 6.25 |
| | Nos. 482-484 (3) | 9.70 | 9.70 |

See Nos. 502-504, 524-526.

Christmas A146

Music for hymn and: 5.50k, Angel. 7k, Candle.

**2006, Nov. 6**    **Litho.**    *Perf. 13¾x13½*

| | | | |
|---|---|---|---|
| 485 | A146 5.50k multi | 2.25 | 2.25 |
| 486 | A146 7k multi | 2.75 | 2.75 |

## Booklet Stamps
## Self-Adhesive
### Serpentine Die Cut 12¼x12

| | | | |
|---|---|---|---|
| 487 | A146 5.50k multi | 2.00 | 2.00 |
| 488 | A146 7k multi | 2.50 | 2.50 |
| a. | Booklet pane, 3 each #487-488 | 13.50 | |
| | Complete booklet, 2 #488a | 27.00 | |

Hydroelectric Power — A147

**2007, Jan. 15**    **Litho.**    *Perf. 13¾x13½*
489 A147 5k multi    1.75 1.75
West Nordic Council, 10th anniv.

---

Crown Prince Frederik, Crown Princess Mary and Prince Christian — A148

**2007, Jan. 15**    *Perf. 13¼x14*
490 A148 14.25k multi    5.00 5.00

Intl. Polar Year A149

Designs: 7.50k, Scientists drilling ice cores. 8k, Urbanization.

### Litho. & Engr.
**2007, Jan. 15**    *Perf. 13x13¼*

| | | | |
|---|---|---|---|
| 491 | A149 7.50k multi | 2.60 | 2.60 |
| 492 | A149 8k multi | 2.75 | 2.75 |
| a. | Souvenir sheet, #491-492 | 5.50 | 5.50 |

Europa — A150

Scouts: 5.75k, And rock pile. 7.50k, At campsite.

**2007, Jan. 15 Litho.**    *Perf. 13¾x13¼*

| | | | |
|---|---|---|---|
| 493 | A150 5.75k multi | 2.00 | 2.00 |
| a. | Sheet of 8 + central label | 16.00 | 16.00 |
| 494 | A150 7.50k multi | 2.60 | 2.60 |
| a. | Sheet of 8 + central label | 21.00 | 21.00 |

## Booklet Stamps
## Self-Adhesive
### Serpentine Die Cut 12¼x12

| | | | |
|---|---|---|---|
| 495 | A150 5.75k multi | 2.00 | 2.00 |
| 496 | A150 7.50k multi | 2.60 | 2.60 |
| a. | Booklet pane, 3 each #495-496 | 14.00 | — |
| | Complete booklet, 2 #496a | 28.00 | |

### Parcel Post Stamp Centenary Type of 2005-06

**2007, May 21 Litho.**    *Perf. 14x13½*
497 A131 100k #Q6    37.50 37.50
   a.    Souvenir sheet, #463, 464a, 497    65.00 65.00

Examples of Nos. 463 and 464a in No. 497a are dated "2007."

A151

Contemporary Art — A152

Unnamed paintings by: 3k, Jens Rosing. 8.50k, Anne-Birthe Hove. 10.50k, Linda Riber Sorensen.
Illustration A151 reduced.

---

**2007, May 21**

| | | | |
|---|---|---|---|
| 498 | A151 3k multi | 1.10 | 1.10 |
| 499 | A152 8.50k multi | 3.25 | 3.25 |
| 500 | A152 10.50k multi | 3.75 | 3.75 |
| | Nos. 498-500 (3) | 8.10 | 8.10 |

Greenlandic Landscape — A153

**2007, Oct. 1**
501 A153 6.50k multi    2.50 2.50

### Science Type of 2006

Designs: 75o, Planting of Greenlandic flag on Tubbiap Qeqertaa. 2k, Soapstone bowl and quarry. 10.25k, Cyanobacteria.

### Litho. & Engr.
**2007, Oct. 1**    *Perf. 13¼x13*

| | | | |
|---|---|---|---|
| 502 | A145 75o multi | .30 | .30 |
| 503 | A145 2k multi | .75 | .75 |
| 504 | A145 10.25k multi | 4.00 | 4.00 |
| | Nos. 502-504 (3) | 5.05 | 5.05 |

Ship Pourquois-Pas? — A154

Paul-Emile Victor (1907-95), Arctic Explorer — A155

**2007, Nov. 8**    **Engr.**    *Perf. 13½*

| | | | |
|---|---|---|---|
| 505 | A154 5.75k multi | 2.25 | 2.25 |
| 506 | A155 7.50k multi | 3.00 | 3.00 |
| a. | Souvenir sheet, #505-506, + label | 5.25 | 5.25 |

See France No. 3369.

Christmas — A156

Snowflakes and: 5.75k, Angel. 7.50k, Star.

**2007, Nov. 8**    **Litho.**    *Perf. 13½x13¾*

| | | | |
|---|---|---|---|
| 507 | A156 5.75k multi | 2.25 | 2.25 |
| 508 | A156 7.50k multi | 3.00 | 3.00 |

## Self-Adhesive
## Booklet Stamps
### Serpentine Die Cut 12x12¼

| | | | |
|---|---|---|---|
| 509 | A156 5.75k multi | 2.25 | 2.25 |
| 510 | A156 7.50k multi | 3.00 | 3.00 |
| a. | Pair, #509-510 | 5.25 | |
| b. | Booklet pane of 12, 6 each #509-510 | 31.50 | |

Europa — A157

Envelope half and: 5.75k, Man. 7.50k, Woman.

**2008, Jan. 31**    **Litho.**    *Perf. 13¾x13½*
511 A157 5.75k multi    2.40 2.40

512 A157 7.50k multi 3.00 3.00

**Booklet Stamps**
**Self-Adhesive**
*Serpentine Die Cut 12¼x12*

513 A157 5.75k multi 2.40 2.40
514 A157 7.50k multi 3.00 3.00
  a. Booklet pane, 6 each #513-514 32.50

Contemporary Art — A158

Unnamed paintings by: 5.50k, Ina Rosing. 14.25k, Buuti Pedersen. 30.50k, Aka Hoegh.

**2008, Jan. 31** **Perf. 14x13½**
515 A158 5.50k multi 2.25 2.25
516 A158 14.25k multi 5.75 5.75
517 A158 30.50k multi 12.50 12.50
  Nos. 515-517 (3) 20.50 20.50

Mythical Places — A159

Myths of: 7k, Kayaker and river rocks. 8k, Bear of the Lake.

**Perf. 13¾x13½**
**2008, Mar. 27** **Litho.**
518 A159 7k multi 3.00 3.00
519 A159 8k multi 3.50 3.50
  a. Souvenir sheet, #518-519 6.50 6.50

Wedding of Prince Joachim and Marie Cavallier — A160

**2008, May 24** **Litho.** **Perf. 13½x14**
520 A160 10.25k multi 4.50 4.50

Fossils A161

Designs: 1k, Halkieria evangelista. 20.50k, Ichthyostega stensioei. 25k, Eudimorphodon cromptonellus.

**Litho. & Engr.**
**2008, May 24** **Perf. 13x13¼**
521 A161 1k multi .45 .45
522 A161 20.50k multi 8.75 8.75
523 A161 25k multi 10.50 10.50
  Nos. 521-523 (3) 19.70 19.70

**Science Type of 2006**

Designs: 6.50k, Scientist, equipment hauler, satellite above Greenland. 10.50k, French station at Scoresbysund. 28k, Danish Arctic station at Nuuk.

**Litho. & Engr.**
**2008, Oct. 20** **Perf. 13¼x13**
524 A145 6.50k multi 2.25 2.25
525 A145 10.50k multi 3.75 3.75
526 A145 28k multi 9.75 9.75
  a. Souvenir sheet, #524-526 16.00 16.00
  Nos. 524-526 (3) 15.75 15.75

International Geophysical Year, 50th anniv. (#524); French station at Scoresbysund, 75th

anniv. (#525); Danish Arctic station at Nuuk, 125th anniv. (#526).

Expedition Ship Sofia — A162

Adolf Erik Nordenskiöld (1832-1901), Arctic Explorer — A163

**2008, Oct. 20** **Perf. 13¼x13**
527 A162 8.50k multi 3.00 3.00
528 A163 16.25k multi 5.75 5.75
  a. Souvenir sheet, #527-528, + label 8.75 8.75

See Finland No. 1321.

Christmas A164

Designs: 5.75k, Reindeer and house. 7.50k, Christmas tree and houses.

**2008, Oct. 20 Litho.** **Perf. 13¾x13¼**
529 A164 5.75k multi 2.00 2.00
530 A164 7.50k multi 2.60 2.60

**Booklet Stamps**
**Self-Adhesive**
*Serpentine Die Cut 12¼x12*

531 A164 5.75k multi 2.00 2.00
532 A164 7.50k multi 2.60 2.60
  a. Pair, #531-532 4.60
  b. Booklet pane of 12, 6 each #531-532 28.00

**SEMI-POSTAL STAMPS**

Catalogue values for unused stamps in this section are for Never Hinged items.

No. 35 Surcharged in Red

**1958, May 22** **Engr.** **Perf. 13**
B1 A7 30o + 10o on 50o 6.00 1.90

The surtax was for the campaign against tuberculosis in Greenland.

No. 32 Surcharged: "Gronlandsfonden 30+10" and Bars

**1959, Feb. 23** **Unwmk.**
B2 A6 30o + 10o on 25o 4.75 4.25

The surtax was for the benefit of the Greenland Fund.

Two Greenland Boys in Round Tower — SP1

**1968, Sept. 12** **Engr.** **Perf. 13**
B3 SP1 60o + 10o dark red 1.25 *1.25*

Surtax for child welfare work in Greenland.

Hans Egede Explaining Bible to Natives — SP2

**1971, July 3** **Engr.** **Perf. 13**
B4 SP2 60o + 10o red brown 2.75 2.75

See footnote after No. 77.

Frederik IX, "Dannebrog" off Umanak — SP3

**1972, Apr. 20**
B5 SP3 60o + 10o dull red 1.75 1.75

King Frederik IX (1899-1972). The surtax was for humanitarian and charitable purposes.

Heimaey Town and Volcano — SP4

**1973, Oct. 18** **Engr.** **Perf. 13**
B6 SP4 70o + 20o gray & red 1.75 1.75

The surtax was for the victims of the eruption of Heimaey Volcano.

Arm Pulling, by Hans Egede — SP5

**1976, Apr. 8** **Engr.** **Perf. 12½**
B7 SP5 100o + 20o multi .70 .70

Surtax for the Greenland Athletic Union.

Rasmussen and Eskimos — SP6

**1979, June 7** **Engr.** **Perf. 13**
B8 SP6 1.30k + 20o brown red .95 .95

Knud Rasmussen (1879-1933), arctic explorer and ethnologist.

Stone Tent Ring, Polar Wolf, King Eider Ducks — SP7

**1981, Sept. 3** **Engr.** **Perf. 13**
B9 SP7 1.60k + 20o lt red brn .90 .90

Surtax was for Peary Land Expeditions.

History Type of 1982

Design: Eric the Red sailing for Greenland.

**1982, Aug. 2** **Engr.** **Perf. 12½**
B10 A39 2k + 40o dk red brn 1.25 1.25

Surtax was for Cultural House, Julianehab.

Blind Man — SP8

**1983, May 19** **Engr.**
B11 SP8 2.50k + 40o multi 1.40 1.40

Surtax was for the handicapped.

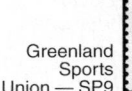

Greenland Sports Union — SP9

**1986, Apr. 17** **Litho.**
B12 SP9 2.80k + 50o Water game 1.50 *1.60*

Surtax for the Sports Union.

Greenland PO, 50th Anniv. — SP10

**1988, Sept. 16 Litho.** **Perf. 12½x13**
B13 SP10 300o +50o multi 2.25 2.25

Surtax for the purchase of postal artifacts.

Sled Dog, Common Eider — SP11

**Litho. & Engr.**
**1990, Sept. 6** **Perf. 13**
B14 SP11 400o + 50o multi 3.50 3.50

Surtax for the Greenland Environmental Foundation.

SP12 SP13

**1991, Sept. 5** **Litho.** **Perf. 13**
B15 SP12 4k +50o multi 15.00 15.00

Blue Cross of Greenland, 75th Anniv. Surtax benefits Blue Cross of Greenland.

**1992, Oct. 8** **Litho.** **Perf. 13**
B16 SP13 4k +50o multi 4.25 4.25

Cancer research in Greenland.

Red Cross — SP14

Boy Scouts in Greenland, 50th Anniv. SP15

**1993, June 17** **Litho.** **Perf. 13**
B17 SP14 4k +50o red & blue 2.50 2.50
B18 SP15 4k +50o multi 2.50 2.50
  a. Souv. sheet, 2 ea #B17-B18 20.00 20.00

1994 Winter Olympics, Lillehammer SP16

**1994, Feb. 10    Litho.    Perf. 13**
B19  SP16  4k +50o Skiers          3.00  3.00
  *a.*    Souvenir sheet of 4      12.00 12.00

Surtax to support Greenlandic athletes.

Natl. Flag, 10th Anniv. — SP17

**1995, June 21    Litho.    Perf. 13**
B20  SP17  4k +50o multi          2.50  2.50
  *a.*    Souvenir sheet of 4     10.00 10.00

Surtax for benefit of Greenland Flag Society.

Handicapped and Disabled in Greenland — SP18

**1996, Sept. 5    Litho.    Perf. 13**
B21  SP18  4.25k +50o multi       1.90  1.90
  *a.*    Souvenir sheet of 4      8.00  8.00

Katuaq Cultural Center, Nuuk SP19

**Litho. & Engr.**

**1997, Jan. 14    Perf. 13**
B22  SP19  4.50k +50o multi       2.25  2.25
  *a.*    Souvenir sheet of 4      9.00  9.00

SP20          SP21

Women's Society of Greenland: Kathrine Chemnitz (1894-1978), first Gen. Secretary.

**1998, May 29    Litho.    Perf. 13**
B23  SP20  4.50k +50o multi       1.75  1.75
  *a.*    Souvenir sheet of 4      7.25  7.25

**1999, May 7    Engr.    Perf. 13**
B24  SP21  4.50k +50o Pincushion, Natl. Museum    1.60  1.60
  *a.*    Souvenir sheet of 4      7.00  7.00

Surtax for the benefit of Greenland National Museum & Archives.

Drum Dance — SP22

**Litho. & Engr.**

**2000, Aug. 18    Perf. 13¼x13**
B25  SP22  4.50k + 1k multi       1.75  1.75
  *a.*    Souvenir sheet of 4      7.00  7.00

Surtax to benefit the Hafnia 01 Philatelic Exhibition, Copenhagen.

2002 Arctic Winter Games — SP23

**2001, Feb. 5    Litho.    Perf. 13¼x13**
B26  SP23  4.50k +50o multi       1.75  1.75
  *a.*    Souvenir sheet of 4      7.00  7.00

SP24

**2002, Mar. 5    Litho.    Perf. 12¾**
B27  SP24  4.50k +50o multi       1.75  1.75
  *a.*    Souvenir sheet of 4      7.00  7.00

Surtax for "Children Are People, Too" Project of Paarisa.

Ornament With Santa Claus, Map of Greenland, House — SP25

**2003, Oct. 20    Litho.    Perf. 13¼**
B28  SP25  5k +50o multi          2.00  2.00
  *a.*    Souvenir sheet of 4      8.00  8.00

Society of Greenlandic Children, 80th Anniv. — SP26

**2004, May 14    Litho.    Perf. 13x13¼**
B29  SP26  5k +50o multi          2.00  2.00
  *a.*    Souvenir sheet of 4      8.00  8.00

Surtax for Society of Greenlandic Children.

Child — SP27

**2005, Jan. 17    Litho.    Perf. 12¾**
B30  SP27  5.25k +50o multi       2.10  2.10
  *a.*    Souvenir sheet of 4      8.50  8.50

Surtax for Save the Children Fund.

Crown Prince Frederik and Crown Princess Mary — SP28

**Perf. 13¼x13¾**
**2006, Mar. 29    Litho.**
B31  SP28  5.50k +50o multi       2.10  2.10
  *a.*    Souvenir sheet of 4      8.50  8.50

Surtax for children's charities.

Amnesty Greenland SP29

**2007, Jan. 15    Litho.    Perf. 13¾x13¼**
B32  SP29  575o +50o multi        2.25  2.25
  *a.*    Souvenir sheet of 4      9.00  9.00

Fight Against Tuberculosis SP30

**2008, May 24    Litho.    Perf. 13¾x13½**
B33  SP30  575o +50o multi        2.75  2.75
  *a.*    Souvenir sheet of 4     11.00 11.00

## PARCEL POST STAMPS

Arms of Greenland — PP1

### Perf. 11, 11½

| 1905-37 | Unwmk. | | Typo. |
|---|---|---|---|
| Q1 | PP1  1o ol grn ('16) | 57.50 | 60.00 |
| *a.* | Perf. 12½ ('05) | 775.00 | 775.00 |
| Q2 | PP1  2o yellow ('16) | 325.00 | 125.00 |
| Q3 | PP1  5o brown ('16) | 125.00 | 125.00 |
| *a.* | Perf. 12½ ('05) | 750.00 | 775.00 |
| Q4 | PP1  10o blue ('37) | 40.00 | 72.50 |
| *a.* | Perf. 12½ ('05) | 950.00 | 625.00 |
| *b.* | Perf. 11½ ('16) | 55.00 | 65.00 |
| Q5 | PP1  15o violet ('16) | 200.00 | 200.00 |
| Q6 | PP1  20o red ('16) | 17.00 | 13.00 |
| *a.* | Perf. 11 ('37) | 40.00 | 60.00 |
| Q7 | PP1  70o violet ('37) | 40.00 | 125.00 |
| *a.* | Perf. 11½ ('30) | 250.00 | 225.00 |
| Q8 | PP1  1k yellow ('37) | 40.00 | 140.00 |
| *a.* | Perf. 11½ ('30) | 52.50 | 65.00 |
| Q9 | PP1  3k brown ('30) | 140.00 | 175.00 |
| | Nos. Q1-Q9 (9) | 984.50 | 1,035. |

| 1937 | Litho. | | Perf. 11 |
|---|---|---|---|
| Q10 | PP1  70o pale violet | 42.50 | 150.00 |
| Q11 | PP1  1k yellow | 40.00 | 77.50 |
| | Nos. Q10-Q11, never hinged | | 125.00 |

On lithographed stamps, PAKKE-PORTO is slightly larger, hyphen has rounded ends and lines in shield are fine, straight and evenly spaced.

On typographed stamps, hyphen has squared ends and shield lines are coarse, uneven and inclined to be slightly wavy.

Used values are for stamps postally used from Denmark. Numeral cancels indicate use as postal savings stamps and are worth less. Greenland village cancels are worth more.

Sheets of 25. Certain printings of Nos. Q1-Q2, Q3a, Q4a and Q5-Q6 were issued without sheet margins. Stamps from the outer rows are straight edged. Some of these sheets were reperfed later.

# GRENADA

grə-'nā-də

LOCATION — Windward Islands, West Indies
GOVT. — Independent nation in the British Commonwealth
AREA — 133 sq. mi.
POP. — 98,600 (1998 est.)
CAPITAL — St. George's

Grenada consists of Grenada Island and the southern Grenadines, including Carriacou. This colony was granted associated statehood with Great Britain in 1967 and became an independent state Feb. 7, 1974.

12 Pence = 1 Shilling
100 Cents = 1 Dollar (1949)

Catalogue values for unused stamps in this country are for Never Hinged items, beginning with Scott 143 in the regular postage section, Scott B1 in the semipostal section, Scott C1 in the air post section, Scott J15 in the postage due section, and Scott O1 in the official section.

## Watermarks

Wmk. 5 — Small Star     Wmk. 6 — Large Star

Wmk. 7 — Large Star with Broad Points

Values for unused stamps are for examples with original gum as defined in the catalogue introduction. Very fine examples of Nos. 1-19, 27-29, and 31-38 will have perforations touching the design on at least one side due to the narrow spacing of the stamps on the plates. Stamps with perfs clear of the design on all four sides are scarce and will command higher prices.

Queen Victoria — A1

### Rough Perf. 14 to 16

| | | | 1861 | Engr. | Unwmk. |
|---|---|---|---|---|---|
| 1 | A1 | 1p green | | 57.50 | 50.00 |
| a. | | 1p blue green | | 5,250. | 350.00 |
| b. | | As No. 1, horiz. pair, imperf. btwn. | | | |
| 2 | A1 | 6p rose | | 1,050. | 110.00 |
| b. | | 6p lake red, perf. 11-12½ | | 1,000. | |

No. 2b was not issued. No. 2 imperf is a proof.

| | | | 1863-71 | | Wmk. 5 |
|---|---|---|---|---|---|
| 3 | A1 | 1p green ('64) | | 100.00 | 15.00 |
| a. | | 1p yellow green | | 125.00 | 30.00 |

| | | | | | |
|---|---|---|---|---|---|
| 4 | A1 | 6p rose | | 775.00 | 20.00 |
| 5 | A1 | 6p vermilion ('71) | | 875.00 | 20.00 |
| a. | | 6p dull red | | 4,000. | 275.00 |
| g. | | Double impression | | | 2,350. |
| i. | | 6p orange red ('66) | | 750.00 | 14.00 |

No. 5a always has sideways watermark. Other colors sometimes have sideways watermark.

### 1873-78    Clean-Cut Perf. about 15

| | | | | | |
|---|---|---|---|---|---|
| 5B | A1 | 1p deep green | | 120.00 | 47.50 |
| j. | | Pair, imperf between | | | 8,750. |
| c. | | 1p blue green ('78) | | 275.00 | 45.00 |
| h. | | Half used as ½p on cover | | | 11,000. |
| 5D | A1 | 6p vermilion ('75) | | 925.00 | 40.00 |
| a. | | 6p dull red | | 950.00 | 40.00 |
| f. | | Double impression | | | 2,350. |

| | | | 1873 | | Wmk. 6 |
|---|---|---|---|---|---|
| 6 | A1 | 1p blue green | | 105.00 | 22.50 |
| a. | | Diagonal half used as ½p on cover | | | 11,000. |
| 7 | A1 | 6p vermilion | | 775.00 | 35.00 |

| | | | 1875 | | Perf. 14 |
|---|---|---|---|---|---|
| 7A | A1 | 1p yellow green | | 90.00 | 9.00 |
| b. | | Half used as ½p on cover | | | 16,000. |
| c. | | Perf. 15 | | 10,000. | 2,600. |

A2            A2a

### Revenue Stamps Surcharged in Black

| | | | 1875-81 | | Perf. 14, 14½ |
|---|---|---|---|---|---|
| 8 | A2 | ½p purple ('81) | | 15.50 | 7.50 |
| a. | | "OSTAGE" | | 225.00 | 150.00 |
| b. | | Imperf., pair | | 350.00 | |
| c. | | "ALF" | | 4,000. | |
| d. | | "PEN" | | | |
| e. | | No hyphen between "HALF" and "PENNY" | | 225.00 | 150.00 |
| f. | | Double surcharge | | 350.00 | 350.00 |
| 9 | A2a | 2½p lake ('81) | | 70.00 | 10.00 |
| a. | | Imperf., pair | | 575.00 | |
| b. | | Imperf. vertically, pair | | 4,500. | |
| c. | | "PENCF" | | 525.00 | 225.00 |
| d. | | No period after "PENNY" | | 290.00 | 90.00 |
| e. | | "PENOE" | | 175.00 | |
| 10 | A2 | 4p blue ('81) | | 120.00 | 10.00 |

### Revenue Stamps Surcharged in Dark Blue

| | | | | | |
|---|---|---|---|---|---|
| 11 | A2 | 1sh purple | | 775.00 | 20.00 |
| a. | | "SHLLIING" | | 6,500. | 800.00 |
| b. | | "NE SHILLING" | | | 3,250. |
| c. | | "OSTAGE" | | 7,250. | 3,000. |
| d. | | Invtd. "S" in "POSTAGE" | | 4,500. | 750.00 |

See Nos. 27-35.

| | | | 1881 | | Wmk. 7 |
|---|---|---|---|---|---|
| 12 | A2 | 2½p lake | | 200.00 | 57.50 |
| a. | | 2½p claret | | 500.00 | 140.00 |
| b. | | As No. 12, "PENCF" | | 875.00 | 325.00 |
| c. | | As No. 12, No period after "PENNY" | | 650.00 | 230.00 |
| d. | | As "a," "PENCF" | | 1,850. | 825.00 |
| e. | | As "a," no period after "PENNY" | | 1,275. | 575.00 |
| 13 | A2 | 4p blue | | 300.00 | 210.00 |

A3           A4

A5           A6

### Revenue Stamp Overprinted "POSTAGE" in Black

| | | | 1883 | | Wmk. 5 |
|---|---|---|---|---|---|
| | | | Denomination & Crown in 2nd Color | | |
| 14 | A3 | ½p orange & grn | | 900.00 | 275.00 |
| a. | | Unsevered pair | | 5,000. | 1,500. |
| b. | | "POSTAGE" omitted | | | 1,500. |

| | | | | | |
|---|---|---|---|---|---|
| 15 | A4 | ½p orange & grn | | 325.00 | 150.00 |
| a. | | Unsevered pair | | 1,750. | 525.00 |
| 16 | A5 | 1p orange & grn | | 400.00 | 65.00 |
| a. | | Inverted overprint | | 3,250. | 2,600. |
| b. | | Double overprint | | 1,625. | 1,275. |
| c. | | Inverted "S" in "Postage" | | | |
| d. | | Diagonal half used as ½p on cover | | 1,150. | 700.00 |
| | | | | | 3,500. |

### "Postage" in Manuscript, Red or Black

| | | | | | |
|---|---|---|---|---|---|
| 18 | A6 | 1p orange & grn (R) | | | 11,000. |
| 19 | A6 | 1p orange & green | | — | 15,000. |

On Nos. 14-19 the words "ONE PENNY" measure from 10-11¼mm in length.
On No. 15, the lower "POSTAGE" is always inverted.
It has been claimed that although Nos. 18 and 19 were used, they were not officially authorized by Grenada's postmaster.

A8            A10

| | | | 1883 | Wmk. 2 | Perf. 14 |
|---|---|---|---|---|---|
| 20 | A8 | ½p green | | 1.50 | 1.25 |
| a. | | Tete beche pair | | 5.00 | 17.50 |
| 21 | A8 | 1p rose | | 80.00 | 4.00 |
| a. | | Tete beche pair | | 260.00 | 290.00 |
| 22 | A8 | 2½p ultra | | 8.00 | 1.25 |
| a. | | Tete beche pair | | 30.00 | 57.50 |
| 23 | A8 | 4p slate | | 5.75 | 2.25 |
| a. | | Tete beche pair | | 21.00 | 65.00 |
| 24 | A8 | 6p red lilac | | 5.00 | 6.50 |
| a. | | Tete beche pair | | 21.00 | 65.00 |
| 25 | A8 | 8p bister | | 10.50 | 14.00 |
| a. | | Tete beche pair | | 37.50 | 87.50 |
| 26 | A8 | 1sh violet | | 140.00 | 65.00 |
| a. | | Tete beche pair | | 1,650. | 1,850. |
| | | Nos. 20-26 (7) | | 250.75 | 94.25 |

Stamps of types A8, A10 and D2 were printed with alternate horizontal rows inverted. For surcharges see Nos. 36-38, J4-J7.

### Revenue Stamps Surcharged

| | | | 1886 | | Wmk. 6 |
|---|---|---|---|---|---|
| 27 | A2 | 1p on 1½ org | | 50.00 | 35.00 |
| a. | | Inverted surcharge | | 350.00 | 350.00 |
| b. | | Diagonal half used as ½ on cover | | | 2,250. |
| c. | | Double surcharge | | 575.00 | 350.00 |
| d. | | "HALH" instead of "HALF" | | 300.00 | 275.00 |
| 28 | A2 | 1p on 1sh org | | 45.00 | 35.00 |
| a. | | "SHILLNG" instead of "SHILLING" | | 525.00 | 450.00 |
| b. | | No period after "POSTAGE" | | 475.00 | |
| c. | | Half used as ½p on cover | | | 2,350. |

| | | | | | Wmk. 5 |
|---|---|---|---|---|---|
| 29 | A2 | 1p on 4p org | | 190.00 | 110.00 |

| | | | 1887 | | Wmk. 2 |
|---|---|---|---|---|---|
| 30 | A10 | 1p rose | | 1.75 | 1.50 |
| a. | | Tete beche pair | | 3.50 | 22.50 |

### Revenue Stamps Surcharged:

h          i

j          k

l

| | | | 1888-91 | Wmk. 5 | Perf. 14½ |
|---|---|---|---|---|---|
| 31 | A2 (h) | ½p on 2sh org ('89) | | 14.00 | 24.00 |
| a. | | Double surcharge | | 350.00 | 375.00 |
| b. | | First "S" in "SHILLINGS" inverted | | 325.00 | 350.00 |
| 32 | A2 (i) | 4p on 2sh org | | 45.00 | 22.50 |
| a. | | "4d" and "POSTAGE" 5mm apart | | 80.00 | 35.00 |
| b. | | "S" inverted, as in #31b | | 550.00 | 400.00 |
| c. | | As "a," inverted "S," as in #31b | | 750.00 | 650.00 |

### "d" Vertical instead of Slanting

| | | | | | |
|---|---|---|---|---|---|
| 33 | A2 (i) | 4p on 2sh org | | 875.00 | 475.00 |
| 34 | A2 (k) | 4p on 2sh org ('90) | | 92.50 | 87.50 |
| a. | | Inverted surcharge | | 875.00 | |
| b. | | "S" inverted | | 825.00 | 750.00 |
| 35 | A2 (l) | 1p on 2sh org ('91) | | 70.00 | 65.00 |
| a. | | Inverted surcharge | | | |
| b. | | No period after "d" | | 450.00 | |
| c. | | "S" inverted | | 575.00 | 575.00 |

No. 25 Surcharged in Black:

| | | | | Wmk. 2 | |
|---|---|---|---|---|---|
| 36 | A8 | 1p on 8p bister | | 12.00 | 15.00 |
| a. | | Tete beche pair | | 50.00 | 70.00 |
| b. | | Inverted surcharge | | 375.00 | 325.00 |
| c. | | No period after "d" | | 300.00 | 300.00 |

### "2" of "½" Upright

| | | | | | |
|---|---|---|---|---|---|
| 37 | A8 | 2½ on 8p bister | | 10.00 | 13.00 |
| a. | | Tete beche pair | | 50.00 | 70.00 |
| b. | | Inverted surcharge | | | |
| c. | | Double surcharge | | 1,000. | 925.00 |
| d. | | Triple surcharge | | | 1,100. |
| e. | | Double surcharge, one inverted | | 650.00 | 575.00 |

### "2" of "½" Italic

| | | | | | |
|---|---|---|---|---|---|
| 38 | A8 | 2½ on 8p bister | | 10.00 | 13.00 |
| a. | | Tete beche pair | | 50.00 | 70.00 |
| b. | | Tete beche pair, #37, 38 | | 125.00 | |
| c. | | Inverted surcharge | | | |
| d. | | Double surcharge | | 875.00 | 925.00 |
| e. | | Triple surcharge | | | 1,050. |
| f. | | Triple surch., two inverted | | | 1,000. |
| g. | | Double surcharge, one inverted | | 625.00 | 575.00 |

Queen Victoria — A17

| | | | 1895-99 | Wmk. 2 Typo. | Perf. 14 |
|---|---|---|---|---|---|
| 39 | A17 | ½p lilac & green | | 3.00 | 2.00 |
| 40 | A17 | 1p lilac & car rose | | 5.25 | .90 |
| 41 | A17 | 2p lilac & brown | | 47.50 | 37.50 |
| 42 | A17 | 2½p lilac & ultra | | 7.50 | 1.75 |
| 43 | A17 | 3p lilac & orange | | 8.00 | 18.00 |
| 44 | A17 | 6p lilac & green | | 15.50 | 35.00 |
| 45 | A17 | 8p lilac & black | | 15.00 | 52.50 |
| 46 | A17 | 1sh green & org | | 22.50 | 52.50 |
| | | Nos. 39-46 (8) | | 124.25 | 200.15 |

Numerals of ½p, 3p, 8p and 1sh of type A17 are in color on colorless tablet.
Issue dates: 1p, May, 1896; ½p, 2p, Sept. 1899; others, Sept. 5, 1895.

Columbus' Flagship, La Concepcion A18     King Edward VII A19

| | | | 1898, Aug. 15 | Engr. | Wmk. 1 |
|---|---|---|---|---|---|
| 47 | A18 | 2½p ultra | | 16.50 | 8.00 |
| a. | | Bluish paper | | 37.50 | 47.50 |

Discovery of the island by Columbus, Aug. 15th, 1498.

| | | | | |
|---|---|---|---|---|
| **1902** | | **Wmk. 2** | | **Typo.** |
| 48 | A19 | ½p violet & grn | 3.75 | 1.50 |
| 49 | A19 | 1p vio & car rose | 5.25 | .35 |
| 50 | A19 | 2p vio & brown | 3.50 | 11.50 |
| 51 | A19 | 2½p vio & ultra | 4.00 | 3.25 |
| 52 | A19 | 3p vio & org | 4.50 | 10.50 |
| 53 | A19 | 6p vio & green | 3.00 | 20.00 |
| 54 | A19 | 1sh green & org | 5.50 | 32.50 |
| 55 | A19 | 2sh grn & ultra | 24.00 | 65.00 |
| 56 | A19 | 5sh car rose | 47.50 | 70.00 |
| 57 | A19 | 10sh green & vio | 140.00 | 300.00 |
| | | Nos. 48-57 (10) | 241.00 | 514.60 |

Numerals of ½p, 3p, 1sh, 2sh and 10sh of type A19 are in color on colorless tablet.

| | | | | |
|---|---|---|---|---|
| **1904-06** | | **Wmk. 3** | | **Perf. 14** |
| 58 | A19 | ½p vio & green | 20.00 | 30.00 |
| 59 | A19 | 1p vio & car rose | 11.00 | 3.00 |
| 60 | A19 | 2p vio & brown | 65.00 | 125.00 |
| 61 | A19 | 2½p vio & ultra | 65.00 | 75.00 |
| 62 | A19 | 3p vio & org | 3.25 | 8.00 |
| 63 | A19 | 6p vio & green | 6.50 | 17.50 |
| 64 | A19 | 1sh green & org | 7.00 | 30.00 |
| 65 | A19 | 2sh grn & ultra | 57.50 | 80.00 |
| 66 | A19 | 5sh car rose | 75.00 | 110.00 |
| 67 | A19 | 10sh green & vio | 175.00 | 300.00 |
| | | Nos. 58-67 (10) | 485.25 | 778.50 |

Nos. 62, 63 and 65 are on both ordinary and chalky paper.
Issued: #58, 60-62, 64, 1905; #63, 65-67, 1906.

Seal of Colony
A20

King George V
A21

| | | | | |
|---|---|---|---|---|
| **1906-11** | | | | **Engr.** |
| 68 | A20 | ½p green | 5.25 | .35 |
| 69 | A20 | 1p carmine | 7.50 | .20 |
| 70 | A20 | 2p yellow | 3.50 | 3.50 |
| 71 | A20 | 2½p blue | 7.00 | 2.00 |
| a. | | 2½p ultramarine | 9.50 | 3.75 |

**Typo.**
**Chalky Paper**
**Numerals white on dark ground**

| | | | | |
|---|---|---|---|---|
| 72 | A20 | 3p vio, yel ('08) | 5.00 | 1.90 |
| 73 | A20 | 6p violet ('08) | 22.50 | 25.00 |
| 74 | A20 | 1sh blk, grn ('11) | 8.00 | 5.00 |
| 75 | A20 | 2sh vio & blue, blue ('08) | 22.50 | 14.00 |
| 76 | A20 | 5sh red & green, yel ('08) | 67.50 | 80.00 |
| | | Nos. 68-76 (9) | 148.75 | 131.95 |

| | | | | |
|---|---|---|---|---|
| **1908** | | | | **Wmk. 2** |
| 77 | A20 | 1sh black, green | 32.50 | 67.50 |
| 78 | A20 | 10sh red & grn, grn | 100.00 | 210.00 |

| | | | | |
|---|---|---|---|---|
| **1913** | | **Ordinary Paper** | | **Wmk. 3** |
| 79 | A21 | ½p green | 1.10 | 1.25 |
| 80 | A21 | 1p carmine | 2.50 | .35 |
| a. | | 1p scarlet ('16) | 5.00 | 1.10 |
| 81 | A21 | 2p orange | 1.90 | .35 |
| 82 | A21 | 2½p ultra | 2.00 | 4.00 |

**Chalky Paper**

| | | | | |
|---|---|---|---|---|
| 83 | A21 | 3p violet, yel | .75 | 1.00 |
| 84 | A21 | 6p dull vio & red vio | 1.75 | 10.00 |
| 85 | A21 | 1sh black, green | 1.10 | 11.50 |
| a. | | 1sh black, emerald | 1.75 | 16.00 |
| b. | | 1sh blk, bl grn, olive back | 52.50 | 90.00 |
| c. | | As "a," olive back | 1.75 | 15.00 |
| 86 | A21 | 2sh vio & ultra, bl | 7.25 | 14.00 |
| 87 | A21 | 5sh grn & red, yel | 20.00 | 67.50 |
| 88 | A21 | 10sh grn & red, grn | 62.50 | 100.00 |
| a. | | 10sh grn & red, emer | 60.00 | 175.00 |
| | | Nos. 79-88 (10) | 100.85 | 209.95 |

| | | | | |
|---|---|---|---|---|
| **1914** | | **Surface-colored Paper** | | |
| 89 | A21 | 3p violet, yel | .70 | 1.60 |
| 90 | A21 | 1sh black, green | 1.40 | 8.50 |

| | | | | |
|---|---|---|---|---|
| **1921-29** | | **Ordinary Paper** | | **Wmk. 4** |
| 91 | A21 | ½p green | 1.40 | .35 |
| 92 | A21 | 1p rose red | .90 | .85 |
| 93 | A21 | 1p brown ('23) | 1.75 | .35 |
| 94 | A21 | 1½p rose red ('22) | 1.75 | 1.75 |
| 95 | A21 | 2p orange | 1.40 | .35 |
| 96 | A21 | 2p gray ('26) | 2.75 | 3.00 |
| 97 | A21 | 2½p ultramarine | 5.25 | 10.00 |
| 98 | A21 | 2½p gray ('22) | 1.10 | 10.00 |
| 99 | A21 | 3p ultra ('22) | 1.75 | 12.50 |

**Chalky Paper**

| | | | | |
|---|---|---|---|---|
| 100 | A21 | 3p vio, yel ('26) | 3.50 | 5.75 |
| 101 | A21 | 4p blk & red, yel ('26) | 1.10 | 4.25 |
| 102 | A21 | 5p gray vio & ol grn ('22) | 1.75 | 4.75 |

| | | | | |
|---|---|---|---|---|
| 103 | A21 | 6p dl vio & red vio | 1.50 | 22.50 |
| 104 | A21 | 6p blk & red ('26) | 2.50 | 2.75 |
| 105 | A21 | 9p gray vio & blk ('22) | 2.50 | 11.00 |
| 106 | A21 | 1sh blk, emer ('23) | 3.00 | 50.00 |
| 107 | A21 | 1sh org brn ('26) | 4.50 | 11.00 |
| 108 | A21 | 2sh vio & ultra, bl ('22) | 7.00 | 19.00 |
| 109 | A21 | 2sh6p blk & red, bl ('29) | 8.00 | 22.50 |
| 110 | A21 | 3sh grn & vio ('22) | 6.75 | 30.00 |
| 111 | A21 | 5sh green & red, yel ('23) | 14.00 | 40.00 |
| 112 | A21 | 10sh green & red, emer ('23) | 57.50 | 150.00 |
| | | Nos. 91-112 (22) | 131.65 | 412.65 |

Grand Anse Beach — A22

Seal of the Colony — A23

View of Grand Etang A24

View of St. George's A25

| | | | | |
|---|---|---|---|---|
| **1934, Oct. 23** | | **Engr.** | | **Perf. 12½** |
| 114 | A22 | ½p green | .20 | 1.25 |
| a. | | Perf. 12½x13 ('36) | 5.00 | 50.00 |

**Perf. 13½x12½**

| | | | | |
|---|---|---|---|---|
| 115 | A23 | 1p blk brn & blk | .65 | .35 |
| a. | | Perf 12½ | 1.10 | 3.50 |

**Perf. 12½x13½**

| | | | | |
|---|---|---|---|---|
| 116 | A24 | 1½p car & black | .90 | .45 |
| a. | | Perf 12½ ('36) | 5.25 | 3.75 |

**Perf. 12½**

| | | | | |
|---|---|---|---|---|
| 117 | A23 | 2p org & black | 1.10 | .80 |
| 118 | A25 | 2½p deep blue | .55 | .55 |
| 119 | A23 | 3p ol grn & blk | 1.10 | 3.25 |
| 120 | A23 | 6p claret & blk | 2.25 | 2.00 |
| 121 | A23 | 1sh brown & blk | 2.25 | 4.50 |
| 122 | A23 | 2sh6p ultra & blk | 9.00 | 30.00 |
| 123 | A23 | 5sh vio & black | 40.00 | 55.00 |
| | | Nos. 114-123 (10) | 58.00 | 98.15 |
| | | Set, never hinged | 125.00 | |

**Common Design Types pictured following the introduction.**

**Silver Jubilee Issue**
**Common Design Type**

| | | | | |
|---|---|---|---|---|
| **1935, May 6** | | | | **Perf. 11x12** |
| 124 | CD301 | ½p green & blk | .80 | 1.25 |
| 125 | CD301 | 1p black & ultra | .80 | 1.90 |
| 126 | CD301 | 1½p car & blue | .80 | 1.90 |
| 127 | CD301 | 1sh brn vio & ind | 7.25 | 19.00 |
| | | Nos. 124-127 (4) | 9.65 | 24.05 |
| | | Set, never hinged | 20.00 | |

**Coronation Issue**
**Common Design Type**

| | | | | |
|---|---|---|---|---|
| **1937, May 12** | | **Wmk. 4** | | **Perf. 11x11½** |
| 128 | CD302 | 1p dark purple | .25 | .25 |
| 129 | CD302 | 1½p dark carmine | .25 | .20 |
| 130 | CD302 | 2½p deep ultra | .50 | .35 |
| | | Nos. 128-130 (3) | 1.00 | .80 |
| | | Set, never hinged | 1.60 | |

George VI — A26

Seal of the Colony — A28

Grand Anse Beach — A27

View of Grand Etang — A29

View of St. George's A30

Seal of the Colony A31

| | | | | |
|---|---|---|---|---|
| **1937, July 12** | | **Photo.** | | **Perf. 14½x14** |
| 131 | A26 | ¼p chestnut | .50 | .75 |
| **1938, Mar. 16** | | **Engr.** | | **Perf. 12½** |
| 132 | A27 | ½p green | .80 | 1.40 |
| 133 | A28 | 1p blk brn & blk | .55 | .55 |
| 134 | A29 | 1½p scarlet & blk | .25 | .95 |
| 135 | A28 | 2p orange & blk | .20 | .55 |
| 136 | A30 | 2½p ultramarine | .20 | .35 |
| 137 | A28 | 3p olive grn & blk | .20 | 2.10 |
| 138 | A28 | 6p red vio & blk | 1.25 | .45 |
| 139 | A28 | 1sh org brn & blk | 2.50 | .45 |
| 140 | A28 | 2sh ultra & black | 10.00 | 2.00 |
| 141 | A28 | 5sh purple & blk | 2.25 | 2.75 |

**Perf. 14**

| | | | | |
|---|---|---|---|---|
| 142 | A31 | 10sh rose car & gray blue | 20.00 | 13.00 |
| a. | | 10sh deep car & gray blue, perf. 12 ('43) | 300.00 | 1,400. |
| b. | | Perf. 12x13 | 42.50 | 12.00 |
| | | Nos. 131-142 (12) | 38.70 | 25.30 |
| | | Set, never hinged | 62.50 | |

| | | | | |
|---|---|---|---|---|
| **1938-42** | | | **Perf. 12½x13½, 13½x12½** | |
| 132a | A27 | ½p | 3.00 | .90 |
| 133a | A28 | 1p | 3.00 | .90 |
| 134a | A29 | 1½p car & blk | 1.25 | .40 |
| 135a | A28 | 2p | 1.40 | .75 |
| 136a | A30 | 2½p | 3,000. | 240.00 |
| 137a | A28 | 3p | 2.50 | 1.00 |
| 138a | A28 | 6p ('42) | 1.25 | .35 |
| 139a | A28 | 1sh ('42) | 1.00 | 1.50 |
| 140a | A28 | 2sh ('41) | 12.50 | 2.00 |
| 141a | A28 | 5sh ('47) | 1.60 | 4.50 |

> **Catalogue values for unused stamps in this section, from this point to the end of the section, are for Never Hinged items.**

**Peace Issue**
**Common Design Type**

| | | | | |
|---|---|---|---|---|
| **1946, Sept. 25** | | | | **Perf. 13½x14** |
| 143 | CD303 | 1½p carmine | .20 | .20 |
| 144 | CD303 | 3½p deep blue | .20 | .20 |

**Silver Wedding Issue**
**Common Design Types**

| | | | | |
|---|---|---|---|---|
| **1948, Oct. 27** | | **Photo.** | | **Perf. 14x14½** |
| 145 | CD304 | 1½p scarlet | .20 | .20 |

**Engr.; Name Typo.**
**Perf. 11½x11**

| | | | | |
|---|---|---|---|---|
| 146 | CD305 | 10sh gray green | 14.50 | 20.00 |

**UPU Issue**
**Common Design Types**
**Engr.; Name Typo. on 6c, 12c**
**Perf. 13½, 11x11½**

| | | | | |
|---|---|---|---|---|
| **1949, Oct. 10** | | | | **Wmk. 4** |
| 147 | CD306 | 5c ultra | .25 | .25 |
| 148 | CD307 | 6c deep olive | 1.40 | 1.75 |
| 149 | CD308 | 12c red lilac | .30 | .50 |
| 150 | CD309 | 24c red brown | .25 | .55 |
| | | Nos. 147-150 (4) | 2.20 | 3.05 |

A32

A33

A34

| | | | | |
|---|---|---|---|---|
| **1951, Jan. 8** | | **Engr.** | | **Perf. 11½** |
| **Center in Black** | | | | |
| 151 | A32 | ½c chestnut | .20 | 1.50 |
| 152 | A32 | 1c blue green | .20 | .60 |
| 153 | A32 | 2c dark brown | .20 | .20 |
| 154 | A32 | 3c carmine | .25 | .20 |
| 155 | A32 | 4c deep orange | .40 | .25 |
| 156 | A32 | 5c purple | .50 | .30 |
| 157 | A32 | 6c olive | .50 | .65 |
| 158 | A32 | 7c blue | 2.00 | .30 |
| 159 | A32 | 12c red violet | 2.25 | .75 |
| **Perf. 11½x12½** | | | | |
| 160 | A33 | 25c dark brown | 2.50 | 1.00 |
| 161 | A33 | 50c ultra | 5.75 | .60 |
| 162 | A33 | $1.50 orange | 8.25 | 8.00 |
| **Perf. 11½x13** | | | | |
| **Center in Gray Blue** | | | | |
| 163 | A34 | $2.50 deep carmine | 7.00 | 6.50 |
| | | Nos. 151-163 (13) | 30.00 | 20.85 |

See #180-183, 202. For overprints see #166-169.

**University Issue**
**Common Design Types**

| | | | | |
|---|---|---|---|---|
| **1951, Feb. 16** | | | | **Perf. 14x14½** |
| 164 | CD310 | 3c dp car & gray blk | .55 | 1.00 |
| 165 | CD311 | 6c olive & black | .65 | .60 |

Nos. 154-156 and 159 Overprinted in Black or Carmine

| | | | | |
|---|---|---|---|---|
| **1951, Sept. 21** | | | | **Perf. 11½** |
| 166 | A32 | 3c carmine & black | .25 | .40 |
| 167 | A32 | 4c dp orange & black | .25 | .40 |
| 168 | A32 | 5c purple & black (C) | .25 | .60 |
| 169 | A32 | 12c red violet & black | .25 | .80 |
| | | Nos. 166-169 (4) | 1.00 | 2.20 |

Adoption of a new constitution for the Windward Islands.

**Coronation Issue**
**Common Design Type**

| | | | | |
|---|---|---|---|---|
| **1953, June 3** | | | | **Perf. 13½x13** |
| 170 | CD312 | 3c carmine & black | .25 | .20 |

Types of 1951 Inscribed "E II R" and

Queen Elizabeth II — A35

| | | | | |
|---|---|---|---|---|
| **1953-59** | | **Engr.** | | **Perf. 11½** |
| **Center in Black** | | | | |
| 171 | A35 | ½c chestnut ('54) | .20 | .20 |
| 172 | A35 | 1c blue green | .20 | .20 |
| 173 | A35 | 2c dark brown | .20 | .20 |
| 174 | A35 | 3c carmine ('54) | .20 | .20 |
| 175 | A35 | 4c dp orange ('54) | .20 | .20 |
| 176 | A35 | 5c purple ('54) | .20 | .20 |
| 177 | A35 | 6c olive | .45 | 1.50 |
| 178 | A35 | 7c blue ('55) | 1.25 | .20 |
| 179 | A35 | 12c red violet | .20 | .20 |
| **Perf. 11½x12½** | | | | |
| 180 | A33 | 25c dark brown ('55) | 1.40 | .35 |
| 181 | A33 | 50c ultra ('55) | 6.00 | .55 |
| 182 | A33 | $1.50 orange ('55) | 12.50 | 14.00 |
| **Perf. 11½x13** | | | | |
| **Center in Gray Blue** | | | | |
| 183 | A34 | $2.50 deep car ('59) | 18.50 | 11.00 |
| | | Nos. 171-183 (13) | 41.50 | 29.00 |

See Nos. 195-202.
No. 182 was locally surcharged "2" and two black horizontal lines and issued Dec. 23, 1965, for revenue use. It was used postally, though not authorized for postal use. The "2" is found in two type faces.

## West Indies Federation
### Common Design Type
*Perf. 11½x11*

**1958, Apr. 22**                    **Wmk. 314**
184 CD313  3c green            .35   .20
185 CD313  6c blue            .55   .70
186 CD313  12c carmine rose    .60   .20
  *Nos. 184-186 (3)*          1.50  1.10

Victoria and Elizabeth II and Mail Truck A36

Queens and: 8c, "La Concepcion" and Dakota plane. 25c, Steam Packet "Solent" and B.O.A.C. plane.

**1961, June 1  Photo.   Perf. 14½x14**
187 A36  3c gray & deep car    .30   .20
188 A36  8c orange & ultra    .60   .25
189 A36  25c blue & maroon     .65   .25
  *Nos. 187-189 (3)*          1.55   .70
Centenary of first Grenada postage stamps.

## Freedom from Hunger Issue
### Common Design Type
**1963, June 4            Perf. 14x14½**
190 CD314  8c green            .30   .20

## Red Cross Centenary Issue
### Common Design Type
**1963, Sept. 2  Litho.    Perf. 13**
191 CD315  3c black & red      .25   .20
192 CD315  25c ultra & red     .55   .20

Types of 1953-55
**Wmk. 314**
**1963-64      Engr.      Perf. 11½**
Center in Black
195 A35  2c dark brown         .20   .20
196 A35  3c carmine            .20   .20
197 A35  4c dp orange          .20   .80
198 A35  5c purple             .20   .20
199 A35  6c olive           200.00  95.00
201 A35  12c red violet        .30   .20
*Perf. 11½x12½*
202 A33  25c dark brown       2.75  1.00
  *Nos. 195-198,201-202 (6)*  3.85  2.60

Issued: 6c, 1963; others, May 12, 1964.

## ITU Issue
### Common Design Type
**1965, May 17  Litho.   Perf. 11x11½**
205 CD317  2c vermilion & olive  .20  .20
206 CD317  50c yellow & ver     .25  .20

## Intl. Cooperation Year Issue
### Common Design Type
**1965, Oct. 25   Litho.    Perf. 14½**
207 CD318  1c blue grn & claret  .20  .20
208 CD318  25c lt violet & green  .20  .20

## Churchill Memorial Issue
### Common Design Type
**1966, Jan. 24  Photo.    Perf. 14**
Design in Black, Gold and Carmine Rose
209 CD319  1c bright blue       .20   .20
210 CD319  3c green            .20   .20
211 CD319  25c brown           .25   .25
212 CD319  35c violet          .35   .35
  *Nos. 209-212 (4)*          1.00  1.00

## Royal Visit Issue
### Common Design Type
**1966, Feb. 4   Litho.    Perf. 11x12**
213 CD320  3c violet blue      .20   .20
214 CD320  35c dark car rose    .60   .20

Careenage, St. George's A37

---

Queen Elizabeth II — A38

Designs: 1c, Hillsborough, Carriacou. 2c, Bougainvillea. 3c, Flamboyant plant. 5c, Levera Beach. 8c, Annandale Falls. 10c, Cacao pods. 12c, Inner Harbor. 15c, Nutmeg. 25c, St. George's. 35c, Grand Anse Beach. 50c, Bananas. $1, Seal of Colony. $3, Map of Grenada.

*Perf. 14½x13½, 14½ (A38)*
**1966, Apr. 1    Photo.    Wmk. 314**
215 A37  1c blue, grn & yel     .20   .80
216 A37  2c dk grn & dp car rose
                                .20   .20
217 A37  3c multicolored        .50   .50
218 A37  5c multicolored       1.00   .20
219 A37  6c ultra, grn & car rose
                                .80   .20
220 A37  8c dp grn, ind & yel   .80   .20
221 A37  10c yel grn, brn & dk car
                                .25   .20
222 A37  12c multicolored       .25   .50
223 A37  15c multicolored       .25   .50
224 A37  25c dk bl, grn & car rose
                                .25   .20
225 A37  35c multicolored       .40   .20
226 A37  50c violet & green    1.25  1.00
227 A38  $1 brn, ultra & dull grn
                               6.75  2.75
228 A38  $2 multicolored       5.00  6.00
229 A38  $3 brt grnsh bl, dk bl & dl yel
                               4.50 12.50
  *Nos. 215-229 (15)*         22.40 25.95

For overprints and surcharges see Nos. 237-261.

## World Cup Soccer Issue
### Common Design Type
**1966, July 1   Litho.    Perf. 14**
230 CD321  5c multicolored      .20   .20
231 CD321  50c multicolored     .45   .70

## WHO Headquarters Issue
### Common Design Type
**1966, Sept. 20  Litho.   Perf. 14**
232 CD322  5c multicolored      .25   .20
233 CD322  25c multicolored     .55   .25

## UNESCO Anniversary Issue
### Common Design Type
**1966, Dec. 1   Litho.    Perf. 14**
234 CD323  2c "Education"       .20   .20
235 CD323  15c "Science"        .20   .20
236 CD323  50c "Culture"        .60   .70
  *Nos. 234-236 (3)*          1.00  1.10

Nos. 216-217, 220 and 224 Overprinted "ASSOCIATED STATEHOOD 1967" in Silver
*Perf. 14½x13½*
**1967, Mar. 3   Photo.    Wmk. 314**
237 A37  2c dk grn & dp car rose  .20  .20
238 A37  3c multicolored       .20   .20
239 A37  8c dp grn, ind & yel   .20   .20
240 A37  25c dk bl, grn & car rose .20 .20
  *Nos. 237-240 (4)*           .80   .80

Nos. 216, 221, 223 and 227-228 Surcharged

*Perf. 14½x13½, 14½ (A38)*
**1967, July 1   Photo.    Wmk. 314**
241 A37  1c on 15c multi        .20   .20
242 A37  2c dk grn & dp car rose .20  .20
243 A37  3c on 10c multi        .20   .20
244 A38  $1 multicolored        .30   .25
245 A38  $2 multicolored        .40   .40
  *Nos. 241-245 (5)*          1.30  1.25

EXPO '67 Intl. Exhib., Montreal, Apr. 28-Oct. 27.

---

Nos. 215-229 Overprinted in Black: "ASSOCIATED STATEHOOD"
**1967-68        Photo.     Wmk. 314**
246 A37  1c multicolored        .20   .20
247 A37  2c multicolored        .20   .20
248 A37  3c multicolored        .20   .20
249 A37  5c multicolored        .20   .20
250 A37  6c multicolored        .20   .20
251 A37  8c multicolored        .20   .20
252 A37  10c multicolored       .20   .20
253 A37  12c multicolored       .20   .20
254 A37  15c multicolored       .20   .20
255 A37  25c multicolored       .20   .20
256 A37  35c multicolored       .60   .20
257 A37  50c multicolored      1.00   .30
258 A38  $1 multicolored       1.40   .75
259 A38  $2 multicolored       1.25  3.00
260 A38  $3 multicolored       2.50  5.00
### Overprinted and Surcharged
261 A38  $5 on $2 multi        1.75  4.50
  *Nos. 246-261 (16)*        10.50 15.75

Issued: $5, 5/18/68; others, 10/19/67.
For surcharges, see Nos. B1A-B1D.

Pres. John F. Kennedy — A39

Pres. Kennedy and: 25c, 50c, Bird-of-paradise flower. 35c, $1, Roses.

*Perf. 14½x14*
**1968, Jan. 13              Unwmk.**
262 A39  1c lt blue & multi     .20   .20
263 A39  15c orange & multi     .20   .20
264 A39  25c violet & multi     .20   .20
265 A39  35c multicolored       .20   .20
266 A39  50c blue & multi       .35   .25
267 A39  $1 multicolored        .50   .70
  *Nos. 262-267 (6)*          1.65  1.75

50th anniv. of the birth of Pres. John F. Kennedy (1917-1963).

Bugler and Jamboree Emblem — A40

Jamboree Emblem and: 2c, 50c, Boy Scouts sitting in tent. 3c, $1, Lord Baden-Powell.

**1968, Feb. 1   Photo.    Perf. 13x14**
268 A40  1c orange & multi      .20   .20
269 A40  2c emer & multi        .20   .20
270 A40  3c yellow & multi      .20   .20
271 A40  35c multicolored       .25   .20
272 A40  50c blue & multi       .40   .35
273 A40  $1 multicolored        .60   .60
  *Nos. 268-273 (6)*          1.85  1.75

12th Boy Scout Jamboree, Farragut State Park, Idaho, Aug. 1-9, 1967.

Seascape, by Winston Churchill — A41

Paintings: 12c, Pine at the shore. 15c, 35c, Houses at the shore. 50c, Churchill painting a seascape.

*Perf. 14x14½*
**1968, Mar. 23              Unwmk.**
274 A41  10c multicolored       .20   .20
275 A41  12c multicolored       .20   .20
276 A41  15c multicolored       .20   .20
277 A41  25c multicolored       .20   .20

---

278 A41  35c multicolored       .30   .20
279 A41  50c multicolored       .45   .25
  *Nos. 274-279 (6)*          1.55  1.25

Winston Churchill as a painter.

Edith McGuire, US, 200m. Dash, 1964 A42

Gold Medal Winners: 2c, 50c, Arthur Wint, Jamaica, 400m run, 1948. 3c, 60c, Adhemar Ferreira da Silva, Brazil, hop, step and jump, 1952 & 1956. 10c, Like 1c.

**1968, Sept. 24  Photo.    Perf. 12½**
280 A42  1c ultra & multi       .20   .30
281 A42  2c lilac & multi       .20   .30
282 A42  3c green & multi       .20   .30
283 A42  10c red org & multi    .20   .30
284 A42  50c Prus blue & multi  .60   .75
285 A42  60c orange & multi     .70   .85
  *Nos. 280-285 (6)*          2.10  2.80

19th Olympic Games, Mexico City, Oct. 12-27. Nos. 280-282 and 283-285 are printed in sheets of 9 (3 of each denomination). For surcharges see Nos. 310-315.

Transplant Operations — A43

*Perf. 13x13½*
**1968, Nov. 25   Photo.    Unwmk.**
286 A43  5c Kidney             .20   .20
287 A43  25c Heart            .35   .20
288 A43  35c Lung             .45   .20
289 A43  50c Cornea           .55   .60
  *Nos. 286-289 (4)*         1.55  1.20

20th anniv. of WHO.

Adoration of the Magi, by Veronese A44

Paintings: 15c, Madonna and Child with St. John and St. Catherine, by Titian. 35c, Adoration of the Magi, by Botticelli. $1, "A Knight Adoring the Infant Christ" by Vincenzo di Biagio Catena.

**1968, Dec. 3              Perf. 12½**
290 A44  5c vio blue & multi    .20   .20
291 A44  15c crimson & multi    .20   .20
292 A44  35c dk green & multi   .20   .20
293 A44  $1 dk blue & multi     .25   .25
  *Nos. 290-293 (4)*           .85   .85

Christmas. For overprints see Nos. 341-344.

Hibiscus and "La Concepcion" — A45

Yacht in St. George's Harbour — A45a

Designs: 2c, Bird-of-paradise flower. 3c, Bougainvillea. 5c, Rock hind (fish; horiz.). 6c, Sailfish. 8c, Red snapper, horiz. 10c, Giant toad, horiz. 12c, Yellowfoot tortoise. No. 302, Tree boa, horiz. No. 302A, Thunbergia. 25c, Mouse opossum. 35c Armadillo, horiz. 50c, Mona monkey. $1, Bananaquit (bird). $2, Brown pelican. $3, Magnificent frigate bird. $5, Bare-eyed thrush.

**Perf. 14x14½, 14½x14; 14x13½ (#302A); 13½x14 (#305A)**
**Photo.; Litho. (#302A, 305A)**

| | | | Unwmk. | |
|---|---|---|---|---|
| 1968-71 | | | | |
| 294 | A45 | 1c dl yel & multi | .20 | .20 |
| 295 | A45 | 2c brt pink & multi | .20 | .20 |
| 296 | A45 | 3c blue & multi | .20 | .20 |
| 297 | A45 | 5c violet & multi | .20 | .20 |
| 298 | A45 | 6c emer & multi | .20 | .20 |
| 299 | A45 | 8c multicolored | .20 | .25 |
| 300 | A45 | 10c multicolored | .20 | .20 |
| 301 | A45 | 12c ver & multi | .20 | .20 |
| 302 | A45 | 15c emer & multi | .90 | .85 |
| 302A | A45 | 15c gray & multi | 5.00 | 3.25 |
| 303 | A45 | 25c multicolored | .30 | .20 |
| 304 | A45 | 35c multicolored | .35 | .20 |
| 305 | A45 | 50c ultra & multi | .45 | .25 |
| 305A | A45a | 75c blue & multi | 10.00 | 8.00 |
| 306 | A45 | $1 multicolored | 3.00 | 2.40 |
| 307 | A45 | $2 multicolored | 4.25 | 10.00 |
| 308 | A45 | $3 yel & multi | 4.25 | 5.00 |
| 309 | A45 | $5 multicolored | 6.00 | 19.00 |
| | | Nos. 294-309 (18) | 36.10 | 50.80 |

Nos. 294-309 vary in size from 25x44mm to 29x46mm.
The overprint "VOTE/FEB. 28 1972" was applied to the 2c, 3c, 6c and 25c in Feb., 1972.
Issued: 5c, 10c, 25c, $2, 2/4/69; 3c, 8c, 35c, $5, 7/1/69; #302A, 1970; 75c, 10/9/71; others, 10/68.
For surcharges see Nos. 462-464. For overprints see Nos. 528-541, C3-C19.

Nos. 280-285 Surcharged in Carmine

| | | | | |
|---|---|---|---|---|
| 1969, Feb. | | | Perf. 12½ | |
| 310 | A42 | 5c on 1c multi | .20 | .20 |
| 311 | A42 | 8c on 2c multi | .20 | .20 |
| 312 | A42 | 25c on 3c multi | .20 | .20 |
| 313 | A42 | 35c on 10c multi | .20 | .20 |
| 314 | A42 | $1 on 50c multi | .25 | .25 |
| 315 | A42 | $2 on 60c multi | .50 | .60 |
| | | Nos. 310-315 (6) | 1.55 | 1.65 |

Gov. Hilda Bynoe and View of St. George's A46

Designs: 15c, Premier Eric M. Gairy, fruits and St. George's. 60c, Emblems of Brussels, New York and Montreal World's Fairs.

| | | | | |
|---|---|---|---|---|
| 1969, May 1 | | Litho. | Perf. 13x13½ | |
| 316 | A46 | 5c multicolored | .20 | .20 |
| 317 | A46 | 15c multicolored | .20 | .20 |
| 318 | A46 | 50c multicolored | .20 | .20 |
| 319 | A46 | 60c multicolored | .20 | .30 |
| | | Nos. 316-319 (4) | .80 | .90 |

Nos. 310-319 issued to publicize CARIFTA (Caribbean Free Trade Area) Exposition, St. George's, Apr. 5-30.

Gov. Hilda Bynoe — A47

Designs: 25c, Dr. Martin Luther King, Jr. $1, Belshazzar's Feast, by Rembrandt, horiz.

**Perf. 13x12½, 12½x13**

| | | | | |
|---|---|---|---|---|
| 1969, June 8 | | Photo. | Unwmk. | |
| 320 | A47 | 5c multicolored | .20 | .20 |
| 321 | A47 | 25c multicolored | .20 | .20 |
| 322 | A47 | 35c multicolored | .20 | .20 |
| 323 | A47 | $1 multicolored | .30 | .40 |
| | | Nos. 320-323 (4) | .90 | 1.00 |

International Human Rights Year.

Batsman Playing Off-drive — A48

Cricket: 10c, Batsman playing defensive stroke. 25c, Batsman sweeping ball. 35c, Batsman playing on-drive.

| | | | | |
|---|---|---|---|---|
| 1969, Aug. 1 | | | Perf. 14x14½ | |
| 324 | A48 | 3c dk blue & multi | .25 | .95 |
| 325 | A48 | 10c fawn & multi | .30 | .40 |
| 326 | A48 | 25c dp green & multi | .55 | .80 |
| 327 | A48 | 35c brt purple & multi | .70 | .85 |
| | | Nos. 324-327 (4) | 1.80 | 3.00 |

Astronaut Collecting Moon Rocks, Landing Module and Earth — A49

Designs: ½c, like $1. 1c, Apollo 11, moon and earth. 2c, Landing module "Eagle." 3c, Memorial tablet left on moon. 8c, Separation of rocket and spaceship. 25c, Take off from Cape Kennedy, vert. 35c, Apollo 11 circling the moon, vert. 50c, Splashdown, vert. ½c, 2c, 25c, 50c, $1 inscribed: "We came in peace for all mankind." 1c, 3c, 8c, 35c inscribed: "Like the moon it shall be established forever" Psalms 89:37.

**Perf. 13x13½ (½c), 12½**

| | | | | |
|---|---|---|---|---|
| 1969, Sept. 24 | | Litho. | Unwmk. | |
| | | Size: 56x35mm | | |
| 328 | A49 | ½c multicolored | .20 | .20 |
| | | Size: 44½x28mm, 28x44½mm | | |
| 329 | A49 | 1c multicolored | .20 | .20 |
| 330 | A49 | 2c multicolored | .20 | .20 |
| 331 | A49 | 3c multicolored | .20 | .20 |
| 332 | A49 | 8c multicolored | .20 | .20 |
| 333 | A49 | 25c multicolored | .20 | .20 |
| 334 | A49 | 35c multicolored | .20 | .20 |
| 335 | A49 | 50c multicolored | .20 | .20 |
| 336 | A49 | $1 multicolored | .40 | .60 |
| a. | | Souvenir sheet of 2 | 2.25 | 2.25 |
| | | Nos. 328-336 (9) | 2.00 | 2.20 |

Man's first moonlanding (Apollo 11), July 20, 1969.
No. 336a contains stamps similar to Nos. 331 and 336 with simulated perforations.
For surcharge and overprints see #349, 379-382.

Mahatma Gandhi — A50

Gandhi in various positions. 15c, 25c are vert.

| | | | | |
|---|---|---|---|---|
| 1969, Oct. 8 | | Perf. 11½x12, 12x11½ | | |
| | | Queen's Head in Gold | | |
| 337 | A50 | 6c multicolored | .20 | .20 |
| 338 | A50 | 15c multicolored | .20 | .20 |
| 339 | A50 | 25c multicolored | .40 | .20 |
| 340 | A50 | $1 multicolored | .75 | .85 |
| a. | | Souvenir sheet of 4 | 3.50 | 3.50 |
| | | Nos. 337-340 (4) | 1.55 | 1.45 |

Mohandas K. Gandhi (1869-1948), leader in India's fight for independence.
No. 340a contains stamps similar to Nos. 337-340 with simulated perforation.

Nos. 290-293 Overprinted in Black or Silver with Bars and "1969"

| | | | | |
|---|---|---|---|---|
| 1969, Dec. 23 | | Photo. | Perf. 12½ | |
| 341 | A44 | 2c on 15c multi | .20 | .75 |
| 342 | A44 | 5c multi (S) | .20 | .20 |
| 343 | A44 | 35c multi (S) | .20 | .20 |
| 344 | A44 | $1 multi (S) | .85 | 1.75 |
| | | Nos. 341-344 (4) | 1.45 | 2.90 |

Christmas.

Edward Teach (Blackbeard) A51

Pirates: 25c, Anne Bonney and sailboats. 50c, Jean Lafitte and sailboats. $1, Mary Read, ships and fighting pirates.

| | | | | |
|---|---|---|---|---|
| 1970, Feb. 1 | | Engr. | Perf. 13x13½ | |
| 345 | A51 | 15c black | .40 | .20 |
| 346 | A51 | 25c emerald | .65 | .20 |
| 347 | A51 | 50c purple | 1.25 | .20 |
| 348 | A51 | $1 carmine | 2.00 | .80 |
| | | Nos. 345-348 (4) | 4.30 | 1.40 |

No. 328 Surcharged

Type I

Type II

| | | | | |
|---|---|---|---|---|
| 1970, Mar. 18 | | Litho. | Perf. 13x13½ | |
| 349 | A49 | 5c on ½c multi (I) | .40 | .40 |
| a. | | Type II | 1.25 | 1.50 |

Christ, from "The Last Supper," by Andrea del Sarto — A52

Paintings: No. 351 (5c), St. John, from Last Supper by Andrea del Sarto. Nos. 352-353 (15c), Christ Crowned with Thorns, by

Anthony Van Dyck. Nos. 354-355 (25c), Passion of Christ, by Hans Memling. Nos. 356-357 (60c), Christ in the Tomb, by Peter Paul Rubens. Nos. 350, 352, 354 and 356 have denomination in lower right corner; others in lower left corner. The stamps of the same denomination are printed se-tenant without separating margin, reproducing continuous picture.

| | | | | |
|---|---|---|---|---|
| 1970, Apr. 13 | | Litho. | Perf. 11½x11 | |
| 350 | A52 | 5c rose car & multi | .20 | .20 |
| 351 | A52 | 5c rose car & multi | .20 | .20 |
| a. | A52 | Pair, #350-351 | .40 | .40 |
| 352 | A52 | 15c ultra & multi | .20 | .25 |
| 353 | A52 | 15c ultra & multi | .20 | .25 |
| a. | A52 | Pair, #352-353 | .40 | .50 |
| 354 | A52 | 25c brt vio & multi | .20 | .25 |
| 355 | A52 | 25c brt vio & multi | .20 | .25 |
| a. | A52 | Pair, #354-355 | .40 | .50 |
| 356 | A52 | 60c dull org & multi | .40 | .55 |
| 357 | A52 | 60c dull org & multi | .40 | .55 |
| a. | A52 | Pair, #354-355 | .85 | 1.10 |
| b. | | Souvenir sheet of 4, #354-357 | 1.40 | 1.40 |
| | | Nos. 350-357 (8) | 2.00 | 2.50 |

Easter.

Girl Pushing Carriage with Kittens — A53

Designs: 15c, Girl playing with puppy and kitten. 30c, Boy fishing and cat. 60c, Children with pets.

| | | | | |
|---|---|---|---|---|
| 1970, May 27 | | Litho. | Perf. 11 | |
| 358 | A53 | 5c multicolored | .20 | .20 |
| 359 | A53 | 15c multicolored | .20 | .20 |
| 360 | A53 | 30c multicolored | .35 | .35 |
| a. | | Souvenir sheet of 2 | 2.50 | 2.50 |
| 361 | A53 | 60c multicolored | .75 | 1.00 |
| a. | | Souvenir sheet of 2 | 2.50 | 2.50 |
| | | Nos. 358-361 (4) | 1.50 | 1.75 |

William Wordsworth (1770-1850). English poet. No. 360a contains stamps similar to Nos. 358 and 360; No. 361a contains stamps similar to Nos. 359 and 361. Sheets have simulated perforations.

Indian Parliament — A54

Commonwealth Parliamentary Association Emblem and: 25c, British Parliament. 50c, Canadian Parliament. 60c, Grenadian Parliament.

| | | | | |
|---|---|---|---|---|
| 1970, June 15 | | Perf. 14½x14 | | |
| 362 | A54 | 5c multicolored | .20 | .20 |
| 363 | A54 | 25c multicolored | .20 | .20 |
| 364 | A54 | 30c multicolored | .20 | .20 |
| 365 | A54 | 60c multicolored | .20 | .20 |
| a. | | Souvenir sheet of 4, #362-365 | 1.25 | 1.25 |
| | | Nos. 362-365 (4) | .80 | .80 |

7th Caribbean Regional Conf. of the Commonwealth Parliamentary Assoc., St. George's. June 13-20.

Sun Tower and EXPO Emblem A55

EXPO Emblem and: 2c, Livelihood Industry pavilion, horiz. 3c, Ikenobo, Japanese floral art, vert. 10c, Adam and Eve, by Tintoretto and Italian pavilion, horiz. 25c, UN pavilion and flags reflected in pool. 50c, Peace statue of St. Francis, San Francisco pavilion, cable car and Golden Gate Bridge, $1, Toshiba-Ihi pavilion, horiz.

| 1970, Aug. 8 | | Litho. | Perf. 13½ |
|---|---|---|---|
| 366 A55 | 1c brt blue & multi | .20 | .20 |
| 367 A55 | 2c multicolored | .20 | .20 |
| 368 A55 | 3c buff & multi | .20 | .20 |
| 369 A55 | 10c multicolored | .20 | .20 |
| 370 A55 | 25c gray & multi | .20 | .20 |
| 371 A55 | 50c gray & multi | .25 | 1.00 |
| Nos. 366-371 (6) | | 1.25 | 2.00 |

**Souvenir Sheet**

| 372 A55 | $1 gold & multi | 1.25 | 1.75 |
|---|---|---|---|

EXPO '70 Intl. Exhib., Osaka, Japan, Mar. 15-Sept. 13.

Pres. Roosevelt and Flag-Raising on Iwo Jima — A56

Designs: 5c, Marshal Georgi K. Zhukov and fall of Berlin. 15c, Winston Churchill and evacuation of Dunkirk. 25c, Charles de Gaulle and liberation of Paris. 50c, General Dwight D. Eisenhower and D-Day landing. 60c, Field Marshal Bernard Montgomery and Battle of Alamein.

| 1970, Sept. 3 | | | Perf. 11 |
|---|---|---|---|
| 373 A56 | ½c multicolored | .20 | .60 |
| 374 A56 | 5c multicolored | 1.00 | .35 |
| 375 A56 | 15c multicolored | 1.50 | .55 |
| 376 A56 | 25c multicolored | 1.75 | .55 |
| 377 A56 | 50c multicolored | 2.00 | 1.60 |
| 378 A56 | 60c multicolored | 2.25 | 3.00 |
| a. | Souv. sheet of 4 #373, 375, 377-378 | 6.75 | 6.75 |
| Nos. 373-378 (6) | | 8.70 | 6.65 |

End of World War II, 25th anniversary.

Nos. 333-336 Overprinted in Black or Silver: "PHILYMPIA / LONDON 1970"

| 1970, Sept. 18 | | | Perf. 12½ |
|---|---|---|---|
| 379 A49 | 25c multicolored | .20 | .20 |
| 380 A49 | 35c multicolored | .20 | .20 |
| 381 A49 | 50c multicolored | .25 | .25 |
| 382 A49 | $1 multi (S) | .50 | .50 |
| Nos. 379-382 (4) | | 1.15 | 1.15 |

Philympia 1970, London philatelic exhibition, Sept. 18-26. The overprint on No. 382 is vertical, reading up.
This overprint was applied in silver to No. 336a. Value $45.

UPU Headquarters, Emblem and Old Transportation — A57

UPU Headquarters, emblem and: 25c, Jet plane, ship and diesel train. 50c, Rowland Hill, vert. $1, Abraham Lincoln, vert.

| 1970, Oct. 17 | | Litho. | Perf. 14½ |
|---|---|---|---|
| 383 A57 | 15c orange & multi | .65 | .25 |
| 384 A57 | 25c blue & multi | .65 | .20 |
| 385 A57 | 50c multicolored | .40 | .40 |
| 386 A57 | $1 rose & multi | .60 | 2.00 |
| a. | Souvenir sheet of 2 | 2.10 | 3.00 |
| Nos. 383-386 (4) | | 2.30 | 2.85 |

Opening of the new UPU Headquarters in Bern. No. 386a contains stamps similar to Nos. 385-386.

Madonna of the Goldfinch, by Tiepolo — A58

Christmas (Paintings): No. 388, 35c, Virgin and Child with Sts. Peter and Paul, by Dirk Bouts. No. 389, $1, Virgin and Child, by Bellini. 3c, Like No. 387. 2c, 50c, Madonna of the Basket, by Correggio.

| 1970, Dec. 5 | | | Perf. 14x13½ |
|---|---|---|---|
| 387 A58 | ½c yel grn & multi | .20 | .20 |
| 388 A58 | ½c pink & multi | .20 | .20 |
| 389 A58 | ½c yellow & multi | .20 | .20 |
| 390 A58 | 2c lt blue & multi | .20 | .20 |
| 391 A58 | 3c dp rose & multi | .20 | .20 |
| 392 A58 | 35c dk green & multi | .30 | .40 |
| 393 A58 | 50c brown & multi | .45 | .50 |
| 394 A58 | $1 purple & multi | .70 | 1.10 |
| a. | Souvenir sheet of 2, #393-394 | 2.75 | 3.00 |
| Nos. 387-394 (8) | | 2.45 | 3.00 |

Nursing in 19th Century A59

Designs: 15c, Horse-drawn ambulance, Northern France, 1918. 25c, First aid station, 1941. 60c, Red Cross truck loaded on plane, 1970 emergency aid.

| 1970, Dec. 12 | | Litho. | Perf. 14½x14 |
|---|---|---|---|
| 395 A59 | 5c red & multi | .20 | .20 |
| 396 A59 | 15c red & multi | .30 | .20 |
| 397 A59 | 25c red & multi | .50 | .35 |
| 398 A59 | 60c red & multi | 1.00 | 1.25 |
| a. | Souvenir sheet of 4, #395-398 | 2.25 | 2.00 |
| Nos. 395-398 (4) | | 2.00 | 2.00 |

Centenary of the British Red Cross Society.

John Dewey, Children Learning to Paint — A60

Designs: 10c, Jean-Jacques Rousseau and students. 50c, Moses Maimonides and biology student. $1, Bertrand Russell and boys.

| 1971, May 8 | | Litho. | Perf. 13½ |
|---|---|---|---|
| 399 A60 | 5c multicolored | .20 | .20 |
| 400 A60 | 10c multicolored | .20 | .20 |
| 401 A60 | 50c multicolored | .50 | .50 |
| 402 A60 | $1 multicolored | 1.10 | .75 |
| a. | Souvenir sheet of 2, #401-402 | 2.00 | 2.25 |
| Nos. 399-402 (4) | | 2.00 | 1.65 |

International Education Year.

Jennifer Hosten and Map of Grenada A61

| 1971, June 1 | | Litho. | Perf. 13½ |
|---|---|---|---|
| 403 A61 | 5c vio blue & multi | .20 | .20 |
| 404 A61 | 10c red lilac & multi | .20 | .20 |
| 405 A61 | 15c brt rose & multi | .30 | .20 |
| 406 A61 | 25c violet & multi | .40 | .30 |

| 407 A61 | 35c blue & multi | .50 | .60 |
|---|---|---|---|
| 408 A61 | 50c red & multi | 1.00 | 1.00 |
| a. | Souvenir sheet of 1 | 2.10 | 2.25 |
| Nos. 403-408 (6) | | 2.60 | 2.50 |

Honoring Miss Jennifer Hosten of Grenada, Miss World, 1971. No. 408a, printed on silk, contains imperf. stamp similar to No. 408.
Nos. 403-408 and 408a were overprinted "INTERPEX/1972" in Mar. 1972. Value $9.50.
For surcharge and overprints #465, C23-C26.

Canadian and French Boy Scouts — A62

Boy Scouts from: 35c, West Germany and US. 50c, Australia and Japan. 75c, Grenada and Great Britain.

| 1971, Aug. | | Litho. | Perf. 11 |
|---|---|---|---|
| 409 A62 | 5c multicolored | .20 | .20 |
| 410 A62 | 35c multicolored | .40 | .40 |
| 411 A62 | 50c multicolored | .50 | .60 |
| 412 A62 | 75c multicolored | .65 | .90 |
| a. | Souvenir sheet of 2, #411-412 | 2.75 | 3.25 |
| Nos. 409-412 (4) | | 1.75 | 2.10 |

13th Boy Scout World Jamboree, Asagiri Plain, Japan, Aug. 2-10.

Napoleon, by Edouard Détaille A63

Paintings of Napoleon: 15c, Outside Madrid, by Carle Vernet. 35c, Crossing the Alps, by Jacques Louis David. $2, Portrait, by David.

| 1971, Sept. | | | Perf. 13x13½ |
|---|---|---|---|
| 413 A63 | 5c multicolored | .20 | .20 |
| 414 A63 | 15c multicolored | .20 | .20 |
| 415 A63 | 35c multicolored | .40 | .40 |
| a. | Souvenir sheet of 1 | 3.25 | 3.50 |
| 416 A63 | $2 multicolored | 1.50 | 1.75 |
| Nos. 413-416 (4) | | 2.30 | 2.55 |

Sesquicentennial of the death of Napoleon Bonaparte (1769-1821).
No. 415a contains stamp similar to No. 415 with simulated perforations.

Grenada No. 1 — A64

15c, Grenada #2 & Queen Elizabeth II. 35c, Grenada #1, 2. 50c, Grenada #1 & scroll.

| 1971, Nov. 6 | | Litho. | Perf. 11 |
|---|---|---|---|
| 417 A64 | 5c dk red & multi | .25 | .20 |
| 418 A64 | 15c multicolored | .35 | .20 |
| 419 A64 | 35c dull org & multi | .55 | .25 |
| 420 A64 | 50c dk green & multi | .75 | 1.75 |
| a. | Souvenir sheet of 2, #419-420 | 1.75 | 1.75 |
| Nos. 417-420 (4) | | 1.90 | 2.40 |

110th anniversary of postal service.

Splashdown, Apollo 13 — A65

Designs: 2c, Capsule and rafts in ocean, Apollo 13. 3c, Separation of landing module from rocket, Apollo 14. 10c, Astronauts collecting moon rocks, Apollo 14. 25c, Astronauts in moon rover, Apollo 15. 50c, $1, Rocket blast-off, Apollo 15, vert.

| 1971, Nov. | | | |
|---|---|---|---|
| 421 A65 | 1c multicolored | .20 | .30 |
| 422 A65 | 2c multicolored | .20 | .30 |
| 423 A65 | 3c black & multi | .20 | .30 |
| 424 A65 | 10c black & multi | .40 | .20 |
| 425 A65 | 25c multicolored | 1.25 | .35 |
| 426 A65 | $1 multicolored | 2.75 | 3.50 |
| Nos. 421-426 (6) | | 5.00 | 4.95 |

**Souvenir Sheet**

| 427 A65 | 50c multicolored | 3.00 | 3.00 |
|---|---|---|---|

US moon missions of Apollo 13, 14 and 15.

67th Regiment of Foot, 1787 — A66

Designs: 1c, 45th Regiment of Foot, 1792. 2c, 29th Regiment of Foot, 1794. 10c, 9th Regiment of Foot, 1801. 25c, 2nd Regiment of Foot, 1815. $1, 70th Regiment of Foot, 1764.

| 1971, Dec. | | | Perf. 13½x14 |
|---|---|---|---|
| 428 A66 | ½c red & multi | .20 | .20 |
| 429 A66 | 1c red & multi | .20 | .20 |
| 430 A66 | 2c red & multi | .20 | .20 |
| 431 A66 | 10c red & multi | .55 | .20 |
| 432 A66 | 25c red & multi | 1.00 | .30 |
| 433 A66 | $1 red & multi | 3.00 | 2.75 |
| a. | Souv. sheet of 2, #432-433, perf. 15 | 4.75 | 4.75 |
| Nos. 428-433 (6) | | 5.15 | 3.85 |

Uniforms of British units stationed in Grenada.
For surcharges see Nos. 439, C1-C2.

Adoration of the Kings, by Memling — A67

Christmas: 25c, Madonna and Child, sculpture by Michelangelo. 35c, Madonna and Child, by Murillo. 50c, Madonna with the Apple, by Memling. $1, Adoration of the Kings, by Jan Mostaert.

| 1971, Dec. | | | Perf. 14x13½ |
|---|---|---|---|
| 434 A67 | 15c gold & multi | .20 | .20 |
| 435 A67 | 25c gold & multi | .30 | .20 |
| 436 A67 | 35c gold & multi | .35 | .20 |
| 437 A67 | 50c gold & multi | .50 | .75 |
| Nos. 434-437 (4) | | 1.35 | 1.35 |

**Souvenir Sheet**

| 438 A67 | $1 gold & multi | 1.10 | 1.10 |
|---|---|---|---|

No. 430 Surcharged with New Value,
Olympic Rings and: "WINTER
OLYMPICS / FEB. 3-13, 1972 /
SAPPORO, JAPAN"

**1972, Feb. 3**      **Perf. 13½x14**
439 A66 $2 on 2c red & multi   2.00 2.00
  *a.* Souvenir sheet of 2      2.50 2.50

11th Winter Olympic Games, Sapporo,
Japan, Feb. 3-13. See Nos. C1-C2.
No. 439a is overprinted in red on No. 433a
(no surcharge); margin inscribed in red: "SAP-
PORO 1972."

King
Arthur,
UNICEF
Emblem
A68

UNICEF Emblem and: 1c, 50c, Robin Hood.
2c, 75c, Robinson Crusoe, vert. 25c, like ½c.
$1, Mary and her Little Lamb, vert.

**1972, Mar. 4**    **Perf. 14½x14, 14x14½**
450 A68 ½c dp blue & multi   .20 .20
451 A68 1c yellow & multi   .20 .20
452 A68 2c dp yel & multi   .20 .20
453 A68 25c salmon & multi   .20 .20
454 A68 50c multicolored   .25 .35
455 A68 75c blue & multi   .35 .60
456 A68 $1 multicolored   .45 .85
  *a.* Souvenir sheet of 1   1.10 1.10
    Nos. 450-456 (7)   1.85 2.60

25th anniv. (in 1971) of UNICEF.

Yachting
A69

1c, 50c, Equestrian. 2c, 35c, Running, vert.

**1972, Sept. 8**    **Litho.**    **Perf. 14**
457 A69 ½c multicolored   .20 .20
458 A69 1c lt blue & multi   .20 .20
459 A69 2c orange & multi   .20 .20
460 A69 35c yellow & multi   .60 .90
461 A69 50c yel grn & multi   .80 1.25
   Nos. 457-461,C20-C21 (7)   3.60 4.00

20th Olympic Games, Munich, Aug. 26-
Sept. 11. See No. C22.

Nos. 294-296, 403 Surcharged with
New Value and Two Bars
**Perf. 14x14½, 13½**
**1972, Oct.**      **Photo.**
462 A45 12c on 1c multi   .50 .55
463 A45 12c on 2c multi   .50 .55
464 A45 12c on 3c multi   .50 .55
465 A61 12c on 5c multi   .50 .55
    Nos. 462-465 (4)   2.00 2.20

**Silver Wedding Issue, 1972**
Common Design Type

Design: Queen Elizabeth II, Prince Philip,
seal of Grenada and myristica fragrans.

**Perf. 14x14½**
**1972, Nov. 20**      **Wmk. 314**
466 CD324 8c olive & multi   .20 .20
467 CD324 $1 multicolored   .45 .45

Boy Scout
Saluting
A70

Designs: 1c, Two Scouts knotting ropes. 2c,
70c, 75c, Scouts from different nations. 3c,
60c, $1, Lord Baden-Powell.

**Unwmk.**
**1972, Dec. 2**    **Litho.**    **Perf. 14**
468 A70 ½c yellow & multi   .20 .20
469 A70 1c red & multi   .20 .20
470 A70 2c yellow & multi   .20 .20
471 A70 3c brt lilac & multi   .20 .20
472 A70 75c lt blue & multi   1.25 1.25
473 A70 $1 multicolored   1.75 1.75
   Nos. 468-473,C27-C28 (8)   5.00 4.90

---

**Souvenir Sheet**
474     Sheet of 2   3.00 3.00
  *a.* A70 60c ocher & multi   1.40 1.40
  *b.* A70 70c pale lilac & multi   1.60 1.60

Boy Scouts, 65th anniversary.

Virgin and Child,
Crosier — A71

Christmas: 3c, 35c, 70c, The Three Kings.
5c, $1, Holy Family. 25c, 60c, Like 1c.

**1972, Dec. 9**    **Litho.**    **Perf. 14x13½**
475 A71 1c blue & multi   .20 .20
476 A71 3c gray & multi   .20 .20
477 A71 5c multicolored   .20 .20
478 A71 25c multicolored   .20 .20
479 A71 35c lt blue & multi   .30 .30
480 A71 $1 ocher & multi   .90 .90
    Nos. 475-480 (6)   2.00 2.00

**Souvenir Sheet**
**Perf. 15**
481     Sheet of 2   1.25 1.25
  *a.* A71 60c blue & multi   .50 .50
  *b.* A71 70c bright pink & multi   .70 .70

Flamingos — A72

**1973, Jan. 5**    **Litho.**    **Perf. 14**
482 A72 25c shown   1.00 .30
483 A72 35c Tapir   .80 .30
484 A72 60c Macaws   1.75 2.00
485 A72 70c Ocelot   1.60 2.50
    Nos. 482-485 (4)   5.15 5.10

National Zoo of Grenada.

Class II Ocean Racing Yacht — A73

**1973, Jan. 26**    **Litho.**    **Perf. 13½x14**
486 A73 25c shown   .40 .35
487 A73 35c Boats in St.
      George's Harbour   .55 .50
488 A73 60c Yacht "Bloodhound"   .90 .85
489 A73 70c St. George's Har-
      bour   .95 1.10
    Nos. 486-489 (4)   2.80 2.80

Yachting off Grenada.

Sun God Helios, Equinoxes and
Solstices — A74

WMO Emblem and: 1c, Poseidon and
Nomad automatic storm detector. 2c, Zeus
and radarscope. 3c, Goddess Iris, rainbow,
weather balloon. 35c, Hermes, ATS 3 satellite.
50c, Zephyr and circulation of atmosphere.
75c, Demeter, space photograph of storm. $1,
Selene, globe showing world rainfall. $2, Com-
puter weather map (42x31mm).

---

**1973, July 6**    **Litho.**    **Perf. 13½**
490 A74 ½c multicolored   .20 .20
491 A74 1c multicolored   .20 .20
492 A74 2c multicolored   .20 .20
493 A74 3c multicolored   .20 .20
494 A74 35c multicolored   .40 .20
495 A74 50c multicolored   .60 .30
496 A74 75c multicolored   .75 .60
497 A74 $1 multicolored   .75 .75
    Nos. 490-497 (8)   3.30 2.65

**Souvenir Sheet**
498 A74 $2 multicolored   2.00 2.00

Intl. meteorological cooperation, cent.

Racing Class Yachts — A75

**1973, Aug. 3**    **Litho.**    **Perf. 13½**
499 A75 ½c shown   .20 .20
500 A75 1c Cruising class   .20 .20
501 A75 2c Open-decked
      sloops   .20 .20
502 A75 35c Sloop Mermaid   .40 .20
503 A75 50c St. George's Har-
      bour   .50 .30
504 A75 75c Map of Carriacou   .75 .75
505 A75 $1 Boat building   .90 .90
    Nos. 499-505 (7)   3.15 2.75

**Souvenir Sheet**
506 A75 $2 End of race   1.75 2.00

Carriacou Regatta, August 1973.

Ignaz Philipp
Semmelweiss
A76

Designs: Physicians and scientists.

**1973, Sept. 17**    **Litho.**    **Perf. 14½**
507 A76 ½c shown   .25 .20
508 A76 1c Louis Pasteur   .25 .20
509 A76 2c Edward Jenner   .25 .20
510 A76 3c Sigmund Freud   .25 .20
511 A76 25c Emil von Behring   .45 .45
512 A76 35c Carl Jung   .60 .60
513 A76 50c Charles Calmette   .90 .90
514 A76 $1 William Harvey   1.75 1.75
    Nos. 507-514 (8)   4.70 4.50

**Souvenir Sheet**
515 A76 $2 Marie Curie   2.50 2.50

WHO, 25th anniv.

Princess Anne and Mark
Phillips — A77

**1973, Nov. 14**    **Wmk. 314**    **Perf. 13½**
516 A77 25c dp orange & multi   .30 .80
517 A77 $2 green & multi   .30 .80
  *a.* Souv. sheet of 2 (75c, $1)   .75 .75

Wedding of Princess Anne and Capt. Mark
Phillips.
Nos. 516-517 were issued only in sheets of
5 plus label. Colors of 75c and $1 are as those
of 25c and $2.

---

Virgin and Child,
by Carlo
Maratti — A78

Christmas (Paintings): 1c, Virgin and Child,
by Carlo Crivelli. 2c, Virgin and Child, by Verrocchio. 3c, Adoration of the Shepherds, by
Roberti. 25c, Holy Family, by Federigo Baroc-
cio. 35c, Holy Family, by Bronzino. 75c, Mystic
Nativity, by Botticelli. $1, Adoration of the
Kings, by Geertgen tot Sint Jans. $2, Adora-
tion of the Kings, by Jan Mostaert (30x45mm).

**1973, Nov.**    **Unwmk.**    **Perf. 14½**
519 A78 ½c lt brown & multi   .20 .20
520 A78 1c citron & multi   .20 .20
521 A78 2c blue & multi   .20 .20
522 A78 3c green & multi   .20 .20
523 A78 25c multicolored   .30 .30
524 A78 35c multicolored   .30 .30
525 A78 75c vio blue & multi   .40 1.10
526 A78 $1 multicolored   .50 1.40
    Nos. 519-526 (8)   2.30 3.90

**Souvenir Sheet**
**Perf. 13½x14**
527 A78 $2 red & multi   2.40 2.40

Nos. 294-297, 299-301, 303-304,
305A-309 Overprinted

**Perf. 14x14½, 14½x14**
**1974, Feb. 7**      **Photo.**
528 A45 1c multicolored   .20 .20
529 A45 2c multicolored   .20 .20
530 A45 3c multicolored   .20 .20
531 A45 5c multicolored   .20 .20
532 A45 8c multicolored   .20 .20
533 A45 10c multicolored   .20 .20
534 A45 12c multicolored   .20 .20
535 A45 25c multicolored   .50 .35
536 A45 35c multicolored   .75 .50

**Litho.**
**Perf. 13½x14**
537 A45a 75c multicolored   2.75 1.25

**Photo.**
**Perf. 14x14½**
538 A45 $1 multicolored   4.75 1.50
539 A45 $2 multicolored   7.25 6.00
540 A45 $3 multicolored   9.25 7.50
541 A45 $5 multicolored   14.50 17.00
    Nos. 528-541 (14)   41.15 35.50

Grenada's independence, Feb. 7, 1974.
Size of overprint on vertical stamps 16x5mm;
on horizontal stamps 20x6mm.

Creative Arts Theater, Jamaica
Campus — A79

Designs: 25c, Marryshow House, University
Center. 50c, Chapel, vert. $1, $2, University
coat of arms, vert.

**1974, Apr. 10**    **Litho.**    **Perf. 13½**
542 A79 10c multicolored   .20 .20
543 A79 25c multicolored   .20 .20
544 A79 50c multicolored   .30 .30
545 A79 $1 multicolored   .45 .45
    Nos. 542-545 (4)   1.15 1.15

**Souvenir Sheet**
546 A79 $2 multicolored   .90 .90

25th anniv. of the University of the West
Indies.

Prime Minister
Eric M.
Gairy — A80

**1974, Aug. 19　Litho.　Perf. 13½**

| | | | | |
|---|---|---|---|---|
| 547 | A80 | 3c Nutmeg and mace | .20 | .20 |
| 548 | A80 | 8c Map of Grenada | .20 | .20 |
| 549 | A80 | 25c shown | .25 | .25 |
| 550 | A80 | 35c Anse Beach and Flag | .35 | .25 |
| 551 | A80 | $1 Coat of arms | .85 | .85 |
| | | Nos. 547-551 (5) | 1.85 | 1.75 |

**Souvenir Sheet**

| | | | | |
|---|---|---|---|---|
| 552 | A80 | $2 Coat of arms | 1.25 | 1.25 |

Grenada's independence.

Soccer, Flags of
West Germany
and Chile — A81

**1974, Sept. 3　Litho.　Perf. 14½**

Soccer Games and Flags: 1c, East Germany and Australia. 2c, Yugoslavia and Brazil. 10c, Scotland and Zaire. 25c, Netherlands and Uruguay. 50c, Sweden and Bulgaria. 75c, Italy and Haiti. $1, Poland and Argentina. $2, Flags of participating nations, horiz.

| | | | | |
|---|---|---|---|---|
| 553 | A81 | ½c multicolored | .20 | .20 |
| 554 | A81 | 1c multicolored | .20 | .20 |
| 555 | A81 | 2c multicolored | .20 | .20 |
| 556 | A81 | 10c multicolored | .20 | .20 |
| 557 | A81 | 25c multicolored | .20 | .20 |
| 558 | A81 | 50c multicolored | .20 | .20 |
| 559 | A81 | 75c multicolored | .40 | .40 |
| 560 | A81 | $1 multicolored | .60 | .60 |
| | | Nos. 553-560 (8) | 2.20 | 2.20 |

**Souvenir Sheet**
**Perf. 13**

| | | | | |
|---|---|---|---|---|
| 561 | A81 | $2 multicolored | 1.75 | 1.75 |

World Cup Soccer Championship, Munich, June 13-July 7.

19th Century US Mail Train, Concorde
and UPU Emblem — A82

UPU Emblem and: 1c, Sailing ship "Caesar," 1839, and helicopter. 2c, Zeppelin, jet and early planes. 8c, Pigeon post, 1480, telephone dial. 15c, Bellman, 18th cent. and radar. 25c, German Imperial messenger, 1450, satellite. 35c, French pillar box and ocean liner. $1, German mailman, 18th cent., and futuristic mail train. $2, St. Gotthard mail coach, 1735, vert.

**1974, Oct. 8　Litho.　Perf. 14½**

| | | | | |
|---|---|---|---|---|
| 562 | A82 | ½c rose & multi | .20 | .20 |
| 563 | A82 | 1c gray & multi | .20 | .20 |
| 564 | A82 | 2c dull pink & multi | .20 | .20 |
| 565 | A82 | 8c yellow & multi | .20 | .20 |
| 566 | A82 | 15c yel grn & multi | .45 | .20 |
| 567 | A82 | 25c dull yel & multi | .50 | .20 |
| 568 | A82 | 35c lilac & multi | .75 | .20 |
| 569 | A82 | $1 lt blue & multi | 2.00 | 1.60 |
| | | Nos. 562-569 (8) | 4.50 | 3.00 |

**Souvenir Sheet**
**Perf. 13**

| | | | | |
|---|---|---|---|---|
| 570 | A82 | $2 multicolored | 1.75 | 2.25 |

UPU, cent.

Sir Winston Churchill — A83

Design: $2, Churchill, different portrait.

**1974, Oct. 28　Litho.　Perf. 13½**

| | | | | |
|---|---|---|---|---|
| 571 | A83 | 35c multicolored | .30 | .30 |
| 572 | A83 | $2 multicolored | 1.00 | 1.00 |

**Souvenir Sheet**

| | | | | |
|---|---|---|---|---|
| 573 | | Sheet of 2 | 1.10 | 1.10 |
| a. | | A83 75c like 35c | .45 | .45 |
| b. | | A83 $1 like $2 | .65 | .65 |

Winston Churchill (1874-1965).

Virgin and Child,
by Botticelli — A84

Christmas: Paintings of the Virgin and Child.

**1974, Nov. 18　　Perf. 14½**

| | | | | |
|---|---|---|---|---|
| 574 | A84 | ½ shown | .20 | .20 |
| 575 | A84 | 1c Niccolo di Pietro | .20 | .20 |
| 576 | A84 | 2c Van der Weyden | .20 | .20 |
| 577 | A84 | 3c Bastiani | .20 | .20 |
| 578 | A84 | 10c Giovanni | .20 | .20 |
| 579 | A84 | 25c Van der Weyden | .20 | .20 |
| 580 | A84 | 50c Botticelli | .25 | .25 |
| 581 | A84 | $1 Mantegna | .40 | .40 |
| | | Nos. 574-581 (8) | 1.85 | 1.85 |

**Souvenir Sheet**
**Perf. 13½**

| | | | | |
|---|---|---|---|---|
| 582 | A84 | $2 Niccolo di Pietro | 1.40 | 1.40 |

Yachts
and Point
Saline
A85

1c, Grenada Yacht Club race, St. George's. 2c, Careenage taxi (boat). 3c, Large working boats. 5c, Deep Water Dock, St. George's. 6c, Cacao beans in drying trays. 8c, Nutmeg branch. 10c, River Antoine Estate rum distillery, c. 1785. 12c, Cacao branch. 15c, Fishermen landing catch at Fontenoy. 20c, Parliament Building, St. George's. 25c, Fort George cannons. 35c, Pearls Airport. 50c, General Post Office. 75c, Carib Leap, Sauteurs Bay. $1, Careenage, St. George's. $2, St. George's harbor at night. $3, Grand Anse Beach. $5, Canoe Bay and Black Bay from Point Saline Lighthouse. $10, Sugar-loaf Island from Levera Beach.

**1975　　Litho.　Perf. 14½**
**Size: 38x25mm**

| | | | | |
|---|---|---|---|---|
| 583 | A85 | ½c multicolored | .20 | .55 |
| 584 | A85 | 1c multicolored | .20 | .20 |
| 585 | A85 | 2c multicolored | .20 | .20 |
| 586 | A85 | 3c multicolored | .20 | .20 |
| 587 | A85 | 5c multicolored | .25 | .20 |
| 588 | A85 | 6c multicolored | .20 | .20 |
| 589 | A85 | 8c multicolored | 1.25 | .20 |
| 590 | A85 | 10c multicolored | .20 | .20 |
| 591 | A85 | 12c multicolored | .35 | .20 |
| 592 | A85 | 15c multicolored | .20 | .20 |
| 593 | A85 | 20c multicolored | .20 | .20 |
| 594 | A85 | 25c multicolored | .25 | .20 |
| 595 | A85 | 35c multicolored | .25 | .20 |
| 596 | A85 | 50c multicolored | .20 | .25 |

**Perf. 13½x14**
**Size: 45x28mm**

| | | | | |
|---|---|---|---|---|
| 597 | A85 | 75c multicolored | .55 | .40 |
| 598 | A85 | $1 multicolored | .60 | .20 |
| 599 | A85 | $2 multicolored | .60 | 1.25 |
| 600 | A85 | $3 multicolored | .65 | 1.75 |
| 601 | A85 | $5 multicolored | .80 | 2.50 |
| 602 | A85 | $10 multicolored | 2.40 | 5.50 |
| | | Nos. 583-602 (20) | 9.75 | 15.20 |

Issue dates: Nos. 583-596, Jan. 13; Nos. 597-601, Jan. 22; No. 602, Mar. 26.
For overprints, see Nos. 965-979.

**1978　　　　　　　　　Perf. 13**

| | | | | |
|---|---|---|---|---|
| 584a | A85 | 1c | .20 | .20 |
| 585a | A85 | 2c | .20 | .20 |
| 586a | A85 | 3c | .20 | .20 |
| 587a | A85 | 5c | .20 | .20 |
| 588a | A85 | 6c | .20 | .25 |
| 590a | A85 | 10c | .20 | .25 |
| 592a | A85 | 15c | .20 | .30 |
| 593a | A85 | 20c | .20 | .40 |
| 594a | A85 | 25c | .20 | .50 |
| 596a | A85 | 50c | .40 | .55 |
| | | Nos. 584a-596a (10) | 2.20 | 3.00 |

Sailfish
A86

Designs: Big game fish.

**1975, Feb. 3　　Perf. 14½**

| | | | | |
|---|---|---|---|---|
| 603 | A86 | ½c shown | .20 | .20 |
| 604 | A86 | 1c Blue marlin | .20 | .20 |
| 605 | A86 | 2c White marlin | .20 | .20 |
| 606 | A86 | 10c Yellowfin tuna | .20 | .20 |
| 607 | A86 | 25c Wahoo | .35 | .30 |
| 608 | A86 | 50c Dolphin | .60 | .40 |
| 609 | A86 | 70c Grouper | .85 | .40 |
| 610 | A86 | $1 Great barracuda | 1.10 | .50 |
| | | Nos. 603-610 (8) | 3.70 | 2.40 |

**Souvenir Sheet**
**Perf. 13**

| | | | | |
|---|---|---|---|---|
| 611 | A86 | $2 Mako shark | 2.40 | 2.40 |

Passiflora Quadrangularis — A87

Designs: Flowers of Grenada.

**1975, Feb. 26　Litho.　Perf. 14½**

| | | | | |
|---|---|---|---|---|
| 612 | A87 | ½c shown | .20 | .20 |
| 613 | A87 | 1c Bleeding heart | .20 | .20 |
| 614 | A87 | 2c Poinsettia | .20 | .20 |
| 615 | A87 | 3c Obroma cacao | .20 | .20 |
| 616 | A87 | 10c Gladioli | .25 | .20 |
| 617 | A87 | 25c Red head-yellow head | .50 | .20 |
| 618 | A87 | 50c Plumbago | .70 | .25 |
| 619 | A87 | $1 Orange blossoms | 1.10 | .50 |
| | | Nos. 612-619 (8) | 3.35 | 1.95 |

**Souvenir Sheet**
**Perf. 13½**

| | | | | |
|---|---|---|---|---|
| 620 | A87 | $2 Barbados gooseberry | 2.10 | 2.10 |

Grenada Flag and
UN
Emblem — A88

Designs: 1c, UN and Grenada flags. 2c, $1, UN emblem and Grenada coat of arms. 35c, UN emblem over map of Grenada. 50c, Grenada flag in front of UN Headquarters. 75c, like ½c. $2, UN emblem and scroll.

**1975, Mar. 19　　　Perf. 14½**

| | | | | |
|---|---|---|---|---|
| 621 | A88 | ½c multicolored | .20 | .20 |
| 622 | A88 | 1c multicolored | .20 | .20 |
| 623 | A88 | 2c multicolored | .20 | .20 |
| 624 | A88 | 35c multicolored | .25 | .25 |
| 625 | A88 | 50c multicolored | .30 | .30 |
| 626 | A88 | $2 multicolored | .70 | .70 |
| | | Nos. 621-626 (6) | 1.85 | 1.85 |

**Souvenir Sheet**
**Perf. 13½**

| | | | | |
|---|---|---|---|---|
| 627 | | Sheet of 2 | 1.60 | 1.60 |
| a. | | A88 75c multicolored | .60 | .60 |
| b. | | A88 $1 multicolored | 1.00 | 1.00 |

Grenada's admission to the United Nations, Sept. 17, 1974.

Remainders of Grenada stamps between Scott Nos. 630 and 872, except Nos. 747-748 and 802-804, were later canceled to order and sold at a fraction of their face value. Our used values for these stamps are for c-t-o examples. Postally used stamps are worth the same as unused, never hinged examples.

Midnight Ride of Paul Revere — A89

1c, Crispus Attucks at Boston Massacre. 2c, Patrick Henry. 3c, Franklin visiting Washington at the front. 5c, Lexington-Concord. 10c, John Paul Jones. #634, Arms of Grenada & US. #635, Flags of Grenada & US.

**1975, May 6　Litho.　Perf. 14½, 13**

| | | | | |
|---|---|---|---|---|
| 628 | A89 | ½c Prus blue & multi | .20 | .20 |
| 629 | A89 | 1c buff & multi | .20 | .20 |
| 630 | A89 | 2c dp org & multi | .20 | .20 |
| 631 | A89 | 3c orange & multi | .20 | .20 |
| 632 | A89 | 5c Prus blue & multi | .20 | .20 |
| 633 | A89 | 10c ultra & multi | .20 | .20 |
| | | Nos. 628-633,C29-C32 (10) | 3.40 | 2.20 |

**Souvenir Sheets**
**Perf. 13½**

| | | | | |
|---|---|---|---|---|
| 634 | A89 | $2 tan & multi | 1.40 | .60 |
| 635 | A89 | $2 gray & multi | 1.40 | .60 |

American Revolution Bicentennial. Size of stamps on Nos. 634-635: 47x34mm.
Nos. 628-633 issued in sheets of 40. Each denomination was also printed in sheets of 5 plus label, perf. 13.

Angel Collecting
Jesus' Blood in
Grail, by
Bellini — A90

Easter (Paintings): 1c, Pieta, by Bellini. 2c, The Deposition, by Rogier van der Weyden. 3c, Pieta, by Bellini. 35c, Descent from the Cross, by Bellini. 75c, Jesus Rising from the Tomb, by Bellini. $1, Descent from the Cross, by Procaccini. $2, Pieta, by Botticelli.

**1975, May 21**

| | | | | |
|---|---|---|---|---|
| 636 | A90 | ½c multicolored | .20 | .20 |
| 637 | A90 | 1c multicolored | .20 | .20 |
| 638 | A90 | 2c multicolored | .20 | .20 |
| 639 | A90 | 3c multicolored | .20 | .20 |
| 640 | A90 | 35c multicolored | .40 | .20 |
| 641 | A90 | 75c multicolored | .50 | .20 |
| 642 | A90 | $1 multicolored | .60 | .20 |
| | | Nos. 636-642 (7) | 2.30 | 1.40 |

**Souvenir Sheet**
**Perf. 13½**

| | | | | |
|---|---|---|---|---|
| 643 | A90 | $2 multicolored | 1.75 | .70 |

Scouts
Studying
Wildlife,
Nordjamb
75
Emblem
A91

Nordjamb 75 Emblem and: 1c, Seamanship; Scouts in sailboat. 2c, Survival; Scouts reading map. 35c, First aid. 40c, Physical fitness; gymnastics. 75c, Mountaineering. $1, Emergency boat building. $2, Scouts singing.

**1975, July 2    Litho.    Perf. 14**

| 644 | A91 | ½c blue & multi | .20 | .20 |
|-----|-----|-----------------|-----|-----|
| 645 | A91 | 1c blue & multi | .20 | .20 |
| 646 | A91 | 2c blue & multi | .20 | .20 |
| 647 | A91 | 35c blue & multi | .60 | .20 |
| 648 | A91 | 40c blue & multi | .70 | .20 |
| 649 | A91 | 75c blue & multi | .80 | .20 |
| 650 | A91 | $2 blue & multi | 1.75 | .40 |
| | | Nos. 644-650 (7) | 4.45 | 1.60 |

**Souvenir Sheet**

| 651 | A91 | $1 blue & multi | 1.60 | .35 |
|-----|-----|-----------------|------|-----|

Nordjamb 75, 14th Boy Scout World Jamboree, Lillehammer, Norway, July 29-Aug. 7.

Leafy Jewel Box — A92

Designs: Sea shells.

**1975, Aug. 1    Litho.    Perf. 14**

| 652 | A92 | ½c shown | .20 | .20 |
|-----|-----|----------|-----|-----|
| 653 | A92 | 1c Emerald nerite | .20 | .20 |
| 654 | A92 | 2c Yellow cockle | .20 | .20 |
| 655 | A92 | 25c Purple sea snail | 1.00 | .20 |
| 656 | A92 | 50c Turkey wing | 2.00 | .40 |
| 657 | A92 | 75c West Indian fighting conch | 2.75 | .50 |
| 658 | A92 | $1 Noble wentletrap | 2.75 | .50 |
| | | Nos. 652-658 (7) | 9.10 | 2.20 |

**Souvenir Sheet**

| 659 | A92 | $2 Music volute | 4.50 | .90 |
|-----|-----|-----------------|------|-----|

Butterflies — A93

**1975, Sept. 22    Litho.    Perf. 14**

| 660 | A93 | ½c Large tiger | .20 | .20 |
|-----|-----|----------------|-----|-----|
| 661 | A93 | 1c Five continents | .20 | .20 |
| 662 | A93 | 2c Large striped blue | .20 | .20 |
| 663 | A93 | 35c Gonatryx | .85 | .25 |
| 664 | A93 | 45c Spear-winged cattle heart | 1.00 | .30 |
| 665 | A93 | 75c Risty nymula | 1.50 | .40 |
| 666 | A93 | $2 Blue night | 3.75 | .75 |
| | | Nos. 660-666 (7) | 7.70 | 2.30 |

**Souvenir Sheet**

| 667 | A93 | $1 Lycrophon | 2.40 | 1.00 |
|-----|-----|--------------|------|------|

Crew Race A94

Young Man, by Michelangelo A95

**1975, Oct. 13    Litho.    Perf. 14**

| 668 | A94 | ½c shown | .20 | .20 |
|-----|-----|----------|-----|-----|
| 669 | A94 | 1c Women's swimming | .20 | .20 |
| 670 | A94 | 2c Steeplechase | .20 | .20 |
| 671 | A94 | 35c Gymnastics | .25 | .20 |
| 672 | A94 | 45c Soccer | .25 | .20 |
| 673 | A94 | 75c Boxing | .35 | .25 |
| 674 | A94 | $2 Bicycling | 2.00 | .45 |
| | | Nos. 668-674 (7) | 3.45 | 1.70 |

**Souvenir Sheet**

| 675 | A94 | $1 Sailing | 2.00 | .45 |
|-----|-----|------------|------|-----|

7th Pan-American Games, Mexico City, Oct. 13-26.

---

**1975, Nov. 3**

Works by Michelangelo (except 50c): ½c, David. 2c, Moses. 40c, Zachariah. 50c, St. John the Baptist (sculpture). 75c, Judith and Holofernes (detail). $1, Madonna (head from Pietà). $2, Doni Madonna (detail from Holy Family).

| 676 | A95 | ½c black & multi | .20 | .20 |
|-----|-----|------------------|-----|-----|
| 677 | A95 | 1c black & multi | .20 | .20 |
| 678 | A95 | 2c black & multi | .20 | .20 |
| 679 | A95 | 40c black & multi | .45 | .20 |
| 680 | A95 | 50c black & multi | .55 | .20 |
| 681 | A95 | 75c black & multi | .85 | .25 |
| 682 | A95 | $2 black & multi | 2.25 | .50 |
| | | Nos. 676-682 (7) | 4.70 | 1.75 |

**Souvenir Sheet**

| 683 | A95 | $1 black & multi | 2.40 | .40 |
|-----|-----|------------------|------|-----|

Michelangelo Buonarroti (1475-1564), Italian painter, sculptor and architect.

Virgin and Child Paintings — A96

Bananaquit — A97

**1975, Dec. 8**

| 684 | A96 | ½c Filippino Lippi | .20 | .20 |
|-----|-----|--------------------|-----|-----|
| 685 | A96 | 1c Mantegna | .20 | .20 |
| 686 | A96 | 2c Luis de Morales | .20 | .20 |
| 687 | A96 | 35c G. M. Morandi | .30 | .20 |
| 688 | A96 | 50c Antonello da Messina | .30 | .20 |
| 689 | A96 | 75c Durer | .35 | .20 |
| 690 | A96 | $1 Velazquez | 1.00 | .40 |
| | | Nos. 684-690 (7) | 1.95 | 1.40 |

**Souvenir Sheet**

| 691 | A96 | $2 Bellini | 2.00 | .50 |
|-----|-----|------------|------|-----|

Christmas.

**1976, Jan. 20    Litho.    Perf. 14**

Designs: 1c, Orange-rumped agouti. 2c, Hawksbill turtle, horiz. 5c, Dwarf poinciana. 35c, Albacores, horiz. 40c, Cardinal's guard flower. $1, Belted kingfisher. $2, Antillean armadillo, horiz.

| 692 | A97 | ½c multicolored | .20 | .20 |
|-----|-----|-----------------|-----|-----|
| 693 | A97 | 1c multicolored | .20 | .20 |
| 694 | A97 | 2c multicolored | .20 | .20 |
| 695 | A97 | 5c multicolored | .20 | .20 |
| 696 | A97 | 35c multicolored | 1.10 | .20 |
| 697 | A97 | 40c multicolored | 1.25 | .20 |
| 698 | A97 | $2 multicolored | 3.00 | .75 |
| | | Nos. 692-698 (7) | 6.15 | 1.95 |

**Souvenir Sheet**

| 699 | A97 | $1 multicolored | 8.00 | 1.00 |
|-----|-----|-----------------|------|------|

Carnival Dancers A98

Designs: 1c, Scuba diving. 2c, Cruise ship in St. George's Harbor. 35c, Game fishing. 50c, St. George's Golf Course. 75c, Tennis. $1, Mount Rich rock carvings. $2, Sailboats.

**1976, Feb. 25    Litho.    Perf. 14**

| 700 | A98 | ½c multicolored | .20 | .20 |
|-----|-----|-----------------|-----|-----|
| 701 | A98 | 1c multicolored | .20 | .20 |
| 702 | A98 | 2c multicolored | .20 | .20 |
| 703 | A98 | 35c multicolored | .90 | .20 |
| 704 | A98 | 50c multicolored | 3.00 | .25 |
| 705 | A98 | 75c multicolored | 3.25 | .35 |
| 706 | A98 | $1 multicolored | 3.50 | .35 |
| | | Nos. 700-706 (7) | 11.25 | 1.75 |

**Souvenir Sheet**

| 707 | A98 | $2 multicolored | 3.00 | .75 |
|-----|-----|-----------------|------|-----|

Tourist publicity.

---

Descent from the Cross, by Master of Okolicsno — A99

Easter (Paintings): 1c, Pieta, by Correggio. 2c, Crucifixion, by van der Weyden. 3c, Burial of Christ, by Dürer. 35c, God the Father Holding Crucified Christ, by unknown master (Florence). 75c, Ascension, by Raphael. $1, Burial of Christ, by Raphael. $2, Pieta, by Crespi.

**1976, Mar. 29**

| 708 | A99 | ½c multicolored | .20 | .20 |
|-----|-----|-----------------|-----|-----|
| 709 | A99 | 1c multicolored | .20 | .20 |
| 710 | A99 | 2c multicolored | .20 | .20 |
| 711 | A99 | 3c multicolored | .20 | .20 |
| 712 | A99 | 35c multicolored | .20 | .20 |
| 713 | A99 | 75c multicolored | .40 | .20 |
| 714 | A99 | $1 multicolored | .55 | .25 |
| | | Nos. 708-714 (7) | 1.95 | 1.45 |

**Souvenir Sheet**

| 715 | A99 | $2 multicolored | 1.25 | 1.25 |
|-----|-----|-----------------|------|------|

Sharpshooters, 1780 — A100

First Stars and Stripes and: 1c, Defense of Liberty Pole. 2c, Men loading muskets. 35c, 75c, Fight for Liberty. 50c, $2, Peace Treaty, 1783. $1, Drumming march on Breed's Hill. $3, Gunboat, c. 1776.

**1976, Apr. 15    Litho.    Perf. 14**

| 716 | A100 | ½c multicolored | .20 | .20 |
|-----|------|-----------------|-----|-----|
| 717 | A100 | 1c multicolored | .20 | .20 |
| 718 | A100 | 2c multicolored | .20 | .20 |
| 719 | A100 | 35c multicolored | .50 | .20 |
| 720 | A100 | 50c multicolored | .65 | .20 |
| 721 | A100 | $1 multicolored | 1.10 | .20 |
| 722 | A100 | $3 multicolored | 2.75 | .30 |
| | | Nos. 716-722 (7) | 5.60 | 1.50 |

**Souvenir Sheet**

| 723 | | Sheet of 2 | 2.25 | 1.50 |
|-----|---|------------|------|------|
| a. | | A100 75c multicolored | .75 | .65 |
| b. | | A100 $2 multicolored | 1.50 | .85 |

American Bicentennial.

Girl Guide Emblems, Nature Study — A101

Volleyball — A102

Various Girl Guide Emblems and: 1c, Cooking. 2c, $2, First aid, diff. 50c, Tenting. 75c, Home economics. $1, Drawing.

**1976, June 1    Litho.    Perf. 14**

| 724 | A101 | ½c multicolored | .20 | .20 |
|-----|------|-----------------|-----|-----|
| 725 | A101 | 1c multicolored | .20 | .20 |
| 726 | A101 | 2c multicolored | .20 | .20 |
| 727 | A101 | 50c multicolored | .65 | .20 |
| 728 | A101 | 75c multicolored | .95 | .30 |
| 729 | A101 | $2 multicolored | 2.40 | .50 |
| | | Nos. 724-729 (6) | 4.60 | 1.60 |

**Souvenir Sheet**

| 730 | A101 | $1 multicolored | 1.75 | .80 |
|-----|------|-----------------|------|-----|

Girl Guides of Grenada, 50th anniv.

---

**1976, June 21    Litho.    Perf. 14**

Olympic Rings and: 1c, Bicycling. 2c, Rowing. 35c, Judo. 45c, Hockey. 75c, Women's gymnastics. $1, High jump. $3, Equestrian.

| 731 | A102 | ½c multicolored | .20 | .20 |
|-----|------|-----------------|-----|-----|
| 732 | A102 | 1c multicolored | .20 | .20 |
| 733 | A102 | 2c multicolored | .20 | .20 |
| 734 | A102 | 35c multicolored | .35 | .20 |
| 735 | A102 | 45c multicolored | .65 | .20 |
| 736 | A102 | 75c multicolored | .70 | .40 |
| 737 | A102 | $1 multicolored | .80 | .40 |
| | | Nos. 731-737 (7) | 3.10 | 1.80 |

**Souvenir Sheet**

| 738 | A102 | $3 multicolored | 2.00 | 1.25 |
|-----|------|-----------------|------|------|

21st Olympic Games, Montreal, Canada, July 17-Aug. 1.

Moulin Rouge, by Toulouse-Lautrec A103

Paintings by Toulouse-Lautrec: 1c, Start of the Quadrille. 2c, Woman's Head. 3c, Hall at the Moulin Rouge. 40c, Man Delivering Laundry. 50c, Dancing the Bolero. $1, Lady with Boa. $2, Signor Boileau at the Cafe.

**1976, July 20    Litho.    Perf. 14**

| 739 | A103 | ½c multicolored | .20 | .20 |
|-----|------|-----------------|-----|-----|
| 740 | A103 | 1c multicolored | .20 | .20 |
| 741 | A103 | 2c multicolored | .20 | .20 |
| 742 | A103 | 3c multicolored | .20 | .20 |
| 743 | A103 | 40c multicolored | .75 | .20 |
| 744 | A103 | 50c multicolored | .95 | .20 |
| 745 | A103 | $2 multicolored | 2.50 | .50 |
| | | Nos. 739-745 (7) | 5.00 | 1.70 |

**Souvenir Sheet**

| 746 | A103 | $1 multicolored | 4.00 | 1.25 |
|-----|------|-----------------|------|------|

Henri de Toulouse-Lautrec (1864-1901), painter, 75th death anniv.

Map of West Indies, Bats, Wicket and Ball A103a

Prudential Cup — A103b

**1976, July 26**

| 747 | A103a | 35c lt blue & multi | .60 | .60 |
|-----|-------|---------------------|-----|-----|
| 748 | A103b | $1 lilac rose & blk | 1.75 | 1.75 |

World Cricket Cup, won by West Indies Team, 1975.

Piper Apache A104

Airplanes: 1c, Beech Twin Bonanza. 2c, D.H. Twin Otter. 40c, Britten Norman Islander. 50c, D.H. Heron. $2, Hawker Siddeley Avro 748. $3, B.A.C. One-Eleven.

**1976, Aug. 18**

| 749 | A104 | ½c multicolored | .20 | .20 |
|-----|------|-----------------|-----|-----|
| 750 | A104 | 1c multicolored | .20 | .20 |
| 751 | A104 | 2c multicolored | .20 | .20 |
| 752 | A104 | 40c multicolored | .75 | .20 |

| | | | | |
|---|---|---|---|---|
| **753** | A104 | 50c multicolored | .80 | .20 |
| **754** | A104 | $2 multicolored | 2.75 | .75 |
| | | *Nos. 749-754 (6)* | 4.90 | 1.75 |

**Souvenir Sheet**

| | | | | |
|---|---|---|---|---|
| **755** | A104 | $3 multicolored | 3.50 | 1.25 |

Helios Mission, Assembly — A105

Designs: 1c, Helios spacecraft in space 2c, Helios assembled. 15c, Helios, system test and checkout. 45c, Viking nearing Mars, horiz. 75c, Viking on Mars. $2, Viking spacecraft assembled. $3, Helios orbiter and Viking lander.

**1976, Sept. 1    Litho.    Perf. 14**

| | | | | |
|---|---|---|---|---|
| **756** | A105 | ½c multicolored | .20 | .20 |
| **757** | A105 | 1c multicolored | .20 | .20 |
| **758** | A105 | 2c multicolored | .20 | .20 |
| **759** | A105 | 15c multicolored | .20 | .20 |
| **760** | A105 | 45c multicolored | .30 | .20 |
| **761** | A105 | 75c multicolored | .45 | .25 |
| **762** | A105 | $2 multicolored | .90 | .40 |
| | | *Nos. 756-762 (7)* | 2.45 | 1.65 |

**Souvenir Sheet**

| | | | | |
|---|---|---|---|---|
| **763** | A105 | $3 multicolored | 1.75 | 1.00 |

Helios (solar probe) mission and Viking Mars missions.

S.S. Geestland, Geest Line Flag — A106

Ships: 1c, M.V. Federal Palm, West Indies Shipping Service. 2c, H.M.S. Blake and ship's crest. 25c, M.V. Vistafjord and Norwegian-American Line flag. 75c, S.S. Canberra and P. & O. Line flag. $1, S.S. Regina and Chandris Line flag. $2, Santa Maria and Spanish flag, 1492. $5, S.S. Arandora and Blue Star Line flag.

**1976, Nov. 3    Litho.    Perf. 14½**

| | | | | |
|---|---|---|---|---|
| **764** | A106 | ½c blue & multi | .20 | .20 |
| **765** | A106 | 1c blue & multi | .20 | .20 |
| **766** | A106 | 2c blue & multi | .20 | .20 |
| **767** | A106 | 25c blue & multi | .65 | .20 |
| **768** | A106 | 75c blue & multi | 1.25 | .25 |
| **769** | A106 | $1 blue & multi | 1.50 | .35 |
| **770** | A106 | $5 blue & multi | 3.00 | .75 |
| | | *Nos. 764-770 (7)* | 7.00 | 2.15 |

**Souvenir Sheet**

| | | | | |
|---|---|---|---|---|
| **771** | A106 | $2 multicolored | 2.50 | 2.50 |

Ships connected with Grenada's development.

Altarpiece of San Barnaba, by Botticelli A107

Christmas (Paintings): 1c, Annunciation, by Botticelli. 2c, Madonna with Chancellor Rolin, by Jan van Eyck. 35c, Annunciation, by Fra Filippo Lippi. 50c, Madonna of the Magnificat, by Botticelli. 75c, Madonna of the Pomegranate, by Botticelli. $2, Gipsy Madonna, by Titian. $3, Madonna with St. Cosmas and Saints, by Botticelli.

**1976, Dec. 8    Litho.    Perf. 14**

| | | | | |
|---|---|---|---|---|
| **772** | A107 | ½c multicolored | .20 | .20 |
| **773** | A107 | 1c multicolored | .20 | .20 |
| **774** | A107 | 2c multicolored | .20 | .20 |
| **775** | A107 | 35c multicolored | .20 | .20 |
| **776** | A107 | 50c multicolored | .30 | .20 |
| **777** | A107 | 75c multicolored | .40 | .20 |
| **778** | A107 | $3 multicolored | 1.00 | .40 |
| | | *Nos. 772-778 (7)* | 2.50 | 1.65 |

**Souvenir Sheet**

| | | | | |
|---|---|---|---|---|
| **779** | A107 | $2 multicolored | 1.60 | .75 |

Globe and Telephone Users A108

Designs: ½c, A. G. Bell, 1876 and modern telephones. 2c, Satellites around globe, world map. 18c, Videophone. 40c, Satellite and ground stations. $1, Satellite and telephone communication with ships. $2, British "Trimphone" and radar station. $5, Flags of the world surrounding globe, and telephone.

**1976, Dec. 17    Litho.    Perf. 14**

| | | | | |
|---|---|---|---|---|
| **780** | A108 | ½c multicolored | .20 | .20 |
| **781** | A108 | 1c multicolored | .20 | .20 |
| **782** | A108 | 2c multicolored | .20 | .20 |
| **783** | A108 | 18c multicolored | .30 | .20 |
| **784** | A108 | 40c multicolored | .40 | .20 |
| **785** | A108 | $1 multicolored | .55 | .30 |
| **786** | A108 | $2 multicolored | .90 | .40 |
| | | *Nos. 780-786 (7)* | 2.75 | 1.80 |

**Souvenir Sheet**

| | | | | |
|---|---|---|---|---|
| **787** | A108 | $2 multicolored | 2.75 | 1.00 |

Centenary of first telephone conversation by Alexander Graham Bell, Mar. 10, 1876.

Coronation of Elizabeth II — A109

Designs: ½c, Coronation. 1c, $1, Orb and scepter. 35c, $3, Trooping of the Guards. 50c, $2, Spoon and ampulla. 35c, (bklt.), $2.50, Elizabeth II and Prince Philip. $5, Royal visit to Grenada.

**1977, Feb. 8    Litho.    Perf. 14, 12**

| | | | | |
|---|---|---|---|---|
| **788** | A109 | ½c multicolored | .20 | .20 |
| **789** | A109 | 1c multicolored | .20 | .20 |
| **790** | A109 | 35c multicolored | .20 | .20 |
| **791** | A109 | 50c multicolored | .50 | .40 |
| **792** | A109 | $2.50 multicolored | .55 | .40 |
| *a.* | | Booklet pane of 6 (35c) | 1.25 | |
| *b.* | | Booklet pane of 3 (50c, $1, $3) | 4.25 | |
| | | *Nos. 788-792 (5)* | 1.65 | 1.40 |

**Souvenir Sheet**

| | | | | |
|---|---|---|---|---|
| **793** | A109 | $5 multicolored | 1.50 | 1.50 |

Reign of Queen Elizabeth II, 25th anniv. Nos. 792a-792b are self-adhesive, roulette x imperf. Marginal inscriptions.

Nos. 788-792 were printed in sheets of 40 (10x4), perf. 14, and sheets of 5 plus label, perf. 12, in changed colors.

For overprints see Nos. 821-826.

Water Skiing, One-ski Slalom A110

Designs: 1c, Speedboat racing around Grand Anse. 2c, Crew racing, St. George's. 22c, Swimming, Grand Anse. 35c, Local work boat races. 75c, Water polo, careenage, St. George's. $2, Game fishing. $3, South Coast yacht race.

**1977, Apr. 13    Litho.    Perf. 14**

| | | | | |
|---|---|---|---|---|
| **794** | A110 | ½c multicolored | .20 | .20 |
| **795** | A110 | 1c multicolored | .20 | .20 |
| **796** | A110 | 2c multicolored | .20 | .20 |
| **797** | A110 | 22c multicolored | .20 | .20 |
| **798** | A110 | 35c multicolored | .35 | .20 |
| **799** | A110 | 75c multicolored | .55 | .20 |
| **800** | A110 | $2 multicolored | 1.10 | .35 |
| | | *Nos. 794-800 (7)* | 2.80 | 1.55 |

**Souvenir Sheet**

| | | | | |
|---|---|---|---|---|
| **801** | A110 | $3 multicolored | 1.75 | 1.25 |

1977 Easter Water Parade.

Tent, OAS Emblem A111

**1977, June 14    Litho.    Perf. 14**

| | | | | |
|---|---|---|---|---|
| **802** | A111 | 35c multicolored | .20 | .20 |
| **803** | A111 | $1 multicolored | .60 | .60 |
| **804** | A111 | $2 multicolored | 1.00 | 1.00 |
| | | *Nos. 802-804 (3)* | 1.80 | 1.80 |

7th Regular Session, General Assembly of Organization of American States.

Scouts on Raft A112

Designs: 1c, Tug-of-war. 2c, Boy Scout regatta. 18c, Scouts around camp fire. 40c, Field kitchen. $1, Boy Scouts and Sea Scouts. $2, Hiking and map reading. $3, Semaphore.

**1977, Sept. 6    Litho.    Perf. 14**

| | | | | |
|---|---|---|---|---|
| **805** | A112 | ½c multicolored | .20 | .20 |
| **806** | A112 | 1c multicolored | .20 | .20 |
| **807** | A112 | 2c multicolored | .20 | .20 |
| **808** | A112 | 18c multicolored | .30 | .20 |
| **809** | A112 | 40c multicolored | .45 | .20 |
| **810** | A112 | $1 multicolored | 1.10 | .35 |
| **811** | A112 | $2 multicolored | 2.00 | .75 |
| | | *Nos. 805-811 (7)* | 4.45 | 1.90 |

**Souvenir Sheet**

| | | | | |
|---|---|---|---|---|
| **812** | A112 | $3 multicolored | 3.00 | 1.25 |

6th Caribbean Jamboree, Kingston, Jamaica, Aug. 5-14.

Annunciation to the Shepherds — A113

Ceiling Paintings, St. Martin's Church, Zillis, Switzerland, 12th Century: 1c, Joseph on his way. 2c, Virgin and Child, Flight into Egypt. 22c, Angel leading the way. 35c, King on way to Herod. 75c, Three horses. $2, Virgin and Child. $3, Adoration of the Kings.

**1977, Nov. 3    Litho.    Perf. 14**

| | | | | |
|---|---|---|---|---|
| **813** | A113 | ½c multicolored | .20 | .20 |
| **814** | A113 | 1c multicolored | .20 | .20 |
| **815** | A113 | 2c multicolored | .20 | .20 |
| **816** | A113 | 22c multicolored | .20 | .20 |
| **817** | A113 | 35c multicolored | .20 | .20 |
| **818** | A113 | 75c multicolored | .20 | .20 |
| **819** | A113 | $2 multicolored | .40 | .30 |
| | | *Nos. 813-819 (7)* | 1.60 | 1.50 |

**Souvenir Sheet**

| | | | | |
|---|---|---|---|---|
| **820** | A113 | $3 multicolored | 1.25 | 1.00 |

Christmas.

Nos. 788-793 Overprinted "Royal Visit W.I. 1977"

**1977, Nov. 10    Perf. 12, 14**

| | | | | |
|---|---|---|---|---|
| **821** | A109 | ½c multicolored | .20 | .20 |
| **822** | A109 | 1c multicolored | .20 | .20 |
| **823** | A109 | 35c multicolored | .20 | .20 |
| **824** | A109 | 50c multicolored | .25 | .40 |
| **825** | A109 | $2.50 multicolored | .30 | .50 |
| | | *Nos. 821-825 (5)* | 1.15 | 1.50 |

**Souvenir Sheet**

**Perf. 14**

| | | | | |
|---|---|---|---|---|
| **826** | A109 | $5 multicolored | .90 | 1.40 |

Caribbean visit of Queen Elizabeth II. Nos. 821-822 are perf. 12, others perf. 12 and 14.

Christjaan Eijkman — A114

Portraits: 1c, Winston Churchill, Literature, 1953. 2c, Woodrow Wilson, Peace, 1919. 35c, Frederic Passy, Peace 1901. $1, Albert Einstein, Physics, 1921. $2, Alfred Nobel, founder. $3, Carl Bosch, Chemistry, 1931.

**1978, Jan. 25    Litho.    Perf. 14**

| | | | | |
|---|---|---|---|---|
| **827** | A114 | ½c multicolored | .20 | .20 |
| **828** | A114 | 1c multicolored | .20 | .20 |
| **829** | A114 | 2c multicolored | .20 | .20 |
| **830** | A114 | 35c multicolored | .30 | .20 |
| **831** | A114 | $1 multicolored | .85 | .30 |
| **832** | A114 | $3 multicolored | 2.25 | .55 |
| | | *Nos. 827-832 (6)* | 4.00 | 1.65 |

**Souvenir Sheet**

| | | | | |
|---|---|---|---|---|
| **833** | A114 | $2 multicolored | 2.00 | 1.00 |

Nobel Prize winners.

Early Zeppelin and Count Zeppelin A115

Designs: 1c, Lindbergh and Spirit of St. Louis. 2c, "Deutschland" airship. 22c, Lindbergh landing in Paris. 35c, Lindbergh in cockpit. 75c, Lindbergh and Spirit of St. Louis in flight. $1, Zeppelin over Alps. $2, Count Zeppelin and early airship. $3, Zeppelin over Capitol.

**1978, Feb. 13    Litho.    Perf. 14**

| | | | | |
|---|---|---|---|---|
| **834** | A115 | ½c multicolored | .20 | .20 |
| **835** | A115 | 1c multicolored | .20 | .20 |
| **836** | A115 | 2c multicolored | .40 | .20 |
| **837** | A115 | 22c multicolored | .40 | .20 |
| **838** | A115 | 75c multicolored | .75 | .20 |
| **839** | A115 | $1 multicolored | .90 | .25 |
| **840** | A115 | $3 multicolored | 2.00 | .50 |
| | | *Nos. 834-840 (7)* | 4.65 | 1.75 |

**Souvenir Sheet**

| | | | | |
|---|---|---|---|---|
| **841** | | Sheet of 2 | 3.25 | 1.00 |
| *a.* | A115 | 35c multicolored | .75 | |
| *b.* | A115 | $2 multicolored | 2.50 | |

Aviation history.

Launching of Space Shuttle — A116    Black-headed Gulls — A117

Space Shuttle: 1c, Booster separation. 2c, External tank separation. 18c, In orbit. 75c, Satellite placement. $2, Landing approach. $3, On landing pad.

**1978, Feb. 28**

| | | | | |
|---|---|---|---|---|
| **842** | A116 | ½c multicolored | .20 | .20 |
| **843** | A116 | 1c multicolored | .20 | .20 |
| **844** | A116 | 2c multicolored | .20 | .20 |
| **845** | A116 | 18c multicolored | .40 | .20 |
| **846** | A116 | 75c multicolored | .90 | .20 |
| **847** | A116 | $2 multicolored | 1.75 | .40 |
| | | *Nos. 842-847 (6)* | 3.65 | 1.40 |

**Souvenir Sheet**

| | | | | |
|---|---|---|---|---|
| **848** | A116 | $3 multicolored | 2.10 | 1.00 |

US space shuttle.

**1978, Mar. 8    Litho.    Perf. 14**

Wild Birds of Grenada and Wildlife Fund Emblem: 1c, Wilson's petrels. 2c, Killdeers. 50c, White-necked jacobin and hibiscus. 75c,

Blue-faced booby. $1, Broad-winged hawk. $2, Scaley-necked pigeon. $3, Scarlet ibis.

| 849 | A117 | ½c multicolored | .30 | .25 |
|-----|------|-----------------|-----|-----|
| 850 | A117 | 1c multicolored | .30 | .25 |
| 851 | A117 | 2c multicolored | .30 | .25 |
| 852 | A117 | 50c multicolored | 3.00 | .40 |
| 853 | A117 | 75c multicolored | 3.50 | .60 |
| 854 | A117 | $1 multicolored | 5.00 | .80 |
| 855 | A117 | $2 multicolored | 7.50 | 1.50 |
| | | Nos. 849-855 (7) | 19.90 | 4.05 |

**Souvenir Sheet**

| 856 | A117 | $3 multicolored | 13.50 | 2.00 |
|-----|------|-----------------|-------|------|

Marquise de Spinola, by Rubens A118

Ludwig van Beethoven A119

Paintings by Peter Paul Rubens (1577-1640): 5c, Reception of Marie de Medicis. 15c, Rubens and Helena Fourment. 25c, Ludovicus Nonnius. 45c, Helena Fourment with her Children. 75c, Child's head. $3, Suzanne Fourment in Velvet Hat.

**1978, Mar. 30    Litho.    Perf. 13½x14**

| 857 | A118 | 5c lt blue & multi | .30 | .20 |
|-----|------|--------------------|-----|-----|
| 858 | A118 | 15c lt blue & multi | .30 | .20 |
| 859 | A118 | 18c lt blue & multi | .30 | .20 |
| 860 | A118 | 25c lt blue & multi | .30 | .20 |
| 861 | A118 | 45c lt blue & multi | .55 | .20 |
| 862 | A118 | 75c lt blue & multi | .80 | .20 |
| 863 | A118 | $3 lt blue & multi | 1.75 | .55 |
| | | Nos. 857-863 (7) | 4.30 | 1.75 |

**Souvenir Sheet**

| 864 | A118 | $5 lt blue & multi | 3.75 | 1.00 |
|-----|------|--------------------|------|------|

**1978, Apr. 24    Perf. 14**

Designs: 15c, Woman violinist playing concerto. 18c, Various musical instruments. 22c, Piano. 50c, Two violins. 75c, Beethoven's piano and score. $2, Beethoven and score. $3, Beethoven and his house. 15c, 18c, 22c, 75c, $2, $3, horiz.

| 865 | A119 | 5c multicolored | .25 | .20 |
|-----|------|-----------------|-----|-----|
| 866 | A119 | 15c multicolored | .25 | .20 |
| 867 | A119 | 18c multicolored | .50 | .20 |
| 868 | A119 | 22c multicolored | .50 | .20 |
| 869 | A119 | 50c multicolored | 1.00 | .40 |
| 870 | A119 | 75c multicolored | 1.75 | .55 |
| 871 | A119 | $3 multicolored | 3.25 | .75 |
| | | Nos. 865-871 (7) | 7.50 | 2.50 |

**Souvenir Sheet**

| 872 | A119 | $2 multicolored | 3.25 | 1.25 |
|-----|------|-----------------|------|------|

Ludwig van Beethoven (1770-1827), composer, death sesquicentennial.

Elizabeth II with Crown, Scepter and Orb — A120

Trooping of the Colors — A121

Designs: 35c, Coronation. $2.50, St. Edward's crown. $5, Elizabeth II and Prince Philip.

**1978, June 2    Litho.    Perf. 14**

| 873 | A120 | 35c multicolored | .20 | .20 |
|-----|------|------------------|-----|-----|
| 874 | A120 | $2 multicolored | .65 | .65 |
| 875 | A120 | $2.50 multicolored | .65 | .65 |
| | | Nos. 873-875 (3) | 1.50 | 1.50 |

**Souvenir Sheet**

| 876 | A120 | $5 multicolored | 1.25 | 1.25 |
|-----|------|-----------------|------|------|

**Imperf**
**Self-adhesive**

35c, Elizabeth II at Maundy Money distribution ceremony. $5, Elizabeth II and Prince Philip.

| 877 | | Souvenir booklet | | 3.25 |
|-----|---|------------------|---|------|
| a. | A121 | Bklt. pane, 3 each 25c, 35c | | 1.00 |
| b. | A121 | Booklet pane of 1, $5 | | 2.50 |

Coronation of Queen Elizabeth II, 25th anniv. Nos. 873-875 were printed in sheets of 40 (10x4), perf. 14, and sheets of 3 plus label, perf. 12, in changed colors. Labels show royal insignia.

No. 877 contains 2 booklet panes printed on peelable paper backing showing coins.

Goalkeeper Reaching for Ball — A122

Designs: Goalkeeper reaching for ball, various stages of motion.

**1978, Aug. 1    Litho.    Perf. 15**

| 878 | A122 | 40c multicolored | .20 | .20 |
|-----|------|------------------|-----|-----|
| 879 | A122 | 60c multicolored | .25 | .25 |
| 880 | A122 | 90c multicolored | .35 | .35 |
| 881 | A122 | $2 multicolored | .85 | .85 |
| | | Nos. 878-881 (4) | 1.65 | 1.65 |

**Souvenir Sheet**

| 882 | A122 | $2.50 multicolored | 1.75 | 1.75 |
|-----|------|--------------------|------|------|

11th World Cup Soccer Championship, Argentina, June 1-25.

Flying Objects, 16th Century Drawing and Flying Saucer, 1962 A123

Designs: 35c, Radar probing skies, and Mars surface. $2, Prime Minister Eric Gairy and UN General Assembly Building. $3, Flying saucer with downwards beam, and UFO photograph.

**1978, Aug. 17**

| 883 | A123 | 5c multicolored | .25 | .20 |
|-----|------|-----------------|-----|-----|
| 884 | A123 | 35c multicolored | .50 | .35 |
| 885 | A123 | $3 multicolored | 3.25 | 3.00 |
| | | Nos. 883-885 (3) | 4.00 | 3.55 |

**Souvenir Sheet**

| 886 | A123 | $2 multicolored | 3.25 | 3.25 |
|-----|------|-----------------|------|------|

Proposal by Prime Minister Eric Gairy of Grenada to the UN General Assembly to study unidentified flying objects, Oct. 7, 1977.

Wright Glider and Allegory of Flight A124

15c, Flyer I, 1903, & eagle. 18c, Flyer III & allegory of flight. 22c, Flyer III & eagle. 50c, Orville Wright, Flyer & allegory of flight. 75c, Flyer, 1908, & eagle. $2, Flyer & allegory of flight. $3, Wilbur Wright, Flyer & allegory of flight.

**1978, Aug. 24    Perf. 14**

| 887 | A124 | 5c multicolored | .20 | .20 |
|-----|------|-----------------|-----|-----|
| 888 | A124 | 15c multicolored | .20 | .20 |
| 889 | A124 | 18c multicolored | .25 | .20 |
| 890 | A124 | 22c multicolored | .25 | .20 |
| 891 | A124 | 50c multicolored | .40 | .30 |
| 892 | A124 | 75c multicolored | .50 | .40 |
| 893 | A124 | $3 multicolored | 1.25 | 1.25 |
| | | Nos. 887-893 (7) | 3.05 | 2.75 |

**Souvenir Sheet**

| 894 | A124 | $2 multicolored | 2.75 | 2.75 |
|-----|------|-----------------|------|------|

75th anniversary of first powered flight by Wright brothers, Dec. 17, 1903.

Hawaiian Feast in Capt. Cook's Honor A125

Capt. Cook and: 35c, Hawaiian warriors' dance. 75c, Honolulu harbor. $3, "Resolution." $4, Death scene.

**1978, Dec. 5    Litho.    Perf. 14**

| 895 | A125 | 18c multicolored | .90 | .50 |
|-----|------|------------------|-----|-----|
| 896 | A125 | 35c multicolored | 1.10 | .60 |
| 897 | A125 | 75c multicolored | 2.00 | 1.90 |
| 898 | A125 | $3 multicolored | 2.75 | 4.50 |
| | | Nos. 895-898 (4) | 6.75 | 7.50 |

**Souvenir Sheet**

| 899 | A125 | $4 multicolored | 5.00 | 5.00 |
|-----|------|-----------------|------|------|

Bicentenary of Capt. Cook's arrival in Hawaii and 250th anniversary of his birth.

Detail from Paumgartner Altar, by Dürer — A126

Convention and Cultural Center — A127

Dürer Paintings: 60c, The Three Kings. 90c, Virgin and Child. $2, Head of the Virgin. $4, Virgin and Child.

**1978, Dec. 20    Litho.    Perf. 14**

| 900 | A126 | 40c multicolored | .25 | .25 |
|-----|------|------------------|-----|-----|
| 901 | A126 | 60c multicolored | .35 | .35 |
| 902 | A126 | 90c multicolored | .40 | .40 |
| 903 | A126 | $2 multicolored | .75 | .75 |
| | | Nos. 900-903 (4) | 1.75 | 1.75 |

**Souvenir Sheet**

| 904 | A126 | $4 multicolored | 2.25 | 2.25 |
|-----|------|-----------------|------|------|

Christmas and 450th death anniv. of Albrecht Dürer (1471-1528), German painter.

**1979, Feb. 8    Litho.    Perf. 14**

18c, Geodesic Dome. 22c, Rowboat race, Easter parade, St. George's. 35c, Prime Minister Eric M. Gairy. $3, Cross at Fort Frederick at night.

| 905 | A127 | 5c multicolored | .20 | .20 |
|-----|------|-----------------|-----|-----|
| 906 | A127 | 18c multicolored | .20 | .20 |
| 907 | A127 | 22c multicolored | .20 | .20 |
| 908 | A127 | 35c multicolored | .20 | .20 |
| 909 | A127 | $3 multicolored | .70 | .70 |
| | | Nos. 905-909 (5) | 1.50 | 1.50 |

5th anniversary of independence.

Chenille Plant — A128

Birds in Flight — A129

Native Flowers: 50c, Red hibiscus. $1, Skyflower. $2, Pink pride of India. $3, Rosebay.

**1979, Feb. 26**

| 910 | A128 | 18c multicolored | .20 | .20 |
|-----|------|------------------|-----|-----|
| 911 | A128 | 50c multicolored | .35 | .30 |
| 912 | A128 | $1 multicolored | .55 | .50 |
| 913 | A128 | $3 multicolored | 1.40 | 1.25 |
| | | Nos. 910-913 (4) | 2.50 | 2.25 |

**Souvenir Sheet**

| 914 | A128 | $2 multicolored | 1.75 | 1.75 |
|-----|------|-----------------|------|------|

**1979, Mar. 15**

$2, Bird in flight & Human Rights emblem.

| 915 | A129 | 15c multicolored | .20 | .20 |
|-----|------|------------------|-----|-----|
| 916 | A129 | $2 multicolored | .75 | .75 |

Universal Declaration of Human Rights, 30th anniversary.

Children Playing Cricket — A130

IYC Emblem and: 22c, Boys playing baseball. $4, Children with model spaceship. $5, Three children.

**1979, Apr. 23    Litho.    Perf. 14**

| 917 | A130 | 18c multicolored | 1.00 | .50 |
|-----|------|------------------|------|-----|
| 918 | A130 | 22c multicolored | .50 | .30 |
| 919 | A130 | $5 multicolored | 4.50 | 6.00 |
| | | Nos. 917-919 (3) | 6.00 | 6.80 |

**Souvenir Sheet**

| 920 | A130 | $4 multicolored | 2.75 | 2.75 |
|-----|------|-----------------|------|------|

Intl. Year of the Child.

Balloon and Space Shuttle A131

Designs: 35c, Octopus holding sailors, nuclear submarine. 75c, Rocket and moon. $3, Imaginary plane and space ship. $4, Multi-propellered ship and US space shuttle.

**1979, May 4**

| 921 | A131 | 18c multicolored | .40 | .20 |
|-----|------|------------------|-----|-----|
| 922 | A131 | 35c multicolored | .70 | .25 |
| 923 | A131 | 75c multicolored | .90 | .65 |
| 924 | A131 | $3 multicolored | 2.40 | 3.00 |
| | | Nos. 921-924 (4) | 4.40 | 4.10 |

**Souvenir Sheet**

| 925 | A131 | $4 multicolored | 2.75 | 2.75 |
|-----|------|-----------------|------|------|

Jules Verne (1828-1905), science fiction writer.

African Mail Runner A132

Sir Rowland Hill (1795-1879), originator of penny postage, and: 40c, American Pony Express. $1, Oriental pigeon post. $3, European mail coach. $5, Tete-beche stamps with revenue surcharge, 1883.

**1979, July 23    Litho.    Perf. 14**

| 926 | A132 | 20c multicolored | .20 | .20 |
|-----|------|------------------|-----|-----|
| 927 | A132 | 40c multicolored | .20 | .20 |
| 928 | A132 | $1 multicolored | .20 | .20 |
| 929 | A132 | $3 multicolored | .60 | .60 |
| | | Nos. 926-929 (4) | 1.20 | 1.20 |

**Souvenir Sheet**

| 930 | A132 | $5 multicolored | 1.10 | 1.10 |
|-----|------|-----------------|------|------|

Nos. 926-929 were printed in sheets of 40, perf. 14, and in sheets of 5 plus label, perf. 12, in changed colors.
For overprints see Nos. 989A-989D.

Boys, Map of
Grenada,
Vaccination
Gun — A133

**1979, Aug. 2      Litho.      Perf. 14**
931  A133  5c multicolored           .20   .20
932  A133  $1 multicolored           .90   .90
Intl. Year of the Child, immunization of
children.

Reef
Shark
A134

Designs: 45c, Spotted eagle ray. 50c, Many-
tooth conger. 60c, Golden olive shells. 70c,
West Indian murex. 75c, Giant tuns. 90c,
Brown boobies. $1, Magnificent frigate bird.
$2.50, Sooty tern.

**1979, Aug. 22     Litho.      Perf. 14**
933  A134  40c multicolored          .40   .35
934  A134  45c multicolored          .40   .35
935  A134  50c multicolored          .45   .40
936  A134  60c multicolored          .75   .60
937  A134  70c multicolored          .90   .70
938  A134  75c multicolored         1.10  1.10
939  A134  90c multicolored         1.90  2.25
940  A134  $1 multicolored          1.90  2.25
        Nos. 933-940 (8)            7.80  8.00
**Souvenir Sheet**
941  A134  $2.50 multicolored        3.50  3.50

Flight into
Egypt,
Tapestry
A135

Tapestries: 25c, Virgin and Child. 30c,
Angel, vert. 40c, Infant Jesus, by Doge Marino
Grimani, vert. 90c, Shepherds, vert. $1, Flight
into Egypt, vert. $2, Virgin in Glory, vert. $4,
Virgin and Child, by Grimani, vert.

**1979, Oct. 16     Litho.      Perf. 14**
942  A135  6c multicolored           .20   .20
943  A135  25c multicolored          .20   .20
944  A135  30c multicolored          .20   .20
945  A135  40c multicolored          .20   .20
946  A135  90c multicolored          .25   .25
947  A135  $1 multicolored           .25   .25
948  A135  $2 multicolored           .55   .55
        Nos. 942-948 (7)            1.85  1.85
**Souvenir Sheet**
949  A135  $4 multicolored           1.50  1.50
Christmas.

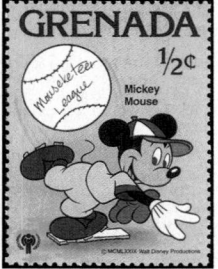

Disney
Characters
and IYC
Emblem
A135a

Designs: Sport scenes.

**1979, Nov. 2      Litho.      Perf. 11**
950  A135a  ½c Mickey Mouse,
                baseball             .20   .20
951  A135a  1c Donald, high
                jump                 .20   .20
952  A135a  2c Goofy, basket-
                ball                 .20   .20
953  A135a  3c Goofy, hurdles       .20   .20

954  A135a  4c Donald Duck,
                golf                 .20   .20
955  A135a  5c Mickey, cricket       .20   .20
956  A135a  10c Mickey, soccer       .20   .20
957  A135a  $2 Mickey, tennis       3.25  3.75
958  A135a  $2.50 Minnie, eques-
                trian               3.25  3.75
        Nos. 950-958 (9)            7.90  8.90
**Souvenir Sheet**
**Perf. 13½**
959  CD329  $3 Goofy in riding
                habit               3.00  3.00
See Nos. 1031-1032.

Hands, Paul P.
Harris, Rotary
Emblem — A136

Rotary Emblem and Hands Holding: 30c,
Caduceus. 90c, Wheat. $2, Family. $4,
Emblem.

**1980, Feb. 25     Litho.      Perf. 14**
960  A136  6c multicolored           .20   .20
961  A136  30c multicolored          .20   .20
962  A136  90c multicolored          .30   .30
963  A136  $2 multicolored           .80   .80
        Nos. 960-963 (4)            1.50  1.50
**Souvenir Sheet**
964  A136  $4 multicolored           1.60  1.60
Rotary International, 75th anniversary.

Nos. 585-586, 588-591, 593-594, 596-
602 Overprinted in Black: PEOPLE'S
REVOLUTION / 13 MARCH 1979

**1980                   Perf. 15, 13½**
965  A85  2c multicolored            .20   .20
966  A85  3c multicolored            .20   .20
967  A85  6c multicolored            .20   .20
968  A85  8c multicolored            .20   .20
969  A85  10c multicolored           .20   .20
970  A85  12c multicolored           .20   .20
971  A85  20c multicolored           .20   .20
972  A85  25c multicolored           .40   .60
973  A85  50c multicolored           .40   .60
974  A85  75c multicolored           .65   .95
975  A85  $1 multicolored           1.00  1.25
976  A85  $2 multicolored           1.75  2.40
977  A85  $3 multicolored           2.25  3.25
978  A85  $5 multicolored           3.00  5.50
979  A85  $10 multicolored          4.25  8.00
        Nos. 965-979 (15)          15.10 23.95
Issue dates: 25c, Apr. 7; others, Feb. 28.

Boxing,
Kremlin,
Olympic
Rings
A137

**1980, Mar. 24     Perf. 14**
980  A137  25c shown                 .20   .20
981  A137  40c Bicycling             .20   .20
982  A137  90c Equestrian            .25   .25
983  A137  $2 Running                .60   .60
        Nos. 980-983 (4)            1.25  1.25
**Souvenir Sheet**
984  A137  $4 Yachting              1.10  1.10
22nd Summer Olympic Games, Moscow,
July 19-Aug. 3.

Tropical
Kingbirds — A138

**1980, Apr. 8**
985  A138  20c shown                1.00   .80
986  A138  40c Rufous-breasted
                hermits             1.40  1.10

987  A138  $1 Troupials            1.90  1.60
988  A138  $2 Ruddy quail doves    2.25  4.00
        Nos. 985-988 (4)            6.55  7.50
**Souvenir Sheet**
989  A138  $3 Prairie warblers     5.25  5.25

Nos. 926-929 Overprinted: "LONDON
1980"

**1980, May 6       Litho.      Perf. 12**
989A  A132  20c multicolored         .20   .20
989B  A132  40c multicolored         .30   .30
989C  A132  $1 multicolored          .50   .50
989D  A132  $3 multicolored         1.75  1.75
        Nos. 989A-989D (4)          2.75  2.75
London '80 Intl. Stamp Exhib., May 6-14.

Free
School
Hot
Lunches
A139

**1980, May 19      Litho.      Perf. 14**
990  A139  10c shown                 .20   .20
991  A139  40c Food canning          .25   .25
992  A139  $1 Health care            .55   .55
993  A139  $2 Housing projects       .85   .85
        Nos. 990-993 (4)            1.85  1.85
**Souvenir Sheet**
994  A139  $5 Prime Minister
                Bishop, vert.       1.50  1.50
People's Revolution, 1st anniv.

Jamb Statues, West Portal, Chartres
Cathedral — A140

Masterpieces: 10c, Les Desmoiselles
d'Avignon, by Picasso. 40c, Winged Victory of
Samothrace. 50c, The Night Watch, by Rembrandt. $1, Edward VI as a Child, by Holbein,
the Younger. $3, Queen Nefertiti. $4, Weier
Haws, by Dürer, vert.

**1980, June       Litho.      Perf. 14**
995  A140  8c multicolored           .20   .20
996  A140  10c multicolored          .20   .20
997  A140  40c multicolored          .25   .25
998  A140  50c multicolored          .25   .25
999  A140  $1 multicolored           .40   .40
1000  A140  $3 multicolored         1.10  1.10
        Nos. 995-1000 (6)           2.40  2.40
**Souvenir Sheet**
1001  A140  $4 multicolored         1.50  1.50

Carib
Canoes
A141

Designs: 1c, Boat building. 2c, Small
workboat. 4c, "Santa Maria." 5c, West India
man barque, 1840. 6c, "Orinoco," 1851. 10c,
Schooner. 12c, Trimaran. 15c, "Petite Amie,"
Spice Island cruising yacht. 20c, Fishing
pirogue. 25c, Harbor police launch. 30c,
Grand Anse speedboat. 40c, "Seimstrand."
50c, "Ariadne," 3-masted schooner. 90c,
"Geestide," banana boat. $1, "Cunard Count-
ess," cruise ship. $3, Rumrunner. $5,
"Statendam." $10, Coast Guard patrol boat.

**1980, Sept. 9      Litho.      Perf. 14**
1002  A141  ½c multicolored          .20   .20
1003  A141  1c multicolored          .20   .20
1004  A141  2c multicolored          .20   .20
1005  A141  4c multicolored          .40   .55
1006  A141  5c multicolored          .40   .55
1007  A141  6c multicolored          .40   .55
1008  A141  10c multicolored         .45   .20
1009  A141  12c multicolored        1.00   .70
1010  A141  15c multicolored         .50   .20
1011  A141  20c multicolored        1.00   .20
1012  A141  25c multicolored        2.00   .45
1013  A141  30c multicolored        1.50   .20
1014  A141  40c multicolored        2.25   .55

1015  A141  50c multicolored         .60   .70
1016  A141  90c multicolored        2.00   .70
1017  A141  $1 multicolored         3.50  1.10
1018  A141  $3 multicolored         3.00  4.00
1019  A141  $5 multicolored         4.25  6.50
1020  A141  $10 multicolored        5.00  8.50
        Nos. 1002-1020 (19)        28.85 26.50
#1017 reprinted inscribed 1982, #1015,
1984.
For overprints see #O1-O10, O12-O13,
O15, O17.

**1982-84               Perf. 12½x12**
1002a  A141  ½c                      .20   .20
1006a  A141  5c                      .60   .60
1008a  A141  10c                     .65   .65
1011a  A141  20c                    1.00  1.00
1012a  A141  25c                    2.00  2.00
1013a  A141  30c                    1.50  1.50
1014a  A141  40c                    2.00  2.00
1015a  A141  50c ('84)               .80   .80
1018a  A141  $3                     3.00  3.00
1019a  A141  $5                     4.25  4.25
1020a  A141  $10 ('84)              9.50  9.50
        Nos. 1002a-1020a (11)      25.50 25.50

Snow White at Well — A142

Christmas: Various scenes from Walt Disney's Snow White and the Seven Dwarfs.

**1980, Sept. 25     Litho.      Perf. 11**
1021  A142  ½c multicolored          .20   .20
1022  A142  1c multicolored          .20   .20
1023  A142  2c multicolored          .20   .20
1024  A142  3c multicolored          .20   .20
1025  A142  4c multicolored          .20   .20
1026  A142  5c multicolored          .20   .20
1027  A142  10c multicolored         .20   .20
1028  A142  $2.50 multicolored      3.25  2.75
1029  A142  $3 multicolored         3.75  3.25
        Nos. 1021-1029 (9)          8.40  7.40
**Souvenir Sheet**
1030  A142  $4 multicolored         5.75  5.75
No. 1030 contains a vertical stamp.

Disney Type of 1980

50th anniversary of Pluto character: $2,
Pluto and birthday cake. $4, Pluto.

**1981, Jan. 19      Litho.      Perf. 14**
1031  A135a  $2 multicolored        2.25  2.25
**Souvenir Sheet**
1032  A135a  $4 multicolored        3.25  3.25
No. 1031 issued in sheets of 8.

Adult Education — A143

**1981, Mar. 13      Litho.      Perf. 12½**
1033  A143  5c Flags of the
                Revolution and
                Grenada             .20   .20
1034  A143  10c shown               .20   .20
1035  A143  15c Food processing
                plant               .20   .20
1036  A143  25c Agriculture         .20   .20
1037  A143  40c Fishing boat,
                crawfish            .25   .25
1038  A143  90c Ships               .65   .65
1039  A143  $1 Palm trees           .70   .70
1040  A143  $3 Map                 2.10  2.10
        Nos. 1033-1040 (8)         4.50  4.50
2nd Festival of the Revolution.

Mickey Mouse and Goofy with Easter Basket
A144

Easter: Various Disney characters with Easter baskets.

| 1981, Apr. 7 | | | Perf. 11 | |
|---|---|---|---|---|
| 1041 | A144 | 35c multi | .30 | .30 |
| 1042 | A144 | 40c multi | .35 | .35 |
| 1043 | A144 | $2 multi | 1.75 | 1.75 |
| 1044 | A144 | $2.50 multi | 2.25 | 2.25 |
| | | Nos. 1041-1044 (4) | 4.65 | 4.65 |
| **Souvenir Sheet** | | | | |
| 1045 | A144 | $4 multi | 3.50 | 3.50 |

Large Heads, by Picasso — A145

Paintings by Pablo Picasso (1881-1973): 25c, Woman-Flower. 30c, Portrait of Madame. 90c, Cavalier with Pipe. $5, Woman on the Bank of the Seine.

| 1981, Apr. 28 | | | Perf. 14 | |
|---|---|---|---|---|
| 1046 | A145 | 25c multicolored | .20 | .20 |
| 1047 | A145 | 30c multicolored | .20 | .20 |
| 1048 | A145 | 90c multicolored | .65 | .65 |
| 1049 | A145 | $4 multicolored | 3.00 | 3.00 |
| | | Nos. 1046-1049 (4) | 4.05 | 4.05 |
| **Souvenir Sheet** | | | | |
| 1050 | A145 | $5 multicolored | 5.50 | 5.50 |

**Royal Wedding Issue**
**Common Design Type**

| 1981, June 16 | | | Litho. | Perf. 15 | |
|---|---|---|---|---|---|
| 1051 | CD331a | 50c Couple | .20 | .20 |
| 1052 | CD331a | $2 Holyrood House | .30 | .30 |
| 1053 | CD331a | $4 Charles | .50 | .50 |
| | | Nos. 1051-1053 (3) | 1.00 | 1.00 |
| **Souvenir Sheet** | | | | |
| 1054 | CD331 | $5 Glass coach | 1.00 | 1.00 |
| **Souvenir Booklet** | | | | |
| 1055 | CD331 | | 9.00 | |
| a. | Pane of 6 (3x$1, Lady Diana, 3x$2, Charles) | | 6.00 | |
| b. | Pane of 1, $5, Couple | | 3.00 | |

No. 1055 contains imperf., self-adhesive stamps.
Sheets of 5 plus label contain 30c, 40c or $4 in changed colors, perf. 14x14½.
For overprints see Nos. O11, O14, O16,

The Bath, by Mary Cassatt (1845-1926)
A146

Decade for Women (Paintings by Women): 40c, Mademoiselle Charlotte du Val d'Ognes, by Constance Marie Charpentier. 60c, Self-portrait, by Mary Beale. $3, Woman in White Stockings, by Suzanne Valadon. $5, The Artist Hesitating between the Arts of Music and Painting, horiz.

---

| 1981, Oct. 13 | | | Litho. | Perf. 14 | |
|---|---|---|---|---|---|
| 1058 | A146 | 15c multicolored | .20 | .20 |
| 1059 | A146 | 40c multicolored | .30 | .30 |
| 1060 | A146 | 60c multicolored | .45 | .45 |
| 1061 | A146 | $3 multicolored | 2.00 | 2.00 |
| | | Nos. 1058-1061 (4) | 2.95 | 2.95 |
| **Souvenir Sheet** | | | | |
| 1062 | A146 | $5 multicolored | 3.25 | 3.25 |

Cinderella and Prince Charming Dancing at the Ball — A147

Christmas: Scenes from Walt Disney's Cinderella.

| 1981, Nov. 2 | | | Litho. | Perf. 14x13½ | |
|---|---|---|---|---|---|
| 1063 | A147 | ½c multi | .20 | .20 |
| 1064 | A147 | 1c multi | .20 | .20 |
| 1065 | A147 | 2c multi | .20 | .20 |
| 1066 | A147 | 3c multi | .20 | .20 |
| 1067 | A147 | 4c multi | .20 | .20 |
| 1068 | A147 | 5c multi | .25 | .25 |
| 1069 | A147 | 10c multi | .25 | .25 |
| 1070 | A147 | $2.50 multi | 3.75 | 3.00 |
| 1071 | A147 | $3 multi | 4.00 | 3.50 |
| | | Nos. 1063-1071 (9) | 9.25 | 8.00 |
| **Souvenir Sheet** | | | | |
| 1072 | A147 | $5 multi | 7.00 | 7.00 |

Columbia Space Shuttle — A148

Views of the Columbia space shuttle.

| 1981, Nov. 12 | | | | |
|---|---|---|---|---|
| 1073 | A148 | 30c multicolored | .20 | .20 |
| 1074 | A148 | 60c multicolored | .40 | .40 |
| 1075 | A148 | 70c multicolored | .50 | .50 |
| 1076 | A148 | $3 multicolored | 2.25 | 2.00 |
| | | Nos. 1073-1076 (4) | 3.35 | 3.10 |
| **Souvenir Sheet** | | | | |
| 1077 | A148 | $5 multicolored | 3.50 | 3.50 |

UPU Membership Centenary — A149

| 1981, Dec. 10 | | | Litho. | Perf. 15 | |
|---|---|---|---|---|---|
| 1078 | A149 | 25c St. George's P.O. | .20 | .20 |
| 1079 | A149 | 30c No. 1 | .20 | .20 |
| 1080 | A149 | 90c No. 384 | .60 | .60 |
| 1081 | A149 | $4 No. 189 | 2.50 | 2.50 |
| | | Nos. 1078-1081 (4) | 3.50 | 3.50 |
| **Souvenir Sheet** | | | | |
| 1082 | A149 | $5 No. 562 | 4.00 | 4.00 |

Intl. Year of the Disabled (1981) — A150

---

| 1982, Feb. 4 | | | Perf. 14 | |
|---|---|---|---|---|
| 1083 | A150 | 30c Artist | .20 | .20 |
| 1084 | A150 | 40c Computer operator | .30 | .30 |
| 1085 | A150 | 70c Teaching Braille | .50 | .50 |
| 1086 | A150 | $3 Drummer | 2.00 | 2.00 |
| | | Nos. 1083-1086 (4) | 3.00 | 3.00 |
| **Souvenir Sheet** | | | | |
| 1087 | A150 | $4 Auto mechanic | 3.75 | 3.75 |

Scouting Year A151

| 1982, Feb. 19 | | | Perf. 15 | |
|---|---|---|---|---|
| 1088 | A151 | 70c Gardening | .60 | .60 |
| 1089 | A151 | 90c Map reading | .75 | .75 |
| 1090 | A151 | $1 Bee keeping | .85 | .80 |
| 1091 | A151 | $4 Hospital reading | 2.75 | 2.75 |
| | | Nos. 1088-1091 (4) | 4.95 | 4.90 |
| **Souvenir Sheet** | | | | |
| 1092 | A151 | $5 Trophy presentation | 4.50 | 4.50 |

Flambeaux A152

| 1982, Mar. 24 | | | Litho. | Perf. 14 | |
|---|---|---|---|---|---|
| 1093 | A152 | 10c shown | .65 | .20 |
| 1094 | A152 | 60c Large orange sulphurs | 2.25 | 1.25 |
| 1095 | A152 | $1 Red anartias | 2.75 | 2.10 |
| 1096 | A152 | $3 Polydamas swallowtails | 7.25 | 7.25 |
| | | Nos. 1093-1096 (4) | 12.90 | 10.80 |
| **Souvenir Sheet** | | | | |
| 1097 | A152 | $5 Caribbean buckeyes | 8.25 | 8.25 |

Norman Rockwell A153

| 1982, Apr. 12 | | | Litho. | Perf. 14x13½ | |
|---|---|---|---|---|---|
| 1098 | A153 | 15c shown | .40 | .20 |
| 1099 | A153 | 30c Card Tricks | .65 | .25 |
| 1100 | A153 | 60c Pharmacist | 1.10 | 1.00 |
| 1101 | A153 | 70c Pals | 1.40 | 1.25 |
| | | Nos. 1098-1101 (4) | 3.55 | 2.70 |

**Princess Diana Issue**
**Common Design Type**

| 1982, July 1 | | | Litho. | Perf. 14½x14 | |
|---|---|---|---|---|---|
| 1101A | CD332 | 50c Kensington Palace | .55 | .75 |
| 1102 | CD332 | 60c like 50c | .60 | .50 |
| 1102A | CD332 | $1 Couple in field | 1.00 | .80 |
| 1103 | CD332 | $2 like $1 | 2.50 | 1.75 |
| 1103A | CD332 | $3 Diana in green dress | 2.75 | 2.75 |
| 1104 | CD332 | $4 like $3 | 3.50 | 3.50 |
| | | Nos. 1101A-1104 (6) | 10.90 | 10.05 |
| **Souvenir Sheet** | | | | |
| 1105 | CD332 | $5 Diana, diff. | 6.75 | 6.75 |

For overprints see Nos. 1115A-1119.

---

Franklin Roosevelt Birth Centenary A154

Designs: 10c, Mary McLeod Bethune, director of Negro Affairs, 1942. 60c, Leadbelly (Huddie Ledbetter, Works Progress Administration). $1.10, Signing Fair Employment Act, 1941. $3, Farm Security Administration.

| 1982, July 27 | | | Litho. | Perf. 14 | |
|---|---|---|---|---|---|
| 1106 | A154 | 10c multi | .20 | .20 |
| 1107 | A154 | 60c multi | .35 | .35 |
| 1108 | A154 | $1.10 multi | .65 | .65 |
| 1109 | A154 | $3 multi | 1.75 | 1.75 |
| | | Nos. 1106-1109 (4) | 2.95 | 2.95 |
| **Souvenir Sheet** | | | | |
| 1110 | A154 | $5 multi | 3.50 | 3.50 |

Easter A155

Details from Raphael's "On the Way to Calvary." 70c, $1.10, $4, $5, vert.

| 1982, Sept. 2 | | | Perf. 14½ | |
|---|---|---|---|---|
| 1111 | A155 | 40c multi | .25 | .25 |
| 1112 | A155 | 70c multi | .35 | .35 |
| 1113 | A155 | $1.10 multi | .60 | .60 |
| 1114 | A155 | $4 multi | 2.50 | 2.50 |
| | | Nos. 1111-1114 (4) | 3.70 | 3.70 |
| **Souvenir Sheet** | | | | |
| 1115 | A155 | $5 multi | 4.25 | 4.25 |

Nos. 1101A-1105 Overprinted:
"ROYAL BABY / 21.6.82"

| 1982, Sept. 27 | | | Litho. | Perf. 14½x14 | |
|---|---|---|---|---|---|
| 1115A | CD332 | 50c multi | .35 | .35 |
| 1116 | CD332 | 60c multi | .40 | .40 |
| 1116A | CD332 | $1 multi | .65 | .65 |
| 1117 | CD332 | $2 multi | 1.40 | 1.40 |
| 1117A | CD332 | $3 multi | 2.25 | 2.00 |
| 1118 | CD332 | $4 multi | 2.75 | 2.75 |
| | | Nos. 1115A-1118 (6) | 7.80 | 7.55 |
| **Souvenir Sheet** | | | | |
| 1119 | CD332 | $5 multi | 5.00 | 5.00 |

Birth of Prince William of Wales, June 21.

Orient Express A156

| 1982, Oct. 4 | | | | |
|---|---|---|---|---|
| 1120 | A156 | 30c shown | .35 | .40 |
| 1121 | A156 | 60c Trans-Siberian Express | .65 | .65 |
| 1122 | A156 | 70c Fleche D'or | .75 | .75 |
| 1123 | A156 | 90c Flying Scotsman | .95 | .95 |
| 1124 | A156 | $1 German Federal Railways | 1.25 | 1.25 |
| 1125 | A156 | $3 German Natl. Railways | 3.00 | 4.00 |
| | | Nos. 1120-1125 (6) | 6.95 | 8.00 |
| **Souvenir Sheet** | | | | |
| 1126 | A156 | $5 20th Century Limited, US | 4.00 | 4.00 |

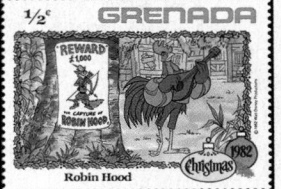

Christmas — A157

Scenes from Walt Disney's Robin Hood.

## 1982, Dec. 7 — Litho. — Perf. 14

| | | | | |
|---|---|---|---|---|
| 1127 | A157 | ½c multi | .20 | .20 |
| 1128 | A157 | 1c multi | .20 | .20 |
| 1129 | A157 | 2c multi | .20 | .20 |
| 1130 | A157 | 3c multi | .20 | .20 |
| 1131 | A157 | 4c multi | .20 | .20 |
| 1132 | A157 | 5c multi | .20 | .20 |
| 1133 | A157 | 10c multi | .20 | .20 |
| 1134 | A157 | $2.50 multi | 3.00 | 3.00 |
| 1135 | A157 | $3 multi | 3.25 | 3.25 |
| | Nos. 1127-1135 (9) | | 7.65 | 7.65 |

**Souvenir Sheet**

| 1136 | A157 | $5 multi | 7.50 | 7.50 |
|---|---|---|---|---|

Italy's Victory in 1982 World Cup A158

## 1982, Dec. 2 — Perf. 14x13½

| 1137 | A158 | 60c Stolen ball | .50 | .50 |
|---|---|---|---|---|
| 1138 | A158 | $4 Captain holding trophy | 3.25 | 3.25 |

**Souvenir Sheet**

| 1139 | A158 | $5 Flags | 3.75 | 3.75 |
|---|---|---|---|---|

Killer Whale — A159

## 1982, Dec. 15 — Perf. 14

| 1140 | A159 | 15c shown | 1.00 | .50 |
|---|---|---|---|---|
| 1141 | A159 | 40c Sperm whale | 2.00 | .75 |
| 1142 | A159 | 70c Blue whale | 2.75 | 2.75 |
| 1143 | A159 | $3 Common dolphins | 5.00 | 6.00 |
| | Nos. 1140-1143 (4) | | 10.75 | 10.00 |

**Souvenir Sheet**

| 1144 | A159 | $5 Humpback whale | 8.75 | 8.75 |
|---|---|---|---|---|

500th Birth Anniv. of Raphael — A160

## 1983, Feb. 15 — Litho. — Perf. 14

| 1145 | A160 | 25c Construction of the Ark | .20 | .20 |
|---|---|---|---|---|
| 1146 | A160 | 30c Jacob's Vision | .25 | .25 |
| 1147 | A160 | 90c Joseph Interprets the Dreams | .60 | .60 |
| 1148 | A160 | $4 Joseph Interprets Pharaoh's Dream | 2.25 | 2.25 |
| | Nos. 1145-1148 (4) | | 3.30 | 3.30 |

**Souvenir Sheet**

| 1149 | A160 | $5 Creation of the Animals | 3.00 | 3.00 |
|---|---|---|---|---|

A161

## 1983, Mar. 14

| 1150 | A161 | 10c Dental care | .20 | .20 |
|---|---|---|---|---|
| 1151 | A161 | 70c Airport runway construction | .45 | .45 |
| 1152 | A161 | $1.10 Beach | .75 | .75 |
| 1153 | A161 | $3 Boat building | 1.50 | 2.00 |
| | Nos. 1150-1153 (4) | | 2.90 | 3.40 |

Commonwealth Day.

World Communication Year — A162

## 1983, Apr. 18

| 1154 | A162 | 30c Ship-satellite communication | .20 | .20 |
|---|---|---|---|---|
| 1155 | A162 | 40c Rural telephone installation | .25 | .25 |
| 1156 | A162 | $2.50 Weather map | 1.60 | 1.60 |
| 1157 | A162 | $3 Airport control tower | 2.00 | 2.00 |
| | Nos. 1154-1157 (4) | | 4.05 | 4.05 |

**Souvenir Sheet**

| 1158 | A162 | $5 Satellite | 3.25 | 3.25 |
|---|---|---|---|---|

For overprints see Nos. 1248-1250.

Franklin Sport Sedan, 1928 A163

## 1983, May 4 — Litho. — Perf. 15

| 1159 | A163 | 6c shown | .20 | .20 |
|---|---|---|---|---|
| 1160 | A163 | 10c Delage D8, 1933 | .20 | .20 |
| 1161 | A163 | 40c Alvis, 1938 | .25 | .25 |
| 1162 | A163 | 60c Invicta S-type Tourer, 1931 | .40 | .40 |
| 1163 | A163 | 70c Alfa-Romeo 1750 Gran Sport, 1930 | .45 | .45 |
| 1164 | A163 | 90c Isotta Fraschini, 1930 | .65 | .60 |
| 1165 | A163 | $1 Bugatti Royal Type 41, 1941 | .70 | .70 |
| 1166 | A163 | $2 BMV 328, 1938 | 1.40 | 1.40 |
| 1167 | A163 | $3 Marmon V-16, 1931 | 2.00 | 2.00 |
| 1168 | A163 | $4 Lincoln KB Saloon, 1932 | 2.75 | 2.75 |
| | Nos. 1159-1168 (10) | | 9.00 | 8.95 |

**Souvenir Sheet**

| 1169 | A163 | $5 Cougar XR-7, 1972 | 3.50 | 3.50 |
|---|---|---|---|---|

Manned Flight Bicentenary — A164

## 1983, July 18 — Litho. — Perf. 14

| 1170 | A164 | 30c Norge blimp | .60 | .60 |
|---|---|---|---|---|
| 1171 | A164 | 60c Gloster-VI sea plane | 1.00 | 1.00 |
| 1172 | A164 | $1.10 Curtiss NC-4 | 1.75 | 1.75 |
| 1173 | A164 | $4 Dornier Do-18 | 4.25 | 4.25 |
| | Nos. 1170-1173 (4) | | 7.60 | 7.60 |

**Souvenir Sheet**

| 1174 | A164 | $5 Hot air ballooning, vert. | 5.00 | 5.00 |
|---|---|---|---|---|

Christmas A165

Designs: Walt Disney's It's Beginning to look a lot like Christmas.

## 1983, Nov. — Perf. 11

| 1175 | A165 | ½c Morty and Patches | .20 | .20 |
|---|---|---|---|---|
| 1176 | A165 | 1c Ludwig von Drake | .20 | .20 |
| 1177 | A165 | 2c Gyro Gearloose | .20 | .20 |
| 1178 | A165 | 3c Pluto and Figaro | .20 | .20 |
| 1179 | A165 | 4c Morty and Ferdy | .20 | .20 |
| 1180 | A165 | 5c Mickey Mouse and Goofy | .30 | .25 |
| 1181 | A165 | 10c Chip'n'Dale | .30 | .25 |
| 1182 | A165 | $2.50 Mickey and Minnie | 3.25 | 3.25 |
| 1183 | A165 | $3 Donald and Grandma Duck | 3.25 | 3.25 |
| | Nos. 1175-1183 (9) | | 8.10 | 8.00 |

**Souvenir Sheet**

| 1184 | A165 | $5 Goofy | 8.25 | 8.25 |
|---|---|---|---|---|

1984 Olympics — A166

Designs: Various Disney characters.

## 1983, Dec. 19 — Litho. — Perf. 13½

| 1185 | A166 | ½c Pommel Horse | .20 | .20 |
|---|---|---|---|---|
| 1186 | A166 | 1c Boxing | .20 | .20 |
| 1187 | A166 | 2c Archery | .20 | .20 |
| 1188 | A166 | 3c Uneven bars | .20 | .20 |
| 1189 | A166 | 4c Hurdles | .20 | .20 |
| 1190 | A166 | 5c Weightlifting | .25 | .25 |
| 1191 | A166 | $1 Kayak | 2.00 | 2.00 |
| 1192 | A166 | $2 Marathon | 2.75 | 2.75 |
| 1193 | A166 | $3 Pole Vault | 3.25 | 3.75 |
| | Nos. 1185-1193 (9) | | 9.25 | 9.75 |

**Souvenir Sheet**

| 1194 | A166 | $5 Medley Relay, vert. | 8.25 | 8.25 |
|---|---|---|---|---|

**Inscribed with Olympic Rings Emblem**

## 1984 — Perf. 12½x12

| 1185a | A166 | ½c | .20 | .20 |
|---|---|---|---|---|
| 1186a | A166 | 1c | .20 | .20 |
| 1187a | A166 | 2c | .20 | .20 |
| 1188a | A166 | 3c | .20 | .20 |
| 1189a | A166 | 4c | .20 | .20 |
| 1190a | A166 | 5c | .25 | .25 |
| 1191a | A166 | $1 | 2.00 | 2.00 |
| 1192a | A166 | $2 | 2.75 | 2.75 |
| 1193a | A166 | $3 | 3.25 | 3.75 |
| | Nos. 1185a-1193a (9) | | 9.25 | 9.75 |

**Souvenir Sheet**

| 1194a | A166 | $5 Olympic rings emblem inscribed | 8.25 | 8.25 |
|---|---|---|---|---|

Nos. 1185a-1193a printed in sheets of 5.

Banana Boat A167

## 1984, July 16 — Litho. — Perf. 15

| 1195 | A167 | 40c shown | 1.00 | .60 |
|---|---|---|---|---|
| 1196 | A167 | 70c Queen Elizabeth 2 | 1.50 | 1.00 |
| 1197 | A167 | 90c Working sailboats | 1.60 | 2.00 |
| 1198 | A167 | $4 Amerikanis | 6.00 | 8.00 |
| | Nos. 1195-1198 (4) | | 10.10 | 11.60 |

**Souvenir Sheet**

| 1199 | A167 | $5 Spanish galleon, flotilla | 7.00 | 7.00 |
|---|---|---|---|---|

King William I, 1066-87 — A168

British Kings or Queens and Years of their reigns: No. 1200b, William II, 1087-1100. c, Henry I, 1100-35. d, Stephen, 1135-54. e, Henry II, 1154-89. f, Richard I, 1189-99. g, John, 1199-1216.

No. 1201a, Henry III, 1216-72. b, Edward I, 1272-1307. c, Edward II, 1307-27. d, Edward III, 1327-77. e, Richard II, 1377-99. f, Henry IV, 1399-1413. g, Henry V, 1413-22.

No. 1202a, Henry VI, 1422-61. b, Edward IV, 1461-83. c, Edward V, 1483. d, Richard III, 1483-85. e, Henry VII, 1485-1509. f, Henry VIII, 1509-47. g, Edward VI, 1547-53.

No. 1203a, Jane Grey, 1553. b, Mary I, 1553-58. c, Elizabeth I, 1558-1603. d, James I, 1603-25. e, Charles I, 1625-49. f, Charles II, 1660-85. g, James II, 1685-88.

No. 1204a, William III, 1688-1702. b, Mary II, 1688-94. c, Anne, 1702-14. d, George I, 1714-27. e, George II, 1727-60. f, George III, 1760-1820. g, George IV, 1820-30.

No. 1205a, William IV, 1830-37. b, Victoria, 1837-1901. c, Edward VII, 1901-10. d, George V, 1910-36. e, Edward VIII, 1936. f, George VI, 1936-52. g, Elizabeth II, since 1952. Size: 141x128mm.

## 1984, Jan. 25 — Litho. — Perf. 14

| 1200 | | Sheet of 7 + label | 21.00 | 21.00 |
|---|---|---|---|---|
| a.-g. | A168 | $4, any single | 3.00 | 3.00 |
| 1201 | | Sheet of 7 + label | 21.00 | 21.00 |
| a.-g. | A168 | $4, any single | 3.00 | 3.00 |
| 1202 | | Sheet of 7 + label | 21.00 | 21.00 |
| a.-g. | A168 | $4, any single | 3.00 | 3.00 |
| 1203 | | Sheet of 7 + label | 21.00 | 21.00 |
| a.-g. | A168 | $4, any single | 3.00 | 3.00 |
| 1204 | | Sheet of 7 + label | 21.00 | 21.00 |
| a.-g. | A168 | $4, any single | 3.00 | 3.00 |
| 1205 | | Sheet of 7 + label | 21.00 | 21.00 |
| a.-g. | A168 | $4, any single | 3.00 | 3.00 |

Local Flowers A169

## 1984, May — Perf. 15

| 1206 | A169 | 25c Lantana | .25 | .20 |
|---|---|---|---|---|
| 1207 | A169 | 30c Plumbago | .35 | .25 |
| 1208 | A169 | 90c Spider lily | .80 | .70 |
| 1209 | A169 | $4 Giant alocasia | 3.00 | 3.00 |
| | Nos. 1206-1209 (4) | | 4.40 | 4.15 |

**Souvenir Sheet**

| 1210 | A169 | $5 Orange trumpet vine | 3.50 | 3.50 |
|---|---|---|---|---|

For overprints see Nos. 1216-1218.

Coral Reef Fish, World Wildlife Fund Emblem A170

## 1984, May — Litho. — Perf. 14

| 1211 | A170 | 10c Blue parrot fish | 4.50 | 1.25 |
|---|---|---|---|---|
| 1212 | A170 | 30c Flame-back cherub fish | 7.00 | 2.25 |
| 1213 | A170 | 70c Painted wrasse | 12.00 | 5.50 |
| 1214 | A170 | 90c Straight-tailed razorfish | 16.00 | 7.00 |
| | Nos. 1211-1214 (4) | | 39.50 | 16.00 |

**Souvenir Sheet**

| 1215 | A170 | $5 Spanish hogfish | 11.00 | 11.00 |
|---|---|---|---|---|

Nos. 1208-1210 Overprinted: "19th U.P.U CONGRESS — HAMBURG"

## 1984 — Litho. — Perf. 15

| 1216 | A169 | 90c multi | .70 | .70 |
|---|---|---|---|---|
| 1217 | A169 | $4 multi | 3.00 | 3.00 |

**Souvenir Sheet**

| 1218 | A169 | $5 multi | 3.75 | 3.75 |
|---|---|---|---|---|

AUSIPEX '84 — A171     Correggio & Degas — A171a

## 1984, Sept. 21 — Perf. 14

| 1219 | A171 | $1.10 Puffing Billy | 1.10 | 1.10 |
|---|---|---|---|---|
| 1220 | A171 | $4 Australia II | 4.50 | 4.50 |

**Souvenir Sheet**

| 1221 | A171 | $5 Melbourne tram | 7.00 | 7.00 |
|---|---|---|---|---|

## 1984, Aug. Litho. Perf. 14

Paintings by Correggio: 10c, The Night (detail). 30c, Virgin Adoring the Child. 90c, Mystical Marriage of St. Catherine with St. Sebastian. $4, Madonna and the Fruit Basket. No. 1230, Madonna at the Spring.
Paintings by Degas: 25c, L'Absinthe. 70c, Pouting, horiz. $1.10, The Millinery Shop. $3, The Bellelli Family. No. 1231, The Cotton Market.

| | | | | |
|---|---|---|---|---|
| 1222 | A171a | 10c multi | .45 | .20 |
| 1223 | A171a | 25c multi | .60 | .30 |
| 1224 | A171a | 30c multi | .80 | .40 |
| 1225 | A171a | 70c multi | 1.25 | 1.00 |
| 1226 | A171a | 90c multi | 1.50 | 1.00 |
| 1227 | A171a | $1.10 multi | 1.75 | 1.75 |
| 1228 | A171a | $3 multi | 3.00 | 4.00 |
| 1229 | A171a | $4 multi | 4.00 | 5.00 |
| | | Nos. 1222-1229 (8) | 13.35 | 13.65 |

### Souvenir Sheets

| | | | | |
|---|---|---|---|---|
| 1230 | A171a | $5 multi | 6.25 | 6.25 |
| 1231 | A171a | $5 multi | 6.25 | 6.25 |

19th Cent. Locomotives — A172

## 1984, Oct. Perf. 14½

| | | | | |
|---|---|---|---|---|
| 1232 | A172 | 30c Locomotion, 1825 | .80 | .35 |
| 1233 | A172 | 40c Novelty, 1829 | .90 | .45 |
| 1234 | A172 | 60c Washington Farmer, 1836 | 1.00 | .70 |
| 1235 | A172 | 70c French Crampton, 1859 | 1.00 | 1.00 |
| 1236 | A172 | 90c Dutch State, 1873 | 1.25 | 1.00 |
| 1237 | A172 | $1.10 Champion, 1882 | 1.50 | 2.00 |
| 1238 | A172 | $2 Webb Compound, 1893 | 2.40 | 3.00 |
| 1239 | A172 | $4 Berlin 74, 1900 | 4.75 | 5.00 |
| | | Nos. 1232-1239 (8) | 13.60 | 13.50 |

### Souvenir Sheets

| | | | | |
|---|---|---|---|---|
| 1240 | A172 | $5 Crampton Phoenix, 1863 | 4.50 | 4.50 |
| 1241 | A172 | $5 2-8-2 Mikado, 1897 | 4.50 | 4.50 |

Christmas and 50th Anniv. of Donald Duck A173

Scenes from various Donald Duck movies.

### Perf. 13½x14, 12 ($2)

## 1984, Nov. Litho.

| | | | | |
|---|---|---|---|---|
| 1242 | A173 | 45c multicolored | 1.00 | .65 |
| 1243 | A173 | 60c multicolored | 1.25 | .95 |
| 1244 | A173 | 90c multicolored | 2.00 | 1.50 |
| 1245 | A173 | $2 multicolored | 3.50 | 3.50 |
| 1246 | A173 | $4 multicolored | 6.75 | 6.75 |
| | | Nos. 1242-1246 (5) | 14.50 | 13.35 |

### Souvenir Sheet

| | | | | |
|---|---|---|---|---|
| 1247 | A173 | $5 multicolored | 8.75 | 8.75 |

Nos. 1155. 1157, and 1158 Overprinted: "OPENING OF / POINT SALINE / INT'L AIRPORT"

## 1984, Oct. 28 Litho. Perf. 14½x14

| | | | | |
|---|---|---|---|---|
| 1248 | A162 | 40c on #1155 | .50 | .50 |
| 1249 | A162 | $3 on #1157 | 3.00 | 3.00 |

### Souvenir Sheet

Same Overprint in Margin in 2 Lines

| | | | | |
|---|---|---|---|---|
| 1250 | A162 | $5 on #1158 | 4.50 | 4.50 |

---

Audubon Birth Bicentenary A174

## 1985, Feb. Litho. Perf. 14

| | | | | |
|---|---|---|---|---|
| 1251 | A174 | 50c Clapper Rail | 2.00 | .75 |
| 1252 | A174 | 70c Hooded Warbler | 2.50 | 1.50 |
| 1253 | A174 | 90c Flicker | 3.25 | 1.75 |
| 1254 | A174 | $4 Bohemian Waxwing | 6.75 | 7.50 |
| | | Nos. 1251-1254 (4) | 14.50 | 11.50 |

### Souvenir Sheet

| | | | | |
|---|---|---|---|---|
| 1255 | A174 | $5 Pigeon Hawk, horiz. | 12.00 | 12.00 |

See Nos. 1352-1356.

Motorcycle Centenary — A175

## 1985, Mar. 11 Litho. Perf. 14

| | | | | |
|---|---|---|---|---|
| 1256 | A175 | 25c Honda XL500R | 1.50 | .75 |
| 1257 | A175 | 50c Suzuki GS1100ES | 1.75 | 1.50 |
| 1258 | A175 | 90c Kawasaki KZ700 | 2.75 | 1.60 |
| 1259 | A175 | $4 BMW K100 | 6.00 | 7.50 |
| | | Nos. 1256-1259 (4) | 12.00 | 11.35 |

### Souvenir Sheet

| | | | | |
|---|---|---|---|---|
| 1260 | A175 | $5 Yamaha 500CC | 9.25 | 9.25 |

Girl Guides, 75th Anniv. A176

## 1985, Apr. 15

| | | | | |
|---|---|---|---|---|
| 1261 | A176 | 25c Nature hike | .65 | .40 |
| 1262 | A176 | 60c Cookout | 1.00 | .90 |
| 1263 | A176 | 90c Singing around campfire | 1.50 | 1.25 |
| 1264 | A176 | $3 Public service | 4.50 | 4.50 |
| | | Nos. 1261-1264 (4) | 7.65 | 7.05 |

### Souvenir Sheet

| | | | | |
|---|---|---|---|---|
| 1265 | A176 | $5 Flags | 5.00 | 5.00 |

Opening of Point Saline Intl. Airport, Oct. 28, 1984 A177

Inaugural flights.

## 1985, Apr. 30

| | | | | |
|---|---|---|---|---|
| 1266 | A177 | 70c From Barbados | 2.75 | 1.40 |
| 1267 | A177 | $1 From New York | 3.75 | 2.00 |
| 1268 | A177 | $4 To Miami | 7.75 | 8.50 |
| | | Nos. 1266-1268 (3) | 14.25 | 11.90 |

### Souvenir Sheet

| | | | | |
|---|---|---|---|---|
| 1269 | A177 | $5 Point Saline Intl. Airport | 8.00 | 8.00 |

Intl. Civil Aviation Org., 40th Anniv. A178

---

## 1985, May 15

| | | | | |
|---|---|---|---|---|
| 1270 | A178 | 10c McDonnell Douglas DC-8 | .40 | .20 |
| 1271 | A178 | 50c Super Constellation | 1.00 | .65 |
| 1272 | A178 | 60c Vickers Vanguard | 1.50 | .80 |
| 1273 | A178 | $4 DeHavilland Twin Otter | 5.00 | 6.50 |
| | | Nos. 1270-1273 (4) | 7.90 | 8.15 |

### Souvenir Sheet

| | | | | |
|---|---|---|---|---|
| 1274 | A178 | $5 Avro 748 Turboprop | 5.25 | 5.25 |

Water Sports A179

## 1985, June 15 Perf. 15

| | | | | |
|---|---|---|---|---|
| 1275 | A179 | 10c Model boat racing | .20 | .20 |
| 1276 | A179 | 50c Snorkeling, Sandy Island carriacou | .40 | .40 |
| 1277 | A179 | $1.10 Sailing, Grand Anse Beach | .90 | .90 |
| 1278 | A179 | $4 Windsurfing | 3.00 | 3.00 |
| | | Nos. 1275-1278 (4) | 4.50 | 4.50 |

### Miniature Sheet

| | | | | |
|---|---|---|---|---|
| 1279 | A179 | $5 Snorkelers, surfers, sailboats | 5.00 | 5.00 |

Island Flowers — A180

½c, Strelitzia reginae. 1c, Passiflora coccinea. 2c, Nerium oleander. 4c, Ananas comosus. 5c, Anthurium andraeanum. 6c, Bougainvillea glabra. 10c, Hibiscus rosasinensis. 15c, Alpinia purpurata. 25c, Euphorbia pulcherrima. 30c, Antigonon leptopus. 40c, Datura candida. 50c, Hippeastrum puniceum. 60c, Opuntia megacantha. 70c, Acalypha hispida. 75c, Cordia sebestina. $1, Catharanthus roseus. $1.10, Ixora macrothyrsa. $3, Justicia brandegeeana. $5, Plumbago capensis. $10, Lantana camara. $20, Jatropha integerrima.

## 1985-88 Perf. 14

| | | | | |
|---|---|---|---|---|
| 1280 | A180 | ½c multi | .20 | .20 |
| 1281 | A180 | 1c multi | .20 | .20 |
| 1282 | A180 | 2c multi | .20 | .20 |
| 1283 | A180 | 4c multi | .20 | .20 |
| 1284 | A180 | 5c multi | .20 | .20 |
| 1285 | A180 | 6c multi | .20 | .20 |
| 1286 | A180 | 10c multi | .20 | .20 |
| 1287 | A180 | 15c multi | .20 | .20 |
| 1288 | A180 | 25c multi | .20 | .20 |
| 1289 | A180 | 30c multi | .20 | .20 |
| 1290 | A180 | 40c multi | .30 | .30 |
| 1291 | A180 | 50c multi | .35 | .35 |
| 1292 | A180 | 60c multi | .40 | .40 |
| 1293 | A180 | 70c multi | .45 | .45 |
| 1293B | A180 | 75c multi | .60 | .60 |
| 1294 | A180 | $1 multi | .70 | .70 |
| 1295 | A180 | $1.10 multi | .75 | .75 |
| 1296 | A180 | $3 multi | 2.00 | 2.00 |
| 1297 | A180 | $5 multi | 3.25 | 3.25 |
| 1297A | A180 | $10 multi | 6.50 | 6.50 |
| 1297B | A180 | $20 multi | 13.00 | 13.00 |
| | | Nos. 1280-1297B (21) | 30.30 | 30.30 |

Issued: #1280-1293, 1294-1297, 7/1; $10, 11/11; $20, 8/1/86; 75c, 1/12/88.
For overprints see #1357-1358, 1558-1560.

## 1986 Perf. 12x12½

| | | | | |
|---|---|---|---|---|
| 1280a | A180 | ½c | .20 | .20 |
| 1281a | A180 | 1c | .20 | .20 |
| 1282a | A180 | 2c | .20 | .20 |
| 1283a | A180 | 4c | .20 | .20 |
| 1284a | A180 | 5c | .20 | .20 |
| 1285a | A180 | 6c | .20 | .20 |
| 1286a | A180 | 10c | .20 | .20 |
| 1287a | A180 | 15c | .20 | .20 |
| 1288a | A180 | 25c | .20 | .20 |
| 1289a | A180 | 30c | .20 | .20 |
| 1290a | A180 | 40c | .30 | .30 |
| 1291a | A180 | 50c | .35 | .35 |
| 1292a | A180 | 60c | .40 | .40 |
| 1293a | A180 | 70c | .45 | .45 |
| 1294a | A180 | $1 | .70 | .70 |
| 1295a | A180 | $1.10 | .75 | .75 |
| 1296a | A180 | $3 | 2.00 | 2.00 |

---

| | | | | |
|---|---|---|---|---|
| 1297c | A180 | $5 | 3.25 | 3.25 |
| 1297d | A180 | $10 | 6.50 | 6.50 |
| | | Nos. 1280a-1297d (19) | 16.70 | 16.70 |

Issued: #1280a-1285a, 1287-1292a, 1294a-1296a, Mar.; 10c, 70c, $5, July; $10, Dec.
Nos. 1289, 1291, 1292 and 1294 reprinted with "1987" imprint, No. 1286 with "1988" imprint.

Queen Mother, 85th Birthday A181

Photographs: $1, At the Royal Opera, vert. $1.50, Playing pool, London Press Club. $2.50, At Epsom for the Oaks Day races, vert. $5, In open carriage with Prince Charles, Thanksgiving Day, 1980, vert.

## 1985, July 5

| | | | | |
|---|---|---|---|---|
| 1298 | A181 | $1 multicolored | .70 | .70 |
| 1299 | A181 | $1.50 multicolored | 1.10 | 1.10 |
| 1300 | A181 | $2.50 multicolored | 1.75 | 1.75 |
| | | Nos. 1298-1300 (3) | 3.55 | 3.55 |

### Souvenir Sheet

| | | | | |
|---|---|---|---|---|
| 1301 | A181 | $5 multicolored | 4.00 | 4.00 |

## 1986, Jan. 20 Litho. Perf. 12x12½

| | | | | |
|---|---|---|---|---|
| 1301A | A181 | 90c like #1298 | .65 | .65 |
| 1301B | A181 | $1 like #1299 | .75 | .75 |
| 1301C | A181 | $3 like #1300 | 2.25 | 2.25 |
| | | Nos. 1301A-1301C (3) | 3.65 | 3.65 |

#1301A-1301C issued in sheets of 5 + label.

Intl. Youth Year — A182

## 1985, Aug. 21 Perf. 15

| | | | | |
|---|---|---|---|---|
| 1302 | A182 | 25c Gardening | .40 | .25 |
| 1303 | A182 | 50c At the beach | .50 | .40 |
| 1304 | A182 | $1.10 Education | 1.00 | 1.00 |
| 1305 | A182 | $3 Health care | 2.40 | 2.40 |
| | | Nos. 1302-1305 (4) | 4.30 | 4.05 |

### Souvenir Sheet

| | | | | |
|---|---|---|---|---|
| 1306 | A182 | $5 Harmonizing | 4.50 | 4.50 |

4th Caribbean Cuboree, Aug. 17-23 A183

## 1985, Sept. 5 Perf. 14

| | | | | |
|---|---|---|---|---|
| 1307 | A183 | 10c Pitching tents | .40 | .20 |
| 1308 | A183 | 50c Swimming | .80 | .65 |
| 1309 | A183 | $1 Stamp collecting | 1.90 | 1.40 |
| 1310 | A183 | $4 Bird watching | 5.25 | 5.25 |
| | | Nos. 1307-1310 (4) | 8.35 | 7.50 |

### Souvenir Sheet

| | | | | |
|---|---|---|---|---|
| 1311 | A183 | $5 Grand Circle ritual | 6.00 | 6.00 |

Johann Sebastian Bach — A184

Portrait, signature, music from Ciaccona and: 25c, Crumhorn. 70c, Oboe d'amore. $1, Violin. $3, Harpsichord. $5, Portrait.

## 1985, Sept. 19
| | | | | |
|---|---|---|---|---|
| 1312 | A184 | 25c multicolored | .80 | .20 |
| 1313 | A184 | 70c multicolored | 1.50 | .85 |
| 1314 | A184 | $1 multicolored | 2.00 | 1.25 |
| 1315 | A184 | $3 multicolored | 3.75 | 3.75 |
| | | Nos. 1312-1315 (4) | 8.05 | 6.05 |

**Souvenir Sheet**
| | | | | |
|---|---|---|---|---|
| 1316 | A184 | $5 multicolored | 6.25 | 6.25 |

The Prince & the Pauper — A185

Walt Disney characters.

## 1985, Oct. 30
| | | | | |
|---|---|---|---|---|
| 1317 | A185 | 25c Prince & Pauper meet | 1.25 | .40 |
| 1318 | A185 | 50c Exchange clothes | 1.50 | .80 |
| 1319 | A185 | $1.10 Prince as the Pauper | 2.00 | 1.75 |
| 1320 | A185 | $1.50 Prince rescued | 2.75 | 2.50 |
| 1321 | A185 | $2 Pauper as the Prince | 4.50 | 4.50 |
| | | Nos. 1317-1321 (5) | 12.00 | 9.95 |

**Souvenir Sheet**
| | | | | |
|---|---|---|---|---|
| 1322 | A185 | $5 Prince & Pauper celebrate | 9.75 | 9.75 |

IYY, Mark Twain (1835-1910), author.

Elizabeth II, Royal Visit to Spice Island — A186

## 1985, Oct. 31          Perf. 14½
| | | | | |
|---|---|---|---|---|
| 1323 | A186 | 50c Flags of Grenada, U.K. | 1.00 | .50 |
| 1324 | A186 | $1 Elizabeth II, vert. | 1.00 | 1.25 |
| 1325 | A186 | $4 HMS Britannia | 3.50 | 3.50 |
| | | Nos. 1323-1325 (3) | 5.50 | 5.25 |

**Souvenir Sheet**
| | | | | |
|---|---|---|---|---|
| 1326 | A186 | $5 Map | 4.25 | 4.25 |

The Brothers Grimm — A187

Disney characters in The Fisherman and His Wife.

## 1985, Nov. 4          Litho.          Perf. 14
| | | | | |
|---|---|---|---|---|
| 1327 | A187 | 30c multicolored | 1.00 | .50 |
| 1328 | A187 | 60c multicolored | 1.50 | 1.00 |
| 1329 | A187 | 70c multicolored | 2.00 | 1.10 |
| 1330 | A187 | $1 multicolored | 3.00 | 1.60 |
| 1331 | A187 | $3 multicolored | 5.25 | 5.25 |
| | | Nos. 1327-1331 (5) | 12.75 | 9.45 |

**Souvenir Sheet**
| | | | | |
|---|---|---|---|---|
| 1332 | A187 | $5 multicolored | 9.75 | 9.75 |

Indigenous Fish and Coral — A188

## 1985, Nov. 15
| | | | | |
|---|---|---|---|---|
| 1333 | A188 | 25c Red-spotted hawkfish | 1.75 | .80 |
| 1334 | A188 | 50c Spotfin butterflyfish | 2.75 | 1.25 |
| 1335 | A188 | $1.10 Fire coral, orange sponge | 5.00 | 3.25 |
| 1336 | A188 | $3 Pillar coral | 8.75 | 8.75 |
| | | Nos. 1333-1336 (4) | 18.25 | 14.05 |

**Souvenir Sheet**
| | | | | |
|---|---|---|---|---|
| 1337 | A188 | $5 Bigeye | 7.00 | 7.00 |

UN, 40th Anniv. A189

UN stamps and famous people: 50c, No. 258, Mary McLeod Bethune (1875-1955), American educator. $2, No. 156, Maimonides (1135-1204), Judaic scholar. $2.50, No. 41, Alexander Graham Bell (1847-1922), inventor of the telephone. $5, Dag Hammarskjold (1905-1961), 2nd UN secretary general.

## 1985, Nov. 22          Perf. 14½
| | | | | |
|---|---|---|---|---|
| 1338 | A189 | 50c multicolored | .75 | .65 |
| 1339 | A189 | $2 multicolored | 3.50 | 3.50 |
| 1340 | A189 | $2.50 multicolored | 3.50 | 4.00 |
| | | Nos. 1338-1340 (3) | 7.75 | 8.15 |

**Souvenir Sheet**
| | | | | |
|---|---|---|---|---|
| 1341 | A189 | $5 multicolored | 4.75 | 4.75 |

Christmas A190

Religious paintings: 25c, Adoration of the Shepherds, by Andre Mantegna (1431-1506). 60c, Journey of the Magi, by Sassetta (d. 1450). 90c, Madonna and Child Enthroned with Saints, by Raphael (1483-1520). $4, Nativity, by Monaco. $5, Madonna and Child Enthroned with Saints, by Agnolo Gaddi (c. 1350-1396).

## 1985, Dec. 23          Perf. 15
| | | | | |
|---|---|---|---|---|
| 1342 | A190 | 25c multicolored | .20 | .20 |
| 1343 | A190 | 60c multicolored | .40 | .40 |
| 1344 | A190 | 90c multicolored | .60 | .60 |
| 1345 | A190 | $4 multicolored | 2.75 | 2.75 |
| | | Nos. 1342-1345 (4) | 3.95 | 3.95 |

**Souvenir Sheet**
| | | | | |
|---|---|---|---|---|
| 1346 | A190 | $5 multicolored | 3.50 | 3.50 |

Statue of Liberty, Cent. A191

Views of New York City.

## 1986, Jan. 6
| | | | | |
|---|---|---|---|---|
| 1347 | A191 | 5c Columbus Circle, 1893 | .50 | .20 |
| 1348 | A191 | 25c Circle, 1986 | 1.00 | .45 |
| 1349 | A191 | 40c Central Park Mounted Police, 1895 | 1.75 | 1.25 |
| 1350 | A191 | $4 Mounted Police, 1986 | 6.50 | 8.00 |
| | | Nos. 1347-1350 (4) | 9.75 | 9.90 |

**Souvenir Sheet**
| | | | | |
|---|---|---|---|---|
| 1351 | A191 | $5 Statue of Liberty | 5.75 | 5.75 |

Nos. 1347-1348, 1351 vert.

### Audubon Type of 1985

## 1986, Jan. 20          Perf. 12x12½
| | | | | |
|---|---|---|---|---|
| 1352 | A174 | 50c Snowy egret | 2.00 | 1.00 |
| 1353 | A174 | 90c Red flamingo | 2.75 | 1.60 |
| 1354 | A174 | $1.10 Barnacle goose | 3.00 | 2.50 |
| 1355 | A174 | $3 Smew | 5.50 | 5.50 |
| | | Nos. 1352-1355 (4) | 13.25 | 10.60 |

**Souvenir Sheet**
**Perf. 14**
| | | | | |
|---|---|---|---|---|
| 1356 | A174 | $5 Brant Goose, horiz. | 16.00 | 16.00 |

Nos. 1291 and 1297 Overprinted "VISIT OF PRES. REAGAN 20 FEB. 1986"

## 1986, Feb. 20          Perf. 14
| | | | | |
|---|---|---|---|---|
| 1357 | A180 | 50c multicolored | .45 | .45 |
| 1358 | A180 | $5 multicolored | 4.50 | 4.50 |

St. George Methodist Church, Bicent. A192

## 1986, Feb. 24          Perf. 15
| | | | | |
|---|---|---|---|---|
| 1359 | A192 | 60c multicolored | .90 | .90 |

**Souvenir Sheet**
| | | | | |
|---|---|---|---|---|
| 1360 | A192 | $5 multicolored | 4.00 | 4.00 |

Heritage Year.

1986 World Cup Soccer Championships, Mexico — A193

Various soccer plays.

## 1986, Mar. 6          Perf. 14
| | | | | |
|---|---|---|---|---|
| 1361 | A193 | 50c multicolored | .80 | .70 |
| 1362 | A193 | 70c multicolored | 1.00 | 1.00 |
| 1363 | A193 | 90c multicolored | 1.50 | 1.50 |
| 1364 | A193 | $4 multicolored | 5.25 | 5.25 |
| | | Nos. 1361-1364 (4) | 8.55 | 8.45 |

**Souvenir Sheet**
| | | | | |
|---|---|---|---|---|
| 1365 | A193 | $5 multicolored | 6.25 | 6.25 |

For overprints see Nos. 1399-1403.

Halley's Comet A194

5c, Clyde Tombaugh, discovered Pluto, 1930, & Dudley Observatory. 20c, US X-24B space shuttle prototype, 1973. 40c, Medallic art, Catholic Church, 1618. $4, Lot & his daughters fleeing Sodom & Gomorrah, 1949 B.C. $5, Comet over Grand Anse Beach.

## 1986, Mar. 20
| | | | | |
|---|---|---|---|---|
| 1366 | A194 | 5c multicolored | .50 | .50 |
| 1367 | A194 | 20c multicolored | .75 | .25 |
| 1368 | A194 | 40c multicolored | 1.00 | .40 |
| 1369 | A194 | $4 multicolored | 4.25 | 4.25 |
| | | Nos. 1366-1369 (4) | 6.50 | 5.40 |

**Souvenir Sheet**
| | | | | |
|---|---|---|---|---|
| 1370 | A194 | $4 multicolored | 8.00 | 8.00 |

For overprints see Nos. 1416-1420.

### Queen Elizabeth II, 60th Birthday
#### Common Design Type

2c, Signing the log, 1951. $1.50, Presenting polo trophy, Windsor, 1965. $4, Derby Day, 1977. $5, Royal family portrait, 1939.

## 1986, Apr. 21          Perf. 14
| | | | | |
|---|---|---|---|---|
| 1371 | CD339 | 2c yel & blk | .20 | .20 |
| 1372 | CD339 | $1.50 pale grn & multi | 1.00 | 1.00 |
| 1373 | CD339 | $4 dl lil & multi | 2.75 | 2.75 |
| | | Nos. 1371-1373 (3) | 3.95 | 3.95 |

**Souvenir Sheet**
| | | | | |
|---|---|---|---|---|
| 1374 | CD339 | $5 tan & blk | 3.50 | 3.50 |

AMERIPEX '86 — A195

Walt Disney characters playing baseball.

## 1986, May 22          Litho.          Perf. 11
| | | | | |
|---|---|---|---|---|
| 1375 | A195 | 1c Pitcher | .20 | .20 |
| 1376 | A195 | 2c Catcher | .20 | .20 |
| 1377 | A195 | 3c Strike | .20 | .20 |
| 1378 | A195 | 4c Force out | .20 | .20 |
| 1379 | A195 | 5c Fly ball | .20 | .20 |
| 1380 | A195 | 6c Third base | .25 | .25 |
| 1381 | A195 | $2 Manager | 2.25 | 1.90 |
| 1382 | A195 | $3 Error | 3.25 | 3.25 |
| | | Nos. 1375-1382 (8) | 6.75 | 6.40 |

**Souvenir Sheets**
**Perf. 14**
| | | | | |
|---|---|---|---|---|
| 1383 | A195 | $5 Batter | 7.00 | 7.00 |
| 1384 | A195 | $5 Grand slam | 7.00 | 7.00 |

### Royal Wedding Issue, 1986
#### Common Design Type

Designs: 2c, Prince Andrew and Sarah Ferguson. $1.10, Andrew. $4, Andrew in flight suit, helicopter. $5, Couple, diff.

## 1986, July 23          Perf. 14
| | | | | |
|---|---|---|---|---|
| 1385 | CD340 | 2c multicolored | .20 | .20 |
| 1386 | CD340 | $1.10 multicolored | .80 | .80 |
| 1387 | CD340 | $4 multicolored | 3.00 | 3.00 |
| | | Nos. 1385-1387 (3) | 4.00 | 4.00 |

**Souvenir Sheet**
| | | | | |
|---|---|---|---|---|
| 1388 | CD340 | $5 multicolored | 4.25 | 4.25 |

Seashells A196

Designs: 25c, Gmelin brown-lined latirus. 60c, Lamarck lamellose wentletrap. 70c, Swainson turkey wing. $4, Linne rooster-tail conch. $5, Linne angular triton.

## 1986, July 15          Litho.          Perf. 15
| | | | | |
|---|---|---|---|---|
| 1389 | A196 | 25c multicolored | .50 | .20 |
| 1390 | A196 | 60c multicolored | .75 | .55 |
| 1391 | A196 | 70c multicolored | .90 | .90 |
| 1392 | A196 | $4 multicolored | 3.75 | 3.75 |
| | | Nos. 1389-1392 (4) | 5.90 | 5.40 |

**Souvenir Sheet**
| | | | | |
|---|---|---|---|---|
| 1393 | A196 | $5 multicolored | 3.75 | 3.75 |

Mushrooms A197

## 1986, Aug. 1          Perf. 15
| | | | | |
|---|---|---|---|---|
| 1394 | A197 | 10c Lepiota roselamellata | .65 | .40 |
| 1395 | A197 | 60c Lentinus bertieri | 1.25 | 1.00 |
| 1396 | A197 | $1 Lentinus retinervis | 2.75 | 2.00 |
| 1397 | A197 | $4 Eccilia cystiophorus | 6.50 | 6.50 |
| | | Nos. 1394-1397 (4) | 11.15 | 9.90 |

**Souvenir Sheet**
| | | | | |
|---|---|---|---|---|
| 1398 | A197 | $5 Cystolepiota eriophora | 14.00 | 14.00 |

Nos. 1361-1365 Ovptd. "WINNERS Argentina 3 / W. Germany 2" in Gold

| | | 1986, Sept. 15 | Litho. | Perf. 14 | |
|---|---|---|---|---|---|
| 1399 | A193 | 50c multicolored | | .95 | .95 |
| 1400 | A193 | 70c multicolored | | 1.25 | 1.25 |
| 1401 | A193 | 90c multicolored | | 1.50 | 1.50 |
| 1402 | A193 | $4 multicolored | | 6.00 | 6.00 |
| | | Nos. 1399-1402 (4) | | 9.70 | 9.70 |

**Souvenir Sheet**

| 1403 | A193 | $5 multicolored | 5.75 | 5.75 |
|---|---|---|---|---|

Disarmament Week and Intl. Peace Year — A198

60c, Mahatma Gandhi, rifles, dove. $4, Martin Luther King, Jr., hands, olive branch.

| | | 1986, Sept. 15 | Perf. 15 | |
|---|---|---|---|---|
| 1404 | A198 | 60c multi, vert. | .45 | .45 |
| 1405 | A198 | $4 multi | 3.25 | 3.25 |

Christmas — A199

Disney characters. Nos. 1406-1407, 1411-1412 vert.

| | | 1986, Nov. 3 | Perf. 11 | |
|---|---|---|---|---|
| 1406 | A199 | 30c Mickey, hearth | .50 | .30 |
| 1407 | A199 | 45c Mickey, Santa | .75 | .45 |
| 1408 | A199 | 60c Donald, Mickey Mouse phone | .90 | .60 |
| 1409 | A199 | 70c Goofy, toy band | 1.10 | .70 |
| 1410 | A199 | $1.10 Daisy, dolls | 1.25 | 1.10 |
| 1411 | A199 | $2 Goofy as Santa | 2.00 | 2.00 |
| 1412 | A199 | $2.50 Goofy playing piano | 2.40 | 2.40 |
| 1413 | A199 | $3 Train ride | 3.00 | 3.00 |
| | | Nos. 1406-1413 (8) | 11.90 | 10.55 |

**Souvenir Sheets**

| 1414 | A199 | $5 Donald, Goofy, Mickey | 7.00 | 7.00 |
|---|---|---|---|---|
| 1415 | A199 | $5 Dewey | 7.00 | 7.00 |

Nos. 1366-1370 Ovptd. with Halley's Comet Emblem

| | | 1986, Oct. 15 | Litho. | Perf. 14 | |
|---|---|---|---|---|---|
| 1416 | A194 | 5c multicolored | | .60 | .60 |
| 1417 | A194 | 20c multicolored | | .85 | .60 |
| 1418 | A194 | 40c multicolored | | 1.25 | .70 |
| 1419 | A194 | $4 multicolored | | 7.25 | 7.25 |
| | | Nos. 1416-1419 (4) | | 9.95 | 9.15 |

**Souvenir Sheet**

| 1420 | A194 | $5 multicolored | 5.50 | 5.50 |
|---|---|---|---|---|

Fauna and Flora A200

| | | 1986, Nov. 17 | Perf. 14 | |
|---|---|---|---|---|
| 1421 | A200 | 10c Chicken, rooster | .25 | .20 |
| 1422 | A200 | 30c Fish-eating bat | .40 | .25 |
| 1423 | A200 | 60c Goat | .85 | .75 |
| 1424 | A200 | 70c Cow | 1.00 | .90 |
| 1425 | A200 | $1 Anthurium | 1.50 | 1.10 |
| 1426 | A200 | $1.10 Royal poinciana | 1.50 | 1.25 |
| 1427 | A200 | $2 Frangipani | 2.50 | 2.50 |
| 1428 | A200 | $4 Orchid | 5.00 | 6.50 |
| | | Nos. 1421-1428 (8) | 13.00 | 13.45 |

**Souvenir Sheets**

| 1429 | A200 | $5 Horse | 4.75 | 4.75 |
|---|---|---|---|---|
| 1430 | A200 | $5 Trees | 4.75 | 4.75 |

Automobile, Cent. — A202

1886 Daimler and modern automobiles.

| | | 1986, Nov. 20 | Perf. 15 | |
|---|---|---|---|---|
| 1431 | A202 | 10c 1984 Maserati Biturbo | .25 | .25 |
| 1432 | A202 | 30c 1960 AC Cobra | .35 | .35 |
| 1433 | A202 | 60c 1963 Corvette | .55 | .55 |
| 1434 | A202 | 70c 1932 Duesenberg SJ7 | .65 | .65 |
| 1435 | A202 | 90c 1957 Porsche | .75 | .75 |
| 1436 | A202 | $1.10 1930 Stoewer | 1.00 | 1.00 |
| 1437 | A202 | $2 1957 VW Beetle | 1.60 | 1.60 |
| 1438 | A202 | $3 1963 Mercedes 600 Limo | 2.40 | 2.75 |
| | | Nos. 1431-1438 (8) | 7.55 | 7.90 |

**Souvenir Sheets**

| 1439 | A202 | $5 1914 Stutz | 4.00 | 4.00 |
|---|---|---|---|---|
| 1440 | A202 | $5 1941 Packard | 4.00 | 4.00 |

Song of Songs, by Marc Chagall (1887-1984) — A203

Paintings: No. 1441, The Rooster. No. 1442, Lovers in the Moonlight. No. 1443, Woman and Haystack. No. 1444, Snow-Covered Church. No. 1445, Peasant Life. No. 1446, Moses Receiving the Tablets. No. 1447, Vitebsk: From Mt. Zadunuv. No. 1449, Song of Songs, diff. No. 1450, The Creation of Man. No. 1451, Spring. No. 1452, Jacob's Struggle with the Angel. No. 1453, Song of Songs (wedding detail). No. 1454, The Painter to the Moon, 1917. No. 1455, Moses Striking the Rock. No. 1456, To My Betrothed, 1911. No. 1457, Sacrifice of Isaac. No. 1458, Monkey Acting as Judge Over Dispute Between Wolf and Fox, 1925. No. 1459, Song of Songs (bride riding Pegasus). No. 1460, Lovers in the Lilac, 1930. No. 1461, Song of Songs (sun, spirits). No. 1462, Jacob's Dream. No. 1463, Purim, 1916. No. 1464, Fantastic Horsecart. No. 1465, Listening to the Cock, 1944. No. 1466, Self-portrait, 1914. No. 1467, The Juggler, 1943. No. 1468, Noah and the Rainbow. No. 1469, Moses Before the Burning Bush. No. 1470, Around Her, 1945. No. 1471, The Trough, 1925. No. 1472, The Poet of Half-Past-Three. No. 1473, The Tree of Life, 1948. No. 1474, Woman with the Blue Face, 1932. No. 1475, Chrysanthemums, 1926. No. 1476, Spoonful of Milk, 1912. No. 1477, The Soldier Drinks, 1911. No. 1478, Noah's Ark. No. 1479, Flowers and Fruit. No. 1480, Adam and Eve Expelled fron Paradise. No. 1481, Return from Synagogue. No. 1482, Aleko: A Fantasy of St. Petersburg. No. 1483, The Orchard. No. 1484, Solitude. No. 1485, Paris Through the Window, 1913. No. 1486, The Wedding, 1910. No. 1487, Paradise. No. 1488, The Dream, 1939. No. 1489, Abraham and the Three Angels. No. 1490, Water Carrier Under the Moon, 1914.

**1986-87**

| 1441-1480 | A203 | $1 each | 1.00 | 1.00 |
|---|---|---|---|---|

**Size: 110x95mm**

*Imperf*

| 1481-1490 | A203 | $5 each | 4.00 | 4.00 |
|---|---|---|---|---|

Nos. 1441-1446, 1450-1452 1455-1458, 1464-1467 and 1470-1479 vert.

A204

America's Cup — A205

| | | 1987, Feb. 5 | Litho. | Perf. 15 | |
|---|---|---|---|---|---|
| 1491 | A204 | 10c Columbia, 1958 | | .20 | .20 |
| 1492 | A204 | 60c Resolute, 1920 | | .50 | .50 |
| 1493 | A204 | $1.10 Endeavor, 1934 | | .90 | .90 |
| 1494 | A204 | $4 Rainbow, 1934 | | 3.25 | 3.25 |
| | | Nos. 1491-1494 (4) | | 4.85 | 4.85 |

**Souvenir Sheet**

| 1495 | A205 | $5 Weatherly, 1962 | 4.00 | 4.00 |
|---|---|---|---|---|

Virgin Mary — A206

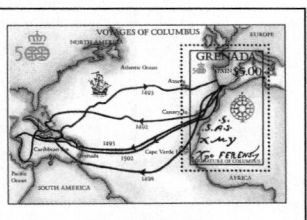

Map of Voyage, Columbus' Signature — A207

| | | 1987, Apr. 27 | Perf. 15 | |
|---|---|---|---|---|
| 1496 | A206 | 10c shown | .30 | .20 |
| 1497 | A206 | 30c Nina, Pinta, Santa Maria | .55 | .25 |
| 1498 | A206 | 50c Columbus, map | .65 | .40 |
| 1499 | A206 | 60c Columbus | .75 | .45 |
| 1500 | A206 | 90c Isabella, Ferdinand | .85 | .70 |
| 1501 | A206 | $1.10 Discovering the Antilles | .90 | .80 |
| 1502 | A206 | $2 Carib Indians | 1.50 | 1.50 |
| a. | | Souv. sheet of 3, 30c, 90c, $2 | 2.40 | 2.40 |
| 1503 | A206 | $3 American Indians, 1493 | 2.25 | 2.25 |
| a. | | Souv. sheet of 5 + label, 10c, 50c, 60c, $1.10, $3 | 4.00 | 4.00 |
| | | Nos. 1496-1503 (8) | 7.75 | 6.55 |

**Souvenir Sheets**

| 1504 | A207 | $5 shown | 3.75 | 3.75 |
|---|---|---|---|---|
| 1505 | A207 | $5 Columbus, Christ child | 3.75 | 3.75 |

Discovery of America 500th anniv. (in 1992). Nos. 1497, 1500 and 1502 horiz.

CAPEX '87 A208

Issued: #1441-1452, 1481-1483, 1986; #1453-1480, 1484-1490, 1987.

Fish. Nos. 1506, 1508 vert.

| | | 1987, June 15 | | |
|---|---|---|---|---|
| 1506 | A208 | 10c Black grouper | .40 | .20 |
| 1507 | A208 | 30c Blue marlin | .60 | .25 |
| 1508 | A208 | 60c White marlin | .75 | .50 |
| 1509 | A208 | 70c Big-eye thresher shark | .85 | .60 |
| 1510 | A208 | $1 Bonefish | 1.25 | 1.00 |
| 1511 | A208 | $1.10 Wahoo | 1.50 | 1.25 |
| 1512 | A208 | $2 Sailfish | 2.25 | 2.00 |
| 1513 | A208 | $4 Albacore | 3.50 | 3.50 |
| | | Nos. 1506-1513 (8) | 11.10 | 9.30 |

**Souvenir Sheets**

| 1514 | A208 | $5 Barracuda | 4.50 | 4.50 |
|---|---|---|---|---|
| 1515 | A208 | $5 Yellowfin tuna, vert. | 4.50 | 4.50 |

Transportation Innovations — A209

| | | 1987, May 18 | Perf. 14 | |
|---|---|---|---|---|
| 1516 | A209 | 10c Cornu's Helicopter, 1907 | .80 | .60 |
| 1517 | A209 | 15c The Monitor and Merrimack, 1862 | .80 | .60 |
| 1518 | A209 | 30c LZ1 Zeppelin, c. 1900 | 1.00 | .80 |
| 1519 | A209 | 50c S.S. Sirius, 1838 | 1.10 | .85 |
| 1520 | A209 | 60c Trans-Siberian Railway | 1.25 | 1.00 |
| 1521 | A209 | 70c USS Enterprise, 1960 | 1.40 | 1.10 |
| 1522 | A209 | 90c Blanchard's Balloon, 1785 | 1.50 | 1.40 |
| 1523 | A209 | $1.50 USS Holland 1, 1900 | 2.25 | 2.25 |
| 1524 | A209 | $2 S.S. Oceanic, 1871 | 3.00 | 3.00 |
| 1525 | A209 | $3 1984 Lamborghini Countach | 4.50 | 4.50 |
| | | Nos. 1516-1525 (10) | 17.60 | 16.10 |

For overprints see Nos. 1599-1602.

Statue of Liberty, Cent. A210

| | | 1987, Aug. 5 | | |
|---|---|---|---|---|
| 1526 | A210 | 10c Computer structural diagrams | .20 | .20 |
| 1527 | A210 | 25c Fireworks around statue | .20 | .20 |
| 1528 | A210 | 50c Fireworks in front of statue | .50 | .50 |
| 1529 | A210 | 60c Statue, boats | .65 | .60 |
| 1530 | A210 | 70c Structural diagram, close-up | 1.00 | .65 |
| 1531 | A210 | $1 Rear of statue, close-up | 1.10 | .95 |
| 1532 | A210 | $1.10 Liberty and Manhattan Isls. | 1.25 | 1.25 |
| 1533 | A210 | $2 Statue, boats, diff. | 2.25 | 2.25 |
| 1534 | A210 | $4 Ocean liner, New York Harbor | 3.75 | 4.50 |
| | | Nos. 1526-1534 (9) | 10.90 | 11.10 |

Nos. 1529, 1531-1534 vert.

Inventors and Innovators A211

Designs: 50c, Sir Isaac Newton (1642-1727), law of gravity. $1.10, Jons Jakob Berzelius (1779-1848), symbols of chemical elements. $2, Robert Boyle (1627-1691), and Boyle's Law of pressure and volume. $3, James Watt (1736-1819), and diagram of steam engine. $5, Wright Flyer, Voyager.

**1987, Sept. 9**

| | | | | |
|---|---|---|---|---|
| 1535 | A211 | 50c multicolored | .90 | .90 |
| 1536 | A211 | $1.10 multicolored | 2.00 | 2.00 |
| 1537 | A211 | $2 multicolored | 2.75 | 2.75 |
| 1538 | A211 | $3 multicolored | 5.00 | 5.00 |
| | *Nos. 1535-1538 (4)* | | 10.65 | 10.65 |

**Souvenir Sheet**

| | | | | |
|---|---|---|---|---|
| 1539 | A211 | $5 multicolored | 5.25 | 5.25 |

No. 1536 inscribed with incorrect spelling of inventors name, "John Jacob Berzelius." No. 1538 inscribed with incorrect caption; James Watt and Watt engine are pictured, not Rudolf Diesel and the Diesel engine.

**Miniature Sheets**

Fairy Tales — A212

Snow White (50th Anniv.): No. 1540a, Snow White scrubs stairs. b, Wicked Queen, looking glass. c, Snow White fleeing. d, Dwarfs, mine. e, Snow White at cottage. f, Snow White, dwarfs. g, Snow White dancing with dwarfs. h, Eating poison apple. i, Prince kissing Snow White.

Sleeping Beauty: No. 1541a, Royal family. b, Maleficent cursing infant (Aurora). c, Merryweather altering curse. d, Three good fairies. e, Briar Rose (Aurora), forest animals. f, Aurora, spinning wheel. g, Sleeping Beauty (Aurora). h, Prince Phillip battling dragon (Maleficent). i, Sleeping Beauty awakes.

Cinderella: No. 1542a, Ella (Cinderella) and father. b, Cinderella sweeping. c, Cinderella, animals in barn. d, Cinderella, stepmother, stepsisters. e, Mice. f, Fairy Godmother. g, Cinderella transformed, coach. h, i, Duke puts glass slipper on Cinderella's foot.

Pinocchio: No. 1543a, Geppetto and puppet. b, Jiminy Cricket. c, Pinocchio, J. Worthington Foulfellow and Gideon. d, Pinocchio, Master Stromboli. e, Blue Fairy rescues Pinocchio. f, Pinocchio, donkeys. g, Pinocchio riding fish. h, Pinocchio and Geppetto at sea. i, Pinocchio transformed into a boy.

Alice in Wonderland: No. 1544a, Alice, rabbit hole. b, Alice in bottle. c, Walrus and Carpenter. d, White Rabbit in pink house. e, Alice, pink butterfly. f, March Hare, Mad Hatter. g, Alice in garden. h, Queen of Hearts. i, Alice on trial.

Peter Pan: No. 1545a, Nana. b, Peter Pan. c, Peter Pan, Tinker Bell, Wendy, John and Michael Darling flying. d, In NeverNever Land. e, Peter Pan and Tiger Lily. f, Captain Hook and First Mate Smee. g, Pater Pan dueling with Captain Hook. h, Tinker Bell, pirate ship. i, Captain Hook, crocodile.

No. 1546, Snow White and Prince riding off into sunset. No. 1547, Aurora and Prince Phillip dancing. No. 1548, Cinderella and Prince Charming marry. No. 1549, Pinocchio, Jiminy Cricket and Gepetto. No. 1550, Alice, cat, mother. No. 1551, Darling children waving goodbye to Peter Pan.

**1987, Sept. 9                Perf. 14x13½**

| | | | |
|---|---|---|---|
| 1540 | Sheet of 9 | 4.25 | |
| | *a.-i.* A212 30c any single | .45 | .45 |
| 1541 | Sheet of 9 | 4.25 | |
| | *a.-i.* A212 30c any single | .45 | .45 |
| 1542 | Sheet of 9 | 4.25 | |
| | *a.-i.* A212 30c any single | .45 | .45 |
| 1543 | Sheet of 9 | 4.25 | |
| | *a.-i.* A212 30c any single | .45 | .45 |
| 1544 | Sheet of 9 | 4.25 | |
| | *a.-i.* A212 30c any single | .45 | .45 |
| 1545 | Sheet of 9 | 4.25 | |
| | *a.-i.* A212 30c any single | .45 | .45 |
| | *Nos. 1540-1545 (6)* | 25.50 | |

**Souvenir Sheets**

| | | | |
|---|---|---|---|
| 1546-1551 | A212 $5 each | 6.75 | 6.75 |

Souvenir Sheet

Baseball All-Star Game, Oakland, July 14 — A213

Athletes, team emblems: a, Wade Boggs, Boston Red Sox. b, Eric Davis, Cincinnati Reds.

**1987, Nov. 2        Litho.        Perf. 14**

| | | | | |
|---|---|---|---|---|
| 1552 | A213 | Sheet of 2 | 1.45 | 1.45 |
| | *a.-b.* $1 any single | | .70 | .70 |

Massachusetts State Crest — A214

Designs: 15c, Independence Hall, Philadelphia. 50c, Benjamin Franklin. $4, Robert Morris (1734-1806), financier of American Revolution. $5, Pres. James Madison.

**1987, Nov. 2**

| | | | | |
|---|---|---|---|---|
| 1553 | A214 | 15c multi, vert. | .20 | .20 |
| 1554 | A214 | 50c multi, vert. | .35 | .35 |
| 1555 | A214 | 60c shown | .45 | .45 |
| 1556 | A214 | $4 multi, vert. | 2.90 | 2.90 |
| | *Nos. 1553-1556 (4)* | | 3.90 | 3.90 |

**Souvenir Sheet**

| | | | | |
|---|---|---|---|---|
| 1557 | A214 | $5 multi, vert. | 3.60 | 3.60 |

US Constitution bicent.

Nos. 1286, 1291 and 1296 Overprinted

**1987, Nov. 2**

| | | | | |
|---|---|---|---|---|
| 1558 | A180 | 10c multicolored | .20 | .20 |
| 1559 | A180 | 50c multicolored | .35 | .35 |
| 1560 | A180 | $3 multicolored | 2.00 | 2.00 |
| | *Nos. 1558-1560 (3)* | | 2.55 | 2.55 |

HAFNIA '87 — A215

Disney animated characters in adaptation of fairy tales by Hans Christian Andersen.

**1987, Nov. 16      Litho.      Perf. 14**

| | | | | |
|---|---|---|---|---|
| 1561 | A215 | 25c The Shadow | .50 | .30 |
| 1562 | A215 | 30c The Storks | .50 | .35 |
| 1563 | A215 | 50c The Emperor's New Clothes | .75 | .60 |
| 1564 | A215 | 60c The Tinderbox | 1.00 | .65 |
| 1565 | A215 | 70c The Shepherdess and the Chimney Sweep | 1.25 | .80 |
| 1566 | A215 | $1.50 The Little Mermaid | 2.25 | 1.75 |
| 1567 | A215 | $3 The Princess and the Pea | 3.25 | 3.25 |
| 1568 | A215 | $4 The Marsh King's Daughter | 4.25 | 4.25 |
| | *Nos. 1561-1568 (8)* | | 13.75 | 11.95 |

**Souvenir Sheets**

| | | | | |
|---|---|---|---|---|
| 1569 | A215 | $5 The Flying Trunk, horiz. | 8.00 | 8.00 |
| 1570 | A215 | $5 The Sandman, horiz. | 8.00 | 8.00 |

Christmas — A216

Religious paintings: 15c, The Annunciation, by Fra Angelico. 30c, The Annunciation, attributed to Hubert van Eyck (c. 1370-1426). 60c, Adoration of the Magi, by Januarius Zick (1730-1797). $4, The Flight Into Egypt, by David. $5, The Circumcision, produced by artists of the Giovanni Bellini Studio, 14th cent.

**1987, Dec. 15**

| | | | | |
|---|---|---|---|---|
| 1571 | A216 | 15c multicolored | .55 | .45 |
| 1572 | A216 | 30c multicolored | 1.00 | .50 |
| 1573 | A216 | 60c multicolored | 1.75 | 1.40 |
| 1574 | A216 | $4 multicolored | 6.75 | 6.75 |
| | *Nos. 1571-1574 (4)* | | 10.05 | 9.10 |

**Souvenir Sheet**

| | | | | |
|---|---|---|---|---|
| 1575 | A216 | $5 multicolored | 8.50 | 8.50 |

T. Albert Marryshow (b. 1887) — A217

**1988, Jan. 22      Litho.      Perf. 14**

| | | | | |
|---|---|---|---|---|
| 1576 | A217 | 25c scarlet, red brn & brn blk | .30 | .30 |

40th Wedding Anniv. of Queen Elizabeth II and Prince Philip — A218

**1988, Feb. 15**

| | | | | |
|---|---|---|---|---|
| 1577 | A218 | 15c Wedding portrait, 1947 | .30 | .20 |
| 1578 | A218 | 50c Elizabeth, Charles, Anne | .60 | .45 |
| 1579 | A218 | $1 Elizabeth, Anne | 1.00 | 1.00 |
| 1580 | A218 | $4 Elizabeth, c. 1980 | 3.25 | 3.25 |
| | *Nos. 1577-1580 (4)* | | 5.15 | 4.90 |

**Souvenir Sheet**

| | | | | |
|---|---|---|---|---|
| 1581 | A218 | $5 Elizabeth, 1947 | 3.75 | 3.75 |

Disney Animated Characters and 1988 Summer Olympics, Seoul A219

**1988, Apr. 13      Litho.      Perf. 13½x14**

| | | | | |
|---|---|---|---|---|
| 1582 | A219 | 1c Lighting torch, Olympia | .20 | .20 |
| 1583 | A219 | 2c Torch bearers | .20 | .20 |
| 1584 | A219 | 3c Flag bearers | .20 | .20 |
| 1585 | A219 | 4c Releasing doves | .20 | .20 |
| 1586 | A219 | 5c Opening ceremony | .20 | .20 |
| 1587 | A219 | 10c Olympic motto | .20 | .20 |
| 1588 | A219 | $6 Tiger character trademark | 6.00 | 5.50 |
| 1589 | A219 | $7 Oldest Korean p.o. | 6.50 | 5.50 |
| | *Nos. 1582-1589 (8)* | | 13.70 | 12.20 |

**Souvenir Sheets**

| | | | | |
|---|---|---|---|---|
| 1590 | A219 | $5 Sportsmanship oath | 5.75 | 5.75 |
| 1591 | A219 | $5 Closing ceremony | 5.75 | 5.75 |

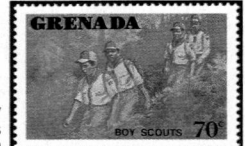

Boy Scouts A220

**1988, May 3      Litho.      Perf. 14**

| | | | | |
|---|---|---|---|---|
| 1592 | A220 | 20c Fishing, vert. | .40 | .20 |
| 1593 | A220 | 70c Hiking | 1.25 | 1.00 |
| 1594 | A220 | 90c First-aid | 1.75 | 1.40 |
| 1595 | A220 | $3 Canoeing, vert. | 4.00 | 4.00 |
| | *Nos. 1592-1595 (4)* | | 7.40 | 6.60 |

**Souvenir Sheet**

| | | | | |
|---|---|---|---|---|
| 1596 | A220 | $5 Scout holding koala, vert. | 3.75 | 3.75 |

Rotary Conference, District 405, St. George, May 5-7 — A221

Rotary Intl. emblem and: $2, Map of District 405 island nations (Grenada, Guyana, Surinam and French Guiana), 15th cent. Spanish galleon Santa Maria, vert. $10, Motto "Service Above Self."

**1988, May 5                Perf. 13½x14**

| | | | | |
|---|---|---|---|---|
| 1597 | A221 | $2 multicolored | 1.50 | 1.50 |

**Souvenir Sheet**

**Perf. 14x13½**

| | | | | |
|---|---|---|---|---|
| 1598 | A221 | $10 shown | 7.50 | 7.50 |

Nos. 1522-1525 Overprinted for Philatelic Exhibitions

a

b

c

d

| | | | | |
|---|---|---|---|---|
| **1988, Apr. 19** | | **Litho.** | **Perf. 14** | |
| 1599 | A209 (a) | 90c multi | 1.25 | .85 |
| 1600 | A209 (b) | $1.50 multi | 1.75 | 1.50 |
| 1601 | A209 (c) | $2 multi | 2.25 | 2.25 |
| 1602 | A209 (d) | $3 multi | 2.75 | 2.75 |
| | Nos. 1599-1602 (4) | | 8.00 | 7.35 |

Birds — A222

| | | | | |
|---|---|---|---|---|
| **1988, May 31** | | | | |
| 1603 | A222 | 10c Roseate tern | .80 | .30 |
| 1604 | A222 | 25c Laughing gull | 1.00 | .30 |
| 1605 | A222 | 50c Osprey | 1.25 | .60 |
| 1606 | A222 | 60c Rose-breasted grosbeak | 1.25 | .60 |
| 1607 | A222 | 90c Purple gallinule | 1.25 | .95 |
| 1608 | A222 | $1.10 White-tailed tropicbird | 1.25 | 1.10 |
| 1609 | A222 | $3 Blue-faced booby | 3.00 | 3.00 |
| 1610 | A222 | $4 Northern shoveler | 4.25 | 4.25 |
| | Nos. 1603-1610 (8) | | 14.05 | 11.10 |

**Souvenir Sheet**

| | | | | |
|---|---|---|---|---|
| 1611 | A222 | $5 Belted kingfisher | 5.00 | 5.00 |
| 1612 | A222 | $5 Rusty-tailed flycatcher | 5.00 | 5.00 |

**Miniature Sheets**

Classic Automobiles
A223

Cars (U.S. unless otherwise stated): No. 1613a, 1934 Tatra Type 77, Czechoslovakia. b, 1938 Rolls-Royce Phantom III, Britain. c, 1947 Studebaker Champion Starlight. d, 1948 Porsche Gmund, Germany. e, 1948 Tucker. f, 1931 Peerless V-16. g, 1931 Minerva AL, Belgium. h, 1933 REO Royale. i, 1933 Pierce-Arrow Silver Arrow. j, 1934 Hupmobile Aerodynamic.

No. 1614a, 1925 Vauxhall Type OE30/98, Britain. b, 1926 Wills Sainte Claire. c, 1928 Bucciali, France. d, 1929 Irving Napier Golden Arrow, Britain. e, 1930 Studebaker President. f, 1907 Thomas Flyer. g, 1908 Isotta-Fraschini Tipo J, Italy. h, 1910 Fiat 10/14HP, Italy. i, 1911 Mercer Type 35 Raceabout. j, 1917 Marmon Model 34 Cloverleaf.

No. 1615a, 1965 Peugeot 404, France. b, 1969 Ford Capri, Britain. c, 1975 Ferrari 312T, Italy. d, 1978 Lotus T-79, Britain. e, 1979 Williams-Cosworth FW07, Britain. f, 1948 H.R.G. 1500 Sports, Britain. g, 1949 Crosley Hotshot. h, 1955 Volvo PV444, Sweden. i, 1960 Maserati Tipo 61, Italy. j, 1963 Saab 96, Sweden.

| | | | | |
|---|---|---|---|---|
| **1988, June 1** | | | **Perf. 13x13½** | |
| 1613 | | Sheet of 10 | 14.50 | 14.50 |
| a.-j. | A223 $2 any single | | 1.40 | 1.40 |
| 1614 | | Sheet of 10 | 14.50 | 14.50 |
| a.-j. | A223 $2 any single | | 1.40 | 1.40 |
| 1615 | | Sheet of 10 | 14.50 | 14.50 |
| a.-j. | A223 $2 any single | | 1.40 | 1.40 |

Paintings by Titian (c. 1488-1576)
A224

Paintings by Titian: 10c, Lavinia Vecellio, c. 1546. 20c, Portrait of a Man, c. 1510. 25c, Andrea De Franceschi, 1532. 90c, Head of a Soldier, 1511. $1, Man With a Flute. $2, Lucrezia and Tarquinius, c. 1515. $3, Duke of Mantua with Dog, 1525. $4, La Bella Di Tiziano, 1536. No. 1624, Allegory of Alfonso D'Avalos. No. 1625, Fall of Man, 1570, horiz.

| | | | | |
|---|---|---|---|---|
| **1988, June 15** | | | **Perf. 13½x14** | |
| 1616 | A224 | 10c multicolored | .20 | .20 |
| 1617 | A224 | 20c multicolored | .20 | .20 |
| 1618 | A224 | 25c multicolored | .20 | .20 |
| 1619 | A224 | 90c multicolored | .60 | .60 |
| 1620 | A224 | $1 multicolored | .65 | .65 |
| 1621 | A224 | $2 multicolored | 1.40 | 1.40 |
| 1622 | A224 | $3 multicolored | 2.10 | 2.10 |
| 1623 | A224 | $4 multicolored | 2.75 | 2.75 |
| | Nos. 1616-1623 (8) | | 8.10 | 8.10 |

**Souvenir Sheets**

| | | | | |
|---|---|---|---|---|
| 1624 | A224 | $5 multicolored | 3.75 | 3.75 |

**Perf. 14x13½**

| | | | | |
|---|---|---|---|---|
| 1625 | A224 | $5 multicolored | 3.75 | 3.75 |

Zeppelins
A225

Designs: 10c, Graf Zeppelin over the Federal Building, Chicago, 1933 World's Fair, vert. 15c, LZ-1 over Lake Constance, 1900. 25c, Washington aerial balloon lifting off the aircraft carrier USS George Washington Parke Custis off Port Royal, South Carolina, 1862, vert. 45c, Hindenburg over a Maybach Zeppelin automobile, Friedrichshaven, 1936. 50c, Goodyear Blimp over the Statue of Liberty, 1986, vert. 60c, Hindenburg passing over the Statue of Liberty during its final flight, 1937. 90c, Experimental docking of aircraft (piloted by Ernst Udet) with the Hindenburg, 1936. $2, Hindenburg over the Olympic stadium, Berlin, 1936, vert. $3, Hindenburg over Christ the Redeemer statue, Rio de Janeiro, 1937, vert. $4, Hindenburg over mail plane catapult ship Bremen, 1936. No. 1636, Zepplin over DLH base, Bathurst, Gambia, 1935. No. 1637, Graf Zeppelin over St. Basil's Cathedral, Moscow, 1930.

| | | | | |
|---|---|---|---|---|
| **1988, July 1** | | | **Perf. 14** | |
| 1626 | A225 | 10c multicolored | .50 | .20 |
| 1627 | A225 | 15c multicolored | .60 | .20 |
| 1628 | A225 | 25c multicolored | .70 | .35 |
| 1629 | A225 | 45c multicolored | .75 | .40 |
| 1630 | A225 | 50c multicolored | .80 | .45 |
| 1631 | A225 | 60c multicolored | .85 | .50 |
| 1632 | A225 | 90c multicolored | 1.00 | .80 |
| 1633 | A225 | $2 multicolored | 1.75 | 1.75 |
| 1634 | A225 | $3 multicolored | 2.50 | 2.50 |
| 1635 | A225 | $4 multicolored | 3.50 | 3.50 |
| | Nos. 1626-1635 (10) | | 12.95 | 10.70 |

**Souvenir Sheets**

| | | | | |
|---|---|---|---|---|
| 1636 | A225 | $5 multicolored | 3.75 | 3.75 |
| 1637 | A225 | $5 multicolored | 3.75 | 3.75 |

The ship name on No. 1628 is incorrect.

SYDPEX '88, Sydney, Australia — A226

Walt Disney characters in Australian settings: 1c, Camping in the Outback, a howling Tasmanian wolf. 2c, Offering peanuts to wallabies. 3c, With a kangaroo and joey against Ayers Rock. 4c, Riding emus, emu-wrens. 5c, Camp and wombat. 10c, Duck-billed platypuses. No. 1644, Photographing a kookaburra. $6, Koala and Mickey waving flags of Grenada, Australia and the United States, map. No. 1646, Flags and candles atop Cake in the shape of Australia. No. 1647, Mickey, Minnie Pluto and Goofy taking a break during a walkabout.

| | | | | |
|---|---|---|---|---|
| **1988, Aug. 1** | | **Litho.** | **Perf. 14x13½** | |
| 1638 | A226 | 1c multicolored | .20 | .20 |
| 1639 | A226 | 2c multicolored | .20 | .20 |
| 1640 | A226 | 3c multicolored | .20 | .20 |
| 1641 | A226 | 4c multicolored | .20 | .20 |
| 1642 | A226 | 5c multicolored | .20 | .20 |
| 1643 | A226 | 10c multicolored | .20 | .20 |

| | | | | |
|---|---|---|---|---|
| 1644 | A226 | $5 multicolored | 5.75 | 5.75 |
| 1645 | A226 | $6 multicolored | 6.75 | 6.75 |
| | Nos. 1638-1645 (8) | | 13.70 | 13.70 |

**Souvenir Sheet**

| | | | | |
|---|---|---|---|---|
| 1646 | A226 | $5 multicolored | 6.75 | 6.75 |
| 1647 | A226 | $5 multicolored | 6.75 | 6.75 |

Mickey Mouse, 60th anniversary.

Intl. Fund for Agricultural Development, 10th Anniv. — A227

| | | | | |
|---|---|---|---|---|
| **1988, Aug. 11** | | **Litho.** | **Perf. 14** | |
| 1648 | A227 | 25c Pineapple, vert. | .40 | .40 |
| 1649 | A227 | 75c Banana, vert. | .80 | .80 |
| 1650 | A227 | $3 Mace, nutmeg | 2.75 | 2.25 |
| | Nos. 1648-1650 (3) | | 3.95 | 3.45 |

Flowering Trees and Shrubs of the Caribbean
A228

| | | | | |
|---|---|---|---|---|
| **1988, Sept. 30** | | | **Litho.** | |
| 1651 | A228 | 15c Lignum vitae | .20 | .20 |
| 1652 | A228 | 25c Saman | .20 | .20 |
| 1653 | A228 | 35c Red frangipani | .25 | .25 |
| 1654 | A228 | 45c Flowering maple | .30 | .30 |
| 1655 | A228 | 60c Yellow poui | .40 | .40 |
| 1656 | A228 | $1 Wild chestnut | .70 | .70 |
| 1657 | A228 | $3 Mountain immortelle | 2.10 | 2.10 |
| 1658 | A228 | $4 Queen of flowers | 2.75 | 2.75 |
| | Nos. 1651-1658 (8) | | 6.90 | 6.90 |

**Souvenir Sheets**

| | | | | |
|---|---|---|---|---|
| 1659 | A228 | $5 Flamboyant | 3.50 | 3.50 |
| 1660 | A228 | $5 Orchid tree | 3.50 | 3.50 |

**Miniature Sheet**

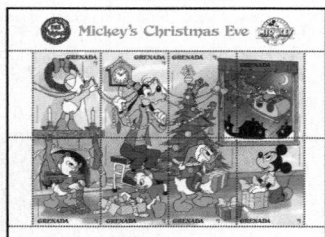

Christmas, Mickey Mouse 60th Anniv. — A229

Designs: a, Huey draping garland. b, Goofy stringing popcorn. c, Chip'n'Dale decorating tree. d, Santa Claus in his sleigh. e, Dewey hanging stockings. f, Louie unpacking decorations. g, Donald Duck. h, Mickey Mouse. No. 1662, Morty and Ferdie leaving milk and cookies for Santa, horiz. No. 1663, Morty and Ferdie dreaming of presents, horiz. Illustration reduced.

| | | | | |
|---|---|---|---|---|
| | | **Perf. 13½x14, 14x13½** | | |
| **1988, Dec. 1** | | | **Litho.** | |
| 1661 | A229 | Sheet of 8 | 7.50 | 7.50 |
| a.-h. | $1 any single | | .90 | .90 |

**Souvenir Sheets**

| | | | | |
|---|---|---|---|---|
| 1662 | A229 | $5 multicolored | 5.50 | 5.50 |
| 1663 | A229 | $5 multicolored | 5.50 | 5.50 |

**Miniature Sheets**

Major League Baseball Players — A230

No. 1664: a, Mickey Mantle. b, Roger Clemens. c, Rod Carew. d, Ryne Sandberg. e, Mike Scott. f, Tim Raines. g, Willie Mays. h, Bret Saberhagen. i, Honus Wagner.

No. 1665: a, Roberto Clemente. b, Cal Ripken, Jr. c, Bob Feller. d, George Bell. e, Mark McGwire. f, Alvin Davis. g, Pete Rose. h, Dan Quisenberry. i, Babe Ruth.

No. 1666: a, Jackie Robinson. b, Dwight Gooden. c, Brooks Robinson, Jr. d, Nolan Ryan. e, Mike Schmidt. f, Gary Gaetti. g, Nellie Fox. h, Tony Gwynn. i, Dizzy Dean.

No. 1667: a, Ernie Banks. b, National League emblem. c, Julio Franco. d, Jack Morris. e, Fernando Valenzuela. f, Lefty Grove. g, Ted Williams. h, Darryl Strawberry. i, Dale Murphy.

No. 1668: a, Johnny Bench. b, Dave Stieb. c, Reggie Jackson. d, Harold Baines. e, Wade Boggs. f, Pete O'Brien. g, Stan Musial. h, Wally Joyner. i, Grover Cleveland Alexander.

No. 1669: a, Jose Cruz. b, American League emblem. c, Al Kaline. d, Chuck Klein. e, Don Mattingly. f, Mike Witt. g, Mark Langston. h, Hubie Brooks. i, Harmon Killebrew.

No. 1670: a, George Brett. b, Joe Carter. c, Frank Robinson. d, Mel Ott. e, Benito Santiago. f, Teddy Higuera. g, Lloyd Moseby. h, Bobby Bonilla. i, Warren Spahn.

No. 1671: a, Gary Carter. b, Hank Aaron. c, Gaylord Perry. d, Ty Cobb. e, Andre Dawson. f, Charlie Hough. g, Kirby Puckett. h, Robin Yount. i, Don Drysdale.

No. 1672: a, Luis Aparicio. b, Paul Molitor. c, Lou Gehrig. d, Jeffrey Leonard. e, Eric Davis. f, Pete Incaviglia. g, Steve Rogers. h, Ozzie Smith. i, Randy Jones.

| | | | | |
|---|---|---|---|---|
| **1988, Nov. 28** | | **Litho.** | **Perf. 14** | |
| 1664 | | Sheet of 9 | 1.90 | |
| a.-i. | A230 30c any single | | .20 | .20 |
| 1665 | | Sheet of 9 | 1.90 | |
| a.-i. | A230 30c any single | | .20 | .20 |
| 1666 | | Sheet of 9 | 1.90 | |
| a.-i. | A230 30c any single | | .20 | .20 |
| 1667 | | Sheet of 9 | 1.90 | |
| a.-i. | A230 30c any single | | .20 | .20 |
| 1668 | | Sheet of 9 | 1.90 | |
| a.-i. | A230 30c any single | | .20 | .20 |
| 1669 | | Sheet of 9 | 1.90 | |
| a.-i. | A230 30c any single | | .20 | .20 |
| 1670 | | Sheet of 9 | 1.90 | |
| a.-i. | A230 30c any single | | .20 | .20 |
| 1671 | | Sheet of 9 | 1.90 | |
| a.-i. | A230 30c any single | | .20 | .20 |
| 1672 | | Sheet of 9 | 1.90 | |
| a.-i. | A230 30c any single | | .20 | .20 |
| | Nos. 1664-1672 (9) | | 17.10 | |

No. 1665 was reprinted with No. 1665g replaced by a label inscribed "U.S. Baseball Series."

Singers — A231

| | | | | |
|---|---|---|---|---|
| **1988, Dec. 5** | | **Litho.** | **Perf. 14** | |
| 1673 | A231 | 10c Tina Turner | .30 | .20 |
| 1674 | A231 | 25c Lionel Ritchie | .30 | .20 |
| 1675 | A231 | 45c Whitney Houston | .45 | .40 |
| 1676 | A231 | 60c Joan Armatrading | .60 | .50 |
| 1677 | A231 | 75c Madonna | 1.00 | .65 |
| 1678 | A231 | $1 Elton John | 1.25 | .85 |
| 1679 | A231 | $3 Bruce Springsteen | 2.50 | 2.50 |
| 1680 | A231 | $4 Bob Marley | 3.25 | 3.25 |
| | Nos. 1673-1680 (8) | | 9.65 | 8.55 |

**Souvenir Sheet**

| | | | | |
|---|---|---|---|---|
| 1681 | | Sheet of 4 (2 55c,2 $1) | 3.50 | 3.50 |
| a. | A231 55c Yoko Minamino | | .75 | .75 |
| b. | A231 $1 Yoko Minamino, diff. | | 2.50 | 2.50 |

Armatrading is misspelled "Ammertrading."

Car Type of 1988
Miniature Sheets

Locomotives.
No. 1682: a, 1889 Canada Atlantic Railway No. 2 0-6-0, Canada. b, 1875 Virginia & Truckee Railroad J.W. Bowker 2-4-0, U.S. c, 1872 Philadelphia & Reading Railway Ariel 2-2-2, U.S. d, 1867 Chicago & Rock Is. Railroad America 4-4-0, U.S. e, 1866 Lehigh Valley Railroad Consolidation No. 63 2-8-0, U.S. f, 1860 Great Western Railway Scotia 0-6-0, Canada. g, 1854 Grand Trunk Railway Birkenhead Class 4-4-0, Canada. h, 1837 Camden & Amboy Railroad Monster 0-8-0, U.S. i, 1834 B&O Railroad Grasshopper Class 0-4-0, U.S. j, 1829 B&O Railroad Tom Thumb 0-2-2, U.S.

No. 1683: a, 1925 United Railways of Yucatan Yucatan 4-4-0, Mexico. b, 1924 Canadian Natl. Railways Class T2 2-10-2, Canada. c, 1919 St. Louis-San Francisco Railroad USRA Light Mikado 2-8-2, U.S. d, 1919 Atlantic Coast

Line Railroad USRA Light Pacific 4-6-2, US. e,
1913 Edaville Railroad (Bridgton & Saco River
Railroad) No. 7 2-4-4-T, US. f, 1903 Denver &
Rio Grande Western Railroad Mudhens Class
K27 2-8-2, US. g, 1902 PRR Class E-2 No.
7002 4-4-2, US. h, 1899 PRR Class H6 2-8-0,
US. i, 1893 Mohawk & Hudson Railroad De
Witt Clinton 0-4-0, US. j, 1891 St. Clair Tunnel
Company No. 598 0-10-0, Canada.

No. 1684: a, 1947 Chesapeake & Ohio Rail-
road M-1 Class No. 500 steam turbine electric,
US. b, 1946 Rutland Railroad No. 93 4-8-2,
US. c, 1942 PRR Class T1 4-4-4-4, US. d,
1942 Chesapeake & Ohio Railroad Class H-8
2-6-6-6, US. e, 1941 Atchison, Topeka &
Santa Fe Railway EMD Model FT Bo-Bo, US.
f, 1940 Gulf, Mobile & Ohio Railroad ALCO
Models S-1 & S-2 Bo-Bo, US. g, 1937 New
York, New Haven & Hartford Railroad Class 15
4-6-4, US. h, 1936 Seaboard Air Line Railroad
Class R 2-6-6-4, US. i, 1930 Newfoundland
Railway Class R-2 2-8-2, Canada. j, 1928
Canadian Natl. Railway No. 9000 2-Do-1 + 1-
Do-2, Canada.

**1989, Jan. 23    Litho.    Perf. 13x13½**

| 1682 |       | Sheet of 10           | 14.50 | 14.50 |
|------|-------|-----------------------|-------|-------|
|      | a.-j. | A223 $2 any single    | 1.40  | 1.40  |
| 1683 |       | Sheet of 10           | 14.50 | 14.50 |
|      | a.-j. | A223 $2 any single    | 1.40  | 1.40  |
| 1684 |       | Sheet of 10           | 14.50 | 14.50 |
|      | a.-j. | A223 $2 any single    | 1.40  | 1.40  |

Medalists of the
1988 Summer
Olympics,
Seoul — A232

Designs: 10c, Jackie Joyner-Kersee, US,
long jump. 25c, Steffi Graf, Federal Republic
of Germany, women's singles tennis. 45c,
Peter Rono, Kenya, 1500m run. 75c, Greg
Barton, US, kayak singles. $1, Italy, women's
team foil. $2, Kristin Otto, German Democratic
Republic, women's 100m freestyle swimming.
$3, Holger Behrendt, German Democratic
Republic, still rings. $4, Japan, duet synchro-
nized swimming. No. 1693, Yukio Iketani,
Japan, men's floor exercise. No. 1694, West
Germany, 400m relay, and (Olympic) flame
over track.

**1989, Apr. 6    Litho.    Perf. 14**

| 1685 | A232 | 10c multicolored  | .30   | .30   |
|------|------|-------------------|-------|-------|
| 1686 | A232 | 25c multicolored  | .70   | .35   |
| 1687 | A232 | 45c multicolored  | .80   | .40   |
| 1688 | A232 | 75c multicolored  | .90   | .60   |
| 1689 | A232 | $1 multicolored   | 1.00  | .75   |
| 1690 | A232 | $2 multicolored   | 1.50  | 1.50  |
| 1691 | A232 | $3 multicolored   | 2.25  | 2.25  |
| 1692 | A232 | $4 multicolored   | 3.00  | 3.00  |
|      |      | Nos. 1685-1692 (8)| 10.45 | 9.15  |

**Souvenir Sheets**

| 1693 | A232 | $6 multicolored | 5.00 | 5.00 |
|------|------|-----------------|------|------|
| 1694 | A232 | $6 multicolored | 5.00 | 5.00 |

"The Fifty-three Stations on the
Tokaido" — A233

Prints by Hiroshige (1797-1858): 10c,
Shinagawa on Edo Bay. 25c, Pine Trees on
the Road to Totsuka. 60c, Kanagawa on Edo
Bay. 75c, Crossing Banyu River to Hiratsuka.
$1, Windy Shore at Odawara. $2, Snow-covered Post Station of Mishima. $3, Full Moon at
Fuchu. $4, Crossing the Stream at Okitsu. No.
1703, Mt. Uzu at Okabe. No. 1704, Mountain
Pass at Nissaka.

**1989, May 15    Litho.    Perf. 14x13½**

| 1695 | A233 | 10c multicolored  | .20  | .20  |
|------|------|-------------------|------|------|
| 1696 | A233 | 25c multicolored  | .20  | .20  |
| 1697 | A233 | 60c multicolored  | .45  | .45  |
| 1698 | A233 | 75c multicolored  | .65  | .65  |
| 1699 | A233 | $1 multicolored   | 1.00 | .75  |
| 1700 | A233 | $2 multicolored   | 1.50 | 1.50 |
| 1701 | A233 | $3 multicolored   | 2.25 | 2.25 |
| 1702 | A233 | $4 multicolored   | 3.00 | 3.00 |
|      |      | Nos. 1695-1702 (8)| 9.25 | 9.00 |

**Souvenir Sheets**

| 1703 | A233 | $5 multicolored | 3.75 | 3.75 |
|------|------|-----------------|------|------|
| 1704 | A233 | $5 multicolored | 3.75 | 3.75 |

Hirohito (1901-1989) and enthronement of
Akihito as emperor of Japan.

Indigenous Birds — A234

**1989, June 6    Litho.    Perf. 14**

| 1705 | A234 | 5c Great blue her-      |       |       |
|------|------|-------------------------|-------|-------|
|      |      | on                      | .75   | 1.00  |
| 1706 | A234 | 10c Green heron         | .75   | .60   |
| 1707 | A234 | 15c Ruddy turn-         |       |       |
|      |      | stone                   | .80   | .60   |
| 1708 | A234 | 25c Blue-winged         |       |       |
|      |      | teal                    | .90   | .30   |
| 1709 | A234 | 35c Ring-necked         |       |       |
|      |      | plover                  | 1.10  | .30   |
| 1710 | A234 | 45c Emerald-throat-     |       |       |
|      |      | ed humming-             |       |       |
|      |      | bird                    | 1.10  | .40   |
| 1711 | A234 | 50c Hairy hermit        | 1.25  | .45   |
| 1712 | A234 | 60c Lesser Antille-     |       |       |
|      |      | an bullfinch            | 1.40  | .55   |
| 1713 | A234 | 75c Brown pelican       | 1.50  | .65   |
| 1714 | A234 | $1 Black-crowned        |       |       |
|      |      | night heron             | 1.60  | 1.00  |
| 1715 | A234 | $3 Sparrow hawk         | 2.40  | 2.40  |
| 1716 | A234 | $5 Barn swallow         | 4.00  | 4.00  |
| 1717 | A234 | $10 Red-billed trop-    |       |       |
|      |      | icbird                  | 8.00  | 8.00  |
| 1718 | A234 | $20 Barn owl            | 21.50 | 21.50 |
|      |      | Nos. 1705-1718 (14)     | 47.05 | 41.75 |

Nos. 1709-1718 vert.

**1990-93    Litho.    Perf. 11½x13**

| 1705a | A234 | 5c  | .70 | .70 |
|-------|------|-----|-----|-----|
| 1706a | A234 | 10c | .70 | .60 |
| 1707a | A234 | 15c | .75 | .60 |
| 1708a | A234 | 25c | .85 | .30 |

**Perf. 13x11½**

| 1709a | A234 | 35c | 1.00  | .30   |
|-------|------|-----|-------|-------|
| 1710a | A234 | 45c | 1.00  | .35   |
| 1711a | A234 | 50c | 1.10  | .45   |
| 1712a | A234 | 60c | 1.25  | .50   |
| 1713a | A234 | 75c | 1.40  | .55   |
| 1714a | A234 | $1  | 1.50  | .90   |
| 1715a | A234 | $3  | 2.40  | 2.40  |
| 1716a | A234 | $5  | 4.00  | 4.00  |
| 1717a | A234 | $10 | 8.00  | 8.00  |
| 1718a | A234 | $20 | 21.50 | 21.50 |
|       |      | Nos. 1705a-1718a (14) | 46.15 | 41.15 |

Issued: #1718a, 1/22/90.

1990 World Cup
Soccer
Championships,
Italy — A235

**1989, June 12    Perf. 14**

| 1719 | A235 | 10c Scotland          | .50   | .30   |
|------|------|-----------------------|-------|-------|
| 1720 | A235 | 25c England vs.       |       |       |
|      |      | Brazil                | .60   | .50   |
| 1721 | A235 | 60c Paolo Rossi, It-  |       |       |
|      |      | aly                   | .80   | .70   |
| 1722 | A235 | 75c Jairzinho of      |       |       |
|      |      | Brazil                | 1.00  | .80   |
| 1723 | A235 | $1 Swedish Strik-     |       |       |
|      |      | er                    | 1.25  | 1.00  |
| 1724 | A235 | $2 Pele, Brazil       | 2.50  | 2.00  |
| 1725 | A235 | $3 Mario Kempes,      |       |       |
|      |      | Argentina             | 3.00  | 3.00  |
| 1726 | A235 | $4 Pat Jennings       | 4.00  | 4.00  |
|      |      | Nos. 1719-1726 (8)    | 13.65 | 12.30 |

**Souvenir Sheets**

| 1727 | A235 | $6 Argentina vs.    |      |      |
|------|------|---------------------|------|------|
|      |      | Holland             | 5.75 | 5.75 |
|      | a.   | $6 1990 score ovptd. in |  |      |
|      |      | margin              | 5.75 | 5.75 |
| 1728 | A235 | $6 Goalie           | 5.75 | 5.75 |

Issue date: No. 1727a, Nov. 30, 1990.

PHILEXFRANCE '89 — A236

19th Cent. ships and cargo: 25c, Chebeck,
sugarcane. 75c, Lugger, cotton. $1, Merchant-
man, cocoa. $4, Ketch, coffee. $6, Vue du Fort
et Ville de St. George dans l'Isle de la Grenade et du Morne, 1779.

**1989, July 7    Perf. 14**

| 1729 | A236 | 25c multicolored | 1.00 | .30  |
|------|------|------------------|------|------|
| 1730 | A236 | 75c multicolored | 1.25 | .85  |
| 1731 | A236 | $1 multicolored  | 1.60 | 1.10 |
| 1732 | A236 | $4 multicolored  | 5.50 | 5.50 |

**Size: 114x71mm**

**Imperf**

| 1733 | A236 | $6 multicolored   | 6.50  | 6.50  |
|------|------|-------------------|-------|-------|
|      |      | Nos. 1729-1733 (5)| 15.85 | 14.25 |

First
Moon
Landing,
20th
Anniv.
A237

Space achievements: 15c, Alan Shepard,
1st American in space, 1961. 35c, Friendship
7, piloted by John Glenn, 1st manned orbit of
the Earth, 1962. 45c, Apollo 8 mission, 1st
manned orbit of the Moon, 1968. 70c, Lunar
rover on Moon, 1972. $1, Apollo 11 mission
emblem and Eagle lunar module on the Moon,
1969. $2, Gemini 8-Agena, 1st space docking,
1969. $3, Edward White, 1st American to walk
in space, 1965. $4, Apollo 7 mission emblem.
No. 1742, Simple flight plan for the Apollo 11
mission. No. 1743, Raising of the American
flag on the Moon.

**1989, July 20    Perf. 14**

| 1734 | A237 | 15c multicolored  | .50   | .40   |
|------|------|-------------------|-------|-------|
| 1735 | A237 | 35c multicolored  | .60   | .45   |
| 1736 | A237 | 45c multicolored  | .80   | .60   |
| 1737 | A237 | 70c multicolored  | 1.00  | .70   |
| 1738 | A237 | $1 multicolored   | 1.50  | 1.10  |
| 1739 | A237 | $2 multicolored   | 2.50  | 2.10  |
| 1740 | A237 | $3 multicolored   | 3.25  | 3.25  |
| 1741 | A237 | $4 multicolored   | 4.25  | 4.25  |
|      |      | Nos. 1734-1741 (8)| 14.40 | 12.85 |

**Souvenir Sheets**

| 1742 | A237 | $5 multicolored | 5.50 | 5.50 |
|------|------|-----------------|------|------|
| 1743 | A237 | $5 multicolored | 5.50 | 5.50 |

Mushrooms      YWCA, Cent.
A238           A239

15c, Hygrocybe occidentalis scarletina. 40c,
Marasmius haemato- cephalus. 50c, Hygrocybe hypohaemacta. 70c, Lepiota pseudoign-
icolor. 90c, Cookeina tricholoma. $1.10,
Leucopaxillus gracillimus. $2.25, Hygrocybe
nigrescens. $4, Clathrus crispus.
#1752, Mycena holoporphyra. #1753, Xer-
omphalina tenuipes.

**1989, Aug. 17    Litho.    Perf. 14**

| 1744-1751 | A238 | Set of 8 | 16.00 | 16.00 |
|-----------|------|----------|-------|-------|

**Souvenir Sheets**

| 1752-1753 | A238 | $6 Set of 2 | 16.00 | 16.00 |
|-----------|------|-------------|-------|-------|

**1989, Sept. 11    Perf. 14**

| 1754 | A239 | 50c shown          | .70 | .70 |
|------|------|--------------------|-----|-----|
| 1755 | A239 | 75c Emblem, horiz. | .90 | .90 |

Butterflies
A240

**1989, Oct. 2    Perf. 14**

| 1756 | A240 | 6c Orion          | .35   | .35   |
|------|------|-------------------|-------|-------|
| 1757 | A240 | 30c Southern      |       |       |
|      |      | daggertail        | .50   | .50   |
| 1758 | A240 | 40c Silver spot   | .65   | .65   |
| 1759 | A240 | 60c Silver spot   | 1.00  | 1.00  |
| 1760 | A240 | $1.10 Gulf fritillary | 1.60 | 1.60 |
| 1761 | A240 | $1.25 Monarch     | 1.90  | 1.90  |
| 1762 | A240 | $4 Polydamas      |       |       |
|      |      | swallowtail       | 4.00  | 4.00  |
| 1763 | A240 | $5 Flambeau       | 4.75  | 4.75  |
|      |      | Nos. 1756-1763 (8)| 14.75 | 14.75 |

**Souvenir Sheets**

| 1764 | A240 | $6 St. Christo-   |      |      |
|------|------|-------------------|------|------|
|      |      | pher hair-        |      |      |
|      |      | streak            | 6.25 | 6.25 |
| 1765 | A240 | $6 White pea-     |      |      |
|      |      | cock              | 6.25 | 6.25 |

Discovery of
America, 500th
Anniv. (in
1992) — A241

Anniv. and UPAE emblems and various pre-
Columbian petroglyphs.

**1989, Oct. 16    Litho.    Perf. 14**

| 1766 | A241 | 45c multicolored     | .90  | .90  |
|------|------|----------------------|------|------|
| 1767 | A241 | 60c multi, diff.     | 1.10 | 1.10 |
| 1768 | A241 | $1 multi, diff.      | 1.25 | 1.25 |
| 1769 | A241 | $4 multi, diff.      | 4.75 | 4.75 |
|      |      | Nos. 1766-1769 (4)   | 8.00 | 8.00 |

**Souvenir Sheet**

| 1770 | A241 | $6 multi, diff. | 5.50 | 5.50 |
|------|------|-----------------|------|------|

World Stamp Expo '89, Scenes from
Ben and Me — A242

Walt Disney characters, story of the American Revolution: 1c, Amos leaves home. 2c,
Amos meets young Benjamin Franklin. 3c,
Invention of the Franklin stove. 4c, Invention of
bifocals. 5c, Pennsylvania Gazette. 6c, Franklin at printing press. 10c, Experimenting with
electricity. $5, As an American diplomat in
England. No. 1779, Amos's "Document of
Agreement." No. 1780, Franklin presiding over
meeting of the Ben Franklin Stamp Club. No.
1781, 2nd Continental Congress, Philadelphia,
1775.

**Perf. 14x13½, 13½x14**

**1989, Nov. 17    Litho.**

| 1771 | A242 | 1c multi  | .20  | .20  |
|------|------|-----------|------|------|
| 1772 | A242 | 2c multi  | .20  | .20  |
| 1773 | A242 | 3c multi  | .20  | .20  |
| 1774 | A242 | 4c multi  | .20  | .20  |
| 1775 | A242 | 5c multi  | .20  | .20  |
| 1776 | A242 | 6c multi  | .20  | .20  |
| 1777 | A242 | 10c multi | .20  | .20  |
| 1778 | A242 | $5 multi  | 6.00 | 6.00 |
| 1779 | A242 | $6 multi  | 6.50 | 6.75 |
|      |      | Nos. 1771-1779 (9) | 13.90 | 14.15 |

**Souvenir Sheets**

| 1780 | A242 | $6 multi, vert. | 5.75 | 5.75 |
|------|------|-----------------|------|------|
| 1781 | A242 | $6 multi        | 5.75 | 5.75 |

Christmas — A243

Paintings by Rubens: 20c, *Christ in the House of Mary and Martha.* 35c, *The Circumcision.* 60c, *Trinity Adored by Duke of Mantua and Family.* $2, *Holy Family with St. Francis.* $3, *The Ildefonso Altarpiece.* $4, *Madonna and Child with Garland and Putti,* by Rubens and Jan Brueghel. No. 1788, *Adoration of the Magi.* No. 1789, *Virgin and Child Adored by Angels.*

| | | | | | |
|---|---|---|---|---|---|
| **1990, Jan. 4** | | **Litho.** | | **Perf. 14** | |
| 1782 | A243 | 20c multicolored | | .50 | .25 |
| 1783 | A243 | 35c multicolored | | .65 | .45 |
| 1784 | A243 | 60c multicolored | | 1.00 | .65 |
| 1785 | A243 | $2 multicolored | | 2.00 | 2.00 |
| 1786 | A243 | $3 multicolored | | 2.50 | 2.50 |
| 1787 | A243 | $4 multicolored | | 3.50 | 3.50 |
| | *Nos. 1782-1787 (6)* | | | 10.15 | 9.35 |
| | **Souvenir Sheets** | | | | |
| 1788 | A243 | $5 multicolored | | 5.00 | 5.00 |
| 1789 | A243 | $5 multicolored | | 5.00 | 5.00 |

Anniversaries and Events (in 1989) — A244

Designs: 10c, Alexander Graham Bell, early telephone, telephone lines. 25c, George Washington, the Capitol Building. 35c, William Shakespeare, birthplace, Stratford-on-Avon. 75c, Jawaharlal Nehru, Mahatma Gandhi. $1, Hugo Eckener, Ferdinand von Zeppelin, zeppelin *Delag.* $2, Charlie Chaplin. $3, Ship in port. $4, Pres. Friedrich Ebert, Heidelberg Gate. No. 1798, Concorde jet. No. 1799, Ship, 13th century, vert.

| | | | | | |
|---|---|---|---|---|---|
| **1990, Feb. 12** | | **Litho.** | | **Perf. 14** | |
| 1790 | A244 | 10c multicolored | | .30 | .20 |
| 1791 | A244 | 25c multicolored | | .30 | .20 |
| 1792 | A244 | 35c multicolored | | 1.00 | .90 |
| 1793 | A244 | 75c multicolored | | 2.00 | 1.50 |
| 1794 | A244 | $1 multicolored | | 1.50 | 1.25 |
| 1795 | A244 | $2 multicolored | | 3.00 | 2.50 |
| 1796 | A244 | $3 multicolored | | 3.25 | 3.25 |
| 1797 | A244 | $4 multicolored | | 4.25 | 4.25 |
| | *Nos. 1790-1797 (8)* | | | 15.60 | 13.65 |
| | **Souvenir Sheets** | | | | |
| 1798 | A244 | $6 multicolored | | 6.25 | 6.25 |
| 1799 | A244 | $6 multicolored | | 6.25 | 6.25 |

Invention of the telephone, 1876 (10c); American presidency, 200th anniv. (25c); 425th birth anniv. of Shakespeare (35c); birth cent. of Nehru (75c); 1st passenger zeppelin, 80th anniv. ($1); birth cent. of Charlie Chaplin ($2); Hamburg, 800th anniv. ($3, No. 1799); Federal Republic of Germany, 40th anniv. ($4); and test flight of the Concorde supersonic jet, 20th anniv. (No. 1798).

Orchids — A245

| | | | | |
|---|---|---|---|---|
| **1990, Mar. 6** | | **Litho.** | **Perf. 14** | |
| 1800 | A245 | 1c *Odontoglossum triumphans* | .20 | .20 |
| 1801 | A245 | 25c *Oncidium splendidum* | .30 | .30 |
| 1802 | A245 | 60c *Laelia anceps* | .65 | .65 |
| 1803 | A245 | 75c *Cattleya trianaei* | .80 | .80 |
| 1804 | A245 | $1 *Odontoglossum rossii* | 1.25 | 1.25 |
| 1805 | A245 | $2 *Brassia gireoudiana* | 1.75 | 1.75 |

| | | | | |
|---|---|---|---|---|
| 1806 | A245 | $3 *Cattleya dowiana* | 2.50 | 2.50 |
| 1807 | A245 | $4 *Sobralia macrantha* | 3.25 | 3.25 |
| | *Nos. 1800-1807 (8)* | | 10.70 | 10.70 |
| | **Souvenir Sheets** | | | |
| 1808 | A245 | $6 *Laelia rubescens* | 5.50 | 5.50 |
| 1809 | A245 | $6 *Oncidium lanceanum* | 5.50 | 5.50 |

EXPO '90 Intl. Garden and Greenery Exposition, Japan.

America Issue — A246

Butterflies, UPAE and discovery of America 500th anniv. emblems: 15c, Southern dagger tail. 25c, Caribbean buckeye. 75c, Malachite. 90c, Orion. $1, St. Lucia mestra. $2, Red rim. $3, Flambeau. $4, Red anartia. No. 1818, Giant hairstreak. No. 1819, Orange-barred sulphur.

| | | | | |
|---|---|---|---|---|
| **1990, Mar. 16** | | **Litho.** | **Perf. 14** | |
| 1810 | A246 | 15c multicolored | .65 | .20 |
| 1811 | A246 | 25c multicolored | .80 | .25 |
| 1812 | A246 | 75c multicolored | 1.25 | .80 |
| 1813 | A246 | 90c multicolored | 1.40 | .95 |
| 1814 | A246 | $1 multicolored | 1.50 | 1.00 |
| 1815 | A246 | $2 multicolored | 2.00 | 2.00 |
| 1816 | A246 | $3 multicolored | 3.00 | 3.00 |
| 1817 | A246 | $4 multicolored | 4.00 | 4.00 |
| | *Nos. 1810-1817 (8)* | | 14.60 | 12.20 |
| | **Souvenir Sheets** | | | |
| 1818 | A246 | $6 multicolored | 6.25 | 6.25 |
| 1819 | A246 | $6 multicolored | 6.25 | 6.25 |

Wildlife A247

| | | | | |
|---|---|---|---|---|
| **1990, Apr. 3** | | **Litho.** | **Perf. 14** | |
| 1820 | A247 | 10c Caribbean monk seal | .50 | .30 |
| 1821 | A247 | 15c Little brown bat | .55 | .30 |
| 1822 | A247 | 45c Norway rat | .65 | .50 |
| 1823 | A247 | 60c Old-world rabbit | .75 | .60 |
| 1824 | A247 | $1 Water opossum | 1.00 | .90 |
| 1825 | A247 | $2 White-nosed ichneumon | 1.60 | 1.60 |
| 1826 | A247 | $3 Little big-eared bat | 2.40 | 2.40 |
| 1827 | A247 | $4 Mouse opossums | 3.25 | 3.25 |
| | *Nos. 1820-1827 (8)* | | 10.70 | 9.85 |
| | **Souvenir Sheets** | | | |
| 1828 | A247 | $6 Old-world rabbit. diff. | 5.50 | 5.50 |
| 1829 | A247 | $6 Water opossum | 5.50 | 5.50 |

No. 1826 is vert. Nos. 1828-1829 have multicolored decorative margins contininiung the designs and picturing little brown bat, prehensile-tailed porcupine and mouse opossum (No. 1828) or four-eyed opossum, West Indies manatee and Norway rat (No. 1829).

World War II A248

Designs: 25c, Operation Battleaxe, June 15, 1941. 35c, Allied landing in southern France, Aug. 15, 1944. 45c, US invasion of Guadalcanal, Aug. 7, 1942. 50c, Allied defeat of Japanese army in New Guinea, Jan. 22, 1943. 60c, US forces secure Leyte, Dec. 11, 1944. 75c, US forces enter Cologne, Mar. 5, 1945. $1, Allied offensive to break out of Anzio, May 23, 1944. $2, Battle of the Bismarck Sea, Mar. 3, 1943. $3, US fleet under Adm. Nimitz, Dec.

17, 1941. $4, Allied landing at Salerno, Sept. 9, 1943. $6, German U-boat.

| | | | | |
|---|---|---|---|---|
| **1990, Apr. 30** | | **Litho.** | **Perf. 14x13½** | |
| 1830 | A248 | 25c multicolored | .40 | .40 |
| 1831 | A248 | 35c multicolored | .50 | .50 |
| 1832 | A248 | 45c multicolored | .60 | .60 |
| 1833 | A248 | 50c multicolored | .70 | .70 |
| 1834 | A248 | 60c multicolored | .80 | .80 |
| 1835 | A248 | 75c multicolored | 1.00 | 1.00 |
| 1836 | A248 | $1 multicolored | 1.50 | 1.50 |
| 1837 | A248 | $2 multicolored | 1.75 | 1.75 |
| 1838 | A248 | $3 multicolored | 2.50 | 2.50 |
| 1839 | A248 | $4 multicolored | 3.50 | 3.50 |
| | *Nos. 1830-1839 (10)* | | 13.25 | 13.25 |
| | **Souvenir Sheet** | | | |
| 1840 | A248 | $6 multicolored | 7.00 | 7.00 |

Souvenir Sheet

Penny Black, 150th Anniv. — A249

| | | | | |
|---|---|---|---|---|
| **1990, May 3** | | **Litho.** | **Perf. 14** | |
| 1841 | A249 | $6 violet | 5.75 | 5.75 |

Stamp World London '90.

Stamp World London '90 — A250

Walt Disney characters and British trains.

| | | | | |
|---|---|---|---|---|
| **1990, June 21** | | | **Perf. 14** | |
| 1844 | A250 | 5c 1925 King Arthur Class | .45 | .20 |
| 1845 | A250 | 10c 1813 Puffing Billy | .45 | .20 |
| 1846 | A250 | 20c 1765 Colliery Tram-wagon | .60 | .20 |
| 1847 | A250 | 45c 1935 No. 2509 Silver Link | 1.00 | .55 |
| 1848 | A250 | $1 1948 No. 60149 Amadis | 1.50 | 1.10 |
| 1849 | A250 | $2 1830 Liverpool | 2.25 | 2.10 |
| 1850 | A250 | $4 1870 Flying Scotsman | 4.25 | 4.25 |
| 1851 | A250 | $5 1972 Advanced Passenger Train | 5.25 | 4.50 |
| | *Nos. 1844-1851 (8)* | | 15.75 | 13.10 |
| | **Souvenir Sheets** | | | |
| 1852 | A250 | $6 Stockton & Darlington Railway Opening, 1825, vert. | 6.75 | 6.75 |
| 1853 | A250 | $6 1809 *Catch-Me-Who-Can* | 6.75 | 6.75 |

Queen Mother, 90th Birthday — A251

| | | | | |
|---|---|---|---|---|
| **1990, July 5** | | **Litho.** | **Perf. 14** | |
| 1854 | A251 | $2 Wearing black hat | 2.25 | 2.25 |
| 1855 | A251 | $2 shown | 2.25 | 2.25 |
| 1856 | A251 | $2 Wearing crown | 2.25 | 2.25 |
| | *Nos. 1854-1856 (3)* | | 6.75 | 6.75 |
| | **Souvenir Sheet** | | | |
| 1857 | A251 | $6 Like No. 1855 | 5.25 | 5.25 |

1992 Summer Olympics, Barcelona — A252

Character trademark and: 10c, Men's steeplechase. 15c, Equestrian. 45c, Men's 200 meter butterfly. 50c, Field hockey. 65c, Balance beam. 75c, Flying Dutchman Class yachting. $2, Freestyle wrestling. $3, Men's diving. $4, Women's cycling. $5, Men's basketball. No. 1863, Three-day equestrian event. No. 1863A, Men's 10,000 M race.

| | | | | |
|---|---|---|---|---|
| **1990, July 9** | | | | |
| 1858 | A252 | 10c multicolored | .35 | .30 |
| 1858A | A252 | 15c multicolored | .45 | .35 |
| 1859 | A252 | 45c multicolored | .55 | .40 |
| 1859A | A252 | 50c multicolored | .80 | .60 |
| 1860 | A252 | 65c multicolored | .80 | .60 |
| 1860A | A252 | 75c multicolored | 1.00 | .80 |
| 1861 | A252 | $2 multicolored | 1.75 | 1.75 |
| 1861A | A252 | $3 multicolored | 2.50 | 2.50 |
| 1862 | A252 | $4 multicolored | 3.75 | 3.75 |
| 1862A | A252 | $5 multicolored | 4.00 | 4.00 |
| | *Nos. 1858-1862A (10)* | | 15.95 | 15.05 |
| | **Souvenir Sheet** | | | |
| 1863 | A252 | $8 multicolored | 6.25 | 6.25 |
| 1863A | A252 | $8 multicolored | 6.25 | 6.25 |

Nos. 1858A, 1859A, 1860A, 1861A, 1862A, 1863A were not available until 1991.

US Airborne, 50th Anniv. A253

| | | | | |
|---|---|---|---|---|
| **1990, July 3** | | | | |
| 1864 | A253 | 75c Mass jump | 2.00 | 2.00 |
| | **Souvenir Sheets** | | | |
| 1865 | A253 | $2.50 Paratrooper landing | 2.50 | 2.50 |
| 1866 | A253 | $6 Paratroopers 1940, 1990 | 5.75 | 5.75 |

Yellow Goatfish A254

| | | | | |
|---|---|---|---|---|
| **1990, Aug. 8** | | | | |
| 1867 | A254 | 10c shown | .40 | .40 |
| 1868 | A254 | 25c Black margate | .60 | .60 |
| 1869 | A254 | 65c Bluehead wrasse | 1.00 | 1.00 |
| 1870 | A254 | 75c Puddingwife | 1.25 | 1.25 |
| 1871 | A254 | $1 Foureye butterflyfish | 1.50 | 1.50 |
| 1872 | A254 | $2 Honey damselfish | 1.90 | 1.90 |
| 1873 | A254 | $3 Queen angelfish | 2.75 | 2.75 |
| 1874 | A254 | $5 Cherubfish | 4.75 | 4.75 |
| | *Nos. 1867-1874 (8)* | | 14.15 | 14.15 |
| | **Souvenir Sheets** | | | |
| 1875 | A254 | $6 Smooth trunkfish | 6.75 | 6.75 |
| 1876 | A254 | $6 Sergeant major | 6.75 | 6.75 |

Birds A255

| | | | | |
|---|---|---|---|---|
| **1990, Sept. 10** | | **Litho.** | **Perf. 14** | |
| 1877 | A255 | 15c Tropical mockingbird | .45 | .45 |
| 1878 | A255 | 25c Gray kingbird | .50 | .50 |
| 1879 | A255 | 65c Bare-eyed thrush | .80 | .80 |
| 1880 | A255 | 75c Antillean crested hummingbird | 1.00 | 1.00 |

| 1881 | A255 | $1 House wren | 1.50 | 1.50 |
|---|---|---|---|---|
| 1882 | A255 | $2 Purple martin | 1.90 | 1.90 |
| 1883 | A255 | $4 Hooded tana- ger | 3.75 | 3.75 |
| 1884 | A255 | $5 Common ground dove | 4.50 | 4.50 |
| | | Nos. 1877-1884 (8) | 14.40 | 14.40 |

**Souvenir Sheets**

| 1885 | A255 | $6 Fork-tailed fly- catcher | 8.00 | 8.00 |
|---|---|---|---|---|
| 1886 | A255 | $6 Smooth-billed ani | 8.00 | 8.00 |

Crustaceans — A256

**1990, Sept. 17**

| 1887 | A256 | 5c Coral crab | .20 | .20 |
|---|---|---|---|---|
| 1888 | A256 | 10c Smoothtail spiny lobster | .20 | .20 |
| 1889 | A256 | 15c Flamestreaked box crab | .20 | .20 |
| 1890 | A256 | 25c Spotted swim- ming crab | .20 | .20 |
| 1891 | A256 | 75c Sally lightfoot rock crab | .60 | .60 |
| 1892 | A256 | $1 Spotted spiny lobster | .80 | .80 |
| 1893 | A256 | $3 Longarm spiny lobster | 2.40 | 2.40 |
| 1894 | A256 | $20 Caribbean spiny lobster | 16.00 | 16.00 |
| | | Nos. 1887-1894 (8) | 20.60 | 20.60 |

**Souvenir Sheets**

| 1895 | A256 | $6 Spanish lob- ster | 6.25 | 6.25 |
|---|---|---|---|---|
| 1896 | A256 | $6 Copper lobster | 6.25 | 6.25 |

World Cup Soccer
Championships,
Italy — A257

Players from participating countries.

**1990, Sept. 24**

| 1897 | A257 | 10c Cameroun | .20 | .20 |
|---|---|---|---|---|
| 1898 | A257 | 25c Spain | .20 | .20 |
| 1899 | A257 | $1 West Germany | .80 | .80 |
| 1900 | A257 | $5 Scotland | 4.00 | 4.00 |
| | | Nos. 1897-1900 (4) | 5.20 | 5.20 |

**Souvenir Sheets**

| 1901 | A257 | $6 Uruguay | 6.00 | 6.00 |
|---|---|---|---|---|
| 1902 | A257 | $6 Italy | 6.00 | 6.00 |

Christmas
A258

Paintings by Raphael: 10c, The Ansidei Madonna. 15c, The Sistine Madonna. $1, Madonna of the Baldacchino. $2, The Large Holy Family. $5, Madonna in the Meadow. No. 1908, Madonna of the Veil. No. 1909, Madonna of the Diadem.

**1990, Dec. 31    Litho.    Perf. 14**

| 1903 | A258 | 10c multicolored | .30 | .20 |
|---|---|---|---|---|
| 1904 | A258 | 15c multicolored | .30 | .20 |
| 1905 | A258 | $1 multicolored | 1.50 | 1.00 |
| 1906 | A258 | $2 multicolored | 2.50 | 2.50 |
| 1907 | A258 | $5 multicolored | 5.25 | 5.25 |
| | | Nos. 1903-1907 (5) | 9.85 | 9.15 |

**Souvenir Sheets**

| 1908 | A258 | $6 multicolored | 6.75 | 6.75 |
|---|---|---|---|---|
| 1909 | A258 | $6 multicolored | 6.75 | 6.75 |

Peter Paul Rubens (1577-1640),
Painter — A259

Entire paintings or different details from: 5c, $1, $4, The Brazen Serpent. 10c, Garden of Love. 25c, Head of Cyrus. 75c, Tournament in Front of a Castle. $2, Judgement of Paris. $5, The Kermesse. No. 1918, The Prodigal Son. No. 1919, Anger of Neptune.

**1991, Jan. 31    Litho.    Perf. 14**

| 1910 | A259 | 5c multicolored | .35 | .20 |
|---|---|---|---|---|
| 1911 | A259 | 10c multicolored | .35 | .20 |
| 1912 | A259 | 25c multicolored | .60 | .20 |
| 1913 | A259 | 75c multicolored | .80 | .60 |
| 1914 | A259 | $1 multicolored | 1.00 | .80 |
| 1915 | A259 | $2 multicolored | 1.60 | 1.60 |
| 1916 | A259 | $4 multicolored | 3.25 | 3.25 |
| 1917 | A259 | $5 multicolored | 4.00 | 4.00 |
| | | Nos. 1910-1917 (8) | 11.95 | 10.85 |

**Souvenir Sheets**

| 1918 | A259 | $6 multicolored | 6.75 | 6.75 |
|---|---|---|---|---|
| 1919 | A259 | $6 multicolored | 6.75 | 6.75 |

Disney Film *Fantasia*, 50th
Anniv. — A260

5c, Mickey as Sorcerer's apprentice, walk-ing broom. 10c, Mushroom Dance Ensemble from The Nutcracker Suite. 20c, Pterodactyls from The Rite of Spring. 45c, Centaurs from The Pastoral Symphony. $1, Bacchus & Jacchus from The Pastoral Symphony. $2, Ostrich ballerina in Dance of the Hours. $4, Elephant dance from Dance of the Hours. $5, Diana, Goddess of the Moon from Dance of the Hours. #1928, Mickey as Sorcerer's apprentice. #1929, Mickey, Leopold Stokow-ski. $12, Mickey as Sorcerer's Apprentice, vert.

**1991, Feb. 4    Litho.    Perf. 14**

| 1920 | A260 | 5c multicolored | .60 | .20 |
|---|---|---|---|---|
| 1921 | A260 | 10c multicolored | .60 | .20 |
| 1922 | A260 | 20c multicolored | .90 | .20 |
| 1923 | A260 | 45c multicolored | 1.00 | .45 |
| 1924 | A260 | $1 multicolored | 1.50 | 1.50 |
| 1925 | A260 | $2 multicolored | 2.25 | 2.25 |
| 1926 | A260 | $4 multicolored | 4.25 | 4.25 |
| 1927 | A260 | $5 multicolored | 5.50 | 5.50 |
| | | Nos. 1920-1927 (8) | 16.60 | 14.55 |

**Souvenir Sheets**

| 1928 | A260 | $6 multicolored | 8.50 | 8.50 |
|---|---|---|---|---|
| 1929 | A260 | $6 multicolored | 8.50 | 8.50 |
| 1930 | A260 | $12 multicolored | 16.50 | 16.50 |

Butterflies
A261

5c, Adelphia iphicla. 10c, Nymphalidae claudina. 15c, Brassolidae polyxena. 20c, Zebra longwing. 25c, Marpesia corinna. 30c, Morpho hecuba. 45c, Morpho rhetenor. 50c, Dismorphia spio. 60c, Prepona omphale. 70c, Morpho anaxibia. 75c, Marpesia iole. $1, Metalmark. $2, Morpho cisseis. $3, Danaidae plexippus. $4, Morpho achilleana. $5, Calliona argenissa. #1947, Anteos clorinde. #1948, Haetera piera. #1949, Papilio cresphontes. #1950, Prepona pheridames.

**1991, Apr. 8    Litho.    Perf. 14**

| 1931 | A261 | 5c multicolored | .45 | .40 |
|---|---|---|---|---|
| 1932 | A261 | 10c multicolored | .50 | .40 |
| 1933 | A261 | 15c multicolored | .55 | .40 |
| 1934 | A261 | 20c multicolored | .60 | .30 |
| 1935 | A261 | 25c multicolored | .65 | .30 |
| 1936 | A261 | 30c multicolored | .70 | .30 |
| 1937 | A261 | 45c multicolored | .80 | .50 |

| 1938 | A261 | 50c multicolored | .85 | .55 |
|---|---|---|---|---|
| 1939 | A261 | 60c multicolored | 1.00 | .65 |
| 1940 | A261 | 70c multicolored | 1.10 | .80 |
| 1941 | A261 | 75c multicolored | 1.25 | 1.25 |
| 1942 | A261 | $1 multicolored | 1.40 | 1.40 |
| 1943 | A261 | $2 multicolored | 1.90 | 1.90 |
| 1944 | A261 | $3 multicolored | 2.75 | 2.75 |
| 1945 | A261 | $4 multicolored | 3.75 | 3.75 |
| 1946 | A261 | $5 multicolored | 4.75 | 4.75 |
| | | Nos. 1931-1946 (16) | 23.00 | 20.40 |

**Souvenir Sheets**

| 1947 | A261 | $6 multicolored | 6.50 | 6.50 |
|---|---|---|---|---|
| 1948 | A261 | $6 multicolored | 6.50 | 6.50 |
| 1949 | A261 | $6 multicolored | 6.50 | 6.50 |
| 1950 | A261 | $6 multicolored | 6.50 | 6.50 |

Voyages
of
Discovery
A262

Explorer's ships: 5c, Vitus Bering, 1728-1729. 10c, Louis de Bougainville, 1766-1769. 25c, Polynesians. 45c, Álvaro de Mendana, 1567-1569. $1, Charles Darwin, 1831-1835. $2, Capt. James Cook, 1768-1771. $4, Capt. Willem Schouten, 1615-1617. $5, Abel Tas-man, 1642-1644. No. 1959, Columbus' ship Santa Maria. No. 1960, Loss of Santa Maria.

**1991, Apr. 29**

| 1951 | A262 | 5c multicolored | .50 | .40 |
|---|---|---|---|---|
| 1952 | A262 | 10c multicolored | .50 | .40 |
| 1953 | A262 | 25c multicolored | .50 | .30 |
| 1954 | A262 | 50c multicolored | .90 | .50 |
| 1955 | A262 | $1 multicolored | 1.50 | 1.25 |
| 1956 | A262 | $2 multicolored | 2.75 | 2.50 |
| 1957 | A262 | $4 multicolored | 3.75 | 3.75 |
| 1958 | A262 | $5 multicolored | 4.75 | 4.75 |
| | | Nos. 1951-1958 (8) | 15.15 | 13.85 |

**Souvenir Sheets**

| 1959 | A262 | $6 multicolored | 6.75 | 6.75 |
|---|---|---|---|---|
| 1960 | A262 | $6 multicolored | 6.75 | 6.75 |

Discovery of America, 500th anniv. (in 1992).

PHILANIPPON '91 — A263

Walt Disney characters celebrating festivals of Japan: 5c, Daisy Duck and Minnie Mouse, Peach Fete, Festival of the Dolls. 10c, Morty and Ferdie, Tango Festival, Boys' Day Festival. 20c, Mickey, Minnie Mouse, Hoshi-Matsuri, Star Festival. 45c, Minnie, Daisy folk dancing at Bon-Odori Summer Festival. $1, Huey, Dewey and Louie wearing Eboshi head-dresses at Yari-Matsuri, Spear Festival of Ohji. $2, Mickey, Goofy pulling Daisy, Minnie in Yamaboko, Gion Festival of Kyoto. $4, Minnie, Daisy preparing rice broth for Nanakusa, Fes-tival of the Seven Plants. $5, Huey, Dewey floating straw boat at O-Bon, Festival of Lan-terns. No. 1969, Goofy, Tori-No-Hichi or Rake Festival, vert. No. 1970, Minnie Mouse, Japa-nese New Year, vert. No. 1971, Mickey, Snow Festival, vert.

**1991, May 6    Litho.    Perf. 13½x14**

| 1961 | A263 | 5c multicolored | .45 | .20 |
|---|---|---|---|---|
| 1962 | A263 | 10c multicolored | .45 | .20 |
| 1963 | A263 | 20c multicolored | .95 | .20 |
| 1964 | A263 | 45c multicolored | 1.25 | .80 |
| 1965 | A263 | $1 multicolored | 2.25 | 1.25 |
| 1966 | A263 | $2 multicolored | 3.00 | 3.00 |
| 1967 | A263 | $4 multicolored | 4.25 | 4.25 |
| 1968 | A263 | $5 multicolored | 5.00 | 5.00 |
| | | Nos. 1961-1968 (8) | 17.60 | 14.90 |

**Souvenir Sheets**

| 1969 | A263 | $6 multicolored | 6.00 | 6.00 |
|---|---|---|---|---|
| 1970 | A263 | $6 multicolored | 6.00 | 6.00 |
| 1971 | A263 | $6 multicolored | 6.00 | 6.00 |

Paintings by Vincent Van
Gogh — A264

Designs: 20c, Blossoming Almond Branch in a Glass, vert. 25c, La Mousme, Sitting, vert. 30c, Still Life with Red Cabbages and Onions. 40c, Japonaiserie: Flowering Plum Tree, vert. 45c, Japonaiserie: Bridge in Rain, vert. 60c, Still Life with Basket of Apples, vert. 75c, Italian Woman (Agostina Segatori), vert. $1, The Painter on His Way to Work, vert. $2, Portrait of Pere Tanguy, vert. $3, Still Life with Plaster Statuette, a Rose and Two Novels, vert. $4, Still Life: Bottle, Lemons and Oranges. $5, Orchard with Blossoming Apricot Trees. No. 1984, Farmhouse in a Wheatfield. No. 1985, The "Roubine du Roi" Canal with Washerwo-man, vert. No. 1986, Japonaiserie: Oiran, vert. No. 1987, The Gleize Bridge over the Viguerat Canal. No. 1988, Rocks with Oak Tree.

**1991, May 13    Litho.    Perf. 13½**

| 1972 | A264 | 20c multicolored | .50 | .25 |
|---|---|---|---|---|
| 1973 | A264 | 25c multicolored | .50 | .25 |
| 1974 | A264 | 30c multicolored | .55 | .30 |
| 1975 | A264 | 40c multicolored | .75 | .40 |
| 1976 | A264 | 45c multicolored | .75 | .50 |
| 1977 | A264 | 60c multicolored | 1.00 | .70 |
| 1978 | A264 | 75c multicolored | 1.10 | 1.00 |
| 1979 | A264 | $1 multicolored | 1.25 | 1.25 |
| 1980 | A264 | $2 multicolored | 1.60 | 1.60 |
| 1981 | A264 | $3 multicolored | 2.40 | 2.40 |
| 1982 | A264 | $4 multicolored | 3.25 | 3.25 |
| 1983 | A264 | $5 multicolored | 4.00 | 4.00 |
| | | Nos. 1972-1983 (12) | 17.65 | 15.90 |

**Size: 100x75mm, 75x100mm**
*Imperf*

| 1984-1988 | A264 | $6 each | 4.75 | 4.75 |
|---|---|---|---|---|

Mushrooms
A265

Designs: 15c, Psilocybe cubensis. 25c, Leptonia caeruleocapitata. 65c, Cystolepiota eriophora. 75c, Chlorophyllum molybdites. $1, Xerocomus hypoxanthus. $2, Volvariella cubensis. $4, Xerocomus coccolobae. $5, Pluteus chrysophlebius. No. 1997, Hygrocybe miniata. No. 1998, Psathyrella tuberculata.

**1991, June 1    Perf. 14**

| 1989 | A265 | 15c multicolored | .70 | .30 |
|---|---|---|---|---|
| 1990 | A265 | 25c multicolored | .85 | .30 |
| 1991 | A265 | 65c multicolored | 1.25 | .75 |
| 1992 | A265 | 75c multicolored | 1.50 | 1.00 |
| 1993 | A265 | $1 multicolored | 1.75 | 1.00 |
| 1994 | A265 | $2 multicolored | 2.00 | 2.00 |
| 1995 | A265 | $4 multicolored | 4.50 | 4.50 |
| 1996 | A265 | $5 multicolored | 5.00 | 5.00 |
| | | Nos. 1989-1996 (8) | 17.55 | 14.85 |

**Souvenir Sheet**

| 1997 | A265 | $6 multicolored | 8.50 | 8.50 |
|---|---|---|---|---|
| 1998 | A265 | $6 multicolored | 8.50 | 8.50 |

**Miniature Sheets**

Exploration of Mars — A266

Designs (all different): No. 1999: a, Johan-nes Kepler, 1571-1630. b, Galileo Galilei, 1564-1642. c, Martian canals drawn by Gio-vanni Schiaparelli, 1886. d, Sir William Her-schel, 1738-1882. e, Mars, planets. f, Percival

Lowell at telescope. g, Mariner 4. h, Mars 2. i, Mars 3.

No. 2000: a, e, Profiles of Mars. b, Olympus Mons. c, Dusty face of Mars. d, Martian moon Phobos. f, Martian moon Deimos. g, Nix Olympica. h, Terrain feature resembling human face. i, South Polar Cap.

No. 2001: a, Mars from Phobus. b, Martian dusk. c, "Voyager descent." d, Viking 2 lander on Mars. e, f, Martian landscape. g, h, i, Panorama view from Viking 2 lander.

No. 2002: a, b, Mariner 9. c, Mars. d, Polar cycle. e, Plain of Sinai. f, South pole. g, Nix Olympica. h, Martian surface. i, Outflow channel.

No. 2003, Phobos spacecraft over Mars. No. 2004, Future spacecraft. No. 2005, Future spacecraft, Mars.

**1991, June 21    Perf. 14x13½**

**Sheets of 9**

| | | | | |
|---|---|---|---|---|
| **1999** | A266 | 75c #a.-i. | 5.50 | 5.50 |
| **2000** | A266 | $1.25 #a.-i. | 9.00 | 9.00 |
| **2001** | A266 | $2 #a.-i. | 14.50 | 14.50 |
| **2002** | A266 | $7 #a.-i. | 50.00 | 50.00 |

**Souvenir Sheets**

| | | | | |
|---|---|---|---|---|
| **2003** | A266 | $6 multicolored | 5.75 | 5.75 |
| **2004** | A266 | $6 multicolored | 5.75 | 5.75 |
| **2005** | A266 | $6 multicolored | 5.75 | 5.75 |

**Royal Family Birthday, Anniversary**
**Common Design Type**

**1991, July 5    Litho.    Perf. 14**

| | | | | |
|---|---|---|---|---|
| **2006** | CD347 | 10c multicolored | .50 | .20 |
| **2007** | CD347 | 15c multicolored | .50 | .20 |
| **2008** | CD347 | 40c multicolored | .95 | .35 |
| **2009** | CD347 | 50c multicolored | 1.50 | .50 |
| **2010** | CD347 | $1 multicolored | 1.75 | 1.50 |
| **2011** | CD347 | $2 multicolored | 2.75 | 1.75 |
| **2012** | CD347 | $4 multicolored | 3.25 | 3.25 |
| **2013** | CD347 | $5 multicolored | 4.00 | 4.00 |
| | | *Nos. 2006-2013 (8)* | 15.20 | 11.75 |

**Souvenir Sheet**

| | | | | |
|---|---|---|---|---|
| **2014** | CD347 | $5 Philip, Elizabeth | 5.75 | 5.75 |
| **2015** | CD347 | $5 Diana, sons, Charles | 5.25 | 5.25 |

10c, 50c, $1, Nos. 2013, 2015, Charles and Diana, 10th Wedding anniversary. Others, Queen Elizabeth II, 65th birthday.

University of West Indies, 40th Anniv. A266a

Designs: 45c, Marryshow House, Grenada. 50c, Administrative Building, Barbados.

**1991, July 19**

| | | | | |
|---|---|---|---|---|
| **2016** | A266a | 45c multicolored | .85 | .50 |
| **2017** | A266a | 50c multicolored | .90 | .90 |

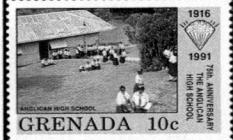

Anglican High School, 75th Anniv. A267

**1991, July 29**

| | | | | |
|---|---|---|---|---|
| **2018** | A267 | 10c Existing school | .35 | .25 |
| **2019** | A267 | 25c New school design | .60 | .25 |

Railways of the World — A269

Railways of Great Britain: No. 2020a, Stephenson's first engine, 1814. b, George Stephenson (1781-1848). c, Stephenson's Killingworth engine, 1816. d, Locomotion No. 1, 1825. e, Locomotion in Darlington, 1825. f, Opening of Stockton & Darlington Railway, 1825. g, Royal George No. 5, 1827. h, Northumbrian Rocket, 1829. i, Planet Class engine, 1830.

No. 2021a, Old Ironsides, US, 1832. b, Wilberforce, Stockton & Darlington Railway, Great Britain, 1832. c, Stephenson's Der Adler, Germany, 1835. d, Stephenson's North Star, Great Britain, 1837. e, London & Birmingham No. 1, Great Britain, 1838. f, Stephenson's 1st Austrian locomotive, 1838. g, Mud Digger, US, 1840. h, Standard Norris, US, 1840. i, Fire Fly Class, Great Britain, 1840.

No. 2022a, Lion, Liverpool and Manchester, Great Britain, 1841. b, Beuth 2-2-2, Berlin-Anhalt Railway, Germany, 1843. c, Derwent No. 25, Stockton & Darlington Railway, Great Britain, 1845. d, MKpV, WCB, Vienna, 1846. e, First railway in Hungary, Budapest to Vac, 1846. f, Stockton & Darlington, 1846. g, Stephenson's long boiler type, Paris, 1847. h, Baldwin 4-4-0, US, 1850. i, 2-4-0, Germany, 1850. No. 2023, Boiler of Locomotion No. 1. No. 2024, Liverpool & Manchester Railway, Great Britain, 1833.

**1991-92    Litho.    Perf. 14**
**Sheets of 9**

| | | | | |
|---|---|---|---|---|
| **2020** | A269 | 75c #a.-i. | 6.75 | 6.75 |
| **2021** | A269 | $1 #a.-i. | 9.00 | 9.00 |
| **2022** | A269 | $2 #a.-i. | 18.00 | 18.00 |

**Souvenir Sheet**

| | | | | |
|---|---|---|---|---|
| **2023** | A269 | $6 multicolored | 8.00 | 8.00 |
| **2024** | A269 | $6 multicolored | 8.00 | 8.00 |

Issued: 75c, #2023, Dec. 2; others, May 7, 1992.

**Miniature Sheet**

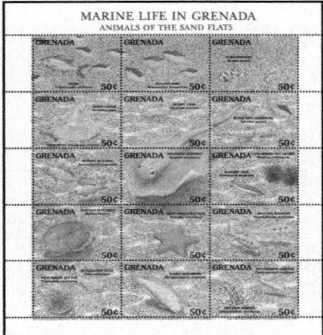

Marine Life in the Sand Flats — A270

Designs: No. 2025a, Barbu. b, Beaugregory. c, Porcupinefish. d, Conchfish, queen conch. e, Hermit crab. f, Bluestripe lizardfish. g, Spotfin mojarra. h, Southern stingray. i, Slippery dick, long-spined sea urchin. j, Peacock flounder. k, West Indian sea star. l, Spotted goatfish. m, West Indian sea egg, reticulated olive. n, Pearly razorfish. o, Mottled and yellowhead jawfish. $6, Shortnose batfish.

**1991, Dec. 5    Litho.    Perf. 14**

| | | | | |
|---|---|---|---|---|
| **2025** | A270 | 50c Sheet of 15, #a.-o. | 12.50 | 12.50 |

**Souvenir Sheet**

| | | | | |
|---|---|---|---|---|
| **2026** | A270 | $6 multicolored | 11.50 | 11.50 |

Christmas A271

Details from paintings by Albrecht Durer: 10c, Adoration of the Magi. 35c, The Madonna with the Siskin. 50c, The Feast of the Rose Garlands. 75c, Madonna and Child (Virgin with the Pear). $1, The Virgin in Half-Length. $2, Madonna and Child. $4, Virgin and Child with St. Anne. $5, Virgin and Child, diff. No. 2035, Virgin with a Multitude of Animals. No. 2036, The Nativity.

**1991, Dec. 9    Perf. 12**

| | | | | |
|---|---|---|---|---|
| **2027** | A271 | 10c multicolored | .40 | .20 |
| **2028** | A271 | 35c multicolored | .60 | .35 |
| **2029** | A271 | 50c multicolored | .65 | .45 |
| **2030** | A271 | 75c multicolored | 1.00 | .70 |
| **2031** | A271 | $1 multicolored | 1.10 | .90 |
| **2032** | A271 | $2 multicolored | 1.75 | 1.75 |

| | | | | |
|---|---|---|---|---|
| **2033** | A271 | $4 multicolored | 4.00 | 4.00 |
| **2034** | A271 | $5 multicolored | 4.50 | 4.50 |
| | | *Nos. 2027-2034 (8)* | 14.00 | 12.85 |

**Souvenir Sheets**
**Perf. 14½**

| | | | | |
|---|---|---|---|---|
| **2035** | A271 | $6 multicolored | 7.50 | 7.50 |
| **2036** | A271 | $6 multicolored | 7.50 | 7.50 |

Thrill Sports — A272

Walt Disney characters enjoying thrill sports.

**1992, Feb. 11    Litho.    Perf. 14x13½**

| | | | | |
|---|---|---|---|---|
| **2037** | A272 | 5c Windsurfing | .45 | .35 |
| **2038** | A272 | 10c Skateboarding | .55 | .35 |
| **2039** | A272 | 20c Gliding | .80 | .35 |
| **2040** | A272 | 45c Stunt kite flying | 1.25 | .35 |
| **2041** | A272 | $1 Mountain biking | 1.50 | 1.00 |
| **2042** | A272 | $2 Parachuting | 2.25 | 2.25 |
| **2043** | A272 | $4 Go-carting | 4.75 | 4.75 |
| **2044** | A272 | $5 Water skiing | 5.50 | 5.50 |
| | | *Nos. 2037-2044 (8)* | 17.05 | 14.90 |

**Souvenir Sheets**

| | | | | |
|---|---|---|---|---|
| **2045** | A272 | $6 Roller blade hockey | 6.00 | 6.00 |
| **2046** | A272 | $6 Bungee jumping | 6.00 | 6.00 |
| **2046A** | A272 | $6 Hang gliding | 6.00 | 6.00 |
| **2046B** | A272 | $6 River rafting | 6.00 | 6.00 |

**Queen Elizabeth II's Accession to the Throne, 40th Anniv.**
**Common Design Type**

**1992, Feb. 6    Perf. 14**

| | | | | |
|---|---|---|---|---|
| **2047** | CD348 | 10c multicolored | .20 | .20 |
| **2048** | CD348 | 50c multicolored | .40 | .40 |
| **2049** | CD348 | $1 multicolored | .80 | .80 |
| **2050** | CD348 | $5 multicolored | 4.00 | 4.00 |
| | | *Nos. 2047-2050 (4)* | 5.40 | 5.40 |

**Souvenir Sheets**

| | | | | |
|---|---|---|---|---|
| **2051** | CD348 | $6 Queen at left | 5.75 | 5.75 |
| **2052** | CD348 | $6 Queen at right | 5.75 | 5.75 |

Spanish Art — A273

Paintings: 10c, The Corpus Christi Procession in Seville, by Manuel Cabral y Aguado, horiz. 35c, The Mancorbo Channel, by Carlos de Haes. 50c, Countess of Vilches, by Federico de Madrazo y Kuntz. 75c, Countess of Santovenia, by Eduardo Rosales Gallina. $1, Queen Maria Isabel de Braganza, by Bernardo Lopez Piquer. $2, $4, The Presentation of Don John of Austria to Charles V (different details), by Gallina. $5, The Testament of Isabella the Catholic, by Eduardo Rosales Gallina, horiz. No. 2061, Meeting of Poets in Antonio Maria Esquivel's Studio, by Antonio Maria Esquivel y Suarez de Urbina. No. 2062, The Horse Corral in the Old Madrid Bullring, by Manuel Castellano, horiz.

**1992, Apr. 30    Litho.    Perf. 13**

| | | | | |
|---|---|---|---|---|
| **2053** | A273 | 10c multicolored | .35 | .20 |
| **2054** | A273 | 35c multicolored | .45 | .35 |
| **2055** | A273 | 50c multicolored | .55 | .45 |
| **2056** | A273 | 75c multicolored | .80 | .65 |
| **2057** | A273 | $1 multicolored | 1.25 | .85 |
| **2058** | A273 | $2 multicolored | 1.75 | 1.75 |
| **2059** | A273 | $4 multicolored | 3.50 | 3.50 |
| **2060** | A273 | $5 multicolored | 4.25 | 4.25 |

**Size: 120x95mm**
**Imperf**

| | | | | |
|---|---|---|---|---|
| **2061** | A273 | $6 multicolored | 5.75 | 5.75 |
| **2062** | A273 | $6 multicolored | 5.75 | 5.75 |
| | | *Nos. 2053-2062 (10)* | 24.40 | 23.50 |

Granada '92.

A274

Discovery of America, 500th Anniv. — A275

**1992, May 7    Litho.    Perf. 14**

| | | | | |
|---|---|---|---|---|
| **2063** | A274 | 10c Green-winged parrot | .50 | .25 |
| **2064** | A274 | 25c Santa Maria | .50 | .25 |
| **2065** | A274 | 35c Columbus | .50 | .45 |
| **2066** | A274 | 50c Hourglass | .70 | .60 |
| **2067** | A274 | 75c Queen Isabella | 1.25 | 1.00 |
| **2068** | A274 | $4 Cantino map, 1502 | 4.50 | 4.50 |
| | | *Nos. 2063-2068 (6)* | 7.95 | 7.05 |

**Souvenir Sheets**

| | | | | |
|---|---|---|---|---|
| **2069** | A274 | $6 Map, ship, fish | 6.25 | 6.25 |
| **2070** | A274 | $6 Map, arms, Genoa | 6.25 | 6.25 |

World Columbian Stamp Expo '92, Chicago.

**1992    Perf. 14½**

| | | | | |
|---|---|---|---|---|
| **2071** | A275 | $1 Coming ashore | 1.10 | 1.10 |
| **2072** | A275 | $2 Native, ships | 2.00 | 2.00 |

Organization of East Caribbean States.

Hummingbirds A276

**1992, May 28**

| | | | | |
|---|---|---|---|---|
| **2073** | A276 | 10c Ruby-throated | .75 | .30 |
| **2074** | A276 | 25c Vervain | .90 | .30 |
| **2075** | A276 | 35c Blue-headed | .95 | .35 |
| **2076** | A276 | 50c Cuban Emerald | 1.25 | .50 |
| **2077** | A276 | 75c Antillean Mango | 1.50 | .75 |
| **2078** | A276 | $2 Purple-throated carib | 1.60 | 1.60 |
| **2079** | A276 | $4 Puerto Rican emerald | 3.25 | 3.25 |
| **2080** | A276 | $5 Green-throated carib | 4.00 | 4.00 |
| | | *Nos. 2073-2080 (8)* | 14.20 | 11.05 |

**Souvenir Sheets**

| | | | | |
|---|---|---|---|---|
| **2081** | A276 | $6 Rufous-breasted hermit | 7.50 | 7.50 |
| **2082** | A276 | $6 Antillean crested | 7.50 | 7.50 |

Genoa '92.

USO, 50th Anniv. — A277        1992 Summer Olympics, Barcelona — A278

**1992, June 1** — **Perf. 14**

| | | | | |
|---|---|---|---|---|
| 2083 | A277 | 15c Gracie Fields | .35 | .25 |
| 2084 | A277 | 25c Jack Benny | .45 | .25 |
| 2085 | A277 | 35c Jinx Falkenburg | .50 | .40 |
| 2086 | A277 | 50c Frances Langford | .65 | .50 |
| 2087 | A277 | 75c Joe E. Brown | 1.00 | 1.00 |
| 2088 | A277 | $1 Phil Silvers | 1.25 | 1.25 |
| 2089 | A277 | $2 Danny Kaye | 2.50 | 2.50 |
| 2090 | A277 | $5 Frank Sinatra | 6.00 | 6.00 |
| | | Nos. 2083-2090 (8) | 12.70 | 12.15 |

**Souvenir Sheets**

| | | | | |
|---|---|---|---|---|
| 2091 | A277 | $6 Anna May Wong | 6.75 | 6.75 |
| 2092 | A277 | $6 Bob Hope | 6.75 | 6.75 |

**1992**

| | | | | |
|---|---|---|---|---|
| 2093 | A278 | 10c Badminton | .50 | .30 |
| 2094 | A278 | 25c Women's long jump | .50 | .20 |
| 2095 | A278 | 35c Women's 100-meter dash | .50 | .30 |
| 2096 | A278 | 50c Cycling | 1.00 | .50 |
| 2097 | A278 | 75c Decathlon (pole vault), horiz. | 1.00 | .70 |
| 2098 | A278 | $2 Judo, horiz. | 1.60 | 1.60 |
| 2099 | A278 | $4 Women's gymnastics | 3.25 | 3.25 |
| 2100 | A278 | $5 Javelin | 4.00 | 4.00 |
| | | Nos. 2093-2100 (8) | 12.35 | 10.85 |

**Souvenir Sheets**

| | | | | |
|---|---|---|---|---|
| 2101 | A278 | $6 Men's floor exercise | 5.75 | 5.75 |
| 2102 | A278 | $6 Men's vault | 5.75 | 5.75 |

Model Trains
A279

Designs: 10c, The Blue Comet, standard gauge, US, 1933. 35c, Switching locomotive, 2-inch gauge, 1906. 40c, B & O Tunnel locomotive, 2-inch gauge, 1905. 75c, Grand Canyon, standard gauge, US, 1931. $1, Lithographed tin streamliner, O gauge, 1930's. $2, Switching locomotive #237, No. 1 gauge, US, 1911. $4, Parlor car, standard gauge, US, 1928. $5, Locomotive #4687 of Improved President's Special, standard gauge, 1927. No. 2111, Engine #3239, No. 1 gauge, US, 1912. No. 2112, Ives engine #1132, 1921.

**1992, Oct. 22** — **Litho.** — **Perf. 14**

| | | | | |
|---|---|---|---|---|
| 2103 | A279 | 10c multicolored | .45 | .25 |
| 2104 | A279 | 35c multicolored | .50 | .30 |
| 2105 | A279 | 40c multicolored | .50 | .35 |
| 2106 | A279 | 75c multicolored | .90 | .50 |
| 2107 | A279 | $1 multicolored | 1.25 | 1.00 |
| 2108 | A279 | $2 multicolored | 1.50 | 1.50 |
| 2109 | A279 | $4 multicolored | 3.00 | 3.00 |
| 2110 | A279 | $5 multicolored | 3.75 | 3.75 |
| | | Nos. 2103-2110 (8) | 11.85 | 10.65 |

**Souvenir Sheet**
**Perf. 13**

| | | | | |
|---|---|---|---|---|
| 2111 | A279 | $6 multicolored | 6.25 | 6.25 |
| 2112 | A279 | $6 multicolored | 6.25 | 6.25 |

Nos. 2111-2112 contains one 51x40mm stamp.

**Souvenir Sheet**

Guggenheim Museum, NYC — A280

**1992, Oct. 28** — **Perf. 14**

| | | | | |
|---|---|---|---|---|
| 2113 | A280 | $6 multicolored | 5.25 | 5.25 |

Postage Stamp Mega Event '92, NYC.

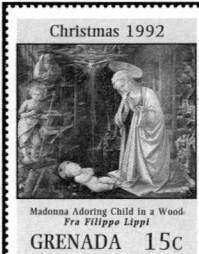

Christmas
A281

Details or entire paintings: 10c, The Adoration of the Magi, by Fra Filippo Lippi. 15c, Madonna Adoring Child in a Wood, by Fra Filippo Lippi. 25c, Adoration of the Magi, by Botticelli. 35c, The Epiphany-Adoration of the Magi, by Hieronymus Bosch. 50c, Adoration of the Magi, by Giovanni de Paolo. 75c, The Adoration of the Magi, by Gentile da Fabriano. 90c, Adoration of the Magi, by Juan Batista Maino. $1, The Adoration of the Child, by Master of Liesborn. $2, The Adoration of the Kings, by Master of Liesborn. $3, The Adoration of the Three Wise Men, by Pedro Berruguete. $4, The Adoration of the Child, by Filippo Lippi. $5, Adoration of the Child, by Correggio. No. 2126, Adoration of Magi, by Hans Memling. No. 2127, Adoration of the Magi, by Andrea Mantegna. No. 2128, Adoration of the Shepherds, by De La Tour.

**1992, Nov. 16** — **Litho.** — **Perf. 13½x14**

| | | | | |
|---|---|---|---|---|
| 2114 | A281 | 10c multicolored | .45 | .20 |
| 2115 | A281 | 15c multicolored | .50 | .20 |
| 2116 | A281 | 25c multicolored | .55 | .20 |
| 2117 | A281 | 35c multicolored | .75 | .40 |
| 2118 | A281 | 50c multicolored | .90 | .50 |
| 2119 | A281 | 75c multicolored | 1.10 | .80 |
| 2120 | A281 | 90c multicolored | 1.25 | .90 |
| 2121 | A281 | $1 multicolored | 1.50 | 1.00 |
| 2122 | A281 | $2 multicolored | 2.00 | 2.00 |
| 2123 | A281 | $3 multicolored | 3.00 | 3.00 |
| 2124 | A281 | $4 multicolored | 4.00 | 4.00 |
| 2125 | A281 | $5 multicolored | 5.00 | 5.00 |
| | | Nos. 2114-2125 (12) | 21.00 | 18.20 |

**Souvenir Sheet**

| | | | | |
|---|---|---|---|---|
| 2126 | A281 | $6 multicolored | 6.25 | 6.25 |
| 2127 | A281 | $6 multicolored | 6.25 | 6.25 |
| 2128 | A281 | $6 multicolored | 6.25 | 6.25 |

Regattas of the
World — A282

Yachts, races: 15c, Matador, Newport News Regatta. 25c, Awesome, Antigua Regatta. 35c, Mistress Quickly, Bermuda Regatta. 50c, Emeraude, St. Tropez Regatta. $1, Diva G, German Admirals Cup. $2, Lady Be, French Admirals Cup. $4, Midnight Sun, Admirals Cup Regatta. $5, Carat, Sardinia Cup Regatta. No. 2137, 1979 Fastnet Race, horiz. No. 2138, Grenada Regatta, horiz.

**1992, Oct.** — **Litho.** — **Perf. 14**

| | | | | |
|---|---|---|---|---|
| 2129 | A282 | 15c multicolored | .20 | .20 |
| 2130 | A282 | 25c multicolored | .20 | .20 |
| 2131 | A282 | 35c multicolored | .30 | .30 |
| 2132 | A282 | 50c multicolored | .75 | .40 |
| 2133 | A282 | $1 multicolored | 1.00 | .75 |
| 2134 | A282 | $2 multicolored | 1.40 | 1.40 |
| 2135 | A282 | $4 multicolored | 3.00 | 3.00 |
| 2136 | A282 | $5 multicolored | 3.75 | 3.75 |
| | | Nos. 2129-2136 (8) | 10.60 | 10.00 |

**Souvenir Sheets**

| | | | | |
|---|---|---|---|---|
| 2137 | A282 | $6 multicolored | 7.00 | 7.00 |
| 2138 | A282 | $6 multicolored | 7.00 | 7.00 |

A283

Anniversaries and
Events — A284

Designs: 25c, LZ1 on maiden flight, 1900. 50c, Endosat, proposed robot plane. 75c, Konrad Adenauer, factory. $1.50, Golden lion tamarin. No. 2143 Mountain gorilla. No. 2144, WHO emblem and "Heartbeat-the Rhythm of Health." $3, Wolfgang Amadeus Mozart. No. 2146, German flag, map, Adenauer. No. 2147, Voyager 2, Neptune. $5, Count Zeppelin, Graf Zeppelin. $6, Lion's Club emblem, Admiral Richard E. Byrd. No. 2150, Scene from "The Magic Flute." No. 2151, Konrad Adenauer. No. 2152, Earth Summit emblem, northern spotted owl. No. 2153, Count Zeppelin. No. 2154, Satellite rescue, vert.

**1992** — **Litho.** — **Perf. 14**

| | | | | |
|---|---|---|---|---|
| 2139 | A283 | 25c multicolored | 1.50 | 1.50 |
| 2140 | A283 | 50c multicolored | 1.50 | 1.50 |
| 2141 | A283 | 75c multicolored | 1.50 | 1.50 |
| 2142 | A283 | $1.50 multicolored | 3.50 | 3.50 |
| 2143 | A283 | $2 multicolored | 4.00 | 4.00 |
| 2144 | A283 | $2 multicolored | 4.75 | 4.75 |
| 2145 | A284 | $3 multicolored | 5.75 | 5.75 |
| 2146 | A283 | $4 multicolored | 4.00 | 4.00 |
| 2147 | A283 | $4 multicolored | 5.50 | 5.50 |
| 2148 | A283 | $5 multicolored | 8.00 | 8.00 |
| 2149 | A283 | $5 multicolored | 5.50 | 5.50 |
| | | Nos. 2139-2149 (11) | 45.50 | 45.50 |

**Souvenir Sheets**

| | | | | |
|---|---|---|---|---|
| 2150 | A284 | $6 multicolored | 6.50 | 6.50 |
| 2151 | A283 | $6 multicolored | 6.00 | 6.00 |
| 2152 | A283 | $6 multicolored | 5.75 | 5.75 |
| 2153 | A283 | $6 multicolored | 6.00 | 6.00 |
| 2154 | A283 | $6 multicolored | 5.75 | 5.75 |

Count Ferdinand von Zeppelin, 75th anniv. of death (#2139, 2148, 2153). Intl. Space Year (#2140, 2147, 2154). Konrad Adenauer, 25th anniv. of death (#2141, 2146, 2151). Earth Summit, Rio de Janeiro (#2142-2143, 2152). Mozart, bicent. of death (in 1991) (#2145, 2150). Lions Intl., 75th anniv. (#2149).

Issue dates: Nos. 2145, 2150, Oct. Nos. 2140-2141, 2144, 2146-2147, 2149, 2151, 2154, Nov. Nos. 2139, 2142-2143, 2148, 2152-2153, Dec.

Grenada
Dove — A285

**1992**

| | | | | |
|---|---|---|---|---|
| 2155 | A285 | 10c multicolored | .85 | .85 |

Entertainers — A286

Gold record award winners: No. 2156a, Cher. b, Michael Jackson. c, Elvis Presley. d, Dolly Parton. e, Johnny Mathis. f, Madonna. g, Nat King Cole. h, Janis Joplin.

No. 2157a, Frank Sinatra. b, Perry Como.
No. 2158a, Chuck Berry. b, James Brown.

**1992, Nov. 19** — **Litho.** — **Perf. 14**
**Miniature Sheet**

| | | | | |
|---|---|---|---|---|
| 2156 | A286 | 90c Sheet of 8, #a.-h. | 11.50 | 11.50 |

**Souvenir Sheets**

| | | | | |
|---|---|---|---|---|
| 2157 | A286 | $3 Sheet of 2, #a.-b. | 8.00 | 8.00 |
| 2158 | A286 | $3 Sheet of 2, #a.-b. | 8.00 | 8.00 |

Care Bears Promote
Conservation — A287

75c, Bear on uncontaminated beachfront. $2, Bear with parasol, butterfly on flower, vert.

**1992, Dec. 15** — **Litho.** — **Perf. 14**

| | | | | |
|---|---|---|---|---|
| 2159 | A287 | 75c multicolored | 1.00 | 1.00 |

**Souvenir Sheet**

| | | | | |
|---|---|---|---|---|
| 2160 | A287 | $2 multicolored | 3.00 | 3.00 |

Dogs
A288

Designs: 10c, Samoyed, St. Basil's Cathedral, Moscow. 15c, Chow chow, Ling Yin Monastery, China. 25c, Boxer, Traitor's Gate, United Kingdom. 90c, Basenji, Yamma Mosque, Niger. $1, Golden Labrador Retriever, Parliament, Ottawa, Canada. $3, Saint Bernard, Parsenn, Switzerland. $4, Rhodesian ridgeback, Melrose House, South Africa. $5, Afghan, Mazar-i-Sharif, Afghanistan. No. 2169, Alaskan malamute, Alaska. No. 2170, Australian cattle dog, Australia.

**1993, Jan. 20** — **Litho.** — **Perf. 14**

| | | | | |
|---|---|---|---|---|
| 2161 | A288 | 10c multicolored | .70 | .40 |
| 2162 | A288 | 15c multicolored | .85 | .40 |
| 2163 | A288 | 25c multicolored | .90 | .40 |
| 2164 | A288 | 90c multicolored | 1.25 | .75 |
| 2165 | A288 | $1 multicolored | 1.50 | 1.00 |
| 2166 | A288 | $3 multicolored | 2.25 | 2.25 |
| 2167 | A288 | $4 multicolored | 3.00 | 3.00 |
| 2168 | A288 | $5 multicolored | 3.75 | 3.75 |
| | | Nos. 2161-2168 (8) | 14.20 | 11.95 |

**Souvenir Sheet**

| | | | | |
|---|---|---|---|---|
| 2169 | A288 | $6 multicolored | 5.75 | 5.75 |
| 2170 | A288 | $6 multicolored | 5.75 | 5.75 |

Miniature Sheet

Louvre Museum, Bicent. — A289

Paintings by Jean-Antoine Watteau (1684-1721): a, The Faux-Pas. b, A Gentleman. c, Young Lady with Archlute. d, Young Man Dancing. e, Autumn. f, The Judgement of Paris. g-h, Pierrot (diff. details).
No. 2172, The Embarkation for Cythera, horiz.

**1993, Mar. 8** — **Litho.** — **Perf. 12**

| | | | | |
|---|---|---|---|---|
| 2171 | A289 | $1 Sheet of 8, #a.-h. + label | 10.00 | 10.00 |

**Souvenir Sheet**
**Perf. 14½**

| | | | | |
|---|---|---|---|---|
| 2172 | A289 | $6 multicolored | 7.50 | 7.50 |

No. 2172 contains one 88x55mm stamp.

Moths
A290

| 1993, Apr. 13 | | Litho. | Perf. 14 | |
|---|---|---|---|---|
| 2173 | A290 | 10c Magnificent | .35 | .25 |
| 2174 | A290 | 35c Metzl's io | .50 | .35 |
| 2175 | A290 | 45c Owl | .60 | .40 |
| 2176 | A290 | 75c Pink-spotted hawk | 1.00 | .60 |
| 2177 | A290 | $1 Faithful beauty | 1.25 | .75 |
| 2178 | A290 | $2 Green geometrid | 2.50 | 1.50 |
| 2179 | A290 | $4 Gaudy sphinx | 3.00 | 3.00 |
| 2180 | A290 | $5 Black witch | 3.75 | 3.75 |
| | | Nos. 2173-2180 (8) | 12.95 | 10.60 |

**Souvenir Sheets**

| 2181 | A290 | $6 Titan hawk, vert. | 5.50 | 5.50 |
|---|---|---|---|---|
| 2182 | A290 | $6 Avocado, vert. | 5.50 | 5.50 |

Flowers — A291

| 1993, May 17 | | Litho. | Perf. 14 | |
|---|---|---|---|---|
| 2183 | A291 | 10c Heliconia | .35 | .25 |
| 2184 | A291 | 35c Pansy | .50 | .35 |
| 2185 | A291 | 45c Water lily | .60 | .40 |
| 2186 | A291 | 75c Bougainvillea | .85 | .60 |
| 2187 | A291 | $1 Calla lily | 1.00 | .75 |
| 2188 | A291 | $2 California poppy | 1.50 | 1.50 |
| 2189 | A291 | $4 Red ginger | 3.00 | 3.00 |
| 2190 | A291 | $5 Anthurium | 3.75 | 3.75 |
| | | Nos. 2183-2190 (8) | 11.55 | 10.60 |

**Souvenir Sheet**

| 2191 | A291 | $6 Christmas rose, horiz. | 5.25 | 5.25 |
|---|---|---|---|---|
| 2192 | A291 | $6 Moth orchids, horiz. | 5.25 | 5.25 |

Baha'i Shrine,
Haifa,
Israel — A292

| 1993, May | | Litho. | Perf. 13½x14 | |
|---|---|---|---|---|
| 2193 | A292 | 75c multicolored | 1.60 | 1.60 |

Baha'i faith in Grenada, cent.

**Miniature Sheet**

Coronation of Queen Elizabeth II, 40th
Anniv. — A293

Designs: a, 35c, Official coronation photograph. b, 70c, Queen Consort's Ivory Rod, Queen Consort's Scepter. c, $1, Elizabeth accepting scepter during ceremony. $5, Queen, family, 1960s.
$6, Portrait, by Peter George Greenham, 1965.

| 1993, June 2 | | | Perf. 13½x14 | |
|---|---|---|---|---|
| 2194 | A293 | Sheet, 2 each #a.-d. | 12.00 | 12.00 |

**Souvenir Sheet**
**Perf. 14**

| 2195 | A293 | $6 multicolored | 6.50 | 6.50 |
|---|---|---|---|---|

No. 2195 contains one 28x42mm stamp.

A294

Anniversaries and Events — A295

Designs: 35c, Telescope. 50c, Willy Brandt, Sen. Edward Kennedy, Mrs. Robert Kennedy, 1973. $4, Astronaut standing on moon. No. 2199, Willy Brandt, Kurt Waldheim. No. 2200, Copernicus. $6, Newspaper headline announcing Brandt's resignation.

| 1993, July 1 | | Litho. | Perf. 14 | |
|---|---|---|---|---|
| 2196 | A294 | 35c multicolored | .50 | .50 |
| 2197 | A294 | 50c black & brown | .75 | .75 |
| 2198 | A294 | $4 multicolored | 4.50 | 4.50 |
| 2199 | A295 | $5 black & brown | 4.25 | 4.25 |
| | | Nos. 2196-2199 (4) | 10.00 | 10.00 |

**Souvenir Sheets**

| 2200 | A294 | $5 multicolored | 5.50 | 5.50 |
|---|---|---|---|---|
| 2201 | A295 | $6 brown & black | 5.75 | 5.75 |

Nicolaus Copernicus, 450th anniv. of death (#2196, 2198, 2200). Willy Brandt, 1st anniv. of death (#2197, 2199, 2201).

Grenada
Carnival,
1992
A296

**1993, July 1**

| 2202 | A296 | 35c Public Library, vert. | .50 | .50 |
|---|---|---|---|---|
| 2203 | A296 | 75c Dancers | .95 | .95 |

Public Library, cent. (in 1992) (#2202).

**Miniature Sheet**

Songbirds
A297

Designs: No. 2204a, 15c, Red-eyed vireo. b, 25c, Scissor-tailed flycatcher (g). c, 35c, Palmchat. d, 35c, Chaffinch. e, 45c, Yellow wagtail. f, 45c Painted bunting. g, 50c, Short-tailed pygmy flycatcher. h, 65c, Rainbow bunting. i, 75c, Red crossbill. j, 75c, Kauai akialoa. k, $1, Yellow-throated wagtail. l, $4, Barn swallow.
No. 2205, Song thrush. No. 2206, White-crested laughing thrush.

**1993, July 13**

| 2204 | A297 | Sheet of 12, #a.-l. | 13.00 | 13.00 |
|---|---|---|---|---|

**Souvenir Sheets**

| 2205 | A297 | $6 multicolored | 5.00 | 5.00 |
|---|---|---|---|---|
| 2206 | A297 | $6 multicolored | 5.00 | 5.00 |

**Miniature Sheet**

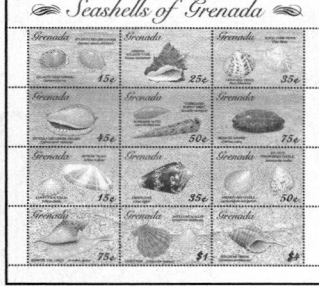

Seashells — A298

Designs: No. 2207a, 15c, Atlantic gray cowrie, Atlantic yellow cowrie. b, 15c, Candy stick tellin, sunrise tellin. c, 25c, Common Atlantic vase. d, 35c, Lightning venus, royal comb venus. e, 35c, Crown cone. f, 45c, Reticulated cowrie-helmet. g, 50c, Barbados miter, variegated turret shell. h, 50c, Common egg cockle, Atlantic strawberry cockle. i, 75c, Measled cowrie. j, 75c, Rooster tail conch. k, $1, Lion's paw, Antillean scallop. l, $4, Dog-head triton.
No. 2208, Dyson's keyhole limpet. No. 2209, Virgin nerite, emerald nerite.

| 1993, July 19 | | Litho. | Perf. 14 | |
|---|---|---|---|---|
| 2207 | A298 | Sheet of 12, #a.-l. | 13.00 | 13.00 |

**Souvenir Sheets**

| 2208 | A298 | $6 multicolored | 7.00 | 7.00 |
|---|---|---|---|---|
| 2209 | A298 | $6 multicolored | 7.00 | 7.00 |

A299

Picasso (1881-1973): 25c, Woman with Loaves, 1906. 90c, Weeping Woman, 1937. $4, Woman Seated in Armchair, 1947. $6, Three Women at the Spring, 1921.

| 1993, July 1 | | Litho. | Perf. 14 | |
|---|---|---|---|---|
| 2210 | A299 | 25c multicolored | .35 | .35 |
| 2211 | A299 | 90c multicolored | 1.25 | 1.00 |
| 2212 | A299 | $4 multicolored | 4.00 | 4.00 |
| | | Nos. 2210-2212 (3) | 5.60 | 5.35 |

**Souvenir Sheet**

| 2213 | A299 | $6 multicolored | 4.75 | 4.75 |
|---|---|---|---|---|

A300

**1993, July 1**

1994 Winter Olympics, Lillehammer, Norway: 35c, Gaeten Boucher, speedskating gold medalist, 1984. $5, Norbert Schramm, figure skater. $6, Michela Figini, Sigrid Wolf, Karen Percy, Super G medalists, 1988, horiz.

| 2214 | A300 | 35c multicolored | .50 | .30 |
|---|---|---|---|---|
| 2215 | A300 | $5 multicolored | 4.50 | 4.50 |

**Souvenir Sheet**

| 2216 | A300 | $6 multicolored | 5.75 | 5.75 |
|---|---|---|---|---|

Polska '93 — A301

Paintings: $1, Portrait of Marii Prohaska, by Tytus Czyzewski, 1923. $3, Marysia et Burek a Geylan, by S.I. Wirkiewicz, 1920-21. $6, Parting, by Witold Wojtkiewicz, 1908.

| 1993, July 1 | | Litho. | Perf. 14 | |
|---|---|---|---|---|
| 2217 | A301 | $1 multicolored | 1.25 | 1.25 |
| 2218 | A301 | $3 multicolored | 3.75 | 3.75 |

**Souvenir Sheet**

| 2219 | A301 | $6 multicolored | 6.25 | 6.25 |
|---|---|---|---|---|

Taipei
'93 — A302

Designs: 35c, Fire-breathing dragon, New Year's Fair, Chongqing. 45c, Stone elephant, Spirit Way to Ming Tomb, Nanjing. $2, Marble peifang, Ming Tombs, Beijing. $4, Stone pillar, Nanjing.
Paintings by Han Meilin: No. 2224a, Ornamental cock. b, Tiger cub. c, Owl. d, Cat. e, Gorillas. f, Leopard.
No. 2225, Orangutan.

| 1993, Aug. 13 | | Litho. | Perf. 14 | |
|---|---|---|---|---|
| 2220 | A302 | 35c multicolored | .25 | .25 |
| 2221 | A302 | 45c multicolored | .75 | .75 |
| 2222 | A302 | $2 multicolored | 3.25 | 3.25 |
| 2223 | A302 | $4 multicolored | 6.25 | 6.25 |
| | | Nos. 2220-2223 (4) | 10.50 | 10.50 |

**Miniature Sheet**

| 2224 | A302 | $1.50 Sheet of 6, #a.-f. | 6.75 | 6.75 |
|---|---|---|---|---|

**Souvenir Sheet**

| 2225 | A302 | $6 multicolored | 5.50 | 5.50 |
|---|---|---|---|---|

**With Bangkok '93 Emblem**

Designs: 35c, Nora Nair, Prasad Phra Thepidon, Wat Phra Kaew. 45c, Stucco deities, Library, Wat Phra Singh. $2, Naga snake, Chiang Mai's Temple. $4, Stucco elephants, Wat Chang Lom.
Thai sculpture: No. 2230a, Horses. b, Wheel of the Law, 7th-8th cent. c, Lanna bronze elephant, 1575. d, Kendi in form of elephant. e, Bronze duck, 14th-15th cent. f, Horseman, 14th-15th cent.
No. 2231, Elephants, horiz.

**1993, Aug. 13**

| 2226 | A302 | 35c multicolored | .25 | .25 |
|---|---|---|---|---|
| 2227 | A302 | 45c multicolored | .35 | .35 |
| 2228 | A302 | $2 multicolored | 1.50 | 1.50 |
| 2229 | A302 | $4 multicolored | 3.00 | 3.00 |
| | | Nos. 2226-2229 (4) | 5.10 | 5.10 |

**Miniature**

| 2230 | A302 | $1.50 Sheet of 6, #a.-f. | 6.75 | 6.75 |
|---|---|---|---|---|

**Souvenir Sheet**

| 2231 | A302 | $6 multicolored | 4.50 | 4.50 |
|---|---|---|---|---|

**With Indopex '93 Emblem**

35c, Megalithic carving, Sumba Island, Indonesia. 45c, Entrance to Gao Gaja (Elephant Cave), Bali. $2, Loving Mother Bridge, Taroko Gorge Natl. Park. $4, Kala head gateway to Balinese Temple, Northern Bali.
Indonesian sculpture - #2236: a, Kris holder and Kris, 19th cent. b, Hanuman protecting Sita, l. Dojotan of Mas. c, Sendi of Visnu mounted on Garuda, 19th cent. d, Wahana (mini vehicle for votive fig.), 20th cent. e, Mercurial monkey warrior Hanuman, Rodja of Mas. f, Singa (polychrome lion).
No. 2237, Loris.

**1993, Aug. 13**       **Perf. 13½x14**

| | | | | |
|---|---|---|---|---|
| 2232 | A302 | 35c multicolored | .25 | .25 |
| 2233 | A302 | 45c multicolored | .35 | .35 |
| 2234 | A302 | $2 multicolored | 1.50 | 1.50 |
| 2235 | A302 | $4 multicolored | 3.00 | 3.00 |
| | | Nos. 2232-2235 (4) | 5.10 | 5.10 |

**Miniature**

| | | | | |
|---|---|---|---|---|
| 2236 | A302 | $1.50 Sheet of 6, #a.-f. | 11.00 | 11.00 |

**Souvenir Sheet**

| | | | | |
|---|---|---|---|---|
| 2237 | A302 | $6 multicolored | 5.50 | 5.50 |

Miniature Sheets of 6

Italian Soccer Assoc. and Genoa Soccer Club, Cent. — A303

Players for Genoa Soccer Club, each $3: No. 2238a, Vittorio Sardelli. b, Juan Carlos Verdeal. c, Fosco Becattini. d, Julio Cesar Abadie. e, Luigi Meroni. f, Roberto Pruzzo.

No. 2239a, each $3: James K. Spensley. b, Renzo de Vecchi. c, Giovanni de Pra. d, Luigi Burlando. e, Felice Levratto. f, Guglielmo Stabile.

Each $15: No. 2240, 1991 Genoa team photo, horiz. No. 2241, Genoa team emblem.

**1993, Sept. 7**    **Litho.**    **Perf. 14**

Sheets of 6, #a-f

| | | | | |
|---|---|---|---|---|
| 2238-2239 | A303 | Set of 2 | 40.00 | 40.00 |

**Souvenir Sheets**

| | | | | |
|---|---|---|---|---|
| 2240-2241 | A303 | Set of 2 | 37.00 | 37.00 |

No. 2240 contains one 48x35mm stamp. No. 2241 contains one 29x45mm stamp.

1994 World Cup Soccer Championships, US — A304

Designs: 10c, Nikolai Larionov, Russia. 25c, Andrea Carnevale, Italy. 35c, Enzo Scifo, Belgium, Soon-Ho Choi, South Korea. 45c, Gary Lineker, England. $1, Diego Maradona, Argentina. $2, Lothar Matthaeus, Germany. $4, Jan Karas, Poland, Julio Cesar Silva, Brazil. $5, Claudio Caniggia, Argentina.

Each $6: No. 2250, Wlodzimierz, Poland. No. 2251, Jose Basualdo, Argentina.

**1993, Sept. 7**    **Litho.**    **Perf. 14**

| | | | | |
|---|---|---|---|---|
| 2242-2249 | A304 | Set of 8 | 12.00 | 12.00 |

**Souvenir Sheets**

| | | | | |
|---|---|---|---|---|
| 2250-2251 | A304 | Set of 2 | 11.00 | 11.00 |

Mickey Mouse, 65th Birthday — A305

Movie clips: 25c, The Band Concert, 1935. 35c, Mickey's Circus, 1936. 50c, Magician Mickey, 1937. 75c, Moose Hunters, 1937. $1, Mickey's Amateurs, 1937. $2, Tugboat Mickey, 1940. $4, Orphan's Benefit, 1941. $5, Mickey's Christmas, 1983.

Each $6: No. 2260, Mickey's Birthday Party, 1942. No. 2261, Mickey's Trailer, 1938.

**1993, Nov. 11**   **Litho.**   **Perf. 14x13½**

| | | | | |
|---|---|---|---|---|
| 2252-2259 | A305 | Set of 8 | 13.00 | 13.00 |

**Souvenir Sheets**

| | | | | |
|---|---|---|---|---|
| 2260-2261 | A305 | Set of 2 | 13.50 | 13.50 |

Christmas A306

Woodcuts by Durer: 10c, The Nativity. 25c, "The Annunciation." $1, "Adoration of the Magi." $5, "The Virgin Mary in the Sun."

Paintings by Leonardo Da Vinci: 35c, The Litta Madonna. 60c, Madonna and Child with St. Anne and the Infant St. John. 90c, Madonna with the Carnation. $4, The Benois Madonna.

Each $6: No. 2270, The Holy Family with Three Hares, by Durer. No. 2271, Adoration of the Magi, by Da Vinci.

The 25c actually shows the Adoration of the Magi. The $1 actually shows The Virgin Mary in the Sun. The $5 actually shows The Annunciation.

**1993, Nov. 22**   **Litho.**   **Perf. 13½x14**

| | | | | |
|---|---|---|---|---|
| 2262-2269 | A306 | Set of 8 | 10.50 | 10.50 |

**Souvenir Sheets**

| | | | | |
|---|---|---|---|---|
| 2270-2271 | A306 | Set of 2 | 10.50 | 10.50 |

Hugo Eckener (1868-1954) — A307

Graf Zeppelin over: 35c, Vienna. 75c, Pyramids at Giza. $5, Rio de Janeiro. #2275, Flensburg.

**1993, Dec. 21**       **Perf. 14**

| | | | | |
|---|---|---|---|---|
| 2272-2274 | A307 | Set of 3 | 5.50 | 5.50 |

**Souvenir Sheet**

| | | | | |
|---|---|---|---|---|
| 2275 | A307 | $6 multicolored | 5.50 | 5.50 |

Royal Air Force, 75th Anniv. A308

**1993, Dec. 21**

| | | | | |
|---|---|---|---|---|
| 2276 | A308 | 50c Lysander | 1.00 | 1.00 |
| 2277 | A308 | $3 Hawker Typhoon | 4.25 | 4.25 |

**Souvenir Sheet**

| | | | | |
|---|---|---|---|---|
| 2278 | A308 | $6 Hawker Hurricane | 5.25 | 5.25 |

Automotive Anniversaries — A309

35c, 1932 Mercedes Benz 370 S Cabriolet. 45c, 1966 Ford Mustang. $3, 1930 Model A Ford Phaeton. $4, Mercedes Benz 300 SL Gullwing.

Each $6: No. 2283, 1903 Ford Model A. No. 2284, 1934 Mercedes Benz 290.

**1993, Dec. 21**    **Litho.**    **Perf. 14**

| | | | | |
|---|---|---|---|---|
| 2279-2282 | A309 | Set of 4 | 10.00 | 10.00 |

**Souvenir Sheets**

| | | | | |
|---|---|---|---|---|
| 2283-2284 | A309 | Set of 2 | 10.50 | 10.50 |

1st Benz 4-wheel car, cent. 1st Ford engine, cent.

First Gas Balloon Flight in America, Bicent. A310

Designs: 45c, Lift-off from Philadelphia. $2, Balloon in flight, vert. $6, Blanchard's balloon in flight, diff., vert.

**1993, Dec. 21**    **Litho.**    **Perf. 14**

| | | | | |
|---|---|---|---|---|
| 2285-2286 | A310 | Set of 2 | 3.00 | 3.00 |

**Souvenir Sheet**

| | | | | |
|---|---|---|---|---|
| 2287 | A310 | $6 multicolored | 6.50 | 6.50 |

Fine Art — A311

Self-portraits, by Matisse: 15c, 1900. 45c, 1918. $2, 1906. $4, 1900, diff.

Self-portraits, by Rembrandt: 35c, 1629. 50c, 1640. 75c, 1652. $5, 1625-31.

No. 2296, The Painter in His Studio, by Matisse. No. 2297, The Sampling Officials of the Draper's Guild, by Rembrandt, horiz.

**1993, Dec. 31**   **Litho.**   **Perf. 13½x14**

| | | | | |
|---|---|---|---|---|
| 2288 | A311 | 15c multicolored | .40 | .20 |
| 2289 | A311 | 35c multicolored | .50 | .25 |
| 2290 | A311 | 45c multicolored | .55 | .40 |
| 2291 | A311 | 50c multicolored | .65 | .45 |
| 2292 | A311 | 75c multicolored | 1.00 | .60 |
| 2293 | A311 | $2 multicolored | 1.75 | 1.60 |
| 2294 | A311 | $4 multicolored | 3.25 | 3.25 |
| 2295 | A311 | $5 multicolored | 4.00 | 4.00 |
| | | Nos. 2288-2295 (8) | 12.10 | 10.75 |

**Souvenir Sheets**

| | | | | |
|---|---|---|---|---|
| 2296 | A311 | $6 multicolored | 5.25 | 5.25 |

**Perf. 14x13½**

| | | | | |
|---|---|---|---|---|
| 2297 | A311 | $6 multicolored | 5.25 | 5.25 |

Spice Islands Billfish Tournament, 25th Anniv. — A312

15c, Blue marlin. 25c, Sailfish with angler. 35c, Yellowfin tuna with angler. 50c, White marlin with angler. 75c, Catching a sailfish.

**1993, Dec.**    **Litho.**    **Perf. 14**

| | | | | |
|---|---|---|---|---|
| 2302-2306 | A312 | Set of 5 | 4.25 | 4.25 |

A313

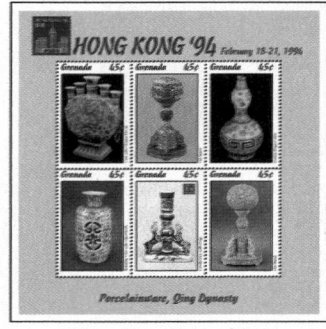

Hong Kong '94 — A314

Stamps, painting, Hong Kong Post Office-1846, by M. Bruce: No. 2307, Hong Kong #263, left detail. No. 2308, Right detail, #1597.

Porcelain ware, Qing Dynasty: No. 2309a, Vase with dragon decor. b, Hat stand. c, Gourd-shaped vase. d, Rotating vase with openwork. e, Candlestick with dogs. f, Hat stand, diff.

**1994, Feb. 18**    **Litho.**    **Perf. 14**

| | | | | |
|---|---|---|---|---|
| 2307 | | 40c multicolored | .65 | .65 |
| 2308 | | 40c multicolored | .65 | .65 |
| a. | A313 | Pair, #2307-2308 | 1.40 | 1.40 |

**Miniature Sheet**

| | | | | |
|---|---|---|---|---|
| 2309 | A314 | 45c Sheet of 6, #a.-f. | 3.75 | 3.75 |

Nos. 2307-2308 issued in sheets of 5 pairs. No. 2308a is a continuous design.

New Year 1994 (Year of the Dog) (#2309e).

Independence, 20th Anniv. — A315

**1994, Feb. 8**    **Litho.**    **Perf. 14**

| | | | | |
|---|---|---|---|---|
| 2310 | A315 | 35c Natl. flag, boat | .85 | .85 |

**Souvenir Sheet**

| | | | | |
|---|---|---|---|---|
| 2311 | A315 | $6 Map of Granada | 6.50 | 6.50 |

Miniature Sheets

Dinosaurs A316

Jurassic: No. 2312a, Germanodactylus. b, Dimorphodon. c, Ramphorhynchus. d, Apatosaurus (h). e, Pterodactylus. f, Stegosaurus. g, Brachiosaurus. h, Allosaurus (l). i, Plesiosaurus. j, Ceratosaurus. k, Compsognathus. l, Elaphosaurus.

Cretaceous: No. 2313a, Quetzalcoatlus. b, Pteranodon ingens (c). c, Tropeognathus. d, Phobetor. e, Alamosaurus (i). f, Triceratops (e). g, Tyrannosaurus rex (h). h, Tyrannosaurus rex (up close) (l). i, Lambeosaurus. j, Spinosaurus. k, Parasaurolophus (l). l, Hadrosaurus.

No. 2314, Plateosaurus, vert. No. 2315, Pteranodon ingens.

**1994, Apr. 13**

Sheets of 12

| | | | | |
|---|---|---|---|---|
| 2312 | A316 | 75c #a.-l. | 7.75 | 7.75 |
| 2313 | A316 | 75c #a.-l. | 7.75 | 7.75 |

**Souvenir Sheets**

| | | | | |
|---|---|---|---|---|
| 2314 | A316 | $6 multicolored | 5.50 | 5.50 |
| 2315 | A316 | $6 multicolored | 5.50 | 5.50 |

Mushrooms
A317

Designs: 35c, Hygrocybe acutoconica. 45c, Leucopaxillus gracillimus. 50c, Leptonia caeruleocapitata. 75c, Leucoprinus birnbaumii. $1, Marasmius atrorubens. $2, Boletellus cubensis. $4, Chlorophyllum molybdites. $5, Psilocybe cubensis.
No. 2324, Mycena pura. No. 2325, Pyrrhoglossum lilaceipes.

**1994, Apr. 6**

| 2316 | A317 | 35c multicolored | .50 | .25 |
|------|------|------------------|------|------|
| 2317 | A317 | 45c multicolored | .60 | .35 |
| 2318 | A317 | 50c multicolored | .70 | .40 |
| 2319 | A317 | 75c multicolored | .90 | .50 |
| 2320 | A317 | $1 multicolored | 1.25 | .75 |
| 2321 | A317 | $2 multicolored | 1.60 | 1.25 |
| 2322 | A317 | $4 multicolored | 3.25 | 3.25 |
| 2323 | A317 | $5 multicolored | 4.00 | 4.00 |
| | | *Nos. 2316-2323 (8)* | 12.80 | 10.75 |

**Souvenir Sheets**

| 2324 | A317 | $6 multicolored | 6.25 | 6.25 |
|------|------|------------------|------|------|
| 2325 | A317 | $6 multicolored | 6.25 | 6.25 |

D-Day,
50th
Anniv.
A318

Designs: 40c, Sherman Dual-Drive swimming tanks. $2, Churchill "Ark" in operation. $3, Churchill "Bobbin" lays path over soft ground.
$6, Churchill "Avre."

**1994, Aug. 4      Litho.      Perf. 14**

| 2326-2328 | A318 | Set of 3 | 6.50 | 6.50 |
|-----------|------|----------|------|------|

**Souvenir Sheet**

| 2329 | A318 | $6 multicolored | 6.25 | 6.25 |
|------|------|------------------|------|------|

Miniature Sheet of 6

First Manned Moon Landing, 25th
Anniv. — A319

Tribute to crew of space shuttle Challenger: No. 2330a, Flame erupting before explosion. b, Judith A. Resnick. c, Aircraft flyover in "Missing Man" formation. d, Dick Scobee. e, Challenger 51-L patch. f, Michael J. Smith.
$6, Crew of mission 51-L.

**1994, Aug. 4**

| 2330 | A319 | $2 #a.-f. | 8.50 | 8.50 |
|------|------|-----------|------|------|

**Souvenir Sheet**

| 2331 | A319 | $6 multicolored | 5.25 | 5.25 |
|------|------|------------------|------|------|

A320

PHILAKOREA '94 — A321

Designs: 40c, Wonson Park & Garden. $1, Port of Pusan. $4, National Theatre, Seoul.
Paintings by Sin Yunbok, Late Choson Dynasty: No. 2335a-2335b, Lady in a Hooded Cloak. c-d, Kiaseng House. e-f, Amorous Youth on a Picnic. g-h, Chasing a Cat.
$6, Roof Tiling, by Kim Hongdo, vert.

**1994, Aug. 4     Perf. 14, 13½ (#2335)**

| 2332-2334 | A320 | Set of 3 | 4.00 | 4.00 |
|-----------|------|----------|------|------|

**Miniature Sheet**

| 2335 | A321 | $1 Sheet of 8, #a.-h. | 6.00 | 6.00 |
|------|------|------------------------|------|------|

**Souvenir Sheet**

| 2336 | A320 | $6 multicolored | 4.50 | 4.50 |
|------|------|------------------|------|------|

A322

Orchids: 15c, Brassavola cuculatta. 25c, Comparettia falcata. 45c, Epidendrum ciliare. 75c, Epidendrum cochleatum. $1, Ionopsis utriculariodes. $2, Oncidium ceboletta. $4, Oncidium luridum. $5, Rodriquezia secunda.
Each $6: #2345, Ionopis utriculariodes, diff. No. 2346, Onicium luridum, diff.

**1994, Aug. 7                    Perf. 14**

| 2337-2344 | A322 | Set of 8 | 10.50 | 10.50 |
|-----------|------|----------|-------|-------|

**Souvenir Sheets**

| 2345-2346 | A322 | Set of 2 | 11.00 | 11.00 |
|-----------|------|----------|-------|-------|

A323

1994 World Cup Soccer Championships, US: No. 2347a, Tony Meola, US. b, Steve Mark, Grenada. c, Gianluigi Lentini, Italy. d, Belloumi, Algeria. e, Nunoz, Spain. f, Lothar Matthaus, Germany.
Each $6: #2348, Steve Mark, diff. #2349, Poster from 1st World Cup Championships, Uruguay, 1930.

**1994, Aug. 11                 Perf. 14**

**Miniature Sheet**

| 2347 | A323 | 75c Sheet of 6, #a.-f. | 5.50 | 5.50 |
|------|------|------------------------|------|------|

**Souvenir Sheet**

| 2348-2349 | A323 | Set of 2 | 10.00 | 10.00 |
|-----------|------|----------|-------|-------|

Fish
A324

Designs: 15c, Yellowtail snapper. 20c, Blue tang. 25c, Porkfish, vert. 75c, Foureye butterflyfish. $1, Longsnout seahorse, vert. $2, Spotted moray eel, vert. $4, Fairy basslet. $5, Queen triggerfish, vert.
Each $6: #2358, Queen angelfish. #2359, Squirrelfish.

**1994, Sept. 1**

| 2350-2357 | A324 | Set of 8 | 10.00 | 10.00 |
|-----------|------|----------|-------|-------|

**Souvenir Sheets**

| 2358-2359 | A324 | Set of 2 | 10.50 | 10.50 |
|-----------|------|----------|-------|-------|

A325

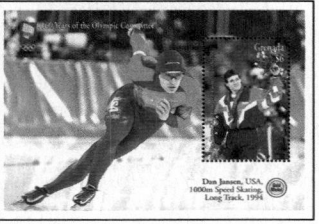

Intl. Olympic Committee,
Cent. — A326

Designs: 50c, Heike Dreschler, Germany, long jump, 1992. $1.50, Nadia Comaneci, Romania, Gymnastics, 1976, 1980.
$6, Dan Jansen, US, 1000-meters long track speed skating, 1994.

**1994, Aug. 4**

| 2360 | A325 | 50c multicolored | 1.00 | 1.00 |
|------|------|------------------|------|------|
| 2361 | A325 | $1.50 multicolored | 2.25 | 2.25 |

**Souvenir Sheet**

| 2362 | A326 | $6 multicolored | 5.00 | 5.00 |
|------|------|------------------|------|------|

1994, Year of the Dog — A327

Scenes from Disney's Society Dog Show: 2c, Mickey bathing Pluto. 3c, Using atomizer. 4c, Having tail "set." 5c, Putting on mascara. 10c, Having nails done. 15c, Mickey using flea powder on Pluto. 20c, On judge's stand. $4, Judge looking at Pluto. $5, Pluto in chair with first prize.
No. 2372, Pluto wearing "13," first prize ribbon. No. 2373, Little dog beside judge. No. 2374, Pluto with first prize ribbon.

**1994, Sept. 22   Litho.   Perf. 14x13½**

| 2363-2371 | A327 | Set of 9 | 10.50 | 10.50 |
|-----------|------|----------|-------|-------|

**Souvenir Sheets**

| 2372-2374 | A327 | $6 each | 5.25 | 5.25 |
|-----------|------|---------|------|------|

Butterflies — A328

**1994, Sept. 28                 Perf. 14**

| 2375 | A328 | 10c Red anartia | .35 | .20 |
|------|------|------------------|------|------|
| 2376 | A328 | 15c Ruddy dag-gerwing | .35 | .20 |
| 2377 | A328 | 25c Fiery skipper | .40 | .20 |
| 2378 | A328 | 35c Caribbean buckeye | .45 | .40 |
| 2379 | A328 | 45c Giant hair-streak | .50 | .40 |
| 2380 | A328 | 50c Zebra longw-ing | .60 | .50 |
| 2381 | A328 | 75c Diadem | .70 | .70 |
| 2382 | A328 | $1 Blue night | 1.00 | 1.00 |
| 2383 | A328 | $2 Orion | 2.00 | 2.00 |
| 2384 | A328 | $3 Orange-barred sulphur | 3.00 | 3.00 |
| 2385 | A328 | $4 Long-tail skipper | 4.00 | 4.00 |
| 2386 | A328 | $5 Polydamas swallowtail | 4.75 | 4.75 |
| 2386A | A328 | $10 Bamboo page | 9.50 | 9.50 |
| 2386B | A328 | $20 Queen cracker | 15.25 | 15.25 |
| | | *Nos. 2375-2386B (14)* | 42.85 | 42.10 |

#2377-2378 exist dated 1996.
See Nos. 2585-2586.

Intl. Year
of the
Family
A329

**1994, Aug. 4**

| 2387 | A329 | $1 multicolored | .95 | .95 |
|------|------|------------------|------|------|

Order of the Caribbean
Community — A330

First award recipients: 15c, Sir Shridath Ramphal, statesman, Guyana. 65c, William Demas, economist, Trinidad & Tobago. $2, Derek Walcott, writer, St. Lucia.

**1994, Sept. 1**

| 2388-2390 | A330 | Set of 3 | 3.00 | 3.00 |
|-----------|------|----------|------|------|

Christmas
A331

Paintings, by Zurbaran: 10c, The Virgin and Child with St. John. 15c, The Circumcision. 25c, Adoration of St. Joseph. 35c, Adoration of the Magi. 75c, The Portiuncula. $1, The Virgin and Child with St. John, 1662. $2, The Virgin and Child with St. John, 1658-64. $4, The Flight into Egypt.
Each $6: No. 2399, Adoration of the Shepherds, horiz. No. 2400, Our Lady of Ransom and Two Mercedarians.

**1994, Dec. 5　Litho.　Perf. 13½x14**
2391-2398　A331　Set of 8　　　　7.50　7.50
**Souvenir Sheets**
2399-2400　A331　Set of 2　　　10.50　10.50

A332　　　　　　　A333

Birds: 25c, Grenada dove, horiz. 35c, Grenada doves, horiz. 45c, Cuban tody. No. 2404, 75c, Grenada dove, diff. No. 2405, 75c, Painted bunting, horiz. No. 2406, $1, Grenada dove, in flight. No. 2407, $1, Red-legged honeycreeper, horiz. No. 2408, $5, Green jay, horiz. Each $6: No. 2409, Chestnut-sided shrike-vireo, horiz. No. 2410, Chaffinch, horiz.

**1995, Jan. 10　　　　　Perf. 14**
2401-2408　A332　Set of 8　　　15.00　15.00
**Souvenir Sheet**
2409-2410　A332　Set of 2　　　13.00　13.00
World Wildlife Fund (#2401-2402, 2404, 2406).

**1995, Jan. 12**
Designs: 25c, Junior Murray, Grenada/W. Indies. 35c, R.B. Richardson, Leeward Isl./W. Indies. $2, A.J. Steward, England, horiz. No. 2414, West Indies team, horiz.

2411-2413　A333　Set of 3　　　　3.00　3.00
**Souvenir Sheet**
2414　A333　$3 multicolored　　4.00　4.00
English Touring Cricket, cent.

Water Birds A334

25c, Hooded merganser. 35c, Teal. $1, Harlequin duck. $3, European wigeon.
No. 2419a, King eider. b, Shoveler. c, Long-tailed duck. d, Chiloe wigeon. e, Red-breasted merganser. f, Falcated teal. g, Vericolor teal. h, Smew. i, Red-crested pochard. j, Northern pintail. k, Barrow's goldeneye. l, Stellar's eider.
No. 2420, European wigeon, diff. No. 2421, Egyptian goose.

**1995, Mar. 27　Litho.　Perf. 14**
2415-2418　A334　Set of 4　　　　5.00　5.00
**Miniature Sheet**
2419　A334　75c Sheet of 12, #a.-l. 9.50 9.50
**Souvenir Sheets**
2420　A334　$5 multicolored　　　4.00　4.00
2421　A334　$6 multicolored　　　4.75　4.75

New Year 1995 (Year of the Boar) — A335

a, 50c, Pig priest, China. b, 75c, Porcelain pig, Scotland. c, $1, Porcelain pig, Italy. $2, Jade pig, China.

**1995, Apr. 21　Litho.　Perf. 14**
2422　A335　Strip of 3, #a.-c.　2.50　2.50
**Souvenir Sheet**
2423　A335　$2 multicolored　　2.75　2.75
No. 2422 was issued in miniature sheets containing 3 #2422.

---

Miniature Sheets of 6 and 8

End of World War II, 50th Anniv. A336

No. 2423A: b, Great Marianas Turkey Shoot. c, Battle of Midway. d, Battle of the Bismarck Sea. e, Musashi sinks at Leyte Gulf. f, Henderson Field. g, Battle of Guadalcanal.
Fighter planes: No. 2424a, Lavochkin LA7, Soviet Air Force. b, Hawker Hurricane, Royal Air Force (RAF). c, North American P-51D, US Army Air Force (USAAF). d, Messerschmitt ME 109F, Luftwaffe. e, Bristol Beaufighter, RAF. f, Messerschmitt ME 262, Luftwaffe. g, Republic P-47D, USAAF. h, Hawker Tempest V, RAF.
No. 2425, Nose of P-47D. No. 2425A, B-29 bomber.

**1995, May 8**
2423A　A336　$2 #b.-g. + label　12.00　12.00
2424　A336　$2 #a.-h. + label　15.00　15.00
**Souvenir Sheets**
2425　A336　$6 multicolored　　7.00　7.00
2425A　A336　$6 multicolored　　6.50　6.50

18th World Scout Jamboree, Holland — A337

Designs: a, 75c, Palm trees, scout. b, $1, Mountain climbing. c, $2, Scout salute, flag. $6, Canoeing.

**1995, May 8**
2426　A337　Strip of 3, #a.-c.　3.25　3.25
**Souvenir Sheet**
2427　A337　$6 multicolored　　5.25　5.25
No. 2426 issued in sheets of 9 stamps.

UN, 50th Anniv. — A338

Designs: a, 75c, Man bending sword into plowshare. b, $1, Earth, dove. c, $2, UN Headquarters. $6, Emblem.

**1995, May 8**
2428　A338　Strip of 3, #a.-c.　3.25　3.25
**Souvenir Sheet**
2429　A338　$6 multicolored　　5.00　5.00
No. 2428 is a continuous design and was issued in sheets of 9 stamps.

Grenada-Republic of China Friendship — A339

Designs: 75c, Flags of Grenada, Republic of China. $1, Prime Minister Nicholas Brathwaite, Grenada, Pres. Lee Teng-hui, Republic of China.

**1995, Apr. 27　Litho.　Perf. 14**
2430　A339　75c multicolored　1.25　1.25
2431　A339　$1 multicolored　　1.50　1.50
　a.　Souvenir sheet, #2430-2431　2.75　2.75

---

Domesticated Animals — A340

Designs: 10c, Cocker spaniel. 15c, Pinto. 25c, Rottweiler. 35c, German shepherd. 45c, Persian. 50c, Snowshoe. 75c, Percheron. $1, Scottish fold. $2, Arabian. $3, Andalusian. $4, C.P. shorthair. $5, Chihuahua.
No. 2444, $5, Manx. No. 2445, $5, Donkey. No. 2446, $6, Shar pei.

**1995, May 3**
2432-2443　A340　Set of 12　　16.00　16.00
**Souvenir Sheets**
2444-2445　A340　Set of 2　　　8.00　8.00
2446　A340　multi　　　　　　5.25　5.25

Miniature Sheets of 9

Sierra Club, Cent. A341

No. 2447, vert, each $1: a, Margay, mouth open. b, Margay seated. c, Margay up close. d, Condor facing left. e, Condor facing right. f, Condor looking back. g, White-faced saki on tree limb. h, White-faced saki, face in light. i, Patagonia Region, South America.
No. 2448, each $1: a, Darwin's rhea, two facing right. b, Darwin's rhea, two facing left. c, One Darwin's rhea. d, Snow covered mountains, Patagonia Region. e, Mountain peaks, Patagonia Region. f, White-faced saki. g, Crested caracara facing right. h, Two crested caracara. i, Crested caracara facing left.

**1995, May 5**
2447-2448　A341　Set of 2　　17.00　17.00

FAO, 50th Anniv. — A342　　Rotary Intl., 90th Anniv. — A343

No. 2449: a, 75c, Woman with baskets. b, $1, Boy with basket. c, $2, Men working in field.
$6, FAO emblem.

**1995, May 8**
2449　A342　Strip of 3, #a.-c.　3.25　3.25
**Souvenir Sheet**
2450　A342　$6 multicolored　　5.00　5.00
No. 2449 was issued in sheets of 9 stamps.

**1995, May 8**
2451　A343　$5 shown　　　　4.25　4.25
**Souvenir Sheet**
2452　A343　$6　Paul Harris, emblem　　　　　　　5.00　5.00

Queen Mother, 95th Birthday — A344

No. 2453: a, Drawing. b, Holding flower. c, Formal portrait. d, Blue hat, white coat.
$6, As younger woman.

---

**1995, May 8　　　　　Perf. 13½x14**
2453　A344　$1.50 Strip or block of 4, #a.-d.　　7.00　7.00
**Souvenir Sheet**
2454　A344　$6 multicolored　　6.25　6.25
No. 2453 was issued in sheets of 8 stamps. Sheets of Nos. 2453 and 2454 exist with black border and text "In Memoriam 1900-2002" overprinted in sheet margins.

1996 Summer Olympics, Atlanta — A345

No. 2455: a, Tian Bingyi, China, badminton. b, Waldemar Leigien, Poland, Frank Wieneke, Germany, judo. c, Nelli Kim, USSR, women's gymnastics. d, Alessandro Andri, Italy, shot put.
No. 2456: a, Jackie Joyner, US, heptathlon. b, Mitsuo Tsukahara, Japan, gymnastics. c, Flo Hyman, US, Zhang Rung Fang, China, volleyball. d, Steffi Graf, Germany, tennis.
Each $6: No. 2457, Sailing. No. 2458, Wilma Rudolph, US, track.

**1995, June 23**
2455　A345　75c Strip of 4, #a.-d.　　　　　　　3.00　3.00
2456　A345　$2 Strip of 4, #a.-d.　　　　　　　7.75　7.75
**Souvenir Sheets**
2457-2458　A345　Set of 2　　10.00　10.00

Anniversaries & Events — A346

25c, Junior Murray, cricket player. 75c, Spices. #2461, $1, Sendall Tunnel, cent. #2462, $1, Caribbean Development Bank, 25th anniv.

**1995, Aug. 18　Litho.　Perf. 14**
2459-2462　A346　Set of 4　　　3.50　3.50

Miniature Sheets of 9

Trains of the World A347

No. 2463: a, ETR 450, Italy. b, Isparta to Bozanonu, Turkey. c, TGV, France. d, ICE Inter-City Express, Germany. e, Nishi Nippon Rail, Japan. f, Bullet Train, Japan. g, Standard 4-4-0, Central Pacific RR, US. h, Amatrak 900 Bo-Bo Electric, US. i, Sir Nigel Gresley LNER, Great Britain.
No. 2464: a, Bi Level Vista Dome, Kinki Nippon Rail, Japan. b, Rolios Rail, South Africa. c, Class 460 Bo-Bo, Switzerland. d, The Central, Peru. e, X2000 Tilt Body Train, Sweden. f, Toronto-Vancouver, Canada. g, Talisman 125 Class 31, Great Britain. h, Flying Scotsman, Great Britain. i, Indian Pacific, Australia.
$5, Diesel Hydraulic, Korea. $6, Trans-Mongolian Beijing to Ulan Bator.

**1995, Sept. 5**
2463-2464　A347　$1 #a.-i., each　8.75　8.75
**Souvenir Sheets**
2465　A347　$5 multicolored　　4.25　4.25
2466　A347　$6 multicolored　　5.00　5.00
Singapore '95 (#2463).

GRENADA

503

Miniature Sheet of 9

Elvis Presley
(1935-77)
A348

Various portraits.

**1995, Sept. 5**      *Perf. 13½x14*
2467 A348 $1 #a.-i.              7.50 7.50

A349

Motion
Picture,
Cent.
A350

No. 2470: a, Film reel, Oscar statuette. b, "HOLLYWOOD" sign. c, Charlie Chaplin. d, Shirley Temple. e, Spencer Tracy, Katherine Hepburn. f, Marilyn Monroe. g, John Wayne. h, Marlon Brando. i, Tom Cruise.
$5, Orson Welles as Citizen Kane, horiz.

**1995, Sept. 5**              *Perf. 14*
2468 A349 75c Marilyn Monroe    1.00 1.00
2469 A349 75c Elvis Presley     1.00 1.00
**Miniature Sheet**
*Perf. 13½x14*
2470 A350 $1 #a.-i.              8.00 8.00
**Souvenir Sheet**
*Perf. 14x13½*
2471 A350 $5 multicolored       8.75 8.75
Nos. 2468-2469 were each issued in miniature sheets of 16. No. 2470 is a continuous design.

Local Entertainers
A351

Designs: No. 2472, 35c, Ajamu, white outfit. No. 2473, 35c, Mighty Sparrow, blue suit. 50c, Mighty Sparrow, black tuxedo. 75c, Ajamu, checkered shirt, sailor hat.

**1995, Sept. 5**      *Litho.*      *Perf. 14*
2472-2475 A351 Set of 4          2.75 2.75

Miniature Sheets

Marine
Life
A352

No. 2476: a, Yellowtail damselfish. b, Bluehead wrasse. c, Balloonfish. d, Shy hamlet. e, Orange tube coral. f, Rock beauty.
No. 2477: a, Creole wrasse. b, Queen angelfish. c, Trumpetfish (e, f). d, Barred hamlet. e, Tube sponge (b, f, h, i). f, Porcupine fish. g, Fire coral (d, e, h). h, Fairy basslet. i, Anemone.
Each $6: No. 2478, Elkhorn coral. No. 2479, Common seahorse, gulfweed.

**1995, Apr. 24**
2476 A352 $1 Sheet of 6, #a.-
f.                  5.25 5.25
2477 A352 $1 Sheet of 9, #a.-
f.                  7.25 7.25
**Souvenir Sheets**
2478-2479 A352 Set of 2          9.00 9.00
Issued: No. 2477, 2478, 4/24/95; Nos. 2476, 2479, 9/19/95.

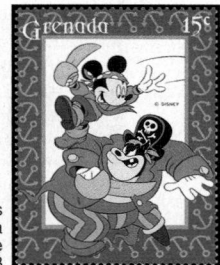

Mickey's
High Sea
Adventure
A353

Designs: 15c, Mickey sword fighting with pirate. 25c, Mickey with treasure chest. 35c, Minnie trying on jewelry from chest. 75c, Pluto with telescope, Mickey over barrel. $3, Pirate. $5, Mickey holding scarf with Minnie's name.
Each $6: No. 2486, Pirate fox fighting on ratlines. No. 2487, Minnie lowered from pirate ship to Mickey.

**1995, Oct. 2**              *Perf. 13½x14*
2480-2485 A353 Set of 6          8.75 8.75
**Souvenir Sheets**
2486-2487 A353 Set of 2          10.50 10.50

Miniature Sheets

Nobel Prize Fund
Established,
Cent. — A354

Recipients: No. 2488a, Albert A. Michelson, physics, 1907. b, Ralph Bunche, peace, 1950. c, Edwin Neher, physiology or medicine, 1991. d, Klaus von Klitzing, physics, 1985. e, Johann Deisenhofer, chemistry, 1988. f, Max Delbrück, physiology or medicine, 1969. g, J. Georg Bednorz, physics, 1987. h, Feodor Lynen, physiology or medicine, 1964. i, Walther Bothe, physics, 1954.
No. 2489: a, Hans G. Dehmelt, physics, 1989. b, Heinrich Böll, literature, 1972. c, Georges Köhler, physiology or medicine, 1984. d, Wolfgang Pauli, physics, 1945. e, Sir Bernard Katz, physiology or medicine, 1970. f, Ernest Ruska, physics, 1986. g, William Golding, literature, 1983. h, Hartmut Michel, chemistry, 1988. i, Hans A. Bethe, physics, 1967.
No. 2490: a, James Franck, physics, 1925. b, Gustav Hertz, physics, 1925. c, Friedrich Bergius, chemistry, 1931. d, Otto Loewi, physiology or medicine, 1936. e, Fritz Lipmann, physiology or medicine, 1953. f, Otto Meyerhof, physiology or medicine, 1922. g, Paul Heyse, literature, 1910. h, Jane Addams, peace, 1931. i, Carl F. Braun, physics, 1909.
Each $6: No. 2491, Winston Churchill, literature, 1953. No. 2492, Woodrow Wilson, peace, 1919. No. 2493, Theodore Roosevelt, peace, 1906.

**1995, Oct. 18**   *Litho.*    *Perf. 14*
2488-2490 A354 $1 Sheets of
9, #a.-i.,
each       8.25 8.25
**Souvenir Sheets**
2491-2493 A354 Set of 3         14.50 14.50

Teresa Teng,
Chinese
Entertainer
A355

Nos. 2495-2496: Various portraits.

**1995, Sept. 29**
2494 A355 75c shown             1.00 1.00
**Miniature Sheets**
2495 A355 35c Sheet of 16, #a.-
p.                  5.50 5.50
2496 A355 75c Sheet of 9, #a.-i. 7.00 7.00
Nos. 2495a-2495p are 24x38mm.

Christmas
A356

Details or entire paintings: 15c, The Madonna, by Montagna. 25c, Sacred Conversation Piece, by dei Pitati. 35c, Nativity, by Van Loo. 75c, The Virgin of the Fountain, Van Eyck. $2, Apparition of the Virgin, by Tiepolo. $5, The Holy Family, by Ribera.
Each $6: No. 1503, Madonna with the Christ Child, by Van Dyck. No. 1504, Vision of St. Anthony, by Van Dyck.

**1995, Nov. 28**  *Litho.*   *Perf. 13½x14*
2497-2502 A356 Set of 6          6.50 6.50
**Souvenir Sheets**
2503-2504 A356 Set of 2          10.50 10.50

Liberation
of
Grenada,
12th
Anniv.
A357

US Pres. Ronald Reagan and: No. 2505: a, Fort George. b, US, Grenada flags. c, St. George. No. 2506, Island scene, map. No. 2507, Waterfall.

**1995, Dec. 8**              *Perf. 14*
2505 A357 75c Strip of 3, #a.-c. 2.50 2.50
**Souvenir Sheets**
2506 A357 $5 multicolored       5.25 5.25
2507 A357 $6 multicolored       6.00 6.00
No. 2505 was issued in sheets of 9 stamps.

Pope John Paul II,
1995 Visit to New
York City — A358

A358a

Pope John Paul II and: No. 2508, Statue of Liberty. No. 2509, St. Patrick's Cathedral. No. 2510, New York skyline.
Illustration A358a reduced.

**1995, Dec. 13**
2508 A358 $1 multicolored       1.00 1.00
2509 A358 $1 multicolored       1.00 1.00
**Souvenir Sheet**
2510 A358 $6 multicolored       5.25 5.25
**Litho. & Embossed**
*Perf. 9*
2510A A358a $30 gold & multi     30.00
Nos. 2508-2509 were each issued in sheets of 9.

New Year 1996 (Year of the
Rat) — A359

Stylized rats: a, green & multi. b, red & multi. c, orange brown & multi.
$1, Two rats, horiz.

**1996, Jan. 2**     *Litho.*    *Perf. 14*
2511 A359 75c Strip of 3, #a.-c. 2.10 2.10
**Miniature Sheet**
2512 A359 75c Sheet of 1 #2511   2.10 2.10
**Souvenir Sheet**
2513 A359 $1 multicolored        1.25 1.25
No. 2511 was issued in sheets of 9 stamps.

Woodcuts
by Dürer
and
Paintings by
Rubens
A360

Details or entire works: 15c, Young Woman, by Dürer. 25c, Four Horsemen from Apocalypse, by Dürer. 35c, Assumption and Coronation of Virgin, by Dürer. 75c, Mulay Ahmed, by Rubens. $1, Anthony Van Dyck Aged 15, by Rubens. $2, Head of a Young Monk, by Rubens. $3, A Scholar Inspired by Nature, by Rubens. $5, Hanns Dürer, by Dürer.
$5, Martyrdom of St. Ursula, by Rubens. $6, The Death and Life of a Virgin, by Dürer.

**1996, Jan. 29**  *Litho.*   *Perf. 13½x14*
2514-2521 A360 Set of 8         10.50 10.50
**Souvenir Sheets**
2522 A360 $5 multicolored        5.00 5.00
2523 A360 $6 multicolored        5.50 5.50

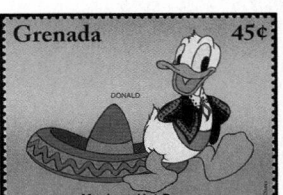

Disney Dancers — A361

Character, dance: 35c, Goofy, tap dance, vert. 45c, Donald, Mexican hat dance. 75c, Daisy, hula, vert. 90c, Mickey, Minnie, tango. $1, Daisy, Donald, jitterbug, vert. $2, Mickey, Minnie, Ukrainian folk dance. $3, Goofy, Pluto, ballet. $4, Minnie, Mickey, line dancing.
$5, Minnie, the can-can. $6, Scrooge McDuck, Scottish sword dance.

*Perf. 13½x14, 14x 13½*

| 1996, Feb. 26 | | Litho. | | |
|---|---|---|---|---|
| 2524-2531 | A361 | Set of 8 | 12.00 | 12.00 |

**Souvenir Sheets**

| 2532 | A361 | $5 multicolored | 5.50 | 5.50 |
|---|---|---|---|---|
| 2533 | A361 | $6 multicolored | 6.50 | 6.50 |

Queen Elizabeth II, 70th Birthday A362

Designs: No. 2534a, 35c, In blue dress. b, 75c, In white hat. c, $4, In black hat.
$6, Younger picture with Prince Phillip.

| 1996, May 8 | Litho. | *Perf. 13½x14* | | |
|---|---|---|---|---|
| 2534 | A362 | Strip of 3, #a.-c. | 4.50 | 4.50 |

**Souvenir Sheet**

| 2535 | A362 | $6 multicolored | 5.25 | 5.25 |
|---|---|---|---|---|

No. 2534 was issued in sheets of 9 stamps.

Ferrari Race Cars — A363

Designs: a, 125-F1. b, Tipo 625. c, P4. d, 312P. e, 312, Formula 1. f, 312B.
$6, F333 SP.

| 1996, May 8 | | *Perf. 14* | | |
|---|---|---|---|---|
| 2536 | A363 | $1.50 Sheet of 6, #a.- f. | 8.00 | 8.00 |

**Souvenir Sheet**

| 2537 | A363 | $6 multicolored | 5.00 | 5.00 |
|---|---|---|---|---|

China '96, 9th Asian Intl. Philatelic Exhibition (#2536). No. 2537 contains one 85x28mm stamp.

Modern Olympic Games, Cent. A364

Designs: 35c, 1896 Olympic Gold Medal, vert. 75c, Olympic Stadium, Athens, 1896. $2, Ancient Greek Olympic runners. $3, Spiridon Louis, 1896 marathon winner.

| 1996, May 8 | | Litho. | *Perf. 14* | |
|---|---|---|---|---|
| 2538-2541 | A364 | Set of 4 | 5.00 | 5.00 |

See Nos. 2599-2602.

Jerusalem, 3000th Anniv. — A365

Various city gates: 75c, $2, $3.
$5, Buildings inside city, horiz.

| 1996, June 26 | | | | |
|---|---|---|---|---|
| 2542-2544 | A365 | Set of 3 | 4.50 | 4.50 |

**Souvenir Sheet**

| 2545 | A365 | $5 multicolored | 4.25 | 4.25 |
|---|---|---|---|---|

UNICEF, 50th Anniv. A366

Designs: 35c, Child writing in book. $2, Child planting seedling. $3, Faces of boy, girl. $5, Boy, vert.

| 1996, June 26 | | | | |
|---|---|---|---|---|
| 2546-2548 | A366 | Set of 3 | 4.25 | 4.25 |

**Souvenir Sheet**

| 2549 | A366 | $5 multicolored | 4.00 | 4.00 |
|---|---|---|---|---|

Radio, Cent. A367

Entertainers: 35c, Jack Benny. 75c, Gertrude Berg. $1, Eddie Cantor. $2, Groucho Marx.
$6, George Burns, Gracie Allen, horiz.

*Perf. 13½x14, 14x13½*

| 1996, June 26 | | | | |
|---|---|---|---|---|
| 2550-2553 | A367 | Set of 4 | 4.25 | 4.25 |

**Souvenir Sheet**

| 2554 | A367 | $6 multicolored | 5.25 | 5.25 |
|---|---|---|---|---|

Classic Cars A368

No. 2555: a, 1939 Type 57C Atalante. b, 1900 Cannstatt-Daimler. c, 1925 Delage. d, 1899 Coventry Daimler. e, 1900 Vauxhall. f, 1912 T-15 Hispano-Suza.
No. 2556: a, 35c, 1929 Mercedes-Benz. b, 1935 J. Duesenberg. c, 1914 Mercer. d, 1927 Bugatti Type 35. e, 1929 Alfa Romeo. f, 1910 Rolls Royce.
Each $6: No. 2557, 1915 L-Head Mercer. No. 2558, 1937 Mercedes.

| 1996, July 25 | | Litho. | *Perf. 14* | |
|---|---|---|---|---|
| 2555 | A368 | $1 Sheet of 6, #a.- f. | 5.00 | 5.00 |
| 2556 | A368 | Sheet of 6, #a.- f. | 6.25 | 6.25 |

**Souvenir Sheets**

| 2557-2558 | A368 | Set of 2 | 10.50 | 10.50 |
|---|---|---|---|---|

Nos. 2557-2558 each contain one 57x43mm stamp.

Ships A369

War ships, No. 2559, each $1: a, Bounty, Britain, 1788. b, Bismark, Germany, 1941. c, Chuii Apoo, China, 1849. d, F224 Lubeck, Germany, 1970. e, Barbary Corsair, France, 1655. f, Augsburg, Germany, 1970. g, Henri Grace A Dieu, 1514, France. h, Prince of Wales, Britain, 1941. i, Santa Anna, Spain, 1512.
Sailing ships, each $1: No. 2560a, Gorch Fock, Germany, 1916. b, Henry B. Hyde, US, 1886. c, Resolution, Britain, 1652. d, USS Constitution, 1797. e, Nippon Maru, Japan, 1930. f, Preussen, Germany, 1902. g, Taeping, Britain, 1852. h, Chariot of Fame, US, 1853. i, Star of India, US, 1861.
$5, Victory, Britain, 1805. $6, Cutty Sark, Britain, 1869.

| 1996, Aug. 14 | | | | |
|---|---|---|---|---|
| **Sheets of 9, #a-i** | | | | |
| 2559-2560 | A368 | Set of 2 | 16.00 | 16.00 |

**Souvenir Sheets**

| 2561 | A369 | $5 multicolored | 4.50 | 4.50 |
|---|---|---|---|---|
| 2562 | A369 | $6 multicolored | 5.25 | 5.25 |

Trains A370

Designs: 35c, C51 Imperial Train, Japan. 75c, Reingold, Germany. $2, Pioneer, US. $3, LA France, France.
Trains of the Orient, each $1: No. 2567: a, C62 4-6-4, Japanese Natl. Railways. b, 4-6-0, Shantung Railways, China. c, C57 Light 4-6-2, Japanese Natl. Railways. d, Diesel Express, Japanese Natl. Railways. e, 4-6-2, Shanghai-Nanking Railway, China. f, 051 2-8-2, Japanese Natl. Railways.
Trains of the world, each $1: No. 2568a, Atlantic Coast Line, US. b, #1619, Pioneer Smith Compound, England. c, 4-8-4 Trans-Siberian Railway, Russia. d, "Atlantic type," Palatinate Railway, Germany. e, 4-6-0 Paris, Lyons and Mediterranean Railway, France. f, 0341 Diesel Electric, Italian State Railways.
$5, Baden State Railways, Germany. $6, C11 2-6-4, Japanese National Railways.

| 1996, Aug. 28 | | | | |
|---|---|---|---|---|
| 2563-2566 | A370 | Set of 4 | 4.50 | 4.50 |
| **Sheets of 6, #a-f** | | | | |
| 2567-2568 | A370 | Set of 2 | 9.00 | 9.00 |

**Souvenir Sheets**

| 2569 | A370 | $5 multicolored | 4.25 | 4.25 |
|---|---|---|---|---|
| 2570 | A370 | $6 multicolored | 5.00 | 5.00 |

Flowers A371

No. 2571, each $1: a, Winter jasmine. b, Chrysanthemum. c, Lilac. d, Japanese iris. e, Hibiscus. f, Sacred lotus. g, Apple blossom. h, Gladiolus. i, Japanese quince.
No. 2572, vert, each $1: a, Canterbury bell. b, Rose. c, Nasturtium. d, Daffodil. e, Tulip. f, Snapdragon. g, Zinnia. h, Sweetpea. i, Pansy.
$5, Aster. $6, Peony, vert.

| 1996, Sept. 9 | | Litho. | *Perf. 14* | |
|---|---|---|---|---|
| **Sheets of 9, #a-i** | | | | |
| 2571-2572 | A371 | Set of 2 | 16.00 | 16.00 |

**Souvenir Sheets**

| 2573 | A371 | $5 multicolored | 5.00 | 5.00 |
|---|---|---|---|---|
| 2574 | A371 | $6 multicolored | 5.75 | 5.75 |

Zeppelins A372

No. 2575: a, 30c, L31, Germany. b, 30c, L35, Germany. c, 50c, L30, Germany. d, 75c, LZ10, Germany. e, $3, L3, Germany. f, $3, Beardmore No. 24, British.
No. 2576: a, Zeppelin L21, Germany. b, Zodiac Type 13 Spiess, France. c, NI "Norge." d, D-LZ 127 "Graf Zeppelin," Germany. e, D-LZ 129 "Hindenburg," Germany. f, Zeppelin NT, Germany, 1996.
Each $6: No. 2577, L13, Germany. No. 2578, Zeppelin ZT, Germany.

| 1996, Sept. 9 | | | | |
|---|---|---|---|---|
| **Sheets of 6** | | | | |
| 2575 | A372 | #a.-f. | 7.50 | 7.50 |
| 2576 | A372 | $1.50 #a.-f. | 8.25 | 8.25 |

**Souvenir Sheets**

| 2577-2578 | A372 | Set of 2 | 10.50 | 10.50 |
|---|---|---|---|---|

Birds A373

No. 2579: a, Horned guan. b, St. Lucia parrot. c, Black penelopina. d, Grenada dove. e, St. Vincent parrot. f, White-breasted thrasher.
$5, Barbados yellow warbler. $6, Semper's warbler.

| 1996 | | | | |
|---|---|---|---|---|
| 2579 | A373 | $1.50 Sheet of 6, #a.- f. | 8.75 | 8.75 |

**Souvenir Sheets**

| 2580 | A373 | $5 multicolored | 4.50 | 4.50 |
|---|---|---|---|---|
| 2581 | A373 | $6 multicolored | 5.25 | 5.25 |

Endangered Species — A374

Designs: a, Blue whale. b, Humpback whale. c, Right whale. d, Hawksbill turtle. e, Leatherback turtle. f, Green turtle.

| 1996, Sept. 18 | | Litho. | *Perf. 14* | |
|---|---|---|---|---|
| 2582 | A374 | $1.50 Sheet of 6, #a.- f. | 8.75 | 8.75 |

Jacqueline Kennedy Onassis (1929-94) — A375

Various portraits.

| 1996, Aug. 26 | | | | |
|---|---|---|---|---|
| 2583 | A375 | $1 Sheet of 9, #a.-i. | 8.75 | 8.75 |

**Souvenir Sheet**

| 2584 | A375 | $6 multicolored | 5.25 | 5.25 |
|---|---|---|---|---|

Butterfly Type of 1994

90c, Tropical chequered skipper. $1.50, Godman's hairstreak.

| 1996, Nov. 7 | | Litho. | *Perf. 12* | |
|---|---|---|---|---|
| 2585 | A328 | 90c multicolored | .80 | .80 |
| 2586 | A328 | $1.50 multicolored | 1.25 | 1.25 |

A376

## 1996, Nov. 7 — Perf. 14

Sea Creatures: No. 2587, each $1: a, Killer whale. b, Dolphin. c, Dolphins. d, Sea lion, royal angelfish. e, Dolphins, hawksbill turtle. f, Hawksbill turtles (e). g, Royal angelfish. h, Pennant butterflyfish. i, Sea lion, squirrel fish.
No. 2588, each $1: a, Brown pelican. b, Killer whale. c, Whale (c). d, Dolphins, sea lion. e, Shortfin pilot whale, blue ringed octopus, sea lion (d, f, h). f, Hammerhead sharks, sea lion. g, Blue striped grunts. h, Stingray, Van Gogh fusiliers (i). i, Van Gogh fusiliers, golden coney, ribbon moray eel (h).
Each $6: No. 2589, Sea lions, horiz. No. 2590, Dolphins, horiz.

### Sheets of 9, #a-i

| 2587-2588 | A376 | Set of 2 | 16.00 | 16.00 |

### Souvenir Sheets

| 2589-2590 | A376 | Set of 2 | 10.50 | 10.50 |

Christmas
A377

Details or entire paintings: 25c, The Visitation, by Tintoretto. 35c, Virgin with the Child, by Palma Vecchio. 50c, The Adoration of the Magi, by Botticeli. 75c, The Annunciation, by Titian. $1, The Flight into Egypt, by Tintoretto. $3, The Holy Family with the Infant Saint John, by Andrea Del Sarto.
Each $6: #2597, Adoration of the Magi, by Paolo Schiavo. #2598, Madonna and Child with Saints, by Vincenzo Foppa.

## 1996, Nov. 18 — Perf. 13½x14

| 2591-2596 | A377 | Set of 6 | 5.50 | 5.50 |

### Souvenir Sheets

| 2597-2598 | A377 | Set of 2 | 10.50 | 10.50 |

## Modern Olympic Games Type of 1996

Marathon medalists: No. 2599: a, Boughera El Quafi, 1928. b, Gustav Jansson, 1952. c, Spiridon Louis, 1896. d, Basil Heatley, 1964. e, Emil Zatopek, 1952. f, Frank Shorter, 1972. g, Alain Mimoun, 1956. h, Kokichi Tsuburaya, 1964. i, Delfo Cabrera, 1948.
Weight lifting medalists: No. 2600: a, Harald Sakata, 1948. b, Tom Kono, 1952. c, Naim Suleymanoglu, 1988. d, Lee Hyung Kun, 1988. e, Vassily Alexeyev, 1972. f, Chen Weiqiang, 1984. g, Ye Huanming, 1988. h, Manfred Nerlinger, 1984. i, Joseph Depietro, 1948.
$5, Manfred Nerlinger, vert. $6, Thomas Hicks, 1904, vert.

## 1996, July 8 — Litho. — Perf. 14

### Sheets of 9

| 2599-2600 | A364 | $1 #a.-i., each | 7.25 | 7.25 |

### Souvenir Sheets

| 2601 | A364 | $5 multicolored | 4.25 | 4.25 |
| 2602 | A364 | $6 multicolored | 5.00 | 5.00 |

US Pres.
Ronald
Reagan
A378

Various portraits.

## 1996, Aug. 26 — Perf. 13½

| 2603 | A378 | $1 Sheet of 9, #a.-i. | 7.00 | 7.00 |

Sylvester
Stallone in
Movie,
"Rocky" — A379

## 1996, Nov. 21 — Litho. — Perf. 14

| 2604 | A379 | $2 Sheet of 3 | 5.25 | 5.25 |

New Year 1997 (Year of the Ox) — A380

Oxen: Nos. 2605a, 2606a, Horns pointed down. Nos. 2605b, 2606b, Horns pointed up. Nos. 2605c, 2606c, Shown.
Illustration reduced.

### Serpentine Die Cut 11

## 1997, Jan. 2 — Litho.

### Self-Adhesive

### Sheets of 3

| 2605 | A380 | $2 #a.-c., gold & multi | 4.50 | 4.50 |
| 2606 | A380 | $2 #a.-c., sil & multi | 4.50 | 4.50 |

Mickey Visits Hong Kong — A381

No. 2607: a, Pet birds. b, Kung-fu tea. c, Chinese Wet Market. d, Handmade grasshopper. e, Mid-Autumn Festival. f, Tai-chi.
No. 2608: a, 35c, Tram. b, 50c, Victoria Harbor. c, 75c, Buddha. d, 90c, Bank of China. e, $2, Bottle gas. f, $3, Seafood restaurant.
No. 2609, Mickey at The Peak, vert. $4, Minnie, Mickey, Hong Kong mail, vert. $5, Mickey pulling rickshaw, vert. $6, Mickey at Peking Noodle Show, vert.

## 1997, Feb. 12 — Litho. — Perf. 14x13½

| 2607 | A381 | $1 Sheet of 6, #a.-f. | 7.00 | 7.00 |
| 2608 | A381 | Sheet of 6, #a.-f. | 8.75 | 8.75 |

### Souvenir Sheets

### Perf. 13½x14

| 2609 | A381 | $3 multicolored | 3.50 | 3.50 |
| 2610 | A381 | $4 multicolored | 4.25 | 4.25 |
| 2611 | A381 | $5 multicolored | 5.50 | 5.50 |
| 2612 | A381 | $6 multicolored | 6.25 | 6.25 |

Hong Kong '97.

UNESCO, 50th Anniv. — A382

Designs: 35c, Kyoto, Japan. 75c, Quedlinburg, Germany. 90c, Dubrovnik, Croatia. $1, Ruins, Delphi, Greece. $2, Tomar, Portugal. $3, Palace of Chaillot, Paris, France.
No. 2619, Chinese sites, vert, each $1: a, Entrance to caves, Desert of Taklamakan. b, House, Taklamakan. c, Monument, Taklamakan. d, Palace of Cielos Purpuras, Wudang. e, House, Wudang. f, Stone Guard, Great Wall. g, Ming Dynasty, Wudang. h, Section, Great Wall.

No. 2620, vert, each $1: a, Bryggen Wharf, Bergen, Norway. b, Old City of Bern, Switzerland. c, Warsaw, Poland. d, Fortress Walls, Luxembourg. e, Palace of Drottningholm, Sweden. f, Petäjävesi Old Church, Finland. g, Vilnius, Lithuania. h, Church of Jelling, Denmark.
No. 2621: a, Cathedral, Segovia, Spain. b, Würzburg, Germany. c, Lakes of Plitvice, Croatia. d, Monastery of Batalha, Portugal. e, River Seine, Paris, France.
Each $6: No. 2622, Monastery of Popocatepetl, Mexico. No. 2623, Shirakami-Sanchi, Japan. No. 2624, Monastery of the Hieronymites and Tower of Belem, Portugal.

## 1997, Apr. 3 — Litho. — Perf. 14

| 2613-2618 | A382 | Set of 6 | 7.50 | 7.50 |

### Sheets of 8 or 5 + Label

| 2619-2620 | A382 | Set of 2 | 15.00 | 15.00 |
| 2621 | A382 | $1.50 #a.-e. | 7.00 | 7.00 |

### Souvenir Sheets

| 2622-2624 | A382 | Set of 2 | 11.00 | 11.00 |

Cats — A383    Dogs — A384

Cats: 35c, Devon rex. 90c, Japanese bobtail. $2, Cornish rex.
No. 2628: a, Turkish van. b, Ragdoll. c, Siberian. d, Egyptian mau. e, American shorthair. f, Bengal. g, Asian longhair. h, Somali. i, Turkish angora.

## 1997, Apr. 10

| 2625-2627 | A383 | Set of 3 | 3.50 | 3.50 |

### Sheet of 9

| 2628 | A383 | $1 #a.-i. | 8.50 | 8.50 |

### Souvenir Sheet

| 2629 | A383 | $6 Singapura | 5.75 | 5.75 |

## 1997, Apr. 10

Dogs: 75c, Cavalier King Charles spaniel. $1, Afghan hound. $3, Pekingese.
No. 2633: a, Lhasa apso. b, Rough collie. c, Norwich terrier. d, America cocker spaniel. e, Chinese crested dog. f, Old English sheepdog. g, Standard poodle. h, German shepherd. i, German shorthaired pointer.
No. 2634, Bernese mountain dog.

| 2630-2632 | A384 | Set of 3 | 4.00 | 4.00 |

### Sheet of 9

| 2633 | A384 | $1 #a.-i. | 8.50 | 8.50 |

### Souvenir Sheet

| 2634 | A384 | $6 multicolored | 5.75 | 5.75 |

Prehistoric Animals — A385

Designs: 35c, Dunkleosteus. 75c, Tyrannosaurus rex. $2, Askeptosaurus, vert. $3, Triceratops, vert.
No. 2639: a, Sordes. b, Dimorphodon. c, Diplodocus. d, Allosaurus. e, Pentaceratops. f, Protoceratops.
Each $6: No. 2640, Maiasaura, vert. No. 2641, Tristychius, Cladoselache, vert.

## 1997, Apr. 15

| 2635-2638 | A385 | Set of 4 | 6.50 | 6.50 |
| 2639 | A385 | $1.50 Sheet of 6, #a.-f. | 8.25 | 8.25 |

### Souvenir Sheets

| 2640-2641 | A385 | Set of 2 | 12.50 | 12.50 |

Marine
Life
A386

Designs: 45c, Porcelain crab. 75c, Humpback whale. 90c, Hermit crab. $1, Great white shark. $3, Green sea turtle. $4, Whale shark.
No. 2648, vert: a, Octopus. b, Lei triggerfish. c, Lionfish. d, Harlequin wrasse. e, Clown fish. f, Moray eel.
Each $6: No. 2649, Pacific barracudas. No. 2650, Scalloped hammerhead shark.

## 1997, May 2

| 2642-2647 | A386 | Set of 6 | 9.00 | 9.00 |
| 2648 | A386 | $1.50 Sheet of 6, | 8.50 | 8.50 |

### Souvenir Sheets

| 2649-2650 | A386 | Set of 2 | 11.50 | 11.50 |

Queen
Elizabeth
II, Prince
Philip,
50th
Wedding
Anniv.
A386a

No. 2651: a, Queen, Prince waving. b, Royal Arms. c, Formal portrait in royal attire. d, Formal portrait in street clothes. e, Windsor Castle. f, Prince Philip.
$6, Formal portrait in royal attire, diff.

## 1997, May 28 — Litho. — Perf. 14

| 2651 | A386a | $1 Sheet of 6, #a.-f. | 5.75 | 5.75 |

### Souvenir Sheet

| 2652 | A386a | $6 multicolored | 5.75 | 5.75 |

Paintings by
Hiroshige
(1797-1858)
A387

No. 2653: a, Nihon Embankment, Yoshiwara. b, Asakusa Ricefields and Torinomachi Festival. c, Senju Great Bridge. d, Dawn Inside the Yoshiwara. e, Tile Kilns and Hasiba Ferry, Sumida River. f, View from Massaki of Suijin Shrine, Uchigawa Inlet and Sekiya.
Each $6: No. 2654, Kinryuzan Temple, Asakusa. No. 2655, Night View of Saruwakamachi.

## 1997, May 28 — Perf. 13½x14

| 2653 | A387 | $1.50 Sheet of 6, #a.-f. | 9.50 | 9.50 |

### Souvenir Sheets

| 2654-2655 | A387 | Set of 2 | 11.50 | 11.50 |

Heinrich
von
Stephan
(1831-97),
Founder
of UPU
A388

No. 2656: a, Postal delivery on motorcycle. b, UPU emblem. c, Postal delivery on skis and snowshoes, Rockies, 1900. $6, Chinese long distance carrier.

## 1997, May 28 — Litho. — Perf. 14

| 2656 | A388 | $2 Sheet of 3, #a.-c. | 6.00 | 6.00 |

### Souvenir Sheet

| 2657 | A388 | $6 multicolored | 6.00 | 6.00 |

PACIFIC 97.

Paul P. Harris (1868-1947), Founder of Rotary, Intl. — A389

Designs: $3, Rotary emblem, vocational training service program, The Philippines, portrait of Harris.

$6, Doves, hands holding globe inscribed "Act with Integrity, Serve with love, Work for Peace".

**1997, May 28**
2658 A389 $3 multicolored          2.75  2.75

**Souvenir Sheet**
2659 A389 $6 multicolored          5.25  5.25

Chernobyl
Disaster,
10th Anniv.
A390

Designs: No. 2660, Chabad's Children of Chernobyl. No. 2661, UNESCO.

**1997, May 28**                        **Perf. 13½x14**
2660 A390 $2 multicolored          2.00  2.00
2661 A390 $2 multicolored          2.00  2.00

Grimm's
Fairy Tales
A391

Mother Goose — A392

Scenes from "Snow White and the Seven Dwarfs:" No. 2662: a, Witch as woman looking into mirror. b, Dwarfs looking at Snow White as she sleeps. c, Snow White awakening, Prince. $6, Witch holding out apple for Snow White.

$5, "Little Johnny" walking in rain with umbrella.

**1997, May 28**                        **Perf. 13½x14**
2662 A391 $2 Sheet of 3, #a.-c.    6.25  6.25

**Souvenir Sheets**
**Perf. 14, 13½x14**
2663 A392 $5 multicolored          4.00  4.00
2664 A391 $6 multicolored          5.00  5.00

1998
Winter
Olympics
Games,
Nagano
A393

Designs: 45c, Luge. 75c, Speed skater in red. $2, Male figure skater. $3, Slalom skier.

No. 2669: a, Luge, diff. b, Ski jumper. c, Downhill skier. d, Speed skater in blue. e, Two-man bobsled. f, Female figure skater. g, Biathlon. h, Hockey. i, Freestyle skier upside down.

Each $6: No. 2670, Downhill skier in air, vert. No. 2671, 4-Man bobsled.

**1997, June 26**                        **Perf. 14**
2665-2668 A393  Set of 4           6.50  6.50
2669 A393 $1 Sheet of 9, #a.-
     i.                            9.00  9.00

**Souvenir Sheets**
2670-2671 A393  Set of 2          11.50 11.50

Return of Hong
Kong to
China — A394

Views of city, Chinese flag as Chinese inscription: 90c, Bank of China, night scene. $1, Skyscrapers. $1.75, "Hong Kong," city in lights, horiz. $2, Deng Xiaoping (1904-97), Hong Kong, horiz.

**1997, July 1**
2672-2675 A394  Set of 4           7.00  7.00

Nos. 2672-2673 were issued in sheets of 4. Nos. 2674-2675 are 59x28mm and were issued in sheets of 3.

Disney's
Hercules
A395

No. 2676: a, Hercules. b, Pegasus. c, Megara. d, Philoctetes. e, Nessus. f, Hydra. g, Pain and Panic. h, Hades.

Each $6: No. 2677, Young Hercules. No. 2678, Calliope surrounded by Terpsichore, Melpomene, Clio, Thalia.

**1997, Aug. 7   Litho.   Perf. 13½x14**
2676 A395 $1 Sheet of 8, #a.-
     h.                           10.00 10.00

**Souvenir Sheets**
2677-2678 A396  Set of 2          13.50 13.50

Butterflies
A396

Designs: 45c, Peacock. 75c, Orange flambeau. 90c, Eastern tailed blue. $2, Black and red. $3, Large white. $4, Oriental swallowtail.

No. 2685: a, Brimstone. b, Mocker swallowtail. c, American painted lady. d, Tiger swallowtail. e, Long wing. f, Sunset moth. g, Australian blue mountain swallowtail. h, Bird wing.

Each $5: No. 2686, Monarch. No. 2687, Blue morpho.

**1997, Aug. 12**                        **Perf. 14**
2679-2684 A396  Set of 6          10.00 10.00
2685 A396 $1 Sheet of 8, #a.-
     h.                            7.50  7.50

**Souvenir Sheets**
2686-2687 A396  Set of 2          10.50 10.50

1998 World Cup Soccer
Championships, France — A397

Various actions scenes from Italy v. West Germany, 1982. 15c, 75c, 90c, $2, $3, $4, vert.

Winning teams: No. 2694, each $1: a, Uruguay. b, Brazil, 1958. c, Germany. d, Argentina. e, Italy. f, West Germany. g, Italy. h, Brazil, 1970.

Soccer players: No. 2695, each $1: a, Seaman, England. b, Klinsmann, Germany. c, Berger, Czech Rep. d, McCoist, Scotland. e, Gascoigne, England. f, Djorkaeff, France. g, Sammer, Germany. h, Futre, Portugal.

Each $6: No. 2696, Beckenbauer, Germany, vert. No. 2697, Moore, England.

**1997**                               **Perf. 13½x14**
2688-2693 A397  Set of 6          10.00 10.00

**Sheets of 8, #a-h**
**Perf. 14x13½**
2694-2695 A397  Set of 2          14.50 14.50

**Souvenir Sheets**
2696-2697 A397  Set of 2          12.00 12.00

Minnie Mouse in Hawaiian
Holiday — A398

Stamps in flip book sequence showing Minnie doing Hula dance: No. 2698: a, 1. b, 2. c, 3. d, 4. e, 5. f, 6. g, 7. h, 8.

No. 2699: a, 9. b, 10. c, 11. d, 12. e, 13. f, 14. g, 15. h, 16. i, 17.

$6, 18.

**1997, Aug. 7   Litho.   Perf. 14x13½**
**Sheets of 8 or 9**
2698 A398 50c #a.-h. + label       6.00  6.00
2699 A398 50c #a.-i.               6.50  6.50

**Souvenir Sheet**
2700 A398 $6 multicolored          8.50  8.50

PACIFIC 97.

Mushrooms — A399

Designs: 35c, Boletus erythropus. 75c, Armillariella mellea. 90c, Amanita flavorubens. $1, Indigo milky. $2, Tylopilus balloui. $4, Boletus parasiticus.

No. 2707, each $1.50: a, Boletus parasiticus, diff. b, Frostis bolete. c, Amanita myscara flavilolvata. d, Volvariella volvacea. e, Stuntz's blue legs. f, Orange-latex milky.

No. 2708, each $1.50: a, Agaricus solidipes. b, Salmon waxy cap. c, Fused marasmius. d, Shellfish-scented russula. e, Red-capped scaber stalk. f, Calocybe tricholoma gambosum.

Each $6: No. 2709, Omphalotus illudens. No. 2710, Agaricus argenteus.

**1997, Sept. 4**                        **Perf. 14**
2701-2706 A399  Set of 6           8.75  8.75

**Sheets of 6, #a-f**
2707-2708 A399  Set of 2          16.50 16.50

**Souvenir Sheets**
2709-2710 A399  Set of 2          11.50 11.50

Orchids
A400

Designs: 20c, Paphiopedilum urbanianum. 35c, Trichoceros parviflorus. 45c, Euanthe sanderiana, vert. 75c, Oncidium macranthum, vert. 90c, Psychopsis kramerianum, vert. $1, Oncidium hastatum, vert. $3, Masdevallia saltatrix, vert. $4, Cattleya luteola.

No. 2719, vert, each $2: a, Odontoglossum crispum. b, Cattleya brabantiae. c, Cattleya bicolor. d, Trichopilia suavia. e, Encyclia mariae. f, Angraecum leonis.

No. 2720, vert, each $2: a, Broughtonia sanguinea. b, Anguloa virginalis. c, Dendrobium Bigibbum. d, T. forcia, L. lucasiana. e, Cymbidium. f, Cymbidium, diff.

Each $6: No. 2721, Oncidium onustum. No. 2722, Laelia milleri.

**1997, Sept. 4**
2711-2718 A400  Set of 8          11.00 11.00

**Sheets of 6, #a-f**
2719-2720 A400  Set of 2          22.00 22.00

**Souvenir Sheets**
2721-2722 A400  Set of 2          11.50 11.50

Diana, Princess of Wales (1961-
97) — A401

Various portraits.

**1997, Oct. 15   Litho.   Perf. 14½**
2723 A401 $1.50 Sheet of 6, #a.-
     f.                            8.75  8.75

**Souvenir Sheet**
2724 A401 $5 multicolored          5.00  5.00

Christmas — A402

Works of art, entire paintings, or details: 35c, Angel, by Matthias Grunewald. 50c, Saint Demetrius (icon). 75c, Reliquary in the Form of a Triptych. $1, Angel of the Annunciation, by Jan van Eyck. $3, The Annunciation, by Simone Martini. $4, Saint Michael (mosaic).

Each $6: No. 2731, The Annunciation, by Titian, horiz. No. 2732, The Coronation of the Virgin, by Fra Angelico.

**1997, Dec. 5   Litho.   Perf. 14**
2725-2730 A402  Set of 6           8.75  8.75

**Souvenir Sheets**
2731-2732 A402  Set of 2          12.50 12.50

New Year 1998 (Year of the
Tiger) — A403

Designs: a, shown. b, With mouth open. c, With ears rolled back. Illustration reduced.

**1998, Jan. 5  Litho.  Die Cut Perf. 9**
**Self-Adhesive**
**Sheets of 3, #a.-c.**
2733  A403  $1.50 gold & multi
2734  A403  $1.50 sil & multi
Nos. 2733b, 2734b have point of triangle down.

Fish
A404

65c, Black-tailed humbug. 90c, Yellow sweetlips. $1, Common squrrelfish. $2, Powder blue surgeon.
No. 2739, each $1.50: a, Blue tang. b, Porkfish. c, Banded butterflyfish. d, Threadfin butterflyfish. e, Red-headed. f, Emperor angelfish.
No. 2740, each $1.50: a, Scribbled angelfish. b, Lemonpeel angelfish. c, Bandit angelfish. d, Bicolor cherub. e, Regal tang. f, Yellow tang.
Each $6: No. 2741, Two-banded anemonefish. No. 2742, Long-nosed butterflyfish.

**1998, Feb. 10  Litho.  Perf. 14**
2735-2738  A404  Set of 4  5.50  5.50
**Sheets of 6, #a.-f.**
2739-2740  A404  Set of 2  17.00  17.00
**Souvenir Sheets**
2741-2742  A404  Set of 2  13.50  13.50

Orchids
A405

No. 2743, each $1.50: a, Arachnis clarkei. b, Cymbidium eburneum. c, Dendrobium chrysotoxum. d, Paphiopedilum insigne. e, Paphiopedilum venustum. f, Renanthera imschootiana.
No. 2744, each $1.50: a, Sophronitis grandiflora. b, Phalaenopsis amboinensis. c, Zygopetalum intermedium. d, Paphiopedilum purpuratum. e, Miltonia regnellii. f, Dendrobium parishii.
Each $6: No. 2745, Lycaste aromatica. No. 2746, Pleione maculata.

**1998, Apr. 21  Litho.  Perf. 14**
**Sheets of 6, #a.-f.**
2743-2744  A405  Set of 2  19.00  19.00
**Souvenir Sheets**
2745-2746  A405  Set of 2  12.50  12.50

Ships
A406

No. 2747, each $1: a, Brig. b, Clipper. c, Caique. d, Mississippi Riverboat. e, Luxury liner. f, The Mayflower. g, Frigate. h, Janggolan. i, Junk.
No. 2748, each $1: a, Dhow. b, Galleon. c, Felucca. d, Schooner. e, Aircraft carrier. f, Knau. g, Destroyer. h, Longship. i, Queen Elizabeth 2.
Each $6: #2749, The Lusitania. #2750, Submarine.

**1998, Apr. 26  Litho.  Perf. 14**
**Sheets of 9, #a-i**
2747-2748  A406  Set of 2  19.00  19.00
**Souvenir Sheets**
2749-2750  A406  Set of 2  12.50  12.50
No. 2749 contains one 85x28mm stamp; No. 2750 one 56x42mm stamp.

Disney's Hercules
A407

Hercules grows up — #2751: a, Hercules, Zeus. b, Hercules and Pegasus walking past creature. c, Phil, Hercules. d, Hercules swinging through air. e, Centaur carrying captured Meg. f, Hercules attacking centaur. g, Hercules fighting lion. h, Hercules, Pegasus looking at prints.
Birth and childhood of Hercules — #2752, each $1: a, Zeus and Hera with newborn Hercules. b, Hades finds baby. c, Hades in the night. d, Baby sleeping. e, Baby swept away by Pain and Panic. f, Old couple with Baby Hercules. g, Hercules pulling cart. h, Hercules looking into mirror.
Hercules triumphant — #2753, each $1: a, Hercules carrying Meg. b, Meg, Hades. c, Hercules being trained by Phil. d, Hercules meeting Hades. e, Monster coming through city. f, Zeus. g, Hercules lifting column off Meg. h, Hercules diving into water.
Each $6: #2754, Hercules with sword, fighting Hydra. #2755, Hades on fire. #2756, Hercules, Meg on Pegasus, horiz. #2757, Zeus, Hercules, horiz. #2758, Hades. #2759, Zeus with baby Pegasus.

**1998, June 16  Litho.  Perf. 13½x14**
**Sheets of 8**
2751  A407  10c #a.-h.  3.75  3.75
2752-2753  A407  Set of 2  18.00  18.00
**Souvenir Sheets**
2754-2759  A407  Set of 6  40.00  40.00

Sea Birds — A408

Designs: 90c, Arctic skua. $1.10, Humboldt penguin. $2, Herring gull. $3, Red knot.
No. 2764, horiz.: a, Northern fulmar. b, Black-legged kittiwake. c, Cape petrel. d, Mediterranean gull. e, Brandt's cormorant (h). f, Greater shearwater. g, Black-footed albatross. h, Red-necked phalarope. i, Black skimmer (f).
Each $5: No. 2765, Black-browed albatross. No. 2766, King penguin.

**1998, June 30  Litho.  Perf. 14**
2760-2763  A408  Set of 4  6.25  6.25
2764  A408  $1 Sheet of 9, #a.-i.  9.25  9.25
**Souvenir Sheets**
2765-2766  A408  Set of 2  10.50  10.50

Diana, Princess of Wales (1961-97) — A409

Portrait of Diana with rose: No. 2767, Wearing hat. No. 2768, Without hat. Illustration reduced.

**Litho. & Embossed**
**1998, July 14  Die Cut 7½**
2767  A409  $20 gold & multi
2768  A409  $20 gold & multi

Supermarine Spitfires — A410

No. 2769, each $1.50: a, MK IX. b, MK XIV. c, MK XII. d, MK XI. e, H.F. MK VIII. f, MK VB.
No. 2770, each $1.50: a, MK I. b, MK VIII. c, MK III. d, MK XVI. e, MK V. f, MK XIX.
Each $6: No. 2771, MK IX. No. 2772, MK IA.

**1998, July 20  Litho.  Perf. 14**
**Sheets of 6, #a.-f.**
2769-2770  A410  Set of 2  15.50  15.50
**Souvenir Sheets**
2771-2772  A410  Set of 2  12.50  12.50
Nos. 2771-2772 each contain one 57x43mm stamp.

Intl. Year of the Ocean
A411

No. 2773: a, Walrus. b, African black footed penguins. c, African black-footed penguin. d, California sea lion. e, Green turtle. f, Redfin anthias. g, Sperm whale. h, French angelfish, Australian sea lion. i, Jellyfish. j, Sawfish. k, Male and female cuckoo wrasse. l, Garibaldi. m, Spinecheek anemonefish. n, Leafy seadragon. o, Blue-spotted goatfish. p, Twospot gobies.
No. 2774, Atlantic spotted dolphins. No. 2775, Octopus.

**1998, Aug. 19**
2773  A411  75c Sheet of 16, #a.-p.  12.50  12.50
**Souvenir Sheets**
2774  A411  $5 multicolored  5.00  5.00
2775  A411  $6 multicolored  6.25  6.25

CARICOM, 25th Anniv. — A412

**1998, Sept. 15  Litho.  Perf. 13½**
2776  A412  $1 multicolored  1.10  1.10

Mahatma Gandhi (1869-1948)
A413

Design: $6, Portrait, head down.

**1998, Sept. 13  Perf. 14**
2777  A413  $1 multicolored  1.50  1.50
**Souvenir Sheet**
2778  A413  $6 multicolored  6.25  6.25
No. 2777 was issued in sheets of 4.

Paintings by Pablo Picasso (1881-1973) — A414

45c, The Bathers, 1918, vert. $2, Luncheon on the Grass, 1960. $3, The Swimmer, 1929. $5, Woman Reading, 1944, vert.

**Perf. 14½x14, 14x14½**
**1998, Sept. 15**
2779-2781  A414  Set of 3  5.25  5.25
**Souvenir Sheet**
2782  A414  $5 multicolored  5.25  5.25

Paintings by Eugéne Delacroix (1798-1863) — A415

No. 2783: a, Horsemen Fighting in the Plain. b, The Assassination of the Bishop of Liege. c, Still-life with Lobsters. d, The Battle of Nancy. e, The Shipwreck of Don Juan. f, The Death of Ophelia. g, Attila and the Barbarians. h, Entertaining the Arabians.
$5, Entry of the Crusaders into Constantinople.

**1998, Sept. 15  Perf. 14**
**Sheet of 8**
2783  A415  $1 #a.-h.  7.75  7.75
**Souvenir Sheet**
2784  A415  $5 multicolored  5.25  5.25

Organization of American States, 50th Anniv.
A416

**1998, Sept. 15  Litho.  Perf. 14**
2785  A416  $1 multicolored  1.10  1.10

Diana, Princess of Wales (1961-97)
A417

**1998  Perf. 14½**
2786  A417  $1 multicolored  1.10  1.10
**Self-Adhesive**
**Serpentine Die Cut Perf. 11½**
**Sheet of 1**
**Size: 52x65mm**
2786A  A417  $6 Diana, buildings  6.00
No. 2786 was issued in sheets of 6. Soaking in water may affect the multi-layer image of No. 2786A.
Issued: $1, 9/15; $6, 11/5/98.

Enzo Ferrari (1898-1988), Automobile Manufacturer — A418

No. 2787: a, 250 GT Berlinetta Lusso. b, 250 GTO. c, 250 GT Boano/Ellena cabriolet. $5, Dino 246 GTS.

**1998, Sept. 15**     **Perf. 14**
2787 A418 $2 Sheet of 3, #a.-c.   5.25 5.25
**Souvenir Sheet**
2788 A418 $5 multicolored   5.25 5.25
No. 2786 was issued in sheets of 6. No. 2788 contains one 91x35mm stamp.

1998 World Scouting Jamboree, Chile — A419

Designs: $2, Scout salute. $3, World Scout flag. $4, Scout first aid. $6, World Scout flag.

**1998, Sept. 15**
2789-2791 A419 Set of 3   8.75 8.75
**Souvenir Sheet**
2792 A419 $6 multi, horiz.   7.00 7.00

Royal Air Force, 80th Anniv. A420

No. 2793, each $2: a, Vickers Supermarine Spitfire Mk2a. b, Vickers Supermarine Spitfire HF Mk1XB flying right. c, Vickers Supermarine Spitfire HF Mk1Xb flying left. d, Hawker Hurricane 11C.
No. 2794, each $2: a, EF-2000 Eurofighter prototype. b, Nimrod MR2P. c, Eurofighter 2000, diff. d, C-47 Dakota.
Each $6: No. 2795, Eurofighter 2000, VC10. No. 2796, Biplane, hawk's head. No. 2797, Biplane, hawk. No. 2798, Eurofighter 2000, Jet Provost.

**1998, Sept. 15**
**Sheets of 4, #a-d**
2793-2794 A420 Set of 2   16.00 16.00
**Souvenir Sheets**
2795-2798 A420 Set of 4   25.00 25.00

Tennis Stars A421

45c, Arthur Ashe. 75c, Martina Hingis. 90c, Chris Evert. $1, Steffi Graf. $1.50, Arantxa Sanchez Vicario. $3, Martina Navratilova. $2, Monica Seles. $6, Martina Hingis, diff.

**1998, Oct. 28**
2799-2805 A421 Set of 7   8.75 8.75
**Souvenir Sheet**
2806 A421 $6 multicolored   7.00 7.00

Peacekeepers, Beirut, Lebanon, 1982-84 — A422

**1998, Nov. 30**    **Litho.**    **Perf. 14**
2807 A422 $1 multicolored   1.25 1.25

Christmas A423

Birds: 45c, Blue-hooded Euphonia. 75c, Black-bellied whistling duck. 90c, Purple martin. $1, Imperial parrot. $2, Adelaide's warbler. $3, Roseate flamingo.
$5, Green-throated carib. $6, Purple-throated carib, Canada #85.

**1998, Dec. 1**
2808-2813 A423 Set of 6   7.75 7.75
**Souvenir Sheet**
2814 A423 $5 multicolored   5.25 5.25
2815 A423 $6 multicolored   8.00 8.00
No. 2815 contains one 38x61mm stamp.

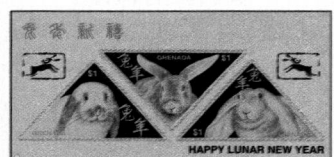
Christmas — A424

Works of art: 35c, Painting, The Angel's Parting from Tobias, by Jean Bilevelt. 45c, Painting, Allegory of Faith, by Moretto da Brescia. 90c, Sculpture, Cross, with Depiction of the Crucifixion, by Ugolino di Tedice. $1, The Triumphal Entry into Jerusalem, Master of the Thuison Altarpiece.

**1998, Dec. 1**
2816-2819 A424 Set of 4   2.75 2.75

New Year 1999 (Year of the Rabbit) — A425

Various rabbits, color of country name: a, green. b, orange. c, red. Illustration reduced.

**1999, Jan. 4 Litho. Die Cut Perf. 9**
**Self-Adhesive**
**Sheet of 3**
2820 A425 $1 sil & multi, #a.-c.   3.50 3.50
No. 2820b has point of triangle down.

A426

Famous People: No. 2821: a, Martin Luther King, Jr. (1929-68). b, Socrates (470-399BC). c, Thomas Moore (1478-1535). d, Chaim Weizmann (1874-1952). e, Alexander Solzhenitsyn (b. 1918). f, Galileo Galilei (1564-1642). g, Michael Servetus (1511-53). h, Salman Rushdie (b. 1947).
$6, Mother Teresa (1910-97).

**1999, Mar. 1 Litho. Perf. 14**
2821 A426 $1 Sheet of 8, #a.-h.   10.00 10.00
**Souvenir Sheet**
2822 A426 $6 multicolored   7.00 7.00
Nos. 2821b-2821c, 2821e-2821f are 53x38mm.

A427

Space Exploration — #2823, each $1.50: a, Robert H. Goddard. b, Werner von Braun. c, Yuri Gagarin. d, Freedom 7 rocket. e, Aleksei Leonov. f, Apollo 11 astronauts on moon.
No. 2824, each $1.50: a, Mariner 9. b, Voyager 1. c, Bruce McCandless. d, Giotto probe. e, Space Shuttle. f, Magellan probe.
Each $6: No. 2825, John H. Glenn, Jr. No. 2826, Neil A. Armstrong.

**1999, Mar. 5**
**Sheets of 6, #a-f**
2823-2824 A427 Set of 2   16.00 16.00
**Souvenir Sheets**
2825-2826 A427 Set of 2   12.00 12.00

Mickey's Dream Wedding A428

No. 2827: a, Goofy. b, Mickey. c, Minnie. d, Daisy Duck. e, Donald Duck. f, Pluto. g, Huey, Dewey & Louie. h, Dog.
Each $6: No. 2828, Mickey eating cake. No. 2829, Mickey, Minnie in back of carriage, horiz.

**1999, Mar. 12 Perf. 13½x14, 14x13½**
2827 A428 $1 Sheet of 8, #a.-h.   8.00 8.00
**Souvenir Sheets**
2828-2829 A428 Set of 2   13.50 13.50
Mickey Mouse, 70th anniv.

Trains A429

Designs: 25c, Grand Trunk Western. 35c, Louisville & Nashville. 45c, Gulf, Mobile & Ohio. 75c, Missouri Pacific. 90c, RTG, French Natl. Railway. $1, Florida East Coast. $3, Kansas City Southern. $4, New Haven.
No. 2838, each $1.50: a, Western Pacific. b, Union Pacific. c, Chesapeake & Ohio. d, Southern Pacific. e, Baltimore & Ohio. f, Wabash.
No. 2839, each $1.50: a, Burlington Route. b, Texas Special, Missouri, Kansas & Texas. c, City of Los Angeles. d, Northwestern. e, Canadian National. f, Rock Island.
No. 2840, each $1.50: a, Rio Grande. b, Erie Lackawanna. c, New York Central. d, Pennsylvania. e, Milwaukee Road. f, Illinois Central.
No. 2841, each $1.50: a, TGV, French National Railways. b, HST, British Railways. c, TEE, Trans Europe Express. d, Ancona Express Itay. e, XPT, Australia. f, APT-P, British Railways.
Each $6: No. 2842, Bullet Train, Japan. No. 2843, Inter City Express, Germany. No. 2844, Santa Fe. No. 2845, ELD 4, Netherlands.

**1999, Mar. 15**    **Perf. 14**
2830-2837 A429 Set of 8   9.75 9.75
**Sheets of 6, #a-f**
2838-2841 A429 Set of 4   36.00 36.00
**Souvenir Sheets**
2842-2845 A429 Set of 4   25.00 25.00

Australia '99, World Stamp Expo A430

Flora and fauna: $1, Orangutan. $2, Dourocouli. $3, Black caiman. $4, Black leopard, vert.
No. 2850, vert, each 75c: a, African binturong. b, Two elephants. c, One elephant. d, Garkulax mitratus. e, Vanda hookeriana (a, f). f, Heron. g, Fur seal (f). h, Pied shag (g). i, Round batfish (e). j, Loggerhead turtle (f, k). k, Three harlequin sweet lips (l). l, Two harlequin sweet lips (k).
No. 2851, each 75c: a, Papilio blumei (d). b, Egret (e). c, Kumarahou (b, f). d, Javan rhinoceros (g). e, Silver eye. f, Kiore (i). g, Cyclorana novaehollandiae. h, Caterpillar. i, Grey duck (h). j, Honey blue-eye. k, Krefft's tortoise. l, Archer fish.
Each $6: No. 2852, Impalas. No. 2853, Ring-tailed lemurs.

**1999, Apr. 12 Litho. Perf. 14**
2846-2849 A430 Set of 4   9.50 9.50
**Sheets of 12, #a-l**
2850-2851 A430 Set of 2   17.50 17.50
**Souvenir Sheets**
2852-2853 A430 Set of 2   12.50 12.50

Paintings by Hokusai (1760-1849) A431

Entire paintings or details — #2854, each $1.50: a, The Actor Ichikawa Danjuro as Tomoe Gozen. b, E-Tehon drawings (washing clothes). c, The Prostitute of Eguchi. d, Sudden Shower from a Fine Sky. e, E-tehon drawings (hanging clothes up to dry). f, Shimada.
No. 2855, each $1.50: a, Head of Old Man. b, Horse Drawings (with head down). c, Girl Making Cord for Binding Hats. d, Li Po Admiring the Waterfall of Lo-Shan. e, Horse drawings (with head up). f, Potted Dwarf Pine with Basin.
Each $6: No. 2856, Women on the Beach at Enoshima. No. 2857, The Guardian God Fudo Myoo and His Two Young Attendants.

**1999, May 24 Litho. Perf. 13½x14**
**Sheets of 6, #a-f**
2854-2855 A431 Set of 2   17.00 17.00
**Souvenir Sheets**
2856-2857 A431 Set of 2   12.50 12.50

Johann Wolfgang von Goethe (1749-1832), Poet — A432

No. 2858: a, Faust contempates the moon in his story. b, Portrait of Goethe and Freidrich von Schiller (1759-1805). c, Faust converses with Wagner outside the town gate.
No. 2860, Margaret Muses in "Faust."

**1999, May 24**    **Perf. 14**
2858 A432 $3 Sheet of 3, #a.-c.   8.75 8.75
**Souvenir Sheet**
2860 A432 $6 multi   6.75 6.75

IBRA '99, World Philatelic Exhibition, Nuremberg — A433

IBRA'99 emblem, 1893 4-4-0 locomotive and: No. 2862, 75c, Prussia #2. No. 2864, $1, Saxony #1.
Emblem, Humboldt sailing ship and: No. 2863, 90c, Mecklenburg-Schwerin #1. No. 2865, $2, Mecklenburg-Strelitz #1.
$6, Saxony #1. Illustration reduced.

| 1999, May 24 | Litho. | | Perf. 14 | |
|---|---|---|---|---|
| 2862-2865 | A433 | Set of 4 | 5.25 | 5.25 |
| **Souvenir Sheet** | | | | |
| 2866 | A433 | $6 multicolored | 7.75 | 7.75 |

Apollo 11 Moon Landing, 30th Anniv. A434

#2867, each $1.50: a, Footprint on moon. b, V2 Rocket. c, Command module, Columbia. d, Lunar rover. e, Lunar lander, Eagle. f, Command module during re-entry.
#2868, each $1.50: a, Moon. b, Edward H. White during first spacewalk. c, Edwin "Buzz" Aldrin. d, Earth. e, Michael Collins. f, Neal A. Armstrong, first man to walk on moon.
Each $6: #2869, Launch of Apollo 11, vert. #2870, US flag, Armstrong on Moon.

| 1999, May 24 | | | | |
|---|---|---|---|---|
| **Sheets of 6, #a-f** | | | | |
| 2867-2868 | A434 | Set of 2 | 19.00 | 19.00 |
| **Souvenir Sheets** | | | | |
| 2869-2870 | A434 | Set of 2 | 12.50 | 12.50 |

Souvenir Sheets

PhilexFrance '99, World Philatelic Exhibition — A435

Designs, each $6: No. 2871, 2-8-0 Heavy freight locomotive, French State Railways. No. 2872, 4 Cylinder Compound Pacific, Paris-Lyons and Mediterranean Railway.
Illustration reduced.

| 1999, May 24 | | | Perf. 13¾ | |
|---|---|---|---|---|
| 2871-2872 | A435 | Set of 2 | 12.50 | 12.50 |

A436

Wedding of Prince Edward and Sophie Rhys-Jones — #2873: a, Edward. b, Sophie and Edward. c, Sophie.
$6, Couple, horiz.

| 1999, June 18 | Litho. | | Perf. 13½ | |
|---|---|---|---|---|
| 2873 | A436 | $3 Sheet of 3, #a.-c. | 8.75 | 8.75 |
| **Souvenir Sheet** | | | | |
| 2874 | A436 | $6 multicolored | 7.00 | 7.00 |

A437

Children: a, Two with fur hats. b, One with pink hat. c, Boy without shirt, girl with shawl. $6, Wearing white shirt.

| 1999, May 24 | Litho. | | Perf. 14 | |
|---|---|---|---|---|
| 2875 | A437 | $3 Sheet of 3, #a.-c. | 8.75 | 8.75 |
| **Souvenir Sheet** | | | | |
| 2876 | A437 | $6 multicolored | 7.00 | 7.00 |

UN Rights of the Child, 10th anniv.

British Comedy "Carry On" — A438

a, Dick. b, Doctor. c, England. d, Matron. e, Round the Bend. f, Up the Jungle. g, Loving. h, Up the Khyber.
$6, Various characters.

| 1999, May 24 | | | Perf. 13½x14 | |
|---|---|---|---|---|
| 2877 | A438 | $1 Sheet of 8, #a.-h. | 8.75 | 8.75 |
| | | | Perf. 13¾ | |
| 2877I | A438 | $6 multicolored | 6.75 | 6.75 |

Variety Club of Great Britain, 50th anniv.

UPU, 125th Anniv. A439

Mail from space: a, Cosmonaut with letter from home. b, Supply and mail ship, "Progress." c, Postmark of space station Mir. d, Buran shuttle, Mir in space.
$6, Space station Mir.

| 1999, May 24 | | | Perf. 14 | |
|---|---|---|---|---|
| 2878 | A439 | $2 Sheet of 4, #a.-d. | 8.75 | 8.75 |
| **Souvenir Sheet** | | | | |
| 2879 | A439 | $6 multicolored | 7.00 | 7.00 |

Queen Mother, 100th Birthday (in 2000) — A440

A440a

**Gold Frames**

No. 2880: a, Queen Mother, Prince Charles, 1948. b, Queen Mother, 1970. c, Queen Mother in Australia, 1958. d, Queen Mother.
$6, Queen Mother, 1953.

| 1999, Aug. 16 | | | | |
|---|---|---|---|---|
| **Sheet of 4** | | | | |
| 2880 | A440 | $2 #a.-d. + label | 8.75 | 8.75 |
| **Souvenir Sheet** | | | | |
| 2881 | A440 | $6 multicolored | 7.00 | 7.00 |
| **Litho. & Embossed** | | | | |
| ***Die Cut Perf. 8¾*** | | | | |
| **Without Gum** | | | | |
| 2881A | A440a | $20 gold & multi | 20.00 | |

No. 2881 contains one 38x50mm stamp. Margins of sheet are embossed.
See Nos. 3212-3213.

Birth of the Silver Screen A441

Musicians — #2882, each $1: a, George Gershwin, 1929. b, Florence Mills, 1928. c, Sam Beckett, 1925. d, Bessie Smith, 1923. e, Billie Holiday, 1933. f, Bert Williams, 1914. g, Cole Porter, 1934. h, Sophie Tucker, 1915.
Actors — #2883, each $1: a, Lon Chaney, 1930. b, Buster Keaton, 1930. c, Norma Shearer, 1934. d, James Cagney, 1930. e, Hedda Hopper, 1933. f, Jean Harlow, 1931. g, Marlene Dietrich, 1930. h, Ramon Novarro, 1928.
Each $6: No. 2884, Louis Armstrong. No. 2885, Clark Gable, 1932.

| 1999, Aug. 18 | | | | |
|---|---|---|---|---|
| **Sheets of 8, #a-h** | | | | |
| 2882-2883 | A441 | Set of 2 | 16.00 | 16.00 |
| **Souvenir Sheets** | | | | |
| 2884-2885 | A441 | Set of 2 | 14.00 | 14.00 |

Star Trek A442

Various starships.

| 1999, July 20 | Litho. | | Perf. 13¼ | |
|---|---|---|---|---|
| 2886 | A442 | $1.50 Sheet of 9, #a.-i. | 14.50 | 14.50 |

Dinosaurs A443

35c, Ouranosaurus. 45c, Struthiomimus, vert. 75c, Parasaurolophus, vert. $2, Triceratops. $3, Stegoceras. $4, Stegosaurus.
No. 2893, each $1: a, Agathaumus. b, Camarosaurus. c, Quetzalcoatlus. d, Alioramus. e, Camptosaurus. f, Albertosaurus. g, Anatosaurus. h, Spinosaurus. i, Centrosaurus.
No. 2894, each $1: a, Archaeopteryx. b, Brachiosaurus. c, Dilophosaurus. d, Dimetrodon. e, Psittacosaurus. f, Acrocanthosaurus. g, Stenonychosaurus. h, Dryosaurus. i, Compsognathus.
Each $6: No. 2895, Velociraptor, vert. No. 2896, Tyrannosaurus, vert.

| 1999, Sept. 1 | Litho. | | Perf. 14 | |
|---|---|---|---|---|
| 2887-2892 | A443 | Set of 6 | 10.00 | 10.00 |
| **Sheets of 9, #a-i** | | | | |
| 2893-2894 | A443 | Set of 2 | 18.00 | 18.00 |
| **Souvenir Sheets** | | | | |
| 2895-2896 | A443 | Set of 2 | 12.50 | 12.50 |

Christmas — A444

Candle and: 20c, Rose. 75c, Tulip. 90c, Pear. $1, Hibiscus. $4, Lily.
$6, The Nativity, by Sandro Botticelli.

| 1999, Dec. 7 | Litho. | | Perf. 14 | |
|---|---|---|---|---|
| 2897-2901 | A444 | Set of 5 | 6.75 | 6.75 |
| **Souvenir Sheet** | | | | |
| 2902 | A444 | $6 multi | 7.00 | 7.00 |

Flowers A445

Various flowers making up a photomosaic of Princess Diana.

| 1999, Dec. 31 | Litho. | | Perf. 13¾ | |
|---|---|---|---|---|
| 2903 | A445 | $1 Sheet of 8, #a.-h. | 8.00 | 8.00 |

See No. 3055.

New Year 2000 (Year of the Dragon) — A446

Inscription color: a, Blue green. b, Red. c, Violet.

| 2000, Feb. 5 | | | Perf. 12½x12¾ | |
|---|---|---|---|---|
| 2904 | A446 | $2 Sheet of 3, #a.-c. | 6.75 | 6.75 |

No. 2904b has point of triangle down.

Birds
A447

Designs: 75c, Roseate spoonbill. 90c, Scarlet ibis. $1.50, Sparkling violet-ear. $2, Northern jacana.

No. 2909, each $1: a, Blue-headed euphonia. b, Troupial. c, Caribbean parakeet. d, Forest thrush. e, Hooded tanager. f, Stripe-headed tanager. g, Ringed kingfisher. h, Zenaida dove.

No. 2910, each $1: a, Adelaide's warbler. b, Hispaniolan trogon. c, Sun parakeet. d, Black-necked stilt. e, Sora rail. f, Fulvous tree duck. g, Blue-headed parrot. h, Tropical mockingbird.

Each $6: No. 2911, Antillean siskin. No. 2912, Cedar waxwing, vert.

**2000, Mar. 1    Litho.    Perf. 14**
2905-2908  A447  Set of 4        5.00  5.00
**Sheets of 8, #a-h**
2909-2910  A447  Set of 2        14.00  14.00
**Souvenir Sheets**
2911-2912  A447  Set of 2        10.00  10.00

No. 2911 contains one 50x37mm stamp. No. 2912 contains one 37x50mm stamp.

Mushrooms
A448

Designs: 35c, Clitocybe geotropa. 45c, Psalliota augusta. $1, Amanita rubescens. $4, Boletus satanas.

No. 2917, each $1.50: a, Ungulina marginata. b, Pleurotus ostreatus. c, Flammula penetrans. d, Morchella crassipes. e, Lepiota procera. f, Tricholoma aurantium.

No. 2918, each $1.50: a, Pholiota spectabilis. b, Mycena polygramma. c, Collybia iocephala. d, Corinus cornatus. e, Amanita muscaria. f, Boletus aereus.

Each $6: No. 2919, Lepiota acutesquamosa. No. 2920, Daedala quercina.

**2000, May 1        Perf. 14**
2913-2916  A448  Set of 4        6.25  6.25
**Sheets of 6, #a-f**
2917-2918  A448  Set of 2        17.00  17.00
**Souvenir Sheets**
2919-2920  A448  Set of 2        12.00  12.00

Paintings of Anthony Van Dyck
A449

No. 2921, each $1: a, Young Woman Resting Her Head on Her Hand. b, Self-portrait. c, Woman Looking Upwards. d, Head of an Old Man, c. 1621. e, Head of a Boy. f, Head of an Old Man, 1616-18.

No. 2922, each $1: a, Charles I on Horseback with Seigneur de St. Antoine. b, St. Martin Dividing His Cloak. c, Giovanni Paolo Balbi on Horseback. d, Marchese Anton Giulio Brignole-Sale on Horseback. e, Study of a Horse. f, An Oriental on Horseback.

No. 2923, each $1.50: a, Portrait of a Man. b, Portrait of a Man Aged Seventy. c, Portrait of a Woman. d, An Elderly Man. e, Portrait of a Young Man. f, Man with a Glove.

No. 2924, each $1.50: a, St. John the Baptist. b, St. Anthony of Padua and the Ass of Rimini. c, The Stoning of St. Stephen. d, The Martyrdom of St. Sebastian. e, St. Sebastian Bound for Martyrdom. f, St. Jerome.

No. 2925, each $1.50: a, Inscribed "Portrait of Anthony Van Dyck," actually a self-portrait of Rubens. b, Inscribed "Self-portrait (after Peter Paul Rubens)." c, Isabella Brant, Wife of Peter Paul Rubens. d, The Penitent Apostle Peter. e, Head of a Robber. f, The Heads of the Apostles, by Rubens.

Each $5: No. 2926, Prince Thomas-Francis of Savoy-Carignan on Horseback. No. 2927, Charles I on Horseback. No. 2928, The Emperor Theodosius Refused Entry in Milan Cathedral, horiz.

Each $6: No. 2929, St. Jerome (in the Wilderness). No. 2930, St. Martin Dividing His Cloak, horiz. No. 2931, Portrait of a Man and His Wife.

**2000, May 1        Perf. 13¾**
**Sheets of 6, #a-f.**
2921-2922  A449  Set of 2        10.50  10.50
2923-2925  A449  Set of 3        22.50  22.50
**Souvenir Sheets**
2926-2928  A449  Set of 3        13.00  13.00
2929-2931  A449  Set of 3        14.50  14.50

Millennium
A450

Highlights of 1650-1700: a, Painter Jan Vermeer dies. b, Birth of microbiology. c, Salem Witch Trials. d, Sir Isaac Newton builds first reflecting telescope. e, Voltaire born. f, Ivan V and Peter become joint rulers of Russia. g, First Qing Dynasty Emperor, Shun Zhi, dies. h, Christiaan Huygens discovers rings of Saturn. i, Robert Hooke identifies cells. j, Wang Shih-min paints "Verdant Peaks." k, René Descartes dies. l, Canal du Midi completed. m, Glorious Revolution. n, King William's War ends. o, Gian Domenico Cassini observes polar caps on Mars. p, Newton formulates law of gravitation (60x40mm). q, Ole Roemer discovers that light moves at a finite speed.

**2000, May 1        Perf. 12½**
2932  A450  50c Sheet of 17, #a-q., + label        8.75  8.75

Orchids — A451

Designs: 75c, Brassolaeliocattleya. 90c, Maxilbera. $1, Isochilius. $2, Oncidium.

No. 2937, each $1.50: a, Laeliocattleya. b, Sophrocattleya (red). c, Epidendrum. d, Cattleya. e, Ionopsis. f, Brassoepidendrum.

No. 2938, each $1.50: a, Lycaste. b, Cochleanthes. c, Brassocattleya. d, Brassolaeliacattleya, diff. e, Iwanagaara. f, Sophrocattleya (orange).

Each $6: No. 2939, Vanilla. No. 2940, Brassocattleya, diff.

**2000, May 15    Litho.    Perf. 14**
2933-2936  A451  Set of 4        4.25  4.25
**Sheets of 6, #a-f.**
2937-2938  A451  Set of 2        17.00  17.00
**Souvenir Sheets**
2939-2940  A451  Set of 2        11.00  11.00

100th Test Match at Lord's Ground — A452

90c, Junior Murray. $5, Rawl Lewis.

$6, Lord's Ground, horiz.

**2000, May 15    Litho.    Perf. 14**
2941-2942  A452  Set of 2        4.75  4.75
**Souvenir Sheet**
2943  A452  $6 multi        5.25  5.25

Prince William, 18th Birthday — A453

No. 2944: a, In suit. b, In suit, with person in tan suit. c, In suit, waving. d, In ski jacket. $6, In suit, diff.
Illustration reduced.

**2000, May 15        Perf. 14**
2944  A453  $1.50 Sheet of 4, #a-d        4.50  4.50
**Souvenir Sheet**
**Perf. 13¾**
2945  A453  $6 multi        4.50  4.50

No. 2944 contains four 28x42mm stamps.

First Zeppelin Flight, Cent. — A454

No. 2946 — Ferdinand von Zeppelin and: a, LZ-130. b, LZ-2. c, LZ-127. $6, LZ-129.
Illustration reduced.

**2000, May 15        Perf. 14**
2946  A454  $3 Sheet of 3, #a-c        8.00  8.00
**Souvenir Sheet**
2947  A454  $6 multi        5.25  5.25

No. 2946 contains three 42x28mm stamps.

Berlin Film Festival, 50th Anniv. — A455

No. 2948: a, Alphaville. b, Rod Steiger. c, Os Fuzis. d, Jean-Pierre Leaud. e, Cul-de-sac. f, Ikiru.
$6, Hsi Yen.
Illustration reduced.

**2000, May 15**
2948  A455  $1.50 Sheet of 6, #a-f  6.75  6.75
**Souvenir Sheet**
2949  A455  $6 multi        4.50  4.50

Apollo-Soyuz Mission, 25th Anniv. — A456

No. 2950, vert.: a, Soyuz launch vehicle. b, Soyuz 19. c, Apollo 18 and Soyuz 19 docked. $6, Valeri Kubasov and Thomas Stafford.
Illustration reduced.

**2000, May 15**
2950  A456  $3 Sheet of 3, #a-c  7.75  7.75
**Souvenir Sheet**
2951  A456  $6 multi        5.75  5.75

**Souvenir Sheets**

2000 Summer Olympics, Sydney — A457

No. 2952: a, Archibald Hahn. b, Show jumping. c, Sports Palace, Rome, and Italian flag. d, Ancient Greek chariot racing.
Illustration reduced.

**2000, May 15**
2952  A457  $2 Sheet of 4, #a-d        7.00  7.00

Public Railways, 175th Anniv. — A458

No. 2953: a, Locomotion No. 1, George Stephenson. b, John Bull.
Illustration reduced.

**2000, May 15**
2953  A458  $3 Sheet of 2, #a-b        5.75  5.75

Johann Sebastian Bach (1685-1750) — A459

Illustration reduced.

**2000, May 15**
2954 A459 $6 multi       4.50 4.50

**Souvenir Sheet**

Albert Einstein (1879-1955) — A460

Illustration reduced.

**2000, May 15   Litho.   Perf. 14¼**
2955 A460 $6 multi       4.50 4.50

Space — A461

No. 2956: a, Luna 4. b, Clementine. c, Luna 12. d, Luna 16. e, Apollo 11 Lunar module. f, Ranger 7.
$6, Apollo command and service modules. Illustration reduced.

**2000, May 15   Litho.   Perf. 14**
2956 A461 $1.50 Sheet of 6, #a-f 7.75 7.75

**Souvenir Sheet**
2957 A461   $6 multi       5.25 5.25

World Stamp Expo 2000, Anaheim

Marine Life A462

Designs: 45c, Porkfish. 75c, Short bigeye. 90c, Red snapper. $1, Creole wrasse. $2, Indigo hamlet. $3, Blue tang.
No. 2964: a, Juvenile French angelfish. b, Beaugregory. c, Queen angelfish. d, Sergeant major. e, Bank butterflyfish. f, Spanish hogfish. g, Porkfish. h, Banded butterflyfish. i, Long-snout seahorse.
No. 2965: a, Hawksbill turtle. b, Foureye butterflyfish. c, Porcupinefish. d, Yellowtail damselfish. e, Adult French angelfish. f, Yellow goatfish. g, Blue-striped grunt. h, Spanish grunt. i, Queen triggerfish.
No. 2966, Queen angelfish. No. 2967, Blue tang.

**2000, Aug. 8**
2958-2963 A462   Set of 5   7.00 7.00

**Sheets of 9, #a-i**
2964-2965 A462 $1 Set of 2   14.50 14.50

**Souvenir Sheets**
2966-2967 A462 $6 Set of 2   9.00 9.00

Grenada National Stadium A463

Designs: $2, Aerial view.
No. 2969: a, Cricket team photo. b, Cricketers playing.

**2000, Aug. 8**
2968 A463 $2 multi       1.50 1.50

**Souvenir Sheet**
2969 A463 $1 Sheet of 2, #a-b   1.50 1.50

European Soccer Championships — A464

No. 2970, horiz. — Belgium: a, Vanderhaege. b, Belgian team. c, Ronny Gaspercic. d, Lorenzo Staelens. e, Stadium Koning Boudewijn. f, Strupar and Mpenza.
No. 2971, horiz. — Spain: a, Sergi Barjuan. b, Spanish team. c, Luis Enrique. d, Hierro. e, De Kuip Stadium. f, Raul Gonzales.
No. 2972, horiz. — Yugoslavia: a, Dejan Savicevic. b, Yugoslavian team. c, Predrag Migatovic. d, Savo Milosevic. e, Jan Breydel Stadium. f, Darko Kovacevic.
No. 2973, Belgian coach Robert Waseige. No. 2974, Spanish coach José Antonio Camacho. No. 2975, Yugoslavian coach Vujadin Boskov.
Illustration reduced.

**2000, Aug. 8   Perf. 13¾**
**Sheets of 6, #a-f**
2970-2972 A464 $1.50 Set of 3   20.00 20.00

**Souvenir Sheets**
2973-2975 A464 $6 Set of 3   13.50 13.50

Ferrari Automobiles — A465

20c, 1953 500 Mondial. 45c, 1948 166 Inter. 75c, 1953 340 MM. 90c, 1964 500 Superfast. $1, 1948 166 MM. $1.50, 1952 250 S. $2, 1957 250 California. $3, 1966 365 California.

**2000, Sept. 5   Perf. 14**
2976-2983 A465   Set of 8   8.00 8.00

Antique Automobiles A466

45c, 1921 Marmon Model 34. 75c, 1917 Buick D44. 90c, 1918 Hudson Runabout Landau. $1, 1915 Chevolet Royal Mail. $2, 1925 Kissel Speedster. $3, 1915 Ford Model T.
No. 2990: a, 1925 Cadillac V63. b, 1939 Plymouth. c, 1934 Franklin Club Sedan. d, 1933 Fiat Ardita. e, 1929 Essex Speedabout. f, 1932 Stutz Bearcat.
No. 2991: a, 1929 Rolls Royce. b, 1932 Graham Convertible. c, 1937 Mercedes-Benz 540K. d, 1948 Jaguar MkV. e, 1939 Lagonda Drophead Coupe. f, 1930 Alfa Romeo Gran Sport.
No. 2992, 1915 Dodge Tourer. No. 2993, 1924 Chrysler.

**2000, Sept. 5**
2984-2989 A466   Set of 6     6.00 6.00

**Sheets of 6, #a-f**
2990-2991 A466 $1.50 Set of 2   13.50 13.50

**Souvenir Sheets**
2992-2993 A466 $6 Set of 2   9.00 9.00

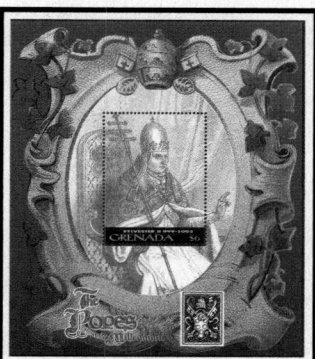

Popes — A467

No. 2994: a, Stephen VIII, 939-42. b, Theodore I, 642-49. c, Theodore II, 897. d, Valentine, 827. e, Vitalian, 657-72. f, Zacharias, 741-52.
$6, Sylvester II, 999-1003.

**2000, Sept. 5   Perf. 13¾**
2994 A467 $1.50 Sheet of 6, #a-f 6.75 6.75

**Souvenir Sheet**
2995 A467   $6 multi       4.50 4.50

Monarchs — A468

No. 2996: a, George III of Great Britain, 1760-1820. b, George IV of Great Britain, 1820-30. c, Duchess Charlotte of Luxembourg, 1964-present. d, Grand Duke Jean of Luxembourg, 1964-present.
$6, Charles VIII of France, 1483-98.

**2000, Sept. 5   Perf. 13¾**
2996 A468 $1.50 Sheet of 4, #a-d   4.50 4.50

**Souvenir Sheet**
2997 A468   $6 multi       4.50 4.50

Shirley Temple in "Heidi" — A469

No. 2998, horiz.: a, With woman holding candle. b, With girl in green dress c, On stairs. d, With Christmas gift.
No. 2999, horiz.: a, Walking with woman. b, Touching bearded man. c, Holding goat. d, With doves. e, With bearded man. f, Seated with woman.
Illustration reduced.

**2000, Oct. 6   Litho.   Perf. 13¾**
2998 A469 $1.50 Sheet of 4, #a-d   4.50 4.50
2999 A469 $1.50 Sheet of 6, #a-f   6.75 6.75

**Souvenir Sheet**
3000 A469   $6 Seated near tree   4.50 4.50

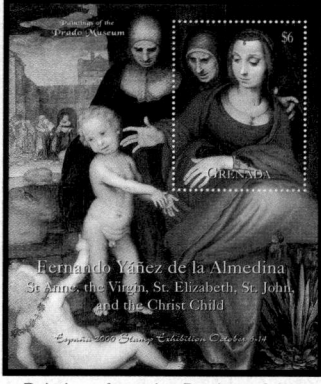

Paintings from the Prado — A470

#3001: a, Monk and king from The Virgin of the Catholic Monarchs, by an Anonymous Castilian. b, Madonna and child from The Virgin of the Catholic Monarchs. c, Monk and queen from The Virgin of the Catholic Monarchs. d, The Flagellation, by Alexo Fernandez. e, The Virgin and Souls in Purgatory, by Pedro Machuca. f, The Holy Trinity, by El Greco.
#3002: a, Playing at Giants, by El Greco. b, The Holy Family Under the Oak Tree, by Raphael. c, Don Gaspar Melchior de Jovellanos, by Francisco de Goya. d, Man with arm on hip from Joseph in the Pharaoh's Palace, by Jacopo Amiconi. e, Man and woman from Joseph in the Pharaoh's Palace. f, Man on bended knee from Joseph in the Pharaoh's Palace.
#3003: a, The Savior Blessing, by Francisco de Zurbarán. b, St. John the Baptist, by Francisco Solimena. c, Noli Me Tangere, by Corregio. d, St. Casilda, by Zurbarán. e, Nicolás Omazur by Bartolomé Esteban Murillo. f, Juan Martínez Montañés, by Diego Velázquez.
#3004, St. Anne, the Virgin, St. Elizabeth, St. John and the Christ child, by Fernando Yáñez de la Almedina. #3005, The Virgin of the Catholic Monarchs. #3006, Joseph in the Pharaoh's Palace, horiz.
Illustration reduced.

**2000, Oct. 19   Perf. 12x12¼, 12¼x12**
**Sheets of 6, #a-f**
3001-3003 A470 $1.50 Set of 3   20.00 20.00

**Souvenir Sheets**
3004-3006 A470 $6 Set of 3   13.50 13.50

Espana 2000 Intl. Philatelic Exhibition.

Battle of Britain, 60th Anniv. — A471

No. 3007: a, Messerschmitt BF 109E and bomb blast. b, Supermarine Spitfire MK XI. c, V1 flying bomb. d, U-boat. e, Ack-ack gun unit. f, Bedford field ambulance.
No. 3008: a, Messerschmitt BF 109E. b, German paratrooper. c, Hawker Hurricane HK 1. d, RAF airfield. e, Heinkel HE 111 H. f, Nose of Supermarine Spitfire MK XI.
No. 3009, Line of Hawker Hurricanes. No. 3010, Supermarine Spitfire MK XI.
Illustration reduced.

**2000, Oct. 30**      *Perf. 14*
**Sheets of 6, #a-f**
3007-3008 A471 $1.50 Set of 2    16.00 16.00
**Souvenir Sheets**
3009-3010 A471 $6 Set of 2    12.00 12.00

A472            A473

Birds: 25c, Purple gallinule. 40c, Limpkin. 50c, Black-necked stilt. 60c, Painted bunting. 75c, Yellow-breasted warbler. $1, Blackburnian warbler. $1.25, Blue grosbeak. $1.50, Black-and-white warbler. $1.60, Blue whistling thrush. $3, Common yellowthroat. $4, Indigo bunting. $5, Gray catbird. $10, Bananaquit. $20, Blue-gray gnatcatcher.

**2000, Oct. 30**      *Perf. 14¾x14*
3011-3024 A472 Set of 14    37.50 37.50

**2000, June 23**    *Litho.*    *Perf. 14*
Dogs: $2, Shetland sheepdog. $3, Central Asian sheepdog.
No. 3027, horiz.: a, Labrador retriever. b, Standard poodle. c, Boxer. d, Rough-coated Jack Russell terrier. e, Tibetan terrier. f, Welsh corgi.
$6, Irish red and white setter, horiz.
3025-3026 A473 Set of 2    3.75 3.75
3027 A473 $1.50 Sheet of 6, #a-f 6.75 6.75
**Souvenir Sheet**
3028 A473 $6 multi    4.50 4.50

Butterflies A474

45c, Marpesia eleuchea bahamaensis. 75c, Pterourus palamedes. 90c, Dryas julia framptoni. $1, Hypna clytemnestra iphegenia.
No. 3033, $1.50: a, Danaus plexippus. b, Anartia amathea. c, Colobura dirce. d, Parides gundiachianus. e, Spiroeta stelenes. f, Hammadrayas feronia.
No. 3034, $1.50: a, Merchantis isthmia. b, Colias eurytheme. c, Papilio troilus d, Junonia coenia. e, Doxocopa laure. f, Pierella hyalinus.
No. 3035, $6, Agraulis vanilae insularis. No. 3036, $6, Danaus gilippus.

**2000, June 26**
3029-3032 A474 Set of 4    3.00 3.00
**Sheets of 6, #a-f**
3033-3034 A474 Set of 2    17.00 17.00
**Souvenir Sheets**
3035-3036 A474 Set of 2    10.00 10.00

A475

Trains — A476

No. 3037, $1.50: a, Diesel-electric locomotive, Royal State Railway of Thailand. b, Diesel-electric locomotive, Danish Railways. c, French-built Turbo train. d, Diesel, Spanish Railways. e, Virgen del Rosario, Spanish Railways. f, 22 Class Co-Co Diesel-electric locomotive, Malayan Railways.
No. 3038, $1.50: a, Class 87 electric locomotive, British Railways. b, Electric-Diesel locomotive, Iraqi Railway. c, Electric locomotive, Austrian Railways. d, 1.4 meter gauge locomotive, South Australia Railways. e, Automated electric locomotive, Black Mesa & Lake Powell Railroad. f, Diesel-electric, Yugoslav Railways.
No. 3039, $1.50: a, Class 10 4-6-2, German Federal Railway. b, Class E.10 Bo-Bo Electric locomotive, German Federal Railways. c, Class 23 2-6-2, German Federal Railway. d, 2-8-4 locomotive, German Federal Railway. e, Rebuilt 01 Class Pacific, East German State Railway. f, High speed Diesel railcar, Deutschen Reichsbahn.
No. 3040, $1.50: a, Borsig Standard 2-2-2. b, Austerity 2-10-0 Series 52, German Federal Railway. c, Adler, facing right, Nuremburg-Furth Railway. d, Bardenia, Baden State Railways. e, Drache. f, Adler, facing left.
No. 3041, $6, Diesel T.E.E. Parsifal. No. 3042, $6, High speed electric, Netherlands Railway. No. 3043, $6, Electric train, Swiss Railway. No. 3044, $6, Silver Fern, New Zealand Railways. No. 3045, $6, Borsig locomotive, Berlin and Anhalt Railway. No. 3046, $6, Krauss-Maffei V.200 Diesel-hydraulic locomotive, German Federal Railway.
Illustrations reduced.

**2000, Sept. 5**
**Sheets of 6, #a-f**
3037-3038 A475 Set of 2    15.00 15.00
3039-3040 A476 Set of 2    15.00 15.00
**Souvenir Sheets**
3041-3044 A475 Set of 4    21.00 21.00
3045-3046 A476 Set of 2    11.00 11.00
Descriptions of trains are in margins on Nos. 3039-3940, 3045-3046.

Nursery Rhymes — A477

No. 3047, Little Bo Peep, $1.50, vert.: a, Crook, tree, dove. b, Little Bo Peep. c, Sheep. d, Geese. e, Goose, Little Bo Peep's leg. f, Dog.
No. 3048, The Old Woman Who Lived in a Shoe, $1.50, vert.: a, Child, roof. b, Child with hat, rainbow. c, Cow, sun, rainbow. d, Child at door. e, Old woman, child. f, Child on shoe.
No. 3049, Little Boy Blue, $1.50, vert.: a, Sheep, house. b, Sun. c, Cow. d, Geese, path. e, Dog, Little Boy Blue's leg. f, Little Boy Blue.
No. 3050, The Cat and the Fiddle, $1.50, vert. a, Bird, house. b, Cow jumping over moon. c, Spoon. d, Dog, house. e, Cat and fiddle. f, Dish.
No. 3051, $6, Little Bo Peep. No. 3052, $6, The Old Woman Who Lived in a Shoe. No. 3053, $6, Little Boy Blue. No. 3054, Cow jumping over the moon.
Illustration reduced.

**2000, Sept. 9**      *Perf. 13¾x13¼*
**Sheets of 6, #a-f**
3047-3050 A477 Set of 4    27.50 27.50
**Souvenir Sheets**
*Perf. 13¼x13¾*
3051-3054 A477 Set of 4    18.00 18.00

**Flower Photomosaic Type of 1999**
**Queen Mother**
Various flowers making up photomosaic.

**2000, Nov. 20**      *Perf. 13¾*
3055 A445 $1 Sheet of 8, #a-h    6.00 6.00

Cats — A478

75c, Maine Coon cat. 90c, Selkirk Rex.
No. 3058, horiz.: a, Spotted tabby British shorthair. b, Burmilla. c, British blue shorthair. d, Siamese. e, Japanese bobtail. f, Oriental shorthair.

**2000, June 23**    *Litho.*    *Perf. 14*
3056-3057 A478 Set of 2    1.75 1.75
3058 A478 $1.50 Sheet of 6, #a-f 8.00 8.00
**Souvenir Sheet**
3059 A478 $6 Scottish Fold    5.75 5.75

Queen Mother, 100th Birthday — A479

**2000, Nov. 20**
3060 A479 $1.50 multi    1.10 1.10
Printed in sheets of 6.

Christmas — A480

Designs: 15c, 50c, No. 3065b, Angel looking left. 25c, $5, No. 3065a, Angel looking right.

**2000, Dec. 4**
3061-3064 A480 Set of 4    4.50 4.50
3065 A480 $2 Sheet, 2 ea #a-b    6.00 6.00
**Souvenir Sheet**
3066 A480 $6 Baby Jesus    4.50 4.50

**Souvenir Sheets**

Betty Boop — A481

Designs: No. 3067, $6, Wearing lei. No. 3068, $6, Holding fishing pole and fish. No. 3069, $6, Wearing polka dot hat. No. 3070, $6, Holding castanets. No. 3071, $6, At Japanese tea ceremony. No. 3072, $6, Wearing pink hat. No. 3073, $6, In mountains, wearing flowered hat. No. 3074, $6, Wearing beret. No. 3075, $6, As Statue of Liberty. No. 3076, $6, In Hollywood. No. 3077, $6, On horse. No. 3078, $6, On camel's back.
Illustration reduced.

**2000, Oct. 11**    *Litho.*    *Perf. 13¾*
3067-3078 A481 Set of 12    60.00 60.00

**Souvenir Sheet**

New Year 2001 (Year of the Snake) — A482

No. 3079: a, Blue green denomination. b, Red denomination. c, Purple denomination.
Illustration reduced.

**2001, Jan. 2**      *Perf. 12½x13*
3079 A482 $2 Sheet of 3, #a-c    4.50 4.50

Rijksmuseum, Amsterdam, Bicent. — A483

No. 3080, $1.50: a, William I, Prince of Orange, by Adriaen Thomasz Key. b, Rutger Jan Schimmelpennick and Family, by Pierre Paul Prud'hon. c, Johan Rudolf Thorbecke, by Johan Heinrich Neuman. d, St. Sebastian, by Joachim Wtewael. e, St. Sebastian, by Hendrick ter Brugghen. f, Portrait of a Man With a Ring, by Werner Van Den Valckert.
No. 3081, $1.50: a, The Syndics of the Amsterdam Goldsmith's Guild, by Thomas de Keyser. b, Portrait of a Gentleman, by de Keyser. c, Portrait of Eva Wtewael, by Wtewael. d, The Cattle Ferry, by Esaias van de Velde. e, Landscape With the Parable of the Tares Among the Wheat, by Abraham Bloemaert. f, Princess Henrietta Marie Stuart, by Bartholomeus van der Helst.
No. 3082, $1.50: a, The Merry Fiddler, by Gerard van Honthorst. b, The Merry Drinker, by Frans Hals. c, Granida and Daifilo, by van Honthorst. d, Vertumnus and Pomona, by Paulus Moreelse. e, Flutist from The Concert, by ter Brugghen. f, A Young Student at His Desk: Melancholy, by Pieter Codde.
No. 3083, $1.50: a, The Haarlem Painter Abraham Casteleyn and His Wife Margarieta van Bancken, by Jan de Bray. b, Two figures from The Concert. c, The Procuress, by Dirck van Baburen. d, Woman Seated at a Virginal, by Johannes Vermeer. e, Dignified Couples Courting, by Willem Buytewech. f, The Young Flute Player, by Judith Leyster.
No. 3084, $6, Interior of the Portuguese Synagogue in Amsterdam, by Emanuel de Witte. No. 3085, $6, The Denial of St. Peter, by Rembrandt, horiz. No. 3086, $6, Winter Landscape With Skaters, by Hendrick Avercamp, horiz. No. 3087, $6, The Raampoortje, by Wouter Johannes van Troostwijk, horiz.
Illustration reduced.

**2001, Jan. 15**      *Perf. 13¾*
**Sheets of 6, #a-f**
3080-3083 A483 Set of 4    27.50 27.50
**Souvenir Sheets**
3084-3087 A483 Set of 4    18.00 18.00

Pokémon — A484

No. 3088: a, Rattata. b, Sandshrew. c, Wartortle. d, Primeape. e, Golduck. f, Persian. Illustration reduced.

**2001, Feb. 1**
3088 A484 $1.50 Sheet of 6, #a-f 6.75 6.75
**Souvenir Sheet**
3089 A484 $6 Jolteon 4.50 4.50

Waterfowl — A485

No. 3090, $1.25: a, African pygmy goose. b, Silver teal. c, Marbled teal. d, Garganey. e, Wandering whistling duck. f, Northern shoveler.
No. 3091, $1.25: a, Female flightless steamer duck. b, Radjah. c, Cape teal. d, Hartlaub's duck. e, Ruddy shelduck. f, White-cheeked pintail.
No. 3092, $1.25, vert.: a, Fulvous whistling duck. b, African black duck. c, Madagascar white-eye. d, Female pygmy goose. e, Female wood duck. f, Male wood duck.
No. 3093, $6, Flightless steamer duck. No. 3094, $6, Flying steamer duck. No. 3095, $6, Australian shelduck, vert.

**Perf. 13¼x13¾, 13¾x13¼**
**2001, Mar. 5** Litho.
**Sheets of 6, #a-f**
3090-3092 A485 Set of 3 17.00 17.00
**Souvenir Sheets**
3093-3095 A485 Set of 3 13.50 13.50
Hong Kong 2001 Stamp Exhibition.

Cricket Players — A486

No. 3096: Various photos of Sir Donald Bradman swinging bat.
No. 3097, Various photos of Shane Warne bowling.
No. 3098, Various photos of Sir Jack Hobbs.
No. 3099, Various photos of Sir Vivian Richards.
No. 3100, Various photos of Sir Garfield Sobers.
No. 3101, oval vignettes: a, Bradman. b, Sobers. c, Hobbs. d, Warne. e, Richards.

**2001, May 15** **Perf. 14**
3096 Sheet of 8, #a-h 6.00 6.00
a.-h. A486 $1 Any single .75 .75
3097 Sheet of 8, #a-h 6.00 6.00
a.-h. A486 $1 Any single .75 .75
3098 Sheet of 4, #a-d 6.00 6.00
a.-d. A486 $2 Any single 1.50 1.50
3099 Sheet of 4, #a-d 6.00 6.00
a.-d. A486 $2 Any single 1.50 1.50
3100 Sheet of 4, #a-d 6.00 6.00
a.-d. A486 $2 Any single 1.50 1.50
3101 Sheet of 5, #a-e 7.50 7.50
a.-e. A486 $2 Any single 1.50 1.50
Nos. 3096-3101 (6) 37.50 37.50

A487

Phila Nippon '01, Japan — A488

Art: 75c, Scenes of Daily Life in Edo, by Miyagawa Choshun. 90c, Twelve Famous Places in Japan, by Kano Isenin Naganobu. $1, After the Rain, by Kawai Gyokudo. $1.25, Ryogoku Bridge Crowded With People, by Kano Kyuei. No. 3106, $2, A Courtesan of Fukagawa, by Katsukawa Shunei. $3, Rite of Bear Killing, by unknown artist.
No. 3108 — Details from the Lotus Sutra, $2, vert.: a, Figure in white at left. b, Figure with flag at lower right. c, Water in center. d, White pagoda at top right.
No. 3109 — Details from the Tale of Genji, $2 (size: 84x28mm): a, Yugao Chapter. b, Suetsumuhana Chapter. c, Wakamurasaki Chapter. d, Momiji-no-ga Chapter.
No. 3110, $6, Pomegranates and a Small Bird, by Onishi Keisai. No. 3111, $6, Bodhisattva from the Lotus Sutra, vert.

**2001, May 1** Litho. **Perf. 14**
3102-3107 A487 Set of 6 6.75 6.75
**Sheets of 4, #a-d**
3108-3109 A488 Set of 2 12.00 12.00
**Souvenir Sheets**
3110-3111 A488 Set of 2 9.00 9.00

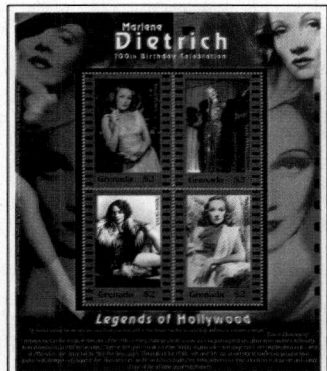

Marlene Dietrich — A489

No. 3112: a, With cigarette. b, Behind microphone. c, Seated, showing legs. d, Seated.

**2001, May 15** **Perf. 13¾**
3112 A489 $2 Sheet of 4, #a-d 6.00 6.00

Queen Victoria (1819-1901) — A490

No. 3113: a, In white, as young girl. b, Wearing crown as young woman. c, Wearing crown as old woman.
$6, On throne.

**2001, May 15** **Perf. 14**
3113 A490 $3 Sheet of 3, #a-c 6.75 6.75
**Souvenir Sheet**
3114 A490 $6 multi 4.50 4.50

Queen Elizabeth II, 75th Birthday — A491

No. 3115: a, Straw hat. b, Red hat. c, Flowered hat. d, Blue hat.
$6, Blue hat with brim.

**2001, May 15** **Perf. 14**
3115 A491 $2 Sheet of 4, #a-d 6.00 6.00
**Souvenir Sheet**
**Perf. 13¾**
3116 A491 $6 multi 4.50 4.50
No. 3116 contains one 38x51mm stamp.

UN Women's Human Rights Campaign — A492

Designs: 90c, Woman, bird, torch. $1, Woman.

**2001, May 15** Litho. **Perf. 14**
3117-3118 A492 Set of 2 1.40 1.40

Mao Zedong (1893-1976) — A493

No. 3119 — background colors: a, Deep purple. b, Pinkish gray. c, Mottled red violet. $6, Mao with cap.

**2001, May 15** **Perf. 13¾**
3119 A493 $2 Sheet of 3, #a-c 4.50 4.50
**Souvenir Sheet**
3120 A493 $3 multi 2.25 2.25

Giuseppe Verdi (1813-1910), Opera Composer — A494

No. 3121: a, Actor with crown. b, Score from Ernani. c, Verdi. d, La Scala Theater, Milan. $6, Verdi with hat.

**2001, May 15** **Perf. 14**
3121 A494 $2 Sheet of 4, #a-d 6.00 6.00
**Souvenir Sheet**
3122 A494 $6 multi 4.50 4.50

Toulouse-Lautrec Paintings — A495

No. 3123: a, Alone. b, Two Half-naked Women. c, The Toilette. d, Justine Dieuhl. $6, Mademoiselle Dihau at the Piano.

**2001, May 15** **Perf. 13¾**
3123 A495 $2 Sheet of 4, #a-d 6.00 6.00
**Souvenir Sheet**
3124 A495 $6 multi 4.50 4.50

A496

Ships — A497

Designs: 45c, Phoenician trading ship. 75c, Portuguese caravel. 90c, Marblehead schooner. No. 3128, Mala pansi. $1.50, US corvette. $2, Racing schooner.

No. 3131, $1: a, English carrack. b, Mediterranean carrack. c, Spanish galleon. d, Elizabeth Grumster. e, British East Indiaman. f, Clipper ship. g, British gunship. h, British flagship. i, English hoy.

No. 3132, $1: a, English cog. b, Roman merchantman. c, Greek war galley. d, Greek merchantman. e, Norse Oseberg ship. f, Egyptian sailboat. g, Egyptian oared ship. h, 16th cent. galleass. i, Norman sailing ship.

No. 3133, $1: a, Gloucester fishing schooner. b, Racing sloop. c, Chinese junk. d, Sambuk. e, Baltimore clipper schooner. f, Schooner yacht. g, US Clipper ship. h, US frigate. i Steam naval packet.

No. 3134, $6, Gulf Streamer. No. 3135, $6, Suhaili.

Illustration A497 reduced.

**2001, June 18**      **Perf. 14**
3125-3130 A496   Set of 6   5.00   5.00
      **Sheets of 9, #a-i**
3131-3133 A496   Set of 3   21.00 21.00
      **Miniature Sheets**
3134-3135 A497   Set of 2   9.00   9.00

Belgica 2001 Intl. Stamp Exhibition, Brussels (Nos. 3131-3133).

A498

Flowers
A499

Designs: 25c, Brassavola nodosa. No. 3137, $1, Allamanda cathartica. No. 3138, $2, Aspasia epidendroides. $3, Oncidium splendidum.

35c, Flor de San Miguel. 75c, Red frangipani. No. 3142, $1, Paper flower. No. 3143, $2, Flor de muerto.

No. 3144, $1.50: a, Candlebush. b, Flamingo flower. c, Bush morning glory. d, Laelia anceps. e, Galeandra baueri. f, Chinese hibiscus.

No. 3145, $1.50: a, Red ginger. b, Bird of paradise. c, Psychlis atropurpurea. d, Cattleya velutina. e, Caularthron bicornutum. f, Cattleya warneri.

No. 3146, $1.50, vert.: a, Mandevilla. b, Tithonia rotundifolia. c, June rose. d, Columnea argentea. e, Chameleon plant. f, Protlandia albiflora.

No. 3147, $1.50, vert.: a, Wild chestnut. b, Jatropha integerrima. c, Fern tree. d, Geiger tree. e, Golden trumpet. f, Saman.

No. 3148, $6, Ipomoea learii, horiz. No. 3149, $6, Anthurium scherzerianum, horiz.

No. 3150, $6, Ladies eardrops. No. 3151, $6, Heliconia psittacorum, vert.

---

**2001**
3136-3139 A498   Set of 4   6.25   6.25
3140-3143 A499   Set of 4   4.75   4.75
      **Sheets of 6, #a-f**
3144-3145 A498   Set of 2   15.00 15.00
3146-3147 A499   Set of 2   15.00 15.00
      **Souvenir Sheets**
3148-3149 A498   Set of 2   11.00 11.00
3150-3151 A499   Set of 2   11.00 11.00

Kane — A500

No. 3152 — Kane: a, In air, above ring ropes. b, On one knee. c, In air. d, With red background. e, With gradiated gray and yellow background. f, Holding up opponent with both hands. g, With spotlight background. h, Holding up shirtless opponent. i, Holding up opponent with one hand.

No. 3153, $5, With red background, diff. No. 3154, $5, With opponent.

**2001**          **Perf. 13¾**
3152 A500 $1 Sheet of 9, #a-i   6.75   6.75
      **Souvenir Sheets**
3153-3154 A500   Set of 2   7.50   7.50

The Three Stooges — A501

No. 3155, $1: a, Larry, Moe, two cowboys. b, Moe and Shemp with hats, Larry. c, Shemp and Larry in drag, Moe with mustache. d, Moe with gun, Larry, Shemp, woman. e, Larry, Moe, Shemp with certificate. f, Shemp, Moe. g, Larry, picture. h, Moe, picture. i, Shemp.

No. 3156, $1: a, Larry, Curly, Moe with tool. b, Joe DeRita eating hay, horse, Larry, Moe. c, Shemp, Larry with flowers, Moe. d, Moe, Shemp, Larry, reading paper. e, Larry, Moe, Shemp with pots. f, Moe, Shemp, Larry with money. g, Shemp with knight. h, Joe DeRita, horse, Moe, Larry. i, Larry with knight.

No. 3157, $5, Larry, Moe, Shemp, woman from movie poster. No. 3158, $5, Shemp pulling Moe's arm. No. 3159, $5, Joe DeRita and Larry. No. 3160, $5, Larry and Joe DeRita, jet engine. No. 3161, $5, Moe, Larry holding woman's hand. No. 3162, $5, Moe listening to jet engine, horiz. No. 3163, $5, Larry, Moe, Shemp and cowboy, horiz. No. 3164, $5, Shemp behind bar, cowboys fighting Larry and Moe, horiz. No. 3165, $5, Curly, Moe, Larry

---

and propeller, horiz. No. 3166, $5, Moe, Larry, woman with drink, horiz. No. 3167, $6, Moe, Larry with knight, horiz. No. 3168, $6, Curly in wringer, Moe, horiz.

**2001**
      **Sheets of 9, #a-i**
3155-3156 A501   Set of 2   13.50 13.50
      **Souvenir Sheets**
3157-3168 A501   Set of 12   47.50 47.50

Lighthouses
A502

Designs: 25c, Montauk Point, NY. 50c, Alcatraz, CA. $1, Barnegat, NJ. $2, St. Augustine, FL.

No. 3173, $1.50: a, Admiralty Head, WA. b, Hooper's Strait, MD. c, Hunting Island, SC. d, Key West Lighthouse Museum, FL. e, Old Point Loma, CA. f, Old Mackinac Moint, MI.

No. 3174, $1.50: a, Point Amour, Canada. b, Inubo-Saki, Japan. c, Belle-Ile. France. d, Faerder, Norway. e, Cape Agulhas, South Africa. f, Minicoy, India.

No. 3175, $1.50: a, Keri, Estonia. b, Anholt, Denmark. c, Porer, Croatia. d, Laotieshan, China. e, Sapientza Methoni, Greece. f, Arkona, Germany.

No. 3176, $6, Boston, MA. No. 3177, $6, Pellworm, Germany. No. 3178, $6, Kvitsoy, Norway. No. 3179, Mahota Pagoda, China.

**2001, Aug. 27**    **Litho.**    **Perf. 14**
3169-3172 A502   Set of 4   2.75   2.75
      **Sheets of 6, #a-f**
3173-3175 A502   Set of 3   20.00 20.00
      **Souvenir Sheets**
3176-3179 A502   Set of 4   18.00 18.00

Marine
Mammals
A503

Designs: 25c, Commerson's dolphin. 50c, Pacific white-sided dolphin. $2, Northern bottlenosed whale. $3, Baird's beaked whale.

No. 3184, $1.50: a, Risso's dolphin. b, Fraser's dolphin. c, Dall's porpoise. d, Right whale. e, Gray whale. f, Minke whale.

No. 3185, $1.50: a, Common dolphin. b, Antillean beaked whale. c, Killer whale. d, Bryde's whale. e, Cuvier's beaked whale. f, Sei whale.

No. 3186, $1.50: a, Harbor porpoise. b, Beluga. c, White-beaked dolphin. d, Narwhal. e, Bowhead whale. f, Fin whale.

No. 3187, $6, Sperm whale. No. 3188, $6, Blue whale. No. 3189, $6, Southern right whale. No. 3190, $6, Humpback whale.

**2001, Sept. 10**
3180-3183 A503   Set of 4   4.25   4.25
      **Sheets of 6, #a-f**
3184-3186 A503   Set of 3   20.00 20.00
      **Souvenir Sheets**
3187-3190 A503   Set of 4   18.00 18.00

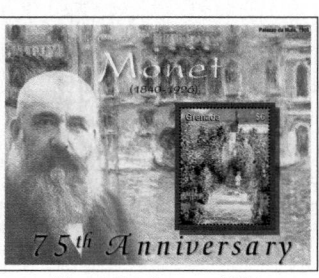

Monet Paintings — A504

No. 3191, horiz.: a, Boats in Winter Quarters, Etretat. b, Regatta at Sainte Adresse. c, The Bridge at Bougival. d, The Beach at Sainte Adresse.

$6, Monet's Garden at Vétheuil.

---

**2001, May 15**   **Litho.**   **Perf. 13¾**
3191 A504 $2 Sheet of 4, #a-d   6.00 6.00
      **Souvenir Sheet**
3192 A504 $6 multi   4.50 4.50

2002 World Cup Soccer
Championships, Japan and
Korea — A505

No. 3193, $1.50: a, Poster, 1950. b, West German championship team, 1954. c, Just Fontaine, 1958. d, Garrincha, Brazil, 1962. e, Bobby Moore, England, 1966. f, Pelé, Brazil, 1970.

No. 3194, $1.50: a, Osvaldo Ardiles, Argentina, 1978. b, Lakhdar Belloumi, Algeria, 1982. c, Diego Maradona, Argentina, 1986. d, Matthäus and Völler, West Germany, 1990. e, Seo Jung Won, South Korea, 1994. f, Ronaldo, Brazil, 1998.

No. 3195, $6, Face from Jules Rimet trophy. No. 3196, $6, Face and globe from World Cup trophy.

**2001, Nov. 29**     **Perf. 13¾x14¼**
      **Sheets of 6, #a-f**
3193-3194 A505   Set of 2   13.50 13.50
      **Souvenir Sheet**
3195-3196 A505   Set of 2   9.00   9.00

Christmas
A506

Santa Claus and: 15c, House, Christmas tree. 50c, Trees, snowman. $1, Tree, ice skates. $4, Children.

$6, Santa eating cookie.

**2001, Dec. 3**      **Perf. 14**
3197-3200 A506   Set of 4   4.25 4.25
      **Souvneir Sheet**
3201 A506 $6 multi   4.50 4.50

A507

Nobel Prizes, Cent. — A508

1901 Laureates: 75c, Emil A. von Behring, Medicine. 90c, Wilhelm C. Röntgen, Physics. $1, Jacobus H. van't Hoff, Chemistry. No. 3205, $1.50, Frederic Passy, Peace. $2, Jean-Henri Dunant, Peace. $3, René Sully-Prudhomme, Literature.

No. 3208, horiz. — Albert Einstein, 1921 Physics laureate, with: a, Dark hair, black suit. b, Pipe. c, Gray suit. d, Pink sweater. e, Gray hair, black suit. f, Blue sweater.
$6, Einstein wearing hat.

**2001, Dec. 13**
| | | | | |
|---|---|---|---|---|
| 3202-3207 | A507 | Set of 6 | 7.00 | 7.00 |
| 3208 | A508 | $1.50 Sheet of 6, #a-f | 6.75 | 6.75 |

**Souvenir Sheet**

| | | | | |
|---|---|---|---|---|
| 3209 | A508 | $6 multi | 4.50 | 4.50 |

Princess Diana (1961-97) — A509

No. 3210: a, Blue gown. b. White gown. c, Red gown.
$6, With pink curtain.

**2001, Dec. 13**
| | | | | |
|---|---|---|---|---|
| 3210 | A509 | $1.50 Sheet, 2 each #a-c | 6.75 | 6.75 |

**Souvenir Sheet**

| | | | | |
|---|---|---|---|---|
| 3211 | A509 | $6 multi | 4.50 | 4.50 |

**Queen Mother Type of 1999**

No. 3212: a, Queen Mother, Prince Charles, 1948. b, Queen Mother, 1970. c, Queen Mother in Australia, 1958. d, Queen Mother. $6, Queen Mother, 1953.

**2001, Dec. 13**      *Perf. 14*
**Yellow Orange Frames**
| | | | | |
|---|---|---|---|---|
| 3212 | A440 | $2 Sheet of 4, #a-d, + label | 6.00 | 6.00 |

**Souvenir Sheet**    *Perf. 13¾*

| | | | | |
|---|---|---|---|---|
| 3213 | A440 | $6 multi | 4.50 | 4.50 |

Queen Mother's 101st birthday. No. 3213 contains one 38x50mm stamp with a redder backdrop than that found on No. 2881. Sheet margins of Nos. 3212-3213 lack embossing and gold arms found on Nos. 2880-2881.

New Year 2002 (Year of the Horse) — A510

Ceramic horses of T'ang dynasty — No. 3214: a, Brown horse with long, tan mane. b, Blue horse with pink hooves. c, Black horse with gray mane. d, Tan horse with round ornaments.
$4, Brown horse with gray and green saddle.

**2001, Dec. 17**      *Perf. 13¾*
| | | | | |
|---|---|---|---|---|
| 3214 | A510 | $1.50 Sheet of 4, #a-d | 4.50 | 4.50 |

**Souvenir Sheet**

| | | | | |
|---|---|---|---|---|
| 3215 | A510 | $4 multi | 3.00 | 3.00 |

A511

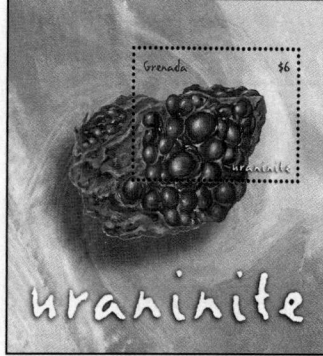

Gemstones and Minerals — A512

Monthly gemstones — No. 3216, $1.50: a, Garnet (January). b, Amethyst (February). c, Aquamarine (March). d, Diamond (April). e, Emerald (May). f, Pearl (June).
No. 3217, $1.50: a, Ruby (July). b, Sardonyx (August). c, Sapphire (September). d, Opal (October). e, Topaz (November). f, Turquoise (December).
Gemstones in mineral form — No. 3218: a, Ruby. b, Diamond. c, Sapphire. d, Opal. e, Turquoise. f, Jade.
No. 3219, $6, Uraninite. No. 3220, $6, Calcite. No. 3221, $6, Quartz, vert.

**2001, Dec. 31**      *Perf. 14*
**Sheets of 6, #a-f**
| | | | | |
|---|---|---|---|---|
| 3216-3217 | A511 | Set of 2 | 14.50 | 14.50 |
| 3218 | A512 | $1.50 Sheet of 6, #a-f | 7.50 | 7.50 |

**Souvenir Sheets**

| | | | | |
|---|---|---|---|---|
| 3219-3221 | A512 | Set of 3 | 14.50 | 14.50 |

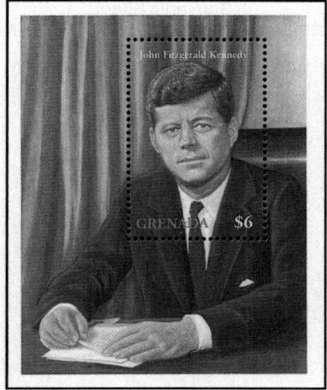

US Presidents — A513

No. 3222, $1.50 — John F. Kennedy and: a, Field. b, Flag, building, microphone. c, Airplane.
No. 3223, $1.50 — Ronald Reagan: a, In uniform with binoculars. b, With red tie. c, With flag.
No. 3224, $6, Kennedy. No. 3225, $6, Reagan.

**2001, Dec. 31**
**Sheets, 2 each #a-c**
| | | | | |
|---|---|---|---|---|
| 3222-3223 | A513 | Set of 2 | 13.50 | 13.50 |

**Souvenir Sheets**

| | | | | |
|---|---|---|---|---|
| 3224-3225 | A513 | Set of 2 | 9.00 | 9.00 |

Souvenir Sheets

I Love Lucy — A514

Designs: No. 3226, $6, Ethel watching Lucy and Desi dance. No. 3227, $6, Desi, Lucy, Fred and Ethel near door. No. 3228, $6, Desi holding Lucy. No. 3229, $6, Lucy in plaid shirt.

**2001**      *Perf. 13¾*
| | | | | |
|---|---|---|---|---|
| 3226-3229 | A514 | Set of 4 | 18.00 | 18.00 |

English Soccer Teams — A515

No. 3230, $1.50 — Arsenal: a, Inside of Highbury Stadium. b, Players celebrate 1994 European Cup and Winner's Cup. c, Players celebrate 1998 premiership. d, East stands, Highbury Stadium. e, Locker rooms. f, Four players with trophies, 1998.
No. 3231, $1.50 — Aston Villa: a, Sign on Villa Park. b, Fans watching night game. c, Empty stadium, field at right. d, Empty stadium, field at left. e, Holte End of stadium. f, Fans in stands.
No. 3232, $1.50 — Bolton Wanderers: a, Empty Reebok Stadium. b, Players celebrating 2001 Division 1 playoff win. c, Promotion to Premier League. d, Fans celebrate. e, Players, coaches with trophy. f, Game played in Reebok Stadium.
No. 3233, $1.50 — Everton: a, 2001-02 team. b, Re-signing of Duncan Ferguson. c, Statue of Wiliam Ralph "Dixie" Dean. d, Fans. e, Goodison Park. f, 1969-70 league championship team.
No. 3234, $1.50 — Ipswich Town: a, Players holding banner and trophy after 2000 Division 1 playoff final. b, 2001-02 team. c, Manager George Burley and Chairman David Sheepshanks. d, Pablo Counago fights for ball. e, Captain Matt Holland. f, George Burley receives Manager of the Year award.
No. 3235, $1.50 — Liverpool: a, Anfield. b, 2000-01 Worthington Cup winners. c, 2000-01 FA Cup winners. d, Fans. e, 2000-01 UEFA Cup winners. f, Treble Cup parade.
No. 3236, $1.50 — Manchester United: a, Legends Meredith, Law and Charlton. b, Three 1998-99 trophies. c, Views of Old Trafford, 1948, 1956. d, Recent views of Old Trafford. e, Third premiership in three years, 2000-01. f, Heroes, Best, Robson and Beckham.
No. 3237, $1.50 — Rangers: a, View of Ibrox Stadium from street. b, 1972 European Cup and Winner's Cup team. c, Scottish FA Cup, Scottish Premier League Trophy. d, Aerial view of Ibrox Stadium. e, Fans in stadium. f, Nine consecutive Scottish League wins.

**2001, Sept. 12**    *Litho.*    *Perf. 13¼*
**Sheets of 6, #a-f**
| | | | | |
|---|---|---|---|---|
| 3230-3237 | A515 | Set of 8 | 55.00 | 55.00 |

Reign of Queen Elizabeth II, 50th Anniv. — A516

No. 3238: a, With Prince Philip. b, Wearing flowered hat. c, Wearing tiara. d, Wearing gray coat with white collar.
$6, Wearing uniform.

**2002, Feb. 6**      *Perf. 14½*
| | | | | |
|---|---|---|---|---|
| 3238 | A516 | $2 Sheet of 4, #a-d | 6.00 | 6.00 |

**Souvenir Sheet**

| | | | | |
|---|---|---|---|---|
| 3239 | A516 | $6 multi | 4.50 | 4.50 |

United We Stand — A517

**2002, Feb.**      *Perf. 13¾x13½*
| | | | | |
|---|---|---|---|---|
| 3240 | A517 | $2 multi | 1.50 | 1.50 |

Issued in sheets of 4.

Dale Earnhardt, Race Car Driver — A518

Years of Winston Cup Championships: No. 3241, $2, 1980. No. 3242, $2, 1986. No. 3243, $2, 1987. No. 3244, $2, 1990. No. 3245, $2, 1991. No. 3246, $2, 1993. No. 3247, $2, 1994.

**2002, Mar. 4**    *Litho.*    *Perf. 14x13¾*
| | | | | |
|---|---|---|---|---|
| 3241-3247 | A518 | Set of 7 | 12.00 | 12.00 |

Mickey Mouse — A519

No. 3249 — Scenes from: a, The Nifty Nineties, 1941. b, Magician Mickey, 1937. c, Steamboat Willie, 1928. d, Fantasia, 1940. e, Mickey Mouse Club, 1955. f, Cactus Kid, 1930. g, The Prince and the Pauper, 1990. h, Brave Little Tailor, 1938. i, Canine Caddy, 1941.

**2002, Apr. 24**     **Perf. 13¾**
3248 A519 $1 shown     .90   .90
3249 A519 $1 Sheet of 9, #a-i    8.75   8.75
   No. 3248 was printed in sheets of nine.

American Civil War Naval
History — A520

   No. 3250, $1: a, CSS Teaser. b, US gun-boats on the James River. c, USS Tyler. d, USS Maratanza. e, USS Metacomet. f, USS Rattler.
   No. 3251, $1.25: a, CSS Tennessee. b, USS Hartford. c, USS Chickasaw. d, USS Ossipee. e, Battle of Mobile Bay. f, USS Chickasaw at Mobile Bay.
   No. 3252, $1.50: a, CSS H.L. Hunley. b, USS Cumberland. c, CSS Old Dominion. d, USS Housatonic. e, USS Hartford. f, USS Essex.
   No. 3253, $1.50: a, CSS Alabama. b, USS Kearsarge and CSS Alabama. c, USS Hatteras. d, CSS Alabama and decoy. e, CSS Sumter. f, USS Kearsarge.
   No. 3254, $6, USS Monitor. No. 3255, $6, CSS Florida. No. 3256, $6, CSS Tennessee. No. 3257, $6, Capt. Raphael Semmes aboard CSS Alabama.

**2002, Apr. 8**   **Litho.**   **Perf. 13¼x13½**
**Sheets of 6, #a-f**
3250-3253 A520   Set of 4    28.00   28.00
**Souvenir Sheets**
3254-3257 A520   Set of 4    22.00   22.00

Chiune Sugihara,
Japanese Diplomat
Who Saved Jews
in World War
II — A521

**2002, July 1**     **Perf. 13½x13¾**
3258 A521 $2 multi     1.50   1.50
   Printed in sheets of 4.

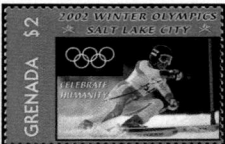

2002
Winter
Olympics,
Salt Lake
City
A522

   Skier with: No. 3259, $2, Red skis. No. 3260, $2, Yellow skis.

**2002, July 1**     **Perf. 13¼x13½**
3259-3260 A522   Set of 2    3.00   3.00
   **a.** Souvenir sheet, #3259-3260   3.00   3.00

Intl. Year of Mountains — A523

   No. 3261: a, Mt. Mawensi, Kenya. b, Mt. Stanley, Uganda. c, Mt. Taweche, Nepal. d, Mt. San Exupery, Argentina.
$6, Mt. Aso, Japan.

**2002, July 1**
3261 A523 $2 Sheet of 4, #a-d   6.00   6.00
**Souvenir Sheet**
3262 A523 $6 multi    4.50   4.50

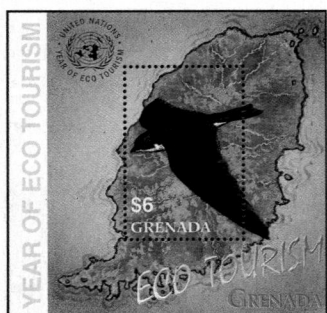

Intl. Year of Ecotourism — A524

   No. 3263, horiz.: a, Tower and pennants. b, Bird. c, Flower, vacationer on chair. d, Diver, fish. e, Fish. f, Sailboats.
$6, Map of Grenada, bird.

**2002, July 1**     **Perf. 13¼x13½**
3263 A524 $1 Sheet of 6, #a-d   4.50   4.50
**Souvenir Sheet**
**Perf. 13½x13¼**
3264 A524 $6 multi    4.50   4.50
   No. 3263 was overprinted in sheet margin "Hurricane Relief 2004" in 2005.

20th World Scout Jamboree,
Thailand — A525

   No. 3265, horiz.: a, Scout in canoe with oar out of water. b, Scout in canoe with oar in water. c, Bugler. d, Scout making Scout sign.
$6, Scout saluting.

**2002, July 1**     **Perf. 13¼x13½**
3265 A525 $2 Sheet of 4, #a-d   7.50   7.50
**Souvenir Sheet**
**Perf. 13½x13¼**
3266 A525 $6 multi    5.00   5.00

Model Heidi Klum — A526

   No. 3267: a, Arms up. b, Arms down. c, No arms shown.
Illustration reduced.

**2002, Aug. 16**   Horiz. strip of    **Perf. 14**
3267 A526 $1.50   3, #a-c    3.50   3.50
   Printed in sheets containing two strips.

Elvis Presley
(1935-77)
A527

**2002, Aug. 26**     **Perf. 13½x13¾**
3268 A527 $1 multi     .75   .75
   Printed in sheets of 9.

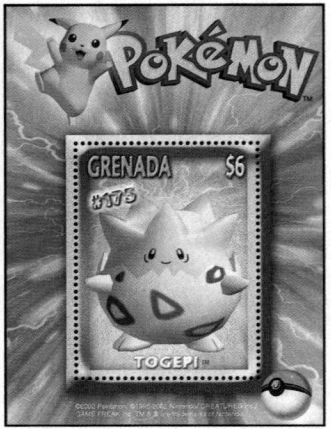

Pokémon — A528

   No. 3269: a, Mareep. b, Sunkern. c, Teddiursa. d, Swinub. e, Murkrow. f, Snubbull.
$6, Togepi.

**2002, Aug. 26**     **Perf. 13¾**
3269 A528 $1.50 Sheet of 6, #a-f 6.75 6.75
**Souvenir Sheet**
3270 A528   $6 multi    4.50   4.50

A529

A530

Teddy Bears, Cent. — A531

   No. 3271: a, 25c, Bear with red hat, lace collar, cheese wheels. b, $1.25, Bear with black cap. c, $3, Bear with wooden shoes. d, $5, Bear with red hat and ribbon.
   No. 3272: a, Army bear. b, Navy bear. c, Air Force bear. d, Marines bear.
   No. 3273: a, Basketball bear. b, Martial arts bear. c, Golf bear. d, Baseball bear.

**2002, Aug. 26**     **Perf. 14**
3271 A529   Sheet of 4, #a-d   7.25   7.25
**Perf. 14¼**
3272 A530 $2 Sheet of 4, #a-d   6.00   6.00
3273 A531 $2 Sheet of 4, #a-d   6.00   6.00

Dutch Nobel Prize Winners — A532

Dutch Lighthouses — A533

Traditional Dutch Women's Costumes — A534

No. 3274: a, Jacobus H. van't Hoff, Chemistry, 1901. b, Nobel Peace medal. c, Pieter Zeeman, Physics, 1902. d, Johannes D. van der Waals, Physics, 1910. e, Tobias M. C. Asser, Peace, 1911. f, Heike Kammerlingh-Onnes, Physics, 1913.

No. 3275: a, Schiermonnikoog. b, Texel. c, Egmond. d, Scheveningen. e, Schouwen. f, Hellevoetsluis.

No. 3276: a, Zeeland (woman with red necklace, patterned dress). b, Noord-Brabant (woman with black shawl). c, Noord-Holland (woman with flowered neckpiece).

**2002, Aug. 29**     *Perf. 13½x13¼*
3274 A532 $1.50 Sheet of 6, #a-f   6.75 6.75
3275 A533 $1.50 Sheet of 6, #a-f   6.75 6.75

*Perf. 13¼*
3276 A534 $3 Sheet of 3, #a-c   6.75 6.75

Amphilex 2002 Intl. Stamp Exhibition, Amsterdam.

Shirley Temple — A535

Scenes from "Our Little Girl" — No. 3277, horiz.: a, With man. b, With man and woman. c, With dog and man. d, With woman and two men. e, On seesaw with dog. f, With dog.

No. 3278: a, With woman. b, with man and clown. c, Kneeling beside chair. d, With man and woman.
$6, In pink dress.

**2002, Sept. 3**     *Perf. 14¼*
3277 A535 $1.50 Sheet of 6, #a-f   6.75 6.75
3278 A535 $2 Sheet of 4, #a-d   6.00 6.00

**Souvenir Sheet**
3279 A535 $6 multi   4.50 4.50

Terrorist Attack on World Trade Center, 1st Anniv. — A536

**2002, Sept. 11**     *Perf. 13¾*
3280 A536 $6 multi   4.50 4.50

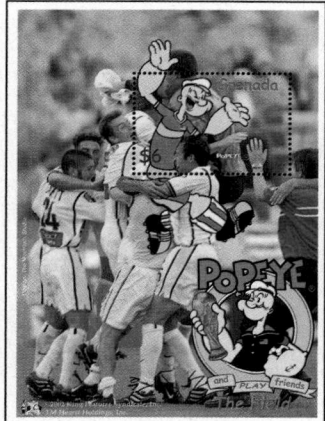

Popeye — A537

No. 3281, vert.: a, Popeye in Florence, Italy. b, Popeye and Brutus in Paris, France. c, Popeye in Athens, Greece. d, Popeye and Olive Oyl in Venice, Italy. e, Popeye in London, England. f, Popeye in Norway.

No. 3282, vert. — At soccer match: a, Swee'Pea. b, Jeep. c, Popeye. d, Brutus.

No. 3283, $6, Popeye playing soccer. No. 3284, $6, Brutus playing soccer. No. 3285, $6, Popeye at Leaning Tower of Pisa, vert.

*Perf. 14¼ (#3281, 3285), 14*
**2002, Sept. 23**
3281 A537 $1.50 Sheet of 6, #a-f   6.75 6.75
3282 A537 $2 Sheet of 4, #a-d   6.00 6.00

**Souvenir Sheets**
3283-3285 A537 Set of 3   13.50 13.50

No. 3218 contains six 38x50mm stamps; No. 3285 contains one 50x75mm stamp.

**English Soccer Teams Type of 2001**
No. 3286, $1.50 — Tottenham Hotspur: a, Fans watching match in White Hart Lane Stadium. b, Sheringham and Anderton in action against Fulham. c, Poyet scoring against Liverpool. d, Tottenham Hotspur wins UEFA Cup, 1972. e, Celebrations after win against Chelsea. f, Fans in stadium, team insignia.

No. 3287, $1.50 — Manchester City: a, Maine Road Stadium from stands. b, Fans celebrate becoming Division One champions. c, Manager Kevin Keegan and trophy. d, Team with trophy. e, Players wearing medals, with trophy. f, Field level view of Maine Road Stadium.

No. 3288, $1.50 — Norwich City: a, Match at the Nest. b, Promotion to the Top Flight, 1971-72. c, Milk Cup win, 1985. d, Carrow Road Stadium. e, Win against Bayern Munich, 1993. f, Action from 1958-59 Cup run.

No. 3289, $1.50 — Arsenal, Double Winners: a, Tony Adams and Patrick Vieira hold FA Cup. b, Team wearing tan shirts, holding championship banners. c, Team without banners, at Premiership trophy presentation. d, Photo of 2001-02 Premiership team, standing and wearing red shirts. e, Four players celebrate winning goal against Chelsea. f, Manager Arsene Wenger and Tony Adams at Double Winners Parade.

No. 3290, $1.50 — Arsenal, Premiership Winners: a, Inside of Highbury Stadium, team emblem and name in red panels. b, Celebrations after Gilberto scores winning goal. c, Team with FA Community Shield sign. d, Team photo, empty stands. e, Gilberto with FA Community Shield. f, Highbury Stadium with fans, team emblem.

No. 3291, $1.50 — Manchester United: a, David Beckham after free kick. b, Team photo,

empty stands. c, Aerial view of Old Trafford Stadium. d, Celebration after Ole Gunnar Solskjaer's 100th goal for Manchester United. e, Fans at Old Trafford Stadium. f, North stand of Old Trafford Stadium.

No. 3292, $1.50 — Liverpool: a, Anfield's Centenary stand, as seen from Main stand. b, 2002-03 team photo. c, Gerard Houllier and Phil Thompson. d, Milan Baros celebrates goal. e, Vladimir Smicer congratulating Danny Murphy. f, The Kop, as seen from Anfield Road end.

No. 3293, $1.50 — Celtic: a, Interior of Celtic Park. b, Martin O'Neill with SPL Trophy. c, Henrik Larsson celebrating goal. d, 2002-03 team photo. e, Players celebrating a goal. f, Exterior of Celtic Park.

No. 3294, $1.50 — Chelsea: a, Night match at Stamford Bridge Stadium. b, Team with 1998 Cup Winners' Cup Final trophy. c, Fans in stadium. d, Sign for the Shed End. e, Field level view of Stamford Bridge Stadium. f, Players celebrating 2000 FA Cup victory.

**2002**     *Perf. 14x13¾*
**Sheets of 6, #a-f**
3286-3294 A515 Set of 9   60.00 60.00
Issued: Nos. 3286-3289, 9/23; Nos. 3290-3294, 11/14.

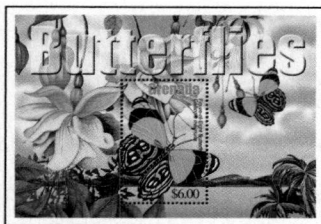

Butterflies, Insects, Mushrooms and Whales — A538

No. 3295, $1.50 — Butterflies: a, Common morpho. b, Blue night. c, Small flambeau. d, Grecian shoemaker. e, Orange-barred sulphur. f, Cramer's mesene.

No. 3296, $1.50 — Insects: a, Honeybees. b, Dragonfly. c, Milkweed bug. d, Bumblebee. e, Migratory grasshopper. f, Monarch caterpillar.

No. 3297, $1.50 — Mushrooms: a, Boletus crocipodius. b, King bolete. c, Velvet shank. d, Death cap. e, Golden cavalier. f, Fly agaric.

No. 3298, $1.50 — Whales: a, Blue. b, Pygmy sperm. c, Humpback. d, Killer. e, Bowhead. f, Gray.

No. 3299, $6, Figure-of-eight butterfly. No. 3300, $6, Hercules beetle. No. 3301, $6, Sharp-scaled parasol mushroom. No. 3302, $6, Blue whale, horiz.

**2002, Oct. 21**     *Perf. 14*
**Sheets of 6, #a-f**
3295-3298 A538 Set of 4   27.50 27.50
**Souvenir Sheets**
3299-3302 A538 Set of 4   18.00 18.00

Sir Norman Wisdom, British Comedian A539

**2002, Nov. 3**     *Perf. 13¾*
3303 A539 $1.50 multi   1.10 1.10
Printed in sheets of 6.

Amerigo Vespucci (1454-1512), Explorer — A540

No. 3304, $3: a, Map of South America, ship. b, Compass rose, ship. c, Map of Europe and Africa.

No. 3305, $3, horiz.: a, Sextant, map of northern South America. b, Vespucci, map of central South America. c, Ship, map of southern South America.

No. 3306, $6, Compass rose. No. 3307, $6, Globe.

**2002, Nov. 4**     *Perf. 13¾*
**Sheets of 3, #a-c**
3304-3305 A540 Set of 2   13.50 13.50
**Souvenir Sheets**
*Perf. 14*
3306-3307 A540 Set of 2   9.00 9.00

No. 3304 contains three 38x50mm stamps; No. 3305 contains three 50x38mm stamps.

Christmas A541

Cimabue paintings: 15c, Madonna and Child, Four Angels and St. Francis, entire. 25c, Madonna and Child and Two Angels, vert. 50c, Madonna Enthroned, detail, vert. $1, Madonna Enthroned, entire, vert. $4, Madonna and Child, Four Angels and St. Francis, detail, vert. $6, Nativity by Perugino, vert.

**2002, Nov. 4**     *Perf. 14*
3308-3312 A541 Set of 5   4.50 4.50
**Souvenir Sheet**
3313 A541 $6 multi   4.50 4.50

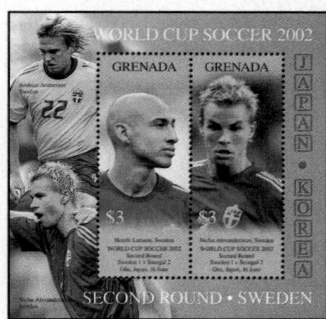

Second Round Matches of 2002 World Cup Soccer Championships, Japan and Korea — A542

No. 3314, $1.50 — Sweden vs. Senegal: a, Johan Mjalby. b, Magnus Hedman. c, Fredrik Ljungberg. d, Khalilou Fadiga. e, El Hadji Diouf. f, Papa Bouba Diop.

No. 3315, $1.50 — Brazil vs. Belgium: a, Roberto Carlos. b, Juninho Paulista. c, Ronaldinho. d, Johan Walem. e, Marc Wilmots. f, Bart Goor.

No. 3316, $3 — Swedish players: a, Henrik Larsson. b, Niclas Alexandersson.

No. 3317, $3 — Senegal players: a, Fadiga. b, Coach Bruno Metsu.

No. 3318, $3 — Brazil players: a, Coach Luiz Felipe Scolari. b, Ronaldo.

No. 3319, $3 — Belgium players: a, Wesley Sonck. b, Coach Robert Waseige.

## 2002, Nov. 18 — Perf. 13¼

**Sheets of 6, #a-f**
3314-3315 A542 Set of 2   13.50 13.50

**Souvenir Sheets of 2, #a-b**
3316-3319 A542 Set of 4   18.00 18.00

**Souvenir Sheet**

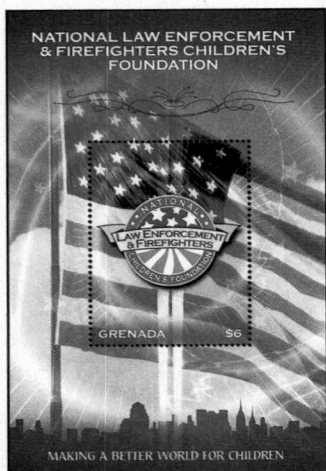

United States Natl. Law Enforcement and Firefighters Children's Foundation — A543

**2002, Nov. 28 — Perf. 14¼**
3320 A543 $6 multi   4.50 4.50

Pres. John F. Kennedy (1917-63) — A544

No. 3321, horiz.: a, Meeting with Cabinet. b, Signing bill into law. c, Meeting civil rights leaders. d, With Astronaut John Glenn. e, On campaign trail. f, Arrival in Dallas, Nov. 22, 1963.
$6, At microphone.

**2002, Dec. 4 — Perf. 14**
3321 A544 $1.50 Sheet of 6, #a-f   6.75 6.75

**Souvenir Sheet**
3322 A544 $6 multi   4.50 4.50

Intl. Federation of Stamp Dealers Associations, 50th Anniv. — A545

**2002, Dec. 16 — Litho.**
3323 A545 $2 multi   1.50 1.50

---

Princess Diana (1961-97) — A546

No. 3324: a, Wearing bow tie. b, Wearing blue dress. c, Wearing red and white hat. d, Holding flowers.
$6, Wearing earphones and microphone.

**2002 — Perf. 14**
3324 A546 $2 Sheet of 4, #a-d   6.00 6.00

**Souvenir Sheet**
3325 A546 $6 multi   4.50 4.50

**I Love Lucy Type of 2001**
Souvenir Sheets

No. 3326, $6, Lucy standing near fireplace. No. 3327, $6, Lucy and Ethel at desk. No. 3328, $6, Fred and Desi standing. No. 3329, $6, Fred and Desi at desk, horiz.

**2002 — Perf. 13¾**
3326-3329 A514 Set of 4   18.00 18.00

New Year 2003 (Year of the Ram) A547

**2003, Jan. 27 — Perf. 13¾**
3330 A547 $1.25 multi   .95 .95
Printed in sheets of 4.

M-Gears — A548

No. 3331: a, Airplane. b, Vehicle. c, Monster. d, Race car.

**2003, Feb. 16 — Litho. — Perf. 14¼**
3331 A548 $2 Sheet of 4, #a-d   6.00 6.00

---

Astronauts Killed in Space Shuttle Columbia Accident — A549

No. 3332: a, Mission Specialist 1 David M. Brown. b, Commander Rick D. Husband. c, Mission Specialist 4 Laurel Blair Salton Clark. d, Mission Specialist 4 Kalpana Chawla. e, Payload Commander Michael P. Anderson. f, Pilot William C. McCool. g, Payload Specialist 4 Ilan Ramon.

**2003, Apr. 7 — Perf. 13¼**
3332 A549 $1 Sheet of 7, #a-g   6.00 6.00

Paintings of Gustav Klimt (1862-1918) A550

Designs: 15c, Jardin aux Tournesols. 25c, L'allée aux Poulets. 75c, Allée dans le Parc du Schloss Kammer. $1, Portrait of Johanna Staude. $1.25, Portrait of Friederike Maria Beer. $3, Portrait of Mäda Primavesi.
No. 3339: a, La Jeune Fille. b, Les Amies. c, Le Berceau. d, La Vie et la Mort.
$6, Portrait of Margaret Stonborough-Wittgenstein.

**2003, Apr. 28 — Perf. 14¼**
3333-3338 A550 Set of 6   5.00 5.00
3339 A550 $2 Sheet of 4, #a-d   6.00 6.00

**Size: 82x103mm**
**Imperf**
3340 A550 $6 multi   4.50 4.50

Art of Yoshitoshi Taiso (1839-92) A551

Designs: 75c, A Harlot in Repose. $1, A "Shakuni," or Geisha, Who Serves Wine or Sake. $1.25, A "Joro," or Low Ranking Prostitute, Having a Snack. $3, A Geisha Known as a "Geiko," or Entertainer Relaxing.
No. 3345: a, Enjoying a Cool Evening Breeze in a Pleasure Boat. b, A Fukagawa Waitress Carrying a Wooden Table Laden With Food. c, A Spoiled Unmarried Woman Pretending to Be Displeased With an Admirer. d, A Coy Young Girl, Biting Her Sleeve Pretending to Be Embarrassed.
$6, A Geisha About to Board a Party Boat.

**2003, Apr. 28 — Perf. 14¼**
3341-3344 A551 Set of 4   4.50 4.50
3345 A551 $2 Sheet of 4, #a-d   6.00 6.00

**Souvenir Sheet**
3346 A551 $6 multi   4.50 4.50

---

Paintings by Lucas Cranach the Elder (1472-1553) — A552

Details from St. Catherine Altarpiece: 50c, Sts. Dorothy, Agnes and Cunigonde. 75c, St. Margaret, vert. $1.25, St. Barbara, vert. $3, Detail from left wing, vert.
No. 3351 — Painting details: a, Lot and His Daughters. b, David and Bathsheba. c, The Agony in the Garden. d, The Adoration of the Magi.
$6, Detail of Samson and Delilah, vert.

**2003, Apr. 28**
3347-3350 A552 Set of 4   4.25 4.25
3351 A552 $2 Sheet of 4, #a-d   6.00 6.00

**Souvenir Sheet**
3352 A552 $6 multi   4.50 4.50

Teddy Bear A553

**2003, Apr. 29 — Embroidered — Imperf.**
**Self-Adhesive**
3353 A553 $15 multi   11.50 11.50
Issued in sheets of 4.

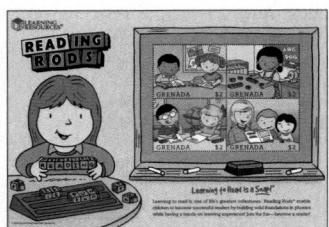

Reading Rods — A554

No. 3354 — Children and: a, Bulletin board. b, Blackboard. c, Globe. d, Teacher.

**2003, May 5 — Litho. — Perf. 13¾**
3354 A554 $2 Sheet of 4, #a-d   6.00 6.00

Tour de France Bicycle Race, Cent. — A555

No. 3355, $2: a, Sylvére Maes, 1939. b, Jean Lazaridés, 1946. c, Jean Robic, 1947. d, Gino Bartali, 1948.
No. 3356, $2: a, Fausto Coppi, 1949. b, Ferdinand Kubler, 1950. c, Hugo Koblet, 1951. d, Coppi, 1952.
No. 3357, $2: a, Roger Walkowiak, 1956. b, Jacques Anquetil, 1957. c, Charly Gaul, 1958. d, Federico Bahamontes, 1959.

No. 3358, $6, Coppi, 1949, diff. No. 3359, $6, Kubler, 1950, diff. No. 3360, $6, Anquetil, 1964.

**2003, June 17**     *Perf. 13¼*
**Sheets of 4, #a-d**
3355-3357 A555   Set of 3    18.00 18.00
**Souvenir Sheets**
3358-3360 A555   Set of 3    13.50 13.50

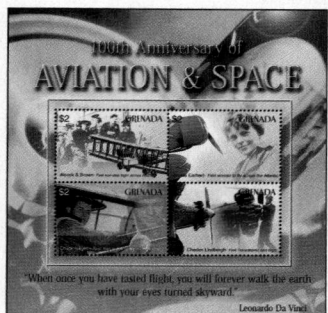

Powered Flight, Cent. — A556

No. 3361, $2: a: First non-stop transatlantic flight by Alcock & Brown. b, Amelia Earhart, first woman to fly across Atlantic. c, Chuck Yeager, first man to break sound barrier. d, Charles Lindbergh, first solo transatlantic flight.
No. 3362, $2: a, Louis Bleriot, first flight across English Channel. b, Johnnie Johnson, ace pilot in World War II. c, Wright Brothers, first powered flight. d, Jacqueline Cochran, first woman to break sound barrier.

**2003, June 24**     *Perf. 13¼x13½*
**Sheets of 4, #a-d**
3361-3362 A556   Set of 2    12.00 12.00

Coronation of Queen Elizabeth II, 50th Anniv. — A557

Designs: No. 3363, $2, Enthroning of the Queen. No. 3364, $2, Duke pays homage to the Queen. No. 3365, $2, Celebration of Holy Communion. No. 3366, $2, Floodlit mall. No. 3367, $2, Queen on balcony. No. 3368, $2, St. Edward's Chair. No. 3369, $2, Official coronation portrait. No. 3370, $2, Queen leaves Abbey.
$6, Queen in coach.

**2003, June 30**     *Perf. 13½x14*
3363-3370 A557   Set of 8    12.00 12.00
**Souvenir Sheet**
3371 A557   $6 multi    4.50 4.50

No. 3371 contains one 38x51mm stamp.

CARICOM, 30th Anniv. — A558

**2003, July 4**     *Perf. 14*
3372 A558   $1 multi    .75 .75

Intl. Year of Fresh Water — A559

No. 3373: a, Levera Pond. b, Concord Falls. c, Lake Antoine.
$6, Lake Grand Etang.

**2003, July 4**     *Perf. 13½x13¼*
3373 A559   $2 Sheet of 3, #a-c    4.50 4.50
**Souvenir Sheet**
3374 A559   $6 multi    4.50 4.50

Circus Performers — A560

No. 3375, $2: a, Clive Andrews. b, Bell Bozo. c, Bumpsy. d, Annie Frattellini.
No. 3376, $2: a, Stag. b, Olga and Regina Kolpensky. c, Brad Byers. d, Tiger.

**2003, July 14**     *Perf. 14*
**Sheets of 4, #a-d**
3375-3376 A560   Set of 2    12.00 12.00

St. George's University School of Medicine A561

Designs: 75c, Aerial view of campus. $1, Campus buildings.

**2003, July 23**
3377-3378 A561   Set of 2    1.40 1.40

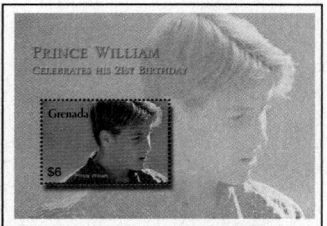

Prince William, 21st Birthday — A562

No. 3379, vert.: a, With bouquet of flowers. b, Wearing blue shirt. c, Wearing blue shirt, close-up.
$6, Wearing plaid shirt.

**2003, Aug. 25**
3379 A562   $3 Sheet of 3, #a-c    6.75 6.75
**Souvenir Sheet**
3380 A562   $6 multi    4.50 4.50

Operation Iraqi Freedom — A563

No. 3381, $1: a, Gazelle helicopter. b, Hovercraft. c, Jaguar. d, HMS Liverpool. e, Harrier GR7. f, Challenger 2 tank. g, Chinook helicopters. h, Tornado F3.
No. 3382, $1: a, Gen. Sir Mike Jackson. b, Air Vice-marshal Glenn Torpy. c, Air Marshal Brian Burridge. d, Maj. Gen. Tony Milton. e, Maj. Gen. Peter Wall. f, Maj. Gen. Barney White-Spunner. g, Adm. Sir Alan West. h, Air Chief Marshal Sir Peter Squire.

**2003, Aug. 29**
**Sheets of 8, #a-h**
3381-3382 A563   Set of 2    12.00 12.00

Pres. Ronald Reagan — A564

No. 3383: a, On Korean demilitarized zone, 1983. b, With British Prime Minister Margaret Thatcher. c, Speaking at the Berlin Wall, 1987. d, Signing IMF treaty with Soviet Secretary General Mikhail Gorbachev. e, With Egyptian President Anwar Sadat, 1981. f, At home with his horse.
$6, Addressing the nation.

**2003**
3383 A564   $1.50 Sheet of 6, #a-f   6.75 6.75
**Souvenir Sheet**
3384 A564   $6 multi    4.50 4.50

Souvenir Sheet

Anatoly Karpov, Chess Champion — A565

**2003**     *Perf. 13¼*
3385 A565   $20 multi    15.00 15.00

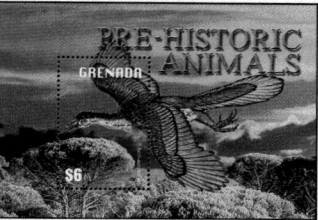

Prehistoric Animals — A566

No. 3386, $2, horiz.: a, Spinosaurus. b, Herrerasaurus. c, Protarchaeopteryx. d, Sinosauropteryx.
No. 3387, $2, horiz.: a, Allosaurus. b, Crylophosaurus. c, Eoraptor. d, Caudipteryx.
No. 3388, $6, Archaeopteryx. No. 3389, $6, Triceratops.

**2003, Oct. 23 Litho.**   *Perf. 13¼x13½*
**Sheets of 4, #a-d**
3386-3387 A566   Set of 2    14.00 14.00
**Souvenir Sheets**
*Perf. 13½x13¼*
3388-3389 A566   Set of 2    10.00 10.00

Flowers A567

Designs: 25c, Yellow allamanda. 50c, Queen of the night. 75c, Anthurium. $3, Oleander.
No. 3394: a, Blue passion flower. b, Chinese hibiscus. c, Poinsettia. d, Bird of paradise.
$6, Shrimp flower.

**2003, Oct. 23**     *Perf. 14*
3390-3393 A567   Set of 4    3.50 3.50
3394 A567   $2 Sheet of 4, #a-d   6.00 6.00
**Souvenir Sheet**
3395 A567   $6 multi    4.50 4.50

Fish A568

Designs: No. 3396, $1, Gold coney. No. 3397, $1, Spotfin butterflyfish. No. 3398, $1, Smallmouth grunt. $3, Night sergeant.
No. 3400: a, Cuban hogfish. b, Bluehead wrasse. c, Black cap gramma. d, Cherubfish.
$6, Banded butterflyfish.

**2003, Oct. 23**
3396-3399 A568   Set of 4    4.50 4.50
3400 A568   $2 Sheet of 4, #a-d   6.00 6.00
**Souvenir Sheet**
3401 A568   $6 multi    4.50 4.50

Birds A569

Designs: No. 3402, $1.25, Osprey. No. 3403, $1.25, Northern oriole. No. 3404, $1.25, Red-eyed vireo. $3, Bahama pintail.
No. 3406: a, Slaty-capped shrike vireor. b, Northern flicker. c, Blackburnian warbler. d, Common tody-flycatcher.
$6, Blue grosbeak, vert.

**2003, Oct. 23**
3402-3405 A569   Set of 4    5.00 5.00
3406 A569   $2 Sheet of 4, #a-d   6.00 6.00
**Souvenir Sheet**
3407 A569   $6 multi    4.50 4.50

Christmas
A570

Paintings by Giotto: 35c, Madonna and Child, from the Church of the Ognissanti. 75c, Ognissanti Madonna. $1, Madonna of the Angels. $4, Madonna and Child, from the Florentine Church of San Giorgio alla Costa. $6, Holy Family with John the Baptist and St. Elizabeth, horiz.

**2003, Nov. 17**      **Perf. 14¼**
3408-3411 A570   Set of 4    4.75   4.75
**Souvenir Sheet**
3412 A570 $6 multi          4.50   4.50
St. Petersburg, Russia, 300th anniv. (#3412).

Paintings by Norman Rockwell (1894-1978) — A571

No. 3413, vert.: a, The Spring Tonic. b, The Facts of Life. c, The Proper Gratuity. d, The Runaway.
$6, Boy with Carriage.

**2003, Dec. 8**      **Perf. 13¼**
3413 A571 $2 Sheet of 4, #a-d   6.00   6.00
**Souvenir Sheet**
3414 A571 $6 multi          4.50   4.50

Paintings in the Hermitage, St. Petersburg, Russia — A572

Designs: 45c, At the Palmist's, by Jean-Baptiste Le Prince, vert. $1, A Visit to Grandmother, by Louis Le Nain. $1.50, Musicale, by Dirck Hals. $3, A Young Woman in the Morning, by Frans van Mieris the Elder, vert.
No. 3419, vert.: a, Louis, Grand Dauphin de France, by Louis Tocqué. b, Count P. A. Stroganov as a Child, by Jean-Baptiste Greuze. c, A Boy with a Book, by Jean-Baptiste Perronneau. d, A Girl with a Doll, by Greuze.
No. 3420, The Lute Player, by Caravaggio.
No. 3421, The Spoiled Child, by Greuze, vert.

**2003, Dec. 8**      **Perf. 13¼**
3415-3418 A572   Set of 4    4.50   4.50
3419 A572 $2 Sheet of 4, #a-d   6.00   6.00
**Imperf**
**Size: 78x65mm**
3420 A572 $6 multi          4.50   4.50
**Size: 67x78mm**
3421 A572 $6 multi          4.50   4.50

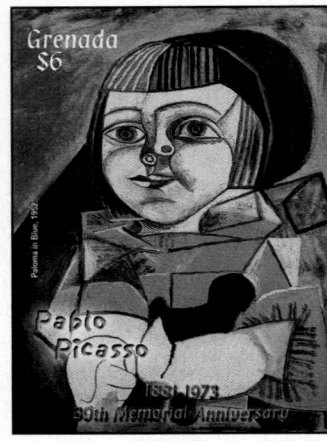

Paintings by Pablo Picasso (1881-1973) — A573

No. 3422: a, Claude Drawing. b, Claude and Paloma at Play. c, Paloma at Three Years Old. d, Paloma with an Orange.
$6, Paloma in Blue.

**2003, Dec. 8**   **Litho.**   **Perf. 13¼**
3422 A573 $2 Sheet of 4, #a-d   6.00   6.00
**Imperf**
3423 A573 $6 multi          4.50   4.50
No. 3422 contains four 37x50mm stamps.

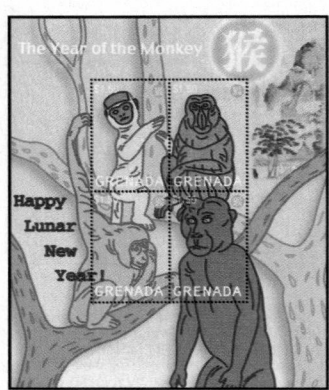

New Year 2004 (Year of the Monkey) — A574

No. 3424: a, Buff monkey with brown features. b, Brown monkey. c, Tan monkey. d, Gray monkey.

**2004, Jan. 4**      **Perf. 14**
3424 A574 $1.50 Sheet of 4, #a-d    4.50   4.50
**Souvenir Sheet**

Training Ship "Lissy" — A575

**2004, Jan. 16**   **Litho.**   **Perf. 14¼**
3425 A575 $6 multi          4.50   4.50
Opening of Weser Tunnel, Dedesdorf, Germany.

Paintings by Pu Hsin-yu (1896-1963) — A576

No. 3426: a, Woman. b, Monkeys in tree. c, Landscape. d, Bird in tree. e, Man seated. f, Man standing.
No. 3427: a, Branch. b, Man.

**2004, Jan. 29**      **Perf. 13½x13¼**
3426 A576 $1.50 Sheet of 6, #a-f    6.75   6.75
3427 A576    $3 Sheet of 2, #a-b    4.50   4.50
2004 Hong Kong Stamp Expo.

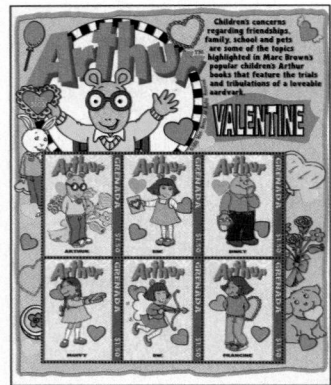

Arthur and Friends — A577

No. 3428, $1.50: a, Arthur. b, D. W. with Valentine's Day card. c, Binky. d, Muffy. e, D. W. as Cupid. f, Francine.
No. 3429, $1.50: a, Muffy giving speech about butterflies. b, Francine giving presentation about butterflies. c, Brain with plants. d, D. W. in space. e, Sue Ellen with insects. f, Arthur with model of solar system.
No. 3430, $2: a, Robinson Crusoe. b, Treasure Island. c, Tom Sawyer. d, Jungle Book.
No. 3431, $2: a, Robin Hood. b, Rumplestiltskin. c, How Arthur Drew Forth His Sword. d, King Arthur.

**2004, Jan. 29**      **Perf. 13¼**
**Sheets of 6, #a-f**
3428-3429 A577   Set of 2   13.50   13.50
**Sheets of 4, #a-d**
3430-3431 A577   Set of 2   12.00   12.00

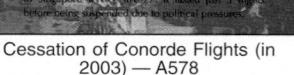

The CONCORDE
(1969-2003)

Cessation of Conorde Flights (in 2003) — A578

No. 3432, $3 — Concorde 210 G-BOAD, British and Singapore flags and: a, Roof line of buildings at UR. b, Curved and jagged lines at UR. c, Dark gray background at UR.
No. 3433, $3 — Concorde 001 F-WTSS, French flag and: a, Concorde above runway. b, Spectators near airport fence. c, Cockpit control panel.
No. 3434, $3 — Concorde 203 F-BVFA and: a, Top of US Capitol. b, Middle part of Capitol dome, head of statue. c, Base of Capitol and statue.

**2004, Feb. 16**      **Perf. 13¼x13½**
**Sheets of 3, #a-c**
3432-3434 A578   Set of 3   21.00   21.00

2004 Summer Olympics, Athens A579

Designs: 75c, Lord Killanin, Intl. Olympic Committee President, 1972-80. $1, 10,000 meter run, 1928 Olympics, horiz. $1.25, Commemorative plaque from 1900 Paris Olympics. $3, Presentation of olive wreath.

**2004, Apr. 8**      **Perf. 13¼**
3435-3438 A579   Set of 4   4.50   4.50

American Indian Chiefs — A580

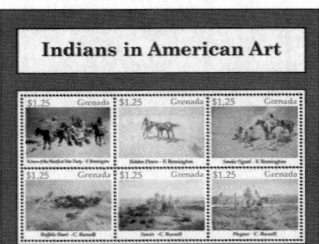

Paintings of American Indians — A581

No. 3439: a, American Horse. b, Blue Bird. c, Crow King. d, Crow Man. e, Gall. f, Good Horse. g, Goose. h, John Grass. i, Rain-in-the-Face. j, Red Cloud. k, Sitting Bull. l, Wild Horse.
No. 3440: a, Return of the Blackfoot War Party, by Frederic Remington. b, Ridden Down, by Remington. c, Smoke Signal, by Remington. d, Buffalo Hunt, by Charles Russell. e, Scouts, by Russell. f, Piegans, by Russell.

**2004, Apr. 19**      **Perf. 13¾**
3439 A580 75c Sheet of 12, #a-l   6.75   6.75
3440 A581 $1.25 Sheet of 6, #a-f   5.75   5.75

## Souvenir Sheet

Deng Xiaoping (1904-97), Chinese
Communist Party Leader — A582

**2004, May 3**     **Perf. 13½x13¼**
3441 A582 $6 multi     4.50 4.50

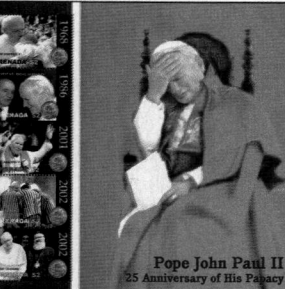

Election of Pope John Paul II, 25th
Anniv. — A583

No. 3442: a, Kissing baby. b, With Mikhail
Gorbachev. c, Waving to crowd. d, Meeting
with Polish deportees. e, Visit to Russia.

**2004, May 3**     **Perf. 13¼x13½**
3442 A583 $2 Sheet of 5, #a-e   7.50 7.50

Marilyn Monroe
(1926-62) — A584

No. 3444: a, Wearing red dress with strap
over shoulder, mouth wide open. b, Wearing
orange red dress, mouth closed. c, Wearing
white dress. d, Wearing red dress, mouth partially open.

**2004, May 3**     **Perf. 14**
3443 A584 50c shown     .60 .60
    **Perf. 13½x13¼**
3444 A584 $2 Sheet of 4, #a-d   7.50 7.50
No. 3443 printed in sheets of 16.

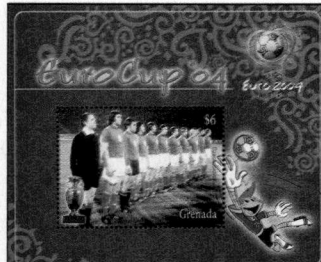

European Soccer Championships,
Portugal — A585

No. 3445, vert.: a, Jan Svehlik. b, Franz
Beckenbauer. c, Karol Dobias. d, Crvena
Zvezda Stadium, Belgrade.
$6, 1976 Czechoslovakian team.

**2004, May 3**     **Perf. 13½x13¼**
3445 A585 $2 Sheet of 4, #a-d   6.00 6.00

## Souvenir Sheet
**Perf. 13¼**
3446 A585 $6 multi     4.50 4.50
No. 3445 contains four 28x42mm stamps.

D-Day,
60th
Anniv.
A586

Designs: 45c, Don Sheppard, Royal Engineers. $1, Air Chief Marshall Sir Arthur Ted-
der. $1.50, Douglas Kay, 13th/18th Royal Hus-
sars. $3, Gen. Bernard Montgomery.
No. 3451, $2: a, Germans detect Allied inva-
sion. b, Germans prepare to engage Allied
invasion fleet. c, Soldier, Merville Battery. d,
Paratroopers capture Merville Battery.
No. 3452, $2: a, HMS Belfast fires on Ger-
man shore batteries. b, Allies pound German
coastal defenses. c, Air strikes over Utah
Beach. d, Allied troops head towards Omaha
Beach.
No. 3453, $6, Fake landing craft. No. 3454,
$6, Pipeline under the ocean.

**2004, May 3**     **Perf. 14**
   **Stamps + Labels (#3447-3450)**
3447-3450 A586 Set of 4   4.50 4.50
   **Sheets of 4, #a-d**
3451-3452 A586 Set of 2   12.00 12.00
   **Souvenir Sheets**
3453-3454 A586 Set of 2   9.00 9.00

Locomotives and Famous
Men — A587

No. 3455, $1: a, Sir Lord Nelson 4-6-0. b,
South African 16CR Class Pacific. c, Florisdorf
0-6-0 Fireless, Austria. d, GWR 57XX Class 0-
6-0. e, GWR Castle Class 4-6-0. f, GWR Saint
Class 4-6-0. g, GWR Star Class 4-6-0. h,
GWR 28XX Class 2-8-0. i, GWR 51XX Class
2-6-2T.
No. 3456, $1, vert.: a, GN Stirling Single 4-
2-2. b, Beyer Peacock Mogul 2-6-0. c, Prus-
sian G8 0-8-0. d, George Stephenson. e,
James Nasmyth. f, Nasmyth's steam hammer.
g, Raven Z Class 4-4-2. h, Sir Vincent Raven.
i, Thomas Cook.
No. 3457, $1, vert.: a, SR Schools Class 4-
4-0. b, Indian Railways SGS Class 0-6-0. c,
Borsig 0-4-0 Tram, Paraguay. d, Richard
Trevithick. e, Herbert Garratt. f, Isambard
Kingdom Brunel. g, Replica of Trevithick's
Coalbrookdale Engine. h, Rhodesian 20th
Class Garratt. i, Train on Brunel's Royal
Saltash Bridge.
No. 3458, $6, California Zephyr. No. 3459,
$6, Indian Pacific. No. 3460, $6, Cumbres and
Toltec.

**2004, July 19**     **Litho.**
   **Sheets of 9, #a-i**
3455-3457 A587 Set of 3   21.00 21.00
   **Souvenir Sheets**
3458-3460 A587 Set of 3   13.50 13.50

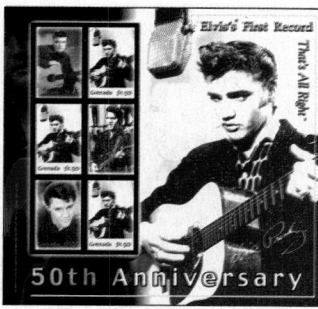

Elvis Presley (1935-77) — A588

No. 3461: a, Holding guitar (brown). b, Playing guitar (green). c, Playing guitar, diff. (red
violet). d, Portrait (brown). e, Like #3461b,
(blue).

**2004, Aug. 3**     **Perf. 14**
3461 A588 $1.50 Sheet, #a-d,
    2 #e     7.25 7.25

Operation Iraqi Freedom — A589

No. 3462: a, Pres. George W. Bush. b, Paul
Bremer. c, Col. James Hickey, US Special
Forces. d, A friendly welcome.

**2004, Aug. 25**     **Perf. 13¼x13½**
3462 A589 $2 Sheet of 4, #a-d   6.00 6.00

Queen Juliana of the Netherlands
(1909-2004) — A590

**2004, Aug. 25**   **Litho.**   **Perf. 13¼**
3463 A590 $2 multi     1.50 1.50
Printed in sheets of 6.

## Miniature Sheet

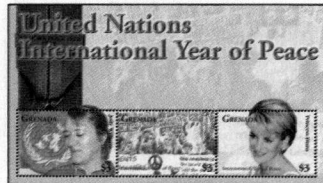

Intl. Year of Peace — A591

No. 3464: a, Jody Williams, 1997 Nobel
Peace laureate. b, Protesters against
landmines. c, Princess Diana.

**2004, Sept. 7**     **Perf. 14**
3464 A591 $3 Sheet of 3, #a-c   6.75 6.75

## Miniature Sheet

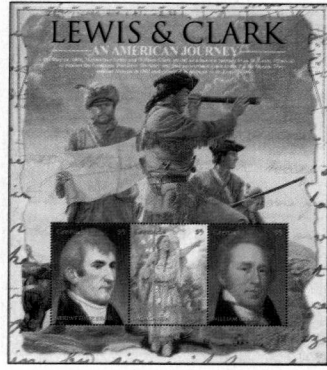

Lewis and Clark Expedition,
Bicent. — A592

No. 3465: a, Meriwether Lewis. b,
Sacajawea. c, William Clark.

**2004, Sept. 7**     **Perf. 14¼**
3465 A592 $3 Sheet of 3, #a-c   6.75 6.75

## Miniature Sheet

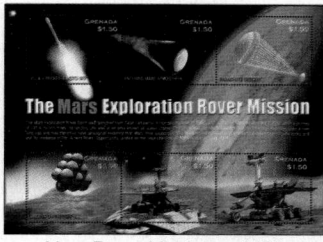

Mars Rover Mission — A593

No. 3466: a, Delta II rocket blasts off. b,
Entering Mars atmosphere. c, Parachute
descent. d, Landing on the surface. e, Rover
leaving lander. f, Rover on Mars surface.

**2004, Sept. 7**
3466 A593 $1.50 Sheet of 6, #a-f 6.75 6.75

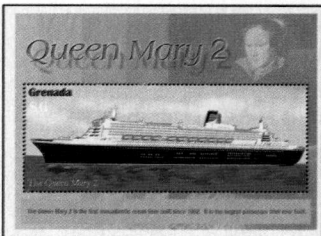

Ocean Liners — A594

No. 3467, $2: a, RMS Titanic. b, TSS Nor-
mandie. c, Mauritania. d, Lusitania.
No. 3468, $2: a, Queen Mary 2. b, Queen
Elizabeth II. c, Queen Mary. d, Queen
Elizabeth.
$6, Queen Mary 2, diff.

**2004, Sept. 7**     **Perf. 13¼x13**
   **Sheets of 4, #a-d**
3467-3468 A594 Set of 2   12.00 12.00
   **Souvenir Sheet**
3469 A594 $6 multi     4.50 4.50

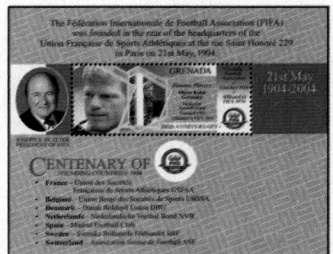

FIFA (Fédération Internationale de
Football Association), Cent. — A595

No. 3470: a, Gabriel Batistuta. b, Cafu. c, Michel Platini. d, Gianluca Vialli. $6, Oliver Kahn.

**2004, Nov. 1**     *Perf. 12¾x12½*
3470 A595 $2 Sheet of 4, #a-d   6.00 6.00
**Souvenir Sheet**
3471 A595 $6 multi     4.50 4.50

National Basketball Association Players — A596

Designs: No. 3472, 75c, Pau Gasol, Memphis Grizzlies. No. 3473, 75c, Allen Iverson, Philadelphia 76ers. No. 3474, 75c, Stephon Marbury, New York Knicks.

**2004**     *Perf. 14*
3472-3474 A596   Set of 3   1.75 1.75
Issued: No. 3472, 11/3; No. 3473, 11/5; No. 3474, 11/6. Each printed in sheets of 12.

Miniature Sheet

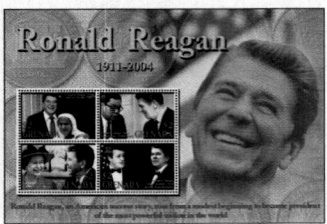

Pres. Ronald Reagan (1911-2004) — A597

No. 3475: a, With Mother Teresa. b, With Colin Powell. c, With Queen Elizabeth II. d, With Brian Mulroney.

**2004**     *Perf. 13½*
3475 A597 $2 Sheet of 4, #a-d   6.00 6.00

A598

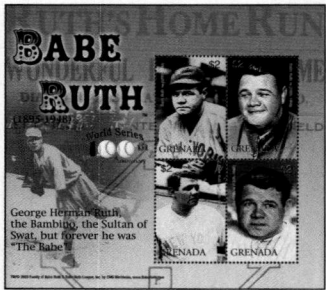

George Herman "Babe" Ruth (1895-1948), Baseball Player — A599

Various portraits.

**2004**     *Perf. 14*
3476 A598 $2 Sheet of 4, #a-d   6.00 6.00
    *Perf. 13¾x13¼*
3477 A599 $2 Sheet of 4, #a-d   6.00 6.00

Christmas A600

Paintings by Norman Rockwell: 35c, Merry Christmas. 75c, Yuletide Merriment. $1, Dressing Up. $4, Christmas. $6, The London Coach.

**2004, Dec. 9**     *Perf. 12*
3478-3481 A600   Set of 4   4.75 4.75
**Souvenir Sheet**
3482 A600 $6 multi     4.50 4.50

New Year 2005 (Year of the Rooster) — A601

Paintings by Qi Baishi: $1, Chrysanthemums, Cocks and Hens. $4, Taro Leaves and Double Hens.

**2005, Jan. 17 Litho.**   *Perf. 11¾x12¼*
3483 A601 $1 multi     .75 .75
**Souvenir Sheet**
    *Perf. 12¾x13*
3484 A601 $4 multi     3.00 3.00
No. 3483 printed in sheets of 4. No. 3484 contains one 22x76mm stamp.

**Basketball Players Type of 2004**
Designs: No. 3485, 75c, Zydrunas Ilgauskas, Cleveland Cavaliers. No. 3486, 75c, Dwyane Wade, Miami Heat. $3, Tracy McGrady, Orlando Magic.

**2005, Feb. 10**     *Perf. 14*
3485-3487 A596   Set of 3   3.50 3.50

Souvenir Sheet

Intl. Year of Rice — A602

No. 3488: a, Detail from Deities Overseeing the Transplanting of Rice, by unknown artist. b, Detail from the Taoist God Overseeing the Rice Planting, by unknown artist. c, Women Transplanting Rice in Late Spring Rain, by Hiroshige.

**2005, Feb. 10**
3488 A602 $3 Sheet of 3, #a-c   6.75 6.75

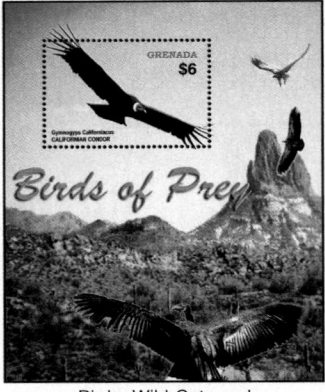

Birds, Wild Cats and Butterflies — A603

No. 3489, $1.50, vert. — Birds: a, Turkey vulture. b, Bald eagle. c, Peregrine falcon. d, Prairie falcon. e, Northern goshawk. f, Cooper's hawk.
No. 3490, $1.50, vert. — Wild cats: a, Cheetah. b, Lion. c, White tiger. d, Leopard. e, Bobcat. f, Bengal tiger.
No. 3491, $1.50 — Butterflies: a, Machaonides's swallowtail. b, Viceroy. c, Glasswing satyr. d, Birdwing. e, Ornithoptera goliath procus. f, Ornithoptera priamus alberio.
No. 3492, $6, California condor. No. 3493, $6, Jaguar, vert. No. 3494, $6, Lime butterfly.

**2005, Feb. 10**     *Litho.*
**Sheets of 6, #a-f**
3489-3491 A603   Set of 3   21.00 21.00
**Souvenir Sheets**
3492-3494 A603   Set of 3   13.50 13.50

A604

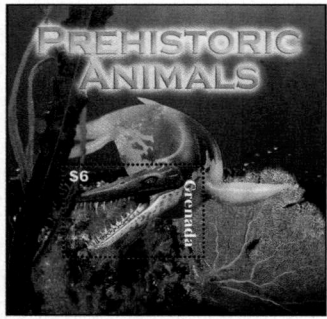

Prehistoric Animals — A605

No. 3495: a, Majungatholus. b, Diplodocus. c, Willo. d, Velociraptor.
No. 3496, $2: a, Archelon. b, Ammonite. c, Plesiosaur. d, Xiphactinus.
No. 3497, $2: a, Pteranodon. b, Dimorphodon. c, Pterodactylus. d, Rhamphorhynchus.
No. 3498, Spinosaurus.
No. 3499, $6, Pliosaur. No. 3500, $6, Tapejara imperator.

**2005, Feb. 10**
3495 A604 $2 Sheet of 4, #a-d   6.00 6.00
**Sheets of 4, #a-d**
3496-3497 A605   Set of 2   12.00 12.00
**Souvenir Sheets**
3498 A604 $6 multi     4.50 4.50
3499-3500 A605   Set of 2   9.00 9.00

Souvenir Sheet

Buildings Damaged in Hurricane Ivan — A606

No. 3501: a, Cathedral of Immaculate Conception. b, Anglican Church. c, York House. d, Springs Sub-office.

**2005, Mar. 8**     *Perf. 12¾*
3501 A606 $2 Sheet of 4, #a-d   6.00 6.00

Elvis Presley (1935-77) — A607

No. 3502, $1.50: a, Singing, 1955. b, Holding microphone, 1957. c, Playing guitar, 1959. d, Singing, 1961. e, Singing, 1968. f, With guitar, 1970.
No. 3503, $1.50: a, Dancing, 1957. b, Playing guitar, 1964. c, On saddle, 1965. d, Playing guitar, 1968. e, Playing piano, 1969. f, Singing, 1970.

**2005, Apr. 4**     *Perf. 13¾*
**Sheets of 6, #a-f**
3502-3503 A607   Set of 2   13.50 13.50

Yasujiro Ozu (1903-63), Film Director — A608

No. 3504: a, Tenement Gentleman, 1947. b, Tokyo Story, 1953. c, A Hen in the Wind, 1948. d, Floating Weeds, 1959.

**2005, Apr. 8**     *Perf. 14¼*
3504 A608 $2 Sheet of 4, #a-d   6.00 6.00

Dutch Royalty — A609

No. 3505: a, King William I. b, King William II. c, King William III. d, Queen Wilhelmina. e, Queen Juliana. f, Queen Beatrix. g, Prince Willem-Alexander. h, Princess Catharina-Amalia.

**2005, Apr. 14     Litho.     Perf. 12**
3505  A609 $2 Sheet of 8, #a-h     12.00 12.00

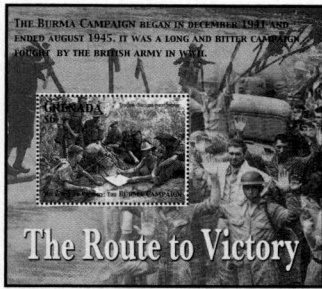

End of World War II, 60th Anniv. — A610

No. 3506, $2 — Burma Campaign: a, "21 Curves" Road. b, British advance through the jungle of Burma. c, Troops at Magwe airstrip. d, Allied troops escorting prisoners.
No. 3507, $2 — Operation Market Garden: a, Allied troops landing behind enemy lines. b, Allied troops fire on German defenders. c, German troops move up to counterattack. d, Bridges still remain in German hands.
No. 3508, $6, Troops discuss next move.
No. 3509, $6, Allied troops meet stiff resistance.

**2005, May 10     Perf. 13¼**
**Sheets of 4, #a-d**
3506-3507  A610  Set of 2     12.00 12.00
**Souvenir Sheets**
3508-3509  A610  Set of 2     9.00 9.00

V-E Day, 60th Anniv. — A611

No. 3510: a, D-Day. b, Allied troops break through enemy lines. c, German troops begin to surrender. d, The war in Europe is over.
$6, Berlin falls to the armies of the Soviet Union.

**2005, May 10     Perf. 14**
3510  A611 $2 Sheet of 4, #a-d     6.00 6.00
**Souvenir Sheet**
3511  A611 $6 multi     4.50 4.50

V-J Day, 60th Anniv. — A612

No. 3512: a, Airplanes over islands of the Pacific. b, Allied forces storm the beaches of Japanese-held islands. c, Gen. Douglas MacArthur returns to the Philippines. d, The Japanese armies surrender.
$6, Allies enjoy victory celebration.

**2005, May 10**
3512  A612 $2 Sheet of 4, #a-d     6.00 6.00
**Souvenir Sheet**
3513  A612 $6 multi     4.50 4.50

Rotary International, Cent. — A613

No. 3514: a, Child receiving polio vaccination. b, District 7030 Governor David Edwards and wife, Donna. c, Paul P. Harris, Rotary International founder.
$6, 2001-02 Rotary President Richard D. King, children.

**2005, May 10     Perf. 14**
3514  A613 $3 Sheet of 3, #a-c     6.75 6.75
**Souvenir Sheet**
3515  A613 $6 multi     4.50 4.50

**Miniature Sheet**

Expo 2005, Aichi, Japan — A614

No. 3516: a, Victoria Falls. b, Bald eagle. c, Caribbean coral reef. d, Childbirth. e, First man on the moon. f, Pollination.

**2005, June 27     Perf. 12**
3516  A614 $1.50 Sheet of 6, #a-f  6.75 6.75

Albert Einstein (1879-1955), Physicist — A615

No. 3517 — Einstein and country name in: a, Blue. b, Black. c, White. d, Red
$6, Einstein with pipe.

**2005, June 27     Perf. 12¾**
3517  A615 $2 Sheet of 4, #a-d     6.00 6.00
**Souvenir Sheet**
3518  A615 $6 multi     4.50 4.50

**Souvenir Sheet**

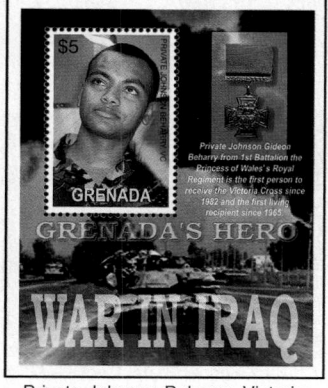

Private Johnson Beharry, Victoria Cross Recipient in Iraq War — A616

**2005, July 11     Litho.**
3519  A616 $5 multi     3.75 3.75

Hans Christian Andersen (1805-75), Author — A617

No. 3520: a, Andersen, with hands shown. b, Photograph of Andersen. c, Andersen, with white tie.
$6, Andersen's tombstone, Copenhagen.

**2005, July 11**
3520  A617 $3 Sheet of 3, #a-c     6.75 6.75
**Souvenir Sheet**
3521  A617 $6 multi     4.50 4.50

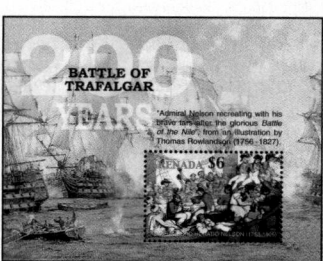

Friedrich von Schiller (1759-1805), Writer — A618

No. 3522, vert.: a, William Tell Memorial, Altdorf, Switzerland. b, Animated movie of William Tell. c, Stage production of William Tell.
$6, Scene from William Tell story.

**2005, July 11     Perf. 14**
3522  A618 $3 Sheet of 3, #a-c     6.75 6.75
**Souvenir Sheet**
3523  A618 $6 multi     4.50 4.50

Jules Verne (1828-1905), Writer — A619

No. 3524: a, Photograph of Verne. b, Photograph of Verne in oval. c, Drawing of Verne.
$6, From the Earth to the Moon.

**2005, July 11     Perf. 12¾**
3524  A619 $3 Sheet of 3, #a-c     6.75 6.75
**Souvenir Sheet**
3525  A619 $6 multi     4.50 4.50

Battle of Trafalgar, Bicent. — A620

No. 3526, vert.: a, Admiral Horatio Nelson. b, Napoleon Bonaparte. c, HMS Victory. d, The Nelson Touch.
$6, Sailors on ship.

**2005, July 11     Perf. 12¾**
3526  A620 $2 Sheet of 4, #a-d     6.00 6.00
**Souvenir Sheet**
3527  A620 $6 multi     4.50 4.50

**Miniature Sheets**

Dennis The Menace, Comic Strip by Hank Ketcham — A621

No. 3528, $2: a, "Grandpa got a new knee. . ." b, "Joey an' me don't have any money. . ." c, "Good news, Mrs. Wilson! . ." d, "I think the boy's. . ."
No. 3529, $2: a, "How 'bout a trade. . ." b, "It's not a good idea. . ." c, "I'll bet you were the top . ." d, "Boy, I'm glad I don't have to. . ."

**2005, July 11     Perf. 14¼**
**Sheets of 4, #a-d**
3528-3529  A621  Set of 2     12.00 12.00

## Souvenir Sheet

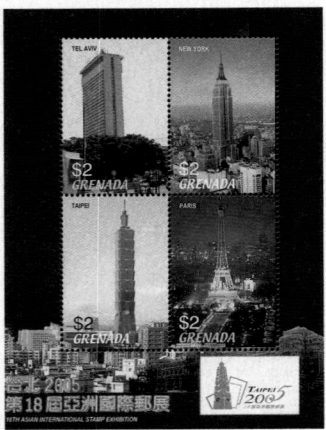

Taipei 2005 Intl. Stamp
Exhibition — A622

No. 3530: a, Shalom Meir Tower, Tel Aviv. b,
Empire State Building, New York. c, Taipei 101
Building, Taipei. d, Eiffel Tower, Paris.

**2005, Aug. 19**     **Perf. 14**
3530 A622 $2 Sheet of 4, #a-d    6.00 6.00

Pope John Paul II
(1920-2005) and
Lech
Walesa — A623

**2005, Aug. 22**     **Perf. 12¾**
3531 A623 $4 multi     3.00 3.00
Printed in sheets of 4.

Wedding of Prince
Charles and
Camilla Parker
Bowles — A624

Various pictures of couple with oval in: No.
3532, $2, Lemon. No. 3533, $2, Light blue.
No. 3534, $2, Pink, horiz.

**2005, Sept. 7**     **Perf. 13½**
3532-3534 A624 Set of 3     4.50 4.50
Each stamp printed in sheets of 4.

Christmas — A625

Designs: 25c, The Nativity, by Correggio.
75c, Virgin and Child, by Lorenzo Lotto. $1,
The Holy Family, by Lotto. $5, Madonna and
Child with the Saints, by Lotto.
$6, Allegory of Music, by Fra Filippo Lippi.

**2005, Nov. 15**     **Perf. 12¾**
3535-3538 A625 Set of 4     5.25 5.25
**Souvenir Sheet**
3539 A625 $6 multi     4.50 4.50

---

## Bird Type of 2000
**2005**    Litho.    **Perf. 12x11¾**
**Size:22x26mm**
3540 A472 10c Purple-throated
Carib     .20 .20

### Miniature Sheets

Chelsea Soccer Team, Cent. — A626

Liverpool Soccer Team — A627

No. 3541: a, Stadium and field. b, Stadium,
field, team emblem and years. c, Players holding English League Championship award. d,
Players in bus with cup and flag. e, Fans with
flag. f, Aerial view of bus carrying players. g,
Players. h, Coach. i, Stadium, field, team
emblem. j, Team with award.
No. 3542: a, Crowd watching bus carrying
players near stadium. b, Player and coach
holding UEFA Cup. c, Gate. d, Aerial view of
stadium. e, Banner. f, Players waving. g, Fans.
h, Soccer match. i, Players celebrating. j,
Crowd cheering players in bus.

**2005, Dec. 28**   Litho.   **Perf. 13¼**
3541 A626 $1.50 Sheet of 10,
#a-j    11.50 11.50
3542 A627 $1.50 Sheet of 10,
#a-j    11.50 11.50

The Two
Hounds,
by Hui-
Tsung
A628

**2006, Jan. 3**
3543 A628 $1 shown     .75 .75
**Souvenir Sheet**
3544 A628 $4 Entire painting    3.00 3.00
No. 3544 contains one 50x37mm stamp.

Pope Benedict
XVI — A629

**2006, Jan. 10**
3545 A629 $2 multi     1.50 1.50
Printed in sheets of 4.

---

A630

Elvis Presley (1935-77) — A631

No. 3546 — Movie posters: a, Girls! Girls!
Girls! b, Jailhouse Rock. c, Paradise - Hawaiian Style. d, It Happened at the World's Fair.

**2006**    Litho.    **Perf. 13¼**
3546 A630 $3 Sheet of 4, #a-
d    9.00 9.00
**Litho. & Embossed**
**Die Cut Perf. 7¾**
**Without Gum**
3547 A631 $20 shown    15.00 15.00
Issued: No. 3546, 7/11, No. 3547, 2/21.

Queen Elizabeth II, 80th
Birthday — A632

No. 3548: a, Wearing necklace, no earrings.
b, Wearing blue jacket. c, Portrait. d, Wearing
jacket and earrings.
$6, Wearing hat.

**2006, Feb. 21**   Litho.   **Perf. 13¼**
3548 A632 $3 Sheet of 4, #a-d    9.00 9.00
**Souvenir Sheet**
**Perf. 12¼x12**
3549 A632 $6 multi     4.50 4.50

Teams Competing in 2006 World Cup
Soccer Championships,
Germany — A633

Designs: No. 3550, $1.50, Angola. No.
3551, $1.50, Argentina. No. 3552, $1.50, Australia. No. 3553, $1.50, Brazil. No. 3554,
$1.50, Costa Rica. No. 3555, $1.50, Croatia.
No. 3556, $1.50, Czech Republic. No. 3557,
$1.50, Ecuador. No. 3558, $1.50, England.
No. 3559, $1.50, France. No. 3560, $1.50,
Germany. No. 3561, $1.50, Ghana. No. 3562,
$1.50, Iran. No. 3563, $1.50, Italy. No. 3564,
$1.50, Ivory Coast. No. 3565, $1.50, Japan.
No. 3566, $1.50, Mexico. No. 3567, $1.50,
Netherlands. No. 3568, $1.50, Paraguay. No.
3569, $1.50, Poland. No. 3570, $1.50, Portugal. No. 3571, $1.50, Saudi Arabia. No. 3572,

---

$1.50, Serbia and Montenegro. No. 3573,
$1.50, South Korea. No. 3574, $1.50, Spain.
No. 3575, $1.50, Sweden. No. 3576, $1.50,
Switzerland. No. 3577, $1.50, Togo. No. 3578,
$1.50, Trinidad and Tobago. No. 3579, $1.50,
Tunisia. No. 3580, $1.50, Ukraine. No. 3581,
$1.50, United States.

**2006, Mar. 29**    **Perf. 12¼x12**
3550-3581 A633 Set of 32   36.00 36.00

Nos. 3550-3581 each printed in sheets of 6.
Stamps other than Nos. 3550, 3553, 3554,
3560, 3561, 3566, 3575, 3579 and 3581,
which have solid color backgrounds, have multicolored backgrounds that vary within the
sheet.

Marilyn Monroe
(1926-62),
Actress — A634

**2006, Mar. 30**    **Perf. 13¼**
3582 A634 $3 multi     2.25 2.25
Printed in sheets of 4.

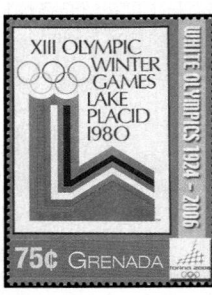

2006 Winter
Olympics,
Turin
A635

Designs: No. 3583, Poster for 1980 Lake
Placid Winter Olympics. No. 3583A, Poster for
2006 Turin Winter Olympics. No. 3584, Switzerland #B173. No. 3584A, Italy #2722. $2,
Poster for 1948 St. Moritz Winter Olympics.
$3, Switzerland #B172.

**2006, May 10**    **Perf. 14¼**
3583   A635 75c multicolored   .55 .55
3583A A635 75c multi   .55 .55
3584   A635 90c multicolored   .70 .70
3584A A635 90c multi   .70 .70
3585   A635 $2 multicolored   1.50 1.50
3586   A635 $3 multicolored   2.25 2.25
   Nos. 3583-3586 (6)   6.25 6.25

Rosa Parks
(1913-2005),
American Civil
Rights
Activist — A636

**2006, May 27**    **Perf. 11½x12**
3587 A636 $3 multi     2.25 2.25
Printed in sheets of 3.

Flags and
Uniforms of
World Cup
Soccer
Champions
A637

Designs: 75c, Brazil, 2002. 90c, Germany, 1990. $3, France, 1998.

**2006, June 9** — *Perf. 13¼*
3588-3590 A637 Set of 3   3.50 3.50

World Cup Trophy — A638

**2006, June 9** — *Die Cut*
**Self-Adhesive**
3591 A638 $6 multi   4.50 4.50

Rembrandt (1606-69), Painter A639

Designs: 50c, The Little Jewish Bride. $1, Young Man in Velvet Cap. $1.50, Old Woman Sleeping. No. 3595, $3, Woman Reading. No. 3596, $6, Portrait of a Seated Man (70x100mm). No. 3597, $6, Portrait of a Scholar (70x100mm).

No. 3598, $3: a, Young Woman with Flowers in Her Hair. b, Portrait of a Seated Woman. c, Alijdt Adriaensor. d, Amalia van Solms.

*Perf. 12, 12½x12¼ (#3596, 3597)*
**2006, June 16**
3592-3597 A639 Set of 6   13.50 13.50
3597a   Imperf.   4.50 4.50
**Miniature Sheet**
*Perf. 13x13¼*
3598 A639 $3 Sheet of 4, #a-d   9.00 9.00

**Souvenir Sheet**

Wolfgang Amadeus Mozart (1756-91), Composer — A640

**2006, June 22** — *Perf. 12¾*
3599 A640 $6 multi   4.50 4.50

**Souvenir Sheet**

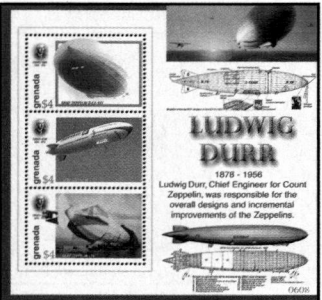

Ludwig Durr (1878-1956), Engineer, and Zeppelins — A641

No. 3600 — Durr and: a, Graf Zeppelin D-LZ-127. b, Graf Zeppelin LT. c, Graf Zeppelin L-26.

**2006, June 22**
3600 A641 $4 Sheet of 3, #a-c   9.00 9.00

Space — A642

No. 3601, $2 — Sputnik 1: a, Sergei Korolev. b, Sputnik 1 in space. c, Inside Sputnik 1. d, Sputnik 1 capsule.

No. 3602, $2, vert. — Apollo-Soyuz: a, Apollo rocket. b, Apollo command module and adapter. c, Soyuz rocket on launchpad. d, Soyuz.

No. 3603 — Giotto Comet Probe: a, Halley's Comet, round head in yellow at right. b, Tip of Giotto Probe launcher Ariane V14. c, Halley's Comet, head at left, thin tail. d, Halley's Comet, head in white at right. e, Bottom of Giotto Probe launcher Ariane V14. f, Halley's Comet, head at left, wide tail.

No. 3604, $6, Stardust Comet Probe. No. 3605, $6, Comet Tempel 1 Deep Impact Mission. No. 3606, $6, Space Shuttle Discovery's return to space.

**2006, Sept. 14** — *Litho.* — *Perf. 12¾*
**Sheets of 4, #a-d**
3601-3602 A642 Set of 2   12.00 12.00
3603 A642 $2 Sheet of 6, #a-f   9.00 9.00
**Souvenir Sheets**
3604-3606 A642 Set of 3   13.50 13.50

Christopher Columbus (1451-1506), Explorer — A643

Designs: $1.50, Sinking of the Santa Maria. $2, Santa Maria, vert. $3, Columbus, sailor and ship, vert. $4, Columbus and ships, vert. $6, Fleet of ships, 1493.

**2006, Oct. 26** — *Perf. 12¾*
3607-3610 A643 Set of 4   8.00 8.00
**Souvenir Sheet**
3611 A643 $6 multi   4.50 4.50

Butterflies A644

Designs: 10c, Mourning cloak butterfly. 25c, Snout butterfly. $1, Tithorea pinthias. $2, Diadem butterfly. $4, Red satyr butterfly. $5, Taygetis chrysogone. $10, Pierella hortona. $20, Morpho aega.

**2006, Dec. 1** — *Litho.* — *Perf. 12½*
3612 A644 10c multi   .20 .20
3613 A644 25c multi   .20 .20
3614 A644 $1 multi   .75 .75
3615 A644 $2 multi   1.50 1.50
3616 A644 $4 multi   3.00 3.00
3617 A644 $5 multi   3.75 3.75
3618 A644 $10 multi   7.50 7.50
3619 A644 $20 multi   15.00 15.00
Nos. 3612-3619 (8)   31.90 31.90

Princess Maxima of the Netherlands — A645

No. 3620: a, Head of Princess Maxima. b, Princess Maxima holding purse.

**2006, Dec. 7** — *Perf. 13½*
3620 A645 $1.50 Pair, #a-b   2.25 2.25
Printed in sheets containing 3 of each stamp.

Christmas — A646

Details of The Adoration of the Shepherds, by Peter Paul Rubens: 25c, Man with hat. 50c, Mary. 75c, Shepherd. $1, Baby Jesus.

No. 3625: a, Like 25c. b, Like 50c. c, Like 75c. d, Like $1.

**2006, Dec. 21** — *Perf. 14*
3621-3624 A646 Set of 4   1.90 1.90
**Souvenir Sheet**
3625 A646 $2 Sheet of 4, #a-d   6.00 6.00

Betty Boop — A647

No. 3626 — Betty Boop: a, Sitting on "E." b, With hands on thighs, between "Y" and "B." c, With one leg elevated. d, With hands clasped, Standing behind "E." e, With arms at side, standing in front of "Y." f, With arms raised upwards.

No. 3627: a, With hands clasped, blue circles. b, With arms at side, red and blue circles. c, With arms raised upwards, pink and blue circles. d, At microphone, blue circles.

No. 3628, $3: a, Holding mirror. b, Wearing fruited hat.

No. 3629, $3, horiz.: a, Head and upper torso. b, Lower torso.

**2006, Dec. 22** — *Perf. 14*
3626 A647 $1.50 Sheet of 6, #a-f   6.75 6.75
3627 A647 $2 Sheet of 4, #a-d   6.00 6.00
**Souvenir Sheets of 2, #a-b**
3628-3629 A647 Set of 2   9.00 9.00

Arsenal Soccer Team — A648

No. 3630: a, $1, Players and crowd. b, $1, Soccer field at night. c, $1, Fans in seats at end of stadium. d, $1, Emirates Stadium exterior. e, $1, Players. f, $2, Players. g, $2, Aerial view of stadium exterior. h, $2, Fans. i, $2, Soccer field and fans. j, $2, Stadium exterior at night.

**2007, Jan. 16**
3630 A648 Sheet of 10, #a-j   11.50 11.50

Concorde Test Pilots and Flags — A649

No. 3631: a, Amore Turcat, French flag. b, Brian Trubshaw, British flag. Illustration reduced.

**2007, Feb. 15**
3631 A649 $2 Pair, #a-b   3.00 3.00
Printed in sheets containing three of each stamp.

Scouting, Cent. — A650

No. 3632 — Scout sign and denomination in: a, Blue. b, Orange. c, Red violet. d, Green $6, Orange.

**2007, Feb. 15**
3632 A650 $3 Sheet of 4, #a-d   9.00 9.00
**Souvenir Sheet**
3633 A650 $6 multi   4.50 4.50

Pres. John F. Kennedy (1917-63) — A651

No. 3634, $2 — First meeting with Soviet Premier Nikita Khrushchev: a, Khrushchev at the Simferopol Space Control Center. b, Kennedy greeting Khrushchev. c, Kennedy and Khrushchev on sofa. d, Kennedy and Khrushchev at residence of US Ambassador in Vienna.

No. 3635, $2 — Cuban Missile Crisis: a, Khrushchev and Fidel Castro. b, Kennedy addressing nation. c, Completed SA-2 missile site. d, Kennedy and Khrushchev shaking hands in Vienna.

**2007, Feb. 15**
**Sheets of 4, #a-d**
3634-3635 A651 Set of 2   12.00 12.00

Souvenir Sheet

New Year 2007 (Year of the Pig) — A652

No. 3636 — Text "Traditional Chinese New Year Paper Cutting" in: a, $1, Black. b, $1, White. c, $2, Beige. d, $2, Yellow.

**2007, Feb. 18**     **Perf. 14**
3636 A652   Sheet of 4, #a-d   4.50 4.50

Pope Benedict XVI — A653

**2007, June 4**   **Litho.**   **Perf. 13¼**
3637 A653 $1 multi     .75 .75
Printed in sheets of 8.

2007 Cricket World Cup, East Indies — A654

Designs: $1, Cricket World Cup emblem, flag and map of Grenada. $2, Rawl Lewis. $3, Queen's Park, horiz. $6, Cricket World Cup emblem.

**2007, June 18**
3638-3640 A654   Set of 3     4.50 4.50
**Souvenir Sheet**
3641 A654   $6 multi     4.50 4.50

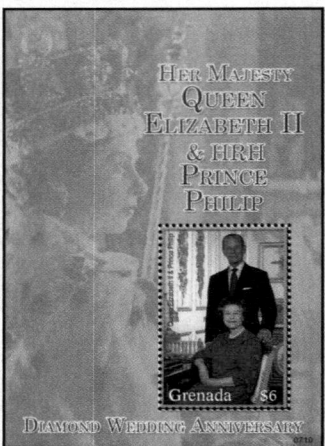

Wedding of Queen Elizabeth II and Prince Philip, 60th Anniv. — A655

No. 3642: a, Queen and Prince, orange panel. b, Queen, orange panel. c, Queen, light blue panel. d, Queen and Prince, light blue panel. e, Queen and Prince, lilac panel. f, Queen, lilac panel.
$6, Queen and Prince, diff.

---

**2007, June 25**
3642 A655 $2 Sheet of 6, #a-f   9.00 9.00
**Souvenir Sheet**
3643 A655 $6 multi     4.50 4.50

Princess Diana (1961-97) — A656

No. 3644 — Diana with: a, Red dress. b, Light blue and white dress. c, White gown. d, Green and white dress.
No. 3645, $6, Scarf on head. No. 3646, $6, Red dress, horiz.

**2007, June 25**
3644 A656 $2 Sheet of 4, #a-d   6.00 6.00
**Souvenir Sheets**
3645-3646 A656   Set of 2    9.00 9.00

Intl. Polar Year — A657

No. 3647, vert.: a, Adult penguin with head raised. b, Three penguins in distance. c, Adult penguin with head lowered. d, Juvenile penguin, ball. e, Juvenile penguin with wings extended. f, Juvenile penguin with head raised.
$6, Penguin on skis.

**2007, June 25**
3647 A657 $2 Sheet of 6, #a-f   9.00 9.00
**Souvenir Sheet**
3648 A657 $6 multi     4.50 4.50

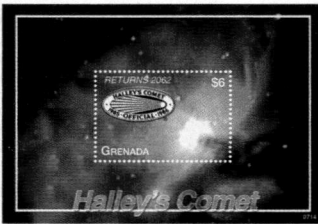

1986 Halley's Comet Merchandising Emblem — A658

No. 3649: a, Orange brown frame. b, Dark blue frame. c, Purple frame. d, Red frame.
$6, Emblem, night sky.

**2007, July 11**
3649 A658 $2 Sheet of 4, #a-d   6.00 6.00
**Souvenir Sheet**
3650 A658 $6 multi     4.50 4.50

---

U.S. Presidents — A659

No. 3651: a, 1c, George Washington. b, 2c, John Adams. c, 3c, Thomas Jefferson. d, 4c, James Madison. e, 5c, James Monroe. f, 6c, John Quincy Adams. g, 7c, Andrew Jackson. h, 8c, Martin Van Buren. i, 9c, William Henry Harrison. j, 10c, John Tyler. k, 11c, James Knox Polk. l, 12c, Zachary Taylor. m, 13c, Millard Fillmore. n, 14c, Franklin Pierce. o, $4, Presidential seal.
No. 3652: a, 15c, James Buchanan. b, 16c, Abraham Lincoln. c, 17c, Andrew Johnson. d, 18c, Ulysses S. Grant. e, 19c, Rutherford B. Hayes. f, 20c, James A. Garfield. g, 21c, Chester A. Arthur. h, 22c, Grover Cleveland. i, 23c, Benjamin Harrison. j, 24c, Grover Cleveland. k, 25c, William McKinley. l, 26c, Theodore Roosevelt. m, 27c, William Howard Taft. n, 28c, Woodrow Wilson. o, $2, Capitol Dome.
No. 3653: a, 29c, Warren G. Harding. b, 30c, Calvin Coolidge. c, 31c, Herbert Hoover. d, 32c, Franklin D. Roosevelt. e, 33c, Harry S Truman. f, 34c, Dwight D. Eisenhower. g, 35c, John F. Kennedy. h, 36c, Lyndon B. Johnson. i, 37c, Richard M. Nixon. j, 38c, Gerald R. Ford. k, 39c, Jimmy Carter. l, 40c, Ronald Reagan. m, 41c, George H. W. Bush. n, 42c, William J. Clinton. o, 43c, George W. Bush.

**2007, July 16**     **Perf. 12**
3651 A659   Sheet of 15, #a-o   3.75 3.75
3652 A659   Sheet of 15, #a-o   3.75 3.75
3653 A659   Sheet of 15, #a-o   4.00 4.00
    Nos. 3651-3653 (3)    11.50 11.50

Worldwide Fund for Nature (WWF) — A660

No. 3654 — Clymene dolphins with denomination in: a, Orange. b, Bluish green. c, Yellow. d, Aquamarine.

**2007, July 23**     **Perf. 13¼**
3654    Strip of 4     3.75 3.75
  a.-d.   A660 $1.20 Any single   .90 .90
  e.   Miniature sheet, 2 each #3654a-3654d    7.50 7.50

Souvenir Sheet

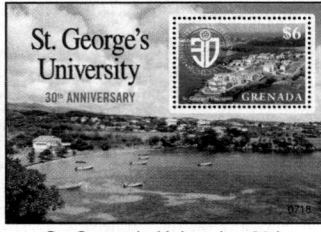

St. George's University, 30th Anniv. — A661

**2007, Oct. 26**     **Perf. 12¾**
3655 A661 $6 multi     4.50 4.50

---

Souvenir Sheet

Susan Bristol, Painting by Bernard Vidal — A662

**2007, Oct. 26**     **Perf. 13¼**
3656 A662 $6 multi     4.50 4.50

Victoria Cross, 150th Anniv. — A663

No. 3657, vert.: a, Corporal Bryan Budd. b, Brigadier General James Forbes-Robertson. c, Private Johnson Beharry. d, Sergeant William J. Gordon. e, Private Henry Tandey. f, Private Jorgen Christian Jensen.
$6, Seaman Jack Mantel.

**2007, Oct. 26**     **Litho.**
3657 A663 $1.50 Sheet of 6, #a-f 6.75 6.75
**Souvenir Sheet**
3658 A663   $6 multi     4.50 4.50

First Helicopter Flight, Cent. — A664

No. 3659, horiz.: a, S-65/RH-53D. b, Autogyro and bird. c, BK 117. d, AS-64.
$6, AH-64 Apache.

**2007, Oct. 26**
3659 A664 $2 Sheet of 4, #a-d   6.00 6.00
**Souvenir Sheet**
3660 A664 $6 multi     4.50 4.50

Miniature Sheets

Intl. Holocaust Remembrance Day — A665

No. 3661 $1.40 — United Nations diplomats and delegates: a, Srgian Kerim, President of 62nd General Assembly. b, Andrei Dapkiunas, Belarus. c, Jean-Marie Ehouzou, Benin. d, Milos Prica, Bosnia & Herzegovina. e, Samuel O. Outlule, Botswana. f, Francis K. Butagira,

Uganda. g, Valeriy P. Kuchinsky, Ukraine. h, Jean Ping, President of 59th General Assembly.

No. 3662, $1.40: a, Erasmo Lara-Peña, Dominican Republic. b, Diego Cordovez, Ecuador. c, Carmen M. Gallardo-Hernandez, El Salvador. d, Lino Sima Ekua Avomo, Equatorial Guinea. e, Tina Intelmann, Estonia. f, Dawit Yohannes, Ethiopia. g, Isikia Rabiei Savua, Fiji. h, Lars Wide, Chef de Cabinet of 60th General Assembly.

No. 3663, $1.40: a, Angus Friday, Grenada. b, Alfredo Lopes Cabral, Guinea-Bissau. c, Samuel Rudolph Insanally, Guyana. d, Lèo Mérorès, Haiti. e, Ivan Romero-Martinez, Honduras. f, Gabor Brodi, Hungary. g, Hjalmar W. Hannesson, Iceland. h, Dan Gillerman, Israel.

No. 3664, $1.40: a, Colin Beck, Solomon Islands. b, Dumisani S. Kumalo, South Africa. c, Juan Antonio Yáñez-Barnueva, Spain. d, Anders Liden, Sweden. e, Peter Maurer, Switzerland. f, K. Laxanachantorn Laohaphan, Thailand. g, José Luis Guterres, East Timor. h, Fekitamoeloa 'Utoikamanu, Tonga.

**2007, Oct. 26**    **Litho.**
**Sheets of 8, #a-h**
3661-3664 A665 Set of 4   35.00 35.00

Christmas A666

Various details from Nativity with the Annunciation to the Shepherds, by Follower of Jan Joest: 25c, 50c, 75c, $1.

**2007, Nov. 1**    **Perf. 14¾x14**
3665-3668 A666 Set of 4   1.90 1.90

New Year 2008 (Year of the Rat) A667

**2007, Dec. 3**   **Litho.**   **Perf. 13x13¼**
3669 A667 $2 multi   1.50 1.50
Printed in sheets of 4.

Souvenir Sheet
Breast Cancer Prevention — A668

**2007, Dec. 11**    **Perf. 14**
3670 A668 $6 multi   4.50 4.50

Princess Diana (1961-97) — A669

Illustration reduced.

**Serpentine Die Cut 7¾**
**2007, Dec. 11**   **Litho. & Embossed**
**Without Gum**
3671 A669 $20 gold & multi   15.00 15.00

---

Miniature Sheets

A670

Elvis Presley (1935-77) — A671

No. 3672 — Presley: a, Holding guitar at neck. b, Singing, not touching microphone. c, Wearing green shirt. d, Facing right, playing guitar. e, Singing, holding microphone. f, Facing right, playing guitar.
No. 3673 — Presley: a, Holding microphone. b, Wearing necktie. c, Holding guitar over shoulder. d, And guitar head.

**2008**   **Litho.**   **Perf. 13¼**
3672 A670 $1.50 Sheet of 6, #a-f 6.75 6.75
3673 A671 $2 Sheet of 4, #a-d 6.00 6.00
Issued: No. 3672, 1/14; No. 3673, 6/13.

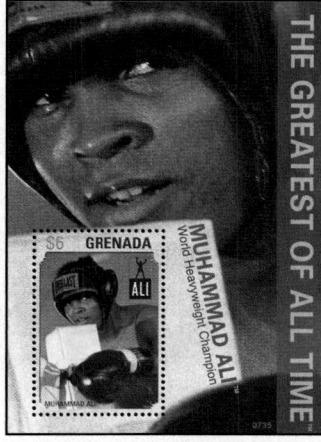
Muhammad Ali, Boxer — A672

No. 3674, $2 — Ali: a, With towel on head, bank of microphones at left. b, With towel on head, bank of microphone at right. c, With fist raised. d, With towel off head, bank of microphones at right.
No. 3675, $2, horiz. — Ali: a, With arms raised. b, Wearing robe. c, At punching bag. d, Boxing.
No. 3676, $6, Ali wearing protective headgear. No. 3677, $2, Ali with fan's hand on shoulder.

**Perf. 12x11½, 11½ (#3675)**
**2008, Jan. 14**
**Sheets of 4, #a-d**
3674-3675 A672 Set of 2 12.00 12.00
**Souvenir Sheets**
**Perf. 13¼**
3676-3677 A672 Set of 2 9.00 9.00

---

Paintings by Qi Baishi (1864-1957) — A673

No. 3678: a, Magnolias and Bees. b, Mother Hen, Chicks and Banana Leaves. c, Fish, Crabs and Watergrass. d, Crows Returning to Wintry Trees.
$4, Morning Glories.

**2008. Feb. 6**    **Perf. 12½**
3678 A673 $1 Sheet of 4, #a-d 3.00 3.00
**Souvenir Sheet**
**Perf. 11¼x11½**
3679 A673 $4 multi 3.00 3.00

Miniature Sheet

2008 Summer Olympics, Beijing — A674

No. 3680: a, Greece #123. b, Poster for 1896 Olympic Games, Athens. c, Germany #B88. d, Poster for 1936 Olympic Games, Berlin.

**2008, Feb. 6**    **Perf. 14¼**
3680 A674 $3 Sheet of 4, #a-d 9.00 9.00

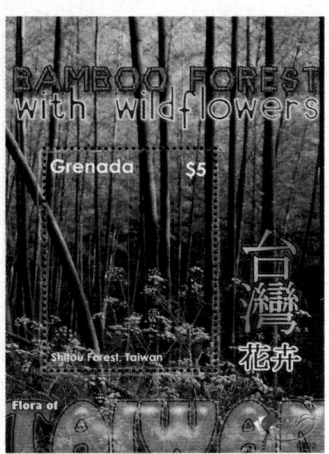
Flora of Taiwan — A675

---

No. 3681, horiz.: a, Oolong tea. b, Pink lotus. c, Japanese maple. d, Bitter melon. e, Rice field. f, Lychees.
$5, Shitou Forest.

**2008, May 8**    **Perf. 11½**
3681 A675 $1 Sheet of 6, #a-f 4.50 4.50
**Souvenir Sheet**
**Perf. 13½**
3682 A675 $5 multi 3.75 3.75
No. 3681 contains six 40x30mm stamps. 2008 Taipei Intl. Stamp Exhibition.

2008 World Stamp Championship, Israel — A676

Illustration reduced.

**2008, May 14**    **Imperf.**
3683 A676 $6 multi 4.50 4.50

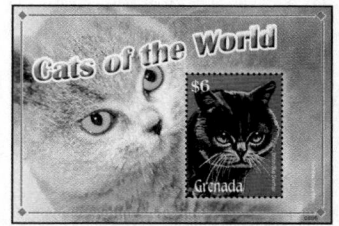
Cats — A677

No. 3684: a, Tortoiseshell. b, Korat. c, Turkish Van. d, Manx.
$6, British blue shorthair.

**2008, June 18**    **Perf. 11½**
3684 A677 $1.40 Sheet of 4, #a-d 4.25 4.25
**Souvenir Sheet**
3685 A677 $6 multi 4.50 4.50

Miniature Sheet

Players on 2008 Los Angeles Lakers Basketball Team — A678

No. 3686: a, Trevor Ariza. b, Jordan Farmar. c, Derek Fisher. d, Pau Gasol. e, Kobe Bryant.

f, Lamar Odom. g, Vladimir Radmanovic. h, Sasha Vujacic. i, Luke Walton.

**2008, June 17      Litho.      Perf. 13½**
3686  A678  $1 Sheet of 9, #a-i      6.75  6.75

### Miniature Sheet

Visit of Pope Benedict XVI to United States — A679

No. 3687 — Pope Benedict XVI and faded background showing: a, Bishop's red zucchetto under LL flourish. b, White ceiling tiles at top. c, Bishop's ear at UL. d, Bishop's hands at R.

**2008, June 18                    Perf. 13½**
3687  A679  $2 Sheet of 4, #a-d      6.00  6.00

### Miniature Sheet

Pres. John F. Kennedy (1917-63) — A680

No. 3688 — Kennedy and background designs of: a, Flag's white stripe and blue field. b, Flag's white and red stripes. c, Necktie. d, Flag's red and white stripes, with blue in UL corner.

**2008, Oct. 10                    Perf. 11½x11¼**
3688  A680  $1.50 Sheet of 4, #a-d      4.50  4.50

### Miniature Sheets

A681

A682

A683

A684

A685

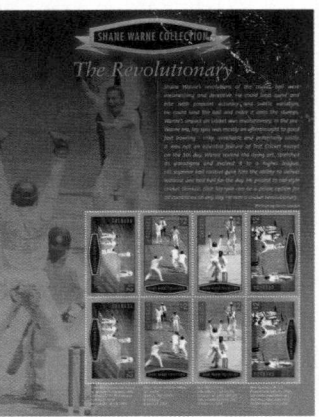

Shane Warne, Cricket Player — A686

No. 3689 — Warne: a, Holding ball, tan frame. b, Waving to crowd, tan frame. c, Close-up, tan frame. d, Wearing white shirt, green frame. e, As "b," green frame. f, As "c," green frame.

No. 3690 — Warne: a, Bowling in Australia uniform, tan frame. b, Holding trophy, tan frame. c, Celebrating, tan frame. d, As "a," green frame. e, As "b," green frame. f, As "c," green frame.

No. 3691 — Drawings of Warne by Phillip Howe: a, The Mastery (tan frame). b, The Revolutionary (tan frame). c, The Appeal (tan frame). d, The Natural (tan frame). e, As "a," green frame. f, As "b," green frame. g, As "c," green frame. h, As "d," green frame. Titles are in sheet margin.

No. 3692 — Warne bowling: a, Left arm horizontal, tan frame. b, Leg lifted, hands even, tan frame. c, Leg lifted, right hand higher than left hand, tan frame. d, Arm above head, tan frame. e, As "a," green frame. f, As "b," green frame. g, As "c," green frame. h, As "d," green frame.

No. 3693 — Warne: a, Celebrating and making fist, tan frame. b, With ball near ear, tan frame. c, After releasing ball, tan frame. d, With arm above head, umpire in background, tan frame. e, As "a," green frame. f, As "b," green frame. g, As "c," green frame. h, As "d," green frame.

No. 3694 — Match scenes: a, Warne bowling against Mike Gatting, tan frame, horiz. b, Warne taking 600th test wicket, tan frame. c, Warne capturing 533rd wicket, tan frame. d, Warne taking 356th test wicket, tan frame. e, As "a," green frame. f, As "b," green frame. g, As "c," green frame. h, As "d," green frame. Match descriptions are in sheet margin.

**2008, Dec. 3     Perf. 14x14½, 14½x14**
3689  A681  $2 Sheet of 6, #a-f    9.25   9.25
3690  A682  $2 Sheet of 6, #a-f    9.25   9.25
3691  A683  $2 Sheet of 8, #a-h   12.50  12.50
3692  A684  $2 Sheet of 8, #a-h   12.50  12.50
3693  A685  $2 Sheet of 8, #a-h   12.50  12.50
3694  A686  $2 Sheet of 8, #a-h   12.50  12.50
      Nos. 3689-3694 (6)          68.50  68.50

### Miniature Sheet

Pope John Paul II (1920-2005) — A687

No. 3695 — Pope John Paul II: a, As child. b, At coronation. c, Holding books. d, With hands raised. e, Wearing biretta, hand on chin. f, Wearing zucchetto, hand touching face.

**2008, Dec. 8                    Perf. 13½**
3695  A687  $2 Sheet of 6, #a-f    9.25   9.25

---

## SEMI-POSTAL STAMPS

Nos. 227-229 Overprinted

| CHILDREN | CHILDREN |
|----------|----------|
| NEED | NEED |
| MILK | MILK |
| 3cts. + 3cts. | 1c. + 3cts. |
| Type I | Type II |

**1968**

**Type I**
B1A  A38  2c + 3c on $2 multi     .20    .20
B1B  A38  3c + 3c on $3 multi     .20    .20

**Type II**
B1C  A38  1c + 3c on $2 multi     .20    .20
B1D  A38  2c + 3c on $3 multi   22.50  50.00
     Nos. B1A-B1D (4)           23.10  50.60

Issued: B1A-B1B, 7/22; B1C-B1D, 8/19.

ESPANA '82 World Cup Soccer SP1

Players and Flags of Winning Countries.

**Unwmk.**
**1981, Nov. 30      Litho.      Perf. 14**
B1   SP1  25c + 10c West Germany, 1974      .50   .50
B2   SP1  40c + 20c Argentina, 1978         .70   .70
B3   SP1  50c + 25c Brazil, 1970          1.00  1.00
B4   SP1  $1 + 50c Grt. Britain, 1966      1.75  1.75
     Nos. B1-B4 (4)                        3.95  3.95

**Souvenir Sheet**
B5   SP1  $5 + 50c World Cup, ESPANA '82   4.00  4.00

Nos. B1-B4 each issued in sheets of 12 with sheet background showing soccer ball.

1988 Seoul Olympics — SP2

**1986, Dec. 1      Litho.      Perf. 15**
B6   SP2  10c + 5c Pole vault          .25   .30
B7   SP2  50c + 20c Balance beam       .55   .65
B8   SP2  70c + 30c Shot put           .85   .85
B9   SP2  $2 + $1 High jump           1.75  2.50
     Nos. B6-B9 (4)                    3.40  4.30

**Souvenir Sheet**
B10  SP2  $3 + $1 Swimming            3.50  3.50

Surtax for natl. Olympic team.

World Philatelic Programs SP3

Halley's Comet or Stamp Collecting emblem and: No. B11, Halley's initial work on nebulae, 1676. No. B12, Experiments at sea (tall ship, manned capsule). No. B13, Halley observes complete lunar cycle, 1720-1738. No. B14, Halley publishes Newton's Principia, 1687. No. B15, Halley charts the southern skies, 1676.

## 1989, Apr. 25    Litho.    *Perf. 14*

| | | | |
|---|---|---|---|
| B11 | SP3 | 25c +5c multi | .75 .75 |
| B12 | SP3 | 75c +5c multi | 1.25 1.25 |
| B13 | SP3 | 90c +5c multi | 1.50 1.50 |
| B14 | SP3 | $2 +5c multi | 2.00 2.00 |

**Size: 111x78mm**
*Imperf*

| | | | |
|---|---|---|---|
| B15 | SP3 | $5 +5c multi | 4.25 4.25 |
| | | *Nos. B11-B15 (5)* | 9.75 9.75 |

### AIR POST STAMPS

Catalogue values for unused stamps in this section are for Never Hinged items.

Nos. 428-429 Surcharged with New Value, Olympic Rings, "Air Mail" and: "WINTER OLYMPICS / FEB. 3-13, 1972 / SAPPORO, JAPAN"

**Perf. 13½x14**

**1972, Feb. 3   Litho.   Unwmk.**

| | | | |
|---|---|---|---|
| C1 | A66 | 35c on ½c multi | .40 .40 |
| C2 | A66 | 50c on 1c multi | .60 .60 |

11th Winter Olympic Games, Sapporo, Japan, Feb. 3-13.

Nos. 294-300, 302A, 303-309 Surcharged Type "a" or Overprinted Type "b"

a

b

**Perfs. as Before**

**1972, May 2    Photo.; Litho.**

| | | | |
|---|---|---|---|
| C3 | A45 | 5c violet & multi | .20 .20 |
| C4 | A45 | 8c multicolored | .20 .20 |
| C5 | A45 | 10c orange & multi | .20 .20 |
| C6 | A45 | 15c gray & multi | .20 .20 |
| C7 | A45 | 25c multicolored | .40 .30 |
| C8 | A45 | 30c on 1c multi | .50 .35 |
| C9 | A45 | 35c multicolored | .55 .40 |
| C10 | A45 | 40c on 2c multi | .60 .45 |
| C11 | A45 | 45c on 3c multi | .65 .50 |
| C12 | A45 | 50c multicolored | .70 .55 |
| C13 | A45 | 60c on 5c multi | .80 .70 |
| C14 | A45 | 70c on 6c multi | .95 .90 |
| C15 | A45 | $1 multicolored | 7.00 1.25 |
| C16 | A45 | $1.35 on 8c multi | 3.50 3.00 |
| C17 | A45 | $2 multicolored | 8.50 7.00 |
| C18 | A45 | $3 multicolored | 11.00 9.00 |
| C19 | A45 | $5 multicolored | 14.00 16.00 |
| | | *Nos. C3-C19 (17)* | 49.95 41.20 |

"AIR MAIL" reading down on 5c, 15c, 25c, 35c, 60c and $5.

### Olympic Type of Regular Issue

Olympic Rings and: 25c, 60c, $1, Boxing. 70c, Equestrian (not inscribed air mail).

**1972, Sept. 8    Litho.    *Perf. 14***

| | | | |
|---|---|---|---|
| C20 | A69 | 25c blue & multi | .60 .40 |
| C21 | A69 | $1 green & multi | 1.00 .85 |

**Souvenir Sheet**

| | | | |
|---|---|---|---|
| C22 | | Sheet of 2 | 1.50 1.50 |
| a. | | A69 60c blue & multi | .50 .50 |
| b. | | A69 70c deep yellow & multi | 1.00 1.00 |

---

Nos. 409-412 Overprinted Vertically, Reading Up "AIR MAIL"

**1972, Oct.    Litho.    *Perf. 11***

| | | | |
|---|---|---|---|
| C23 | A62 | 5c multicolored | .60 .20 |
| C24 | A62 | 35c multicolored | 1.50 .60 |
| C25 | A62 | 50c multicolored | 1.75 1.00 |
| C26 | A62 | 75c multicolored | 2.50 2.00 |
| | | *Nos. C23-C26 (4)* | 6.35 3.80 |

### Boy Scout Type of Regular Issue

Designs: 25c, Scout saluting. 35c, Two Scouts knotting ropes.

**1972, Nov.        *Perf. 14***

| | | | |
|---|---|---|---|
| C27 | A70 | 25c dp blue & multi | .50 .45 |
| C28 | A70 | 35c brn org & multi | .70 .65 |

John Hancock — AP1

Designs: 50c, Benjamin Franklin. 75c, John Adams. $1, Marquis de Lafayette.

**1975, May 6    Litho.    *Perf. 14½, 13***

| | | | |
|---|---|---|---|
| C29 | AP1 | 40c multicolored | .30 .20 |
| C30 | AP1 | 50c multicolored | .50 .25 |
| C31 | AP1 | 75c multicolored | .65 .25 |
| C32 | AP1 | $1 multicolored | .75 .30 |
| | | *Nos. C29-C32 (4)* | 2.20 1.00 |

American Revolution Bicentennial. Nos. C29-C32 issued in sheets of 40. Each denomination was also printed in sheets of 5 plus label, perf. 13.

### POSTAGE DUE STAMPS

D1       D2

**1892    Typo.    Wmk. 2    Perf. 14**

| | | | |
|---|---|---|---|
| J1 | D1 | 1p black | 30.00 2.75 |
| J2 | D1 | 2p black | 190.00 3.25 |
| J3 | D1 | 3p black | 190.00 4.00 |
| | | *Nos. J1-J3 (3)* | 410.00 10.00 |

**Black Surcharge**

| | | | |
|---|---|---|---|
| J4 | D2 | 1p on 6p red lilac | 92.50 2.25 |
| a. | | Tete beche pair | 1,400. *1,800.* |
| b. | | Double surcharge | 190.00 |
| c. | | Same as "b," tete beche pair | |
| J5 | D2 | 1p on 8p bister | 875.00 6.00 |
| a. | | Tete beche pair | *4,000. 1,600.* |
| J6 | D2 | 2p on 6p red lilac | 190.00 4.50 |
| a. | | Tete beche pair | *2,000. 1,275.* |
| J7 | D2 | 2p on 8p bister | 3,200. 12.00 |
| a. | | Tete beche pair | *7,500. 3,500.* |
| | | *Nos. J4-J7 (4)* | 4,357. 24.75 |

Nos. J4-J7 were printed with alternate horizontal rows inverted.

**1906-11        Wmk. 3**

| | | | |
|---|---|---|---|
| J8 | D1 | 1p black ('11) | 3.75 *5.00* |
| J9 | D1 | 2p black | 12.50 3.75 |
| J10 | D1 | 3p black | 15.00 6.50 |
| | | *Nos. J8-J10 (3)* | 31.25 15.25 |

D3

---

**1921-22        Wmk. 4**

| | | | |
|---|---|---|---|
| J11 | D3 | 1p black | 1.40 *1.40* |
| J12 | D3 | 1½p black | 10.00 *20.00* |
| J13 | D3 | 2p black | 3.00 *4.50* |
| J14 | D3 | 3p black | 3.00 *4.75* |
| | | *Nos. J11-J14 (4)* | 17.40 *30.65* |

Issued: 1½p, Dec. 15, 1922, others, Dec. 1921.

Catalogue values for unused stamps in this section, from this point to the end of the section, are for Never Hinged items.

**1952, Mar. 1**

| | | | |
|---|---|---|---|
| J15 | D3 | 2c black | .50 9.00 |
| a. | | Wmk. 4a (error) | 25.00 |
| J16 | D3 | 4c black | .50 9.00 |
| a. | | Wmk. 4a (error) | 25.00 |
| J17 | D3 | 6c black | .65 13.00 |
| a. | | Wmk. 4a (error) | 42.50 |
| J18 | D3 | 8c black | .60 11.00 |
| a. | | Wmk. 4a (error) | 50.00 |
| | | *Nos. J15-J18 (4)* | 2.25 42.00 |

### WAR TAX STAMPS

Nos. 80a, 80 Overprinted

**1916    Wmk. 3    *Perf. 14***

| | | | |
|---|---|---|---|
| MR1 | A21 | 1p carmine | 2.50 2.00 |
| a. | | 1p scarlet | 3.00 3.00 |
| b. | | Double overprint | 325.00 |
| c. | | Inverted overprint | 325.00 |

No. 80 Overprinted

| | | | |
|---|---|---|---|
| MR2 | A21 | 1p scarlet | .30 .20 |

### OFFICIAL STAMPS

Catalogue values for unused stamps in this section are for Never Hinged items.

Nos. 1006-1018, 1020, 1051-1053 Overprinted: "P.R.G."

**1982, July 15    Litho.    *Perf. 14, 15***

| | | | |
|---|---|---|---|
| O1 | A141 | 5c multicolored | .20 .20 |
| O2 | A141 | 6c multicolored | .20 .20 |
| O3 | A141 | 10c multicolored | .20 .20 |
| O4 | A141 | 12c multicolored | .20 .20 |
| O5 | A141 | 15c multicolored | .20 .20 |
| O6 | A141 | 20c multicolored | .20 .20 |
| O7 | A141 | 25c multicolored | .20 .20 |
| O8 | A141 | 30c multicolored | .25 .25 |
| O9 | A141 | 40c multicolored | .30 .30 |
| O10 | A141 | 50c multicolored | .40 .40 |
| O11 | CD331 | 50c multicolored | .40 .40 |
| O12 | A141 | 90c multicolored | .75 .75 |
| O13 | A141 | $1 multicolored | .80 .80 |
| O14 | CD331 | $2 multicolored | 2.00 2.00 |
| O15 | A141 | $3 multicolored | 2.50 2.50 |
| O16 | CD331 | $4 multicolored | 4.50 4.50 |
| O17 | A141 | $10 multicolored | 8.00 8.00 |
| | | *Nos. O1-O17 (17)* | 21.30 21.30 |

PRG stands for People's Revolutionary Government.

## GRENADA GRENADINES

grə-'nä-də ˌgre-nə-'dēnz

LOCATION — North of Grenada
GOVT. — Part of Grenada
CAPITAL — None

---

Main islands are Carriacou and Ronde.

Catalogue values for all unused stamps in this country are for Never Hinged items.

All stamps are a type of Grenada unless otherwise noted or illustrated. Nos. 15-58 have the additional inscription Grenadines.

Grenada Nos. 516-517a Overprinted

**Perf. 13½x14**

**1973, Dec. 23   Litho.   Wmk. 314**

| | | | |
|---|---|---|---|
| 1 | A77 | 25c dp orange & multi | .20 .20 |
| 2 | A77 | $2 green & multi | .60 .50 |
| a. | | Souvenir sheet of 2 (75c, $1) | .80 .50 |

Grenada Nos. 294-297, 299-301, 303, 306-309 Overprinted

**Perf. 14x14½, 14½x14**

**1974, May 29    Photo.    Unwmk.**

**Size: 25x44mm**

| | | | |
|---|---|---|---|
| 3 | A45 | 1c multicolored | .20 .20 |
| 4 | A45 | 2c multicolored | .20 .20 |
| 5 | A45 | 3c multicolored | .20 .20 |
| 6 | A45 | 5c multicolored | .20 .20 |
| 7 | A45 | 8c multicolored | .20 .20 |
| 8 | A45 | 10c multicolored | .20 .20 |
| 9 | A45 | 12c multicolored | .20 .20 |
| 10 | A45 | 25c multicolored | .30 .30 |

**Size: 25x47mm**

| | | | |
|---|---|---|---|
| 11 | A45 | $1 multicolored | 3.00 1.40 |
| 12 | A45 | $2 multicolored | 4.75 2.00 |
| 13 | A45 | $3 multicolored | 4.75 2.90 |
| 14 | A45 | $5 multicolored | 5.50 3.50 |
| | | *Nos. 3-14 (12)* | 19.70 11.50 |

### World Cup Soccer Type

Designs: Soccer matches and flags. ½c, West Germany-Chile. 1c, East Germany-Australia. 2c, Yugoslavia-Brazil. 10c, Scotland-Zaire. 25c, Netherlands-Uruguay. 50c, Sweden-Bulgaria. 75c, Italy-Haiti. $1, Poland-Argentina. $2, Flags of participating nations.

**1974, Sept. 17    Litho.    *Perf. 14½***

| | | | |
|---|---|---|---|
| 15 | A81 | ½c multicolored | .20 .20 |
| 16 | A81 | 1c multicolored | .20 .20 |
| 17 | A81 | 2c multicolored | .20 .20 |
| 18 | A81 | 10c multicolored | .25 .20 |
| 19 | A81 | 25c multicolored | .35 .20 |
| 20 | A81 | 50c multicolored | .45 .25 |
| 21 | A81 | 75c multicolored | .45 .25 |
| 22 | A81 | $1 multicolored | .50 .30 |
| | | *Nos. 15-22 (8)* | 2.60 1.80 |

**Souvenir Sheet**

| | | | |
|---|---|---|---|
| 23 | A81 | $2 multicolored | 2.25 2.25 |

### UPU Centenary Type

UPU Emblem and: 8c, Mailboat *Caesar*, 1839, helicopter. 25c, German messenger, 1540, satellite. 35c, Biplanes, zeppelin, jet. No. 27, US Mail train, 19th cent., Concorde. No. 28a, Bellman, 18th cent., radar. $2, German postman, 18th cent., mail train, 1980's.

**1974, Oct. 8        *Perf. 14½***

| | | | |
|---|---|---|---|
| 24 | A82 | 8c multicolored | .20 .20 |
| 25 | A82 | 25c multicolored | .20 .20 |
| 26 | A82 | 35c multicolored | .25 .20 |
| 27 | A82 | $1 multicolored | 1.10 .50 |
| | | *Nos. 24-27 (4)* | 1.75 1.10 |

### Souvenir Sheet
### Perf. 13

| 28 | | Sheet of 2 | 2.25 | 2.25 |
|----|----|----|----|----|
| a. | | A82 $1 multicolored | .50 | .50 |
| b. | | A82 $2 multicolored | 1.25 | 1.25 |

### Churchill Type

Design: $2, Churchill, different portrait.

### 1974, Nov. 11     Perf. 13½

| 29 | A83 | 35c multicolored | .20 | .20 |
|----|----|----|----|----|
| 30 | A83 | $2 multicolored | .50 | .50 |

### Souvenir Sheet

| 31 | | Sheet of 2 | .80 | .80 |
|----|----|----|----|----|
| a. | | A82 75c like 35c | .30 | .30 |
| b. | | A82 $1 like $2 | .35 | .35 |

### Christmas Type

Paintings of the Virgin and Child.

### 1974, Nov. 27     Perf. 14½

| 32 | A84 | ½c Botticelli | .20 | .20 |
|----|----|----|----|----|
| 33 | A84 | 1c Niccolo di Pietro | .20 | .20 |
| 34 | A84 | 2c Van der Weyden | .20 | .20 |
| 35 | A84 | 3c Bastiani | .20 | .20 |
| 36 | A84 | 10c Giovanni | .20 | .20 |
| 37 | A84 | 25c Van der Weyden, diff. | .20 | .20 |
| 38 | A84 | 50c Botticelli | .20 | .20 |
| 39 | A84 | $1 Mantegna | .30 | .25 |
| | | Nos. 32-39 (8) | 1.70 | 1.65 |

### Souvenir Sheet
### Perf. 13½

| 40 | A84 | $2 Niccolo di Pietro | 1.10 | 1.10 |
|----|----|----|----|----|

### Big Game Fish Type

### 1975, Feb. 17     Perf. 14½

| 41 | A86 | ½c Sailfish | .20 | .20 |
|----|----|----|----|----|
| 42 | A86 | 1c Blue marlin | .20 | .20 |
| 43 | A86 | 2c White marlin | .20 | .20 |
| 44 | A86 | 10c Yellowfin tuna | .20 | .20 |
| 45 | A86 | 25c Wahoo | .25 | .20 |
| 46 | A86 | 50c Dolphin | .40 | .20 |
| 47 | A86 | 70c Grouper | .50 | .30 |
| 48 | A86 | $1 Great barracuda | .75 | .50 |
| | | Nos. 41-48 (8) | 2.70 | 2.00 |

### Souvenir Sheet
### Perf. 13

| 49 | A86 | $2 Mako shark | 2.25 | 2.25 |
|----|----|----|----|----|

### Flowers of Grenada Type

### 1975, Mar. 11     Perf. 14½

| 50 | A87 | ½c Grandilla barbadine | .20 | .20 |
|----|----|----|----|----|
| 51 | A87 | 1c Bleeding heart | .20 | .20 |
| 52 | A87 | 2c Poinsettia | .20 | .20 |
| 53 | A87 | 3c Cocoa | .20 | .20 |
| 54 | A87 | 10c Gladioli | .20 | .20 |
| 55 | A87 | 25c Red head-yellow head | .20 | .20 |
| 56 | A87 | 50c Plumbago | .40 | .35 |
| 57 | A87 | $1 Orange blossoms | .75 | .55 |
| | | Nos. 50-57 (8) | 2.35 | 2.10 |

### Souvenir Sheet
### Perf. 13½

| 58 | A87 | $2 Barbados gooseberry | 1.75 | 1.75 |
|----|----|----|----|----|

Remainders of Grenada Grenadines stamps between Scott Nos. 59 and 269, except Nos. 109-128, 217-220, 237-240 and some souvenir sheets, were later canceled to order and sold at a fraction of their face value. Our used values for these stamps are for c-t-o examples. Postally used stamps are worth the same as unused, never hinged examples.

Christ Crowned with Thorns, by Titian — G1

Easter paintings of the Crucifixion by various artists.

### 1975, June 24     Perf. 14½

| 59 | G1 | ½c shown | .20 | .20 |
|----|----|----|----|----|
| 60 | G1 | 1c Giotto | .20 | .20 |
| 61 | G1 | 2c Tintoretto | .20 | .20 |
| 62 | G1 | 3c Cranach | .20 | .20 |
| 63 | G1 | 35c Caravaggio | .20 | .20 |
| 64 | G1 | 75c Tiepolo | .25 | .20 |
| 65 | G1 | $2 Velasquez | .30 | .20 |
| | | Nos. 59-65 (7) | 1.50 | 1.40 |

### Souvenir Sheet
### Perf. 13½

| 66 | G1 | $1 Titian, diff. | 1.25 | 1.25 |
|----|----|----|----|----|

Works by Michelangelo (1475-1564) — G2    Butterflies — G3

Designs: ½c, Dawn (sculpture, detail from Medici tomb). 1c, Delphic Sibyl. 2c, Giuliano de Medici (sculpture). 40c, The Creation. 50c, Lorenzo de Medici (sculpture). 75c, Persian Sibyl. $1, The Prophet Jeremiah. $2, Head of Christ (sculpture).

### 1975, July 16     Perf. 14½

| 67 | G2 | ½c violet & multi | .20 | .20 |
|----|----|----|----|----|
| 68 | G2 | 1c multicolored | .20 | .20 |
| 69 | G2 | 2c green & multi | .20 | .20 |
| 70 | G2 | 40c multicolored | .25 | .20 |
| 71 | G2 | 50c brt red & multi | .35 | .20 |
| 72 | G2 | 75c multicolored | .50 | .20 |
| 73 | G2 | $2 brt blue & multi | .80 | .20 |
| | | Nos. 67-73 (7) | 2.50 | 1.40 |

### Souvenir Sheet
### Perf. 13½

| 74 | G2 | $1 multicolored | 1.40 | .75 |
|----|----|----|----|----|

### 1975, Aug. 12     Perf. 15

| 75 | G3 | ½c Emperor | .20 | .20 |
|----|----|----|----|----|
| 76 | G3 | 1c Queen | .20 | .20 |
| 77 | G3 | 2c Tiger pierid | .20 | .20 |
| 78 | G3 | 35c Cracker | .45 | .20 |
| 79 | G3 | 45c Scarlet bamboo page | .60 | .20 |
| 80 | G3 | 75c Apricot | 1.00 | .20 |
| 81 | G3 | $2 Purple king shoemaker | 2.75 | .20 |
| | | Nos. 75-81 (7) | 5.40 | 1.40 |

### Souvenir Sheet
### Perf. 13½

| 82 | G3 | $1 Bamboo page | 5.50 | 5.50 |
|----|----|----|----|----|

Jamboree Scenes and Badges G4

Nordjamb 75 Emblem and: ½c, Progress badge. 1c, Boating badge. 2c, Coxswain badge. 35c, Interpreter badge. 45c, Ambulance badge. 75c, Chief scout's award. $1, Venture award. $2, Queen's scout award.

### 1975, Aug. 22     Perf. 15

| 83 | G4 | ½c lemon yel & multi | .20 | .20 |
|----|----|----|----|----|
| 84 | G4 | 1c vio blue & multi | .20 | .20 |
| 85 | G4 | 2c green & multi | .20 | .20 |
| 86 | G4 | 35c dull vio & multi | .20 | .20 |
| 87 | G4 | 45c org brown & multi | .20 | .20 |
| 88 | G4 | 75c brown & multi | .30 | .20 |
| 89 | G4 | $2 green & multi | .70 | .20 |
| | | Nos. 83-89 (7) | 2.00 | 1.40 |

### Souvenir Sheet
### Perf. 13½

| 90 | G4 | $1 dull vio & multi | 1.25 | .40 |
|----|----|----|----|----|

Nordjamb 75, 14th Boy Scout World Jamboree, Lillehammer, Norway, July 29-Aug. 7.

Surrender of Lord Cornwallis G5

Designs: 1c, Minuteman. 2c, Paul Revere's Ride. 3c, Battle of Bunker Hill. 5c, Spirit of '76. 45c, Backwoodsman. 75c, Boston Tea Party. No. 98, Naval engagement. No. 99, George Washington. No. 100, White House, flags.

### 1975, Sept. 30     Perf. 14
### Size: 39x25mm

| 91 | G5 | ½c multicolored | .20 | .20 |
|----|----|----|----|----|
| 92 | G5 | 1c multicolored | .20 | .20 |
| 93 | G5 | 2c multicolored | .20 | .20 |
| 94 | G5 | 3c multicolored | .20 | .20 |
| 95 | G5 | 5c multicolored | .20 | .20 |
| 96 | G5 | 45c multicolored | .20 | .20 |
| 97 | G5 | 75c multicolored | .25 | .20 |
| 98 | G5 | $2 multicolored | .55 | .45 |

### Size: 59x39mm
### Perf. 11

| 99 | G5 | $2 multicolored, vert. | .55 | .45 |
|----|----|----|----|----|
| a. | | Souvenir sheet of 1, imperf. | 1.10 | 1.10 |
| 100 | G4 | $2 multicolored | .55 | .45 |
| a. | | Souvenir sheet of 1, imperf. | 1.10 | 1.10 |
| | | Nos. 91-100 (10) | 3.10 | 2.75 |

American Revolution Bicentennial. Nos. 99a, 100a have simulated perfs.

Fencing G6

### 1975, Oct. 27     Perf. 15

| 101 | G6 | ½c shown | .20 | .20 |
|----|----|----|----|----|
| 102 | G6 | 1c Hurdling | .20 | .20 |
| 103 | G6 | 2c Pole vault | .20 | .20 |
| 104 | G6 | 35c Weightlifting | .20 | .20 |
| 105 | G6 | 45c Javelin | .20 | .20 |
| 106 | G6 | 75c Discus | .20 | .20 |
| 107 | G6 | $2 Diving | .35 | .25 |
| | | Nos. 101-107 (7) | 1.55 | 1.45 |

### Souvenir Sheet

| 108 | G6 | $1 Sprinter | .80 | .80 |
|----|----|----|----|----|

Pan American Games, Mexico City, Oct. 12-26, 1975.

### Type of 1975

Designs: ½c, Cruising Yachts, Point Saline. 1c, Yacht Club race, St. George's. 2c, Careenage Taxi. 3c, Working boats. 5c, Deep water dock, St. George's. 6c, Cocoa beans drying. 8c, Nutmegs. 10c, Rum distillery, River Antoine Estate. 12c, Cocoa tree. 15c, Landing catch at Fontenoy. 20c, Parliament building, St. George's. 25c, Fort George cannons. 35c, Pearls airport. 50c, General Post Office. 75c, Caribs Leap, Sauteurs Bay. $1, Careenage, St. George's. $2, St. George's harbor at night. $3, Grand Anse beach. $5, Canoe and Black Bays from Point Saline lighthouse. $10, Sugar Loaf Island from Levera beach.

### 1975-76     Perf. 14½
### Size: 38x25mm

| 109 | A85 | ½c multicolored | .20 | .35 |
|----|----|----|----|----|
| 110 | A85 | 1c multicolored | .20 | .20 |
| 111 | A85 | 2c multicolored | .20 | .20 |
| 112 | A85 | 3c multicolored | .20 | .20 |
| 113 | A85 | 5c multicolored | .20 | .20 |
| 114 | A85 | 6c multicolored | .20 | .20 |
| 115 | A85 | 8c multicolored | .20 | .20 |
| 116 | A85 | 10c multicolored | .20 | .20 |
| 117 | A85 | 12c multicolored | .20 | .20 |
| 118 | A85 | 15c multicolored | .20 | .20 |
| 119 | A85 | 20c multicolored | .20 | .65 |
| 120 | A85 | 25c multicolored | .20 | .20 |
| 121 | A85 | 35c multicolored | 1.00 | .20 |
| 122 | A85 | 50c multicolored | .25 | 1.00 |

### Perf. 13½x14
### Size: 45x28mm

| 123 | A85 | 75c multicolored | .55 | .65 |
|----|----|----|----|----|
| 124 | A85 | $1 multicolored | .85 | .95 |
| 125 | A85 | $2 multicolored | 1.25 | 2.25 |
| 126 | A85 | $3 multicolored | 1.50 | 2.75 |
| 127 | A85 | $5 multicolored | 1.75 | 5.50 |
| 128 | A85 | $10 multicolored | 3.00 | 6.00 |
| | | Nos. 109-128 (20) | 12.55 | 22.30 |

Issued: #109-127, 11/5/75; #128, 1/1/76. For overprints see Nos. 360-372.

Madonna and Child by Durer — G8

Christmas: Paintings showing Madonna and Child by various artists.

### 1975, Dec. 17     Perf. 14

| 129 | G8 | ½c shown | .20 | .20 |
|----|----|----|----|----|
| 130 | G8 | 1c Durer, diff. | .20 | .20 |
| 131 | G8 | 2c Correggio | .20 | .20 |
| 132 | G8 | 40c Botticelli | .20 | .20 |
| 133 | G8 | 50c Niccolo da Cremona | .20 | .20 |
| 134 | G8 | 75c Correggio, diff. | .20 | .20 |
| 135 | G8 | $2 Correggio, diff. | .35 | .20 |
| | | Nos. 129-135 (7) | 1.55 | 1.40 |

### Souvenir Sheet

| 136 | G8 | $1 Bellini | .80 | .60 |
|----|----|----|----|----|

Sea Shells G9

### 1976, Jan. 13

| 137 | G9 | ½c Bleeding Tooth | .20 | .20 |
|----|----|----|----|----|
| 138 | G9 | 1c Wedge clam | .20 | .20 |
| 139 | G9 | 2c Hawk wing conch | .20 | .20 |
| 140 | G9 | 3c Distorsio clathrata | .20 | .20 |
| 141 | G9 | 25c Scotch bonnet | .50 | .20 |
| 142 | G9 | 50c King helmet | .95 | .20 |
| 143 | G9 | 75c Queen conch | 1.60 | .20 |
| | | Nos. 137-143 (7) | 3.85 | 1.40 |

### Souvenir Sheet

| 144 | G9 | $2 Atlantic triton | 2.75 | 1.00 |
|----|----|----|----|----|

Lignum Vitae G10

Designs: 1c, Cocoa thrush. 2c, Tarantula. 35c, Hooded tanager. 50c, Nyctaginaceae. 75c, Grenada dove. $1, Marine toad. $2, Blue-hooded euphonia.

### 1976, Feb. 4

| 145 | G10 | ½c multicolored | .20 | .20 |
|----|----|----|----|----|
| 146 | G10 | 1c multicolored | .20 | .20 |
| 147 | G10 | 2c multicolored | .20 | .20 |
| 148 | G10 | 35c multicolored | 1.25 | .20 |
| 149 | G10 | 50c multicolored | 1.25 | .20 |
| 150 | G10 | 75c multicolored | 2.50 | .30 |
| 151 | G10 | $1 multicolored | 2.50 | .30 |
| | | Nos. 145-151 (7) | 8.10 | 1.60 |

### Souvenir Sheet

| 152 | G10 | $2 multicolored | 5.75 | 1.25 |
|----|----|----|----|----|

Hooked Sailfish G11

Designs: 1c, Careened schooner, Carriacou. 2c, Annual regatta. 18c, Boat building. 22c, Workboat race. 75c, Cruising off Petit Martinique. $1, Water skiing. $2, Yacht racing.

### 1976, Feb. 17

| 153 | G11 | ½c multicolored | .20 | .20 |
|----|----|----|----|----|
| 154 | G11 | 1c multicolored | .20 | .20 |
| 155 | G11 | 2c multicolored | .20 | .20 |
| 156 | G11 | 18c multicolored | .30 | .20 |
| 157 | G11 | 22c multicolored | .30 | .20 |
| 158 | G11 | 75c multicolored | .50 | .20 |
| 159 | G11 | $1 multicolored | .65 | .25 |
| | | Nos. 153-159 (7) | 2.35 | 1.50 |

### Souvenir Sheet

| 160 | G11 | $2 multicolored | 1.00 | 1.00 |
|----|----|----|----|----|

Making a Camp Fire G12

50th anniv. of Girl Guides of Grenada: 1c, First aid. 2c, Nature study. 50c, Cooking. $1, Drawing. $2, Playing guitar.

### 1976, Mar. 17

| 161 | G12 | ½c multicolored | .20 | .20 |
|----|----|----|----|----|
| 162 | G12 | 1c multicolored | .20 | .20 |
| 163 | G12 | 2c multicolored | .20 | .20 |

| | | | |
|---|---|---|---|
| **164** | G12 | 50c multicolored | .55 .20 |
| **165** | G12 | $1 multicolored | 1.25 .30 |
| | | *Nos. 161-165 (5)* | 2.40 1.10 |

**Souvenir Sheet**

| | | | |
|---|---|---|---|
| **166** | G12 | $2 multicolored | 1.40 1.00 |

Christ Mocked by
Bosch — G13

Easter Paintings: 1c, Christ Crucified by Messina. 2c, Adoration by Durer. 3c, Lamentation of Christ by Durer. 35c, The Entombment by Van Der Weyden. $2, Blood of the Redeemer by Bellini. $3, The Deposition by Raphael.

**1976, Apr. 28**

| | | | |
|---|---|---|---|
| **167** | G13 | ½c multicolored | .20 .20 |
| **168** | G13 | 1c multicolored | .20 .20 |
| **169** | G13 | 2c multicolored | .20 .20 |
| **170** | G13 | 3c multicolored | .20 .20 |
| **171** | G13 | 35c multicolored | .20 .20 |
| **172** | G13 | $3 multicolored | .40 .30 |
| | | *Nos. 167-172 (6)* | 1.40 1.30 |

**Souvenir Sheet**

| | | | |
|---|---|---|---|
| **173** | G13 | $2 multicolored | .90 .90 |

Frigate
South
Carolina
G14

1c, Schooner Lee. 2c, HMS Roebuck. 35c, Andrew Doria. 50c, Sloop Providence. $1, Flagship Alfred. $2, Frigate Confederacy. $3, Cutter Revenge.

**1976, May 18**

| | | | |
|---|---|---|---|
| **174** | G14 | ½c multicolored | .20 .20 |
| **175** | G14 | 1c multicolored | .20 .20 |
| **176** | G14 | 2c multicolored | .20 .20 |
| **177** | G14 | 35c multicolored | .80 .20 |
| **178** | G14 | 50c multicolored | 1.00 .20 |
| **179** | G14 | $1 multicolored | 1.60 .20 |
| **180** | G14 | $2 multicolored | 2.50 .40 |
| | | *Nos. 174-180 (7)* | 6.50 1.65 |

**Souvenir Sheet**

| | | | |
|---|---|---|---|
| **181** | G14 | $3 multicolored | 3.00 1.25 |

American Revolution Bicentennial.

Piper
Apache
G15

Designs: 1c, Beech Twin Bonanza. 2c, de Havilland Twin Otter. 40c, Britten Norman Islander. 50c, de Havilland Heron. $2, Hawker Siddeley Avro 748. $3, BAC 1-11.

**1976, June 10**

| | | | |
|---|---|---|---|
| **182** | G15 | ½c multicolored | .20 .20 |
| **183** | G15 | 1c multicolored | .20 .20 |
| **184** | G15 | 2c multicolored | .20 .20 |
| **185** | G15 | 40c multicolored | .50 .20 |
| **186** | G15 | 50c multicolored | .65 .20 |
| **187** | G15 | $2 multicolored | 1.75 .30 |
| | | *Nos. 182-187 (6)* | 3.50 1.30 |

**Souvenir Sheet**

| | | | |
|---|---|---|---|
| **188** | G15 | $3 multicolored | 3.00 1.50 |

Olympic
Games,
Montreal
G16

**1976, July 1**

| | | | |
|---|---|---|---|
| **189** | G16 | ½c Cycling | .20 .20 |
| **190** | G16 | 1c Gymnastics | .20 .20 |
| **191** | G16 | 2c Hurdling | .20 .20 |
| **192** | G16 | 35c Shot put | .20 .20 |
| **193** | G16 | 45c Diving | .20 .20 |
| **194** | G16 | 75c Sprinting | .25 .20 |
| **195** | G16 | $2 Rowing | .75 .30 |
| | | *Nos. 189-195 (7)* | 2.00 1.50 |

**Souvenir Sheet**

| | | | |
|---|---|---|---|
| **196** | G16 | $3 Sailing | 1.25 1.00 |

Virgin and Child
by Cima — G17

Christmas: 1c, 2c, The Nativity by Romanino. 35c, Adoration of the Kings by Brueghel. 50c, Madonna and Child by Girolamo. 75c, Adoration of the Magi by Giorgione, horiz. $2, The Adoration of the Kings by Angelico, horiz. $3, The Holy Family by Garofalo.

**1976, Oct. 19**

| | | | |
|---|---|---|---|
| **197** | G17 | ½c multicolored | .20 .20 |
| **198** | G17 | 1c multicolored | .20 .20 |
| **199** | G17 | 2c multicolored | .20 .20 |
| **200** | G17 | 35c multicolored | .20 .20 |
| **201** | G17 | 50c multicolored | .25 .20 |
| **202** | G17 | 75c multicolored | .30 .25 |
| **203** | G17 | $2 multicolored | .90 .35 |
| | | *Nos. 197-203 (7)* | 2.25 1.60 |

**Souvenir Sheet**

| | | | |
|---|---|---|---|
| **204** | G17 | $3 multicolored | 1.75 1.75 |

Alexander
Graham
Bell, First
Telephone
G18

Portraits of Bell and Telephone from: 1c, 1895. 2c, 1900. 35c, 1915. 75c, 1920. $1, 1929. $2, 1963. $3, 1976.

**1977, Jan. 28**

| | | | |
|---|---|---|---|
| **205** | G18 | ½c multicolored | .20 .20 |
| **206** | G18 | 1c multicolored | .20 .20 |
| **207** | G18 | 2c multicolored | .20 .20 |
| **208** | G18 | 35c multicolored | .20 .20 |
| **209** | G18 | 75c multicolored | .20 .20 |
| **210** | G18 | $1 multicolored | .35 .20 |
| **211** | G18 | $2 multicolored | .65 .25 |
| | | *Nos. 205-211 (7)* | 2.00 1.45 |

**Souvenir Sheet**

| | | | |
|---|---|---|---|
| **212** | G18 | $3 multicolored | 2.00 1.00 |

Centenary of 1st telephone conversation, Mar. 10, 1876.

Coronation Coach — G19

Royal
Visit — G20

Designs: 50c, Crown of St. Edward. No. 214, Queen entering Abbey. No. 219, Queen and Prince Charles. $4, Queen is crowned.

No. 216, Mall on Coronation Night. No. 220, Queen's Flag.

**Litho. and Embossed**

**1977, Feb. 7**       **Perf. 13½**

| | | | |
|---|---|---|---|
| **213** | G19 | 35c multicolored | .20 .20 |
| **214** | G19 | $2 multicolored | .25 .20 |
| **215** | G19 | $4 multicolored | .35 .25 |
| | | *Nos. 213-215 (3)* | .80 .65 |

**Souvenir Sheet**
**Perf. 14**

| | | | |
|---|---|---|---|
| **216** | G19 | $5 multicolored | .90 .90 |

**Booklet Stamps**
**Roulette x imperf.**
**Self-adhesive**

| | | | |
|---|---|---|---|
| **217** | G20 | 35c multicolored | .20 .20 |
| *a.* | | Booklet pane of 6 | .75 |
| **218** | G20 | 50c multicolored | .35 .35 |
| **219** | G20 | $2 multicolored | .55 .55 |
| **220** | G20 | $5 multicolored | .65 .65 |
| *a.* | | Bklt. pane of 3, #218, #219, #220 | 1.25 |

Reign of Queen Elizabeth II, 25th anniv. Nos. 213-215, perf. 11, have different background colors and come from sheetlets of 3 stamps plus label.
For overprints see Nos. 237-240.

Easter — G21     Adoration of Jesus
by
Correggio — G22

Paintings of the Crucifixion by various artists.

**1977, July 5**    **Litho.**    **Perf. 14**

| | | | |
|---|---|---|---|
| **221** | G21 | ½c Fra Angelico | .20 .20 |
| **222** | G21 | 1c Fra Angelico, diff. | .20 .20 |
| **223** | G21 | 2c El Greco | .20 .20 |
| **224** | G21 | 18c El Greco, diff. | .20 .20 |
| **225** | G21 | 35c Fra Angelico, diff. | .20 .20 |
| **226** | G21 | 50c Giottino | .20 .20 |
| **227** | G21 | $2 da Messina | .30 .25 |
| | | *Nos. 221-227 (7)* | 1.50 1.45 |

**Souvenir Sheet**

| | | | |
|---|---|---|---|
| **228** | G21 | $3 Fra Angelico, diff. | 1.25 .90 |

**1977, Nov. 17**       **Perf. 14**

Christmas: Paintings of the Madonna and Child by various artists.

| | | | |
|---|---|---|---|
| **229** | G22 | ½c shown | .20 .20 |
| **230** | G22 | 1c Giorgione | .20 .20 |
| **231** | G22 | 2c Morales | .20 .20 |
| **232** | G22 | 18c Raphael | .20 .20 |
| **233** | G22 | 35c Van Dyck | .20 .20 |
| **234** | G22 | 50c Filippo Lippi | .20 .20 |
| **235** | G22 | $2 Filippo Lippi, diff. | .30 .25 |
| | | *Nos. 229-235 (7)* | 1.50 1.45 |

**Souvenir Sheet**

| | | | |
|---|---|---|---|
| **236** | G22 | $3 Ghirlandaio | 1.25 .90 |

**Nos. 213-216 Overprinted**

**1977, Nov. 23**       **Perf. 13½**

| | | | |
|---|---|---|---|
| **237** | G19 | 35c multicolored | .20 .20 |
| **238** | G19 | $2 multicolored | .30 .30 |
| **239** | G19 | $4 multicolored | .65 .65 |
| | | *Nos. 237-239 (3)* | 1.15 1.15 |

**Souvenir Sheet**

| | | | |
|---|---|---|---|
| **240** | G19 | $5 multicolored | .90 .90 |

Caribbean visit of Queen Elizabeth II. Nos. 237-239 exist perf. 11.

Swimming
and Life
Saving
G23

6th Caribbean Jamboree, Kingston, Jamaica, Aug. 5-14: 1c, Hiking. 2c, Ropes and Knots. 22c, Erecting Tent. 35c, Limbo dance. 75c, Cooking. $2, Pioneer bridge building. $3, Sea Scouts' race.

**1977, Dec. 7**       **Perf. 14**

| | | | |
|---|---|---|---|
| **241** | G23 | ½c multicolored | .20 .20 |
| **242** | G23 | 1c multicolored | .20 .20 |
| **243** | G23 | 2c multicolored | .20 .20 |
| **244** | G23 | 22c multicolored | .20 .20 |
| **245** | G23 | 35c multicolored | .40 .20 |
| **246** | G23 | 75c multicolored | .80 .20 |
| **247** | G23 | $3 multicolored | 1.50 .40 |
| | | *Nos. 241-247 (7)* | 3.50 1.60 |

**Souvenir Sheet**

| | | | |
|---|---|---|---|
| **248** | G23 | $2 multicolored | 1.90 1.25 |

Space
Shuttle
Blast-off
G24

Designs: 1c, Booster separation. 2c, External tank separation. 22c, Working in orbit. 50c, Re-entry. $2, Towing in. $3, Landing.

**1978, Feb. 3**

| | | | |
|---|---|---|---|
| **249** | G24 | ½c multicolored | .20 .20 |
| **250** | G24 | 1c multicolored | .20 .20 |
| **251** | G24 | 2c multicolored | .20 .20 |
| **252** | G24 | 22c multicolored | .20 .20 |
| **253** | G24 | 50c multicolored | .20 .20 |
| **254** | G24 | $3 multicolored | 1.50 .60 |
| | | *Nos. 249-254 (6)* | 2.50 1.50 |

**Souvenir Sheet**

| | | | |
|---|---|---|---|
| **255** | G24 | $2 multicolored | 1.00 1.00 |

US Space Shuttle.

Alfred
Nobel,
Medicine
Medal
G25

Alfred Nobel and: 1c, Physics, Chemistry Medal. 2c, Peace Medal. 22c, Nobel Institute, Oslo. 75c, Peace Prize committee. $2, Peace Medal, Nobel's will. $3, Literature Medal.

**1978, Feb. 22**

| | | | |
|---|---|---|---|
| **256** | G25 | ½c multicolored | .20 .20 |
| **257** | G25 | 1c multicolored | .20 .20 |
| **258** | G25 | 2c multicolored | .20 .20 |
| **259** | G25 | 22c multicolored | .35 .20 |
| **260** | G25 | 75c multicolored | .80 .20 |
| **261** | G25 | $3 multicolored | 2.75 .40 |
| | | *Nos. 256-261 (6)* | 4.50 1.40 |

**Souvenir Sheet**

| | | | |
|---|---|---|---|
| **262** | G25 | $2 multicolored | 1.75 .90 |

Nobel Prize awards.

Germany No. C37 — G26

15c, France #C43. 25c, Liechtenstein #C8 specimen. 35c, Panama #257. 50c, Russia #C15. 75c, US #C10. $2, Germany #C57. $3, Spain #C56.

**1978, Mar. 15**

| | | | |
|---|---|---|---|
| **263** | G26 | 5c multicolored | .20 .20 |
| **264** | G26 | 15c multicolored | .75 .20 |
| **265** | G26 | 25c multicolored | .30 .20 |
| **266** | G26 | 35c multicolored | .50 .20 |
| **267** | G26 | 50c multicolored | .85 .20 |
| **268** | G26 | $3 multicolored | 2.25 .40 |
| | | *Nos. 263-268 (6)* | 4.85 1.40 |

## Souvenir Sheet

| | | | |
|---|---|---|---|
| **269** | Sheet of 2 | 2.75 | 1.25 |
| a. | G26 75c multicolored | .60 | .30 |
| b. | G26 $2 multicolored | 1.60 | .80 |

50th anniv. of Lindbergh's solo trans-Atlantic flight. 75th anniv. of 1st Zeppelin flight.

Coronation Ring — G27

Designs: $2, Queen's Orb. $2.50, Imperial State Crown. $5, Queen Elizabeth II.

**1978, Apr. 12**        *Perf. 14*

| | | | |
|---|---|---|---|
| **270** | G27 50c multicolored | .20 | .20 |
| **271** | G27 $2 multicolored | .25 | .25 |
| **272** | G27 $2.50 multicolored | .35 | .35 |
| | Nos. 270-272 (3) | .80 | .80 |

## Souvenir Sheet

| | | | |
|---|---|---|---|
| **273** | G27 $5 multicolored | .90 | .90 |

Nos. 270-272, perf 12, printed in sheets of 3 + label, have different background colors. Issue date; June 2, 1978.

G28

Designs: 18c, Drummer, Royal Regiment of Fusiliers. 50c, Drummer, Royal Anglian Regiment. $5, Drum Major, Queen's Regiment.

**1978, Apr. 12**      *Roulette x imperf.*
### Booklet Stamps
### Self-Adhesive

| | | | |
|---|---|---|---|
| **274** | Souvenir booklet | 2.50 | 3.00 |
| a. | G28 Pane of 6 (3 ea 18c, 50c) | .75 | .75 |
| b. | G28 Pane of 1 ($5) | 1.50 | 1.50 |

G29

**1978, May 18**        *Perf. 14*

Paintings by Rubens: 5c, Le Chapeau de Paille. 15c, Hector Killed by Achilles. 18c, Helene Fourment and Her Children. 22c, Rubens and Isabella Brandt. 35c, Ildefonso Altarpiece. $2, Self-portrait. $3, Four Negro Heads.

| | | | |
|---|---|---|---|
| **275** | G29 5c multicolored | .20 | .20 |
| **276** | G29 15c multicolored | .20 | .20 |
| **277** | G29 18c multicolored | .20 | .20 |
| **278** | G29 22c multicolored | .30 | .20 |

| | | | |
|---|---|---|---|
| **279** | G29 35c multicolored | .30 | .20 |
| **280** | G29 $3 multicolored | 2.40 | 1.50 |
| | Nos. 275-280 (6) | 3.60 | 2.50 |

## Souvenir Sheet

| | | | |
|---|---|---|---|
| **281** | G29 $2 multicolored | 1.60 | 1.60 |

400th birth anniv. of Rubens.

Wright Flyer G30

Designs: 15c, Orville Wright, vert. 18c, Wilbur Wright, vert. 25c, 35c, 75c, $2, $3, various Wright airplanes.

**1978, Aug. 10**

| | | | |
|---|---|---|---|
| **282** | G30 5c multicolored | .20 | .20 |
| **283** | G30 15c multicolored | .20 | .20 |
| **284** | G30 18c multicolored | .20 | .20 |
| **285** | G30 25c multicolored | .20 | .20 |
| **286** | G30 35c multicolored | .20 | .20 |
| **287** | G30 75c multicolored | .25 | .25 |
| **288** | G30 $3 multicolored | 1.00 | 1.00 |
| | Nos. 282-288 (7) | 2.25 | 2.25 |

## Souvenir Sheet

| | | | |
|---|---|---|---|
| **289** | G30 $2 multicolored | 1.75 | 1.75 |

75th anniv. of first powered flight by the Wright brothers, Dec. 17, 1903.

Audubon's Shearwater G31     Players, Soccer Ball G32

10c, Northern ring-necked plover. 18c, Garnet-throated hummingbird. 22c, Black-bellied tree duck. 40c, Purple martin. $1, Yellow-bellied tropic bird. $2, Long-billed curlew. $5, Snowy egret.

**1978, Sept. 28**

| | | | |
|---|---|---|---|
| **290** | G31 5c multi | 1.00 | .25 |
| **291** | G31 10c multi | 1.25 | .25 |
| **292** | G31 18c multi, horiz. | 1.50 | .30 |
| **293** | G31 22c multi, horiz. | 2.00 | .30 |
| **294** | G31 40c multi, horiz. | 3.00 | .50 |
| **295** | G31 $1 multi | 4.25 | .60 |
| **296** | G31 $2 multi | 5.75 | 1.10 |
| | Nos. 290-296 (7) | 18.75 | 3.30 |

## Souvenir Sheet

| | | | |
|---|---|---|---|
| **297** | G31 $5 multicolored | 16.00 | 16.00 |

**1978, Nov. 2**

Soccer players in action.

| | | | |
|---|---|---|---|
| **298** | G32 15c multicolored | .20 | .20 |
| **299** | G32 35c multicolored | .20 | .20 |
| **300** | G32 50c multicolored | .25 | .20 |
| **301** | G32 $3 multicolored | .75 | .75 |
| | Nos. 298-301 (4) | 1.40 | 1.35 |

## Souvenir Sheet

| | | | |
|---|---|---|---|
| **302** | G32 $2 multicolored | 1.60 | 1.60 |

World Cup Soccer Championships, Argentina, June 1-25.

Captain Cook, Kalaniopu (King of Hawaii), 1778 G33

22c, Cook, Hawaiian native. 50c, Cook, death scene, 2/14/79. $3, Cook and offering ceremony. $4, Cook, HMS Resolution.

**1978, Dec. 13**

| | | | |
|---|---|---|---|
| **303** | G33 18c multicolored | .55 | .20 |
| **304** | G33 22c multicolored | .70 | .25 |
| **305** | G33 50c multicolored | 1.25 | .50 |
| **306** | G33 $3 multicolored | 3.00 | 2.00 |
| | Nos. 303-306 (4) | 5.50 | 2.95 |

## Souvenir Sheet

| | | | |
|---|---|---|---|
| **307** | G33 $4 multicolored | 3.50 | 3.50 |

250th birth anniv. of Captain James Cook and Bicentennial of his discovery of the Hawaiian Islands.

Durer Paintings — G34

Christmas: 40c, The Virgin at Prayer. 60c, Dresden Alterpiece. 90c, Madonna and Child. $2, Madonna and Child. $4, Salvator Mundi.

**1978, Dec 20**

| | | | |
|---|---|---|---|
| **308** | G34 40c multicolored | .20 | .20 |
| **309** | G34 60c multicolored | .20 | .20 |
| **310** | G34 90c multicolored | .25 | .25 |
| **311** | G34 $2 multicolored | .80 | .80 |
| | Nos. 308-311 (4) | 1.45 | 1.45 |

## Souvenir Sheet

| | | | |
|---|---|---|---|
| **312** | G34 $4 multicolored | 1.50 | 1.50 |

Strelitzia Reginae — G35

**1979, Feb. 15**

| | | | |
|---|---|---|---|
| **313** | G35 22c shown | .20 | .20 |
| **314** | G35 40c Euphorbia pulcher-rima | .35 | .35 |
| **315** | G35 $1 Heliconia humilis | .70 | .40 |
| **316** | G35 $3 Thunbergia alata | 1.25 | .75 |
| | Nos. 313-316 (4) | 2.50 | 1.70 |

## Souvenir Sheet

| | | | |
|---|---|---|---|
| **317** | G35 $2 Bougainvillea glabra | 1.60 | 1.60 |

Children with Pig G36

International Year of the Child: 50c, Children with donkey. $1, Children with goats. $3, Children fishing. $4, Child with coconuts.

**1979, Mar. 22**

| | | | |
|---|---|---|---|
| **318** | G36 18c multicolored | .20 | .20 |
| **319** | G36 50c multicolored | .20 | .20 |
| **320** | G36 $1 multicolored | .60 | .60 |
| **321** | G36 $3 multicolored | .80 | .80 |
| | Nos. 318-321 (4) | 1.80 | 1.80 |

## Souvenir Sheet

| | | | |
|---|---|---|---|
| **322** | G36 $4 multicolored | 1.10 | 1.10 |

150th Birth Anniv. of Jules Verne G37

Designs: 18c, 20,000 Leagues Under the Sea. 38c, From the Earth to the Moon. 75c, From the Earth to the Moon, diff. $3, Five Weeks in a Balloon. $4, Around the World in 80 Days.

**1979, Apr. 20**

| | | | |
|---|---|---|---|
| **323** | G37 18c multicolored | .75 | .20 |
| **324** | G37 38c multicolored | .85 | .25 |
| **325** | G37 75c multicolored | 1.00 | .40 |
| **326** | G37 $3 multicolored | 2.00 | 2.00 |
| | Nos. 323-326 (4) | 4.60 | 2.85 |

## Souvenir Sheet

| | | | |
|---|---|---|---|
| **327** | G37 $4 multicolored | 4.00 | 4.00 |

Sir Rowland Hill, Mail Truck G38

Designs: $1, Ocean liner. $2, Mail train. $3, Concorde. $4, Sir Rowland Hill.

**1979, July 30**        *Perf. 14*

| | | | |
|---|---|---|---|
| **328** | G38 15c multicolored | .20 | .20 |
| **329** | G38 $1 multicolored | .20 | .20 |
| **330** | G38 $2 multicolored | .75 | .75 |
| **331** | G38 $3 multicolored | 1.10 | 1.10 |
| | Nos. 328-331 (4) | 2.25 | 2.25 |

## Souvenir Sheet

| | | | |
|---|---|---|---|
| **332** | G38 $4 multicolored | 1.50 | 1.50 |

Death centenary of Sir Rowland Hill. Nos. 328-331, perf. 12, printed in sheets of 5 + label, have different colored backgrounds.

Virgin and Child Enthroned (Byzantine Era, 11th Cent.) — G39

Christmas sculptures: 25c, Presentation in the Temple by Beauneveu c. 1390. 30c, Flight to Egypt (Utrecht, c. 1510). 40c, Madonna and Child by della Quercia, 1047-48. 90c, Madonna della Mela by della Robbia, c. 1455. $1, Madonna and Child by Rossellino, 1461-66. $2, Madonna (Antwerp, 1700). $4, Virgin (Krumau, 1390).

**1979, Oct. 23**        *Perf. 14*

| | | | |
|---|---|---|---|
| **333** | G39 6c multicolored | .20 | .20 |
| **334** | G39 25c multicolored | .20 | .20 |
| **335** | G39 30c multicolored | .20 | .20 |
| **336** | G39 40c multicolored | .20 | .20 |
| **337** | G39 90c multicolored | .20 | .20 |
| **338** | G39 $1 multicolored | .25 | .25 |
| **339** | G39 $2 multicolored | .40 | .40 |
| | Nos. 333-339 (7) | 1.65 | 1.65 |

## Souvenir Sheet

| | | | |
|---|---|---|---|
| **340** | G39 $4 multicolored | 1.00 | 1.00 |

Great Hammerhead Shark — G40

Designs: 45c, Banded butterflyfish. 50c, Permit. 60c, Threaded turban. 70c, Milk conch. 75c, Great blue heron. 90c, Colored Atlantic natica. $1, Red footed booby. $2.50, Collared plover.

**1979, Nov. 9**

| | | | |
|---|---|---|---|
| **341** | G40 40c multicolored | .55 | .55 |
| **342** | G40 45c multicolored | .60 | .60 |
| **343** | G40 50c multicolored | .70 | .70 |
| **344** | G40 60c multicolored | .80 | .80 |
| **345** | G40 70c multicolored | 1.00 | 1.00 |
| **346** | G40 75c multicolored | 1.60 | 1.10 |
| **347** | G40 90c multicolored | 1.40 | 1.40 |
| **348** | G40 $1 multicolored | 2.00 | 2.00 |
| | Nos. 341-348 (8) | 8.65 | 8.15 |

## Souvenir Sheet

| | | | |
|---|---|---|---|
| **349** | G40 $2.50 multicolored | 2.25 | 2.25 |

Doctor Goofy G41

International Year of the Child: 1c, Admiral Mickey Mouse. 2c, Fireman Goofy. 3c, Nurse Minnie Mouse. 4c, Drum Major Mickey Mouse. 5c, Policeman Donald Duck. 10c, Pilot Donald Duck. $2, Mailman Goofy, horiz. $2.50 Engineer Donald Duck, horiz. $3, Fireman Mickey Mouse.

**1979, Dec. 12**       *Perf. 11*

| | | | | |
|---|---|---|---|---|
| 350 | G41 | ½c multicolored | .20 | .20 |
| 351 | G41 | 1c multicolored | .20 | .20 |
| 352 | G41 | 2c multicolored | .20 | .20 |
| 353 | G41 | 3c multicolored | .20 | .20 |
| 354 | G41 | 4c multicolored | .20 | .20 |
| 355 | G41 | 5c multicolored | .25 | .25 |
| 356 | G41 | 10c multicolored | .25 | .25 |
| 357 | G41 | $2 multicolored | 2.50 | 2.50 |
| 358 | G41 | $2.50 multicolored | 3.00 | 3.00 |
| | | Nos. 350-358 (9) | 7.00 | 7.00 |

**Souvenir Sheet**
*Perf. 13½*

| | | | | |
|---|---|---|---|---|
| 359 | G41 | $3 multicolored | 3.50 | 3.50 |

Nos. 114, 117-128 Overprinted

**1980, Mar. 10**       *Perf. 15*

| | | | | |
|---|---|---|---|---|
| 360 | A85 | 6c multicolored | .20 | .20 |
| 361 | A85 | 12c multicolored | .20 | .20 |
| 362 | A85 | 15c multicolored | .20 | .20 |
| 363 | A85 | 20c multicolored | .20 | .20 |
| 364 | A85 | 25c multicolored | .20 | .20 |
| 365 | A85 | 30c multicolored | .20 | .20 |
| 366 | A85 | 50c multicolored | .30 | .35 |

*Perf. 13½x14*

| | | | | |
|---|---|---|---|---|
| 367 | A85 | 75c multicolored | .35 | .40 |
| 368 | A85 | $1 multicolored | .50 | .60 |
| 369 | A85 | $2 multicolored | .75 | .90 |
| 370 | A85 | $3 multicolored | 1.40 | 1.60 |
| 371 | A85 | $5 multicolored | 2.00 | 2.40 |
| 372 | A85 | $10 multicolored | 3.25 | 3.75 |
| | | Nos. 360-372 (13) | 9.75 | 11.20 |

Classroom G42

Rotary Intl., 75th anniv.: 30c, Rotary emblem, people. 60c, Rotary executive making contribution to physician. $3, Young patients, nurses. $4, Paul P. Harris, founder of Rotary.

**1980, Mar. 12**       *Perf. 14*

| | | | | |
|---|---|---|---|---|
| 373 | G42 | 6c multicolored | .20 | .20 |
| 374 | G42 | 30c multicolored | .25 | .25 |
| 375 | G42 | 60c multicolored | .45 | .45 |
| 376 | G42 | $3 multicolored | 2.10 | 1.60 |
| | | Nos. 373-376 (4) | 3.00 | 2.50 |

**Souvenir Sheet**

| | | | | |
|---|---|---|---|---|
| 377 | G42 | $4 multicolored | 1.40 | 1.40 |

Yellow-bellied Seedeater — G43

---

40c, Blue-hooded euphonia. 90c, Yellow warbler. $2, Tropical mockingbird. $3, Barn owl.

**1980, Apr. 14**

| | | | | |
|---|---|---|---|---|
| 378 | G43 | 25c multicolored | .65 | .20 |
| 379 | G43 | 40c multicolored | .70 | .25 |
| 380 | G43 | 90c multicolored | 1.60 | .85 |
| 381 | G43 | $2 multicolored | 2.25 | 1.60 |
| | | Nos. 378-381 (4) | 5.20 | 2.90 |

**Souvenir Sheet**

| | | | | |
|---|---|---|---|---|
| 382 | G43 | $3 multicolored | 5.50 | 5.50 |

Running G44

Designs: 40c, Soccer. 90c, Boxing. $2, Wrestling. $4, Runners in silhouette.

**1980, Apr. 21**

| | | | | |
|---|---|---|---|---|
| 383 | G44 | 30c multicolored | .20 | .20 |
| 384 | G44 | 40c multicolored | .20 | .20 |
| 385 | G44 | 90c multicolored | .40 | .40 |
| 386 | G44 | $2 multicolored | .85 | .85 |
| | | Nos. 383-386 (4) | 1.65 | 1.65 |

**Souvenir Sheet**

| | | | | |
|---|---|---|---|---|
| 387 | G44 | $4 multicolored | .90 | .90 |

22nd Summer Olympic Games, Moscow, July 19-Aug. 3.

Nos. 328-331 Overprinted

**1980, May 6**       *Perf. 12*

| | | | | |
|---|---|---|---|---|
| 388 | G38 | 15c multicolored | .20 | .20 |
| 389 | G38 | $1 multicolored | 1.10 | .50 |
| 390 | G38 | $2 multicolored | 2.25 | 1.75 |
| 391 | G38 | $3 multicolored | 3.75 | 3.00 |
| | | Nos. 388-391 (4) | 7.30 | 5.45 |

Issued in sheets of 5 + label.

Longspine Squirrelfish — G45

Designs: 1c, Blue chromis. 2c, Foureye butterflyfish. 4c, Sergeant major. 5c, Yellowtail snapper. 6c, Mutton snapper. 10c, Cocoa damselfish. 12c, Royal gramma. 15c, Cherubfish. 20c, Blackbar soldierfish. 25c, Comb grouper. 30c, Longsnout butterflyfish. 40c, Pudding wife. 50c, Midnight parrotfish. 90c, Redspotted hawkfish. $1, Hogfish. $3, Beau gregory. $5, Rock beauty. $10, Barred hamlet.

**1980, Aug. 6**       *Perf. 14*

| | | | | |
|---|---|---|---|---|
| 392 | G45 | ½c multicolored | .20 | .20 |
| a. | | Perf. 12, inscribed 1982 | 10.00 | 10.00 |
| 393 | G45 | 1c multicolored | .20 | .20 |
| 394 | G45 | 2c multicolored | .20 | .20 |
| 395 | G45 | 4c multicolored | .20 | .20 |
| 396 | G45 | 5c multicolored | .20 | .20 |
| 397 | G45 | 6c multicolored | .20 | .20 |
| 398 | G45 | 10c multicolored | .20 | .20 |
| 399 | G45 | 12c multicolored | .20 | .20 |
| 400 | G45 | 15c multicolored | .20 | .20 |
| 401 | G45 | 20c multicolored | .20 | .20 |
| 402 | G45 | 25c multicolored | .20 | .20 |
| 403 | G45 | 30c multicolored | .20 | .20 |
| 404 | G45 | 40c multicolored | .25 | .25 |
| 405 | G45 | 50c multicolored | .30 | .35 |
| 406 | G45 | 90c multicolored | .45 | .50 |
| 407 | G45 | $1 multicolored | .55 | .60 |
| 408 | G45 | $3 multicolored | 1.50 | 1.75 |
| 409 | G45 | $5 multicolored | 2.00 | 2.25 |
| 410 | G45 | $10 multicolored | 3.25 | 3.75 |
| | | Nos. 392-410 (19) | 10.70 | 11.85 |

No. 398 exists with 1984 date below design.

---

Bambi with Mother — G46

Various scenes from Walt Disney's Bambi.

**1980, Oct. 7**       *Perf. 11*

| | | | | |
|---|---|---|---|---|
| 411 | G46 | ½c multicolored | .20 | .20 |
| 412 | G46 | 1c multicolored | .20 | .20 |
| 413 | G46 | 2c multicolored | .20 | .20 |
| 414 | G46 | 3c multicolored | .20 | .20 |
| 415 | G46 | 4c multicolored | .20 | .20 |
| 416 | G46 | 5c multicolored | .20 | .20 |
| 417 | G46 | 10c multicolored | .20 | .20 |
| 418 | G46 | $2.50 multicolored | 1.75 | 1.75 |
| 419 | G46 | $3 multicolored | 1.75 | 1.75 |
| | | Nos. 411-419 (9) | 4.90 | 4.90 |

**Souvenir Sheet**

| | | | | |
|---|---|---|---|---|
| 420 | G46 | $4 multicolored | 3.00 | 3.00 |

Christmas.

The Unicorn in Captivity by Unknown 15th Cent. Artist — G47

Designs: 10c, The Fighting Temeraire by J.M.W. Turner. 25c, Sunday Afternoon on the Ile De La Grande-Jatte by Seurat. 90c, Max Schmitt in a Single Scull by Eakins. $2, The Burial of the Count of Orgaz by El Greco. $3, George Washington by Stuart. $5, Kaiser Karl the Great by Durer. Nos. 425-427 are vert.

**1981, Jan. 25**       *Perf. 14*

| | | | | |
|---|---|---|---|---|
| 421 | G47 | 6c multicolored | .20 | .20 |
| 422 | G47 | 10c multicolored | .20 | .20 |
| 423 | G47 | 25c multicolored | .20 | .20 |
| 424 | G47 | 90c multicolored | .50 | .50 |
| 425 | G47 | $2 multicolored | .90 | .90 |
| 426 | G47 | $3 multicolored | 1.25 | 1.25 |
| | | Nos. 421-426 (6) | 3.25 | 3.25 |

**Souvenir Sheet**

| | | | | |
|---|---|---|---|---|
| 427 | G47 | $5 multicolored | 2.75 | 2.75 |

Disney Type of 1979

50th anniv. of Pluto character: $2, Mickey Mouse, Pluto and birthday cake. $4, Pluto.

**1981, Jan. 26**

| | | | | |
|---|---|---|---|---|
| 428 | A135a | $2 multicolored | 1.00 | 1.00 |

**Souvenir Sheet**

| | | | | |
|---|---|---|---|---|
| 429 | A135a | $4 multicolored | 2.75 | 2.75 |

No. 428 issued in sheets of 8.

Chip Coloring Easter Eggs — G48

Easter: Various Disney characters coloring Easter eggs.

**1981, Apr. 14**       *Perf. 11*

| | | | | |
|---|---|---|---|---|
| 430 | G48 | 35c multicolored | .20 | .20 |
| 431 | G48 | 40c multicolored | .20 | .20 |
| 432 | G48 | $2 multicolored | 1.00 | 1.00 |
| 433 | G48 | $2.50 multicolored | 1.40 | 1.40 |
| | | Nos. 430-433 (4) | 2.80 | 2.80 |

---

**Souvenir Sheet**
*Perf. 14*

| | | | | |
|---|---|---|---|---|
| 434 | G48 | $4 multicolored | 2.75 | 2.75 |

Bust of a Woman — G49     Diana — G50

Paintings by Pablo Picasso (1881-1973): 40c, Woman (Study for Les Demoiselles d'Avignon). 90c, Nude with Raised Arms (The Dancer of Avignon). $4, The Dryad. $5, Les Demoiselles d'Avignon.

**1981, May 5**       *Perf. 14*

| | | | | |
|---|---|---|---|---|
| 435 | G49 | 6c multicolored | .20 | .20 |
| 436 | G49 | 40c multicolored | .20 | .20 |
| 437 | G49 | 90c multicolored | .35 | .35 |
| 438 | G49 | $4 multicolored | 1.75 | 1.75 |

**Size: 103x128mm**
*Imperf*

| | | | | |
|---|---|---|---|---|
| 439 | G49 | $5 multicolored | 2.75 | 2.40 |
| | | Nos. 435-439 (5) | 5.25 | 4.90 |

Common Design Types pictured following the introduction.

**Royal Wedding Issue**
Common Design Type

**1981, June 16**       *Perf. 15*

| | | | | |
|---|---|---|---|---|
| 440 | CD331a | 40c Couple | .20 | .20 |
| 441 | CD331a | $2 Balmoral Castle | .30 | .30 |
| 442 | CD331a | $4 Charles | .50 | .50 |
| | | Nos. 440-442 (3) | 1.00 | 1.00 |

**Souvenir Sheet**

| | | | | |
|---|---|---|---|---|
| 443 | CD331a | $5 Royal Coach | 1.40 | 1.40 |

Sheets of 5 plus label contain 30c (like No. 440), 40c (like No. 441), or $4 in changed colors, perf 15x14½.

*Roulette x imperf. (#444a), Imperf. (#444b)*

**1981, June 16**

$1, Diana. $2, Charles. $5, Diana and Charles.

**Booklet**
**Self-Adhesive**

| | | | | |
|---|---|---|---|---|
| 444 | G50 | Souvenir Booklet | 3.50 | |
| a. | | Pane of 6 (3 each $1, $2) | 2.00 | |
| b. | | Pane of 1, $5 | 1.50 | |

Royal wedding.

Amy Johnson, Pilot of 1st Britain-Australia Solo Flight by a Woman, May 1930 — G51

Decade for Women: 70c, Mme. la Baronne de Laroche, 1st qualified aviatrix, May 1910. $1.10, Ruth Nichols. $3, Amelia Earhart, 1st Atlantic solo flight by woman, May 1932. $5, Valentina Tereshkova, 1st woman in space, June 1963.

**1981, Oct. 13**       *Perf. 14*

| | | | | |
|---|---|---|---|---|
| 445 | G51 | 30c multicolored | .45 | .45 |
| 446 | G51 | 70c multicolored | .70 | .70 |
| 447 | G51 | $1.10 multicolored | .85 | .85 |
| 448 | G51 | $3 multicolored | 1.75 | 1.75 |
| | | Nos. 445-448 (4) | 3.75 | 3.75 |

**Souvenir Sheet**

| | | | | |
|---|---|---|---|---|
| 449 | G51 | $5 multicolored | 2.00 | 2.00 |

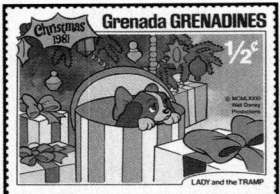

Lady and the Tramp — G52

Christmas. Various scenes from Walt Disney's film Lady and the Tramp.

**1981, Nov. 2**
| | | | | |
|---|---|---|---|---|
| 450 | G52 | ½c multicolored | .20 | .20 |
| 451 | G52 | 1c multicolored | .20 | .20 |
| 452 | G52 | 2c multicolored | .20 | .20 |
| 453 | G52 | 3c multicolored | .20 | .20 |
| 454 | G52 | 4c multicolored | .20 | .20 |
| 455 | G52 | 5c multicolored | .20 | .20 |
| 456 | G52 | 10c multicolored | .25 | .20 |
| 457 | G52 | $2.50 multicolored | 4.00 | 1.75 |
| 458 | G52 | $3 multicolored | 4.00 | 2.25 |
| | | Nos. 450-458 (9) | 9.45 | 5.40 |

**Souvenir Sheet**
| | | | | |
|---|---|---|---|---|
| 459 | G52 | $5 multicolored | 7.25 | 6.25 |

747 Carrying Space Shuttle — G53

Designs: 40c, Re-entry. $1.10, External tank separation. $3, Touchdown. $5, Lift-off.

**1981, Nov. 2**       *Perf. 14½*
| | | | | |
|---|---|---|---|---|
| 460 | G53 | 10c multicolored | .40 | .20 |
| 461 | G53 | 40c multicolored | .85 | .30 |
| 462 | G53 | $1.10 multicolored | 1.60 | .80 |
| 463 | G53 | $3 multicolored | 2.40 | 1.50 |
| | | Nos. 460-463 (4) | 5.25 | 2.80 |

**Souvenir Sheet**
| | | | | |
|---|---|---|---|---|
| 464 | G53 | $5 multicolored | 5.50 | 4.00 |

Soccer Player — G54

World Cup Soccer Championships, Spain, 1982: Soccer players in various positions.

**1981, Nov. 30**       *Perf. 14*
| | | | | |
|---|---|---|---|---|
| 465 | G54 | 20c multicolored | .20 | .20 |
| 466 | G54 | 40c multicolored | .20 | .20 |
| 467 | G54 | $1 multicolored | .45 | .30 |
| 468 | G54 | $2 multicolored | .90 | .60 |
| | | Nos. 465-468 (4) | 1.75 | 1.30 |

**Souvenir Sheet**
| | | | | |
|---|---|---|---|---|
| 469 | G54 | $4 multicolored | 1.75 | 1.50 |

Stagecoach, Mail Truck — G55

UPU Membership Cent.: 40c, UPU Emblem. $2.50, Sailing ship, ocean liner. $4, Biplane, Concorde. $5, Steam train, high-speed trains.

**1982, Jan. 13**       *Perf. 15*
| | | | | |
|---|---|---|---|---|
| 470 | G55 | 30c multicolored | .40 | .20 |
| 471 | G55 | 40c multicolored | .40 | .20 |
| 472 | G55 | $2.50 multicolored | 2.00 | 1.00 |
| 473 | G55 | $4 multicolored | 3.25 | 2.00 |
| | | Nos. 470-473 (4) | 6.05 | 3.40 |

**Souvenir Sheet**
| | | | | |
|---|---|---|---|---|
| 474 | G55 | $5 multicolored | 5.25 | 4.50 |

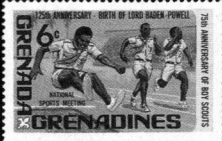

Sprinting G56

90c, Sea scouts sailing. $1.10, Hand crafts. $3, Animal husbandry. $5, Music around campfire.

**1982, Feb. 19**
| | | | | |
|---|---|---|---|---|
| 475 | G56 | 6c multicolored | .20 | .20 |
| 476 | G56 | 90c multicolored | .75 | .60 |
| 477 | G56 | $1.10 multicolored | 1.00 | .70 |
| 478 | G56 | $3 multicolored | 2.10 | 2.10 |
| | | Nos. 475-478 (4) | 4.05 | 3.60 |

**Souvenir Sheet**
| | | | | |
|---|---|---|---|---|
| 479 | G56 | $5 multicolored | 3.25 | 3.25 |

Boy Scouts, 75th anniv. Lord Baden-Powell, 125th birth anniv.

White Peacock G57

Designs: 40c, St. Vincent long-tail skipper. $1.10, Painted lady. $3, Orion. $5, Silver spot.

**1982, Mar. 24**       *Perf. 14*
| | | | | |
|---|---|---|---|---|
| 480 | G57 | 30c multicolored | .95 | .45 |
| 481 | G57 | 40c multicolored | 1.00 | .65 |
| 482 | G57 | $1.10 multicolored | 2.25 | 1.75 |
| 483 | G57 | $3 multicolored | 4.00 | 4.00 |
| | | Nos. 480-483 (4) | 8.20 | 6.85 |

**Souvenir Sheet**
| | | | | |
|---|---|---|---|---|
| 484 | G57 | $5 multicolored | 4.25 | 4.25 |

**Princess Diana Issue**
**Common Design Type**

**1982, July 1**       *Perf. 14½x14*
| | | | | |
|---|---|---|---|---|
| 485 | CD332 | 50c Blenheim Palace | 1.25 | 1.25 |
| 486 | CD332 | 60c Like 50c | .75 | .75 |
| 487 | CD332 | $1 Couple in field | 1.75 | 1.75 |
| 488 | CD332 | $2 Like $1 | 1.90 | 1.90 |
| 489 | CD332 | $3 Diana | 2.50 | 2.50 |
| 490 | CD332 | $4 Like $3 | 2.50 | 2.50 |
| | | Nos. 485-490 (6) | 10.65 | 10.65 |

**Souvenir Sheet**
| | | | | |
|---|---|---|---|---|
| 491 | CD332 | $5 Diana, diff. | 7.25 | 7.25 |

50c, $1, $3 issued in sheets of 5 plus label.

Overprinted

**1982, Aug. 30**
| | | | | |
|---|---|---|---|---|
| 492 | CD332 | 50c multicolored | .75 | .75 |
| 493 | CD332 | 60c multicolored | .80 | .80 |
| 494 | CD332 | $1 multicolored | 1.00 | 1.00 |
| 495 | CD332 | $2 multicolored | 1.50 | 1.50 |
| 496 | CD332 | $3 multicolored | 1.90 | 1.90 |
| 497 | CD332 | $4 multicolored | 2.25 | 2.25 |
| | | Nos. 492-497 (6) | 8.20 | 8.20 |

**Souvenir Sheet**
| | | | | |
|---|---|---|---|---|
| 498 | CD332 | $5 multicolored | 5.25 | 5.25 |

Birth of Prince William of Wales, June 21.

**Roosevelt Type of 1982**

Designs: 30c, New Deal soil conservation. 40c, Roosevelt, George Washington Carver. 70c, Civilian Conservation Corps. $3, Roosevelt, Liberian Pres. Edwin Barclay. $5, Roosevelt addressing Howard University.

**1982, July 27**       *Perf. 14*
| | | | | |
|---|---|---|---|---|
| 499 | A154 | 30c multicolored | .50 | .20 |
| 500 | A154 | 40c multicolored | .50 | .20 |
| 501 | A154 | 70c multicolored | .60 | .30 |
| 502 | A154 | $3 multicolored | 1.40 | 1.40 |
| | | Nos. 499-502 (4) | 3.00 | 2.10 |

**Souvenir Sheet**
| | | | | |
|---|---|---|---|---|
| 503 | A154 | $5 multicolored | 3.50 | 3.50 |

Presentation of Christ in the Temple — G58

Easter Paintings by Rembrandt: 60c, Descent from the Cross. $2, Raising of the Cross. $4, Resurrection of Christ. $5, The Risen Christ.

**1982, Sept. 2**       *Perf. 14½*
| | | | | |
|---|---|---|---|---|
| 504 | G58 | 30c multicolored | .55 | .20 |
| 505 | G58 | 60c multicolored | .70 | .20 |
| 506 | G58 | $2 multicolored | 1.00 | 1.00 |
| 507 | G58 | $4 multicolored | 1.75 | 1.75 |
| | | Nos. 504-507 (4) | 4.00 | 3.15 |

**Souvenir Sheet**
| | | | | |
|---|---|---|---|---|
| 508 | G58 | $5 multicolored | 3.50 | 3.50 |

G59

**1982, Oct. 4**       *Perf. 15*
| | | | | |
|---|---|---|---|---|
| 509 | G59 | 10c Santa Fe | .70 | .20 |
| 510 | G59 | 40c Mistral | 1.00 | .30 |
| 511 | G59 | 70c Rheingold | 1.10 | .65 |
| 512 | G59 | $1 ET 403 | 1.40 | .70 |
| 513 | G59 | $1.10 Mallard | 1.75 | .75 |
| 514 | G59 | $2 Tokaido | 2.00 | 1.25 |
| | | Nos. 509-514 (6) | 7.95 | 3.85 |

**Souvenir Sheet**
| | | | | |
|---|---|---|---|---|
| 515 | G59 | $5 Settebello | 3.75 | 3.75 |

Soccer Players G60

Italy, World Cup Soccer Champions: $4, Soccer players, diff. $5, Map of Italy.

**1982, Dec. 2**       *Perf. 14*
| | | | | |
|---|---|---|---|---|
| 516 | G60 | 60c multicolored | 1.00 | .45 |
| 517 | G60 | $4 multicolored | 3.00 | 3.00 |

**Souvenir Sheet**
| | | | | |
|---|---|---|---|---|
| 518 | G60 | $5 multicolored | 2.50 | 2.50 |

**Christmas Type of 1982**

Scenes from Walt Disney's film The Rescuers.

**1982, Dec. 14**       *Perf. 13½*
| | | | | |
|---|---|---|---|---|
| 519 | A157 | ½c multicolored | .20 | .20 |
| 520 | A157 | 1c multicolored | .20 | .20 |
| 521 | A157 | 2c multicolored | .20 | .20 |
| 522 | A157 | 3c multicolored | .20 | .20 |
| 523 | A157 | 4c multicolored | .20 | .20 |
| 524 | A157 | 5c multicolored | .20 | .20 |
| 525 | A157 | 10c multicolored | .20 | .20 |
| 526 | A157 | $2.50 multicolored | 3.75 | 3.25 |
| 527 | A157 | $3 multicolored | 3.75 | 3.25 |
| | | Nos. 519-527 (9) | 8.90 | 7.90 |

**Souvenir Sheet**
| | | | | |
|---|---|---|---|---|
| 528 | A157 | $5 multicolored | 7.25 | 6.25 |

**Whales Type of 1982**

Designs: 10c, Pilot whale. 60c, Dall porpoise. $1.10, Humpback whale. $3, Bowfin whale. $5, Spotted dolphin.

**1983, Jan. 10**       *Perf. 14*
| | | | | |
|---|---|---|---|---|
| 529 | A159 | 10c multicolored | 1.00 | .90 |
| 530 | A159 | 60c multicolored | 2.50 | 2.25 |
| 531 | A159 | $1.10 multicolored | 4.50 | 3.75 |
| 532 | A159 | $3 multicolored | 7.50 | 6.00 |
| | | Nos. 529-532 (4) | 15.50 | 12.90 |

**Souvenir Sheet**
| | | | | |
|---|---|---|---|---|
| 533 | A159 | $5 multicolored | 7.50 | 6.00 |

**Raphael Paintings Type**

Designs: 25c, David and Goliath. 30c, David Sees Bathsheba. 90c, Triumph of David. $4, Anointing of Solomon. $5, Anointing of David.

**1983, Feb. 15**       *Perf. 14*
| | | | | |
|---|---|---|---|---|
| 534 | A160 | 25c multicolored | .25 | .25 |
| 535 | A160 | 30c multicolored | .25 | .25 |
| 536 | A160 | 90c multicolored | .40 | .40 |
| 537 | A160 | $4 multicolored | .90 | .90 |
| | | Nos. 534-537 (4) | 1.80 | 1.80 |

**Souvenir Sheet**
| | | | | |
|---|---|---|---|---|
| 538 | A160 | $5 multicolored | 1.40 | 1.40 |

Audio and Video Communication — G61

World Communications Year: 60c, Ambulance. $1.10, Helicopters. $3, Satellite. $5, Diver, bottle-nose porpoise.

**1983, Apr. 7**       *Perf. 14*
| | | | | |
|---|---|---|---|---|
| 539 | G61 | 30c multicolored | .25 | .25 |
| 540 | G61 | 60c multicolored | .45 | .45 |
| 541 | G61 | $1.10 multicolored | .80 | .80 |
| 542 | G61 | $3 blk, red & blue | 1.50 | 1.50 |
| | | Nos. 539-542 (4) | 3.00 | 3.00 |

**Souvenir Sheet**
| | | | | |
|---|---|---|---|---|
| 543 | G61 | $5 multicolored | 3.50 | 3.00 |

For overprints see Nos. 629-630A.

**Car Type of 1983**

Designs: 10c, 1931 Chrysler Imperial Roadster. 30c, 1925 Doble Steam Car. 40c, 1965 Ford Mustang. 60c, 1930 Packard Tourer. 70c, 1913 Mercer Raceabout. 90c, 1963 Corvette Stingray. $1.10, 1935 Auburn 851 Supercharger Speedster. $2.50, 1933 Pierce Arrow Silver Arrow. $3, 1929 Duesenberg Dual Cowl Phaeton. $4, 1928 Mercedes-Benz SSK. $5, 1923 McFarlan Knickerbocker Cabriolet.

**1983, May 4**       *Perf. 14½*
| | | | | |
|---|---|---|---|---|
| 544 | A163 | 10c multicolored | .20 | .20 |
| 545 | A163 | 30c multicolored | .35 | .35 |
| 546 | A163 | 40c multicolored | .35 | .35 |
| 547 | A163 | 60c multicolored | .50 | .50 |
| 548 | A163 | 70c multicolored | .50 | .50 |
| 549 | A163 | 90c multicolored | .50 | .50 |
| 550 | A163 | $1.10 multicolored | .55 | .55 |
| 551 | A163 | $2.50 multicolored | .90 | .90 |
| 552 | A163 | $3 multicolored | 1.10 | 1.10 |
| 553 | A163 | $4 multicolored | 1.10 | 1.10 |
| | | Nos. 544-553 (10) | 6.05 | 5.95 |

**Souvenir Sheet**
| | | | | |
|---|---|---|---|---|
| 554 | A163 | $5 multicolored | 3.50 | 3.50 |

**Anniversary of Manned Flight Type**

Designs: 40c, Short Solent flying boat. 70c, Curtiss R3C-2 seaplane. 90c, Hawker Nimrod biplane. $4, Montgolfier balloon. $5, Victoria Luise airship.

**1983, July 18**       *Perf. 14*
| | | | | |
|---|---|---|---|---|
| 555 | A164 | 40c multicolored | 1.00 | .25 |
| 556 | A164 | 70c multicolored | 1.25 | .50 |
| 557 | A164 | 90c multicolored | 1.50 | 1.50 |
| 558 | A164 | $4 multicolored | 3.75 | 3.25 |
| | | Nos. 555-558 (4) | 7.50 | 5.50 |

**Souvenir Sheet**
| | | | | |
|---|---|---|---|---|
| 559 | A164 | $5 multicolored | 3.50 | 3.50 |

Christmas G62

Walt Disney characters in scenes from "Jingle Bells."

**1983, Nov. 7**       *Perf. 11*
| | | | | |
|---|---|---|---|---|
| 560 | G62 | ½c multicolored | .20 | .20 |
| 561 | G62 | 1c multicolored | .20 | .20 |
| 562 | G62 | 2c multicolored | .20 | .20 |
| 563 | G62 | 3c multicolored | .20 | .20 |
| 564 | G62 | 4c multicolored | .20 | .20 |
| 565 | G62 | 5c multicolored | .20 | .20 |
| 566 | G62 | 10c multicolored | .20 | .20 |
| 567 | G62 | $2.50 multicolored | 5.75 | 5.75 |
| 568 | G62 | $3 multicolored | 6.25 | 6.25 |
| | | Nos. 560-568 (9) | 13.40 | 13.40 |

## Souvenir Sheet
### Perf. 13½
**569** G62 $5 multicolored 12.00 12.00

G63

### 1984, Jan. 9 — Perf. 14
| | | | | | |
|---|---|---|---|---|---|
| **570** | G63 | 30c Weightlifting | | .25 | .20 |
| **571** | G63 | 60c Gymnastics | | .55 | .50 |
| **572** | G63 | 70c Archery | | .75 | .60 |
| **573** | G63 | $4 Sailing | | 2.75 | 2.75 |
| | | Nos. 570-573 (4) | | 4.30 | 4.05 |

### Souvenir Sheet
**574** G63 $5 Basketball 4.00 4.00

Olympic Games, Los Angeles.

G64

### 1984, Apr. 9 — Perf. 15
Designs: 15c, Frangipani. 40c, Dwarf poinciana. 70c, Walking iris. $4, Lady's slipper. $5, Brazilian glory vine.

| | | | | | |
|---|---|---|---|---|---|
| **575** | G64 | 15c multicolored | | .20 | .20 |
| **576** | G64 | 40c multicolored | | .30 | .30 |
| **577** | G64 | 70c multicolored | | .75 | .55 |
| **578** | G64 | $4 multicolored | | 2.75 | 2.75 |
| | | Nos. 575-578 (4) | | 4.00 | 3.80 |

### Souvenir Sheet
**579** G64 $5 multicolored 3.75 3.75

For overprints see Nos. 598-600.

Easter
G65

Walt Disney characters with Easter hats.

### 1984, May 1 — Perf. 11
| | | | | | |
|---|---|---|---|---|---|
| **580** | G65 | ½c multicolored | | .20 | .20 |
| **581** | G65 | 1c multicolored | | .20 | .20 |
| **582** | G65 | 2c multicolored | | .20 | .20 |
| **583** | G65 | 3c multicolored | | .20 | .20 |
| **584** | G65 | 4c multicolored | | .20 | .20 |
| **585** | G65 | 5c multicolored | | .20 | .20 |
| **586** | G65 | 10c multicolored | | .20 | .20 |
| **587** | G65 | $2 multicolored | | 2.00 | 2.00 |
| **588** | G65 | $4 multicolored | | 2.90 | 2.90 |
| | | Nos. 580-588 (9) | | 6.30 | 6.30 |

### Souvenir Sheet
**589** G65 $5 multicolored 5.25 5.25

Bobolink
G66

Birds: 50c, Eastern kingbird. 60c, Barn swallow. 70c, Yellow warbler. $1, Rose-breasted grosbeak. $1.10, Yellowthroat. $2, Catbird. $5, Fork-tailed flycatcher.

### 1984, May 21 — Perf. 14
| | | | | | |
|---|---|---|---|---|---|
| **590** | G66 | 40c multicolored | | 2.50 | 2.00 |
| **591** | G66 | 50c multicolored | | 2.90 | 2.25 |
| **592** | G66 | 60c multicolored | | 3.25 | 2.90 |
| **593** | G66 | 70c multicolored | | 3.25 | 2.90 |
| **594** | G66 | $1 multicolored | | 3.50 | 3.50 |
| **595** | G66 | $1.10 multicolored | | 4.00 | 4.00 |
| **596** | G66 | $2 multicolored | | 5.00 | 5.00 |
| | | Nos. 590-596 (7) | | 24.40 | 22.55 |

### Souvenir Sheet
**597** G66 $5 multicolored 11.00 11.00

Nos. 577-579
Overprinted

### 1984, June 19 — Perf. 15
| | | | | | |
|---|---|---|---|---|---|
| **598** | G64 | 70c multicolored | | 1.25 | 1.25 |
| **599** | G64 | $4 multicolored | | 5.50 | 5.50 |

### Souvenir Sheet
**600** G64 $5 multicolored 5.00 5.00

Geeststar
G67

### 1984, July 16 — Perf. 15
| | | | | | |
|---|---|---|---|---|---|
| **601** | G67 | 30c shown | | .85 | .85 |
| **602** | G67 | 60c Daphne | | 1.10 | 1.10 |
| **603** | G67 | $1.10 Schooner Southwind | | 1.40 | 1.40 |
| **604** | G67 | $4 Oceanic | | 2.40 | 2.40 |
| | | Nos. 601-604 (4) | | 5.75 | 5.75 |

### Souvenir Sheet
**605** G67 $5 Privateer 5.75 5.75

### Correggio Paintings Type
Designs: 10c, The Hunt — Blowing the Horn. 30c, St. John the Evangelist, horiz. 90c, The Hunt — The Deer's Head. $4, The Virgin Crowned by Christ, horiz. $5, Martyrdom of the Four Saints.

### 1984, Aug. 22 — Perf. 14
| | | | | | |
|---|---|---|---|---|---|
| **606** | A171a | 10c multicolored | | .20 | .20 |
| **607** | A171a | 30c multicolored | | .25 | .25 |
| **608** | A171a | 90c multicolored | | .70 | .70 |
| **609** | A171a | $4 multicolored | | 3.00 | 3.00 |
| | | Nos. 606-609 (4) | | 4.15 | 4.15 |

### Souvenir Sheet
**610** A171a $5 multicolored 4.00 4.00

The Song of the
Dog — G68

Paintings by Edgar Degas: 70c, Cafe-Concert. $1.10, The Orchestra of the Opera. $3, The Dance Lesson. $5, Madame Camus at the Piano.

### 1984, Aug. 22
| | | | | | |
|---|---|---|---|---|---|
| **611** | G68 | 25c multicolored | | .45 | .20 |
| **612** | G68 | 70c multicolored | | .75 | .60 |
| **613** | G68 | $1.10 multicolored | | 1.60 | 1.60 |
| **614** | G68 | $3 multicolored | | 3.00 | 3.00 |
| | | Nos. 611-614 (4) | | 5.80 | 5.40 |

### Souvenir Sheet
**615** G68 $5 multicolored 4.00 4.00

150th birth anniv. of Degas.

Queen
Victoria
Gardens
G69

$4, Ayers Rock. $5, Yarra River, Melbourne.

### 1984, Sept. 21
| | | | | | |
|---|---|---|---|---|---|
| **616** | G69 | $1.10 multicolored | | .85 | .85 |
| **617** | G69 | $4 multicolored | | 3.25 | 3.25 |

### Souvenir Sheet
**618** G69 $5 multicolored 4.00 4.00

AUSIPEX International Stamp Exhibition, Melbourne, Australia.

Colonel
Steven's
Model,
"1825"
G70

Locomotives: 50c, Royal George, 1827. 60c, Stourbridge Lion, 1829. 70c, Liverpool, 1830. 90c, South Carolina, 1832. $1.10, Monster, 1836. $2, Lafayette, 1837. $4, Lion, 1838.

### 1984, Oct. 3 — Perf. 15
| | | | | | |
|---|---|---|---|---|---|
| **619** | G70 | 20c multicolored | | .80 | .30 |
| **620** | G70 | 50c multicolored | | 1.00 | .60 |
| **621** | G70 | 60c multicolored | | 1.10 | .75 |
| **622** | G70 | 70c multicolored | | 1.25 | 1.25 |
| **623** | G70 | 90c multicolored | | 1.40 | 1.40 |
| **624** | G70 | $1.10 multicolored | | 1.40 | 1.40 |
| **625** | G70 | $2 multicolored | | 1.75 | 1.75 |
| **626** | G70 | $4 multicolored | | 2.25 | 2.25 |
| | | Nos. 619-626 (8) | | 10.95 | 9.70 |

### Souvenir Sheets
| | | | | | |
|---|---|---|---|---|---|
| **627** | G70 | $5 Sequin's Engine, 1829 | | 4.25 | 4.25 |
| **628** | G70 | $5 Der Adler, 1835 | | 4.25 | 4.25 |

Nos. 539, 541, 543 Overprinted

### 1984, Oct. 28 — Perf. 14
| | | | | | |
|---|---|---|---|---|---|
| **629** | G61 | 30c multicolored | | .35 | .25 |
| **630** | G61 | $1.10 multicolored | | 1.25 | .95 |

### Souvenir Sheet
**630A** G61 $5 multicolored 6.50 5.25

Opening of the Point Saline International Airport. No. 630A is overprinted in the margin.

### Christmas Type of 1984
Scenes from various Donald Duck movies.

### 1984, Nov. 26 — Perf. 13½x14
| | | | | | |
|---|---|---|---|---|---|
| **631** | A173 | 45c multicolored | | .95 | .55 |
| **632** | A173 | 60c multicolored | | 1.10 | .75 |
| **633** | A173 | 90c multicolored | | 1.60 | 1.25 |
| **634** | A173 | $2 multi, perf. 12 | | 2.50 | 2.50 |
| **635** | A173 | $4 multicolored | | 4.75 | 4.75 |
| | | Nos. 631-635 (5) | | 10.90 | 9.80 |

### Souvenir Sheet
**636** A173 $5 multicolored 6.50 6.00

No. 634 issued in sheets of 8.

### Audubon Type of 1985
Designs: 50c, Blue-winged teal. 90c, White ibis. $1.10, Swallow-tailed kite. $3, Common Gallinule. $5, Mangrove cuckoo.

### 1985, Feb. 11 — Perf. 14
| | | | | | |
|---|---|---|---|---|---|
| **637** | A174 | 50c multicolored | | 2.25 | .90 |
| **638** | A174 | 90c multicolored | | 2.75 | 1.60 |
| **639** | A174 | $1.10 multicolored | | 3.75 | 2.10 |
| **640** | A174 | $3 multicolored | | 4.75 | 4.75 |
| | | Nos. 637-640 (4) | | 13.50 | 9.35 |

### Souvenir Sheet
**641** A174 $5 multicolored 6.25 6.25

See Nos. 732-736.

Motorcycle
Centenary — G71

Anniv. emblem and: 30c, Kawasaki 750, 1972. 60c, Honda Goldwing GL1000, 1974, horiz. 70c, Kawasaki Z650, 1976, horiz. $4, Honda CBX, 1977. $5, BMW R100RS, 1978.

### 1985, Mar. 11
| | | | | | |
|---|---|---|---|---|---|
| **642** | G71 | 30c multicolored | | .75 | .50 |
| **643** | G71 | 60c multicolored | | 1.00 | 1.00 |
| **644** | G71 | 70c multicolored | | 1.25 | 1.25 |
| **645** | G71 | $4 multicolored | | 5.00 | 5.00 |
| | | Nos. 642-645 (4) | | 8.00 | 7.75 |

### Souvenir Sheet
**646** G71 $5 multicolored 6.00 6.00

Intl. Youth
Year
G72

Designs: 50c, Folding bandages (health). 70c, Diver, turtle (environment). $1.10, Sailing (leisure). $3, Boys playing chess (education). $5, Hands touching globe.

### 1985, Apr. 15
| | | | | | |
|---|---|---|---|---|---|
| **647** | G72 | 50c multicolored | | .65 | .45 |
| **648** | G72 | 70c multicolored | | 1.00 | .85 |
| **649** | G72 | $1.10 multicolored | | 1.50 | 1.40 |
| **650** | G72 | $3 multicolored | | 7.50 | 7.50 |
| | | Nos. 647-650 (4) | | 10.65 | 10.20 |

### Souvenir Sheet
**651** G72 $5 multicolored 5.00 5.00

Intl. Civil
Aviation
Org., 40th
Anniv.
G73

Designs: 5c, Lockheed Lodestar. 70c, Avro 748 Turboprop. $1.10, Boeing 727. $4, Boeing 707. $5, Pilatus Britten-Norman Islander.

### 1985, Apr. 30
| | | | | | |
|---|---|---|---|---|---|
| **652** | G73 | 5c multicolored | | .50 | .20 |
| **653** | G73 | 70c multicolored | | 2.25 | .70 |
| **654** | G73 | $1.10 multicolored | | 2.75 | 1.10 |
| **655** | G73 | $4 multicolored | | 4.50 | 3.25 |
| | | Nos. 652-655 (4) | | 10.00 | 5.25 |

### Souvenir Sheet
**656** G73 $5 multicolored 5.75 5.00

### Girl Guides Type
Designs: 30c, Lady Baden-Powell, Guide leaders. 50c, Botany field trip. 70c, Making camp, vert. $4, Sailing, vert. $5, Lord and Lady Baden-Powell, vert.

### 1985, May 30
| | | | | | |
|---|---|---|---|---|---|
| **657** | A176 | 30c multicolored | | .50 | .25 |
| **658** | A176 | 50c multicolored | | 1.25 | .35 |
| **659** | A176 | 70c multicolored | | 1.25 | .55 |
| **660** | A176 | $4 multicolored | | 5.00 | 2.75 |
| | | Nos. 657-660 (4) | | 8.00 | 3.90 |

### Souvenir Sheet
**661** A176 $5 multicolored 5.50 5.50

Grenadine
Grizzled
Skipper
G74

Butterflies: 1c, Red anartia. 2c, Lesser Antillean giant hairstreak. 4c, Santa Domingo long-tail skipper. 5c, Spotted Manuel's skipper. 6c, Grenada's polydamus swallowtail. 10c, Palmira sulphur. 12c, Pupillated orange sulphur. 15c, Migrant sulphur. 20c, St. Christopher's hairstreak. 25c, St. Lucia mestra. 30c, Insular gulf fritillary. 40c, Michael's Caribbean buckeye. 60c, Frampton's flambeau. 70c, Bamboo page. $1.10, Antillean cracker. $2.50, Red crescent hairstreak. $5, Single colored Antillean white. $10, Lesser whirlabout. $20, Blue night.

### 1985-86                    *Perf. 14*

| | | | | |
|---|---|---|---|---|
| 662 | G74 | ½c multicolored | .20 | .20 |
| 663 | G74 | 1c multicolored | .20 | .20 |
| 664 | G74 | 2c multicolored | .20 | .20 |
| 665 | G74 | 4c multicolored | .20 | .20 |
| 666 | G74 | 5c multicolored | .20 | .20 |
| 667 | G74 | 6c multicolored | .20 | .20 |
| 668 | G74 | 10c multicolored | .30 | .20 |
| 669 | G74 | 12c multicolored | .50 | .20 |
| 670 | G74 | 15c multicolored | .50 | .20 |
| 671 | G74 | 20c multicolored | .65 | .20 |
| 672 | G74 | 25c multicolored | .65 | .20 |
| 673 | G74 | 30c multicolored | .65 | .25 |
| 674 | G74 | 40c multicolored | .80 | .50 |
| 675 | G74 | 60c multicolored | 1.10 | .75 |
| 676 | G74 | 70c multicolored | 1.25 | .80 |
| 677 | G74 | $1.10 multicolored | 2.00 | 1.50 |
| 678 | G74 | $2.50 multicolored | 3.50 | 3.00 |
| 679 | G74 | $5 multicolored | 5.50 | 5.00 |
| 680 | G74 | $10 multicolored | 9.00 | 9.00 |
| 681 | G74 | $20 multicolored | 12.50 | 12.50 |
| | | Nos. 662-681 (20) | 40.10 | 35.50 |

Issued: #662-679, 6/17; #680, 11/11; #681, 1/8/86.

For overprints see Nos. 737-738.

### 1986                 *Perf. 12½x12*

| | | | | |
|---|---|---|---|---|
| 662a | G74 | ½c multicolored | .20 | .20 |
| 663a | G74 | 1c multicolored | .20 | .20 |
| 664a | G74 | 2c multicolored | .20 | .20 |
| 665a | G74 | 4c multicolored | .20 | .20 |
| 666a | G74 | 5c multicolored | .20 | .20 |
| 667a | G74 | 6c multicolored | .20 | .20 |
| 668a | G74 | 10c multicolored | .20 | .20 |
| 669a | G74 | 12c multicolored | .20 | .20 |
| 670a | G74 | 15c multicolored | .20 | .20 |
| 671a | G74 | 20c multicolored | .20 | .20 |
| 672a | G74 | 25c multicolored | .20 | .20 |
| 673a | G74 | 30c multicolored | .30 | .30 |
| 674a | G74 | 40c multicolored | .35 | .35 |
| 675a | G74 | 60c multicolored | .60 | .60 |
| 676a | G74 | 70c multicolored | .65 | .65 |
| 677a | G74 | $1.10 multicolored | 1.00 | 1.00 |
| 678a | G74 | $2.50 multicolored | 3.50 | 3.50 |
| 679a | G74 | $5 multicolored | 6.00 | 6.00 |
| 680a | G74 | $10 multicolored | 10.00 | 10.00 |
| 681a | G74 | $20 multicolored | 13.00 | 13.00 |
| | | Nos. 662a-681a (20) | 37.60 | 37.60 |

Issued: #662a-677a, 679a, 1986; #678a, 680a, 9/1986; #681a, 5/1989.

### Queen Mother Birthday Type

$1, Portrait. $1.50, At Ascot, horiz. $2.50, Queen Mother, Prince Charles. $5, Portrait, diff.

### 1985, July 3             *Perf. 14*

| | | | | |
|---|---|---|---|---|
| 682 | A181 | $1 multicolored | .65 | .65 |
| 683 | A181 | $1.50 multicolored | 1.10 | 1.10 |
| 684 | A181 | $2.50 multicolored | 1.75 | 1.75 |
| | | Nos. 682-684 (3) | 3.50 | 3.50 |

**Souvenir Sheet**

| | | | | |
|---|---|---|---|---|
| 685 | A181 | $5 multicolored | 3.75 | 3.75 |

### 1986, Jan. 28         *Perf. 12x12½*

| | | | | |
|---|---|---|---|---|
| 686 | A181 | 70c like #682 | .60 | .60 |
| 687 | A181 | $1.10 like #683 | .75 | .75 |
| 688 | A181 | $3 like #684 | 2.50 | 2.50 |
| | | Nos. 686-688 (3) | 3.85 | 3.85 |

Issued in sheets of 5 plus label.

### Water Sports Type

Designs: 15c, Scuba diving. 70c, Playing in waterfall. 90c, Water skiing. $4, Swimming. $5, Skin diver, sailboat.

### 1985, July 15         *Perf. 15*

| | | | | |
|---|---|---|---|---|
| 689 | A179 | 15c multicolored | .20 | .20 |
| 690 | A179 | 70c multicolored | .55 | .55 |
| 691 | A179 | 90c multicolored | 1.00 | 1.00 |
| 692 | A179 | $4 multicolored | 3.50 | 3.50 |
| | | Nos. 689-692 (4) | 5.25 | 5.25 |

**Souvenir Sheet**

| | | | | |
|---|---|---|---|---|
| 693 | A179 | $5 multicolored | 4.50 | 4.50 |

Queen Conch
G75

Marine Life: 90c, Porcupine fish, fire coral. $1.10, Ghost crab. $4, West Indies spiny lobster. $5, Long-spined urchin.

### 1985, Aug. 1             *Perf. 14*

| | | | | |
|---|---|---|---|---|
| 694 | G75 | 60c multicolored | .75 | .60 |
| 695 | G75 | 90c multicolored | 1.25 | .85 |
| 696 | G75 | $1.10 multicolored | 1.50 | 1.00 |
| 697 | G75 | $4 multicolored | 3.75 | 3.75 |
| | | Nos. 694-697 (4) | 7.25 | 6.20 |

**Souvenir Sheet**

| | | | | |
|---|---|---|---|---|
| 698 | G75 | $5 multicolored | 7.25 | 7.25 |

### Bach Anniversary Type

Portrait, signature, music from Invention No. 9 and: 15c, Natural trumpet. 60c, Bass viol. $1.10, Flute. $3, Double flageolet. $5, Portrait.

### 1985, Sept. 3         *Perf. 14*

| | | | | |
|---|---|---|---|---|
| 699 | A184 | 15c multicolored | .65 | .20 |
| 700 | A184 | 60c multicolored | 1.10 | .60 |
| 701 | A184 | $1.10 multicolored | 2.00 | 1.00 |
| 702 | A184 | $3 multicolored | 3.00 | 2.50 |
| | | Nos. 699-702 (4) | 6.75 | 4.30 |

**Souvenir Sheet**

| | | | | |
|---|---|---|---|---|
| 703 | A184 | $5 multicolored | 4.50 | 4.50 |

### Royal Visit Type

10c, Arms of Great Britain, Grenada. $1, Queen Elizabeth II. $4, HMY Britannia. $5, Map.

### 1985, Nov. 4        *Perf. 14½*

| | | | | |
|---|---|---|---|---|
| 704 | A186 | 10c multicolored | .25 | .20 |
| 705 | A186 | $1 multi, vert. | 1.50 | 1.50 |
| 706 | A186 | $4 multicolored | 4.50 | 4.50 |
| | | Nos. 704-706 (3) | 6.25 | 6.20 |

**Souvenir Sheet**

| | | | | |
|---|---|---|---|---|
| 707 | A186 | $5 multicolored | 5.25 | 5.25 |

### UN Anniversary Type

UN stamps and famous people: $1, #373, Neil Armstrong. $2, #221, Mahatma Gandhi. $2.50, #43, Maimonides. $5, Ralph Bunche.

### 1985, Nov. 22

| | | | | |
|---|---|---|---|---|
| 708 | A189 | $1 multicolored | 1.50 | 1.25 |
| 709 | A189 | $2 multicolored | 4.25 | 4.25 |
| 710 | A189 | $2.50 multicolored | 5.00 | 5.00 |
| | | Nos. 708-710 (3) | 10.75 | 10.50 |

**Souvenir Sheet**

| | | | | |
|---|---|---|---|---|
| 711 | A189 | $5 multicolored | 5.25 | 5.25 |

### Twain & Disney Type

Walt Disney characters in scenes from "Letters From Hawaii": 25c, Mickey, Minnie on beach. 60c, Donald Duck surfing. $1.50, Donald roasting marshmallow. $3, Mickey canoeing. $5, Mickey, cat.

### 1985, Nov. 27       *Perf. 14x13½*

| | | | | |
|---|---|---|---|---|
| 712 | A185 | 25c multicolored | .85 | .40 |
| 713 | A185 | 50c multicolored | 1.25 | .90 |
| 714 | A185 | $1.50 multicolored | 3.25 | 3.25 |
| 715 | A185 | $3 multicolored | 5.50 | 5.50 |
| | | Nos. 712-715 (4) | 10.85 | 10.05 |

**Souvenir Sheet**

| | | | | |
|---|---|---|---|---|
| 716 | A185 | $5 multicolored | 7.00 | 7.00 |

### Brothers Grimm & Disney Type

Walt Disney characters in scenes from "The Elves and the Shoemaker": 30c, Mickey as shoemaker. 60c, Elves helping. 70c, Mickey, new shoes. $4, Minnie at sewing machine. $5, Minnie & Mickey.

### 1985, Nov. 27       *Perf. 13½x14*

| | | | | |
|---|---|---|---|---|
| 717 | A187 | 30c multicolored | .85 | .45 |
| 718 | A187 | 60c multicolored | 1.25 | 1.00 |
| 719 | A187 | 70c multicolored | 1.60 | 1.25 |
| 720 | A187 | $4 multicolored | 5.25 | 5.25 |
| | | Nos. 717-720 (4) | 8.95 | 7.95 |

**Souvenir Sheet**

| | | | | |
|---|---|---|---|---|
| 721 | A187 | $5 multicolored | 7.50 | 7.50 |

Madonna and Child by Titian — G76

Christmas paintings: 70c, Madonna and Child with St. Mary and John the Baptist by Bugiardini. $1.10, Adoration of the Magi by Di Fredi. $3, Madonna and Child with Young St. John the Baptist by Bartolomeo. $5, The Annunciation by Botticelli.

### 1985, Dec. 23        *Perf. 15*

| | | | | |
|---|---|---|---|---|
| 722 | G76 | 50c multicolored | .60 | .45 |
| 723 | G76 | 70c multicolored | .75 | .55 |
| 724 | G76 | $1.10 multicolored | 1.25 | .90 |
| 725 | G76 | $3 multicolored | 2.40 | 2.40 |
| | | Nos. 722-725 (4) | 5.00 | 4.30 |

**Souvenir Sheet**

| | | | | |
|---|---|---|---|---|
| 726 | G76 | $5 multicolored | 4.00 | 4.00 |

### Statue of Liberty Type of 1985

Designs: 5c, Croton Reservoir, 1875. 10c, NY Public Library, 1986. 70c, Old Boathouse, Central Park, 1894. $4, Boating, Central Park, 1986. $5, Statue of Liberty, vert.

### 1986, Jan. 6         *Perf. 15*

| | | | | |
|---|---|---|---|---|
| 727 | A191 | 5c multicolored | .20 | .20 |
| 728 | A191 | 10c multicolored | .20 | .20 |
| 729 | A191 | 70c multicolored | .40 | .40 |
| 730 | A191 | $4 multicolored | 2.75 | 2.75 |
| | | Nos. 727-730 (4) | 3.55 | 3.55 |

**Souvenir Sheet**

| | | | | |
|---|---|---|---|---|
| 731 | A191 | $5 multicolored | 5.00 | 5.00 |

### Audubon Type of 1985

Designs: 50c, Louisiana heron. 70c, Black-crowned night heron. 90c, Bittern. $4, Glossy ibis. $5, King eider.

### 1986, Jan. 28       *Perf. 12½x12*

| | | | | |
|---|---|---|---|---|
| 732 | A174 | 50c multicolored | 2.25 | 1.10 |
| 733 | A174 | 70c multicolored | 2.75 | 1.60 |
| 734 | A174 | 90c multicolored | 3.00 | 2.40 |
| 735 | A174 | $4 multicolored | 5.50 | 5.50 |
| | | Nos. 732-735 (4) | 13.50 | 10.60 |

**Souvenir Sheet**
                  *Perf. 14*

| | | | | |
|---|---|---|---|---|
| 736 | A174 | $5 multicolored | 8.00 | 8.00 |

Nos. 732-735 issued in sheets of 5 plus label.

### Nos. 676, 679 Overprinted

### 1986, Feb. 20        *Perf. 14*

| | | | | |
|---|---|---|---|---|
| 737 | G74 | 70c multicolored | 1.50 | 1.50 |
| 738 | G75 | $5 multicolored | 6.50 | 6.50 |

World Cup Soccer Championships, Mexico — G77

Various soccer plays.

### 1986, Mar. 18

| | | | | |
|---|---|---|---|---|
| 739 | G77 | 10c multicolored | .65 | .40 |
| 740 | G77 | 70c multicolored | 1.90 | 1.40 |
| 741 | G77 | $1 multicolored | 2.25 | 1.90 |
| 742 | G77 | $4 multicolored | 5.50 | 5.50 |
| | | Nos. 739-742 (4) | 10.30 | 9.20 |

**Souvenir Sheet**

| | | | | |
|---|---|---|---|---|
| 743 | G77 | $5 multicolored | 6.25 | 6.25 |

For overprints see Nos. 772-776.

### Halley's Comet Type

Designs: 5c, Nicolaus Copernicus, Earl of Rossi's six foot reflector. 20c, Sputnik. 40c, Tycho Brahe's notes, sketch of comet of 1577. $4, Edmond Halley, comet of 1682. $5, Halley's comet. Captions on 40c and $4 are reversed.

### 1986, Mar. 26

| | | | | |
|---|---|---|---|---|
| 744 | A194 | 5c multicolored | .50 | .50 |
| 745 | A194 | 20c multicolored | .80 | .50 |
| 746 | A194 | 40c multicolored | 1.00 | .75 |
| 747 | A194 | $4 multicolored | 5.00 | 5.00 |
| | | Nos. 744-747 (4) | 7.30 | 6.75 |

**Souvenir Sheet**

| | | | | |
|---|---|---|---|---|
| 748 | A194 | $5 multicolored | 4.75 | 4.75 |

"Tycho," on 40c, and "Nicolaus" on 5c misspelled.
For overprints see Nos. 787-791. Compare No. 748 with No. 913.

### Queen Elizabeth II, 60th Birthday
#### Common Design Type

Designs: 2c, At Windsor Park, 1933. $1.50, Queen Elizabeth II. $4, In Sydney, Australia, 1970. $5, Family portrait, Coronation Day, 1937.

### 1986, Apr. 21

| | | | | |
|---|---|---|---|---|
| 749 | CD339 | 2c yel & blk | .20 | .20 |
| 750 | CD339 | $1.50 pale grn & multi | 1.00 | 1.00 |
| 751 | CD339 | $4 dl lil & multi | 2.75 | 2.75 |
| | | Nos. 749-751 (3) | 3.95 | 3.95 |

**Souvenir Sheet**

| | | | | |
|---|---|---|---|---|
| 752 | CD339 | $5 tan & blk | 3.75 | 3.75 |

### AMERIPEX '86 Type

Walt Disney characters visiting: 30c, Grand Canyon. 60c, Golden Gate Bridge. $1, Chicago Watertower. $3, The White House. $5, NY Harbor, Statue of Liberty.

### 1986, May 22        *Perf. 11*

| | | | | |
|---|---|---|---|---|
| 753 | A195 | 30c multicolored | .80 | .50 |
| 754 | A195 | 60c multicolored | 1.20 | 1.20 |
| 755 | A195 | $1 multicolored | 2.00 | 2.00 |
| 756 | A195 | $3 multicolored | 4.00 | 4.00 |
| | | Nos. 753-756 (4) | 8.00 | 7.70 |

**Souvenir Sheet**
                *Perf. 14*

| | | | | |
|---|---|---|---|---|
| 757 | A195 | $5 multicolored | 6.25 | 6.25 |

### Royal Wedding Issue, 1986
#### Common Design Type

Designs: 60c, Prince Andrew and Sarah Ferguson. 70c, Andrew. $4, Andrew in dress uniform, helicopter. $5, Couple, diff.

### 1986, July 1         *Perf. 14*

| | | | | |
|---|---|---|---|---|
| 758 | CD340 | 60c multicolored | .45 | .45 |
| 759 | CD340 | 70c multicolored | .55 | .55 |
| 760 | CD340 | $4 multicolored | 3.00 | 3.00 |
| | | Nos. 758-760 (3) | 4.00 | 4.00 |

**Souvenir Sheet**

| | | | | |
|---|---|---|---|---|
| 761 | CD340 | $5 multicolored | 5.00 | 5.00 |

Mushrooms G78      Seashells G79

Designs: 15c, Hygrocybe firma. 50c, Xerocomus coccolobae. $2, Volvariella cubensis. $3, Lactarius putidus. $5, Leponia caeruleocapitata.

### 1986, July 15        *Perf. 15*

| | | | | |
|---|---|---|---|---|
| 762 | G78 | 15c multicolored | .90 | .45 |
| 763 | G78 | 50c multicolored | 1.90 | 1.25 |
| 764 | G78 | $2 multicolored | 3.75 | 3.75 |
| 765 | G78 | $3 multicolored | 5.00 | 5.00 |
| | | Nos. 762-765 (4) | 11.55 | 10.45 |

**Souvenir Sheet**

| | | | | |
|---|---|---|---|---|
| 766 | G78 | $5 multicolored | 11.00 | 11.00 |

### 1986, Aug. 1

Designs: 15c, Giant Atlantic pyram. 50c, Beau's murex. $1.10, West Indian fighting conch. $4, Alphabet coral. $5, Brown-lined paper bubble.

| | | | | |
|---|---|---|---|---|
| 767 | G79 | 15c multicolored | 1.10 | .55 |
| 768 | G79 | 50c multicolored | 2.50 | 1.50 |
| 769 | G79 | $1.10 multicolored | 2.75 | 2.75 |
| 770 | G79 | $4 multicolored | 4.75 | 4.75 |
| | | Nos. 767-770 (4) | 11.10 | 9.55 |

**Souvenir Sheet**

| | | | | |
|---|---|---|---|---|
| 771 | G79 | $5 multicolored | 10.00 | 10.00 |

Nos. 739-743 Overprinted in Gold: WINNERS / Argentina 3 / W.Germany 2

### 1986, Sept. 15       *Perf. 14*

| | | | | |
|---|---|---|---|---|
| 772 | G77 | 10c multicolored | .75 | .45 |
| 773 | G77 | 70c multicolored | 1.50 | 1.25 |
| 774 | G77 | $1 multicolored | 2.00 | 1.50 |
| 775 | G77 | $4 multicolored | 4.75 | 4.75 |
| | | Nos. 772-775 (4) | 9.00 | 7.95 |

**Souvenir Sheet**

| | | | | |
|---|---|---|---|---|
| 776 | G77 | $5 multicolored | 8.00 | 8.00 |

Manicou
G80

Wildlife.

**1986, Sept. 15**     *Perf. 15*

| | | | | |
|---|---|---|---|---|
| 777 | G80 | 10c shown | .20 | .20 |
| 778 | G80 | 30c Giant toad | .40 | .40 |
| 779 | G80 | 60c Land tortoise | .85 | .85 |
| 780 | G80 | 70c Murine opossum | .90 | .90 |
| 781 | G80 | 90c Burmese mongoose | 1.00 | 1.00 |
| 782 | G80 | $1.10 Antillean armadillo | 1.25 | 1.25 |
| 783 | G80 | $2 Agouti | 1.90 | 1.90 |
| 784 | G80 | $3 Humpback whale | 4.75 | 4.75 |
| | | *Nos. 777-784 (8)* | 11.25 | 11.25 |

**Souvenir Sheets**

| | | | | |
|---|---|---|---|---|
| 785 | G80 | $5 Mona monkey | 6.50 | 6.50 |
| 786 | G80 | $5 Iguana | 6.50 | 6.50 |

Nos. 744-748 Overprinted in Silver or Black

**1986, Oct. 15**     *Perf. 14*

| | | | | |
|---|---|---|---|---|
| 787 | A194 | 5c multicolored (Bk) | .65 | .65 |
| 788 | A194 | 20c multicolored | .85 | .55 |
| 789 | A194 | 40c multicolored (Bk) | 1.00 | .65 |
| 790 | A194 | $4 multicolored | 5.50 | 5.50 |
| | | *Nos. 787-790 (4)* | 8.00 | 7.35 |

**Souvenir Sheet**

| | | | | |
|---|---|---|---|---|
| 791 | A194 | $4 multicolored | 6.50 | 6.50 |

Christmas Type of 1986

**1986 Nov. 3**     *Perf. 11*

| | | | | |
|---|---|---|---|---|
| 792 | A199 | 25c Chip 'n' Dale | .50 | .20 |
| 793 | A199 | 30c Mickey Mouse | .50 | .25 |
| 794 | A199 | 50c Piglet, Pooh, Jose Carioca | .65 | .35 |
| 795 | A199 | 60c Daisy | .75 | .45 |
| 796 | A199 | 70c A kiss under the mistletoe | .85 | .55 |
| 797 | A199 | $1.50 Huey, Dewey, and Louie | 1.50 | 1.50 |
| 798 | A199 | $3 Mickey Mouse, Morty | 1.75 | 1.75 |
| 799 | A199 | $4 Kittens on the keys | 3.00 | 3.00 |
| | | *Nos. 792-799 (8)* | 9.50 | 8.05 |

**Souvenir Sheets**

| | | | | |
|---|---|---|---|---|
| 800 | A199 | $5 Mickey Mouse | 5.00 | 5.00 |
| 801 | A199 | $5 Bambi | 5.00 | 5.00 |

Nos. 793, 795-796, 799 vert.

Automobile Centenary Type

Designs: 10c, 1984 Aston-Martin Volante. 30c, 1948 Jaguar Mk V. 60c, 1956 Nash Ambassador. 70c, 1984 Toyota Supra. 90c, 1985 Ferrari Testarossa. $1, 1955 BMW 501B. $2, 1968 Mercedes-Benz 280SL. $3, 1932 Austro-Daimler ADR8.

**1986, Nov. 20**     *Perf. 15*

| | | | | |
|---|---|---|---|---|
| 802 | A202 | 10c multicolored | .30 | .30 |
| 803 | A202 | 30c multicolored | .55 | .55 |
| 804 | A202 | 60c multicolored | .75 | .75 |
| 805 | A202 | 70c multicolored | .75 | .75 |
| 806 | A202 | 90c multicolored | .90 | .90 |
| 807 | A202 | $1 multicolored | .90 | .90 |
| 808 | A202 | $2 multicolored | 1.25 | 1.25 |
| 809 | A202 | $3 multicolored | 1.60 | 1.60 |
| | | *Nos. 802-809 (8)* | 7.00 | 7.00 |

**Souvenir Sheets**

| | | | | |
|---|---|---|---|---|
| 810 | A202 | $5 1977 Morgan +8 | 4.25 | 4.25 |
| 811 | A202 | $5 Checker Taxi | 4.25 | 4.25 |

Chagall Type

Paintings: No. 812, The Mirror. No. 813, Dancer with a Fan. No. 814, The Acrobat. No. 815, Abraham's Sacrifice. No. 816, The Fruit Seller. No. 817, The Rooster. No. 818, The Wedding. No. 819, Horsewoman. No. 820, The Aged Lion from Fables of La Fontaine. No. 821, The Fruit Basket. No. 822, The Satyr and the Wayfarer. No. 823, Self-portrait with Seven Fingers. No. 824, Fruit and Flowers. No. 825, Lovers and Flowers. No. 826, The Wedded with an Angel. No. 827, In the Cafe, 1936. No. 828, The Equestrian. No. 829, Blue

Violinist, 1947. No. 830, I and the Village. No. 831, Portrait of Vava, 1955. No. 832, To Russia, Asses and Cattle, 1911. No. 833, The Accordion Player. No. 834, The Violinist, 1913. No. 835, Mother and Child, 1968. No. 836, Sunday, 1953. No. 837, Red and Black World, 1951. No. 838, Double Portrait with Wineglass, 1917. No. 839, Homage to Apollinaire. No. 840, Time is a River without Banks, 1930. No. 841, The Rue de La Paix, 1953. No. 842, Bonjour Paris. No. 843, The Blue Home, 1926, horiz. No. 844, Still-life, 1912, horiz. No. 845, Autumn Village. No. 846, Aleko: Scene I (Costume Design). No. 847, The Jew in Pink, 1914. No. 848, The Clown Musician, 1927. No. 849, War, 1943. No. 850, The Artist Angel. No. 851, Woman at Window, 1961. No. 852, Birthday, 1915. No. 853, Wheatfield on a Summer Afternoon, 1942. No. 854, The Nude Above Vitebsk. No. 855, Aleko and Zemphira by Moonlight. No. 856, The Family Dinner. No. 857, Life. No. 858, The Flying Carriage, 1913. No. 859, The Studio. No. 860, Birth. No. 861, Rain.

**1986-87**     *Perf. 14x13½*

| | | | | |
|---|---|---|---|---|
| 812-851 | A203 | $1.10 each | 1.00 | 1.00 |

**Size: 110x95mm**

*Imperf*

| | | | | |
|---|---|---|---|---|
| 852-861 | A203 | $5 each | 3.75 | 3.75 |

Issued: Nos. 824-851, 855-861, 1987.

America's Cup Type

**1987, Feb. 5**     *Perf. 15*

| | | | | |
|---|---|---|---|---|
| 862 | A204 | 25c Defender, 1895 | .85 | .55 |
| 863 | A204 | 45c Caleta, 1886 | 1.10 | .85 |
| 864 | A204 | 70c Azzurra, 1981 | 1.40 | 1.40 |
| 865 | A204 | $4 Australia II, 1983 | 3.00 | 3.00 |
| | | *Nos. 862-865 (4)* | 6.35 | 5.80 |

**Souvenir Sheet**

| | | | | |
|---|---|---|---|---|
| 866 | A204 | $5 Columbia, Shamrock, 1899 | 7.00 | 7.00 |

Discovery of America Type

**1987, Apr. 27**

| | | | | |
|---|---|---|---|---|
| 867 | A206 | 15c Columbus | .20 | .20 |
| 868 | A206 | 30c Queen Isabella | .20 | .20 |
| 869 | A206 | 50c Santa Maria | .35 | .35 |
| 870 | A206 | 60c Landing in New World | .40 | .40 |
| 871 | A206 | 90c Lesser Antilles | .65 | .65 |
| 872 | A206 | $1 King Ferdinand | .70 | .70 |
| 873 | A206 | $2 Fort of La Navidad | 1.50 | 1.50 |
| 874 | A206 | $3 Galley off Hispaniola | 2.10 | 2.10 |
| a. | | Sheet of 8 | 7.00 | 7.00 |
| | | *Nos. 867-874 (8)* | 6.10 | 6.10 |

**Souvenir Sheets**

| | | | | |
|---|---|---|---|---|
| 875 | A207 | $5 Native Canoe | 5.00 | 5.00 |
| 876 | A207 | $5 Santa Maria at anchor | 5.00 | 5.00 |

Transportation Innovations Type

Designs: 10c, Saunders Roe SR-N1 Hovercraft, 1959. 15c, Bugatti Royale, 1931. 30c, Aleksei Leonov, 1st space walk, 1965. 50c, CSS Hunley, submarine, 1864. 60c, Rolls Royce Flying Bedstead, VTOL aircraft, 1954. 70c, Jenny Lind, locomotive, 1854. 90c, Duryea, 1893. $1.50, Steam locomotive, London subway, 1863. $2, SS Great Britain, screw-driven steamship, 1843. $3, Budweiser rocket, 1979.

**1987, May 18**     *Perf. 14*

| | | | | |
|---|---|---|---|---|
| 877 | A209 | 10c multicolored | .55 | .30 |
| 878 | A209 | 15c multicolored | .60 | .40 |
| 879 | A209 | 30c multicolored | .80 | .50 |
| 880 | A209 | 50c multicolored | 1.10 | .75 |
| 881 | A209 | 60c multicolored | 1.25 | .90 |
| 882 | A209 | 70c multicolored | 1.40 | 1.25 |
| 883 | A209 | 90c multicolored | 1.50 | 1.25 |
| 884 | A209 | $1.50 multicolored | 2.25 | 2.25 |
| 885 | A209 | $2 multicolored | 2.75 | 2.75 |
| 886 | A209 | $3 multicolored | 3.00 | 3.00 |
| | | *Nos. 877-886 (10)* | 15.20 | 13.35 |

Capex '87 Type

Fish.

**1987, June 15**

| | | | | |
|---|---|---|---|---|
| 887 | A208 | 6c Yellow chub | .20 | .20 |
| 888 | A208 | 30c Kingfish | .50 | .35 |
| 889 | A208 | 50c Mako shark | .70 | .60 |
| 890 | A208 | 60c Dolphinfish | .80 | .80 |
| 891 | A208 | 90c Bonito | 1.00 | 1.00 |
| 892 | A208 | $1.10 Cobia | 1.25 | 1.25 |
| 893 | A208 | $3 Great tarpon | 3.00 | 3.00 |
| 894 | A208 | $4 Swordfish | 3.25 | 3.25 |
| | | *Nos. 887-894 (8)* | 10.70 | 10.45 |

**Souvenir Sheets**

| | | | | |
|---|---|---|---|---|
| 895 | A208 | $5 Jewfish | 5.00 | 5.00 |
| 896 | A208 | $5 Amberjack | 5.00 | 5.00 |

Statue of Liberty Type

10c, Washing statue's face. 15c, Commemorative medals. 25c, Band facing right. 30c, Band facing forward. 45c, Liberty's face. 50c, Washing statue's hair, horiz. 60c, Commemorative statuettes, horiz. 70c, Boats in NY Harbor, horiz. $1, Re-opening. $1.10, Blimps, Liberty & Manhattan Islands. $2, Warship. $3, Commemorative flags.

**1987, Aug. 5**

| | | | | |
|---|---|---|---|---|
| 897 | A210 | 10c multicolored | .20 | .20 |
| 898 | A210 | 15c multicolored | .30 | .30 |
| 899 | A210 | 25c multicolored | .45 | .45 |
| 900 | A210 | 30c multicolored | .50 | .50 |
| 901 | A210 | 45c multicolored | .55 | .55 |
| 902 | A210 | 50c multicolored | .60 | .60 |
| 903 | A210 | 60c multicolored | .70 | .70 |
| 904 | A210 | 70c multicolored | .80 | .80 |
| 905 | A210 | $1 multicolored | .95 | .95 |
| 906 | A210 | $1.10 multicolored | 1.00 | 1.00 |
| 907 | A210 | $2 multicolored | 1.90 | 1.90 |
| 908 | A210 | $3 multicolored | 2.10 | 2.10 |
| | | *Nos. 897-908 (12)* | 10.05 | 10.05 |

Inventors Type

Designs: 60c, Isaac Newton, Newton Medal. $1, Louis Daguerre, inventor of Daguerreotype. $2, Antoine Lavoisier, French chemist, apparatus. $3, Rudolf Diesel, German engineer, Diesel engine. $5, Halley's comet.

**1987, Sept. 9**

| | | | | |
|---|---|---|---|---|
| 909 | A211 | 60c multicolored | .90 | .70 |
| 910 | A211 | $1 multicolored | 1.10 | 1.10 |
| 911 | A211 | $2 multicolored | 2.25 | 2.25 |
| 912 | A211 | $3 multicolored | 5.25 | 5.25 |
| | | *Nos. 909-912 (4)* | 9.50 | 9.30 |

**Souvenir Sheet**

| | | | | |
|---|---|---|---|---|
| 913 | A211 | $5 multicolored | 7.25 | 7.25 |

No. 913 inscribed "Great Scientific Discoveries" in margin.

No. 912 incorrectly inscribed "James Watt, Steam Engine." See Grenada No. 1538.

US Constitution Bicentennial Type

10c, Constitutional Convention, Philadelphia. 50c, Georgia state flag. 60c, Capitol, vert. $4, Thomas Jefferson, vert. $5, Alexander Hamilton, vert.

**1987, Nov. 1**

| | | | | |
|---|---|---|---|---|
| 914 | A214 | 10c multicolored | .25 | .20 |
| 915 | A214 | 50c multicolored | .85 | .75 |
| 916 | A214 | 60c multicolored | .85 | .80 |
| 917 | A214 | $4 multicolored | 4.75 | 4.75 |
| | | *Nos. 914-917 (4)* | 6.70 | 6.50 |

**Souvenir Sheet**

| | | | | |
|---|---|---|---|---|
| 918 | A214 | $5 multicolored | 4.25 | 4.25 |

Hafnia '87 Type

Walt Disney characters in adaptations of Hans Christian Andersen Fairy Tales: 25c, The Swineherd. 30c, What the Good Man Does is Always Right. 50c, Little Tuk. 60c, The World's Fairest Rose. 70c, The Garden of Paradise. $1.50, The Naughty Boy. $3, What the Moon Saw. $4, Thumbelina. No. 927, Hans Clodhopper. No. 928, Elder Tree Mother.

**1987, Nov. 16**

| | | | | |
|---|---|---|---|---|
| 919 | A215 | 25c multicolored | .55 | .30 |
| 920 | A215 | 30c multicolored | .60 | .40 |
| 921 | A215 | 50c multicolored | .80 | .80 |
| 922 | A215 | 60c multicolored | .80 | .80 |
| 923 | A215 | 70c multicolored | .85 | .85 |
| 924 | A215 | $1.50 multicolored | 2.25 | 2.25 |
| 925 | A215 | $3 multicolored | 3.00 | 3.00 |
| 926 | A215 | $4 multicolored | 3.50 | 3.50 |
| | | *Nos. 919-926 (8)* | 12.35 | 11.90 |

**Souvenir Sheets**

| | | | | |
|---|---|---|---|---|
| 927 | A215 | $5 multicolored | 6.50 | 6.50 |
| 928 | A215 | $5 multicolored | 6.50 | 6.50 |

Christmas — G81

Paintings by El Greco: 10c, Virgin and Child with Saints Martin and Agnes. 50c, Detail from Virgin and Child with Saints Martin and Agnes. 60c, The Annunciation. $4, Holy Family with St. Anne. $5, Adoration of the Shepherds.

**1987, Dec. 15**

| | | | | |
|---|---|---|---|---|
| 929 | G81 | 10c multicolored | .45 | .20 |
| 930 | G81 | 50c multicolored | 1.40 | .95 |
| 931 | G81 | 60c multicolored | 1.40 | 1.10 |
| 932 | G81 | $4 multicolored | 5.50 | 5.50 |
| | | *Nos. 929-932 (4)* | 8.75 | 7.75 |

**Souvenir Sheet**

| | | | | |
|---|---|---|---|---|
| 933 | G81 | $5 multicolored | 9.25 | 9.25 |

Wedding Anniv. Type

**1988, Feb. 15**

| | | | | |
|---|---|---|---|---|
| 934 | A218 | 20c Elizabeth, Anne | .25 | .20 |
| 935 | A218 | 30c Wedding portrait | .25 | .25 |
| 936 | A218 | $2 Elizabeth, Charles, Anne | 1.50 | 1.50 |
| 937 | A218 | $3 Elizabeth wearing tiara | 2.25 | 2.25 |
| | | *Nos. 934-937 (4)* | 4.25 | 4.20 |

**Souvenir Sheet**

| | | | | |
|---|---|---|---|---|
| 938 | A218 | $5 Elizabeth in wedding gown | 4.25 | 4.25 |

1988 Summer Olympics Type

Walt Disney characters in modern and ancient events.

**1988, Apr. 13**     *Perf. 13½x14, 14x13½*

| | | | | |
|---|---|---|---|---|
| 939 | A219 | 1c Rhythmic gymnastics | .20 | .20 |
| 940 | A219 | 2c Pankration | .20 | .20 |
| 941 | A219 | 3c Synchronized swimming | .20 | .20 |
| 942 | A219 | 4c Hoplite race | .20 | .20 |
| 943 | A219 | 5c Baseball | .20 | .20 |
| 944 | A219 | 10c Horse race | .25 | .20 |
| 945 | A219 | $6 Windsurfing | 5.00 | 5.00 |
| 946 | A219 | $7 Chariot race | 5.75 | 5.75 |
| | | *Nos. 939-946 (8)* | 12.00 | 12.00 |

**Souvenir Sheet**

| | | | | |
|---|---|---|---|---|
| 947 | A219 | $5 Tennis | 5.00 | 5.00 |
| 948 | A219 | $5 Pentathlon | 5.00 | 5.00 |

Boy Scout Type

**1988, May 3**     *Perf. 14*

| | | | | |
|---|---|---|---|---|
| 949 | A220 | 50c Semaphore, vert. | .50 | .50 |
| 950 | A220 | 70c Canoeing, vert. | .60 | .60 |
| 951 | A220 | $1 Cook-out | .90 | .90 |
| 952 | A220 | $3 Campfire | 2.75 | 2.75 |
| | | *Nos. 949-952 (4)* | 4.75 | 4.75 |

**Souvenir Sheet**

| | | | | |
|---|---|---|---|---|
| 953 | A220 | $5 Pitching tent | 4.50 | 4.50 |

Bird Type

**1988, May 31**

| | | | | |
|---|---|---|---|---|
| 954 | A222 | 20c Yellow-crowned night heron | .25 | .25 |
| 955 | A222 | 25c Brown pelican | .25 | .25 |
| 956 | A222 | 45c Audubon's shearwater | .40 | .35 |
| 957 | A222 | 60c Red-footed booby | .55 | .40 |
| 958 | A222 | 70c Bridled tern | .55 | .50 |
| 959 | A222 | 90c Red-billed tropicbird | .75 | .75 |
| 960 | A222 | $3 Blue-winged teal | 2.25 | 2.25 |
| 961 | A222 | $4 Sora | 3.00 | 3.00 |
| | | *Nos. 954-961 (8)* | 8.00 | 7.75 |

**Souvenir Sheets**

| | | | | |
|---|---|---|---|---|
| 962 | A222 | $5 Little blue heron | 4.25 | 4.25 |
| 963 | A222 | $5 Purple-throated carib | 4.25 | 4.25 |

Titian Type

Paintings by Titian: 15c, Man with Blue Eyes, 1545. 30c, The Three Ages of Man, 1512. 60c, Don Diego Mendoza, 1545. 75c, Emperor Charles V Seated, 1548. $1, A Young Man in a Fur, 1515. $2, Tobias and the Angel, 1543. $3, Pietro Bembo, 1540. $4, Pier Luigi Farnese, 1546. No. 972, Sacred and Profane Love. No. 973, Venus and Adonis.

**1988, June 15**     *Perf. 13½x14*

| | | | | |
|---|---|---|---|---|
| 964 | A224 | 15c multicolored | .20 | .20 |
| 965 | A224 | 30c multicolored | .25 | .25 |
| 966 | A224 | 60c multicolored | .40 | .40 |
| 967 | A224 | 75c multicolored | .55 | .55 |
| 968 | A224 | $1 multicolored | .75 | .75 |
| 969 | A224 | $2 multicolored | 1.50 | 1.50 |
| 970 | A224 | $3 multicolored | 2.25 | 2.25 |
| 971 | A224 | $4 multicolored | 3.00 | 3.00 |
| | | *Nos. 964-971 (8)* | 8.90 | 8.90 |

**Souvenir Sheet**

| | | | | |
|---|---|---|---|---|
| 972 | A224 | $5 multicolored | 5.25 | 5.25 |
| 973 | A224 | $5 multicolored | 5.25 | 5.25 |

Airship Type

Historic flights: 10c, Hindenburg over Rio de Janeiro, 1937. 20c, Hindenburg over NYC, 1937. 30c, US Navy airships, WWII convoy to Europe, 1944. 40c, Hindenburg docking at Lakehurst, NJ, 1937, vert. 50c, Joint flight, Hindenburg and Graf Zeppelin, 1936, vert. 70c, DC-3, Hindenburg, Los Angeles at Lakehurst, 1936. $1, Graf Zeppelin II over England, 1939, vert. $2, Deutschland, 1st passenger flight, 1912. $3, Graf Zeppelin over Dome of the Rock, Jerusalem, 1931. $4, Hindenburg Olympic flight, 1936. No. 984, Graf Zeppelin over Vatican City, 1933, vert. No. 985, Graf Zeppelin Polar flight, 1931.

**1988, July 1**     *Perf. 14*

| | | | | |
|---|---|---|---|---|
| 974 | A225 | 10c multicolored | .20 | .20 |
| 975 | A225 | 20c multicolored | .20 | .20 |
| 976 | A225 | 30c multicolored | .25 | .25 |
| 977 | A225 | 40c multicolored | .35 | .35 |
| 978 | A225 | 60c multicolored | .80 | .60 |
| 979 | A225 | 90c multicolored | 1.10 | .80 |

| | | | | |
|---|---|---|---|---|
| 980 | A225 | $1 multicolored | 1.10 | .90 |
| 981 | A225 | $2 multicolored | 1.75 | 1.75 |
| 982 | A225 | $3 multicolored | 2.50 | 2.50 |
| 983 | A225 | $4 multicolored | 3.25 | 3.25 |
| | | Nos. 974-983 (10) | 11.50 | 10.80 |

**Souvenir Sheets**

| | | | | |
|---|---|---|---|---|
| 984 | A225 | $5 multicolored | 6.00 | 6.00 |
| 985 | A225 | $5 multicolored | 6.00 | 6.00 |

### Fairy Tales Type
### Miniature Sheets

*Bambi:* No. 986a, Newborn Bambi, mother and forest animals. b, Bambi, Flower and Thumper. c, Bambi and opossum family hanging from tree. d, Bambi, his mother, and Faline, a female fawn. e, Foraging in a snow storm. f, Meeting his father, the Great Stag. g, Competing for Faline's attention. h, The Great Stag leading animals to safety during forest fire. i, Bambi, grown, becomes the Great Stag.

*The Fox and the Hound:* No. 987a, Big Mama, consoling the orphaned baby fox, Tod. b, Widow Tweed feeding Tod. c, Tod playing with Copper, the hound. d, Copper leashed. e, Copper and Chief. f, Chief barking at Tod, Copper shocked. g, Porcupine. h, Vixey, a female fox. i, Bear attacking Copper.

*101 Dalmatians:* No. 988a, Pongo, Perdita and their masters. b, Pongo and Perdita, courting. c, Three puppies. d, Cruella de Ville and henchmen. e, Captain the Horse, Colonel the Sheepdog and Tibbs the Cat. f, Dalmatians following Tibbs to freedom. g, Cruella racing car in pursuit. h, Dalmatians disguised in soot. i, Nanny dusting off the soot.

*Dumbo:* No. 989a, Stork delivering Dumbo. b, Elephant making fun of Dumbo's large ears. c, Dumbo, Mrs. Jumbo performing. d, Timothy the Mouse. e, Timothy and Dumbo. f, Crows pushing Dumbo off a cliff. g, Dumbo flying away from burning building. h, Dumbo flying with the crows. i, Dumbo and Mrs. Jumbo on train.

*Lady and the Tramp:* No. 990a, Darling holding Lady. b, Lady meets the Tramp. c, Lady looking in bassinet. d, Siamese cats, Lady. e, Lady, Tramp, crocodiles. f, Tramp kisses Lady. g, Lady in dog catcher's carriage. h, Lady and Tramp attacking rat. i, Trusty and Jock overturning dog catcher's carriage where Tramp is imprisoned.

*The Aristocats:* No. 991a, Edgar driving Madame Mornfamille's carriage. b, Dutchess and kittens. c, Edgar feeding the cats cream spiked with sleeping pills. d, Edgar transporting cats on motorcycle. e, Walter O'Malley discovers the abandoned cats. f, Three geese. g, Scat Cat and friends holding a jam session. h, Edgar attacks O'Malley with a pitch fork. i, Frau-Frau kicking Edgar.

No. 992, Faline and newborn twin fawns. No. 993, Tod and Vixey. No. 994, Pongo, Perdita and puppies. No. 995, Dumbo flying with Timothy the Mouse. No. 996, Lady and Tramp's puppies. No. 997, Walter O'Malley, Dutchess and kittens.

| | | | | |
|---|---|---|---|---|
| **1988, July 25** | | | **Perf. 14x13½** | |
| 986 | | Sheet of 9 | 4.25 | 4.25 |
| | a.-i. | A212 30c any single | .40 | .40 |
| 987 | | Sheet of 9 | 4.25 | 4.25 |
| | a.-i. | A212 30c any single | .40 | .40 |
| 988 | | Sheet of 9 | 4.25 | 4.25 |
| | a.-i. | A212 30c any single | .40 | .40 |
| 989 | | Sheet of 9 | 4.25 | 4.25 |
| | a.-i. | A212 30c any single | .40 | .40 |
| 990 | | Sheet of 9 | 4.25 | 4.25 |
| | a.-i. | A212 30c any single | .40 | .40 |
| 991 | | Sheet of 9 | 4.25 | 4.25 |
| | a.-i. | A212 30c any single | .40 | .40 |
| | | Nos. 986-991 (6) | 25.50 | 25.50 |

**Souvenir Sheets**

| | | | | |
|---|---|---|---|---|
| 992-997 | A212 | $5 each | 6.50 | 6.50 |

### SYDPEX '88 Type

Walt Disney characters: 1c, Conducting at Sydney Opera House. 2c, Climbing Ayers Rock. 3c, Working at a sheep station. 4c, Visiting Lone Pine Koala Sanctuary. 5c, Playing Australian football. 10c, Racing camels. No. 1004, Lawn bowling. $6, America's Cup trophy and Australia II. No. 1006, The Great Barrier Reef. No. 1007, Beach party.

| | | | | |
|---|---|---|---|---|
| **1988, Aug. 1** | | | **Perf. 14x13½** | |
| 998 | A226 | 1c multicolored | .20 | .20 |
| 999 | A226 | 2c multicolored | .20 | .20 |
| 1000 | A226 | 3c multicolored | .20 | .20 |
| 1001 | A226 | 4c multicolored | .20 | .20 |
| 1002 | A226 | 5c multicolored | .20 | .20 |
| 1003 | A226 | 10c multicolored | .20 | .20 |
| 1004 | A226 | 5c multicolored | 5.50 | 5.50 |
| 1005 | A226 | 6c multicolored | 6.50 | 6.50 |
| | | Nos. 998-1005 (8) | 13.20 | 13.20 |

**Souvenir Sheets**

| | | | | |
|---|---|---|---|---|
| 1006 | A226 | $5 multicolored | 5.00 | 5.00 |
| 1007 | A226 | $5 multicolored | 5.00 | 5.00 |

### Flowering Trees Type

| | | | | |
|---|---|---|---|---|
| **1988, Sept. 30** | | | **Perf. 14** | |
| 1008 | A228 | 10c Potato tree, vert. | .20 | .20 |
| 1009 | A228 | 20c Wild cotton | .20 | .20 |
| 1010 | A228 | 30c Shower of gold, vert. | .25 | .25 |
| 1011 | A228 | 60c Napoleon's button, vert. | .50 | .45 |
| 1012 | A228 | 90c Geiger tree | .75 | .65 |
| 1013 | A228 | $1 Fern tree | .85 | .85 |
| 1014 | A228 | $2 French cashew | 1.75 | 1.75 |
| 1015 | A228 | $4 Amherstia, vert. | 3.00 | 3.00 |
| | | Nos. 1008-1015 (8) | 7.50 | 7.35 |

**Souvenir Sheets**

| | | | | |
|---|---|---|---|---|
| 1016 | A228 | $5 African tulip tree, vert. | 3.75 | 3.75 |
| 1017 | A228 | $5 Swamp immortelle | 3.75 | 3.75 |

### Car Type
### Miniature Sheets

Designs: No. 1018a, 1925 Doble Series E, US. b, 1926 Alvis 12/50, United Kingdom. c, 1927 Sunbeam 3-liter, UK. d, 1928 Franklin Airman, US. e, 1929 Delage D8S, France. f, 1897 Mors, France. g, 1904 Peerless Green Dragon, US. h, 1909 Pope-Hartford, US. i, 1920 Daniels Submarine Speedster, US. j, 1922 McFarlan 9.3 liter, US.

No. 1019a, 1949 Frazer Nash Lemans Replica, UK. b, 1953 Pegaso Z102, Spain. No. 1019c, 1953 Siata Spyder V-8, Italy. d, 1953 Kurtis-Offenhauser, US. No. 1019e, 1954 Kaiser-Darrin, US. f, 1930 Tracta, France. g, 1932 Maybach Zeppelin, Germany. h, 1934 Railton Light Sports, UK. i, 1936 Hotchkiss, France. j, 1939 Mercedes-Benz W163, Germany.

No. 1020a, 1982 Aston Martin Vantage V8, UK. b, 1982 Porsche 956, Germany. No. 1020c, 1983 Lotus Esprit Turbo, UK. d, 1984 McLaren MP4/2, UK. e, 1985 Mercedes-Benz 190E 2-3-16, Germany. f, 1963 Ferrari 250 GT Lusso, Italy. g, 1964 Porsche 904, Germany. h, 1967 Volvo P1800, Sweden. i, 1970 McLaren-Chevrolet M8D, US. j, 1981 Jaguar XJ6, UK.

| | | | | |
|---|---|---|---|---|
| **1988, Oct. 7** | | | **Perf. 13x13½** | |
| 1018 | | Sheet of 10 | 15.00 | 15.00 |
| | a.-j. | A223 $2 any single | 1.50 | 1.50 |
| 1019 | | Sheet of 10 | 15.00 | 15.00 |
| | a.-j. | A223 $2 any single | 1.50 | 1.50 |
| 1020 | | Sheet of 10 | 15.00 | 15.00 |
| | a.-j. | A223 $2 any single | 1.50 | 1.50 |

### Christmas and Mickey Mouse 60th
### Anniv. Type
### Miniature Sheet

"Mickey's Christmas Parade": No. 1021a, Dumbo. b, Goofy. c, Minnie Mouse. d, Morty, Ferdy and Clarabelle Cow. e, Huey, Dewey and Louie. f, Donald Duck. g, Wooden soldiers marching. h, Mickey Mouse leading parade. No. 1022, Capt. Hook on float. No. 1023, Mickey and Donald on float.

| | | | | |
|---|---|---|---|---|
| **1988, Dec. 1** | | | **Perf. 13½x14** | |
| 1021 | | Sheet of 8 | 6.00 | 6.00 |
| | a.-h. | A229 $1 any single | .75 | .75 |

**Souvenir Sheets**
**Perf. 14x13**

| | | | | |
|---|---|---|---|---|
| 1022 | A229 | $7 multicolored | 6.50 | 6.50 |
| 1023 | A229 | $7 multicolored | 6.50 | 6.50 |

### Japanese Painting Type

"The Fifty-three Stations on the Tokaido" by Hiroshige (1979-1858): 15c, Crossing the Oi at Shimada by Ferry. 20c, Daimyo and Entourage at Arai. 45c, Cargo Portage through Goyu. 75c, Snowfall at Fujigawa. $1, Horses for the Emperor at Chirifu. $2, Rainfall at Tsuchiyama. $3, At Inn of Ishibe. $4, On the Shore of Lake Biwa at Otsu. No. 1032, Pilgrimage to Atsuta Shrine at Miya. No. 1033, Fishing Village of Yokkaichi on the Mie.

| | | | | |
|---|---|---|---|---|
| **1989, May 15** | | | **Perf. 14x13½** | |
| 1024 | A233 | 15c multicolored | .30 | .30 |
| 1025 | A233 | 20c multicolored | .35 | .35 |
| 1026 | A233 | 45c multicolored | .60 | .60 |
| 1027 | A233 | 75c multicolored | 1.00 | 1.00 |
| 1028 | A233 | $1 multicolored | 1.00 | 1.00 |
| 1029 | A233 | $2 multicolored | 1.75 | 1.75 |
| 1030 | A233 | $3 multicolored | 2.75 | 2.75 |
| 1031 | A233 | $4 multicolored | 3.75 | 3.75 |
| | | Nos. 1024-1031 (8) | 11.50 | 11.50 |

**Souvenir Sheets**

| | | | | |
|---|---|---|---|---|
| 1032 | A233 | $5 multicolored | 4.50 | 4.50 |
| 1033 | A233 | $5 multicolored | 4.50 | 4.50 |

### 1988 Olympic Medalists Type

Designs: 15c, Henry Maske, East Germany, boxing (165 lbs.). 50c, Andreas Schroeder, East Germany, freestyle wrestling (286 lbs.). 60c, East German team, women's gymnastics. 75c, Greg Louganis, US, men's springboard and platform diving. $1, Mitsuru Sato, Japan, freestyle wrestling (115 lbs.). $2, West German team, 4x200m freestyle relay. $3, Dieter Baumann, West Germany, 5000m race. $4, Jackie Joyner-Kersee, US, heptathlon. No. 1042, Joachim Kunz, East Germany, weight lifting (149 lbs.). No. 1043, West German equestrian team, 3-day event.

**World Cup Soccer Championships,**
**Italy — G82**

Designs: 15c, World Cup, vert. 45c, Kaiser Franz, West Germany, vert. 75c, Like 20c, flag of Italy, 1982 champions. $1, Pele, Brazil, vert. $2, Like 20c, flag of West Germany, 1974 champions. $3, Like 20c, flag of Brazil, 1970 champions. $4, Jules Rimet Cup, vert. No. 1052, Pele, Jules Rimet Cup, vert. No. 1053, Goalie.

| | | | | |
|---|---|---|---|---|
| **1989, June 12** | | | | |
| 1044 | G82 | 15c multicolored | .20 | .20 |
| 1045 | G82 | 20c multicolored | .20 | .20 |
| 1046 | G82 | 45c multicolored | .30 | .30 |
| 1047 | G82 | 75c multicolored | .55 | .55 |
| 1048 | G82 | $1 multicolored | 1.40 | 1.40 |
| 1049 | G82 | $2 multicolored | 2.75 | 2.75 |
| 1050 | G82 | $3 multicolored | 2.10 | 2.10 |
| 1051 | G82 | $4 multicolored | 2.75 | 2.75 |
| | | Nos. 1044-1051 (8) | 10.25 | 10.25 |

**Souvenir Sheets**

| | | | | |
|---|---|---|---|---|
| 1052 | G82 | $6 multicolored | 4.75 | 4.75 |
| 1053 | G82 | $6 multicolored | 4.75 | 4.75 |

### Car Type of 1988
### Miniature Sheets

North American locomotives: No. 1054a, Morris & Essex, Dover, 1841. No. 1054b, B&O, Memmon No. 57, 1848. No. 1054c, Camden & Amboy, John Stevens, 1849. No. 1054d, Lawrence Machine Shop, Lawrence, 1853. No. 1054e, South Carolina, James S. Corry, 1859. No. 1054f, Mine Hill & Schuylkill Haven, Flexible Beam No. 3, 1860. No. 1054g, DL&W, Montrose, 1861. No. 1054h, Central Pacific, Pequop No. 68, 1868. No. 1054i, Boston & Providence, Daniel Nason, 1863. No. 1054j, Morris & Essex, Joe Scranton, 1870.

No. 1055a, Central Railroad of New Jersey, No. 124, 1871. No. 1055b, Baldwin Steam Motor for Street Railways, 1876. No. 1055c, Lackawanna & Bloomsburg, Luzerne, 1878. No. 1055d, Central Mexicano, No. 150, 1892. No. 1055e, Denver, South Park & Pacific, Breckenridge No. 15, 1879. No. 1055f, Miles Planting & Manufacturing Co., "Daisy" Plantation locomotive, 1894. No. 1055g, Central of Georgia, Baldwin 854 No. 1136, 1895. No. 1055h, Savannah, Florida & Western, No. 111, 1900. No. 1055i, Douglas, Gilmore & Co. No. 3, 1902. No. 1055j, Lehigh Valley Coal Co., Compressed Air locomotive No. 900, 1903.

No. 1056a, Morgan's Louisiana & Texas, McKeen Motorcar, 1908. No. 1056b, Clear Lake Lumber Co., Type B Climax, 1910. No. 1056c, Blue Jay Lumber Co., Heisler No. 10, 1912. No. 1056d, Stewartstown, Gasoline Engine No. 6, 1920's. No. 1056e, Bangor & Aroostook, Class G No. 186, 1921. No. 1056f, Hammond Lumber Co., No. 6, 1923. No. 1056g, Central Railroad of New Jersey, No. 1000, 1925. No. 1056h, Atchison, Topeka & Santa Fe, Super Chief No. 1-1A, 1935. No. 1056i, Norfolk & Western, Class Y-6, 1948. No. 1056i, Boston & Maine, Budd Railcar, 1949.

| | | | | |
|---|---|---|---|---|
| **1989, June 28** | | | **Perf. 13x13½** | |
| 1054 | | Sheet of 10 | 20.00 | 20.00 |
| | a.-j. | A223 $2 any single | 1.75 | 1.75 |
| 1055 | | Sheet of 10 | 20.00 | 20.00 |
| | a.-j. | A223 $2 any single | 1.75 | 1.75 |
| 1056 | | Sheet of 10 | 20.00 | 20.00 |
| | a.-j. | A223 $2 any single | 1.75 | 1.75 |

| | | | | |
|---|---|---|---|---|
| **1989, Apr. 13** | | | **Perf. 14** | |
| 1034 | A232 | 15c multicolored | .30 | .20 |
| 1035 | A232 | 50c multicolored | .40 | .35 |
| 1036 | A232 | 60c multicolored | .50 | .40 |
| 1037 | A232 | 75c multicolored | .70 | .55 |
| 1038 | A232 | $1 multicolored | .85 | .75 |
| 1039 | A232 | $2 multicolored | 1.50 | 1.50 |
| 1040 | A232 | $3 multicolored | 2.25 | 2.25 |
| 1041 | A232 | $4 multicolored | 3.00 | 3.00 |
| | | Nos. 1034-1041 (8) | 9.50 | 9.00 |

**Souvenir Sheets**

| | | | | |
|---|---|---|---|---|
| 1042 | A232 | $6 multicolored | 4.75 | 4.75 |
| 1043 | A232 | $6 multicolored | 4.75 | 4.75 |

**PHILEXFRANCE '89 — G83**

Walt Disney characters in Paris.

| | | | | |
|---|---|---|---|---|
| **1989, July 7** | | **Perf. 14x13½, 13½x14** | | |
| 1057 | G83 | 1c Military school | .20 | .20 |
| 1058 | G83 | 2c Conciergerie | .20 | .20 |
| 1059 | G83 | 3c Hotel de Ville, vert. | .20 | .20 |
| 1060 | G83 | 4c Genie of the Bastille, vert. | .20 | .20 |
| 1061 | G83 | 5c The Opera | .20 | .20 |
| 1062 | G83 | 10c Gardens of Luxembourg | .25 | .25 |
| 1063 | G83 | $5 Arche de la Defense, vert. | 7.00 | 7.00 |
| 1064 | G83 | $6 Place Vendome, vert. | 7.00 | 7.00 |
| | | Nos. 1057-1064 (8) | 15.25 | 15.25 |

**Souvenir Sheets**

| | | | | |
|---|---|---|---|---|
| 1065 | G83 | $6 Riding moped | 7.00 | 7.00 |
| 1066 | G83 | $6 Hot air ballooning | 7.00 | 7.00 |

### Moon Landing Anniv. Type

Apollo 11 mission, 1969: 25c, Liftoff, vert. 50c, Splashdown. 60c, Spacecraft approaching moon, vert. 75c, Buzz Aldrin conducting experiment on lunar surface. $1, Leaving Earth orbit. $2, Transport of launch vehicle to pad, vert. $3, Lunar module liftoff. $4, Eagle lands on moon, vert. No. 1075, Footprint on moon. No. 1076, Armstrong stepping onto the moon, vert.

| | | | | |
|---|---|---|---|---|
| **1989, July 20** | | | **Perf. 14** | |
| 1067 | A237 | 25c multicolored | .30 | .30 |
| 1068 | A237 | 50c multicolored | .50 | .50 |
| 1069 | A237 | 60c multicolored | .60 | .60 |
| 1070 | A237 | 75c multicolored | .75 | .75 |
| 1071 | A237 | $1 multicolored | .90 | .90 |
| 1072 | A237 | $2 multicolored | 2.00 | 2.00 |
| 1073 | A237 | $3 multicolored | 2.50 | 2.50 |
| 1074 | A237 | $4 multicolored | 3.50 | 3.50 |
| | | Nos. 1067-1074 (8) | 11.05 | 11.05 |

**Souvenir Sheets**

| | | | | |
|---|---|---|---|---|
| 1075 | A237 | $5 multicolored | 5.00 | 5.00 |
| 1076 | A237 | $5 multicolored | 5.00 | 5.00 |

### Mushroom Type

| | | | | |
|---|---|---|---|---|
| **1989, Aug. 17** | | | | |
| 1078 | A238 | 6c Collybia aurea | .40 | .25 |
| 1079 | A238 | 10c Podaxis pistillaris | .40 | .25 |
| 1080 | A238 | 20c Hygrocybe firma | .65 | .50 |
| 1081 | A238 | 30c Agaricus rufoaurantiacus | .75 | .65 |
| 1082 | A238 | 75c Leptonia howellii | 1.60 | 1.60 |
| 1083 | A238 | $2 Marasmiellus purpureus | 3.00 | 3.00 |
| 1084 | A238 | $3 Marasmius trinitatis | 3.50 | 3.50 |
| 1085 | A238 | $4 Hygrocybe martinicensis | 4.00 | 4.00 |
| | | Nos. 1078-1085 (8) | 14.30 | 13.75 |

**Souvenir Sheets**

| | | | | |
|---|---|---|---|---|
| 1086 | A238 | $6 Lentinus crinitus | 8.00 | 8.00 |
| 1087 | A238 | $6 Agaricus purpurellus | 8.00 | 8.00 |

### Butterflies Type

| | | | | |
|---|---|---|---|---|
| **1989, Oct. 2** | | | **Perf. 14** | |
| 1088 | A239 | 25c Androgeus swallowtail | .50 | .50 |
| 1089 | A239 | 35c Cloudless sulpher | .60 | .60 |
| 1090 | A239 | 45c Cracker | .65 | .65 |
| 1091 | A239 | 50c Painted lady | .65 | .65 |
| 1092 | A239 | 75c Great southern white | 1.00 | 1.00 |
| 1093 | A239 | 90c Little sulpher | 1.10 | 1.10 |
| 1094 | A239 | $2 Migrant sulpher | 2.50 | 2.50 |
| 1095 | A239 | $3 Mimic | 3.00 | 3.00 |
| | | Nos. 1088-1095 (8) | 10.00 | 10.00 |

**Souvenir Sheets**

| | | | | |
|---|---|---|---|---|
| 1096 | A239 | $6 Giant hairstreak | 6.50 | 6.50 |
| 1097 | A239 | $6 Red anartia | 6.50 | 6.50 |

### World Stamp Expo Type

Scenes from Walt Disney animated films and quotes from Poor Richard's Almanack by Benjamin Franklin: 1c, "Beware of little expenses, a small leak will sink a great ship."

2c, "Trust thyself and another shall not betray thee." 3c, "A spoonful of honey will catch more flies than a gallon of vinegar." 4c, "No gain without pain." 5c, "A true friend is the best possession." 6c, "Haste makes waste." 8c, "A quiet conscience sleeps in thunder, but rest and guilt live far asunder." 10c, "The muses love the morning." $5, "An egg today is better than a hen tomorrow." No. 1107, "He that riseth late, must trot all day." No. 1108, "If you'd be belov'd, make yourself amiable." No. 1109, "In Christmas feasting pray take care; let not your table be a snare; but with the poor God's bounty share. Adieu my friends! Till the next year," vert.

### 1989, Nov.    Litho.    Perf. 14x13½

| | | | | |
|---|---|---|---|---|
| 1098 | A242 | 1c multicolored | .20 | .20 |
| 1099 | A242 | 2c multicolored | .20 | .20 |
| 1100 | A242 | 3c multicolored | .20 | .20 |
| 1101 | A242 | 4c multicolored | .20 | .20 |
| 1102 | A242 | 5c multicolored | .20 | .20 |
| 1103 | A242 | 6c multicolored | .20 | .20 |
| 1104 | A242 | 8c multicolored | .20 | .20 |
| 1105 | A242 | 10c multicolored | .20 | .20 |
| 1106 | A242 | $5 multicolored | 4.50 | 4.50 |
| 1107 | A242 | $6 multicolored | 5.50 | 5.50 |
| | | Nos. 1098-1107 (10) | 11.60 | 11.60 |

#### Souvenir Sheet

| | | | | |
|---|---|---|---|---|
| 1108 | A242 | $6 multicolored | 7.50 | 7.50 |
| 1109 | A242 | $6 multicolored | 7.50 | 7.50 |

World Stamp Expo '89, Washington, D.C.

Shakespearean Actors and Theater Masks — G84

15c, Ethel Barrymore (1879-1959). $1.10, Richard Burton (1925-1984). $2, John Barrymore (1882-1942). $3, Paul Robeson (1898-1976). $6, Bando Tamasaburo & Nakamura Kanzaburo.

### 1989, Oct. 9    Litho.    Perf. 14

| | | | | |
|---|---|---|---|---|
| 1110 | G84 | 15c multicolored | .40 | .30 |
| 1111 | G84 | $1.10 multicolored | 1.75 | 1.50 |
| 1112 | G84 | $2 multicolored | 2.75 | 2.75 |
| 1113 | G84 | $3 multicolored | 3.00 | 3.00 |
| | | Nos. 1110-1113 (4) | 7.90 | 7.55 |

#### Souvenir Sheet

| | | | | |
|---|---|---|---|---|
| 1114 | G84 | $6 multicolored | 7.00 | 7.00 |

20th Century Musicians — G85

### 1989, Oct. 9

| | | | | |
|---|---|---|---|---|
| 1115 | G85 | 10c Buddy Holly | .40 | .30 |
| 1116 | G85 | 25c Jimi Hendrix | .65 | .50 |
| 1117 | G85 | 75c Mighty Sparrow | .95 | .95 |
| 1118 | G85 | $4 Katsutoji Kineya | 4.25 | 4.25 |
| | | Nos. 1115-1118 (4) | 6.25 | 6.00 |

#### Souvenir Sheet

| | | | | |
|---|---|---|---|---|
| 1119 | G85 | $6 Lotte Lenya, Kurt Weill | 6.25 | 6.25 |

Jimi is spelled incorrectly as "Jimmy."

#### Discovery of America Type

### 1989, Oct. 16

| | | | | |
|---|---|---|---|---|
| 1120 | A241 | 15c Canoeing | .40 | .30 |
| 1121 | A241 | 75c Cooking | 1.25 | 1.25 |
| 1122 | A241 | 90c Using stone tools | 1.75 | 1.75 |
| 1123 | A241 | $3 Eating | 4.50 | 4.50 |
| | | Nos. 1120-1123 (4) | 7.90 | 7.80 |

#### Souvenir Sheet

| | | | | |
|---|---|---|---|---|
| 1124 | A241 | $6 Building fire | 6.25 | 6.25 |

#### Christmas Type

Religious paintings by Rubens: 10c, The Annunciation. 15c, The Flight of the Holy Family into Egypt. 25c, The Presentation in the Temple. 45c, The Holy Family Under the Apple Tree. $2, Madonna and Child with Saints. $4, The Virgin and Child Enthroned with Saints. No. 1132, The Holy Family. No. 1132, Adoration of the Magi. No. 1133, Adoration of the Magi, diff.

---

### 1990, Jan. 4    Perf. 14

| | | | | |
|---|---|---|---|---|
| 1125 | A243 | 10c multicolored | .40 | .20 |
| 1126 | A243 | 15c multicolored | .45 | .20 |
| 1127 | A243 | 25c multicolored | .65 | .20 |
| 1128 | A243 | 45c multicolored | .85 | .40 |
| 1129 | A243 | $2 multicolored | 2.40 | 2.40 |
| 1130 | A243 | $4 multicolored | 3.50 | 3.50 |
| 1131 | A243 | $5 multicolored | 3.50 | 3.50 |
| | | Nos. 1125-1131 (7) | 11.75 | 10.40 |

#### Souvenir Sheets

| | | | | |
|---|---|---|---|---|
| 1132 | A243 | $5 multicolored | 7.00 | 7.00 |
| 1133 | A243 | $5 multicolored | 7.00 | 7.00 |

America Issue (Insects) G86

### 1990, Mar. 16    Perf. 14

| | | | | |
|---|---|---|---|---|
| 1134 | G86 | 35c Hercules beetle | .40 | .40 |
| 1135 | G86 | 40c Click beetle | .40 | .40 |
| 1136 | G86 | 50c Harlequin beetle | .50 | .50 |
| 1137 | G86 | 60c Gold rim butterfly | .90 | .90 |
| 1138 | G86 | $1 Red skimmer dragonfly | 1.10 | 1.10 |
| 1139 | G86 | $2 Buprestid beetle | 2.00 | 2.00 |
| 1140 | G86 | $3 Mimic butterfly | 3.00 | 3.00 |
| 1141 | G86 | $4 Scarab beetle | 3.00 | 3.00 |
| | | Nos. 1134-1141 (8) | 11.30 | 11.30 |

#### Souvenir Sheets

| | | | | |
|---|---|---|---|---|
| 1142 | G86 | $6 Canna skipper butterfly | 5.50 | 5.50 |
| 1143 | G86 | $6 Monarch butterfly | 5.50 | 5.50 |

Orchids — G87

### 1990, Mar. 6    Litho.    Perf. 14

| | | | | |
|---|---|---|---|---|
| 1144 | G87 | 15c Brassocattleya thalie | .30 | .30 |
| 1145 | G87 | 20c Odontocidium tigersun | .30 | .30 |
| 1146 | G87 | 50c Odontioda hambuhren | .45 | .45 |
| 1147 | G87 | 75c Paphiopedium delrosi | .55 | .55 |
| 1148 | G87 | $1 Vuylstekeara yokara | .90 | .90 |
| 1149 | G87 | $2 Paphiopedilum geelong | 1.75 | 1.75 |
| 1150 | G87 | $3 Wilsonara tigerwood | 2.25 | 2.25 |
| 1151 | G87 | $4 Cymbidium ormoulu | 3.00 | 3.00 |
| | | Nos. 1144-1151 (8) | 9.50 | 9.50 |

#### Souvenir Sheets

| | | | | |
|---|---|---|---|---|
| 1152 | G87 | $6 Odontonia sappho | 6.00 | 6.00 |
| 1153 | G87 | $6 Cymbidium vieux rose | 6.00 | 6.00 |

EXPO '90 Intl. Garden and Greenery Exposition, Osaka, Japan.

#### Wildlife Type

### 1990, Apr. 3

| | | | | |
|---|---|---|---|---|
| 1154 | A247 | 5c West Indies giant rice rat | .25 | .25 |
| 1155 | A247 | 25c Agouti | .40 | .40 |
| 1156 | A247 | 30c Humpback whale | .85 | .80 |
| 1157 | A247 | 40c Pilot whale | .85 | .80 |
| 1158 | A247 | $1 Spotted dolphin | 1.10 | 1.10 |
| 1159 | A247 | $2 Mongoose | 2.10 | 2.10 |
| 1160 | A247 | $3 Prehensile-tailed porcupine | 2.75 | 2.75 |
| 1161 | A247 | $4 West Indies manatee | 3.00 | 3.00 |
| | | Nos. 1154-1161 (8) | 11.30 | 11.20 |

#### Souvenir Sheets

| | | | | |
|---|---|---|---|---|
| 1162 | A247 | $6 Caribbean monk seal | 5.50 | 5.50 |
| 1163 | A247 | $6 Mongoose | 5.50 | 5.50 |

#### World War II Type

Designs: 6c, First British troops arrive in France, Sept. 6, 1939. 10c, British launch "Operation Crusader", Nov. 18, 1941. 20c,

---

Rommel begins retreat from El Alamein, Nov. 4, 1942. 45c, US forces land on Aleutian Islands, May 11, 1943. 50c, US Marines land on Tarawa, Nov. 20, 1943. 60c, US 5th Army enters Rome, June 4, 1944. 75c, US troops reach River Seine, Aug. 19, 1944. $1, Battle of the Bulge, Dec. 16, 1944. $5, Allies launch final phase of Italian Campaign, Apr. 9, 1945. No. 1173, Atom bomb dropped on Hiroshima, Aug. 6, 1945. No. 1174, St. Paul's Catherdral during London blitz, Battle of Britain, 1940.

### 1990, Apr. 30

| | | | | |
|---|---|---|---|---|
| 1164 | A248 | 6c multicolored | .40 | .40 |
| 1165 | A248 | 10c multicolored | .40 | .40 |
| 1166 | A248 | 20c multicolored | .65 | .65 |
| 1167 | A248 | 45c multicolored | .70 | .70 |
| 1168 | A248 | 50c multicolored | .80 | .80 |
| 1169 | A248 | 60c multicolored | .85 | .85 |
| 1170 | A248 | 75c multicolored | .95 | .95 |
| 1171 | A248 | $1 multicolored | 1.25 | 1.25 |
| 1172 | A248 | $5 multicolored | 4.00 | 4.00 |
| 1173 | A248 | $5 multicolored | 5.00 | 5.00 |
| | | Nos. 1164-1173 (10) | 15.00 | 15.00 |

#### Souvenir Sheets

| | | | | |
|---|---|---|---|---|
| 1174 | A248 | $6 multicolored | 7.50 | 7.50 |

#### Disney Type

Disney characters portraying Shakespearian characters: 15c, Daisy Duck at Ann Hathaway's Cottage, Shottery. 30c, Minnie Mouse and a young Shakespeare walking in Stratford birthplace, vert. 50c, Minnie as Mary Arden, Shakespeare's mother in Wilmcote, vert. 60c, Mickey in front of New Place, Stratford. $1, Mickey walking in Great Garden of New Place. $2, Mickey at Guild Chapel, Scholars Lane, vert. $4, Mickey at the Royal Shakespeare Theater, Stratford, vert. $5, Ludwig von Drake instructing Shakespeare. No. 1183, Mickey at Edge Hill, Stratford, vert. No. 1184, Mickey and Minnie rowing past Holy Trinity Church, Stratford-Upon-Avon.

### 1990, May    Perf. 14x13½

| | | | | |
|---|---|---|---|---|
| 1175 | A250 | 15c multicolored | .50 | .25 |
| 1176 | A250 | 30c multicolored | .65 | .45 |
| 1177 | A250 | 50c multicolored | .95 | .85 |
| 1178 | A250 | 60c multicolored | 1.10 | 1.10 |
| 1179 | A250 | $1 multicolored | 1.50 | 1.50 |
| 1180 | A250 | $2 multicolored | 2.75 | 2.75 |
| 1181 | A250 | $4 multicolored | 4.00 | 4.00 |
| 1182 | A250 | $5 multicolored | 4.00 | 4.00 |
| | | Nos. 1175-1182 (8) | 15.45 | 14.90 |

#### Souvenir Sheets    Perf. 14

| | | | | |
|---|---|---|---|---|
| 1183 | A250 | $6 multicolored | 8.00 | 8.00 |
| 1184 | A250 | $6 multicolored | 8.00 | 8.00 |

#### Penny Black Type
#### Souvenir Sheet

### 1990, May 3    Litho.    Perf. 14

| | | | | |
|---|---|---|---|---|
| 1185 | A249 | $6 Globe with South America | 8.00 | 8.00 |

Stamp World London '90.

#### Queen Mother, 90th Birthday Type

### 1990, July 5

| | | | | |
|---|---|---|---|---|
| 1186 | A251 | $2 Pink hat | 1.60 | 1.60 |
| 1187 | A251 | $2 With Charles | 1.60 | 1.60 |
| 1188 | A251 | $2 Blue outfit | 1.60 | 1.60 |
| | | Nos. 1186-1188 (3) | 4.80 | 4.80 |

#### Souvenir Sheet

| | | | | |
|---|---|---|---|---|
| 1189 | A251 | $6 like #1187 | 4.75 | 4.75 |

#### Bird Type

### 1990, Sept. 10    Litho.    Perf. 14

| | | | | |
|---|---|---|---|---|
| 1190 | A255 | 25c Yellow-bellied seedeater | .40 | .40 |
| 1191 | A255 | 45c Carib grackle | .60 | .60 |
| 1192 | A255 | 50c Black-whiskered vireo | .70 | .70 |
| 1193 | A255 | 75c Bananaquit | .80 | .80 |
| 1194 | A255 | $1 Collared swift | 1.10 | 1.10 |
| 1195 | A255 | $2 Yellow-bellied elaenia | 1.75 | 1.75 |
| 1196 | A255 | $3 Blue-hooded euphonia | 2.25 | 2.25 |
| 1197 | A255 | $5 Eared dove | 4.00 | 4.00 |
| | | Nos. 1190-1197 (8) | 11.60 | 11.60 |

#### Souvenir Sheets

| | | | | |
|---|---|---|---|---|
| 1198 | A255 | $6 Mangrove cuckoo | 5.75 | 5.75 |
| 1199 | A255 | $6 Scaly-breasted thrasher | 5.75 | 5.75 |

#### Crustaceans

### 1990, Sept. 17

| | | | | |
|---|---|---|---|---|
| 1200 | A256 | 10c Slipper lobster | .25 | .25 |
| 1201 | A256 | 25c Green reef crab | .35 | .35 |
| 1202 | A256 | 65c Caribbean lobsterette | .70 | .70 |
| 1203 | A256 | 75c Blind deep sea lobster | .80 | .80 |
| 1204 | A256 | $1 Flattened crab | 1.10 | 1.10 |
| 1205 | A256 | $2 Ridged slipper lobster | 2.00 | 2.00 |

---

| | | | | |
|---|---|---|---|---|
| 1206 | A256 | $3 Land crab | 2.50 | 2.50 |
| 1207 | A256 | $4 Mountain crab | 3.00 | 3.00 |
| | | Nos. 1200-1207 (8) | 10.70 | 10.70 |

#### Souvenir Sheets

| | | | | |
|---|---|---|---|---|
| 1208 | A256 | $6 Caribbean king crab | 5.25 | 5.25 |
| 1209 | A256 | $6 Purse crab | 5.25 | 5.25 |

G88     G89

Players from participating countries.

### 1990, Sept. 24

| | | | | |
|---|---|---|---|---|
| 1210 | G88 | 15c England | .25 | .25 |
| 1211 | G88 | 45c Argentina | .50 | .50 |
| 1212 | G88 | $2 Sweden | 2.00 | 2.00 |
| 1213 | G88 | $4 South Korea | 3.25 | 3.25 |
| | | Nos. 1210-1213 (4) | 6.00 | 6.00 |

#### Souvenir Sheets

| | | | | |
|---|---|---|---|---|
| 1214 | G88 | $6 Yugoslavia | 5.00 | 5.00 |
| 1215 | G88 | $6 United States | 5.00 | 5.00 |

World Cup Soccer Championships, Italy.

### 1990, Nov. 11    Litho.    Perf. 14

| | | | | |
|---|---|---|---|---|
| 1216 | G89 | 10c Boxing | .20 | .20 |
| 1217 | G89 | 25c Olympic flame | .25 | .25 |
| 1218 | G89 | 50c Soccer | .55 | .55 |
| 1219 | G89 | 75c Discus | .75 | .75 |
| 1220 | G89 | $1 Pole vault | 1.00 | 1.00 |
| 1221 | G89 | $2 Equestrian 3-day event | 2.25 | 2.25 |
| 1222 | G89 | $4 Women's basketball | 4.25 | 4.25 |
| 1223 | G89 | $5 Men's gymnastics | 3.75 | 3.75 |
| | | Nos. 1216-1223 (8) | 13.00 | 13.00 |

#### Souvenir Sheets

| | | | | |
|---|---|---|---|---|
| 1224 | G89 | $6 Sailboarding | 6.50 | 6.50 |
| 1225 | G89 | $6 Decathlon | 6.50 | 6.50 |

1992 Summer Olympics, Barcelona.

#### Rubens Type

Entire paintings or different details from: 5c, 25c, Adam and Eve, vert. 15c, Esther before Ahasuerus. 50c, Expulsion from Eden. $1, Cain Slaying Abel, vert. $2, Lot's Flight. $4, Samson and Delilah. $5, Abraham and Melchizedek. No. 1234, The Meeting of David and Abigail. No. 1235, Daniel in the Lions Den.

### 1991, Jan. 31    Litho.    Perf. 14

| | | | | |
|---|---|---|---|---|
| 1226 | A259 | 5c multicolored | .25 | .20 |
| 1227 | A259 | 15c multicolored | .40 | .20 |
| 1228 | A259 | 25c multicolored | .50 | .25 |
| 1229 | A259 | 50c multicolored | .85 | .65 |
| 1230 | A259 | $1 multicolored | 1.50 | 1.25 |
| 1231 | A259 | $2 multicolored | 2.00 | 2.00 |
| 1232 | A259 | $4 multicolored | 3.00 | 3.00 |
| 1233 | A259 | $5 multicolored | 3.50 | 3.50 |
| | | Nos. 1226-1233 (8) | 12.00 | 11.05 |

#### Souvenir Sheets

| | | | | |
|---|---|---|---|---|
| 1234 | A259 | $6 multicolored | 6.00 | 6.00 |
| 1235 | A259 | $6 multicolored | 6.00 | 6.00 |

#### Fish Type of 1990

### 1991, Feb. 5

| | | | | |
|---|---|---|---|---|
| 1236 | A254 | 15c Barred hamlet | .50 | .25 |
| 1237 | A254 | 35c Squirrelfish | .85 | .55 |
| 1238 | A254 | 45c Red-spotted hawkfish | .90 | .65 |
| 1239 | A254 | 75c Bigeye | 1.40 | 1.10 |
| 1240 | A254 | $1 Spiny puffer | 1.60 | 1.40 |
| 1241 | A254 | $2 Smallmouth grunt | 2.50 | 2.50 |
| 1242 | A254 | $3 Harlequin bass | 3.00 | 3.00 |
| 1243 | A254 | $4 Creole fish | 3.25 | 3.25 |
| | | Nos. 1236-1243 (8) | 14.00 | 12.70 |

#### Souvenir Sheets

| | | | | |
|---|---|---|---|---|
| 1244 | A254 | $6 Fairy basslet | 6.00 | 6.00 |
| 1245 | A254 | $6 Copper sweeper | 6.00 | 6.00 |

Hummel
Figurines — G90 / Orchids — G91

## 1991, Mar. 1 — Litho. — Perf. 14

| | | | | | |
|---|---|---|---|---|---|
| 1246 | G90 | 10c Angel, star | | .25 | .20 |
| 1247 | G90 | 15c Angel, guitar, Christ Child | | .35 | .20 |
| 1248 | G90 | 25c Shepherd | | .50 | .20 |
| 1249 | G90 | 50c Angel, lantern, horn | | 1.00 | .55 |
| 1250 | G90 | $1 Angel, children, Christ Child | | 1.50 | 1.00 |
| 1251 | G90 | $2 Angel, candle, Christ Child | | 2.50 | 2.50 |
| 1252 | G90 | $4 Angel with baskets | | 3.50 | 3.50 |
| 1253 | G90 | $5 Angels singing | | 3.75 | 3.75 |
| | | *Nos. 1246-1253 (8)* | | 13.35 | 11.90 |

### Souvenir Sheets

| | | | | |
|---|---|---|---|---|
| 1254 | | Sheet of 4 | 5.00 | 5.00 |
| a. | | G90 5c like No. 1247 | .20 | .20 |
| b. | | G90 40c like No. 1249 | .30 | .30 |
| c. | | G90 60c like No. 1250 | .50 | .50 |
| d. | | G90 $3 like No. 1253 | 2.75 | 2.75 |
| 1255 | | Sheet of 4 | 8.00 | 8.00 |
| a. | | G90 20c like No. 1246 | .20 | .20 |
| b. | | G90 30c like No. 1248 | .25 | .25 |
| c. | | G90 75c like No. 1251 | .70 | .70 |
| d. | | G90 $6 like No. 1252 | 5.50 | 5.50 |

Christmas 1990.

## 1991-92 — Litho. — Perf. 14

Designs: 5c, Brassia maculata. 10c, Oncidium lanceanum. 15c, Broughtonia sanguinea. 25c, Diacrium bicornutum. 35c, Cattleya labiata. 45c, Epidendrum fragrans. 50c, Oncidium papilio. 75c, Neocogniauxia monophylla. $1, Epidendrum polybulbon. $2, Spiranthes speciosa. $4, Epidendrum ciliare. $5, Phais tankervilliae. $10, Brassia caudata. $20, Brassavola cordata.

| | | | | |
|---|---|---|---|---|
| 1256 | G91 | 5c multicolored | .45 | .45 |
| 1257 | G91 | 10c multicolored | .45 | .45 |
| 1258 | G91 | 15c multicolored | .50 | .20 |
| 1259 | G91 | 25c multicolored | .60 | .20 |
| 1260 | G91 | 35c multicolored | .60 | .20 |
| 1261 | G91 | 45c multicolored | .75 | .30 |
| 1262 | G91 | 50c multicolored | .80 | .35 |
| 1263 | G91 | 75c multicolored | 1.00 | .55 |
| 1264 | G91 | $1 multicolored | 1.25 | .75 |
| 1265 | G91 | $2 multicolored | 2.10 | 2.10 |
| 1266 | G91 | $4 multicolored | 3.50 | 3.50 |
| 1267 | G91 | $5 multicolored | 3.75 | 3.75 |
| 1268 | G91 | $10 multicolored | 7.00 | 7.00 |
| 1269 | G91 | $20 multicolored | 14.00 | 14.00 |
| | | *Nos. 1256-1269 (14)* | 36.75 | 33.80 |

Issued: $20, 6/92; others, 4/1/91.

### Butterfly Type

Designs: 5c, Crimson-patched longwing. 10c, Morpho helena. 15c, Morpho sulkowskyi. 20c, Dynastor napoleon. 25c, Pieridae callinira. 30c, Anartia amathea. 35c, Heliconiidae dido. 45c, Papilionidae columbus. 50c, Nymphalidae praeneste. 60c, Panacea prola. 75c, Julia. $1, Papilionidae orthosilaus. $2, Pyrrhopyge cometes. $3, Papilionidae paeon. $4, Morpho cypris. $5, Choringa. No. 1286, Caligo idomenides. No. 1287, Monarch. No. 1287A, Nymphalidae amydon. No. 1287B, Papilio childrenae.

## 1991, Apr. 8 — Litho. — Perf. 14

| | | | | | |
|---|---|---|---|---|---|
| 1270 | A261 | 5c multicolored | | .50 | .35 |
| 1271 | A261 | 10c multicolored | | .50 | .35 |
| 1272 | A261 | 15c multicolored | | .70 | .40 |
| 1273 | A261 | 20c multicolored | | .75 | .45 |
| 1274 | A261 | 25c multicolored | | .75 | .50 |
| 1275 | A261 | 30c multicolored | | .85 | .55 |
| 1276 | A261 | 35c multicolored | | .85 | .55 |
| 1277 | A261 | 45c multicolored | | 1.00 | .75 |
| 1278 | A261 | 50c multicolored | | 1.10 | .80 |
| 1279 | A261 | 60c multicolored | | 1.25 | .90 |
| 1280 | A261 | 75c multicolored | | 1.25 | 1.00 |
| 1281 | A261 | $1 multicolored | | 1.60 | 1.25 |
| 1282 | A261 | $2 multicolored | | 2.25 | 2.25 |
| 1283 | A261 | $3 multicolored | | 2.75 | 2.75 |
| 1284 | A261 | $4 multicolored | | 3.25 | 3.25 |
| 1285 | A261 | $5 multicolored | | 4.00 | 4.00 |
| | | *Nos. 1270-1285 (16)* | | 23.35 | 20.10 |

### Souvenir Sheets

| | | | | |
|---|---|---|---|---|
| 1286 | A261 | $6 multicolored | 4.75 | 4.75 |
| 1287 | A261 | $6 multicolored | 4.75 | 4.75 |
| 1287A | A261 | $6 multicolored | 4.75 | 4.75 |
| 1287B | A261 | $6 multicolored | 4.75 | 4.75 |

Save Our Planet — G100

Walt Disney characters and ecology themes: 10c, Daisy and Donald, alternate forms of transportation. 15c, Goofy saving water. 25c, Donald, Daisy camping simply. 45c, Donald protecting birds. $1, Donald holding ascending balloons. $2, Minnie, Daisy using natural coolers. $4, Mickey, nephews cleaning beaches. $5, Scrooge McDuck using pedal power. No. 1296, Little Hiawatha and Iron Eyes Cody viewing destroyed forest. No. 1297, Donald, recycling. No. 1298, Minnie, Mickey planting trees.

## 1991, Apr. 22 — Litho. — Perf. 14

| | | | | |
|---|---|---|---|---|
| 1288 | G100 | 10c multicolored | .65 | .20 |
| 1289 | G100 | 15c multicolored | .75 | .20 |
| 1290 | G100 | 25c multicolored | 1.00 | .40 |
| 1291 | G100 | 45c multicolored | 1.40 | .60 |
| 1292 | G100 | $1 multicolored | 2.25 | 1.40 |
| 1293 | G100 | $2 multicolored | 3.25 | 3.00 |
| 1294 | G100 | $4 multicolored | 4.00 | 4.00 |
| 1295 | G100 | $5 multicolored | 4.00 | 4.00 |
| | | *Nos. 1288-1295 (8)* | 17.30 | 13.80 |

### Souvenir Sheets

| | | | | |
|---|---|---|---|---|
| 1296 | G100 | $6 multicolored | 6.50 | 6.50 |
| 1297 | G100 | $6 multicolored | 6.50 | 6.50 |
| 1298 | G100 | $6 multicolored | 6.50 | 6.50 |

### Voyages of Discovery Type

Discovery of America, 500th anniv. (in 1992).: 15c, Ferdinand Magellan, 1519-1521. 20c, Sir Francis Drake, 1577-1580. 50c, Capt. James Cook, 1768-1771. 60c, Douglas World Cruiser, 1924. $1, Sputnik, 1957. $2, Yuri Gagarin, 1961. $4, John Glenn, 1962. $5, Space Shuttle, 1981. No. 1307, Columbus' fleet. No. 1308, The Pinta, vert.

## 1991, Apr. 29 — Litho. — Perf. 14

| | | | | |
|---|---|---|---|---|
| 1299 | A262 | 15c multicolored | .35 | .20 |
| 1300 | A262 | 20c multicolored | .25 | .25 |
| 1301 | A262 | 50c multicolored | .50 | .50 |
| 1302 | A262 | 60c multicolored | .60 | .60 |
| 1303 | A262 | $1 multicolored | .95 | .95 |
| 1304 | A262 | $2 multicolored | 1.90 | 1.90 |
| 1305 | A262 | $4 multicolored | 3.75 | 3.75 |
| 1306 | A262 | $5 multicolored | 4.50 | 4.50 |
| | | *Nos. 1299-1306 (8)* | 12.80 | 12.65 |

### Souvenir Sheets

| | | | | |
|---|---|---|---|---|
| 1307 | A262 | $6 multicolored | 6.00 | 6.00 |
| 1308 | A262 | $6 multicolored | 6.00 | 6.00 |

### Disney Phila Nippon '91 Type

Walt Disney characters demonstrating arts, crafts and industries of Japan: 15c, Minnie, silkworms. 30c, Mickey, Minnie, Morty and Ferdie photographing the Torii. 50c, Donald, Mickey, origami. 60c, Mickey, Minnie diving for pearls. $1, Minnie modeling kimono. $2, Mickey making masks. $4, Donald, Mickey making paper. $5, Minnie, Pluto, pottery. #1317, Mickey making prints, vert. #1318, Mickey arranging flowers, vert. #1319, Mickey, tea ceremony, vert. #1320, Mickey carving ivory and wood into netsukes, vert.

## 1991, May 6

| | | | | |
|---|---|---|---|---|
| 1309 | A263 | 15c multi | .50 | .20 |
| 1310 | A263 | 30c multi | .85 | .35 |
| 1311 | A263 | 50c multi | 1.00 | .55 |
| 1312 | A263 | 60c multi | 1.10 | .60 |
| 1313 | A263 | $1 multi | 2.00 | 1.00 |
| 1314 | A263 | $2 multi | 2.75 | 2.50 |
| 1315 | A263 | $4 multi | 3.75 | 3.75 |
| 1316 | A263 | $5 multi | 4.50 | 4.50 |
| | | *Nos. 1309-1316 (8)* | 16.45 | 13.45 |

### Souvenir Sheets

| | | | | |
|---|---|---|---|---|
| 1317 | A263 | $6 multi | 5.00 | 5.00 |
| 1318 | A263 | $6 multi | 5.00 | 5.00 |
| 1319 | A263 | $6 multi | 5.00 | 5.00 |
| 1320 | A263 | $6 multi | 5.00 | 5.00 |

### Mushrooms Type

## 1991, June 1 — Litho. — Perf. 14

| | | | | |
|---|---|---|---|---|
| 1321 | A265 | 5c Pyrrhoglossum pyrrhum | .40 | .25 |
| 1322 | A265 | 45c Agaricus purpurellus | 1.00 | .55 |
| 1323 | A265 | 50c Amanita crase-oderma | 1.00 | .60 |
| 1324 | A265 | 90c Hygrocybe acutoconica | 1.75 | 1.25 |
| 1325 | A265 | $1 Limacella guttata | 1.75 | 1.25 |
| 1326 | A265 | $2 Lactarius hygropho-roides | 2.50 | 2.50 |

| | | | | |
|---|---|---|---|---|
| 1327 | A265 | $4 Boletellus cubensis | 4.00 | 4.00 |
| 1328 | A265 | $5 Psilocybe caerulescens | 4.00 | 4.00 |
| | | *Nos. 1321-1328 (8)* | 16.40 | 14.40 |

### Souvenir Sheets

| | | | | |
|---|---|---|---|---|
| 1329 | A265 | $6 Marasmius haemato-cephalus | 7.50 | 7.50 |
| 1330 | A265 | $6 Lepiota spicu-lata | 7.50 | 7.50 |

### Royal Family Birthday, Anniversary
#### Common Design Type

## 1991, July 5 — Litho. — Perf. 14

| | | | | |
|---|---|---|---|---|
| 1331 | CD347 | 5c multi | .50 | .30 |
| 1332 | CD347 | 20c multi | .30 | .30 |
| 1333 | CD347 | 25c multi | .30 | .20 |
| 1334 | CD347 | 60c multi | 1.25 | .75 |
| 1335 | CD347 | $1 multi | 1.25 | 1.00 |
| 1336 | CD347 | $2 multi | 2.00 | 2.00 |
| 1337 | CD347 | $4 multi | 3.25 | 3.25 |
| 1338 | CD347 | $5 multi | 5.00 | 5.00 |
| | | *Nos. 1331-1338 (8)* | 13.85 | 12.80 |

### Souvenir Sheet

| | | | | |
|---|---|---|---|---|
| 1339 | CD347 | $5 Elizabeth, Philip | 6.00 | 6.00 |
| 1340 | CD347 | $5 Diana, Charles, with sons | 6.00 | 6.00 |

5c, 60c, $1, Nos. 1338, 1340, Charles and Diana, 10th wedding anniversary. Others, Queen Elizabeth II, 65th birthday.

### Van Gogh Painting Type

Designs: 5c, Two Thistles, vert. 10c, The Baby Marcelle Roulin, vert. 15c, Still Life: Basket with Six Oranges. 25c, Orchard in Blossom, vert. 45c, Portrait of Armand Roulin, vert. 50c, Wood Gatherers in the Snow (detail). 60c, Almond Tree in Blossom, vert. $1, Portrait of an Old Man, vert. $2, The Seine Bridge at Asnieres. $3, Vase with Lilacs, Daisies & Anemones, vert. $4, Self-portrait, vert. $5, Portrait of Patience Escalier, vert. No. 1353, Les Alyscamps, vert. No. 1354, Quay with Men Unloading Sand Barges. No. 1355, Sunset: Wheat Fields Near Arles.

### Perf. 13½x14, 14x13½

| | | | | |
|---|---|---|---|---|
| 1341 | A264 | 5c multicolored | .35 | .20 |
| 1342 | A264 | 10c multicolored | .35 | .20 |
| 1343 | A264 | 15c multicolored | .35 | .20 |
| 1344 | A264 | 25c multicolored | .35 | .20 |
| 1345 | A264 | 45c multicolored | .45 | .35 |
| 1346 | A264 | 50c multicolored | .55 | .45 |
| 1347 | A264 | 60c multicolored | .60 | .50 |
| 1348 | A264 | $1 multicolored | 1.00 | .90 |
| 1349 | A264 | $2 multicolored | 1.75 | 1.75 |
| 1350 | A264 | $3 multicolored | 2.25 | 2.25 |
| 1351 | A264 | $4 multicolored | 3.25 | 3.25 |
| 1352 | A264 | $5 multicolored | 3.75 | 3.75 |
| | | *Nos. 1341-1352 (12)* | 15.00 | 14.00 |

### Size: 102x127mm, 127x102mm
#### Imperf

| | | | | |
|---|---|---|---|---|
| 1353 | A264 | $6 multicolored | 5.00 | 5.00 |
| 1354 | A264 | $6 multicolored | 5.00 | 5.00 |
| 1355 | A264 | $6 multicolored | 5.00 | 5.00 |

### Marine Life Type
#### Miniature Sheet

Marine life of the deeper reef: No. 1356a, Sargassum triggerfish. b, Tobaccofish. c, Longsnout butterflyfish. d, Cherubfish. e, Black jack head. f, Black jack tail, masked goby. g, Spotfin hogfish. h, Fairy basslet. i, Orangeback bass. j, Candy basslet. k, Blackcap basslet. l, Longspine squirrelfish. m, Jackknife fish. n, Bigeye. o, Short Bigeye. $6, Caribbean flashlight fish.

## 1991, Dec. 5 — Litho. — Perf. 14

| | | | | |
|---|---|---|---|---|
| 1356 | A270 | 50c Sheet of 15, #a.-o. | 16.00 | 16.00 |

### Souvenir Sheet

| | | | | |
|---|---|---|---|---|
| 1357 | A270 | $6 multicolored | 12.00 | 12.00 |

### Christmas Art Type

Details, entire paintings or engravings by Martin Schongauer: 10c, Angel of the Annunciation. 35c, Madonna of the Rose Hedge. 50c, Madonna of the Rose Hedge, diff. 75c, Nativity. $1, Adoration of the Shepherds. $2, Nativity, diff. $4, Nativity, diff. $5, Symbol of St. Matthew. No. 1366, Nativity, diff. No. 1367, Adoration of the Shepherds.

## 1991, Dec. 9 — Perf. 12

| | | | | |
|---|---|---|---|---|
| 1358 | A271 | 10c multicolored | .45 | .20 |
| 1359 | A271 | 35c multicolored | .80 | .35 |
| 1360 | A271 | 50c multicolored | 1.10 | .45 |
| 1361 | A271 | 75c multicolored | 1.40 | .75 |
| 1362 | A271 | $1 multicolored | 1.50 | 1.25 |
| 1363 | A271 | $2 multicolored | 2.40 | 2.40 |
| 1364 | A271 | $4 multicolored | 3.00 | 3.00 |
| 1365 | A271 | $5 multicolored | 3.00 | 3.00 |
| | | *Nos. 1358-1365 (8)* | 13.65 | 11.30 |

### Souvenir Sheets
#### Perf. 14½

| | | | | |
|---|---|---|---|---|
| 1366 | A271 | $6 multicolored | 6.75 | 6.75 |
| 1367 | A271 | $6 multicolored | 6.75 | 6.75 |

### Queen Elizabeth II's Accession to the Throne, 40th Anniv.
#### Common Design Type

## 1992, Feb. 6 — Litho. — Perf. 14

| | | | | |
|---|---|---|---|---|
| 1368 | CD348 | 60c multicolored | .90 | .35 |
| 1369 | CD348 | 75c multicolored | 1.00 | .40 |
| 1370 | CD348 | $2 multicolored | 2.10 | 1.60 |
| 1371 | CD348 | $4 multicolored | 3.00 | 3.00 |
| | | *Nos. 1368-1371 (4)* | 7.00 | 5.35 |

### Souvenir Sheets

| | | | | |
|---|---|---|---|---|
| 1372 | CD348 | $6 Queen, rural scene | 5.00 | 5.00 |
| 1373 | CD348 | $6 Queen, harbor | 5.00 | 5.00 |

### Railways of the World Type

Steam locomotives: No. 1379a, Medoc Class, Switzerland, 1857. b, Sterling, Great Britain, 1870. c, No. 90, France, 1877. d, Standard, US, 1880. e, Vittorio Emanuel II, Italy, 1884. f, Johnson Single, Great Britain, 1887. g, No. 999, US, 1893. h, Q1 Class, Great Britain, 1896. i, Claud Hamilton, Great Britain, 1900.
No. 1380a, Class P8, Germany, 1906. b, Class P, Denmark, 1935. c, Class Ps, US, 1926. d, Class 4-4-0, Ireland, 1932. e, Class GS, US, 1937. f, Class 12, Belgium, 1938. g, Class J, US, 1941. h, PA series, US, 1946. i, Class 4E1, South Africa, 1954.
No. 1381a, Tee 4-car train, Europe, 1957. b, FL9B, US, 1960. c, Shin-Kansen 16-car train, Japan, 1964. d, Class 103.1, Germany 1970. e, RTG 4-car train set, France, 1972. f, ETR 401 Pendolino 4-car train, Italy, 1976. g, Class 370, Great Britain, 1981. h, LRC, Canada, 1982. i, Mav BZMOT 601 1B1, Hungary, 1983.
No. 1382, ETR 401 four-car train, Italy, 1976. No. 1382A, Werner von Siemens' first electric locomotive, Germany, 1879.

## 1992, Feb. 13 — Litho. — Perf. 14
### Sheets of 9

| | | | | |
|---|---|---|---|---|
| 1379 | A269 | 75c #a.-i. | 6.25 | 6.25 |
| 1380 | A269 | $1 #a.-i. | 8.25 | 8.25 |
| 1381 | A269 | $2 #a.-i. | 17.00 | 17.00 |
| | | *Nos. 1379-1381 (3)* | 31.50 | 31.50 |

### Souvenir Sheets

| | | | | |
|---|---|---|---|---|
| 1382 | A269 | $6 multicolored | 5.50 | 5.50 |
| 1382A | A269 | $6 multicolored | 5.50 | 5.50 |

1992 Summer Olympics, Barcelona — G101

Designs: 10c, Women's 100-meter backstroke. 15c, Women's handball. 25c, 4x100-meter relay. 35c, Hammer throw. 50c, 110-meter hurdles. 75c, Pole vault. $1, Volleyball. $2, Weight lifting. $5, Stationary rings. $6, Soccer. No. 1393, Baseball. No. 1394, Finn class single-handed dinghy.

## 1992, Mar. 23 — Litho. — Perf. 14

| | | | | |
|---|---|---|---|---|
| 1383 | G101 | 10c multicolored | .65 | .30 |
| 1384 | G101 | 15c multicolored | .70 | .30 |
| 1385 | G101 | 25c multicolored | .80 | .30 |
| 1386 | G101 | 35c multicolored | .85 | .35 |
| 1387 | G101 | 50c multicolored | 1.00 | .65 |
| 1388 | G101 | 75c multicolored | 1.40 | .85 |
| 1389 | G101 | $1 multicolored | 1.50 | 1.10 |
| 1390 | G101 | $2 multicolored | 2.75 | 2.75 |
| 1391 | G101 | $5 multicolored | 3.75 | 3.75 |
| 1392 | G101 | $6 multicolored | 4.00 | 4.00 |
| | | *Nos. 1383-1392 (10)* | 17.40 | 14.35 |

### Souvenir Sheets

| | | | | |
|---|---|---|---|---|
| 1393 | G101 | $15 multicolored | 11.50 | 11.50 |
| 1394 | G101 | $15 multicolored | 11.50 | 11.50 |

### Spanish Art Type

Paintings: 10c, The Surrender of Seville, by Francisco de Zurbaran. 35c, The Liberation of Saint Peter by an Angel, by Antonio de Pereda. 50c, Joseph Explains the Dreams of the Pharaoh, by Antonio del Castillo Saavedra, horiz. 75c, The Flower Vase, by Juan de Arellano. $1, The Duke of Pastrana, by Juan Carreno de Miranda. $2, $4, The Annunciation (diff. details), by Francisco Rizi. $5, Old Woman Seated, attributed to Antonio Puga. No. 1403, The Triumph of Saint Hermenegildo, by Francisco de Herrera, the Younger, vert. No. 1404, Relief of Genoa by the Second Marquis of Santa Cruz, by de Pereda, horiz.

| 1992, Apr. 30 | | | Perf. 13 | |
|---|---|---|---|---|
| 1395 | A273 | 10c multicolored | .30 | .20 |
| 1396 | A273 | 35c multicolored | .50 | .35 |
| 1397 | A273 | 50c multicolored | .75 | .60 |
| 1398 | A273 | 75c multicolored | 1.00 | .75 |
| 1399 | A273 | $1 multicolored | 1.25 | .90 |
| 1400 | A273 | $2 multicolored | 2.00 | 2.00 |
| 1401 | A273 | $4 multicolored | 3.00 | 3.00 |
| 1402 | A273 | $5 multicolored | 3.00 | 3.00 |
| | *Nos. 1395-1402 (8)* | | 11.80 | 10.80 |

**Size: 95x110mm**
**Imperf**

| 1403 | A273 | $6 multicolored | 5.25 | 5.25 |
|---|---|---|---|---|
| 1404 | A273 | $6 multicolored | 5.25 | 5.25 |

Granada '92.

Discovery
of
America,
500th
Anniv.
G102

Designs: 10c, Don Isaac Abarbanel (1437-1508), Spanish Minister of Finance. 25c, Columbus. 35c, Crewman sighting land. 50c, King Ferdinand and Queen Isabella. 60c, Columbus and Queen Isabella. $5, Santa Maria and map. No. 1411, Portrait of Columbus. No. 1412, Columbus at first landfall.

| 1992, May 7 | | Litho. | Perf. 14 | |
|---|---|---|---|---|
| 1405 | G102 | 10c multicolored | .20 | .20 |
| 1406 | G102 | 25c multicolored | .30 | .25 |
| 1407 | G102 | 35c multicolored | .45 | .35 |
| 1408 | G102 | 50c multicolored | .75 | .75 |
| 1409 | G102 | 60c multicolored | .80 | .80 |
| 1410 | G102 | $5 multicolored | 6.00 | 6.00 |
| | *Nos. 1405-1410 (6)* | | 8.50 | 8.35 |

**Souvenir Sheets**

| 1411 | G102 | $6 multicolored | 4.75 | 4.75 |
|---|---|---|---|---|
| 1412 | G102 | $6 multicolored | 4.75 | 4.75 |

World Columbian Expo '92, Chicago.

**USO Anniv. Type of 1992**

| 1992, May 7 | | | | |
|---|---|---|---|---|
| 1413 | A277 | 10c James Cagney | .55 | .25 |
| 1414 | A277 | 15c Ann Sheridan | .55 | .25 |
| 1415 | A277 | 35c Jerry Colonna | .55 | .25 |
| 1416 | A277 | 50c Spike Jones | .65 | .35 |
| 1417 | A277 | 75c Edgar Bergen, Charlie Mc-Carthy | .80 | .50 |
| 1418 | A277 | $1 Andrews Sisters | 1.25 | .75 |
| 1419 | A277 | $2 Dinah Shore | 1.90 | 1.90 |
| 1420 | A277 | $5 Bing Crosby | 4.25 | 4.25 |
| | *Nos. 1413-1420 (8)* | | 10.50 | 8.50 |

**Souvenir Sheets**

| 1421 | A277 | $6 Marlene Dietrich | 5.25 | 5.25 |
|---|---|---|---|---|
| 1422 | A277 | $6 Fred Astaire | 5.25 | 5.25 |

**Hummingbird Type of 1992**

Designs: 5c, Blue-headed male. 10c, Rufous-breasted hermit female. 20c, Blue-headed female. 45c, Green-throated carib male. 90c, Antillean crested male. $2, Purple-throated carib male. $4, Purple-throated carib female. $5, Antillean crested female. No. 1431, Rufous-breated hermit female. No. 1432, Green-throated carib female.

| 1992, May 7 | | | | |
|---|---|---|---|---|
| 1423 | A276 | 5c multicolored | .20 | .20 |
| 1424 | A276 | 10c multicolored | .20 | .20 |
| 1425 | A276 | 20c multicolored | .20 | .20 |
| 1426 | A276 | 45c multicolored | .30 | .30 |
| 1427 | A276 | 90c multicolored | .65 | .65 |
| 1428 | A276 | $2 multicolored | 1.50 | 1.50 |
| 1429 | A276 | $4 multicolored | 3.00 | 3.00 |
| 1430 | A276 | $5 multicolored | 3.75 | 3.75 |
| | *Nos. 1423-1430 (8)* | | 9.80 | 9.80 |

**Souvenir Sheets**

| 1431 | A276 | $6 multicolored | 6.00 | 6.00 |
|---|---|---|---|---|
| 1432 | A276 | $6 multicolored | 6.00 | 6.00 |

Genoa '92.

**Discovery of America Type**

| 1992 | | | Perf. 14½ | |
|---|---|---|---|---|
| 1433 | A275 | $1 Coming ashore | .75 | .75 |
| 1434 | A275 | $2 Natives, ships | 1.50 | 1.50 |

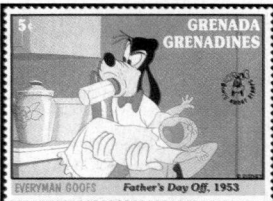

Walt Disney's Goofy, 60th
Anniv. — G103

Scenes from Disney cartoon films: 5c, Father's Day Off, 1953. 10c, Cold War, 1951. 15c, Home Made Home, 1951. 25c, Get Rich Quick, 1951. 50c, Man's Best Friend, 1952. 75c, Aquamania, 1961. 90c, Tomorrow We Diet, 1951. $1, Teachers Are People, 1952. $2, The Goofy Success Story, 1955. $3, Double Dribble, 1946. $4, Hello Aloha, 1952. $5, Father's Lion, 1952. No. 1447, Father's Weekend, 1953, vert. No. 1448, Motor Mania, 1950. No. 1449, Hold That Pose, 1950, vert.

| 1992, Nov. 24 | | Litho. | Perf. 14x13½ | |
|---|---|---|---|---|
| 1435 | G103 | 5c multicolored | .20 | .20 |
| 1436 | G103 | 10c multicolored | .20 | .20 |
| 1437 | G103 | 15c multicolored | .20 | .20 |
| 1438 | G103 | 25c multicolored | .20 | .20 |
| 1439 | G103 | 50c multicolored | .40 | .40 |
| 1440 | G103 | 75c multicolored | .60 | .60 |
| 1441 | G103 | 90c multicolored | .70 | .70 |
| 1442 | G103 | $1 multicolored | .75 | .75 |
| 1443 | G103 | $2 multicolored | 1.50 | 1.50 |
| 1444 | G103 | $3 multicolored | 2.25 | 2.25 |
| 1445 | G103 | $4 multicolored | 3.00 | 3.00 |
| 1446 | G103 | $5 multicolored | 3.75 | 3.75 |
| | *Nos. 1435-1446 (12)* | | 13.75 | 13.75 |

**Souvenir Sheets**
**Perf. 13½x14**

| 1447 | G103 | $6 multicolored | 4.50 | 4.50 |
|---|---|---|---|---|
| 1448 | G103 | $6 multicolored | 4.50 | 4.50 |
| 1449 | G103 | $6 multicolored | 4.50 | 4.50 |

**Model Trains Type of 1992**

Designs: 15c, #2220 Switcher locomotive, 2-inch gauge, US, 1910. 25c, 0-4-0 Engine, Bridge Port Line, O gauge, US, 1907. 50c, First Ives Co. electric toy locomotive, O gauge, US, 1910. 75c, J. C. Penney Special, standard gauge, US, 1920. $1, Cast metal locomotive, O gauge, US, 1916. $2, Copper-plated cast iron locomotive & tender pull toy, US, 1900. $4, Chromium plated locomotive #4689, standard gauge, US, 1928. $5, Ives long cab locomotive of the Olympian set, standard gauge, US, 1929.
No. 1458, Clockwork model, O gauge, US, 1910. No. 1459, American Flyer Statesman passenger train.

| 1992, Oct. 22 | | Litho. | Perf. 14 | |
|---|---|---|---|---|
| 1450 | A279 | 15c multicolored | .25 | .20 |
| 1451 | A279 | 25c multicolored | .40 | .20 |
| 1452 | A279 | 50c multicolored | .70 | .45 |
| 1453 | A279 | 75c multicolored | .90 | .65 |
| 1454 | A279 | $1 multicolored | 1.00 | .90 |
| 1455 | A279 | $2 multicolored | 2.00 | 2.00 |
| 1456 | A279 | $4 multicolored | 3.50 | 3.50 |
| 1457 | A279 | $5 multicolored | 3.50 | 3.50 |
| | *Nos. 1450-1457 (8)* | | 12.25 | 11.40 |

**Souvenir Sheet**
**Perf. 13**

| 1458 | A279 | $6 multicolored | 5.25 | 5.25 |
|---|---|---|---|---|
| 1459 | A279 | $6 multicolored | 5.25 | 5.25 |

Nos. 1458-1459 contain one 51x40mm stamp.

**New York City Type**
**Souvenir Sheet**

| 1992, Oct. 28 | | | Perf. 14 | |
|---|---|---|---|---|
| 1460 | A280 | $6 Brooklyn Bridge | 5.00 | 5.00 |

Postage Stamp Mega Event '92, New York City.

**Christmas Type of 1992**

Details or entire paintings of The Annunciation by: 5c, Robert Campin. 15c, Melchior Broederlam. 25c, The Annunciation (2 panels), by Fra Filippo Lippi. 35c, Simone Martini. 50c, Fra Filippo Lippi, detail of angel. 75c, The Annunciation (Mary), by Fra Filippo Lippi. 90c, Albert Bouts. $1, D. Di Michelino. $2, Van der Weyden. $3, Sandro Botticelli, detail of angel. $4, Botticelli, detail of Mary. $5, Bernardo Daddi, horiz. No. 1472, Rogier Van der Weyden, vert. No. 1473, Hubert Van Eyck. No. 1474, Botticelli.

**Perf. 13½x14, 14x13½**
**1992, Nov. 16**

| 1461 | A281 | 5c multicolored | .20 | .20 |
|---|---|---|---|---|
| 1462 | A281 | 15c multicolored | .30 | .20 |
| 1463 | A281 | 25c multicolored | .35 | .20 |
| 1464 | A281 | 35c multicolored | .45 | .30 |

| 1464A | A281 | 50c multicolored | .65 | .50 |
|---|---|---|---|---|
| 1465 | A281 | 75c multicolored | .85 | .70 |
| 1466 | A281 | 90c multicolored | 1.00 | 1.00 |
| 1467 | A281 | $1 multicolored | 1.10 | 1.10 |
| 1468 | A281 | $2 multicolored | 2.10 | 2.10 |
| 1469 | A281 | $3 multicolored | 2.75 | 2.75 |
| 1470 | A281 | $4 multicolored | 3.25 | 3.25 |
| 1471 | A281 | $5 multicolored | 3.50 | 3.50 |
| | *Nos. 1461-1471 (12)* | | 16.50 | 15.80 |

**Souvenir Sheets**

| 1472 | A281 | $6 multicolored | 5.00 | 5.00 |
|---|---|---|---|---|
| 1473 | A281 | $6 multicolored | 5.00 | 5.00 |
| 1474 | A281 | $6 multicolored | 5.00 | 5.00 |

America's Cup
Yacht
Race — G104

Designs: 15c, Atalanta, Mischief, 1881. 25c, Valkyrie III, Defender. 35c, Shamrock IV, Resolute. 75c, Endeavour II, Ranger, 1937. $1, Sceptre, Columbia, 1958. $2, Australia II, Liberty. $4, Stars and Stripes, Kookaburra III. $5, New Zealand, Stars and Stripes, 1988. No. 1483, America, Aurora, 1851. No. 1484, Emblems of 1992 participants.

| 1992, Oct. | | | Perf. 14 | |
|---|---|---|---|---|
| 1475 | G104 | 15c multicolored | .55 | .20 |
| 1476 | G104 | 25c multicolored | .70 | .25 |
| 1477 | G104 | 35c multicolored | .85 | .40 |
| 1478 | G104 | 75c multicolored | 1.25 | .70 |
| 1479 | G104 | $1 multicolored | 1.40 | .90 |
| 1480 | G104 | $2 multicolored | 2.00 | 2.00 |
| 1481 | G104 | $4 multicolored | 3.00 | 3.00 |
| 1482 | G104 | $5 multicolored | 3.25 | 3.25 |
| | *Nos. 1475-1482 (8)* | | 13.00 | 10.70 |

**Souvenir Sheets**

| 1483 | G104 | $6 multicolored | 6.00 | 6.00 |
|---|---|---|---|---|
| 1484 | G104 | $6 multicolored | 6.00 | 6.00 |

Nos. 1483-1484 contains one 58x43mm stamp.

G105

GRENADA
GRENADINES
$3

Anniversaries and
Events — G106

Designs: 25c, Zeppelin Viktoria Luise over Kiel Harbor. 50c, Space Shuttle Columbia. 75c, Flag, arms of Germany, Konrad Adenauer. $1.50, Giant anteater. No. 1489, Scarlet macaw, vert. No. 1490, Emblem of Intl. Conf. on Nutrition. $3, Wolfgang Amadeus Mozart. No. 1492, Berlin airlift. No. 1493, Space Shuttle Endeavour crew repairing Intelsat VI. $5, Hindenburg disaster. No. 1495, Adm. Richard E. Byrd's Ford Trimotor flying over North Pole, 1926. No. 1496, Map of Federal Republic of Germany, vert. No. 1497, Zeppelin Z.4 above clouds. No. 1498, First flight of space shuttle Endeavour. No. 1499, Scene from "The Marriage of Figaro." No. 1500, Jaguar.

| 1992 | | Litho. | Perf. 14 | |
|---|---|---|---|---|
| 1485 | G105 | 25c multicolored | .65 | .25 |
| 1486 | G105 | 50c multicolored | .75 | .35 |
| 1487 | G105 | 75c multicolored | .75 | .60 |
| 1488 | G105 | $1.50 multicolored | 1.10 | 1.10 |
| 1489 | G105 | $2 multicolored | 2.50 | 2.00 |
| 1490 | G106 | $2 multicolored | 1.50 | 1.50 |
| 1491 | G106 | $3 multicolored | 2.25 | 2.25 |
| 1492 | G105 | $3 multicolored | 3.00 | 3.00 |
| 1493 | G105 | $4 multicolored | 3.00 | 3.00 |
| 1494 | G105 | $4 multicolored | 3.75 | 3.75 |
| 1495 | G105 | $5 multicolored | 3.75 | 3.75 |
| | *Nos. 1485-1495 (11)* | | 23.00 | 21.55 |

**Souvenir Sheets**
**Perf. 13½**

| 1496 | G105 | $6 multicolored | 4.50 | 4.50 |
|---|---|---|---|---|
| 1497 | G105 | $6 multicolored | 4.50 | 4.50 |
| 1498 | G105 | $6 multicolored | 4.50 | 4.50 |

**Perf. 14**

| 1499 | G106 | $6 multicolored | 4.50 | 4.50 |
|---|---|---|---|---|
| 1500 | G106 | $6 multicolored | 4.50 | 4.50 |

Count Zeppelin, 75th anniv. of death (#1485, 1494, 1497). Intl. Space Year (#1486, 1493). Konrad Adenauer, 25th anniv. of death (#1487, 1492, 1496). Earth Summit, Rio de Janeiro (#1488-1489, 1500). Intl. Conf. on Nutrition, Rome (#1490). Wolfgang Amadeus Mozart, bicent. of death (in 1991) (#1491, 1499). Intl. Lions Intl., 75th anniv. (#1495). Space Year (#1498).

Issue dates: Nos. 1491, 1499, Oct. Nos. 1485-1486, 1490, 1493-1495, 1497, Nov. Nos. 1487-1489, 1492, 1496, 1500, Dec.

No. 1496 contains one 39x50mm stamp, Nos. 1497-1498 one 50x39mm stamp, No. 1500 one 52x40mm stamp.

**Miniature Sheet**
**Entertainers Type of 1992**

Grammy award winners: No. 1501a, Leonard Bernstein. b, Ray Charles. c, Bob Dylan. d, Barbra Streisand. e, Frank Sinatra. f, Harry Belafonte. g, Aretha Franklin. h, Garth Brooks. No. 1502a, Johnny Cash. b, Willie Nelson. No. 1503a, Charlie Parker. b, Miles Davis.

| 1992, Nov. 19 | | | Perf. 14 | |
|---|---|---|---|---|
| 1501 | A286 | 90c Sheet of 8, | | |
| | | #a.-h. | 12.50 | 12.50 |

**Souvenir Sheets**

| 1502 | A286 | $3 Sheet of 2, | | |
|---|---|---|---|---|
| | | #a.-b. | 5.50 | 5.50 |
| 1503 | A286 | $3 Sheet of 2, | | |
| | | #a.-b. | 5.50 | 5.50 |

Dogs — G107          Butterflies — G108

Designs: 35c, Irish Setter, Glendalough, Ireland. 50c, Boston terrier, State House, Boston, US. 75c, Beagle, Temple to Athena, Greece. $1, Weimaraner, Nesselwang, Germany. $3, Norwegian elkhound, Urnes Stave Church, Norway. $4, Mastiff, Great Sphinx, Egypt. No. 1510, Akita, Kyoto torii, Japan. No. 1511, Saluki, Rub'al Khali, Saudi Arabia. No. 1512, Shar pei, China. No. 1513, Bulldog, United Kingdom.

| 1993, Jan. 20 | | Litho. | Perf. 14 | |
|---|---|---|---|---|
| 1504 | G107 | 35c multicolored | .65 | .35 |
| 1505 | G107 | 50c multicolored | .90 | .65 |
| 1506 | G107 | 75c multicolored | 1.25 | .75 |
| 1507 | G107 | $1 multicolored | 1.60 | 1.10 |
| 1508 | G107 | $3 multicolored | 3.25 | 3.25 |
| 1509 | G107 | $4 multicolored | 3.50 | 3.50 |
| 1510 | G107 | $5 multicolored | 3.50 | 3.50 |
| 1511 | G107 | $5 multicolored | 3.50 | 3.50 |
| | *Nos. 1504-1511 (8)* | | 18.15 | 16.60 |

**Souvenir Sheets**

| 1512 | G107 | $6 multicolored | 4.75 | 4.75 |
|---|---|---|---|---|
| 1513 | G107 | $6 multicolored | 4.75 | 4.75 |

**Louvre Painting Type**
**Miniature Sheet**

Details or entire paintings: No. 1514a, The Virgin and Child with Young St. John the Baptist, by Botticelli. b, The Buffet, by Chardin. c, The Provider, by Chardin. d, Erasmus, by Durer. e, Self-Portrait, by Durer. f, Jeanne of Aragon, by Raphael. g-h, La Belle Jardiniere (diff. details), by Raphael.
$6, Charles I, King of England, Hunting, by Van Dyck.

| 1993, Mar. 8 | | Litho. | Perf. 12 | |
|---|---|---|---|---|
| 1514 | A289 | $1 Sheet of 8, #a.- | | |
| | | h. + label | 11.50 | 11.50 |

**Souvenir Sheet**
**Perf. 14½**

| 1515 | A289 | $6 multicolored | 7.50 | 7.50 |
|---|---|---|---|---|

No. 1515 contains one 55x88mm stamp.

## 1993, Apr. 13　　Litho.　　Perf. 14

| 1516 | G108 | 15c | Polydamas swallowtail | .20 | .20 |
| 1517 | G108 | 35c | Guaraguao skipper | .30 | .30 |
| 1518 | G108 | 45c | Giant hairstreak | .35 | .35 |
| 1519 | G108 | 75c | Malachite | .60 | .60 |
| 1520 | G108 | $1 | Cloudless sulphur | .75 | .75 |
| 1521 | G108 | $2 | Silver spot | 1.50 | 1.50 |
| 1522 | G108 | $4 | St. Christopher's hairstreak | 3.00 | 3.00 |
| 1523 | G108 | $5 | Common longtail skipper | 3.75 | 3.75 |
| | | Nos. 1516-1523 (8) | | 10.45 | 10.45 |

### Souvenir Sheets

| 1524 | G108 | $6 | Orion | 5.00 | 5.00 |
| 1525 | G108 | $6 | Zebra | 5.00 | 5.00 |

### Flowers Type of 1993

## 1993, May

| 1526 | A291 | 35c | Hibiscus | .65 | .30 |
| 1527 | A291 | 35c | Columbine | .65 | .30 |
| 1528 | A291 | 45c | Red ginger | .65 | .35 |
| 1529 | A291 | 75c | Bougainvillea | .90 | .60 |
| 1530 | A291 | $1 | Crown imperial | 1.00 | .75 |
| 1531 | A291 | $2 | Fairy orchid | 1.75 | 1.75 |
| 1532 | A291 | $4 | Heliconia | 3.00 | 3.00 |
| 1533 | A291 | $5 | Tulip | 3.25 | 3.25 |
| | | Nos. 1526-1533 (8) | | 11.85 | 10.30 |

### Souvenir Sheets

| 1534 | A291 | $6 | Balloonflower, horiz. | 5.00 | 5.00 |
| 1535 | A291 | $6 | Blackberry lily, horiz. | 5.00 | 5.00 |

No. 1536 will not be assigned.

### Coronation of Queen Elizabeth II Type of 1993
### Miniature Sheet

Designs: a, 35c, Official coronation photograph. b, 50c, Ampulla, spoon. c, $2, Queen, following coronation. d, $4, Queen, Prince Charles and his family, c. 1984.
$6, Portrait, by Pietro Annigoni, 1954.

## 1993, June 2　　Litho.　　Perf. 13½x14

| 1537 | A293 | Sheet, 2 each #a.-d. | | 10.50 | 10.50 |

### Souvenir Sheet
### Perf. 14

| 1538 | A293 | $6 | multicolored | 5.50 | 5.50 |

No. 1538 contains one 28x42mm stamp.

### Anniversaries and Events Types of 1993

Designs: 50c, Telescope. 75c, Willy Brandt, Lyndon Johnson, 1961. $4, Radio telescope. $5, Willy Brandt, Eleanor Hulles, 1957. No. 1543, Copernicus. No. 1544, Willy, Rut Brandt.

## 1993, July 1　　Litho.　　Perf. 14

| 1539 | A294 | 50c | multicolored | 1.40 | .50 |
| 1540 | A295 | $1 | multicolored | 1.60 | 1.60 |
| 1541 | A294 | $4 | multicolored | 4.00 | 4.00 |
| 1542 | A295 | $5 | multicolored | 4.00 | 4.00 |
| | | Nos. 1539-1542 (4) | | 11.00 | 10.10 |

### Souvenir Sheets

| 1543 | A294 | $6 | multicolored | 5.50 | 5.50 |
| 1544 | A295 | $6 | multicolored | 5.50 | 5.50 |

Copernicus, 450th death anniv. (#1539, 1541, 1543). Willy Brandt, 1st death anniv. (#1540, 1542, 1544).

### Songbird Type of 1993
### Miniature Sheet

Designs: No. 1545a, 15c, Painted bunting. b, 15c, White-throated sparrow. c, 25c, Common grackle. d, 25c, Royal flycatcher. e, 25c, Swallow tanager. f, 35c, Vermilion flycatcher. g, 45c, Black headed bunting. h, 50c, Rosebreasted grosbeak. i, 75c, Corn bunting. j, 75c, Rosebreasted thrush tanager. k, $1, Buff-throated saltator. l, $4, Plush-capped finch.
No. 1546, Bohemian waxwing. No. 1547, Pine grosbeak.

## 1993, July 13

| 1545 | A297 | Sheet of 12, #a.-l. | | 13.00 | 13.00 |

### Souvenir Sheets

| 1546 | A297 | $6 | multicolored | 6.50 | 6.50 |
| 1547 | A297 | $6 | multicolored | 6.50 | 6.50 |

### Seashell Type of 1993
### Miniature Sheet

Designs: No. 1548a, 15c, Hawk wing conch. b, 15c, Music volute. c, 25c, Globe vase, deltoid rock shell. d, 35c, Spiny vase. e, 35c, Common sundial, common purple snail. f, 45c, Caribbean donax, gaudy asaphis. g, 45c, Mouse cone. h, 50c, Gold-mouthed triton. i,

75c, Tulip mussel, trigonal tivela. j, 75c, Common dove shell, chestnut latirus. k, $1, Widemouthed purpura. l, $4, Atlantic thorny oyster, Atlantic wing oyster.
No. 1549, Turkey wing. No. 1550, Zebra periwinkle.

## 1993, July 19　　Litho.　　Perf. 14

| 1548 | A298 | Sheet of 12, #a.-l. | | 13.00 | 13.00 |

### Souvenir Sheet

| 1549 | A298 | $6 | multicolored | 6.50 | 6.50 |
| 1550 | A298 | $6 | multicolored | 6.50 | 6.50 |

### Picasso Type of 1993

Paintings: 15c, Painter and Model, 1928. $1, The Artist and His Model, 1963. $4, The Drawing Lession, 1925. $6, Picasso seated in front of canvas, 1956.

## 1993, July 1　　Litho.　　Perf. 14

| 1551 | A299 | 15c | multi, horiz. | .60 | .35 |
| 1552 | A299 | $1 | multi, horiz. | 1.50 | 1.50 |
| 1553 | A299 | $4 | multi, horiz. | 3.75 | 3.75 |
| | | Nos. 1551-1553 (3) | | 5.85 | 5.60 |

### Souvenir Sheet

| 1554 | A299 | $6 | multi, horiz. | 5.00 | 5.00 |

### Olympics Type of 1993

Design: $6, Emil Zogragski, ski jump.

## 1993, July 1

| 1554A | A300 | 35c | multi | .30 | .30 |
| 1554B | A300 | $5 | multi | 3.75 | 3.75 |
| 1555 | A300 | $6 | multicolored | 5.00 | 5.00 |
| | | Nos. 1554A-1555 (3) | | 9.05 | 9.05 |

### Polska '93 Type of 1993

Paintings: 75c, Gra w Gudziki, by Ludomir Slerdinski, 1928. $2, Pocalunek Mongoskiego Ksiecia, by S.I. Witkiewicz, 1915. $6, Allegory, by Jan Wydra, 1929.

## 1993, July 1

| 1556 | A301 | 75c | multi, horiz. | 1.25 | 1.25 |
| 1557 | A301 | $2 | multi, horiz. | 3.50 | 3.50 |

### Souvenir Sheet

| 1558 | A301 | $6 | multicolored | 5.25 | 5.25 |

### Taipei '93 Type

Designs: 35c, Macao Palace, Hong Kong. 45c, Stone pixie, Ming Tomb, Nanjing. $1, Stone camels, Ming Tomb, Nanjing. $5, Stone lion and elephant, Ming Tomb, Nanjing.
Sculpture: No. 1563a, Nesting quail incense burner. b, Standing quail incense burner. c, Seated qilin incense burner. d, Pottery horse, Han Dynasty. e, Seated caparisoned elephant. f, Cow (imitation delft).
No. 1564, Sumatran tiger.

## 1993　　Litho.　　Perf. 14x13½

| 1559 | A302 | 35c | multi, horiz. | .25 | .25 |
| 1560 | A302 | 45c | multi, horiz. | .35 | .35 |
| 1561 | A302 | $1 | multi, horiz. | .75 | .75 |
| 1562 | A302 | $5 | multi, horiz. | 3.75 | 3.75 |
| | | Nos. 1559-1562 (4) | | 5.10 | 5.10 |

### Miniature Sheet

| 1563 | A302 | $1.50 | Sheet of 6, #a.-f. | 11.00 | 11.00 |

### Souvenir Sheet
### Perf. 13½x14

| 1564 | A302 | $6 | multicolored | 5.25 | 5.25 |

Nos. 1563a-1563f are horiz.

### With Bangkok '93 Emblem

Designs: 35c, Naga snakes, Chiang Mai's Temple, Thailand. 45c, Sri Mariamman Temple, Singapore. $1, Topiary, Hua Hin Resort, Thailand. $5, Pak Tai Temple, Cheung Chau Island.
Thai paintings: No. 1569a, Buddha's victory over Mara. b, Mythological elephant. c, Battle with Mara. d, Untitled work, by Panya Wijinthanasarn, 1984. e, Temple mural. f, Elephants in Pahcekha Buddha's Heaven.
No. 1570, Monkey.

## 1993　　　　Perf. 14x13½

| 1565 | A302 | 35c | multi, horiz. | .25 | .25 |
| 1566 | A302 | 45c | multi, horiz. | .35 | .35 |
| 1567 | A302 | $1 | multi, horiz. | .75 | .75 |
| 1568 | A302 | $5 | multi, horiz. | 3.75 | 3.75 |
| | | Nos. 1565-1568 (4) | | 5.10 | 5.10 |

### Miniature Sheet

| 1569 | A302 | $1.50 | Sheet of 6, #a.-f. | 11.00 | 11.00 |

### Souvenir Sheet
### Perf. 13½x14

| 1570 | A302 | $6 | multicolored | 5.25 | 5.25 |

Nos. 1569a-1569f are horiz.

### Indopex '93 Type

Designs: 35c, Natl. Museum, Central Jakarta, Indonesia. 45c, Sacred Wheel &

Deer, Monastery. $1, Ramayana relief, Panataran Temple. $5, Candi Tikus, Trawulan, East Java.
Paintings: No. 1575a, Bullock Carts, bu Batara Lubis, 1951. b, Surat Irsa II, by A.D. Pirous, 1983. c, Self-portrait with Goat, by Kartika, 1987. d, The Cow-est Cow, by Ivan Sagito, 1987. e, Rain Storm, by Sudjana Kerton, 1984. f, Story of Pucuk Flower, by Effendi, 1972.
No. 1576, Banteng cattle.

## 1993, Aug. 13　　Litho.　　Perf. 14x13½

| 1571 | A302 | 35c | multicolored | .25 | .25 |
| 1572 | A302 | 45c | multicolored | .35 | .35 |
| 1573 | A302 | $1 | multicolored | .75 | .75 |
| 1574 | A302 | $5 | multicolored | 3.75 | 3.75 |
| | | Nos. 1571-1574 (4) | | 5.10 | 5.10 |

### Miniature Sheet

| 1575 | A302 | $1.50 | Sheet of 6, #a.-f. | 11.00 | 11.00 |

### Souvenir Sheet

| 1576 | A302 | $6 | multicolored | 5.25 | 5.25 |

Nos. 1571-1576 are horiz.

1994 World Cup Soccer Championships, US — G109

Designs: 15c, Stuart McCall, Carlos Verri. 25c, Carlos Verri, Diego Maradona. 35c, S. Schillaci, J.P. Saldana. 45c, Ruud Gullit, Mark Wright. $1, Carlos Verri, Diego Maradona. $2, Zubizarreta, Fernandez, Albert. $4, Gheorghe Hagi, Paul McGrath. $5, Alberto Gorriz, Enzo Scifo. No. 1585, Schaefer Stadium, Foxboro, MA. No. 1586, Rudi Voeller, vert.

## 1993, Sept. 7　　Litho.　　Perf. 14

| 1577 | G109 | 15c | multicolored | .45 | .20 |
| 1578 | G109 | 25c | multicolored | .45 | .20 |
| 1579 | G109 | 35c | multicolored | .45 | .20 |
| 1580 | G109 | 45c | multicolored | .45 | .40 |
| 1581 | G109 | $1 | multicolored | .75 | .75 |
| 1582 | G109 | $2 | multicolored | 1.50 | 1.50 |
| 1583 | G109 | $4 | multicolored | 3.00 | 3.00 |
| 1584 | G109 | $5 | multicolored | 3.75 | 3.75 |
| | | Nos. 1577-1584 (8) | | 10.80 | 10.00 |

### Souvenir Sheets

| 1585 | G109 | $6 | multicolored | 5.00 | 5.00 |
| 1586 | G109 | $6 | multicolored | 5.00 | 5.00 |

### Mickey Mouse, 65th Anniv. Type

Movie clips: 15c, The Worm Turns, 1937. 35c, Mickey's Rival, 1936. 50c, The Pointer, 1939. 75c, Society Dog Show, 1939. $1, A Gentleman's Gentleman, 1941. $2, The Little Whirlwind, 1941. $4, Mickey Down Under, 1948. $5, R'coon Dawg, 1951.
No. 1595, Mickey's Garden, 1935, vert. No. 1596, Lonesome Ghosts, 1937.

### Perf. 13½x14, 14x13½

## 1993, Nov. 11　　　　Litho.

| 1587 | A305 | 15c | multicolored | .60 | .25 |
| 1588 | A305 | 35c | multicolored | .80 | .35 |
| 1589 | A305 | 50c | multicolored | 1.00 | .60 |
| 1590 | A305 | 75c | multicolored | 1.40 | 1.00 |
| 1591 | A305 | $1 | multicolored | 1.60 | 1.10 |
| 1592 | A305 | $2 | multicolored | 2.25 | 2.25 |
| 1593 | A305 | $4 | multicolored | 3.25 | 3.25 |
| 1594 | A305 | $5 | multicolored | 3.25 | 3.25 |
| | | Nos. 1587-1594 (8) | | 14.15 | 12.05 |

### Souvenir Sheets

| 1595 | A305 | $6 | multicolored | 5.50 | 5.50 |
| 1596 | A305 | $6 | multicolored | 5.50 | 5.50 |

### Christmas Type of 1993

Various details from Adoration of the Shepherds by Durer: 10c, 75c, $1, $4. No. 1605, $6, horiz.
Various details from Oddi Altarpiece by Raphael: 25c, 35c, 50c, $5. No. 1606, $6.

### Perf. 13½x14, 14x13½ (#1605)

## 1993, Nov. 22　　　　Litho.

| 1597-1604 | A306 | Set of 8 | | 11.00 | 11.00 |

### Souvenir Sheets

| 1605-1606 | A306 | Set of 2 | | 11.00 | 11.00 |

### Eckener Type of 1993

Designs: 50c, Graf Zeppelin over Rio De Janeiro. 75c, Dr. Hugo Eckener. $5, Eckener commanding Graf Zeppelin. $6, Eckener, Pres. Herbert Hoover.

## 1993, Dec. 21　　Litho.　　Perf. 14

| 1607-1609 | A307 | Set of 3 | | 5.25 | 5.25 |

### Souvenir Sheet

| 1610 | A307 | $6 | multicolored | 5.00 | 5.00 |

### Royal Air Force Anniv. Type of 1993

Designs: 15c, Avro Lancaster. $5, Short Sunderland. $6, Supermarine Spitfire.

## 1993, Dec. 21

| 1611 | A308 | 15c | multicolored | .35 | .20 |
| 1612 | A308 | $5 | multicolored | 6.50 | 6.50 |

### Souvenir Sheet

| 1613 | A308 | $6 | multicolored | 7.00 | 7.00 |

### Automobile Anniv. Type

Designs: 25c, 1955 Mercedes Benz 300SLR. 45c, 1957 Ford Thunderbird. $4, 1929 Ford 150A Station Wagon. $5, Mercedes Benz 540K.
Each $6: No. 1618, 1929 Mercedes Benz SSK. No. 1619, 1924 Ford Model T.

## 1993, Dec. 21　　Litho.　　Perf. 14

| 1614-1617 | A309 | Set of 4 | | 10.00 | 10.00 |

### Souvenir Sheets

| 1618-1619 | A309 | Set of 2 | | 11.00 | 11.00 |

1st Benz 4-wheel car, 1st Ford engine, cent.

### First Gas Balloon Flight in America Type

Designs: 35c, Blanchard's balloon crossing Delaware River. $3, Blanchard delivering Washington's passport of introduction. $6, Balloon in flight, vert.

## 1993, Dec. 21　　Litho.　　Perf. 14

| 1620-1621 | A310 | Set of 2 | | 3.50 | 3.50 |

### Souvenir Sheet

| 1622 | A310 | $6 | multicolored | 5.00 | 5.00 |

### Fine Art Type

Details or entire paintings by Rembrandt: 15c, Hendrickje Stoffels as Flora. 35c, Lady & Gentlemen in Black. 50c, Aristotle with Bust of Homer. $5, Christ & the Woman of Samaria.
Details or entire paintings by Matisse: 75c, Interior: Flowers and Parakeets. $1, Goldfish. $2, The Girl with Green Eyes. $3, Still Life with a Plaster Figure.
Each $6: No. 1631, Anna Accused of Stealing the Kid, by Rembrandt. No. 1632, Tea in the Garden by Matisse, horiz.

### Perf. 13½x14, 14x13½

## 1993, Dec. 31　　　　Litho.

| 1623-1630 | A311 | Set of 8 | | 11.00 | 11.00 |

### Souvenir Sheets

| 1631-1632 | A311 | Set of 2 | | 11.00 | 11.00 |

### Hong Kong '94 Type

Designs: No. 1633, Hong Kong #426, jet at Kai Tak Airport. No. 1634, Junk, Kwaloon Bay, #975.
Chinese jade: No. 1635a, White jade brush washer. b, Archaic jade brush washer. c, Dark green jade brush washer. d, Green jade alms bowl. e, Archaic jade dog. f, Yellow jade brush washer.

## 1994, Feb. 18　　Litho.　　Perf. 14

| 1633 | A313 | 40c | multicolored | .90 | .90 |
| 1634 | A313 | 40c | multicolored | .90 | .90 |
| a. | | Pair, #1633-1634 | | 2.40 | 2.40 |

### Miniature Sheet

| 1635 | A314 | 45c | Sheet of 6, #a.-f. | 5.00 | 5.00 |

Nos. 1633-1634 issued in sheets of of 5 pairs. No. 1634a is a continuous design. Nos. 1635a-1635f are horiz.
New Year 1994 (Year of the Dog) (#1635e).

Dinosaurs G110

15c, Spinosaurus. 35c, Apatosaurus. 45c, Tyrannosaurus rex. 55c, Triceratops. $1, Pachycephalosaurus. $2, Pteranodon. $4, Parasaurolophus. $5, Brachiosaurus.
Each $6: No. 1644, Brachiosaurus, vert. No. 1645, Tyrannosaurus, spinosaurus, vert.

## 1994　　Litho.　　Perf. 14

| 1636-1643 | G110 | Set of 8 | | 11.00 | 11.00 |

### Souvenir Sheets

| 1644-1645 | G110 | Set of 2 | | 9.50 | 9.50 |

Mushrooms
G111

Designs: 35c, Hygrocybe hypohaemacta. 45c, Cantherellus cinnabarinus. 50c, Marasmius haematocephalus. 75c, Mycena pura. $1, Gymnopilus russipes. $2, Galocybe cyanocephala. $4, Pleuteus chrysophlebius. $5, Chlorophyllum molybdites.
Each $6: No. 1654, Collybia fibrosipes. No. 1655, Xeromphalina tenuipes.

**1994**
1646-1653  G111  Set of 8    10.50 10.50
**Souvenir Sheets**
1654-1655  G111  Set of 2    9.50 9.50

D-Day Type of 1994

40c, Churchill bridgelayer in action. $2, Sherman "Firefly" attacks beach. $3, Churchill Crocodile flame thrower. $6, Sherman "Crab" flail tank.

**1994, Aug. 4    Litho.    Perf. 14**
1656-1658  A318  Set of 3    5.00 5.00
**Souvenir Sheet**
1659  A318  $6 multicolored    5.25 5.25

First Manned Moon Landing, 25th Anniv. Type of 1994
Miniature Sheet of 6

Tribute to Challenger crew: No. 1660a, Slidewire escape training. b, Christa A. McAuliffe. c, Challenger 51-L on pad LC39B. d, Gregory B. Jarvis. e, Ellison S. Onizuka. f, Ronald E. McNair.
$6, Judith A. Resnick, vert.

**1994, Aug. 4**
1660  A319  $1.10 #a.-f.    7.50 7.50
**Souvenir Sheet**
1661  A319  $6 multicolored    6.50 6.50

PHILAKOREA '94 Type

Designs: 40c, Onung Tomb, Korea. $1, Stone pogoda, Mt. Nansan, Kyongju. $4, Pusan Port.
Paintings, by Sin Yunbok, late Choson Dynasty, 1758: No. 1665a-1665b, Admiring spring in the Country. c-d, Women on Dano Day. e-f, Enjoying Lotuses While Listening to Music. g-h, Women by a Crystal Stream.
$6, Blacksmith's Shop, by Kim Duksin (1754-1822).

**1994, Aug. 4    Perf. 14, 13½ (#1665)**
1662-1664  A320  Set of 3    4.25 4.25
**Miniature Sheet of 8**
1665  A321  $1 #a.-h.    9.50 9.50
**Souvenir Sheet**
1666  A320  $6 multicolored    5.00 5.00

Orchid Type of 1994

15c, Cattleya aurantiaca. 25c, Blettia patula. 45c, Sobralia macrantha. 75c, Encyclia belizensis. $1, Sophrolaeliocattleya. $2, Encyclia frangrans. $4, Schombocattleya. $5, Brassolaeliocattleya.
Each $6: No. 1675, Brassavola nodosa. No. 1676, Ornithidium coccineum.

**1994, Aug. 7    Perf. 14**
1667-1674  A322  Set of 8    11.00 11.00
**Souvenir Sheets**
1675-1676  A322  Set of 2    10.00 10.00

1994 World Cup Soccer Type
Miniature Sheet of 6

Designs: No. 1677a, Steve Mark, Grenada. b, Jurgen Kohler, Germany. c, Almir, Brazil. d, Michael Windiscmann, US. e, Guiseppe Giannini, Italy. f, Rashidi Yekini, Nigeria.
Each $6: No. 1678, Kemari. No. 1679, The World Cup.

**1994, Aug. 11    Perf. 14**
1677  A323  $1½ #a.-f.    5.25 5.25
**Souvenir Sheets**
1678-1679  A323  Set of 2    9.50 9.50

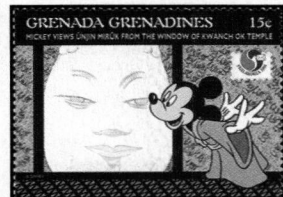

Disney's PHILAKOREA '94 — G112

15c, Mickey, Unjin Miruk, Kwanch Ok Temple. 35c, Goofy, statue of Admiral Yi, Chonju. 50c, Cousin Gus, Donald. 75c, Mickey playing flute. $1, Goofy, Tolharubang Grandfather statue. $2, Mickey, Minnie, Hyang-Wonjong. $4, Mickey, Unsan Pyolshin Festival. $5, Minnie, ceremonial fan.
Each $6: No. 1688, Minnie, Buk drum, vert. No. 1689, Mickey, Pugok Hawaii, vert.

**1994, Aug. 16    Litho.    Perf. 14x13½**
1680-1687  G112  Set of 8    15.00 15.00
**Souvenir Sheets**
**Perf. 13½x14**
1688-1689  G112  Set of 2    12.00 12.00
This set exists with very low face values.

Fish Type of 1994

Designs, each 75c: No. 1690a, Yellowtail snapper (b, e). b, Caribbean reef shark (a). c, Great barracuda. d, Redtail parrotfish. e, Blue tang. f, Queen angelfish. g, Red hind (h). h, Rock beauty. i, Queen parrotfish. j, Spanish hogfish. k, Spotted moray. l, Queen triggerfish (i).
Each 75c: No. 1691a, Pork fish (b). b, Blue chromis (a). c, Caribbean reef shark. d, Longspine squirrelfish. e, Foureye butterflyfish. f, Blue head. g, Royal gramma. h, Sharpnose puffer. i, Longsnout seahorse. j, Blackbar soldierfish (g, k). k, Redlip blenny. l, Rainbow wrasse.
Each $6: No. 1692, Rainbow wrasse, diff. No. 1693, Queen angelfish, diff.

**1994, Sept. 1    Perf. 14**
**Miniature Sheets of 12**
1690-1691  A324  Set of 2    21.00 21.00
**Souvenir Sheets**
1692-1693  A324  Set of 2    11.00 11.00

Intl. Olympic Committe Type of 1994

Designs: 50c, Silke Renk, Germany, javelin, 1992. $1.50, Mark Spitz, US, swimming, 1972. $6, Team Japan, Nordic combined, 1994.

**1994    Perf. 14**
1694  A325  50c multi, horiz.    .40 .40
1695  A325  $1.50 multi, horiz.    1.10 1.10
**Souvenir Sheet**
1696  A326  $6 multicolored    5.00 5.00

Intl. Year of the Family Type of 1994
**1994**
1697  A329  $1 Family of 5    .80 .80

Order of the Caribbean Community Type

Designs: 25c, Sir Shridath Ramphal, statesman, Guyana. 50c, William Demas, economist, Trinidad & Tobago. $2, Derek Walcott, writer, St. Lucia.

**1994, Sept. 1**
1698-1700  A330  Set of 3    3.00 3.00

Christmas Type of 1994

Paintings, by Bartolome Murillo: 15c, The Annunciation. 35c, The Adoration of the Shepherds. No. 1703, 50c, Flight into Egypt. No. 1704, 50c, Virgin and Child with St. Rose. 75c, Virgin and Child. $1, Virgin of the Rosary. $4, The Holy Family.
Each $6: No. 1708, Adoration of the Shepherds. No. 1709, The Holy Family with a Little Bird.

**1994, Dec. 5    Litho.    Perf. 13½x14**
1701-1707  A331  Set of 7    7.50 7.50
**Souvenir Sheets**
1708-1709  A331  Set of 2    10.00 10.00

Bird Type of 1995

25c, Ground dove. 50c, White-winged dove, horiz. $2, Inca dove. $4, Mourning dove, horiz.

**1995, Jan. 10    Perf. 14**
1710-1713  A332  Set of 4    9.50 9.50

English Touring Cricket, Cent. Type

Designs: 50c, M.A. Atherton, England, horiz. 75c, C.E.L. Ambrose, Leeward Isl./W. Indies. $1, B.C. Lara, Trinidad/W. Indies. $3, West Indies Team, horiz.

**1995, Jan. 12**
1714-1717  A333  Set of 3    4.00 4.00
**Souvenir Sheet**
1718  A333  $3 multicolored    4.00 4.00

Miniature Sheet of 10

Capitals of the World — G113

Designs: a, London. b, Cairo. c, Vienna. d, Paris. e, Rome. f, Budapest. g, Moscow. h, Beijing. i, Tokyo. j, Wasington.

**1995, Mar. 10    Litho.    Perf. 14**
1719  G113  $1 #a.-j.    10.00 10.00

New Year 1995 (Year of the Boar) — G114

Various stylized boars with different Chinese inscriptions: a, Smiling, purple legs. b, Smiling, red legs. c, Brown legs. d, Red legs.
$2, Two boars, horiz.

**1995, Apr. 21    Litho.    Perf. 14½**
1720  G114  75c Block or horiz.
    strip of 4, #a.-d.    2.25 2.25
e.    Souvenir sheet of 4, #1720a-
    1720d    3.00 3.00
**Souvenir Sheet**
1721  G114  $2 multicolored    2.25 2.25
No. 1720 was issued in miniature sheets of 16 stamps.

VE Day Type of 1995
Miniature Sheets of 6 and 8

#1721A: b, Mitsubishi G4M1 "Betty." c, Aircraft carrying submarine I-14. d, Mitsubishi G3M1. e, Destroyer Akizuki. f, Battleship Kirishima. g, Cruiser Asigari.
Bombers: #1722: a, Avro Lancaster, Tallboy bomb. b, Junkers JU-88. c, B-25 Mitchell. d, B-17 Flying Fortress. e, Petlyakov Pe-2. f, Martin B-26 Marauder. g, Henkel He-111. h, Consolidated B-24 Liberator.
#1723, Pres. Truman displaying newspaper headline. #1723A, Aichi D3A1 "Val" dive bomber.

**1995, May 8    Perf. 14**
1721A  A336  $2 #b.-g. + label    9.50 9.50
1722  A336  $2 #a.-h. + label    13.00 13.00
**Souvenir Sheets**
1723  A336  $6 multicolored    4.75 4.75
1723A  A336  $6 multicolored    5.50 5.50
Inscription in central label of No. 1721A misidentifies a Yokosuka MXY-7 Okha kamikaze plane.
No. 1723 contains one 57x42mm stamp.

Scout Jamboree Type of 1995

a, 75c, Beach scene, scout. b, $1, Mountains, sea, scout with pole. c, $2, Flag, scout salute.
$6, Snorkeling, fish.

**1995, May 8**
1724  A337  Strip of 3, #a.-c.    3.00 3.00
**Souvenir Sheet**
1725  A337  $6 multicolored    5.50 5.50
No. 1724 was issued in sheets of 9 stamps.

UN, 50th Anniv. Type of 1995

Designs: a, 75c, Building, UN flag. b, $1, Trygve Lie (1896-1968), Norway, 1st Secretary General. c, $2, Flag, member of UN peacekeeping force.
$6, Dove, emblem.

**1995, May 8**
1726  A338  Strip of 3, #a.-c.    3.00 3.00
**Souvenir Sheet**
1727  A338  $6 multicolored    4.75 4.75
No. 1726 is a continuous design and was issued in sheets of 9 stamps.

Marine Life of the Caribbean
G115

No. 1728, each $1: a, Dolphins. b, Scorpion fish. c, Sea turtle, rock beauty. d, Butterflyfish, nurse shark. e, Angel fish. f, Grouper coney. g, Rainbow eel, moray eel. h, Sun flower-star, coral crab. i, Octopus.
No. 1729, each $1: a, Bull shark. b, Big white shark. c, Octopus. d, Barracuda (e). e, Moray eel (f, h, i). f, Spotted eagle ray. g, Goldspotted snake. h, Stingray. i, Grouper.
$5, French angelfish. $6, Hammerhead shark.

**1995, May 3    Litho.    Perf. 14**
**Miniature Sheets of 9, #a-i**
1728-1729  G115  Set of 2    16.00 16.00
**Souvenir Sheets**
1730  G115  $5 multicolored    3.75 3.75
1731  G115  $6 multicolored    4.50 4.50

Domesticated Animals — G116

Horses: 15c, Suffolk punch. 25c, Shetland pony. $1, Arab. $3, Shire horse.
Dogs, each 75c: No. 1736a, Shetland sheepdog. b, Bull terrier. c, Afghan. d, Scottish terrier. e, Labrador retriever. f, English springer spaniel. g, Samoyed. h, Irish setter. i, Border collie. j, Pekingese. k, Dachshund. l, Weimaraner.
Cats, each 75c: No. 1737a, Blue persian. b, Sorrel abyssinian. c, White angora. d, Brown burmese. e, Red tabby exotic shorthair. f, Seal-point birman. g, Korat. h, Norwegian forest cat. i, Lilac-point Balinese. j, British shorthair. k, Red self longhair. l, Calico manx.
Each $6: No. 1738, English setter. No. 1739, Seal-point colorpoint.

**1995, May 3**
1732-1735  G116  Set of 4    3.50 3.50
**Miniature Sheets of 12, #a-l**
1736-1737  G116  Set of 2    14.00 14.00
**Souvenir Sheets**
1738-1739  G116  Set of 2    11.00 11.00

Sierra Club, Cent. G117

No. 1740, each $1: a, Brown pelican. b, Northern spotted owl. c, Northern spotted owl in winter. d, Jaguarundi. e, Central American spider monkeys facing forward. f, Two Central American spider monkeys. g, Central American spider monkey. h, Wood stork. i, Maned wolves.
No. 1741, each $1, vert: a, Northern spotted owl. b, Brown pelican. c, Brown pelican up close. d, Jaguarundi up close. e, Jaguarundi. f, Maned wolf. g, Wood stork facing right. h, Wood stork facing left. i, Maned wolf up close.

**1995, May 5**
**Miniature Sheets of 9, #a-i**
1740-1741  G117  Set of 2    15.00 15.00

FAO, 50th Anniv. — G118

No. 1742: a, 75c, Man working in field. b, $1, Woman working in field. c, $2, Two workers in field.
$6, Child with chopsticks.

**1995, May 8**
1742 G118 Strip of 3, #a.-c.    3.00 3.00
**Souvenir Sheet**
1743 G118 $6 multicolored    4.50 4.50
No. 1742 was issued in sheets of 9 stamps.

Rotary Intl., 90th Anniv. G119

**1995, May 8**
1744 G119 $5 Paul Harris, emblem    3.75 3.75
**Souvenir Sheet**
1745 G119 $6 Old, new emblems 4.50 4.50

Queen Mother, 95th Anniv. Type of 1995

No. 1746: a, Drawing. b, In black outfit. c, Formal portrait. d, In green outfit.
No. 1747, Speaking at Blitz Memorial.

**1995, May 8**
1746 A344 $1.50 Strip or block of 4, #a.-d.    5.00 5.00
**Souvenir Sheet**
1747 A344 $6 multicolored    5.00 5.00
No. 1746 was issued in sheets of 8 stamps.
Sheets of Nos. 1746-1747 exist with black border and text "In Memoriam - 1900-2002" in sheet margins.

1996 Summer Olympics Type

No. 1748, horiz: a, Rosemary Ackerman, East Germany, high jump. b, Li Ning, China, gymnastics. c, Denise Parker, US, archery.
No. 1749, horiz: a, Terry Carlisle, US, skeet shooting. b, Kathleen Nord, East Germany, 200-meter butterfly. c, Brigit Schmidt, East Germany, kayaking.
Each $6: No. 1750, George Foreman, US, boxing. No. 1751, Dan Gable US, Kikuo Wada, Japan, wrestling.

**1995, June 23**
1748 A345 15c Strip of 3, #a.-c.    .60 .60
1749 A345 $3 Strip of 3, #a.-c.    9.50 9.50
**Souvenir Sheets**
1750-1751 A345 Set of 2    11.00 11.00

G120

Designs: 10c, Brown pelican. 15c, Common stilt. 25c, Cuban trogan. 35c, Flamingo. 75c, Parrot. $1, Pintail duck. $2, Ringed kingfisher. $3, Strip-headed tanager.
No. 1760: a, Great blue heron. b, Jamaican tody. c, Laughing gull. d, Purple-throated carib. e, Red-legged thrush. f, Ruddy duck. g, Shoveler duck. h, West Indian red-bellied woodpecker.
Each $5: No. 1761, Blue-hooded Euphania. No. 1762, Village weaver.

**1995, Sept. 5    Litho.    Perf. 14**
1752-1759 G120 Set of 8    8.00 8.00

**Miniature Sheet of 8**
1760 G120 $1 #a.-h.    8.00 8.00
**Souvenir Sheets**
1761-1762 G120 Set of 2    10.50 10.50
Singapore '95 (#1760-1762). No. 1760d is mis-spelled.

Mickey's High Sea Adventure — G121

10c, Goofy carrying treasure chests, Donald. 35c, Mickey, Minnie at helm. 75c, Mickey, Donald, Goofy opening treasure chest. $1, Pirates confronting Mickey. $2, Mickey, Goofy, Donald in life boat. $5, Goofy using mop to fight enemy.
Each $6: No. 1769, Cannonballs being shot at Goofy, vert. No. 1770, Mickey on island, monkey pinching his nose, vert.

**1995, Oct. 2    Litho.    Perf. 14x13½**
1763-1768 G121 Set of 6    7.00 7.00
**Souvenir Sheets**
**Perf. 13½x14**
1769-1770 G121 Set of 2    10.00 10.00

Nobel Prize Recipients Type of 1995

No. 1770A, Derek Walcott, literature, 1992. No. 1770B, W. Arthur Lewis, economics, 1979.
No. 1771, each $1: a, Heike Kamerlingh Onnes, physics, 1913. b, Fridtjof Nanson, 1922. c, Sir Ronald Ross, physiology or medicine, 1902. d, Paul Müller, physiology or medicine, 1948. e, Allvar Gullstrand, physiology or medicine, 1911. f, Gerhart Hauptmann, literature, 1912. g, Hans Spemann, physiology or medicine, 1935. h, Cecil F. Powell, physics, 1950. i, Walther Bothe, physics, 1954.
No. 1772, each $1: a, Jules Bordet, physiology or medicine, 1919. b, René Cassin, peace, 1968. c, Verner von Heidenstam, literature, 1916. d, Jose Echegaray, literature, 1904. e, Otto Wallach, chemistry, 1910. f, Corneille Heymans, physiology or medicine, 1938. g, Ivar Giaever, physics, 1973. h, Sir William Cremer, peace, 1903. i, John W. Strutt, physics, 1904.
No. 1773, each $1: a, James Franck, physics, 1925. b, Tobias M.C. Asser, peace, 1911. c, Carl F.G. Spitteler, literature, 1919. d, Christiaan Eijkman, physiology or medicine, 1929. e, Ragnar Granit, physiology or medicine, 1967. f, Frederic Passy, peace, 1901. g, Louis Neel, physics, 1970. h, Sir William Ramsay, chemistry, 1904. i, Philip Noel-Baker, peace, 1959.
Each $6: No. 1774, Albert Schweitzer, peace, 1952. No. 1775, Willy Brandt, peace, 1971. No. 1776, Winston Churchill, literature, 1953.

**1995, Oct. 18    Litho.    Perf. 14**
1770A A354 75c multicolored    .55 .55
1770B A354 75c multicolored    .55 .55
**Miniature Sheets of 9, #a-i**
1771-1773 A354 Set of 3    20.00 20.00
**Souvenir Sheets**
1774-1776 A354 Set of 3    16.50 16.50

Motion Pictures, Cent. G122

Actresses, each $1: No. 1777a, Marion Davies. b, Marlene Dietrich. c, Lillian Gish. d, Bette Davis. e, Elizabeth Taylor. f, Veronica Lake. g, Ava Gardner. h, Grace Kelly. i, Kim Novak.
Romantic couples, each $1: No. 1778a, Nita Naldi, Rudolph Valentino. b, Ramon Navaro, Alice Terry. c, Frederic March, Joan Crawford.

d, Clark Gable, Vivien Leigh. e, Barbara Stanwyck, Burt Lancaster. f, Warren Beatty, Natalie Wood. g, Spencer Tracy, Katharine Hepburn. h, Humphrey Bogart, Lauren Bacall. i, Omar Sharif, Julie Christie.
Each $6: No. 1779, Sophia Loren. No. 1780, Greta Garbo, John Gilbert, horiz.

**1995, Nov. 3    Perf. 13½x14**
**Miniature Sheets of 9, #a-i**
1777-1778 G122 Set of 2    14.00 14.00
**Souvenir Sheets**
**Perf. 13½x14, 14x13½**
1779-1780 G122 Set of 2    10.00 10.00

Classic Racing Cars G123

Designs: 10c, 1990's Williams-Renault Formula 1. 25c, 1980's Le Mans Porsche 956. 35c, 1970's Lotus "John Player Special." 75c, 1960's Ford GT 40. $2, 1950's Mercedes Benz W196. $3, 1920's Mercedes SSK.
$6, 1971 Tyrrell-Ford Fourmula 1.

**1995, Nov. 7    Perf. 14**
1781-1786 G123 Set of 6    6.50 6.50
**Souvenir Sheet**
1787 G123 $6 multicolored    6.00 6.00

Local Transportation — G124

**1995, Nov. 7**
1788 G124 35c Donkey    .40 .25
1789 G124 75c Bus    1.00 .90

Miniature Sheet

Sailing Ships G125

Designs: No. 1790a, Preussen. b, Japanese junk. c, Pirate ship. d, Mayflower. e, Chinese junk. f, Santa Maria.
$5, Spanish galleon.

**1995, Nov. 7**
1790 G125 $1 Sheet of 6, #a.-f.    6.00 6.00
**Souvenir Sheet**
1791 G125 $5 multicolored    5.00 5.00
No. 1791 contains one 57x42mm stamp.

Christmas Type of 1995

Details or entire paintings: 10c, Immaculate Conception, by De Cosimo. 15c, St. Michel Dedicating Arms to the Madonna, by Le Nain. 35c, Annunciation, by de Credi. 50c, The Holy Family, by Jordaens. $3, Madonna and Child, by Lippi. $5, Madonna and Child with Ten Saints, by Fiorentino.
Each $6: No. 1798, Adoration of the Shepherds, by Van Oost. No. 1799, Holy Family, by Del Sart.

**1995, Nov. 28    Perf. 13½x14**
1792-1797 A356 Set of 6    8.00 8.00
**Souvenir Sheets**
1798-1799 A356 Set of 2    11.00 11.00

New Year 1996 (Year of the Rat) — G126

Stylized rats: No. 1800: a, blue & multi. b, violet & multi. c, red & multi. d, green & multi.
$2, Two rats, horiz.

**1996, Jan. 2    Litho.    Perf. 14½**
1800 G126 75c Block of 4, #a.-d. 2.25 2.25
**Miniature Sheet**
1801 G126 75c Sheet of 1 #1800 2.25 2.25
**Souvenir Sheet**
1802 G126 $2 multicolored    1.75 1.75
No. 1800 was issued in sheets of 16 stamps.

Works by Dürer and Rubens Type of 1996

Details or entire work: 15c, The Centaur Family, by Dürer. 35c, Oriental Ruler Seated, by Dürer. 50c, The Entombment, by Dürer. 75c, Man in Armor, by Rubens. $1, Peace Embracing Plenty, by Rubens. $2, Departure of Lot, by Rubens. $3, The Four Evangelists, by Rubens. No. 1810, $5, Knight, Death and Devil, by Dürer.
No. 1811, The Father of the Church, by Rubens. $6, St. Jerome, 1514 engraving, by Dürer.

**1996, Jan. 29    Litho.    Perf. 14**
1803-1810 A360 Set of 8    10.00 10.00
**Souvenir Sheets**
1811 A360 $5 multicolored    4.50 4.50
1812 A360 $6 multicolored    4.50 4.50

Disney Holidays — G127

Disney characters celebrating: 25c, New Year's Day, "Hopping John" Feast. 50c, May Day. 75c, Independence Day. 90c, Halloween. $3, Thanksgiving. $4, Hanukkah.
Each $6: No. 1819, Caribbean Carnival. No. 1820, St. Patrick's Day Parade, vert.

**1996, Apr. 17    Litho.    Perf. 14x13½**
1813-1818 G127 Set of 6    10.00 10.00
**Souvenir Sheets**
**Perf. 14x13½, 13½x14**
1819-1820 G127 Set of 2    13.00 13.00

Sites in China — G128

No. 1821, each $1: a, Entryway to hall, Imperial Palace. b, Great Wall's eastern end, Shanhaiguan. c, Fortress in Great Wall, Shanhaiguan. d, Gate of Heavenly Peace, Tiananmen, main entrance to Imperial City.
No. 1822, each $1: a, Mausoleum of Dr. Sun Yat-Sen, Nanjing. b, Summer Palace,

Beijing. c, Temple of Heaven, Beijing. d, Hall of Supreme Harmony, Forbidden City, Beijing. Each $6: No. 1823, Great Wall of China. No. 1824, Marble boat, Summer Palace, Beijing. Illustration reduced.

**1996, May 8**     **Perf. 13**
**Sheets of 4, #a-d**
1821-1822  G128  Set of 2  13.00 13.00
**Souvenir Sheets**
1823-1824  G128  Set of 2  10.50 10.50

China '96, 9th Asian Intl. Philatelic Exhibition (#1821-1822).
No. 1823 contains one 40x51mm stamp, No. 1824 one 51x40mm stamp.
See No. 1881.

**Queen Elizabeth II, 70th Birthday Type of 1996**

Designs: a, 35c, Portrait in blue dress. b, $2, Wearing crown. c, $4, Windsor Castle. $6, Standing in front of palace.

**1996, May 8**   **Litho.**   **Perf. 13½x14**
1825  A362  Strip of 3, #a.-c.  4.75 4.75
**Souvenir Sheet**
1826  A362  $6 multicolored  4.50 4.50

No. 1825 was issued in sheets of 9 stamps with each strip in a different order.

Flowers — G129

35c, Camellia "Apple Blossom." 90c, Camellia japonica "Extravaganza." $1, Chrysanthemum "Primrose Dorothy Else." $2, Dahlia "Brandaris."
No. 1831: a, Odontoglossum. b, Cattleya. c, Paphiopedilum "Venus's Slipper." d, Laeliocattleya "Marysville."
No. 1832: a, Fuschia "Citation." b, Fuchsia "Amy Lye." c, Clysonimus butterfly. d, Digitalis purpurea "Foxglove" (h). e, Lilium martagon "Martagon Lily." f, Tulip "Couleur Cardinal." g, Galanthus nivalis "Snowdrop." h, Rose "Superstar." i, Crocus "Dutch Yellow Mammouth." j, Lilium speciosum Japanese lily. k, Lilium "Joan Evans." l, Rose "Rosemary Harkness."
$5, Narcissus "Rembrandt." $6, Gladiollus "Flowersong."

**1996, June 12**   **Litho.**   **Perf. 14**
1827-1830  G129  Set of 4  4.50 4.50
1831  G129  75c Strip of 4, #a.-d.  3.00 3.00
1832  G129  75c Strip of 12, #a.-l.  8.50 8.50
**Souvenir Sheets**
1833  G129  $5 multicolored  4.00 4.00
1834  G129  $6 multicolored  4.50 4.50

No. 1831 issued in sheets of 12 stamps.

UNICEF, 50th Anniv. G130

Letters spelling UNICEF and: 75c, Child smiling. $2, Child eating. $3, Child reading. $6, Child on mother's back.

**1996, June 26**
1836-1838  G130  Set of 3  4.50 4.50
**Souvenir Sheet**
1839  G130  $6 multicolored  4.50 4.50
#1838 is unassigned.

Jerusalem, 3000th Anniv. G131

Flowers and: a, $1, Pool of Bethesda. b, $2, Damascus Gate. c, $3, Church of All Nations, Gethsemane.
$6, Church of the Holy Sepulchre.

**1996, June 26**
1840  G131  Sheet of 3, #a.-c.  4.50 4.50
**Souvenir Sheet**
1841  G131  $6 multicolored  4.50 4.50

Radio, Cent. Type of 1996

Entertainers: 35c, Ed Wynn. 75c, Red Skelton. $1, Joe Penner. $3, Jerry Colonna.
$6, Bob Elliot, Ray Goulding, horiz.

**1996, June 26**   **A367**   **Perf. 13½x14**
1842-1845  A367  Set of 4  3.75 3.75
**Souvenir Sheet**
**Perf. 14x13½**
1846  A367  $6 multicolored  4.50 4.50

Olympics Type of 1996

35c, Memorial Coliseum, Los Angeles, 1994. 75c, Connie Carpenter-Phinney, US. $2, Mohamed Bouchighe, Algeria, vert. $3, Jackie Joyner-Kersee, US.
No. 1851, Gymnasts, vert, each $1: a, Julianne McNamara, US. b, Takuti Hayato, Japan. c, Nikolai Adrianov, Russia. d, Mitch Gaylord, US. e, Ludmilla Tourischeva, Russia. f, Karin Janz, Germany. g, Peter Kormann, US. h, Sawao Kato, Japan. i, Nadia Comaneci, Romania.
No. 1852, Equestrian participants, vert, each $1: a, Josef Neckermann, Germany. b, Harry Boldt, Germany. c, Elena Petouchkova, Russia. d, Alwin Schockemoehle, Germany. e, Hans Winkler, Germany. f, Joe Fargis, US. g, David Broome, Great Britain. h, Reiner Klimke, Germany. i, Richard Meade, Great Britain.
No. 1853, Young Japanese girl, vert. No. 1854, William Steinkraus, US.

**1996, July 15**     **Perf. 14**
1847-1850  A364  Set of 4  4.50 4.50
**Sheets of 9, #a-i**
1851-1852  A364  Set of 2  13.50 13.50
**Souvenir Sheets**
1853  A364  $5 multicolored  3.75 3.75
1854  A364  $6 multicolored  4.50 4.50

Classic Cars — G132

No. 1855: a, Delaunay-Belleville HB6, France. b, Bugatti Type-15, Italy. c, Mazda Type 800, Japan. d, Mercedes 24/100/140 Sport, Germany. e, MG K3 Rover, England. f, Plymouth Fury, US.
No. 1856: a, 35c, Chevrolet Belair Convertible, US. b, 75c, Rolls Royce Torpedo, England. c, $1, Nissan Type "Cepric," Japan. d, VIP car. e, Mercedes Benz 500k, Germany. f, Bugatti Type-13, Italy.
$5, Bugatti "Roadster" Type-55. $6, Lincoln Type-L, US.

**1996, July 25**   **Litho.**   **Perf. 14**
1855  G132  $1 Sheet of 6, #a.-f.  4.50 4.50
1856  G132  Sheet of 6, #a.-f.  5.75 5.75
**Souvenir Sheets**
1857  G132  $5 multicolored  3.75 3.75
1858  G132  $6 multicolored  4.50 4.50
Nos. 1857-1858 each contain one 51x39mm stamp.

Ships G133

Traditional Grenada schooners: 35c, Red and white. 75c, Blue and white.
No. 1861, Ancient ships, each $1: a, Anthenian war triremes, 1000BC. b, Egyptian Nile trader, 30BC. c, Bangladesh dinghi, 3100BC. d, Queen Hatshepsut warship, 1476BC. e, Chinese junk, 200BC. f, Polynesian voyager, 600BC.
No. 1862, Ocean liners, each $1: a, Europa, Germany, 1957. b, Lusitania, England, 1906.

c, Queen Mary, England, 1936. d, Bianca C, Italy. e, SS France, 1932. f, Orion, England, 1915.
$5, Queen Elizabeth 2, England, 1969. $6, Viking ship, 610BC.

**1996, Aug. 14**
1859  G133  35c multicolored  .25 .25
1860  G133  75c multicolored  .55 .55
**Sheets of 6, #a-f**
1861-1862  G133  Set of 2  9.00 9.00
**Souvenir Sheets**
1863  G133  $5 multicolored  3.75 3.75
1864  G133  $6 multicolored  4.50 4.50

No. 1863 contains one 51x42mm stamp, No. 1864 one 42x51mm stamp.

Famous Composers G134

Composer, work illustrated: No. 1865, each $1: a, Bèla Bartòk, "Mikrokosmos," 1926. b, Giacomo Puccini, "Madame Butterfly," 1904. c, George Gershwin, "Rhapsody in Blue," 1923. d, Leonard Bernstein, "West Side Story," 1957. e, Kurt Weill, "Three Penny Opera," 1928. f, John Cage, "Music of Changes," 1951. g, Aaron Copland, "El Salón Mexico," 1936. h, Sergei Prokofiev, "Peter and the Wolf," 1936. i, Igor Stravinsky, "Rite of Spring," 1913.
No. 1866, each $1: a, Felix Mendelssohn, overture to "Midsummer Night's Dream," 1826. b, Franz Schubert, "Die Forelle" (The Trout) D.550, 1817. c, Franz Joseph Haydn, "String Quartet in D Major," Op. 64 No. 5 (Lark), 1790. d, Robert Schumann, "Spring," Symphony No. 1, Op. 38, 1841. e, Ludwig Van Beethoven, "Moonlight" sonata Op. 27, No. 2. f, Gioacchino Rossini, "William Tell," 1829. g, George Frederick Handel, "Royal Fireworks Music," 1749. h, Peter Ilyich Tchaikovsky, "Swan Lake," Op.20, 1876. i, Frederic Chopin, "Fantasia," in F minor, Op. 49, 1840-41.
$5, Richard Strauss. $6, Mozart, "Jupiter" symphony in C major.

**1996, Aug. 26**
**Sheets of 9, #a-i**
1865-1866  G134  Set of 2  14.00 14.00
**Souvenir Sheets**
1867  G134  $5 multicolored  3.75 3.75
1868  G134  $6 multicolored  4.50 4.50

Trains G135

No. 1869, each $1.50: a, Pacific Blue Peter, British Eastern. b, Class P36 4-8-4, Russia. c, Class OJ 2-10-2, China. d, Class 12 4-4-2, Belgium. e, Challenger Class 4-6-6-4, US. f, Class 25 4-8-4 Condenser, South Africa.
No. 1870, each $1.50: a, Federal Railways Class 38 4-6-0, Germany. b, Duchess of Hamilton Class 4-6-2, London & Glasgow. c, Class WP 4-6-2, Indian State Railways. d, Class 141R "L'Americane" 282, France (American-built). e, Class A4 4-6-2 Mallard, England. f, Deutche Reichsbahn Class 18 4-6-2, Germany.
$5, Cornish Rivera Express, King Class 4-6-2, Britain. $6, Caledonian "Royal Scot Class," 4-6-0, Britain.

**1996, Aug. 28**
**Sheets of 6, #a-f**
1869-1870  G135  Set of 2  13.50 13.50
**Souvenir Sheets**
1871  G135  $5 multicolored  3.75 3.75
1872  G135  $6 multicolored  4.50 4.50

Christmas Type of 1996

Details of painting, Suffer Little Children to Come Unto Me, by Van Dyck: 15c, Child with beads over shoulder. 25c, Christ anointing head of child. $1, Mother holding infant, father, children. $1.50, Christ, disciples. $2, Father, infant. $4, Christ, children, family.

Each $6: No. 1879, Entire painting, horiz. No. 1880, Adoration of the Shepherds, by Bernaldo Strozzi, horiz.

**1996, Nov. 18**   **Litho.**   **Perf. 13½x14**
1873-1878  A377  Set of 6  7.00 7.00
**Souvenir Sheets**
1879-1880  A377  Set of 2  9.00 9.00

Souvenir Sheet

China '96 — G136

Painting depicting scene from "Hong Lou Meng." Illustration reduced.

**1996, May 8**   **Litho.**   **Perf. 13x13½**
1881  G136  $2 multicolored  1.10 1.10
No. 1881 was not available until March 1997.

Hong Kong Past and Present G137

No. 1882, Man Ho Temple, each $3: a, 1841. b, 1983.
No. 1883, City of Victoria with view of St. John's Cathedral, each $3: a, 1886. b, 1983.
No. 1884, Victoria Harbor, Hong Kong, each $3: a, 1858. b, 1983.
No. 1885, each $3: a, Treaty of Nanking, 1842. b, Margaret Thatcher signing Joint Declaration, 1984.
No. 1886, Victoria Harbor, each $3: a, Older black & white photograph. b, Modern photograph.

**1997, Feb. 12**   **Litho.**   **Perf. 14**
**Sheets of 2, #a-b**
1882-1886  G137  Set of 5  22.50 22.50
Hong Kong '97.

**UNESCO Type of 1997**

Designs: 15c, Kyoto, Japan. 25c, Roman ruins at Trier, Germany. $1, Mount Taishan, China. $1.50, Scandola Nature Reserve, France. $2, Fortress Wall, Dubrovnik, Croatia. $4, Angra Do Heroismo, Portugal.
No. 1893, vert, each $1: a, Sanctuary of Congonhas, Brazil. b, Cartagena, Colombia. c, City of Puebla, Mexico. d, Mayan Ruins, Copan, Honduras. e, Monastery of Popocatepetl, Mexico. f, Galapagos Islands, Ecuador. g, Waterfall, La Amisted Natl. Park, Costa Rica. h, Glaciares Natl. Park, Argentina.
No. 1894, vert, each $1: a, b, c, Kyoto, Japan. d, Ayutthaya, Thailand. e, Temple of Borobudur, Indonesia. f, Monuments, Pattadakal, India. g, Polonnaruwa, Sri Lanka. h, Sagarmatha Natl. Park, Nepal.
No. 1895, each $1.50: a, Cathedral of Notre Dame, France. b, Timbered house, Maulbronn, Germany. c, Himeji-Jo, Japan. d, Ruins, Delphi, Greece. e, Palace of Fontainebleau, France.
Each $6: No. 1896, Temple, Chengde, China. No. 1897, Pre-hispanic city of Teotihuacan, Mexico. No. 1898, Mont St. Michel, France.

**1997, Apr. 3**   **Litho.**   **Perf. 14**
1887-1892  A382  Set of 6  6.75 6.75
**Sheets of 8**
1893-1894  A382  Set of 2  12.00 12.00
**Sheet of 5 + Label**
1895  A382  #a.-e.  5.75 5.75
**Souvenir Sheets**
1896-1898  A382  Set of 3  15.00 15.00

Dogs and Cats G138

Dogs: 35c, Springer spaniel. 75c, Doberman pinscher. $1, Italian spinone, vert. $2, Cocker spaniel, vert.

No. 1903: a, Leonberger. b, Newfoundland. c, Boxer. d, St. Bernard. e, Silky terrier. f, Miniature schnauzer.

No. 1904, Golden retriever puppy.

**1997, Apr. 10**

| | | | | |
|---|---|---|---|---|
| 1899-1902 | G138 | Set of 4 | 3.00 | 3.00 |

**Sheet of 6**

| | | | | |
|---|---|---|---|---|
| 1903 | G138 | $1.50 #a.-f. | 6.75 | 6.75 |

**Souvenir Sheet**

| | | | | |
|---|---|---|---|---|
| 1904 | G138 | $6 multicolored | 6.75 | 6.75 |

**1997, Apr. 10**

Cats: 45c, Abyssinian blue. 50c, Bermese cream, vert. 90c, Persian tortoiseshell and white. $3, Oriental shorthair red Agouti tabby, vert.

No. 1909: a, Siamese chocolate point. b, Oriental shorthair white. c, Burmese sable. d, Abysinian tabby. e, Persian shaded silver. f, Tonkinese natural mink.

| | | | | |
|---|---|---|---|---|
| 1905-1908 | G138 | Set of 4 | 3.75 | 3.75 |

**Sheet of 6**

| | | | | |
|---|---|---|---|---|
| 1909 | G138 | $1.50 #a.-f. | 6.75 | 6.75 |

**Souvenir Sheet**

| | | | | |
|---|---|---|---|---|
| 1910 | G138 | $6 Sphinx, vert. | 6.75 | 6.75 |

**Prehistoric Animal Type of 1997**

Designs: 45c, Stegosaurus. 90c, Diplodocus. $1, Pteranodon, vert. $2, Deinonychus, ankylasaurus, vert.

No. 1915: a, Rhamphorhynchus, brachiosaurus (c, d, e,). b, Archaeopteryx. c, Anurognathus. d, Albertosaurus (f). e, Herrerasaurus. f, Platyhystrix.

Each $6: No. 1916, Hypacrosaurus. No. 1917, Apatosaurus, allosaurus, vert.

**1997, Apr. 15    Litho.    Perf. 14**

| | | | | |
|---|---|---|---|---|
| 1911-1914 | A385 | Set of 4 | 3.00 | 3.00 |
| 1915 | A385 | $1.50 Sheet of 6, #a.-f. | 6.75 | 6.75 |

**Souvenir Sheets**

| | | | | |
|---|---|---|---|---|
| 1916-1917 | A385 | Set of 2 | 9.00 | 9.00 |

**Queen Elizabeth II, Prince Philip, 50th Wedding Anniv. Type of 1997**

No. 1918: a, Colored portrait. b, Royal Arms. c, Black and white portrait. d, Black and white portrait in royal attire. e, Sandringham House. f, Queen in blue dress, Prince in uniform.

$6, Wedding portrait.

**1997, May 28    Litho.    Perf. 14**

| | | | | |
|---|---|---|---|---|
| 1918 | A386a | $1 Sheet of 6, #a.-f. | 4.50 | 4.50 |

**Souvenir Sheet**

| | | | | |
|---|---|---|---|---|
| 1919 | A386a | $6 multicolored | 4.50 | 4.50 |

**Paintings by Hiroshige Type of 1997**

No. 1920: a, Koume Embankment. b, Azuma Shrine and the Entwined Camphor. c, Yanagishima. d, Inside Akiba Shrine, Ukeji. e, Distant View of Kinryuzan Temple and Azuma Bridge. f, Night View of Matsuchiyama and the San'ya Canal.

Each $6: No. 1921, Five Pines, Onagi Canal. No. 1922, Spiral Hall, Five Hundred Rakan Temple.

**1997, May 28    Perf. 13½x14**

| | | | | |
|---|---|---|---|---|
| 1920 | A387 | $1.50 Sheet of 6, #a.-f. | 8.50 | 8.50 |

**Souvenir Sheets**

| | | | | |
|---|---|---|---|---|
| 1921-1922 | A387 | Set of 2 | 11.00 | 11.00 |

**Heinrich von Stephan Type of 1997**

**1997, May 28    Litho.    Perf. 14**

Portrait of Von Stephan and: No. 1923: a, The Pony Express, 1860-61. b, UPU emblem. c, Steam locomotive postal delivery, 1800's. $6, Camel courier, Baghdad.

| | | | | |
|---|---|---|---|---|
| 1923 | A388 | $1.50 Sheet of 3, #a.-c. | 2.50 | 2.50 |

**Souvenir Sheet**

| | | | | |
|---|---|---|---|---|
| 1924 | A388 | $6 multicolored | 4.50 | 4.50 |

PACIFIC 97.

**Paul P. Harris Type of 1997**

**1997, May 28**

Designs: $3, Women in Burkina Faso pumping well water, portrait of Harris. $6, Early Rotary parade float.

| | | | | |
|---|---|---|---|---|
| 1925 | A389 | $3 multicolored | 2.25 | 2.25 |

**Souvenir Sheet**

| | | | | |
|---|---|---|---|---|
| 1926 | A389 | $6 multicolored | 4.50 | 4.50 |

**Grimm's Fairy Tale and Mother Goose Types of 1997**

**1997, May 28    Perf. 13½x14**

Scenes from "The Fox and the Geese:" No. 1927: a, Fox, geese. b, Geese singing as fox waves knife, fork. c, Fox asleep, geese celebrating. No. 1928, Fox lurking in forest, horiz.

No. 1929, Girl with black sheep.

| | | | | |
|---|---|---|---|---|
| 1927 | A391 | $2 Sheet of 3, #a.-c. | 4.50 | 4.50 |

**Souvenir Sheets**

**Perf. 14x13½, 14**

| | | | | |
|---|---|---|---|---|
| 1928 | A391 | $6 multicolored | 4.50 | 4.50 |
| 1929 | A392 | $6 multicolored | 4.50 | 4.50 |

1998 Winter Olympic Games, Nagano G139

Designs: 90c, Downhill skier. $2, Luge. $3, Male figure skater. $5, Speed skater in blue hat.

No. 1934: a, Downhill skier in air. b, Freestyle skier. c, Curling. d, Ski jumper. e, Bobsled. f, Biathlon. g, Speed skater in yellow and red hat. h, Hockey. i, Cross-country skier.

Each $6: No. 1935, Luge, diff., vert. No. 1936, Female figure skater.

**1997, June 26    Perf. 14**

| | | | | |
|---|---|---|---|---|
| 1930-1933 | G139 | Set of 4 | 8.25 | 8.25 |
| 1934 | G139 | $1 Sheet of 9, #a.-i. | 6.75 | 6.75 |

**Souvenir Sheets**

| | | | | |
|---|---|---|---|---|
| 1935-1936 | G139 | Set of 2 | 9.00 | 9.00 |

**Return of Hong Kong to China Type**

Chinese flag in foreground, "Hong Kong" in English and Chinese with city scene showing through words: $1, Night scene. $1.25, Daytime view of skyscrapers. $1.50, Skyline at night, horiz. $2, View of harbor, horiz.

**1997, July 1**

| | | | | |
|---|---|---|---|---|
| 1937-1940 | A394 | Set of 4 | 4.50 | 4.50 |

Nos. 1937-1938 were issued in sheets of 4. Nos. 1939-1940 are 59x28mm and were issued in sheets of 3.

Fish G140

Designs: 10c, Wimplefish. 15c, Clown triggerfish. 25c, Ringed emperor angelfish. 35c, Hooded butterfly fish. 45c, Semicircle angelfish. 75c, Scribbled angelfish. 90c, Threadfin butterfly fish. $1, Clown surgeonfish.

**1997, July 22    Litho.    Perf. 14**

| | | | | |
|---|---|---|---|---|
| 1941 | G140 | 10c multicolored | .20 | .20 |
| 1942 | G140 | 15c multicolored | .20 | .20 |
| 1943 | G140 | 25c multicolored | .20 | .20 |
| 1944 | G140 | 35c multicolored | .25 | .25 |
| 1945 | G140 | 45c multicolored | .35 | .35 |
| 1946 | G140 | 75c multicolored | .55 | .55 |
| 1947 | G140 | 90c multicolored | .70 | .70 |
| 1948 | G140 | $1 multicolored | .75 | .75 |
| | | Nos. 1941-1948 (8) | 3.20 | 3.20 |

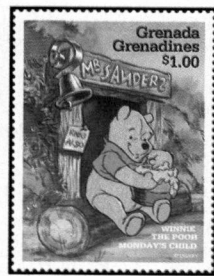

Winnie the Pooh G141

#1949: a, Winnie the Pooh. b, Kanga & Roo. c, Eeyore. d, Tigger. e, Piglet & Gopher. f, Rabbit.

$6, Christopher Robin.

**1997, Aug. 7    Litho.    Perf. 13½x14**

| | | | | |
|---|---|---|---|---|
| 1949 | G141 | $1 Sheet of 6, #a.-f. | 4.50 | 4.50 |

**Souvenir Sheet**

| | | | | |
|---|---|---|---|---|
| 1950 | G141 | $6 multicolored | 4.50 | 4.50 |

**1998 World Cup Soccer Type of 1997**

Team pictures: 10c, Italy, 1934. 20c, Angola. 45c, Brazil, 1958. $1, Uruguay, 1950. $1.50, West Germany, 1974. $5, Italy, 1938.

World Cup winners: No. 1951: a, England. b, W. Germany, 1954. c, Uruguay. d, West Germany, 1990. e, Argentina, 1986. f, Brazil. g, Argentina, 1978. h, W. Germany 1974.

Tournament stars, vert.: No. 1952: a, Ademir, Brazil. b, Kocsis, Hungary. c, Leonidas, Brazil. d, Nejedly, Czechoslovakia. e, Schiavio, Italy. f, Stabile, Uruguay. g, Pele, Brazil. h, Fritzwalter, W. Germany.

Each $6: No. 1953, Shearer, England, vert. No. 1954, Paulao, Angola.

**1997, Aug. 11**

| | | | | |
|---|---|---|---|---|
| 1950A-1950F | A397 | Set of 6 | 6.25 | 6.25 |

**Sheets of 8, #a-h**

| | | | | |
|---|---|---|---|---|
| 1951-1952 | A397 | Set of 2 | 12.00 | 12.00 |

**Souvenir Sheets**

| | | | | |
|---|---|---|---|---|
| 1953-1954 | A397 | Set of 2 | 9.00 | 9.00 |

**Fish Type of 1997**

$2, Tursiops truncatus. $5, Balistes vetula. $10, Pterois volitans. $20, Equetus lanceolatus.

**1997, July 22    Litho.    Perf. 14**

| | | | | |
|---|---|---|---|---|
| 1955 | G140 | $2 multicolored | 1.50 | 1.50 |
| 1956 | G140 | $5 multicolored | 3.75 | 3.75 |
| 1957 | G140 | $10 multicolored | 7.50 | 7.50 |
| 1958 | G140 | $20 multicolored | 15.00 | 15.00 |
| | | Nos. 1955-1958 (4) | 27.75 | 27.75 |

Sealed with a Kiss — G142

Characters from Disney's classic animated films: No. 1959: a, Snow White, 1937. b, Pinocchio, 1940. c, Peter Pan, 1953. d, Cinderella, 1950. e, The Little Mermaid, 1989. f, Beauty and the Beast, 1991. g, Aladdin, 1992. h, Pocahontas, 1995. i, Hunchback of Notre Dame, 1996.

$5, The Aristocats, 1970, vert.

**1997, Aug. 7    Litho.    Perf. 14x13½**

| | | | | |
|---|---|---|---|---|
| 1959 | G142 | $1 Sheet of 9, #a.-i. | 6.75 | 6.75 |

**Souvenir Sheet**

**Perf. 13½x14**

| | | | | |
|---|---|---|---|---|
| 1960 | G142 | $5 multicolored | 3.75 | 3.75 |

Butterflies of the World G143

75c, Polyura dehaani. 90c, Polyura dolon. $1, Charaxes candiope. $1.50, Pantaporia punctata. $2, Charaxes etesippe. $3, Charaxes castor.

No. 1967, Euphaedra, each $1.50: a, Francina. b, Eleus. c, Harpalyce. d, Cyparissa. e, Gausape. f, Imperialis.

No. 1968, each $1.50: a, Euthalia confucius. b, Euthalia kardama. c, Limenitis albomaculata. d, Hestina assimilis. e, Kalima inachus. f, Euthalia teutoides.

Each $6: No. 1969, Charaxes numenes, vert. No. 1970, Charaxes nobilis, vert.

**1997, Aug. 12    Perf. 14**

| | | | | |
|---|---|---|---|---|
| 1961-1966 | G143 | Set of 6 | 6.75 | 6.75 |

**Sheets of 6, #a-f**

| | | | | |
|---|---|---|---|---|
| 1967-1968 | G143 | Set of 2 | 13.50 | 13.50 |

**Souvenir Sheets**

| | | | | |
|---|---|---|---|---|
| 1969-1970 | G143 | Set of 2 | 9.00 | 9.00 |

James Dean (1931-55), Actor G144

Various portraits.

**1997, Aug. 22    Perf. 14x13½**

| | | | | |
|---|---|---|---|---|
| 1971 | G144 | $1 Sheet of 9, #a.-i. | 6.75 | 6.75 |

Mushrooms — G145

Designs: 75c, Clitocybe metachroa. 90c, Clavulinopsis helvola. $1, Lycoperdon pyriforme. $1.50, Auricularia auricula-judae. $2, Clathrus archeri. $3, Lactarius trivialis.

No. 1978: a, Entoloma incanum. b, Coprinus atramentarius. c, Mycena polygramma. d, Lepista nuda. e, Pleurotis cornucopiae. f, Laccaria amethystina.

Each $6: No. 1979, Amanita muscaria. No. 1980, Morchella esculenta.

**1997, Sept. 4    Perf. 14**

| | | | | |
|---|---|---|---|---|
| 1972-1977 | G145 | Set of 6 | 6.75 | 6.75 |
| 1978 | G145 | $1.50 Sheet of 6, #a.-f. | 6.75 | 6.75 |

**Souvenir Sheets**

| | | | | |
|---|---|---|---|---|
| 1979-1980 | G145 | Set of 2 | 9.00 | 9.00 |

G146      Orchids — G147

Designs: 35c, Symphyglossum sanguineum. 45c, Doritaenopsis "Mythic Beauty." 75c, Odontoglossum cervantesii. 90c, Cattleya "Pumpernickel." $1, Vanda "Patricia Law." $1.50, Odontonia "Debutante." $2, Laeliocattleya "Mini Purple." $3, Phragmipedium "Dominiarium."

No. 1989, each $1: a, Cymbidium "Showgirl." b, Disa "Blackii." c, Phalaenopsis aphrodite. d, Iwanagaara "Apple Blossom." e, Masdevallia "Copper Angel." f, Paphiopedilum micranthum. g, Paphiopedilum "Claire de Lune." h, Cattleya forbesii. i, Dendrobium "Dawn Maree."

No. 1990, each $1: a, Lycaste "Aquila." b, Brassolaeliocattleya "Dorothy Bertsch." c, Phalaenopsis "Zuma Urchin." d, Promenaea xanthina. e, Amesiella philippinensis. f, Brassocattleya "Angel Lace." g, Brassoepidsendrum "Peggy Ann." h, Miltonia seine. i, Sophralaeliocattleya "Precious Stones."

No. 1991, each $1.50: a, Miltoniosis "Jean Sabourin." b, Cymbididium "Red Beauty." c, Brassocattleya "Green Dragon." d, Phalaenopsis hybrid. e, Laelio cattleya "Mary Ellen Carter." f, Disa hybrid.

No. 1992, each $1.50: a, Lycaste macrobulbon. b, Cochleanthes discolor. c, Cymbidium "Nang Carpenter." d, Paphiopedilum "Clair de Lune." e, Masdevallia caudata. f, Cymbidum "Showgirl."

$5, Phalenopsis "Medford Star." $6, Brassolaeliocattleya "Mem. Dorothy Bertsch."

**1997, Sept. 4**

| | | | | |
|---|---|---|---|---|
| 1981-1988 | G146 | Set of 8 | 7.50 | 7.50 |

**Sheets of 9, #a-i**

| | | | | |
|---|---|---|---|---|
| 1989-1990 | G147 | Set of 2 | 13.50 | 13.50 |

**Sheets of 6, #a-f**

| | | | | |
|---|---|---|---|---|
| 1991-1992 | G146 | Set of 2 | 13.50 | 13.50 |

## Souvenir Sheets

| | | | | |
|---|---|---|---|---|
| 1993 | G146 | $5 multicolored | 3.75 | 3.75 |
| 1994 | G146 | $6 multicolored | 4.50 | 4.50 |

Famous Composers, Musicians G148

No. 1995, each $1: a, Beethoven. b, Tchaikovsky. c, J.S. Bach. d, Chopin. e, Stravinsky. f, Haydn. g, Mahler. h, Rossini.
Each $6: No. 1996, Mozart. No. 1997, Schubert.

**1997, Oct. 10   Litho.   Perf. 14½x14**
### Sheet of 8

| | | | | |
|---|---|---|---|---|
| 1995 | G148 | #a.-h. + label | 6.00 | 6.00 |

### Souvenir Sheets

| | | | | |
|---|---|---|---|---|
| 1996-1997 | G148 | Set of 2 | 9.00 | 9.00 |

Diana, Princess of Wales (1961-97) G149

Various portraits of Diana wearing various hats, scenes following her death: No. 1998: a, Buckingham Palace. b, Island, Spencer Estate, Althorp. c, Westminster Abbey. d, Gate, Spencer Estate. e, Gate, Kensington Palace. g, Spencer Estate, Althorp.
$6, Diana smelling flowers in front of Kensington Palace.

**1997, Nov. 10   Perf. 14**

| | | | | |
|---|---|---|---|---|
| 1998 | G149 | $1.50 Sheet of 6, #a.-f. | 6.75 | 6.75 |

### Souvenir Sheet

| | | | | |
|---|---|---|---|---|
| 1999 | G149 | $6 multicolored | 4.50 | 4.50 |

No. 1999 contains one 60x40mm stamp.

### Christmas Art Type of 1997

Entire paintings, details, or sculptures: 20c, Choir of Angels, by Simon Marmion. 75c, The Annunciation, by Giotto. 90c, Festival of the Rose Garlands, by Albrecht Durer. $1.50, Madonna with Two Angels, by Hans Memling. $2, The Ognissanti Madonna, by Giotto. $3, Angel with Candlestick, by Michelangelo.
Each $6: No. 2006, Cupid Commemorating a Marriage by Incising on a Table, by Jean-Baptiste Huet, horiz. No. 2007, The Rising of the Sun, by Francois Boucher, horiz.

**1997, Dec. 5   Litho.   Perf. 14**

| | | | | |
|---|---|---|---|---|
| 2000-2005 | A402 | Set of 6 | 12.50 | 12.50 |

### Souvenir Sheets

| | | | | |
|---|---|---|---|---|
| 2006-2007 | A402 | Set of 2 | 9.00 | 9.00 |

### Marine Life Type of 1997

No. 2008, each $1: a, Holocanthus ciliaris. b, Ballstoides conspicillum. c, Chaetodon quadrimaculatus. d, Microspathodon chrysurus. e, Halichoeres garnoti. f, Gramma loreto. g, Liopropoma carmabi. h, Lactophrys triqueter. i, Cephalopolis miniatus.
Each $6: No. 2009, Carcharhinus melanopterus. No. 2010, Obistognathus aurifrons, vert.

**1997, Dec. 12   Litho.   Perf. 14**

| | | | | |
|---|---|---|---|---|
| 2008 | A386 | Sheet of 9, #a.-i. | 6.75 | 6.75 |

### Souvenir Sheets

| | | | | |
|---|---|---|---|---|
| 2009-2010 | A386 | Set of 2 | 9.00 | 9.00 |

New Year 1998 (Year of the Tiger) — G150

---

**Die Cut Perf. 11**
**1998, Feb. 10   Litho.**
### Self-Adhesive

| | | | |
|---|---|---|---|
| 2011 | G150 | $1.50 Hologram | 1.10 |

### Souvenir Sheet

| | | | |
|---|---|---|---|
| 2012 | G150 | $3 like #2011 | 2.25 |

No. 2011 was issued in sheets of 4. No. 2012 contains one 52x65mm stamp.

Great Ships, Shipwrecks — G151

Ships — #2013: a, CSS Alabama. b, Persia. c, Ariel. d, CSS Florida. e, Great Eastern. f, Jacob Bell. g, Star of India. h, Robert E. Lee. i, US Monitor Passaic. j, Madagascar. k, HMS Devastation. l, General Grant.
"Gone with the Wind," vert. — #2014: a, Clark Gable. b, Blockade runner wrecked on Sullivan's Island, North Carolina, 1863. c, Margaret Mitchell. d, George Alfred Trenholm, model for character Rhett Butler. e, Dock Street Theater, confiscated from Trenholm after Civil War. f, Howlet sinks off Charleston, South Carolina, 1865. g, USS Tecumseh sunk by Confederate gunboats, 1864. h, City jail, where Trenholm was imprisoned, 1865.
Each $6: No. 2015, Nashville sinks the Union clipper, Harvey Birch, vert. No. 2016, Dr. Lee Spence, expert on shipwrecks and sunken treasures, Alabama sinking Hatteras off Texas coast.

**1998, May 7   Litho.   Perf. 14**

| | | | | |
|---|---|---|---|---|
| 2013 | G151 | 75c Sheet of 12, #a.-l. | 6.75 | 6.75 |
| 2014 | G151 | $1 Sheet of 8, #a.-h. | 6.00 | 6.00 |

### Souvenir Sheets

| | | | | |
|---|---|---|---|---|
| 2015-2016 | G151 | Set of 2 | 9.00 | 9.00 |

#2015-2016 contain one 57x43mm stamp.

Modern, Future Aircraft G152

70c, Concept strike fighter. 90c, Concept space shuttle. $2, Concept air & space jet. $3, V Jet II.
No. 2021: a, Velocity 173 RG Elite. b, Davis DA 9. c, Concorde. d, Voyager. e, Factimobile. f, RAF 2000. g, Boomerang. h, N1M Flying Wing.
Each $6: No. 2022, Gee-Bee replica. No. 2023, Concept Aeropod.

**1998, May 13**

| | | | | |
|---|---|---|---|---|
| 2017-2020 | G152 | Set of 4 | 5.00 | 5.00 |
| 2021 | G152 | $1 Sheet of 8, #a.-h. | 6.00 | 6.00 |

### Souvenir Sheets

| | | | | |
|---|---|---|---|---|
| 2022-2023 | G152 | Set of 2 | 9.00 | 9.00 |

No. 2022 is inscribed "Delmar."

Orchids — G153

Designs: $1, Laclia tenebrosa. $1.50, Phragmipedium besseae. $2, Pschopsis papilio. $3, Masdevallia coccinea.
No. 2028, each $1: a, Lycaste deppei. b, Dendrobium victoriae. c, Dendrobium nobile. d, Cymbidium danyanum. e, Cymbidium starbright. f, Cymbidium giganteum. g, Chysis aurea. h, Broughtonia sanguinea. i, Cattleya guttata.
No. 2029, each $1: a, Calanthe vestita. b, Cattleya bicolor. c, Laelia anceps. d, Epidendrum prismatocarpum. e, Coelogyne ochcracea. f, Doritaenopsis eclantant. g, Laelia gouldiana. h, Encyclia vitellina. i, Maxillaria praestans.

---

Each $6: No. 2030, Masdevallia ignea. No. 2031, Encyclia brassavolae.

**1998, May 19**

| | | | | |
|---|---|---|---|---|
| 2024-2027 | G153 | Set of 4 | 5.75 | 5.75 |

### Sheets of 9, #a-i

| | | | | |
|---|---|---|---|---|
| 2028-2029 | G153 | Set of 2 | 13.50 | 13.50 |

### Souvenir Sheets

| | | | | |
|---|---|---|---|---|
| 2030-2031 | G153 | Set of 2 | 9.00 | 9.00 |

### Sea Birds Type of 1998

75c, Bonaparte's gull. 90c, Western sandpiper. $2, Great black-backed gull. $3, Dotterell.
No. 2036, each $1.50: a, Terns. b, Brown pelican. c, Black-legged kittiwake. d, Herring gull. e, Lesser noddy. f, Kittiwake.
No. 2037, each $1.50: a, Whimbrels. b, Golden white-tailed tropic bird. c, Arctic tern. d, Ruddy turnstones. e, Imperial shag. f, Magellan gull.
Each $5: No. 2038, Yellow-nosed albatross, vert. No. 2039, Broad-billed prion.

**1998, June 30   Litho.   Perf. 14**

| | | | | |
|---|---|---|---|---|
| 2032-2035 | A408 | Set of 4 | 5.00 | 5.00 |

### Sheets of 6, #a-f

| | | | | |
|---|---|---|---|---|
| 2036-2037 | A408 | Set of 2 | 13.50 | 13.50 |

### Souvenir Sheets

| | | | | |
|---|---|---|---|---|
| 2038-2039 | A408 | Set of 2 | 7.50 | 7.50 |

Diana, Princess of Wales (1961-97) — G155

Diana in front of Kensington Palace: No. 2040, Wearing tiara, ruffled dress. No. 2041, Wearing white dress, pearls.

### Litho. & Embossed
**1998, July 14   Die Cut 7½**

| | | | |
|---|---|---|---|
| 2040 | G155 | $20 gold | |
| 2041 | G155 | $20 gold & multi | |

### Intl. Year of the Ocean Type

No. 2042: a, Great black-backed gull. b, Common dolphin. c, Seal. d, Amazonian catfish. e, Shark. f, Goldfish. g, Cyathopharynx. h, Whale. i, Telmatochromis. j, Crab. k, Octopus. l, Turtle.
No. 2043: a, Dolphins. b, Seal. c, Turtle. d, Leopard shark. e, Flame angelfish. f, Syndontis. g, Lamprologus. h, Kryptopterus bicirrhus. i, Pterophyllum scalare. j, Swimming pancake. k, Cowfish. l, Sea horse.
Each $6: No. 2044, Tetraodon mbu. No. 2045, Goldfish.

**1998, Aug. 19   Litho.   Perf. 14**
### Sheets of 12

| | | | | |
|---|---|---|---|---|
| 2042 | A411 | 75c #a.-l. | 6.75 | 6.75 |
| 2043 | A411 | 90c #a.-l. | 8.00 | 8.00 |

### Souvenir Sheets

| | | | | |
|---|---|---|---|---|
| 2044-2045 | A411 | Set of 2 | 9.00 | 9.00 |

### Gandhi Type of 1998

Portraits of Gandhi.

**1998, Sept. 15   Litho.   Perf. 14**

| | | | | |
|---|---|---|---|---|
| 2046 | A413 | $1 multicolored | .75 | .75 |

### Souvenir Sheet

| | | | | |
|---|---|---|---|---|
| 2047 | A413 | $6 multicolored | 4.50 | 4.50 |

No. 2046 was issued in sheets of 4.

---

### Picasso Type of 1998

Paintings: 45c, Bust of a Woman, 1943, vert. $2, Three Musicians, 1921. $3, Studio at La Californie, 1956.
$5, Woman with a Blue Hat, 1901.

**Perf. 14½x14, 14x14½**
**1998, Sept. 15**

| | | | | |
|---|---|---|---|---|
| 2048-2050 | A414 | Set of 3 | 4.25 | 4.25 |

### Souvenir Sheet

| | | | | |
|---|---|---|---|---|
| 2051 | A414 | $5 multicolored | 3.75 | 3.75 |

### Delacroix Type of 1998

Paintings — #2052: a, The Natchez. b, Christ and His Disciples Crossing the Sea of Galilee. c, Sunset. d, Moroccans Outside the Walls of Tangier. e, The Fireplace. f, Forest View with a Oak Tree. g, View of the Harbor at Dieppe. h, Arabs Skirmishing in the Mountains.
$5, Orphan Girl in a Cemetary, vert.

**1998, Sept. 15   Litho.   Perf. 14**

| | | | | |
|---|---|---|---|---|
| 2052 | A415 | $1 Sheet of 8, #a.-h. | 6.00 | 6.00 |

### Souvenir Sheet

| | | | | |
|---|---|---|---|---|
| 2053 | A415 | $5 multicolored | 4.50 | 4.50 |

### Organization of American States Type

**1998, Sept. 15**

| | | | | |
|---|---|---|---|---|
| 2054 | A416 | $1 multicolored | .75 | .75 |

### Diana Type of 1998

**1998   Perf. 14½**

| | | | | |
|---|---|---|---|---|
| 2055 | A417 | $1.50 multicolored | 1.10 | 1.10 |

### Self-Adhesive
**Serpentine Die Cut Perf. 11½**
### Sheet of 1
**Size: 53x65mm**

| | | | |
|---|---|---|---|
| 2055A | A417 | $8 Diana, buildings | |

No. 2055 was issued in sheets of 6. Soaking in water may affect the multi-layer image of No. 2055A.
Issued: $1.50, 9/15; $8, 11/5/98.

### Ferrari Type of 1998

No. 2056: a, 275 GTB. b, 340 MM. c, 250 GT SWB Berlinetta SEFAC "Hot Rod."
$5, First Ferrari Cabriolet (011-S).

**1998, Sept. 15   Perf. 14**

| | | | | |
|---|---|---|---|---|
| 2056 | A418 | $2 Sheet of 3, #a.-c. | 4.50 | 4.50 |

### Souvenir Sheet

| | | | | |
|---|---|---|---|---|
| 2057 | A418 | $5 multicolored | 4.50 | 4.50 |

No. 2057 contains one 91x35mm stamp.

### Scout Jamboree Type of 1998

Designs: 90c, Scout sign. $1.50, Lord Baden-Powell. $5, Scout salute.
$6, Lord Baden-Powell, diff., vert.

**1998, Sept. 15**

| | | | | |
|---|---|---|---|---|
| 2058-2060 | A419 | Set of 3 | 5.75 | 5.75 |

### Souvenir Sheet

| | | | | |
|---|---|---|---|---|
| 2061 | A419 | $6 multicolored | 4.50 | 4.50 |

### Royal Air Force Type of 1998

No. 2062, each $2: a, Chinook. b, BAe Harrier GR5. c, Panavia Tornado F3 ADV. d, Chinook HC2 carrying 105mm light gun.
No. 2063, each $2: a, Tornado GR1. b, BAe Hawk TIA. c, Sepecat Jaguar GRI. d, Harrier GR7.
Each $6: No. 2064, Eurofighter 2000, Hunter. No. 2065, Biplane, hawk in flight. No. 2066, Head of hawk, biplane. No. 2067, Eurofighter 2000, Tornado.

**1998, Sept. 15**
### Sheets of 4, #a-d

| | | | | |
|---|---|---|---|---|
| 2062-2063 | A420 | Set of 2 | 12.00 | 12.00 |

### Souvenir Sheets

| | | | | |
|---|---|---|---|---|
| 2064-2067 | A420 | Set of 2 | 9.00 | 9.00 |

Disney Christmas Trains — G156

Silly Symphony Railroad — #2068, each $1: a, Santa in locomotive, rabbit. b, Giraffe, elephant, tiger. c, Wolf, Three Little Pigs. d, Robin Hood blowing horn, Jiminy Cricket, penguins, children. e, Geese, Indian boy, turtle in caboose.

Mickey's Toontown Christmas Train — #2069, each $1: a, Mickey in locomotive. b, Pluto, chipmunks in coal car. c, Donald, Daisy Duck in passenger car. d, Goofy leading Huey, Dewey, & Louie in caroling. e, Minnie in caboose.

Pooh's Railroad — #2070, each $1: a, Piglet as engineer. b, Winnie the Pooh shoveling honey. c, Rabbit, Owl. d, Kanga, Roo, Christopher Robin. e, Eeyore, Tigger.

Each $6: No. 2071, Santa setting up toy train under Christmas tree. No. 2072, Mickey as engineer. No. 2073, Winnie the Pooh reading paper, Rabbit, Piglet.

**1998, Oct. 15**      *Perf. 14x13½*
**Sheets of 5, #a-e**
2068-2070 G156 Set of 3     11.50 11.50
**Souvenir Sheets**
2071-2073 G156 Set of 3     13.50 13.50

**New Year 1999 (Year of the Rabbit) Type**

Various rabbits, color of country name: a, green. b, orange. c, red.

**1999, Jan. 4**   **Litho.**   *Die Cut Perf. 9*
**Self-Adhesive**
**Sheet of 3**
2074 A425 $1.50 gold & multi,
      #a.-c.            3.50 3.50

No. 2074b has point of triangle down.

Queen Elizabeth II and Prince Philip, 50th Wedding Anniv. — G157

**Litho. & Embossed**
**1999, Jan. 8**     *Die Cut Perf. 7*
**Without Gum**
2075 G157 $20 gold & multi

Australia '99, World Stamp Expo G158

Dinosaurs — #2076: a, Troodon. b, Camptosaurus. c, Parasaurolophus. d, Dryosaurus. e, Gallimimus. f, Camarasaurus (all vert.).

#2077: a, Duckbill. b, Lambeosaurus. c, Iguanodon. d, Euoplocephalus. e, Triceratops. f, Brachiosaurus. g, Ponoptosaurus. h, Stegosaurus.

Each $6: #2078, Edmontosaurus. #2079, Tyrannosaurus, vert. #2080, Halticosaurus, vert.

**1999, Mar. 1**   **Litho.**   *Perf. 14*
2076 G158 $1 Sheet of 6,
     #a.-f.          4.50 4.50
2077 G158 $1.50 Sheet of 8,
     #a.-h.          9.25 9.25
**Souvenir Sheets**
2078-2080 G158 Set of 3     13.50 13.50

Trains G159

Designs: 15c, India, 4-4-0 express passenger and mail engine. 75c, Ireland, 4-4-0. 90c, Canada, 4-6-0. $1.50, India, 4-4-0 express. $2, Australia, 4-6-2. $3, Great Britain, Stirling 0-4-2.

No. 2087, each $2: a, Belgium, type 4-4-0. b, Sweden, class "Cc" type 4-4-0. c, Chile, 0-6-0. d, Bolivia, Fairlie-type double engine.

No. 2088, each $2: a, Belgium, 4-cylinder 4-6-0. b, England, 4-cylinder 4-6-0. c, Northern Ireland, 2-cylinder compound 4-4-0. d, Holland, 4-4-0.

No. 2089, each $2: a, Switzerland, 0-8-0. b, Ireland, 0-6-0. c, US 4-6-0. d, Great Britain, Prince of Wales class 4-2-2.

No. 2090, each $2: a, Ireland, narrow gauge 2-4-2. b, Russia, 0-8-0. c, England, Ivatt large-boilered Atlantic. d, Germany, Atlantic type express.

No. 2091, each $2: a, France, 4-6-0. b, New Zealand, 2-6-4. c, Burma, 4-4-4. d, Malaya, 4-6-0.

Each $6: No. 2092, France, 4-4-0. No. 2093, Italy, 0-6-4.

**1999, Apr. 12**   **Litho.**   *Perf. 14*
2081-2086 G159 Set of 6    6.25 6.25
**Sheets of 4, #a-d**
2087-2091 G159 Set of 5    30.00 30.00
**Souvenir Sheets**
2092-2093 G159 Set of 2    9.00 9.00

**Flora and Fauna Type of 1999**

Designs: 75c, Porkfish. 90c, Leatherback turtle. $1.50, Ruby-throated hummingbird. $2, Theope eudocia.

No. 2098, vert, each $1: a, White-tailed tropicbird. b, Laughing gull. c, Palm tree. d, Humpback whale. e, Painted bunting. f, Common grackle. g, Green anole. h, Morpho peleides. i, Prepoua meandor.

No. 2099, vert, each $1: a, Common dolphin. b, Catonephele numiti. c, Sooty tern. d, Vermilion flycatcher. e, Blue grosbeak. f, Great egret. g, Actinote pellenea. h, Anteos clorinade. i, Common iguana.

Each $6: No. 2100, Bannaquit. No. 2101, Beay gregory.

**1999, Apr. 26**
2094-2097 A430 Set of 4    3.75 3.75
**Sheets of 9, #a-i**
2098-2099 A430 Set of 2   13.50 13.50
**Souvenir Sheets**
2100-2101 A430 Set of 2    9.00 9.00

**Hokusai Type of 1999**

Entire paintings or details, horiz. — #2102, each $1.50: a, A Breeze on a Fine Day. b, Ejiri. c, Horse drawings (kicking up hind legs). d, Horse drawings (with head down). e, View Along the Bank of the Sumida River. f, Thunderstorm Below the Mountain.

No. 2103, each $1.50: a, Fuchû. b, Doll Fair at Fikkendana. c, Sumo Wrestlers (with arms locked). d, Sumo Wrestlers (one head butting). e, Sōjō Henjō. f, Twin Gardens Gateway of the Asakusa Kannon Temple.

Each $6: No. 2104 Kôbô Daishi Exorcising Demon that Causes Sickness. No. 2105, Stretching Cloth.

**1999, May 24**   **Litho.**   *Perf. 14x13½*
**Sheets of 6, #a-f**
2102-2103 A431 Set of 2   13.50 13.50
**Souvenir Sheet**
2104-2105 A431 Set of 2    9.00 9.00

John H. Glenn's Return to Space G160

Portraits — #2106: a, Thumbs up, 1998 flight. b, Receiving NASA Service Award from Pres. Kennedy, 1962. c, Talking to Ground Control from Discovery, 1998. d, Climbing out of Friendship 7, 1962. e, Being checked for balance, 1998. f, Climbing into Friendship 7, 1962.

No. 2107, vert.: a, Portrait as Ohio Senator, 1974. b, Official portrait, 1962. c, Suit-up test, 1998. d, Suiting up for Discovery, 1998. e,

Meeting press after Discovery flight, 1998. f, Smiling aboard Discovery, 1998. g, Medical research, 1998. h, Official portrait, 1998.

**1999, May 24**      *Perf. 14x14½*
**Sheets of 6 and 8**
2106 G160 $1 #a.-f.      4.50 4.50
2107 G160 $1 #a.-h.      6.00 6.00

**Hokusai Type of 1999**

No. 2108: a, Peasants dancing under the linden tree. b, Faust dreams of soaring above the mortal.

No. 2109, Portrait of Goethe.

**1999, May 24**      *Perf. 14*
2108 A432 $3 Sheet of 3, #a.-b.,
     Grenada #2858b     6.75 6.75
**Souvenir Sheet**
2109 A432 $6 multi      4.50 4.50

**IBRA '99 World Stamp Expo Type of 1999**

IBRA '99 emblem, Luckenbach sailing ship and: No. 2110, 35c, Thurn and Taxis #1. No. 2113, $3, North German Confederation #1.

Emblem, Leipzig-Dresden Railway and: No. 2111, 45c, Schleswig-Holstein #1. No. 2112, $1.50, Oldenburg #4.

$6, Cover showing pair of Thurn & Taxis #1. Illustration reduced.

**1999, May 24**   **Litho.**   *Perf. 14*
2110-2113 A433 Set of 4    4.00 4.00
**Souvenir Sheet**
2114 A433 $6 multicolored    4.50 4.50

**Philexfrance '99 Type**
**Souvenir Sheets**

Designs, each $6: No. 2115, Co-co 7000 class high speed electric locomotive. No. 2116, Cha Pelon 4-8-0. Illustration reduced.

**1999, May 24**   **Litho.**   *Perf. 14*
2115-2116 A435 Set of 2    7.00 7.00

Beginning with Nos. 2117-2118, stamps from Grenada Grenadines will be inscribed GRENADA / Carriacou & Petite Martinique.

**Wedding of Prince Edward and Sophie Rhys-Jones Type**

No. 2117: a, Edward. b, Sophie. Edward. c, Sophie.
$6, Couple.

**1999, June 18**   **Litho.**   *Perf. 13½*
2117 A436 $3 Sheet of 3, #a.-c.   6.75 6.75
**Souvenir Sheet**
2118 A436 $6 multicolored    4.50 4.50

**UN Rights of the Child Type of 1999**

No. 2119: a, Boy. b, Liv Ullman, UNICEF's first woman ambassador. c, Woman.
$6, Maurice Pate, founding director of UNICEF.

**1999, May 24**   **Litho.**   *Perf. 14*
2119 A437 $3 Sheet of 3, #a.-c.   6.75 6.75
**Souvenir Sheet**
2120 A437 $6 multicolored    4.50 4.50

**Queen Mother Type of 1999**
**Gold frames**

No. 2121: a, Lady Elizabeth Bowles-Lyon. b, Queen Elizabeth in Rhodesia, 1957. c, Queen Elizabeth, Princess Elizabeth, and Princess Anne, 1950. d, Queen Mother, 1988.

$6, Queen Mother, Berlin.

**1999, Aug. 16**
**Sheet of 4**
2121 A440 $2 #a.-d. + label    6.00 6.00
**Souvenir Sheet**
2122 A440 $6 multicolored    4.50 4.50

No. 2122 contains one 38x50mm stamp. Margins of sheets are embossed. See Nos. 2369-2370.

**Litho. & Embossed**
*Die Cut Perf. 8¾*
**Without Gum**
2122A A440a $20 gold & multi

**Famous People Type of 1999**

Actors — #2123: a, George Raft (1895-1980). b, Raft in movie scene. c, Fatty Arbuckle (1887-1933) in movie scene. d, Portrait of Arbuckle. e, Buster Keaton (1895-

1966). f, Keaton in movie scene. g, Harold Lloyd (1893-1971) in movie scene. h, Portrait of Lloyd.

No. 2124: a, James Cagney (1899-1986). b, Cagney in movie scene. c, Edward G. Robinson (1893-1973). d, Robinson in movie scene. $6, Charlie Chaplin (1889-1977).

**1999, Aug. 20**   **Litho.**   *Perf. 14*
2123 A426 $1 Sheet of 8, #a.-h.   6.00 6.00
2124 A426 $2 Sheet of 4, #a.-d.   6.00 6.00
**Souvenir Sheet**
2125 A426 $6 multicolored    4.50 4.50

Space Exploration — G161

No. 2126, each $1.50: a, Sputnik I. b, Explorer I. c, Telstar I. d, Marisat I. e, Long Duration Exposure Facility. f, Hubble Space Telescope.

No. 2127, vert, each $1.50: a, X-15. b, Mercury Redstone 3 rocket, Freedom 7. c, Mercury Atlas 6 rocket, Friendship 7. d, Gemini 4, Edward H. White II. e, Saturn V rocket, Edwin Aldrin. f, Lunar rover.

Each $6: No. 2128, Space Shuttle Columbia. No. 2129, Mars Pathfinder.

**1999, Oct. 8**   **Litho.**   *Perf. 14*
**Sheets of 6, #a.-f.**
2126-2127 G161 Set of 2   13.50 13.50
**Souvenir Sheets**
2128-2129 G161 Set of 2    9.00 9.00

**Christmas Type of 1999**

Christmas plants: 15c, Poinsettia. 35c, Holly. 75c, Fir tree. $3, Geranium. $6, The Adoration of the Magi.

**1999, Nov. 23**   **Litho.**   *Perf. 13¾*
2130-2134 A444 Set of 5    4.25 4.25
**Souvenir Sheet**
2135 A444 $6 multicolored    4.50 4.50

Kirk Douglas (b. 1916), Actor G162

Douglas in various poses.

**1999**   **Litho.**   *Perf. 13¾*
2136 G162 $1.50 Sheet of 6, #a.-f.   6.75 6.75
**Souvenir Sheet**
2137 G162 $6 multi    4.50 4.50

Elvis Presley G163

Presley in various poses.

**1999**
**Sheet of 6**
2138 G163 $1.50 #a.-f.    6.75 6.75

**Millennium Type of 2000**

Highlights of 1970s — No. 2139: a, Salvador Allende elected Pres. of Chile. b, Earth Day. c, CAT scan introduced. d, Pres. Nixon goes to China. e, Massacre at Olympics. f, Gas shortages. g, Sydney Opera House opens. h, Pres. Nixon resigns. i, New theory of black holes. j, US bicentennial. k, 1st "Test tube" baby. l, Pope John Paul II visits Poland. m, Iran's Islamic Revolution. n, Concorde makes 1st flight. o, Charles de Gaulle dies. p, Camp David agreements (60x40mm). q, Mother Teresa wins Nobel Peace Prize.

Highlights of 1300-1350 — No. 2140: a, Robert the Bruce crowned King of Scotland. b, Giotto paints frescoes. c, Mansa Musa rules Mali. d, Dante completes "The Divine Comedy." e, Noh theater developed in Japan. f, Tenochtitlan founded by Aztecs. g, Ibn Battutah journeys to Africa and Asia. h, Munich fire. i, Ivan I of Russia increases Moscow's importance. j, Hundred Years' War begins. k, First use of cannons in Europe. l, Black Death devastates Europe. m, Boccaccio begins writing "Decameron." n, Eyeglasses developed in Italy. o, Plate armor replaces chain mail. p, Grand Canal of China completed. (60x40mm). q, Migration of Maoris to New Zealand.

Sea Exploration — No. 2141: a, Ferdinand Magellan. b, Restless seas. c, Queen Elizabeth I. d, Albatrosses. e, Penguins. f, Tahiti. g, Breadfruit. h, Easter Island. i, Maori carving. j, Lobster. k, Orchid. l, Walrus. m, Kangaroo. n, The Beagle. o, Frigatebird. p, Strait of Magellan (60x40mm). q, Capt. James Cook.

| 2000 | Litho. | Perf. 12¾x12½ |
|------|--------|----------------|

**Sheets of 17**

| 2139 | A450 | 20c #a.-q., + label | 2.50 | 2.50 |
| 2140 | A450 | 50c #a.-q. + label | 6.25 | 6.25 |
| 2141 | A450 | 50c #a.-q. + label | 6.25 | 6.25 |

Issued: #2139, 3/28; #2140-2141, 2/1.

**Souvenir Sheet**

New Year 2000 (Year of the Dragon) — G164

| 2000, Feb. 5 | | Perf. 13¾ |
|------|------|------|
| 2142 | G164 | $4 multi | 3.00 | 3.00 |

G165

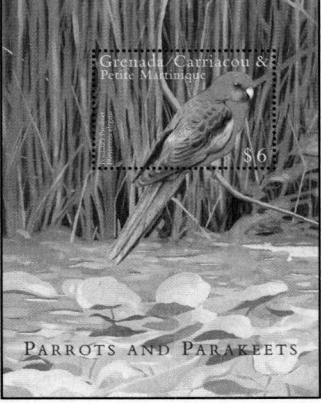

Birds — G166

Designs: 75c, Barn swallow. 90c, Caribbean coot. $2, Common moorhen. $3, Orange-winged parrot.

No. 2147, each $1: a, Red-collared lorikeet. b, Citron-crested cockatoo. c, Stella's lorikeet. d, Leadbeator's cockatoo. e, Golden conure. f, Red-spotted parakeet. g, Nobel macaw. h, Goffins cockatoo. i, Sun conure.

No. 2148, each $1: a, Turquoise parakeet. b, Scarlet-chested parakeet. c, Red-capped parakeet. d, Eastern rosella. e, Budgerigar. f, Orange-flanked parakeet. g, Mallee ringneck. h, Red-rumped parakeet. i, Yellow-fronted parakeet.

No. 2149, each $1.50: a, Puerto Rican emerald. b, Green mango. c, Red-legged

thrush. d, Red-crowned parrot. e, Hispaniolan parrot. f, Yellow-crowned parrot.

No. 2150, each $1.50: a, Yellow-shouldered blackbird. b, Troupial. c, Green-throated Carib. d, Black-hooded parakeet. e, Scarlet tanager. f, Yellow-crowned bishop.

Each $6: No. 2151, Puerto Rican lizard-cuckoo. No. 2152, Pin-tailed whydah, vert. No. 2153, Pennant's parakeet. No. 2154, Scarlet macaw, vert.

Illustration G166 reduced.

| 2000, Mar. 1 | Litho. | Perf. 14 |
|------|------|------|
| 2143-2146 | G165 | Set of 4 | 5.00 | 5.00 |

**Sheets of 9, #a.-i.**

| 2147-2148 | G166 | Set of 2 | 13.50 | 13.50 |

**Sheets of 6, #a.-f.**

| 2149-2150 | G165 | Set of 2 | 13.50 | 13.50 |

**Souvenir Sheets**

*Perf. 13¾*

| 2151-2152 | G165 | Set of 2 | 9.00 | 9.00 |

*Perf. 14*

| 2153-2154 | G166 | Set of 2 | 9.00 | 9.00 |

No. 2151 contains one 48x32mm stamp; No. 2152 contains one 32x48mm stamp.

Tropical Fish G167

35c, Slender mbuna. 45c, Pygoplite diacanthus. #2157, 75c, Siamese fighting fish. #2158, 75c, Pomacanthus semicirclatus. 90c, Zanclus canescens. #2160, $1, Dwarf pencilfish. #2161, $1, Xiphophorus maculatus. #2162, $2, Wimplefish. #2163, $2, Gramma loreto. #2164, $3, Zebrasoma xanthurum.

#2165, each $1: a, Emperor angelfish. b, Strawberryfish. c, Jackknife fish. d, Flame angelfish. e, Clarke's anemonefish. f, Flashback dottyback. g, Coral trout. h, Foxface.

#2166, each $1: a, Bumbelbee goby. b, Black-headed blenny. c, Boarfish. d, Achilles tang. e, Swordtail. f, Moorish idol. g, Banded pipefish. h, Striped sea catfish.

#2167, each $1.65: a, Bodianus rufus. b, Coris aygula. c, Centropyge bicolor. d, Balistoides conspicillum. e, Poecilia reticulata. f, Heniochus acuminatus.

#2168, each $1.65: a, Plectorhynchus chaetodonoids. b, Bodianus puchellus. c, Acanthurus leucosternon. d, Chromileptis altivelis. e, Pterophyllum scalare f, Premnas biaculeatus.

Each $6: #2169, Equetus punctatus. #2170, Harlequin tuskfish. #2171, Purplequeen. #2172, Pomacanthus imperator, vert.

| 2000, Mar. 28 | | Perf. 14 |
|------|------|------|
| 2155-2164 | G167 | Set of 10 | 9.00 | 9.00 |

**Sheets of 8, #a.-h.**

| 2165-2166 | G167 | Set of 2 | 12.00 | 12.00 |

**Sheets of 6, #a.-f.**

| 2167-2168 | G167 | Set of 2 | 15.00 | 15.00 |

**Souvenir Sheets**

| 2169-2172 | G167 | Set of 4 | 18.00 | 18.00 |

**Van Dyck Painting Type of 2000**

No. 2173, each $1.50: a, Cardinal Bentivoglio. b, Cardinal Infante Ferdinand. c, Cesare Alessandro Scaglia. d, A Roman Clergyman. e, Jean-Charles della Faille. f, Cardinal Domenico Rivarola.

No. 2174, each $1.50: a, Portrait of an Elderly Woman. b, Head of a Young Woman. c, Portrait of a Man. d, Jan van den Wouwer. e, Portrait of a Young Man. f, Portrait of Everhard Jabach.

No. 2175, each $1.50: a, A Man in Armor. b, Portrait of a Young General. c, Emanuele Filiberto, Prince of Savoy. d, Donna Polixena Spinola Guzman de Leganes. e, Luigia Cattaneo Gentile. f, Portrait of Giovanni Battista Cattaneo.

No. 2176, each $1.50: a, Marchesa Paolina Adorno Brignole-Sale, 1623-25. b, Marchesa Geronima Spinola. c, Marchesa Paolina Adorno Broignole-Sale, 1627. d, Marcello Durazzo. e, Marchesa Grimaldi Cattaneo with a Black Page. f, Young Man of the House of Spinola.

No. 2176G: h, A Man in Armor. i, Portrait of a Young General. j, Emanuele Filiberto, Prince of Savoy. k, Donna Polixena Spinola Guzman de Leganes. l, Luigia Cattaneo Gentile. m, Giovanni Battista Cattaneo.

Each $5: No. 2177, Portrait of Jacques le Roy. No. 2178, Hendrik van der Bergh.

Each $6: No. 2179, Frederik Hendrik, Prince of Orange. No. 2180, Justus van Meerstraeten. No. 2181, The Abbot Scaglia Adoring the Virgin and Child, horiz. No. 2182, Maria Louisa de Tassis, horiz.

| 2000, May 1 | | Perf. 13¾ |
|------|------|------|

**Sheets of 6, #a.-f.**

| 2173-2176 | A449 | Set of 4 | 27.00 | 27.00 |
| 2176G | A449 | $1.50 Sheet of 6, #a-f | 6.75 | 6.75 |

**Souvenir Sheets**

| 2177-2178 | A449 | Set of 2 | 7.50 | 7.50 |
| 2179-2182 | A449 | Set of 4 | 18.00 | 18.00 |

**Prince William Type of 2000**

No. 2183: a, Wearing scarf. b, Wearing suit with vest. c, Wearing casual shirt. d, Wearing gray suit.

$6, Wearing sweater.

| 2000, May 15 | Litho. | Perf. 14 |
|------|------|------|
| 2183 | A453 | $1.50 Sheet of 4, #a-d | 4.50 | 4.50 |

**Souvenir Sheet**

*Perf. 13¾*

| 2184 | A453 | $6 multi | 4.50 | 4.50 |

No. 2183 contains four 28x42mm stamps.

**Zeppelin Type of 2000**

No. 2185 — Ferdinand von Zeppelin and: a, LZ-3. b, LZ-56. c, LZ-88.

$6, LZ-1.

| 2000, May 15 | | Perf. 14 |
|------|------|------|
| 2185 | A454 | $3 Sheet of 3, #a-c | 6.75 | 6.75 |

**Souvenir Sheet**

| 2186 | A454 | $6 multi | 4.50 | 4.50 |

No. 2185 contains three 42x28mm stamps.

**Berlin Film Festival Type of 2000**

No. 2187: a, James Stewart. b, Sachiko Hidari. c, Juliette Mayniel. d, Le Bonheur. e, La Notte. f, Lee Marvin.

$6, The Thin Red Line.

| 2000, May 15 | | |
|------|------|------|
| 2187 | A455 | $1.50 Sheet of 6, #a-f | 6.75 | 6.75 |

**Souvenir Sheet**

| 2188 | A455 | $6 multi | 4.50 | 4.50 |

**Souvenir Sheets**

**Olympics Type of 2000**

No. 2189: a, Frantz Reichel. b, Discus throw. c, Seoul Sports Complex and Korean flag. d, Ancient Greek wrestlers.

| 2000, May 15 | | |
|------|------|------|
| 2189 | A457 | $2 Sheet of 4, #a-d | 6.00 | 6.00 |

**Public Railways Type of 2000**

No. 2190: a, Locomotion No. 1 and George Stephenson. b, Rocket.

| 2000, May 15 | | |
|------|------|------|
| 2190 | A458 | $3 Sheet of 2, #a-b | 4.50 | 4.50 |

**Bach Type of 2000**

| 2000, May 15 | | |
|------|------|------|
| 2191 | A459 | $6 Statue of Bach | 4.50 | 4.50 |

G168

Butterflies and Moths — G169

No. 2192, each $1.50: a, Clara satin moth. b, Spanish festoon. c, Giant silkmoth. d, Oak eggar. e, Common wall. f, Large oak blue.

No. 2193, each $1.50: a, Jersey tiger. b, Boisduval's autumnal moth. c, Orange swallow-tailed moth. d, Regent skipper. e, Hoop pine moth. f, Coppery oysphania.

No. 2194, each $1.50: a, Grecian shoemaker. b, 88. c, Cramer's mesene. d, Salt marsh moth. e, Ruddy dagger wing. f, Blue night.

No. 2195, each $1.50: a, Heliconius charitonius. b, Tiger pierid. c, Hewiton's blue hairstreak. d, Esmeralda. e, California dogface. f, Orange theope.

No. 2196, each $2: a, Hummingbird gleariwing. b, Gold-drop helicopis. c, Great tiger moth. d, Staudinger's longtail.

No. 2197, each $2: a, Common map. b, Papilio machaon. c, Purple emperor. d, Red-lined geometrid.

Each $6: No. 2198, Peacock royal. No. 2199, Queen Alexandra's birdwing. No. 2200, Giant leopard moth. No. 2201, Robin moth, vert.

Illustrations reduced.

| 2000, May 29 | | Perf. 14 |
|------|------|------|

**Sheets of 6, #a-f**

| 2192-2193 | G168 | Set of 2 | 13.50 | 13.50 |
| 2194-2195 | G169 | Set of 2 | 13.50 | 13.50 |

**Sheets of 4, #a-d**

| 2196-2197 | G168 | Set of 2 | 12.00 | 12.00 |

**Souvenir Sheets**

| 2198-2199 | G168 | Set of 2 | 9.00 | 9.00 |
| 2200-2201 | G169 | Set of 2 | 9.00 | 9.00 |

**Apollo-Soyuz Type**

No. 2202, vert.: a, Thomas P. Stafford. b, Mission badge. c, Donald K. Slayton.

$6, Alexei Leonov, vert.

| 2000, May 15 | Litho. | Perf. 14 |
|------|------|------|
| 2202 | A456 | $3 Sheet of 3, #a-c | 6.75 | 6.75 |

**Souvenir Sheet**

| 2203 | A456 | $6 Alexei Leonov | 4.50 | 4.50 |

**Einstein Type**

**Souvenir Sheet**

| 2000, May 15 | | Perf. 14¼ |
|------|------|------|
| 2204 | A460 | $6 multi | 4.50 | 4.50 |

**Space Type**

Nos. 2205, each $1.50: a, Foton (green and orange background). b, Sub-satellite and comet tail. c, NEAR Eros (green background). d, Explorer 16 and sun. e, Astro Challenger (green and orange background). f, Giotto (green background).

No. 2206, each $1.50: a, Foton and asteroid. b, Sub-satellite and asteroid. c, NEAR Eros and asteroid. d, Explorer 16 and planet surface. e, Space Shuttle. f, Giotto (blue background).

Each $6: No. 2207, Lunar Prospector. No. 2208, Pegasus Saturn.

| 2000, May 15 | | Perf. 14 |
|------|------|------|

**Sheets of 6, #a-f**

| 2205-2206 | A461 | Set of 2 | 13.50 | 13.50 |

**Souvenir Sheets**

| 2207-2208 | A461 | Set of 2 | 9.00 | 9.00 |

Nos. 2205-2206 depict different satellites, but have the same inscriptions. World Stamp Expo 2000, Anaheim.

Trains G170

Designs: 90c, Golsdorf 2-6-2, Vienna Metropolitan Railways. $1, Forrester 2-2-0, Dublin & Kingstown Railway. $2, Metro-Cammell Co-

Co, Nigerian Railways. $3, TGV 001, French Natl. Railways.

No. 2213, each $1.50: a, Braithwait 0-4-0, Eastern Counties Railway. b, The Philadelphia, Austria. c, Stephenson 2-2-2, Russia. d, L'aigle, Western Railway of France. e, Borsig Standard 2-2-2, Germany. f, The Ajax, Great Western Railway.

No. 2214, each $1.50: a, Co-Co locomotive, Norwegian State Railways. b, Diesel-electric locomotive, Jamaica Railway. c, Diesel-electric locomotive, Railway of the People's Republic of China. d, Electric locomotive, Portuguese Railways. e, Re 6/6, Swiss Federal Railways. f, Dual-purpose Electric locomotive, Turkish State Railways.

No. 2215, each $1.50: a, 4-4-0 engine, Perak Government Railway. b, 2-4-2 tank engine, Rhondda & Swansea Railway. c, 2-4-2 tank engine, Lancashire & Yorkshire Railway. d, 2-8-2 tank engine, Northwestern Railway of India. e, 4-2-2 Imperial Yellow Mail engine, Shanghai-Nanking Railway. f, 2-4-2 tank engine, Danish State Railway.

No. 2216, each $1.50: a, Electric railcar, South Jersey Transit. b, Metroliner, US. c, HSST Mag-lev train. d, E60C, Amtrak. e, TEE Express "Parsifal." f, 2-Co-Co-2 electric, Amtrak.

No. 2217, $6, The Experiment, US. No. 2218, 2-8-2 locomotive, Central South African Railway. No. 2219, $6, The Prospector, Western Australian Government Railways. No. 2220, Diesel-electric locomotive, South African Railways.

**2000, June 13**
| | | | | |
|---|---|---|---|---|
| 2209-2212 | G170 | Set of 4 | 5.25 | 5.25 |

**Sheets of 6, #a-f**
| | | | | |
|---|---|---|---|---|
| 2213-2216 | G170 | Set of 4 | 26.00 | 26.00 |

**Souvenir Sheets**
| | | | | |
|---|---|---|---|---|
| 2217-2220 | G170 | Set of 4 | 18.00 | 18.00 |

**European Soccer Championships Type**

No. 2221, horiz., each $1.50 — Denmark: a, Tofting. b, Team photo. c, Michael Laudrup. d, Jorgensen. e, Philips Stadium, Eindhoven. f, Moller.

No. 2222, horiz., each $1.50 — France: a, Thuram. b, Team photo. c, Barthez. d, Zidane. e, Jan Breydel Stadium, Brugge. f, Michel Platini.

No. 2223, horiz., each $1.50 — Netherlands: a, Giovanni Van Bronckhorst. b, Team photo. c, Patrick Kluivert. d, Johan Cruyff. e, Amsterdam Arena Stadium. f, Zenden.

Each $6: No. 2224, Denmark coach Bo Johansson. No. 2225, France coach Roger Lemerre. No. 2226, Netherlands coach Frank Rijkaard.

**2000, Aug. 8                    Perf. 13¾**
**Sheets of 6, #a-f**
| | | | | |
|---|---|---|---|---|
| 2221-2223 | A464 | Set of 3 | 20.00 | 20.00 |

**Souvenir Sheets**
| | | | | |
|---|---|---|---|---|
| 2224-2226 | A464 | Set of 3 | 13.50 | 13.50 |

**Popes Type**

No. 2227, each $1.50: a, Adrian VI, 1522-23. b, Paul II, 1464-71. c, Calixtus III, 1455-58. d, Eugenius IV, 1431-47.

**2000, Aug. 22**
| | | | | |
|---|---|---|---|---|
| 2227 | A467 | Sheet of 4, #a-d | 4.50 | 4.50 |

**Souvenir Sheet**
| | | | | |
|---|---|---|---|---|
| 2228 | A467 | $6 Gregory IX, 1370-78 | 4.50 | 4.50 |

**Monarchs Type**

No. 2229, each $1.50: a, Louis XVI of France, 1774-92. b, Louis XVIII of France, 1814-24. c, Queen of Kublai Khan, China. d, Mary Tudor of England, 1553-58. e, Mohammed Ali of Iran, 1907-09. f, Ch'ien-lung (Qian-long, Hung-li) of China, 1735-96.

$6, Vladimir I, Grand Prince of Kiev, 980-1015.

**2000, Aug. 22**
| | | | | |
|---|---|---|---|---|
| 2229 | A468 | Sheet of 6, #a-f | 6.75 | 6.75 |

**Souvenir Sheet**
| | | | | |
|---|---|---|---|---|
| 2230 | A468 | $6 Vladimir I | 4.50 | 4.50 |

Fauna
G171

Designs: 75c, St. Lucia Amazon. 90c, Three-toed sloth. $1, Hispaniolan solenodon. $2,Thick-billed parrot.

No. 2235, each $1.50: a, Jaguarundi. b, Andean condor. c, Darwin's rhea. d, Central American tapir. e, Jaguar. f, Jamaican hutia.

No. 2236, each $1.50: a, Red vakari. b, San Andreas vireo. c, Golden lion tamarin. d, American crocodile. e, Spectacled caiman. f, Rhinoceros iguana.

Each $6: No. 2237, Pronghorn. No. 2238, Kemp Ridley sea turtle.

**2000, Sept. 5                    Perf. 14**
| | | | | |
|---|---|---|---|---|
| 2231-2234 | G171 | Set of 4 | 3.50 | 3.50 |

**Sheets of 6, #a-f**
| | | | | |
|---|---|---|---|---|
| 2235-2236 | G171 | Set of 2 | 13.50 | 13.50 |

**Souvenir Sheets**
| | | | | |
|---|---|---|---|---|
| 2237-2238 | G171 | Set of 2 | 9.00 | 9.00 |

The Stamp Show 2000, London (Nos. 2235-2238).

Souvenir Sheet

David Copperfield, Magician — G172

No. 2239, each $1.50: a, Copperfield's face at L, legs at R. b, Upper torso at L, face at R. c, Legs at L, face at R. d, Face at L, upper torso at R.
Illustration reduced.

**2000, Sept. 14**
| | | | | |
|---|---|---|---|---|
| 2239 | G172 | Sheet of 4, #a-d | 4.50 | 4.50 |

**Prado Paintings Type**

#2240, each $1.50: a, St. John the Baptist and the Franciscan Maestro Henricus Werl, by Robert Campin. b, Justice and Peace, by Corrado Giaquinto. c, St. Barbara, by Campin. d, John Fane, 10th Count of Westmoreland, by Thomas Lawrence. e, The Marchioness of Manzanedo, by Jean-Louis-Ernest Meissonier. f, Mr. Storer, by Martin Archer Shee.

#2241, each $1.50: a, Isabella Carla Eugenia, by Alonso Sánchez Coello. b, Portrait of a Nobleman with His Hand on His Chest, by El Greco. c, Philip III, by Juan Pantoja de la Cruz. d, Madonna & child from The Holy Family with Saints Ildefons & John the Evangelist, & the Master Alonso de Villegas, by Blas del Prado. e, The Last Supper, by Bartolomé Carducci. f, Man with goblet from The Holy Family with Saints Ildefons & John the Evangelist, & the Master Alonso de Villegas.

#2242, each $1.50: a, Dominic of Silos, by Bartolomé Bermejo. b, Head of a Prophet, by Jaime Huguet. c, Christ Giving His Blessing, by Fernando Gallego. d, The Mystic Marriage of St. Catherine, by Alonso Sánchez Coello. e, St. Catherine of Alexandria, by Fernando Yáñez de la Almedina. f, Virgin and Child, by Luis de Morales.

Each $6: #2243, The Holy Family with Saints Ildefons & John the Evangelist, & the Master Alonso de Villegas. #2244, The Last Supper, horiz. #2245, The Coronation of the Virgin, by El Greco, horiz.

**2000, Oct. 19    Perf. 12x12¼, 12¼x12**
**Sheets of 6, #a-f**
| | | | | |
|---|---|---|---|---|
| 2240-2242 | A470 | Set of 3 | 20.00 | 20.00 |

**Souvenir Sheets**
| | | | | |
|---|---|---|---|---|
| 2243-2245 | A470 | Set of 3 | 13.50 | 13.50 |

Espana 2000, Intl. Philatelic Exhibition.

**Mushroom Type of 2000**

No. 2246, $2: a, Cinnabar chanterelle. b, Blackening wax cap. c, Edible cort. d, Orange scaber-stalk bolete.

No. 2247, $2: a, Crab russula. b, Steel blue entoloma. c, Tiger lentinus. d, Yellow-white mycena.

No. 2248, $2, horiz.: a, Le Gal's bolete. b, Emetic russula. c, Silvery violet cort. d, Tree volvariella.

No. 2249, $6, Scaly vase chanterelle, horiz. No. 2250, $6, Common collybia, horiz.

**2000, Mar. 3        Litho.        Perf. 14**
**Sheets of 4, #a-d**
| | | | | |
|---|---|---|---|---|
| 2246-2248 | A448 | Set of 3 | 18.00 | 18.00 |

**Souvenir Sheets**
| | | | | |
|---|---|---|---|---|
| 2249-2250 | A448 | Set of 2 | 9.00 | 9.00 |

**Dog Type of 2000**

Designs: 45c, Irish setter. 90c, Dalmatian. $2, German shepherd.

No. 2254, $1.50: a, Alaskan malamute. b, Golden retriever. c, Afghan hound. d, Long-haired dachshund. e, Irish terrier. f, Miniature poodle.

No. 2255, $1.50: a, Great Dane. b, Newfoundland. c, Rottweiler. d, Bulldog. e, Japanese spitz. f, Bull terrier.

No. 2256, $6, Labrador retriever. No. 2257, $6, Basset hound, horiz.

**2000, June 23**
| | | | | |
|---|---|---|---|---|
| 2251-2253 | A473 | Set of 3 | 2.50 | 2.50 |

**Sheets of 6, #a-f**
| | | | | |
|---|---|---|---|---|
| 2254-2255 | A473 | Set of 2 | 13.50 | 13.50 |

**Souvenir Sheets**
| | | | | |
|---|---|---|---|---|
| 2256-2257 | A473 | Set of 2 | 9.00 | 9.00 |

**Cat Type of 2000**

Designs: 75c, Blue point snowshoe. $3, Black and white Maine coon cat. $4, Brown tabby British shorthair.

No. 2261, $1.50: a, California spangled cat. b, Russian blue. c, Seal point Siamese. d, Black Devon rex. e, Silver tabby British shorthair. f, Tricolor Japanese bobtail.

No. 2262, $1.50: a, British white shorthair. b, Blue cream American shorthair. c, Bombay. d, Red Burmese. e, Sorrel Abyssinian. f, Ocicat.

$5, Silver classic tabby Persian, horiz. No. 2263A, $5, Red-white bicolored British shorthair.

**2000, June 23**
| | | | | |
|---|---|---|---|---|
| 2258-2260 | A478 | Set of 3 | 5.75 | 5.75 |

**Sheets of 6, #a-f**
| | | | | |
|---|---|---|---|---|
| 2261-2262 | A478 | Set of 2 | 13.50 | 13.50 |

**Souvenir Sheet**
| | | | | |
|---|---|---|---|---|
| 2263 | A478 | $5 multi | 3.75 | 3.75 |
| 2263A | A478 | $5 multi | 3.75 | 3.75 |

**Battle of Britain Type of 2000**

No. 2264, each $1: a, Women fire fighters, London. b, Family leaving after the Blitz. c, Searchlights, London. d, Winston Churchill in Coventry after German raid. e, Rescue after German bombing. f, Rescue after London bombing. g, Terror hits Buckingham Gate. h, After a German raid on Coventry.

No. 2265, each $1: a, Pilots scramble to their planes. b, Balloons to catch low-flying planes. c, Spitfire B. d, Speech by Princess Elizabeth. e, Fire Watchers, auxiliary fire service. f, Painting stripes to see at night. g, Bombed buildings in Britain. h, Air raid wardens, auxiliary police force.

Each $6: No. 2266, Hawker Hurricane. No. 2267, British family survives German bombing, vert.

**2000, Oct. 30**
**Sheets of 8, #a-h**
| | | | | |
|---|---|---|---|---|
| 2264-2265 | A471 | Set of 2 | 12.00 | 12.00 |

**Souvenir Sheets**
| | | | | |
|---|---|---|---|---|
| 2266-2267 | A471 | Set of 2 | 9.00 | 9.00 |

**Queen Mother Type of 2000**
**2000, Oct. 30**
| | | | | |
|---|---|---|---|---|
| 2268 | A479 | $1.50 multi | 1.10 | 1.10 |

Printed in sheets of 6.

**Photomosaic Type of 1999**

No. 2269, $1: Various flowers making up a photomosaic of the Queen Mother.

No. 2270, $1: Various photographs with religious theme making up a photomosaic of Pope John Paul II.

**2000, Oct. 30                    Perf. 13¾**
| | | | | |
|---|---|---|---|---|
| 2269-2270 | A445 | Set of 2 | 12.00 | 12.00 |

Harry Houdini, Magician — G173

**2000        Litho.        Perf. 14**
| | | | | |
|---|---|---|---|---|
| 2271 | G173 | $1.50 multi | 1.10 | 1.10 |

Issued in sheets of 4.

Souvenir Sheet

Barbara Taylor Bradford, Author — G174

Illustration reduced.

**2000        Litho.        Perf. 12¼**
| | | | | |
|---|---|---|---|---|
| 2272 | G174 | $6 multi | 4.50 | 4.50 |

Souvenir Sheet

Hong Kong Comic Strip "The Storm Riders" — G175

No. 2273: a, Character with arms folded. b, Character with sword. c, Character in brown cape. d, Character in green.
Illustration reduced.

**2000                            Perf. 13½**
| | | | | |
|---|---|---|---|---|
| 2273 | G175 | $4 Sheet of 4, #a-d | 9.00 | 9.00 |

New Year 2001 (Year of the Snake) — G176

No. 2274: a, Rat snake. b, Mangrove snake. c, Boomslang. d, Emerald tree boa. e, African egg-eating snake. f, Chinese green tree viper.
Illustration reduced.

**2001, Jan. 2                    Perf. 14**
| | | | | |
|---|---|---|---|---|
| 2274 | G176 | 90c Sheet of 6, #a-f | 4.00 | 4.00 |

**Souvenir Sheet**
| | | | | |
|---|---|---|---|---|
| 2275 | G176 | $4 King cobra | 3.00 | 3.00 |

## Rijksmuseum Type of 2001

No. 2276, $1.50: a, Person with red shirt from Dune Landcape, by Jan van Goyen. b, The Raampoortje, by Wouter Johannes van Troostwijk. c, House and horse from The Cattle Ferry, by Esaias van de Velde. d, The Departure of a Senior Functionary from Middleburg, by Adriaen van de Venne. e, Steeple and ferry from The Cattle Ferry. f, Four people near rock from Dune Landscape.

No. 2277, $1.50: a, Building, statue and dog from Garden Party, by Dirck Hals. b, Still Life with Gilt Cup, by Willem Claesz Heda. c, Cloud of smoke from Orestes and Pylades Disputing at the Altar, by Pieter Lastman. d, Buildings from Orestes and Pylades Disputing at the Altar. e, Self-portrait in a Yellow Robe, by Jan Lievens. f, Birds in sky from Garden Party.

No. 2278, $1.50: a, Beatrix from Marriage Portrait of Isaac Massa and Beatrix van der Laen, by Frans Hals. b, Winter Landscape With Ice Skaters, by Hendrick Avercamp. c, Man and woman from The Spendthrift, by Cornelis Troost. d, Men in brown from The Spendthrift. e, Men and woman from The Art Gallery of Jan Gildermeester Jansz, by Adriaan de Lelie. f, Three men from The Art Gallery of Jan Gildermeester Jansz.

No. 2279, $1.50: a, Man from A Music Party, by Rembrandt. b, Woman from A Music Party. c, Girl and boy from Rutger Jan Schimmelpennick With His Wife and Children, by Pierre-Paul Prud'hon. d, Girl from Rutger Jan Schimmelpennick With His Wife and Children. e, Two men from The Syndics, by Thomas de Keyser. f, Isaac and Beatrix from Marriage Portrait of Isaac Massa and Beatrix van der Laen.

No. 2280, $6, A Music Party. No. 2281, $6, Anna Accused by Tobit of Stealing a Kid, by Rembrandt. No. 2282, $6, Cleopatra's Banquet, by Gerard Lairesse, horiz. No. 2283, $6, View of Tivoli, by Isaac de Moucheron.

**2001, Jan. 15          Perf. 13¾**
**Sheets of 6, #a-f**
2276-2279  A483  Set of 4       27.50 27.50
**Souvenir Sheets**
2280-2283  A483  Set of 4       18.00 18.00

### Pokémon Type of 2001

No. 2284, each $1.50: a, Bellsprout. b, Vulpix. c, Dewgong. d, Oddish. e, Dratini. f, Jigglypuff.

**2001, Feb. 1**
2284  A484  Sheet of 6, #a-f    6.75 6.75
**Souvenir Sheet**
2285  A484  $6 Pikachu          4.50 4.50

Animals
of the
Tropics
G177

Designs: 75c, Greater flamingo, vert. 90c, Cuban crocodile. $1, Jaguarundi, vert. $2, Wedge-capped capuchin monkey.

No. 2290, $1.50, vert.: a, Cuban pygmy owl. b, Woody spider monkey. c, Bee hummingbirds. d, Dragonfly, poison dart frog. e, Red brocket deer. f, Cuban stream anole.

No. 2291, $1.50, vert.: a, Red-breasted toucan. b, Mexican black howler monkey. c, Fleck's pygmy boa. d, Red-eyed tree frog. e, Caiman. f, Jaguar.

No. 2292, $6, Ocelot, vert. No. 2293, $6, Western knight anole, vert.

**2001, Feb. 1          Perf. 14**
2286-2289  A177  Set of 4       3.50   3.50
**Sheets of 6, #a-f**
2290-2291  G177  Set of 2       13.50 13.50
**Souvenir Sheets**
2292-2293  G177  Set of 2       9.00  9.00
Hong Kong 2001 Stamp Exhibition.

### Fish Type of 2000 with Added WWF Emblem

No. 2294: a, Sparisoma rubripinne. b, Scarus vetula. c, Scarus taeniopterus. d, Sparisoma viride.

**2001, Mar. 28  Litho.  Perf. 14**
2294  G167  75c Strip of 4, #a-d   5.25 5.25

---

Waterfowl — G178

No. 2295, horiz, each $1.50: a, Falklands streamer duck. b, Black-crowned night heron. c, Muscovy duck. d, Ruddy duck. e, Black-necked screamer. f, White-faced whistling duck.

**2001, Mar. 28**
2295  G178  Sheet of 6, #a-f    6.75 6.75
**Souvenir Sheet**
2296  G178  $6 Great egret      4.50 4.50

Scenes From "The Littlest Rebel,"
Starring Shirley Temple — G179

Temple with — No. 2297, horiz.: a, Pointing soldier. b, Black woman. c, Soldier in carriage. d, Pres. Lincoln.
No. 2298.: a, Spoon. b, Woman near tree. c, Soldier with hat. d, Woman. e, Black man and soldier. f, Man.
$6, Black man.

**2001, Apr. 25          Perf. 13¾**
2297  G179  $2 Sheet of 4, #a-d   6.00 6.00
2298  G179  $2 Sheet of 6, #a-f   9.00 9.00
**Souvenir Sheet**
2299  G179  $6 multi           4.50 4.50

Clark Gable (1901-60) — G180

No. 2300, $1.50 — Color of photo: a, Purple. b, Sepia (wearing suit and tie). c, Yellow. d, Sepia (wearing sweater). e, Blue. f, Sepia (wearing bow tie).
No. 2301, $1.50 — Signature of Gable and Gable with: a, Cigar. b, Vest. c, Chair. d, Pen. e, Suit and tie. f, Pinstriped suit.
No. 2302, $6, Blue background. No. 2303, $6, Gable in uniform.

---

**2001, Apr. 25          Perf. 14**
**Sheets of 6, #a-f**
2300-2301  G180  Set of 2       13.50 13.50
**Souvenir Sheets**
2302-2303  G180  Set of 2       9.00  9.00

### Betty Boop Type of 2000

No. 2304 — Boop: a, With crown. b, With veil. c, With lei. d, At carnival. e, With flower in hair. f, With cowboy hat. g, With beret. h, In automobile. i, As Statue of Liberty.
No. 2305, $6, In sari. No. 2306, $6, In gondola.

**2001, Apr. 25          Perf. 13¾**
2304  A481  $1 Sheet of 9, #a-i   6.75 6.75
**Souvenir Sheets**
2305-2306  A481  Set of 2        9.00 9.00

### Phila Nippon Type of 2001

Designs: 75c, Scenes of Daily Life in Edo, by Choshun Miyagawa. 90c, Twelve Famous Places in Japan, by Eisenin Naganobu Kano. $1, Scenery Along the Length of the Sumida River, by Kyuei Kano. $1.25, Cranes, by Eisenin Michinobu Kano. No. 2311, $2, A Courtesan of Yoshiwara, by Shunei Katsukawa. $3, Rite of Bear Killing: Praying to the Bear's Spirit, by unknown artist.

No. 2313, $2, vert. — Bodhisattva Samantabhadra from the Lotus Sutra: a, Surrounding rings, yellow elephant. b, White elephant. c, Temple at left. d, Surrounding rings with rays.

No. 2314, $2 (85x28mm) — Chapter illustrations from Genji Monogatari Emaki, by Ryusetsu Hidenobu Kano: a, Kiritsubo. b, Akashi. c, Hatsune. d, E-Awase.

No. 2315, $6, A Sage Pointing at the Moon, by Ranseki Katagiri. No. 2316, $6, Frontispiece for Devadatta, Lotus Sutra, vert.

**2001, May 1          Perf. 14**
2307-2312  A487  Set of 6       6.75  6.75
**Sheets of 4, #a-d**
2313-2314  A488  Set of 2       12.00 12.00
**Souvenir Sheets**
2315-2316  A488  Set of 2       9.00  9.00

### Marlene Dietrich Type of 2001

Dietrich with: a, Microphone. b, Robe. c, Flowered dress. d, Hat.

**2001, May 15          Perf. 13¾**
2317  A489  $2 Sheet of 4, #a-d   6.00 6.00

### Queen Victoria Type of 2001

No. 2318 — Queen Victoria with: a, Scepter. b, Flower. c, Sash.
$6, Sash, diff.

**2001, May 15          Perf. 14**
2318  A490  $3 Sheet of 3, #a-c   6.75 6.75
**Souvenir Sheet**
2319  A490  $6 multi           4.50 4.50

### Queen Elizabeth II Type of 2001

No. 2320, each $1.25 — Predominant background colors: a, Brown and yellow. b, Green. c, Blue. d, Black. e, Red and violet. f, Red and light blue.
No. 2320G, each $2: a, Green background. b, Purple background. c, Brown background.
$6, Tan.

**2001, May 15          Perf. 14**
2320   A491  Sheet of 6, #a-f    5.75 5.75
2320G  A491  Sheet of 3, #h-j    4.50 4.50
**Souvenir Sheet**
**Perf. 13¾**
2321  A491  $6 multi           3.75 3.75
No. 2321 contains one 38x51mm stamp.

### Ship Type of 2001

Designs: 90c, Creole. $1, Britannia. $2, Ariel. $3, Sindia.
No. 2326, $1.25: a, William Fawcett. b, Sirius. c, S.S. Great Britain. d, Oriental. e, Lightning. f, Great Eastern.
No. 2327, $1.25: a, Santa Maria and Christopher Columbus. b, Sao Gabriel and Vasco da Gama. c, Victoria and Ferdinand Magellan. d, Golden Hind and Sir Francis Drake. e, Endeavour and Capt. James Cook. f, HMS Erebus and John Franklin.
No. 2328, $1.25, vert.: a, Mayflower. b, Gabriel. c, Beagle. d, Challenger. e, Vega. f, Fram.
No. 2329, $6, Challenge. No. 2330, $6, Cutty Sark.

**2001, June 18          Perf. 14**
2322-2325  A497  Set of 4       5.25   5.25

---

**Sheets of 6, #a-f**
2326-2328  A497  Set of 3       17.00 17.00
**Miniature Sheets**
2329-2330  A497  Set of 2       9.00  9.00

### Magician Type of Grenada Grenadines of 2000

Designs: No. 2331, $1.50, Howard Thurston. No. 2332, $1.50, Harry Kellar.

**2001**
2331-2332  G173  Set of 2       2.25 2.25
Issued in sheets of 4.

### Mao Zedong Type of 2001

No. 2333, horiz.: a, Mao on stairs. b, Mao at right, with soldiers. c, Mao at left, with peasants. d, Mao seated, with officers.
$3, Portrait.

**2001, May 15   Litho.   Perf. 14**
2333  A493  $1.50 Sheet of 4,   4.50 4.50
          #a-d
**Souvenir Sheet**
2334  A493  $3 multi           2.25 2.25

### Verdi Type of 2001

No. 2335 — Verdi and score: a, 25c. b, 75c. c, $2. d, $3.
$6, Portrait.

**2001, May 15          Perf. 14**
2335  A494  Sheet of 4, #a-d    4.50 4.50
**Souvenir Sheet**
2336  A494  $6 multi           4.50 4.50

### Toulouse-Lautrec Type of 2001

No. 2337, horiz.: a, Helene V. b, The Clownesse. c, Madame Berthe Bady. d, The Woman With The Black Boa.
$6, Loie Fuller at the Folies Bergére.

**2001, May 15          Perf. 13¾**
2337  A495  $1 Sheet of 4, #a-d   3.00 3.00
**Souvenir Sheet**
2338  A495  $6 multi           4.50 4.50

### Monet Type of 2001

No. 2339, horiz.: a, The Magpie. b, La Pointe de la Hève at Low Tide. c, Boats: Regatta at Argenteuil. d, La Grenouillère.
$6, Portrait of J. F. Jaquemart with Parasol.

**2001, May 15**
2339  A504  $1 Sheet of 4, #a-d   3.00 3.00
**Souvenir Sheet**
2340  A504  $6 multi           4.50 4.50

Orchids
G181

Designs: 25c, Vanda Singapore. 50c, Vanda Joan Warne. 75c, Vanda lamellata. $2, Vanda merrillii.

No. 2345, $1.50: a, Papilionanthe teres. b, Vanda flabellata. c, Vanda tessellata (name at LL). d, Vanda pumila. e, Rhynchostylis gigantea. f, Vandopsis gigantea.

No. 2346, $1.50: a, Vanda tessellata (name at center left). b, Vanda helvola. c, Vanda brunnea. d, Vanda stangeana. e, Vanda limbata. f, Vandopsis tricolor.

No. 2347, $6, Vanda insignis. No. 2348, $6, Vandopsis lissochiloides.

**2001, Oct. 15          Perf. 14**
2341-2344  G181  Set of 4       2.60   2.60
**Sheets of 6, #a-f**
2345-2346  G181  Set of 2       13.50 13.50
**Souvenir Sheets**
2347-2348  G181  Set of 2       9.00  9.00

## Souvenir Sheets

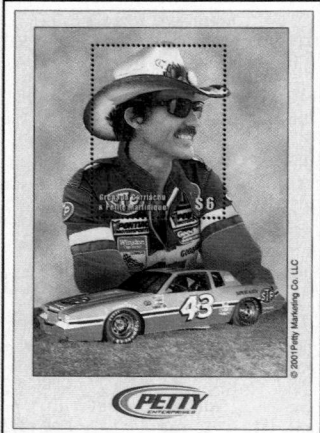

Richard Petty, Stock Car
Racer — G182

Designs: No. 2349, $6, shown. No. 2350,
$6, Petty speaking into microphone.

**2001, Oct. 15**                          **Perf. 13¾**
2349-2350  G182  Set of 2                  9.00  9.00

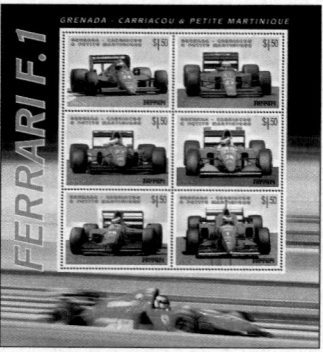

Ferrari Formula 1 Racing
Cars — G183

No. 2351: a, 1986 F1 86. b, 1989 F1 89. c,
1992 F92A. d, 1993 F1 93. e, 1994 412T1. f,
1996 F310.

**2001, Nov. 19**                          **Perf. 13¾**
2351  G183  $1.50 Sheet of 6,
                #a-f                       6.75  6.75

**World Cup Soccer Championships
Type of 2001**

No. 2352, $1.50 — World Cup posters and
badges from: a, 1950. b, 1954. c, 1958. d,
1962. e, 1966. f, 1970.
No. 2353, $1.50 — World Cup posters and
badges from: a, 1978. b, 1982. c, 1986. d,
1990. e, 1994. f, 1998.
No. 2354, $6, World Cup poster and badge,
1930. No. 2355, $6, Head and globe from
World Cup trophy.

**2001, Nov. 29**                          **Perf. 13¾x14¼**
**Sheets of 6, #a-f**
2352-2353  A505  Set of 2                  13.50 13.50
**Souvenir Sheets**
2354-2355  A505  Set of 2                  9.00  9.00

Christmas — G184

Designs: 25c, Coronation of the Virgin, by
Filippo Lippi. 75c, Virgin and Child, by Mantegna. $1.50, Madonna and Child, by Masaccio.
$3, Madonna and Child, by Raphael.
$6, Virgin and child Enthroned with Angels,
by Mantegna.

**2001, Dec. 3**                           **Perf. 14**
2356-2359  G184  Set of 4                  4.25  4.25
**Souvenir Sheet**
2360  G184  $6 multi                       4.50  4.50

Royal Navy
Ships — G185

Designs: 75c, HMS Renown in Portsmouth
Harbor, 1922. 90c, Battle of the Saintes, 1782.
$2, Battle of Trafalgar, 1805. $3, Embarkation
at Dover, 1520.
No. 2365, $1.50, horiz.: a, Battle of Solebay,
1672. b, HMS Royal Prince, 1679. c, Battle of
Texel, 1673. d, Battle of Scheveningen, 1653.
e, Barbary Pirates, 1600s. f, Royal Charles,
1667.
No. 2366, $1.50, horiz.: a, Skirmishing pre-
ceding the Battle of the First of June. b, Moonlight Battle, 1780. c, Great ships of the Jaco-
bean Navy, 1623. d, Battle of the Gulf of
Genoa, 1795. e, Battle of the Nile, 1798. f, St.
Lucia, 1778.
No. 2367, $6, Battle of Navarino, 1827,
horiz. No. 2368, $6, HMS Repulse, 1924,
horiz.

**2001, Dec. 10**                          **Litho.**
2361-2364  G185  Set of 4                  5.00  5.00
**Sheets of 6, #a-f**
2365-2366  G185  Set of 2                  13.50 13.50
**Souvenir Sheets**
2367-2368  G185  Set of 2                  9.00  9.00

**Queen Mother Type of 1999
Redrawn**

No. 2369: a, Lady Elizabeth Bowles-Lyon. b,
In Rhodesia, 1957. c, With Princesses Elizabeth and Anne, 1950. d, In 1988.
$6, In Berlin.

**2001, Dec. 13**                          **Perf. 14**
**Yellow Orange Frames**
2369  A440  $2 Sheet of 4, #a-d, +
                label                      6.00  6.00
**Souvenir Sheet**
**Perf. 13¾**
2370  A440  $6 multi                       4.50  4.50

Queen Mother's 101st birthday. No. 2370
contains one 38x50mm stamp with a slightly
darker appearance than that found on No.
2122. Sheet margins of Nos. 2369-2370 lack
embossing and gold arms and frames found
on Nos. 2121-2122.

**Princess Diana Type of 2001**
**Souvenir Sheet**

Diana in: a, Yellow dress. b, Red jacket. c,
White pinstriped suit.

**2001, Feb. 15**                          **Perf. 14**
2371  A509  $1.50 Sheet of 2 each
                #a-c                       6.75  6.75

Pres. John F. Kennedy — G187

No. 2372, vert. — Pres. Kennedy: a, In boat.
b, In chair. c, Profile. d, Close-up, smiling. e,
Close-up. f, Looking down.
$6, With Nikita Khrushchev.

**2001, Dec. 15**                          **Perf. 13¾**
2372  G187  $1.50 Sheet of 6,
                #a-f                       6.75  6.75
**Souvenir Sheet**
2373  G187  $6 multi                       4.50  4.50

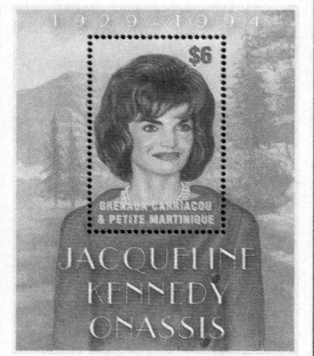

Jacqueline Kennedy Onassis (1929-
94) — G188

No. 2374: a, Blue jacket, blue blouse. b, Red
jacket, blue blouse. c, Green dress. d, Blue
cape. e Pink and blue jacket. f, Blue jacket,
yellow blouse.
No. 2375, $6, Mountain in background. No.
2376, $6, Beige background.

**2001, Dec. 15**                          **Perf. 14**
2374  G188  $1.50 Sheet of 6,
                #a-f                       6.75  6.75
**Souvenir Sheets**
2375-2376  G188  Set of 2                  9.00  9.00

G189

US Generals and Admirals — G190

No. 2377: a, Gen. Omar N. Bradley. b, Gen.
George C. Marshall. c, Gen. Douglas MacAr-
thur. d, Adm. William F. Halsey. e, Gen.
Dwight D. Eisenhower. f, Adm. Chester Nimitz.
g, Adm. William D. Leahy. h, Gen. Henry H.
Arnold. i, Adm. Ernest J. King. j, Gen. George
Washington. k, Gen. John J. Pershing.
No. 2378: a, Gen. George S. Patton, Jr. b,
Gen. Joseph W. Stilwell. c, Adm. Thomas C.
Kinkaid. d, Gen. Jonathan Wainwright. e, Lt.
Gen. James H. Doolittle. f, Gen. Matthew B.
Ridgway. g, Gen. Maxwell D. Taylor. h, Adm.
Richmond Kelly Turner. i, Gen. Curtis E.
LeMay. j, Gen. Hoyt S. Vandenberg. k, Gen.
Carl Spaatz. l, Adm. Raymond Spruance.
No. 2379, $6, Eisenhower. No. 2380, $6,
Douglas MacArthur.

**2001, Dec. 15**                          **Perf. 14**
2377  G189  75c Sheet of 11, #a-
                k, + label                 6.25  6.25
2378  G189  75c Sheet of 12, #a-l          6.75  6.75
**Souvenir Sheets**
**Perf. 13¾**
2379-2380  G190  Set of 2                  9.00  9.00

Moths
G191

Designs: 75c, Pine emperor. 90c, Inquisitive
monkey. $2, Oak eggar. $3, Madagascan sun-
set moth.
No. 2385, $1.50: a, Spanish moon moth. b,
Coppery dysphania. c, Io moth. d, Large
agarista. e, Millar's tiger. f, Tropical fruit-
piercer.
No. 2386, $1.50: a, Indian moon moth. b,
Beautiful tiger. c, Regal moth. d, Great tiger
moth. e, Venus moth. f, Zodiac moth.
No. 2387, $6, Diva moth, vert. No. 2388, $6,
African moon moth, vert.

**2001, Dec. 17**                          **Perf. 14**
2381-2384  G191  Set of 4                  5.00  5.00
**Sheets of 6, #a-f**
2385-2386  G191  Set of 2                  13.50 13.50
**Souvenir Sheets**
2387-2388  G191  Set of 2                  9.00  9.00
                Vegaspex (#2386).

**Reign of Queen Elizabeth II, 50th
Anniv. Type of 2002**

No. 2389: a, White hat. b, Red hat. c, Tiara.
d, Hatless.
$6, With Princes Philip, Charles, Princess
Anne.

**2002, Feb. 6**                           **Perf. 14¼**
2389  A516  $2 Sheet of 4, #a-d            6.00  6.00
**Souvenir Sheet**
2390  A516  $6 multi                       4.50  4.50

New Year 2002 (Year of the
Horse) — G192

Various horses with background colors of —
No. 2391: a, 75c, Light brown and light
orange. b, $1.25, Light blue and olive green. c,
$2, Tan and bister.
$6, Light orange and orange.

**2002, Mar. 4**          **Litho.**       **Perf. 13¾**
2391  G192  Sheet of 3, #a-c               3.00  3.00
**Souvenir Sheet**
2392  G192  $6 multi                       4.50  4.50

United We
Stand — G193

**2002, May 21**                           **Perf. 14**
2393  G193  80c multi                       .60   .60
                Printed in sheets of 4.

## Chiune Sugihara Type of 2002
### Souvenir Sheets

Sugihara and: No. 2394, $6, Map of Asia. No. 2395, $6, Pink background.

**2002, July 1**    *Perf. 13½x13¼*
2394-2395 A521   Set of 2    9.00 9.00

## Winter Olympics Type of 2002

Montages of: No. 2396, $3, Skier in air, course flag, vert. No. 2397, $3, Skier, no flag, vert.

**2002, July 1**    *Perf. 13½x13¼*
2396-2397 A522   Set of 2    4.50 4.50
2397a    Souvenir sheet, #2396-
     2397         4.50 4.50

## Intl. Year of Mountains Type of 2002

No. 2398: a, Mt. Kilimanjaro, Tanzania. b, Mt. Kenya, Kenya. c, Mauna Kea, Hawaii. d, Mt. Fuji, Japan.
$6, Koolau Mountains, Hawaii.

**2002, July 1**    *Perf. 13¼x13½*
2398 A523 $2 Sheet of 4, #a-d   6.00 6.00
### Souvenir Sheet
2399 A523 $6 multi        4.50 4.50

## Intl. Year of Ecotourism Type of 2002

No. 2400, horiz.: a, Tourists at waterfall. b, Bird. c, Butterfly. d, Fish. e, Cactus. f, Orchid.
$6, Birds, horiz.

**2002, July 1**    *Perf. 13¼x13½*
2400 A524 $1.50 Sheet of 6, #a-f 6.75 6.75
### Souvenir Sheet
2401 A524 $6 multi        4.50 4.50
Nos. 2400-2401 were each overprinted in sheet margins "Hurricane Relief 2004" in 2005.

## Scout Jamboree Type of 2002

No. 2402, horiz.: a, Campfire, Scout emblem. b, Scout with walking stick and backpack. c, Scout feeding calf. d, Girl giving Scout sign.
No. 2403, $6, Scout with hat.

**2002, July 1**    *Perf. 13¼x13½*
2402 A525 $2 Sheet of 4, #a-d   6.00 6.00
### Souvenir Sheet
*Perf. 13½x13¼*
2403 A525 $2 multi        1.50 1.50

Amerigo Vespucci (1454-1512), Explorer — G194

Various portraits with background colors of: $1, Purple. $2, Orange brown. $3, Green. $6, Vespucci and map.

**2002, July 1**    *Perf. 13½x13¼*
2404-2406 G194   Set of 3   4.50 4.50
### Souvenir Sheet
2407 G194 $6 multi       4.50 4.50

## Butterflies, Insects, Mushrooms and Whales Type of 2002

No. 2408, $1 — Whales: a, Sperm. b, Bottlenose. c, Sei. d, Killer. e, Humpback. f, Pygmy sperm.
No. 2409, $1 — Insects: a, Bumblebee. b, Dragonfly. c, Hercules beetle. d, Ladybug. e, Figure-of-eight butterfly. f, Praying mantis.
No. 2410, $2 — Butterflies: a, White peacock. b, Orange-barred sulphur. c, Blue night. d, Banded king shoemaker. e, Cramer's mesene. f, Common morpho.
No. 2411, $2 — Mushrooms: a, Shaggy mane. b, Shaggy parasol. c, Purple coincap. d, Sharp-scaled parasol. e, Thick-footed morel. f, Rosy-gill fairy helmet.
No. 2412, $6, Blue whale, horiz. No. 2413, $6, Dragonfly, horiz. No. 2414, $6, Blue night butterfly, horiz. No. 2415, $6, Death cap mushroom.

**2002, Aug. 12**    *Perf. 14*
### Sheets of 6, #a-f
2408-2411 A538   Set of 4   27.50 27.50
### Souvenir Sheets
2412-2415 A538   Set of 4   18.00 18.00

### Elvis Presley Type of 2002 and

Elvis Presley — G195

No. 2416, Color portrait.
No. 2417: a, Wearing light plaid shirt. b, Holding microphone. c, Wearing dark shirt. d, Holding guitar with neck up. e, Wearing suit, holding guitar. f, Wearing short-sleeve shirt, holding guitar. g, Wearing shirt with flowers on shoulders. h, Wearing wrist watch and short-sleeve shirt. i, Wearing dark plaid shirt, holding guitar.

**2002, Aug. 26**    *Perf. 13¾*
2416 A527 $1 multi     .75 .75
2417 G195 $1 Sheet of 9, #a-i   6.75 6.75
No. 2416 printed in sheets of 9.

## Dutch Nobel Prize Winners, Lighthouses and Women's Costumes Types of 2002

No. 2418 — Nobel Prize winners: a, Paul Crutzen, Chemistry, 1995. b, Nobel Medal for Physics, Chemistry, Physiology or Medicine, and Literature. c, Martinus J. G. Veltman, Physics, 1999. d, Hendrik A. Lorentz, Physics, 1902. e, Christiaan Eijkman, Physiology or Medicine, 1929. f, Gerardus 't Hooft, Physics, 1999.
No. 2419 — Lighthouses: a, Ameland. b, Vlieland. c, Julianadorp. d, Noordwijk. e, Hoek van Holland. f, Goeree.
No. 2420 — Women's costumes: a, Noord-Holland (woman with child). b, Overijssel (woman with blue dress and plaid neckerchief). c, Zeeland (woman with necklace).

**2002, Aug. 29**    *Perf. 13½x13¼*
2418 A532 $1.50 Sheet of 6,
     #a-f    6.75   6.75
2419 A533 $1.50 Sheet of 6,
     #a-f    6.75   6.75
*Perf. 13¼*
2420 A534 $3 Sheet of 3,
     #a-c    6.75   6.75
Amphilex 2002 Intl. Stamp Exhibition, Amsterdam.

## Teddy Bear Centenary Types of 2002

No. 2421 — Bear with: a, 15c, Tasseled helmet. b, $2, Black hat with red bullseye. c, $3, Hat and neck ruffle. d, $4, Gray hat.
No. 2422 — Bear with: a, 50c, Happy birthday heart. b, $1, Flower, vest, hat, and violin case. c, $2, Hat and trench coat. d, $5, Shorts.

**2002, Sept. 23**    *Perf. 14*
2421 A529   Sheet of 4, #a-d   7.00 7.00
2422 A530   Sheet of 4, #a-d   6.50 6.50

## Christmas Type of 2002

Carpaccio paintings: 15c, The Redeemer and the Four Apostles. 25c, The Miracle of the Relic of the Cross, vert. 50c, The Presentation in the Temple. $2, The Visitation. $3, The Birth of the Virgin.
$6, Madonna and Child and Two Angels, by Cimabue, vert.

---

**2002, Nov. 4**    *Perf. 14*
2423-2427 A541   Set of 5   4.50 4.50
### Souvenir Sheet
2428 A541 $6 multi     4.50 4.50

## World Cup Soccer Matches Type of 2002

No. 2429, $1.50: a, Oliver Neuville, Eddie Pope. b, Claudio Reyna, Miroslav Klose. c, Christian Ziege, Frankie Hejduk. d, Nadal, Jung Hwan Ahn. e, Luis Enrique, Chong Gug Song. f, Park Ji Sung, Mendieta Gaizka.
No. 2430, $1.50: a, Danny Mills, Ronaldo. b, Roque Junior, Emile Heskey. c, Sol Campbell, Rivaldo. d, Lamine Diatta, Hakan Sukur. e, Umit Davala, Khalilou Fadiga. f, El Hadji Diouf, Tugay Kerimoglu.
No. 2431, $3: a, Oliver Kahn. b, Brad Friedel.
No. 2432, $3: a, Chun Soo Lee. b, Juan Carlos Valeron.
No. 2433, $3: a, David Beckham, Roberto Carlos. b, Ronaldinho, Nicky Butt.
No. 2434, $3: a, Alpay Ozalan. b, Fadiga.

**2002, Nov. 18**    *Perf. 13¼*
### Sheets of 6, #a-f
2429-2430 A542   Set of 2   13.50 13.50
### Souvenir Sheets of 2, #a-b
2431-2434 A542   Set of 4   18.00 18.00

## Dale Earnhardt Type of 2002

No. 2435: a, $2, 1980 photo. b, $2, 1986 photo. c, $2, 1987 photo. d, $2, 1990 photo. e, $2, 1991 photo. f, $2, 1993 photo. g, $2, 1994 photo. h, $4, Two cars (75x50mm).

**2002**    *Perf. 13½x13¾*
2435 A518   Sheet of 8, #a-h   13.50 13.50

New Year 2003 (Year of the Ram) — G196

**2003, Jan. 27**    *Perf. 14*
2436 G196 $1.25 multi    .95 .95
Printed in sheets of 4.

G197

---

Coronation of Queen Elizabeth II, 50th Anniv. — G198

No. 2437: a, As child. b, In blue dress. c, On horse.
$6, Wearing sash and tiara.
$20, Wearing tiara.

**2003**    *Litho.*    *Perf. 14*
2437 G197 $3 Sheet of 3, #a-
     c    6.75 6.75
### Souvenir Sheet
2438 G197 $6 multi    4.50 4.50
### Miniature Sheet
*Litho. & Embossed*
*Perf. 13¼x13*
2439 G198 $20 gold & multi   15.00 15.00
Issued: Nos. 2437-2438, 8/25; No. 2439, 2/24.

## Space Shuttle Columbia Type of 2003

No. 2440: a, Mission Specialist 1 David M. Brown. b, Commander Rick D. Husband. c, Mission Specialist 4 Laurel Blair Salton Clark. d, Mission Specialist 4 Kalpana Chawla. e, Payload Commander Michael P. Anderson. f, Pilot William C. McCool. g, Payload Specialist 4 Ilan Ramon.

**2003, Apr. 7**    *Litho.*    *Perf. 13¼*
2440 A549 $1 Sheet of 7, #a-g   5.25 5.25

## Klimt Paintings Type of 2003

Designs: 15c, Le Chapeau de Plumes Noires. 25c, Le Schloss Kammer am Attersee. 50c, Malcesine sue le Lac de Garde. 75c, Ferme en Haute Autriche. $1.25, Portrait d'une Dame. $4, La Frise Beethoven.
No. 2447: a, Portrait de la Baronne Elisabeth Bachofen-Echt. b, Portrait d'une Dame, diff. c, Portrait d'Emilie Floge. d, Portrait d'Adele Bloch-Bauer.
$6, Le Baiser.

**2003, Apr. 28**    *Perf. 14¼*
2441-2446 A550   Set of 6   5.25 5.25
*Perf. 13¼*
2447 A550 $2 Sheet of 4, #a-d   6.00 6.00
### Size: 83x103mm
*Imperf*
2448 A550 $6 multi    4.50 4.50

## Japanese Art Type of 2003

Paintings by Kunichika Toyohara: 50c, The Actor Danjuro Ichikawa IX as the Beggar Kagekiyo Akushichibyoe. 75c, The Actor Danjuro Ichikawa IX as the Female Demon Uwanari. $1.25, The Actor Tossho Sawamura II as Sutewakamaru. $3, The Actor Hikosaburo Bando V as Danjo Nikki.
No. 2453: a, The Actor Shikan Nakamura IV as Rokusuke Keyamura. b, The Actor Hikosaburo Bando V as Ichimisair No Musume Osono. c, The Actor Sadanji Ichikawa I as Wada No Shimobe Busuke. d, The Actor Sandanji Ichikawa I as Kiyomizu no Yoshitaka.
$6, The Actor Kikugoro Onoe V as Tsuneemon Torii Retruning to Mikawa, horiz.

**2003, Apr. 28**    *Perf. 14¼*
2449-2452 A551   Set of 4   4.25 4.25
2453 A551 $2 Sheet of 4, #a-d   6.00 6.00
### Souvenir Sheet
2454 A551 $6 multi    4.50 4.50

## Cranach Paintings Type of 2003

Details from paintings by Lucas Cranach the Elder: 25c, The St. Mary Altarpiece, vert. $1, The St. Mary Altarpiece, diff., vert. $1.25, Duke John with St. James the Greater, from Altarpiece of the Princes, vert. $3, Frederick the Wise with St. Bartholomew, vert.

No. 2459: a, Judith at the Table of Holofernes. b, Central panel of St. Catherine Altarpeice. c, Judith Killing Holofernes. d, The Martyrdom of St. Catherine.
$6, Cardinal Albrecht of Brandenbourg as St. Jerome in the Wilderness, vert.

**2003, Apr. 28**
2455-2458  A552    Set of 4      4.25  4.25
2459  A552  $2 Souvenir sheet, #a-d  6.00  6.00
**Souvenir Sheet**
2460  A552  $6 multi      4.50  4.50

**Teddy Bear Type of 2003**
**2003, Apr. 29    Embroidered    Imperf.**
**Self-Adhesive**
2461  A553  $15 multi      11.50  11.50
Issued in sheets of 4.

**Tour de France Type of 2003**
No. 2462, $2: a, Ferdinand Kubler, 1950. b, Hugo Koblet, 1951. c, Fausto Coppi, 1952. d, Louison Bobet, 1953.
No. 2463, $2: a, Bobet, 1954. b, Bobet, 1955. c, Roger Walkowiak, 1956. d, Jacques Anquetil, 1957.
No. 2464, $2: a, Gastone Nencini, 1960. b, Anquetil, 1961. c, Anquetil, 1962. d, Anquetil, 1963.
No. 2465, $6, Bobet, 1953-55. No. 2466, $6, Anquetil, 1957, diff. No. 2467, $6, Eddy Merckx, 1969.

**2003, June 17    Perf. 13¼**
**Sheets of 4, #a-d**
2462-2464  A555    Set of 3      18.00  18.00
**Souvenir Sheets**
2465-2467  A555    Set of 3      13.50  13.50

**John F. Kennedy Type of 2002**
No. 2468, $2: a, As Choate graduate, 1935. b, As congressman, 1946. c, With wife, Jacqueline, on tennis court. d, With son, John, Jr.
No. 2469, $2: a, With wife, Jacqueline. b, Announcing Cuban blockade, 1962. c, Seated in White House, 1962. d, Wife and children at funeral, 1963.

**2003, July 1    Perf. 14**
**Sheets of 4, #a-d**
2468-2469  A544    Set of 2      12.00  12.00

**Intl. Year of Fresh Water Type of 2003**
No. 2470 — Flag and: a, La Sagesse. b, Annadale Falls. c, Grand Etang.
$6, Flag and St. George, horiz.

**2003, July 4    Perf. 13½x13¼**
2470  A559  $2 Sheet of 3, #a-c  4.50  4.50
**Souvenir Sheet**
**Perf. 13¼x13½**
2471  A559  $6 multi      4.50  4.50

**Circus Performers Type of 2003**
No. 2472, $2 — Clowns: a, Anton Pilossian. b, Victor Vashnikov. c, Dan Rice. d, Tom Comet.
No. 2473, $2: a, Dog. b, Macaw. c, Monique. d, Vassily Trofimov.

**2003, July 14    Perf. 14**
**Sheets of 4, #a-d**
2472-2473  A560    Set of 2      12.00  12.00

**Powered Flight Type of 2003**
No. 2474, $2: a, Wright Brothers Flyer. b, NC-4. c, Douglas World Cruiser. d, Fokker Eindecker.
No. 2475, $2: a, Hawker Hart. b, Martin B-10. c, Armstrong Whitworth Siskin IIIA. d, Loening OL-8.
No. 2476, $2: a, Hansa-Brandenburg D.1. b, B.E. 2e. c, Handley Page 0/400. d, Avro 504.
No. 2477, $6, Wright Brothers No. 3 glider. No. 2478, $6, Wright Brothers Flyer No. 2. No. 2479, $6, Gloster Gamecock.

**2003, July 14**
**Sheets of 4, #a-d**
2474-2476  A556    Set of 3      18.00  18.00
**Souvenir Sheets**
2477-2479  A556    Set of 3      13.50  13.50

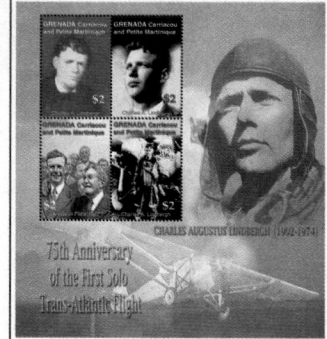

First Nonstop Solo Transatlantic Flight, 75th Anniv. — G199

No. 2480, $2: a, Charles Lindbergh (white denomination, blue background). b, Lindbergh (blue denomination, brown background. c, Lindbergh's arrival in Paris, 1927. d, Lindbergh and Spirit of St. Louis (white denomination, country name in blue).
No. 2481, $2: a, Lindbergh (blue denomination and background). b, Lindbergh and Spirit of St. Louis, blue denomination, red violet background). c, Lindbergh and Spirit of St. Louis (white denomination and country name). d, Lindbergh (white denomination and blue country name).

**2003, July 14**
**Sheets of 4, #a-d**
2480-2481  G199    Set of 2      12.00  12.00

**Prince William Type of 2003**
No. 2482, vert.: a, Looking right. b, Looking forward. c, Looking left.
$6, In ski jacket, vert.

**2003, Sept. 22**
2482  A562  $3 Sheet of 3, #a-c  6.75  6.75
**Souvenir Sheet**
2483  A562  $6 multi      4.50  4.50

**Flowers Type of 2003**
Designs: 75c, Wild rhododendron, vert. $1, Peony, vert. $1.25, Camellia, vert. No. 2487, $2, Laurel, vert.
No. 2488, $2, vert.: a, Apple blossom. b, Mock orange. c, Wild rose. d, Hibiscus.
$6, Violets, vert.

**2003, Oct. 23    Perf. 13½**
2484-2487  A567    Set of 4      3.75  3.75
2488  A567  $2 Sheet of 4, #a-d  6.00  6.00
**Souvenir Sheet**
2489  A567  $6 multi      4.50  4.50
ASDA Postage Stamp Mega-event (#2489).

**Fish Type of 2003**
Designs: 25c, Domino damsel. 75c, Porcupine fish. $1.25, Damselfish. No. 2493, $2, Clownfish.
No. 2494, $2: a, Triggerfish. b, Half-and-half wrasse. c, Long-fin bannerfish. d, Butterflyfish.
$6, Blue-girdled angelfish.

**2003, Oct. 23**
2490-2493  A568    Set of 4      3.25  3.25
2494  A568  $2 Sheet of 4, #a-d  6.00  6.00
**Souvenir Sheet**
2495  A568  $6 multi      4.50  4.50

**Birds Type of 2003**
Designs: 25c, Rose-breasted grosbeak. No. 2497, 50c, Gray catbird. No. 2498, 50c, Bullock's oriole. $1, Blue grosbeak.
No. 2500, $2, vert.: a, Lazuli bunting. b, Indigo bunting. c, Broad-tailed hummingbird. d, Scarlet tanager.
$6, Barn swallow.

**2003, Oct. 23**
2496-2499  A569    Set of 4      1.75  1.75
2500  A569  $2 Sheet of 4, #a-d  6.00  6.00
**Souvenir Sheet**
2501  A569  $6 multi      4.50  4.50

**Christmas Type of 2003**
Designs: 35c, Madonna and Child, from Carnesecchi Tabernacle, by Domenico Veneziano. 75c, Madonna and Child, from Magnoli altarpiece, by Veneziano. 90c, Crevole Madonna, by Duccio di Buoninsegna. $3, Madonna and Child, by Veneziano.
$6, Madonna and Child by the Fireplace, by Robert Campin.

**2003, Nov. 17    Perf. 14¼**
2502-2505  A570    Set of 4      3.75  3.75
**Souvenir Sheet**
2506  A570  $6 multi      4.50  4.50

**Hermitage Paintings Type of 2003**
Designs: 75c, Abraham and Isaac, by Rembrandt, vert. $1, David and Jonathan, by Rembrandt, vert. $1.25, St. Onuphrius, by Jusepe de Ribera, vert. No. 2510, $2, Pope Paul III, by Titian, vert.
No. 2511, $2: a, Rest on the Flight into Egypt, by Bartolomé Estéban Murillo. b, Esther Before Ahasuerus, by Nicolas Poussin. c, Abraham's Servant and Rebecca, by Jacob Hogers. d, The Prophet Elisha and Naaman, by Lambert Jacobsz.
No. 2512, Hagar Flees Abram's House, by Peter Paul Rubens. No. 2513, The Building of Noah's Ark, by Guido Reni, vert.

**2003, Dec. 8    Perf. 13½**
2507-2510  A572    Set of 4      3.75  3.75
2511  A572  $2 Sheet of 4, #a-d  6.00  6.00
**Imperf**
**Size: 78x65mm**
2512  A572  $6 multi      4.50  4.50
**Size: 67x78mm**
2513  A572  $6 multi      4.50  4.50

**Norman Rockwell Type of 2003**
No. 2514, vert.: a, The Trumpeter. b, Waiting for the Vet. c, The Diving Board. d, The Discovery.
$6, Day in a Boy's Life.

**2003, Dec. 8    Litho.    Perf. 13¼**
2514  A571  $2 Sheet of 4, #a-d  6.00  6.00
**Souvenir Sheet**
2515  A571  $6 multi      4.50  4.50

**Pablo Picasso Type of 2003**
No. 2516: a, Jacqueline Sitting. b, Jacqueline with Flower. c, Seated Nude. d, Woman in Armchair.
$6, Head of a Woman.

**2003, Dec. 8    Perf. 13¼**
2516  A573  $2 Sheet of 4, #a-d  6.00  6.00
**Imperf**
2517  A573  $6 multi      4.50  4.50
No. 2516 contains four 37x50mm stamps.

**New Year (Year of the Monkey) Type of 2004**
No. 2518: a, White, blue and orange monkey. b, Blue monkey. c, Brown monkey. d, Monkey with orange face.

**2004, Jan. 4    Perf. 14**
2518  A574  $1.50 Sheet of 4, #a-d  4.50  4.50

Zhoa Mengfu (1254-1322), Artist — G200

No. 2519: a, The Mind Landscape of Xie Youyu. b, Scroll with green backround and large mountains at left and right. c, Twin Pines. d, Scroll with brown background and large mountain at left.
$6, Autumn.

**2004, Jan. 29   Litho.   Perf. 13½x13¼**
2519  G200  $2 Sheet of 4, #a-d  6.00  4.50
**Souvenir Sheet**
2520  G200  $6 multi      4.50  4.50

**Arthur and Friends Type of 2004**
No. 2521: a, Brain. b, Binky. c, Francine. d, Prunella. e, Arthur. f, Muffy.
No. 2522, $2: a, Francine, diff. b, Buster. c, Muffy, diff. d, Sue Ellen.
No. 2523, $2: a, Francine and butterfly. b, Binky and map. c, Brain and blackboard. d, Arthur and model of solar system.

**2004, Jan. 29    Perf. 13¼**
2521  A577  $1.50 Sheet of 6, #a-f  6.75  6.75
**Sheets of 4, #a-d**
2522-2523  A577    Set of 2      12.00  12.00

**Olympics Type of 2004**
Designs: 25c, Long jumper, 1924 Paris Olympics. 50c, Avery Brundage, Intl. Olympic Committee President, 1952-72. $1, Commemorative medal for 1972 Munich Olympics. $4, Paidotribai.

**2004, Apr. 8    Litho.**
2524-2527  A579    Set of 4      4.50  4.50

**Deng Xiaoping Type of 2004**
**Souvenir Sheet**
**2004, May 3    Perf. 13½x13¼**
2528  A582  $6 Wearing cap      4.50  4.50

**Pope John Paul II Type of 2004**
No. 2529: a, With Lech Walesa. b, With Meir Lau, Chief Rabbi of Israel. c, Blessing children. d, At computer. e, Wearing miter.

**2004, May 3    Perf. 13½**
2529  A583  $2 Sheet of 5, #a-e  7.50  7.50

**Marilyn Monroe Type of 2004**
Designs: 50c, Portrait, diff.
No. 2531 — Various portraits with color and location of denomination of: a, Black, UL. b, Black, UR. c, White, UR. d, White, UL.

**2004, May 3    Perf. 13½x13¼**
2530  A584  50c multi      .40  .40
2531  A584  $2 Sheet of 4, #a-d  6.00  6.00
No. 2530 was printed in sheets of 16.

**D-Day Type of 2004**
Designs: 25c, Admiral Sir Bertram Ramsay. 50c, Lt. Gen. Miles Dempsey. 75c, Bob Shrimpton, Submarine Detector on HMS Belfast. $4, Denis Edwards, 6th Airborne Division.
No. 2536, $2: a, Sir Winston Churchill without hat. b, Churchill with hat. c, British link up with Airborne troops. d, Link up at Orne River.
No. 2537, $2: a, US troops move inland. b, Troops move inland from Omaha Beach. c, Heavy fighting on Sword Beach. d, German generals meet.
No. 2538, $6, Assault landing craft head for invasion beaches. No. 2539, $6, Gunner in a British bomber.

**2004, July 19    Perf. 14**
**Stamps + Labels (#2532-2535)**
2532-2535  A586    Set of 4      4.25  4.25
**Sheets of 4, #a-d**
2536-2537  A586    Set of 2      12.00  12.00
**Souvenir Sheets**
2538-2539  A586    Set of 2      9.00  9.00

**Locomotives Type of 2004**
No. 2540, $1: a, Liner V2 Class 2-6-2. b, Sudan Railways 2-8-2. c, China Railways DF4 Co-Co. d, LMS 2F 0-6-0 with Black 5 4-6-0. e, LMS Lickey Banker 0-10-0. f, LMS Princess Royal Pacific. g, LMS Reboilered Claughton Class 4-6-0. h, LMS Stanier 8F 2-8-0. i, Midland Railway Compound 4-4-0.
No. 2541, $1: a, Britannia Class 4-6-2. b, Indian Railways XD Class 2-8-2. c, China Railways KD6 2-8-0 (USATC S160). d, SE+CR 01 Class 0-6-0. e, Battle of Britain Light Pacific. f, SR King Arthur Class 4-6-0. g, SR Marsh 13 Class 4-4-2T. h, SR N Class 2-6-0. i, SR School Class 4-4-0.
No. 2542, $1: a, SR Merchant Navy Pacific 4-6-2. b, Gazira Cotton Railway, Sudan. c, Spanish Railways 4-8-4. d, LNER 04-1 Class 2-8-0. e, LNER A1 4-6-2 Pacific. f, LNER A3 Class 4-6-2. g, LNER A4 Class 4-6-2 Pacific. h, LNER B1 Class 4-6-0. i, LNER Ivatt Large Atlantic 4-4-2 A4 Pacific 4-4-0.
No. 2543, $6, Aberdeen to Penzance train. No. 2544, $6, London to Holyhead train. No. 2545, $6, Dublin to Tralee train.

**2004, July 19    Perf. 14**
**Sheets of 9, #a-i**
2540-2542  A587    Set of 3      21.00  21.00
**Souvenir Sheets**
2543-2545  A587    Set of 3      13.50  13.50

**Queen Juliana Type of 2004**
**2004, Aug. 25    Litho.    Perf. 13¼**
2546  A590  $2 1937 portrait      1.50  1.50
Printed in sheets of 6.

Carriacou
Regatta
Festival,
40th
Anniv.
G201

Designs: 75c, Parade. 90c, People, boats in water. $1, Sailboats, vert.

**2004, Oct. 11**     *Perf. 14*
2547-2549 G201   Set of 3    2.00 2.00

**FIFA Type of 2004**
No. 2550: a, David Beckham. b, Marcel Desailly. c, Guido Buchwald. d, Alfonso. $6, Bobby Charlton.

**2004, Nov. 1**     *Perf. 12¾x12½*
2550 A595 $2 Sheet of 4, #a-d   6.00 6.00
**Souvenir Sheet**
2551 A595 $6 multi     4.50 4.50

Ocean Liners — G202

Designs: 25c, Titanic. 75c, Michelangelo. $1, America. $1.25, Vaterland. $2, Deutschland. $3, Mauritania. $6, Ile de France.

**2004, Nov. 29**     *Perf. 14¼*
2552-2557 G202   Set of 6   6.25 6.25
**Souvenir Sheet**
2558 G202 $6 multi     4.50 4.50

**Elvis Presley Type of 2004**
No. 2559, $2: a, Wearing purple shirt. b, Playing guitar, wearing polka dot shirt, "Elvis Presley" at right. c, With guitar hanging from neck, "Elvis Presley" at right. d, Wearing patterned shirt.
No. 2560, $2: a, Wearing brown shirt. b, Playing guitar, wearing polka dot shirt, "Elvis Presley" at left. c, With guitar hanging from neck, "Elvis Presley" at left. d, Wearing gray suit and black shirt, playing guitar.

**2004, Nov. 29**     *Perf. 13¼*
**Sheets of 4, #a-d**
2559-2560 A588   Set of 2   12.00 12.00

**Christmas Type of 2004**
Paintings by Norman Rockwell: 35c, Follow Me in Merry Measure. 75c, The Merrie Old Coach Driver. 90c, Joy to the World. $3, Santa Reading His Mail. $6, Wartime Santa.

**2004, Dec. 9**     *Perf. 12*
2561-2564 A600   Set of 4   3.75 3.75
**Size: 63x81mm**
*Imperf*
2565 A600 $6 multi     4.50 4.50

**Babe Ruth Type of 2004**
No. 2566: a, Blue background. b, White background.
No. 2567: a, Swinging bat. b, Looking forward. c, Looking to right. d, With glove.

**2004, Jan. 29**   *Litho.*   *Perf. 14*
2566 A598 50c Pair, #a-b    .75 .75
2567 A598 $2 Sheet of 4, #a-d   6.00 6.00

Moths —
G202a

Designs: 75c, Scarlet-bodied wasp moth. 90c, Bella moth. $1, Sphinx moth. $3, Faithful beauty moth.
$6, Empyreuma affinis.

**2004, Nov. 17**     *Perf. 12¾*
2568-2571 G202a   Set of 4   4.25 4.25
**Souvenir Sheet**
2572 G202a $6 multi    4.50 4.50

**Ronald Reagan Type of 2004**
No. 2573: a, With Press Secretary James Brady. b, With German Chancellor Helmut Kohl. c, With family. d, With Princess Diana.

**2004, Nov. 29**     *Perf. 13¼x13½*
2573 A597 $2 Sheet of 4, #a-d   6.00 6.00

**Year of the Rooster Type of 2005**
Paintings by Ren Yi: 75c, Double Chickens and Peony. $3, A Rooster, horiz.

**2005, Jan. 17**     *Perf. 12¾x13*
2574 A601 75c multi    .60 .60
**Souvenir Sheet**
2575 A601 $3 multi    2.25 2.25
No. 2574 printed in sheets of 4. No. 2575 contains one 56x35mm stamp.

**Intl. Year of Rice Type of 2005 and**

Screen Panels by Oshen
Maruyama — G203

No. 2576 — Various panels depicting rice plants and birds.
$6, Rice Farming in Bali, by unknown artist, horiz.

**2005, Feb. 10**     *Perf. 14*
2576 G203 $1.50 Sheet of 6, #a-f 6.75 6.75
**Souvenir Sheet**
2577 A602 $6 multi    4.50 4.50

**Prehistoric Animals Type of 2005**
No. 2578: a, Psittacosaurus. b, Deinonychus. c, Suchomimus. d,Smilodon. $6, Tenotosaurus.

**2005, Feb. 10**     *Perf. 13¼x13½*
2578 A604 $2 Sheet of 4, #a-d   6.00 6.00
**Souvenir Sheet**
2579 A604 $6 multi    4.50 4.50
See Nos. 2598-2601.

Reptiles and Amphibians — G204

No. 2580: a, Poison dart frog. b, Western Antillean anole. c, Black iguana. d, American crocodile.
$6, Anolis lizard.

**2005, Feb. 10**     *Perf. 12¾*
2580 G204 $2 Sheet of 4, #a-d   6.00 6.00
**Souvenir Sheet**
2581 G204 $6 multi    4.50 4.50

Carnivorous Plants — G205

No. 2582: a, Heliamphora tatei. b, Sarracenia flava, Genlisea pygmaea. c, Nepenthes bicalcarata. d, Utricularia intermedia.
$6, Dionaea muscipula.

**2005, Feb. 10**
2582 G205 $2 Sheet of 4, #a-d   6.00 6.00
**Souvenir Sheet**
2583 G205 $6 multi    4.50 4.50

**Elvis Presley Type of 2005**
No. 2584, $1.50: a, With guitar, 1955. b, Singing, 1956. c, With hand on chin, 1958. d, In suit, 1962. e, With guitar, 1968. f, Singing, 1972.
No. 2585, $1.50: a, In Army uniform, 1958. b, Wearing Hawaiian shirt, 1961. c, Wearing cap, 1963. d, Wearing turban, 1965. e, Sitting on sports car, 1966. f, With stethoscope, 1969.

**2005, Apr. 4**     *Perf. 13½*
**Sheets of 6, #a-f**
2584-2585 A607   Set of 2   13.50 13.50

Battle of Trafalgar,
Bicent. — G206

Designs: 75c, Swiftsure. $1, British sail near Cape Trafalgar, horiz. $2, Capt. Alexander Ball. $3, Vice-Admiral Francedillaois Brueys d'Aigalliers.
$6, Admiral Aristide du Petit-Thouars.

**2005, Apr. 4**     *Perf. 14*
2586-2589 G206   Set of 4   5.25 5.25
**Souvenir Sheet**
2590 G206 $6 multi    4.50 4.50

**Yasujiro Ozu Type of 2005**
No. 2591: a, A Mother Should Be Loved, 1934. b, An Inn in Tokyo, 1935. c, Dragnet Girl, 1933. d, There Was a Father, 1942.

**2005, Apr. 8**     *Perf. 14¼*
2591 A608 $2 Sheet of 4, #a-d   6.00 6.00

**Basketball Players Type of 2004**
Designs: No. 2592, 75c, Steve Francis, Orlando Magic. No. 2593, 75c, Allan Houston, New York Knicks. No. 2594, 75c, Tracy McGrady, Houston Rockets. No. 2595, 75c, Steve Nash, Phoenix Suns. No. 2596, 75c, Shaquille O'Neal, Miami Heat. No. 2597, 75c, Chris Webber, Sacramento Kings.

**2005, Mar. 8**   *Litho.*   *Perf. 14*
2592-2597 A596   Set of 6   3.50 3.50
Each stamp printed in sheets of 12.

**Prehistoric Animals Type of 2005**
No. 2598, $2: a, Europholis. b, Ichthyosaurus. c, Plesiosaur. d, Varnerxiphactinus.
No. 2599, $2: a, Pterosaurus. b, Archaeopteryx. c, Pterosaurian. d, Micoraptor.
No. 2600, $6, Uintatherium. No. 2601, $6, Mammoth, vert.

**Perf. 13¼x13¾, 13¾x13¼**
**2005, Apr. 15**
**Sheets of 4, #a-d**
2598-2599 A604   Set of 2   12.00 12.00
**Souvenir Sheets**
2600-2601 A604   Set of 2   9.00 9.00

**End of World War II Type of 2005**
No. 2602, $2 — Battle of El Alamein: a, Field Marshal Bernard Montgomery directs troops forward. b, Field Marshal Erwin Rommel ready for battle. c, Troops move forward into battle. d, Line of German prisoners after battle.
No. 2603, $2 — Fall of Berlin: a, Russians at the gates of Berlin. b, German soldiers surrender. c, Berlin in ruins. d, Picking up the pieces.
No. 2604, $6, German soldier. No. 2605, $6, Sign with quote by Adolf Hitler, vert.

**2005, May 10**     *Perf. 13¼*
**Sheets of 4, #a-d**
2602-2603 A610   Set of 2   12.00 12.00
**Souvenir Sheets**
2604-2605 A610   Set of 2   9.00 9.00

**Albert Einstein Type of 2005**
No. 2606, vert.: a, Einstein, planet, diagram of Earth and Moon. b, Einstein. c, Israeli Prime Minister David Ben Gurion.

**2005, June 27**     *Perf. 13¼*
2606 A615 $3 Sheet of 3, #a-c   6.75 6.75
No. 2606 contains three 38x50mm stamps.

**V-J Day Type of 2005**
No. 2607, $2: a, P-38J Lightning. b, P-51D Mustang. c, F-4 fighter plane. d, Douglas C-47 Skytrain.
No. 2608, $2: a, Officer reads V-J Day message to his troops. b, Chaplain's prayer. c, Rejoicing the victory. d, USS Missouri in Tokyo Bay.

**2005, July 11**     *Perf. 12¾*
**Sheets of 4, #a-d**
2607-2608 A612   Set of 2   12.00 12.00

**Rotary International Type of 2005**
No. 2609, horiz.: a, People in front of National Polio Laboratory. b, People in National Polio Laboratory. c, Rotary International emblem.

**2005, July 11**     *Perf. 14*
2609 A613 $3 Sheet of 3, #a-c   6.75 6.75

Pope John Paul II (1920-
2005) — G207

**2005, Sept. 22**     *Perf. 13¼x13½*
2610 G207 $3 multi    2.25 2.25
Printed in sheets of 6.

Maimonides (1135-1204),
Philosopher — G208

**2005**     *Perf. 12*
2611 G208 $2 multi    1.50 1.50

**Christmas Type of 2005**
Designs: 35c, Madonna and Child, by Andrea del Sarto. 75c, Madonna Pesaro, by Titian. 90c, Madonna and Child, by Titian. $3, Madonna and Child, by Peter Paul Rubens.
$6, Madonna and Child, by Domenico Veneziano.

**2005**     *Perf. 12¾*
2612-2615 A625   Set of 4   3.75 3.75
**Souvenir Sheet**
2616 A625 $6 multi    4.50 4.50

Dog, by Chang Dai-Chien G209

**2006, Jan. 3    Litho.    Perf. 11½x11¼**
2617  G209  $1 multi                    .75   .75
New Year 2006 (Year of the Dog). Printed in sheets of 4.

**Pope Benedict XVI Type of 2006**
**2006, Jan. 10                     Perf. 13¼**
2618  A629  $2 Pope, diff.          1.50  1.50
Printed in sheets of 4.

**Elvis Presley Type of 2006**
*Variable Die Cut Perf.*
**2006, Feb. 21    Litho. & Embossed**
**Without Gum**
2619  A631  $20 multi              15.00  15.00

**Queen Elizabeth II, 80th Birthday Type of 2006**
No. 2620: a, Queen wearing hat, sepia photograph. b, Queen wearing tiara. c, Queen with Princess Anne. d, Queen wearing hat, color photograph.
$6, Portrait of Queen in robe.

**2006, Feb. 21    Litho.    Perf. 13¼**
2620  A632  $3 Sheet of 4, #a-d      9.00  9.00
**Souvenir Sheet**
**Perf. 12**
2621  A632  $6 multi               4.50  4.50

**Marilyn Monroe Type of 2006**
**2006, Mar. 30                     Perf. 13½**
2622  A634  $3 Monroe, diff.        2.25  2.25
Printed in sheets of 4.

**Rembrandt Type of 2006**
Designs: 75c, The Strolling Musicians. 90c, The Great Jewish Bride. $1, Old Haaringh. $4, Beggars Receiving Alms at the Door of a House. No. 2627, $6, Young Woman in a Pearl-trimmed Beret (70x100mm). No. 2628, $6, Portrait of a Boy (70x100mm).
No. 2629: a, Man from Lady and Gentleman in Black. b, Woman from Lady and Gentleman in Black. c, Man from The Shipbuilder and His Wife. d, Woman from The Shipbuilder and His Wife.

**Perf. 12, 12½x12¼ (#2627-2628)**
**2006, June 16**
2623-2628  A639  Set of 6          14.00  14.00
**Miniature Sheet**
2629  A639  $3 Sheet of 4, #a-d     9.00  9.00

**Mozart Type of 2006**
**2006, June 22    Litho.    Perf. 12¾**
2630  A640  $6 Don Giovanni         4.50  4.50

**Space Type of 2006**
No. 2631 — First Flight of Space Shuttle Columbia: a, Columbia on launchpad. b, Astronauts John W. Young and Robert L. Crippen. c, Liftoff of Columbia. d, Columbia in space. e, Crew in cabin. f, Columbia landing.
No. 2632, $3 — Apollo-Soyuz: a, Liftoff of Soyuz 19. b, Apollo-Soyuz crew. c, Crew in cabin. d, Soyuz 19.
No. 2633, $3 — Space Shuttle Discovery's return to space: a, Discovery on launchpad. b, Crew of Mission STS-114. c, Discovery and International Space Station. d, STS-114 space walk.
No. 2634, $6, Luna 9. No. 2635, $6, Venus Express. No. 2636, $6, Mars Reconnaissance Orbiter.

**2006, Sept. 14**
2631  A642  $2 Sheet of 6, #a-f     9.00  9.00
**Sheets of 4, #a-d**
2632-2633  A642  Set of 2          18.00  18.00
**Souvenir Sheets**
2634-2636  A642  Set of 3          13.50  13.50

**Columbus Type of 2006**
Designs: 75c, Pinta, vert. $1.50, Nina, Pinta and Santa Maria set sail. $2, Ship and map. $3, Columbus discovers San Salvador.
$6, Columbus.

---

**2006, Oct. 26**
2637-2640  A643  Set of 4           5.50  5.50
**Souvenir Sheet**
2641  A643  $6 multi               4.50  4.50

**Christmas Type of 2006**
Details of St. Willibrod in Adoration Before Mary, Mother of God, by Peter Paul Rubens: 25c, Man. 50c, Angels. 75c, Mary and Jesus. $1, St. Willibrod.
No. 2646: a, Like 25c. b, Like 50c. c, Like 75c. d, Like $1.

**2006, Dec. 21                     Perf. 14**
2642-2645  A646  Set of 4           1.90  1.90
**Souvenir Sheet**
2646  A646  $2 Sheet of 4, #a-d     6.00  6.00

Souvenir Sheet

Airships — G210

No. 2647: a, LZ-127. b, Dining room of the Hindenburg. c, Marine airship L53.

**2007, Jan. 16                     Perf. 13¼**
2647  G210  $3 Sheet of 3, #a-c     6.75  6.75

Souvenir Sheet

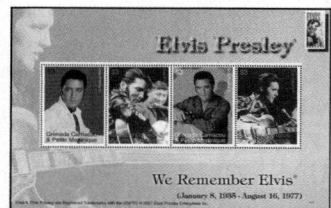

Elvis Presley (1935-77) — G211

No. 2648 — Various portraits with: a, Black denomination. b, Red denomination, playing guitar. c, White denomination. d, Red denomination, hands off guitar.

**2007, Jan. 16                     Perf. 14¼**
2648  G211  $3 Sheet of 4, #a-d     9.00  9.00

Pres. John F. Kennedy (1917-63) — G212

No. 2649, $2: a, On crutches, running for Congress. b, Campaigning for Congress. c, Campaigning in New Hampshire. d, As president.
No. 2650, $2.50: a, Naru Island. b, As Navy lieutenant on Solomon Islands, wearing cap. c, As lieutenant on Solomon Islands, without cap. d, SOS coconut carved by Kennedy.

**2007, Jan. 16                     Perf. 13½**
**Sheets of 4, #a-d**
2649-2650  G212  Set of 2          13.50  13.50

**Scouting Type of 2007**
Scout fleur-de-lis, "100," years "1907 / 2007," and background colors of: $2, Blue and green, horiz. $6, Orange and green, horiz.

---

**2007, Jan. 16**
2651  A650  $2 multi               1.50  1.50
**Souvenir Sheet**
2652  A650  $6 multi               4.50  4.50
No. 2651 printed in sheets of 4.

**Year of the Pig Type of 2007**
*Miniature Sheet*
No. 2653 — Wild Boar, by Liu Jiyou and painting name in: a, $1, Black. b, $1, Brown. c, $2, Black. d, $2, Red.

**2007, Feb. 15    Litho.    Perf. 14**
2653  A652  Sheet of 4, #a-d       4.50  4.50

G213

G214

Mushrooms — G215

Designs: 75c, Morchella semilibera. No. 2655, $1, Ganoderma resinaceum. No. 2656, $1, Helvella crispa. $4, Ganoderma sp.
No. 2658, $2: a, Russula sardonia. b, Amanita cruzii. c, Macrocybe titans. d, Amanita microspora.
No. 2659, $2: a, Aleuria aurantia. b, Boletus sp. c, Boletellus russellii. d, Otidea onotica.
No. 2660, $5, Amanita polypyramis. No. 2661, $5, Boletellus ananas. No. 2662, $5, Cantharellus cibarius.

**2007, May 16    Litho.    Perf. 14**
2654-2657  G213  Set of 4           5.25  5.25
**Sheets of 4, #a-d**
2658-2659  G214  Set of 2          12.00  12.00
**Souvenir Sheets**
2660  G214  $5 multi               3.75  3.75
2661-2662  G215  Set of 2           7.50  7.50

Birds — G216

Designs: 75c, Pied-billed grebe. No. 2664, $1, Black-crowned night heron. No. 2665, $1, Turkey vulture. $4, Green honeycreeper.
No. 2667, $2, horiz.: a, Caspian tern. b, Scarlet tanager. c, Common nighthawk. d, Osprey.
No. 2668, $2, horiz.: a, Hooded warbler. b, Northern flicker. c, Mockingbird. d, Blue tit.
No. 2669, $5, White-winged parakeet. No. 2670, $5, Blackpoll warbler. No. 2671, $5, Yellow-green vireo, horiz.

---

**2007, May 16**
2663-2666  G216  Set of 4           5.25  5.25
**Sheets of 4, #a-d**
2667-2668  G216  Set of 2          12.00  12.00
**Souvenir Sheets**
2669-2671  G216  Set of 3          11.50  11.50

Orchids — G217

Designs: 75c, Goodyera tesselata. $1.50, Oncidium floridanum. No. 2674, $2, Hexalectris spicata. $3, Pogonia ophioglossoides.
No. 2676, $2: a, Platanthera blephariglottis. b, Epipactis helleborine. c, Cypripedium alaskanum. d, Zeuxine strateumatica.
No. 2677, $2: a, Platanthera grandiflora. b, Platanthera peramoena. c, Cyrtopodium punctatum. d, Spiranthes odorata.
No. 2678, $6, Platanthera chapmanii. No. 2679, $6, Bletilla striata, horiz. No. 2680, $6, Macradenia lutescens, horiz.

**2007, May 16                     Perf. 12¾**
2672-2675  G217  Set of 4           5.50  5.50
**Sheets of 4, #a-d**
2676-2677  G217  Set of 2          12.00  12.00
**Souvenir Sheets**
2678-2680  G217  Set of 3          13.50  13.50

Betty Boop in "Snow White" — G218

No. 2681, horiz.: a, Queen looking at ring in snow. b, Green witch looking at mirror, dog and clown. c, Dancing ghost. d, Betty Boop asleep, frozen skull.
No. 2682, horiz.: a, $1, Queen looking in mirror. b, $1, Angry queen. c, $1, Knights and tree stump. d, $2, Betty Boop with alarm clock. e, $2, Betty Boop with mirror, dog, clown. f, $2, Betty Boop in snow.
$6, Betty Boop running.

**2007, June 4                     Perf. 13½**
2681  G218  $2 Sheet of 4, #a-d     6.00  6.00
2682  G218  Sheet of 6, #a-f        6.75  6.75
**Souvenir Sheet**
2683  G218  $6 multi               4.50  4.50

**Intl. Polar Year Type of 2007**
No. 2684, vert. — Royal penguins with: a, Country name at UR, denomination at LR. b, Country name at top, denomination at LR. c, Country name at UR, denomination at UL. d, Country name at bottom, denomination at UL. e, Country name at bottom, denomination at UR. f, Country name at UL, denomination at LR.
$6, African penguin, vert.

**2007, June 25                     Perf. 13½**
2684  A657  $2 Sheet of 6, #a-f     9.00  9.00
**Souvenir Sheet**
2685  A657  $6 multi               4.50  4.50

**First Helicopter Flight, Cent. Type of 2007**
No. 2686, horiz.: a, BK 117. b, UH-1 Iroquois. c, S-65/RH-53D. d, UH-1B/C Iroquois. e, Autogyro. f, BO 105.
$6, AH-64 Apache, horiz.

**2007, June 25**
2686  A664  $1.50 Sheet of 6, #a-f  6.75  6.75
**Souvenir Sheet**
2687  A664  $6 multi               4.50  4.50

## Pope Benedict XVI Type of 2007

**2007, July 11**
2688 A653 $1 Pope, diff.   .75 .75
Printed in sheets of 8.

Christmas
G219

Paintings: 25c, Virgin and Child with Saints Jerome and Bartholomew, by Alessandro Bonvicino. 50c, Virgin and Child Between Saints Thomas and Jerome, by Guido Reni. 75c, Virgin and Child, by Giovanni Batista Salvi. $1, Madonna of Decemviri, by Pietro Perugino.

**2007, Oct. 26      Perf. 14¼x14¾**
2689-2692 G219   Set of 4   1.90 1.90

## Wedding of Queen Elizabeth II and Prince Philip, 60th Anniv. Type of 2007
### Miniature Sheet

No. 2693: a, Couple, denomination at left, dull maroon panel. b, Queen, denomination at right, dull maroon panel. c, Queen, denomination at left, maroon panel. d, Couple, denomination at right, maroon panel. e, Couple, denomination at left, maroon panel. f, Queen, denomination at right, maroon panel.

**2007, June 25   Litho.   Perf. 13¼**
2693 A655 $1.50 Sheet of 6, #a-f 6.75 6.75

### Year of the Rat Type of 2007

**2007, Dec. 3      Perf. 13x13¼**
2694 A667 $1 multi   .75 .75
Printed in sheets of 4.

### Princess Diana Type of 2007

No. 2695 — Diana wearing: a, Plaid jacket. b, Purple feathered hat. c, Green dress. d, Plaid jacket, close-up in frame. e, Purple feathered hat, close-up in frame. f, Green dress, close-up in frame.
$6, Princess Diana, Prince Charles and infant, horiz.

**2008, Jan. 14      Perf. 13¼**
2695 A656 $1.50 Sheet of 6, #a-f 6.75 6.75

### Souvenir Sheet
2696 A656 $6 multi   4.50 4.50

### Elvis Presley Type of 2008

No. 2697 — Presley: a, Silhouette, holding microphone, gray background. b, Wearing green shirt. c, Silhouette, holding microphone, olive green background. d, Playing guitar. e, Silhouette, playing guitar. f, Wearing orange shirt.

**2008, Jan. 14      Perf. 13¼**
2697 A671 $1.50 Sheet of 6, #a-f 6.75 6.75

## World Stamp Championship Type of 2008

Design: Aerial view of Jerusalem, horiz. (149x125mm).

**2008, May 14      Imperf.**
2698 A676 $6 multi   4.50 4.50

### Basketball Type of 2008
#### Miniature Sheet

No. 2699 — Members of 2008 Boston Celtics basketball team: a, Ray Allen. b, Rajon Rondo. c, Paul Pierce. d, Kendrick Perkins. e, Kevin Garnett. f, Leon Powe. g, James Posey. h, Sam Cassell. i, P. J. Brown.

**2008, June 17   Litho.   Perf. 13½**
2699 A678 $1 Sheet of 9, #a-i   6.75 6.75

### Cats Type of 2008

No. 2700: a, Havana. b, Scottish Fold. c, American Curl. d, American Bobtail. e, Balinese. f, Singapura.
$6, Burmese, horiz.

**2008, June 18      Perf. 11½**
2700 A677 $1 Sheet of 6, #a-f   4.50 4.50
### Souvenir Sheet
2701 A677 $6 multi   4.50 4.50

---

## Elvis Presley Type of 2008
### Miniature Sheet

No. 2702 — Presley: a, Wearing lei, holding microphone in right hand. b, Playing guitar, red striped background. c, Wearing lei, holding microphone in left hand, right arm extended with hand in fist. d, Playing guitar, olive green and black background. e, Wearing lei, holding microphone in left hand, right hand at side. f, Wearing red shirt.

**2008, Oct. 10      Perf. 13¼**
2702 A670 $1.50 Sheet of 6, #a-f 6.75 6.75

## SEMI-POSTAL STAMPS

### 1988 Seoul Olympics Type

**1986, Dec. 1      Perf. 15**
B1 SP2 10c +5c Cycling   .90 .45
B2 SP2 50c +20c Sailing   .90 .90
B3 SP2 70c +30c Uneven Parallel Bars   .90 .90
B4 SP2 $2 +$1 Dressage   2.75 2.75
     Nos. B1-B4 (4)   5.45 5.00
### Souvenir Sheet
B5 SP2 $3 +$1 Marathon   4.50 4.50

## OFFICIAL STAMPS

Grenada Grenadines Nos. 396-408, 410, 440-442, 465-468 Overprinted "P.R.G."

**1982, June      Perf. 14, 15**
O1 G45 5c multicolored   .20 .20
O2 G45 6c multicolored   .20 .20
O3 G45 10c multicolored   .20 .20
O4 G45 12c multicolored   .20 .20
O5 G45 15c multicolored   .20 .20
O6 G45 20c multicolored   .20 .20
O7 G54 20c multicolored   .20 .20
O8 G45 25c multicolored   .20 .20
O9 G45 30c multicolored   .20 .20
O10 G45 40c multicolored   .25 .25
O11 CD331 40c multicolored   .25 .25
O12 G54 40c multicolored   .25 .25
O13 G45 50c multicolored   .30 .30
O14 G45 90c multicolored   .60 .60
O15 G45 $1 multicolored   .70 .70
O16 G54 $1 multicolored   .70 .70
O17 CD331 $2 multicolored   1.40 1.40
O18 G54 $2 multicolored   1.40 1.40
O19 G45 $3 multicolored   2.10 2.10
O20 CD331 $4 multicolored   2.75 2.75
O21 G45 $10 multicolored   7.00 7.00
     Nos. O1-O21 (21)   19.50 19.50

Royal Wedding stamps in changed colors, perf 15x14½ were also overprinted.

---

# GRIQUALAND WEST

ˈgri-kwə-ˌland ˈwest

LOCATION — In South Africa west of the Orange Free State and north of the Orange River
GOVT. — British Crown Colony
AREA — 15,197 sq. mi.
POP. — 83,375 (1891)
CAPITAL — Kimberley

Originally a territorial division of the Cape of Good Hope Colony, Griqualand West was declared a British Crown Colony in 1873 and together with Griqualand East was annexed to the Cape Colony in 1880.

12 Pence = 1 Shilling

---

Beware of forgeries.

---

Stamps of Cape of Good Hope 1864-65 (Type I, 4p, 6p, 1sh) and 1871-76 (Type II, ½p, 1p, 4p, 5sh) Surcharged or Overprinted

Type I — With frame line around stamp.
Type II — Without frame line.

"Hope" — A1

---

## Manuscript Surcharge in Dark Red

**1874      Wmk. 1      Perf. 14**
1  A1  1p on 4p blue (type I)   1,350. 2,250.

Overprinted          G. W.

**1877                  Black Overprint**
2      1p rose   575.00 95.00
a.   Double overprint         2,250.
### Red Overprint
3      4p blue (type II)   450.00 85.00

Overprinted

| | | |
|---|---|---|
| G | G | G | G |
| a | b | c | d |
| G | G | G | |
| e | f | g | |

### In Black on the One Penny, in Red on the Other Values

| | | | | |
|---|---|---|---|---|
| 4 | (a) | ½p gray black | 26.00 | 30.00 |
| 5 | (a) | 1p rose | 27.50 | 20.00 |
| 6 | (a) | 4p blue (type I) | 300.00 | 42.50 |
| 7 | (a) | 4p blue (type II) | 225.00 | 27.50 |
| 8 | (a) | 6p dull violet | 150.00 | 29.00 |
| 9 | (a) | 1sh green | 190.00 | 26.00 |
| a. | | Inverted overprint | | 550.00 |
| 10 | (a) | 5sh orange | 700.00 | 32.50 |
| 11 | (b) | ½p gray black | 30.00 | 35.00 |
| 12 | (b) | 1p rose | 30.00 | 22.50 |
| 13 | (b) | 4p blue (type I) | 425.00 | 50.00 |
| 14 | (b) | 4p blue (type II) | 275.00 | 30.00 |
| 15 | (b) | 6p dull violet | 300.00 | 35.00 |
| 16 | (b) | 1sh green | 375.00 | 27.50 |
| 17 | (b) | 5sh orange | 1,000. | 35.00 |
| 18 | (c) | ½p gray black | 65.00 | 75.00 |
| 19 | (c) | 1p rose | 70.00 | 42.50 |
| 20 | (c) | 4p blue (type I) | 750.00 | 125.00 |
| 21 | (c) | 4p blue (type II) | 500.00 | 80.00 |
| 22 | (c) | 6p dull violet | 350.00 | 85.00 |
| 23 | (c) | 1sh green | 425.00 | 65.00 |
| 24 | (c) | 5sh orange | 1,100. | 75.00 |
| 25 | (d) | ½p gray black | 35.00 | 42.50 |
| 26 | (d) | 1p rose | 32.50 | 27.50 |
| 27 | (d) | 4p blue (type I) | 475.00 | 65.00 |
| 28 | (d) | 4p blue (type II) | 350.00 | 37.50 |
| 29 | (d) | 6p dull violet | 225.00 | 42.50 |
| 30 | (d) | 1sh green | 325.00 | 32.50 |
| 31 | (d) | 5sh orange | 900.00 | 42.50 |
| 32 | (e) | ½p gray black | 65.00 | 80.00 |
| 33 | (e) | 1p rose | 70.00 | 42.50 |
| 34 | (e) | 4p blue (type I) | 750.00 | 125.00 |
| 35 | (e) | 4p blue (type II) | 475.00 | 85.00 |
| 36 | (e) | 6p dull violet | 350.00 | 90.00 |
| 37 | (e) | 1sh green | 425.00 | 65.00 |
| a. | | Inverted overprint | | 900.00 |
| 38 | (e) | 5sh orange | 1,100. | 75.00 |
| 39 | (f) | ½p gray black | 75.00 | 82.50 |
| 40 | (f) | 1p rose | 80.00 | 50.00 |
| 41 | (f) | 4p blue (type I) | 850.00 | 130.00 |
| 42 | (f) | 4p blue (type II) | 550.00 | 100.00 |
| 43 | (f) | 6p dull violet | 425.00 | 105.00 |
| 44 | (f) | 1sh green | 500.00 | 75.00 |
| 45 | (f) | 5sh orange | 1,600. | 85.00 |
| 46 | (g) | ½p gray black | 32.00 | 35.00 |
| 47 | (g) | 1p rose | 27.50 | 21.00 |
| 48 | (g) | 4p blue (type I) | 375.00 | 55.00 |
| 49 | (g) | 4p blue (type II) | 325.00 | 35.00 |
| 50 | (g) | 6p dull violet | 200.00 | 40.00 |
| 51 | (g) | 1sh green | 300.00 | 30.00 |
| a. | | Inverted overprint | — | 650.00 |
| 52 | (g) | 5sh orange | 850.00 | 37.50 |

There are minor varieties of types e and f.

Overprinted in Black

---

| | |
|---|---|
| G | G | G | G | G |
| i | k | l | m | n |
| G | G | G | G | |
| o | p | q | r | |

**1878**
| | | | | |
|---|---|---|---|---|
| 54 | (g) | 4p blue (type II) | 375.00 | 70.00 |
| 55 | (g) | 6p dull violet | 500.00 | 110.00 |
| 56 | (i) | 1p rose | 28.00 | 20.00 |
| 57 | (i) | 4p blue (type II) | 140.00 | 26.00 |
| 58 | (i) | 6p dull violet | 275.00 | 60.00 |
| a. | | Double overprint | | 900.00 |
| 59 | (k) | 1p rose | 65.00 | 32.50 |
| 60 | (k) | 4p blue (type II) | 350.00 | 55.00 |
| 61 | (k) | 6p dull violet | 475.00 | 95.00 |
| 62 | (l) | 1p rose | 30.00 | 21.00 |
| 63 | (l) | 4p blue (type II) | 160.00 | 27.50 |
| 64 | (l) | 6p dull violet | 325.00 | 70.00 |
| a. | | Double overprint | | 900.00 |
| 65 | (m) | 1p rose | 80.00 | 70.00 |
| 66 | (m) | 4p blue (type II) | 400.00 | 82.50 |
| 67 | (m) | 6p dull violet | 550.00 | 150.00 |
| 68 | (n) | 1p rose | 85.00 | 75.00 |
| 69 | (n) | 4p blue (type II) | 425.00 | 85.00 |
| 70 | (n) | 6p dull violet | 600.00 | 150.00 |
| a. | | Double overprint | | 1,100. |
| 71 | (o) | 1p rose | 75.00 | 47.50 |
| 72 | (o) | 4p blue (type II) | 375.00 | 75.00 |
| 73 | (o) | 6p dull violet | 500.00 | 110.00 |
| 74 | (p) | 1p rose | 77.50 | 67.50 |
| 75 | (p) | 4p blue (type II) | 375.00 | 75.00 |
| 76 | (p) | 6p dull violet | 500.00 | 130.00 |
| 77 | (q) | 1p rose | 125.00 | 100.00 |
| 78 | (q) | 4p blue (type II) | 600.00 | 160.00 |
| 79 | (q) | 6p dull violet | 800.00 | 225.00 |
| 80 | (r) | 1p rose | 425.00 | 325.00 |
| 81 | (r) | 4p blue (type II) | 2,000. | 475.00 |
| 82 | (r) | 6p dull violet | 2,400. | 625.00 |

There are two minor varieties of type i and one of type p.

Overprinted in Red

| | |
|---|---|
| G | G |
| s | t |

**1878**
| | | | | |
|---|---|---|---|---|
| 83 | (s) | ½p gray black | 14.50 | 14.50 |
| a. | | Double overprint | 52.50 | 67.50 |
| b. | | Inverted overprint | 17.00 | 17.00 |
| c. | | Double overprint, inverted | 100.00 | 125.00 |
| 84 | (s) | 4p blue (type II) | 350.00 | 100.00 |
| a. | | Inverted overprint | 900.00 | 100.00 |
| 85 | (t) | ½p gray black | 15.00 | 15.00 |
| a. | | Double overprint | 85.00 | 85.00 |
| b. | | Inverted overprint | 14.00 | 16.00 |
| 86 | (t) | 4p blue (type II) | | 90.00 |
| a. | | Inverted overprint | 400.00 | 90.00 |

### Black Overprint

| | | | | |
|---|---|---|---|---|
| 87 | (s) | ½p gray black | 225.00 | 125.00 |
| a. | | Inverted overprint | 250.00 | |
| b. | | With 2nd ovpt. (s) in red, invtd. | 425.00 | |
| c. | | With 2nd ovpt. (t) in red, invtd. | 200.00 | |
| 88 | (s) | 1p rose | 15.00 | 13.00 |
| a. | | Double overprint | 225.00 | 60.00 |
| b. | | Inverted overprint | 16.00 | 11.00 |
| c. | | Double overprint, both inverted | 225.00 | 80.00 |
| d. | | With second overprint (s) in red, both inverted | 45.00 | 47.50 |
| 89 | (s) | 4p blue (type I) | | 160.00 |
| 90 | (s) | 4p blue (type II) | 150.00 | 32.50 |
| a. | | Double overprint | — | 240.00 |
| b. | | Inverted overprint | 250.00 | 95.00 |
| c. | | Double overprint, both inverted | — | 300.00 |
| 91 | (s) | 6p dull violet | 145.00 | 30.00 |
| 92 | (t) | ½p gray black | 52.50 | 52.50 |
| a. | | Inverted overprint | 115.00 | 85.00 |
| b. | | With 2nd ovpt. inverted | 200.00 | |
| 93 | (t) | 1p rose | 15.00 | 13.50 |
| a. | | Double overprint | — | 100.00 |
| b. | | Inverted overprint | 92.50 | 34.00 |
| c. | | Double overprint, both inverted | — | 125.00 |
| d. | | With 2nd ovpt. (t) in red, both invtd. | 92.50 | 92.50 |
| 94 | (t) | 4p blue (type I) | | 160.00 |
| 95 | (t) | 4p blue (type II) | 170.00 | 15.00 |
| a. | | Double overprint | — | 210.00 |
| b. | | Inverted overprint | 275.00 | 32.50 |
| c. | | Double overprint, both inverted | — | 300.00 |
| 96 | (t) | 6p dull violet | | 32.50 |

Overprinted in Black

Overprinted in Black

| | | | | |
|---|---|---|---|---|
| **97** | ½p gray black | | 18.50 | 8.75 |
| *a.* | Double overprint | | 425.00 | 275.00 |
| **98** | 1p rose | | 19.50 | 6.50 |
| *a.* | Double overprint | | — | 150.00 |
| *b.* | Triple overprint | | — | 240.00 |
| *c.* | Inverted overprint | | — | 92.50 |
| **99** | 4p blue (type II) | | 37.50 | 6.50 |
| *a.* | Double overprint | | — | 125.00 |
| **100** | 6p brt violet | | 150.00 | 9.50 |
| *a.* | Double overprint | | 725.00 | 190.00 |
| *b.* | Inverted overprint | | — | 40.00 |
| **101** | 1sh green | | 135.00 | 7.00 |
| *a.* | Double overprint | | 400.00 | 97.50 |
| **102** | 5sh orange | | 475.00 | 15.00 |
| *a.* | Double overprint | | 650.00 | 87.50 |
| *b.* | Triple overprint | | — | 325.00 |

These stamps were declared obsolete in 1880 and the remainders were used in Cape of Good Hope offices as ordinary stamps. Prices for used stamps are for examples with such cancels.

# GUADELOUPE

ˈgwä-dəl-ˌüp

LOCATION — In the West Indies lying between Montserrat and Dominica
GOVT. — French colony
AREA — 688 sq. mi.
POP. — 271,262 (1946)
CAPITAL — Basse-Terre

Guadeloupe consists of two large islands, Guadeloupe proper and Grande-Terre, together with five smaller dependencies. Guadeloupe became an integral part of the Republic, acquiring the same status as the departments in metropolitan France, under a law effective Jan. 1, 1947.

100 Centimes = 1 Franc

Catalogue values for unused stamps in this country are for Never Hinged items, beginning with Scott 168 in the regular postage section, Scott B12 in the semi-postal section, Scott C1 in the airpost section, and Scott J38 in the postage due section.

See France Nos. 850, 909, 1280, 1913 for French stamps inscribed "Guadeloupe."

Stamps of French Colonies Surcharged

| | | | | |
|---|---|---|---|---|
| **1884** | | **Unwmk.** | | **Imperf.** |
| **1** | A8 20c on 30c brn, *bis* | | 72.50 | 60.00 |
| *a.* | Large "2" | | 325.00 | 260.00 |
| **2** | A8 25c on 35c blk, *org* | | 60.00 | 60.00 |
| *a.* | Large "2" | | 325.00 | 260.00 |
| *b.* | Large "5" | | 160.00 | 125.00 |

The 5c on 4c (French Colonies No. 40) was not regularly issued. Three examples exist. Value $42,500.

The 5c on 4c also exists as an essay, surcharge similar to the issued values. Value $1,000.

     c                d

| | | | | |
|---|---|---|---|---|
| **1889** | | **Perf. 14x13½** | | |
| | **Surcharged Type c** | | | |
| **3** | A9 3c on 20c red, *grn* | | 5.25 | 5.25 |
| **4** | A9 15c on 20c red, *grn* | | 32.50 | 27.50 |
| **5** | A9 25c on 20c red, *grn* | | 32.50 | 27.50 |
| | *Nos. 3-5 (3)* | | 70.25 | 60.25 |
| | **Surcharged Type d** | | | |
| **6** | A9 5c on 1c blk, *lil bl* | | 14.50 | 13.50 |
| *a.* | Inverted surcharge | | — | 1,400. |
| *b.* | Double surcharge | | 450.00 | 450.00 |
| **7** | A9 10c on 40c red, *straw* | | 40.00 | 35.00 |
| *a.* | Double surcharge | | 475.00 | 475.00 |
| **8** | A9 15c on 20c red, *grn* | | 32.50 | 30.00 |
| *a.* | Double surcharge | | 475.00 | 475.00 |
| **9** | A9 25c on 30c brn, *bis* | | 52.50 | 45.00 |
| *a.* | Double surcharge | | 475.00 | 475.00 |
| | *Nos. 6-9 (4)* | | 139.50 | 123.50 |

The word "centimes" in surcharges "b" and "c" varies from 10 to 12½mm.
Issue dates: No. 6, June 25, others, Mar. 22.

| | | | | |
|---|---|---|---|---|
| **1891** | | | | |
| **10** | A9 5c on 10c blk, *lav* | | 15.00 | 12.50 |
| **11** | A9 5c on 1fr brnz grn, *straw* | | 17.00 | 12.50 |

Stamps of French Colonies Overprinted in Black

| | | | | |
|---|---|---|---|---|
| **1891** | | | | **Imperf.** |
| **12** | A7 30c brn, *yelsh* | | 350.00 | *375.00* |
| *a.* | Double overprint | | 725.00 | 725.00 |
| **13** | A7 80c car, *pnksh* | | 1,100. | *1,300.* |
| | | **Perf. 14x13½** | | |
| **14** | A9 1c blk, *lil bl* | | 1.75 | 1.60 |
| *a.* | Double overprint | | 40.00 | 40.00 |
| *b.* | Inverted overprint | | 150.00 | 150.00 |
| **15** | A9 2c brn, *buff* | | 2.60 | 2.00 |
| *a.* | Double overprint | | 45.00 | 40.00 |
| **16** | A9 4c claret, *lav* | | 6.00 | 5.25 |
| **17** | A9 5c grn, *grnsh* | | 8.75 | 7.25 |
| *a.* | Double overprint | | 45.00 | 40.00 |
| *b.* | Inverted overprint | | 160.00 | 160.00 |
| **18** | A9 10c blk, *lavender* | | 17.00 | 13.50 |
| **19** | A9 15c blue | | 52.50 | 6.00 |
| *a.* | Double overprint | | — | 110.00 |
| **20** | A9 20c red, *grn* | | 45.00 | 30.00 |
| *a.* | Double overprint | | 240.00 | 240.00 |
| **21** | A9 25c blk, *rose* | | 47.50 | 5.25 |
| *a.* | Double overprint | | 240.00 | 240.00 |
| *b.* | Inverted overprint | | 225.00 | 225.00 |
| **22** | A9 30c brn, *bister* | | 45.00 | 30.00 |
| *a.* | Double overprint | | 240.00 | 240.00 |
| **23** | A9 35c dp vio, *org* | | 87.50 | 72.50 |
| *a.* | Double overprint | | 675.00 | 675.00 |
| **24** | A9 40c red, *straw* | | 65.00 | 52.50 |
| *a.* | Double overprint | | 675.00 | 675.00 |
| **25** | A9 75c car, *rose* | | 130.00 | 125.00 |
| **26** | A9 1fr brnz grn, *straw* | | 92.50 | 72.50 |
| | *Nos. 14-26 (13)* | | 601.10 | 423.35 |

The following errors may be found in all values: "GNADELOUPE," "GUADELOUEP," "GUADELONPE" and "GUADBLOUPE."

Navigation and Commerce — A7

| | | | | |
|---|---|---|---|---|
| | **Perf. 14x13½** | | | |
| **1892-1901** | **Typo.** | | | **Unwmk.** |
| | **Colony Name in Blue or Carmine** | | | |
| **27** | A7 1c blk, *lil bl* | | 1.40 | 1.40 |
| **28** | A7 2c brn, *buff* | | 1.50 | 1.40 |
| **29** | A7 4c claret, *lav* | | 1.75 | 1.50 |
| **30** | A7 5c grn, *grnsh* | | 3.50 | 1.50 |
| **31** | A7 5c yel grn ('01) | | 6.00 | 1.60 |
| **32** | A7 10c blk, *lavender* | | 10.00 | 3.25 |
| **33** | A7 10c red ('00) | | 8.75 | 2.40 |
| *a.* | Imperf. | | 120.00 | |
| **34** | A7 15c blue, quadrille paper | | 18.00 | 1.75 |
| **35** | A7 15c gray, *lt gray* ('00) | | 13.00 | 1.60 |
| **36** | A7 20c red, *grn* | | 11.00 | 6.50 |
| **37** | A7 25c blk, *rose* | | 11.00 | 4.00 |
| **38** | A7 25c blue ('00) | | 100.00 | 100.00 |
| **39** | A7 30c brn, *bister* | | 24.00 | 15.00 |
| **40** | A7 40c red, *straw* | | 24.00 | 15.00 |
| **41** | A7 50c car, *rose* | | 32.50 | 16.00 |

| | | | | |
|---|---|---|---|---|
| **42** | A7 50c brn, *az* ('00) | | 45.00 | 42.50 |
| **43** | A7 75c dp vio, *org* | | 32.50 | 22.50 |
| **44** | A7 1fr brnz grn, *straw* | | 32.50 | 30.00 |
| | *Nos. 27-44 (18)* | | 376.40 | 266.90 |

Perf. 13½x14 stamps are counterfeits.
For surcharges see Nos. 45-53, 83-85.

Nos. 39-41, 43-44 Surcharged in Black:

    f                  g

     h

| | | | | |
|---|---|---|---|---|
| **1903** | | | | |
| **45** | A7 (f) 5c on 30c | | 4.00 | 4.00 |
| *a.* | "C" instead of "G" | | 32.50 | 32.50 |
| *b.* | Inverted surcharge | | 45.00 | 45.00 |
| *c.* | Double surcharge | | 140.00 | 140.00 |
| *d.* | Double surch., inverted | | 160.00 | |
| **46** | A7 (g) 10c on 40c | | 9.50 | 9.50 |
| *a.* | "C" instead of "G" | | 40.00 | 40.00 |
| *b.* | "1" inverted | | 60.00 | 60.00 |
| *c.* | Inverted surcharge | | 55.00 | 55.00 |
| **47** | A7 (f) 15c on 50c | | 13.00 | 13.00 |
| *a.* | "C" instead of "G" | | 40.00 | 40.00 |
| *b.* | Inverted surcharge | | 110.00 | 110.00 |
| *c.* | "15" inverted | | 375.00 | 375.00 |
| **48** | A7 (g) 40c on 1fr | | 13.00 | 13.00 |
| *a.* | "C" instead of "G" | | 52.50 | 52.50 |
| *b.* | "4" inverted | | 120.00 | 120.00 |
| *c.* | Inverted surcharge | | 110.00 | 110.00 |
| *d.* | Double surcharge | | 240.00 | 240.00 |
| **49** | A7 (h) 1fr on 75c | | 42.50 | 42.50 |
| *a.* | "C" instead of "G" | | 160.00 | 160.00 |
| *b.* | "1" inverted | | 160.00 | 160.00 |
| *c.* | Value above "G & D" | | 300.00 | 300.00 |
| *d.* | Inverted surcharge | | 125.00 | 125.00 |
| | *Nos. 45-49 (5)* | | 82.00 | 82.00 |

Letters and figures from several fonts were used for these surcharges, resulting in numerous minor varieties.

Nos. 48-49 With Additional Overprint "1903" in a Frame

| | | | | |
|---|---|---|---|---|
| **1904, Mar.** | | | | |
| | **Red Overprint** | | | |
| **50** | A7 (g) 40c on 1fr | | 65.00 | 72.50 |
| **51** | A7 (h) 1fr on 75c | | 92.50 | 100.00 |
| | **Blue Overprint** | | | |
| **52** | A7 (g) 40c on 1fr | | 52.50 | 55.00 |
| **53** | A7 (h) 1fr on 75c | | 87.50 | 95.00 |
| | *Nos. 50-53 (4)* | | 297.50 | 322.50 |

The date "1903" may be found in 19 different positions and type faces within the frame. These stamps may also be found with the minor varieties of Nos. 48-49.
The 40c exists with black overprint. Value, $500 unused or used.

Harbor at Basse-Terre — A8

View of La Soufrière A9

Pointe-à-Pitre, Grand-Terre — A10

| | | | | |
|---|---|---|---|---|
| **1905-27** | **Typo.** | **Perf. 14x13½** | | |
| **54** | A8 1c blk, *bluish* | | .30 | .30 |
| **55** | A8 2c vio brn, *straw* | | .30 | .30 |
| **56** | A8 4c bis brn, *az* | | .30 | .30 |
| **57** | A8 5c green | | 2.10 | .65 |
| **58** | A8 5c dp blue ('22) | | .25 | .25 |
| **59** | A8 10c rose | | 2.10 | .65 |

| | | | | |
|---|---|---|---|---|
| **60** | A8 10c green ('22) | | 1.25 | 1.25 |
| **61** | A8 10c red, *bluish* ('25) | | .25 | .25 |
| **62** | A8 15c violet | | .55 | .50 |
| **63** | A9 20c red, *grn* | | .55 | .40 |
| **64** | A9 20c bl grn ('25) | | .65 | .65 |
| **65** | A9 25c blue | | .95 | .65 |
| **66** | A9 25c ol grn ('22) | | .65 | .65 |
| **67** | A9 30c black | | 4.50 | 3.00 |
| **68** | A9 30c rose ('22) | | .70 | .70 |
| **69** | A9 30c brn ol, *lav* ('25) | | .55 | .55 |
| **70** | A9 35c blk, *yel* ('06) | | .80 | .80 |
| **71** | A9 40c red, *straw* | | .80 | .80 |
| **72** | A9 45c ol gray, *lil* ('07) | | 1.25 | .80 |
| **73** | A9 45c rose ('25) | | .80 | .80 |
| **74** | A9 50c gray grn, *straw* | | 4.75 | 3.25 |
| **75** | A9 50c dp bl ('22) | | 1.10 | 1.10 |
| **76** | A9 50c violet ('25) | | .70 | .70 |
| **77** | A9 65c blue ('27) | | .70 | .70 |
| **78** | A9 75c car, *bl* | | .80 | .80 |
| **79** | A10 1fr blk, *green* | | 1.50 | 1.50 |
| **80** | A10 1fr lt bl ('25) | | .95 | .95 |
| **81** | A10 2fr car, *org* | | 2.00 | 2.00 |
| **82** | A10 5fr dp bl, *org* | | 6.50 | 6.50 |
| | *Nos. 54-82 (29)* | | 38.60 | 31.65 |

Nos. 57 and 59 exist imperf. Value, each $60.
For surcharges see #86-95, 167, B1-B2.

Nos. 29, 39 and 40 Surcharged in Carmine or Black

     a                  b

| | | | | |
|---|---|---|---|---|
| **1912, Nov.** | | | | |
| **83** | A7 5c on 4c claret, *lav* (C) | | 1.50 | 1.50 |
| **84** | A7 5c on 30c brn, *bis* (C) | | 1.90 | 1.90 |
| **85** | A7 10c on 40c red, *straw* | | 2.25 | 2.25 |
| | *Nos. 83-85 (3)* | | 5.65 | 5.65 |

Two spacings between the surcharged numerals are found on Nos. 83 to 85. For detailed listings, see the Scott Classic Specialized Catalogue of Stamps and Covers.

Stamps and Types of 1905-27 Surcharged with New Value and Bars

| | | | | |
|---|---|---|---|---|
| **1924-27** | | | | |
| **86** | A10 25c on 5fr dp bl, *org* | | .70 | .70 |
| **87** | A10 65c on 1fr gray grn | | 1.25 | 1.25 |
| **88** | A10 85c on 1fr gray grn | | 1.40 | 1.40 |
| **89** | A9 90c on 75c dl red | | 1.25 | 1.25 |
| **90** | A10 1.05fr on 2fr ver (Bl) | | .85 | .85 |
| **91** | A10 1.25fr on 1fr lt bl (R) | | .65 | .65 |
| **92** | A10 1.50fr on 1fr dk bl | | 1.25 | 1.25 |
| **93** | A10 3fr on 5fr org brn | | 1.50 | 1.50 |
| **94** | A10 10fr on 5fr vio rose, *org* | | 11.00 | 11.00 |
| **95** | A10 20fr on 5fr rose lil, *pnksh* | | 13.00 | 13.00 |
| | *Nos. 86-95 (10)* | | 32.85 | 32.85 |

Years issued: Nos. 87-88, 1925. Nos. 90-91, 1926. Nos. 89, 92-95, 1927.

Sugar Mill — A11

Saints Roadstead A12

Harbor Scene A13

| | | | | |
|---|---|---|---|---|
| | **Perf. 14x13½** | | | |
| **1928-40** | **Unwmk.** | | | **Typo.** |
| **96** | A11 1c yel & vio | | .25 | .25 |
| **97** | A11 2c blk & lt red | | .25 | .25 |
| **98** | A11 3c yel & red vio ('40) | | .30 | .30 |
| **99** | A11 4c yel grn & org brn | | .25 | .25 |
| **100** | A11 5c ver & grn | | .25 | .25 |
| **101** | A11 10c bis brn & dp bl | | .25 | .25 |
| **102** | A11 15c brn red & blk | | .30 | .30 |
| **103** | A11 20c lil & ol brn | | .50 | .50 |
| **104** | A12 25c grnsh bl & olvn | | .55 | .55 |
| **105** | A12 30c gray grn & yel grn | | .40 | .40 |

| | | | | |
|---|---|---|---|---|
| 106 | A12 | 35c bl grn ('38) | .40 | .40 |
| 107 | A12 | 40c yel & vio | .40 | .40 |
| 108 | A12 | 45c vio brn & slate | .95 | .80 |
| 109 | A12 | 45c bl grn & dl grn ('40) | 1.00 | 1.00 |
| 110 | A12 | 50c dl grn & org | .30 | .30 |
| 111 | A12 | 55c ultra & car ('38) | 1.25 | 1.25 |
| 112 | A12 | 60c ultra & car ('40) | .65 | .65 |
| 113 | A12 | 65c gray blk & ver | .55 | .55 |
| 114 | A12 | 70c gray blk & ver ('40) | .70 | .70 |
| 115 | A12 | 75c dl red & bl grn | .70 | .70 |
| 116 | A12 | 80c car & brn ('38) | .85 | .65 |
| 117 | A12 | 90c dl red & dl rose | 1.90 | 1.75 |
| 118 | A12 | 90c rose red & bl ('39) | 1.10 | 1.10 |
| 119 | A13 | 1fr lt rose & lt bl | 4.75 | 3.50 |
| 120 | A13 | 1fr rose red & org ('38) | 1.60 | 1.50 |
| 121 | A13 | 1fr bl gray & blk brn ('40) | .70 | .70 |
| 122 | A13 | 1.05fr lt bl & rose | 1.10 | 1.10 |
| 123 | A13 | 1.10fr lt red & grn | 3.50 | 2.75 |
| 124 | A13 | 1.25fr bl gray & blk brn ('33) | .65 | .65 |
| 125 | A13 | 1.25fr brt rose & red org ('39) | .95 | .95 |
| 126 | A13 | 1.40fr lt bl & lil rose ('40) | .70 | .70 |
| 127 | A13 | 1.50fr dl bl & bl | .40 | .40 |
| 128 | A13 | 1.60fr lil rose & yel brn ('40) | .70 | .70 |
| 129 | A13 | 1.75fr lil rose & yel brn ('33) | 5.00 | 3.25 |
| 130 | A13 | 1.75fr vio bl ('38) | 5.25 | 4.00 |
| 131 | A13 | 2fr bl grn & dk brn | .40 | .40 |
| 132 | A13 | 2.25fr vio bl ('39) | 1.10 | 1.10 |
| 133 | A13 | 2.50fr pale org & grn ('40) | 1.10 | 1.10 |
| 134 | A13 | 3fr org brn & sl | .65 | .65 |
| 135 | A13 | 5fr dl bl & org | 1.10 | 1.00 |
| 136 | A13 | 10fr vio & ol brn | 1.10 | 1.10 |
| 137 | A13 | 20fr green & mag | 1.40 | 1.40 |
| | | Nos. 96-137 (42) | 46.20 | 40.50 |

Nos. 96-103, 110, 119, 123, 134, 137 exist imperf. Values each $30-$60.
For surcharges see Nos. 161-166.
For 10c, type A11, without "RF", see No. 163A.

Common Design Types pictured following the introduction.

**Colonial Exposition Issue**
Common Design Types
**1931, Apr. 13     Engr.     Perf. 12½**
Name of Country in Black

| | | | | |
|---|---|---|---|---|
| 138 | CD70 | 40c deep green | 4.75 | 4.75 |
| 139 | CD71 | 50c violet | 4.75 | 4.75 |
| 140 | CD72 | 90c red orange | 4.75 | 4.75 |
| 141 | CD73 | 1.50fr dull blue | 4.75 | 4.75 |
| | | Nos. 138-141 (4) | 19.00 | 19.00 |

Cardinal Richelieu Establishing French Antilles Co., 1635 — A14

Victor Hugues and his Corsairs — A15

**1935     Perf. 13**

| | | | | |
|---|---|---|---|---|
| 142 | A14 | 40c gray brown | 10.00 | 10.00 |
| 143 | A14 | 50c dull red | 10.00 | 10.00 |
| 144 | A14 | 1.50fr dull blue | 10.00 | 10.00 |
| 145 | A15 | 1.75fr lilac rose | 10.00 | 10.00 |
| 146 | A15 | 5fr dark brown | 10.00 | 10.00 |
| 147 | A15 | 10fr blue green | 10.00 | 10.00 |
| | | Nos. 142-147 (6) | 60.00 | 60.00 |

Tercentenary of the establishment of the French colonies in the West Indies.

**Paris International Exposition Issue**
Common Design Types
**1937     Perf. 13**

| | | | | |
|---|---|---|---|---|
| 148 | CD74 | 20c deep violet | 1.90 | 1.90 |
| 149 | CD75 | 30c dark green | 1.75 | 1.75 |
| 150 | CD76 | 40c car rose | 1.50 | 1.50 |
| 151 | CD77 | 50c dk brn & blk | 1.50 | 1.50 |

| | | | | |
|---|---|---|---|---|
| 152 | CD78 | 90c red | 1.50 | 1.50 |
| 153 | CD79 | 1.50fr ultra | 1.90 | 1.90 |
| | | Nos. 148-153 (6) | 10.05 | 10.05 |

**Colonial Arts Exhibition Issue**
Souvenir Sheet
Common Design Type
**1937     Imperf.**

| | | | | |
|---|---|---|---|---|
| 154 | CD75 | 3fr dark blue | 9.50 | 11.00 |

**New York World's Fair Issue**
Common Design Type
**1939     Engr.     Perf. 12½x12**

| | | | | |
|---|---|---|---|---|
| 155 | CD82 | 1.25fr car lake | 1.25 | 1.25 |
| 156 | CD82 | 2.25fr ultra | 1.25 | 1.25 |

For surcharges see Nos. 159-160.

La Soufrière View and Marshal Pétain A16

**1941     Engr.     Perf. 12½x12**

| | | | | |
|---|---|---|---|---|
| 157 | A16 | 1fr lilac | | .80 |
| 158 | A16 | 2.50fr blue | | .80 |

Nos. 157-158 were issued by the Vichy government in France, but were not placed on sale in Guadeloupe.
For surcharges, see Nos. B11A-B11B.

Nos. 155, 156, 113, 117 and 118
Surcharged with New Values in Black
**1943     Perf. 14x13½, 12½x12**

| | | | | |
|---|---|---|---|---|
| 159 | CD82 | 40c on 1.25fr | .80 | .80 |
| 160 | CD82 | 50c on 2.25fr | 1.60 | 1.60 |
| 161 | A12 | 50c on 65c | 1.00 | 1.00 |
| 162 | A12 | 1fr on 90c (#117) | 1.40 | 1.40 |
| 163 | A12 | 1fr on 90c (#118) | 1.25 | 1.25 |
| | | Nos. 159-163 (5) | 6.05 | 6.05 |

Type of 1928 Without "RF"
**1943     Perf. 14x13½**

| | | | | |
|---|---|---|---|---|
| 163A | A11 | 10c bis brn & dp blue | | .65 |

No. 163A was issued by the Vichy government in France, and was not placed on sale in Guadeloupe.

Nos. 104, 106, 113 and 90
Surcharged with New Values in Black
**1944     Perf. 14x13½**

| | | | | |
|---|---|---|---|---|
| 164 | A12 | 40c on 35c | 1.10 | 1.10 |
| 165 | A12 | 50c on 25c | .30 | .30 |
| 166 | A12 | 1fr on 65c | 1.25 | 1.25 |
| a. | | Double surcharge | 200.00 | 150.00 |
| 167 | A10 | 4fr on 1.05fr on 2fr | 1.75 | 1.75 |
| | | Nos. 164-167 (4) | 4.40 | 4.40 |

The surcharge on No. 166 is spelled out.

> **Catalogue values for unused stamps in this section, from this point to the end of the section, are for Never Hinged items.**

Dolphins A17

**1945     Unwmk.     Photo.     Perf. 11½**

| | | | | |
|---|---|---|---|---|
| 168 | A17 | 10c chlky bl & red org | .30 | .25 |
| 169 | A17 | 30c lt yel grn & red | .30 | .25 |
| 170 | A17 | 40c lt bl & car | .80 | .65 |
| 171 | A17 | 50c red org & yel grn | .40 | .30 |
| 172 | A17 | 60c ol bis & lt bl | .40 | .30 |
| 173 | A17 | 70c lt gray & yel grn | .80 | .65 |
| 174 | A17 | 80c lt bl grn & yel | .80 | .65 |
| 175 | A17 | 1fr brn vio & grn | .40 | .30 |
| 176 | A17 | 1.20fr brt red vio & yel grn | .40 | .30 |
| 177 | A17 | 1.50fr dl brn & car | .80 | .55 |
| 178 | A17 | 2fr cer & bl | .80 | .55 |
| 179 | A17 | 2.40fr sal & yel grn | 1.40 | |
| 180 | A17 | 3fr gray brn & bl vio | .80 | .55 |
| 181 | A17 | 4fr ultra & buff | .65 | .30 |
| 182 | A17 | 4.50fr brn org & grn | .80 | .55 |
| 183 | A17 | 5fr dk vio & grn | .95 | .65 |
| 184 | A17 | 10fr gray grn & red vio | .95 | .65 |
| 185 | A17 | 15fr sl gray & org | 1.25 | .85 |

| | | | | |
|---|---|---|---|---|
| 186 | A17 | 20fr pale gray & dl org | 2.10 | 1.00 |
| | | Nos. 168-186 (19) | 15.10 | 10.25 |

**Eboue Issue**
Common Design Type
**1945     Engr.     Perf. 13**

| | | | | |
|---|---|---|---|---|
| 187 | CD91 | 2fr black | .65 | .50 |
| 188 | CD91 | 25fr Prussian green | 1.40 | 1.10 |

Basse-Terre Harbor and Woman A18

Cutting Sugar Cane — A19

Pineapple Bearer — A20

Guadeloupe Woman — A21

Gathering Coffee — A22

Guadeloupe Woman — A23

**1947     Unwmk.     Engr.     Perf. 13**

| | | | | |
|---|---|---|---|---|
| 189 | A18 | 10c red brown | .30 | .25 |
| 190 | A18 | 30c sepia | .30 | .25 |
| 191 | A18 | 50c blue grn | .40 | .30 |
| 192 | A19 | 60c black brn | .65 | .50 |
| 193 | A19 | 1fr dp carmine | .95 | .65 |
| 194 | A19 | 1.50fr dk gray bl | 1.40 | .85 |
| 195 | A20 | 2fr blue grn | 1.40 | .85 |
| 196 | A20 | 2.50fr dp car | 1.25 | .95 |
| 197 | A20 | 3fr deep blue | 1.40 | .95 |
| 198 | A21 | 4fr violet | 1.25 | .95 |
| 199 | A21 | 5fr blue grn | 1.25 | .95 |
| 200 | A21 | 6fr red | 1.25 | .95 |
| 201 | A22 | 10fr deep blue | 1.25 | .95 |
| 202 | A22 | 15fr dk vio brn | 1.90 | 1.10 |
| 203 | A22 | 20fr rose red | 2.10 | 1.40 |
| 204 | A23 | 25fr blue green | 5.50 | 2.75 |
| 205 | A23 | 40fr red green | 6.50 | 3.50 |
| | | Nos. 189-205 (17) | 29.05 | 18.10 |

**SEMI-POSTAL STAMPS**

Nos. 59 and 62 Surcharged in Red

**1915-17     Unwmk.     Perf. 14 x 13½**

| | | | | |
|---|---|---|---|---|
| B1 | A8 | 10c + 5c rose | 5.25 | 3.50 |
| B2 | A8 | 15c + 5c violet | 5.25 | 3.50 |
| a. | | Double surcharge | 225.00 | 225.00 |

**Curie Issue**
Common Design Type
**1938, Oct. 24     Perf. 13**

| | | | | |
|---|---|---|---|---|
| B3 | CD80 | 1.75fr + 50c brt ultra | 11.00 | 11.00 |

**French Revolution Issue**
Common Design Type
Name and Value Typo. in Black
**1939, July 5     Photo.     Perf. 13**

| | | | | |
|---|---|---|---|---|
| B4 | CD83 | 45c + 25c green | 10.00 | 10.00 |
| B5 | CD83 | 70c + 30c brown | 10.00 | 10.00 |
| B6 | CD83 | 90c + 35c red org | 10.00 | 10.00 |
| B7 | CD83 | 1.25fr + 1fr rose pink | 10.00 | 10.00 |
| B8 | CD83 | 2.25fr + 2fr blue | 10.00 | 10.00 |
| | | Nos. B4-B8 (5) | 50.00 | 50.00 |

Common Design Type and

Colonial Artillery SP1

Colonial Infantry — SP2

**1941     Photo.     Perf. 13½**

| | | | | |
|---|---|---|---|---|
| B9 | SP1 | 1fr + 1fr red | | 1.00 |
| B10 | CD86 | 1.50fr + 3fr maroon | | 1.00 |
| B11 | SP2 | 2.50fr + 1fr blue | | 1.50 |
| | | Nos. B9-B11 (3) | | 3.50 |

Nos. B9-B11 were issued by the Vichy government in France, but were not placed on sale in Guadeloupe.

Nos. 157-158
Surcharged in Black or Red

**1944     Engr.     Perf. 12½x12**

| | | | | |
|---|---|---|---|---|
| B11A | | 50c + 1.50fr on 2.50fr blue (R) | | .80 |
| B11B | | + 2.50fr on 1fr lilac | | .80 |

Colonial Development Fund.
Nos. B11A-B11B were issued by the Vichy government in France, but were not placed on sale in Guadeloupe.

> **Catalogue values for unused stamps in this section, from this point to the end of the section, are for Never Hinged items.**

**Red Cross Issue**
Common Design Type
**1944     Perf. 14½x14**

| | | | | |
|---|---|---|---|---|
| B12 | CD90 | 5fr + 20fr ultra | 1.40 | 1.00 |

The surtax was for the French Red Cross and national relief.

**AIR POST STAMPS**

> **Catalogue values for unused stamps in this section are for Never Hinged items.**

Common Design Type
**1945     Unwmk.     Photo.     Perf. 14½x14**

| | | | | |
|---|---|---|---|---|
| C1 | CD87 | 50fr green | 1.50 | 1.00 |
| C2 | CD87 | 100fr deep plum | 2.25 | 1.50 |

**Victory Issue**
Common Design Type
**1946, May 8     Engr.     Perf. 12½**

| | | | | |
|---|---|---|---|---|
| C3 | CD92 | 8fr redsh brn | 1.25 | 1.00 |

## Chad to Rhine Issue
### Common Design Types
**1946, June 6**

| | | | | |
|---|---|---|---|---|
| C4 | CD93 | 5fr dk slate grn | 1.90 | 1.60 |
| C5 | CD94 | 10fr deep blue | 1.90 | 1.60 |
| C6 | CD95 | 15fr brt violet | 1.90 | 1.60 |
| C7 | CD96 | 20fr brown car | 1.90 | 1.60 |
| C8 | CD97 | 25fr black | 1.90 | 1.60 |
| C9 | CD98 | 50fr red brown | 1.90 | 1.60 |
| | | Nos. C4-C9 (6) | 11.40 | 9.60 |

Gathering Bananas — AP1

Seaplane at Roadstead — AP2

Pointe-a-Pitre Harbor and Guadeloupe Woman — AP3

**1947    Unwmk.    Perf. 13**

| | | | | |
|---|---|---|---|---|
| C10 | AP1 | 50fr dk brown violet | 6.00 | 2.75 |
| C11 | AP2 | 100fr deep blue | 8.75 | 5.25 |
| C12 | AP3 | 200fr red | 11.50 | 5.50 |
| | | Nos. C10-C12 (3) | 26.25 | 13.50 |

## AIR POST SEMI-POSTAL STAMPS

Mother & Nurse with Children — SPAP1

**1942, June 22    Engr.    Perf. 13**

| | | | |
|---|---|---|---|
| CB1 | SPAP1 | 1.50fr + 3.50fr green | 1.00 |
| CB2 | SPAP1 | 2fr + 6fr brown & red | 1.00 |

Native children's welfare fund.

Nos. CB1-CB2 were issued by the Vichy government in France, but were not placed on sale in Guadeloupe.

### Colonial Education Fund
#### Common Design Type
**1942, June 22**

| | | | |
|---|---|---|---|
| CB3 | CD86a | 1.20fr + 1.80fr blue & red | 1.10 |

No. CB3 was issued by the Vichy government in France, but was not placed on sale in Guadeloupe.

## POSTAGE DUE STAMPS

D1    D2    D3

---

**1876    Unwmk.    Typeset    Imperf.**

| | | | | |
|---|---|---|---|---|
| J1 | D1 | 25c black | 1,350. | 925.00 |
| J2 | D2 | 40c black, blue | | 37,500. |
| J3 | D3 | 40c black | 1,500. | 1,200. |

Twenty varieties of each.

Nos. J1 and J3 have been reprinted on thinner and whiter paper than the originals.

D4    D5

**1879**

| | | | | |
|---|---|---|---|---|
| J4 | D4 | 15c black, blue | 55.00 | 52.50 |
| a. | | Period after "c" omitted | 175.00 | 175.00 |
| J5 | D4 | 30c black | 110.00 | 87.50 |
| a. | | Period after "c" omitted | 240.00 | 225.00 |

Twenty varieties of each.

**1884**

| | | | | |
|---|---|---|---|---|
| J6 | D5 | 5c black | 35.00 | 35.00 |
| J7 | D5 | 10c black, blue | 75.00 | 65.00 |
| J8 | D5 | 15c black, violet | 110.00 | 87.50 |
| J9 | D5 | 20c black, rose | 160.00 | 100.00 |
| a. | | Italic "2" in "20" | 1,000. | 950.00 |
| J10 | D5 | 30c black, yellow | 160.00 | 160.00 |
| J11 | D5 | 35c black, gray | 60.00 | 52.50 |
| J12 | D5 | 50c black, green | 32.50 | 27.50 |
| | | Nos. J6-J12 (7) | 632.50 | 527.50 |

There are ten varieties of the 35c, and fifteen of each of the other values, also numerous wrong font and missing letters.

### Postage Due Stamps of French Colonies Surcharged in Black

**1903**

| | | | | |
|---|---|---|---|---|
| J13 | D1 | 30c on 60c brn, cr | 325.00 | 325.00 |
| a. | | "3" with flat top | 325.00 | 325.00 |
| b. | | Inverted surcharge | 1,100. | 1,100. |
| c. | | As "a," inverted | 2,000. | 2,000. |
| J14 | D1 | 30c on 1fr rose, cr | 400.00 | 400.00 |
| a. | | Inverted surcharge | 1,200. | 1,200. |
| b. | | "3" with flat top | 1,200. | 1,200. |
| c. | | As "b," inverted | 2,250. | 2,250. |

Gustavia Bay — D6    Avenue of Royal Palms — D7

**1905-06    Typo.    Perf. 14x13½**

| | | | | |
|---|---|---|---|---|
| J15 | D6 | 5c blue | .55 | .55 |
| J16 | D6 | 10c brown | .55 | .55 |
| J17 | D6 | 15c green | 1.00 | 1.00 |
| J18 | D6 | 20c black, yel ('06) | 1.00 | 1.00 |
| J19 | D6 | 30c rose | 1.25 | 1.25 |
| J20 | D6 | 50c black | 3.25 | 3.25 |
| J21 | D6 | 60c brown orange | 1.75 | 1.75 |
| J22 | D6 | 1fr violet | 3.25 | 3.25 |
| | | Nos. J15-J22 (8) | 12.60 | 12.60 |

Type of 1905-06 Issue Surcharged

**1926-27**

| | | | | |
|---|---|---|---|---|
| J23 | D6 | 2fr on 1fr gray | 2.00 | 2.00 |
| J24 | D6 | 3fr on 1fr ultra ('27) | 2.75 | 2.75 |

**1928, June 18**

| | | | | |
|---|---|---|---|---|
| J25 | D7 | 2c olive brn & lil | .25 | .25 |
| J26 | D7 | 4c bl & org brn | .25 | .25 |
| J27 | D7 | 5c gray grn & dk brn | .25 | .25 |
| J28 | D7 | 10c dl vio & yel | .30 | .30 |
| J29 | D7 | 15c rose & olive grn | .30 | .30 |
| J30 | D7 | 20c brn org & ol grn | .50 | .50 |
| J31 | D7 | 25c brn red & bl grn | .50 | .50 |
| J32 | D7 | 30c slate & olivine | .80 | .80 |
| J33 | D7 | 50c ol brn & lt red | .80 | .80 |
| J34 | D7 | 60c dp bl & blk | .80 | .80 |
| J35 | D7 | 1fr green & orange | 2.60 | 2.60 |

---

| | | | | |
|---|---|---|---|---|
| J36 | D7 | 2fr bis brn & lt red | 1.90 | 1.90 |
| J37 | D7 | 3fr vio & bl blk | 1.10 | 1.10 |
| | | Nos. J25-J37 (13) | 10.35 | 10.35 |

### Type of 1928 Without "RF"
**1944**

| | | | |
|---|---|---|---|
| J37A | D7 | 60c dp bl & blk | .30 |
| J37B | D7 | 1fr green & orange | .65 |
| J37C | D7 | 2fr bis brn & lt red | .65 |
| | | Nos. J37A-J37C (3) | 1.60 |

Nos. J37A-J37C were issued by the Vichy government in France, but were not placed on sale in Guadeloupe.

> Catalogue values for unused stamps in this section, from this point to the end of the section, are for Never Hinged items.

D8

**Perf. 14x13**

**1947, June 2    Unwmk.    Engr.**

| | | | | |
|---|---|---|---|---|
| J38 | D8 | 10c black | .30 | .25 |
| J39 | D8 | 30c dull blue green | .40 | .30 |
| J40 | D8 | 50c bright ultra | .40 | .30 |
| J41 | D8 | 1fr dark green | .65 | .50 |
| J42 | D8 | 2fr dark blue | .85 | .70 |
| J43 | D8 | 3fr black brown | 1.25 | 1.00 |
| J44 | D8 | 4fr lilac rose | 1.40 | 1.25 |
| J45 | D8 | 5fr purple | 1.90 | 1.60 |
| J46 | D8 | 10fr red | 2.60 | 2.10 |
| J47 | D8 | 20fr dark violet | 3.00 | 2.25 |
| | | Nos. J38-J47 (10) | 12.75 | 10.25 |

---

# GUATEMALA

ˌgwä-lə-ˈmä-lə

LOCATION — Central America, bordering on Atlantic and Pacific Oceans
GOVT. — Republic
AREA — 42,042 sq. mi.
POP. — 12,335,580 (1999 est.)
CAPITAL — Guatemala City

100 Centavos = 8 Reales = 1 Peso
100 Centavos de Quetzal = 1 Quetzal (1927)

> Catalogue values for unused stamps in this country are for Never Hinged items, beginning with Scott 316 in the regular postage section, Scott B5 in the semi-postal section, Scott C137 in the air post section, Scott CB5 in the air post semi-postal section and Scott E2 in the special delivery section.

Coat of Arms
A1    A2

Two types of 10c:
Type I — Both zeros in "10" are wide.
Type II — Left zero narrow.

**Perf. 14x13½**

**1871, Mar. 1    Typo.    Unwmk.**

| | | | | |
|---|---|---|---|---|
| 1 | A1 | 1c ocher | .75 | 10.00 |
| a. | | Imperf., pair | 5.00 | |
| b. | | Printed on both sides, imperf. | 75.00 | |
| 2 | A1 | 5c lt bister brn | 4.00 | 7.50 |
| a. | | Imperf. pair | 35.00 | |
| b. | | Tête bêche pair | 150.00 | |
| c. | | Tête bêche pair, imperf. | 2,600. | |
| 3 | A1 | 10c blue (I) | 5.00 | 8.00 |
| a. | | Imperf. pair (I) | 45.00 | |
| b. | | Type II | 8.00 | 10.00 |
| c. | | Imperf. pair (II) | 60.00 | |

---

| | | | | |
|---|---|---|---|---|
| 4 | A1 | 20c rose | 4.00 | 7.50 |
| a. | | Imperf., pair | 45.00 | |
| b. | | 20c blue (error) | 125.00 | 125.00 |
| c. | | As "b," imperf. | 800.00 | |
| | | Nos. 1-4 (4) | 13.75 | 33.00 |

Forgeries exist. Forged cancellations abound. See No. C458.

**1873    Litho.    Perf. 12**

| | | | | |
|---|---|---|---|---|
| 5 | A2 | 4r dull red vio | 325.00 | 85.00 |
| 6 | A2 | 1p dull yellow | 175.00 | 115.00 |

Forgeries exist.

Liberty
A3    A4

A5    A6

**1875, Apr. 15    Engr.**

| | | | | |
|---|---|---|---|---|
| 7 | A3 | ¼r black | 1.00 | 3.50 |
| 8 | A4 | ½r blue green | 1.00 | 3.00 |
| 9 | A5 | 1r blue | 1.00 | 3.00 |
| a. | | Half used as ½r on cover | | 1,700. |
| 10 | A6 | 2r dull red | 1.00 | 3.00 |
| | | Nos. 7-10 (4) | 4.00 | 12.50 |

Nos. 7-10 normally lack gum. Unused values are for examples without gum.
Forgeries and forged cancellations exist.

Indian Woman — A7    Quetzal — A8

### Typographed on Tinted Paper
**1878, Jan. 10    Perf. 13**

| | | | | |
|---|---|---|---|---|
| 11 | A7 | ½r yellow grn | .75 | 3.00 |
| 12 | A7 | 2r carmine rose | 1.25 | 4.00 |
| 13 | A7 | 4r violet | 1.25 | 4.50 |
| 14 | A7 | 1p yellow | 2.00 | 9.00 |
| c. | | Half used as 4r on cover | | 2,200. |
| | | Nos. 11-14 (4) | 5.25 | 20.50 |

Some sheets of Nos. 11-14 have papermaker's watermark, "LACROIX FRERES," in double-lined capitals appearing on six stamps.
Part perforate pairs of Nos. 11, 12 and 14 exist. Value for each, about $100.
Forgeries of Nos. 11-14 are plentiful. Forged cancellations exist.
For surcharges see Nos. 18, 20.

**Imperf., Pairs**

| | | | |
|---|---|---|---|
| 11a | A7 | ½r yellow green | 50.00 |
| 12a | A7 | 2r carmine rose | 50.00 |
| 13a | A7 | 4r violet | 50.00 |
| 14a | A7 | 1p yellow | 50.00 |

**1879    Engr.    Perf. 12**

| | | | | |
|---|---|---|---|---|
| 15 | A8 | ¼r brown & green | 2.50 | 2.75 |
| 16 | A8 | 1r black & green | 2.50 | 3.75 |

For similar types see A11, A72, A103, A121, A146. For surcharges see Nos. 17, 19.

Nos. 11, 12, 15, 16 Surcharged in Black

**1881    Perf. 12 and 13**

| | | | | |
|---|---|---|---|---|
| 17 | A8 | 1c on ¼r brn & grn | 11.25 | 15.00 |
| a. | | "ecntavo," | 37.50 | 45.00 |
| b. | | Pair, one without surcharge | 200.00 | |
| 18 | A7 | 5c on ½r yel grn | 5.00 | 5.00 |
| a. | | "ecntavos," | 35.00 | 35.00 |
| b. | | "5" omitted | 100.00 | |
| c. | | Double surcharge | 90.00 | 110.00 |

| 19 | A8 | 10c on 1r blk & grn | 16.00 | 22.50 |
|---|---|---|---|---|
| a. | | "s" of "centavos" missing | 75.00 | 75.00 |
| b. | | "ecntavos" | 40.00 | 45.00 |
| 20 | A7 | 20c on 2r car rose | 30.00 | 40.00 |
| a. | | Horiz. pair, imperf. between | 425.00 | |
| | | Nos. 17-20 (4) | 62.25 | 85.00 |

The 5c had three settings.
Surcharge varieties found on Nos. 17-20 include: Period omitted; comma instead of period; "ecntavo." or "ecntavos."; "s" omitted; spaced "centavos."; wider "0" in "20."
Counterfeits of Nos. 17-20 are plentiful.

Quetzal — A11

**1881, Nov. 7  Engr.  Perf. 12**

| 21 | A11 | 1c black & grn | 2.75 | 1.90 |
|---|---|---|---|---|
| 22 | A11 | 2c brown & grn | 2.75 | 1.90 |
| a. | | Center inverted | 400.00 | |
| 23 | A11 | 5c red & grn | 5.75 | 2.50 |
| a. | | Center inverted | 3,000. | 1,300. |
| 24 | A11 | 10c gray vio & grn | 2.75 | 1.90 |
| 25 | A11 | 20c yellow & grn | 2.75 | 2.25 |
| a. | | Center inverted | 500.00 | |
| | | Nos. 21-25 (5) | 16.75 | 10.45 |

Gen. Justo Rufino Barrios — A12

**1886, Mar. 6**

| 26 | A12 | 25c on 1p ver | .70 | .70 |
|---|---|---|---|---|
| a. | | "centovos" | 1.50 | |
| b. | | "centanos" | 1.50 | |
| c. | | "255" instead of "25" | 150.00 | |
| d. | | Inverted "S" in "Nacionales" | 20.00 | |
| f. | | "cen avos" | 20.00 | |
| h. | | "Corre cionales" | 20.00 | |
| i. | | Inverted surcharge | 75.00 | |
| 27 | A12 | 50c on 1p ver | .70 | .70 |
| a. | | "centovos" | 1.50 | |
| b. | | "centanos" | 1.50 | |
| c. | | "Carreos" | 1.50 | |
| d. | | Inverted surcharge | 50.00 | |
| e. | | Double surcharge | 75.00 | |
| f. | | Inverted "S" in "Nacionales" | 10.00 | |
| g. | | "cen avos" | 20.00 | |
| h. | | "cen avos" | 20.00 | |
| 28 | A12 | 75c on 1p ver | .70 | .70 |
| a. | | "centovos" | 1.50 | |
| b. | | "centanos" | 1.50 | |
| c. | | "Carreos" | 1.50 | |
| d. | | "50" for "75" at upper right | 2.00 | |
| e. | | Inverted "S" in "Nacionales" | 10.00 | |
| f. | | Double surcharge | 75.00 | |
| g. | | "ales" inverted | 100.00 | |
| 29 | A12 | 100c on 1p ver | 1.40 | 1.40 |
| a. | | "110" at upper left and "á" at lower left, instead of "100" | 5.00 | |
| b. | | Inverted surcharge | 75.00 | |
| c. | | "Guatemala" bolder; 23mm instead of 18½mm wide | 2.25 | |
| d. | | Double surcharge, one diagonal | 100.00 | |
| 30 | A12 | 150c on 1p ver | 1.40 | 1.40 |
| a. | | Inverted "G" | 5.00 | |
| b. | | "Guatemala" and italic "5" in upper 4 numerals | 5.00 | |
| c. | | Inverted surcharge | 90.00 | |
| e. | | Pair, one without surcharge | 100.00 | |
| f. | | Double surcharge | 100.00 | |
| | | Nos. 26-30 (5) | 4.90 | 4.90 |

There are many other minor varieties, such as wrong font letters, etc. The surcharge on Nos. 29 and 30 has different letters and ornaments. On No. 29, "Guatemala" normally is 18½mm wide.
Used values of Nos. 26-30 are for canceled to order stamps. Postally used sell for much more.

National Emblem — A13

**1886, July 1  Litho.  Perf. 12**

| 31 | A13 | 1c dull blue | 5.00 | 2.00 |
|---|---|---|---|---|
| 32 | A13 | 2c brown | 5.00 | 3.00 |
| 33 | A13 | 5c purple | 37.50 | .75 |
| 34 | A13 | 10c red | 10.00 | .75 |
| 35 | A13 | 20c emerald | 15.00 | 1.25 |
| 36 | A13 | 25c orange | 15.00 | 1.50 |
| 37 | A13 | 50c olive green | 10.00 | 2.00 |
| 38 | A13 | 75c carmine rose | 10.00 | 3.00 |
| 39 | A13 | 100c red brown | 10.00 | 3.00 |
| 40 | A13 | 150c dark blue | 15.00 | 3.75 |
| 41 | A13 | 200c orange yellow | 17.50 | 4.75 |
| | | Nos. 31-41 (11) | 150.00 | 25.75 |

Used values of Nos. 38-41 are for canceled to order stamps. Postally used sell for more.
See Nos. 43-50, 99-107. For surcharges see Nos. 42, 51-59, 75-85, 97-98, 108-110, 124-130.

No. 32 Surcharged in Black

Two settings:
I — "1886" (no period).
II — "1886." (period).

**1886, Nov. 12**

| 42 | A13 | 1c on 2c brown, I | 2.00 | 2.50 |
|---|---|---|---|---|
| a. | | Date inverted, I | 75.00 | |
| b. | | Date double, I | 75.00 | |
| c. | | Date omitted, I | 60.00 | |
| d. | | Date double, one invtd., I | 100.00 | |
| e. | | Date triple, one inverted, I | 100.00 | |
| f. | | Setting II | 1.50 | 1.00 |
| g. | | Inverted surcharge, II | 4.00 | |
| h. | | Double surcharge, II | 100.00 | |

Forgeries exist.

Type I          Type II

Two types of 5c:
I — Thin "5"
II — Larger, thick "5"

**1886-95  Engr.  Perf. 12**

| 43 | A13 | 1c blue | .75 | .20 |
|---|---|---|---|---|
| 44 | A13 | 2c yellow brn | 2.25 | .20 |
| a. | | Half used as 1c on cover | 100.00 | |
| 45 | A13 | 5c purple (I) | 50.00 | 1.00 |
| 46 | A13 | 5c vio (II) ('88) | 1.50 | .20 |
| 47 | A13 | 6c lilac ('95) | .60 | .20 |
| 48 | A13 | 10c red ('90) | 1.50 | .20 |
| 49 | A13 | 20c green ('93) | 3.00 | .75 |
| 50 | A13 | 25c red org ('93) | 7.50 | 1.25 |
| | | Nos. 43-44,46-49 (7) | 17.10 | 3.00 |

The impression of the engraved stamps is sharper than that of the lithographed. On the engraved stamps the top four lines at left are heavier than those below them. (This is also true of the 1c litho., which is distinguished from the engraved only by a slight color difference and the impression.)
The "2" and "5" (I) are more open than the litho. numerals. The "10" of the engraved is wider. The 20c and 25c of the engraved have a vertical line at right end of the "centavos" ribbon.

No. 38 Surcharged in Blue Black

"1894" 14½mm wide

**1894, Apr. 25**

| 51 | A13 | 10c on 75c car rose | 4.50 | 4.50 |
|---|---|---|---|---|
| a. | | Double surcharge | 75.00 | |
| b. | | Inverted surcharge | 100.00 | |

Same on Nos. 38-41 in Blue or Red "1894" 14mm wide

**1894, June 13**

| 52 | A13 | 2c on 100c | 7.50 | 4.25 |
|---|---|---|---|---|
| 53 | A13 | 6c on 150c (R) | 7.50 | 3.50 |
| 54 | A13 | 10c on 75c | 550.00 | 500.00 |
| 55 | A13 | 10c on 200c | 7.50 | 4.25 |
| c. | | Inverted surcharge | | |

Nos. 54-55 exist with thick or thin "1" in new value.

Same on Nos. 39-41 in Black or Red "1894" 12mm wide

**1894, July 14**

| 52a | A13 | 2c on 100c red brn (Bk) | 4.00 | 3.50 |
|---|---|---|---|---|
| b. | | Vert. pair, one without surcharge | 150.00 | |
| 53a | A13 | 6c on 150c dk bl (R) | 4.50 | 3.50 |
| 55a | A13 | 10c on 200c org yel (Bk) | 5.00 | 3.50 |
| d. | | Inverted surcharge | 100.00 | |
| e. | | Vert. pair, one without surcharge | 150.00 | |

Nos. 44 and 46 Surcharged in Black, Blue Black, or Red:

b                c

d                e

**1894-96**

| 56 | A13 (b) | 1c on 2c (Bk) | .75 | .30 |
|---|---|---|---|---|
| a. | | "Centav" | 5.00 | 5.00 |
| b. | | Double surcharge | 75.00 | |
| c. | | As "a," dbl. surcharge | 150.00 | |
| d. | | Blue black surcharge | 20.00 | 20.00 |
| e. | | Dbl. surch., one inverted | 150.00 | |
| 57 | A13 (c) | 1c on 5c (R) ('95) | .50 | .20 |
| a. | | Inverted surcharge | 3.00 | 3.00 |
| b. | | "1894" instead of "1895" | 3.50 | 3.00 |
| c. | | Double surcharge | 50.00 | |
| 58 | A13 (d) | 1c on 5c (R) ('95) | .75 | .20 |
| a. | | Inverted surcharge | 50.00 | 50.00 |
| b. | | Double surcharge | 50.00 | |
| 59 | A13 (e) | 1c on 5c (R) ('96) | 1.25 | .40 |
| a. | | Inverted surcharge | 50.00 | 50.00 |
| b. | | Double surcharge | 50.00 | |
| | | Nos. 56-59 (4) | 3.25 | 1.10 |

Nos. 56-58 may be found with thick or thin "1" in the new value.

National Arms and President J. M. Reyna Barrios A21

**1897, Jan. 1  Engr.  Unwmk.**

| 60 | A21 | 1c blk, lil gray | .50 | .50 |
|---|---|---|---|---|
| 61 | A21 | 2c blk, grnsh gray | .50 | .50 |
| 62 | A21 | 6c blk, brn org | .50 | .50 |
| 63 | A21 | 10c blk, dl bl | .50 | .50 |
| 64 | A21 | 12c blk, rose red | .50 | .50 |
| 65 | A21 | 18c blk, grysh white | 9.25 | 9.25 |
| 66 | A21 | 20c blk, scarlet | 1.00 | 1.00 |
| 67 | A21 | 25c blk, bis brn | 1.50 | 1.00 |
| 68 | A21 | 50c blk, redsh brn | 1.00 | 1.00 |
| 69 | A21 | 75c blk, gray | 50.00 | 50.00 |
| 70 | A21 | 100c blk, bl grn | 1.00 | 1.00 |
| 71 | A21 | 150c blk, dl rose | 100.00 | 125.00 |
| 72 | A21 | 200c blk, magenta | 1.00 | 1.00 |
| 73 | A21 | 300c blk, yel grn | 1.00 | 1.00 |
| | | Nos. 60-73 (14) | 168.25 | 192.75 |

Issued for Central American Exposition.
Stamps often sold as Nos. 65, 69 and 71 are copies with telegraph overprint removed.
Used values for Nos. 60-73 are for canceled-to-order copies. Postally used examples are worth more.
The paper of Nos. 64 and 66 was originally colored on one side only, but has "bled through" on some copies.

No. 64 Surcharged in Violet

**1897, Nov.**

| 74 | A21 | 1c on 12c rose red | 1.00 | 1.00 |
|---|---|---|---|---|
| a. | | Inverted surcharge | 30.00 | 30.00 |
| b. | | Pair, one without surcharge | 75.00 | |
| c. | | Dbl. surch., one invtd. | 100.00 | |

Stamps of 1886-93 Surcharged in Red

f                g

**1898**

| 75 | (f) | 1c on 5c violet | 1.00 | 1.00 |
|---|---|---|---|---|
| a. | | Inverted surcharge | 75.00 | |
| 76 | (f) | 1c on 50c ol grn | 1.50 | 1.25 |
| a. | | Inverted surcharge | 100.00 | 100.00 |
| 77 | (f) | 6c on 5c violet | 4.50 | 1.50 |
| 78 | (f) | 6c on 150c dk bl | 4.50 | 3.25 |
| 79 | (g) | 10c on 20c emerald | 5.00 | 4.00 |
| a. | | Double surch., one inverted | 125.00 | 125.00 |
| | | Nos. 75-79 (5) | 16.50 | 11.00 |

**Black Surcharge**

| 80 | (f) | 1c on 25c red org | 2.00 | 2.00 |
|---|---|---|---|---|
| 81 | (f) | 1c on 75c car rose | 1.50 | 1.50 |
| a. | | Double surcharge | 100.00 | |
| 82 | (f) | 6c on 10c red | 10.00 | 9.00 |
| 83 | (f) | 6c on 20c emer | 5.00 | 4.00 |
| 84 | (f) | 6c on 100c red brn | 5.00 | 4.00 |
| 85 | (f) | 6c on 200c org yel | 5.00 | 4.00 |
| a. | | Inverted surcharge | 50.00 | 50.00 |
| | | Nos. 80-85 (6) | 28.50 | 24.50 |

Information that we have see indicates that No. 77 inverted and double surcharges are counterfeits.

National Emblem
A24    A25
Revenue Stamp Overprinted or Surcharged in Carmine
**Perf. 12, 12x14, 14x12**

**1898, Oct. 8  Litho.**

| 86 | A24 | 1c dark blue | 1.40 | 1.40 |
|---|---|---|---|---|
| a. | | Inverted overprint | 12.50 | 12.50 |
| 87 | A24 | 2c on 1c dk bl | 2.25 | 2.25 |
| a. | | Inverted surcharge | 12.50 | 12.50 |

Counterfeits exist.
See type A26.

Revenue Stamps Surcharged in Carmine

**1898  Engr.  Perf. 12½ to 16**

| 88 | A25 | 1c on 10c bl gray | .75 | .75 |
|---|---|---|---|---|
| a. | | "ENTAVO" | 5.00 | 5.00 |
| 89 | A25 | 2c on 5c pur | 1.25 | 1.00 |
| 90 | A25 | 2c on 10c bl gray | 6.50 | 7.00 |
| a. | | Double surch., car & blk | 100.00 | 75.00 |
| 91 | A25 | 2c on 50c dp bl | 9.25 | 9.25 |
| a. | | Double surch., car & blk | 100.00 | 100.00 |
| | | Nos. 88-91 (4) | 17.75 | 18.00 |

**Black Surcharge**

| 92 | A25 | 2c on 1c lil rose | 3.50 | 2.00 |
|---|---|---|---|---|
| 93 | A25 | 2c on 25c red | 7.50 | 8.00 |
| 94 | A25 | 6c on 1c purple | 4.00 | 4.50 |
| 95 | A25 | 6c on 5p gray vio | 7.50 | 7.50 |
| 96 | A25 | 6c on 10p emer | 7.50 | 7.50 |
| | | Nos. 92-96 (5) | 30.00 | 29.50 |

Nos. 88 and 90 are found in shades ranging from Prussian blue to slate blue.
Varieties other than those listed are bogus.
Counterfeits exist of No. 92.
Soaking in water causes marked fading.
See type A27.

No. 46 Surcharged in Red

**1899, Sept.  Perf. 12**

| 97 | A13 | 1c on 5c violet | .40 | .25 |
|---|---|---|---|---|
| a. | | Inverted surcharge | 7.50 | 7.50 |
| b. | | Double surcharge | 15.00 | 15.00 |
| c. | | Double surcharge, one inverted | 15.00 | 15.00 |

No. 48 Surcharged
in Black

**1900, Jan.**

| | | | | |
|---|---|---|---|---|
| **98** | A13 | 1c on 10c red | .65 | .50 |
| *a.* | | Inverted surcharge | 10.00 | 10.00 |
| *b.* | | Double surcharge | 75.00 | 75.00 |

Quetzal Type of 1886

| **1900-02** | | | **Engr.** | |
|---|---|---|---|---|
| **99** | A13 | 1c dark green | .60 | .25 |
| **100** | A13 | 2c carmine | .60 | .25 |
| **101** | A13 | 5c blue (II) | 2.25 | 1.25 |
| **102** | A13 | 6c lt green | .75 | .25 |
| **103** | A13 | 10c bister brown | 7.50 | 1.00 |
| **104** | A13 | 20c purple | 7.50 | 7.50 |
| **105** | A13 | 20c bister brn ('02) | 7.50 | 7.50 |
| **106** | A13 | 25c yellow | 7.50 | 7.50 |
| **107** | A13 | 25c blue green ('02) | 7.50 | 7.50 |
| | | *Nos. 99-107 (9)* | 41.70 | 33.00 |

No. 49 Surcharged in
Black

**1901, May**

| | | | | |
|---|---|---|---|---|
| **108** | A13 | 1c on 20c green | .50 | .50 |
| *a.* | | Inverted surcharge | 22.50 | 22.50 |
| *b.* | | Double surch., one diagonal | 50.00 | |
| **109** | A13 | 2c on 20c green | 1.50 | 1.50 |

No. 50 Surcharged in
Black

**1901, Apr.**

| | | | | |
|---|---|---|---|---|
| **110** | A13 | 1c on 25c red org | .60 | .60 |
| *a.* | | Inverted surcharge | 25.00 | 25.00 |
| *b.* | | Double surcharge | 50.00 | 50.00 |

A26          A27

Revenue Stamps Surcharged in
Carmine or Black

| **1902, July** | | **Perf. 12, 14x12, 12x14** | | |
|---|---|---|---|---|
| **111** | A26 | 1c on 1c dk blue | 1.10 | 1.10 |
| *a.* | | Double surcharge | 20.00 | |
| *b.* | | Inverted surcharge | 20.00 | |
| **112** | A26 | 2c on 1c dk blue | 1.10 | 1.10 |
| *a.* | | Double surcharge | 90.00 | |
| *b.* | | Inverted surcharge | 25.00 | |

| | | **Perf. 14, 15** | | |
|---|---|---|---|---|
| **113** | A27 | 6c on 25c red (Bk) | 2.50 | 2.50 |
| *a.* | | Double surch., one invtd | 75.00 | 75.00 |
| | | *Nos. 111-113 (3)* | 4.70 | 4.70 |

National
Emblem — A28

Statue of Justo
Rufino
Barrios — A29

"La Reforma"
Palace — A30

Temple of
Minerva — A31

Lake
Amatitlán — A32

Cathedral in
Guatemala — A33

Columbus
Theater — A34

Artillery
Barracks — A35

Monument to
Columbus — A36

School for
Indians — A37

| **1902** | | **Engr.** | **Perf. 12 to 16** | |
|---|---|---|---|---|
| **114** | A28 | 1c grn & claret | .20 | .20 |
| *a.* | | Horiz. pair, imperf. vert. | 100.00 | |
| **115** | A29 | 2c lake & blk | .20 | .20 |
| *a.* | | Horiz. or vert. pair, imperf. btwn. | 150.00 | |
| **116** | A30 | 5c blue & blk | .30 | .20 |
| *a.* | | 5c ultra & blk | .75 | .40 |
| *b.* | | Imperf., pair | 100.00 | 100.00 |
| *c.* | | Horiz. pair, imperf. vert. | 100.00 | |
| **117** | A31 | 6c bister & grn | .30 | .20 |
| *a.* | | Horiz. pair, imperf. btwn. | 150.00 | |
| **118** | A32 | 10c orange & bl | .40 | .40 |
| *a.* | | Horiz. pair, imperf. vert. | 100.00 | |
| **119** | A33 | 20c rose lil & blk | .60 | .40 |
| *a.* | | Horiz. pair, imperf. vert. | 100.00 | |
| **120** | A34 | 50c red brn & bl | .45 | .40 |
| *a.* | | Vert. pair, imperf. btwn. | 350.00 | |
| **121** | A35 | 75c gray lil & blk | .55 | .40 |
| *a.* | | Horiz. pair, imperf. btwn. | 150.00 | |
| *b.* | | Horiz. pair, imperf. vert. | 100.00 | |
| **122** | A36 | 1p brown & blk | .85 | .40 |
| *a.* | | Horiz. pair, imperf. btwn. | 150.00 | |
| **123** | A37 | 2p ver & blk | 1.00 | .85 |
| | | *Nos. 114-123 (10)* | 4.85 | 3.65 |

See Nos. 210, 212-214, 219, 223, 239-241,
243. For overprints and surcharges see Nos.
133, 135-139, 144-157, 168, 170-171, 178,
192-194, 298-299, 301, C19, C27, C123.

Issues of 1886-1900
Surcharged in Black
or Carmine

| **1903, Apr. 18** | | | **Perf. 12** | |
|---|---|---|---|---|
| **124** | A13 | 25c on 1c dk grn | 1.25 | .55 |
| *a.* | | Inverted surcharge | 50.00 | 50.00 |
| **125** | A13 | 25c on 2c carmine | 1.50 | .55 |
| **126** | A13 | 25c on 6c lt grn | 2.50 | 1.75 |
| *a.* | | Inverted surcharge | 40.00 | 40.00 |
| **127** | A13 | 25c on 10c bis brn | 7.50 | 7.00 |
| **128** | A13 | 25c on 75c rose | 10.00 | 10.00 |
| **129** | A13 | 25c on 150c dk bl (C) | 9.00 | 9.00 |
| **130** | A13 | 25c on 200c yellow | 10.00 | 10.00 |
| | | *Nos. 124-130 (7)* | 41.75 | 38.85 |

Forgeries and bogus varieties exist.

Declaration of
Independence
A38

| **1907, Jan. 1** | | | **Perf. 13½ to 15** | |
|---|---|---|---|---|
| **132** | A38 | 12½c ultra & blk | .45 | .45 |
| *a.* | | Horiz. pair, imperf. btwn. | 150.00 | |

For surcharge see No. 134.

Nos. 118, 119 and
132 Surcharged in
Black or Red

| **1908, May** | | | | |
|---|---|---|---|---|
| **133** | A32 | 1c on 10c org & bl | .30 | .30 |
| *a.* | | Double surcharge | 25.00 | |
| *b.* | | Inverted surcharge | 15.00 | 15.00 |
| *c.* | | Pair, one without surcharge | 50.00 | |
| **134** | A38 | 2c on 12½c ultra & blk (R) | .25 | .25 |
| *a.* | | Horiz. or vert. pair, imperf. btwn. | 100.00 | |
| *b.* | | Inverted surcharge | 15.00 | 10.00 |
| *c.* | | Double surcharge | 30.00 | |
| **135** | A33 | 6c on 20c rose lil & blk | .45 | .25 |
| *a.* | | Inverted surcharge | 20.00 | 20.00 |
| | | *Nos. 133-135 (3)* | 1.00 | .80 |

Similar Surcharge, Dated 1909, in Red
or Black on Nos. 121 and 120

| **1909, Apr.** | | | | |
|---|---|---|---|---|
| **136** | A35 | 2c on 75c (R) | .55 | .55 |
| **137** | A34 | 6c on 50c (R) | 62.50 | 62.50 |
| *a.* | | Double surcharge | 125.00 | 125.00 |
| **138** | A34 | 6c on 50c (Bk) | .30 | .30 |
| | | *Nos. 136-138 (3)* | 63.35 | 63.35 |

Counterfeits exist of Nos. 137, 137a.

No. 123
Surcharged in
Black

| | | | | |
|---|---|---|---|---|
| **139** | A37 | 12½c on 2p ver & blk | .30 | .30 |
| *a.* | | Inverted surcharge | 25.00 | 25.00 |
| *b.* | | Period omitted after "1909" | 12.50 | 12.50 |

Counterfeits exist.

Gen. Miguel García
Granados, Birth
Cent. (in
1909) — A39

| **1910, Feb. 11** | | | **Perf. 14** | |
|---|---|---|---|---|
| **140** | A39 | 6c bis & indigo | .55 | .40 |
| *a.* | | Imperf., pair | 55.00 | |

Some sheets used for this issue contained a
two-line watermark, "SPECIAL POSTAGE
PAPER / LONDON." For surcharge see No.
143.

General Post
Office — A40

Pres. Manuel
Estrada
Cabrera — A41

| **1911, June** | | | **Perf. 12** | |
|---|---|---|---|---|
| **141** | A40 | 25c bl & blk | .55 | .25 |
| *a.* | | Center inverted | 1,750. | 900.00 |
| **142** | A41 | 5p red & blk | .65 | .65 |
| *a.* | | Center inverted | 30.00 | 27.50 |

Nos. 116, 118 and 140 Surcharged in
Black or Red:

h

i

j

| **1911** | | | **Perf. 14** | |
|---|---|---|---|---|
| **143** | A39 (h) | 1c on 6c | 25.00 | 9.75 |
| *a.* | | Double surcharge | 75.00 | 75.00 |
| **144** | A30 (i) | 2c on 5c (R) | 1.60 | .85 |
| **145** | A32 (j) | 6c on 10c | 1.25 | 1.25 |
| *a.* | | Double surcharge | 50.00 | |
| | | *Nos. 143-145 (3)* | 27.85 | 11.85 |

See watermark note after No. 140. Forgeries exist.

Nos. 119-121 Surcharged in Black:

k

l

m

| **1912, Sept.** | | | | |
|---|---|---|---|---|
| **147** | A33 (k) | 1c on 20c | .40 | .40 |
| *a.* | | Inverted surcharge | 12.50 | 12.50 |
| *b.* | | Double surcharge | 15.00 | 15.00 |
| **148** | A34 (l) | 2c on 50c | .40 | .40 |
| *a.* | | Inverted surcharge | 12.50 | 12.50 |
| *b.* | | Double surcharge | 12.50 | |
| *c.* | | Double inverted surcharge | 25.00 | |
| **149** | A35 (m) | 5c on 75c | .80 | .80 |
| *a.* | | "191" for "1912" | 7.50 | 7.50 |
| *b.* | | Double surcharge | 15.00 | 15.00 |
| *c.* | | Inverted surcharge | 10.00 | |
| | | *Nos. 147-149 (3)* | 1.60 | 1.60 |

Forgeries exist.

Nos. 120, 122 and 123 Surcharged in
Blue, Green or Black:

n

o

p

| **1913, July** | | | | |
|---|---|---|---|---|
| **151** | A34 (n) | 1c on 50c (Bl) | .25 | .25 |
| *a.* | | Inverted surcharge | 10.00 | |
| *b.* | | Double surcharge | 17.50 | |
| *c.* | | Horiz. pair, imperf. btwn. | 100.00 | |

| 152 | A36 (o) | 6c on 1p (G) | .30 | .30 |
|---|---|---|---|---|
| 153 | A37 (p) | 12½c on 2p (Bk) | .30 | .30 |
| a. | | Inverted surcharge | 15.00 | 15.00 |
| b. | | Double surcharge | 40.00 | |
| c. | | Horiz. pair, imperf. btwn. | 100.00 | |
| | | Nos. 151-153 (3) | .85 | .85 |

Forgeries exist.

**Nos. 114 and 115 Surcharged in Black:**

 q

 r

 s

 t

**1916-17**

| 154 | A28 (q) | 2c on 1c ('17) | .25 | .25 |
|---|---|---|---|---|
| 155 | A28 (r) | 6c on 1c | .25 | .25 |
| 156 | A28 (s) | 12½c on 1c | .25 | .25 |
| 157 | A29 (t) | 25c on 2c | .25 | .25 |
| | | Nos. 154-157 (4) | 1.00 | 1.00 |

Numerous errors of value and color, inverted and double surcharges and similar varieties are in the market. They were not regularly issued, but were surreptitiously made and sold.

Counterfeit surcharges abound.

"Liberty" and President Estrada Cabrera — A51

Estrada Cabrera and Quetzal — A52

**1917, Mar. 15** — **Perf. 14, 15**

| 158 | A51 | 25c dp blue & brown | .25 | .20 |
|---|---|---|---|---|

Re-election of President Estrada Cabrera.

**1918** — **Perf. 12**

| 161 | A52 | 1.50p dark blue | .30 | .25 |
|---|---|---|---|---|

Radio Station — A54
"Joaquina" Maternity Hospital — A55

"Estrada Cabrera" Vocational School — A56
National Emblem — A57

**1919, May 3** — **Perf. 14, 15**

| 162 | A54 | 30c red & blk | 2.75 | .75 |
|---|---|---|---|---|
| 163 | A55 | 60c ol grn & blk | .80 | .50 |
| 164 | A56 | 90c red brn & blk | .80 | .75 |
| 165 | A57 | 3p dp grn & blk | 1.75 | .50 |
| | | Nos. 162-165 (4) | 6.10 | 2.50 |

See Nos. 215, 227. For surcharges see Nos. 166-167, 179-185, 188, 195-198, 245-246, C8-C11, C21-C22.

No. 162 Surcharged

**Blue Overprint and Black Surcharge**
**1920, Jan.** — **Unwmk.**

| 166 | A54 | 2c on 30c red & blk | .30 | .25 |
|---|---|---|---|---|
| a. | | Inverted surcharge | 12.50 | 12.50 |
| b. | | "1920" double | 10.00 | 10.00 |
| c. | | "1920" omitted | 15.00 | 15.00 |
| d. | | "2 centavos" omitted | 20.00 | |
| e. | | Imperf, pair | 100.00 | |
| f. | | Pair, imperf. btwn. | 100.00 | |

**Nos. 123 and 163 Surcharged:**

 u

 v

**1920**

| 167 | A55 | 2c on 60c (Bk & R) | .25 | .25 |
|---|---|---|---|---|
| a. | | Inverted surcharge | 10.00 | 10.00 |
| b. | | "1920" inverted | 7.50 | 7.00 |
| c. | | "1920" omitted | 10.00 | 10.00 |
| d. | | "1920" only | 10.00 | |
| e. | | Double surcharge | 25.00 | |
| 168 | A37 | 25c on 2p (Bk) | .30 | .25 |
| a. | | "35" for "25" | 10.00 | 10.00 |
| b. | | Large "5" in "25" | 10.00 | 10.00 |
| c. | | Inverted surcharge | 15.00 | 15.00 |
| d. | | Double surcharge | 25.00 | |

A61

**1920**

| 169 | A61 | 25c green | .25 | .20 |
|---|---|---|---|---|
| a. | | Double overprint | 50.00 | |
| b. | | Double overprint, inverted | 75.00 | |

See types A65-A66.

No. 119 Surcharged

**1921, Apr.**

| 170 | A33 | 12½c on 20c | .25 | .20 |
|---|---|---|---|---|
| a. | | Double surcharge | 15.00 | |
| b. | | Inverted surcharge | 15.00 | |

No. 121 Surcharged
1921 Cincuenta centavos

**1921, Apr.**

| 171 | A35 | 50c on 75c lil & blk | .50 | .30 |
|---|---|---|---|---|
| a. | | Double surcharge | 22.50 | |
| b. | | Inverted surcharge | 25.00 | 25.00 |

Mayan Stele at Quiriguá — A62

Monument to President Granados — A63
"La Penitenciaria" Bridge — A64

**1921, Sept. 1** — **Perf. 13½, 14, 15**

| 172 | A62 | 1.50p blue & org | .85 | .25 |
|---|---|---|---|---|
| 173 | A63 | 5p brown & grn | 2.75 | 1.25 |
| 174 | A64 | 15p black & ver | 22.50 | 12.50 |
| | | Nos. 172-174 (3) | 26.10 | 14.00 |

See Nos. 216, 228, 229. For surcharges see Nos. 186-187, 189-191, 199-201, 207, 231, 247-251, C1-C5, C12, C23-C24.

A65   A66

**Telegraph Stamps Overprinted or Surcharged in Black or Red**
**1921** — **Perf. 14**

| 175 | A65 | 25c green | .25 | .20 |
|---|---|---|---|---|
| 176 | A66 | 12½c on 25c grn (R) | .25 | .20 |
| 177 | A66 | 12½c on 25c grn | 15.00 | 15.00 |
| | | Nos. 175-177 (3) | 15.50 | 15.40 |

**Nos. 119, 163 and 164 Surcharged in Black or Red:**

w

1922 DOCE Y MEDIO CENTAVOS

x

1922 25 CENTAVOS

**1922, Mar.**

| 178 | A33(w) | 12½c on 20c | .25 | .25 |
|---|---|---|---|---|
| a. | | Inverted surcharge | 10.00 | |
| 179 | A55(w) | 12½c on 60c (R) | .50 | .50 |
| a. | | Inverted surcharge | 25.00 | |
| 180 | A56(w) | 12½c on 90c | .50 | .50 |
| a. | | Inverted surcharge | 25.00 | |
| 181 | A55(x) | 25c on 60c | 1.00 | 1.00 |
| a. | | Inverted surcharge | 20.00 | |
| 182 | A55(x) | 25c on 60c (R) | 125.00 | 125.00 |
| a. | | Inverted surcharge | 25.00 | |
| 183 | A56(x) | 25c on 90c | 1.00 | 1.00 |
| 184 | A56(x) | 25c on 90c (R) | 4.00 | 4.00 |
| | | Nos. 178-181,183-184 (6) | 7.25 | 7.25 |

Counterfeits exist.

**Nos. 165, 173-174 Surcharged in Red or Dark Blue**

1922 DOCE Y MEDIO CENTAVOS

**1922, May**

| 185 | A57 | 12½c on 3p grn & blk (R) | .25 | .25 |
|---|---|---|---|---|
| 186 | A63 | 12½c on 5p brn & grn | .50 | .50 |
| 187 | A64 | 12½c on 15p blk & ver | .50 | .45 |
| | | Nos. 185-187 (3) | 1.25 | 1.15 |

**Nos. 165, 173-174 Surcharged in Red or Black**

1922 25 CENTAVOS

25  25  25  25
I    II   III  IV

**1922**

| 188 | A57 | 25c on 3p (I) (R) | .20 | .20 |
|---|---|---|---|---|
| a. | | Type II | .60 | .60 |
| b. | | Type III | .60 | .60 |
| c. | | Type IV | .30 | .30 |
| d. | | Inverted surcharge | 40.00 | |
| e. | | Horiz. or vert. pair, imperf. btwn. (I) | 125.00 | |
| 189 | A63 | 25c on 5p (I) | 1.00 | 2.00 |
| a. | | Type II | 2.00 | 3.00 |
| b. | | Type III | 2.00 | 3.00 |
| c. | | Type IV | 1.00 | 2.00 |
| 190 | A64 | 25c on 15p (I) | 1.00 | 1.50 |
| a. | | Type II | 2.00 | 3.00 |
| b. | | Type III | 2.00 | 3.00 |
| c. | | Type IV | 1.00 | 1.50 |
| 191 | A64 | 25c on 15p (I) (R) | 22.50 | 30.00 |
| a. | | Type II | 40.00 | 45.00 |
| b. | | Type III | 45.00 | 45.00 |
| c. | | Type IV | 30.00 | 35.00 |
| | | Nos. 188-191 (4) | 24.70 | 33.70 |

**Stamps of 1902-21 Surcharged in Dark Blue or Red**

1922 25 CENTAVOS

25  25  25
V    VI   VII
25   25
VIII  IX

**1922, Aug.** — **On Nos. 121-123**

| 192 | A35 | 25c on 75c (V) | .40 | .40 |
|---|---|---|---|---|
| a. | | Type VI | .40 | .40 |
| b. | | Type VII | 1.75 | 1.75 |
| c. | | Type VIII | 5.50 | 4.75 |
| d. | | Type IX | 6.50 | 6.00 |
| 193 | A36 | 25c on 1p (V) | .30 | .30 |
| a. | | Type VI | .30 | .30 |
| b. | | Type VII | 1.25 | 1.25 |
| c. | | Type VIII | 2.50 | 2.50 |
| d. | | Type IX | 4.00 | 4.00 |
| e. | | Inverted surcharge | 40.00 | |
| 194 | A37 | 25c on 2p (V) | .45 | .45 |
| a. | | Type VI | .45 | .45 |
| b. | | Type VII | 1.25 | 1.25 |
| c. | | Type VIII | 4.00 | 4.00 |
| d. | | Type IX | 6.50 | 6.50 |

**On Nos. 162-165**

| 195 | A54 | 25c on 30c (V) | .45 | .45 |
|---|---|---|---|---|
| a. | | Type VI | .45 | .45 |
| b. | | Type VII | 1.25 | 1.25 |
| c. | | Type VIII | 5.50 | 5.50 |
| d. | | Type IX | 6.50 | 6.50 |
| 196 | A55 | 25c on 60c (V) | 1.00 | 1.50 |
| a. | | Type VI | 1.25 | 1.50 |
| b. | | Type VII | 6.25 | 7.75 |
| c. | | Type VIII | 8.50 | 9.50 |
| d. | | Type IX | 10.00 | 11.00 |
| 197 | A56 | 25c on 90c (V) | 1.00 | 1.50 |
| a. | | Type VI | 1.50 | 2.00 |
| b. | | Type VII | 6.00 | 6.75 |
| c. | | Type VIII | 8.50 | 9.50 |
| d. | | Type IX | 10.00 | 11.00 |
| 198 | A57 | 25c on 3p (R) (V) | .40 | .40 |
| a. | | Type VI | .40 | .40 |
| b. | | Type VII | 1.25 | 1.00 |
| c. | | Type VIII | 6.00 | 4.50 |
| d. | | Type IX | 6.50 | 6.00 |
| e. | | Inverted surcharge | 50.00 | |

**On Nos. 172-174**

| 199 | A62 | 25c on 1.50p (V) | .30 | .30 |
|---|---|---|---|---|
| a. | | Type VI | .30 | .30 |
| b. | | Type VII | 1.25 | 1.00 |
| c. | | Type VIII | 3.00 | 3.00 |
| d. | | Type IX | 4.50 | 4.50 |
| e. | | Inverted surcharge | 40.00 | |

| 200 | A63 | 25c on 5p (V) | .75 | .90 |
|---|---|---|---|---|
| a. | | Type VI | .80 | 1.00 |
| b. | | Type VII | 3.00 | 3.50 |
| c. | | Type VIII | 5.50 | 6.00 |
| d. | | Type IX | 8.00 | 8.50 |
| 201 | A64 | 25c on 15p (V) | .85 | .90 |
| a. | | Type VI | 1.50 | 1.50 |
| b. | | Type VII | 5.00 | 5.50 |
| c. | | Type VIII | 6.50 | 6.50 |
| d. | | Type IX | 12.00 | 12.00 |
| | | Nos. 192-201 (10) | 5.90 | 7.10 |

Centenary Palace — A69

National Palace at Antigua — A70

**1922**     **Perf. 14, 14½**
**Printed by Waterlow & Sons**

| 202 | A69 | 12½c green | .30 | .20 |
|---|---|---|---|---|
| a. | | Horiz. or vert. pair, imperf. btwn. | 100.00 | |
| 203 | A70 | 25c brown | .30 | .20 |

See Nos. 211, 221, 234.

Columbus Theater A71

Quetzal A72

Granados Monument — A73

**Litho. by Castillo Bros.**
**1924, Feb.**     **Perf. 12**

| 204 | A71 | 50c rose | .50 | .20 |
|---|---|---|---|---|
| a. | | Imperf., pair | 7.50 | |
| b. | | Horiz. or vert. pair, imperf. btwn. | 25.00 | |
| 205 | A72 | 1p dark green | 2.25 | .20 |
| a. | | Imperf. vertically | 15.00 | |
| b. | | Vert. pair, imperf. btwn. | 20.00 | |
| c. | | Imperf., pair | 7.50 | |
| 206 | A73 | 5p orange | 1.25 | .50 |
| a. | | Imperf., pair | 8.50 | |
| b. | | Horiz. pair, imperf. btwn. | 20.00 | |
| | | Nos. 204-206 (3) | 4.00 | .90 |

For surcharges see Nos. 208-209.

Nos. 172 and 206 Surcharged

**1924, July**

| 207 | A62 | 1p on 1.50p bl & org | .30 | .20 |
|---|---|---|---|---|
| 208 | A73 | 1.25p on 5p orange | .50 | .50 |
| a. | | "UN PESO 25 Cents." omitted | 40.00 | |
| b. | | Horiz. pair, imperf. btwn. | 25.00 | |

#208 with two bars over "25 Cents."
**1924**

| 209 | A73 | 1p on 5p orange | .50 | .50 |
|---|---|---|---|---|

Types of 1902-22 Issues
**Engr. by Perkins Bacon & Co.**
**1924, Aug.**   **Re-engraved**   **Perf. 14**

| 210 | A31 | 6c bister | .20 | .20 |
|---|---|---|---|---|
| 211 | A70 | 25c brown | .20 | .20 |
| 212 | A34 | 50c red | .25 | .20 |
| 213 | A36 | 1p orange brn | .25 | .20 |
| 214 | A37 | 2p orange | .35 | .25 |
| 215 | A57 | 3p deep green | 2.00 | .50 |
| 216 | A64 | 15p black | 5.00 | 2.75 |
| | | Nos. 210-216 (7) | 8.25 | 4.30 |

The designs of the stamps of 1924 differ from those of the 1902-22 issues in many details which are too minute to illustrate. The re-engraved issue may be readily distinguished by the imprint "Perkins Bacon & Co. Ld. Londres."

Pres. Justo Rufino Barrios A74

Lorenzo Montúfar A75

**1924, Aug.**

| 217 | A74 | 1.25p ultra | .20 | .20 |
|---|---|---|---|---|
| 218 | A75 | 2.50p dk violet | 1.00 | .25 |

See Nos. 224, 226. For surcharges see Nos. 232, C6, C20.

Aurora Park — A76

National Post Office — A77

National Observatory A78

Types of 1921-24 Re-engraved and New Designs Dated 1926
**Engraved by Waterlow & Sons, Ltd.**
**1926, July-Aug.**    **Perf. 12½**

| 219 | A31 | 6c ocher | .20 | .20 |
|---|---|---|---|---|
| 220 | A76 | 12½c green | .20 | .20 |
| 221 | A70 | 25c brown | .20 | .20 |
| 222 | A77 | 50c red | .20 | .20 |
| 223 | A36 | 1p orange brn | .20 | .20 |
| 224 | A74 | 1.50p dk blue | .20 | .20 |
| 225 | A78 | 2p orange | 1.25 | 1.00 |
| 226 | A75 | 2.50p dk violet | 1.50 | 1.25 |
| 227 | A57 | 3p dark green | .45 | .20 |
| 228 | A63 | 5p brown vio | 1.00 | .40 |
| 229 | A64 | 15p black | 6.00 | 2.75 |
| | | Nos. 219-229 (11) | 11.40 | 6.80 |

These stamps may be distinguished from those of the same designs in preceding issues by the imprint "Waterlow & Sons, Limited, Londres," the date, "1926," and the perforation.
See Nos. 233, 242. For surcharge see No. 230.

Nos. 225-226, 228 Surcharged in Various Colors

**1928**

| 230 | A78 | ½c on 2p (Bl) | .65 | .50 |
|---|---|---|---|---|
| a. | | Inverted surcharge | 12.50 | |
| 231 | A63 | ½c on 5p (Bk) | .35 | .20 |
| a. | | Inverted surcharge | 10.00 | 10.00 |
| b. | | Double surcharge | 50.00 | |
| c. | | Blue surcharge | 45.00 | 45.00 |
| d. | | Blue and black surcharge | 50.00 | 50.00 |
| 232 | A75 | 1c on 2.50p (R) | .35 | .20 |
| b. | | Double surcharge | 50.00 | |
| | | Nos. 230-232 (3) | 1.35 | .90 |

Barrios — A79

Montúfar — A80

Granados A81

General Orellana A82

Coat of Arms of Guatemala City — A83

**Engraved by T. De la Rue & Co.**
**1929, Jan.**     **Perf. 14**

| 233 | A78 | ½c yellow grn | .75 | .20 |
|---|---|---|---|---|
| 234 | A70 | 1c dark brown | .25 | .20 |
| 235 | A79 | 2c deep blue | .25 | .20 |
| 236 | A80 | 3c dark violet | .20 | .20 |
| 237 | A81 | 4c orange | .25 | .20 |
| 238 | A82 | 5c dk carmine | .50 | .20 |
| 239 | A31 | 10c brown | .40 | .20 |
| 240 | A36 | 15c ultra | .50 | .20 |
| 241 | A29 | 25c brown org | 1.00 | .25 |
| 242 | A76 | 30c green | .90 | .30 |
| 243 | A32 | 50c pale rose | 2.00 | .60 |
| 244 | A83 | 1q black | 3.00 | .40 |
| | | Nos. 233-244 (12) | 10.00 | 3.15 |

Nos. 233, 234 and 239 to 243 differ from the illustrations in many minor details, particularly in the borders.
See No. 300 for bisect of No. 235. For overprints and surcharges see Nos. 297, C13, C17-C18, C25-C26, C28, E1, RA17-RA18.

No. 227 Surcharged in Black or Red

**1929, Dec. 28**    **Perf. 12½, 13**

| 245 | A57 | 3c on 3p dk grn (Bk) | 1.25 | 1.90 |
|---|---|---|---|---|
| a. | | Inverted surcharge | 15.00 | 15.00 |
| 246 | A57 | 5c on 3p dk grn (R) | 1.25 | 1.90 |
| a. | | Inverted surcharge | 15.00 | 15.00 |

Inauguration of the Eastern Railroad connecting Guatemala and El Salvador.

No. 229 Surcharged in Red

**1930, Mar. 30**     **Unwmk.**

| 247 | A64 | 1c on 15p black | 1.25 | 1.40 |
|---|---|---|---|---|
| 248 | A64 | 2c on 15p black | 1.25 | 1.40 |
| 249 | A64 | 3c on 15p black | 1.25 | 1.40 |
| 250 | A64 | 5c on 15p black | 1.25 | 1.40 |
| 251 | A64 | 15c on 15p black | 1.25 | 1.40 |
| | | Nos. 247-251 (5) | 6.25 | 7.00 |

Opening of Los Altos electric railway.

Hydroelectric Dam — A85

Los Altos Railway A86

Railroad Station A87

**1930, Mar. 30**    **Typo.**    **Perf. 12**

| 252 | A85 | 2c brn vio & blk | 1.40 | 1.90 |
|---|---|---|---|---|
| a. | | Horiz. pair, imperf. btwn. | 125.00 | |
| 253 | A86 | 3c dp red & blk | 2.75 | 2.75 |
| a. | | Vert. pair, imperf. btwn. | 125.00 | |
| 254 | A87 | 5c buff & dk bl | 2.75 | 2.75 |
| | | Nos. 252-254 (3) | 6.90 | 7.40 |

Opening of Los Altos electric railway. Exist imperf.

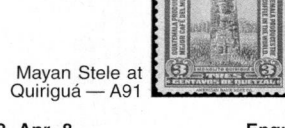

Mayan Stele at Quiriguá — A91

**1932, Apr. 8**     **Engr.**

| 258 | A91 | 3c carmine rose | 1.90 | .40 |
|---|---|---|---|---|

See Nos. 302-303.

Flag of the Race, Columbus and Tecum Uman A92

**1933, Aug. 3**    **Litho.**    **Perf. 12½**

| 259 | A92 | ½c dark green | .75 | .75 |
|---|---|---|---|---|
| 260 | A92 | 1c dull brown | 1.25 | 1.10 |
| 261 | A92 | 2c deep blue | 1.25 | 1.10 |
| 262 | A92 | 3c dull violet | 1.25 | .75 |
| 263 | A92 | 5c rose | 1.25 | 1.10 |
| | | Nos. 259-263 (5) | 5.75 | 4.80 |

Day of the Race and 441st anniv. of the sailing of Columbus from Palos, Spain, Aug. 3, 1492, on his 1st voyage to the New World. The 3c and 5c exist imperf.

Birthplace of Barrios A93

View of San Lorenzo A94

Justo Rufino Barrios A95

National Emblem and Locomotive A96

General Post Office — A97

Telegraph Building and Barrios
A98

Military Academy
A99

National Police Headquarters — A100

Jorge Ubico and J. R. Barrios
A101

**1935, July 19**     **Photo.**

| | | | |
|---|---|---|---|
| 264 | A93 | ½c yel grn & mag | .40 .45 |
| 265 | A94 | 1c org red & pck bl | .40 .45 |
| 266 | A95 | 2c orange & blk | .40 .55 |
| 267 | A96 | 3c car rose & pck bl | 4.50 2.25 |
| 268 | A97 | 4c pck bl & org red | 4.50 10.00 |
| 269 | A98 | 5c bl grn & brn | 3.25 4.25 |
| 270 | A99 | 10c slate grn & rose lake | 4.50 5.50 |
| 271 | A100 | 15c ol grn & org brn | 4.50 4.75 |
| 272 | A101 | 25c scarlet & bl | 4.50 4.75 |
| | | Nos. 264-272 (9) | 26.95 32.95 |

General Barrios. See Nos. C29-C31.

Lake Atitlán
A102

Quetzal
A103

Legislative Building — A104

**1935, Oct. 10**

| | | | |
|---|---|---|---|
| 273 | A102 | 1c brown & crim | .25 .20 |
| 274 | A103 | 3c rose car & pck grn | .70 .20 |
| 275 | A103 | 3c red org & pck grn | .70 .20 |
| 276 | A104 | 4c brt bl & dp rose | .35 .20 |
| | | Nos. 273-276 (4) | 2.00 .80 |

See No. 277. For surcharges see Nos. B1-B3.

**No. 273 perforated diagonally through the center**

**1936, June**     **Perf. 12½x12**
| | | | |
|---|---|---|---|
| 277 | A102 | (½c) brown & crimson | .20 .20 |
| a. | | Unsevered pair | .50 .60 |

Bureau of Printing — A105

Map of Guatemala
A106

**1936, Sept. 24**     **Perf. 12½**
| | | | |
|---|---|---|---|
| 278 | A105 | ½c green & pur | .25 .20 |
| 279 | A106 | 5c blue & dk brn | .90 .20 |

For surcharge see No. B4.

Quetzal
A107

Union Park, Quezaltenango
A108

Gen. Jorge Ubico on Horseback
A109

1c, Tower of the Reformer. 3c, National Post Office. 4c, Government Building, Retalhuleu. 5c, Legislative Palace entrance. 10c, Custom House. 15c, Aurora Airport Custom House. 25c, National Fair. 50c, Residence of Presidential Guard. 1.50q, General Ubico, portrait standing, no cap.

**1937, May 20**
| | | | |
|---|---|---|---|
| 280 | A107 | ½c pck bl & car rose | .70 .45 |
| 281 | A107 | 1c ol gray & red brn | .70 .35 |
| 282 | A108 | 2c vio & car rose | .60 .35 |
| 283 | A108 | 3c brn vio & brt bl | .50 .25 |
| 284 | A108 | 4c yel & dl ol grn | 2.00 2.00 |
| 285 | A107 | 5c crim & brt vio | 2.10 1.75 |
| 286 | A107 | 10c mag & brn blk | 3.00 3.50 |
| 287 | A108 | 15c ultra & cop red | 2.50 3.50 |
| 288 | A108 | 25c red org & vio | 3.00 3.75 |
| 289 | A108 | 50c dk grn & org red | 4.50 5.50 |
| 290 | A109 | 1q magenta & blk | 22.50 22.50 |
| 291 | A109 | 1.50q red brn & blk | 22.50 22.50 |
| | | Nos. 280-291 (12) | 64.60 66.40 |

Second term of President Ubico.

Mayan Calendar
A119

Natl. Flower (White Nun Orchid)
A120

Quetzal — A121

Map of Guatemala
A122

**1939, Sept. 7**     **Perf. 13x12, 12½**
| | | | |
|---|---|---|---|
| 292 | A119 | ½c grn & red brn | .25 .20 |
| 293 | A120 | 2c bl & gray blk | 1.50 .30 |
| 294 | A121 | 3c red org & turq grn | 2.00 .55 |
| 295 | A121 | 3c ol bis & turq grn | 2.00 .55 |
| 296 | A122 | 5c blue & red | 1.75 1.75 |
| | | Nos. 292-296 (5) | 7.50 3.35 |

For overprints see Nos. 324, C157.

**No. 235 Surcharged with New Value in Red**

**1939, Sept.**     **Perf. 14**
| | | | |
|---|---|---|---|
| 297 | A79 | 1c on 2c deep blue | .25 .20 |

Stamps of 1929 Surcharged in Blue:

y

z

**1940, June**
| | | | |
|---|---|---|---|
| 298 | A29 | (y) 1c on 25c brn org | .25 .20 |
| 299 | A32 | (z) 5c on 50c pale rose (bar 10x¾mm) | .25 .20 |
| a. | | Bar 12½x2mm | .30 .20 |
| b. | | Bar 12½x1mm | 50.00 5.00 |

**No. 235 perforated diagonally through the center**

**1941, Aug. 16**     **Perf. 14x11½**
| | | | |
|---|---|---|---|
| 300 | A79 | (1c) deep blue | .30 .20 |
| a. | | Unsevered pair | .80 .80 |

No. 241 Surcharged in Black

**1941, Dec. 24**     **Perf. 14**
| | | | |
|---|---|---|---|
| 301 | A29 | ½c on 25c brn org | .30 .30 |

**Type of 1932 Inscribed "1942"**
**1942**     **Engr.**     **Perf. 12**
| | | | |
|---|---|---|---|
| 302 | A91 | 3c green | .95 .25 |
| 303 | A91 | 3c deep blue | .95 .25 |

Issued to publicize the coffee of Guatemala.

Vase of Guastatoya
A123

Home for the Aged
A124

**1942, July 13**     **Unwmk.**
| | | | |
|---|---|---|---|
| 304 | A123 | ½c red brown | .35 .20 |
| 305 | A124 | 1c carmine rose | .35 .20 |

National Printing Works
A125

Rafael Maria Landivar
A126

**1943, Jan. 25**     **Engr.**     **Perf. 11, 12**
| | | | |
|---|---|---|---|
| 307 | A125 | 2c scarlet | .25 .20 |
| a. | | Vert. pair, imperf. horiz. | 35.00 |

**1943, Aug.**     **Perf. 11**
| | | | |
|---|---|---|---|
| 308 | A126 | 5c brt ultra | .25 .20 |

Death of Rafael Landivar, poet, 150th anniv.

National Palace
A127

**1944, June 30**     **Perf. 11**
| | | | |
|---|---|---|---|
| 309 | A127 | 3c dk blue green | .20 .20 |

Inauguration of the Natl. Palace, Nov. 10, 1943.
See Nos. C137A-C139. For overprints see Nos. 311-311A, C133.

Ruins of Zakuleu
A128

**1945, Jan. 6**
| | | | |
|---|---|---|---|
| 310 | A128 | ½c black brown | .20 .20 |

**Type of 1944 Overprinted in Blue**

**1945, Jan. 15**
| | | | |
|---|---|---|---|
| 311 | A127 | 3c deep blue | .30 .25 |

**Overprint Bar 1mm Thick**
| | | | |
|---|---|---|---|
| 311A | A127 | 3c deep blue | 1.00 .70 |

Allegory of the Revolution
A129

Torch
A130

**1945, Feb. 20**
| | | | |
|---|---|---|---|
| 312 | A129 | 3c grayish blue | .30 .25 |
| | | Nos. 312,C128-C131 (5) | 2.30 1.25 |

Revolution of 10/20/44.

**1945, Oct. 20**
| | | | |
|---|---|---|---|
| 313 | A130 | 3c deep blue | .25 .20 |

1st anniv. of the Revolution of Oct. 20, 1944.
See No. C135-C136.

José Milla y
Vidaurre
A131

Payo
Enriquez de
Rivera
A132

**1945**　　　　　　　　**Perf. 11, 12½**
314 A131 1c deep green　　　.20　.20
315 A132 2c dull lilac　　　　.20　.20
　　Nos. 314-315,C134-C134A (4) 2.10 1.70

See Nos. 343-346, 379, C137, C269, C311-C315.

> Catalogue values for unused stamps in this section, from this point to the end of the section, are for Never Hinged items.

José Batres y
Montufar
A133

UPU Monument
Bern, Switzerland
A134

**1946**　　　　　　　　　**Unwmk.**
316 A133 ½c sepia　　　　.25　.20
317 A133 3c deep blue　　　.25　.20

See Nos. 319, C142.

**1946, Aug. 5　Photo.　Perf. 14x13**
318 A134 1c vio & gray brn　.30　.20
　　Nos. 318,C140-C141 (3)　1.45　.75

Centenary of the first postage stamp.

Batres Type of 1946
**1947, Nov. 11　Engr.　Perf. 11, 12½**
319 A133 3c dull green　　.25　.25

Symbolical of
Labor — A135

Bartolomé de
las Casas and
Indian — A136

**1948, May 14　Unwmk.　Perf. 11**
320 A135 1c deep green　　.40　.25
　a.　Perf. 12½　　　　5.00
321 A135 2c sepia　　　　.40　.25
　a.　Perf. 12½　　　　5.00
322 A135 3c deep ultra　　.40　.25
　a.　Perf. 12½　　　　5.00
323 A135 5c rose carmine　.40　.25
　a.　Perf. 12½　　　　5.00
　　Nos. 320-323 (4)　　1.60 1.00

Labor Day, May 1, 1948. Other perfs. and compound perfs. exist.

No. 296 Overprinted "1948" in
Carmine at Lower Right
**1948, May 14　　　　Perf. 12½**
324 A122 5c blue & red　　.40　.30

**1949, Oct. 8　Engr.　Perf. 12½, 13½**
325 A136 ½c red　　　　.25　.20
326 A136 1c black brown　　.25　.20
327 A136 2c dk blue grn　　.25　.20
　a.　2c green, perf. 11, 11½ ('60)　.25　.20
328 A136 3c rose pink　　.25　.20
　a.　3c car, perf. 11, 12½, 13½ ('64)　.30　.20
329 A136 4c ultra　　　　.25　.20
　　Nos. 325-329 (5)　　1.25 1.00

See Nos. 384-386.

Gathering
Coffee — A137

1c, Poptun Agricultural Colony. 2c, Banana trees. 3c, Sugar cane field. 6c, Intl. Bridge.

**1950, Feb.　Photo.　Perf. 14**
330 A137 ½c vio bl, pink & ol
　　gray　　　　　　.25　.20
331 A137 1c red brn, yel &
　　grnsh gray　　　　.25　.20
332 A137 2c ol grn, pink & bl
　　gray　　　　　　.25　.20
333 A137 3c pur, bl & org brn　.25　.20
334 A137 6c dp org, aqua & vio　.50　.20
　　Nos. 330-334 (5)　　1.50 1.00

See Nos. 347-349.

Badge of Public
and Social
Assistance
Ministry — A138

Nurse — A139

Map Showing
Hospitals — A140

**1950-51　Litho.　Perf. 12, 12½x12**
335 A138 1c car rose & bl　.25　.20
336 A139 3c dl grn & rose red　.35　.20

**Perf. 12**
337 A140 5c dk bl & choc ('51)　.50　.25
　a.　Souvenir sheet, #335-337　2.75　2.75
　　Nos. 335-337 (3)　　1.10　.65

Issued to publicize the National Hospitals Fund.

No. 337a exists perf. and imperf., same values.

A perforated souvenir sheet is known which is similar to No. 337a, but with the 5c stamp like the basic stamp of No. C232 (with "BRITISH HONDURAS" inscription).

See #C177-C180a. For overprint see #C232.

Motorcycle
Messenger
A141

**1951, May 22　　　　Perf. 14x12½**
337B A141 4c bl grn & gray blk　.55　.25

Issued for regular postage, although inscribed "Expreso." See No. E2.

Souvenir Sheet

A142

**Typographed and Engraved**
**1951, Oct. 22　　　　Imperf.**
338 A142　Sheet of 2　　5.00 5.00
　a.　1c rose carmine　　2.00 1.50
　b.　10c deep ultramarine　2.00 1.50

75th anniv. (in 1949) of the UPU.
For overprint see No. 419.

A143

Modern
Model
Schools
A144

**1951, Oct. 22　Photo.　Perf. 13½x14**
339 A143 ½c purple & sepia　.35　.20
340 A144 1c brn car & dl grn　.35　.20
341 A143 2c grnsh bl & red brn　.35　.25
342 A144 4c blk brn & rose vio　.35　.25
　　Nos. 339-342 (4)　　1.40　.90

Enriquez de Rivera Type of 1945
Re-engraved
**1952, June 4　　　　Perf. 12½**
343 A132 ½c violet　　　　.25　.20
344 A132 1c rose carmine　.25　.20
345 A132 2c green　　　　.25　.20
346 A132 4c orange　　　.45　.20
　　Nos. 343-346 (4)　　1.20　.80

A panel containing the dates "1660-1951" has been added below the portrait.

Produce Type of 1950
Designs: ½c, Sugar cane field. 1c, Banana trees. 2c, Poptun Agricultural Colony.

**1953, Feb. 11　Photo.　Perf. 13½**
347 A137 ½c dk brn & dp bl　.70　.20
348 A137 1c red org & ol grn　.70　.20
349 A137 2c dk car & gray blk　.70　.20
　　Nos. 347-349 (3)　　2.10　.60

Issued to publicize farming.

Rafael
Alvarez
Ovalle and
José
Joaquin
Palma
A145

**1953, May 13**
350 A145 ½c purple & blk　.55　.40
351 A145 1c dk grn & org brn　.55　.40
352 A145 2c org brn & ol grn　.55　.40
353 A145 3c dk bl & ol brn　.55　.40
　　Nos. 350-353 (4)　　2.20 1.60

Authors of Guatemala's national anthem.
For overprints see Nos. 374-378.

Quetzal — A146

**1954, Sept. 27　Engr.　Perf. 12½, 11**
354 A146 1c dp violet blue　1.00　.25

See Nos. 367-373, 380-382A, 434-444. For overprint see No. 395.

Mario
Camposeco
A147

Globe and Red Cross
A148

10c, Carlos Aguirre Matheu. 15c, Goalkeeper.

**1955-56　　Unwmk.　Perf. 12½**
355 A147 4c violet　　　　1.00　.25
356 A147 4c carmine ('56)　1.00　.25
357 A147 4c blue grn ('56)　1.00　.25

358 A147 10c bluish grn　3.25　.75
359 A147 15c dark blue　3.25 2.00
　　Nos. 355-359 (5)　　9.50 3.50

50 years of Soccer in Guatemala.

**1956, May 23　　　　Perf. 13x12½**
Designs: 3c, Red Cross, Telephone and "5110." 4c, Nurse, patient and Red Cross flag.

360 A148 1c brown & car　.25　.20
361 A148 3c dk green & red　.25　.20
362 A148 4c dk sl grn & red　.30　.20
　　Nos. 360-362 (3)　　.80　.60

Red Cross. See Nos. B5-B7, CB5-CB7. For surcharges see Nos. CB8-CB10.

Dagger-Cross of the
Liberation — A149

1c, Map showing 2,000 km. (1,243 miles) of new roads. 3c, Oil production.

**1956　　Engr.　　Perf. 12½**
363 A149 ½c violet　　　.20　.20
364 A149 1c dk blue grn　.20　.20

**Perf. 11**
365 A149 3c sepia　　　.20　.20
　　Nos. 363-365 (3)　　.60　.60

Liberation of 1954-55. Issue dates: ½c, 1c, July 27; 3c, Oct. 31. See Nos. C210-C218.

Quetzal Type of 1954
**1957-58　　　　Perf. 11, 12½**
367 A146 2c violet　　　.55　.25
368 A146 3c carmine rose　.70　.25
369 A146 3c ultra　　　.70　.25
　a.　3c dark blue, perf. 11½ ('72)　—
370 A146 4c orange　　1.10　.25
371 A146 5c brown　　1.50　.25
372 A146 5c org ver ('58)　1.50　.25
373 A146 6c yellow grn　2.00　.25
　　Nos. 367-373 (7)　　8.05 1.75

No. 368 is only perf. 12½. The 2c, 4c and No. 369 are found in perf. 11 and 12½. Other values are only perf. 11.

No. 350 Overprinted in Blue, Black,
Carmine, Red Orange or Green:

**1958, Nov.-Dec.　Photo.　Perf. 13½**
374 A145 ½c purple & blk (Bl)　.40　.40
375 A145 ½c purple & blk (Bk)　.40　.40
376 A145 ½c purple & blk (C)　.40　.40
377 A145 ½c purple & blk (RO)　.40　.40
378 A145 ½c purple & blk (G)　.40　.40
　　Nos. 374-378 (5)　　2.00 2.00

Cent. of the birth of Rafael Alvarez Ovalle, composer of Guatemala's national anthem.

Re-engraved Rivera Type of 1945
**1959, Sept. 12　Engr.　Perf. 11, 12½**
379 A132 4c gray blue　　.30　.20

See note after No. 346.

Quetzal Type of 1954
**1960-63　　Unwmk.　Perf. 11**
380 A146 2c brown ('61)　.55　.25
381 A146 4c lt violet　　1.00　.25
382 A146 5c blue green　1.10　.25

**Perf. 12½**
382A A146 5c slate gray ('63)　2.00　.40
　　Nos. 380-382A (4)　　4.65 1.15

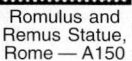

Romulus and
Remus Statue,
Rome — A150

1871
Stamp — A151

**1961**          **Photo.**          **Perf. 14**
383  A150  3c blue          .65  .20
Inauguration of the Plaza Italia.

Las Casas Type of 1949
*Perf. 11, 11½, 12½, 13½*

**1962-64**          **Engr.**
384  A136  ½c blue          .25  .20
385  A136  1c brt violet ('64)          .25  .20
386  A136  4c brown ('64)          .25  .20
          Nos. 384-386 (3)          .75  .60

**1963-66**          **Unwmk.**          **Perf. 11**
387  A151  10c carmine          .40  .25
388  A151  10c slate ('64)          .40  .25

          **Perf. 11½**
389  A151  10c olive brn ('66)          .40  .25
390  A151  20c dp purple ('64)          .65  .30
391  A151  20c dk blue ('65)          .65  .30
          Nos. 387-391 (5)          2.50  1.35

For souvenir sheet, see No. C310.

Pedro
Bethancourt
Comforting Sick
Man — A152

**1964, Jan. 6**          **Engr.**          **Perf. 11**
394  A152  2½c olive bister          .45  .25
Beatification (1962-63) of Pedro
Bethancourt (1626-67). See Nos. C319-C322.
For overprints see Nos. C381-C382.

Quetzal Type of 1957-
58 Overprinted in Blue

**1964, Dec. 29**          **Engr.**          **Perf. 12½**
395  A146  4c orange          .45  .25
15th anniv. (in 1963) of the Intl. Soc. of Guatemala Collectors.

Map of
Guatemala
and British
Honduras
A153

**1967, Apr. 28**          **Litho.**          **Perf. 14x13½**
396  A153  4c ol, vio bl & dp rose          .55  .30
397  A153  5c ocher, vio bl & dp
          org          .45  .30
398  A153  6c dp org, vio bl & gray          .45  .30
          Nos. 396-398 (3)          1.45  .90

Issued to state Guatemala's claim to British
Honduras.
For overprints see Nos. C411-C413.

Quetzal, Mayan Ball
Game Goal — A154

**Lithographed and Engraved**
**1968, Oct. 15**          **Perf. 11½**
399  A154  1c blk, lt grn & red          .40  .20
400  A154  5c yel, lt grn & red          .55  .25
401  A154  8c org, lt grn & red          .65  .25
402  A154  15c bl, lt grn & red          1.10  .25
403  A154  30c lt vio, lt grn & red          2.00  1.10
          Nos. 399-403 (5)          4.70  2.05

19th Olympic Games, Mexico City, 10/12-27.
The 1c, 5c, 8c, 15c also exist perf 12½-12.7; 1c,
8c, perf 13½.
See Nos. 412-415. For overprints see Nos.
408-411, C431-C435.

Child and
Poinsettia — A155

**1968-70**          **Typo.**          **Perf. 13½**
404  A155  2½c grn, dp bis & car          .30  .20
405  A155  2½c grn, org & car
          ('70)          .45  .55
406  A155  5c green, gray & car          .45  .20
407  A155  21c green, lil & car          1.00  .85
          Nos. 404-407 (4)          2.20  1.80

Issued to help abandoned children.

Type of 1968
Overprinted in Black
or Red

**1970, Mar. 19**          **Litho.**          **Perf. 13½**
408  A154  8c org, lt grn & red          .45  .20
409  A154  8c org, lt grn & red
          (R)          .45  .20

          **Perf. 12½**
410  A154  15c bl, lt grn & red          .70  .25
411  A154  15c bl, lt grn & red (R)          .70  .25
          Nos. 408-411 (4)          2.30  .90

50th anniv. of ILO. Gold overprint believed
to be a trial color.

Type of 1968
**1971**          **Typo. & Engr.**          **Perf. 11½**
412  A154  1c gray, yel grn & red          .30  .25

          **Typo.**
413  A154  5c brt pink, yel grn &
          red          .55  .25
414  A154  5c brown, grn & red          .55  .25
415  A154  5c dk bl, grn & red          .55  .55
          Nos. 412-415 (4)          1.95  1.30

Mayas and CARE
Package — A156

**1971-72**          **Typo.**          **Perf. 13½**
416  A156  1c black & multi          .25  .25

          **Perf. 11½**
417  A156  1c violet & multi ('72)          .25  .25
418  A156  1c brown & multi ('72)          .25  .25
          Nos. 416-418 (3)          .75  .75

10th anniv. of CARE in Guatemala, a US-
Canadian Cooperative for American Relief
Everywhere. Exist imperf. See No. C459.

No. 338 (trimmed) Overprinted in
Orange
with Olympic Rings and: "JUEGOS
OLIMPICOS / MUNICH 1972"
Souvenir Sheet
**Typo. & Engr.**

**1972, Oct. 23**          **Imperf.**
419  A142  Sheet of 2          1.50  1.50
  a.     1c rose carmine ("Munich")          .40  .40
  b.     10c deep ultra ("1972")          .50  .50

20th Olympic Games, Munich, Aug. 26-
Sept. 11. Commemorative inscriptions on No.
338 at left, top and right have been trimmed
off.  Size:  61x45mm (approximately).  Many
varieties exist.  Gold overprints probably are
proofs.

Pres.
Carlos
Arana
Osorio
A157

Designs:  3c, 5c, President Osorio seated,
vert.  8c, Pres. Osorio standing, vert.

**1973-74**          **Typo.**          **Perf. 12½**
420  A157  2c blue & blk          .20  .20
421  A157  3c orange & brn          .25  .20
422  A157  5c rose car & blk          .30  .20
423  A157  8c black & brt grn          .55  .20
  a.     Lithographed ('74)          .40  .20
          Nos. 420-423 (4)          1.30  .80

8th population and 3rd dwellings census,
Mar. 26-Apr. 7, 1973.

Francisco
Ximenez — A158

**Typographed, Lithographed (#426)**
**1973-77**          **Perf. 11½, 13½ (#426)**
424  A158  2c black & emer          .20  .20
425  A158  3c dk brn & org          .20  .20
426  A158  3c black & yellow          .25  .20
427  A158  6c black & brt bl          .25  .20
          Nos. 424-427 (4)          .90  .80

Brother Francisco Ximenez, discoverer and
translator of National Book of Guatemala. No.
427 issued for Intl. Book Year 1972.
Issued:  6c, 8/2; 2c, 1/14/75; #425, 3/5/75;
#426, 9/26/77.

Sculpture of Christ, by Pedro de
Mendoza, 1643 — A159

8c, Sculpture by Lanuza Brothers, 18th
century.

**1977, Apr. 4**          **Litho.**          **Perf. 11**
428  A159  6c purple & multi          .40  .20
429  A159  8c purple & multi          .40  .20
          Nos. 428-429,C614-C619 (8)          4.65  2.70

Holy Week 1977.

INTERFER 77
Emblem — A160

**1977, Oct. 31**          **Litho.**          **Perf. 11½**
430  A160  7c black & multi          .40  .20

INTERFER 77, 4th International Fair, Guatemala, Oct. 31-Nov. 13.

Rotary Intl.,
75th Anniv.
A161

**1980, July 31**          **Litho.**          **Perf. 11½**
431  A161  4c shown          .80  .25
432  A161  6c Diamond and
          Quetzal          .80  .25
433  A161  10c Paul P. Harris          .95  .60
          Nos. 431-433 (3)          2.55  1.10

Quetzal Type of 1954

**1984-86**          **Engr.**          **Perf. 12½**
434  A146  1c deep green          .25  .20
435  A146  2c deep blue          .25  .20
436  A146  3c olive green          .20  .20
437  A146  3c sepia          .20  .20
438  A146  3c blue          .20  .20
439  A146  3c red          .20  .20
440  A146  3c orange          .20  .20
441  A146  3c vermilion          .25  .20
442  A146  4c lt red brn          .25  .20
443  A146  5c magenta          .25  .20
444  A146  6c deep blue          .30  .20
          Nos. 434-444 (11)          2.55  2.20

Issued: #436-439, 2/20; #441, 6c, 4/25/86;
1c, 4c, 5c, 2/16/87; 2c, 3/25/87.

Miguel Angel
Asturias Cultural
Center — A162

*Perf. 12½, 11½ (5c, 9c), 12½x11½
(4c), 13x12½ (6c)*

**1987-96**          **Litho.**
445  A162  1c light blue          .25  .20
446  A162  2c bister brown          .25  .20
447  A162  3c ultra          .25  .20
448  A162  4c bright pink          .25  .20
449  A162  5c orange          .25  .20
450  A162  6c pale green          .25  .20
451  A162  7c vermilion          .25  .20
452  A162  8c brt pink          .25  .20
453  A162  9c black          .25  .20
454  A162  10c pale green          .30  .20
          Nos. 445-454 (10)          2.55  2.00

Miguel Angel Asturias (1899-1974), 1967
Nobel laureate in literature.
Issued: 3c, 11/24; 7c, 11/17; 8c, 11/27; 10c,
12/8; 2c, 3/2/88; 5c, 3/23/90; 9c, 10/1/91; 4c,
6c, 3/16/93; 1c, 7/9/96.

Central
American
and
Caribbean
University
Games
A163

Toucan as a participant in various events.

**1990**          **Litho.**          **Perf. 12½**
455  A163  15c shown          .30  .20
456  A163  20c Torch bearer,
          vert.          .45  .20
457  A163  25c Volleyball          .65  .20
458  A163  30c Soccer          .70  .20
459  A163  45c Karate          1.10  .30
460  A163  1q Baseball          2.50  .70

| 461 | A163 | 2q Basketball | 4.50 | 1.50 |
|---|---|---|---|---|
| 462 | A163 | 3q Hurdles | 7.50 | 2.50 |
| | | Nos. 455-462 (8) | 17.70 | 5.80 |

Issued: 20c, 8/22; 30c, 3q, 7/10; others, 4/25.

A164

A166

Oct. 20 Revolution, 50th Anniv. — A165

Designs: 1q, Student holding book, rifle. 2q, Constitution, city buildings, San Carlos University, social security building.

**1994, Nov. 8**   **Litho.**   **Perf. 11½**

| 463 | A164 | 40c multicolored | .30 | .20 |
|---|---|---|---|---|
| 464 | A165 | 60c multicolored | .50 | .35 |
| 465 | A164 | 1q multicolored | .95 | .65 |
| 466 | A166 | 2q multicolored | 1.75 | 1.25 |
| 467 | A166 | 3q multicolored | 3.00 | 1.75 |
| | | Nos. 463-467 (5) | 6.50 | 4.20 |

UNICEF, 50th Anniv. — A167

Designs: 10c, Soldier hugging child, vert. 20c, Children flying on doves.

**1997, May 21**   **Litho.**   **Perf. 12½**

| 468 | A167 | 10c multicolored | .25 | .20 |
|---|---|---|---|---|

**Perf. 11½x12½**

| 469 | A167 | 20c multicolored | .25 | .20 |
|---|---|---|---|---|

Landmark Buildings A168

Designs: 50c, Paraninfo University. 1q, Central American Services Building, vert.

**1997, Mar. 6**   **Perf. 12½**

| 470 | A168 | 50c multicolored | .30 | .30 |
|---|---|---|---|---|
| 471 | A168 | 1q multicolored | .65 | .65 |

Famous Guatemalans With 1999 Birth Anniversaries A169

Designs: 3q, Francisco Marroquín (b. 1499), first Guatemalan bishop. 4q, Jacinto Rodriguez Diaz (b. 1899), aviator. 8.75q, Miguel Angel Asturias (1899-1974), 1967 Nobel Laureate for Literature. 10q, Cesar Brañas (b. 1899), writer.

**2001, Oct. 9**   **Litho.**   **Perf. 12½x11½**

| 472-475 | A169 | Set of 4 | 17.50 | 9.00 |
|---|---|---|---|---|

Visit of Pope John Paul II and Canonization of St. Peter of San José Betancur (1626-67) — A170

Designs: Nos. 476, 483a, 20c, Saint and churches, vert. Nos. 477, 483b, 25c, Saint and bell, vert. Nos. 478, 483c, 50c, Pope, Saint and church. Nos. 479, 483d, 1q, Saint, painting of nativity, and bell, vert. Nos. 480, 483e, 2q, Pope and Guatemala Archbishop Quezada Toruño. Nos. 481, 483f, 5q, Pope, fountain and church decoration. Nos. 482, 483g, 8.75q, Pope and churches.

**2002, July 16**   **Litho.**   **Perf. 12½**

| 476-482 | A170 | Set of 7 | 11.00 | 5.00 |
|---|---|---|---|---|

**Souvenir Sheet**

**Rouletted 8½**

| 483 | A170 | Sheet of 7, #a-g | 11.00 | 11.00 |
|---|---|---|---|---|

Universal Postal Union, 125th Anniv. (in 1999) — A171

Designs: 20c, Quetzal, air mail envelopes, globe, flags. 2q, UPU emblem, quetzal, envelopes. 3q, Globe, quetzal, UPU emblem. 5q, Map of Guatemala, globe, envelopes and flags.

**2002, Oct. 31**   **Litho.**   **Perf. 12½**

| 484-487 | A171 | Set of 4 | 5.00 | 2.50 |
|---|---|---|---|---|

2001 Ascent of Mt. Everest by Jaime Viñals — A172

**2002, Nov. 22**

| 488 | A172 | 3q multi | 1.50 | .75 |
|---|---|---|---|---|

Pan-American Health Organization, Cent. — A173

**2002, Dec. 18**

| 489 | A173 | 4q multi | 2.00 | 1.00 |
|---|---|---|---|---|

St. Josemaría Escrivá de Balaguer (1902-75) A174

Balaguer and: 20c, Farmer. 50c, Fisherman with boatful of fish. 3q, Fisherman, mountain. 10q, Church.

**2003**   **Litho.**   **Perf. 12¼**

| 490-493 | A174 | Set of 4 | 7.00 | 3.50 |
|---|---|---|---|---|

Masks for Dances — A175

Mask for: 20c, Dance of the Conquest. 2q, Dance of the Moors and Christians. 3q, Dance of the Deer. 4q, Dance of the Jaguar. 5q, Dance of Paabanc.

**2003, July 9**   **Litho.**   **Perf. 12½**

| 494-497 | A175 | Set of 4 | 5.25 | 2.50 |
|---|---|---|---|---|

**Souvenir Sheet**

**Rouletted 8½**

| 498 | A175 | 5q multi | 3.25 | 3.25 |
|---|---|---|---|---|

No. 498 was issued in sheets of 18 and has perf. 12½ margins.

Regional Sanitary Agricultural Organization, 50th Anniv. — A176

Designs: 20c, Banana picker. 1q, Hands in corn. 2q, Cow. 4q, Cultivated field. 5q, Sliced meat. 10q, Eye, map, ear of corn. 3q, Basket of vegetables.

**2003, Dec. 8**   **Litho.**   **Perf. 12½**

| 499-504 | A176 | Set of 6 | 9.50 | 4.50 |
|---|---|---|---|---|

**Souvenir Sheet**

**Rouletted 8¼**

| 505 | A176 | 3q multi | 1.25 | .60 |
|---|---|---|---|---|

Tourist Attractions of Izabal Department A177

Designs: 20c, Punta de Manabique. 50c, Siete Altares. 1q, Las Escobas. 1.50q, View between Barrios and Pichilingo. 2q, Acropolis, Quiriguá. 3q, Livingston on the Río Dulce. No. 512, 4q, Castle of San Felipe. 5q, El Estor. 8.75q, Agua Caliente. 10q, Río Polochic. No. 516, Quiriguá.

**2004, Jan. 30**   **Perf. 12½**

| 506-515 | A177 | Set of 10 | 16.00 | 7.25 |
|---|---|---|---|---|

**Souvenir Sheet**

**Rouletted 6½**

| 516 | A177 | 4q multi | 2.50 | 1.10 |
|---|---|---|---|---|

Elevation to Cardinal of Archbishop Rodolfo Quezada Toruño A178

Designs: 20c, Cardinal, cathedral. 25c, Cardinal holding crucifix, cathedral. 50c, Cardinal wearing biretta kneeling before Pope John Paul II. 1q, Cardinal wearing zucchetto kneeling before Pope. 2q, Cardinal holding biretta, wearing zucchetto. No. 522, 3q, Cardinal wearing zucchetto. 4q, Cardinal wearing miter. 5q, Cardinal kissing hand of Pope. 8.75q, Cardinal and bishops. 10q, Coat of arms No. 527, 3q, Statue of Virgin Mary.

**2004, Nov. 5**   **Litho.**   **Perf. 12½**

| 517-526 | A178 | Set of 10 | 15.00 | 7.50 |
|---|---|---|---|---|

**Souvenir Sheet**

**Rouletted 6½**

| 527 | A178 | 3q multi | 1.25 | .65 |
|---|---|---|---|---|

America Issue, Flora and Fauna — A179

Designs: 50c, Sarcoranphus papa. 3q, Heliconia collinsiana, vert. 5q, Felis concolor. 10q, Heliconius petiveranus. 12q, Tapirus vairdii.

**2005, Apr. 29**   **Litho.**   **Perf. 12½**

| 528 | A179 | 50c multi | .25 | .25 |
|---|---|---|---|---|
| 529 | A179 | 3q multi | 1.40 | 1.40 |
| 530 | A179 | 5q multi | 2.25 | 2.25 |
| 531 | A179 | 10q multi | 4.50 | 4.50 |

**Souvenir Sheet**

**Rouletted 6½**

| 532 | A179 | 12q multi | 5.25 | 5.25 |
|---|---|---|---|---|

Diplomatic Relations Between Guatemala and Japan A180

Flags of Guatemala and Japan and: 1q, Child, flowing well pipe, San Pedro La Laguna. 8q, Child, hospital, Puerto Barrios. 14q, Mt. Fuji.

**2005, July 29**   **Litho.**   **Perf. 12½**

| 533-534 | A180 | Set of 2 | 3.50 | 3.50 |
|---|---|---|---|---|

**Souvenir Sheet**

**Rouletted 8½**

| 535 | A180 | 14q multi | 5.50 | 5.50 |
|---|---|---|---|---|

Majolica A181

Designs: 1q, Incense burner. 2q, Jars. 6.50q, Bowls. 8q, Lantern. 12q, Covered jar and sugar bowls.

**2005, Oct. 4**   **Perf. 12½**

| 536-539 | A181 | Set of 4 | 6.75 | 6.75 |
|---|---|---|---|---|

**Souvenir Sheet**

**Rouletted 8½**

| 540 | A181 | 12q multi | 5.00 | 5.00 |
|---|---|---|---|---|

Rotary International, Cent. — A182

Designs: 2q, Emblem, handshake, Western Hemisphere. 6.50q, Emblem, Polio Plus emblem.
8q, Emblem.

**2005, Nov. 15**     *Perf. 12½*
541-542 A182   Set of 2    3.25 3.25
**Souvenir Sheet**
***Rouletted 8½***
543 A182 8q multi     3.25 3.25

America Issue, Fight Against Poverty — A183

No. 544, 50c: a, Open hands. b, Two children
No. 545, 5q: a, Clasped hands. b, Two children, diff.
Illustration reduced.

**2006, Feb. 22**     *Perf. 12½*
**Horiz. Pairs, #a-b**
544-545 A183   Set of 2    4.50 4.50

Prof. José Joaquín Pardo, Historian, Cent. of Birth — A184

**2006, Feb. 28**
546 A184 3q multi     1.25 1.25

Churches A185

Designs: 50c, Santa Cruz Hermitage, Antigua Guatemala. 1q, San Jacinto Church, Salcajá. 2q, San Andres Xecul Church, Totonicapan, vert. 3q, El Calvario Church, Chichicastenango, vert. 4q, San Cristobal Acasaguastlán, El Progreso, vert. 5q, Antigua Cathedral, Antigua Guatemala. 8q, San Pedro Church and Hospital, Antigua Guatemala. 10q, San Pedro Las Huertas Church, Antigua Guatemala.
14q, Metropolitan Cathedral, Guatemala City.

**2006, Mar. 15**     *Perf. 12½*
547-554 A185   Set of 8    13.00 13.00
**Souvenir Sheet**
***Rouletted 8½***
555 A185 14q multi     5.50 5.50

Christmas A186

Various ceramic creche figurines: 20c, 6.50q.

**2006, Nov. 27**   **Litho.**   *Perf. 12½*
556-557 A186   Set of 2    2.75 2.75

Coffee Growing Regions A187

Designs: 50c, Acatenango. 1q, Antigua. 2q, Atitlán. 6.50q, Cobán. 8q, Fraijanes. 10q, Huehue.
No. 564: a, 5q, Oriente. b, 20q, San Marcos.

**2006, Nov. 29**     *Perf. 12½*
558-563 A187   Set of 6    11.00 11.00
**Souvenir Sheet**
***Rouletted 6½***
564 A187   Sheet of 2, #a-b    10.00 10.00

America Issue, Energy Conservation A188

Designs: 3q, Oil wells, gasoline pump nozzle. 10q, Light switch, solar panels.

**2006, Dec. 7**     *Perf. 12½*
565-566 A188   Set of 2    5.25 5.25

Diplomatic Relations Between Guatemala and Brazil, Cent. — A189

No. 567: a, Baile de la Conquista dancers. b, Maracatu dancers.
Illustration reduced.

**2006, Dec. 12**
567 A189 4q Horiz. pair, #a-b    3.25 3.25

Nos. 453, C850-C852, C863, C865, C870-C871 Surcharged

**Methods and Perfs As Before**
**2007, Jan. 23**
568 AP186 50c on 40c #C850   .20   .20
569 AP188 50c on 40c #C863   .20   .20
570 AP186 1q on 60c #C851   .40   .40
571 AP191 2q on 80c #C871   .85   .85
572 AP188 3q on 60c #C865   1.25   1.25
573 A162 5q on 9c #453   2.40   2.40
574 AP186 8q on 80c #C852   3.25   3.25
575 AP191 10q on 60c #C870   4.00   4.00
    *Nos. 568-575 (8)*    12.55 12.55

"Aereo" on Nos. 568-572, 574-575 is not obliterated.

Year of Transparency (in 2006) — A190

Designs: 20c, Hand holding ball with map of Guatemala. 6.50q, Magnifying glass, fingerprint (45x25mm).

**2007, Jan. 23**   **Litho.**   *Perf. 12½*
576-577 A190   Set of 2    2.75 2.75
Dated 2006.

Guatemala Philatelic Association, 75th Anniv. — A191

Designs: 1q, Guatemala #21. 3q, Guatemala #22. 6.50q, Guatemala #23. 8q, Guatemala #24.
25q, Guatemala #25.

**2007, July 19**   **Litho.**   *Perf. 12½*
578-581 A191   Set of 4    5.25 5.25
**Souvenir Sheet**
582 A191 25q multi     7.25 7.25

Diplomatic Relations Between Guatemala and Uruguay, Cent. — A192

No. 583: a, Santa Catarina Arch, Antigua, Guatemala. b, City gate, Colonia del Sacramento, Uruguay.
Illustration reduced.

**2007, Sept. 7**
583 A192 4q Horiz. pair, #a-b    2.40 2.40
   See Uruguay No. 2205.

America Issue, Education For All — A193

No. 584 — Stick figure children and: a, Blue panel. b, Red panel. c, Yellow orange panel. d, Green panel.
Illustration reduced.

**2007, Oct. 25**
584 A193 4q Block of 4, #a-d    4.75 4.75

Christmas A194      Scouting, Cent. A195

Creche figures: 20c, Holy Family. 6.50q, Magi, horiz. (36x31mm).

**2007, Dec. 4**
585-586 A194   Set of 2    2.00 2.00

**2007, Dec. 5**
587 A195 20c multi     .20   .20

Institute For Municipal Development, 50th Anniv. (in 2007) — A196

**2008, Jan. 30**
588 A196 3q multi     .90   .90
   Dated 2007.

Monsignor Juan Gerardi Conedera (1922-98) A197

**2008, Apr. 25**   **Litho.**   *Perf. 12½*
589 A197 8q multi     2.25 2.25

19th Cent. Defensive Bulwarks of Guatemala City — A198

No. 590: a, San Rafael de Matamoros. b, San José de Buena Vista.
Illustration reduced.

**2008, June 27**
590 A198 1q Horiz. pair, #a-b    .55   .55

### SEMI-POSTAL STAMPS

Regular Issues of 1935-36 Surcharged in Blue or Red similar to illustration

**1937, Mar. 15**   **Unwmk.**   *Perf. 12½*
B1 A102 1c + 1c brn & crim   .75   1.00
B2 A103 3c + 1c rose car & pck     grn   .75   1.00
B3 A103 3c + 1c red org & pck     grn   .75   1.00
B4 A106 5c + 1c bl & dk brn (R)   .75   1.00
    *Nos. B1-B4 (4)*    3.00 4.00

1st Phil. Exhib. held in Guatemala, Mar. 15-20.

> **Catalogue values for unused stamps in this section, from this point to the end of the section, are for Never Hinged items.**

Type of Regular Issue, 1956

Designs: 5c+15c, Nurse, Patient and Red Cross Flag. 15c+50c, Red Cross, telephone and "5110." 25c+50c, Globe and Red Cross.

**1956, June 19**   **Engr.**   *Perf. 13x12½*
B5 A148 5c + 15c ultra & red   1.00 *1.40*
   *a.*   Imperf. pair     75.00
B6 A148 15c + 50c dk vio &     red   2.25 *2.75*
B7 A148 25c + 50c bluish blk &     car   2.25 *2.75*
    *Nos. B5-B7 (3)*    5.50 *6.90*

The surtax was for the Red Cross.

Jesus and Esquipulas Cathedral — SP1

**1957, Oct. 29**     *Perf. 13*
B8 SP1 1½c + ½c blk & brn   .55 .25
The surtax was for the Esquipulas highway.

See Nos. CB12-CB14.

Type of Air Post Semi-Postal Stamps and

Arms — SP2

3c+3c, Wounded man, Battle of Solferino.

**1960, Apr. 9   Photo.   Perf. 13½x14**
**Cross in Rose Red**

| | | | | |
|---|---|---|---|---|
| B9 | SP2 | 1c + 1c red brn & bl | .30 | .25 |
| B10 | SPAP2 | 3c + 3c lil, bl & pink | .30 | .25 |
| B11 | SP2 | 4c + 4c blk & bl | .30 | .25 |
| | | Nos. B9-B11 (3) | .90 | .75 |

Cent. (in 1959) of the Red Cross idea. The surtax went to the Red Cross. Exist imperf. See Nos. CB15-CB21.

---

## AIR POST STAMPS

Surcharged in Red on No. 229

**1929, May 20   Unwmk.   Perf. 12½**

| | | | | |
|---|---|---|---|---|
| C1 | A64 | 3c on 15p blk | 1.10 | 1.40 |
| C2 | A64 | 5c on 15p blk | .55 | .45 |
| C3 | A64 | 15c on 15p blk | 1.50 | .45 |
| a. | | Double surcharge (G & R) | 100.00 | |
| C4 | A64 | 20c on 15p blk | 2.25 | 2.25 |
| a. | | Inverted surcharge | 100.00 | |
| b. | | Double surcharge | 100.00 | |

Surcharged in Red on No. 216

**1929, May 20   Perf. 14**

| | | | | |
|---|---|---|---|---|
| C5 | A64 | 5c on 15p black | 3.25 | 2.25 |
| | | Nos. C1-C5 (5) | 8.65 | 6.80 |

Surcharged in Black on No. 218

**1929, Oct. 9**

| | | | | |
|---|---|---|---|---|
| C6 | A75 | 3c on 2.50p dk vio | 1.00 | 1.00 |

Airplane and Mt. Agua AP3

**1930, June 4   Litho.   Perf. 12½**

| | | | | |
|---|---|---|---|---|
| C7 | AP3 | 6c rose red | .60 | .40 |
| a. | | Double impression | 25.00 | 25.00 |
| b. | | Imperf., pair | 350.00 | |

For overprint see No. C14.

Nos. 227, 229 Surcharged in Black or Red

**1930, Dec. 9   Perf. 12½**

| | | | | |
|---|---|---|---|---|
| C8 | A57 | 1c on 3p grn (Bk) | .40 | .40 |
| a. | | Double surcharge | 100.00 | |
| C9 | A57 | 2c on 3p grn (Bk) | 1.10 | 1.50 |
| C10 | A57 | 3c on 3p grn (R) | 1.10 | 1.50 |
| C11 | A57 | 4c on 3p grn (R) | 1.10 | 1.50 |
| C12 | A64 | 10c on 15p blk (R) | 5.00 | 5.00 |
| a. | | Double surcharge | 125.00 | |
| | | Nos. C8-C12 (5) | 8.70 | 9.90 |

---

No. 237 Overprinted

**1931, May 19   Perf. 14**

| | | | | |
|---|---|---|---|---|
| C13 | A81 | 4c orange | .40 | .30 |
| a. | | Double overprint | 40.00 | 50.00 |

No. C7 Overprinted

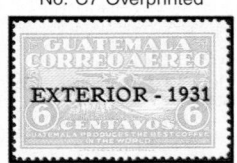

**Perf. 12½**

| | | | | |
|---|---|---|---|---|
| C14 | AP3 | 6c rose red | 1.50 | 1.40 |
| a. | | On No. C7a | 30.00 | 30.00 |
| b. | | Inverted overprint | 7.00 | 7.00 |

Nos. 240, 242 Overprinted in Red

**1931, Oct. 21   Perf. 14**

| | | | | |
|---|---|---|---|---|
| C15 | A36 | 15c ultra | 2.00 | .25 |
| a. | | Double overprint | 125.00 | 125.00 |
| C16 | A76 | 30c green | 3.00 | .95 |
| a. | | Double overprint | 75.00 | 75.00 |

Nos. 235-236 Overprinted in Red or Green

**1931, Dec. 5**

| | | | | |
|---|---|---|---|---|
| C17 | A79 | 2c dp bl (R) | 2.50 | 3.00 |
| C18 | A80 | 3c dk vio (G) | 2.50 | 3.00 |

No. 240 Overprinted in Red

| | | | | |
|---|---|---|---|---|
| C19 | A36 | 15c ultra | 2.75 | 3.00 |

Nos. C17-C19 were issued in connection with the 1st postal flight from Barrios to Miami.

No. 224 Surcharged in Red

**1932-33   Perf. 12½**

| | | | | |
|---|---|---|---|---|
| C20 | A74 | 2c on 1.50p dk bl | .80 | .55 |

Nos. 227, 229 Surcharged in Violet, Red or Blue

| | | | | |
|---|---|---|---|---|
| C21 | A57 | 3c on 3p grn (V) | .80 | .25 |
| a. | | Inverted surcharge | 45.00 | 45.00 |
| b. | | Vert. pair, imperf. horiz. | 900.00 | |
| C22 | A57 | 3c on 3p grn (R) | .80 | .25 |
| C23 | A64 | 10c on 15p blk (R) | 7.75 | 6.25 |
| b. | | First "I" of "Interior" missing | 10.00 | 10.00 |
| C24 | A64 | 15c on 15p blk (Bl) | 9.00 | 8.50 |
| a. | | First "I" of "Interior" missing | 15.00 | 15.00 |
| | | Nos. C20-C24 (5) | 19.15 | 15.80 |

Issued: #C22, 1/1/33; others, 2/11/32.

---

No. 237 Overprinted in Green

**1933, Jan. 1   Perf. 14**

| | | | | |
|---|---|---|---|---|
| C25 | A81 | 4c orange | .40 | .35 |
| a. | | Double overprint | 40.00 | 40.00 |

Nos. 235, 238 and 240 Overprinted in Red or Black

**1934, Aug. 7**

| | | | | |
|---|---|---|---|---|
| C26 | A82 | 5c dk car (Bk) | 1.50 | .25 |
| C27 | A36 | 15c ultra (R) | 1.50 | .25 |

Overprinted in Red

| | | | | |
|---|---|---|---|---|
| C28 | A79 | 2c deep blue | .55 | .20 |

View of Port Barrios — AP7

Designs: 15c, Tomb of Barrios. 30c, Equestrian Statue of Barrios.

**1935, July 19   Photo.   Perf. 12½**

| | | | | |
|---|---|---|---|---|
| C29 | AP7 | 10c yel brn & pck grn | 6.00 | 4.50 |
| C30 | AP7 | 15c gray & brn | 1.50 | 1.75 |
| C31 | AP7 | 30c car rose & bl vio | 1.50 | 1.25 |
| | | Nos. C29-C31 (3) | 9.00 | 7.50 |

Birth cent. of Gen. Justo Rufino Barrios.

Lake Amatitlán AP10

#C36, C37, C45, C46. Different views of Lake Amatitlan. 3c, Port Barrios. #C34, C35, Ruins of Port San Felipe. 10c, Port Livingston. #C39, C40, Port San Jose. #C41, C42, View of Atitlan. #C43, C44, Aurora Airport.

## Overprinted with Quetzal in Green

**1935-37   Size: 37x17mm**

| | | | | |
|---|---|---|---|---|
| C32 | AP10 | 2c org brn | .25 | .20 |
| C33 | AP10 | 3c blue | .25 | .20 |
| C34 | AP10 | 4c black | .25 | .20 |
| C35 | AP10 | 4c ultra ('37) | .25 | .20 |
| C36 | AP10 | 6c yel grn | .25 | .20 |
| C37 | AP10 | 6c blk vio ('37) | 4.00 | .20 |
| C38 | AP10 | 10c claret | .50 | .25 |
| C39 | AP10 | 15c red org | .65 | .40 |
| C40 | AP10 | 15c yel grn ('37) | .65 | .65 |
| C41 | AP10 | 30c olive grn | 6.00 | 6.50 |
| C42 | AP10 | 30c ol bis ('37) | .75 | .50 |
| C43 | AP10 | 50c rose vio | 17.50 | 15.00 |
| C44 | AP10 | 50c Prus bl ('36) | 4.00 | 3.00 |
| C45 | AP10 | 1q scarlet | 17.50 | 20.00 |
| C46 | AP10 | 1q car ('36) | 4.50 | 3.00 |
| | | Nos. C32-C46 (15) | 57.30 | 50.50 |

Issue dates follow No. C69.
For overprints and surcharges see Nos. C70-C79, CB1-CB2.

Central Park, Antigua AP11

Designs: 1c, Guatemala City. 2c, Central Park, Guatemala City. 3c, Monastery. Nos. C50-C51, Mouth of Dulce River. Nos. C52-

---

C53, Plaza Barrios. Nos. C54-C55, Los Proceres Monument. No. C56, Central Park, Antigua. No. C57, Dulce River. Nos. C58-C59, Quezaltenango. Nos. C60-C61, Ruins at Antigua. Nos. C62-C63, Dock at Port Barrios. Nos. C64-C65, Port San Jose. Nos. C66-C67, Aurora Airport. 2.50q, Island off Atlantic Coast. 5q, Atlantic Coast view.

## Overprinted with Quetzal in Green
**Size: 34x15mm**

| | | | | |
|---|---|---|---|---|
| C47 | AP11 | 1c yel brn | .25 | .20 |
| C48 | AP11 | 2c vermilion | .25 | .20 |
| C49 | AP11 | 3c magenta | .50 | .25 |
| C50 | AP11 | 4c org yel ('36) | 1.75 | 1.40 |
| C51 | AP11 | 4c car lake ('37) | 1.00 | .75 |
| C52 | AP11 | 5c dl bl | .25 | .20 |
| C53 | AP11 | 5c org ('37) | .25 | .20 |
| C54 | AP11 | 10c red brn | .50 | .40 |
| C55 | AP11 | 10c ol grn ('37) | .50 | .30 |
| C56 | AP11 | 15c rose red | .25 | .20 |
| C57 | AP11 | 15c ver ('37) | .25 | .20 |
| C58 | AP11 | 20c ultra | 2.50 | 3.00 |
| C59 | AP11 | 20c dp cl ('37) | .50 | .25 |
| C60 | AP11 | 25c gray blk | 3.00 | 3.50 |
| C61 | AP11 | 25c bl grn ('37) | .45 | .25 |
| a. | | Quetzal omitted | | 1,100. |
| C62 | AP11 | 30c yel grn | 1.50 | 1.50 |
| C63 | AP11 | 30c rose red ('37) | 1.00 | 2.00 |
| C64 | AP11 | 50c car rose | 7.00 | 8.00 |
| C65 | AP11 | 50c pur ('36) | 6.50 | 7.50 |
| C66 | AP11 | 1q dk bl | 22.50 | 25.00 |
| C67 | AP11 | 1q dk grn ('36) | 7.50 | 7.50 |

**Size: 46x20mm**

| | | | | |
|---|---|---|---|---|
| C68 | AP11 | 2.50q rose red & ol grn ('36) | 5.00 | 3.00 |
| C69 | AP11 | 5q org & ind ('36) | 7.00 | 4.00 |
| a. | | Quetzal omitted | 1,500. | 1,250. |
| | | Nos. C47-C69 (23) | 70.20 | 68.00 |

Issued: #C32-C69, 11/1/35; 10/1/36; 1/1/37. Value for No. C61a is for a sound example. For overprints and surcharges see Nos. C80-C91, CB3-CB4.

Types of Air Post Stamps, 1935
Overprinted with Airplane in Blue

2c, Quezaltenango. 3c, Lake Atitlan. 4c, Progressive Colony, Lake Amatitlan. 6c, Carmen Hill. 10c, Relief map. 15c, National University. 30c, Espana Plaza. 50c, Police Station, Aurora Airport. 75c, Amphitheater, Aurora Airport. 1q, Aurora Airport.

**1937, May 18**
**Center in Brown Black**

| | | | | |
|---|---|---|---|---|
| C70 | AP10 | 2c carmine | .25 | .20 |
| C71 | AP10 | 3c blue | 1.00 | 1.25 |
| C72 | AP10 | 4c citron | .25 | .20 |
| C73 | AP10 | 6c yel grn | .35 | .25 |
| C74 | AP10 | 10c red vio | 2.00 | 2.25 |
| C75 | AP10 | 15c orange | 1.50 | 1.00 |
| C76 | AP10 | 30c ol grn | 3.75 | 3.00 |
| C77 | AP10 | 50c pck bl | 5.00 | 4.25 |
| C78 | AP10 | 75c dk vio | 10.00 | 11.00 |
| C79 | AP10 | 1q dp rose | 11.00 | 12.00 |
| | | Nos. C70-C79 (10) | 35.10 | 35.40 |

Overprinted with Airplane in Black

1c, 7th Ave., Guatemala City. 2c, Los Proceres Monument. 3c, Natl. Printing Office. 5c, Natl. Museum. 10c, Central Park. 15c, Escuintla. 20c, Motorcycle Police. 25c, Slaughterhouse, Escuintla. 30c, Exhibition Hall. 50c, Barrios Plaza. 1q, Polytechnic School. 1.50q, Aurora Airport.

**Size: 33x15mm**

| | | | | |
|---|---|---|---|---|
| C80 | AP11 | 1c yel brn & brt bl | .25 | .20 |
| C81 | AP11 | 2c crim & dp vio | .25 | .20 |
| C82 | AP11 | 3c red vio & red brn | .50 | .50 |
| C83 | AP11 | 5c pck grn & cop red | 4.00 | 3.00 |
| C84 | AP11 | 10c car & grn | 1.25 | 1.00 |
| C85 | AP11 | 15c rose & dl ol grn | .50 | .25 |
| C86 | AP11 | 20c ultra & blk | 3.00 | 1.75 |
| C87 | AP11 | 25c dk gray & scar | 2.50 | 2.50 |
| C88 | AP11 | 30c grn & dp vio | 1.25 | 1.25 |
| C89 | AP11 | 50c magenta & ultra | 10.00 | 12.00 |

**Size: 42x19mm**

| | | | | |
|---|---|---|---|---|
| C90 | AP11 | 1q ol grn & red vio | 10.00 | 12.00 |
| C91 | AP11 | 1.50q scar & ol brn | 10.00 | 12.00 |
| | | Nos. C80-C91 (12) | 43.50 | 46.65 |

Second term of President Ubico.

## Souvenir Sheet

HOMENAJE
A LOS
ESTADOS UNIDOS DE NORTE AMERICA

1787 — 1789    1937 — 1939

EN EL
CL. ANIVERSARIO
DE SU CONSTITUCION POLITICA

AP12

**1938, Jan. 10**          **Perf. 12½**
C92  AP12  Sheet of 4        8.00  8.00
  a.    15c George Washington       1.50  1.50
  b.    4c Franklin D. Roosevelt    1.50  1.50
  c.    4c Map of the Americas      1.50  1.50
  d.    15c Pan American Union Build-
        ing, Washington, DC          .75   .75

150th anniv. of US Constitution.

President
Arosemena,
Panama
AP13

PRIMERA EXPOSICION FILATELICA CENTRO-AMERICANA
EN GUATEMALA DEL 20 AL 27 NOV. 1938

CONFRATERNIDAD CENTRO-AMERICANA

Flags of Central American
Countries — AP19

Designs: 2c, Pres. Cortés Castro, Costa
Rica. 3c, Pres. Somoza, Nicaragua. 4c, Pres.
Carias Andino, Honduras. 5c, Pres. Martinez,
El Salvador. 10c, Pres. Ubico, Guatemala.

**1938, Nov. 20**          **Unwmk.**
C93  AP13  1c org & ol brn     .25   .20
C94  AP13  2c scar, pale pink &
           sl grn              .30   .20
C95  AP13  3c grn, buff & ol brn  .40   .30
C96  AP13  4c dk cl, pale lil &
           brn                 .55   .35
C97  AP13  5c bis, pale grn & ol
           brn                 .50   .60
C98  AP13  10c ultra, pale bl &
           brn                1.00  1.25
       Nos. C93-C98 (6)        3.00  2.90

### Souvenir Sheet
C99  AP19  Sheet of 6         8.00  8.00
  a.    1c Guatemala           .80   .80
  b.    2c El Salvador         .80   .80
  c.    3c Honduras           1.10  1.10
  d.    4c Nicaragua          1.40  1.40
  e.    5c Costa Rica         1.40  1.40
  f.    10c Panama            2.40  2.40

1st Central American Phil. Exhib., Guatemala City, Nov. 20-27.
For overprints see Nos. CO1-CO7.

La Merced
Church,
Antigua
AP20

Designs: 2c, Ruins of Christ School, Antigua. 3c, Aurora Airport. 4c, Drill ground, Guatemala City. 5c, Cavalry barracks. 6c, Palace
of Justice. 10c, Customhouse, San José.
15c, Communications Building, Retalhuleu.
30c, Municipal Theater, Quezaltenango. 50c,
Customhouse, Retalhuleu. 1q, Departmental
Building.

## Inscribed "Aéreo Interior"
### Overprinted with Quetzal in Green

**1939, Feb. 14**
C100  AP20  1c ol bis & chnt    .20   .20
C101  AP20  2c rose red & sl
            grn                 .20   .20
C102  AP20  3c dl bl & bis      .25   .20
C103  AP20  4c rose pink &
            yel grn             .25   .20
C104  AP20  5c brn lake & brt
            ultra               .30   .20
C105  AP20  6c org & gray brn   .35   .20
C106  AP20  10c bis brn & gray
            blk                 .50   .20
C107  AP20  15c dl vio & blk    .75   .20
C108  AP20  30c dp bl & dk car 1.10   .20
C109  AP20  50c org & brt vio  1.50   .40
  a.     Quetzal omitted            1,750.
C110  AP20  1q yel grn & brt
            ultra              2.50  1.25
       Nos. C100-C110 (11)     7.90  3.50

See Nos. C111-C122. For overprint and
surcharge see No. C124, C132.

**1939, Feb. 14**

Designs: 1c, Mayan Altar, Aurora Park. 2c,
Sanitation Building. 3c, Lake Amatitlan. 4c,
Lake Atitlan. 5c, Tamazulapa River bridge.
10c, Los proceres Monument. 15c, Palace of
Captains General. 20c, Church on Carmen
Hill. 25c, Barrios Park. 30c, Mayan Altar.
50c, Charles III fountain. 1q, View of Antigua.

## Inscribed "Aéreo International" or "Aérea Exterior"
### Overprinted with Quetzal in Green

C111  AP20  1c ol grn & gldn
            brn                 .20   .20
C112  AP20  2c lt grn & blk     .30   .20
C113  AP20  3c ultra & cob bl   .20   .20
C114  AP20  4c org brn & yel
            grn                 .20   .20
C115  AP20  5c sage grn & red
            org                 .35   .20
C116  AP20  10c lake & sl blk  1.75   .20
C117  AP20  15c ultra & brt rose 1.75 .20
C118  AP20  20c yel grn & ap
            grn                 .60   .20
C119  AP20  25c dl vio & lt ol grn .60 .20
C120  AP20  30c dl rose & blk   .80   .20
C121  AP20  50c scar & brt yel 1.50   .20
C122  AP20  1q org & yel grn   2.50   .35
       Nos. C111-C122 (12)    10.75  2.55

No. 240
Overprinted in
Carmine

**1940, Apr. 14**          **Perf. 14**
C123  A36  15c ultra           .60   .25

Pan American Union, 50th anniversary.

## No. C112 Overprinted in Carmine

DICIEMBRE 2
1941
SEGUNDO DIA PAN
AMERICANO DE LA SALUD

**1941, Dec. 2**          **Perf. 12½**
C124  AP20  2c lt grn & blk     .40   .25

Second Pan American Health Day.

San Carlos
University,
Antigua
AP21

**1943, June 25**   **Engr.**   **Perf. 11**
C125  AP21  15c dk red brn      .55   .20
  a.     Imperf., pair         100.00

Don Pedro
de
Alvarado
AP22

Type I — Diagonal shading lines at inner
edges of commemorative tablet.
Type II — Overall shading added to tablet.

**1943, Mar. 10   Unwmk.   Perf. 11½**
C126  AP22  15c dp ultra (II)   .55   .25
  a.     Type I               16.00 11.00

400th anniv. of the founding of Antigua.

National
Police
Building
AP23

**1943, Aug. 3**          **Perf. 11**
C127  AP23  10c dp rose vio     .35   .20

## Allegory of Revolution Type

**1945, Apr. 27**          **Engr.**
C128  A129  5c dp rose         .50   .25
C129  A129  6c dk bl grn       .50   .25
  a.     Imperf., pair        110.00
C130  A129  10c violet         .50   .25
C131  A129  15c aqua           .50   .25
       Nos. C128-C131 (4)     2.00  1.00

1945
FERIA DEL LIBRO
2½ CENTAVOS

No. C113
Surcharged
in Red

**1945, July 25**          **Perf. 12½**
C132  AP20  2½c on 3c         1.50  1.50

The 1945 Book Fair.

## Type of 1944 Overprinted "PALACIO NACIONAL" in Carmine

**1945, Aug.   Engr.   Perf. 11**
C133  A127  5c rose car        .30   .20
  a.     Triple ovpt., one inverted  50.00 25.00
  b.     Double ovpt., one inverted  65.00

See Nos. C137A-C139.

## José Milla y Vidaurre Type

**1945**
C134  A131  7½c sepia         1.10  1.00
C134A A131  7½c dark blue      .60   .30

Issued: #C134, Sept. 28; #C134A, Dec. 6.
For overprint see No. C230.

## Torch Type

**1945, Oct. 19**
C135  A130  5c brt red vio     .40   .25

### Souvenir Sheet
*Imperf*
C136  A130  Sheet of 2        1.40  1.10
  a.     5c bright red violet  .40   .40

1st anniv. of the Revolution of Oct. 20, 1944.
See Nos. C147-C150.

Catalogue values for unused
stamps in this section, from this
point to the end of the section, are
for Never Hinged items.

## Payo Enriquez de Rivera Type

**1946, Jan. 22   Unwmk.   Perf. 11**
C137  A132  5c rose pink       .50   .20

See Nos. C269, C311-C315.

## Palace Type of 1944

**1946-47**
C137A A127  5c rose car ('47)  .55   .25
C138  A127  10c deep lilac     .25   .25
  a.     Imperf., pair        100.00
C139  A127  15c blue           .55   .25
  a.     Imperf., pair        100.00
       Nos. C137A-C139 (3)    1.35   .75

See No. C133 for #C137A without overprint.

Sir Rowland          Globes,
Hill — AP30          Quetzal — AP31

**1946, Aug. 5   Photo.   Perf. 14x13**
C140  AP30  5c slate & brn
            (blk ovpt.)        .50   .25
  a.     Without "AEREO" ovpt.  400.00 400.00
C141  AP31  15c car lake, ul-
            tra & emer         .65   .30

Centenary of the first postage stamp.

José Batres y
Montufar — AP32

Signing the
Declaration of
Independence
AP33

**1946, Sept. 16   Engr.   Perf. 11**
C142  AP32  10c Prus grn       .45   .25
  a.     Perf. 12½           10.00   .20

**1946, Dec. 19**          **Perf. 11**
C143  AP33  5c rose car        .20   .20
C144  AP33  6c ol brn          .25   .20
C145  AP33  10c violet         .30   .25
C146  AP33  20c blue           .40   .25
       Nos. C143-C146 (4)     1.15   .90

125th anniv. of the signing of the Declaration of Independence.

## Torch Type of 1945
Dated 1944-1946

**1947, Feb. 3**          **Engr.**
C147  A130  1c green           .40   .25
C148  A130  2c carmine         .40   .25
C149  A130  3c violet          .40   .25
C150  A130  5c dp bl           .40   .25
       Nos. C147-C150 (4)     1.60  1.00

Inscribed "II Aniversario de la Revolucion."
"Aereo" in color on a white background.
2nd anniv. of the Revolution of 10/20/44.

Franklin D.
Roosevelt — AP34

**1947, June 6**
C151  AP34  5c rose car        .25   .25
C152  AP34  6c blue            .25   .25
C153  AP34  10c dp ultra       .35   .25
C154  AP34  30c gray blk      1.60   .90
C155  AP34  50c lt violet     2.50  2.25
  a.     Imperf., pair        125.00
C156  AP34  1q gray grn       4.25  3.75
  a.     Imperf., pair        125.00
       Nos. C151-C156 (6)     9.20  7.65

1948

AEREO

No. 296 Overprinted in Carmine

**1948, May 14**          **Perf. 12½**
C157  A122  5c blue & red      .35   .25

Soccer
Game
AP35

**1948, Aug. 31**       **Engr.**
**Center in Black**

| | | | | |
|---|---|---|---|---|
| C158 | AP35 | 3c brt carmine | .75 | .30 |
| C159 | AP35 | 5c blue green | .90 | .40 |
| C160 | AP35 | 10c dk violet | 1.00 | .95 |
| C161 | AP35 | 30c dp blue | 2.25 | 3.50 |
| C162 | AP35 | 50c bister | 4.50 | 4.50 |
| | | Nos. C158-C162 (5) | 9.40 | 9.65 |

4th Central American and Caribbean Soccer
Championship, Mar. 1948.

Seal, University of
Guatemala — AP36

**1949, Nov. 29**       **Perf. 12½**
**Center in Blue**

| | | | | |
|---|---|---|---|---|
| C163 | AP36 | 3c carmine | .70 | .40 |
| C164 | AP36 | 10c green | 1.00 | .75 |
| C165 | AP36 | 50c yellow | 3.75 | 3.25 |
| | | Nos. C163-C165 (3) | 5.45 | 4.40 |

1st Latin American Cong. of Universities.

Lake
Atitlan — AP37

Tecum Uman
Monument — AP38

Designs: 8c, San Cristobal Church. 13c,
Weaver. 35c, Momostenango Cliffs.

**1950, Feb. 17**     **Photo.**    **Perf. 14**
**Multicolored Centers**

| | | | | |
|---|---|---|---|---|
| C166 | AP37 | 3c car rose | .35 | .25 |
| C167 | AP38 | 5c red brn | .35 | .25 |
| C168 | AP37 | 8c dk sl grn | .40 | .25 |
| C169 | AP37 | 13c brown | .70 | .25 |
| C170 | AP37 | 35c purple | 2.50 | 3.00 |
| | | Nos. C166-C170 (5) | 4.30 | 4.00 |

See No. C181.

Soccer — AP39

Pole
Vault — AP40

Designs: 3c, Foot race. 8c, Tennis. 35c,
Diving. 65c, Stadium.

---

**1950, Feb. 25**     **Engr.**    **Perf. 12½**
**Center in Black**

| | | | | |
|---|---|---|---|---|
| C171 | AP39 | 1c purple | .65 | .25 |
| C172 | AP39 | 3c carmine | .70 | .25 |
| C173 | AP40 | 4c orange brn | .95 | .30 |
| C174 | AP39 | 8c red violet | 1.10 | .40 |
| C175 | AP40 | 35c lt blue | 2.50 | 3.25 |

**Center in Green**

| | | | | |
|---|---|---|---|---|
| C176 | AP40 | 65c dk slate grn | 5.00 | 5.50 |
| | | Nos. C171-C176 (6) | 10.90 | 9.95 |

6th Central American and Caribbean Games.

Nurse
and
Patient
AP41

Designs: 10c, School of Nurses. 50c,
Zacapa Hospital. 1q, Roosevelt Hospital.

**1950, Sept. 6**    **Litho.**    **Perf. 12**
**Quetzal in Blue Green**

| | | | | |
|---|---|---|---|---|
| C177 | AP41 | 5c rose vio & car | .25 | .25 |
| a. | | Double impression (frame) | 25.00 | |
| C178 | AP41 | 10c ol brn & emer | .70 | .35 |
| C179 | AP41 | 50c ver & red vio | 2.50 | 2.50 |
| C180 | AP41 | 1q org yel & sage grn | 3.00 | 2.75 |
| a. | | Souv. sheet, #C177-C180 | 7.50 | 7.50 |
| | | Nos. C177-C180 (4) | 6.45 | 5.85 |

National Hospital Fund.
Nos. C177-C180 exist with colors reversed,
perf. and imperf. These are proofs.

No. C168 perf. 12½ or 12 diagonally
through center

**1951, Apr.**       **Perf. 14**

| | | | | |
|---|---|---|---|---|
| C181 | AP37 | (4c) multi | 15.00 | 9.00 |
| a. | | Unserved pair | 36.00 | 22.50 |

Counterfeits of diagonal perforation exist.

Ceremonial Stone
Ax — AP42

National Flag and
Emblem — AP43

**1953, Feb. 11**    **Photo.**    **Perf. 14x13½**

| | | | | |
|---|---|---|---|---|
| C182 | AP42 | 3c dk bl & ol gray | .45 | .45 |
| C183 | AP42 | 5c dk gray & hn brn | .55 | .45 |
| C184 | AP42 | 10c dk pur & slate | .75 | .45 |
| | | Nos. C182-C184 (3) | 1.75 | 1.35 |

**1953, Mar. 14**       **Perf. 13½**
**Multicolored Center**

| | | | | |
|---|---|---|---|---|
| C185 | AP43 | 1c maroon | .25 | .20 |
| C186 | AP43 | 2c slate green | .25 | .20 |
| C187 | AP43 | 4c dark brown | .30 | .20 |
| | | Nos. C185-C187 (3) | .80 | .60 |

Issued to mark the passing of the presidency from J. J. Arevalo to Col. Jacobo
Arbenz Guzman.

Regional
Dance — AP44

---

Horse
Racing
AP45

Designs: 4c, White nun — national flower.
5c, Allegory of the fair. 20c, Zakuleu ruins.
30c, Symbols of Agriculture. 50c, Champion
bull. 65c, Bicycle racing. 1q, Quetzal.

**1953, Dec. 18**    **Engr.**    **Perf. 12½**

| | | | | |
|---|---|---|---|---|
| C188 | AP44 | 1c dp ultra & car | .25 | .25 |
| C189 | AP44 | 4c org & grn | 1.25 | .30 |
| C190 | AP44 | 5c emer & choc | .80 | .40 |
| C191 | AP45 | 15c choc & dk pur | 1.10 | 1.00 |
| C192 | AP45 | 20c car & ultra | 1.00 | 1.00 |
| C193 | AP44 | 30c dp ultra & choc | 1.25 | 1.25 |
| C194 | AP45 | 50c pur & blk | 1.25 | 1.25 |
| C195 | AP45 | 65c lt bl & dk grn | 2.50 | 2.50 |
| C196 | AP44 | 1q dk bl grn & dk red | 25.00 | 15.00 |
| | | Nos. C188-C196 (9) | 34.40 | 22.95 |

National Fair, Oct. 20, 1953.

Indian — AP46

**1954, Apr. 21**    **Unwmk.**    **Perf. 12½**

| | | | | |
|---|---|---|---|---|
| C197 | AP46 | 1c carmine | .30 | .25 |
| C198 | AP46 | 2c dp blue | .30 | .25 |
| C199 | AP46 | 4c yellow grn | .30 | .25 |
| C200 | AP46 | 5c aqua | .55 | .25 |
| C201 | AP46 | 6c orange | .55 | .25 |
| C202 | AP46 | 10c violet | 1.10 | .30 |
| C203 | AP46 | 20c black brn | 3.25 | 3.25 |
| | | Nos. C197-C203 (7) | 6.35 | 4.80 |

Guatemala and
ODECA
Flags — AP47

Rotary Emblem,
Map of
Guatemala
AP48

**1954, Oct. 13**    **Photo.**    **Perf. 14x13½**

| | | | | |
|---|---|---|---|---|
| C204 | AP47 | 1c multicolored | .55 | .50 |
| C205 | AP47 | 2c multicolored | .55 | .50 |
| C206 | AP47 | 4c multicolored | .55 | .50 |
| | | Nos. C204-C206 (3) | 1.65 | 1.50 |

3rd anniv. of the formation of the Organization of Central American States.

**1956, Sept. 8**       **Engr.**

| | | | | |
|---|---|---|---|---|
| C207 | AP48 | 4c bl & dl yel | .30 | .25 |
| C208 | AP48 | 6c lt bl grn & dl yel | .30 | .20 |
| C209 | AP48 | 35c pur & dl yel | 1.50 | 1.75 |
| | | Nos. C207-C209 (3) | 2.10 | 2.20 |

50th anniv. of Rotary Intl. (in 1955).

---

Mayan Warrior
Holding Dagger
Cross of the
Liberation
AP49

4c, Family looking into the sun. 5c, The dagger of the Liberation destroying communist
symbols. 6c, Hands holding cogwheel & map
of Guatemala. 20c, Monument to the victims of
communism & flag. 30c, Champerico harbor.
65c, Radio tower, Mercury & map of Guatemala. 1q, Flags of the American nations. 5q,
Pres. Carlos Castillo Armas.

**1956, Oct. 10**    **Photo.**    **Perf. 14x13½**

| | | | | |
|---|---|---|---|---|
| C210 | AP49 | 2c dp grn, red, bl & brn | .25 | .25 |
| C211 | AP49 | 4c dp car & gray blk | .25 | .25 |
| C212 | AP49 | 5c bl & red brn | .25 | .25 |
| C213 | AP49 | 6c dk brn & dp ultra | .30 | .25 |
| C214 | AP49 | 20c vio, brn & bl | 1.40 | 1.75 |
| C215 | AP49 | 30c dp bl & ol | 1.75 | 2.00 |
| C216 | AP49 | 65c chnt brn & grn | 2.50 | 3.00 |
| C217 | AP49 | 1q dk brn & multi | 3.50 | 4.00 |
| C218 | AP49 | 5q multi | 14.00 | 15.00 |
| | | Nos. C210-C218 (9) | 24.20 | 26.75 |

Liberation of 1954-55.
For overprints see Nos. C233, C243, C265-
C266, C417.

Red Cross,
Map and
Quetzal
AP50

Designs: 2c, José Ruiz Augulo and woman
with child, vert 3c, Pedro de Bethancourt with
sick man. 4c, Rafael Ayau.

**Perf. 13½x14, 14x13½**
**1958, May 13**       **Unwmk.**

| | | | | |
|---|---|---|---|---|
| C219 | AP50 | 1c multicolored | .75 | .40 |
| C220 | AP50 | 2c multicolored | .45 | .20 |
| C221 | AP50 | 3c multicolored | .45 | .20 |
| C222 | AP50 | 4c multicolored | .45 | .20 |
| | | Nos. C219-C222 (4) | 2.10 | 1.00 |

Issued in honor of the Red Cross.
For overprints and surcharges see Nos.
C235-C242, C251-C254, C283-C298, C390-
C394.

Col. Carlos
Castillo
Armas — AP51

Galleon of 1532
and Freighter
"Quezaltenango"
AP52

**1959, Feb. 27**       **Perf. 14x13½**
**Center in Dark Blue and Yellow**

| | | | | |
|---|---|---|---|---|
| C223 | AP51 | 1c black | .30 | .25 |
| C224 | AP51 | 2c rose red | .30 | .25 |
| C225 | AP51 | 4c brown | .30 | .25 |
| C226 | AP51 | 6c dk bl grn | .30 | .25 |
| C227 | AP51 | 10c dk purple | .45 | .30 |
| C228 | AP51 | 20c blue grn | 1.25 | .75 |
| C229 | AP51 | 35c gray | 1.75 | 1.40 |
| | | Nos. C223-C229 (7) | 4.65 | 3.45 |

Pres. Carlos Castillo Armas (1914-1957).

No. C134A Overprinted in Carmine:
"HOMENAJE A LAS NACIONES
UNIDAS"

**1959, Mar. 4    Engr.    Perf. 11**
C230 A131 7½c dk blue    1.25  *1.25*
Issued to honor the United Nations.

**1959, May 15    Litho.    Perf. 11**
C231 AP52 6c ultra & rose red    1.00  .30
Issued to honor the formation of the Guate-
mala-Honduras merchant fleet.
For overprint see No. C467.

Type of 1950
Overprinted in Dark
Blue

**1959, Oct. 9    Perf. 12**
C232 A140 5c dk bl & lt brn    .65  .20
a.   Inverted overprint    200.00  35.00

Issued to state Guatemala's claim to British
Honduras. Overprint reads: "Belize is ours."
Map includes "BRITISH HONDURAS" and its
borderline, and excludes bit extending above
"A" of "GUATEMALA" on No. 337.
No. C232 is known without overprint in
multiples.

No. C213 Overprinted in Red:
"1859 Centenario Primera Exportacion
de Cafe 1959"

**1959, Oct. 26    Photo.    Perf. 14x13½**
C233 AP49 6c dk brn & dp ultra    .60  .30
Centenary of coffee export.

Pres. and
Mrs.
Villeda of
Honduras
AP53

**1959, Nov. 3    Litho.    Perf. 11**
C234 AP53 6c pale brown    .40  .30
Visit of President Ramon Villeda Morales of
Honduras, Oct. 12, 1958.
For overprint see No. C415.

Nos. C219-C222 Overprinted: "AÑO
MUNDIAL DE REFUGIADOS" in
Green, Violet, Blue or Brown
**Perf. 13½x14, 14x13½**

**1960, Apr. 23    Photo.    Unwmk.**
C235 AP50 1c multi (G)    2.00  1.75
C236 AP50 2c multi (V)    .95  .95
C237 AP50 3c multi (Bl)    .95  .95
C238 AP50 4c multi (Br)    .95  .95

**Nos. C219-C222 Overprinted as
Above and Surcharged with New
Value**
C239 AP50 6c on 1c multi    5.00  2.50
C240 AP50 7c on 2c multi    2.50  2.25
C241 AP50 10c on 3c multi    4.00  4.25
C242 AP50 20c on 4c multi    4.50  4.50
   Nos. C235-C242 (8)    20.85  18.10

Nos. C235-C242 issued to publicize World
Refugee Year, July 1, 1959-June 30, 1960.

No. C213 Overprinted in Red:
"Fundacion de la ciudad Melchor de
Mencos, 30-IV-1960"

**1960, Apr. 30    Perf. 14x13½**
C243 AP49 6c dk brn & dp ultra    1.25  1.25
Founding of the city of Melchor de Mencos.

UNESCO
and Eiffel
Tower, Paris
AP54

**1960, Nov. 4    Photo.    Perf. 12½**
C244 AP54 5c dp mag & vio    .25  .25
C245 AP54 6c ultra & vio brn    .25  .25
C246 AP54 8c emer & magenta    .40  .25
C247 AP54 20c red brn & dl bl    1.40  1.40
   Nos. C244-C247 (4)    2.30  2.15
Issued to honor UNESCO.
For overprints see Nos. C258, C267-C268.

Abraham
Lincoln — AP55

**1960, Oct. 29    Engr.    Perf. 11**
C248 AP55 5c violet blue    .20  .20
C249 AP55 30c violet    1.10  1.40
C250 AP55 50c gray    5.50  6.50
   Nos. C248-C250 (3)    6.80  8.10

Sesquicentenary of the birth of Abraham
Lincoln.
An 8c was also printed, but was not issued
and all copies were destroyed.

Nos. C219-C222 Overprinted "Mayo
de 1960" in Green, Blue or Brown
**Perf. 13½x14, 14x13½**

**1961, Apr. 20    Photo.    Unwmk.**
C251 AP50 1c multi (G)    .60  .45
C252 AP50 2c multi (Bl)    .60  .45
C253 AP50 3c multi (Bl)    .60  .45
C254 AP50 4c multi (Br)    .60  .45
   Nos. C251-C254 (4)    2.40  1.80
Issued to honor the Red Cross.

Proclamation of
Independence — AP56

**1962    Engr.    Perf. 11**
C255 AP56 4c sepia    .20  .20
C256 AP56 5c violet blue    .40  .20
C257 AP56 15c brt violet    1.40  .65
   Nos. C255-C257 (3)    2.00  1.05
140th anniv. of Independence (in 1961).
Issue dates: 4c, 5c, May 23; 15c, Aug. 10.

No. C245 Overprinted in Red: "1962 /
EL MUNDO UNIDO / CONTRA LA
MALARIA"

**1962, Oct. 4    Photo.    Perf. 12½**
C258 AP54 6c ultra & vio brn    1.00  1.40
WHO drive to eradicate malaria.

Dr. José
Luna — AP57

Guatemalan physicians: 4c, Rodolfo Robles.
5c, Narciso Esparragoza y Gallardo. 6c, Juan
J. Ortega. 10c, Dario Gonzalez. 20c, José
Felipe Flores.

**1962, Dec. 12    Photo.    Perf. 14x13½**
C259 AP57 1c ol bis & dl pur    .80  .20
C260 AP57 4c org yel & gray
   ol    .80  .20
C261 AP57 5c pale bl & red
   brn    .80  .20
C262 AP57 6c salmon & blk    .80  .20
C263 AP57 10c pale grn & red
   brn    1.10  .20
C264 AP57 20c pale pink & bl    1.25  .80
   Nos. C259-C264 (6)    5.55  1.80

No. C213 Overprinted in Red:
"PRESIDENTE/ YDIGORAS/
FUENTES/ RECORRE POR TIERRA/
CENTRO AMERICA/ 14 A 20 DIC.
1962"

**1962, Dec.    Photo.    Perf. 14x13½**
C265 AP49 6c dk brn & dp ultra    1.10  .80
Pres. Ydigoras' tour of Central America,
Dec. 14-20, 1962.

No. C213 Overprinted in Vermilion:
"Reunion Presidents: Kennedy, EE.
UU. — Ydigoras F., Guat. — Rivera.
Salv. — Villeda M., Hond. — Somoza,
Nic. — Orlich, C. R. — Chiari,
Panama — San Jose, Costa Rica, 18
A 21 de Marzo de 1963"
**Perf. 14x13½**

**1963, Mar. 18    Unwmk.**
C266 AP49 6c dk brn & dp ultra    6.00  3.00
Meeting of Pres. John F. Kennedy with the
Presidents of the Central American Republics,
San Jose, Costa Rica, Mar. 18-21.

Nos. C245-C246 Overprinted
"CONMEMORA / CION FIRMA /
NUEVA CARTA / ODECA. — 1962" in
Magenta or Black

**1963, Mar. 14    Perf. 12½**
C267 AP54 6c ultra & vio brn (M)    .50  .20
C268 AP54 8c emerald & mag    .55  .20
Signing of the new charter of the Organiza-
tion of Central American States (ODECA).

Enriquez de Rivera Type of 1946
**Perf. 11, 11½, 12½**

**1963, Mar. 26    Engr.**
C269 A132 5c olive bister    .30  .20

Woman Carrying Fruit
Basket — AP58

**1963, Mar. 14    Litho.    Perf. 11, 12½**
C270 AP58 1c multicolored    .20  .20
Spring Fair, 1960.

Reaper — AP59

**1963, July 25    Photo.    Perf. 14**
C271 AP59 5c Prus green    .30  .20
C272 AP59 10c dark blue    .60  .30
FAO "Freedom from Hunger" campaign.

Ceiba
Tree — AP60

**1963    Unwmk.    Perf. 12**
C273 AP60 4c brown & green    1.40  .20

Patzun
Palace
AP61

Buildings: 3c, Coban. 4c, Retalhuleu. 5c,
San Marcos. 6c, Captains General of Antigua.

**1964, Jan. 15    Perf. 13½x14**
C274 AP61 1c rose red & brn    .50  .20
C275 AP61 3c rose cl & Prus grn    .50  .20
C276 AP61 4c vio bl & rose lake    .50  .20
C277 AP61 5c brown & blue    .65  .20
C278 AP61 6c green & slate    .65  .20
   Nos. C274-C278 (5)    2.80  1.00

City Hall,
Guatemala
City
AP62

Design: 4c, Social Security Institute.

**1964, Jan. 15    Photo.    Perf. 12x11½**
C279 AP62 3c brt bl & brn    .40  .20
C280 AP62 4c brn & brt bl    .50  .20
See Nos. C281-C282A. For overprints see
Nos. C360-C361, C421.

**1964-65    Engr.    Perf. 11½**
Designs: 3c, Social Security Institute. 4c,
University administration building. No. C282,
City Hall, Guatemala City. No. C282A, Engi-
neering School.

**Different Frames**
C281 AP62 3c dull green    .55  .20
C281A AP62 4c gray ('65)    .55  .20
C282 AP62 7c blue    .60  .20
C282A AP62 7c olive bis ('65)    .60  .20
   Nos. C281-C282A (4)    2.30  .80

Nos. C219-C222 Overprinted in
Green, Blue or Black with Olympic
Rings and: "OLIMPIADAS / TOKIO —
1964"

**1964    Photo.    Perf. 13½x14, 14x13½**
C283 AP50 1c multi (G)    1.25  1.40
C284 AP50 2c multi (Bl)    1.25  1.40
C285 AP50 3c multi (Bl)    1.25  1.40
C286 AP50 4c multi (Bk)    1.25  1.40
   Nos. C283-C286 (4)    5.00  5.60
18th Olympic Games, Tokyo, 10/10-25/64.

Nos. C219-C222 Surcharged in Green,
Blue or Black with New Value and:
"HABILITADA — 1964"

**1964**
C287 AP50 7c on 1c multi (G)    .30  .20
C288 AP50 9c on 2c multi (Bl)    .40  .40
C289 AP50 13c on 3c multi (Bl)    .55  .45
C290 AP50 21c on 4c multi (Bk)    1.00  .85
   Nos. C287-C290 (4)    2.25  1.90

Nos. C219-C222 Overprinted "FERIA
MUNDIAL / DE NEW YORK" in Green,
Blue or Black

**1964, June 25**
C291 AP50 1c multi (G)    .80  .85
C292 AP50 2c multi (Bl)    .80  .85
C293 AP50 3c multi (G)    .80  .85
C294 AP50 4c multi (Bk)    .80  .85
   Nos. C291-C294 (4)    3.20  3.40
New York World's Fair.

Nos. C219-C222 Overprinted in
Green, Blue or Black: "VIII VUELTA /
CICLISTICA"

**1964**
C295 AP50 1c multi (G)    1.60  1.40
C296 AP50 2c multi (Bl)    1.60  1.40
C297 AP50 3c multi (G)    1.60  1.40
C298 AP50 4c multi (Bk)    2.50  2.25
   Nos. C295-C298 (4)    7.30  6.45
Eighth Bicycle Race.

Pres. John F.
Kennedy — AP63

**1964**     **Engr.**     *Perf. 11½*
| | | | | |
|---|---|---|---|---|
| **C299** | AP63 | 1c violet | 1.10 | .70 |
| **C300** | AP63 | 2c yellow grn | 1.10 | .70 |
| **C301** | AP63 | 3c brown | 1.10 | .70 |
| **C302** | AP63 | 7c deep blue | 1.10 | .70 |
| **C303** | AP63 | 50c dk gray | 8.50 | *7.50* |
| | *Nos. C299-C303 (5)* | | 12.90 | *10.30* |

Minute letters "TEOK" are in lower right corner of 1c, 2c, 3c and 50c.
Issue dates: 7c, July 10; others, Aug. 21.

Centenary Emblem — AP64

*Perf. 11x12*

**1964, Sept. 9**    **Unwmk.**    **Photo.**
| | | | | |
|---|---|---|---|---|
| **C304** | AP64 | 7c ultra, sil & red | .90 | .25 |
| **C305** | AP64 | 9c org, sil & red | .90 | .40 |
| **C306** | AP64 | 13c pur, sil & red | 1.40 | .55 |
| **C307** | AP64 | 21c brt grn, sil & red | 1.10 | *1.00* |
| **C308** | AP64 | 35c brn, sil & red | 2.10 | *1.40* |
| **C309** | AP64 | 1q lem, sil & red | 3.75 | 3.00 |
| | *Nos. C304-C309 (6)* | | 10.15 | *6.60* |

Centenary (in 1963) of the Intl. Red Cross.
For overprints see Nos. C323-C327, C395-C400.

Type of Regular Issue 1963
Souvenir Sheet

**1964**     **Engr.**     *Imperf.*
| | | | | |
|---|---|---|---|---|
| **C310** | | Sheet of 2 | 9.50 | 10.00 |
| ***a.*** | | A151 10c violet blue | 4.00 | 4.00 |
| ***b.*** | | A151 20c carmine | 4.00 | 4.00 |

15th UPU Congress, Vienna, May-June, 1964.

Enriquez de Rivera Type of 1946

**1964, Dec. 18**   **Engr.**   *Perf. 11½*
| | | | | |
|---|---|---|---|---|
| **C311** | A132 | 5c gray | .30 | .20 |
| **C312** | A132 | 5c orange | .30 | .20 |
| **C313** | A132 | 5c lt green | .30 | .20 |
| **C314** | A132 | 5c lt ultra | .30 | .20 |
| **C315** | A132 | 5c dull violet | .30 | .20 |
| | *Nos. C311-C315 (5)* | | 1.50 | 1.00 |

Bishop Francisco Marroquin AP65

Guatemalan Boy Scout Emblem — AP66

**1965, Jan. 21**   **Photo.**   **Unwmk.**
| | | | | |
|---|---|---|---|---|
| **C316** | AP65 | 4c lilac & brn | .20 | .20 |
| **C317** | AP65 | 7c gray & sepia | .60 | .20 |
| **C318** | AP65 | 9c vio bl & blk | .70 | .20 |
| | *Nos. C316-C318 (3)* | | 1.50 | .60 |

Issued to honor Bishop Francisco Marroquin.

Bethancourt Type of Regular Issue, 1964

**1965, Apr. 20**   **Engr.**   *Perf. 11½*
| | | | | |
|---|---|---|---|---|
| **C319** | A152 | 2½c violet blue | .20 | .20 |
| **C320** | A152 | 3c orange | .20 | .20 |
| **C321** | A152 | 4c purple | .20 | .20 |
| **C322** | A152 | 5c yellow grn | .30 | .20 |
| | *Nos. C319-C322 (4)* | | .90 | .80 |

For overprints see Nos. C381-C382.

---

Nos. C304-C308 Overprinted in Red:
"AYUDENOS / MAYO 1965"

**1965, June 18**   **Photo.**   *Perf. 11x12*
| | | | | |
|---|---|---|---|---|
| **C323** | AP64 | 7c ultra, sil & red | .45 | .45 |
| **C324** | AP64 | 9c org, sil & red | .55 | .55 |
| **C325** | AP64 | 13c pur, sil & red | .60 | .55 |
| **C326** | AP64 | 21c brt grn, sil & red | .85 | .80 |
| **C327** | AP64 | 35c brn, sil & red | 1.00 | *1.25* |
| | *Nos. C323-C327 (5)* | | 3.45 | 3.60 |

**1966, Mar. 3**   **Photo.**   *Perf. 14x13½*

Designs: 9c, Campfire and Scouts. 10c, Scout emblem and Scout carrying torch and flag. 15c, Scout emblem, flags and Scout giving Scout sign. 20c, Lord Baden-Powell.
| | | | | |
|---|---|---|---|---|
| **C328** | AP66 | 5c multicolored | .60 | .55 |
| **C329** | AP66 | 9c multicolored | .75 | .70 |
| **C330** | AP66 | 10c multicolored | .95 | .85 |
| **C331** | AP66 | 15c multicolored | 1.25 | 1.10 |
| **C332** | AP66 | 20c multicolored | 1.75 | 1.50 |
| | *Nos. C328-C332 (5)* | | 5.30 | 4.70 |

5th Interamerican Regional Training Conf., Guatemala City, Mar. 1-3.
For overprints see Nos. C376-C380.

**Central American Independence Issue**

Flags of Central American States — AP67

**1966, Mar. 9**     *Perf. 12½x13½*
| | | | | |
|---|---|---|---|---|
| **C333** | AP67 | 6c multicolored | .40 | .20 |

Queen Nefertari Temple, Abu Simbel AP68

**1966, Oct. 3**   **Photo.**   *Perf. 12*
| | | | | |
|---|---|---|---|---|
| **C334** | AP68 | 21c violet & ocher | .85 | .45 |

UNESCO world campaign to save historic monuments in Nubia.

Coat of Arms — AP69

**1966-70**    **Engr.**    *Perf. 13½*
| | | | | |
|---|---|---|---|---|
| **C335** | AP69 | 5c orange | .30 | .20 |
| **C336** | AP69 | 5c green | .30 | .20 |
| ***a.*** | | 5c yel grn, perf. 11½ ('69) | .30 | .20 |

*Perf. 11½*
| | | | | |
|---|---|---|---|---|
| **C337** | AP69 | 5c blue ('67) | .30 | .20 |
| ***a.*** | | 5c dk bl, perf. 12½ ('69) | .30 | .20 |

*Perf. 12½*
| | | | | |
|---|---|---|---|---|
| **C338** | AP69 | 5c gray ('67) | .30 | .20 |
| **C339** | AP69 | 5c purple ('67) | .30 | .20 |
| ***a.*** | | 5c bright violet ('69) | .30 | .20 |

*Perf. 11½*
| | | | | |
|---|---|---|---|---|
| **C339B** | AP69 | 5c dp mag ('70) | .55 | .20 |
| **C339C** | AP69 | 5c grn, *yel* ('70) | .60 | .20 |
| | *Nos. C335-C339C (7)* | | 2.65 | 1.40 |

Issued: #C335, 10/31; #C336, 12/15/66; #C337, 2/9/67; #C338-C339, 4/28/67; #C336a, 12/3/69; #C339a, 12/11/69; #C339B, 7/8/70; #C339C, 10/16/70.

---

Msgr. Mariano Rossell y Arellano AP70

**1966, Nov. 3**   **Engr.**   *Perf. 13½*
| | | | | |
|---|---|---|---|---|
| **C340** | AP70 | 1c dp violet | .20 | .20 |
| **C341** | AP70 | 2c green | .30 | .20 |
| **C342** | AP70 | 3c brown | .30 | .20 |
| **C343** | AP70 | 7c blue | .45 | .40 |
| **C344** | AP70 | 50c gray | 2.00 | 2.00 |
| | *Nos. C340-C344 (5)* | | 3.25 | 3.00 |

Issued to honor Msgr. Mariano Rossell y Arellano, apostolic delegate.

Mario Mendez Montenegro AP71

**1966-67**      *Perf. 13½*
| | | | | |
|---|---|---|---|---|
| **C345** | AP71 | 2c rose red ('67) | .20 | .20 |
| **C346** | AP71 | 3c orange ('67) | .30 | .20 |
| **C347** | AP71 | 4c rose claret ('67) | .40 | .20 |
| **C348** | AP71 | 5c gray | .55 | .20 |
| **C349** | AP71 | 5c lt ultra ('67) | .55 | .20 |
| **C350** | AP71 | 5c green ('67) | .55 | .20 |
| **C351** | AP71 | 5c bluish blk ('67) | .55 | .20 |
| | *Nos. C345-C351 (7)* | | 3.10 | 1.40 |

Mario Mendez Montenegro (1910-65), founder of the Revolutionary Party.

Morning Glory and Map of Guatemala AP72

Flowers: 8c, Bird of paradise, horiz. 10c, White nun orchid, national flower, horiz. 20c, Nymphs of Amatitlan.

**1967, Jan. 12**   **Photo.**   *Perf. 12*
**Flowers in Natural Colors**
| | | | | |
|---|---|---|---|---|
| **C352** | AP72 | 4c orange | 1.40 | .60 |
| **C353** | AP72 | 8c green | 1.40 | .60 |
| **C354** | AP72 | 10c dk blue | 1.60 | 1.10 |
| **C355** | AP72 | 20c dk red | 3.50 | 2.40 |
| | *Nos. C352-C355 (4)* | | 7.90 | 4.70 |

Pan-American Institute Emblem — AP73

**1967, Apr. 13**   **Photo.**   *Perf. 13½*
| | | | | |
|---|---|---|---|---|
| **C356** | AP73 | 4c lt brn, lil & blk | .40 | .20 |
| **C357** | AP73 | 5c ol, bl & blk | .75 | .20 |
| **C358** | AP73 | 7c org yel, bl & blk | 1.10 | .40 |
| | *Nos. C356-C358 (3)* | | 2.25 | .80 |

8th Gen. Assembly of the Pan-American Geographical and Historical Institute in 1965.

---

No. C281 Overprinted

**1967, Apr. 28**   **Engr.**   *Perf. 11½*
| | | | | |
|---|---|---|---|---|
| **C360** | AP62 | 3c dull green | 1.60 | 1.10 |

Guatemala's victory in the 3rd Norceca Soccer Games (Caribbean, Central and North American).

No. C281A Overprinted in Red:
"REUNION JEFES DE ESTADO / AMERICANO, PUNTA DEL ESTE, / MONTEVIDEO, URUGUAY 1967"

**1967, June 28**   **Engr.**   *Perf. 11½*
| | | | | |
|---|---|---|---|---|
| **C361** | AP62 | 4c gray | 1.10 | 1.10 |

Meeting of American Presidents, Punta del Este, Apr. 10-12.

Handshake AP74

**1967, June 28**   **Photo.**   *Perf. 12*
| | | | | |
|---|---|---|---|---|
| **C362** | AP74 | 7c pink, brn & grn | .55 | .25 |
| **C363** | AP74 | 21c lt bl, grn & brn | .85 | .55 |

"Peace and Progress through Cooperation."
For overprint see No. C416.

Church of Santo Domingo AP75

1c, Yurrita Church, vert. 3c, Church of St. Francis. 4c, Antonio José de Irisarri, vert. 5c, Church of the Convent, vert. 7c, Mercy Church, Antigua. 10c, Metropolitan Cathedral.

**1967, Aug.**    *Perf. 11½x12, 12x11½*
| | | | | |
|---|---|---|---|---|
| **C364** | AP75 | 1c grn, lt bl & dk brn | .40 | .25 |
| **C365** | AP75 | 2c plum, sal pink & brn | .45 | .25 |
| **C366** | AP75 | 3c brt rose, gray & blk | .45 | .25 |
| **C367** | AP75 | 4c mar, sl grn & org | .45 | .25 |
| **C368** | AP75 | 5c lil, pale grn & dk brn | .45 | .25 |
| **C369** | AP75 | 7c ultra, lil rose & blk | .55 | .25 |
| **C370** | AP75 | 10c pur, yel & blk | .95 | .30 |
| | *Nos. C364-C370 (7)* | | 3.70 | 1.80 |

Abraham Lincoln (1809-1865) AP76

**1967**    **Engr.**   *Perf. 13½, 11½ (9c)*
| | | | | |
|---|---|---|---|---|
| **C371** | AP76 | 7c gray & dp org | .45 | .25 |
| **C372** | AP76 | 9c dk grn & grysh | .55 | .25 |
| **C373** | AP76 | 11c brn org & slate | .45 | .30 |
| **C374** | AP76 | 15c ultra & vio brn | .65 | .40 |
| **C375** | AP76 | 30c magenta & grn | 1.50 | 1.50 |
| | *Nos. C371-C375 (5)* | | 3.60 | 2.70 |

Issued: 7c, 9c, Oct. 9; others, Dec. 12.
For surcharge see No. C554.

Nos. C328-C332 Overprinted: "VIII Camporee Scout / Centroamericano / Diciembre 1-8/1967"

**1967, Dec. 1**   **Photo.**   *Perf. 14x13½*
| | | | | |
|---|---|---|---|---|
| **C376** | AP66 | 5c multicolored | .40 | .40 |
| **C377** | AP66 | 9c multicolored | .65 | .65 |
| **C378** | AP66 | 10c multicolored | .85 | .55 |

| | | | | |
|---|---|---|---|---|
| C379 | AP66 | 15c multicolored | .85 | .85 |
| C380 | AP66 | 20c multicolored | 1.00 | 1.00 |
| | | Nos. C376-C380 (5) | 3.75 | 3.75 |

Issued to commemorate the 8th Central American Boy Scout Camporee, Dec. 1-8.

Nos. C320-C321 Overprinted in Four Lines: "Premio Nóbel de Literatura - 10 diciembre 1967 - Miguel Angel Asturias"

**1967, Dec. 11     Engr.     Perf. 11½**

| | | | | |
|---|---|---|---|---|
| C381 | A152 | 3c orange | .55 | .55 |
| C382 | A152 | 4c purple | .55 | .55 |

Awarding of the Nobel Prize for Literature to Miguel Angel Asturias, Guatemalan writer.

Institute Emblem — AP77

**1967, Dec. 12     Engr.     Perf. 11½**

| | | | | |
|---|---|---|---|---|
| C383 | AP77 | 9c black & grn | .80 | .80 |
| C384 | AP77 | 25c car & brn | 1.50 | 1.50 |
| C385 | AP77 | 1q ultra & bl | 4.00 | 4.00 |
| | | Nos. C383-C385 (3) | 6.30 | 6.30 |

Inter-American Agriculture Institute, 25th anniv.

UNESCO Emblem and Children AP78

**1967, Dec. 12**

| | | | | |
|---|---|---|---|---|
| C386 | AP78 | 4c blue green | .30 | .20 |
| C387 | AP78 | 5c blue | .35 | .20 |
| C388 | AP78 | 7c gray | .50 | .35 |
| C389 | AP78 | 21c brt rose lil | 1.10 | 1.10 |
| | | Nos. C386-C389 (4) | 2.25 | 1.85 |

20th anniv. (in 1966) of UNESCO.

Nos. C219-C221 and C304-C308 Overprinted in Black or Yellow Green: "III REUNION DE / PRESIDENTES / Nov. 15-18, 1967"

**Perf. 13½x14, 14x13½, 11x12**

**1968, Jan. 23                    Photo.**

| | | | | |
|---|---|---|---|---|
| C390 | AP50 | 1c multi | .80 | .55 |
| C391 | AP50 | 1c multi (G) | .80 | .80 |
| C392 | AP50 | 2c multi | .80 | .80 |
| C393 | AP50 | 2c multi (G) | .80 | .80 |
| C394 | AP50 | 3c multi | .80 | .80 |
| C395 | AP64 | 3c multi (G) | .80 | .80 |
| C396 | AP64 | 7c multi | .80 | .80 |
| C397 | AP64 | 9c multi | 1.10 | 1.10 |
| C398 | AP64 | 13c multi | 1.60 | 1.10 |
| C399 | AP64 | 21c multi | 2.25 | 1.10 |
| C400 | AP64 | 35c multi | 1.90 | 1.90 |
| | | Nos. C390-C400 (11) | 12.45 | 10.55 |

3rd meeting of Central American Presidents, Nov. 15-18, 1967.

Our Lady of the Coro — AP79

Miguel Angel Asturias, Flags of Guatemala and Sweden — AP80

**1968-74     Engr.     Perf. 13½, 11½**

| | | | | |
|---|---|---|---|---|
| C403 | AP79 | 4c ultra | .55 | .25 |
| C404 | AP79 | 7c slate | .50 | .25 |
| C405 | AP79 | 9c green | .50 | .25 |
| C406 | AP79 | 9c lilac ('74) | .55 | .25 |
| C407 | AP79 | 10c brick red | .95 | .25 |
| C408 | AP79 | 10c gray | .60 | .25 |
| C408A | AP79 | 10c vio bl ('74) | .40 | .20 |

| | | | | |
|---|---|---|---|---|
| C409 | AP79 | 1q vio brn | 4.00 | 3.50 |
| C410 | AP79 | 1q org yel | 4.00 | 3.50 |
| | | Nos. C403-C410 (9) | 12.05 | 8.70 |

Perf. 13½ applies to 4c and Nos. C407, C409-C410; perf. 11½ to 4c, 7c, 9c and Nos. C408, C408A.

Nos. 396-398 Overprinted: "AEREO / XI VUELTA / CICLISTICA / 1967"

**1968, Mar. 25     Litho.     Perf. 14x13½**

| | | | | |
|---|---|---|---|---|
| C411 | A153 | 4c multicolored | .85 | .85 |
| C412 | A153 | 5c multicolored | .85 | .85 |
| C413 | A153 | 15c multicolored | .70 | .70 |
| | | Nos. C411-C413 (3) | 2.40 | 2.40 |

The 11th Bicycle Race.

**1968, June 18     Engr.     Perf. 11½**

| | | | | |
|---|---|---|---|---|
| C414 | AP80 | 20c ultra | 1.10 | .40 |

Awarding of the Nobel Prize for Literature to Miguel Angel Asturias.

No. C234 Overprinted in Carmine: "1968. — AÑO INTERNACIONAL / DERECHOS HUMANOS. — ONU"

**1968, July 18     Litho.     Perf. 11**

| | | | | |
|---|---|---|---|---|
| C415 | AP53 | 6c pale brown | .75 | .40 |

International Human Rights Year.

No. C362 Overprinted: "AYUDA A CONSERVAR / LOS BOSQUES. — 1968"

**1968, July 18     Photo.     Perf. 12**

| | | | | |
|---|---|---|---|---|
| C416 | AP74 | 7c pink, brn & grn | .65 | .40 |

Issued to publicize forest conservation.

No. C213 Overprinted in Brown: "Expedición / Científica / Nahakín / Guatemala-Peru / Ruta de los / Mayas"

**1968, Aug. 23     Photo.     Perf. 14x13½**

| | | | | |
|---|---|---|---|---|
| C417 | AP49 | 6c dk brn & dp ultra | .65 | .65 |

Nahakin scientific expedition along the route of the Mayas undertaken jointly with Peru.

Views, Quetzal and White Nun Orchid — AP81

**1968, Aug. 23     Engr.     Perf. 13½**

| | | | | |
|---|---|---|---|---|
| C418 | AP81 | 10c dp cl & grn | .55 | .25 |
| C419 | AP81 | 20c dp org & blk | .85 | .60 |
| C420 | AP81 | 50c ultra & car | 1.50 | 1.50 |
| | | Nos. C418-C420 (3) | 2.90 | 2.35 |

Issued for tourist publicity.

No. C281A Overprinted in Carmine: "CONFEDERACION / DE UNIVERSIDADES / CENTROAMERICANAS / 1948 1968"

**1968, Nov. 4                    Perf. 11½**

| | | | | |
|---|---|---|---|---|
| C421 | AP62 | 4c gray | .55 | .55 |

20th anniv. of the Federation of Central American Universities.

Presidents Gustavo Diaz Ordaz and Julio Cesar Mendez Montenegro AP82

**1968, Dec. 3     Litho.     Perf. 14x13½**

| | | | | |
|---|---|---|---|---|
| C422 | AP82 | 5c multicolored | .25 | .25 |
| C423 | AP82 | 10c multicolored | .40 | .25 |
| C424 | AP82 | 25c multicolored | .95 | .85 |
| | | Nos. C422-C424 (3) | 1.60 | 1.35 |

Mutual visits of the Presidents of Mexico and Guatemala.

ITU Emblem, Old and New Communication Equipment — AP83

**Engraved and Photogravure**

**1968-74     Perf. 11½, 12½ (21c)**

| | | | | |
|---|---|---|---|---|
| C425 | AP83 | 7c violet blue | .25 | .20 |
| C426 | AP83 | 15c gray & emer | .45 | .20 |
| C426A | AP83 | 15c vio brn & org ('74) | .55 | .25 |
| C427 | AP83 | 21c magenta | .70 | .45 |
| C428 | AP83 | 35c rose red & emer | .95 | .45 |
| C429 | AP83 | 75c green & red | 2.40 | 2.40 |
| C430 | AP83 | 3q brown & red | 9.25 | 7.75 |
| | | Nos. C425-C430 (7) | 14.55 | 11.70 |

Cent. (in 1965) of the ITU.

Nos. C425, C427 are engr. only; on others denominations are photo. No. C426A is on thin, toned paper.

Issued: #C426A, 2/18/74; others 12/13/68.

For surcharges see Nos. C454, C516.

Nos. 399-403 Overprinted in Red, Black or Gold

**Lithographed and Engraved**

**1969                    Perf. 11½, 13½ (1c)**

| | | | | |
|---|---|---|---|---|
| C431 | A154 | 1c blk, lt grn & red (R) | .80 | .40 |
| C432 | A154 | 5c yel, lt grn & red | 1.00 | .55 |
| C433 | A154 | 8c org, lt grn & red | .95 | .85 |
| C434 | A154 | 15c bl, lt grn & red | 1.10 | 1.00 |
| C435 | A154 | 30c lt vio, lt grn & red (G) | 1.60 | 1.40 |
| | | Nos. C431-C435 (5) | 5.45 | 4.20 |

Dante Alighieri — AP84

**1969, July 17     Engr.     Perf. 12½**

| | | | | |
|---|---|---|---|---|
| C436 | AP84 | 7c rose vio & ultra | .40 | .25 |
| C437 | AP84 | 10c dk blue | .45 | .25 |
| C438 | AP84 | 20c green | .70 | .25 |
| C439 | AP84 | 21c gray & brn | 1.10 | .80 |
| C440 | AP84 | 35c pur & brt grn | 2.75 | 1.75 |
| | | Nos. C436-C440 (5) | 5.40 | 3.30 |

Dante Alighieri (1265-1321), Italian poet.

Map of Latin America — AP85

Design: 9c, Seal of University.

**1969, Oct. 29     Typo.     Perf. 13**

**Size: 44x27mm**

| | | | | |
|---|---|---|---|---|
| C441 | AP85 | 2c brt pink & blk | .25 | .20 |

**Size: 35x27mm**

| | | | | |
|---|---|---|---|---|
| C442 | AP85 | 9c gray & blk | .55 | .25 |

**Souvenir Sheet**

*Imperf*

| | | | | |
|---|---|---|---|---|
| C443 | AP85 | Sheet of 2 | 1.40 | 1.40 |
| a. | | 2c light blue & black | .60 | .60 |
| b. | | 9c orange & black | .60 | .60 |

20th anniv. of the Union of Latin American Universities.

**Moon Landing Issue**

Moon Landing — AP86

**1969-70     Engr.     Perf. 11½**

| | | | | |
|---|---|---|---|---|
| C444 | AP86 | 50c maroon & blk | 2.75 | 2.75 |
| C445 | AP86 | 1q ultra & blk | 4.75 | 4.75 |

**Souvenir Sheet**

*Imperf*

| | | | | |
|---|---|---|---|---|
| C446 | AP86 | 1q yel grn & ultra | 6.75 | 6.75 |

See note after US No. C76. No. C446 contains one stamp with simulated perforations.

Issued: #C445-C446, 12/19/69; #C444, 1/6/70.

Giant Grebe Family on Lake Atitlan AP87

Designs: 4c, Lake Atitlan. 20c, Grebe chick, eggs atop floating nest, vert.

**1970, Mar. 31     Litho.     Perf. 13½**

| | | | | |
|---|---|---|---|---|
| C447 | AP87 | 4c red & multi | .95 | .25 |
| C448 | AP87 | 9c red & multi | 1.40 | .30 |
| a. | | Souv. sheet of 2, #C447-C448 | 15.00 | 15.00 |
| C449 | AP87 | 20c red & multi | 2.40 | .85 |
| | | Nos. C447-C449 (3) | 4.75 | 1.40 |

Protection of zambullidor ducks.

Dr. Victor Manuel Calderon — AP88

Hand Holding Bible — AP89

**1970     Litho. & Engr.     Perf. 13, 12½**

| | | | | |
|---|---|---|---|---|
| C450 | AP88 | 1c lt bl & blk | .20 | .20 |
| C451 | AP88 | 2c pale grn & blk | .25 | .20 |

**Perf. 13**

| | | | | |
|---|---|---|---|---|
| C452 | AP88 | 9c yellow & blk | .55 | .20 |
| | | Nos. C450-C452 (3) | 1.00 | .60 |

Dr. Victor Manuel Calderon (1889-1969), who described microfilaria, a blood parasite.

**1970     Litho. & Typo.     Perf. 13x13½**

| | | | | |
|---|---|---|---|---|
| C453 | AP89 | 5c red & multi | .30 | .25 |

Fourth centenary of the Bible in Spanish.

No. C430 Surcharged

**1971, Mar. 11     Engr.     Perf. 11½**

| | | | | |
|---|---|---|---|---|
| C454 | AP83 | 50c on 3q brn & red | 2.00 | 2.00 |

Arms of Guatemala,
Newspapers — AP90

Official Decree of First Issue — AP91

**1971**     **Litho.**     **Perf. 11½, 12½**
C455 AP90 2c dk bl & red    .20   .20
C456 AP90 5c brn & red    .20   .20
C457 AP90 25c brt bl & red    .65   .40
    Nos. C455-C457 (3)    1.05   .80

**Souvenir Sheet**

**Lithographed and Engraved**

*Imperf*

C458 AP91   Sheet of 5    2.00 2.00

Cent. of Guatemala's postage stamps.
Nos. C456-C457 have white value tablet.
No. C458 contains a litho. 4c black and
engr. reproductions of Nos. 1-4 in colors similar to 1871 issue. Simulated perforations.
In 1974 No. C458 was overprinted "Conmemorativa / al Campeonato Mundial de Foot
Ball / Munich 1974" and Munich Games
emblem in black. Value $12. Overprint in gold
or other colors was not authorized,
See Nos. C569-C570.

Mayas with CARE Package — AP92

**1971**     **Typo.**     **Perf. 11½**
C459 AP92 5c multi    .40   .40
   a.    Souv. sheet of 2    2.50 2.50

25th aniversary of CARE, a US-Canadian
Cooperative for American Relief Everywhere.
No. C459a contains imperf. stamps similar
to Nos. 416 and C459.

J. Rufino Barrios, M. Garcia
Granados, Map of Guatemala,
Quetzal — AP93

**1971, June 30**     **Perf. 11½**
C460 AP93 2c multi, perf
         13½    .80   .20
   a.    Value in pink ('72)    .70   .20
C461 AP93 10c multi    1.50   .30
   a.    Value in pink, perf. 12½
        ('72)    1.50   .30
C462 AP93 50c multi    8.00 3.25
C463 AP93 1q multi    12.00 6.50
    Nos. C460-C463 (4)    22.30 10.25

Centenary of the liberal revolution of 1871.

Chavarry Arrué and León
Bilak — AP94

**Perf. 11½, 11x12½, 12½**
**1971-72**            **Engr.**
C464 AP94 1c grn & blk ('72)   .25   .20
C465 AP94 2c lt brn & blk ('72)   .30   .25
C466 AP94 5c grn & blk    .45   .30
    Nos. C464-C466 (3)    1.00   .75

Honoring J. Arnoldo Chavarry Arrué, stamp
engraver; León Bilak, philatelist.

No. C231
Overprinted

**1971, Oct. 25**    **Litho.**    **Perf. 11½**
C467 AP52 6c ultra & rose red   .50   .20
   INTERFER 71, Intl. Fair, Guatemala, Oct.
30-Nov. 21.

Flag and Map of
Guatemala
AP95

UNICEF Emblem
and Mayan
Figure — AP96

**Perf. 13½ (1c), 12½ (3c, 9c), 11 (5c)**
**1971-75**            **Typo.**
C468 AP95 1c blk, bl & lil   .25   .25
   a.    Lithographed ('75)    .25   .25
C469 AP95 3c brn, brt pink & bl   .25   .25
C470 AP95 5c brn, org & bl   .25   .25
   a.    Lithographed, perf. 12½ ('74)   .25   .25
C471 AP95 9c blk, emer & bl   .25   .25
    Nos. C468-C471 (4)    1.00 1.00

Central American independence, sesqui.
Date of issue: #C469-C471, July 10, 1972.

**1971-75**        **Engr.**     **Perf. 11½**
C472 AP96 1c yel grn    .25   .25
C472A AP96 2c purple    .25   .25
C473 AP96 50c vio brn    1.90 1.90
C474 AP96 1q ultra    3.00 3.00
    Nos. C472-C474 (4)    5.40 5.40

25th anniv. UNICEF.
Issued: 2c, 2/24/75; others, 11/71.

Early Boeing Planes — AP97

Design: 10c, Bleriot's plane.

**1972**     **Typo.**     **Perf. 11½**
C475 AP97 5c lt brn & brt bl   .75   .30
C476 AP97 10c dark blue    1.25   .30

Military aviation in Guatemala, 50th anniv.

Arches, Antigua — AP98

**1972-73**     **Typo.**     **Perf. 11½**
**Dark Blue and Light Blue**
C480 AP98 1c shown    .25   .20
C481 AP98 1c Cathedral    .25   .20
C482 AP98 1c Fountain,
         Central Park   .25   .20
C483 AP98 1c Capuchin
         Monastery   .25   .20
C484 AP98 1c Fountain and
         Santa Clara   .25   .20
C485 AP98 1c Portal of San
         Francisco   .25   .20
   a.    Block of 6, #C480-C485   1.75 1.60
**Black, Lilac Rose, and Silver**
C486 AP98 2½c shown    .45   .20
C487 AP98 2½c Catherdral   .45   .20
C488 AP98 2½c Fountain and
         Santa Clara   .45   .20
C489 AP98 2½c Portal of San
         Francisco   .45   .20
C490 AP98 2½c Fountain    .45   .20
C491 AP98 2½c Capuchin
         Monastery   .45   .20
   a.    Block of 6, #C3486-C491   3.00 1.60
**Blue, Orange and Black**
C492 AP98 5c shown    .95   .25
C493 AP98 5c Cathedral    .95   .25
C494 AP98 5c Santa Clara   .95   .25
C495 AP98 5c Portal of San
         Francisco   .95   .25
C496 AP98 5c Fountain    .95   .25
C497 AP98 5c Capuchin
         Monastery   .95   .25
   a.    Block of 6, #C492-C497   6.00 3.00
   Nos. C492-C497 exist perf. 12½, same
value.

**Perf. 12½**
**Red, Blue and Black**
C498 AP98 1q Fountain    4.75 2.50
C499 AP98 1q Capuchin
         Monastery   4.75 2.50
C500 AP98 1q shown    4.75 2.50
C501 AP98 1q Cathedral    4.75 2.50
C502 AP98 1q Fountain and
         Santa Clara   4.75 2.50
C503 AP98 1q Portal of San
         Francisco   4.75 2.50
   a.    Block of 6, #C498-C503   27.50 15.00
    Nos. C480-C503 (24)    38.40 18.90

Earthquake ruins of Antigua. 1c printed se-
tenant in sheets of 90 (10x9); 2½c, 5c se-
tenant in sheets of 30 (5x6); 1q se-tenant in
sheets of 6 (3x2).
On Nos. C498-C503 the inks were applied
by a thermographic process giving a shiny
raised effect.
Issued: #C480-C485, 12/14; #C486-C491,
1/22/73; #C492-C497, 3/12/73; #C498-C503,
8/22/73.
Nos. C480-C485 were overprinted "II Feria
Internacional / INTERFER/73 / 31 Octubre —
Noviembre 18 / 1973 / GUATEMALA" in black
or lilac rose and issued 11/3/73. Value $3.
The same overprint exists in black on Nos.
C480-C485, but these stamps were not
decreed or issued.
See Nos. C528-C545, C770-C775F. For
overprints see Nos. C517-C523.

Simon Bolivar
and Map of
Americas
AP99

**1973-74**     **Perf. 11½**
C504 AP99 3c brt lil rose & blk   .25   .25
C505 AP99 3c org & dk bl ('74)   .25   .25
C506 AP99 5c yel & multi    .25   .25
C507 AP99 5c brt grn & blk   .25   .25
    Nos. C504-C507 (4)    1.00 1.00

Indian with
CARE
Package,
World Map
AP100

CARE Package
AP101

**1973, June 14**    **Typo.**    **Perf. 12½**
C508 AP100 2c blk & multi   .25   .20
C509 AP101 10c blk & multi   .55   .40
   a.    Souvenir sheet of 2   1.50 1.50

25th anniversary of CARE (in 1971), a US-
sponsored relief organization and 10th anniversary of its work in Guatemala.
No. C509a contains 2 stamps similar to
Nos. C508-C509 with simulated perforations.

Guatemala
No. 1,
Laurel
AP102

**1973-74**   **Engr.**   **Perf. 12½, 11½ (1q)**
C510 AP102 1c brt brn ('74)   .25   .20
C511 AP102 1q rose claret   3.00 2.50

Centenary (in 1971) of Guatemala postage
stamps. See Nos. C574-C576A.

Oak
Wreath
and Star
AP103

**1973, Aug. 22**    **Typo.**    **Perf. 12½**
C512 AP103 5c brn, yel & bl   .30   .25

Centenary of Escuela Politecnica, Guatemala's military academy.
See Nos. C552-C553.

Eleanor Roosevelt
AP104

## Perf. 11½, 12½
**1973, Sept. 11**  **Engr.**
C513 AP104 7c blue .40 .20
Eleanor Roosevelt (1884-1962), lecturer, writer, UN delegate.

Boys' School, Chiquimula AP105

**1973-74**  **Typo.**  **Perf. 12½**
C514 AP105 3c blk & bl .30 .25
C515 AP105 5c blk & dp lil rose .30 .25
Centenary of the Instituto Varones in Chiquimula.
Issued: 5c, 12/5/73; 3c, 6/13/74.

No. C430 Surcharged in Red:
"Desvalorizadas a Q0.50" and Ornamental Obliteration of Old Denomination
**1974**  **Engr. & Photo.**  **Perf. 11½**
C516 AP83 50c on 3q brn & red 2.00 2.00

Nos. C480-C485 and C509a Overprinted with UPU Emblem, "UPU / HOMENAJE CENTENARIO / 1874 1974"
**1974, June 13**  **Typo.**  **Perf. 11½**
C517 AP98 1c dk bl & lt bl .40 .30
C518 AP98 1c dk bl & lt bl .40 .30
C519 AP98 1c dk bl & lt bl .40 .30
C520 AP98 1c dk bl & lt bl .40 .30
C521 AP98 1c dk bl & lt bl .40 .30
C522 AP98 1c dk bl & lt bl .40 .30
Nos. C517-C522 (6) 2.40 1.80
### Souvenir Sheet
C523 Sheet of 2 13.50 13.50
Centenary of Universal Postal Union.
No. C523 consists of an overprint on No. C509a, including "UNIVERSAL POSTAL UNION" instead of "UPU."
The overprint on No. C523 in red was not authorized by the Post Office. Value $28.

Antigua Type of 1972-73
**1974, Oct. 8**  **Typo.**  **Perf. 11½**
### Black and Light Brown
C528 AP98 2c Capuchin Monastery .25 .25
C529 AP98 2c Arches .25 .25
C530 AP98 2c Cathedral .25 .25
C531 AP98 2c Fountain and Santa Clara .25 .25
C532 AP98 2c Portal of San Francisco .25 .25
C533 AP98 2c Fountain .25 .25
Nos. C528-C533 (6) 1.50 1.50

**1974, Sept. 24**
### Black and Yellow
C540 AP98 20c Capuchin Monastery .55 .55
C541 AP98 20c Arches .55 .55
C542 AP98 20c Cathedral .55 .55
C543 AP98 20c Fountain and Santa Clara .55 .55
C544 AP98 20c Portal of San Francisco .55 .55
C545 AP98 20c Fountain .55 .55
Nos. C540-C545 (6) 3.30 3.30
Earthquake ruins of Antigua. Each group of six printed se-tenant in sheets of 30 (5x6). Value $2.
Nos. C528-C533 were printed in 1975 in black and bister se-tenant in sheets of 24 (4x6) on whiter paper. Value $5.

Generals Justo Rufino Barrios and M. Garcia Granados — AP106

---

Polytechnic School AP107

**1974-75 Typo.**  **Perf. 12½, 11½ (25c)**
C552 AP106 6c red, gray & bl .25 .25
C553 AP107 25c multi .45 .30
Centenary (in 1973) of Escuela Politecnica, Guatemala's military academy.
Issued: 6c, 9/17; 25c, 1/1/75.

No. C373 Surcharged in Black and Green

**1974, Dec. 3**  **Engr.**  **Perf. 13½**
C554 AP76 10c on 11c multi 1.10 .50
Nature protection. The quetzal, Guatemala's national bird.

Costume San Martin Sacatepequez AP108

Costumes of Women: 2c, Solola. 9c, Coban. 20c, Chichicastenango.

**1974-75**  **Typo.**  **Perf. 12½**
C556 AP108 2c car & multi .25 .25
C557 AP108 2½c bl, car & brn .20 .20
C559 AP108 9c bl & multi .30 .25
a. Perf. 12½x13½ .30 .25
C561 AP108 20c red & multi .55 .25
Nos. C556-C561 (4) 1.30 .95
Issue dates: 2½c, Dec. 16, 1974; 20c, Jan. 14, 1975; 2c, 9c, May 19, 1975.

Quetzals and Maya Quekchi Woman Wearing Huipil — AP109

**1975, June 25**  **Litho.**  **Perf. 13½**
C565 AP109 8c bl & multi .70 .25
C566 AP109 20c red & multi 1.25 .40
International Women's Year 1975.

Rotary Emblem AP110

---

**1975-76**  **Typo.**  **Perf. 13½**
C567 AP110 10c bl & multi .40 .20
**Perf. 11½**
C568 AP110 15c bl & multi .45 .20
Guatemala City Rotary Club, 50th anniv.
Issued: 10c, 10/1; 15c, 12/21/76.

Gaceta Type of 1971 Redrawn
**1975-76**  **Typo.**  **Perf. 12½**
C569 AP90 5c brn & red .25 .25
C570 AP90 50c brt rose & brn 1.40 .55
The white background around numeral and on right of arms has been filled in.
Issued: 5c, 12/12; 50c, 12/1/76.

IWY Emblem and White Nun Orchid — AP111

**1975-76**  **Perf. 12½x13½, 11½ (8c)**
C571 AP111 1c multi .30 .25
C572 AP111 8c yel & multi .40 .25
C573 AP111 26c rose & multi .95 .30
Nos. C571-C573 (3) 1.65 .80
International Women's Year 1975.
Issued: 1c, 12/19; 8c, 12/12; 26c, 5/10/76.

Stamp Centenary Type of 1973
**1975-77**  **Engr.**  **Perf. 11½**
C574 AP102 6c orange .25 .25
C575 AP102 6c green ('76) .25 .25
C576 AP102 6c gray ('77) .25 .25
C576A AP102 6c vio bl ('77) .25 .25
Nos. C574-C576A (4) 1.00 1.00
Issued: #C574, 12/31; #C575, 5/10; others, 8/10.

Destroyed Joyabaj Village — AP112

Designs (Guatemala Flag and): 3c, Emergency food distribution. 5c, Jaguar Temple, Tikal. 10c, Destroyed bridge. 15c, Outdoors emergency hospital. 25c, Sugar cane harvest. 25c, Destroyed house. 30c, New building, Tecpan. 50c, Destroyed Cerro del Carmen church. 75c, Cleaning up debris. 1q, Military help. 2q, Lake Atitlan.

**1976, June 4**  **Litho.**  **Perf. 12½**
C577 AP112 1c red & multi .20 .20
C578 AP112 3c multi .20 .20
C579 AP112 5c pink & multi .20 .20
C580 AP112 10c red & multi .30 .20
C581 AP112 15c multi .45 .20
C582 AP112 20c pink & multi .45 .30
C583 AP112 25c red & multi .80 .35
C584 AP112 30c multi .95 .30
C585 AP112 50c red & multi 1.25 .45
C586 AP112 75c multi 2.00 1.00
C587 AP112 1q multi 3.00 1.25
C588 AP112 2q multi 5.75 3.00
Nos. C577-C588 (12) 15.55 7.65
Earthquake of Feb. 4, 1976, and gratitude for foreign help. Inscriptions in colored panels vary. 3 imperf. souvenir sheets exist (50c, 1q, 2q). Size: 112x83mm.

Allegory of Independence — AP113

Designs: 2c, Boston Tea Party. 3c, Thomas Jefferson, vert. 4c, 20c, 35c, Allegory of Independence (each different; 4c, 35c, vert.). 5c,

---

Warren's Death at Bunker Hill. 10c, Washington at Valley Forge. 15c, Washington at Monmouth. 25c, The Generals at Yorktown. 30c, Washington Crossing the Delaware. 40c, Declaration of Independence. 45c, Patrick Henry, vert. 50c, Congress Voting Independence. 1q, Washington, vert. 2q, Lincoln, vert. 3q, Franklin, vert. 5q, John F. Kennedy, vert. The historical designs and portraits are after paintings.

**1976, July 30**  **Litho.**  **Perf. 12½**
### Size: 46x27mm, 27x46mm
C592 AP113 1c multicolored .25 .20
C593 AP113 2c multicolored .20 .20
C594 AP113 3c multicolored .20 .20
C595 AP113 4c multicolored .25 .20
C596 AP113 5c multicolored .25 .20
C597 AP113 10c multicolored .25 .20
C598 AP113 15c multicolored .30 .20
C599 AP113 20c multicolored .45 .25
C600 AP113 25c multicolored .45 .25
C601 AP113 30c multicolored .80 .25
C602 AP113 35c multicolored .85 .45
C603 AP113 40c multicolored .85 .55
C604 AP113 45c multicolored 1.00 .65
C605 AP113 50c multicolored 1.40 .45
C606 AP113 1q multicolored 2.40 2.00
a. Souvenir sheet 2.75 2.75
C607 AP113 2q multicolored 4.00 4.00
a. Souvenir sheet 5.00 5.00
C608 AP113 3q multicolored 5.50 5.50
a. Souvenir sheet 6.25 6.25
### Size: 35x55mm
C609 AP113 5q multicolored 9.50 3.50
a. Souvenir sheet 12.00 12.00
Nos. C592-C609 (18) 28.85 19.25
American Bicentennial. Souvenir sheets contain one imperf. stamp each.

1974 Quetzal Coin AP114

### Lithographed and Engraved
**1976, Dec. 1**  **Perf. 11½**
C610 AP114 8c org, blk & bl .25 .20
**Perf. 13½**
C611 AP114 20c brt rose, bl & blk .70 .25
50th anniv. of introduction of Quetzal currency.

Engineers at Work AP115

**1976, Dec. 21**  **Engr.**  **Perf. 11½**
C612 AP115 9c ultra .30 .20
C613 AP115 10c green .30 .20
School of Engineering, Guatemala City, centenary.

Holy Week Type of 1977
Designs: Sculptures of Christ from various Guatemalan churches. 4c, 7c, 9c, 20c, vert.

**1977, Apr. 4**  **Litho.**  **Perf. 11**
C614 A159 3c pur & multi .40 .25
C615 A159 4c pur & multi .40 .25
C616 A159 7c pur & multi .40 .25
C617 A159 9c pur & multi .45 .25
C618 A159 20c pur & multi .95 .60
C619 A159 26c pur & multi 1.25 .70
Nos. C614-C619 (6) 3.85 2.30
### Souvenir Sheet
### Roulette 7½
C620 A159 30c pur & multi 4.00 4.00
Holy Week 1977.

City Hall and Bank of Guatemala — AP116

Designs: 6c, Deed to original site, vert. 8c, Church and farm house, site of first legislative session. 9c, Coat of arms of Pedro Cortes, first archbishop. 22c, Arms of Guatemala City, vert.

### Perf. 13½ (6c); 11½ (others)
**1977, Aug. 10**     Litho.

| | | | | |
|---|---|---|---|---|
| C621 | AP116 | 6c multicolored | .40 | .25 |
| C622 | AP116 | 7c multicolored | .40 | .25 |
| C623 | AP116 | 8c multicolored | .40 | .25 |
| C624 | AP116 | 9c multicolored | .55 | .25 |
| a. | | Souvenir sheet | .80 | .80 |
| C625 | AP116 | 22c multicolored | .85 | .25 |
| a. | | Souvenir sheet | 1.10 | 1.10 |
| | | Nos. C621-C625 (5) | 2.60 | 1.25 |

Bicentenary of the founding of Nueva Guatemala de la Asuncion (Guatemala City). Nos. C624a-C625a contain one stamp each with simulated perforations.

Arms of Quetzaltenango AP117

City Hall and Torch AP118

**1977, Sept. 11**   Litho.   Perf. 11½

| | | | | |
|---|---|---|---|---|
| C626 | AP117 | 7c blk & sil | .25 | .20 |
| C627 | AP118 | 30c bl & yel | .85 | .30 |

Founding of Quetzaltenango, 150th anniv.

Mayan Bas-relief — AP119

**1977, Nov. 7**

| | | | | |
|---|---|---|---|---|
| C628 | AP119 | 10c brt car & blk | .30 | .20 |

14th Intl. Cong. of Latin Notaries.

Children Bringing Gifts to Christ Child — AP120

Christmas: 1c, Mother and children, horiz. 4c, Guatemalan children's Nativity scene.

**1977, Dec. 16**   Litho.   Perf. 11½

| | | | | |
|---|---|---|---|---|
| C629 | AP120 | 1c multicolored | .25 | .25 |
| C630 | AP120 | 2c multicolored | .25 | .25 |
| C631 | AP120 | 4c multicolored | .25 | .25 |
| | | Nos. C629-C631 (3) | .75 | .75 |

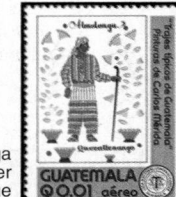

Almolonga Costume, Cancer League Emblem — AP121

---

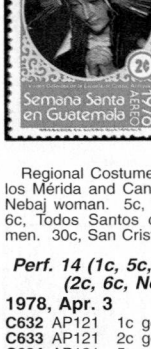

Virgin of Sorrows, Antigua — AP122

Regional Costumes after Paintings by Carlos Mérida and Cancer League Emblem: 2c, Nebaj woman. 5c, San Juan Cotzal couple. 6c, Todos Santos couple. 20c, Regidores men. 30c, San Cristobal woman.

### Perf. 14 (1c, 5c, No. C636); Perf. 12 (2c, 6c, No. C636a, 30c)
**1978, Apr. 3**     Litho.

| | | | | |
|---|---|---|---|---|
| C632 | AP121 | 1c gold & multi | .20 | .20 |
| C633 | AP121 | 2c gold & multi | .20 | .20 |
| C634 | AP121 | 5c gold & multi | .20 | .20 |
| C635 | AP121 | 6c gold & multi | .30 | .20 |
| C636 | AP121 | 20c gold & multi | 1.10 | 1.10 |
| a. | | Souv. sheet of 1 | 1.25 | 1.25 |
| C637 | AP121 | 30c gold & multi | 1.10 | .90 |
| | | Nos. C632-C637 (6) | 3.10 | 1.35 |

Part of proceeds from sale of stamps went to National League to Fight Cancer.

**1978**     Litho.     Perf. 11½

Statues from Various Churches: 4c, Virgin of Mercy, Antigua. 5c, Virgin of Anguish, Yurrita. 6c, Virgin of the Rosary, Santo Domingo. 8c, Virgin of Sorrows, Santo Domingo. 9c, Virgin of the Rosary, Quetzaltenango. 10c, Virgin of the Immaculate Conception, Church of St. Francis. 20c, Virgin of the Immaculate Conception, Cathedral Church.

| | | | | |
|---|---|---|---|---|
| C638 | AP122 | 2c multicolored | .40 | .25 |
| C639 | AP122 | 4c multicolored | .40 | .25 |
| C640 | AP122 | 5c multicolored | .40 | .25 |
| C641 | AP122 | 6c multicolored | .40 | .25 |
| C642 | AP122 | 8c multicolored | .40 | .25 |
| C643 | AP122 | 9c multicolored | .40 | .25 |
| C644 | AP122 | 10c multicolored | .40 | .25 |
| C645 | AP122 | 20c multicolored | 1.00 | .25 |
| | | Nos. C638-C645 (8) | 3.80 | 2.00 |

Holy Week 1978. A 30c imperf. souvenir sheet shows the Pietà from Calvary Church, Antigua. Size: 71x101mm. Value $3.
Issued: 6c, 10c, 20c, 9/28; others, 5/22.

Soccer Player, Argentina '78 Emblem AP123

**1978, July 3**   Litho.   Perf. 12

| | | | | |
|---|---|---|---|---|
| C646 | AP123 | 10c multicolored | .50 | .20 |

11th World Cup Soccer Championship, Argentina, June 1-25.

Gymnastics AP124

**1978, Sept. 4**     Perf. 12

| | | | | |
|---|---|---|---|---|
| C647 | AP124 | 6c shown | .25 | .25 |
| C648 | AP124 | 6c Volleyball | .25 | .25 |
| C649 | AP124 | 6c Target shooting | .25 | .25 |
| C650 | AP124 | 6c Weight lifting | .25 | .25 |
| a. | | Block of 4, #C647-C650 | 1.00 | 1.00 |
| C651 | AP124 | 8c Track & field | .25 | .25 |
| | | Nos. C647-C651 (5) | 1.25 | 1.25 |

13th Central American and Caribbean Games, Medellin, Colombia.

---

Cattleya Pachecoi AP125

Designs: Orchids.

**1978, Dec. 7**   Litho.   Perf. 12

| | | | | |
|---|---|---|---|---|
| C652 | AP125 | 1c shown | 1.40 | 1.25 |
| C653 | AP125 | 1c Sobralia | 1.40 | 1.25 |
| C654 | AP125 | 1c Cypripedium | 1.40 | 1.25 |
| C655 | AP125 | 1c Oncidium | 1.40 | 1.25 |
| a. | | Block of 4, #C652-C655 | 20.00 | 20.00 |
| C656 | AP125 | 3c Cattleya bowrigiana | 1.60 | 1.25 |
| C657 | AP125 | 3c Encyclia | 1.60 | 1.25 |
| C658 | AP125 | 3c Epidendrum | 1.60 | 1.25 |
| C659 | AP125 | 3c Barkeria | 1.60 | 1.25 |
| a. | | Block of 4, #C656-C659 | 35.00 | 35.00 |
| C660 | AP125 | 8c Spiranthes | 3.50 | 2.50 |
| C661 | AP125 | 20c Lycaste | 12.50 | 10.50 |
| | | Nos. C652-C661 (10) | 28.00 | 23.00 |

Seal of University AP126

Students of Different Departments AP127

Designs: 12c, Student in 17th cent. clothes. 14c, Students, 1978, and molecular model.

**1978, Dec. 7**

| | | | | |
|---|---|---|---|---|
| C662 | AP126 | 6c multicolored | .20 | .20 |
| C663 | AP127 | 7c multicolored | .25 | .20 |
| C664 | AP126 | 12c multicolored | .30 | .20 |
| C665 | AP126 | 14c multicolored | .45 | .20 |
| | | Nos. C662-C665 (4) | 1.20 | .80 |

San Carlos University of Guatemala, tercentenary.

Brown and White Children AP128

A Helping Hand — AP129

Designs: 7c, Child at play. 14c, Hands sheltering Indian girl.

---

**1978, Dec. 7**

| | | | | |
|---|---|---|---|---|
| C666 | AP128 | 6c multicolored | .20 | .20 |
| C667 | AP128 | 7c multicolored | .25 | .20 |
| C668 | AP129 | 12c multicolored | .30 | .20 |
| C669 | AP129 | 14c multicolored | .45 | .20 |
| | | Nos. C666-C669 (4) | 1.20 | .80 |

Year of the Children of Guatemala.

Tree Planting and FAO Emblem — AP130

Forest protection: 8c, Burnt forest. 9c, Watershed, river and trees. 10c, Sawmill. 26c, Forests, river and cultivated terraces.

**1979, Apr. 16**     Perf. 13½

| | | | | |
|---|---|---|---|---|
| C670 | AP130 | 6c multicolored | .30 | .25 |
| C671 | AP130 | 8c multicolored | .30 | .25 |
| C672 | AP130 | 9c multicolored | .30 | .25 |
| C673 | AP130 | 10c multicolored | .30 | .25 |
| C674 | AP130 | 26c multicolored | .55 | .25 |
| a. | | Souv. sheet of 5, #C670-C674 | 2.00 | 2.00 |
| | | Nos. C670-C674 (5) | 1.75 | 1.25 |

Peten Wild Turkey — AP131

Clay Jar, 50-100 A.D. — AP132

Wildlife conservation: 3c, White-tailed deer, horiz. 5c, King buzzard. 7c, Horned owl. 9c, Young wildcat. 30c, Quetzal.

**1979, June 14**   Litho.   Perf. 13½

| | | | | |
|---|---|---|---|---|
| C675 | AP131 | 1c multicolored | 1.90 | .70 |
| C676 | AP131 | 3c multicolored | 1.10 | .70 |
| C677 | AP131 | 5c multicolored | 5.75 | .70 |
| C678 | AP131 | 7c multicolored | 12.50 | 2.75 |
| C679 | AP131 | 9c multicolored | 2.75 | .70 |
| | | Nos. C675-C679 (5) | 24.00 | 5.55 |

### Souvenir Sheet

| | | | | |
|---|---|---|---|---|
| C680 | AP131 | 30c multicolored | 16.00 | 16.00 |

**1979, Sept. 19**   Litho.   Perf. 13

Archaeological Treasures from Tikal: 3c, Mayan woman, ceramic head, 900 A.D. 4c, Earring, 50-100 A.D. 5c, vase, 700 A.D. 6c, Boy, 200-50 B.C. 7c, Bone carving, 700 A.D. 8c, Striped vase, 700 A.D. 10c, Covered vase on tripod, 450 B.C.

| | | | | |
|---|---|---|---|---|
| C681 | AP132 | 2c multi | .40 | .25 |
| C682 | AP132 | 3c multi | .55 | .40 |
| C683 | AP132 | 4c multi | .80 | .55 |
| C684 | AP132 | 5c multi | .95 | .55 |
| C685 | AP132 | 6c multi | 1.25 | .80 |
| C686 | AP132 | 7c multi | 1.25 | .95 |
| C687 | AP132 | 8c multi | 1.50 | 1.00 |
| C688 | AP132 | 10c multi | 2.00 | 1.25 |
| | | Nos. C681-C688 (8) | 8.70 | 5.75 |

Presidential Guard Patches AP133

Presidential Guard, 30th anniv.: 10c, Guard Headquarters.

**1979, Dec. 6    Litho.    Perf. 11½**
| C689 | AP133 | 8c multi | .25 | .25 |
| C690 | AP133 | 10c multi | .25 | .25 |

National Coat of Arms — AP134

Arms of Guatemalan Municipalities.

**1979, Dec. 27    Litho.    Perf. 13½**
| C691 | AP134 | 8c shown | .45 | .25 |
| C692 | AP134 | 8c Alta Verapaz | .45 | .25 |
| C693 | AP134 | 8c Baja Verapaz | .45 | .25 |
| C694 | AP134 | 8c Chimal Tenango | .45 | .25 |
| C695 | AP134 | 8c Chiquimula | .45 | .25 |
| C696 | AP134 | 8c Escuintla | .45 | .25 |
| C697 | AP134 | 8c Flores | .45 | .25 |
| C698 | AP134 | 8c Guatemala | .45 | .25 |
| C699 | AP134 | 8c Huehuetenango | .45 | .25 |
| C700 | AP134 | 8c Izabal | .45 | .25 |
| C701 | AP134 | 8c Jalapa | .45 | .25 |
| C702 | AP134 | 8c Jutiapa | .45 | .25 |
| C703 | AP134 | 8c Mazatenango | .45 | .25 |
| C704 | AP134 | 8c Progreso | .45 | .25 |
| C705 | AP134 | 8c Quezaltenan-go | .45 | .25 |
| C706 | AP134 | 8c Quiche | .45 | .25 |
| C707 | AP134 | 8c Retalhuleu | .45 | .25 |
| C708 | AP134 | 8c Sacatepequez | .45 | .25 |
| C709 | AP134 | 8c San Marcos | .45 | .25 |
| C710 | AP134 | 8c Santa Rosa | .45 | .25 |
| C711 | AP134 | 8c Solola | .45 | .25 |
| C712 | AP134 | 8c Totonicapan | .45 | .25 |
| C713 | AP134 | 8c Zacapa | .45 | .25 |
| *Nos. C691-C713 (23)* | | | 10.35 | 5.75 |

**Miniature Sheet**
*Imperf*
| C714 | AP134 | 50c 1st & current natl. arms | 3.50 | 3.50 |

No. C714 is horizontal.

The Creation of the World — AP135

Designs: Scenes from The Creation, Popul Vuh (Sacred Book of the Ancient Quiches of Guatemala): No. C716, Origin of the Twin Semi-gods. No. C717, Populating the earth. No. C718, Balam Quitze. No. C719, Quiche monarch Cotuha. No. C720, Birth of the Stick Men. No. C721, Princess Xquic's punishment. No. C722, Caha Paluma. No. C723, Cotuha and Iztayul invincible. No. C724, Odyssey of Hun Ahpu and Xbalanque. No. C725, Balam Acab. No. C726, Chief of all Nations. No. C727, Destruction of the Stick Men. No. C728, The Test in Xibalba. No. C729, Chomiha. No. C730, Warrior with captive. No. C731, Creation of the Corn Men. No. C732, Multiplication of the Prodigies. No. C733, Mahucutah. No. C734, Undefeatable king. No. C735, Thanksgiving. No. C736, Deification of Hun Ahpu and Xbalanque. No. C737, Tzununiha. No. C738, Greatness of the Quiches (battle scene).

**1981    Litho.    Perf. 12**
| C715 | AP135 | 1c multi | .20 | .20 |
| C716 | AP135 | 1c multi | .20 | .20 |
| C717 | AP135 | 2c multi | .20 | .20 |
| C718 | AP135 | 2c multi | .20 | .20 |
| C719 | AP135 | 3c multi | .20 | .20 |
| C720 | AP135 | 4c multi | .25 | .20 |
| C721 | AP135 | 4c multi | .25 | .20 |
| C722 | AP135 | 4c multi | .25 | .20 |
| C723 | AP135 | 4c multi | .25 | .20 |
| C724 | AP135 | 6c multi | .30 | .25 |
| C725 | AP135 | 6c multi | .30 | .25 |
| C726 | AP135 | 6c multi | .30 | .25 |
| C727 | AP135 | 8c multi | .45 | .30 |
| C728 | AP135 | 8c multi | .45 | .30 |
| C729 | AP135 | 8c multi | .45 | .30 |
| C730 | AP135 | 8c multi | .45 | .30 |
| C731 | AP135 | 10c multi | .55 | .40 |
| C732 | AP135 | 10c multi | .55 | .40 |
| C733 | AP135 | 10c multi | .55 | .40 |
| C734 | AP135 | 10c multi | .55 | .40 |
| C735 | AP135 | 22c multi | 1.25 | .85 |
| C736 | AP135 | 26c multi | 1.40 | .95 |
| C737 | AP135 | 30c multi | 1.75 | 1.10 |
| C738 | AP135 | 50c multi | 2.75 | 2.00 |
| *Nos. C715-C738 (24)* | | | 14.05 | 10.25 |

Issued: #C715, C717, 3c, C731, 22c, 1/29; #C716, C718, C721-C722, C724-C725, C728-C729, C732-C733, 26c, 30c, 3/16; others, 1981.

Thomas Edison (Phonograph Centenary) AP136

Talking Movies, 50th Anniv. — AP137

Telephone Centenary (1976) — AP138

Lindbergh's Atlantic Flight, 50th Anniv. (1977) AP139

12c, Jose Cecilio del Valle, patriot. 25c, Jesus Castillo (1877-1949), composer.

**Perf. 11½, 12½ (25c)**
**1981, June 1    Litho.**
| C739 | AP136 | 3c multi | .25 | .25 |
| C740 | AP137 | 5c multi | .30 | .25 |
| C741 | AP138 | 6c multi | .40 | .25 |
| C742 | AP139 | 7c multi | .45 | .30 |
| C743 | AP139 | 12c multi | .80 | .45 |
| C744 | AP139 | 25c multi | 1.50 | 1.00 |
| *Nos. C739-C744 (6)* | | | 3.70 | 2.50 |

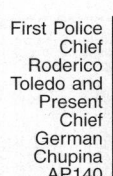

First Police Chief Roderico Toledo and Present Chief German Chupina AP140

**1981, Sept. 12    Litho.    Perf. 11½**
| C745 | AP140 | 2c shown | .40 | .25 |
| C746 | AP140 | 4c Headquarters | .40 | .25 |

Mayan Rock of the Sun Calendar AP141

**1981, Oct. 9**
| C747 | AP141 | 1c multi | .25 | .25 |

Gen. Jose Gervasio Artigas of Uruguay AP142

Liberators of the Americas: 2c, Bernardo O'Higgins (Chile). 4c, Jose de San Martin (Argentina). 10c, Miguel Garcia Granados. 2c, 4c, 10c, 31x47mm.

**1982, Apr. 2    Litho.    Perf. 11½**
| C748 | AP142 | 2c multi | .25 | .25 |
| C749 | AP142 | 3c multi | .25 | .25 |

**Perf. 12½**
| C750 | AP142 | 4c multi | .25 | .25 |
| C751 | AP142 | 10c tan & blk | .25 | .25 |
| *Nos. C748-C751 (4)* | | | 1.00 | 1.00 |

Occidents Bank Centenary (1981) AP143

1c, Justo Rufino Barrios (1st pres.), Main Office, Quezaltenango. 2c, Main Office, 3c, Emblem, vert. 4c, Commemorative medals, vert.

**1982, July 28    Litho.    Perf. 11½**
| C752 | AP143 | 1c multi | .30 | .25 |
| C753 | AP143 | 2c multi | .30 | .25 |
| C754 | AP143 | 3c multi | .30 | .25 |
| C755 | AP143 | 4c multi | .30 | .25 |
| *Nos. C752-C755 (4)* | | | 1.20 | 1.00 |

50th Anniv. of Natl. Mortgage Bank (1980) AP144

Various emblems. 5c vert.

**1982, Oct. 18    Litho.    Perf. 11½**
| C756 | AP144 | 1c multi | .30 | .25 |
| C757 | AP144 | 2c multi | .30 | .25 |
| C758 | AP144 | 5c multi | .30 | .25 |
| C759 | AP144 | 10c multi | .30 | .25 |
| *Nos. C756-C759 (4)* | | | 1.20 | 1.00 |

AP145

AP146

**1983, May 16    Litho.    Perf. 11½**
| C760 | AP145 | 1c Portrait | .20 | .20 |
| C761 | AP145 | 20c Aparition, horiz. | .60 | .40 |

20th Anniv. of Beatification of Pedro Bethancourt (1626-1667).

**1983, July 25    Litho.    Perf. 11½**
| C762 | AP146 | 10c multi | .30 | .25 |

World Telecommunications and Health Day, May 17, 1981

Evangelical Church Centenary (1982) — AP147

**1983, Aug. 9**
| C763 | AP147 | 3c Hands holding bible | .40 | .25 |
| C764 | AP147 | 5c Church | .40 | .25 |

Natl. Railroad Centenary — AP148

10c, 1st locomotive crossing Puenta de Las Vacas. 25c, General Justo Rufino Barrios, Railroad Yard. 30c, Spanish Diesel, Amatitlan crossing.

**1983, Sept. 28    Litho.    Perf. 11½**
| C765 | AP148 | 10c multi | 1.00 | .80 |
| C766 | AP148 | 25c multi | 2.75 | 1.75 |
| C767 | AP148 | 30c multi | 3.00 | 2.00 |
| *Nos. C765-C767 (3)* | | | 6.75 | 4.55 |

World Food Day AP149

**1983, Oct. 16    Photo.    Perf. 11½**
| C768 | AP149 | 8c Globe, wheat, vert. | .25 | .20 |
| C769 | AP149 | 1q shown | 2.75 | 1.75 |

Architecture Type of 1972

**1984, Feb. 20    Typo.    Perf. 12½**
**Black and Green**
| C770 | AP98 | 1c like #C480 | .20 | .20 |
| C771 | AP98 | 1c like #C481 | .20 | .20 |
| C772 | AP98 | 1c like #C482 | .20 | .20 |
| C773 | AP98 | 1c like #C483 | .20 | .20 |
| C774 | AP98 | 1c like #C484 | .20 | .20 |
| C775 | AP98 | 1c like #C485 | .20 | .20 |
| g. | | Strip of 6, #C770-C775 | 1.00 | 1.00 |

**Black, Brown and Orange Brown**
| C775A | AP98 | 5c like #C484 | .25 | .20 |
| C775B | AP98 | 5c like #C485 | .25 | .20 |
| C775C | AP98 | 5c like #C482 | .25 | .20 |
| C775D | AP98 | 5c like #C483 | .25 | .20 |
| C775E | AP98 | 5c like #C480 | .25 | .20 |
| C775F | AP98 | 5c like #C481 | .25 | .20 |
| h. | | Strip of 6, #C775A-C775F | 1.75 | 1.75 |

Visit of Pope John Paul II, Mar. 8-9, 1983
AP150

**1984, Mar. 26** **Litho.** *Perf. 11½*
C776 AP150 4c Pope, arms .45 .35
C777 AP150 8c Receiving Mayan indian .45 .35

Rafael Landivar (1731-93), Poet — AP151

Cardinal Mario Casariego y Acevedo AP152

**1984, Aug. 6** **Litho.** *Perf. 11½*
C778 AP151 2c Portrait, vert. .30 .25
C779 AP151 4c Tomb .30 .25

**1984, Aug. 6**
C780 AP152 10c 16th archbishop of Guat. (1909-83) .40 .25

Central American Bank for Economic Integration, 20th Anniv. — AP153

**1984, Sept. 10** **Litho.** *Perf. 11½*
C781 AP153 30c Bank emblem, map 1.10 .60

Coffee Production, 1870 AP154

Modern Coffee Production AP155

Designs: 1c, Planting coffee. 2c, Harvesting. 3c, Drying beans. 4c, Loading beans on steamer. 5c, Reyna plant grafting method. 10c, Picking beans, coffee cup. 12c, Drying unripened beans, Gardiola Freeze-drying machine. 25c, Cargo transports.

**1984, Dec. 19** *Perf. 11½*
C782 AP154 1c sep & pale brn .25 .25
C783 AP154 2c sep & pale org brn .25 .25
C784 AP154 3c sep & beige .25 .25

---

C785 AP154 4c sep & pale yel brn .25 .25
C786 AP155 5c multi .30 .25
C787 AP155 10c multi .60 .40
C788 AP155 12c multi .80 .45
C789 AP155 25c multi 1.50 1.00
*Nos. C782-C789 (8)* 4.20 3.10

Natl. coffee production and export. An 86x112mm 25c stamp of Type AP154 and a 105x85mm 30c stamp of Type AP155 exist, value $110 and $140 respectively.

Natl. Scouting Assoc. — AP156

Scouting emblems and: 5c, Beaver scout, Pyramid of Tikal. 6c, Wolf scout, Palace of the Captains-General and Ahua Volcano. 8c, Scout, San Pedro Volcano and Marimba player. 10c, Rover scout and conquest mask dance. 20c, Lord Baden-Powell and Col. Carlos Cipriani, natl. founder.

**1985, July 1**
C792 AP156 5c multi .30 .20
C793 AP156 6c multi .40 .25
C794 AP156 8c multi .45 .30
C795 AP156 10c multi .45 .40
C796 AP156 20c multi 1.25 .85
*Nos. C792-C796 (5)* 2.85 2.00

Inter-American Family Unity Year — AP157

Central American Aeronautics Admin., 25th Anniv. — AP158

**1985, Oct. 16**
C797 AP157 10c multi .45 .30

**1985, Nov. 11**
C798 AP158 10c multi .40 .25

Natl. Telegraph, Cent. — AP159

Portraits: Samuel Morse, telegraph inventor, and Justo Rufino Barrios, communications pioneer.

**1985, Nov. 20** *Perf. 12*
C799 AP159 4c brn & blk .25 .25

---

Intl. Olympic Committee, 90th Anniv. — AP160

Designs: 8c, Mayan bust of ancient sportsman. 10c, Baron Pierre de Coubertin (1863-1937), father of modern Games, 1st committee president.

**1986, Jan. 28** **Litho.** *Perf. 11½*
C800 AP160 8c multi .55 .45
C801 AP160 10c multi .75 .45

Volunteer Fire Department AP161

**1986, Feb. 6** **Litho.** *Perf. 11½*
C802 AP161 6c multi .65 .25

Temple of Minerva — AP162

Quetzeltenango Coat of Arms, City Hall — AP163

**1986, July 16** **Litho.** *Perf. 12½, 11½*
C803 AP162 8c multi .25 .20
C804 AP163 10c multi .30 .25

Quetzeltenango Independence Fair, cent.

Volunteer Fire Department AP164

**1986, Oct. 10** **Litho.** *Perf. 11½*
C805 AP164 8c Rescue .85 .30
C806 AP164 10c Ruins .85 .30

Assoc. of Telegraphers and Radio-Telegraph Operators, 25th Anniv. — AP165

**1986, Oct. 10** *Perf. 12*
C807 AP165 6c multi .50 .20

---

San Carlos University School of Architecture, 25th Anniv. — AP166

**1987, Feb. 16** **Litho.** *Perf. 11½*
C808 AP166 10c multi .50 .20

ICAO, 40th Anniv. (in 1984) AP167

**1987, Apr. 2** **Litho.** *Perf. 11½*
C809 AP167 8c Aviateca Airlines jet .25 .20
C810 AP167 10c Jet, vert. .30 .20

Chixoy Hydroelectric Power Plant — AP168

**1987, May 18** **Litho.** *Perf. 11½*
C811 AP168 2c multi .40 .40

Nat'l. Electrification Institute inauguration (in 1985).

San Jose de los Infantes College, 200th Anniv. (in 1981) AP169

8c, Portrait of Archbishop Cayetano Francos y Monroy, founder. 10c, College crest.

**1987, June 10**
C812 AP169 8c multi, vert. .25 .20
C813 AP169 10c multi .30 .25

Promotion of Literacy in Latin America and Caribbean AP170

**1987, Aug. 20** **Litho.** *Perf. 11½*
C814 AP170 12c apple grn, blk & brt org .40 .25

19th Natl. Folklore Carnival of Coban, Alta Verapaz, July 25 — AP171

**1987, Oct. 12**
C815 AP171 1q Three girls from Tamahu    5.50  2.00

**1987, Dec. 8**
C816 AP171 50c Girl weaving    2.75  .95
See No. C831.

9th Pan American Games, Caracas AP172

**1987, Nov. 5**    *Perf. 12½*
C817 AP172 10c blk & sky blue    .30  .20

Writers and Historians AP173

Esquipulas II — AP174

Designs: 1c, Flavio Herrera, poet, novelist. 2c, Rosendo Santa Cruz, novelist. 3c, Werner Ovalle Lopez, poet. 4c, Enrique A. Hidalgo, poet, humorist. 5c, Enrique Gomez Carrillo (1873-1927), novelist. 6c, Cesar Branas (1899-1976), journalist. 7c, Clemente Marroquin Rojas, historian. 8c, Rafael Arevalo Martinez (1884-1975), poet. 9c, Jose Milla y Vidaurre (1822-1882), historian. 10c, Miguel Angel Asturias, Nobel laureate for literature.

**1987-90**    *Perf. 11½*
C818 AP173 1c blk & lil    .30  .25
C819 AP173 2c blk & dl org    .30  .25
C820 AP173 3c blk & brt bl    .30  .25
C821 AP173 4c blk & ver    .30  .25
C822 AP173 5c blk & org brn    .30  .25
C823 AP173 6c blk & org    .30  .25
C824 AP173 7c blk & grn    .30  .25
C825 AP173 8c blk & brt red    .30  .25
C826 AP173 9c blk & brt rose lil    .30  .25
C827 AP173 10c blk & yel    .30  .25
    Nos. C818-C827 (10)    3.00  2.50

Issued: 6c, 8c, 9c, 11/5/87; 4c, 5c, 1/13/88; 7c, 3/23/90; 1c, 2c, 3c, 10c, 4/9/90.

**1988, Jan. 15**    *Perf. 12½*
C828 AP174 10c dark olive grn    .40  .25
C829 AP174 40c plum    1.50  1.00
C830 AP174 60c deep blue vio    2.40  1.50
    Nos. C828-C830 (3)    4.30  2.75

2nd Meeting of the Central American Peace Plan. Nos. C828-C829 horiz.

Folklore Festival Type of 1987
**1988, Dec. 6**    *Imperf.*
**Souvenir Sheet**
C831 AP171 2q Music ensemble, horiz.    10.00  10.00

St. John Bosco (1815-1888), Educator AP175

**1989, Feb. 1**    *Litho.*    *Perf. 11½*
C832 AP175 40c gold & blk    .95  .55

French Revolution, Bicent. AP176

**1989, Oct. 18**    *Litho.*    *Perf. 11½*
C833 AP176 1q dark red, blk & deep blue    5.00  2.00

America Issue — AP177

UPAE emblem and: 10c, Detail of the *Madrid Codex.* 20c, Temple of the Gran Jaguar of Tikal, Tikal Natl. Park.

**1990, Jan. 25**    *Litho.*    *Perf. 11½*
C834 AP177 10c shown    1.75  1.10
C835 AP177 20c brown & multi    3.50  2.40

Institute of Nutrition of Central America and Panama, 40th Anniv. AP178

**1990, May 18**
C837 AP178 20c multicolored    .55  .25

Red Cross, Red Crescent Societies, 125th Anniv. AP179

**1990, June 8**
C838 AP179 50c multicolored    1.25  .40

Defense Ministry General Staff, Cent. AP180

**1991, May 8**    *Litho.*    *Perf. 11½*
C839 AP180 20c multicolored    .45  .20

America AP181

UPAE: 10c, Pacaya Volcano Erupting at Night. 60c, Lake Atitlan.

**1991, July 30**    *Litho.*    *Perf. 11½*
C840 AP181 10c multicolored    .25  .25
C841 AP181 60c multicolored    2.25  .50

America Issue AP182

Designs: 40c, Pinzon brothers, Nina. 60c, Columbus, Santa Maria, vert.

**1992, July 27**    *Litho.*    *Perf. 11½*
C842 AP182 40c green & black    .95  .45
C843 AP182 60c green & black    1.40  .70

AP183

AP184

**1992, Oct. 6**    *Litho.*    *Perf. 12½*
C844 AP183 10c multicolored    .55  .25

Interamerican Institute for Agricultural Cooperation, 50th anniv.

**1992, Dec. 1**    *Photo.*    *Perf. 11½*
C845 AP184 1q multicolored    2.50  .80

World campaign against AIDS.

Orchids — AP185

20c, Phragmipedium caudatum. 50c, Encyclia cochleata. 1q, Encyclia vitellina. 1.50q, Odontoglossum laeve 2q, Odontoglossum uroskinneri.

**1994, Aug. 9**    *Litho.*    *Perf. 11½*
C845A AP185 20c multi    .60  .60
C846 AP185 50c multi    1.10  .80
C847 AP185 1q multi    2.40  .80
C847A AP185 1.50q multi    4.75  4.75
C848 AP185 2q multi    4.25  1.50
    Nos. C845A-C848 (5)    13.10  8.45

#C845A, C847A put on sale 8/16/96.

Tourism — AP186

Designs: 20c, Rafting. 40c, Water sports. 60c, Boats on Lake Atitlan, volcanic mountain. 80c, Tourist boat on Lake Atitlan. 1q, Mt. Pacaya erupting. 2q, Guatemala City. 3q, Macaws, vert. 4q, Temple of the Gran Jaguar, vert. 5q, Holy Week procession from Antigua, carpet of colored saw dust, vert.

**1995-96**    *Litho.*    *Perf. 12½*
C849 AP186 20c multicolored    .40  .25
C850 AP186 40c multicolored    .40  .25
C851 AP186 60c multicolored    .55  .30
C852 AP186 80c multicolored    .60  .40
C853 AP186 1q multicolored    .60  .30
C854 AP186 2q multicolored    1.25  .60
C855 AP186 3q multicolored    1.75  .85
C856 AP186 4q multicolored    2.50  1.25
C857 AP186 5q multicolored    3.00  1.75
    Nos. C849-C857 (9)    11.05  5.95

Issued: #C850, 7/5/96; #C852, 7/9/96.

Visit of Pope John Paul II — AP187

Papal arms, quotation, Pope John Paul II: 10c, With arms outstreached, dove, "That all the people join hands for peace." 1q, Kissing infant, "Let the children come unto me." 1.75q, Holding crucifix, "The house of the Lord is my house." 1.90q, Looking forward, "Blessed is he who comes in the name of the Lord." 2.90q, Waving hand, "Remember that all men are our brothers."

**1996, Jan. 5**    *Litho.*    *Perf. 12½*
C858 AP187 10c multicolored    .20  .20
C859 AP187 1q multicolored    .45  .45
C860 AP187 1.75q multicolored    .85  .85
C861 AP187 1.90q multicolored    .95  .95
C862 AP187 2.90q multicolored    1.50  1.50
    Nos. C858-C862 (5)    3.95  3.95

Distinguished Guatemalans AP188

Designs: 40c, Carlos Merida (Self-portrait). 50c, José Eulalio Samayoa. 60c, Manuel Montufar y Coronado.

**1996, Oct. 21**    *Litho.*    *Perf. 12½*
C863 AP188 40c multicolored    .25  .25
C864 AP188 50c multicolored    .25  .25
C865 AP188 60c multicolored    .30  .30
    Nos. C863-C865 (3)    .80  .80

Mother Breastfeeding — AP190

**1997, Mar. 6**    *Perf. 11½*
C868 AP190 1q multicolored    .60  .60

Public Finance Projects — AP191

Designs: 20c, Education. 60c, Health care. 80c, Road construction. 1q, Family security.

**1997, Oct. 6**    *Litho.*    *Perf. 11½x12½*
C869 AP191 20c multicolored    .20  .20
C870 AP191 60c multicolored    .30  .25
C871 AP191 80c multicolored    .45  .40
C872 AP191 1q multicolored    .60  .45
    Nos. C869-C872 (4)    1.55  1.30

Jorge Rybar and Machine — AP192

**1998　　Litho.　　Perf. 12½**
C873　AP192　10c multi　　　.25　.25
Plastics industry in Guatemala, 50th anniv.

Intl. Society of Guatemala Collectors,
50th Anniv. — AP193

**1999, May 14　Litho.　Perf. 11½x12½**
C874　AP193　1q Quetzel note　.60　.60

1993
Census
AP194

**2001, Dec. 6　Litho.　Perf. 11½**
C875　AP194　10c multi　　50.00　50.00
No. C875 was withdrawn from sale 12/11/01.

**AIR POST SEMI-POSTAL STAMPS**

Air Post Stamps of 1937 Surcharged
in Red or Blue

**1937, Mar. 15　Unwmk.　Perf. 12½**
CB1　AP10　4c + 1c ultra (R)　　.90　1.25
CB2　AP10　6c + 1c blk vio (R)　.90　1.25
CB3　AP11　10c + 1c ol grn (Bl)　.90　1.25
CB4　AP11　15c + 1c ver (Bl)　　.90　1.25
　　　Nos. CB1-CB4 (4)　　　3.60　5.00
1st Phil. Exhib. held in Guatemala, 3/15-20.

> **Catalogue values for unused
> stamps in this section, from this
> point to the end of the section, are
> for Never Hinged items.**

Type of Regular Issue, 1956
Designs: 35c+1q, Red Cross, Ambulance
and Volcano. 50c+1q, Red Cross, Hospital
and Nurse. 1q+1q, Nurse and Red Cross.

**Perf. 13x12½**
**1956, June 19　Engr.　Unwmk.**
CB5　A148　35c + 1q red & ol
　　　　　　　grn　　　　5.50　5.75
CB6　A148　50c + 1q ultra & red　5.50　5.75
CB7　A148　1q + 1q dk grn &
　　　　　　　dk red　　5.50　5.75
　　　Nos. CB5-CB7 (3)　　16.50　17.25
The surtax was for the Red Cross.

---

Nos. B5-B7
Overprinted

**1957, May 11**
CB8　A148　5c + 15c　　　7.00　8.00
　a.　　Imperf., pair　　225.00
CB9　A148　15c + 50c　　　7.00　8.00
　a.　　Overprint inverted　275.00
CB10　A148　25c + 50c　　　7.00　8.00
　　　Nos. CB8-CB10 (3)　21.00　24.00
The surtax was for the Red Cross.

Type of Semi-Postal Stamps, 1957
and

Esquipulas
Cathedral
SPAP1

15c+1q, Cathedral & crucifix. 20c+1q, Christ
with crown of thorns and part of globe.
25c+1q, Archbishop Mariano Rossell y
Arellano.

**Perf. 13½x14½, 13**
**1957, Oct. 29　Engr.　Unwmk.**
CB11　SPAP1　10c + 1q choc &
　　　　　　　emer　　　7.00　7.50
CB12　SP1　15c + 1q dl grn
　　　　　　　& sep　　7.00　7.50
CB13　SP1　20c + 1q bl gray
　　　　　　　& brn　　7.00　7.50
CB14　SP1　25c + 1q lt vio &
　　　　　　　car　　　7.00　7.50
　　　Nos. CB11-CB14 (4)　28.00　30.00
The tax was for the Esquipulas highway.

Wounded
Man, Battle
of Solferino
SPAP2

Designs: 6c+6c, 20c+20c, Flood disaster.
10c+10c, 25c+25c, Earth, moon and stars.
15c+15c, 30c+30c, Red Cross headquarters.

**1960, Apr. 9　Photo.　Perf. 13½x14**
CB15　SPAP2　5c + 5c multi　2.50　2.75
CB16　SPAP2　6c + 6c multi　2.50　2.75
CB17　SPAP2　10c + 10c multi　2.50　2.75
CB18　SPAP2　15c + 15c multi　2.50　2.75
CB19　SPAP2　20c + 20c multi　2.50　2.75
CB20　SPAP2　25c + 25c multi　2.50　2.75
CB21　SPAP2　30c + 30c multi　2.50　2.75
　　　Nos. CB15-CB21 (7)　17.50　19.25
Cent. (in 1959) of the Red Cross idea. The
surtax went to the Red Cross. Exist imperf.

---

**AIR POST OFFICIAL STAMPS**

Nos. C93-C98 Overprinted in Black

**1939, Apr. 29　Unwmk.　Perf. 12½**
CO1　AP13　1c org & ol brn　1.10　1.10
CO2　AP13　2c multi　　　1.10　1.10
CO3　AP13　3c multi　　　1.10　1.10
CO4　AP13　4c multi　　　1.10　1.10
CO5　AP13　5c multi　　　1.10　1.10
CO6　AP13　10c multi　　1.10　1.10
　　　Nos. CO1-CO6 (6)　6.60　6.60

No. C99 with Same Overprint on each
Stamp

**1939**
CO7　AP19　Sheet of 6　　3.75　3.75
　a.　　1c yel org, blue & blk　.60　.60
　b.　　2c lake, org, blue & blk　.60　.60

---

　c.　　3c olive, blue & orange　.60　.60
　d.　　4c dk claret, bl, org & blk　.60　.60
　e.　　5c grnsh bl, bl, red, org & blk　.60　.60
　f.　　10c olive bister, red & org　.60　.60

**SPECIAL DELIVERY STAMPS**

No. 237 Overprinted
in Red

**1940, June　Unwmk.　Perf. 14**
E1　A81　4c orange　　　1.50　.35
No. E1 paid for express service by motorcy-
cle messenger between Guatemala City and
Coban.

> **Catalogue values for unused
> stamps in this section, from this
> point to the end of the section, are
> for Never Hinged items.**

Motorcycle
Messenger
SD1

Black Surcharge
**1948, Sept. 3　Photo.　Perf. 14x12½**
E2　SD1　10c on 4c bl grn & gray
　　　　　　blk　　　3.25　.85
No. E2 without surcharge was issued for
regular postage, not special delivery. See No.
337B.

---

**OFFICIAL STAMPS**

O1　　　　　National
　　　　　Emblem — O2

**1902, Dec. 18　Typeset　Perf. 12**
O1　O1　1c green　　　5.50　3.50
O2　O1　2c carmine　　5.50　3.50
O3　O1　5c ultra　　　5.50　2.75
O4　O1　10c brown violet　7.50　2.75
O5　O1　25c orange　　7.50　2.75
　a.　　Horiz. pair, imperf. between　100.00
　　　Nos. O1-O5 (5)　31.50　15.25
Nos. O1-O5 printed on thin paper with sheet
watermark "AMERICAN LINEN BOND." Nos.
O1-O3 also printed on thick paper with sheet
watermark "ROYAL BANK BOND." Values are
for copies that do not show the watermark.
Counterfeits of Nos. O1-O5 exist.

During the years 1912 to 1926 the
Post Office Department perforated the
word "OFICIAL" on limited quantities of
the following stamps: Nos. 114-123,
132, 141-149, 151-153, 158, 202, 210-
229 and RA2. The perforating was
done in blocks of four stamps at a time
and was of two types.
A rubber handstamp "OFICIAL" was
also used during the same period and
was applied in violet, red, blue or black
to stamps No. 117-118, 121-123, 163-
165, 172 and 202-218.
Both perforating and handstamping
were done in the post office at Guatemala City and use of the stamps was
limited to that city.

---

**1929, Jan.　　Engr.　　Perf. 14**
O6　O2　1c pale grnsh bl　.30　.30
O7　O2　2c dark brown　　.30　.30
O8　O2　3c green　　　　.30　.30
O9　O2　4c deep violet　　.40　.35
O10　O2　5c brown car　　.40　.35
O11　O2　10c brown orange　.70　.70
O12　O2　25c dark blue　　1.40　1.10
　　　Nos. O6-O12 (7)　3.80　3.40

**POSTAL TAX STAMPS**

National
Emblem — PT1

**Perf. 13½, 14, 15**
**1919, May 3　Engr.　Unwmk.**
RA1　PT1　12½c carmine　　.30　.20
Tax for rebuilding post offices.

G. P. O. and
Telegraph
Building — PT2

**1927, Nov. 10　Typo.　Perf. 14**
RA2　PT2　1c olive green　　.55　.25
Tax to provide a fund for building a post
office in Guatemala City.

No. RA2
Overprinted in
Green

**1936, June 30**
RA3　PT2　1c olive green　　.70　.55
Liberal revolution, 65th anniversary.

No. RA2
Overprinted in
Blue

**1936, Sept. 15**
RA4　PT2　1c olive green　　.55　.55
Independence of Guatemala, 115th anniv.

No. RA2
Overprinted in
Red Brown

**1936, Nov. 15**
RA5　PT2　1c olive green　　.55　.45
National Fair.

No. RA2
Overprinted in
Red

**1937, Mar. 15**
RA6　PT2　1c olive green　　.55　.55

No. RA2
Overprinted in
Blue

**1938, Jan. 10**      *Perf. 14x14½*
RA7 PT2 1c olive green    .30   .25
    *a.* "1937-1939" omitted    110.00
    150th anniv. of the US Constitution.

No. RA2
Overprinted in
Blue or Red

**1938**      *Perf. 14*
RA8 PT2 1c olive green (Bl)    .40   .30
RA9 PT2 1c olive green (R)    .40   .30

No. RA2
Overprinted in
Violet

**1938, Nov. 20**
RA10 PT2 1c olive green    .40   .25
    1st Central American Philatelic Exposition.

No. RA2
Overprinted in
Green or Black

**1939**
RA11 PT2 1c olive green (G)    .40   .25
RA12 PT2 1c olive green (Bk)    .40   .25

No. RA2
Overprinted in
Violet or Brown

**1940**
RA13 PT2 1c olive green (V)    .40   .25
RA14 PT2 1c olive green (Br)    .40   .25

No. RA2
Overprinted in
Red

**1940, Apr. 14**
RA15 PT2 1c olive green    .40   .25
    Pan American Union, 50th anniversary.

No. RA2
Overprinted in
Red

**1941**
RA16 PT2 1c olive green    .55   .25

---

No. 235 Surcharged
in Red

RA17 A79 1c on 2c deep blue    .30   .25

No. 235 Surcharged
in Carmine

**1942, Jan.**
RA18 A79 1c on 2c deep blue    .55   .25

Arch of Communications Building
PT3          PT4
With Imprint Below Design
**1942, June 3   Engr.   Perf. 11, 12x11**
RA19 PT3 1c black brown    5.50   2.00

No imprint; Thin Paper
*Perf. 11, 12x11, 11x12, 11x12x11x11*
**1942, July 18**
RA20 PT3 1c black brown    .40   .25

**1943**      *Perf. 11, 12x11, 12*
RA21 PT4 1c orange    .40   .25

PT5

*Perf. 11, 12½ and Compound*
**1945, Feb.**      **Unwmk.**
RA22 PT5 1c orange    .30   .25

**1949**      *Perf. 12½*
RA23 PT5 1c deep ultra    .30   .25

---

# GUINEA

'gi-nē

LOCATION — Coast of West Africa, between Guinea-Bissau and Sierra Leone
GOVT. — Republic
AREA — 94,926 sq. mi.
POP. — 7,538,953 (1999 est.)
CAPITAL — Conakry

This former French Overseas Territory of French West Africa proclaimed itself an independent republic on October 2, 1958.

100 Centimes = 1 Franc
100 Caury = 1 Syli (1973)
100 Centimes = 1 Guinean Franc (1986)

**Catalogue values for all unused stamps in this country are for Never Hinged items.**

Common Design Types pictured following the introduction.

French West Africa No. 79 Overprinted

**1959 Unwmk. Photo. Perf. 12x12½**
168 CD104 10fr multi      4.00 2.50

French West Africa No. 78 Surcharged in Red

**Engr.**
**Perf. 13**
169 A33 45fr on 20fr multi    4.50 2.25

Map, Dove and Pres. Sékou Touré A12

**1959 Unwmk. Engr. Perf. 13**
170 A12   5fr rose car     .40 .20
171 A12   10fr ultramarine   .60 .20
172 A12   20fr orange    1.00 .30
173 A12   65fr slate green   3.00 .95
174 A12   100fr violet    5.00 2.10
    Nos. 170-174 (5)   10.00 3.75

Proclamation of independence, Oct. 2, 1958.

Bananas — A13

---

Flag Raising, Labé — A15

Fishing Boats and Tamara Lighthouse A14

**1959 Litho. Perf. 11½**
175 A13   10fr shown     .20 .20
176 A13   15fr Grapefruit    .40 .20
177 A13   20fr Lemons     .70 .20
178 A13   25fr Avocados    .80 .20
179 A13   50fr Pineapple    1.75 .20
    Nos. 175-179 (5)    3.85 1.00

For overprints see Nos. 209-213.

**1959 Engr. Perf. 13½**

5fr, Coco palms & sailboat, vert. 10fr, Launching fishing pirogue. 15fr, Elephant's head. 20fr, Pres. Sékou Touré & torch, vert. 25fr, Elephant.

180 A14   1fr rose     .20 .20
181 A14   2fr green     .20 .20
182 A14   3fr brown     .20 .20
183 A14   5fr blue     .80 .20
184 A14   10fr claret     .90 .20
185 A14   15fr light brn    1.10 .20
186 A14   20fr claret     1.60 .20
187 A14   25fr red brown   2.00 .20
    Nos. 180-187 (8)    7.00 1.60

**1959 Litho. Perf. 12**
188 A15   50fr multicolored   1.10 .20
189 A15   100fr multicolored   2.40 .50

For overprints see Nos. 201-202.

UN Headquarters, New York, and People of Guinea — A16

**1959 Perf. 12**
190 A16   1fr vio blue & org   .20 .20
191 A16   2fr red lil & emer   .20 .20
192 A16   3fr brn & crimson   .20 .20
193 A16   5fr brn & grnsh bl   .20 .20
    Nos. 190-193,C22-C23 (6)   3.40 2.45

Guinea's admission to the UN, first anniv.
For overprints see Nos. 205-208, C27-C28.

Uprooted Oak Emblem — A17

**1960 Photo. Perf. 11½**
**Granite Paper**
194 A17   25fr multicolored   .80 .20
195 A17   50fr multicolored   1.10 .20

World Refugee Year, 7/1/59-6/30/60.
For surcharges see Nos. B17-B18.

UPU Monument, Bern — A18

---

**1960 Granite Paper Unwmk.**
196 A18   10fr gray brn & blk   .20 .20
197 A18   15fr lil & purple   .45 .20
198 A18   20fr ultra & dk blue   .75 .20
199 A18   25fr yel grn & sl grn   .95 .20
200 A18   50fr red org & brown   1.00 .20
    Nos. 196-200 (5)    3.35 1.00

Nos. 199-200 are vertical.
Admission to the UPU, first anniv.

Nos. 188-189 Overprinted in Black, Orange or Carmine: "Jeux Olympiques Rome 1960" and Olympic Rings

**1960 Litho. Perf. 12**
201 A15   50fr multi (Bk)   8.00 6.00
202 A15   100fr multi (O or C)   12.50 9.00
    Nos. 201-202,C24-C26 (5)   92.25 67.25

17th Olympic Games, Rome, 8/25-9/11.

Map and Flag of Guinea — A19

**1960 Photo. Perf. 11½**
203 A19   25fr multicolored   .60 .30
204 A19   30fr multicolored   .80 .30

Second anniversary of independence.

Nos. 190-193 Overprinted

**1961 Litho. Perf. 12**
205 A16   1fr vio blue & org   .20 .20
206 A16   2fr red lil & emer   .20 .20
207 A16   3fr brn & crimson   .20 .20
208 A16   5fr brn & grnsh bl   .20 .20

Nos. 175-179 Overprinted in Black or Orange

**Perf. 11½**
**Fruits in Natural Colors**
209 A13   10fr red     .20 .20
210 A13   15fr grn & pink   .40 .20
211 A13   20fr red brn & bl   .50 .20
212 A13   25fr bl & yel (O)   .50 .25
213 A13   50fr dk vio blue   1.00 .40
    Nos. 205-213,C27-C28 (11)   5.90 3.00

15th anniversary of United Nations.

Defassa Waterbuck A20

**1961, Sept. 1 Photo. Perf. 11½**
**Multicolored Design; Granite Paper**
214 A20   5fr bright grn    .20 .20
215 A20   10fr emerald    .35 .20
216 A20   25fr lilac     .40 .20
217 A20   40fr orange    .75 .20
218 A20   50fr red orange   1.75 .30
219 A20   75fr ultramarine   2.50 .30
    Nos. 214-219 (6)    5.95 1.40

For surcharges see Nos. B19-B24.

---

Exhibition Hall — A21

**1961, Oct. 2 Perf. 11½**
**Flag in Red, Yellow & Green**
**Granite Paper**
220 A21   5fr ultra & red   .30 .20
221 A21   10fr brown & red   .30 .20
222 A21   25fr gray grn & red   .30 .20
    Nos. 220-222 (3)    .90 .60

First Three-Year Plan.

Gray-breasted Helmet Guinea Fowl — A22

**1961 Unwmk. Perf. 13x14**
223 A22   5fr rose lil, sepia & bl   .30 .20
224 A22   10fr dp org, sepia & bl   .35 .20
225 A22   25fr cerise, sepia & bl   .55 .20
226 A22   40fr ocher, sepia & bl   .95 .20
227 A22   50fr lemon, sepia & bl   1.25 .20
228 A22   75fr apple grn, sep & bl   2.50 .30
    Nos. 223-228 (6)    5.90 1.30

For surcharges see Nos. B30-B35.

Patrice Lumumba and Map of Africa — A23

**1962, Feb. 13 Photo. Perf. 11½**
229 A23   10fr multicolored   .65 .25
230 A23   25fr multicolored   .80 .25
231 A23   50fr multicolored   .50 .25
    Nos. 229-231 (3)    1.95 .75

Death anniv. (on Feb. 12, 1961) of Patrice Lumumba, Premier of the Congo Republic.

King Mohammed V of Morocco and Map of Africa — A24

**1962, Mar. 15 Litho. Perf. 13**
232 A24   25fr multicolored   1.10 .20
233 A24   75fr multicolored   2.75 .60

First anniv. of the conference of African heads of state at Casablanca.
For surcharges see Nos. B36-B37.

**African Postal Union Issue**

Map of Africa and Post Horn — A25

**1962, Apr. 23 Photo. Perf. 13½x13**
234 A25   25fr org, blk & grn   1.00 .20
235 A25   100fr deep brn & org   2.40 .55

Establishment of African Postal Union.

Bolon Player A26

Musical Instruments: 30c, 25fr, 50fr, Bote, vert. 1fr, 10fr, Flute, vert. 1.50fr, 3fr, Koni. 2fr, 20fr, Kora. 4fr, 75fr, Bolon.

### Perf. 13½x13, 13x13½
### 1962, June 15

| | | | | |
|---|---|---|---|---|
| 236 | A26 | 30c bl, dk grn & red | .20 | .20 |
| 237 | A26 | 50c sal, brn & brt grn | .20 | .20 |
| 238 | A26 | 1fr yel grn, grn & lil | .20 | .20 |
| 239 | A26 | 1.50fr yel, red & bl | .20 | .20 |
| 240 | A26 | 2fr rose lil, red lil & grn | .20 | .20 |
| 241 | A26 | 3fr brn grn, grn & lil | .20 | .20 |
| 242 | A26 | 10fr org, brn & bl | .20 | .20 |
| 243 | A26 | 20fr ol, dk ol & car | .45 | .20 |
| 244 | A26 | 25fr ol, dk & lil | .55 | .20 |
| 245 | A26 | 40fr bl, grn & red lil | .80 | .20 |
| 246 | A26 | 50fr rose, dp rose & Prus bl | 1.10 | .25 |
| 247 | A26 | 75fr dl yel, brn & Prus bl | 1.50 | .60 |
| | | Nos. 236-247,C32-C34 (15) | 18.95 | 8.60 |

Hippopotamus — A27

25fr, 75fr, Lion. 30fr, 100fr, Leopard.

### 1962, Aug. 25    Litho.    Perf. 13x13½

| | | | | |
|---|---|---|---|---|
| 248 | A27 | 10fr org, grn & brn | .35 | .20 |
| 249 | A27 | 25fr emer, blk & brn | .90 | .20 |
| 250 | A27 | 30fr yel grn, dk brn & yel | 1.00 | .20 |
| 251 | A27 | 50fr vio bl, dk brn & grn | 1.25 | .30 |
| 252 | A27 | 75fr lil, lt lil & red brn | 1.90 | .40 |
| 253 | A27 | 100fr grnsh bl, dk brn & yel | 2.40 | .60 |
| | | Nos. 248-253 (6) | 7.80 | 1.90 |

See Nos. 340-345.

Child at Blackboard — A28

Designs: 10fr, 20fr, Adult class.

### 1962, Sept. 19    Photo.    Perf. 13½x13

| | | | | |
|---|---|---|---|---|
| 254 | A28 | 5fr yel, dk brn & org | .20 | .20 |
| 255 | A28 | 10fr org & dk brn | .20 | .20 |
| 256 | A28 | 15fr yel grn, dk brn & red | .40 | .20 |
| 257 | A28 | 20fr bl & dk brn | .50 | .20 |
| | | Nos. 254-257 (4) | 1.30 | .80 |

Campaign against illiteracy.

### Imperforates
From late 1962 onward, most Guinea stamps exist imperforate.

Alfa Yaya — A29

### 1962, Oct. 2    Perf. 13½
30fr, King Behanzin. 50fr, King Ba Bemba. 75fr, Almamy Samory. 100fr, Tierno Aliou.

### Gold Frame

| | | | | |
|---|---|---|---|---|
| 258 | A29 | 25fr brt bl & sepia | .35 | .20 |
| 259 | A29 | 30fr yel & sepia | .60 | .20 |
| 260 | A29 | 50fr brt pink & sepia | .70 | .30 |
| 261 | A29 | 75fr grn & sepia | 1.75 | .45 |
| 262 | A29 | 100fr org, red & sepia | 2.10 | .70 |
| | | Nos. 258-262 (5) | 5.50 | 1.85 |

Heroes and martyrs of Africa.

Gray Parrot A30

Birds: 30c, 3fr, 50fr, Crowned crane (vert). 1fr, 20fr, Abyssinian ground hornbill. 1.50fr, 25fr, White spoonbill. 2fr, 40fr, Bateleur eagle.

### 1962, Dec.    Perf. 13½x13, 13x13½

| | | | | |
|---|---|---|---|---|
| 263 | A30 | 30c multicolored | .20 | .20 |
| 264 | A30 | 50c multicolored | .20 | .20 |
| 265 | A30 | 1fr multicolored | .20 | .20 |
| 266 | A30 | 1.50fr multicolored | .20 | .20 |
| 267 | A30 | 2fr multicolored | .65 | .20 |
| 268 | A30 | 3fr multicolored | .80 | .20 |
| 269 | A30 | 10fr multicolored | .90 | .20 |
| 270 | A30 | 20fr multicolored | .95 | .20 |
| 271 | A30 | 25fr multicolored | 1.10 | .20 |
| 272 | A30 | 40fr multicolored | 1.60 | .35 |
| 273 | A30 | 50fr multicolored | 2.10 | .50 |
| 274 | A30 | 75fr multicolored | | |
| | | Nos. 263-274,C41-C43 (15) | 29.60 | 11.10 |

Wheat Emblem and Globe A31

### 1963, Mar. 21    Photo.    Perf. 13x14

| | | | | |
|---|---|---|---|---|
| 275 | A31 | 5fr red & yellow | .20 | .20 |
| 276 | A31 | 10fr emerald & yel | .20 | .20 |
| 277 | A31 | 15fr brown & yel | .20 | .20 |
| 278 | A31 | 25fr dark ol & yel | .20 | .20 |
| | | Nos. 275-278 (4) | .80 | .80 |

FAO "Freedom from Hunger" campaign.

Basketball — A32

50c, 4fr, 30fr, Boxing. 1fr, 5fr, Running. 1.50fr, 10fr, Bicycling. 2fr, 20fr, Single sculls.

### 1963, Mar. 16    Unwmk.    Perf. 14

| | | | | |
|---|---|---|---|---|
| 279 | A32 | 30c ver, dp claret & grn | .20 | .20 |
| 280 | A32 | 50c lilac & blue | .20 | .20 |
| 281 | A32 | 1fr dl org, sep & grn | .20 | .20 |
| 282 | A32 | 1.50fr org, ultra & mag | .20 | .20 |
| 283 | A32 | 2fr aqua, dk bl & mag | .20 | .20 |
| 284 | A32 | 3fr ol, dp cl & grn | .20 | .20 |
| 285 | A32 | 4fr car rose, pur & bl | .20 | .20 |
| 286 | A32 | 5fr brt grn, ol & mag | .20 | .20 |
| 287 | A32 | 10fr lil rose, ultra & mag | .20 | .20 |
| 288 | A32 | 20fr red org, dk bl & crim | .20 | .20 |
| 289 | A32 | 25fr emer, dp cl & dk grn | .25 | .20 |
| 290 | A32 | 30fr gray, pur & bl | .30 | .20 |
| | | Nos. 279-290,C44-C46 (15) | 18.05 | 8.95 |

For overprints and surcharges see Nos. 312-314, C58-C60.

A33

Various Butterflies.

### 1963, May 10    Photo.    Perf. 12

| | | | | |
|---|---|---|---|---|
| 291 | A33 | 10c dp rose, blk & gray | .20 | .20 |
| 292 | A33 | 30c rose, blk & yel | .20 | .20 |
| 293 | A33 | 40c yel grn, brn & yel | .20 | .20 |
| 294 | A33 | 50c pale vio, blk & grn | .20 | .20 |
| 295 | A33 | 1fr yel, blk & emer | .40 | .20 |
| 296 | A33 | 1.50fr bluish grn, blk & sep | .40 | .20 |
| 297 | A33 | 2fr multi | .40 | .20 |
| 298 | A33 | 3fr multi | 1.10 | .20 |
| 299 | A33 | 10fr rose lil, blk & grn | 1.25 | .20 |
| 300 | A33 | 20fr gray, blk & grn | 1.40 | .20 |
| 301 | A33 | 25fr grn, blk & gray | 1.60 | .20 |
| 302 | A33 | 40fr multi | 2.00 | .45 |
| 303 | A33 | 50fr ultra, blk & yel | 2.50 | .55 |
| 304 | A33 | 75fr yel, blk & grn | 3.25 | .80 |
| | | Nos. 291-304,C47-C49 (17) | 33.85 | 11.25 |

Handshake, Map and Dove — A34

### 1963, May 22    Perf. 13½x14

| | | | | |
|---|---|---|---|---|
| 305 | A34 | 5fr bluish grn & dk brn | .20 | .20 |
| 306 | A34 | 10fr org yel & dk brn | .20 | .20 |
| 307 | A34 | 15fr ol & dk brn | .25 | .20 |
| 308 | A34 | 25fr bis brn & dk brn | .30 | .20 |
| | | Nos. 305-308 (4) | .95 | .80 |

Conference of African heads of state for African Unity, Addis Ababa.

Globe Encircled by Satellite — A35

### 1963, July 25    Engr.    Perf. 10½

| | | | | |
|---|---|---|---|---|
| 309 | A35 | 5fr green & car | .20 | .20 |
| 310 | A35 | 10fr vio bl & car | .40 | .20 |
| 311 | A35 | 15fr yellow & car | .50 | .20 |
| | | Nos. 309-311,C50 (4) | 2.00 | .80 |

Centenary of the International Red Cross.

Nos. 279-281 Surcharged in Carmine, Yellow or Orange: "COMMISSION PRÉPARATOIRE AUX JEUX OLYMPIQUES À CONAKRY," New Value and Olympic Rings

### 1963, Nov. 20    Photo.    Perf. 14

| | | | | |
|---|---|---|---|---|
| 312 | A32 | 40fr on 30c (C or Y) | 1.40 | 1.10 |
| 313 | A32 | 50fr on 50c (C or O) | 2.10 | 1.75 |
| 314 | A32 | 75fr on 1fr (C or O) | 3.50 | 2.50 |
| | | Nos. 312-314,C58-C60 (6) | 18.90 | 13.75 |

Meeting of the Olympic Games Preparatory Commission at Conakry. The overprint is in a circular line on #312, in 3 lines on each side on #313-314.

Jewelfish A36

Fish: 40c, 30fr, Golden pheasant. 50c, 40fr, Blue gularis. 1fr, 75fr, Banded Jewelfish. 1.50fr, African lyretail. 2fr, Six-barred epiplatys. 5fr, Jewelfish.

### 1964, Feb. 15    Litho.    Perf. 14x13½

| | | | | |
|---|---|---|---|---|
| 315 | A36 | 30c car rose & multi | .20 | .20 |
| 316 | A36 | 40c pur & multi | .20 | .20 |
| 317 | A36 | 50c car rose & multi | .20 | .20 |
| 318 | A36 | 1fr blue & multi | .20 | .20 |
| 319 | A36 | 1.50fr blue & multi | .20 | .20 |
| 320 | A36 | 2fr pur & multi | .60 | .20 |
| 321 | A36 | 5fr blue & multi | .65 | .20 |
| 322 | A36 | 30fr grn & multi | .85 | .20 |
| 323 | A36 | 40fr grn & multi | 1.75 | .40 |
| 324 | A36 | 75fr multi | 2.50 | .55 |
| | | Nos. 315-324,C54-C55 (12) | 17.35 | 4.50 |

John F. Kennedy A37

### 1964, Mar. 5    Engr.    Perf. 10½
### Flag in Red and Blue

| | | | | |
|---|---|---|---|---|
| 325 | A37 | 5fr blk & pur | .20 | .20 |
| 326 | A37 | 25fr grn & pur | .40 | .20 |
| 327 | A37 | 50fr brn & pur | .85 | .30 |
| | | Nos. 325-327,C56 (4) | 3.20 | 1.50 |

Issued in sheets of 20 with marginal quotations in English and French. Two sheets for each denomination. See No. C56.

Workers Welding Pipe — A38

5fr, Pipe line over mountains, vert. 10fr, Waterworks. 30fr, Transporting pipe. 50fr, Laying pipe.

### 1964, May 1    Photo.    Perf. 11½

| | | | | |
|---|---|---|---|---|
| 328 | A38 | 5fr deep mag | .20 | .20 |
| 329 | A38 | 10fr bright pur | .20 | .20 |
| 330 | A38 | 20fr org red | .50 | .20 |
| 331 | A38 | 30fr ultra | .65 | .20 |
| 332 | A38 | 50fr yel grn | .75 | .20 |
| | | Nos. 328-332 (5) | 2.30 | 1.00 |

Completion of the water-supply pipeline to Conakry, Mar. 1964.

Ice Hockey — A39

### 1964, May 15    Perf. 13x12½

| | | | | |
|---|---|---|---|---|
| 333 | A39 | 10fr shown | .40 | .20 |
| 334 | A39 | 25fr Ski jump | .60 | .20 |
| 335 | A39 | 50fr Slalom | 1.10 | .40 |
| | | Nos. 333-335,C57 (4) | 4.35 | 1.20 |

9th Winter Olympic Games, Innsbruck, Jan. 29-Feb. 9, 1964.

Eleanor Roosevelt Reading to Children — A40

**1964, June 1　　Engr.　　Perf. 10½**

| 336 | A40 | 5fr green | .25 | .20 |
|---|---|---|---|---|
| 337 | A40 | 10fr red org | .25 | .20 |
| 338 | A40 | 15fr bright bl | .25 | .20 |
| 339 | A40 | 25fr car rose | .25 | .20 |
| | | Nos. 336-339,C61 (5) | 1.90 | 1.05 |

Eleanor Roosevelt, 15th anniv. of the Universal Declaration of Human Rights (in 1963).

**Animal Type of 1962**

Designs: 5fr, 30fr, Striped hyenas. 40fr, 300fr, Black buffaloes. 75fr, 100fr, Elephants.

**1964, Oct. 8　　Litho.　　Perf. 13x13½**

| 340 | A27 | 5fr yellow & blk | .20 | .20 |
|---|---|---|---|---|
| 341 | A27 | 30fr light bl & blk | .35 | .20 |
| 342 | A27 | 40fr lil rose & blk | .80 | .20 |
| 343 | A27 | 75fr yel grn & blk | 1.90 | .35 |
| 344 | A27 | 100fr bister & blk | 2.25 | .60 |
| 345 | A27 | 300fr orange & blk | 6.50 | 2.40 |
| | | Nos. 340-345 (6) | 12.00 | 3.95 |

Guinea Exhibit, World's Fair — A41

**1964, Oct. 26　　Engr.　　Perf. 10½**

| 346 | A41 | 30fr vio & emerald | .35 | .20 |
|---|---|---|---|---|
| 347 | A41 | 40fr red lil & emer | .50 | .20 |
| 348 | A41 | 50fr sepia & emer | .70 | .20 |
| 349 | A41 | 75fr rose red & dk bl | 1.10 | .25 |
| | | Nos. 346-349 (4) | 2.65 | .85 |

New York World's Fair, 1964-65.
See Nos. 372-375, C62-C63, C69-C70.

Queen Nefertari Crowned by Isis and Hathor — A42

Designs: 25fr, Ramses II in battle. 50fr, Submerged sphinxes, sailboat, Wadies-Sebua. 100fr, Ramses II holding crook and flail, Abu Simbel. 200fr, Feet and legs of Ramses statues, Abu Simbel.

**1964, Nov. 19　　Photo.　　Perf. 12**

| 350 | A42 | 10fr dk bl, red brn & cit | .20 | .20 |
|---|---|---|---|---|
| 351 | A42 | 25fr blk, dl red & brn | .60 | .20 |
| 352 | A42 | 50fr dk brn, bl & vio | .75 | .20 |
| 353 | A42 | 100fr dk brn, yel & pur | 1.25 | .40 |
| 354 | A42 | 200fr pur, dl grn & buff | 2.75 | .75 |
| | | Nos. 350-354,C64 (6) | 10.30 | 3.15 |

UNESCO campaign to preserve Nubian monuments.
For overprint see No. 415.

Weight Lifter and Caucasian, Japanese and Negro Children — A43

**1965, Jan. 18　　Photo.　　Perf. 13x12½**

10fr, Runner carrying torch. 25fr, Pole vaulting and flags. 40fr, Runners. 50fr, Judo. 75fr, Japanese woman, flags and stadium.

| 355 | A43 | 5fr gold, claret & blk | .20 | .20 |
|---|---|---|---|---|
| 356 | A43 | 10fr gold, blk, ver & bl | .40 | .20 |
| 357 | A43 | 25fr gold, blk, yel grn & red | .45 | .20 |
| 358 | A43 | 40fr gold, blk, brn & yel | .50 | .20 |
| 359 | A43 | 50fr gold, blk & grn | .80 | .30 |
| 360 | A43 | 75fr gold & multi | 1.50 | .40 |
| | | Nos. 355-360,C65 (7) | 5.60 | 1.85 |

18th Olympic Games, Tokyo, 10/10-25/64.
For overprints see Nos. 410-414.

Doudou Mask, Boké — A44

Designs: 40c, 1fr, 15fr, Various Niamou masks, N'Zérékoré region. 60c, "Yoki," wood-carved statuette of a girl, Boke. 80c, Masked woman dancer from Guekedou. 2fr, Masked dancer from Macenta. 20fr, Beater from Tam-tam. 60fr, Bird dancer from Macenta. 80fr, Bassari dancer from Koundara. 100fr, Sword dancer from Karana.

**1965, Feb. 15　　Unwmk.　　Perf. 14**

| 361 | A44 | 20c multicolored | .20 | .20 |
|---|---|---|---|---|
| 362 | A44 | 40c multicolored | .20 | .20 |
| 363 | A44 | 60c multicolored | .20 | .20 |
| 364 | A44 | 80c multicolored | .20 | .20 |
| 365 | A44 | 1fr multicolored | .20 | .20 |
| 366 | A44 | 2fr multicolored | .50 | .20 |
| 367 | A44 | 15fr multicolored | .55 | .20 |
| 368 | A44 | 20fr multicolored | .55 | .20 |
| 369 | A44 | 60fr multicolored | 1.25 | .40 |
| 370 | A44 | 80fr multicolored | 1.50 | .50 |
| 371 | A44 | 100fr multicolored | 1.75 | .50 |
| | | Nos. 361-371,C68 (12) | 12.75 | 5.75 |

**World's Fair Type of 1964 Inscribed "1965"**

**1965, Mar. 24　　Engr.　　Perf. 10½**

| 372 | A41 | 30fr grn & orange | .40 | .20 |
|---|---|---|---|---|
| 373 | A41 | 40fr car & brt grn | .50 | .20 |
| 374 | A41 | 50fr brt grn & vio | .70 | .25 |
| 375 | A41 | 75fr brown & vio | 1.00 | .35 |
| | | Nos. 372-375 (4) | 2.60 | 1.00 |

See Nos. C69-C70.

Blacksmith — A45

Handicrafts: 20fr, Potter. 60fr, Cloth dyers. 80fr, Basketmaker.

**1965, May 1　　Photo.　　Perf. 14**

| 376 | A45 | 15fr multicolored | .20 | .20 |
|---|---|---|---|---|
| 377 | A45 | 20fr multicolored | .50 | .20 |
| 378 | A45 | 60fr multicolored | .80 | .30 |
| 379 | A45 | 80fr multicolored | .95 | .40 |
| | | Nos. 376-379,C71-C72 (6) | 9.20 | 2.70 |

ITU Emblem, Old and New Communication Equipment — A46

**1965, May 17　　Unwmk.**

| 380 | A46 | 25fr yel, gray, gold & blk | .45 | .20 |
|---|---|---|---|---|
| 381 | A46 | 25fr yel, grn, gold & blk | .70 | .25 |
| | | Nos. 380-381,C73-C74 (4) | 5.40 | 1.50 |

ITU centenary.

Maj. Virgil I. Grissom — A47

Moon from 258mi. — A48

Sputnik Over Earth — A49

American Achievements in Space: 10fr, Lt. Com. John W. Young. 25fr, Moon from 115mi. 30fr, Moon from 58mi. 100fr, Grissom and Young in Gemini 2 spaceship.

**1965, July 19　　Photo.　　Perf. 13**

**Size: 21x29mm**

| 382 | A47 | 5fr dk red & multi | .20 | .20 |
|---|---|---|---|---|
| 383 | A47 | 10fr dk red & multi | .20 | .20 |
| 384 | A48 | 15fr gold, bl & dk bl | .20 | .20 |

**Size: 39x28mm**

| 385 | A48 | 25fr gold, bl & dk bl | .20 | .20 |

**Size: 21x29mm**

| 386 | A48 | 30fr gold, bl & dk bl | .20 | .20 |

**Size: 39x28mm**

| 387 | A47 | 100fr multi & dk red | .50 | .40 |
|---|---|---|---|---|
| a. | | Sheet of 15, #382-387 | 9.00 | |

Russian Achievements in Space: 5fr, Col. Pavel Belyayev. 10fr, Lt. Col. Alexei Leonov. 15fr, Vostoks 3 & 4 in space. 30fr, Vostoks 5 & 6 over Earth. 100fr, Leonov floating in space.

**Size: 21x29mm**

| 388 | A47 | 5fr bl & multi | .20 | .20 |
|---|---|---|---|---|
| 389 | A47 | 10fr bl & multi | .20 | .20 |
| 390 | A49 | 15fr bl & multi | .20 | .20 |

**Size: 39x28mm**

| 391 | A49 | 25fr bl & multi | .20 | .20 |

**Size: 21x29mm**

| 392 | A49 | 30fr bl & multi | .20 | .20 |

**Size: 39x28mm**

| 393 | A47 | 100fr blk, dk red & gold | .50 | .40 |
|---|---|---|---|---|
| a. | | Sheet of 15, #388-393 | 9.00 | |
| | | Nos. 382-393 (12) | 3.00 | 2.80 |

American and Russian achievements in space. Nos. 387a and 393a contain five triptychs each: four rows with 5fr, 100fr and 10fr, and a center row with 15fr, 25fr and 30fr stamps each.

ICY Emblem, UN Headquarters and Skyline, New York — A50

**1965, Sept. 8　　Perf. 10½**

| 394 | A50 | 25fr yel grn & ver | .35 | .20 |
|---|---|---|---|---|
| 395 | A50 | 45fr vio & orange | .40 | .20 |
| 396 | A50 | 75fr red brn & org | .65 | .25 |
| | | Nos. 394-396,C75 (4) | 2.65 | 1.00 |

Intl. Cooperation Year, 1965.

Polytechnic Institute, Conakry — A51

New Projects, Conakry: 30fr, Hotel Camayenne. 40fr, Gbessia Airport. 75fr, Stadium "28 September."

**1965, Oct. 2　　Photo.　　Perf. 13½**

| 397 | A51 | 25fr multicolored | .30 | .20 |
|---|---|---|---|---|
| 398 | A51 | 30fr multicolored | .35 | .20 |
| 399 | A51 | 40fr multicolored | .60 | .30 |
| 400 | A51 | 75fr multicolored | .75 | .40 |
| | | Nos. 397-400,C76-C77 (6) | 10.10 | 5.10 |

Seventh anniversary of independence.

Photographing Far Side of Moon — A52

10fr, Trajectories of Ranger VII on flight to moon. 25fr, Relay satellite. 45fr, Vostoks I & II & globe.

**1965, Nov. 15　　Litho.　　Perf. 14x13½**

| 401 | A52 | 5fr blk, pur & ocher | .20 | .20 |
|---|---|---|---|---|
| 402 | A52 | 10fr red brn, lt grn & yel | .20 | .20 |
| 403 | A52 | 25fr blk, bl & bis | .50 | .20 |
| 404 | A52 | 45fr blk, lt ultra & bis | 1.00 | .20 |
| | | Nos. 401-404,C78-C79 (6) | 5.40 | 2.30 |

For overprints and surcharges see Nos. 529-530, C112-C112B.

Sword Dance, Karana — A53

Designs: 30c, Dancing girls, Lower Guinea. 50c, Behore musicians of Tiekere playing "Eyoro," horiz. 5fr, Doundouba dance of Kouroussa. 40fr, Bird man's dance of Macenta.

**1966, Jan. 5　　Photo.　　Perf. 13½**

**Size: 26x36mm**

| 405 | A53 | 10c multicolored | .20 | .20 |
|---|---|---|---|---|
| 406 | A53 | 30c multicolored | .20 | .20 |

**Size: 36x28½mm**

| 407 | A53 | 50c multicolored | .45 | .20 |

**Size: 26x36mm**

| 408 | A53 | 5fr multicolored | .45 | .20 |
|---|---|---|---|---|
| 409 | A53 | 40fr multicolored | .75 | .20 |
| | | Nos. 405-409,C80 (6) | 3.55 | 1.50 |

Festival of African Art and Culture. See Nos. 436-441.

Engraved Overprint in Red or Orange on Nos. 355-356 and Nos. 358-360

**1966, Mar. 14　　Perf. 13x12½**

| 410 | A43 | 5fr multi (R) | .40 | .20 |
|---|---|---|---|---|
| 411 | A43 | 10fr multi (R) | .50 | .20 |
| 412 | A43 | 40fr multi (O) | .85 | .25 |
| 413 | A43 | 50fr multi (R) | 1.10 | .40 |
| 414 | A43 | 75fr multi (R) | 2.00 | .65 |
| | | Nos. 410-414,C81 (6) | 6.10 | 2.15 |

4th Pan Arab Games, Cairo, Sept. 2-11, 1965. The same overprint was also applied to imperf. sheets of No. 357.

Engraved Red Orange Overprint on No. 352:
"CENTENAIRE DU TIMBRE CAIRE 1966"

**1966, Mar. 14　　Perf. 12**

| 415 | A42 | 50fr dk brn, bl & vio | 1.00 | .50 |
|---|---|---|---|---|

1st Egyptian postage stamps, cent. See #C82.

Vonkou Rock, Telimélé — A54

Views: 25fr, Artificial lake, Coyah. 40fr, Kalé waterfalls. 50fr, Forécariah bridge. 75fr, Liana bridge.

**1966, Apr. 4    Photo.    Perf. 13½**
| 416 | A54 | 20fr multicolored | .20 | .20 |
| 417 | A54 | 25fr multicolored | .45 | .20 |
| 418 | A54 | 40fr multicolored | .50 | .20 |
| 419 | A54 | 50fr multicolored | .70 | .20 |
| 420 | A54 | 75fr multicolored | .90 | .30 |
| | | Nos. 416-420,C83 (6) | 4.15 | 1.70 |

See Nos. 475-478, C90-C91. For overprints see Nos. 482-488, C93-C95.

UNESCO Emblem — A55

**1966, May 2    Photo.    Unwmk.**
| 421 | A55 | 25fr multicolored | .70 | .20 |

20th anniv. of UNESCO. See Nos. C84-C85.

Woman of Guinea and Morning Glory — A56

Symbolic Water Cycle and UNESCO Emblem — A57

Designs: Women and Flowers of Guinea.

**1966, May 30    Photo.    Perf. 13½**
**Size: 23x34mm**
| 422 | A56 | 10c multicolored | .20 | .20 |
| 423 | A56 | 25c multicolored | .20 | .20 |
| 424 | A56 | 30c multicolored | .20 | .20 |
| 425 | A56 | 40c multicolored | .20 | .20 |
| 426 | A56 | 3fr multicolored | .20 | .20 |
| 427 | A56 | 4fr multicolored | .20 | .20 |
| 428 | A56 | 10fr multicolored | .20 | .20 |
| 429 | A56 | 25fr multicolored | .65 | .20 |

**Size: 28x43mm**
| 430 | A56 | 30fr multicolored | .80 | .20 |
| 431 | A56 | 50fr multicolored | 1.00 | .35 |
| 432 | A56 | 80fr multicolored | 1.50 | .45 |
| | | Nos. 422-432,C86-C87 (13) | 14.35 | 5.40 |

**1966, Sept. 26    Engr.    Perf. 10½**
| 433 | A57 | 5fr bl & dp org | .30 | .20 |
| 434 | A57 | 25fr grn & dp org | .35 | .20 |
| 435 | A57 | 100fr brt rose lil & dp org | .95 | .35 |
| | | Nos. 433-435 (3) | 1.60 | .75 |

Hydrological Decade (UNESCO), 1965-74.

Dance Type of 1966
Various folk dances. 25fr, 75fr, horizontal.

**1966, Oct. 24    Photo.    Perf. 13½**
**Sizes: 26x36mm, 36x28½mm**
| 436 | A53 | 60c multicolored | .20 | .20 |
| 437 | A53 | 1fr multicolored | .20 | .20 |
| 438 | A53 | 1.50fr multicolored | .20 | .20 |
| 439 | A53 | 25fr multicolored | .75 | .20 |
| 440 | A53 | 50fr multicolored | 1.25 | .20 |
| 441 | A53 | 75fr multicolored | 1.75 | .50 |
| | | Nos. 436-441 (6) | 4.35 | 1.50 |

Guinean National Dancers.

Child's Drawing and UNICEF Emblem — A58

Children's Drawings: 2fr, Elephant. 3fr, Girl. 20fr, Village, horiz. 25fr, Boy playing soccer. 40fr, Still life. 50fr, Bird in a tree.

**1966, Dec. 12    Photo.    Perf. 13½**
| 442 | A58 | 2fr multicolored | .20 | .20 |
| 443 | A58 | 3fr multicolored | .20 | .20 |
| 444 | A58 | 10fr multicolored | .20 | .20 |
| 445 | A58 | 20fr multicolored | .20 | .20 |
| 446 | A58 | 25fr multicolored | .40 | .20 |
| 447 | A58 | 40fr multicolored | .45 | .20 |
| 448 | A58 | 50fr multicolored | .65 | .20 |
| | | Nos. 442-448 (7) | 2.30 | 1.40 |

20th anniv. of UNICEF. Printed in sheets of 10 stamps and 2 labels with ornamental borders and inscriptions.

Laboratory Technician — A59

WHO Emblem and: 50fr, Physician examining infant. 75fr, Pre-natal care & instruction. 80fr, WHO Headquarters, Geneva.

**1967, Jan. 20    Photo.    Perf. 13½**
| 449 | A59 | 30fr multicolored | .30 | .20 |
| 450 | A59 | 50fr multicolored | .40 | .20 |
| 451 | A59 | 75fr multicolored | .60 | .25 |
| 452 | A59 | 80fr multicolored | .70 | .35 |
| | | Nos. 449-452 (4) | 2.00 | 1.00 |

Inauguration (in 1966) of WHO Headquarters, Geneva.

Niamou Mask, N'Zerekore — A60

Designs: 10c, 1fr, 30fr, Small Banda mask, Kanfarade, Boké region. 1.50fr, 50fr, Like 30c. 50c, 5fr, 75fr, Bearded Niamou mask. 60c, 25fr, 100fr, Horned Yinadjinkele mask, Kankan region.

**1967, Mar. 25    Photo.    Perf. 14x13**
| 453 | A60 | 10c org & multi | .20 | .20 |
| 454 | A60 | 30c cit & brn blk | .20 | .20 |
| 455 | A60 | 50c dp lil rose, blk & red | .20 | .20 |
| 456 | A60 | 60c dp org, blk & bis | .20 | .20 |
| 457 | A60 | 1fr yel grn & multi | .20 | .20 |
| 458 | A60 | 1.50fr sal pink & brn blk | .20 | .20 |
| 459 | A60 | 5fr ap grn, blk & red | .20 | .20 |
| 460 | A60 | 25fr red lil, blk & bis | .45 | .20 |
| 461 | A60 | 30fr bis & multi | .50 | .20 |
| 462 | A60 | 50fr grnsh bl & brn blk | .80 | .20 |
| 463 | A60 | 75fr yel, blk & red | 1.25 | .35 |
| 464 | A60 | 100fr lt ultra, blk & bis | 1.90 | .55 |
| | | Nos. 453-464 (12) | 6.30 | 2.90 |

Ball Python — A61

20c, Pastoria Research Institute. 50c, 75fr, Extraction of snake venom. 1fr, 50fr, Rock python. 2fr, Men holding rock python. 5fr, 30fr, Gaboon viper. 20fr, West African mamba.

**1967, May 15    Litho.    Perf. 13½**
**Size: 43½x20mm**
| 465 | A61 | 20c multicolored | .20 | .20 |
| 466 | A61 | 30c multicolored | .20 | .20 |
| 467 | A61 | 50c multicolored | .20 | .20 |
| 468 | A61 | 1fr multicolored | .20 | .20 |
| 469 | A61 | 2fr multicolored | .20 | .20 |
| 470 | A61 | 5fr multicolored | .20 | .20 |

**Size: 56x26mm**
| 471 | A61 | 20fr multicolored | .65 | .20 |
| 472 | A61 | 30fr multicolored | 1.10 | .20 |
| 473 | A61 | 50fr multicolored | 1.25 | .20 |
| 474 | A61 | 75fr multicolored | 2.00 | .20 |
| | | Nos. 465-474,C88-C89 (12) | 14.95 | 5.50 |

Research Institute for Applied Biology of Guinea (Pastoria). For souvenir sheet see No. C88a.

Scenic Type of 1966
Views: 5fr, Loos Island. 30fr, Tinkisso Waterfalls. 70fr, "The Elephant's Trunk" Hotel, Mt. Kakoulima. 80fr, Evening at the shore, Ratoma.

**1967, June 20    Photo.    Perf. 13½**
| 475 | A54 | 5fr multicolored | .20 | .20 |
| 476 | A54 | 30fr multicolored | .20 | .20 |
| 477 | A54 | 70fr multicolored | .60 | .20 |
| 478 | A54 | 80fr multicolored | .85 | .20 |
| | | Nos. 475-478,C90-C91 (6) | 5.55 | 2.35 |

People's Palace, Conakry — A62

Elephant A63

**1967, Sept. 28    Photo.    Perf. 13½**
| 479 | A62 | 5fr silver & multi | .20 | .20 |
| 480 | A63 | 30fr silver & multi | .30 | .20 |
| 481 | A62 | 55fr gold & multi | .50 | .20 |
| | | Nos. 479-481 (3) | 1.00 | .60 |

20th anniv. of the Democratic Party of Guinea and the opening of the People's Palace, Conakry. See No. C92.

Nos. 418-420 and 475-478 Overprinted with Lions Emblem and: "AMITIE DES PEUPLES GRACE AU TOURISME 1917-1967"

**1967, Nov. 6**
| 482 | A54 | 5fr multicolored | .45 | .20 |
| 483 | A54 | 30fr multicolored | .90 | .20 |
| 484 | A54 | 40fr multicolored | .75 | .20 |
| 485 | A54 | 50fr multicolored | 1.00 | .20 |
| 486 | A54 | 70fr multicolored | 1.25 | .30 |
| 487 | A54 | 75fr multicolored | 1.75 | .50 |
| 488 | A54 | 80fr multicolored | 2.25 | .50 |
| | | Nos. 482-488,C93-C95 (10) | 18.35 | 5.40 |

50th anniversary of Lions International.

WHO Office for Africa — A64

**1967, Dec. 4    Photo.    Perf. 13½**
| 489 | A64 | 30fr lt ol grn, bis & dk grn | .55 | .20 |
| 490 | A64 | 75fr red org, bis & dk bl | 1.10 | .30 |

Inauguration of the WHO Regional Office for Africa in Brazzaville, Congo.

Human Rights Flame — A65

**1968, Jan. 15    Photo.    Perf. 13½**
| 491 | A65 | 30fr ocher, grn & dk car | .50 | .20 |
| 492 | A65 | 40fr vio, grn & car | .60 | .20 |

International Human Rights Year, 1968.

Coyah, Dubréka Region A66

Homes and People: 30c, 30fr, Kankan Region. 40c, Kankan, East Guinea. 50c, 15fr, Woodlands Region. 60c, Fulahmori, Gaoual Region. 5fr, Cognagui, Kundara Region. 40fr, Fouta Djallon, West Guinea. 100fr, Labé, West Guinea.

**1968, Apr. 1    Photo.    Perf. 13½x14**
**Size: 36x27mm**
| 493 | A66 | 20c gold & multi | .20 | .20 |
| 494 | A66 | 30c gold & multi | .20 | .20 |
| 495 | A66 | 40c gold & multi | .20 | .20 |
| 496 | A66 | 50c gold & multi | .20 | .20 |

**Perf. 14x13½**
**Size: 57x36mm**
| 497 | A66 | 60c gold & multi | .20 | .20 |
| 498 | A66 | 5fr gold & multi | .20 | .20 |
| 499 | A66 | 15fr gold & multi | .20 | .20 |
| 500 | A66 | 20fr gold & multi | .35 | .20 |
| 501 | A66 | 30fr gold & multi | .40 | .20 |
| 502 | A66 | 40fr gold & multi | .55 | .20 |
| 503 | A66 | 100fr gold & multi | 1.50 | .30 |
| | | Nos. 493-503,C100 (12) | 8.70 | 3.55 |

The Storyteller — A67

African Legends: 15fr, The Little Genie of Mt. Nimba. No. 506, The Legend of the Moons and the Stars. No. 507, Lan, the Child Buffalo, vert. 40fr, Nianablas and the Crocodiles. 50fr, Leuk the Hare Playing the Drum, vert. 75fr, Leuk the Hare Selling his Sister, vert. 80fr, The Hunter and the Antelope-woman. The designs are from paintings by students of the Academy of Fine Arts in Bellevue.

**1968    Photo.    Perf. 13½**
| 504 | A67 | 15fr multicolored | .20 | .20 |
| 505 | A67 | 25fr multicolored | .20 | .20 |
| 506 | A67 | 30fr multicolored | .25 | .20 |
| 507 | A67 | 40fr multicolored | .25 | .20 |
| 508 | A67 | 50fr multicolored | .40 | .20 |
| 509 | A67 | 50fr multicolored | .65 | .20 |
| a. | | Souv. sheet of 4 | 5.50 | 5.50 |
| 510 | A67 | 75fr multicolored | .65 | .25 |
| 511 | A67 | 80fr multicolored | 1.10 | .25 |
| | | Nos. 504-511,C101-C104 (12) | 12.75 | 4.45 |

Issued in sheets of 10 plus 2 labels. No. 509a contains 4 imperf. stamps similar to Nos. 508-509, C101 and C104. "Poste Aerienne" omitted on the 70fr and 300fr of the souvenir sheet.
Issued: #505-506, 510-511, 5/16; #504, 507-509, 9/16.

Anubius Baboon — A68

African Animals: 10fr, Leopards. 15fr, Hippopotami. 20fr, Nile crocodile. 30fr, Ethiopian wart hog. 50fr, Defassa waterbuck. 75fr, Cape buffaloes.

**1968, Nov. 25**    **Photo.**    *Perf. 13½*
**Size: 44x31mm**

| | | | | |
|---|---|---|---|---|
| 512 | A68 | 5fr gold & multi | .20 | .20 |
| 513 | A68 | 10fr gold & multi | .60 | .20 |
| 514 | A68 | 15fr gold & multi | .65 | .20 |
| *a.* | | Souv. sheet of 3, #512-514 | 1.50 | 1.50 |
| 515 | A68 | 20fr gold & multi | .80 | .20 |
| 516 | A68 | 30fr gold & multi | 1.00 | .20 |
| 517 | A68 | 50fr gold & multi | 1.25 | .20 |
| *a.* | | Souv. sheet of 3, #515-517 | 3.75 | 3.75 |
| 518 | A68 | 75fr gold & multi | 2.00 | .30 |
| *a.* | | Souv. sheet of 3 | 10.50 | 10.50 |
| | | Nos. 512-518,C105-C106 (9) | 14.00 | 4.15 |

No. 518a contains one No. 518 and one each similar to Nos. C105-C106 without "POSTE AERIENNE" inscription. The three souvenir sheets contain 3 stamps and one green and gold label inscribed "FAUNE AFRICAINE."

Senator Robert F. Kennedy A69

Portraits: 75fr, Rev. Martin Luther King, Jr. 100fr, Pres. John F. Kennedy.

**1968, Dec. 16**

| | | | | |
|---|---|---|---|---|
| 519 | A69 | 30fr yel & multi | .55 | .20 |
| 520 | A69 | 75fr multicolored | 1.25 | .20 |
| 521 | A69 | 100fr multicolored | 1.75 | .30 |
| | | Nos. 519-521,C107-C109 (6) | 11.90 | 2.35 |

Robert F. Kennedy, John F. Kennedy and Martin Luther King, Jr., martyrs for freedom.
The stamps are printed in sheets of 15 (3x5) containing 10 stamps and five yellow-green and gold center labels. Sheets come either with English or French inscriptions on label.

Sculpture and Runner A70

Sculpture and Soccer — A71

Designs (Sculpture and): 10fr, Boxing. 15fr, Javelin. 30fr, Steeplechase. 50fr, Hammer throw. 75fr, Bicycling.

**1969, Feb. 18**    **Photo.**    *Perf. 13½*

| | | | | |
|---|---|---|---|---|
| 522 | A70 | 5fr multicolored | .20 | .20 |
| 523 | A70 | 10fr multicolored | .20 | .20 |
| 524 | A70 | 15fr multicolored | .40 | .20 |
| 525 | A71 | 25fr multicolored | .40 | .20 |
| 526 | A70 | 30fr multicolored | .40 | .20 |
| 527 | A70 | 50fr multicolored | .65 | .20 |
| 528 | A70 | 75fr multicolored | .90 | .20 |
| | | Nos. 522-528,C110-C111A (10) | 11.65 | 3.70 |

19th Olympic Games, Mexico City, 10/12-27.

No. 404 Surcharged and Overprinted in Red

**1969, Mar. 17**    **Litho.**    *Perf. 14x13½*

| | | | | |
|---|---|---|---|---|
| 529 | A52 | 30fr on 45fr multi | .60 | .35 |
| 530 | A52 | 45fr multicolored | .60 | .35 |
| | | Nos. 529-530,C112-C112B (5) | 5.35 | 2.55 |

US Apollo 8 mission, the first men in orbit around the moon, Dec. 21-27, 1968.
Nos. 529-530 also exist with surcharge and overprint in black. These sell for about 10% more.

Tarzan — A72

Designs: 30fr, Tarzan sitting in front of Pastoria Research Institute gate. 75fr, Tarzan and his family. 100fr, Tarzan sitting in a tree.

**1969, June 6**    **Photo.**    *Perf. 13½*

| | | | | |
|---|---|---|---|---|
| 531 | A72 | 25fr orange & multi | .45 | .20 |
| 532 | A72 | 30fr bl grn & multi | .60 | .20 |
| 533 | A72 | 75fr yel grn & multi | 1.25 | .20 |
| 534 | A72 | 100fr yellow & multi | 1.90 | .35 |
| | | Nos. 531-534 (4) | 4.20 | .95 |

Tarzan was a Guinean chimpanzee with superior intelligence and ability.

Campfire A73

25fr, Boy Scout & tents. 30fr, Marching Boy Scouts. 40fr, Basketball. 45fr, Senior Scouts, thatched huts & mountain. 50fr, Guinean Boy Scout badge.

**1969, July 1**

| | | | | |
|---|---|---|---|---|
| 535 | A73 | 5fr gold & multi | .20 | .20 |
| 536 | A73 | 25fr gold & multi | .35 | .20 |
| 537 | A73 | 30fr gold & multi | .35 | .20 |
| 538 | A73 | 40fr gold & multi | .55 | .20 |
| 539 | A73 | 45fr gold & multi | .70 | .20 |
| 540 | A73 | 50fr gold & multi | .75 | .20 |
| *a.* | | Min. sheet of 6, #535-540 | 4.00 | 4.00 |
| | | Nos. 535-540 (6) | 2.90 | 1.20 |

Issued to honor the Boy Scouts of Guinea.

Launching Apollo 11 — A74

Designs: 30fr, Earth showing Africa as seen from moon. 50fr, Separation of lunar landing module and spaceship. 60fr, Astronauts and module on moon. 75fr, Module on moon and earth. 100fr, Module leaving moon. 200fr, Splashdown. "a" stamps are inscribed in French. "b" stamps are inscribed in English.

**1969, Aug. 20**    **Photo.**    *Perf. 13½*
**Size: 34x55mm**

| | | | | |
|---|---|---|---|---|
| 541 | A74 | 25fr Pair, #541a, 541b | .40 | .20 |
| 542 | A74 | 30fr Pair, #542a, 542b | .50 | .20 |
| 543 | A74 | 50fr Pair, #543a, 543b | .75 | .20 |
| 544 | A74 | 60fr Pair, #544a, 544b | 1.25 | .35 |
| 545 | A74 | 75fr Pair, #545a, 545b | 1.50 | .40 |

**Size: 34x71mm**

| | | | | |
|---|---|---|---|---|
| 546 | A74 | 100fr Pair, #546a, 546b | 2.50 | .60 |

**Size: 34x55mm**

| | | | | |
|---|---|---|---|---|
| 547 | A74 | 200fr Pair, #547a, 547b | 5.00 | 1.50 |
| | | Nos. 541-547 (7) | 11.90 | 3.45 |

Man's 1st landing on the moon, 7/20/69.

Harvest and ILO Emblem A75

ILO, 50th Anniv.: 25fr, Power lines and blast furnaces. 30fr, Women in broadcasting studio. 200fr, Potters.

**1969, Oct. 28**    **Photo.**    *Perf. 13½*

| | | | | |
|---|---|---|---|---|
| 548 | A75 | 25fr gold & multi | .20 | .20 |
| 549 | A75 | 30fr gold & multi | .30 | .20 |
| 550 | A75 | 75fr gold & multi | .75 | .20 |
| 551 | A75 | 200fr gold & multi | 2.25 | .60 |
| | | Nos. 548-551 (4) | 3.50 | 1.20 |

Mother and Sick Child — A76

25fr, Sick child. 40fr, Girl receiving vaccination. 50fr, Boy receiving vaccination. 60fr, Mother receiving vaccination. 200fr, Edward Jenner, M.D.

**1970, Jan. 15**    **Photo.**    *Perf. 13½*

| | | | | |
|---|---|---|---|---|
| 552 | A76 | 25fr multicolored | .20 | .20 |
| 553 | A76 | 30fr multicolored | .35 | .20 |
| 554 | A76 | 40fr multicolored | .40 | .20 |
| 555 | A76 | 50fr multicolored | .60 | .20 |
| 556 | A76 | 60fr multicolored | .70 | .20 |
| 557 | A76 | 200fr multicolored | 2.40 | 1.00 |
| | | Nos. 552-557 (6) | 4.65 | 2.00 |

Campaign against smallpox and measles.

Map of Africa — A77

**1970, Feb. 3**    **Litho.**    *Perf. 14½x14*

| | | | | |
|---|---|---|---|---|
| 558 | A77 | 30fr lt bl & multi | .25 | .20 |
| 559 | A77 | 200fr lt vio & multi | 1.75 | .75 |

Meeting of statesmen of countries bordering on Senegal River: Mali, Guinea, Senegal and Mauritania.

Open Book and Radar A78

**1970, July 6**    **Litho.**    *Perf. 14*

| | | | | |
|---|---|---|---|---|
| 560 | A78 | 5fr lt bl & blk | .20 | .20 |
| 561 | A78 | 10fr rose & blk | .20 | .20 |
| 562 | A78 | 50fr yellow & blk | .60 | .20 |
| 563 | A78 | 200fr lilac & blk | 2.10 | .90 |
| | | Nos. 560-563 (4) | 3.10 | 1.50 |

International Telecommunications Day.

Lenin — A79

Designs: 20fr, Meeting with Lenin, by V. Serov. 30fr, Lenin Addressing Workers, by V. Serov. 40fr, Lenin with Red Guard Soldier and Sailor, by P. V. Vasiliev. 100fr, Lenin Speaking from Balcony, by P. V. Vasiliev. 200fr, Like 5fr.

**1970, Nov. 16**    **Photo.**    *Perf. 13*

| | | | | |
|---|---|---|---|---|
| 564 | A79 | 5fr gold & multi | .20 | .20 |
| 565 | A79 | 20fr gold & multi | .40 | .20 |
| 566 | A79 | 30fr gold & multi | .50 | .20 |
| 567 | A79 | 40fr gold & multi | .80 | .20 |
| 568 | A79 | 100fr gold & multi | 1.60 | .30 |
| 569 | A79 | 200fr gold & multi | 3.25 | .75 |
| | | Nos. 564-569 (6) | 6.75 | 1.85 |

Lenin (1870-1924), Russian communist leader.

Phenecogrammus Interruptus — A80

Designs: Various fish from Guinea.

**1971, Apr. 1**    **Photo.**    *Perf. 13*

| | | | | |
|---|---|---|---|---|
| 570 | A80 | 5fr gold & multi | .20 | .20 |
| 571 | A80 | 10fr gold & multi | .25 | .20 |
| 572 | A80 | 15fr gold & multi | .30 | .20 |
| 573 | A80 | 20fr gold & multi | .30 | .20 |
| 574 | A80 | 25fr gold & multi | .45 | .20 |
| 575 | A80 | 30fr gold & multi | .65 | .20 |
| 576 | A80 | 40fr gold & multi | .85 | .20 |
| 577 | A80 | 45fr gold & multi | 1.00 | .20 |
| 578 | A80 | 50fr gold & multi | 1.40 | .25 |
| 579 | A80 | 75fr gold & multi | 2.40 | .55 |
| 580 | A80 | 100fr gold & multi | 3.25 | .65 |
| 581 | A80 | 200fr gold & multi | 7.00 | 1.10 |
| | | Nos. 570-581 (12) | 18.05 | 4.15 |

Violet-crested Touraco — A81

Birds: 20fr, European golden oriole. 30fr, Blue-headed coucal. 40fr, Northern shrike. 75fr, Vulturine guinea fowl. 100fr, Southern ground hornbill.

**1971, June 18**    **Photo.**    *Perf. 13*
**Size: 34x34mm**

| | | | | |
|---|---|---|---|---|
| 582 | A81 | 5fr gold & multi | .20 | .20 |
| 583 | A81 | 20fr gold & multi | .45 | .20 |
| 584 | A81 | 30fr gold & multi | .70 | .20 |
| 585 | A81 | 40fr gold & multi | .85 | .25 |
| 586 | A81 | 75fr gold & multi | 2.50 | .55 |
| 587 | A81 | 100fr gold & multi | 3.25 | .80 |
| | | Nos. 582-587,C113-C113B (9) | 18.10 | 4.65 |

UNICEF Emblem, Map of Africa — A82

**1971, Dec. 24 Perf. 12x12½**
**Map in Olive**

| 588 | A82 | 25fr orange & blk | .20 | .20 |
|---|---|---|---|---|
| 589 | A82 | 30fr pink & black | .35 | .20 |
| 590 | A82 | 50fr gray grn & blk | .60 | .20 |
| 591 | A82 | 60fr gray bl & blk | .70 | .20 |
| 592 | A82 | 100fr lil rose & blk | 1.10 | .20 |
| | | Nos. 588-592 (5) | 2.95 | 1.00 |

UNICEF, 25th anniv.
For overprints see Nos. 625-629.

Imaginary Prehistoric Space Creature — A83

Various imaginary prehistoric space creatures.

**1972, Apr. 1 Perf. 13½x13**

| 593 | A83 | 5fr multicolored | .20 | .20 |
|---|---|---|---|---|
| 594 | A83 | 20fr multicolored | .20 | .20 |
| 595 | A83 | 30fr multicolored | .45 | .20 |
| 596 | A83 | 40fr multicolored | .50 | .20 |
| 597 | A83 | 100fr multicolored | 1.10 | .35 |
| 598 | A83 | 200fr multicolored | 2.75 | .75 |
| | | Nos. 593-598 (6) | 5.20 | 1.90 |

Black Boy, Men of 4 Races, Emblem — A84

Designs: 20fr, Oriental boy. 30fr, Indian youth. 50fr, Caucasian girl. 100fr, Men of 4 races and Racial Equality emblem.

**1972, May 14 Perf. 13x13½**

| 599 | A84 | 15fr gold & multi | .20 | .20 |
|---|---|---|---|---|
| 600 | A84 | 20fr gold & multi | .20 | .20 |
| 601 | A84 | 30fr gold & multi | .35 | .20 |
| 602 | A84 | 50fr gold & multi | .50 | .20 |
| 603 | A84 | 100fr gold & multi | 1.00 | .30 |
| | | Nos. 599-603,C119 (6) | 3.75 | 2.10 |

Intl. Year Against Racial Discrimination, 1971.

Map of Africa, Syncom Satellite — A85

Designs (Map of Africa and Satellites): 30fr, Relay. 75fr, Early Bird. 80fr, Telstar.

**1972, May 17 Litho. Perf. 13**

| 604 | A85 | 15fr multicolored | .20 | .20 |
|---|---|---|---|---|
| 605 | A85 | 30fr red org & multi | .20 | .20 |
| 606 | A85 | 75fr grn & multi | 1.00 | .20 |
| 607 | A85 | 80fr multicolored | 1.10 | .45 |
| | | Nos. 604-607,C120-C121 (6) | 6.90 | 3.15 |

4th World Telecommunications Day.

Carrier Pigeon, UPAF Emblem — A86

**1972, July 10**

| 608 | A86 | 15fr brt bl & multi | .20 | .20 |
|---|---|---|---|---|
| 609 | A86 | 30fr multicolored | .20 | .20 |
| 610 | A86 | 75fr lil & multi | .75 | .20 |
| 611 | A86 | 80fr multicolored | .90 | .45 |
| | | Nos. 608-611,C122-C123 (6) | 4.95 | 2.85 |

Book Year Emblem, Reading Child — A87

Designs (Book Year Emblem and): 15fr, Book as sailing ship. 40fr, Young woman with flower and book. 50fr, Book as key. 75fr, Man reading and globe. 200fr, Book and laurel.

**1972, Aug. 2 Photo. Perf. 14x13½**

| 612 | A87 | 5fr red & multi | .20 | .20 |
|---|---|---|---|---|
| 613 | A87 | 15fr multicolored | .20 | .20 |
| 614 | A87 | 40fr yel & multi | .45 | .20 |
| 615 | A87 | 50fr blue & multi | .65 | .20 |
| 616 | A87 | 75fr dk red & multi | 1.10 | .45 |
| 617 | A87 | 200fr org & multi | 2.10 | .90 |
| | | Nos. 612-617 (6) | 4.70 | 2.15 |

International Book Year 1972.

Javelin, Olympic Emblems, Arms of Guinea A88

**1972, Aug. 26 Photo. Perf. 13**

| 618 | A88 | 5fr shown | .20 | .20 |
|---|---|---|---|---|
| 619 | A88 | 10fr Pole vault | .20 | .20 |
| 620 | A88 | 25fr Hurdles | .40 | .20 |
| 621 | A88 | 30fr Hammer throw | .60 | .20 |
| 622 | A88 | 40fr Boxing | .75 | .20 |
| 623 | A88 | 50fr Vaulting | .80 | .35 |
| 624 | A88 | 75fr Running | 1.90 | .45 |
| | | Nos. 618-624,C124-C125 (9) | 11.00 | 3.50 |

20th Olympic Games, Munich, 8/26-9/11.

Dimitrov at Leipzig Trial — A89

**1972, Sept. 28 Perf. 13**
**Gold, Dark Green & Black**

| 630 | A89 | 5fr shown | .20 | .20 |
|---|---|---|---|---|
| 631 | A89 | 25fr In Moabit Prison, 1933 | .45 | .20 |
| 632 | A89 | 40fr Writing his memoirs | .50 | .20 |
| 633 | A89 | 100fr Portrait | 1.25 | .30 |
| | | Nos. 630-633 (4) | 2.40 | .90 |

George Dimitrov (1882-1949), Bulgarian Communist party leader and Premier.

Emperor Haile Selassie — A90

Design: 200fr, Emperor facing right.

**1972, Oct. 2**

| 634 | A90 | 40fr blk & multi | .55 | .20 |
|---|---|---|---|---|
| 635 | A90 | 200fr multicolored | 2.75 | .95 |

Syntomeida Epilais — A91

**1973, Mar. 5 Photo. Perf. 14x13½**

Designs: Various insects.

| 636 | A91 | 5fr shown | .30 | .20 |
|---|---|---|---|---|
| 637 | A91 | 15fr Ladybugs | .35 | .20 |
| 638 | A91 | 30fr Green locust | .95 | .20 |
| 639 | A91 | 40fr Honey bee | 1.60 | .35 |
| 640 | A91 | 50fr Photinus pyralis | 2.25 | .50 |
| 641 | A91 | 200fr Ancyluris formosissima | 6.00 | 1.60 |
| | | Nos. 636-641 (6) | 11.45 | 3.05 |

Kwame Nkrumah A92

Various portraits of Kwame Nkrumah.

**1973, May 25 Photo. Perf. 13½**

| 642 | A92 | 1.50s lt grn, gold & brn | .20 | .20 |
|---|---|---|---|---|
| 643 | A92 | 2.50s lt grn, gold & brn | .35 | .20 |
| 644 | A92 | 5s lt grn, gold & brn | .60 | .20 |
| 645 | A92 | 10s gold & dark vio | 1.75 | .45 |
| | | Nos. 642-645 (4) | 2.90 | 1.05 |

OAU, 10th anniversary.

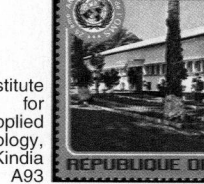

Institute for Applied Biology, Kindia A93

WHO Emblem and: 2.50s, Technicians inoculating egg. 3s, Filling vaccine into ampules. 4s, Sterilization of vaccine. 5s, Assembling of vaccine and vaccination gun. 10s, Inoculation of steer. 20s, Vaccination of woman.

**1973, Nov. 16 Photo. Perf. 13½**
**Size: 40x36mm**

| 646 | A93 | 1s gold & multi | .20 | .20 |
|---|---|---|---|---|
| 647 | A93 | 2.50s gold & multi | .40 | .20 |
| 648 | A93 | 3s gold & multi | .55 | .20 |
| 649 | A93 | 4s gold & multi | .75 | .20 |

**Size: 47½x31mm**

| 650 | A93 | 5s gold & multi | .90 | .20 |
|---|---|---|---|---|
| 651 | A93 | 10s gold & multi | 1.40 | .40 |
| 652 | A93 | 20s gold & multi | 3.25 | 1.00 |
| | | Nos. 646-652 (7) | 7.45 | 2.40 |

WHO, 25th anniversary.

Copernicus, Heliocentric System, Primeval Landscape — A94

Nicolaus Copernicus — A95

Designs (Copernicus and): 2s, Sun rising over volcanic desert, and spacecraft. 4s, Earth, moon and spacecraft. 5s, Moon scape and spacecraft. 10s, Jupiter and spacecraft. 20s, Saturn and heliocentric system.

**1973, Dec. 17 Photo. Perf. 13½**

| 653 | A94 | 50c gold & multi | .20 | .20 |
|---|---|---|---|---|
| 654 | A94 | 2s gold & multi | .30 | .20 |
| 655 | A94 | 4s gold & multi | .40 | .20 |
| 656 | A94 | 5s gold & multi | .60 | .20 |
| 657 | A94 | 10s gold & multi | 1.50 | .40 |
| 658 | A94 | 20s gold & multi | 3.00 | .90 |
| | | Nos. 653-658 (6) | 6.00 | 2.10 |

**Souvenir Sheet**

| 659 | | Sheet of 4 | 20.00 | 20.00 |
|---|---|---|---|---|
| a. | A95 | 20s Single stamp | 3.25 | 3.25 |

Nicolaus Copernicus (1473-1543), Polish astronomer. No. 659 contains center label showing rocket and heliocentric system in gold margin.

Loading Bauxite on Freighter — A96

**1974, Mar. 1 Litho. Perf. 13½**

| 660 | A96 | 4s shown | .75 | .20 |
|---|---|---|---|---|
| 661 | A96 | 6s Freight train | 2.00 | .20 |
| 662 | A96 | 10s Mining | 3.25 | .65 |
| | | Nos. 660-662 (3) | 6.00 | 1.05 |

Bauxite mining, Boke.

Nos. 588-592 Overprinted

**1972, Sept. 28 Photo. Perf. 12x12½**
**Map in Olive**

| 625 | A82 | 25fr org & blk | .50 | .20 |
|---|---|---|---|---|
| 626 | A82 | 30fr pink & blk | .70 | .20 |
| 627 | A82 | 50fr gray grn & blk | 1.10 | .25 |
| 628 | A82 | 60fr gray bl & blk | 1.75 | .25 |
| 629 | A82 | 100fr lil rose & blk | 2.50 | .80 |
| | | Nos. 625-629 (5) | 6.55 | 1.70 |

UN Conference on Human Environment, Stockholm, June 5-16.

Clappertonia Ficifolia — A97

**1974, May 20    Photo.    Perf. 13**
**Size: 25x36mm**

| | | | | |
|---|---|---|---|---|
| 663 | A97 | 50c shown | .20 | .20 |
| 664 | A97 | 1s Rothmannia longiflora | .20 | .20 |
| 665 | A97 | 2s Oncoba spinosa | .20 | .20 |
| 666 | A97 | 3s Venidium fastuosum | .40 | .20 |

**Size: 31x42mm**

| | | | | |
|---|---|---|---|---|
| 667 | A97 | 4s Bombax costatum | .50 | .20 |
| 668 | A97 | 5s Clerodendrum splendens | .95 | .20 |
| 669 | A97 | 7.50s Combretuni grandiflorum | 1.10 | .30 |
| 670 | A97 | 10s Mussaendra erythrophylla | 1.25 | .35 |

**Size: 38x38mm (Diamond)**

| | | | | |
|---|---|---|---|---|
| 671 | A97 | 12s Argemone mexicana | 1.60 | .45 |

Nos. 663-671,C127-C129 (12)    24.15   7.10

Drummers, Pigeon, UPAF and UPU Emblems — A98

Designs (Carrier Pigeon, African Postal Union and UPU Emblems): 6s, Runner with letter stick. 7.50s, Monorail and mail truck. No. 675, Jet and ocean liner. No. 676, Balloon and dugout canoe. 20s, Satellites over earth.

**1974, Oct. 16    Photo.    Perf. 13½x14**

| | | | | |
|---|---|---|---|---|
| 672 | A98 | 5s mag & multi | .60 | .20 |
| 673 | A98 | 6s grn & multi | .80 | .20 |
| 674 | A98 | 7.50s ver & multi | 1.25 | .35 |
| 675 | A98 | 10s Prus bl & multi | 1.75 | .60 |

Nos. 672-675 (4)    4.40   1.35

**Souvenir Sheets**
**Perf. 13½**

| | | | | |
|---|---|---|---|---|
| 676 | A98 | 10s ocher & multi | 6.00 | 6.00 |
| 677 | | Sheet of 4, multi | 12.00 | 12.00 |
| a. | | 20s Single stamp | 1.60 | 1.60 |

Centenary of Universal Postal Union. No. 676 contains one 70x60mm stamp.

Rope Bridge — A99

Designs (Pioneers): 2s, Field observation. 4s, Communication. 5s, Cooking in camp. 7.50s, Salute. 10s, Basketball.

**1974, Nov. 22    Photo.    Perf. 14x13½**

| | | | | |
|---|---|---|---|---|
| 678 | A99 | 50c multicolored | .20 | .20 |
| 679 | A99 | 2s multicolored | .35 | .20 |
| 680 | A99 | 4s multicolored | .45 | .20 |
| 681 | A99 | 5s multicolored | .75 | .20 |
| 682 | A99 | 7.50s multicolored | 1.10 | .20 |
| 683 | A99 | 10s multicolored | 1.90 | .45 |
| a. | | Souv. sheet of 2, #682-683 | 4.00 | 4.00 |

Nos. 678-683 (6)    4.75   1.45

National Pioneer Movement.

Souvenir Sheet

Fruit — A100

**1974, Nov. 22    Photo.    Perf. 13x14**

| | | | | |
|---|---|---|---|---|
| 684 | A100 | Sheet of 5 | 7.00 | 7.00 |
| a. | | 4s Limes | .70 | .70 |
| b. | | 4s Oranges | .70 | .55 |
| c. | | 5s Bananas | 1.00 | 1.00 |
| d. | | 5s Mangos | 1.00 | 1.00 |
| e. | | 12s Pineapple | 2.10 | 2.10 |

Chimpanzee — A101

**1975, May 14    Photo.    Perf. 13½**

| | | | | |
|---|---|---|---|---|
| 685 | A101 | 1s shown | .45 | .20 |
| 686 | A101 | 2s Impala | .65 | .20 |
| 687 | A101 | 3s Wart hog | .75 | .20 |
| 688 | A101 | 4s Kobus defassa | .75 | .20 |
| a. | | Souv. sheet of 4, #685-688 | 9.00 | 9.00 |
| 689 | A101 | 5s Leopard | 1.25 | .25 |
| 690 | A101 | 6s Greater kudu | 1.25 | .25 |
| 691 | A101 | 6.50s Zebra | 1.50 | .25 |
| 692 | A101 | 7.50s Cape buffalo | 1.90 | .25 |
| a. | | Souv. sheet of 4, #689-692 | 4.00 | 9.00 |
| 693 | A101 | 8s Hippopotamus | 3.00 | .75 |
| 694 | A101 | 10s Lion | 3.00 | .75 |
| 695 | A101 | 12s Black rhinoceros | 3.75 | .90 |
| 696 | A101 | 15s Elephant | 5.25 | 1.25 |
| a. | | Souv. sheet of 4, #693-696 | 26.50 | 26.50 |

Nos. 685-696 (12)    23.50   5.35

Sheets exist perf. and imperf. Stamps in Nos. 692a, 696a are inscribed "Poste Aerienne."

Lions, Pipe Line and ADB Emblem A102

Designs (African Development Bank Emblem, Pipe Line and): 7s, Elephants. 10s, Male lions. 20s, Elephant and calf.

**1975, June 16    Photo.    Perf. 13½**

| | | | | |
|---|---|---|---|---|
| 697 | A102 | 5s gold & multi | .90 | .20 |
| 698 | A102 | 7s gold & multi | 1.25 | .20 |
| 699 | A102 | 10s gold & multi | 1.60 | .35 |
| 700 | A102 | 20s gold & multi | 3.25 | .70 |

Nos. 697-700 (4)    7.00   1.45

African Development Bank, 10th anniv.

Women Musicians, IWY Emblem A103

IWY Emblem and: 7s, Women banjo & guitar players. 9s, Woman railroad shunter & train. 15s, Woman physician examining infant. 20s, Male & female symbols.

**1976, Apr. 12    Photo.    Perf. 13½**

| | | | | |
|---|---|---|---|---|
| 701 | A103 | 5s multicolored | .60 | .20 |
| 702 | A103 | 7s multicolored | .90 | .20 |
| 703 | A103 | 9s blue & multi | 1.50 | .45 |
| 704 | A103 | 15s multicolored | 2.25 | .75 |
| a. | | Souvenir sheet | 3.00 | 3.00 |
| 705 | A103 | 20s vio bl & multi | 2.75 | 1.00 |
| a. | | Souvenir sheet of 4 | 13.00 | 13.00 |

Nos. 701-705 (5)    8.00   2.60

International Women's Year 1975. No. 704a contains one stamp similar to No. 704 with gold frame. No. 705a contains 4 stamps similar to No. 705 with gold frame.

Woman Gymnast A104

Montreal Olympic Games Emblem and: 4s, Long jump. 5s, Hammer throw. 6s, Discus. 6.50s, Hurdles. 7s, Javelin. 8s, Running. 8.50s, Bicycling. 10s, High jump. 15s, Shot put. 20s, Pole vault. #717, Soccer. #718, Swimming.

**1976, May 17    Photo.    Perf. 13½**
**Size: 38x38mm**

| | | | | |
|---|---|---|---|---|
| 706 | A104 | 3s multicolored | .40 | .20 |
| 707 | A104 | 4s grn & multi | .60 | .20 |
| 708 | A104 | 5s yel & multi | .60 | .20 |
| 709 | A104 | 6s multicolored | .70 | .20 |
| 710 | A104 | 6.50s plum & multi | .70 | .20 |
| 711 | A104 | 7s blue & multi | .95 | .30 |
| 712 | A104 | 8s ultra & multi | .95 | .30 |
| 713 | A104 | 8.50s org & multi | 1.50 | .35 |
| 714 | A104 | 10s multicolored | 1.60 | .40 |
| 715 | A104 | 15s multicolored | 2.50 | .75 |
| 716 | A104 | 20s multicolored | 3.25 | .95 |
| 717 | A104 | 25s grn & multi | 3.75 | 1.00 |

Nos. 706-717 (12)    17.50   5.05

**Souvenir Sheet**

| | | | | |
|---|---|---|---|---|
| 718 | A104 | 25s multicolored | 5.00 | 5.00 |

21st Olympic Games, Montreal, Canada, July 17-Aug. 1. No. 718 contains one 32x32mm stamp. See No. C130.

A. G. Bell, Telephone, 1900 — A105

7s, Wall telephone, 1910. 12s, Syncom telecommunications satellite. #722, Telstar satellite. #723, Telephone switchboard operator, 1914.

**1976, Nov. 15    Photo.    Perf. 13**

| | | | | |
|---|---|---|---|---|
| 719 | A105 | 5s multicolored | .65 | .20 |
| 720 | A105 | 7s multicolored | 1.00 | .20 |
| 721 | A105 | 12s multicolored | 1.60 | .45 |
| 722 | A105 | 15s multicolored | 2.25 | .60 |
| a. | | Souvenir sheet of 4, #719-722 | 7.00 | 7.00 |

Nos. 719-722 (4)    5.50   1.45

**Souvenir Sheet**

| | | | | |
|---|---|---|---|---|
| 723 | A105 | 15s multicolored | 2.50 | 2.50 |

Centenary of first telephone call by Alexander Graham Bell, Mar. 10, 1876.

Collybia Fusipes — A106

Mushrooms: 7s, Lycoperdon perlatum. 9s, Boletus edulis. 9.50s, Lactarius deliciosus. 11.50s, Agaricus campestris.

**1977, Feb. 6    Photo.    Perf. 13**
**Size: 48x26mm**

| | | | | |
|---|---|---|---|---|
| 724 | A106 | 5s multicolored | 1.90 | .25 |
| 725 | A106 | 7s multicolored | 3.00 | .25 |
| 726 | A106 | 9s multicolored | 3.50 | .55 |
| 727 | A106 | 9.50s multicolored | 3.50 | .65 |
| a. | | Souvenir sheet of 2, #724, 726 | 7.50 | 7.50 |

**Size: 48x31mm**

| | | | | |
|---|---|---|---|---|
| 728 | A106 | 11.50s multicolored | 6.25 | 1.10 |

Nos. 724-728,C131-C133 (8)    37.15   6.50

Hexaplex Hoplites — A107

Sea Shells: 2s, Perrona lineata. 4s, Marginella pseudofaba. 5s, Tympanotonos radula. 7s, Marginella strigata. 8s, Harpa doris. 10s, Demoulia pinguis. 20s, Bursa scrobiculator. 25s, Marginella adansoni.

**1977, Apr. 25    Photo.    Perf. 13**
**Size: 50x25mm**

| | | | | |
|---|---|---|---|---|
| 729 | A107 | 1s gold & multi | .25 | .20 |
| 730 | A107 | 2s gold & multi | .40 | .20 |
| 731 | A107 | 4s gold & multi | 1.00 | .30 |
| 732 | A107 | 5s gold & multi | 1.50 | .35 |
| 733 | A107 | 7s gold & multi | 2.10 | .40 |
| 734 | A107 | 8s gold & multi | 2.50 | .60 |

**Size: 50x30mm**

| | | | | |
|---|---|---|---|---|
| 735 | A107 | 10s gold & multi | 3.25 | .90 |
| 736 | A107 | 20s gold & multi | 6.50 | 1.25 |
| 737 | A107 | 25s gold & multi | 8.50 | 1.75 |

Nos. 729-737 (9)    26.00   5.95

Farmers and Ox Plow A108

Designs: 5s, Pres. Touré addressing rally. 20s, Soldier driving farm tractor. 25s, Pres. Touré addressing UN General Assembly. 30s, 40s, Pres. Sékou Touré, vert.

**1977, May 14    Perf. 13½x13, 13x13½**

| | | | | |
|---|---|---|---|---|
| 738 | A108 | 5s gold & multi | .70 | .20 |
| 739 | A108 | 10s gold & multi | 1.10 | .40 |
| 740 | A108 | 20s gold & multi | 2.75 | .90 |
| 741 | A108 | 25s gold & multi | 3.25 | 1.25 |
| a. | | Souvenir sheet of 4, #738-741 | 10.50 | 10.50 |
| 742 | A108 | 30s gold & dk brn | 4.00 | 1.25 |
| 743 | A108 | 40s gold & sl grn | 4.75 | 1.50 |
| a. | | Souvenir sheet of 2, #742-743 | 13.00 | 13.00 |

Nos. 738-743 (6)    16.55   5.50

Democratic Party of Guinea, 30th anniv.

Nile Monitor — A109

Reptiles and Snakes: 4s, Frogs. 5s, Lizard (uromastix). 6s, Sand skink. 6.50s, Agama. 7s, Black-lipped spitting cobra. 8.50s, Ball python. 20s, Toads.

**1977, Oct. 10  Photo.  Perf. 13½**
Size: 46x20mm

| | | | | |
|---|---|---|---|---|
| 744 | A109 | 3s multi | .65 | .20 |
| 745 | A109 | 4s multi | .95 | .20 |
| 746 | A109 | 5s multi | .95 | .20 |

Size: 46x30mm

| | | | | |
|---|---|---|---|---|
| 747 | A109 | 6s multi | 1.50 | .25 |
| 748 | A109 | 6.50s multi | 1.90 | .25 |
| 749 | A109 | 7s multi | 2.40 | .55 |
| 750 | A109 | 15s multi | 2.75 | .65 |
| 751 | A109 | 20s multi | 6.50 | 1.40 |
| | Nos. 744-751,C134-C136 (11) | | 35.35 | 7.20 |

Eland — A110

Endangered Animals: 2s, Chimpanzee. 2.50s, Pygmy elephant. 3s, Lion. 4s, Palm squirrel. 5s, Hippopotamus. Each animal shown male, female and young.

**1977, Dec. 12  Photo.  Perf. 14x13½**

| | | | | |
|---|---|---|---|---|
| 752 | A110 | Strip of 3 | 1.10 | .20 |
| a.-c. | | 1s any single | | .20 |
| 753 | A110 | Strip of 3 | 1.75 | .25 |
| a.-c. | | 2s any single | | .40 |
| 754 | A110 | Strip of 3 | 2.25 | .30 |
| a.-c. | | 2.50s any single | | .60 |
| 755 | A110 | Strip of 3 | 2.75 | .40 |
| a.-c. | | 3s any single | | .70 |
| 756 | A110 | Strip of 3 | 3.50 | .55 |
| a.-c. | | 4s any single | | 1.10 |
| 757 | A110 | Strip of 3 | 4.50 | .65 |
| a.-c. | | 5s any single | | 1.40 |
| | Nos. 752-757,C137-C142 (12) | | 58.10 | 22.35 |

Russian October Revolution, 60th Anniv. — A111

Designs: 2.50s, First Lenin debate, Moscow. 5s, Lenin speaking, 1917. 7.50s, Lenin and people. 8s, Lenin in first parade on Red Square.

**1978, Feb. 27  Photo.  Perf. 14**

| | | | | |
|---|---|---|---|---|
| 758 | A111 | 2.50s gold & multi | .60 | .20 |
| 759 | A111 | 5s gold & multi | 1.00 | .20 |
| 760 | A111 | 7.50s gold & multi | 1.50 | .30 |
| 761 | A111 | 8s gold & multi | 1.60 | .35 |
| | Nos. 758-761,C143-C144 (6) | | 15.45 | 3.95 |

Pres. Giscard d'Estaing at Microphones — A112

Pres. Valery Giscard d'Estaing of France and Pres. Sekou Toure of Guinea: 5s, 10s, In conference. 6.50s, Signing agreement. 7s, Attending official meeting. 8.50s, With their wives. 20s, Drinking a toast.

**1979, Sept. 14  Photo.  Perf. 13**

| | | | | |
|---|---|---|---|---|
| 762 | A112 | 3s lt brn & brn | .85 | .20 |
| 763 | A112 | 5s green & brn | 1.50 | .20 |
| 764 | A112 | 6.50s red lil & brn | 1.75 | .20 |
| 765 | A112 | 7s ultra & brn | 1.90 | .30 |
| 766 | A112 | 8.50s dk red & brn | 2.40 | .55 |
| 767 | A112 | 10s vio & brown | 2.75 | .80 |
| 768 | A112 | 20s yel grn & brn | 6.00 | 1.10 |
| | Nos. 762-768,C145 (8) | | 24.15 | 5.40 |

Visit of Pres. Valery Giscard d'Estaing to Guinea.

Twenty Thousand Leagues Under the Sea — A113

Jules Verne Stories: 3s, Children of Capt. Grant. 5s, Mysterious Island. 7s, A Captain at Fifteen. 10s, The Borsac Mission.

**1979, Nov. 8  Litho.  Perf. 12x12½**

| | | | | |
|---|---|---|---|---|
| 769 | A113 | 1s multicolored | .40 | .20 |
| 770 | A113 | 3s multicolored | .45 | .20 |
| 771 | A113 | 5s multicolored | .85 | .20 |
| 772 | A113 | 7s multicolored | 1.25 | .30 |
| 773 | A113 | 10s multicolored | 1.75 | .40 |
| | Nos. 769-773,C146-C147 (7) | | 11.70 | 3.80 |

Jules Verne (1828-1905), French science fiction writer.

"Aerial Steam Carriage," 1842 — A114

Aviation Retrospect: 5s, Wright's Flyer 1 1903. 6.50s, Caudron, 1934. 7s, Spirit of St. Louis, 1927. 8.50s, Bristol Beaufighter, 1940. 10s, Bleriot XI, 1909. #780, Concorde. #781, Boeing 727, 1963.

**1979, Nov. 22  Photo.  Perf. 14**

| | | | | |
|---|---|---|---|---|
| 774 | A114 | 3s multi | .50 | .20 |
| 775 | A114 | 5s multi | .90 | .20 |
| 776 | A114 | 6.50s multi | 1.10 | .35 |
| 777 | A114 | 7s multi | 1.25 | .35 |
| 778 | A114 | 8.50s multi | 1.50 | .45 |
| 779 | A114 | 10s multi | 1.75 | .45 |
| 780 | A114 | 20s multi | 3.50 | .95 |
| 781 | A114 | 20s multi | 3.50 | .95 |
| | Nos. 774-781 (8) | | 14.00 | 3.90 |

Hafia Soccer Team — A115

Designs: 2s, Players and Sekou Touré cup, vert. 5s, Pres. Touré presenting cup. 7s, Pres. Touré and player holding cup, vert. 8s, Sekou Touré cup, vert. 10s, Team captains and referees, vert. 20s, The winning goal.

**Perf. 12½x12, 12x12½**
**1979, Dec. 18  Litho.**

| | | | | |
|---|---|---|---|---|
| 782 | A115 | 1s multicolored | .20 | .20 |
| 783 | A115 | 2s multicolored | .20 | .20 |
| 784 | A115 | 5s multicolored | .80 | .20 |
| 785 | A115 | 7s multicolored | 1.10 | .35 |
| 786 | A115 | 8s multicolored | 1.25 | .40 |
| 787 | A115 | 10s multicolored | 1.75 | .45 |
| 788 | A115 | 20s multicolored | 3.25 | .75 |
| | Nos. 782-788 (7) | | 8.55 | 2.55 |

Hafia Soccer Team, African triple champions, 1977.

Train, IYC Emblem A116

IYC Emblem and: 2s, Children dancing around tree, vert. 4s, "1979" and leaves, vert. 7s, Village. 10s, Boy climbing tree. 25s, Boys of different races, flowers, sun.

**1980, Jan. 14  Perf. 13x13½, 13½x13**

| | | | | |
|---|---|---|---|---|
| 789 | A116 | 2s multicolored | .30 | .20 |
| 790 | A116 | 4s multicolored | .65 | .20 |
| 791 | A116 | 5s multicolored | .80 | .20 |
| 792 | A116 | 7s multicolored | 1.00 | .30 |
| 793 | A116 | 10s multicolored | 1.75 | .40 |
| 794 | A116 | 25s multicolored | 4.00 | 1.10 |
| | Nos. 789-794 (6) | | 8.50 | 2.40 |

International Year of the Child (1979).

Butterflyfish — A117

**1980, Apr. 1  Perf. 12½x12, 12x12½**

| | | | | |
|---|---|---|---|---|
| 795 | A117 | 1s shown | .20 | .20 |
| 796 | A117 | 2s Porgy | .65 | .20 |
| 797 | A117 | 3s Zeus conchifer, vert. | .70 | .20 |
| 798 | A117 | 4s Grouper | .90 | .20 |
| 799 | A117 | 5s Sea horse, vert. | 1.25 | .20 |
| 800 | A117 | 6s Hatchet fish | 1.50 | .30 |
| 801 | A117 | 7s Pisodonophis semicinctus | 1.60 | .35 |
| 802 | A117 | 8s Flying gurnard, vert. | 1.90 | .45 |
| 803 | A117 | 9s Squirrelfish | 2.25 | .60 |
| 804 | A117 | 10s Psettus sebae, vert. | 2.50 | .60 |
| 805 | A117 | 12s Abudefuf hoeffleri | 3.25 | .70 |
| 806 | A117 | 15s Triggerfish | 4.50 | .90 |
| | Nos. 795-806 (12) | | 21.20 | 4.90 |

Apollo 11 Take-Off — A118

**1980, July 20  Photo.  Perf. 14**

| | | | | |
|---|---|---|---|---|
| 807 | A118 | 1s shown | .20 | .20 |
| 808 | A118 | 2s Earth from moon | .20 | .20 |
| 809 | A118 | 4s Armstrong leaving module | .75 | .20 |
| 810 | A118 | 5s Armstrong on moon | .90 | .20 |
| 811 | A118 | 7s Collecting samples | 1.25 | .35 |
| 812 | A118 | 8s Re-entry | 1.40 | .45 |
| 813 | A118 | 12s Recovery | 2.25 | .75 |
| 814 | A118 | 20s Crew | 3.50 | 1.10 |
| | Nos. 807-814 (8) | | 10.45 | 3.45 |

Apollo 11 moon landing, 10th anniv. (1979).

Intl. Palestinian Solidarity Day — A119

**1981, Nov. 21  Photo.  Perf. 13½**

| | | | | |
|---|---|---|---|---|
| 815 | A119 | 8s multicolored | 1.50 | .45 |
| 816 | A119 | 11s multicolored | 2.25 | .60 |

Soccer — A120

**1982  Litho.  Perf. 12½x12**

| | | | | |
|---|---|---|---|---|
| 817 | A120 | 1s shown | .20 | .20 |
| 818 | A120 | 2s Basketball | .20 | .20 |
| 819 | A120 | 3s Diving | .50 | .20 |
| 820 | A120 | 4s Gymnast | .65 | .20 |
| 821 | A120 | 5s Boxing | .90 | .20 |
| 822 | A120 | 6s Pole vault | 1.10 | .30 |
| 823 | A120 | 7s Running | 1.25 | .35 |
| 824 | A120 | 8s Long jump | 1.50 | .40 |
| | Nos. 817-824,C148-C152 (13) | | 20.80 | 6.00 |

22nd Summer Olympic Games, Moscow, July 19-Aug. 3, 1980.

5th Anniv. of West African Economic Community — A121

**1982, May 14  Perf. 13½**

| | | | | |
|---|---|---|---|---|
| 825 | A121 | 6s multicolored | 1.10 | .25 |
| 826 | A121 | 7s multicolored | 1.50 | .35 |
| 827 | A121 | 9s multicolored | 2.00 | .55 |
| | Nos. 825-827 (3) | | 4.60 | 1.15 |

Kemal Ataturk Birth Centenary A122

**1982, July 19  Photo.  Perf. 13½**

| | | | | |
|---|---|---|---|---|
| 828 | A122 | 7s multi | 1.25 | .35 |
| 829 | A122 | 10s multi, diff. | 2.00 | .45 |
| 830 | A122 | 25s multi, horiz. | 4.75 | 1.10 |
| | Nos. 828-830,C153 (4) | | 13.00 | 3.15 |

1982 World Cup A123

Designs: Various soccer players.

**1982, Aug. 23**

| | | | | |
|---|---|---|---|---|
| 831 | A123 | 6s multicolored | 1.25 | .30 |
| 832 | A123 | 8s multicolored | 1.75 | .40 |
| 833 | A123 | 9s multicolored | 1.90 | .45 |
| 834 | A123 | 10s multicolored | 2.10 | .45 |
| | Nos. 831-834,C154-C156 (7) | | 21.60 | 7.40 |

Soccer Type of 1982
#831-834 Overprinted in Red and Green:
"CHAMPION ITALIE-11 JUILLET 1982" and Italian Flag

**1982, Aug. 23  Photo.  Perf. 13½**

| | | | | |
|---|---|---|---|---|
| 835 | A123 | 6s multicolored | 1.25 | .30 |
| 836 | A123 | 8s multicolored | 1.75 | .40 |
| 837 | A123 | 9s multicolored | 1.90 | .45 |
| 838 | A123 | 10s multicolored | 2.10 | .45 |
| | Nos. 835-838,C157-C159 (7) | | 20.40 | 6.10 |

Italy's victory in 1982 World Cup.

23rd
Olympic
Games, Los
Angeles,
July 28-Aug.
12, 1984
A124

| 1983, July 1 | | Litho. | *Perf. 13½* | |
|---|---|---|---|---|
| 839 | A124 | 5s Wrestling | 1.50 | .20 |
| 840 | A124 | 7s Weightlifting | 1.90 | .30 |
| 841 | A124 | 10s Gymnastics | 2.75 | .55 |
| 842 | A124 | 15s Discus | 4.25 | .95 |
| 843 | A124 | 20s Kayak | 6.00 | 1.40 |
| 844 | A124 | 25s Equestrian | 6.75 | 1.60 |
| | | *Nos. 839-844 (6)* | 23.15 | 5.00 |

**Litho. & Embossed**
**Size: 39x58mm**

| 844A | A124 | 100s Running | 45.00 | 37.50 |
|---|---|---|---|---|

**Souvenir Sheets**
**Litho.**

| 845 | A124 | 30s Running | 5.00 | 1.60 |
|---|---|---|---|---|

**Litho. & Embossed**

| 845A | A124 | 100s Show jumping | 15.00 | 12.50 |
|---|---|---|---|---|

Nos. 844A, 845A are airmail. No. 845A contains one 58x39mm stamp.

First Manned
Balloon Flight,
200th
Anniv. — A125

Designs: 5s, Marquis D'Arlandes, Pilatre de Rozier. 7s, Marie Antoinette Balloon, Rozier. 10s, Dirigible, Dupuy De Lome, horiz. 15s, Dirigible, Major A. Perseval, horiz.

| 1983, Aug. 1 | | Litho. | *Perf. 13½* | |
|---|---|---|---|---|
| 846 | A125 | 5s multicolored | .80 | .20 |
| 847 | A125 | 7s multicolored | 1.10 | .30 |
| 848 | A125 | 10s multicolored | 1.50 | .55 |
| 849 | A125 | 15s multicolored | 2.40 | .65 |
| | | *Nos. 846-849,C160-C161 (6)* | 12.80 | 4.70 |

Intl. Year of the Handicapped — A126

| 1983, Aug. 24 | | | Litho. | |
|---|---|---|---|---|
| 850 | A126 | 10s multicolored | 3.75 | .80 |
| 851 | A126 | 20s multicolored | 7.75 | 1.40 |

Dr. Robert
Koch (1843-
1910), TB
Bacillus
A127

Various phases of research.

| 1983, Aug. 24 | | | Litho. | |
|---|---|---|---|---|
| 852 | A127 | 6s multicolored | 1.75 | .25 |
| 853 | A127 | 10s multicolored | 2.75 | .40 |
| 854 | A127 | 11s multicolored | 3.00 | .40 |
| 855 | A127 | 12s multicolored | 3.50 | .80 |
| 856 | A127 | 15s multicolored | 4.50 | .95 |

| 857 | A127 | 20s multicolored | 6.00 | 1.10 |
|---|---|---|---|---|
| 858 | A127 | 25s multicolored | 6.75 | 1.40 |
| | | *Nos. 852-858 (7)* | 28.25 | 5.30 |

Mosque,
Conakry
A128

| 1983, Oct. 2 | | Litho. | *Perf. 13½* | |
|---|---|---|---|---|
| 859 | A128 | 1s multicolored | .40 | .20 |
| 860 | A128 | 2s multicolored | .55 | .20 |
| 861 | A128 | 5s multicolored | .95 | .20 |
| 862 | A128 | 10s multicolored | 1.90 | .55 |
| | | *Nos. 859-862 (4)* | 3.80 | 1.15 |

**Souvenir Sheet**

| 863 | A128 | 25s multicolored | 4.00 | 1.90 |
|---|---|---|---|---|

Natl. independence, 25th anniv. No. 863 airmail.

Mano
River
Union,
10th
Anniv.
A129

2s, Development program graduates. 7s, Emblem. 8s, Pres. Toure of Guinea, Stevens of Sierra Leone, Doe of Liberia. 10s, 20s, Signing treaty.

| 1983, Oct. 3 | | | | |
|---|---|---|---|---|
| 864 | A129 | 2s multicolored | .40 | .20 |
| 865 | A129 | 7s multicolored | .85 | .20 |
| 866 | A129 | 8s multicolored | 1.25 | .30 |
| 867 | A129 | 10s multicolored | 1.50 | .35 |
| | | *Nos. 864-867 (4)* | 4.00 | 1.05 |

**Souvenir Sheet**

| 868 | A129 | 20s multicolored | 3.25 | 1.75 |
|---|---|---|---|---|

No. 868 airmail.

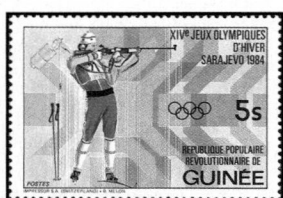

14th Winter Olympics, Sarajevo, Feb.
8-19, 1984 — A130

| 1983, Dec. 5 | | Litho. | *Perf. 13½* | |
|---|---|---|---|---|
| 869 | A130 | 5s Biathlon | .75 | .20 |
| 870 | A130 | 7s Bobsledding | .95 | .30 |
| 871 | A130 | 10s Downhill skiing | 1.40 | .40 |
| 872 | A130 | 15s Speed skating | 2.25 | .65 |
| 873 | A130 | 20s Ski jumping | 3.00 | .85 |
| 874 | A130 | 25s Figure skating | 3.50 | 1.10 |
| | | *Nos. 869-874 (6)* | 11.85 | 3.50 |

**Litho. & Embossed**
**Size: 58x39mm**

| 874A | A130 | 100s Downhill skiing | 40.00 | 32.50 |
|---|---|---|---|---|

**Souvenir Sheets**
**Litho.**

| 875 | A130 | 30s Hockey | 5.00 | 1.60 |
|---|---|---|---|---|

**Litho. & Embossed**

| 875A | A130 | 100s 4-man bobsled | 15.00 | 12.50 |
|---|---|---|---|---|

Nos. 873-875A airmail. No. 875A contains one 58x39mm stamp.

Self-portrait
and Virgin
with Blue
Diadem, by
Raphael
A131

Designs: 7s, Self-portrait and Holy Family, by Rubens. 10s, Self-portrait and Portrait of Saskia, by Rembrandt. 15s, Portrait of Goethe and scene from Young Werther. 20s, Scouting Year. 25s, Paul Harris, Rotary emblem. 30s, J.F. Kennedy, Apollo XI. 100s, Paul Harris, 3 other men in Rotary meeting.

| 1984, Jan 2 | | Litho. | *Perf. 13* | |
|---|---|---|---|---|
| 876 | A131 | 5s multicolored | 1.00 | .35 |
| 877 | A131 | 7s multicolored | 1.75 | .45 |
| 878 | A131 | 10s multicolored | 2.25 | .60 |
| 879 | A131 | 15s multicolored | 2.25 | .75 |
| 880 | A131 | 20s multicolored | 3.00 | .85 |
| 881 | A131 | 25s multicolored | 4.00 | 1.25 |
| | | *Nos. 876-881 (6)* | 14.25 | 4.25 |

**Souvenir Sheets**

| 882 | A131 | 30s multicolored | 6.00 | 2.75 |
|---|---|---|---|---|

**Litho. & Embossed**
*Perf. 13½*

| 882A | A131 | 100s gold & multi | 12.00 | 8.00 |
|---|---|---|---|---|

Nos. 880-882A airmail. No. 882A contains one 51x42mm stamp.
For overprints see Nos. C164-C165.

Transportation — A132

| 1984, May 7 | | Litho. | *Perf. 13½* | |
|---|---|---|---|---|
| 883 | A132 | 5s Congo River steamer | .75 | .20 |
| 884 | A132 | 7s Graf Zeppelin LZ 127 | 1.25 | .20 |
| 885 | A132 | 10s Daimler automobile, 1886 | 1.60 | .30 |
| 886 | A132 | 15s E. African RR Beyer-Garrat | 2.25 | .50 |
| 887 | A132 | 20s Latecoere 28, 1929 | 3.25 | .65 |
| 888 | A132 | 25s Sial Marchetti S.M. 73, 1934 | 4.25 | .85 |
| | | *Nos. 883-888 (6)* | 13.35 | 2.70 |

**Souvenir Sheet**

| 889 | A132 | 30s Series B locomotive | 6.00 | 3.00 |
|---|---|---|---|---|

Nos. 887-889 airmail.

Anniversaries and Events — A133

Famous men: 5s, Abraham Lincoln, log cabin, the White House. 7s, Jean-Henri Dunant, Red Cross at Battle of Solferino. 10s, Gottlieb Daimler, 1892 Motor Carriage. 15s, Louis Bleriot, monoplane. 20s, Paul Harris, Rotary Intl. 25s, Auguste Piccard, bathyscaphe Trieste. 30s, Anatoly Karpov, world chess champion, chessboard and knight. 100s, Paul Harris, Rotary Intl. emblem.

| 1984, Aug. 20 | | Litho. | *Perf. 13½* | |
|---|---|---|---|---|
| 890 | A133 | 5s multicolored | .80 | .20 |
| 891 | A133 | 7s multicolored | 1.10 | .20 |
| 892 | A133 | 10s multicolored | 1.60 | .35 |
| 893 | A133 | 15s multicolored | 2.40 | .50 |
| 894 | A133 | 20s multicolored | 3.00 | .65 |
| 895 | A133 | 25s multicolored | 4.00 | .80 |
| | | *Nos. 890-895 (6)* | 12.90 | 2.70 |

**Litho. & Embossed**
**Size: 60x30mm**

| 895A | A133 | 100s gold & multi | — | — |
|---|---|---|---|---|
| *b.* | | Min. sheet of 1, 91x70mm | 60.00 | |
| *c.* | | Min. sheet of 1, 121x70mm | 16.00 | 12.50 |

**Souvenir Sheet**

| 896 | A133 | 30s multicolored | 6.00 | 2.40 |
|---|---|---|---|---|

Nos. 894-896 are airmail.
For overprints see Nos. C163, C166.

The Holy Family,
by Durer — A134

Painting details: 5s, The Mystic Marriage of St. Catherine and St. Sebastian, by Correggio. 10s, The Veiled Woman, by Raphael. 15s, Portrait of a Young Man, by Durer. 20s, Portrait of Soutine, by Modigliani. 25s, Esterhazy Madonna, by Raphael. 30s, Impannata Madonna, by Raphael.

| 1984, Aug. 23 | | | | |
|---|---|---|---|---|
| 897 | A134 | 5s multicolored | .75 | .20 |
| 898 | A134 | 7s multicolored | 1.25 | .30 |
| 899 | A134 | 10s multicolored | 1.75 | .35 |
| 900 | A134 | 15s multicolored | 2.25 | .75 |
| 901 | A134 | 20s multicolored | 3.50 | 1.10 |
| 902 | A134 | 25s multicolored | 4.50 | 1.25 |
| | | *Nos. 897-902 (6)* | 14.00 | 3.95 |

**Souvenir Sheet**

| 903 | A134 | 30s multicolored | 6.00 | 2.40 |
|---|---|---|---|---|

Nos. 901-903 airmail.

1984 Winter
Olympics,
Sarajevo
A135

Gold medalists: 5s, East German two-man bobsled. 7s, Thomas Wassberg, Sweden, 50-kilometer cross-country. 10s, Gaetan Boucher, Canada, 1000 and 1500-meter speed skating. 15s, Katarina Witt, DDR, singles figure skating. 20s, Bill Johnson, US, men's downhill. 25s, Soviet Union, ice hockey. 30s, Jens Weissflog, DDR, 70-meter ski jump. No. 909A, Phil Mahre, US, slalom skiing. No. 910A, Jayne Torvill & Christopher Dean, Great Britain, ice dancing.

| 1985, Sept. 23 | | Litho. | *Perf. 13½* | |
|---|---|---|---|---|
| 904 | A135 | 5s multicolored | .75 | .20 |
| 905 | A135 | 7s multicolored | .95 | .20 |
| 906 | A135 | 10s multicolored | 1.50 | .30 |
| 907 | A135 | 15s multicolored | 2.10 | .45 |
| 908 | A135 | 20s multicolored | 2.75 | .60 |
| 909 | A135 | 25s multicolored | 3.75 | .75 |
| | | *Nos. 904-909 (6)* | 11.80 | 2.50 |

**Litho. & Embossed**
**Size: 51x36mm**

| 909A | A135 | 100s gold & multi | 60.00 | 30.00 |
|---|---|---|---|---|

**Souvenir Sheets**
**Litho.**

| 910 | A135 | 30s multicolored | 6.00 | 2.10 |
|---|---|---|---|---|

**Litho. & Embossed**

| 910A | A135 | 100s gold & multi | 18.00 | 15.00 |
|---|---|---|---|---|

Nos. 908A-910A are airmail. No. 910A contains one 51x36mm stamp.

1984 Los Angeles Summer
Olympics — A136

Medalists and various satellites: 5s, T. Ruiz and C. Costie, US, synchronized swimming.

7s, West Germany, team dressage. 10s, US, yachting, flying Dutchman class. 15s, Mark Todd, New Zealand, individual 3-day equestrian event. 20s, Daley Thompson, G.B., decathlon. 25s, US, team jumping. 30s, Carl Lewis, US, long jump, 100 and 200-meter run, 4x100 relay.

**1985, Mar. 18**    **Litho.**    *Perf. 13½*

| | | | | |
|---|---|---|---|---|
| 911 | A136 | 5s multicolored | .45 | .20 |
| 912 | A136 | 7s multicolored | .70 | .20 |
| 913 | A136 | 10s multicolored | .90 | .25 |
| 914 | A136 | 15s multicolored | 1.40 | .40 |
| 915 | A136 | 20s multicolored | 1.60 | .45 |
| 916 | A136 | 25s multicolored | 2.40 | .60 |
| | | *Nos. 911-917 (7)* | 13.45 | 4.20 |

**Souvenir Sheet**

| | | | | |
|---|---|---|---|---|
| 917 | A136 | 30s multicolored | 6.00 | 2.10 |

Nos. 915-917 airmail.

Fungi — A137

**1985, Mar. 21**    **Litho.**    *Perf. 13½*

| | | | | |
|---|---|---|---|---|
| 918 | A137 | 5s Rhodophyllus callidermus | .90 | .20 |
| 919 | A137 | 7s Agaricus niger | 1.60 | .20 |
| 920 | A137 | 10s Thermitomyces globulus | 2.25 | .45 |
| 921 | A137 | 15s Amanita robusta | 3.50 | .60 |
| 922 | A137 | 20s Lepiota subradicans | 4.75 | .90 |
| 923 | A137 | 25s Cantharellus rhodophyllus | 6.00 | 1.25 |
| | | *Nos. 918-923 (6)* | 19.00 | 3.60 |

**Souvenir Sheet**

| | | | | |
|---|---|---|---|---|
| 924 | A137 | 30s Phlebopus sylvaticus | 6.75 | 2.50 |

Nos. 922-924 airmail.
For surcharges see Nos. 962-968.

Scientist Herman J. Oberth, and Two-Stage Rocket A138

Space achievements: 10s, Lunik 1, USSR, 1959. 15s, Lunik 2 on the Moon, 1959. 20s, Lunik 3 photographing the Moon, 1959. 30s, US astronauts Armstrong, Aldrin, Collins and Apollo 11, 1969. 35s, Sally Ride, 1st American woman in space, 1983. 50s, Recovering a Palapa B satellite, 1984. No. 930A, Guion S. Bluford, 1st black American astronaut. No. 931A, Viking probe on Mars.

**1985, May 26**    **Litho.**    *Perf. 13½*

| | | | | |
|---|---|---|---|---|
| 925 | A138 | 7s multicolored | 1.10 | .20 |
| 926 | A138 | 10s multicolored | 1.40 | .25 |
| 927 | A138 | 15s multicolored | 2.10 | .40 |
| 928 | A138 | 20s multicolored | 2.40 | .45 |
| 929 | A138 | 30s multicolored | 4.75 | .85 |
| 930 | A138 | 35s multicolored | 5.50 | .90 |
| | | *Nos. 925-930 (6)* | 17.25 | 3.05 |

**Litho. & Embossed**
**Size: 51x36mm**

| | | | | |
|---|---|---|---|---|
| 930A | A138 | 200s gold & multi | 47.50 | — |

**Souvenir Sheet**
**Litho.**

| | | | | |
|---|---|---|---|---|
| 931 | A138 | 50s multicolored | 8.00 | 3.25 |

**Litho. & Embossed**

| | | | | |
|---|---|---|---|---|
| 931A | A138 | 200s gold & multi | 32.50 | — |

Nos. 929-931A are airmail. No. 931A contains one 51x36mm stamp.

Maimonides (1135-1204), Jewish Scholar, Cordoba Jewish Quarter — A139

Anniversaries and events: 10s, Christopher Columbus departing from Palos for New World, 1492. 15s, Frederic Auguste Bartholdi (1834-1904), sculptor, architect, and Statue of Liberty, cent. 20s, Queen Mother, 85th birthday. 30s, Ulf Merbold, German physicist, US space shuttle Columbia. 35s, Wedding of Prince Charles and Lady Diana, 1981. 50s, Charles, Diana, Princes Henry and William. 100s, Queen Mother Elizabeth's 85th birthday.

**1985, Sept. 23**

| | | | | |
|---|---|---|---|---|
| 932 | A139 | 7s multicolored | 1.00 | .20 |
| 933 | A139 | 10s multicolored | 1.40 | .25 |
| 934 | A139 | 15s multicolored | 2.10 | .40 |
| 935 | A139 | 20s multicolored | 2.75 | .55 |
| 936 | A139 | 30s multicolored | 4.00 | .80 |
| 937 | A139 | 35s multicolored | 5.00 | .90 |
| | | *Nos. 932-937 (6)* | 16.25 | 3.10 |

**Litho. & Embossed**
**Size: 42x51mm**

| | | | | |
|---|---|---|---|---|
| 937A | A139 | 100s gold & multi | 16.00 | 12.50 |

**Souvenir Sheet**
**Litho.**

| | | | | |
|---|---|---|---|---|
| 938 | A139 | 50s multicolored | 8.00 | 3.25 |

Nos. 936-938 airmail. No. 938 contains one 51x36mm stamp. Nos. 934 and 937A exist in souvenir sheets of one.

Audubon Birth Bicent. — A140

Illustrations of bird species from Birds of America.

**1985, Sept. 23**    **Litho.**    *Perf. 13½*

| | | | | |
|---|---|---|---|---|
| 939 | A140 | 7s Coccizus erythrophthalmus | .90 | .20 |
| 940 | A140 | 10s Conuropsis carolinensis | 1.40 | .30 |
| 941 | A140 | 15s Anhinga anhinga | 2.40 | .50 |
| 942 | A140 | 20s Buteo lineatus | 3.00 | .70 |
| 943 | A140 | 30s Otus asio | 5.00 | 1.25 |
| 944 | A140 | 35s Toxostoma rufum | 5.25 | 1.50 |
| | | *Nos. 939-944 (6)* | 17.95 | 4.45 |

**Souvenir Sheet**

| | | | | |
|---|---|---|---|---|
| 945 | A140 | 50s Zenaidura macroura | 7.50 | 3.00 |

Nos. 941, 944 vert. Nos. 943-945 are airmail. No. 945 contains one 51x36mm stamp. Nos. 939-944 exist in souvenir sheets of one. Value, set $80.

1986 World Cup Soccer Championships, Mexico — A141

Famous soccer players: 7s, Bebeto, Brazil. 10s, Rinal Dassaev, USSR. 15s, Phil Neal, Great Britain. 20s, Jean Tigana, France. 30s, Fernando Chalana, Portugal. 35s, Michel Platini, France. 50s, Karl Heinz Rummenigge, West Germany.

**1985, Oct. 26**

| | | | | |
|---|---|---|---|---|
| 946 | A141 | 7s multicolored | 1.10 | .20 |
| 947 | A141 | 10s multicolored | 1.50 | .25 |
| 948 | A141 | 15s multicolored | 2.25 | .40 |
| 949 | A141 | 20s multicolored | 3.00 | .60 |
| 950 | A141 | 30s multicolored | 4.25 | .85 |
| 951 | A141 | 35s multicolored | 5.25 | .95 |
| | | *Nos. 946-951 (6)* | 17.35 | 3.25 |

**Souvenir Sheet**

| | | | | |
|---|---|---|---|---|
| 952 | A141 | 50s multicolored | 7.50 | 3.00 |

Nos. 950-952 airmail.

Cats and Dogs A142

**1985, Oct. 26**

| | | | | |
|---|---|---|---|---|
| 953 | A142 | 7s Blue-point Siamese | 1.10 | .20 |
| 954 | A142 | 10s Cocker spaniel | 1.50 | .25 |
| 955 | A142 | 15s Poodles | 2.25 | .40 |
| 956 | A142 | 20s Blue Persian | 3.00 | .60 |
| 957 | A142 | 25s European red-and-white tabby | 3.75 | .70 |
| 958 | A142 | 30s German shepherd | 4.25 | .85 |
| 959 | A142 | 35s Abyssinians | 5.50 | .95 |
| 960 | A142 | 40s Boxer | 6.50 | 1.25 |
| | | *Nos. 953-960 (8)* | 27.85 | 5.20 |

**Souvenir Sheet**

| | | | | |
|---|---|---|---|---|
| 961 | A142 | 50s Pyrenean mountain dog, chartreux cat | 7.50 | 3.00 |

Nos. 958-961 airmail. No. 961 contains one 51x30mm stamp.

**Nos. 918-924 Surcharged with 4 Bars**

**1985, Nov. 15**

| | | | | |
|---|---|---|---|---|
| 962 | A137 | 1s on 5s multi | .80 | .20 |
| 963 | A137 | 2s on 7s multi | .85 | .20 |
| 964 | A137 | 8s on 10s multi | 1.75 | .40 |
| 965 | A137 | 30s on 15s multi | 7.00 | 1.60 |
| 966 | A137 | 35s on 20s multi | 8.50 | 2.25 |
| 967 | A137 | 40s on 25s multi | 10.00 | 2.75 |
| | | *Nos. 962-967 (6)* | 28.90 | 7.40 |

**Souvenir Sheet**

| | | | | |
|---|---|---|---|---|
| 968 | A137 | 50s on 30s multi | 9.50 | 4.00 |

Nos. 966-968 airmail.

Locomotives — A143

Designs: 7s, 8F Class steam, Great Britain. 15s, Bobo 5500 Series III electric, German Fed. Railways. 25s, Pacific A Mazout No. 270, African Railways. 35s, Serie 420 electric train set, Suburban S-Bahn, Germany. 50s, ICE high-speed train, German Fed. Railways.

**1985, Dec. 18**    **Litho.**    *Perf. 13½*

| | | | | |
|---|---|---|---|---|
| 969 | A143 | 7s multicolored | 1.10 | .20 |
| 970 | A143 | 15s multicolored | 2.40 | .70 |
| 971 | A143 | 25s multicolored | 4.50 | .90 |
| 972 | A143 | 35s multicolored | 6.00 | 1.25 |
| | | *Nos. 969-972 (4)* | 14.00 | 3.05 |

**Souvenir Sheet**

| | | | | |
|---|---|---|---|---|
| 973 | A143 | 50s multicolored | 8.00 | 3.25 |

Nos. 972-973 airmail.
For surcharges see Nos. 991-995.

Columbus Discovering America, 1492 — A144

**1985, Dec. 18**

| | | | | |
|---|---|---|---|---|
| 974 | A144 | 10s Pinta | 1.40 | .25 |
| 975 | A144 | 20s Santa Maria | 3.00 | .65 |
| 976 | A144 | 30s Nina | 4.75 | .95 |
| 977 | A144 | 40s Santa Maria, sighting land | 6.75 | 1.25 |
| | | *Nos. 974-977 (4)* | 15.90 | 3.10 |

**Souvenir Sheet**

| | | | | |
|---|---|---|---|---|
| 978 | A144 | 50s Columbus and Nina | 7.50 | 3.00 |

Nos. 976-979 airmail.

Intl. Youth Year — A145

**1986, Jan. 21**

| | | | | |
|---|---|---|---|---|
| 979 | A145 | 10s Chopin | 1.40 | .40 |
| 980 | A145 | 20s Botticelli | 2.75 | .85 |
| 981 | A145 | 25s Picasso | 3.50 | 1.10 |
| 982 | A145 | 35s Rossini | 5.00 | 1.50 |
| | | *Nos. 979-982 (4)* | 12.65 | 3.85 |

**Souvenir Sheet**

| | | | | |
|---|---|---|---|---|
| 983 | A145 | 50s Michelangelo | 7.50 | 3.00 |

Nos. 981, 983 airmail.
For surcharges see Nos. 996-1000.

Halley's Comet — A146

Sightings: 5fr, Bayeux Tapestry (detail), c. 1092, France. 30fr, Arab, astrolabe, 1400. 40fr, Montezuma II, Aztec deity. 50fr, Edmond Halley, trajectory diagram. 300fr, Halley, Sir Isaac Newton. 500fr, Giotto, Soviet and NASA space probes, comet. 600fr, Hally commemorative medal, Giotto probe.

**1986, July 1**    **Litho.**    *Perf. 13½*
**5fr-500fr Surcharged with New**
**Currency in Silver or Black**

| | | | | |
|---|---|---|---|---|
| 984 | A146 | 5fr multi | .20 | .20 |
| 985 | A146 | 30fr multi | .35 | .20 |
| 986 | A146 | 40fr multi | .40 | .20 |
| 987 | A146 | 50fr multi | .50 | .20 |
| 988 | A146 | 300fr multi | 2.75 | 1.00 |
| 989 | A146 | 500fr multi | 4.75 | 1.75 |
| | | *Nos. 984-989 (6)* | 8.95 | 3.55 |

**Souvenir Sheet**

| | | | | |
|---|---|---|---|---|
| 990 | A146 | 600fr multi | 6.50 | 2.50 |

Nos. 988-990 are airmail. Nos. 984-989 not issued without surcharge.

**Nos. 969-973 Surcharged in Black or**
**Black on Silver**

**1986, Aug. 25**    **Litho.**    *Perf. 13½*

| | | | | |
|---|---|---|---|---|
| 991 | A143 | 2fr on 7s multi (B on S) | .55 | .20 |
| 992 | A143 | 25fr on 15s multi | .65 | .20 |
| 993 | A143 | 50fr on 25s multi | 1.00 | .20 |
| 994 | A143 | 90fr on 35s multi | 1.75 | .55 |
| | | *Nos. 991-994 (4)* | 3.95 | 1.15 |

**Souvenir Sheet**

| | | | | |
|---|---|---|---|---|
| 995 | A143 | 500fr on 50s multi | 6.00 | 2.10 |

**Nos. 979-983 Surcharged**

**1986, Aug. 25**

| | | | | |
|---|---|---|---|---|
| 996 | A145 | 5fr on 10s multi | .40 | .20 |
| 997 | A145 | 35fr on 20s multi | .50 | .20 |
| 998 | A145 | 50fr on 25s multi | .75 | .20 |
| 999 | A145 | 90fr on 35s multi | 1.25 | .40 |
| | | *Nos. 996-999 (4)* | 2.90 | 1.00 |

**Souvenir Sheet**

| | | | | |
|---|---|---|---|---|
| 1000 | A145 | 500fr on 50s multi | 6.00 | 2.10 |

Locomotives — A147

Designs: 20fr, Dietrich 640 CV. 100fr, T.13 7906. 300fr, Vapeur 01220. 400fr, ABH Type 3 5020. 600fr, Renault ABH 3 (300 CV).

**1986, Nov. 1**
| | | | | |
|---|---|---|---|---|
| **1001** | A147 | 20fr multi | .35 | .20 |
| **1002** | A147 | 100fr multi | 1.00 | .35 |
| **1003** | A147 | 300fr multi | 3.00 | .95 |
| **1004** | A147 | 400fr multi | 4.25 | 1.25 |
| | *Nos. 1001-1004 (4)* | | 8.60 | 2.75 |

**Souvenir Sheet**
| | | | | |
|---|---|---|---|---|
| **1005** | A147 | 600fr multi | 7.00 | 2.50 |

Nos. 1004-1005 are airmail.

Discovery of America, 500th Anniv. (in 1992) — A148

Designs: 40fr, Columbus at Ft. Navidad construction, Santa Maria, 1492. 70fr, Landing at Hispaniola, 2nd voyage, 1494. 200fr, Aboard ship, 3rd voyage, 1498. 500fr, Trading with Indians. 600fr, At court of Ferdinand and Isabella, 1493.

**1986, Nov. 1**
| | | | | |
|---|---|---|---|---|
| **1006** | A148 | 40fr multi | .50 | .20 |
| **1007** | A148 | 70fr multi | .80 | .20 |
| **1008** | A148 | 200fr multi | 2.25 | .70 |
| **1009** | A148 | 500fr multi | 5.50 | 1.75 |
| | *Nos. 1006-1009 (4)* | | 9.05 | 2.85 |

**Souvenir Sheet**
| | | | | |
|---|---|---|---|---|
| **1010** | A148 | 600fr multi | 7.00 | 2.50 |

Nos. 1009-1010 are airmail.

Anniversaries & Events A149

30fr, Prince Charles and Diana, 5th wedding anniv. 40fr, Alain Prost, San Marino, 1985 Formula 1 Grand Prix world champion. 100fr, Wedding of Prince Andrew and Sarah Ferguson. 300fr, Elvis Presley. 500fr, Michael Jackson. 600fr, M. Dassault (1892-1986), aerospace engineer.

**1986, Nov. 12**
| | | | | |
|---|---|---|---|---|
| **1011** | A149 | 30fr multi | .40 | .20 |
| **1012** | A149 | 40fr multi | .55 | .20 |
| **1013** | A149 | 100fr multi | 1.25 | .40 |
| **1014** | A149 | 300fr multi | 3.50 | 1.25 |
| **1015** | A149 | 500fr multi | 6.00 | 2.40 |
| | *Nos. 1011-1015 (5)* | | 11.70 | 4.45 |

**Souvenir Sheet**
| | | | | |
|---|---|---|---|---|
| **1016** | A149 | 600fr multi | 8.00 | 2.75 |

Nos. 1015-1016 are airmail.

1986 World Cup Soccer Championships — A150

Various players and final scores.

**1986, Nov. 12**
| | | | | |
|---|---|---|---|---|
| **1017** | A150 | 100fr Pfaff | 1.00 | .35 |
| **1018** | A150 | 300fr Platini | 3.00 | .95 |
| **1019** | A150 | 400fr Matthaus | 4.00 | 1.50 |
| **1020** | A150 | 500fr D. Maradona | 5.00 | 2.10 |
| | *Nos. 1017-1020 (4)* | | 13.00 | 4.90 |

**Souvenir Sheet**
| | | | | |
|---|---|---|---|---|
| **1021** | A150 | 600fr Maradona, trophy | 7.00 | 2.50 |

Nos. 1020-1021 are airmail. No. 1021 contains one 51x42mm stamp.
For surcharge see No. 1182A.

1988 Summer Olympics, Seoul — A151

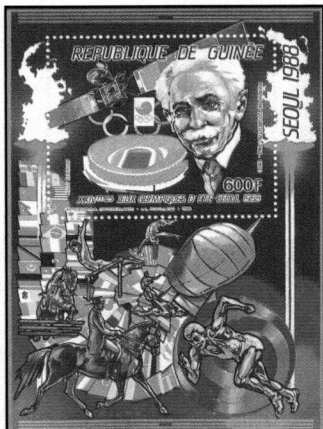

Pierre de Coubertin (1863-1937), Seoul Stadium, Telecommunications Satellite — A151a

| **1987, Jan. 17** | | **Litho.** | **Perf. 13½** | |
|---|---|---|---|---|
| **1022** | A151 | 20fr Judo | .20 | .20 |
| **1023** | A151 | 30fr High jump | .35 | .20 |
| **1024** | A151 | 40fr Team handball | .45 | .20 |
| **1025** | A151 | 100fr Women's gymnastics | 1.00 | .20 |
| **1026** | A151 | 300fr Javelin | 3.00 | .90 |
| **1027** | A151 | 500fr Equestrian | 5.00 | 2.10 |
| | *Nos. 1022-1027 (6)* | | 10.00 | 3.80 |

**Souvenir Sheet**
| | | | | |
|---|---|---|---|---|
| **1028** | A151a | 600fr multi | 7.00 | 2.50 |

Dated 1986. Nos. 1026-1028 are airmail.

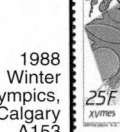

1988 Winter Olympics, Calgary — A152

| **1987, Mar. 23** | | **Litho.** | **Perf. 13½** | |
|---|---|---|---|---|
| **1029** | A152 | 50fr on 40fr Biathlon | .50 | .20 |
| **1030** | A152 | 100fr Cross-country skiing | 1.00 | .35 |
| **1031** | A152 | 400fr Ski jumping | 4.00 | 2.50 |
| **1032** | A152 | 500fr Two-man bobsled | 5.00 | 2.10 |
| | *Nos. 1029-1032 (4)* | | 10.50 | 5.15 |

**Souvenir Sheet**
| | | | | |
|---|---|---|---|---|
| **1033** | A152 | 600fr Woman skater, satellite | 7.00 | 2.50 |

No. 1029 not issued without overprint. Nos. 1031-1033 are airmail.

1988 Winter Olympics, Calgary A153

Telecommunications satellite, athletes and emblem.

**1987, May 1**
| | | | | |
|---|---|---|---|---|
| **1034** | A153 | 25fr Women's slalom | .30 | .20 |
| **1035** | A153 | 50fr Hockey | .50 | .20 |
| **1036** | A153 | 100fr Men's figure skating | .95 | .30 |
| **1037** | A153 | 150fr Men's downhill skiing | 1.50 | .45 |
| **1038** | A153 | 300fr Speed skating | 3.00 | 1.25 |
| **1039** | A153 | 500fr Four-man bobsled | 4.75 | 2.10 |
| | *Nos. 1034-1039 (6)* | | 11.00 | 4.50 |

**Souvenir Sheet**
| | | | | |
|---|---|---|---|---|
| **1040** | A153 | 600fr Ski jumping | 7.00 | 2.50 |

Nos. 1038-1040 are airmail.

Famous Men — A154

Intl. Cardiology Congresses in Chicago, Washington and New York — A155

Designs: 50fr, Lafayette, military leader during American and French revolutions. 100fr, Ettore Bugatti (1881-1947), Italian automobile manufacturer. 200fr, Garri Kasparov, Russian chess champion. 300fr, George Washington. 400fr, Boris Becker, 1987 Wimbledon tennis champion. 500fr, Sir Winston Churchill.

| **1987, Nov. 1** | | **Litho.** | **Perf. 13½** | |
|---|---|---|---|---|
| **1041** | A154 | 50fr multi | .45 | .20 |
| **1042** | A154 | 100fr multi | 1.00 | .40 |
| **1043** | A154 | 200fr multi | 1.90 | .80 |
| **1044** | A154 | 300fr multi | 2.75 | 1.25 |
| **1045** | A154 | 400fr multi | 3.75 | 1.60 |
| **1046** | A154 | 500fr multi | 4.75 | 2.00 |
| | *Nos. 1041-1046 (6)* | | 14.60 | 6.25 |

**Souvenir Sheet**
| | | | | |
|---|---|---|---|---|
| **1047** | A155 | 1500fr multi | 16.00 | 12.50 |

Nos. 1045-1047 are airmail. Stamp in No. 1047 divided into three sections by simulated perforations.
For surcharge see No. 1182B.

Prehistoric Animals — A157

**1987, Nov. 1**
| | | | | |
|---|---|---|---|---|
| **1048** | A156 | 50fr Dimetrodon | .80 | .20 |
| **1049** | A156 | 100fr Iguanodon | 1.60 | .50 |
| **1050** | A156 | 200fr Tylosaurus | 3.25 | 1.00 |
| **1051** | A156 | 300fr shown | 4.75 | 1.50 |
| **1052** | A156 | 400fr Saber-tooth tiger | 6.25 | 2.10 |
| **1053** | A156 | 500fr Stegosaurus | 8.25 | 2.50 |
| | *Nos. 1048-1053 (6)* | | 24.90 | 7.80 |

**Souvenir Sheet**
| | | | | |
|---|---|---|---|---|
| **1054** | A157 | 600fr Triceratops | 8.00 | 2.75 |

Nos. 1052-1054 are airmail.
For surcharge see No. 1182C.

1988 Summer Olympics, Seoul — A158

Male and female tennis players in action.

**1987, Nov. 28**
| | | | | |
|---|---|---|---|---|
| **1055** | A158 | 50fr multi | .45 | .20 |
| **1056** | A158 | 100fr multi, diff. | 1.00 | .35 |
| **1057** | A158 | 150fr multi, diff. | 1.50 | .60 |
| **1058** | A158 | 200fr multi, diff. | 1.90 | .75 |
| **1059** | A158 | 300fr multi, diff. | 3.00 | 1.25 |
| **1060** | A158 | 500fr multi, diff. | 5.00 | 1.90 |
| | *Nos. 1055-1060 (6)* | | 12.85 | 5.05 |

**Souvenir Sheet**
| | | | | |
|---|---|---|---|---|
| **1061** | A158 | 600fr multi | 7.00 | 2.75 |

Reintroduction of tennis as an Olympic event. Nos. 1059-1061 are airmail.

1992 Summer Olympics, Barcelona A159

Athletes participating in events, Barcelona highlights: 50fr, Discus, courtyard of St. Croix and St. Paul Hospital. 100fr, High jump, Pablo Casals playing cello. 150fr, Long jump, Labyrinth of Horta. 170fr, Javelin, lizard from Guell Park. 400fr, Gymnastics, Mercy Church. 500fr, Tennis, Picasso Museum. 600fr, Running, tapestry by Miro.

| **1987, Dec. 28** | | **Litho.** | **Perf. 13½** | |
|---|---|---|---|---|
| **1062** | A159 | 50fr multi | .50 | .20 |
| **1063** | A159 | 100fr multi | 1.00 | .35 |
| **1064** | A159 | 150fr multi | 1.50 | .55 |
| **1065** | A159 | 170fr multi | 1.75 | .60 |
| **1066** | A159 | 400fr multi | 3.75 | 1.40 |
| **1067** | A159 | 500fr multi | 5.00 | 1.75 |
| | *Nos. 1062-1067 (6)* | | 13.50 | 4.85 |

**Souvenir Sheet**
| | | | | |
|---|---|---|---|---|
| **1068** | A159 | 600fr multi | 6.50 | 4.50 |

Nos. 1066-1068 are airmail.
For surcharges see Nos. 1182D-1182E.

Cave Bear — A156

Wildlife
A160

**1987, Dec. 28**
| | | | | |
|---|---|---|---|---|
| 1069 | A160 | 50fr African wild dog pups | 1.75 | .75 |
| 1070 | A160 | 70fr Adult | 2.25 | 1.00 |
| 1071 | A160 | 100fr Adults circling gazelle | 2.75 | 1.25 |
| 1072 | A160 | 170fr Chasing gazelle | 3.25 | 1.50 |
| 1073 | A160 | 400fr Crown cranes | 4.75 | 1.40 |
| 1074 | A160 | 500fr Derby elands | 5.75 | 2.50 |
| | | Nos. 1069-1074 (6) | 20.50 | 8.40 |

**Souvenir Sheet**
| | | | | |
|---|---|---|---|---|
| 1075 | A160 | 600fr Vervet monkeys | 9.00 | 7.00 |

Nos. 1069-1072 picture World Wildlife Fund emblem; Nos. 1073, 1075, picture Scouting trefoil and No. 1074 pictures Rotary Intl. emblem. Nos. 1073-1075 are airmail.
For surcharges see Nos. 1182F-1182G.

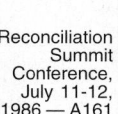

Reconciliation Summit Conference, July 11-12, 1986 — A161

Heads of state and natl. flags: Dr. Samuel Kanyon Doe of Liberia, Colonel Lansana Conte of Guinea and Maj.-Gen. Joseph Saidu Momoh of Sierra Leone.

**1987          Litho.          Perf. 13½**
| | | | | |
|---|---|---|---|---|
| 1076 | A161 | 40fr multi | .40 | .20 |
| 1077 | A161 | 50fr multi | .55 | .20 |
| 1078 | A161 | 75fr multi | .90 | .40 |
| 1079 | A161 | 100fr multi | 1.10 | .55 |
| 1080 | A161 | 150fr multi | 1.75 | .85 |
| | | Nos. 1076-1080 (5) | 4.70 | 2.20 |

Space Exploration — A162

**1988, Apr. 16**
| | | | | |
|---|---|---|---|---|
| 1081 | A162 | 50fr Galaxie-Grasp | .60 | .20 |
| 1082 | A162 | 150fr Energia-Mir | 1.50 | .50 |
| 1083 | A162 | 200fr NASA Space Station | 2.00 | .70 |
| 1084 | A162 | 300fr Ariane 5-E.S.A. | 3.00 | 1.00 |
| 1085 | A162 | 400fr Mars-Rover | 3.75 | 1.40 |
| 1086 | A162 | 450fr Venus-Vega | 5.00 | 1.60 |
| | | Nos. 1081-1086 (6) | 15.85 | 5.40 |

**Souvenir Sheet**
| | | | | |
|---|---|---|---|---|
| 1087 | A162 | 500fr Mars-Phobos | 8.00 | 6.00 |

Nos. 1085-1087 are airmail.

A163

A163a

Boy Scouts watching birds and butterflies.

**1988, July 5          Litho.          Perf. 13½**
| | | | | |
|---|---|---|---|---|
| 1088 | A163 | 50fr Spermophaga ruficapilla | .60 | .20 |
| 1089 | A163 | 100fr Medon nymphalidae | 1.25 | .35 |
| 1090 | A163 | 150fr Euplecte orix | 1.75 | .60 |
| 1091 | A163 | 300fr Nectarinia pulchella | 3.50 | 1.25 |
| 1092 | A163 | 400fr Sophia nymphalidae | 4.50 | 1.50 |
| 1093 | A163 | 450fr Rumia nymphalidae | 5.25 | 1.75 |
| | | Nos. 1088-1093 (6) | 16.85 | 5.65 |

**Souvenir Sheet**
| | | | | |
|---|---|---|---|---|
| 1094 | A163 | 750fr Opis nymphalidae, Psittacula krameri | 9.00 | 6.50 |

**1990, Aug. 3          Litho. & Embossed**
| | | | | |
|---|---|---|---|---|
| 1094A | A163a | 1500fr Druya antimachus | 20.00 | 12.50 |

Nos. 1092-1094A are airmail. No. 1094 contains one 35x50mm stamp.
#1094A exists in souvenir sheet of 1. Value $45.
For surcharge and overprints see Nos. 1182H, 1240-1246.

A164

Famous People: 200fr, Queen Elizabeth II, Prince Philip and crown jewels. 250fr, Fritz von Opel (1899-1971), German automotive industrialist, and 1928 RAK 2 Opel. 300fr, Wolfgang Amadeus Mozart, composer, and Masonic emblem. 400fr, Steffi Graf, tennis champion. 450fr, Buzz Aldrin and Masonic emblem. 500fr, Paul Harris, Rotary Intl. founder, and organization emblem. 750fr, Thomas Jefferson, horiz.

**1988, July 5**
| | | | | |
|---|---|---|---|---|
| 1095 | A164 | 200fr multi | 2.00 | .75 |
| 1096 | A164 | 250fr multi | 2.50 | .95 |
| 1097 | A164 | 300fr multi | 3.25 | 1.25 |
| 1098 | A164 | 400fr multi | 4.25 | 1.50 |
| 1099 | A164 | 450fr multi | 4.75 | 1.60 |
| 1100 | A164 | 500fr multi | 5.25 | 1.90 |
| | | Nos. 1095-1100 (6) | 22.00 | 7.95 |

**Souvenir Sheet**
| | | | | |
|---|---|---|---|---|
| 1101 | A164 | 750fr multi | 8.00 | 2.75 |

40th wedding anniv. of Queen Elizabeth II and Prince Philip (200fr).
Nos. 1099-1101 are airmail. No. 1101 contains one 42x36mm stamp.
For surcharges see Nos. 1182I, 1182Q.

1988 Winter Olympics Gold Medalists
A165

Designs: 50fr, Vreni Schneider, Switzerland, women's giant slalom and slalom. 100fr, Frank-Peter Roetsch, East Germany, 10 and 20-kilometer biathlon. 150fr, Matti Nykaenen,

Finland, 70 and 90-meter ski jumping. 250fr, Marina Kiehl, West Germany, women's downhill. 400fr, Frank Piccard, France, super giant slalom. 450fr, Katarina Witt, East Germany, women's figure skating. 750fr, Pirmin Zurbriggen, Switzerland, men's downhill.

**1988, Oct. 2          Litho.          Perf. 13½**
| | | | | |
|---|---|---|---|---|
| 1102 | A165 | 50fr multi, vert. | .45 | .20 |
| 1103 | A165 | 100fr multi, vert. | .90 | .35 |
| 1104 | A165 | 150fr multi, vert. | 1.50 | .60 |
| 1105 | A165 | 250fr multi, vert. | 2.50 | .95 |
| 1106 | A165 | 400fr multi, vert. | 3.75 | 1.50 |
| 1107 | A165 | 450fr multi, vert. | 4.50 | 1.60 |
| | | Nos. 1102-1107 (6) | 13.60 | 5.20 |

**Souvenir Sheet**
| | | | | |
|---|---|---|---|---|
| 1108 | A165 | 750fr multi | 8.00 | 2.75 |

Nos. 1103, 1107-1108 are airmail.
For surcharge see No. 1182J.

African Postal Union, 25th Anniv.
A165a

**1988          Litho.          Perf. 13½**
| | | | | |
|---|---|---|---|---|
| 1108A | A165a | 50fr multicolored | .45 | .20 |
| 1108B | A165a | 75fr multicolored | .75 | .35 |
| 1108C | A165a | 100fr multicolored | 1.00 | .40 |
| 1108D | A165a | 150fr multicolored | 1.60 | .65 |
| | | Nos. 1108A-1108D (4) | 3.80 | 1.60 |

World Health Day — A165b

**1988, Oct. 2          Litho.          Perf. 13½**
| | | | | |
|---|---|---|---|---|
| 1108E | A165b | 50fr Medical research | .50 | .20 |
| 1108F | A165b | 150fr Immunization | 1.50 | .65 |
| 1108G | A165b | 500fr Dentistry | 4.75 | 2.25 |
| | | Nos. 1108E-1108G (3) | 6.75 | 3.10 |

For surcharge see No. 1182K.

Opening of MT 20 Intl. Communications Center — A165c

**1988, Dec. 8          Litho.          Perf. 13½**
| | | | | |
|---|---|---|---|---|
| 1108H | A165c | 50fr multicolored | .50 | .20 |
| 1108I | A165c | 100fr multicolored | 1.00 | .20 |
| 1108J | A165c | 150fr multicolored | 1.50 | .65 |

Pierre de Coubertin, Founder of Intl. Olympic Committee
A165d

**1988          Litho.          Perf. 13½y**
| | | | | |
|---|---|---|---|---|
| 1108K | A165d | 50fr multi | .45 | .40 |
| 1108L | A165d | 100fr multi | .95 | .80 |
| 1108M | A165d | 150fr multi | 1.50 | 1.40 |
| 1108N | A165d | 500fr multi | 5.00 | 4.00 |
| | | Nos. 1108K-1108N (4) | 7.90 | 6.60 |

For surcharge see No. 1182L.

1992 Summer Olympics, Barcelona — A166

**1989, May 3          Litho.          Perf. 13½**
| | | | | |
|---|---|---|---|---|
| 1109 | A166 | 50fr Diving | .55 | .20 |
| 1110 | A166 | 100fr Running, vert. | 1.25 | .55 |
| 1111 | A166 | 150fr Shooting | 2.10 | .95 |
| 1112 | A166 | 250fr Tennis, vert. | 3.25 | 1.50 |
| 1113 | A166 | 400fr Soccer | 5.25 | 2.40 |
| 1114 | A166 | 500fr Equestrian, vert. | 6.50 | 3.00 |
| | | Nos. 1109-1114 (6) | 18.90 | 8.60 |

**Souvenir Sheet**
| | | | | |
|---|---|---|---|---|
| 1115 | A166 | 750fr Yachting, vert. | 7.50 | 2.50 |

Nos. 1113-1115 are airmail.
For surcharge see No. 1182M.

French Revolution, Bicent. — A167

Personalities of and scenes from the revolution: 250fr, Jean-Sylvain Bailly (1736-1793) leading proceedings in Tennis Court, June 20, 1789. 300fr, Count Mirabeau (1749-1791) at royal session, June 23, 1789. 400fr, Lafayette (1757-1834), federation anniversary celebration, July 18, 1790. 450fr, Jerome Petion de Villeneuve (1756-1794), king's arrest at Varennes-en-Argonne, June 21, 1791. 750fr, Camille Desmoulins (1760-1794), destruction of the Bastille, July 1789.

**1989, July 7          Litho.          Perf. 13½**
| | | | | |
|---|---|---|---|---|
| 1116 | A167 | 250fr multi | 3.00 | .80 |
| 1117 | A167 | 300fr multi | 3.50 | 1.00 |
| 1118 | A167 | 400fr multi | 4.50 | 1.40 |
| 1119 | A167 | 450fr multi | 5.00 | 1.50 |
| | | Nos. 1116-1119 (4) | 16.00 | 4.70 |

**Souvenir Sheet**
| | | | | |
|---|---|---|---|---|
| 1120 | A167 | 750fr multi | 8.00 | 2.50 |

Nos. 1119-1120 airmail.
Nos. 1116-1119 exist in souvenir sheets of 1. Sold for 100fr extra.
For surcharge and overprints see Nos. 1182N, 1216-1220.

Planting
A168

**1989          Litho.          Perf. 13½**
| | | | | |
|---|---|---|---|---|
| 1121 | A168 | 25fr shown | .25 | .20 |
| 1122 | A168 | 50fr Irrigation | .50 | .20 |
| 1123 | A168 | 75fr Milking | .70 | .25 |
| 1124 | A168 | 100fr Fishing | .95 | .35 |
| 1125 | A168 | 150fr Farmers in corn field | 1.40 | .55 |
| 1126 | A168 | 300fr Public well | 3.00 | 1.10 |
| | | Nos. 1121-1126 (6) | 6.80 | 2.65 |

Natl. Campaign for Self-sufficiency in Food Production and 10th anniv. of the Intl. Fund for Agricultural Development (in 1988). Dated 1988.

African Development Bank, 25th Anniv. — A169

**1989, Nov. 4　　Litho.　　Perf. 13½**
1127　A169　300fr multicolored　　3.00　1.10

Mano River Union, 15th Anniv. A170

Design: 300fr, Map of Guinea, Sierra Leone and Liberia, leaders' portraits.

**1989, Nov. 4**
1128　A170　150fr multicolored　　1.50　.65
1129　A170　300fr multicolored　　3.00　1.25

World Cup Soccer, Italy — A171

Various soccer plays and: 200fr, Spire of San Domenico, Naples. 250fr, Piazza San Carlo, Turin. 300fr, Church of San Cataldo. 450fr, Church of San Francesco, Utine. 750fr, Statue of Dante, Florence and World Cup Soccer Trophy.

**1990, Aug. 3　　Litho.　　Perf. 13½**
1130　A171　200fr multicolored　　1.90　.80
1131　A171　250fr multicolored　　2.50　1.00
1132　A171　300fr multicolored　　3.25　1.25
1133　A171　450fr multicolored　　5.00　1.90
　　　Nos. 1130-1133 (4)　　12.65　4.95

**Souvenir Sheet**
1134　A171　750fr multicolored　　7.25　2.75
　　　No. 1133-1134 airmail.
For overprints see Nos. 1221-1225.

Concorde, TGV Atlantic — A172

**1990, Aug. 3**
1135　A172　400fr multicolored　　4.00　1.50
　　No. 1135 exists in a souvenir sheet of 1.
For surcharge see No. 1182O.

Pope John Paul II, Pres. Gorbachev — A173

**1990, Aug. 3**
1136　A173　300fr multicolored　　3.25　1.10
　Summit Meeting, Dec. 2, 1989. No. 1136 exists in a souvenir sheet of 1. Value $10.

1992 Winter Olympics, Albertville — A174

**1990, Aug. 3**
1137　A174　150fr Downhill skiing　　1.40　.65
1138　A174　250fr Cross country skiing　　2.50　1.10
1139　A174　400fr Two-man bobsled　　3.75　1.60
1140　A174　500fr Speedskating　　5.00　2.00
　　　Nos. 1137-1140 (4)　　12.65　5.35

**Souvenir Sheet**
1141　A174　750fr Slalom skiing　　8.00　3.00
　Nos. 1140-1141 airmail. Nos. 1137-1140 exist in souvenir sheets of 1.
　For overprints and surcharge see Nos. 1182P, 1225-1230.

Pres. Bush, Pres. Gorbachev — A175

**1990, Aug. 3　　Litho.　　Perf. 13½**
1142　A175　200fr multicolored　　1.75　.75
　Summit Meeting Dec. 3, 1989. No. 1142 exists in a souvenir sheet of 1.

De Gaulle's Call for French Resistance, 50th Anniv. — A176

**1990**
1143　A176　250fr multi　　2.50　1.00
　No. 1143 exists in a souvenir sheet of 1.

A177

World Cup Soccer Championships, Italy 1990 — A178

No. 1152, Player, Chateau Saint-Ange.

**1991, Apr. 1　　Litho.　　Perf. 13½**
1144　A177　200fr Rudi Voller　　1.75　.80
1145　A177　250fr Uwe Bein　　2.25　1.00
1146　A177　300fr Pierre Littbarski　　2.75　1.25
1147　A177　400fr Jurgen Klinsmann　　4.00　1.90
1148　A177　450fr Lothar Matthaus　　4.00　1.90
1149　A177　500fr Andreas Brehme　　4.50　2.00
　　　Nos. 1144-1149 (6)　　19.25　8.85

**Litho. & Embossed**
1150　A178　1500fr gold & multi　24.00　18.00

**Souvenir Sheets**
**Litho.**
1151　A177　750fr Brehme, diff.　　8.00　3.00

**Litho. & Embossed**
1152　A178　1500fr gold & multi　16.00　12.50
　Nos. 1148-1152 are airmail. Nos. 1144-1150 exist in souvenir sheets of 1.

Christmas A179

Paintings by Raphael: 50fr, Della Tenda Madonna. 100fr, Cowper Madonna. 150fr, Tempi Madonna. 250fr, Niccolini Madonna. 300fr, Orleans Madonna. 500fr, Solly Madonna. 750fr, Madonna of the Fish.

**1991, Apr. 1　　　　　　Litho.**
1153　A179　50fr multi　　.50　.20
1154　A179　100fr multi　　.85　.45
1155　A179　150fr multi　　1.40　.65
1156　A179　250fr multi　　2.25　1.00
1157　A179　300fr multi　　2.75　1.25
1158　A179　500fr multi　　4.50　2.00
　　　Nos. 1153-1158 (6)　　12.25　5.55

**Souvenir Sheet**
1159　A179　750fr multi　　8.00　3.00
　Nos. 1157-1159 are airmail. Nos. 1153-1158 exist in souvenir sheets of 1.

A180

World War II Battles — A181

Designs: No. 1160, Sinking of the Bismarck, May 27, 1941, Adm. Raeder and Adm. Tovey. No. 1161, Battle of Midway, June 3, 1942, Adm. Yamamoto and Adm. Nimitz. 200fr, Guadalcanal, Oct. 7, 1942, Adm. Kondo and Adm. Halsey. 250fr, Battle of El Alamein, Oct. 23, 1942, Field Marshal Erwin Rommel, Field Marshal Montgomery. 300fr, Battle of the Bulge, Dec. 16, 1944, Gen. Guderian and Gen. Patton. 450fr, Sinking of the Yamato, Apr. 7, 1945, Adm. Kogo and Gen. MacArthur. No. 1166, Review of Free French Forces, July 14, 1940, Gen. Charles De Gaulle. 750fr, Boeing B-17G, Gen. Dwight Eisenhower. No. 1168, De Gaulle's Call for French Resistance, June 18, 1940.

**1991, Apr. 8　　Litho.　　Perf. 13½**
1160　A180　100fr multicolored　　.90　.45
1161　A180　150fr multicolored　　1.25　.70
1162　A180　200fr multicolored　　1.75　.90
1163　A180　250fr multicolored　　2.25　1.10
1164　A180　300fr multicolored　　2.75　1.25
1165　A180　450fr multicolored　　6.00　3.00
　a.　Sheet of 6, #1160-1165　16.00　8.00

**Litho. & Embossed**
1166　A181　1500fr gold & multi　17.00　11.00

**Souvenir Sheets**
**Litho.**
1167　A180　750fr multicolored　　8.00　3.00

**Litho. & Embossed**
1168　A181　1500fr gold & multi　15.00　10.00
　Nos. 1164-1168 are airmail. No. 1160-1166 exist in souvenir sheets of 1. Value, set $32.
　For overprint see No. C177.

Doctors Without Borders A182

**1991, Feb. 22　　Litho.　　Perf. 13½**
1169　A182　300fr multicolored　　3.25　1.50

Telecom '91 A183

**1991, Jan. 15**
1170　A183　150fr multi, vert.　　1.50　1.25
1171　A183　300fr shown　　2.75　2.40
　6th World Forum and Exposition on Telecommunications, Geneva, Switzerland.

American Entertainers and Films — A184

Designs: 100fr, Nat King Cole Trio. 150fr, Yul Brynner, The Magnificent Seven. 250fr, Judy Garland, The Wizard of Oz. 300fr, Steve McQueen, Papillon. 500fr, Gary Cooper, Sergeant York. 600fr, Bing Crosby, High Society. 750fr, John Wayne, How the West Was Won.

**1991, Oct. 2　　Litho.　　Perf. 13½**
1172　A184　100fr multicolored　　.75　.45
1173　A184　150fr multicolored　　1.10　.60
1174　A184　250fr multicolored　　2.00　1.00
1175　A184　300fr multicolored　　2.40　1.25
1176　A184　500fr multicolored　　4.00　2.00
1177　A184　600fr multicolored　　8.75　4.25
　　　Nos. 1172-1177 (6)　　19.00　9.55

**Souvenir Sheet**
1178　A184　750fr multicolored　　8.00　3.00
　Nos. 1176-1178 are airmail. No. 1172-1177 exist in souvenir sheets of 1.

Care Bears Promoting Environmental Protection — A184a

Designs: 50fr, Care Bears circling earth, vert. 100fr, Save water, vert. 200fr, Recycle, vert. 300fr, Control noise, vert. 400fr, Elephant. 500fr, Care Bear emblem, end of rainbow. 600fr, Scout, tent, Lord Baden-Powell.

**1991　　　　　　　　　Perf. 13½**
1178A　A184a　50fr multi　　.40　.25
1178B　A184a　100fr multi　　.85　.40
1178C　A184a　200fr multi　　1.75　.85
1178D　A184a　300fr multi　　2.50　1.25
1178E　A184a　400fr multi　　3.50　1.75
　　Nos. 1178A-1178E (5)　　9.00　4.50

## Souvenir Sheets

| | | | | |
|---|---|---|---|---|
| 1178F | A184a | 500fr multi | 4.25 | 2.25 |
| 1178G | A184a | 600fr multi | 5.00 | 2.50 |

Nos. 1178F-1178G each contain one 39x27mm stamp. No. 1178G is airmail.

African Tourism Year A185

**1991, Aug. 16   Litho.   Perf. 13½**

| | | | | |
|---|---|---|---|---|
| 1179 | A185 | 100fr Dancer, vert. | 1.25 | .60 |
| 1180 | A185 | 150fr Baskets | 2.00 | .90 |
| 1181 | A185 | 250fr Drum | 3.25 | 1.25 |
| 1182 | A185 | 300fr Flute player, vert. | 3.50 | 1.60 |
| *Nos. 1179-1182 (4)* | | | 10.00 | 4.35 |

Stamps of 1986-92 Surcharged in Black or Silver (#1182A-1182B, 1182D, 1182H-1182I, 1182M-1182N, 1182P)

**1991   Litho.   Perfs. as Before**

| | | | | |
|---|---|---|---|---|
| 1182A | A150 | 100fr on 400fr #1019 | .85 | .40 |
| 1182B | A154 | 100fr on 400fr #1045 | .85 | .40 |
| 1182C | A156 | 100fr on 400fr #1052 | .85 | .40 |
| 1182D | A159 | 100fr on 170fr #1065 | .85 | .40 |
| 1182E | A159 | 100fr on 400fr #1066 | .85 | .40 |
| 1182F | A160 | 100fr on 170fr #1072 | 90.00 | — |
| 1182G | A160 | 100fr on 400fr #1073 | 4.00 | 1.00 |
| 1182H | A163 | 100fr on 400fr #1092 | .85 | .40 |
| 1182I | A164 | 100fr on 400fr #1098 | .85 | .40 |
| 1182J | A165 | 100fr on 400fr #1106 | .85 | .40 |
| 1182K | A165b | 100fr on 500fr #1108G | .85 | .40 |
| 1182L | A165d | 100fr on 500fr #1108N | .85 | .40 |
| 1182M | A166 | 100fr on 400fr #1113 | .85 | .40 |
| 1182N | A167 | 100fr on 250fr #1116 | .85 | .40 |
| 1182O | A172 | 100fr on 400fr #1135 | .85 | .40 |
| 1182P | A174 | 100fr on 400fr #1139 | .85 | .40 |
| 1182Q | A164 | 300fr on 450fr #1099 | 2.50 | 1.25 |
| 1182R | AP14 | 300fr on 400fr #C170 | 2.50 | 1.25 |
| *Nos. 1182A-1182R (18)* | | | 110.90 | 9.10 |

Nos. 1182B-1182C, 1182E, 1182G, 1182M, 1182Q-1182R are airmail.

Visit by Pope John Paul II — A185a

**1992, Feb. 24   Litho.   Perf. 13½**

| | | | | |
|---|---|---|---|---|
| 1182S | A185a | 150fr multicolored | 3.50 | 1.75 |

1994 World Cup Soccer, US — A186

A186a

Player, World Cup Trophy and scenes of Atlanta: 100fr, Little Five Points. 300fr, Fulton County Stadium. 400fr, Inman Park. 500fr, High Museum of Art. 1000fr, Intelsat VI, Capitol.
#1187A, Player in white shirt. #1187B, Player in red.

**1992, Apr. 27   Litho.   Perf. 13½**

| | | | | |
|---|---|---|---|---|
| 1183 | A186 | 100fr multi | 1.25 | .40 |
| 1184 | A186 | 300fr multi | 4.00 | 1.25 |
| 1185 | A186 | 400fr multi | 5.75 | 1.75 |
| 1186 | A186 | 500fr multi | 7.00 | 2.25 |
| *Nos. 1183-1186 (4)* | | | 18.00 | 5.65 |

**Souvenir Sheet**

| | | | | |
|---|---|---|---|---|
| 1187 | A186 | 1000fr multi | 10.00 | 6.00 |

**Litho. & Embossed**

| | | | | |
|---|---|---|---|---|
| 1187A | A186a | 1500fr gold & multi | 24.00 | 14.00 |

**Souvenir Sheet**

| | | | | |
|---|---|---|---|---|
| 1187B | A186a | 1500fr gold & multi | 20.00 | 12.00 |

Nos. 1186-1187B are airmail. Nos. 1183-1186A exist in souvenir sheets of 1.

Lions Intl., 75th Anniv. — A187

**1992, May 22   Litho.   Perf. 13½**

| | | | | |
|---|---|---|---|---|
| 1188 | A187 | 150fr blue & multi | 1.50 | .75 |
| 1188A | A187 | 400fr lilac rose & multi | 4.00 | 2.00 |

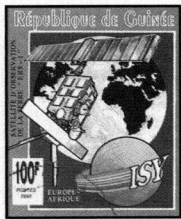

Anniversaries and Events — A188

Designs: 100fr, Satellite ERS-1 in orbit. 150fr, Vase with Fourteen Sunflowers, by Vincent van Gogh. 200fr, Napoleon Bonaparte. 250fr, Henri Dunant, Red Cross workers. 300fr, Brandenburg Gate. 400fr, Pope John Paul II. 450fr, Garry Kasparov, Anatoly Karpov, chess pieces. 500fr, African child, dove, emblems of Rotary and Lions Clubs.

**1992, Nov. 10   Litho.   Perf. 13½**

| | | | | |
|---|---|---|---|---|
| 1189 | A188 | 100fr multicolored | 1.00 | .45 |
| 1190 | A188 | 150fr multicolored | 1.50 | .75 |
| 1191 | A188 | 200fr multicolored | 2.25 | 1.00 |
| 1192 | A188 | 250fr multicolored | 2.50 | 1.25 |
| 1193 | A188 | 300fr multicolored | 3.25 | 1.50 |
| 1194 | A188 | 400fr multicolored | 4.25 | 2.10 |
| 1195 | A188 | 450fr multicolored | 4.75 | 2.25 |
| 1196 | A188 | 500fr multicolored | 5.50 | 2.50 |
| *Nos. 1189-1196 (8)* | | | 25.00 | 11.80 |

Intl. Space Year (#1189). Vincent van Gogh, cent. of death (in 1990) (#1190). Napolean Bonaparte, 170th anniv. of death (in 1991) (#1191). Founding of Red Cross (in 1864) (#1192). Brandenburg Gate, bicent. (#1193). Pope John Paul II's visit to Africa in 1989 (#1194). World Chess Championships (#1195). Lions Intl., 75th anniv. (#1196).
Nos. 1195-1196 are airmail. Nos. 1189-1196 exist in souvenir sheets of one.
For overprint see No. C178.

Anniversaries and Events — A189

Designs: 200fr, The Devil and Kate, Antonin Dvorak. 300fr, Antonio Vivaldi. 350fr, Graf Zeppelin, flying boat, Count Ferdinand von Zeppelin. 400fr, English Channel Euro-Tunnel Train. 450fr, Konrad Adenauer, Brandenburg Gate. 500fr, Japanese naval ensign, Emperor Hirohito. 750fr, Tunnel Train, diff.

**1992, Nov. 10**

| | | | | |
|---|---|---|---|---|
| 1197 | A189 | 200fr multicolored | 2.25 | .90 |
| 1198 | A189 | 300fr multicolored | 3.25 | 1.40 |
| 1199 | A189 | 350fr multicolored | 3.75 | 1.50 |
| 1200 | A189 | 400fr multicolored | 4.00 | 1.90 |
| 1201 | A189 | 450fr multicolored | 5.00 | 2.00 |
| *a.* | | Souvenir sheet of 2, #1199, 1201 | 8.00 | 3.25 |
| 1202 | A189 | 500fr multicolored | 5.50 | 2.25 |
| *Nos. 1197-1202 (6)* | | | 23.75 | 9.95 |

**Souvenir Sheet**

| | | | | |
|---|---|---|---|---|
| 1203 | A189 | 750fr multicolored | 8.00 | 3.75 |

Antonin Dvorak, 90th anniv. of death (in 1994) (#1197). Antonio Vivaldi, 250th anniv. of death (in 1991) (#1198). Count Ferdinand von Zeppelin, 75th anniv. of death (#1199). Opening of English Channel Tunnel (in 1994) (#1200, 1203). Konrad Adenauer, 25th anniv. of death, Brandenburg Gate, bicent. (#1201). Death of Emperor Hirohito (in 1989) (#1202).
Nos. 1201-1203 are airmail. Nos. 1197-1202 exist imperf. and in souvenir sheets of one. No. 1203 exists imperf. and contains one 60x42mm stamp.

Anniversaries and Events A190

Designs: 50fr, Modern Times, film by Charlie Chaplin. 100fr, Expo '92 Seville, Columbus. 150fr, St. Peter's Square, Rome. 200fr, Marlene Dietrich, roses. 250fr, Michael Schumacher, Benetton Ford B192. 300fr, Mercury rocket, John Glenn. 400fr, Bill Koch, America 3. 450fr, Mark Rypien, quarterback of Washington Redskins. 500fr, Rescue of Intelsat VI by shuttle Endeavour.

**1992, Dec. 3**

| | | | | |
|---|---|---|---|---|
| 1204 | A190 | 50fr multicolored | .45 | .20 |
| 1205 | A190 | 100fr multicolored | .90 | .40 |
| 1206 | A190 | 150fr multicolored | 1.40 | .65 |
| 1207 | A190 | 200fr multicolored | 1.90 | .85 |
| 1208 | A190 | 250fr multicolored | 2.25 | 1.10 |
| 1209 | A190 | 300fr multicolored | 2.75 | 1.25 |
| 1210 | A190 | 400fr multicolored | 3.50 | 1.75 |
| 1211 | A190 | 450fr multicolored | 4.00 | 1.90 |
| 1212 | A190 | 500fr multicolored | 4.50 | 2.10 |
| *Nos. 1204-1212 (9)* | | | 21.65 | 10.20 |

Discovery of America, 500th anniv. (#1205). First US orbital space flight, 30th anniv. (#1209). Americas Cup yacht race (#1210). Super Bowl XXVI football game (#1211).
Nos. 1210-1212 are airmail. Nos. 1204-1212 exist in souvenir sheets of one.

Intl. Conference on Nutrition, Rome — A191

**1992, Nov. 10   Litho.   Perf. 13½**

| | | | | |
|---|---|---|---|---|
| 1213 | A191 | 150fr multi | 1.50 | .70 |
| 1214 | A191 | 400fr multi | 3.50 | 1.90 |
| 1215 | A191 | 500fr multi | 4.50 | 2.25 |
| *Nos. 1213-1215 (3)* | | | 9.50 | 4.85 |

Nos. 1116-1120 Ovptd. in Silver "BICENTAIRE / DE L'AN I / DE LA REPUBLIQUE / FRANCAISE"

**1992, Feb. 24   Litho.   Perf. 13½**

| | | | | |
|---|---|---|---|---|
| 1216 | A167 | 250fr multicolored | 3.00 | 1.10 |
| 1217 | A167 | 300fr multicolored | 3.75 | 1.40 |
| 1218 | A167 | 400fr multicolored | 5.00 | 1.75 |
| 1219 | A167 | 450fr multicolored | 5.75 | 2.00 |
| *Nos. 1216-1219 (4)* | | | 17.50 | 6.25 |

**Souvenir Sheet**

| | | | | |
|---|---|---|---|---|
| 1220 | A167 | 750fr multicolored | 9.00 | 4.50 |

Nos. 1219-1220 are airmail. Nos. 1216-1219 exist in souvenir sheets of 1. Sold for 100fr extra.

Nos. 1130-1134 Ovptd. in Gold "1. ALLEMAGNE / 2. ARGENTINE / 3. ITALIE"

**1992, Feb. 24   Litho.   Perf. 13½**

| | | | | |
|---|---|---|---|---|
| 1221 | A171 | 200fr multicolored | 2.00 | .80 |
| 1222 | A171 | 250fr multicolored | 2.50 | 1.00 |
| 1223 | A171 | 300fr multicolored | 3.00 | 1.25 |
| 1224 | A171 | 450fr multicolored | 5.00 | 2.00 |
| *Nos. 1221-1224 (4)* | | | 12.50 | 5.05 |

**Souvenir Sheet**

| | | | | |
|---|---|---|---|---|
| 1225 | A171 | 750fr multicolored | 8.00 | 3.00 |

Nos. 1137-1141 Ovptd. in Gold

**1992   Litho.   Perf. 13½**

| | | | | |
|---|---|---|---|---|
| 1226 | A174 | 150fr multicolored | 1.75 | .70 |
| 1227 | A174 | 250fr multicolored | 2.50 | 1.10 |
| 1228 | A174 | 400fr multicolored | 4.00 | 1.75 |
| 1229 | A174 | 500fr multicolored | 5.25 | 2.10 |
| *Nos. 1226-1229 (4)* | | | 13.50 | 5.65 |

**Souvenir Sheet**

| | | | | |
|---|---|---|---|---|
| 1230 | A174 | 750fr multicolored | 6.25 | 3.00 |

Overprints read: 150fr, 750fr, "SLALOM GEANT / Alberto Tomba, Italie." 250fr, "SKI NORDIQUE / Vegard Ulvang, Norvege." 400fr, "BOB A DEUX / G. Weder / D Acklin, Suisse." 500fr, "PATINAGE DE VITESSE / Olaf Zinke 1000m., Allemagne."

A192

1994 World Cup Soccer Championships, US — A192a

Soccer player, city skyline: 100fr, San Francisco. 300fr, Washington, DC. 400fr, Detroit. 500fr, Dallas. 1000fr, New York.

**1993, Sept. 24    Litho.    Perf. 13½**
| | | | | |
|---|---|---|---|---|
| 1233 | A192 | 100fr multicolored | 1.10 | .45 |
| 1234 | A192 | 300fr multicolored | 3.50 | 1.50 |
| 1235 | A192 | 400fr multicolored | 4.50 | 1.90 |
| 1236 | A192 | 500fr multicolored | 5.75 | 2.40 |
| | *Nos. 1233-1236 (4)* | | 14.85 | 6.25 |

**Souvenir Sheet**
| | | | | |
|---|---|---|---|---|
| 1237 | A192 | 1000fr multicolored | 10.00 | 5.50 |

**Litho. & Embossed**
| | | | | |
|---|---|---|---|---|
| 1237A | A192a | 1500fr gold & multi | 16.00 | 12.50 |

Nos. 1236-1237A are airmail. No. 1237A exists in a souvenir sheet of 1.

**Miniature Sheet**

Dinosaurs — A193

No. 1238: a, 50fr, Euparkeria. b, 50fr, Plateosaurus. c, 50fr, Anchisaurus. d, 50fr, Ornithosuchus. e, 100fr, Megalosaurus. f, 100fr, Scelidosaurus. g, 100fr, Camptosaurus. h, 100fr, Ceratosaurus. i, 250fr, Ouranosaurus. j, 250fr, Dicraeosaurus. k, 250fr, Tarbosaurus. l, 250fr, Gorgosaurus. m, 250fr, Polacanthus. n, 250fr, Deinonychus. o, 250fr, Corythosaurus. p, 250fr, Spinosaurus. 1000fr, Tyrannosaurus rex.

**1993, Oct. 27**
| | | | | |
|---|---|---|---|---|
| 1238 | A193 | Sheet of 16, #a.-p. | 30.00 | 15.00 |

**Souvenir Sheet**
| | | | | |
|---|---|---|---|---|
| 1239 | A193 | 1000fr multicolored | 10.00 | 4.50 |

No. 1239 is airmail and contains one 50x60mm stamp.

Nos. 1088-1094 Ovptd. in Silver "50eme ANNIVERSAIRE DE LA MORT DE BADEN POWEL"

A194

**1993, Feb. 24    Litho.    Perf. 13½**
| | | | | |
|---|---|---|---|---|
| 1240 | A163 | 50fr multicolored | .45 | .20 |
| 1241 | A163 | 100fr multicolored | 1.10 | .50 |
| 1242 | A163 | 150fr multicolored | 1.75 | .65 |
| 1243 | A163 | 300fr multicolored | 3.25 | 1.40 |
| 1244 | A163 | 400fr multicolored | 3.75 | 1.90 |
| 1245 | A163 | 450fr multicolored | 4.75 | 2.00 |
| | *Nos. 1240-1245 (6)* | | 15.05 | 6.65 |

**Souvenir Sheet**
| | | | | |
|---|---|---|---|---|
| 1246 | A163 | 750fr multicolored | 8.00 | 3.25 |

Nos. 1244-1246 are airmail.

1994 Winter Olympic Games, Lillehammer A195

Views of Lillehammer: 150fr, Ice hockey. 250fr, Bobsled. 400fr, Biathlon. 450fr, Ski jump.
1000fr, Slalom skiing. 1500fr, Ice skating.

**1993, July 16    Litho.    Perf. 13½**
| | | | | |
|---|---|---|---|---|
| 1247 | A194 | 150fr multicolored | 1.25 | .65 |
| 1248 | A194 | 250fr multicolored | 2.75 | 1.25 |
| 1249 | A194 | 400fr multicolored | 4.25 | 2.10 |
| 1250 | A194 | 450fr multicolored | 4.75 | 2.25 |
| | *Nos. 1247-1250 (4)* | | 13.00 | 6.25 |

**Souvenir Sheet**
| | | | | |
|---|---|---|---|---|
| 1251 | A194 | 1000fr multicolored | 10.00 | 5.00 |

**Litho. & Embossed**
| | | | | |
|---|---|---|---|---|
| 1252 | A195 | 1500fr gold & multi | 16.00 | 12.50 |

Nos. 1249-1252 are airmail.
For overprints see #1267A-1267E.

A196

1996 Summer Olympic Games, Atlanta — A197

Event, scenes of Atlanta: 150fr, Soccer, "Little White House." 250fr, Cycling, Georgia World Congress Center. 400fr, Basketball, underground Atlanta. 500fr, Baseball, new Georgia Railroad.
1000fr, Tennis, Atlanta at night. 1500fr, Running, Georgia State Capitol, Olympic torch.

**1993, July 16    Litho.    Perf. 13½**
| | | | | |
|---|---|---|---|---|
| 1253 | A196 | 150fr multi | 1.50 | .65 |
| 1254 | A196 | 250fr multi | 2.75 | 1.25 |
| 1255 | A196 | 400fr multi | 4.75 | 2.10 |
| 1256 | A196 | 500fr multi | 6.00 | 2.50 |
| | *Nos. 1253-1256 (4)* | | 15.00 | 6.50 |

**Souvenir Sheet**
| | | | | |
|---|---|---|---|---|
| 1257 | A196 | 1000fr multi | 10.00 | 5.00 |

**Litho. & Embossed**
| | | | | |
|---|---|---|---|---|
| 1257A | A197 | 1500fr gold & multi | 16.00 | 12.50 |

Nos. 1256-1257A are airmail.
#1253-1256 exist in souvenir sheets of 1.

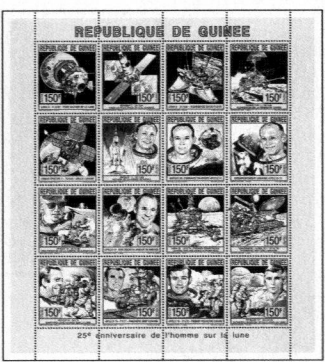

First Manned Moon Landing, 25th Anniv. — A197a

d, Luna 3, 1959. e, Ranger 7, 1964. f, Luna 9, 1966. g, Surveyor 1, 1966. h, Lunar Orbiter 1, 1966. i, Launch of Apollo 11, Neil Armstrong, 1969. j, Michael Collins, Apollo 11 command module. k, Apollo 11 landing on Moon, "Buzz" Aldrin. l, Apollo 12, 1969. m, Apollo 13, 1969. n, Luna 16, 1970. o, Luna 17, 1970. p, Apollo 14, 1971. q, Apollo 15, 1971. r, Apollo 16, 1972. s, Apollo 17, 1972.

**1993, July 27    Litho.    Perf. 13½**
**Sheet of 16**
| | | | | |
|---|---|---|---|---|
| 1257B | A197a | 150fr d.-s. | 25.00 | 12.25 |

D-Day Landings, Normandy, 50th Anniv. — A198

Battle scenes and: No. 1258a, 150fr, Field Marshal Irwin Rommel (1891-1944), Germany. b, 600fr, Gen. Dwight D. Eisenhower (1890-1969), Allies. c, 150fr, Gen. George S. Patton, Jr. (1885-1945), Allies.
Battle of the Bulge, 1944: No. 1259a, 150fr, Lt. Gen. William H. Simpson. b, 600fr, Battle scene. c, 150fr, Gen. Heinz Guderian (1888-1954).
Austerlitz, Dec. 2, 1805: No. 1260a, 150fr, John I, Prince of Liechtenstein (1760-1836). b, 600fr, Napoleon I. c, 150fr, Marshal Joachim Murat (1767-1815).
Battle of Borodino, Sept. 7, 1812: No. 1261a, 150fr, Marshal Michael Ney (1769-1815). b, 600fr, Battle scene. c, 150fr, Prince Pytor Ivanovich Bagration (1765-1812).

**1994, Jan. 26    Litho.    Perf. 13½**
| | | | | |
|---|---|---|---|---|
| 1258 | A198 | Strip of 3, #a.-c. | 11.00 | 4.75 |
| 1259 | A198 | Strip of 3, #a.-c. | 11.00 | 4.75 |
| 1260 | A198 | Strip of 3, #a.-c. | 11.00 | 4.75 |
| 1261 | A198 | Strip of 3, #a.-c. | 11.00 | 4.75 |
| | *Nos. 1258-1261 (4)* | | 44.00 | 19.00 |

No. 1258b, 1259b, 1260b, 1261b are 60x46mm. Nos. 1258-1261 are each a continuous design.

Astronomers and Spacecraft A199

Designs: a, 300fr, Johannes Kepler, Pluto probe. b, 500fr, Copernicus, Galileo probe. b, 300fr, Sir Isaac Newton, Voyager.

**1994, Jan. 26**
| | | | | |
|---|---|---|---|---|
| 1262 | A199 | Strip of 3, #a.-c. | 15.00 | 6.75 |

No. 1262b is 60x46mm. No. 1262 has a continuous design.

Nos. 1233-1237 Ovptd. in Silver "1. BRESIL / 2. ITALIE / 3. SUEDE"

**1994, Sept. 14    Litho.    Perf. 13½**
| | | | | |
|---|---|---|---|---|
| 1263 | A192 | 100fr multicolored | 1.00 | .50 |
| 1264 | A192 | 300fr multicolored | 3.00 | 1.75 |
| 1265 | A192 | 400fr multicolored | 4.00 | 2.25 |
| 1266 | A192 | 500fr multicolored | 4.75 | 2.50 |
| | *Nos. 1263-1266 (4)* | | 12.75 | 7.00 |

**Souvenir Sheet**
| | | | | |
|---|---|---|---|---|
| 1267 | A192 | 1000fr multicolored | 10.00 | 5.00 |

Nos. 1266-1267 are airmail.

Nos. 1247-1251 Overprinted in Gold

**1994, Sept. 14    Litho.    Perf. 13½**
| | | | | |
|---|---|---|---|---|
| 1267A | A194 | 150fr multi | 1.25 | .65 |
| 1267B | A194 | 250fr multi | 2.40 | 1.25 |
| 1267C | A194 | 400fr multi | 3.75 | 1.90 |
| 1267D | A194 | 450fr multi | 4.50 | 2.10 |
| | *Nos. 1267A-1267D (4)* | | 11.90 | 5.90 |

**Souvenir Sheet**
| | | | | |
|---|---|---|---|---|
| 1267E | A194 | 1000fr multi | 10.00 | 5.00 |

Overprints read: 150fr, MEDAILLE D'OR / SUEDE. 250fr, G. WEDER / D. ACKLIN / SUISSE. 400fr, F.B. LUNDBERG / NORVEGE. 450fr, J. WEISSFLOG / ALLEMAGNE. 1000fr, T. MOE / U.S.A.
Nos. 1267C-1267E are airmail.

Birds — A200

150fr, Carduelis carduelis. 250fr, Luscinia megarhynchos. #1270, Serinus canaria. #1271, Fringilla coelebs. #1272, Carduelis chloris.
No. 1273, Erithacus rubecula.

**1995, Aug. 31    Litho.    Perf. 13**
| | | | | |
|---|---|---|---|---|
| 1268 | A200 | 150fr multicolored | .50 | .25 |
| 1269 | A200 | 250fr multicolored | .80 | .35 |
| 1270 | A200 | 500fr multicolored | 1.60 | .80 |
| 1271 | A200 | 500fr multicolored | 1.60 | .80 |
| 1272 | A200 | 500fr multicolored | 1.60 | .80 |
| | *Nos. 1268-1272 (5)* | | 6.10 | 3.00 |

**Souvenir Sheet**
| | | | | |
|---|---|---|---|---|
| 1273 | A200 | 1000fr multicolored | *6.00* | *3.00* |

No. 1273 contains one 32x40mm stamp.

1996 Summer Olympics, Atlanta — A201

**1995, Aug. 5**
| | | | | |
|---|---|---|---|---|
| 1274 | A201 | 150fr Javelin | .50 | .25 |
| 1275 | A201 | 250fr Boxing | .80 | .40 |
| 1276 | A201 | 500fr Basketball | 1.60 | .80 |
| 1277 | A201 | 500fr Weight lifting | 1.60 | .80 |
| 1278 | A201 | 500fr Soccer | 1.60 | .80 |
| | *Nos. 1274-1278 (5)* | | 6.10 | 3.05 |

**Souvenir Sheet**
| | | | | |
|---|---|---|---|---|
| 1279 | A201 | 1000fr Archery | *4.75* | *2.50* |

No. 1279 contains one 32x40mm stamp.

African Animals A202

Designs: 150fr, Cercopithecus mona, vert. 250fr, Cercopithecus aethiops, vert. No. 1282, Galagoides demidovi, vert. No. 1283, Manis gigantea. No. 1284, Lepus crawshayi. 1000fr, Aonyx capensis, vert.

**1995, Sept. 25**

| | | | | |
|---|---|---|---|---|
| **1280** | A202 | 150fr multicolored | .50 | .25 |
| **1281** | A202 | 250fr multicolored | .80 | .35 |
| **1282** | A202 | 500fr multicolored | 1.60 | .80 |
| **1283** | A202 | 500fr multicolored | 1.60 | .80 |
| **1284** | A202 | 500fr multicolored | 1.60 | .80 |
| | | Nos. 1280-1284 (5) | 6.10 | 3.00 |

**Souvenir Sheet**

| | | | | |
|---|---|---|---|---|
| **1285** | A202 | 1000fr multicolored | 6.00 | 3.00 |

1998 World Cup Soccer Championships, France — A203

Opposing two players wearing: No. 1288, Yellow shirt & blue shorts, red shirt & white shorts. No. 1289, Red & white uniform, red shirt & white shorts. No. 1290, Striped shirt & blue shorts, red & yellow shirt & green shorts. 1000fr, Three players.

**1995, Oct. 30**    **Litho.**    **Perf. 13**

| | | | | |
|---|---|---|---|---|
| **1286** | A203 | 150fr multicolored | .50 | .25 |
| **1287** | A203 | 250fr multicolored | .80 | .35 |
| **1288** | A203 | 500fr multicolored | 1.60 | .80 |
| **1289** | A203 | 500fr multicolored | 1.60 | .80 |
| **1290** | A203 | 500fr multicolored | 1.60 | .80 |
| | | Nos. 1286-1290 (5) | 6.10 | 3.00 |

**Souvenir Sheet**

| | | | | |
|---|---|---|---|---|
| **1291** | A203 | 1000fr multicolored | 6.00 | 3.00 |

No. 1291 contains one 32x40mm stamp.

Domestic Cats A204

150fr, Tortoiseshell. 250fr, Tabby and white. #1294, Tortoiseshell and white longhair. #1295, Red tabby. #1296, Smoke long-haired. 1000fr, Chinchilla.

**1995, July 25**

| | | | | |
|---|---|---|---|---|
| **1292** | A204 | 150fr multicolored | .80 | .40 |
| **1293** | A204 | 250fr multicolored | 1.25 | .55 |
| **1294** | A204 | 500fr multicolored | 2.50 | 1.25 |
| **1295** | A204 | 500fr multicolored | 2.50 | 1.25 |
| **1296** | A204 | 500fr multicolored | 2.50 | 1.25 |
| | | Nos. 1292-1296 (5) | 9.55 | 4.70 |

**Souvenir Sheet**
**Perf. 12½**

| | | | | |
|---|---|---|---|---|
| **1297** | A204 | 1000fr multicolored | 6.00 | 3.00 |

No. 1297 contains one 40x32mm stamp.

Production of Electrical Power — A205

Designs: 100fr, Banéa Dam. 150fr, Water Chamber, Donkea. 200fr, Tinkisso Spillway, vert. 250fr, Cascades of Grand Falls. 500fr, Building, Kinkon.

**1995, July 18**    **Perf. 12½**

| | | | | |
|---|---|---|---|---|
| **1298** | A205 | 100fr multicolored | .50 | .25 |
| **1299** | A205 | 150fr multicolored | .75 | .35 |
| **1300** | A205 | 200fr multicolored | 1.00 | .50 |
| **1301** | A205 | 250fr multicolored | 1.25 | .65 |
| **1302** | A205 | 500fr multicolored | 2.50 | 1.25 |
| | | Nos. 1298-1302 (5) | 6.00 | 3.00 |

FAO, 50th Anniv. A206

Designs: 200fr, Man, oxen, boy. 750fr, Instructing women, children on nutrition.

**1995, Oct. 16**    **Perf. 13**

| | | | | |
|---|---|---|---|---|
| **1303** | A206 | 200fr multicolored | 1.00 | .55 |
| **1304** | A206 | 750fr multicolored | 4.00 | 2.00 |

Light Aircraft — A207

100fr, Pup-150, UK. 150fr, Gardan GY-80 Horizon, France. 250fr, Piper Cub J-3, US. No. 1308, Valmet L-90TP Redigo, Finland. No. 1309, Pilatus PC-6 Porter, Switzerland. No. 1310, Piper PA-28 Cherokee Arrow, US. 1000fr, Stol DO-27, Germany.

**1995, Oct. 1**    **Perf. 12½**

| | | | | |
|---|---|---|---|---|
| **1305** | A207 | 100fr multicolored | .45 | .20 |
| **1306** | A207 | 150fr multicolored | .75 | .35 |
| **1307** | A207 | 250fr multicolored | 1.25 | .65 |
| **1308** | A207 | 500fr multicolored | 2.40 | 1.10 |
| **1309** | A207 | 500fr multicolored | 2.40 | 1.10 |
| **1310** | A207 | 500fr multicolored | 2.40 | 1.10 |
| | | Nos. 1305-1310 (6) | 9.65 | 4.50 |

**Souvenir Sheet**

| | | | | |
|---|---|---|---|---|
| **1311** | A207 | 1000fr multicolored | 5.50 | 2.75 |

No. 1311 contains one 40x32mm stamp.

Flowers — A208

100fr, Sprekelia formosissima. 150fr, Rudbeckia purpurea. 250fr, Meconopsis betonicifolia. #1314, Gail Borden rose. #1315, Lathyrus odoratus. #1316, Iris starshine. 1000fr, Cypripedium alma gaevert.

**1995, Oct. 12**

| | | | | |
|---|---|---|---|---|
| **1312** | A208 | 100fr multicolored | .45 | .20 |
| **1313** | A208 | 150fr multicolored | .75 | .35 |
| **1314** | A208 | 250fr multicolored | 1.25 | .60 |
| **1315** | A208 | 500fr multicolored | 2.40 | 1.10 |
| **1316** | A208 | 500fr multicolored | 2.40 | 1.10 |
| **1317** | A208 | 500fr multicolored | 2.40 | 1.10 |
| | | Nos. 1312-1317 (6) | 9.65 | 4.45 |

**Souvenir Sheet**

| | | | | |
|---|---|---|---|---|
| **1318** | A208 | 1000fr multicolored | 5.50 | 2.75 |

No. 1318 contains one 32x40mm stamp.

Historic Buses — A209

250fr, 1832 Omnibus. 300fr, 1898 Daimler. 400fr, 1904 V.H. Bussing. 450fr, 1906 Autobus M.A.N. 500fr, 1904 Autocar M.A.N.

**1995, Dec. 3**    **Litho.**    **Perf. 12½**

| | | | | |
|---|---|---|---|---|
| **1319** | A209 | 250fr multicolored | .75 | .35 |
| **1320** | A209 | 300fr multicolored | .90 | .45 |
| **1321** | A209 | 400fr multicolored | 1.25 | .60 |
| **1322** | A209 | 450fr multicolored | 1.40 | .70 |
| **1323** | A209 | 500fr multicolored | 1.50 | .75 |
| | | Nos. 1319-1323 (5) | 5.80 | 2.85 |

Arabian Horses A210

Various horses.

**1995**
**Background Colors**

| | | | | |
|---|---|---|---|---|
| **1324** | A210 | 100fr dk bl, vert. | .30 | .20 |
| **1325** | A210 | 150fr tan, vert. | .55 | .20 |
| **1326** | A210 | 250fr lt bl, vert. | .90 | .40 |
| **1327** | A210 | 500fr pink, vert. | 1.75 | .90 |
| **1328** | A210 | 500fr lilac, vert. | 1.75 | .90 |
| **1329** | A210 | 500fr sage | 1.75 | .90 |
| | | Nos. 1324-1329 (6) | 7.00 | 3.50 |

**Souvenir Sheet**

| | | | | |
|---|---|---|---|---|
| **1330** | A210 | 1000fr white & gray | 6.00 | 3.00 |

No. 1330 contains one 32x40mm stamp.

Mushrooms A211

150fr, Leccinum nigrescens. 250fr, Boletus rhodoxanthus. #1333, Paxillus involutus. #1334, Cantharellus lutescens. #1335, Xerocomus rubellus. 1000fr, Gymnopilus junonius.

**1995**    **Litho.**    **Perf. 12½**

| | | | | |
|---|---|---|---|---|
| **1331** | A211 | 150fr multicolored | .45 | .20 |
| **1332** | A211 | 250fr multicolored | .75 | .40 |
| **1333** | A211 | 500fr multicolored | 1.50 | .75 |
| **1334** | A211 | 500fr multicolored | 1.50 | .75 |
| **1335** | A211 | 500fr multicolored | 1.50 | .75 |
| | | Nos. 1331-1335 (5) | 5.70 | 2.85 |

**Souvenir Sheet**

| | | | | |
|---|---|---|---|---|
| **1336** | A211 | 1000fr multicolored | 6.00 | 3.00 |

No. 1336 contains one 32x40mm stamp.

Tourism — A212

**1996, Sept. 5**    **Litho.**    **Perf. 12½**

| | | | | |
|---|---|---|---|---|
| **1337** | A212 | 200fr Mountain cliff | 1.00 | .50 |
| **1338** | A212 | 750fr Young child | 3.75 | 1.75 |
| **1339** | A212 | 1000fr Women carrying wood | 4.75 | 2.50 |
| | | Nos. 1337-1339 (3) | 9.50 | 4.75 |

Dogs — A213

**1996, Oct. 20**

| | | | | |
|---|---|---|---|---|
| **1340** | A213 | 200fr Bull terrier | .85 | .50 |
| **1341** | A213 | 250fr Elkhound | 1.10 | .70 |
| **1342** | A213 | 300fr Akita | 1.40 | .75 |
| **1343** | A213 | 400fr Collie | 1.75 | 1.00 |
| **1344** | A213 | 450fr Rottweiler | 2.00 | 1.00 |
| **1345** | A213 | 500fr Boxer | 2.40 | 1.10 |
| | | Nos. 1340-1345 (6) | 9.50 | 5.05 |

**Souvenir Sheet**
**Perf. 13**

| | | | | |
|---|---|---|---|---|
| **1346** | A213 | 1000fr German pointer | 5.00 | 2.50 |

No. 1346 contains one 32x40mm stamp.

Mushrooms A214

**1996, Dec. 20**    **Litho.**    **Perf. 12½**

| | | | | |
|---|---|---|---|---|
| **1347** | A214 | 200fr Chestnut | .85 | .45 |
| **1348** | A214 | 250fr Granular | 1.10 | .55 |
| **1349** | A214 | 300fr Destroying angel | 1.40 | .70 |
| **1350** | A214 | 400fr Milky blue | 1.75 | .95 |
| **1351** | A214 | 450fr Violet cortinarius | 2.00 | 1.00 |
| **1352** | A214 | 500fr Rough-stemmed | 2.40 | 1.10 |
| | | Nos. 1347-1352 (6) | 9.50 | 4.75 |

**Souvenir Sheet**
**Perf. 13**

| | | | | |
|---|---|---|---|---|
| **1353** | A214 | 1000fr Hygrophorus | 5.00 | 2.50 |

No. 1353 contains one 32x40mm stamp.

Locomotives — A215

Designs: 200fr, Tom Thumb, 1829. 250fr, Genf, 1858. 300fr, Dübs and Company, 1873. 400fr, W.G. Bagnall of Castle Engine Works, 1932. 450fr, Werner von Siemens, 1879. 500fr, North London Tramways Co., 1885-89. 1000fr, General, 1862.

**1996, Aug. 30**    **Perf. 12½**

| | | | | |
|---|---|---|---|---|
| **1354** | A215 | 200fr multicolored | .85 | .45 |
| **1355** | A215 | 250fr multicolored | 1.10 | .60 |
| **1356** | A215 | 300fr multicolored | 1.40 | .70 |
| **1357** | A215 | 400fr multicolored | 2.00 | .95 |
| **1358** | A215 | 450fr multicolored | 2.25 | 1.00 |
| **1359** | A215 | 500fr multicolored | 2.40 | 1.10 |
| | | Nos. 1354-1359 (6) | 10.00 | 4.80 |

**Souvenir Sheet**

| | | | | |
|---|---|---|---|---|
| **1360** | A215 | 1000fr multicolored | 5.50 | 2.75 |

Nos. 1355, 1358 are each 68x27mm. No. 1360 contains one 40x32mm stamp.

Cats A216

200fr, Tortoiseshell short-hair. 250fr, Black and white short-hair. 300fr, Japanese. 400fr, Himalayan. 450fr, Brown long-hair. 500fr, Blue Persian. 1000fr, Tortoiseshell long-hair.

**1996, Nov. 15**    **Perf. 12½**

| | | | | |
|---|---|---|---|---|
| **1361** | A216 | 200fr multicolored | .85 | .45 |
| **1362** | A216 | 250fr multicolored | 1.10 | .60 |
| **1363** | A216 | 300fr multicolored | 1.40 | .70 |
| **1364** | A216 | 400fr multicolored | 2.00 | .95 |
| **1365** | A216 | 450fr multicolored | 2.25 | 1.00 |
| **1366** | A216 | 500fr multicolored | 2.40 | 1.10 |
| | | Nos. 1361-1366 (6) | 10.00 | 4.80 |

**Souvenir Sheet**

| | | | | |
|---|---|---|---|---|
| **1367** | A216 | 1000fr multicolored | 5.00 | 2.50 |

No. 1367 contains one 32x40mm stamp.

Birds — A217

Designs: 200fr, Carduelis cucullata. 250fr, Uraeginthus bengalus. 300fr, Lonchura castaneothorax. 400fr, Amadina erythrocephala. 450fr, Chloebia gouldiae. 500fr, Euplectes orix.
1000fr, Poephila guttata.

| | | | | |
|---|---|---|---|---|
| **1996, Sept. 28** | | | **Perf. 12½** | |
| 1368 | A217 | 200fr multicolored | .85 | .45 |
| 1369 | A217 | 250fr multicolored | 1.10 | .60 |
| 1370 | A217 | 300fr multicolored | 1.40 | .70 |
| 1371 | A217 | 400fr multicolored | 2.00 | .95 |
| 1372 | A217 | 450fr multicolored | 2.25 | 1.00 |
| 1373 | A217 | 500fr multicolored | 2.40 | 1.10 |
| | | *Nos. 1368-1373 (6)* | 10.00 | 4.80 |
| | | **Souvenir Sheet** | | |
| 1374 | A217 | 1000fr multicolored | *5.00* | *2.50* |

No. 1374 contains one 32x40mm stamp.

Orchids
A218

Designs: 200fr, Paphiopedilum millmoore. 250fr, Paphiopedilum ernest read. 300fr, Paphiopedilum harrisianum. 400fr, Paphiopedilum gaudianum. 450fr, Paphiopedilum papa röhl. 500fr, Paphiopedilum sea cliffl.
1000fr, Paphiopedilum gowenanum.

| | | | | |
|---|---|---|---|---|
| **1997, Mar. 3** | | **Litho.** | **Perf. 12½** | |
| 1375 | A218 | 200fr multicolored | .90 | .50 |
| 1376 | A218 | 250fr multicolored | 1.10 | .60 |
| 1377 | A218 | 300fr multicolored | 1.25 | .65 |
| 1378 | A218 | 400fr multicolored | 1.75 | .90 |
| 1379 | A218 | 450fr multicolored | 2.25 | 1.00 |
| 1380 | A218 | 500fr multicolored | 2.50 | 1.10 |
| | | *Nos. 1375-1380 (6)* | 9.75 | 4.75 |
| | | **Souvenir Sheet** | | |
| 1381 | A218 | 1000fr multicolored | *5.00* | *2.50* |

No. 1381 contains one 32x40mm stamp.

1998 World Cup Soccer
Championships, France — A219

Various soccer plays.

| | | | | |
|---|---|---|---|---|
| **1997, Jan. 15** | | | | |
| 1382 | A219 | 200fr multi, vert. | .90 | .50 |
| 1383 | A219 | 250fr multi, vert. | 1.10 | .60 |
| 1384 | A219 | 300fr multi, vert. | 1.25 | .65 |
| 1385 | A219 | 400fr multicolored | 1.75 | .90 |
| 1386 | A219 | 450fr multicolored | 2.25 | 1.00 |
| 1387 | A219 | 500fr multicolored | 2.50 | 1.10 |
| | | *Nos. 1382-1387 (6)* | 9.75 | 4.75 |
| | | **Souvenir Sheet** | | |
| 1388 | A219 | 1000fr Goalie at net | 5.00 | 2.50 |

No. 1388 contains one 32x40mm stamp.

Wild
Animals
A220

Designs: 200fr, Giraffa camelopardalis. 250fr, Cerothoterium simun, vert. 300fr, Phacochoerus aethiopicus. 400fr, Acinonyx jubatus. 450fr, Loxodonta africana, vert. 500fr, Choeropsis liberiensis.
1000fr, Okapia johnstoni.

| | | | | |
|---|---|---|---|---|
| **1997, Apr. 15** | | **Litho.** | **Perf. 12½** | |
| 1389 | A220 | 200fr multicolored | .95 | .45 |
| 1390 | A220 | 250fr multicolored | 1.25 | .55 |
| 1391 | A220 | 300fr multicolored | 1.40 | .75 |
| 1392 | A220 | 400fr multicolored | 1.90 | .95 |
| 1393 | A220 | 450fr multicolored | 2.10 | 1.00 |
| 1394 | A220 | 500fr multicolored | 2.40 | 1.25 |
| | | *Nos. 1389-1394 (6)* | 10.00 | 4.95 |
| | | **Souvenir Sheet** | | |
| 1395 | A220 | 1000fr multicolored | *5.00* | *2.50* |

19th Century Warships — A221

Designs: 200fr, Captain, England, 1870. 250fr, Konig Wilhelm, Germany, 1869. 300fr, Téméraire, England, 1877. 400fr, Mouillage, Italy, 1866. 450fr, Inflexible, England, 1881. 500fr, Magenta, France, 1862.
1000fr, Redoutable, France, 1878.

| | | | | |
|---|---|---|---|---|
| **1997, May 20** | | **Litho.** | **Perf. 12½** | |
| 1396 | A221 | 200fr multicolored | .95 | .45 |
| 1397 | A221 | 250fr multicolored | 1.10 | .55 |
| 1398 | A221 | 300fr multicolored | 1.40 | .75 |
| 1399 | A221 | 400fr multicolored | 1.90 | .95 |
| 1400 | A221 | 450fr multicolored | 2.10 | 1.00 |
| 1401 | A221 | 500fr multicolored | 2.40 | 1.10 |
| | | *Nos. 1396-1401 (6)* | 9.85 | 4.80 |
| | | **Souvenir Sheet** | | |
| 1402 | A221 | 1000fr multicolored | *5.00* | *2.50* |

No. 1402 contains one 32x40mm stamp.

Fish
A222

Designs: 200fr, Siganus trispilos. 250fr, Scarus niger. 300fr, Choerodon fasciata. 400fr, Naso lituratus. 450fr, Hypoplectrus gemma. 500fr, Acanthurus achilles.
1000fr, Zebrasoma flavescens.

| | | | | |
|---|---|---|---|---|
| **1997, June 15** | | **Litho.** | **Perf. 13** | |
| 1403 | A222 | 200fr multicolored | .50 | .25 |
| 1404 | A222 | 250fr multicolored | 1.10 | .50 |
| 1405 | A222 | 300fr multicolored | 1.40 | .60 |
| 1406 | A222 | 400fr multicolored | 2.00 | .80 |
| 1407 | A222 | 450fr multicolored | 2.25 | .90 |
| 1408 | A222 | 500fr multicolored | 2.25 | .95 |
| | | *Nos. 1403-1408 (6)* | 9.50 | 4.00 |
| | | **Souvenir Sheet** | | |
| | | **Perf. 12½** | | |
| 1409 | A222 | 1000fr multicolored | *5.00* | *2.50* |

No. 1409 contains one 40x32mm stamp.

Chess Pieces
A222a

200fr, Thailand, 14th cent. 250fr, China, 1930. 300fr, Portugal, 1920. 400fr, Germany. 450fr, Russia. 500fr, Pieces by Max Ernst.
1000fr, France, 18th cent.

| | | | | |
|---|---|---|---|---|
| **1997, Oct. 20** | | | **Perf. 13** | |
| 1409A | A222a | 200fr multi | .95 | .45 |
| 1409B | A222a | 250fr multi | 1.10 | .55 |
| 1409C | A222a | 300fr multi | 1.40 | .70 |
| 1409D | A222a | 400fr multi | 1.75 | .90 |
| 1409E | A222a | 450fr multi | 2.10 | 1.00 |
| 1409F | A222a | 500fr multi | 2.25 | 1.10 |
| | | *Nos. 1409A-1409F (6)* | 9.55 | 4.70 |
| | | **Souvenir Sheet** | | |
| | | **Perf. 12½** | | |
| 1409G | A222a | 1000fr multi | 5.50 | 2.75 |

No. 1409G contains one 32x40mm stamp.

Dogs
A223

| | | | | |
|---|---|---|---|---|
| **1997, Nov. 10** | | **Litho.** | **Perf. 12½** | |
| | | **Stamp plus Label** | | |
| 1410 | A223 | 200fr Siberian husky | .70 | .35 |
| 1411 | A223 | 250fr Dachshund | .85 | .45 |
| 1412 | A223 | 300fr Boston terrier | 1.00 | .50 |
| 1413 | A223 | 400fr Basset hound | 1.40 | .70 |
| 1414 | A223 | 450fr Dalmatian | 1.50 | .75 |
| 1415 | A223 | 500fr Rottweiler | 1.70 | .85 |
| | | *Nos. 1410-1415 (6)* | 7.15 | 3.60 |
| | | **Souvenir Sheet** | | |
| 1416 | A223 | 1000fr Golden retriever | 5.50 | 2.75 |

Nos. 1410-1415 are each printed with se-tenant label.

Prehistoric Animals — A224

200fr, Dilophosaurus. 250fr, Psittacosaurus. 300fr, Dromiceiomimus. 400fr, Stenonychosaurus. 450fr, Opisthocoelicaudia. 500fr, Ornitholestes.
1000fr, Anchiceratops.

| | | | | |
|---|---|---|---|---|
| **1997** | | **Litho.** | **Perf. 12½** | |
| 1417 | A224 | 200fr multi | .75 | .40 |
| 1418 | A224 | 250fr multi, vert. | .90 | .50 |
| 1419 | A224 | 300fr multi | 1.10 | .55 |
| 1420 | A224 | 400fr multi, vert. | 1.50 | .75 |
| 1421 | A224 | 450fr multi | 1.60 | .80 |
| 1422 | A224 | 500fr multi | 1.90 | .90 |
| | | *Nos. 1417-1422 (6)* | 7.75 | 3.90 |
| | | **Souvenir Sheet** | | |
| 1423 | A224 | 1000fr multicolored | 4.25 | 2.10 |

No. 1423 contains one 40x32mm stamp.

UNICEF —
A224a

Design: 200fr, Children at school, horiz. 300fr, Baby receiving inoculation, horiz. 750fr, Mother nursing child. 1500fr, Women reading, horiz.

| | | | | |
|---|---|---|---|---|
| **1997** | | **Litho.** | **Perf. 13¼** | |
| 1423A | A224a | 200fr multi | — | — |
| 1423B | A224a | 300fr multi | — | — |
| 1423C | A224a | 750fr multi | — | — |
| 1423D | A224a | 1500fr multi | — | — |

Butterflies — A225

200fr, Eueides cleobaea. 250fr, Danaus cleophile. 300fr, Dryas julia. 400fr, Dismorphia cubana. 450fr, Pyrrhocalles antiga. 500fr, Phoebis orbis.
1000fr, Morpho adonis.

| | | | | |
|---|---|---|---|---|
| **1998** | | | | |
| 1424 | A225 | 200fr multicolored | .75 | .40 |
| 1425 | A225 | 250fr multicolored | .90 | .50 |
| 1426 | A225 | 300fr multicolored | 1.10 | .55 |
| 1427 | A225 | 400fr multicolored | 1.50 | .75 |
| 1428 | A225 | 450fr multicolored | 1.60 | .80 |
| 1429 | A225 | 500fr multicolored | 1.90 | .90 |
| | | *Nos. 1424-1429 (6)* | 7.75 | 3.90 |
| | | **Souvenir Sheet** | | |
| 1430 | A225 | 1000fr multicolored | 4.25 | 2.10 |

No. 1430 contains one 40x32mm stamp.

Environmental Protection Week—
A225a

Mount Nimba and frame in: 200fr, Brown. 300fr, Blue. 750fr, Green.

| | | | | |
|---|---|---|---|---|
| **1998** | | **Litho.** | **Perf. 13¼x13½** | |
| 1430A-1430C | A225a | Set of 3 | — | — |

Domestic
Cats — A226

200fr, English shorthair bicolor. 250fr, Scottish fold. 300fr, Birman. 400fr, American coarse hair. 450fr, Snowshoe. 500fr, Maine coon.
1000fr, Malaysian.

| | | | | |
|---|---|---|---|---|
| **1998** | | **Litho.** | **Perf. 12½** | |
| 1431 | A226 | 200fr multicolored | .65 | .30 |
| 1432 | A226 | 250fr multicolored | 1.00 | .45 |
| 1433 | A226 | 300fr multicolored | 1.10 | .60 |
| 1434 | A226 | 400fr multicolored | 1.50 | .75 |
| 1435 | A226 | 450fr multicolored | 1.75 | .90 |
| 1436 | A226 | 500fr multicolored | 2.00 | 1.00 |
| | | *Nos. 1431-1436 (6)* | 8.00 | 4.00 |

## Souvenir Sheet
### Perf. 13

**1437** A226 1000fr multicolored   4.25 2.10

No. 1437 contains one 32x40mm stamp.

Diana, Princess of Wales (1961-97) A227

Various portraits.

| 1998 | Litho. | Perf. 13½ |

### Sheets of 9

| **1438** A227 | 200fr #a.-i. | 8.00 | 4.00 |
| **1439** A227 | 300fr #a.-i. | 12.00 | 6.00 |
| **1440** A227 | 750fr #a.-i. | 30.00 | 15.00 |

### Souvenir Sheets

| **1441** A227 | 1500fr multicolored | 10.00 | 5.00 |
| **1442** A227 | 2000fr multicolored | 10.00 | 5.00 |

Dated 1997.

1998 World Cup Soccer Championships, France — A228

Various soccer plays.

| 1998 | Litho. | Perf. 12½ |

| **1443** A228 | 200fr multi, vert. | .75 | .40 |
| **1444** A228 | 250fr multi, vert. | .90 | .50 |
| **1445** A228 | 300fr multi, vert. | 1.10 | .55 |
| **1446** A228 | 400fr multi, vert. | 1.50 | .75 |
| **1447** A228 | 450fr multi | 1.60 | .80 |
| **1448** A228 | 500fr multi | 1.90 | .90 |
| *Nos. 1443-1448 (6)* | | 7.75 | 3.90 |

### Souvenir Sheet
### Perf. 13

| **1449** A228 | 1000fr multi | 5.50 | 2.75 |

No. 1449 contains one 32x40mm stamp.

Old Germanic Military Uniforms A228a

Designs: 200fr, Officer, Von Witerfeldt's Regiment. 250fr, Non-commissioned officer, Von Kanitz's Regiment. 300fr, Private, Prince Franz von Anhalt-Dessau's Regiment. 400fr, Private, Von Kalnein's Regiment. 450fr, Grenadier, Duke Ferdinand of Brunswick's Regiment. 500fr, Musician, Rekow's Guards Battalion.
1000fr, Pioneer.

| 1997, Aug. 17 | Litho. | Perf. 12½ |
| **1449A-1449F** A228a | Set of 6 | 10.00 5.00 |

### Souvenir Sheet

| **1449G** | A228a 1000fr multi | 5.00 2.25 |

No. 1449G contains one 32x40mm stamp.

Steam Locomotives — A229

200fr, Baldwin Locomotive Works, 0-4-2. 250fr, American Locomotive Co., 0-6-0. 300fr, Vulcan Iron Works, 0-6-0. 400fr, Baldwin Locomotive Works, 0-6-0. 450fr, H.K. Porter Co., 0-6-0. 500fr, Vulcan Iron Works, 0-6-0, diff.
1000fr, Baldwin Locomotive Works, 0-6-0, diff.

| 1997, Sept. 10 | Litho. | Perf. 12½ |
| **1450-1455** A229 | Set of 6 | 10.00 4.75 |

### Souvenir Sheet

| **1456** A229 | 1000fr multicolored | 7.00 3.50 |

No. 1456 contains one 40x32mm stamp.

Nectophrynoides Occidentalis — A230

Color of border: 200fr, green. 300fr, blue. 750fr, pale rose.

| 1998 | | Perf. 13½ |
| **1457-1459** A230 | Set of 3 | 5.50 2.75 |

Intl. Year of the Ocean A231

Marine life — #1460: a, Physeter macrocephalus, neophova cinerea. b, Melanogrammus aeglefinus. c, Delphinapterus leucas. d, Megaptera novaeangliae. e, Notorhynchus cependianus. f, Manta birostris. g, Delphinaterusleucas, macrozoarces americanus. h, Physalia physalis, pollachius virens. i, Manta birostris. j, Odontapis taurus. k, Thalassoma ruppelli, octopus vulgaris. l, Sebestes marinus.
1500fr, Megaptera novaeangliae, diff.

**1998**
| **1460** A231 | 200fr Sheet of 12, #a.-l. | 8.00 4.00 |

### Souvenir Sheet
| **1461** A231 | 1500fr multicolored | 9.00 4.25 |

Antique Cars A232

200fr, 1932 Chrysler, 8 cylinders, US. 300fr, 1907 Napier, 60HP, England. 450fr, 1903 Mercedes, 60HP, Germany. 750fr, 1925 Fiat 509, Italy.
No. 1466: a, 1929 Alfa Romeo 6C 1750 Zagato, Italy. b, 1932 Hispano-Suiza Type 68, Spain. c, 1931 Horsch V12, Germany. d, 1909 Rolland Pilain, 16hp, France. e, 1920 McLaughlin, Canada. f, 1930 Walter 6B, Czechoslovakia.
No. 1467: a, 1914 Fischer SS, Switzerland. b, 1922 Excelsior Adex C, Belgium. c, 1912 Pilain Torpedo, France. d, 1932 Franklin, 6 cylinders, US. e, 1912 Abadal 18/24hp, Spain. f, 1923 Alvis 12/50, England.
Each 1500fr: No. 1468, 1925 Rolls Royce Phantom 1, England. No. 1468A, 1932 Ford V8, US.

| 1998, Aug. 21 | | |
| **1462-1465** A232 | Set of 4 | 8.50 4.25 |

### Sheets of 6
| **1466** A232 | 450fr #a.-f. | 13.00 6.50 |

| **1467** A232 | 750fr #a.-f. | 24.00 11.50 |

### Souvenir Sheets
| **1468-1468A** A232 | Set of 2 | 18.00 8.50 |

Nos. 1468-1468A each contain one 56x42mm stamp.

Greenpeace — A233

Designs: a, Albatross looking left. b, Albatross in flight. c, Stern of Greenpeace ship, helicopter. d, Bow of Greenpeace ship. e, Albatross nesting. f, Albatross looking right.
2000fr, Albatross with chick.

| 1998 | Litho. | Perf. 13½ |
| **1469** A233 | 450fr Sheet of 6, #a.-f. | 10.00 8.00 |

### Souvenir Sheet
| **1470** A233 | 2000fr multicolored | 9.50 4.75 |

No. 1470 contains one 40x46mm stamp.

Endangered Species — A234

Designs, vert: 200fr, Lynx pardellus. 300fr, Lepilemur mustelinus. 450fr, Canis rufus. 750fr, Bison bonasus.
No. 1475: a, Leopard. b, Civet (f). c, Bird (d). d, Hawk. e, Rhinoceros, impala. f, Okapi (e, h, i). g, Lion. h, Chimpanzee. i, Gorilla. j, Bird (long, curved beak). k, Hippopotamus (l). l, Antelope (h).
No. 1476: a, Falco peregrinus. b, Acinonyx jubatus. c, Antilocapre americana. d, Mustela nigripes. e, Ursus maritimus. f, Rhinoceros unicornis.
No. 1477: a, Gymnobelideus leadbeater. b, Felis concolor. c, Felis pardalis. d, Panthera pardus. e, Bufo hemiophyrs. f, Mustela rutorius.
Each 1500fr: No. 1478, Muscardinus avellanarius. No. 1479, Aepyceros melampus, vert. No. 1480, Panthera uncia.

| 1998, Sept. 8 | | |
| **1471-1474** A234 | Set of 4 | 9.00 4.50 |

### Sheets of 12 & 6
| **1475** A234 | 200fr #a.-f. | 10.00 5.00 |
| **1476** A234 | 450fr #a.-f. | 12.00 5.75 |
| **1477** A234 | 750fr #a.-f. | 18.00 9.00 |

### Souvenir Sheets
| **1478-1480** A234 | Set of 3 | 24.00 12.00 |

Locomotives of the World — A235

No. 1481: a, Sir Nigel Gresley, England. b, Switzerland. c, Canada. d, EMU 102-6 Tobu Railway Spacia, Japan. e, Krauss Maffei V200, Germany. f, IC 580 Portugal. g, Amtrak No. 5, US. h, TGV, France.
No. 1482: a, Nippon Pacific No. 82, Middle East. b, Russia. c, Freight train, Albania. d, Dart No. 8319, Ireland. e, No. 141-F-177, France. f, EMU No. 69625, Norway. g, Bo-Bo, New Zealand. h, Azusa, Japan.
No. 1483: a, Syrian Railways 2-8-0, Iraq. b, The Irish Mail, England. c, Four car EMU, Italy. d, Sprinter, England. e, Van Golu Express, Turkey. f, No. 11.2110, Norway. g, Two-car EMU, New Zealand. h, Grey Mouse, France.
No. 1484: a, The Flying Scotman, United Kingdom. b, National Railways, Japan. c, North Africa. d, F-40M Winnebago, US. e, Federal Railways Class 10, three cylinder 4-6-2, Germany. f, DX5500, New Zealand. g, CIE, Ireland. h, Intercity class 43, England.
Each 1500fr: No. 1485, D2157, New Zealand. No. 1486, 140.7410, German Railways.

No. 1487, JR Shinkansen 221-204, Japan. No. 1488, Egyptian Railways, Bo-Bo.

| 1998, Oct. 30 | | |
### Sheets of 8
| **1481** A235 | 200fr #a.-h. | 8.00 3.75 |
| **1482** A235 | 300fr #a.-h. | 12.00 5.75 |
| **1483** A235 | 450fr #a.-h. | 16.00 7.75 |
| **1484** A235 | 750fr #a.-h. | 24.00 12.00 |

### Souvenir Sheets
| **1485-1488** A235 | Set of 4 | 30.00 15.00 |

Aircraft A236

Amphibians & flying boats — #1489: a, Boeing Model 1, 1916. b, Grumman G-21 Goose, 1937. c, Latecoere 631, 1942. d, Cessna Model 205. e, Sikorsky S-42, 1934. f, Boeing Model 314 Clipper. g, De Havilland Canada DHC-2 Beaver, 1947. h, Lake Buccaneer, 1979.
Balloons and Dirigibles — #1490: a, Henri Giffard, 1852. b, Santos-Dumont "Baladeuse," 1903. c, Zeppelin L37. d, R101, 1930. e, Santos-Dumont, 1898. f, Baldwin, 1908. g, Norge, 1926. h, Hindenburg, 1936.
Helicopters — #1491: a, Sikorsky VS-300, 1940. b, Sikorsky S-61, 1957. c, Bell Long Ranger, 1966. d, Dauphin SA 365, 1972. e, Bell 47, 1946. f, Boeing Vertol 243LR, 1958. g, Aerospatial SA 315 Blama. h, Bell Model 222, 1981.
Spacecraft — #1492: a, Mercury Capsule, 1961. b, Gemini 8, 1966. c, Apollo Lunar Module, 1968. d, Soviet Vostok, 1961. e, Apollo Command Module, 1968. f, Soviet Soyuz, 1975.
Each 1500fr: No. 1493, Cessna 208 Caravan, 1980. No. 1494, Goodyear Blimp. No. 1495, Miles Mi-26, 1983. No. 1496, Space Shuttle Columbia, 1981.

| 1998, Oct. 30 | | |
### Sheets of 8 & 6
| **1489** A236 | 200fr #a.-h. | 9.00 4.25 |
| **1490** A236 | 300fr #a.-h. | 13.00 6.25 |
| **1491** A236 | 450fr #a.-h. | 18.00 9.00 |
| **1492** A236 | 750fr #a.-f. | 22.50 11.00 |

### Souvenir Sheets
| **1493-1496** A236 | Set of 4 | 20.00 10.00 |

No. 1489a incorrectly inscribed "1961."

Dinosaurs A237

No. 1497: a, Dicraeosaurus. b, Parasaurolophus. c, Sauronithoides. d, Dilophosaurus. e, Titanosaurus, bagaceratops. f, Iguanodon. g, Tenontosaurus. h, Dryosaurus. i, Ceratosaurus.
1500fr, Yangchuanosaurus, brachiosaurus.

| 1998 | Litho. | Perf. 13½ |
| **1497** A237 | 750fr Sheet of 9, #a.-i. | 27.50 13.50 |

### Souvenir Sheet
| **1498** A237 | 1500fr multicolored | 6.00 3.00 |

Minerals — A238

a, Calcite. b, Wolframite. c, Spodumene. #1500D: e, Psilomelane. f, Heterosite. g, Columbo-tantalite.

**1998**     **Litho.**     *Perf. 13½*

**Strip of 3**

| 1499 | A238 | 750fr | Green background, #a.-c. | 10.50 | 5.25 |

**Souvenir Sheets of 3**

| 1500 | A238 | 750fr | Gray blue background, #a.-c. | 10.50 | 5.25 |
| 1500D | A238 | 1500fr | #e-g | 21.00 | 21.00 |

Sailing Ships — A239

No. 1501, each 450fr: a, "Theseus." b, "Euphrates." c, Phoenician War Galley. d, Chinese Junk.

No. 1502, each 450fr: a, "Juan Sebastian." b, "Santa Maria." c, Frigate. d, Madurese Jukung rig.

No. 1503, vert, each 750fr: a, Windjammer, "Wavertree." b, British frigate, "Rose." c, Tromp's flagship, "Golden Leeuw." d, Danish Timber Barque.

No. 1504, vert, each 750fr: a, Kraeck. b, Clipper ship, "Golden State." c, English ship, "Resolution." d, "Eagle."

Each 1500fr: No. 1505, British barque, "Garthpool." No. 1506, HMS Victory.

**1998, Nov. 10**     *Perf. 14*

**Sheets of 4, #a.-d.**

| 1501-1502 | A239 | Set of 2 | 16.00 | 7.75 |
| 1503-1504 | A239 | Set of 2 | 30.00 | 15.00 |

**Souvenir Sheets**

| 1505-1506 | A239 | Set of 2 | 15.00 | 15.00 |

Novotel Hotel, Conakry — A239a

**1998**     **Litho.**     *Perf. 13x13½*

| 1506A | A239a | 200fr multi | — | — |
| 1506B | A239a | 750fr multi | — | — |

The editors suspect that additional stamps may have been issued in this set and would like to examine any examples. Numbers may change.

**Modern Guinean Arts**

A239b

A239c

A239d

A239e

A239f

A239g

A239h

A239i

**1998, Dec. 8**     **Litho.**     *Perf. 13¼x13*

| 1506D | A239b | 750fr | Dance | — | — |
| 1506E | A239c | 750fr | Painting | — | — |
| 1506F | A239d | 750fr | Ceramics | — | — |
| 1506G | A239e | 750fr | Sculpture | — | — |
| 1506H | A239f | 750fr | Sculpture | — | — |
| 1506I | A239g | 750fr | Dance | — | — |
| 1506J | A239h | 750fr | Painting | — | — |
| 1506K | A239i | 750fr | Painting | — | — |

Horses A240

Designs: 150fr, Trotteur Russe. 200fr, Brabant. 300fr, Camargue. No. 1510, 450fr, Unidentified breed. No. 1511, 450fr, Dales pony. No. 1512, 750fr, Fjord.

No. 1513, vert.: a, Kabardin. b, Shire. c, Arabian. d, Mustang. e, Quarter horse. f, Appaloosa.

No. 1514, vert.: a, Thoroughbred. b, Lipizzaner. c, Belgian. d, Palomino. e, Haflinger. f, Fjord, diff.

Each 1500fr: No. 1515, Mustang, diff. No. 1516, Thoroughbred colt.

**1999, May 1**     **Litho.**     *Perf. 14*

| 1507-1512 | A240 | Set of 6 | 11.00 | 11.00 |

**Sheets of 6**

| 1513 | A240 | 450fr | #a.-f. | 12.00 | 12.00 |
| 1514 | A240 | 750fr | #a.-f. | 21.00 | 21.00 |

**Souvenir Sheets**

| 1515-1516 | A240 | Set of 2 | 17.00 | 17.00 |

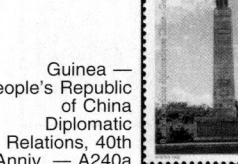

Guinea — People's Republic of China Diplomatic Relations, 40th Anniv. — A240a

Designs: 200fr, Shown. 300fr, Building with flat roof, horiz. 750fr, Building with slanted roof, horiz.

**1999**     **Litho.**     *Perf. 13¼x13*

| 1516A | A240a | 200fr multi | — | — |
| 1516B | A240a | 300fr multi | — | — |
| 1516C | A240a | 750fr multi | — | — |

Dogs A241

Designs: 200fr, Newfoundland. No. 1518, 750fr, St. Bernard.

No. 1519, vert.: a, Bulldog. b, Miniature schnauzer. c, Dachshund. d, Beagle. e, Bloodhound. f, Miniature pinscher.

1500fr, Irish setter.

**1999, May 1**

| 1517-1518 | A241 | Set of 2 | 5.00 | 5.00 |

**Sheet of 6**

| 1519 | A241 | 750fr | #a.-f. | 18.00 | 18.00 |

**Souvenir Sheet**

| 1520 | A241 | 1500fr multi | 8.00 | 8.00 |

Modern Guinean Sculptures — A241a

Various sculptures.

**1999, Aug. 9**     **Litho.**     *Perf. 13¼x13*

| 1520A | A241a | 200fr multi | 2.40 | 2.40 |
| 1520B | A241a | 250fr multi | 2.40 | 2.40 |
| 1520C | A241a | 300fr multi | 2.40 | 2.40 |
| 1520D | A241a | 500fr shown | 2.40 | 2.40 |
| 1520E | A241a | 750fr multi | 2.40 | 2.40 |

PhilexFrance '99.

Dinosaurs & Prehistoric Animals — A243

Designs: 300fr, Ouranosaurus. No. 1522, 450fr, Centrosaurus. No. 1523, 450fr, Dilophosaurus, vert.

No. 1524: a, Cymbospondylus. b, Kronosaurus. c, Ichthyosaurus. d, Eurhinosaurus. e, Stenopterygius. f, Ophthalmosaurus. g, Shonisaurus. h, Temnodontosaurus. i, Mixosaurus.

No. 1525, vert.: a, Eudimorphodon. b, Sordes. c, Dimorphodon. d, Albertosaurus. e, Triceratops. f, Alioramus. g, Mesosaurus. h, Labidosaurus. i, Struthiomimus.

No. 1526: a, Saltosaurus. b, Corythosaurus. c, Protoceratops. d, Baryonyx. e,

Pachycephalosaurus. f, Maiasaurus. g, Spinosaurus. h, Lambeosaurus.

2500fr, Elasmosaurus, vert. No. 1528, Tyrannosaurus Rex. No. 1529, Utahraptor. No. 1530, Parasaurolophus, vert.

**1999, Aug. 12**

| 1521-1523 | A242 | Set of 3 | 5.00 | 5.00 |

**Sheets of 9**

| 1524 | A243 | 350fr | #a.-i. | 15.00 | 15.00 |
| 1525 | A243 | 450fr | #a.-i. | 18.00 | 18.00 |

**Sheet of 8**

| 1526 | A242 | 450fr | #a.-h | 18.00 | 18.00 |

**Souvenir Sheets**

| 1527 | A243 | 2500fr multi | 13.00 | 13.00 |
| 1528 | A243 | 3000fr multi | 13.00 | 13.00 |
| 1529-1530 | A242 | 3000fr | Set of 2 | 28.00 | 28.00 |

No. 1527 contains one 42x56mm stamp. No. 1528 contains one 56x42mm stamp.

Return of Macao to People's Republic of China, Dec. 20, 1999 A244

No. 1531, each 650fr: a, Current view of Nam Van (tall buildings). b, Nam Van in 1850s (hilltop and bay). c, Current view of Largo de Senado. d, Largo de Senado in 1900s.

No. 1532, each 650fr: a, Current view of Nam Van (highway). b, Nam Van in 1850s (buildings at water's edge). c, Current view of Nam Van (boat). d, Nam Van in 1850s (ships).

**1999, Aug. 20**     *Perf. 14¼x14½*

**Sheets of 4, #a.-d.**

| 1531-1532 | A244 | Set of 2 | 24.00 | 24.00 |

China 1999 World Philatelic Exhibition.

Paintings of Zhang Daqian (1899-1983) — A245

No. 1533: a, Ink Lotus. b, Ink Peony. c, Red Cliff Excursion at Night. d, Poetic Landscape. e, Landscape in the Evening. f, Spring Landscape. g, Chatting at Leisure in Mountains. h, Pine Nesting. i, Pine in Thunder. j, Blue and Green Landscape.

No. 1534: a, Landscape. b, Versing in the Landscape.

**1999, Aug. 20**     **Litho.**     *Perf. 13¼*

| 1533 | A245 | 330fr | Sheet of 10, #a.-j. | 15.00 | 15.00 |

**Souvenir Sheet of 2**

*Perf. 13*

| 1534 | A245 | 1150fr | #a.-b. | 4.50 | 4.50 |

No. 1534 contains two 51x39mm stamps. China 1999 World Philatelic Exhibition

First French Postage Stamp, 150th Anniv. — A245a

**Litho. with Hologram Applied**

**1999, Sept. 10**     *Perf. 13*

| 1534C | A245a | 750fr multi | 4.75 | 4.75 |

Trains
A246

100fr, Diesel TGV, East Germany. No. 1536, 200fr, 1900 horsepower Diesel-electric, Finland. No. 1537, 200fr, Type MLW 3000 horsepower Diesel-electric. No. 1538, 250fr, A-4, Britain. No. 1539, 250fr, Class R 4-6-4. No. 1540, 250fr, Class M, 4-6-2, Tasmania. No. 1541, 450fr, Class 68000 Diesel-electric, France. No. 1542, 450fr, 4-8-4 Daylight Express. No. 1543, 450fr, Electric TGV, Italy. No. 1544, 450fr, Western Class Hydraulic-Diesel.

No. 1545: a, Class 10 3-cylinder 4-6-2. b, SD18 Diesel-electric. c, Hikari Super Express Train, Japan. d, Diesel-electric No. 10000. e, PA-1 Diesel-electric. f, 2500 horsepower experimental gas turbine locomotive.

No. 1546: a, YP Class, India. b, Class 47, Standard Type 4 Diesel-electric. c, DSI Class 2-8-2, Japan. d, Class D-341 Diesel-electric. e, S1 Class 2-6-4. f, 3600 horsepower locomotive, India.

No. 1547: a, 2000 horsepower GP-20 Diesel-electric. b, Class C-53 3-cylinder, Japan. c, Multiple-unit Diesel, Japan. d, Royal Scot Class 4-6-0. e, Deltic electric prototype. f, W.P. Standard 4-6-2.

No. 1548: 2500fr, Class 40 electric, England.

Each 3000fr: No. 1549, GP-40 Diesel-electric. No. 1550, 9780 horsepower DM-3, Sweden. No. 1551, 1750 horsepower Diesel-electric, Denmark.

**1999, Oct. 25**        **Perf. 14**
1535-1544 A246 Set of 10    13.00 13.00

**Sheets of 6**
1545 A246 300fr #a.-f.    8.50 8.50
1546 A246 450fr #a.-f.    12.00 12.00
1547 A246 750fr #a.-f.    21.00 21.00

**Souvenir Sheets**
1548 A246 2500fr multi    11.00 11.00
1549-1551 A246 Set of 3    40.00 40.00

Mushrooms and Insects — A247

Mushrooms and unidentified insects: No. 1552, 100fr, Lentinellus cochleatus. No. 1553, 100fr, Lactarius blennius. No. 1554, Lactarius sanguifluus. No. 1555, 150fr, Leucocortinarius bulbiger. No. 1556, 300fr, Clitocybe phyllophila. No. 1557, 300fr, Calocybe ionides. No. 1558, 300fr, Lactarius porninsis. No. 1559, 300fr, Cystoderma amianthinum. No. 1560, 300fr, Limacella guttata. No. 1561, 300fr, Suillus placidus. No. 1562, 450fr, Suillus grevillei. No. 1563, 450fr, Suillus luteus. No. 1564, 450fr, Suillus granulatus. No. 1565, 450fr, Pleurotus cornuscopiae. No. 1566, 450fr, Calocybe carnea. No. 1567, 450fr, Panus tigrinus.

Mushrooms and insects — No. 1568: a, Hygrocybe nigreseens, Argynnis paphia. b, Hygrocybe subglobispora, Pterophoridae. c, Oudemansiella mucida, Tettigonia viridissima. d, Amanita rubescens, unidentified insect. e, Amanita muscaria, Oedipoda caerulescens. f, Suillus luteus, Happarchia fagi. g, Coprinus picaceus, Aphantopus hyperantus. h, Gymnopilus junonius, Ourapteryx sambucaria. i, Amanita muscaria, Catocala nupta.

No. 1569: a, Macrolepiota procera, Pieris brassicae. b, Lactarius britannicus, Pyrochroa cocci. c, Cortinarius sanguineus, Tabicina haematodes. d, Amanita muscaria, Sympetrum. e, Aerocomus badius, Issoria lathonia. f, Laccaria amethystea, Sympetrum. g, Paxillus atrotomentosus, Inachis io. h, Armillaria mellea, Chrystoxum cautum. i, Amanita echinocephala, Vanessa atalanta.

Each 2500fr: No. 1570, Lactarius brittanicus, Coccinella punctala. No. 1571, Amanita phalloides, Ochlodes venatus. No. 1572, Coprinus atramentarius, unidentified insect. Each 3000fr: No. 1573, Amanita citrina, unidentified insect. No. 1574, Amanita pantherina, Aperia syringaria.

---

**1999, Nov. 11**
1552-1567 A247 Set of 16    24.00 24.00

**Sheets of 9**
1568 A247 300fr #a.-i.    12.00 12.00
1569 A247 450fr #a.-i.    18.00 18.00

**Souvenir Sheets**
1570-1572 A247 Set of 3    35.00 35.00
1573-1574 A247 Set of 2    24.00 24.00

Birds
A248        A249

Designs: No. 1575, 200fr, Catamblyrhychus diadema. No. 1576, 200fr, Tichodrome. No. 1577, 300fr, Turtle dove. No. 1578, 300fr, Flamingo. No. 1579, 300fr, Duck. No. 1580, 300fr, Woodpecker. No. 1581, 450fr, Warbler. No. 1582, 450fr, Bullfinch.

No. 1583: a, Wild turkey. b, Ring-necked pheasant. c, Gray partridge. d, Woodcock. e, Capercaillie. f, Rock partridge.

No. 1584: a, Cuban hummingbird. b, Rufous-breated hermit. c, Green-throated hummingbird. d, Bee-eater. e, Puerto Rican hummingbird. f, Antillean hummingbird.

No. 1585: a, Gould's finch. b, Oriole. c, Psarismus dalhousiae. d, Woodchat shrike. e, Pitta guajana. f, Neodreponis coruscans.

No. 1586, horiz.: a, Purple-throated Carib. b, Bahamas hummingbird. c, Blue-bearded hummingbird. d, Green hummingbird. e, Jamaican hummingbird. f, Vervaine.

Each 2500fr: No. 1587, Spotted waxwing. No. 1588, Red-banded bee-eater.

Each 2500fr: No. 1589, Bahamas hummingbird, horiz. No. 1590, Antillean crested hummingbird.

No. 1591, 3000fr, Emerald hummingbird.

**1999, Nov. 22**
1575-1582 A248 Set of 8    10.00 10.00

**Sheets of 6**
1583 A248 450fr #a.-f.    12.00 12.00
1584 A249 500fr #a.-f.    15.00 15.00
1585 A248 600fr #a.-f.    16.00 16.00
1586 A249 750fr #a.-f.    20.00 20.00

**Souvenir Sheets**
1587-1588 A248 Set of 2    24.00 24.00
1589-1590 A249 Set of 2    24.00 24.00
1591 A249 3000fr multi    14.00 14.00

Butterflies
A250

Designs: No. 1592, 300fr, Acraea acerata. No. 1593, 300fr, Charaxes protoclea. No. 1594, 300fr, Charaxes hadrianus. No. 1595, 300fr, Colotis halimede. No. 1596, 300fr, Colotis eucharis. No. 1597, Papilio dardanus.

No. 1598, vert.: a, Papilio charopus. b, Papilio dardanus. c, Acraea zetes. d, Hypolimnas salmacis. e, Cymothoe beckeri. f, Papilio nobilis.

No. 1599, vert.: a, Iolaus lalos. b, Graphium gudenusi. c, Hewitsonia boisduvalii. d, Graphium ucalegon. e, Danaus chrysippus. f, Acraea satis.

Each 2500fr: No. 1600, Euxanthe tiberius. No. 1601, Colotis danae.

**1999, Nov. 22**
1592-1597 A250 Set of 6    7.50 7.50

**Sheets of 6**
1598 A250 450fr #a.-f.    12.00 12.00
1599 A250 750fr #a.-f.    20.00 20.00

**Souvenir Sheets**
1600-1601 A250 Set of 2    24.00 24.00

---

Wedding of Prince Edward and Sophie Rhys-Jones
A251

No. 1602: a, Edward in blue striped shirt. b, Sophie with scarf. c, Edward looking left. d, Sophie looking right. e, Edward with blue checked shirt. f, Sophie with black blouse.
3000fr, Couple.

**1999, Dec. 6**
1602 A251 750fr Sheet of 6,
     #a.-f.    21.00 21.00

**Souvenir Sheet**
1603 A251 3000fr multi    14.00 14.00

Hokusai Paintings
A252

No. 1604, each 750fr: a, Actor Ichikawa Ebizo. b, Drawings (man with fan). c, Actor Sakata Hangoro. d, Geisha and Madam. e, Drawings (man with sword). f, Kabuki Actor Hanshiro IV.

No. 1605, each 750fr: a, Kintaro and Wild Animals. b, Drawings (man with clasped hands). c, Lady Walking in the Snow. d, Lady and Maiden on an Outing. e, Drawings (man with incense burner). f, Girls at Their Toilette.

Each 3000fr: No. 1606, Sumo Wrestlers. No. 1607, Geisha House and Madam at Leisure with Child.

**1999, Dec. 6**        **Perf. 12¼**

**Sheets of 6, #a.-f.**
1604-1605 A252 Set of 2    35.00 35.00

**Souvenir Sheets**
1606-1607 A252 Set of 2    27.50 27.50

Johann Wolfgang von Goethe (1749-1832), German Poet — A253

No. 1608, each 1000fr: a, Mephistopheles tempts Faust with Margaret. b, Goethe and Friedrich von Schiller. c, The witches' kitchen, a potion brewed.
3000fr, Euphorion.

**1999, Dec. 6**        **Perf. 14**
1608 A253 Sheet of 3, #a.-c.    14.00 14.00

**Souvenir Sheet**
1609 A253 3000fr multi    14.00 14.00

A254

---

A255

Space Exploration — A256

Designs: No. 1610, 300fr, Pioneer 10. No. 1611, 300fr, Viking 1.

No. 1612: a, Takao Doi. b, Frank Borman. c, Alan B. Shepard, Jr. d, M. Scott Carpenter. e, Ulf Merbold. f, David R. Scott. g, Mamoru Mohri, h, Gherman Titov. i, Sally K. Ride. j, Walter M. Schirra. k, John L. Swigert, Jr. l, Yuri A. Gagarin.

No. 1613, each 500fr: a, Venus. b, Neptune. c, Jupiter. d, Uranus. e, Saturn. f, Mercury.

No. 1614, each 500fr: a, Mariner 4. b, HL-20. c, Mariner 2. d, Voyager 1. e, Venture Star. f, Phobos.

No. 1615, each 750fr: a, 1961 drawing of lunar ferry. b, 1960 drawing of lunar lander. c, 1959 drawing of lunar lander. d, 1962 drawing of lunar lander. e, 1962 drawing of lunar lander trainer. f, 1961 drawing of lunar lander.

No. 1616, vert.: a, Apollo 5. b, Apollo 6, c, Apollo 7. d, Apollo escape test. e, Apollo "Little Joe." f, Apollo 4.

No. 1617, 1500fr, John Glenn.

Each 1500fr: No. 1618, Apollo 11 command module, vert. No. 1619, Collecting moon rocks.

Each 2000fr: No. 1620, Viking, diff. No. 1621, Mars Global Surveyor. No. 1622, Sojourner.

**1999, Dec. 9**
1610-1611 A254 Set of 2    3.00 3.00

**Sheet of 12, #a.-l.**
1612 A255 450fr multi    27.50 27.50

**Sheets of 6, #a.-f.**
1613-1614 A254 Set of 2    24.00 24.00
1615-1616 A256 Set of 2    40.00 40.00

**Souvenir Sheets**
1617 A255 1500fr multi    8.00 8.00
1618-1619 A256 Set of 2    15.00 15.00
1620-1622 A254 Set of 3    26.50 26.50

Nos. 1620-1622 each contain one 50x37mm stamp.

Queen Mother (b. 1900) — A257

No. 1623: a, In 1934. b, With tiara. c, Lady of the Garter. d, In 1997.
3000fr, With tiara, diff.

**1999, Dec. 6**        **Perf. 14**
1623 A257 1000fr Sheet of 4,
     #a.-d., + label    19.00 19.00

**Souvenir Sheet**
**Perf. 13¾**
1624 A257 3000fr multi    14.00 14.00

No. 1624 contains one 38x50mm stamp.

Cats
A257a

Designs: 300fr, Ragdoll. No. 1626, 400fr, Egyptian Mau.

No. 1627, vert.: a, Tonkinese. b, Korat. c, Siamese. d, British Shorthair. e, Bengal. f, Persian.

1500fr, Calico Shorthair, vert.

| 1999 | | | **Perf. 14** | |
|---|---|---|---|---|
| **1625-1626** | A257a | Set of 2 | 3.25 | 3.25 |
| | | **Sheet of 6** | | |
| **1627** | A257a | 450fr #a.-f. | 12.00 | 12.00 |
| | | **Souvenir Sheet** | | |
| **1628** | A257a | 1500fr multi | 8.00 | 8.00 |

Romance of
the Three
Kingdoms
A258

No. 1629, each 460fr: a, Archer and four men. b, Two men and tea pot. c, Spear carrier, man, woman. d, Horsemen jousting. e, Four men.

No. 1630, each 460fr: a, Swordsman on white horse. b, Spear carrier on black horse. c, Bed chamber. d, Man being speared. e, At sea.

2000fr, Three men with tea cups.

| 1999 | | | **Perf. 13¼** | |
|---|---|---|---|---|
| | | **Sheets of 5, #a.-e.** | | |
| **1629-1630** | A258 | Set of 2 | 20.00 | 20.00 |
| | | **Souvenir Sheet** | | |
| **1631** | A258 | 2000fr multi | 9.00 | 9.00 |

No. 1631 contains one 48x58mm stamp.

Millennium — A354

No. 1823 — Marco Polo's Voyages: a, Young Marco Polo. b, Piazza San Marco. c, Polo's ship. d, Priest buying incense. e, Houses in Syria. f, Ruins of Saveh. g, Persian ventilator. h, Moncia costume. i, Ulan Bator Abbey. j, Buddha, 5th cent. k, Great Wall of China. l, Warrior of Kublai Khan's Army. m, Ship on the Yangtze. n, Japanese archer. o, Golden plate. p, Medallion of Marco Polo, horiz. (60x40mm). q, Kublai Khan.

No. 1824 — Expansion of Knowledge: a, Election of King Sigismund I of Hungary as Holy Roman Emperor, 1411. b, Filippo Brunelleschi wins architectural contest to build the dome of the Santa Maria di Fiore, 1420. c, Lorenzo Ghiberti sculpts human forms on doors of the Florence Baptistry, 1425. d, Death of Juliana of Norwich, c. 1443. e, Chinese Ming capital moves from Nanjing to Beijing, 1420. f, Europeans begin to use Chinese method of black printing, 1423. g, King Henry V of England defeats French at Battle of Agincourt, 1415. h, Tamerlane defeats Ottomans at Battle of Ankyra, 1402. i, Joan of Arc leads French forces at Siege of Orleans, 1429. j, Korea prospers under rule of King Sejong, 1419. k, Thomas à Kempis writes *The Imitation of Christ*, 1427. l, King Casimir IV of Poland unites Polish Kingdom with Grand Duchy of Lithuania, 1447. m, End of the Great Schism, 1417. n, John Hus burnt at the stake,

1415. o, Medici family dominates the government of Florence, 1434. p, Chaucer completes *Canterbury Tales*, 1400, horiz. (60x40mm). q, Shogun Yoshima Ashikaga begins rule in Japan, 1449.

No. 1825 — Across the Continents: a, Engraving, c. 1598. b, Caribbean warriors. c, Viking ship, 12th cent. d, Ship of Vasco da Gama. e, Detail from Italian engraving. f, Columbus's letter of 1493. g, Kokyrboom tree, h, Megalzina virens. i, Details from a map, Moon between Earth and Sun. j, Details from a map, Earth between Sun and Moon. k, Maori wood carving. l, Astrolabes. m, Frilled lizard (inscribed "Gila monster"). n, White ibises. o, Tahitian utensils. p, Ocean monsters, horiz. (60x40mm). q, Samoan boat.

| | | **Perf. 12¾x12½** | | |
|---|---|---|---|---|
| **2000, Feb. 18** | | | | **Litho.** |
| | | **Sheets of 17, #a-q, + Label** | | |
| **1823** | A354 | 200fr multi | 16.00 | 16.00 |
| **1824** | A354 | 250fr multi | 21.00 | 21.00 |
| **1825** | A354 | 300fr multi | 24.00 | 24.00 |
| | | *Nos. 1823-1825 (3)* | 61.00 | 61.00 |

New Year 2000 (Year of the
Dragon) — A355

No. 1826 — Dragon with background in: a, Red, claws near "Office." b, Green. c, Blue. d, Red, tail near "Office."

2000fr, Light blue.

| **2000, Feb. 18** | | | **Perf. 13¾** | |
|---|---|---|---|---|
| **1826** | A355 | 400fr Sheet of 4, #a-d | 7.50 | 7.50 |
| | | **Souvenir Sheet** | | |
| **1827** | A355 | 2000fr multi | 9.50 | 9.50 |

No. 1826 contains four 48x32mm stamps.

Miniature Sheet

Vacation Photographs — A356

No. 1828: Various photographs making up a photomosaic of the Titanic.

| **2000, Feb. 18** | | | | |
|---|---|---|---|---|
| **1828** | A356 | 750fr Sheet of 8, #a-h | 27.50 | 27.50 |

2000 Summer Olympics,
Sydney — A357

No. 1829: a, Women's discus. b, Javelin. c, Men's discus. d, Shot put. e, Hammer throw.

No. 1830: a, Women's volleyball. b, Water polo. c, Women's beach volleyball. d, Handball. e, Women's soccer.

No. 1831: a, Women's judo. b, Wrestling. c, Men's judo. d, Boxing, pink background. e, Boxing, green background.

No. 1832: a, Women's diving. b, Synchronized swimming. c, Women's swimming. d, Women's sailing. e, Kayaking.

No. 1833: a, Badminton. b, Field hockey. c, Baseball. d, Fencing. e, Weight lifting.

No. 1834: a, Dressage. b, Archery. c, Show jumping. d, Rifle shooting. e, Pistol shooting.

No. 1835: a, Table tennis, two men. b, Table tennis, one man, blue and purple background. c, Table tennis, one man, green and yellow background. d, Women's table tennis. e, Table tennis, four players.

No. 1836: a, Women's tennis, blue background. b, Men's tennis, green background. c, Women's tennis, bister background. d, Men's tennis, gray background. e, Men's tennis, blue background.

No. 1837: a, Women's basketball. b, Men's basketball (Michael Jordan dunking basketball). c, Men's basketball, two players. d, Men's basketball (Jordan dribbling). e, Men's basketball, blue background.

No. 1838: a, Cycling Road Race (Route). b, Cycling Sprint Race (Vitesse). c, Cycling Team Pursuit. d, Cycling Points Race (Kilometre). e, Cycling Time Trial (Contre la montre).

| **2000, Nov. 14** | | | **Perf. 13¼** | |
|---|---|---|---|---|
| | | **Sheets of 5, #a-e, + Label** | | |
| **1829** | A357 | 150fr multi | 3.50 | 3.50 |
| **1830** | A357 | 150fr multi | 3.50 | 3.50 |
| **1831** | A357 | 200fr multi | 4.50 | 4.50 |
| **1832** | A357 | 200fr multi | 4.50 | 4.50 |
| **1833** | A357 | 300fr multi | 7.00 | 7.00 |
| **1834** | A357 | 300fr multi | 7.00 | 7.00 |
| **1835** | A357 | 600fr multi | 13.50 | 13.50 |
| **1836** | A357 | 600fr multi | 13.50 | 13.50 |
| **1837** | A357 | 750fr multi | 17.00 | 17.00 |
| **1838** | A357 | 750fr multi | 17.00 | 17.00 |
| | | *Nos. 1829-1838 (10)* | 91.00 | 91.00 |

Sports and Chess — A358

No. 1839 — Golf: a, Golfer with purple cap. b, Golfer with white pants. c, Golfer with white cap. d, Golfer with green shirt.

No. 1840 — Soccer: a, Marcel Dessally. b, Zinedine Zidane. c, Youri Djorkaeff. d, Thierry Henry.

No. 1841 — Auto racing: a, Ayrton Senna. b, Mika Hakkinen. c, Alain Prost. d, Michael Schumacher.

No. 1842 — Chess: a, Player with hands on forehead. b, Player with blue jacket. c, Player with gray jacket. d, Female player.

| **2000, Nov. 14** | | | | |
|---|---|---|---|---|
| | | **Sheets of 4, #a-d** | | |
| **1839** | A358 | 450fr multi | 8.00 | 8.00 |
| **1840** | A358 | 450fr multi | 8.00 | 8.00 |
| **1841** | A358 | 750fr multi | 14.00 | 14.00 |
| **1842** | A358 | 750fr multi | 14.00 | 14.00 |
| | | *Nos. 1839-1842 (4)* | 44.00 | 44.00 |

Locomotives — A359

No. 1843, horiz.: a, De Witt Clinton. b, American 220. c, Triplet Mallet. d, Philadelphia & Reading 422 Baldwin. e, Mason Bogie. f, Promontory Point 220 No. 119. g, Mogul. h, Best Friend of Charleston. i, John Bull.

No. 1844, horiz.: a, Union Pacific Bo-Bo-Bo-Bo. b, Bipolar No. 2. c, Burlington Northern-Series SD 40-2 No. 7044. d, Amtrak Metroliner No. 880. e, Rio Grande Western Series F. f, Union Pacific Series DD 40AX. g, Lake Superior & Ishpeming Co-Co 025C No. 2500. h, Chicago, Milwaukee, St. Paul & Pacific Bipolar 3000V No. 4. i, Southern Pacific Krauss-Maffei C-C No. 9006.

No. 1845, horiz.: a, Southern Pacific GM-EMD Series F No. 98. b, Union Pacific M-10001. c, Union Pacific Switcher No. 4466. d, Chesapeake & Ohio Series M No. 500. e, Amtrak Series P32 No. 513. f, Southern Pacific EMD SD 40-2 No. 9368. g, Great Northern Series W-1 No. 5018. h, Grand Canyon 140. i, Pennsylvania Railroad 6100.

No. 1846, horiz.: a, Burlington Northern Santa Fe No. 4326. b, Conrail Series GP EMD No. 8194. c, Kansas City Southern No. 6639. d, Southern Pacific No. 9800. e, Pennsylvania Railroad 661 No. 4835. f, Union Pacific No. 8182. g, Burlington Northern No. 2917. h, Gulf, Mobile & Ohio Railroad Series F. i, Santa Fe No. 627.

No. 1847, horiz.: a, Norfolk Southern No. 6627. b, Grand Trunk No. 6219. c, Soo Line No. 6401. d, Santa Fe BNSF No. 2512. e, Chessie System No. 6035. f, Utah Railway No. 9010. g, Chicago & Northwestern No. 6866. h, Norfolk Southern No. 3328. i, Canadian National No. 4634.

No. 1848, horiz.: a, Canadian Pacific Budd Autorail Diesel No. 9112. b, New York Central 2-Do-2 No. 113. c, British Columbia Railway Series C630 No. 703. d, Chesapeake & Ohio Series GP9 No. 6137. e, Amtrak 661 No. 902. f, Santa Fe GP9 No. 2293. g, Trainmaster Type Co-Co. h, Chicago, Burlington & Quincy Pioneer Zephyr. i, Denver & Rio Grande Western No. 5350.

No. 1849, 2000fr, Tom Thumb, 2-2-0. No. 1850, 2000fr, Norfolk & Western Class J. No. 1851, 2000fr, Royal Gorge CC No. 403. No. 1852, 2000fr, Hudson 4-6-4 No. 490.

| **2000, Dec. 7** | | | | |
|---|---|---|---|---|
| | | **Sheets of 9, #a-i** | | |
| **1843** | A359 | 200fr multi | 8.00 | 8.00 |
| **1844** | A359 | 300fr multi | 12.50 | 12.50 |
| **1845** | A359 | 350fr multi | 15.00 | 15.00 |
| **1846** | A359 | 400fr multi | 16.00 | 16.00 |
| **1847** | A359 | 450fr multi | 18.00 | 18.00 |
| **1848** | A359 | 500fr multi | 21.00 | 21.00 |
| | | *Nos. 1843-1848 (6)* | 90.50 | 90.50 |
| | | **Souvenir Sheets** | | |
| **1849-1852** | A359 | Set of 4 | 32.50 | 32.50 |

Nos. 1843-1848 each contain nine 51x36mm stamps.

A360

First Zeppelin flight, Cent. — A361

No. 1853: a, Zeppelin LZ-11 Viktoria Luise. b, E. T. Willows. c, Hindenburg. d, Astra-Torres 1. e, Beta. f, Schutte-Lanz SL3.

No. 1854: a, Gross-Basenach M1. b, Schutte-Lanz SL1. c, Parseval PL25. d, Siemens-Schuckert. e, Delta. f, Parseval PL VIII.

No. 1855: a, LZ-9. b, LZ-10 Schwaben. c, LZ-11 Viktoria Luise, diff. d, LZ-127 Graf Zeppelin. e, LZ-129 Hindenburg. f, LZ-130.

No. 1856: a, LZ-1. b, LZ-2. c, LZ-3. d, LZ-4. e, LZ-5. f, LZ-6.

No. 1857, Graf Zeppelin and airplane. No. 1858, LZ-1, diff.

**2000, Dec. 11**　　　　　　**Perf. 14**
**Sheets of 6, #a-f**
| | | | | |
|---|---|---|---|---|
| 1853 | A360 | 300fr multi | 8.50 | 8.50 |
| 1854 | A360 | 450fr multi | 12.00 | 12.00 |
| 1855 | A361 | 1000fr multi | 27.50 | 27.50 |
| 1856 | A361 | 1000fr multi | 27.50 | 27.50 |
| | *Nos. 1853-1856 (4)* | | 75.50 | 75.50 |

**Souvenir Sheets**
| | | | | |
|---|---|---|---|---|
| 1857 | A360 | 4000fr multi | 20.00 | 20.00 |
| 1858 | A361 | 4000fr multi | 20.00 | 20.00 |

**Miniature Sheet**

Flowers — A362

No. 1859: Various photographs making up a photomosaic of Queen Mother Elizabeth.

**2000, Dec. 11**
| | | | | |
|---|---|---|---|---|
| 1859 | A362 | 750fr Sheet of 8, #a-h | 26.00 | 26.00 |

Prince William of Wales, 18th Birthday — A363

No. 1860: a, Wearing red tie. b, Wearing black and white checked tie. c, With Prince Harry. d, Wearing blue sweater.
4000fr, Wearing scarf.

**2000, Dec. 11**　　　　　　**Perf. 14**
| | | | | |
|---|---|---|---|---|
| 1860 | A363 | 1000fr Sheet of 4, #a-d | 18.00 | 18.00 |

**Souvenir Sheet**
**Perf. 13¾**
| | | | | |
|---|---|---|---|---|
| 1861 | A363 | 4000fr multi | 19.00 | 19.00 |

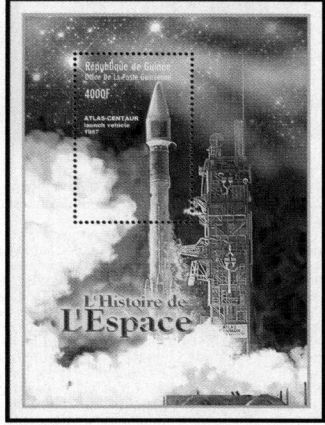

History of Space Exploration — A364

No. 1862, 200fr: a, Discovery of gunpowder. b, Fire arrows. c, Wan Hu's rocket glider. d, Konstantin Tsiolkovsky. e, Telescope of William Herschel. f, Galileo Galilei. g, Nicolaus Copernicus. h, Robert H. Goddard. i, Paper hot air balloons. j, Wernher von Braun. k, Launch of first rocket by Goddard. l, V-1 missile buzz-bomb.

No. 1863, 200fr: a, First American spacewalk by Ed White, Gemini 4. b, First man on the Moon, Apollo 11. c, Space Shuttle Atlantis. d, Voskhod 2. e, Sputnik 1. f, Apollo-Soyuz. g, John Glenn, first American to orbit Earth. h, Valentina Tereshkova, first woman in space. i, Yuri Gagarin, first man in space. j, Apollo 17. k, Robotic lunar explorer. l, Hubble Space Telescope.

No. 1864, 4000fr, Atlas-Centaur launch vehicle. No. 1865, 4000fr, International Space Station.

**2000, Dec. 11**　　　　　　**Perf. 14**
**Sheets of 12, #a-l**
| | | | | |
|---|---|---|---|---|
| 1862-1863 | A364 | Set of 2 | 17.00 | 17.00 |

**Souvenir Sheets**
| | | | | |
|---|---|---|---|---|
| 1864-1865 | A364 | Set of 2 | 12.00 | 12.00 |

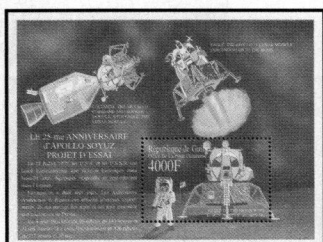

Apollo-Soyuz Mission, 25th Anniv. — A365

No. 1866, 1000fr: a, Saturn IB rocket. b, Apollo 18 command and service modules with docking adapter. c, Apollo 18 Commander Thomas P. Stafford. d, A-2 Soyuz rocket. e, Soyuz 19 spacecraft. f, Soyuz 19 Commander Alexei Leonov.

No. 1867, 1000fr, vert.: a, Lunar Module Eagle, upside-down. b, Lunar Module Eagle, with thrusters firing. c, Apollo 11 command module Columbia. d, Edwin E. Aldrin, Jr. on lunar module ladder. e, Apollo 11 Saturn V rocket. f, Re-entry of Apollo 11 capsule.

4000fr, Aldrin and lunar module on Moon.

**2000, Dec. 11**
**Sheets of 6, #a-f**
| | | | | |
|---|---|---|---|---|
| 1866-1867 | A365 | Set of 2 | 42.50 | 42.50 |

**Souvenir Sheet**
| | | | | |
|---|---|---|---|---|
| 1868 | A365 | 4000fr multi | 6.00 | 6.00 |

Marine Life — A367

Designs: No. 1873, 400fr, Coral grouper. No. 1874, 400fr, Candy cane sea star. 450fr, Hippocampus kuda.

No. 1876, 750fr: a, Chromis caerulea. b, Brittle star. c, Calloplesiops altivelis. d, Ewa blenny. e, Coral polyp. f, Butterflyfish.

No. 1877, 750fr: a, Chelonia mydas. b, Ptereleotris evides. c, Halichoeres iridis. d, Sea fan. e, Florometra serratissima. f, Gramma loreto.

No. 1878, 5000fr, Clownfish. No. 1879, 5000fr, Bigeye scad, horiz.

**Perf. 13½x13¼, 13¼x13½**
**2001, Feb. 28**
| | | | | |
|---|---|---|---|---|
| 1873-1875 | A367 | Set of 3 | 5.50 | 5.50 |

**Sheets of 6, #a-f**
| | | | | |
|---|---|---|---|---|
| 1876-1877 | A367 | Set of 2 | 40.00 | 40.00 |

**Souvenir Sheets**
| | | | | |
|---|---|---|---|---|
| 1878-1879 | A367 | Set of 2 | 42.50 | 42.50 |

Marine Life A368

Designs: No. 1880, 400fr, Chaetodon semilarvatus. No. 1881, 400fr, Amphiprion ocellarus. No. 1882, 450fr, Gramma malecara. No. 1883, 450fr, Amphiprion bicinctuc.

No. 1884, 200fr: a, Diodon hystrix. b, Synchiropus splendidos. c, Lactoria cornuta. d, Canthigaster solandri. e, Gymnothorax tesselatus. f, Gramma loreto.

No. 1885, 200fr: a, Synchiropus picturatus. b, Pygoplytes diacanthus. c, Pomocanthus imperator. d, Holocanthus ciliaris. e, Phinecanthus aculeatus. f, Lienardella fasciatus.

No. 1886, 5000fr, Pterois antennata, vert. No. 1887, 5000fr, Hippocampus kuda, vert.

**Perf. 13¼x13½, 13½x13¼**
**2001, Feb. 28**
| | | | | |
|---|---|---|---|---|
| 1880-1883 | A368 | Set of 4 | 7.50 | 7.50 |

**Sheets of 6, #a-f**
| | | | | |
|---|---|---|---|---|
| 1884-1885 | A368 | Set of 2 | 11.00 | 11.00 |

**Souvenir Sheets**
| | | | | |
|---|---|---|---|---|
| 1886-1887 | A368 | Set of 2 | 42.50 | 42.50 |

Marine Life — A369

No. 1888, 1000fr: a, Jackknife fish. b, Requiem shark. c, Great white shark (Grand blanc). d, Holocanthus ciliaris. e, Brain coral. f, Bluehead wrasse.

No. 1889, 1000fr: a, Sergeant major. b, Bottlenose dolphin. c, Swordfish. d, Sea horse. e, Slate pencil urchin. f, Gold-spotted snake eel.

No. 1890, 1000fr: a, Great white shark (Grand requin blanc). b, Baird's beaked whale. c, Butterflyfish. d, Turtle. e, Solenostomus paradoxus. f, Australian pineapple fish.

No. 1891, 1000fr: a, Hawksbill turtle. b, Killer whale. c, Manta ray. d, Filefish. e, Graysby. f, Striped-eel catfish.

No. 1892, 5000fr, Smooth trunkfish. No. 1879, 5000fr, Dolphin.

**2001, Feb. 28**　　　　　**Perf. 13¼x13½**
**Sheets of 6, #a-f**
| | | | | |
|---|---|---|---|---|
| 1888-1891 | A369 | Set of 4 | 100.00 | 100.00 |

**Souvenir Sheets**
| | | | | |
|---|---|---|---|---|
| 1892-1893 | A369 | Set of 2 | 42.50 | 42.50 |

Flora and Fauna — A370

No. 1894, 300fr — Bears: a, Spectacled bear. b, Giant panda. c, Silver bear. d, Cannelle (Pyreneean bear). e, Syrian bear. f, Grizzly bear.

No. 1895, 300fr — Primates: a, Howler monkey. b, Macaque. c, Drill. d, Yellow baboon. e, Anubis baboon. f, Gelada.

No. 1896, 300fr, vert. — Lemurs: a, Crowned lemur (couronné). b, Black lemur (macao). c, Albifrons lemur. d, Mongoz lemur. e, Sanfordi lemur. f, Fulvus lemur.

No. 1897, 300fr, vert. — Fish: a, Sebastes nigrocinctus. b, Lampris guttatus. c, Cyclopterus lumpus. d, Carnegiella strigata. e, Parosphromenus dreissneri. f, Syncniropus splendidus.

No. 1898, 300fr, vert. — Flowers: a, Peony (Pivoine des rocheuses). b, Hypericum richeri. c, Flamboyant. d, Bird of paradise (oiseau du paradis). e, Hesperantha petitiana. f, Moraea neopavonia.

No. 1899, 750fr — Lemurs: a, Lepilemur leucopus. b, Wooly avahi (avahi laineux). c, Black lemur (macao). d, Verreaux's sifaka (Propithecus verreauxi deckeni). e, Phaner. f, Verreaux's sifaka (Propithecus verrauxi majori).

No. 1900, 750fr — Flowers: a, Thunia alba. b, Eulophia guineensis. c, Polystacha bella. d, Oeceoclades maculata. e, Serapias cordigera. f, Angraecum distichum.

No. 1901, 750fr — Birds: a, Black cockatoo. b, Rosalbin cockatoo. c, Leadbetter's cockatoo. d, Goffin's cockatoo. e, Gray parrot. f, Senegal parrot.

No. 1902, 750fr, vert. — Owls: a, Hibou des marais. b, Hibou petit duc. c, Grand duc Americain. d, Chouette chevechette perlée. e, Hibou grand duc. f, Harphang des neiges.

No. 1903, 750fr, vert. — Insects: a, Giant Himalayan bee. b, Phyllium. c, Magicicada septemdecim. d, Petasida ephippigera. e, Graphosoma semipunctatum. f, Honeybee.

**2001, Mar. 28**　　**Litho.**　　**Perf. 13¼**
**Sheets of 6, #a-f**
| | | | | |
|---|---|---|---|---|
| 1894-1903 | A370 | Set of 10 | 140.00 | 140.00 |

Guinean Railways Locomotive A371

Design: 200fr, Front view. 300fr, Side view, horiz. 750fr, Rear view.

**2001, May 16**
| | | | | |
|---|---|---|---|---|
| 1904-1906 | A371 | Set of 3 | 5.50 | 5.50 |

Nos. 1904-1906 each exist in souvenir sheets of 1, containing stamps lacking printer's inscription.

Locomotives — A372

Designs: 300fr, Union Pacific Jupiter. 400fr, No. 7200 Philadelphia. 600fr, C-28 Type 2-8-0. 800fr, Wainwright P Type 0-6-0. 1300fr, Union Pacific Rogers 119. 1600fr, Northwestern 4-6-0 steam engine.

No. 1913, 950fr: a, Oliver Cromwell. b, Big Boy 4-8-8-4 No. 4019. c, 1858 Rogers. d, Gray Lady. e, Old No. 1. f, Jones Goods 4-6-0.

No. 1914, 950fr: a, Jubilee Type No. SS96. b, Iron Horse. c, 4-6-0. d, Type OS2 2-10-0. e, Single Driver 1887 Johnson. f, King George V 4-6-0.

No. 1915, 950fr: a, Hardwicke Western 2-4-0, No. 790. b, High-wheeled Pacific, Texas State Railroad. c, Longhorne. d, City of Truro 4-4-0 No. 3440. e, Leander Type Jubilee. f, The American.

No. 1916, 4000fr, Stanier Black 5-4-6-0. No. 1917, 4000fr, LMS 5305. No. 1918, 4000fr, Duchess of Hamilton.

**2001, June 8**      **Perf. 13¼x13½**
1907-1912 A372   Set of 6     21.00 21.00
**Sheets of 6, #a-f**
1913-1915 A372   Set of 3     70.00 70.00
**Souvenir Sheets**
1916-1918 A372   Set of 3     55.00 55.00

Locomotives — A373

Designs: 500fr, Ae 6/6 Co-Co electric. 750fr, Hikari Super Express. 1000fr, Krauss-Maffei V200 Diesel-electric. 1250fr, 46 Type electric.

No. 1923, 950fr: a, EW Type Bo-Bo-Bo electric. b, 68000 Type Diesel-electric. c, Type Ge 6/6 electric. d, 19,000 horsepower Diesel-electric. e, Express Co-Co electric. f, AL6 Bo-Bo electric.

No. 1924, 950fr: a, 1,750 horsepower Diesel-electric. b, 7000 Co-Co electric. c, Type E10 Bo-Bo electric. d, D341 Type Diesel-electric. e, Diesel-hydraulic express. f, 5E1 electric.

No. 1925, 4000fr, Santa Fe F9 Diesel-electric. No. 1926, 4000fr, Type SSI Co-Co electric. No. 1918, 4000fr, Union Pacific electric.

**2001, June 8**
1919-1922 A373   Set of 4     15.00 15.00
**Sheets of 6, #a-f**
1923-1924 A373   Set of 2     45.00 45.00
**Souvenir Sheets**
1925-1927 A373   Set of 3     55.00 55.00
Belgica 2001 Intl. Stamp Exhibition, Brussels.

Locomotives — A374

Designs: 750fr, Type 18 4-6-2. 1000fr, ICE. 1250fr, Type G.

No. 1931, 950fr: a, Type WP 4-6-2. b, ETR 450. c, EU-07 Bo-Bo. d, Type 25 4-8-4. e, TGV. f, Type 345 Bo-Bo.

No. 1932, 950fr: a, Type SY 2-6-2. b, GM F7 War Bonnet. c, Type 4-4-0. d, Type A2/1 4-6-2. e, Type BB 22200. f, Type OL-49 4-6-2.

No. 1933, 4000fr, VT601. No. 1934, 4000fr, Type QJ 2-10-2.

**2001, June 8**
1928-1930 A374   Set of 3     13.00 13.00
**Sheets of 6, #a-f**
1931-1932 A374   Set of 2     45.00 45.00
1933-1934 A374   Set of 2     37.50 37.50
Belgica 2001 Intl. Stamp Exhibition, Brussels.

Famous People — A375

No. 1935 — Explorers: a, Vasco da Gama. b, Sir Francis Drake. c, Ferdinand Magellan. d, Capt. James Cook. e, Jacques Cartier. f, Christopher Columbus.

No. 1936: a, Albert Einstein. b, Albert Schweitzer. c, Henri Dunant. d, Sir Alexander Fleming. e, Marie Curie. f, Louis Pasteur.

No. 1937 — Space pioneers: a, Yuri Gagarin. b, John Glenn. c, Edward White. d, Neil Armstrong. e, John Young. f, Thomas Stafford and Alexei Leonov.

No. 1938 — Pope John Paul II: a, As baby, with mother and dove. b, Wearing miter and holding crucifix. c, In garden. d, Kneeling. e, Holding crucifix, with dove. f, With arms raised.

No. 1939 — Lord Robert Baden-Powell, Scouts and: a, Psittacus enthacus. b, Charaxes eupale. c, Pluvianus aegyptius. d, Catacroptera cloanthe. e, Merops albicollis. f, Euphaedra eupalus.

**2001, June 14**      **Perf. 13¼**
**Sheets of 6, #a-f**
1935 A375   350fr multi    10.00 10.00
1936 A375   450fr multi    12.00 12.00
1937 A375   475fr multi    13.00 13.00
1938 A375   600fr multi    16.00 16.00
1939 A375   750fr multi    21.00 21.00
     *Nos. 1935-1939 (5)*    72.00 72.00

Nos. 1936a-1936f and 1939a-1939f each exist in souvenir sheets of one.

Birds — A377

Designs: 200fr, Guinea fowl (pintade vulturine). 250fr, African fish eagle (pygarve vocifer). 300fr, Striped hoopoe (huppe fasciée). 350fr, Jacana. 400fr, Secretary bird (serpentaire). 450fr, Wild Guinea fowl (pintade sauvage).

No. 1948, 950fr: a, Verreaux's eagle (aigle de verreaux). b, White pelican. c, Swallow (hirondelle de rivage). d, Egyptian geese (ouette d'Egypte). e, Crane (grue cendrée). f, Heron.

No. 1949, 950fr: a, Swallow (hirondelle de fenetre). b, Dwarf bee-eater (guepier nain). c, Blue rock thrush (merle solitaire rouge). d, Senegal jabiru. e, Ibis. f, Purple swamphen (talève sultane).

No. 1950, 950fr: a, Vulture (vautour chaugoun). b, Red and yellow barbet (barbican à tete rouge). c, Buzzard (buse rounoir). d, Tufted lark (cochevis). e, Gray wagtail (bergeronnette des ruisseaux). f, Red-heades shrike (pie grieche à tete rouge).

No. 1951, 4000fr, Flamingo (petit flamant). No. 1952, 4000fr, Anhinga. No. 1953, 4000fr, Marabout. No. 1954, 4000fr, Ostrich (autriche).

**2001, Aug. 27**      **Perf. 13½x13¼**
1942-1947 A377   Set of 6     8.50 8.50
**Sheets of 6, #a-f**
1948-1950 A377   Set of 3     52.50 52.50
**Souvenir Sheets**
1951-1954 A377   Set of 4     16.50 16.50
Phila Nippon '01, Japan (#1948-1954).

Birds — A378

Designs: 200fr, Heron. 300fr, Ibis. 500fr, Stonechat (tarier patre). 550fr, Sparrow (hirondelle striée). 600fr, Egyptian courser (pluvian fluviatile). 650fr, Jacana.

No. 1961, 750fr: a, Variable sunbird (souimanga à ventre jaune). b, Long-tailed sunbird (soui-manga à longue queue). c, Scarlet-chested sunbird (soui-manga à poitrine rouge). d, Abyssinian roller (rollier d'Abyssinie). e, Blue-breasted roller (rollier à ventre bleu). f, Broad-billed roller (rolle violet).

No. 1962, 750fr: a, Black bee-eater (guepier noir). b, Blue-headed bee-eater (guepier à tete bleue). c, White-throated bee-eater (guepier à gorge blanche). d, Red-throated bee-eater (guepier à gorge rouge). e, Rosy bee-eater (guepier gris-rose). f, Carmine bee-eater (guepier supreme).

No. 1963, 750fr: a, Blue-breasted kingfisher (martin-chasseur à poitrine bleue). b, Gray-headed kingfisher (martin-chasseur à tete grise). c, Chocolate-backed kingfisher (martin-chasseur marron). d, Dwarf kingfisher (martin-pécheur à tete rousse). e, Malachite kingfisher (martin-pécheur huppé). f, Giant kingfisher (alcyon géant).

No. 1964, 4000fr, Touraco. No. 1965, 4000fr, White-faced whistling duck (dendrocygne veuf). No. 1966, 4000fr, Denham's bustard (outarde du Denham).

**2001, Aug. 27**
1955-1960 A378   Set of 6     11.00 11.00
**Sheets of 6, #a-f**
1961-1963 A378   Set of 3     55.00 55.00
**Souvenir Sheets**
1964-1966 A378   Set of 3     52.50 52.50
Phila Nippon '01, Japan (#1961-1966).

A379

Butterflies — A380

Designs: 700fr, Icolotis zoe. 750fr, Catopsilia florella. 800fr, Kallimoides rumia. 850fr, Charaxes eupale. No. 1971, 950fr, Physcaeneura leda. 1000fr, Mylothris chloris.

No. 1973, 900fr: a, Papilio demodocus. b, Anaphaeis auroto. c, Charaxes superbus. d, Amauris echeria. e, Euxanthe wakefieldi. f, Papilio dardana.

No. 1974, 900fr: a, Hypolimnas salmacis. b, Myrena silenus. c, Charaxes smagardus. d, Papilio zalmoxis. e, Salamis parnassus. f, Charaxes bohemani.

No. 1975, 900fr: a, Charaxes fournierae. b, Eurema floricola. c, Mimacraea marshalli. d, Charaxes candiope. e, Catacroptera cloanthe. f, Danaus chrysippus.

No. 1976, 950fr: a, Castalius isis. b, Axioceres amanga. c, Eurema brenda. d, Epamera stenogrammica. e, Pseudaletis agrippina. f, Alaena margaritalea.

No. 1977, 950fr: a, Papilio dardanus, diff. b, Charaxes eupale, diff. c, Acraea cerasa. d, Precis clelia. e, Colotis celimene. f, Pseudacraea poggei.

No. 1978, 4000fr, Papilio antimachus. No. 1979, 4000fr, Acraea zetes. No. 1980, 4000fr, Colotis danae.

No. 1981, 4000fr, Hypolimnas deceptor. No. 1982, 4000fr, Euphaedra perseis.

**2001, Aug. 27**      **Perf. 13¼x13½**
1967-1972 A379   Set of 6     20.00 20.00
**Sheets of 6, #a-f**
1973-1975 A379   Set of 3     21.00 21.00
1976-1977 A380   Set of 2     35.00 35.00
**Souvenir Sheets**
1978-1980 A379   Set of 3     52.50 52.50
1981-1982 A380   Set of 2     35.00 35.00

Phila Nippon '01, Japan (#1973-1982). Rectangles replace the accented "e's" on all stamps of type A280.

Hummingbirds — A387

Designs: No. 2038, 900fr, Anthracothorax manga. No. 2039, 900fr, Eulampis holosericeus. No. 2040, 1000fr, Archilochus colubris. No. 2041, 1000fr, Chlorostilbon ricordii.

No. 2042, 1000fr: a, Selasphorus rufus. b, Mellisuga helenae. c, Eutoxeres aquila. d, Anthracothorax viridis. e, Allamanda cathartica. f, Orthorhynchus cristatus.

No. 2043, 1000fr: a, Archilochus alexandri. b, Calliphlox evelynae. c, Chlorostilbon maugaeus. d, Musta ornata. e, Phaethornis superciliosus. f, Eulampis jugularis.

No. 2044, 1000fr: a, Cyanophaia bicolor. b, Glaucis hirsuta. c, Chlorostilbon swainsonn. d, Heliconia. e, Heliconia bihai. f, Anthracothorax dominicus.

No. 2045, 4000fr, Amazilia violiceps. No. 2046, 4000fr, Trochilus scitulus. No. 2047, 4000fr, Trochilus polytmus, vert.

**Perf. 13¼x13½, 13½x13¼**
**2001**               **Litho.**
2038-2041 A387   Set of 4     14.00 14.00
**Sheets of 6, #a-f**
2042-2044 A387   Set of 3     65.00 65.00
**Souvenir Sheets**
2045-2047 A387   Set of 3     47.50 47.50

Trains of Africa A390

Designs: No. 2050, 750fr, 0-6-4, Z.A.S.M, Transvaal, 1858. No. 2051, 750fr, 4-6-2, Central South Africa, 1858. No. 2052, 750fr, 4-4-0, Cape Province, 1903. No. 2053, 750fr, 4-8-2 Class 12, South Africa, 1920. No. 2054, 750fr, 4-6-2 Class 10 RB, South Africa, 1950. No. 2055, 750fr, 4-8-2, Benguela, 1951. No. 2056, 750fr, 4-6-4+4-6-4 Class 15A, South Africa, 1952. No. 2057, 750fr, 4-8-4 Class 25 NC, South Africa, 1953.

No. 2058, 200fr: a, Cape Province locomotive, 1895. b, 2-8-2, Central South Africa, 1920. c, 4-4-2, Cape Province, 1898. d, 4-8-2 Class 23, South Africa, 1930. e, Natal Province locomotive, 1901. f, 2-8-4 Class 24, South Africa, 1940.

No. 2059, 300fr: a, 4-6-2 Class 16E, South Africa, 1935. b, 4-8-4 Class 25, South Africa, 1953. c, 2-D-1+1-D-2 Class 20, South Africa, 1954. d, 4-8-2+2-8-4 Class 59, East Africa, 1955. e, 1-Co-Co-1 Class 92, East Africa, 1971. f, 2-D-2 Class 26, South Africa, 1982.

No. 2060, 750fr: a, 4-8-2 Class 15F, South Africa, 1948. b, 4-8-2+2-8-4 GEA Beyer-Garret, South Africa, 1950. c, 4-8-2 Class 11, South Africa, 1951. d, 4-8-2+2-8-4 GEA Beyer-Garret, South Africa, 1954. e, 1-Co-Co-1 Class 4E, South Africa, 1954. f, Co-Co Class 9E, South Africa, 1978.

No. 2061, 4000fr, Umtali-Salisbury Class 4-4-0, 1897. No. 2062, 4000fr, Bo-Bo Class 5E, Blue Train, South Africa, 1969.

**2002, Feb. 8**   **Litho.**   **Perf. 13¼x13½**
2050-2057 A390   Set of 8     21.00 21.00
**Sheets of 6, #a-f**
2058-2060 A390   Set of 3     26.50 26.50
**Souvenir Sheets**
2061-2062 A390   Set of 2     12.00 12.00

Watercraft — A391

Designs: No. 2063, 750fr, Three-masted schooner, 1866. No. 2064, 750fr, Two-masted schooner, 1932. No. 2065, 750fr, Bark, 1968. No. 2066, 750fr, Sailboard. No. 2067, 750fr, Galleass, 16th cent., horiz. No. 2068, 750fr, Sailboat, horiz.

No. 2069, 750fr: a, Galleon, 16th cent. b, 17th cent. ship. c, Corvette, 18th cent. d, Gaff-rig yacht. e, Dinghy. f, Catamaran.

No. 2070, 4000fr, Full-rigged ship, 20th cent., horiz. No. 2071, 4000fr, Pinnace, 17th cent., horiz.

**Perf. 13½x13¼, 13¼x13½**

**2002, Feb. 8**

| 2063-2068 | A391 | Set of 6 | 16.00 | 16.00 |
| 2069 | A391 | 750fr Sheet of 6, #a-f | 17.00 | 17.00 |

**Souvenir Sheet**

| 2070-2071 | A391 | Set of 2 | 12.00 | 12.00 |

Nos. 2070-2071 each contain one 56x42mm stamp.

Airplanes and Ships — A392

No. 2072, 750fr: a, Wright Brothers Flyer. b, Super Sabre F-100. c, Junkers J1. d, De Havilland Comet. e, Douglas DC-3. f, Boeing 747.

No. 2073, 750fr: a, Egyptian wooden boat. b, 18th cent. sailboat. c, Viking longboat. d, Great Eastern. e, Spanish galleon, 16th cent. f, Savannah.

No. 2074, 4000fr, Concorde. No. 2075, 4000fr, Ocean Princess.

**2002, Feb. 8     Perf. 13¼x13½**

**Sheets of 6, #a-f**

| 2072-2073 | A392 | Set of 2 | 9.25 | 9.25 |

**Souvenir Sheets**

| 2074-2075 | A392 | Set of 2 | 8.25 | 8.25 |

First Zeppelin Flight, Cent. — A393

No. 2076: a, LZ-3. b, LZ-5. c, USS Macon. d, Zeppelin NT.

No. 2077, 4000fr, LZ-4. No. 2078, 4000fr, LZ-129.

**2002, Feb. 8**

| 2076 | A393 | 750fr Sheet of 4, #a-d | 12.00 | 12.00 |

**Souvenir Sheets**

| 2077-2078 | A393 | Set of 2 | 12.00 | 12.00 |

Airplanes — A394

No. 2079: a, Lockheed Streamliner. b, Dornier Do-X. c, Lockheed Vega. d, Boeing 707. e, Douglas DC-3. f, De Havilland Comet. 4000fr, Concorde.

**2002, Feb. 8**

| 2079 | A394 | 750fr Sheet of 6, #a-f | 17.00 | 17.00 |

**Souvenir Sheet**

| 2080 | A394 | 4000fr multi | 6.00 | 6.00 |

Airplanes A395

Designs: No. 2081, 750fr, Tupelov TU-144. No. 2082, 750fr, Tri-star L-1011. No. 2083, 750fr, Airbus A-300-B. No. 2084, 750fr, Boeing 777-200.

No. 2085, 750fr: a, Junkers G-24. b, Armstrong Whitworth XV Atalanta. c, Aerospatiale SE 210 Caravelle III. d, De Havilland D. H. 106 Comet 4B. e, Armstrong Havilworth 650 Argosy 100. f, Douglas DC-9.

No. 2086, 750fr: a, Wright Brothers Flyer. b, Vickers Vimy. c, Spirit of St. Louis. d, Junkers G-38. e, Douglas DC-3. f, Vickers-Armstrong Viscount 700.

No. 2087, 4000fr, Boeing 747. No. 2088, 4000fr, Airbus A-3XX.

**2002, Feb. 8**

| 2081-2084 | A395 | Set of 4 | 11.00 | 11.00 |

**Sheets of 6, #a-f**

| 2085-2086 | A395 | Set of 2 | 32.50 | 32.50 |

**Souvenir Sheets**

| 2087-2088 | A395 | Set of 2 | 12.00 | 12.00 |

Military Aircraft A396

Designs: No. 2089, 750fr, Sopwith Camel. No. 2090, 750fr, Fokker Dr-1. No. 2091, 750fr, Messerschmitt Bf-109 E. No. 2092, 750fr, Mitsubishi Zero. No. 2093, 750fr, Northrop F-20 Tigershark. No. 2094, 750fr, Dassault-Breguet Mirage 2000.

No. 2095, 750fr: a, S.E. 5A. b, Fokker D-VII. c, Thomas Morse S4C. d, De Havilland D.H. 2. e, Boeing PW-9D. f, Spad XIII.

No. 2096, 750fr: a, Mustang P-51. b, Junkers Ju-87R. c, Curtiss Hawk 75A. d, Hawker Hurricane. e, Nakajima Ki-43 Hayabusa. f, Macchi M.C. 200 Saetta.

No. 2097, 750fr: a, Panavia Tornado Gr. Mk1. b, Mikoyan-Gurevich MiG-15. c, Vought A-7D Corsair 11. d, BAe Sea Harrier FRS Mk1. e, General Dynamics F-111. f, Dassault/Breguet Dornier Alpha Jet.

No. 2098, 4000fr, Saab Draken J35. No. 2099, 4000fr, Supermarine Spitfire.

**2002, Feb. 8**

| 2089-2094 | A396 | Set of 6 | 16.00 | 16.00 |

**Sheets of 6, #a-f**

| 2095-2097 | A396 | Set of 3 | 52.50 | 52.50 |

**Souvenir Sheets**

| 2098-2099 | A396 | Set of 2 | 12.00 | 12.00 |

Antique Automobiles — A397

No. 2100, 1000fr: a, 1920 Rolls-Royce. b, 1896 Ford. c, 1930 Hispano-Suiza. d, 1924 Stoewer Allemagne D10 D12. e, 1924 Chrysler. f, 1912 Hudson.

No. 2101, 1000fr: a, 1930 Bugatti SIA. b, 1901 Mercedes. c, 1926 Jordan Playboy. d, 1936 Cadillac V-16. e, 1914 Stutz Bearcat. f, 1904 Daimler.

No. 2102, 4000fr, 1886 Daimler-Benz. No. 2103, 4000fr, 1903 Ford Model A.

**2002, Feb. 8     Perf. 13¼x13½**

**Sheets of 6, #a-f**

| 2100-2101 | A397 | Set of 2 | 42.50 | 42.50 |

**Souvenir Sheets**

| 2102-2103 | A397 | Set of 2 | 12.00 | 12.00 |

Race Cars A398

Designs: No. 2104, 750fr, Marmon Wasp, 1911 Indianapolis 500. No. 2105, 750fr, Ferrari Dino 246, 1958 French Grand Prix. No. 2106, 750fr, Lotus 49, 1967 German Grand Prix. No. 2107, Tyrell 003, 1971 American Grand Prix.

No. 2108, 750fr: a, Mercedes, 1914 French Grand Prix. b, Duesenberg, 1921 French Grand Prix. c, Bugatti, 1924 French Grand Prix. d, Alfa Romeo P3, 1934 French Grand Prix. e, Auto Union, 1937 Nürburgring Rally. f, Maserati 8C, 1939 German Grand Prix.

No. 2109, 750fr: a, Vanwall, 1957 British Grand Prix. b, Cooper T43, 1958 Argentine Grand Prix. c, Lotus 25, 1965 British Grand Prix. d, Brabham-Repro BT-19, 1966 French Grand Prix. e, Renault RS 01, 1977 British Grand Prix. f, Ferrari 640, 1989 Brazilian Grand Prix.

No. 2110, 4000fr, Coventry Daimler, 1899 Paris-Ostende Race. No. 2111, 4000fr, Penske PC-23, 1994 Portland Race.

**2002, Feb. 8**

| 2104-2107 | A398 | Set of 4 | 11.00 | 11.00 |

**Sheets of 6, #a-f**

| 2108-2109 | A398 | Set of 2 | 17.00 | 17.00 |

**Souvenir Sheets**

| 2110-2111 | A398 | Set of 2 | 12.00 | 12.00 |

Pres. John F. Kennedy (1917-63) — A400

No. 2113: a, With ship's wheel. b, With doves. c, With arch. 4000fr, At podium with flag and map. Illustration reduced.

**Perf. 13½x13¼**

**2002, Feb. 20     Litho.**

| 2113 | A400 | 750fr Horiz. strip of 3, #a-c | 8.00 | 8.00 |

**Souvenir Sheet**

| 2114 | A400 | 4000fr multi | 7.00 | 7.00 |

No. 2113 printed in sheets of 2 strips.

Pres. Ronald Reagan (1911-2004) — A401

No. 2115: a, With stars. b, With curtain. c, With US Capitol. 4000fr, With Statue of Liberty and Presidential seal. Illustration reduced.

**2002, Feb. 20**

| 2115 | A401 | 750fr Horiz. strip of 3, #a-c | 8.00 | 8.00 |

**Souvenir Sheet**

| 2116 | A401 | 4000fr multi | 7.00 | 7.00 |

No. 2115 printed in sheets of 2 strips.

Princess Diana (1961-97) — A402

No. 2117: a, Wearing tiara. b, Holding flowers. c, Wearing hat. 4000fr, Wearing black dress. Illustration reduced.

**2002, Feb. 20**

| 2117 | A402 | 750fr Horiz. strip of 3, #a-c | 8.00 | 8.00 |

**Souvenir Sheet**

| 2118 | A402 | 4000fr multi | 7.00 | 7.00 |

No. 2117 printed in sheets of 2 strips.

Prince William of Wales — A403

No. 2119, 750fr: a, Wearing brown checked shirt. b, Wearing jacket and bow tie. c, Wearing green sweater. d, Wearing lilac sweater. e, Wearing brown suit, white shirt and blue tie. f, Wearing brown suit, striped shirt and blue gray tie.

No. 2120, 750fr: a, Wearing blue shirt. b, Wearing blue suit, blue background. c, Wearing riding helmet. d, Wearing blue suit, white background. e, Wearing blue sweater. f, Wearing ski gear.

No. 2121, 4000fr, With Prince Harry. No. 2122, 4000fr, With Prince Charles, horiz.

**Perf. 13½x13¼, 13¼x13½**

**2002, Feb. 20**

**Sheets of 6, #a-f**

| 2119-2120 | A403 | Set of 2 | 32.50 | 32.50 |

**Souvenir Sheets**

| 2121-2122 | A403 | Set of 2 | 14.00 | 14.00 |

Queen Elizabeth II, 50th Anniv. of Reign — A404

No. 2123: a, Wearing blue coat and gloves. b, With Prince Philip. c, Wearing gray coat and hat. d, Wearing yellow suit and hat. 4000fr, Wearing red uniform.

**2002, Feb. 20**      **Perf. 14¼**
2123 A404 1400fr Sheet of 4,
     #a-d      12.00 12.00

**Souvenir Sheet**
2124 A404 4000fr multi      7.00 7.00

A405

A406

Elvis Presley (1935-77) — A407

No. 2125 — Background color: a, Blue. b, Yellow. c, Red. d, Pink. e, Lilac. f, Yellow green.
No. 2126: a, Red and white shirt. b, Blue shirt. c, Black and brown shirt. d, Purple shirt. e, Red jacket with neckerchief. f, Red shirt.
No. 2127: a, Wearing red and white shirt with scarf. b, Wearing black jacket and gray shirt. c, Holding guitar on shoulder. d, With hands resting on guitar. e, Singing. f, Wearing army uniform.

**2002, Feb. 20**      **Perf. 13½x13¼**
2125 A405 750fr Sheet of 6,
     #a-f      18.00 18.00
2126 A406 750fr Sheet of 6,
     #a-f      18.00 18.00
2127 A407 750fr Sheet of 6,
     #a-f      18.00 18.00

Nobel Prize Physics Laureates — A408

No. 2128, each 750fr: a, Hendrik Lorentz, 1902. b, Pieter Zeeman, 1902. c, Sir Joseph Thomson, 1906. d, Gabriel Lippman, 1908. e, Max von Laue, 1914. f, Jean B. Perrin, 1926.
No. 2129, each 750fr: a, Owen Richardson, 1928. b, Sir Chandrasekhara Venkata Raman, 1930. c, Victor F. Hess, 1936. d, Carl D. Anderson, 1936. e, Sir George Thompson, 1937. f, Clinton Davisson, 1937.
No. 2130, each 750fr: a, Enrico Fermi, 1938. b, Ernest Lawrence, 1939. c, Isidor I. Rabi, 1944. d, Patrick Blackett, 1948. e, Fritz Zernike, 1953. f, Donald A. Glaser, 1960.
No. 2131, each 750fr: a, Alfred Kastler, 1966. b, Luis W. Alvarez, 1968. c, Murray Gell-Mann, 1969. d, John Bardeen, 1972. e, Leon N. Cooper, 1972. f, John R, Schrieffer, 1972.
No. 2132: 4000fr, Wilhelm Röntgen, 1901. No. 2133, 4000fr, Marie Curie, 1903. No. 2134, 4000fr, Pierre Curie, 1903. No. 2135, 4000fr, Antoine Henri Becquerel, 1903.

**2002, Feb. 20**      **Litho.**
**Sheets of 6, #a-f**
2128-2131 A408   Set of 4    72.50 72.50
**Souvenir Sheets**
2132-2135 A408   Set of 4    27.50 27.50
Nobel Prizes, cent. (in 2001).

Albert Einstein (1879-1955), Physicist — A409

No. 2136: a, Smoking pipe. b, Wearing black jacket and tie, facing left. c, Wearing blue sweater. d, Wearing black jacket and tie, facing right. e, Wearing black sweater. f, Wearing brown jacket.
4000fr, With wife, Elsa.

**2002, Feb. 20**
2136 A409   750fr Sheet of 6,
     #a-f      17.00 17.00
**Souvenir Sheet**
2137 A409 4000fr multi      7.00 7.00

Pres. Theodore Roosevelt (1858-1919) — A410

No. 2138: a, As Assistant Navy Secretary. b, In Cuba, 1898. c, In Yellowstone Park, 1903. d, As President, 1901-09. e, Campaigning for war preparedness, 1916. f, In 1917.
4000fr, As colonel in Rough Riders.

**2002, Feb. 20**      **Perf. 13¼**
2138 A410   950fr Sheet of 6,
     #a-f      21.00 21.00
**Souvenir Sheet**
2139 A410 4000fr multi      7.00 7.00

Jacqueline Kennedy Onassis (1929-94), First Lady — A411

Designs: No. 2140, 1000fr, Wearing white blouse, yellow background. 2000fr, With Pres. John F. Kennedy, horiz. No. 2142, 4000fr, Wearing Inaugural Ball gown.
No. 2143: a, Wearing necklace, shoulders showing, green background. b, Wearing hat. c, Facing left, green background. d, Wearing necklace, orange background. e, Wearing necklace, shoulders covered, green background. f, Wearing sunglasses.
No. 2144, 4000fr, As child.

**Perf. 13½x13¼, 13¼x13½**
**2002, Feb. 20**
2140-2142 A411   Set of 3    26.00 26.00
2143 A411 1000fr Sheet of 6,
     #a-f      24.00 24.00
**Souvenir Sheet**
2144 A411 4000fr multi      7.00 7.00

Famous People — A412

Designs: No. 2145, 750fr, Pres. John F. Kennedy (1917-63). No. 2146, 750fr, Pres. Ronald Reagan (1911-2004). No. 2147, 750fr, Chiune Sugihara, Japanese diplomat who saved Jews in World War II. No. 2148, 750fr, Queen Elizabeth II as younger woman, denomination at right. No. 2149, 750fr, Queen Elizabeth II wearing tiara, denomination at left. No. 2150, 750fr, Princess Diana (1961-97). No. 2151, 750fr, Queen Mother Elizabeth (1900-2002). No. 2152, 750fr, Prince William of Wales, denomination in red. No. 2153, 750fr, Prince William of Wales, denomination in yellow. No. 2154, 750fr, Prince William of Wales, denomination in violet. No. 2155, 750fr, Hereditary Prince Haakon and Princess Mette-Marie of Norway, horiz. No. 2156, 750fr,

Prince Philippe and Princess Mathilde of Belgium, horiz.
**2002, Feb. 20**      **Perf. 14**
2145-2156 A412   Set of 12   32.50 32.50

2002 Winter Olympic Games, Salt Lake City A413

Designs: No. 2157, 750fr, Biathlon. No. 2158, 750fr, Luge. No. 2159, 750fr, Skiing. No. 2160, 750fr, Snowboarding, vert.

**Perf. 13¼x13½, 13½x13¼**
**2002, Feb. 20**
2157-2160 A413   Set of 4    11.00 11.00

Japanese Entertainment — A414

No. 2161, 750fr — Film stars: a, Miyoshi Umeki. b, Kimiko Ikegami. c, Masahiro Takashima. d, Sessue Hayakawa. e, Toshiro Mifune. f, Kaho Minami.
No. 2162, 750fr — Kabuki actors: a, Shinnosuke as Sukeroku. b, Kikugoro as Genkuro Kitsune. c, Ganjiro as Izaemon. d, Kikunosuke as Shiratama. e, Kikunosuke as Keisei. f, Shinnosuke as Matsuomaru.
No. 2163, 4000fr, Akira Kurosawa, film director. No. 2164, 4000fr, Danjuro as Kampei and Tamasaburo as Okaru, horiz.

**Perf. 13½x13¼, 13¼x13½**
**2002, Feb. 20**
**Sheets of 6, #a-f**
2161-2162 A414   Set of 2    32.50 32.50
**Souvenir Sheets**
2163-2164 A414   Set of 2    14.00 14.00

Scouts — A422

No. 2208 — Scouts and shells: a, 200fr, Cypraea caurica. b, 300fr, Olivella nana. c, 5000fr, Marginella persicula.
No. 2209 — Scouts and sea mammals: a, 200fr, Balaena mysticetus. b, 300fr, Tursiops truncatus. c, 5000fr, Delphinus delphis.
No. 2210 — Scouts and dinosaurs: a, 200fr, Spinosaurus. b, 300fr, Ouranosaurus. c, 5000fr, Kentrosaurus.
No. 2211 — Scouts and dogs: a, 200fr, Bouvier Bernois. b, 750fr, Chihuahua. c, 5000fr, Irish wolfhound.
No. 2212 — Scouts and meteorites from: a, 200fr, Tatahouine. b, 750fr, Gao-Guenie. c, 5000fr, Great Sand Sea.
No. 2213 — Scouts and cats: a, 300fr, Japanese bobtail. b, 750fr, Egyptian Mau. c, 5000fr, Bombay.
No. 2214 — Scouts and minerals: a, 300fr, Anglesite. b, 750fr, Brucite. c, 5000fr, Beudantite.
No. 2215 — Scouts and mushrooms: a, 300fr, Aseroe rubra. b, 750fr, Boletus edulis. c, 5000fr, Hygrocybe punicea.

No. 2216 — Scouts and butterflies: a, 300fr, Anaphe panda. b, 750fr, Eurema brigitta. c, 5000fr, Acraea zetes.

**2002, Dec. 27**    **Litho.**    **Perf. 13¼**
**Sheets of 3, #a-c**
2208-2216   A422   Set of 9   62.50   62.50
Each stamp exists in souvenir sheet of 1.

Nicolaus August Otto (1832-91), Engineer A423

Wright Brothers and Wright Flyer A424

Astronaut Spacewalking — A425

Pierre de Coubertin (1863-1937), Intl. Olympic Committee President A426

Winston Churchill, Franklin D. Roosevelt and Joseph Stalin A427

Newspaper Mastheads A428

Ferris Wheels on Film A429

**2002**    **Perf. 13½x13¼, 13¼x13½**
2217   A423   200fr multi   1.60   1.60
2218   A424   300fr multi   1.60   1.60
2219   A425   750fr multi   1.60   1.60
2220   A426   1000fr multi   1.60   1.60
2221   A427   1250fr multi   1.60   1.60
2222   A428   1500fr multi   1.60   1.60
2223   A429   2000fr multi   1.60   1.60

Space — A430

Designs: No. 2224, 3000fr, Multi-scout Mars Lander. No. 2225, 3000fr, Stardust Probe. No. 2226, 3000fr, Mars Rover. No. 2227, 3000fr, Ceres-Vesta Probe. No. 2228, 3000fr, Deep Space Probe. No. 2229, 3000fr, NGST Space Telescope. No. 2230, 3000fr, Rosetta Probe. No. 2231, 3000fr, NEAR Probe.
No. 2232, 1500fr, horiz.: a, Newton Space Telescope. b, Darwin Space Telescope. c, Kepler Space Telescope. d, Herschel Space Telescope. e, Plank Space Telescope. f, Xeus Space Telescope. g, Mars Orbiter. h, Net Lander.
No. 2233, 1500fr, horiz.: a, Mission Specialist 4 Kalpana Chawla. b, Payload Commander Michael P. Anderson. c, Mission Specialist 1 David M. Brown. d, Pilot William C. McCool. e, Mission Specialist 4 Laurel B. Clark. f, Payload Specialist 4 Ilan Ramon. g, Commander Rick D. Husband. h, Columbia Space Shuttle.
No. 2234, 3000fr, Chawla, diff. No. 2235, 3000fr, Anderson, diff. No. 2236, 3000fr, Brown, diff. No. 2237, 3000fr, McCool, diff. No. 2238, 3000fr, Clark, diff. No. 2239, 3000fr, Ramon, diff. No. 2240, 3000fr, Husband, diff. No. 2241, 3000fr, Columbia Space Shuttle, diff. No. 2242, 6000fr, Corot Space Telescope, horiz. No. 2243, 6000fr, Crew of ill-fated Columbia Space Shuttle mission STS-107, horiz.

**2003, Mar. 3**    **Perf. 13¼**
2224-2231   A430   Set of 8   25.00   25.00
**Sheets of 8, #a-h**
2232-2233   A430   Set of 2   30.00   30.00
**Souvenir Sheets**
2234-2243   A430   Set of 10   37.50   37.50
Nos. 2242 and 2243 each contain one 50x41mm stamp. Nos. 2224-2231 each exist in souvenir sheets of 1.

2004 Summer Olympics, Athens — A431

Designs: No. 2244, 750fr, No. 2252, 3000fr, Triathlon and Pentathlon. No. 2245, 750fr, No. 2253, 3000fr, Archery. No. 2246, 1500fr, No. 2254, 3000fr, Table tennis. No. 2247, 1500fr, No. 2255, 3000fr, Taekwondo and Judo. No. 2248, 1500fr, No. 2256, 3000fr, Equestrian. No. 2249, 1500fr, No. 2257, 3000fr, Women's tennis. No. 2250, 1500fr, No. 2258, 3000fr, Swimming. No. 2251, 1500fr, No. 2259, 3000fr, Track and field. No. 2260, 6000fr, Soccer.

**2003, Nov. 12**    **Perf. 13¼**
2244-2251   A431   Set of 8   15.00   15.00
**Souvenir Sheets**
2252-2260   A431   Set of 9   30.00   30.00
*2259a*    Souvenir sheet, #2252, 2257-2259   12.00   12.00
No. 2260 contains one 36x51mm stamp.

Pope John Paul II (1920-2005) — A433

Pope: 100fr, Hugging man. 150fr, In vestments, with open arms. 200fr, Face. 300fr, Praying at microphone. 450fr, Blessing bishop. 500fr, Kissing ground and with arms raised. 550fr, With Black Madonna of Czestochowa.

600fr, Wounded in assassination attempt. 650fr, With man. 1000fr, With children and Virgin Mary. 1500fr, Handshake. 2000fr, With Lech Walesa. 2500fr, With people tearing down Berlin Wall. 7500fr, With crowd.

**2004**    **Litho.**    **Perf. 13x13¼**
2263-2276   A433   Set of 14   12.50   12.50

## SEMI-POSTAL STAMPS

Eye Examination — SP1

Microscopic Examination SP2

#B13, Medical laboratory. #B14, Insect control. #B16, Surgical operation.

**Engraved and Lithographed**
**1960**    **Unwmk.**    **Perf. 11½**
B12   SP1   20fr + 10fr ultra & car   1.25   .60
B13   SP1   30fr + 20fr brn org & violet   1.25   .60
B14   SP1   40fr + 20fr rose lil & blue   1.60   .80
B15   SP2   50fr + 50fr grn & brn   2.50   1.25
B16   SP2   100fr + 100fr lil & grn   3.00   1.50
   *Nos. B12-B16 (5)*   9.60   4.75
Issued for national health propaganda. For overprints see Nos. B25-B29.

**Nos. 194-195 Surcharged "1961" and New Value in Red or Orange**
**1961, June 6**    **Photo.**
B17   A17   25fr + 10fr (R or O)   7.00   3.50
B18   A17   50fr + 20fr (R or O)   7.00   3.50
Nos. B17-B18 exist with orange surcharges transposed: "1961 + 10FRS." on 50fr and "1961 + 20FRS." on 25fr.

**Nos. 214-219 Surcharged in Green, Lilac, Orange or Blue: "POUR LA PROTECTION DE NOS ANIMAUX +5 FRS"**
**Photo., Surcharge Engr.**
**1961, Dec. 8**
**Multicolored Design; Granite Paper**
B19   A20   5fr + 5fr brt grn (G)   .40   .20
B20   A20   10fr + 5fr emer (G)   .50   .20
B21   A20   25fr + 5fr lilac (L)   .75   .35
B22   A20   40fr + 5fr org (O)   1.00   .45
B23   A20   50fr + 5fr red org (O)   1.40   .65
B24   A20   75fr + 5fr ultra (B)   2.00   .90
   *Nos. B19-B24 (6)*   6.05   2.75
The surtax was for animal protection.

Nos. B12-B16 Overprinted in Red or Orange

**Engr. & Litho.**
**1962, Feb.**    **Perf. 11½**
B25   SP1   20fr + 10fr (R or O)   .50   .25
B26   SP1   30fr + 20fr (R or O)   .70   .35
B27   SP1   40fr + 20fr (R or O)   .80   .40
B28   SP2   50fr + 50fr (R or O)   1.60   .80
B29   SP2   100fr + 100fr (R or O)   3.25   1.60
   *Nos. B25-B29 (5)*   6.85   3.40
WHO drive to eradicate malaria. No. B25 also exists with black overprint.

**Nos. 223-228 Surcharged in Red: "POUR LA PROTECTION DE NOS OISEAUX + 5 FRS"**
**Photo., Surcharge Engr.**
**1962, May 14**    **Perf. 13x14**
B30   A22   5fr + 5fr multi   .40   .20
B31   A22   10fr + 5fr multi   .50   .20
B32   A22   25fr + 5fr multi   .65   .20
B33   A22   40fr + 5fr multi   .90   .45
B34   A22   50fr + 5fr multi   1.50   .75
B35   A22   75fr + 5fr multi   3.50   1.75
   *Nos. B30-B35 (6)*   7.45   3.55
The surtax was for bird protection.

**Nos. 232-233 Surcharged in Orange or Red and Overprinted: "Aide aux Réfugiés Algeriens"**
**1962, Nov. 1**    **Litho.**    **Perf. 13**
B36   A24   25fr + 15fr multi   .90   .45
B37   A24   75fr + 25fr multi   1.75   .90
Issued to help Algerian refugees.

Astronomers and Space Phenomena — SP3

**1989, Mar. 7**    **Litho.**    **Perf. 13½**
B38   SP3   100fr +25fr Helical nebula   1.00   .40
B39   SP3   150fr +25fr Orion nebula   1.50   .80
B40   SP3   200fr +25fr Eagle nebula   2.25   1.00
B41   SP3   250fr +25fr Trifide nebula   2.75   1.10
B42   SP3   300fr +25fr Eta-carinae nebula   3.25   1.50
B43   SP3   500fr +25fr NGC-2264 nebula   5.25   2.40
   *Nos. B38-B43 (6)*   16.00   7.20
**Souvenir Sheet**
B44   SP3   750fr +50fr Horse's Head nebula   7.25   3.00
Nos. B42-B44 are airmail.

## AIR POST STAMPS

Lockheed Constellation — AP1

Design: 500fr, Plane on ground.

**Lithographed and Engraved**
**1959, July 13**    **Unwmk.**    **Perf. 11½**
**Size: 52½x24mm**
C14   AP1   100fr dp car, ultra & emer   2.75   1.00
C15   AP1   200fr emer, brn & lil   3.75   2.00
**Size: 56½x26mm**
C16   AP1   500fr multicolored   9.50   3.50
   *Nos. C14-C16 (3)*   16.00   6.50
For overprints see Nos. C24-C26, C52-C53.

Doves with Letter and Olive Twig — AP2

**1959, Oct. 16**    **Engr.**    **Perf. 13½**
C17   AP2   40fr blue   .40   .20
C18   AP2   50fr emerald   .80   .40
C19   AP2   100fr dk car rose   1.40   1.00

C20 AP2 200fr rose red 2.50 1.75
C21 AP2 500fr red orange 7.00 3.00
*Nos. C17-C21 (5)* 12.10 6.35

For overprints see Nos. C35-C38.

## Admission to UN Type of 1959
### Engr. & Litho.
**1959, Dec. 12** *Perf. 12*
Size: 44x26mm
C22 A16 50fr multicolored 1.10 .75
C23 A16 100fr multicolored 1.50 .90

For overprints see Nos. C27-C28.

## Nos. C14-C16 Overprinted in Carmine, Orange or Blue: "Jeux Olympiques Rome 1960" and Olympic Rings
**1960** **Litho. & Engr.** *Perf. 11½*
Size: 52½x24mm
C24 AP1 100fr multi (C or O) 9.75 4.25
C25 AP1 200fr multi (Bl) 17.00 8.00
Size: 56½x26mm
C26 AP1 500fr multi (C or O) 45.00 40.00
*Nos. C24-C26 (3)* 71.75 52.25

17th Olympic Games, Rome, 8/25-9/11.

Nos. C22-C23 Overprinted

### Engr. & Litho.
**1961, Oct. 24** *Perf. 12*
C27 A16 50fr multicolored 1.00 .40
C28 A16 100fr multicolored 1.50 .55

United Nations, 15th anniversary.

Mosquito and Malaria Eradication Emblem AP3

**1962, Apr. 7** **Engr.** *Perf. 10½*
C29 AP3 25fr orange & blk .65 .20
C30 AP3 50fr car rose & blk 1.00 .35
C31 AP3 100fr green & blk 1.75 .60
*Nos. C29-C31 (3)* 3.40 1.15

WHO drive to eradicate malaria.
A souvenir sheet exists containing a 100fr green & sepia stamp, imperf. Sepia coat of arms in margin. Size: 102x76mm. Value $10.

## Musician Type of Regular Issue
Musical Instruments: 100fr, 200fr, Kora. 500fr, Balafon.
**1962, June 15** **Photo.** *Perf. 13x13½*
C32 A26 100fr brt pink, dk car & Prus bl 1.40 .50
C33 A26 200fr lt & dk ultra & car rose 2.75 1.25
C34 A26 500fr dl org, pur & Prus bl 9.00 4.00
*Nos. C32-C34 (3)* 13.15 5.75

## Nos. C17-C20 Overprinted in Carmine, Orange or Black: "La Conquête De L'Espace"
*Perf. 13½*
**1962, Nov. 15** **Unwmk.** **Engr.**
C35 AP2 40fr blue (C or O) .80 .25
C36 AP2 50fr emer (C or O) .80 .35
C37 AP2 100fr dk car rose (B) 1.75 .70
C38 AP2 200fr rose red (B) 3.00 1.25
*Nos. C35-C38 (4)* 6.35 2.55

The conquest of space. Two types of overprint: Straight lines on 40fr and 50fr in carmine, 100fr (black). Curved lines on 40fr and 50fr in orange, 200fr (black).

## Bird Type of Regular Issue
Birds: 100fr, Hornbill. 200fr, White spoonbill. 500fr, Bateleur eagle.
**1962, Dec.** **Photo.** *Perf. 13x13½*
C41 A30 100fr multicolored 3.00 1.10
C42 A30 200fr multicolored 5.00 2.40
C43 A30 500fr multicolored 12.50 4.75
*Nos. C41-C43 (3)* 20.50 8.25

## Sports Type of Regular Issue, 1963
Designs: 100fr, Running. 200fr, Bicycling. 500fr, Single sculls.
**1963, Mar. 16** *Perf. 14*
C44 A32 100fr dp rose, sep & grn 2.00 .80
C45 A32 200fr ol bis, ultra & mag 4.50 2.00
C46 A32 500fr ocher, dk bl & red 9.00 3.75
*Nos. C44-C46 (3)* 15.50 6.55

## Butterfly Type of Regular Issue
Various Butterflies.
**1963, May 10** **Unwmk.** *Perf. 12*
C47 A33 100fr cit, dk brn & gray 2.00 .35
C48 A33 200fr sal pink, blk & green 6.25 2.40
C49 A33 500fr multicolored 10.50 4.50
*Nos. C47-C49 (3)* 18.75 7.25

## Red Cross Type of Regular Issue
**1963, July 25** **Engr.** *Perf. 10½*
C50 A35 25fr black & car .90 .20
**Souvenir Sheet**
*Imperf*
C51 A35 100fr green & car 4.00 3.00

Nos. C14-C15 Overprinted:

### Lithographed and Engraved
**1963, Oct. 28** *Perf. 11½*
C52 AP1 100fr dp car, ultra & emer 1.90 .70
C53 AP1 200fr emer, brn & lil 4.50 1.25

1st Pan American air service from Conakry to New York, July 30, 1963.

## Fish Type of Regular Issue, 1964
100fr, African lyretail. 300fr, Six-barred epiplatys.
**1964, Feb. 15** **Litho.** *Perf. 14x13½*
C54 A36 100fr grn & multi 2.25 .55
C55 A36 300fr brn & multi 7.75 1.40

## Kennedy Type of Regular Issue, 1964
**1964, Mar. 5** **Engr.** *Perf. 10½*
C56 A37 100fr multicolored 1.75 .80

See note after No. 327.

## Olympic Type of Regular Issue
Design: 100fr, Women's ice skating.
**1964, May 15** **Photo.** *Perf. 13x12½*
C57 A39 100fr gold, brn org & ind 2.25 .40

## Nos. C44-C46 Overprinted in Carmine or Orange: "Jeux Olympiques Tokyo 1964" and Olympic Rings
**1964, May 15** **Unwmk.** *Perf. 14*
C58 A32 100fr (C or O) 1.90 1.40
C59 A32 200fr (C or O) 3.00 2.00
C60 A32 500fr (C or O) 7.00 5.00
*Nos. C58-C60 (3)* 11.90 8.40

18th Olympic Games, Tokyo, Oct. 10-25.

## Mrs. Roosevelt Type of Regular Issue
**1964, June 1** **Engr.** *Perf. 10½*
C61 A40 50fr violet .90 .25

## Souvenir Sheets

Unisphere, "Rocket Thrower" and Guinea Pavilion — AP4

**1964, Oct. 26** **Engr.** *Imperf.*
C62 AP4 100fr dk bl & org 1.60 .80
C63 AP4 200fr rose red & emer 3.75 1.90

NY World's Fair, 1964-65. See Nos. C69-C70.

## Nubian Monuments Type of Regular Issue
300fr, Queen Nefertari, Abu Simbel.
**1964, Nov. 19** **Photo.** *Perf. 12*
C64 A42 300fr gold, dl red brn & sal 4.75 1.40

For overprint see No. C82.

Japanese Hostess, Plane and Map of Africa AP5

**1965, Jan. 18** *Perf. 12½x13*
C65 AP5 100fr gold, blk & red lil 1.75 .35

18th Olympic Games, Tokyo, Oct. 10-25, 1964. Two multicolored souvenir sheets (200fr vert. and 300fr horiz.) exist, showing different views of Mt. Fuji. Sizes: 86x119mm, 119x86mm. Value, both: $12.50 perf; $40 imperf.

For overprint see No. C81.

## Mask Type of Regular Issue
300fr, Niamou mask from N'Zérékoré.
**1965, Feb. 15** **Photo.** *Perf. 14*
C68 A44 300fr multicolored 6.25 2.75

## World's Fair Type of 1964 Souvenir Sheets
**1965, Mar. 24** **Engr.** *Imperf.*
C69 AP4 100fr green & brn 2.40 1.00
C70 AP4 200fr rose red & car rose 4.75 2.50

## Handicraft Type of Regular Issue
100fr, Cabinetmaker. 300fr, Ivory carver.
**1965, May 1** **Photo.** *Perf. 14*
C71 A45 100fr multicolored 1.50 .35
C72 A45 300fr multicolored 5.25 1.25

## ITU Type of Regular Issue, 1965
**1965, May 17** **Unwmk.**
C73 A46 100fr multicolored 1.25 .30
C74 A46 200fr multicolored 3.00 .75

Exist imperf.

## ICY Type of Regular Issue, 1965
**1965, Sept. 8** **Engr.** *Perf. 10½*
C75 A50 100fr bl & yel org 1.25 .35

West Facade, Polytechnic Institute — AP6

Design: 200fr, North facade.
**1965, Oct. 2** **Photo.** *Perf. 13½*
C76 AP6 200fr gold & multi 2.10 1.00
C77 AP6 500fr gold & multi 6.00 3.00

Seventh anniversary of independence.

For overprints see Nos. C84-C85.

## Moon Type of 1965
100fr, Ranger VII approaching moon, vert. 200fr, Launching of Ranger VII, Cape Kennedy, vert.
**1965, Nov. 15** **Litho.** *Perf. 13½x14*
C78 A52 100fr rose red, yel & dk brown 1.00 .50
C79 A52 200fr multicolored 2.50 1.00

For overprints & surcharge see #C112-C112B.

## Dancer Type of Regular Issue, 1966
100fr, Kouyate Kandia, national singer.
**1966, Jan. 5** **Photo.** *Perf. 13½*
Size: 36x28½mm
C80 A53 100fr multi, horiz. 1.50 .50

Engraved Overprint on No. C65

**1966, Mar. 14 Photo.** *Perf. 12½x13*
C81 AP5 100fr gold, blk & red lil 1.25 .45

Fourth Pan Arab Games, Cairo, Sept. 2-11, 1965. The same overprint was applied to two souvenir sheets noted after No. C65 (red ovpt. on 200fr, black ovpt. on 300fr).

## Engraved Dark Blue Overprint on No. C64:
"CENTENAIRE DU TIMBRE / CAIRE 1966"
**1966, Mar. 14** *Perf. 12*
C82 A42 300fr gold, dl red brn & sal 2.75 1.50

Centenary of first Egyptian postage stamp.

## Scenic Type of Regular Issue
View: Boulbinet Lighthouse.
**1966, Apr. 4** *Perf. 13½*
C83 A54 100fr multicolored 1.40 .60

See #C90-C91. For overprints see #C93-C95.

Nos. C76-C77 Overprinted in Blue or Yellow

**1966, May 2** **Photo.** *Perf. 13½*
C84 AP6 200fr multi (Bl) 2.25 1.10
C85 AP6 500fr multi (Y) 5.75 2.75

UNESCO, 20th anniv.

## Woman-Flower Type of Regular Issue
Designs: Women and flowers of Guinea.
**1966, May 30** **Photo.** *Perf. 13½*
Size: 28x34mm
C86 A56 100fr multicolored 3.50 .70
C87 A56 300fr multicolored 5.50 2.10

## Snake Type of Regular Issue
Designs: 200fr, Pastoria Research Institute. 300fr, Men holding rock python.
**1967, May 15** **Litho.** *Perf. 13½*
Size: 56x20mm
C88 A61 200fr multicolored 3.25 1.25
*a.* Souv. sheet of 3, #471, 474, C88 9.00 6.50
C89 A61 300fr multicolored 5.50 2.25

## Scenic Type of Regular Issue
Views: 100fr, House of explorer Olivier de Sanderval. 200fr, Conakry.
**1967, June 20** **Photo.** *Perf. 13½*
C90 A54 100fr multicolored .95 .45
C91 A54 200fr multicolored 2.75 1.10

For overprints see Nos. C94-C95.

## Elephant Type of Regular Issue, 1967

**1967, Sept. 28**    **Photo.**    *Perf. 13½*
C92   A63   200fr gold & multi    1.60   .75

Nos. C83 and C90-C91 Overprinted
with Lions Emblem and: "AMITIE DES
PEUPLES GRACE AU TOURISME
1917-1967"

**1967, Nov. 6**
C93   A54   100fr multi (#C83)    2.50   .90
C94   A54   100fr multi (#C90)    2.50   .90
C95   A54   200fr multi (#C91)    5.00   1.50
   *Nos. C93-C95 (3)*    10.00   3.30

50th anniversary of Lions International.

Detail from Mural by José Vela
Zanetti — AP7

Family, Mural by
Per
Krohg — AP8

The designs of the 30fr, 50fr and 200fr show
mankind's struggle for a lasting peace after
the mural in the lobby of the UN Conference
Building, NY. The designs of the 100fr and of
Nos. C98a-C98b show mankind's hope for the
future after a mural in the UN Security Council
Chamber.

**1967, Nov. 11**
C96   AP7   30fr multicolored    .40   .20
C97   AP7   50fr multicolored    .50   .20
C98   AP8   100fr multicolored    1.10   .35
   *a.*   Souv. sheet of 3, English inscription    3.00   3.00
   *b.*   As "a," French inscription    3.00   3.00
C99   AP7   200fr multi    2.50   .50
   *Nos. C96-C99 (4)*    4.50   1.25

Nos. C98a and C98b each contain a 100fr
stamp similar to No. C98 and two 50fr stamps
showing festival scenes. The 50fr stamps
have not been issued individually.

## People and Dwellings Type of Regular Issue

Design: 300fr, People and village of Les
Bassari, Kundara Region.

**1968, Apr. 1**    **Photo.**    *Perf. 14x13½*
   **Size: 57x36mm**
C100   A66   300fr gold & multi    4.50   1.25

## Legends Type of Regular Issue

70fr, The Girl and the Hippopotamus. 100fr,
Old Faya's Inheritance, vert. 200fr,
Soumangourou Kante Killed by Djegue
(woman on horseback). 300fr, Little Gouné,
Son of the Lion, vert.

**1968**    **Photo.**    *Perf. 13½*
C101   A67   70fr multicolored    .90   .20
C102   A67   100fr multicolored    1.40   .30
C103   A67   200fr multicolored    2.75   1.00
   *a.*   Souv. sheet of 4    7.00   7.00
C104   A67   300fr multicolored    4.00   1.25
   *Nos. C101-C104 (4)*    9.05   2.75

Issued in sheets of 10 plus 2 labels. No.
C103a contains 4 imperf. stamps similar to
Nos. 510-511 and C102-C103.;
For souvenir sheet see No. 509a.
Issued: #C102-C103, 5/16; #C101, C104,
9/16.

## African Animal Type of Regular Issue

**1968, Nov. 25**    **Photo.**    *Perf. 13½*
   **Size: 49x35mm**
C105   A68   100fr Lions    2.75   .55
C106   A68   200fr Elephant    4.75   2.10

For souvenir sheet see No. 518a.

## Robert F. Kennedy Type of Regular Issue, 1968

Portraits: 50fr, Senator Robert F. Kennedy.
100fr, Rev. Martin Luther King, Jr. 200fr,
Pres. John F. Kennedy.

**1968, Dec. 16**
C107   A69   50fr yel & multi    1.10   .20
C108   A69   100fr multicolored    2.25   .20
C109   A69   200fr multicolored    5.00   1.25
   *Nos. C107-C109 (3)*    8.35   1.65

The stamps are printed in sheets of 15 (3x5)
containing 10 stamps and five green and gold
center labels. Sheets come either with
English or French inscriptions on label.

## Olympic Type of Regular Issue

Sculpture &: 100fr, Gymnast on vaulting
horse. 200fr, Gymnast on rings. 300fr, High
jump.

**1969, Feb. 1**    **Photo.**    *Perf. 13½*
C110   A71   100fr multicolored    1.25   .30
C111   A71   200fr multicolored    2.75   .90
C111A   A71   300fr multicolored    4.50   1.10
   *Nos. C110-C111A (3)*    8.50   2.30

Nos. C78-C79
Surcharged and
Overprinted in
Red

**1969, Mar. 17**    **Litho.**    *Perf. 13½x14*
C112   A52   25fr on 200fr multi    .50   .20
C112A   A52   100fr multicolored    1.25   .65
C112B   A52   200fr multicolored    2.40   1.00
   *Nos. C112-C112B (3)*    4.15   1.85

See note after No. 530.
Nos. C112-C112B also exist with surcharge
and overprint in orange (25fr, 200fr) or black
(100fr). These sell for a small premium.

## Bird Type of Regular Issue

Birds: 50fr, Violet-crested touraco. 100fr,
European golden oriole. 200fr, Vulturine
guinea fowl.

**1971, June 18**    **Photo.**    *Perf. 13*
   **Size: 41x41mm**
C113   A81   50fr gold & multi    1.40   .40
C113A   A81   100fr gold & multi    2.75   .80
C113B   A81   200fr gold & multi    6.00   1.25
   *Nos. C113-C113B (3)*    10.15   2.45

John and Robert Kennedy, Martin
Luther King, Jr. — AP9

**Embossed on Metallic Foil**
**1972**    *Die Cut Perf. 10½*
C114   AP9   300fr silver    35.00   35.00
**Embossed & Typo.**
C114A   AP9   1500fr gold, cream    55.00   55.00
     & green

Jules Verne, Moon Rocket — AP10

**Embossed on Metallic Foil**
**1972**    *Die Cut Perf. 10½*
C115   AP10   300fr silver    35.00   35.00
C115A   AP10   1200fr gold    85.00   85.00

Richard
Nixon — AP11

Nixon and Mao — AP12

Nixon's Trip to People's Republic of China:
a, Nixon. b, Chinese table tennis player. c,
American table tennis player, Capitol dome. d,
Mao Tse-tung.

**Embossed on Metallic Foil**
**1972**    *Die Cut Perf. 10½*
C116   AP11   90fr Block of 4,        27.50   27.50
     #a.-d., silver
C117   AP11   290fr Block of 4,        45.00   45.00
     #a.-d., gold
**Embossed & Typo.**
C118   AP12   1200fr gold & red    60.00   60.00

Perforations within blocks of 4 are perf. 11.

## Racial Equality Year Type of Regular Issue

Design: 100fr, Men of 4 races and racial
equality emblem (like No. 603).

**1972, May 14**    **Photo.**    *Perf. 13x13½*
C119   A84   100fr gold & multi    1.50   1.00

## Satellite Type of Regular Issue

Designs: 100fr, Map of Africa and Relay.
200fr, Map of Africa and Early Bird.

**1972, May 17**    **Litho.**    *Perf. 13*
C120   A85   100fr yel & multi    1.40   .70
C121   A85   200fr multicolored    3.00   1.40

## African Postal Union Type of Regular Issue

Air mail envelope and UPAF emblem.

**1972, July 10**
C122   A86   100fr multicolored    1.00   .55
C123   A86   200fr multicolored    1.90   1.25

## Olympic Type of Regular Issue

**1972, Aug. 26**    **Photo.**    *Perf. 13*
C124   A88   100fr Gymnast on    2.40   .60
     rings
C125   A88   200fr Bicycling    3.75   1.10
**Souvenir Sheet**
C126   A88   300fr Soccer    7.00   7.00

## Flower Type of 1974

**1974, May 20**    **Photo.**    *Perf. 13*
   **Size: 38x38mm (Diamond)**
C127   A97   20s Thunbergia alata    3.50   .95
C128   A97   25s Diascia barberae    4.25   1.10
C129   A97   50s Kigelia africana    10.00   2.75
   *Nos. C127-C129 (3)*    17.75   4.80

## Olympic Games Type of 1976
## Souvenir Sheet

**1976, May 17**    **Photo.**    *Perf. 13½*
C130    Sheet of 4    16.00   12.50
   *a.*   A104 25s Soccer    2.50   2.50

No. C130 contains 32x32mm stamps.

## Mushroom Type of 1977

Mushrooms: 10s, Morchella esculenta. 12s,
Lepiota procera. 15s, Cantharellus cibarius.

**1977, Feb. 6**    **Photo.**    *Perf. 13*
   **Size: 48x31mm**
C131   A106   10s multicolored    4.50   .70
C132   A106   12s multicolored    6.25   .90
C133   A106   15s multicolored    8.25   2.10
   *Nos. C131-C133 (3)*    19.00   3.70

## Reptile Type of 1977

Reptiles: 10s, Flap-necked chameleon.
15s, Nile crocodiles. 25s, Painted tortoise.

**1977, Oct. 10**    **Photo.**    *Perf. 13½*
   **Size: 46x30mm**
C134   A109   10s multicolored    4.25   .80
C135   A109   15s multicolored    5.50   1.10
C136   A109   25s multicolored    8.00   1.60
   *Nos. C134-C136 (3)*    17.75   3.50

## Animal Type of 1977

Endangered Animals: 5s, Eland. 8s,
Pygmy elephant. 9s, Hippopotamus. 10s,
Chimpanzee. 12s, Palm squirrel. 13s, Lion.
Male, female and young of each animal
shown.

**1977, Dec. 12**    **Photo.**    *Perf. 14x13½*
C137   A110   Strip of 3    4.00   1.75
   *a.-c.*   5s any single    1.10
C138   A110   Strip of 3    6.25   2.75
   *a.-c.*   8s any single    1.90
C139   A110   Strip of 3    6.75   3.00
   *a.-c.*   9s any single    2.00
C140   A110   Strip of 3    7.00   3.50
   *a.-c.*   10s any single    2.10
C141   A110   Strip of 3    8.50   4.00
   *a.-c.*   12s any single    2.50
C142   A110   Strip of 3    9.75   5.00
   *a.-c.*   13s any single    3.00
   *Nos. C137-C142 (6)*    42.25   20.00

## Russian Revolution Type, 1978

10s, Russian ballet. 30s, Pushkin
Monument.

**1978, Feb. 27**    **Photo.**    *Perf. 14*
C143   A111   10s gold & multi    2.75   .80
C144   A111   30s gold & multi    8.00   2.10

## Giscard d'Estaing Type of 1979

Pres. Valery Giscard d'Estaing of France,
vert.

**1979, Sept. 14**    **Photo.**    *Perf. 13*
C145   A112   25s multicolored    7.00   2.00

## Jules Verne Type of 1979

Designs: 20s, Five Weeks in a Balloon.
25s, Robur the Conqueror.

**1979, Nov. 8**    **Litho.**    *Perf. 12x12½*
C146   A113   20s multicolored    3.50   1.25
C147   A113   25s multicolored    3.50   1.25

## Olympic Type of 1982

**1982**    **Litho.**    *Perf. 12½x12, 12x12½*
C148   A120   9s Fencing    1.60   .45
C149   A120   10s Soccer, vert.    1.90   .45
C150   A120   11s Basketball, vert.    2.25   .45
C151   A120   20s Diving, vert.    4.00   1.10
C152   A120   25s Boxing, vert.    4.75   1.50
   *Nos. C148-C152 (5)*    14.50   3.95

## Ataturk Type of 1982

**1982, July 19**    **Photo.**    *Perf. 13½*
C153   A122   25s like #830    5.00   1.25

## World Cup Type of 1982

Designs: Various soccer players.

**1982, Aug. 23**
C154   A123   10s multicolored    2.60   .95
C155   A123   20s multicolored    5.50   2.10
C156   A123   25s multicolored    6.50   2.75
   *Nos. C154-C156 (3)*    14.60   5.80

## Nos. C154-C156 Overprinted like #835-838

**1982, Aug. 23**    **Photo.**    *Perf. 13½*
C157   A123   10s multicolored    2.40   .75
C158   A123   20s multicolored    5.00   1.75
C159   A123   25s multicolored    6.00   2.00
   *Nos. C157-C159 (3)*    13.40   4.50

Location of flag in overprint varies.

## Balloon Type

Designs: 20s, Graf Zeppelin, Airship, horiz.
25s, Double Eagle II, L. Newman, B. Abruzzo,
M. Anderson. 30s, Le Geant Hot Air Balloon,
Nadar; Dirigible, Dumont.

**1983, Aug. 1**    **Litho.**    *Perf. 13½*
C160   A125   20s multicolored    3.25   1.25
C161   A125   25s multicolored    3.75   1.75
**Souvenir Sheet**
C162   A125   30s multicolored    5.00   1.90

## Nos. 894, 880-881 and 896
### Overprinted

**1985, Nov. 5**    Litho.    *Perf. 13½*
C163 A133 20s "80c Anniver-
saire / 1905-
1985"    2.75 1.25
C164 A131 20s "Rassemble-
ment /
Jambville-
1985"    2.75 1.25
C165 A131 25s "80e Anniversaire / 1905-
1985"    3.50 1.50
Nos. C163-C165 (3)    9.00 4.00

### Souvenir Sheet

C166 A133 30s "Kasparov /
champion /
du Monde"    15.00 10.00

US Space Shuttle Challenger
Explosion, Jan. 28, 1986 — AP13

Designs: 100fr, Lift-off, crew names. 170fr, Shuttle design, Christa McAuliffe holding shuttle model. 600fr, Lift-off, vert.

**1986, July 1**
**100fr, 170fr Surcharged in Silver and Black**
C167 AP13 100fr multicolored    1.10 .30
C168 AP13 170fr multicolored    1.90 .50

### Souvenir Sheet

C169 AP13 600fr multicolored    7.00 2.75

#C167-C168 not issued without surcharge. Souvenir sheets of one exist containing Nos. C167 and C168.

Robin Yount, Milwaukee Brewers
Baseball Player — AP14

**1990, Aug. 3**    Litho.    *Perf. 13½*
C170 AP14 450fr multicolored    5.00 2.10

No. C170 exists in a souvenir sheet of 1.
For surcharge see No. 1182R.

### Souvenir Sheet

Armstrong, Aldrin, Collins and Apollo
11 Emblem — AP15

**1990, Aug. 3**    Litho.    *Perf. 13½*
C171 AP15 750fr multicolored    8.00 3.25

---

Galileo Spacecraft — AP16

**1990, Aug. 3**
C172 AP16 500fr multicolored    5.25 2.25

No. C172 exists as a souvenir sheet of 1.

Pope John
Paul II,
Visit to
Africa
AP18

Portrait and: No. C174, Raising hand in benediction. No. C175, Child.

### Litho. & Embossed
**1992, Oct. 26**    *Perf. 13½*
C174 AP18 1500fr gold & multi    24.00 19.00

### Souvenir Sheet
C175 AP18 1500fr gold & multi    18.00 15.00

No. C175 exists imperf.

Elvis Presley, 15th Anniv. of
Death — AP19

**1992, Nov. 10**
C176 AP19 1500fr gold & multi    24.00 20.00

No. C176 exists in miniature sheet of one.

### De Gaulle Type of 1991 Overprinted "6 JUNE 1944 / DEBARQUEMENT"
**1994**   Litho. & Embossed   *Perf. 13½*
C177 A181 1500fr like #1168    15.00 12.50

### No. 1195 Ovptd. in Silver "RENCONTHE / FISCHER-SPASSKY / 4 SEPT au 5 NOV 1992 / AU MONTENEGRO"
**1993, Feb. 24**    Litho.    *Perf. 13½*
C178 A188 450fr multicolored    4.50 2.25

No. C178 exists in souvenir sheet of 1.

---

## POSTAGE DUE STAMPS

D5           D6

**1959**   Unwmk.   Litho.   *Perf. 11½*
J36 D5 1fr emerald    .30 .20
J37 D5 2fr lilac rose    .30 .20
J38 D5 3fr brown    .55 .20
J39 D5 5fr blue    1.40 .20

---

J40 D5 10fr orange    2.10 .55
J41 D5 20fr rose lilac    4.25 .95
Nos. J36-J41 (6)    8.90 2.30

**1960**    Engr.    *Perf. 13½*
J42 D6 1fr dark carmine    .20 .20
J43 D6 2fr brown orange    .20 .20
J44 D6 3fr dark car rose    .30 .20
J45 D6 5fr bright green    .70 .35
J46 D6 10fr dark brown    1.50 .55
J47 D6 20fr dull blue    3.00 1.25
Nos. J42-J47 (6)    5.90 2.75

---

# GUINEA-BISSAU

ˈgi-nē-bi-ˈsauⁿ̦

LOCATION — West coast of Africa
between Senegal and Guinea
GOVT. — Republic
AREA — 13,948 sq. mi.
POP. — 1,234,555 (1999 est.)
CAPITAL — Bissau

Guinea-Bissau, the former Portuguese Guinea, attained independence September 10, 1974. The state includes the Bissagos Islands.

100 Centavos = 1 Escudo
100 Centavos = 1 Peso

> **Catalogue values for all unused stamps in this country are for Never Hinged items.**

Amilcar Cabral, Map of Africa and
Flag — A27

Design: Flag of the PAIGC (African Party of Independence of Guinea-Bissau and Cape Verde) shows location of Guinea-Bissau on map of Africa.

### Perf. 11x10½
**1974, Sept. 10**   Litho.   Unwmk.
345 A27 1p brown & multi    1.00 .55
346 A27 2.50p brown & multi    1.40 .80
347 A27 5p brown & multi    22.50 9.00
348 A27 10p brown & multi    3.75 2.10
Nos. 345-348 (4)    28.65 12.45

First anniv. of Proclamation of Independence, Sept. 24, 1973.

WMO
Emblem — A28

Portuguese Guinea No. 344
Overprinted in Black

**1975**    Litho.    *Perf. 13*
349 A28 2c brown & multi    1.40 1.40

No. 349 exists with overprint in brown.
Value, $5.

Amilcar Cabral, Map of Africa,
Flag — A29

---

**1975, Sept.**    Litho.    *Perf. 11*
350 A29 1p brown & multi
351 A29 2.50p brown & multi
352 A29 5p brown & multi
353 A29 10p brown & multi
Nos. 350-353 (4)    14.00 7.50

Nos. 350-353 are dated Sept. 24, 1973, in the design. Also exist dated Sept. 21, 1973. Value of latter set, $10.

Flag and Arms of Guinea-Bissau and
Amilcar Cabral — A30

Flag, Arms and: 2e, #358, Family. 3e, 5e, Pres. Luiz Cabral. #359, like 1e.

**1975, Sept.**      *Perf. 14*
354 A30 1e yel & multi    2.00 1.00
355 A30 2e multicolored    2.00 1.25
356 A30 3e red & multi    3.00 1.50
357 A30 5e yel & multi    8.00 4.00
358 A30 10e red & multi    12.00 5.00
359 A30 10e brt grn & multi    12.00 5.00
Nos. 354-359 (6)    39.00 17.75

Amilcar Cabral's 51st birth anniv. (1e, No. 359); African Party of Independence of Guinea-Bissau and Cape Verde, 19th anniv. (2e, No. 358); Proclamation of Independence, 2nd anniv. (3e, 5e).
For surcharges see Nos. 367-367E.

Henry Knox, Cannons of
Ticonderoga — A30a

Designs: 10e, Israel Putnam, Battle of Bunker Hill. 15e, Washington crossing the Delaware. 20e, Tadeusz Kosciuszko, Battle of Saratoga. 30e, Von Steuben, winter at Valley Forge. 40e, Lafayette, Washington rallying troops at Monmouth. 50e, Signing the Declaration of Independence.

**1976, May 5**    Litho.    *Perf. 13½*
360 A30a 5e multicolored
360A A30a 10e multicolored
360B A30a 15e multicolored
360C A30a 20e multicolored
360D A30a 30e multicolored
360E A30a 40e multicolored
Nos. 360-360E (6)    12.00 3.75

### Souvenir Sheet
360F A30a 50e multicolored    16.00

American Revolution, bicentennial. Nos. 360D-360F are airmail. Nos. 360-360E exist in miniature sheets of 1, perf. and imperf. No. 360F contains one 75x45mm stamp and exists imperf.
See Nos. 371-371A.

Masked
Dancer
A30b

**1976, May 10**      *Perf. 11*
**Denomination in Black on Silver Block**

361 A30b 2p shown
361A A30b 3p Dancer, drummer
361B A30b 5p Dancers on stilts

**361C** A30b 10p Dancer with
     spear, bow
**361D** A30b 15p Masked dancer,
     diff.
**361E** A30b 20p Dancer with
     striped cloak
   *Nos. 361-3601 (6)*     9.00 3.00
    **Souvenir Sheet**
**361F** A30b 50p Like No. 361E   8.00 8.00

Nos. 361C-361F are airmail. Silver block obliterates original denomination. Not issued without surcharge.

**Nos. 361-361F Ovptd. in Black**

**1976, June 8**         **Perf. 11**
**362** A30b  2p on No. 361
**362A** A30b  3p on No. 361A
**362B** A30b  5p on No. 361B
**362C** A30b 10p on No. 361C
**362D** A30b 15p on No. 361D
**362E** A30b 20p on No. 361E
   *Nos. 362-362E (6)*    9.50 2.80
    **Souvenir Sheet**
**362F** A30b 50p on No. 361F   5.00 5.00

Nos. 362C-362F are airmail. UPU cent. (in 1974). Nos. 362-362F exist imperf, and Nos. 362-362E in imperf miniature sheets of 1, all with black or red overprints.

Cabral, Guinean Mother and Children — A31

**1976, Aug.**   **Litho.**   **Perf. 13½**
**363** A31  3p multicolored   .20 .20
**364** A31  5p multicolored   .20 .20
**365** A31  6p multicolored   .55 .20
**366** A31 10p multicolored   .70 .20
   *Nos. 363-366 (4)*    1.65 .80

3rd anniv. of assassination of Amilcar Cabral (1924-1973), revolutionary leader.

Nos. 354-359 Surcharged in Black on Silver

**1976, Sept. 12**   **Litho.**   **Perf. 14**
**367** A30  1p on 1e No. 354
**367A** A30  2p on 2e No. 355
**367B** A30  3p on 3e No. 356
**367C** A30  5p on 5e No. 357
**367D** A30 10p on 10e No. 358
**367E** A30 10p on 10e No. 359
   *Nos. 367-367E (6)*    6.50 1.40

1876 Bell Telephone and Laying First Trans-Atlantic Cable — A31a

Telephones of: 3p, France, 1890, and first telephone booth, 1893. 5p, Germany, 1903, and automatic telephone, 1898. 10p, England, 1910, and relay station, 1963. 15p, France, 1924, and communications satellite. 20p, Modern telephone, 1970, and Molniya satellite. 50p, Picture phone.

**1976, Oct. 18**      **Perf. 13½**
**368** A31a  2p multicolored
**368A** A31a  3p multicolored
**368B** A31a  5p multicolored
**368C** A31a 10p multicolored
**368D** A31a 15p multicolored
**368E** A31a 20p multicolored
   *Nos. 368-368E (6)*    6.00 2.75
    **Souvenir Sheet**
**368F** A31a 50p multicolored   6.00 6.00

Nos. 368C-368F are airmail. No. 368F contains one 68x42mm stamp. No. 368F exists imperf. Nos. 368-368E exist in souvenir sheets of one, perf. and imperf.

1976 Winter Olympics, Innsbruck — A31b

**1976, Nov. 3**     **Perf. 14x13½**
**369** A31b  1p Women's figure
     skating
**369A** A31b  3p Ice hockey
**369B** A31b  5p Two-man bobsled
**369C** A31b 10p Pairs figure skat-
     ing
**369D** A31b 20p Cross country
     skiing
**369E** A31b 30p Speed skating
   *Nos. 369-369E (6)*    7.50 2.50
    **Souvenir Sheet**
**369F** A31b 50p Downhill skiing  5.50 5.50

Nos. 369C-369F are airmail. No. 369F exists imperf. Nos. 369-369E exist in souvenir sheets of one, perf. and imperf.

1976 Summer Olympics, Montreal — A31c

**1976, Nov. 24**      **Perf. 13½**
**370** A31c  1p Soccer
**370A** A31c  3p Pole vault
**370B** A31c  5p Women's hurdles
**370C** A31c 10p Discus
**370D** A31c 20p Sprinting
**370E** A31c 30p Wrestling
   *Nos. 370-370E (6)*    7.00 2.25
    **Souvenir Sheet**
**370F** A31c 50p Cycling, horiz.  6.50 6.50

Nos. 370E-370F are airmail. No. 370F contains one 47x38mm stamp. No. 370F exists imperf. Nos. 370-370E exist in souvenir sheets of one, perf. and imperf.

**American Revolution Type of 1976**

Designs: 3.50p, Crispus Attucks, Boston Massacre. 5p, Martin Luther King, US Capitol.

**1977, Jan. 27**     **Perf. 13½**
**Denomination in Black on Gold Block**
**371** A30a 3.50p multicolored
**371A** A30a  5p multicolored
   *Nos. 371-371A (2)*    .80 .40

Gold block obliterates original denomination. Not issued without surcharge. Exist in souvenir sheets of one, perf. and imperf.

Cabral Addressing UN General Assembly — A32

Design: 50c, Cabral and guerrilla fighters.

**1977, July**   **Litho.**   **Perf. 13½**
**372** A32  50c multicolored   .20 .20
**373** A32 3.50p multicolored   .30 .20

For surcharges see Nos. C12-C13.

Henri Dunant, Nobel Peace Prize, 1901 A32a

Nobel Prize Winners: 5p, Einstein, Physics, 1921. 6p, Irene and Frederic Joliot-Curie, Chemistry, 1935. 30p, Fleming, Medicine, 1945. 35p, Hemingway, Literature, 1954. 40p, J. Tinbergen, Economics, 1969. 50p, Nobel Prize Medal.

**1977, July 27**
**374** A32a 3.50p multicolored
**374A** A32a  5p multicolored
**374B** A32a  6p multicolored
**374C** A32a 30p multicolored
**374D** A32a 35p multicolored
**374E** A32a 40p multicolored
   *Nos. 374-374E (6)*   15.00 5.25
    **Souvenir Sheet**
**374F** A32a 50p multicolored  5.50 5.50

Nos. 374D-374F are airmail. No. 374F contains one 57x39mm stamp. No. 374F exists imperf. Nos. 374-374E exist in souvenir sheets of one, perf. and imperf.

Postal Runner, Telstar Satellite — A32b

UPU Centenary (in 1974): 5p, Biplane, satellites encircle globe. 6p, Mail truck, satelite control room. 30p, Stagecoach, astronaut canceling letters on Moon. 35p, Steam locomotive, communications satellite. 40p, Space shuttle, Apollo-Soyuz link-up. 50p, Semaphore signalling system, satellite dish.

**1977, Sept. 30**
**375** A32b 3.50p multicolored
**375A** A32b  5p multicolored
**375B** A32b  6p multicolored
**375C** A32b 30p multicolored
**375D** A32b 35p multicolored
**375E** A32b 40p multicolored
   *Nos. 375-375E (6)*   10.00 4.25
    **Souvenir Sheet**
**375F** A32b 50p multicolored  5.00 5.00

Nos. 375D-375F are airmail. No. 375F exists imperf. Nos. 375-375E exist in souvenir sheets of one, perf. and imperf.

Torch and Party Emblem — A33

**1977, Sept.**   **Litho.**   **Perf. 14**
**376** A33  3p yel & multi   .25 .20
**377** A33 15p sal & multi   1.25 .60
**378** A33 50p lt grn & multi  3.00 1.50
   *Nos. 376-378 (3)*    4.50 2.30

African Party of Independence of Guinea-Bissau and Cape Verde, 20th anniversary.

Queen Elizabeth II, Silver Jubilee — A33a

Designs: 5p, Coronation ceremony. 10p, Yeoman of the Guard, Crown Jewels. 20p, Trumpeter. 25p, Royal Horse Guard. 30p, Royal Family. 50p, Queen Elizabeth II.

**1977, Oct. 15**
**379** A33a 3.50p multicolored
**379A** A33a  5p multicolored
**379B** A33a 10p multicolored
**379C** A33a 20p multicolored
**379D** A33a 25p multicolored
**379E** A33a 30p multicolored
   *Nos. 379-379E (6)*   11.00 2.75
    **Souvenir Sheet**
**379F** A33a 50p multicolored  5.00 5.00

Nos. 379D-379F are airmail. No. 379F contains one 42x39mm stamp. No. 379F exists imperf. Nos. 379-379E exist in souvenir sheets of one, perf. and imperf.

Massacre of the Innocents by Rubens A33b

Paintings by Peter Paul Rubens: 5p, Rape of the Daughters of Leukippos. 6p, Lamentation of Christ, horiz. 30p, Francisco IV Gonzaga, Prince of Mantua. 35p, The Four Continents. 40p, Marquise Brigida Spinola Doria. 50p, The Wounding of Christ.

**1977, Nov. 15**
**380** A33b 3.50p multicolored
**380A** A33b  5p multicolored
**380B** A33b  6p multicolored
**380C** A33b 30p multicolored
**380D** A33b 35p multicolored
**380E** A33b 40p multicolored
   *Nos. 380-380E (6)*   11.00 5.00
    **Souvenir Sheet**
**380F** A33b 50p multicolored  5.50 5.50

Nos. 380D-380F are airmail. Nos. 380-380F exist imperf. Nos. 380-380E exist in souvenir sheets of one, perf. and imperf.

Congress Emblem — A34

**1977, Nov. 15    Litho.    Perf. 14**
381 A34 3.50p multicolored          .30  .20
3rd PAIGC Congress, Bissau, Nov. 15-20.

Santos-Dumont's Airship, 1901 — A34a

Airships: 5p, R-34 crossing the Atlantic, 1919. 10p, Norge over North Pole, 1926. 20p, Graf Zeppelin over Abu Simbel, 1931. 25p, Hindenburg over New York, 1937. 30p, Graf Zeppelin, Concorde, space shuttle. 50p, Ferdinand von Zeppelin, horiz.

**1978, Feb. 27**
382 A34a 3.50p multicolored
382A A34a 5p multicolored
382B A34a 10p multicolored
382C A34a 20p multicolored
382D A34a 25p multicolored
382E A34a 30p multicolored
    Nos. 382-382E (6)          8.00 3.75
**Souvenir Sheet**
382F A34a 50p multicolored       5.00 5.00
Nos. 382D-382F are airmail. No. 382F exists imperf. Nos. 382-382E exist in souvenir sheets of one, perf. and imperf.

World Cup Soccer Championships, Argentina — A34b

Soccer players and posters from previous World Cup Championships: 3.50p, 1930. 5p, 1938. 10p, 1950. 20p, 1962. 25p, 1970. 30p, 1974. 50p, Argentina '78 emblem.

**1978, Mar. 15**
383 A34b 3.50p multicolored
383A A34b 5p multicolored
383B A34b 10p multicolored
383C A34b 20p multicolored
383D A34b 25p multicolored
383E A34b 30p multicolored
    Nos. 383-383E (6)          8.00 3.75
**Souvenir Sheet**
383F A34b 50p multicolored       5.00 5.00
Nos. 383D-383F are airmail. Nos. 383-383F exist imperf. Nos. 383-383E exist in miniature sheets of one, perf. and imperf.
For surcharges see Nos. 393-393F.

Endangered Species — A34c

**1978, Apr. 17**
384 A34c 3.50p Black antelope
384A A34c 5p Fennec
384B A34c 6p Secretary bird
384C A34c 30p Hippopotami
384D A34c 35p Cheetahs
384E A34c 40p Gorillas
    Nos. 384-384E (6)         13.00 6.00
**Souvenir Sheet**
384F A34c 50p Cercopithecus erythotis       6.50 6.50
Nos. 384D-384F are airmail. No. 384F contains one 39x42mm stamp. No. 384F exists imperf. Nos. 384-384E exist in souvenir sheets of one, perf. and imperf.

Antenna, ITU Emblem A35

**1978, May 17    Litho.    Perf. 13½**
385 A35 3.50p silver & multi       .20  .20
386 A35 10p gold & multi           .90  .30
10th World Telecommunications Day.

Boy — A36

3p, Infant and grandfather. 5p, Boys. 30p, Girls.

**1978    Perf. 14**
387 A36 50c yel grn & dk bl        .20  .20
388 A36 3p claret & car rose       .20  .20
389 A36 5p ocher & brown           .40  .20
390 A36 30p car & ocher           2.10  .80
    Nos. 387-390 (4)             2.90 1.40
Children's Day.

Queen Elizabeth II, Silver Jubilee A36a

Elizabeth, Imperial State Crown — A36b

Designs: 5p, Queen, Prince Philip in Coronation Coach. 10p, Queen, Prince Philip. 20p, Mounted drummer. 25p, Imperial State Crown,

St. Edward's Crown. 30p, Queen holding orb and scepter. 50p, Queen on Throne flanked by Archbishops. No. 391H, Coronation Coach.

**1978, June 15**
391 A36a 3.50p multicolored
391A A36a 5p multicolored
391B A36a 10p multicolored
391C A36a 20p multicolored
391D A36a 25p multicolored
391E A36a 30p multicolored
    Nos. 391-391E (6)          7.00 2.75
**Litho. & Embossed**
391F A36b 100p gold & multi 20.00  —
**Souvenir Sheets**
391G A36a 50p multicolored     5.00 5.00
**Litho. & Embossed**
391H A36b 100p gold & multi 14.00  —
Nos. 391D-391H are airmail. Nos. 391-391E exist in souvenir sheets of one, perf. and imperf. Nos. 391F-391H exist imperf.

History of Aviation — A36c

**1978, June 15    Litho.    Perf. 13½**
392 A36c 3.50p Wright Brothers
392A A36c 10p Santos-Dumont
392B A36c 15p Bleriot
392C A36c 20p Lindbergh, Spirit of St. Louis
392D A36c 25p Lunar module
392E A36c 30p Space shuttle
    Nos. 392-392E (6)          8.50 3.25
**Souvenir Sheet**
392F A36c 50p Concorde         5.50 5.50
Nos. 392D-392F are airmail. Nos. 392-392E exist in souvenir sheets of one, perf. and imperf. No. 392F exists imperf.

Nos. 383-383F Ovptd. in Gold

**1978, Oct. 2**
393 A34b 3.50p on No. 383
393A A34b 5p on No. 383A
393B A34b 10p on No. 383B
393C A34b 20p on No. 383C
393D A34b 25p on No. 383D
393E A34b 30p on No. 383E
    Nos. 393-393E (6)          8.00
**Souvenir Sheet**
393F A34b 50p on No. 383F      5.00 5.00
Nos. 393D-393F are airmail. Nos. 393-393E exist imperf. Nos. 393-393E exist in miniature sheets of 1 perf. and imperf. No. 393F exists overprinted in silver.

Virgin and Child by Albrecht Durer — A36d

Different Paintings of the Virgin and Child (Virgin only on 30p) by Durer.

**1978, Nov. 14**
394 A36d 3.50p multicolored
394A A36d 5p multicolored
394B A36d 6p multicolored
394C A36d 30p multicolored
394D A36d 35p multicolored
394E A36d 40p multicolored
    Nos. 394-394E (6)         10.00 4.00
**Souvenir Sheet**
394F A36d 50p multicolored     5.50 5.50
Nos. 394D-394F are airmail. No. 394F contains one 51x56mm stamp. Nos. 394-394E exist in souvenir sheets of one, perf. and imperf. No. 394F exists imperf.

Sir Rowland Hill (1795-1879), Wurttemberg No. 53 — A36e

Hill and: 5p, Belgium #1. 6p, Monaco #10. 30p, Spain 2r stamp of 1851 in blue. 35p, Switzerland #5. 40p, Naples #8. 50p, Portuguese Guinea #13 in brown.

**1978, Dec. 15**
395 A36e 3.50p multicolored
395A A36e 5p multicolored
395B A36e 6p multicolored
395C A36e 30p multicolored
395D A36e 35p multicolored
395E A36e 40p multicolored
    Nos. 395-395E (6)         17.00 2.00
**Souvenir Sheet**
395F A36e 50p multicolored     5.50 5.50
Nos. 395D-395F are airmail. No. 395F contains one 51x42mm stamp. Nos. 395-395E exist in souvenir sheets of one, perf. and imperf. No. 395F exists imperf.

Intl. Day of the Child — A36f

**1979, Jan. 15    Perf. 14**
396 A36f 3.50p shown
396A A36f 10p Children drinking
396B A36f 15p Child with book
396C A36f 20p Space plane
396D A36f 25p Skylab
396E A36f 30p Children playing chess
    Nos. 396-396E (6)         10.00 3.50
**Souvenir Sheet**
396F A36f 50p Children watching spaceship       5.50 5.50
Nos. 396C-396F are airmail. Nos. 396-396E exist in souvenir sheets of one, perf. and imperf. No. 396F exists imperf.

A36g

A36h

**1979    Litho.    Perf. 13**
397 A36g 4.50p multicolored        .45  .20
Massacre of Pindjiguiti, 20th anniv.

**1979		Litho.		Perf. 14**
397A  A36h  50c shown						.20  .20
397B  A36h  4p People, rainbow,
				diff.					.30  .20

World Telecommunications Day.

Family
A37

**1979, May	Litho.		Perf. 12x11½**
398  A37  50c multicolored					.45  .20
399  A37  2p multicolored					.95  .20
400  A37  4p multicolored					.45  .20
		Nos. 398-400 (3)				1.85  .60

General population census, Apr. 16-30.

Ernst Udet
and Fokker
D.VII — A38

**1980		Litho.		Perf. 13½**
401  A38  3.50p shown						.45  .20
401A  A38  5p Charles Nun-
				gesser, Nieu-
				port 17				.45  .20
401B  A38  6p von Richthofen,
				Fokker DR.1			.55  .20
401C  A38  30p Francesco
				Baracca,
				Spad XIII			2.25  .70
		Nos. 401-401C,C14-C14A (6)	10.20  3.55

Lake Placid Emblem, Speed
Skating — A39

**1980**
402  A39  3.50p shown						.45  .20
402A  A39  5p Downhill skiing				.45  .20
402B  A39  6p Luge						.55  .20
402C  A39  30p Cross-country
				skiing				2.25  .70
		Nos. 402-402C,C15-C16 (6)		9.95  3.55

13th Winter Olympic Games, Lake Placid,
NY, Feb. 12-24.

Shot-put
A40

**1980, Aug.	Litho.		Perf. 13½**
403  A40  3.50p shown						.30  .20
403A  A40  5p Athlete on
				rings				.70  .20
403B  A40  6p Running						.90  .25
403C  A40  30p Fencing					3.50  .70
		Nos. 403-403C,C18-C19 (6)		14.65  3.60

22nd Summer Olympic Games, Moscow,
7/19-8/3.

Pres. Luis
Caral,
Children
and
Workers
A41

5p, Pres. Caral holding books.

**1980, Aug.	Litho.		Perf. 13½**
404  A41  3.50p multicolored					.45  .20
405  A41  5p multicolored					.75  .20

Literacy campaign. See Nos. C21-C22.

Cooperation Among Developing
Countries — A42

**1980, Aug.**
406  A42  3.50p multicolored					.80  .20
407  A42  6p multicolored					.80  .20
408  A42  10p multicolored					1.60  .20
		Nos. 406-408 (3)				3.20  .60

Baskets — A43

**1980, Aug.	Litho.		Perf. 13½**
409  A43  3p Bird, family wood
				statues, vert.			.35  .20
410  A43  6p shown						.35  .20
411  A43  20p Head, doll carvings			1.25  .45
		Nos. 409-411 (3)				1.95  .85

Infant and Toy
Train,
Locomotive,
IYC Emblem
A44

**1980**
412  A44  6p Classroom, horiz.				.50  .30
412A  A44  10p Boy reading Jules
				Verne story			.90  .55
412B  A44  25p shown						1.75  .80
412C  A44  35p Archer, boy with
				bow				2.75  1.25
		Nos. 412-412C (4)				5.90  2.90

**Souvenir Sheet**
412D  A44  50p Students in lab				4.50  4.50

International Year of the Child (1979).

Columbia
Space Shuttle
and
Crew — A45

Space Exploration:  3.50p, Galileo, satellites.  5p, Wernher von Braun.  6p, Jules
Verne, rocket.

**1981, May	Litho.		Perf. 13½**
413  A45  3.50p multicolored					.40  .20
413A  A45  5p multicolored					.45  .20
413B  A45  6p multicolored					.50  .20
413C  A45  30p multicolored					2.50  .90
		Nos. 413-413C,C23-C24 (6)		11.10  4.25

Soccer Players, World Cup, Argentina
'78 and Espana '82 Emblems — A46

Soccer scenes and famous players: 3.50p,
Platini, France. 5p, Bettega, Italy. 6p, Rensen-
brink, Netherlands. 30p, Rivelino, Brazil.

**1981, May**
414  A46  3.50p multicolored					.40  .25
414A  A46  5p multicolored					.45  .25
414B  A46  6p multicolored					.50  .25
414C  A46  30p multicolored					2.50  .80
		Nos. 414-414C,C26-C27 (6)		11.10  4.30

Prince
Charles
and Lady
Diana, St.
Paul's
Cathedral
A47

Royal Wedding (Couple and): 3.50p, Diana
leading horse. 5p, Charles crowned Prince of
Wales. 6p, Diana with kindergarten children.

**1981		Litho.		Perf. 13½**
415  A47  3.50p multicolored					.40  .20
415A  A47  5p multicolored					.55  .20
415B  A47  6p multicolored					.60  .20
415C  A47  30p multicolored					2.10  .90
		Nos. 415-415C,C29-C30 (6)		12.40  4.25

Woman
Before a
Mirror, by
Picasso
(1881-1973)
A48

Picasso Birth Cent.: Various paintings.

**1981, Dec.	Litho.		Perf. 13½**
416  A48  3.50p multi						.50  .20
417  A48  5p multi						.65  .20
418  A48  6p multi						.75  .20
419  A48  30p multi						3.75  .90
		Nos. 416-419,C32-C33 (6)		18.15  4.35

Henrique
Vermelho
and his
Ship,
Drakkar
A49

Navigators and their ships: 5p, Vasco de
Gama, St. Gabriel. 6p, Ferdinand Magellan,
Victoria. 30p, Jacques Cartier, Emerillon.

**1981		Litho.		Perf. 13½**
420  A49  3.50p multicolored					.30  .20
421  A49  5p multicolored					.45  .20
422  A49  6p multicolored					.65  .20
423  A49  30p multicolored					3.00  1.00
		Nos. 420-423,C35-C36 (6)		13.15  4.75

Christmas — A50

Designs:  Virgin and Child paintings.

**1981**
424  A50  3.50p Mantegna					.30  .20
425  A50  5p Bellini						.45  .20
426  A50  6p Mantegna, diff.				.65  .20
427  A50  25p Correggio					3.00  1.00
		Nos. 424-427,C38-C39 (6)		13.15  4.75

Scouting
Year — A51

**1982, June 9	Litho.		Perf. 13½**
428  A51  3.50p Archery					.40  .20
429  A51  5p First aid training				.40  .20
430  A51  6p Bugler						.55  .20
431  A51  30p Cub scouts					3.00  .65
		Nos. 428-431,C41-C42 (6)		12.10  3.35

1982 World Cup — A52

Various soccer players and cup.

**1982, June 13	Litho.		Perf. 13½**
432  A52  3.50p Keegan					.40  .20
433  A52  5p Rossi						.40  .20
434  A52  6p Zico						.55  .20
435  A52  30p Arconada					3.00  .65
		Nos. 432-435,C44-C45 (6)		12.10  3.35

21st Birthday of Princess Diana — A53

Portraits and scenes of Diana.

**1982**
436  A53  3.50p multicolored					.40  .20
437  A53  5p multicolored					.40  .20
438  A53  6p multicolored					.55  .20
439  A53  30p multicolored					3.00  .65
		Nos. 436-439,C47-C48 (6)		12.10  3.35

For overprints see Nos. 450-456.

Visit by Portuguese President Eanes — A54

4.50p, Portugal and Guinea-Bissau flags.

| 1982 | | Litho. | Perf. 13½ | |
|---|---|---|---|---|
| 440 | A54 | 4.50p multicolored | .40 | .20 |
| 441 | A54 | 20p multicolored | 1.60 | 1.10 |

Manned Flight Bicentenary — A55

Various hot air balloons.

| 1983, Jan. 15 | | Litho. | Perf. 11 | |
|---|---|---|---|---|
| 442 | A55 | 50c multicolored | .20 | .20 |
| 443 | A55 | 2.50p multicolored | .20 | .20 |
| 444 | A55 | 3.50p multicolored | .40 | .20 |
| 445 | A55 | 5p multicolored | .65 | .20 |
| 446 | A55 | 10p multicolored | .70 | .20 |
| 447 | A55 | 20p multicolored | 1.75 | .35 |
| 448 | A55 | 30p multicolored | 2.50 | .45 |
| | | Nos. 442-448 (7) | 6.40 | 1.80 |

**Souvenir Sheet**
**Perf. 12½**

| 449 | A55 | 50p multicolored | 5.50 | .90 |
|---|---|---|---|---|

No. 449 contains one 47x47mm stamp.

Nos. 436-439, C47-C48, C49A-C49B Overprinted: "21 DE JULHO . GUILHERMO ARTUR FILIPE LUIS PRINCIPE DE GALES"

| 1982 | | Litho. | Perf. 13½ | |
|---|---|---|---|---|
| 450 | A53 | 3.50p multicolored | .70 | .20 |
| 451 | A53 | 5p multicolored | .80 | .20 |
| 452 | A53 | 6p multicolored | .95 | .20 |
| 453 | A53 | 30p multicolored | 4.25 | .65 |
| 454 | A53 | 35p multicolored | 5.25 | .80 |
| 455 | A53 | 40p multicolored | 5.75 | 1.10 |
| | | Nos. 450-455 (6) | 17.70 | 3.15 |

**Souvenir Sheet**

| 456 | A53 | 50p multicolored | 9.00 | 1.25 |
|---|---|---|---|---|

**Litho. & Embossed**

| 456A | A53a | 200p gold & multi | 18.00 | |
|---|---|---|---|---|

**Souvenir Sheet**

| 456B | A53a | 200p gold & multi, vert. | 40.00 | |
|---|---|---|---|---|

Nos. 454-456A are airmail.

African Apes and Monkeys A56

| 1983, Mar. 15 | | Litho. | Perf. 13½ | |
|---|---|---|---|---|
| 457 | A56 | 1p Comopithecus hamadryas | .20 | .20 |
| 458 | A56 | 1.50p Gorilla gorilla | .20 | .20 |
| 459 | A56 | 3.50p Theropithecus gelada | .45 | .20 |
| 460 | A56 | 5p Mandrillus sphinx | .55 | .20 |
| 461 | A56 | 8p Pan trogladytes | 1.25 | .20 |
| 462 | A56 | 20p Colobus abyssinicus | 2.00 | .30 |
| 463 | A56 | 30p Cercopithecus diana | 2.75 | .45 |
| | | Nos. 457-463 (7) | 7.40 | 1.75 |

Souvenir Sheet

TEMBAL '83, Stamp Exhibition, Basel — A57

**1983, May 21**
| 464 | A57 | 50p Space shuttle | 6.00 | 1.10 |
|---|---|---|---|---|

A58

Designs: Various telecommunications satellites and space shuttles.

| 1983, May 25 | | Litho. | Perf. 13½ | |
|---|---|---|---|---|
| 465 | A58 | 1p multicolored | .20 | .20 |
| 466 | A58 | 1.50p multicolored | .20 | .20 |
| 467 | A58 | 3.50p multicolored | .20 | .20 |
| 468 | A58 | 5p multicolored | .40 | .20 |
| 469 | A58 | 8p multicolored | .60 | .20 |
| 470 | A58 | 20p multicolored | 1.50 | .40 |
| 471 | A58 | 30p multicolored | 2.25 | .65 |
| | | Nos. 465-471 (7) | 5.35 | 2.05 |

**Souvenir Sheet**

| 472 | A58 | 50p multicolored | 4.50 | .90 |
|---|---|---|---|---|

History of Chess — A59

Early Chess Game — A60

Various chess pieces.

| 1983, June 13 | | Litho. | Perf. 12 | |
|---|---|---|---|---|
| 473 | A59 | 1p multicolored | .20 | .20 |
| 474 | A59 | 1.50p multicolored | .20 | .20 |
| 475 | A59 | 3.50p multicolored | .20 | .20 |
| 476 | A59 | 5p multicolored | .45 | .20 |
| 477 | A59 | 10p multicolored | .95 | .20 |
| 478 | A59 | 20p multicolored | 1.75 | .20 |
| 479 | A59 | 40p multicolored | 4.25 | .60 |
| | | Nos. 473-479 (7) | 8.00 | 1.80 |

**Souvenir Sheet**

| 480 | A60 | 50p brown & blk | 5.50 | .85 |
|---|---|---|---|---|

Raphael, 500th Birth Anniv. A61

Various paintings.

| 1983, June 30 | | Litho. | Perf. 12½ | |
|---|---|---|---|---|
| 481 | A61 | 1p gold & multi | .20 | .20 |
| 482 | A61 | 1.50p gold & multi | .20 | .20 |
| 483 | A61 | 3.50p gold & multi | .20 | .20 |
| 484 | A61 | 5p gold & multi | .50 | .20 |
| 485 | A61 | 8p gold & multi | .65 | .20 |
| 486 | A61 | 15p gold & multi | 1.25 | .20 |
| 487 | A61 | 30p gold & multi | 2.40 | .45 |
| | | Nos. 481-487 (7) | 5.40 | 1.65 |

**Souvenir Sheet**

| 488 | A61 | 50p gold & multi | 4.50 | 1.25 |
|---|---|---|---|---|

1984 Summer Olympics, Los Angeles — A62

| 1983, July 20 | | Litho. | Perf. 12½ | |
|---|---|---|---|---|
| 489 | A62 | 1p Swimming | .20 | .20 |
| 490 | A62 | 1.50p Jumping | .20 | .20 |
| 491 | A62 | 3.50p Fencing | .50 | .20 |
| 492 | A62 | 5p Weightlifting | .50 | .20 |
| 493 | A62 | 10p Running | .65 | .20 |
| 494 | A62 | 20p Equestrian | 1.40 | .25 |
| 495 | A62 | 40p Bicycling | 2.75 | .70 |
| | | Nos. 489-495 (7) | 6.20 | 1.95 |

**Souvenir Sheet**

| 496 | A62 | 50p Stadium | 4.50 | 1.25 |
|---|---|---|---|---|

Souvenir Sheet

BRASILIANA '83, Philatelic Exhibition — A63

| 1983, July 29 | | Litho. | Perf. 13 | |
|---|---|---|---|---|
| 497 | A63 | 50p multicolored | 10.00 | 7.50 |

Local Fish — A64

**Perf. 12x11½, 11½x12**

| 1983, Dec. 8 | | | Litho. | |
|---|---|---|---|---|
| 498 | A64 | 1p Monodactylus sebae, vert. | .20 | .20 |
| 499 | A64 | 1.50p Botia macracanthus | .20 | .20 |
| 500 | A64 | 3.50p Ctenopoma acutirostre | .45 | .20 |
| 501 | A64 | 5p Roloffia bertholdi | .50 | .20 |
| 502 | A64 | 8p Aphyosemion bualanum | .75 | .20 |
| 503 | A64 | 10p Aphyosemion bivittatum | 1.10 | .20 |
| 504 | A64 | 30p Aphyosemion australe | 3.25 | .95 |
| | | Nos. 498-504 (7) | 6.45 | 2.15 |

1984 Winter Olympics, Sarajevo — A65

| 1983, Oct. 10 | | Litho. | Perf. 13 | |
|---|---|---|---|---|
| 505 | A65 | 1p Speed skating | .20 | .20 |
| 506 | A65 | 1.50p Ski jumping | .20 | .20 |
| 507 | A65 | 3p Biathlon | .50 | .20 |
| 508 | A65 | 5p Bobsledding | .65 | .20 |
| 509 | A65 | 10p Hockey | .75 | .20 |
| 510 | A65 | 15p Figure skating | 1.50 | .20 |
| 511 | A65 | 20p Luge | 2.00 | .30 |
| | | Nos. 505-511 (7) | 5.80 | 1.50 |

**Souvenir Sheet**

| 512 | A65 | 50p Downhill skiing | 6.00 | 6.00 |
|---|---|---|---|---|

No. 512 contains one 31x40mm stamp.

A66

A67

| 1983, Nov. 7 | | | Perf. 12½ | |
|---|---|---|---|---|
| 513 | A66 | 4.50p Emblem | .60 | .20 |
| 514 | A66 | 7.50p Woman, flag | .80 | .20 |
| 515 | A66 | 9p Sewing | 1.10 | .20 |
| 516 | A66 | 12p Farm workers | 1.50 | .20 |
| | | Nos. 513-516 (4) | 4.00 | .80 |

First anniv. of Women's Federation.

| 1983, Nov. 12 | | Litho. | Perf. 13 | |
|---|---|---|---|---|

Designs: Local flowers.

| 517 | A67 | 1p Canna coccinea | .20 | .20 |
| 518 | A67 | 1.50p Bouganville litoralis | .20 | .20 |
| 519 | A67 | 3.50p Euphorbia milii | .30 | .20 |
| 520 | A67 | 5p Delonix regia | .40 | .20 |
| 521 | A67 | 8p Bauhinia variegata | .70 | .20 |
| 522 | A67 | 10p Spathodea campanulata | .95 | .20 |
| 523 | A67 | 30p Hibiscus rosa sinensis | 2.75 | .80 |
| | | Nos. 517-523 (7) | 5.50 | 2.00 |

JAAC Congress, Sept. 8-12 — A68

| 1983, Sept. 1 | | Litho. | Perf. 13 | |
|---|---|---|---|---|
| 524 | A68 | 4p shown | 1.25 | .20 |
| 524A | A68 | 5p Emblem | 1.25 | .20 |

World Food Day A69

**1983, Oct. 16    Litho.    Perf. 12½x12**
| | | | |
|---|---|---|---|---|
| 525 | A69 | 1.50p multicolored | .20 | .20 |
| 526 | A69 | 2p multicolored | .35 | .20 |
| 527 | A69 | 4p multicolored | .50 | .20 |

**Imperf**
**Size: 61x62mm**
| | | | |
|---|---|---|---|---|
| 528 | A69 | 10p Hoeing | 3.00 | 1.00 |
| | | *Nos. 525-528 (4)* | 4.05 | 1.60 |

1984 Winter Olympics, Sarajevo A70

**1984, Feb. 8    Perf. 12**
| | | | |
|---|---|---|---|---|
| 529 | A70 | 50c Ski jumping | .20 | .20 |
| 530 | A70 | 2.50p Speed skating | .50 | .20 |
| 531 | A70 | 3.50p Hockey | .65 | .20 |
| 532 | A70 | 5p Biathlon | .75 | .20 |
| 533 | A70 | 6p Downhill skiing | .80 | .20 |
| 534 | A70 | 20p Figure skating | 2.25 | .40 |
| 535 | A70 | 30p Bobsledding | 3.75 | .45 |
| | | *Nos. 529-535 (7)* | 8.90 | 1.85 |

**Souvenir Sheet**
**Perf. 11½**
| | | | |
|---|---|---|---|---|
| 536 | A70 | 50p Skiing | 8.50 | 3.25 |

No. 536 contains one 32x43mm stamp.

World Communications Year — A71

**1983, Aug. 30    Litho.    Perf. 12½**
| | | | |
|---|---|---|---|---|
| 537 | A71 | 50c Rowland Hill | .40 | .20 |
| 538 | A71 | 2.50p Samuel Morse | .50 | .20 |
| 539 | A71 | 3.50p H.R. Hertz | .60 | .20 |
| 540 | A71 | 5p Lord Kelvin | .75 | .20 |
| 541 | A71 | 10p Alex. Graham Bell | 1.50 | .20 |
| 542 | A71 | 20p G. Marconi | 3.00 | .60 |
| 543 | A71 | 30p V. Zworykin | 4.25 | .75 |
| | | *Nos. 537-543 (7)* | 11.00 | 2.35 |

**Souvenir Sheet**
| | | | |
|---|---|---|---|---|
| 544 | A71 | 50p Satellites | 8.50 | 3.25 |

No. 544 contains one stamp 31x39mm.

Vintage Cars A72

**1984, Mar. 20    Perf. 12**
| | | | |
|---|---|---|---|---|
| 545 | A72 | 5p Duesenberg, 1928 | .45 | .20 |
| 546 | A72 | 8p MG Midget, 1932 | .80 | .20 |
| 547 | A72 | 15p Mercedes, 1928 | 1.10 | .20 |
| 548 | A72 | 20p Bentley, 1928 | 1.25 | .30 |
| 549 | A72 | 22p Alfa Romeo, 1929 | 1.50 | .35 |
| 550 | A72 | 30p Datsun, 1932 | 2.10 | .50 |
| 551 | A72 | 35p Lincoln, 1932 | 2.50 | .55 |
| | | *Nos. 545-551 (7)* | 9.70 | 2.30 |

**Souvenir Sheet**
| | | | |
|---|---|---|---|---|
| 552 | A72 | 100p Gottlieb Daimler | 11.00 | 4.25 |

No. 552 contains one stamp 50x42mm.

Madonna and Child, by Morales — A73

Paintings by Spanish Artists (Espana '84): 6p, Dona Tadea Arias de Enriquez, by Goya. 10p, Santa Cassilda, by Zurbaran. 12p, Saints Andrew and Francis, by El Greco. 15p, Infanta Isabel Clara Eugenia, by Coello. 35p, Queen Maria of Austria, by Velazquez. 40p, Holy Trinity, by El Greco. 100p, Clothed Maja, by Goya.

**1984, Apr. 20**
| | | | |
|---|---|---|---|---|
| 553 | A73 | 3p multicolored | .35 | .20 |
| 554 | A73 | 6p multicolored | .55 | .20 |
| 555 | A73 | 10p multicolored | .85 | .20 |
| 556 | A73 | 12p multicolored | 1.10 | .20 |
| 557 | A73 | 15p multicolored | 1.40 | .25 |
| 558 | A73 | 35p multicolored | 3.50 | .60 |
| 559 | A73 | 40p multicolored | 4.25 | .65 |
| | | *Nos. 553-559 (7)* | 12.00 | 2.30 |

**Souvenir Sheet**
| | | | |
|---|---|---|---|---|
| 560 | A73 | 100p multicolored | 11.00 | 4.75 |

No. 560 contains one stamp 29x50mm.

Carnivorous Animals — A74

**1984, June 28**
| | | | |
|---|---|---|---|---|
| 561 | A74 | 3p Panthera tigris | .40 | .20 |
| 562 | A74 | 6p Panthera leo | .60 | .20 |
| 563 | A74 | 10p Neofelis nebulosa | .70 | .20 |
| 564 | A74 | 12p Acinonyx jubatus | .85 | .20 |
| 565 | A74 | 15p Lynx lynx | .95 | .20 |
| 566 | A74 | 35p Panthera pardus | 2.25 | .45 |
| 567 | A74 | 40p Uncia uncia | 2.75 | .45 |
| | | *Nos. 561-567 (7)* | 8.75 | 1.90 |

Intl. Civil Aviation Org., 40th Anniv. — A75

**1984, Apr. 4    Litho.    Perf. 12½**
| | | | |
|---|---|---|---|---|
| 568 | A75 | 8p Caravelle | .75 | .20 |
| 569 | A75 | 22p DC-6B | 1.50 | .35 |
| 570 | A75 | 80p IL-76 | 5.25 | 1.25 |
| | | *Nos. 568-570 (3)* | 7.50 | 1.80 |

1984 Summer Olympics, Los Angeles — A76

**1984, May 24    Perf. 12**
| | | | |
|---|---|---|---|---|
| 571 | A76 | 6p Soccer | .45 | .20 |
| 572 | A76 | 8p Dressage | .55 | .20 |
| 573 | A76 | 15p Yachting | 1.10 | .20 |
| 574 | A76 | 20p Field hockey | 1.40 | .25 |
| 575 | A76 | 22p Women's team handball | 1.50 | .25 |
| 576 | A76 | 30p Canoeing | 2.25 | .40 |
| 577 | A76 | 40p Boxing | 2.75 | .80 |
| | | *Nos. 571-577 (7)* | 10.00 | 2.30 |

**Souvenir Sheet**
**Perf. 11½**
| | | | |
|---|---|---|---|---|
| 578 | A76 | 100p Windsurfing | 10.00 | 3.75 |

World Heritage — A77

Wood sculptures: 3p, Pearl throne, Cameroun and Central Africa. 6p, Antelope, South Sudan. 10p, Kneeling woman, East Africa. 12p, Mask, West African coast. 15p, Leopard, Guinea coast. 35p, Standing woman, Zaire. 40p, Funerary statues, Southeast Africa and Madagascar.

**1984, Aug. 15    Perf. 12½**
| | | | |
|---|---|---|---|---|
| 579 | A77 | 3p multicolored | .65 | .20 |
| 580 | A77 | 6p multicolored | .75 | .20 |
| 581 | A77 | 10p multicolored | .85 | .20 |
| 582 | A77 | 12p multicolored | 1.40 | .25 |
| 583 | A77 | 15p multicolored | 1.75 | .30 |
| 584 | A77 | 35p multicolored | 3.50 | .65 |
| 585 | A77 | 40p multicolored | 3.75 | .70 |
| | | *Nos. 579-585 (7)* | 12.65 | 2.50 |

Amilcar Cabral, 60th Birth Anniv. — A78

**1984, Sept. 12    Perf. 13**
| | | | |
|---|---|---|---|---|
| 586 | A78 | 5p Public speaking | .85 | .20 |
| 587 | A78 | 12p In combat fatigues | .95 | .20 |
| 588 | A78 | 20p Memorial building, Bafata | 1.75 | .35 |
| 589 | A78 | 50p Mausoleum, Bissau | 4.25 | .80 |
| | | *Nos. 586-589 (4)* | 7.80 | 1.55 |

Independence, 11th Anniv. — A79

**1984, Sept. 24**
| | | | |
|---|---|---|---|---|
| 590 | A79 | 3p Mechanic | .60 | .20 |
| 591 | A79 | 6p Student | .70 | .20 |
| 592 | A79 | 10p Mason | .90 | .20 |
| 593 | A79 | 12p Health care, vert. | 1.25 | .30 |
| 594 | A79 | 15p Seamstress, vert. | 1.50 | .30 |
| 595 | A79 | 35p Telecommunications | 2.75 | .70 |
| 596 | A79 | 40p PAIGC building | 3.25 | .75 |
| | | *Nos. 590-596 (7)* | 10.95 | 2.65 |

Whales A80

**1984, Sept. 30    Perf. 12**
| | | | |
|---|---|---|---|---|
| 597 | A80 | 5p Eschrichtius gibbosus | .80 | .20 |
| 598 | A80 | 8p Balaenoptera musculus | 1.10 | .20 |
| 599 | A80 | 15p Tursiops truncatus | 1.60 | .35 |
| 600 | A80 | 20p Physeter macrocephalus | 2.25 | .35 |
| 601 | A80 | 24p Orcinus orca | 3.00 | .45 |
| 602 | A80 | 30p Balaena mysticetus | 3.50 | .55 |
| 603 | A80 | 35p Balaenoptera borealis | 3.75 | .60 |
| | | *Nos. 597-603 (7)* | 16.00 | 2.70 |

Butterflies A81

**1984, Oct. 6    Perf. 12½x13**
| | | | |
|---|---|---|---|---|
| 604 | A81 | 3p Hypolimnas dexithea | .50 | .20 |
| 605 | A81 | 6p Papilio arcturus | .65 | .20 |
| 606 | A81 | 10p Morpho menelaus terrestris | .75 | .20 |
| 607 | A81 | 12p Apaturina erminea papuana | 1.00 | .25 |
| 608 | A81 | 15p Prepona praeneste | 1.25 | .35 |
| 609 | A81 | 35p Ornithoptera paradisea | 2.10 | .65 |
| 610 | A81 | 40p Morpho hecuba obidona | 2.75 | .75 |
| | | *Nos. 604-610 (7)* | 9.00 | 2.60 |

1984 Olympic Winners — A82

National flag, medal and: 6p, Carl Lewis, 4x100 relay, US. 8p, Koji Gushiken, gymnastics, Japan. 15p, Reiner Klimke, equestrian, Federal Republic of Germany. 20p, Tracie Ruiz, synchronized swimming, US. 22p, Mary Lou Retton, gymnastics, US. 30p, Michael Gross, swimming, Federal Republic of Germany. 40p, Edwin Moses, hurdler, US. 100p, Daley Thompson, decathlon, Great Britain.

**1984, Nov. 27    Perf. 13**
| | | | |
|---|---|---|---|---|
| 611 | A82 | 6p multicolored | .45 | .20 |
| 612 | A82 | 8p multicolored | .65 | .20 |
| 613 | A82 | 15p multicolored | 1.00 | .25 |
| 614 | A82 | 20p multicolored | 1.50 | .25 |
| 615 | A82 | 22p multicolored | 1.60 | .30 |
| 616 | A82 | 30p multicolored | 2.50 | .45 |
| 617 | A82 | 40p multicolored | 3.25 | .65 |
| | | *Nos. 611-617 (7)* | 10.95 | 2.30 |

**Souvenir Sheet**
**Perf. 12½**
| | | | |
|---|---|---|---|---|
| 618 | A82 | 100p multicolored | 10.00 | 3.75 |

No. 618 contains one stamp 32x40mm.

Locomotives — A83

**1984, Dec. 15    Perf. 13**
| | | | |
|---|---|---|---|---|
| 619 | A83 | 5p White Mountain Central No. 4 | .60 | .20 |
| 620 | A83 | 8p Kessler 2-6-OT, 1886 | .70 | .20 |
| 621 | A83 | 15p Langen tram, 1901 | .95 | .30 |
| 622 | A83 | 20p Gurjao No. 6 | 1.25 | .35 |
| 623 | A83 | 24p Achenseebahn | 1.50 | .40 |
| 624 | A83 | 30p Vitznau-Rigi steam locomotive | 1.90 | .55 |
| 625 | A83 | 35p Riggenbach rackrail, 1873 | 2.10 | .85 |
| | | *Nos. 619-625 (7)* | 9.00 | 2.85 |

**Souvenir Sheet**
**Perf. 12½**
| | | | |
|---|---|---|---|---|
| 625A | A83 | 100p like #621 | 9.50 | 3.25 |

No. 625A contains one stamp 40x32mm.

Native
Crafts — A83a

LUBRAPEX '84: a, Numbe mask. b, Sono statue. c, Erande statue. d, Kokumba arms. e, Oma mask. f, Koni mask.

**1984** **Litho.** **Perf. 13½**
626 A83a 7.50p Strip of 6, #a.-f. 5.50 3.50

Motorcycle Cent. — A84

**1985, Feb. 20** **Perf. 13x12½**
627 A84 5p Harley-Davidson .65 .20
628 A84 8p Kawasaki .95 .20
629 A84 15p Honda 1.40 .20
630 A84 20p Yamaha 2.25 .35
631 A84 25p Suzuki 3.25 .40
632 A84 30p BMW 3.75 .55
633 A84 35p Moto Guzzi 5.75 .60
*Nos. 627-633 (7)* 18.00 2.55

**Souvenir Sheet**
**Perf. 12½**
634 A84 100p Daimler Motorized Bicycle,
1885, vert. 16.00 5.50
No. 634 contains one 32x40mm stamp.

Miniature Sheet

Mushrooms
A85

**1985, May 15** **Perf. 13**
635 Sheet of 6 8.00 2.10
a. A85 7p Clitocybe gibba .50 .20
b. A85 9p Morchella elata .55 .25
c. A85 12p Lepista nuda .75 .30
d. A85 20p Lactarius deliciosus 1.25 .35
e. A85 30p Russula virescens 1.75 .45
f. A85 35p Chroogomphus rutilus 2.00 .55

Henri Dunant (1828-1910), Red Cross
Founder, Plane — A87

**1985, June 12** **Perf. 12½**
643 A87 20p shown .90 .20
644 A87 25p Ambulance 1.10 .20
645 A87 40p Helicopter 2.25 .45
646 A87 80p Speed boat 4.75 .65
*Nos. 643-646 (4)* 9.00 1.50

Cats — A88

**1985, July 5** **Perf. 13**
647 A88 7p multicolored .20 .20
648 A88 10p multicolored .30 .20
649 A88 12p multicolored .50 .20
650 A88 15p multicolored .80 .20
651 A88 20p multicolored 1.10 .20
652 A88 40p multicolored 1.60 .25
653 A88 45p multicolored 2.50 .40
*Nos. 647-653 (7)* 7.00 1.65

**Souvenir Sheet**
654 A88 100p multicolored 7.50 5.50
ARGENTINA '85. No. 654 contains one
40x32mm stamp.

Composers
and Musical
Instruments
A89

Designs: 4p, Vincenzo Bellini (1801-1835),
harp, 1820, and descant viol, 16th cent. 5p,
Schumann (1810-1856) and Viennese pyramid piano, 1829. 7p, Chopin (1810-1849) and
piano-forte, 1817. 12p, Luigi Cherubini (1760-
1842) and 18th cent. Baryton violin and
Quinton viol. 20p, G. B. Pergolesi (1710-1736)
and double-manual harpsichord, 1734. 30p,
Handel (1685-1759), valve trumpet, 1825, and
timpani drum, 18th cent. 50p, Heinrich Schutz
(1585-1672), bass viol and two-stop oboe,
17th cent. 100s, Bach (1685-1750) and St.
Thomas Church organ, Leipzig.

**1985, Aug. 5** **Perf. 12**
655 A89 4p multicolored .45 .20
656 A89 5p multicolored .55 .20
657 A89 7p multicolored .75 .20
658 A89 12p multicolored 1.25 .20
659 A89 20p multicolored 1.75 .20
660 A89 30p multicolored 2.75 .30
661 A89 50p multicolored 4.50 .60
*Nos. 655-661 (7)* 12.00 1.90

**Souvenir Sheet**
**Perf. 11½**
662 A89 100p multicolored 11.00 4.25
No. 662 contains one 30x50mm stamp.

Santa Maria,
15th Cent.,
Spain — A90

Ships: 15p, Carack, 16th cent., Netherlands.
20p, Mayflower, 17th cent., Great Britain. 30p,
St. Louis, 17th cent., France. 35p, Royal Sovereign, 1635, Great Britain. 45p, Soleil Royal,
17th cent., France. 80p, English brig, 18th-
19th cent.

**1985, Sept. 12** **Perf. 13**
663 A90 8p multicolored .50 .20
664 A90 15p multicolored .75 .20
665 A90 20p multicolored 1.00 .20
666 A90 30p multicolored 1.60 .20
667 A90 35p multicolored 1.90 .30
668 A90 45p multicolored 2.50 .45
669 A90 80p multicolored 4.75 .75
*Nos. 663-669 (7)* 13.00 2.40

UN, 40th
Anniv.
A91

**1985, Oct. 17**
670 A91 10p Emblem, doves,
vert. .80
671 A91 20p Emblem, 40 1.60

Venus and
Mars, by
Sandro Botticelli
(1445-1510)
A92

Botticelli paintings (details): 7p, Virgin with
Child and St. John. 12p, St. Augustine in the
Work Hall. 15p, Awakening of Spring. 20p,
Virgin and Child. 40p, Virgin with Child and St.
John, diff. 45p, Birth of Venus. 100p, Virgin
and Child with Two Angels.

**1985, Oct. 25** **Perf. 12½x13**
672 A92 7p multicolored .50 .20
673 A92 10p multicolored .55 .20
674 A92 12p multicolored .70 .20
675 A92 15p multicolored .80 .20
676 A92 20p multicolored 1.10 .20
677 A92 40p multicolored 2.25 .40
678 A92 45p multicolored 2.75 .45

**Size: 73x106mm**
*Imperf*
679 A92 100p multicolored 8.50 5.50
*Nos. 672-679 (8)* 17.15 7.35
ITALIA '85.

Intl.
Youth
Year
A93

**1985, Nov. 29** **Litho.** **Perf. 12½**
680 A93 7p Dance .45 .20
681 A93 13p Wind surfing .55 .20
682 A93 15p Rollerskating .60 .20
683 A93 25p Hang gliding 1.10 .20
684 A93 40p Surfing 1.75 .30
685 A93 50p Skateboarding 2.25 .50
686 A93 80p Parachuting 3.75 .70
*Nos. 680-686 (7)* 10.45 2.30

**Souvenir Sheet**
**Perf. 13**
687 A93 100p Self-defense 7.50 5.50
No. 687 contains one 40x32mm stamp.

Miniature Sheet

Halley's Comet — A94

1986 World Cup Soccer
Championships, Mexico — A95

24th
Summer
Olympics,
Seoul,
1988
A96

Italian
Automobile
Industry,
Cent.
A97

German
Railways,
150th
Anniv.
A98

Discovery
of America,
500th
Anniv. (in
1992)
A99

First American Manned Space Flight,
25th Anniv. — A100

1986 Wimbledon Tennis
Championships — A101

1986 Masters Tennis
Championships — A102

Giotto Space Probe — A103

Designs: a, Comet tail. b, Comet. c, Trophy. d, Trophy base. e, Five-ring Olympic emblem. f, Alfa Tourer, Italy, c. 1905. g, Railway station, Frankfurt-on Main, c. 1914. h, Barcelona, site of Discovery of America exhibition and 1992 Olympics. i, Space station solar panels and tanks. j, Space station. k, Removing cargo from space shuttle. l, Docking facility, station panels. m, Boris Becker swinging tennis racket. n, Becker, diff. o, Ivan Lendl holding racket. p, Lendl, diff.

**1986, Dec. 30     Litho.     Perf. 13½**
688     Sheet of 16                           125.00
  **a.-p.** A94-A102 15p any single       7.50     3.25
**Souvenir Sheet**
689     A103  100p multicolored      14.00   10.00
Nos. 688a-688b, 688c-688d, 688i-688l, 688m-688n, 688o-688p are se-tenant in continuous designs. Inscription on Nos. 688i-688l incorrect; should read "TRIPULADO MERCURY / 5-5-1961."

Discovery of
America, 500th
Anniv. (in
1992) — A104

Designs: No. 690, Christopher Columbus aboard caravelle. No. 691, Guadalquivir Port, Seville, c. 1490. No. 692, Pedro Alvars Cabral landing at Bahia, Brazil. No. 693, Bridge over the Guadalquivir River, Seville. No. 694, Port, Lisbon, 15th cent.

**1987, Feb. 27**
690     A104  50p multicolored        4.00     1.00
691     A104  50p multicolored        4.00     1.00
692     A104  50p multicolored        4.00      .70
693     A104  50p multicolored        4.00     1.00
  Nos. 690-693 (4)              16.00     3.70
**Souvenir Sheet**
694     A104  150p multicolored      18.00   10.00
No. 694 exists with pink or yellow anniv. emblem pictured in vignette. Values are the same.

---

Portuguese Guinea Nos. 306-309,
313, 316-317, Ovptd., Guinea-Bissau
No. 349 Surcharged

**1987, July     Litho.     Perf. 13½**
696     A21   100p on 20c #306    1.75     .60
697     A21   200p on 35c #307    3.25    1.25
698     A21   300p on 70c #308    5.00    1.60
699     A21   400p on 80c #309    5.50    2.00
700     A21   500p on 3.50e
           #313        7.75    2.75
701     A21  1000p on 15e #316   20.00    5.50
702     A21  2000p on 20e #317   40.00   13.50
**Perf. 13**
703     CD61 2500p on 2e
           #349       50.00   14.50
  Nos. 696-703 (8)          133.25   41.70
Placement of "Bissau," new denomination and obliterating bar varies.

1988 Winter Olympics,
Calgary — A106

**1988, Jan. 15     Litho.     Perf. 13**
704     A106   5p Pairs figure
          skating              .50     .20
705     A106  10p Luge               .80     .20
706     A106  50p Skiing            1.00     .20
707     A106 200p Slalom skiing     1.25     .35
708     A106 300p Skibobbing        2.25     .50
709     A106 500p Ski jumping,
          vert.               3.25     .65
710     A106 800p Speed skating,
          vert.               5.75    2.25
  Nos. 704-710 (7)           14.80    4.35
**Souvenir Sheet**
710A    A106 900p Two-man luge      9.00    3.25
No. 710A contains one 40x32mm stamp.

Soccer — A107

Various soccer plays.

**1988, Apr. 14     Litho.     Perf. 13**
711     A107   5p multi             .20     .20
712     A107  10p multi, diff.      .20     .20
713     A107  50p multi, diff.      .75     .20
714     A107 200p multi, diff.     1.60     .40
715     A107 300p multi, diff.     2.50     .50
716     A107 500p multi, diff.     3.50     .65
717     A107 800p multi, diff.     6.00    1.60
  Nos. 711-717 (7)          14.75    3.75
**Souvenir Sheet**
718     A107 900p multi, diff.    11.00    4.25
ESSEN '88 stamp exhibition. No. 718 contains one 32x40mm stamp.

---

1988 Summer Olympics,
Seoul — A108

**Perf. 12½x12, 12x12½**
**1988, Feb. 26                          Litho.**
719     A108   5p Yachting, vert.     .20     .20
720     A108  10p Equestrian          .20     .20
721     A108  50p High jump           .50     .20
722     A108 200p Shooting           1.60     .40
723     A108 300p Long jump,
          vert.               2.50     .50
724     A108 500p Tennis, vert.      3.75     .65
725     A108 800p Women's arch-
          ery, vert.          6.25    1.25
  Nos. 719-725 (7)           15.00    3.40
**Souvenir Sheet**
**Perf. 12½**
726     A108 900p Soccer            7.00    2.25
No. 726 contains one 40x32mm stamp.

Ancient Ships — A109

Designs: 5p, Egyptian, c. 3300 B.C. 10p, Pharaoh Sahure's ship, c. 2700 B.C. 50p, Queen Hatsepsowe's ship, c. 1500 B.C. 200p, Ramses III's ship, c. 1200 B.C. 300p, Greek trireme, 480 B.C. 500p, Etruscan bireme, 600 B.C. 800p, Venetian galley, 12th cent.

**1988                     Litho.     Perf. 13x12½**
727     A109   5p multi             .20     .20
728     A109  10p multi             .20     .20
729     A109  50p multi             .65     .20
730     A109 200p multi            1.50     .20
731     A109 300p multi            2.10     .30
732     A109 500p multi            3.50     .50
733     A109 800p multi            5.75     .85
  Nos. 727-733 (7)           13.90    2.45

FINLANDIA
'88 — A110

Chess champions, board and chessmen.

**1988         Litho.     Perf. 12x12½**
734     A110   5p Philidor          .20     .20
735     A110  10p Staunton          .20     .20
736     A110  50p Anderssen         .70     .20
737     A110 200p Morphy           1.75     .20
738     A110 300p Steinitz         2.25     .30
739     A110 500p Lasker           4.25     .40
740     A110 800p Capablanca       6.25     .65
  Nos. 734-740 (7)           15.60    2.15
**Souvenir Sheet**
**Perf. 13**
741     A110 900p Ruy Lopez       12.00    4.50
No. 741 contains one 40x32mm stamp.

---

Dogs
A111

**1988                      Perf. 13x12½**
742     A111   5p Basset hound      .35     .20
743     A111  10p Great blue of
         Gascony              .45     .20
744     A111  50p Sabujo of Italy   .45     .20
745     A111 200p Yorkshire terrier 1.10     .55
746     A111 300p Small muster-
         lander              1.75     .80
747     A111 500p Pointer          2.75    1.40
748     A111 800p German setter    4.50    2.25
  Nos. 742-748 (7)          11.35    5.60
**Souvenir Sheet**
**Perf. 12½**
749     A111 900p German shep-
         herd                7.00    2.50
No. 749 contains one 40x32mm stamp.

Intl. Red Cross and Red Crescent
Organizations, 125th Anniv. — A112

**1988                            Perf. 13**
750     A112  10p Jean-Henri Dunant  .70    .20
751     A112  50p Dr. T. Maunoir      .30    .20
752     A112 200p Dr. Louis Appia    1.25    .20
753     A112 800p Gustave Moynier    5.75    .65
  Nos. 750-753 (4)           8.00    1.25

Maps and Fauna — A113

**1988               Perf. 12½x13, 13x12½**
754     A113   5p Panthera leo       .20    .20
755     A113  10p Glaucidium
         brasilianum         .20    .20
756     A113  50p Upupa epops        .70    .20
757     A113 200p Equus burchelli
         antiquorum         1.50    .20
758     A113 300p Loxodonta afri-
         cana               2.25    .30
759     A113 500p Acryllium vul-
         turinum            3.50   1.60
760     A113 800p Diceros
         bicornis           6.00    .65
  Nos. 754-760 (7)          14.35   3.35
Nos. 754-755, 758-760 vert. The genus "Upupa" is misspelled on the 50p and "Loxodonta" is misspelled on the 300p.

Samora Machel
(1933-1986),
Pres. of
Mozambique
A114

**1988                            Perf. 13**
761     A114  10p shown             .20    .20
762     A114  50p Raising fist      .45    .20
763     A114 200p With sentry      1.50    .20
764     A114 300p Wearing ear-
         phones at UN       2.50    .25
  Nos. 761-764 (4)           4.65    .85

Mushrooms — A115

| 1988 | | Litho. | | Perf. 13x12½ | |
|---|---|---|---|---|---|
| 765 | A115 | 370p | Peziza aurantia | 2.50 | .35 |
| 766 | A115 | 470p | Morchella | 3.00 | .40 |
| 767 | A115 | 600p | Amanita caes- | | |
| | | | area | 4.50 | .60 |
| 768 | A115 | 780p | Amanita mus- | | |
| | | | caria | 6.50 | .70 |
| 769 | A115 | 800p | Amanita phal- | | |
| | | | loides | 6.50 | .70 |
| 770 | A115 | 900p | Agaricus | | |
| | | | bisporus | 7.75 | .90 |
| 771 | A115 | 945p | Cantharellus | | |
| | | | cibarius | 7.25 | .95 |
| | | Nos. 765-771 (7) | | 38.00 | 4.60 |

1992 Winter Olympics,
Albertville — A116

| 1989, Oct. 12 | | Litho. | | Perf. 12½x12 | |
|---|---|---|---|---|---|
| 772 | A116 | 50p | Speed skat- | | |
| | | | ing | .70 | .20 |
| 773 | A116 | 100p | Women's fig- | | |
| | | | ure skating | .90 | .20 |
| 774 | A116 | 200p | Ski jumping | 1.75 | .20 |
| 775 | A116 | 350p | Skiing | 2.10 | .40 |
| 776 | A116 | 500p | Skiing, diff. | 3.50 | .55 |
| 777 | A116 | 800p | Bobsled | 5.50 | .95 |
| 778 | A116 | 1000p | Ice hockey | 7.00 | 1.10 |
| | | Nos. 772-778 (7) | | 21.45 | 3.60 |

**Souvenir Sheet**
**Perf. 12½**

| 779 | A116 | 1500p | Ice hockey, | | |
|---|---|---|---|---|---|
| | | | diff. | 11.00 | 5.00 |

No. 779 contains one 32x40mm stamp.

World Cup Soccer Championships,
Italy — A117

Various soccer players.

| 1989 | | Litho. | | Perf. 12½ | |
|---|---|---|---|---|---|
| 780 | A117 | 50p | multicolored | .20 | .20 |
| 781 | A117 | 100p | multicolored | .65 | .20 |
| 782 | A117 | 200p | multicolored | .90 | .20 |
| 783 | A117 | 350p | multicolored | 1.50 | .35 |
| 784 | A117 | 500p | multicolored | 1.75 | .45 |
| 785 | A117 | 800p | multicolored | 3.50 | .80 |
| 786 | A117 | 1000p | multicolored | 4.50 | .90 |
| | | Nos. 780-786 (7) | | 13.00 | 3.10 |

**Souvenir Sheet**
**Perf. 13**

| 786A | A117 | 1500p | multicolored | 7.50 | 2.75 |
|---|---|---|---|---|---|

No. 786A contains one 40x32mm stamp.

Lilies
(Lilium) — A118

| 1989 | | | | Perf. 12½ | |
|---|---|---|---|---|---|
| 787 | A118 | 50p | Limelight | .20 | .20 |
| 788 | A118 | 100p | Candidum | .50 | .20 |
| 789 | A118 | 200p | Pardalinum | .90 | .35 |
| 790 | A118 | 350p | Auratum | 1.50 | .65 |
| 791 | A118 | 500p | Canadense | 1.75 | .70 |
| 792 | A118 | 800p | Enchantment | 3.50 | 1.50 |
| 793 | A118 | 1000p | Black Dragon | 4.50 | 1.90 |
| | | Nos. 787-793 (7) | | 12.85 | 5.50 |

**Souvenir Sheet**

| 794 | A118 | 1500p | Lilium pyrena- | | |
|---|---|---|---|---|---|
| | | | icum | 7.50 | 2.75 |

No. 794 contains one 32x40mm stamp.

Trains
A119

Various railroad engines.

| 1989, May 24 | | Litho. | | Perf. 13 | |
|---|---|---|---|---|---|
| 795 | A119 | 50p | multicolored | .20 | .20 |
| 796 | A119 | 100p | multicolored | .45 | .20 |
| 797 | A119 | 200p | multicolored | .75 | .35 |
| 798 | A119 | 350p | multicolored | 1.60 | .70 |
| 799 | A119 | 500p | multicolored | 2.25 | .95 |
| 800 | A119 | 800p | multicolored | 3.25 | 1.60 |

**Perf. 12½**
**Size: 68x27mm**

| 801 | A119 | 1000p | multicolored | 4.00 | .85 |
|---|---|---|---|---|---|
| | | Nos. 795-801 (7) | | 12.50 | 4.85 |

**Souvenir Sheet**
**Perf. 12½**

| 802 | A119 | 1500p | multicolored | 7.00 | 3.25 |
|---|---|---|---|---|---|

No. 802 contains one 32x40mm stamp.

La Marseillaise by Francois
Rude — A120

Paintings: 100p, Armed mob. 200p, Storm-
ing the Bastille. 350p, Lafayette, Liberty, vert.
500p, Dancing around the Liberty tree. 800p,
Rouget de Lisle singing La Marseillaise by
Pils. 1000p, Storming the Bastille, diff. 1500p,
Arms of the Republic of France.

**Perf. 12½, 12½x12½ (350p)**

| 1989, July 5 | | | | | |
|---|---|---|---|---|---|
| 803 | A120 | 50p | shown | .20 | .20 |
| 804 | A120 | 100p | multicolored | .40 | .20 |
| 805 | A120 | 200p | multicolored | .80 | .40 |
| 806 | A120 | 350p | multicolored, | | |
| | | | 27x44mm | 1.60 | .75 |
| 807 | A120 | 500p | multicolored | 2.25 | 1.00 |
| 808 | A120 | 800p | multicolored | 3.50 | 1.60 |
| 809 | A120 | 1000p | multicolored | 4.25 | 2.00 |
| | | Nos. 803-809 (7) | | 13.00 | 6.15 |

**Souvenir Sheet**
**Perf. 13**

| 810 | A120 | 1500p | multicolored | 7.50 | 2.75 |
|---|---|---|---|---|---|

Birds
A121

Designs: 50p, Alectroenas pulcherrima.
100p, Streptopelia senegalensis. 200p, Oena
capensis. 350p, Claravis mondetoura. 500p,
Streptopelia roseogrisea. 800p, Otidiphaps
nobilis. 1000p, Chalophapa indica. 1500p,
Reinwardtoena Reinwardtsi.

| 1989 | | Litho. | | Perf. 12½ | |
|---|---|---|---|---|---|
| 811 | A121 | 50p | multicolored | .20 | .20 |
| 812 | A121 | 100p | multicolored | .45 | .20 |
| 813 | A121 | 200p | multicolored | .85 | .40 |
| 814 | A121 | 350p | multicolored | 1.50 | .65 |
| 815 | A121 | 500p | multicolored | 2.25 | .90 |
| 816 | A121 | 800p | multicolored | 3.50 | 1.60 |
| 817 | A121 | 1000p | multicolored | 4.25 | 1.90 |
| | | Nos. 811-817 (7) | | 13.00 | 5.85 |

**Souvenir Sheet**

| 818 | A121 | 1500p | multicolored | 6.50 | 3.50 |
|---|---|---|---|---|---|

Pioneers Organization — A122

| 1989 | | | | Perf. 13 | |
|---|---|---|---|---|---|
| 819 | A122 | 10p | Children present- | | |
| | | | ing flag, vert. | .20 | .20 |
| 820 | A122 | 50p | Children saluting, | | |
| | | | vert. | .60 | .20 |
| 821 | A122 | 200p | Children shown | 2.50 | .95 |
| 822 | A122 | 300p | Children playing | | |
| | | | ball | 3.50 | 1.50 |
| | | Nos. 819-822 (4) | | 6.80 | 2.85 |

Town of
Cacheu,
400th
Anniv.
A123

| 1989, Nov. 30 | | | | | |
|---|---|---|---|---|---|
| 823 | A123 | 10p | Monument, vert. | .20 | .20 |
| 824 | A123 | 50p | shown | .20 | .20 |
| 825 | A123 | 200p | Old building | 1.00 | .20 |
| 826 | A123 | 300p | Church | 1.60 | .30 |
| | | Nos. 823-826 (4) | | 3.00 | .90 |

Dated 1988.

A124

Designs: Prehistoric creatures.

**Perf. 13, 12½x12 (100p)**

| 1989, Sept. 15 | | | | | |
|---|---|---|---|---|---|
| 827 | A124 | 50p | Trachodon | .20 | .20 |
| 828 | A124 | 100p | Edaphosaurus, | | |
| | | | 68x27mm | .50 | .20 |
| 829 | A124 | 200p | Mesosaurus | .90 | .35 |
| 830 | A124 | 350p | Elephas | | |
| | | | primigenius | 1.60 | .65 |
| 831 | A124 | 500p | Tyrannosau- | | |
| | | | rus | 2.75 | .90 |
| 832 | A124 | 800p | Stegosaurus | 4.25 | 1.50 |
| 833 | A124 | 1000p | Cervus | | |
| | | | megaceros | 4.75 | 1.75 |
| | | Nos. 827-833 (7) | | 14.95 | 5.55 |

Nos. 828, 831-833 horiz.

A125

| 1989, Apr. 10 | | Litho. | | Perf. 13 | |
|---|---|---|---|---|---|
| | | Designs: Musical instruments. | | | |
| 834 | A125 | 50p | Bombalon | .40 | .20 |
| 835 | A125 | 100p | Flauta | .60 | .20 |
| 836 | A125 | 200p | Tambor | 1.25 | .30 |
| 837 | A125 | 350p | Dondon | 2.00 | .40 |

| 838 | A125 | 500p | Balafon | 2.50 | .45 |
|---|---|---|---|---|---|
| 839 | A125 | 800p | Kora | 3.00 | .60 |
| 840 | A125 | 1000p | Nhanhero | 3.25 | .70 |
| | | Nos. 834-840 (7) | | 13.00 | 2.85 |

A126

| 1989, July 13 | | | | Perf. 12x12½ | |
|---|---|---|---|---|---|
| | | Designs: Indian artifacts. | | | |
| 841 | A126 | 50p | Teotihuacan | .25 | .20 |
| 842 | A126 | 100p | Mochica | .40 | .20 |
| 843 | A126 | 200p | Jaina | .75 | .35 |
| 844 | A126 | 350p | Nayarit | 1.60 | .70 |
| 845 | A126 | 500p | Inca | 2.25 | 1.00 |
| 846 | A126 | 800p | Hopewell | 3.50 | 1.60 |
| 847 | A126 | 1000p | Taina | 4.25 | 1.90 |
| | | Nos. 841-847 (7) | | 13.00 | 5.95 |

**Souvenir Sheet**
**Perf. 12½**

| 848 | A126 | 1500p | Indian statu- | | |
|---|---|---|---|---|---|
| | | | ette | 7.50 | 2.50 |

Brasiliana '89 Philatelic Exhibition. Nos.
841-847 printed se-tenant with multicolored
label showing scenes of colonization. No. 848
contains one 32x40mm stamp.

1992
Summer
Olympics,
Barcelona
A127

| 1989, June 3 | | | | Perf. 12½x13 | |
|---|---|---|---|---|---|
| 849 | A127 | 50p | Hurdles | .30 | .20 |
| 850 | A127 | 100p | Boxing | .55 | .20 |
| 851 | A127 | 200p | High jump | .80 | .20 |
| 852 | A127 | 350p | Sprinters in | | |
| | | | the blocks | 1.25 | .35 |
| 853 | A127 | 500p | Woman | | |
| | | | sprinter | 2.10 | .55 |
| 854 | A127 | 800p | Gymnastics | 3.25 | .95 |
| 855 | A127 | 1000p | Pole vault | 4.25 | 1.25 |
| | | Nos. 849-855 (7) | | 12.50 | 3.70 |

**Souvenir Sheet**

| 856 | A127 | 1500p | Soccer | 6.50 | 2.40 |
|---|---|---|---|---|---|

No. 856 contains one 32x40mm stamp.

Wild
Animals — A128

| 1989, Nov. 24 | | | | Perf. 12½ | |
|---|---|---|---|---|---|
| 857 | A128 | 50p | Syncerus caf- | | |
| | | | fer | .45 | .20 |
| 858 | A128 | 100p | Equus quag- | | |
| | | | ga | .70 | .20 |
| 859 | A128 | 200p | Diceros | | |
| | | | bicornis | .95 | .25 |
| 860 | A128 | 350p | Okapia john- | | |
| | | | stoni | 1.50 | .40 |
| 861 | A128 | 500p | Macaca mu- | | |
| | | | latta | 2.00 | .60 |
| 862 | A128 | 800p | Hippopota- | | |
| | | | mus | | |
| | | | amphibius | 3.25 | 1.00 |
| 863 | A128 | 1000p | Acinonyx | | |
| | | | jubatus | 3.75 | 1.25 |
| 864 | A128 | 1500p | Panthera leo | 5.75 | 1.75 |
| | | Nos. 857-864 (8) | | 18.35 | 5.65 |

Christmas
A129

Paintings of the Madonna and Child (50p) and the Adoration of the Magi.

| 1989, Dec. 10 | | | Perf. 13 | |
|---|---|---|---|---|
| 865 | A129 | 50p Fra Filippo Lippi | .60 | .20 |
| 866 | A129 | 100p Pieter Brueghel | .80 | .20 |
| 867 | A129 | 200p Mostaert | 1.10 | .20 |
| 868 | A129 | 350p Durer | 1.75 | .35 |
| 869 | A129 | 500p Rubens | 3.00 | .60 |
| 870 | A129 | 800p Van der Weyden | 4.75 | .90 |
| 871 | A129 | 1000p Francia, horiz. | 6.00 | 1.25 |
| | Nos. 865-871 (7) | | 18.00 | 3.70 |

Womens' Hairstyles
A130

Various hairstyles.

| 1989, Mar. 8 | | | Perf. 12½x13 | |
|---|---|---|---|---|
| 872 | A130 | 50p multicolored | .20 | .20 |
| 873 | A130 | 100p multicolored | .55 | .20 |
| 874 | A130 | 200p multicolored | .85 | .35 |
| 875 | A130 | 350p multicolored | 1.50 | .65 |
| 875A | A130 | 500p multicolored | 2.00 | .90 |
| 876 | A130 | 800p multicolored | 3.50 | 1.50 |
| 877 | A130 | 1000p multicolored | 4.25 | 1.75 |
| | Nos. 872-877 (7) | | 12.85 | 5.55 |

Vegetables — A131

| 1989, May 20 | | | Perf. 12½ | |
|---|---|---|---|---|
| 878 | A131 | 50p Capisium annum | .20 | .20 |
| 879 | A131 | 100p Solanium | .20 | .20 |
| 880 | A131 | 200p Curcumis peco | .85 | .20 |
| 881 | A131 | 350p Solanium licopersicum | 1.50 | .40 |
| 882 | A131 | 500p Solanium itiopium | 2.10 | .60 |
| 883 | A131 | 800p Hibiscus esculentus | 3.25 | .95 |
| 884 | A131 | 1000p Oseille de guine | 4.25 | 1.25 |
| | Nos. 878-884 (7) | | 12.35 | 3.80 |

Visit of Pope John Paul II — A132

| 1990, Jan. 27 | | Litho. | Perf. 13½ | |
|---|---|---|---|---|
| 885 | A132 | 500p shown | 2.25 | 1.60 |
| 886 | A132 | 1000p multi, diff. | 4.50 | 3.25 |
| | **Souvenir Sheet** | | | |
| 887 | A132 | 1500p multi, diff., vert. | 7.50 | 6.25 |

Souvenir Sheet

Belgica '90 — A133

| 1990, June 1 | | | Perf. 14½ | |
|---|---|---|---|---|
| 888 | A133 | 3000p multicolored | 7.00 | 3.50 |

World Meteorology Day — A134

| 1990, Oct. 1 | | Litho. | Perf. 13 | |
|---|---|---|---|---|
| 889 | A134 | 1000p Radar weather map | 1.75 | .70 |
| 890 | A134 | 3000p Heliograph | 7.25 | 2.50 |

LUBRAPEX '90 — A135

| 1990, Sept. 21 | | | Perf. 14 | |
|---|---|---|---|---|
| 891 | A135 | 500p Rooster, hen | 1.10 | .50 |
| 892 | A135 | 800p Turkey | 1.90 | .75 |
| 893 | A135 | 1000p Duck, ducklings | 2.50 | .90 |
| | Nos. 891-893 (3) | | 5.50 | 2.15 |
| | **Souvenir Sheet** | | | |
| | **Perf. 13½** | | | |
| 894 | A135 | 1500p Rooster, turkey, ducks | 6.00 | 2.40 |

UN Development Program, 40th Anniv. — A136

| 1990 | | Litho. | Perf. 14 | |
|---|---|---|---|---|
| 895 | A136 | 1000p multicolored | 2.50 | .75 |

Fight against AIDS.

Textile Manufacturing
A137

No. 896: a, Gossypium hirsutum. b, Processing cotton. c, Spinning thread. d, Picking cotton. e, Moth, silkworms. f, Dyeing thread. g, Weaving. h, Animal design. i, Multicolored stripes design. j, Stripes, dots design.

| 1990 | | | | |
|---|---|---|---|---|
| 896 | | Sheet of 10 | 2.00 | |
| a.-j. | A137 | 150p any single | .25 | .25 |

| 897 | A137 | 400p like #896a | .35 | .20 |
|---|---|---|---|---|
| 898 | A137 | 500p like #896g | .45 | .20 |
| 899 | A137 | 600p like #896h | .55 | .35 |
| | Nos. 896-899 (4) | | 3.35 | .75 |

Carnival Masks
A138

| 1990 | | Litho. | Perf. 14 | |
|---|---|---|---|---|
| 900 | A138 | 200p Mickey Mouse | .45 | .20 |
| 901 | A138 | 300p Hippopotamus | .65 | .20 |
| 902 | A138 | 600p Bull | 1.25 | .35 |
| 903 | A138 | 1200p Bull, diff. | 2.50 | .50 |
| | Nos. 900-903 (4) | | 4.85 | 1.25 |

Fish
A139

Designs: 300p, Pentanemus quinquarius. 400p, Psettias sabae. 500p, Chaetodipterus goreensis. 600p, Trachinotus goreensis.

| 1991, Mar. 10 | | Litho. | Perf. 14 | |
|---|---|---|---|---|
| 904 | A139 | 300p multicolored | .65 | .35 |
| 905 | A139 | 400p multicolored | 1.00 | .45 |
| 906 | A139 | 500p multicolored | 1.10 | .55 |
| 907 | A139 | 600p multicolored | 1.25 | .70 |
| | Nos. 904-907 (4) | | 4.00 | 2.05 |

Fire Trucks
A140

| 1991, Aug. 19 | | Litho. | Perf. 14 | |
|---|---|---|---|---|
| 908 | A140 | 200p shown | .40 | .20 |
| 909 | A140 | 500p Ladder truck | .85 | .45 |
| 910 | A140 | 800p Rescue vehicle | 1.25 | .70 |
| 911 | A140 | 1500p Ambulance | 2.50 | 1.25 |
| | Nos. 908-911 (4) | | 5.00 | 2.60 |

Birds — A141

Designs: 100p, Kaupifalco monogrammicus. 250p, Balearica pavonina. 350p, Bucorvus abyssinicus. 500p, Ephippiorhynchus senegalensis. 1500p, Kaupifalco monogrammicus, diff.

| 1991, Sept. 10 | | | | |
|---|---|---|---|---|
| 912 | A141 | 100p multicolored | .75 | .20 |
| 913 | A141 | 250p multicolored | 1.10 | .20 |
| 914 | A141 | 350p multicolored | 1.75 | .55 |
| 915 | A141 | 500p multicolored | 2.40 | .75 |
| | Nos. 912-915 (4) | | 6.00 | 1.70 |
| | **Souvenir Sheet** | | | |
| | **Perf. 14½** | | | |
| 916 | A141 | 1500p multicolored | 5.00 | 5.00 |

No. 916 contains one 40x50mm stamp.

Messages
A142

| 1991, Oct. 28 | | Litho. | Perf. 14 | |
|---|---|---|---|---|
| 917 | A142 | 250p Congratulations | .40 | .20 |
| 918 | A142 | 400p With love | .75 | .40 |
| 919 | A142 | 800p Happiness | 1.25 | .80 |
| 920 | A142 | 1000p Seasons Greetings | 1.60 | .95 |
| | Nos. 917-920 (4) | | 4.00 | 2.35 |

Fruits — A143

Designs: 500p, Landolfia owariensis. 1500p, Dialium guineensis. 2000p, Adansonia digitata. 3000p, Parkia biglobosa.

| 1992, Mar. 25 | | Litho. | Perf. 14 | |
|---|---|---|---|---|
| 921 | A143 | 500p multicolored | .30 | .30 |
| 922 | A143 | 1500p multicolored | .75 | .75 |
| 923 | A143 | 2000p multicolored | 1.10 | 1.10 |
| 924 | A143 | 3000p multicolored | 1.75 | 1.75 |
| | Nos. 921-924 (4) | | 3.90 | 3.90 |

Healthy Hearts — A144

| 1992, Apr. 7 | | | | |
|---|---|---|---|---|

Designs: 1500p, Cigarette butts, healthy heart. 4000p, Heart running over junk food.

| 925 | A144 | 1500p multicolored | 1.75 | .80 |
|---|---|---|---|---|
| 926 | A144 | 4000p multicolored | 3.75 | 2.10 |

Traditional Costumes
A145

Designs: a, 400p, Fula. b, 600p, Balanta. c, 1000p, Fula, diff. d, 1500p, Manjaco.

| 1992, Feb. 28 | | Litho. | Perf. 14 | |
|---|---|---|---|---|
| 927 | A145 | Strip of 4, #a.-d. | 3.00 | 2.10 |

Canoes
A146

Designs: Nos. 928-931, Various types of canoes. No. 932, Alcedo cristata galerita.

| 1992, May 10 | | | | |
|---|---|---|---|---|
| 928 | A146 | 750p multicolored | .40 | .40 |
| 929 | A146 | 800p multicolored | .55 | .55 |
| 930 | A146 | 1000p multicolored | .70 | .70 |
| 931 | A146 | 1300p multicolored | .90 | .90 |
| | Nos. 928-931 (4) | | 2.55 | 2.55 |
| | **Souvenir Sheet** | | | |
| | **Perf. 13½** | | | |
| 932 | A146 | 1500p multicolored | 6.00 | 6.00 |

Trees — A147

a, 100p, Cassia alata. b, 400p, Perlebia purpurea. c, 1000p, Caesalpina pulcherrima. d, 1500p, Adenanthera pavonina. 3000p, Caesalpina pulcherrima, diff.

**1992, May 8**     **Perf. 14**
933 A147 Block of 4, #a.-d.    5.50 5.50

**Souvenir Sheet**
**Perf. 13½**
934 A147 3000p multicolored    5.00 5.00

1992 Summer Olympics, Barcelona A148

**1992, July 28**    **Litho.**    **Perf. 14**
935 A148 600p Basketball    .25 .20
936 A148 1000p Volleyball    .60 .20
937 A148 1500p Team handball    .90 .20
938 A148 2000p Soccer    1.25 .20
    Nos. 935-938 (4)    3.00 .80

Trees A149

Designs: 1000p, Afzelia africana Smith. 1500p, Kaya senegalenses. 2000p, Militia regia. 3000p, Pterocarpus erinaceus.

**1992, Sept. 11**     **Perf. 12**
939 A149 1000p multicolored    .50 .45
940 A149 1500p multicolored    .65 .60
941 A149 2000p multicolored    .95 .80
942 A149 3000p multicolored    1.40 1.25
    Nos. 939-942 (4)    3.50 3.10

Souvenir Sheet

Discovery of America, 500th Anniv. — A150

**1992, Sept. 18**
943 A150 5000p multicolored    3.50 3.50
    Genoa '92.

Procolobus Badius Temminckii A151

Designs: a, Pair in tree. b, Adult seated in vegetation c, Adult seated in tree fork. d, Female with young.

**1992**    **Litho.**    **Perf. 12x11½**
944 A151 2000p Strip of 4, #a.-d.   4.75 4.75
    World Wildlife Fund.

Reptiles A152

**1993, May 18**    **Litho.**    **Perf. 14**
945 A152 1500p Bitis sp.    .50 .25
946 A152 3000p Osteolaemus te-traspis    1.10 .55
947 A152 4000p Varanus nitolicus    1.50 .70
948 A152 5000p Agama agama    1.90 .85
    a.   Souvenir sheet of 4, #945-948   6.00 2.50
    Nos. 945-948 (4)    5.00 2.35

Souvenir Sheet

Union of Portuguese Speaking Capitals — A153

**1993, July 30**    **Litho.**    **Perf. 13½**
949 A153 6000p Fort    1.50 1.50
    Brasiliana '93.

Tourism — A154

Designs: a, 1000p. b, 2000p. c, 4000p. d, 5000p. Illustration reduced.

**1993, Nov. 15**    **Litho.**    **Perf. 14**
950 A154 Block of 4, #a.-d.    4.00 4.00

Traditional Jewelry A155

**1993, Nov. 30**     **Perf. 14½**
951 A155 1500p Bracelet    .45 .20
952 A155 3000p Mask pendant    1.10 .50
953 A155 4000p Circle pendant    1.50 .65
954 A155 5000p Filigree pendant   1.75 .80
    Nos. 951-954 (4)    4.80 2.15

**1994, Nov. 30**

**Souvenir Sheet**
955 A155 18,000p like #952    8.00 8.00
    Hong Kong '94 (No. 955). No. 955 has continuous design.

1994 World Cup Soccer Championships, US — A156

Various stylized designs of player, ball, net.

**1994, June 17**    **Litho.**    **Perf. 14**
956 A156 4000p multicolored    1.50 .85
957 A156 5000p multicolored    2.00 1.10
958 A156 5500p multicolored    2.50 1.25
959 A156 6500p multicolored    3.00 1.60
    Nos. 956-959 (4)    9.00 4.80

Flowering Plants — A157

Designs: 2000p, Erythrina senegalensis. 3000p, Cassia occidentalis. 4000p, Gardenia ternifolia. 6000p, Cochlospermum tinctorium.

**1994, May 30**    **Litho.**    **Perf. 14**
960 A157 2000p multicolored    .90 .45
961 A157 3000p multicolored    1.25 .70
962 A157 4000p multicolored    1.60 .90
963 A157 6000p multicolored    2.75 1.50
    Nos. 960-963 (4)    6.50 3.55

Snakes — A158

#964: a, Dasypeltis scabra. b, Philothamnus. c, Naja melanoleuca. d, Python sebae.
15,000p, Thelotornis kirtlandii.

**1994, Aug. 16**    **Litho.**    **Perf. 14**
964 A158 5000p Block of 4, #a.-d.   8.00 8.00

**Souvenir Sheet**
**Perf. 13½**
965 A158 15,000p multicolored    6.50 6.50
    PHILAKOREA '94, SINGPEX '94. No. 965 contains one 60x50mm stamp.

Palmeira Dendem — A159

3000p, Climbing tree to pick fruit. 6500p, Hand processing palm fruit into baskets. 7500p, Mechanical processing. 8000p, Palm oil, uses.

**1995, Feb. 27**    **Litho.**    **Perf. 14**
966 A159 3000p multicolored    .75 .35
967 A159 6500p multicolored    1.50 .70
968 A159 7500p multicolored    1.75 .80
969 A159 8000p multicolored    2.00 .85
    Nos. 966-969 (4)    6.00 2.70

FAO, 50th Anniv. A160

**1995**    **Litho.**    **Perf. 13½**
970 A160 3000p Net fishing    .75 .45
971 A160 6500p Disking field    1.50 .85
972 A160 7500p Hands holding fruit    1.75 1.00
973 A160 8000p Vendors along road    2.00 1.10
    a.   Souvenir sheet of 2, #973-973   4.50 2.25
    Nos. 970-973 (4)    6.00 3.40

UN, 50th
Anniv. — A161

**1995, Oct. 24**    **Litho.**    **Perf. 13½**
974 A161   4000p shown    1.00   .55
975 A161   5500p UN flag    1.25   .75
976 A161   7500p Natl. flag    1.75 1.00
977 A161   8000p Hand on dove    2.00 1.10
    *Nos. 974-977 (4)*    6.00 3.40

**Souvenir Sheet**
978 A161 15,000p UN emblem    5.00 5.00

100 Centimes = 1 Franc (1997)

Endangered Animals — A166

No. 995: a, 5000p, Hippopotamus. b, 7500p, Crocodile. c, 10,000p, Chelonia mydas. d, 12,000p, Trichechus senegalensis. Illustration reduced.

**1997**    **Litho.**    **Perf. 12x11¾**
995 A166   Block of 4, #a-d    —   —

Despite change to franc currency on May 2, 1997, Nos. 995-997 have denominations in pesos.

Venomous Animals — A167

No. 996: a, 7500p, Pandinus imperator. b, 8000p, Naja nigricollis. c, 10,000p, Scolopendra morsitans. d, 11,000p, Lycosa tarentula. Illustration reduced.

**1997**
996 A167   Block of 4, #a-d    —   —

Economic Community of West African States, 20th Anniv. (in 1995) — A168

**1997, Dec. 26**
997 A168 25,000p multi    —   —

Native
Foods
A169

---

Designs: 100fr, Caldo branco. 120fr, Siga. 160fr, Caldo de amendoin. 190fr, Caldo de chabeu.

**1998, June 1**
998-1001 A169   Set of 4    —   —

No. 1001 Overprinted in Brown

**1998, Sept. 4**    **Litho.**    **Perf. 12x11¾**
1002 A169 190fr on No. 1001    —   —

Maritime Discoveries — A170

**1998, Oct. 9**    **Perf. 12x11¾**
1003 A170 200fr multi    —   —
   *a.*    Souvenir sheet of 1, perf. 12½    —   —

Marine
Life
A171

Designs: 150fr, Cultellus tenuis. 170fr, Penaeus keraethurus. 200fr, Periophthalmus papilio. 250fr, Istiophorus albicans.

**1998, Dec. 28**    **Perf. 12x11¾**
1004-1007 A171   Set of 4    —   —
*1007a*   Souvenir sheet, #1004-
    1007, perf. 12½    —   —

Souvenir Sheet

España 2000 World Philatelic
Exhibition — A174

**2000**    **Litho.**    **Perf. 13x12¾**
1016 A174 1000fr multi    —   —

No. 924
Surcharged

---

**Methods and Perfs As Before
2000 ?**
1027 A143 1000fr on 3000p #924    —

At least 12 other surcharges were issued in this set. The editors would like to examine any examples.

---

## AIR POST STAMPS

Liftoff of
Soyuz
Spacecraft
AP1

Apollo-Soyuz mission: 10p, Launch of Apollo spacecraft. 15p, Leonov, Stafford and meeting in space. 20p, Eclipse of the sun. 30p, Infra-red photo of Earth. 40p, Return to Earth. 50p, Apollo and Soyuz docked, horiz.

**1976, Oct. 4**    **Perf. 13½**
C10   AP1   5p multicolored
C10A   AP1   10p multicolored
C10B   AP1   15p multicolored
C10C   AP1   20p multicolored
C10D   AP1   30p multicolored
C10E   AP1   40p multicolored
   *Nos. C10-C10E (6)*    11.50   6.50

**Souvenir Sheet**
C10F   AP1   50p multicolored    5.00 5.00

No. C10F contains one 60x42mm stamp. Nos. C10-C10E exist in souvenir sheets of one, perf. and imperf.

Viking
Spacecraft
Orbiting
Mars
AP2

35p, Viking gathering Martian soil samples.

**1977, Jan. 27**
C11   AP2   25p multicolored    2.50 1.00
C11A   AP2   35p multicolored    2.50 1.00

Nos. 372-373 Surcharged with New
Value and "CORREIO AEREO" in
Black on Silver Panels

**1978**    **Litho.**    **Perf. 13½**
C12   A32   15p on 3.50p multi    1.10 .40
C13   A32   30p on 50c multi    1.50 .60

History of Aviation Type of 1980

**1980**    **Litho.**    **Perf. 13½**
C14   A38   35p Willy de
    Houthulst,
    Hanriot HD.1    2.75 1.00
C14A   A38   40p Charles
    Guynemer,
    Spad S. VII    3.75 1.25

**Souvenir Sheet**
C14B   A38   50p Comdr. de Rose,
    Nieuport    6.50 4.50

No. C14B contains one stamp 37x55mm.

Winter Olympics Type of 1980

**1980**
C15   A39   35p Slalom    2.75 1.00
C16   A39   40p Figure skating    3.50 1.25

**Souvenir Sheet**
C17   A39   50p Ice hockey, horiz.    7.00 4.50

---

Summer Olympics Type of 1980
**1980, Aug.**    **Litho.**    **Perf. 13½**
C18   A40   35p Somersault    4.25 1.00
C19   A40   40p Running    5.00 1.25

**Souvenir Sheet**
C20   A40   50p Emblem    7.00 4.50

Literacy Type of 1980
**1980, Aug.**    **Litho.**    **Perf. 13½**
C21   A41   15p like #391    2.25 .50
C22   A41   25p like #392    3.75 .60

Space Type of 1981
35p, Viking 1 & 2. 40p, Apollo-Soyuz craft & crew. 50p, Apollo 11 crew, craft & emblem.

**1981, May**    **Litho.**    **Perf. 13½**
C23   A45   35p multicolored    3.50 1.25
C24   A45   40p multicolored    3.75 1.50

**Souvenir Sheet**
C25   A45   50p multicolored    9.00 6.00

No. C25 contains one stamp 60x42mm.

Soccer Type of 1981
Designs: 35p, Rummenigge, Germany. 40p, Kempes, Argentina. 50p, Juanito, Spain.

**1981, May**
C26   A46   35p multicolored    3.50 1.25
C27   A46   40p multicolored    3.75 1.50

**Souvenir Sheet**
C28   A46   50p multicolored    11.00 7.25

No. C28 contains one stamp 56x40mm.

Royal Wedding Type of 1981
**1981**    **Litho.**    **Perf. 13½**
C29   A47   35p Palace    4.00 1.25
C30   A47   40p Prince of Wales
    arms    4.75 1.50

**Souvenir Sheet**
C31   A47   50p Couple    9.00 6.00

Picasso Type of 1981
**1981, Dec.**    **Litho.**    **Perf. 13½**
C32   A48   35p multicolored    5.50 1.25
C33   A48   40p multicolored    7.00 1.60

**Souvenir Sheet**
C34   A48   50p multicolored    9.00 6.00

No. C34 contains one stamp 41x50mm.

Navigator Type of 1981
35p, Francis Drake, Golden Hinde. 40p, James Cook, Endeavor. 50p, Columbus, Santa Maria.

**1981**    **Litho.**    **Perf. 13½**
C35   A49   35p multicolored    3.75 1.40
C36   A49   40p multicolored    5.00 1.75

**Souvenir Sheet**
C37   A49   50p multicolored    12.00 7.50

Christmas Type of 1981
**1981**
C38   A50   30p Memling    4.00 1.40
C39   A50   35p Bellini, diff.    4.75 1.75

**Souvenir Sheet**
C40   A50   50p Fra Angelico    9.00 6.00

No. C40 contains one 35x59mm stamp.

Scout Type of 1982
**1982, June 9**    **Litho.**    **Perf. 13½**
C41   A51   35p Canoeing    3.50 .85
C42   A51   40p Flying model
    planes    4.25 1.25

**Souvenir Sheet**
C43   A51   50p Playing chess    18.00 8.25

No. C43 contains one 48x38mm stamp.

Soccer Type of 1982
**1982, June 13**    **Litho.**    **Perf. 13½**
C44   A52   35p Kempes    3.50 .85
C45   A52   40p Kaltz    4.25 1.25

**Souvenir Sheet**
C46   A52   50p Stadium    9.00 3.75

Princess Diana, 21st Birthday — AP3

**1982**
| | | | | |
|---|---|---|---|---|
| C47 | A53 | 35p multicolored | 3.50 | .85 |
| C48 | A53 | 40p multicolored | 4.25 | 1.25 |

**Souvenir Sheet**
| | | | | |
|---|---|---|---|---|
| C49 | A53 | 50p multi, vert. | 9.00 | 3.75 |

**1982, Oct. 1   Litho. & Embossed**
| | | | |
|---|---|---|---|
| C49A | AP3 | 200p gold & multi | 18.00 |

**Souvenir Sheet**
| | | | |
|---|---|---|---|
| C49B | AP3 | 200p gold & multi, vert. | 40.00 |

For overprints see Nos. 456A-456B.

Audubon Birth Bicent. — AP4

**1985, Apr. 16   Litho.   Perf. 12**
| | | | |
|---|---|---|---|
| C50 | AP4 | 5p Brown pelican | 1.00 |
| C51 | AP4 | 10p American white pelican | 1.60 |
| C52 | AP4 | 20p Great blue heron | 2.10 |
| C53 | AP4 | 40p American flamingo | 4.25 |
| | | Nos. C50-C53 (4) | 8.95 |

# GUYANA

gī-'a-nə

LOCATION — Northeast coast of South America
GOVT. — Republic
AREA — 83,000 sq. mi.
POP. — 705,156 (1999 est.)
CAPITAL — Georgetown

The former Crown Colony of British Guiana became an independent member of the British Commonwealth May 26, 1966, taking the name Guyana. On February 23, 1970, Guyana became a republic, remaining a Commonwealth nation.

100 Cents = 1 Dollar

> Catalogue values for all unused stamps in this country are for Never Hinged items.

**Watermark**

Wmk. 364 — Lotus Bud Multiple

---

British Guiana #254-256, 258-260, 267 Overprinted

**Perf. 12½x13, 13**
**1966, May 26    Wmk. 4    Engr.**
| | | | | |
|---|---|---|---|---|
| 1 | A60 | 2c dark green | .50 | .30 |
| 1A | A60 | 3c red brn & ol | 4.75 | 5.00 |
| 2 | A61 | 4c violet | 2.75 | .75 |
| 3 | A60 | 6c yellow green | .75 | .20 |
| 4 | A60 | 8c ultra | 2.50 | 1.00 |
| 5 | A61 | 12c brn & blk | 3.00 | 1.00 |
| 6 | A61 | $5 blk & ultra | 40.00 | 57.50 |
| | | Nos. 1-6 (7) | 54.25 | 65.75 |

Same Overprint on British Guiana Stamps and Types of 1954

**Engr.; Center Litho. on $1**
**1966-67    Wmk. 314 Upright**
| | | | | |
|---|---|---|---|---|
| 7 | A60 | 1c black ('67) | .35 | .40 |
| 8 | A60 | 3c red brn & ol (#279) | 2.00 | .30 |
| 9 | A61 | 4c violet ('67) | .35 | .75 |
| 10 | A60 | 5c blk & red (#280) | .50 | .30 |
| 10A | A60 | 6c yel green ('67) | .35 | .30 |
| 11 | A60 | 8c ultra ('67) | .90 | 1.75 |
| 12 | A61 | 12c brn & blk (#281) | .35 | .30 |
| 13 | A60 | 24c org & blk (#282) | 7.25 | .50 |
| 14 | A60 | 36c blk & rose (#283) | .75 | .60 |
| 15 | A61 | 48c red brn & ultra (#284) | 6.75 | 8.00 |
| 16 | A61 | 72c emer & rose (#285) | 1.00 | 1.00 |
| 17 | A60 | $1 blk & multi (#286) | 4.25 | .90 |
| 18 | A60 | $2 mag (#287) | 3.75 | 1.60 |
| 19 | A61 | $5 black & ultra | 3.00 | 5.00 |
| | | Nos. 7-19 (14) | 31.55 | 21.70 |

For surcharges see Nos. 543, 544A, 625-626, 1446.

**1966-67    Wmk. 314 Sideways**
| | | | | |
|---|---|---|---|---|
| 7a | A60 | 1c black | .35 | .35 |
| 9a | A61 | 4c violet | .35 | .35 |
| 11a | A60 | 8c ultramarine | .35 | .35 |
| 12a | A61 | 12c brown & black ('67) | .35 | .35 |
| 13a | A60 | 24c orange & black | 3.75 | .90 |
| 14a | A60 | 36c black & rose ('67) | .60 | 2.25 |
| 15a | A61 | 48c red brown & ultra | .60 | .45 |
| 16a | A61 | 72c emerald & rose ('67) | 3.00 | 5.50 |
| 17a | A60 | $1 black & multi ('67) | 4.00 | 5.50 |
| 18a | A60 | $2 magenta ('67) | 4.75 | 5.50 |
| 19a | A61 | $5 black & ultra ('67) | 3.00 | 4.75 |
| | | Nos. 7a-19a (11) | 21.10 | 26.25 |

See Nos. 32-32T and note. For surcharges see Nos. 544, 627-628, 1447.

Flag and Map of Guyana — A1

Designs: 25c, $1, Arms of Guyana.

**Unwmk.**
**1966, May 26    Photo.    Perf. 14**
| | | | | |
|---|---|---|---|---|
| 20 | A1 | 5c violet & multi | .30 | .30 |
| 21 | A1 | 15c dk red brown & multi | .30 | .30 |
| 22 | A1 | 25c brt blue & multi | .35 | .35 |
| 23 | A1 | $1 sepia & multi | 1.25 | 1.25 |
| | | Nos. 20-23 (4) | 2.20 | 2.20 |

Guyana's independence, May 26, 1966.

Bank of Guyana A2

**1966, Oct. 11    Perf. 13½x14**
| | | | | |
|---|---|---|---|---|
| 24 | A2 | 5c yel grn, blue, blk & gold | .20 | .20 |
| 25 | A2 | 25c blue, black & gold | .20 | .20 |

Establishment of the Bank of Guyana.

---

British Guiana No. 13 — A3

**1967, Feb. 23    Litho.    Perf. 12½**
| | | | | |
|---|---|---|---|---|
| 26 | A3 | 5c multicolored | .20 | .20 |
| 27 | A3 | 25c multicolored | .20 | .20 |
| *a.* | | Imperf., pair | | |

Issued to honor the unique British Guiana 1c black on magenta stamp of 1856.

**Canceled to Order**
Remainders of Nos. 26-30, 33-38 and 54-67 were canceled and sold by the Post Office in 1969. Values are for these canceled to order stamps. Postally used copies do not command a significant premium.

Chateau Margot — A4

Designs: 15c, Independence Arch. 25c, Guyana Fort, Fort Island, horiz. $1, Parliament, National Assembly Hall, horiz.

**Perf. 14, 14½x14, 14x14½**
**1967, May 26    Photo.    Unwmk.**
| | | | | |
|---|---|---|---|---|
| 28 | A4 | 6c multicolored | .20 | .20 |
| 29 | A4 | 15c multicolored | .20 | .20 |
| 30 | A4 | 25c multicolored | .20 | .20 |
| 31 | A4 | $1 multicolored | .30 | .20 |
| | | Nos. 28-31 (4) | .90 | .80 |

First anniversary of independence.

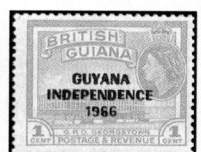

British Guiana Stamps and Types of 1954 Locally Overprinted

**1967    Wmk. 4**
| | | | | |
|---|---|---|---|---|
| 32 | A60 | 1c black | .20 | .20 |
| 32A | A60 | 2c dark green | .20 | .20 |
| 32B | A60 | 3c red brown & ol | .90 | .20 |
| 32C | A61 | 4c violet | .30 | .20 |
| 32D | A60 | 6c yellow green | .30 | .20 |
| 32E | A60 | 8c ultramarine | .30 | .20 |
| 32F | A61 | 12c brown & black | .30 | .20 |
| 32G | A60 | $2 magenta | 3.25 | 2.50 |
| 32H | A61 | $5 black & ultra | 4.25 | 2.75 |
| | | Nos. 32-32H (9) | 10.00 | 6.65 |

The 24c with Wmk. 4 also exists with this overprint. Value $325.

**1967-68    Wmk. 314 Upright**
| | | | | |
|---|---|---|---|---|
| 32I | A60 | 1c black ('68) | .20 | .70 |
| 32J | A60 | 2c dk green ('68) | .45 | 1.40 |
| 32K | A60 | 3c red brown & ol | .35 | .20 |
| 32L | A61 | 4c violet ('68) | .20 | 1.25 |
| 32M | A60 | 5c black & red | 1.50 | 2.00 |
| 32N | A60 | 6c yel green ('68) | .40 | .90 |
| 32O | A60 | 24c orange & blk | 3.25 | .25 |
| 32P | A60 | 36c black & rose | 1.25 | .20 |
| 32Q | A61 | 48c red brn & ultra | 1.25 | .75 |
| 32R | A61 | 72c emer & rose | 2.50 | .85 |
| 32S | A60 | $1 black & multi | 4.75 | 1.00 |
| 32T | A60 | $2 magenta | 5.00 | 4.00 |
| | | Nos. 32I-32T (12) | 21.10 | 13.50 |

The 1c, 4c, 6c, 8c and $5 with Wmk. 314 were not issued without overprint.
For surcharges see Nos. 540, 542, 543A.

---

"Millie," the Bilingual Macaw — A5

Wicketkeeper, Emblem of West Indies Cricket Team — A6

**Christmas Issues**
**1967, Nov. 6    Perf. 14½x14**
| | | | | |
|---|---|---|---|---|
| 33 | A5 | 5c olive green & multi | .20 | .20 |
| 33A | A5 | 25c purple & multi | .30 | .20 |

**1968, Jan. 22**
| | | | | |
|---|---|---|---|---|
| 34 | A5 | 5c multi | .20 | .20 |
| 35 | A5 | 25c yel green & multi | .30 | .20 |

**1968, Jan. 8    Photo.    Perf. 14**
Designs: 6c, Batsman and emblem of Marylebone Cricket Club. 25c, Bowler and emblem of West Indies Cricket Team.
| | | | | |
|---|---|---|---|---|
| 36 | A6 | 5c multicolored | .20 | .20 |
| 37 | A6 | 6c multicolored | .20 | .20 |
| 38 | A6 | 25c multicolored | .40 | .20 |
| *a.* | | Strip of 3, #36-38 | 1.00 | 1.00 |

Visit of the Marylebone Cricket Club to the West Indies, Jan.-Feb. 1968. Printed in sheets of 9.

Pike Cichlid — A7

Marail Guan — A8

Christ of St. John of the Cross, by Salvador Dali — A9

Designs: 2c, Piranha. 3c, Cichla ocellaris (fish). 5c, Armored catfish. 6c, Two-spotted cichlid. 15c, Harpy eagle. 20c, Hoatzin. 25c, Andean cock-of-the-rock. 40c, Great kiskadee. 50c, Agouti. 60c, Peccary. $1, Paca. $2, Armadillo. $5, Ocelot.

**Perf. 14x14½, 14½x14**
**1968, Mar. 4    Photo.    Unwmk.**
| | | | | |
|---|---|---|---|---|
| 39 | A7 | 1c chalky blue & multi | .25 | .20 |
| 40 | A7 | 2c gray & multi | .25 | .20 |
| 41 | A7 | 3c grnsh bl & multi | .25 | .20 |
| 42 | A7 | 5c ultra & multi | .25 | .20 |
| 43 | A7 | 6c brt olive & multi | .75 | .20 |
| 44 | A8 | 10c yel green & multi | .85 | .20 |
| 45 | A8 | 15c green & multi | 1.75 | .20 |
| 46 | A8 | 20c ap grn & multi | .90 | .20 |
| 47 | A8 | 25c brt green & multi | .90 | .20 |
| 48 | A8 | 40c pale brn & multi | 1.60 | .80 |
| 49 | A7 | 50c rose brn & multi | 1.25 | .75 |
| 50 | A7 | 60c lilac rose & multi | 1.40 | .25 |
| 51 | A7 | $1 dp orange & multi | 1.75 | .25 |
| 52 | A7 | $2 ocher & multi | 2.25 | 3.25 |
| 53 | A7 | $5 red & multi | 3.00 | 4.00 |
| | | Nos. 39-53 (15) | 17.40 | 11.10 |

See Nos. 68-82.
For overprints & surcharges see #357, 410-413, 603, 752, 756, 761a, 1463, 1501, 1839, 2045.

**1968, Mar. 25    Perf. 14x14½**
| | | | | |
|---|---|---|---|---|
| 54 | A9 | 5c car rose & multi | .20 | .20 |
| 55 | A9 | 25c brt violet & multi | .30 | .20 |

Easter.

"Efficiency Year" — A10

Designs: 30c, 40c, "Savings bonds."

**1968, July 22     Litho.     Perf. 14**
| | | | | |
|---|---|---|---|---|
| 56 | A10 | 6c green & multi | .20 | .20 |
| 57 | A10 | 25c fawn & multi | .20 | .20 |
| 58 | A10 | 30c multicolored | .20 | .20 |
| 59 | A10 | 40c multicolored | .20 | .20 |
| | | Nos. 56-59 (4) | .80 | .80 |

Issued to promote the sale of savings bonds and to publicize Efficiency Year.

Open Koran A11

**Perf. 14x13½**
**1968, Oct. 9     Photo.     Unwmk.**
| | | | | |
|---|---|---|---|---|
| 60 | A11 | 6c sal pink, gold & blk | .20 | .20 |
| 61 | A11 | 25c pale vio, gold & blk | .20 | .20 |
| 62 | A11 | 30c pale yel grn, gold & blk | .20 | .20 |
| 63 | A11 | 40c pale blue, gold & blk | .20 | .20 |
| | | Nos. 60-63 (4) | .80 | .80 |

Koran's 1400th anniversary.
For overprints & surcharges see #354, 355, 441, 445, 487-488, 575, 630, 1464-1465.

Dish Aerials, Thomas Lands, Guyana — A12

Designs: 30c, 40c, Map showing connection between Guyana and Trinidad. All stamps are inscribed: "Guyana Sends Christmas Greetings to the World."

**Wmk. 364**
**1968, Nov. 11     Litho.     Perf. 14**
| | | | | |
|---|---|---|---|---|
| 64 | A12 | 6c blue, gray, ocher & emer | .20 | .20 |
| 65 | A12 | 25c rose lil, brn & emer | .20 | .20 |
| 66 | A12 | 30c blue grn & dk blue grn | .20 | .20 |
| 67 | A12 | 40c blue grn & red | .20 | .20 |
| | | Nos. 64-67 (4) | .80 | .80 |

Christmas; communications link with Trinidad by the tropospheric scatter system.

**Types of 1968**
Designs as before.

**Perf. 14x14½, 14½x14**
**1968     Photo.     Wmk. 364**
| | | | | |
|---|---|---|---|---|
| 68 | A7 | 1c chalky bl & multi | .20 | .20 |
| 69 | A7 | 2c gray & multi | .20 | .25 |
| 70 | A7 | 3c grnsh bl & multi | .20 | .55 |
| 71 | A7 | 5c ultra & multi | .20 | .20 |
| 72 | A7 | 6c brt olive & multi | .20 | .55 |
| 73 | A8 | 10c yel grn & multi | .65 | .55 |
| 74 | A8 | 15c green & multi | .65 | .20 |
| 75 | A8 | 20c apple grn & multi | .65 | .65 |
| 76 | A8 | 25c brt green & multi | .65 | .20 |
| 77 | A8 | 40c pale brn & multi | 1.25 | .65 |
| 78 | A7 | 50c rose brn & multi | .70 | .20 |
| 79 | A7 | 60c lilac rose & multi | .75 | .90 |
| 80 | A7 | $1 dp org & multi | 1.50 | 1.10 |
| 81 | A7 | $2 ocher & multi | 2.10 | 3.00 |
| 82 | A7 | $5 red & multi | 2.10 | 4.50 |
| | | Nos. 68-82 (15) | 12.00 | 13.70 |

For overprints & surcharges see #373, 376-377, 413D, 565-566, 633, 635, 704-705, 744, 749, 752a, 757-758, 761-762, 1862-1863, 1981, O2.

Celebrants Spraying Perfumed Powder — A13

Phagwah (Holi) Hindu Festival: 25c, 40c, Two celebrants spraying colored water.

**1969, Feb. 26     Litho.     Perf. 13½**
| | | | | |
|---|---|---|---|---|
| 83 | A13 | 6c multicolored | .20 | .20 |
| 84 | A13 | 25c multicolored | .20 | .20 |
| 85 | A13 | 30c multicolored | .20 | .20 |
| 86 | A13 | 40c multicolored | .20 | .20 |
| | | Nos. 83-86 (4) | .80 | .80 |

The Last Supper, by Salvador Dali A14

**1969, Mar. 10     Photo.     Perf. 13**
| | | | | |
|---|---|---|---|---|
| 87 | A14 | 6c dp carmine & multi | .20 | .20 |
| 88 | A14 | 25c green & multi | .20 | .20 |
| 89 | A14 | 30c org brown & multi | .20 | .20 |
| 90 | A14 | 40c dp violet & multi | .20 | .20 |
| | | Nos. 87-90 (4) | .80 | .80 |

Easter. For overprints and surcharges see Nos. 393-394, 482-485, 572, 576, 634, 765, 772, 1407-1410, 1813, 1815-1817, 2050.

Map of Caribbean — A15     Prow of Aluminum Ship — A16

Design: 25c, "Strength in Unity," horiz.

**Wmk. 364**
**1969, Apr. 30     Litho.     Perf. 13½**
| | | | | |
|---|---|---|---|---|
| 91 | A15 | 6c violet blue & multi | .20 | .20 |
| 92 | A15 | 25c brt rose, yel & brown | .20 | .20 |

1st anniv. of CARIFTA (Caribbean Free Trade Area).

**1969, Apr. 30     Perf. 12x11, 11x12**
50th Anniv. of the ILO: 40c, Bauxite processing plant, horiz.
| | | | | |
|---|---|---|---|---|
| 93 | A16 | 30c black, blue & silver | .40 | .20 |
| 94 | A16 | 40c multicolored | .50 | .25 |

Flag Raising A17

Designs: 8c, 30c, Campfire.

**1969, Aug. 13     Litho.     Perf. 13½x13**
| | | | | |
|---|---|---|---|---|
| 95 | A17 | 6c pale green & multi | .20 | .20 |
| 96 | A17 | 8c orange & multi | .20 | .20 |
| 97 | A17 | 25c pale brown & multi | .20 | .20 |
| 98 | A17 | 30c multicolored | .20 | .20 |
| 99 | A17 | 50c rose & multi | .20 | .20 |
| | | Nos. 95-99 (5) | 1.00 | 1.00 |

60th anniv. of Scouting in Guyana; 3rd Caribbean Scout Jamboree, Georgetown, Aug. 13-22. For overprints and surcharges see Nos. 392, 395, 397, 402, 404-405, 453.

Gandhi and Spinning Wheel A18

**1969, Oct. 1     Perf. 14½x14**
| | | | | |
|---|---|---|---|---|
| 100 | A18 | 6c olive, blk & lt brn | .30 | .65 |
| 101 | A18 | 15c rose lilac, blk & lt brn | 1.00 | .65 |

Mohandas K. Gandhi (1868-1948), leader in India's fight for independence.

Mother Sally Troupe — A19     City Hall, Georgetown — A20

**1969, Nov. 17     Perf. 14½x13½**
| | | | | |
|---|---|---|---|---|
| 102 | A19 | 5c multicolored | .20 | .20 |
| 103 | A20 | 6c blue & multi | .20 | .20 |
| 104 | A19 | 25c multicolored | .20 | .20 |
| 105 | A20 | 60c orange & multi | .20 | .20 |
| | | Nos. 102-105 (4) | .80 | .80 |

Christmas. The 5c, 6c, and 25c exist without the "Christmas 1969" overprint.

Prime Minister Forbes Burnham and Map — A21     Descent from the Cross, by Rubens — A22

6c, "Rural Self Help Project" (man & woman building house). 15c, University of Guyana, horiz. 25c, President's Residence, horiz.

**1970, Feb. 23     Litho.     Perf. 14**
| | | | | |
|---|---|---|---|---|
| 106 | A21 | 5c blue, brn & ocher | .20 | .20 |
| 107 | A21 | 6c blue, blk ocher & brn | .20 | .20 |
| 108 | A21 | 15c apple grn & multi | .20 | .20 |
| 109 | A21 | 25c multicolored | .20 | .20 |
| | | Nos. 106-109 (4) | .80 | .80 |

Issued for Republic Day, Feb. 23, 1970.

**1970, Mar. 24     Perf. 14x14½**
Easter: 6c, 25c, Christ on the Cross, by Rubens.
| | | | | |
|---|---|---|---|---|
| 110 | A22 | 5c blue & multi | .20 | .20 |
| 111 | A22 | 6c rose lilac & multi | .20 | .20 |
| 112 | A22 | 15c dark red & multi | .20 | .20 |
| 113 | A22 | 25c yellow & multi | .30 | .20 |
| | | Nos. 110-113 (4) | .90 | .80 |

"Peace" and UN Emblem A23

UN 25th Anniv.: 6c, 25c, UN emblem, panning for gold and drilling for minerals.

**1970, Oct. 26     Perf. 14½x14**
| | | | | |
|---|---|---|---|---|
| 114 | A23 | 5c red & multi | .20 | .20 |
| 115 | A23 | 6c blue & multi | .20 | .20 |
| 116 | A23 | 15c multicolored | .20 | .20 |
| 117 | A23 | 25c brown & multi | .20 | .20 |
| | | Nos. 114-117 (4) | .80 | .80 |

Mother and Child, by Philip Moore — A24

**1970, Dec. 8     Litho.     Perf. 13½**
| | | | | |
|---|---|---|---|---|
| 118 | A24 | 5c violet & multi | .20 | .20 |
| 119 | A24 | 6c brown & multi | .20 | .20 |
| 120 | A24 | 15c dk green & multi | .20 | .20 |
| 121 | A24 | 25c maroon & multi | .20 | .20 |
| | | Nos. 118-121 (4) | .80 | .80 |

Christmas.

National Cooperative Bank — A25

**1971, Feb. 23     Wmk. 364     Perf. 14**
| | | | | |
|---|---|---|---|---|
| 122 | A25 | 6c red & multi | .20 | .20 |
| 123 | A25 | 15c yellow & multi | .20 | .20 |
| 124 | A25 | 25c ultra & multi | .20 | .20 |
| | | Nos. 122-124 (3) | .60 | .60 |

Republic Day.

"Togetherness, Vision, Understanding" A26

Volunteer Felling Tree, by John Criswick — A27

**1971, Mar. 22     Perf. 14½x14**
| | | | | |
|---|---|---|---|---|
| 125 | A26 | 5c yel grn & multi | .20 | .20 |
| 126 | A26 | 6c lil rose & multi | .20 | .20 |
| 127 | A26 | 15c multicolored | .20 | .20 |
| 128 | A26 | 25c yellow & multi | .20 | .20 |
| | | Nos. 125-128 (4) | .80 | .80 |

Intl. year against racial discrimination.

**1971, July 19     Perf. 14**
| | | | | |
|---|---|---|---|---|
| 129 | A27 | 5c blue & multi | .20 | .20 |
| 130 | A27 | 20c green & multi | .20 | .20 |
| 131 | A27 | 25c yellow & multi | .20 | .20 |
| 132 | A27 | 50c brown & multi | .40 | 1.25 |
| | | Nos. 129-132 (4) | 1.00 | 1.85 |

1st anniv. of the Natl. Self-help Road Project.

Yellow Allamanda — A28

Flora: 1c, Pitcher plant of Mt. Roraima. 3c, Hanging heliconia. 5c, Annatto tree. 6c, Cannonball tree. 10c, Cattleya violacea. 15c, Christmas orchid. 20c, Paphinia cristata. 25c, Gongora quinquinervis. 40c, Tiger beard. 50c, Guzmania lingulata. 60c, Soldier's cap. $1,

Chelonanthus uliginoides. $2, Norantea gui-
anensis. $5, Odontadenia grandiflora.

**1971-76      Litho.      Perf. 13x13½**

| | | | | |
|---|---|---|---|---|
| 133 | A28 | 1c multi ('72) | .20 | .20 |
| 134 | A28 | 2c lilac & multi | .20 | .20 |
| 135 | A28 | 3c multicolored | .20 | .20 |
| 136 | A28 | 5c lt blue & multi | .20 | .20 |
| 137 | A28 | 6c dull rose & multi | .20 | .20 |

**Perf. 13½**

| | | | | |
|---|---|---|---|---|
| 138 | A28 | 10c multi ('72) | 4.25 | .20 |
| a. | | Perf. 13 | 5.25 | .20 |
| 139 | A28 | 15c multi ('72) | 1.00 | .20 |
| a. | | Perf. 13 ('76) | .75 | .20 |
| 140 | A28 | 20c multi ('72) | 4.00 | .40 |
| a. | | Perf. 13 | 7.00 | .40 |
| 141 | A28 | 25c multi, 25c at center ('72) | 6.50 | 9.00 |
| 141A | A28 | 25c multi, 25c right of center ('73) | .45 | .55 |
| b. | | Perf. 13 ('76) | .45 | .30 |
| 142 | A28 | 40c multi ('72) | 4.50 | |
| 143 | A28 | 50c multi ('73) | .50 | .80 |
| 144 | A28 | 60c multi ('73) | .40 | .65 |
| 145 | A28 | $1 multi ('73) | .40 | .40 |
| 146 | A28 | $2 multi ('73) | .60 | .60 |
| 147 | A28 | $5 multi ('73) | 1.00 | 1.00 |
| | | Nos. 133-147 (16) | 24.60 | 15.00 |

No. 141 has 2 blossoms at left, 3 at right;
this is reversed on No. 141A.

The overprint "REVENUE / ONLY" between
rules was applied to Nos. 134-136, 141A, 142-
147 in 1975. Postal use was permitted in Nov.-
Dec., 1975. Value, set $20.

See Nos. 433-434, 731-732.

For overprints and surcharges see Nos.
192, 209, 234, 331-335, 351, 358-359, 367,
370, 372, 374-375A, 379-383, 385-390A, 401,
407, 422-425, 433-434, 438-440, 447, 450,
451, 457-458, 460-461, 464-466, 497-500,
545-546, 550, 563-564, 597, 602, 618, 631-
632, 641-642, 666-667, 727, 747-748, 750-
751, 753-754, 759-760, 803, 805, 807-808,
810-812, 847-848, 910-911, 995, 1361, 1382-
1383, 1385-1386, 1391-1392, 1452, 1454,
1456-1460, 1466, 1499, 1778-1779, 1781-
1784, 1837-1838, 1870-1872, 1898-1900,
2046-2049, 2225-2227, C2-C4, O1, O3-O5,
O7, O13-O14, Q1-Q4, QO1.

The Lord's Prayer, by School Girl
Veronica Bassoo — A29

Guyana Masker,
by School Boy
Michael
Austin — A30

**Perf. 13½x14, 14x13½**

**1971, Nov. 15      Litho.      Wmk. 364**

| | | | | |
|---|---|---|---|---|
| 148 | A29 | 5c brt green & multi | .20 | .20 |
| 149 | A29 | 20c brt green & multi | .20 | .20 |
| 150 | A30 | 25c multicolored | .20 | .20 |
| 151 | A30 | 50c multicolored | .30 | .30 |
| | | Nos. 148-151 (4) | .90 | .90 |

Christmas.

Guyana
Dollar — A31

Handclasp and
Mosque — A32

**1972, Feb. 23      Litho.      Perf. 14½x14**

| | | | | |
|---|---|---|---|---|
| 152 | A31 | 5c blk, dp org & silver | .20 | .20 |
| 153 | A31 | 20c blk, dp lil rose & sil | .20 | .20 |
| 154 | A31 | 25c black, ultra & silver | .20 | .20 |
| 155 | A31 | 50c black, emerald & silver | .35 | .35 |
| | | Nos. 152-155 (4) | .95 | .95 |

Republic Day.

**1972, Apr. 3                Perf. 14**

| | | | | |
|---|---|---|---|---|
| 156 | A32 | 5c brown & multi | .20 | .20 |
| 157 | A32 | 25c blue & multi | .20 | .20 |
| 158 | A32 | 30c green & multi | .20 | .20 |
| 159 | A32 | 60c yellow brn & multi | .30 | .30 |
| | | Nos. 156-159 (4) | .90 | .90 |

Youman Nabi (Peaceful Prophet), Moham-
medan festival.

Map of South
America, Emblem
of Non-aligned
Countries — A33

CARIFESTA '72
Emblem — A34

**1972, July 20**

| | | | | |
|---|---|---|---|---|
| 160 | A33 | 8c violet & multi | .20 | .20 |
| 161 | A33 | 25c yellow grn & multi | .20 | .20 |
| 162 | A33 | 40c orange & multi | .20 | .20 |
| 163 | A33 | 50c red brown & multi | .25 | .25 |
| | | Nos. 160-163 (4) | .85 | .85 |

Conf. of Foreign Ministers of Nonaligned
Countries, Georgetown, Aug. 7-12.
For overprints & surcharges see #573, 611,
O17.

**1972, Aug. 25**

| | | | | |
|---|---|---|---|---|
| 164 | A34 | 8c orange & multi | .20 | .20 |
| 165 | A34 | 25c orange & multi | .20 | .20 |
| 166 | A34 | 40c orange & multi | .20 | .25 |
| 167 | A34 | 50c orange & multi | .25 | .35 |
| | | Nos. 164-167 (4) | .85 | 1.00 |

Caribbean Festival of Arts (CARIFESTA),
Georgetown, Aug. 25-Sept. 15.

Holy Family — A35

**1972, Oct. 18      Litho.      Perf. 13x13½**

| | | | | |
|---|---|---|---|---|
| 168 | A35 | 8c blue & multi | .20 | .20 |
| 169 | A35 | 25c blue & multi | .20 | .20 |
| 170 | A35 | 40c blue & multi | .20 | .25 |
| 171 | A35 | 50c blue & multi | .20 | .30 |
| | | Nos. 168-171 (4) | .80 | .95 |

Christmas.

Umana Yana
(Meeting Place of
Wai Wai
Chiefs) — A36

**1973, Feb. 23      Litho.      Perf. 14x14½**

Designs: 25c, 40c, Bethel Chapel.

| | | | | |
|---|---|---|---|---|
| 172 | A36 | 8c brt blue & multi | .20 | .20 |
| 173 | A36 | 25c rose red & multi | .20 | .20 |
| 174 | A36 | 40c emerald & multi | .25 | .20 |
| 175 | A36 | 50c black & multi | .35 | .25 |
| | | Nos. 172-175 (4) | 1.00 | .85 |

Republic Day.

Pomegranate, Fertility and Church
Symbol — A37

Map of
Guyana and
People
Looking to
the
Cross — A38

**1973, Apr. 19      Perf. 14x14½, 13½**

| | | | | |
|---|---|---|---|---|
| 176 | A37 | 8c pink & multi | .20 | .20 |
| 177 | A38 | 25c yellow & multi | .20 | .20 |
| 178 | A38 | 40c ultra & multi | .20 | .20 |
| 179 | A37 | 50c yellow & multi | .20 | .20 |
| | | Nos. 176-179 (4) | .80 | .80 |

Easter.

Symbolic of Blood
Donation — A39

**Perf. 14x14½**

**1973, Oct. 1                Wmk. 364**

| | | | | |
|---|---|---|---|---|
| 180 | A39 | 8c red & black | .20 | .20 |
| 181 | A39 | 25c red & lilac | .25 | .20 |
| 182 | A39 | 40c red & vio blue | .40 | .50 |
| 183 | A39 | 50c red & brown | .65 | .90 |
| | | Nos. 180-183 (4) | 1.50 | 1.80 |

Guyana Red Cross, 25th anniversary.

Steel Band, Star,
Pegasus
Hotel — A40

Madonna
and Child,
St. Philip's
Anglican
Church,
Georgetown
A41

**1973, Nov. 20      Litho.      Perf. 14x14½**

| | | | | |
|---|---|---|---|---|
| 184 | A40 | 8c lilac & multi | .20 | .20 |
| 185 | A40 | 25c lilac & multi | .25 | .20 |

**Perf. 13½x14**

| | | | | |
|---|---|---|---|---|
| 186 | A41 | 40c violet blue & multi | .40 | .70 |
| 187 | A41 | 50c violet blue & multi | .40 | .70 |
| | | Nos. 184-187 (4) | 1.25 | 1.80 |

Christmas.

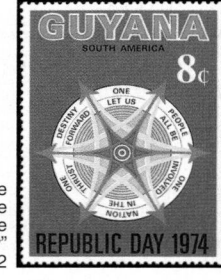

"One
People, One
Nation, One
Destiny"
A42

Designs: 25c, 50c, Wai Wai Indian.

**1974, Feb. 23      Litho.      Perf. 13½**

| | | | | |
|---|---|---|---|---|
| 188 | A42 | 8c multicolored | .20 | .20 |
| 189 | A42 | 25c multicolored | .20 | .20 |
| 190 | A42 | 40c multicolored | .20 | .30 |
| 191 | A42 | 50c multicolored | .20 | .40 |
| | | Nos. 188-191 (4) | .80 | 1.10 |

Republic Day.

No. 137 Surcharged with New Value
and 2 Bars

**Perf. 13x13½**

**1974, Mar. 18                Wmk. 364**

| | | | | |
|---|---|---|---|---|
| 192 | A28 | 8c on 6c multi | .35 | .35 |

For overprints and surcharges see Nos.
424, 459, 474-478, 1453, 1500, 1780.

Crucifix Super-imposed on Eddy Bow
Kite — A43

Crucifix in Pre-Columbian Timehri
Style — A44

"Efficiency Year" — A10

Designs: 30c, 40c, "Savings bonds."

**1968, July 22      Litho.      Perf. 14**
56 A10  6c green & multi            .20 .20
57 A10  25c fawn & multi           .20 .20
58 A10  30c multicolored           .20 .20
59 A10  40c multicolored           .20 .20
        Nos. 56-59 (4)             .80 .80

Issued to promote the sale of savings bonds and to publicize Efficiency Year.

Open Koran A11

**Perf. 14x13½**
**1968, Oct. 9      Photo.      Unwmk.**
60 A11  6c sal pink, gold & blk    .20 .20
61 A11  25c pale vio, gold & blk   .20 .20
62 A11  30c pale yel grn, gold &
        blk                        .20 .20
63 A11  40c pale blue, gold & blk  .20 .20
        Nos. 60-63 (4)             .80 .80

Koran's 1400th anniversary.
For overprints & surcharges see #354, 355, 441, 445, 487-488, 575, 630, 1464-1465.

Dish Aerials, Thomas Lands, Guyana — A12

Designs: 30c, 40c, Map showing connection between Guyana and Trinidad. All stamps are inscribed: "Guyana Sends Christmas Greetings to the World."

**Wmk. 364**
**1968, Nov. 11      Litho.      Perf. 14**
64 A12  6c blue, gray, ocher &
        emer                       .20 .20
65 A12  25c rose lil, brn & emer   .20 .20
66 A12  30c blue grn & dk blue grn .20 .20
67 A12  40c blue grn & red         .20 .20
        Nos. 64-67 (4)             .80 .80

Christmas; communications link with Trinidad by the tropospheric scatter system.

**Types of 1968**
Designs as before.

**Perf. 14x14½, 14½x14**
**1968            Photo.          Wmk. 364**
68 A7   1c chalky bl & multi       .20 .20
69 A7   2c gray & multi            .20 .25
70 A7   3c grnsh bl & multi        .20 .55
71 A7   5c ultra & multi           .20 .20
72 A7   6c brt olive & multi       .20 .55
73 A8   10c yel grn & multi        .65 .55
74 A8   15c green & multi          .65 .20
75 A8   20c apple grn & multi      .65 .65
76 A8   25c brt green & multi      .65 .20
77 A8   40c pale brn & multi       1.25 .65
78 A7   50c rose brn & multi       .70 .20
79 A7   60c lilac rose & multi     .75 .90
80 A7   $1 dp org & multi          1.50 1.10
81 A7   $2 ocher & multi           2.10 3.00
82 A7   $5 red & multi             2.10 4.50
        Nos. 68-82 (15)            12.00 13.70

For overprints & surcharges see #373, 376-377, 413D, 565-566, 633, 635, 704-705, 744, 749, 752a, 757-758, 761-762, 1862-1863, 1981, O2.

Celebrants Spraying Perfumed Powder — A13

Phagwah (Holi) Hindu Festival: 25c, 40c, Two celebrants spraying colored water.

**1969, Feb. 26      Litho.      Perf. 13½**
83 A13  6c multicolored            .20 .20
84 A13  25c multicolored           .20 .20
85 A13  30c multicolored           .20 .20
86 A13  40c multicolored           .20 .20
        Nos. 83-86 (4)             .80 .80

The Last Supper, by Salvador Dali A14

**1969, Mar. 10      Photo.      Perf. 13**
87 A14  6c dp carmine & multi      .20 .20
88 A14  25c green & multi          .20 .20
89 A14  30c org brown & multi      .20 .20
90 A14  40c dp violet & multi      .20 .20
        Nos. 87-90 (4)             .80 .80

Easter. For overprints and surcharges see Nos. 393-394, 482-485, 572, 576, 634, 765, 772, 1407-1410, 1813, 1815-1817, 2050.

Map of Caribbean — A15     Prow of Aluminum Ship — A16

Design: 25c, "Strength in Unity," horiz.

**Wmk. 364**
**1969, Apr. 30      Litho.      Perf. 13½**
91 A15  6c violet blue & multi     .20 .20
92 A15  25c brt rose, yel & brown  .20 .20

1st anniv. of CARIFTA (Caribbean Free Trade Area).

**1969, Apr. 30      Perf. 12x11, 11x12**
50th Anniv. of the ILO: 40c, Bauxite processing plant, horiz.
93 A16  30c black, blue & silver   .40 .20
94 A16  40c multicolored           .50 .25

Flag Raising A17

Designs: 8c, 30c, Campfire.

**1969, Aug. 13      Litho.      Perf. 13½x13**
95 A17  6c pale green & multi      .20 .20
96 A17  8c orange & multi          .20 .20
97 A17  25c pale brown & multi     .20 .20
98 A17  30c multicolored           .20 .20
99 A17  50c rose & multi           .20 .20
        Nos. 95-99 (5)             1.00 1.00

60th anniv. of Scouting in Guyana; 3rd Caribbean Scout Jamboree, Georgetown, Aug. 13-22. For overprints and surcharges see Nos. 392, 395, 397, 402, 404-405, 453.

Gandhi and Spinning Wheel A18

**1969, Oct. 1      Perf. 14½x14**
100 A18  6c olive, blk & lt brn    .30 .65
101 A18  15c rose lilac, blk & lt
         brn                       1.00 .65

Mohandas K. Gandhi (1868-1948), leader in India's fight for independence.

Mother Sally Troupe — A19     City Hall, Georgetown — A20

**1969, Nov. 17      Perf. 14½x13½**
102 A19  5c multicolored           .20 .20
103 A20  6c blue & multi           .20 .20
104 A19  25c multicolored          .20 .20
105 A20  60c orange & multi        .20 .20
         Nos. 102-105 (4)          .80 .80

Christmas. The 5c, 6c, and 25c exist without the "Christmas 1969" overprint.

Prime Minister Forbes Burnham and Map — A21     Descent from the Cross, by Rubens — A22

6c, "Rural Self Help Project" (man & woman building house). 15c, University of Guyana, horiz. 25c, President's Residence, horiz.

**1970, Feb. 23      Litho.      Perf. 14**
106 A21  5c blue, brn & ocher      .20 .20
107 A21  6c blue, blk ocher & brn  .20 .20
108 A21  15c apple grn & multi     .20 .20
109 A21  25c multicolored          .20 .20
         Nos. 106-109 (4)          .80 .80

Issued for Republic Day, Feb. 23, 1970.

**1970, Mar. 24      Perf. 14x14½**
Easter: 6c, 25c, Christ on the Cross, by Rubens.
110 A22  5c blue & multi           .20 .20
111 A22  6c rose lilac & multi     .20 .20
112 A22  15c dark red & multi      .20 .20
113 A22  25c yellow & multi        .30 .20
         Nos. 110-113 (4)          .90 .80

"Peace" and UN Emblem A23

UN 25th Anniv.: 6c, 25c, UN emblem, panning for gold and drilling for minerals.

**1970, Oct. 26      Perf. 14½x14**
114 A23  5c red & multi            .20 .20
115 A23  6c blue & multi           .20 .20
116 A23  15c multicolored          .20 .20
117 A23  25c brown & multi         .20 .20
         Nos. 114-117 (4)          .80 .80

Mother and Child, by Philip Moore — A24

**1970, Dec. 8      Litho.      Perf. 13½**
118 A24  5c violet & multi         .20 .20
119 A24  6c brown & multi          .20 .20
120 A24  15c dk green & multi      .20 .20
121 A24  25c maroon & multi        .20 .20
         Nos. 118-121 (4)          .80 .80

Christmas.

National Cooperative Bank — A25

**1971, Feb. 23      Wmk. 364      Perf. 14**
122 A25  5c red & multi            .20 .20
123 A25  15c yellow & multi        .20 .20
124 A25  25c ultra & multi         .20 .20
         Nos. 122-124 (3)          .60 .60

Republic Day.

"Togetherness, Vision, Understanding" A26

**1971, Mar. 22      Perf. 14½x14**
125 A26  5c yel grn & multi        .20 .20
126 A26  6c lil rose & multi       .20 .20
127 A26  15c multicolored          .20 .20
128 A26  25c yellow & multi        .20 .20
         Nos. 125-128 (4)          .80 .80

Intl. year against racial discrimination.

Volunteer Felling Tree, by John Criswick — A27

**1971, July 19      Perf. 14**
129 A27  5c blue & multi           .20 .20
130 A27  20c green & multi         .20 .20
131 A27  25c yellow & multi        .20 .20
132 A27  50c brown & multi         .40 1.25
         Nos. 129-132 (4)          1.00 1.85

1st anniv. of the Natl. Self-help Road Project.

Yellow Allamanda — A28

Flora: 1c, Pitcher plant of Mt. Roraima. 3c, Hanging heliconia. 5c, Annatto tree. 6c, Cannonball tree. 10c, Cattleya violacea. 15c, Christmas orchid. 20c, Paphinia cristata. 25c, Gongora quinquinervis. 40c, Tiger beard. 50c, Guzmania lingulata. 60c, Soldier's cap. $1,

Chelonanthus uliginoides. $2, Norantea gui-
anensis. $5, Odontadenia grandiflora.

**1971-76　　　Litho.　　Perf. 13x13½**

| | | | | |
|---|---|---|---|---|
| 133 | A28 | 1c multi ('72) | .20 | .20 |
| 134 | A28 | 2c lilac & multi | .20 | .20 |
| 135 | A28 | 3c multicolored | .20 | .20 |
| 136 | A28 | 5c lt blue & multi | .20 | .20 |
| 137 | A28 | 6c dull rose & multi | .20 | .20 |

**Perf. 13½**

| | | | | |
|---|---|---|---|---|
| 138 | A28 | 10c multi ('72) | 4.25 | .20 |
| a. | | Perf. 13 | 5.25 | .20 |
| 139 | A28 | 15c multi ('72) | 1.00 | .20 |
| a. | | Perf. 13 ('76) | .75 | .20 |
| 140 | A28 | 20c multi ('72) | 4.00 | .40 |
| a. | | Perf. 13 | 7.00 | .40 |
| 141 | A28 | 25c multi, 25c at center ('72) | 6.50 | 9.00 |
| 141A | A28 | 25c multi, 25c right of center ('73) | .45 | .55 |
| b. | | Perf. 13 ('76) | .45 | .30 |
| 142 | A28 | 40c multi ('72) | 4.50 | .20 |
| 143 | A28 | 50c multi ('73) | .50 | .80 |
| 144 | A28 | 60c multi ('73) | .40 | .65 |
| 145 | A28 | $1 multi ('73) | .40 | .40 |
| 146 | A28 | $2 multi ('73) | .60 | .60 |
| 147 | A28 | $5 multi ('73) | 1.00 | 1.00 |
| | | Nos. 133-147 (16) | 24.60 | 15.00 |

No. 141 has 2 blossoms at left, 3 at right;
this is reversed on No. 141A.

The overprint "REVENUE / ONLY" between
rules was applied to Nos. 134-136, 141A, 142-
147 in 1975. Postal use was permitted in Nov.-
Dec., 1975. Value, set $20.

See Nos. 433-434, 731-732.

For overprints and surcharges see Nos.
192, 209, 234, 331-335, 351, 358-359, 367,
370, 372, 374-375A, 379-383, 385-390A, 401,
407, 422-425, 433-434, 438-440, 447, 450,
451, 457-458, 460-461, 464-466, 497-500,
545-546, 550, 563-564, 597, 602, 618, 631-
632, 641-642, 666-667, 727, 747-748, 750-
751, 753-754, 759-760, 803, 805, 807-808,
810-812, 847-848, 910-911, 995, 1361, 1382-
1383, 1385-1386, 1391-1392, 1452, 1454,
1456-1460, 1466, 1499, 1778-1779, 1781-
1784, 1837-1838, 1870-1872, 1898-1900,
2046-2049, 2225-2227, C2-C4, O1, O3-O5,
O7, O13-O14, Q1-Q4, QO1.

The Lord's Prayer, by School Girl
Veronica Bassoo — A29

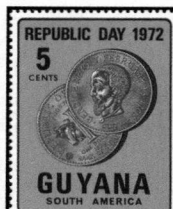

Guyana Masker,
by School Boy
Michael
Austin — A30

**Perf. 13½x14, 14x13½**

**1971, Nov. 15　　Litho.　　Wmk. 364**

| | | | | |
|---|---|---|---|---|
| 148 | A29 | 5c brt green & multi | .20 | .20 |
| 149 | A29 | 20c brt green & multi | .20 | .20 |
| 150 | A30 | 25c multicolored | .20 | .20 |
| 151 | A30 | 50c multicolored | .30 | .30 |
| | | Nos. 148-151 (4) | .90 | .90 |

Christmas.

Handclasp and
Mosque — A32

**1972, Feb. 23　Litho.　Perf. 14½x14**

| | | | | |
|---|---|---|---|---|
| 152 | A31 | 5c blk, dp org & silver | .20 | .20 |
| 153 | A31 | 20c blk, dp lil rose & sil | .20 | .20 |
| 154 | A31 | 25c black, ultra & silver | .20 | .20 |
| 155 | A31 | 50c black, emerald & silver | .35 | .35 |
| | | Nos. 152-155 (4) | .95 | .95 |

Republic Day.

**1972, Apr. 3　　　　　Perf. 14**

| | | | | |
|---|---|---|---|---|
| 156 | A32 | 5c brown & multi | .20 | .20 |
| 157 | A32 | 25c blue & multi | .20 | .20 |
| 158 | A32 | 30c green & multi | .20 | .20 |
| 159 | A32 | 60c yellow brn & multi | .30 | .30 |
| | | Nos. 156-159 (4) | .90 | .90 |

Youman Nabi (Peaceful Prophet), Moham-
medan festival.

Map of South
America, Emblem
of Non-aligned
Countries — A33

CARIFESTA '72
Emblem — A34

**1972, July 20**

| | | | | |
|---|---|---|---|---|
| 160 | A33 | 8c violet & multi | .20 | .20 |
| 161 | A33 | 25c yellow grn & multi | .20 | .20 |
| 162 | A33 | 40c orange & multi | .20 | .20 |
| 163 | A33 | 50c red brown & multi | .25 | .25 |
| | | Nos. 160-163 (4) | .85 | .85 |

Conf. of Foreign Ministers of Nonaligned
Countries, Georgetown, Aug. 7-12.

For overprints & surcharges see #573, 611,
O17.

**1972, Aug. 25**

| | | | | |
|---|---|---|---|---|
| 164 | A34 | 8c orange & multi | .20 | .20 |
| 165 | A34 | 25c orange & multi | .20 | .20 |
| 166 | A34 | 40c orange & multi | .20 | .25 |
| 167 | A34 | 50c orange & multi | .25 | .35 |
| | | Nos. 164-167 (4) | .85 | 1.00 |

Caribbean Festival of Arts (CARIFESTA),
Georgetown, Aug. 25-Sept. 15.

Holy Family — A35

**1972, Oct. 18　Litho.　Perf. 13x13½**

| | | | | |
|---|---|---|---|---|
| 168 | A35 | 8c blue & multi | .20 | .20 |
| 169 | A35 | 25c blue & multi | .20 | .20 |
| 170 | A35 | 40c blue & multi | .20 | .25 |
| 171 | A35 | 50c blue & multi | .20 | .30 |
| | | Nos. 168-171 (4) | .80 | .95 |

Christmas.

Umana Yana
(Meeting Place of
Wai Wai
Chiefs) — A36

**1973, Feb. 23　Litho.　Perf. 14x14½**

Designs: 25c, 40c, Bethel Chapel.

| | | | | |
|---|---|---|---|---|
| 172 | A36 | 8c brt blue & multi | .20 | .20 |
| 173 | A36 | 25c rose red & multi | .20 | .20 |
| 174 | A36 | 40c emerald & multi | .25 | .20 |
| 175 | A36 | 50c black & multi | .35 | .25 |
| | | Nos. 172-175 (4) | 1.00 | .85 |

Republic Day.

Pomegranate, Fertility and Church
Symbol — A37

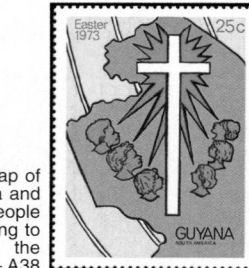

Map of
Guyana and
People
Looking to
the
Cross — A38

**1973, Apr. 19　　Perf. 14x14½, 13½**

| | | | | |
|---|---|---|---|---|
| 176 | A37 | 8c pink & multi | .20 | .20 |
| 177 | A38 | 25c yellow & multi | .20 | .20 |
| 178 | A38 | 40c ultra & multi | .20 | .20 |
| 179 | A37 | 50c yellow & multi | .20 | .20 |
| | | Nos. 176-179 (4) | .80 | .80 |

Easter.

Symbolic of Blood
Donation — A39

**Perf. 14x14½**

**1973, Oct. 1　　　　Wmk. 364**

| | | | | |
|---|---|---|---|---|
| 180 | A39 | 8c red & black | .20 | .20 |
| 181 | A39 | 25c red & lilac | .25 | .20 |
| 182 | A39 | 40c red & vio blue | .40 | .50 |
| 183 | A39 | 50c red & brown | .65 | .90 |
| | | Nos. 180-183 (4) | 1.50 | 1.80 |

Guyana Red Cross, 25th anniversary.

Steel Band, Star,
Pegasus
Hotel — A40

Madonna
and Child,
St. Philip's
Anglican
Church,
Georgetown
A41

**1973, Nov. 20　Litho.　Perf. 14x14½**

| | | | | |
|---|---|---|---|---|
| 184 | A40 | 8c lilac & multi | .20 | .20 |
| 185 | A40 | 25c lilac & multi | .25 | .20 |

**Perf. 13½x14**

| | | | | |
|---|---|---|---|---|
| 186 | A41 | 40c violet blue & multi | .40 | .70 |
| 187 | A41 | 50c violet blue & multi | .40 | .70 |
| | | Nos. 184-187 (4) | 1.25 | 1.80 |

Christmas.

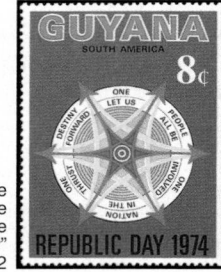

"One
People, One
Nation, One
Destiny"
A42

Designs: 25c, 50c, Wai Wai Indian.

**1974, Feb. 23　Litho.　Perf. 13½**

| | | | | |
|---|---|---|---|---|
| 188 | A42 | 8c multicolored | .20 | .20 |
| 189 | A42 | 25c multicolored | .20 | .20 |
| 190 | A42 | 40c multicolored | .20 | .30 |
| 191 | A42 | 50c multicolored | .20 | .40 |
| | | Nos. 188-191 (4) | .80 | 1.10 |

Republic Day.

No. 137 Surcharged with New Value
and 2 Bars

**Perf. 13x13½**

**1974, Mar. 18　　　　Wmk. 364**

| | | | | |
|---|---|---|---|---|
| 192 | A28 | 8c on 6c multi | .35 | .35 |

For overprints and surcharges see Nos.
424, 459, 474-478, 1453, 1500, 1780.

Crucifix Super-imposed on Eddy Bow
Kite — A43

Crucifix in Pre-Columbian Timehri
Style — A44

**1974, Apr. 8**     **Perf. 13½x14**
| | | | | |
|---|---|---|---|---|
| 193 | A43 | 8c green & multi | .20 | .20 |
| 194 | A44 | 25c black, green & gray | .20 | .20 |
| 195 | A44 | 40c black, gray & car | .20 | .20 |
| 196 | A43 | 50c gold & multi | .20 | .20 |
| | | Nos. 193-196 (4) | .80 | .80 |

Easter.

UPU Emblem and British Guiana Type of 1863 — A45

Mailman and UPU Emblem A46

**1974, June 18   Litho.   Perf. 14, 14½**
| | | | | |
|---|---|---|---|---|
| 197 | A45 | 8c rose & multi | .50 | .25 |
| 198 | A46 | 25c yellow green & multi | .60 | .25 |
| 199 | A46 | 40c blue & multi | .60 | .40 |
| 200 | A46 | 50c yellow green & multi | .80 | .55 |
| | | Nos. 197-200 (4) | 2.50 | 1.45 |

Centenary of Universal Postal Union.

Girl Guides Holding Banner A47

Designs: 25c, 40c, Guides in camp cooking and carrying water. 50c, Like 8c.

**1974, Aug. 1**     **Perf. 14½**
| | | | | |
|---|---|---|---|---|
| 201 | A47 | 8c multicolored | .25 | .20 |
| 202 | A47 | 25c multicolored | .35 | .20 |
| 203 | A47 | 40c multicolored | .60 | .40 |
| 204 | A47 | 50c multicolored | .60 | .50 |
| a. | | Souvenir sheet of 4, #201-204 | 2.50 | 2.50 |
| | | Nos. 201-204 (4) | 1.80 | 1.30 |

Girl Guides of Guyana, 50th anniv. For overprints see Nos. 574, 1352.

Buck Toyeau — A48

Christmas (Fruit): 35c, Carambola (starfruit) and awaras. 50c, Pawpaw and tangerine. $1, Pineapple and sapodillas.

**1974, Nov. 18   Litho.   Perf. 14x13½**
| | | | | |
|---|---|---|---|---|
| 205 | A48 | 8c multicolored | .20 | .20 |
| 206 | A48 | 25c multicolored | .20 | .20 |
| 207 | A48 | 50c multicolored | .25 | .20 |
| 208 | A48 | $1 multicolored | .40 | .75 |
| a. | | Souvenir sheet of 4, #205-208 | 1.40 | 3.00 |
| | | Nos. 205-208 (4) | 1.05 | 1.35 |

For overprints & surcharges see #551, 612, 716.

No. 135 Surcharged with New Value and Two Bars

**1975, Jan. 20   Litho.   Perf. 13x13½**
| | | | | |
|---|---|---|---|---|
| 209 | A28 | 8c on 3c multi | .40 | .40 |

For surcharge see No. 423.

Golden Arrow of Courage — A49

Republic Day: 35c, Cacique's Crown of Honour. 50c, Cacique's Crown of Valour. $1, Order of Excellence.

**1975, Feb. 23**     **Perf. 13x13½**
| | | | | |
|---|---|---|---|---|
| 210 | A49 | 10c brown & multi | .20 | .20 |
| 211 | A49 | 35c brown red & multi | .20 | .20 |
| 212 | A49 | 50c green & multi | .20 | .25 |
| 213 | A49 | $1 violet bl & multi | .35 | .50 |
| | | Nos. 210-213 (4) | .95 | 1.15 |

For overprints and surcharges see Nos. 360, 368, 398, 637, 1359.

Old Sluice Gate — A50

Modern Sluice Gate A51

**1975, May 2**     **Perf. 14**
| | | | | |
|---|---|---|---|---|
| 214 | A50 | 10c bister & multi | .20 | .20 |
| 215 | A51 | 35c brown & multi | .20 | .20 |
| 216 | A50 | 50c bister & multi | .20 | .25 |
| 217 | A51 | $1 green & multi | .35 | .50 |
| a. | | Souvenir sheet of 4, #214-217 | 1.25 | 2.50 |
| | | Nos. 214-217 (4) | .95 | 1.15 |

Intl. Commission on Irrigation and Drainage, 25th anniv.
For overprints see Nos. 361, 592, 794-795, 1374-1375.

IWY Emblem, Symbolic Man and Woman A52

Designs: IWY emblem and petroglyph designs of men and women.

**1975, July 1   Litho.   Wmk. 364**
| | | | | |
|---|---|---|---|---|
| 218 | A52 | 10c yellow & dull grn | .20 | .20 |
| 219 | A52 | 35c Prus blue & pur | .20 | .20 |
| 220 | A52 | 50c orange & dk blue | .25 | .25 |
| 221 | A52 | $1 ultra & brown | .40 | .40 |
| a. | | Souvenir sheet of 4, #218-221, perf. 14½ | 1.75 | 3.00 |
| | | Nos. 218-221 (4) | 1.05 | 1.05 |

Intl. Women's Year. For overprints and surcharges see Nos. 362, 399, 555.

Freedom Monument, Georgetown A53

"GNS," Flower and Clasped Hands A54

Designs: Various views of Freedom Monument, Georgetown.

**1975, Aug. 26   Litho.   Perf. 14**
| | | | | |
|---|---|---|---|---|
| 222 | A53 | 10c gray & multi | .20 | .20 |
| 223 | A53 | 35c yellow & multi | .20 | .20 |
| 224 | A53 | 50c lilac & multi | .25 | .25 |
| 225 | A53 | $1 olive & multi | .35 | .35 |
| | | Nos. 222-225 (4) | 1.00 | 1.00 |

Namibia Day (independence for South-West Africa).
For overprints and surcharges see Nos. 330, 582, 593, 619, 1360.

**1975, Oct. 2   Wmk. 364   Perf. 14**

"GNS" and Clasped hands: 35c, Wheel. 50c, Soccer ball. $1, Uniform cap.
| | | | | |
|---|---|---|---|---|
| 226 | A54 | 10c violet, yel & grn | .20 | .20 |
| 227 | A54 | 35c brt bl, org & grn | .20 | .20 |
| 228 | A54 | 50c lt brn, brt bl & grn | .25 | .25 |
| 229 | A54 | $1 grn, vio & brt grn | .35 | .35 |
| a. | | Souvenir sheet of 4, #226-229 | 1.25 | 2.00 |
| | | Nos. 226-229 (4) | 1.00 | 1.00 |

Guyana National Service, 1st anniv. For overprint & surcharges see #448, 636, 638.

Foresters' Building and Badge A55

35c, Rock painting of hunter. 50c, Crossed axes and hunting horn. $1, Bow and arrow.

**1975, Nov. 14   Litho.   Wmk. 364**
| | | | | |
|---|---|---|---|---|
| 230 | A55 | 10c red, black & gold | .20 | .20 |
| 231 | A55 | 35c red, black & gold | .20 | .20 |
| 232 | A55 | 50c gold & multi | .25 | .25 |
| 233 | A55 | $1 gold & multi | .35 | .35 |
| a. | | Souvenir sheet of 4, #230-233 | 1.25 | 2.25 |
| | | Nos. 230-233 (4) | 1.00 | 1.00 |

Ancient Order of Foresters, centenary.
For overprints and surcharges see Nos. 356, 363, 400, 422, 583.

No. 144 Surcharged

**1976, Feb. 10**     **Perf. 13½**
| | | | | |
|---|---|---|---|---|
| 234 | A28 | 35c on 60c multi | .40 | .40 |

For overprints see Nos. 703-703b, 852.

St. John Ambulance Emblem — A56

Independence Arch, 1966 — A57

**1976, Mar. 29   Litho.   Perf. 14**
| | | | | |
|---|---|---|---|---|
| 235 | A56 | 8c black, lil rose & sil | .20 | .20 |
| 236 | A56 | 15c black, orange & sil | .20 | .20 |
| 237 | A56 | 35c black, emer & silver | .25 | .25 |
| 238 | A56 | 40c black, blue & sil | .30 | .30 |
| | | Nos. 235-238 (4) | .95 | .95 |

Guyana St. John Ambulance, 50th anniv. For surcharges see Nos. 715, 717, 1411.

**1976, May 25**     **Perf. 13½**

Stylized Designs: 15c, Victoria regia. 35c, Letter "S" for socialism. 40c, Worker with pitchfork.
| | | | | |
|---|---|---|---|---|
| 239 | A57 | 8c silver & multi | .20 | .20 |
| 240 | A57 | 15c silver & multi | .20 | .20 |
| 241 | A57 | 35c silver & multi | .20 | .20 |

| | | | | |
|---|---|---|---|---|
| 242 | A57 | 40c silver & multi | .20 | .20 |
| a. | | Souvenir sheet of 4, #239-242, perf. 14 | 1.00 | 1.50 |
| | | Nos. 239-242 (4) | .80 | .80 |

10th anniv. of independence. For surcharges see Nos. 567, 639, 1444.

Map of West Indies, Bats, Wicket and Ball A57a

Prudential Cup — A57b

**Unwmk.**

**1976, Aug. 3   Litho.   Perf. 14**
| | | | | |
|---|---|---|---|---|
| 243 | A57a | 15c light blue & multi | 1.25 | 1.75 |
| 244 | A57b | 15c lilac rose & black | 1.25 | 1.75 |

World Cricket Cup, won by West Indies Team, 1975.
For overprints & surcharges see #352-353, 653-654.

Lamp — A58

Guitar-Sitar, Benin Head — A59

Designs: 15c, Hand and flame. 35c, Flame. 40c, Lakshmi, Hindu goddess of wealth.

**1976, Oct. 21**     **Perf. 14**
| | | | | |
|---|---|---|---|---|
| 245 | A58 | 8c multicolored | .20 | .20 |
| 246 | A58 | 15c orange & multi | .20 | .20 |
| 247 | A58 | 35c purple & multi | .25 | .25 |
| 248 | A58 | 40c ultra & multi | .30 | .30 |
| a. | | Souvenir sheet of 4, #245-248 | 1.40 | 1.75 |
| | | Nos. 245-248 (4) | .95 | .95 |

Deepavali, Hindu Festival of Lights. For surcharges see Nos. 719-721.

**1977, Feb. 1   Litho.   Perf. 14½**
| | | | | |
|---|---|---|---|---|
| 249 | A59 | 10c gold & multi | .20 | .20 |
| 250 | A59 | 35c gold & multi | .20 | .20 |
| 251 | A59 | 50c gold & multi | .35 | .35 |
| 252 | A59 | $1 gold & multi | .50 | .50 |
| a. | | Souvenir sheet of 4, #249-252 | 1.60 | 3.50 |
| | | Nos. 249-252 (4) | 1.25 | 1.25 |

2nd World Black and African Festival, Lagos, Nigeria, Jan. 15-Feb. 12. Nos. 249-252a were not issued without black bar.
For overprints see Nos. 364, 369, 584.

1c and 5c Coins A60

Coins (Obverse): 15c, 10c and 25c. 35c, 50c and $1. 40c, $5 and $10. $1, $50 and $100. $2, Reverse, Coat of arms.

**1977, May 26**     **Perf. 14**
| | | | | |
|---|---|---|---|---|
| 253 | A60 | 8c multicolored | .35 | .35 |
| 254 | A60 | 15c multicolored | .40 | .40 |
| 255 | A60 | 35c multicolored | .70 | .70 |
| 256 | A60 | 40c multicolored | .85 | .85 |

**257** A60 $1 multicolored 1.25 1.25
**258** A60 $2 multicolored 2.00 2.00
*Nos. 253-258 (6)* 5.55 5.55

New coinage. For overprints and surcharges see Nos. 539-541, 568, 594, O18, O20, Q5.

Hand Pump, c. 1850 A61

National Fire Prevention Week: 15c, Steam engine, c. 1860. 35c, Fire engine, c. 1930. 40c, Fire engine, 1977.

*Perf. 14x14½*
**1977, Nov. 15 Litho. Wmk. 364**
**259** A61 8c multicolored 1.25 .20
**260** A61 15c multicolored 2.00 .20
**261** A61 35c multicolored 2.25 1.10
**262** A61 40c multicolored 2.50 1.25
*Nos. 259-262 (4)* 8.00 2.75

For surcharges see Nos. 1370-1371.

Cuffy Monument — A62

8c, 35c, Cuffy statue from monument.

**1977, Dec. 7 Litho. Perf. 14**
**263** A62 8c multicolored .20 .20
**264** A62 15c multicolored .20 .20
**265** A62 35c multicolored .20 .20
**266** A62 40c multicolored .20 .20
*Nos. 263-266 (4)* .80 .80

Cuffy, Guyana's national hero, led a slave revolution in 1763. The monument was unveiled in 1976. For overprints see Nos. 446, 569, 613.

Wildlife Protection — A63

**1978, Feb. 15 Perf. 14**
**267** A63 8c Manatee 1.00 .20
**268** A63 15c Giant sea turtle 1.25 .30
**269** A63 35c Harpy eagle 5.25 2.25
**270** A63 40c Iguana 5.00 2.25
*Nos. 267-270 (4)* 12.50 5.00

8c, 15c are horiz. For overprints and surcharges see Nos. 443, 722-723, 1416.

Parliament and Prime Minister Burnham — A64

Prime Minister and: 15c, Student and school children. 35c, Bauxite mine. 40c, Cooperative village.

**1978, Apr. 27 Litho. Perf. 13½x14**
**271** A64 8c violet & black .20 .20
**272** A64 15c gray, blk & bl .20 .20
**273** A64 35c multicolored .20 .20

**274** A64 40c gray, blk & org .20 .20
**a.** Souvenir sheet of 4, #271-274 1.10 1.75
*Nos. 271-274 (4)* .80 .80

Prime Minister Linden Forbes Burnham, 25th anniv. of his entry into parliament. For surcharges see Nos. 648-649.

Dr. George Giglioli, Anopheles Mosquito — A65

Agrias Claudina — A66

30c, Institute of Applied Science & Technology, proposed for University of Guyana. 50c, Map of Guyana & National Science Research Council emblem. 60c, Commonwealth Science Council emblem.

*Perf. 13½x14, 14x13½*
**1978, Sept. 4 Litho. Wmk. 364**
**275** A65 10c multi .20 .20
**276** A65 30c multi, horiz. .20 .20
**277** A65 50c multi .30 .30
**278** A65 60c multi, horiz. .40 .40
*Nos. 275-278 (4)* 1.10 1.10

For overprints see Nos. 577, 585, 590.

**1978-80 Perf. 14x13½**
**Size: 22x16mm**
**279** A66 5c Prepona pheridamas 2.25 .20
**280** A66 10c Archonias bellona 2.25 .20
**281** A66 15c Eryphanis polyxena 2.25 .20
**282** A66 20c Helicopis cupido 2.25 .20
**283** A66 25c Nessaea batesli 2.25 .20
**283A** A66 30c Nymphidium mantus ('80) 1.75 2.75
**284** A66 35c Siderone galanthis 2.25 .20
**285** A66 40c Morpho rethenor, male 2.25 .20
**286** A66 50c Hamadryas amphinone 2.25 .25
**286A** A66 60c Papilio androgeus ('80) 2.00 1.50

*Perf. 13½x13*
**287** A66 $1 Agrias claudina 5.25 .30
**288** A66 $2 Morpho rethenor, female 7.75 .60
**289** A66 $5 Morpho deidamia 8.75 1.25
**289A** A66 $10 Elbella patrobas, perf. 14 ('80) 6.75 5.25
*Nos. 279-289A (14)* 50.25 13.30

Issued: #279-283, 284-286, 287-289, 10/1/78. For overprints and surcharges see Nos. 391, 406, 436-436A, 481, 486, 554, 668-670, 733-743, 871, 936-939, 944, 969, 1373, 1418, 1455, 1786, 1812, 1814, 1832-1833, 1873, 1901, 1912-1913, 1984-1988, 2051, 2053, 2054C, 2055, 2057, 2057B-2057C, 2058-2059, 2082-2111, C5-C6, O15-O16, O23-O29.

Indian Making Stone Chip Grater — A67

UNESCO Emblem and: 30c, Arawak Cassiri jar and decorated Amerindian jar. 50c, Gate to old Dutch fort, Kykover-al. 60c, Fort Island, Dutch ruins.

**1978, Dec. 27 Wmk. 364 Perf. 14**
**290** A67 10c green & multi .20 .20
**291** A67 30c green & multi .20 .20
**292** A67 50c green & multi .25 .25
**293** A67 60c green & multi .25 .25
*Nos. 290-293 (4)* .90 .90

National and International Heritage Year. For surcharges see Nos. 604-606.

Earth Station at Dawn, Georgetown A68

Designs: 30c, Earth Station in daylight, Georgetown. 50c, Intelsat V. $3, Intelsat IVa.

**1979, Feb. 7 Litho. Perf. 14x14½**
**294** A68 10c multicolored .20 .20
**295** A68 30c multicolored .25 .20
**296** A68 50c multicolored .40 .20
**297** A68 $3 multicolored 1.40 1.40
*Nos. 294-297 (4)* 2.25 2.00

For surcharges see Nos. 384, 655, 714, 1376-1377, 1380, O9.

British Guyana No. 5 — A69

Designs: 30c, British Guiana No. 13, vert. 50c, British Guiana No. 152. $3, Printing press used for 1c Magenta, vert.

**1979, June 11 Wmk. 364 Perf. 14**
**298** A69 10c multicolored .20 .20
**299** A69 30c multicolored .30 .20
**300** A69 50c multicolored .40 .20
**301** A69 $3 multicolored .60 .60
*Nos. 298-301 (4)* 1.50 1.20

Sir Rowland Hill (1795-1879), originator of penny postage.
For overprints & surcharges see #409, 426, 428, 449, 479, 480, 578, 586, 598, 614, O6.

"Fun with the Fowls" and IYC Emblem — A70

Children's Drawings and IYC Emblem: 10c, "Me and my sister," vert. 50c, "Two boys catching ducks." $3, "Mango season."

**1979, Aug. 20 Litho. Perf. 13½**
**302** A70 10c multicolored .20 .20
**303** A70 30c multicolored .20 .20
**304** A70 50c multicolored .35 .35
**305** A70 $3 multicolored 1.00 1.50
*Nos. 302-305 (4)* 1.75 2.25

Intl. Year of the Child. For overprints and surcharges see Nos. 435, 579, 587, 599, 615, 943.

H. N. Critchlow, Worker Hauling Sack — A71

Critchlow and: 30c, Baker, horiz. 50c, Flag and crowd. $3, Portrait only.

**1979, Sept. 27 Litho. Perf. 14**
**306** A71 10c multicolored .20 .20
**307** A71 30c multicolored .20 .20
**308** A71 50c multicolored .25 .25
**309** A71 $3 multicolored .60 .90
*Nos. 306-309 (4)* 1.25 1.55

Guyana Labor Union, 60th anniversary. For surcharges see Nos. 403, 429, 718.

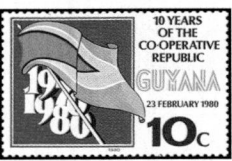

Cooperative Republic, 10th Anniv. — A72

**Wmk. 364**
**1980, Feb. 23 Litho. Perf. 14**
**313** A72 10c shown .20 .20
**314** A72 35c Demerara River Bridge .30 .20
**315** A72 60c Kaieteur Falls .50 .20
**316** A72 $3 Makanaima, American Indian .75 .75
*Nos. 313-316 (4)* 1.75 1.35

For overprints and surcharges see Nos. 365, 371, 450A, 442, 591, 656.

Miniature Sheet

Snoek, London 1980 Emblem A73

London 80 Emblem and Fish; a, Snoek. b, Haimara. c, Electric eel. d, Golden rivulus. e, Pencil fish. f, Four-eyed fish. g, Pirai. h, Smoking hassar. i, Devil ray. j, Flying patwa. k, Arapaima. l, Lukanani.

**1980, May 6 Wmk. 373 Perf. 14**
**317** Sheet of 12 6.50 6.50
**a.-l.** A73 35c any single .40 .40

London 1980 Intl. Stamp Exhib., May 6-14. For overprints & surcharges see #444, 725-726, 1414.

Children's Convalescent Home, Rotary Emblem — A74

Rotary International, 75th anniversary (Emblem and): 30c, Georgetown club emblem. 50c, District 404 emblem (hibiscus), vert. $3, Anniversary emblem, vert.

*Perf. 14x14½, 14½x14*
**1980, June 23 Litho. Wmk. 364**
**318** A74 10c multicolored .20 .20
**319** A74 30c multicolored .20 .20
**320** A74 50c multicolored .45 .50
**321** A74 $3 multicolored 1.25 1.25
*Nos. 318-321 (4)* 2.10 2.15

For overprints and surcharges see Nos. 552, 580, 601, C1.

Emblem and Caduceus A75

**Wmk. 364**
**1980, Sept. 23 Litho. Perf. 13½**
**322** A75 10c shown .20 .20
**323** A75 60c Scientist, beach scene .60 .30

| | | | |
|---|---|---|---|
| **324** | A75 | $3 Emblems over is-land | 1.50 1.25 |
| | | Nos. 322-324 (3) | 2.30 1.75 |

Commonwealth Caribbean Medical Research Council, 25th anniversary. For overprints and surcharges see Nos. 366, 427, 430, 494, 553.

Virola Surinamensis (Christmas 1980) — A76

| | | | |
|---|---|---|---|
| **1980, Nov. 1** | | **Wmk. 373** | **Perf. 14** |
| **325** | A76 | 10c shown | .20 .20 |
| **326** | A76 | 30c Hymenaea courbaril | .30 .20 |
| **327** | A76 | 50c Mora excelsa | .50 .35 |
| **328** | A76 | $3 Peltogyne venosa | 1.60 1.60 |
| | | Nos. 325-328 (4) | 2.60 2.35 |

For overprints and surcharges see Nos. 431, 773, 790, 792-793.

### Miniature Sheet

A77

Designs: a, Tree porcupine. b, Howler monkeys. c, Squirrel monkeys. d, Two-toed sloth. e, Tapir. f, Collared peccary. g, Six-banded armadillo. h, Anteater. i, Great anteaters. j, Mouse opossums. k, Four-eyed opossum. l, Orange-rumped agouti.

| | | | |
|---|---|---|---|
| **1981, Mar. 2** | | **Wmk. 364** | **Perf. 14** |
| **329** | | Sheet of 12 | 8.75 8.75 |
| **a.-l.** | A77 | 30c any single | .65 .65 |
| **m.** | | As #329g, perf. 12 | 3.25 .40 |

For overprints see #581, 819, 1399, 1503, 1844.

During 1981-91, there were numerous sources creating stamps for Guyana, with as many as 5-7 parties being active at any given time.

### No. 222 Surcharged

| | | | |
|---|---|---|---|
| **1981, May 4** | | | |
| **330** | A53 | $1.05 on 10c multi | 1.75 |

For surcharges see Nos. 396, 620.

### Nos. 135, 146-147 Surcharged

Nos. 145 and 147 Surcharged in Blue or Black

| | | | |
|---|---|---|---|
| **1981** | | **Litho.** | **Wmk. 364** | **Perf. 13½** |
| **331** | A28 | 60c on 3c #135 | 1.25 |
| **332** | A28 | 75c on $5 #147 | 1.50 |
| **333** | A28 | $1.10 on $2 #146 | 1.00 |

---

| | | | |
|---|---|---|---|
| **334** | A28 | $3.60 on $5 #147 (Blk) | 3.50 |
| **a.** | | Blue overprint | 3.50 |
| **335** | A28 | $7.20 on $1 #145 (Bl) | 3.50 |
| **a.** | | Black overprint | 5.00 |

No. 333 is airmail. Issue dates: $3.60, $7.20, May 6. Others July 22. Diagonal overprint on No. 332. Vertical overprint on No. 333. Location of surcharge varies.

See Nos. 621, 666-667, Q4, QO5. For overprints and surcharges see Nos. 378, 489-496, 547, 549, 646, 818, 867-868, O11, Q3, QO3.

Map of Guyana — A78

| | | | |
|---|---|---|---|
| **1981, May 11** | | **Photo.** | **Perf. 13½** |
| **336** | A78 | 10c on 3c multi | 1.00 |
| **337** | A78 | 30c on 2c multi | 1.00 |
| **338** | A78 | 50c on 2c multi | 1.00 |
| **339** | A78 | 60c on 2c multi | 1.00 |
| **340** | A78 | 75c on 3c multi | 1.00 |
| | | Nos. 336-340 (5) | 5.00 |

Revenue stamps surcharged for postal use. For similar stamp, see #934a. For surcharge see #503.

### Nos. J5-J8 Surcharged in Red, Black, or Brown

| | a | b |
|---|---|---|

| | | | |
|---|---|---|---|
| **1981, June 8** | | **Typo.** | **Perf. 13½x14** |

**Type "a"**

| | | | |
|---|---|---|---|
| **341** | D1 | 10c on 2c #J6 | |
| **342** | D1 | 15c on 12c #J8 (Blk) | |
| **343** | D1 | 20c on 1c #J5 | |
| **344** | D1 | 45c on 2c #J6 | |
| **345** | D1 | 55c on 4c #J7 | |
| **346** | D1 | 60c on 4c #J7 (Brn) | |
| **347** | D1 | 65c on 2c #J6 | |
| **348** | D1 | 70c on 4c #J7 | |
| **349** | D1 | 80c on 4c #J7 | |
| | | Nos. 341-349 (9) | 11.00 |

**Type "b"**

| | | | |
|---|---|---|---|
| **341a** | D1 | 10c on 2c #J6 | |
| **342a** | D1 | 15c on 12c #J8 (Blk) | |
| **343a** | D1 | 20c on 1c #J5 | |
| **344a** | D1 | 45c on 2c #J6 | |
| **345a** | D1 | 55c on 4c #J7 | |
| **347a** | D1 | 65c on 2c #J6 | |
| **348a** | D1 | 70c on 4c #J7 | |
| **349a** | D1 | 80c on 4c #J7 | |
| | | Nos. 341a-349a (8) | 11.00 |

Pairs with types a and b exist for all values except the 60c.

Nos. 48, 61-62, 74, 139, 142-143, 145-147, 212-213, 216, 220, 231-232, 243-244, 251-252, 315-316, and 323 Overprinted in Black or Red

| | | | |
|---|---|---|---|
| **1981** | | | **Perfs. as Before** |
| **Watermarks & Printing Methods as Before** | | | |
| **350** | A8 | 15c on #74 (R) | 17.50 |
| **351** | A28 | 15c on #139 | |
| **a.** | | Red overprint | 7.00 |
| **b.** | | On #139a, red overprint | 8.00 |
| **352** | A57a | 15c on #243 | 8.50 |
| **353** | A57b | 15c on #244 | 5.00 |
| **354** | A11 | 25c on #61 (R) | .75 |
| **355** | A11 | 30c on #62 (R) | .75 |
| **356** | A55 | 35c on #231 (R) | 3.00 |
| **357** | A8 | 40c on #48 | 12.00 |
| **358** | A28 | 40c on #142 | |
| **359** | A28 | 40c on #143 | 4.00 |
| **360** | A49 | 50c on #212 | 3.25 |
| **361** | A50 | 50c on #216 | 1.50 |
| **362** | A52 | 50c on #220 | 27.50 |
| **363** | A55 | 50c on #232 | 3.25 |

---

| | | | |
|---|---|---|---|
| **364** | A59 | 50c on #251 | 15.00 |
| **365** | A72 | 60c on #315 | .90 |
| **366** | A75 | 60c on #323 | .90 |
| **367** | A28 | $1 on #145 | 3.50 |
| **a.** | | Red overprint | 2.00 |
| **368** | A49 | $1 on #213 | 7.50 |
| **369** | A59 | $1 on #252 | 6.50 |
| **370** | A28 | $2 on #146 | 8.00 |
| **a.** | | Red overprint | 2.00 |
| **b.** | | Black ovpt. with serifs | 25.00 |
| **371** | A72 | $3 on #316 | 3.00 |
| **372** | A28 | $5 on #147 | 4.25 |
| | | Nos. 350-372 (23) | 50.00 |

Issued: #354-356, 367, 6/8; #350, 357, 370, 7/1; #351-353, 359-366, 368-369, 371-372, 7/7.

Location and size of overprint varies. Refer to second paragraph in footnote following No. 147 for Nos. 358-359.

For surcharges and overprints see Nos. 556, 607, 659, 745, 849-850, 1362.

Nos. 68, 135-136, 139, 145-147, 297, 333 Surcharged or Overprinted

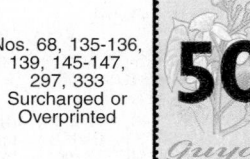

| | | | |
|---|---|---|---|
| **1981** | | **Litho.** | **Perfs. as Before** |
| **Watermarks & Printing Methods as Before** | | | |
| **373** | A8 | 15c on 1c #68 | 1.10 |
| **374** | A28 | 50c on 5c #136 | 2.50 |
| **375** | A28 | 75c on 5c #136 | 30.00 |
| **375A** | A28 | 80c on 15c #139 | |
| **376** | A8 | 100c on 1c #68 | 1.00 |
| **377** | A8 | 110c on 1c #68 | 1.00 |
| **a.** | | Strip of 3, #373, 376-377 | 7.00 |
| **378** | A28 | $1.10 on #333 | 17.50 |
| **379** | A28 | 120c on $1 #145 | 2.50 |
| **380** | A28 | 140c on $1 #145 | 2.50 |
| **381** | A28 | 150c on $2 #146 | 2.50 |
| **382** | A28 | 210c on $5 #147 | 30.00 |
| **383** | A28 | 220c on 5c #136 | 30.00 |
| **384** | A68 | 220c on $3 #297 | 4.50 |
| **385** | A28 | 250c on $5 #147 | 2.75 |
| **386** | A28 | 280c on $5 #147 | 2.75 |
| **387** | A28 | 360c on $2 #146 | 3.50 |
| **388** | A28 | 375c on $5 #147 | 3.00 |
| **389** | A28 | $7.20 on $5 #135 | 110.00 |
| **390** | A28 | 720c on 60c #144 | 3.75 |
| **390A** | A28 | $20 on 5c #136 | |

Location and size of surcharge and obliterator varies. Obliterator is an "X" on Nos. 381-388, 390, two solid boxes on Nos. 379-380, and five bars on No. 389. Numeral "7" is placed before 5 make surcharge on No. 375. "Royal Wedding 1981" obliterated by three bars on No. 378. New denomination on No. 375A does not have cent sign. Obliterator on No. 390A is three horizontal bars.

Refer to second paragraph in footnote following No. 147 for Nos. 381, 387 and 390. Nos. 376-378 are airmail.

Issued: #375, 382, 6/8; #373-374, 376-388, 390, 7/1.

For overprint and surcharges see Nos. 408, 788, 859-860, 863-864, 1379, 1417.

### No. 281 Overprinted "ESSEQUIBO / IS OURS"

| | | | |
|---|---|---|---|
| **1981, July** | | **Litho.** | **Perf. 14x13½** |
| **391** | A66 | 15c on #281 | 6.75 |
| **a.** | | Ovpt. without serifs | |

Nos. 87, 95-96, 142, 146, 210, 218, 230, 309, 330, O15 Surcharged

| | | | |
|---|---|---|---|
| **1981** | | | **Perfs. as Before** |
| **Watermarks & Printing Methods as Before** | | | |
| **392** | A17 | 55c on 6c #95 | 4.50 |
| **393** | A14 | 70c on 6c #87 | 1.25 |
| **394** | A14 | 100c on 6c #87 | 1.50 |
| **395** | A17 | 100c on 8c #96 | 4.50 |
| **396** | A53 | 100c on #330 | |
| | | (surcharge reading down | 40.00 |
| **a.** | | Surcharge reading up | 50.00 |
| **397** | A17 | 110c on 6c #95 | 3.00 |
| **398** | A49 | 110c on 10c #210 | 3.00 |
| **399** | A52 | 110c on 10c #218 | 7.25 |
| **400** | A55 | 110c on 10c #230 | 7.25 |
| **401** | A28 | 125c on $2 #146 | 16.50 |

---

| | | | |
|---|---|---|---|
| **402** | A17 | 180c on 6c #95 | 4.50 |
| **403** | A71 | 240c on $3 #309 | 10.50 |
| **404** | A17 | 400c on 6c #95 | 4.50 |
| **405** | A17 | $4.40 on 6c #95 | 2.25 |
| **a.** | | Fours same size | 11.00 |
| **406** | A66 | 550c on $10 #O15 | 10.00 |
| **407** | A28 | 625c on 40c #142 | 17.50 |

Issued: #392, 394-395, 397-399, 405, 405a, 407, July 7; #393, 402-404, 406, Sept. 15. Refer to 2nd paragraph in footnote following #147 for #407. For overprints and surcharges see #651-652, 996, 1858-1859, 1861, O8, O10, O12.

No. 383 Ovptd. "Espana 82"
No. 301 Surcharged "1831-1981 / Von Stephan"

**Perfs. as Before**

| | | | |
|---|---|---|---|
| **1981, July 22** | | **Litho.** | **Wmk. 364** |
| **408** | A28 | 220c on #383 | 2.50 |
| **409** | A69 | 330c on $3 #301 | 3.00 |

For surcharges see Nos. 616, 622.

### Nos. 43, 72 Surcharged

| | | | |
|---|---|---|---|
| **1981** | | **Photo. Unwmk.** | **Perf. 14x14½** |
| **410** | A7 | 12c on 12c on 6c #43 | |
| **411** | A7 | Pair, #a.-b. | |
| **a.** | | 15c on 10c on 6c #43 | |
| **b.** | | 15c on 30c on 6c #43 | |
| **412** | A7 | Pair, #a.-b. | |
| **a.** | | 15c on 50c on 6c #43 | |
| **b.** | | 15c on 60c on 6c #43 | |
| **413** | A7 | Strip of 3, #a.-c. | |
| **a.** | | 12c on 6c #43 | |
| **b.** | | 50c on 6c #43 | |
| **c.** | | $1 on 6c #43 | |

**Wmk. 364**

| | | | |
|---|---|---|---|
| **413D** | A7 | Strip of 3, #e.-g. | |
| **e.** | | 12c On 6c #72 | |
| **f.** | | 50c On 6c #72 | |
| **g.** | | $1 On 6c #72 | |

Issue dates: Nos. 410-412, Aug. 24. No. 413-413D, Nov. 10.

Nos. 410-412 were not issued without large numeral surcharges. Obliterator is black box on Nos. 410-412, "X" on Nos. 413a & 413De. Nos. 413b-413c, 413Df-g are airmail.

For overprints and surcharges see Nos. 728-728a, 914, 994, 994a, 1400-1401.

16th Anniv. of the
Guyana Defense
Force — A79

**1981, Oct. 1　Wmk. 364　Perf. 13½**
414 A79　15c on 10c Armed
　　　　　Ranger, 1772　　　.25　.20
415 A79　50c Private, Foot Reg-
　　　　　iment, 1825　　　.65　.40
416 A79　$1 on 30c Marine
　　　　　Private, 1775　　1.25　1.25
417 A79 $1.10 on $3 Defense
　　　　　Force officers,
　　　　　1966　　　　　1.50　1.50
　　　Nos. 414-417 (4)　　　3.65　3.35
　Nos. 414, 416-417 not issued without
surcharge. For overprints see Nos. 570, 588,
595, 1368-1369.

Louis Braille and Boy Reading
Braille — A80

　Intl. Year of the Disabled: 50c, Helen Keller
and Rajkumari Singh. $1, Beethoven and
Sonny Thomas. $1.10, Renoir and painting.

**1981, Nov. 2　　　　Perf. 13½x14**
418 A80　15c on 10c multi　　.20　.20
419 A80　50c multi　　　　　.50　.40
420 A80　$1 on 60c multi　　.90　.80
421 A80 $1.10 on $3 multi　1.10　1.10
　　　Nos. 418-421 (4)　　　2.70　2.50
　Nos. 418, 420-421 not issued without
surcharge. For overprints and surcharge see
#571, 589, 596, 1913A.

Nos. 192, 209, 230, 298, 301, 309,
322, 324, 328, O1 Surcharged in Blue
or Red

**1981, Nov. 14　　　Perfs. as Before**
**Watermarks & Printing Methods as
Before**
422 A55　110c on 10c #230　　5.00
423 A28　110c on #209　　　5.00
424 A28　110c on #192　　　5.00
425 A28　110c on #O1　　　3.75
426 A69　110c on 10c #298 (R)　2.75
427 A75　110c on 10c #322　15.00
428 A69　110c on $3 #301 (R)　2.50
429 A71　110c on $3 #309　　8.00
430 A75　110c on $3 #324　　3.00
　a.　Red surcharge　　　　8.00
431 A76　110c on $3 #328　　6.00
　a.　Red surcharge　　　　55.00
　　　Nos. 422-431 (10)　　56.00
　Nos. 423-424 were issued with two 110c
surcharges of different sizes. Refer to second
paragraph in footnote below No. 147 for No.
425. For overprints and surcharges see Nos.
791, 820, 855, 1000, 1364-1366.

Flower Type of 1971-76 Surcharged
**1981, Nov. 24　Photo.　Perf. 15x14**
**Size: 20x23mm**
**Coil Stamps**
433 A28　15c on 2c like #134　　.35
434 A28　15c on 8c Mazaruni
　　　　　Pride　　　　　　.35
　a.　Pair, #433-434　　　　1.10
　Nos. 433-434 were not issued without
surcharge. See Nos. 731-732.

No. 305 Surcharged
"U.N.I.C.E.F. / 1946-1981"
**Wmk. 364**
**1981, Nov. 14　Litho.　Perf. 13½**
435 A70 125c on $3 #305　　3.25
　For surcharge see No. 942.

---

No. 279 Surcharged "Nov. 81" (#436)
or "Cancun 81" (#436A)
**1981, Nov. 14　　　Perf. 14x13½**
436 A66　50c on 5c #279
436A A66　50c on 5c #279　　6.50

Conversion to
Metric System,
Jan. 2 — A81

　a, Tape measure. b, Juggler. c, Man, envelope. d, Baby on scale. e, Canje Bridge. f, Liter
bucket.

**Perf. 14½x14**
**1982, Jan. 18　　　　Wmk. 364**
437 A81 15c Sheet of 6, #a.-f.　3.25　3.25
　For surcharge see No. 557.

Nos. 61, 63, 139, 140, 141A, 143-144,
146-147, 228, 266, 269, 300, 314 and
316-317 Ovptd. "1982" Vertically or
Horizontally in Blue or Violet

**1982-83　　　　Perfs. as Before**
**Watermarks & Printing Methods as
Before**
438 A28　15c on #139　　　8.00
　a.　On #139a　　　　65.00
439 A28　20c on #140　　　4.00
440 A28　25c on #141A　　6.50
441 A11　25c on #61 (V)　　2.00
442 A72　35c on #314　　　1.00
443 A63　35c on #269　　　6.00
444 A73　35c on block of 6,
　　　　　#317a-317f　　20.00
445 A11　40c on #63 (V)　　1.00
446 A62　40c on #266　　　1.00
447 A28　50c on #143　　　3.00
448 A54　50c on #228　　　2.00
449 A69　50c on #300　　　1.00
449A A28　60c on #144　　　7.00
450 A28　$2 on #146　　　1.50
450A A72　$3 on #316　　　2.25
451 A28　$5 on #147　　　1.50
　　　Nos. 438-451 (16)　　67.75
　Issued: #439-441, 2/8; #450-451, 4/23;
#445-446, 4/27; #438, 6/17; #443-444, 8/16;
#442, 9/15; #447-449, 10/11; #449A, 7/1/83;
#450A, 11/3/83.
　For other stamps overprinted "1982" only,
see Nos 482-483, 555.
　For overprints and surcharges see Nos.
600, 806, 809, 813-814, 851, 999, 1354, 1415.

Nos. 97, O3, O4, O9-O10 Ovptd.
"POSTAGE" in Blue
**1982　　　　　Perfs. as Before**
**Watermarks and Printing Methods
as Before**
452 A28　15c on #O3　　　10.00
453 A17　25c on #97　　　6.00
454 A28　50c on #O4　　　1.50
455 A68 100c on #O9　　　2.50
456 A17 110c on #O10　　　3.00
　For surcharge see No. 853. For similar overprints see Nos. 729-730. Refer to second paragraph in footnote following No. 147 for No.
454.

Nos. 133, 137, 142, and 192
Surcharged in Blue or Green

**Perfs. as Before**
**1982　　Litho.　　Wmk. 364**
457 A28　20c on 6c #137　　.90
458 A28　20c on 6c #137 (G)　.90
459 A28 125c on #192　　　.90

---

460 A28 180c on #142 ovpt.
　　　　　"1982"　　　5.75
461 A28 220c on 1c #133　　2.00
　　　Nos. 457-461 (5)　　10.45
　No. 458 has no obliterator, "20c" is 23mm
long.
　Issued: #457-459, 2/8; #460, 4/8; #461,
4/23.
　Refer to 2nd paragraph in footnote following
#147 for #460.
　For overprints see #755, 856, 862.

Savings
Campaign
A81a

**1982　　Litho.　　Perf. 14½**
462 A81a　$1 Soldier & flag　　.60
463 A81a $1.10 on $5, two
　　　　　soldiers, flag　　7.00
　a.　Inverted comma before "OURS"
　Size of obliterator differs on Nos. 463 and
463a. Nos. 462-463a are revenue stamps
ovptd. for postal use.
　Issued: #462, 2/8; #463, 3/3; #463a, 7/13.

Nos. 134, 136, & 192 Surcharged in
Black or Green
"BADEN-POWELL / 1857-1982"
(#464a, 465a, 466a)
"Scout Movement / 1907-1982"
(#464b, 465b, 466b)
"1907-1982" (#464c, 465c, 466c)
"1857-1982" (#464d, 465d, 466d)
"1982" (#464e, 465e, 466e)

**Perf. 13x13½**
**1982, Feb. 22　Litho.　Wmk. 364**
**Sheets of 25**
464　　8 #a.-b., 4 #c.-d., 1
　　　　#e.　　　　　　9.00
　a.-e.　A28 15c on 2c #134, any sin-
　　　　gle　　　　　　　.40
465　　8 #a.-b., 4 #c.-d., 1
　　　　#e.　　　　　　20.00
　a.-e.　A28 110c on 5c #136, any
　　　　single　　　　　　.80
466　　8 #a.-b., 4 #c.-d., 1
　　　　#e.　　　　　　20.00
　a.-e.　A28 125c on #192, any single
　　　　(G)　　　　　　.80
　Lord Robert Baden-Powell, 125th anniv. of
birth. Boy Scout Movement, 75th anniv.
　For overprints and surcharges see Nos.
558, 778-784, 836-837, 1347.

Nos. 289, 299, 301 Surcharged or
Overprinted in Black or Blue

**Perfs. as Before**
**1982, Feb. 15　Litho.　Wmk. 364**
479 A69 100c on $3 #301　1.75　.50
480 A69 400c on 30c #299　2.50　2.00
481 A66　$5 #289 (Bl)　11.50　7.50
　　　Nos. 479-481 (3)　　15.75
　For surcharges see Nos. 617, 904-906, 937-
939, O22-O29.

Nos. 88-89 Ovptd. "1982" in Blue and
Nos. 87, 90 Surcharged in Blue or
Red
**1982, Mar. 15　Photo.　Perf. 13**
482 A14　25c on #88
483 A14　30c on #89
484 A14　45c on 6c #87
485 A14　75c on 40c #90 (R)
　　　Nos. 482-485 (4)　　2.50
　For overprints see Nos. 766-767.

---

Nos. 60, 284, 324, and 331-333
Surcharged in Black or Blue

**1982　　　　　Perfs. as Before**
**Watermarks & Printing Methods as
Before**
486 A66　20c on 35c #284　　7.50
487 A11　80c on 6c #60 (Bl)　3.00
488 A11　85c on 6c #60 (Bl)　3.00
489 A28　85c on #331　　　5.00
490 A28　130c on #331　　　3.00
491 A28 160c on #333 (Bl)　3.00
　a.　Black surcharge　　　5.00
492 A28　170c on #333　　15.00
493 A28　210c on #332 (Bl)　3.00
494 A75　210c on $3 #324 (Bl)　4.00
495 A28　235c on #332　　　4.00
　a.　Blue surcharge　　　9.00
496 A28 330c on #333　　　3.50
　　　Nos. 486-496 (11)　　54.00
　Nos. 491-491a, 492, & 496 are airmail.
Obliterators differ.
　Issue dates: #486, Mar. 15. Others, Apr. 27.
　For surcharges see Nos. 647, 1367.

Nos. 135, 137, 144 & 145 Overprinted
or Surcharged in Blue or Black
"ESPANA / 1982" or "ESPANA / 1982"
and "ITALY" (#499)
**Wmk. 364**
**1982, May 15　Litho.　Perf. 13½**
497 A28　$1 on #145 (Blk)　1.50
498 A28　110c on 3c #135　　1.50
499 A28 $2.35 on 180c on 60c
　　　　　#144　　　14.00
500 A28　250c on 6c #137　　2.00
　Refer to second paragraph in footnote below
No. 147 for No. 499.
　#499 not issued without $2.35 surcharge.
　See No. 597 for stamp with one-line Espana
1982 overprint. For surcharges see #774-777.

Map Revenue Type A78 Surcharged in
Black, Blue, or Red
**1982-83　Photo.　Wmk. 364　Perf. 13**
501 A78　15c on 2c (Bl)
502 A78　20c on 2c (Bl)
503 A78　20c on 10c #336
　　　　　(Bl)
504 A78　25c on 2c
　a.　Blue surcharge
　b.　Red surcharge　　　1.00
505 A78　30c on 2c (Bl)
506 A78　40c on 2c
　a.　Blue surcharge
507 A78　45c on 2c (Bl)
508 A78　50c on 2c (Bl)
509 A78　60c on 2c (Bl)
510 A78　75c on 2c (Bl)
511 A78　80c on 2c (Bl)
512 A78　85c on 2c (Bl)
513 A78　$1.00 on 3c
514 A78　$1.10 on 3c
515 A78　$1.20 on 3c
516 A78　$1.25 on 3c
517 A78　$1.30 on 3c
518 A78　$1.50 on 3c
519 A78　$1.60 on 3c
520 A78　$1.70 on 3c
521 A78　$1.75 on 3c
522 A78　$1.80 on 3c
523 A78　$2.00 on 3c
524 A78　$2.10 on 3c
525 A78　$2.20 on 3c
526 A78　$2.35 on 3c
527 A78　$2.40 on 3c
528 A78　$2.50 on 3c
529 A78　$3.00 on 3c
530 A78　$3.30 on 3c
531 A78　$3.75 on 3c
532 A78　$4.00 on 3c
533 A78　$4.40 on 3c
534 A78　$5.00 on 3c
535 A78　$5.50 on 3c
536 A78　$6.25 on 3c
537 A78　$15 on 2c (R)
538 A78　$20 on 3c (R)
　　　Nos. 501-538 (38)　　210.00
　Revenue stamps surcharged for postal use.
Issue dates: Nos. 501-502, 504-538, May 17,
1982; No. 503, Mar. 14, 1983.
　For surcharge see No. 935.

British Guiana Nos. 254, 255, 279, Guyana 10A, 13, 13a, 32J, 32K, 32N Surcharged "H.R.H. / Prince William / 21st June 1982" in Blue

British Guiana stamps also have "GUYANA."

**1982, July 12    Perfs. as Before**
**Watermarks & Printing Methods as Before**

| | | | | |
|---|---|---|---|---|
| 539 | A60 | 50c on 2c #254 | 1.00 | .45 |
| 540 | A60 | 50c on 2c #32J | 20.00 | 4.50 |
| 541 | A60 | $1.10 on 3c #279 | 3.00 | .65 |
| 541A | A60 | $1.10 on 3c #255 | 2.00 | .55 |
| 542 | A60 | $1.10 on 3c #32K | 32.50 | 4.50 |
| 543 | A60 | $1.25 on 6c #10A | .85 | .85 |
| 543A | A60 | $1.25 on 6c #32N | .85 | .85 |
| 544 | A60 | $2.20 on 24c #13a | 3.00 | |
| 544A | A60 | $2.20 on 24c #13 | 2.00 | 2.00 |

For surcharges see Nos. 797-800.

Nos. 133-134 Surcharged "C.A. & CARIB / Games / 1982"

**Perf. 13x13½**
**1982, Aug. 16    Litho.    Wmk. 364**

| | | | | |
|---|---|---|---|---|
| 545 | A28 | 50c on 2c #134 | 2.25 | .40 |
| 546 | A28 | 60c on 1c #133 | 2.75 | .25 |
| | | Nos. 545-546 (2) | 5.00 | |

Central American and Caribbean Games, Havana. For overprint see No. 816.

Nos. 331, C2 Surcharged
**1982, Sept. 15**

| | | | | |
|---|---|---|---|---|
| 547 | A28 | 130c on #331 | 2.00 | |
| 548 | A28 | 170c on #C2 | 2.50 | |
| 549 | A28 | 440c on #331 ovptd. "1982" | 3.00 | |
| a. | | Without "1982" | 75.00 | |
| | | Nos. 547-549 (3) | 7.50 | |

For surcharge see No. 802.

No. 137 Surcharged "Commonwealth / GAMES / AUSTRALIA / 1982" in Blue
**1982, Sept. 27**

| | | | | |
|---|---|---|---|---|
| 550 | A28 | $1.25 on 6c #137 | 2.25 | .50 |

For surcharge see No. 789.

No. 207 Ovptd. "INT. / FOOD DAY / 1982" in Dark Blue
No. 320 Ovptd. "INT. YEAR / OF THE / ELDERLY" in Dark Blue
No. 323 Ovptd. "Dr. R. KOCH / CENTENARY / TBC BACILLUS / DISCOVERY" in Dark Blue
No. 287 Ovptd. "F.D. ROOSEVELT / 1882-1982 " in Green
No. 221 Ovptd. "1982" in Blue
No. 332 Surcharged "GAC Inaug. Flight / Georgetown- / Boa Vista, Brasil" in Blue and "1982" in Blue Green

**1982, Oct. 15    Perfs. as Before**
**Watermarks & Printing Methods as Before**

| | | | | |
|---|---|---|---|---|
| 551 | A48 | 50c on #207 | 21.00 | 1.00 |
| 552 | A74 | 50c on #320 | 14.00 | 1.00 |
| 553 | A75 | 60c on #323 | 5.00 | .55 |
| 554 | A66 | $1 on #287 | 6.00 | 1.00 |
| 555 | A52 | $1 on #221 | 6.00 | 1.25 |
| 556 | A28 | 200c on #332 | 20.00 | 2.75 |
| | | Nos. 551-556 (6) | 72.00 | |

For surcharges see Nos. 895, 902, 936, 1363.

No. 437 Surcharged "CARICOM / Heads of Gov't / Conference / July 1982"

**Perf. 14½x14**
**1982, Jan. 18    Litho.    Wmk. 364**

| | | | | |
|---|---|---|---|---|
| 557 | | Sheet of 6 | 15.00 | 12.50 |
| a.-f. | A81 | 50c on 15c, any single | 2.25 | .50 |

Nos. 464 Ovptd. "CHRISTMAS / 1982" in Red

**1982, Dec. 1    Perf. 13x13½**

| | | | | |
|---|---|---|---|---|
| 558 | | Sheet of 25, 8 #a.-b., 4 #c.-d., 1 #e. | 17.00 | 17.00 |
| a.-b. | A28 | 15c on #464a-464b, either single | .50 | .25 |
| c.-d. | A28 | 15c on #464c-464d, either single | 1.10 | .25 |
| e. | A28 | 15c on #464e | 12.50 | 12.50 |

---

Nos. 134, 137 Surcharged

**Perf. 13x13½**
**1982-83    Litho.    Wmk. 364**

| | | | |
|---|---|---|---|
| 563 | A28 | 15c on 2c #134 (Bl) | .50 |
| a. | | Red surcharge | 2.00 |
| b. | | Black surcharge | .75 |
| 564 | A28 | 20c on 6c #137 (Bk) | .50 |
| a. | | Green surcharge | .75 |

Issued: #563, Dec. 15; #564, Jan. 5, 1983. Compare No. 564 with Nos. 631-632. For surcharges see Nos. 846, 846a, 846b.

No. 72 Surcharged
**1982, Dec. 15    Perf. 14x14½**

| | | | | |
|---|---|---|---|---|
| 565 | A7 | 50c on 6c #72 | .75 | .25 |
| 566 | A7 | $1.00 on 6c #72 | 1.25 | .45 |
| | | Nos. 565-566 (2) | 2.00 | .70 |

Nos. 62, 88-89, 144, 161, 202, 217, 224-225, 232, 240, 251, 254, 257, 264, 276-278, 299-301, 303-305, 315, 319, 321, 329m, 414-416, and 418-420 Ovptd. "1983" Vertically or Horizontally

**1983    Perfs. as Before**
**Watermarks & Printing Methods as Before**

| | | | |
|---|---|---|---|
| 567 | A57 | 15c on #240 | 6.00 |
| 568 | A60 | 15c on #254 | 1.50 |
| 569 | A62 | 15c on #264 | 1.00 |
| 570 | A79 | 15c on 10c #414 | 1.00 |
| 571 | A80 | 15c on 10c #418 | .25 |
| 572 | A14 | 25c on #88 | .50 |
| 573 | A33 | 25c on #161 | 14.00 |
| 574 | A47 | 25c on #202 | |
| 575 | A11 | 30c on #62 | 1.50 |
| 576 | A14 | 30c on #89 | .50 |
| 577 | A65 | 30c on #276 | 12.50 |
| 578 | A69 | 30c on #299 | 5.00 |
| 579 | A70 | 30c on #303 | 10.00 |
| 580 | A74 | 30c on #319 | 6.00 |
| 581 | A77 | 30c on #329m | 3.00 |
| 582 | A53 | 50c on #224 | 2.00 |
| 583 | A55 | 50c on #232 | 5.00 |
| 584 | A59 | 50c on #251 | 7.00 |
| 585 | A65 | 50c on #277 | 5.00 |
| 586 | A69 | 50c on #300 | 5.00 |
| 587 | A70 | 50c on #304 | 30.00 |
| 588 | A79 | 50c on #415 | 1.00 |
| 589 | A80 | 50c on #419 | 2.00 |
| 590 | A65 | 60c on #278 | 5.50 |
| 591 | A72 | 60c on #315 | 7.00 |
| 592 | A51 | $1 on #217 | 10.00 |
| 593 | A53 | $1 on #225 | 10.00 |
| 594 | A60 | $1 on #257 | 6.00 |
| 595 | A79 | $1 on 30c #416 | 2.75 |
| 596 | A80 | $1 on 60c #420 | 7.50 |
| 597 | A28 | 180c on 60c #144 | 2.00 |
| 598 | A69 | $3 on #301 | 12.00 |
| 599 | A70 | $3 on #305 | 15.00 |
| 600 | A74 | $3 on #321 | 75.00 |
| 601 | A28 | 360c on $2 #146 | 2.25 |

Issued: #567-571, 583, 585-586, 2/1; #596, 3/7; #573, 3/11; #572, 576, 3/17; #582, 584, 587, 588, 589, 592-595, 598-599, 601, 4/1; #574, 5/23; #575, 577-580, 590-591, 7/1; #602, 11/3; #581, 11/15; #597, 12/14.

Refer to the second paragraph in footnote under No. 147 for Nos. 597 & 602. No. 597 contains unissued overprint, "ESPANA 1982."

For overprints and surcharges see Nos. 724, 901, 940, 943A.

No. O2 Ovptd. "POSTAGE" in Red

**Perf. 14½x14**
**1983, Feb. 1    Photo.    Wmk. 364**

| | | | | |
|---|---|---|---|---|
| 603 | A7 | 15c on #O2 | 16.00 | .50 |

For surcharge see Nos. 746-746a.

Nos. 291-293, 356 Surcharged in Blue or Black

**Wmk. 364**
**1983, Feb. 8    Litho.    Perf. 14**

| | | | | |
|---|---|---|---|---|
| 604 | A67 | 90c on 30c #291 (Blk) | 2.00 | 1.00 |
| 605 | A67 | 90c on 50c #292 | 1.25 | .30 |
| 606 | A67 | 90c on 60c #293 | 2.00 | 1.00 |
| 607 | A55 | 90c on #356 | 4.75 | .50 |
| | | Nos. 604-607 (4) | 10.00 | 2.80 |

For overprints and surcharges see Nos. 763-764, 768-769, 770-771.

---

Flag
A82

Cooperative Youth Palace — A83

**1983, Feb. 19    Perf. 14½x14**

| | | | | |
|---|---|---|---|---|
| 608 | A82 | Pair | .60 | .60 |
| a. | | 25c Flag flying right | .30 | .30 |
| b. | | 25c Flag flying left | .30 | .30 |

**Perf. 13½**

| | | | | |
|---|---|---|---|---|
| 609 | A83 | $1.30 shown | 1.00 | 1.00 |

**Size: 43x25mm**
**Perf. 14½**

| | | | | |
|---|---|---|---|---|
| 610 | A83 | $6 Map | 3.25 | 3.25 |

60th birthday of Pres. Linden Forbes Burnham. No. 608a inscribed for birthday; No. 608b for Burnham's 30th anniv. of election to parliament.

See #660, 913. For overprints & surcharges see #826-835, 924-926, 1404-1406.

**1983    Litho.    Perfs. as Before**
**Watermarks & Printing Methods as Before**

| | | | |
|---|---|---|---|
| 611 | A33 | 50c on 8c #160 (R) | 25.00 |
| 612 | A48 | 50c on 8c #205 | 2.25 |
| 613 | A62 | 50c on 8c #263 | 8.00 |
| 614 | A69 | 50c on 10c #298 (R) | 1.50 |
| 615 | A70 | 50c on 10c #302 | 4.00 |
| 616 | A69 | 50c on #409 | 4.50 |
| 617 | A69 | 50c on #480 | 2.00 |
| 618 | A28 | 50c on #O1 | 5.00 |
| 619 | A53 | $1 on #222 | 8.50 |
| 620 | A53 | $1 on #330 | 5.00 |
| 621 | A28 | $1 on #333 | 5.00 |
| 622 | A28 | $1 on #408 | 10.00 |
| 623 | A28 | $1 on #C4 | 1.50 |
| 624 | A28 | $1 on #Q3 | 25.00 |

#621 has Royal Wedding ovpt. similar to #331. #624 also ovptd. "1982." See #648-649 for similar surcharges. For overprint see #815, 941. Issued: #614, 617, 619-624, 3/7; #611, 3/11; others, 4/1.

Nos. 10A, 13a Surcharged "Commonwealth / Day / 14 March 1983" and Emblem in Blue or Black

**Wmk. 314 Upright**
**1983, Mar. 14    Engr.    Perf. 12½x13**

| | | | |
|---|---|---|---|
| 625 | A60 | 25c on 6c #10A | |
| 626 | A60 | $1.20 on 6c #10A (Bl) | |

**Wmk. 314 Sideways**

| | | | |
|---|---|---|---|
| 627 | A60 | $1.30 on 24c #13a | |
| 628 | A60 | $2.40 on 24c #13a (Bl) | |
| | | Nos. 625-628 (4) | 5.00 |

For overprints see Nos. 1823-1825.

Intl. Maritime Organization, 25th Anniv. — A84

**Perf. 14**
**1983, Mar. 17    Typo.    Wmk. 3**
**Red Overprint on British Guiana Revenue Stamp**

| | | | |
|---|---|---|---|
| 629 | A84 | $4.80 grn & blue | 9.00 |

---

Nos. 60, 72, 87 & 137 Surcharged in Black or Blue

**1983    Perfs. as Before**
**Watermarks & Printing Methods as Before**

| | | | |
|---|---|---|---|
| 630 | A11 | 15c on 6c #60 | .75 |
| a. | | Blue surcharge | 1.00 |
| 631 | A28 | 20c on 6c #137, two obliterators | 1.00 |
| 632 | A28 | 20c on 6c #137 | 1.00 |
| 633 | A7 | 50c on 6c #72 | .75 |
| 634 | A14 | 50c on 6c #87 | 1.00 |
| | | Nos. 630-634 (5) | 4.50 |

Issued: #630, 632-633, 5/23; #630a, 631, 634, 5/2.
Surcharge on No. 632 has "c" after value. No. 564 does not.
For surcharge see No. 916.

No. 72 Surcharged in Black or Red

**Perf. 14x14½**
**1983    Photo.    Wmk. 364**

| | | | |
|---|---|---|---|
| 635 | A7 | $1 on 6c #72 | 1.60 |
| a. | | Red overprint, 4mm high | 6.50 |

Issue dates: #635, May 2. #635a, May 23. For surcharge see No. 916A.

Nos. 142, 147, 211, 226-227, 239 & 249 Surcharged in Blue

**1983    Perfs. as Before**
**Watermarks & Printing Methods as Before**

| | | | |
|---|---|---|---|
| 636 | A54 | 110c on 10c #226 | 3.00 |
| 637 | A49 | 120c on 35c #211 | 4.50 |
| 638 | A54 | 120c on 35c #227 | 4.50 |
| 639 | A57 | 120c on 8c #239 | 4.50 |
| 640 | A59 | 120c on 10c #249 | 4.50 |
| 641 | A28 | 250c on 40c #142 | 12.00 |
| 642 | A28 | 400c on $5 #147 | 9.00 |
| | | Nos. 636-642 (7) | 42.00 |

Issue dates: Nos. 636, 641-642, May 2. Others, July 1. For surcharge see No. 865.

Nos. 332, 495a, C3 Surcharged in Red or Blue
"ITU / 1983" or (#643)
"WHO / 1983" or (#644)
"17 MAY '83 / ITU/WHO /" (#645)
"ITU/WHO / 17 MAY / 1983" (#646-647)

**1983, May 17    Perfs. as Before**
**Watermarks & Printing Methods as Before**

| | | | | |
|---|---|---|---|---|
| 643 | A28 | 25c on #C3 | 4.00 | .90 |
| 644 | A28 | 25c on #C3 | 4.00 | .90 |
| 645 | A28 | 25c on #C3 | 4.00 | .90 |
| a. | | Strip of 3, #643-645 | 22.50 | 10.00 |
| 646 | A28 | $4.50 on #332 (Bl) | 16.00 | 2.00 |
| 647 | A28 | $4.50 on #495a (Bl) | | |

Nos. 643-645 issued in sheets of 25 with 8 each Nos. 643-644 and 9 No. 645.

Nos. 272, 274 Surcharged in Dark Blue

**Perf. 13½x14**
**1983, May 18    Litho.    Wmk. 364**

| | | | | |
|---|---|---|---|---|
| 648 | A64 | $1 on 15c #272 | 7.50 | 1.00 |
| 649 | A64 | $1 on 40c #274 | 12.50 | 1.00 |
| | | Nos. 648-649 (2) | 20.00 | 2.00 |

Surcharge on No. 648 also contains overprint "1983."

Nos. 402, 404, O8 Surcharged or Overprinted "CANADA 1983"

**1983, June 15    Perf. 13½x13**

| | | | | |
|---|---|---|---|---|
| 650 | A17 | $1.30 on #O8 | 4.50 | 3.00 |
| 651 | A17 | 180c on #402 | 4.50 | 4.50 |
| 652 | A17 | $3.90 on #404 | 10.00 | 1.00 |
| | | Nos. 650-652 (3) | 19.00 | 17.50 |

For surcharge see No. 1860.

Nos. 243-244 Surcharged

**1983, June 22    Unwmk.    Perf. 14**

| | | | | |
|---|---|---|---|---|
| 653 | A57a | 60c on 15c #243 | 15.00 | 1.00 |
| 654 | A57b | $1.50 on 15c #244 | 22.50 | 2.50 |
| | | Nos. 653-654 (2) | 37.50 | 3.50 |

Nos. 297, 313 Surcharged

**Perfs. as Before**
**1983, July 1    Wmk. 364**

| | | | | |
|---|---|---|---|---|
| 655 | A68 | 120c on #297 | 7.50 | 1.25 |
| 656 | A72 | 120c on 10c #313 (R) | 7.50 | 1.25 |

No. 655 has unissued surcharge, "INTERNATIONAL / SCIENCE YEAR / 375."

British Guiana No. J1 and Guyana No. J5 Surcharged "120 / GUYANA" in Dark Blue

**1983, July 1   Wmk. 4   Perf. 13½x14**
657 D1 120c on 1c #J1    6.00 1.25

**Wmk. 364**
658 D1 120c on 1c #J5    6.00 1.25

No. 371 Surcharged in Red "CARICOM DAY 1983"

**1983, July 1   Wmk. 364   Perf. 14**
659 A72 60c on $3 #371    3.00

Type A82 Without Inscription

**1983, July 1   Litho.   Perf. 14½x14**
660 A82   Pair    .30 .30
   a.   25c, Flag flying right    .20 .20
   b.   25c, Flag flying left    .20 .20

River Steamers A85

**1983, July 11   Litho.   Perf. 14**
661 A85 30c Kurupukari    .20 .20
662 A85 60c Makouria    .40 .40
   a.   Tete-beche pair
663 A85 120c Powis    .85 .85
   a.   Tete-beche pair
664 A85 120c Pomeroon    .95 .95
665 A85 150c Lukanani    1.10 1.10
   Nos. 661-665 (5)    3.50 3.50

No. 146 Surcharged in Dark Blue

**1983, July 22   Perf. 13½**
666 A28 $2.30 on $1.10 on $2   
667 A28 $3.20 on $1.10 on $2   
   Nos. 666-667 (2)    6.00

Nos. 666-667 have unissued surcharge of "$1.10 / Royal Wedding / 1981" similar to No. 331.

Nos. 282-283 & 283A Overprinted as Shown or with Various Initials in Red or Blue

Overprints: No. 668a, BW. b, LM. c, GY 1963 / 1983. d, JW. e, CU. f. Mont Golfier / 1783-1983.

No. 669a, BGI. b, GEO. c, MIA. d, BVB. e, PBM. f, Mont Golfier / 1783-1983. g, POS. h, JFK.

No. 670a, AHL. b, BCG. c, BMJ. d, EKE. e, GEO. f, GFO. g, IBM. h, Mont Golfier / 1783-1983. i, KAI. j, KAR. k, KPG. l, KRG. m, KTO. n, LTM. o, MHA. p, MWI. q, MYM. r, NAI. s, ORJ. t, USI. u, VEG.

**1983, Sept. 5   Perf. 14x13½**

**Sheets of 25**
668 A66 20c 4 each #a.-e., 5 #f    30.00
669 A66 25c 2 each #a., c.-e., g.-h., 8 #b., 5 #f.    45.00
670 A66 30c #a.-e., g.-u., 5 #f., (BI)    40.00

Manned flight, bicentennial and Guyana Airways, 20th anniv. For ovpts. see #871, 969.

No. 234 Surcharged in Dark Blue

**1983, Sept. 14   Perf. 13½**
703 A28 240c on #234    3.00 1.25
   a.   "4" with serif    3.50 1.50

Nos. 703, 703a appear in same sheet.

Nos. 68, 70 Surcharged "FAO 1983" in Red

**Perf. 14x14½**

**1983, Sept. 15   Photo.   Wmk. 364**
704 A7 30c on 1c #68    .50 .20
705 A7 $2.60 on 3c #70    2.25 2.25
   Nos. 704-705 (2)    2.75 2.45

For overprints see Nos. 1497-1498.

---

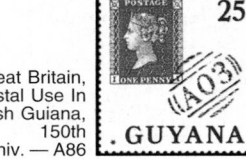

Great Britain, Postal Use In British Guiana, 150th Anniv. — A86

Stamps: a, #20. b, #26. c, #27. d, #28.

**1983, Oct. 1   Litho.   Perf. 14**

**Inscribed in Black**
706 A86 25c #20    .25 .25
707 A86 30c #26    .25 .25
708 A86 60c #27    .45 .45
709 A86 120c #28    1.00 1.00

**Inscribed in Blue**
710   Block of 4    .80 .80
   a.-d.   A86 25c any single    .20 .20
711   Block of 4    1.00 1.00
   a.-d.   A86 30c any single    .20 .20
712   Block of 4    1.75 1.75
   a.-d.   A86 45c any single    .40 .40
713   Block of 4    5.00 5.00
   a.   A86 120c #20    .80 .80
   b.   A86 130c #26, Demerara    .85 .85
   c.   A86 150c #27, Berbice    1.00 1.00
   d.   A86 200c #28, Essequibo    1.50 1.50
   Nos. 706-713 (8)    10.50 10.50

Nos. 706-709 printed in sheets with bottom two rows inverted. Nos. 710-712 printed in sheets of 60. No. 713 printed in sheets with blue marginal text.

For overprints and surcharges see Nos. 796, 903, 912, 1448, 1982.

#235 & 238 Surcharged
#297 Surcharged "INT. / COMMUNICATIONS / YEAR"
#206 Surcharged "Int. Food Day / 1983"
#309 Surcharged "1918-1983 / I.L.O."

**1983, Oct. 15   Perfs. as Before**
**Watermarks & Printing Methods as Before**
714 A68 50c on 375c on $3 #297    6.00
715 A56 75c on 8c #235    7.00
716 A48 $1.20 on 35c #206    1.75
717 A56 $1.20 on 40c #238    7.00
718 A71 240c on $3 #309    2.00
   Nos. 714-718 (5)    23.75

No. 714 was not issued without 375c surcharge. For overprint see No. 821.

Nos. 245, 247-248 Surcharged
**Unwmk.**

**1983, Nov. 1   Litho.   Perf. 14**
719 A58 25c on 8c #245    .35 .20
720 A58 $1.50 on 35c #247    2.40 1.00
721 A58 $1.50 on 40c #248    1.25 1.00
   Nos. 719-721 (3)    4.00 2.20

Nos. 268 & 270 Surcharged

**1983, Nov. 15   Wmk. 364**
722 A63 60c on 15c #268    2.50 .50
723 A63 $1.20 on 40c #270    2.50 .90

No. 601 Ovptd. "Human Rights / Day"

**1983, Dec. 1   Perf. 14½x14**
724 A74 $3 on #601    3.25 1.75

For surcharge see footnote following No. 998.

Nos. 317 and 726 Surcharged "LOS ANGELES / 1984"

**1983, Dec. 6   Wmk. 373**
725   Sheet of 12   
   a.-l.   A73 55c on 125c on 35c #726a-726l, any single
726   Sheet of 12   
   a.-l.   A73 125c on 35c #317a-317l, any single

For surcharge see No. 1897.

No. 133 Surcharged
"COMMONWEALTH / HEADS OF GOV'T / MEETING--INDIA / 1983"

**Perf. 13x13½**

**1983, Dec. 14   Wmk. 364**
727 A28 150c on 1c #133    4.00 1.00

Nos. 413a, 413e Surcharged "CHRISTMAS / 1983"

**1983, Dec. 14   Photo.   Perf. 14x14½**
**Watermarks as before**
728 A7 20c on #413a    1.50 .20
   a.   20c on #413De    .50 .20

---

Nos. 146, O15 Ovptd. "POSTAGE" in Blue

**1984, Jan. 8   Perfs. as before**
729 A28 $2 on #146    4.25 1.00
730 A66 550c on $10 #O15    22.00 10.00

Refer to second paragraph in footnote following No. 147 for No. 729.

Flower Type of 1971-76 Surcharged in Blue

**Perf. 15x14**

**1984, Jan.   Photo.   Unwmk.**
**Size: 20x23mm**
**Coil Stamps**
731 A28 17c on 2c, like #134    4.50 2.75
732 A28 17c on 8c, Mazaruni Pride    4.50 2.75
   a.   Pair, #731-732    10.00 10.00

Nos. 731-732 were intended for use on 8c envelopes to increase postage rate to 25c and were not issued without surcharge.

Nos. 284, 286A Surcharged in Black or Overprinted in Dark Blue
(1) "ALL / OUR HERITAGE"
(2) "1984" 7mm long
(3) "REPUBLIC / DAY"
(4) "BERBICE"
(5) "DEMERARA"
(6) "ESSEQUIBO"
(7) "1984" 18mm long

**Perf. 14x13½**

**1984, Feb. 24   Litho.   Wmk. 364**
733 A66 25c on 35c (1)    .75 .20
734 A66 25c on 35c (2)    1.25 .50
735 A66 25c on 35c (3)    1.25 .50
736 A66 25c on 35c #284    1.25 .50
737 A66 25c on 35c (4)    6.00 4.50
738 A66 25c on 35c (5)    6.00 4.50
739 A66 25c on 35c (6)    6.00 4.50
740 A66 25c on 35c (7)    14.00 14.00
741 A66 60c on #286A (1) (DBl)    3.50 1.00
742 A66 60c on #286A (3) (DBl)    3.50 1.00
743 A66 60c on #286A (2) (DBl)    3.50 1.00

Nos. 733-740 were issued in sheets of 25, 6 #733, 4 each #734-736, 2 each #737-739, 1 #740. Nos. 741-743 were issued in sheets of 25, 8 each #741-742, 9 #743.

Nos. 49-50, 52, 73-74, 77-80, 82, 139, 141A-143, 350, 603 Surcharged or Overprinted in Black and/or Blue "Protecting Our Heritage"

**1984, Mar. 5   Perfs. as Before**
**Watermarks & Printing Methods as Before**
744 A8 20c on 15c #74    8.50 .50
   a.   Blue surcharge (value and words)    20.00
745 A8 20c on 15c #350    8.50 .50
746 A8 20c on 15c #603 (BI)    17.50 2.00
   a.   "Protecting our Heritage" in black
747 A28 25c on #141A    14.50 .50
   a.   25c on #141b    65.00 .60
748 A28 30c on 15c #139    24.00 .60
749 A8 40c on #77    12.50 .60
750 A28 50c on #143    1.50 .60
751 A28 50c on #143 (Revenue Ovpt.)    .50 .60
752 A7 60c on #50    18.50 .60
   a.   60c on #79    100.00
753 A28 90c on 40c #142    19.50 .90
754 A28 90c on 40c #142 (Revenue ovpt.)    140.00
755 A28 180c on #460    14.50 1.50
756 A7 $2 on #52    80.00 2.25
757 A28 225c on 10c on #73    25.00 1.75
758 A28 260c on $1 #80    17.50 1.50
759 A28 320c on 40c #142    17.50 3.25
760 A28 350c on 40c #142    24.00 4.25
761 A7 390c on 50c #78    9.50 4.00
   a.   390c on #49    125.00
762 A7 450c on $5 #82    12.50 4.00
   Nos. 744-762 (19)    467.00

Nos. 748, 753-754, 759-760 use row of "X", 6mm high, as obliterator. Nos. 744-746, 757 have new value printed vertically over old value. Nos. 758, 761-762 have new value printed horizontally over old value. Refer to second paragraph in footnote under No. 147 for Nos. 751, 754-755.

---

Nos. 89, 484-485, 606 Overprinted or Surcharged in Dark Blue "1984"
No. 87 Surcharged
No. 606 Surcharged "INT. / CHESS / FED. / 1924-1984" in Dark Blue (#764a, 769a, 771a)

**1984   Perfs. as Before**
**Watermarks & Printing Methods as Before**
763 A67 25c on #606    2.00
764 A67 25c on #606    4.00
   a.   Pair, #763-764    10.00
765 A14 30c on #89    .50
766 A14 45c on 6c #484    .50
767 A14 75c on 40c #485    .50
768 A67 75c on #606    1.00
769 A67 75c on #606    3.00
   a.   Pair, #768-769    8.00
770 A67 90c on #606    1.00
771 A67 90c on #606    3.00
   a.   Pair, #770-771    9.00
772 A14 130c on 6c #87    2.50
773 A76 $3 on #328    3.00
   Nos. 763-773 (11)    19.00

Issued: #765-767, 772, Mar. 17; #773, June 15; #763-764, 768-769, 770-771, July 20.

No. 767 exists with surcharge either above old value or in center of stamp.

Nos. 497-500 Surcharged

**1984, Apr. 2   Litho.   Perf. 13½**
774 A28 75c on #497    11.00 .55
775 A28 75c on #498    13.00 .55
776 A28 225c on #500    3.50 1.75
777 A28 230c on #499    4.00 1.25
   Nos. 774-777 (4)    31.50 4.10

Nos. 464e, 465a, 465b, 465e, 466a, 466b, 466e Surcharged Like No. 748

**1984, May 2**
778 A28 20c on #464e    2.25 .50
779 A28 75c on #465e    11.50 1.00
780 A28 90c on #465a    7.00 1.25
781 A28 90c on #465b    9.50 1.25
782 A28 120c on #466a    11.00 1.50
783 A28 120c on #466e    11.00 1.50
784 A28 120c on #466b    3.50 1.50

No. C3 Surcharged "ITU DAY / 1984" (#785)
No. C3 Surcharged "WHO DAY / 1984" (#786)
Nos. C3, 386 Surcharged "ITU/WHO / DAY / 1984" (#787-788)

**1984, May 17**
785 A28 25c on #C3    1.60 1.60
786 A28 25c on #C3    1.60 1.60
787 A28 25c on #C3    1.60 1.60
788 A28 $4.50 on #386    2.50 2.50
   Nos. 785-788 (4)    7.30 7.30

The surcharge is vertical on Nos. 785-787, horizontal on No. 788.

No. 550 Surcharged

**1984, June 11**
789 A28 120c on #550    8.75 1.00

Nos. 325-327, 431 Surcharged in Blue or Black

**Wmk. 373**

**1984, June 15   Litho.   Perf. 14**
790 A76 55c on 30c #326 (Blk)    5.00 .50
791 A76 75c on #431    1.10 .75
792 A76 160c on 50c #327    1.50 1.25
793 A76 260c on 50c #325    2.50 1.75
   Nos. 790-793 (4)    10.10 4.25

No. 214 Surcharged

**1984, June 18   Litho.   Wmk. 364**
794 A50 55c on 110c on 10c    1.25 .50
795 A50 90c on 110c on 10c    1.25 .75

No. 214 surcharged 110c only was never issued.

No. 713 Ovptd. "UPU / Congress 1984 / Hamburg"

**1984, June 19**
796   Block of 4    5.00 5.00
   a.   A86 120c on #713a    .75 .75
   b.   A86 130c on #713b    .90 .90
   c.   A86 150c on #713c    1.00 1.00
   d.   A86 200c on #713d    1.25 1.25

Nos. 539, 541, 543-544 Surcharged in Black, Blue or Dark Green

**1984, June 21   Perfs. as Before**
**Watermarks & Printing Methods as Before**
797 A60 45c on #539    .50 .50
798 A60 60c on #541 (DkG)    2.50 .60
   a.   60c on British Guiana #255 (DkG)

| 799 | A60 120c on #543 | .75 | .55 |
| 800 | A60 200c on #544 (Bl) | 6.75 | 1.50 |
| | Nos. 797-800 (4) | 10.50 | 3.15 |

Nos. 135, 548, C2-C3 Surcharged in
Blue or Black
No. C4 Overprinted "1984"
Perf. 13x13½

| 1984, June 30 | Litho. | Wmk. 364 |
|---|---|---|
| 801 | A28 75c on #C2 (Blk) | 1.50 | .50 |
| 802 | A28 120c on #548 (Blk) | 1.90 | .75 |
| 803 | A28 150c on #135 | 1.60 | .80 |
| 804 | A28 200c on #C3 | 17.50 | 2.50 |
| 804A | A28 330c on #C4 | 3.00 | 3.00 |
| | Nos. 801-804A (5) | 25.50 | 7.55 |

Surcharge on Nos. 801-802, 804 is like No.
748. Surcharge on No. 803 is like No. 457.

No. 135 Surcharged "CARICOM /
HEADS OF GOV'T / CONFERENCE /
JULY 1984"
No. 450A Surcharged "CARICOM DAY
1984"

| 1984, June 30 | Perfs. as Before |
| Watermarks & Printing Methods as Before |
|---|
| 805 | A28 60c on 3c #135 | 1.40 | .60 |
| 806 | A72 60c on #450A | 1.40 | .60 |

Nos. 140-141, 141A, 329, 334, 427,
439a-440, 546, 611, 718, O13 Ovptd.
"1984" in Black or Blue

| 1984 | Perfs. as Before |
| Watermarks & Printing Methods as Before |
|---|
| 807 | A28 20c on #140 | 12.50 |
| a. | On #140a | 150.00 |
| 808 | A28 20c on #140 | 55.00 |
| a. | On #140a | 150.00 |
| 809 | A28 20c on #439, 1984 omitted | 60.00 |
| 810 | A28 25c on #141 | 100.00 |
| a. | 1984 omitted | 100.00 |
| 811 | A28 25c on #141 (Revenue Only) | 6.00 |
| 812 | A28 25c on #141A | |
| 813 | A28 25c on #141, 1982 ovpt., 1984 omitted | 40.00 |
| 814 | A28 25c on #440, 1984 omitted | |
| 815 | A33 50c on #611 (Bl) | 10.00 |
| 816 | A28 60c on #546 (Bl) | 1.00 |
| 817 | A28 $2 on #O13 (Bl) | 2.50 |
| 818 | A28 $3.60 on #834 | 4.00 |
| c. | As #818, fleur-de-lis omitted | 10.00 |
| d. | On #334a (Bl) | 4.00 |
| e. | As "d," fleur-de-lis omitted | 5.00 |
| 819 | Sheet of 12 | 4.00 |
| a.-l. | A77 30c on #329a-329l, any single | |
| 820 | A71 240c on #429 | 4.75 |
| 821 | A71 240c on #438 | 4.75 |

Overprint on Nos. 808-814, 818 contains
fleur-de-lis. Refer to second paragraph in footnote below No. 147 for Nos. 811-812, 817.
Issued: #819, Sept. 15; #820-821, Oct. 15.

Teachers' Assoc.
Centenary — A87

| 1984, July 16 | Wmk. 364 | Perf. 14 |
|---|---|---|
| 822 | A87 25c Children dancing | .25 | .25 |
| 823 | A87 25c Torch, graduate | .25 | .25 |
| 824 | A87 25c Torch concentric circles | .25 | .25 |
| 825 | A87 25c Teachers, school | .25 | .25 |
| a. | Block of 4 | 1.00 | 1.00 |

No. 609 Surcharged in Blue:
"CYCLING" (#826, 831)
"TRACK / AND / FIELD" (#827, 832)
"OLYMPIC / GAMES / 1984" (#828, 833)
"BOXING" (#829, 834)
"OLYMPIC / GAMES / 1984 / LOS
ANGELES" (#830, 835)
Perf. 14½x14

| 1984, July 28 | Litho. | Wmk. 364 |
|---|---|---|
| 826 | A83 25c on $1.30 | 1.00 | .80 |
| 827 | A83 25c on $1.30 | 1.00 | .80 |
| 828 | A83 25c on $1.30 | 1.00 | .80 |
| 829 | A83 25c on $1.30 | 3.75 | 2.00 |
| 830 | A83 25c on $1.30 | 3.75 | 2.00 |
| 831 | A83 $1.20 on $1.30 | 3.00 | 2.50 |
| 832 | A83 $1.20 on $1.30 | 3.00 | 2.50 |
| 833 | A83 $1.20 on $1.30 | 3.00 | 2.50 |
| 834 | A83 $1.20 on $1.30 | 5.50 | 3.00 |
| 835 | A83 $1.20 on $1.30 | 5.50 | 4.00 |

Nos. 826-828 and 831-833 exist in strips of
3. Nos. 827, 829-830 and 832, 834-835 exists
in booklets.

Nos. 465-466 Surcharged "GIRL /
GUIDES / 1924-1984" in Blue

| 1984, Aug. 15 | Perf. 13x13½ |
| Sheets of 25 |
|---|
| 836 | 8 #a.-b., 4 #c.-d., 1 #e. | |
| a.-e. | A28 25c on #465a-465e, any single | |
| 837 | 8 #a.-b., 4 #c.-d., 1 #e. | |
| a.-e. | A28 25c on #466a-466e, any single | |
| | Nos. 836-837 (2) | 35.00 |

Nos. 138-139, 234, 335, 351, 378,
380, 388, 401, 423, 438, 452, 459,
461, 563, 642, O3, O11-O12, O14
Surcharged

| 1984 | Perfs. as Before |
| Watermarks & Printing Methods as Before |
|---|
| 846 | A28 20c on #563 | 1.00 |
| a. | 20c on #563a (Blk over R) | 1.00 |
| b. | 20c on #563b (Blk over Bl) | 1.00 |
| 847 | A28 25c on #138 | 27.50 |
| a. | 25c on #138a | 55.00 |
| 848 | A28 25c on #139 | 150.00 |
| 849 | A28 25c on #351a | 20.00 |
| a. | 25c on #351 | 70.00 |
| 850 | A28 25c on #351b | 8.50 |
| 851 | A28 25c on #438 | 8.00 |
| a. | 25c on #438a | 150.00 |
| 852 | A28 25c on #234 | 100.00 |
| 853 | A28 25c on #452 | 8.00 |
| 854 | A28 25c on #O3 | 8.00 |
| 855 | A28 60c on #423, two obliterators, small 110 only | 45.00 |
| a. | Single obliterator, small 110 only | |
| 856 | A28 120c on #459 | 5.00 |
| 857 | A28 120c on #401 | 35.00 |
| 858 | A28 120c on #O12 | 2.00 |
| 859 | A28 120c on #380 | 6.00 |
| 860 | A28 130c on #378 | 100.00 |
| 861 | A28 130c on #O11 | 12.50 |
| 862 | A28 200c on #461 | 5.00 |
| 863 | A28 320c on #378 | 5.50 |
| 864 | A28 350c on #388 | 5.00 |
| 865 | A28 390c on #642 | 6.00 |
| 866 | A28 450c on #O14 | 5.75 |
| 867 | A28 600c on #335 | 15.00 |
| a. | 600c on #335a | 17.50 |
| 868 | A28 600c on #335a | 3.00 |
| a. | 600c on #335 | 4.00 |
| | Nos. 846-868 (23) | 581.75 |

Nos. 860-861 are airmail. Obliterator on
Nos. 846, 856-859, 862-866 is row of
"X", on Nos. 847, 850, 852 is single line, on Nos. 848-849, 851, 853-854 is fleur-de-lis, on No. 855 is a block of 6 lines, on No. 867 is 3 lines, on No. 868 is 3 lines and fleur-de-lis.

Nos. 556, 670, C4 Overprinted in Blue
or Surcharged in Blue and Black

Overprints: #a-f, ICAO on #670a-670f. g,
IMB/ICAO on #g. h, KCV/ICAO on #h. i,
KAI/ICAO on #i. j-k, ICAO on #670j-670k. l,
1984 on #h. m, KPM/ICAO on #h. n-p, ICAO
on #670 l-670n. q, PMT/ICAO on #h. r-x, ICAO
on #670o-670u.

Perf. 14x13½

| 1984, Sept. 6 | Litho. | Wmk. 364 |
|---|---|---|
| 871 | A66 30c Sheet of 25, #a.-k., m.-x., 2 #l | 65.00 | 65.00 |
| 895 | A28 200c ICAO on #556 | 5.50 | 2.25 |
| 896 | A28 200c ICAO on #C4 (Bl & Blk) | 3.00 | 2.00 |

No. 896 is airmail with unissued "GAC" overprint. For surcharge see No. 1470.

Nos. J3-J4, J7-J8 Surcharged "120 /
GUYANA" in Blue
Perf. 13½x14

| 1984, Oct. 1 | Typo. | Wmk. 314 |
|---|---|---|
| 897 | D1 120c on 4c #J3 | 3.00 | .80 |
| 898 | D1 120c on 12c #J4 | 3.00 | .80 |
| | | Wmk. 364 |
| 899 | D1 120c on 4c #J7 | 8.00 | .80 |
| 900 | D1 120c on 12c #J8 | 28.50 | 1.25 |
| | Nos. 897-900 (4) | 42.50 | 3.65 |

Nos. 551, 571 Surcharged in Black or
Blue
Perfs. as Before

| 1984, Oct. 15 | Wmk. 364 |
|---|---|
| 901 | A80 $1.50 on #571 (Bl) | 14.00 | 1.50 |
| 902 | A48 150c on #551 | 4.50 | .75 |

Obliterator is "X" on No. 901. Surcharge on
No. 902 places "1" before existing 50c value,
obliterates "1982" and adds "1984."

Nos. 712, 479-481 Surcharged

| 1984, Oct. 22 | Perf. 14 |
|---|---|
| 903 | Block of 4 | 1.25 | 1.25 |
| a.-d. | A86 25c on #712a-712d, any single | .20 | .20 |
| 904 | A69 120c on #479 | 9.50 | .75 |
| 905 | A69 120c on #480 | 1.25 | .75 |
| 906 | A66 320c on #481 | 20.00 | 2.75 |
| | Nos. 903-906 (4) | 32.00 | 5.50 |

Nos. 135-136 Surcharged "MAHA
SABHA / 1934-1984" in Blue

| 1984, Nov. 1 | Perf. 13x13½ |
|---|---|
| 910 | A28 25c on 5c #136 | .75 | .20 |
| 911 | A28 $1.50 on 3c #135 | 4.25 | 1.50 |
| | Nos. 910-911 (2) | 5.00 | 1.70 |

No. 713 Ovptd. "Philatelic Exhibition /
New York 1984" in Red

| 1984, Nov. 15 | Perf. 14 |
|---|---|
| 912 | Block of 4 | 5.00 | 5.00 |
| a. | A86 120c on No. 713a | 1.00 | .80 |
| b. | A86 130c on No. 713b | 1.10 | .90 |
| c. | A86 150c on No. 713c | 1.25 | 1.00 |
| d. | A86 200c on No. 713d | 1.50 | 1.25 |

Type A83 Inscribed with Olympic
Rings and
"OLYMPIC GAMES 1984 / LOS
ANGELES"

| 1984, Nov. 16 | Perf. 13½ |
|---|---|
| 913 | A83 $1.20 multicolored | 5.00 | 5.00 |

Copies with numbers stamped on back are
coils.
For similar stamp overprinted see No. 923.
For surcharges see Nos. 1953-1957.

Nos. 410, 413e, 633, 635a
Surcharged

| 1984, Nov. 24 | Photo. | Perf. 14x14½ |
| Watermarks as Before |
|---|---|
| 914 | A7 20c on #410 | 1.00 | .20 |
| 915 | A7 20c on #413De | 92.50 | 7.50 |
| 916 | A7 25c on #633 | .50 | .20 |
| 916A | A7 60c on #635a | .70 | .45 |

No. 914 has an "X" obliterating a "1" and no
obliterating lines. No. 1400 has obliterating
lines and small "20" in UR.

Elanoides
Forficatus
A88

Designs: a, Pair in tree. b, Landing on
branch. c, In flight, wings up. d, In flight, wings
down. e, In flight, wings outstretched.

| 1984, Dec. 3 | Wmk. 364 | Perf. 14½ |
|---|---|---|
| 917 | A88 60c Strip of 5, #a.-e. | 22.50 | 22.50 |

Inscribed "Christmas 1982."
For surcharges see Nos. 1502, 1840.

High Street Architecture — A89

Designs: 25c, St. George's Cathedral, 1892,
Colonial Life Insurance Co. 60c, No. 920a,
Demerara Mutual Life Assurance Soc., Ltd.
No. 920b, 200c, Town Hall, 1888, City Engineers Office. No. 920c, 300c, Victoria Law
Courts, 1887.

| 1985, Feb. 8 | Perf. 14 |
|---|---|
| 918 | A89 25c multi | .20 | .20 |
| 919 | A89 60c multi | .40 | .40 |
| 920 | Triptych | 1.40 | 1.40 |
| a.-c. | A89 120c, any single | .45 | .45 |
| d. | Triptych, unwmkd. | 1.75 | 1.75 |
| e.-g. | As "d," any single | .60 | .60 |
| 921 | A89 200c multi | 1.25 | 1.25 |
| 922 | A89 300c multi | 1.75 | 1.75 |
| | Nos. 918-922 (5) | 5.00 | 5.00 |

For surcharge see No. 1850.

Type A83 Ovptd. "INTERNATIONAL /
YOUTH YEAR 1985"
Wmk. 364

| 1985, Feb. 15 | Litho. | Perf. 14½ |
|---|---|---|
| 923 | A83 $1.20 multi | 3.00 | .75 |

Bars obliterate Olympic Games inscription
with second line spelled "LOS ANGELLES."
No. 913 spells "Los Angeles" correctly.

Nos. 608, 610 Ovptd. in Red "Republic
/ Day / 1970-1985" or
"1970 / 1985 / Republic / Day"

| 1985, Feb. 22 | Perfs. as Before |
|---|---|
| 924 | A82 25c on #608 | |
| 925 | A83 120c on $6 #610 | |
| 926 | A83 130c on $6 #610 | |
| | Nos. 924-926 (3) | 3.00 | 2.25 |

Ocelot Cub
Xica — A90

Macaw
Nena — A90a

Perf. 12½x13

| 1985, Mar. 11 | Wmk. 364 |
|---|---|
| 927 | A90 25c multi | 2.00 | .30 |
| 928 | A90 60c multi | .60 | .60 |
| 929 | Triptych | 3.50 | 3.50 |
| a.-c. | A90 120c, like #927-928, 930 | 1.10 | 1.10 |
| 930 | A90 130c multi | 1.25 | 1.25 |
| | | Perf. 14½ |
| 931 | A90a 320c shown | 4.25 | 2.00 |
| 932 | A90a 330c Cub on hind legs | 2.50 | 2.00 |
| | Nos. 927-932 (6) | 14.10 | 9.65 |

No. 929, perf. 14, inscribed "1986," were
from the liquidation of stock held by the printer,
value 75c.
For overprints see #1903-1905, 1983, 2032.

Map Revenue Type A78 and Nos. 481,
501, 554, O6 Surcharged in Black or
Blue

| 1985 | Perfs as Before |
| Watermarks & Printing Methods as Before |
|---|
| 933 | A69 30c on 50c on #O6 (Bl) | 1.00 | .20 |
| 934 | A78 55c on 2c multi | 1.00 | .25 |
| a. | "ESSEQUIBO IS OURS" omitted | 15.00 |
| 935 | A78 55c on #501 | 1.00 | .40 |
| 936 | A66 90c on #554 (Bl) | 7.00 | .65 |
| 937 | A66 225c on #481 | 10.00 | 2.00 |
| 938 | A66 230c on #481 (Bl) | 10.00 | 2.25 |
| 939 | A66 260c on #481 (Bl) | 10.00 | 2.50 |
| | Nos. 933-939 (7) | 40.00 | 8.25 |

Issued: #933-936, 938-939, 3/11; #937, 4/11.
Obliterator on Nos. 934-935 is fleur-de-lis.

Nos. 305, 435, 587, 599, & 615 Ovptd.
"INTERNATIONAL / YOUTH YEAR /
1985" in Black
Wmk. 364

| 1985, Apr. 15 | Litho. | Perf. 13½ |
|---|---|---|
| 940 | A70 50c on #587 | 2.00 | .30 |
| 941 | A70 50c on #615 | 7.00 | .30 |
| 942 | A70 120c on #435 | 2.25 | .55 |
| 943 | A70 $3 on #305 | 10.00 | |
| 943A | A70 $3 on #599 | 2.25 | 1.25 |
| | Nos. 940-943A (5) | 23.50 | 2.40 |

No. 280 Surcharged with Names of
1860 Post Offices or Postal Agencies
in Blue

Overprints: a, Airy Hall. b, Belfield / Arab.
Coast. c, Belfield / E.C. Dem. d, Belladrum. e,
Beterver- / wagting. f, Blairmont / Ferry. g,
Boeraserie. h, Brahn. i, Bushlot. j, De /
Kinderen. k, Fort / Wellington. l, Georgetown.
m, Hague. n, Leguan. o, Mahaica. p, Mahaicony. q, New / Amsterdam. r, Plaisance. s,

No. 6 Police / Station. t, Queenstown. u, Verte-noegen. v, Vigilance. w, Vreed-en- / Hoop. x, Wakenaam. y, Windsor / Castle.

### Perf. 14x13½
**1985, May 2    Litho.    Wmk. 364**
### Sheet of 25
944  A66  25c on 10c, #a.-y.    27.50  27.50

Colonial Post Office, 125th anniv.

### Nos. 670 Ovptd. "1985" or with Letters in Red

Overprints: a-f, 1985 on #670a-670f. g, I on #670g. h, T on #670h. i, U on #670i. j-k, 1985 on #670j-670k. l, W on #670h. m, H on #670h. n, O on #670h. o-p, 1985 on #670 l-670m. q, D on #670n. r, A on #670h. s, Y on #670o. t-y, 1985 on #670p-#670u.

**1985, May 17**
### Sheet of 25
969  A66  30c #a.-y.    20.00  20.00

### Nos. 413a & 413e Surcharged
**1985, May 21    Photo.    Perf. 14x14½**
### Watermarks as Before
994  A7  20c on #413a    10.00  .30
  a.  20c on #413De    14.00  .20

#994a has "20" at left and 11 obliterating lines. #1401 has "20" at right and 12 lines.

### No. 135 Surcharged "CARDI / 1975-1985"
### Perf. 13x13½
**1985, May 21    Litho.    Wmk. 364**
995  A28  60c on 3c #135    1.75  .40

Caribbean Agricultural Research Development Institute, 10th anniv.

### No. 407 Surcharged
**1985, June 3**
996  A28  600c on #407    30.00  3.75

### Nos. 288, 724, C1 Surcharged "ROTARY / INTERNATIONAL / 1905-1985" in Red
**1985, June 21    Perfs. as Before**
### Watermarks & Printing Methods as Before
997  A74  120c on #C1    14.50  1.00
998  A66  300c on #288    10.00  3.50

No. 724 with a similar surcharge is usually found on first day covers.

### No. 450A Surcharged "CARICOM DAY / 1985" and
### No. 426 Surcharged "135th Anniversary / Cotton Reel / 1850-1985" in Red
**1985, June 28    Perfs. as Before**
### Watermarks & Printing Methods as Before
999  A72  60c on #450A    1.00  .50
1000  A69  120c on #426    1.00  .50

Orchids from Reichenbachia, by Sanders — A91

**1985-87    Perf. 14**
**Wmk. 364 (#1027, 1031, 1036, 1046, 1049, 1052, 1054, 1071, 1074, 1076, 1079, 1084, 1091, 1108), Unwmkd.**
### Series 1
| | | | | |
|---|---|---|---|---|
| 1021 | A91 | 120c Plate No. 1 | .90 | .60 |
| 1022 | A91 | 60c Plate No. 2 | .30 | .30 |
| 1023 | A91 | 130c Plate No. 3 | 1.00 | .65 |
| 1024 | A91 | 200c Plate No. 4 | 1.75 | 1.00 |
| 1025 | A91 | 60c like #1025 | .45 | .45 |
| 1026 | A91 | 75c like #1025 | .40 | .40 |
| a. | | Wmk. 364 ('87) | 7.50 | 7.50 |
| 1027 | A91 | 100c Plate No. 6 | .75 | .75 |
| 1028 | A91 | 130c like #1027 | 1.00 | .65 |
| a. | | Wmk. 364 ('86) | .65 | .65 |

| | | | | |
|---|---|---|---|---|
| 1029 | A91 | 60c Plate No. 7 | .30 | .30 |
| 1030 | A91 | 25c Plate No. 8 | .20 | .20 |
| 1031 | A91 | 50c Plate No. 9 | .40 | .40 |
| 1032 | A91 | 55c like #1031 | .30 | .30 |
| a. | | Wmk. 364 ('86) | .30 | .30 |
| 1033 | A91 | 60c Plate No. 10 | .30 | .30 |
| 1034 | A91 | 120c Plate No. 11 | .90 | .60 |
| 1035 | A91 | 25c Plate No. 12 | .20 | .20 |
| 1036 | A91 | 100c Plate No. 13 | .75 | .75 |
| 1037 | A91 | 130c like #1036 | 1.00 | .65 |
| a. | | Wmk. 364 ('86) | 1.00 | .65 |
| 1038 | A91 | 200c Plate No. 14 | 1.75 | 1.00 |
| 1039 | A91 | 55c Plate No. 15 | .45 | .45 |
| 1040 | A91 | 180c like #1039 | 1.60 | .90 |
| | | Nos. 1021-1040 (20) | 14.70 | 10.85 |

Issued: #1022-1024, 1028-1029, 1033, 1035, 1037, 7/9; #1032, 8/12; #1021, 1030, 1034, 1038, 9/16; #1026, 2/26/86; #1040, 7/24/86; #1025, 1027, 1031, 1036, 1039, 8/21/86.

Nos. 1021, 1034 horiz.

| | | | | |
|---|---|---|---|---|
| 1041 | A91 | 130c Plate No. 16 | 1.00 | .65 |
| 1042 | A91 | 55c Plate No. 17 | .30 | .30 |
| a. | | Wmk. 364 ('87) | 4.25 | 4.25 |
| 1043 | A91 | 80c like #1042 | .40 | .40 |
| 1044 | A91 | 130c Plate No. 18 | 1.00 | .65 |
| 1045 | A91 | 130c Plate No. 19 | .30 | .30 |
| 1046 | A91 | 100c Plate No. 20 | .75 | .75 |
| 1047 | A91 | 130c like #1046 | 1.00 | .65 |
| a. | | Wmk. 364 ('86) | 1.00 | .65 |
| 1048 | A91 | 200c Plate No. 21 | 1.75 | 1.00 |
| 1049 | A91 | 50c Plate No. 22 | .40 | .40 |
| 1050 | A91 | 55c like #1049 | .30 | .30 |
| a. | | Wmk. 364 ('86) | .30 | .30 |
| 1051 | A91 | 25c Plate No. 23 | .20 | .20 |
| 1052 | A91 | 50c Plate No. 24 | .40 | .40 |
| 1053 | A91 | 225c like #1052 | 2.00 | 1.10 |
| a. | | Wmk. 364 ('86) | 2.00 | 1.10 |
| 1054 | A91 | 100c Plate No. 25 | .75 | .75 |
| 1055 | A91 | 130c like #1054 | 1.00 | .65 |
| a. | | Wmk. 364 ('86) | 1.00 | .65 |
| 1056 | A91 | 150c Plate No. 26 | 1.40 | .65 |
| 1057 | A91 | 120c Plate No. 27 | .90 | .60 |
| 1058 | A91 | 120c Plate No. 28 | .90 | .60 |
| 1059 | A91 | 130c Plate No. 29 | 1.00 | .65 |
| 1060 | A91 | 130c Plate No. 30 | 1.00 | .65 |
| | | Nos. 1041-1060 (20) | 16.75 | 11.75 |

Issued: #1044-1045, 1047, 1055, 1057, 1059-1060, 7/9; #1041, 1050, 8/12; #1048, 1051, 1058, 9/16; #1042, 1053, 1056, 7/10/86; #1046, 1049, 1052, 1054, 8/21/86; #1043, 11/25/86.

Nos. 1048, 1058 horiz.

| | | | | |
|---|---|---|---|---|
| 1061 | A91 | 60c Plate No. 31 | .30 | .30 |
| 1062 | A91 | 150c Plate No. 32 | 1.25 | .75 |
| 1063 | A91 | 200c Plate No. 33 | 1.75 | 1.00 |
| 1064 | A91 | 150c Plate No. 34 | 1.40 | .75 |
| 1065 | A91 | 150c Plate No. 35 | 1.40 | .75 |
| 1066 | A91 | 120c Plate No. 36 | .90 | .60 |
| 1067 | A91 | 130c Plate No. 37 | .90 | .60 |
| 1068 | A91 | 130c Plate No. 38 | .90 | .65 |
| 1069 | A91 | 80c Plate No. 39 | .65 | .65 |
| 1070 | A91 | 260c like #1069 | 2.50 | 1.25 |
| a. | | Wmk. 364 ('87) | 4.75 | 4.25 |
| 1071 | A91 | 100c Plate No. 40 | .75 | .75 |
| 1072 | A91 | 150c like #1071 | 1.25 | .75 |
| a. | | Wmk. 364 ('86) | 1.25 | .75 |
| 1073 | A91 | 150c Plate No. 41 | 1.25 | .75 |
| 1074 | A91 | 100c Plate No. 42 | .75 | .75 |
| 1075 | A91 | 150c like #1075 | 1.25 | .75 |
| a. | | Wmk. 364 ('86) | 1.25 | .75 |
| 1076 | A91 | 100c Plate No. 43 | .75 | .75 |
| 1077 | A91 | 200c like #1076 | 1.75 | 1.00 |
| a. | | Wmk. 364 ('86) | 1.75 | 1.00 |
| 1078 | A91 | 60c Plate No. 44 | .30 | .30 |
| 1079 | A91 | 100c Plate No. 45 | .75 | .75 |
| 1080 | A91 | 150c like #1079 | 1.25 | .75 |
| a. | | Wmk. 364 ('86) | 1.25 | .75 |
| | | Nos. 1061-1080 (20) | 21.95 | 14.55 |

Issued: #1061, 7/9; #1062, 1064-1066, 1068, 1073, 1078, 8/12; #1072, 1075, 1077, 1080, 9/16; #1063, 1067, 1070, 7/10/86; #1069, 1071, 1074, 1076, 1079, 8/21/86.

Nos. 1063, 1071-1072, 1074-1077, 1079-1080 horiz.

| | | | | |
|---|---|---|---|---|
| 1081 | A91 | 120c Plate No. 46 | .80 | .60 |
| 1082 | A91 | 60c Plate No. 47 | .30 | .30 |
| 1083 | A91 | 150c Plate No. 48 | 1.25 | .75 |
| 1084 | A91 | 50c Plate No. 49 | 1.00 | 1.00 |
| 1085 | A91 | 55c like #1084 | .30 | .30 |
| a. | | Wmk. 364 ('86) | .30 | .30 |
| 1086 | A91 | 60c Plate No. 50 | .40 | .40 |
| 1087 | A91 | 320c like #1086 | 3.00 | 1.60 |
| a. | | Wmk. 364 ('87) | 8.00 | 7.50 |
| 1088 | A91 | 25c Plate No. 51 | .20 | .20 |
| 1089 | A91 | 25c Plate No. 52 | .20 | .20 |
| 1090 | A91 | 30c Plate No. 53 | .20 | .20 |
| a. | | Wmk. 364 ('86) | .20 | .20 |
| 1091 | A91 | 50c Plate No. 54 | .40 | .40 |
| 1092 | A91 | 45c Plate No. 54 | .25 | .25 |
| a. | | Wmk. 364 ('87) | 7.50 | 7.50 |
| 1093 | A91 | 45c Plate No. 54 | .45 | .45 |
| 1094 | A91 | 50c Plate No. 55 | 1.00 | 1.00 |
| 1095 | A91 | 60c like #1094 | 1.25 | 1.25 |
| 1096 | A91 | 75c like #1094 | .40 | .40 |
| a. | | Wmk. 364 | .40 | .40 |
| 1097 | A91 | 120c Plate No. 56 | .90 | .60 |
| 1098 | A91 | 60c Plate No. 57 | .30 | .30 |
| 1099 | A91 | 120c Plate No. 58 | .90 | .60 |
| 1100 | A91 | 120c Plate No. 59 | .20 | .20 |
| a. | | Dark red flowers ('86) | .20 | .20 |
| | | Nos. 1081-1100 (20) | 13.70 | 11.00 |

Issued: #1082-1083, 1085, 1089, 8/12; #1088, 9/16; #1095, 10/7; #1087, 1092, 2/26/86; #1081, 1090, 1096-1100, 7/10/86; #1086, 1091, 1093, 8/21/86; #1084, 12/22/86; #1094, 1/16/87.

No. 1098 horiz.

| | | | | |
|---|---|---|---|---|
| 1101 | A91 | 75c Plate No. 60 | .55 | .55 |
| 1102 | A91 | 225c like #1101 | 2.00 | 1.10 |
| a. | | Wmk. 364 ('87) | 9.00 | 8.50 |
| 1103 | A91 | 25c Plate No. 61 | .20 | .20 |
| 1104 | A91 | 150c Plate No. 62 | 1.25 | .75 |
| 1105 | A91 | 25c Plate No. 63 | .20 | .20 |
| 1106 | A91 | 50c Plate No. 64 | 1.00 | 1.00 |
| a. | | Wmk. 364 | — | — |
| 1107 | A91 | 55c like #1106 | .30 | .30 |
| a. | | Wmk. 364 ('86) | .30 | .30 |
| 1108 | A91 | 50c Plate No. 65 | .40 | .40 |
| 1109 | A91 | 100c like #1108 | .50 | .50 |
| a. | | Wmk. 364 | .50 | .50 |
| 1110 | A91 | 130c Plate No. 66 | 1.00 | .65 |
| 1111 | A91 | 120c Plate No. 67 | .90 | .60 |
| 1112 | A91 | 40c Plate No. 68 | 1.00 | 1.00 |
| 1113 | A91 | 100c like #1112 | .50 | .50 |
| a. | | Wmk. 364 ('87) | 4.25 | 4.25 |
| 1114 | A91 | 60c Plate No. 69 | .45 | .45 |
| 1115 | A91 | 120c like #1114 | .90 | .60 |
| a. | | Wmk. 364 ('87) | 8.25 | 8.25 |
| 1116 | A91 | 25c Plate No. 70 | .20 | .20 |
| 1117 | A91 | 25c Plate No. 71 | .20 | .20 |
| a. | | Wmk. 364 ('87) | 8.25 | 8.25 |
| 1118 | A91 | 60c like #1117 | .45 | .45 |
| 1119 | A91 | 25c Plate No. 72 | .20 | .20 |
| 1120 | A91 | 60c Plate No. 73 | .45 | .45 |
| | | Nos. 1101-1120 (20) | 12.50 | 10.15 |

Issued: #1104, 1107, 8/12; #1103, 1105, 1116, 9/16; #1102, 1115, 1117, 4/4/86; #1109-1111, 1113, 1120, 7/10/86; #1101, 1108, 1114, 1118, 8/21/86; #1112, 11/25/86.

No. 1114-1115, 1117-1118, 1120 horiz.

| | | | | |
|---|---|---|---|---|
| 1121 | A91 | 80c Plate No. 74 | .60 | .60 |
| 1122 | A91 | 250c like #1121 | 2.25 | 1.25 |
| a. | | Wmk. 364 ('87) | 4.50 | 4.25 |
| 1123 | A91 | 60c Plate No. 75 | .30 | .30 |
| 1124 | A91 | 65c Plate No. 76 | .50 | .50 |
| 1125 | A91 | 150c Plate No. 124 | 1.25 | .75 |
| a. | | Wmk. 364 ('87) | 8.50 | 8.00 |
| 1126 | A91 | 40c Plate No. 77 | .20 | .20 |
| a. | | Wmk. 364 ('87) | 7.50 | 7.50 |
| 1127 | A91 | 45c like #1126 | .35 | .35 |
| 1128 | A91 | 45c Plate No. 78 | .35 | .35 |
| 1129 | A91 | 150c like #1128 | 1.25 | .75 |
| a. | | Wmk. 364 ('87) | 7.75 | 7.50 |
| 1130 | A91 | 60c Plate No. 79 | .45 | .45 |
| 1131 | A91 | 200c like #1130 | 1.75 | 1.00 |
| a. | | Wmk. 364 ('87) | 7.75 | 7.50 |
| 1132 | A91 | 65c Plate No. 80 | .50 | .50 |
| 1133 | A91 | 330c like #1132 | 3.00 | 1.60 |
| a. | | Wmk. 364 ('87) | 8.25 | 8.00 |
| 1134 | A91 | 45c Plate No. 81 | .25 | .25 |
| a. | | Wmk. 364 ('87) | 8.00 | 8.00 |
| 1135 | A91 | 55c like #1134 | .45 | .45 |
| 1136 | A91 | 55c Plate No. 82 | .45 | .45 |
| 1137 | A91 | 320c like #1136 | 3.00 | 1.60 |
| a. | | Wmk. 364 ('87) | 8.25 | 8.00 |
| 1138 | A91 | 75c Plate No. 83 | .55 | .55 |
| 1139 | A91 | 300c like #1138 | 2.75 | 1.50 |
| a. | | Wmk. 364 ('87) | 8.50 | 8.25 |
| 1140 | A91 | 45c like #1134 | .35 | .35 |
| 1141 | A91 | 90c like #1140 | .45 | .45 |
| | | Wmk. 364 | 7.50 | 7.50 |
| | | Nos. 1121-1141 (21) | 21.00 | 14.20 |

Issued: #1126, 1129, 1131, 1139, 1141, 2/26/86; #1122-1123, 7/10/86; #1125, 1133-1134, 1137, 7/24/86; #1121, 1124, 1127-1128, 1130, 1132, 1135-1136, 1138, 1140, 8/21/86.

No. 1123 horiz.

| | | | | |
|---|---|---|---|---|
| 1142 | A91 | 45c Plate No. 85 | .35 | .35 |
| 1143 | A91 | 360c like #1142 | 3.00 | 1.75 |
| a. | | Wmk. 364 ('87) | 8.00 | 7.50 |
| 1144 | A91 | 30c Plate No. 86 | .20 | .20 |
| a. | | Wmk. 364 ('87) | 4.25 | 4.25 |
| 1145 | A91 | 40c like #1144 | 1.00 | 1.00 |
| 1146 | A91 | 60c Plate No. 87 | .45 | .45 |
| 1147 | A91 | 150c like #1146 | 1.25 | .75 |
| a. | | Wmk. 364 ('87) | 9.00 | 8.25 |
| 1148 | A91 | 65c Plate No. 88 | .45 | .45 |
| 1149 | A91 | 100c like #1148 | .50 | .50 |
| a. | | Wmk. 364 ('87) | 8.00 | 8.00 |
| 1150 | A91 | 55c Plate No. 89 | .40 | .40 |
| 1151 | A91 | 90c like #1150 | .45 | .45 |
| a. | | Wmk. 364 ('87) | 8.00 | 8.00 |
| 1152 | A91 | 40c Plate No. 90 | .30 | .30 |
| 1153 | A91 | 375c like #1152 | 1.90 | 1.90 |
| a. | | Wmk. 364 ('87) | 4.25 | 4.25 |
| 1154 | A91 | 40c Plate No. 91 | 1.75 | 1.75 |
| 1155 | A91 | 130c like #1154 | 1.25 | .65 |
| a. | | Wmk. 364 ('87) | 4.50 | 4.25 |
| 1156 | A91 | 50c Plate No. 92 | .25 | .25 |
| a. | | Wmk. 364 ('87) | 8.25 | 8.25 |
| 1157 | A91 | 75c Plate No. 93 | .55 | .55 |
| 1158 | A91 | 60c like #1156 | .30 | .30 |
| a. | | Wmk. 364 ('87) | 4.25 | 4.25 |
| 1159 | A91 | 80c like #1158 | .60 | .60 |
| 1160 | A91 | 45c Plate No. 94 | .45 | .45 |
| 1161 | A91 | 350c like #1160 | 3.25 | 1.75 |
| a. | | Wmk. 364 ('87) | 8.50 | 8.25 |
| 1162 | A91 | 60c Plate No. 95 | .30 | .30 |
| a. | | Wmk. 364 ('87) | 8.25 | 8.25 |
| 1163 | A91 | 75c Plate No. 96 | .55 | .55 |
| 1164 | A91 | 40c Plate No. 96 | .20 | .20 |
| 1165 | A91 | 65c like #1164 | .50 | .50 |
| | | Nos. 1142-1165 (24) | 20.20 | 16.35 |

See note below #1341. Issued: #1143, 1156, 1162, 2/26/86; #1147, 1161, 4/4/86; #1144, 1153, 1155, 1158, 7/10/86; #1149, 1150, 1152, 1157, 1159-1160, 1163, 1165, 8/21/86, 9/26/86; #1145, 10/23/86.

Some stamps printed in sheets of 25, blocks of 4 each of different stamps separated by gutter containing 2 #1337 and strip of 5 #1339. Margin contains separation marks for #1337, 1339.

Nos. 1146-1147, 1160-1161 horiz.

Nos. 1025, 1027, 1031, 1036, 1039, 1046, 1049, 1052, 1054, 1069, 1071, 1074, 1076, 1079, 1086, 1091, 1093, 1101, 1108, 1114, 1118, 1121, 1124, 1127-1128, 1130, 1132, 1135-1136, 1138, 1140, 1142, 1146, 1148, 1150, 1152, 1157, 1159-1160, 1163, 1165 sold as singles in booklets only. Two booklets of 48 stamps each contain these numbers and previous values issued in the series.

See #1372. For overprints and surcharges see #1342-1346, 1393, 1402-1403, 1412-1413, 1494, 1511-1670F, 1731-1740, 1742-1750, 1755-1759, 1761, 1764-1773, 1785, 1845-1849, 1906-1909, 1914-1933, 1939-1941, 1943-1947, 1958-1959, 1960-1979, 2000, C7, C9-C12, E2, E4.

**1986-89    Litho.    Unwmk.    Perf. 14**
### Series 2
| | | | | |
|---|---|---|---|---|
| 1166 | A91 | 175c Plate No. 1 | 1.50 | .65 |
| 1167 | A91 | 560c like #1166 | 4.50 | 1.60 |
| 1168 | A91 | 90c Plate No. 2 | 1.00 | 1.00 |
| 1169 | A91 | 200c like #1168 | 1.75 | 1.00 |
| 1170 | A91 | 50c Plate No. 3 | .20 | .20 |
| 1171 | A91 | 90c like #1170 | .45 | .45 |
| 1172 | A91 | 90c Plate No. 4 | .45 | .45 |
| 1173 | A91 | 140c like #1172 | 1.25 | .50 |
| 1174 | A91 | 130c Plate No. 5 | 1.10 | .50 |
| 1175 | A91 | 160c like #1174 | 1.50 | .80 |
| 1176 | A91 | 50c Plate No. 6 | .20 | .20 |
| 1177 | A91 | 390c like #1176 | 3.50 | 2.00 |
| 1178 | A91 | 30c Plate No. 7 | .20 | .20 |
| 1179 | A91 | 40c like #1178 | .20 | .20 |
| 1180 | A91 | 70c Plate No. 8 | .25 | .25 |
| 1181 | A91 | 75c like #1180 | .40 | .40 |
| 1182 | A91 | 70c Plate No. 9 | .25 | .25 |
| 1183 | A91 | 200c like #1182 | 1.75 | 1.00 |
| 1184 | A91 | 90c Plate No. 10 | 1.25 | 1.25 |
| 1185 | A91 | 320c like #1184 | 2.75 | 1.60 |
| | | Nos. 1166-1185 (20) | 24.45 | 14.50 |

Issued: #1172, 1175, 1181, 1183, 9/23; #1184, 10/23; #1177, 1185, 10/31; #1169, 11/25; #1171, 1179, 12/27; #1168, 1/5/87; #1167, 4/24/87; #1166, 1170, 1173-1174, 1176, 1178, 1180, 1182, 8/23/88.
Nos. 1174-1175 horiz.

| | | | | |
|---|---|---|---|---|
| 1186 | A91 | 200c Plate No. 11 | 1.75 | .75 |
| 1187 | A91 | 70c Plate No. 12 | .25 | .25 |
| 1188 | A91 | 320c like #1187 | 2.75 | 1.60 |
| 1189 | A91 | 50c Plate No. 13 | 1.25 | 1.25 |
| 1190 | A91 | 90c like #1189 | .45 | .45 |
| 1191 | A91 | 30c Plate No. 14 | .20 | .20 |
| 1192 | A91 | 120c like #1191 | 1.00 | .60 |
| 1193 | A91 | 50c Plate No. 15 | 3.75 | 3.75 |
| 1194 | A91 | 85c like #1193 | .45 | .45 |
| 1195 | A91 | 260c like #1193 | 2.00 | .55 |
| 1196 | A91 | 320c like #1195 | 3.00 | 1.25 |
| 1197 | A91 | 45c Plate No. 17 | .20 | .20 |
| 1198 | A91 | 70c like #1197 | .25 | .25 |
| 1199 | A91 | 85c like #1197 | .45 | .45 |
| 1200 | A91 | 320c like #1199 | 3.00 | 1.60 |
| 1201 | A91 | 175c Plate No. 19 | 1.50 | .75 |
| 1202 | A91 | 450c like #1201 | 3.75 | 1.25 |
| 1203 | A91 | 25c Plate No. 20 | .20 | .20 |
| 1204 | A91 | 50c like #1203 | .20 | .20 |
| 1205 | A91 | 45c Plate No. 21 | 1.50 | 1.50 |
| | | Nos. 1186-1205 (20) | 27.90 | 17.40 |

Issued: #1188, 1205, 9/23; #1190, 1197, 10/31; #1189, 12/3; #1192, 1194, 1200, 1203, 12/27; #1193, 1199, 1/5/87; #1202, 4/24/87; #1196, 6/1/88; #1186-1187, 1191, 1198, 1201, 1204, 8/23/88; #1195, 7/7/89.
Nos. 1201-1202, 1205, horiz.

| | | | | |
|---|---|---|---|---|
| 1206 | A91 | 30c Plate No. 22 | .20 | .20 |
| 1207 | A91 | 150c like #1206 | 1.25 | .75 |
| 1208 | A91 | 200c Plate No. 23 | 1.75 | .75 |
| 1209 | A91 | 85c like #1209 | 1.00 | 1.00 |
| 1210 | A91 | 225c like #1209 | 3.25 | 3.25 |
| 1211 | A91 | 140c Plate No. 25 | 1.10 | .50 |
| 1212 | A91 | 230c like #1211 | 2.00 | .60 |
| 1213 | A91 | 200c Plate No. 26 | 1.75 | .75 |
| 1214 | A91 | 60c like #1214 | .30 | .30 |
| 1215 | A91 | 90c like #1214 | 1.00 | 1.00 |
| 1216 | A91 | 30c Plate No. 28 | .20 | .20 |
| 1217 | A91 | 330c like #1216 | 3.00 | 1.60 |
| 1218 | A91 | 130c Plate No. 29 | 1.00 | .50 |
| 1219 | A91 | 350c like #1218 | 3.25 | 1.75 |
| 1220 | A91 | 50c Plate No. 30 | 2.50 | 2.50 |
| 1221 | A91 | 875c like #1220 | 6.00 | 3.50 |
| 1222 | A91 | 50c Plate No. 32 | .25 | .25 |
| 1223 | A91 | 130c like #1222 | 1.00 | .60 |
| 1224 | A91 | 50c Plate No. 33 | .25 | .25 |
| 1225 | A91 | 100c like #1224 | .75 | .75 |
| | | Nos. 1206-1225 (20) | 31.75 | 21.00 |

Issued: #1219, 1220, 9/23; #1214, 1224, 10/31; #1210, 11/25; #1209, 1215, 12/15; #1207, 1217, 1223, 12/27; #1212, 2/14/87; #1221, 6/15/88; #1206, 1208, 1211, 1213, 1216, 1218, 1222, 1225, 8/23/88.
Nos. 1218-1219 horiz.

| | | | | |
|---|---|---|---|---|
| 1226 | A91 | 140c Plate No. 34 | 1.10 | .50 |
| 1227 | A91 | 360c like #1226 | 3.00 | 1.75 |
| 1228 | A91 | 380c Plate No. 35 | 3.25 | 1.40 |
| 1229 | A91 | 525c like #1228 | 4.00 | 2.25 |
| 1230 | A91 | 175c Plate No. 37 | 1.25 | .65 |
| 1231 | A91 | 390c like #1230 | 3.00 | 1.25 |
| 1232 | A91 | 130c Plate No. 38 | 1.00 | .65 |
| 1233 | A91 | 140c like #1232 | 1.10 | .50 |
| 1234 | A91 | 175c Plate No. 39 | 1.50 | .65 |
| 1235 | A91 | 260c like #1234 | 2.00 | .75 |
| 1236 | A91 | 250c Plate No. 40 | 2.00 | .90 |
| 1237 | A91 | $10 like #1236 | 5.50 | 4.25 |
| 1238 | A91 | 140c Plate No. 41 | 1.10 | .50 |
| 1239 | A91 | 180c like #1238 | 1.40 | .45 |

| | | | | | |
|---|---|---|---|---|---|
| 1240 | A91 | 80c Plate No. 42 | | .40 | .40 |
| 1241 | A91 | 130c like #1240 | | 1.10 | .50 |
| 1242 | A91 | 200c Plate No. 43 | | 1.75 | .55 |
| 1243 | A91 | 100c Plate No. 44 | | .75 | .75 |
| 1244 | A91 | 200c Plate No. 43 | | 1.75 | 1.00 |
| 1245 | A91 | 35c Plate No. 45 | | .20 | .20 |
| 1246 | A91 | 85c Plate No. 1245 | | .40 | .40 |
| | | Nos. 1226-1246 (21) | | 37.55 | 20.25 |

Issued: #1227, 1232, 1240, 9/23; #1244, 1246, 10/31; #1245, 1/5/87; #1239, 2/14/87; #1231, 1235, 4/24/87; #1242, 9/29/87; #1237, 3/24/88; #1229, 6/1/88; #1226, 1228, 1230, 1233-1234, 1236, 1238, 1241, 1243, 8/23/88. Nos. 1230-1231, 1240-1241 horiz.

| | | | | | |
|---|---|---|---|---|---|
| 1247 | A91 | 225c Plate No. 46 | | 1.50 | .80 |
| 1248 | A91 | 175c Plate No. 47 | | 1.25 | .65 |
| 1249 | A91 | 240c like #1248 | | 1.75 | .70 |
| 1250 | A91 | 200c Plate No. 48 | | 1.40 | .55 |
| 1251 | A91 | 200c Plate No. 49 | | 1.40 | .55 |
| 1252 | A91 | 720c like #1251 | | 4.00 | 3.00 |
| 1253 | A91 | 160c Plate No. 50 | | 1.00 | .55 |
| 1254 | A91 | 300c like #1253 | | 2.00 | 1.50 |
| 1255 | A91 | 175c Plate No. 51 | | 1.10 | .60 |
| 1256 | A91 | 500c like #1255 | | 3.00 | 1.50 |
| 1257 | A91 | 140c Plate No. 52 | | 1.00 | .40 |
| 1258 | A91 | 590c like #1257 | | 3.00 | 1.50 |
| 1259 | A91 | 200c Plate No. 53 | | 1.25 | .55 |
| 1260 | A91 | 290c like #1259 | | 2.00 | 1.25 |
| 1261 | A91 | 175c Plate No. 54 | | 1.25 | .60 |
| 1261A | A91 | 460c like #1261 | | 2.75 | 1.40 |
| 1262 | A91 | 120c Plate No. 55 | | .90 | .35 |
| 1263 | A91 | 75c Plate No. 56 | | .40 | .40 |
| 1264 | A91 | 100c Plate No. 1263 | | .30 | .30 |
| 1265 | A91 | 225c Plate No. 57 | | 1.25 | .60 |
| | | Nos. 1247-1265 (20) | | 32.50 | 17.75 |

Issued: #1254, 1263, 10/31; #1258, 2/14/87; #1249, 1256, 1261A, 4/24/87; #1262, 9/29/87; #1252, 1260, 11/23/87; #1247-1248, 8/23/88; #1253, 1255, 11/3/88; #1251, 1257, 1259, 1261-1262, 1264-1265, 1/3/89. Nos 1261, 1261A horiz.

| | | | | | |
|---|---|---|---|---|---|
| 1266 | A91 | 175c Plate No. 58 | | 1.25 | .50 |
| 1267 | A91 | 275c like #1266 | | 2.00 | .85 |
| 1268 | A91 | 775c Plate No. 59 | | 4.00 | 3.25 |
| 1269 | A91 | 200c Plate No. 60 | | 1.50 | .55 |
| 1270 | A91 | 575c like #1269 | | 2.75 | 1.50 |
| 1271 | A91 | 255c Plate No. 61 | | 2.00 | 1.00 |
| 1272 | A91 | 280c like #1271 | | 1.40 | .95 |
| 1273 | A91 | 700c like #1272 | | 3.50 | 3.00 |
| 1274 | A91 | 285c Plate No. 63 | | 1.40 | 1.00 |
| 1275 | A91 | 200c Plate No. 64 | | 1.00 | .55 |
| 1276 | A91 | 680c like #1275 | | 3.25 | 2.75 |
| 1277 | A91 | 140c Plate No. 65 | | .70 | .40 |
| 1278 | A91 | 650c like #1277 | | 3.00 | 1.60 |
| 1279 | A91 | 280c like #1275 | | 1.25 | .75 |
| 1280 | A91 | 750c like #1279 | | 3.50 | 3.00 |
| 1281 | A91 | 280c Plate No. 67 | | 1.25 | .75 |
| 1282 | A91 | $15 like #1281 | | 7.00 | 6.25 |
| 1283 | A91 | 325c Plate No. 68 | | 1.75 | .85 |
| 1284 | A91 | 530c Plate No. 69 | | 2.50 | 2.25 |
| 1285 | A91 | 550c Plate No. 70 | | 2.75 | 2.75 |
| | | Nos. 1266-1285 (20) | | 47.75 | 34.50 |

Issued: #1278, 2/14/87; #1267, 4/24/87; #1270, 1283, 10/26/87; #1271, 1276, 1280, 11/23/87; #1282, 1288, 6/1/88; #1268, 1273, 6/15/88; #1285, 8/15/88; #1272, 1274, 11/3/88; #1266, 1269, 1275, 1277, 1279, 1281, 1/3/89. No. 1266-1267, 1283, 1285 horiz.

| | | | | | |
|---|---|---|---|---|---|
| 1286 | A91 | 670c Plate No. 71 | | 3.50 | 3.25 |
| 1287 | A91 | 300c Plate No. 72 | | 1.50 | .80 |
| 1288 | A91 | $25 like #1287 | | 7.50 | 6.50 |
| 1289 | A91 | 130c like #1289 | | .80 | .25 |
| 1290 | A91 | 475c like #1289 | | 2.25 | 2.00 |
| 1291 | A91 | 350c Plate No. 74 | | 1.75 | 1.50 |
| 1291A | A91 | 900c like #1291 | | 4.50 | 4.00 |
| 1291B | A91 | 600c on 900c #1291A | | | |
| 1292 | A91 | 200c Plate No. 75 | | 1.00 | .70 |
| 1293 | A91 | 250c like #1293 | | 1.25 | .65 |
| 1294 | A91 | 850c like #1293 | | 4.00 | 3.50 |
| 1295 | A91 | 300c Plate No. 77 | | 1.50 | .80 |
| 1296 | A91 | 480c like #1295 | | 2.25 | 1.25 |
| 1297 | A91 | 280c Plate No. 78 | | 1.40 | .75 |
| 1298 | A91 | 950c like #1298 | | 4.50 | 4.00 |
| 1299 | A91 | 250c Plate No. 79 | | 1.25 | .90 |
| 1300 | A91 | 800c like #1299 | | 4.00 | 3.25 |
| 1301 | A91 | 800c Plate No. 80 | | 1.50 | .80 |
| 1302 | A91 | 400c like #1301 | | 2.00 | 1.10 |
| 1303 | A91 | 305c Plate No. 81 | | 1.50 | .80 |
| 1304 | A91 | 250c Plate No. 82 | | 1.25 | .65 |
| 1305 | A91 | 330c like #1304 | | 1.60 | .85 |
| | | Nos. 1286-1291A,1292-1305 (21) | | 50.80 | 38.30 |

Issued: #1305, 2/14/87; #1288, 1296, 1302, 7/22/87; #1291A-1291B, 10/9/87; #1294, 1300, 11/23/87; #1290, 6/1/88; #1298, 6/15/88; #1291, 6/22/88; #1286, 8/15/88; #1292, 1299, 11/3/88; #1287, 1293, 1295, 1297, 1301, 1303-1304, 1/3/89; #1289, 7/7/89. No. 1286 horiz.

| | | | | | |
|---|---|---|---|---|---|
| 1306 | A91 | 350c Plate No. 83 | | 1.75 | .95 |
| 1307 | A91 | $20 like #1306 | | 7.50 | 5.25 |
| 1308 | A91 | 360c Plate No. 84 | | 1.90 | 1.75 |
| 1309 | A91 | 250c Plate No. 85 | | 1.25 | .65 |
| 1310 | A91 | 300c like #1309 | | 1.50 | .75 |
| 1311 | A91 | 350c Plate No. 86 | | 1.75 | .95 |
| 1312 | A91 | 500c like #1311 | | 2.25 | 1.25 |
| 1313 | A91 | 250c Plate No. 87 | | 1.25 | .65 |
| 1314 | A91 | 425c like #1313 | | 2.00 | 1.00 |
| 1315 | A91 | 250c Plate No. 88 | | 1.25 | .65 |
| 1316 | A91 | 440c like #1315 | | 2.00 | 1.10 |
| 1317 | A91 | 350c Plate No. 89 | | 1.75 | .95 |
| 1318 | A91 | 520c like #1317 | | 2.60 | 1.40 |
| 1319 | A91 | 270c Plate No. 90 | | 1.25 | 1.25 |

| | | | | | |
|---|---|---|---|---|---|
| 1320 | A91 | 250c Plate No. 91 | | 1.10 | .65 |
| 1321 | A91 | $12 like #1320 | | 5.50 | 5.00 |
| 1322 | A91 | 200c Plate No. 92 | | 1.00 | .55 |
| 1323 | A91 | 200c Plate No. 93 | | 1.00 | .70 |
| 1324 | A91 | 300c Plate No. 94 | | 1.50 | .80 |
| 1325 | A91 | 600c like #1324 | | 2.75 | 1.60 |
| 1326 | A91 | 420c Plate No. 95 | | 2.00 | 1.25 |
| 1327 | A91 | 200c Plate No. 96 | | 1.00 | .40 |
| 1328 | A91 | 375c like #1327 | | 1.75 | 1.50 |
| | | Nos. 1306-1328 (23) | | 47.60 | 31.00 |

Issued: #1310, 1314, 1316, 2/14/87; #1307, 1312, 1318, 6/2/87; #1325, 7/22/87/ #1322, 9/29/87; #1326, 10/26/87; #1328, 11/23/87; #1321, 3/24/88; #1308, 1319, 8/15/88; #1323, 11/3/88; #1306, 1309, 1311, 1313, 1315, 1317, 1320, 1324, 1/3/89; #1327, 7/7/89. No. 1326, horiz.

Nos. 1166, 1170, 1174, 1176, 1178, 1180, 1182, 1187, 1191, 1193, 1198, 1201, 1204, 1206, 1211, 1216, 1218, 1222, 1225-1226, 1230, 1233-1234, 1236, 1238, 1248, 1257, 1261, 1264, 1266, 1277, 1279, 1281, 1287, 1293, 1295, 1297, 1301, 1304, 1306, 1308-1309, 1311, 1313, 1315, 1317, 1320, 1324 sold as singles in booklets only. Two booklets of 48 stamps each contain these numbers and previous values issued in the series.

### Miniature Sheets of 4

Designs: Nos. 1329a, 1330b, 1331b, like #1303. Nos. 1329b, 1330a, 1332a, like #1265. Nos. 1329c, 1330c, 1332b, like #1247. Nos. 1330d, 1331a, 1332c, like #1262.

| | | | | |
|---|---|---|---|---|
| 1329 | | #1262, 1329a-1329c | 2.25 | 2.25 |
| a.-c. | A91 | 120c any single | .50 | .50 |
| 1330 | | #a.-d. | 2.50 | 2.50 |
| a.-d. | A91 | 150c any single | .55 | .55 |
| 1331 | | #1247, 1265, 1331a-1331b | 4.25 | 4.25 |
| a.-b. | A91 | 225c any single | .80 | .80 |
| 1332 | | #1303, 1332a-1332c | 4.50 | 4.50 |
| a.-c. | A91 | 305c any single | .90 | .90 |
| 1333 | | | 6.00 | 6.00 |
| a. | A91 | 320c like #1262 | 1.10 | 1.10 |
| b. | A91 | 330c like #1247 | 1.10 | 1.10 |
| c. | A91 | 350c like #1303 | 1.25 | 1.25 |
| d. | A91 | 500c like #1265 | 2.00 | 2.00 |
| 1334 | | | 6.00 | 6.00 |
| a. | A91 | 320c like #1247 | 1.10 | 1.10 |
| b. | A91 | 330c like #1262 | 1.10 | 1.10 |
| c. | A91 | 350c like #1265 | 1.25 | 1.25 |
| d. | A91 | 500c like #1303 | 2.00 | 2.00 |
| 1335 | | | 6.00 | 6.00 |
| a. | A91 | 320c like #1303 | 1.10 | 1.10 |
| b. | A91 | 330c like #1265 | 1.10 | 1.10 |
| c. | A91 | 350c like #1262 | 1.25 | 1.25 |
| d. | A91 | 500c like #1247 | 2.00 | 2.00 |
| 1336 | | | 6.00 | 6.00 |
| a. | A91 | 320c like #1265 | 1.10 | 1.10 |
| b. | A91 | 330c like #1303 | 1.10 | 1.10 |
| c. | A91 | 350c like #1247 | 1.25 | 1.25 |
| d. | A91 | 500c like #1262 | 2.00 | 2.00 |

Issued: #1329-1332, 7/7/89; others, 2/26/88.
For surcharges & overprints see #1671-1727, 1776-1777, 1834-1835, 1942, 1948-1952, 1998-1999, 2031, 2033-2044, 2064, 2907A-2907G, 2928A-2928D, E3, E5, O40-O56.

Natl. Arms — A92

| | | | | |
|---|---|---|---|---|
| **1985-87** | | | **Perf. 14 Vert.** | |
| 1337 | A92 | 25c multi | .20 | .50 |
| 1338 | A92 | 25c multi ('87) | 1.25 | .75 |
| | | **Perf. 14 Horiz.** | | |
| 1339 | A92 | 25c multi | .20 | .20 |
| 1340 | A92 | 25c multi ('87) | 1.25 | .75 |
| | | Nos. 1337-1340 (4) | 2.90 | 2.20 |
| | | **Perf. 14** | | |
| 1341 | A92 | 25c multi | | |

Nos. 1337-1340 were cut from orchid sheet gutters. Stamps vary considerably in size. Nos. 1338, 1340 are Nos. 1337 and 1339 redrawn to include black border.

Issue dates: Nos. 1337, 1339, 1341, July 1985. No. 1338, 1340 June 2, 1987.

See Nos. 1467-1468. For surcharges see Nos. 1777A-1777C.

Nos. 1024, 1044, 1047, 1059, 1060 Surcharged or Overprinted in Blue or Black "QUEEN MOTHER 1900-1985" on 1 or 2 Lines

| | | | | |
|---|---|---|---|---|
| **1985** | | | **Perfs. as Before** | |
| 1342 | A91 | 130c on #1044 | | |
| 1343 | A91 | 130c on #1059 | | |
| 1344 | A91 | 130c on #1060 | | |
| | | Nos. 1342-1344 (3) | 6.25 | |

#### Miniature sheets

| | | | | |
|---|---|---|---|---|
| 1345 | | Sheet of 4 | 7.50 | |
| a.-d. | A91 | 200c on #1024, any single | | |
| 1346 | | Sheet of 4 | 11.00 | |
| a.-d. | A91 | 200c on 130c #1047, any single (Bk) | | |

Issued: #1342-1345, July 9; #1346, Sept. 12. Nos. 1345a, 1346a overprinted "LADY BOWES-LYON 1900-1923". Nos. 1345b, 1346b overprinted "DUCHESS OF YORK 1923-1937". Nos. 1345c, 1346c overprinted "QUEEN ELIZABETH 1937-1952". Surcharge on No. 1346 sans serif.

For overprints see #1741, 1751-1754, 1774-1775.

Nos. 465 Surcharged in Red "INTERNATIONAL / YOUTH YEAR / 1985"
**Perf. 13x13½**

| | | | | |
|---|---|---|---|---|
| **1985, July 18** | | **Litho.** | **Wmk. 364** | |
| 1347 | | Sheet of 25, 8 #a.-b., 4 #c.-d., 1 #e. | 175.00 | |
| a.-e. | A28 | 25c on #465a-465e, any single | | |

No. 203 Surcharged "1910-1985" and

No. 443 Surcharged

| | | | | |
|---|---|---|---|---|
| **1985, July 26** | | | **Perfs. as Before** | |
| **Watermarks & Printing Methods as Before** | | | | |
| 1352 | A47 | 225c on #203 | 30.00 | 4.00 |
| 1354 | A63 | 240c on #443 | 20.00 | 5.00 |

Girl Guides, 75th anniv. (#1352), John J. Audubon, bicentennial of birth. No. 203 surcharged only with 350c, $2.25 or surcharged with both was not issued.

Abolition of Slavery, Sesquicent. — A93

Designs: 25c, Revolution leaders, 1763. 60c, Damon's execution, 1834. 130c, Demerara Uprising, 1823. 150c Den Arendt slave ship.

| | | | | |
|---|---|---|---|---|
| | | **Unwmk.** | | |
| **1985, July 29** | | **Litho.** | **Perf. 14** | |
| 1355 | A93 | 25c gray & black | .25 | .25 |
| 1356 | A93 | 60c pink & black | .65 | .65 |
| 1357 | A93 | 130c blue grn & blk | 1.40 | 1.40 |
| 1358 | A93 | 150c lilac & blk | 1.60 | 1.60 |
| | | Nos. 1355-1358 (4) | 3.90 | 3.90 |

See Nos. 1994-1997 for changed colors.

No. 210 Surcharged "Guyana/Libya / Friendship 1985"
No. 223 Surcharged in Brown
No. 135 Surcharged "Mexico / 1986"

| | | | | |
|---|---|---|---|---|
| **1985, Aug. 16** | | | **Perfs. as Before** | |
| **Watermarks and Printing Methods as Before** | | | | |
| 1359 | A49 | 150c on #210 | 9.00 | 3.00 |
| 1360 | A53 | 150c on #223 | 2.75 | .85 |
| 1361 | A28 | 275c on 3c #135 | 9.00 | 1.75 |
| | | Nos. 1359-1361 (3) | 20.75 | |

Refer to 2nd paragraph under No. 147 for No. 1361. See No. 1452 for 225c Mexico 1986 surcharge.

Nos. 366, 427, 430, 430a, 494, & 553 Ovptd. or Surcharged "1955-1985" Vertically or Horizontally
**Wmk. 364**

| | | | | |
|---|---|---|---|---|
| **1985, Sept. 23** | | **Litho.** | **Perf. 13½** | |
| 1362 | A75 | 60c on #366 | .50 | .50 |
| 1363 | A75 | 60c on #553 | .50 | .50 |
| 1364 | A75 | 120c on #427 | 1.00 | 1.00 |
| 1365 | A75 | 120c on #430 | 1.00 | 1.00 |
| 1366 | A75 | 120c on #430a | 1.00 | 1.00 |
| 1367 | A75 | 120c on #494 | 1.00 | 1.00 |
| | | Nos. 1362-1367 (6) | 5.00 | |

No. 417 Surcharged "1965-1985" Vertically

| | | | | |
|---|---|---|---|---|
| **1985, Sept. 30** | | | | |
| 1368 | A79 | 25c on #417 | .75 | .30 |
| 1369 | A79 | 225c on #417 | 2.50 | 1.50 |
| | | Nos. 1368-1369 (2) | 3.25 | |

Nos. 260 & 262 Surcharged "1985"

| | | | | |
|---|---|---|---|---|
| **1985, Oct. 5** | | **Litho.** | **Perf. 14x14½** | |
| 1370 | A61 | 25c on #262 | 11.00 | .40 |
| 1371 | A61 | 320c on 15c #260 | 20.00 | 3.75 |

Orchid Type of 1985 Surcharged in Red "CRISTOBAL COLON / 1492-1992"

| | | | | |
|---|---|---|---|---|
| **1985, Oct. 12** | | | **Perf. 14** | |
| 1372 | A91 | 350c on 120c like #1108 | 8.75 | 3.25 |

No. 1372 not issued without surcharge. For overprint see No. E1. For surcharge see No. 1591A.

No. 288 Overprinted "SIR WINSTON CHURCHILL / 1965-1985"

| | | | | |
|---|---|---|---|---|
| **1985, Oct. 15** | | | **Perf. 13½x13** | |
| 1373 | A66 | $2 on #288 | 12.00 | 3.75 |

No. 214 Surcharged "1950-1985"

| | | | | |
|---|---|---|---|---|
| **1985, Oct. 15** | | | **Perf. 14** | |
| 1374 | A50 | 25c on 110c on 10c | .30 | .20 |
| 1375 | A50 | 200c on 110c on 10c | 1.25 | 1.25 |
| | | Nos. 1374-1375 (2) | 1.55 | |

#214 with 110c surcharge only was not issued.

Nos. 295-297, 384, and O9 Overprinted or Surcharged "United / Nations / 1945-1985"

| | | | | |
|---|---|---|---|---|
| **1985, Oct. 28** | | | **Perf. 14x14½** | |
| 1376 | A68 | 30c on #295 | 1.75 | .20 |
| 1377 | A68 | 50c on #296 | 1.75 | .30 |
| 1378 | A68 | 100c on #O9 | 1.75 | .50 |
| 1379 | A68 | 225c on #384 | 18.50 | 1.25 |
| 1380 | A68 | $3 on #297 | 4.00 | 2.75 |
| | | Nos. 1376-1380 (5) | 27.75 | |

Nos. 142-144, 289A, O4-O5, O7, O15, and QO1-QO2 Ovptd. "POSTAGE"

| | | | | |
|---|---|---|---|---|
| **1985, Oct. 29** | | | **Perfs. as Before** | |
| **Watermarks and Printing Methods as Before** | | | | |
| 1381 | A28 | 30c on #O4 | 1.00 | .30 |
| 1382 | A28 | 40c on #142 | 60.00 | .90 |
| 1383 | A28 | 50c on #143 | 1.00 | .50 |
| 1384 | A28 | 50c on #O5 | 1.00 | .40 |
| 1385 | A28 | 60c on #144 | 4.25 | .50 |
| 1386 | A28 | 60c on #144 (Revenue Only) | 1.50 | .35 |
| 1387 | A28 | 60c on #O7 | 3.75 | .40 |
| 1388 | A66 | $10 on #O15 | 17.50 | 7.00 |
| 1389 | A28 | $15 on #QO1 | 17.50 | 12.00 |
| 1390 | A28 | $20 on #QO2 | 17.50 | 13.00 |
| | | Nos. 1381-1390 (10) | 125.00 | |

Refer to 2nd paragraph in footnote following #147 for #1381, 1384, 1386-1387.

Nos. 133-134 Surcharged "Deepavali / 1985"

| | | | | |
|---|---|---|---|---|
| **1985, Nov. 1** | | | | |
| 1391 | A28 | 25c on 2c #134 | 1.00 | .35 |
| 1392 | A28 | 150c on 1c #133 | 3.00 | 1.00 |
| | | Nos. 1391-1392 (2) | 4.00 | |

Miniature Sheet
No. 1050 Ovptd. in Red

Overprinted: a, "Christmas 1985." b, "Happy New Year." c, "Merry Christmas." d, "Happy Holidays."

| | | | | |
|---|---|---|---|---|
| **1985, Nov. 3** | | **Unwmk.** | **Perf. 14** | |
| 1393 | A91 | 55c Sheet of 4, #a.-d. | 12.00 | 7.00 |

For surcharge see No. 1670F.

Clive Lloyd, Cricketer — A94

Lloyd Holding Intl. Cup — A95

Designs: #a, $2.25, Lloyd playing cricket. #b, $1.30, Lloyd, bat and wicket. #c, 60c, Gloves, wicket, bat, natl. flag.

| | | | | | |
|---|---|---|---|---|---|
| **1985, Nov. 7** | | | **Perf. 14½x14** | | |
| 1394 | | Triptych | | .75 | .75 |
| a.-c. | A94 25c any single | | | .20 | .20 |

**Size: 30x38mm**
**Perf. 14x14½**

| | | | | | |
|---|---|---|---|---|---|
| 1395 | A94 | 60c multi | | .45 | .45 |
| 1396 | A94 | $1.30 multi | | .90 | .90 |
| 1397 | A94 | $2.25 multi | | 1.60 | 1.60 |
| 1398 | A95 | $3.50 multi | | 2.60 | 2.60 |
| | Nos. 1394-1398 (5) | | | 6.30 | 6.30 |

For surcharge see No. 1504.

Miniature Sheet
No. 329 Ovptd. "1985" in Red
**Wmk. 364**

| | | | | | |
|---|---|---|---|---|---|
| **1985, Nov. 15** | | **Litho.** | **Perf. 14** | | |
| 1399 | A77 | 30c Sheet of 12, #a.-l. | | 17.50 | 17.50 |

Nos. 410 and 413e Surcharged

| | | | | | |
|---|---|---|---|---|---|
| **1985, Dec. 23** | **Photo.** | | **Perf. 14x14½** | | |

**Watermarks as Before**

| | | | | | |
|---|---|---|---|---|---|
| 1400 | A7 | 20c on #410 | | 6.00 | .50 |
| 1401 | A7 | 20c on #413De | | 6.00 | .50 |
| | Nos. 1400-1401 (2) | | | 12.00 | 1.00 |

Compare No. 1400 with No. 914 and 1401 with No. 994a.

Nos. 1075, 1077 Ovptd.
"REICHENBACHIA 1886-1986" in Purple

| | | | | | |
|---|---|---|---|---|---|
| **1986, Jan. 13** | **Litho.** | | **Perf. 14** | | |
| 1402 | A91 | 150c on #1075 | | 9.00 | 1.00 |
| 1403 | A91 | 200c on #1077 | | 9.00 | 1.10 |

For surcharge and overprints see Nos. 1553, 1760, 1762-1763.

Nos. 608, 610 Surcharged "Republic Day / 1986"
**Perfs. as Before**

| | | | | | |
|---|---|---|---|---|---|
| **1986, Feb. 22** | | | **Wmk. 364** | | |
| 1404 | A82 | 25c on #608 | | | |
| 1405 | A83 | 120c on $6 #610 | | | |
| 1406 | A83 | 225c on $6 #610 | | | |
| | Nos. 1404-1406 (3) | | | 2.00 | |

No. 87 Surcharged "1986"

| | | | | | |
|---|---|---|---|---|---|
| **1986, Mar. 24** | **Photo.** | | **Perf. 13** | | |
| 1407 | A14 | 25c on 6c #87 | | .30 | .25 |
| 1408 | A14 | 50c on 6c #87 | | .50 | .45 |
| 1409 | A14 | 100c on 6c #87 | | .90 | .85 |
| 1410 | A14 | 200c on 6c #87 | | 1.75 | 1.50 |
| | Nos. 1407-1410 (4) | | | 3.45 | 3.05 |

No. 237 Surcharged "1926 / 1986"

| | | | | | |
|---|---|---|---|---|---|
| **1986, Mar. 27** | **Litho.** | | **Perf. 14** | | |
| 1411 | A56 | 150c on 35c #237 | | 5.50 | 1.00 |

St. John Ambulance, 60th anniv.

Nos. 1028, 1037 Surcharged "Queen Elizabeth / 1926 1986"

| | | | | | |
|---|---|---|---|---|---|
| **1986, Apr. 21** | | | **Unwmk.** | | |
| 1412 | A91 | Sheet of 4 | | 8.50 | 8.50 |
| a. | | 130c on 130c #1028 | | 2.00 | 1.50 |
| b. | | 200c on 130c #1028 | | 2.00 | 1.50 |

| | | | | | |
|---|---|---|---|---|---|
| c. | | 260c on 130c #1028 | | 2.00 | 1.50 |
| d. | | 330c on 130c #1028 | | 2.00 | 1.50 |
| 1413 | A91 | 130c on #1037 | | 2.00 | .75 |

Location of overprint on No. 1413 differs from No. 1412.
For overprints & surcharges see #1670A, 1738B.

Nos. 267, 317g-317 I, 444a-444f
Surcharged "Protect the"
**Wmk. 373**

| | | | | | |
|---|---|---|---|---|---|
| **1986, May 3** | **Litho.** | | **Perf. 14** | | |
| 1414 | A73 | 60c on 35c #317g-317I, block of 6, #a.-f. | | 3.00 | 3.00 |
| 1415 | A73 | 60c on 35c #444, block of 6, #a.-f. | | 50.00 | 17.50 |

**Wmk. 364**

| | | | | | |
|---|---|---|---|---|---|
| 1416 | A63 | $6 on 8c #267 | | 4.00 | 3.75 |

No. 390 Surcharged

| | | | | | |
|---|---|---|---|---|---|
| **1986, May 5** | **Litho.** | | **Perf. 13** | | |
| 1417 | A28 | 600c on #390 | | 15.00 | 1.25 |

No. 283A Surcharged

Overprints: a, Abary. b, Anna Regina. c, Aurora. d, Bartica Grove. e, Bel Air. f, Belle Plaine. g, Clonbrook. h, T.P.O. Dem. / Railway. i, Enmore. j, Fredericks / burg: k, Good Success. l, 1986. m, Mariabba. n, Massaruni. o, Nigg. p, No. 50. q, No. 63 / Benab. r, Philadelphia. s, Sisters. t, Skeldon. u, Suddie. v, Taymouth / Manor. w, Wales. x, Whim.

**Perf. 14x13½**

| | | | | | |
|---|---|---|---|---|---|
| **1986, May 15** | | | **Wmk. 364** | | |
| 1418 | | Sheet of 25, #a.-k., m.-x., 2 #l. | | 27.50 | 27.50 |
| a.-x. | A66 25c on 30c, any single | | | 1.00 | .75 |

British Guiana No. 254 Surcharged "GUYANA / INDEPENDENCE 1966-1986"
Nos. 10A and 13a Surcharged "1986"
No. 237 Surcharged
No. 713a-713d Surcharged "INDEPENDENCE / 1966-1986"

| | | | | | |
|---|---|---|---|---|---|
| **1986, May 26** | | | **Perfs. as Before** | | |

**Watermarks and Printing Methods as Before**

| | | | | | |
|---|---|---|---|---|---|
| 1443 | A60 | 25c on 2c British Guiana #254 | | .25 | .20 |
| 1444 | A57 | 25c on 35c #241 | | .25 | .20 |
| 1445 | A60 | 60c on 2c British Guiana #254 | | .45 | .30 |
| 1446 | A60 | 120c on 6c #10A | | .50 | .35 |
| 1447 | A60 | 130c on 24c #13a | | 9.00 | .75 |
| 1448 | | Block of 4 | | 1.75 | 1.75 |
| a. | A86 | 25c on 120c #713a | | .35 | .20 |
| b. | A86 | 25c on 130c #713b | | .35 | .20 |
| c. | A86 | 25c on 150c #713c | | .35 | .20 |
| d. | A86 | 225c on 200c #713d | | .70 | .70 |
| | Nos. 1443-1448 (6) | | | 12.20 | |

No. 135 Surcharged "MEXICO / 1986" in Blue
**Perf. 13x13½**

| | | | | | |
|---|---|---|---|---|---|
| **1986, May 31** | **Litho.** | | **Wmk. 364** | | |
| 1452 | A28 | 225c on 3c #135 | | 20.00 | 3.75 |

World Cup Soccer Championships, Mexico City.

Nos. 135 and 192 Surcharged "CARICOM HEADS OF GOV'T / CONFERENCE / JULY 1986" in Blue
No. 286A Ovptd. "CARICOM / DAY 1986" in Blue

| | | | | | |
|---|---|---|---|---|---|
| **1986** | | | **Perfs. as Before** | | |

**Watermarks and Printing Methods as Before**

| | | | | | |
|---|---|---|---|---|---|
| 1453 | A28 | 25c on #192 | | 2.75 | .75 |
| 1454 | A28 | 60c on 3c #135 | | 3.50 | .30 |
| 1455 | A66 | 60c on #286A | | 11.00 | .75 |
| | Nos. 1453-1455 (3) | | | 17.25 | |

Issued: #1455, June 28; #1453-1454, July 1.

Nos. 133 and 137 Surcharged "INT. YEAR / OF PEACE" in Black or Blue

| | | | | | |
|---|---|---|---|---|---|
| **1986, July 14** | **Litho.** | | **Perf. 13x13½** | | |
| 1456 | A28 | 25c on 1c #133 (Bl) | | .75 | .45 |
| 1457 | A28 | 60c on 6c #137 | | 1.75 | 1.75 |
| 1458 | A28 | 120c on 6c #137 | | 1.75 | 1.75 |
| 1459 | A28 | 130c on 6c #137 | | 1.75 | 1.75 |
| 1460 | A28 | 150c on 6c #137 | | 1.75 | 1.75 |
| | Nos. 1456-1460 (5) | | | 7.75 | |

Halley's Comet — A96

Designs: a, Br. Guiana #172. b, Guyana #931.

| | | | | | |
|---|---|---|---|---|---|
| **1986, July 19** | | | **Perf. 14** | | |
| 1461 | A96 | 320c Pair, #a.-b. | | 3.00 | 3.00 |
| c. | | Imperf. | | 7.50 | |

No. 1461 has continuous design. No. 1461 exists imperf. between. Most were overprinted. For overprints and surcharges see Nos. 1822, 1836, 2029, E5-E6, E11, E14.

No. 43 Surcharged

| | | | | | |
|---|---|---|---|---|---|
| **1986, July 28** | **Photo.** | | **Perf. 14x14½** | | |
| 1463 | A7 | 20c on 6c #43 | | 8.00 | .40 |

Nos. 60-61 Surcharged "GUSIA / 1936-1986"
**Perf. 14x13½**

| | | | | | |
|---|---|---|---|---|---|
| **1986, Aug. 15** | **Photo.** | | **Unwmk.** | | |
| 1464 | A11 | 25c on #61 | | 5.25 | .45 |
| 1465 | A11 | $1.50 on 6c #60 | | 10.00 | 3.25 |
| | Nos. 1464-1465 (2) | | | 14.75 | |

No. 136 Surcharged "REGIONAL / PHARMACY / CONFERENCE / 1986" in Blue
**Perf. 13x13½**

| | | | | | |
|---|---|---|---|---|---|
| **1986, Aug. 15** | | | **Wmk. 364** | | |
| 1466 | A28 | 130c on 5c #136 | | 12.00 | 1.75 |

Nos. 1337, 1339, 1341 Inscribed "1966-1986"
**Perfs. as Before**

| | | | | | |
|---|---|---|---|---|---|
| **1986, Sept. 23** | | | **Unwmk.** | | |
| 1467 | A92 | 25c on #1337 | | 2.50 | .30 |
| 1468 | A92 | 25c on #1339 | | 2.50 | .30 |
| 1469 | A92 | 25c on #1341 | | 2.50 | .30 |

No. 871 Surcharged
**Perf. 14x13½**

| | | | | | |
|---|---|---|---|---|---|
| **1986, Oct. 1** | **Litho.** | | **Wmk. 364** | | |
| **Sheet of 25** | | | | | |
| 1470 | | #a.-k., m.-x., 2 #l | | 55.00 | 40.00 |
| a.-x. | A66 120c any single | | | 2.00 | 1.25 |

No. 1145 Surcharged "12th World Orchid Conference" / "TOKYO JAPAN MARCH 1987"
**Unwmk.**

| | | | | | |
|---|---|---|---|---|---|
| **1986, Oct. 6** | **Litho.** | | **Perf. 14** | | |
| 1494 | A91 | 650c on 40c #1145 | | 17.50 | 6.00 |

For overprint see No. 1851.

Orchid Type like No. 1052 Surchd. "1492-1992" and "CHRISTOPHER COLUMBUS" in Black and Red or Red

| | | | | | |
|---|---|---|---|---|---|
| **1986, Oct.** | | | | | |
| 1495 | A91 | 320c on 150c | | 11.50 | 3.00 |
| 1496 | A91 | 320c on 150c (R) | | 11.50 | 3.00 |
| | Nos. 1495-1496 (2) | | | 23.00 | |

Issued: #1495, 10/10; #1496, 10/30. #1495-1496 not issued without surcharge.

Nos. 704 and 705 Surcharged "1986"

| | | | | | |
|---|---|---|---|---|---|
| **1986, Oct. 15** | **Photo.** | | **Perf. 14x14½** | | |
| | | | | **Wmk. 364** | |
| 1497 | A7 | 50c on #704 | | 4.75 | .60 |
| 1498 | A7 | 225c on #705 | | 13.50 | 3.25 |
| | Nos. 1497-1498 (2) | | | 18.25 | |

Nos. 134, 192 Surcharged "Deepavali /1986"

| | | | | | |
|---|---|---|---|---|---|
| **1986, Nov. 3** | **Litho.** | | **Perf. 13x13½** | | |
| 1499 | A28 | 25c on 2c #134 | | 3.00 | .50 |
| 1500 | A28 | 200c on #192 | | 10.00 | 3.00 |
| | Nos. 1499-1500 (2) | | | 13.00 | |

No. 43 Surcharged "CHRISTMAS / 1986" in Red
No. 917 Surcharged in Red

| | | | | | |
|---|---|---|---|---|---|
| **1986, Nov. 26** | | | **Perfs. as Before** | | |

**Watermarks and Printing Methods as Before**

| | | | | | |
|---|---|---|---|---|---|
| 1501 | A7 | 20c on 6c #43 | | 4.75 | .30 |

**Miniature Sheet**

| | | | | | |
|---|---|---|---|---|---|
| 1502 | A88 | 120c on 60c #a.-e. | | 8.50 | 8.50 |

No. 1502 is surcharged on an unissued miniature sheet containing No. 917.

No. 329 Ovptd. "1986" in Blue
**Wmk. 364**

| | | | | | |
|---|---|---|---|---|---|
| **1986, Nov. 26** | **Litho.** | | **Perf. 14** | | |
| 1503 | A77 | 30c Sheet of 12, #a.-l. | | 25.00 | 25.00 |

No. 1398 Surcharged in Red

| | | | | | |
|---|---|---|---|---|---|
| **1986, Dec. 1** | **Litho.** | | **Perf. 14x14½** | | |
| 1504 | A95 | $15 on $3.50 #1398 | | 45.00 | 20.00 |

L.F.S. Burnham, President 1980-85 A97

| | | | | | |
|---|---|---|---|---|---|
| **1986, Dec. 13** | **Litho.** | | **Perf. 12½x13** | | |
| 1505 | A97 | 25c Tomb | | .20 | .20 |
| 1506 | A97 | 120c Flags, map | | .35 | .35 |
| 1507 | A97 | 130c Government building | | .40 | .40 |
| 1508 | A97 | $6 Portrait, necklace, vert. | | 1.90 | 1.90 |
| | Nos. 1505-1508 (4) | | | 2.85 | 2.85 |

Orchid Type of 1985-87 Surcharged "GPOC / 1977 - 1987"

| | | | | | |
|---|---|---|---|---|---|
| **1987, Jan. 19** | | | **Perf. 14** | | |
| 1509 | A91 | 225c on 25c like #1090 | | 4.50 | 1.00 |
| 1510 | A91 | $10 on 50c like #1052 | | 11.00 | 11.00 |

Nos. 1509-1510 not issued without surcharge. No. 1509 adds "2" to 25c value, No. 1510 uses flower as obliterator.

Stamps of Type A91 Surcharged in Black or Red

a

b

c

d

e

f

g

h

i

j

k

l

**1987-89**     *Perfs. as Before*
**Design A91**
**Series 1**
**(Plate Number in Parentheses)**
**On Nos. 1022-1039**

| | | | |
|---|---|---|---|
| 1511 | (a) | 120c on 60c (2) | 2.50 |
| 1512 | (b) | 120c on 60c (2) | 1.00 |
| 1513 | (a) | 120c on 60c (5) | 2.00 |
| 1514 | (c) | 200c on 60c (5) | 1.00 |
| 1515 | (c) | 200c on 75c (5) | 1.00 |

Obliterator invtd. in surch. on #1514-1515.

| | | | |
|---|---|---|---|
| 1516 | (d) | 200c on 60c (7) | 1.00 |
| 1517 | (d) | 200c on 25c (8) | 1.50 |
| 1518 | (e) | 200c on 25c (8) | 1.00 |
| 1519 | (a) | 120c on 50c (9) | 1.00 |
| 1520 | (b) | 120c on 50c (9) | |
| 1521 | (f) | 120c on 50c (9) | 1.00 |
| 1522 | (g) | 120c on 50c (9) | |
| 1523 | (a) | 120c on 55c (9) | 2.00 |
| 1524 | (d) | 200c on 55c (9) | 1.50 |
| *a.* | | 120c on 55c #1032a | 1.50 |
| 1525 | (g) | 120c on 55c (9) | 1.00 |
| 1526 | (a) | 120c on 60c (10) | 2.00 |
| 1527 | (d) | 200c on 60c (10) | 1.00 |
| 1528 | (h) | $2 on 25c (12) | |

Surcharge on No. 1528 lacks obliterator.

| | | | |
|---|---|---|---|
| 1529 | (f) | 120c on 55c (15) | 1.25 |
| 1530 | (a) | 200c on 55c (15) | 5.00 |

Issued: #1518, 1528, 3/6; #1514-1515, 3/17; #1516-1517, 1522, 1525, 1527, 3/87; #1521, 1524, 1529, 7/87; #1511, 1513, 1519, 1523, 1526, 1530, 9/87; #1512, 1520, 7/88.

**On Nos. 1042-1061**

| | | | |
|---|---|---|---|
| 1531 | (b) | 120c on 55c (17) | |
| 1532 | (d) | 200c on 55c (17) | 1.50 |
| 1533 | (a) | 600c on 80c (17) | 3.00 |
| 1534 | (a) | 120c on 60c (19) | 2.00 |
| 1535 | (d) | 200c on 60c (19) | 1.00 |
| 1536 | (a) | 120c on 50c (22) | |
| 1537 | (b) | 120c on 50c (22) | |
| 1538 | (f) | 120c on 50c (22) | 1.00 |
| 1539 | (c) | 200c on 50c (22) | 1.00 |
| 1540 | (i) | 225c on 50c (22) | 1.50 |
| 1541 | (a) | 120c on 55c | |
| | | #1050a (22) | 2.00 |
| 1542 | (f) | 120c on 55c | |
| | | #1050a (22) | 1.50 |
| 1543 | (c) | 200c on 55c | |
| | | #1050a (22) | 1.00 |
| 1544 | (h) | $2 on 25c (23) | 1.25 |
| 1545 | (a) | 120c on 50c (24) | 2.00 |
| 1546 | (a) | 200c on 50c (24) | |
| 1547 | (d) | 200c on 50c (24) | 1.00 |
| 1548 | (a) | 120c on 60c (31) | 2.00 |
| 1549 | (d) | 200c on 60c (31) | 1.00 |

Issued: #1544, 3/6; #1539, 1543, 3/17; #1532, 1535, 1547, 1549, 3/87; #1540, 6/87; #1538, 1542, 7/87; #1533-1534, 1536, 1541, 1545-1546, 1548, 9/87; #1531, 1537, 7/88.

**On Nos. 1069-1091**

| | | | |
|---|---|---|---|
| 1550 | (b) | 120c on 80c (39) | |
| 1551 | (a) | 600c on 80c (39) | 3.00 |
| 1552 | (g) | $15 on 80c (39) | 4.00 |
| 1553 | (i) | 225c on #1402 (42) | 1.50 |
| 1554 | (d) | 200c on 60c (44) | 1.00 |
| 1555 | (d) | 200c on 60c (47) | 1.00 |
| 1556 | (a) | 120c on 50c (49) | |
| 1557 | (f) | 120c on 50c (49) | 1.50 |
| 1558 | (a) | 120c on 55c | |
| | | #1085a (49) | 2.00 |
| 1559 | (f) | 120c on 55c (49) | 1.25 |
| *a.* | | 120c on 55c on #1085a | 1.50 |
| 1560 | (d) | 200c on 55c (49) | 1.00 |
| *a.* | | 200c on 55c on #1085a | 2.50 |
| 1561 | (a) | 120c on 60c (50) | 2.00 |
| 1562 | (b) | 120c on 60c (50) | |
| 1563 | (e) | 200c on 25c (51) | 1.25 |
| 1564 | (d) | 200c on 25c (52) | 1.00 |
| 1565 | (b) | 120c on 30c (53) | |
| *a.* | | 120c on 30c on #1090a | |
| 1566 | (a) | 120c on 50c (53) | 2.00 |
| 1567 | (d) | 200c on 30c | |
| | | #1090a (53) | 1.00 |
| 1568 | (a) | 200c on 50c (53) | |
| 1569 | (d) | 200c on 50c (53) | 1.00 |
| 1570 | (g) | $10 on 25c (53) | 3.25 |
| 1571 | (g) | $25 on 25c (53) | 6.00 |

Surcharge on #1571 lacks obliterator and places a "$" in front of original denomination. #1570-1571 not issued without surcharge.

Issued: #1563, 3/6; #1552, 1554-1555, 1560, 1564, 1567, 1569-1571, 3/87; #1553, 6/87; #1557, 1559, 7/87; #1551, 1556, 1561, 1566, 1568, 9/87; #1550, 1562, 1565, 7/88.

**On Nos. 1092-1108, 1372**

| | | | |
|---|---|---|---|
| 1572 | (b) | 120c on 45c (54) | |
| 1573 | (a) | 120c on 60c (54) | 2.00 |
| 1574 | (b) | 120c on 60c (54) | 1.00 |
| 1575 | (a) | 200c on 55c (55) | |
| 1576 | (i) | 225c on 50c (55) | 1.50 |
| 1577 | (b) | 120c on 60c (57) | 1.00 |
| *a.* | | New value at bottom | |
| 1578 | (d) | 200c on 60c (57) | 1.00 |
| 1579 | (b) | 120c on 25c (59) | 1.00 |
| 1580 | (a) | 120c on 75c (60) | 2.00 |
| 1581 | (c) | 200c on 75c (60) | 2.50 |
| 1582 | (b) | 120c on 25c (61) | |
| 1583 | (b) | 120c on 25c (63) | 1.00 |
| 1584 | (a) | 120c on 50c (64) | |
| 1585 | (f) | 120c on 50c (64) | 1.50 |
| 1586 | (a) | 120c on 55c, wmkd. | |
| | | (64) | 2.00 |
| 1587 | (f) | 120c on 55c (64) | 1.00 |
| *a.* | | 120c on 55c on #1107a | 1.25 |
| 1588 | (g) | 120c on 55c (64) | 1.00 |
| *a.* | | 120c on 55c on #1107a | 1.00 |

Surcharge on Nos. 1522, 1525, 1588-1588a does not contain date.

| | | | |
|---|---|---|---|
| 1589 | (a) | 120c on 50c (65) | 2.00 |
| 1590 | (a) | 200c on 50c (65) | |
| 1591 | (d) | 200c on 50c (65) | 1.00 |
| 1591A | (i) | 225c on #1372 (65) | |

Issued: #1581, 3/17; #1578, 1588, 1591, 3/87; #1576, 6/87; #1585, 1587, 7/87; #1573, 1575, 1580, 1584, 1586, 1589-1590, 9/87; #1591A, 10/9/87; #1572, 1574, 1577, 1579, 1582-1583, 7/88.

**On Nos. 1112-1124**

| | | | |
|---|---|---|---|
| 1592 | (b) | 120c on 40c (68) | 1.00 |
| *a.* | | New value at LL | |
| 1593 | (c) | 200c on 40c (68) | 1.00 |
| *a.* | | Obliterator inverted | 1.00 |
| 1594 | (a) | 225c on 40c (68) | 2.50 |
| 1595 | (a) | 120c on 60c (69) | |
| 1596 | (b) | 120c on 60c (69) | 1.00 |
| 1597 | (b) | 120c on 25c (70) | |
| 1598 | (b) | 120c on 25c (71) | |
| 1599 | (a) | 120c on 60c (71) | 2.00 |
| 1600 | (d) | 200c on 25c (71) | 1.00 |
| 1601 | (d) | 200c on 60c (71) | 1.00 |
| 1602 | (j) | 120c on 25c (72) | |
| 1603 | (d) | 200c on 25c (72) | 1.00 |
| 1604 | (b) | 120c on 60c (73) | |
| 1605 | (d) | 200c on 60c (73) | .75 |
| 1606 | (b) | 120c on 80c (74) | |
| 1607 | (a) | 600c on 80c (74) | 3.00 |
| 1608 | (g) | $12 on 80c (74) | 3.50 |
| 1609 | (b) | 120c on 60c (75) | |
| *a.* | | New value at bottom | |
| 1610 | (d) | 200c on 60c (75) | 1.00 |
| 1611 | (a) | 225c on 65c (76) | 2.50 |

Issued: #1593, 3/17; #1600-1601, 1603, 1605, 1608, 1610, 3/87; #1594-1595, 1599,

1611, 9/87; #1592, 1596-1598, 1604, 1606-1607, 1609, 7/88; #1602, 9/88.

**On Nos. 1126-1142**

| | | | |
|---|---|---|---|
| 1612 | (b) | 120c on 40c (77) | |
| *a.* | | New value at UL | |
| 1613 | (d) | 200c on 40c (77) | 1.00 |
| 1614 | (a) | 200c on 45c (77) | 3.00 |
| 1615 | (d) | 200c on 45c (77) | 1.00 |
| 1616 | (a) | 200c on 45c (78) | 3.00 |
| 1617 | (a) | 120c on 60c (78) | 1.00 |
| 1618 | (a) | 120c on 60c (79) | 3.00 |
| 1619 | (b) | 120c on 60c (79) | |
| 1620 | (a) | 225c on 65c (80) | 3.00 |
| 1621 | (b) | 120c on 45c (81) | |
| 1622 | (f) | 120c on 55c (81) | 1.25 |
| 1623 | (d) | 200c on 55c (81) | 1.00 |
| 1624 | (a) | 200c on 55c (81) | 4.00 |
| 1625 | (f) | 120c on 55c (82) | 1.50 |
| 1626 | (a) | 200c on 55c (82) | 10.00 |
| 1627 | (a) | 120c on 75c (83) | 3.00 |
| 1628 | (b) | 120c on 90c (84) | |
| 1629 | (a) | 200c on 45c (84) | 3.00 |
| 1630 | (a) | 200c on 45c (85) | 3.00 |
| 1631 | (d) | 200c on 45c (85) | 1.00 |

Issued: #1613, 1615, 1617, 1623, 1631, 3/87; #1622, 1625, 7/87; #1614, 1616, 1618, 1620, 1624, 1626-1627, 1629-1630, 9/87; #1612, 1619, 1621, 1628, 7/88.

**On Nos. 1144-1153**

| | | | |
|---|---|---|---|
| 1632 | (b) | 120c on 30c (86) | |
| 1633 | (b) | 120c on 40c (86) | 1.00 |
| 1634 | (d) | 200c on 30c (86) | 1.00 |
| 1635 | (d) | 200c on 40c (86) | |
| 1636 | (a) | 225c on 40c (86) | 3.00 |
| *a.* | | Inscribed "ONTOGLOS- | |
| | | SUM" | 2.50 |
| 1637 | (a) | 120c on 60c (87) | 2.00 |
| *a.* | | Surcharge reading up | |
| 1638 | (d) | 200c on 60c (87) | 1.00 |
| 1639 | (a) | 225c on 65c (88) | 2.50 |
| 1640 | (f) | 120c on 55c (89) | 1.25 |
| 1641 | (b) | 120c on 90c (89) | |
| 1642 | (a) | 200c on 55c (89) | 5.00 |
| 1643 | (d) | 225c on 90c (89) | 1.00 |
| 1644 | (a) | 120c on 40c (90) | 2.00 |
| 1645 | (b) | 120c on 40c (90) | 1.00 |
| 1646 | (c) | 200c on 40c (90) | 1.00 |
| 1647 | (d) | 200c on 40c (R) | |
| | | (90) | 1.25 |
| 1648 | (c) | 200c on 375c (90) | 1.00 |
| *a.* | | 200c on 375c #1153a | 3.00 |
| 1649 | (a) | 225c on 40c (90) | 2.50 |
| 1650 | (i) | 225c on 40c (90) | 1.50 |
| 1651 | (k) | 260c on 375c (90) | 1.00 |

Issued: #1647, 2/9/87; #1646, 1648, 3/17/87; #1634-1635, 1638, 1643, 3/87; #1650, 6/87; #1640, 7/87; #1636-1637, 1639, 1642, 1644, 1649, 9/87; #1632-1633, 1641, 1645, 7/88; #1651, 10/88.

Surcharge on #1651 is placed over original value and has no obliterator.

**On Nos. 1154-1165**

| | | | |
|---|---|---|---|
| 1652 | (a) | 120c on 40c (91) | 2.00 |
| 1653 | (b) | 120c on 40c (91) | 1.00 |
| *a.* | | New value at LR | |
| 1654 | (a) | 225c on 40c (91) | 3.00 |
| 1655 | (i) | 225c on 40c (91) | 1.50 |
| 1656 | (b) | 120c on 50c (92) | |
| 1657 | (a) | 120c on 75c (92) | 2.50 |
| 1658 | (c) | 200c on 50c (92) | |
| 1659 | (c) | 200c on 75c (92) | 1.00 |
| 1660 | (b) | 120c on 60c (93) | |
| 1661 | (b) | 120c on 80c (93) | |
| 1662 | (i) | 225c on 60c (93) | 1.50 |
| 1663 | (i) | 225c on 80c (93) | 1.50 |
| 1664 | (a) | 600c on 80c (93) | |
| 1665 | (a) | 120c on 60c (94) | |
| 1666 | (b) | 120c on 60c (94) | |
| 1667 | (b) | 120c on 60c (95) | |
| 1668 | (a) | 120c on 75c (95) | 3.00 |
| 1669 | (b) | 120c on 40c (96) | |
| 1670 | (a) | 225c on 65c (96) | 2.50 |

**Miniature Sheets**

| | | | |
|---|---|---|---|
| 1670A | | Sheet of 4 | 20.00 |
| *b.* | (a) | 600c on 130c #1412a (6) | |
| *c.* | (a) | 600c on 200c #1412b (6) | |
| *d.* | (a) | 600c on 260c #1412c (6) | |
| *e.* | (a) | 600c on 330c #1412d (6) | |
| 1670F | | Sheet of 4 | 10.00 |
| *g.* | (i) | 225c on #1393a (22) | |
| *h.* | (i) | 225c on #1393b (22) | |
| *i.* | (i) | 225c on #1393c (22) | |
| *j.* | (i) | 225c on #1393d (22) | |

Issued: #1658-1659, 3/17/87; #1655, 1662-1663, 6/87; #1652, 1654, 1657, 1664-1665, 1668, 1670, 9/87; #1670F, 11/9/87; #1670A, 11/20/87; #1653, 1656, 1660-1661, 1666-1667, 1669, 7/88.

For overprints see Nos. 1975, 1979.

**Series 2**
**On Nos. 1168-1204**

| | | | |
|---|---|---|---|
| 1671 | (b) | 120c on 90c (2) | 1.00 |
| 1672 | (b) | 120c on 50c (3) | 1.00 |
| 1673 | (f) | 120c on 50c (3) | 1.00 |
| 1674 | (b) | 200c on 90c (4) | |
| 1675 | (b) | 120c on 50c (6) | 1.00 |
| 1676 | (f) | 120c on 50c (6) | 1.00 |
| 1677 | (b) | 120c on 30c (7) | 1.00 |
| 1678 | (b) | 120c on 70c (8) | 1.00 |
| 1679 | (b) | 120c on 70c (9) | |
| *a.* | | New value at LR | |

| | | | |
|---|---|---|---|
| 1680 | (b) | 120c on 90c (10) | 1.00 |
| 1681 | (b) | 120c on 70c (12) | 1.00 |
| **a.** | | New value at LL | |
| 1682 | (b) | 120c on 50c (13) | 1.00 |
| 1683 | (b) | 120c on 90c (13) | 1.00 |
| 1684 | (b) | 120c on 30c (14) | 1.00 |
| **a.** | | New value at UR | |
| 1685 | (b) | 120c on 50c (15) | 1.00 |
| 1686 | (b) | 120c on 85c (15) | 1.00 |
| 1687 | (b) | 120c on 70c (17) | 11.00 |
| 1688 | (b) | 120c on 85c (18) | 1.00 |
| 1689 | (c) | 200c on 85c (18) | |
| 1690 | (b) | 120c on 50c (20) | 1.00 |
| 1691 | (f) | 120c on 50c (20) | 1.50 |

Issued: #1689, 3/17/87; #1673, 1676, 1691, 7/87; #1671-1672, 1674-1675, 1677-1688, 1690, 7/88.

### On Nos. 1205-1240

| | | | |
|---|---|---|---|
| 1692 | (b) | 120c on 45c (21) | 1.00 |
| 1693 | (b) | 120c on 30c (22) | 1.00 |
| 1694 | (l) | 350c on 330c #O52 (23) | 1.00 |
| 1695 | (b) | 120c on 85c (24) | 1.00 |
| 1696 | (j) | 120c on 140c (R) (25) | 1.00 |
| 1697 | (l) | 250c on 225c #O46 (26) | 1.00 |
| **a.** | | New value at UL | |
| 1698 | (b) | 120c on 60c (27) | 1.50 |
| 1699 | (b) | 120c on 90c (27) | 1.00 |
| 1700 | (b) | 120c on 30c (28) | 1.00 |
| **a.** | | New value at UL | 1.00 |
| 1701 | (b) | 120c on 30c (30) | 1.00 |
| 1702 | (k) | 240c on 140c (30) | 1.00 |

No. 1702 not issued without surcharge.

| | | | |
|---|---|---|---|
| 1703 | (l) | 150c on 175c #O44 (31) | 1.00 |
| 1704 | (b) | 120c on 50c (32) | 1.00 |
| 1705 | (f) | 120c on 50c (32) | 1.00 |
| 1706 | (k) | 240c on 140c (34) | 1.00 |
| 1707 | (l) | 125c on 140c #O42 (36) | 1.00 |
| 1708 | (k) | 120c on 140c (38) | 1.00 |
| 1709 | (k) | 120c on 140c (41) | 1.00 |
| 1710 | (k) | 200c on 80c (42) | 1.00 |
| 1711 | (l) | #O43 (43) | 1.00 |

Issued: #1705, 7/87; #1692-1693, 1695, 1698-1701, 1704, 1710, 7/88; #1702, 1706, 10/88; #1696, 1708-1709, 2/22/89; #1694, 1697, 1703, 1707, 1711, 3/89.

### On Nos. 1245-1314

| | | | |
|---|---|---|---|
| 1712 | (b) | 120c on 35c (45) | 1.00 |
| 1713 | (b) | 120c on 85c (45) | 1.00 |
| 1714 | (j) | 120c on 140c (R) (52) | 1.00 |
| 1715 | (k) | 300c on 290c (53) | 1.00 |
| 1716 | (j) | 120c on 175c (R) (54) | 1.00 |
| 1717 | (k) | 170c on 175c (58) | 1.00 |
| 1718 | (l) | 250c on #O48 (59) | 1.00 |
| 1719 | (j) | 120c on 140c (R) (65) | 1.00 |
| 1720 | (k) | 250c on 280c (66) | 1.00 |
| 1721 | (k) | 250c on 280c (67) | 1.00 |
| 1722 | (l) | 250c on 230c #O47 (68) | 1.00 |
| 1723 | (l) | 250c on 260c #O49 (69) | 1.00 |
| **a.** | | New value at UR | 1.00 |
| 1724 | (l) | 600c on #O54 (70) | 1.00 |
| 1725 | (l) | $12 on #O55 (71) | 1.00 |
| 1726 | (l) | $15 on #O56 (84) | 1.00 |
| 1727 | (k) | 240c on 425c (87) | 1.00 |
| 1728 | (l) | 300c on 275c #O50 (90) | 1.00 |
| 1729 | (l) | 125c on 130c #O41 (92) | 1.00 |
| 1730 | (l) | 350c on #O53 (95) | 1.00 |

On No. 1730 "Postage" reads up or down.
Issued: #1712-1713, 7/88; #1727, 10/88; #1714, 1716, 1719, 2/22/89; #1715, 1717-1718, 1720-1726, 1728-1730, 3/89.
Obliterator on Nos. 1708-1709, 1715, 1717, 1720-1721 has two thick bars.

Stamps of Type A91 Overprinted

m

---

n

o

p

**1987**      **Perfs. as Before**

### Series 1

| | | | |
|---|---|---|---|
| 1731 | (m) | 120c on #1021 (1) | 5.00 |
| 1732 | (n) | 130c on #1023 (3) | 1.00 |
| 1733 | (m) | 130c on #1028a (6) | 3.00 |
| 1734 | (n) | 130c on #1028 (6) | 1.25 |
| **a.** | | 130c on #1028a | 1.25 |
| 1735 | (m) | 120c on #1034 (11) | 3.00 |
| 1736 | (n) | 130c on #1037a (13) | 3.00 |
| 1737 | (n) | 130c on #1413 (13) | 2.50 |
| 1738 | (o) | 130c on #1037 (13) | 1.00 |
| **a.** | | 130c on #1037a | 1.00 |
| 1738B | (p) | 130c on #1413 (13) | |
| 1739 | (n) | 200c on #1038 (14) | 1.50 |
| 1740 | (n) | 130c on #1041 (16) | 1.00 |
| 1741 | (n) | 130c on #1342 (18) | 1.00 |
| 1742 | (p) | 130c on #1342 (18) | 1.00 |
| 1743 | (m) | 130c on #1047a (20) | 2.00 |
| 1744 | (n) | 130c on #1047a (20) | 1.00 |
| **a.** | | 130c on #1047 | 1.25 |
| 1745 | (n) | 200c on #1048 (21) | 1.00 |
| 1746 | (n) | 200c on #1048 (21) | 1.00 |
| 1747 | (n) | 130c on #1055a (25) | 2.50 |
| 1748 | (o) | 130c on #1055 (25) | 1.00 |
| **a.** | | 130c on #1055a | 1.00 |
| 1749 | (p) | 150c on #1056 (26) | 1.00 |
| 1750 | (m) | 120c on #1058 (28) | 4.00 |
| 1751 | (n) | 130c on #1343 (29) | 1.00 |
| 1752 | (p) | 130c on #1343 (29) | 1.00 |

Issued: #1732, 1734, 1737-1741, 1744, 1746, 1748, 1751, Mar; #1731, 1733, 1735-1736, 1743, 1745, 1747, 1750, July; #1738B, Nov. 20; #1742, 1749, 1752, Dec.

| | | | |
|---|---|---|---|
| 1753 | (n) | 130c on #1344 (30) | 1.00 |
| 1754 | (p) | 130c on #1344 (30) | 1.00 |
| 1755 | (n) | 200c on #1063 (33) | 1.00 |
| 1756 | (m) | 120c on #1067 (37) | 1.50 |
| 1757 | (n) | 260c on #1070 (39) | 2.00 |
| 1758 | (m) | 150c on #1072a, ovpt. reading up (40) | 1.50 |
| **a.** | | 150c on #1072 | 2.50 |
| 1759 | (m) | 150c on #1075a (42) | 3.00 |
| 1760 | (m) | 150c on #1402 (42) | 5.00 |
| 1761 | (m) | 200c on #1077a (43) | 5.00 |
| 1762 | (m) | 200c on #1403 (43) | 5.00 |
| 1763 | (n) | 200c on #1403 (43) | 3.00 |
| 1764 | (m) | 150c on #1080 reading down (45) | 2.00 |
| **a.** | | 150c on #1080a reading up | 2.50 |
| 1765 | (m) | 120c on #1081 (46) | 8.00 |
| 1766 | (m) | 120c on #1097 (56) | 3.00 |
| 1767 | (m) | 120c on #1099 (58) | 3.00 |
| 1768 | (n) | 130c on #1110 (66) | 3.00 |
| 1769 | (p) | 130c on #1110 (66) | 1.00 |
| 1770 | (p) | 120c on #1111 (67) | 1.00 |
| 1771 | (n) | 250c on #1122 (74) | 1.25 |
| 1772 | (n) | 200c on #1131 (79) | 1.25 |
| 1773 | (o) | 130c on #1155 (91) | 1.00 |

### Miniature Sheets of 4

| | | | |
|---|---|---|---|
| 1774 | (n) | 200c on #1345 (4) | 3.00 |

---

| | | | |
|---|---|---|---|
| 1775 | (n) | 200c on 130c #1346 (20) | 4.00 |

### Series 2

| | | | |
|---|---|---|---|
| 1776 | (n) | 200c on #1169 (2) | 5.00 |
| 1777 | (n) | 200c on #1183 (9) | 1.00 |

Issued: #1753, 1755, 1757, 1763, 1768, 1771-1777, Mar.; #1756, 1758, 1759-1762, 1764-1767, July. #1754, 1769-1770, Dec.
Overprint reads up on #1759, 1761. Overprint reads down on #1731, 1735, 1745, 1750, 1755, 1758a, 1760, 1762, 1763.
See Nos. 1813-1814, 1844 for other stamps overprinted "1987" only.

### Nos. 1337, 1339, 1341 Surcharged

**1987, Mar. 6**      **Perfs. as Before**

| | | | | |
|---|---|---|---|---|
| 1777A | A92 | 200c on #1337 | 6.00 | 2.00 |
| 1777B | A92 | 200c on #1339 | 6.00 | 2.00 |
| 1777C | A92 | 200c on #1341 | 6.00 | 2.00 |

See note following No. 1341.

### Nos. 134, 136, 139a, and 192 Surcharged "Post Office / Corp. / 1977-1987" in Blue

**Perfs. as Before**

**1987, Feb. 17**    **Litho.**    **Wmk. 364**

| | | | | |
|---|---|---|---|---|
| 1778 | A28 | 25c on 2c #134 | .25 | .20 |
| 1779 | A28 | 25c on 5c #136 | .25 | .20 |
| 1780 | A28 | 25c on #192 | .25 | .20 |
| 1781 | A28 | 25c on 15c #139a | 5.00 | .50 |
| 1782 | A28 | 60c on 15c #139a | 10.00 | .40 |
| 1783 | A28 | $1.20 on 2c #134 | .85 | .85 |
| 1784 | A28 | $1.30 on 15c #139a | 11.00 | 2.75 |
| | | Nos. 1778-1784 (7) | 27.60 | 5.10 |

### Nos. 1032, 1032a Surcharged "12th World Orchid Conference" and "TOKYO JAPAN"

**1987, Mar. 12**    **Unwmk.**    **Perf. 14**

| | | | | |
|---|---|---|---|---|
| 1785 | A91 | 650c on 55c #1032 | 11.00 | 6.50 |
| **a.** | | 650c on 55c #1032a | 11.00 | 6.50 |

### No. 280 Surcharged with Names of Post Offices Operating in 1885

Overprints: a, AGRICOLA. b, BAGOTVILLE. c, BOURDA. d, BUXTON. e, CABACABURI. f, CAR- / MICHAEL STREET. g, COTTON / TREE. h, DUNOON. i, FELLOW- / SHIP. j, GROVE. k, HACKNEY. l, LEONORA. m, 1987. n, MALLALI. o, PROVI- / DENCE. p, RELI-ANCE. q, SPARTA. r, STEWART- / VILLE. s, TARLOGY. t, T.P.O. / BERBICE RIV. u, T.P.O. / DEM. RIV. v, T.P.O. / ESSEQ. RIV. w, T.P.O. / MASSARUNI / RIV. x, TUSCHEN / (De / VRIENDEN). y, ZORG.

**Perf. 14x13½**

**1987, Mar. 17**      **Wmk. 364**

| | | | | |
|---|---|---|---|---|
| 1786 | | Sheet of 25, #a.-y. | 42.50 | 35.00 |
| **a.-y.** | | A66 25c on 10c, any single | 1.50 | 1.25 |

British Guiana Post Office, 125th Anniv.

Columbus' Discovery of America, 500th Anniv. (in 1992) — A98

Paintings: 120c, Discovery of America, by Dali. 225c, Preparations Before the Journey, by unknown artist. 360c, Catholic Kings from Prado Museum.
$6, Columbus' Fleet, by R. Monleon.

**1987, Mar. 30**    **Litho.**    **Perf. 13½**

| | | | | |
|---|---|---|---|---|
| 1787 | A98 | 120c multicolored | 1.75 | 1.00 |
| 1788 | A98 | 225c multicolored | 4.00 | 3.00 |
| 1789 | A98 | 360c multicolored | 6.25 | 3.00 |
| **a.** | | Strip of 3, #1787-1789 | 13.50 | 13.50 |

### Souvenir Sheet

| | | | | |
|---|---|---|---|---|
| 1790 | A98 | $6 gold & multi | 15.00 | 15.00 |

No. 1790 exists with silver border.

### No. 289A Ovptd. "28 MARCH 1927 / PAA / GEO-POS"

**1987, Mar. 28**      **Perf. 13½x13**

| | | | | |
|---|---|---|---|---|
| 1811 | A66 | $10 on #289A | 24.00 | 13.00 |

First Georgetown to Port-of-Spain Flight, 50th Anniv.

---

### No. 285 Surcharged

**1987, Apr. 6**      **Perf. 14x13½**

| | | | | |
|---|---|---|---|---|
| 1812 | A66 | 25c on 40c #285 | 12.50 | .40 |

### Nos. 87-88, 90, 287 Surcharged or Overprinted "1987"

**1987, Apr.**      **Perfs. as Before**

**Watermarks and Printing Methods as Before**

| | | | | |
|---|---|---|---|---|
| 1813 | A14 | 25c on #88 | .75 | .10 |
| 1814 | A66 | $1 on #287 | 15.00 | 1.00 |
| 1815 | A14 | 120c on 6c #87 | .90 | .20 |
| 1816 | A14 | 320c on 6c #87 | 1.50 | .75 |
| 1817 | A14 | 500c on 40c #90 | 2.00 | 1.40 |
| | | Nos. 1813-1817 (5) | 20.15 | 3.45 |

Issued: #1813, 1815-1817, Apr. 21; #1814, Apr.

### No. 1461 Ovptd. "CAPEX '87"

**1987, June 10**    **Litho.**    **Perf. 14**

| | | | | |
|---|---|---|---|---|
| 1822 | A96 | 320c Pair, #a.-b. | 5.50 | 5.50 |
| **c.** | | on #1461, imperf. between | 11.00 | |

For surcharges see Nos. 2030, E15.

### Nos. 626-628 Ovptd. "1987"

**Wmk. 314 Upright**

**1987, July 15**    **Engr.**    **Perf. 12½x13**

| | | | | |
|---|---|---|---|---|
| 1823 | A60 | $1.20 on #626 | .90 | .25 |

**Wmk. 314 Sideways**

| | | | | |
|---|---|---|---|---|
| 1824 | A60 | $1.30 on #627 | 10.00 | .75 |
| 1825 | A60 | $2.40 on #628 | 12.00 | 3.75 |
| | | Nos. 1823-1825 (3) | 22.90 | 4.75 |

A99

A100

Locomotives — A101

#1826a, 1827a, Alexandra 4. #1826b, 1827b, Diesel locomotive facing right. #1826c, 1827c, Steam locomotive facing right. #1826d, 1827d, Diesel locomotive No. 21 facing left. #1829a, 1830a, Alexandra 4. #1829b, 1830b, Diesel locomotive. #1829c, 1830c, Steam locomotive facing right. #1829d, 1830c, Diesel locomotive No. 21. #1830e, Photograph of trains in Georgetown Station. #1831, Steam locomotive pulling cattle cars, map of routes from Parika to Vreedenhoop and from Georgetown to Rosignol.

**1987, Aug. 3**      **Perf. 15**

| | | | | |
|---|---|---|---|---|
| 1826 | | Block of 4 | 1.50 | 1.50 |
| **a.-d.** | | A99 $1.20 green, any single | .30 | .30 |
| 1827 | | Block of 5 | 4.00 | 4.00 |
| **a.-d.** | | A99 $3.20 blue, any single | .70 | .70 |
| **e.** | | A100 $3.20 blue | .70 | .70 |
| 1828 | A101 | $12 shown | 3.00 | 3.00 |
| | | Nos. 1826-1828 (3) | 8.50 | 8.50 |

**1987, Dec. 4**

| | | | | |
|---|---|---|---|---|
| 1829 | | Block of 4 | 1.60 | 1.60 |
| **a.-d.** | | A99 $1.20 rose lake, any single | .35 | .35 |
| 1830 | | Block of 5 | 4.25 | 4.25 |
| **a.-d.** | | A99 $3.30 blk, any single | .80 | .80 |
| **e.** | | A100 $3.30 black | .80 | .80 |
| 1831 | A101 | $10 multi | 3.00 | 3.00 |
| | | Nos. 1829-1831 (3) | 8.85 | 8.85 |

Sizes: #1827e, 1830e, 84x57mm. #1828, 1831, 90x40mm.
For surcharges see #E12-E13. For overprints see #1910-1911, 1935-1938, 2024-2028F, 2054, 2056.

No. 287 Ovptd. "FAIREY NICHOLL / 15 AUG 1927 / GEO-MAB" or "FAIREY NICHOLL / 8 AUG 1927 / GEO-MAZ"

| | | | | |
|---|---|---|---|---|
| **1987, Aug. 7** | | **Litho.** | **Perf. 13½x13** | |
| **1832** A66 | $1 "MAB" on #287 | | 12.00 | 11.00 |
| **1833** A66 | $1 "MAZ" on #287 | | 12.00 | 11.00 |
| a. | Pair, #1832-1833 | | 30.00 | 27.50 |

No. 1291A Surcharged "CRISTOVAO COLOMBO / 1492 — 1992" (#1834) or "CHRISTOPHE COLOMB / 1492 — 1992" (#1835)

No. 1461c Surcharged "THE PASSING OF HALLEY'S COMET: / PROPHESY OF THE ARRIVAL OF / HERNAN CORTES 1519. / V CENTENARY OF THE LANDING OF / CHRISTOPHER COLUMBUS / IN THE AMERICAS"

| | | | | |
|---|---|---|---|---|
| | **Unwmk.** | | | |
| **1987, Oct. 9** | | **Litho.** | **Perf. 14** | |
| **1834** A91 | 950c on 900c #1291A | | 3.00 | 3.00 |
| **1835** A91 | 950c on 900c #1291A | | 3.00 | 3.00 |
| a. | Pair, #1834-1835 | | 7.00 | 7.00 |
| | *Imperf* | | | |
| **1836** A96 | $20 on 320c #1461c | | 8.50 | 8.50 |

Nos. 135-136 Surcharged "DEEPAVALI / 1987"

| | | | | |
|---|---|---|---|---|
| **1987, Nov. 2** | | **Litho.** | **Perf. 13x13½** | |
| **1837** A28 | 25c on 3c #135 | | 2.25 | .40 |
| **1838** A28 | $3 on 5c #136 | | 8.00 | 3.50 |

No. 43 Surcharged "CHRISTMAS / 1987" in Red

No. 1502 Surcharged "1987" in Blue

| | | | |
|---|---|---|---|
| **1987, Nov. 9** | | **Perfs. as Before** | |
| **Watermarks and Printing Methods as Before** | | | |
| **1839** A7 | 20c on 6c #43 | | |
| | **Miniature Sheet** | | |
| **1840** A88 | 120c on 60c #1502 | | |

No. 329 Overprinted "1987"

No. 920 Surcharged "Protect Our Heritage '87" in Red

Nos. 1037, 1040, 1056, 1110-1111, 1494 Surcharged "PROTECT OUR HERITAGE '87"

| | | | | |
|---|---|---|---|---|
| **1987, Dec. 9** | | **Perfs. as Before** | | |
| **Watermarks and Printing Methods as Before** | | | | |
| **1844** A77 | 30c Sheet of 12, | | | |
| | #a.-l, on #329 | | 7.00 | 7.00 |
| **1845** A91 | 120c on #1111 | | 1.50 | 1.50 |
| **1846** A91 | 130c on #1110 | | 1.75 | 1.75 |
| **1847** A91 | 150c on #1056 | | 2.25 | 2.25 |
| **1848** A91 | 180c on #1040 | | 2.50 | 2.50 |
| **1849** A91 | 320c on #1137 | | 3.00 | 3.00 |
| **1850** A89 | 320c Triptych, #a.-c, | | | |
| | on 120c #920 | | 9.00 | 9.00 |
| **1851** A91 | 650c on #1494 | | 5.00 | 5.00 |

1988 Summer Olympics, Seoul — A102

| | | | | |
|---|---|---|---|---|
| **1987, Dec. 30** | | **Litho.** | **Perf. 13½x14** | |
| **1852** A102 | $2 Jumping | | 2.25 | 2.00 |
| **1853** A102 | $3 Discus | | 3.50 | 3.00 |
| **1854** A102 | $5 Vase | | 6.00 | 5.00 |
| a. | Strip of 3, #1852-1854 | | 12.50 | 12.50 |
| | **Souvenir Sheet** | | | |
| | **Perf. 14** | | | |
| **1855** A102 | $3.50 Olympic Rings, horiz. | | 5.50 | 5.50 |

Christmas 1987 — A103

Paintings: #a, The Virgin of the Rocks, by Da Vinci. #b, Virgin with Grapes, by Mignard. #c, Sacred Family, by Raphael. #d, Virgin Mary, by Lucas Cranach. No. 1857, Adoration of Three Kings, by Rubens.

| | | | | |
|---|---|---|---|---|
| **1988, Jan. 7** | | **Litho.** | **Perf. 14** | |
| **1856** A103 | $2 Strip of 4, #a.-d. | | 7.75 | 7.75 |
| | **Souvenir Sheet** | | | |
| **1857** A103 | $10 Sheet of 1 | | 13.50 | 13.50 |
| | Dated 1987. | | | |

Nos. 397, 405 and 651 Ovptd. or Surcharged "*AUSTRALIA* / 1987 JAMBOREE 1988" in Red

| | | | | |
|---|---|---|---|---|
| **1988, Jan. 7** | | **Litho.** | **Perf. 13½x13** | |
| **1858** A17 | $4.40 on #405 | | | |
| **1859** A17 | $10 on #397 | | | |
| **1860** A17 | $10 on #651 | | | |
| **1861** A17 | $10 on #405 | | | |
| a. | $10 on #405a | | | |
| | Nos. 1858-1861 (4) | | 10.00 | |

Obliterator on Nos. 1859-1861 is red fleur-de-lis. Size and location of overprint varies.

Nos. 68 and 70 Surcharged "IFAD / For a World / Without Hunger"

**Perf. 14x14½**

| | | | | |
|---|---|---|---|---|
| **1988, Jan. 26** | | **Photo.** | **Wmk. 364** | |
| **1862** A68 | 25c on 1c #68 | | 2.00 | .30 |
| **1863** A68 | $5 on 3c #70 | | 7.00 | 3.00 |
| | Nos. 1862-1863 (2) | | 9.00 | 3.30 |

No. 1862 uses new denomination as obliterator and No. 1863 uses "X."

Flora and Fauna — A104

Mushrooms — #1864: a, Corprinus comatus. b, Amanita muscaria. c, Pholiota aurivella. d, Laccaria amethstina.

Birds — #1865: a, Starling. b, Reed warbler. c, Kingfisher. d, Goldcrest.

Cats — #1866: a, Himalayan. b, American shorthaired. c, Maine coon. d, Abyssinian.

Cactus flowers — #1866: e, Sulcorebutia densiseta. f, Subutia hyalacantha. g, Echinopsis. h, Lobivia polycephala.

Nos. 1866a-1866h horiz.

| | | | |
|---|---|---|---|
| **1988, Jan. 28** | | **Perf. 14** | |
| **1864** A104 | $2 Strip of 4, #a.-d. | 8.00 | 8.00 |
| **1865** A104 | $2 Strip of 4, #a.-d. | 7.00 | 7.00 |
| | **Miniature Sheet** | | |
| | **Perf. 14x13½** | | |
| **1866** A104 | $2 Sheet of 8, #a.-h. | 13.00 | 13.00 |
| | Dated 1987. | | |

Santa Maria — A105

Ships: a, Santa Maria. b, Grande Francoise. #1869, San Martin, horiz.

| | | | | |
|---|---|---|---|---|
| **1988, Feb. 10** | | **Litho.** | **Perf. 13½x14** | |
| **1867** A105 | $7 Pair, #a.-b., pale yel & multi | | 6.00 | 6.00 |
| **1868** A105 | $7 Pair, #a.-b., bl & multi | | 6.00 | 6.00 |
| | Nos. 1867-1868 (2) | | 12.00 | 12.00 |
| | **Souvenir Sheet** | | | |
| | **Perf. 14** | | | |
| **1869** A105 | $7 silver & multi | | 12.00 | 12.00 |

Discovery of America, 500th anniv. (in 1992). Nos. 1867-1868 printed checkerwise with se-tenant labels describing ship dimensions. No. 1869 exists with gold border.

Nos. 136, 139a, and 146 Surcharged "Republic / Day / 1988" in Blue

| | | | | |
|---|---|---|---|---|
| | **Perfs. as Before** | | | |
| **1988, Feb. 23** | | **Litho.** | **Wmk. 364** | |
| **1870** A28 | 25c on 5c #136 | | .20 | .20 |
| **1871** A28 | 120c on 15c #139a | | 6.50 | .75 |
| **1872** A28 | $10 on $2 #146 | | 2.00 | 2.00 |
| | Nos. 1870-1872 (3) | | 8.70 | 2.95 |

No. 283A Surcharged with Names of Post Offices Operating in 1900

Overprints: a, Albouystown. b, Anns Grove. c, Amacura. d, Arakaka. e, Baramanni. f, Cuyuni. g, Hope Placer. h, HMPS. i, Kitty. j, M'M'Zorg. k, Maccaseema. l, 1988. m, Morawhanna. n, Naamryck. o, Purini. p, Potaro / Landing. q, Rockstone. r, Rosignol. s, Stanleytown. t, Santa Rosa. u, Tumatumari. v, Weldaad. w, Wismar. x, TPO Berbice / Railway.

| | | | |
|---|---|---|---|
| **1988, Apr. 5** | | **Perf. 14x13½** | |
| **1873** A66 | 25c Sheet of 25, #a.-k., m.-x., 2 #l. | 32.50 | 32.50 |

British Guiana Post Office, 125th Anniv.

No. 725 Surcharged "Olympic / Games / 1988"

**Perf. 14½x14**

| | | | | |
|---|---|---|---|---|
| **1988, May 3** | | **Litho.** | **Wmk. 373** | |
| **1897** A73 | 120c Sheet of 12, #a.-l. | | 18.00 | 18.00 |

Nos. 136-137 and 146 Surcharged "Caricom Day / 1988"

**Perf. 13x13½**

| | | | | |
|---|---|---|---|---|
| **1988, June 15** | | **Litho.** | **Wmk. 364** | |
| **1898** A28 | 25c on 5c #136 | | .90 | .20 |
| **1899** A28 | $1.20 on 6c #137 | | .90 | .20 |
| **1900** A28 | $10 on $2 #146 | | 4.50 | 4.00 |
| | Nos. 1898-1900 (3) | | 6.30 | 4.40 |

No. 286A Overprinted

Overprints: a, 1988. b, WHO / 1948-1988.

| | | | |
|---|---|---|---|
| **1988, June 17** | **Litho.** | **Perf. 14x13½** | |
| **1901** | Sheet of 25, 24 #a., 1 #b. | 27.50 | 25.00 |
| a. | A28 60c any single | .40 | .20 |
| b. | A28 60c | 17.50 | 17.50 |

World Health Day, 40th anniv.

Nos. 929d Overprinted as Indicated Nos. 1053a, 1063, 1131, and 1161 Overprinted "CONSERVE / WATER"

Overprints: No. 1903, "CONSERVE TREES" on ocher stamp, "CONSERVE ELECTRICITY on green stamp, "CONSERVE WATER on brown stamp. No. 1904, "CONSERVE WATER on ocher stamp, "CONSERVE ELECTRICITY" on ocher stamp, "CONSERVE WATER on green stamp, "CONSERVE TREES on brown stamp. No. 1905, "CONSERVE WATER" on ocher stamp, "CONSERVE TREES on green stamp, "CONSERVE ELECTRICITY on brown stamp.

| | | | |
|---|---|---|---|
| | **Perfs. as Before** | | |
| **1988, July 15** | | **Litho.** | |
| | **Watermarks as Before** | | |
| **1903** | Triptych | 3.00 | 3.00 |
| a.-c. | A90 120c any single | .80 | .50 |
| **1904** | Triptych | 3.00 | 3.00 |
| a.-c. | A90 120c any single | .80 | .50 |
| **1905** | Triptych | 3.00 | 3.00 |
| a.-c. | A90 120c any single | .80 | .50 |
| **1906** A91 | 200c on #1063 | 1.00 | 1.00 |
| **1907** A91 | 200c on #1131 | 1.00 | 1.00 |
| **1908** A91 | 225c on #1053a | 1.00 | 1.00 |
| **1909** A91 | 350c on #1161 | 1.00 | 1.00 |
| | Nos. 1903-1909 (7) | 13.00 | 13.00 |

Location and size of overprint varies.

Nos. 1826a and 1829a Ovptd. "BEWARE / OF ANIMALS" (a.)

Nos. 1826b and 1829b Ovptd. "BEWARE / OF CHILDREN" (b.)

Nos. 1826c and 1829c Ovptd. "DRIVE SAFELY" (c.)

Nos. 1826d and 1829d Ovptd. "DO NOT / DRINK AND DRIVE" (d.)

| | | | | |
|---|---|---|---|---|
| | **Unwmk.** | | | |
| **1988, July 15** | | **Litho.** | **Perf. 15** | |
| | **Block of 4, #a.-d.** | | | |
| **1910** A99 | $1.20 on #1826 | | 7.50 | 7.50 |
| **1911** A99 | $1.20 on #1829 | | 7.50 | 7.50 |
| | Nos. 1910-1911 (2) | | 15.00 | 15.00 |

No. 287 Ovptd. or Surcharged

**Perf. 13½x13**

| | | | | |
|---|---|---|---|---|
| **1988, July** | | **Litho.** | **Wmk. 364** | |
| **1912** A66 | $1 "1988" on #287 | | 8.00 | 1.50 |
| **1913** A66 | 120c on $1 #287 | | 8.00 | 1.50 |

No. 421 Surcharged with New Value and "1988"

| | | | | |
|---|---|---|---|---|
| **1988?** | | **Litho.** | **Perf. 13½x14** | |
| **1913A** A80 | $1.20 on $1.10 on $3 #421 | | | |

Nos. 1037a, 1047a, 1056-1057, 1066-1068, 1097, 1099, 1109-1109a, 1110-1111, 1113, 1115, 1122, 1125, 1129, 1147, 1149, and 1155 Ovptd. "CONSERVE / OUR RESOURCES"

| | | | |
|---|---|---|---|
| **1988, July** | | **Perf. 14** | |
| **Watermarks as Before** | | | |
| **Series 1** | | | |
| **Plate Numbers in Parentheses** | | | |
| **1914** | 130c on #1037a (13) | 1.00 | .75 |
| a. | Overprint inverted | 15.00 | |

#1914a probably is as common as #1914.

| | | | |
|---|---|---|---|
| **1915** A91 | 130c on #1047a (20) | 1.00 | .75 |
| **1916** A91 | 150c on #1056 (26) | 1.00 | .75 |
| **1917** A91 | 120c on #1057 (27) | 1.00 | .75 |
| **1918** A91 | 120c on #1066 (36) | 1.00 | .75 |
| **1919** A91 | 120c on #1067 (37) | 1.00 | .75 |
| **1920** A91 | 130c on #1068 (38) | 1.00 | .75 |
| **1921** A91 | 120c on #1097 (56) | 1.00 | .75 |
| **1922** A91 | 120c on #1099 (58) | 1.00 | .75 |
| **1923** A91 | 100c on #1109 (65) | 1.00 | .75 |
| a. | 100c on #1109a | | |
| **1924** A91 | 130c on #1110 (66) | 1.00 | .75 |
| **1925** A91 | 120c on #1111 (67) | 1.00 | .75 |
| **1926** A91 | 100c on #1113 (68) | 1.00 | .75 |
| **1927** A91 | 120c on #1115 (69) | 1.00 | .75 |
| **1928** A91 | 250c on #1122 (74) | 1.00 | .75 |
| **1929** A91 | 150c on #1125 (76) | 1.00 | .75 |
| **1930** A91 | 150c on #1129 (78) | 1.00 | .75 |
| **1931** A91 | 150c on #1147 (87) | 1.00 | .75 |
| **1932** A91 | 100c on #1149 (88) | 1.00 | .75 |
| **1933** A91 | 100c on #1155 (91) | 1.00 | .75 |

Nos. 1827a-1827d and 1830a-1830d Ovptd. with Red Cross

| | | | | |
|---|---|---|---|---|
| **1988, Aug. 3** | | **Litho.** | **Perf. 15** | |
| **1935** A99 | $3.20 Pair, #a.-b., on #1827a, 1827c | | 3.00 | 3.00 |
| **1936** A99 | $3.20 Pair, #a.-b., on #1827b, 1827d | | 3.00 | 3.00 |
| **1937** A99 | $3.30 Pair, #a.-b., on #1830a, 1830c | | 3.00 | 3.00 |
| **1938** A99 | $3.30 Pair, #a.-b., on #1830b, 1830d | | 3.00 | 3.00 |
| | Nos. 1935-1938 (4) | | 12.00 | 12.00 |

Nos. 1038, 1131 Ovptd. and Nos. 1147, 1175 Surcharged "1928-1988 / CRICKET / JUBILEE"

| | | | |
|---|---|---|---|
| **1988, Sept. 5** | | **Litho.** | **Perf. 14** |
| **Watermarks as Before** | | | |
| **Plate Numbers in Parentheses** | | | |
| **1939** A91 | 200c on #1038 (14) | 22.50 | 22.50 |
| **1940** A91 | 200c on #1131 (79) | 1.25 | .50 |
| **1941** A91 | 800c on 150c #1147 (87) | 9.50 | 9.50 |
| **1942** A91 | 800c on 160c #1175 (5) | 3.75 | 3.75 |
| | Nos. 1939-1942 (4) | 37.00 | 36.25 |

Nos. 1063, 1081, 1139, 1147, 1161, 1185, 1219, 1232, and 1305 Ovptd. and No. 1227 Surcharged "OLYMPIC GAMES / 1988"

| | | | |
|---|---|---|---|
| **1943** A91 | 200c on #1063 (53) | .70 | .70 |
| **1944** A91 | 120c on #1081 (46) | .70 | .70 |
| **1945** A91 | 300c on #1139 (83) | .70 | .70 |
| **1946** A91 | 150c on #1147 (87) | .70 | .70 |
| **1947** A91 | 350c on #1161 (94) | .90 | .90 |
| **1948** A91 | 320c on #1185 (10) | .90 | .90 |
| **1949** A91 | 350c on #1219 (29) | .90 | .90 |

**1950** A91 300c on 360c #1227
(34) .90 .90
**1951** A91 130c on #1232 (38) .90 .90
**1952** A91 330c on #1305 (82) .90 .90
Overprint reads up on No. 1947.

Type A83 Ovptd. or Surcharged
"OLYMPICS 1988" (a.) or
"KOREA 1988" (b.)

| | | | | |
|---|---|---|---|---|
| **1988** | Litho. | Wmk. 364 | *Perf. 13½* | |
| **1953** | A83 | $1.20 Pair, #a.-b. | 1.25 | 1.25 |
| **1954** | A83 | 130c on $1.20, pair, #a.-b. | 1.25 | 1.25 |
| **1955** | A83 | 150c on $1.20, pair, #a.-b. | 1.25 | 1.25 |
| **1956** | A83 | 200c on $1.20, pair, #a.-b. | 1.50 | 1.50 |
| **1957** | A83 | 350c on $1.20, pair, #a.-b. | 1.75 | 1.75 |
| *c.* | | Strip of 5, #1953a-1957a | 7.00 | 7.00 |
| *d.* | | Strip of 5, #1953b-1957b | 7.00 | 7.00 |

Overprint obliterates inscription spelled
"LOS ANGELES."

No. 1087 Ovptd. and No. 1143
Surcharged "V CENTENARY OF /
THE LANDING OF / CHRISTOPHER
COLUMBUS / IN THE AMERICAS"

**Unwmk.**

| | | | | |
|---|---|---|---|---|
| **1988, Oct. 12** | Litho. | *Perf. 14* | | |
| **1958** | A91 | 320c on #1087 | 2.75 | .75 |
| **1959** | A91 | $15 on 360c #1143 | 5.00 | 5.00 |
| | *Nos. 1958-1959 (2)* | | 7.75 | 5.75 |

Nos. 1027, 1036, 1040, 1046, 1054,
1062, 1070, 1071, 1074, 1076, 1079,
1102, 1104, 1133, 1137 and 1143
Surcharged "SEASON'S /
GREETINGS" in Blue or Black

Nos. 1053, 1053a, 1102, 1591A and
1670F Ovptd. or Surcharged
"SEASON'S / GREETINGS / 1988" in
Blue

**1988, Nov. 10** *Perfs. as Before*
**Watermarks and Printing Methods
as Before**
**Plate Numbers in Parentheses**

| | | | |
|---|---|---|---|
| **1960** | A91 | 120c on 100c #1027 (6) | 2.00 |
| **1961** | A91 | 120c on 100c #1036 (13) | 2.00 |
| **1962** | A91 | 240c on 180c #1040 (15) (Bk) | 1.00 |
| **1963** | A91 | 120c on 100c #1046 (20) | 2.00 |
| **1964** | A91 | 225c on #1053 (24) | 1.00 |
| *a.* | | 225c on #1053a | 2.50 |
| **1965** | A91 | 120c on 100c #1054 (25) | 2.00 |
| **1966** | A91 | 150c on 100c #1062 (32) (Bk) | 1.00 |
| **1967** | A91 | 260c on #1070 (39) (Bk) | 1.00 |
| **1968** | A91 | 120c on 100c #1071 (40) | 2.00 |
| **1969** | A91 | 120c on 100c #1074 (42) | 2.00 |
| **1970** | A91 | 120c on 100c #1076 (43) | 2.00 |
| **1971** | A91 | 120c on 100c #1079 (45) | 2.00 |
| **1972** | A91 | 225c on #1102 (60) (Bk) | 1.00 |
| **1973** | A91 | 225c on #1102 (60) (Bk) | 1.00 |
| **1974** | A91 | 150c on #1104 (62) (Bk) | 1.00 |
| **1975** | A91 | 225c on #1591A (65) | 1.50 |
| **1976** | A91 | 330c on #1133 (80) (Bk) | 1.00 |
| **1977** | A91 | 320c on #1137 (82) (Bk) | 1.00 |
| **1978** | A91 | 360c on #1143 (85) (Bk) | 1.00 |
| | *Nos. 1960-1978 (19)* | | 27.50 |

**Miniature Sheet**

**1979** A91 225c on #1670F (22) 4.75 4.75
Size and location of overprint varies.

Nos. 72, 713 and 932 Surcharged or
Ovptd. "CHRISTMAS / 1988" in Red
or Black

**1988, Nov. 16** *Perfs. as Before*
**Watermarks and Printing Methods
as Before**

| | | | | |
|---|---|---|---|---|
| **1981** | A7 | 20c on 6c #72 | .30 | .20 |
| **1982** | A86 | Block of 4 (Bk) | 2.25 | 2.25 |
| *a.* | | 120c on #713a | .50 | .50 |
| *b.* | | 120c on 130c #713b | .50 | .50 |
| *c.* | | 120c on 150c #713c | .50 | .50 |
| *d.* | | 120c on 200c #713d | .50 | .50 |
| **1983** | A90a | 500c on 330c #932 | 2.50 | 2.50 |
| | *Nos. 1981-1983 (3)* | | 5.05 | 4.95 |

Overprint reads up on No. 1983.

---

Nos. 288, 289, and 289A Surcharged
or Ovptd. for Prevention of AIDS

Beginnning of overprint reads: Nos. 1984a,
1985e, "Get information..." Nos. 1984b,
1985a, "Get the facts..." Nos. 1984c, 1985b,
"Say no to drugs..." Nos. 1984d, 1985c, $2,
$5, $10, "Protect yourself..." Nos. 1984e,
1985d, "Be compassionate..."

| | | | | |
|---|---|---|---|---|
| *Perf. 13½x13* | | | | |
| **1988, Dec. 1** | Litho. | Wmk. 364 | | |
| **1984** | A66 | 120c Strip of 5, #a.-e., on #289 | 18.50 | 18.50 |
| **1985** | A66 | 120c Strip of 5, #a.-e., on #289A | 18.50 | 18.50 |
| **1986** | A66 | $2 on #288 | 12.00 | 3.00 |
| **1987** | A66 | $5 on #289 | 14.00 | 7.50 |
| **1988** | A66 | $10 on #289A | 16.00 | 12.00 |
| | *Nos. 1984-1988 (5)* | | 79.00 | 59.50 |

1988 Winter
Olympics,
Calgary
A106

Design: $3.50, Olympic rings.

**1988, Dec. 1** *Perf. 14*
**1989** A106 $7 Downhill ski-
ing 11.00 11.00

**Souvenir Sheet**

**1990** A106 $3.50 Sheet of 1 6.00 6.00
No. 1989 exists in souvenir sheet of 1. Value
$11.

Christmas — A107

Paintings: No. 1991a, Virgin and Child
Between St. George and St. Catherine, by
Titian. No. 1992a, Adoration of the Magi, by Titian.
No. 1992a, Holy Family, by Rubens. b. Ado-
ration of the Shepherds, by Rubens.
$8, The Madonna, by Titian.

| | | | | |
|---|---|---|---|---|
| *Perf. 14x13½, 13½x14* | | | | |
| **1988, Dec. 15** | Litho. | | | |
| **1991** | A107 | $2 Pair, #a.-b. | 7.00 | 7.00 |
| **1992** | A107 | $2 Pair, #a.-b. | 7.00 | 7.00 |

**Souvenir Sheet**
*Perf. 13½x14*

**1993** A107 $8 multicolored 17.50 17.50
Nos. 1991a-1991b, 1992a-1992b exist in
souvenir sheets of 1.

Abolition of Slavery Type of 1985

**1988, Dec. 16** Litho. *Perf. 14*
**Designs as Before**

| | | | | |
|---|---|---|---|---|
| **1994** | A93 | 25c brown & black | .25 | .25 |
| **1995** | A93 | 60c magenta & black | .50 | .50 |
| **1996** | A93 | 130c green & black | 1.00 | 1.00 |
| **1997** | A93 | 150c blue & black | 1.25 | 1.25 |
| | *Nos. 1994-1997 (4)* | | 3.00 | 3.00 |

Nos. 1087, 1167, and 1200
Surcharged "SALUTING WINNERS /
OLYMPIC GAMES / 1988"

**Unwmk.**

| | | | | |
|---|---|---|---|---|
| **1989, Jan. 3** | Litho. | *Perf. 14* | | |
| **1998** | A91 | $5.50 on 560c #1167 | 1.75 | 1.25 |
| **1999** | A91 | $9 on 320c #1200 | 2.25 | 2.25 |
| **2000** | A91 | $10.50 on 320c #1087 | 3.00 | 3.00 |
| | *Nos. 1998-2000 (3)* | | 7.00 | 6.50 |

---

Miniature Sheets

Red Cross, 125th Anniv. — A108

Designs: No. 2001, Henri Dunant, vert. No.
2002, First maritime ambulance. No. 2003,
Red Cross hospital ship in African War. No.
2004, Red Cross air ambulance. No. 2005,
Red Cross train.
Nos. 2001-2004 printed with red cross in
center of sheet. Each stamp contains part of
the red cross at the: a, LR. b, LL. c, UR. d, UL.

*Perf. 13½x14, 14x13½*
**1989, Jan. 5** Litho.

| | | | | |
|---|---|---|---|---|
| **2001** | A108 | $2 Sheet of 4, #a.-d. | 10.00 | 10.00 |
| **2002** | A108 | $2 Sheet of 4, #a.-d. | 10.00 | 10.00 |
| **2003** | A108 | $2 Sheet of 4, #a.-d. | 10.00 | 10.00 |
| **2004** | A108 | $2 Sheet of 4, #a.-d. | 10.00 | 10.00 |
| | *Nos. 2001-2004 (4)* | | 40.00 | 40.00 |

**Souvenir Sheet**
*Perf. 14x13½*

**2005** A108 $7 Sheet of 1 11.00 11.00
Dated 1988.

Trains — A109

Designs: a, Hernalser sleeping carriage. b,
5 Forney locomotive. c, Austrian sleeping carriage. d, Pacific 231 locomotive.
$10, First Japanese imperial train.

**1989, Jan. 5** Litho. *Perf. 14*
**2006** A109 $2 Sheet of 4,
#a.-d. 15.00 15.00

**Souvenir Sheet**

**2007** A109 $10 multicolored 11.00 11.00
Nos. 2006a-2006d exist in souvenir sheets
of 1. Value, each $3.75.
Dated 1988.

Naval Airship LZ 92, 1916 — A110

#2008: a, Astronaut on moon. b, Graf
Zeppelin over San Francisco Bay, 1929. c,
Testu-Brissy on horseback ascending in bal-
loon, 1798.
#2009, Graf Zeppelin LZ 127.

**1989, Jan. 26** *Perf. 14*
**2007A** A110 $2 black 3.00 3.00
**2008** A110 $2 Strip of 3, #a.-c. 8.00 8.00
*Nos. 2007A-2008 (2)* 11.00

**Souvenir Sheet**

**2009** A110 $2 Sheet of 1 10.00 6.00
Nos. 2007A, 2008b, 2009, Ferdinand von
Zeppelin, 150th birth anniv. in 1988. No.
2008a, 1st moon landing, 20th anniv. in 1989.
The inscriptions on Nos. 2007A and 2009 are
in error. Dated 1988.

---

Mushrooms — A111

#2010: a, Cortinarius bolaris. b, Cortinarius
laniger. c, Tricholoma sulphureum. d, Lepiota
cristata.
#2011, Sarcoscypha coccinea, vert.

**1989, Feb. 1** *Perf. 14x13½*
**2010** A111 $2 Block of 4, #a.-
d. 15.00 15.00

**Souvenir Sheet**
*Perf. 13½x14*

**2011** A111 $5 Sheet of 1 11.00 11.00
Dated 1988.

Boy Scout Jamboree,
Australia — A112

Design: $8, Scouts of different races.

**1989, Feb. 10**
**2012** A112 $10 grn, black &
yel 15.00 15.00

**Souvenir Sheet**

**2013** A112 $8 Sheet of 1 15.00 15.00
Dated 1988. #2012 exists in souvenir sheet
of 1.

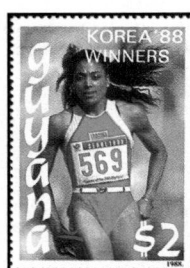

1988 Summer
Olympics,
Seoul — A113

Emblem of
South
American
Soccer
Federation —
A113a

Designs: No. 2014, Florence Griffith-Joyner.
No. 2015, Carl Lewis. No. 2016, Equestrian.
No. 2017, Runners, horiz. No. 2018, City skyline, Olympic Rings, horiz. No. 2019, 1988 &
1992 Olympic mascots, horiz. No. 2022, Griffith-Joyner, Lewis, horiz. No. 2023, Cosmic
Athlete by Dali, horiz.

**1989, Feb. 15** Litho. *Perf. 14*

| | | | | |
|---|---|---|---|---|
| **2014** | A113 | $2 multicolored | 3.50 | 3.50 |
| **2015** | A113 | $2 multicolored | 3.50 | 3.50 |
| **2016** | A113 | $2 multicolored | 3.50 | 3.50 |
| **2017** | A113 | $2 multicolored | 3.50 | 3.50 |
| **2018** | A113 | $2 multicolored | 3.50 | 3.50 |
| **2019** | A113 | $2 multicolored | 3.50 | 3.50 |
| **2020** | A113a | $2 multicolored | 3.50 | 3.50 |

## Souvenir Sheets

**2022** A113 $3.50 multicolored 15.00 15.00
**2023** A113 $3.50 multicolored 15.00 15.00
 Nos. 2022-2023 (2) 30.00 30.00

No. 2023 exists with gold border and inscriptions. Nos. 2014-2020 inscribed 1988. An additional stamp was issued in this set. The editors would like to examine any examples.

### Nos. 1826, 1829 and 1831 Ovptd. "REPUBLIC DAY 1989" in Red

**1989, Feb. 22** Litho. Perf. 15
**2024** A99 $1.20 Block of 4,
 #a.-d., on
 #1826 3.00 3.00
**2025** A99 $1.20 Block of 4,
 #a.-d., on
 #1829 3.00 3.00
**2026** A101 $10 on #1831 5.00 5.00
 Nos. 2024-2026 (3) 11.00

### Nos. 1827a-1827d and 1830a-1830d Surcharged in Red

**1989, Feb. 22**
**2027** A99 $5 Pair, #a.-b., on
 $3.20 #a., c. 7.50 7.50
**2028** A99 $5 Pair, #a.-b., on
 $3.20 #b., d. 7.50 7.50
**2028C** A99 $5 Pair, #d.-e., on
 $3.30 #a., c. 7.50 7.50
**2028F** A99 $5 Pair, #g.-h., on
 $3.30 #b., d. 7.50 7.50

### Nos. 1461, 1822 Surcharged in Red

**1989, Feb. 22** Litho. Perf. 14
**2029** A96 $10 #a.-b. on #1461 10.00 10.00
**2030** A96 $10 #a.-b. on #1822 10.00 10.00
 Nos. 2029-2030 (2) 20.00

### No. 1188 Surcharged "EASTER"

**1989, Mar. 22** Perf. 14
**2031** A91 Sheet of 4 on #1188 5.00 5.00
 **b.** 125c on 320c #1188 .50 .50
 **b.** 250c on 320c #1188 1.00 1.00
 **c.** 300c on 320c #1188 1.25 1.25
 **d.** 350c on 320c #1188 1.50 1.50

### No. 927 Surcharged

**1989, Mar.** Wmk. 364 Perf. 14
**2032** A90 250c on 25c #927 6.00 1.25
 Inscribed "1986."

### No. 1197 Surcharged "RED CROSS / 1948 / 1988"

**1989, Apr.** Unwmk. Perf. 14
**2033** A91 375c on 45c #1197 5.50 5.50
**2034** A91 425c on 45c #1197 5.50 5.50
 Nos. 2033-2034 (2) 11.00

Guyana Red Cross, 40th anniv.

### #1263 & 1252 Surcharged in Pairs "ALL FOR / HEALTH" (a.) or "HEALTH / FOR ALL" (b.)

**1989, Apr. 3**
**2035** A91 250c on 75c #1263
 (56), pair 8.00 8.00
**2036** A91 675c on 720c #1252
 (49), pair 10.00 10.00
 Nos. 2035-2036 (2) 18.00 18.00

For surcharge see No. 2052.

### Nos. 1224-1225, and 1254 Overprinted or Surcharged "BOY SCOUTS / 1909 1989" (a.) or "GIRL GUIDES / 1924 1989" (b.) Nos. 1272-1273 Surcharged "LADY BADEN POWELL / 1889-1989"

**1989, Apr. 11**
**2037** A91 250c on 100c, pair,
 #a.-b. 5.00 5.00
**2038** A91 $2.50 on 50c, pair, #a.-
 b. 5.00 5.00
**2039** A91 300c Pair, #a.-b. 5.00 5.00
 **c.** Pair, #d.-e., Prussian bl ovpt.
**2040** A91 $25 on 280c #1272 7.00 7.00
 **a.** Prussian blue overprint
**2041** A91 $25 on 700c #1273 7.00 7.00
 **a.** Prussian blue overprint

Nos. 2037-2039, Boy Scouts in Guyana, 80th anniversary and Girl Guides, 65th anniversary. Nos. 2040-2041, Lady Baden Powell, birth centenary.

### No. 1177 Surcharged "PHOTOGRAPHY / 1839-1989"

**1989, Apr. 15**
**2042** A91 550c on 390c 7.00 7.00
**2043** A91 650c on 390c, 2 bar
 obliterator 7.00 7.00
 **a.** 6 bar obliterator 7.00 7.00
 Nos. 2042-2043, 2043a (3) 21.00 21.00

Nos. 2042-2043 printed in sheets of 4 with alternating overprints.

### No. 1263 Surcharged "I.L.O. / 1919-1989"

**1989, May 2**
**2044** A91 300c on 75c #1263 12.00 2.25

Intl. Labor Organization, 70th anniversary.

Nos. 43, 87, 134-137, 279-280, 284-285, and 286A 288, 1827, 1830, and 2035-2036 Surcharged in Black or Blue

q

s

r

t

**1989-92** Perfs. as Before
**Watermarks and Printing Methods as Before**
**2045** A7(q) 80c on 6c #43 .60 .35
 **a.** A7 80c on 6c #43 .60 .35
**2046** A28(q) $1 on 2c
 #134 .60 .35
 **a.** A28(r) $1 on 2c #134 .60 .35
**2047** A28(q) $2.05 on 3c
 #135 .60 .35
 **a.** A28(q) $2.55 on 5c
 #136 .60 .35
**2048** A28(q) $2.55 on 5c
 #136 .60 .35
 **a.** A28(r) $2.55 on 5c #136 .60 .35
**2049** A28(q) $3.25 on 6c
 #137 .60 .40
 **a.** A28(r) $3.25 on 6c #137 .60 .40
**2050** A14(q) $5 on 6c #87 .60 .35
 **a.** A14(s) $5 on 6c #87 .60 .35
 **b.** A14(r) $5 on 6c #87
**2051** A66(q) $6 on 5c
 #279
**2052** A91 640c Pair,
 #2036 5.00 5.00
**2053** A66(q) $6.40 on 10c
 #280 6.00 .90
 **a.** A66 $6.40 on 10c #280 6.00 .90
 **b.** A66(r) $6.40 on 10c #280 6.00 .90
**2054** Block of 5, #a.-e. on
 #1830 42.50 42.50
 **a.-d.** A99(t) $6.40 on $3.30
 #a.-d. 5.00 2.00
 **e.** A100(t) $190 on $3.30
 #e. 22.50 20.00
**2054F** A66(r) $7.65 on 35c
 #284 7.25 1.50
**2055** A66 $7.65 on 40c
 #285 8.25 1.50
**2056** Block of 5, #a.-e. on
 #1827 42.50 42.50
 **a.-d.** A99(t) $7.65 on $3.20
 #a.-d. 5.00 2.00
 **e.** A100(t) $225 on $3.20
 #e. 22.50 20.00
**2057** A66(q) $8.90 on 60c
 #286A 9.00 1.50
 **a.** A66 $8.90 on 60c #286A 9.00 1.50

**2057B** A66(q) $30 on 10c
 #280
**2057C** A66(q) $35 on 35c
 #284
**2058** A66(r) $50 on $2
 #288 (Bl) 20.00 10.00
**2059** A66(r) $100 on $2
 #288 27.50 20.00

Issued: #2045a, 2053-2053a, 2054F, 2055, May 18; #2057, May 26; #2058-2059, June 5; #2045, 2049, 2046a, 2048a, 2049a, June 15; #2050-2050a, 2051, 2052, 2054, 2056, Aug. 16; #2050b, 1992.

Nos. 2045a, 2053a, 2055, 2057a have no obliterator. New denominations are larger on Nos. 2045a, 2053a and 2057a. No. 2045a has no cent sign. Denomination on No. 2050b is above "X" obliterator.

Nos. 2054e, 2056b additionally overprinted "SPECIAL DELIVERY."

### No. 1244 Surcharged "CARICOM / DAY"

**1989, June 26** Unwmk. Litho. Perf. 14
**2064** A91 125c on 200c #1244,
 2 bar obliterator 8.00 1.50
 **a.** 6 bar obliterator 10.00 1.75

### No. 280 Ovptd. in Gold or Silver for Gold Medalists at 1988 Summer Olympics

Overprints read: Nos. 2082a, 2083a, "SEOUL / OLYMPICS." Nos. 2082b, 2083b, "Men's 800M / Ereng / Kenya." Nos. 2082c, 2083c, "KOREA." Nos. 2082d, 2083d, "Men's / Gymnastics / Artemov / USSR." Nos. 2082e, 2083e, "Men's / Swimming / Louganis / USA." Nos. 2082f, 2083f, "Woman's / Swimming / Otto / DDR." Nos. 2082g, 2083g, "Men's Fencing / Lamour / France." Nos. 2082h, 2083h, "Men's / Gymnastics / Lou / China." Nos. 2082i, 2083i, "Women's / Cycling / Knol / Holland." Nos. 2082j, 2083j, "Men's / Swimming / Szabo / Hungary." Nos. 2082k, 2083k, "1988." Nos. 2082l, 2083l, "Men's / Swimming / Nesty / Suriname." Nos. 2082m, 2083m, "Men's Boxing / Lewis / Canada." Nos. 2082n, 2083n, "Men's Javelin / Korjus / Finland." Nos. 2082o, 2083o, "Basketball / USA." Nos. 2082p, 2083p, "Men's / Equestrian / Klimke / W. Germany." Nos. 2082q, 2083q, "Men's Boxing / Park / Korea." Nos. 2082r, 2083r, "Women's / Marathon / Mota / Portugal." Nos. 2082s, 2083s, "Men's / Swimming / Suzuki / Japan." Nos. 2084a, 2085a, "Men's 100M / Lewis / USA." Nos. 2084b, 2085b, "Men's / Pole Vault / Bubka / USSR." Nos. 2084c, 2085c, "Women's / 100-200m / Joyner / USA." Nos. 2084d, 2085d, "Men's Pentathlon / Martinek / Hungary." Nos. 2084e, 2085e, "Men's Wrestling / Sako / Japan." Nos. 2084f, 2085f, "Men's Judo / Saito / Japan." Nos. 2084g, 2085g, "Women's 800M / Wodars / DDR." Nos. 2084h, 2085h, "Men's Boxing / Gross / W. Germany." Nos. 2084i, 2085i, "Men's Boxing / Maske / DDR." Nos. 2084j, 2085j, "Men's Boxing / Kim / Korea." Nos. 2084k, 2085k, "Woman's / Swimming / Evans / USA." Nos. 2084l, 2085l, "Soccer / USSR." Nos. 2084m, 2085m, "Woman's / Gymnastics / Silivas / Romania." Nos. 2084n, 2085n, "Men's Boxing / Mercer / USA." Nos. 2084o, 2085o, "Men's Marathon / Bordin / Italy." Nos. 2084p, 2085p, "Women's Tennis / Graf / W. Germany."

Perf. 14x13½
**1989, Apr.** Litho. Wmk. 364
**Sheets of 25**
**2082** 5 #a., 3 #c., #b., d.-s. 12.50 12.50
**2083** 5 #a., 3 #c., #b., d.-s.
 (S) 12.50 12.50
 **a.-s.** A66 10c on #280, any single .45 .45
**2084** #a.-p., 5 #2082a, 3
 #2082c, #2082k 12.50 12.50
 **a.-p.** A66 10c on #280, any single .45 .45
**2085** #a.-p., 5 #2083a, 3
 #2083c, #2083k (S) 12.50 12.50
 **a.-p.** A66 10c on #280, any single .45 .45

### Nos. 280 Ovptd. in Gold or Silver for Gold Medalists at 1988 Winter Olympics

Overprints read: Nos. 2086a, 2087a, "Gold Medal / Winners." Nos. 2086b, 2087b, "Ice Hockey / USSR." Nos. 2086c, 2087c, "CALGARY / OLYMPICS." Nos. 2086d, 2087d, "Bobsled / Kipours-Kozlov / USSR." Nos. 2086e, 2087e, "Women's Skating / 1500-3000-5000M / Gennip / Netherlands." Nos. 2086f, 2087f, "Men's / Speed / Skating / 5000-10000M / Gustafson / Sweden." Nos. 2086g, 2087g, "Men's Figure / Skating / Boitano / USA." Nos. 2086h, 2087h, "Women's / 500M Skating / Blair / USA." Nos. 2086i, 2087i, "Women's / Figure Skating / Witt / DDR." Nos. 2086j, 2087j, "Men's Giant / Slalom / Tomba / Italy." Nos. 2086k, 2087k, "CANADA." Nos. 2086l, 2087l, "Men's Super / Giant Slalom / Picard / France." Nos. 2086m, 2087m,

"Women's / Downhill Skiing / Kiehl / W. Germany." Nos. 2086n, 2087n, "Men's 50km Skiing Svan / Sweden." Nos. 2086o, 2087o, "Men's Nordic / Combined Skiing / Mueller-Pohl / Schwarz / W. Germany." Nos. 2086p, 2087p, "Women's / Giant Slalom / Schneider / Switzerland." Nos. 2086q, 2087q, "Women's / 5-km Skiing / Matikainen / Finland." Nos. 2086r, 2087r, "Men's Downhill / Alpine Skiing / Zurbriggen / Switzerland." Nos. 2086s, 2087s, "Men's Ski / Jumping / Nykanen / Finland."

**1989, Apr.**
**2086** 4 #a., 3 #c., #b., d.-s.,
 #2082k 12.50 12.50
 **a.-s.** A66 10c on #280, any single .45 .45
**2087** 4 #a., 3 #c., #b., d.-s.,
 #2083k (S) 12.50 12.50
 **a.-s.** A66 10c on #280, any single .45 .45

### No. 281 Ovptd. in Gold or Silver in Memory of Hirohito, Emperor of Japan

Overprints read: Nos. 2088a, 2089a, "Emperor / Hirohito." Nos. 2088b, 2089b, "Showa / Era." Nos. 2088c, 2089c, "Chrysanthemum / Dynasty." Nos. 2088d, 2089d, "Emperor / of Japan." Nos. 2088e, 2089e, "1901." Nos. 2088f, 2089f, "1989." Nos. 2088g, 2089g, "Emperor / Hirohito / 1901-1989."

**1989, Apr.**
**2088** 5 #a., 4 #c.-d., 9 #b.,
 #e.-g. 12.50 12.50
 **a.-g.** A66 15c on #281, any single .45 .45
**2089** 5 #a., 4 #c.-d., 9 #b.,
 #e.-g. (S) 12.50 12.50
 **a.-g.** A66 15c on #281, any single .45 .45

### No. 280 Ovptd. in Gold or Silver for Enthronment of Akihito, Emperor of Japan

Overprints reads: Nos. 2090a, 2091a, "Honoring / His / Majesty." Nos. 2090b, 2091b, "Emperor / of / Japan." Nos. 2090c, 2091c, "1989." Nos. 2090d, 2091d, "HEISI / ERA."

**1989, Apr.**
**2090** 12 #a, 8 #b., 4 #c., #d. 12.50 12.50
 **a.-d.** A66 10c on #280, any single .45 .45
**2091** 12 #a., 8 #b., 4 #c., #d.
 (S) 12.50 12.50
 **a.-d.** A66 10c on #280, any single .45 .45

Overprint is 10mm long on #2090c, 2091c.

### Nos. 280-281 and 283 Ovptd. with Emblems of Scouts, Rotary Intl., and Lions Intl. in Gold, Silver, Metallic Red, Metallic Green and Black

Overprints: Nos. 2092a, 2093a, 2094a, 2095a, 2096b, 2097b, 2098b, 2099b, 2100c, 2101c, 2102c, 2103c, Scouting emblem. Nos. 2092b, 2093b, 2094b, 2095b, 2096a, 2097a, 2098a, 2099a, 2100b, 2101b, 2102b, 2103b, Rotary emblem. Nos. 2092c, 2093c, 2094c, 2095c, 2096c, 2097c, 2098c, 2099c, 2100a, 2101a, 2102a, 2103a, Lions emblem. Nos. 2092d, 2093d, 2094d, 2095d, 2096d, 2097d, 2098d, 2099d, 2100d, 2101d, 2102d, 2103d, "1989." Nos. 2092e, 2093e, 2094e, 2095e, Large scouting emblem. Nos. 2096e, 2097e, 2098e, 2099e, Large Rotary emblem. Nos. 2100e, 2101e, 2102e, 2103e, Large Lions emblem.

**1989, Apr.**
**2092** 8 #a.-b., 6 #c., 2 #d.,
 #e. 12.50 12.50
 **a.-e.** A66 10c on #280, any single .45 .45
**2093** 8 #a.-b., 6 #c., 2 #d.,
 #e. (S) 12.50 12.50
 **a.-e.** A66 10c on #280, any single .45 .45
**2094** 8 #a.-b., 6 #c., 2 #d.,
 #e. (R) 12.50 12.50
 **a.-e.** A66 10c on #280, any single .45 .45
**2095** 8 #a.-b., 6 #c., 2 #d.,
 #e. (Bk) 12.50 12.50
 **a.-e.** A66 10c on #280, any single .45 .45
**2096** 8 #a.-b., 6 #c., 2 #d.,
 #e. 12.50 12.50
 **a.-e.** A66 15c on #281, any single .45 .45
**2097** 8 #a.-b., 6 #c., 2 #d.,
 #e. (S) 12.50 12.50
 **a.-e.** A66 15c on #281, any single .45 .45
**2098** 8 #a.-b., 6 #c., 2 #d.,
 #e. (R) 12.50 12.50
 **a.-e.** A66 15c on #281, any single .45 .45
**2099** 8 #a.-b., 6 #c., 2 #d.,
 #e. (Gr) 12.50 12.50
 **a.-e.** A66 15c on #281, any single .45 .45
**2100** 8 #a.-b., 6 #c., 2 #d.,
 #e. 12.50 12.50
 **a.-e.** A66 25c on #283, any single .45 .45
**2101** 8 #a.-b., 6 #c., 2 #d.,
 #e. (S) 12.50 12.50
 **a.-e.** A66 25c on #283, any single .45 .45
**2102** 8 #a.-b., 6 #c., 2 #d.,
 #e. (R) 12.50 12.50
 **a.-e.** A66 25c on #283, any single .45 .45
**2103** 8 #a.-b., 6 #c., 2 #d.,
 #e. (Gr) 12.50 12.50
 **a.-e.** A66 25c on #283, any single .45 .45

"1989" overprints are 7½mm long.

## No. 280 Ovptd. in Gold or Silver for Halley's Comet

Overprints read: Nos. 2104a, 2105a, "Halley's / Comet." Nos. 2104b, 2105b, "Famous / Space Event." Nos. 2104c, 2105c, "Edmund / Halley / 1656-1742." Nos. 2104d, 2105d, "1910." Nos. 2104e, 2105e, "1986."

**1989, Apr.**

| | | | | |
|---|---|---|---|---|
| 2104 | | 11 #a., 6 #b., 4 #c., 2 #d.-e. | 12.50 | 12.50 |
| a.-e. | A66 10c on #280, any single | | .45 | .45 |
| 2105 | | 11 #a., 6 #b., 4 #c., 2 #d.-e. (S) | 12.50 | 12.50 |
| a.-e. | A66 10c on #280, any single | | .45 | .45 |

## No. 280 Ovptd. in Gold or Silver for Space Achievements

Overprints read: Nos. 2106a, 2107a, "Sputnik I / Oct. 4, 1957." Nos. 2106b, 2107b, "Explorer I / Jan. 31, 1958." Nos. 2106c, 2107c, "Sputnik II / Laika / Spacedog / Nov. 3, 1957." Nos. 2106d, 2107d, "Alan Shepard, Jr. / Mercury III / May 5, 1961." Nos. 2106e, 2107e, "Yuri Gagarin / Vostok I / April 12, 1961." Nos. 2106f, 2107f, "John Glenn / Mercury VI / Feb. 20, 1962." Nos. 2106g, 2107g, "Vostok III / Aug. 12, 1962." Nos. 2106h, 2107h, "Grissom-Young / Gemini III / March 23, 1965." Nos. 2106i, 2107i, "Luna III / Oct. 4, 1959." Nos. 2106j, 2107j, "Edward H. White II / Gemini IV / June 3, 1965." Nos. 2106k, 2107k, "V. Tereshkova / First Woman / in Space / June 16-19, 1963." Nos. 2106 l, 2107 l, "Surveyor I / June 2, 1966." Nos. 2106m, 2107m, "Space / Achievements." Nos. 2106n, 2107n, "Voskod I / First 3 Man Crew / Oct. 12-13, 1964." Nos. 2106o, 2107o, "Apollo I / Jan. 27, 1967." Nos. 2106p, 2107p, "Alexei A. Leonov / First Walk in Space / March 18-19, 1965." Nos. 2106q, 2107q, "Apollo VIII / Dec. 21-27, 1968." Nos. 2106r, 2107r, "V. Komarov / Soyuz I / April 24, 1967." Nos. 2106s, 2107s, "Apollo XI / First Man on Moon / July 20, 1969." Nos. 2106t, 2107t, "Lunokhod I / Dec. 10, 1970." Nos. 2106u, 2107u, "Apollo XIII / April 11-17, / 1970." Nos. 2106v, 2107v, "Soyuz XI / June 30, 1971." Nos. 2106w, 2107w, "Viking I / July 20, 1976." Nos. 2106x, 2107x, "Vega I / March 6, 1986." Nos. 2106y, 2107y, "Columbia Sts-1 / April 12-14, / 1981."

**1989, Apr.**

| | | | | |
|---|---|---|---|---|
| 2106 | | #a.-y. | 12.50 | 12.50 |
| a.-y. | A66 10c on #280, any single | | .45 | .45 |
| 2107 | | #a.-y. (S) | 12.50 | 12.50 |
| a.-y. | A66 10c on #280, any single | | .45 | .45 |

## No. 280 Ovptd. in Gold or Silver

Overprints read: Nos. 2108a, 2109a, "1969-/ 1989." Nos. 2108b, 2109b, "Apollo XI." Nos. 2108c, 2109c, "First Man / on Moon." Nos. 2108d, 2109d, "USA." Nos. 2108e, 2109e, "Neil A. / Armstrong." Nos. 2108f, 2109f, "Col. Edwin E. / Aldrin, Jr." Nos. 2108g, 2109g, "Lt. Col. / Michael / Collins."

**1989, Apr.**

| | | | | |
|---|---|---|---|---|
| 2108 | | 5 #a., 7 b, 4 c, 6 d, e-g | 12.50 | 12.50 |
| a.-g. | A66 10c on #280, any single | | .45 | .45 |
| 2109 | | 5 #a., 7 b, 4 c, 6 d, e-g (S) | 12.50 | 12.50 |
| a.-g. | A66 10c on #280, any single | | .45 | .45 |

Moon Landing, 20th anniv.

## No. 281 Ovptd. in Gold or Silver for Space Shuttle Program

Overprints read: Nos. 2110a, 2111a, "Enterprise / Aug. 12, 1977." Nos. 2110b, 2111b, "Columbia / April 12, 1981." Nos. 2110c, 2111c, "Space / Shuttles." Nos. 2110d, 2111d, "Discovery / Aug. 30, 1984." Nos. 2110e, 2111e, "Atlantis / Oct. 3, 1985." Nos. 2110f, 2111f, "Challenger / Heroes." Nos. 2110g, 2111g, "Resnik / McAuliffe / Jarvis." Nos. 2110h, 2111h, "In Memoriam / Challenger / Jan. 28, 1986." Nos. 2110i, 2111i, "Onizuka / Smith / McNair / Scobee."

**1989, Apr.**

| | | | | |
|---|---|---|---|---|
| 2110 | | 4 #a.-e., 2 #f., #g.-i. | 12.50 | 12.50 |
| a.-i. | A66 15c on #281, any single | | .45 | .45 |
| 2111 | | 4 #a.-e., 2 #f., #g.-i. (S) | 12.50 | 12.50 |
| a.-i. | A66 15c on #281, any single | | .45 | .45 |

Butterflies — A115    A116

---

**1989, Sept. 7**    *Litho.*    *Perf. 14*

| | | | | |
|---|---|---|---|---|
| 2208 | A115 | 80c Stalachtis calliope | .50 | .25 |
| 2209 | A115 | $2.25 Morpho rhetenor | .60 | .25 |
| 2210 | A115 | $5 Agrias claudia | .75 | .40 |
| 2211 | A115 | $6.40 Marpesia marcella | .85 | .70 |
| 2212 | A115 | $7.65 Papilio zagreus | 1.00 | .90 |
| 2213 | A115 | $8.90 Chorinea faunus | 1.25 | 1.10 |
| 2214 | A115 | $25 Cepheuptychia cephus | 4.00 | 3.00 |
| 2215 | A115 | $100 Nessaea regina | 13.50 | 12.50 |
| | | Nos. 2208-2215 (8) | 22.45 | 19.10 |

See Nos. E16-E17. For overprints see Nos. 2251-2254, 2256-2257, 2260-2261, 2283-2290, E19-E22, E24, E26-E27, E31.

**1989, Nov. 8**

Women in Space, 25th Anniv. (in 1988): $6.40, Kathryn Sullivan, 1st US woman to walk in space. $12.80, Svetlana Savitskaya, 1st Soviet woman to walk in space. $15.30, Judy Resnik & Christa McAuliffe, astronauts killed in Challenger explosion. $100, Sally Ride, 1st US woman astronaut.

| | | | | |
|---|---|---|---|---|
| 2216 | A116 | $6.40 multicolored | 1.00 | .25 |
| 2217 | A116 | $12.80 multicolored | 1.75 | 1.25 |
| 2218 | A116 | $15.30 multicolored | 2.00 | 1.50 |
| 2219 | A116 | $100 multicolored | 11.50 | 11.50 |
| | | Nos. 2216-2219 (4) | 16.25 | 14.50 |

See No. E18. For overprints see Nos. 2255, 2258-2259, 2262, E23, E25, E28, E32.

1990 World Cup Soccer Championships, Italy — A117

Various soccer players.

*Perf. 14x13½, 13½x14*

**1989, Nov. 20**

| | | | | |
|---|---|---|---|---|
| 2220 | A117 | $2.55 shown | 5.00 | 5.00 |
| 2221 | A117 | $2.55 Yellow shirt, vert. | 5.00 | 5.00 |
| 2222 | A117 | $2.55 Goalie | 5.00 | 5.00 |
| 2223 | A117 | $2.55 Green shirt, vert. | 5.00 | 5.00 |
| | | Nos. 2220-2223 (4) | 20.00 | 20.00 |

**Souvenir Sheet**

| | | | | |
|---|---|---|---|---|
| 2224 | A117 | $20 Championships emblem, vert. | 17.50 | 17.50 |

#2220-2223 exist in souvenir sheets of 1. For surcharges see Nos. 2263-2267.

## No. 134-136 Surcharged "AHMADIYYA / CENTENARY / 1889-1989"

*Perf. 13x13½*

**1989, Nov. 22**    *Litho.*    *Wmk. 364*

| | | | | |
|---|---|---|---|---|
| 2225 | A28 | 80c on 2c #134 | 4.50 | .60 |
| 2226 | A28 | $6.40 on 3c #135 | 13.50 | 5.50 |
| 2227 | A28 | $8.90 on 5c #136 | 15.00 | 8.00 |
| | | Nos. 2225-2227 (3) | 33.00 | 14.10 |

1992 Summer Olympics, Barcelona A118

**1989, Dec. 5**    *Perf. 13½x14, 14x13½*

| | | | | |
|---|---|---|---|---|
| 2228 | A118 | $2.55 shown | 4.00 | 4.00 |
| 2229 | A118 | $2.55 Boxing, horiz. | 4.00 | 4.00 |
| 2230 | A118 | $2.55 Chariot racing, horiz. | 4.00 | 4.00 |
| 2231 | A118 | $2.55 Javelin, horiz. | 4.00 | 4.00 |
| 2232 | A118 | $2.55 Running, horiz. | 4.00 | 4.00 |

---

| | | | | |
|---|---|---|---|---|
| 2233 | A118 | $2.55 Wrestling | 4.00 | 4.00 |
| | | Nos. 2228-2233 (6) | 24.00 | 24.00 |

**Souvenir Sheets**

| | | | | |
|---|---|---|---|---|
| 2234 | A118 | $10 Running, horiz., diff. | 15.00 | 15.00 |
| 2235 | A118 | $10 Columbus Walk by Picasso | 15.00 | 15.00 |
| | | Nos. 2234-2235 (2) | 30.00 | 30.00 |

#2228-2233 exist in souvenir sheets of 1.

Christmas — A119

Paintings: No. 2236, Child Declaring in Favor of His Mother, by Titian. No. 2237, The Sacred Family, by Rubens. No. 2238, Saint Anne, the Virgin and Child, by Durer. No. 2239, Madonna Enthroned, Surrounded by Saints, by Rubens. $20, Saint Ildefonso, by Rubens.

**1989, Dec. 26**    *Perf. 14x13½, 13½x14*

| | | | | |
|---|---|---|---|---|
| 2236 | A119 | $2.55 multi | 4.00 | 4.00 |
| 2237 | A119 | $2.55 multi, vert. | 4.00 | 4.00 |
| 2238 | A119 | $2.55 multi, vert. | 4.00 | 4.00 |
| 2239 | A119 | $2.55 multi, vert. | 4.00 | 4.00 |
| | | Nos. 2236-2239 (4) | 16.00 | 16.00 |

**Souvenir Sheet**

| | | | | |
|---|---|---|---|---|
| 2240 | A119 | $20 multi, vert. | 20.00 | 20.00 |

#2236-2239 exist in souvenir sheets of 1.

Harpy Eagle — A120

Channel-billed Toucan — A121

**1990, Jan. 23**    *Litho.*    *Perf. 14*

| | | | | |
|---|---|---|---|---|
| 2241 | A120 | $2.25 Eagle's head | 1.25 | .50 |
| 2242 | A120 | $5 Eagle with prey | 1.75 | .75 |
| 2243 | A120 | $8.90 Eagle facing right | 2.75 | 1.00 |
| 2244 | A121 | $15 shown | 1.75 | .90 |
| 2245 | A121 | $25 Blue & yellow macaw | 2.25 | 1.00 |
| 2246 | A120 | $30 Eagle facing left | 5.25 | 4.50 |
| 2247 | A121 | $50 Wattled jacana, horiz. | 4.00 | 3.00 |
| 2248 | A121 | $60 Hoatzin, horiz. | 4.50 | 3.25 |
| | | Nos. 2241-2248 (8) | 23.50 | 14.90 |

**Souvenir Sheets**

| | | | | |
|---|---|---|---|---|
| 2249 | A121 | $100 Great kiskadee, horiz. | 7.00 | 7.00 |
| 2250 | A121 | $100 Amazon kingfisher, horiz. | 7.00 | 7.00 |

Nos. 2241-2243, 2246, World Wildlife Fund.

## Nos. 2208-2184 Ovptd. in Silver with Rotary Emblem and "ROTARY INTERNATIONAL 1905-1990" on 2 or 3 Lines

**1990, Mar. 15**

| | | | | |
|---|---|---|---|---|
| 2251 | A115 | 80c on #2208 | | |
| 2252 | A115 | $2.25 on #2209 | | |
| 2253 | A115 | $5 on #2210 | | |
| 2254 | A115 | $6.40 on #2211 | | |

---

| | | | | |
|---|---|---|---|---|
| 2255 | A116 | $6.40 on #2216 | | |
| 2256 | A115 | $7.65 on #2212 | | |
| 2257 | A115 | $8.90 on #2213 | | |
| 2258 | A116 | $12.80 on #2217 | | |
| 2259 | A116 | $15.30 on #2218 | | |
| 2260 | A115 | $25 on #2214 | | |
| 2261 | A115 | $100 on #2215 | | |
| 2262 | A116 | $100 on #2219 | | |
| | | Nos. 2251-2262 (12) | 37.50 | |

## Nos. 2220-2222, 2224 Surcharged "GERMANY / CHAMPION"
## No. 2223 Surcharged "GERMANY / CHAMPION / ARGENTINA / SUB-CHAMPION"

**1990**    *Perfs. as Before*

| | | | | |
|---|---|---|---|---|
| 2263 | A117 | $75 on #2220 | | |
| 2264 | A117 | $75 on #2221 | | |
| 2265 | A117 | $75 on #2222 | | |
| 2266 | A117 | $75 on #2223 | | |
| | | Nos. 2263-2266 (4) | 10.00 | |

**Souvenir Sheet**

| | | | | |
|---|---|---|---|---|
| 2267 | A117 | $225 on #2224 | 8.00 | |

#2263-2266 exist in souvenir sheets of 1.

## Miniature Sheets

Penny Black, 150th Anniv., 500th Anniv. of Thurn & Taxis Postal Service A122

No. 2268: a, Banghy Post runner, 1832. b, Penny Black, Sir Rowland Hill. c, Dutch mail ship. d, Paddle steamer Monarch, 1830. e, Paddle steamer Hindostan, 1842. f, Mail steamer Chusan. g, Sailing ship Madagascar, 1853. h, Paddle steamer Orinoco, 1855. i, Packet Orpheus, 1835.

No. 2269: a, Imperial postal messenger. b, Swiss messenger, 1499. c, River messenger, 15th century. d, Russian courier, Middle Ages. e, Oldenburg postilions, 1820. f, Indian mail coach, 1829. g, Baden mail coach postilions, 1820. h, Pony Express, 1860. i, Camel rider.

No. 2270: a, Mail coach, 1840. b, Danish Ball Post, 1815. c, Australian Bush mailman, 1838. d, Japanese postmen, 1870. e, Mail cart, 1857. f, Russian mail troika. g, Wells, Fargo Overland Express. h, Phantoms of the Night, 1853. i, Cobb & Co. coach, Australia.

No. 2271: a, Postilions, 1850. b, Mounted postilion, Holland. c, Paddle steamer Arctic, 1850. d, Peruvian swimming couriers. e, First London post box, 1855. f, Indian mail cart, 1870. g, Balloon post, 1870. h, Bath Mail Coach. i, Postrider, 1837.

No. 2272: a, Northeastern Railway post office. b, Traveling post office, 1838. c, American Express. d, Graf Zeppelin. e, Columbia Post airplane, 1925. f, Calcutta flying boat. g, Junkers JU-52/3M mail plane. h, Douglas M2 mail plane. i, US air mail service, DH-4.

No. 2273: a, First Atlantic Airways. b, Morris post office van, 1931. c, Swiss post-passenger bus. d, Westland-Sikorsky S51 helicopter mail flight. e, Union Pacific Railway. f, Boeing Model 314 flying boat, Yankee Clipper. g, Boeing 747. h, Concorde. i, Apollo 11, US #C76.

No. 2274, Mounted postilion. No. 2275, Thurn & Taxis #7. No. 2276, Thurn & Taxis #45.

**1990, May 3**

| | | | | |
|---|---|---|---|---|
| 2268 | A122 | $15.30 Sheet of 9, #a.-i. | 9.00 | 9.00 |
| 2269 | A122 | $15.30 Sheet of 9, #a.-i. | 9.00 | 9.00 |
| 2270 | A122 | $15.30 Sheet of 9, #a.-i. | 9.00 | 9.00 |
| 2271 | A122 | $17.80 Sheet of 9, #a.-i. | 10.00 | 10.00 |
| 2272 | A122 | $20 Sheet of 9, #a.-i. | 11.00 | 11.00 |
| 2273 | A122 | $20 Sheet of 9, #a.-i. | 11.00 | 11.00 |
| | | Nos. 2268-2273 (6) | 59.00 | 59.00 |

**Souvenir Sheets**

| | | | | |
|---|---|---|---|---|
| 2274 | A122 | $150 multi | 7.50 | 7.50 |
| 2275 | A122 | $150 multi | 7.50 | 7.50 |
| 2276 | A122 | $150 multi | 7.50 | 7.50 |

For overprint see No. 2551.

Nos. 1028, 1032, 1055, 1085, 1107
Surcharged "ROTARY / DISTRICT 405
/ 9th CONFERENCE / MAY 1990 /
GEORGETOWN"
Unwmk.

**1990, May 8    Litho.    Perf. 14**
Design A91
Plate Numbers in Parentheses

| | | |
|---|---|---|
| 2277 | 80c on 55c #1032 (9) | |
| 2278 | 80c on 55c #1085 (49) | |
| 2279 | 80c on 55c #1107 (64) | |
| 2280 | $6.40 on 130c #1028 (6) | |
| 2281 | $6.40 on 130c #1055 (25) | |
| 2282 | $7.65 on 130c #1055 (25) | |
| | Nos. 2277-2282 (6) | 10.00 |

Nos. 2208-2215 Overprinted
**90th Birthday**
H.M. The Queen Mother

**1990, June 8    Litho.    Perf. 14**

| | | | | |
|---|---|---|---|---|
| 2283 | A115 | 80c on #2208 | 1.75 | .45 |
| 2284 | A115 | $2.25 on #2209 | 2.00 | .45 |
| 2285 | A115 | $5 on #2210 | 2.50 | .65 |
| 2286 | A115 | $6.40 on #2211 | 2.75 | .65 |
| 2287 | A115 | $7.65 on #2212 | 3.00 | .90 |
| 2288 | A115 | $8.90 on #2213 | 3.25 | 1.00 |
| 2289 | A115 | $25 on #2214 | 6.00 | 6.00 |
| 2290 | A115 | $100 on #2215 | 15.00 | 15.00 |
| | Nos. 2283-2290 (8) | | 36.25 | 25.10 |

See Nos. E26-E27.

Locomotives — A123

**1990, July 15    Perf. 14x13½**

| | | | |
|---|---|---|---|
| 2291 | A123 | $2.55 Class 3F | |
| 2292 | A123 | $2.55 Class A4 | |
| 2293 | A123 | $2.55 Liner Class A34 | |
| 2294 | A123 | $2.55 Pacific Class | |
| 2295 | A123 | $2.55 Grange Class | |
| | Nos. 2291-2295 (5) | | 13.50 |

**Souvenir Sheets**
**Perf. 13½x14, 14x13½**

| | | | |
|---|---|---|---|
| 2296 | A123 | $20 Castle Class, vert. | |
| 2297 | A123 | $20 Southern Railway | |
| | Nos. 2296-2297 (2) | | 22.50 |

Still Life with Guitar, by
Picasso — A124

Paintings: No. 2299, Horseman, by Velazquez. No. 2300, Sunflowers, by Van Gogh, vert. No. 2301, Man Wearing Striped Shirt, by Miro, vert. No. 2302, Franz von Taxis, by Durer, vert. No. 2303, Virgin and Child, by Titian, vert. No. 2304, Presentation of Marie de Medici, by Rubens, vert.

**Perf. 14x13½, 13½x14**

**1990, Aug. 1    Litho.**

| | | |
|---|---|---|
| 2298 | A124 | $2.55 multicolored |
| 2299 | A124 | $2.55 multicolored |
| 2300 | A124 | $2.55 multicolored |
| 2301 | A124 | $2.55 multicolored |
| 2302 | A124 | $2.55 multicolored |
| | Nos. 2298-2302 (5) | 11.50 |

**Souvenir Sheets**

| | | |
|---|---|---|
| 2303 | A124 | $20 multicolored |
| 2304 | A124 | $20 multicolored |
| | Nos. 2303-2304 (2) | 18.00 |

Postal System of Thurn and Taxis, 500th anniv. (#2302). Titian, 500th birth anniv. (#2303). Rubens, 350th death anniv. (#2304).

Birds — A125

Designs: 80c, Guiana partridge, horiz. $2.55, Collared trogon. $3.25, Derby aracari. $5, Black-necked aracari. $5.10, Green aracari. $5.80, Ivory-billed aracari. $6.40, Guiana toucanet. $6.50, Sulphur-breasted toucan. $7.55, Red-billed toucan. $7.65, Toco toucan. $8.25, Natterers toucanet. $8.90, Welcome trogon. $9.75, Doubtful trogon. $11.40, Banded aracari. $12.65, Golden-headed train bearer. $12.80, Band-tail barbthroat. $13.90, Band-tail barbthroat. $15.30, White-tipped sickle bill. $17.80, Black jacobin. $19.20, Fiery topaz. $22.95, Tufted coquette. $26.70, Ecuadorian pied-tail. $30, Quetzal. $50, Green-crowned brilliant. $100, Emerald-chinned hummingbird. $190, Lazuline sabrewing. $225, Berylline hummingbird.

**1990, Sept. 12    Litho.    Perf. 14**

| | | | | |
|---|---|---|---|---|
| 2305 | A125 | 80c multi | .25 | .25 |
| 2306 | A125 | $2.55 multi | .25 | .25 |
| 2307 | A125 | $3.25 multi | .25 | .25 |
| 2308 | A125 | $5 multi | .25 | .25 |
| 2309 | A125 | $5.10 multi | .25 | .25 |
| 2310 | A125 | $5.80 multi | .25 | .25 |
| 2311 | A125 | $6.40 multi | .25 | .25 |
| 2312 | A125 | $6.50 multi | .25 | .25 |
| 2313 | A125 | $7.55 multi | .35 | .35 |
| 2314 | A125 | $7.65 multi | .45 | .45 |
| 2315 | A125 | $8.25 multi | .55 | .55 |
| 2316 | A125 | $8.90 multi | .65 | .65 |
| 2317 | A125 | $9.75 multi | .65 | .65 |
| 2318 | A125 | $11.40 multi | .70 | .70 |
| 2319 | A125 | $12.65 multi | .75 | .75 |
| 2320 | A125 | $12.80 multi | .80 | .80 |
| 2321 | A125 | $13.90 multi | .90 | .90 |
| 2322 | A125 | $15.30 multi | 1.10 | 1.10 |
| 2323 | A125 | $17.80 multi | 1.25 | 1.25 |
| 2324 | A125 | $19.20 multi | 1.40 | 1.40 |
| 2325 | A125 | $22.95 multi | 1.60 | 1.60 |
| 2326 | A125 | $26.70 multi | 1.90 | 1.90 |
| 2327 | A125 | $30 multi | 2.00 | 2.00 |
| 2328 | A125 | $50 multi | 3.25 | 3.25 |
| 2329 | A125 | $100 multi | 6.00 | 6.00 |
| 2330 | A125 | $190 multi | 11.50 | 11.50 |
| 2331 | A125 | $225 multi | 14.00 | 14.00 |
| | Nos. 2305-2331 (27) | | 51.80 | 51.80 |

Butterflies — A126

No. 2340: a, Thecla falerina. b, Pheles heliconides. c, Echenais leucocyana. d, Heliconius xanthocles. e, Mesopthalma idotea. f, Parides aeneas. g, Heliconius numata. h, Thecla critola. i, Themone pais. j, Nymula agle. k, Adelpha cocala. l, Anaea eribotes. m, Prepona demophon. n, Selenophanes cassiope. o, Consul hippona. p, Antirrhaea avernus.

No. 2341: a, Thecla telemus. b, Thyridia confusa. c, Heliconius burneyi. d, Parides lysander. e, Eunica orphise. f, Adelpha melona. g, Morpho menelaus. h, Nymula phylleus. i, Stalachtis phlegia. j, Theope barea. k, Morpho perseus. l, Lycorea ceres. m, Archonias bellona. n, Caerois chorinaeus. o, Vila azeca. p, Nessaea batesii.

No. 2342: a, Heliconius silvana. b, Eunica alcmena. c, Mechanitis polymnia. d, Mesosemia ephyne. e, Thecla erema. f, Callizona acesta. g, Stalachtis phaedusa. h, Battus belus. i, Nymula phliasus. j, Parides childrenae. k, Stalachtis euterpe. l, Dysmathia portia. m, Tithorea hermias. n, Prepona pheridamas. o, Dismorphia fortunata. p, Hamadryas amphinome.

No. 2343: a, Heliconius vetustus. b, Mesosemia eumene. c, Parides phosphorus. d, Polystichtis emylius. e, Xanthocleis aedesia. f, Doxocopa agathina. g, Adelpha plesaure. h, Heliconius wallacei. i, Notheme eumeus. j, Melinaea mediatrix. k, Theritas coronata. l, Dismorphia orise. m, Phyciodes ianthe. n, Morpho aega. o, Zaretis isidora. p, Pierella lena.

Nos. 2340-2341 are horiz.

**1990, Sept. 26    Litho.    Perf. 14**

| | | | | |
|---|---|---|---|---|
| 2332 | A126 | 80c Melinaea idae | .75 | .75 |
| 2333 | A126 | $2.55 Rhetus dysonii | .75 | .75 |
| 2334 | A126 | $5 Actinote anteas | .75 | .75 |
| 2335 | A126 | $6.40 Heliconius tales | .75 | .75 |
| 2336 | A126 | $7.65 Thecla telemus | .75 | .75 |
| 2337 | A126 | $8.90 Theope eudoica | 1.00 | 1.00 |
| 2338 | A126 | $50 Heliconius vicini | 4.00 | 4.00 |
| 2339 | A126 | $100 Amarynthis meneria | 8.50 | 8.50 |
| | Nos. 2332-2339 (8) | | 17.25 | 17.25 |

**Miniature Sheets**

| | | | | |
|---|---|---|---|---|
| 2340 | A126 | $10 Sheet of 16, #a.-p. | 13.00 | 13.00 |
| 2341 | A126 | $10 Sheet of 16, #a.-p. | 13.00 | 13.00 |
| 2342 | A126 | $10 Sheet of 16, #a.-p. | 13.00 | 13.00 |
| 2343 | A126 | $10 Sheet of 16, #a.-p. | 13.00 | 13.00 |

**Souvenir Sheets**

| | | | | |
|---|---|---|---|---|
| 2344 | A126 | $150 Heliconius aoede | 9.00 | 9.00 |
| 2345 | A126 | $150 Phyciodes clio, horiz. | 9.00 | 9.00 |
| 2346 | A126 | $190 Nymphidium caricae | 13.00 | 13.00 |
| 2347 | A126 | $190 Thecla hemon | 13.00 | 13.00 |

For surcharges see #2415-2425, 2596-2606.

Mushrooms
A127

**1990, Oct. 12**

| | | | |
|---|---|---|---|
| 2348 | A127 | $2.55 Oudeman-seilla mucida | |
| 2349 | A127 | $2.55 Pholiota squarosa | |
| 2350 | A127 | $2.55 Coprinus comatus | |
| 2351 | A127 | $2.55 Anellaria semiovaja | |
| | Nos. 2348-2351 (4) | | 14.00 |

**Souvenir Sheet**

| | | | |
|---|---|---|---|
| 2352 | A127 | $20 Phallus impudicus | 14.00 |

Sailing
Ships — A128

**1990, Oct. 12**

| | | | |
|---|---|---|---|
| 2353 | A128 | $2.55 Brig century | |
| 2354 | A128 | $2.55 Dutch marine ship | |
| 2355 | A128 | $2.55 Galleon, 1588 | |
| 2356 | A128 | $2.55 Warship, 16th cent. | |
| 2357 | A128 | $2.55 Hulk, 17th cent. | |
| | Nos. 2353-2357 (5) | | 13.00 |

**Souvenir Sheet**

| | | | |
|---|---|---|---|
| 2358 | A128 | $20 Dutch ships, 16th-17th cent. | 14.00 |

No. 2358 printed in continuous design. Discovery of America, 500th anniv. (in 1992).

Flora — A129

Orchids: $7.65, Vanilla inodora. $8.90, Epidendrum ibaguense. No. 858, Maxillaria parkeri. $15.30, Epidendrum nocturnum. $17.80, Catasetum discolor. $20, Scuticaria hadwenii. $25, Epidendrum fragrans. $100, Epistephium parviflorum.

No. 2367: a, Dichea muricata. b, Octomeria erosilabia. c, Spiranthes orchiodes. d, Brassavola nodosa. e, Epidendrum rigidum. f, Brassia caudata. g, Pleurothallis diffusa. h, Aspasia variegata. i, Stenia pallida. j, Cyrtopodium punctatum. k, Cattleya deckeri. l, Cryptarrhena lunata. m, Cattleya violacea. n, Caularthron bicornutum. o, Oncidium carthagenense. p, Galeandra devoniana.

No. 2368: a, Bifrenaria aurantiaca. b, Epidendrum ciliare. c, Dichaea picta. d, Scaphyglottis violacea. e, Cattleya percivaliana. f, Map of Guyana (no flower). g, Epidendrum difforme. h, Eulophia maculata. i, Spiranthes tenuis. j, Peristeria guttata. k, Pleurothallis pruinosa. l, Cleistes rosea. m, Maxillaria variabilis. n, Brassavola cucullata. o, Epidendrum moyobambae. p, Oncidium orthostates.

No. 2369: a, Brassavola martiana. b, Paphinia cristata. c, Aganisia pulchella. d, Oncidium lanceanum. e, Lockhartia imbricata. f, Caularthron bilamellatum. g, Oncidium nanum. h, Pleurothallis ovalifolia. i, Galeandra dives. j, Cycnoches loddigesii. k, Ada aurantiaca. l, Catasetum barbatum. m, Palmorchis pubescens. n, Epidendrum anceps. o, Huntleya meleagris. p, Sobralia sessilis.

No. 2370: a, Maxillaria camaridii. b, Vanilla pompona. c, Stanhopea grandiflora. d, Oncidium pusillum. e, Polycycnis vittata. f, Cattleya lawrenceana. g, Menadenium labiosum. h, Rodriguezia secunda. i, Mormodes buccinator. j, Otostylis brachystalix. k, Maxillaria discolor. l, Liparis elata. m, Gongora maculata. n, Koellensteinia graminea. o, Rudolfiella aurantiaca. p, Scuticaria steelei.

Flowering Trees: No. 2371: a, Cochlospermum vitifolium. b, Eugenia malaccensis. c, Plumiera rubra. d, Erythrina glauca. e, Spathodea campanulata. f, Jacaranda filicifolia. g, Samanea saman. h, Cassia fistula. i, Abutilon integerrimum. j, Lagerstroemia speciosa. k, Tabebuia serratifolia. l, Guaiacum officinale. m, Solanum macranthum. n, Peltophorum roxburghii. o, Bauhinia variegata. p, Plumiera alba.

Flowering Vines: No. 2372: a, Gloriosa rothschildiana. b, Pseudocalymma alliaceum. c, Callichlamys latifolia. d, Distictis riversii. e, Maurandya barclaiana. f, Beaumontia fragrans. g, Phaseolus caracalla. h, Mandevilla splendens. i, Solandra longiflora. j, Passiflora coccinea. k, Allamanda cathartica. l, Bauhinia galpini. m, Verbena maritima. n, Mandevilla suaveolens. o, Phryganocydia corymbosa. p, Jasminum sambac.

**1990, Oct. 16    Litho.    Perf. 14**

| | | | | |
|---|---|---|---|---|
| 2359 | A129 | $7.65 multicolored | .40 | .40 |
| 2360 | A129 | $8.90 multicolored | .55 | .55 |
| 2361 | A129 | $12.80 multicolored | .85 | .85 |
| 2362 | A129 | $15.30 multicolored | .90 | .90 |
| 2363 | A129 | $17.80 multicolored | 1.00 | 1.00 |
| 2364 | A129 | $20 multicolored | 1.25 | 1.25 |
| 2365 | A129 | $25 multicolored | 1.50 | 1.50 |
| 2366 | A129 | $100 multicolored | 6.50 | 6.50 |
| | Nos. 2359-2366 (8) | | 12.95 | 12.95 |

**Miniature Sheets**

| | | | | |
|---|---|---|---|---|
| 2367 | A129 | $10 Sheet of 16, #a.-p. | 8.00 | 8.00 |
| 2368 | A129 | $10 Sheet of 16, #a.-p. | 8.00 | 8.00 |
| 2369 | A129 | $12.80 Sheet of 16, #a.-p. | 12.00 | 12.00 |
| 2370 | A129 | $12.80 Sheet of 16, #a.-p. | 12.00 | 12.00 |
| 2371 | A129 | $12.80 Sheet of 16, #a.-p. | 12.00 | 12.00 |
| 2372 | A129 | $12.80 Sheet of 16, #a.-p. | 12.00 | 12.00 |
| | Nos. 2367-2372 (6) | | 64.00 | 64.00 |

**Souvenir Sheets**

| | | | | |
|---|---|---|---|---|
| 2373 | A129 | $150 Coleandra devoniana | 9.00 | 9.00 |
| 2374 | A129 | $150 Delonix regia | 9.00 | 9.00 |
| 2375 | A129 | $150 Hexisea bidentata | 9.00 | 9.00 |
| 2376 | A129 | $150 Lecythis olaria | 9.00 | 9.00 |

2377 A129 $190 Ionopsis
  utricu-
  larioides          11.00 11.00
  Nos. 2373-2377 (5)   47.00 47.00
  Nos. 2370-2375 are horiz. For surcharges
see Nos. 2593-2595.

## Souvenir Sheet

Cenozoic Era
Wildlife — A130

Designs: a, Palaelodus. b, Archaeotrogon.
c, Vulture. d, Bradyrus tridactylus. e, Natalus
stramineus bat. f, Cebidae. g, Cuvieronius. h,
Phororhacos. i, Smilodectes. j, Megatherium.
k, Titanotylopus. l, Teleoceras. m,
Macrauchenia. n, Mylodon. o, Smilodon. p,
Glyptodon. q, Protohydrocherus. r,
Archaeohyrax. s, Pyrotherium. t,
Platypittamys.

### 1990, Nov. 6
2378 A130 $12.80 Sheet of 20,
  #a.-t.               15.00 15.00

### Miniature Sheets

Endangered
Wildlife — A131

#2379: a, Ivory-billed woodpecker. b, Cauca
guan. c, Sun conure. d, Quetzal. e, Long-wat-
tled umbrellabird. f, Banded cotinga. g, Blue-
chested parakeet. h, Rufous-bellied
chachalaca. i, Yellow-faced amazon. j, Toucan
barbet. k, Red siskin. l, Cock-of-the-rock. m,
Hyacinth macaw. n, Yellow cardinal. o, Bare-
necked umbrellabird. p, Saffron toucanette. q,
Red-billed curassow. r, Spectacled parrotlet.
s, Lovely cotinga. t, Black-breasted gnateater.
#2380: a, Swallow-tailed kite. b, Hoatzin. c,
Ruby topaz hummingbird. d, Black vulture. e,
Rufous-tailed jacamar. f, Scarlet macaw. g,
Rose-breasted thrush tanager. h, Toco toucan.
i, Bearded bellbird. j, Blue-crowned motmot. k,
Green oropendola. l, Pompadour cotinga. m,
Vermilion flycatcher. n, Blue and yellow
macaw. o, White-barred piculet. p, Great
razor-billed curassow. q, Ruddy quail-dove. r,
Paradise tanager. s, Anhinga. t, Greater
flamingo.
#2381: a, Harpy eagle. b, Andean condor. c,
Amazonian umbrellabird. d, Spider monkeys.
e, Hyacinth macaw, diff. f, Red siskin, diff. g,
Toucan barbet, diff. h, Three-toed sloth. i,
Guanaco. j, Spectacled bear. k, White-lipped
peccary. l, Maned wolf. m, Jaguar. n, Spectacled caiman. o, Giant armadillo. p, Giant anteater. q, South American river otter. r, Yapok.
s, Central American river turtle. t, Cauca guan,
diff.

### Perf. 14x13½, 13½x14
### 1990, Nov. 6          Litho.
2379 A131 $12.80 Sheet of 20,
  #a.-t.               15.00 15.00
2380 A131 $12.80 Sheet of 20,
  #a.-t.               15.00 15.00
2381 A131 $12.80 Sheet of 20,
  #a.-t.               15.00 15.00
  #2381a-2381t are horiz. #2380s incorrectly
inscribed Anhigna. See #E29-E30.
  Numbers have been reserved for additional
values in this set.

Independence, 25th Anniv. — A132

---

Illustration reduced.
### 1991, June 25    Litho.    Imperf.
2389 A132 $225 multicolored   10.00 10.00

### Miniature Sheets

Olympic
Gold
Medal
Winners
A133

No. 2390: a, Ramon Fonst. b, Lucien
Gaudin. c, Ole A. Lilloe-Olsen. d, Morris
Fisher. e, Ray C. Ewry. f, Hubert Van Innes. g,
Alvin Kraenzlein. h, Johnny Weissmuller. i,
Hans Winkler.
No. 2391: a, Viktor Chukarin. b, Agnes
Keleti. c, Barbel Wochel. d, Eric Heiden. e,
Alvodar Gerevich. f, Guiseppe Delfino. g, Alex-
ander Tikhonov. h, C.F. Pahud de Mortanges.
i, Patricia McCormick.
No. 2392: a, Nelli Kim. b, Viktor Krovopus-
kov. c, Viktor Sidiak. d, Nikolai Andrianov. e,
Nadia Comaneci. f, Mitsuo Tsukahara. g,
Yelena Novikova-Belova. h, John Naber. i,
Kornelia Ender.
No. 2393: a, Olga Korbut. b, Lyudmila Turis-
cheva. c, Lasse Viren. d, George Miez. e,
Roland Matthes. f, Pal Kovaks. g, Jesse
Owens. h, Mark Spitz. i, Eduardo Mangiarotti.
No. 2394: a, Sawao Kato. b, Rudolf Karpati.
c, Jeno Fuchs. d, Emil Zatopek. e, Fanny
Blankers-Koen. f, Melvin Sheppard. g, Gert
Fredriksson. h, Paul Elvstrom. i, Harrison W.
Dillard.
No. 2395: a, Lydia Skoblikova. b, Ivar Bal-
langrud. c, Clas Thunberg. d, Anton Heida. e,
Akinori Nakayama. f, Sixten Jernberg. g,
Yevgeniy Grischin. h, Paul Radmilovic. i,
Charles Daniels.
No. 2396: a, Betty Cuthbert. b, Vera Caslav-
ska. c, Galina Kulakova. d, Yukio Endo. e,
Vladimir Morozov. f, Boris Shaklin. g, Don
Schollander. h, Gyozo Kulscar. i, Christian
D'Oriola.
No. 2397: a, Al Oerter. b, Polina Astakhova.
c, Takashi Ono. d, Valentin Muratov. e, Henri
St. Cyr. f, Iain Murray Rose. g, Larissa
Latynina. h, Carlo Pavesi. i, Dawn Fraser.
No. 2398, Paavo Nurmi, vert. No. 2399,
Johannes Kolehmainen, vert. $190. Nedo
Nadi, vert.

### 1991, Aug. 12    Litho.    Perf. 14x13½
2390 A133 $15.30 Sheet of 9,
  #a.-i.                5.75  5.75
2391 A133 $17.80 Sheet of 9,
  #a.-i.                6.75  6.75
2392 A133 $20 Sheet of 9,
  #a.-i.                7.25  7.25
2393 A133 $20 Sheet of 9,
  #a.-i.                7.25  7.25
2394 A133 $25 Sheet of 9,
  #a.-i.                9.50  9.50
2395 A133 $25 Sheet of 9,
  #a.-i.                9.50  9.50
2396 A133 $30 Sheet of 9,
  #a.-i.               11.50 11.50
2397 A133 $30 Sheet of 9,
  #a.-i.               11.50 11.50
  Nos. 2390-2397 (8)  69.00 69.00

### Souvenir Sheets
### Perf. 13x13½
2398 A133 $150 multicolored   5.50  5.50
2399 A133 $150 multicolored   5.50  5.50
2400 A133 $190 multicolored   7.00  7.00
  For overprints see Nos. 2552-2557.

Discovery of
America,
500th Anniv.
(in
1992) — A134

Birds: $6.40, Phoenicopterus ruber. $7.65,
Ostinops decumanus. $50, Falco peregrinus.
$100, Nymphicus hollandicus. $190, Vultur fer-
iphus. $260, Merganetta armata, horiz.

### 1991, Sept. 15    Litho.    Perf. 13½x14
2401 A134 $6.40 multicolored
2402 A134 $7.65 multicolored
2403 A134 $50 multicolored
2404 A134 $100 multicolored
2405 A134 $190 multicolored
  Nos. 2401-2405 (5)    16.50

---

## Souvenir Sheet
### Perf. 14x13½
2406 A134 $260 multicolored   15.00

A135

Various orchids.

### Perf. 13½x14, 14x13½
### 1991, Sept. 30
2407 A135 $6.40 multicolored
2408 A135 $7.65 multi, horiz.
2409 A135 $50 multicolored
2410 A135 $100 multicolored
2411 A135 $190 Odontoglos-
  sum
  Nos. 2407-2411 (5)    8.00

### Souvenir Sheets
2412 A135 $360 multicolored
2413 A135 $360 Cycnoches
  ventricosum
2414 A135 $360 Miltonia
  hibrida,
  horiz.
  Nos. 2412-2414 (3)    22.50

### Nos. 2332-2339, 2343-2345 Ovptd. or Surcharged

Overprints: 80c, $2.55, Nos. 2421-2422,
2423a, 2423p, Rotary emblem and "1905-
1990." $5.00, $6.40, $7.65, Nos. 2420, 2423d,
2423m, Rotary emblem and "Paul Percy Harris
Founder 1868-1947" on 2 or 3 lines. Nos.
2423b, 2423l, 2423n, Boy Scout emblem and
"1907-1992." Nos. 2423c, 2423i, 2423o, Lions
Intl. emblem and "1917-1992." Nos. 2423e,
2423h, Red Cross emblem and "125 Years /
Red Cross." Nos. 2423f-2423g, 2423j-2423k
have parts of larger Rotary emblem. Nos.
2424-2425 ovptd. with service emblems in
sheet margins.

### 1991, Oct. 29        Perfs. as Before
2415 A126 80c on #2332      .25   .25
2416 A126 $2.55 on #2333    .25   .25
2417 A126 $5 on #2334       .25   .25
2418 A126 $6.40 on #2335    .25   .25
2419 A126 $7.65 on #2336    .25   .25
2420 A126 $100 on $8.90
  #2337              2.75  2.75
2421 A126 $190 on $50
  #2338              5.00  5.00
2422 A126 $225 on $100
  #2339              5.75  5.75
  Nos. 2415-2422 (8)  14.75 14.75

### Miniature Sheet
2423 A126 Sheet of 16      12.00 12.00
  a.-l. $10 any single      .25   .25
  m. $50 on $10 #2343m     1.25  1.25
  n. $75 on $10 #2343n     1.75  1.75
  o. $100 on $10 #2343o    2.25  2.25
  p. $190 on $10 #2343p    4.25  4.25

### Souvenir Sheets
2424 A126 $400 on $150
  #2344             12.00 12.00
2425 A126 $500 on $150
  #2345             14.00 14.00

Swiss
Confederation,
700th
Anniv. — A136

Designs: $6.40, Painting by Diego
Giacometti. $7.65, Swiss puppets. $50, Man in
top hat by Goya. $100, Stained glass window
of Mary & Joseph. $190, Stained glass win-
dow of Jesus healing the sick.
No. 2431, Ship's cross-section, by Le
Corbusier. No. 2432, Portrait of Giovanna
Tornabuoni.

---

### 1991, Oct. 30        Perf. 13½x14
2426 A136 $6.40 multicolored
2427 A136 $7.65 multicolored
2428 A136 $50 multicolored
2429 A136 $100 multicolored
2430 A136 $190 multicolored
  a. Sheet of 5 + label, #2426-
  2430               12.00

### Souvenir Sheets
2431 A136 $360 multicolored
2432 A136 $360 multicolored
  Nos. 2431-2432 (2)    25.00

Phila Nippon '91 — A137

Trains: $6.40, Class 581 12-car. $7.65,
Class EF-81. $50, Class 381 9-car. $100,
Kodama 8-car. $190, Shin-Kansen 16-car. No.
2438, Shin-Kansen 16-car, diff. No. 2439, Japanese locomotives in Calcutta.

### 1991, Nov. 16        Perf. 14x13½
2433 A137 $6.40 multicolored
2434 A137 $7.65 multicolored
2435 A137 $50 multicolored
2436 A137 $100 multicolored
2437 A137 $190 multicolored
  Nos. 2433-2437 (5)    16.50

### Souvenir Sheets
2438 A137 $360 multicolored
2439 A137 $360 multicolored
  Nos. 2438-2439 (2)    32.50

Swiss Confederation, 700th anniv., #2439.

---

Common Design Types
pictured following the introduction.

### Royal Family Birthday, Anniversary
### Common Design Type
### 1991, Nov.    Litho.    Perf. 14
2440 CD347 $8.90 multi    .35   .20
2441 CD347 $12.80 multi   .35   .30
2442 CD347 $15.30 multi   .35   .30
2443 CD347 $50 multi     1.25  1.10
2444 CD347 $75 multi     1.75  1.75
2445 CD347 $100 multi    2.50  2.50
2446 CD347 $130 multi    3.00  3.00
2447 CD347 $150 multi    3.75  3.75
2448 CD347 $190 multi    5.00  5.00
2449 CD347 $200 multi    5.25  5.25
  Nos. 2440-2449 (10)   23.55 23.15

### Souvenir Sheets
2450 CD347 $225 Elizabeth   6.50  6.50
2451 CD347 $225 Charles,
  Diana,
  sons         7.00  7.00

$8.90, $50, $75, $190, No. 2451, Charles
and Diana, 10th wedding anniversary. $130,
$150, Prince Philip, 70th birthday. Others,
Queen Elizabeth II, 65th birthday.

### Miniature Sheet

Japanese
Attack on
Pearl
Harbor,
50th Anniv.
A138

No. 2452: a, Akagi launches attack planes.
b, Sakamaki's midget submarine beached. c,
Mistubishi ASM Zero fighter. d, USS Arizona
under attack. e, Aichi D3A1 Val dive bomber. f,
USS California. g, P40 defends Pearl Harbor.
h, USS Cassin and Downes hit at dry dock. i,
B17 crash lands at Bellows Field. j, USS
Nevada burns at Hospital Point.

### 1991, Dec. 7        Perf. 14½x15
2452 A138 $50 Sheet of 10,
  #a.-j.               17.00 17.00

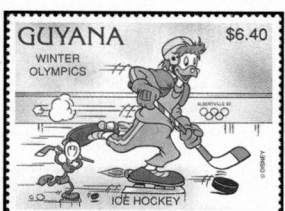

1992 Winter Olympics,
Albertville — A139

Walt Disney characters at the Olympics:
$6.40, Gus Gander playing ice hockey. $7.65,
Mickey, Minnie in bobsled. $8.90, Huey,
Dewey, Louie pretending to luge. $12.80,
Goofy freestyle skiing. $50, Goofy ski jumping.
$100, Donald, Daisy Duck speed skating.
$130, Pluto cross-country skiing. $190,
Mickey, Minnie ice dancing. No. 2461,
Scrooge McDuck slalom skiing. No. 2462,
Huey curling.

| 1991, Dec. 12 | | | Perf. 13½x13 | |
|---|---|---|---|---|
| 2453 | A139 | $6.40 multi | .40 | .40 |
| 2454 | A143 | $7.65 multi | .45 | .45 |
| 2455 | A139 | $8.90 multi | .50 | .50 |
| 2456 | A143 | $12.80 multi | .70 | .70 |
| 2457 | A143 | $50 multi | 1.50 | 1.50 |
| 2458 | A139 | $100 multi | 2.50 | 2.50 |
| 2459 | A143 | $130 multi | 3.00 | 3.00 |
| 2460 | A143 | $190 multi | 4.50 | 4.50 |
| | | Nos. 2453-2460 (8) | 13.55 | 13.55 |

**Souvenir Sheets**

| 2461 | A139 | $225 multi | 7.00 | 7.00 |
|---|---|---|---|---|
| 2462 | A143 | $225 multi | 7.00 | 7.00 |

Mushrooms — A140

Designs: $6.40, Boletus satanoides. $7.65,
Russula nigricans. $50, Cortinarius
glaucopus. $100, Lactarius camphoratus.
$190, Cortinarius callisteus. No. 2468, Rus-
sula integra. No. 2469, Coprinus micaceus,
vert.

| 1991, Dec. 16 | Litho. | | Perf. 14x13½ | |
|---|---|---|---|---|
| 2463 | A140 | $6.40 multicolored | | |
| 2464 | A140 | $7.65 multicolored | | |
| 2465 | A140 | $50 multicolored | | |
| 2466 | A140 | $100 multicolored | | |
| 2467 | A140 | $190 multicolored | | |
| | | Nos. 2463-2467 (5) | 16.00 | 16.00 |

**Souvenir Sheets**
**Perf. 14x13½, 13½x14**

| 2468 | A140 | $360 multicolored | | |
|---|---|---|---|---|
| 2469 | A140 | $360 multicolored | | |
| | | Nos. 2468-2469 (2) | 30.00 | |

Walt Disney Christmas Cards — A141

Designs and year of issue: 80c, Mickey,
friends singing carols, 1989. $2.55, Mickey,
friends riding trolley car, 1962. $5, Donald,
Pluto wrapping package, 1971. $6.40, Mickey
holding candle, 1948. $7.65, Mickey with
Santa mask, 1947. $8.90, Pinocchio's
shadow, 1939. $50, Three Little Pigs, dancing
on wolf's back, 1933. $200, Mickey, mice sing-
ing carols, 1949.
No. 2478: a, Conductor, Donald. b, Elephant with book. c, Goofy, centaurs. d, Snow
White, dwarfs. e, Pluto, dinosaur.
No. 2479: a, Mickey in sleigh. b, Three little
pigs, Winnie-the-Pooh, Bambi. c, Dalmatian,
bear, monkey, Lady and the Tramp. d, Alice,
Goofy, Mad Hatter. e, Pinocchio, Tinker Bell,
Peter Pan, Seven Dwarfs, Donald Duck. f,
Pluto, 1974.
No. 2480, Mickey and friends riding in
coach, 1932. No. 2481, Mickey, Pluto greeting

friends, 1935. No. 2482, Donald, Jose Cari-
oca, 1944. No. 2483, Couple dancing, baseball batter, 1945. No. 2484, Mickey, Donald,
Goofy, 1946. No. 2485, Santa in chimney,
1969. No. 2486, Portrait of Winnie-the-Pooh
hanging on wall, 1969. No. 2487, Mickey,
1978.

| 1991, Dec. 17 | | | Perf. 14x13½ | |
|---|---|---|---|---|
| 2470 | A141 | 80c multi | .25 | .20 |
| 2471 | A141 | $2.55 multi | .25 | .20 |
| 2472 | A141 | $5 multi | .25 | .25 |
| 2473 | A141 | $6.40 multi | .35 | .25 |
| 2474 | A141 | $7.65 multi | .35 | .25 |
| 2475 | A141 | $8.90 multi | .35 | .25 |
| 2476 | A141 | $50 multi | 1.40 | 1.40 |
| 2477 | A141 | $200 multi | 5.25 | 5.25 |
| 2478 | A141 | $50 Strip of 5, #a.-e. | 7.00 | 7.00 |
| 2479 | A141 | $50 Strip of 6, #a.-f. | 8.50 | 8.50 |
| | | Nos. 2470-2479 (10) | 23.95 | 23.55 |

**Souvenir Sheets**

| 2480 | A141 | $260 multi | 6.00 | 6.00 |
|---|---|---|---|---|
| 2481 | A141 | $260 multi | 6.00 | 6.00 |
| 2482 | A141 | $260 multi | 6.00 | 6.00 |
| 2483 | A141 | $260 multi | 6.00 | 6.00 |
| 2484 | A141 | $260 multi | 6.00 | 6.00 |
| 2485 | A141 | $260 multi | 6.00 | 6.00 |
| 2486 | A141 | $260 multi | 6.00 | 6.00 |
| 2487 | A141 | $260 multi | 6.00 | 6.00 |
| | | Nos. 2480-2487 (8) | 48.00 | 48.00 |

Nos. 2478a-2478e, 2479a-2479f, 2480-
2481, 2485 and 2487 are vert.

No. 2377 Surcharged

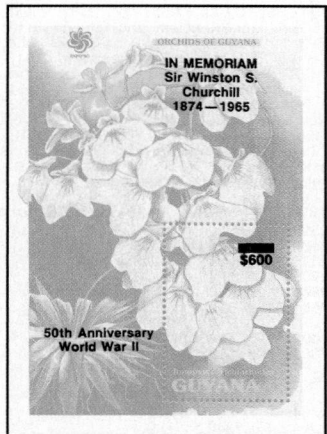

| 1991, Dec. 19 | Litho. | Perf. 14 | |
|---|---|---|---|
| 2487B | A129 | $600 on $190 #2377 | — — |

An additional sheet was issued in this set.
The editors would like to examine it.

Christmas
A142

Paintings: $6.40, Madonna and Child with
Angels, by Titian, horiz. $7.65, Madonna and
Child with Angels, by Rubens. $50, Madonna
and Child, by Raphael. $100, Madonna and
Child, by Durer. $190, Madonna, by Durer. No.
2493, Madonna and Child, by Rubens, horiz.
No. 2494, Madonna, by Durer, diff.

| 1991, Dec. 30 | | Perf. 14x13½, 13½x14 | |
|---|---|---|---|
| 2488 | A142 | $6.40 multicolored | |
| 2489 | A142 | $7.65 multicolored | |
| 2490 | A142 | $50 multicolored | |
| 2491 | A142 | $100 multicolored | |
| 2492 | A142 | $190 multicolored | |
| | | Nos. 2488-2 92(5) | 15.00 |

**Souvenir Sheets**

| 2493 | A142 | $360 multicolored | |
|---|---|---|---|
| 2494 | A142 | $360 multicolored | |
| | | Nos. 2493-2494 (2) | 35.00 |

Brandenburg Gate, Bicent. — A143

Designs: $10, Map of Berlin. $25, US Pres.
George Bush, Polish Pres. Lech Walesa.
$100, German Chancellor Helmut Kohl, For-
eign Minister Hans-Dietrich Genscher. $190,
Armored helmet.

| 1991, Dec. | | | Perf. 14 | |
|---|---|---|---|---|
| 2495 | A143 | $10 multicolored | .40 | .40 |
| 2496 | A143 | $25 multicolored | .90 | .90 |
| 2497 | A143 | $100 multicolored | 3.25 | 3.25 |
| | | Nos. 2495-2497 (3) | 4.55 | 4.55 |

**Souvenir Sheet**

| 2498 | A143 | $190 multicolored | 6.50 | 6.50 |
|---|---|---|---|---|

Wolfgang
Amadeus
Mozart,
Death
Bicent.
A144

Portrait of Mozart and: $75, Laxenburg. $80,
Death of Leopold II. $100, Mozart's birthplace,
Salzburg.

| 1991, Dec. | | | | |
|---|---|---|---|---|
| 2499 | A144 | $75 multicolored | 2.50 | 2.50 |
| 2500 | A144 | $80 multicolored | 2.75 | 2.75 |
| 2501 | A144 | $100 multicolored | 3.00 | 3.00 |
| | | Nos. 2499-2501 (3) | 8.25 | 8.25 |

**Souvenir Sheet**

| 2502 | A144 | $190 Bust of Mo-zart, vert. | 6.00 | 6.00 |
|---|---|---|---|---|

17th World Scout Jamboree,
Korea — A145

Designs: $30, Scouts hiking. $40, Emblems,
flag. $100, Lord Baden-Powell, vert. $190,
Rocket cover with US No. 1145.

| 1991, Dec. | | | | |
|---|---|---|---|---|
| 2503 | A145 | $25 multicolored | 1.00 | 1.00 |
| 2504 | A145 | $30 multicolored | 1.10 | 1.10 |
| 2505 | A145 | $40 multicolored | 1.25 | 1.25 |
| 2506 | A145 | $100 multicolored | 3.25 | 3.25 |
| | | Nos. 2503-2506 (4) | 6.60 | 6.60 |

**Souvenir Sheet**

| 2507 | A145 | $190 multicolored | 6.50 | 6.50 |
|---|---|---|---|---|

Charles
de Gaulle
A146

De Gaulle: $60, In Venice, 1944. $75, With
Khrushchev, 1960. $80, In Algiers, 1958.
$100, With Pope Paul VI, 1967.

| 1991, Dec. | | | | |
|---|---|---|---|---|
| 2508 | A146 | $60 multicolored | 2.00 | 2.00 |
| 2509 | A146 | $75 multicolored | 2.50 | 2.50 |
| 2510 | A146 | $80 multicolored | 2.75 | 2.75 |
| 2511 | A146 | $100 multicolored | 3.25 | 3.25 |
| | | Nos. 2508-2511 (4) | 10.50 | 10.50 |

**Souvenir Sheets**

| 2512 | A146 | $150 Portrait, vert. | 7.50 | 7.50 |
|---|---|---|---|---|
| 2513 | A146 | $190 Portrait, diff, vert. | 9.75 | 9.75 |

Anniversaries and Events — A147

Designs: No. 2515, Caroline Herschel,
astronomer, Old Town Hall, Hanover. No.
2516, Map of Switzerland, woman in traditional dress. $80, Otto Lilienthal's glider No. 3.
$100, Locomotive. $190, Arms of Bern and
Solothurn.

| 1991, Dec. | | | | |
|---|---|---|---|---|
| 2515 | A147 | $75 multicolored | 4.00 | 4.00 |
| 2516 | A147 | $75 multicolored | 3.25 | 3.25 |
| 2517 | A147 | $80 multicolored | 3.75 | 3.75 |
| 2518 | A147 | $100 multicolored | 5.00 | 5.00 |
| | | Nos. 2515-2518 (4) | 16.00 | 16.00 |

**Souvenir Sheet**

| 2519 | A147 | $190 multicolored | 5.75 | 5.75 |
|---|---|---|---|---|

Hanover, 750th anniv. (#2515), Swiss Confederation, 700th anniv. (#2516, 2519), first
glider flight, cent. (#2517), Trans-Siberian Railway, cent. (#2518).

Discovery
of
America,
500th
Anniv.
A148

Designs: $6.40, Columbus lands on Trini-
dad. $7.65, Columbus, globe. $8.90, Ships
blown off course by hurricane. $12.80, Map,
hands in chains. $15.30, Land sighted. $50,
Nina, Pinta. $75, Santa Maria. $100, Columbus trading with natives. $125, Superstitions &
sea monsters. $130, Map, Columbus ashore.
$140, Priest & natives. $150, Columbus kneeling before King Ferdinand and Queen Isabella. #2532, Map of New World. #2533, One
of Columbus' ships, vert. #2534, Columbus.

| 1992, Jan. 2 | | | Perf. 14 | |
|---|---|---|---|---|
| 2520 | A148 | $6.40 multi | .40 | .35 |
| 2521 | A148 | $7.65 multi | .45 | .40 |
| 2522 | A148 | $8.90 multi | .50 | .45 |
| 2523 | A148 | $12.80 multi | .55 | .50 |
| 2524 | A148 | $15.30 multi | .60 | .55 |
| 2525 | A148 | $50 multi | 1.75 | 1.75 |
| 2526 | A148 | $75 multi | 2.25 | 2.25 |
| 2527 | A148 | $100 multi | 3.00 | 3.00 |
| 2528 | A148 | $125 multi | 3.75 | 3.75 |
| 2529 | A148 | $130 multi | 4.00 | 4.00 |
| 2530 | A148 | $140 multi | 4.25 | 4.25 |
| 2531 | A148 | $150 multi | 4.50 | 4.50 |
| | | Nos. 2520-2531 (12) | 26.00 | 25.75 |

**Souvenir Sheets**

| 2532 | A148 | $280 multi | 8.50 | 8.50 |
|---|---|---|---|---|
| 2533 | A148 | $280 multi | 8.50 | 8.50 |
| 2534 | A148 | $280 multi | 8.50 | 8.50 |

Movie
Posters — A149

Designs: $8.90, The Great K & A Train Rob-
bery. $12.80, Cimarron. $15.30, Buzzin'
Around. $25, Adventures of Captain Marvel.
$30, The Mummy. $50, A Sainted Devil. $75,
A Tale of Two Cities. $100, A Tugboat Romeo.
$130, Thief of Bagdad. $150, Bacon Grab-
bers. $190, A Night at the Opera. $200, Citizen Kane. No. 2547, She Done Him Wrong.
No. 2548, The Circus. No. 2549, Babe Comes
Home. No. 2550, Zeppelin, horiz.

| 1992, Mar. 11 | Litho. | | Perf. 14 | |
|---|---|---|---|---|
| 2535 | A149 | $8.90 multi | .60 | .50 |
| 2536 | A149 | $12.80 multi | .65 | .55 |
| 2537 | A149 | $15.30 multi | .70 | .65 |
| 2538 | A149 | $25 multi | .80 | .75 |
| 2539 | A149 | $30 multi | .90 | .85 |
| 2540 | A149 | $50 multi | 1.50 | 1.40 |
| 2541 | A149 | $75 multi | 2.25 | 2.00 |
| 2542 | A149 | $100 multi | 3.00 | 2.75 |
| 2543 | A149 | $130 multi | 3.75 | 3.50 |
| 2544 | A149 | $150 multi | 4.50 | 4.25 |

| | | | | |
|---|---|---|---|---|
| 2545 | A149 | $190 multi | 5.75 | 5.50 |
| 2546 | A149 | $200 multi | 6.00 | 5.75 |
| | *Nos. 2535-2546 (12)* | | 30.40 | 28.45 |

**Size: 70x100mm, 100x70mm**

*Imperf*

| | | | | |
|---|---|---|---|---|
| 2547 | A149 | $225 multi | 6.75 | 6.75 |
| 2548 | A149 | $225 multi | 6.75 | 6.75 |
| 2549 | A149 | $225 multi | 6.75 | 6.75 |
| 2550 | A149 | $225 multi | 6.75 | 6.75 |

No. 2273 Overprinted or Surcharged with Olympic Rings and "ALBERTVILLE '92" or "XVIth Olympic Winter / Games in Albertville" (No. 2551e)

**1992**

| | | | *Perfs. as Before* |
|---|---|---|---|
| 2551 | A122 | Sheet of 9 | |
| *a.-f.* | $20 on #2273a-2273f | | |
| *g.* | $70 on $20 #2273g | | |
| *h.* | $100 on $20 #2273h | | |
| *i.* | $190 on $20 #2273i | | |

Nos. 2391g, 2395c, 2396c, 2398, 2400 Ovptd. "ALBERTVILLE '92" No. 2399 Ovptd. "Barcelona '92" and emblems in Sheet Margin

**1992**

| | | | *Perfs. as Before* | |
|---|---|---|---|---|
| 2552 | A133 | $17.80 on #2391g | 12.00 | 12.00 |
| 2553 | A133 | $25 on #2395c | 12.00 | 12.00 |
| 2554 | A133 | $30 on #2396c | 12.00 | 12.00 |

**Souvenir Sheets**

| | | | | |
|---|---|---|---|---|
| 2555 | A133 | $150 on #2398 | 7.00 | 7.00 |
| 2556 | A133 | $150 on #2399 | 7.00 | 7.00 |
| 2557 | A133 | $190 on #2400 | 7.00 | 7.00 |

Nos. 2552-2554 printed in sheets of 9, overprint applied to only one stamp per sheet. Overprint on Nos. 2555, 2557 applied to sheet margin.

Easter
A150

Various details from paintings by Durer: $6.40, $12.80, $50, $130, No. 2567, The Martyrdom of Ten Thousand. $7.65, $15.30, $100, $190, No. 2566, Adoration of the Trinity.

**1992** **Litho.** *Perf. 13½x14*

| | | | | |
|---|---|---|---|---|
| 2558 | A150 | $6.40 multi | .30 | .20 |
| 2559 | A150 | $7.65 multi | .30 | .20 |
| 2560 | A150 | $12.80 multi | .45 | .25 |
| 2561 | A150 | $15.30 multi | .55 | .45 |
| 2562 | A150 | $50 multi | 1.50 | 1.25 |
| 2563 | A150 | $100 multi | 2.75 | 2.75 |
| 2564 | A150 | $130 multi | 3.75 | 3.75 |
| 2565 | A150 | $190 multi | 5.75 | 5.75 |
| | *Nos. 2558-2565 (8)* | | 15.35 | 14.60 |

**Souvenir Sheets**

| | | | | |
|---|---|---|---|---|
| 2566 | A150 | $225 multi | 6.75 | 6.75 |
| 2567 | A150 | $225 multi | 6.75 | 6.75 |

Queen Elizabeth II's Accession to the Throne, 40th Anniv.
A151

Queen Elizabeth II: $8.90, With Prince Philip. $12.80, In uniform. $100, At coronation. $130, Wearing black cape and hat. No. 2572, Coronation portrait. No. 2573, Fortieth anniv. portrait.

**1992** **Litho.** *Perf. 14*

| | | | | |
|---|---|---|---|---|
| 2568 | A151 | $8.90 multicolored | 1.00 | .50 |
| 2569 | A151 | $12.80 multicolored | 1.50 | .60 |
| 2570 | A151 | $100 multicolored | 5.25 | 4.00 |
| 2571 | A151 | $130 multicolored | 6.25 | 5.00 |
| | *Nos. 2568-2571 (4)* | | 14.00 | 10.10 |

**Souvenir Sheets**

| | | | | |
|---|---|---|---|---|
| 2572 | A151 | $225 multicolored | 7.25 | 7.25 |
| 2573 | A151 | $225 multicolored | 7.25 | 7.25 |

Diocese of Guyana, 150th Anniv.
A152

Designs: $6.40, Holy Cross Church, Annai Bupununi. $50, St. Peter's Church. $100, St. George's Cathedral, interior, vert. $190, Map, vert. $225, Religious symbols.

**1992** **Litho.** *Perf. 14*

| | | | | |
|---|---|---|---|---|
| 2574 | A152 | $6.40 multicolored | .40 | .30 |
| 2575 | A152 | $50 multicolored | 1.25 | 1.10 |
| 2576 | A152 | $100 multicolored | 2.75 | 2.75 |
| 2577 | A152 | $190 multicolored | 4.50 | 4.50 |
| | *Nos. 2574-2577 (4)* | | 8.90 | 8.65 |

**Souvenir Sheet**

| | | | | |
|---|---|---|---|---|
| 2578 | A152 | $225 multicolored | 7.00 | 7.00 |

**Miniature Sheet**

Horses — A153

No. 2579: a, Palomino. b, Appaloosa. c, Clydesdale. d, Arab. e, Morgan. f, Friesian. g, Pinto. h, Thoroughbred. No. 2580, Lipizzaner.

**1992, Aug. 10**

| | | | | |
|---|---|---|---|---|
| 2579 | A153 | $190 Sheet of 8, | 40.00 | 40.00 |
| | | #a.-h. | | |

**Souvenir Sheet**

| | | | | |
|---|---|---|---|---|
| 2580 | A153 | $190 multicolored | 8.00 | 8.00 |

No. 2580 contains one 58x29mm stamp.

Cats — A154

No. 2588A: b, Russian blue. c, Havana brown. d, Himalayan. e, Manx. f, Cornish rex. g, Black Persian. h, Scottish fold. i, Siamese.

**1992, Aug. 10** *Perf. 14½x14*

| | | | | |
|---|---|---|---|---|
| 2581 | A154 | $5 Burmese | .30 | .20 |
| 2582 | A154 | $6.40 Turkish van | .30 | .20 |
| 2583 | A154 | $12.80 American shorthair | .40 | .35 |
| 2584 | A154 | $15.30 Egyptian | .55 | .50 |
| 2585 | A154 | $50 Egyptian mau | 1.75 | 1.50 |
| 2586 | A154 | $100 Japanese bobtail | 3.25 | 3.25 |
| 2587 | A154 | $130 Abyssinian | 4.00 | 4.00 |
| 2588 | A154 | $225 Oriental shorthair | 7.50 | 7.50 |
| | *Nos. 2581-2588 (8)* | | 18.05 | 17.50 |

**Miniature Sheet**

*Perf. 14x13½*

| | | | | |
|---|---|---|---|---|
| 2588A | A154 | $50 Sheet of 8, #b.-i. | 12.00 | 12.00 |

**Souvenir Sheets**

*Perf. 14x14½*

| | | | | |
|---|---|---|---|---|
| 2589 | A152 | $250 Chartreuse, vert. | 7.25 | 7.25 |

| | | | | |
|---|---|---|---|---|
| 2590 | A154 | $250 Turkish angora | 7.25 | 7.25 |
| 2591 | A154 | $250 Maine coon | 7.25 | 7.25 |
| 2592 | A154 | $250 Chinchilla | 7.25 | 7.25 |

No. 2589 has continuous design. Nos. 2590-2592 are vert. and have continous design.

Nos. 2368-2369 Surcharged on 4 stamps and Overprinted in Red "PHILA NIPPON '91 / WORLD STAMP EXHIBITION NIPPON '91" and Show Emblem in Sheet Margin
No. 2376 Surcharged in Red

**1992** *Perfs. as Before*

| | | | | |
|---|---|---|---|---|
| 2593 | A129 | Sheet of 12, #a.-d., #2368a-2368l | | 19.00 |
| *a.* | $25 on $10 #2368m | | | |
| *b.* | $50 on $10 #2368n | | | |
| *c.* | $75 on $10 #2368o | | | |
| *d.* | $130 on $10 #2368p | | | |
| 2594 | A129 | Sheet of 16, #a.-d., 2369a-2369l | | 19.00 |
| *a.* | $25 on $12.80 #2369m | | | |
| *b.* | $50 on $12.80 #2369n | | | |
| *c.* | $75 on $12.80 #2369o | | | |
| *d.* | $100 on $12.80 #2369p | | | |

**Souvenir Sheet**

| | | | |
|---|---|---|---|
| 2595 | A129 | $250 on $150 #2376 | |

Nos. 2332-2340, 2346-2347 Overprinted or Surcharged

Overprints: 80c, $2.55, Nos. 2602-2603, Lions emblem and "Lions International / 1917-1992." $5, $6.40, $7.65, Nos. 2601, 2604d, 2604m, Lions emblem and "Melvin Jones Founder 1880-1961" on 2 or 3 lines. Nos. 2604a, 2604p, Lions emblem and "1917-1992." Nos. 2604b, 2604i, 2604o, Rotary emblem and "1905-1990." Nos. 2604c, 2604l, 2604n, Boy Scout emblem and "1907-1992." Nos. 2604e, 2604h, Red Cross emblem and "125 Years Red Cross." Nos. 2604f-2604g, 2604j-2604k have parts of larger Lions emblem. Nos. 2605-2606 have service organization emblems in sheet margins.

**1992** *Perfs. as Before*

| | | | |
|---|---|---|---|
| 2596 | A126 | 80c on #2332 | |
| 2597 | A126 | $2.55 on #2333 | |
| 2598 | A126 | $5 on #2334 | |
| 2599 | A126 | $6.40 on #2335 | |
| 2600 | A126 | $7.65 on #2336 | |
| 2601 | A126 | $100 on $8.90 #2337 | |
| 2602 | A126 | $190 on $50 #2338 | |
| 2603 | A126 | $225 on $100 #2339 | |

**Miniature Sheet**

| | | | | |
|---|---|---|---|---|
| 2604 | | Sheet of 16 | 45.00 | |
| *a.-l.* | A126 $10 any single | | | |
| *m.* | A126 $50 on $10 #2340m | | | |
| *n.* | A126 $75 on $10 #2340n | | | |
| *o.* | A126 $100 on $10 #2340o | | | |
| *p.* | A126 $190 on $10 #2340p | | | |

**Souvenir Sheets**

| | | | |
|---|---|---|---|
| 2605 | A126 | $400 on $190 #2346 | |
| 2606 | A126 | $500 on $190 #2347 | |

Elephants — A155

No. 2607: a, Mammoth, Oligocene Epoch. b, Stegodon, mid- Miocene Epoch. c, Mammoth, Pliocene Epoch. d, Hannibal's army crossing Alps. e, Royal elephant of the Maharaja of Mysore, India. f, Elephant pulling tree trunks, Burma. g, Tiger hunt, India. h, Elephant towing raft on River Kwai, Thailand. $225, African elephants, Kenya.

**1992, Aug. 10** **Litho.** *Perf. 14*

| | | | | |
|---|---|---|---|---|
| 2607 | A155 | $50 Sheet of 8, #a.-h. | 16.00 | 16.00 |

**Souvenir Sheet**

| | | | | |
|---|---|---|---|---|
| 2608 | A155 | $225 multicolored | 11.00 | 11.00 |

No. 2607 has continuous design.

Animals of Guyana
A156

**1992, Aug. 10**

| | | | | |
|---|---|---|---|---|
| 2609 | A156 | $8.90 Red howler monkey | .25 | .20 |
| 2610 | A156 | $12.80 Ring-tailed coati | .30 | .25 |
| 2611 | A156 | $15.30 Jaguar | .40 | .35 |
| 2612 | A156 | $25 Two-toed sloth | .65 | .60 |
| 2613 | A156 | $50 Giant armadillo | 1.40 | 1.25 |
| 2614 | A156 | $75 Giant anteater | 2.00 | 2.00 |
| 2615 | A156 | $100 Capybara | 2.75 | 2.75 |
| 2616 | A156 | $130 Ocelot | 3.50 | 3.50 |
| | *Nos. 2609-2616 (8)* | | 11.25 | 10.90 |

**Souvenir Sheets**

| | | | | |
|---|---|---|---|---|
| 2617 | A156 | $225 Wooly opossum, vert. | 7.00 | 7.00 |
| 2618 | A156 | $225 Night monkey, vert. | 7.00 | 7.00 |

**Souvenir Sheet**

Statue of Liberty, New York — A157

**1992, Oct. 28**

| | | | | |
|---|---|---|---|---|
| 2619 | A157 | $325 multicolored | 11.00 | 11.00 |

Postage Stamp Mega Event '92, New York City.

**Miniature Sheets**

Model Trains
A158

Marklin toy locomotives: No. 2620a, 2-4-4-2 Crocodile locomotive, 1 gauge, 1933. b, French prototype streetcar, 1 gauge, 1933. c, British prototype Flatiron 2-4-4 tank engine, O gauge, 1913. d, German National Railways 0-6-0 switching engine, Z gauge, 1970. e, Smoking/non-smoking third class car, 1 gauge, 1909. f, American style 0-4-0 locomotive, O gauge, 1904. g, Zurich, Switzerland prototype streetcar, O gauge, 1928. h, Central London Railway Bo-Bo, 1 gauge, 1904. i, "The Great Bear" Pacific, 1 gauge, 1909.

No. 2621: a, 0-4-4 American style locomotive, 2 gauge, 1907. b, German first and second class passenger car, 1 gauge, 1908. c, British Great Eastern Railway 4-4-0, 1 gauge, 1908. d, English prototype steeplecab, O gauge, 1904. e, Santa Fe Railroad diesel, 1962. f, British Great Northern 4-4-0, 3 gauge, live steam model, 1903. g, Caledonian Railway "Cardean" of Scotland, 1 gauge, 1904. h, British LNWR passenger car, 1 gauge, 1903. i, Swiss Gotthard Rwy. 0-4-0 locomotive, O gauge, 1920.

No. 2622: a, British LB & SCR tank engine, O gauge, 1920. b, Central London Railway, tunnel locomotive, 1 gauge, 1904. c, "Borsig" 4-6-4 streamliner, O gauge, 1935. d, French PLM first class car, 1 gauge, 1929. e, American style 0-4-0 locomotive #1021, 1 gauge, 1904. f, "Paris-Orsay" long-nose steeplecab, 1 gauge, 1920. g, British "Cock O' The North," 1 gauge, 1936. h, Prussian State Railways P8 4-6-0 live steam model, 1 gauge, 1975. i, 1937 German "Schnell Treibwagen," O gauge, 1937.

No. 2623: a, Marklin North British Railway "Atlantic," 1 gauge, 1913. b, Bing British London & Western Railway 4-4-2 "Precursor," O gauge, clockwork model, 1916. c, Marklin British Great Western "King George V," O gauge, 1937. d, Marklin passenger car, "Kaiser Train," 1 gauge, 1901. e, Bing 4-4-0 side tank engine, 1 gauge, live steam model, 1904. f, Marklin short-nose steeplecab, 1 gauge, 1912. g, Marklin "Der Adler," 1 gauge, 1935. h, Bing British Great Western Railway "County of Northampton," 1 gauge, live steam model, 1909. i, Bing British Midland Railway "Black Prince," 3 gauge, live steam model, 1908.

Bing toy locomotives: No. 2624: a, Midland Railway "Deeley Type" 4-4-0, 1 gauge clockwork model, 1909. b, No. 2631, British Midland Railway 0-4-0, 3 gauge clockwork model, 1903. c, German 4-6-2 Pacific, O gauge clockwork model, 1927. d, British Great Western Railway, third class coach, O gauge, 1926. e, British London & Southwestern "M7" 0-4-4, 1 gauge clockwork model, 1909. f, "Pilot" 4-4-0 side tank engine, 3 gauge live steam model, 1901. g, British London & Northwestern Railway Webb "Cauliflower," O gauge clockwork model, 1912. h, No. 112, 4-4-0 side tank locomotive, 1 gauge live steam model, 1910. i, British Great Northern Railway, "Stirling Single," 2 gauge live steam model, 1904.

Carette toy locomotives: No. 2625: a, Lithographed tin "Penny Bazaar" train, 1904. b, Winteringham 0-4-0 locomotive, O gauge, 1917. c, British Northeastern Railway, Smith Compound, 3 gauge, 1905. d, SE & CR 2-2-4 steam railcar, 1 gauge, live steam model, 1908. e, No. 776 British Great Northern Railway Stirling "Single," 3 gauge, live steam model, 1903. f, British Midland Railway 4-4-0, O gauge, clockwork model, 1911. g, London Metropolitan Railway "Westinghouse," 1 gauge, 1908. h, Clestory coach, 1 gauge, 1907. i, Steam railcar No. 1, O gauge, live steam model, 1906.

Marklin toy locomotives: No. 2626: a, LMS "Precursor" 4-4-2 tank engine, O gauge clockwork model, 1923. b, American "Congressional Limited" passenger car, 1 gauge, 1908. c, Swiss prototype "Ae 3/6" locomotive, O gauge, 1934. d, German National Railways class 80, 0-6-0, 1 gauge, 1975. e, British Southern Railway third class coach, O gauge, 1926. f, "Bowen-Cooke" 4-6-2 tank engine, O gauge, 1913. g, First electric prototype model, "Two Penny Tube," London, 1 gauge clockwork model, 1901. h, "Paris-Orsay" steeplecab, 1 gauge, 1920. i, 0-2-2 Passenger engine, O gauge clockwork model, 1895.

Bing toy locomotives: No. 2627: a, 2-2-0 engine and tender, 2 gauge live steam model, 1895. b, British Midland Railway "single," O gauge clockwork model, 1913. c, #524/510 reversible express passenger locomotive, 1 gauge, 1916. d, "Kaiser Train" passenger car with Gothic windows, 1 gauge, 1902. e, Tinplate model, British rural station, 1 gauge, 1915. f, British LSMR "M7" side tank locomotive, O gauge clockwork model, 1909. g, 4-4-4 "Windcutter," 1 gauge live steam model, 1912. h, British Great Central Railway "Sir Sam Fay," 1 gauge clockwork model, 1914. i, "Dunalastair" locomotive Caledonian Railway, 1 gauge clockwork model, 1910.

No. 2628, German National Railroad class 0-1 Pacific, O gauge, 1937. No. 2629, Bing 0-4-0 Contractor's locomotive, 4 gauge, 1904. No. 2630, Rack Railway "Steeplecab" locomotive, 2 gauge, 1908. No. 2631, Bing Pabst Blue Ribbon Beer refrigerator car, O gauge, 1925. No. 2632, Marklin "Commodore Vanderbilt," O gauge, 1937. No. 2633, Bing British Great Western Railway "County of Northampton," 1 gauge, live steam model, 1909. No. 2634, Marklin French Prototype PLM Pacific, 1 gauge, live steam model, 1912. No. 2635, Marklin "Mountain Etat" second series, O gauge, 1933.

**1992, Nov. 19**     **Perf. 14**
| | | | | |
|---|---|---|---|---|
|2620|A158|$45 Sheet of 9, #a.-i.|8.00|8.00|
|2621|A158|$45 Sheet of 9, #a.-i.|8.00|8.00|
|2622|A158|$45 Sheet of 9, #a.-i.|8.00|8.00|
|2623|A158|$45 Sheet of 9, #a.-i.|8.00|8.00|
|2624|A158|$45 Sheet of 9, #a.-i.|8.00|8.00|
|2625|A158|$45 Sheet of 9, #a.-i.|8.00|8.00|
|2626|A158|$45 Sheet of 9, #a.-i.|8.00|8.00|
|2627|A158|$45 Sheet of 9, #a.-i.|8.00|8.00|

**Souvenir Sheets**
| | | | | |
|---|---|---|---|---|
|2628|A158|$350 multicolored|7.00|7.00|
|2629|A158|$350 multicolored|7.00|7.00|

**Perf. 14x13½**
| | | | | |
|---|---|---|---|---|
|2630|A158|$350 multicolored|7.00|7.00|

**Perf. 13x13½, 13½x13**
| | | | | |
|---|---|---|---|---|
|2631|A158|$350 multicolored|7.00|7.00|
|2632|A158|$350 multicolored|7.00|7.00|
|2633|A158|$350 multicolored|7.00|7.00|
|2634|A158|$350 multicolored|7.00|7.00|
|2635|A158|$350 multicolored|7.00|7.00|

Genoa '92. Nos. 2628-2635 each contain one 50x39mm stamp.

While Nos. 2622-2623 & 2631 have the issue date as Nos. 2620-2621 & 2628-2630, the face value of of Nos. 2622-2623 & 2631 was lower when they were released.

Anniversaries and Events — A159

Designs: $12.80, Zeppelin over Lake Constance, 1909. No. 2638, Voyager 1, Jupiter. No. 2639, Konrad Adenauer, John F. Kennedy. No. 2640, Aeromedical airlift. No. 2641, Amazon dolphins. No. 2642, Lift-off of Voyager 1, 1977. No. 2643, Baby gorilla. No. 2644, America's Cup yacht Stars and Stripes. No. 2644A, Eye screening van, doctor with patient. $190, Adenauer, Charles de Gaulle. $225, Zeppelin preparing for takeoff. No. 2647, Count Zeppelin, vert. No. 2648 View of Earth from space, vert. No. 2649, Konrad Adenauer, vert. No. 2650, Tree frog, vert.

**1993, Jan.**   **Litho.**   **Perf. 14**
| | | | | |
|---|---|---|---|---|
|2637|A159|$12.80 multi|.75|.75|
|2638|A159|$50 multi|1.75|1.75|
|2639|A159|$50 multi|2.00|2.00|
|2640|A159|$100 multi|4.50|4.50|
|2641|A159|$100 multi|3.00|3.00|
|2642|A159|$130 multi|4.25|4.25|
|2643|A159|$130 multi|3.75|3.75|
|2644|A159|$130 multi|4.75|4.75|
|2644A|A159|$130 multi|4.75|4.75|
|2645|A159|$190 multi|6.00|6.00|
|2646|A159|$225 multi|6.50|6.50|
|Nos. 2637-2646 (11)||42.00|42.00|

**Souvenir Sheets**
| | | | | |
|---|---|---|---|---|
|2647|A159|$225 multi|7.50|7.50|
|2648|A159|$225 multi|7.00|7.00|
|2649|A159|$225 multi|7.00|7.00|
|2650|A159|$225 multi|7.00|7.00|

Count Zeppelin, 75th anniv. of death (#2637, 2646-2647). Intl. Space Year (#2638, 2642, 2648). Konrad Adenauer, 25th anniv. of death (#2639, 2645, 2649). World Health Organization (#2640). Earth Summit, Rio (#2641, 2643, 2650). America's Cup Yacht Race (#2644). Lions Intl., 75th anniv. (#2644A).

**Miniature Sheet**

Biblical Story of David and Goliath — A160

No. 2651: a, City of Jerusalem, two birds in flight. b, City, bird in flight at right. c, City, sun above. d, City, bird in flight at left. e, City with clouds above. f, Philistine army (i-k, q-r). g, Goliath. h, Goliath's arm, spear shaft (b, i, n). l, Goliath's leg (m, q-s), shield. n, David (r-t, w) with slingshot. o, Jewish soldiers with spears or swords (p-y).

**1992, Dec. 29**   **Litho.**   **Perf. 14**
| | | | | |
|---|---|---|---|---|
|2651|A160|$25 Sheet of 25, #a.-y.|19.00|19.00|

No. 2651 has a continuous design.

Parrots A161

**1993, Mar. 10**
| | | | | |
|---|---|---|---|---|
|2652|A161|80c Hyacinth macaw|.35|.20|
|2653|A161|$6.40 Scarlet macaw|.60|.30|
|2654|A161|$7.65 Green macaw, vert.|.60|.30|
|2655|A161|$15.30 Tovi parakeet|.80|.60|
|2656|A161|$50 Blue & yellow macaw|1.25|.95|
|2657|A161|$100 Military macaw, vert.|2.50|2.40|
|2658|A161|$130 Red & green macaw, vert.|3.25|3.25|
|2659|A161|$190 Severa macaw, vert.|3.75|3.75|
|Nos. 2652-2659 (8)||13.10|11.75|

**Souvenir Sheet**
| | | | | |
|---|---|---|---|---|
|2660|A161|$225 Scarlet macaw, diff.|6.00|6.00|
|2661|A161|$225 Green parakeet, vert.|6.00|6.00|

While Nos. 2654-2656, 2659, 2661 have the same issue date as Nos. 2652-2653, 2657-2658, 2660, the value of Nos. 2654-2656, 2659, 2661 was lower when released.

**Miniature Sheets**

Dinosaurs — A162

No. 2662: a, Archaeopteryx. b, Pteranodon. c, Quetzalcoatlus. d, Protoavis. e, Dicraeosaurus. f, Moschops. g, Lystrosaurus. h, Dimetrondon. i, Staurikosaurus. j, Cacops. k, Diarthrognathus. l, Estemmenosuchus.

No. 2663: a, Pteranodon. b, Cearadactylus. c, Eudimorphodon. d, Pterodactylus. e, Stauirkosaurus. f, Euoplocephalus. g, Tuojiangosaurus. h, Oviraptor. i, Protoceratops. j, Panaoplosaurus. k, Psittacosaurus. l, Corythosaurus.

No. 2664: a, Sordes. b, Quetzalcoatlus. c, Archaeopteryx. d, Rhamphorynchus. e, Spinosaurus. f, Anchisaurus. g, Stegosaurus. h, Leaellynosaurus. i, Minmi. j, Heterdontosaurus. k, Lesothosaurus. l, Deninonychus.

**1993, Mar. 10**   **Litho.**   **Perf. 14**
| | | | | |
|---|---|---|---|---|
|2662|A162|$30 Sheet of 12, #a.-l.|8.75|8.75|
|2663|A162|$30 Sheet of 12, #a.-l.|8.75|8.75|
|2664|A162|$30 Sheet of 12, #a.-l.|8.75|8.75|

**Miniature Sheet**

Signs of the Zodiac A163

No. 2665: a, Aquarius. b, Pisces. c, Aries. d, Taurus. e, Gemini. f, Cancer. g, Leo. h, Virgo. i, Libra. j, Scorpio. k, Sagittarius. l, Capricorn.

**1992, Dec. 29**   **Litho.**   **Perf. 14x13½**
**Sheet of 12**
| | | | | |
|---|---|---|---|---|
|2665|A163|$30 Sheet of 12, #a.-l.|19.00|19.00|

Caribbean Manatee A164

Designs: $6.40, Adult sticking head out of water. $7.65, Adult, eating, with young. $8.90, Adult swimming underwater. $50, Adult swimming with young.

**1993, Mar. 10**   **Litho.**   **Perf. 15x14½**
| | | | | |
|---|---|---|---|---|
|2666|A164|$6.40 multicolored|1.25|1.10|
|2667|A164|$7.65 multicolored|1.25|1.10|
|2668|A164|$8.90 multicolored|1.25|1.10|
|2669|A164|$50 multicolored|4.75|4.75|
|Nos. 2666-2669 (4)||8.50|8.05|

World Wildlife Federation. Exists imperf. Value, set $36.

Fauna — A165

No. 2670: a, Southern tamandua. b, Three-toed sloth. c, Red howler monkey. d, Four-eyed opossum. e, Black spider monkey. f, Giant otter. g, Red brocket. h, Tree porcupine. i, Tayra. j, Tapir. k, Ocelot. l, Giant armadillo.

No. 2671: a, Crimson topaz hummingbird. b, Bearded bellbird (f). c, Amazonian umbrellabird. d, Paradise jacamar (h). e, Paradise tanager. f, White-tailed trogon (i-j). g, Scarlet macaw (k). h, Red fan parrot. i, Red-billed toucan. j, White plumed antbird. k, Crimson-hooded manakin. l, Guyanan cock-of-the-rock.

No. 2672, Paca. No. 2673, Tufted coquettes, horiz.

**1993, Mar. 10**   **Perf. 14**
| | | | | |
|---|---|---|---|---|
|2670|A165|$50 Sheet of 12, #a.-l.|14.00|14.00|
|2671|A165|$50 Sheet of 12, #a.-l.|13.75|13.75|

**Souvenir Sheets**
| | | | | |
|---|---|---|---|---|
|2672|A165|$325 multicolored|8.25|8.25|
|2673|A165|$325 multicolored|9.00|9.00|

Coronation of Queen Elizabeth II, 40th Anniv. A166

No. 2674: a, $25, Official coronation photograph. b, $50, Gems from royal collection. c, $75, Queen, Duke of Edinburgh. d, $130, Queen opening Parliament. $325, State Portrait, by Sir James Gunn, 1954-56.

**1993, June 2**   **Litho.**   **Perf. 13½x14**
| | | | | |
|---|---|---|---|---|
|2674|A166|Sheet, 2 each #a.-d.|16.00|16.00|

**Souvenir Sheet**
**Perf. 14**
| | | | | |
|---|---|---|---|---|
|2675|A166|$325 multicolored|10.00|10.00|

No. 2675 contains one 28x42mm stamp. For overprints see Nos. 2793-2795.

A167

Famous People A168

Athletes: No. 2676: a, O. J. Simpson, football. b, Rohan B. Kanhai, cricket. c, Gabriela Sabatini, tennis. d, Severiano Ballesteros, golf. e, Peace dove, blue background. f, Franz Beckenbauer, soccer. g, Pele, soccer. h, Wilt Chamberlain, basketball. i, Nadia Comaneci, gymnastics.

Scientists: No. 2677: a, Louis Leakey, archaeology. b, Jonas Salk, polio vaccine. c, Hideyo Noguchi, yellow fever. d, Karl Landsteiner, blood transfusions. e, Peace dove, blue green background. f, Sigmund Freud, psychoanalysis. g, Louis Pasteur. h, Madame Curie, radium tubes. i, Jean Baptiste Perrin, physics.

Artists, entertainers: No. 2678: a, Gabriel Marquez, writer. b, Pablo Picasso, artist. c, Cecil DeMille, film director. d, Martha Graham, dance. e, Peace dove, purple background. f, Charles Chaplin, actor. g, Paul Robeson, singer. h, Rudolph Dunbar, musician. i, Louis Armstrong, musician.

Politicians: No. 2679: a, Jawaharlal Nehru. b, Dr. Eric Williams, first prime minister of Trinidad and Tobago. c, John F. Kennedy. d, Hugh Desmond Hoyte, president of Guyana. e, Peace dove over map. f, Friedrich Ebert. g, Franklin D. Roosevelt. h, Mikhail Gorbachev. i, Winston Churchill.

Humanitarians: No. 2680: a, Gandhi. b, Dalai Lama, c, Michael Manley, prime minister of Jamaica. d, Javier Perez de Cuellar, former UN Secretary General. e, Peace dove, globe. f, Mother Teresa. g, Martin Luther King, Jr. h, Nelson Mandela. i, Raoul Wallenberg.

Transportation, communication: No. 2681: a, DC-3 cargo plane. b, Space shuttle. c, Concorde. d, Ferdinand von Zeppelin. e, Peace dove. f, Guglielmo Marconi. g, Adrian Thompson, mountaineer. h, Bullet train, Japan. i, John von Neuman, mathematician.

No. 2682, UN Flag, natl. flags. No. 2683, Jackie Robinson. No. 2684, Einstein's formula. No. 2685, Elvis Presley. No. 2686, Nobel Peace Prize certificate. No. 2687, Apollo Moon Landing.

**1993, July 26    Litho.    Perf. 14**

| | | | | | |
|---|---|---|---|---|---|
| 2676 | A167 | $50 Sheet of 9, | | | |
| | | #a.-i. | | 16.00 | 16.00 |
| 2677 | A167 | $50 Sheet of 9, | | | |
| | | #a.-i. | | 16.00 | 16.00 |
| 2678 | A167 | $50 Sheet of 9, | | | |
| | | #a.-i. | | 16.00 | 16.00 |
| 2679 | A168 | $100 Sheet of 9, | | | |
| | | #a.-i. | | 16.00 | 16.00 |
| 2680 | A168 | $100 Sheet of 9, | | | |
| | | #a.-i. | | 16.00 | 16.00 |
| 2681 | A168 | $100 Sheet of 9, | | | |
| | | #a.-i. | | 16.00 | 16.00 |

**Souvenir Sheets**

| | | | | |
|---|---|---|---|---|
| 2682 | A168 | $250 multi, vert. | 8.00 | 8.00 |
| 2683 | A167 | $250 multi, vert. | 8.00 | 8.00 |
| 2684 | A167 | $250 multi, vert. | 8.00 | 8.00 |
| 2685 | A167 | $250 multi, vert. | 8.00 | 8.00 |
| 2686 | A168 | $250 multi, vert. | 8.00 | 8.00 |
| 2687 | A168 | $250 multi | 8.00 | 8.00 |

Willy Brandt (1913-1992), German Chancellor — A169

Designs: $25, Brandt, Golda Meir, 1969. $190, Brandt at steel mill, 1969. $325, Brandt.

**1993, Aug. 16    Litho.    Perf. 14**

| | | | | |
|---|---|---|---|---|
| 2688 | A169 | $25 multicolored | .90 | .90 |
| 2689 | A169 | $190 multicolored | 6.50 | 6.50 |

**Souvenir Sheet**

| | | | | |
|---|---|---|---|---|
| 2690 | A169 | $325 multicolored | 9.00 | 9.00 |

Armillary Sphere — A170

Copernicus (1473-1543): $190, Satellite antenna. $300, Copernicus.

**1993, Aug. 16**

| | | | | |
|---|---|---|---|---|
| 2691 | A170 | $50 multicolored | 1.75 | 1.75 |
| 2692 | A170 | $190 multicolored | 6.25 | 6.25 |

**Souvenir Sheet**

| | | | | |
|---|---|---|---|---|
| 2693 | A170 | $300 multicolored | 8.00 | 8.00 |

Georg Hackl, Luge Gold Medalist, 1992 — A171

**1993, Aug. 16**

1994 Winter Olympics, Lillehammer, Norway: $130, Karen Magnussen, figure skater, 1972. $325, German bobsled team, 1992.

| | | | | |
|---|---|---|---|---|
| 2694 | A171 | $50 multicolored | 1.75 | 1.75 |
| 2695 | A171 | $130 multicolored | 4.25 | 4.25 |

**Souvenir Sheet**

| | | | | |
|---|---|---|---|---|
| 2696 | A171 | $325 multicolored | 9.50 | 9.50 |

A172

World War II — A173

Designs: $6.40, Audie Murphy. $7.65, British, US forces link up in France, June 8, 1944. $8.90, Monte Cassino falls to Allies, May 18, 1944. $12.80, Battleship Yamato attacked by US in Battle of East China Sea, Apr. 7, 1945. $15.30, St. Basil's Cathedral, Moscow, Foreign Ministers Conf., Oct. 19, 1943. $50, US forces cross Rhine River, Mar. 7, 1945. $130, Gen. George S. Patton, Jr., Battle of Sicily ends, Aug. 17, 1943. $190, Battleship Tirpitz sunk, Nov. 12, 1944. $200, US Sherman tank, US forces enter Brittany after taking Normandy, Aug. 1, 1944. $100, B-29s begin bombing raids on Japan from China, June 15, 1944. $225, End of fighting in Italy, May 2, 1945.

No. 2708 — War at Sea, 1943: a, Adm. Yamamoto launches air offensive, Apr. 7. b, PT-109 in Blackett Strait, Aug. 1. c, USS Enterprise. d, Allied ships attack Rabaul, Oct. 12. e, US troops land at Cape Gloucester, Dec. 26. f, USS Bogue enters service, Feb. 9. g, Wildcat fighters sink U-118. h, Battle of Atlantic reaches peak, U-boats sink 108 ships. i, Italian fleet surrenders at Malta, Sept. 10. j, Battleship Duke of York sinks Scharnhorst, Dec. 26.

No. 2709 — War in the Air, 1943: a, Royal Australian Air Force Beaufighter, Battle of Bismark Sea, Mar. 2-4. b, P-38 Lightening shoots down Adm. Yamamoto's plane over Bougainville, Apr. 7. c, B-24 Liberators bomb Tarawa prior to landings, Sept. 17-19. d, B-25 Mitchell of Fifth Air Force bombs Rabaul, Oct. 12. e, US Navy aircraft attack Makin, Nov. 19. f, US Army Air Force's first daylight raid over Germany, Jan. 27. g, Royal Air Force Mosquito bombers make first daylight raid on Berlin, Jan. 30. h, Allies devastate Hamburg with first firestorm, July 24-30. i, B-24 bombers raid Ploesti oil refineries in Romania, Aug. 1. j, Battle of Berlin begins, Nov. 18.

No. 2710, $325, US, Russian infantry meeting at Elbe River, Apr. 25, 1945.

**1993, Oct. 18    Litho.    Perf. 14**

| | | | | |
|---|---|---|---|---|
| 2697 | A172 | $6.40 multicolored | .80 | .30 |
| 2698 | A172 | $7.65 multicolored | .85 | .35 |
| 2699 | A172 | $8.90 multicolored | .90 | .40 |
| 2700 | A172 | $12.80 multicolored | .95 | .60 |
| 2701 | A172 | $15.30 multicolored | 1.00 | .70 |
| 2702 | A172 | $50 multicolored | 1.75 | 1.25 |
| 2703 | A172 | $100 multicolored | 2.75 | 2.50 |
| 2704 | A172 | $130 multicolored | 4.00 | 4.00 |
| 2705 | A172 | $190 multicolored | 5.50 | 5.50 |
| 2706 | A172 | $200 multicolored | 5.75 | 5.75 |
| 2707 | A172 | $225 multicolored | 6.50 | 6.50 |
| | | Nos. 2697-2707 (11) | 30.75 | 27.85 |

**Miniature Sheets**
**Perf. 15**

| | | | | |
|---|---|---|---|---|
| 2708 | A173 | $50 Sheet of 10, | | |
| | | #a.-j. | 14.00 | 14.00 |
| 2709 | A172 | $50 Sheet of 10, | | |
| | | #a.-j. | 14.00 | 14.00 |
| | | Nos. 2709a-2709j are 35 ½x22mm. | | |

**Souvenir Sheet**
**Perf. 14**

| | | | | |
|---|---|---|---|---|
| 2710 | A172 | $325 multicolored | 12.00 | 12.00 |

1994 World Cup Soccer Championships, U.S. — A174

Player, country: $5, Stuart Pearce, England. $6.40, Ronald Koeman, Holland. $7.65, Gianluca Vialli, Italy. $12.80, McStay, Scotland, Alemao, Brazil. $15.30, Ceulemans, Belgium, Butcher, England. $50, Dragan Stojkovic, Yugoslovia. $100, Ruud Gullit, Holland. $130, Miloslav Kadlec, Czechoslovakia. $150, Ramos, Uruguay, Berthold, Germany. $190, Baggio, Italy; Wright, England. $200, Yarentchuck, Russia, Renquin, Belgium. $225, Timofte, Romania; Aleinikov, Russia. No. 2724, Rene Higuita, Colombia. No. 2723, Salvatore Schillaci, Italy, horiz.

**1993, Oct. 18    Litho.    Perf. 14**

| | | | | |
|---|---|---|---|---|
| 2711 | A174 | $5 multicolored | .25 | .25 |
| 2712 | A174 | $6.40 multicolored | .25 | .25 |
| 2713 | A174 | $7.65 multicolored | .35 | .25 |
| 2714 | A174 | $12.80 multicolored | .40 | .25 |
| 2715 | A174 | $15.30 multicolored | .45 | .30 |
| 2716 | A174 | $50 multicolored | 1.60 | .90 |
| 2717 | A174 | $100 multicolored | 2.50 | 2.50 |
| 2718 | A174 | $130 multicolored | 3.00 | 3.00 |
| 2719 | A174 | $150 multicolored | 3.50 | 3.50 |
| 2720 | A174 | $190 multicolored | 4.25 | 4.25 |
| 2721 | A174 | $200 multicolored | 5.00 | 5.00 |
| 2722 | A174 | $225 multicolored | 5.25 | 5.25 |
| | | Nos. 2711-2722 (12) | 26.80 | 25.70 |

**Souvenir Sheets**

| | | | | |
|---|---|---|---|---|
| 2723 | A174 | $325 multicolored | 8.50 | 8.50 |
| 2724 | A174 | $325 multicolored | 8.50 | 8.50 |

Order of the Caribbean Community A175

**1993, Sept. 27    Litho.    Perf. 14**

| | | | | |
|---|---|---|---|---|
| 2725 | A175 | $7.65 William Demas | 1.00 | .75 |
| 2726 | A175 | $7.65 Derek Walcott | 1.00 | .75 |
| 2727 | A175 | $7.65 Sir Shridath | | |
| | | Ramphal | 2.00 | 1.00 |
| | | Nos. 2725-2727 (3) | 4.00 | 2.50 |

Christmas A176

Details from Holy Family Under the Apple Tree, by Rubens: No. 2728, $6.40, No. 2730, $12.80, No. 2733, $130, No. 2734, $190.

Details from The Virgin in Glory, by Durer: No. 2729, $7.65, No. 2731, $15.30, No. 2732, $50, No. 2735, $250.

No. 2736, Holy Family Under the Apple Tree (entire). No. 2737, The Virgin in Glory (entire).

**1993, Dec. 1    Perf. 13½x14**

| | | | | |
|---|---|---|---|---|
| 2728-2735 | A176 | Set of 8 | 14.00 | 14.00 |

**Souvenir Sheets**

| | | | | |
|---|---|---|---|---|
| 2736 | A174 | $325 multicolored | 7.00 | 7.00 |
| 2737 | A174 | $325 multicolored | 7.00 | 7.00 |

Louvre Museum, Bicent. A177

Details or entire paintings: No. 2738, Mona Lisa, by Da Vinci.

No. 2739, $50: a, La Femme à la Puce, by Crespi. b, La Femme Hydropique, by Dou. c, Portrait d'un Couple, by Ittenbach. d, Cléopâtre Assise, Demi Face, sur un Trône Elevé , by Moreau. e, La Richesse, by Vouet. f, Vieillard et Jeune Garçon, by Ghirlandaio. g, Louis XIV, by Rigaud. h, La Buveuse, by Pieter De Hooch.

No. 2740, $50: a, La Femme à la Puce, by Chardin. b, L'Infante Marie-Thérèse, by Velasquez. c, Le Printemps, by Arcimboldo. d, La Vierge de Douleur, by Bouts. e, L'Etude, by Fragonard. f. François 1er, by Clouet. g, Le Condottière, by Antonello Da Messina. h, La Bohémienne, by Hals.

No. 2741, $50: a, La Femme à la Puce, entire, by Crespi. b, Autoportrait au Chevalet, by Rembrandt. c, Femmes d'Alger dans Leur Appartement, by Delacroix. d, Tête de Jeune Homme, by Raphael. e, Vénus et les Grâces, by Botticelli. f, Nature Morte à l'Échiquier, by Lubin Baugin. g, Lady MacBeth Somnambule, by Fussli. h, La Tabagie, by Chardin.

Nos. 2742, $50: a-c, L'Accordée de Village (left, center, right), by Greuze. d, Autoportrait, by Melendez. e, Le Chevalier, La Jeune Fille et La Mont, by Baldung-Grien. f, Le Jeune Mendiant, by Murillo. g-h, Les Pèlerins d'Emmas (left, right), by Mathieu Le Nain.

No. 2743, $50: a-b, Le Vierge au Lapin (diff. details), by Titian. c, La Belle Jardinière, by Raphael. d, La Dentellière, by Vermeer. e, Jeanne d'Aragon, by Raphael. f, L'Astronome, by Vermeer. g, Le Pont du Rialto, by Canaletto. h, Sigismond Malatesta, by Piero Della Francesca.

No. 2744, $325, Cour de Ferme, by Jan Brueghel, the Younger. No. 2745, $325, Le Pont du Rialto, by Canaletto. No. 2746, $325, Le Sacre de Napoléon 1er, by David. No. 2747, $325, Details and painting of Mona Lisa. No. 2748, $325, La Diseuse de Bonne Aventure, by Caravaggio. No. 2749, $325, Les Noces de Cana, by Veronese.

**1993, Dec. 6    Litho.    Perf. 13½x14**

| | | | | |
|---|---|---|---|---|
| 2738 | A177 | $50 multicolored | .90 | .90 |
| a. | | Sheet of 8 + label | 8.00 | 8.00 |

**Sheets of 8, #a-h, + Label**

| | | | | |
|---|---|---|---|---|
| 2739-2743 | A177 | Set of 5 | 40.00 | 40.00 |

**Souvenir Sheets**
**Perf. 12**

| | | | | |
|---|---|---|---|---|
| 2744-2749 | A177 | Set of 6 | 37.50 | 37.50 |

Nos. 2744-2746 each contain one 80x47mm stamp. Nos. 2747-2749 one 80x53mm stamp.

Christmas A177a

Entire paintings or details: $7.65, St. Anne with Mary and the Child Jesus, by Dürer. $8.90, Mary Being Crowned by Two Angels, by Dürer. $50, Pentecost, by Titian. $100, Samson and Delilah, by Rubens. $250, Origin of the Milky Way, by Rubens.

No. 2749F, $500, The Descent from the Cross, by Rubens, horiz. No. 2749G, $500, The Descent from the Cross, by Dürer, horiz.

**1993    Litho.    Perf. 13½x14, 14x13½**

| | | | | |
|---|---|---|---|---|
| 2749A-2749E | A177a | Set of 5 | 13.50 | 13.50 |

**Souvenir Sheets**

| | | | | |
|---|---|---|---|---|
| 2749F-2749G | A177a | Set of 2 | 16.00 | 16.00 |

Polska '93 (Paintings) — A178

Designs: $50, $130, Pantaloons, by Tadeusz Brzozowski, 1966. $75, Fortress, by Miedzyrecz. $325, Children in the Garden, by Wladyslaw Podkowinski, 1892, horiz.

**1993** **Perf. 14**
| 2750 | A178 | $50 multicolored | 1.75 | 1.75 |
| 2751 | A178 | $75 multicolored | 2.25 | 2.25 |
| 2752 | A178 | $130 multicolored | 4.00 | 4.00 |
| a. | | Pair, #2750, #2752 | 6.00 | 6.00 |
| | | Nos. 2750-2752 (3) | 8.00 | 8.00 |

**Souvenir Sheet**
| 2753 | A178 | $325 multicolored | 8.00 | 8.00 |

Picasso (Paintings) — A179

Designs: $15.30, Bather, Paris, 1909. $100, Two Nudes, 1906. $190, Nude Seated on a Rock, 1921. $325, The Rescue, 1922.

**1993, Nov.** **Litho.** **Perf. 14**
| 2754 | A179 | $15.30 multicolored | .40 | .40 |
| 2755 | A179 | $100 multicolored | 2.60 | 2.60 |
| 2756 | A179 | $190 multicolored | 5.00 | 5.00 |
| | | Nos. 2754-2756 (3) | 8.00 | 8.00 |

**Souvenir Sheet**
| 2756A | A179 | $325 multicolored | 8.00 | 8.00 |

Rebirth of Democracy, 1st Anniv. — A180

Designs: $6.40, Dr. Cheddie B. Jagan, Guyana Pres. $325, Sunburst, "REBIRTH OF DEMOCRACY," horiz.

**1993, Dec. 17** **Litho.** **Perf. 13½x14**
| 2757 | A180 | $6.40 multicolored | .80 | .80 |

**Souvenir Sheet**
**Perf. 13**
| 2757A | A180 | $325 multicolored | 7.50 | 7.50 |

Aladdin — A181

Nos. 2758: a-h, Various characters from Disney animated film, vert.
Nos. 2759: a-i, Various film scenes.
Nos. 2760: a-i, Various scenes from Disney animated film.
No. 2761, Genie, Jasmine, and Aladdin. No. 2762, Aladdin, the Genie, Abu, Magic Carpet. No. 2763, Aladdin as Prince Ali Ababwa. No. 2764, Aladdin, Abu, Jasmine.

**1993, Dec. 20** **Litho.** **Perf. 14x13½**
| 2758 | A181 | $7.65 | Sheet of 8, #a.-h. | 2.00 | 2.00 |
| 2759 | A181 | $50 | Sheet of 9, #a.-i. | 12.00 | 12.00 |
| 2760 | A181 | $65 | Sheet of 9, #a.-i. | 14.00 | 14.00 |
| | | | Nos. 2758-2760 (3) | 28.00 | 28.00 |

**Souvenir Sheets**
| 2761 | A181 | $325 multicolored | 7.50 | 7.50 |
| 2762 | A181 | $325 multicolored | 7.50 | 7.50 |
| 2763 | A181 | $325 multicolored | 7.50 | 7.50 |
| 2764 | A181 | $325 multicolored | 7.50 | 7.50 |

A182

Hong Kong '94 — A183

Stamps, photograph of Happy Valley Horse Race Course: No. 2765, Hong Kong #437, scoreboard. No. 2766, Track, horses, #2545.
No. 2767 — Snuff boxes, Qing Dynasty: a, Painted enamel in shape of bamboo. b, Painted enamel with human figure. c, Amber with lions playing ball. d, Agate in shape of two gourds. e, Glass overlay with dog. f, Glass, foliage design.
No. 2768 — Porcelain, Ch'ing Dynasty: a, Covered jar with dragon. b, Rotating brush holder. c, Covered jar with horses. d, Amphora vase with bats & peaches. e, Tea caddy with Fo dogs. f, Vase with wild camellia & peaches.

**1994, Feb. 18** **Perf. 14**
| 2765 | A182 | $50 multicolored | .80 | .80 |
| 2766 | A182 | $50 multicolored | .80 | .80 |
| a. | | Pair, #2765-2766 | 1.60 | 1.60 |

**Miniature Sheets**
| 2767 | A183 | $20 Sheet of 6, #a.-f. | 8.00 | 8.00 |
| 2768 | A183 | $20 Sheet of 6, #a.-f. | 8.00 | 8.00 |

Nos. 2765-2766 issued in sheets of 5 pairs. No. 2766a is continuous design.
New Year 1994 (Year of the Dog) (#2767e, #2768e).

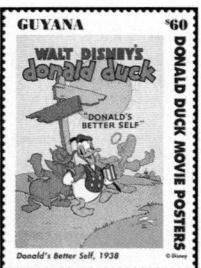

Vintage Donald Duck — A184

No. 2769, $60 — Movie posters: a, Donald's Better Self, 1938. b, Donald's Golf Game, 1938. c, Sea Scouts, 1939. d, Donald's Penguin, 1939. e, A Good Time for a Dime, 1941. f, Truant Officer Donald. g, Orphan's Benefit, 1941. h, Chef Donald, 1941.
No. 2770, $60: a, The Village Smithy, 1942. b, Donald's Snow Fight, 1942. c, Donald's Garden, 1942. d, Donald's Gold Mine, 1942. e, The Vanishing Private, 1942. f, Sky Trooper, 1942. g, Bellboy Donald, 1942. h, The New Spirit, 1942.
No. 2771, $60: a, Saludos Amigos, 1943. b, The Eyes Have It, 1945. c, Donald's Crime, 1945. d, Straight Shooters, 1947. e, Donald's Dilemma, 1947. f, Bootle Beetle, 1947. g, Daddy Duck, 1948. h, Soup's On, 1948.
No. 2772 — Story boards from Pirate Gold, horiz.: a, Pirate ship. b, Carrying treasure chest. c, Donald Duck with map. d, Donald,

souvenir shop. e, Donald following Aracuan bird. f, Angry Donald.
No. 2773, $80 — Movie posters: a, Donald's Happy Birthday, 1949. b, Sea Salts, 1949. c, Honey Harvester, 1949. d, All in a Nutshell, 1949. e, The Greener Yard, 1949. f, Slide, Donald, Slide, 1949. g, Lion Around, 1950. h, Trailer Horn, 1950.
No. 2774, $80: a, Bee at the Beach, 1950. b, Out on a Limb, 1950. c, Corn Chips, 1951. d, Test Pilot Donald, 1951. e, Lucky Number, 1951. f, Out of Scale, 1951. g, Bee on Guard, 1951. h, Let's Stick Together, 1952.
No. 2775, $80: a, Trick or Treat, 1952. b, Don's Fountain of Youth, 1953. c, Rugged Bear, 1953. d, Canvas Back Duck, 1953. e, Dragon Around, 1954. f, Grin and Bear It, 1954. g, The Flying Squirrel, 1954. h, Up a Tree, 1955.
No. 2776, Studio Fan Card, Melody Time, 1948.
No. 2777, $500, Scene from picture book of first movie, The Wise Little Hen, 1944, horiz. No. 2778, $500, Sketch for closing scene of Timber, 1941. No. 2779, $500, Donald Duck, horiz. No. 2780, $500, Studio fan card, The Three Caballeros, 1945, horiz.
Movie posters contained in No. 2780A are listed as designs for Nos. 2769-2771, 2774-2775, 2777, 2780.

**Perf. 14x13½, 13½x14**
**1993, Dec. 6** **Litho.**
**Sheets of 8, #a-h**
| 2769-2771 | A184 | Set of 3 | 28.50 | 28.50 |
| 2772 | A184 | $80 Sheet of 6, #a.-f. | 9.00 | 9.00 |

**Sheets of 8, #a-h**
| 2773-2775 | A184 | Set of 3 | 34.50 | 34.50 |

**Size: 130x104mm**
**Imperf**
| 2776 | A184 | $500 multi | 10.00 | 10.00 |

**Souvenir Sheets**
**Perf. 14x13½, 13½x14**
| 2777-2780 | A184 | Set of 4 | 40.00 | 40.00 |

**Imperf**
**Self-Adhesive**
**Size: 64x89mm**
| 2780A | A184 | $60 Set of 10 | 70.00 | |

No. 2780A exists with backing labels printed in English or French. Value is for either set. No. 2780A was printed on thin card and sold in sealed cellophane packages containing 10 stamps. To affix stamps, backing containing film information must be removed.
#2769-2771, 2773-2775 exist in sheets of 7 $5 stamps + label. The label replaces #2769f, 2770b, 2771h, 2773a, 2774d, 2775e. These sheets became available Nov. 20, 1996.

Tropical Flowers A185

Designs: $6.40, Cestrum parqui. $7.65, Brunfelsia calycina. $12.80, Datura rosei. $15.30, Ruellia macrantha. No. 2785, $50, Portlandia albiflora. $130, Pachystachys coccinea. $190, Beloperone guttata. $250, Ferdinandusa speciosa.
No. 2789, $50: a, Clusia grandiflora. b, Begonia haageana. c, Fuchsia simplicicaulis. d, Guaiacum officinale (a). e, Pithecoctenium cynanchoides. f, Sphaeralcea umbellata. g, Erythrina poeppigiana. h, Steriphoma paradoxa. i, Allemanda violacea (f). j, Centropogon cornutus (g). k, Passiflora quadrangularis. l, Victoria amazonica.
No. 2790, $50: a, Cobaea scandens. b, Pyrostegia venusta (c). c, Petrea kohautiana (b). d, Hippobroma longiflora (a). e, Cleome hassleriana (b, d, f, h, i). f, Verbena peruviana (c). g, Tropaeolum peregrinum. h, Plumeria rubra (g, i). i, Selenicereus grandiflorus. j, Mandevilla splendens (g). k, Pereskia aculeata. l, Ipomoea learii.
No. 2791, $325, Columnea fendleri. No. 2792, $325, Lophospermum erubescens.

**1994, Feb. 10** **Litho.** **Perf. 13½**
| 2781-2788 | A185 | Set of 8 | 13.75 | 13.75 |

**Sheets of 12, #a-l**
**Perf. 14**
| 2789-2790 | A185 | Set of 2 | 27.00 | 27.00 |

**Souvenir Sheets**
**Perf. 13**
| 2791-2792 | A185 | Set of 2 | 14.00 | 14.00 |

Nos. 2674-2675 Ovptd. "ROYAL VISIT FEB 19-22, 1994" in One or Two Lines
**1994** **Litho.** **Perf. 13½x14**
| 2793 | A166 | Sheet, 2 each #a.-f. | 14.00 | 14.00 |

**Souvenir Sheet**
**Perf. 14**
| 2794 | A166 | $325 multicolored | 9.00 | 9.00 |

Hummel Figurines — A186

Designs: No. 2795, $20, No. 2803a, $30, Girl holding basket and heart. No. 2796, $25, Boy holding heart. No. 2797, $35, No. 2804a, $20, Chef holding dessert. No. 2798, $50, No. 2804b, $130, Girl holding planter of mushrooms. No. 2799, $60, Girl holding plant, horn. No. 2800, $130, No. 2803b, $6, Four girls. No. 2801, $190, Two girls, boy and puppy. No. 2802, $250, No. 2804c, $35, Boy holding covered dish, puppy.

**1994, May 5** **Litho.** **Perf. 14**
| 2795-2802 | A186 | Set of 8 | 18.00 | 18.00 |

**Souvenir Sheets**
| 2803 | A186 | Sheet of 4, #a.-b, #2796, 2801 | 5.50 | 5.50 |
| 2804 | A186 | Sheet of 4, #a.-c, #2799 | 5.50 | 5.50 |

Sierra Club, Cent. A187

No. 2805 — Various animals or scenic places: a-b, American alligator. c-d, Italian Alps. e-f, Mono Lake.
No. 2806: a, Red kangaroo. b-d, Whooping crane. e-f, Alaskan brown bear. g, Bald eagle. h, Giant panda.
No. 2807, vert.: a-b, Red kangaroo. c, American alligator. d, Alaskan brown bear. e-f, Bald eagle. g-h, Giant panda.
No. 2808, vert.: a-c, Sea lion. d, Mono Lake. e, Sierra Club centennial emblem. f, Italian Alps. g-i, Matterhorn.

**1994, May 20** **Litho.** **Perf. 14**
| 2805 | A187 | $70 Sheet of 6, #a.-f. | 8.50 | 8.50 |
| 2806 | A187 | $70 Sheet of 8, #a.-h. | 11.50 | 11.50 |
| 2807 | A187 | $70 Sheet of 8, #a.-h. | 11.50 | 11.50 |
| 2808 | A187 | $70 Sheet of 9, #a.-i. | 14.50 | 14.50 |
| | | Nos. 2805-2808 (4) | 46.00 | 46.00 |

First Manned Moon Landing, 25th Anniv. A188

No. 2809, $60: a, Robert R. Gilruth, Apollo 16. b, Ernst Stuhlinger, Apollo 17. c, Christopher C. Kraft, X-30 National Aero-Space Plane. d, Rudolf Opitz, Me-163, July 24, 1943. e, Clyde W. Tombaugh, "Face on Mars." f, Hermann Oberth, Scene from "The Girl in the Moon."
No. 2810, $60: a, Werner von Braun, Apollo 11. b, Rocco A. Petrone, Apollo 11. c, Eberhard Rees, Apollo 12. d, Charles A. Berry, Apollo 13. e, Thomas O. Paine, Apollo 14. f, A.F. Staats, Apollo 15.
No. 2811, $60: a, Walter Dornberger, 1st A-4 launch. b, Rudolph Nebel, Surveyor 1. c, Robert H. Goddard, Apollo 7. d, Kurt Debus, Apollo 8. e, James T. Webb, Apollo 9. f, George E. Mueller, Apollo 10.
No. 2812, Frank J. Everest, Jr.

**1994, July 20**    Litho.    *Perf. 14*
**Sheets of 6, #a-f**
2809-2811 A188 Set of 3    22.00 22.00
**Souvenir Sheet**
2812 A188 $325 multicolored    8.50 8.50

A189

World War II — A190

Designs: $6, Photo reconnaissance Spitfire. $35, 226 Squadron B-25. $190, 76 Squadron P-47 Thunderbolts.

No. 2816 — Europe and North Africa, 1944: a, Allied landings, Anzio, Jan. 22. b, RAF bombs Amiens prison, Feb. 18. c, Sevastopol falls to Red Army, May 9. d, Allies breach Gustav Line, May 19. e, D-Day, June 6. f, V-1 attacks on London begin, June 13. g, Cease fire declared for Paris, Aug. 19. h, Germany launches V-2 rockets, Sept. 8. i, German battleship Tirpitz sunk, Nov. 12. j, Siege of Bastogne lifted, Dec. 29.

No. 2817 — D-Day: a, Paratroops drop behind enemy lines. b, Glider-born commandos land behind enemy lines. c, USS Arkansas shells Omaha beach defenses. d, Allied aircraft attack enemy movements. e, Allied landing craft hit the beach. f, Allied troops pinned down by enemy fire. g, Commandos exit landing craft. h, Specialized Allied tanks destroy enemy mines. i, Allies break through beach defenses. j, Consolidation of position.

No. 2818, RAF Lancaster bomber.

**1994, June 20**      *Perf. 14*
2813 A189 $6 multicolored    .40 .40
2814 A189 $35 multicolored    1.10 1.10
2815 A189 $190 multicolored    5.00 5.00
   Nos. 2813-2815 (3)    6.50 6.50
         *Perf. 13*
2816 A190 $60 Sheet of 10, #a.-j.    14.00 14.00
2817 A190 $60 Sheet of 10, #a.-j.    14.00 14.00
**Souvenir Sheet**
         *Perf. 14*
2818 A189 $325 multicolored    9.00 9.00

A191

Butterflies A192

Designs: $6, Heliconius melpomene. $20, Helicopius cupido. $25, Agrias claudina. $30, Parides coelus. $50, Heliconius hecale. $60, Morpho diana. $190, Dismorphia orise. $250, Morpho deidamia.

No. 2827 — a, Anaea marthesia. b, Brassolis astyra. c, Heliconius melpomene. d, Haetera piera. e, Morpho diana dixey. f, Parides coelus. g, Catagramma pitheas. h, Nessaea obrinus. i, Automeris janus. j, Papilio torquatus. k, Eunica sophonisba. l, Ceratinia nise. m, Panacea procilla. n, Pyrrhogyra neaerea. o, Morpho deidamia. p, Dismorphia orise.

No. 2829, $325, Eunica sophonisba. No. 2830, $325, Anaea eribotes.
No. 2831, $325, Hamadryas velutina. No. 2832, $325, Agrias claudina.

**1994, July 5**    Litho.    *Perf. 14*
2819-2826 A191 Set of 8    16.00 16.00
2827 A192 $50 Sheet of 16, #a.-p.    22.00 22.00

**Souvenir Sheets**
2829-2830 A191 Set of 2    15.00 15.00
2831-2832 A192 Set of 2    15.00 15.00
   Nos. 2829-2830 each contain one 43x28mm stamp.

Bible Stories — A193

No. 2833 — Story of Ruth and Naomi: a-f: Ruth & Naomi preparing to leave Moab & return to Israel. g-l: Ruth harvesting grain in fields of Boaz. m-r: Boaz receives a man's sandal, finalizing sale of Naomi's field. s-x: Naomi, Boaz, Ruth and Obed, who was David's grandfather.

No. 2834 — Story of Joseph: a-d, Jacob made Joseph a coat of many colors. e-h, Joseph's brothers take his coat and cast him into pit. i-l, Joseph is sold to the Ishmaelites. m-p, Joseph is accused by Potiphar's wife and thrown into prison. q-t, Joseph interprets Pharoah's dreams. u-x, Joseph is reunited with his brothers.

No. 2835 — Parting of the Red Sea: a-x, Moses leading Israelites through sea, Pharoah's army drowning.

No. 2836 — Daniel and the Lions: a-x, Daniel in lion's den surrounded by various animals, angel.

**1994, Aug. 4**    Litho.    *Perf. 14*
**Sheets of 24, #a-x**
2833-2836 A193 $20 Set of 4    52.00 52.00
   Nos. 2835-2836 have continuous design.

A194            A195

Philakorea '94: $6, Statues of socialist ideals, Pyongyang. $25, Statue of Adm. Yi Sun-sin. $120, Sokkat'ap Pagoda, Pulguksa. $130, Village guardian, Chejudo Island.

No. 2841, $60 — Ten-fold screens: a, Shown. b-e, Cranes. h-i, Deer. j, Deer, mushrooms, waterfall.

No. 2842, $60: b-d, Cranes. f-h, Deer. c, h, Waterfalls. i-j, Mushrooms.

No. 2843, $325, Falled Rock, horiz. No. 2844, $325, Westerners at Korean Court, horiz.

**1994, June 20**    Litho.    *Perf. 14*
2837-2840 A194 Set of 4    6.00 6.00
**Sheets of 10, #a-j**
         *Perf. 13*
2841-2842 A195 Set of 2    26.00 26.00
**Souvenir Sheets**
         *Perf. 14*
2843-2844 A194 Set of 2    14.00 14.00
   Nos. 2841-2842 have continuous design.

Entertainers of Takarazuka Revue, Japan A196

No. 2845: a, $60, Mira Anju. b, $60, Yuki Amami. c, $60, Maki Ichiro. d, $60, Yu Shion. e, $20, Miki Maya. f, $20, Fubuki Takane. g, $20, Seika Juze. h, $20, Saki Asaji.

**1994**             *Perf. 14½*
2845 A196 Sheet of 8, #a.-h. + 4 labels    9.00 9.00
   Nos. 2845a-2845d are 34x47mm.

A197

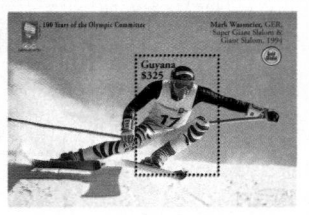

Intl. Olympic Committee, Cent. — A198

Designs: $20, Nancy Kerrigan, US, figure skating, 1994. $35, Sawao Kato, Japan, gymnastics, 1976. $130, Florence Griffith-Joyner, US, 100-, 200-meters, 1988.

$325, Mark Wasmeier, Germany, super giant & giant slalom, 1994.

**1994, June 20**
2846-2848 A197 Set of 3    4.50 4.50
**Souvenir Sheet**
2849 A198 $325 multicolored    8.00 8.00

1994 World Cup Soccer Championships, U.S. — A199

Player, country: $6, Paulo Futre, Portugal. $35, Lyndon Hooper, Canada. $60, Enzo Francescoli, Uruguay. $190, Freddy Rincon, Colombia.

No. 2854, $60: a, Paolo Maldini, Italy. b, Guyana player. c, Bwalya Kalusha, Zambia. d, Diego Maradona, Argentina. e, Andreas Brehme, Germany. f, Eric Wynalda, US.

No. 2855, $60: a, John Doyle, US. b, Eric Wynalda, US, diff. c, Thomas Dooley, US. d, Ernie Stewart, US. f, Marcelo Balboa, US. g, Coach Bora Milutinovic, US.

No. 2856, $325, 1994 World Cup program cover. No. 2857, $325, Oiler Watson.

**1994, Aug. 8**
2850-2853 A199 Set of 4    7.00 7.00
**Sheets of 6, #a-f**
2854-2855 A199 Set of 2    18.00 18.00
**Souvenir Sheets**
2856-2857 A199 Set of 2    17.00 17.00

Birds — A200

No. 2858, $35: a, Goshawk. b, Lapwing. c, Ornate umbrellabird. d, Slatey-headed parakeet. e, Regent bowerbird. f, Egytian goose. g, White-winged crossbill. h, Waxwing. i, Ruff. j, Hoopoe. k, Superb starling. l, Great jacamar.

No. 2859, $35: a, Peregrine falcon. b, Great spotted woodpecker. c, White-throated kingfisher. d, Peruvian cock-of-the-rock. e, Yellow-headed Amazon. f, Victoria crowned pigeon. g, Little owl. h, Pheasant. i, Goldfinch. j, Jay. k, Sulphur-brasted toucan. l, Japanese blue flycatcher.

No. 2860, $325, Gould's violet-ear. No. 2861, $325, Bald eagle.

**1994, Sept. 15**
**Sheets of 12, #a.-i.**
2858-2859 A200 Set of 2    22.00 22.00
**Souvenir Sheets**
2860-2861 A200 Set of 2    19.00 19.00
   PHILAKOREA '94.

1996 Summer Olympics, Atlanta — A201

**1994, Sept. 28**

German athletes: $6, Anja Fichtel, fencing, 1988, horiz. $25, Annegret Richter, 100-meter dash, 1976. $30, Heike Henkel, high jump, 1982. $35, Armin Hary, 100-meter dash, 1960. $50, Heike Drechsler, long jump, 1972. $60, Josef Neckermann, equestrian grand prix, 1968. $130, Heide Rosendahl, long jump, 1988. $190, Ulrike Mayfarth, high jump, 1984. $250, Michael Gross, swimming, 1984, horiz.

No. 2870A: b, $135, Markus Wasmeier, skiing, 1994. c, $190, Katja Seizinger, skiing, 1994.

No. 2871, $325, Franziska van Almsick, swimming, 1992. No. 2872, $325, Steffi Graf, tennis, 1992.

2862-2870 A201 Set of 9    18.00 18.00
**Souvenir Sheets**
2870A A201 Sheet of 2, #b.-c.    7.25 7.25
2871-2872 A201 Set of 2    14.50 14.50

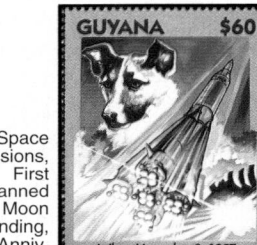

Space Missions, First Manned Moon Landing, 25th Anniv. A202

No. 2873, $60: a, Laika, first dog in space. b, Yuri Gagarin, first man in space. c, John Glenn, first American to orbit earth. d, Edward White, first American to walk in space. e, Neil Armstrong, first to step foot onto moon. f, Luna 16. g, Luna 17. h, Skylab 1. i, 1975 Apollo-Soyuz.

No. 2874, $60 — Unmanned probes: a, Mars 3, Mars. b, Mariner 10, Mercury. c, Voyager, planetary grand tour. d, Pioneer, Venus. e, Giotto, Halley's Comet. f, Megellan, Venus. g, Galileo, Jupiter. h, Ulysses, Sun. i, Cassini, Titan.

No. 2875, $325, "Buzz" Aldrin, Neil Armstrong, Michael Collins. No. 2876, $325, Pioneer 1, 2.

**1994, Nov. 10**    Litho.    *Perf. 13½*
**Sheets of 9, #a-i**
2873-2874 A202 Set of 2    26.00 26.00
**Souvenir Sheets**
2875-2876 A202 Set of 2    17.00 17.00

Steam Locomotives — A203

Designs: No. 2877, $25, South Eastern Railway #285, 1882. No. 2878, $25, West Point Foundry, 1830. No. 2879, $300, Mt. Washington Cog Railway, 1886. No. 2880, $300, Stroudley-Brighton, 1872.

No. 2881, $30: a, "John Bull," 1831. b, Stephenson, 1837. c, "Atlantic," 1832. d, Stourbridge Lion, 1829. e, Polonceau, 1854. f, Rogers, 1848. g, "Vulcan," 1858. h, "Namur," 1846.

No. 2882, $30: a, West Point Foundry, 1832. b, Sequin, 1830. c, Stephenson's Planet, 1830. d, Norris 4-2-0, 1840. e, Union

Iron Works os San Francisco, 1867. f, Andrew Jackson, 1832. g, Herald, 1831. h, Cumberland, 1845.

No. 2883, $30: a, Pennsylvania's Class K, 1880. b, Cooke, 1885. c, John B. Turner, 1867. d, Baldwin, 1871. e, Richard Trevithick, 1804. f, John Stephens, 1825. g, John Blenkinsop, 1814. h, Pennsylvania, 1803.

$250, Est Railway, 1878. $300, "Claud Hamilton," 1840.

**1994, Nov. 15** — **Perf. 14**
2877-2880  A203  Set of 4 — 15.00 15.00
**Sheets of 8, #a-h, + Label**
2881-2883  A203  Set of 3 — 19.00 19.00
**Souvenir Sheets**
2884  A203  $250 multicolored — 8.00 8.00
2885  A203  $300 multicolored — 10.00 10.00

English Touring Cricket, Cent. A204

Designs: $20, C.H. Lloyd, Guyana/West Indies, vert. $35, C.W. Hooper, Guyana/West Indies, Wisden Trophy. $60, G.A. Hick, England, Wisden Trophy.
$200, First English Team, 1895.

**1994, June 20  Litho.  Perf. 14**
2886-2888  A204  Set of 3 — 4.00 4.00
**Souvenir Sheet**
2889  A204  $200 multicolored — 6.00 6.00

Christmas A205

Paintings: $6, Joseph with the Christ Child, by Guido Reni. $20, Adoration of the Christ Child, by Girolamo Romanino. $25, Adoration of the Christ Child with St. Barbara and St. Martin, by Raffaello Botticini. $30, Holy Family, by Pompeo Girolam Batoni. $35, Flight into Egypt, by Bartolommeo Carducci. $60, Holy Family and the Baptist, by Andrea del Sarto. $120, Sacred Conversation, by Cesare de Sesto. $190, Madonna and Child with Sts. Joseph & John the Baptist, by Pontormo.
No. 2898, $325, Holy Family and St. Elizabeth and St. John the Baptist, by Francisco Primaticcio. No. 2899, $325, Presentation of Christ in the Temple, by Fra Bartolommeo.

**1994, Dec. 5  Perf. 13½x14**
2890-2897  A205  Set of 8 — 13.50 13.50
**Souvenir Sheets**
2898-2899  A205  Set of 2 — 18.00 18.00

Order of the Caribbean Community — A206

First award recipients: No. 2900, $60, Sir Shridath Ramphal, statesman, Guyana. No. 2901, $60, William Demas, economist, Trinidad & Tobago. No. 2902, $60, Derek Walcott, writer, St. Lucia.

**1994  Perf. 14**
2900-2902  A206  Set of 3 — 5.00 5.00

Motion Picture, Star Trek Generations A207

A207a

No. 2903, "Boldly Go," Starship Enterprise.
No. 2904, $100: a, Capt. Picard. b, Cmdr. Riker. c, Capt. Kirk. d, Villain with phaser. e, Kirk, Picard on horseback. f, Klingons L'rsa and B'tor. g, Kirk, Picard, diff. h, Counselor Troi. i, Picard, Lt. Cmdr. Data.
No. 2905, $100: a, Troi, Riker. b, Worf. c, Picard. d, Worf, Lt. Cmdr. LaForge. e, Sailing ship, Enterprise. f, Picard, Riker. g, Data. h, Worf. i, Dr. Crusher.
No. 2906, Like No. 2903, horiz.
$1000, Kirk and Picard.
No. 2906D: e, Capt. Picard. f, Capt. Kirk. Illustration A207a reduced.

**1994  Litho.  Perf. 13½x14**
2903  A207  $100 multicolored — 3.25 3.25
**Sheets of 9, #a-i**
2904-2905  A207  Set of 2 — 58.50 58.50
**Souvenir Sheet**
**Perf. 14x13½**
2906  A207  $500 multicolored — 12.00 12.00
**Litho. & Embossed**
**Die Cut Perf. 9**
2906C  A207a  $1000 gold & multi — 30.00 30.00
**Souvenir Sheet**
**Die Cut Perf. 9 on Outside**
2906D  A207a  $500 Sheet of 2, #e.-f. — 30.00 30.00

Issued: No. 2906C, 11/18, others 12/7. No. 2903 was issued in sheets of 9. Nos. 2906e-2906f are imperf.

Sisters of Mercy of Guyana, Cent. — A208

**1994, Dec. 12  Perf. 14**
2907  A208  $60 multicolored — 1.90 1.90

Nos. 1037a, 1097, 1099 Surcharged "ILO / 75th Anniversary / 1919-1994"
**Perfs & Printing Methods as Before**
**1994**
2907A  A91  $6 on 130c #1037a
2907B  A91  $30 on 120c #1099
2907C  A91  $35 on 120c #1097

Nos. 1063, 1098, 1120, 1123 Surcharged in Blue "CENTENARY / Sign For The / MAHDI / 1894-1994"
**Perfs. & Printing Methods as Before**
**1994**
2907D  A91  $6 on 60c #1120
2907E  A91  $20 on 200c #1063
2907F  A91  $30 on 60c #1098
2907G  A91  $35 on 60c #1123

Cricket A209

Designs: $20, Sobers congratulates Lara. $30, Brian Lara setting world record, vert. $375, Lara, Chanderpaul.
$300, Brian Lara walking under "avenue of bats," vert.

**1995, Feb. 3  Litho.  Perf. 14**
2908-2910  A209  Set of 3 — 8.25 8.25
**Souvenir Sheet**
2911  A209  $300 multicolored — 7.00 7.00

A210

A211

Babe Ruth (1895-1948) — A212

Type A211 various portraits like #2914. $2000, Portrait, Ruth holding bat, vert. Type A212 illustration reduced.

**1995, Feb. 6  Litho.  Perf. 14**
2912  A210  $65 multi — 1.40 1.40
**Self-Adhesive (#2913)**
**Size: 64x89mm (#2913)**
2913  A211  $350 Set of 12 — 70.00 70.00
**Litho. & Embossed**
**Perf. 12**
2914  A212  $1000 gold & sep 25.00
**Embossed**
2914A  A212  $2000 gold — 29.00
**Litho.**
**Perf. 14**
2915  A211  $65 Sheet of 12, #a.-l. — 14.00 14.00
**Souvenir Sheet**
2916  A211  $500 like #2912a, horiz. — 12.00 12.00

No. 2912 issued in sheets of 9. Portraits of Babe Ruth in No. 2913 are same as in No. 2915, but surrounded by gold frame, gold autograph, baseballs, and simulated perfs. No. 2913 was sold in sealed cellophane package. To affix stamps, backing containing biographical information must be removed.

Disney Characters at Work — A213

No. 2917, $30 — Animal workers: a, Veterinarian. b, Animal trainer. c, Animal psychiatrist. d, Ornithologist. e, Dog groomer. f, Herpetologist. g, Pet shop keeper. h, Park ranger. i, Aquarist.
No. 2918, $30 — Arts & crafts: a, Mickey the animator, Pluto. b, Goofy the tailor, Mickey. c, Pete the glass blower, Morty. d, Clarabelle modeling for Minnie the artist. e, Daisy sculpts Donald. f, Donald, nephews working with clay. g, Watchmakers, Chip & Dale. h, Locksmith Donald, nephews. i, Grandma Duck makes a quilt.
No. 2919, $30 — Medical group: a, Family doctor. b, Optometrist. c, Nurse. d, Psychiatrist. e, Physical therapist. f, Dentist. g, Radiologist. h, Pharmacist. i, Chiropractor.
No. 2920, $35 — Hard hat & company, vert.: a, Mickey, Pluto in truck. b, Mickey at work. c, Goofy jackhammer. d, Minnie at work. e, Forklifters. f, Construction contractor. g, Carpenter. h, Bulldozer.
No. 2921, $35 — Home services, vert.: a, Mickey, plumber. b, Mickey, paperboy. c, Huey, Dewey, Louie, moving service. d, Pete, handyman. e, Donald, newphews' house painting service. f, Goofy, washer repairman. g, Minnie, babysitter. h, Daisy cares for Grandma Duck.
No. 2922, $35 — Public service workers, vert.: a, Policeman. b, Fireman. c, Ambulance driver. d, Crossing guard. e, Museum docent. f, Census taker. g, Street maintenance workers. h, Sanitation worker.
No. 2923, $200, Goofy, zoo keeper. No. 2924, $200, Camera, Pluto, vert. No. 2925, $200, Goofy, surgeon. No. 2926, $200, Minnie, pups, tool chest. No. 2927, $200, Minnie, maid. No. 2928, $200, Horace, politician.

**1995, Feb. 23  Litho.  Perf. 13½x14**
**Sheets of 9, #a-i**
2917-2919  A213  Set of 3 — 18.00 18.00
**Sheets of 8, #a-h**
**Perf. 14x13½**
2920-2922  A213  Set of 3 — 19.00 19.00
**Souvenir Sheets**
2923-2928  A213  Set of 6 — 39.00 39.00

Nos. 2917-2922 exist in sheets of 7 or 8 $5 stamps + label. The label replaces Nos. 2917e, 2918e, 2919g, 2920h, 2921h, 2922e. These sheets became available Nov. 20, 1996.

Nos. 1022, 1033, 1045, 1061 Surcharged in Red "SALVATION / ARMY / 1895-1995"
**1995, Apr. 24  Litho.  Perf. 14**
2928A  A91  $6 on 60c #1033
2928B  A91  $20 on 60c #1045
2928C  A91  $30 on 60c #1022
2928D  A91  $35 on 60c #1061

New Year 1995 (Year of the Boar) — A214

No. 2929 — Stylized boars: a, $20. b, $30. c, $50, Facing forward. denomination LR. d, $100. f, $50, "Abundant Year of the Pig." g,

$50, "Fortunate Year of the Pig." h, $50, Facing forward, denomination LL.
$150, Face, Chinese inscriptions.

**1995, May 4    Litho.    Perf. 14½**

| | | | | |
|---|---|---|---|---|
| 2929 | A214 | Block of 4, #a.-d. | 6.00 | 6.00 |
| e. | | Souvenir sheet of 4, #c, f.-h. | 8.00 | 8.00 |

**Souvenir Sheet**

| | | | | |
|---|---|---|---|---|
| 2930 | A214 | $150 multicolored | 6.00 | 6.00 |

No. 2929 was issued in miniature sheets of 4.

A215

Birds: $5, Goshawk. $6, Lapwing. $8, Ornate umbrellabird. $15, Slatey-headed parakeet. $19, Regent bowerbird. $20, Egyptian goose. $25, White-winged crossbill. $30, Waxwing. $35, Ruff. $60, Hoopoe. $100, Superb starling. $500, Great jacamar.

**1995, May 8    Litho.    Perf. 14½x13½**

| | | | | |
|---|---|---|---|---|
| 2931 | A215 | $5 multicolored | .20 | .20 |
| 2932 | A215 | $6 multicolored | .25 | .20 |
| 2933 | A215 | $8 multicolored | .30 | .20 |
| 2934 | A215 | $15 multicolored | .40 | .25 |
| 2935 | A215 | $19 multicolored | .50 | .25 |
| 2936 | A215 | $20 multicolored | .55 | .35 |
| 2937 | A215 | $25 multicolored | .65 | .40 |
| 2938 | A215 | $30 multicolored | .75 | .45 |
| 2939 | A215 | $35 multicolored | .90 | .55 |
| 2940 | A215 | $60 multicolored | 1.10 | 1.00 |
| 2941 | A215 | $100 multicolored | 1.75 | 1.75 |
| 2942 | A215 | $500 multicolored | 8.50 | 8.00 |
| | | Nos. 2931-2942 (12) | 15.85 | 13.60 |

Nolan Ryan, Baseball Player — A216

No. 2943: a, Looking left, Mets. b, With bat, Mets. c, Pitching, Mets. d, Looking toward home plate, Angels. e, Pitching, Angels. f, Without hat, Angels. g, In red cap, Astros. h, Pitching, Astros. i, In black cap, Astros. j, Pitching, Rangers. k, Getting ready to pitch, Rangers. l, Up close, Rangers.

**1995    Litho.    Imperf.**
**Self-Adhesive**
**Size: 64x89mm**

| | | | | |
|---|---|---|---|---|
| 2943 | A216 | $350 Set of 12, #a.-l. | 70.00 | 70.00 |

Nos. 2943a-2943l are printed on thin cards, distributed in boxed sets containing certificate of aunthenticity and sealed in celophane packages. To affix stamps, backing containing biographical information must be removed.

Miniature Sheets of 12

Singapore '95 — A217

No. 2944, $35 — Dogs: a, Gordon setter. b, Long-haired chihuahua. c, Dalmation. d, Afghan. e, English bulldog. f, Miniature schnauzer. g, Clumber spaniel. h, Pekingese. i, St. Bernard. j, English cocker spaniel. k, Alaskan malamute. l, Rottweiler.
No. 2945, $35 — Cats: a, Norwegian forest cat. b, Scottish fold. c, Red burmese. d, British blue-hair. e, Abyssinian. f, Siamese. g, Exotic shorthair. h, Turkish van cat. i, Black Persian. j, Black-tipped burmilla. k, Singapura. l, Calico shorthair.
No. 2946, $35 — Horses: a, Chestnut thoroughbred colt. b, Liver chestnut quarter horse. c, Black Freisian. d, Chestnut Belgian. e, Appaloosa. f, Lipizzanas. g, Chestnut hunter. h, British shire. i, Palomino. j, Seal brown point. k, Arab. l, Afghanistan Kabardin.
No. 2947, $300, Golden retriever. No. 2948, $300, Maine coon. No. 2949, $300, American Anglo-Arab.

**1995, June 1    Perf. 14**
**Sheets of 12, #a-l**

| | | | | |
|---|---|---|---|---|
| 2944-2946 | A217 | Set of 3 | 30.00 | 30.00 |

**Souvenir Sheets**

| | | | | |
|---|---|---|---|---|
| 2947-2949 | A217 | Set of 3 | 18.00 | 18.00 |

Pocahontas
A218

No. 2950 — Characters from Disney animated film: a, Pocahontas, Meeko. b, John Smith. c, Chief Powhatan. d, Kocoum. e, Ratcliffe. f, Wiggins. g, Nakoma. h, Thomas.
No. 2951, Meeko, horiz.

**1995, June 23    Litho.    Perf. 13½x14**

| | | | | |
|---|---|---|---|---|
| 2950 | A218 | $50 Sheet of 8, #a.-h. | 17.00 | 17.00 |

**Souvenir Sheet**
**Perf. 14x13½**

| | | | | |
|---|---|---|---|---|
| 2951 | A218 | $300 multicolored | 10.00 | 10.00 |

See Nos. 2985-2990.

UN, 50th Anniv. — A219

No. 2952 — Map of: a, $35, North, South America. b, $60, Europe, Africa. c, $200, Asia, Australia.
$300, Secretary General Boutros Boutros-Ghali.

**1995, July 6    Perf. 14**

| | | | | |
|---|---|---|---|---|
| 2952 | A219 | Strip of 3, #a.-c. | 5.50 | 5.50 |

**Souvenir Sheet**

| | | | | |
|---|---|---|---|---|
| 2953 | A219 | $300 multicolored | 5.00 | 5.00 |

End of World War II, 50th Anniv. A220

No. 2954: a, P61 Black Widow. b, PT boat. c, B26 Marauder. d, Cruiser USS San Juan. e, US Gato class submarine. f, US destroyer.
No. 2955: a, Jan. 1945, Battle of Bulge is over. b, Sigfried Line is breached. c, Liberation of concentration camps. d, Operation "Manna," Allies drop food to starving Dutch. e, GIs looking for snipers at end of Italian campaign. f, Newspaper headline announces Hitler's suicide. g, Soviet tanks pour into Berlin. h, U-858, first German warship to surrender in US waters.

No. 2956, $300, Battleship, aircraft carrier. No. 2957, $300, Top of Brandenburg Gate.

**1995, July 6**

| | | | | |
|---|---|---|---|---|
| 2954 | A220 | $60 Sheet of 6, #a.-f. + label | 7.25 | 7.25 |
| 2955 | A220 | $60 Sheet of 8, #a.-h. + label | 9.50 | 9.50 |

**Souvenir Sheets**

| | | | | |
|---|---|---|---|---|
| 2956-2957 | A220 | Set of 2 | 10.00 | 10.00 |

No. 2957 contains one 57x42mm stamp.

FAO, 50th Anniv. — A221

No. 2958: a, $35, Girl carrying sack on head. b, $60, Man carrying sack, woman sorting sacks. c, $200, Woman lifting sack.
$300, Pouring from ladle into bowl.

**1995, July 6    Litho.    Perf. 14**

| | | | | |
|---|---|---|---|---|
| 2958 | A221 | Strip of 3, #a.-c. | 5.75 | 5.75 |

**Souvenir Sheet**

| | | | | |
|---|---|---|---|---|
| 2959 | A221 | $300 multicolored | 5.00 | 5.00 |

No. 2958 is a continuous design.

Rotary Intl., 90th Anniv. A222

Designs: $200, Paul Harris, Rotary emblem. $300, Old, new Rotary emblems.

**1995, July 6**

| | | | | |
|---|---|---|---|---|
| 2960 | A222 | $200 multicolored | 4.50 | 4.50 |

**Souvenir Sheet**

| | | | | |
|---|---|---|---|---|
| 2961 | A222 | $300 multicolored | 5.25 | 5.25 |

1995 Boy Scout Jamboree, Netherlands — A223

Slogan, emblem, and: $20, Campfire. $25, Scout, beach. $30, Hiking. $35, Snorkeling. $60, Natl. flag, scout salute. $200, Fishing from boat.
No. 2968, $300, Canoeing. No. 2969, $300, Camping.

**1995, July 6**

| | | | | |
|---|---|---|---|---|
| 2962-2967 | A223 | Set of 6 | 7.00 | 7.00 |

**Souvenir Sheets**

| | | | | |
|---|---|---|---|---|
| 2968-2969 | A223 | Set of 2 | 10.00 | 10.00 |

Queen Mother, 95th Birthday A224

No. 2970: a, Drawing. b, Violet hat. c, Formal portrait. d, Green blue hat.
$325, As younger woman.

**1995, July 6    Perf. 13½x14**

| | | | | |
|---|---|---|---|---|
| 2970 | A224 | $100 Strip or block of 4, #a.-d. | 8.25 | 8.25 |

**Souvenir Sheet**

| | | | | |
|---|---|---|---|---|
| 2971 | A224 | $325 multicolored | 7.00 | 7.00 |

No. 2970 issued in sheets of 2.
Sheets of Nos. 2970 and 2971 exist with black border in margin with text "In Memoriam/1900-2002."

Holidays of the World A225

No. 2972: a, Thanksgiving, US. b, Christmas, Germany. c, Hanukkah, Israel. d, Easter, Spain. e, Carnivale, brazil. f, Bastill Day, France. g, Independence Day, India. h, St. Patrick's Day, Ireland.
$300, Chinese New Year, China.

**1995, Aug. 8    Litho.    Perf. 14**

| | | | | |
|---|---|---|---|---|
| 2972 | A225 | $60 Sheet of 8, #a.-h. | 9.75 | 9.75 |

**Souvenir Sheet**

| | | | | |
|---|---|---|---|---|
| 2973 | A225 | $300 multicolored | 5.00 | 5.00 |

Marine Life A226

No. 2974, vert: a, Cocoa damselfish. b, Sergeant major. c, Beau gregory. d, Yellowtail damselfish.
No. 2975: a, $30, Butterflyfish. b, $35, Bluehead. c, $60, Yellow damselfish. d, $200, Clown wrasse.
No. 2976: a, $30, Lemon shark. b, $35, Green turtle. c, $60, Sawfish. d, $200, Stingray.
No. 2977, $60: a, Tiger shark. b, Needlefish. c, Horse-eye jack. d, Princess parrotfish. e, Yellowtail snapper. f, Spotted snake eel. g, Trunkfish. h, Cherubfish. i, French angelfish.
No. 2978, $60: a, Sei whale. b, Barracuda. c, Mutton snapper. d, Hawksbill turtle. e, Spanish hogfish. f, Queen angelfish. g, Porkfish. h, Trumpetfish. i, Electric ray.
No. 2979, $300, Carcharodon carcharias. No. 2980, $300, Dermochelys coriacea.

**1995, Sept. 5    Litho.    Perf. 14**

| | | | | |
|---|---|---|---|---|
| 2974 | A226 | $80 Strip of 4, #a.-d. | 6.00 | 6.00 |

**Sheets of 4, #a-d**

| | | | | |
|---|---|---|---|---|
| 2975-2976 | A226 | Set of 2 | 12.00 | 12.00 |

**Sheets of 9, #a-i**

| | | | | |
|---|---|---|---|---|
| 2977-2978 | A226 | Set of 2 | 26.00 | 26.00 |

**Souvenir Sheets**

| | | | | |
|---|---|---|---|---|
| 2979-2980 | A226 | Set of 2 | 16.00 | 16.00 |

No. 2974 was issued in sheets of 4.

Miniature Sheets of 8

1996 Summer Olympics, Atlanta — A227

No. 2981 $60: a, Shot put. b, Relay. c, Balance beam. d, Cycling. e, Synchronized swimming. f, Hurdles. g, Pommel horse. h, Discus thrower, head down.
No. 2982, $60: a, Pole vault. b, Long jump. c, Track. d, Wrestling. e, Discus thrower, head up. f, Basketball. g, Boxing. h, Weight lifting.
No. 2983, $300, Long jump. No. 2984, $300, Runners.

**1995, Oct. 2**    **Litho.**    *Perf. 14*
**Sheets of 8, #a-h**
2981-2982 A227 Set of 2    16.00 16.00
**Souvenir Sheets**
2983-2984 A227 Set of 2    10.00 10.00

### Pocahontas Type of 1995
#### Miniature Sheets

Nos. 2985-2987: Various scenes from Disney animated picture, horiz.
No. 2988, $325, Pocahontas behind tree branch, horiz. No. 2989, Pocahontas, Powhatan, horiz. No. 2990, $325, Pocahontas kneeling.

*Perf. 14x13½, 13½x14 (#2990)*
**1995, Oct. 9**       **Litho.**
2985 A218 $8 Sheet of 9,
    #a.-i.    3.50 3.50
2986 A218 $30 Sheet of 9,
    #a.-i.    11.50 11.50
2987 A218 $35 Sheet of 9,
    #a.-i.    15.00 15.00

**Souvenir Sheets**
2988-2990 A218 Set of 3    32.50 32.50

Fauna — A228

No. 2991: a, $35, House martin. b, $60. Hobby. c, $20, Sand martin (a). d, $200, Long-tailed skua (b).
No. 2992: a, Olive colobus. b, Violet-backed starling. c, Diana monkey. d, African palm civet. e, Giraffe, zebras. f, African linsang. g, Royal antelope (fawn). h, Royal antelope (adult, fawn) (g, i). i, Palm squirrel.
No. 2993, $300, Brush pig. No. 2994, $300, Chimpanzee.

**1995, Oct. 18**    **Litho.**    *Perf. 14*
2991 A228 Block of 4, #a.-d.    7.00 7.00
2992 A228 $60 Sheet of 9,
    #a.-i.    9.00 9.00
**Souvenir Sheets**
2993-2994 A228 Set of 2    10.00 10.00
No. 2991 was issued in sheets of 16 stamps.

Queenstown Holy Mosque, Georgetown, Cent. — A229

**1995, Dec. 1**    **Litho.**    *Perf. 14*
2995 A229 $60 multicolored    1.00 1.00

Christmas
A230

Details or entire paintings, by Carracci: $25, The Angel of Annunciation. $30, Annunciation of the Virgin. $35, Assumption of the Virgin. $60, Baptism of Christ. $100, Madonna and Child. $300, Birth by the Virgin.
No. 3002, $325, Madonna and Ten Saints, by Fiorentino. No. 3003, $325, Mystical Marriage of St. Catherine, by Carracci.

**1995, Dec. 4**      *Perf. 13½x14*
2996-3001 A230 Set of 6    9.25 9.25
**Souvenir Sheets**
3002-3003 A230 Set of 2    11.00 11.00

Guyana Defense Force, 30th Anniv. — A231

**1995, Dec. 7**        *Perf. 14*
3004 A231 $6 Woman with gun    .20 .20
3005 A231 $60 Man with gun    .90 .90

John Lennon
(1940-80) — A232

**1995**
3006 A232 $35 multicolored    1.00 1.00
No. 3006 was issued in sheets of 16.

Nobel Prize Fund Established, Cent. — A233

No. 3007, $35: a, Henri Becquerel, physics, 1903. b, Igor Tamm, physics, 1958. c, Georges Köhler, medicine, 1984. d, Gerhard Domagk, medicine, 1939. e, Yasunari Kawabata, literature, 1968. f, Maurice Allais, economics, 1988. g, Aristide Briand, peace, 1926. h, Pavel Cherenkov, physics, 1958. i, Feodor Lynen, medicine, 1964.
No. 3008 $35: a, Adolf von Baeyer, chemistry, 1905. b, Hideki Yukawa, physics, 1949. c, George W. Beadle, medicine, 1958. d, Edwin M. McMillian, chemistry, 1951. e, Samuel C.C. Ting, physics, 1976. f, Saint-John Perse, literature, 1960. g, John F. Enders, medicine, 1954. h, Felix Bloch, physics, 1952. i, P.B. Medawar, medicine, 1960.
No. 3009, $35: a, Albrecht Kossel, medicine, 1910. b, Arthur H. Compton, physics, 1927. c, N.M. Butler, peace, 1931. d, Charles Laveran, medicine, 1907. e, George R. Minot, medicine, 1934. f, Henry H. Dale, medicine, 1936. g, Jacques Monod, medicine, 1965. h, Alfred Hershey, medicine, 1969. i, Pär Lagerkvist, literature, 1951.
No. 3010, $35: a, Francis Crick, medicine, 1962. b, Manne Siegbahn, physics, 1924. c, Eisaku Sato, peace, 1974. d, Robert Koch, medicine, 1905. e, Edgar D. Adrian, medicine, 1932. f, Erwin Neher, medicine, 1991. g, Henry Taube, chemistry, 1983. h, Norman Angell, peace, 1933. i, Robert Robinson, chemistry, 1947.
No. 3011, $35: a, Nikolai Basov, physics, 1964. b, Klas Arnoldson, peace, 1908. c, René Sully-Prudhomme, literature, 1901. d, Robert W. Wilson, physics, 1978. e, Hugo Theorell, medicine, 1955. f, Nelly Sachs, literature, 1966. g, Hans von Euler-Chelpin, chemistry, 1929. h, Mairead Corrigan, peace, 1976. i, Willis E. Lamb, Jr, physics, 1955.
No. 3012 $35: a, Norman F. Ramsey, physics, 1989. b, Chen Ning Yang, physics, 1957. c, Earl W. Sutherland, Jr., medicine, 1971. d, Paul Karrer, chemistry, 1937. e, Harmut Michel, chemistry, 1988. f, Richard Kuhn, chemistry, 1938. g, P.A.M. Dirac, physics, 1933. h, Victor Grignard, chemistry, 1912. i, Richard Willstätter, chemistry, 1915.
No. 3013, $300, Le Duc Tho, peace, 1973. No. 3014, $300, Yasunari Kawabata, literature, 1968. No. 3015, $300, Heinrich Böll, literature, 1972. No. 3016, $300, Henry Kissinger, peace, 1973. No. 3017, $300, Kenichi Fukui, chemistry, 1981. No. 3018, $300, Lech Walesa, peace, 1983.

**1995, Dec. 20**    **Litho.**    *Perf. 14*
**Sheets of 9, #a-i**
3007-3012 A233 Set of 6    57.00 57.00
**Souvenir Sheets**
3013-3018 A233 Set of 6    36.00 36.00

Caribbean Development Bank, 25th Anniv. — A234

**1995, Dec. 29**    **Litho.**    *Perf. 14*
3019 A234 $60 multicolored    1.00 1.00

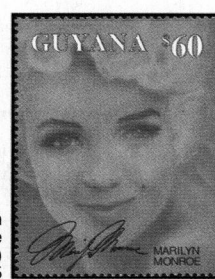

Marilyn Monroe (1926-62) A235

No. 3020, Various portraits. No. 3021, Portrait, horiz.

**1995, Dec. 29**      *Perf. 13½x14*
3020 A235 $60 Sheet of 9, #a.-
    i.    9.00 9.00
**Souvenir Sheet**
*Perf. 14x13½*
3021 A235 $300 multicolored    5.00 5.00

David Copperfield, Magician A236

Nos. 3022-3023, Various portraits, magic acts.

**1995, Dec. 29**      *Perf. 13½x14*
3022 A236 $60 Sheet of 9,
    #a.-i.    10.00 10.00
**Souvenir Sheet**
3023 A236 $300 multicolored    5.00 5.00

New Year 1996 (Year of the Rat) — A237

No. 3024 — Stylized rats: a, $20. b, $30. c, $50, light brown & multi. d, $100.
No. 3025: a, Like #3024a, b, Like #3024b. c, Like #3024c, darker brown & multi. d, Like #3024d.
No. 3026, Rat facing forward.

**1996, Jan. 2**       *Perf. 14½*
3024 A237 Block of 4, #a.-d.    4.00 4.00
**Miniature Sheet**
3025 A237 $50 Sheet of 4, #a.-
    d.    3.50 3.50
**Souvenir Sheet**
3026 A237 $150 multicolored    3.50 3.50
No. 3024 was issued in sheets of 16 stamps.

UNICEF, 50th Anniv. A238

No. 3027: a, Children, building in background. b, Man, boy, tree in background. c, Children behind tree. d, Man, children.

**1996, Jan. 2**       *Perf. 14*
3027 A238 $1100 Sheet of 4,
    #a.-d.    70.00 70.00
No. 3027 is a continuous design.

Paintings by Peter Paul Rubens A239

Details or entire paintings: $6, The Garden of Love. $10, Two Sleeping Children. $20, All Saints Day. $25, Sacrifice of Abraham. $30, The Last Supper. $35, The Birth of Henry of Navarre. $40, Standing Female Saint Study. $50, $60, The Garden of Love, each diff. No. 3037, $200, The Martyrdom of St. Livinus. No. 3038, $200, Der Heilige Franz Von Paula. $300, The Union of Maria de Medici and Henry IV.
No. 3039, $325, The Three Crosses. No. 3040, $325, Decius Mus Addressing the Legions, horiz. No. 3041, $325, Triumph of Henry IV, horiz.

**1996, Jan. 29**    **Litho.**    *Perf. 14*
3028-3038A A239 Set of 11    19.00 19.00
**Souvenir Sheets**
3039-3041 A239 Set of 3    18.50 18.50
Nos. 3039-3041 each contain one 57x85mm or 85x57mm stamp.

### Miniature Sheets

A240

Prehistoric Animals — A241

No. 3042: a, Tarbosaurus. b, Hadrosaurus. c, Polacanthus. d, Psittacosaurus. e, Ornitholestes. f, Yangchuanosaurus. g, Scelidosaurus. h, Kentrosaurus. i, Coelophysis. j, Lesothosaurus. k, Plateosaurus. l, Staurikosaurus.
No. 3043, $35: a, Eudimorphodon. b, Criorynchus. c, Elasmosaurus. d, Rhomaleosaurus. e, Ceresiosaurus. f, Mesosaurus. g, Grendelius. h, Nothosaurus. i, Mixosaurus. j, Placodus. k, Coelacanth. l, Mosasaurus.
No. 3044, $35: a, Ornithomimus. b, Pteranodon. c, Rhamphorynchus. d, Ornitholestes. e, Brachiosaurus. f, Parasaurolophus. g, Ceratosaurus. h, Camarasaurus. i, Euoplocephalus. j, Scutellosaurus. k, Compsognathus. l, Stegoceras.
No. 3045, $35: a, Apatosaurus. b, Archaeopteryx. c, Dimorphodon. d, Deinonychus. e, Coelophysis. f, Tyrannosaurus. g, Triceratops. h, Anatosaurus. i, Saltasaurus. j, Allosaurus. k, Oviraptor. l, Stegosaurus.
No. 3046, $60: a, Heterodontosaurus (b). b, Compsognathus (c). c, Ornithomimus (b).

No. 3047, $60: a, Saurolophus. b, Muttaburrasaurus (a). c, Dicraeosaurus (b).
No. 3048, $300, Apatosaurus, allosaurus, horiz. No. 3049, $300, Tyrannosaurus rex.
No. 3050, $300, Quetzalcoatlus. No. 3051, $300, Lagosuchus. No. 3052, $300Struthiomimus.

**1996, Feb. 12**
| | | | | |
|---|---|---|---|---|
| 3042 | A240 | $35 Sheet of 12, | | |
| | | #a.-l. | 8.00 | 8.00 |

**Sheets of 12, #a-l**
| | | | | |
|---|---|---|---|---|
| 3043-3045 | A241 | Set of 3 | 24.00 | 24.00 |

**Sheets of 3, #a-c**
| | | | | |
|---|---|---|---|---|
| 3046-3047 | A240 | Set of 2 | 7.00 | 7.00 |

**Souvenir Sheets**
| | | | | |
|---|---|---|---|---|
| 3048-3049 | A240 | Set of 2 | 12.00 | 12.00 |
| 3050-3052 | A241 | Set of 3 | 18.00 | 18.00 |

Pandas — A242

No. 3053 — In tree: a, Lying on back, looking right. b, Arms, legs around branch. c, Paws holding onto tree. d, Sitting, looking left.
No. 3054 — On rocks by stream: a, Standing. b, Sitting, holding bamboo stick. c, Holding bamboo to mouth. d, Lying on stomach.

**1996, Apr. 12    Litho.    Perf. 14**
| | | | | |
|---|---|---|---|---|
| 3053 | A242 | $60 Sheet of 4, #a.-d. | 5.00 | 5.00 |
| 3054 | A242 | $60 Sheet of 4, #a.-d. | 5.00 | 5.00 |

China '96, 9th Asian Intl. Philatelic Exhibtion.

Mushrooms, Insects and Coral — A243

Designs: $20, Yellow morce, leaf beetle. $25, Green spored mushroom. $30, Leaf beetle, common mushroom. $35, Monarch caterpillars, pine cone mushroom.
No. 3059, $60: a, Green-beaded jelly club. b, Aspic puffball. c, Stalkless paxillus. d, Stout-stalked amanita.
No. 3060, $60: a, Fly agaric. b, Graying yellow russula, click beetle. c, Netted stinkhorn, housefly. d, Butterfly hunter, strophania.
No. 3061, $60: a, Cockle-shell lentinus. b, Parasitic volvariella. c, Deadly lepiota. d, Shaggy-stalked boleta.
No. 3062: a, Armillauella mellea. b, Sealy vase chanterelle. c, Bitter pholiota. d, Flute white helvella. e, Fading scarlet waxy cap. f, Jask's lantern. g, Hygzocybe acutoconica. h, Mycena viscosa.
No. 3063, $300, Orange mycena. No. 3064, $300, Violet-branched coral, Red raspberry slime, Yellow-tipped coral, horiz.

**1996, May 3    Litho.    Perf. 14**
| | | | | |
|---|---|---|---|---|
| 3055-3058 | A243 | Set of 4 | 3.50 | 3.50 |

**Strips of 4, #a-d**
| | | | | |
|---|---|---|---|---|
| 3059-3061 | A243 | Set of 3 | 13.50 | 13.50 |
| 3062 | A243 | $60 Sheet of 8, #a.-h. | 9.00 | 9.00 |

**Souvenir Sheets**
| | | | | |
|---|---|---|---|---|
| 3063-3064 | A243 | Set of 2 | 11.50 | 11.50 |

Nos. 3059-3061 were issued in sheets of 8 stamps.

Deng Xiaoping, Chinese Communist Leader — A244

No. 3065: a, Painting inscription. b, With dignitaries, waving. c, Signing autograph. d, Waving.
$300, Wearing white shirt, vert.

**1996    Perf. 13**
| | | | | |
|---|---|---|---|---|
| 3065 | A244 | $30 Strip or block of 4, #a.-d. | 2.00 | 2.00 |

**Souvenir Sheet**
| | | | | |
|---|---|---|---|---|
| 3066 | A244 | $300 multicolored | 5.00 | 5.00 |

No. 3065 issued in sheets of 16 stamps.

Queen Elizabeth II, 70th Birthday A245

No. 3067: a, Portrait wearing blue dress. b, Wearing blue green dress, hat. c, On throne, opening Parliament.
$325, In ceremonial attire.

**1996, May 3    Litho.    Perf. 13½x14**
| | | | | |
|---|---|---|---|---|
| 3067 | A245 | $100 Strip of 3, #a.-c. | 5.00 | 5.00 |

**Souvenir Sheet**
| | | | | |
|---|---|---|---|---|
| 3068 | A245 | $325 multicolored | 5.25 | 5.25 |

No. 3067 was issued in sheets of 9 stamps, with each strip having a different order.

Jerusalem, 3000th Anniv. — A246

No. 3069: a, $30. The Hulda Gates. b, $35, Old City, View from Mt. of Olives. c, $200, Absalom's Memorial, Kidron Valley. $300, Children's Memorial.

**1996    Litho.    Perf. 14**
| | | | | |
|---|---|---|---|---|
| 3069 | A246 | Sheet of 3, #a.-d. | 5.00 | 5.00 |

**Souvenir Sheet**
| | | | | |
|---|---|---|---|---|
| 3070 | A246 | $300 multicolored | 5.00 | 5.00 |

Birds — A247

No. 3071: a, Blue & yellow macaw. b, Andean condor. c, Crested eagle. d, White-tailed trogon. e, Toco toucan. f, Great horned owl. g, Andean cock-of-the-rock. h, Great curassow.
No. 3071I — Hummingbirds: j, Long-billed starthroat. k, Velvet-purple coronet. l, Racket-tailed coquette. m, Violet-tailed sylph. n,

Broad-tailed hummingbird. o, Blue-tufted starthroat. p, White-necked jacobin. q, Ruby-throated hummingbird.
No. 3072, Ornate hawk eagle, horiz. No. 3073, Gould's violet-ear.

**1996, July 10**
| | | | | |
|---|---|---|---|---|
| 3071 | A247 | $60 Sheet of 8, #a.-h. | 7.50 | 7.50 |
| 3071I | A247 | $60 Sheet of 8, #j.-q. | 7.50 | 7.50 |

**Souvenir Sheets**
| | | | | |
|---|---|---|---|---|
| 3072 | A247 | $300 multicolored | 5.50 | 5.50 |
| 3073 | A247 | $300 multicolored | 5.50 | 5.50 |

Radio, Cent. A248

Entertainers: $20, Frank Sinatra. $35, Gene Autry. $60, Groucho Marx. $200, Red Skelton. $300, Burl Ives.

**1996, July 25**
| | | | | |
|---|---|---|---|---|
| 3074-3077 | A248 | Set of 4 | 5.00 | 5.00 |

**Souvenir Sheet**
| | | | | |
|---|---|---|---|---|
| 3078 | A248 | $300 multicolored | 5.00 | 5.00 |

1996 Summer Olympic Games, Atlanta A249

Designs: $20, Pancratium. $30, Olympic Stadium, 1956. $60, Leonid Spirin, 20k walk, 1956, vert. $200, Lars Hall, modern pentathlon, 1952, 1956, vert.
No. 3083, $50, vert.: a, Florence Griffith-Joyner. b, Ines Geissler. c, Nadia Comaneci. d, Tatiana Gutsu. e, Olga Korbut. f, Barbara Krause. g, Olga Bryzgina. h, Fanny Blankers-Koen. i, Irena Szewinska.
No. 3084, $50, vert.: a, Gerd Wessig. b, Jim Thorpe. c, Norman Read. d, Lasse Viren. e, Milt Campbell. f, Abebe Bikila. g, Jesse Owens. h, Viktor Saneev. i, Waldemer Cierpinski.
No. 3085, $50, vert.: a, Ditmar Schmidt. b, Pam Shriver. c, Zina Garrison. d, Hyun Jung-Hua. e, Steffi Graf. f, Michael Jordan. g, Karch Kiraly. h, "Magic" Johnson. i, Ingolf Weigert.
No. 3086, $50: a, Volleyball. b, Basketball. c, Tennis. d, Table tennis. e, Baseball. f, Handball. g, Field hockey. h, Water polo. i, Soccer.
No. 3087, $50, vert.: a, Cycling. b, Hurdles. c, High jump. d, Diving. e, Weight lifting. f, Canoeing. g, Wrestling. h, Gymnastics. i, Running.
No. 3088, $300, Carl Lewis, track and field gold medalist. No. 3089, $300, US defeats Korea for gold medal in baseball, 1988.

**1996, July 25**
| | | | | |
|---|---|---|---|---|
| 3079-3082 | A249 | Set of 4 | 5.00 | 5.00 |

**Sheets of 9, #a-i**
| | | | | |
|---|---|---|---|---|
| 3083-3087 | A249 | Set of 5 | 35.00 | 35.00 |

**Souvenir Sheets**
| | | | | |
|---|---|---|---|---|
| 3088-3089 | A249 | Set of 2 | 9.75 | 9.75 |

Olymphilex '96 (#3088).

Disney Cartoons — A250

No. 3090 — Mickey outdoors: a, Mickey's Bait Shop. b, Ol' Mickey, The Lumbercamp Legend and Pluto the Yellow Dog. c, For All Men Are Equal Before Fish.

No. 3091, vert. — Super sports: a, BMX Championships. b, Goofy, Hockey Superstar. c, Malibu Surf City.
No. 3092, vert. — Nautical Mickey: a, The Path to Adventure is Shown in the Stars. b, Captain Mickey's Steamship School. c, Ahoy, Follow the Wind on Waves of Fortune.
No. 3093, $250, M. Mouse, ESQ, Lawman, vert.: No. 3094, $250, All Aboard, Ride the Great American Transcontinental Railroad. No. 3095, $250, Mouse and Pinkerton, Wild West Detective Agency, vert.
$300, Donald's Rock & Ice Mountaineers. $325, Guided by The Great Spirit, vert.

**1996, July 26    Perf. 14x13½, 13½x14**
| | | | | |
|---|---|---|---|---|
| 3090 | A250 | $60 Strip of 3, #a.-c. | 4.50 | 4.50 |
| 3091 | A250 | $80 Strip of 3, #a.-c. | 6.00 | 6.00 |
| 3092 | A250 | $100 Strip of 3, #a.-c. | 8.50 | 8.50 |

**Souvenir Sheets**
| | | | | |
|---|---|---|---|---|
| 3093-3095 | A250 | Set of 3 | 22.50 | 22.50 |
| 3096 | A250 | $300 multi | 7.50 | 7.50 |
| 3097 | A250 | $325 multi | 8.50 | 8.50 |

Nos. 3090-3092 were issued in sheets of 9 stamps.

Disney Antique Toys — A251

No. 3098: a, Two-Gun Mickey. b, Wood-jointed Mickey doll. c, Donald Jack-in-the Box. d, Rocking Minnie. e, Fireman Donald Duck. f, Long-billed Donald Duck. g, Painted wood Mickey doll. h, Wind-up Jiminy Cricket.
No. 3099, $300, Mickey doll. No. 3100, $300, Carousel train.

**1996, July 26    Perf. 13½x14**
| | | | | |
|---|---|---|---|---|
| 3098 | A251 | $6 Sheet of 8, #a.-h. | 7.00 | 7.00 |

**Souvenir Sheets**
| | | | | |
|---|---|---|---|---|
| 3099-3100 | A251 | Set of 2 | 18.00 | 18.00 |

Elvis Presley's First "Hit" Year, 40th Anniv. A252

Various portraits.

**1996, Sept. 8    Litho.    Perf. 13½x14**
| | | | | |
|---|---|---|---|---|
| 3101 | A252 | $100 Sheet of 6, #a.-f. | 11.00 | 11.00 |

Domestic Cats A253

No. 3102, $60: a, Birman. b, American curl. c, Turkish Angora. d, European shorthair. e, Persian. f, Scottish fold. g, Sphynx. h, Malayan. i, Cornish rex.
No. 3103, $60, vert: a, Norwegian forest. b, Russian shorthair. c, European shorthair. d, Birman. e, Ragdoll. f, Egyptian mau. g, Persian. h, Angora. i, Siamese.
No. 3104, $300, Maine coon, vert. No. 3105, $300, Himalayan.

**1996, Sept. 18**      **Perf. 14**
**Sheets of 9, #a-i**
3102-3103 A253   Set of 2    19.00 19.00
**Souvenir Sheets**
3104-3105 A253   Set of 2    11.00 11.00

Deep Ocean Exploration — A254

No. 3106: a, Goblin shark, coelacanth. b, Remote operated vehicle, JASON. c, Deep water invertebrates. d, Submarine NR1 (e). e, Giant squid (b, c, f, g, h, j, m). f, Sperm whale (b, c). g, Volcanic vents, submersible ALVIN. h, Air-recycling pressure suit, shipwreck. i, Bacteria survey, submersible SHINKAI 6500. j, Giant tube worms. k, Anglerfish. l, Six-gill shark (k). m, Autonomous underwater vehicle ABE. n, Viperfish. o, Swallower, hatchetfish.
$300, Sea anemone.

**1996, Dec. 2**    **Litho.**     **Perf. 14**
3106 A254   $30 Sheet of 15,
         #a.-o.         7.50 7.50
**Souvenir Sheet**
3107 A254   $300 multicolored   5.25 5.25

Characters from Disney's Snow White in Christmas Scenes A255

Designs: $6, Snow White. $20, Doc. $25, Dopey, Sneezy. $30, Sleepy, Happy, Bashful. $35, Dopey, Santa. $60, Dopey, fireplace. $100, Dopey, Grumpy. $200, Dopey as Santa. No. 3116, $300, Snow White looking at squirrel in box. No. 3117, $300, Dopey placing star on tree.

**1996, Dec. 16**      **Perf. 13½x14**
3108-3115 A255   Set of 8    17.50 17.50
**Souvenir Sheets**
3116-3117 A255   Set of 2    22.00 22.00

Marine Life A256

No. 3118: a, Red gorgonians. b, Plexaura homomalla, butterflyfish (a, c). c, Dendronephtbya. d, Common clownfish, anemone, mushroom coral (a). e, Anemone, horse-eyed jack (d, g-h). f, Slender snappers (c), splendid coral trout. g, Anemones. h, Brain coral, Indo-Pacific hard coral. i, Cup coral (f, h).

**1996, Dec. 2**    **Litho.**     **Perf. 14**
3118 A256   $60 Sheet of 9, #a.-i.   9.00 9.00

New Year 1997 (Year of the Ox) — A257

No. 3119 — Denomination at: a, $20, LR. b, $30, LL. c, $35, UR. d, $50, UL.
No. 3120: a, Like #3119a. b, Like #3119b. c, Like #3119c.
$150, Ox, facing.

**1997, Jan. 2**   **Litho.**    **Perf. 14½**
3119 A257   Block of 4, #a.-d.   3.75 3.75
3120 A257   $50 Sheet of 4, #a.-
        c. + #3119d      4.00 4.00
**Souvenir Sheet**
3121 A257   $150 multicolored   3.00 3.00
No. 3119 was issued in sheets of 16 stamps.

Mickey and Friends Celebrate Chinese Lunar New Year — A258

No. 3122: a, $6, Mickey. b, $20, Home visit. c, $25, Fortune lantern. d, $30, Silhouette. e, $35, Flower market. f, $60, Harmonious man, woman.
No. 3123: a, Red-pocket money. b, Lion dance. c, Calligraphy. d, Surplus every year. e, Fireworks. f, Ox.
$150, Mickey marching, vert. $200, Mickey, ox.

**1997, Jan. 2**      **Perf. 14x13½**
3122 A258   Sheet of 6, #a.-
        f.           4.75 4.75
3123 A258   $30 Sheet of 6, #a.-
        f.           5.25 5.25
**Souvenir Sheets**
**Perf. 13½x14, 14x13½**
3124 A258   $150 multicolored   5.00 5.00
3125 A258   $200 multicolored   5.50 5.50

Marine Life A259

No. 3126, $6, Angelfish. No. 3127, $6, Hyed snapper. $20, Box fish. $25, Golden damselfish. $35, Clown triggerfish. $200, Harlequin tuskfish.
$300, Caribbean flower coral.

**1996**     **Litho.**     **Perf. 14**
3126-3131 A259   Set of 6    6.50 6.50
**Souvenir Sheet**
3132 A259   $300 multicolored   5.75 5.75

Hotel Tower, 50th Anniv. — A260

**1996, Dec. 28**
3133 A260   $30 multicolored   1.00 1.00

Souvenir Sheet

The Summer Palace, Beijing — A261

Illustration reduced.

**1996, Apr. 12**   **Litho.**    **Perf. 13**
3134 A261   $60 multicolored   2.00 2.00
China '96. No. 3134 was not available until March 1997.

Transfer of Hong Kong — A262

No. 3135, $80: a, Tortoise. b, Dragon. c, Unicorn. d, Phoenix.
No. 3136, $80, vert.: a, Swallow & willow. b, Kingfisher & chrysanthemum. c, Crane & pine. d, Peacock & peony.
No. 3137, $80, vert.: a-d, Various kites.
No. 3138, vert.: a-b, Paintings of mountains and lakes.

**1997, Feb. 12**      **Perf. 14**
**Sheets of 4 , #a-d**
3135-3137 A262   Set of 3    15.00 15.00
3138 A262   $200 Sheet of 2,
        #a.-b.        6.00 6.00
Hong Kong '97. No. 3138 contains two 70x44mm stamps.

Motion Pictures, Cent. A263

No. 3139 — Movie star, World War II films: a, Burgess Meredith, "The Story of GI Joe." b, M.E. Clifton-James, "I Was Monty's Double." c, Audie Murphy, "To Hell and Back." d, Gary Cooper, "The Story of Dr. Wassell." e, James Mason, "The Desert Fox." f, Manart Kippen, "Mission to Moscow." g, Robert Taylor, "Above and Beyond." h, James Cagney, "The Gallant Hours." i, John Garfield, "Pride of the Marines."
$300, George C. Scott, "Patton," horiz.

**1997, Feb. 21**      **Perf. 13½x14**
3139 A263   $50 Sheet of 9,
        #a.-i.       10.00 10.00
**Souvenir Sheet**
**Perf. 14x13½**
3140 A263   $300 multicolored   9.00 9.00

Pres. John F. Kennedy (1917-63) — A264

**1997, Mar. 14**   **Litho.**    **Perf. 14**
3141 A264   $50 blue     1.25 1.25

George Washington A265

Designs from works of art: No. 3142: a, Washington in battle. b, Washington taking oath. c, Washington Seated in Armchair, from engraving after Chappel. d, Col. Washington of Virginia Militia, by Charles W. Peale. e, George Washington, by Rembrandt Peale. f, Washington Addressing Constitutional Convention, by Junius Brutus Stearns. g, Washington on His Way to the Continental Congress. h, Washington on a White Charger, by

John Faed. i, Washington as a Surveyor, from an engraving by G.R. Hall after Darley's drawing. j, Bas-relief of Washington Praying at Valley Forge. k, Death of Gen. Mercer at Battle of Princeton, by John Trumbull. l, Washington Taking Command of the Continental Army at Cambridge. m, George Washington, by Gilbert Stuart.
No. 3143: a, Washington Before the Battle of Trenton, by John Trumbull. b, Washington, His Family at Mt. Vernon, by Alonzo Chappel. c, Inauguration of Washington in New York City, by Chappel. d, Washington, by Adolph Ulrich Wertmuller. e, Washington Accepts His Commission as Commander-in-Chief, June 1775, Currier & Ives lithograph. f, Washington from a mezzotint by Sartain. g, On the Lawn at Mt. Vernon after the War. h, Washington Conversing with a Farmhand During the Baling Season with Nelly and Washington Custus Playing Nearby, from anonymous print after Junius Brutus Stearns. i, Nellie Custis' Wedding on Washington's Last Birthday, by Ogden. j, Washington Crossing the Delaware, by Leutze. k, Washington Receives Orders from Mortally Wounded Gen. Braddock at 1755 Battle of Monongahela. l, Washington Birthplace (supposed) on the Potomac, Currier & Ives lithograph. m, Washington at Yorktown, by James Peale.

**1997, Mar. 14**   **Litho.**    **Perf. 14**
3142     Sheet of 13    17.50 17.50
  *a.-l.*   A265 $60 any single   1.00 1.00
  *m.*    A265 $300 imperf.    5.00 5.00
3143     Sheet of 13    17.50 17.50
  *a.-l.*   A265 $60 any single   1.00 1.00
  *m.*    A265 $300 imperf.    5.00 5.00
Nos. 3142m, 3143m are each 66x91mm and have simulated perforations.
No. 3142m exists perf. 14½.

Mushrooms A266

Designs: $6, Morchella hortensis. $20, Boletus chyrsenteron. $25, Hygrophorus agathosmus. $30, Cortinarius violaceus. $35, Acanthocystis geogenius. $60, Mycena polygramma. $80, Hebeloma radicosum. $300, Coprinus comatus.
No. 3152, $80: a, Coprinus picaceus. b, Stropharia umbonatescens. c, Paxillus involutus. d, Amanita inaurata. e, Lepiota rhacodes. f, Russula amoena.
No. 3153, $80: a, Volvaria volvacea. b, Psalliota augusta. c, Tricholoma aurantium. d, Pholiota spectabilis. e, Cortinarius armillatus. f, Agrocybe dura.
No. 3154, $300, Pholiota mutabilis. No. 3155, $300, Amanita muscaria.

**1997, Apr. 2**   **Litho.**    **Perf. 14**
3144-3151 A266   Set of 8   10.50 10.50
**Sheets of 6, #a-f**
3152-3153 A266   Set of 2   16.00 16.00
**Souvenir Sheets**
3154-3155 A266   Set of 2   10.00 10.00

Flowers — A267

Designs: No. 3156, $6, Pineapple lily. No. 3157, $6, Blue columbine. $20, Petunia. $25, Lily of the Nile. $30, Bird of Paradise. $35, African daisy. $60, Cape daisy. $80, Gazania. $100, Cape water lily. $200, Insigne lady's slipper.
No. 3166: a, Monarch supperwart. b, Passion flower. c, Butterfly iris. d, Red-hot poker. e, Dir. G.T. Moore water lily. f, Superbissima painted tongue. g, Orchid. h, Annual chrysanthemum.
No. 3167: a, Tulips. b, Liatris. c, Roses. d, Gerber daisies. e, Sunflowers. f, Chrysanthemums.
No. 3168, Petunia.

**1997, Apr. 2**

| | | | | |
|---|---|---|---|---|
| 3156-3165 | A267 | Set of 10 | 9.00 | 9.00 |
| 3166 | A267 | $60 Sheet of 8, #a.-h. | 8.50 | 8.50 |
| 3167 | A267 | $80 Sheet of 6, #a.-f. | 8.50 | 8.50 |

**Souvenir Sheet**

| | | | | |
|---|---|---|---|---|
| 3168 | A267 | $300 multicolored | 5.00 | 5.00 |

Deng Xiaoping (1904-97) — A268

Illustration reduced.

**1997, May 1**

| | | | | |
|---|---|---|---|---|
| 3169 | A268 | $100 shown | 1.75 | 1.75 |

**Souvenir Sheet**

| | | | | |
|---|---|---|---|---|
| 3170 | A268 | $150 Portrait, diff. | 2.75 | 2.75 |

No. 3169 was issued in sheets of 3.

UNESCO, 50th Anniv. — A269

Designs: $20, Horyu-Ji, Japan. $25, Scandola Nature Reserve, France. $30, Great Wall Defenses, China. $35, Wurzburg, Germany. $60, Monastery of Batalha, Portugal. $200, Dubrovnik, Croatia.

No. 3177, $60, vert. — Sites in Germany: a, Cathedral of Aquisgran, Aachen. b, Cathedral at Trier. c, Column of Augusta Treveror, Trier. d, f, Residences, Wurzburg. e, Church interior, Wurzburg. g, House of the River at Inselstadt, Bamberg. h, Cathedral interior, Speyer.

No. 3178, $60, Sites in Greece, vert: No. 3178: a, Monastery of Thessaloniki. b, d, e, Monastery at Mystras. c, Church of Santa Sofia, Thessaloniki. f, City, Thessaloniki. g, Painting, Mystras. h, Museum of Byzantine Art, Thessaloniki.

No. 3179, $60, vert.: a, Monastery of Poblet Catalonia, Spain. b, Old City of Salamanca, Spain. c, Toledo, Spain. d, Cathedral of Florence, Italy. e, Tower of Pisa, Italy. f, g, h, Convent of Christ, Tomar, Portugal.

No. 3180, $80 — Sites in Japan: a, d, e, Horyu-Ji. b, c, Kyoto.

No. 3181, $80 — Sites in the Americas: a, Cuzco, Peru. b, Potosi, Bolivia. c, Fortress, San Lorenzo, Panama. d, Sangay Natl. Park, Ecuador. e, Los Glaciares Natl. Park, Argentina.

No. 3182, $80 — Sites in US: a, Monticello. b, Yosemite Natl. Park. c, Yellowstone Natl. Park. d, Olympic Natl. Park. e, Everglades.

No. 3183, $300, Mount Taishan Shrine, China. No. 3184, $300, Monastery of Batalha, Portugal. No. 3185, $300, Bamberg Cathedral (detail), Germany. No. 3186, $300, Monastery, Mount Athos, Greece.

**1997, May 20**

| | | | | |
|---|---|---|---|---|
| 3171-3176 | A269 | Set of 6 | 6.00 | 6.00 |

**Sheets of 8, #a-h + Label**

| | | | | |
|---|---|---|---|---|
| 3177-3179 | A269 | Set of 3 | 22.50 | 22.50 |

**Sheets of 5**

| | | | | |
|---|---|---|---|---|
| 3180-3182 | A269 | Set of 3 | 17.50 | 17.50 |

**Souvenir Sheets**

| | | | | |
|---|---|---|---|---|
| 3183-3186 | A269 | Set of 4 | 18.50 | 18.50 |

Queen Elizabeth II, Prince Philip, 50th Wedding Anniv. A270

No. 3187: a, Queen. b, Royal Arms. c, Wedding portrait. d, Queen, Prince. e, Broadlands House. f, Prince Philip.
$300, Queen Elizabeth II.

**1997, May 20**      Litho.     Perf. 14

| | | | | |
|---|---|---|---|---|
| 3187 | A270 | $60 Sheet of 6, #a.-f. | 7.00 | 7.00 |

**Souvenir Sheet**

| | | | | |
|---|---|---|---|---|
| 3188 | A270 | $300 multicolored | 5.50 | 5.50 |

Paintings, by Hiroshige (1797-1858) A271

No. 3189: a, Oumayagashi. b, Ryogoku Ekoin & Moto-Yanagibashi Bridge. c, Pine of Success and Oumayagashi Asakusa River. d, Fireworks at Ryogoku. e, Dyers' Quarter, Kanda. f, Cotton-goods Lane, Odenma-cho.
No. 3190, $300, Suruga-cho. No. 3191, $300, Yatsukoji, inside Sujikai Gate.

**1997, May 20**     Perf. 13½x14

| | | | | |
|---|---|---|---|---|
| 3189 | A271 | $80 Sheet of 6, #a.-f. | 6.75 | 6.75 |

**Souvenir Sheets**

| | | | | |
|---|---|---|---|---|
| 3190-3191 | A271 | Set of 2 | 10.00 | 10.00 |

Heinrich von Stephan (1831-97), Founder of UPU A272

No. 3192: a, Frieze of Roman post service. b, UPU emblem. c, Cable car, Boston, 1907. $300, Von Stephan, Egyptian messenger.

**1997, May 20**     Litho.     Perf. 14

| | | | | |
|---|---|---|---|---|
| 3192 | A272 | $100 Sheet of 3, #a.-c. | 8.00 | 8.00 |

**Souvenir Sheet**

| | | | | |
|---|---|---|---|---|
| 3193 | A272 | $300 multicolored | 9.00 | 9.00 |

PACIFIC 97.

Paul P. Harris (1868-1947), Founder of Rotary, Intl. — A273

Designs: $200, Health, hunger and humanity, portrait of Harris. $300, Mutual respect among all faiths, races and cultures.

**1997, May 20**

| | | | | |
|---|---|---|---|---|
| 3194 | A273 | $200 multicolored | 2.75 | 2.75 |

**Souvenir Sheet**

| | | | | |
|---|---|---|---|---|
| 3195 | A273 | $300 multicolored | 4.25 | 4.25 |

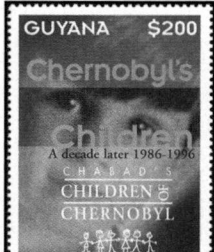

Chernobyl Disaster, 10th Anniv. A274

Designs: No. 3196, Chabad's Children of Chernobyl. No. 3197, UNESCO.

**1997, May 20**     Perf. 13½x14

| | | | | |
|---|---|---|---|---|
| 3196 | A274 | $200 multicolored | 3.00 | 3.00 |
| 3197 | A274 | $200 multicolored | 3.00 | 3.00 |

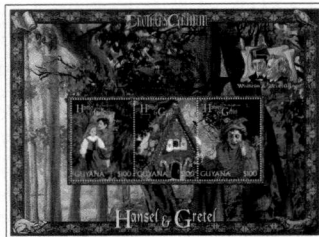

Grimm's Fairy Tales — A275

Mother Goose — A276

Scenes from "Hansel & Gretel:" No. 3198: a, Hansel & Gretel in forest. b, Gingerbread house. c, Wicked witch. $500, Witch trying to capture Gretel, horiz.
$300, Rooster from "Cock-A-Doodle-Doo."

**1997, May 20**     Perf. 13½x14

| | | | | |
|---|---|---|---|---|
| 3198 | A275 | $100 Sheet of 3, #a.-c. | 5.50 | 5.50 |

**Souvenir Sheets**
**Perf. 14, 14x13½**

| | | | | |
|---|---|---|---|---|
| 3199 | A276 | $300 multicolored | 5.00 | 5.00 |
| 3200 | A275 | $500 multicolored | 8.25 | 8.25 |

US Pres. Bill Clinton's Visit to Caribbean, May 1997 — A277

Designs: $30, Guyana Pres. Cheddi Jagan, Pres. Clinton, map of Caribbean, vert. $100, Clinton, Jagan, flags of US, Guyana, palm trees, beach.

**Perf. 13½x14, 14x13½**
**1997, June 23**

| | | | | |
|---|---|---|---|---|
| 3201 | A277 | $30 multicolored | .50 | .50 |
| 3202 | A277 | $100 multicolored | 1.50 | 1.50 |

Nos. 3201-3202 each issued in sheets of 9. See Nos. 3237-3238.

1998 Winter Olympic Games, Nagano

A278            A279

Medalists: $30, Georg Thoma. $35, Katja Seizinger. $60, Georg Hackl. $200, Katarina Witt.

No. 3207, $60: a, Gunda Niemann, 3000- & 5000-m speed skating, 1992. b, Tony Nash,

Robin Dixon, 2-man bobsled, 1964. c, Switzerland 4-man bobsled, 1988. d, Piet Kleine, speed skating, 1976.

No. 3208, $60: a, Oksana Baiul, figure skating, 1994. b, Cathy Turner, 500-m short track speed skating, 1994. c, Brian Boitano, figure skating, 1988. d, Nancy Kerrigan, figure skating, 1994.

No. 3209: a, Markus Wasmeier. b, Jens Weissflog. c, Erhard Keller. d, Rosi Mittermaier. e, Gunda Niemann. f, Peter Angerer.

No. 3210, Swiss 4-Man bobsled team.

No. 3211, $300, Jean-Claude Killy, slalom, 1968. No. 3212, $300, Chen Lu, figure skating, 1992.

**1997, July 1**         Perf. 14

| | | | | |
|---|---|---|---|---|
| 3203-3206 | A278 | Set of 4 | 4.75 | 4.75 |

**Strips or Blocks of 4, #a-d**

| | | | | |
|---|---|---|---|---|
| 3207-3208 | A279 | Set of 2 | 12.00 | 12.00 |
| 3209 | A278 | $30 Sheet of 6, #a.-f. | 3.00 | 3.00 |

**Souvenir Sheets**

| | | | | |
|---|---|---|---|---|
| 3210 | A278 | $300 multicolored | 6.00 | 6.00 |
| 3211-3212 | A279 | Set of 2 | 12.00 | 12.00 |

Nos. 3207-3208 issued in sheets of 8 stamps.

**Souvenir Sheet**

Return of Hong Kong to China — A280

**Litho. & Embossed**
**1997, July 1**         Perf. 14

| | | | | |
|---|---|---|---|---|
| 3213 | A280 | $500 gold & multi | 7.50 | 7.50 |

Domestic Cats A281

Designs, vert.: $30, Norwegian forest cat. $35, Oriental spotted tabby. $200, Asian smoke.

No. 3217: a, Abyssinian. b, Chocolate colorpoint shorthair. c, Silver tabby. d, Persian. e, Maine coon cat & kitten. f, Brown shaded Burmese. g, Persian kitten. h, Siamese. i, British shorthair.
$300, Manx, vert.

**1997, July 29**

| | | | | |
|---|---|---|---|---|
| 3214-3216 | A281 | Set of 3 | 4.25 | 4.25 |
| 3217 | A281 | $60 Sheet of 9, #a.-i. | 8.50 | 8.50 |

**Souvenir Sheet**

| | | | | |
|---|---|---|---|---|
| 3218 | A281 | $300 multi | 5.50 | 5.50 |

Birds A282

Designs: $25, Verdin. $30, Wood thrush, vert. $60, Rofous-sided towhee. $200, Pygmy nuthatch, vert.

No. 3223, $80: a, Groove-billed ani. b, Green honeycreeper. c, Toucanet. d, Wire-tailed manakin. e, Hoatzin. f, Tiger heron.

No. 3224, $80 — Hummingbirds: a, Magenta-throated woodstar. b, Long-tailed hermit. c, Red-footed plumeleteer. d, Anna's. e, White-tipped sicklebill. f, Fiery-throated.

No. 3225, $300, Pinnated bittern. No. 3226, $300, Keel-billed toucan.

**1997, Aug. 12    Litho.    Perf. 14**
3219-3222 A282 Set of 4         5.00  5.00

**Sheets of 6, #a-f**
3223-3224 A282 Set of 6        15.00 15.00

**Souvenir Sheets**
3225-3226 A282 Set of 2        11.00 11.00

Dogs — A283

Designs: $20, Chihuahua. $25, Norfolk terrier. $60, Welsh terrier.
No. 3230: a, Shar-pei. b, Chihuahua. c, Chow chow. d, Sealyham terrier. e, Collie. f, German shorthair pointer. g, Bulldog. h, German shepherd. i, Old English sheepdog.
$300, Tibetan spaniel.

**1997, July 29    Litho.    Perf. 14**
3227-3229 A283 Set of 3         2.25  2.25
3230 A283 $60 Sheet of 9, #a.-
             i.                  8.50  8.50

**Souvenir Sheet**
3231 A283 $300 multicolored     5.50  5.50

Pres. Cheddi Jagan's 1st Election to Parliament, 50th Anniv. — A284

**1997, Oct. 6    Litho.    Perf. 14**
3232 A284 $6 green & multi       .20   .20
3233 A284 $30 pale yellow &
             multi              4.25  4.25

Nos. 3232-3233 each issued in sheets of 9.

Diana, Princess of Wales (1961-97) — A285

No. 3234: a-f, Various portraits.
No. 3235, $300, Wearing red dress. No. 3236, $300, With longer hair.

**1997, Oct. 15**
3234 A285 $80 Sheet of 6,
             #a.-f.            8.25  8.25

**Souvenir Sheets**
**Perf. 14½**
3235-3236 A285 Set of 2       10.00 10.00

Nos. 3235-3236 each contain one 34x52mm stamp.

US Pres. Bill Clinton's Visit Type of 1997

Designs: $6, Like #3201. No. 3238, Clinton, Jagan, flags, sun on horizon.

**Perf. 13½x14, 14x13½**
**1997, Nov. 10**
3237 A277 $6 multi               .20   .20
3238 A277 $30 multi              .50   .50

Nos. 3237-3238 each issued in sheets of 9.

Souvenir Sheets

Chinese Pres. Jiang Zemin's Visit to New York — A286

Pres. Zemin, New York skyline, and: $200, Flags of China, UN, US. $300, Flags of China, US.

**1997, Nov. 10    Perf. 14**
3239 A286 $200 multicolored     3.00  3.00
3240 A286 $300 multicolored     4.50  4.50

Buildings in Guyana — A287

**1997, Dec. 8    Litho.    Perf. 14**
3241 A287 $6 W. Fogarty #1       .20   .20
3242 A287 $30 Public building    .60   .60

Christmas A288

Entire paintings, details, or sculptures: $24, $30, Diff. angels from The Triumph of Galatea, by Raphael. $35, Primavera, by Botticelli. $60, Angel Musicians, by Agostino di Duccio, (bas relief). $100, From cover of Life Magazine, #1212, 1906. $200, Madonna and Saints, by Rosso Fiorentino.
No. 3249, $300, The Gardens of Love, by Rubens. No. 3250, $300, Cherubs, by Philippe de Champaigne.

**1997, Dec. 8**
3243-3248 A288 Set of 6         7.50  7.50

**Souvenir Sheets**
3249-3250 A288 Set of 2        12.00 12.00

Historical Events A289

Designs: No. 3251, $60, Explorers discover tomb of Tutankhamun, 1922. No. 3252, $60, Lincoln Memorial dedicated, Washington, DC, 1922. No. 3253, $60, Alexander Graham Bell dies, 1922. No. 3254, $60, Calvin Coolidge becomes President, 1923. No. 3255, $60, John L. Baird develops 1st experimental television, 1923. No. 3256, $60, Warren G. Harding dies, 1923. No. 3257, $60, First Winter Olympic Games, Chamonix, France, 1924. No. 3258, $60, Tennessee bans teaching of evolution in schools, 1925. No. 3259, $60, Chinese leader Sun Yat-Sen dies, 1925. No. 3260, $60, Robert Goddard launches 1st liquid fuel rocket, 1926. No. 3261, $60, Richard E. Byrd is 1st to fly over North Pole, 1926. No.

3262, $60, Sesquicentennial Exposition, Philadelphia, 1926.

**1997. Dec. 8**
3251-3262 A289 Set of 12       12.50 12.50

New Year 1998 (Year of the Tiger) — A290

No. 3263 — Various stylized tigers with denomination in: a, LR. b, LL. c, UR. d, UL. $150, Tiger, red background.

**1998, Jan. 5    Litho.    Perf. 14½**
3263 A290 $50 Sheet of 4, #a.-
             d.                 2.75  2.75

**Souvenir Sheet**
3264 A290 $150 multicolored     2.10  2.10

Prehistoric Wildlife — A291

Designs: $25, Kentrosaurus. $30, Lesothosaurus. $35, Stegoceras. $60, Lagosuchus. $100, Herrerasaurus. $200, Iguanodon.
No. 3271, $55: a, Quetzalcoatlus (d). b, Pteranodon (a, c). c, Peteinosaurus. d, Criorhychus (g). e, Pterodaustro. f, Eudimorphodon. g, Archeopteryx. h, Dimorphodon. i, Sharovipteryx.
No. 3272, $55: a, Ceresiosaurus. b, Nothosaurus. c, Rhomaleosaurus. d, Grendelius. e, Mixosaurus. f, Mesosaurus. g, Placodus. h, Stethacanthus. i, Coelacanth.
No. 3273, $300, Styracosaurus, vert. No. 3274, $300, Yangchuanosaurus, vert.

**1998, Feb. 23    Litho.    Perf. 14**
3265-3270 A291 Set of 6         7.00  7.00

**Sheets of 9, #a-i**
3271-3272 A291 Set of 2        16.00 16.00

**Souvenir Sheets**
3273-3274 A291 Set of 2         8.50  8.50

1998 World Cup Soccer Championships, France — A292

Group A: No. 3275, $30, Brazil. No. 3276, $30, Morocco. No. 3277, $30, Norway. No. 3278, $30, Scotland.
Group B: No. 3279, $30, Austria. No. 3280, $30, Cameroun. No. 3281, $30, Chile. No. 3282, $30, Italy.
Group C: No. 3283, $30, Denmark. No. 3284, $30, France. No. 3285, $30, Saudi Arabia. No. 3286, $30, South Africa.
Group D: No. 3287, $30, Bulgaria. No. 3288, $30, Nigeria. No. 3289, $30, Paraguay. No. 3290, $30, Spain.
Group E: No. 3291, $30, Belgium. No. 3292, $30, Holland. No. 3293, $30, S. Korea. No. 3294, $30, Mexico.
Group F: No. 3295, $30, Germany. No. 3296, $30, Iran. No. 3297, $30, US. No. 3298, $30, Yugoslavia.
Group G: No. 3299, $30, Colombia. No. 3300, $30, England. No. 3301, $30, Romania. No. 3302, $30, Tunisia.
Group H: No. 3303, $30, Argentina. No. 3304, $30, Croatia. No. 3305, $30, Jamaica. No. 3306, $30, Japan.
Japanese players, vert.: No. 3306A, $300, Okada. No. 3306B, $300, Nakata.

**1998, Apr. 8    Litho.    Perf. 14x13½**
3275-3306 A292 Set of 32       14.00 14.00

**Perf. 13½x14**
**Souvenir Sheets**
3306A-
3306B       A292 Set of 2       8.50  8.50

Nos. 3275-3306 were each issued in sheets of 8 + 1 label.
For overprints see Nos. 3317-3324.

The Titanic A293

No. 3307: a, J. Bruce Ismay, managing director, White Star Line. b, Jack Phillips, radio operator. c, Margaret "Unsinkable Molly" Brown, passenger. d, Capt. Edward J. Smith. e, Frederick Fleet, lookout. f, Thomas Andrews, managing director of Harland and Wolff.
$300, Titanic sinking.

**1998, June 17    Litho.    Perf. 14**
3307 A293 $80 Sheet of 6, #a.-
             f.                 6.75  6.75

**Souvenir Sheet**
3308 A293 $300 multicolored     4.25  4.25

Sailing Ships A294

No. 3309, $80: a, Viking double-ended ship, 14th cent. b, Portuguese caravel. c, "Nina." d, Fannie, 1896. e, "Victoria," 1519. f, Arab samboke.
No. 3310, $80: a, "Dutch Fluyt." b, "Alastor." c, "Falcon." d, "Red Rover." e, "British Anglesey." f, "Archibald Russel."
No. 3311, $300, Oseberg ship. No. 3312, $300, "Half Moon," 1609.

**1998, June 17    Litho.    Perf. 14**
**Sheets of 6, #a-f**
3309-3310 A294 Set of 2        13.50 13.50

**Souvenir Sheets**
3311-3312 A294 Set of 2         8.50  8.50

Diana, Princess of Wales (1961-97) — A295

Designs: No. 3313, $1500, Diana in black and brown fur trimmed hat and coat. No. 3314, $1500, Diana wearing suit and hat.

**Litho. & Embossed**
**1998, Aug. 3    Die Cut 7½**
3313-3314 A295 $1500 Set of
             2                  150.00

Queen
Mother
A296

**1998, Aug. 4**                          **Perf. 13½**
3315 A296 $90 multicolored                  1.40 1.40

CARICOM, 25th Anniv. — A297

**1998, July 4    Litho.    Perf. 13½**
3316 A297 $20 multicolored        .40 .40

Nos. 3275, 3282-3286, 3289, 3304
Ovptd. "FRANCE WINNERS" in Gold

**1998, Aug. 20    Litho.    Perf. 14x13½**
3317    A292 $30 on #3275    .45    .45
3318    A292 $30 on #3282    .45    .45
3319    A292 $30 on #3283    .45    .45
3320    A292 $30 on #3284    .45    .45
3321    A292 $30 on #3285    .45    .45
3322    A292 $30 on #3286    .45    .45
3323    A292 $30 on #3289    .45    .45
3324    A292 $30 on #3304    .45    .45
   *Nos. 3317-3324 (8)*         3.60 3.60

Nos. 3317-3324 were each issued in sheets
of 8+label. Each sheet contains additional
overprints in sheet margins.

National Hockey League
Players — A298

No. 3325: a, Bryan Berard. b, Ray Bourque.
c, Martin Brodeur. d, Pavel Bure. e, Chris Che-
lios. f, Sergei Fedorov. g, Peter Forsberg. h,
Wayne Gretzky. i, Dominik Hasek. j, Brett Hull.
k, Jarome Iginla. l, Jaromir Jagr. m, Paul
Kariya. n, Saku Koivu. o, John LeClair. p,
Brian Leetch. q, Eric Lindros. r, Patrick Mar-
leau. s, Mark Messier. t, Mike Modano. u,
Chris Osgood. v, Zigmund Palffy. w, Felix
Potvin. x, Jeremy Roenick. y, Patrick Roy. z,
Joe Sakic. aa, Sergei Samsonov. ab, Teemu
Selanne. ac, Brendan Shanahan. ad, Ryan
Smyth. ae, Jocelyn Thibault. af, Joe Thornton.
ag, Keith Tkachuk. ah, John Vanbiesbrouck.
ai, Steve Yzerman. aj, Dainius Zubrus.

**1998, Apr. 1    Litho.    Perf. 13½**
3325 A298 $35 Sheet of 36,
       #a.-aj.                18.00 18.00

Aircraft
A299

No. 3326, $80 — Military aircraft: a, A7K
Corsair II. b, A6E Intruder. c, U2 Spy plane. d,
Blackhawk. e, F-16. f, Phantom II.
No. 3327, $80 — Pioneers of aviation: a,
Wright Brothers, 1903. b, Bleriot, 1911. c, Cur-
tiss Jenny, 1919. d, Airship Schwaben, 1911.
e, W-8B, 1923. f, DH-66, 1926.
No. 3328, $300, A-10 Warthog. No. 3329,
$300HH-65A Dolphin.

---

**1998, Sept. 28**                        **Perf. 14**
**Sheets of 6, #a-f**
3326-3327 A299  Set of 2    13.50 13.50
**Souvenir Sheets**
3328-3329 A299  Set of 2    8.50 8.50

Endangered
Species — A300

Nos. 3330, $80, 3332, $300, Various pictures of the giant panda.
Nos. 3331, $80, 3333, $300, Various pictures of the mountain gorilla.

**1998, Oct. 8**
**Sheets of 6, a-f**
3330-3331 A300  Set of 2    14.00 14.00
**Souvenir Sheets**
3332-3333 A300  Set of 2    8.75 8.75

Donald Duck Adventures, Christmas
on Bear Mountain — A301

No. 3334 — Cartoon panels: a, 1-8. b, 9-16.
c, 17-24. d, 25-32. e, 33-40. f, 41-48. g, 49-56.
h, 57-64. i, 65-72. j, 73-80. k, Pane of 2, Carl
Barks, vert., bears and duck.
   Illustration reduced.

**1998, Oct. 15    Perf. 14x13½, 13½x14**
3334    Complete booklet    45.00 45.00
   *a.-j.* A301 $35 Any pane of 4    2.75    2.75
   *k.* A301 $300 Pane of 2    10.00 10.00

Disney's Uncle Scrooge, by Carl Barks,
50th anniv.

Organization
of American
States, 50th
Anniv.
A302

**1998, Oct. 29**                        **Perf. 14**
3335 A302 $40 multicolored      .55 .55

Ferrari Automobiles — A302a

No. 3335A: c, 212 Export. d, 410 Super-
america chassis. e, 125 S.
$300, 512 S Racer.
   Illustration reduced.

**1998, Oct. 29    Litho.    Perf. 14**
3335A   A302a $100 Sheet of 3,
       #c-e                    5.00 5.00
**Souvenir Sheet**
3335B   A302a $300 multi       5.00 5.00
No. 3335A contains three 39x25mm stamps.

---

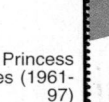

Diana, Princess
of Wales (1961-
97)
A303

**1998, Oct. 29**
3336    A303 $60 multicolored    1.00 1.00
**Self-Adhesive**
*Serpentine Die Cut Perf. 11½*
**Sheet of 1**
**Size: 53x65mm**
3336A   A303 $300 Diana, build-
       ings, bridge    65.00

No. 3336 was issued in sheets of 6.
Soaking in water may affect the multi-layer
image of No. 3336A.
Issued: $60, 10/29; $300, 11/5/98.

Grand Prix Champion Racing Cars
and Drivers—A304 — 3337

No. 3337, $80: a, 1914 Grand Prix Merce-
des, Christian Lautenschlager. b, 1930 Bugati
Type 35B, P. Etancelin. c, 1934 Alfa Romeo
P3, Louis Chiron. d, 1938 Mercedes Benz
W154, Richard Seaman. e, 1938 Auto Union
D Type, Tazio Nuvolari. f, 1951 Alfa Romeo
158, Juan Manuel Fangio.
No. 3338, $80: a, 1955 Mercedes Benz
W196, Stirling Moss. b, 1960 Ferrari Dino 246,
Phil Hill. c, 1966 Brabham-Repco BT19, Jack
Brabham. d, 1970 Lotus Ford 72, John Miles.
e, 1983 Renault RE40, Alain Prost. f, 1998
McLaren Mercedes MP4/13, David Coulthard.
No. 3339, $300, 1906 Grand Prix Renault,
Ferenc Szisz. No. 3340, $300, 1956 Maserati
250F, Stirling Moss.

**1998, Oct. 29**
**Sheets of 6, #a-f**
3337-3338 A304  Set of 2    13.50 13.50
**Souvenir Sheets**
3339-3340 A304  Set of 2    8.50 8.50
Nos. 3339-3340 contain one 57x42mm
stamp.

Tigger's Happy New Year — A304a

No. 3340A, vert. — Tigger: d, Giving gift to
Winnie the Pooh. e, With fireworks. f, Giving
flowers to Kanga. g, With Piglet. h, At door. i,
With Eeyore.
No. 3340B, $300, Tigger beating drum. No.
3340C, $300, Tigger carrying staff for dragon.

**1998, Oct. 29    Litho.    Perf. 13¼**
3340A   A304a $60 Sheet of 6, #a-
       f                        5.75 5.75
**Souvenir Sheets**
3340B-3340C A304a  Set of 2    8.50 8.50

---

Gandhi — A305

No. 3341: a, Age 37, 1906. b, Age 77, 1946.
c, Age 78, 1948. d, Age 77, 1947.
$300, Age 76, 1946, horiz.

**1998, Oct. 29**
3341 A305 $100 Sheet of 4, #a.-
       d.                       5.50 5.50
**Souvenir Sheet**
3342 A305 $300 multicolored    4.25 4.25
No. 3341b-3341c are each 53x38mm.

Pablo
Picasso
A306

Paintings, details: $25, Sleeping Peasants,
1919. $60, Large Nude in Red Armchair,
1929, vert. $200, Sculpture, "Female Head,"
1931, vert.
$300, Man and Woman, 1971, vert.

**1998, Oct. 29**                        **Perf. 14½**
3343-3345 A306  Set of 3    4.00 4.00
**Souvenir Sheet**
3346 A306 $300 multicolored    4.50 4.50

Royal Air
Force,
80th
Anniv.
A307

No. 3347, $100: a, Avro Lancaster B2. b,
PBY-5A Catalina Amphibian. c, BAe Hawk TIA
trainers (Red Arrows). d, Avro Lancaster,
DeHavilland Mosquito.
No. 3348, $100: a, BAe Hawk TIA. b, C130
Hercules. c, Panavia Tornado GRI. d, BAe
Hawk 200.
No. 3349, $150: a, BAe Nimrod RIP. b,
Panavia Tornado F3 ADV. c, CH-47 Chinook
helicopter. d, Panavia Tornado GRIA.
No. 3350, $200, Biplane, hawks in flight. No.
3351, $200, Eurofighter, Spitfire. No. 3352,
$300, Eurofighters. No. 3353, $300, Head of
hawk, hawk spreading wings, biplane. No.
3354, $300, Tiger Moth, Eurofighter. No.
3355, $300, Hawk spreading wings, biplane.

**1998, Oct. 29**                        **Perf. 14**
**Sheets of 4, #a.-d.**
3347-3349 A307  Set of 3    20.00 20.00
**Souvenir Sheets**
3350-3355 A307  Set of 6    22.50 22.50

1998 World Scout Jamboree,
Chile — A308

No. 3356: a, James E. West, 1st scout executive with early Eagle Scouts. b, Pres. Kennedy greets Explorers, 51st Scouts anniv.,
1961. c, Astronaut Walter Schirra receives a
special merit badge, 1962.

**1998, Oct. 29    Litho.    Perf. 14**
3356    A308 $160 Sheet of 3, #a.-
       c.                       7.00 7.00

Paintings by Eugene Delacroix (1798-1863) A309

No. 3357, $60: a, The Sultan of Morocco Receives the Count de Mornay. b, Armed Indian with a Gurkha Scimitar. c, Portrait presumed to be of the Singer Baroihet in Turkish Dress. d, Moroccan Notebook: Studies of Jewish Women. e, Arab Horseman Giving a Signal. f, Arab Cavalry Practicing a Charge. g, A Seated Moor. h, Jewish Woman in Traditional Dress.

No. 3358, $60: a, Corner of the Studio; the Stove. b, Room in the Apartment the Count de Mornay. c, Hamlet and Horatio in the Graveyard. d, George Sand. e, The Bride of Abydos. f, Elysian Fields. g, A Lioness Standing by a Tree. h, Monsieur Alfred Bruyas.

No. 3359, $300, Moroccan Jewish Wedding, horiz. No. 3360, $300, Death of Sardanapulus, horiz.

**1998, Oct. 29**
**Sheets of 8, #a-h.**
3357-3358  A309  Set of 2      13.50  13.50
**Souvenir Sheets**
3359-3360  A309  Set of 2       8.50   8.50

St. Andrew's Church, Georgetown, 180th Anniv. — A310

Various views of front of church: $6, $30, $60.

**1998**          **Litho.**       **Perf. 14**
3361-3363  A310  Set of 3       1.25   1.25

New Year 1999 (Year of the Rabbit) — A311

No. 3364 — Various stylized rabbits with denomination at: a, LR. b, LL. c, UR. d, UL. $150, Red background, Chinese inscription.

**1999, Jan. 4**    **Litho.**     **Perf. 14½**
3364  A311  $50 Sheet of 4, #a-d.      3.00   3.00
**Souvenir Sheet**
3365  A311  $150 multicolored         2.25   2.25

Disney Characters in Sporting Activities A312

No. 3366, $80 — Skateboarding: a, Huey. b, Mickey. c, Dewey. d, Louie. e, Goofy. f, Donald.
No. 3367, $80 — Rollerblading: a, Minnie. b, Goofy. c, Daisy. d, Baby Duck. e, Donald. f, Mickey.
No. 3368, $80 — Skateboarding, rollerblading, red, white & blue background:: a, Baby

Duck. b, Daisy. c, Mickey. d, Goofy. e, Dewey. f, Donald.
No. 3369, $300, Dewey. No. 3370, $300, Daisy. No. 3371, $300, Goofy, horiz.

**Perf. 13½x14, 14X13½**
**1999, Mar. 1**    **Litho.**
**Sheets of 6, #a-f**
3366-3368  A312  Set of 3      25.00  25.00
**Souvenir Sheets**
3369-3371  A312  Set of 3      18.50  18.50
Mickey Mouse, 70th anniv.

Disney Characters in Trains — A313

No. 3372, $100 — 101 Dalmatians Express: a, Locomotive. b, Flatcar. c, Car with pillars. d, "Basket" car. e, Caboose.
No. 3373, $100 — Robin Hood Train: a, Engine. b, Marian, Robin Hood. c, Royal coach. d, Flatcar. e, Caboose.
No. 3374, $100 — Snow White, Diamond Mine Railroad: a, Engine. b, Flatcar. c, Snow White, Prince Charming. d, Passenger car. e, Pump car.
No. 3375, $100 — Little Mermaid Railroad: a, Engine. b, Fish holding pearls. c, Little Mermaid. d, Various marine life in car. e, "Bah Hum Bug!"
No. 3376: a, Dwarf from Diamond Mine Railroad driving locomotive. b, Dwarf on pump car.
No. 3377, $300, Bandits, Cruela De Vil. No. 3378, $300, Robin Hood, Bear. No. 3379, $300, Little Mermaid kissing Prince under mistletoe. No. 3380, $300, Little Mermaid holding starfish.

**1999, Mar. 1**    **Perf. 13½x14**
**Sheets of 5, #a-e**
3372-3375  A313  Set of 4      36.00  36.00
3376  A313  $200 Sheet of 2, #a-b.    9.00   9.00
**Souvenir Sheets**
3377-3380  A313  Set of 4      22.00  22.00

Caribbean Butterflies — A314

No. 3381, $80: a, Scarce Bamboo Page. b, Spicebush swallowtail. c, Isabella. d, The mosaic. e, Gulf fritillary. f, Figure-of-eight.
No. 3382, $80: a, Hewitson's blue hairstreak. b, Polydamas swallowtail. c, Common morpho. d, Blue-green reflector. e, Malachite. f, Grecian shoemaker.
No. 3383, $300, Giant swallowtail, vert. No. 3384, $300, Pipevine swallowtail, vert.

**1999, Mar. 15**        **Perf. 14**
**Sheets of 6, #a-f**
3381-3382  A314  Set of 2      14.50  14.50
**Souvenir Sheets**
3383-3384  A314  Set of 2       9.00   9.00

Flowers A315

No. 3385, $60: a, Geranium. b, Oncidium macranthum. c, Bepi orchidglades. d, Sunflowers (2). e, Cattleya walkeriana. f, Cattleya frasquita. g, Helianthus maximilani (one). h, Paphiopedilum insigne sanderae, lily. i, Lily (2).

No. 3386, $60: a, Dendrobium nobile. b, Phalaenopsis schilleriana. c, Cymbidium alexette. d, Rhododendron. e, Phragmipedium besseae, laelia cinnabarina. f, Masdevallia veitchiana. g, Calochortus nuttallii. h, Brassolaeliocattleya pure gold. i, Laelia cinnabarina.
No. 3387: a, Leptotes bicolor, masdevallia ignea. b, Sophrolaeliocattleya, anguloa clowesii. c, Laelia pumila. d, Masdevallia ignea. e, Dendrodium phalaenopsis. f, Anguloa clowesii.
No. 3388, $300, Ascocentrum miniatum, vert. No. 3389, $300, Iris pseudacorus.

**1999, Mar. 15**   **Litho.**    **Perf. 14**
**Sheets of 9, #a-i**
3385-3386  A315  Set of 2      16.00  16.00
3387  A315  $90 Sheet of 6, #a.-f.    7.50   7.50
**Souvenir Sheet**
3388-3389  A315  Set of 2       8.50   8.50

Akira Kurosawa (1910-98), Film Director — A316

No. 3390 — Films, vert.: a, "The Dream." b, "Rashomon." c, "Kagemusha." d, "Red Beard." e, "Seven Samurai." f, "Yojimbo."
No. 3391 — Portraits: a, Pointing. b, Hand on face. c, Standing. d, With cameraman. $300, Scene from "Dreams."

**1999, Mar. 22**
3390  A316  $80 Sheet of 6, #a.-f.    6.75   6.75
3391  A316  $130 Sheet of 4, #a.-d.   7.25   7.25
**Souvenir Sheet**
3392  A316  $300 multicolored         4.25   4.25

Mushrooms A317

Designs: $25, Coprinus atramentarius. $35, Hebeloma crustuliniforme. $100, Russula nigricans. $200, Tricholoma aurantium.
No. 3397, $60: a, Boletus aereus. b, Coprinus comatus. c, Inocybe godeyi. d, Morchella crassipes. e, Lepiota acutesquamosa. f, Amanita phalloides. g, Boletus spadiceus. h, Cortinarius collinitus. i, Lepiota procera.
No. 3398, $60: a, Russula ochroleuca. b, Hygrophorus hypotheius. c, Amanita rubescens. d, Boletus satanas. e, Amanita echinocephala. f, Amanita muscaria. g, Boletus badius. h, Hebeloma radicosum. i, Mycena polygramma.
No. 3399, $300, Lepiota acutequamoso. No. 3400, $300, Pluteus cervinus.

**1999, May 6**   **Litho.**      **Perf. 14**
3393-3396  A317  Set of 4       4.25   4.25
**Sheets of 9, #a-i**
**Perf. 14½**
3397-3398  A317  Set of 2      16.50  16.50
**Souvenir Sheet**
3399-3400  A317  Set of 2       9.00   9.00
Nos. 3397-3398 each contain nine 32x41mm stamps. Nos. 3399-3400 each contain one 32x41mm stamp.

Trains — A318

No. 3401, $80: a, Burlington Northern GP 39-2, 1974. b, CSX GP40-2, 1967. c, Erie Lackawana Railroad GP 9, 1956. d, Amtrak P 42 Genesis, 1993. e, Erie Railroad S-2, 1948. f, Pennsylvania Railroad S-1, 1947.
No. 3402, $80: a, Northern and Western #610, c. 1933. b, Pennsylvania Railroad M1B Mountain, 1930. c, Reading Railroad FP7A, 1951. d, New York Central 2-8-4, c. 1940. e, Union Pacific Challenger Big Boy, 1963. f, GP 15-1, 1956.
No. 3403, $80: a, Shinkansen Bullet 100 series, 1984, Japan. b, Ukranian Diesel ZMGR, 1983, Russia. c, Rhatische Bahn GE 6/6 II, Germany. d, Eurostar TGV, 1986, France. e, Atlantique TGV, 1989, France. f, Class 86-6, UK.
No. 3404, $80: a, Joseph Clark 0-4-0, 1868. b, Diamond Stack Bethel 4-4-0, 1863. c, New York Central #999, 1890. d, Boston & Maine Ballardville 0-4-0, 1876. e, Atlantic 4-4-0 Portland Rochester Railroad, 1863. f, America 4-4-0 Baltimore & Ohio Railroad, 1881.
Railroad pioneers: No. 3405, $300, George Stephen, vert. No. 3406, $300, Alfred de Glehn, vert. No. 3407, $300, George Nagelmackers, vert. No. 3408, $300, R.F. Trevithick, vert.

**1999, May 10**          **Perf. 14**
**Sheets of 6, #a.-f.**
3401-3404  A318  Set of 4      29.00  29.00
**Souvenir Sheets**
3405-3408  A318  Set of 4      17.00  17.00
Australia '99 World Stamp Expo.

Wedding of Prince Edward and Sophie Rhys-Jones — A319

Various portraits: Nos. 3409, $150, 3411, $300, rose lilac sheet margin. Nos. 3410, $150, 3412, $300, yellow brown sheet margin.

**1999, June 19**   **Litho.**    **Perf. 14¼**
**Sheets of 4, #a.-d.**
3409-3410  A319  Set of 2      17.00  17.00
**Souvenir Sheets**
3411-3412  A319  Set of 2       8.50   8.50
Nos. 3411-3412 are horiz.

Johann Wolfgang von Goethe (1749-1832), Poet — A320

No. 3413: a, Lynceus sings from the watchtower. b, Portaits of Von Goethe and Friedrich von Schiller (1759-1805), poet. c, The fallen Icarus.

$300, Mephistopheles appears as salamander, vert.

**1999, June 22    Litho.    Perf. 14**
3413  A320  $150 Sheet of 3, #a.-
c.                                6.25  6.25
**Souvenir Sheet**
3414  A320  $300 multicolored     4.25  4.25

IBRA '99, World Philatelic Exhibition, Nuremberg — A321

Designs: $60, Class E10 Bo-bo electric locomotive, BMW offices, Munich, 1952, vert. $200, Class 01, 4-6-2 steam express train, 1926.
Illustration reduced.

**1999, June 22**
3415  A321  $60 multicolored      .90   .90
3416  A321  $200 multicolored    2.75  2.75

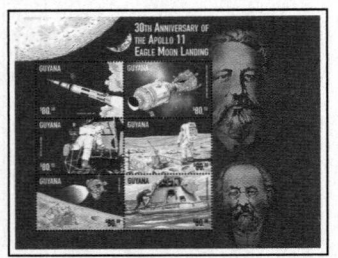

Apollo 11 Moon Landing, 30th Anniv. — A322

No. 3417, $80: a, Blast off. b, Command Module docked with Lunar Lander. c, First man on moon. d, Seismic experiments package. e, Back to the orbiter. f, Astronauts being picked up.
No. 3418, $80, vert: a, Sputnik, 1959, Konstantin Tsiolkovsky. b, Apollo 11 liftoff. c, On the moon. d, Collecting samples of lunar rocks. e, Apollo 11 Lunar Module. f, Splashdown.
No. 3419, $300, Salute to the flag. No. 3420, $300, Michael Collins.

**1999, June 22**
**Sheets of 6, #a-f**
3417-3418  A322  Set of 2        13.00 13.00
**Souvenir Sheet**
3419-3420  A322  Set of 2         8.50  8.50

Souvenir Sheets

PhilexFrance '99, World Philatelic Exhibition — A323

Designs: No. 3421, $300, Co-Co 7000 Class High Speed 1949-55. No. 3422, $300, 241-P Class 4-8-2 Express 1947-49.
Illustration reduced.

**1999, June 22**
3421-3422  A323  Set of 2         9.00  9.00

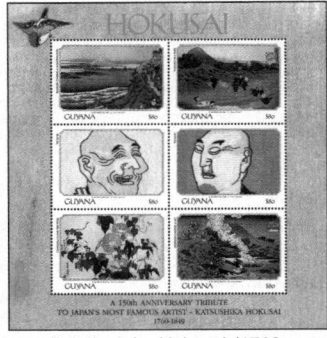

Paintings by Hokusai (1760-1849) — A324

No. 3423, $80: a, Travelers Climbing a Mountain Path. b, Washing in a River. c, The Blind (eyes & mouth open). d, The Blind (eyes & mouth shut). e, Convolvulus and Tree-Frog. f, Fishermen Hauling a Net.
No. 3424, $80: a, Hibiscus and Sparrow. b, Hydrangea and Swallow. c, The Blind (eyes shut, mouth open). d, The Blind (eyes open, mouth shut). e, Irises. f, Lilies.
No. 3425, $300, Flowering Cherries at Mount Yoshino, vert. No. 3426, $300, A View of a Stone Causeway, vert.

**1999, June 22    Litho.    Perf. 14x13¾**
**Sheets of 6, #a-f**
3423-3424  A324  Set of 2        13.50 13.50
**Souvenir Sheets**
**Perf. 13¾x14**
3425-3426  A324  Set of 2         8.50  8.50

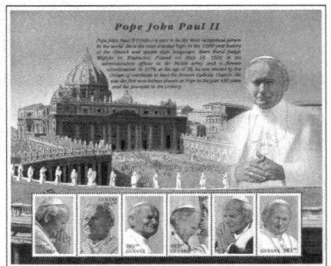

Pope John Paul II — A325

**1999, June 22    Perf. 14**
3427  A325  $80 Sheet of 6, #a.-f. 7.50 7.50

John Glenn's Return to Space — A326

No. 3428: a, In space suit, 1962. b, After landing, 1962. c, As Senator. d, With helmet, 1998. e, Without helmet, 1998.

**1999, June 22    Perf. 14½x14¼**
3428  A326  $100 Sheet of 5, #a.-
e.                                7.00  7.00

Parrots and Parakeets — A327

No. 3429, $60: a, Hyacinth macaw. b, Blue and gold macaw. c, Blue-fronted Amazon parrot. d, Amazon parrot. e, Sun Conure. f, Tivi parakeet. g, Bavaria's conure. h, Fairy lorikeet.
No. 3430, $60: a, Marron macaw. b, Thick-billed parrot. c, Golden-crowned canure. d, Yellow-naped macaw. e, Double yellow-headed parrot. f, Golden-fronted parakeet. g, Maroon-billed conure. h, Nandaya conure.
No. 3431, $300, Jendaya conure, horiz. No. 3432, $300, Gray-cheeked parakeet.

**1999, Aug. 3    Perf. 14**
**Sheets of 8, #a.-h.**
3429-3430  A327  Set of 2        14.00 14.00
**Souvenir Sheets**
3431-3432  A327  Set of 2         8.50  8.50

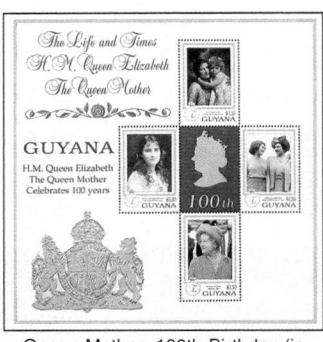

Queen Mother, 100th Birthday (in 2000) — A328

No. 3433: a, Duchess of York, Princess Elizabeth, 1928. b, Lady Elizabeth Bowles-Lyon, 1914. c, Queen Elizabeth, Princess Elizabeth, 1940. d, Queen Mother, Venice, 1984.
$400, Queen Mother, Canada, 1988.

**1999, Aug. 4**
**Gold Frames**
3433  A328  $130 Sheet of 4, #a.-
d. + label                        8.00  8.00
**Souvenir Sheet**
**Perf. 13¾**
3434  A328  $400 multicolored     5.50  5.50
No. 3434 contains one 38x50mm stamp. Margins of sheets are embossed.
See Nos. 3689-3690.

China Soccer League Superstars A329

Nos. 3435a-3435g, 3436a-3436g, Various players. Nos. 3435h, 3436h, League emblem.

**1999, Aug. 16    Perf. 14½x14¼**
3435  A329  $50 Sheet of 8, #a.-h. 5.25  5.25
3436  A329  $60 Sheet of 8, #a.-h. 6.25  6.25

Rights of the Child — A330

No. 3437: a, Denomination at LL, flag at UR. b, Denomination at UL, flag at LL. c, Denomination at UL, flag at UR.
$300, Prince Talal.

**1999, June 22    Litho.    Perf. 14**
3437  A330  $150 Sheet of 3, #a.-
c.                                5.50  5.50
**Souvenir Sheet**
3438  A330  $300 multicolored     4.00  4.00

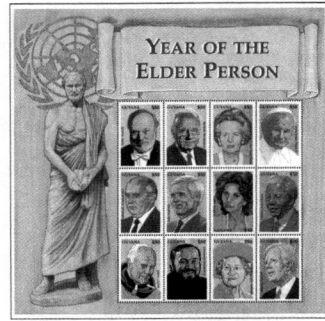

Intl. Year of the Elderly — A331

No. 3439: a, Kurt Masur. b, Rupert Murdoch. c, Margaret Thatcher. d, Pope John Paul II. e, Mikhail Gorbachev. f, Ted Turner. g, Sophia Loren. h, Nelson Mandela. i, John Glenn. j, Luciano Pavarotti. k, Queen Mother. l, Jimmy Carter.
No. 3440 — Ronald Reagan: a, As young man. b, In uniform. c, Feeding chimp. d, With campaign poster. e, With cowboy hat. f, With wine glass.

$300, Reagan in star.

**1999, June 22    Litho.    Perf. 14**
3439  A331  $50 Sheet of 12,
#a.-l.                            8.50  8.50
3440  A331  $100 Sheet of 6, #a.-
f.                                7.00  7.00
**Souvenir Sheet**
3441  A331  $300 multicolored     3.50  3.50

Souvenir Sheet

Mei Lan Fang, Chinese Actor — A332

**1999, Aug. 16    Litho.    Perf. 13¾**
3442  A332  $400 multicolored     4.50  4.50

First Balloon Flight Around the World — A333

No. 3443: a, Orbiter 3. b, Emblem. c, Bertrand Piccard. d, Brian Jones.
$300, Orbiter 3, flight path.

**1999, Aug. 16    Litho.    Perf. 14**
3443  A333  $150 Sheet of 4, #a.-
d.                                    7.25  7.25
**Souvenir Sheet**
3444  A333  $300 multicolored        4.00  4.00

The Kennedy Family
A334

No. 3445: a, Jacqueline and John, Jr. b. John and John, Jr. c, John and Jacqueline. d, Jacqueline. e, John, Jr. and Caroline. f, John. No. 3445G: h, John, Jr. as adult and child. i, John, Jr. and Jacqueline. j, John Jr.

**1999, Oct. 4    Litho.    Perf. 13¾**
3445  A334  $80 Sheet of 6,
#a.-f.                                6.25  6.25
3445G A334  $160 Sheet of 3,
#h.-j.                                5.75  5.75

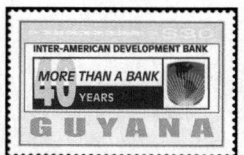

Inter-American Development Bank, 40th Anniv. — A335

**1999, Nov. 15    Litho.    Perf. 14**
3446  A335  $30 multicolored         .40   .40

Ferrari Automobiles — A336

Designs: $30, 312 T2. $35, 553 F.1. $60, D 50. $200, 246 F.1. $300, 126/C2. $400, 312/B2.

**1999    Litho.    Perf. 14**
3447-3452 A336  Set of 6            11.50 11.50

Sidney Sheldon, Novelist — A337

**1999    Litho.    Perf. 14**
3453  A337  $80 multicolored         1.00  1.00
Issued in sheets of 4.

A338

No. 3454: a, During World War II. b, Wedding photo. c, As child. d, At coronation of George VI. e, In 1971. f, In 1991. g, in 1914. h, In 1988. i, At Royal Agricultural show. j, On 60th birthday.
$1,000, Portrait.

**1999    Litho.    Perf. 12**
3454  A338  $60 Sheet of 10,
#a.-j.                                8.75  8.75
**Imperf**
**Size: 51x76mm**
3455  A338  $1000 multicolored      12.00 12.00
Sheets of #3454 exist with black border in margin with text "In Memoriam/1900-2002."

Queen Mother (b. 1900) — A339

**Litho. & Embossed**
**1999, Aug. 4    Die Cut Perf. 8¾**
3456  A339  $1500 gold & multi      35.00

Millennium A340

No. 3457, Founding of first university, 1088.
No. 3458 — Highlights of the 11th Century: a, Anasazi trade center. b, "Black Virgin." c, Seljuk warrior. d, Appearance of Halley's Comet. e, Battle of Hastings. f, William of Normandy crowned King of England. g, Power of the Fujiwara is checked. h, Holy Roman Emperor Henry IV. i, Muslims build Timbuktu. j, Like No. 3457. k, Gondolas come into use in Venice. l, El Cid. m, First crusade. n, Crusaders capture Jerusalem. o, Chinese statue of Guanyin. p, Rubiyat of Omar Khayyam (60x40mm). q, Syrian storage jar.
No. 3459 — Highlights of the 1910s: a, Manet and Post-impressionists show, Grafton Gallery, London. b, Standard Oil loses Supreme Court antitrust suit. c, Harriet Quimby, 1st female pilot in US d, US enters World War I. e, Titanic sinks. f, Pu Yi resigns as Chinese Emperor. g, Grand Central Station built in NYC. h, Assassination of Archduke Francis Ferdinand. i, Panama Canal opens. j, Lawrence of Arabia. k, Easter Uprising, Ireland. l, 1917 Russian Revolution. m, Execution of the Romanovs. n, Treaty of Versailles ends World War I. o, Influenza epidemic. p, Leo Tolstoy & Mark Twain die (60x40mm). q, Bauhaus opens, Weimar, Germany.

**1999, Dec. 20    Litho.    Perf. 13¼x13**
3457  A340  $35 multi                .50   .50
**Perf. 12¾x12½**
3458  A340  $35 Sheet of 17,
#a.-q.                                7.50  7.50
3459  A340  $35 Sheet of 17,
#a.-q., + label                      7.50  7.50

Flowers — A341

#3460: Various flowers making up a photomosaic of Princess Diana.
#3461: Various details of paper money of the world making up a photomosaic of George Washington's portrait on $1 bill.

**1999-2000    Litho.    Perf. 13¾**
3460  A341  $80 Sheet of 8, #a.-h.  8.50  8.50
3461  A341  $80 Sheet of 8, #a.-h.  8.50  8.50
Issued: #3460, 12/31; #3461, 3/27/00.
See Nos. 3568-3569.

New Year 2000 (Year of the Dragon) — A342

No. 3462 — Dragons with denomination in: a, LR. b, LL. c, UR, d, UL.
$300, LR.

**2000, Feb. 5    Perf. 14¾**
3462  A342  $100 Sheet of 4,
#a.-d.                                5.00  5.00
**Souvenir Sheet**
3463  A342  $300 multi               3.50  3.50

A343

Automobiles — A344

No. 3464, $100: a, Nicholas Cugnot's steam-powered Fardier, 1769. b, Siegfried Marcus's motor carriage, 1875. c, Karl Benz's Velo, 1894. d, Virgilio Bordino's steam carriage, 1854. e, 1886 Benz. f, 1908 Ford Model T.
No. 3465, $100: a,1926 Duesenberg Model A Phaeton. b, 1927 Mercedes-Benz Model K. c, 1928, Rolls-Royce Phantom I limousine. d, 1935 Auburn 851 Speedster. e, 1936 Mercedes-Benz 540K Cabriolet B. f, 1949, Volkswagen Cabriolet Beetle.
No. 3466, $100: a, 1957 Ford Thunderbird. b, 1957 Jaguar XK150. c, 1968 Chevrolet Corvette Stingray. d, 1973 BMW 2002 Turbo. e, 1975 Porsche 911 Turbo. f, 1999 Volkswagen Beetle.
No. 3467, $100: a, 1886 Daimler motor car. b, 1898 Opel Luzman. c, 1899 Benz Landaulet coupe. d, 1892 Peugeot Vis-a-vis. e, 1886 Benz. f, 1894 Benz Velo, diff.
No. 3468, $100: a, 1896 Ford. b, 1903 De Dion-Bouton Populare. c, 1900 Adler. d, 1904 Vauxhall. e, 1908 Rolls-Royce Silver Ghost. f, 1908 Ford Model T, diff.
No. 3469, $400, 1904 Mercedes-Benz 60/70. No. 3470, $400, 1939 Mercedes-Benz Type 320 Cabriolet. No. 3471, $400, 1954 Mercedes-Benz 300SL Gullwing.
No. 3472, $400, 1904 Turner-Miesse. No. 3473, $400, 1910 Runabout.

**2000, Mar. 13    Litho.    Perf. 13½**
**Sheets of 6, #a.-f.**
3464-3466 A343  Set of 3            22.00 22.00
**Perf. 14**
3467-3468 A344  Set of 2            14.00 14.00
**Souvenir Sheets**
**Perf. 14½**
3469-3471 A343  Set of 3            13.50 13.50
**Perf. 14¼**
3472-3473 A344  Set of 2             9.00  9.00
Size of stamps from Nos. 3463-3466, 41x25mm; from Nos. 3467-3468, 42x28mm.

Marine Life A345

Designs: $30, Lachnolaimus maximus. $35, Cyphoma gibbosum. $60, Trachinotus falcatus. $100, Bodianus pulchellus. $200, Anisotremus virginicus. $300, Etheostoma spectabile.
No. 3480, $80: a, Hypoplectrus indigo. b, Chlamys hastata. c, Sebastes rubrivinctus. d, Selene vomer. e, Marginella carnea. f, Phoca vitulina. g, Coryphaena hippurus. h, Epinephelus fulvus.
No. 3481, $80: a, Sphyraena barracuda. b, Saccopharynx sp. c, Chromodoris amoena. d, Makaira nigricans. e, Orcinus orca. f, Hippocampus reidi. g, Chelonia mydas. h, Emblemaria pandionis.
No. 3482, $80, vert.: a, Pterois volitans. b, Tursiops truncatus. c, Diplulmaris antarctica. d, Pomacanthus arcuatus. e, Aetobatus narinari. f, Carcharhinus amblyrhynchos. g, Sacura margaritacea. h, Octopus dolfeini.
No. 3483, $400, Asteroschema tenue, vert. No. 3484, $400, Apodichthys flavidus, vert. No. 3485, $400, Periclimenes pedersoni.

**2000, May 15    Perf. 14**
3474-3479 A345  Set of 6            8.50  8.50
**Sheets of 8, #a.-h.**
3480-3482 A345  Set of 3            25.00 25.00
**Souvenir Sheets**
3483-3485 A345  Set of 3            14.00 14.00
No. 3485 contains one 57x42mm stamp.

*1999 Return of Macao to People's Republic of China*

A346

No. 3486: a, Flag. b, Skyline.
Illustration reduced.

**2000, May 15**
3486  A346  $150  Sheet of 2, #a.-
　　b.　　　　　　　　　3.75 3.75

100th Test Match
at Lord's
Ground — A347

Designs: $100, Rohan Kanhai. $300, Clive
Lloyd.
$400, Lord's Ground, horiz.

**2000, May 15**　**Litho.**　**Perf. 14**
3487-3488  A347  Set of 2
　　　　　　　　　　　　5.00 5.00
**Souvenir Sheet**
3489  A347  $400 multi　　　5.25 5.25

Prince William, 18th Birthday — A348

No. 3490: a, With Prince Harry. b, Wearing
sweater. c, In profile. d, In suit.
$400, In ski wear.
Illustration reduced.

**2000, May 15**　　　　　　**Perf. 14**
3490  A348  $100 Sheet of 4, #a-d 5.50 5.50
**Souvenir Sheet**
**Perf. 13¾**
3491  A348  $400 multi　　　5.25 5.25
No. 3490 contains four 28x42mm stamps. It
exists imperf.

First Zeppelin Flight, Cent. — A349

No. 3492 — Ferdinand von Zeppelin and: a,
LZ-1. b, LZ-2. c, LZ-9.
$400, LZ-127.

**2000, May 15**　　　　　　**Perf. 14**
3492  A349  $200 Sheet of 3, #a-c 7.25 7.25
**Souvenir Sheet**
3493  A349  $400 multi　　　4.75 4.75
No. 3492 contains three 40x24mm stamps.

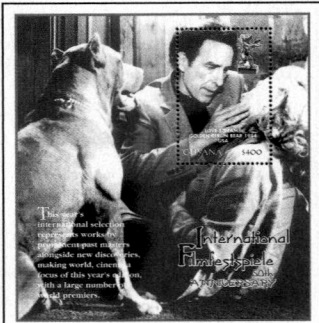

Berlin Film Festival, 50th
Anniv. — A350

No. 3494: a, Das Boot Ist Voll. b, David. c,
Hong Gao Liang (Red Sorghum). d, Die Ehe
der Maria Braun. e, Edith Evans.  f, Michel
Simon.
$400, Love Streams.
Illustration reduced.

**2000, May 15**
3494  A350  $100 Sheet of 6, #a-f  7.00 7.00
**Souvenir Sheet**
3495  A350  $400 multi　　　4.50 4.50

Apollo-Soyuz Mission, 25th
Anniv. — A351

No. 3496: a, Vance D. Brand, Thomas P.
Stafford. b, Apollo 18, docking adapter. c, Staf-
ford, Valeri Kubasov.
$400, Stafford, Donald K. Slayton.
Illustration reduced.

**2000, May 15**
3496  A351  $200 Sheet of 3, #a-c  7.25 7.25
**Souvenir Sheet**
3497  A351  $400 multi　　　4.50 4.50

2000 Summer Olympics,
Sydney — A352

No. 3498: a, Henry Robert Pearce. b, Volleyball. c, Olympic Park, Montreal, and Canadian flag. d, Ancient Greek runners.
Illustration reduced.

**2000, May 15**
3498  A352  $160 Sheet of 4, #a-d 7.50 7.50

Public Railways, 175th Anniv. — A353

No. 3499: a, Timothy Hackworth. b, Sans
Pareil. c, Branhope Tunnel.
Illustration reduced.

**2000, May 15**
3499  A353  $200 Sheet of 3, #a-c  7.00 7.00

Johann Sebastian Bach (1685-
1750) — A354

Illustration reduced.

**2000, May 15**
3500  A354  $400 multi　　　4.75 4.75

Albert Einstein (1879-1955) — A355

Illustration reduced.

**2000, May 15**　**Litho.**　**Perf. 14¼**
3501  A355  $400 multi　　　5.00 5.00

Space — A356

No. 3502, $100: a, Amsat IIIc. b, SRET. c,
Inspector. d, Stardust. e, Temisat. f, Arsene.
No. 3503, $100, horiz.: a, Sun and Echo
satellite (inscribed Apollo 11). b, Saturn, and-
Pioneer. c, Moon and Apollo 11 (inscribed
Echo satellite). d, Mars and Mars Explorer. e,
Space Shuttle, Intl. Space Station. f, Halley's
Comet and Giotto.
No. 3504, $100, horiz.: a, Cesar, Argentine,
Spanish flags. b, Sirio 2, Italian flag. c, Taos
S.80, French flag. d, Viking, Swedish flag. e,
SCD 1, Brazilian flag. f, Offeq 1, Israeli flag.
No. 3505, $400, Clementine. No. 3506,
$400, Solar Max, horiz.
Illustration reduced.

**2000, May 15**　**Litho.**　**Perf. 14**
**Sheets of 6, #a-f**
3502-3504  A356  Set of 3　　22.00 22.00
**Souvenir Sheets**
3505-3506  A356  Set of 2　　9.25 9.25
World Stamp Expo 2000, Anaheim.

The Three Stooges — A357

No. 3507: a, Shemp, Moe, Larry, man with
glasses. b, Skeleton, Larry, Moe. c, Shemp. d,
Stooges with fingers in mouths. e, Stooges
reading book. f, Stooges attacking man. g,
Stooges with candle. h, Stooges, man, fire
bucket. i, Moe, Shemp, man in window.

No. 3508, $400, Moe in doorway. No. 3509, $400, Larry, skeleton.
Illustration reduced.

**2000, July 27**     **Perf. 13¾**
3507 A357 $80 Sheet of 9, #a-i   8.75 8.75
**Souvenir Sheets**
3508-3509 A357 Set of 2    9.00 9.00

See Nos. 3542-3544.

Betty Boop — A358

No. 3510: a, In striped blouse. b, With shopping bags. c, On cushion. d, As belly dancer. e, In red lingerie. f, In cutoff shorts. g, With musical notes. h, In flowered pants. i, In black dress.
No. 3511, $400, In fur coat. No. 3512, $400, In polka dot bathing suit, with flamingos.
Illustration reduced.

**2000, July 27**     **Perf. 13¾**
3510 A358 $80 Sheet of 9, #a-i   9.00 9.00
**Souvenir Sheets**
3511-3512 A358 Set of 2    9.00 9.00

See Nos. 3545-3552.

Third Annual
Caribbean Media
Conference
A359

**2000, Aug. 14**     **Perf. 14**
3513 A359 $100 multi    1.25 1.25

European Soccer
Championships — A360

No. 3514, $80, horiz.: a, Denmark. b, Germany. c, Italy. d, Netherlands. e, Portugal. f, Romania. g, Czech Republic. h, Norway.

No. 3515, $80, horiz.: a, Turkey. b, Slovenia. c, Yugoslavia. d, Sweden. e, Belgium. f, Spain. g, France. h, England.
No. 3516, $400, Jurgen Klinsmann. No. 3517, $400, Stefan Kuntz.
Illustration reduced.

**2000, Aug. 21**     **Perf. 13¾**
**Sheets of 8, #a-h, + label**
3514-3515 A360 Set of 2   16.00 16.00
**Souvenir Sheets**
3516-3517 A360 Set of 2    9.50 9.50

Mushrooms — A361

No. 3518, $100, horiz.: a, Sealy vase chanterelle. b, Caesar's mushroom. c, Greenheaded jelly club. d, Salmon unicorn entoloma. e, White oysterette. f, Variable cort.
No. 3519, $100, horiz.: a, Coccora. b, Winter polypore. c, Turpentine waxy cap. d, Aeryginosa. e, Fly agaric. f, Honey mushroom.
No. 3520, $100, horiz.: a, Salmon waxy cap. b, Shellfish-scented russula. c, Scarlet waxy cap. d, Stuntz's blue legs. e, Netted rhodotus. f, Indigo milky.
No. 3521, $400, Tiny volvariella. No. 3522, $400, Turkey tail, horiz. No. 3523, $400, Pinwheel marasmius, horiz.
Illustration reduced.

**2000, Oct. 4**     **Perf. 14**
**Sheets of 6, #a-f**
3518-3520 A361 Set of 3   22.50 22.50
**Souvenir Sheets**
3521-3523 A361 Set of 3   14.00 14.00

The Stamp Show 2000, London.

A362

Flowers — A363

Designs: No. 3524, $35, Bougainvillea spectabilis. No. 3525, $60, Euphorbia milii. No. 3526, $200, Catharanthus roseus. No. 3527, $300, Ipomoea carnea.
No. 3528, $35, Russelia equisetiformis. No. 3529, $60, Sprekelia formosissima. No. 3530, $200, Passiflora quadrangularis. No. 3531, $300, Mirabilis jalapa.
No. 3532, $100: a, Lantana camara. b, Jatropha integerrima. c, Plumeria alba. d, Strelitzia reginae. e, Clerodendrum splendens. f, Thunbergia grandiflora.
No. 3533, $100, vert.: a, Cordia sebestena. b, Heliconia wagneriana. c, Dendrobium phalaenopsis. d, Passiflora caerulea. e, Oncidium nubigenum. f, Hibiscus rosa-sinensis.

No. 3534, $100: a, Ipomoea tricolor. b, Lantana camara (inscribed canara). c, Cantua buxifolia. d, Fuchsia. e, Eichornia crassipes. f, Cosmos sulphureus.
No. 3535, $100: a, Bignonia capreolata. b, Calceolaria herbeo-hybrida. c, Canna generalis. d, Bauhinia grandiflora. e, Amaranthus caudatus. f, Aoutilon megapotamicum.
No. 3536, $100, Guzmania lingulata. No. 3537, $400, Cattleya granulosa, vert.
No. 3538, $400, Tacsonia van-volxemii. No. 3539, $400, Oeceoclades maculata.

**2000, Oct. 30**     **Perf. 14**
3524-3527 A362 Set of 4   6.75 6.75
3528-3531 A363 Set of 4   6.75 6.75
**Sheets of 6, #a-f**
3532-3533 A362 Set of 2   14.00 14.00
3534-3535 A363 Set of 2   14.00 14.00
**Souvenir Sheets**
3536-3537 A362 Set of 2    9.50 9.50
3538-3539 A363 Set of 2    9.50 9.50

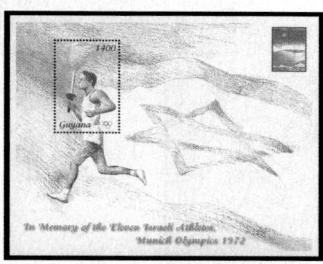

Munich Olympics Massacre — A364

No. 3540: a, Yaakov Springer. b, Andrei Schpitzer. c, Amitsur Shapira. d, David Berger. e, Ze'ev Friedman. f, Joseph Gottfreund. g, Moshe Weinberg. h, Kahat Shor. i, Mark Slavin. j, Eliezer Halefin. k, Joseph Romano. l, Poster of Munich Olympics.
Illustration reduced.

**2000, Oct. 30**
3540 A364 $40 Sheet of 12,
   #a-l     7.00 7.00
**Souvenir Sheet**
3541 A364 $400 Torch bearer   5.50 5.50

**Three Stooges Type of 2000**

No. 3542: a, Moe with seltzer bottle, Shemp, Larry. b, As cave men trying to break rock. c, Moe with cow. d, Two women, Shemp, Moe. e, As cave men, seated. f, As cave men, Shemp holding large rock. g, Stooges wearing pith helmets. h, Stooges, picture frames. i, Stooges with fake beards.
No. 3543, $400, Larry, woman, vert. No. 3544, $400, Moe in plaid shirt, vert.

**2000, July 27**    **Litho.**   **Perf. 13¾**
3542 A357 $80 Sheet of 9, #a-i   8.75 8.75
**Souvenir Sheets**
3543-3544 A357 Set of 2    9.00 9.00

**Betty Boop Type of 2000**
**Souvenir Sheets**

#3545, At football field. #3546, With tennis racquet. #3547, With ankh earrings, winking. #3548, With red swimsuit. #3549, As portrait of queen. #3550, As Can-can girl. #3551, Standing on shell. #3552, As Mona Lisa, horiz.

**2000, July 27**
3545-3552 A358 $400 Set of 8   40.00 40.00

I Love Lucy — A365

No. 3553: a, Lucy reading book. b, Ricky, Lucy with book. c, Ricky kissing Lucy. d, Lucy near window. e, Lucy grabbing Ethel. f, Ricky holding scarf, Lucy in bed. g, Ethel, Lucy, frying pan. h, Ricky with frying pan. i, Lucy, Ethel, coffee table.
No. 3554, $400, Lucy in pink robe. No. 3555, $400, Lucy with garbage can lid.
Illustration reduced.

**2000, July 27**
3553 A365 $80 Sheet of 9, #a-i   6.75 6.75
**Souvenir Sheets**
3554-3555 A365 Set of 2    9.00 9.00

FIN. K. L — A366

No. 3556: a, Lee Hyo-Ri. b, Ok Ju-Hyun. c, Lee Jin. d, Lee Jin. e, Group. f, Sung Yu-Ri. g, Lee Hyo-Ri. h, Sung Yu-Ri. i, Ok Ju-Hyun. #d, f, i, full color, others, sepia tone.

**2000, Sept. 7**     **Perf. 13½**
3556 A366 $80 Sheet of 9, #a-i   9.00 9.00

Queen Mother,
100th
Birthday — A367

**2000, Dec. 1**     **Perf. 14**
3557 A367 $100 multi    1.40 1.40

Printed in sheets of 6.

Christmas — A368

$60, #3562b, Heads of 2 angels, org background. $90, #3562a, 2 full angels, bl background. $120, #3562c, Heads of 2 angels, bl background. #3561, $400, #3562d, 2 full angels, org background.
No. 3563, Baby Jesus, horiz.

**2000, Dec. 18**
3558-3561 A368 Set of 4   8.50 8.50
3562 A368 $180 Sheet of 4, #a-d 8.25 8.25
**Souvenir Sheet**
3563 A368 $400 multi    4.75 4.75

New Year 2001 (Year of the
Snake) — A369

No. 3564: a, Green snake head. b, Red snake head. c, Blue snake head. d, Yellow snake head.
$250, Purple snake head, vert.

**2001, Jan. 2**    **Litho.**   **Perf. 13½x13**
3564 A369 $80 Sheet of 4, #a-d 4.25 4.25

## Souvenir Sheet
**Perf. 13x13½**

3565 A369 $250 multi          3.00 3.00

Tourist Attractions — A370

Designs: No. 3566, $90, Prime Minister's residence. No. 3567, $90, Kaiteur Falls, vert.

**2001, Jan. 30**          **Perf. 13¼**
3566-3567 A370 Set of 2          2.25 2.25

### Flower Photomosaic Type of 1999

No. 3568, $80: Various photographs of flowers making up a photomosaic of the Queen Mother.

No. 3569, $100: Various photographs of religious sites making up a photomosaic of Pope John Paul II.

**2001, Feb. 13**          **Perf. 13¾**
**Sheets of 8, #a-h**
3568-3569 A341 Set of 2          19.00 19.00

## Souvenir Sheet

Chow Yun-Fat, Actor — A371

Background color: a, Blue green. b, Dark red. c, Olive brown. d, Red violet. e, Dark blue. f, Purple.

**2001, Feb. 13**          **Perf. 13¾x13¼**
3570 A371 $60 Sheet of 6, #a-f          4.25 4.25

Pokémon — A372

No. 3571: a, Staryu. b, Seaking. c, Tentacool. d, Magikarp. e, Seadra. f, Goldeen. Illustration reduced.

**2001, Feb. 13**          **Perf. 13¾**
3571 A372 $100 Sheet of 6, #a-f          7.50 7.50

### Souvenir Sheet
3572 A372 $400 Horsea          4.50 4.50

### Betty Boop Type of 2000

Designs: No. 3573, $400, In pink hat. No. 3574, $400, As singer on stage. No. 3575, $400, With red top and necklace, on beach.

No. 3576, $400, In orange and black hat, horiz.

**2001 ?**          **Litho.**          **Perf. 13¾**
3573-3576 A358 Set of 4          18.00 18.00

### I Love Lucy Type of 2000

Designs: No. 3577, $400, Dressed like Carmen Miranda. No. 3578, $400, With blue hat and gloves. No. 3579, $400, As knife thrower's target. No. 3580, $400, At table, wearing blue hat. No. 3581, $400, Wearing glasses with thick black frames.

**2001 ?**
3577-3581 A365 Set of 5          22.50 22.50

A373

A374

Cats and Dogs — A375

Designs: No. 3582, $35, Boxer. No. 3583, $60, Cinnamon ocicat. No. 3584, $100, Smooth dachshund. $300, White Manx.

No. 3586, $35, Chihuahua. No. 3587, $60, Persian tabby. No. 3588, $100, Colorpoint shorthair. $200, Cocker spaniel.

No. 3590 — Names of dogs (border color and location of denomination), $100: a, Pup (pink, bottom). b, Yogi (orange, bottom). c, Hooch (yellow, bottom) d, Huxley Blu (orange, top) e, Snowflake (yellow, top). f, Red (pink, top).

No. 3591 — Names of cats (border color and location of denomination), $100: a, Tom (orange, bottom). b, Puff (yellow, bottom). c, Jag (pink, bottom). d, Fritz (yellow, top). e, Smokey (pink, top). f, Thor, (orange, top).

No. 3592, $60: a, Devon rex. b, Egyptian mau. c, Turkish angora. d, Sphynx. e, Persian. f, American wirehair. g, Exotic shorthair. h, American curl.

No. 3593, $80: a, Airedale terrier. b, Greyhound. c, Afghan hound. d, Samoyed. e, Field spaniel. f, Scottish terrier. g, Brittany spaniel. h, Boston terrier.

No. 3594, $80: a, American shorthair. b, Somali. c, Singapura. d, Balinese. e, Egyptian mau. f, Scottish fold. g, Sphynx. h, Korat.

No. 3595, $80: a, Rottweiler. b, German shepherd. c, Bernese mountain dog. d, Sharpei. e, Dachshund. f, Jack Russell terrier. g, Boston terrier. h, Welsh corgi.

No. 3596, $400, Dalmatian. No. 3597, $400, Birman. No. 3598, $400, Abyssinian. No. 3599, $400, Beagle. No. 3600, $400, German shepeherd named Baron of Fillmore. No. 3601, $400, Cat named Spike.

**2001, Mar. 1**          **Perf. 14**
3582-3585 A373 Set of 4          6.25 6.25
3586-3589 A374 Set of 4          5.25 5.25
**Sheets of 6, #a-f**
3590-3591 A375 Set of 2          16.00 16.00

### Sheets of 8, #a-h
3592-3593 A373 Set of 2          15.00 15.00
3594-3595 A374 Set of 2          16.50 16.50
### Souvenir Sheets
3596-3597 A373 Set of 2          9.50 9.50
3598-3599 A374 Set of 2          9.50 9.50
3600-3601 A375 Set of 2          9.50 9.50

Hong Kong 2001 Stamp Exhibition (Nos. 3592-3593, 3596-3597).

### Souvenir Sheets

Hello Kitty — A376

Western children's stories with Hello Kitty characters: No. 3602, $400, Cinderella. No. 3603, $400, The Wizard of Oz. No. 3604, $400, Little Red Riding Hood. No. 3605, $400, Peter Pan. No. 3606, $400, Heidi. No. 3607, $400, Alice in Wonderland.

Oriental children's stories with Hello Kitty characters: No. 3608, $400, The Fishermen. No. 3609, $400, In the Snow. No. 3610, $400, Bamboo Princess. No. 3611, $400, Three in a Boat. No. 3612, $400, Up a Tree. No. 3613, $400, On a Bear.

**2001, Mar. 28**          **Litho.**          **Perf. 13¾**
3602-3613 A376 Set of 12          55.00 55.00

Phila Nippon '01, Japan — A377

Designs: No. 3614, $25, Hanaogi with Maidservant, by Choki Eishosai. No. 3615, $25, Girl at a Hot Spring Resort, by Goyo Hashiguchi. No. 3616, $30, Morokoshi of the Echizenya, by Eiri Rekisentei. No. 3617, $30, Courtesan Receiving Letter of Invitation, by Harunobu Suzuki. No. 3618, $35, Two Girls on Their Way to or from the Bathhouse, by Suzuki. No. 3619, $35, Mother and Daughter on an Outing, by Hokusai. No. 3620, $60, Matron in Love, by Utamaro. No. 3621, $60, Girl and Frog, by Suzuki. No. 3622, $100, The Courtesan Midorigi, by Eisho Chokosai. No. 3623, $100, Three Beauties of High Fame, by Utamaro. No. 3624, $200, Maiko, by Bakusen Tsuchida. No. 3625, $200, Girl Breaking Off the Branch of a Flowering Tree, by Suzuki.

No. 3626 — Paintings by Jakuchu Ito (28x84mm): a, Insects, Reptiles and Amphibians at a Pond. b, Rose Mallows and Fowl. c, Rooster, Sunflower and Morning Glories. d, A Group of Roosters. e, Black Rooster and Nandina. f, Birds and Autumn Maples. g, Wagtail and Roses. h, Cockatoos in a Pine.

No. 3627 — Predominate features of sections of Procession to the Shugakuin Imperial Villa, by Sesshin Kakimoto (28x84mm): a, Bridge. b, High mountain, road and bridge. c, Large tree in foreground. d, Small island in foreground. e, Building at bottom. f, Building and large tree at bottom.

No. 3628 — Paintings of Women (28x84mm): a, Girls After the Bath, by Utamaro. b, Summer Evening on the Riverbank at Hama-cho, by Kiyonaga Torii. c, A Beauty in a Wind, by Ando Kaigetsudo. d, Sisters by Shoen Uemura. e, Kasamori Osen, by Suzuki.

No. 3629 — Details from Backstage at a Kabuki Theater, by Moronobu Hishikawa (30x38mm): a, Top of screen. b, Man with red kimono. c, Man with stringed instrument. e, Man on chair.

No. 3630, $400, Portrait of Senseki Takami, by Kazan Watanabe. No. 3631, $400, Fish and Octopus From the Colorful Realm of Living Beings, by Ito. No. 3632, $400, Woman Holding a Flower, by Hisako Kajiwara, horiz. No. 3633, $400, Palace of Immortals in an Autumn Valley, by Yako Okochi, horiz. No. 3634, $400, Wintry Sky, by Hosen Higashibara, horiz.

**2001, June 18**          **Perf. 14**
3614-3625 A377 Set of 12          11.00 11.00
3626 A377 $80 Sheet of 8, #a-h          8.25 8.25
3627 A377 $100 Sheet of 6, #a-f          7.50 7.50
3628 A377 $120 Sheet of 5, #a-e          6.75 6.75
3629 A377 $160 Sheet of 4, #a-d          7.50 7.50
**Sizes: 90x120mm, 120x90mm**
*Imperf*
3630-3634 A377 Set of 5          22.50 22.50

Giuseppe Verdi (1813-1901), Opera Composer — A378

No. 3635: a, Verdi, score at LR. b, Actor, score from Rigoletto. c, Actor, score from Ernani. d, Verdi, scores at left. $400, Verdi and scores.

**2001, June 18**          **Perf. 14**
3635 A378 $160 Sheet of 4, #a-d 8.25 8.25
### Souvenir Sheet
3636 A378 $400 multi          5.50 5.50

Toulouse-Lautrec Paintings — A379

No. 3637, horiz.: a, Maurice Joyant in the Baie de Somme. b, Monsieur Boileau. c, Monsieur, Madame and the Dog. $300, Man from Monsieur, Madame and the Dog.

**2001, June 18**          **Perf. 13¾**
3637 A379 $160 Sheet of 3, #a-c 5.50 5.50
### Souvenir Sheet
3638 A379 $300 multi          5.25 5.25

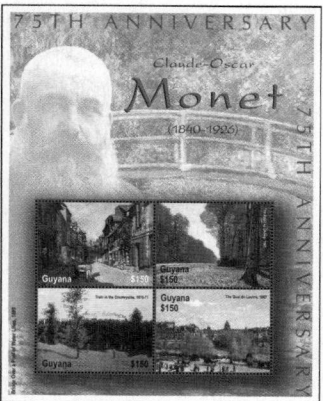

Monet Paintings — A380

No. 3639, horiz.: a, Village Street in Normandy, Near Honfleur. b, The Road to Chailly. c, Train in the Countryside. d, The Quai du Louvre.
$400, Flowering Garden.

**2001, June 18**
3639 A380 $150 Sheet of 4, #a-d 7.50 7.50

**Souvenir Sheet**
3640 A380 $400 multi      5.25 5.25

Queen Victoria (1819-1901) — A381

Pictures of Victoria from — No. 3641, $200: a, 1829. b, 1837. c, 1840. d, 1897 (with crown).
No. 3642, $200: a, 1850. b, 1843. c, 1859. d, 1897 (with hat).
No. 3643, $400, 1885 (with crown). No. 3644, $400, Undated.

**2001, June 18**      **Perf. 14**
**Sheets of 4, #a-d**
3641-3642 A381 Set of 2   19.00 19.00

**Souvenir Sheets**
3643-3644 A381 Set of 2   9.50 9.50

Queen Elizabeth II, 75th
Birthday — A382

No. 3645: a, Pink hat. b, Red hat. c, White hat. d, Tiara.

**2001, June 18**      **Perf. 14**
3645 A382 $150 Sheet of 4, #a-d 7.50 7.50

**Souvenir Sheet**
**Perf. 13¾**
3646 A382 $400 shown    5.25 5.25

No. 3645 contains four 28x42mm stamps.

Photomosaic of
Queen Elizbeth
II — A383

**2001, June 18**      **Perf. 14**
3647 A383 $80 multi     .90 .90

Printed in sheets of 8, with and without inscription reading "In Celebration of the 50th Anniversary of H.M. Queen Elizabeth II's Accession to the Throne."

**Flower Photomosaic Type of 1999-2000**

No. 3648: Various pictures of American scenes making up a photomosaic of Pres. John F. Kennedy.

**2001, June 18**
3648 A341 $80 Sheet of 8, #a-h 7.50 7.50

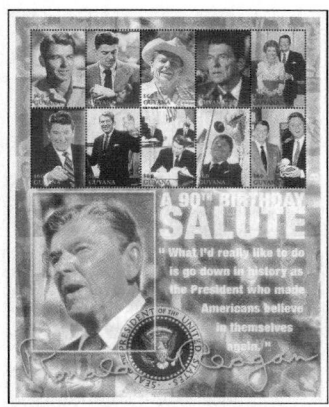

Pres. Ronald Reagan — A384

Reagan: a, In checked shirt. b, With Bonzo. c, With cowboy hat. d, With dark tie. e, With wife, Nancy. f, With striped tie. g, Waving. h, Signing treaty with Mikhail Gorbachev. i, With hammer and chisel. j, With Pres. Clinton.

**2001, June 18**
3649 A384 $60 Sheet of 10, #a-j 8.25 8.25

**Betty Boop Type of 2000**

Designs: No. 3650, $400, With swimsuit and sunglasses. No. 3651, $400, With lilac headdress. No. 3652, $400, With purple top and pirate's hat. No. 3653, $400, Dancing on radio, horiz.

**2001**      **Perf. 13¾**
3650-3653 A358 Set of 4   18.00 18.00

**Betty Boop Type of 2000**

Designs: No. 3654, $400, In orange and yellow polka dot swimsuit, holding gift. No. 3655, $400, Holding on to anchor. No. 3556, $400, In red bikini, surfing. No. 3557, $400, Wearing birthday hat, horiz.

**2001**    **Litho.**   **Perf. 13¾**
3654-3657 A358 Set of 4   18.00 18.00

**Historical Events Type of 1997**

No. 3658: a, Securities and Exchange Commission formed, 1934. b, Herbert Hoover is elected president, 1928. c, The Jazz Singer is first talking movie, 1927. d, J. Edgar Hoover becomes director of FBI, 1924. e, Alexander Fleming discovers penicillin, 1928. f, FCC established to regulate broadcasting, 1934. g, Lindbergh becomes first to fly solo across

Atlantic, 1927. h, Albert Einstein is awarded Nobel Prize for Physics, 1921. i, Hindenburg dies and Hitler becomes German Führer, 1934. j, Social Security Act provides safety for Americans, 1935. k, Earhart is first to fly solo from Hawaii to California, 1935. l, Marcus Garvey's prison sentence is commuted, 1927.

**2001, Mar. 28**      **Perf. 14¼x14¾**
3658 A289 $60 Sheet of 12, #a-l 9.50 9.50

Prehistoric
Animals — A385

Designs: $20, Allosaurus. $30, Spinosaurus. $35, Pteranodon. $60, Cetiosaurus. $200, Archaeopteryx. $300, Parasaurolophus.
No. 3665, $100, horiz.: a, Alamosaurus. b, Archaeopteryx, diff. c, Pachycephalosaurus. d, Parasaurolophus, diff. e, Edmontosaurus. f, Triceratops.
No. 3666, $100, horiz.: a, Brachiosaurus and two palm trees. b, Dimorphodon. c, Coelophysis. d, Velociraptor. e, Antrodemus. f, Euparkeria.
No. 3667, $100, horiz.: a, Ichthyostega. b, Eryops. c, Ichthyosaur. d, Pliosaur. e, Dunklosteus. f, Eogyrinus.
No. 3668, $100, horiz.: a, Brachiosaurus and palm tree. b, Pteranodon, diff. c, Compsognathus. d, Corythosaurus. e, Allosaurus, diff. f, Torosaurus.
No. 3669, $400, Brachiosaurus, diff. No. 3670, $400, Torosaurus, diff., horiz. No. 3671, $400, Ichthyosaur, diff., horiz. No. 3672, $400, Pteranodon, diff., horiz.

**2001, Oct. 15**      **Perf. 14**
3659-3664 A385 Set of 6  7.25 7.25

**Sheets of 6, #a-f**
3665-3668 A385 Set of 4  27.50 27.50

**Souvenir Sheets**
3669-3672 A385 Set of 4  18.00 18.00

Vegaspex (#3665-3672).

Animals of
Tropical
Rainforests
A386

Designs: $35, Mandrill, vert. $100, Leaf cutting ants.
No. 3675, $80: a, Elephant. b, Impala. c, Leopard. d, Gray parrot. e, Hippopotamus. f, Pygmy chimp. g, African green python. h, Mountain gorilla.
No. 3676, $80: a, Three-toed sloth. b, Lion tamarin. c, Ringtail lemur. d, Sugar glider. e, Toucan. f, Trogons. g, Pygmy marmoset. h, Poison arrow frog.
No. 3677, $400, Tapir, vert. No. 3678, $400, Sable antelope, vert.

**2001, Oct. 15**
3673-3674 A386 Set of 2  1.50 1.50

**Sheets of 8, #a-h**
3675-3676 A386 Set of 2  14.50 14.50

**Souvenir Sheets**
3677-3678 A386 Set of 2  9.00 9.00

Tropical Birds — A387

No. 3679, $100, horiz.: a, Rainbow lorikeet. b, King bird of paradise. c, Yellow-chevroned parakeet. d, Masked lovebird. e, Scarlet ibis. f, Toco toucan.
No. 3680, $100, horiz.: a, Hyacinth macaw. b, Wire-tailed manakin. c, Scarlet macaw. d, Sun parakeet. e, Roseate spoonbill. f, Red-billed toucan.
No. 3681, $400, Eclectus parrot. No. 3682, $400, Sulfur-crested cockatoo.

**2001, Oct. 15**      **Litho.**
**Sheets of 6, #a-f**
3679-3680 A387 Set of 2  13.50 13.50

**Souvenir Sheets**
3681-3682 A387 Set of 2  9.00 9.00

New Year 2002 (Year of the
Horse) — A388

No. 3683 — Evolution of Chinese character for "horse": a, Two characters outside, one character inside parentheses at UR. b, Three characters outside, one character inside parentheses at UR. c, Four characters outside, one character inside parentheses at UR. d, Three characters outside, two characters inside parentheses at UR.
No. 3684 — Figure on horse: a, Denomination at UL. b, Denomination at UR.

**2001, Oct. 15**      **Perf. 13**
3683 A388 $100 Sheet of 4, #a-d 4.50 4.50
**Perf. 13¼**
3684 A388 $150 Sheet of 2, #a-b 3.50 3.50

No. 3684 contains two 38x50mm stamps.

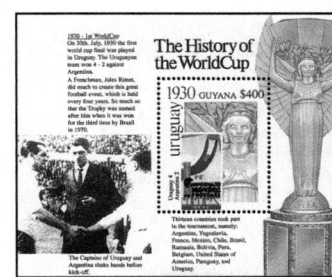

2002 World Cup Soccer
Championships, Japan and
Korea — A389

No. 3685, $100 — Posters from: a, 1950, and player. b, 1954, and Jules Rimet. c, 1958, Pelé and teammates. d, 1962, and Zito scoring goal. e, 1966, and English players celebrating. f, 1970, and Jairzinho.

No. 3686, $100 — Posters from: a, 1978, and Daniel Passarella. b, 1982, and Paolo Rossi. c, 1986, and Diego Maradona. d, 1990, and German players celebrating. e, 1994, and Brazilian players celebrating. f, 1998, and Zinedine Zidane.

No. 3687, $400, 1930 poster, head from Jules Rimet Trophy. No. 3688, $400, Head and globe from World Cup trophy.

**2001, Dec. 26**     *Perf. 13³⁄₄x14¹⁄₄*

**Sheets of 6, #a-f**

3685-3686   A389   Set of 2    14.00 14.00

**Souvenir Sheets**

*Perf. 14¹⁄₄*

3687-3688   A389   Set of 2    9.00 9.00

**Queen Mother Type of 1999 Redrawn**

No. 3689: a, With Princess Elizabeth, 1928. b, Lady Elizabeth-Bowles Lyon, 1914. c, With Princess Elizabeth, 1950. d, In Venice, 1984. $400, In Canada, 1988.

**2001, Dec.**      *Perf. 14*

**Yellow Orange Frames**

3689   A328   $130 Sheet of 4, #a-d, + label    5.75 5.75

**Souvenir Sheet**

*Perf. 13³⁄₄*

3690   A328   $400 multi    4.50 4.50

Queen Mother's 101st birthday. No. 3690 contains one 38x50mm stamp with a bluer cast than that found on No. 3434. Sheet margins of Nos. 3689-3690 lack embossing and gold arms and frames found on Nos. 3433-3434.

**I Love Lucy Type of 2000**

**Souvenir Sheets**

Designs: No. 3691, $400, Lucy wearing leis, with hands up. No. 3692, $400, Lucy with checked shirt and apron, with mouth open.

**2001 ?**      *Perf. 13³⁄₄*

3691-3692   A365   Set of 2    9.00 9.00

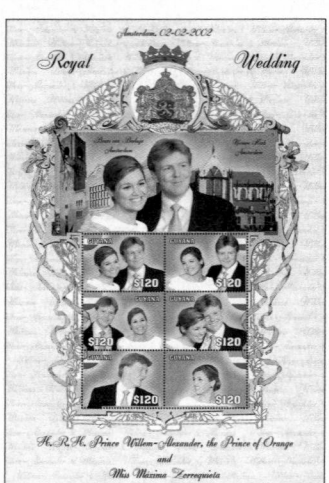

Wedding of Netherlands Prince Willem-Alexander and Máxima Zorreguieta — A390

No. 3693: a, Couple (Máxima at left), flag colors at left. b, Couple (heads apart), flag colors at right. c, Couple (Máxima at right), flag colors at left. d, Couple (heads together), flag colors at right. e, Willem-Alexander. f, Máxima.

**2002, Jan. 7**   Litho.   *Perf. 14³⁄₄x14¹⁄₄*

3693   A390   $120 Sheet of 6, #a-f   8.00 8.00

**2002, Feb. 6**     *Perf. 13¹⁄₂x13¹⁄₄*

3694   A391   $200 multi    2.25 2.25

Printed in sheets of four.

United We Stand — A391

Reign of Queen Elizabeth II, 50th Anniv. — A392

No. 3695: a, Blue hat. b, Feathered hat. c, Waving. d, With horse at right. $400, With horse at left.

**2002, Feb. 6**     *Perf. 14¹⁄₂*

3695   A392   $150 Sheet of 4, #a-d   6.75 6.75

**Souvenir Sheet**

3696   A392   $400 multi    4.50 4.50

**Flower Photomosaic Type of 1999-2000**

No. 3697: Various science photographs making up a photomosaic of Albert Einstein.

**2002, Feb. 25**     *Perf. 13³⁄₄*

3697   A341   $80 Sheet of 8, #a-h   7.25 7.25

Nobel Prizes, Cent. (in 2001) — A393

No. 3698, $100 — Chemistry laureates: a, Harold C. Urey, 1934. b, Willard F. Libby, 1960. c, Frederick Sanger, 1958 and 1980. d, Theodor Svedberg, 1926. e, Cyril N. Hinshelwood, 1956. f, Nikolai Semenov, 1956.

No. 3699, $100: a, Alexander Todd, Chemistry, 1957. b, John Steinbeck, Literature, 1962. c, Edward C. Kendall, Physiology or Medicine, 1950. d, Frederick G. Banting, Physiology or Medicine, 1923. e, Charles Nicolle, Physiology or Medicine, 1928. f, Charles Richet, Physiology or Medicine, 1913.

No. 3700, $400, International Red Cross, Peace, 1917. No. 3701, $400, John J. R. MacLeod, Physiology or Medicine, 1923. No. 3702, $400, Derek H. R. Barton, Chemistry, 1969.

**2002, Feb. 25**     *Perf. 14*

**Sheets of 6, #a-f**

3698-3699   A393   Set of 2   13.50 13.50

**Souvenir Sheets**

3700-3702   A393   Set of 3   13.50 13.50

2002 Winter Olympics, Salt Lake City A394

Designs: No. 3703, $200, Skier. No. 3704, $200, Figure skater.

**2002, July 1**   Litho.   *Perf. 13¹⁄₄x13¹⁄₂*

3703-3704   A394   Set of 2   4.50 4.50

a.   Souvenir sheet, #3703-3704    4.50 4.50

Guyana — People's Republic of China Diplomatic Relations, 30th Anniv. — A395

Designs: No. 3705, $100, Chinese flag, Kaieteur Falls, Guyana. No. 3706, $100, Guyanese flag, Great Wall of China.

**2002, July 1**     *Perf. 14*

3705-3706   A395   Set of 2   2.25 2.25

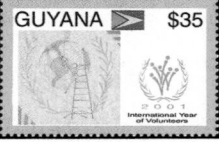

Intl. Volunteers Year (in 2001) A396

Emblem, Guyanese flag and: $35, Person on ladder touching Guyana on map. $60, Map of Guyana and IVY emblem. $300, People.

**2002, July 1**

3707-3709   A396   Set of 3   4.50 4.50

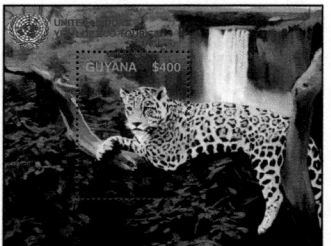

Intl. Year of Ecotourism — A397

No. 3710: a, Owl. b, Waterfall and tourists. c, Baboon. d, Butterfly. e, Flower. f, Otter. $400, Leopard.

**2002, July 1**

3710   A397   $100 Sheet of 6, #a-f   6.75 6.75

**Souvenir Sheet**

3711   A397   $400 multi    4.50 4.50

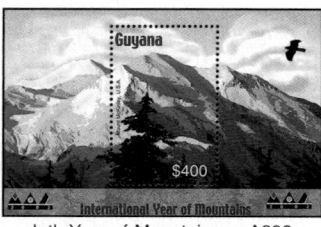

Intl. Year of Mountains — A398

No. 3712: a, Devil's Tower, US. b, Schreckhorn, Switzerland. c, Mt. Rainier, US. d, Mt. Everest, Nepal and Tibet. No. 3713: Mt. McKinley, U.S.

**2002, July 1**     *Perf. 13¹⁄₂x13¹⁄₄*

3712   A398   $200 Sheet of 4, #a-d   14.00 14.00

**Souvenir Sheet**

3713   A398   $400 multi    7.00 7.00

See Nos. 3848-3851.

20th World Scout Jamboree, Thailand — A399

No. 3714: a, Environmental Science merit badge. b, Citizenship in the World merit badge. c, Life Saving merit badge. $400, Mascot, Scout emblem.

**2002, July 1**

3714   A399   $200 Sheet of 3, #a-c   6.75 6.75

**Souvenir Sheet**

3715   A399   $400 multi    4.50 4.50

Flora and Fauna — A400

No. 3716, $100 — Butterflies: a, Sweet oil. b, Swallowtail. c, Southern white admiral. d, Prepona pheridamas. e, Plain tiger. f, Common eggfly.

No. 3717, $100 — Moths: a, Burgena varia. b, Lime hawkmoth. c, Spurge hawkmoth. d, Eligma laetipicta. e, Io moth. f, Pine hawkmoth.

No. 3718, $100 — Birds: a, Flycatcher. b, Barbary shrike. c, Red-faced mousebird. d, Red-footed booby. e, White-fronted goose. f, Great crested grebe.

No. 3719, $100 — Whales: a, Sperm. b, Pygmy sperm. c, Blue. d, Bottlenose. e, Killer. f, True's beaked.

No. 3720, $100, vert. — Orchids: a, Masdevallia tovarensis. b, Encyclia vitellina. c, Dendrobium nobile. d, Masdevallia falcata. e, Calanthe vestita. f, Brassolaeliacattleya Rising Sun.

No. 3721, $400, Zebra butterfly. No. 3722, $400, Callimorpha quadripuntaria. No. 3723, $400, Whiskered tern. No. 3724, $400, Beluga whale. No. 3725, $400, Brassavola nodosa.

**2002, Aug. 7**     *Perf. 14*

**Sheets of 6, #a-f**

3716-3720   A400   Set of 5   37.50 37.50

**Souvenir Sheets**

3721-3725   A400   Set of 5   25.00 25.00

Elvis Presley (1935-77) A401

Designs: No. 3726, $60, In army uniform. No. 3727, $60, Singing.

**2002, Aug. 16**     *Perf. 13³⁄₄*

3726-3727   A401   Set of 2   1.75 1.75

Each stamp was printed in a sheet of nine.

Popeye — A402

No. 3728: a, Popeye. b, Olive Oyl. c, Wimpy. d, Jeep. e, Swee'Pea and Olive Oyl. f, Swee'Pea.
$400, Popeye, diff.

**2002, Oct. 7**      **Perf. 14**
3728 A402 $100 Sheet of 6, #a-f   7.50 7.50
**Souvenir Sheet**
3729 A402 $400 multi      5.50 5.50

New Year 2003 (Year of the Ram) — A403

Rams and background color of: a, Red. b, Orange. c, Bright pink. d, Yellow green.

**2003, Jan. 27 Litho.**   **Perf. 14¼x14½**
3730 A403 $100 Sheet of 4, #a-d 5.50 5.50

Pres. John F. Kennedy (1917-63) — A404

No. 3731, vert.: a, Pres. Kennedy, Presidential seal. b, Pres. Kennedy, Dr. Martin Luther King, Jr. c, Pres. Kennedy, space capsule. d, Pres. Kennedy, US flag, White House. e, Pres. Kennedy, map of Cuba, missile. f, Jacqueline and John F. Kennedy, Jr., US flag.
$400, Pres. Kennedy and wife, Jacqueline.

**2003, Jan. 27**      **Perf. 14**
3731 A404 $100 Sheet of 6, #a-f   7.00 7.00
**Souvenir Sheet**
3732 A404 $400 multi      5.50 5.50

Pres. Ronald Reagan — A405

No. 3733, vert. — Pres. Reagan: a, And eagle. b, As actor. c, And Mt. Rushmore. d, And wife Nancy. e, And White House. f, Riding horse.
$400, With Mikhail Gorbachev.

**2003, Jan. 27**
3733 A405 $100 Sheet of 6, #a-f   8.00 8.00
**Souvenir Sheet**
3734 A405 $400 multi      7.00 7.00

Princess Diana (1961-97) — A406

No. 3735: a-f, Various depictions of Princess wearing tiaras or bridal veils.
$400, Wearing pink and yellow dress.

**2003, Jan. 27**
3735 A406 $100 Sheet of 6, #a-f   7.00 7.00
**Souvenir Sheet**
3736 A406 $400 multi      5.00 5.00

Paintings of Lucas Cranach the Elder (1472-1553) A407

Designs: $35, Portrait of a Man. $60, Portrait of a Woman. $100, Duchess Catherine of Mecklenburg. $200, Portrait of Duke Henry of Saxony.
No. 3741: a, The Virgin, c. 1518. b, The Virgin and Child Under the Apple Tree. c, The Virgin, c. 1535. d, The Virgin, c. 1525.
$400, The Virgin and Child Holding a Piece of Bread.

**2003, June 17 Litho.**   **Perf. 14¼**
3737-3740 A407   Set of 4    4.50 4.50
3741 A407 $150 Sheet of 4, #a-d 6.75 6.75
**Souvenir Sheet**
3742 A407 $400 multi      4.50 4.50

Art by Kunichika Toyohara (1835-1900) A408

Designs: $60, The Actor Shikan Nakamura IV. $80, The Actor Danjuro Ichikawa IX as Sukeroku, 1883. $100, The Actor Tatsunosuke Onoe. $300, The Actor Sadanji Ichikawa I as Kyusuke.
No. 3747: a, The Actor Sansho Kawarazaki as Watonai. b, The Actor Danjuro Ichikawa IX as Gongoru Kagemasa Kamakura. c, The Actor Sadanji Ichikawa I as Sadakuro. d, The Actor Danjuro Ichikawa IX as Sukeroku, 1898.
$400, The Actor Danjuro Ichikawa IX as Shukeigashira Kiyomasa Kato, horiz.

**2003, June 17**
3743-3746 A408   Set of 4    6.00 6.00
3747 A408 $150 Sheet of 4, #a-d 6.75 6.75
**Souvenir Sheet**
3748 A408 $400 multi      4.50 4.50

Paintings by Wassily Kandinsky (1866-1944) — A409

Designs: $25, Tension in Red. $30, Black Accompaniment. $35, Calm Tension. $60, Hard and Soft. $100, Yellow Point, horiz. $300, Composition VIII, horiz.
No. 3755: a, Red Oval. b, On the White II. c, Mutual Agreement. d, Inclination.
No. 3756, $400, White Center, horiz. No. 3757, $400, Black Weft, horiz.

**2003, June 17**
3749-3754 A409   Set of 6    6.25 6.25
3755 A409 $150 Sheet of 4, #a-d 6.75 6.75
**Size: 104x84mm**
*Imperf*
3756-3757 A409   Set of 2    9.00 9.00

Caribbean Community, 30th Anniv. — A410

Anniversary emblem and: $20, Map of Guyana, vert. $60, Bank of Guyana Building. $100, Hands with torch, vert. $160, Stethoscope and AIDS ribbon, vert.

**2003, July 7**      **Perf. 14**
3758-3761 A410   Set of 4    3.75 3.75

A411

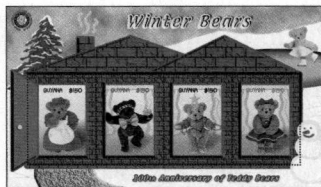

Teddy Bears, Cent. (in 2002) — A412

No. 3762 — Background color: a, Lilac. b, Dull greenish blue. c, Light blue. d, Dull yellow green. e, Dull blue green. f, Dull gray green. h, Gray. i, Dull green. j, Gray blue.
No. 3763 — Bear with: a, Red dress. b, Menorah. c, Christmas lights. d, Blue dress.

**2003, Aug. 25**
3762 A411  $80 Sheet of 9, #a-i   8.50 8.50
3763 A412 $150 Sheet of 4, #a-d   7.00 7.00

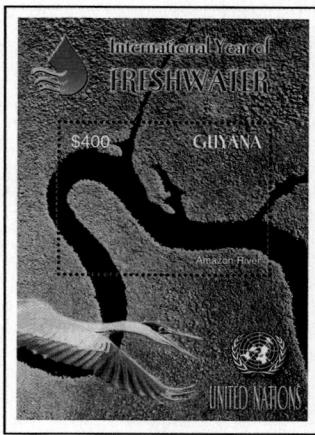

Intl. Year of Fresh Water — A413

No. 3764 — Kaieteur Falls: a, Top. b, Middle. c, Base.
$400, Amazon River.

**2003, Aug. 25**      **Perf. 13¾**
3764 A413 $200 Sheet of 3, #a-c 6.75 6.75
**Souvenir Sheet**
3765 A413 $400 multi      4.50 4.50

Tour de France Bicycle Race, Cent. — A414

No. 3766: a, Jacques Anquetil, 1964. b, Felice Gimondi, 1965. c, Lucien Aimar, 1966. d, Roger Pingeon, 1967.
$400, Jan Janssen, 1968.

**2003, Aug. 25**      **Perf. 13½x13**
3766 A414 $150 Sheet of 4, #a-d 6.75 6.75
**Souvenir Sheet**
3767 A414 $400 multi      4.50 4.50

Coronation of Queen Elizabeth II, 50th Anniv. — A415

No. 3768: a, Wearing tiara. b, Wearing dark blue dress. c, Wearing lilac dress.
$400, Wearing crown.

**2003, Aug. 25**      **Perf. 14**
3768 A415 $200 Sheet of 3, #a-c 6.75 6.75
**Souvenir Sheet**
3769 A415 $400 multi      4.50 4.50

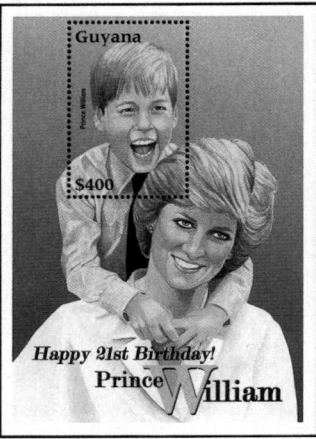

Prince William, 21st Birthday — A416

No. 3770: a, As toddler. b, As adult. c, As infant.
$400, As young boy.

**2003, Aug. 25**
3770 A416 $200 Sheet of 3, #a-c 7.00 7.00
**Souvenir Sheet**
3771 A416 $400 multi 5.50 5.50

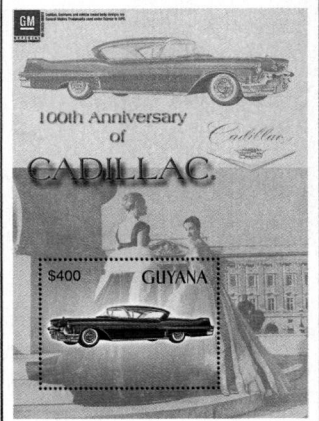

General Motors Automobiles — A418

No. 3776, $150 — Cadillacs: a, 1948 Sixty Special. b, 1966 Fleetwood Sixty Special. c, 1967 Eldorado. d, 1976 Eldorado convertible.
No. 3777, $150 — Corvettes: a, 1964 Stingray. b, 1963 Stingray. c, 1966 Stingray. 4. d, 1969.
No. 3778, $400, Undescribed Cadillac (1957 Coupe de Ville). No. 3779, $400, 1971 Corvette.

**2003, Aug. 25   Sheets of 4, #a-d**
3776-3777 A418 Set of 2 14.50 14.50
**Souvenir Sheets**
3778-3779 A418 Set of 2 9.50 9.50

Butterflies — A419

Designs: $20, Grecian shoemaker. $55, Clorinde. $80, Orange-barred sulphur. $100, Atala. $160, White peacock. $200, Polydamus swallowtail. $300, Giant swallowtail. $400, Banded king shoemaker. $500, Blue night. $1000, Orange theope. $2000, Small lacewing. $3000, Common morpho.

**2003, Nov. 4   Litho.   Perf. 13¼**
3780 A419 $20 multi .25 .25
3781 A419 $55 multi .70 .70
3782 A419 $80 multi 1.00 1.00
3783 A419 $100 multi 1.25 1.25
3784 A419 $160 multi 1.90 1.90
3785 A419 $200 multi 2.40 2.40
3786 A419 $300 multi 3.50 3.50
3787 A419 $400 multi 4.75 4.75
3788 A419 $500 multi 6.00 6.00
3789 A419 $1000 multi 11.50 11.50
3790 A419 $2000 multi 23.00 23.00
3791 A419 $3000 multi 34.00 34.00
Nos. 3780-3791 (12) 90.25 90.25

Worldwide Fund for Nature (WWF) A420

No. 3792: a, Head of channel-billed toucan. b, Two toco toucans on branch. c, Channel-billed toucan on branch. d, Toco toucan and chick.

**2003, Dec. 1   Perf. 14**
3792 Horiz. strip of 4, #a-d 5.00 5.00
 a.-d. A420 $100 Any single 1.20 1.20
 e. Souvenir sheet, 2 each #3792a-3792d 10.50 10.50

Mushrooms — A421

Designs: No. 3793, $20, Clitocybe gibba. No. 3794, $20, Clitocybe clavipes. $30, Calocybe carnea. $300, Marasmius.

No. 3797: a, Amanita spissa. b, Boletus aestivalis. c, Boletus rubellus. d, Clathrus archeri.
$400, Volvariella bombycina.

**2003, Dec. 1**
3793-3796 A421 Set of 4 4.50 4.50
3797 A421 $150 Sheet of 4, #a-d 7.25 7.25
**Souvenir Sheet**
3798 A421 $400 multi 5.75 5.75

Mammals A422

Designs: $25, Common tenrec. $60, Humboldt's woolly monkey, vert. $100, Gundi. $200, Harbor seal.
No. 3803: a, Prevost's squirrel. b, Mountain tapir. c, Sea otter. d, Indus dolphin.
$400, Peter's disk-winged bat, vert.

**2003, Dec. 1**
3799-3802 A422 Set of 4 4.25 4.25
3803 A422 $150 Sheet of 4, #a-d 6.75 6.75
**Souvenir Sheet**
3804 A422 $400 multi 4.50 4.50

Flowers — A423

Designs: $20, Begonia sedeni. $30, Dahlia. $35, Eschecholzia californica. $300, Lupinus perennis.
No. 3809: a, Agapanthus africanus. b, Hyacinth cultivars. c, Protea linearis. d, Hippestrum aulicum.
$400, Crocus sativus, horiz.

**2003, Dec. 1**
3805-3808 A423 Set of 4 4.25 4.25
3809 A423 $150 Sheet of 4, #a-d 6.75 6.75
**Souvenir Sheet**
3810 A423 $400 multi 5.00 5.00

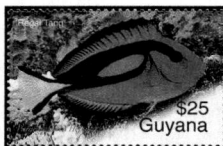

Fish A424

Designs: $25, Regal tang. $60, Pajama tang. $100, Coral beauty. $200, Emperor angelfish.
No. 3815: a, High hat. b, Regal angelfish. c, Fire clown. d, Domino damselfish.
$400, Tomato clown.

**2003, Dec. 1**
3811-3814 A424 Set of 4 4.25 4.25
3815 A424 $150 Sheet of 4, #a-d 8.00 8.00
**Souvenir Sheet**
3816 A424 $400 multi 5.00 5.00

Guyana — Brazil Diplomatic Relations, 35th Anniv. A425

**2003, Dec. 18**
3817 A425 $20 multi .20 .20

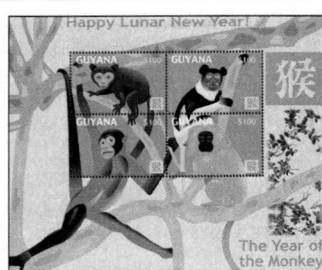

New Year 2004 (Year of the Monkey) — A426

No. 3818: a, Dark brown monkey with orange face. b, Dark brown and white monkey with brown face. c, Brown monkey with orange face. d, Orange monkey with black face.

**2004, Jan. 5**
3818 A426 $100 Sheet of 4, #a-d 4.75 4.75

Paintings by Tang Yin (1470-1524) — A427

No. 3819, vert.: a, Concubines of Emperor Chu. b, Lady. c, Untitled painting depicting woman. d, Untitled painting depicting landscape.
$400, Mountain Scene.

**2004, Jan. 21   Litho.   Perf. 13¼**
3819 A427 $150 Sheet of 4, #a-d 6.75 6.75
**Souvenir Sheet**
3820 A427 $400 multi 4.50 4.50

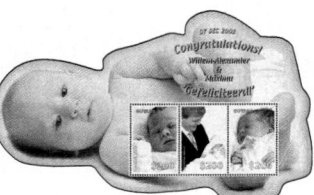

Birth of Princess Catherina Amalia of the Netherlands — A428

No. 3821: a, Princess, one hand shown. b, Princess and father, Prince Willem-Alexander. c, Princess, two hands shown.

**2004, Feb. 15   Perf. 14¼**
3821 A428 $200 Sheet of 3, #a-c 7.00 7.00

FIFA (Fédération Internationale de Football Association), Cent. — A429

World Cup championship teams: No. 3822, $80, Uruguay, 1930. No. 3823, $80, Italy, 1934. No. 3824, $80, Italy, 1938. No. 3825, $80, Uruguay, 1950. No. 3826, $80, Germany, 1954. No. 3827, $80, Brazil, 1958. No. 3828, $80, Brazil, 1962. No. 3829, $80, England, 1966. No. 3830, $80, Brazil, 1970.

**2004, Feb. 16   Perf. 13¼**
3822-3830 A429 Set of 9 8.25 8.25

---

**Celebrating 100 Years of Aviation**

Powered Flight, Cent. — A417

Designs: $100, Airplane of Sir Alliot Verdon Roe. $160, Airplane of Samuel Franklin Cody.
No. 3772, $150: a, Wright Flyer. b, Spad 13. c, Sopwith F-1. d, Albatros D.II.
No. 3773, $150: a, Nieuport 17. b, S. E. 5a. c, D. H. 4. d, German biplane.
No. 3774, $400, Wright Flyer making first flight. No. 3775, $400, Fokker D.VIIs.

**2003, Aug. 25**
3771A A417 $100 multi 1.10 1.10
3771B A417 $160 multi 1.75 1.75
**Sheets of 4, #a-d**
3772-3773 A417 Set of 2 13.50 13.50
**Souvenir Sheets**
3774-3775 A417 Set of 2 10.00 10.00

Paintings by Norman Rockwell (1894-1978) — A430

No. 3831, vert.: a, Doctor and Doll. b, Baby-sitter with Screaming Infant. c, Girl with Black Eye. d, Checkup.
$400, Girl Running with Wet Canvas (Wet Paint).

**2004, Feb. 16**          **Perf. 14¼**
3831 A430 $150 Sheet of 4, #a-d 6.75 6.75
**Souvenir Sheet**
3832 A430 $400 multi          4.50 4.50

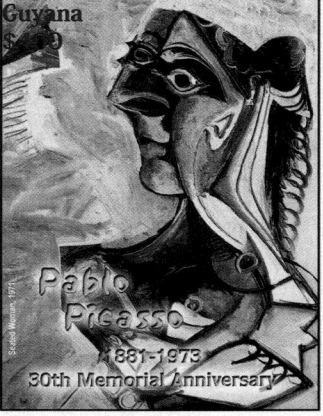

Paintings by Pablo Picasso (1881-1973) — A431

No. 3833: a, Woman in Yellow Hat. b, Seated Woman, 1962. c, Head of a Woman. d, Large Profile.
$400, Seated Woman, 1971.

**2004, Feb. 16**          **Perf. 14¼**
3833 A431 $150 Sheet of 4, #a-d 6.75 6.75
**Imperf**
3834 A431 $400 multi          4.50 4.50
No. 3833 contains four 38x50mm stamps.

Rembrandt Paintings A432

Designs: $35, A Woman Bathing. $60, Flora. $100, The Poet, Jan Hermansz Krul. $200, Portrait of a Young Man.
No. 3839: a, The Apostle James. b, The Apostle Bartholemew. c, The Evangelist Matthew Inspired by an Angel. d, The Apostle Peter Standing.
$400, Balaam and the Ass.

**2004, Feb. 16**          **Perf. 14¼**
3835-3838 A432     Set of 4      4.50 4.50
3839 A432 $150 Sheet of 4, #a-d 6.75 6.75
**Souvenir Sheet**
3840 A432 $400 multi          4.75 4.75

Paintings in the Hermitage, St. Petersburg, Russia — A433

Designs: $35, Mercury Giving Bacchus to Nymphs to Raise, by Laurent de La Hyre. $60, Satyr and Bacchante, by Nicolas Poussin, vert. $100, Parting of Abelard and Eloisa, by Angelica Kauffmann. $200, Pastoral Scene, by François Boucher.
No. 3845, vert.: a, The Union of Earth and Water, by Peter Paul Rubens. b, Hercules Between Love and Wisdom, by Pompeo Girolano Batoni. c, Innocence Choosing Love Over Wealth, by Pierre-Paul Prud'hon. d, Mars and Venus, by Joseph Marie Vien.
No. 3846, Allegory of Virtuous Life, by Hendrik Van Balen. No. 3847, Statue of Ceres, by Rubens, vert.

**2004, Feb. 16**          **Perf. 14¼**
3841-3844 A433     Set of 4      4.50 4.50
3845 A433 $150 Sheet of 4, #a-d 7.00 7.00
**Imperf**
**Size: 77x55mm**
3846 A433 $400 multi          5.50 5.50
**Size: 56x77mm**
3847 A433 $400 multi          5.50 5.50

**Intl. Year of Mountains Type of 2002**

Designs: $80, Mt. Kosciuszko, Australia. $100, Mt. Elbrus, Russia. $150, Mt. Vinson, Antarctica.
$400, Mt. Everest, Nepal.

**2004**                **Perf. 14**
3848-3850 A398     Set of 3      3.75 3.75
**Souvenir Sheet**
3851 A398 $400 multi          4.50 4.50

**Miniature Sheet**

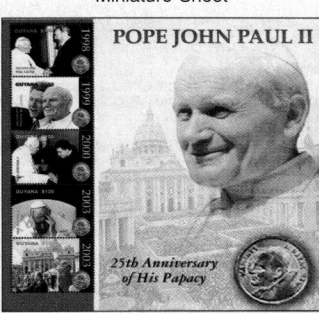

Election of Pope John Paul II, 25th Anniv. (in 2003) — A434

No. 3852: a, With Fidel Castro, 1998. b, With Pres. Bill Clinton, 1999. c, With bishop and man, 2000. d, With hands on head, 2003. e, In Popemobile, 2003.

**2004, Sept. 27  Litho.  Perf. 14**
3852 A434 $100 Sheet of 5, #a-e 5.75 5.75

2004 Summer Olympics, Athens A435

Designs: $60, Poster for 1912 Stockholm Olympics. $80, High jump, 1932 Los Angeles Olympics, horiz. $100, Commemorative medal for 1932 Olympics. $200, Ancient Greek runners, horiz.

**2004, Sept. 27**          **Perf. 14¼**
3853-3856 A435     Set of 4      6.75 6.75

European Soccer Championships, Portugal — A436

No. 3857, vert.: a, Michel Platini. b, Luis Arconada. c, Bruno Bellone. d, Parc des Princes, Paris.
$400, 1984 France team.

**2004, Sept. 27**          **Litho.**
3857 A436 $150 Sheet of 4, #a-d 8.00 8.00
**Souvenir Sheet**
3858 A436 $400 multi          5.00 5.00
No. 3857 contains four 28x47mm stamps.

FIFA (Fédération Internationale de Football Association), Cent. — A437

No. 3859: a, Alf Ramsey. b, Pele. c, Lothar Matthaus. d, Dennis Bergkamp.
$400, Fabien Barthez.

**2004, Sept. 27**          **Perf. 12¾x12½**
3859 A437 $150 Sheet of 4, #a-d 7.00 7.00
**Souvenir Sheet**
3860 A437 $400 multi          5.00 5.00

A438

D-Day, 60th Anniv. — A439

No. 3861, $150: a, Operation Overlord begins. b, Troops in landing craft storm the beaches of Normandy. c, Troops deep behind enemy lines. d, Churchill announces landings a success.
No. 3862, $150: a, Royal Scots Fusiliers. b, 2nd Company, 101st Heavy Tank Battalion. c, Anti-tank gun of 7th Green Howards. d, 229th Engineer Combat Battalion.
No. 3863, $150, vert.: a, Michael Wittmann. b, Lt. Robert Edlin. c, CSM Stanley Hollis. d, Kurt Meyer.
No. 3864, vert.: a, Rear Admiral John L. Hall. b, Rear Admiral Carlton F. Bryant. c, General Dwight D. Eisenhower. d, General Hap Arnold.
No. 3865, $400, Tank battle, Cotentin Peninsula. No. 3866, $400, Seaforth Highlanders of Canada. No. 3867, $400, Sgt. Clifton Barker.

No. 3868, Major General Maxwell D. Taylor.

**2004, Sept. 27**          **Perf. 13½**
**Sheets of 4, #a-d**
3861-3863 A438     Set of 3    21.00 21.00
3864 A439 $150 Sheet of 4, #a-d 7.00 7.00
**Souvenir Sheets**
3865-3867 A438     Set of 3    15.00 15.00
3868 A439 $400 multi          5.00 5.00

A440

A441

A442

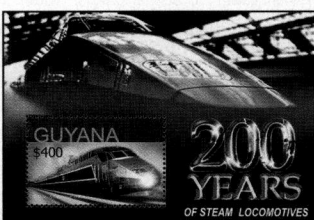

Locomotives — A443

No. 3869: a, Santa Fe Depot. b, LD Porta. c, D9000 Royal Scots Gray. d, TGV.
No. 3870, $150: a, Hercules 4-4-0. b, Sterling 8 ft Single Class 4-2-2. c, Class YP 4-6-2. d, Class 01.10 4-6-2.
No. 3871, $150: a, GWR King Class 4-6-0. b, 4500 Class 4-6-2. c, Class F 4-6-2. d, Class 231C 4-6-2.
No. 3872, $150: a, Western Railway, France, 1856. b, Dutch State Railway, 1880. c, Southern Railway, England, 1890. d, Madras and Southern Mahratta Railway, India, 1891.
No. 3873, $150: a, Baltimore and Ohio Railroad, US, 1856. b, Utica and Schenectady Railroad, US, 1837. c, Great Southern Railway, Spain, 1913. d, Victorian Government Railway, Australia, 1906.
No. 3874, $150: a, Shantung Railway, China, 1919. b, Great Indian Peninsula Railway, 1898. c, Cumberland Valley Railroad,

US, 1851. d, Central Pacific Railroad, US, 1863.

No. 3875, $150: a, Great Northern Railway, Ireland, 1876. b, London and Northwestern Railways, 1873. c, Shanghai-Nanking Railway, China, 1910. d, London, Brighton and South Coast Railway, 1846.

No. 3876, $400, No. 990, 4-4-0. No. 3877, $400, Northumbrian 0-2-2, vert.

No. 3878, $400, Netherlands State Railway, 1888. No. 3879, $400, Austrian State Railway, 1868. No. 3880, $400, London, Midland and Scottish Railway, 1923. No. 3881, $400, Pennsylvania Railroad, 1848.

No. 3882, TGV Atlantique.

| 2004, Sept. 27 | | | Perf. 13½ | |
|---|---|---|---|---|
| 3869 | A440 | $150 Sheet of 4, #a-d | 7.00 | 7.00 |
| **Sheets of 4, #a-d** | | | | |
| 3870-3871 | A441 | Set of 2 | 14.00 | 14.00 |
| 3872-3875 | A442 | Set of 4 | 30.00 | 30.00 |
| **Souvenir Sheets** | | | | |
| 3876-3877 | A441 | Set of 2 | 10.00 | 10.00 |
| 3878-3881 | A442 | Set of 4 | 20.00 | 20.00 |
| 3882 | A443 | $400 multi | 5.00 | 5.00 |

**Souvenir Sheet**

Deng Xiaoping (1904-97), Chinese Leader — A444

| 2004 | | | Perf. 14 | |
|---|---|---|---|---|
| 3883 | A444 | $400 multi | 4.75 | 4.75 |

South American Reptiles, Fish, Bats and Flowers — A445

No. 3884, $160 — Reptiles: a, Red-foot tortoise. b, Emerald tree boa. c, Green iguana. d, Cuvier's dwarf caiman.

No. 3885, $160 — Fish: a, Velvet cichlid. b, Freshwater sting ray. c, Splash tetra. d, Red piranha.

No. 3886, $160 — Bats: a, Mexican funnel-eared bat. b, Greater bulldog bat. c, Vampire bat. d, Doffroy's tailless bat.

No. 3887, $160, vert. — Flowers: a, Blue passion flower. b, Scarlet passion flower. c, Passion vine. d, Bromeliad flower.

No. 3888, $400, Eyelash viper. No. 3889, $400, Tambaqui, vert. No. 3890, $400, Short-tailed fruit bat, vert. No. 3891, $400, Epiphytic blueberry, vert.

| Perf. 13¼x13½, 13½x13¼ | | | | |
|---|---|---|---|---|
| **2005, Jan. 10** | | | **Litho.** | |
| **Sheets of 4, #a-d** | | | | |
| 3884-3887 | A445 | Set of 4 | 36.00 | 36.00 |
| **Souvenir Sheets** | | | | |
| 3888-3891 | A445 | Set of 4 | 19.50 | 19.50 |

New Year 2005 (Year of the Rooster) — A446

No. 3892: a, Rooster with dark feathers. b, Rooster with white feathers.
Illustration reduced.

| 2005, Jan. 24 | | | Perf. 12¾ | |
|---|---|---|---|---|
| 3892 | A446 | $50 Pair, #a-b | 1.40 | 1.40 |

Printed in sheets containing two pairs.

Prehistoric Animals — A447

No. 3893, $150: a, Eustreptospondylus. b, Rhamphorhynchus. c, Utahraptor. d, Entelodonts.

No. 3894, $150: a, Moeritherium. b, Deinonychus. c, Ophthalmosaurus. d, Grendelius.

No. 3895, $150: a, Spinosaurus. b, Tarbosaurus. c, Coelophysis. d, Sinosauropteryx prima.

No. 3896, $400, Velociraptor babies. No. 3897, $400, Ophthalmosaurus baby. No. 3898, $400, Iguanodon bernissartensis, vert.

| 2005, Jan. 24 | | Litho. | Perf. 12¾ | |
|---|---|---|---|---|
| **Sheets of 4, #a-d** | | | | |
| 3893-3895 | A447 | Set of 3 | 20.00 | 20.00 |
| **Souvenir Sheets** | | | | |
| 3896-3898 | A447 | Set of 3 | 15.00 | 15.00 |

Eddy Grant, Musician — A448

Designs: $20, Grant at UR. $80, Grant at UL.

No. 3901 — Portrait in: a, Blue. b, Yellow green. c, Blue violet. d, Red violet.
$400, Grant with guitar.

| 2005, Feb. 17 | | | Perf. 12¾ | |
|---|---|---|---|---|
| 3899-3900 | A448 | Set of 2 | 1.25 | 1.25 |
| 3901 | A448 | $190 Sheet of 4, #a-d | 9.75 | 9.75 |
| **Souvenir Sheet** | | | | |
| 3902 | A448 | $400 multi | 4.75 | 4.75 |

Pope John Paul II (1920-2005) and Pres. Ronald Reagan (1911-2004) A449

| 2005, Aug. 12 | | Litho. | Perf. 13½ | |
|---|---|---|---|---|
| 3903 | A449 | $300 multi | 3.25 | 3.25 |

Battle of Trafalgar, Bicent. A450

Designs: $25, Vice-admiral Cuthbert Collingwood. $35, Admiral Horatio Nelson injured at Battle of Santa Cruz. $60, Nelson's funeral car arriving at St. Paul's Cathedral, horiz. $80, Nelson and Flag Captain Thomas M. Hardy. $100, First shots of Battle of Trafalgar, horiz. $300, British ship hoists signals to begin pincer movement.
$400, Nelson.

| 2005, Aug. 12 | | | Perf. 13¼ | |
|---|---|---|---|---|
| 3904-3909 | A450 | Set of 6 | 6.50 | 6.50 |
| **Souvenir Sheet** | | | | |
| | | **Perf. 12** | | |
| 3910 | A450 | $400 multi | 5.00 | 5.00 |

V-E Day, 60th Anniv. — A451

No. 3911, horiz.: a, Neville Chamberlain makes peace with Adolf Hitler, 1938. b, The Royal Air Force hits back. c, Victory, 1945.
$400, Netherlands #277.

| 2005, Aug. 12 | | | Perf. 12¾ | |
|---|---|---|---|---|
| 3911 | A451 | $200 Sheet of 3, #a-c | 7.25 | 7.25 |
| **Souvenir Sheet** | | | | |
| 3912 | A451 | $400 multi | 5.00 | 5.00 |

V-J Day, 60th Anniv. — A452

No. 3913: a, Japan attacks Pearl Harbor, 1941. b, Iwo Jima War Memorial, Harlington, Texas. c, Newspaper announcing Japanese surrender, 1945.
$400, Seebees celebrate Japanese surrender.

| 2005, Aug. 12 | | | | |
|---|---|---|---|---|
| 3913 | A452 | $200 Sheet of 3, #a-c | 7.25 | 7.25 |
| **Souvenir Sheet** | | | | |
| 3914 | A452 | $400 multi | 5.00 | 5.00 |

Rotary International, Cent. — A453

No. 3915: a, Dentist examining patient's mouth. b, 2005 Rotary President-elect Carl-Wilhelm Stenhammar. c, Rotary District of Guyana first couple.
$400, Homer Wood, founder of second Rotary Club.

| 2005, Aug. 12 | | | | |
|---|---|---|---|---|
| 3915 | A453 | $150 Sheet of 3, #a-c | 6.25 | 6.25 |
| **Souvenir Sheet** | | | | |
| 3916 | A453 | $400 multi | 4.75 | 4.75 |

Friedrich von Schiller (1759-1805), Writer — A454

Designs: $400, Schiller and Ludwig van Beethoven.

No. 3918: a, Schiller. b, Schiller and his house. c, Beethoven.
Illustration reduced.

| 2005, Aug. 12 | | | | |
|---|---|---|---|---|
| 3917 | A454 | $400 multi | 4.75 | 4.75 |
| **Souvenir Sheet** | | | | |
| 3918 | A454 | $200 Sheet of 3, #a-c | 7.00 | 7.10 |

No. 3918 contains three 42x28mm stamps.

Hans Christian Andersen (1805-75), Author — A455

No. 3919: a, The Traveling Companion. b, The Shadow. c, The Drop of Water.
$400, The Emperor's New Suit.

| 2005, Aug. 12 | | | Perf. 12¾ | |
|---|---|---|---|---|
| 3919 | A455 | $200 Sheet of 3, #a-c | 7.00 | 7.00 |
| **Souvenir Sheet** | | | | |
| | | **Perf. 12** | | |
| 3920 | A455 | $400 multi | 4.75 | 4.75 |

No. 3919 contains three 42x28mm stamps.

Jules Verne (1828-1905), Writer — A456

No. 3921, vert.: a, Verne. b, Book illustration. c, Space capsule as imagined by Verne. d, Space capsule.
$400, Man on the Moon.

| 2005, Aug. 12 | | | Perf. 12¾ | |
|---|---|---|---|---|
| 3921 | A456 | $150 Sheet of 4, #a-d | 6.50 | 6.50 |
| **Souvenir Sheet** | | | | |
| 3922 | A456 | $400 multi | 5.00 | 5.00 |

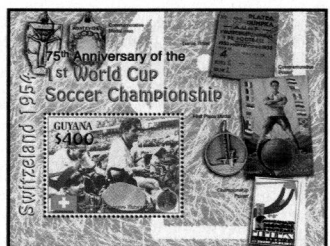

World Cup Soccer Championships, 75th Anniv. — A457

No. 3923: a, 1954 Germany team. b, Final goal in 1954 German victory over Hungary. c, Wankdorf Stadium. d, Helmut Rahn.
$400, German players celebrating victory.

**2005, Aug. 12**     *Perf. 12*
3923 A457 $150 Sheet of 4, #a-d   8.00 8.00
**Souvenir Sheet**
3924 A457 $400 multi      4.75 4.75

Space — A458

No. 3925: a, Luna 9 in space. b, Luna 9 capsule. c, Oceanus Procellarum region of Moon. d, Sergei Korolev. e, First images of the Moon. f, Launch of Molniya 8K78M rocket.
No. 3926, $200: a, Space Shuttle Discovery docked with International Space Station Destiny Laboratory. b, Astronaut Stephen K. Robinson attached to Canadarm 2. c, View of Discovery during docking operation. d, Discovery and stairway truck.
No. 3927, $200, vert.: a, First launch of Space Shuttle Columbia. b, Astronaut Robert C. Crippen. c, Astronaut John W. Young. d, Mission control.
No. 3928, $200, vert.: a, Launch vehicle MV-5 rocket. b, Hayabusa satellite. c, Composite color image of Itokawa asteroid. d, Projected return to Earth of satellite.
No. 3929, $400, Venus Express. No. 3930, $400, Lunar Reconnaissance Orbiter. No. 3931, $400, Calipso satellite. No. 3932, $400, Hayabusa satellite over Itokawa asteroid.

**2006**     **Litho.**     *Perf. 14*
3925 A458 $160 Sheet of 6,
    #a-f      12.50 12.50
**Sheets of 4, #a-d**
3926-3928 A458 Set of 3    28.00 28.00
**Souvenir Sheets**
3929-3932 A458 Set of 4    17.00 17.00
Issued: Nos. 3925, 3926, 3930, 7/10, Nos. 3928, 3932, 7/27.

**Souvenir Sheet**

"Penny Magenta" Stamp, 150th Anniv. — A459

**2006, July 27**     *Perf. 12x11½*
3933 A459 $400 multi     4.50 4.50

**Souvenir Sheet**

Christopher Columbus (1451-1506), Explorer — A460

No. 3934: a, Nina. b, Pinta. c, Santa Maria.

**2006, July 27**     *Perf. 13¼*
3934 A460 $300 Sheet of 3,
    #a-c     11.00 11.00

Airships — A461

No. 3935: a, De Beers Zeppelin NT. b, Lockheed Martin LTA 2004. c, Strattelite concept airship.
$400, Skybus Airship.

**2006, July 27**     *Perf. 13¼*
3935 A461 $200 Sheet of 3, #a-c   7.25 7.25
**Souvenir Sheet**
3936 A461 $400 multi     4.50 4.50

Rembrandt (1606-69), Painter — A462

No. 3937 — Details from The Music Makers: a, Man with viola. b, Woman with shawl. c, Man with harp. d, Woman with tiara.
$400, Old Man with a Jewelled Cross.

**2006, July 27**     *Perf. 13¼*
3937 A462 $160 Sheet of 4, #a-d 8.25 8.25
**Imperf**
3938 A462 $400 shown     4.50 4.50
No. 3937 contains four 37x50mm stamps.

Queen Elizabeth II, 80th Birthday — A463

No. 3939: a, Queen and Guyana Parliament Building. b, Queen wearing black and white hat.
$400, Queen and flags of Guyana and Great Britain.
Illustration reduced.

**2006, July 27**     *Perf. 13¼*
3939 A463 $200 Pair, #a-b    4.50 4.50
**Souvenir Sheet**
3940 A463 $400 multi     5.25 5.25
No. 3939 printed in sheets containing two pairs.

**Souvenir Sheet**

2006 World Cup Soccer Championships, Germany — A464

No. 3941 — 2006 World Cup emblem, World Cup and: a, $80, Man in Japanese clothing. b, $100, Kemari players. c, $160, Tsuchu players. d, $300, People's Republic of China #2073.

**2006, Sept. 14**    **Litho.**    *Perf. 13¼*
3941 A464   Sheet of 4, #a-d    7.00 7.00

Betty Boop — A465

No. 3942, vert.: a, With top hat and cane. b, Holding mirror. c, Holding flower bouquet. d, In city. e, At microphone. f, Lifting dress.
No. 3943: a, Sitting with legs crossed. b, In car.

**2006, Dec. 14**    **Litho.**    *Perf. 14*
3942 A465 $100 Sheet of 6, #a-f 6.50 6.50
**Souvenir Sheet**
3943 A465 $200 Sheet of 2, #a-b 4.25 4.25

Marilyn Monroe (1926-62), Actress — A466

No. 3944: a, Wearing beret. b, Wearing red dress, horizontal post at both sides of neck. c,

Wearing red dress, horizontal post at left of neck. d, With eyes closed.
$400, With eyes partially closed.

**2007, Feb. 15**     *Perf. 13¼*
3944 A466 $200 Sheet of 4, #a-d 8.00 8.00
**Souvenir Sheet**
3945 A466 $400 multi     4.00 4.00

Dogs — A467

No. 3946: a, Papillon. b, Dogue de Bordeaux. c, Cavalier King Charles spaniel. d, Neapolitan mastiff.
$400, Basset hound.

**2007, Feb. 15**     *Perf. 14*
3946 A467 $160 Sheet of 4, #a-d 6.50 6.50
**Souvenir Sheet**
3947 A467 $400 multi     4.00 4.00

Cats A468

Designs: $25, Chartreux. $35, Seal snowshoe. $60, Maine coon cat. $300, Turkish Angora.
$400, Blue Burmese, vert.

**2007, Feb. 15**
3948-3951 A468 Set of 4    4.25 4.25
**Souvenir Sheet**
3952 A468 $400 multi     4.00 4.00

Birds A469

Designs: $25, Summer tanager. $35, Graycheeked thrush. $60, Blackpoll warbler. $300, Thick-billed parrot.
No. 3957, vert.: a, Golden-tailed warbler. b, Blue-crowned parakeet. c, White-winged parakeet. d, Yellow-green vireo.
No. 3958, $400, Pacific golden plover, vert. No. 3959, $400, Bobolink, vert.

**2007, Feb. 15**
3953-3956 A469 Set of 4     4.25 4.25
3957 A469 $160 Sheet of 4, #a-d 6.50 6.50
**Souvenir Sheets**
3958-3959 A469 Set of 2    8.00 8.00

Butterflies A470

Designs: $25, Morpho vitrea. $35, Rothschildia hesperus. $60, Anaea nessus. $300, Dryas iulia.

No. 3964: a, Callithea sapphira. b, Prepona buckleyana. c, Lycorea pasinutia. d, Danaus eresimus.

No. 3965, $400, Cithaerias aurorina. No. 3966, $400, Eurytides protesilaus.

**2007, Feb. 15**
3960-3963 A470 Set of 4   4.25 4.25
3964 A470 $160 Sheet of 4, #a-d 6.50 6.50
**Souvenir Sheets**
3965-3966 A470 Set of 2   8.00 8.00

Orchids — A471

Designs: $25, Bletia florida. $35, Basiphyllaea corallicola. $60, Calopogon multiflorus. $300, Bletia purpurea.

No. 3971: a, Cypripedium acaule. b, Calopogon tuberosus. c, Calopogon pallidus. d, Bletia patula.

$400, Cypripedium reginae.

**2007, Feb. 15**
3967-3970 A471 Set of 4   4.25 4.25
3971 A471 $160 Sheet of 4, #a-d 6.50 6.50
**Souvenir Sheet**
3972 A471 $400 multi   4.00 4.00

Souvenir Sheet

New Year 2007 (Year of the Pig) — A472

No. 3973 — Pig at: a, $55, Right. b, $80, Left. c, $100, Right. d, $160, Left.

**2007, Mar. 21**    **Perf. 13¼**
3973 A472   Sheet of 4, #a-d 4.00 4.00

Souvenir Sheet

Wolfgang Amadeus Mozart (1756-91), Composer — A473

No. 3974 — Mozart: a, In 1770. b, In 1762. c, Circa 1789. d, Portrait by Joseph Grassi.

**2007, Mar. 21**
3974 A473 $190 Sheet of 4, #a-d 7.50 7.50

Scouting, Cent. — A474

No. 3975, horiz.: a, Lord Robert Baden-Powell and dove. b, Scouts on raft. c, Scouts pulling tug-of-war rope.

$400, Dove and hand of Baden-Powell.

**2007, Mar. 21**
3975 A474 $180 Sheet of 3, #a-c 5.50 5.50
**Souvenir Sheet**
3976 A474 $400 multi   4.00 4.00

Souvenir Sheets

Pres. John F. Kennedy (1917-63) — A475

No. 3977: a, $80, Taking oath of office. b, $100, Giving inaugural speech. c, $160, Portrait. d, $190, With wife at inaugural ball.

No. 3978: a, $80, Peace Corps. b, $100, Space program. c, $160, Civil rights. d, $190, Portrait, diff.

**2007, Mar. 21**    **Perf. 13¼**
**Sheets of 4, #a-d**
3977-3978 A475 Set of 2 10.50 10.50

Elvis Presley (1935-77) — A476

No. 3979, $160: a, Wearing glasses, blue panel at top. b, Without glasses, red background.

No. 3980, $160: a, Without glasses, orange panel at bottom. b, With glasses, red background.

**2007, Mar. 21**    **Perf. 14**
**Pairs, #a-b**
3979-3980 A476 Set of 2 6.50 6.50
Nos. 3979-3980 each were printed in sheets containing two pairs.

2007 Cricket World Cup, West Indies — A477

Designs: $100, Cricket World Cup emblem, map and flag of Guyana. $200, Guyana cricket team, horiz. $500, Cricket World Cup emblem.

**2007, Mar. 28**    **Perf. 13¼**
3981-3982 A477 Set of 2 3.00 3.00
**Souvenir Sheet**
3983 A477 $500 multi   5.00 5.00

A478

Pope Benedict XVI — A479

Illustration A479 reduced.

**2007, Apr. 17**   **Litho.**   **Perf. 13¼**
3984 A478 $80 multi   .80 .80
**Litho. & Embossed**
***Serpentine Die Cut***
**Without Gum**
3985 A479 $1500 multi 15.00 15.00
No. 3984 was printed in sheets of 8.

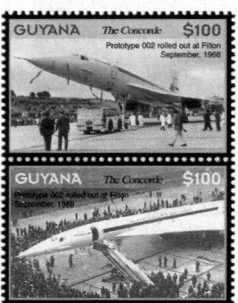

Concorde A480

No. 3986, $100: a, Concorde Prototype 002 and towing vehicle. b, Concorde Prototype 002 and stairway.

No. 3987, $100: a, Concorde and Royal Air Force Red Arrows. b, Concorde, Red Arrows and Queen Elizabeth 2.

**2007, Apr. 17**   **Litho.**   **Perf. 13¼**
**Pairs, #a-b**
3986-3987 A480 Set of 2   4.00 4.00
Nos. 3986-3987 were each printed in sheets containing 3 pairs.

Miniature Sheet

2008 Summer Olympics, Beijing — A481

No. 3988: a, Field hockey. b, Basketball. c, Judo. d, Shooting.

**2008, Apr. 22**   **Litho.**   **Perf. 13¼x13**
3988 A481 $100 Sheet of 4, #a-d 4.00 4.00

10th Caribbean Festival of Arts — A482

Map in: $20, Yellow and white, frame in red. $55, White, frame in green. $80, Yellow and white, frame in blue green. $160, Green, frame in white and yellow.

**2008, Aug. 19**    **Perf. 14¼**
3989-3992 A482 Set of 4 3.25 3.25

Jesuits in Guyana, 150th Anniv. A483

Designs: $80, St. Stanislaus College. $100, Sacred Heart Church. $160, Father Cuthbert Cary-Elwes, missionary, and indigenous people.

**2008, Aug. 25**   **Litho.**   **Perf. 13x13¼**
3993-3995 A483 Set of 3 3.50 3.50

Souvenir Sheet

Sir James Douglas (1803-77), First Governor of British Columbia — A484

**2008, Aug. 25**    **Perf. 13¼**
3996 A484 $160 multi   1.60 1.60

### AIR POST STAMPS

No. 321 Surcharged in Blue "HUMAN RIGHTS / DAY / 1981 / 110 AIR"

**1981, Nov. 14**   **Perfs. as Before**
C1 A74 110c on $3 No. 321   3.50
For surcharge see No. 997.

Nos. 133, 136 and 146 Surcharged in Red, Black or Blue "AIR / Princess / of Wales / 1961-1982"

**1982, June 25**   **Perfs. as Before**
**Printing Methods as Before**
C2 A28 110c on 5c No. 136   2.50 .40
    (R)
C3 A28 220c on 1c No. 133   2.75 1.00
C4 A28 330c on $2 No. 146   2.75 1.60
    (Bl)
    *Nos. C2-C4 (3)*   7.25

For surcharges see Nos. 623, 785-787, 801, 804-804A, O19, O21, O30-O39.

No. 287 Surcharged in Dark Blue
"UNICEF / 1946-1986 / AIR" or
"UNESCO / 1946-1986 / AIR"

**Perfs. as Before**

| | | | |
|---|---|---|---|
| **1986, Oct. 24** | | **Litho.** | |
| C5 | A66 | 120c on $1 UNICEF | 11.00 |
| C6 | A66 | 120c on $1 UNESCO | 11.00 |
| a. | Pair, #C5-C6 | | 24.00 |

Nos. 1026, 1095, 1096, 1096a, 1100,
1138, 1163 Surcharged "AIR"

**1987-88    Litho.    Perf. 14**
**Design A91**
**Plate Numbers in Parentheses**

| | | | | |
|---|---|---|---|---|
| C7 | 75c on 25c No. 1100 (59) | 13.50 | 1.50 |
| C8 | 60c on No. 1095 (55) | 11.00 | 10.00 |
| C9 | 75c on No. 1026 (5) | 1.25 | .65 |
| C10 | 75c on No. 1096 (55) | 1.25 | .65 |
| a. | 75c on No. 1096a | | |
| C11 | 75c on No. 1138 (83) | 1.25 | .65 |
| C12 | 75c on No. 1163 (55) | 1.25 | .65 |

Issued: #C7, 11/87; #C8, 12/87; #C9-C12,
8/88.

---

## SPECIAL DELIVERY STAMPS

Orchid Type of 1985 Overprinted or
Surcharged "EXPRESS"

**1986-87    Litho.    Perf. 14**
**Plate Numbers in Parentheses**

| | | | | |
|---|---|---|---|---|
| E1 | A91 | $12 on #1372 (65) | 12.00 | 12.00 |
| E2 | A91 | $15 on 40c #1145 (86) | 12.00 | 12.00 |
| E3 | A91(p) | $15 on #E2 (86) | 11.00 | 11.00 |
| E4 | A91 | $25 on 25c like #1090 (53) | 15.00 | 15.00 |
| | | Nos. E1-E4 (4) | 50.00 | |

Issue dates: $12, $25, #E2, Nov. 10. #E3,
Dec. 1987. #E4 not issued without surcharge.

No. 1461c Surcharged "EXPRESS"

**1986-87    Litho.    Imperf.**

| | | | | |
|---|---|---|---|---|
| E5 | A96 | $20 on 320c #1461c | 12.00 | 12.00 |

No. E5 Ovptd. with Maltese Cross

**1987, Mar. 3**

| | | | | |
|---|---|---|---|---|
| E6 | A96 | $20 on No. E5 | 12.00 | 12.00 |

Orchid Type of 1985 Inscribed
"Express"

**1987-88    Litho.    Perf. 14**
**Series 2**
**Plate Numbers in Parentheses**

| | | | | |
|---|---|---|---|---|
| E7 | A91 | $15 like #1186 (11) | 4.00 | 4.00 |
| E8 | A91 | $20 like #1323 (93) | 7.50 | 7.50 |
| E9 | A91 | $25 like #1274 (63) | 6.50 | 6.50 |
| E10 | A91 | $45 like #1228 (35) | 12.00 | 12.00 |
| | | Nos. E7-E10 (4) | 30.00 | 30.00 |

Issued: $45, 9/1; $15, 9/29; $25, 10/26; $20,
5/17/88.

No. "1461" Surcharged "EXPRESS /
FORTY DOLLARS"

**1987, Nov.    Perf. 14**

| | | | | |
|---|---|---|---|---|
| E11 | A96 | $40 on 320c No. 1461, imperf. btwn. | 15.00 | 15.00 |

A five-pointed star appears between the
lines of the surcharge on #E11. See #E14.

Nos. 1827e, 1830e Surcharged in Red
"SPECIAL DELIVERY"

**1988, Aug. 10    Perf. 15**

| | | | | |
|---|---|---|---|---|
| E12 | A100 | $40 on $3.20 #1827e | 12.00 | 12.00 |
| E13 | A100 | $45 on $3.30 #1830e | 12.00 | 12.00 |

See Nos. 2054b, 2056b.

Nos. "1461," 1822c Surcharged in Red
"EXPRESS / FORTY DOLLARS"

**1989, Mar.    Perf. 14**

| | | | | |
|---|---|---|---|---|
| E14 | A96 | $40 on 320c #1461, imperf. btwn. | 7.00 | 7.00 |
| E15 | A96 | $40 on 320c #1822c, imperf. btwn. | 7.00 | 7.00 |

---

Butterflies Type of 1989 Inscribed
"EXPRESS"
Souvenir Sheets

**1989, Sept. 7    Litho.    Perf. 14**

| | | | | |
|---|---|---|---|---|
| E16 | A115 | $130 Phareas coeleste | 7.75 | 7.75 |
| E17 | A115 | $190 Papilio torquatus | 12.50 | 12.50 |

For overprints see #E19-E22, E24, E26-
E27, E31.

Women in Space Type of 1989
Inscribed "EXPRESS"
Souvenir Sheets

**1989, Nov. 8**

| | | | | |
|---|---|---|---|---|
| E18 | A116 | $190 Valentina Tereshkova | 12.50 | 12.50 |

For overprints see No. E23, E25, E28, E32.

Nos. E16-E17 Ovptd. with World
Stamp Expo '89 Emblem

**1989, Nov. 17**

| | | | | |
|---|---|---|---|---|
| E19 | A115 | $130 on No. E16 | 7.00 | 7.00 |
| E20 | A115 | $190 on No. E17 | 7.00 | 7.00 |

Nos. E16-E18 Ovptd. in Sheet Margin
"Stamp World London 90" and Show
Emblem

**1990, May 3**

| | | | | |
|---|---|---|---|---|
| E21 | A115 | $130 on No. E16 | | |
| E22 | A115 | $190 on No. E17 | | |
| E23 | A116 | $190 on No. E18 | | |
| | | Nos. E21-E23 (3) | 30.00 | |

Nos. E17-E18 Ovptd. in Sheet Margin
with Rotary Emblem and "ROTARY /
INTERNATIONAL / 1905-1990"

**1990, Mar.**

| | | | | |
|---|---|---|---|---|
| E24 | A115 | $190 on No. E17 | | |
| E25 | A116 | $190 on No. E18 | | |
| | | Nos. E24-E25 (2) | 22.50 | |

Nos. E16-E18 Ovptd. in Sheet Margin
"90th BIRTHDAY / H.M. THE / QUEEN
MOTHER"

**1990, June 8    Litho.    Perf. 14**

| | | | | |
|---|---|---|---|---|
| E26 | A115 | $130 on No. E16 | 7.75 | 7.75 |
| E27 | A115 | $190 on No. E17 | 12.50 | 12.50 |
| E28 | A116 | $190 on No. E18 | 12.50 | 12.50 |
| | | Nos. E26-E28 (3) | 32.75 | 32.75 |

Endangered Wildlife Type
Souvenir Sheets

**1990, Nov. 6    Litho.    Perf. 14**

| | | | | |
|---|---|---|---|---|
| E29 | A131 | $130 Harpy eagle | 7.00 | 7.00 |
| E30 | A131 | $150 Ocelot | 7.50 | 7.50 |

Nos. E29-E30 each contain one 43x57mm
stamp.

Nos. E16, E18 Ovptd. in Sheet Margin
with "BELGICA PHILATELIC /
EXPOSITION 1990" and Scout, Lions,
Rotary and Show Emblems

**1990, June 2**

| | | | | |
|---|---|---|---|---|
| E31 | A131 | $130 on No. E16 | 7.50 | 7.50 |
| E32 | A116 | $190 on No. E18 | 7.50 | 7.50 |

No. E31 has Scout and Lions emblems. No.
E32 has Scout and Rotary emblems.

---

## POSTAGE DUE STAMPS

Type of British Guiana Inscribed
"Guyana"
**Perf. 13½x14**

| | | | | |
|---|---|---|---|---|
| **1967-68** | | **Wmk. 314** | **Typo.** | |
| J2 | D1 | 2c black ('68) | .75 | .75 |
| J3 | D1 | 4c ultramarine | .30 | .30 |
| J4 | D1 | 12c carmine | .50 | .50 |
| | | Nos. J2-J4 (3) | 1.55 | 1.55 |

For surcharges see Nos. 897-898.

| | | | | |
|---|---|---|---|---|
| **1973** | | **Wmk. 364** | | |
| J5 | D1 | 1c green | .35 | 2.00 |
| J6 | D1 | 2c black | .35 | 2.00 |
| J7 | D1 | 4c ultramarine | .35 | 2.00 |
| J8 | D1 | 12c carmine | .40 | 2.00 |
| | | Nos. J5-J8 (4) | 1.45 | 8.00 |

For surcharges see #341-349, 658, 899-900.

---

## OFFICIAL STAMPS

Nos. 74, 139, 141, 143-144, 146-147,
289A, 297, 300, 333, 395, 397, 401
Surcharged in Black, Red, or Black
and Red

**1981-82    Perfs. as Before**
**Printing Methods as Before**

| | | | | |
|---|---|---|---|---|
| O1 | A28 | 10c on 25c #141 (Bk & R) | 4.00 | 2.25 |
| O2 | A8 | 15c on #74 | 10.00 | 2.00 |
| O3 | A28 | 15c on #139 | 13.50 | 1.00 |
| O4 | A28 | 30c on $2 #146 (Bk & R) | 1.00 | .50 |
| O5 | A28 | 50c on #143 (R) | 2.00 | .75 |
| O6 | A69 | 50c on #300 | 1.50 | .40 |
| O7 | A28 | 60c on #144 (R) | 1.50 | .25 |
| O8 | A17 | 100c on #395 | 2.00 | 2.00 |
| O9 | A68 | 100c on $3 #297 (Bk & R) | 3.50 | .75 |
| O10 | A17 | 110c on #397 | 3.50 | 3.50 |
| O11 | A28 | $1.10 on #333 (R) | | |
| O12 | A28 | 125c on #401 (R) | 1.50 | .80 |
| O13 | A28 | $2 on #146 (R) | 12.50 | |
| O14 | A28 | $5 on #147 (R) | 3.00 | 3.00 |
| O15 | A66 | $10 on #289A | 17.50 | |

Issued: #O1, O5, O7, O15, 6/8; #O2, O4,
O9, O11-O12, 7/1; #O13, 7/12/82; others, 7/7.
Surcharge on Nos. O3, O6, O8, O10, O13-
O14 have no obliterator. No. O11 is airmail.
Refer to 2nd paragraph in footnote following
#147 for #O1, O4-O5, O7 and O13.
For overprints and surcharges see No. 406,
425, 452, 454-456, 603, 618, 650, 817, 854,
861, 866, 933, 1378, 1381, 1384, 1387-1388.

Nos. 162, 256, 258, 282, 480, C2-C3
Surcharged in Blue or Black

**1982    Perfs. as Before**
**Printing Methods as Before**

| | | | | |
|---|---|---|---|---|
| O16 | A66 | 20c on #282 | 10.00 | 1.25 |
| O17 | A33 | 40c on #162 | 1.50 | .75 |
| O18 | A60 | 40c on #256 | 2.00 | 1.00 |
| O19 | A28 | 110c on #C2 (Bk) | 3.00 | 1.00 |
| O20 | A60 | $2 on #258 | 18.00 | 3.50 |
| O21 | A28 | 220c on #C3 | 3.00 | .80 |
| O22 | A69 | 250c on #480 | 1.75 | .80 |
| | | Nos. O16-O22 (7) | 39.25 | |

Issue dates: 110c, Sept. 15; others, May 17.
Nos. O19, O21 are airmail.

No. 481 Surcharged "OPS" Reading
Up in Blue Violet or Blue Violet and
Black

**1984, Apr. 2    Perfs. as Before**

| | | | | |
|---|---|---|---|---|
| O23 | A66 | 150c on $5 | 6.00 | 3.00 |
| O24 | A66 | 200c on $5 | 6.50 | 3.25 |
| O25 | A66 | 225c on $5 (BV & Bk) | 6.50 | 3.25 |
| O25A | A66 | 230c on $5 | 6.75 | 3.50 |
| O26 | A66 | 260c on $5 | 7.00 | 3.75 |
| O27 | A66 | 320c on $5 | 7.00 | 3.75 |
| O28 | A66 | 350c on $5 | 7.50 | 3.75 |
| O29 | A66 | 600c on $5 | 8.00 | 4.25 |
| | | Nos. O23-O29 (8) | 10.00 | 6.00 |

Nos. C2-C3 Surcharged "OPS" in
Black and Blue, Black or Blue

**1984, June 25    Perfs. as Before**

| | | | | |
|---|---|---|---|---|
| O30 | A28 | 25c on No. C2 (Bk) | | |
| O31 | A28 | 30c on No. C2 | 1.00 | .50 |
| O32 | A28 | 45c on No. C3 | 1.00 | .50 |
| O33 | A28 | 55c on No. C2 (Bk) | 1.25 | .50 |
| O34 | A28 | 60c on No. C3 | 1.50 | .60 |
| O35 | A28 | 75c on No. C3 | 2.00 | .70 |
| O36 | A28 | 90c on No. C3 (Bl) | 2.00 | .70 |
| O37 | A28 | 120c on No. C3 | 2.25 | .90 |
| O38 | A28 | 130c on No. C3 (Bl) | 2.25 | 1.25 |
| O39 | A28 | 330c on No. C3 (Bl) | 4.00 | 1.25 |
| | | Nos. O30-O39 (10) | 17.25 | |

Overprint reads up on No. O39.

---

Orchid Type of 1985

**1987-88    Litho.    Unwmk.    Perf. 14**
**Series 2**
**Plate Numbers in Parentheses**

| | | | | |
|---|---|---|---|---|
| O40 | A91 | 120c like #1250 (48) | 1.50 | .40 |
| O41 | A91 | 130c like #1322 (92) | 1.50 | .40 |
| O42 | A91 | 140c like #1229 (36) | 1.00 | .40 |
| O43 | A91 | 150c like #1242 (43) | 1.50 | .50 |
| O44 | A91 | 175c like #1221 (31) | 1.00 | .50 |
| O45 | A91 | 200c like #1271 (61) | 1.50 | .60 |
| O46 | A91 | 225c like #1213 (26) | 1.50 | .60 |
| O47 | A91 | 230c like #1283 (68) | .75 | .60 |
| O48 | A91 | 250c like #1268 (59) | .75 | .60 |
| O49 | A91 | 260c like #1284 (69) | .75 | .60 |
| O50 | A91 | 275c like #1319 (90) | 1.75 | .75 |
| O51 | A91 | 320c like #1292 (75) | 1.75 | .85 |
| O52 | A91 | 330c like #1208 (23) | 2.00 | 1.00 |
| O53 | A91 | 350c like #1326 (95) | 1.00 | 1.00 |
| O54 | A91 | 600c like #1285 (70) | 1.50 | 1.50 |
| O55 | A91 | $12 like #1286 (71) | 2.50 | 2.50 |
| O56 | A91 | $15 like #1308 (84) | 3.00 | 3.00 |
| | | Nos. O40-O56 (17) | 25.25 | 15.80 |

Nos. O47, O53-O56 horiz.
Issued: #O42, O44, O48, O49, 10/5/88;
others, 10/5/87.
For overprints & surcharges see #1694,
1697, 1703, 1707, 1722-1726, 1728-1730.

---

## PARCEL POST STAMPS

No. 145 Surcharged "PARCEL POST"

**1981, June 8    Perf. 13½**

| | | | | |
|---|---|---|---|---|
| Q1 | A28 | $15 on $1 No. 145 | 19.50 | 3.50 |
| Q2 | A28 | $20 on $1 No. 145 | 19.00 | 7.00 |
| | | Nos. Q1-Q2 (2) | 38.00 | |

For overprints see Nos. QO1-QO2.

No. 333 Surcharged "PARCEL POST"
in Blue

**1983, Jan. 15**

| | | | | |
|---|---|---|---|---|
| Q3 | A28 | $12 on No. 333 | 12.50 | 2.00 |

For surcharge see No. 624.

No. 146 Surcharged "Parcel Post"

**1983, Sept. 14**

| | | | | |
|---|---|---|---|---|
| Q4 | A28 | $12 on $1.10 on $2 | 2.50 | 2.50 |

No. Q4 has a horizontal Royal Wedding /
1981 surcharge similar to No. 331. For overprint see No. QO5.

No. 255 Surcharged in Red
"TWENTY FIVE DOLLARS / PARCEL
POST 25.00"

**1985, Apr. 25    Perf. 14**

| | | | | |
|---|---|---|---|---|
| Q5 | A60 | $25 on 35c No. 255 | 33.00 | 27.50 |

---

## PARCEL POST OFFICIAL STAMPS

Nos. Q1-Q2 Overprinted "OPS" in Red

**1981, June 8**

| | | | | |
|---|---|---|---|---|
| QO1 | A28 | $15 on No. Q1 | 18.00 | 2.50 |
| QO2 | A28 | $20 on No. Q2 | 17.00 | 3.25 |

For surcharges see Nos. 1389-1390.

No. 333 Surcharged in Blue
"OPS / 1982 / Parcel Post / $12.00"

**1983, Jan. 15**

| | | | | |
|---|---|---|---|---|
| QO3 | A28 | $12 on No. 333 | 115.00 | 20.00 |

No. QO3 Overprinted "OPS" in Black

**1983, Aug. 22**

| | | | | |
|---|---|---|---|---|
| QO4 | A28 | $12 on No. QO3 | 42.50 | 4.00 |

No. Q4 Overprinted "OPS" in Blue

**1983, Nov. 3**

| | | | | |
|---|---|---|---|---|
| QO5 | A28 | $12 on No. Q4 | 15.00 | 4.00 |

# HAITI
'hä-tē

LOCATION — Western part of Hispaniola
GOVT. — Republic
AREA — 10,714 sq. mi.
POP. — 6,884,264 (1999 est.)
CAPITAL — Port-au-Prince

100 Centimes = 1 Piaster (1906)
100 Centimes = 1 Gourde

Catalogue values for unused stamps in this country are for Never Hinged items, beginning with Scott 370 in the regular postage section, Scott B2 in the semipostal section, Scott C33 in the air post section, Scott CB9 in the air post semi-postal section, Scott CO6 in the air post official section, Scott CQ1 in the air post parcel post seciton, Scott E1 in the special delivery section, Scott J21 in the postage due section, Scott Q1 in the parcel post section, Scott RA1 in the postal tax section, and Scott RAC1 in the air post postal tax section.

## Watermark

Wmk. 131 — RH

Liberty Head — A1

A3      A4

On A3 (#18, 19) there are crossed lines of dots on face. On A4 the "5" is 3mm wide, on A1 2½mm wide.

| 1881 | | Unwmk. | Typo. | Imperf. | |
|---|---|---|---|---|---|
| 1 | A1 | 1c vermilion, *yelsh* | | 9.00 | 5.50 |
| 2 | A1 | 2c dk violet, *pale lil* | | 11.00 | 5.50 |
| 3 | A1 | 3c bister, *pale bis* | | 20.00 | 8.00 |
| 4 | A1 | 5c green, *grnsh* | | 32.50 | 16.00 |
| 5 | A1 | 7c blue, *grysh* | | 22.00 | 4.00 |
| 6 | A1 | 20c red brown, *yelsh* | | 82.50 | 30.00 |
| | | *Nos. 1-6 (6)* | | 177.00 | 69.00 |

Nos. 1-6 were printed from plate I, Nos. 7-13 from plates II and III.

| 1882 | | | | Perf. 13½ | |
|---|---|---|---|---|---|
| 7 | A1 | 1c ver, *yelsh* | | 5.75 | 2.10 |
| c. | | Horiz. pair, imperf. btwn. | | 190.00 | |
| d. | | Vert. pair imperf. btwn. | | 200.00 | 160.00 |
| 8 | A1 | 2c dk vio, *pale lil* | | 11.00 | 3.25 |
| a. | | 2c dark violet | | 11.00 | 6.50 |
| b. | | 2c red violet, *pale lilac* | | 7.25 | 2.60 |
| c. | | Horiz. pair, imperf. vert. | | 150.00 | |
| d. | | Vert. pair, imperf. horiz. | | 150.00 | |
| e. | | Horiz. pair, imperf. between | | 175.00 | 175.00 |
| 9 | A1 | 3c bister, *pale bis* | | 11.50 | 3.25 |
| 10 | A1 | 5c grn, *grnsh* | | 8.25 | 1.60 |
| a. | | 5c yellow green, *greenish* | | 7.75 | 1.40 |
| b. | | 5c deep green, *greenish* | | 7.75 | 1.40 |
| c. | | Horiz. pair, imperf. vert. | | 250.00 | |
| d. | | Horiz. or vert. pair, imperf. btwn. | | | 190.00 |
| 11 | A1 | 7c blue, *grysh* | | 10.50 | 2.10 |
| a. | | Horiz. pair, imperf. between | | 150.00 | 140.00 |
| 12 | A1 | 7c ultra, *grysh* | | 16.00 | 3.25 |
| a. | | Vert. pair, imperf. between | | | |
| b. | | Horiz. pair, imperf. vert. | | | |
| 13 | A1 | 20c pale brn, *yelsh* | | 15.00 | 4.50 |
| a. | | 20c red brown, *yellowish* | | 20.00 | 8.00 |
| b. | | Horiz. pair, imperf. vert | | | 140.00 |

| c. | | Vert. pair, imperf. horiz. | | | 160.00 |
|---|---|---|---|---|---|
| d. | | Horiz. or vert. pair, imperf. btwn. | | 175.00 | 160.00 |
| | | *Nos. 7-13 (7)* | | 78.00 | 20.05 |

Stamps perf. 14, 16 are postal forgeries.

| 1886-87 | | | | Perf. 13½ | |
|---|---|---|---|---|---|
| 18 | A3 | 1c vermilion, *yelsh* | | 5.75 | 2.00 |
| a. | | Horiz. pair, imperf. vert. | | | 175.00 |
| b. | | Horiz. pair, imperf. between | | 200.00 | 190.00 |
| 19 | A3 | 2c dk violet, *lilac* | | 42.50 | 7.00 |
| 20 | A4 | 5c green ('87) | | 20.00 | 2.75 |
| | | *Nos. 18-20 (3)* | | 68.25 | 11.75 |

General Louis Etienne Félicité Salomon — A5

| 1887 | | Engr. | | Perf. 14 | |
|---|---|---|---|---|---|
| 21 | A5 | 1c lake | | .40 | .30 |
| 22 | A5 | 2c violet | | 1.00 | .70 |
| 23 | A5 | 3c blue | | .70 | .70 |
| 24 | A5 | 5c green | | 4.50 | .55 |
| a. | | Double impression | | 150.00 | |
| | | *Nos. 21-24 (4)* | | 6.60 | 2.00 |

Some experts believe the imperfs. of Nos. 21-24 are plate proofs. Value per pair, $30.

No. 23 Handstamp Surcharged in Red

**1890**

| 25 | A5 | 2c on 3c blue | | .65 | .55 |
|---|---|---|---|---|---|

This surcharge being handstamped is to be found double, inverted, etc. This applies to succeeding surcharged issues.

Coat of Arms
A7

Coat of Arms
(Leaves Drooping)
A9

| 1891 | | | | Perf. 13 | |
|---|---|---|---|---|---|
| 26 | A7 | 1c violet | | .50 | .30 |
| 27 | A7 | 2c blue | | .70 | .30 |
| 28 | A7 | 3c gray lilac | | 1.00 | .45 |
| a. | | 3c slate | | .90 | .55 |
| 29 | A7 | 5c orange | | 3.50 | .50 |
| 30 | A7 | 7c red | | 7.50 | 2.75 |
| | | *Nos. 26-30 (5)* | | 13.20 | 4.30 |

Nos. 26-30 exist imperf. Value of unused pairs, each $50.
The 2c, 3c and 7c exist imperf. vertically.

No. 28 Surcharged Like No. 25 in Red

**1892**

| 31 | A7 | 2c on 3c gray lilac | | 1.40 | .95 |
|---|---|---|---|---|---|
| a. | | 2c on 3c slate | | 1.60 | 1.00 |

| 1892-95 | | Engr., Litho. (20c) | | Perf. 14 | |
|---|---|---|---|---|---|
| 32 | A9 | 1c lilac | | .40 | .20 |
| a. | | Imperf, pair | | | |
| b. | | Double impression | | — | |
| 33 | A9 | 2c deep blue | | .50 | .20 |
| 34 | A9 | 3c gray | | .70 | .45 |
| 35 | A9 | 5c orange | | 2.75 | .50 |
| 36 | A9 | 7c red | | .50 | .20 |
| a. | | Imperf., pair | | 30.00 | |
| 37 | A9 | 20c brown | | 1.40 | 1.00 |
| | | *Nos. 32-37 (6)* | | 6.25 | 2.55 |

Nos. 32, 33, 35 exist in horiz. pairs, imperf vert., Nos. 33, 35, in vert. pairs, imperf horiz.

| 1896 | | Engr. | | Perf. 13½ | |
|---|---|---|---|---|---|
| 38 | A9 | 1c light blue | | .55 | .70 |
| 39 | A9 | 2c red brown | | .65 | 1.20 |
| 40 | A9 | 3c lilac brown | | .55 | 1.20 |
| 41 | A9 | 5c slate green | | .65 | 1.20 |
| 42 | A9 | 7c dark gray | | .90 | 1.75 |
| 43 | A9 | 20c orange | | 1.10 | 2.25 |
| | | *Nos. 38-43 (6)* | | 4.40 | 8.30 |

Nos. 32-37 are 23¾mm high, Nos. 38-43 23¼mm to 23½mm. The "C" is closed on Nos. 32-37, open on Nos. 38-43. Other differences

exist. The stamps of the two issues may be readily distinguished by their colors and perfs. Nos. 38-43 exist imperf. and in horiz. pairs, imperf. vert. The 1c, 3c, 5c, 7c exist in vert. pairs, imperf. horiz. or imperf. between. The 5c, 7c exist in horiz. pairs, imperf. between. Value of unused pairs, $9 and up.

#37, 43 Surcharged Like #25 in Red
**1898**

| 44 | A9 | 2c on 20c brown | | 1.40 | 3.00 |
|---|---|---|---|---|---|
| 45 | A9 | 2c on 20c orange | | .90 | .65 |

No. 45 exists in various part perf. varieties.

Coat of Arms — A11

| 1898 | | Wmk. 131 | | Perf. 11 | |
|---|---|---|---|---|---|
| 46 | A11 | 1c ultra | | 2.50 | 2.50 |
| 47 | A11 | 2c brown carmine | | .55 | .40 |
| 48 | A11 | 3c dull violet | | 2.50 | 2.50 |
| 49 | A11 | 5c dark green | | .55 | .40 |
| 50 | A11 | 7c gray | | 5.00 | 5.00 |
| 51 | A11 | 20c orange | | 10.00 | 10.00 |
| | | *Nos. 46-51 (6)* | | 21.10 | 20.80 |

All values exist imperforate. They are plate proofs.

Pres. T.
Augustin Simon
Sam — A12

Coat of
Arms — A13

| 1898-99 | | Unwmk. | | Perf. 12 | |
|---|---|---|---|---|---|
| 52 | A12 | 1c ultra | | .20 | .20 |
| 53 | A13 | 1c yel green ('99) | | .20 | .20 |
| 54 | A12 | 2c deep orange | | .20 | .20 |
| 55 | A13 | 2c car lake ('99) | | .20 | .20 |
| 56 | A12 | 3c green | | .20 | .20 |
| 57 | A13 | 4c red | | .20 | .20 |
| 58 | A13 | 5c red brown | | .20 | .20 |
| 59 | A13 | 5c pale blue ('99) | | .20 | .20 |
| 60 | A12 | 7c gray | | .20 | .20 |
| 61 | A13 | 8c carmine | | .20 | .20 |
| 62 | A13 | 10c orange red | | .20 | .20 |
| 63 | A13 | 15c olive green | | .60 | .45 |
| 64 | A12 | 20c black | | .60 | .45 |
| 65 | A12 | 50c rose brown | | 1.00 | .50 |
| 66 | A12 | 1g red violet | | 2.25 | 2.60 |
| | | *Nos. 52-66 (15)* | | 6.65 | 5.60 |

For overprints see Nos. 67-81, 110-124, 169, 247-248.

Stamps of 1898-99
Handstamped in
Black

**1902**

| 67 | A12 | 1c ultra | | .60 | .45 |
|---|---|---|---|---|---|
| 68 | A13 | 1c yellow green | | .45 | .30 |
| 69 | A13 | 2c deep orange | | .80 | .70 |
| 70 | A13 | 2c carmine lake | | .45 | .30 |
| 71 | A13 | 3c green | | .45 | .45 |
| 72 | A13 | 4c red | | .60 | .55 |
| 73 | A13 | 5c red brown | | 1.25 | 1.10 |
| 74 | A13 | 5c pale blue | | .45 | .45 |
| 75 | A12 | 7c gray | | .95 | .90 |
| 76 | A13 | 8c carmine | | .95 | .90 |
| 77 | A13 | 10c orange red | | .95 | .90 |
| 78 | A13 | 15c olive green | | 4.50 | 4.50 |
| 79 | A12 | 20c black | | 4.50 | 4.50 |
| 80 | A12 | 50c rose brown | | 10.50 | 10.50 |
| 81 | A12 | 1g red violet | | 16.50 | 16.50 |
| | | *Nos. 67-81 (15)* | | 43.90 | 43.00 |

Many forgeries exist of this overprint.

## Centenary of Independence Issues

Coat of Arms
A14

Pierre D.
Toussaint
L'Ouverture
A15

Emperor Jean
Jacques
Dessalines
A16

Pres. Alexandre
Sabes Pétion
A17

| 1904 | | Engr. | | Perf. 13½, 14 | |
|---|---|---|---|---|---|
| 82 | A14 | 1c green | | .35 | .35 |

**Center Engr., Frame Litho.**

| 83 | A15 | 2c rose & blk | | .35 | .35 |
|---|---|---|---|---|---|
| 84 | A15 | 5c dull blue & blk | | .35 | .35 |
| 85 | A16 | 7c plum & blk | | .35 | .35 |
| 86 | A16 | 10c yellow & blk | | .35 | .35 |
| 87 | A17 | 20c slate & blk | | .35 | .35 |
| 88 | A17 | 50c olive & blk | | .35 | .35 |
| | | *Nos. 82-88 (7)* | | 2.45 | 2.45 |

Nos. 82 to 88 exist imperforate. Nos. 83-88 exist with centers inverted. Some are known with head omitted. Forgeries exist.

Same Handstamped
in Blue

**1904**

| 89 | A14 | 1c green | | .50 | 1.50 |
|---|---|---|---|---|---|
| 90 | A15 | 2c rose & blk | | .50 | 1.50 |
| 91 | A15 | 5c dull blue & blk | | .50 | 1.50 |
| 92 | A16 | 7c plum & blk | | .50 | 1.50 |
| 93 | A16 | 10c yellow & blk | | .50 | 1.50 |
| 94 | A17 | 20c slate & blk | | .50 | 1.50 |
| 95 | A17 | 50c olive & blk | | .50 | 1.50 |
| | | *Nos. 89-95 (7)* | | 3.50 | 10.50 |

Two dies were used for the handstamped overprint on Nos. 89-95. Letters and figures are larger on one than on the other. All values exist imperforate.

Pres. Pierre Nord-
Alexis — A18

| 1904 | | Engr. | | Perf. 13½, 14 | |
|---|---|---|---|---|---|
| 96 | A18 | 1c green | | .35 | .35 |
| 97 | A18 | 2c carmine | | .35 | .35 |
| 98 | A18 | 5c dark blue | | .35 | .35 |
| 99 | A18 | 10c orange brown | | .35 | .35 |
| 100 | A18 | 20c orange | | .35 | .35 |
| 101 | A18 | 50c claret | | .35 | .35 |
| a. | | Tête bêche pair | | 350.00 | |
| | | *Nos. 96-101 (6)* | | 2.10 | 2.10 |

Used values are for c-t-o's. Postally used examples are worth more.
Nos. 96-101 exist imperforate. Value, set $10.
This issue, and the overprints and surcharges, exist in horiz. pairs, imperf. vert., and in vert. pairs, imperf. horiz.
For overprints and surcharges see Nos. 102-109, 150-161, 170-176, 217-218, 235-238, 240-242, 302-303.
Forgeries of Nos. 96, 101, 101a exist.
*Reprints or very accurate imitations of this issue exist, including No. 101a.*

*Some are printed in very bright colors on very white paper and are found both perforated and imperforate. Generally the original stamps are perf. 13¼, the reprints perf 13½.*

**Same Handstamped in Blue like #89-95**

**1904**
| | | | | |
|---|---|---|---|---|
| 102 | A18 | 1c green | .60 | 1.50 |
| 103 | A18 | 2c carmine | .60 | 1.50 |
| 104 | A18 | 5c dark blue | .60 | 1.50 |
| 105 | A18 | 10c orange brown | .60 | 1.50 |
| 106 | A18 | 20c orange | .60 | 1.50 |
| 107 | A18 | 50c claret | .60 | 1.50 |
| | | Nos. 102-107 (6) | 3.60 | 9.00 |

The note after No. 95 applies also to Nos. 102-107. All values exist imperf.
Forgeries exist.

**Regular Issue of 1904 Handstamp Surcharged in Black:**

**1906, Feb. 20**
| | | | | |
|---|---|---|---|---|
| 108 | A18 | 1c on 20c orange | .35 | .20 |
| a. | | 1c on 50c claret | 950.00 | |
| 109 | A18 | 2c on 50c claret | .35 | .20 |

No. 108a is known only with inverted surcharge.
Forgeries exist.

Nos. 52-66
Handstamped in Red

**1906**
| | | | | |
|---|---|---|---|---|
| 110 | A12 | 1c ultra | 1.25 | .85 |
| 111 | A13 | 1c yellow green | .65 | .65 |
| 112 | A13 | 2c deep orange | 2.25 | 2.10 |
| 113 | A13 | 2c carmine lake | 1.25 | 1.10 |
| 114 | A13 | 3c green | 1.25 | 1.10 |
| 115 | A13 | 4c red | 5.25 | 4.00 |
| 116 | A12 | 5c red brown | 6.50 | 5.00 |
| 117 | A12 | 5c pale blue | .95 | .55 |
| 118 | A12 | 7c gray | 4.50 | 4.00 |
| 119 | A13 | 8c carmine | .95 | .90 |
| 120 | A13 | 10c orange red | 1.75 | 1.10 |
| 121 | A13 | 15c olive green | 2.25 | 1.10 |
| 122 | A12 | 20c black | 5.25 | 4.00 |
| 123 | A12 | 50c rose brown | 5.00 | 3.25 |
| 124 | A12 | 1g red violet | 10.50 | 6.50 |
| | | Nos. 110-124 (15) | 49.55 | 36.20 |

Forgeries of this overprint are plentiful.

Coat of Arms — A19

President Nord-Alexis A20

Market at Port-au-Prince A21

---

Sans Souci Palace — A22

Independence Palace at Gonaives — A23

Entrance to Catholic College at Port-au-Prince A24

Monastery and Church at Port-au-Prince A25

Seat of Government at Port-au-Prince A26

Presidential Palace at Port-au-Prince A27

**For Foreign Postage (centimes de piastre)**

**1906-13**                    *Perf. 12*
| | | | | |
|---|---|---|---|---|
| 125 | A19 | 1c de p green | .35 | .20 |
| 126 | A20 | 2c de p ver | .45 | .20 |
| 127 | A21 | 3c de p brown | .60 | .25 |
| 128 | A21 | 3c de p org yel | | |
| | | ('11) | 6.00 | 4.00 |
| 129 | A22 | 4c de p car lake | .60 | .35 |
| 130 | A22 | 4c de p lt ol grn | | |
| | | ('13) | 12.50 | 9.00 |
| 131 | A20 | 5c de p dk blue | 2.50 | .30 |
| 132 | A23 | 7c de p gray | 1.75 | .85 |
| 133 | A23 | 7c de p org red | | |
| | | ('13) | 32.50 | 22.50 |
| 134 | A24 | 8c de p car rose | 1.75 | .80 |
| 135 | A24 | 8c de p ol grn | | |
| | | ('13) | 25.00 | 19.00 |
| 136 | A25 | 10c de p org red | 1.25 | .30 |
| 137 | A25 | 10c de p red brn | | |
| | | ('13) | 25.00 | 19.00 |
| 138 | A26 | 15c de p sl grn | 2.25 | .90 |
| 139 | A26 | 15c dp p yel ('13) | 13.00 | 7.50 |
| 140 | A20 | 20c de p blue grn | 2.25 | .90 |
| 141 | A19 | 50c de p red | 3.25 | 2.25 |
| 142 | A19 | 50c de p org yel | | |
| | | ('13) | 13.00 | 7.50 |
| 143 | A27 | 1p claret | 7.25 | 4.50 |
| 144 | A27 | 1p red ('13) | 13.00 | 11.00 |
| | | Nos. 125-144 (20) | 164.25 | 111.30 |

All 1906 values exist imperf. These are plate proofs.
For overprints and surcharges see Nos. 177-195, 213-216, 239, 245, 249-260, 263, 265-277, 279-284, 286-301, 304.

Nord-Alexis A28

Coat of Arms — A29

---

**For Domestic Postage (centimes de gourde)**

**1906-10**
| | | | | |
|---|---|---|---|---|
| 145 | A28 | 1c de g blue | .35 | .20 |
| 146 | A29 | 2c de g org yel | .45 | .20 |
| 147 | A29 | 2c de g lemon ('10) | .65 | .25 |
| 148 | A29 | 3c de g slate | .40 | .20 |
| 149 | A29 | 7c de g green | 1.25 | .45 |
| | | Nos. 145-149 (5) | 3.10 | 1.30 |

For overprints see Nos. 196-197.

**Regular Issue of 1904 Handstamp Surcharged in Red like #108-109**

**1907**
| | | | | |
|---|---|---|---|---|
| 150 | A18 | 1c on 5c dk bl | .40 | .35 |
| 151 | A18 | 1c on 20c org | .40 | .20 |
| 152 | A18 | 2c on 10c org brn | .40 | .40 |
| 153 | A18 | 2c on 50c claret | .50 | .40 |

**Black Surcharge**
| | | | | |
|---|---|---|---|---|
| 154 | A18 | 1c on 5c dk bl | .50 | .40 |
| 155 | A18 | 1c on 10c org brn | .50 | .20 |
| 156 | A18 | 2c on 20c org | .40 | .40 |

**Brown Surcharge**
| | | | | |
|---|---|---|---|---|
| 157 | A18 | 1c on 5c dk bl | 1.50 | 1.25 |
| 158 | A18 | 1c on 10c org brn | 1.50 | 1.25 |
| 159 | A18 | 2c on 20c org | 5.00 | 4.00 |
| 160 | A18 | 2c on 50c claret | 27.50 | 22.50 |

**Violet Surcharge**
| | | | | |
|---|---|---|---|---|
| 161 | A18 | 1c on 20c org | | 150.00 |

The handstamps are found sideways, diagonal, inverted and double.
Forgeries exist.

A30

President Antoine T. Simon — A31

**For Foreign Postage**

**1910**
| | | | | |
|---|---|---|---|---|
| 162 | A30 | 2c de p rose red & blk | .65 | .50 |
| 163 | A30 | 5c de p bl & blk | 13.00 | 1.00 |
| 164 | A30 | 20c de p yel grn & blk | 12.50 | 7.50 |

**For Domestic Postage**

| | | | | |
|---|---|---|---|---|
| 165 | A31 | 1c de g lake & blk | .30 | .20 |
| | | Nos. 162-165 (4) | 26.45 | 9.20 |

For overprint and surcharges see Nos. 198, 262, 278, 285.

A32

A33

Pres. Cincinnatus Leconte — A34

**1912**
| | | | | |
|---|---|---|---|---|
| 166 | A32 | 1c de g car lake | .40 | .40 |
| 167 | A33 | 2c de g dp org | .50 | .40 |

**For Foreign Postage**
| | | | | |
|---|---|---|---|---|
| 168 | A34 | 5c de p dp blue | .90 | .40 |
| | | Nos. 166-168 (3) | 1.80 | 1.20 |

For overprints see Nos. 199-201.

---

Stamps of Preceding Issues Handstamped Vertically

**1914**

**On No. 61**
| | | | | |
|---|---|---|---|---|
| 169 | A13 | 8c carmine | 13.00 | 10.00 |

**On Nos. 96-101**
| | | | | |
|---|---|---|---|---|
| 170 | A18 | 1c green | 35.00 | 30.00 |
| 171 | A18 | 2c carmine | 35.00 | 30.00 |
| 172 | A18 | 5c dk blue | .65 | .40 |
| 173 | A18 | 10c orange brn | .65 | .40 |
| 174 | A18 | 20c orange | 1.10 | .50 |
| 175 | A18 | 50c claret | 2.50 | 1.25 |
| | | Nos. 170-175 (6) | 74.90 | 62.55 |

Perforation varieties of Nos. 172-175 exist.
No. 175 overprinted "T. M." is a revenue stamp. The letters are the initials of "Timbre Mobile."

**On No. 107**
| | | | | |
|---|---|---|---|---|
| 176 | A18 | 50c claret | 10,000. | 13,000. |

**Horizontally on Stamps of 1906-13**
| | | | | |
|---|---|---|---|---|
| 177 | A19 | 1c de p green | .50 | .40 |
| 178 | A20 | 2c de p ver | .65 | .40 |
| 179 | A21 | 3c de p brown | 1.10 | .60 |
| 180 | A21 | 3c de p org yel | .50 | .40 |
| 181 | A22 | 4c de p car lake | 1.10 | .60 |
| 182 | A22 | 4c de p lt ol grn | 2.75 | 1.40 |
| 183 | A23 | 7c de p gray | 2.50 | 2.40 |
| 184 | A23 | 7c de p org red | 6.50 | 6.00 |
| 185 | A24 | 8c de p car rose | 4.50 | 4.00 |
| 186 | A24 | 8c de p ol grn | 8.25 | 8.00 |
| 187 | A25 | 10c de p org red | 1.30 | .60 |
| 188 | A25 | 10c de p red brn | 3.50 | 2.10 |
| 189 | A26 | 15c de p sl grn | 3.75 | 3.25 |
| 190 | A26 | 15c de p yellow | 2.75 | 1.40 |
| 191 | A20 | 20c de p bl grn | 3.25 | 1.25 |
| 192 | A19 | 50c de p red | 5.75 | 5.50 |
| 193 | A19 | 50c de p org yel | 9.75 | 9.00 |
| 194 | A27 | 1p claret | 5.75 | 5.50 |
| 195 | A27 | 1p red | 10.50 | 9.75 |
| 196 | A29 | 2c de g lemon | .50 | .40 |
| 197 | A29 | 3c de g slate | .50 | .40 |
| | | Nos. 177-197 (21) | 75.65 | 63.35 |

**On No. 164**
| | | | | |
|---|---|---|---|---|
| 198 | A30 | 20c de p yel grn & blk | 3.75 | 3.50 |

**Vertically on Nos. 166-168**
| | | | | |
|---|---|---|---|---|
| 199 | A32 | 1c de g car lake | .50 | .40 |
| 200 | A33 | 2c de g dp org | .65 | .50 |
| 201 | A34 | 5c de p dp blue | 1.10 | .40 |
| | | Nos. 199-201 (3) | 2.25 | 1.30 |

Two handstamps were used for the overprints on Nos. 169-201. They may be distinguished by the short and long foot of the "L" of "GL" and the position of the first "1" in "1914" with regard to the period above it. Both handstamps are found on all but #176, 294, 295, 308.

Handstamp Surcharged

**On Nos. 141 and 143**
| | | | | |
|---|---|---|---|---|
| 213 | A19 | 1c de p on 50c de p red | .50 | .40 |
| 214 | A27 | 1c de p on 1p claret | .65 | .50 |

**On Nos. 142 and 144**
| | | | | |
|---|---|---|---|---|
| 215 | A19 | 1c de p on 50c de p org yel | .65 | .50 |
| 216 | A27 | 1c de p on 1p red | .65 | .50 |

Handstamp Surcharged

**On Nos. 100 and 101**
| | | | | |
|---|---|---|---|---|
| 217 | A18 | 7c on 20c orange | .50 | .20 |
| 218 | A18 | 7c on 50c claret | .45 | .20 |

The initials on the preceding handstamps are those of Gen. Oreste Zamor; the date is that of his triumphal entry into Port-au-Prince.

Pres. Oreste Zamor

Coat of Arms

Pres. Tancrède Auguste

Owing to the theft of a large quantity of this 1914 issue, while in transit from the printers, the stamps were never placed on sale at post offices. A few copies have been canceled through carelessness or favor. Value, set of 10, $8.50.

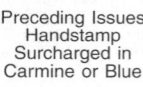

Preceding Issues Handstamp Surcharged in Carmine or Blue

**On Nos. 98-101**

**1915-16**
| | | | | |
|---|---|---|---|---|
| 235 | A18 | 1c on 5c dk bl (C) | 2.00 | 2.25 |
| 236 | A18 | 1c on 10c org brn | .60 | .75 |
| 237 | A18 | 1c on 20c orange | .60 | .75 |
| 238 | A18 | 1c on 50c claret | .60 | .75 |

**On No. 132**
| | | | | |
|---|---|---|---|---|
| 239 | A23 | 1c on 7c de p gray (C) | .60 | .75 |

**On Nos. 106-107**
| | | | | |
|---|---|---|---|---|
| 240 | A18 | 1c on 20c orange | 1.50 | 1.50 |
| 241 | A18 | 1c on 50c claret | 3.50 | 1.50 |
| 242 | A18 | 1c on 50c cl (C) | 45.00 | 35.00 |
| | | Nos. 235-242 (8) | 54.40 | 43.25 |

Nos. 240-242 are known with two types of the "Post Paye" overprint. No. 237 with red surcharge and any stamps with violet surcharge are unofficial.

Values for Nos. 245-308 are for examples with the boxed "Gourde" surcharge partially on the stamp. Examples upon which this surcharge is fully present on the stamp command substantial premiums.

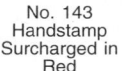

No. 143 Handstamp Surcharged in Red

**1917-19**
| | | | | |
|---|---|---|---|---|
| 245 | A27 | 2c on 1p claret | .50 | .50 |

Stamps of 1906-14 Handstamp Surcharged in Various Colors

1c, 5c

**On Nos. 123-124**
| | | | | |
|---|---|---|---|---|
| 247 | A12 | 1c on 50c (R) | 35.00 | 30.00 |
| 248 | A12 | 1c on 1g (R) | 35.00 | 30.00 |

**On #127, 129, 134, 136, 138, 140-141**
| | | | | |
|---|---|---|---|---|
| 249 | A22 | 1c on 4c de p (Br) | .65 | .75 |
| 250 | A25 | 1c on 10c de p (Bl) | .65 | .75 |
| 252 | A20 | 1c on 20c de p (R) | .65 | .75 |
| 253 | A20 | 1c on 20c de p (Bk) | .65 | .75 |
| 254 | A19 | 1c on 50c de p (R) | .65 | .75 |
| 255 | A19 | 1c on 50c de p (Bk) | .65 | .75 |
| 256 | A21 | 2c on 3c de p (R) | .65 | .75 |
| 257 | A24 | 2c on 8c de p (R) | .65 | .75 |
| 258 | A24 | 2c on 8c de p (Bk) | .65 | .75 |
| 259 | A26 | 2c on 15c de p (R) | .65 | .75 |
| 260 | A20 | 2c on 20c de p (R) | .65 | .75 |
| | | Nos. 249-260 (11) | 7.15 | 8.25 |

The 1c on 10c de p stamp in black is actually a blue ink which bled into the stamps.

**On Nos. 164, 128**
| | | | | |
|---|---|---|---|---|
| 262 | A30 | 1c on 20c de p (Bk) | 3.75 | 3.50 |
| 263 | A21 | 2c on 3c de p (R) | .60 | .75 |

**On #130, 133, 135, 137, 139, 142, 144**
| | | | | |
|---|---|---|---|---|
| 265 | A22 | 1c on 4c de p (R) | .60 | .75 |
| 266 | A23 | 1c on 7c de p (Br) | .60 | .75 |
| 267 | A26 | 1c on 15c de p (R) | .60 | .75 |
| 268 | A19 | 1c on 50c de p (Bk) | 2.00 | 2.50 |
| 269 | A27 | 1c on 1p (Bk) | 2.00 | 2.50 |
| 270 | A24 | 2c on 8c de p (R) | .60 | .75 |
| 271 | A25 | 2c on 10c de p (Br) | .60 | .75 |
| 272 | A26 | 2c on 15c de p (R) | .60 | .75 |
| 273 | A25 | 5c on 10c de p (Bl) | 2.00 | 2.50 |
| 274 | A25 | 5c on 10c de p (VBk) | .60 | .75 |
| 275 | A26 | 5c on 15c de p (R) | 5.00 | 6.00 |
| | | Nos. 265-275 (11) | 15.20 | 18.75 |

"O. Z." Stamps of 1914 Handstamp Surcharged in Red or Brown

| | | | | |
|---|---|---|---|---|
| 276 | A26 | 1c on 15c de p sl grn | .60 | .75 |
| 277 | A20 | 1c on 20c de p bl grn | .60 | .75 |
| 278 | A30 | 1c on 20c de p yel grn & blk | .60 | .75 |
| 279 | A27 | 1c on 1p claret (Br) | .60 | .75 |
| 280 | A27 | 1c on 1p claret | 2.00 | 2.50 |
| 281 | A27 | 5c on 1p red (Br) | .60 | .75 |
| | | Nos. 276-281 (6) | 5.00 | 6.25 |

"O. Z." Stamps of 1914 Handstamp Surcharged in Violet, Green, Red, Magenta or Black
1 ct and 2 cts as in 1917-19 and

**1919-20**
| | | | | |
|---|---|---|---|---|
| 282 | A22 | 2c on 4c de p car lake (V) | .60 | .75 |
| 283 | A24 | 2c on 8c de p car rose (G) | .60 | .75 |
| 284 | A24 | 2c on 8c de p ol grn (R) | .60 | .75 |
| 285 | A30 | 2c on 20c de p yel grn & blk (R) | .75 | 1.00 |
| 286 | A19 | 2c on 50c de p red (G) | .60 | .75 |
| 288 | A19 | 2c on 50c de p red | .60 | .75 |
| 289 | A19 | 2c on 50c de p org yel (R) | .60 | .75 |
| 290 | A27 | 2c on 1pi claret (R) | 3.00 | 3.50 |
| 291 | A27 | 2c on 1pi red (R) | 2.00 | 2.50 |
| 292 | A21 | 3c on 3c de p brn (R) | .60 | .75 |
| 293 | A23 | 3c on 7c de p org red (R) | .60 | .75 |
| 294 | A21 | 3c on 3c de p brn (R) | .60 | .75 |
| 295 | A21 | 5c on 3c de p org yel (R) | 2.00 | 2.50 |
| 296 | A22 | 5c on 4c de p car lake (R) | .60 | .75 |
| 297 | A22 | 5c on 4c de p ol grn (R) | .60 | .75 |
| 298 | A23 | 5c on 7c de p gray (V) | .60 | .75 |
| 299 | A23 | 5c on 7c de p org red (R) | .60 | .75 |
| 300 | A25 | 5c on 10c de p org red (V) | .60 | .75 |
| 301 | A26 | 5c on 15c de p yel (M) | .60 | .75 |
| | | Nos. 282-301 (19) | 16.75 | 20.75 |

Nos. 217 and 218 Handstamp Surcharged with New Value in Magenta
| | | | | |
|---|---|---|---|---|
| 302 | A18 | 5c on 7c on 20c orange | .60 | .75 |
| 303 | A18 | 5c on 7c on 50c claret | 3.50 | 4.00 |

No. 187 Handstamp Surcharged in Magenta

| | | | | |
|---|---|---|---|---|
| 304 | A25 | 5c de p on 10c de p | .60 | .75 |

Postage Due Stamps of 1906-14 Handstamp Surcharged in Black or Magenta (#308)

**On Stamp of 1906**
| | | | | |
|---|---|---|---|---|
| 305 | D2 | 5c on 50c ol gray | 15.00 | 15.00 |

**On Stamp of 1914**
| | | | | |
|---|---|---|---|---|
| 306 | D2 | 5c on 10c violet | .60 | .75 |
| 307 | D2 | 5c on 50c olive gray | .60 | .75 |
| 308 | D2 | 5c on 50c ol gray (M) | 2.50 | 2.00 |
| | | Nos. 305-308 (4) | 18.70 | 18.50 |

Nos. 299 with red surcharge and 306-307 with violet are trial colors or essays.

Allegory of Agriculture A40

Allegory of Commerce A41

**1920, Apr.        Engr.        Perf. 12**
| | | | | |
|---|---|---|---|---|
| 310 | A40 | 3c deep orange | .40 | .40 |
| 311 | A40 | 5c green | .40 | .40 |
| 312 | A41 | 10c vermilion | .50 | .40 |
| 313 | A41 | 15c violet | .50 | .40 |
| 314 | A41 | 25c deep blue | .65 | .50 |
| | | Nos. 310-314 (5) | 2.45 | 2.10 |

Nos. 311-313 overprinted "T. M." are revenue stamps. The letters are the initials of "Timbre Mobile."

President Louis J. Borno — A42

Christophe's Citadel — A43

Old Map of West Indies — A44

Borno — A45

National Capitol — A46

**1924, Sept. 3**
| | | | | |
|---|---|---|---|---|
| 315 | A42 | 5c deep green | .40 | .20 |
| 316 | A43 | 10c carmine | .40 | .20 |
| 317 | A44 | 20c violet blue | .90 | .40 |
| 318 | A45 | 50c orange & blk | .90 | .40 |
| 319 | A46 | 1g olive green | 1.60 | .50 |
| | | Nos. 315-319 (5) | 4.20 | 1.70 |

For surcharges see Nos. 359, C4A.

Coffee Beans and Flowers — A47

**1928, Feb. 6**
| | | | | |
|---|---|---|---|---|
| 320 | A47 | 35c deep green | 3.75 | .60 |

For surcharge see No. 337.

Pres. Louis Borno — A48

**1929, Nov. 4**
| | | | | |
|---|---|---|---|---|
| 321 | A48 | 10c carmine rose | .50 | .40 |

Signing of the "Frontier" treaty between Haiti and the Dominican Republic.

Presidents Salomon and Vincent — A49

Pres. Sténio Vincent — A50

## 1931, Oct. 16

| | | | | | |
|---|---|---|---|---|---|
| 322 | A49 | 5c deep green | | 1.30 | .50 |
| 323 | A50 | 10c carmine rose | | 1.30 | .50 |

50th anniv. of Haiti's joining the UPU.

President Vincent — A52

Aqueduct at Port-au-Prince A53

Fort National — A54

Palace of Sans Souci — A55

Christophe's Chapel at Milot — A56

King's Gallery Citadel — A57

Vallières Battery — A58

## 1933-40

| | | | | | |
|---|---|---|---|---|---|
| 325 | A52 | 3c orange | | .30 | .20 |
| 326 | A52 | 3c dp ol grn ('39) | | .30 | .20 |
| 327 | A53 | 5c green | | .30 | .20 |
| a. | | 5c emerald ('38) | | .30 | .20 |
| b. | | 5c bright green ('39) | | .30 | .20 |
| c. | | 5c brown olive ('40) | | .50 | .20 |
| 329 | A54 | 10c rose car | | .50 | .20 |
| a. | | 10c vermilion | | .65 | .20 |
| 330 | A54 | 10c red brn ('40) | | .50 | .20 |
| 331 | A55 | 25c blue | | .90 | .20 |
| 332 | A56 | 50c brown | | 2.50 | .55 |
| 333 | A57 | 1g dark green | | 2.50 | .55 |
| 334 | A58 | 2.50g olive bister | | 4.50 | .90 |
| | | Nos. 325-334 (9) | | 12.30 | 3.20 |

For surcharges see Nos. 357-358, 360.

Alexandre Dumas, His Father and Son — A59

## 1935, Dec. 29   Litho.   Perf. 11½

| | | | | | |
|---|---|---|---|---|---|
| 335 | A59 | 10c rose pink & choc | | .90 | .40 |
| 336 | A59 | 25c blue & chocolate | | 1.60 | .40 |
| | | Nos. 335-336,C10 (3) | | 7.00 | 3.40 |

Visit of a delegation from France to Haiti.

---

No. 335 exists imperf and in horiz. pair, imperf. between. #336 exists as pair, imperf horiz.

### No. 320 Surcharged in Red

## 1939, Jan. 24   Perf. 12

| | | | | | |
|---|---|---|---|---|---|
| 337 | A47 | 25c on 35c dp grn | | .90 | .40 |

Statue of Liberty, Map of Haiti and Flags of American Republics A60

## 1941, June 30   Engr.   Perf. 12

| | | | | | |
|---|---|---|---|---|---|
| 338 | A60 | 10c rose carmine | | 1.00 | .50 |
| 339 | A60 | 25c dark blue | | .90 | .40 |
| | | Nos. 338-339,C12-C13 (4) | | 8.40 | 2.40 |

3rd Inter-American Caribbean Conf., held at Port-au-Prince.

Patroness of Haiti, Map and Coat of Arms — A61

## 1942, Dec. 8

### Size: 26x36¼mm

| | | | | | |
|---|---|---|---|---|---|
| 340 | A61 | 3c dull violet | | .40 | .20 |
| 341 | A61 | 5c brt green | | .50 | .20 |
| 342 | A61 | 10c rose car | | .50 | .20 |
| 343 | A61 | 15c orange | | .65 | .50 |
| 344 | A61 | 20c brown | | .65 | .50 |
| 345 | A61 | 25c deep blue | | 1.40 | .50 |
| 346 | A61 | 50c red orange | | 1.75 | .70 |
| 347 | A61 | 2.50g olive black | | 4.75 | 1.10 |

### Size: 32x45mm

| | | | | | |
|---|---|---|---|---|---|
| 348 | A61 | 5g purple | | 11.50 | 4.50 |
| | | Nos. 340-348,C14-C18 (14) | | 27.80 | 10.40 |

Issued in honor of Our Lady of Perpetual Help, patroness of Haiti.
For surcharges see Nos. 355-356.

Adm. Hammerton Killick and Destruction of "La Crête-à-Pierrot" — A62

## 1943, Sept. 6

| | | | | | |
|---|---|---|---|---|---|
| 349 | A62 | 3c orange | | .40 | .20 |
| 350 | A62 | 5c turq green | | .50 | .40 |
| 351 | A62 | 10c carmine rose | | .50 | .40 |
| 352 | A62 | 25c deep blue | | .65 | .40 |
| 353 | A62 | 50c olive | | 1.40 | .50 |
| 354 | A62 | 5g brown black | | 5.75 | 3.00 |
| | | Nos. 349-354,C22-C23 (8) | | 11.45 | 6.90 |

### Nos. 343 and 345 Surcharged with New Value and Bars in Red

## 1944, July 19

| | | | | | |
|---|---|---|---|---|---|
| 355 | A61 | 10c on 15c orange | | .40 | .20 |
| 356 | A61 | 10c on 25c dp blue | | .40 | .20 |

---

### Nos. 319, 326 and 334 Surcharged with New Values and Bars in Red

## 1944-45

| | | | | | |
|---|---|---|---|---|---|
| 357 | A52 | 2c on 3c dp ol grn | | .30 | .20 |
| 358 | A52 | 5c on 3c dp ol grn | | .40 | .20 |
| 359 | A46 | 10c on 1g ol grn | | .50 | .40 |
| a. | | Surcharged "01.0" | | | 1.50 |
| 360 | A58 | 20c on 2.50g ol bis | | .50 | .40 |
| | | Nos. 357-360 (4) | | 1.70 | 1.40 |

Nurse and Wounded Soldier on Battlefield — A63

## 1945, Feb. 20

### Cross in Rose

| | | | | | |
|---|---|---|---|---|---|
| 361 | A63 | 3c gray black | | .20 | .20 |
| 362 | A63 | 5c dk blue grn | | .20 | .20 |
| 363 | A63 | 10c red orange | | .30 | .20 |
| 364 | A63 | 20c black brn | | .30 | .20 |
| 365 | A63 | 25c deep blue | | .40 | .20 |
| 366 | A63 | 35c orange | | .50 | .20 |
| 367 | A63 | 50c car rose | | .50 | .20 |
| 368 | A63 | 1g olive green | | .90 | .40 |
| 369 | A63 | 2.50g pale violet | | 2.50 | .50 |
| | | Nos. 361-369,C25-C32 (17) | | 18.65 | 7.00 |

Issued to honor the Intl. Red Cross. 20c, 1g, 2.50g, Aug. 14. Others, Feb. 20. For overprints and surcharges see Nos. 456-457, C153-C160.

> Catalogue values for unused stamps in this section, from this point to the end of the section, are for Never Hinged items.

Col. François Capois A64     Jean Jacques Dessalines A65

### Unwmk.

## 1946, July 18   Engr.   Perf. 12

| | | | | | |
|---|---|---|---|---|---|
| 370 | A64 | 3c red orange | | .25 | .20 |
| 371 | A64 | 5c Prus green | | .25 | .20 |
| 372 | A64 | 10c red | | .25 | .20 |
| 373 | A64 | 20c olive black | | .25 | .20 |
| 374 | A64 | 25c deep blue | | .30 | .20 |
| 375 | A64 | 35c orange | | .40 | .20 |
| 376 | A64 | 50c red brown | | .50 | .40 |
| 377 | A64 | 1g olive brown | | .50 | .40 |
| 378 | A64 | 2.50g gray | | 1.30 | .50 |
| | | Nos. 370-378,C35-C42 (17) | | 9.50 | 5.60 |

For surcharges see Nos. 383, 392, C43-C45, C49-C51, C61-C62.

## 1947-54

| | | | | | |
|---|---|---|---|---|---|
| 379 | A65 | 3c orange yel | | .20 | .20 |
| 380 | A65 | 5c green | | .20 | .20 |
| 380A | A65 | 5c dp vio ('54) | | .65 | .20 |
| 381 | A65 | 10c carmine rose | | .25 | .20 |
| 382 | A65 | 25c deep blue | | .40 | .20 |
| | | Nos. 379-382,C46 (6) | | 2.10 | 1.20 |

### No. 375 Surcharged with New Value and Rectangular Block in Black

## 1948

| | | | | | |
|---|---|---|---|---|---|
| 383 | A64 | 10c on 35c orange | | .40 | .20 |

Arms of Port-au-Prince A66

---

### Engraved and Lithographed

## 1950, Feb. 12   Perf. 12½

| | | | | | |
|---|---|---|---|---|---|
| 384 | A66 | 10c multicolored | | .40 | .20 |
| | | Nos. 384,C47-C48 (3) | | 2.20 | 1.20 |

200th anniv. (in 1949) of the founding of Port-au-Prince.

### Nos. RA10-RA12 and RA16 Surcharged or Overprinted in Black

## 1950, Oct. 4   Unwmk.   Perf. 12

| | | | | | |
|---|---|---|---|---|---|
| 385 | PT2 | 3c on 5c ol gray | | .20 | .20 |
| 386 | PT2 | 5c green | | .40 | .20 |
| 387 | PT2 | 10c on 5c car rose | | .40 | .20 |
| 388 | PT2 | 20c on 5c blue | | .50 | .50 |
| | | Nos. 385-388,C49-C51 (7) | | 4.25 | 3.40 |

75th anniv. (in 1949) of the UPU. Exist with inverted or double surcharge and 10c on 5c green.

Cacao — A67

Pres. Paul E. Magloire and Day Nursery, Saline — A68

## 1951, Sept. 3   Photo.   Perf. 12½

| | | | | | |
|---|---|---|---|---|---|
| 389 | A67 | 5c dark green | | .40 | .20 |
| | | Nos. 389,C52-C54 (4) | | 27.15 | 4.70 |

## 1953, May 4   Engr.   Perf. 12

Design: 10c, Applying asphalt.

| | | | | | |
|---|---|---|---|---|---|
| 390 | A68 | 5c green | | .20 | .20 |
| 391 | A68 | 10c rose carmine | | .30 | .20 |
| | | Nos. 390-391,C57-C60 (6) | | 3.75 | 2.15 |

No. 375 Surcharged in Black

## 1953, Apr. 7

| | | | | | |
|---|---|---|---|---|---|
| 392 | A64 | 50c on 35c orange | | .50 | .40 |

Gen. Pierre Dominique Toussaint L'Ouverture, 1743-1803, liberator.

J. J. Dessalines and Paul E. Magloire — A69

Alexandre Sabes Pétion — A70

Battle of Vertieres — A71

Design: No. 395, Larmartiniere. No. 396, Boisrond-Tonnerre. No. 397, Toussaint L'Ouverture. No. 399, Capois. No. 401, Marie Jeanne and Lamartinière leading attack.

**1954, Jan. 1　　Photo.　　Perf. 11½**
**Portraits in Black**

| | | | | |
|---|---|---|---|---|
| 393 | A69 | 3c blue gray | .20 | .20 |
| 394 | A70 | 5c yellow green | .30 | .20 |
| 395 | A70 | 5c yellow green | .30 | .20 |
| 396 | A70 | 5c yellow green | .40 | .30 |
| 397 | A70 | 5c yellow green | .30 | .20 |
| 398 | A69 | 10c crimson | .30 | .20 |
| 399 | A70 | 15c rose lilac | .40 | .20 |

**Perf. 12½**

| | | | | |
|---|---|---|---|---|
| 400 | A71 | 25c dark gray | .40 | .20 |
| 401 | A71 | 25c deep orange | .40 | .20 |
| | Nos. 393-401 (9) | | 3.00 | 1.90 |
| | Nos. 393-401,C63-C74 (21) | | 14.90 | 10.45 |

150th anniv. of Haitian independence. See Nos. C95-C96.

Mme. Yolette Magloire — A72

**1954, Jan. 1　　　　Perf. 11½**
| | | | | |
|---|---|---|---|---|
| 402 | A72 | 10c orange | .30 | .20 |
| 403 | A72 | 10c blue | .30 | .20 |
| | Nos. 402-403,C75-C80 (8) | | 6.70 | 5.05 |

Henri Christophe, Paul Magloire and Citadel A73

Zim Waterfall A80

Tomb and Arms of Henri Christophe — A74

**Perf. 13½x13**
**1954, Dec. 6　　Litho.　　Unwmk.**
| | | | | |
|---|---|---|---|---|
| 404 | A73 | 10c carmine | .25 | .20 |

**Perf. 13**
| | | | | |
|---|---|---|---|---|
| 405 | A74 | 10c red, blk & car | .30 | .20 |
| | Nos. 404-405,C81-C90 (12) | | 15.10 | 8.65 |

Restoration of Christophe's Citadel.

J. J. Dessalines A75

Pres. Magloire and Dessalines Memorial, Gonaives A76

**1955-57　　Photo.　　Perf. 11½**
| | | | | |
|---|---|---|---|---|
| 406 | A75 | 3c ocher & blk | .20 | .20 |
| 407 | A75 | 5c pale vio & blk ('56) | .20 | .20 |
| 408 | A75 | 10c rose & blk | .25 | .20 |
| a. | 10c salmon pink & black ('57) | | .20 | |
| 409 | A75 | 25c chalky bl & blk ('56) | .30 | .20 |
| a. | 25c blue & black ('57) | | .30 | .20 |
| | Nos. 406-409,C93-C94 (6) | | 1.45 | 1.20 |

For surcharges, see Nos. 454-455.

---

**1955, Aug. 1**
| | | | | |
|---|---|---|---|---|
| 410 | A76 | 10c deep blue & blk | .40 | .20 |
| 411 | A76 | 10c crimson & blk | .40 | .20 |
| | Nos. 410-411,C97-C98 (4) | | 2.10 | .80 |

21st anniv. of the new Haitian army. Nos. 410-411 were printed in a single sheet of 20 (5x4). The two upper rows are of No. 410, the two lower No. 411, providing five se-tenant pairs. Value 85 cents.

Flamingo A77

Mallard A78

**1956, Apr. 14　　Photo.　　Perf. 11½**
**Granite Paper**
| | | | | |
|---|---|---|---|---|
| 412 | A77 | 10c blue & ultra | 2.50 | .30 |
| 413 | A78 | 25c dk grn & bluish grn | 3.50 | .45 |
| | Nos. 412-413,C99-C104 (8) | | 46.45 | 6.80 |

Immanuel Kant — A79

**1956, July 19　　　　Perf. 12**
**Granite Paper**
| | | | | |
|---|---|---|---|---|
| 414 | A79 | 10c brt ultra | .30 | .20 |
| | Nos. 414,C105-C107 (4) | | 2.45 | 1.30 |

10th anniv. of the 1st Inter-American Philosophical Congress.

**1957, Dec. 16　　Unwmk.　　Perf. 11½**
**Granite Paper**
| | | | | |
|---|---|---|---|---|
| 415 | A80 | 10c orange & blue | .30 | .20 |
| | Nos. 415,C108-C111 (5) | | 4.70 | 2.90 |

For surcharge & overprint see #CB49, CQ2.

**1958, July 1　　　　　Photo.**
| | | | | |
|---|---|---|---|---|
| 416 | A81 | 5c yel grn & blk | .25 | .20 |

Bicentenary of birth of J. J. Dessalines. See Nos. 470-471, C112, C170. For overprints see Nos. 480-482, C183-C184, CQ1, Q1-Q3.

"Atomium" — A82

View of Brussels Exposition A83

---

**Perf. 13x13½, 13½x13**
**1958, July 22　　Litho.　　Unwmk.**
| | | | | |
|---|---|---|---|---|
| 417 | A82 | 50c brown | .40 | .20 |
| 418 | A83 | 75c brt green | .40 | .20 |
| 419 | A82 | 1g purple | .75 | .20 |
| 420 | A83 | 1.50g red orange | .75 | .40 |
| | Nos. 417-420,C113-C114 (6) | | 5.05 | 2.35 |

Issued for the Universal and International Exposition at Brussels.
For surcharges see Nos. B2-B3, CB9.

Sylvio Cator — A84

U. S. Satellite — A85

**1958, Aug. 16　　Photo.　　Perf. 11½**
**Granite Paper**
| | | | | |
|---|---|---|---|---|
| 421 | A84 | 5c green | .20 | .20 |
| 422 | A84 | 10c brown | .20 | .20 |
| 423 | A84 | 20c lilac | .25 | .20 |
| | Nos. 421-423,C115-C118 (7) | | 4.05 | 2.25 |

30th anniversary of the world championship record broad jump of Sylvio Cator.

**1958, Oct. 8　　　　Perf. 14x13½**

Designs: 20c, Emperor penguins. 50c, Modern observatory. 1g, Ocean exploration.
| | | | | |
|---|---|---|---|---|
| 424 | A85 | 10c brt bl & brn red | .30 | .20 |
| 425 | A85 | 20c black & dp org | 1.40 | .50 |
| 426 | A85 | 50c grn & rose brn | .75 | .30 |
| 427 | A85 | 1g black & blue | .80 | .30 |
| | Nos. 424-427,C119-C121 (7) | | 9.35 | 2.70 |

Issued for the International Geophysical Year 1957-58.

President François Duvalier — A86

**Engraved and Lithographed**
**1958, Oct. 22　　Unwmk.　　Perf. 11½**
**Commemorative Inscription in Ultramarine**
| | | | | |
|---|---|---|---|---|
| 428 | A86 | 10c blk & dp pink | .30 | .20 |
| 429 | A86 | 50c blk & lt grn | .40 | .20 |
| 430 | A86 | 1g blk & brick red | .50 | .40 |
| 431 | A86 | 5g blk & sal | 2.40 | 1.50 |
| | Nos. 428-431,C122-C125 (8) | | 10.90 | 6.35 |

1st anniv. of the inauguration of Pres. Dr. François Duvalier. See note on souvenir sheets after No. C125.

**1958 Nov. 20**
**Without Commemorative Inscription**
| | | | | |
|---|---|---|---|---|
| 432 | A86 | 5c blk & lt vio bl | .20 | .20 |
| 433 | A86 | 10c blk & dp pink | .20 | .20 |
| 434 | A86 | 20c blk & yel | .20 | .20 |
| 435 | A86 | 50c blk & lt grn | .30 | .20 |
| 436 | A86 | 1g blk & brick red | .50 | .40 |
| 437 | A86 | 1.50g blk & rose pink | .65 | .50 |
| 438 | A86 | 2.50g blk & gray vio | .90 | .50 |
| 439 | A86 | 5g blk & sal | 1.60 | 1.10 |
| | Nos. 432-439,C126-C132 (15) | | 13.20 | 7.90 |

For surcharges see Nos. B13, B22-B24.

Map of Haiti — A87

---

**1958, Dec. 5　　Photo.　　Perf. 11½**
**Granite Paper**
| | | | | |
|---|---|---|---|---|
| 440 | A87 | 10c rose pink | .20 | .20 |
| 441 | A87 | 25c green | .30 | .20 |
| | Nos. 440-441,C133-C135 (5) | | 1.80 | 1.20 |

Tribute to the UN. See No. C135a. For overprints and surcharges see Nos. 442-443, B4-B5, CB11-CB12.

Nos. 440-441 Overprinted "10th ANNIVERSARY OF THE / UNIVERSAL DECLARATION / OF HUMAN RIGHTS" in English (a), French (b), Spanish (c) or Portuguese (d)

**1959, Jan. 28**
| | | | | |
|---|---|---|---|---|
| 442 | | Block of 4 | .35 | .35 |
| a.-d. | A87 10c any single | | .20 | .20 |
| 443 | | Block of 4 | .90 | .70 |
| a.-d. | A87 25c any single | | .20 | .20 |
| | Nos. 442-443,C136-C138 (5) | | 14.75 | 14.55 |

10th anniv. of the signing of the Universal Declaration of Human Rights.

Pope Pius XII and Children — A88

50c, Pope praying. 2g, Pope on throne.

**1959, Feb. 28　　Photo.　　Perf. 14x13½**
| | | | | |
|---|---|---|---|---|
| 444 | A88 | 10c vio bl & ol | .20 | .20 |
| 445 | A88 | 50c green & dp brn | .40 | .20 |
| 446 | A88 | 2g dp claret & dk brn | .90 | .50 |
| | Nos. 444-446,C139-C141 (6) | | 3.40 | 1.90 |

Issued in memory of Pope Pius XII. For surcharges see Nos. B6-B8.

Abraham Lincoln — A89

**1959, May 12　　Photo.　　Perf. 12**
| | | | | |
|---|---|---|---|---|
| 447 | A89 | 50c lt bl & deep claret | .40 | .20 |
| | Nos. 447,C142-C144 (5) | | 2.50 | 1.50 |

Sesquicentennial of the birth of Abraham Lincoln. Imperf. pairs exist.
For surcharges see #B9, CB16-CB18.

Chicago's Skyline and Dessables House — A90

Jean Baptiste Dessables and Map of American Midwest, c. 1791 — A91

Design: 50c, Discus thrower and flag of Haiti.

**1959, Aug. 27    Unwmk.    Perf. 14**
448  A90  25c blk brn & lt bl          .40    .20
449  A90  50c multicolored             .50    .40
450  A91  75c brown & blue             .65    .50
     Nos. 448-450,C145-C147 (6)       4.70   2.25

3rd Pan American Games, Chicago, 8/27-9/7.

For surcharges see #B10-B12, CB19-CB21.

No. 449 Overprinted

**1960, Feb. 29**
451  A90  50c multicolored            1.60   1.20
     Nos. 451,C148-C150 (4)           7.65   7.25

8th Olympic Winter Games, Squaw Valley, Calif., Feb. 18-29, 1960.

Uprooted Oak Emblem and Hands — A92

**1960, Apr. 7    Litho.    Perf. 12½x13**
452  A92  10c salmon & grn            .20    .20
453  A92  50c violet & mag            .40    .20
     Nos. 452-453,C151-C152 (4)      1.50   1.00

World Refugee Year, July 1, 1959-June 30, 1960. See Nos. 489-490, C191-C192. For surcharges see Nos. B14-B17, B28-B29, CB24-CB27, CB45-CB46.

No. 406 Surcharged with New Values

**1960, Apr. 27    Photo.    Perf. 11½**
454  A75  5c on 3c ocher & blk        .25    .20
455  A75  10c on 3c ocher & blk       .35    .20

No. 369 Surcharged or Overprinted in Red: "28eme ANNIVERSAIRE"

**1960, May 8    Engr.    Perf. 12**
Cross in Rose
456  A63  1g on 2.50g pale vio        .90    .50
457  A63  2.50g pale violet          1.40   1.00
     Nos. 456-457,C153-C160 (10)     7.30   5.30

28th anniversary of the Haitian Red Cross.

Claudinette Fouchard, Miss Haiti, Sugar Queen — A93

Sugar Queen and: 20c, Sugar harvest. 50c, Beach. 1g, Sugar plantation.

**Perf. 11½**
**1960, May 30    Photo.    Unwmk.**
Granite Paper
458  A93  10c ol bis & vio           .25    .20
459  A93  20c red brn & blk          .30    .20
460  A93  50c brt bl & brn           .75    .20
461  A93  1g green & brn            1.75    .20
     Nos. 458-461,C161-C162 (6)     6.20   1.50

Haitian sugar industry.

Olympic Victors, Athens, 1896, Melbourne Stadium and Olympic Torch
A94

Designs: 20c, Discus thrower and Rome stadium. 50c, Pierre de Coubertin and victors, Melbourne, 1956. 1g, Athens stadium, 1896.

**1960, Aug. 18    Photo.    Perf. 12**
462  A94  10c black & org            .20    .20
463  A94  20c dk blue & crim         .20    .20
464  A94  50c green & ocher          .40    .20
465  A94  1g dk brn & grnsh bl       .50    .40
     Nos. 462-465,C163-C165 (7)     3.50   1.75

17th Olympic Games, Rome, Aug. 25-Sept. 11. For surcharges see Nos. B18-B19, CB28-CB29.

Occide Jeanty and Score from "1804" A95

20c, Occide Jeanty and National Capitol.

**1960, Oct. 19    Perf. 14x14½**
466  A95  10c orange & red lilac     .25    .20
467  A95  20c blue & red lilac       .35    .20
468  A95  50c green & sepia          .50    .40
     Nos. 466-468,C166-C167 (5)     2.35   1.25

Cent. of the birth of Occide Jeanty, composer. Printed in sheets of 12 (3x4) with commemorative inscription and opening bars of "1804," Jeanty's military march, in top margin.

UN Headquarters, NYC — A96

**1960, Nov. 25    Engr.    Perf. 10½**
469  A96  1g green & blk             .50    .40
     Nos. 469,C168-C169 (3)        1.40   1.00

15th anniv. of the UN. For surcharges see Nos. B20-B21, CB30-CB31, B35-CB36. Exists with center inverted.

Dessalines Type of 1958
**Perf. 11½**
**1960, Nov. 5    Unwmk.    Photo.**
Granite Paper
470  A81  10c red org & blk          .25    .20
471  A81  25c ultra & blk            .35    .20
     Nos. 470-471,C170 (3)          .85    .60

Alexandre Dumas Père and Musketeer — A97

5c, Map of Haiti & birthplace of General Alexandre Dumas, horiz. 50c, Alexandre Dumas, father & son, French & Haitian flags, horiz.

**1961, Feb. 10    Perf. 11½**
Granite Paper
472  A97  5c lt blue & choc          .20    .20
473  A97  10c rose, blk & sep        .20    .20
474  A97  50c dk blue & crim         .40    .20
     Nos. 472-474,C177-C179 (6)     3.25   1.40

Gen. Dumas (Alexandre Davy de la Pailleterie), born in Jeremie, Haiti, and his son and grandson, French authors.

Three Pirates — A98

Tourist publicity: 5c, Map of Tortuga. 15c, Pirates. 20c, Privateer in battle. 50c, Pirate with cutlass in rigging.

**1961, Apr. 4    Litho.    Perf. 12**
475  A98  5c blue & yel              .20    .20
476  A98  10c lake & yel             .20    .20
477  A98  15c ol grn & org           .20    .20
478  A98  20c choc & org             .30    .20
479  A98  50c vio bl & org           .40    .20
     Nos. 475-479,C180-C182 (8)     2.60   1.85

For surcharges and overprints see Nos. 484-485, C186-C187.

Nos. 416, 470-471 and 378
Overprinted: "Dr. F. Duvalier / Président / 22 Mai 1961"

**1961, May 22    Photo.    Perf. 11½**
480  A81  5c yel grn & blk           .20    .20
481  A81  10c red org & blk          .20    .20
482  A81  25c ultra & blk            .25    .20
Engr.
**Perf. 12**
483  A64  2.50g gray                1.10    .60
     Nos. 480-483,C183-C185 (7)    2.60   2.00

Re-election of Pres. Francois Duvalier.

No. 475 Surcharged: "EXPLORATION SPATIALE JOHN GLENN," Capsule and New Value

**1962, May 10    Litho.**
484  A98  50c on 5c bl & yel         .50    .40
485  A98  1.50g on 5c bl & yel      1.40   1.00
     Nos. 484-485,C186-C187 (4)     3.80   2.80

U.S. achievement in space exploration and for the 1st orbital flight of a US astronaut, Lt. Col. John H. Glenn, Jr., Feb. 20, 1962.

Malaria Eradication Emblem — A99

Design: 10c, Triangle pointing down.

**Unwmk.**
**1962, May 30    Litho.    Perf. 12**
486  A99  5c crimson & dp bl         .20    .20
487  A99  10c red brn & emer         .20    .20
488  A99  50c blue & crimson         .40    .20
     Nos. 486-488,C188-C190 (6)     1.90   1.40

WHO drive to eradicate malaria. Sheets of 12 with marginal inscription.
For surcharges see Nos. B25-B27, CB42-CB44.

WRY Type of 1960 Dated "1962"
**1962, June 22    Perf. 12½x13**
489  A92  10c lt blue & org          .20    .20
490  A92  50c rose lil & ol grn      .40    .40
     Nos. 489-490,C191-C192 (4)    1.35   1.25

Issued to publicize the plight of refugees. For souvenir sheet see note after #C191-C192.

Haitian Scout Emblem — A100

5c, 50c, Scout giving Scout sign. 10c, Lord and Lady Baden-Powell, horiz.

**Perf. 14x14½, 14½x14**
**1962, Aug. 6    Photo.**
491  A100  3c blk, ocher & pur       .20    .20
492  A100  5c cit, red brn & blk     .20    .20
493  A100  10c ocher, blk & grn      .20    .20
494  A100  25c maroon, ol & bl       .25    .20
495  A100  50c violet, grn & red     .40    .20
     Nos. 491-495,C193-C195 (8)     2.60   2.00

22nd anniv. of the Haitian Boy Scouts.
For surcharges and overprints see Nos. B31-B34, C196-C199.

TIMBRE MOBILE, etc.
From 1970 through 1979 postage and airmail stamps were overprinted for use as revenue stamps. The overprints used were: "TIMBRE MOBILE," "TIMBRE DE SOLIDARITE," "SOLIDARITE," "TIMBRE SOLIDARITE," "OBLIGATION PELIGRE."

Space Needle, Space Capsule and Globe — A101

**1962, Nov. 19    Litho.    Perf. 12½**
496  A101  10c red brn & lt bl       .20    .20
497  A101  20c vio bl & pink         .20    .20
498  A101  50c emerald & yel         .40    .20
499  A101  1g car & lt grn           .50    .40
     Nos. 496-499,C200-C202 (7)     3.00   2.00

"Century 21" International Exposition, Seattle, Wash., Apr. 21-Oct. 21.
For overprints see #503-504, C206-C207.

Plan of Duvalier Ville and Stamp of 1904 — A102

**1962, Dec. 10    Photo.    Perf. 14x14½**
500  A102  5c vio, yel & blk         .20    .20
501  A102  10c car rose, yel & blk   .20    .20
502  A102  25c bl gray, yel & blk    .35    .20
     Nos. 500-502,C203-C205 (6)     3.15   1.70

Issued to publicize Duvalier Ville.
For surcharge see No. B30.

Nos. 498-499 with Vertical Overprint in Black Similar to

**1963, Jan. 23    Litho.    Perf. 12½**
503  A101  50c emerald & yel         .65    .40
 a.    Claret overprint, horiz.      .65    .40
504  A101  1g car & lt grn          1.40    .50
 a.    Claret overprint, horiz.     1.40    .50
     Nos. 503-504,C206-C207 (4)     5.20   2.60
     Nos. 503a-504a,C206a-C207a (4) 5.20   2.60

"Peaceful Uses of Outer Space." The black vertical overprint has no outside frame lines and no broken shading lines around capsule. Nos. 503a and 504a were issued Feb. 20.

Symbolic Harvest A103

**1963, July 12 Photo. Perf. 13x14**
505 A103 10c orange & blk .20 .20
506 A103 20c bluish grn & blk .20 .20
 Nos. 505-506,C208-C209 (4) 1.30 1.00

FAO "Freedom from Hunger" campaign.

J. J. Dessalines A104    Weight Lifter A105

**1963, Oct. 17 Perf. 14x14½**
507 A104 5c tan & ver .25 .20
508 A104 10c yellow & blue .25 .20
 Nos. 507-508,C214-C215 (4) 1.00 .80

For overprints see Nos. 509, C216-C217.

**No. 508 Overprinted: "FETE DES MERES / 1964"**

**1964, July 22**
509 A104 10c yellow & blue .25 .20
 Nos. 509,C216-C218 (4) 1.65 1.00

Issued for Mother's Day, 1964.

**1964, Nov. 12 Photo. Perf. 11½**
**Granite Paper**

Design: 50c, Hurdler.
510 A105 10c lt bl & dk brn .20 .20
511 A105 25c salmon & dk brn .25 .20
512 A105 50c pale rose lil & dk brn .40 .20
 Nos. 510-512,C223-C226 (7) 2.80 1.90

18th Olympic Games, Tokyo, Oct. 10-25. Printed in sheets of 50 (10x5), with map of Japan in background extending over 27 stamps.
For surcharges see #B35-B37, CB51-CB54.

Madonna of Haiti and International Airport, Port-au-Prince A106

**1964, Dec. 15 Perf. 14½x14**
513 A106 10c org yel & blk .20 .20
514 A106 25c bl grn & blk .25 .20
515 A106 50c brt yel grn & blk .40 .20
516 A106 1g vermilion & blk .50 .40
 Nos. 513-516,C227-C229 (7) 3.80 2.25

**Same Overprinted "1965"**

**1965, Feb. 11**
517 A106 10c org, yel & blk .20 .20
518 A106 25c blue grn & blk .25 .20
519 A106 50c brt yel grn & blk .40 .20
520 A106 1g vermilion & blk .50 .40
 Nos. 517-520,C230-C232 (7) 3.40 2.30

Unisphere, NY World's Fair — A107

**1965, Mar. 22 Photo. Perf. 13½**
20c, "Rocket Thrower" by Donald De Lue.
521 A107 10c grn, yel ol & dk red .20 .20
522 A107 20c plum & orange .25 .20
523 A107 50c dk brn, dk red, yel & grn .40 .20
 Nos. 521-523,C233-C235 (6) 4.15 3.10

New York World's Fair, 1964-65.

Merchantmen — A108

**1965, May 13 Unwmk. Perf. 11½**
524 A108 10c blk, lt grn & red .20 .20
525 A108 50c blk, lt bl & red .40 .20
 Nos. 524-525,C236-C237 (4) 1.75 1.10

The merchant marine.

ITU Emblem, Old and New Communication Equipment — A109

**1965, Aug. 16 Litho. Perf. 13½**
526 A109 10c gray & multi .20 .20
527 A109 25c multicolored .40 .20
528 A109 50c multicolored .50 .20
 Nos. 526-528,C242-C245 (7) 4.50 2.30

Cent. of the ITU.
For overprints see #537-539, C255-C256.

Statue of Our Lady of the Assumption A110

Designs: 5c, Cathedral of Port-au-Prince, horiz. 10c, High altar.

**Perf. 14x13, 13x14**
**1965, Nov. 19 Photo.**
**Size: 39x29mm, 29x39mm**
529 A110 5c multicolored .20 .20
530 A110 10c multicolored .25 .20
531 A110 25c multicolored .30 .20
 Nos. 529-531,C246-C248 (6) 4.55 3.45

200th anniv. of the Metropolitan Cathedral of Port-au-Prince.

Passionflower A111

Flowers: 5c, 15c, American elder. 10c, Okra.

**1965, Dec. 20 Photo. Perf. 11½**
**Granite Paper**
532 A111 3c dk vio, lt vio bl & grn .20 .20
533 A111 5c grn, lt bl & yel .20 .20
534 A111 10c multicolored .20 .20
 a. "0.10" omitted
535 A111 15c grn, pink & yel .25 .20
536 A111 50c dk vio, yel & grn .50 .40
 Nos. 532-536,C249-C254 (11) 5.95 4.30

For surcharges see Nos. 566, B38-B40, CB55-CB56.

**Nos. 526-528 Overprinted in Red: "20e. Anniversaire / UNESCO"**

**1965, Aug. 27 Litho. Perf. 13½**
537 A109 10c gray & multi .30 .20
538 A109 25c yel brn & multi .35 .35
539 A109 50c pale grn & multi .70 .70
 Nos. 537-539,C255-C256 (5) 5.35 2.60

20th anniversary of UNESCO.

Amulet — A112

Ceremonial Stool — A113

**Perf. 14x½x14, 14x14½**
**1966, Mar. 14 Photo. Unwmk.**
540 A112 5c grnsh bl, blk & yel .20 .20
541 A113 10c multi .20 .20
542 A112 50c scar, yel & blk .40 .20
 Nos. 540-542,C257-C259 (6) 3.35 2.15

For overprints and surcharges see Nos. 543, 567-570, C260-C261, C280-C281.

**No. 541 Overprinted in Red: "Hommage / a Hailé Sélassiéler / 24-25 Avril 1966"**

**1966, Apr. 24**
543 A113 10c multi .30 .20
 Nos. 543,C260-C262 (4) 2.35 1.60

Visit of Emperor Haile Selassie of Ethiopia, Apr. 24-25.

Space Rendezvous of Gemini VI and VII, Dec. 15, 1965 A114

**1966, May 3 Perf. 13½**
544 A114 5c vio bl, brn & lt bl .20 .20
545 A114 10c pur, brn & lt bl .20 .20
546 A114 25c grn, brn & lt bl .30 .20
547 A114 50c dk red, brn & lt bl .40 .20
 Nos. 544-547,C263-C265 (7) 2.65 1.90

Walter M. Shirra, Thomas P. Stafford, Frank A. Borman, James A. Lovell and Gemini VI.
For overprint see No. 584.

Soccer Ball within Wreath and Pres. Duvalier A115

Design: 10c, 50c, Soccer player within wreath and Duvalier.

**Lithographed and Photogravure**
**1966, June 16 Perf. 13x13½**
**Portrait in Black; Gold Inscription; Green Commemorative Inscription in Two Lines**
548 A115 5c pale sal & grn .20 .20
549 A115 10c lt ultra & grn .20 .20
550 A115 15c lt grn & grn .25 .20
551 A115 50c pale lil rose & grn .40 .20

**Green Commemorative Inscription in 3 Lines; Gold Inscription Omitted**
552 A115 5c pale sal & grn .20 .20
553 A115 10c lt ultra & grn .20 .20
554 A115 15c lt grn & grn .20 .20
555 A115 50c pale lil rose & grn .40 .20
 Nos. 548-555,C266-C269 (12) 4.15 3.20

Caribbean Soccer Festival, June 10-22. Nos. 548-551 also for the Natl. Soccer Championships, May 8-22.
For surcharges and overprint see Nos. 578-579, C288, CB57.

"ABC," Boy and Girl — A116

10c, Scout symbols. 25c, Television set, book and communications satellite, horiz.

**Perf. 14x13½, 13½x14**
**1966, Oct. 18 Litho. & Engr.**
556 A116 5c grn, sal pink & brn .20 .20
557 A116 10c red brn, lt brn & blk .20 .20
558 A116 25c grn, bl & dk vio .25 .20
 Nos. 556-558,C270-C272 (6) 2.20 1.70

Issued to publicize education through literacy, Scouting and by audio-visual means.

Dr. Albert Schweitzer, Maps of Alsace and Gabon — A117

Designs: 10c, Dr. Schweitzer and pipe organ. 20c, Dr. Schweitzer and Albert Schweitzer Hospital, Deschapelles, Haiti.

**Perf. 12½x13**
**1967, Apr. 20 Photo. Unwmk.**
559 A117 5c pale lil & multi .20 .20
560 A117 10c buff & multi .20 .20
561 A117 20c gray & multi .40 .20
 Nos. 559-561,C273-C276 (7) 3.35 2.60

Issued in memory of Dr. Albert Schweitzer (1875-1965), medical missionary to Gabon, theologian and musician.

Watermelon and J. J. Dessalines — A118

**1967, July 4 Photo. Perf. 12½**
562 A118 5c shown .20 .20
563 A118 10c Cabbage .20 .20
564 A118 20c Tangerine .25 .20
565 A118 50c Chayote .40 .20
 Nos. 562-565,C277-C279 (7) 2.60 1.90

No. 532 Surcharged

**1967, Aug. 21 Photo. Perf. 11½**
566 A111 50c on 3c multi .30 .20
 Nos. 566,B38-B40,CB55-CB56 (6) 1.70 1.40

12th Boy Scout World Jamboree, Farragut State Park, Idaho, Aug. 1-9.

Nos. 540-542
Overprinted and
Surcharged

**Perf. 14½x14, 14x14½**

| 1967, Aug. 30 | | | Photo. | |
|---|---|---|---|---|
| 567 | A112 | 5c grnsh bl, blk & yel | .20 | .20 |
| 568 | A113 | 10c multi | .20 | .20 |
| 569 | A112 | 50c scar, yel & blk | .25 | .20 |
| 570 | A112 | 1g on 5c multi | .50 | .40 |
| | | Nos. 567-570,C280-C281 (6) | 2.50 | 1.95 |

EXPO '67 Intl. Exhibition, Montreal, 4/28-10/27.

Pres.
Duvalier
and Brush
Turkey
A119

| 1967, Sept. 22 | | | Photo. | **Perf. 14x13** |
|---|---|---|---|---|
| 571 | A119 | 5c car rose & gold | .20 | .20 |
| 572 | A119 | 10c ultra & gold | .20 | .20 |
| 573 | A119 | 25c dk red brn & gold | .25 | .20 |
| 574 | A119 | 50c dp red lil & gold | .40 | .20 |
| | | Nos. 571-574,C282-C284 (7) | 3.30 | 2.40 |

10th anniversary of Duvalier revolution.

Writing
Hands
A120

Designs: 10c, Scout emblem and Scouts, vert. 25c, Audio-visual teaching of algebra.

| 1967, Dec. 11 | | | Litho. | **Perf. 11½** |
|---|---|---|---|---|
| 575 | A120 | 5c multicolored | .20 | .20 |
| 576 | A120 | 10c multicolored | .20 | .20 |
| 577 | A120 | 25c dk grn, lt bl & yel | .25 | .20 |
| | | Nos. 575-577,C285-C287 (6) | 2.05 | 1.70 |

Issued to publicize the importance of education.
For surcharges see Nos. CB58-CB60.

Nos. 552 and 554 Surcharged

**Lithographed and Photogravure**

| 1968, Jan. 18 | | | | **Perf. 13x13½** |
|---|---|---|---|---|
| 578 | A115 | 50c on 15c | .40 | .40 |
| 579 | A115 | 1g on 5c | .50 | .40 |
| | | Nos. 578-579,C288,CB57 (4) | 3.15 | 2.35 |

19th Olympic Games, Mexico City, Oct. 12-27.
The 1968 date is missing on 2 stamps in every sheet of 50.

Caiman
Woods, by
Raoul
Dupoux
A121

| 1968, Apr. 22 | | | Photo. | **Perf. 12** |
|---|---|---|---|---|
| | | **Size: 36x26mm** | | |
| 580 | A121 | 5c multi | .20 | .20 |
| 581 | A121 | 10c rose red & multi | .20 | .20 |
| 582 | A121 | 25c multi | .20 | .20 |
| 583 | A121 | 50c dl lil & multi | .40 | .20 |
| | | Nos. 580-583,C289-C295 (11) | 6.45 | 4.70 |

Caiman Woods ceremony during the Slaves' Rebellion, Aug. 14, 1791.

No. 547 Overprinted

| 1968, Apr. 19 | | | Photo. | **Perf. 13½** |
|---|---|---|---|---|
| 584 | A114 | 50c dk red, brn & lt bl | .90 | .80 |
| | | Nos. 584,C296-C298 (4) | 5.40 | 2.90 |

10th Winter Olympic Games, Grenoble, France, Feb. 6-18, 1968.

Monument to the
Unknown
Maroon — A122

Palm Tree and
Provincial Coats of
Arms — A123

Madonna, Papal Arms and Arms of
Haiti — A124

| 1968, May 22 | | | | **Perf. 11½** |
|---|---|---|---|---|
| | | **Granite Paper** | | |
| 585 | A122 | 5c bl & blk | .20 | .20 |
| 586 | A122 | 10c rose brn & blk | .20 | .20 |
| 587 | A122 | 20c vio & blk | .20 | .20 |
| 588 | A122 | 25c lt ultra & blk | .25 | .20 |
| 589 | A122 | 50c brt bl grn & blk | .40 | .20 |
| | | Nos. 585-589,C299-C301 (8) | 2.95 | 2.10 |

Unveiling of the monument to the Unknown Maroon, Port-au-Prince.
For surcharges see Nos. C324-C325.

**Perf. 13x14, 12½x13½**

| 1968, Aug. 16 | | | | Photo. |
|---|---|---|---|---|

Design: 25c, Cathedral, arms of Pope Paul VI and arms of Haiti.

| 590 | A123 | 5c grn & multi | .20 | .20 |
|---|---|---|---|---|
| 591 | A124 | 10c brn & multi | .20 | .20 |
| 592 | A124 | 25c multi | .20 | .20 |
| | | Nos. 590-592,C302-C305 (7) | 3.55 | 2.80 |

Consecration of the Bishopric of Haiti, 10/28/66.

Air Terminal, Port-au-Prince — A125

| 1968, Sept. 22 | | | Photo. | **Perf. 11½** |
|---|---|---|---|---|
| | | **Portrait in Black** | | |
| 593 | A125 | 5c brn & lt ultra | .20 | .20 |
| 594 | A125 | 10c brn & lt bl | .20 | .20 |
| 595 | A125 | 25c brn & pale lil | .25 | .20 |
| | | Nos. 593-595,C306-C308 (6) | 2.60 | 2.10 |

Inauguration of the Francois Duvalier Airport in Port-au-Prince.

Slave Breaking
Chains, Map
of Haiti, Torch,
Conch — A126

| 1968, Oct. 28 | | | Litho. | **Perf. 14½x14** |
|---|---|---|---|---|
| 596 | A126 | 5c brn, lt bl & brt pink | .20 | .20 |
| 597 | A126 | 10c brn, lt ol & brt pink | .20 | .20 |
| 598 | A126 | 25c brn, bis & brt pink | .25 | .20 |
| | | Nos. 596-598,C310-C313 (7) | 3.00 | 2.30 |

Slaves' Rebellion, of 1791.

Children
Learning to
Read
A127

10c, Children watching television. 50c, Hands setting volleyball and sports medal.

| 1968, Nov. 14 | | | | **Perf. 11½** |
|---|---|---|---|---|
| 599 | A127 | 5c multi | .20 | .20 |
| 600 | A127 | 10c multi | .20 | .20 |
| 601 | A127 | 50c multi | .40 | .20 |
| | | Nos. 599-601,C314-C316 (6) | 2.35 | 1.70 |

Issued to publicize education through literacy, audio-visual means and sport.
For surcharges see #B41-B42, CB61-CB62.

Winston Churchill — A128

Churchill: 5c, as painter. 10c, as Knight of the Garter. 15c, and soldiers at Normandy. 20c, and early seaplane. 25c, and Queen Elizabeth II. 50c, and Big Ben, London.

| 1968, Dec. 23 | | | Photo. | **Perf. 13** |
|---|---|---|---|---|
| 602 | A128 | 3c gold & multi | .20 | .20 |
| 603 | A128 | 5c gold & multi | .20 | .20 |
| 604 | A128 | 10c gold & multi | .20 | .20 |
| 605 | A128 | 15c gold & multi | .20 | .20 |
| 606 | A128 | 20c gold & multi | .20 | .20 |
| 607 | A128 | 25c gold & multi | .25 | .20 |
| 608 | A128 | 50c gold & multi | .40 | .20 |
| | | Nos. 602-608,C319-C322 (11) | 4.00 | 3.10 |

Exist imperf. For surcharge see No. 828.

1968
Winter
Olympics,
Grenoble
A128a

Designs: 5c, 1.50g, Peggy Fleming, US, figure skating. 10c, Harold Groenningen, Norway, cross-country skiing. 20c, Belousova &

Protopopov, USSR, pairs figure skating. 25c, Toini Gustafsson, Sweden, cross country skiing. 50c, Eugenio Monti, Italy, 4-man bobsled. 2g, Erhard Keller, Germany, speed skating. 4g, Jean-Claude Killy, France, downhill skiing.

| 1968 | | | Litho. | **Perf. 14x13½** |
|---|---|---|---|---|
| 609 | A128a | 5c brt bl & multi | .20 | .20 |
| 609A | A128a | 10c bl grn & multi | .20 | .20 |
| 609B | A128a | 20c brt rose & multi | .20 | .20 |
| 609C | A128a | 25c sky bl & multi | .25 | .20 |
| 609D | A128a | 50c ol bis & multi | .45 | .30 |
| 609E | A128a | 1.50g vio & multi | 1.10 | .65 |
| | | **Size: 36x65mm** | | |
| | | **Perf. 12x12½** | | |
| 609F | A128a | 2g emer grn & multi | 2.25 | 2.25 |
| | | Nos. 609-609F (7) | 4.65 | 4.00 |
| | | **Souvenir Sheet** | | |
| 609G | A128a | 4g brn & multi | 12.00 | 12.00 |

No. 609G contains one 36x65mm stamp. Nos. 609F-609G are airmail. No. 609G exists imperf. with green, brown and blue margin.

No. 589 Surcharged with New Value and Rectangle

| 1969, Feb. 21 | | | Photo. | **Perf. 11½** |
|---|---|---|---|---|
| 610 | A122 | 70c on 50c | .50 | .40 |
| | | Nos. 610,C324-C325 (3) | 1.80 | 1.30 |

Blue-headed
Euphonia — A129

Birds of Haiti: 10c, Hispaniolan trogon. 20c, Palm chat. 25c, Stripe-headed tanager. 50c, Like 5c.

| 1969, Feb. 26 | | | | **Perf. 13½** |
|---|---|---|---|---|
| 611 | A129 | 5c lt grn & multi | 2.00 | .50 |
| 612 | A129 | 10c yel & multi | 2.00 | .50 |
| 613 | A129 | 20c cream & multi | 2.25 | .50 |
| 614 | A129 | 25c lt lil & multi | 2.50 | .60 |
| 615 | A129 | 50c lt gray & multi | 3.50 | .60 |
| | | Nos. 611-615,C326-C329 (9) | 28.50 | 9.45 |

For overprints see Nos. C344A-C344D.

Olympic Marathon Winners, 1896-1968 — A130

Designs: Games location, date, winner, country and time over various stamp designs. Souvenir sheets do not show location, date, country or time.

| 1969, May 16 | | | | **Perf. 12½x12** |
|---|---|---|---|---|
| | | **Size: 66x35mm (Nos. 616, 616C, 616F, 616O)** | | |
| 616 | A130 | 5c like Greece #124 | .20 | .20 |
| 616A | A130 | 10c like France #124 | .25 | .20 |
| 616B | A130 | 15c like US #327 | .25 | .20 |
| 616C | A130 | 20c like Great Britain #142 | .50 | .25 |
| 616D | A130 | 20c like Sweden #68 | .50 | .25 |
| 616E | A130 | 25c Belgium #B49 | .80 | .35 |
| 616F | A130 | 25c like France #198 | .80 | .35 |
| 616G | A130 | 25c Netherlands #B30 | .80 | .35 |
| 616H | A130 | 30c US #718 | .90 | .40 |
| 616I | A130 | 50c Germany #B86 | 1.40 | .60 |
| 616J | A130 | 60c Great Britain #274 | 1.75 | .85 |
| 616K | A130 | 75c like Finland #B110 | 2.50 | 1.25 |
| 616L | A130 | 75c like Australia #277 | 2.50 | 1.25 |

| | | | | | |
|---|---|---|---|---|---|
| 616M | A130 | 90c Italy #799 | | 2.75 | 1.40 |
| 616N | A130 | 1g like Japan #822 | | 3.75 | 1.60 |
| 616O | A130 | 1.25g like Mexico #C328 | | 5.00 | 2.50 |
| | | Nos. 616-616O (16) | | 24.65 | 12.00 |

**Souvenir Sheets**

| | | | | | |
|---|---|---|---|---|---|
| 616P | A130 | 1.50g US #718, diff. | | 16.00 | 9.00 |

*Imperf*

| | | | | | |
|---|---|---|---|---|---|
| 616Q | A130 | 1.50g Germany #B86, diff. | | 16.00 | 9.00 |

Nos. 616H-616O are airmail. Nos. 616P-616Q contain one 66x35mm stamp. A 2g souvenir sheet exists, perf. & imperf. Value, each $9.

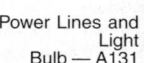

Power Lines and Light Bulb — A131

**1969, May 22    Litho.    Perf. 13x13½**

| | | | | |
|---|---|---|---|---|
| 617 | A131 | 20c lilac & blue | .20 | .20 |

Issued to publicize the Duvalier Hydroelectric Station. See Nos. C338-C340.

Learning to Write — A132

Designs: 10c, children playing, vert. 50c, Peace poster on educational television, vert.

**1969, Aug. 12    Litho.    Perf. 13½**

| | | | | |
|---|---|---|---|---|
| 618 | A132 | 5c multi | .20 | .20 |
| 619 | A132 | 10c multi | .20 | .20 |
| 620 | A132 | 50c multi | .25 | .20 |
| | | Nos. 618-620,C342-C344 (6) | 2.25 | 1.70 |

Issued to publicize national education.

ILO Emblem A133

**1969, Sept. 22    Perf. 14**

| | | | | |
|---|---|---|---|---|
| 621 | A133 | 5c bl grn & blk | .20 | .20 |
| 622 | A133 | 10c brn & blk | .20 | .20 |
| 623 | A133 | 20c vio bl & blk | .25 | .20 |
| | | Nos. 621-623,C345-C347 (6) | 2.95 | 1.70 |

50th anniv. of the ILO.

Apollo Space Missions — A133a

Designs: 10c, Apollo 7 rendezvous of command module, third stage. 15c, Apollo 7, preparation for re-entry. 20c, Apollo 8, separation of third stage. 25c, Apollo 8, mid-course correction. 70c, Apollo 8, approaching moon. 1g, Apollo 8, orbiting moon, Christmas 1968, vert. 1.25, Apollo 8, leaving moon. 1.50g, Apollo 8, crew, vert. 1.75g, 2g, Apollo 11, first lunar landing.

**1969, Oct. 6    Perf. 12x12½**

| | | | | |
|---|---|---|---|---|
| 624 | A133a | 10c brt rose & multi | .20 | .20 |
| 624A | A133a | 15c vio & multi | .20 | .20 |
| 624B | A133a | 20c ver & multi | .25 | .20 |
| 624C | A133a | 25c emer grn & multi | .25 | .20 |
| 624D | A133a | 70c brt bl & multi | .25 | .20 |
| 624E | A133a | 1g bl grn & multi | .55 | .30 |
| 624F | A133a | 1.25g dk bl & multi | .65 | .40 |

| | | | | |
|---|---|---|---|---|
| 624G | A133a | 1.50g dp rose lil & multi | .80 | .50 |

**Souvenir Sheets**

| | | | | |
|---|---|---|---|---|
| 624H | A133a | 1.75g grn & multi | 12.00 | 8.00 |
| 624I | A133a | 2g sky bl & multi | 12.00 | 8.00 |
| | | Nos. 624-624I (10) | 27.15 | 18.20 |

Nos. 624D-624I are airmail. Nos. 624-624I exist imperf. in different colors.

Papilio Zonaria — A134

Butterflies: 20c, Zerene cesonia cynops. 25c, Papilio machaonides.

**1969, Nov. 14    Photo.    Perf. 13½**

| | | | | |
|---|---|---|---|---|
| 625 | A134 | 10c pink & multi | 5.00 | .75 |
| 626 | A134 | 20c gray & multi | 10.00 | 2.00 |
| 627 | A134 | 25c lt bl & multi | 15.00 | 2.10 |
| | | Nos. 625-627,C348-C350 (6) | 150.00 | 15.60 |

Martin Luther King, Jr. A135

**1970, Jan. 12    Litho.    Perf. 12½x13½**

| | | | | |
|---|---|---|---|---|
| 628 | A135 | 10c bis, red & blk | .20 | .20 |
| 629 | A135 | 20c grnsh bl, red & blk | .20 | .20 |
| 630 | A135 | 25c brt rose, red & blk | .20 | .20 |
| | | Nos. 628-630,C351-C353 (6) | 3.05 | 2.25 |

Martin Luther King, Jr. (1929-1968), American civil rights leader.

Laeliopsis Dominguensis — A136

UPU Monument and Map of Haiti — A137

Haitian Orchids: 20c, Oncidium Haitiense. 25c, Oncidium calochilum.

**1970, Apr. 3    Litho.    Perf. 13x12½**

| | | | | |
|---|---|---|---|---|
| 631 | A136 | 10c yel, lil & blk | .20 | .20 |
| 632 | A136 | 20c lt bl grn, yel & brn | .35 | .35 |
| 633 | A136 | 25c bl & multi | .45 | .35 |
| | | Nos. 631-633,C354-C356 (6) | 3.00 | 2.20 |

**1970, June 23    Photo.    Perf. 11½**

Designs: 25c, Propeller and UPU emblem, vert. 50c, Globe and doves.

| | | | | |
|---|---|---|---|---|
| 634 | A137 | 10c blk, brt grn & ol bis | .20 | .20 |
| 635 | A137 | 25c blk, brt rose & ol bis | .20 | .20 |
| 636 | A137 | 50c blk & bl | .35 | .25 |
| | | Nos. 634-636,C357-C359 (6) | 2.70 | 1.95 |

16th Cong. of the UPU, Tokyo, Oct. 1-Nov. 16, 1970.
For overprints see Nos. 640, C360-C362.

Map of Haiti, Dam and Generator A138

Design: 25c, Map of Haiti, dam and pylon.

**1970    Litho.    Perf. 14x13½**

| | | | | |
|---|---|---|---|---|
| 637 | A138 | 20c lt grn & multi | .20 | .20 |
| 638 | A138 | 25c lt bl & multi | .25 | .20 |

François Duvalier Central Hydroelectric Plant.
For surcharges see #B43-B44, RA40-RA41.

Apollo 12 — A138a

**1970, Sept. 7    Perf. 13½x14**

| | | | | |
|---|---|---|---|---|
| 639 | A138a | 5c Lift-off | .20 | .20 |
| 639A | A138a | 10c 2nd stage ignition | .20 | .20 |
| 639B | A138a | 15c Docking preparations | .25 | .20 |
| 639C | A138a | 20c Heading for moon | .35 | .20 |
| 639D | A138a | 25c like 639B | .45 | .20 |
| 639E | A138a | 25c Lunar exploration | .25 | .20 |
| 639F | A138a | 30c Landing on Moon | .65 | .25 |
| 639G | A138a | 30c Lift-off from Moon | .45 | .25 |
| 639H | A138a | 40c 3rd stage separation | .90 | .35 |
| 639I | A138a | 40c Lunar module, crew | .55 | .25 |
| 639J | A138a | 50c Lunar orbital activities | 1.10 | .35 |
| 639K | A138a | 50c Leaving Moon orbit | .65 | .35 |
| 639L | A138a | 75c In Earth orbit | 1.10 | .40 |
| 639M | A138a | 1g Re-entry | 1.50 | .50 |
| 639N | A138a | 1.25g Landing at sea | 2.25 | .75 |
| 639O | A138a | 1.50g Docking with lunar module | 2.40 | .75 |
| | | Nos. 639-639O (16) | 13.25 | 5.40 |

Nos. 639E, 639G, 639I, 639K-639O are airmail. Nos. 639-639O exist imperf. with brighter colors. Value, unused $16.
For overprints see Nos. 656-656O.

No. 636 Overprinted in Red with UN Emblem and: "XXVe ANNIVERSAIRE / O.N.U."

**1970, Dec. 14    Photo.    Perf. 11½**

| | | | | |
|---|---|---|---|---|
| 640 | A137 | 50c blk & bl | .35 | .20 |
| | | Nos. 640,C360-C362 (4) | 2.30 | 1.50 |

UN, 25th anniv.

Fort Nativity, Drawing by Columbus — A139

Ascension, by Castera Bazile — A140

**1970, Dec. 22**

| | | | | |
|---|---|---|---|---|
| 641 | A139 | 3c dk brn & buff | .20 | .20 |
| 642 | A139 | 5c dk grn & pale grn | .30 | .20 |

Christmas 1970.

**1971, Apr. 29    Litho.    Perf. 12x12½**

Paintings: 5c, Man with Turban, by Rembrandt. 20c, Iris in a Vase, by Van Gogh. 50c, Baptism of Christ, by Castera Bazile. No. 647, Young Mother Sewing, by Mary Cassatt. No. 648, The Card Players, by Cezanne.

**Size: 20x40mm**

| | | | | |
|---|---|---|---|---|
| 643 | A140 | 5c multi | .20 | .20 |
| 644 | A140 | 10c multi | .20 | .20 |

**Perf. 13x12½**
**Size: 25x37mm**

| | | | | |
|---|---|---|---|---|
| 645 | A140 | 20c multi | .20 | .20 |

**Perf. 12x12½**
**Size: 20x40mm**

| | | | | |
|---|---|---|---|---|
| 646 | A140 | 50c multi | .35 | .20 |
| | | Nos. 643-646,C366-C368 (7) | 2.65 | 2.00 |

**Souvenir Sheets**
*Imperf*

| | | | | |
|---|---|---|---|---|
| 647 | A140 | 3g multi | 1.50 | 1.50 |
| 648 | A140 | 3g multi | 1.50 | 1.50 |

No. 647 contains one stamp, size: 20x40mm, No. 648 size: 25x37mm.
Nos. 643-646, C366-C368 exist imperf in changed colors.

Soccer Ball — A141

Design: No. 651, 1g, 5g, Jules Rimet cup.

**1971, June 14    Photo.    Perf. 11½**

| | | | | |
|---|---|---|---|---|
| 649 | A141 | 5c salmon & blk | .20 | .20 |
| 650 | A141 | 50c tan & blk | .50 | .35 |
| 651 | A141 | 50c rose pink, blk & gold | .50 | .35 |
| 652 | A141 | 1g lil, blk & gold | .65 | .45 |
| 653 | A141 | 1.50g gray & blk | .80 | .55 |
| 654 | A141 | 5g gray, blk & gold | 2.40 | 1.60 |
| | | Nos. 649-654 (6) | 5.05 | 3.50 |

**Souvenir Sheet**
*Imperf*

| | | | | |
|---|---|---|---|---|
| 655 | | Sheet of 2 | 12.00 | 8.50 |
| a. | A141 | 70c light violet & black | 4.00 | 3.00 |
| b. | A141 | 1g light green, blue & gold | 4.00 | 3.00 |

9th World Soccer Championships for the Jules Rimet Cup, Mexico City, May 30-June 21, 1971. The surface tint of the sheets of 50 (10x5) of Nos. 649-654 includes a map of Brazil covering 26 stamps. Positions 27, 37 and 38 inscribed "Brasilia," "Santos," "Rio de Janeiro" respectively. On soccer ball design the 4 corner stamps are inscribed "Pele."
Nos. 655a and 655b have portions of map of Brazil in background; No. 655a inscribed "Pele" and "Santos," No. 655b "Brasilia."

Nos. 639-639O Ovptd. in Gold

**1971, Mar. 15**

| | | | | |
|---|---|---|---|---|
| 656 | A138a | 5c multi | .20 | .20 |
| 656A | A138a | 10c multi | .20 | .20 |
| 656B | A138a | 15c multi | .25 | .20 |
| 656C | A138a | 20c multi | .35 | .20 |
| 656D | A138a | 25c multi | .45 | .20 |
| 656E | A138a | 25c multi | .25 | .20 |
| 656F | A138a | 30c multi | .65 | .25 |
| 656G | A138a | 30c multi | .45 | .25 |
| 656H | A138a | 40c multi | .90 | .35 |
| 656I | A138a | 40c multi | .55 | .35 |
| 656J | A138a | 50c multi | 1.10 | .35 |
| 656K | A138a | 50c multi | .65 | .35 |
| 656L | A138a | 75c multi | 1.10 | .40 |
| 656M | A138a | 1g multi | 1.50 | .50 |
| 656N | A138a | 1.25g multi | 2.25 | .75 |
| 656O | A138a | 1.50g multi | 2.40 | .75 |
| | | Nos. 639-639O (16) | 13.25 | 5.40 |

Nos. 656E, 656G, 656I, 656K-656O are airmail.
Exist overprinted in silver. Value, unused $16.

J. J. Dessalines — A142

**1972, Apr. 28**    **Photo.**    **Perf. 11½**
657 A142   5c grn & blk   .20   .20
658 A142   10c brt bl & blk   .20   .20
659 A142   25c org & blk   .20   .20
   Nos. 657-659,C378-C379 (5)   2.05   1.45

See Nos. 697-700, C448-C458, 727, C490-C493, C513-C514. For surcharges see Nos. 692, 705-709, 724-726, C438, C512.

"Sun" and EXPO '70 Emblem — A143

**1972, Oct. 27**    **Photo.**    **Perf. 11½**
660 A143   10c ocher, brn & grn   .20   .20
661 A143   25c ocher, brn & mar   .20   .20
   Nos. 660-661,C387-C390 (6)   2.90   1.95

EXPO '70 International Exposition, Osaka, Japan, Mar. 15-Sept. 13, 1970.

Gold Medalists, 1972 Summer Olympics, Munich — A143a

Designs: 5c, L. Linsenhoff, dressage, W. Ruska, judo. 10c, S. Kato, gymnastics, S.Gould, women's swimming. 20c, M. Peters, women's pentathlon, K. Keino, steeplechase. 25c, L. Viren, 5,000, 10,000m races, R. Milburn, 110m hurdles. No. 662D, D. Morelon, cycling, J. Akii-Bua, 400m hurdles. No. 662E, R. Williams, long jump. 75c, G. Mancinelli, equestrian. 1.50g, W. Nordwig, pole vault. 2.50g, K. Wolferman, javelin. 5g, M. Spitz, swimming.

**1972, Dec. 29**      **Perf. 13½**
662   A143a   5c multicolored   .20   .20
662A   A143a   10c multicolored   .20   .20
662B   A143a   20c multicolored   .20   .20
662C   A143a   25c multicolored   .20   .20
662D   A143a   50c multicolored   .25   .20
662E   A143a   50c multicolored   .25   .20
662F   A143a   75c multicolored   .35   .20
662G   A143a   1.50g multicolored   .55   .25
662H   A143a   2.50g multicolored   1.10   .40
662I   A143a   5g multicolored   2.00   .60
   Nos. 662-662I (10)   5.30   2.65

Nos. 662E-662I are airmail.

Basket Vendors A144

Designs: 80c, 2.50g, Postal bus.

**1973, Jan.**    **Photo.**    **Perf. 11½**
665 A144   50c blk & multi   .35   .20
666 A144   80c blk & multi   .45   .35
667 A144   1.50g blk & multi   .70   .45
668 A144   2.50g blk & multi   1.50   .80
   Nos. 665-668 (4)   3.00   1.80

20th anniv. of Caribbean Travel Assoc.

### Space Exploration
A set of 12 stamps for US-USSR space exploration, the same overprinted for the centenary of the UPU and 3 overprinted in silver for Apollo 17 exist but we have no evidence that they were printed with the approval of the Haitian postal authorities. Value, $10 and $6, respectively.

Micromelo Undata A145

Designs: Marine life; 50c horizontal.

**1973, Sept. 4**    **Litho.**    **Perf. 14**
669 A145   5c shown   .25   .20
670 A145   10c Nemaster rubiginosa   .25   .20
671 A145   25c Cyerce cristallina   .50   .20
672 A145   50c Desmophyllum risei   1.00   .20
   Nos. 669-672,C395-C398 (8)   8.90   1.90

For surcharge see No. C439.

Gramma Loreto — A146

**1973**      **Perf. 13½**
673 A146   10c shown   .35   .20
674 A146   50c Acanthurus coeruleus   .45   .35
   Nos. 673-674,C399-C402 (6)   5.55   3.30

For surcharges see Nos. 693, C440.

Soccer Stadium A147

Design: 20c, Haiti No. 654.

**1973, Nov. 29**      **Perf. 14x13**
675 A147   10c bis, blk & emer   .20   .20
676 A147   20c rose lil, blk & tan   .20   .20
   Nos. 675-676,C407-C410 (6)   5.40   3.65

Caribbean countries preliminary games of the World Soccer Championships, Munich, 1974.

Jean Jacques Dessalines A148      Nicolaus Copernicus A149

**1974, Apr. 22**    **Photo.**    **Perf. 14**
677 A148   10c lt bl & emer   .20   .20
678 A148   20c rose & blk   .20   .20
679 A148   25c yel & vio   .20   .20
   Nos. 677-679,C411-C414 (7)   2.90   2.15

For surcharges see Nos. 694, C443.

**1974, May 24**    **Litho.**    **Perf. 14x13½**
Design: 10c, Symbol of heliocentric system.
680 A149   10c multi   .20   .20
681 A149   25c brt grn & multi   .20   .20
   Nos. 680-681,C415-C419 (7)   3.05   2.15

For overprint and surcharges see Nos. 695, C444, C460-C463.

Pres. Jean-Claude Duvalier — A151

**1974**    **Photo.**    **Perf. 14x13½**
689 A151   10c grn & gold   .25   .20
690 A151   20c car rose & gold   .30   .20
691 A151   50c bl & gold   .40   .20
   Nos. 689-691,C421-C426 (9)   7.40   4.40

For surcharge and overprints see Nos. C445, C487-C489.

### Audubon Birds
In 1975 or later various sets of bird paintings by Audubon were produced by government employees without official authorization. They were not sold by the Haiti post office and were not valid for postage. The first set consisted of 23 values and was sold in 1975. A second set containing some of the original stamps and some new stamps appeared unannounced several years later. More sets may have been printed as there are 75 different stamps. These consist of 5 denominations each for the 15 designs.

Perf and imperf souvenir sheets picturing Audubon were also produced.

Nos. 659, 673 and 679-680 Surcharged with New Value and Bar
**Perf. 11½, 13½, 14, 14x13½**
**1976**      **Photo.; Litho.**
692 A142   80c on 25c   .55   .35
693 A146   80c on 10c   .55   .35
694 A148   80c on 25c   .55   .35
695 A149   80c on 10c   .55   .35
   Nos. 692-695 (4)   2.20   1.40

Haiti No. C11 and Bicentennial Emblem — A152

**1976, Apr. 22**    **Photo.**    **Perf. 11½**
**Granite Paper**
696 A152   10c multi   .25   .20
   Nos. 696,C434-C437 (5)   4.70   3.20

American Bicentennial.

### Dessalines Type of 1972
**1977**    **Photo.**    **Perf. 11½**
697 A142   10c rose & blk   .20   .20
698 A142   20c lemon & blk   .20   .20
699 A142   50c vio & blk   .35   .20
700 A142   50c tan & blk   .35   .20
   Nos. 697-700 (4)   1.10   .80

### Dessalines Type of 1972 Surcharged in Black or Red
**1978**    **Photo.**    **Perf. 11½**
705 A142   1g on 20c (#698)   .65   .35
706 A142   1g on 1.75g (#C454)   .65   .35
707 A142   1.25g on 75c (#C448)   .65   .35
708 A142   1.25g on 1.50g (#C453)   .65   .35
709 A142   1.25g on 1.50g (#C453; R)   .65   .35
   Nos. 705-709 (5)   3.25   1.75

Rectangular bar obliterates old denomination on Nos. 705-709 and "Par Avion" on Nos. 706-709.

J. C. Duvalier Earth Telecommunications Station — A153

Designs: 20c, Video telephone. 50c, Alexander Graham Bell, vert.

**1978, June 19**    **Litho.**    **Perf. 13½**
710 A153   10c multi   .25   .20
711 A153   25c multi   .25   .20
712 A153   50c multi   .35   .20
   Nos. 710-712,C466-C468 (6)   2.70   1.95

Centenary of first telephone call by Alexander Graham Bell, Mar. 10, 1876.

Athletes' Inaugural Parade — A154

**1978, Sept. 4**    **Litho.**    **Perf. 13½x13**
713 A154   5c shown   .20   .20
714 A154   25c Bicyclists   .20   .20
715 A154   50c Pole Vault   .35   .20
   Nos. 713-715,C469-C471 (6)   5.80   3.65

21st Olympic Games, Montreal, 7/17-8/1/76.

Mother Nursing Child — A155      Mother Feeding Child — A156

**1979, Jan. 15**    **Photo.**    **Perf. 14x14½**
716 A155   25c multi   .25   .20
   Nos. 716,C472-C473 (3)   1.60   1.10

Inter-American Children's Inst., 50th anniv.

**1979, May 11**    **Photo.**    **Perf. 11½**
717 A156   25c multi   .20   .20
718 A156   50c multi   .35   .20
   Nos. 717-718,C474-C476 (5)   3.55   2.45

30th anniversary of CARE (Cooperative for American Relief Everywhere).

Human Rights Emblem — A157

**1979, July 20**    **Litho.**    **Perf. 14**
719 A157   25c multi   .30   .20
   Nos. 719,C477-C479 (4)   3.30   2.25

30th anniversary of declaration of human rights.

Anti-Apartheid Year Emblem, Antenor Firmin, "On the Equality of Human Races" A158

**1979, Nov. 22    Photo.    *Perf. 12x11½***
720  A158  50c tan & black            .50   .20
     *Nos. 720,C480-C482 (4)*       4.35  2.25
Anti-Apartheid Year (1978).

Children
Playing, IYC
Emblem
A159

**1979, Dec. 19    Photo.    *Perf. 12***
721  A159  10c multi                  .25   .20
722  A159  25c multi                  .25   .20
723  A159  50c multi                  .40   .20
     *Nos. 721-723,C483-C486 (7)*     8.50  4.50
International Year of the Child.

Nos. C379, C449,
C454 Surcharged

**1980          Photo.    *Perf. 11½***
              Granite Paper
724  A142  1g on 2.50g lil & blk      .55   .45
725  A142  1.25g on 80c emer &
              blk                      .65   .55
726  A142  1.25g on 1.75g rose &
              blk                      .65   .55
     *Nos. 724-726 (3)*               1.85  1.55

Dessalines Type of 1972

**1980, Aug. 27    Photo.    *Perf. 11½***
              Granite Paper
727  A142  25c org yel & blk          .30   .20
     *Nos. 727,C490-C493 (5)*         5.10  3.65

Henry Christophe Citadel — A160

**1980, Dec. 2    Litho.    *Perf. 12½x12***
728  A160  5c shown                   .20   .20
729  A160  25c Sans Souci Palace      .20   .20
730  A160  50c Vallieres market       .35   .20
     *Nos. 728-730,C494-C498 (8)*     5.50  4.10
World Tourism Conf., Manila, Sept. 27.
For surcharges see Nos. 738, C511.

Soccer Players, World Cup, Flag of
Uruguay (1930 Champion) — A161

**1980, Dec. 30    Litho.    *Perf. 14***
731  A161  10c shown                  .20   .20
732  A161  20c Italy, 1934            .20   .20
733  A161  25c Italy, 1938            .20   .20
     *Nos. 731-733,C499-C506 (11)*   10.10  6.70
World Cup Soccer Championship, 50th
anniv.
For surcharges see Nos. 741, 829.

Going to
Church, by
Gregoire
Etienne
A162

Paintings: 5c, Woman with Birds and Flowers, by Hector Hyppolite, vert. 20c, Street
Market, by Petion Savain. 25c, Market Vendors, by Michele Manuel.

**1981, May 12    Photo.    *Perf. 11½***
734  A162  5c multi                   .20   .20
735  A162  10c multi                  .20   .20
736  A162  20c multi                  .20   .20
737  A162  25c multi                  .20   .20
     *Nos. 734-737,C507-C510 (8)*     5.45  4.00

For surcharges see Nos. 739-740.

Nos. 728, 734-735, 732 Surcharged
     *Perf. 12½x12, 14, 11½*
**1981, Dec. 30        Litho., Photo.**
738  A160  1.25g on 5c multi          .65   .55
739  A162  1.25g on 5c multi          .65   .55
740  A162  1.25g on 10c multi         .65   .55
741  A161  1.25g on 20c multi         .65   .55
     *Nos. 738-741,C511-C512 (6)*     4.45  3.60

10th Anniv. of
Pres. Duvalier
Reforms — A163

**1982, June 21    Photo.    *Perf. 11½x12***
              Granite Paper
742  A163  25c yel grn & blk          .20   .20
743  A163  50c olive & blk            .35   .20
744  A163  1g rose & blk              .55   .45
745  A163  1.25g bl & blk             .65   .55
746  A163  2g org red & blk           1.10  .85
747  A163  5g org & blk               2.40  1.60
     *Nos. 742-747 (6)*               5.25  3.85

Nos. 742, 744-746 Overprinted in
Blue: "1957-1982 / 25 ANS DE
REVOLUTION"
**1982, Nov. 29    Photo.    *Perf. 11½x12***
              Granite Paper
748  A163  25c yel grn & blk          .20   .20
749  A163  1g rose & blk              .55   .45
750  A163  1.25g blue & blk           .65   .55
751  A163  2g org red & blk           1.10  .85
     *Nos. 748-751 (4)*               2.50  2.05

25th anniv. of revolution.

Scouting
Year
A164

     *Perf. 13½x14, 14x13½*
**1983, Feb. 26                     Litho.**
752  A164  5c Building campfire       .20   .20
753  A164  10c Baden-Powell,
              vert.                    .20   .20
754  A164  25c Boat building          .20   .20
755  A164  50c like 10c               .50   .20
756  A164  75c like 25c               1.25  .25
757  A164  1g like 5c                 1.50  .30
758  A164  1.25g like 25c             2.00  .35
759  A164  2g like 10c                2.75  .60
     *Nos. 752-759 (8)*               8.60  2.30
     Nos. 756-759 airmail.
For surcharge see No. 827.

Patroness of Haiti — A165

**1983, Mar. 9        Litho.    *Perf. 14***
760  A165  10c multi                  .20   .20
761  A165  20c multi                  .20   .20
762  A165  25c multi                  .20   .20
763  A165  50c multi                  .20   .20
764  A165  75c multi                  .35   .20
765  A165  1g multi                   .60   .20
766  A165  1.25g multi                .70   .20
767  A165  1.50g multi                1.00  .35
768  A165  1.75g multi                1.40  .40

769  A165  2g multi                   1.75  .50
770  A165  5g multi                   2.75  1.00
     a.  Souvenir sheet, 116x90mm     7.50  7.50
     j.  Souvenir sheet, 90x116mm     7.50  7.50
     *Nos. 760-770 (11)*              9.35  3.75
Centenary of the Miracle of Our Lady of Perpetual Help. Nos. 764-770 airmail.
For surcharge see No. 875.

UPU
Admission,
100th
Anniv.
A165a

**1983, June 10    Litho.    *Perf. 15x14***
770B  A165a  5c shown                 .50   .20
770C  A165a  10c L.F. Salo-
                mon, J.C.
                Duvalier              .50   .20
770D  A165a  25c No. 1, UPU
                emblem                .50   .20
770E  A165a  50c like 5c              .50   .20
770F  A165a  75c like 10c             .60   .25
770G  A165a  1g like 5c               .80   .25
770H  A165a  1.25g like 25c           1.00  .30
770I  A165a  2g like 25c              1.60  .40
     *Nos. 770B-770I (8)*             6.00  2.00
     Nos. 770F-770I airmail.
For surcharge see No. 825.

1982 World
Cup — A166

Games and scores. Nos. 776-780 airmail,
horiz.

**1983, Nov. 22          Litho.    *Perf. 14***
771  A166  5c Argentina, Belgi-
              um                      .20   .20
772  A166  10c Northern Ireland,
              Yugoslavia              .20   .20
773  A166  20c England, France       .20   .20
774  A166  25c Spain, Northern
              Ireland                 .20   .20
775  A166  50c Italy (champion)      .35   .20
776  A166  1g Brazil, Scotland       .55   .45
777  A166  1.25g Northern Ireland,
              France                  .65   .55
778  A166  1.50g Poland, Came-
              roun                    .95   .65
779  A166  2g Italy, Germany         1.10  .85
780  A166  2.50g Argentina, Brazil   1.40  1.10
     *Nos. 771-780 (10)*              5.80  4.60

For surcharge see No. 826.

Haiti Postage Stamp
Centenary — A167

**1984, Feb. 28        Litho.    *Perf. 14½***
781  A167  5c #1                      .30   .20
782  A167  10c #2                     .30   .20
783  A167  25c #3                     .30   .20
784  A167  50c #5                     .30   .25
785  A167  75c Liberty, Salomon       .45   .25
786  A167  1g Liberty, Salomon        .60   .35
787  A167  1.25g Liberty, Duvalier    .70   .40
788  A167  2g Liberty, Duvalier       1.10  .75
     *Nos. 781-788 (8)*               4.05  2.60
     Nos. 785-788 airmail.
For surcharge see No. 826A.

A168                    A169

**1984, May 30    Photo.    *Perf. 11½***
              Granite Paper
789  A168  25c Broadcasting
              equipment,
              horiz.                   .20   .20
790  A168  50c like 25c               .35   .20
791  A168  1g Drum                    .55   .45
792  A168  1.25g like 1g              .65   .55
793  A168  2g Globe                   1.10  .85
794  A168  2.50g like 2g              1.40  1.10
     *Nos. 789-794 (6)*               4.25  3.35
World Communications Year.

**1984, July 27**
              Granite Paper
795  A169  5c Javelin, running,
              pole vault,
              horiz.                   .20   .20
796  A169  10c like 5c                .20   .20
797  A169  25c Hurdles, horiz.        .20   .20
798  A169  50c like 25c               .35   .20
799  A169  1g Long jump               .55   .45
800  A169  1.25g like 1g              .80   .55
801  A169  2g like 1g                 1.10  .85
     *Nos. 795-801 (7)*               3.40  2.65

**Souvenir Sheet**
802  A169  2.50g like 1g              2.00  1.10
     1984 Summer Olympics. No. 802 exists
imperf. Value $15.
For surcharge see No. 874.

Arrival of Europeans in America, 500th
Anniv. — A170

The Unknown Indian, detail or full perspec-
tive of statue. Nos. 807-809 are vert. and
airmail.

**1984, Dec. 5        Litho.    *Perf. 14***
803  A170  5c multi                   .45   .35
804  A170  10c multi                  .45   .35
805  A170  25c multi                  .45   .35
806  A170  50c multi                  .75   .50
807  A170  1g multi                   .90   .60
808  A170  1.25g multi                1.40  .75
809  A170  2g multi                   5.00  2.50
     a.  Souvenir sheet of #806, 809  12.50 12.50
     *Nos. 803-809 (7)*               9.40  5.40

For surcharge see No. 881.

Simon Bolivar and Alexander
Petion — A171

Designs: 25c, 1.25g, 7.50g, Portraits
reversed. 50c, 4.50g, Bolivar, flags of Grand
Colombian Confederation member nations.

**1985, Aug. 30                   *Perf. 13½x14***
810  A171  5c multi                   .30   .25
811  A171  25c multi                  .30   .25
812  A171  50c multi                  .35   .25
813  A171  1g multi                   .55   .30
814  A171  1.25g multi                .60   .45
815  A171  2g multi                   1.10  .85
816  A171  7.50g multi                3.25  2.10
     *Nos. 810-816 (7)*               6.45  4.45

**Souvenir Sheet**
              *Imperf*
817  A171  4.50g multi                3.50  2.50
     Nos. 813-817 airmail.
For surcharge see No. 876.

Arrival of Europeans in America, 500th Anniv. — A172

Designs: 10c, 25c, 50c, Henri, cacique of Bahoruco, hero of the Spanish period, 1492-1625. 1g, 1.25g, 2g, Henri in tropical forest.

**1986, Apr. 11    Litho.    Perf. 14**
| | | | | |
|---|---|---|---|---|
| 818 | A172 | 10c multi | .85 | .20 |
| 819 | A172 | 25c multi | .85 | .20 |
| 820 | A172 | 50c multi | .85 | .20 |
| 821 | A172 | 1g multi | 1.50 | .35 |
| 822 | A172 | 1.25g multi | 2.00 | .40 |
| 823 | A172 | 2g multi | 3.00 | .60 |
| | | Nos. 818-823 (6) | 9.05 | 1.95 |

Nos. 821-823 are airmail. A 3g souvenir sheet exists picturing Henri in tropical forest. Value $16.
For surcharge see No. 883.

**Nos. 770B, 771, 781, 756, C322, C500 Surcharged**

**1986, Apr. 18**
| | | | | |
|---|---|---|---|---|
| 825 | A165a | 25c on 5c No. 770B | .30 | .20 |
| 826 | A166 | 25c on 5c No. 771 | .30 | .20 |
| 826A | A167 | 25c on 5c No. 781 | .30 | .20 |
| 827 | A164 | 25c on 75c No. 756 | .30 | .20 |
| 828 | A128 | 25c on 1.50g No. C322 | .30 | .20 |
| 829 | A161 | 25c on 75c No. C500 | .30 | .20 |
| | | Nos. 825-829 (6) | 1.80 | 1.20 |

Intl. Youth Year — A173

UNESCO, 40th Anniv. (in 1986) — A174

**1986, May 20    Litho.    Perf. 14x15**
| | | | | |
|---|---|---|---|---|
| 830 | A173 | 10c Afforestation | .20 | .20 |
| 831 | A173 | 25c IYY emblem | .20 | .20 |
| 832 | A173 | 50c Girl Guides | .35 | .20 |
| 833 | A173 | 1g like 10c | .55 | .45 |
| 834 | A173 | 1.25g like 25c | .65 | .55 |
| 835 | A173 | 2g like 50c | 1.10 | .85 |
| | | Nos. 830-835 (6) | 3.05 | 2.45 |

**Souvenir Sheet**
| | | | | |
|---|---|---|---|---|
| 836 | A173 | 3g multi | 7.00 | 7.00 |

Nos. 833-836 are airmail.
For surcharge see No. 873.

**1987, May 29    Photo.    Perf. 11½**
**Granite Paper**
| | | | | |
|---|---|---|---|---|
| 837 | A174 | 10c multi | .20 | .20 |
| 838 | A174 | 25c multi | .20 | .20 |
| 839 | A174 | 50c multi | .35 | .20 |
| 840 | A174 | 1g multi | .55 | .45 |
| 841 | A174 | 1.25g multi | .70 | .55 |
| 842 | A174 | 2.50g multi | 1.40 | 1.10 |
| | | Nos. 837-842 (6) | 3.40 | 2.70 |

**Souvenir Sheet**
**Granite Paper**
| | | | | |
|---|---|---|---|---|
| 843 | A174 | 2g multi | 2.00 | 2.00 |

Nos. 840-842 are airmail.
For surcharge see No. 882.

Charlemagne Peralte, Resistance Leader — A175

**1988, Oct. 18    Litho.    Perf. 14**
| | | | | |
|---|---|---|---|---|
| 844 | A175 | 25c multi | .20 | .20 |
| 845 | A175 | 50c multi | .35 | .20 |
| 846 | A175 | 1g multi | .55 | .45 |
| 847 | A175 | 2g multi | 1.10 | .85 |
| a. | | Souvenir sheet of 1 | 2.50 | 2.25 |
| 848 | A175 | 3g multi | 1.75 | 1.40 |
| | | Nos. 844-848 (5) | 3.95 | 3.10 |

Nos. 846-848, 847a are airmail.

Slave Rebellion, 200th Anniv. A176

Design: 1g, 2g, 3g, Slaves around fire, vert.

**1991, Aug. 22    Litho.    Perf. 12x11½**
| | | | | |
|---|---|---|---|---|
| 849 | A176 | 25c brt green & multi | .40 | .20 |
| 850 | A176 | 50c pink & multi | .70 | .40 |

**Perf. 11½x12**
| | | | | |
|---|---|---|---|---|
| 851 | A176 | 1g blue & multi | 1.40 | .75 |
| 852 | A176 | 2g yellow & multi | 2.50 | 1.50 |
| a. | | Souv. sheet of 2, #850 & 852 | 14.00 | 14.00 |
| 853 | A176 | 3g buff & multi | 4.00 | 2.25 |
| | | Nos. 849-853 (5) | 9.00 | 5.10 |

Nos. 851-853 are airmail.

Discovery of America, 500th Anniv. A177

Designs: 25c, 50c, Ships at anchor, men coming ashore, native. 1g, 2g, 3g, Ships, beached long boats, vert.

**1993, July 30    Litho.    Perf. 11½**
| | | | | |
|---|---|---|---|---|
| 854 | A177 | 25c green & multi | .35 | .20 |
| 855 | A177 | 50c yellow & multi | .55 | .20 |
| 856 | A177 | 1g blue & multi | .85 | .45 |
| 857 | A177 | 2g pink & multi | 1.75 | .85 |
| a. | | Souvenir sheet of 2, #856-857 | | |
| 858 | A177 | 3g orange yellow & multi | 2.75 | 1.50 |
| | | Nos. 854-858 (5) | 6.25 | 3.20 |

Nos. 856-858, 857a are airmail.

25th Genl. Assembly of the Organization of American States A178

Designs: 50c, 75c, 7.50g, Emblem, map of Haiti. 1g, 2g, 3g, 5g, Emblems, map of North, South America, vert.

**Perf. 14x12½, 12½x14**
**1995, June 25                    Litho.**
| | | | | |
|---|---|---|---|---|
| 859 | A178 | 50c violet & multi | .40 | .20 |
| 860 | A178 | 75c green & multi | .60 | .30 |
| 861 | A178 | 1g gray blue & multi | .75 | .45 |
| 862 | A178 | 2g lilac rose & multi | 1.50 | .85 |
| 863 | A178 | 3g green & multi | 2.00 | 1.40 |
| 864 | A178 | 5g violet & multi | 3.25 | 1.90 |
| | | Nos. 859-864 (6) | 8.50 | 5.10 |

**Souvenir Sheet**
**Imperf**
| | | | | |
|---|---|---|---|---|
| 865 | A178 | 7.50g green blue & multi | 7.00 | 7.00 |

UN, 50th Anniv. A179

Designs: 50c, 75c, Dove holding UN, Haitian flags. 1g, 2g, 3g, 5g, Haitian, UN flags, dove carrying olive branch.

**1995, Nov. 24    Litho.    Perf. 12x11½**
| | | | | |
|---|---|---|---|---|
| 866 | A179 | 50c blue & multi | .50 | .30 |
| 867 | A179 | 75c lilac & multi | .75 | .40 |
| 868 | A179 | 1g apple green & multi | 1.00 | .60 |
| 869 | A179 | 2g yellow & multi | 2.25 | 1.00 |
| 870 | A179 | 3g orange brown & multi | 3.50 | 1.50 |
| 871 | A179 | 5g blue green & multi | 5.75 | 3.00 |
| | | Nos. 866-871 (6) | 13.75 | 6.80 |

**Souvenir Sheet**
| | | | | |
|---|---|---|---|---|
| 872 | A179 | 5g multicolored | 10.00 | 9.00 |

Nos. 868-872 are airmail.

Nos. 766, 800, 814, 834 Surcharged

**1996              Perfs., Etc., as Before**
| | | | | |
|---|---|---|---|---|
| 873 | A173 | 1g on 1.25g #834 | .75 | .60 |
| 874 | A169 | 2g on 1.25g #800 | 1.50 | 1.00 |
| 875 | A165 | 3g on 1.25g #766 | 2.25 | 1.50 |
| 876 | A171 | 3g on 1.25g #814 | 2.50 | 1.50 |
| | | Nos. 873-876 (4) | 7.00 | 4.60 |

Size and location of surcharge varies. Nos. 873, 875-876 are airmail.

1996 Summer Olympic Games, Atlanta — A180

**1996, Aug. 2    Litho.    Perf. 14**
| | | | | |
|---|---|---|---|---|
| 877 | A180 | 3g Hurdler | .75 | .45 |
| 878 | A180 | 10g Athlete up close | 2.50 | 1.60 |

Volleyball Federation, 1996 Summer Olympics, Atlanta — A181

#879: a, 50c, Three players in yellow shirts. b, 75c, Three players in red shirts. c, 1g, Two players in white shirts, torch. d, 2g, Players in yellow, in red.
15g, Player in red.

**1996, Aug. 2**
| | | | | |
|---|---|---|---|---|
| 879 | A181 | Sheet of 4, #a.-d. | 12.50 | 12.50 |

**Souvenir Sheet**
| | | | | |
|---|---|---|---|---|
| 880 | A181 | 15g multicolored | 12.50 | 12.50 |

Volleyball, cent. (#880).

Nos. 803, 818, 837 Surcharged

**1996, Nov.    Litho.    Perfs. as Before**
| | | | | |
|---|---|---|---|---|
| 881 | A170 | 1g on 5c #803 | .75 | .60 |
| 882 | A174 | 4g on 10c #837 | 3.00 | 2.00 |
| 883 | A172 | 6g on 10c #818 | 4.00 | 3.00 |
| | | Nos. 881-883 (3) | 7.75 | 5.60 |

Size and location of surcharge varies.

Christmas A182

Paintings: 2g, The Virgin and Infant, by Jacopo Bellini. 3g, Adoration of the Shepherds, by Strozzi. 6g, Virgin and the Infant, by Giovanni Bellini. 10g, Virgin and the Infant, by Francesco Mazzola. #888, Adoration of the Magi, by Gentile da Fabriano.
#889 The Nativity, by Jan de Beer, horiz.

**1996, Dec. 16    Litho.    Perf. 13½x14**
| | | | | |
|---|---|---|---|---|
| 884 | A182 | 2g multicolored | .50 | .30 |
| 885 | A182 | 3g multicolored | .75 | .60 |
| 886 | A182 | 6g multicolored | 1.50 | 1.25 |
| 887 | A182 | 10g multicolored | 3.00 | 1.50 |
| 888 | A182 | 25g multicolored | 6.50 | 4.25 |
| | | Nos. 884-888 (5) | 12.25 | 7.90 |

**Souvenir Sheet**
**Perf. 14x13½**
| | | | | |
|---|---|---|---|---|
| 889 | A182 | 25g multicolored | 7.00 | 7.00 |

UNICEF, 50th Anniv. — A183

**1997, Jan. 28              Perf. 14**
| | | | | |
|---|---|---|---|---|
| 890 | A183 | 4g green & multi | 1.00 | .75 |
| 891 | A183 | 5g pink & multi | 1.25 | 1.00 |
| 892 | A183 | 6g blue & multi | 1.75 | 1.10 |
| 893 | A183 | 10g brown & multi | 2.75 | 1.75 |
| 894 | A183 | 20g bister & multi | 5.50 | 2.75 |
| | | Nos. 890-894 (5) | 12.25 | 7.35 |

**Souvenir Sheet**
| | | | | |
|---|---|---|---|---|
| 895 | A183 | 25g like #890-894, vert. | 6.50 | 5.50 |

#890-894 were each issued in sheets of 6.

Grimm's Fairy Tales — A184

2g, #902a, Sleeping Beauty. 3g, #902b, Snow White. 4g, #902c, Prince awakening Sleeping Beauty. 6g, #902d, Old man sleeping from "The Drink of Life." 10g, #902e, Cinderella. 20g, #902f, Old man awakened after taking drink.
No. 903, Cottage of the Seven Dwarfs, horiz.

**1998, Jan. 5    Litho.    Perf. 13½**
| | | | | |
|---|---|---|---|---|
| 896-901 | A184 | Set of 6 | 24.00 | 23.00 |

**Size: 38x50mm**
**Perf. 14**

902 A184 Sheet of 6, #a.-f.          25.00 25.00
**Souvenir Sheet**
903 A184 25g multicolored               22.50 22.50

Abstract
paintings
A185

**1998, Oct. 30    Litho.    Perf. 12½**
2g, "Coconut on Pastel Stairs," by Luce
Turnier. 3g, "Ogou," by Rose Marie Desruis-
seau. 5g, "Lantern," by Hilda Williams. 6g,
Woman using artist's brush and palette.
15g, Fish, flower and geometric design with
faces, snakes by Philippe Dodar.

904 A185 2g multicolored          1.50  1.00
905 A185 3g multicolored          2.25  1.50
906 A185 5g multicolored          3.25  2.00
907 A185 6g multicolored          5.00  3.00
   Nos. 904-907 (4)              12.00  7.50
**Souvenir Sheet**
**Perf. 13**
908 A185 15g multicolored        20.00 18.00
Tourism. Nos. 904-907 exist in imperf. souvenir sheet of 4. No. 908 contains one
28x36mm stamp.

Birds
A186

Designs: 2g, Priotelus roseigaster. 4g,
Xenoligeo mantana. 10g, Phoenicophilus
poliocephalus. 20g, Phoenicopterus ruber.

**1999, Aug. 27    Litho.    Perf. 14**
909 A186 2g multicolored          .75   .75
910 A186 4g multicolored         1.50  1.50
911 A186 10g multicolored        4.00  4.00
912 A186 20g multicolored        7.00  7.00
   a.    Souvenir sheet, #909-912  15.00 15.00
   Nos. 909-912 (4)              13.25 13.25

Nos. 911-912 are airmail.

Worldwide Fund for Nature — A187

No. 913: a, 2g, Hyla vasta. b, 4g, Head of
Hyla vasta. c, 2g, Cyclura ricordii. d, 4g, Head
of Cyclura ricordii.

**1999, Aug. 27    Litho.    Perf. 14**
913 A187 Block of 4, #a.-d.       3.00  3.00
Issued in sheets of 16 (4x4) and 8 (2x4).

---

Souvenir Sheet

Protection of Natural
Resources — A188

**1999          Litho.    Perf. 13¾**
914 A188 20g multicolored         5.00  5.00

A188a           Christmas
                A188b

**1999          Photo.    Perf. 11¾**
**Panel Color**
914A A188a 1g Prussian blue       .20   .20
914B A188a 3g red brown           .50   .50
914C A188a 5g dark blue          1.00  1.00
914D A188b 10g dk purple         2.25  2.25
914E A188b 15g red               3.00  3.00
914F A188b 20g blue              4.25  4.25
   Nos. 914A-914F (6)           11.20 11.20
914Fg    Souvenir sheet, #915A-
         915F                   12.50 12.50

Nos. 914D-914F are airmail.

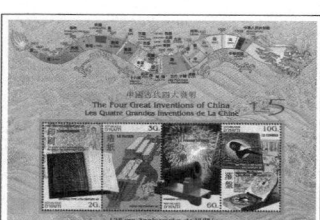

Chinese Inventions — A189

No. 915, 2g, Movable type. No. 916, 3g,
Paper. No. 917, 6g, Gunpowder, cannon. No.
918, 10g, Compass.

**1999, Dec. 20    Litho.    Perf. 13¾**
915-918 A189 Set of 4            7.50  7.50
   a.    Souv. sheet, #915-918   12.00 12.00

UPU, 125th anniv.

Tourism
A190

Designs: 2g, Pirogue. 3g, Smiling girl. 4g,
Zim Pond, vert. 5g, Ardadins Island, vert. 6g,
Gingerbread House. 10g, National Pal-
ace.20g, Peligre Reservoir, vert.

**Perf. 14¼x14½, 14½x14¼**
**2000, June 5              Litho.**
919-925 A190 Set of 7           11.00 11.00
   a.    Souv. sheet, #919-925 + label  12.50 12.50
**Souvenir Sheet**
926 A190 25g Boat "Pays,"
         vert.                   11.00 11.00

---

1801
Constitution,
Bicent.
A191

Designs: 1g, 2g, 5g, 10g, 25g, 50g, Tous-
saint L'Ouverture and 1801 Constitution.
No. 933: a, Toussaint L'Ouverture. b, 1801
Constitution.

**2001          Litho.    Perf. 13¾x13¼**
927 A191 1g multi                1.00  1.00
928 A191 2g multi                1.50  1.50
929 A191 5g multi                3.00  3.00
930 A191 10g multi               6.00  6.00
931 A191 25g multi               9.00  9.00
932 A191 50g multi              10.00 10.00
   Nos. 927-932 (6)             30.50 30.50
**Souvenir Sheet**
**Perf. 12¾**
933 A191 25g Sheet of 2, #a-b   25.00 25.00
Nos. 929-932 are airmail. No. 933 contains
two 25x29mm stamps.

Toussaint
L'Ouverture
(c. 1743-
1803)
A192

Background color: 1g, Green. 2g, Brown.
3g, Yellow green. 5g, Red brown. 6g, blue.
10g, Violet.

**2003, Apr. 7    Litho.    Perf. 13**
934-939 A192 Set of 6           25.00 25.00
**Souvenir Sheet**
**Imperf**
940 A192 15g multi              10.00 10.00

**Pope John Paul II and**
**Pope Benedict XVI Stamps**

In 2005 a set of 8 face-different
stamps with the image of John Paul II
and 8 face different stamps with the
image of Benedict XVI were printed
without official authorization. They were
printed in sheetlets numbered 1-40,
with either three or six stamps per
sheet. Selvage of various sheets containing the same stamps bear text in
either French, English, Latin, Polish,
Italian or Spanish. They were not sold
by the Haiti post office and were not
valid for postage.

---

The following items inscribed
"Republic of Haiti" have been declared
"illegal" by Haitian postal authorities:
   Sheets of six 8g stamps depicting
Pope John Paul II, and Pope Benedict
XVI.
   Sheets of six 10g stamps depicting
Pope John Paul II, and Pope Benedict
XVI.
   Sheets of six 15g stamps depicting
Pope John Paul II, and Pope Benedict
XVI.
   Sheet of three 20g stamps depicting
Pope John Paul II.
   Sheet of three 30g stamps depicting
Pope John Paul II.
   Sheets of two 25g stamps depicting
Pope Benedict XVI (2 different).

---

**SEMI-POSTAL STAMPS**

Pierre de
Coubertin
SP1

**Engraved & Litho (flag)**
**1939, Oct. 3    Unwmk.    Perf. 12**
B1  SP1 10c + 10c multi         27.50 27.50
   Nos. B1,CB1-CB2 (3)          77.50 77.50
Pierre de Coubertin, organizer of the modern Olympic Games. The surtax was used to
build a Sports Stadium at Port-au-Prince.

> **Catalogue values for unused
> stamps in this section, from this
> point to the end of the section, are
> for Never Hinged items.**

Nos. 419-420
Surcharged in Deep
Carmine

**Perf. 13x13½, 13½x13**
**1958, Aug. 30    Litho.    Unwmk.**
B2  A82 1g + 50c purple          2.50  2.40
B3  A83 1.50g + 50c red org      2.50  2.40
   Nos. B2-B3,CB9 (3)            7.50  7.20
The surtax was for the Red Cross. Overprint
arranged horizontally on No. B3.

Similar Surcharge in Red on One Line
on Nos. 440-441

**1959, Apr. 7    Photo.    Perf. 11½**
**Granite Paper**
B4  A87 10c + 25c rose pink       .40   .25
B5  A87 25c + 25c green           .40   .35

Nos. 444-446 Surcharged Like Nos.
B2-B3 in Red
**Perf. 14x13½**
B6  A88 10c + 50c vio bl & ol     .75   .50
B7  A88 50c + 50c grn & dp brn    .75   .60
B8  A88 2g + 50c dp cl & dk
        brn                      1.25  1.00
   Nos. B6-B8,CB10-CB15 (9)      7.65  7.00
The surtax was for the Red Cross.

No. 447 Surcharged Diagonally

**Unwmk.**
**1959, July 23    Photo.    Perf. 12**
B9  A89 50c + 20c lt bl & dp cl   .85   .85
   Nos. B9,CB16-CB18 (4)         4.05  4.05
Issued for the World Refugee Year, July 1,
1959-June 30, 1960.

Nos. 448-450 Surcharged in Dark Carmine

**1959, Oct. 30**      **Perf. 14**
B10 A90 25c + 75c blk brn & lt bl   .65   .60
B11 A90 50c + 75c multi   .90   .60
B12 A91 75c + 75c brn & bl   .90   .60
    Nos. B10-B12,CB19-CB21 (6)   5.45   4.80

The surtax was for Haitian athletes.
On No. B12, surcharge lines are spaced to total depth of 16mm.

No. 436 Surcharged in Red:
"Hommage a l'UNICEF +G. 0,50"

**Engraved and Lithographed**
**1960, Feb. 2**      **Perf. 11½**
B13 A86 1g + 50c blk & brick red   .90   .90
    Nos. B13,CB22-CB23 (3)   3.65   3.65

UNICEF.

Nos. 452-453 Surcharged with Additional Value and Overprinted "ALPHABETISATION" in Red or Black

**Perf. 12½x13**
**1960, July 12**    **Litho.**    **Unwmk.**
B14 A92 10c + 20c sal & grn (R)   .35   .20
B15 A92 10c + 30c sal & grn   .40   .20
B16 A92 50c + 20c vio & mag (R)   .40   .20
B17 A92 50c + 30c vio & mag   .55   .50
    Nos. B14-B17,CB24-CB27 (8)   4.55   3.55

**Olympic Games Issue**
Nos. 464-465 Surcharged with Additional Value

**1960, Sept. 9**    **Photo.**    **Perf. 12**
B18 A94 50c + 25c grn & ocher   .40   .20
B19 A94 1g + 25c dk brn & grnsh bl   .50   .40
    Nos. B18-B19,CB28-CB29 (4)   1.95   1.40

No. 469 Surcharged:
"UNICEF +25 centimes"

**1961, Jan. 14**    **Engr.**    **Perf. 10½**
B20 A96 1g + 25c grn & blk   .50   .40
    Nos. B20,CB30-CB31 (3)   1.55   1.20

UNICEF.

No. 469 Surcharged:
"OMS SNEM +20 CENTIMES"

**1961, Dec. 11**
B21 A96 1g + 20c grn & blk   .55   .50
    Nos. B21,CB35-CB36 (3)   4.40   4.35

Haiti's participation in the UN malaria eradication drive.

Nos. 434, 436 and 438 Surcharged in Black or Red:

(Surcharge arranged to fit shape of stamp.)

**1961-62**    **Engr. & Litho.**    **Perf. 11½**
B22 A86 20c + 25c blk & yel   .30   .20
B23 A86 1g + 50c blk & brick red (R) ('62)   .50   .50
B24 A86 2.50g + 50c blk & gray vio (R) ('62)   .90   .60
    Nos. B22-B24,CB37-CB41 (8)   5.55   5.15

The surtax was for the benefit of the urban rehabilitation program in Duvalier Ville.

Nos. 486-488 Surcharged: "+25 centimes"

**1962, Sept. 13**    **Litho.**    **Perf. 12**
B25 A99 5c + 25c crim & dp bl   .30   .20
B26 A99 10c + 25c red brn & emer   .30   .20
B27 A99 50c + 25c bl & crim   .40   .20
    Nos. B25-B27,CB42-CB44 (6)   2.15   1.40

Nos. 489-490 Surcharged in Red:
"+0.20"

**1962**    **Unwmk.**    **Perf. 12½x13**
B28 A92 10c + 20c bl & org   .30   .20
B29 A92 50c + 20c rose lil & ol grn   .40   .40
    Nos. B28-B29,CB45-CB46 (4)   1.60   1.40

No. 502 Surcharged:
"ALPHABETISATION" and "+0,10"

**1963, Mar. 15**    **Photo.**    **Perf. 14x14½**
B30 A102 25c + 10c bl gray, yel & blk   .25   .20
    Nos. B30,CB47-CB48 (3)   1.15   .80

Nos. 491-494 Surcharged and Overprinted in Black or Red With Olympic Emblem and: "JEUX OLYMPIQUES / D'HIVER / INNSBRUCK 1964"

**Perf. 14x14½, 14½x14**
**1964, July 27**    **Unwmk.**
B31 A100 50c + 10c on 3c (R)   .60   .40
B32 A100 50c + 10c on 5c   .60   .40
B33 A100 50c + 10c on 10c (R)   .60   .40
B34 A100 50c + 10c on 25c   .60   .40
    Nos. B31-B34,CB49 (5)   3.30   2.40

9th Winter Olympic Games, Innsbruck, Austria, Jan. 20-Feb. 9, 1964. The 10c surtax went for charitable purposes.

Nos. 510-512 Surcharged: "+ 5c." in Black

**1965, Mar. 15**    **Photo.**    **Perf. 11½**
**Granite Paper**
B35 A105 10c + 5c lt bl & dk brn   .20   .20
B36 A105 25c + 5c sal & dk brn   .20   .20
B37 A105 50c + 5c pale rose lil & dk brn   .50   .40
    Nos. B35-B37,CB51-CB54 (7)   3.10   2.25

Nos. B35-B37 and CB51-CB54 also exist with this surcharge (without period after "c") in red. They also exist with a similar black surcharge which lacks the period and is in a thinner, lighter type face.

Nos. 533 and 535-536 Surcharged and Overprinted with Haitian Scout Emblem and "12e Jamboree / Mondial 1967" Like Regular Issue

**1967, Aug. 21**    **Photo.**    **Perf. 11½**
B38 A111 10c + 10c on 5c multi   .20   .20
B39 A111 15c + 10c multi   .20   .20
B40 A111 50c + 10c multi   .30   .20
    Nos. B38-B40,CB55-CB56 (5)   1.85   1.50

12th Boy Scout World Jamboree, Farragut State Park, Idaho, Aug. 1-9. The surcharge on No. B38 includes 2 bars through old denomination.

Nos. 600-601 Surcharged in Red with New Value, Red Cross and: "50ème. Anniversaire / de la Ligue des / Sociétés de la / Croix Rouge"

**1969, June 25**    **Litho.**    **Perf. 11½**
B41 A127 10c + 10c multi   .20   .20
B42 A127 50c + 20c multi   .50   .40
    Nos. B41-B42,CB61-CB62 (4)   2.10   1.60

50th anniv. of the League of Red Cross Societies.

Nos. 637-638 Surcharged with New Value and: "INAUGURATION / 22-7-71"

**1971, Aug. 3**    **Litho.**    **Perf. 14x13½**
B43 A138 20c + 50c multi   .45   .35
B44 A138 25c + 1.50g multi   .80   .45

Inauguration of the François Duvalier Central Hydroelectric Plant, July 22, 1971.

## AIR POST STAMPS

Plane over Port-au-Prince — AP1

**1929-30**    **Unwmk.**    **Engr.**    **Perf. 12**
C1 AP1 25c dp gro ('30)   .50   .40
C2 AP1 50c dp vio   .65   .40
C3 AP1 75c red brn ('30)   1.75   1.25
C4 AP1 1g dp ultra   1.90   1.60
    Nos. C1-C4 (4)   4.80   3.65

AP1a

Red Surcharge
**1933, July 6**
C4A AP1a 60c on 20c blue   75.00   80.00

Non-stop flight of Capt. J. Errol Boyd and Robert G. Lyon from New York to Port-au-Prince.

Plane over Christophe's Citadel — AP2

**1933-40**
C5 AP2 50c org brn   5.25   1.00
C6 AP2 50c ol grn ('35)   4.00   1.00
C7 AP2 50c car rose ('37)   3.50   2.00
C8 AP2 50c blk ('38)   2.00   1.00
C8A AP2 60c choc ('40)   1.10   .50
C9 AP2 1g ultra   1.75   .50
    Nos. C5-C9 (6)   17.60   6.00

For surcharge see No. C24.

Dumas Type of Regular Issue
**1935, Dec. 29**    **Litho.**    **Perf. 11½**
C10 A59 60c brt vio & choc   4.50   2.50

Visit of delegation from France to Haiti.

Arms of Haiti and Portrait of George Washington — AP4

**1938, Aug. 29**    **Engr.**    **Perf. 12**
C11 AP4 60c deep blue   .70   .40

150th anniv. of the US Constitution.

Caribbean Conference Type of Regular Issue
**1941, June 30**
C12 A60 60c olive   3.25   .85
C13 A60 1.25g purple   3.25   .65

Madonna Type of Regular Issue
**1942, Dec. 8**      **Perf. 12**
C14 A61 10c dk olive   .40   .20
C15 A61 25c brt ultra   .50   .40
C16 A61 50c turq grn   .90   .40
C17 A61 60c rose car   1.40   .50
C18 A61 1.25g black   2.50   .50
    Nos. C14-C18 (5)   5.70   2.00

**Souvenir Sheets**
C19 A61 Sheet of 2, #C14, C16   5.00   5.00
    a.   Imperf   25.00   25.00

C20 A61 Sheet of 2, #C15, C17   5.00   5.00
    a.   Imperf   25.00   25.00
C21 A61 Sheet of 1, #C18   5.00   5.00
    a.   Imperf   25.00   25.00

Our Lady of Perpetual Help, patroness of Haiti.

Killick Type of Regular Issue
**1943, Sept. 6**
C22 A62 60c purple   .65   .40
C23 A62 1.25g black   1.60   1.60

No. C8A Surcharged with New Value and Bars in Red
**1944, Nov. 25**
C24 AP2 10c on 60c choc   .50   .40
    a.   Bars at right vertical   2.40
    b.   Double surcharge   65.00

Red Cross Type of Regular Issue
**1945**           **Cross in Rose**
C25 A63 20c yel org   .40   .20
C26 A63 25c brt ultra   .40   .20
C27 A63 50c ol blk   .40   .20
C28 A63 60c dl vio   .50   .20
C29 A63 1g yellow   1.40   .40
C30 A63 1.25g carmine   1.25   .40
C31 A63 1.35g green   1.25   .60
C32 A63 5g black   7.25   2.50
    Nos. C25-C32 (8)   12.85   4.70

Issue dates: 1g, Aug. 14; others, Feb. 20. For surcharges see Nos. C153-C160.

> Catalogue values for unused stamps in this section, from this point to the end of the section, are for Never Hinged items.

Franklin D. Roosevelt — AP11

**1946, Feb. 5**    **Unwmk.**    **Perf. 12**
C33 AP11 20c black   .40   .20
C34 AP11 60c black   .50   .20

Capois Type of Regular Issue
**1946, July 18**          **Engr.**
C35 A64 20c car rose   .20   .20
C36 A64 25c dk grn   .20   .20
C37 A64 50c orange   .25   .20
C38 A64 60c purple   .40   .20
C39 A64 1g gray blk   .50   .20
C40 A64 1.25g red vio   .75   .40
C41 A64 1.35g black   .80   .50
C42 A64 5g rose car   2.40   1.20
    Nos. C35-C42 (8)   5.50   3.10

For surcharges see Nos. C43-C45, C49-C51, C61-C62.

Nos. C37 and C41 Surcharged with New Value and Bar or Block in Red or Black
**1947-48**
C43 A64 5c on 1.35g (R) ('48)   .60   .40
C44 A64 30c on 50c   .50   .40
C45 A64 30c on 1.35g (R)   .50   .40
    Nos. C43-C45 (3)   1.60   1.20

Dessalines Type of 1947-54 Regular Issue
**1947, Oct. 17**          **Engr.**
C46 A65 20c chocolate   .40   .20

Christopher Columbus and Fleet — AP14

Pres. Dumarsais Estiméand Exposition Buildings — AP15

**1950, Feb. 12**     *Perf. 12½*
C47 AP14 30c ultra & gray    .90   .50
C48 AP15 1g black    .90   .50
   200th anniversary (in 1949) of the founding of Port-au-Prince.

Nos. C36, C39 and C41 Surcharged or Overprinted in Carmine

**1950, Oct. 4**     *Perf. 12*
C49 A64   30c on 25c dk grn    .40   .30
  a.    30c on 1g gray black    75.00
C50 A64   1g gray blk    .40   .50
  a.    "P" of overprint omitted    65.00   60.00
C51 A64 1.50g on 1.35g blk    1.75   1.50
   Nos. C49-C51 (3)    2.75   2.30
   75th anniv. (in 1949) of the UPU.

Bananas AP16     Coffee AP17

Sisal AP18     Isabella I AP19

**1951, Sept. 3**   **Photo.**   *Perf. 12½*
C52 AP16 30c dp org    2.25   .40
C53 AP17 80c dk grn & sal pink    5.50   .60
C54 AP18 5g gray    19.00   3.50
   Nos. C52-C54 (3)    26.75   4.50
   For surcharge see No. C218.

**1951, Oct. 12**     *Perf. 13*
C55 AP19 15c brown    .30   .20
C56 AP19 30c dull blue    .40   .20
   Queen Isabella I of Spain, 500th birth anniv.

Type of Regular Issue
**1953, May 4**   **Engr.**   *Perf. 12*
   20c, Cap Haitien Roadstead. 30c, Workers' housing, St. Martin. 1.50g, Restored cathedral. 2.50g, School lunchroom.
C57 A68   20c dp bl    .25   .20
C58 A68   30c red brn    .40   .20
C59 A68 1.50g gray blk    .85   .50
C60 A68 2.50g violet    1.75   .85
   Nos. C57-C60 (4)    3.25   1.75

Nos. C38 and C41 Surcharged in Black

**1953, May 18**
C61 A64 50c on 60c pur    .40   .20
  a.    Double surcharge    50.00   50.00
C62 A64 50c on 1.35g blk    .40   .20
  a.    Double surcharge    50.00   50.00
   150th anniv. of the adoption of the natl. flag.

Dessalines and Magloire Type and:

Henri Christophe — AP21

**1954, Jan. 1**   **Photo.**   *Perf. 11½*
C63 AP21 50c shown    .50   .25
C64 AP21 50c Toussaint L'Ouverture    .50   .25
C65 AP21 50c Dessalines    .50   .25
C66 AP21 50c Petion    .50   .25
C67 AP21 50c Boisrond-Tonerre    .50   .25
C68 AP21   1g Petion    .80   .50
C69 AP21 1.50g Lamartiniere    1.50   1.00
C70 A69 7.50g shown    5.50   5.00
   Nos. C63-C70 (8)    10.30   7.75
   See Nos. C95-C96.

Marie Jeanne and Lamartinière Leading Attack — AP23

Design: Nos. C73, C74, Battle of Vertieres.
**1954, Jan. 1**     *Perf. 12½*
C71 AP23 50c black    .40   .20
C72 AP23 50c carmine    .40   .20
C73 AP23 50c ultra    .40   .20
C74 AP23 50c sal pink    .40   .20
   Nos. C71-C74 (4)    1.60   .80
   150th anniv. of Haitian independence.

Mme. Magloire Type of Regular Issue
**1954, Jan. 1**     *Perf. 11½*
C75 A72   20c red org    .20   .20
C76 A72   50c brown    .40   .40
C77 A72   1g gray grn    .50   .40
C78 A72 1.50g crimson    .75   .50
C79 A72 2.50g bl grn    1.25   .90
C80 A72   5g gray    3.00   2.25
   Nos. C75-C80 (6)    6.10   4.65

Christophe Types of Regular Issue
**1954, Dec. 6**   **Litho.**   *Perf. 13½x13*
**Portraits in Black**
C81 A73   50c orange    .40   .20
C82 A73   1g blue    .80   .50
C83 A73 1.50g green    1.10   .65
C84 A73 2.50g gray    1.75   .90
C85 A73   5g rose car    3.25   1.90
     *Perf. 13*
**Flag in Black and Carmine**
C86 A74   50c orange    .40   .20
C87 A74   1g dp bl    .75   .45
C88 A74 1.50g bl grn    1.10   .65
C89 A74 2.50g gray    1.75   .90
C90 A74   5g red org    3.25   1.90
   Nos. C81-C90 (10)    14.55   8.25

Fort Nativity, Drawing by Christopher Columbus — AP27

**1954, Dec. 14**   **Engr.**   *Perf. 12*
C91 AP27 50c dk rose car    .65   .50
C92 AP27 50c dk gray    .65   .50

Dessalines Type of 1955-57 Issue
     *Perf. 11½*
**1955, July 14**   **Unwmk.**   **Photo.**
C93 A75 20c org & blk    .25   .20
C94 A75 20c yel grn & blk    .25   .20
   For overprint see No. C183a.

Portrait Type of 1954
Dates omitted
Design: J. J. Dessalines.

**1955, July 19**
**Portrait in Black**
C95 AP21 50c gray    .40   .20
C96 AP21 50c blue    .40   .20

Dessalines Memorial Type of Regular Issue
**1955, Aug. 1**
C97 A76 1.50g gray & blk    .65   .20
C98 A76 1.50g grn & blk    .65   .20

Types of 1956 Regular Issue and

Car and Coastal View — AP30

Designs: No. C100, 75c, Plane, steamship and Haiti map. 1g, Car and coastal view. 2.50g, Flamingo. 5g, Mallard.

**1956, Apr. 14**   **Unwmk.**   *Perf. 11½*
**Granite Paper**
C99 AP30   50c hn brn & lt bl    .70   .25
C100 AP30   50c blk & gray    .45   .25
C101 AP30   75c dp grn & bl grn    1.00   .50
C102 AP30   1g ol grn & lt bl    .80   .30
C103 A77 2.50g dp org & org    15.00   1.75
C104 A78   5g red & buff    22.50   3.00
   Nos. C99-C104 (6)    40.45   6.05
   For overprint see No. C185.

Kant Type of Regular Issue
**1956, July 19**   **Photo.**   *Perf. 12*
**Granite Paper**
C105 A79   50c chestnut    .40   .20
C106 A79   75c dp yel grn    .50   .40
C107 A79 1.50g dp magenta    1.25   .50
  a.    Miniature sheet of 3    8.00   5.00
   Nos. C105-C107 (3)    2.15   1.10
   No. C107a exists both perf. and imperf. Each sheet contains Nos. C105, C106 and a 1.25g gray black of same design.

Waterfall Type of Regular Issue
**1957, Dec. 16**     *Perf. 11½*
**Granite Paper**
C108 A80   50c grn & grnsh bl    .25   .20
C109 A80 1.50g ol grn & grnsh bl    .65   .40
C110 A80 2.50g dk bl & brt bl    1.00   .60
C111 A80   5g bluish blk & saph    2.50   1.50
   Nos. C108-C111 (4)    4.40   2.70
   For surcharge and overprint see Nos. CB49, CQ2.

Dessalines Type of Regular Issue
**1958, July 2**
C112 A81 50c org & blk    .65   .40
   For overprints see Nos. C184, CQ1.

Brussels Fair Types of Regular Issue, 1958
   *Perf. 13x13½, 13½x13*
**1958, July 22**   **Litho.**   **Unwmk.**
C113 A82 2.50g pale car rose    1.25   .50
C114 A83   5g bright blue    1.50   .85
  a.    Souv. sheet of 2, #C113-C114, imperf.    5.50   5.00
   For surcharge see No. CB9.

Sylvio Cator — AP33

**1958, Aug. 16**   **Photo.**   *Perf. 11½*
**Granite Paper**
C115 AP33 50c green    .25   .20
C116 AP33 50c blk brn    .25   .20
C117 AP33   1g org brn    .50   .40
C118 AP33   5g gray    2.40   .85
   Nos. C115-C118 (4)    3.40   1.65
   30th anniversary of the world championship record broad jump of Sylvio Cator.

IGY Type of Regular Issue, 1958
Designs: 50c, US Satellite. 1.50g, Emperor penguins. 2g, Modern observatory.
**1958, Oct. 8**     *Perf. 14x13½*
C119 A85   50c dp ultra & brn red    .60   .25
C120 A85 1.50g brn & crim    3.25   .75
C121 A85   2g dk bl & crim    2.25   .40
  a.    Souv. sheet of 4, #427, C119-C121, imperf.    8.00   7.50
   Nos. C119-C121 (3)    6.10   1.40

President Francois Duvalier AP34

**Engraved and Lithographed**
**1958, Oct. 22**   **Unwmk.**   *Perf. 11½*
**Commemorative Inscription in Ultramarine**
C122 AP34   50c blk & rose    1.00   .20
C123 AP34 2.50g blk & ocher    1.40   .60
C124 AP34   5g blk & rose lil    1.90   1.25
C125 AP34 7.50g blk & lt bl grn    3.00   2.00
   Nos. C122-C125 (4)    7.30   4.05
   See note after No. 431.
   Souvenir sheets of 3 exist, perf. and imperf., containing one each of Nos. C124-C125 and No. 431. Sheets measure 132x77mm. with marginal inscription in ultramarine. Value, $6.25 each.
   For surcharges see Nos. CB37-CB39.

Same Without Commemorative Inscription
**1958, Nov. 20**
C126 AP34   50c blk & rose    .40   .20
C127 AP34   1g blk & vio    .50   .25
C128 AP34 1.50g blk & pale brn    .75   .40
C129 AP34   2g blk & rose pink    1.00   .40
C130 AP34 2.50g blk & ocher    1.00   .50
C131 AP34   5g blk & rose lil    2.00   1.25
C132 AP34 7.50g blk & lt bl grn    3.00   1.60
   Nos. C126-C132 (7)    8.65   4.60
   For surcharges see #CB22-CB23, CB40-CB41.

Type of Regular Issue and

Flags of Haiti and UN — AP35

     *Perf. 11½*
**1958, Dec. 5**   **Unwmk.**   **Photo.**
**Granite Paper**
C133 AP35 50c pink, car & ultra    .40   .20
C134 A87   75c brt bl    .40   .20
C135 A87   1g brown    .50   .40
  a.    Souv. sheet of 2, #C133, C135, imperf.    3.50   3.50
   Nos. C133-C135 (3)    1.30   .80
   For surcharges see Nos. CB10-CB12.

Nos. C133-C135 Overprinted: "10th ANNIVERSARY OF THE UNIVERSAL DECLARATION OF HUMAN RIGHTS," in English (a), French (b), Spanish (c) or Portuguese (d)
**1959, Jan. 28**
C136    Block of 4    2.75   2.75
  a.-d.    AP35 50c any single    .60   .60
C137    Block of 4    3.75   3.75
  a.-d.    A87 75c any single    .80   .80
C138    Block of 4    7.00   7.00
  a.-d.    A87 1g any single    1.50   1.50
   Nos. C136-C138 (3)    13.50   13.50

Pope Pius XII — AP36

1.50g, Pope praying. 2.50g, Pope on throne.

**1959, Feb. 28   Photo.   *Perf. 14x13½***
C139  AP36   50c grn & lil         .25   .20
C140  AP36   1.50g ol & red brn    .65   .40
C141  AP36   2.50g pur & dk bl     1.00   .40
   Nos. C139-C141 (3)             1.90  1.00

Issued in memory of Pope Pius XII.
For surcharges see Nos. CB13-CB15.

### Lincoln Type of Regular Issue, 1959

Designs: Various Portraits of Lincoln.

**1959, May 12                     *Perf. 12***
C142  A89   1g lt grn & chnt       .50   .20
C143  A89   2g pale lem & sl
              grn                  .75   .50
C144  A89  2.50g buff & vio bl     .85   .40
   a.  Min. sheet of 4, #447, C142-
       C144, imperf.              3.00  2.75
   Nos. C142-C144 (3)             2.10  1.30

Imperf. pairs exist.
For surcharges see Nos. CB16-CB18.

### Pan American Games Types of Regular Issue

Designs: 50c, Jean Baptiste Dessables and
map of American Midwest, c. 1791. 1g, Chicago's skyline and Dessables house. 1.50g,
Discus thrower and flag of Haiti.

**1959, Aug. 27   Photo.   *Perf. 14***
   Unwmk.
C145  A91   50c hn brn & aqua      .75   .25
C146  A90   1g lil & aqua         1.00   .40
C147  A90  1.50g multi            1.40   .50
   Nos. C145-C147 (3)             3.15  1.15

For surcharges see Nos. CB19-CB21.

### Nos. C145-C147 Overprinted like No. 451

**1960, Feb. 29**
C148  A91   50c hn brn & aqua     1.40  1.40
C149  A90   1g lil & aqua         1.90  1.90
C150  A90  1.50g multi            2.75  2.75
   Nos. C148-C150 (3)             6.05  6.05

### WRY Type of Regular Issue, 1960

**1960, Apr. 7   Litho.   *Perf. 12½x13***
C151  A92   50c bl & blk           .40   .20
C152  A92   1g lt grn & mar        .50   .40
   a.  Souv. sheet of 4, #452-453,
       C151-C152, imperf.         6.50  6.00

See Nos. C191-C192. For surcharges
see Nos. CB24-CB27, CB45-CB46.

### Nos. C31, C28 and 369 Surcharged or Overprinted in Red: "28ème ANNIVERSAIRE"

**1960, May 8   Engr.   *Perf. 12***
   Cross in Rose
C153  A63   20c on 1.35g grn       .40   .20
C154  A63   50c on 60c dl vio      .65   .40
C155  A63   50c on 1.35g grn       .40   .40
C156  A63   50c on 2.50g pale
              vio                  .40   .40
C157  A63   60c dl vio             .40   .40
C158  A63   1g on 1.35g grn        .70   .50
C159  A63   1.35g green            .65   .50
C160  A63   2g on 1.35g grn       1.40  1.00
   Nos. C153-C160 (8)             5.00  3.80

28th anniv. of the Haitian Red Cross. Additional overprint "Avion" on No. C156.

### Sugar Type of Regular Issue

Miss Fouchard &: 50c, Harvest. 2.50g,
Beach.

***Perf. 11½***
**1960, May 30   Unwmk.   Photo.**
   Granite Paper
C161  A93   50c lil rose & brn     .90   .20
C162  A93  2.50g ultra & brn      2.25   .50

### Olympic Type of Regular Issue

Designs: 50c, Pierre de Coubertin, Melbourne stadium and torch. 1.50g, Discus
thrower and Rome stadium. 2.50g, Victors'
parade, Athens, 1896, and Melbourne, 1956.

**1960, Aug. 18                     *Perf. 12***
C163  A94   50c mar & bis          .40   .20
C164  A94  1.50g rose car & yel
              grn                  .80   .25
C165  A94  2.50g sl grn & mag     1.00   .30
   a.  Souv. sheet of 2, #465, C165,
       imperf.                    3.50  3.50
   Nos. C163-C165 (3)             2.20   .75

For surcharges see Nos. CB28-CB29.

### Jeanty Type of Regular Issue

50c, Occide Jeanty and score from "1804."
1.50g, Occide Jeanty and National Capitol.

---

**1960, Oct. 19            *Perf. 14x14½***
C166  A95   50c yel & bl           .50   .20
C167  A95  1.50g lil rose & sl grn .75   .25

Printed in sheets of 12 (3x4) with inscription
and opening bars of "1804," Jeanty's military
march, in top margin.

### UN Type of Regular Issue, 1960

**1960, Nov. 25   Engr.   *Perf. 10½***
C168  A96   50c red org & blk      .40   .20
C169  A96  1.50g dk bl & blk       .50   .40
   a.  Souv. sheet of 3, #469, C168-
       C169, imperf.              2.50  2.50

For surcharges see #CB30-CB31, CB35-
CB36.
Nos. C168-C169 exist with centers inverted.

### Dessalines Type of Regular Issue

**1960, Nov. 5   Photo.   *Perf. 11½***
   Granite Paper
C170  A81   20c gray & blk         .25   .20

For overprint see No. C183.

Sud-Caravelle Jet Airliner and
Orchid — AP37

Designs: 50c, Boeing 707 jet airliner, facing
left, and Kittyhawk.  1g, Sud-Caravelle jet airliner and Orchid.  1.50g, Boeing 707 jet airliner
and air post stamp of 1933.

**1960, Dec. 17   Photo.   Unwmk.**
   Granite Paper
C171  AP37   20c dp ultra & car    .20   .20
C172  AP37   50c rose brn & grn    .50   .25
C173  AP37   50c brt grnsh bl &
                ol grn             .50   .25
C174  AP37   50c gray & grn        .50   .25
C175  AP37   1g gray ol & ver     1.60   .25
C176  AP37  1.50g brt pink & dk bl 1.25   .30
   a.  Souv. sheet of 3, #C174-
       C176, imperf.              3.00  3.00
   Nos. C171-C176 (6)             4.55  1.50

Issued for Aviation Week, Dec. 17-23.
#C172-C174 are dated 17 Decembre 1903.
For overprints and surcharges see Nos.
CB32-CB34, CO1-CO5.

### Dumas Type of Regular Issue.

Designs: 50c, The Three Musketeers and
Dumas père, horiz 1g, The Lady of the Camel-
lias and Dumas fils.  1.50g, The Count of
Monte Cristo and Dumas père.

**1961, Feb. 10   Photo.   *Perf. 11½***
   Granite Paper
C177  A97   50c brt bl & blk       .60   .20
C178  A97   1g blk & red           .75   .25
C179  A97  1.50g brt grn & bl blk 1.10   .35
   Nos. C177-C179 (3)             2.45   .80

### Type of Regular Issue, 1961

Tourist publicity:  20c, Privateer in Battle.
50c, Pirate with cutlass in rigging. 1g, Map of
Tortuga.

**1961, Apr. 4   Litho.   *Perf. 12***
C180  A98   20c dk bl & yel        .30   .20
C181  A98   50c brt pur & org      .55   .25
C182  A98   1g Prus grn & yel      .45   .40
   Nos. C180-C182 (3)             1.30   .85

For overprint and surcharge see #C186-
C187.

### Nos. C170, C112 and C101 Overprinted: "Dr. F. Duvalier Président 22 Mai 1961"

**1961, May 22   Photo.   *Perf. 11½***
C183  A81   20c gray & blk         .20   .20
   a.  On No. C93
C184  A81   50c org & blk          .25   .20
C185  AP30   75c dp grn & bl grn   .40   .40
   Nos. C183-C185 (3)             .85   .80

Re-election of Pres. Francois Duvalier.

### No. C182 Overprinted or Surcharged: "EXPLORATION SPATIALE JOHN GLENN" and Capsule

**1962, May 10   Litho.   *Perf. 12***
C186  A98   1g Prus grn & yel      .50   .40
C187  A98   2g on 1g Prus grn &
              yel                 1.40  1.00

See note after No. 485.

---

### Malaria Type of Regular Issue

Designs: 20c, 1g, Triangle pointing down.
50c, Triangle pointing up.

**1962, May 30                     Unwmk.**
C188  A99   20c lilac & red        .20   .20
C189  A99   50c emer & rose car    .40   .40
C190  A99   1g org & dk vio        .50   .40
   a.  Souv. sheet of 3           2.50  2.50
   Nos. C188-C190 (3)             1.10   .80

Sheets of 12 with marginal inscription.
No. C190a contains stamps similar to Nos.
488 and C189-C190 in changed colors and
imperf. Issued July 16.
A similar sheet without the "Contribution . . ."
inscription was issued May 30.
For surcharges see Nos. CB42-CB44.

### WRY Type of 1960 Dated "1962"

**1962, June 22            *Perf. 12½x13***
C191  A92   50c lt bl & red brn    .35   .25
C192  A92   1g bister & blk        .40   .40

A souvenir sheet exists containing one each
of #489-490, C191-C192, imperf. Value,
$2.50.
For surcharges see Nos. CB45-CB46.

### Boy Scout Type of 1962

Designs: 20c, Scout giving Scout sign. 50c,
Haitian Scout emblem.  1.50g, Lord and Lady
Baden-Powell, horiz.

**Perf. 14x14½, 14½x14**
**1962, Aug. 6   Photo.   Unwmk.**
C193  A100   20c multi             .20   .20
C194  A100   50c multi             .50   .20
C195  A100  1.50g multi            .65   .40
   Nos. C193-C195 (3)             1.35  1.00

A souvenir sheet contains one each of Nos.
C194-C195 imperf. Value, $1.60.
A similar sheet inscribed in gold, "Epreuves
De Luxe," was issued Dec. 10. Value $3.

### Nos. 495 and C193-C195 Overprinted: "AÉROPORT INTERNATIONAL 1962"

**1962, Oct. 26   *Perf. 14x14½, 14½x14***
C196  A100   20c multi, #C193      .25   .20
C197  A100   50c multi, #495       .40   .20
C198  A100   50c multi, #C194      .40   .20
C199  A100  1.50g multi, #C195     .60   .40
   Nos. C196-C199 (4)             1.65  1.00

Proceeds from the sale of Nos. C196-C199
were for the construction of new airport at
Port-au-Prince.   The overprint on No. C197
has "Poste Aérienne" added.

### Seattle Fair Type of 1962

Design:  Denomination at left, "Avion" at
right.

**1962, Nov. 19   Litho.   *Perf. 12½***
C200  A101   50c blk & pale lil    .40   .20
C201  A101   1g org brn & gray     .60   .40
C202  A101  1.50g red lil & org    .70   .40
   Nos. C200-C202 (3)             1.70  1.00

An imperf. sheet of two exists containing
one each of Nos. C201-C202 with simulated
gray perforations. Size: 133x82mm. Value,
$3.50.

Street in Duvalier Ville and Stamp of
1881 — AP38

**1962, Dec. 10   Photo.   *Perf. 14x14½***
   Stamp in Dark Brown
C203  AP38   50c orange            .50   .20
C204  AP38   1g blue               .90   .40
C205  AP38  1.50g green           1.00   .50
   Nos. C203-C205 (3)             2.40  1.10

Issued to publicize Duvalier Ville.
For surcharges see Nos. CB47-CB48.

---

Nos. C201-C202 Overprint in Black

**1963, Jan. 23   Litho.   *Perf. 12½***
C206  A101   1g org brn & gray    1.40   .60
   a.  Claret overprint, horiz.   1.40   .60
C207  A101  1.50g red lil & org   1.75  1.10
   a.  Claret overprint, horiz.   1.75  1.10

"Peaceful Uses of Outer Space." The black
vertical overprint has no outside frame lines
and no broken shading lines around capsule.
Nos. C206a and C207a were issued Feb. 20.

### Hunger Type of Regular Issue

**Perf. 13x14**
**1963, July 12   Unwmk.   Photo.**
C208  A103   50c lil rose & blk    .40   .20
C209  A103   1g lt ol grn & blk    .50   .40

Dag Hammarskjold and UN
Emblem — AP39

### Lithographed and Photogravure

**1963, Sept. 28            *Perf. 13½x14***
   Portrait in Slate
C210  AP39   20c buff & brn        .20   .20
C211  AP39   50c lt bl & car       .40   .20
   a.  Souvenir sheet of 2        2.00  2.00
C212  AP39   1g pink & bl          .40   .20
C213  AP39  1.50g gray & grn       .65   .50
   Nos. C210-C213 (4)             1.65  1.10

Dag Hammarskjold, Sec. Gen. of the UN,
1953-61. Printed in sheets of 25 (5x5) with
map of Sweden extending over 9 stamps in
second and third vertical rows. No. C211a
contains 2 imperf. stamps: 50c blue and carmine and 1.50g ocher and brown with map of
southern Sweden in background.
For overprints see Nos. C219-C222, C238-
C241, CB50.

### Dessalines Type of Regular Issue, 1963

**1963, Oct. 17   Photo.   *Perf. 14x14½***
C214  A104   50c bl & lil rose     .25   .20
C215  A104   50c org & grn         .25   .20

### Nos. C214-C215 and C53 Overprinted in Black or Red: "FETE DES MÈRES / 1964"

**1964, July 22   *Perf. 14x14½, 12½***
C216  A104   50c bl & lil rose     .40   .20
C217  A104   50c org & grn         .40   .20
C218  AP17  1.50g on 80c dk grn
              & sal pink (R)       .60   .40
   Nos. C216-C218 (3)             1.40   .80

Issued for Mother's Day, 1964.

Nos. C210-C213 Overprinted in Red

## Lithographed and Engraved
**1964, Oct. 2**     *Perf. 13½x14*
### Portrait in Slate
| | | | | |
|---|---|---|---|---|
| C219 | AP39 | 20c buff & brn | .40 | .20 |
| C220 | AP39 | 50c lt bl & car | .40 | .20 |
| C221 | AP39 | 1g pink & bl | .60 | .40 |
| C222 | AP39 | 1.50g gray & grn | .70 | .50 |
| | | *Nos. C219-C222,CB50 (5)* | 3.50 | 2.55 |

Cent. (in 1963) of the Intl. Red Cross.

### Olympic Type of Regular Issue
#C223, Weight lifter. #C224-C226, Hurdler.

**1964, Nov. 12**   **Photo.**   *Perf. 11½*
### Granite Paper
| | | | | |
|---|---|---|---|---|
| C223 | A105 | 50c pale lil & dk brn | .40 | .20 |
| C224 | A105 | 50c pale grn & dk brn | .40 | .20 |
| C225 | A105 | 75c buff & dk brn | .50 | .40 |
| C226 | A105 | 1.50g gray & dk brn | .65 | .50 |
| a. | | Souv. sheet of 4 | 2.60 | 2.50 |
| | | *Nos. C223-C226 (4)* | 1.95 | 1.30 |

Printed in sheets of 50 (10x5), with map of Japan in background extending over 27 stamps.

No. C226a contains four imperf. stamps similar to Nos. C223-C226 in changed colors and with map of Tokyo area in background.

For surcharges see Nos. CB51-CB54.

### Airport Type of Regular Issue, 1964
**1964, Dec. 15**     *Perf. 14½x14*
| | | | | |
|---|---|---|---|---|
| C227 | A106 | 50c org & blk | .40 | .20 |
| C228 | A106 | 1.50g brt lil rose & blk | .65 | .45 |
| C229 | A106 | 2.50g lt vio & blk | 1.40 | .60 |
| | | *Nos. C227-C229 (3)* | 2.45 | 1.25 |

### Same Overprinted "1965"
**1965, Feb. 11**     **Photo.**
| | | | | |
|---|---|---|---|---|
| C230 | A106 | 50c org & blk | .40 | .20 |
| C231 | A106 | 1.50g brt lil rose & blk | .65 | .40 |
| C232 | A106 | 2.50g lt vio & blk | 1.00 | .70 |
| | | *Nos. C230-C232 (3)* | 2.05 | 1.30 |

### World's Fair Type of Regular Issue, 1965
Designs: 50c, 1.50g, "Rocket Thrower" by Donald De Lue. 5g, Unisphere, NY World's Fair.

**1965, Mar. 22**   **Unwmk.**   *Perf. 13½*
| | | | | |
|---|---|---|---|---|
| C233 | A107 | 50c dp bl & org | .40 | .20 |
| C234 | A107 | 1.50g gray & org | .50 | .40 |
| C235 | A107 | 5g multi | 2.40 | 1.90 |
| | | *Nos. C233-C235 (3)* | 3.30 | 2.50 |

### Merchant Marine Type of Regular Issue, 1965
**1965, May 13**   **Photo.**   *Perf. 11½*
| | | | | |
|---|---|---|---|---|
| C236 | A108 | 50c blk, lt grnsh bl & red | .40 | .20 |
| C237 | A108 | 1.50g blk, lt vio & red | .75 | .50 |

Nos. C210-C213 Overprinted

## Lithographed and Photogravure
**1965, June 26**     *Perf. 13½x14*
### Portrait in Slate
| | | | | |
|---|---|---|---|---|
| C238 | AP39 | 20c buff & brn | .20 | .20 |
| C239 | AP39 | 50c lt bl & car | .40 | .20 |
| C240 | AP39 | 1g pink & bl | .50 | .40 |
| C241 | AP39 | 1.50g gray & grn | .65 | .50 |
| | | *Nos. C238-C241 (4)* | 1.75 | 1.30 |

20th anniversary of the United Nations.

### ITU Type of Regular Issue
*Perf. 13½*
**1965, Aug. 16**   **Unwmk.**   **Litho.**
| | | | | |
|---|---|---|---|---|
| C242 | A109 | 50c multi | .40 | .20 |
| C243 | A109 | 1g multi | .50 | .40 |
| C244 | A109 | 1.50g bl & multi | 1.00 | .50 |
| C245 | A109 | 2g pink & multi | 1.50 | .60 |
| | | *Nos. C242-C245 (4)* | 3.40 | 1.70 |

A souvenir sheet, released in 1966, contains 50c and 2g stamps resembling Nos. C242 and C245, with simulated perforations. Value $15.00.

For overprints see Nos. C255-C256.

---

### Cathedral Type of Regular Issue, 1965
Designs: 50c, Cathedral, Port-au-Prince, horiz. 1g, High Altar. 7.50g, Statue of Our Lady of the Assumption.

*Perf. 14x13, 13x14*
**1965, Nov. 19**     **Photo.**
### Size: 39x29mm, 29x39mm
| | | | | |
|---|---|---|---|---|
| C246 | A110 | 50c multi | .40 | .20 |
| C247 | A110 | 1g multi | .65 | .40 |

### Size: 38x52mm
| | | | | |
|---|---|---|---|---|
| C248 | A110 | 7.50g multi | 2.75 | 2.25 |
| | | *Nos. C246-C248 (3)* | 3.80 | 2.85 |

### Flower Type of Regular Issue
#C249, 5g, Passionflower. #C250, C252, Okra. #C251, C253, American elder.

**1965, Dec. 20**   **Photo.**   *Perf. 11½*
### Granite Paper
| | | | | |
|---|---|---|---|---|
| C249 | A111 | 50c dk vio, yel & grn | .40 | .20 |
| C250 | A111 | 50c multi | .40 | .20 |
| C251 | A111 | 50c grn, gray & yel | .40 | .20 |
| C252 | A111 | 1.50g multi | .70 | .50 |
| C253 | A111 | 1.50g grn, tan & yel | .70 | .50 |
| C254 | A111 | 5g dk vio, yel grn & grn | 2.00 | 1.50 |
| | | *Nos. C249-C254 (6)* | 4.60 | 3.10 |

For surcharges see Nos. CB55-CB56.

### Nos. C242-C243 Overprinted in Red: "20e. Anniversaire / UNESCO"
**1965, Aug. 27**   **Litho.**   *Perf. 13½*
| | | | | |
|---|---|---|---|---|
| C255 | A109 | 50c lt vio & multi | 1.40 | .50 |
| C256 | A109 | 1g citron & multi | 2.60 | .85 |

20th anniversary of UNESCO.

The souvenir sheet noted below No. C245 was also overprinted "20e. Anniversaire / UNESCO" in red. Value, $25.00.

### Culture Types of Regular Issue and

Modern Painting — AP40

Designs: 50c, Ceremonial stool. 1.50g, Amulet.

*Perf. 14x14½, 14½x14, 14*
**1966, Mar. 14**   **Photo.**   **Unwmk.**
| | | | | |
|---|---|---|---|---|
| C257 | A113 | 50c lil, brn & brnz | .40 | .20 |
| C258 | A112 | 50c brt rose lil, yel & blk | .65 | .50 |
| C259 | AP40 | 2.50g multi | 1.50 | .85 |
| | | *Nos. C257-C259 (3)* | 2.55 | 1.55 |

For overprints and surcharge see Nos. C260-C262, C280-C281.

### Nos. C257-C259 Overprinted in Black or Red: "Hommage / a Hailé Sélassiéler / 24-25 Avril 1966"
**1966, Apr. 24**
| | | | | |
|---|---|---|---|---|
| C260 | A112 | 50c (R) | .40 | .20 |
| C261 | A113 | 1.50g (vert. ovpt.) | .65 | .50 |
| C262 | AP40 | 2.50g (R) | 1.00 | .70 |
| | | *Nos. C260-C262 (3)* | 2.05 | 1.40 |

See note after No. 543.

Walter M. Schirra, Thomas P. Stafford, Frank A. Borman, James A. Lovell and Gemini VI and VII — AP41

**1966, May 3**     *Perf. 13½*
| | | | | |
|---|---|---|---|---|
| C263 | AP41 | 50c vio bl, brn & lt bl | .40 | .20 |
| C264 | AP41 | 1g grn, brn & lt bl | .50 | .40 |
| C265 | AP41 | 1.50g car, brn & bl | .65 | .50 |
| | | *Nos. C263-C265 (3)* | 1.55 | 1.10 |

See No. 547.
For overprints see Nos. C296-C298.

---

### Soccer Type of Regular Issue
Designs: 50c, Pres. Duvalier and soccer ball within wreath. 1.50g, President Duvalier and soccer player within wreath.

### Lithographed and Photogravure
**1966, June 16**     *Perf. 13x13½*
### Portrait in Black; Gold Inscription; Green Commemorative Inscription in Two Lines
| | | | | |
|---|---|---|---|---|
| C266 | A115 | 50c lt ol grn & plum | .40 | .20 |
| C267 | A115 | 1.50g rose & plum | .65 | .50 |

### Green Commemorative Inscription in 3 Lines; Gold Inscription Omitted
| | | | | |
|---|---|---|---|---|
| C268 | A115 | 50c lt ol grn & plum | .40 | .40 |
| C269 | A115 | 1.50g rose & plum | .65 | .50 |
| | | *Nos. C266-C269 (4)* | 2.10 | 1.60 |

Caribbean Soccer Festival, June 10-22. Nos. C266-C267 also for the National Soccer Championships, May 8-22.

For overprint and surcharge see Nos. C288, CB57.

### Education Type of Regular Issue
Designs: 50c, "ABC", boy and girl. 1g, Scout symbols. 1.50g, Television set, book and communications satellite, horiz.

*Perf. 14x13½, 13½x14*
### Litho. and Engraved
**1966, Oct. 18**
| | | | | |
|---|---|---|---|---|
| C270 | A116 | 50c grn, yel & brn | .40 | .20 |
| C271 | A116 | 1g dk brn, org & blk | .50 | .40 |
| C272 | A116 | 1.50g grn, bl grn & dk bl | .65 | .50 |
| | | *Nos. C270-C272 (3)* | 1.55 | 1.10 |

### Schweitzer Type of Regular Issue
Designs (Schweitzer and): 50c, 1g, Albert Schweitzer Hospital, Deschapelles, Haiti. 1.50g, Maps of Alsace and Gabon. 2g, Pipe organ.

*Perf. 12½x13*
**1967, Apr. 20**   **Photo.**   **Unwmk.**
| | | | | |
|---|---|---|---|---|
| C273 | A117 | 50c multi | .50 | .40 |
| C274 | A117 | 1g multi | .50 | .40 |
| C275 | A117 | 1.50g lt bl & multi | .65 | .50 |
| C276 | A117 | 2g multi | .90 | .70 |
| | | *Nos. C273-C276 (4)* | 2.55 | 2.00 |

### Fruit-Vegetable Type of Regular Issue, 1967
**1967, July 4**   **Photo.**   *Perf. 12½*
| | | | | |
|---|---|---|---|---|
| C277 | A118 | 50c Watermelon | .40 | .20 |
| C278 | A118 | 1g Cabbage | .50 | .40 |
| C279 | A118 | 1.50g Tangerine | .65 | .50 |
| | | *Nos. C277-C279 (3)* | 1.55 | 1.10 |

### No. C258 Overprinted or Surcharged Like EXPO '67 Regular Issue
**1967, Aug. 30**   **Photo.**   *Perf. 14½x14*
| | | | | |
|---|---|---|---|---|
| C280 | A112 | 1.50g multi | .60 | .40 |
| C281 | A112 | 1g on 1.50g multi | .75 | .55 |

Issued to commemorate EXPO '67 International Exhibition, Montreal, Apr. 28-Oct. 27.

### Duvalier Type of Regular Issue, 1967
**1967, Sept. 22**   **Photo.**   *Perf. 14x13*
| | | | | |
|---|---|---|---|---|
| C282 | A119 | 1g brt grn & gold | .50 | .40 |
| C283 | A119 | 1.50g vio & gold | .65 | .50 |
| C284 | A119 | 2g org & gold | 1.10 | .70 |
| | | *Nos. C282-C284 (3)* | 2.25 | 1.60 |

### Education Type of Regular Issue, 1967
50c, Writing hands. 1g, Scout emblem and Scouts, vert. 1.50g, Audio-visual teaching of algebra.

**1967, Dec. 11**   **Litho.**   *Perf. 11½*
| | | | | |
|---|---|---|---|---|
| C285 | A120 | 50c multi | .25 | .20 |
| C286 | A120 | 1g multi | .50 | .40 |
| C287 | A120 | 1.50g multi | .65 | .50 |
| | | *Nos. C285-C287 (3)* | 1.40 | 1.10 |

For surcharges see Nos. CB58-CB60.

No. C269 Overprinted

---

## Lithographed and Photogravure
**1968, Jan. 18**     *Perf. 13x13½*
| | | | | |
|---|---|---|---|---|
| C288 | A115 | 1.50g rose & plum | .65 | .50 |

See note after No. 579.

### Caiman Woods Type of Regular Issue
**1968, Apr. 22**   **Photo.**   *Perf. 12*
### Size: 36x26mm
| | | | | |
|---|---|---|---|---|
| C289 | A121 | 50c multi | .40 | .20 |
| C290 | A121 | 1g multi | .50 | .40 |

*Perf. 12½x13½*
### Size: 49x36mm
| | | | | |
|---|---|---|---|---|
| C291 | A121 | 50c multi | .40 | .20 |
| C292 | A121 | 1g multi | .50 | .40 |
| C293 | A121 | 1.50g multi | .75 | .60 |
| C294 | A121 | 2g gray & multi | .90 | .70 |
| C295 | A121 | 5g multi | 2.00 | 1.40 |
| | | *Nos. C289-C295 (7)* | 5.45 | 3.90 |

Nos. C263-C265 Overprinted

**1968, Apr. 19**     *Perf. 13½*
| | | | | |
|---|---|---|---|---|
| C296 | AP41 | 50c multi | .70 | .40 |
| C297 | AP41 | 1g multi | 1.40 | .60 |
| C298 | AP41 | 1.50g multi | 2.40 | 1.10 |
| | | *Nos. C296-C298 (3)* | 4.50 | 2.10 |

See note after No. 584.

### Monument Type of Regular Issue
**1968, May 22**     *Perf. 11½*
### Granite Paper
| | | | | |
|---|---|---|---|---|
| C299 | A122 | 50c ol bis & blk | .40 | .20 |
| C300 | A122 | 1g brt rose & blk | .50 | .40 |
| C301 | A122 | 1.50g org & blk | .80 | .50 |
| | | *Nos. C299-C301 (3)* | 1.70 | 1.10 |

For surcharges see Nos. C324-C325.

### Types of Regular Bishopric Issue
50c, Palm tree & provincial coats of arms. 1g, 2.50g, Madonna, papal arms & arms of Haiti. 1.50g, Cathedral, arms of Pope Paul VI & arms of Haiti.

*Perf. 13x14, 12½x13½*
**1968, Aug. 16**     **Photo.**
| | | | | |
|---|---|---|---|---|
| C302 | A123 | 50c lil & multi | .40 | .20 |
| C303 | A124 | 1g multi | .50 | .40 |
| C304 | A124 | 1.50g multi | .65 | .50 |
| C305 | A124 | 2.50g multi | 1.40 | 1.10 |
| | | *Nos. C302-C305 (4)* | 2.95 | 2.20 |

### Airport Type of Regular Issue
50c, 1.50g, 2.50g, Front view of air terminal.

**1968, Sept. 22**   **Photo.**   *Perf. 11½*
### Portrait in Black
| | | | | |
|---|---|---|---|---|
| C306 | A125 | 50c rose lake & pale vio | .40 | .20 |
| C307 | A125 | 1.50g rose lake & bl | .65 | .50 |
| C308 | A125 | 2.50g rose lake & lt grnsh bl | .90 | .80 |
| | | *Nos. C306-C308 (3)* | 1.95 | 1.50 |

Pres. François Duvalier — AP42

### Embossed & Typo. on Gold Foil
**1968, Sept. 22**     *Die Cut Perf. 14*
| | | | | |
|---|---|---|---|---|
| C309 | AP42 | 30g black & red | 40.00 | 35.00 |

### Freed Slaves' Type of Regular Issue
**1968, Oct. 28**   **Litho.**   *Perf. 14½x14*
| | | | | |
|---|---|---|---|---|
| C310 | A126 | 50c brn, lil & brt pink | .40 | .20 |
| C311 | A126 | 1g brn, yel grn & brt pink | .50 | .40 |
| C312 | A126 | 1.50g brn, lt vio bl & brt pink | .65 | .50 |
| C313 | A126 | 2g brn, lt grn & brt pink | .80 | .60 |
| | | *Nos. C310-C313 (4)* | 2.35 | 1.70 |

## Education Type of Regular Issue, 1968

50c, 1.50g, Children watching television. 1g, Hands throwing ball, and sports medal.

**1968, Nov. 14**     *Perf. 11½*
| | | | | |
|---|---|---|---|---|
| C314 | A127 | 50c multi | .40 | .20 |
| C315 | A127 | 1g multi | .50 | .40 |
| C316 | A127 | 1.50g multi | .65 | .50 |
| | | *Nos. C314-C316 (3)* | 1.55 | 1.10 |

For surcharges see Nos. CB61-CB62.

Jan Boesman and his Balloon — AP43

**1968, Nov. 28**    Litho.    *Perf. 13½*
| | | | | |
|---|---|---|---|---|
| C317 | AP43 | 70c lt yel grn & sepia | .65 | .50 |
| C318 | AP43 | 1.75g grnsh bl & sepia | 1.40 | 1.00 |

Dr. Jan Boesman's balloon flight, Mexico City, Nov. 1968.

### Miniature Sheet

Cachet of May 2, 1925 Flight — AP44

**1968, Nov. 28**   Litho.   *Perf. 13½x14*
**Black Cachets, Magenta Inscriptions and Rose Lilac Background**
| | | | | |
|---|---|---|---|---|
| C318A | | Sheet of 12 | 10.00 | 10.00 |
| b. | | AP44 70c 2 Mai 1925 | .50 | .60 |
| c. | | AP44 70c 2 Septembre 1925 | .50 | .60 |
| d. | | AP44 70c 28 Mars 1927 | .50 | .60 |
| e. | | AP44 70c 12 Juillet 1927 | .50 | .60 |
| f. | | AP44 70c 13 Septembre 1927 | .50 | .60 |
| g. | | AP44 70c 6 Février 1928 | .50 | .60 |

Galiffet's 1784 balloon flight and pioneer flights of the 1920's. No. C318A contains 2 each of Nos. C318b-C318g. The background of the sheet shows in white outlines a balloon and the inscription "BALLON GALIFFET 1784." The design of each stamp shows a different airmail cachet, date of a special flight and part of the white background design.

### Churchill Type of Regular Issue

Churchill: 50c, and early seaplane. 75c, and soldiers at Normandy. 1g, and Queen Elizabeth II. 1.50g, and Big Ben, London. 3g, and coat of arms, horiz.

**1968, Dec. 23**    Photo.    *Perf. 13*
| | | | | |
|---|---|---|---|---|
| C319 | A128 | 50c gold & multi | .40 | .20 |
| C320 | A128 | 75c gold & multi | .50 | .40 |
| C321 | A128 | 1g gold & multi | .65 | .50 |
| C322 | A128 | 1.50g gold & multi | .80 | .60 |
| | | *Nos. C319-C322 (4)* | 2.35 | 1.70 |

**Souvenir Sheet**
*Perf. 12½x13, Imperf.*
| | | | | |
|---|---|---|---|---|
| C323 | A128 | 3g sil, blk & red | 6.00 | 6.00 |

Nos. C319-C322 exist imperf. Value, $6. No. C323 contains one horizontal stamp. For surcharge, see No. C515. size: 38x25½mm.

### Nos. C299-C300 Surcharged with New Value and Rectangle

**1969, Feb. 21**    Photo.    *Perf. 11½*
| | | | | |
|---|---|---|---|---|
| C324 | A122 | 70c on 50c | .50 | .40 |
| C325 | A122 | 1.75g on 1g | .80 | .50 |

### Bird Type of Regular Issue

Birds of Haiti: 50c, Hispaniolan trogon. 1g, Black-cowled oriole. 1.50g, Stripe-headed tanager. 2g, Striated woodpecker.

**1969, Feb. 26**    *Perf. 13½*
| | | | | |
|---|---|---|---|---|
| C326 | A129 | 50c multi | 3.00 | .85 |
| C327 | A129 | 1g lt bl & multi | 3.75 | 1.40 |
| C328 | A129 | 1.50g multi | 4.50 | 2.00 |
| C329 | A129 | 2g gray & multi | 16.25 | 6.75 |
| | | *Nos. C326-C329 (4)* | 16.25 | 6.75 |

For overprints see Nos. C344A-C344D.

### Electric Power Type of 1969

**1969, May 22**    Litho.    *Perf. 13x13½*
| | | | | |
|---|---|---|---|---|
| C338 | A131 | 20c dk bl & lil | .25 | .20 |
| C339 | A131 | 25c grn & rose red | .25 | .20 |
| C340 | A131 | 25c rose red & grn | .25 | .20 |
| | | *Nos. C338-C340 (3)* | .75 | .60 |

### Education Type of 1969

Designs: 50c, Peace poster on educational television, vert. 1g, Learning to write. 1.50g, Playing children, vert.

**1969, Aug. 12**    Litho.    *Perf. 13½*
| | | | | |
|---|---|---|---|---|
| C342 | A132 | 50c multi | .30 | .20 |
| C343 | A132 | 1g multi | .50 | .40 |
| C344 | A132 | 1.50g multi | .80 | .50 |
| | | *Nos. C342-C344 (3)* | 1.60 | 1.10 |

Nos. C326-C329 Overprinted

**1969, Aug. 29**    Photo.    *Perf. 13½*
| | | | | |
|---|---|---|---|---|
| C344A | A129 | 50c multi | 1.25 | 1.25 |
| C344B | A129 | 1g lt bl & multi | 2.40 | 2.40 |
| C344C | A129 | 1.50g multi | 4.50 | 4.50 |
| C344D | A129 | 2g gray & multi | 5.75 | 5.75 |
| | | *Nos. C344A-C344D (4)* | 13.90 | 13.90 |

### ILO Type of Regular Issue

**1969, Sept. 22**    *Perf. 14*
| | | | | |
|---|---|---|---|---|
| C345 | A133 | 25c red & blk | .30 | .20 |
| C346 | A133 | 70c org & blk | .65 | .20 |
| C347 | A133 | 1.75g brt pur & blk | 1.40 | .70 |
| | | *Nos. C345-C347 (3)* | 2.35 | 1.10 |

### Butterfly Type of Regular Issue

50c, Danaus eresimus kaempfferi. 1.50g, Anaea marthesia nemesis. 2g, Prepona antimache.

**1969, Nov. 14**    Photo.    *Perf. 13½*
| | | | | |
|---|---|---|---|---|
| C348 | A134 | 50c multi | 20.00 | 2.50 |
| C349 | A134 | 1.50g multi | 40.00 | 3.25 |
| C350 | A134 | 2g yel & multi | 60.00 | 5.00 |
| | | *Nos. C348-C350 (3)* | 120.00 | 10.75 |

### King Type of Regular Issue

**1970, Jan. 12**    Litho.    *Perf. 12½x13½*
| | | | | |
|---|---|---|---|---|
| C351 | A135 | 50c emer, red & blk | .45 | .20 |
| C352 | A135 | 1g brick red, red & blk | .80 | .60 |
| C353 | A135 | 1.50g brt bl, red & blk | 1.20 | .85 |
| | | *Nos. C351-C353 (3)* | 2.45 | 1.65 |

### Orchid Type of Regular Issue

Haitian Orchids: 50c, Tetramicra elegans. 1.50g, Epidendrum truncatum. 2g, Oncidium desertorum.

**1970, Apr. 3**    Litho.    *Perf. 13x12½*
| | | | | |
|---|---|---|---|---|
| C354 | A136 | 50c buff, brn & mag | .35 | .20 |
| C355 | A136 | 1.50g multi | .65 | .45 |
| C356 | A136 | 2g lilac & multi | 1.00 | .65 |
| | | *Nos. C354-C356 (3)* | 2.00 | 1.30 |

### UPU Type of Regular Issue

Designs: 50c, Globe and doves. 1.50g, Propeller and UPU emblem, vert. 2g, UPU Monument and map of Haiti.

**1970, June 23**    Photo.    *Perf. 11½*
| | | | | |
|---|---|---|---|---|
| C357 | A137 | 50c blk & vio | .35 | .20 |
| C358 | A137 | 1.50g multi | .65 | .45 |
| C359 | A137 | 2g multi | .95 | .65 |
| a. | | Souvenir sheet of 3, #C357-C359, imperf. | 2.50 | 2.25 |
| | | *Nos. C357-C359 (3)* | 1.95 | 1.30 |

### Nos. C357-C359a Overprinted in Red with UN Emblem and: "XXVe ANNIVERSAIRE / O.N.U."

**1970, Dec. 14**    Photo.    *Perf. 11½*
| | | | | |
|---|---|---|---|---|
| C360 | A137 | 50c blk & vio | .35 | .20 |
| C361 | A137 | 1.50g multi | .65 | .45 |
| C362 | A137 | 2g multi | .95 | .65 |
| a. | | Souvenir sheet of 3 | 2.50 | 2.25 |
| | | *Nos. C360-C362 (3)* | 1.95 | 1.30 |

United Nations, 25th anniversary.

Haitian Nativity AP45

**1970, Dec. 22**
| | | | | |
|---|---|---|---|---|
| C363 | AP45 | 1.50g sepia & multi | .65 | .45 |
| C364 | AP45 | 1.50g ultra & multi | .65 | .45 |
| C365 | AP45 | 2g multi | 1.10 | .65 |
| | | *Nos. C363-C365 (3)* | 2.40 | 1.55 |

Christmas 1970.

### Painting Type of Regular Issue

Paintings: 50c, Nativity, by Rigaud Benoit. 1g, Head of a Negro, by Rubens. 1.50g, Ascension, by Castera Bazile (like No. 648).

**1971, Apr. 29**   Litho.   *Perf. 12x12½*
**Size: 20x40mm**
| | | | | |
|---|---|---|---|---|
| C366 | A140 | 50c multi | .35 | .20 |
| C367 | A140 | 1g multi | .55 | .45 |
| C368 | A140 | 1.50g multi | .80 | .55 |
| | | *Nos. C366-C368 (3)* | 1.70 | 1.20 |

Nos. C366-C368 exist imperf in changed colors.

Balloon and Haiti No. C2 — AP46

No. C370, as #C369. No. C373, Haiti #C2. 1g, 1.50g, Supersonic transport & Haiti #C2.

**1971, Dec. 22**    Photo.    *Perf. 11½*
| | | | | |
|---|---|---|---|---|
| C369 | AP46 | 20c bl, red org & blk | .30 | .20 |
| C370 | AP46 | 50c ultra, red org & blk | .50 | .25 |
| C371 | AP46 | 1g org & blk | 1.25 | .35 |
| C372 | AP46 | 1.50g lil rose & blk | 1.90 | .45 |
| | | *Nos. C369-C372 (4)* | 3.95 | 1.25 |

**Souvenir Sheet**
*Imperf*
| | | | | |
|---|---|---|---|---|
| C373 | AP46 | 50c brt grn & blk | 9.00 | 4.50 |

40th anniv. (in 1969) of air post service in Haiti.
For overprints see #C374-C377, C380-C386.

### Nos. C369-C372 Overprinted

**1972, Mar. 17**    *Perf. 11½*
| | | | | |
|---|---|---|---|---|
| C374 | AP46 | 20c multi | .20 | .20 |
| C375 | AP46 | 50c multi | .35 | .35 |
| C376 | AP46 | 1g org & blk | .55 | .45 |
| C377 | AP46 | 1.50g lil rose & blk | .65 | .55 |
| | | *Nos. C374-C377 (4)* | | 1.75 |

14th INTERPEX, NYC, Mar. 17-19.

### Dessalines Type of Regular Issue

**1972, Apr. 28**    Photo.    *Perf. 11½*
| | | | | |
|---|---|---|---|---|
| C378 | A142 | 50c yel grn & blk | .35 | .20 |
| C379 | A142 | 2.50g lil & blk | 1.10 | .65 |

For surcharge see No. C438.

### Nos. C369-C372 Overprinted

**1972, May 4**
| | | | | |
|---|---|---|---|---|
| C380 | AP46 | 20c multi | .20 | .20 |
| C381 | AP46 | 50c multi | .35 | .20 |
| C382 | AP46 | 1g org & blk | .45 | .45 |
| C383 | AP46 | 1.50g lil rose & blk | .65 | .45 |
| | | *Nos. C380-C383 (4)* | 1.65 | 1.20 |

HAIPEX, 5th Congress.

### Nos. C370-C372 Overprinted

**1972, July**
| | | | | |
|---|---|---|---|---|
| C384 | AP46 | 50c multi | .35 | .20 |
| C385 | AP46 | 1g org & blk | .45 | .35 |
| C386 | AP46 | 1.50g lil rose & blk | .65 | .45 |
| | | *Nos. C384-C386 (3)* | 1.45 | 1.00 |

Belgica '72, International Philatelic Exhibition, Brussels, June 24-July 9.

Tower of the Sun, EXPO '70 Emblem AP47

**1972, Oct. 27**
| | | | | |
|---|---|---|---|---|
| C387 | AP47 | 50c bl, plum & dk bl | .35 | .20 |
| C388 | AP47 | 1g bl, plum & red | .55 | .35 |
| C389 | AP47 | 1.50g bl, lil rose & blk | .65 | .45 |
| C390 | AP47 | 2.50g bl, plum & grn | .95 | .55 |
| | | *Nos. C387-C390 (4)* | 2.50 | 1.55 |

EXPO '70 International Exposition, Osaka, Japan, Mar. 15-Sept. 13, 1970.
For surcharges see Nos. C447-C447A.

### Souvenir Sheets

1972 Summer Olympics, Munich — AP47a

Designs: 2.50g, Israeli delegation, opening ceremony in Munich Stadium. 5g, Assassinated Israeli athlete David Berger.

**1973**    *Perf. 13½*
| | | | | |
|---|---|---|---|---|
| C390A | AP47a | 2.50g multi | 2.00 | 2.00 |
| C390B | AP47a | 5g multi | 2.25 | 1.50 |

No. C390B contains one 22½x34mm stamp.

Headquarters and Map of Americas — AP48

**1973, May 11**    Litho.    *Perf. 14½*
| | | | | |
|---|---|---|---|---|
| C391 | AP48 | 50c dk bl & multi | .35 | .20 |
| C392 | AP48 | 80c multi | .50 | .35 |
| C393 | AP48 | 1.50g vio & multi | .60 | .45 |
| C394 | AP48 | 2g brn & multi | .85 | .55 |
| | | *Nos. C391-C394 (4)* | 2.30 | 1.55 |

70th anniversary (in 1972) of the Panamerican Health Organization.

## Marine Life Type of Regular Issue

50c, 1.50g horizontal.

**1973, Sept. 4**     **Perf. 14**

| | | | | |
|---|---|---|---|---|
| C395 | A145 | 50c Platypodia spectabilis | 1.00 | .20 |
| C396 | A145 | 85c Goniaster tessellatus | 1.40 | .20 |
| C397 | A145 | 1.50g Stephanocyathus diadema | 2.00 | .30 |
| C398 | A145 | 2g Phyllangia americana | 2.50 | .40 |
| | | Nos. C395-C398 (4) | 6.90 | 1.10 |

For surcharge see No. C439.

## Fish Type of Regular Issue

Designs: Tropical fish.

**1973**     **Perf. 13½**

| | | | | |
|---|---|---|---|---|
| C399 | A146 | 50c Gramma melacara | .45 | .35 |
| C400 | A146 | 85c Holacanthus tricolor | .55 | .45 |
| C401 | A146 | 1.50g Liopropoma rubre | 1.00 | .55 |
| C402 | A146 | 5g Clepticus parrai | 2.75 | 1.40 |
| | | Nos. C399-C402 (4) | 4.75 | 2.75 |

For surcharge see No. C440.

Haitian Flag
AP49

Nos. C404, C405, Haitian flag and coat of arms. No. C406, Flag and Pres. Jean-Claude Duvalier.

**1973, Nov. 18**     **Perf. 14½x14**
**Size: 35x22½mm**

| | | | | |
|---|---|---|---|---|
| C403 | AP49 | 80c blk & red | .45 | .35 |
| C404 | AP49 | 80c red & blk | .45 | .35 |

**Perf. 14x13½**
**Size: 42x27mm**

| | | | | |
|---|---|---|---|---|
| C405 | AP49 | 1.85g blk & red | .95 | .65 |
| C406 | AP49 | 1.85g red & blk | .95 | .65 |
| | | Nos. C403-C406 (4) | 2.80 | 2.00 |

For overprints and surcharges see Nos. C427-C428, C432-C433, C441-C442.

## Soccer Type of Regular Issue

50c, 80c, Soccer Stadium. 1.75g, 10g, Haiti #654.

**1973, Nov. 29**     **Perf. 14x13**

| | | | | |
|---|---|---|---|---|
| C407 | A147 | 50c multi | .35 | .20 |
| C408 | A147 | 80c multi | .45 | .35 |
| C409 | A147 | 1.75g multi | .95 | .45 |
| C410 | A147 | 10g multi | 3.25 | 2.25 |
| | | Nos. C407-C410 (4) | 5.00 | 3.25 |

## Dessalines Type of 1974

**1974, Apr. 22**     **Photo.**     **Perf. 14**

| | | | | |
|---|---|---|---|---|
| C411 | A148 | 50c brn & grnsh bl | .35 | .20 |
| C412 | A148 | 80c gray & brn | .45 | .35 |
| C413 | A148 | 1g lt grn & mar | .55 | .45 |
| C414 | A148 | 1.75g lil & ol brn | .95 | .55 |
| | | Nos. C411-C414 (4) | 2.30 | 1.55 |

For surcharge see No. C443.

## Copernicus Type of 1974

Designs: No. C415, 80c, 1.50g, 1.75g, Symbol of heliocentric system. No. C416, 1g, 2.50g, Nicolaus Copernicus.

**1974, May 24**     **Litho.**     **Perf. 14x13½**

| | | | | |
|---|---|---|---|---|
| C415 | A149 | 50c org & multi | .35 | .20 |
| C416 | A149 | 50c yel & multi | .35 | .20 |
| C417 | A149 | 80c multi | .45 | .35 |
| C418 | A149 | 1g multi | .55 | .45 |
| C419 | A149 | 1.75g brn & multi | .95 | .55 |
| | | Nos. C415-C419 (5) | 2.65 | 1.75 |

**Souvenir Sheet**
**Imperf**

| | | | | |
|---|---|---|---|---|
| C420 | | Sheet of 2 | 2.50 | 2.50 |
| a. | | A149 1.50g light green & multi | .90 | .90 |
| b. | | A149 2.50g deep orange & multi | 1.40 | 1.40 |

For overprint and surcharges see Nos. C444, C460-C463.

## Pres. Duvalier Type of 1974

**1974**     **Photo.**     **Perf. 14x13½**

| | | | | |
|---|---|---|---|---|
| C421 | A151 | 50c vio brn & gold | .35 | .20 |
| C422 | A151 | 80c rose red & gold | .45 | .35 |
| C423 | A151 | 1g red lil & gold | .65 | .45 |
| C424 | A151 | 1.50g Prus bl & gold | 1.00 | .65 |

---

| | | | | |
|---|---|---|---|---|
| C425 | A151 | 1.75g brt vio & gold | 1.25 | .65 |
| C426 | A151 | 5g ol grn & gold | 2.75 | 1.50 |
| | | Nos. C421-C426 (6) | 6.45 | 3.80 |

For surcharge and overprints see Nos. C445, C487-C489.

### Nos. C405-C406 Surcharged in Violet Blue

**1975, July 15**     **Litho.**     **Perf. 14x13½**

| | | | | |
|---|---|---|---|---|
| C427 | AP49 | 80c on 1.85g, #C405 | 1.50 | 1.50 |
| C428 | AP49 | 80c on 1.85g, #C406 | 1.50 | 1.50 |

### Nos. C405-C406 Overprinted in Blue

**1975, July 15**     **Litho.**     **Perf. 14x13½**

| | | | | |
|---|---|---|---|---|
| C432 | AP49 | 1.85g blk & red | .95 | .65 |
| C433 | AP49 | 1.85g red & blk | .95 | .65 |

Centenary of Universal Postal Union. "100 ANS" in 2 lines on No. C433.

Names of Haitian Participants at Siege of Savannah — AP50

**1976, Apr. 22**     **Photo.**     **Perf. 11½**
**Granite Paper**

| | | | | |
|---|---|---|---|---|
| C434 | AP50 | 50c multi | .35 | .20 |
| C435 | AP50 | 80c multi | .55 | .35 |
| C436 | AP50 | 1.50g multi | .80 | .55 |
| C437 | AP50 | 7.50g multi | 2.75 | 1.90 |
| | | Nos. C434-C437 (4) | 4.45 | 3.00 |

American Bicentennial.

### Stamps of 1972-74 Surcharged with New Value and Bar in Black or Violet Blue

**Photogravure; Lithographed**

**1976**     **Perf. 11½, 13½, 14x13½, 14**

| | | | | |
|---|---|---|---|---|
| C438 | A142 | 80c on 2.50g, #C379 | .55 | .35 |
| C439 | A145 | 80c on 85c, #C396 | .55 | .35 |
| C440 | A146 | 80c on 85c, #C400 | .55 | .35 |
| C441 | AP49 | 80c on 1.85g, #C405 | .55 | .35 |
| C442 | AP49 | 80c on 1.85g, #C406 | .55 | .35 |
| C443 | A148 | 80c on 1.75g, #C414 (VB) | .55 | .35 |
| C444 | A149 | 80c on 1.75g, #C419 (VB) | .55 | .35 |
| C445 | A151 | 80c on 1.75g, #C425 | .55 | .35 |
| C446 | AP50 | 80c on 1.50g, #C436 | .55 | .35 |
| C447 | AP47 | 80c on 1.50g, #C389 | .55 | .35 |
| C447A | AP47 | 80c on 2.50g #C390 | .55 | .35 |
| | | Nos. C438-C447A (11) | 6.05 | 3.85 |

Black surcharge of Nos. C441-C442 differs from the violet blue surcharge of Nos. C427-C428 in type face, arrangement of denomination and bar, and size of bar (10x6mm).

### Dessalines Type of 1972

**1976-77**     **Perf. 11½**
**Granite Paper**

| | | | | |
|---|---|---|---|---|
| C448 | A142 | 75c yel & blk | .35 | .35 |
| C449 | A142 | 80c emer & blk | .35 | .35 |
| C450 | A142 | 1g bl & blk | .45 | .35 |
| C451 | A142 | 1g red brn & blk | .55 | .45 |

---

| | | | | |
|---|---|---|---|---|
| C452 | A142 | 1.25g yel grn & blk | .45 | .35 |
| C453 | A142 | 1.50g bl gray & blk | .45 | .35 |
| C454 | A142 | 1.75g rose & blk | .55 | .45 |
| C455 | A142 | 2g yel & blk | .65 | .55 |
| C457 | A142 | 5g bl grn & blk | 1.75 | 1.10 |
| C458 | A142 | 10g ocher & blk | 3.50 | 2.10 |
| | | Nos. C448-C458 (10) | 9.05 | 6.40 |

Issued: 75c, 80c, #C451, 1.75g, 5g, 10g, 1977.

Nos. C415-C416, C418-C419 Overprinted or Surcharged in Black, Dark Blue or Green

**1977, July 6**     **Litho.**     **Perf. 14x13½**

| | | | | |
|---|---|---|---|---|
| C460 | A149 | 1g (Bk) | .45 | .35 |
| C461 | A149 | 1.25g on 50c (DB) | .55 | .45 |
| C462 | A149 | 1.25g on 50c (G) | .55 | .45 |
| C463 | A149 | 1.25g on 1.75g (Bk) | .55 | .45 |
| | | Nos. C460-C463 (4) | 2.10 | 1.70 |

Charles A. Lindbergh's solo transatlantic flight from NY to Paris, 50th anniv.

## Telephone Type of 1978

Designs: 1g, Telstar over globe. 1.25g, Duvalier Earth Telecommunications Station. 2g, Wall telephone, 1890, vert.

**1978, June 19**     **Litho.**     **Perf. 13½**

| | | | | |
|---|---|---|---|---|
| C466 | A153 | 1g multi | .45 | .35 |
| C467 | A153 | 1.25g multi | .55 | .45 |
| C468 | A153 | 2g multi | .85 | .55 |
| | | Nos. C466-C468 (3) | 1.85 | 1.35 |

## Olympic Games Type of 1978

Montreal Olympic Games' Emblem and: 1.25g, Equestrian. 2.50g,Basketball. 5g, Yachting.

**1978, Sept. 4**     **Litho.**     **Perf. 13½x13**

| | | | | |
|---|---|---|---|---|
| C469 | A154 | 1.25g multi | .65 | .55 |
| C470 | A154 | 2.50g multi | 1.40 | 1.10 |
| C471 | A154 | 5g multi | 3.00 | 1.40 |
| | | Nos. C469-C471 (3) | 5.05 | 3.05 |

## Children's Institute Type, 1979

Designs: 1.25g, Mother nursing child. 2g, Nurse giving injection.

**1979, Jan. 15**     **Photo.**     **Perf. 14x14½**

| | | | | |
|---|---|---|---|---|
| C472 | A155 | 1.25g multi | .55 | .35 |
| C473 | A155 | 2g multi | .80 | .55 |

Haitians Spinning Cotton, CARE Workshop AP51

**1979, May 11**     **Photo.**     **Perf. 11½**

| | | | | |
|---|---|---|---|---|
| C474 | AP51 | 1g multi | .65 | .55 |
| C475 | AP51 | 1.25g multi | .95 | .65 |
| C476 | AP51 | 2g multi | 1.40 | .85 |
| | | Nos. C474-C476 (3) | 3.00 | 2.05 |

30th anniversary of CARE.

## Human Rights Type of 1979

**1979, July 20**     **Litho.**     **Perf. 14**

| | | | | |
|---|---|---|---|---|
| C477 | A157 | 1g multi | .65 | .55 |
| C478 | A157 | 1.25g multi | .95 | .65 |
| C479 | A157 | 2g multi | 1.40 | .85 |
| | | Nos. C477-C479 (3) | 3.00 | 2.05 |

## Anti-Apartheid Year Type of 1979

**1979, Nov. 22**     **Photo.**     **Perf. 12x11½**

| | | | | |
|---|---|---|---|---|
| C480 | A158 | 1g yel grn & blk | 1.00 | .55 |
| C481 | A158 | 1.25g bl & blk | 1.10 | .65 |
| C482 | A158 | 2g gray olive | 1.75 | .85 |
| | | Nos. C480-C482 (3) | 3.85 | 2.05 |

## IYC Type of 1979

**1979, Dec. 19**     **Photo.**     **Perf. 12**

| | | | | |
|---|---|---|---|---|
| C483 | A159 | 1g multi | .65 | .55 |
| C484 | A159 | 1.25g multi | .95 | .65 |
| C485 | A159 | 2.50g multi | 2.50 | 1.10 |
| C486 | A159 | 5g multi | 3.50 | 1.60 |
| | | Nos. C483-C486 (4) | 7.60 | 3.90 |

---

Nos. C421, C424-C425 Overprinted:

**1980, May 17**     **Photo.**     **Perf. 14x13½**

| | | | | |
|---|---|---|---|---|
| C487 | A151 | 50c multi | .35 | .20 |
| C488 | A151 | 1.50g multi | .95 | .45 |
| C489 | A151 | 1.75g multi | 1.20 | .55 |
| | | Nos. C487-C489 (3) | 2.50 | 1.20 |

Wedding of Pres. Duvalier, May 27.

## Dessalines Type of 1972

**1980, Aug. 27**     **Photo.**     **Perf. 11½**
**Granite Paper**

| | | | | |
|---|---|---|---|---|
| C490 | A142 | 1g gray vio & blk | .55 | .45 |
| C491 | A142 | 1.25g sal pink & blk | .65 | .55 |
| C492 | A142 | 2g pale grn & blk | 1.20 | .85 |
| C493 | A142 | 5g lt bl & blk | 2.40 | 1.60 |
| | | Nos. C490-C493 (4) | 4.80 | 3.45 |

For surcharge see No. C512.

## Tourism Type

**1980, Dec. 2**     **Litho.**     **Perf. 12½x12**

| | | | | |
|---|---|---|---|---|
| C494 | A160 | 1g like #728 | .55 | .45 |
| C495 | A160 | 1.25g like #729 | .65 | .55 |
| C496 | A160 | 1.50g Carnival dancers | .95 | .55 |
| C497 | A160 | 2g Vendors | 1.20 | .85 |
| C498 | A160 | 2.50g like #C497 | 1.40 | 1.10 |
| | | Nos. C494-C498 (5) | 4.75 | 3.50 |

For surcharge see No. C511.

## Soccer Type of 1980

**1980, Dec. 30**     **Litho.**     **Perf. 14**

| | | | | |
|---|---|---|---|---|
| C499 | A161 | 50c Uruguay, 1950 | .35 | .20 |
| C500 | A161 | 75c Germany, 1954 | .45 | .35 |
| C501 | A161 | 1g Brazil, 1958 | .65 | .45 |
| C502 | A161 | 1.25g Brazil, 1962 | .80 | .55 |
| C503 | A161 | 1.50g Gt. Britain, 1966 | 1.10 | .65 |
| C504 | A161 | 1.75g Brazil, 1970 | 1.25 | .85 |
| C505 | A161 | 2g Germany, 1974 | 1.40 | .95 |
| C506 | A161 | 5g Argentina, 1978 | 3.50 | 2.10 |
| | | Nos. C499-C506 (8) | 9.50 | 6.10 |

## Painting Type of 1981

**1981, May 12**     **Photo.**     **Perf. 11½**

| | | | | |
|---|---|---|---|---|
| C507 | A162 | 50c like #734 | .35 | .20 |
| C508 | A162 | 1.25g like #735 | .65 | .55 |
| C509 | A162 | 2g like #736 | 1.25 | .85 |
| C510 | A162 | 5g like #737 | 2.40 | 1.60 |
| | | Nos. C507-C510 (4) | 4.65 | 3.20 |

### Nos. C496, C493 Surcharged

**Perf. 12½x12, 11½**

**1981, Dec. 30**     **Litho., Photo.**

| | | | | |
|---|---|---|---|---|
| C511 | A160 | 1.25g on 1.50g multi | .65 | .55 |
| C512 | A142 | 2g on 5g multi | 1.20 | .85 |

## Dessalines Type of 1972

**1982, Jan. 25**     **Photo.**     **Perf. 11½**
**Granite Paper**

| | | | | |
|---|---|---|---|---|
| C513 | A142 | 1.25g lt brn & blk | .65 | .55 |
| C514 | A142 | 2g lilac & blk | 1.20 | .85 |

No. C320 Surcharged

**2000?**     **Photo.**     **Perf. 13**

| | | | | |
|---|---|---|---|---|
| C515 | A128 | 3g on 75c #C320 | — | — |

## AIR POST SEMI-POSTAL STAMPS

### Coubertin Semipostal Type of 1939
**Unwmk.**

| 1939, Oct. 3 | | Engr. | Perf. 12 |
|---|---|---|---|
| CB1 | SP1 | 60c + 40c multi | 25.00 25.00 |
| CB2 | SP1 | 1.25g + 60c multi | 25.00 25.00 |

Mosquito and National
Sanatorium — SPAP2

| 1949, July 22 | | Cross in Carmine | |
|---|---|---|---|
| CB3 | SPAP2 | 20c + 20c sep | 11.00 6.00 |
| CB4 | SPAP2 | 30c + 30c dp grn | 11.00 6.00 |
| CB5 | SPAP2 | 45c + 45c lt red brn | 11.00 6.00 |
| CB6 | SPAP2 | 80c + 80c pur | 11.00 6.00 |
| CB7 | SPAP2 | 1.25g + 1.25g car rose | 11.00 6.00 |
| a. | | Souvenir sheet | 40.00 25.00 |
| CB8 | SPAP2 | 1.75g + 1.75g bl | 11.00 6.00 |
| a. | | Souvenir sheet | 40.00 25.00 |
| | | Nos. CB3-CB8 (6) | 66.00 36.00 |

The surtax was used for fighting tuberculosis and malaria.

> Catalogue values for unused stamps in this section, from this point to the end of the section, are for Never Hinged items.

No. C113
Surcharged in Deep
Carmine

| 1958, Aug. 30 | | Litho. | Perf. 13x13½ |
|---|---|---|---|
| CB9 | A82 | 2.50g + 50c | 2.50 2.40 |

The surtax was for the Red Cross.

Similar Surcharge in Red on One Line
on Nos. C133-C135

| 1959, Apr. 7 | | Photo. | Perf. 11½ |
|---|---|---|---|
| | | Granite Paper | |
| CB10 | AP35 | 50c + 25c pink, car & ultra | .40 .40 |
| CB11 | A87 | 75c + 25c brt bl | .50 .50 |
| CB12 | A87 | 1g + 25c brn | .75 .75 |

### Nos. C139-C141 Surcharged Like No. CB9 in Red

| 1959 | | | |
|---|---|---|---|
| CB13 | AP36 | 50c + 50c grn & lil | 1.00 1.00 |
| CB14 | AP36 | 1.50g + 50c ol & red brn | 1.00 1.00 |
| CB15 | AP36 | 2.50g + 50c pur & dk bl | 1.25 1.25 |
| | | Nos. CB10-CB15 (6) | 4.90 4.90 |

Surtax for the Red Cross.

Nos. C142-C144 Surcharged
Diagonally

---

| 1959, July 23 | | Unwmk. | Perf. 12 |
|---|---|---|---|
| CB16 | A89 | 1g + 20c | 1.00 1.00 |
| CB17 | A89 | 2g + 20c | 1.10 1.10 |
| CB18 | A89 | 2.50g + 20c | 1.10 1.10 |
| | | Nos. CB16-CB18 (3) | 3.20 3.20 |

World Refugee Year, July 1, 1959-June 30, 1960. A similar surcharge of 50c was applied horizontally to stamps in No. C144a. Value $25.

C145-C147 Surcharged in Dark
Carmine

| 1959, Oct. 30 | | Photo. | Perf. 14 |
|---|---|---|---|
| CB19 | A91 | 50c + 75c hn brn & aqua | 1.00 1.00 |
| CB20 | A90 | 1g + 75c lil & aqua | 1.00 1.00 |
| CB21 | A90 | 1.50g + 75c multi | 1.00 1.00 |
| | | Nos. CB19-CB21 (3) | 3.00 3.00 |

The surtax was for Haitian athletes.
On No. CB19, surcharge lines are spaced to total depth of 16mm.

### Nos. C129-C130 Surcharged in Red: "Hommage a l'UNICEF +G. 0,50"
### Engraved and Lithographed

| 1960, Feb. 2 | | | Perf. 11½ |
|---|---|---|---|
| CB22 | AP34 | 2g + 50c | 1.00 1.00 |
| CB23 | AP34 | 2.50g + 50c | 1.75 1.75 |

Issued to honor UNICEF.

### Nos. C151-C152 Surcharged and Overprinted: "ALPHABETISATION" in Red or Black.

| 1960, July 12 | | Litho. | Perf. 12½x13 |
|---|---|---|---|
| CB24 | A92 | 50c + 20c (R) | .40 .40 |
| CB25 | A92 | 50c + 30c | .65 .55 |
| CB26 | A92 | 1g + 20c (R) | .90 .75 |
| CB27 | A92 | 1g + 30c | .90 .75 |
| | | Nos. CB24-CB27 (4) | 2.85 2.45 |

### Olympic Games Issue
Nos. C163-C164 Surcharged

| 1960, Sept. 9 | | Photo. | Perf. 12 |
|---|---|---|---|
| CB28 | A94 | 50c + 25c | .40 .25 |
| CB29 | A94 | 1.50g + 25c | .65 .55 |

### Nos. C168-C169 Surcharged: "UNICEF +25 centimes"

| 1961, Jan. 14 | | Engr. | Perf. 10½ |
|---|---|---|---|
| CB30 | A96 | 50c + 25c red org & blk | .40 .25 |
| CB31 | A96 | 1.50g + 25c dk bl & blk | .65 .55 |

### Nos. C171, C175-C176 Surcharged with Additional Value, Scout Emblem and: "18e Conference Internationale du Scoutisme Mondial Lisbonne Septembre 1961"

| 1961, Sept. 30 | | | Perf. 11½ |
|---|---|---|---|
| CB32 | AP37 | 20c + 25c | .40 .30 |
| CB33 | AP37 | 1g + 25c | .50 .40 |
| CB34 | AP37 | 1.50g + 25c | .60 .60 |
| | | Nos. CB32-CB34 (3) | 1.50 1.30 |

Issued to commemorate the 18th Boy Scout World Conference, Lisbon, Sept. 19-24, 1961. The surtax was for the Red Cross. Additional proceeds from the sale of Nos. CB32-CB34 benefited the Port-au-Prince airport project.
The same surcharge was also applied to No. C176a. Value $3.

### Nos. C168-C169 Surcharged: "OMS SNEM +20 CENTIMES"

| 1961, Dec. 11 | | Engr. | Perf. 10½ |
|---|---|---|---|
| CB35 | A96 | 50c + 20c | 1.60 1.60 |
| CB36 | A96 | 1.50g + 20c | 2.25 2.25 |

Issued to publicize Haiti's participation in the UN malaria eradication drive.

---

Nos. C123, C126-C127 and C131-C132 Surcharged in Black or Red:

### Engraved and Lithographed

| 1961-62 | | | Perf. 11½ |
|---|---|---|---|
| CB37 | AP34 | 50c + 25c | .25 .25 |
| CB38 | AP34 | 1g + 50c | .35 .35 |
| CB39 | AP34 | 2.50g + 50c (R) ('62) | .65 .65 |
| CB40 | AP34 | 5g + 50c | 1.10 1.10 |
| CB41 | AP34 | 7.50g + 50c (R) ('62) | 1.50 1.50 |
| | | Nos. CB37-CB41 (5) | 3.85 3.85 |

The surtax was for the benefit of the urban rehabilitation program in Duvalier Ville.

### Nos. C188-C190 Surcharged: "+25 centimes"

| 1962, Sept. 13 | | Litho. | Perf. 12 |
|---|---|---|---|
| CB42 | A99 | 20c + 25c | .25 .20 |
| CB43 | A99 | 50c + 25c | .40 .20 |
| CB44 | A99 | 1g + 25c | .50 .40 |
| | | Nos. CB42-CB44 (3) | 1.15 .80 |

### #C191-C192 Surcharged in Red: "+0.20"

| 1962 | | | Perf. 12½x13 |
|---|---|---|---|
| CB45 | A92 | 50c + 20c | .40 .40 |
| CB46 | A92 | 1g + 20c | .50 .40 |

### Nos. C203 and C205 Surcharged: "ALPHABETISATION" and "+0, 10"

| 1963, Mar. 15 | | Photo. | Perf. 14x14½ |
|---|---|---|---|
| CB47 | AP38 | 50c + 10c | .40 .20 |
| CB48 | AP38 | 1.50g + 10c | .50 .40 |

### No. C110 Surcharged in Red with Olympic Emblem and: "JEUX OLYMPIQUES / D'HIVER / INNSBRUCK 1964"

| 1964, July 27 | | Photo. | Perf. 11½ |
|---|---|---|---|
| CB49 | A80 | 2.50g + 50c + 10c | .90 .80 |

See note after No. B34. The 50c+10c surtax went for charity.

No. C213 Surcharged in Red

### Engraved and Photogravure

| 1964, Oct. 2 | | | Perf. 13½x14 |
|---|---|---|---|
| CB50 | AP39 | 2.50g + 1.25g on 1.50g | 1.40 1.25 |

Issued to commemorate the centenary (in 1963) of the International Red Cross.

### Nos. C223-C226 Surcharged: "+ 5c."

| 1965, Mar. 15 | | Photo. | Perf. 11½ |
|---|---|---|---|
| CB51 | A105 | 50c + 5c pale lil & dk brn | .40 .20 |
| CB52 | A105 | 50c + 5c pale grn & dk brn | .40 .20 |
| CB53 | A105 | 75c + 5c buff & dk brn | .50 .40 |
| CB54 | A105 | 1.50g + 5c gray & dk brn | .80 .65 |
| | | Nos. CB51-CB54 (4) | 2.10 1.45 |

The souvenir sheet No. C226a was surcharged "+25c." Value, $8.
See note following No. B37.

### Nos. C251 and C253 Surcharged and Overprinted with Haitian Scout Emblem and "12e Jamboree / Mondial 1967" Like Regular Issue

| 1967, Aug. 21 | | Photo. | Perf. 11½ |
|---|---|---|---|
| CB55 | A111 | 50c + 10c multi | .50 .40 |
| CB56 | A111 | 1.50g + 50c multi | .65 .50 |

See note after No. B40.

---

No. C269 Surcharged Like Regular Issue

**Lithographed and Photogravure**

| 1968, Jan. 18 | | | Perf. 13x13½ |
|---|---|---|---|
| CB57 | A115 | 2.50g + 1.25g on 1.50g | 1.60 1.25 |

See note after No. 579.

### #C285-C287 Surcharged "CULTURE + 10"

| 1968, July 4 | | Litho. | Perf. 11½ |
|---|---|---|---|
| CB58 | A120 | 50c + 10c multi | .40 .20 |
| CB59 | A120 | 1g + 10c multi | .50 .40 |
| CB60 | A120 | 1.50g + 10c multi | .65 .50 |
| | | Nos. CB58-CB60 (3) | 1.55 1.10 |

### Nos. C314 and C316 Surcharged in Red with New Value, Red Cross and: "50ème. Anniversaire / de la Ligue des / Sociétés de la / Croix Rouge"

| 1969, June 25 | | Litho. | Perf. 11½ |
|---|---|---|---|
| CB61 | A127 | 50c + 20c multi | .50 .40 |
| CB62 | A127 | 1.50g + 25c multi | .90 .50 |

League of Red Cross Societies, 50th anniv.

---

## AIR POST OFFICIAL STAMPS

Nos. C172-C176 and C176a
Overprinted: "OFFICIEL"
Perf. 11½

| 1961, Mar. | | Unwmk. | Photo. |
|---|---|---|---|
| CO1 | AP37 | 50c rose brn & grn | .60 |
| CO2 | AP37 | 50c brt grnsh bl & ol grn | .60 |
| CO3 | AP37 | 50c gray & grn | .60 |
| CO4 | AP37 | 1g gray ol & ver | .85 |
| CO5 | AP37 | 1.50g brt pink & dk bl | 1.40 |
| a. | | Sheet of 3 | 3.75 |
| | | Nos. CO1-CO5 (5) | 4.05 |

Nos. CO1-CO5a only available canceled.

> Catalogue values for unused stamps in this section, from this point to the end of the section, are for Never Hinged items.

Jean Jacques
Dessalines — OA1

| 1962, Mar. 7 | | Photo. | Perf. 14x14½ |
|---|---|---|---|
| | | Size: 20½x38mm | |
| CO6 | OA1 | 50c dk bl & sepia | .50 .40 |
| CO7 | OA1 | 1g lt bl & maroon | .80 .50 |
| CO8 | OA1 | 1.50g bister & bl | 1.00 .70 |
| | | Size: 30x40mm | |
| CO9 | OA1 | 5g rose & ol grn | 2.75 2.40 |
| | | Nos. CO6-CO9 (4) | 5.05 4.00 |

Inscription at bottom of #CO9 is in 2 lines.

---

## AIR POST PARCEL POST STAMPS

> Catalogue values for unused stamps in this section are for Never Hinged items.

Nos. C112 and C111
Overprinted in Red

Perf. 11½

| 1960, Nov. 21 | | Unwmk. | Photo. |
|---|---|---|---|
| CQ1 | A81 | 50c orange & black | .50 .40 |
| CQ2 | A80 | 5g bluish blk & saph | 3.50 2.60 |

## Type of Parcel Post Stamps, 1961
Inscribed "Poste Aerienne"

**1961, Mar. 24** — *Perf. 14*
CQ3 PP1 2.50g yel grn & mar 2.00 1.40
CQ4 PP1 5g org & green 2.50 1.60

### SPECIAL DELIVERY STAMP

> The catalogue value for the unused stamp in this section is for Never Hinged.

Postal Administration Building — SD1

**Unwmk.**
**1953, May 4 Engr.** *Perf. 12*
E1 SD1 25c vermilion .70 .50

### POSTAGE DUE STAMPS

D1      D2

**1898, May Unwmk. Engr. Perf. 12**
J1 D1 2c black 1.00 .75
J2 D1 5c red brown 1.50 1.00
J3 D1 10c brown orange 2.00 1.50
J4 D1 50c slate 3.00 2.50
    *Nos. J1-J4 (4)* 7.50 5.75

For overprints see Nos. J5-J9, J14-J16.

Stamps of 1898 Handstamped like #67-81

**1902** **Black Overprint**
J5 D1 2c black 2.50 1.50
J6 D1 5c red brown 2.50 1.50
J7 D1 10c brown orange 2.50 1.50
J8 D1 50c slate 12.00 7.00
**Red Overprint**
J9 D1 2c black 3.50 3.50
    *Nos. J5-J9 (5)* 23.00 15.00

**1906**
J10 D2 2c dull red 1.50 1.00
J11 D2 5c ultra 2.75 2.50
J12 D2 10c violet 2.75 2.50
J13 D2 50c olive gray 11.50 7.50
    *Nos. J10-J13 (4)* 18.50 13.50

For surcharges and overprints see Nos. 305-308, J17-J20.

Preceding Issues Handstamped like #169-201

**1914** **On Stamps of 1898**
J14 D1 5c red brown 1.50 1.10
J15 D1 10c brown orange 1.50 1.10
J16 D1 50c slate 6.00 5.50
    *Nos. J14-J16 (3)* 9.00 7.70
**On Stamps of 1906**
J17 D2 2c dull red 1.25 1.00
J18 D2 5c ultra 2.25 2.25
J19 D2 10c violet 7.50 5.50
J20 D2 50c olive gray 35.00 35.00
    *Nos. J17-J20 (4)* 46.00 43.75

The note after No. 201 applies to Nos. J14-J20 also.

> Catalogue values for unused stamps in this section, from this point to the end of the section, are for Never Hinged.

---

Unpaid Letter — D3

**1951, July Litho.** *Perf. 11½*
J21 D3 10c carmine .20 .20
J22 D3 20c red brown .25 .20
J23 D3 40c green .40 .40
J24 D3 50c orange yellow .50 .50
    *Nos. J21-J24 (4)* 1.35 1.30

### PARCEL POST STAMPS

> Catalogue values for unused stamps in this section are for Never Hinged items.

Nos. 416, 470-471 and 378 Overprinted in Red

**Photogravure, Engraved**
*Perf. 11½, 12*
**1960, Nov. 21** **Unwmk.**
Q1 A81 5c yel grn & blk .20 .20
Q2 A81 10c red org & blk .20 .20
Q3 A81 25c ultra & black .40 .25
Q4 A64 2.50g gray 2.75 2.40
    *Nos. Q1-Q4 (4)* 3.55 3.05

Coat of Arms — PP1

**Unwmk.**
**1961, Mar. 24 Photo.** *Perf. 14*
Q5 PP1 50c bister & purple .50 .40
Q6 PP1 1g pink & dark blue .80 .50
    See Nos. CQ3-CQ4.

### POSTAL TAX STAMPS

> Catalogue values for unused stamps in this section, are for Never Hinged items.

Haitian Woman, War Invalids and Ruined Buildings PT1

**Unwmk.**
**1944, Aug. 16 Engr.** *Perf. 12*
RA1 PT1 5c dull purple 1.40 .60
RA2 PT1 5c dark blue 1.40 .60
RA3 PT1 5c olive green 1.40 .60
RA4 PT1 5c black 1.40 .60

**1945, Dec. 17**
RA5 PT1 5c dark green 1.40 .60
RA6 PT1 5c sepia 1.40 .60
RA7 PT1 5c red brown 1.40 .60
RA8 PT1 5c rose carmine 1.40 .60
    *Nos. RA1-RA8 (8)* 11.20 4.80

The proceeds from the sale of Nos. RA1 to RA8 were for United Nations Relief.

---

George Washington, J.J. Dessalines and Simón Bolivar — PT2

**1949, Sept. 20**
RA9 PT2 5c red brown .50 .40
RA10 PT2 5c olive gray .50 .40
RA11 PT2 5c blue .50 .40
RA12 PT2 5c green .50 .40
RA13 PT2 5c violet .50 .40
RA14 PT2 5c black .50 .40
RA15 PT2 5c orange .50 .40
RA16 PT2 5c carmine rose .50 .40
    *Nos. RA9-RA16 (8)* 4.00 3.20

Bicentenary of Port-au-Prince.
For overprint and surcharges see #385-388.

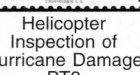

Helicopter Inspection of Hurricane Damage PT3    Helicopter PT4

**1955, Jan. 3 Photo.** *Perf. 11½*
RA17 PT3 10c bright green .25 .20
RA18 PT3 10c bright blue .25 .20
RA19 PT3 10c gray black .25 .20
RA20 PT3 10c orange .25 .20
RA21 PT3 20c rose carmine .35 .20
RA22 PT3 20c deep green .35 .20
    *Nos. RA17-RA22 (6)* 1.70 1.20

**1955, May 3**
RA23 PT4 10c black, *gray* .25 .20
RA24 PT4 20c violet blue, *blue* .30 .20

The surface tint of the sheets of 50, (10x5) of #RA23-RA24, RAC1-RAC2 includes a map of Haiti's southern peninsula which extends over the three center rows of stamps.
The tax was for reconstruction.
See Nos. RAC1-RAC2.

PT5

**1959-60 Unwmk. Photo.** *Perf. 11½*
    **Size: 38x22½mm**
RA25 PT5 5c green .20 .20
RA26 PT5 5c black ('60) .20 .20
RA27 PT5 10c red .20 .20
    *Nos. RA25-RA27 (3)* .60 .60

**1960-61**
    **Size: 28x17mm**
RA28 PT5 5c green .20 .20
RA29 PT5 10c red .20 .20
RA30 PT5 10c blue ('61) .20 .20
    *Nos. RA28-RA30 (3)* .60 .60

PT6

**1963, Sept.** *Perf. 14½x14*
    **Size: 13½x21mm**
RA31 PT6 10c red orange .20 .20
RA32 PT6 10c bright blue .20 .20
RA33 PT6 10c olive .20 .20
   *Nos. RA31-RA33,RAC6-RAC8 (6)* 1.20 1.20

---

**1966-69 Photo.** *Perf. 14x14½*
    **Size: 17x25mm**
RA34 PT6 10c bright green .20 .20
RA35 PT6 10c violet .20 .20
RA36 PT6 10c violet blue .20 .20
RA37 PT6 10c brown ('69) .20 .20
   *Nos. RA34-RA37,RAC9-RAC15 (11)* 2.20 2.20

Nos. RA25-RA37 represent a tax for a literacy campaign.
See Nos. RA42-RA45, RAC20-RAC22.

Duvalier de Peligre Hydroelectric Works — PT7

**1970-72**
RA38 PT7 20c violet & olive .20 .20
RA39 PT7 20c ultra & blk ('72) .20 .20
    See Nos. RA46, RAC16-RAC19, RAC23.

Nos. 637-638 Surcharged: "ALPHABETISATION +10"
**1971, Dec. 23 Litho.** *Perf. 14x13½*
RA40 A138 20c + 10c multi .35 .20
   a. Inverted surcharge 2.00
RA41 A138 25c + 10c multi .35 .20
    Tax was for the literacy campaign.

"CA" Type of 1963
**1972-74 Photo.** *Perf. 14x14½*
    **Size: 17x25mm**
RA42 PT6 5c violet blue .20 .20
RA43 PT6 5c deep carmine .20 .20
RA44 PT6 5c ultra ('74) .20 .20
RA45 PT6 5c carmine rose ('74) .20 .20
    *Nos. RA42-RA45 (4)* .80 .80

Tax was for literacy campaign.

Hydroelectric Type of 1970
**1980 Photo.** *Perf. 14x14½*
RA46 PT7 25c choc & green .25 .20

---

### AIR POST POSTAL TAX STAMPS

> Catalogue values for unused stamps in this section, are for Never Hinged items.

Helicopter Type of 1955
**1955 Unwmk. Photo.** *Perf. 11½*
RAC1 PT4 10c red brn, *pale sal* .30 .20
RAC2 PT4 20c rose pink, *pink* .35 .20
    See note after No. RA24.

Type of Postal Tax Stamps, 1960-61
**1959**
    **Size: 28x17mm**
RAC3 PT5 5c yellow .20 .20
RAC4 PT5 5c dull salmon .20 .20
RAC5 PT5 10c blue .20 .20
    *Nos. RAC3-RAC5 (3)* .60 .60

Type of Postal Tax Stamps, 1963
**1963, Sept.** *Perf. 14½x14*
    **Size: 13½x21mm**
RAC6 PT6 10c dark gray .20 .20
RAC7 PT6 10c violet .20 .20
RAC8 PT6 10c brown .20 .20
    *Nos. RAC6-RAC8 (3)* .60 .60

**1966-69** *Perf. 14x14½*
    **Size: 17x25mm**
RAC9 PT6 10c orange .20 .20
RAC10 PT6 10c sky blue .20 .20
RAC11 PT6 10c yellow ('69) .20 .20
RAC12 PT6 10c carmine ('69) .20 .20
RAC13 PT6 10c gray grn ('69) .20 .20
RAC14 PT6 10c lilac ('69) .20 .20
RAC15 PT6 10c dp claret ('69) .20 .20
    *Nos. RAC9-RAC15 (7)* 1.40 1.40

Nos. RAC3-RAC15, RAC20-RAC21 represent a tax for a literacy campaign.

Hydroelectric Type of 1970
**1970-74**
RAC16 PT7 20c tan & slate .20 .20
RAC17 PT7 20c brt bl & dl vio .20 .20
RAC18 PT7 25c sal & bluish blk ('74) .25 .20

RAC19 PT7 25c yel ol & bluish
blk ('74) .25 .20
*Nos. RAC16-RAC19 (4)* .90 .80

### "CA" Type of 1963

**1973** **Photo.** **Perf. 14x14½**
**Size: 17x26mm**
RAC20 PT6 10c brn & blue .35 .20
RAC21 PT6 10c brn & green .35 .20
RAC22 PT6 10c brn & orange .35 .20
*Nos. RAC20-RAC22 (3)* 1.05 .60

### Hydroelectric Power Type of 1970

**1979(?)** **Photo.** **Perf. 14x14½**
RAC23 PT7 25c blue & vio brn .25 .20

# HATAY

hä-'tī

LOCATION — Northwest of Syria, bordering on Mediterranean Sea
GOVT. — Semi-independent republic
AREA — 10,000 sq. mi. (approx.)
POP. — 273,350 (1939)
CAPITAL — Antioch

Alexandretta, a semi-autonomous district of Syria under French mandate, was renamed Hatay in 1938 and transferred to Turkey in 1939.

100 Santims = 1 Kurush

40 Paras = 1 Kurush (1939)

Stamps of Turkey, 1931-38,
Surcharged in Black:

On A77     On A78

**1939** **Unwmk.** **Perf. 11½x12**
1 A77 10s on 20pa dp
org 1.25 .35
a. "Sent" instead of
"Sant" 90.00 22.50
2 A78 25s on 1ku dk sl
grn 1.40 .35
a. Small "25" 11.00 1.50
3 A78 50s on 2ku dk vio 1.40 .35
a. Small "50" 5.00 2.00
4 A77 75s on 2½ku
green 1.25 .40
5 A78 1ku on 4ku slate 8.00 4.25
6 A78 1ku on 5ku rose
red 4.50 1.40
7 A78 1½ku on 3ku brn org 2.00 .60
8 A78 2½ku on 4ku slate 3.00 .60
9 A78 5ku on 8ku brt
blue 5.00 .90
10 A77 12½ku on 20ku ol grn 6.00 2.00
11 A77 20ku on 25ku Prus
bl 11.00 5.00
*Nos. 1-11 (11)* 44.80 16.20
Set, never hinged 100.00

Map of
Hatay — A1

Lions of
Antioch
A2

Flag of
Hatay
A3

Post Office
A4

**1939** **Unwmk.** **Typo.** **Perf. 12**
12 A1 10p orange & aqua 2.00 .75
13 A1 30p lt vio & aqua 2.00 .75
14 A1 1½ku olive & aqua 2.00 .75
15 A2 2½ku turq grn 2.50 1.00
16 A2 3ku light blue 2.50 1.00
17 A2 5ku chocolate 2.50 1.00
18 A3 6ku brt blue & car 3.25 1.25
19 A3 7½ku dp green &
car 3.75 1.40
20 A3 12ku violet & car 4.50 1.40
21 A3 12½ku dk blue & car 3.50 1.50
22 A4 17½ku brown car 7.00 3.00
23 A4 25ku olive brn 8.00 3.50
24 A4 50ku slate blue 16.50 8.50
*Nos. 12-24 (13)* 60.00 25.80
Set, never hinged 120.00

Stamps of 1939
Overprinted in
Black

**1939**
25 A1 10p orange & aqua 1.50 .75
a. Overprint reading up 20.00
26 A1 30p lt vio & aqua 1.50 .75
27 A1 1½ku ol & aqua 2.00 .80
28 A2 2½ku turq grn 2.00 .80
29 A2 3ku light blue 2.25 .80
30 A2 5ku chocolate 3.00 1.25
a. Overprint inverted 20.00
31 A3 6ku brt bl & car 3.25 1.25
32 A3 7½ku dp grn & car 3.50 1.25
33 A3 12ku vio & car 3.50 1.25
34 A3 12½ku dk bl & car 4.00 1.25
35 A4 17½ku brn car 5.00 2.25
a. Overprint inverted 20.00
36 A4 25ku olive brn 8.00 4.25
37 A4 50ku slate blue 17.50 10.00
*Nos. 25-37 (13)* 57.00 26.65
Set, never hinged 110.00

The overprint reads "Date of annexation to the Turkish Republic, June 30, 1939."
On Nos. 25-27, the overprint reads down. On Nos. 28-37, it is horizontal.

## POSTAGE DUE STAMPS

Postage Due Stamps of
Turkey, 1936,
Surcharged or
Overprinted in Black

**1939** **Unwmk.** **Perf. 11½**
J1 D6 1ku on 2ku lt bl 2.75 .45
J2 D6 3ku bright violet 3.25 .90
J3 D6 4ku on 5ku Prus bl 3.25 .90
J4 D6 5ku on 12ku brt rose 3.75 1.25
J5 D6 12ku bright rose 50.00 27.50
*Nos. J1-J5 (5)* 63.00 31.00
Set, never hinged 120.00

Castle at
Antioch
D1

**1939** **Typo.** **Perf. 12**
J6 D1 1ku red orange 3.25 1.00
J7 D1 3ku dk olive brown 3.75 1.00
J8 D1 4ku turqoise green 4.25 1.50
J9 D1 5ku slate black 5.00 2.00
*Nos. J6-J9 (4)* 16.25 5.50
Set, never hinged 30.00

Nos. J6-J9 Overprinted in Black like
Nos. 25-37

**1939**
J10 D1 1ku red orange 3.25 1.25
J11 D1 3ku dk olive brown 4.00 1.50
J12 D1 4ku turqoise green 4.00 1.75
J13 D1 5ku slate black 6.00 2.00
a. Overprint inverted 20.00
*Nos. J10-J13 (4)* 17.25 6.50
Set, never hinged 30.00

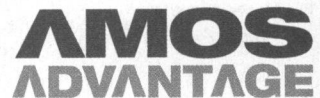

# HELIGOLAND

'he-lə-gō-,land

LOCATION — An island in the North Sea near the northern coast of Germany
GOVT. — Former British Possession
AREA — ¼ sq. mi.
POP. — 2,307 (1900)

Great Britain ceded Heligoland to Germany in 1890. It became part of Schleswig-Holstein province. Stamps of Heligoland were superseded by those of the German Empire.

16 Schillings = 1 Mark
100 Pfennig = 1 Mark = 1 Schilling (1875)

## REPRINTS

Most Heligoland issues were extensively reprinted between 1875 and 1895, and these comprise the great majority of Heligoland stamps in the marketplace. Such reprints sell for much less than the originals, usually for $1-$2 each. Expertization of Heligoland issues is strongly recommended by the editors.

A1

A2

A3

A4

Queen Victoria

HALF SCHILLING
A1: Curl below chignon is rounded.
A2: Curl resembles hook or comma.

### Typo., Head Embossed

| | | | Unwmk. | Rouletted |
|---|---|---|---|---|
| 1 | A1 | ½sch bl grn & rose | 325.00 | 875.00 |
| 1A | A2 | ½sch bl grn & rose | 775.00 | 1,400. |
| 2 | A1 | 1sch rose & dp grn | 175.00 | 200.00 |
| 3 | A3 | 2sch rose & pale green | 14.50 | 60.00 |
| 4 | A3 | 6sch gray green & rose | 16.50 | 275.00 |

*Reprints of No. 2 lack the large curl, those of No. 1A are not in blue green, and those of Nos. 3 and 4 are on slightly porous paper and the colors are either too deep or too bright. The 2sch and 6sch perforated exist only as reprints.*

**1869-71**  Perf. 13½x14½
### Thick Soft Paper

| 5 | A2 | ½sch ol grn & car | 150.00 | 200.00 |
|---|---|---|---|---|
| a. | | ½sch blue green & salmon | 210.00 | 225.00 |
| b. | | ½sch yellow green & rose | 350.00 | 325.00 |
| 6 | A2 | 1sch rose & yel grn | 175.00 | 250.00 |

*Reprints are on thinner paper and in too dark colors.*

**1873**  Thick Quadrille Paper

| 7 | A4 | ¼sch pale rose & pale grn | 31.00 | 2,000. |
|---|---|---|---|---|
| a. | | ¼sch deep rose & pale grn | 250.00 | 2,000. |
| 8 | A4 | ¼sch yel grn & rose | 135.00 | 3,300. |
| 9 | A2 | ½sch brt grn & rose | 125.00 | 210.00 |
| 10 | A4 | ¾sch gray grn & pale rose | 35.00 | 1,300. |
| a. | | ¾sch gray green & dp rose | 35.00 | 1,300. |

| 11 | A2 | 1sch rose & pale grn | 210.00 | 350.00 |
|---|---|---|---|---|
| 12 | A4 | 1½sch yel grn & rose | 72.50 | 275.00 |

*Reprints are never on quadrille paper.*

**1874**  Thin Wove Paper

| 13 | A4 | ¼sch rose & yel grn | 16.00 | |
|---|---|---|---|---|

*Originals have the large curl. The early reprints have the small curl. The later reprints are on thin hard paper with smooth white gum and the colors are too bright.*

A5

A6

A7

Coat of Arms — A8

**1875**  Wove Paper

| 14 | A5 | 1pf dk rose & dk grn | 14.50 | 575.00 |
|---|---|---|---|---|
| 15 | A5 | 2pf yel grn & dk rose | 14.50 | 875.00 |
| 16 | A6 | 5pf dk rose & dk grn | 13.50 | 21.00 |
| 17 | A6 | 10pf blue grn & red | 13.00 | 37.50 |
| a. | | 10pf yel green & dark rose | 110.00 | 27.50 |
| b. | | 10pf lt green & pale red | 140.00 | 25.00 |
| 18 | A7 | 25pf rose & dk grn | 16.50 | 30.00 |
| a. | | 25pf dk rose & dk green | 16.50 | 30.00 |
| 19 | A7 | 50pf grn & brick red | 22.50 | 85.00 |
| a. | | 50pf dl grn & dk rose | 57.50 | 37.50 |

*The 1pf and 2pf have been reprinted on very white paper with white gum. The colors are too bright and too light.*

**1876-88**  Typo.

| 20 | A8 | 3pf grn & bright red ('77) | 250.00 | 1,300. |
|---|---|---|---|---|
| a. | | 3pf dp grn & dl red | 175.00 | 950.00 |
| 21 | A8 | 20pf ver & brt grn ('88) | 14.50 | 30.00 |
| a. | | 20pf brn org & grn ('87) | 425.00 | 42.50 |
| b. | | 20pf vio car & yel grn ('80) | 240.00 | 125.00 |
| c. | | 20pf anil rose & dk grn ('85) | 425.00 | 65.00 |
| d. | | 20pf lilac rose & dk green | 240.00 | 125.00 |
| e. | | 20pf rose red & dk grn ('80) | 240.00 | 125.00 |

*The coat-of-arms on Nos. 20, 21 and subvarieties is printed in three colors: varying shades of yellow, red and green.*

*The 3pf has been reprinted. The colors are usually too pale, especially the red, which is either orange or orange red.*

A9

A10

**1879**  Typo.

| 22 | A9 | 1m dp green & car | 200.00 | 200.00 |
|---|---|---|---|---|
| a. | | 1m blue green & salmon | 210.00 | 200.00 |
| b. | | 1m dark green & vermilion | 70.00 | |
| 23 | A10 | 5m dp green & sal | 190.00 | 1,050. |

Perf. 11½

| 24 | A9 | 1m dp grn & car | 1,600. | 5,000. |
|---|---|---|---|---|
| 25 | A10 | 5m bl grn & rose red | 1,300. | 10,500. |
| a. | | Horiz. pair, imperf. vert. | 5,000. | |

Nos. 13, 22b, 24 and 25 were never placed in use. Forged cancellations of Nos. 1-23 are plentiful.

Heligoland stamps were replaced by those of the German Empire in 1890.

---

# HONDURAS

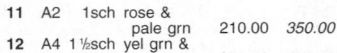

hän-'dur-əs

LOCATION — Central America, between Guatemala on the north and Nicaragua on the south
GOVT. — Republic
AREA — 43,277 sq. mi.
POP. — 5,997,327 (1999 est.)
CAPITAL — Tegucigalpa

8 Reales = 1 Peso
100 Centavos = 1 Peso (1878)
100 Centavos = 1 Lempira (1933)

Catalogue values for unused stamps in this country are for Never Hinged items, beginning with Scott 344 in the regular postage section, Scott B1 in the semipostal section, Scott C144 in the airpost section, Scott CB5 in the airpost semi-postal section, Scott CE3 in the airpost special delivery section, Scott CO110 in the airpost official section, and Scott RA6 in the postal tax section.

Values for unused stamps are for examples with original gum as defined in the catalogue introduction. Very fine examples of the locally printed Nos. 95-110, 127, 140, 151-210C, and 218-279 will have margins clear of the perforations but will be noticeably off center.

**Watermark**

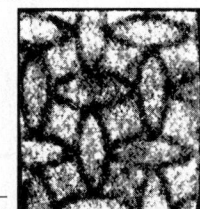

Wmk. 209 — Multiple Ovals

Coat of Arms — A1

**1865, Dec.**  Unwmk.  Litho.  Imperf.

| 1 | A1 | 2r black, green | .65 | — |
|---|---|---|---|---|
| 2 | A1 | 2r black, pink | .65 | — |

Comayagua

Tegucigalpa

Medio real = ½ real
Un real = 1 real
Dos reales = 2 reales

## Comayagua Issue

**1877, May**

### Red Surcharge

| 3 | A1 | ½r on 2r blk, grn | 70.00 | |
|---|---|---|---|---|

### Blue Surcharge

| 5 | A1 | 2r on 2r blk, grn | — | |
|---|---|---|---|---|
| 6 | A1 | 2r on 2r blk, pink | 475.00 | — |

### Black Surcharge

| 7 | A1 | 1r on 2r blk, grn | 150.00 | |
|---|---|---|---|---|
| 8 | A1 | 2r on 2r blk, grn | 800.00 | |
| 9 | A1 | 2r on 2r blk, pink | 500.00 | |

No. 5 may exist only as the base for No. 13a.

## Tegucigalpa Issue

**1877, July**

### Black Surcharge

| 13 | A1 | 1r on 2r blk, grn | 15.00 | 35.00 |
|---|---|---|---|---|
| a. | | Surcharged on #5 | 1,000. | |
| 14 | A1 | 1r on 2r blk, pink | 80.00 | |
| 16 | A1 | 2r on 2r blk, pink | — | |

### Blue Surcharge

| 18 | A1 | ½r on 2r blk, grn | 80.00 | |
|---|---|---|---|---|
| 19 | A1 | ½r on 2r blk, pink | 25.00 | |
| 20 | A1 | ½r on 2r blk, pink | 35.00 | |
| 23 | A1 | 2r on 2r blk, pink | 15.00 | 25.00 |

### Red Surcharge

| 24 | A1 | ½r on 2r blk, grn | 15.00 | 35.00 |
|---|---|---|---|---|
| 25 | A1 | ½r on 2r blk, pink | 60.00 | |

Only the stamps valued or dashed used are known to have been postally used. Nos. 3 and 7 may have been postally used, but to date no examples are recorded used. The other listed stamps were sold as remainders. No covers bearing Nos. 13 to 25 are known.

The blue surcharges range from light blue to violet black. The black surcharge has no tinge of blue. The red surcharges range from light to dark carmine. Some exist double or inverted, but genuine errors are rare. Normal cancel is a blue or black 7-bar killer. Target cancels on Nos. 1-24 are forgeries and surcharges with target cancels also are forgeries. Surcharges and cancels have been extensively forged.

### Regular Issue

President Francisco Morazán — A4

Thin, hard paper, colorless gum
Various Frames

**1878, July**  Engr.  Perf. 12
**Printed by National Bank Note Co. of N.Y.**

| 30 | A4 | 1c violet | .50 | .50 |
|---|---|---|---|---|
| 31 | A4 | 2c brown | .50 | .50 |
| 32 | A4 | ½r black | 5.00 | .50 |
| 33 | A4 | 1r green | 25.00 | .50 |
| 34 | A4 | 2r deep blue | 3.00 | 5.00 |
| 35 | A4 | 4r vermilion | 5.00 | 10.00 |
| 36 | A4 | 1p orange | 6.00 | 25.00 |
| | | Nos. 30-36 (7) | 45.00 | 42.00 |

Various counterfeit cancellations exist on Nos. 30-36. Most used copies of Nos. 35-36 offered are actually 35a-36a with fake or favor cancels.

### Re-Issue

Soft paper, yellowish gum
Various Frames

**1889**
**Printed by American Bank Note Co. of N.Y.**

| 30a | A4 | 1c deep violet | 10.00 | |
|---|---|---|---|---|
| 31a | A4 | 2c red brown | .25 | |
| 32a | A4 | ½r black | .25 | |
| 33a | A4 | 1r blue green | .30 | |
| 34a | A4 | 2r ultramarine | 5.00 | |
| 35a | A4 | 4r scarlet vermilion | .25 | |
| 36a | A4 | 1p orange yellow | .25 | |
| | | Nos. 30a-36a (7) | 16.25 | |

Although Nos. 30a-36a were not intended for postal use, they were valid, and genuine cancels are known on Nos. 31a-34a.

Arms of Honduras — A5

**1890, Jan. 6**

| 40 | A5 | 1c yellow green | .30 | .30 |
|---|---|---|---|---|
| 41 | A5 | 2c red | .30 | .30 |
| 42 | A5 | 5c blue | .30 | .30 |
| 43 | A5 | 10c orange | .35 | .40 |
| 44 | A5 | 20c ocher | .35 | .40 |
| 45 | A5 | 25c rose red | .35 | .40 |
| 46 | A5 | 30c purple | .50 | .60 |
| 47 | A5 | 40c dark blue | .50 | .80 |
| 48 | A5 | 50c brown | .55 | .80 |
| 49 | A5 | 75c blue green | .55 | 2.00 |
| 50 | A5 | 1p carmine | .70 | 2.25 |
| | | Nos. 40-50 (11) | 4.75 | 8.55 |

The tablets and numerals of Nos. 40 to 50 differ for each denomination.
For overprints see Nos. O1-O11.

Used values of Nos. 1-110 are for stamps with genuine cancellations applied while the stamps were valid. Various counterfeit cancellations exist.

A6

President Luis
Bográn — A7

## 1891, July 31
| | | | | |
|---|---|---|---|---|
| 51 | A6 | 1c dark blue | .30 | .30 |
| 52 | A6 | 2c yellow brown | .30 | .30 |
| 53 | A6 | 5c blue green | .30 | .30 |
| 54 | A6 | 10c vermilion | .30 | .30 |
| 55 | A6 | 20c brown red | .30 | .30 |
| 56 | A6 | 25c magenta | .40 | .55 |
| 57 | A6 | 30c slate | .40 | .55 |
| 58 | A6 | 40c blue green | .40 | .55 |
| 59 | A6 | 50c black brown | .50 | .80 |
| 60 | A6 | 75c purple | .50 | 1.25 |
| 61 | A6 | 1p brown | .75 | 1.60 |
| 62 | A7 | 2p brn & black | 2.25 | 5.00 |
| a. | | Head inverted | 225.00 | |
| 63 | A7 | 5p pur & black | 2.00 | 5.75 |
| a. | | Head inverted | 60.00 | |
| 64 | A7 | 10p green & blk | 2.00 | 5.75 |
| a. | | Head inverted | 75.00 | |
| | | Nos. 51-64 (14) | 10.70 | 23.30 |

#62, 64 exist with papermakers watermark.
For overprints see Nos. O12-O22.

Columbus
Sighting
Honduran
Coast — A8

General
Trinidad
Cabañas — A9

## 1892, July 31
| | | | | |
|---|---|---|---|---|
| 65 | A8 | 1c slate | .40 | .45 |
| 66 | A8 | 2c deep blue | .40 | .45 |
| 67 | A8 | 5c yellow green | .40 | .45 |
| 68 | A8 | 10c blue green | .40 | .45 |
| 69 | A8 | 20c red | .40 | .45 |
| 70 | A8 | 25c orange brown | .50 | .55 |
| 71 | A8 | 30c ultramarine | .50 | .60 |
| 72 | A8 | 40c orange | .50 | .90 |
| 73 | A8 | 50c brown | .60 | .85 |
| 74 | A8 | 75c lake | .60 | 1.25 |
| 75 | A8 | 1p purple | .60 | 1.40 |
| | | Nos. 65-75 (11) | 5.30 | 7.80 |

Discovery of America by Christopher
Columbus, 400th anniv.

## 1893, Aug.
| | | | | |
|---|---|---|---|---|
| 76 | A9 | 1c green | .25 | 1.50 |
| 77 | A9 | 2c scarlet | .25 | 1.50 |
| 78 | A9 | 5c dark blue | .25 | 1.50 |
| 79 | A9 | 10c orange brn | .25 | 1.50 |
| 80 | A9 | 20c brown red | .25 | 1.50 |
| 81 | A9 | 25c dark blue | .30 | 1.50 |
| 82 | A9 | 30c red orange | .45 | 1.50 |
| 83 | A9 | 40c black | .45 | 1.50 |
| 84 | A9 | 50c olive brn | .45 | 1.50 |
| 85 | A9 | 75c purple | .60 | 1.50 |
| 86 | A9 | 1p deep magenta | .60 | 1.75 |
| | | Nos. 76-86 (11) | 4.10 | 16.75 |

"Justice"
A10

President Celio
Arias
A11

## 1895, Feb. 15
| | | | | |
|---|---|---|---|---|
| 87 | A10 | 1c vermilion | .30 | .30 |
| 88 | A10 | 2c deep blue | .30 | .30 |
| 89 | A10 | 5c slate | .35 | .50 |
| 90 | A10 | 10c brown rose | .45 | .50 |
| 91 | A10 | 20c violet | .45 | .50 |
| 92 | A10 | 30c deep violet | .45 | .85 |
| 93 | A10 | 50c olive brown | .55 | 1.25 |
| 94 | A10 | 1p dark green | .60 | 1.60 |
| | | Nos. 87-94 (8) | 3.45 | 5.80 |

The tablets and numerals of Nos. 76-94 differ for each denomination.

## 1896, Jan. 1    Litho.    Perf. 11½
| | | | | |
|---|---|---|---|---|
| 95 | A11 | 1c dark blue | .30 | .35 |
| 96 | A11 | 2c yellow brn | .30 | .35 |
| 97 | A11 | 5c purple | 1.10 | .30 |
| a. | | 5c red violet | .60 | 1.10 |
| 98 | A11 | 10c vermilion | .40 | .40 |
| a. | | 10c red | 4.50 | 4.50 |
| 99 | A11 | 20c emerald | .75 | .50 |
| a. | | 20c deep green | | |
| 100 | A11 | 30c ultramarine | .65 | .70 |
| 101 | A11 | 50c rose | .90 | 1.00 |
| 102 | A11 | 1p black brown | 1.25 | 1.50 |
| | | Nos. 95-102 (8) | 5.65 | 5.10 |

Counterfeits are plentiful. Nos. 95-102 exist
imperf. between horiz. or vertically.
*Originals of Nos. 95 to 102 are on both thin,
semi-transparent paper and opaque paper;
reprints are on thicker, opaque paper and usually have a black cancellation "HONDURAS"
between horizontal bars.*

Railroad
Train — A12

## 1898, Aug. 1
| | | | | |
|---|---|---|---|---|
| 103 | A12 | 1c brown | .50 | .20 |
| 104 | A12 | 2c rose | .50 | .20 |
| 105 | A12 | 5c dull ultra | 1.00 | .25 |
| b. | | 5c red violet (error) | 1.50 | .70 |
| 106 | A12 | 6c red violet | .90 | .25 |
| b. | | 6c dull rose (error) | | |
| 107 | A12 | 10c dark blue | 1.00 | .30 |
| 108 | A12 | 20c dull orange | 1.25 | .75 |
| 109 | A12 | 50c orange red | 2.00 | 1.25 |
| 110 | A12 | 1p blue green | 4.00 | 3.00 |
| | | Nos. 103-110 (8) | 11.15 | 6.20 |

Excellent counterfeits of Nos. 103-110 exist.
For overprints see Nos. O23-O27.

### Laid Paper
| | | | | |
|---|---|---|---|---|
| 103a | A12 | 1c | 1.00 | .50 |
| 104a | A12 | 2c | 1.25 | .50 |
| 105a | A12 | 5c | 1.60 | .50 |
| 106a | A12 | 6c | 1.60 | .75 |
| 107a | A12 | 10c | 1.60 | 1.00 |
| | | Nos. 103a-107a (5) | 7.05 | 3.25 |

General Santos
Guardiola
A13

President José
Medina
A14

## 1903, Jan. 1    Engr.    Perf. 12
| | | | | |
|---|---|---|---|---|
| 111 | A13 | 1c yellow grn | .35 | .20 |
| 112 | A13 | 2c carmine rose | .35 | .30 |
| 113 | A13 | 5c blue | .35 | .30 |
| 114 | A13 | 6c dk violet | .35 | .30 |
| 115 | A13 | 10c brown | .40 | .30 |
| 116 | A13 | 20c dull ultra | .45 | .40 |
| 117 | A13 | 50c vermilion | 1.25 | 1.10 |
| 118 | A13 | 1p orange | 1.25 | 1.10 |
| | | Nos. 111-118 (8) | 4.75 | 4.00 |

"PERMITASE" handstamped on stamps of
1896-1903 was applied as a control mark by
the isolated Pacific Coast post office of
Amapala to prevent use of stolen stamps.

## 1907, Jan. 1    Perf. 14
| | | | | |
|---|---|---|---|---|
| 119 | A14 | 1c dark green | .20 | .20 |
| 120 | A14 | 2c scarlet | .25 | .25 |
| 120A | A14 | 2c carmine | 9.00 | 5.50 |
| 121 | A14 | 5c blue | .30 | .30 |
| 122 | A14 | 6c purple | .35 | .30 |
| a. | | 6c dark violet | .80 | .60 |
| 123 | A14 | 10c gray brown | .40 | .35 |
| 124 | A14 | 20c ultra | .90 | .85 |
| a. | | 20c blue violet | 110.00 | 110.00 |

| | | | | |
|---|---|---|---|---|
| 125 | A14 | 50c deep lake | 1.10 | 1.10 |
| 126 | A14 | 1p orange | 1.50 | 1.50 |
| a. | | 1p orange yellow | — | |
| | | Nos. 119-126 (9) | 14.00 | 10.35 |

All values of the above set exist imperforate,
imperforate horizontally and in horizontal
pairs, imperforate between. No. 124a imperf is
worth only 10% of the listed perforated variety.
For surcharges see Nos. 128-130.

## 1909    Typo.    Perf. 11½
| | | | | |
|---|---|---|---|---|
| 127 | A14 | 1c green | 1.25 | 1.00 |
| a. | | Imperf., pair | 4.00 | 3.50 |
| b. | | Printed on both sides | 7.50 | 10.00 |

The 1909 issue is roughly typographed in
imitation of the 1907 design. It exists pin perf.
8, 13, etc.

No. 124 Handstamp Surcharged in
Black, Green or Red:

## 1910, Nov.    Perf. 14
| | | | | |
|---|---|---|---|---|
| 128 | A14 | 1c on 20c ultra | 7.50 | 6.00 |
| 129 | A14 | 5c on 20c ultra (G) | 7.50 | 6.00 |
| 130 | A14 | 10c on 20c ultra (R) | 7.50 | 6.00 |
| | | Nos. 128-130 (3) | 22.50 | 18.00 |

As is usual with handstamped surcharges
inverts and double exist.

Honduran
Scene — A15

## 1911, Jan.    Litho.    Perf. 14, 12 (1p)
| | | | | |
|---|---|---|---|---|
| 131 | A15 | 1c violet | .35 | .20 |
| 132 | A15 | 2c green | .35 | .20 |
| a. | | Perf. 12 | 5.00 | 1.25 |
| 133 | A15 | 5c carmine | .40 | .20 |
| a. | | Perf. 12 | 8.00 | 3.50 |
| 134 | A15 | 6c ultramarine | .50 | .30 |
| 135 | A15 | 10c blue | .60 | .40 |
| 136 | A15 | 20c yellow | .60 | .50 |
| 137 | A15 | 50c brown | 2.00 | 1.75 |
| 138 | A15 | 1p olive green | 2.50 | 2.00 |
| | | Nos. 131-138 (8) | 7.30 | 5.55 |

For overprints and surcharges see Nos.
139, 141-147, O28-O47.

No. 132a
Overprinted in Red

## 1911, Sept. 19    Perf. 12
| | | | | |
|---|---|---|---|---|
| 139 | A15 | 2c green | 20.00 | 18.00 |
| a. | | Inverted overprint | 24.00 | 22.50 |

90th anniversary of Independence.
Counterfeit overprints on perf. 14 stamps
exist.

President Manuel
Bonilla — A16

## 1912, Feb. 1    Typo.    Perf. 11½
| | | | | |
|---|---|---|---|---|
| 140 | A16 | 1c orange red | 12.00 | 12.00 |

Election of Pres. Manuel Bonilla.

Stamps of 1911 Surcharged in Black,
Red or Blue:

a          b

## 1913    Litho.    Perf. 14
| | | | | |
|---|---|---|---|---|
| 141 | A15(a) | 2c on 1c violet | 1.25 | .75 |
| a. | | Double surcharge | | 3.25 |
| b. | | Inverted surcharge | 4.50 | |
| c. | | Double surch., one invtd. | 6.75 | |
| d. | | Red surcharge | 40.00 | 40.00 |
| 142 | A15(b) | 2c on 1c violet | 7.00 | 5.75 |
| a. | | Inverted surcharge | 14.00 | |
| 143 | A15(b) | 2c on 10c blue | 2.75 | 2.25 |
| a. | | Double surcharge | 5.75 | 5.75 |
| b. | | Inverted surcharge | | |
| 144 | A15(b) | 2c on 20c yellow | 7.00 | 6.75 |
| 145 | A15(b) | 5c on 1c violet | 2.50 | .75 |
| 146 | A15(b) | 5c on 10c bl (Bl) | 2.75 | 1.50 |
| 147 | A15(b) | 6c on 1c violet | 2.75 | 2.25 |
| | | Nos. 141-147 (7) | 26.00 | 20.00 |

Counterfeit surcharges exist.

Terencio
Sierra — A17

Bonilla — A18

ONE CENTAVO:
Type I — Solid border at sides below
numerals.
Type II — Border of light and dark stripes.

## 1913-14    Typo.    Perf. 11½
| | | | | |
|---|---|---|---|---|
| 151 | A17 | 1c dark brn, I | .20 | .20 |
| a. | | 1c brown, type II | .75 | .45 |
| 152 | A17 | 2c carmine | .25 | .20 |
| 153 | A18 | 5c blue | .40 | .20 |
| 154 | A18 | 5c ultra ('14) | .40 | .20 |
| 155 | A18 | 6c gray vio | .50 | .25 |
| 156 | A18 | 6c purple ('14) | .40 | .25 |
| a. | | 6c red lilac | .60 | .35 |
| 157 | A17 | 10c blue | .75 | .75 |
| 158 | A17 | 10c brown ('14) | 1.25 | .50 |
| 159 | A17 | 20c brown | 1.00 | .75 |
| 160 | A18 | 50c rose | 2.00 | 2.00 |
| 161 | A18 | 1p gray green | 2.25 | 2.25 |
| | | Nos. 151-161 (11) | 9.40 | 7.55 |

For overprints and surcharges see Nos.
162-173, O48-O57.

Surcharged in Black
or Carmine

## 1914
| | | | | |
|---|---|---|---|---|
| 162 | A17 | 1c on 2c carmine | .75 | .75 |
| 163 | A17 | 5c on 2c carmine | 1.25 | .90 |
| 164 | A18 | 5c on 6c gray vio | 2.00 | 2.00 |
| 165 | A17 | 10c on 2c carmine | 2.00 | 2.00 |
| 166 | A18 | 10c on 6c gray vio | 2.00 | 2.00 |
| a. | | Double surcharge | 10.00 | |
| 167 | A18 | 10c on 6c gray vio (C) | 2.00 | 2.00 |
| 168 | A18 | 10c on 50c rose | 6.50 | 5.00 |
| | | Nos. 162-168 (7) | 16.50 | 14.65 |

## No. 158 Surcharged with New Value
### 1915
173 A17 5c on 10c brown    2.50 1.75

Ulua Bridge — A19    Bonilla Theater — A20

### 1915-16      Typo.
| | | | | |
|---|---|---|---|---|
| 174 | A19 | 1c chocolate | .20 | .20 |
| 175 | A19 | 2c carmine | .20 | .20 |
| a. | | Tête bêche pair | 1.00 | 1.00 |
| 176 | A20 | 5c bright blue | .25 | .20 |
| 177 | A20 | 6c deep purple | .35 | .20 |
| 178 | A19 | 10c dull blue | .75 | .20 |
| 179 | A19 | 20c red brown | 1.25 | 1.00 |
| a. | | Tête bêche pair | 4.00 | 4.00 |
| 180 | A20 | 50c red | 1.50 | 1.50 |
| 181 | A20 | 1p yellow grn | 2.50 | 2.50 |
| | | Nos. 174-181 (8) | 7.00 | 6.00 |

For overprints & surcharges see #183, 231-232, 237, 239-240, 285, 292, C1-C13, C25, C28, C31, C36, C57, CO21, CO30-CO32, CO42, O58-O65.

### Imperf., Pairs
| | | | | |
|---|---|---|---|---|
| 174a | A19 | 1c | 2.00 | 2.00 |
| 175b | A19 | 2c | 2.00 | 2.00 |
| 176a | A20 | 5c | 3.50 | |
| 178a | A19 | 10c | 3.50 | |
| 179b | A19 | 20c | 5.25 | |
| 180b | A20 | 50c | 7.00 | |
| 181a | A20 | 1p | 8.75 | 8.75 |

Francisco Bertrand A21    Statue to Francisco Morazán A22

### 1916, Feb. 1
182 A21 1c orange    2.00 2.00

Election of Pres. Francisco Bertrand.
Unauthorized reprints exist.

## Official Stamp No. O60 Overprinted

### 1918
| | | | | |
|---|---|---|---|---|
| 183 | A20 | 5c bright blue | 2.00 | 1.50 |
| a. | | Inverted overprint | 5.00 | 5.00 |

### 1919      Typo.
| | | | | |
|---|---|---|---|---|
| 184 | A22 | 1c brown | .20 | .20 |
| a. | | Printed on both sides | 2.00 | |
| b. | | Imperf., pair | .70 | |
| 185 | A22 | 2c carmine | .25 | .20 |
| 186 | A22 | 5c lilac rose | .25 | .20 |
| 187 | A22 | 6c brt violet | .25 | .20 |
| 188 | A22 | 10c dull blue | .25 | .25 |
| 189 | A22 | 15c light blue | .75 | .20 |
| 190 | A22 | 15c dark violet | .60 | .20 |
| 191 | A22 | 20c orange brn | 1.00 | .30 |
| a. | | 20c gray brown | 10.00 | .30 |
| b. | | Imperf., pair | 2.75 | |
| 192 | A22 | 50c light brown | 4.00 | 2.50 |
| a. | | Imperf. pair | 15.00 | |
| 193 | A22 | 1p yellow green | 7.50 | 20.00 |
| a. | | Imperf., pair | 20.00 | |
| b. | | Printed on both sides | 9.00 | |
| c. | | Tête bêche pair | 15.00 | |
| | | Nos. 184-193 (10) | 15.05 | 24.25 |

See note on handstamp following No. 217.
Unauthorized reprints exist.
For overprints and surcharges see Nos. 201-210C, 230, 233, 235-236, 238, 241-243, 287, 289, C58, C61, CO23, CO25, CO33, CO36-CO38, CO39, CO40, O66-O74.

"Dawn of Peace" — A23

---

### 1920, Feb. 1
#### Size: 27x21mm
| | | | | |
|---|---|---|---|---|
| 194 | A23 | 2c rose | 2.50 | 2.50 |
| a. | | Tête bêche pair | 15.00 | 12.50 |
| b. | | Imperf., pair | 15.00 | 12.50 |

#### Size: 51x40mm
| | | | | |
|---|---|---|---|---|
| 195 | A23 | 2c gold | 10.00 | 10.00 |
| 196 | A23 | 2c silver | 10.00 | 10.00 |
| 197 | A23 | 2c bronze | 10.00 | 10.00 |
| 198 | A23 | 2c red | 12.00 | 12.00 |
| | | Nos. 194-198 (5) | 44.50 | 44.50 |

Assumption of power by Gen. Rafael Lopez Gutierrez.
Nos. 195-198 exist imperf.
Unauthorized reprints of #195-198 exist.

#### Type of 1919, Dated "1920"
### 1921
| | | | | |
|---|---|---|---|---|
| 201 | A22 | 6c dark violet | 10.00 | 5.00 |
| a. | | Tête bêche pair | 15.00 | |
| b. | | Imperf., pair | 15.00 | |

Unauthorized reprints exist.

## No. 185 Surcharged in Antique Letters

### 1922
| | | | | |
|---|---|---|---|---|
| 202 | A22 | 6c on 2c carmine | .40 | .40 |
| a. | | "ALE" for "VALE" | 2.00 | 2.00 |
| b. | | Comma after "CTS" | 2.00 | 2.00 |
| c. | | Without period after "CTS" | 2.00 | 2.00 |
| d. | | "CT" for "CTS" | 2.00 | 2.00 |
| e. | | Double surcharge | 4.25 | |
| f. | | Inverted surcharge | 4.25 | |

## Stamps of 1919 Surcharged in Roman Figures and Antique Letters in Green

### 1923
| | | | | |
|---|---|---|---|---|
| 203 | A22 | 10c on 1c brown | 1.50 | 1.50 |
| 204 | A22 | 50c on 2c carmine | 2.00 | 2.00 |
| a. | | Inverted surcharge | 10.00 | 10.00 |
| b. | | "HABILTADO" | 6.00 | 6.00 |

## Surcharged in Black or Violet Blue

| | | | | |
|---|---|---|---|---|
| 205 | A22 | 1p on 5c lil rose (Bk) | 3.50 | 3.50 |
| a. | | "PSEO" | 20.00 | 20.00 |
| b. | | Inverted surcharge | 20.00 | 20.00 |
| 206 | A22 | 1p on 5c lil rose (VB) | 20.00 | 20.00 |
| a. | | "PSEO" | 70.00 | |

On Nos. 205-206, "Habilitado Vale" is in Antique letters, "Un Peso" in Roman.

## No. 185 Surcharged in Roman Letters in Green

207 A22 6c on 2c carmine    3.50 2.75

## Nos. 184-185 Surcharged in Roman Letters in Green

| | | | | |
|---|---|---|---|---|
| 208 | A22 | 10c on 1c brown | 1.75 | 1.25 |
| a. | | "DIES" | 6.00 | |
| b. | | "DEIZ" | 6.00 | |
| c. | | "DEIZ CAS" | 6.00 | |
| d. | | "TTS" for "CTS" | 6.00 | |
| e. | | "HABILTADO" | 6.00 | |
| f. | | "HABILTAD" | 6.00 | |
| g. | | "HABILITA" | 6.00 | |
| h. | | Inverted surcharge | 30.00 | |

---

| | | | | |
|---|---|---|---|---|
| 209 | A22 | 50c on 2c carmine | 3.75 | 2.75 |
| a. | | "CAT" for "CTA" | 10.00 | |
| b. | | "TCA" for "CTA" | 10.00 | |
| c. | | "TTS" for "CTS" | 10.00 | |
| d. | | "CAS" for "CTS" | 10.00 | |
| e. | | "HABILTADO" | 10.00 | |

Surcharge on No. 209 is found in two spacings between value and HABILITADO: 5mm (illustrated) and 1½mm.

## No. 186 Surcharged in Antique Letters in Black

$ 1.00
HABILITADO
VALE
UN PESO

| | | | | |
|---|---|---|---|---|
| 210 | A22 | 1p on 5c lil rose | 25.00 | 25.00 |
| a. | | "PFSO" | 75.00 | |

In the surcharges on Nos. 202 to 210 there are various wrong font, inverted and omitted letters.

## No. 184 Surcharged in Large Antique Letters in Green

$ 0.10
HABILITADO
VALE
DIEZ CTS

| | | | | |
|---|---|---|---|---|
| 210C | A22 | 10c on 1c brown | 15.00 | 15.00 |
| d. | | "DIFZ" | 55.00 | 55.00 |

Dionisio de Herrera A24    Pres. Miguel Paz Baraona A25

### 1924, June    Litho.    Perf. 11, 11½
| | | | | |
|---|---|---|---|---|
| 211 | A24 | 1c olive green | .30 | .20 |
| 212 | A24 | 2c deep rose | .35 | .20 |
| 213 | A24 | 6c red violet | .40 | .20 |
| 214 | A24 | 10c blue | .40 | .20 |
| 215 | A24 | 20c yellow brn | .80 | .35 |
| 216 | A24 | 50c vermilion | 1.75 | 1.10 |
| 217 | A24 | 1p emerald | 4.00 | 2.75 |
| | | Nos. 211-217 (7) | 8.00 | 5.00 |

In 1924 a facsimile of the signatures of Santiago Herrera and Francisco Caceres, covering four stamps, was handstamped in violet to prevent the use of stamps that had been stolen during a revolution.
Imperfs exist.
For overprints and surcharges see Nos. 280-281, 290-291, C14-C24, C26-C27, C29-C30, C32-C35, C56, C60, C73-C76, CO1-CO5, CO22, CO24, CO28-CO29, CO34-CO35, CO38A, CO39A, CO41, CO43, O75-O81.

### 1925, Feb. 1    Typo.    Perf. 11½
| | | | | |
|---|---|---|---|---|
| 218 | A25 | 1c dull blue | 2.00 | 2.00 |
| a. | | 1c dark blue | 2.00 | 2.00 |
| 219 | A25 | 1c car rose | 5.00 | 5.00 |
| a. | | 1c brown carmine | 5.00 | 5.00 |
| 220 | A25 | 1c olive brn | 14.00 | 14.00 |
| a. | | 1c orange brown | 14.00 | 14.00 |
| b. | | 1c dark brown | 14.00 | 14.00 |
| c. | | 1c black brown | 14.00 | 14.00 |
| 221 | A25 | 1c buff | 12.00 | 12.00 |
| 222 | A25 | 1c red | 60.00 | 60.00 |
| 223 | A25 | 1c green | 40.00 | 40.00 |
| | | Nos. 218-223 (6) | 133.00 | 133.00 |

#### Imperf
| | | | | |
|---|---|---|---|---|
| 225 | A25 | 1c dull blue | 5.50 | 5.50 |
| a. | | 1c dark blue | 5.50 | 5.50 |
| 226 | A25 | 1c car rose | 8.75 | 8.75 |
| a. | | 1c brown carmine | 8.75 | 8.75 |
| 227 | A25 | 1c olive brn | 8.75 | 8.75 |
| a. | | 1c orange brown | 8.75 | 8.75 |
| b. | | 1c deep brown | 8.75 | 8.75 |
| c. | | 1c black brown | 8.75 | 8.75 |
| 228 | A25 | 1c buff | 8.75 | 8.75 |
| 229 | A25 | 1c red | 60.00 | 60.00 |
| 229A | A25 | 1c green | 27.50 | 27.50 |
| | | Nos. 225-229A (6) | 119.25 | 119.25 |

Inauguration of President Baraona.
Counterfeits and unauthorized reprints exist.

---

## No. 187 Overprinted in Black and Red

### 1926, June      Perf. 11½
230 A22 6c bright violet    1.50 1.25

Many varieties of this two-part overprint exist: one or both inverted or double, and various combinations. Value, each $10.

## Nos. 177 and 187 Overprinted in Black or Red

### 1926
| | | | | |
|---|---|---|---|---|
| 231 | A20 | 6c deep pur (Bk) | 2.00 | 2.00 |
| a. | | Inverted overprint | 5.50 | 5.50 |
| b. | | Double overprint | 5.50 | 5.50 |
| 232 | A20 | 6c deep pur (R) | 2.50 | 2.50 |
| a. | | Double overprint | 5.00 | 5.00 |
| 233 | A22 | 6c lilac (Bk) | .60 | .60 |
| a. | | 6c violet | .75 | .75 |
| b. | | Inverted overprint | 5.00 | 5.00 |
| c. | | Double overprint | 5.00 | 5.00 |
| d. | | Double ovpt., one inverted | 5.00 | 5.00 |
| e. | | "192" | 7.50 | 7.50 |
| f. | | Double ovpt., both inverted | 7.50 | 7.50 |

#### Same Overprint on No. 230
| | | | | |
|---|---|---|---|---|
| 235 | A22 | 6c violet | 20.00 | 20.00 |
| a. | | "1926" inverted | 20.00 | 20.00 |
| b. | | "Habilitado" triple, one invtd. | 20.00 | 20.00 |

## No. 188 Surcharged in Red or Black

| | | | | |
|---|---|---|---|---|
| 236 | A22 | 6c on 10c blue (R) | .50 | .20 |
| c. | | Double surcharge | 5.00 | 4.00 |
| d. | | Without bar | | |
| e. | | Inverted surcharge | 4.00 | 3.50 |
| f. | | "Vale" omitted | | |
| g. | | "6cts" omitted | | |
| h. | | "cts" omitted | | |
| k. | | Black surcharge | 55.00 | 55.00 |

## Nos. 175 and 185 Overprinted in Green

| | | | | |
|---|---|---|---|---|
| 237 | A19 | 2c carmine | .20 | .20 |
| a. | | Tête bêche pair | 4.00 | 4.00 |
| b. | | Double overprint | 2.00 | 1.40 |
| c. | | "HABILITADO" | 2.00 | 1.40 |
| d. | | "1926" only | 2.75 | 2.75 |
| e. | | Double overprint, one inverted | 2.75 | 2.75 |
| f. | | "1926" omitted | 3.50 | 3.50 |
| g. | | Triple overprint, two inverted | 5.25 | 5.25 |
| h. | | Double on face, one on back | 5.25 | 5.25 |
| 238 | A22 | 2c carmine | .20 | .20 |
| a. | | "HARILITADO" | .90 | .90 |
| b. | | Double overprint | 1.40 | 1.40 |
| c. | | Inverted overprint | 2.00 | 2.00 |

## No. 177 Overprinted in Red 1926

Large Numerals, 12x5mm
### 1927
| | | | | |
|---|---|---|---|---|
| 239 | A20 | 6c deep purple | 25.00 | 25.00 |
| a. | | "1926" over "1927" | 35.00 | 35.00 |
| b. | | Invtd. ovpt. on face of stamp, normal ovpt. on back | 30.00 | |

## No. 179 Surcharged

### 1927
| | | | | |
|---|---|---|---|---|
| 240 | A19 | 6c on 20c brown | .75 | .75 |
| a. | | Tête bêche pair | 2.75 | 2.75 |
| c. | | Inverted surcharge | 2.50 | 2.50 |
| d. | | Double surcharge | 8.50 | 8.50 |

Nos. 8 and 10 in the setting have no period after "cts" and No. 50 has the "t" of "cts" inverted.

## Same Surcharge on Nos. 189-191

| | | | |
|---|---|---|---|
| **241** A22 | 6c on 15c blue | 27.50 | 27.50 |
| *a.* | "c" of "cts" omitted | | |
| **242** A22 | 6c on 15c vio | .70 | .70 |
| *a.* | Double surcharge | 1.75 | 1.75 |
| *b.* | Double surch., one invtd. | 2.00 | 2.00 |
| *c.* | "L" of "Vale" omitted | | |
| **243** A22 | 6c on 20c yel brn | .60 | .60 |
| *a.* | 6c on 20c deep brown | | |
| *b.* | "6" omitted | 1.75 | 1.75 |
| *c.* | "Vale" and "cts" omitted | 3.50 | 3.50 |
| | Nos. 240-243 (4) | 29.55 | 29.55 |

On Nos. 242 and 243 stamps Nos. 12, 16 and 43 in the setting have no period after "cts" and No. 34 often lacks the "s." On No. 243 the "c" of "cts" is missing on stamp No. 38. On No. 241 occur the varieties "ct" or "ts" for "cts." and no period.

Southern Highway — A26

Ruins of Copán — A27

Pine Tree — A28

Presidential Palace — A29

Ponciano Leiva — A30

Pres. M.A. Soto — A31

Lempira — A32

Map of Honduras — A33

President Juan Lindo — A34

Statue of Columbus — A35

### 1927-29 Typo. Wmk. 209

| | | | |
|---|---|---|---|
| **244** A26 | 1c ultramarine | .30 | .20 |
| *a.* | 1c blue | .30 | .20 |
| **245** A27 | 2c carmine | .30 | .20 |
| **246** A28 | 5c dull violet | .30 | .20 |
| **247** A28 | 5c bl gray ('29) | 25.00 | 7.00 |
| **248** A29 | 6c blue black | .75 | .50 |
| *a.* | 6c gray black | .75 | .50 |
| **249** A29 | 6c dark bl ('29) | .40 | .20 |
| *a.* | 6c light blue | .40 | .20 |
| **250** A30 | 10c blue | .70 | .20 |
| **251** A31 | 15c deep blue | 1.00 | .50 |
| **252** A32 | 20c dark blue | 1.25 | .60 |
| **253** A33 | 30c dark brown | 1.50 | 1.00 |
| **254** A34 | 50c light blue | 2.50 | 1.50 |
| **255** A35 | 1p red | 5.00 | 2.50 |
| | Nos. 244-255 (12) | 39.00 | 14.60 |

In 1929 a quantity of imperforate sheets of No. 249 were stolen from the Litografia Nacional. Some of them were perforated by sewing machine and a few copies were passed through the post. To prevent the use of stolen stamps of the 1927-29 issues they were declared invalid and the stock on hand was overprinted "1929 a 1930."

For overprints and surcharges see Nos. 259-278, CO19-CO20B.

Pres. Vicente Mejia Colindres and Vice-Pres. Rafael Diaz Chávez — A36

President Mejia Colindres — A37

### 1929, Feb. 25

| | | | |
|---|---|---|---|
| **256** A36 | 1c dk carmine | 3.00 | 3.00 |
| **257** A37 | 2c emerald | 3.00 | 3.00 |

Installation of Pres. Vicente Mejia Colindres. Printed in sheets of ten.

Nos. 256 and 257 were surreptitiously printed in transposed colors. They were not regularly issued.

Stamps of 1927-29 Overprinted in Various Colors

### 1929, Oct.

| | | | |
|---|---|---|---|
| **259** A26 | 1c blue (R) | .20 | .20 |
| *a.* | 1c ultramarine (R) | .50 | .20 |
| *b.* | Double overprint | 2.50 | 1.75 |
| *c.* | As "a," double overprint | 2.50 | 1.75 |
| **260** A26 | 1c blue (Bk) | 6.50 | 6.50 |
| *a.* | 1c ultramarine (Bk) | | |
| **261** A27 | 2c car (R Br) | 3.50 | 3.50 |
| *a.* | Double overprint | | |
| **262** A27 | 2c car (Bl Gr) | 1.00 | 1.00 |
| *a.* | Double overprint | | |
| **263** A27 | 2c car (Bk) | 1.00 | .50 |
| **264** A27 | 2c car (V) | .50 | .25 |
| *a.* | Double overprint | | |
| *b.* | Double ovpt., one inverted | | |
| **265** A27 | 2c org red (V) | 1.50 | |
| **266** A28 | 5c dl vio (R) | .40 | .30 |
| *a.* | Double overprint (R+V) | | |
| **267** A28 | 5c bl gray (R) | 1.00 | .75 |
| *a.* | Double overprint (R+Bk) | | |
| **269** A29 | 6c gray blk (R) | 2.50 | 2.00 |
| *a.* | Double overprint | 6.00 | 6.00 |
| **272** A29 | 6c dk blue (R) | .40 | .20 |
| *a.* | 6c light blue (R) | .40 | .20 |
| *b.* | Double overprint | 2.00 | 2.00 |
| *c.* | Double overprint (R+V) | | |
| **273** A30 | 10c blue (R) | .40 | .20 |
| *a.* | Double overprint | 2.50 | 1.75 |
| **274** A31 | 15c dp blue (R) | .50 | .25 |
| *a.* | Double overprint | 3.50 | 2.50 |
| **275** A32 | 20c dark bl (R) | .50 | .35 |
| **276** A33 | 30c dark brn (R) | .75 | .60 |
| *a.* | Double overprint | 3.50 | 2.50 |
| **277** A34 | 50c light bl (R) | 2.00 | 1.00 |
| **278** A35 | 1p red (V) | 5.00 | 2.50 |
| | Nos. 259-278 (17) | 27.65 | |

Nos. 259-278 exist in numerous shades. There are also various shades of the red and violet overprints. The overprint may be found reading upwards, downwards, inverted, double, triple, tête bêche or combinations.

Status of both 6c stamps with overprint in black is questioned.

A38

### 1929, Dec. 10

| | | | |
|---|---|---|---|
| **279** A38 | 1c on 6c lilac rose | .70 | .70 |
| *a.* | "1992" for "1929" | | |
| *b.* | "9192" for "1929" | | |
| *c.* | Surcharge reading down | 8.00 | |
| *d.* | Dbl. surch., one reading down | | |

Varieties include "1992" reading down and pairs with one surcharge reading down, double or with "1992."

No. 214 Surcharged in Red

### Perf. 11, 11½

**1930, Mar. 26 Unwmk.**

| | | | |
|---|---|---|---|
| **280** A24 | 1c on 10c blue | .35 | .30 |
| *a.* | "1093" for "1930" | 1.40 | |
| *b.* | "tsc" for "cts" | 1.40 | |
| **281** A24 | 2c on 10c blue | .35 | .30 |
| *a.* | "tsc" for "cts" | 2.00 | |
| *b.* | "Vale 2" omitted | | |

Official Stamps of 1929 Overprinted in Red or Violet

### 1930, Mar. Wmk. 209 Perf. 11½

| | | | |
|---|---|---|---|
| **282** O1 | 1c blue (R) | .50 | .50 |
| *a.* | Double overprint | 2.00 | 2.00 |
| **284** O1 | 2c carmine (V) | .90 | .90 |

Stamps of 1915-26 Overprinted in Blue

### On No. 174

**1930, July 19 Unwmk.**

| | | | |
|---|---|---|---|
| **285** A19 | 1c chocolate | .30 | .25 |
| *a.* | Double overprint | 1.00 | 1.00 |
| *b.* | Inverted overprint | 1.40 | 1.40 |
| *c.* | Dbl. ovpt., one inverted | 1.40 | 1.40 |

### On No. 184

| | | | |
|---|---|---|---|
| **287** A22 | 1c brown | 15.00 | 15.00 |
| *a.* | Double overprint | | |
| *c.* | Inverted overprint | | |

### On No. 204

| | | | |
|---|---|---|---|
| **289** A22 | 50c on 2c carmine | 100.00 | 90.00 |
| *b.* | Inverted surcharge | | |

### On Nos. 211 and 212

| | | | |
|---|---|---|---|
| **290** A24 | 1c olive green | .20 | .20 |
| *a.* | Double overprint | 1.75 | 1.75 |
| *b.* | Inverted overprint | 1.75 | 1.75 |
| *d.* | On No. O75 | 12.00 | |
| **291** A24 | 2c carmine rose | .25 | .25 |
| *a.* | Double overprint | 1.75 | 1.75 |
| *b.* | Inverted overprint | 1.75 | 1.75 |

### On No. 237

| | | | |
|---|---|---|---|
| **292** A19 | 2c car (G & Bl) | 100.00 | 100.00 |

From Title Page of Government Gazette, First Issue — A39

### 1930, Aug. 11 Typo. Wmk. 209

| | | | |
|---|---|---|---|
| **295** A39 | 2c orange | .90 | .90 |
| **296** A39 | 2c ultramarine | .90 | .90 |
| **297** A39 | 2c red | .90 | .90 |
| | Nos. 295-297 (3) | 2.70 | 2.70 |

Publication of the 1st newspaper in Honduras, cent. The stamps were on sale and available for postage on Aug. 11th, 1930, only. Not more than 5 copies of each color could be purchased by an applicant.

Nos. 295-297 exist imperf. and part-perforate. Unauthorized reprints exist.

For surcharges see Nos. CO15-CO18A.

Paz Baraona — A40

Manuel Bonilla — A41

Lake Yojoa — A42

View of Palace at Tegucigalpa A43

City of Amapala A44

Mayan Stele at Copán A45

Christopher Columbus A46

Discovery of America A47

Loarque Bridge A48

### Unwmk.

**1931, Jan. 2 Engr. Perf. 12**

| | | | |
|---|---|---|---|
| **298** A40 | 1c black brown | .75 | .20 |
| **299** A41 | 2c carmine rose | .75 | .20 |
| **300** A42 | 5c dull violet | 1.00 | .20 |
| **301** A43 | 6c deep green | 1.00 | .20 |
| **302** A44 | 10c brown | 1.50 | .25 |
| **303** A45 | 15c dark blue | 2.00 | .30 |
| **304** A46 | 20c black | 3.50 | .40 |
| **305** A47 | 50c olive green | 4.50 | 1.50 |
| **306** A48 | 1p slate black | 9.00 | 2.50 |
| | Nos. 298-306 (9) | 24.00 | 5.75 |

Regular Issue of 1931 Overprinted in Black or Various Colors

## 1931

| | | | | |
|---|---|---|---|---|
| **307** | A40 | 1c black brown | .40 | .30 |
| **308** | A41 | 2c carmine rose | .60 | .30 |
| **309** | A45 | 15c dark blue | 1.00 | .30 |
| **310** | A46 | 20c black | 2.50 | .40 |

Overprinted

| | | | | |
|---|---|---|---|---|
| **311** | A42 | 5c dull violet | .50 | .30 |
| **312** | A43 | 6c deep green | .50 | .30 |
| **315** | A44 | 10c brown | 1.50 | .35 |
| **316** | A47 | 50c olive green | 8.00 | 5.00 |
| **317** | A48 | 1p slate black | 10.00 | 7.50 |
| | | Nos. 307-317 (9) | 25.00 | 14.75 |
| | | Nos. 307-317,C51-C55 (14) | 50.00 | 35.75 |

The overprint is a control mark. It stands for "Tribunal Superior de Cuentas" (Superior Tribunal of Accounts).

Overprint varieties include: inverted; double; double, one or both inverted; on back; pair, one without overprint; differing colors (6c exists with overprint in orange, yellow and red).

President Carías and Vice-President Williams — A49

## 1933, Apr. 29

| | | | | |
|---|---|---|---|---|
| **318** | A49 | 2c carmine rose | .50 | .35 |
| **319** | A49 | 6c deep green | .75 | .40 |
| **320** | A49 | 10c deep blue | 1.00 | .50 |
| **321** | A49 | 15c red orange | 1.25 | .75 |
| | | Nos. 318-321 (4) | 3.50 | 2.00 |

Inauguration of Pres. Tiburico Carias Andino and Vice-Pres. Abraham Williams, Feb. 1, 1933.

Columbus' Fleet and Flag of the Race — A50

**Wmk. 209**

### 1933, Aug. 3    Typo.    Perf. 11½

| | | | | |
|---|---|---|---|---|
| **322** | A50 | 2c ultramarine | 1.00 | .65 |
| **323** | A50 | 6c yellow | 1.00 | .65 |
| **324** | A50 | 10c lemon | 1.40 | .85 |

**Perf. 12**

| | | | | |
|---|---|---|---|---|
| **325** | A50 | 15c violet | 2.00 | 1.50 |
| **326** | A50 | 50c red | 4.00 | 3.50 |
| **327** | A50 | 1 l emerald | 7.00 | 7.00 |
| | | Nos. 322-327 (6) | 16.40 | 14.15 |

"Day of the Race," an annual holiday throughout Spanish-American countries. Also for the 441st anniv. of the sailing of Columbus to the New World, Aug. 3, 1492.

Masonic Temple, Tegucigalpa — A51

Designs: 2c, President Carias. 5c, Flag. 6c, Tomás Estrada Palma.

**Unwmk.**

### 1935, Jan. 12    Engr.    Perf. 12

| | | | | |
|---|---|---|---|---|
| **328** | A51 | 1c green | .40 | .20 |
| **329** | A51 | 2c carmine | .40 | .20 |
| **330** | A51 | 5c dark blue | .40 | .25 |
| **331** | A51 | 6c black brown | .40 | .25 |
| **a.** | | Vert. pair, imperf. btwn. | 20.00 | 20.00 |
| | | Nos. 328-331 (4) | 1.60 | .90 |
| | | Nos. 328-331,C77-C83 (11) | 15.15 | 6.25 |

Gen. Carías Bridge — A55

### 1937, June 4

| | | | | |
|---|---|---|---|---|
| **332** | A55 | 6c car & ol green | .90 | .40 |
| **333** | A55 | 21c grn & violet | 1.50 | .65 |
| **334** | A55 | 46c orange & brn | 2.10 | 1.50 |
| **335** | A55 | 55c ultra & black | 3.00 | 2.40 |
| | | Nos. 332-335 (4) | 7.50 | 4.95 |

Prolongation of the Presidential term to Jan. 19, 1943.

Seal of Honduras A56

Central District Palace — A57

Designs: 3c, Map of Honduras. 5c, Bridge of Choluteca. 8c, Flag.

### 1939, Mar. 1    Perf. 12½

| | | | | |
|---|---|---|---|---|
| **336** | A56 | 1c orange yellow | .20 | .20 |
| **337** | A57 | 2c red orange | .20 | .20 |
| **338** | A57 | 3c carmine | .30 | .20 |
| **339** | A57 | 5c orange | .30 | .20 |
| **340** | A56 | 8c dark blue | .50 | .20 |
| | | Nos. 336-340 (5) | 1.50 | 1.00 |
| | | Nos. 336-340,C89-C98 (15) | 15.30 | 8.45 |

Nos. 336-340 exist imperf.
For overprints see #342-343.

Nos. 336 and 337 Overprinted in Green

### 1944    Perf. 12½

| | | | | |
|---|---|---|---|---|
| **342** | A56 | 1c orange yellow | .30 | .30 |
| **a.** | | Inverted overprint | 5.00 | 5.00 |
| **343** | A57 | 2c red orange | 1.25 | .75 |
| **a.** | | Inverted overprint | 5.00 | 5.00 |

**Catalogue values for unused stamps in this section, from this point to the end of the section, are for Never Hinged items.**

International Peace Movement — A58

### 1984, Feb. 15    Litho.    Perf. 12

| | | | | |
|---|---|---|---|---|
| **344** | A58 | 78c multi | .85 | .65 |
| **345** | A58 | 85c multi | .95 | .30 |
| **346** | A58 | 95c multi | 1.00 | .35 |
| **347** | A58 | 1.50 l multi | 1.75 | .55 |
| **348** | A58 | 2 l multi | 2.10 | .70 |
| **349** | A58 | 5 l multi | 5.50 | 1.75 |
| | | Nos. 344-349 (6) | 12.15 | 4.30 |

Central American Aeronautics Corp., 25th Anniv. — A59

Designs: 2c, Edward Warner Award issued by the Intl. Civil Aviation Organization, vert. 5c, Corp. emblem, flags of Guatemala, Honduras, El Salvador, Costa Rica and Panama. 60c, Transmission tower, plane. 75c, Corp. emblem, vert. 1 l, 1.50 l, Emblem, flags, diff.

### 1987, Feb. 26    Litho.    Perf. 12

| | | | | |
|---|---|---|---|---|
| **350** | A59 | 2c multi | .20 | .20 |
| **351** | A59 | 5c multi | .20 | .20 |
| **352** | A59 | 60c multi | .75 | .35 |
| **353** | A59 | 75c multi | .95 | .40 |
| **354** | A59 | 1 l multi | 1.25 | .55 |
| | | Nos. 350-354 (5) | 3.35 | 1.70 |

**Souvenir Sheet**

| | | | | |
|---|---|---|---|---|
| **355** | A59 | 1.50 l multi | 3.00 | 3.00 |

Housing Institute (INVA), 30th Anniv. A60

### 1987, Oct. 9    Litho.    Perf. 13½

| | | | | |
|---|---|---|---|---|
| **356** | A60 | 5c shown | .30 | .20 |
| **357** | A60 | 95c Map, emblem, text | 1.00 | .40 |

EXFILHON '88 — A61

### 1988, Sept. 11    Litho.    Imperf.

| | | | | |
|---|---|---|---|---|
| **358** | A61 | 3 l dull red brn & brt ultra | 4.50 | 4.50 |

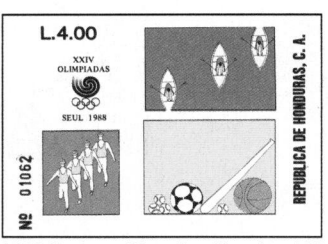

1988 Summer Olympics, Seoul — A62

### 1988, Sept. 30    Litho.    Imperf.

| | | | | |
|---|---|---|---|---|
| **359** | A62 | 4 l multi | 4.75 | 4.75 |
| | | Nos. 359,C772-C773 (3) | 7.05 | 5.65 |

Luis Bogran Technical Institute, Cent. A63

85c, Cogwheel, map, flag of Honduras.

### 1990, Sept. 28    Litho.    Perf. 10½

| | | | | |
|---|---|---|---|---|
| **360** | A63 | 20c multicolored | | .20 |
| **361** | A63 | 85c multicolored | | .55 |

**Size: 114x82mm**

**Imperf**

| | | | | |
|---|---|---|---|---|
| **362** | A63 | 2 l like #360 | | 2.00 |
| | | Nos. 360-362 (3) | | 2.75 |

Nos. 360-361 are airmail.

America Issue A64

UPAE emblem, land and seascapes showing produce and fish.

### 1990, Oct. 31    Litho.    Perf. 13½

| | | | | |
|---|---|---|---|---|
| **363** | A64 | 20c multi, vert. | .30 | .20 |
| **364** | A64 | 1 l multicolored | .80 | .30 |

A65

A66

### 1992, Feb. 17

| | | | | |
|---|---|---|---|---|
| **365** | A65 | 50c shown | .40 | |
| **366** | A65 | 3 l Cross-country skiing | 2.00 | |

1992 Winter Olympics, Albertville.

### 1992, May 21    Litho.    Perf. 13½

Mother's Day (Paintings): 20c, Saleswoman, by Manuel Rodriguez. 50c, The Grandmother and Baby, by Rodriguez. 5 l, Saleswomen, by Maury Flores.

| | | | | |
|---|---|---|---|---|
| **367** | A66 | 20c shown | .25 | |
| **368** | A66 | 50c multicolored | .40 | |
| **369** | A66 | 5 l multicolored | 3.25 | |
| | | Nos. 367-369 (3) | 3.90 | |

Butterflies A67

Designs: 25c, Melitaeinae chlosyne janais. 85c, Heliconiinae agrilus vanillae. 3 l, Morphinae morpho granadensis. 5 l, Heliconiinae dryadula phalusa.

### 1992, June 22

| | | | | |
|---|---|---|---|---|
| **370** | A67 | 25c multicolored | .50 | |
| **371** | A67 | 85c multicolored | 1.25 | |
| **372** | A67 | 3 l multicolored | 4.25 | |

**Size: 108x76mm**

**Imperf**

| | | | | |
|---|---|---|---|---|
| **373** | A67 | 5 l multicolored | 6.00 | |
| | | Nos. 370-373 (4) | 12.00 | |

1992 Summer Olympics, Barcelona — A68

### 1992, Mar. 16    Litho.    Perf. 13½

| | | | | |
|---|---|---|---|---|
| **374** | A68 | 20c Running | .20 | |
| **375** | A68 | 50c Tennis | .30 | |
| **376** | A68 | 85c Soccer | .50 | |
| | | Nos. 374-376 (3) | 1.00 | |

Japanese Overseas Cooperation Volunteers in Honduras, 20th Anniv. — A69

Designs: 1.40 l, Volunteers working on Japanese letter, vert. 4.30 l, Folding screen showing Mayan Gods. 5.40 l, Men, women of Honduras in traditional costumes, volunteer.

**1995, Sept. 20    Litho.    Perf. 13½**
| | | | |
|---|---|---|---|
| 377 | A69 1.40 l multicolored | .50 | .40 |
| 378 | A69 4.30 l multicolored | 1.50 | 1.25 |
| 379 | A69 5.40 l multicolored | 1.75 | 1.50 |
| | Nos. 377-379 (3) | 3.75 | |

Nos. 378-379 are airmail.

Birds — A70

Designs: 1.40 l, Buteo jamaicensis. 1.50 l, Ramphastos sulfuratus. 2 l, Dendrocygna autumnalis. 2.15 l, Micrastur semitorguatus. 3 l, Polyporus plancus. 5.40 l, 10 l, Sacroamphus papa.

**1997, Apr. 29    Litho.    Perf. 13½**
| | | | |
|---|---|---|---|
| 380 | A70 1.40 l multicolored | .55 | |
| 381 | A70 1.50 l multicolored | .60 | |
| 382 | A70 .80 l multicolored | .80 | |
| 383 | A70 2.15 l multicolored | .90 | |
| a. | Pair, #382, 383 | 3.00 | |
| 384 | A70    3 l multicolored | 1.20 | |
| a. | Pair, #380, 384 | 3.00 | |
| 385 | A70 5.40 l multicolored | 2.00 | |
| a. | Pair, #381, 385 | 4.00 | |
| | Nos. 380-385 (6) | 6.05 | |

**Size: 50x73mm**
*Imperf*
| | | | |
|---|---|---|---|
| 386 | A70    20 l multicolored | 6.50 | |

Nos. 380-385 were printed in panes of 30 (5x6), with one value compring the top three rows and another the bottom three rows. Thus, each pane contains five setenant pairs.
No. 386 is airmail.

No. RA8 Surcharged in Gold

**1999, June 25    Litho.    Perf. 13½**
| | | | |
|---|---|---|---|
| 387 | PT6  2.60 l on 1c | .65 | .35 |
| 388 | PT6  7.85 l on 1c | 1.90 | .95 |
| 389 | PT6 10.65 l on 1c | 2.60 | 1.25 |
| 390 | PT6 11.55 l on 1c | 2.75 | 1.40 |
| 391 | PT6 12.45 l on 1c | 3.00 | 1.50 |
| 392 | PT6 13.85 l on 1c | 3.50 | 1.75 |
| | Nos. 387-392 (6) | 14.40 | 7.20 |

For surcharges, see C1199//C1206.

## SEMI-POSTAL STAMPS

**Catalogue values for unused stamps in this section are for Never Hinged items.**

Indiginous Musical Instruments SP1

No. B1: a, Garífuna drum. b, Flutes. c, Toltec drum. d, Hornpipe. e, Maya drum. f, Conch shell.

**2000, Apr. 7    Litho.    Perf. 13¼**
| | | | |
|---|---|---|---|
| B1 | Sheet of 6, "Pro filatelia" in black | 16.00 | 16.00 |
| a.-f. | SP1 10 l + 1 l Any single | 2.50 | 2.50 |
| g. | As #B1, "Pro filatelia" in gold | 17.50 | 17.50 |

See Nos. C1073, C1209.

## AIR POST STAMPS

Regular Issue of 1915-16 Overprinted in Black, Blue or Red

**1925    Unwmk.    Perf. 11½**
| | | | |
|---|---|---|---|
| C1 | A20   5c lt blue (Bk) | 87.50 | 87.50 |
| C2 | A20   5c lt blue (Bl) | 300.00 | 300.00 |
| a. | Inverted overprint | 400.00 | |
| b. | Vertical overprint | 600.00 | |
| c. | Double overprint | 800.00 | |
| C3 | A20   5c lt blue (R) | 7,250. | |

Value for No. C3 is for copy without gum.
| | | | |
|---|---|---|---|
| C4 | A19 10c dk blue (R) | 175.00 | |
| a. | Inverted overprint | 325.00 | |
| b. | Overprint tête bêche, pair | 800.00 | |
| C5 | A19 10c dk blue (Bk) | 1,100. | |
| C6 | A19 20c red brn (Bk) | 175.00 | 175.00 |
| a. | Inverted overprint | 250.00 | |
| b. | Tête bêche, pair | 400.00 | |
| c. | Overprint tête bêche, pair | 725.00 | |
| d. | "AFRO" | 1,400. | |
| e. | Double overprint | 600.00 | |
| C7 | A19 20c red brn (Bl) | 175.00 | 175.00 |
| a. | Inverted overprint | 700.00 | |
| b. | Tête bêche pair | 1,000 | |
| c. | Vertical overprint | 900.00 | |
| C8 | A20 50c red (Bk) | 450.00 | 300.00 |
| a. | Overprint tête bêche, pair | 550.00 | |
| b. | Overprint tête bêche, pair | 900.00 | |
| C9 | A20   1p yel grn (Bk) | 600.00 | 600.00 |

Surcharged in Black or Blue

| | | | |
|---|---|---|---|
| C10 | A19 25c on 1c choc | 125.00 | 125.00 |
| a. | Inverted surcharge | 700.00 | |
| C11 | A20 25c on 5c lt bl (Bl) | 225.00 | 225.00 |
| a. | Inverted surcharge | 700.00 | |
| b. | Double inverted surcharge | 675.00 | |
| C12 | A19 25c on 10c dk bl | 75,000. | |
| C13 | A19 25c on 20c brn (Bl) | 200.00 | 200.00 |
| a. | Inverted surcharge | 325.00 | |
| b. | Tête bêche pair | 450.00 | |

Counterfeits of Nos. C1-C13 are plentiful.

Monoplane and Lisandro Garay AP1

**1929, June 5    Engr.    Perf. 12**
| | | | |
|---|---|---|---|
| C13C | AP1 50c carmine | 2.00 | 1.75 |

No. 216 Surcharged in Blue

**1929    Perf. 11, 11½**
| | | | |
|---|---|---|---|
| C14 | A24 25c on 50c ver | 5.00 | 3.50 |

In the surcharges on Nos. C14 to C40 there are various wrong font and defective letters and numerals, also periods omitted.

Nos. 215-217 Surcharged in Green, Black or Red

**1929, Oct.**
| | | | |
|---|---|---|---|
| C15 | A24   5c on 20c yel brn (G) | 1.40 | 1.40 |
| a. | Double surcharge (R+G) | 45.00 | |
| C16 | A24 10c on 50c ver (Bk) | 2.25 | 1.90 |
| C17 | A24 15c on 1p emer (R) | 3.50 | 3.50 |
| | Nos. C15-C17 (3) | 7.15 | 6.80 |

a            b

Nos. 214 and 216 SurchargedVertically in Red or Black

**1929, Dec. 10**
| | | | |
|---|---|---|---|
| C18 | A24(a)   5c on 10c bl (R) | .60 | .60 |
| C19 | A24(b) 20c on 50c ver | 1.00 | 1.00 |
| a. | "1299" for "1929" | 190.00 | |
| b. | "cts. cts." for "cts. oro." | 190.00 | |
| c. | "r" of "Aereo" omitted | 2.00 | |
| d. | Horiz. pair, imperf. btwn. | 20.00 | |

Nos. 214, 215 and 180 Surcharged in Various Colors

**1930, Feb.**
| | | | |
|---|---|---|---|
| C20 | A24   5c on 10c (R) | .50 | .50 |
| a. | "1930" reading down | 3.50 | |
| b. | "1903" for "1930" | 3.50 | |
| c. | Surcharge reading down | 10.00 | |
| d. | Double surcharge | 14.00 | |
| e. | Dbl. surch., one downward | 14.00 | |
| C21 | A24   5c on 10c (Y) | 450.00 | 450.00 |
| C22 | A24   5c on 20c (Bl) | 125.00 | 125.00 |
| C23 | A24 10c on 20c (Bk) | .70 | .70 |
| a. | "0" for "10" | 3.50 | |
| b. | Double surcharge | 8.75 | |
| c. | Dbl. surch., one downward | 12.00 | |
| d. | Horiz. pair, imperf. btwn. | 70.00 | |
| C24 | A24 10c on 20c (V) | 750.00 | 750.00 |
| a. | "0" for "10" | 1,600. | |
| C25 | A20 25c on 50c (Bk) | .95 | .95 |
| a. | "Internaoicnal" | 3.50 | |
| b. | "o" for "oro" | 3.50 | |
| c. | Inverted surcharge | 17.50 | |
| d. | As "a," invtd. surch. | 175.00 | |
| e. | As "b," invtd. surch. | 175.00 | |

Surcharge on Nos. C20-C24 are vertical.

Nos. 214, 215 and 180 Surcharged

**1930, Apr. 1**
| | | | |
|---|---|---|---|
| C26 | A24   5c on 10c blue | .50 | .50 |
| a. | Double surcharge | 9.50 | |
| b. | "Servicioa" | 3.50 | |
| C27 | A24 15c on 20c yel brn | .55 | .55 |
| a. | Double surcharge | 7.00 | |
| C28 | A20 20c on 50c red, surch. reading down | .95 | .95 |
| a. | Surcharge reading up | 7.00 | |
| | Nos. C26-C28 (3) | 2.00 | 2.00 |

Nos. C22 and C23 Surcharged Vertically in Red

**1930**
| | | | |
|---|---|---|---|
| C29 | A24 10c on 5c on 20c (Bl+R) | .90 | .90 |
| a. | "1930" reading down | 9.00 | 9.00 |
| b. | "1903" for "1930" | 9.00 | 9.00 |
| c. | Red surcharge, reading down | 14.00 | |
| C30 | A24 10c on 10c on 20c (Bk+R) | 87.50 | 87.50 |
| a. | "0" for "10" | 190.00 | |

No. 181 Surcharged as No. C25 and Re-surcharged

| | | | |
|---|---|---|---|
| C31 | A20 50c on 25c on 1p grn | 4.25 | 4.25 |
| a. | "Internaoicnal" | 7.00 | |
| b. | "o" for "oro" | 7.00 | |
| c. | 25c surcharge inverted | 17.50 | 17.50 |
| d. | 50c surcharge inverted | 17.50 | 17.50 |
| e. | As "a" and "c" | | |
| f. | As "a" and "d" | | |
| g. | As "b" and "c" | | |
| h. | As "b" and "d" | | |
| | Nos. C29-C31 (3) | 92.65 | 92.65 |

No. 215 Surcharged in Dark Blue

**1930, May 22**
| | | | |
|---|---|---|---|
| C32 | A24   5c on 20c yel brn | 1.25 | 1.00 |
| a. | Double surcharge | 5.25 | 5.25 |
| b. | Horiz. pair, imperf. btwn. | 60.00 | 60.00 |
| c. | Vertical pair, imperf. between | 20.00 | 20.00 |

Nos. O78-O80 Surcharged like Nos. C20 to C25 in Various Colors

**1930**
| | | | |
|---|---|---|---|
| C33 | A24   5c on 10c (R) | 450.00 | 350.00 |
| a. | "1930" reading down | 875.00 | |
| b. | "1903" for "1930" | 875.00 | |
| C34 | A24   5c on 20c (Bl) | 400.00 | 400.00 |
| C35 | A24 25c on 50c (Bk) | 225.00 | 225.00 |
| a. | 55c on 50c vermilion | 325.00 | 325.00 |

No. C35 exists with inverted surcharge.

No. O64 Surcharged like No. C28
| | | | |
|---|---|---|---|
| C36 | A20 20c on 50c red, surcharge reading down | 350.00 | 350.00 |
| a. | Surcharge reading up | 350.00 | 350.00 |
| b. | Dbl. surch., reading down | 350.00 | 350.00 |
| c. | Dbl. surch., reading up | 350.00 | 350.00 |

No. O87 Overprinted

**1930, Feb. 21    Wmk. 209    Perf. 11½**
| | | | |
|---|---|---|---|
| C37 | O1 50c yel, grn & blue | 1.40 | 1.25 |
| a. | "Internaoical" | 5.25 | |
| b. | "Iuternacional" | 5.25 | |
| c. | Double overprint | 5.25 | |

Nos. O86-O88 Overprinted in Various Colors

**1930, May 23**
| | | | |
|---|---|---|---|
| C38 | O1 20c dark blue (R) | 1.10 | .85 |
| a. | Double overprint | 8.75 | |
| b. | Triple overprint | 12.00 | |
| C39 | O1 50c org, grn & bl (Bk) | 1.10 | .90 |
| C40 | O1   1p buff (Bl) | 1.40 | 1.25 |
| a. | Double overprint | 10.50 | |
| | Nos. C38-C40 (3) | 3.60 | 3.00 |

National Palace AP3

**Unwmk.**

**1930, Oct. 1**    **Engr.**    **Perf. 12**

| | | | | |
|---|---|---|---|---|
| **C41** | AP3 | 5c yel orange | .50 | .30 |
| **C42** | AP3 | 10c carmine | .75 | .60 |
| **C43** | AP3 | 15c green | 1.00 | .75 |
| **C44** | AP3 | 20c dull violet | 1.25 | .60 |
| **C45** | AP3 | 1p light brown | 4.00 | 4.00 |
| | | *Nos. C41-C45 (5)* | 7.50 | 6.25 |

**Same Overprinted in Various Colors**

**1931**            **Perf. 12**

| | | | | |
|---|---|---|---|---|
| **C51** | AP3 | 5c yel orange (R) | 2.00 | 1.50 |
| **C52** | AP3 | 10c carmine (Bk) | 3.00 | 2.50 |
| **C53** | AP3 | 15c green (Br) | 5.00 | 4.00 |
| **C54** | AP3 | 20c dull vio (O) | 5.00 | 4.25 |
| **C55** | AP3 | 1p lt brown (G) | 10.00 | 8.75 |
| | | *Nos. C51-C55 (5)* | 25.00 | 21.00 |

See note after No. 317.

**Stamps of Various Issues Surcharged in Blue or Black (#C59)**

**1931, Oct.**      **Perf. 11½**

**On No. 215**

| | | | | |
|---|---|---|---|---|
| **C56** | A24 | 15c on 20c yel brn | 3.50 | 2.75 |
| *a.* | | Horiz. pair, imperf. btwn. | 42.50 | |
| *b.* | | Green surcharge | 20.00 | 20.00 |

**On No. O64**

| | | | | |
|---|---|---|---|---|
| **C57** | A20 | 15c on 50c red | 4.25 | 3.50 |
| *a.* | | Inverted surcharge | 10.50 | 10.50 |

**On No. O72**

| | | | | |
|---|---|---|---|---|
| **C58** | A22 | 15c on 20c brn | 4.25 | 4.25 |
| *a.* | | Vert. pair, imperf. between | 12.00 | |

On Nos. C57 and C58 the word "OFICIAL" is canceled by two bars.

**On No. O88**

**Wmk. 209**

| | | | | |
|---|---|---|---|---|
| **C59** | O1 | 15c on 1p buff | 4.25 | 4.25 |
| *a.* | | Vert. pair, imperf. horiz. | 25.00 | |
| *b.* | | "Sevricio" | 14.00 | 14.00 |

The varieties "Vaie" for "Vale," "aereo" with circumflex accent on the first "e" and "Interior" with initial capital "I" are found on #C56, C58-C59. #C57 is known with initial capital in "Interior."

A similar surcharge, in slightly larger letters and with many minor varieties, exists on Nos. 215, O63, O64 and O73. The authenticity of this surcharge is questioned.

**Nos. 215, O73, O87-O88 Surcharged in Green, Red or Black**

**1931, Nov.**      **Unwmk.**

| | | | | |
|---|---|---|---|---|
| **C60** | A24 | 15c on 20c (G) | 3.50 | 2.75 |
| *a.* | | Inverted surcharge | 6.25 | |
| *b.* | | "XI" omitted | 6.25 | |
| *c.* | | "X" for "XI" | 6.25 | |
| *d.* | | "PI" for "XI" | 6.25 | |
| **C61** | A22 | 15c on 50c (R) | 3.50 | 2.75 |
| *a.* | | "XI" omitted | 6.75 | |
| *b.* | | "PI" for "XI" | 6.75 | |
| *c.* | | Double surcharge | 20.00 | 20.00 |

On No. C61 the word "OFICIAL" is not barred out.

**Wmk. 209**

| | | | | |
|---|---|---|---|---|
| **C62** | O1 | 15c on 50c (Bk) | 2.75 | 2.50 |
| *a.* | | "1391" for "1931" | 10.50 | 10.50 |
| *b.* | | Double surcharge | 8.75 | 8.75 |
| **C63** | O1 | 15c on 1p (Bk) | 2.50 | 2.25 |
| *a.* | | "1391" for "1931" | 12.50 | |
| *b.* | | Surcharged on both sides | 7.00 | |

**Nos. O76-O78 Surcharged in Black or Red**

**1932**      **Unwmk.**      **Perf. 11, 11½**

| | | | | |
|---|---|---|---|---|
| **C73** | A24 | 15c on 2c | .80 | .80 |
| *a.* | | Double surcharge | 5.50 | |
| *b.* | | Inverted surcharge | 4.25 | |
| *c.* | | "Ae" of "Aero" omitted | 1.00 | |
| *d.* | | On No. 212 (no "Official") | | |
| **C74** | A24 | 15c on 6c | .80 | .80 |
| *a.* | | Double surcharge | 3.50 | |
| *b.* | | Horiz. pair, imperf. btwn. | 17.50 | |
| *c.* | | "Aer" omitted | | |
| *d.* | | "A" omitted | 1.00 | |
| *e.* | | Inverted surcharge | 3.50 | |
| **C75** | A24 | 15c on 10c (R) | .80 | .80 |
| *a.* | | Double surcharge | 5.50 | |
| *b.* | | Inverted surcharge | 3.50 | |
| *c.* | | "r" of "Aereo" omitted | 1.00 | |

**Same Surcharge on No. 214 in Red**

| | | | | |
|---|---|---|---|---|
| **C76** | A24 | 15c on 10c dp bl | *150.00* | *100.00* |

There are various broken and missing letters in the setting.

A similar surcharge with slightly larger letters exists.

**View of Tegucigalpa — AP5**

Designs: 15c, Map of Honduras. 20c, Mayol Bridge. 40c, View of Tegucigalpa. 50c, Owl. 1 l, Coat of Arms.

**1935, Jan. 10**      **Perf. 12**

| | | | | |
|---|---|---|---|---|
| **C77** | AP4 | 8c blue | .20 | .20 |
| **C78** | AP5 | 10c gray | .25 | .20 |
| **C79** | AP5 | 15c olive gray | .40 | .20 |
| **C80** | AP5 | 20c dull green | .50 | .20 |
| **C81** | AP5 | 40c brown | .70 | .20 |
| **C82** | AP4 | 50c yellow | 8.25 | 1.60 |
| **C83** | AP4 | 1 l green | 3.25 | 2.75 |
| | | *Nos. C77-C83 (7)* | 13.55 | 5.35 |

**Flags of US and Honduras — AP11**

**Engr. & Litho.**

**1937, Sept. 17**      **Unwmk.**

| | | | | |
|---|---|---|---|---|
| **C84** | AP11 | 46c multicolored | 2.75 | 1.40 |

US Constitution, 150th anniv..

**Comayagua Cathedral AP12**

**Founding of Comayagua AP13**

**Alonzo Cáceres and Pres. Carías AP14**

**Lintel of Royal Palace AP15**

**1937, Dec. 7**      **Engr.**

| | | | | |
|---|---|---|---|---|
| **C85** | AP12 | 2c copper red | .20 | .20 |
| **C86** | AP13 | 8c dark blue | .35 | .20 |
| **C87** | AP14 | 15c slate black | .70 | .70 |
| **C88** | AP15 | 50c dark brown | 4.25 | 2.75 |
| | | *Nos. C85-C88 (4)* | 5.50 | 3.85 |

City of Comayagua founding, 400th anniv. For surcharges see Nos. C144-C146.

**Mayan Stele at Copán AP16**

**Mayan Temple, Copán AP17**

Designs: 15c, President Carias. 30c, José C. de Valle. 40c, Presidential House. 46c, Lempira. 55c, Church of Our Lady of Suyapa. 66c, J. T. Reyes. 1 l, Hospital at Choluteca. 2 l, Ramón Rosa.

**1939, Mar. 1**      **Perf. 12½**

| | | | | |
|---|---|---|---|---|
| **C89** | AP16 | 10c orange brn | .20 | .20 |
| **C90** | AP16 | 15c grnsh blue | .30 | .20 |
| **C91** | AP17 | 21c gray | .50 | .20 |
| **C92** | AP16 | 30c dk blue grn | .55 | .20 |
| **C93** | AP17 | 40c dull violet | 1.00 | .25 |
| **C94** | AP16 | 46c dk gray brn | 1.00 | .65 |
| **C95** | AP16 | 55c green | 1.25 | 1.00 |
| *a.* | | Imperf., pair | 22.50 | |
| **C96** | AP16 | 66c black | 1.75 | 1.25 |
| **C97** | AP16 | 1 l olive grn | 3.00 | 1.00 |
| **C98** | AP16 | 2 l henna red | 4.25 | 2.50 |
| | | *Nos. C89-C98 (10)* | 13.80 | 7.45 |

For surcharges see #C118-C119, C147-C152.

**Souvenir Sheets**

**AP26**

14c, Francisco Morazan. 16c, George Washington. 30c, J. C. de Valle. 40c, Simon Bolivar.

**1940, Apr. 13**    **Engr.**    **Perf. 12**
**Centers of Stamps Lithographed**

| | | | | |
|---|---|---|---|---|
| **C99** | AP26 | Sheet of 4 | 10.00 | 10.00 |
| *a.* | | 14c black, yellow, ultra & rose | 1.40 | 1.40 |
| *b.* | | 16c black, yellow, ultra & rose | 1.75 | 1.75 |
| *c.* | | 30c black, yellow, ultra & rose | 2.40 | 2.40 |
| *d.* | | 40c black, yellow, ultra & rose | 2.75 | 2.75 |

**Imperf**

| | | | | |
|---|---|---|---|---|
| **C100** | AP26 | Sheet of 4 | 16.00 | 16.00 |
| *a.* | | 14c black, yellow, ultra & rose | 2.25 | 2.25 |
| *b.* | | 16c black, yellow, ultra & rose | 2.75 | 2.75 |
| *c.* | | 30c black, yellow, ultra & rose | 4.00 | 4.00 |
| *d.* | | 40c black, yellow, ultra & rose | 4.50 | 4.50 |

Pan American Union, 50th anniv. For overprints see Nos. C153-C154, C187.

**Air Post Official Stamps of 1939 Overprinted in Red**

**1940, Oct. 12**      **Perf. 12½**

| | | | | |
|---|---|---|---|---|
| **C101** | OA2 | 2c dp bl & green | .20 | .20 |
| **C102** | OA2 | 5c dp blue & org | .25 | .25 |
| **C103** | OA2 | 8c deep bl & brn | .30 | .30 |
| **C104** | OA2 | 15c dp blue & car | .50 | .50 |
| **C105** | OA2 | 46c dp bl & ol grn | .80 | .80 |
| **C106** | OA2 | 50c dp bl & vio | .90 | .90 |
| **C107** | OA2 | 1 l dp bl & red brn | 3.75 | 3.75 |
| **C108** | OA2 | 2 l dp bl & red org | 7.50 | 7.50 |
| | | *Nos. C101-C108 (8)* | 14.20 | 14.20 |

Erection and dedication of the Columbus Memorial Lighthouse.

**Air Post Official Stamps of 1939 Overprinted in Black**

**1941, Aug. 2**

| | | | | |
|---|---|---|---|---|
| **C109** | OA2 | 5c deep bl & org | 3.00 | .25 |
| **C110** | OA2 | 8c dp blue & brn | 5.00 | .25 |
| *a.* | | Overprint inverted | | 225.00 |

**Nos. CO44, CO47-CO51 Surcharged in Black**

**1941, Oct. 28**

| | | | | |
|---|---|---|---|---|
| **C111** | OA2 | 3c on 2c | .40 | .20 |
| **C112** | OA2 | 8c on 2c | .50 | .50 |
| **C113** | OA2 | 8c on 15c | .50 | .20 |
| **C114** | OA2 | 8c on 46c | .60 | .60 |
| **C115** | OA2 | 8c on 50c | .75 | .50 |
| **C116** | OA2 | 8c on 1 l | 1.25 | .70 |
| **C117** | OA2 | 8c on 2 l | 2.00 | 1.50 |
| | | *Nos. C111-C117 (7)* | 6.00 | 4.20 |

Once in each sheet a large "h" occurs in "ocho."

**Nos. C90, C94 Surcharged in Red**

**1942, July 14**

| | | | | |
|---|---|---|---|---|
| **C118** | AP16 | 8c on 15c | .70 | .30 |
| *a.* | | "Cerreo" | 2.00 | 2.00 |
| *b.* | | Double surcharge | 25.00 | 25.00 |
| *c.* | | As "a," double surcharge | 175.00 | |
| **C119** | AP16 | 16c on 46c | .70 | .30 |
| *a.* | | "Cerreo" | 2.00 | 2.00 |

**Plaque AP27**

Morazán's Tomb, San Salvador — AP28

Designs: 5c, Battle of La Trinidad. 8c, Morazán's birthplace. 16c, Statue of Morazán. 21c, Church where Morazán was baptized. 1 l, Arms of Central American Federation. 2 l, Gen. Francisco Morazán.

**1942, Sept. 15**       **Perf. 12**

| | | | | |
|---|---|---|---|---|
| C120 | AP27 | 2c red orange | .20 | .20 |
| C121 | AP27 | 5c turq green | .20 | .20 |
| C122 | AP27 | 8c sepia | .20 | .20 |
| C123 | AP28 | 14c black | .40 | .30 |
| C124 | AP27 | 16c olive gray | .25 | .20 |
| C125 | AP27 | 21c light blue | 1.00 | .65 |
| C126 | AP27 | 1 l brt ultra | 3.00 | 2.25 |
| C127 | AP28 | 2 l dl ol brn | 7.50 | 7.25 |
| | | *Nos. C120-C127 (8)* | 12.75 | 11.25 |

Gen. Francisco Morazan (1799-1842).
For surcharges see Nos. C349-C350.

Coat of Arms AP35

Cattle AP36

Bananas — AP37    Pine Tree — AP38

Tobacco Plant AP39

Orchid AP40

Coco Palm — AP41

Map of Honduras AP42

---

Designs: 2c, Flag. 8c, Rosario. 16c, Sugar cane. 30c, Oranges. 40c, Wheat. 1 l, Corn. 2 l, Map of Americas.

**1943, Sept. 14**       **Perf. 12½**

| | | | | |
|---|---|---|---|---|
| C128 | AP35 | 1c light grn | .20 | .20 |
| C129 | AP35 | 2c blue | .20 | .20 |
| C130 | AP36 | 5c green | .30 | .20 |
| C131 | AP37 | 6c dark bl grn | .25 | .20 |
| C132 | AP36 | 8c lilac | .30 | .20 |
| C133 | AP38 | 10c lilac brn | .30 | .20 |
| C134 | AP39 | 15c dp claret | .35 | .20 |
| C135 | AP38 | 16c dark red | .35 | .20 |
| C136 | AP40 | 21c deep blue | .75 | .20 |
| C137 | AP39 | 30c org brown | .60 | .20 |
| C138 | AP40 | 40c red orange | .60 | .20 |
| C139 | AP41 | 55c black | 1.10 | .60 |
| C140 | AP41 | 1 l dark olive | 1.75 | 1.40 |
| C141 | AP37 | 2 l brown red | 5.25 | 4.00 |
| C142 | AP42 | 5 l orange | 13.00 | 13.00 |
| a. | | Vert. pair, imperf. btwn. | 150.00 | |
| | | *Nos. C128-C142 (15)* | 25.30 | 21.20 |

Pan-American School of Agriculture AP50

**1944, Oct. 12**       **Perf. 12**

| | | | | |
|---|---|---|---|---|
| C143 | AP50 | 21c dk blue grn | .40 | .20 |

Inauguration of the Pan-American School of Agriculture, Tegucigalpa.

> **Catalogue values for unused stamps in this section, from this point to the end of the section, are for Never Hinged items.**

Air Post Stamps of 1937-39 Surcharged in Red or Green

**1945, Mar. 13**       **Perf. 11, 12½**

| | | | | |
|---|---|---|---|---|
| C144 | AP15 | 1c on 50c dk brn | .20 | .20 |
| C145 | AP12 | 2c on 2c cop red | .20 | .20 |
| C146 | AP14 | 8c on 15c sl blk | .25 | .20 |
| C147 | AP16 | 10c on 10c org brown (G) | .45 | .30 |
| C148 | AP16 | 15c on 15c grnsh blue (G) | .30 | .25 |
| C149 | AP17 | 30c on 21c gray (G) | 4.50 | 3.00 |
| C150 | AP17 | 40c on 40c dull violet (G) | 2.25 | 1.25 |
| C151 | AP16 | 1 l on 46c dk gray brown (G) | 2.25 | 1.75 |
| C152 | AP16 | 2 l on 66c blk (G) | 4.50 | 3.00 |
| | | *Nos. C144-C152 (9)* | 14.90 | 10.15 |

Souvenir Sheets
Nos. C99 and C100 Overprinted in Red

"VICTORIA DE LAS NACIONES UNIDAS, ALEMANIA SE RINDE INCONDICIONALMENTE 8 DE MAYO DE 1945. ACDO. No. 1231 QUE AUTORIZA LA CONTRAMARCA"

**1945, Oct. 1**       **Perf. 12**

| | | | | |
|---|---|---|---|---|
| C153 | AP26 | Sheet of 4 | 4.00 | 3.00 |

**Imperf**

| | | | | |
|---|---|---|---|---|
| C154 | AP26 | Sheet of 4 | 6.50 | 4.25 |

Allied Nations' victory and Germany's unconditional surrender, May 8, 1945.

Seal of Honduras AP51

Arms of Gracias and Trujillo AP52

---

Franklin D. Roosevelt ("F.D.R." under Column) AP53

Arms of San Miguel de Heredia de Tegucigalpa AP54

Designs (Coats of Arms): 5c, Comayagua and San Jorge de Olancho. 15c, Province of Honduras and San Juan de Puerto Caballas. 21c, Comayagua and Tencoa. 1 l, Jerez de la Frontera de Choluteca and San Pedro de Zula.

**1946, Oct. 15**    **Unwmk.**    **Engr.**

| | | | | |
|---|---|---|---|---|
| C155 | AP51 | 1c red | .20 | .20 |
| a. | | Vert. pair, imperf. between | 17.50 | |
| b. | | Imperf., pair | 70.00 | |
| C156 | AP52 | 2c red orange | .20 | .20 |
| a. | | Imperf., pair | 70.00 | |
| C157 | AP52 | 5c violet | .45 | .20 |
| C158 | AP53 | 8c brown | 1.60 | .50 |
| a. | | Horiz. pair, imperf. btwn. | 70.00 | |
| C159 | AP52 | 15c sepia | .80 | .20 |
| C160 | AP52 | 21c deep blue | .90 | .30 |
| a. | | Horiz. pair, imperf. btwn. | 15.00 | |
| b. | | Imperf., pair | 70.00 | |
| C161 | AP52 | 1 l green | 3.25 | 1.25 |
| C162 | AP52 | 2 l dark grn | 5.00 | 2.00 |
| | | *Nos. C155-C162 (8)* | 12.40 | 4.85 |

No. C158 commemorates the death of Franklin D. Roosevelt and the Allied victory over Japan in World War II.

Type AP53 Redrawn ("Franklin D. Roosevelt" under Column) AP59

**1947, Oct.**       **Perf. 12½**

| | | | | |
|---|---|---|---|---|
| C163 | AP59 | 8c brown | .50 | .35 |
| a. | | Vert. pair, imperf. between | 87.50 | |
| b. | | Horiz. pair, imperf. btwn. | 175.00 | |
| c. | | Perf. 12x6 | 175.00 | |

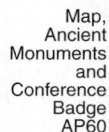

Map, Ancient Monuments and Conference Badge AP60

**1947, Oct. 20**       **Perf. 11x12½**
**Various Frames**

| | | | | |
|---|---|---|---|---|
| C164 | AP60 | 16c green | .40 | .20 |
| C165 | AP60 | 22c orange yel | .30 | .20 |
| C166 | AP60 | 40c orange | .65 | .35 |
| C167 | AP60 | 1 l deep blue | 1.10 | .90 |
| C168 | AP60 | 2 l lilac | 4.00 | 3.50 |
| C169 | AP60 | 5 l brown | 10.50 | 8.00 |
| | | *Nos. C164-C169 (6)* | 16.95 | 13.15 |

1st Intl. Archeological Conf. of the Caribbean.
For overprints and surcharges see Nos. C181-C186, C351, C353-C354, C379, C544.

Flag and Arms of Honduras AP61    Juan Manuel Galvez AP62

---

J. M. Galvez, Gen. Tiburcio Carias A. and Julio Lozano AP63

National Stadium AP64

Designs: 5c, 15c, Julio Lozano. 9c, Juan Manuel Galvez. 40c, Custom House. 1 l, Recinto Hall. 2 l, Gen. Tiburcio Carias A. 5 l, Galvez and Lozano.
Various frames inscribed: "Conmemorativa de la Sucesion Presidencial para el Periodo de 1949-1955."

**1949, Sept. 17**    **Engr.**    **Perf. 12**

| | | | | |
|---|---|---|---|---|
| C170 | AP61 | 1c deep blue | .20 | .20 |
| C171 | AP62 | 2c rose car | .20 | .20 |
| C172 | AP62 | 5c deep blue | .20 | .20 |
| C173 | AP62 | 9c sepia | .20 | .20 |
| C174 | AP62 | 15c red brown | .25 | .20 |
| C175 | AP63 | 21c gray black | .45 | .20 |
| C176 | AP64 | 30c olive gray | .60 | .20 |
| C177 | AP64 | 40c slate gray | .90 | .20 |
| C178 | AP61 | 1 l red brown | 1.40 | .40 |
| C179 | AP62 | 2 l violet | 3.25 | 1.50 |
| C180 | AP64 | 5 l rose car | 9.25 | 5.50 |
| | | *Nos. C170-C180 (11)* | 16.90 | 9.00 |

Presidential succession for the 1949-1955 term.
For overprints and surcharges see Nos. C188-C197, C206-C208, C346, C355, C419-C420, C478, C545.

Nos. C164-C169 Overprinted in Carmine

**1951, Feb. 26**       **Perf. 11x12½**

| | | | | |
|---|---|---|---|---|
| C181 | AP60 | 16c green | .50 | .40 |
| a. | | Inverted overprint | 45.00 | 45.00 |
| C182 | AP60 | 22c orange yel | .65 | .55 |
| a. | | Inverted overprint | 45.00 | |
| C183 | AP60 | 40c orange | .65 | .55 |
| C184 | AP60 | 1 l deep blue | 2.00 | 1.75 |
| C185 | AP60 | 2 l lilac | 3.75 | 3.25 |
| a. | | Inverted overprint | 60.00 | |
| C186 | AP60 | 5 l brown | 32.50 | 29.00 |
| | | *Nos. C181-C186 (6)* | 40.05 | 35.50 |

**Souvenir Sheets**
**Same Overprint in Carmine on Nos. C99 and C100**
**Perf. 12**

| | | | | |
|---|---|---|---|---|
| C187 | AP26 | Sheet of 4 | 8.00 | 4.75 |
| a. | | Imperf. | 250.00 | 250.00 |

UPU, 75th anniv. (in 1949).

Nos. C170 to C179 Overprinted in Carmine

**1951, Feb. 27**       **Perf. 12**

| | | | | |
|---|---|---|---|---|
| C188 | AP61 | 1c deep blue | .20 | .20 |
| C189 | AP62 | 2c rose car | .20 | .20 |
| C190 | AP62 | 5c deep blue | .20 | .20 |
| C191 | AP62 | 9c sepia | .20 | .20 |
| C192 | AP62 | 15c red brown | .20 | .20 |
| C193 | AP63 | 21c gray black | .25 | .20 |
| C194 | AP64 | 30c olive gray | .60 | .30 |
| C195 | AP64 | 40c slate gray | .90 | .60 |
| C196 | AP61 | 1 l red brown | 2.25 | 1.50 |
| C197 | AP62 | 2 l violet | 7.25 | 5.00 |
| | | *Nos. C188-C197 (10)* | 12.25 | 8.60 |

Founding of Central Bank, July 1, 1950.

Discovery of America
AP65

Queen Isabella
I — AP66

2c, 1 l, Columbus at court. 8c, Surrender of Granada. 30c, Queen Isabella offering her jewels.

### Perf. 13½x14, 14x13½

| | | | Unwmk. | |
|---|---|---|---|---|
| **1952, Oct. 11** | | **Engr.** | | |
| C198 | AP65 | 1c red org & blk | .20 | .20 |
| C199 | AP65 | 2c bl & red brn | .20 | .20 |
| C200 | AP65 | 8c dk grn & dk brown | .20 | .20 |
| C201 | AP66 | 16c dk bl & blk | .40 | .25 |
| C202 | AP65 | 30c pur & dk grn | .70 | .70 |
| C203 | AP65 | 1 l dp car & blk | 1.75 | 1.40 |
| C204 | AP65 | 2 l brn & vio | 4.25 | 3.50 |
| C205 | AP66 | 5 l rose lil & ol | 9.25 | 8.75 |
| | | Nos. C198-C205 (8) | 16.95 | 15.20 |

500th birth anniv. of Isabella I of Spain.
For overprints and surcharges see Nos. C209-C221, C377-C378, C404-C406, C489, CO52-CO59.

HABILITADO 1953 L 0.05

No. C175 Surcharged in Carmine

| | | | **Perf. 12** | |
|---|---|---|---|---|
| **1953, May 13** | | | | |
| C206 | AP63 | 5c on 21c gray blk | .25 | .20 |
| C207 | AP63 | 12c on 21c gray blk | .55 | .20 |
| C208 | AP63 | 16c on 21c gray blk | .95 | .20 |
| | | Nos. C206-C208 (3) | 1.75 | .60 |

### Nos. CO52-CO54 Surcharged "HABILITADO 1953" and New Value in Red

| **1953, Dec. 8** | | **Perf. 13½x14, 14x13½** | | |
|---|---|---|---|---|
| C209 | AP65 | 10c on 1c | .20 | .20 |
| a. | | Inverted surcharge | 50.00 | 50.00 |
| C210 | AP65 | 12c on 1c | .20 | .20 |
| C211 | AP65 | 15c on 2c | .30 | .20 |
| C212 | AP65 | 20c on 2c | .50 | .30 |
| C213 | AP65 | 24c on 2c | .50 | .30 |
| a. | | Inverted surcharge | 50.00 | 50.00 |
| C214 | AP65 | 25c on 2c | .50 | .30 |
| C215 | AP65 | 30c on 8c | .60 | .30 |
| C216 | AP65 | 35c on 8c | .70 | .45 |
| C217 | AP65 | 50c on 8c | .80 | .45 |
| C218 | AP65 | 60c on 8c | 1.00 | .90 |

### Same Overprint on Nos. CO57-CO59

| C219 | AP65 | 1 l dk grn & dk brown | 3.00 | 2.25 |
|---|---|---|---|---|
| C220 | AP65 | 2 l bl & red brn | 6.75 | 5.50 |
| C221 | AP66 | 5 l red org & blk | 16.00 | 13.00 |
| a. | | Date inverted | 150.00 | |
| | | Nos. C209-C221 (13) | 31.05 | 24.35 |

Flags of UN and Honduras
AP67

2c, UN emblem. 3c, UN building. 5c, Shield. 15c, Juan Manuel Galvez. 30c, UNICEF. 1 l, UNRRA. 2 l, UNESCO. 5 l, FAO.

### Engraved; Center of 1c Litho.

| **1953, Dec. 18** | | **Perf. 12½** | | |
|---|---|---|---|---|
| | | **Frames in Black** | | |
| C222 | AP67 | 1c ultra & vio bl | .20 | .20 |
| C223 | AP67 | 2c blue | .20 | .20 |
| C224 | AP67 | 3c rose lilac | .20 | .20 |
| C225 | AP67 | 5c green | .25 | .20 |
| C226 | AP67 | 15c red brown | .40 | .25 |
| C227 | AP67 | 30c brown | .85 | .50 |
| C228 | AP67 | 1 l dp carmine | 6.75 | 4.50 |
| C229 | AP67 | 2 l orange | 8.75 | 6.25 |
| C230 | AP67 | 5 l blue green | 19.00 | 15.00 |
| | | Nos. C222-C230 (9) | 36.60 | 27.30 |

Issued to honor the United Nations.
For overprints and surcharges see Nos. C231-C249, C331-C335, C472, C490, CO60-CO68.

Nos. CO60-CO66 Overprinted in Red

| **1955, Feb. 23** | | **Unwmk.** | **Perf. 12½** | |
|---|---|---|---|---|
| | | **Frames in Black** | | |
| C231 | AP67 | 1c ultra & vio bl | .20 | .20 |
| C232 | AP67 | 2c dp blue grn | .20 | .20 |
| C233 | AP67 | 3c orange | .20 | .20 |
| C234 | AP67 | 5c dp carmine | .25 | .25 |
| C235 | AP67 | 15c dk brown | .35 | .35 |
| C236 | AP67 | 30c purple | 1.00 | .90 |
| C237 | AP67 | 1 l olive gray | 20.00 | 15.00 |

Overprint exists inverted on 1c, 3c.

### Nos. C231 to C233 Surcharged with New Value in Black

| C238 | AP67 | 8c on 1c | .20 | .20 |
|---|---|---|---|---|
| C239 | AP67 | 10c on 2c | .20 | .20 |
| C240 | AP67 | 12c on 3c | .20 | .20 |
| | | Nos. C231-C240 (10) | 22.80 | 17.70 |

50th anniv. of the founding of Rotary International (Nos. C231-C240).

O N U
X ANIVERSARIO
1945 - 1955

Nos. CO60-CO63, C226-C230 Overprinted

| **1956, July 14** | | **Unwmk.** | **Perf. 12½** | |
|---|---|---|---|---|
| | | **Frames in Black** | | |
| C241 | AP67 | 1c ultra & vio bl | .20 | .20 |
| C242 | AP67 | 2c dp bl grn | .20 | .20 |
| C243 | AP67 | 3c orange | .25 | .20 |
| C244 | AP67 | 5c dp car | .30 | .25 |
| C245 | AP67 | 15c red brn | .35 | .30 |
| C246 | AP67 | 30c brown | .55 | .40 |
| C247 | AP67 | 1 l dp car | 4.00 | 2.75 |
| C248 | AP67 | 2 l orange | 5.75 | 4.75 |
| C249 | AP67 | 5 l bl brown | 15.00 | 14.00 |
| | | Nos. C241-C249 (9) | 26.60 | 23.05 |

10th anniv. of UN (in 1955). The red "OFICIAL" overprint was not obliterated.
The "ONU" overprint exists inverted on 1c, 3c, 5c and 1-lempira.

Basilica of Suyapa
AP68

Pres. Julio Lozano Diaz — AP69

3c, Southern Highway. 4c, Genoveva Guardiola de Estrada Palma. 5c, Maria Josefa Lastiri de Morazan. 8c, Landscape and cornucopia (5-Year Plan). 10c, National Stadium. 12c, US School. 15c, Central Bank. 20c, Legislative Palace. 25c, Development Bank (projected). 30c, Toncontin Airport. 40c, Juan Ramon Molina Bridge. 50c, Peace Monument. 60c, Treasury Palace. 1 l, Blood bank. 2 l, Communications Building. 5 l, Presidential Palace.

### Engraved; #C255 Litho.

| **1956, Oct. 3** | | **Perf. 13x12½, 12½x13** | | |
|---|---|---|---|---|
| C250 | AP68 | 1c black & vio bl | .20 | .20 |
| C251 | AP69 | 2c black & dk bl | .20 | .20 |
| C252 | AP68 | 3c black & brown | .20 | .20 |
| C253 | AP69 | 4c black & lilac | .20 | .20 |
| C254 | AP69 | 5c black & dk red | .20 | .20 |
| C255 | AP68 | 8c brown & multi | .20 | .20 |
| C256 | AP69 | 10c black & emer | .20 | .20 |
| C257 | AP68 | 12c black & green | .20 | .20 |
| C258 | AP68 | 15c dk red & blk | .30 | .20 |
| C259 | AP68 | 20c black & ultra | .30 | .20 |
| C260 | AP69 | 24c black & lil | .35 | .20 |
| C261 | AP68 | 25c black & green | .40 | .25 |
| C262 | AP68 | 30c black & car rose | .40 | .25 |
| C263 | AP68 | 40c black & red brn | .50 | .25 |
| C264 | AP69 | 50c black & bl grn | .60 | .35 |
| C265 | AP68 | 60c black & orange | .80 | .45 |
| C266 | AP68 | 1 l black & rose vio | 2.00 | 1.00 |
| C267 | AP69 | 2 l black & mag | 3.75 | 2.25 |
| C268 | AP69 | 5 l black & brn car | 9.00 | 5.00 |
| | | Nos. C250-C268 (19) | 20.00 | 12.00 |

Issued to publicize the Five-Year Plan.
For overprints and surcharges see Nos. C414-C418, C491-C493, C537-C538, C542, C550.

Types AP68 and AP69 in different colors, overprinted "OFICIAL," see Nos. CO69-CO87.

Flag of Honduras
AP70

Designs: 2c, 8c, Monument and mountains. 10c, 15c, 1 l, Lempira. 30c, 2 l, Coat of arms.

| **1957, Oct. 21** | | **Litho.** | **Perf. 13** | |
|---|---|---|---|---|
| | | **Frames in Black** | | |
| C269 | AP70 | 1c buff & ultra | .20 | .20 |
| C270 | AP70 | 2c org, pur & emerald | .20 | .20 |
| C271 | AP70 | 5c pink & ultra | .20 | .20 |
| C272 | AP70 | 8c org, vio & ol | .20 | .20 |
| C273 | AP70 | 10c violet & brown | .20 | .20 |
| C274 | AP70 | 12c lt grn & ultra | .25 | .20 |
| C275 | AP70 | 15c green & brown | .30 | .20 |
| C276 | AP70 | 30c pink & slate | .45 | .25 |
| C277 | AP70 | 1 l blue & brown | 2.00 | 1.50 |
| C278 | AP70 | 2 l lt grn & slate | 3.75 | 3.00 |
| | | Nos. C269-C278 (10) | 7.75 | 6.15 |

First anniv. of the October revolution.
For overprints and surcharge, see Nos. C551, CO88-CO97.

---

Control marks were handstamped in violet on many current stamps in July and August, 1958, following fire and theft of stamps at Tegucigalpa in April.

All post offices were ordered to honor only stamps overprinted with the facsimile signature of their departmental revenue administrator. Honduras has 18 departments.

---

Flags of Honduras and US — AP71

| **1958, Oct. 2** | | **Engr.** | **Perf. 12** | |
|---|---|---|---|---|
| | | **Flags in National Colors** | | |
| C279 | AP71 | 1c light blue | .20 | .20 |
| C280 | AP71 | 2c red | .20 | .20 |
| C281 | AP71 | 5c green | .20 | .20 |
| C282 | AP71 | 10c brown | .25 | .20 |
| C283 | AP71 | 20c orange | .40 | .20 |
| C284 | AP71 | 30c deep rose | .45 | .25 |
| C285 | AP71 | 50c gray | .60 | .40 |
| C286 | AP71 | 1 l orange yel | 1.25 | 1.00 |

| C287 | AP71 | 2 l gray olive | 2.40 | 2.00 |
|---|---|---|---|---|
| C288 | AP71 | 5 l vio blue | 5.50 | 4.00 |
| | | Nos. C279-C288 (10) | 11.45 | 8.65 |

Honduras Institute of Inter-American Culture. The proceeds were intended for the Binational Center, Tegucigalpa.
For overprints see Nos. C320-C324.

Abraham Lincoln — AP72

Lincoln's Birthplace
AP73

Designs: 3c, 50c, Gettysburg Address. 5c, 1 l, Freeing the slaves. 10c, 2 l, Assassination. 12c, 5 l, Memorial, Washington.

| **1959, Feb. 12** | | **Unwmk.** | **Perf. 13½** | |
|---|---|---|---|---|
| | | **Flags in National Colors** | | |
| C289 | AP72 | 1c green | .20 | .20 |
| C290 | AP73 | 2c dark blue | .20 | .20 |
| C291 | AP73 | 3c purple | .25 | .20 |
| C292 | AP73 | 5c dk carmine | .25 | .20 |
| C293 | AP73 | 10c black | .30 | .20 |
| C294 | AP73 | 12c dark brown | .30 | .20 |
| C295 | AP72 | 15c red orange | .40 | .25 |
| C296 | AP73 | 25c dull pur | .60 | .40 |
| C297 | AP73 | 50c ultra | .75 | .65 |
| C298 | AP73 | 1 l red brown | 1.50 | 1.40 |
| C299 | AP73 | 2 l gray olive | 2.40 | 1.75 |
| C300 | AP73 | 5 l ocher | 5.50 | 5.00 |
| a. | | Miniature sheet | 10.00 | 10.00 |
| | | Nos. C289-C300 (12) | 12.65 | 10.65 |

Birth sesquicentennial of Abraham Lincoln.
No. C300a contains one each of the 1c, 3c, 10c, 25c, 1 l and 5 l, imperf.
For overprints and surcharges see Nos. C316-C319, C325-C330, C345, C347-C348, C352, C356-C364, C494-C495, C539-C541, C552-C553.

Types AP72 and AP73 in different colors, overprinted "OFICIAL," see Nos. CO98-CO109.

Constitution
AP74

Designs: 2c, 12c, Inauguration of Pres. Villeda Morales, horiz. 3c, 25c, Pres. Ramon Villeda Morales. 5c, 50c, Allegory of Second Republic (Torch and olive branches).

### Engr.; Seal Litho. on 1c, 10c

| **1959, Dec. 21** | | **Perf. 13½** | | |
|---|---|---|---|---|
| C301 | AP74 | 1c red brn, car & ultra | .20 | .20 |
| C302 | AP74 | 2c bister brn | .20 | .20 |
| C303 | AP74 | 3c ultra | .20 | .20 |
| C304 | AP74 | 5c orange | .20 | .20 |
| C305 | AP74 | 10c dull green, car & ultra | .25 | .20 |
| C306 | AP74 | 12c rose red | .35 | .20 |
| C307 | AP74 | 25c dull lilac | .85 | .20 |
| C308 | AP74 | 50c dark blue | 1.40 | .50 |
| | | Nos. C301-C308 (8) | 3.65 | 1.90 |

Second Republic of Honduras, 2nd anniv.
For surcharge see No. C543.

King Alfonso XIII and Map
AP75

Designs: 2c, 1906 award of King Alfonso XIII of Spain. 5c, Arbitration commission delivering its award, 1907. 10c, Intl. Court of Justice. 20c, Verdict of the Court, 1960. 50c, Pres. Morales, Foreign Minister Puerto and map. 1 l, Pres. Davila and Pres. Morales.

**1961, Nov. 18    Engr.    Perf. 14½x14**

| C309 | AP75 | 1c dark blue | .20 | .20 |
|------|------|-------------|-----|-----|
| C310 | AP75 | 2c magenta | .20 | .20 |
| C311 | AP75 | 5c deep green | .20 | .20 |
| C312 | AP75 | 10c brn orange | .20 | .20 |
| C313 | AP75 | 20c vermilion | .40 | .35 |
| C314 | AP75 | 50c brown | 1.00 | .55 |
| C315 | AP75 | 1 l vio black | 1.50 | 1.00 |
| | | Nos. C309-C315 (7) | 3.70 | 2.70 |

Judgment of the Intl. Court of Justice at The Hague, Nov. 18, 1960, returning a disputed territory to Honduras from Nicaragua.

Nos. C295-C297 and CO105 Surcharged

**1964, Apr. 7    Perf. 13½**

**Flags in National Colors**

| C316 | AP72 | 6c on 15c red org | .25 | .20 |
|------|------|-------------------|-----|-----|
| C317 | AP73 | 8c on 25c dull pur | .25 | .20 |
| C318 | AP73 | 10c on 50c ultra | .30 | .20 |
| C319 | AP73 | 20c on 25c black | .75 | .40 |
| | | Nos. C316-C319 (4) | 1.55 | 1.00 |

The red "OFICIAL" overprint on No. C319 was not obliterated.
See Nos. C345-C355, C419-C421.

Nos. C279-C281, C284 and C287 Overprinted: "FAO / Lucha Contra / el Hambre"

**1964, Mar. 23    Unwmk.    Perf. 12**

**Flags in National Colors**

| C320 | AP71 | 1c light blue | .20 | .20 |
|------|------|---------------|-----|-----|
| C321 | AP71 | 2c red | .20 | .20 |
| C322 | AP71 | 5c green | .25 | .20 |
| C323 | AP71 | 30c deep rose | 1.10 | .75 |
| C324 | AP71 | 1 l gray olive | 5.75 | 5.50 |
| | | Nos. C320-C324 (5) | 7.50 | 6.85 |

FAO "Freedom from Hunger Campaign" (1963).

Nos. CO98-CO101, CO104 and CO106 Overprinted in Blue or Black: "IN MEMORIAM / JOHN F. KENNEDY / 22 NOVEMBRE 1963"

**1964, May 29    Perf. 13½**

**Flags in National Colors**

| C325 | AP72 | 1c ocher (Bl) | .20 | .20 |
|------|------|---------------|-----|-----|
| C326 | AP73 | 2c gray ol (Bl) | .20 | .20 |
| C327 | AP73 | 3c red brn (Bl) | .35 | .20 |
| C328 | AP73 | 5c ultra (Bk) | .50 | .30 |
| C329 | AP72 | 15c dk brn (Bl) | 2.00 | 1.25 |
| C330 | AP73 | 50c dk car (Bl) | 10.50 | 6.25 |
| | | Nos. C325-C330 (6) | 13.75 | 8.40 |

Pres. John F. Kennedy (1917-63). The red "OFICIAL" overprint was not obliterated. The same overprint was applied to the stamps in miniature sheet No. C300a and seal of Honduras and Alliance for Progress emblem added in margin. Value \$65.

Nos. C222-C224, C226 and CO67 Overprinted with Olympic Rings and "1964"

**Engr.; Center of 1c Litho.**

**1964, July 23    Perf. 12½**

**Frames in Black**

| C331 | AP67 | 1c ultra & vio bl | .20 | .20 |
|------|------|-------------------|-----|-----|
| C332 | AP67 | 2c blue | .20 | .20 |
| C333 | AP67 | 3c rose lilac | .25 | .25 |
| C334 | AP67 | 15c red brown | .50 | .50 |
| C335 | AP67 | 2 l lilac rose | 6.25 | 6.25 |
| | | Nos. C331-C335 (5) | 7.40 | 7.40 |

18th Olympic Games, Tokyo, Oct. 10-25. The red "OFICIAL" overprint on No. C335 was not obliterated.
The same overprint was applied in black to the 6 stamps in #CO108a, with additional rings and "1964" in margins of souvenir sheet. Value \$50.

View of Copan AP76

Designs: 2c, 12c, Stone marker from Copan. 5c, 1 l, Mayan ball player (stone). 8c, 2 l, Olympic Stadium, Tokyo.

**Unwmk.**

**1964, Nov. 27    Photo.    Perf. 14**

**Black Design and Inscription**

| C336 | AP76 | 1c yellow grn | .20 | .20 |
|------|------|---------------|-----|-----|
| C337 | AP76 | 2c pale rose lil | .20 | .20 |
| C338 | AP76 | 5c light ultra | .25 | .20 |
| C339 | AP76 | 8c bluish green | .30 | .25 |
| C340 | AP76 | 10c buff | .40 | .30 |
| C341 | AP76 | 12c lemon | .60 | .35 |
| C342 | AP76 | 1 l light ocher | 1.60 | 1.25 |
| C343 | AP76 | 2 l pale ol grn | 4.25 | 3.50 |
| C344 | AP76 | 3 l rose | 4.75 | 4.00 |
| | | Nos. C336-C344 (9) | 12.55 | 10.25 |

18th Olympic Games, Tokyo, Oct. 10-25. Perf. and imperf. souvenir sheets of four exist containing one each of Nos. C338-C339, C341 and C344. Size: 129x110mm. Values: perf \$40; imperf \$50.
For overprints, see Nos. CO111-CO119.

Nos. C292, C174, CO106, CO104, C124-C125, C165, C167-C168 and C178 Surcharged

**1964-65**

| C345 | AP73 | 4c on 5c dk car, bl & red | .20 | .20 |
|------|------|------|-----|-----|
| C346 | AP62 | 10c on 15c red brn | .20 | .20 |
| C347 | AP73 | 10c on 50c dk car, bl & red | .20 | .20 |
| C348 | AP72 | 12c on 15c dk brn, bl & red | .30 | .20 |
| C349 | AP27 | 12c on 16c ol gray | .30 | .20 |
| C350 | AP27 | 12c on 21c lt blue | .30 | .20 |
| C351 | AP60 | 12c on 22c org yel | .30 | .20 |
| C352 | AP73 | 12c on 25c blk, bl & red | .30 | .20 |
| C353 | AP60 | 30c on 1 l dp blue | .50 | .50 |
| C354 | AP60 | 40c on 2 l lilac ('65) | .70 | .50 |
| C355 | AP61 | 40c on 1 l red brown ('65) | .70 | .30 |
| | | Nos. C345-C355 (11) | 4.00 | 2.65 |

The red "OFICIAL" overprint on Nos. C347-C348 and C352 was not obliterated.

Nos. C289, CO99, C291-C292, C295-C296, CO106 and C299-C300 Overprinted in Black or Green: "Toma de Posesión / General / Oswaldo López A. / Junio 6, 1965"

**1965, June 6    Engr.    Perf. 13½**

**Flags in National Colors**

| C356 | AP72 | 1c green | .25 | .25 |
|------|------|----------|-----|-----|
| C357 | AP73 | 2c gray ol (G) | .25 | .25 |
| C358 | AP73 | 3c purple (G) | .25 | .25 |
| C359 | AP73 | 5c dk car (G) | .25 | .25 |
| C360 | AP72 | 15c red orange | .35 | .35 |
| C361 | AP73 | 25c dull pur (G) | .50 | .50 |
| C362 | AP73 | 50c dk carmine (G) | 1.00 | 1.00 |
| C363 | AP73 | 2 l gray olive (G) | 4.00 | 4.00 |
| C364 | AP73 | 5 l ocher (G) | 9.50 | 9.50 |
| | | Nos. C356-C364 (9) | 16.35 | 16.35 |

Inauguration of Gen. Oswaldo López Arellano as president. The red "OFICIAL" overprint on Nos. C357 and C362 was not obliterated.

Ambulance and Maltese Cross AP77

Designs (Maltese Cross and): 5c, Hospital of Knights of Malta. 12c, Patients treated in village. 1 l, Map of Honduras.

**1965, Aug. 30    Litho.    Perf. 12x11**

| C365 | AP77 | 1c ultra | .35 | .20 |
|------|------|----------|-----|-----|
| C366 | AP77 | 5c dark green | .40 | .30 |
| C367 | AP77 | 12c dark brown | .55 | .50 |
| C368 | AP77 | 1 l brown | 2.25 | 1.90 |
| | | Nos. C365-C368 (4) | 3.55 | 2.90 |

Knights of Malta; campaign against leprosy.

Father Manuel de Jesus Subirana — AP78

Designs: 1c, Jicaque Indian. 2c, Preaching to the Indians. 10c, Msgr. Juan de Jesus Zepeda. 12c, Pope Pius IX. 20c, Tomb of Father Subirana, Yore. 1 l, Mission church. 2 l, Jicaque mother and child.

**Perf. 13½x14**

**1965, July 27    Litho.    Unwmk.**

| C369 | AP78 | 1c multicolored | .20 | .20 |
|------|------|-----------------|-----|-----|
| C370 | AP78 | 2c multicolored | .20 | .20 |
| C371 | AP78 | 8c multicolored | .20 | .20 |
| C372 | AP78 | 10c multicolored | .20 | .20 |
| C373 | AP78 | 12c multicolored | .20 | .20 |
| C374 | AP78 | 20c multicolored | .45 | .30 |
| C375 | AP78 | 1 l multicolored | 2.00 | 1.50 |
| C376 | AP78 | 2 l multicolored | 4.00 | 3.00 |
| a. | | Souv. sheet of 4, #C371, C373, C375-C376 | 20.00 | 20.00 |
| | | Nos. C369-C376 (8) | 7.45 | 5.80 |

Centenary (in 1964) of the death of Father Manuel de Jesus Subirana (1807-64), Spanish missionary to the Central American Indians.
For overprints and surcharges see Nos. C380-C386, C407-C413, C487-C488, C554.

Nos. C198-C199 and C168 Overprinted: "IN MEMORIAM / Sir Winston Churchill / 1874-1965."

**1965, Dec. 20    Engr.    Perf. 13½x14**

| C377 | AP65 | 1c red org & blk | .30 | .30 |
|------|------|------------------|-----|-----|
| C378 | AP65 | 2c blue & red brn | .80 | .80 |
| C379 | AP60 | 2 l lilac | 7.00 | 7.00 |
| | | Nos. C377-C379 (3) | 8.10 | 8.10 |

Sir Winston Spencer Churchill (1874-1965), statesman and World War II leader.

Nos. C369-C375 Overprinted

**1966, Mar. 10    Litho.    Perf. 13½x14**

| C380 | AP78 | 1c multicolored | .20 | .20 |
|------|------|-----------------|-----|-----|
| C381 | AP78 | 2c multicolored | .20 | .20 |
| C382 | AP78 | 8c multicolored | .25 | .20 |
| C383 | AP78 | 10c multicolored | .25 | .20 |
| C384 | AP78 | 12c multicolored | .30 | .20 |
| C385 | AP78 | 20c multicolored | .35 | .35 |
| C386 | AP78 | 1 l multicolored | 3.25 | 3.25 |
| | | Nos. C380-C386 (7) | 4.80 | 4.60 |

Visit of Pope Paul VI to the UN, New York City, Oct. 4, 1965.

Stamp of 1866, #1 — AP79

Tomas Estrada Palma — AP80

Post Office, Tegucigalpa AP81

Designs: 2c, Air post stamp of 1925, #C1. 5c, Locomotive. 6c, 19th cent. mail transport with mules. 7c, 19th cent. mail room. 8c, Sir Rowland Hill. 9c, Modern mail truck. 10c, Gen. Oswaldo Lopez Arellano. 12c, Postal emblem. 15c, Heinrich von Stephan. 20c, Mail plane. 30c, Flag of Honduras. 40c, Coat of Arms. 1 l, UPU monument, Bern. 2 l, José Maria Medina.

**Perf. 14½x14, 14x14½**

**1966, May 31    Litho.    Unwmk.**

| C387 | AP79 | 1c gold, blk & grnsh gray | .20 | .20 |
|------|------|------|-----|-----|
| C388 | AP79 | 2c org, blk & lt bl | .20 | .20 |
| C389 | AP80 | 3c brt rose, gold & dp plum | .20 | .20 |
| C390 | AP81 | 4c bl, gold & blk | .20 | .20 |
| C391 | AP81 | 5c pink, gold & blk | .75 | .20 |
| C392 | AP81 | 6c lil, gold & blk | .20 | .20 |
| C393 | AP81 | 7c lt bl grn, gold & black | .20 | .20 |
| C394 | AP80 | 8c lt bl, gold & blk | .20 | .20 |
| C395 | AP81 | 9c lt ultra, gold & black | .20 | .20 |
| C396 | AP80 | 10c cit, gold & blk | .20 | .20 |
| C397 | AP79 | 12c gold, blk, yel & emerald | .20 | .20 |
| C398 | AP80 | 15c brt pink, gold & dp claret | .40 | .40 |
| C399 | AP81 | 20c org, gold & blk | .45 | .45 |
| C400 | AP80 | 30c gold & bl | .55 | .55 |
| C401 | AP79 | 40c multi | .90 | .80 |
| C402 | AP79 | 1 l emer, gold & dk green | 2.00 | 1.50 |
| C403 | AP80 | 2 l gray, gold & black | 4.25 | 4.25 |
| a. | | Souv. sheet of 6, #C387-C388, C396-C397, C402-C403 | 6.75 | 6.75 |
| | | Nos. C387-C403 (17) | 11.30 | 10.15 |

Centenary of the first Honduran postage stamp. #C403a exists perf. and imperf. See #CE3. For surcharges see #C473-C474, C479, C486, C496.

Nos. CO53, C201 and C204 Overprinted: "CAMPEONATO DE FOOTBALL Copa Mundial 1966 Inglaterra-Alemania Wembley, Julio 30"

**Perf. 13½x14, 14x13½**

**1966, Nov. 25    Engr.**

| C404 | AP65 | 2c brown & vio | .20 | .20 |
|------|------|----------------|-----|-----|
| C405 | AP66 | 16c dk bl & blk | .30 | .30 |
| C406 | AP65 | 2 l brn & vio | 8.50 | 8.50 |
| | | Nos. C404-C406 (3) | 9.00 | 9.00 |

Final game between England and Germany in the World Soccer Cup Championship, Wembley, July 30, 1966. The overprint on the 2c and 2 l is in 6 lines, it is in 8 lines on the 16c. There is no hyphen between "Inglaterra" and "Alemania" on the 16c.

Nos. C369-C371 and C373-C376 Overprinted in Red: "CONMEMORATIVA / del XX Aniversario / ONU 1966"

**1967, Jan. 31    Litho.    Perf. 13½x14**

| C407 | AP78 | 1c multicolored | .20 | .20 |
|------|------|-----------------|-----|-----|
| C408 | AP78 | 2c multicolored | .20 | .20 |
| C409 | AP78 | 8c multicolored | .30 | .30 |
| C410 | AP78 | 12c multicolored | .50 | .40 |
| C411 | AP78 | 20c multicolored | .65 | .55 |
| C412 | AP78 | 1 l multicolored | 1.50 | 1.50 |
| C413 | AP78 | 2 l multicolored | 3.50 | 3.25 |
| | | Nos. C407-C413 (7) | 6.85 | 6.40 |

UN, 20th anniversary.

Nos. C250, C252, C258, C261 and C267 Overprinted in Red: "Siméon Cañas y Villacorta / Libertador de los esclavos / en Centro America / 1767-1967"

**1967, Feb. 27**      Engr.

| | | | | |
|---|---|---|---|---|
| C414 | AP68 | 1c blk & vio bl | .20 | .20 |
| C415 | AP68 | 3c blk & brown | .25 | .25 |
| C416 | AP68 | 15c dk red & blk | .35 | .35 |
| C417 | AP68 | 25c blk & grn | 1.00 | .70 |
| C418 | AP69 | 2 l blk & mag | 2.75 | 2.50 |
| | | Nos. C414-C418 (5) | 4.55 | 4.00 |

Birth bicentenary of Father José Siméon Canas y Villacorta, D.D. (1767-1838), emancipator of the Central American slaves. The overprint is in 6 lines on the 2 l, in 4 lines on all others.

Nos. C178-C179 and CE2 Surcharged

**1967**

| | | | | |
|---|---|---|---|---|
| C419 | AP61 | 10c on 1 l | .35 | .20 |
| C420 | AP62 | 10c on 2 l | .35 | .20 |
| C421 | APSD1 | 10c on 20c | .35 | .20 |
| | | Nos. C419-C421 (3) | 1.05 | .60 |

José Cecilio del Valle, Honduras AP82

Designs: 12c, Ruben Dario, Nicaragua. 14c, Batres Montufar, Guatemala. 20c, Francisco Antonio Gavidia, El Salvador. 30c, Juan Mora Fernandez, Costa Rica. 40c, Federation Emblem with map of Americas. 50c, Map of Central America.

**1967, Aug. 4**   Litho.   Perf. 13

| | | | | |
|---|---|---|---|---|
| C422 | AP82 | 11c gold, ultra & blk | .20 | .20 |
| C423 | AP82 | 12c lt bl, yel & blk | .20 | .20 |
| C424 | AP82 | 14c sil, grn & blk | .20 | .20 |
| C425 | AP82 | 20c pink, grn & blk | .25 | .25 |
| C426 | AP82 | 30c bluish lil, yel & black | .40 | .40 |
| C427 | AP82 | 40c pur, lt bl & gold | .70 | .70 |
| C428 | AP82 | 50c lem, grn & car rose | .70 | .70 |
| | | Nos. C422-C428 (7) | 2.65 | 2.60 |

Founding of the Federation of Central American Journalists.
For surcharges see Nos. C475-C476.

Olympic Rings, Flags of Mexico and Honduras AP83

Olympic Rings and Winners of 1964 Olympics: 2c, Like 1c. 5c, Italian flag and boxers. 10c, French flag and women skiers. 12c, German flag and equestrian team. 50c, British flag and women runners. 1 l, US flag and runners (Bob Hayes).

**1968, Mar. 4**   Litho.   Perf. 14x13½

| | | | | |
|---|---|---|---|---|
| C429 | AP83 | 1c gold & multi | .20 | .20 |
| C430 | AP83 | 2c gold & multi | .20 | .20 |
| C431 | AP83 | 5c gold & multi | .25 | .25 |
| C432 | AP83 | 10c gold & multi | .30 | .25 |
| C433 | AP83 | 12c gold & multi | .50 | .25 |
| C434 | AP83 | 50c gold & multi | 3.25 | 3.25 |
| C435 | AP83 | 1 l gold & multi | 6.25 | 6.25 |
| | | Nos. C429-C435 (7) | 10.95 | 10.65 |

19th Olympic Games, Mexico City, Oct. 12-27.
Exist imperf. Value $45.
Perf. and imperf. souvenir sheets of 2 exist containing 20c and 40c stamps in design of 1c. Values: perf $8; imperf $16.
For surcharge see No. C499.

---

John F. Kennedy, Rocket at Cape Kennedy AP84

ITU Emblem and: 2c, Radar and telephone. 3c, Radar and television set. 5c, Radar and globe showing Central America. 8c, Communications satellite. 10c, 20c, like 1c.

**1968, Nov. 28**     Perf. 14x13½

| | | | | |
|---|---|---|---|---|
| C436 | AP84 | 1c vio & multi | .20 | .20 |
| C437 | AP84 | 2c sil & multi | .20 | .20 |
| C438 | AP84 | 3c multicolored | .35 | .35 |
| C439 | AP84 | 5c org & multi | .40 | .40 |
| C440 | AP84 | 8c multicolored | .50 | .50 |
| C441 | AP84 | 10c olive & multi | .55 | .55 |
| C442 | AP84 | 20c multicolored | .70 | .70 |
| | | Nos. C436-C442 (7) | 2.90 | 2.90 |

ITU, cent. A 30c in design of 2c, a 1 l in design of 5c and a 1.50 l in design of 1c exist; also two souvenir sheets, one containing 10c, 50c and 75c, the other one 1.50 l.
For overprints see Nos. C446-C453.

Nos. C436, C441-C442 Overprinted: "In Memoriam / Robert F. Kennedy / 1925-1968"

**1968, Dec. 23**

| | | | | |
|---|---|---|---|---|
| C446 | AP84 | 1c vio & multi | .20 | .20 |
| C447 | AP84 | 10c olive & multi | .50 | .50 |
| C448 | AP84 | 20c multicolored | .80 | .80 |
| | | Nos. C446-C448 (3) | 1.50 | 1.50 |

In memory of Robert F. Kennedy. Same overprint was also applied to a 1.50 l and to a souvenir sheet containing one 1.50 l. Value, souvenir sheet $6.

Nos. C437-C440 Overprinted in Blue or Red with Olympic Rings and: "Medalias de Oro / Mexico 1968"

**1969, Mar. 3**

| | | | | |
|---|---|---|---|---|
| C450 | AP84 | 2c multi (Bl) | .50 | .50 |
| C451 | AP84 | 3c multi (Bl) | 1.00 | 1.00 |
| C452 | AP84 | 5c multi (Bl) | 1.50 | 1.50 |
| C453 | AP84 | 8c multi (R) | 2.00 | 2.00 |
| | | Nos. C450-C453 (4) | 5.00 | 5.00 |

Gold medal winners in 19th Olympic Games, Mexico City. The same red overprint was also applied to a 30c and a 1 l. The souvenir sheet of 3 noted after No. C442 exists with this overprint in black. Value, souvenir sheet $6.

Rocket Blast-off AP85

Designs: 10c, Close-up view of moon. 12c, Spacecraft, horiz. 20c, Astronaut and module on moon, horiz. 24c, Lunar landing module.

**Perf. 14½x13½, 13½x14**

**1969, Oct. 29**

| | | | | |
|---|---|---|---|---|
| C454 | AP85 | 5c multicolored | .20 | .20 |
| C455 | AP85 | 10c multicolored | .30 | .30 |
| C456 | AP85 | 12c multicolored | .40 | .40 |
| C457 | AP85 | 20c multicolored | .50 | .50 |
| C458 | AP85 | 24c multicolored | 1.00 | 1.00 |
| | | Nos. C454-C458 (5) | 2.40 | 2.40 |

Man's first landing on the moon, July 20, 1969. A 30c showing re-entry of capsule, a 1 l in design of 20c and a 1.50 l in design of 24c exist. Two souvenir sheets exist, one containing #C454-C455 and 1.50 l, and the other #C456, 30c and 1 l.
For the safe return of Apollo 13, overprints were applied in 1970 to #C454-C458, the 3 unlisted denominations and the 2 souvenir sheets. Value of 2 souvenir sheets $20.
For overprints and surcharges see Nos. C500-C504, C555.

---

Nos. C224, C393, C395, C422, C424, CE2 and C178 Surcharged with New Value

**1970, Feb. 20**    Engr.; Litho.

| | | | | |
|---|---|---|---|---|
| C472 | AP67 | 4c on 3c blk & rose lil | .20 | .20 |
| C473 | AP81 | 5c on 7c multi | .25 | .20 |
| C474 | AP81 | 10c on 9c multi | .30 | .20 |
| C475 | AP82 | 10c on 11c multi | .30 | .20 |
| C476 | AP82 | 12c on 14c multi | .35 | .20 |
| C477 | APSD1 | 12c on 20c blk & red | .35 | .20 |
| C478 | AP61 | 12c on 1 l red brn | .35 | .20 |
| | | Nos. C472-C478 (7) | 2.10 | 1.40 |

No. CE3 Overprinted "HABILITADO"

**1970**    Litho.    Perf. 14x14½

| | | | | |
|---|---|---|---|---|
| C479 | AP81 | 20c bis brn, brn & gold | .75 | .35 |

Julio Adolfo Sanhueza AP86

Emblems, Map and Flag of Honduras — AP87

Designs: 8c, Rigoberto Ordoñez Rodriguez. 12c, Forest Fire Brigade emblem (with map of Honduras) and emblems of fire fighters, FAO and Alliance for Progress, horiz. 1 l, Flags of Honduras, UN and US, Arms of Honduras and emblems as on 12c.

**Perf. 14½x14, 14x14½**

**1970, Aug. 15**    Litho.

| | | | | |
|---|---|---|---|---|
| C480 | AP86 | 5c gold, emer & ind | .30 | .20 |
| C481 | AP86 | 8c gold, org brn & indigo | .40 | .20 |
| C482 | AP87 | 12c bl & multi | .50 | .20 |
| C483 | AP87 | 20c yel & multi | .70 | .25 |
| C484 | AP87 | 1 l gray & multi | 3.50 | 1.75 |
| a. | | Souvenir sheet of 5 | 3.00 | 2.00 |
| | | Nos. C480-C484 (5) | 5.40 | 2.60 |

Campaign against forest fires and in memory of the men who lost their lives fighting forest fires. No. C484a contains 5 imperf. stamps with simulated perforations and without gum similar to Nos. C480-C484. Sold for 1.45 l.
For surcharges see Nos. C497-C498.

Hotel Honduras Maya AP88

**1970, Oct. 24**    Litho.    Perf. 14

| | | | | |
|---|---|---|---|---|
| C485 | AP88 | 12c sky blue & blk | .30 | .25 |

Hotel Honduras Maya, Tegucigalpa, opening.

Stamps of 1952-1968 Surcharged

**1971**       Litho.; Engr.

| | | | | |
|---|---|---|---|---|
| C486 | AP79 | 4c on 1c (#C387) | .20 | |
| C487 | AP78 | 5c on 1c (#C369) | .20 | |
| C488 | AP78 | 8c on 2c (#C370) | .25 | |
| C489 | AP65 | 10c on 2c (#C199) | .35 | |
| C490 | AP67 | 10c on 3c (#C224) | .35 | |
| a. | | Inverted surcharge | | |
| C491 | AP68 | 10c on 3c (#C252) | .35 | |
| C492 | AP68 | 10c on 3c (#CO71) | .35 | |
| C493 | AP69 | 10c on 2c (#C251) | .35 | |
| C494 | AP73 | 10c on 3c (#CO99) | .35 | |
| C495 | AP73 | 10c on 3c (#CO100) | .35 | |
| C496 | AP80 | 10c on 3c (#C389) | .35 | |
| C497 | AP87 | 15c on 12c (#C482) | .50 | |
| C498 | AP87 | 30c on 12c (#C482) | 1.00 | |
| C499 | AP83 | 40c on 50c (#C434) | 1.25 | |
| C500 | AP85 | 40c on 24c (#C458) | 1.25 | |
| | | Nos. C486-C500 (15) | 7.45 | |

Red "OFICIAL" overprint was not obliterated on Nos. C492, C494-C495.

---

No. C491 exists with inverted surcharge.

Nos. C454, C456-C458 Overprinted and Surcharged

**Perf. 14½x13½, 13½x14½**

**1972, May 15**     Litho.

| | | | | |
|---|---|---|---|---|
| C501 | AP85 | 5c multi | .70 | .40 |
| C502 | AP85 | 12c multi | 1.50 | .75 |
| C503 | AP85 | 1 l on 20c multi | 3.50 | 3.00 |
| C504 | AP85 | 2 l on 24c multi | 6.00 | 5.00 |
| | | Nos. C501-C504 (4) | 11.70 | 9.15 |

Masonic Grand Lodge of Honduras, 50th anniv. Overprint varies to fit stamp shape.

Soldier's Bay, Guanaja AP89

Designs: 5c, 7c, 9c, 10c, 2 l, vertical.

**1972, May 19**     Perf. 13

| | | | | |
|---|---|---|---|---|
| C505 | AP89 | 4c shown | .20 | .20 |
| C506 | AP89 | 5c Taps | .20 | .20 |
| C507 | AP89 | 6c Yojoa Lake | .20 | .20 |
| C508 | AP89 | 7c Banana Carrier, by Roberto Aguilar | .20 | .20 |
| C509 | AP89 | 8c Military parade | .20 | .20 |
| C510 | AP89 | 9c Orchid, national flower | .25 | .20 |
| C511 | AP89 | 10c like 9c | .25 | .20 |
| C512 | AP89 | 12c Soldier with machine gun | .20 | .20 |
| C513 | AP89 | 15c Sunset over beach | .30 | .20 |
| C514 | AP89 | 20c Litter bearers | .30 | .20 |
| C515 | AP89 | 30c Landscape, by Antonio Velasquez | .50 | .25 |
| C516 | AP89 | 40c Ruins of Copan | .75 | .40 |
| a. | | Souv. sheet of 4, #C508, C513, C515-C516 | 2.00 | 2.00 |
| C517 | AP89 | 50c Girl from Huacal, by Pablo Zelaya Sierra | .60 | .35 |
| a. | | Souv. sheet of 4, #C506-C507, C514, C517 | 2.00 | 2.00 |
| C518 | AP89 | 1 l Trujillo Bay | 1.50 | 1.00 |
| a. | | Souv. sheet of 4, #C505, C509, C512, C518 | 2.75 | 2.75 |
| C519 | AP89 | 2 l Orchid, national flower | 4.00 | 3.00 |
| a. | | Souv. sheet of 3, #C510-C511, C519 | 6.50 | 6.50 |
| | | Nos. C505-C519,CE4 (16) | 10.35 | 7.35 |

Sesquicentennial of independence (stamps inscribed 1970).
For surcharge see No. CE5.

Sister Maria Rosa and Child — AP90

Designs: 15c, SOS Children's Village emblem, horiz. 30c, Father José Trinidad Reyes. 40c, Kennedy Center, first SOS village in Central America, horiz. 1 l, Boy.

**Perf. 13½x13, 13x13½**

**1972, Nov. 10**     Photo.

| | | | | |
|---|---|---|---|---|
| C520 | AP90 | 10c grn, gold & brn | .20 | .20 |
| C521 | AP90 | 15c grn, gold & brn | .25 | .20 |
| C522 | AP90 | 30c grn, gold & brn | .40 | .20 |
| C523 | AP90 | 40c grn, gold & brn | .50 | .20 |
| C524 | AP90 | 1 l grn, gold & brn | 2.00 | 1.50 |
| | | Nos. C520-C524 (5) | 3.35 | 2.30 |

Children's Villages in Honduras (Intl. SOS movement to save homeless children).

For overprints and surcharges see #C531, C534-C536, C546-C549, C556, C560-C561.

Map of Honduras and Society Emblem AP91

Design: 12c, Map of Honduras, emblems of National Geographic Institute and Interamerican Geodesic Service.

**1973, Mar. 27    Litho.    Perf. 13**

| | | | | |
|---|---|---|---|---|
| C525 | AP91 | 10c multicolored | .55 | .30 |
| C526 | AP91 | 12c multicolored | .65 | .30 |

25th anniv. of Natl. Cartographic Service (10c) and of joint cartographic work (12c).
For overprints and surcharges see Nos. C532-C533, C557-C558.

Juan Ramón Molina AP92

Designs: 8c, Illustration from Molina's book "Habitante de la Osa." 1 l, Illustration from "Tierras Mares y Cielos." 2 l, "UNESCO."

**1973, Apr. 17    Litho.    Perf. 13½**

| | | | | |
|---|---|---|---|---|
| C527 | AP92 | 8c brn org, blk & red brn | .20 | .20 |
| C528 | AP92 | 20c brt bl & multi | .65 | .25 |
| C529 | AP92 | 1 l green & multi | 1.50 | 1.00 |
| C530 | AP92 | 2 l org & multi | 3.25 | 2.75 |
| a. | | Sheet of 4 | 6.00 | 6.00 |
| | | Nos. C527-C530 (4) | 5.60 | 4.20 |

Molina (1875-1908), poet, and 25th anniv. (in 1971) of UNESCO. #C530a contains 4 stamps similar to #C527-C530. Exists perf. & imperf.
For surcharge see No. C559.

Nos. C520-C523, C525-C526 Overprinted in Red or Black: "Censos de Población y Vivienda, marzo 1974. 1974, Año Mundial de Población"

**1973, Dec. 28    Photo; Litho.**
Perf. 13½x13, 13x13½

| | | | | |
|---|---|---|---|---|
| C531 | AP90 | 10c multi (R) | .20 | .20 |
| C532 | AP90 | 10c multi (B) | .20 | .20 |
| C533 | AP91 | 12c multi (B) | .20 | .20 |
| C534 | AP90 | 15c multi (R) | .20 | .20 |
| C535 | AP90 | 30c multi (R) | .30 | .25 |
| C536 | AP90 | 40c multi (R) | .35 | .35 |
| | | Nos. C531-C536 (6) | 1.45 | 1.40 |

1974 population and housing census; World Population Year. The overprint is in 7 lines on vertical stamps, in 5 lines on horizontal.

Issues of 1947-59 Surcharged in Red or Black
**Perf. 13x12½, 13½, 11x12½, 12**

**1974, June 28    Engr.**

| | | | | |
|---|---|---|---|---|
| C537 | AP68 | 2c on 1c (#C250) (R) | .20 | .20 |
| C538 | AP68 | 2c on 1c (#CO69) | .20 | .20 |
| C539 | AP72 | 2c on 1c (#C289) | .20 | .20 |
| C540 | AP72 | 2c on 1c (#CO98) | .20 | .20 |
| C541 | AP72 | 3c on 1c (#C289) | .20 | .20 |
| C542 | AP68 | 3c on 1c (#C250) (R) | .20 | .20 |
| C543 | AP74 | 1 l on 50c (#C308) | 1.40 | 1.40 |
| C544 | AP60 | 1 l on 2 l (#C168) | 1.40 | 1.40 |
| C545 | AP62 | 1 l on 2 l (#C179) | 1.40 | 1.40 |
| | | Nos. C537-C545 (9) | 5.40 | 5.40 |

Red "OFICIAL" overprint was not obliterated on Nos. C538 and C540.

Nos. C520-C523 Overprinted in Bright Green: "1949-1974 SOS Kinderdorfer International Honduras-Austria"

**1974, July 25    Photo.**

| | | | | |
|---|---|---|---|---|
| C546 | AP90 | 10c grn, gold & brn | .20 | .20 |
| C547 | AP90 | 15c grn, gold & brn | .20 | .20 |
| C548 | AP90 | 30c grn, gold & brn | .25 | .25 |
| C549 | AP90 | 40c grn, gold & brn | .35 | .35 |
| | | Nos. C546-C549 (4) | 1.00 | 1.00 |

25th anniversary of Children's Villages in Honduras. Overprint in 6 lines on 10c and 30c, in 4 lines on 15c and 40c.

Stamps of 1956-73 Surcharged
**1975, Feb. 24    Litho.; Engr.**

| | | | | |
|---|---|---|---|---|
| C550 | AP68 | 16c on 1c (#C250) | .20 | .20 |
| C551 | AP70 | 16c on 1c (#C269) | .20 | .20 |
| C552 | AP72 | 16c on 1c (#C289) | .20 | .20 |
| C553 | AP72 | 16c on 1c (#CO98) | .20 | .20 |
| C554 | AP78 | 16c on 1c (#C369) | .30 | .30 |
| C555 | AP85 | 18c on 12c (#C456) | .40 | .25 |
| C556 | AP90 | 18c on 10c (#C520) | .25 | .20 |
| C557 | AP91 | 18c on 10c (#C525) | .25 | .20 |
| C558 | AP91 | 18c on 12c (#C526) | .25 | .20 |
| C559 | AP92 | 18c on 8c (#C527) | .25 | .20 |
| C560 | AP90 | 50c on 30c (#C522) | .75 | .50 |
| C561 | AP90 | 1 l on 40c (#C522) | 1.25 | .90 |
| | | Nos. C550-C561,CE5 (13) | 5.50 | 4.80 |

Denominations not obliterated on Nos. C551, C553-C558, C560-C561; "OFICIAL" overprint not obliterated on No. C553.
For surcharges, see Nos. C1197, C1198, C1200.

Flags of Germany and Austria AP93

Designs (Flags): 2c, Belgium & Denmark. 3c, Spain & France. 4c, Hungary & Russia. 5c, Great Britain & Italy. 10c, Norway & Sweden. 12c, Honduras. 15c, US & Switzerland. 20c, Greece & Portugal. 30c, Romania & Serbia. 1 l, Egypt & Netherlands. 2 l, Luxembourg & Turkey.

**1975, June 18    Litho.    Perf. 13**
**Gold & Multicolored; Colors Listed are for Shields**

| | | | | |
|---|---|---|---|---|
| C562 | AP93 | 1c lilac | .20 | .20 |
| C563 | AP93 | 2c gold | .20 | .20 |
| C564 | AP93 | 3c rose gray | .20 | .20 |
| C565 | AP93 | 4c light blue | .20 | .20 |
| C566 | AP93 | 5c yellow | .20 | .20 |
| C567 | AP93 | 10c gray | .20 | .20 |
| C568 | AP93 | 12c lilac rose | .25 | .25 |
| C569 | AP93 | 15c bluish green | .35 | .35 |
| C570 | AP93 | 20c bright blue | .40 | .40 |
| C571 | AP93 | 30c pink | .75 | .75 |
| C572 | AP93 | 1 l salmon | 1.75 | 1.75 |
| C573 | AP93 | 2 l yellow green | 3.75 | 3.75 |
| | | Nos. C562-C573 (12) | 8.45 | 8.45 |

**Souvenir Sheet**

| | | | | |
|---|---|---|---|---|
| C574 | AP93 | Sheet of 12 | 12.00 | 12.00 |

UPU, cent. (in 1974). No. C574 contains 12 stamps similar to Nos. C562-C573 with shields in different colors.

Humuya Youth Center and Mrs. Arellano AP94

Designs (Portrait of First Lady, Gloria de Lopez Arellano, IWY Emblem and): 16c, Jalteva Youth Center. 18c, Mrs. Arellano (diff. portrait) and IWY emblem. 30c, El Carmen de San Pedro Sula Youth Center. 55c, Flag of National Social Welfare Organization, vert. 1 l, La Isla sports and recreational facilities. 2 l, Women's Social Center.

**1976, Mar. 5    Litho.    Perf. 13½**

| | | | | |
|---|---|---|---|---|
| C575 | AP94 | 8c sal & multi | .20 | .20 |
| C576 | AP94 | 16c yel & multi | .20 | .20 |
| C577 | AP94 | 18c pink & multi | .20 | .20 |
| C578 | AP94 | 30c org & multi | .45 | .45 |
| C579 | AP94 | 55c multicolored | .70 | .70 |
| C580 | AP94 | 1 l multicolored | 1.50 | 1.50 |
| C581 | AP94 | 2 l multicolored | 2.75 | 2.75 |
| | | Nos. C575-C581 (7) | 6.00 | 6.00 |

International Women's Year (1975).
For surcharges see #C736-C737, C781, C798, C885, C887, C919, C1203.

"CARE" and Globe AP95

Designs: 1c, 16c, 30c, 55c, 1 l, Care package and globe, vert. Others like 5c.

**1976, May 24    Litho.    Perf. 13½**

| | | | | |
|---|---|---|---|---|
| C582 | AP95 | 1c blk & lt blue | .20 | .20 |
| C583 | AP95 | 5c rose brn & blk | .20 | .20 |
| C584 | AP95 | 16c black & org | .20 | .20 |
| C585 | AP95 | 18c lemon & blk | .25 | .25 |
| C586 | AP95 | 30c blk & blue | .35 | .35 |
| C587 | AP95 | 50c yel grn & blk | .50 | .50 |
| C588 | AP95 | 55c blk & buff | .50 | .50 |
| C589 | AP95 | 70c brt rose & blk | .70 | .70 |
| C590 | AP95 | 1 l blk & lt grn | 1.25 | 1.25 |
| C591 | AP95 | 2 l ocher & blk | 2.40 | 2.40 |
| | | Nos. C582-C591 (10) | 6.55 | 6.55 |

20th anniversary of CARE in Honduras.
For surcharges see Nos. C735, C738, C788, C888, C922.

Fawn in Burnt-out Forest — AP96

"Sons of Liberty" — AP97

Forest Protection: 16c, COHDEFOR emblem (Corporacion Hondureña de Desarollo Forestal). 18c, Forest, horiz. 30c, 2 l, Live and burning trees. 50c, like 10c. 70c, Emblem. 1 l, Young forest, horiz.

**1976, May 28    Litho.    Perf. 13½**

| | | | | |
|---|---|---|---|---|
| C592 | AP96 | 10c multicolored | .20 | .20 |
| C593 | AP96 | 16c multicolored | .25 | .20 |
| C594 | AP96 | 18c multicolored | .25 | .20 |
| C595 | AP96 | 30c grn & multi | .50 | .20 |
| C596 | AP96 | 50c multicolored | .75 | .30 |
| C597 | AP96 | 70c brn & multi | 1.00 | .40 |
| C598 | AP96 | 1 l yel & multi | 2.00 | .75 |
| C599 | AP96 | 2 l vio & multi | 3.50 | 3.50 |
| | | Nos. C592-C599,CE6 (9) | 9.20 | 6.25 |

For surcharges see Nos. C784, C787, C917.

**1976, Aug. 29    Litho.    Perf. 12**

American Bicentennial: 2c, Raising flag of "Liberty and Union." 3c, Bunker Hill flag. 4c, Washington's Cruisers' flag. 5c, 1st Navy Jack. 6c, Flag of Honduras over Presidential Palace, Tegucigalpa. 18c, US flag over Capitol. 55c, Grand Union flag. 2 l, Bennington flag. 3 l, Betsy Ross and her flag.

| | | | | |
|---|---|---|---|---|
| C601 | AP97 | 1c multicolored | .20 | .20 |
| C602 | AP97 | 2c multicolored | .20 | .20 |
| C603 | AP97 | 3c multicolored | .20 | .20 |
| C604 | AP97 | 4c multicolored | .20 | .20 |
| C605 | AP97 | 5c multicolored | .20 | .20 |
| C606 | AP97 | 6c multicolored | .20 | .20 |
| C607 | AP97 | 18c multicolored | .30 | .35 |
| C608 | AP97 | 55c multicolored | .75 | .70 |
| a. | | Souv. sheet of 4, #C603, C606-C608 | 2.00 | 2.00 |
| C609 | AP97 | 2 l multicolored | 2.25 | 2.25 |
| a. | | Souv. sheet of 3, #C601, C604, C609 | 4.50 | 4.50 |
| C610 | AP97 | 3 l multicolored | 4.75 | 4.75 |
| a. | | Souv. sheet of 3, #C602, C605, C610 | 5.50 | 5.50 |
| | | Nos. C601-C610 (10) | 9.25 | 9.25 |

For surcharges see Nos. C883-C884, C885, C889.

King Juan Carlos of Spain — AP98

Designs: 16c, Queen Sophia. 30c, Queen Sophia and King Juan Carlos. 2 l, Arms of Honduras and Spain, horiz.

**1977, Sept. 13    Litho.    Perf. 14**

| | | | | |
|---|---|---|---|---|
| C611 | AP98 | 16c multicolored | .20 | .20 |
| C612 | AP98 | 18c multicolored | .20 | .20 |
| C613 | AP98 | 30c multicolored | .30 | .25 |
| C614 | AP98 | 2 l multicolored | 2.10 | 2.10 |
| | | Nos. C611-C614 (4) | 2.80 | 2.75 |

Visit of King and Queen of Spain.
For surcharges see Nos. C890, C918.

Mayan Steles, Exhibition Emblems AP99

Designs: 18c, Giant head. 30c, Statue. 55c, Sun god. 1.50 l, Mayan pelota court.

**1978, Apr. 28    Litho.    Perf. 12**

| | | | | |
|---|---|---|---|---|
| C615 | AP99 | 15c multi | .20 | .20 |
| C616 | AP99 | 18c multi | .45 | .45 |
| C617 | AP99 | 30c multi | .65 | .65 |
| C618 | AP99 | 55c multi | 1.25 | 1.25 |

**Imperf**

| | | | | |
|---|---|---|---|---|
| C619 | AP99 | 1.50 l multi | 4.00 | 4.00 |
| | | Nos. C615-C619 (5) | 6.55 | 6.55 |

Honduras '78 Philatelic Exhibition.
For overprints and surcharges see Nos. C642-C645, C786, C920, C924, CB6.

Del Valle's Birthplace AP100

Designs: 14c, La Merced Church, Choluteca, where del Valle was baptized. 15c, Baptismal font, vert. 20c, Del Valle reading independence acts. 25c, Portrait, documents, map of Central America. 40c, Portrait, vert. 1 l, Monument, Central Park, Choluteca. 3 l, Bust, vert.

**1978, Apr. 11    Litho.    Perf. 14**

| | | | | |
|---|---|---|---|---|
| C620 | AP100 | 8c multicolored | .20 | .20 |
| C621 | AP100 | 14c multicolored | .20 | .20 |
| C622 | AP100 | 15c multicolored | .20 | .20 |
| C623 | AP100 | 20c multicolored | .20 | .20 |
| C624 | AP100 | 25c multicolored | .30 | .30 |
| C625 | AP100 | 40c multicolored | .40 | .40 |
| C626 | AP100 | 1 l multicolored | 1.25 | 1.25 |
| C627 | AP100 | 3 l multicolored | 4.00 | 4.00 |
| | | Nos. C620-C627 (8) | 6.75 | 6.75 |

Bicentenary of the birth of José Cecilio del Valle (1780-1834), Central American patriot and statesman.
For surcharges see Nos. C739, C793, C795, C886A.

Rural Health Center AP101

Designs: 6c, Child at water pump. 10c, Los Laureles Dam, Tegucigalpa. 20c, Rural aqueduct. 40c, Teaching hospital, Tegucigalpa. 2 l, Parents and child. 3 l, National vaccination campaign. 5 l, Panamerican Health Organization Building, Washington, DC.

**1978, May 10    Litho.    Perf. 14**

| | | | | |
|---|---|---|---|---|
| C628 | AP101 | 5c multicolored | .20 | .20 |
| C629 | AP101 | 6c multicolored | .20 | .20 |
| C630 | AP101 | 10c multicolored | .20 | .20 |
| C631 | AP101 | 20c multicolored | .25 | .25 |
| C632 | AP101 | 40c multicolored | .45 | .45 |
| C633 | AP101 | 2 l multicolored | 1.90 | 1.90 |
| C634 | AP101 | 3 l multicolored | 3.00 | 3.00 |
| C635 | AP101 | 5 l multicolored | 4.50 | 4.50 |
| | | Nos. C628-C635 (8) | 10.70 | 10.70 |

75th anniv. of Panamerican Health Organization (in 1977).
For surcharge see No. C783.

Luis Landa and his "Botanica" AP102

Designs (Luis Landa and): 16c, Map of Honduras showing St. Ignacio. 18c, Medals received by Landa. 30c, Landa's birthplace in St. Ignacio. 2 l, Brassavola (orchid), national flower. 3 l, Women's Normal School.

**1978, Aug. 29    Photo.    Perf. 13x13½**

| | | | | |
|---|---|---|---|---|
| C636 | AP102 | 14c multicolored | .20 | .20 |
| C637 | AP102 | 16c multicolored | .20 | .20 |
| C638 | AP102 | 18c multicolored | .20 | .20 |
| C639 | AP102 | 30c multicolored | .40 | 1.00 |
| C640 | AP102 | 2 l multicolored | 3.00 | 1.00 |
| C641 | AP102 | 3 l multicolored | 3.50 | 3.50 |
| | | Nos. C636-C641 (6) | 7.50 | 5.30 |

Prof. Luis Landa (1875-1975), botanist.
For surcharges see Nos. C740, C794, C888A, C923.

Nos. C615-C618 Overprinted in Red with Argentina '78 Soccer Cup Emblem and:
"Argentina Campeon / Holanda Sub-Campeon / XI Campeonato Mundial / de Football"

**1978, Sept. 6    Litho.    Perf. 12**

| | | | | |
|---|---|---|---|---|
| C642 | AP99 | 15c multicolored | .20 | .20 |
| C643 | AP99 | 18c multicolored | .35 | .20 |
| C644 | AP99 | 30c multicolored | .45 | .40 |
| C645 | AP99 | 55c multicolored | 1.00 | .65 |
| | | Nos. C642-C645 (4) | 2.00 | 1.45 |

Argentina's victory in World Cup Soccer Championship. Same overprint was applied to No. C619. Value $45.
For surcharges, see No. C924, C1079.

Central University and Coat of Arms — AP103

Designs show for each denomination a 19th century print and a contemporary photograph of same area (except 1.50 l, 5 l): No. C647, University City. 8c, Manuel Bonilla Theater. No. C650, Court House, vert. No. C651, North Boulevard highway intersection, vert. No. C652, Natl. Palace. No. C653, Presidential Palace. 20c, Hospital. 40c, Cathedral. 50c, View of Tegucigalpa. 1.50 l, Aerial view of Tegucigalpa. No. C660, Arms of San Miguel de Tegucigalpa, 18th cent., vert. No. C661, Pres. Marco Aurelio Soto (1846-1908) (painting), vert.

**1978, Sept. 29**

| | | | | |
|---|---|---|---|---|
| C646 | AP103 | 6c black & brn | .20 | .20 |
| C647 | AP103 | 6c multicolored | .20 | .20 |
| a. | | Pair, #C646-C647 | .20 | .20 |
| C648 | AP103 | 8c black & brn | .20 | .20 |
| C649 | AP103 | 8c multicolored | .20 | .20 |
| a. | | Pair, #C648-C649 | .25 | .25 |
| C650 | AP103 | 10c black & brn | .20 | .20 |
| C651 | AP103 | 10c multicolored | .20 | .20 |
| a. | | Pair, #C650-C651 | .30 | .30 |
| C652 | AP103 | 16c black & brn | .25 | .25 |
| C653 | AP103 | 16c multicolored | .25 | .25 |
| a. | | Pair, #C652-C653 | .50 | .50 |
| C654 | AP103 | 20c black & brn | .30 | .30 |
| C655 | AP103 | 20c multicolored | .30 | .30 |
| a. | | Pair, #C654-C655 | .60 | .60 |

| | | | | |
|---|---|---|---|---|
| C656 | AP103 | 40c black & brn | .75 | .45 |
| C657 | AP103 | 40c multicolored | .75 | .45 |
| a. | | Pair, #C656-C657 | 1.60 | 1.60 |
| C658 | AP103 | 50c black & brn | 1.00 | .50 |
| C659 | AP103 | 50c multicolored | 1.00 | .50 |
| a. | | Pair, #C658-C659 | 2.10 | 2.10 |
| C660 | AP103 | 5 l black & brn | 6.75 | 6.75 |
| C661 | AP103 | 5 l multicolored | 6.75 | 6.75 |
| a. | | Pair, #C660-C661 | 14.00 | 14.00 |
| | | Nos. C646-C661 (16) | 19.30 | 17.40 |

**Souvenir Sheet**

| | | | | |
|---|---|---|---|---|
| C662 | AP103 | 1.50 l multi | 2.75 | 2.75 |

400th anniv. of the founding of Tegucigalpa. In the listing the first number is for the 19th cent. design, the second for the 20th cent. design.
For overprints and surcharges see #C724-C725, C740A-C746, C766-C769, C779-C780.

REP. DE HONDURAS, C.A.
Goalkeeper — AP104

Designs: Various soccer scenes.

**1978, Nov. 26    Litho.    Perf. 12**

| | | | | |
|---|---|---|---|---|
| C663 | AP104 | 15c multi, vert. | .20 | .20 |
| C664 | AP104 | 30c multi | .30 | .30 |
| C665 | AP104 | 55c multi, vert. | .60 | .60 |
| C666 | AP104 | 1 l multi | 1.40 | 1.40 |
| C667 | AP104 | 2 l multi | 2.50 | 2.50 |
| | | Nos. C663-C667 (5) | 5.00 | 5.00 |

7th Youth Soccer Championship, Nov. 26.
For surcharge see No. C797.

UPU Emblem — AP105

2c, Postal emblem of Honduras. 25c, Dr. Ramon Rosa, vert. 50c, Pres. Marco Aurelio Soto, vert.

**1979, Apr. 1    Litho.    Perf. 12**

| | | | | |
|---|---|---|---|---|
| C668 | AP105 | 2c multicolored | .20 | .20 |
| C669 | AP105 | 15c multicolored | .20 | .20 |
| C670 | AP105 | 25c multicolored | .20 | .20 |
| C671 | AP105 | 50c multicolored | .40 | .40 |
| | | Nos. C668-C671 (4) | 1.00 | 1.00 |

Centenary of Honduras joining UPU.

Rotary Emblem and "50" AP106

**1979, Apr. 26    Litho.    Perf. 14**

| | | | | |
|---|---|---|---|---|
| C672 | AP106 | 3c multi | .20 | .20 |
| C673 | AP106 | 5c multi | .20 | .20 |
| C674 | AP106 | 50c multi | .50 | .50 |
| C675 | AP106 | 2 l multi | 1.75 | 1.75 |
| | | Nos. C672-C675 (4) | 2.65 | 2.65 |

Rotary Intl. of Honduras, 50th anniv.
For surcharge see No. C884A.

Map of Caratasca Lagoon AP107

Designs: 10c, Fort San Fernando de Omoa. 24c, Institute anniversary emblem, vert. 5 l, Map of Santanilla islands.

**1979, Sept. 15    Litho.    Perf. 13½**

| | | | | |
|---|---|---|---|---|
| C676 | AP107 | 5c multi | .20 | .20 |
| C677 | AP107 | 10c multi | .20 | .20 |
| C678 | AP107 | 24c multi | .25 | .20 |
| C679 | AP107 | 5 l multi | 4.00 | 4.00 |
| | | Nos. C676-C679 (4) | 4.65 | 4.60 |

Panamerican Institute of History and Geography, 50th anniversary.
For surcharge see No. C891.

General Post Office, 1979 — AP108

UPU Membership Cent.: 3 l, Post Office, 19th cent.

**1980, Feb. 20    Litho.    Perf. 12**

| | | | | |
|---|---|---|---|---|
| C680 | AP108 | 24c multi | .20 | .20 |
| C681 | AP108 | 3 l multi | 2.75 | 2.75 |

For surcharge see No. C925.

Workers in the Field, IYC Emblem AP109

**1980, Dec. 9    Litho.    Perf. 14½**

| | | | | |
|---|---|---|---|---|
| C682 | AP109 | 1c shown | .20 | .20 |
| C683 | AP109 | 5c Landscape, vert. | .20 | .20 |
| C684 | AP109 | 15c Sitting boy, vert. | .20 | .20 |
| C685 | AP109 | 20c IYC emblem, vert. | .25 | .25 |
| C686 | AP109 | 30c Beach scene | .45 | .45 |
| | | Nos. C682-C686 (5) | 1.30 | 1.30 |

**Souvenir Sheet**

| | | | | |
|---|---|---|---|---|
| C687 | AP109 | 1 l UNICEF and IYC emblems, vert. | 1.50 | 1.50 |

International Year of the Child (1979).

Maltese Cross, Hill AP110

**1980, Dec. 17**

| | | | | |
|---|---|---|---|---|
| C688 | AP110 | 1c shown | .25 | .25 |
| C689 | AP110 | 2c Penny Black | .25 | .25 |
| C690 | AP110 | 5c Honduras type A1 | .25 | .25 |
| C691 | AP110 | 10c Honduras type A1 | .25 | .25 |

**Size: 47x34mm**

| | | | | |
|---|---|---|---|---|
| C692 | AP110 | 15c Postal emblem | .25 | .25 |
| C693 | AP110 | 20c Flags of Honduras, Gt. Britain | .25 | .25 |
| | | Nos. C688-C693 (6) | 1.50 | 1.50 |

**Souvenir Sheet**

| | | | | |
|---|---|---|---|---|
| C694 | AP110 | 1 l Honduras #C402 | 2.50 | 2.50 |

Sir Rowland Hill (1795-1879), originator of penny postage. No. C694 contains one stamp 47x34mm.

Intibucana Mother and Child — AP111

Inter-American Women's Commission, 50th Anniv.: 2c, Visitacion Padilla, Honduras Section founder. 10c, Maria Trinidad del Cid, Section member. 1 l, Emblem, horiz.

**1981, June 15    Litho.    Perf. 14½**

| | | | | |
|---|---|---|---|---|
| C695 | AP111 | 2c multicolored | .20 | .20 |
| C696 | AP111 | 10c multicolored | .20 | .20 |
| C697 | AP111 | 40c multicolored | .30 | .30 |
| C698 | AP111 | 1 l multicolored | .80 | .80 |
| | | Nos. C695-C698 (4) | 1.50 | 1.50 |

Bernardo O'Higgins, by Jose Gil de Castro — AP112

**1981, June 29**

Paintings of O'Higgins: 16c, Liberation of Chile, by Cosme San Martin, horiz. 20c, Portrait of Ambrosio O'Higgins (father). 1 l, Abdication of Office, by Antonio Caro, horiz.

| | | | | |
|---|---|---|---|---|
| C699 | AP112 | 16c multicolored | .20 | .20 |
| C700 | AP112 | 20c multicolored | .20 | .20 |
| C701 | AP112 | 30c multicolored | .25 | .25 |
| C702 | AP112 | 1 l multicolored | 1.00 | .50 |
| | | Nos. C699-C702 (4) | 1.65 | 1.15 |

For surcharges see Nos. C785, C888B.

CONCACAF 81 Soccer Cup — AP113

**1981, Dec. 30    Litho.    Perf. 14**

| | | | | |
|---|---|---|---|---|
| C703 | AP113 | 20c Emblem | .60 | .25 |
| C704 | AP113 | 50c Player | 1.25 | .35 |
| C705 | AP113 | 70c Flags | 1.90 | 1.00 |
| C706 | AP113 | 1 l Stadium | 2.75 | 1.50 |
| | | Nos. C703-C706 (4) | 6.50 | 3.10 |

**Souvenir Sheet**

| | | | | |
|---|---|---|---|---|
| C707 | AP113 | 1.50 l like #C703 | 1.75 | 1.75 |

For overprint see No. C797.

50th Anniv. of Air Force (1981) AP114

Designs: 3c, Curtiss CT-32 Condor. 15c, North American NA-16. 25c, Chance Vought F4U-5. 65c, Douglas C47. 1 l Cessna A37-B. 2 l, Super Mister SMB-11.

**1983, Jan. 14    Litho.    Perf. 12**

| | | | | |
|---|---|---|---|---|
| C708 | AP114 | 3c multi | .20 | .20 |
| C709 | AP114 | 15c multi | .20 | .20 |
| C710 | AP114 | 25c multi | .35 | .20 |
| C711 | AP114 | 65c multi | .65 | .35 |
| C712 | AP114 | 1 l multi | 1.00 | .50 |
| C713 | AP114 | 2 l multi | 2.00 | 1.75 |
| | | Nos. C708-C713 (6) | 4.40 | 3.20 |

**Souvenir Sheet**

| | | | | |
|---|---|---|---|---|
| C714 | AP114 | 1.55 l Helicopter | 4.00 | 4.00 |

For surcharge see No. C884B.

UPU Executive Council Membership, 3rd Anniv. — AP115

**1983, Jan. 14**
C715 AP115 16c UPU monument .20 .20
C716 AP115 18c 18th UPU Con-
gress emblem .20 .20
C717 AP115 30c Natl. Postal
Service em-
blem .35 .35
C718 AP115 55c Rio de Janeiro .50 .50
C719 AP115 2 l Dove on globe 2.00 2.00
Nos. C715-C719 (5) 3.25 3.25
**Souvenir Sheet**
C720 AP115 1 l like 2 l 2.50 2.50
For surcharges see Nos. C921, C1204.

Natl.
Library and
Archives
Centenary
(1980)
AP116

**1983, Feb. 11    Litho.    Perf. 12**
C721 AP116 9c Library .30 .20
C722 AP116 1 l Books 1.10 .40

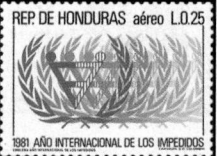

Intl. Year of
the
Disabled
(1979)
AP117

**1983, Feb. 11**
C723 AP117 25c Emblem .40 .25

No. C657a Overprinted in Red:
"CONMEMORATIVA DE LA VISITA /
DE SS. JUAN PABLO II / 8 de marzo
de 1983"

**1983, Mar. 8**
C724 AP103 40c multicolored 3.00 2.50
C725 AP103 40c multicolored 3.00 2.50
a. Pair, #C724-C725 6.00 5.00

Visit of Pope John Paul II.

Literacy
Campaign
(1980) — AP118

World Food Day,
Oct. 16,
1981 — AP119

**1983, May 18    Litho.    Perf. 12**
C726 AP118 40c Hands, open
book .50 .45
C727 AP118 1.50 l People holding books 2.00 1.90

**1983, May 18**
C728 AP119 65c Produce, emblem 1.00 1.00

20th Anniv. of
Inter-American
Development
Bank
(1980) — AP120

**1983, June 17    Litho.    Perf. 12**
C729 AP120 1 l Comayagua Riv-
er Bridge 1.50 .50
C730 AP120 2 l Luis Bogran
Technical Insti-
tute of Physics 2.75 1.00

2nd Anniv. of Return to Constitutional
Government — AP121

**1984, Jan. 27    Litho.    Perf. 12**
C731 20c Arms, text .20 .20
C732 20c Pres. Suazo Cordova .20 .20
a. AP121 Pair, #C731-C732 .65 .55

La Gaceta Newspaper
Sesquicentenary (1980) — AP122

**1984, May 25    Litho.    Perf. 12**
C733 AP122 10c multicolored .35 .35
C734 AP122 20c multicolored .35 .35

Nos. C582 and C575-C576
Surcharged

**1985, June 26    Litho.    Perf. 13½**
C735 AP95 5c on 1c #C582 .20 .20
C736 AP94 10c on 8c #C575 .20 .20
C737 AP94 20c on 16c #C576 .20 .20
C738 AP95 1 l on 1c #C582 1.00 .40
Nos. C735-C738 (4) 1.60 1.00

Nos. C621, C636, C647a Surcharged
Litho., Photo. (No. C740)

**1986, Aug. 21    Perfs. as before**
C739 AP100 50c on 14c #C621 .45 .25
C740 AP102 60c on 14c #C636 .55 .30
C740A AP103 85c on 6c #C646 .80 .55
C740B AP103 85c on 6c #C647 .80 .55
c. Pair, #C740A-C740B 1.75 1.50
C741 AP103 95c on 6c #C646 .90 .60
C742 AP103 95c on 6c #C647 .90 .60
a. Pair, #C741-C742 2.00 1.75
Nos. C739-C742 (6) 4.40 2.85

Black bar obliterating old values on #C739-
C740 also cover "aereo."

Nos. C656-C657 Ovptd. in Red
"EXFILHON '86," "MEXICO '86" and:
No. C743 "ARGENTINA CAMPEON"
No. C744 "ALEMANIA FEDERAL
Sub Campeon"
No. C745 "FRANCIA TERCER
LUGAR"
No. C746 "BELGICA CUARTO
LUGAR"

**1986, Sept. 12    Litho.    Perf. 12**
C743 AP103 40c No. C656 .40 .20
C744 AP103 40c No. C657 .40 .20
C745 AP103 40c No. C657 .40 .20
C746 AP103 40c No. C656 .40 .20
a. Block of 4, #C743-C746 2.00

AP123

San Fernando de Omoa
Castle — AP124

20c, Phulapanzak Falls. 78c, Bahia Isls.
beach. 85c, Bahia Isls. cove. 95c, Yojoa
Lake. 1 l, Woman painting pottery.

**Perf. 13½x14, 14x13½**
**1986, Nov. 10    Litho.**
C747 AP123 20c multi, vert. .20 .20
C748 AP123 78c multi 1.10 .55
C749 AP123 85c multi 1.25 .55
C750 AP123 95c multi, vert. 1.40 .65
C751 AP123 1 l multi, vert. 1.50 .70
**Size: 84x59mm**
**Imperf**
C752 AP124 1.50 l multi 2.75 2.75
Nos. C747-C752 (6) 8.20 5.40
For overprint see No. C782.

AP125

**1987, Feb. 2    Litho.    Perf. 13½**
National flag, Pres. Jose Azcona Hoyo.
C753 AP125 20c multicolored .30 .25
C754 AP125 85c multicolored 1.25 .85
Democratic government, 1st anniv.

Flora — AP126

**1987, July 8    Litho.    Perf. 13½x14**
C755 AP126 10c Eupatorium
cyrillinelsonii .25 .25
C756 AP126 20c Salvia ernesti-
vargasii .45 .45
C757 AP126 95c Robinsonella
erasmi-sosae 1.40 .75
Nos. C755-C757 (3) 2.10 1.45

Birds — AP127

AP128

**1987, Sept. 10    Litho.    Perf. 13½x14**
C758 AP127 50c Eumomota
superciliosa 1.75 .50
C759 AP127 60c Ramphastos
sulfuratus 2.00 .50

C760 AP127 85c Amazona
autumnalis 3.50 1.10
Nos. C758-C760 (3) 7.25 2.10

**1987, Dec. 10    Litho.    Perf. 13½**
C761 AP128 1 l blk, brt yel &
dark red 1.25 .50
Natl. Autonomous University of Honduras,
30th anniv.

AP129

AP130

**1987, Dec. 23    Litho.    Perf. 13½**
C762 AP129 20c red & dk ultra .50 .20
Natl. Red Cross, 50th anniv.

**1988, Jan. 27    Perf. 13½**
C763 AP130 95c brt blue & org
yel 1.10 .45
17th regional meeting of Lions Intl.

Atlantida
Bank, 75th
Anniv.
AP131

Main offices: 10c, La Ceiba, Atlantida,
1913. 85c, Tegucigalpa, 1988.

**1988, Feb. 10**
C764 AP131 10c multi .25 .20
C765 AP131 85c mutli .90 .40
a. Souv. sheet of 2, #358-359,
imperf. 1.25 1.25
No. C765a sold for 1 l.

No. C649a Surcharged

**1988, June 9    Litho.    Perf. 12**
C766 AP103 20c on 8c #C648 .90 .90
C767 AP103 20c on 8c #C649 .90 .90
a. Pair, #C766-C767 2.00 2.00

No. C647a Surcharged

**1988, July 8    Litho.    Perf. 12**
C768 AP103 5c on 6c #C646 .30 .30
C769 AP103 5c on 6c #C647 .30 .30
a. Pair, #C768-C769 .80 .80

Postman
AP132

Tegucigalpa Postmark on Stampless
Cover, 1789 — AP133

**1988, Sept. 11    Litho.    Perf. 13½**
C770   AP132 85c dull red brn    1.10   .40
C771   AP133 2 l   dull red brn &  
               ver        2.50   1.00

EXFILHON '88.

**Summer Olympics Type of 1988**

**1988, Sept. 30    Litho.    Perf. 13½**
**Size: 28x33mm**
C772   A62   85c   Running, vert.    1.10   .40
**Size: 36x27mm**
C773   A62   1 l   Baseball, soccer,
                basketball      1.20   .50

Discovery
of America,
500th
Anniv. (in
1992)
AP134

Pre-Colombian pottery artifacts: 10c,
Footed vase, vert. 25c, Bowl. 30c, Footed
bowl. 50c, Pitcher, vert. 1 l, Rectangular footed
bowl.

**1988      Litho.      Perf. 13½**
C774   AP134 10c multicolored    .30   .20
C775   AP134 25c multicolored    .75   .25
C776   AP134 30c multicolored    .90   .30
C777   AP134 50c multicolored    1.50   .50
     Nos. C774-C777 (4)     3.45   1.25
**Size: 115x83mm**
***Imperf***
C778   AP134 1 l   multicolored    3.25   3.25

**Nos. C653a and C576 Surcharged**
**1988      Litho.    Perf. 12, 13½**
C779   AP103 10c on 16c #C652   .20   .20
C780   AP103 10c on 16c #C653   .25   .20
   a.    Pair, #C779-C780       .50   .50
C781   AP94   50c on 16c #C576   .80   .40
     Nos. C779-C781 (3)     1.25   .80
Nos. C779-C780 exist with double surcharge.
Issued: 10c, Apr. 7, 50c, May 25.

**No. C752 Overprinted**

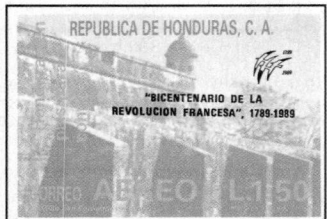

**1989, July 14    Litho.    Imperf.**
C782   AP124 1.50 l   multi    2.75   2.75
French revolution, bicent.

---

**Nos. C629 and C593 Surcharged**

I

II

**1989      Litho.    Perf. 14, 13½**
C783   AP101 15c on 6c, I     .20
C783A   AP101 15c on 6c, II    1.00
C784   AP96   1 l   on 16c      1.25
     Nos. C783-C784 (3)     2.45
       Issue date: 1 l, June 15.

**Nos. C699 and C616 Surcharged**
**1989, Dec. 15    Litho.    Perf. 14½, 12**
C785   AP112 20c on 16c #C699   .20
C786   AP99   95c on 18c #C616   1.40
No. C786 exists with inverted surcharge.
Issued: #C785, Dec. 15; #C786, Dec. 28.

**Nos. C594 and C585 Surcharged with**
**New Denomination and "IV Juegos /**
**Olimpicos / Centroamericanos"**
**1990, Jan. 12      Perf. 13½**
C787   AP96 75c on 18c #C594
             (S)      1.10   .85
C788   AP95 85c on 18c #C585   1.25   .95
No. C787 exists with double and inverted
surcharge.

World Wildlife
Fund — AP135

Various *Mono ateles.*

**1990, Apr. 18    Litho.    Perf. 13½**
C789   AP135 10c shown    3.75   2.50
C790   AP135 10c Adult, young   3.75   2.50
C791   AP135 20c Adult hang-
              ing, diff.    6.00   4.00
C792   AP135 20c Adult, young,
              diff.    6.50   4.50
     Nos. C789-C792 (4)    20.00   13.50

**No. C621 Surcharged**
**1990, Feb. 8    Litho.    Perf. 14**
C793   AP100 20c on 14c multi    .20

**Nos. C621 and C636 Surcharged "50**
**Aniversario / IHCI" / 1939-1989**
**1990, Mar. 29**
C794   AP102 20c on 14c No. 636   .20
C795   AP100 1 l   on 14c No. 621   .45

---

**No. C665 Surcharged**

**1990, June 14    Litho.    Perf. 12**
C796   AP104 1 l   on 55c multi    .75
World Cup Soccer Championships, Italy.

**No. C707 Ovptd. in Margin**
**"CAMPEONATO MUNDIAL DE**
**FUTBOL Italia '90," and Character**
**Trademark**
**Souvenir Sheet**
**1990, June 14      Perf. 14**
C797   AP113 1.50 l   multi    .80

**No. C577 Surcharged in Black**

**1990, Feb. 22    Litho.    Perf. 13½**
C798   AP94 20c on 18c multi    .40

FAO, 45th
Anniv. — AP136

**1990, Oct. 16    Litho.    Perf. 13½**
C799   AP136 95c yel, blk, bl, grn   .85   .75

17th Interamerican Congress of
Industry and Construction — AP137

**1990, Nov. 21    Litho.    Perf. 13½**
C800   AP137 20c Map, vert.    .25
C801   AP137 1 l   Jose Cecilio
              Del Valle Pal-
              ace        .65

AP138

---

Christmas — AP139

**1990, Nov. 30    Litho.    Perf. 13½**
C802   AP138 20c shown      .40
C803   AP138 95c Madonna and
              Child, vert.    .80
**Size: 112x82mm**
***Imperf***
C804   AP139 3 l   Poinsettia    2.50
     Nos. C802-C804 (3)    3.70

Salesian
Order in
Honduras,
80th Anniv.
AP140

**1990, Dec. 28    Litho.    Perf. 13½**
C805   AP140 75c St. John Bosco   .50
C806   AP140 1 l   Natl. Youth
              Sanctuary    .65

Pres. Rafael
Leonardo
Callejas — AP141

**1991, Jan. 31**
C807   AP141 30c Taking oath    .20
C808   AP141 2 l   Portrait    1.20

Moths and
Butterflies
AP142

**1991, Feb. 28    Litho.    Perf. 13½**
C809   AP142   85c Strymon me-
                linus      1.25
C810   AP142   90c Diorina sp.   1.50
C811   AP142 1.50 l   Hyalophora
                cecropia    2.50
**Size: 114x82mm**
***Imperf***
C812   AP142   5 l   Papilio polix-
                enes      4.00
     Nos. C809-C812 (4)    9.25

Notary
Day — AP143

**1991, May 22    Litho.    Perf. 13½**
C813   AP143 50c multicolored    .40

Rafael Heliodoro Valle, Birth Cent. — AP144

**1991, July 26    Litho.    Perf. 13½**
C815 AP144 2 l pale pink & blk    1.40

Churches AP145

Discovery of America, 500th Anniv. emblem and: 30c, Church of St. Manuel of Colohete, Gracias. 95c, Church of Our Lady of Mercy, Gracias. 1 l, Comayagua Cathedral.

**1991, Aug. 30    Litho.    Perf. 13½**
C816 AP145 30c multicolored    .20    .20
C817 AP145 95c multicolored    .70    .20
C818 AP145 1 l multicolored    .85    .45
    Nos. C816-C818 (3)    1.75    .85

Latin American Institute, 25th Anniv. AP146

**1991, June 20**
C819 AP146 1 l multicolored    .70

Flowers AP147

**1991, Apr. 30**
C820 AP147 30c Rhyncholaelia
    glauca    .25    .20
C821 AP147 50c Oncidium
    splendidum,
    vert.    .50    .40
C822 AP147 95c Laelia
    anceps, vert.    .75    .70
C823 AP147 1.50 l Cattleya skin-
    neri    1.25    1.10
    Nos. C820-C823 (4)    2.75    2.40

Espamer '91, Buenos Aires AP148

**1991, July 1**
C824 AP148 2 l multicolored    2.25
    **Size: 101x82mm**
    *Imperf*
C825 AP148 5 l like #C824    3.50
Discovery of America, 500th anniv. (in 1992).

11th Pan American Games, Havana AP149

**1991, Aug. 8**
C826 AP149 30c Equestrian    .25
C827 AP149 85c Judo    .60
C828 AP149 95c Men's swim-
    ming    .75
    **Size: 114x83mm**
    *Imperf*
C829 AP149 5 l Women's swim-
    ming    3.50
    Nos. C826-C829 (4)    5.10

Pre-Columbian Culture — AP150

UPAEP emblem, artifacts and: 25c, ears of corn. 40c, ear of corn, map. 1.50 l, map.

**1991, Sept. 30    Litho.    Perf. 13½**
C830 AP150 25c multicolored    .25    .20
C831 AP150 40c multicolored    .75    .40
C832 AP150 1.50 l multicolored    1.50    .60
    Nos. C830-C832 (3)    2.50    1.20

4th Intl. Congress on Control of Insect Pests AP151

Designs: 30c, Tactics to control pests. 75c, Integration of science. 1 l, Cooperation between farmers and scientists. 5 l, Pests and biological controls.

**1991, Nov. 22**
C833 AP151 30c multicolored    .40    .20
C834 AP151 75c multicolored    1.10    .55
C835 AP151 1 l multicolored    2.10    .85
    **Size: 115x83mm**
    *Imperf*
C836 AP151 5 l multicolored    3.25
    Nos. C833-C836 (4)    6.85    1.60

America Issue AP152

**1992, Jan. 27    Litho.    Perf. 13½**
C837 AP152 90c Sighting land    .75    .60
C838 AP152 1 l Columbus'
    ships    .85    .75
C839 AP152 2 l Ship, map,
    birds    1.60    1.25
    Nos. C837-C839 (3)    3.20    2.60

Christmas AP153

**1991, Dec. 19**
C840 AP153 1 l shown    .60
C841 AP153 2 l Poinsettias in
    rooster vase    1.25

Honduran Savings Insurance Company, 75th Anniv. AP154

**1992, Jan. 17**
C842 AP154 85c multicolored    .55
C843 AP154 1 l Priest saying
    mass    .65
    **Size: 115x83mm**
    *Imperf*
C844 AP154 5 l like #C842    3.25
    Nos. C842-C844 (3)    4.45

First mass in New World, 490th anniv. (No. C843). Taking possession of new continent, 490th anniv. (Nos. C842, C844).

Pres. Rafael Leonardo Callejas, 2nd Year in Office AP155

Callejas with: 20c, Italian president Francesco Cossiga. 2 l, Pope John Paul II.

**1992, Jan. 27    Litho.    Perf. 13½**
C845 AP155 20c black & purple    .25
C846 AP155 2 l black & multi    1.40

Flowers AP156

**1992, July 25    Litho.    Perf. 13½**
C847 AP156 20c Bougainvillea
    glabra    .20
C848 AP156 30c Canna indica    .20
C849 AP156 75c Epiphyllum    .70
C850 AP156 95c Sobralia
    macrantha    .90
    Nos. C847-C850 (4)    2.00

Gen. Francisco Morazan Hydroelectric Complex — AP157

**1992, Aug. 17**
C851 AP157 85c Dam face, vert.    .50
C852 AP157 4 l Rear of dam    2.40

AP158

AP159

**1992, Aug. 24**
C853 AP158 95c black & multi    .65    .55
C854 AP158 95c multicolored    .65    .55

Intl. Conference on Agriculture, 50th anniv.

**1992, Sept. 18    Litho.    Perf. 13½**
Gen. Francisco Morazan (1792-1842): 5c, Morazan mounted on horseback. 10c, Statue of Morazan. 50c, Watch and sword, horiz. 95c,

Portrait of Josefa Lastiri de Morazan. 5 l, Portrait of Morazan in uniform.

C855 AP159 5c multicolored    .20    .20
C856 AP159 10c multicolored    .20    .20
C857 AP159 50c multicolored    .35    .20
C858 AP159 95c multicolored    .60    .30
    **Size: 76x108mm**
    *Imperf*
C859 AP159 5 l multicolored    3.00    2.25
    Nos. C855-C859 (5)    4.35    3.15

Children's Day — AP160

Paintings of children: 25c, Musicians. 95c, Boy, dog standing in doorway. 2 l, Flower girl.

**1992, Sept. 7**
C860 AP160 25c multicolored    .20
C861 AP160 95c multicolored    .60
C862 AP160 2 l multicolored    1.25
    Nos. C860-C862 (3)    2.05

Intl. Conference on Nutrition AP161

**1992, Sept. 30    Litho.    Perf. 13½**
C863 AP161 1.05 l multicolored    .70

Pan-American Agricultural School, 50th Anniv. — AP162

**1992, Oct. 9**
C864 AP162 20c Bee keepers    .20
C865 AP162 85c Woman, goats    .50
C866 AP162 1 l Plowing    .60
C867 AP162 2 l Man with tool,
    vert.    1.25
    Nos. C864-C867 (4)    2.55

Exfilhon '92 — AP163

Birds: 1.50 l, F. triquilidos. 2.45 l, Ara macao. 5 l, Quetzal pharomachrus mocinno.

**1992, Oct. 2**
C868 AP163 1.50 l multicolored    1.75    1.50
C869 AP163 2.45 l multicolored    2.75    2.40
    **Size: 76x108mm**
    *Imperf*
C870 AP163 5 l multicolored    3.25    3.25
    Nos. C868-C870 (3)    7.75    7.15

Discovery of America, 500th anniv.

America
Issue — AP164

Discovery of
America, 500th
Anniv. — AP165

UPAEP emblem and: 35c, Native settlement. 5 l, Explorers meeting natives in boats.

**1992, Oct. 30      Litho.      Perf. 13½**
C871  AP164  35c multicolored      .20  .20
C872  AP164  5 l multicolored      2.75  2.00

Printed on both thick and thin paper.

**1992, Oct. 30**
Details from First Mass, by Roque Zelaya: 95c, Ships off-shore. 1 l, Holding services with natives, horiz. 2 l, Natives, countryside, temples, horiz.

C873  AP165  95c multicolored      .50
C874  AP165  1 l multicolored      .55
C875  AP165  2 l multicolored      1.10
      Nos. C873-C875 (3)      2.15

City of El
Progreso,
Cent.
AP166

**1992, Oct. 17**
C876  AP166  1.55 l multicolored      .90  .55

First Road Conservation Congress of
Panama and Central
America — AP167

**1992, Nov. 16      Perf. 13½**
C878  AP167  20c shown      .20
C879  AP167  85c Bulldozer on
            highway      .45

Pan-American Health Organization,
90th Anniv. — AP168

**1992, Nov. 27**
C880  AP168  3.95 l multicolored      2.25

Christmas
AP169

Paintings by Roque Zelaya: 20c, Crowd watching people climb pole in front of church, vert. 85c, Nativity scene.

**1992, Nov. 24**
C881  AP169  20c multicolored      .20
C882  AP169  85c multicolored      .45

Surcharges on:

No. C601

Nos. C606-C607

Nos. C584, C612, C637

Nos. C672, C678, C708

Nos. C575-C576, C603, C620, C699

**1992-93**
**Perfs. and Printing Methods as
Before**

C883  AP97  20c on 1c #C601      .20
C884  AP97  20c on 3c #C603      .20
C884A  AP106  20c on 3c #C672      .20
C884B  AP114  20c on 3c #C708      .20
C885  AP97  20c on 6c #C606      .20
C886  AP94  20c on 8c #C575      .20
C886A  AP100  20c on 8c #C620      .20
C887  AP94  50c on 16c #C576      .40
C888  AP95  50c on 16c #C584      .25
C888A  AP102  50c on 16c #C637      .25
C888B  AP112  50c on 16c #C699      .40
C889  AP97  85c on 18c #C607      .45
C890  AP98  85c on 18c #C612      .45
C891  AP107  85c on 24c #C678      .40
      Nos. C883-C891 (14)      4.00

Size and location of surcharge varies.
Issued: #C883, 12/18/92; #C889, 1/22/93; #C885, 3/8/93; #C888A, 9/7/93; #C888, 9/13/93; #C890, 9/24/93; #C891, 10/1/93; #C884A, 10/5/93; #C884B, 10/8/93; #C884, C886A, 10/21/93; #C886, 10/29/93; #C887, C888B, 11/3/93.

Intl. Court of Justice Decision on
Border Dispute Between Honduras &
El Salvador
AP170

Designs: 90c, Pres. of El Salvador and Pres. Callejas of Honduras, vert. 1.05 l, Country flags, map of Honduras and El Salvador.

**1993, Feb. 24      Litho.      Perf. 13½**
C893  AP170  90c multicolored      .50
C894  AP170  1.05 l multicolored      .65

Third year of Pres. Callejas' term.

Mother's
Day — AP171

Endangered
Animals — AP172

Paintings of a mother and child, by Sandra Pendrey.

**1993, May 5      Litho.      Perf. 13½**
C895  AP171  50c Red blanket      .30
C896  AP171  95c Green blanket      .55

**1993, May 14      Perf. 13½**
C897  AP172  85c Manatee,
            horiz.      .65  .50
C898  AP172  2.45 l Puma, horiz.      1.75  1.25
C899  AP172  10 l Jaguar      6.50  4.00
      Nos. C897-C899 (3)      8.90  5.75

Natl. Symbols
AP173

**1993, June 25      Litho.      Perf. 13½**
C900  AP173  25c Ara macao      1.00
C901  AP173  95c Odocoileus
            virginianus      1.50

First
Brazilian
Postage
Stamps,
150th
Anniv.
AP174

**1993, Sept. 10      Litho.      Perf. 13½**
C902  AP174  20c Brazil No. 1      .20
C903  AP174  50c Brazil No. 2      .25
C904  AP174  95c Brazil No. 3      .45
      Nos. C902-C904 (3)      .90

Departments in Honduras — AP175

Various scenes, department name: No. C905a, Atlantida. b, Colon. c, Cortes. d, Choluteca. e, El Paraiso. f, Francisco Morazan.
No. C906a, Comayagua. b, Copan. c, Intibuca. d, Islas de la Bahia. e, Lempira. f, Ocotepeque.
No. C907a, La Paz. b, Olancho. c, Santa Barbara. d, Valle. e, Yoro. f, Gracias a Dios.

**1993, Sept. 20      Litho.      Perf. 13½**
C905  AP175  20c Strip of 6,
            #a.-f.      .65
C906  AP175  50c Strip of 6,
            #a.-f.      1.50
C907  AP175  1.50 l Strip of 6,
            #a.-f.      4.25
      Nos. C905-C907 (3)      6.40

No. C906 is vert.

Endangered
Birds — AP176

UN Development
Program
AP177

**1993, Oct. 11      Litho.      Perf. 13½**
C908  AP176  20c Spizaetus
            ornatus      .25  .20
C909  AP176  80c Cairina mos-
            chata, horiz.      1.00  .50
C910  AP176  2 l Harpia harpija,
            horiz.      2.25  1.50
      Nos. C908-C910 (3)      3.50  2.20

**1993, Oct. 19**
C911  AP177  95c multicolored      .50  .35

Christmas
AP178

**1993, Nov. 5**
C912  AP178  20c Church      .25
C913  AP178  85c Woman, flowers      .45

Nos. C577, C585,
C593, C611,
C616, C638,
C643, C680,
C716 Surcharged

## 1993
### Perfs. and Printing Methods as Before

| | | | |
|---|---|---|---|
| **C917** | AP96 | 50c on 16c #C593 | .25 |
| **C918** | AP98 | 50c on 16c #C611 | .25 |
| **C919** | AP94 | 50c on 18c #C577 | .25 |
| **C920** | AP99 | 50c on 18c #C616 | .25 |
| **C921** | AP115 | 50c on 18c #C716 | .40 |
| **C922** | AP95 | 85c on 18c #C585 | .40 |
| **C923** | AP102 | 85c on 18c #C638 | .40 |
| **C924** | AP99 | 85c on 18c #C643 | .40 |
| **C925** | AP108 | 85c on 24c #C680 | .40 |
| | *Nos. C917-C925 (9)* | | 3.00 |

Size and location of surcharge varies. This is an expanding set. Numbers may change. Issued: #C917-C918, 11/12; #C920, C924, 11/23; #C921, C925, 11/30; #C922-C923, 12/3; #C919, 12/10.

Fish
AP179

### 1993, Dec. 7    Litho.    Perf. 13½

| | | | | |
|---|---|---|---|---|
| **C931** | AP179 | 20c | Pomacanthus arcuatus | .30 |
| **C932** | AP179 | 85c | Holacanthus ciliaris | .80 |
| **C933** | AP179 | 3 l | Chaetodon striatus | 2.50 |
| | *Nos. C931-C933 (3)* | | | 3.60 |

Famous Men — AP180

### 1993, Nov. 17

| | | | | |
|---|---|---|---|---|
| **C934** | AP180 | 25c | Ramon Rosa | .20 |
| **C935** | AP180 | 65c | Jesus Aguilar Paz | .30 |
| **C936** | AP180 | 85c | Augusto C. Coello | .40 |
| | *Nos. C934-C936 (3)* | | | .90 |

Pres. Rafael Leonardo Callejas, 4th Year in Office AP181

95c, Wife, Norma, planting tree, vert.

### 1994, Jan. 21    Litho.    Perf. 13½

| | | | |
|---|---|---|---|
| **C937** | AP181 | 95c multicolored | .45 |
| **C938** | AP181 | 1 l multicolored | .50 |

AP182

AP183

### 1994, Mar. 8    Litho.    Perf. 13½

| | | | |
|---|---|---|---|
| **C939** | AP182 | 1 l multicolored | .45 |

Intl. Year of the Family.

### 1994, Oct. 24    Litho.    Perf. 13½

| | | | |
|---|---|---|---|
| **C940** | AP183 | 1 l multicolored | .45 |

Intl. Conference on Peace and Development in Central America, Tegucigalpa.

Christmas
AP184

UN, 50th Anniv. — AP185

Paintings by Gelasio Gimenez: 95c, Madonna and Child. 1 l, Holy Family.

### 1994, Dec. 15    Litho.    Perf. 13½

| | | | |
|---|---|---|---|
| **C941** | AP184 | 95c multicolored | .45 |
| **C942** | AP184 | 1 l multicolored | .55 |

### 1995, Jan. 17

Designs: 1 l, The Sowing: Ecological Family, by Elisa Dulcey. 2 l, Family Scene, by Delmer Mejia. 3 l, UN emblem, "50."

| | | | |
|---|---|---|---|
| **C943** | AP185 | 1 l multicolored | .50 |
| **C944** | AP185 | 2 l multicolored | .85 |
| **C945** | AP185 | 3 l multicolored | 1.25 |
| | *Nos. C943-C945 (3)* | | 2.60 |

Pres. Carlos Roberto Reina, 1st Anniv. of Taking Office AP186

Designs: 80c, Beside flag, vert. 1 l, Summit meeting of area presidents & vice presidents.

### 1995, Jan. 27

| | | | |
|---|---|---|---|
| **C946** | AP186 | 80c multicolored | .30 |
| **C947** | AP186 | 95c multicolored | .35 |
| **C948** | AP186 | 1 l multicolored | .40 |
| | *Nos. C946-C948 (3)* | | 1.05 |

America Issue AP187

Postal vehicles.

### 1995, Feb. 28    Litho.    Perf. 13½

| | | | |
|---|---|---|---|
| **C949** | AP187 | 1.50 l | Van | .55 |
| **C950** | AP187 | 2 l | Motorcycle | .75 |

Miniature Sheet of 30

Mushrooms AP188

1 l: a, Marasmius cohaerens. b, Lepista nuda. c, Polyporus pargamenus. d, Fomes. e, Paneolus sphinctrinus. f, Hygrophorus aurantiaca.

1.50 l, vert: g, Psathyrella. h, Amanita rubescens. i, Boletellus russelli. j, Boletus frostii. k, Marasmius spegazzinii. l, Fomes annosus.

2 l, vert: m, Craterellus cornucopioides. n, Amanita. o, Auricularia delicata. p, Psllocybe cubensis. q, Clavariadelphus pistilaris. r, Boletus regius.

2.50 l: s, Scleroderma aurantium. t, Amanita praegraveolens. u, Cantharellus cibarius. v, Geastrum triplex. w, Russula emetica. x, Boletus pinicola.

3 l: y, Fomes versicolor. z, Cantharellus pupurascens. aa, Lyophyllum decastes. ab, Pleurotus ostreatus. ac, Boletus ananas. ad, Amanita caesarea.

### 1995, Apr. 7

| | | | |
|---|---|---|---|
| **C951** | AP188 | #a.-ad. | 35.00 |

FAO, 50th Anniv. AP189

### 1995, May 25    Litho.    Perf. 13½

| | | | |
|---|---|---|---|
| **C952** | AP189 | 3 l multicolored | .70    .40 |

CARE, 50th Anniv. AP190

Designs: 1.40 l, Family, farm. No. C954, Orchid, wildlife, couple working in soil. No. C955, Couple in vegetable garden.

### 1995, Aug. 4    Litho.    Perf. 13½

| | | | |
|---|---|---|---|
| **C953** | AP190 | 1.40 l multicolored | .50    .50 |
| **C954** | AP190 | 5.40 l multicolored | 2.10 2.10 |
| **C955** | AP190 | 5.40 l multicolored | 2.10 2.10 |
| | *Nos. C953-C955 (3)* | | 4.70 4.70 |

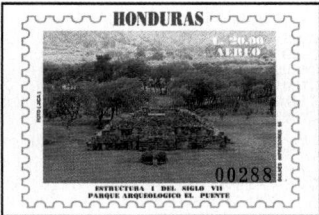

El Puente Archaeological Park — AP191

Illustration reduced.

### 1995, Aug. 8    Imperf.

| | | | |
|---|---|---|---|
| **C956** | AP191 | 20 l multicolored | 6.25 6.25 |

America Issue AP192

1.40 l, Kinosternon scorpioides. 4.54 l, Alpinia purpurata, vert. 10 l, Polyborus plancus, vert.

### 1995, Oct. 10    Litho.    Perf. 13½

| | | | |
|---|---|---|---|
| **C957** | AP192 | 1.40 l multicolored | .50    .50 |
| **C958** | AP192 | 4.54 l multicolored | 1.60 1.60 |
| **C959** | AP192 | 10 l multicolored | 3.50 3.50 |
| | *Nos. C957-C959 (3)* | | 5.60 5.60 |

Reptiles AP193

### 1995, Nov. 10    Litho.    Perf. 13

| | | | | |
|---|---|---|---|---|
| **C960** | AP193 | 5.40 l | Iguana iguana | 2.10 2.00 |
| **C961** | AP193 | 5.40 l | Agalychnis | 2.10 2.00 |

Christmas AP194

### 1995, Dec. 4    Litho.    Perf. 13½

| | | | | |
|---|---|---|---|---|
| **C962** | AP194 | 1.40 l | Bell, vert. | .50    .60 |
| **C963** | AP194 | 5.40 l | Nativity figurines | 2.25 2.25 |
| **C964** | AP194 | 6.90 l | Carved deer, vert. | 2.50 2.50 |
| | *Nos. C962-C964 (3)* | | | 5.25 5.35 |

Integration System of Central America AP195

1.40 l, Map of Central America, Tegucigalpa Protocol, 1991. 4.30 l, Functions listed, 1993. 5.40 l, 17th Summit of Presidents of Central America.

### 1996, Feb. 19    Litho.    Perf. 13½

| | | | |
|---|---|---|---|
| **C965** | AP195 | 1.40 l multicolored | .50    .50 |
| **C966** | AP195 | 4.30 l multicolored | 1.60 1.60 |
| **C967** | AP195 | 5.40 l multicolored | 2.00 2.00 |
| | *Nos. C965-C967 (3)* | | 4.10 4.10 |

UN Fight Against Drug Trafficking and Abuse, 10th Anniv. AP196

Designs: 1.40 l, Stylized picture of minds on drugs. 5.40 l, Person with butterfly for brain, vert. 10 l, Musical score, "Viva la Vida."

### 1996, May 3

| | | | |
|---|---|---|---|
| **C968** | AP196 | 1.40 l multicolored | .40    .40 |
| **C969** | AP196 | 5.40 l multicolored | 1.75 1.75 |
| **C970** | AP196 | 10 l multicolored | 2.75 2.75 |
| | *Nos. C968-C970 (3)* | | 4.90 4.90 |

Arrival of the Garifunas in Honduras, Bicent. AP197

Designs: 1.40 l, Headdress, vert. 5.40 l, Dancers, men playing drums. 10 l, Drums.

### 1996, June 13    Litho.    Perf. 13½

| | | | |
|---|---|---|---|
| **C971** | AP197 | 1.40 l multicolored | .40    .20 |
| **C972** | AP197 | 5.40 l multicolored | 1.50 1.00 |
| **C973** | AP197 | 10 l multicolored | 2.75 1.50 |
| | *Nos. C971-C973 (3)* | | 4.65 2.70 |

EXFILHON '96, 7th Philatelic Exhibition AP198

**1996, July 12    Litho.    Perf. 13½**
C974 AP198 5.40 l Steam locomotive    2.00    2.00
C975 AP198 5.40 l Passenger railcar    2.00    2.00

**73x52mm**
*Imperf*
C976 AP198 20 l +2 l like #C974    7.50    7.50
Nos. C974-C976 (3)    11.50    11.50

6th Central American Games AP199

**1996, Aug. 30    Litho.    Perf. 13½**
C977 AP199 4.30 l Soccer    1.40    .60
C978 AP199 4.54 l Volleyball    1.40    .65
C979 AP199 5.40 l Mascot, vert.    1.60    .75
Nos. C977-C979 (3)    4.40    2.00

Scouting in Honduras, 75th Anniv. AP200

**1996, Oct. 25    Litho.    Perf. 13½**
C980 AP200 2.15 l Emblems    .50    .20
C981 AP200 5.40 l Emblem, vert.    1.40    .60
C982 AP200 6.90 l Scout feeding deer, vert.    2.10    .80
Nos. C980-C982 (3)    4.00    1.60

Christmas AP201

Poinsettia and: 1.40 l, Candles. 5.40 l, Candles, vert.

**1996, Dec. 23    Litho.    Perf. 13½**
C983 AP201 1.40 l multicolored    .65    .20
C984 AP201 3 l shown    1.25    .50
C985 AP201 5.40 l multicolored    2.10    .95
Nos. C983-C985 (3)    4.00    1.65

Traditional Costumes AP202

America issue: 4.55 l, Man in costume. 5.40 l, Woman in costume. 10 l, Couple in costumes.

**1997, Jan. 17    Litho.    Perf. 13½**
C986 AP202 4.55 l multicolored    1.10    .50
C987 AP202 5.40 l multicolored    1.40    .65
C988 AP202 10 l multicolored    3.50    1.10
Nos. C986-C988 (3)    6.00    2.25

Honduras Plan, 20th Anniv., Intl. Plan, 60th Anniv. AP203

Children's paintings: 1.40 l, Outdoor scene, children swimming, vert. 5.40 l, Girl standing beside lake, fish. 9.70 l, People working between buildings.

**1997, Feb. 7    Litho.    Perf. 13½**
C989 AP203 1.40 l multicolored    .50    .20
C990 AP203 5.40 l multicolored    1.50    .70
C991 AP203 9.70 l multicolored    3.00    2.50
Nos. C989-C991 (3)    5.00    3.40

Heinrich von Stephan (1831-97) AP205

**1997, May 9    Litho.    Perf. 13½**
C995 AP205 5.40 l multicolored    1.25    .55

World Population Day AP206

Designs: 6.90 l, Child's drawing of people outside, trees, houses.

**1997, July 11    Litho.    Perf. 13½**
C996 AP206 1.40 l shown    .50    .50
C997 AP206 6.90 l multicolored    2.50    1.25

Butterflies AP207

Designs: 1 l, Rothchildia forbesi. 1.40 l, Parides photinus. 2.15 l, Morpho peleides. 3 l, Eurytides marcellus. 4.30 l, Parides iphidamas. 5.40 l, Danaus plexippus. 20 l+2 l, Hamadryas arinome.

**1997, July 31**
C998 AP207 1 l multi    .50    .20
C999 AP207 1.40 l multi    .50    .20
C1000 AP207 2.15 l multi    .90    .20
C1001 AP207 3 l multi    1.25    .20
C1002 AP207 4.30 l multi    1.60    .65
C1003 AP207 5.40 l multi    2.25    .85

*Imperf*
**Size: 80x53mm**
C1004 AP207 20 l +2 l multi    7.50    5.50
Nos. C998-C1004 (7)    14.50    7.80

St. Teresa of Jesus, Death Cent. — AP208

**1997, Aug. 20    Litho.    Perf. 13½**
C1005 AP208 1.40 l shown    .30    .20
C1006 AP208 5.40 l Portrait, diff.    1.25    .60

Astronomical Observatory AP209

Designs: 5.40 l, Statue of Father Jose Trinidad Reyes. 10 l, Woman with book leading child up steps.

**1997, Sept. 19    Litho.    Perf. 13½**
C1007 AP209 1.40 l multicolored    .30    .20
C1008 AP209 5.40 l multicolored    1.25    .60
C1009 AP209 10 l multicolored    2.25    1.10
Nos. C1007-C1009 (3)    3.80    1.90

Alma Mater Foundation, 150th anniv., Autonomous University, 40th anniv.

Alcoholics Anonymous in Honduras, 37th anniv. — AP210

**1997, Oct. 27**
C1010 AP210 5.40 l multicolored    1.60    .60

Diana, Princess of Wales (1961-97) AP211

1.40 l, Portrait, vert. 5.40 l, Diana dressed to walk through mine field, warning sign. 20 l, Mother Teresa, Princess Diana.

**1997, Oct. 15**
C1011 AP211 1.40 l multi    .40    .20
C1012 AP211 5.40 l multi    1.60    .70

**Size: 51x78mm**
*Imperf*
C1013 AP211 20 l multicolored    6.00    4.25
Nos. C1011-C1013 (3)    8.00    5.15

Christmas AP212

**1997, Dec. 2    Litho.    Perf. 13½**
C1014 AP212 1.40 l Christ of Picacho    .40    .40
C1015 AP212 5.40 l Virgin of Suyapa    1.60    .85

Mascot — AP213

C1016: a, Basketball. b, At bat, baseball. c, Soccer. d, Racquetball. e, Spiking volleyball. f, Setting volleyball. g, Bowling. h, Table tennis. i, Rings over map of Central America. j, Pitching, baseball.

No. C1017: a, Kicking, karate. b, Chopping, karate. c, Bowing, karate. d, Wrestling. e, Weight lifting. f, Boxing. g, Body building. h, Fencing. i, Program cover. j, Shooting.
No. C1018: a, Riding bicycle. b, Riding bicycle by shoreline. c, Swimming. d, Water polo. e, Hurdles. f, Gymnastics. g, Riding horse. h, Tennis. i, Program cover with mascot. j, Chess.

**1997**
**Sheets of 10**
C1016 AP213 1.40 l #a.-j.    3.50    3.50
C1017 AP213 1.50 l #a.-j.    3.75    3.75
C1018 AP213 2.15 l #a.-j.    5.00    5.00
6th Central American Games, San Pedro Sula.

Fish AP214

1.40 l, Cichlasoma dovii. 2 l, Cichlasoma spilurum. 3 l, Cichlasoma spilurum facing right. 5.40 l, Astyanay fasciatus.

**1997    Litho.    Perf. 13½**
C1019 AP214 1.40 l multicolored    .30    .30
C1020 AP214 2 l multicolored    .40    .40
C1021 AP214 3 l multicolored    .60    .50
C1022 AP214 5.40 l multicolored    1.10    .90
Nos. C1019-C1022 (4)    2.40    2.10

Marine Life, Islas de la Bahía (Bay Islands) — AP215

Designs: a, Balistes vetula. b, Haemudon plumieri. c, Pomacanthus paru. d, Juvenile halichoeres garnoti. e, Pomacanthus arcuatus. f, Holacanthus ciliaris. g, Diver's face, pseud opterogorgia. h, Diver's oxygen tanks, pseud opterogorgia. i, Dendrogya cylindrus. j, Holocentrus adscensionis. k, Dendrogya cylindrus, diff. l, Stegastes fuscus. m, Gorgonia mariae. n, Pillar coral. o, Pomacanthus arcuatus, diff. p, Holocentrus adscensionis, diff. q, Eusmilia fastigiata. r, Scarus coelestinus. s, Pillar coral, diff. t, Lachnolaimus masimus.

**1998, Mar. 13    Litho.    Perf. 13½**
**Sheet of 20**
C1023 AP215 2.50 l #a.-t.    16.00    16.00
Bancahsa, 50th anniv.
Exists imperf.

America Issue AP216

**1998, May 29    Litho.    Perf. 13½**
C1024 AP216 5.40 l Post Office headquarters    1.60    .80
C1025 AP216 5.40 l Postman on motorcycle    1.60    .80

Maya Artifacts — AP217

Designs: 1 l, Large carving on temple. 1.40 l, Stele of Mayan king. 2.15 l, Large stelae. 5.40 l, Small ornamental carving.

20 l, Maya Ruins, Copán.

| 1998, June 19 | Litho. | | Perf. 13½ | |
|---|---|---|---|---|
| C1026 | AP217 | 1 l multi | .20 | .20 |
| C1027 | AP217 | 1.40 l multi | .55 | .20 |
| C1028 | AP217 | 2.15 l multi | .90 | .20 |
| C1029 | AP217 | 5.40 l multi | 2.10 | .55 |

**Size: 78x52mm**

***Imperf***

| C1030 | AP217 | 20 l multicolored | 6.50 | 3.00 |
|---|---|---|---|---|
| | *Nos. C1026-C1030 (5)* | | 10.25 | 4.15 |

1998 World Cup Soccer Championships, France — AP218

No. C1033: a, Stadium, Tegucigalpa. b, St. Denis Stadium, France.

| 1998, July 3 | Litho. | | Perf. 13½ | |
|---|---|---|---|---|
| C1031 | AP218 | 5.40 l shown | 1.50 | .70 |
| C1032 | AP218 | 10 l Players, vert. | 3.00 | 1.50 |

***Imperf***

| C1033 | AP218 | 10 l Pair, #a.- | | |
|---|---|---|---|---|
| | | b. | 8.25 | 7.00 |

No. C1033 contains two 53x42mm stamps. No. C1033 also issued rouletted between the stamps; value the same.

Reptiles AP219

Designs: 1.40 l, Green iguana. 2 l, Rattlesnake. 3 l, Two iguanas. 5.40 l, Coral snake. 20 l + 2 l, Marine turtle.

| 1998, July 31 | Litho. | | Perf. 13½ | |
|---|---|---|---|---|
| C1034 | AP219 | 1.40 l multi | .40 | .35 |
| C1035 | AP219 | 2 l multi | .75 | .60 |
| C1036 | AP219 | 3 l multi | .95 | .75 |
| C1037 | AP219 | 5.40 l multi | 1.90 | 1.25 |

**Size: 77x52mm**

***Imperf***

| C1038 | AP219 | 20 l +2 l multi | 7.00 | 4.50 |
|---|---|---|---|---|
| | *Nos. C1034-C1038 (5)* | | 11.00 | 7.45 |

Christmas AP220

Designs: 3 l, Girl taking ornament from bird, vert. 5.40 l, Christ Child asleep on bed of holly, dove, stars. 10 l, Boy with lantern leading donkey, cabin in the snow, vert.

| 1998, Dec. 8 | Litho. | | Perf. 13½ | |
|---|---|---|---|---|
| C1039 | AP220 | 3 l multicolored | .70 | .30 |
| C1040 | AP220 | 5.40 l multicolored | 1.25 | .60 |
| C1041 | AP220 | 10 l multicolored | 2.25 | 1.25 |
| | *Nos. C1039-C1041 (3)* | | 4.20 | 2.15 |

Pres. Carlos Roberto Flores, 1st Anniv. of Taking Office AP221

Designs: 5.40 l, Pres. and Mrs. Flores, Pope John Paul II. 10 l, Portrait of Pres., Mrs. Flores, vert.

| 1999, Jan. 27 | Litho. | | Perf. 13½ | |
|---|---|---|---|---|
| C1042 | AP221 | 5.40 l multicolored | 1.10 | .55 |
| C1043 | AP221 | 10 l multicolored | 2.00 | 1.00 |

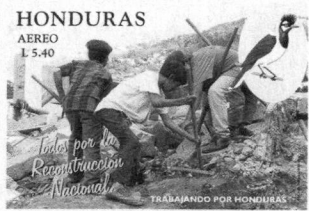

Hurricane Mitch — AP222

No. C1044: a, Men working to clean up. b, Helicopter distributing aid. c, Vehicles under water, North Zone. d, Tipper Gore, Mary de Flores cleaning. e, Working to save banana crop. f, Destruction of Tegucigalpa. g, Cars, buses, trucks blocked by rock slide. h, Destruction of Comayagüela. i, Streets of Comayagüela. j, Oriental Zone. k, Loading debris, help from Mexico. l, Streets of Limpieza. m, Pres. Flores with Pres. Chirac of Fance. n, Business district of Comayagüela. o, Flooding, Tegucigalpa. p, Car in street, Comayagüela.

No. C1045: a, Central Zone. b, South Zone. c, Prince Felipe de Borbon, Mary de Flores. d, Small child crying. e, Cleaning up debris, Comayagüela. f, Families, man carrying baby, North Zone. g, Two men looking at destruction of building, Tegucigalpa. h, Man, child, woman wading in water, North Zone. i, Destruction in rural area. j, Cars piled up, concrete abutment along roadway. k, Cars, buildings along roadway. l, Mexican troops, airplane. m, Boys swimming. n, Pres. & Mrs. Flores, Hillary Clinton. o, People walking over rubble and debris, South Zone. p, Pres. Flores, former US Pres. George Bush.

Illustration reduced.

| 1999, Feb. 19 | | | *Rouletted* | |
|---|---|---|---|---|
| **Sheets of 16** | | | | |
| C1044 | AP222 | 5.40 l #a.-p. | 18.00 | 18.00 |
| C1045 | AP222 | 5.40 l #a.-p. | 18.00 | 18.00 |

For surcharges, see Nos. C1207, C1208.

Famous Honduran Women — AP223

America Issue: 2.60 l, Maria del Pilar Salinas (b. 1914), scholar. 7.30 l, Clementina Suarez (1902-91), poet, writer. 10.65 l, Mary Flake de Flores, first lady of Honduras.

| 1999, Apr. 20 | Litho. | | Perf. 13½ | |
|---|---|---|---|---|
| C1046 | AP223 | 2.60 l multi | .55 | .25 |
| C1047 | AP223 | 7.30 l multi | 1.50 | .75 |
| C1048 | AP223 | 10.65 l multi | 2.25 | 1.10 |
| | *Nos. C1046-C1048 (3)* | | 4.30 | 2.10 |

Dated 1998.

Mother's Day AP224

Designs: 20 l, Police officer Orellana breastfeeding baby, vert. 30 l, Paphiopedilum urbanianum. 50 l, Miltoniopsis vexillaria.

| 1999, May 14 | Litho. | | Perf. 13½ | |
|---|---|---|---|---|
| C1049 | AP224 | 20 l multicolored | 4.25 | 3.50 |
| C1050 | AP224 | 30 l multicolored | 6.25 | 4.25 |
| C1051 | AP224 | 50 l multicolored | 10.50 | 7.25 |
| | *Nos. C1049-C1051 (3)* | | 21.00 | 15.00 |

Endangered Birds — AP225

No. C1052, 5 l: a, Sarcorampohus papa. b, Leucopternis albicollis. c, Harpia harpyja. d, Pulsatrix perspicallata. e, Spizaetus ornatus. f, Pharomarchrus mocinno. g, Aulacorhynchus prasinus. h, Amazilia luciae. i, Ara macao. j, Centurus pygmaeus.

3 l: k, Aratinga canicularis. l, Amazona albifrons. m, Amazona auropalliata. n, Amazona autumnalis. o, Eurypyga helias. p, Crax rubra. q, Brotogeris jugularis. r, Pionus senilis. s, Aratinga rubritorques. t, Tinamus major.

No. C1053: a, Jaberu mycteria. b, Chondrohierax uncinatus. c, Pharomachrus mocinno. d, Ramphastos sulfuratus.

| 1999, July 8 | | | | |
|---|---|---|---|---|
| C1052 | AP225 | Sheeet of 20, #a.-t. | 17.50 | 17.50 |
| C1053 | AP225 | 10 l Sheet of 4, #a.-d. | 9.00 | 7.50 |

Banco Sogerin, 30th anniv.

Inter-American Development Bank, 40th Anniv. — AP226

| 1999, Nov. 22 | Litho. | | Perf. 13½ | |
|---|---|---|---|---|
| C1054 | AP226 | 18.30 l multi | 3.75 | 2.00 |

Blessed Josemaría Escrivá de Balaguer (1902-75), Founder of Opus Dei — AP227

| 1999, Nov. 29 | | | | |
|---|---|---|---|---|
| C1055 | AP227 | 2.60 l multi | .60 | .30 |
| C1056 | AP227 | 16.40 l multi | 3.25 | 2.00 |

Millennium AP228

Designs: 2 l, Salvador Moncada, discoverer of nitric oxide in blood, vert. 8.65 l, Albert Einstein, vert. 10 l, Wilhelm Röntgen, vert. 14.95 l, George Stephenson and locomotive "Rocket."

| 1999, Oct. 18 | | | | |
|---|---|---|---|---|
| C1057 | AP228 | 2 l multi | .40 | .20 |
| C1058 | AP228 | 8.65 l multi | 1.60 | .80 |
| C1059 | AP228 | 10 l multi | 1.90 | .95 |
| C1060 | AP228 | 14.95 l multi | 2.75 | 1.40 |
| | *Nos. C1057-C1060 (4)* | | 6.65 | 3.35 |

National Congress, 175th Anniv. AP229

Designs: 4.30, Statue of Francisco Morazán. 10 l, Congress President Rafael Pineda Ponce, Congress Building.

| 1999, Dec. 17 | Litho. | | Perf. 13¼ | |
|---|---|---|---|---|
| C1061 | AP229 | 4.30 l multi | 1.00 | .50 |
| C1062 | AP229 | 10 l multi | 2.25 | 1.10 |

AP230

Holy Year 2000 — AP231

Holy Year Emblem and: 4 l, Pope John Paul II, people. 4.30 l, St. Peter. 6.90 l, Jesus, Jerusalem, horiz. 7.30 l, John Paul II, crowd, horiz. 10 l, John Paul II giving blessing. 14 l, Pres. Carlos Roberto Flores, John Paul II.

| 2000, Jan. 1 | Litho. | | Perf. 13¼ | |
|---|---|---|---|---|
| C1063 | AP230 | 4 l multi | .90 | .40 |
| C1064 | AP230 | 4.30 l shown | 1.40 | .70 |
| C1065 | AP230 | 6.90 l multi | 1.50 | .80 |
| C1066 | AP230 | 7.30 l multi | 1.60 | .85 |
| C1067 | AP230 | 10 l multi | 2.25 | 1.10 |
| C1068 | AP231 | 14 l multi | 4.25 | 1.75 |

**Nos. C1064, C1068 Redrawn**

| C1069 | AP230 | 4.30 l multi | 1.25 | .50 |
|---|---|---|---|---|
| C1070 | AP231 | 14 l multi | 3.50 | 1.50 |
| | *Nos. C1063-C1070 (8)* | | 16.65 | 7.60 |

#C1067 issued in sheets of 6, with picture of John Paul II in selvage. #C1069 has "HONDURAS" in yellow; #C1064 in white. #C1070 has "HONDURAS" at right, reading up; #C1068 at top.

2nd Anniv. of Inauguration of Pres. Flores — AP232

Pres. Flores and: 10 l, Conference delegates. 10.65 l, Mario Hung Pacheco.

| 2000, Jan. 27 | | | | |
|---|---|---|---|---|
| C1071 | AP232 | 10 l multi | 2.50 | 1.25 |
| C1072 | AP232 | 10.65 l multi | 3.00 | 1.40 |

**Musical Instruments Type of Semipostals of 2000**

No. 1073: a, 1.40 l, Marimba, denomination at L. b, 1.40 l, Marimba, denomination at L. c, 1.40 l, Ayotl. d, 10 l, Maya drum. e, 10 l, Teponaxtle. f, 2.60 l, Maracas. g, 2.60 l, Güiro. h, 2.60 l, Chinchín. i, 2.60 l, Raspador. j, 2.60 l, Horse's jawbone. k, 3 l, Green zoomorphic whistle. l, 3 l, Aztec drum. m, 3 l, One-tone zoomorphic whistle. n, 3 l, Two-tone zoomorphic whistle. o, 3 l, Tun. p, 4 l, Gourd. q, 4 l, Deer hide drum. r, 4 l, Guacalitos. s, 4 l, Five musicians, marimba. t, 4 l, Four musicians, marimba.

| 2000, Apr. 7 | Litho. | | Perf. 13¼ | |
|---|---|---|---|---|
| C1073 | SP1 | Sheet of 20, #a-t | 21.00 | 21.00 |

Paintings of Pablo Zelaya Sierra — AP233

No. C1074: a, 2 l, Green City (building and tree). b, 2 l, Old Woman With Rosary. c, 2 l, Rural Women (women with jars). d, 2 l, Woman With Green Robe. e, 2 l, City. f, 1.40 l, Shoulders of a Man. g, 1.40 l, Goat. h, 1.40 l, Spanish City. i, 1.40 l, Woman With Chignon. j, 1.40 l, Woman With Calabash. k, 2.60 l, Goat and Birds. l, 2.60 l, Tree Trunks. m, 2.60 l, Nuns. n, 2.60 l, Archers. o, 2.60 l, Moon and Boats. p, 2.60 l, Bust. q, 10 l, Still-life. r, 10 l, Composition With Books. s, 2.60 l, Landscape. t, 2.60 l, Head, Fan and Book.

**2000, July 1**
C1074 AP233 Sheet of 20,
#a-t 22.50 22.50

**Airmail Anniv. Type of Semi-postals**

Designs: 7.30 l, #C12. 10 l, Thomas Canfield Pounds, owner of Central American Airline, vert. 10.65 l, Pres. Rafael López Gutiérrez, signer of first airmail contract, vert.

**2000, July 7**
**Size: 35x25mm**
C1075 SP2 7.30 l multi 1.60 .85
**Size: 25x35mm**
C1076 SP2 10 l multi 2.25 1.10
C1077 SP2 10.65 l multi 2.40 1.25
Nos. C1075-C1077 (3) 6.25 3.20

America Issue, A New Millennium Without Arms — AP234

Designs: 10 l, Sobralia macrantha, No guns, vert. 10.65 l, Peace dove, No soldiers, vert. 14 l, Train, No bombs, no more terrorism.

**2000, July 28 Litho. Perf. 13¼**
C1078-C1080 AP234 Set of 3 9.00 7.00

2000 Summer Olympics, Sydney AP235

Designs: 2.60 l, Soccer players Ivan Guerrero, Mario Chirinos. 10.65 l, Swimmer Ramon Valle, vert. 12.45 l, Runner Gina Coello.
No. C1084: a, 4.30 l, Swimmer. b, 4.30 l, Soccer player Danilo Turcios. c, 10.65 l, Runner Pedro Ventura. d, 12.45 l, Soccer player David Suazo.

**2000, Sept. 13**
C1081-C1083 AP235 Set of 3 10.00 8.50
**Souvenir Sheet**
C1084 AP235 Sheet of 4, #a-d 11.00 11.00

No. C1084 exists imperf.

Intl. Voluntarism Year — AP236

Emblem, people and: 2.60 l, White-crowned parrot. 10.65 l, Telipogon ampliflorus.

**2000, Dec. 5**
C1085-C1086 AP236 Set of 2 3.25 2.25

Christmas AP237

Designs: 2.60 l, Madonna and child. 7.30 l, Nativity, vert. 14 l, Carpet painter.

**2000, Dec. 18**
C1087-C1089 AP237 Set of 3 5.00 3.25

America Issue, Birds — AP238

Designs: 2.60 l, Amazona auropalliata caribea. 4.30 l, Columbina passerina, horiz. 10.65 l, Ara macao. 20 l, Aguila harpia.

**2001, Feb. 16 Litho. Perf. 13¼**
C1090-C1093 AP238 Set of 4 10.00 8.25

Nos. C584, C593, C606, C611, C646-C647, C652-C653, C699 Surcharged — c

Nos. C620, C672, C708, C721 Surcharged — d

No. C637 Surcharged — e

**Methods and Perfs. as Before**
**2001**

| | | | | |
|---|---|---|---|---|
| C1094 | AP103(c) | 2 l on 16c #C652 | .35 | .20 |
| C1095 | AP103(c) | 2 l on 16c #C653 | .35 | .20 |
| a. | Pair, #C1094-C1095 | | .70 | .35 |
| C1096 | AP106(d) | 2.60 l on 3c #C672 | .45 | .20 |
| C1097 | AP114(d) | 2.60 l on 3c #C708 | .45 | .20 |
| C1098 | AP100(d) | 2.60 l on 8c #C620 | .45 | .20 |
| C1099 | AP102(e) | 2.60 l on 16c #C637 | .45 | .20 |
| C1100 | AP96(c) | 3 l on 16c #C593 | .55 | .25 |
| C1101 | AP116(d) | 4 l on 9c #C721 | .70 | .35 |
| C1102 | AP97(c) | 4.30 l on 6c #C606 | .75 | .35 |
| C1103 | AP103(c) | 7.30 l on 6c #C646 | 1.25 | .60 |
| C1104 | AP103(c) | 7.30 l on 6c #C647 | 1.25 | .60 |
| a. | Pair, #C1103-C1104 | | 2.50 | 1.20 |
| C1105 | AP95(c) | 10 l on 16c #C584 | 1.75 | .90 |
| C1106 | AP112(c) | 10.65 l on 16c #C699 | 1.90 | .95 |
| C1107 | AP98(c) | 14 l on 16c #C611 | 3.00 | 1.25 |

Nos. C1094-C1107 (14) 13.65 6.45
Size and location of surcharge varies. Issued: Nos. C1096-C1099, 3/26; others, 4/3.

**2001**
C1110-C1111 AP241 Set of 2 4.00 3.00

Oscar Cardinal Rodriguez — AP239

No. C1108: a, 2.60 l, With father, 1946. b, 2.60 l, In Sanctuary of Our Lady of Suyapa. c, 2.60 l, As seminarian, 1964. d, 2.60 l, Installation as archbishop. e, 2.60 l, Ordination, 1960. f, 2.60 l, At Vatican, Feb. 21, 2001. g, 2.60 l, At mass in Guatemala, 1970. h, 2.60 l, Standing behind Honduran flag. i, 2.60 l, With Pope John Paul II, 1993. j, 2.60 l, Returning to Honduras as Cardinal. k, 2.60 l, Giving address as Cardinal, Mar. 10, 2001. l, 10.65 l, With Pope and woman, 1993. m, 10.65 l, Papal audience, Feb. 23, 2001. n, 10.65 l, Celebration of the Eucharist. o, 10.65 l, Kneeling before Pope, 1993. p, 10.65 l, Installation as Cardinal, Feb. 21, 2001. q, 15 l, Installation as Cardinal, St. Peter's Square.

**2001, May 9 Litho. Perf. 13¼**
C1108 AP239 Sheet of 17, #a-q 30.00 30.00

Stamp sizes: Nos. C1108a-C1108j, 29x40mm; C1108k-C1108p, 49x40mm; C1108q, 163x131mm. No. C1108 exists imperf. Value $30.

Banco de Occidente, S.A., 50th Anniv. — AP240

Mayan ceramics: a, 2 l, Flower pot. b, 2 l, Anthropomorphic jar. c, 2 l, Anthropomorphic cover. d, 2 l, Cylindrical vase. e, 2 l, Censer tripod. f, 3 l, Scribe. g, 3 l, Cylindrical jar with anthropomorphic figures. h, 3 l, Three-part container. i, 3 l, Ceramic face. j, 3 l, Anthropomorphic jar, diff. k, 5 l, Three-legged vessel. l, 5 l, Pot with handles. m, 5 l, Censer. n, 5 l, Anthropomorphic cover. o, 5 l, Anthropomorphic jar, diff. p, 6.90 l, Pot with handles, diff. q, 6.90 l, Anthropomorphic cover, diff. r, 6.90 l, Anthropomorphic jar, diff. s, 6.90 l, Red cylindrical container. t, 6.90 l, Decorated container.

**2001, Sept. 1 Litho. Perf. 13¼**
C1109 AP240 Sheet of 20, #a-t 26.00 26.00

UN High Commissioner for Refugees, 50th Anniv. — AP241

Designs: 2.60 l, Refugee and child, vert. 10.65 l, Refugees running.

Juan Ramon Molina Bridge — AP242

No. C1112: a, 2.60 l, Aerial view from end. b, 10 l, Close-up view from side. c, 10.65 l, Aerial view from side. d, 13.65 l, Side view showing river.

**2001, Dec. 20 Litho. Rouletted 6½**
C1112 AP242 Sheet of 4, #a-d 15.00 15.00

Stamp sizes: No. C1112b, 152x93mm; others, 40x30mm.

America Issue — Wildlife AP243

Designs: 10 l, Bird, Yojoa Lake. 10.65 l, Iguana, Cisne Islands. 20 l, Chrysina quetzalcoatli, Morpho sp., Pulaphanzhak Cataracts.

**2002, Jan. 31 Perf. 13¼**
C1113-C1115 AP243 Set of 3 13.00 13.00

Pan-American Health Organization, Cent. — AP244

**2002, Apr. 7**
C1116 AP244 10 l multi 3.25 3.25

Miguel R. Pastor, Central District Mayor — AP245

Central District emblem and: a, 1.40 l, Cathedral of San Miguel, statues, birds (57x35mm). b, 1.40 l, Chimpanzee throwing banana peel in trash can (57x35mm). c, 1.40 l, Municipal building (57x35mm). d, 2.60 l, Mayor Pastor, flags (27x35mm). e, 2.60 l, Mayor Pastor under tree (27x35mm). f, 2.60 l, Mayor Pastor with old woman (27x35mm). g, 2.60 l, Mayor Pastor with crowd (27x35mm). h, 2.60 l, Mayor Pastor planting seedling (27x35mm). i, 2.60 l, Mayor Pastor and family (27x35mm). j, 10 l, Municipal council (57x35mm). k, 10 l, Mayor with guests (57x35mm). l, 10.65 l, Cathedral of San Miguel, statues, birds (114x75mm).

**2002, June 13 Litho. Perf. 13¼**
C1117 AP245 Sheet of 12, #a-l 16.00 16.00

## Souvenir Sheet

Discovery of Honduras, 500th Anniv. — AP246

No. C1118: a, 10.65 l, Boat on shore, jungle. b, 12.45 l, Natives on shore. c, 13.65 l, Spaniards coming ashore. d, 20 l, Spanish ship.

**2002, Aug. 14**
C1118  AP246  Sheet of 4, #a-d    9.00  9.00
Exfilhon 2002.

## Souvenir Sheet

Christianity in Honduras, 500th Anniv. — AP247

No. C1119: a, 2.60 l, Natives and cross. b, 3 l, Santa Barbara Trujillo Fort. c, 10 l, 400 Years of History, by Mario Castillo. d, 10 l, Spaniards on shore, ships at sea.

**2002, Aug. 14**
C1119  AP247  Sheet of 4, #a-d    5.00  5.00
America issue.

Banco del Pais, 10th Anniv. AP248

**2002, Sept. 5    Litho.    Perf. 13¼**
C1120  AP248    2 l multi    .25    .25
  a.    Block of 10    3.00    3.00
C1121  AP248    2.60 l multi    .50    .50
  a.    Block of 10    4.25    4.25
C1122  AP248    10 l multi    1.75    1.75
  a.    Sheet of 30    45.00    45.00
C1123  AP248    10.65 l multi    2.00    2.00
  a.    Sheet of 30    50.00    50.00
  Nos. C1120-C1123 (4)    4.50    4.50

Backgrounds of Nos. C1120-C1123 show a flag on a staff and clouds in the blocks and and the flag on the sheets, giving each stamp a different background.

Orchids AP249

Designs: 1.40 l, Vanilla planifolia. 2.60 l, Lycaste viriginalis. 3 l, Coelia bella. 4.30 l, Chysis laevis. 8.65 l, Myrmecophila bryslana. 10 l, Rhyncolaelia digbyana. 20 l, Mormodes aromatica.

**2002, Sept. 25    Litho.    Perf. 13¼**
C1124-C1129  AP249  Set of 6    7.00  7.00
**Size: 96x66mm**
*Imperf*
C1130  AP249  20 l multi    6.00  6.00

Christmas AP250

Designs: 2.60 l, Creche scene. 10.65 l, Holy Family. 14 l, People at recreation of nativity scene.

**2002, Nov. 25**
C1131-C1133  AP250  Set of 3    4.00  4.00

National Children's Foundation AP251

Designs: 2.60 l, Children. 10 l, Elderly people. 10.65 l, Symbols of Honduras, vert.

**2002, Dec. 6**
C1134-C1136  AP251  Set of 3    3.50  3.50

Insects — AP252

No. C1137: a, 2 l, Chrysina spectabilis. b, 2 l, Chrysina strasseni. c, 2 l, Viridimicus omoaensis. d, 2 l, Hoplopyga liturata. e, 2.60 l, Chrysina cusuquensis. f, 2.60 l, Calomacraspis haroldi. g, 2.60 l, Pelidnota strigosa. h, 2.60 l, Odontocheila tawahka. i, 3 l, Chrysina cavei. j, 3 l, Macropoides crassipes. k, 3 l, Pelidnota velutipes. l, 3 l, Tragidion cyanovestis. m, 4 l, Chrysina pastori. n, 4 l, Platycoelia humeralis. o, 4 l, Phanaeus eximius. p, 4 l, Acanthoderes cavei. q, 10.65 l, Chrysina quetzalcoatli. r, 10.65 l, Cyclocephala abrelata. s, 10.65 l, Aegithus rufipennis. t, 10.65 l, Callipogon barbatum.
No. C1138 — Chrysina spp.: a, Eggs. b, Larva. b, Pupa.

**2003, Feb. 20**
C1137  AP252    Sheet of 20,
    #a-t    17.00  17.00
**Souvenir Sheet**
C1138  AP252  10 l  Sheet of 3,
    #a-c    6.00  6.00
Banco Atlantida, 90th anniv. (#C1137).

World Food Program AP253

Designs: 2.60 l, Children with food. 6.90 l, Child with food. 10.65 l, Child with bowl and spoon.

**2003, May 15**
C1139-C1141  AP253  Set of 3    3.50  3.50

**Souvenir Sheet**

Pontificate of John Paul II, 25th Anniv., and 20th Anniv. of Visit to Honduras — AP254

No. C1142: a, 13.65 l, Pope giving blessing. b, 14.55 l, Pope at airport. c, 15.45 l, Pope with staff. d, 16.65 l, Pope with rosary beads.

**2003, Oct. 10    Perf. 10½**
C1142  AP254    Sheet of 4, #a-
    d    11.00  11.00

Regional Sanitary Agricultural Organization, 50th Anniv. — AP255

Designs: 2.60 l, Eggs, sliced meat. 10 l, Eye, map of Central America, corn. 10.65 l, Emblem, map of Central America. 14 l, Vegetables. 20 l, Corn, tomato, fish.

**2003, Oct. 24    Perf. 13¼**
C1143-C1147  AP255  Set of 5    10.00  10.00

Bridges Built by Japan — AP256

No. C1148: a, 3 l, Ilama Bridge, Santa Bárbara. b, 3 l, Sol Naciente Bridge, Choluteca. c, 4.30 l, Río Hondo Bridge, Francisco Morazán. d, 4.30 l, El Chile Bridge, Central District. e, 4.30 l, Iztoca Bridge, Choluteca. f, 10 l, La Democracia Bridge, near El Progreso. g, 10 l, Guasaule Bridge, Honduras-Nicaragua border. 20 l, Juan Ramón Molina Bridge, Tegucigalpa (168x109mm).

**2003, Nov. 25    Litho.    Perf. 13¼**
C1148  AP256    Sheet of 7, #a-
    h + label    10.00  10.00

Telethon Honduras AP257

Telethon emblem and: 1.40 l, Flag on staff. 2.60 l, Hand, flag in light blue. 7.30 l, Hand, flag in dark blue. 10 l, Map.

**2003, Dec. 4**
C1149-C1152  AP257  Set of 4    3.50  3.50

Christmas AP258

Designs: 10.65 l, Angel. 14 l, Holy Family in manger.

**2003, Dec. 8**
C1153-C1154  AP258  Set of 2    4.00  4.00

**Souvenir Sheet**

Endangered Birds — AP259

No. C1155: a, 10 l, Arantinga strenua. b, 10.65 l, Falco deiroleucus. c, 14 l, Spizaetus melanoleucos. d, 20 l, Amazona xantholora.

**2004, May 13**
C1155  AP259    Sheet of 4, #a-
    d    10.00  10.00
Exfilhon 2004.

Endangered Animals — AP260

Designs: 85c, Pecari tajacu. 1.40 l, Mazama americana. 2 l, Mazama mexicana, vert. 2.60 l, Felis concolor. No. C1160, Tamandua mexicana, vert. No. C1161, Felis concolor. No. C1162, Mazama americana. No. C1163, Bradypus variegatus. 4.30 l, Pecari tajacu. 7.85 l, Agalychinis challidryas, vert. 10.65 l, Bradypus variegatus. 14.95 l, Agalchinis challidryas, vert.
No. C1168, vert.: a, Mono titi. b, Cebus capucinus. c, Ateles geoffroyi. d, Alouatta palliata.

**2004, May 24    Litho.    Perf. 13¼**
C1156  AP260    85c multi    .20    .20
C1157  AP260    1.40 l multi    .20    .20
C1158  AP260    2 l multi    .40    .40
C1159  AP260    2.60 l multi    .45    .45
C1160  AP260    3 l multi    .55    .55
C1161  AP260    3 l multi    .55    .55
C1162  AP260    4 l multi    .60    .60
C1163  AP260    4 l multi    .60    .60
C1164  AP260    4.30 l multi    .65    .65
C1165  AP260    7.85 l multi    1.40    1.40
C1166  AP260    10.65 l multi    2.10    2.10
C1167  AP260    14.95 l multi    3.00    3.00
  Nos. C1156-C1167 (12)    10.70    10.70
C1168  AP260    10 l  Sheet of
    4, #a-d    7.50    7.50

Nos. C1156-C1158, C1161, C1163, and C1165 were each printed in souvenir sheets of 4.

Shells AP261

Designs: Nos. C1169, C1174f, Voluta polypleura. Nos. C1170, C1174d, Strombus gallus. Nos. C1171, C1174a, Charonia variegata, Terebra taurina. Nos. C1172, C1174e, Spondylus americanus. Nos. C1173, C1174c, Strombus raninus. No. C1174b, Man blowing conch shell.

**2004, July 19    Litho.    Perf. 13¼**
C1169  AP261    85c multi    .20    .20
C1170  AP261    1.40 l multi    .20    .20
C1171  AP261    2 l multi    .20    .20
C1172  AP261    2.60 l multi    .55    .55
C1173  AP261    10.65 l multi    2.10    2.10
  Nos. C1169-C1173 (5)    3.25    3.25
**Miniature Sheet**
C1174    Sheet of 6    11.00    11.00
  a.-b.  AP261  4 l  Either single    .75    .75
  c.-d.  AP261  5 l  Either single    .95    .95
  e.-f.  AP261  20 l  Either single    3.75    3.75

## No. C1004 Surcharged in Red

Illustration reduced.

**2004, Aug. 13** **Litho.** *Imperf.*
C1175 AP207 50 l on 20 l+2 l
multi      9.00 9.00

### Miniature Sheet

Banco Ficohsa, Sponsor of National
Soccer Team — AP262

No. C1176: a, 4.30 l, Players, Honduras
flag. b, 10.65 l, Team. c, 14 l, Saúl Martinez,
David Suazo. d, 20 l, Amado Guevara.

**2004, Sept. 3** **Litho.** *Perf. 13¼*
C1176 AP262 Sheet of 4, #a-d   6.50 6.50

Christmas
AP263

Designs: 2.60 l, Flight into Egypt. 7.85 l,
Santa Claus on ornament. 10.65 l, Three
Kings. 20 l, Holy Family.

**2004, Nov. 23** **Litho.** *Perf. 13¼*
C1177-C1180 AP263 Set of 4   7.50 7.50
C1178a   Sheet of 4 #C1178   6.50 6.50

AP264

National
Unity — AP265

**2005, Feb. 3**
C1181 AP264 10 l multi     1.10 1.10
C1182 AP265 20 l multi     2.25 2.25

---

Rotary International, Cent. — AP266

Rotary International emblem and: 2.60 l,
Rafael Díaz Chávez, Paul Harris and Jorge
Fidel Durón. 5 l, "100 años," vert. 8 l, Globe
and arrows. 10.65 l, Map of Honduras,
PolioPlus emblem. 14 l, Mayan sculpture.

**2005, Feb. 23**
C1183-C1187 AP266 Set of 5   5.25 5.25

Pope John Paul
II (1920-2005)
AP267

Pope: 10 l, Wearing white vestments. 15 l,
Wearing colored vestments.
20 l, Holding crucifix.

**2005, Apr. 15** **Litho.** *Perf. 13¼*
C1188-C1189 AP267 Set of 2   3.25 3.25
### Souvenir Sheet
C1190   Sheet of 2 #C1190a   5.25 5.25
   a.   AP267 20 l multi, 29x42mm   2.50 2.50

Honduran
Medical Review,
75th
Anniv. — AP268

Designs: 3 l, House. 5 l, Bird. 12 l, Jaguar.
30 l, Flowers.
No. C1195: a, Macaws. b, Macaw in banana
tree. c, Rooster. d, Turkeys and hens.

**2005, May 18**
C1191-C1194 AP268 Set of 4   6.50 6.50
### Souvenir Sheet
C1195 AP268 25 l Sheet of 4,
#a-d   13.00 13.00

Nos. 390-392, B1, C550, C552, C553,
C576, C715, C1044-C1045 and
C1140 Surcharged

"X" Obliterators — f

Box Obliterator
and "Aereo" —
g

---

Box Obliterator — h

Illustration "h" reduced.

### Methods and Perfs as Before
**2005, June 3**

| Cat | Type | Surcharge | | |
|---|---|---|---|---|
| C1196 | AP253(f) | 3 l on 6.90 l #C1140 | .30 | .30 |
| C1197 | AP72(f) | 5 l on 16c on 1c #C552 | .55 | .55 |
| C1198 | AP72(f) | 5 l on 16c on 1c #C553 | .55 | .55 |
| C1199 | PT6(g) | 10 l on 13.85 l on 1c #392 | 1.10 | 1.10 |
| C1200 | AP68(f) | 14 l on 16c on 1c #C550 | 1.50 | 1.50 |
| C1201 | PT6(g) | 20 l on 13.85 l on 1c #392 | 2.10 | 2.10 |
| C1202 | PT6(g) | 25 l on 11.55 l on 1c #390 | 2.75 | 2.75 |
| C1203 | AP94(f) | 30 l on 16c #C576 | 3.25 | 3.25 |
| C1204 | AP115(f) | 35 l on 16c #C715 | 3.75 | 3.75 |
| C1205 | PT6(g) | 40 l on 11.55 l on 1c #390 | 4.25 | 4.25 |
| C1206 | PT6(g) | 50 l on 12.45 l on 1c #391 | 5.50 | 5.50 |
| | Nos. C1196-C1206 (11) | | 25.60 | 25.60 |

### Sheets

| Cat | | | | |
|---|---|---|---|---|
| C1207 | Sheet of 16 (#C1044) | | 15.00 | 15.00 |
| a.-p. | AP222(h) 8 l on 5.40 l any single | | .90 | .90 |
| C1208 | Sheet of 16 (#C1045) | | 15.00 | 15.00 |
| a.-p. | AP222(h) 8 l on 5.40 l any single | | .90 | .90 |
| C1209 | Sheet of 6 (#B1) | | 10.00 | 10.00 |
| a.-f. | SP1(f) 15 l on 10 l +1 l any single | | 1.60 | 1.60 |
| g. | As No. C1209, on No. B1a | | 10.00 | 10.00 |

Size, location and font of surcharges and
obliterators vary on types "f" and "h."

Honduras
— Japan
Diplomatic
Relations,
70th Anniv.
AP269

Designs: 8 l, Actors in play. 15 l, Emblem of
Japanese-Central American Year. 30 l,
National Congress, Japanese Princess
Sayako.
No. C1213: a, Japanese ceramics. b, Flowers. c, Mayan ceramics. d, Mount Fuji, Japan
and Pico Bonito National Park, Honduras.

**2005, Aug. 9** **Litho.** *Perf. 13¼*
C1210-C1212 AP269 Set of 3   7.00 7.00
### Souvenir Sheet
C1213 AP269 25 l Sheet of 4,
#a-d   13.00 13.00

Gen. José
Trinidad Cabañas
(1805-71)
AP270

---

Cabañas: 3 l, With green panel at bottom.
8 l, With university buildings, horiz. 15 l, In oval
frame.

**2005, Sept. 12**
C1214-C1216 AP270 Set of 3   3.25 3.25

Honduras, Water
Capital — AP271

Water droplet and: 30 l, Heart, butterfly,
Sanaa and Ras-hon emblems. 50 l, Heart.

**2005, Sept. 28**
C1217 AP271 30 l multi   4.00 4.00
### Souvenir Sheet
C1218 AP271 50 l multi   7.00 7.00

### Souvenir Sheet

America Issue — Endangered
Mushrooms — AP272

No. C1219: a, 20 l, Hygrophorus marzuolus.
b, 25 l, Lactarius deliciosus. c, 30 l, Boletus
pinophilus. d, 50 l, Gyromitra esculenta.

**2005**
C1219 AP272 Sheet of 4, #a-
d   17.00 17.00

AP273

Mail
Transport
AP274

Designs: 5 l, Charles Lindbergh, PAA
emblem. 25 l, Postal rail car, 1920. 30 l, First
Honduran postal car, 1914.
50 l, Sikorsky S-38 airplane, PAA emblem,
horiz.

**2005, Dec. 6** **Litho.** *Perf. 13¼*
C1220 AP273 5 l multi     .65 .65
C1221 AP274 25 l multi     3.00 3.00
C1222 AP274 30 l multi     3.75 3.75
   Nos. C1220-C1222 (3)   7.40 7.40
*Imperf*
**Size: 89x64mm**
C1223 AP273 50 l multi   6.50 6.50

Nos. C1177-
C1179
Surcharged

**2005**     **Litho.**     **Perf. 13¼**
**C1224** AP263   3 l on 2.60 l
       #C1177       .35   .35
**C1225** AP263   15 l on 7.85 l
       #C1178     1.90   1.90
**C1226** AP263   25 l on 7.85 l
       #C1178     3.50   3.50
**C1227** AP263   50 l on 10.65 l
       #C1179     6.75   6.75
  *Nos. C1224-C1227 (4)*   12.50   12.50

No. C1226 has a thick wavy line obliterator
and was issued in sheets of four.

2006 Winter
Olympics,
Turin — AP275

Skier and: 20 l, Turin Olympics emblem,
Olympic rings. 50 l, Olympic rings.

**2006, Jan. 24**
**C1228-C1229** AP275   Set of 2    9.00   9.00

Forgiveness of Honduran Debts by
Foreign Nations — AP276

Designs: 14 l, Structure 4, Copán Ruins.
15 l, Flags of nations forgiving debts. 30 l,
Honduras Pres. Ricardo Maduro, vert.

**2006, Jan. 26**
**C1230-C1232** AP276   Set of 3   12.50   12.50

Cortés Chamber
of Commerce
and Industry,
75th
Anniv. — AP277

Anniversary and Chamber of Commerce
emblem and: 20 l, Gears. 35 l, The Forger,
sculpture by J. Zelaya, horiz. 50 l, El Industrial,
mural by A. Martínez.

**2006**
**C1233-C1235** AP277   Set of 3   13.00   13.00

Diplomatic
Relations
Between
Honduras
and Brazil,
Cent.
AP278

Designs: 20 l, Flags of Honduras and Brazil.
30 l, Baron of Rio Branco (1845-1912) Brazilian diplomat, vert.

**2006**     **Litho.**     **Perf. 13¼**
**C1236-C1237** AP278   Set of 2   6.50   6.50

---

**Miniature Sheet**

Honduran Friendship With
Japan — AP279

No. C1238: a, 10 l, Children learning about
Chagas disease. b, 15 l, Teacher and children.
c, 20 l, Japanese naval vessels and flag. d,
25 l, Sailors in dress uniforms.

**2006**
**C1238** AP279   Sheet of 4, #a-d   7.50   7.50

Nos. C1054, C1124-C1125, C1127-
C1128, C1149-C1151, C1159, C1162,
C1164, C1166-C1167, C1169-C1170,
C1172-C1173 Surcharged

**Methods and Perfs As Before**
**2007 ?**
**C1239** AP260   2 l on 2.60 l
       #C1159     .25   .25
**C1240** AP260   2 l on 4 l #C1162   .25   .25
**C1241** AP249   2 l on 8.65 l
       #C1128     .25   .25
**C1242** AP260   2 l on 10.65 l
       #C1166     .25   .25
**C1243** AP249   3 l on 1.40 l
       #C1124     .35   .35
**C1244** AP257   3 l on 1.40 l
       #C1149     .35   .35
**C1245** AP257   3 l on 2.60 l
       #C1150     .35   .35
**C1246** AP261   3 l on 2.60 l
       #C1172     .35   .35
**C1247** AP257   3 l on 7.30 l
       #C1151     .35   .35
**C1248** AP261   3 l on 10.65 l
       #C1173     .35   .35
**C1249** AP226   3 l on 18.30 l
       #C1054     .35   .35
**C1250** AP261   5 l on 85c #C1169   .55   .55
**C1251** AP261   5 l on 1.40 l
       #C1170     .55   .55
**C1252** AP249   5 l on 2.60 l
       #C1125     .55   .55
**C1253** AP249   5 l on 4.30 l
       #C1127     .55   .55
**C1254** AP260   5 l on 4.30 l
       #C1164     .55   .55
**C1255** AP260   5 l on 14.95 l
       #C1167     .55   .55
  *Nos. C1239-C1255 (17)*   6.75   6.75

Constitution, 25th Anniv. — AP280

Designs: 5 l, Leaders of the Legislative,
Executive and Judicial branches of government. 10 l, 1824 Constituent Assembly Building. 15 l, Presidential House, 1922-91, vert.
20 l, Legislative Building.

**2007**     **Litho.**     **Perf. 13¼**
**C1256-C1259** AP280   Set of 4   5.50   5.50

---

**Miniature Sheet**

Central Bank of Honduras, 50th
Anniv. — AP281

No. C1260 — Central Bank of Honduras
emblem and paintings: a, 5 l, Holocausto, by
César Rendón. b, 10 l, La Novia, by Miguel
Angel Ruiz Matute. c, 15 l, Ayer, Hoy y
Mañana, by Felipe Bouchard. d, 20 l, Paisaje
de Tegucigalpa, by Mario Castillo. e, 25 l,
Dinamismo, by Benigno Gómez. f, 30 l, Guitar-
ras en Descanso, by Dante Lazzaroni.

**2007**
**C1260** AP281   Sheet of 6, #a-f   11.50   11.50

Adjudication of "Four Cardinal Points"
Police Torture Case — AP282

**2007, Oct. 18**     **Litho.**     **Perf. 13¼**
**C1261** AP282   50 l multi     5.50   5.50

  Printed in sheets of 2.

**Miniature Sheets**

Launch of Sputnik I, 50th
Anniv. — AP283

No. C1262: a, 25 l, Sputnik launch vehicle,
pale blue background (30x40mm). b, 35 l,
Sputnik I, yellow background (30x40mm). c,
50 l, Sputnik orbiting Earth, pale green background (60x40mm).
No. C1263: a, 25 l, As #C1262a, pale green
background. b, 35 l, As #C1262b, pale blue
background. c, 50 l, As #C1262c, yellow
background.

**2007, Nov. 30**
**C1262** AP283   Sheet of 3,
        #a-c    12.00   12.00
**C1263** AP283   Sheet of 3,
        #a-c    12.00   12.00

---

**Miniature Sheet**

Paintings by Gaye-Darléne Bidart de
Satulsky — AP284

No. C1264: a, 3 l, Medusa de las Islas. b,
3 l, Nido de Amor. c, 3 l, Guitarrista Isleño. d,
5 l, "M" Hombre Cruz. e, 5 l, Amor a Martil-
lazos. f, 5 l, Sor María Rosa. g, 5 l, Isleña,
Luna y Mar. h, 5 l, Clementina Suárez. i, 5 l,
La Naranjera.

**2008**
**C1264** AP284   Sheet of 9, #a-i   4.25   4.25

**Miniature Sheet**

America Issue — AP285

No. C1265: a, 2 l, Factory workers and sewing machine. b, 3 l, Energy savings mascot. c,
5 l, School children. d, 10 l, Children in native
costumes.

**2008**
**C1265** AP285   Sheet of 4, #a-d   2.10   2.10

---

**AIR POST SEMI-POSTAL STAMPS**

No. C13C Surcharged with Plus Sign
and Surtax in Black
**Unwmk.**
**1929, June 5**     **Engr.**     **Perf. 12**
**CB1** AP1   50c + 5c carmine     .50   .30
**CB2** AP1   50c + 10c carmine    .60   .35
**CB3** AP1   50c + 15c carmine    .85   .55
**CB4** AP1   50c + 20c carmine   1.25   .75
  *Nos. CB1-CB4 (4)*    3.20   1.95

> **Catalogue values for unused
> stamps in this section, from this
> point to the end of the section, are
> for Never Hinged items.**

## Souvenir Sheet

Airmail Pilot Sumner B. Morgan and Airplane — SP2

**2000, July 7**
CB5 SP2 50 l + 5 l multi    11.00 11.00

First airmail flight in Honduras, 75th anniv., EXFILHON 2000. See Nos. C1075-C1077.

No. C619 Surcharged With New Value in Black and 2000 Sydney Olympics Emblem in Red

**2000, Sept. 13**   **Litho.**   *Imperf.*
CB6 AP99 48.50 l +1.50 l multi   10.00 10.00

## AIR POST SPECIAL DELIVERY STAMPS

No. CO52 Surcharged in Red

*Perf. 13½x14*
**1953, Dec. 8**   **Engr.**   **Unwmk.**
CE1 AP65 20c on 1c    3.00 1.50

Transport Plane APSD1

**1956, Oct. 3**   *Perf. 13x12½*
CE2 APSD1 20c black & red    .80 .50

Surcharges on No. CE2 (see Nos. C421, C477) eliminate its special delivery character.

> **Catalogue values for unused stamps in this section, from this point to the end of the section, are for Never Hinged items.**

### Stamp Centenary Type of Air Post Issue

Design: 20c, Mailman on motorcycle.

**1966, May 31**   **Litho.**   *Perf. 14x14½*
CE3 AP81 20c bis brn, brn & gold   1.00 .50

Centenary (in 1965) of the first Honduran postage stamp.
The "HABILITADO" overprint on No. CE3 (see No. C479) eliminates its special delivery character.

### Independence Type of Air Post Issue

**1972, May 19**   **Litho.**   *Perf. 13*
CE4 AP89 20c Corsair plane    .70 .35

### Same Surcharged

**1975**
CE5 AP89 60c on 20c    1.00 .65

### Forest Protection Type of Air Post

**1976, May 28**   **Litho.**   *Perf. 13½*
CE6 AP96 60c Stag in forest    .75 .50

---

## AIR POST OFFICIAL STAMPS

Official Stamps Nos. O78 to O81 Overprinted in Red, Green or Black

**1930**    *Perf. 11, 11½*
CO1 A24 10c deep blue (R)   1.25 1.25
CO2 A24 20c yellow brown   1.25 1.25
  *a.* Vert. pair, imperf. btwn.   14.00
CO3 A24 50c vermilion (Bk)   1.40 1.40
CO4 A24 1p emerald (R)   1.25 1.25
  *Nos. CO1-CO4 (4)*   5.15 5.15

OA1

### Green Surcharge
CO5 OA1 5c on 6c red vio   1.00 1.00
  *a.* "1910" for "1930"   2.75 2.75
  *b.* "1920" for "1930"   2.75 2.75

The overprint exists in other colors and on other denominations but the status of these is questioned.

Official Stamps of 1931 Overprinted

**1931**   **Unwmk.**   *Perf. 12*
CO6 O2 1c ultra   .35 .35
CO7 O2 2c black brown   .85 .85
CO8 O2 5c olive gray   1.00 1.00
CO9 O2 6c orange red   1.00 1.00
  *a.* Inverted overprint   24.00 24.00
CO10 O2 10c dark green   1.25 1.25
CO11 O2 15c olive brown   2.00 1.75
  *a.* Inverted overprint   20.00 20.00
CO12 O2 20c red brown   2.00 1.75
CO13 O2 50c gray violet   1.40 1.40
CO14 O2 1p deep orange   2.00 1.75
  *Nos. CO6-CO14 (9)*   11.85 11.10

In the setting of the overprint there are numerous errors in the spelling and punctuation, letters omitted and similar varieties.
This set is known with blue overprint. A similar overprint is known in larger type, but its status has not been fully determined.

Postage Stamps of 1918-30 Surcharged Type "a" or Type "b" (#CO22-CO23) in Green, Black, Red and Blue

| Aereo Oficial Vale L. 0.70 1933 | Aéreo oficial Vale L. o.90 1933 |
|---|---|
| a | b |

**1933**    **Wmk. 209, Unwmk.**
CO15 A39 20c on 2c #295
    (G)   3.25 3.25
CO16 A39 20c on 2c #296
    (G)   3.25 3.25
CO17 A39 20c on 2c #297
    (G)   3.25 3.25
CO17A A39 40c on 2c #295   2.00 2.00
CO18 A39 40c on 2c #297
    (G)   7.00 7.00
CO18A A39 40c on 2c #297   4.25 4.25
CO19 A28 40c on 5c #246   4.25 4.25
CO19A A28 40c on 5c #247   7.00 7.00
CO20 A28 40c on 5c #266   15.00 15.00
CO20A A28 40c on 5c #267   9.00 9.00
CO20B A28 40c on 5c #267
    (R)   14.00 14.00
CO21 A20 70c on 5c #183   3.00 3.00
CO22 A24 70c on 10c
    #214 (R)   3.25 3.25
CO23 A22 1 l on 20c
    #191 (Bl)   3.25 3.25
CO24 A24 1 l on 50c
    #216 (Bl)   14.00 14.00

---

CO25 A22 1.20 l on 1p #193
    (Bl)   1.00 1.00
  *Nos. CO15-CO25 (16)*   96.75 96.75

**Official Stamps of 1915-29 Surcharged Type "a" or Type "b" (#CO28-CO29, CO33-CO41, CO43) in Black, Red, Green, Orange, Carmine or Blue**

CO26 O1 40c on 5c #O84
    (Bk)   1.00 1.00
CO27 O1 40c on 5c #O84
    (R)   25.00 25.00
CO28 A24 60c on 6c #O77
    (Bk)   .70 .70
CO29 A24 60c on 6c #O77
    (G)   25.00 25.00
CO30 A20 70c on 5c #O60
    (Bk)   5.25 5.25
CO31 A19 70c on 10c #O62
    (R)   9.00 9.00
CO32 A19 70c on 10c #O62
    (Bk)   7.75 7.75
CO33 A22 70c on 10c #O70
    (R)   4.50 4.00
CO34 A24 70c on 10c #O78
    (R)   3.50 3.50
CO35 A24 70c on 10c #O78
    (O)   4.50 4.50
CO36 A22 70c on 15c #O71
    (C)   87.50 87.50
CO37 A22 90c on 10c #O70
    (R)   5.25 5.25
CO38 A22 90c on 15c #O71
    (R)   8.00 8.00
CO38A A24 1 l on 2c #O76
    (R)   1.40 1.40
CO39 A22 1 l on 20c #O72
    (R)   2.50 2.50
CO39A A24 1 l on 20c #O79
    (R)   3.75 3.75
CO40 A22 1 l on 50c #O73
    (R)   1.90 1.90
CO41 A24 1 l on 50c #O80
    (R)   4.25 4.25
CO42 A20 1.20 l on 1p #O65
    l   9.00 7.00
CO43 A24 1.20 l on 1p #O81
    l   3.00 3.00
  *Nos. CO26-CO43 (20)*   212.75 210.25

Varieties of foregoing surcharges exist.

Merchant Flag and Seal of Honduras OA2

**1939, Feb. 27**   **Unwmk.**   *Perf. 12½*
CO44 OA2 2c dp blue & grn   .20 .20
CO45 OA2 5c dp blue & org   .20 .20
CO46 OA2 8c dp blue & brn   .20 .20
CO47 OA2 15c dp blue & car   .30 .20
CO48 OA2 46c dp blue & ol grn   .40 .30
CO49 OA2 50c dp blue & vio   .50 .30
CO50 OA2 1 l dp blue & red brn   1.75 1.25
CO51 OA2 2 l dp blue & red org   3.75 2.25
  *Nos. CO44-CO51 (8)*   7.30 4.90

For overprints and surcharges see #C101-C117.

Types of Air Post Stamps of 1952 Overprinted in Red

*Perf. 13½x14, 14x13½*
**1952**   **Engr.**   **Unwmk.**
CO52 AP65 1c rose lil & ol   .20 .20
CO53 AP65 2c brown & vio   .20 .20
CO54 AP65 8c dp car & blk   .20 .20
CO55 AP66 16c pur & dk grn   .25 .25
CO56 AP65 30c dk bl & blk   .50 .50
CO57 AP65 1 l dk grn & dk brown   1.75 1.75

---

CO58 AP65 2 l bl & red brn   3.50 3.50
CO59 AP66 5 l red org & blk   8.50 8.50
  *Nos. CO52-CO59 (8)*   15.10 15.10

Queen Isabella I of Spain, 500th birth anniv. For overprints and surcharge, see Nos. CE1, CO110.

No. C222 and Types of Air Post Stamps of 1953 Overprinted in Red

### Engraved; Center of 1c Litho.
**1953, Dec. 18**   *Perf. 12½*
### Frames in Black
CO60 AP67 1c ultra & vio bl   .20 .20
CO61 AP97 2c dp blue grn   .20 .20
CO62 AP67 3c orange   .20 .20
CO63 AP67 5c dp carmine   .20 .20
CO64 AP67 15c dk brown   .25 .20
CO65 AP67 30c purple   .45 .35
CO66 AP67 1 l olive gray   4.00 2.25
CO67 AP67 2 l lilac rose   5.00 3.00
CO68 AP67 5 l ultra   11.50 7.00
  *Nos. CO60-CO68 (9)*   22.00 13.60

Issued to honor the United Nations.

Types of Air Post Stamps Overprinted in Red

### Engraved; 8c Lithographed
**1956, Oct. 3**   *Perf. 13x12½*
CO69 AP68 1c blk & brn car   .20 .20
CO70 AP69 2c black & mag   .20 .20
CO71 AP68 3c blk & rose vio   .20 .20
CO72 AP69 4c black & org   .20 .20
CO73 AP69 5c black & bl grn   .20 .20
CO74 AP68 8c violet & multi   .20 .20
CO75 AP68 10c blk & red brn   .20 .20
CO76 AP68 12c blk & car rose   .20 .20
CO77 AP68 15c carmine & blk   .20 .20
CO78 AP68 20c black & ol brn   .20 .20
CO79 AP68 24c black & blue   .20 .20
CO80 AP68 25c blk & rose vio   .20 .20
CO81 AP68 30c black & grn   .20 .20
CO82 AP68 40c blk & red org   .25 .25
CO83 AP69 50c blk & brn red   .30 .30
CO84 AP68 60c blk & rose vio   .40 .40
CO85 AP69 1 l black & brn   1.40 1.10
CO86 AP69 2 l black & dk bl   2.75 2.25
CO87 AP69 5 l black & vio bl   5.75 5.25
  *Nos. CO69-CO87 (19)*   13.45 12.15

OFICIAL

Nos. C269-C278 Overprinted Vertically in Red (Horizontally on Nos. CO89 and CO91)

**1957, Oct. 21**   **Litho.**   *Perf. 13*
### Frames in Black
CO88 AP70 1c buff & aqua   .20 .20
CO89 AP70 2c org, pur & emer   .20 .20
CO90 AP70 5c pink & ultra   .20 .20
  *a.* Inverted overprint
CO91 AP70 8c orange, vio & ol   .20 .20
CO92 AP70 10c violet & brn   .20 .20
CO93 AP70 12c lt grn & ultra   .20 .20
CO94 AP70 15c green & brn   .20 .20
CO95 AP70 30c pink & sl   .55 .25
CO96 AP70 1 l blue & brn   1.40 1.00
CO97 AP70 2 l lt grn & sl   2.75 2.25
  *Nos. CO88-CO97 (10)*   6.10 4.90

Types of Lincoln Air Post Stamps 1959 Overprinted in Red

**1959**    Engr.    *Perf. 13½*
**Flags in National Colors**

| | | | | |
|---|---|---|---|---|
| CO98 | AP72 | 1c ocher | .20 | .20 |
| CO99 | AP73 | 2c gray olive | .20 | .20 |
| a. | | Inverted overprint | | |
| CO100 | AP73 | 3c red brown | .20 | .20 |
| CO101 | AP73 | 5c ultra | .20 | .20 |
| CO102 | AP73 | 10c dull purple | .20 | .20 |
| a. | | Overprint omitted | | |
| CO103 | AP73 | 12c red orange | .20 | .20 |
| CO104 | AP72 | 15c dark brown | .20 | .20 |
| CO105 | AP73 | 25c black | .20 | .20 |
| CO106 | AP73 | 50c dark car | .30 | .25 |
| CO107 | AP73 | 1 l purple | .75 | .65 |
| CO108 | AP73 | 2 l dark blue | 1.40 | 1.10 |
| a. | | Min. sheet of 6, 2c, 5c, 12c, 15c, 50c, 2 l, imperf. | 3.00 | 3.00 |
| CO109 | AP73 | 5 l green | 4.50 | 3.75 |
| | | *Nos. CO98-CO109 (12)* | 8.55 | 7.35 |

> **Catalogue values for unused stamps in this section, from this point to the end of the section, are for Never Hinged items.**

No. CO55 Overprinted: "IN MEMORIAM / Sir Winston / Churchill / 1874-1965"

**1965, Dec. 20**    *Perf. 14x13½*
CO110 AP66 16c purple & dk grn 1.00 1.00

See note after No. C379.

Nos. C336-C344 Overprinted in Red:

**1965**    Photo.    *Perf. 14*
**Black Design and Inscription**

| | | | | |
|---|---|---|---|---|
| CO111 | AP76 | 1c yellow green | .20 | .20 |
| CO112 | AP76 | 2c pale rose lil | .20 | .20 |
| CO113 | AP76 | 5c light ultra | .20 | .20 |
| CO114 | AP76 | 8c bluish grn | .25 | .25 |
| CO115 | AP76 | 10c buff | .30 | .30 |
| CO116 | AP76 | 12c lemon | .35 | .35 |
| CO117 | AP76 | 1 l light ocher | 4.00 | 4.00 |
| CO118 | AP76 | 2 l pale olive grn | 8.75 | 8.75 |
| CO119 | AP76 | 3 l rose | 11.00 | 11.00 |
| | | *Nos. CO111-CO119 (9)* | 25.25 | 25.25 |

## OFFICIAL STAMPS

Type of Regular Issue of 1890 Overprinted in Red

**1890**    Unwmk.    *Perf. 12*

| | | | |
|---|---|---|---|
| O1 | A5 | 1c pale yellow | .20 |
| O2 | A5 | 2c pale yellow | .20 |
| O3 | A5 | 5c pale yellow | .20 |
| O4 | A5 | 10c pale yellow | .20 |
| O5 | A5 | 20c pale yellow | .20 |
| O6 | A5 | 25c pale yellow | .20 |
| O7 | A5 | 30c pale yellow | .20 |
| O8 | A5 | 40c pale yellow | .20 |
| O9 | A5 | 50c pale yellow | .20 |
| O10 | A5 | 75c pale yellow | .20 |
| O11 | A5 | 1p pale yellow | .20 |
| | | *Nos. O1-O11 (11)* | 2.20 |

Type of Regular Issue of 1891 Overprinted in Red

**1891**

| | | | |
|---|---|---|---|
| O12 | A6 | 1c yellow | .20 |
| O13 | A6 | 2c yellow | .20 |
| O14 | A6 | 5c yellow | .20 |
| O15 | A6 | 10c yellow | .20 |
| O16 | A6 | 20c yellow | .20 |
| O17 | A6 | 25c yellow | .20 |
| O18 | A6 | 30c yellow | .20 |
| O19 | A6 | 40c yellow | .20 |
| O20 | A6 | 50c yellow | .20 |
| O21 | A6 | 75c yellow | .20 |
| O22 | A6 | 1p yellow | .20 |
| | | *Nos. O12-O22 (11)* | 2.20 |

Nos. O1 to O22 were never placed in use. Cancellations were applied to remainders. They exist with overprint inverted, double, triple and omitted; also, imperf. and part perf.

Regular Issue of 1898 Overprinted

**1898-99**    *Perf. 11½*

| | | | |
|---|---|---|---|
| O23 | A12 | 5c dl ultra | .20 |
| O24 | A12 | 10c dark bl | .20 |
| O25 | A12 | 20c dull org | .30 |
| O26 | A12 | 50c org red | .35 |
| O27 | A12 | 1p blue grn | .60 |
| | | *Nos. O23-O27 (5)* | 1.65 |

Counterfeits of basic stamps and of overprint exist.

Regular Issue of 1911 Overprinted

**1911-15**    *Perf. 12, 14*
**Carmine Overprint**

| | | | | |
|---|---|---|---|---|
| O28 | A15 | 1c violet | 1.50 | .65 |
| a. | | Inverted overprint | 2.00 | |
| b. | | Double overprint | 2.00 | |
| O29 | A15 | 6c ultra | 2.50 | 2.00 |
| a. | | Inverted overprint | 2.50 | |
| O30 | A15 | 10c blue | 1.50 | 1.25 |
| a. | | "OFICAIL" | 2.50 | |
| b. | | Double overprint | 3.50 | |
| O31 | A15 | 20c yellow | 15.00 | 12.00 |
| O32 | A15 | 50c brown | 8.00 | 7.00 |
| O33 | A15 | 1p ol grn | 12.00 | 10.00 |
| | | *Nos. O28-O33 (6)* | 40.50 | 32.90 |

**Black Overprint**

| | | | | |
|---|---|---|---|---|
| O34 | A15 | 2c green | 1.00 | .70 |
| a. | | "CFICIAL" | 5.00 | |
| O35 | A15 | 5c carmine | 1.50 | 1.00 |
| a. | | Perf. 12 | 7.50 | 5.00 |
| O36 | A15 | 6c ultra | 4.50 | 4.50 |
| O37 | A15 | 10c blue | 4.00 | 4.00 |
| O38 | A15 | 20c yellow | 5.00 | 5.00 |
| O39 | A15 | 50c brown | 5.50 | 5.00 |
| | | *Nos. O34-O39 (6)* | 21.50 | 19.20 |

Counterfeits of overprint of Nos. O28-O39 exist.

With Additional Surcharge

**1913-14**

| | | | | |
|---|---|---|---|---|
| O40 | A15 | 1c on 5c car | 1.75 | 1.50 |
| O41 | A15 | 2c on 5c car | 2.00 | 1.50 |
| O42 | A15 | 10c on 1c vio | 4.00 | 3.50 |
| a. | | "OFICIAL" inverted | 7.50 | |
| O43 | A15 | 20c on 1c vio | 3.00 | 2.50 |
| | | *Nos. O40-O43 (4)* | 10.75 | 9.00 |

On No. O40 the surcharge reads "1 cent." Nos. O40-O43 exist with double surcharge.

No. O43 Surcharged Vertically in Black, Yellow or Maroon

**1914**

| | | | | |
|---|---|---|---|---|
| O44 | A15 | 10c on 20c on 1c | 20.00 | 20.00 |
| a. | | Maroon surcharge | 20.00 | 20.00 |
| O45 | A15 | 10c on 20c on 1c (Y) | 40.00 | 40.00 |

No. O35 Surcharged

**1915**
O46 A15 10c on 5c car 20.00 20.00

No. O39 Surcharged

O47 A15 20c on 50c brn 5.00 5.00

Regular Issues of 1913-14 Overprinted in Red or Black

**1915**    *Perf. 11½*

| | | | | |
|---|---|---|---|---|
| O48 | A17 | 1c brn (R) | .40 | .40 |
| a. | | "OFICIAL" | 5.00 | |
| O49 | A17 | 2c car (Bk) | .40 | .40 |
| a. | | "OFICIAL" | 5.00 | |
| b. | | Double overprint | 4.00 | |
| O50 | A18 | 5c ultra (Bk) | .45 | .45 |
| a. | | "OFIC" | 4.00 | |
| O51 | A18 | 5c ultra (R) | 1.00 | 1.00 |
| a. | | "OFIC" | | |
| b. | | "OFICIAIL" | 5.00 | |
| c. | | 6c red lil (Bk) | | |
| O52 | A18 | 6c pur (Bk) | 1.50 | 1.50 |
| O53 | A17 | 10c brn (Bk) | 1.25 | 1.25 |
| O54 | A17 | 20c brn (Bk) | 3.00 | 3.00 |
| O55 | A17 | 20c brn (R) | 3.00 | 3.00 |
| a. | | Double overprint (R+Bk) | 10.00 | |
| b. | | "OFICIAL" | 5.00 | |
| O56 | A18 | 50c rose (Bk) | 6.00 | 6.00 |
| | | *Nos. O48-O56 (9)* | 17.00 | 17.00 |

The 10c blue has the overprint "OFICIAL" in different type from the other stamps of the series. It is stated that forty stamps were overprinted for the Postmaster General but the stamp was never put in use or on sale at the post office.

No. 152 Surcharged

| | | | | |
|---|---|---|---|---|
| O57 | A17 | 1c on 2c car | 2.00 | 2.00 |
| a. | | "0.10" for "0.01" | 4.25 | 4.25 |
| b. | | "0.20" for "0.01" | 4.25 | 4.25 |
| c. | | Double surcharge | 8.50 | 8.50 |
| d. | | As "a," double surcharge | 77.50 | |
| e. | | As "b," double surcharge | 77.50 | |

Regular Issue of 1915-16 Overprinted in Black or Red.

**1915-16**

| | | | | |
|---|---|---|---|---|
| O58 | A19 | 1c choc (Bk) | .20 | .20 |
| O59 | A19 | 2c car (Bk) | .20 | .20 |
| a. | | Tête bêche pair | 1.25 | 1.25 |
| b. | | Double overprint | 2.00 | |
| c. | | Double overprint, one inverted | 2.00 | |
| d. | | "b" and "c" in tête bêche pair | | |
| O60 | A20 | 5c brt blue (R) | .30 | .30 |
| a. | | Inverted overprint | 3.00 | |
| O61 | A20 | 6c deep pur (R) | .40 | .40 |
| a. | | Black overprint | 3.00 | |
| b. | | Inverted overprint | 2.00 | 2.00 |
| O62 | A19 | 10c dl bl (R) | .40 | .40 |
| O63 | A19 | 20c red brn (Bk) | .60 | .60 |
| a. | | Tête bêche pair | | |
| O64 | A20 | 50c red (Bk) | 1.75 | 1.75 |
| O65 | A20 | 1p yel grn (C) | 3.75 | 3.75 |
| | | *Nos. O58-O65 (8)* | 7.60 | 7.60 |

The 6c, 10c and 1p exist imperf.

Regular Issue of 1919 Overprinted

**1921**

| | | | | |
|---|---|---|---|---|
| O66 | A22 | 1c brown | 2.25 | 2.25 |
| a. | | Inverted overprint | 3.00 | 3.00 |
| O67 | A22 | 2c carmine | 6.50 | 6.50 |
| a. | | Inverted overprint | 3.00 | 3.00 |
| O68 | A22 | 5c lilac rose | 6.50 | 6.50 |
| a. | | Inverted overprint | 3.00 | |
| O69 | A22 | 6c brt vio | .50 | .50 |
| a. | | Inverted overprint | | |
| O70 | A22 | 10c dull blue | .60 | .60 |
| a. | | Double overprint | | |
| O71 | A22 | 15c light blue | .70 | .70 |
| a. | | Inverted overprint | 2.00 | |
| b. | | Double ovpt., one inverted | 4.00 | |
| O72 | A22 | 20c brown | 1.00 | 1.00 |
| O73 | A22 | 50c light brown | 1.50 | 1.50 |
| O74 | A22 | 1p yellow green | 3.00 | 3.00 |
| | | *Nos. O66-O74 (9)* | 22.55 | 22.55 |

Regular Issue of 1924 Overprinted

**1924**    *Perf. 11, 11½*

| | | | | |
|---|---|---|---|---|
| O75 | A24 | 1c olive brn | .20 | .20 |
| O76 | A24 | 2c deep rose | .20 | .20 |
| O77 | A24 | 6c red vio | .30 | .30 |
| O78 | A24 | 10c deep bl | .45 | .45 |
| O79 | A24 | 20c yel brn | .60 | .60 |
| O80 | A24 | 50c vermilion | 1.25 | 1.25 |
| O81 | A24 | 1p emerald | 2.00 | 2.00 |
| | | *Nos. O75-O81 (7)* | 5.00 | 5.00 |

J. C. del Valle — O1

Designs: 2c, J. R. Molina. 5c, Coffee tree. 10c, J. T. Reyes. 20c, Tegucigalpa Cathedral. 50c, San Lorenzo Creek. 1p, Radio station.

**1929**    Litho.    Wmk. 209    *Perf. 11½*

| | | | | |
|---|---|---|---|---|
| O82 | O1 | 1c blue | .20 | .20 |
| O83 | O1 | 2c carmine | .20 | .20 |
| a. | | 2c rose | .20 | .20 |
| O84 | O1 | 5c purple | .35 | .35 |
| O85 | O1 | 10c emerald | .50 | .35 |
| O86 | O1 | 20c dk bl | .60 | .60 |
| O87 | O1 | 50c org, grn & bl | 1.00 | 1.00 |
| O88 | O1 | 1p buff | 1.75 | 1.75 |
| | | *Nos. O82-O88 (7)* | 4.60 | 4.45 |

Nos. O82-O88 exist imperf.
For overprints and surcharges see Nos. 282, 284, C37-C40, C59, C62-C63, CO26-CO27.

View of Tegucigalpa O2

**1931**    Unwmk.    Engr.    *Perf. 12*

| | | | | |
|---|---|---|---|---|
| O89 | O2 | 1c ultra | .30 | .30 |
| O90 | O2 | 2c black brn | .30 | .20 |
| O91 | O2 | 5c olive gray | .35 | .25 |
| O92 | O2 | 6c orange red | .40 | .30 |
| O93 | O2 | 10c dark green | .50 | .35 |
| O94 | O2 | 15c olive brn | .65 | .40 |
| O95 | O2 | 20c red brown | .75 | .50 |
| O96 | O2 | 50c gray vio | 1.00 | .65 |
| O97 | O2 | 1p dp orange | 1.75 | 1.75 |
| | | *Nos. O89-O97 (9)* | 6.00 | 4.60 |

For overprints see #CO6-CO14, O98-O105.

## HONDURAS

Official Stamps of 1931 Overprinted in Black

**1936-37**

| | | | | |
|---|---|---|---|---|
| O98 | O2 | 1c ultra | .25 | .25 |
| O99 | O2 | 2c black brn | .25 | .25 |
| a. | | Inverted overprint | 10.00 | |
| O100 | O2 | 5c olive gray | .30 | .30 |
| O101 | O2 | 6c red orange | .40 | .40 |
| O102 | O2 | 10c dark green | .40 | .40 |
| O103 | O2 | 15c olive brown | .50 | .50 |
| a. | | Inverted overprint | 5.00 | |
| O104 | O2 | 20c red brown | 1.00 | 1.00 |
| a. | | "1938-1935" | | |
| O105 | O2 | 50c gray violet | 4.00 | 3.00 |
| | | Nos. O98-O105 (8) | 7.10 | 6.10 |

Double overprints exist on 1c and 2c. No. O97 with this overprint is fraudulent.

### POSTAL TAX STAMPS

Red Cross PT1

Francisco Morazán PT2

**Engr.; Cross Litho.**

**1941, Aug. 1    Unwmk.    Perf. 12**
RA1 PT1 1c blue & carmine    .25  .20

Obligatory on all domestic or foreign mail, the tax to be used by the Honduran Red Cross.

**1941, Aug. 1    Engr.**
RA2 PT2 1c copper brown    .40  .20

Francisco Morazan, 100th anniv. of death.

Mother and Child — PT3

Henri Dunant — PT4

**1945    Engr.; Cross Litho.**
RA3 PT3 1c ol brn, car & bl    .25  .20

The tax was for the Honduran Red Cross.

Similar to Type of 1945 Large Red Cross

**1950**
RA4 PT3 1c olive brn & red    .25  .20

The tax was for the Honduran Red Cross.

**1959    Perf. 13x13½**
RA5 PT4 1c blue & red    .25  .20

The tax was for the Red Cross.

Catalogue values for unused stamps in this section, from this point to the end of the section, are for Never Hinged items.

Henri Dunant — PT5

---

No. RA7, as PT5, but redrawn; country name panel at bottom, value at right, "El poder . . ." at top.

**1964, Dec. 15    Litho.    Perf. 11**
RA6 PT5 1c brt grn & red    .25  .20
RA7 PT5 1c brown & red    .25  .20

The tax was for the Red Cross.

Nurse and Patient — PT6

**1969, June    Litho.    Perf. 13½**
RA8 PT6 1c light blue & red    .25  .20

The tax was for the Red Cross. For surcharges see Nos. 387-391.

---

# HONG KONG

ˈhäŋˌkäŋ

LOCATION — A peninsula and island in southeast China at the mouth of the Canton River
GOVT. — Special Administrative Area of China (PRC) (as of 7/1/97)
AREA — 426 sq. mi.
POP. — 6,847,125 (1999 est.)
CAPITAL — Victoria

100 Cents = 1 Dollar

Catalogue values for unused stamps in this country are for Never Hinged items, beginning with Scott 174 in the regular postage section, Scott B1 in the semipostal section and Scott J13 in the postage due section.

**Watermark**

Wmk. 340

Values for unused stamps are for examples with original gum as defined in the catalogue introduction. Very fine examples of Nos. 1-25, 29-48, 61-66d and 69-70a will have perforations touching the design on at least one side due to the narrow spacing of the stamps on the plates. Stamps with perfs clear of the design on all four sides are scarce and will command higher prices.

Queen Victoria — A1

**Unwmk.**

**1862, Dec. 8    Typo.    Perf. 14**

| | | | | |
|---|---|---|---|---|
| 1 | A1 | 2c pale brown | 525.00 | 110.00 |
| a. | | 2c deep brown | 650.00 | 140.00 |
| 2 | A1 | 8c buff | 775.00 | 82.50 |
| 3 | A1 | 12c blue | 700.00 | 70.00 |
| 4 | A1 | 18c lilac | 700.00 | 65.00 |
| 5 | A1 | 24c green | 1,200. | 140.00 |
| 6 | A1 | 48c rose | 3,000. | 400.00 |
| 7 | A1 | 96c gray | 4,000. | 525.00 |

**1863-80    Wmk. 1**

| | | | | |
|---|---|---|---|---|
| 8 | A1 | 2c brown ('65) | 145.00 | 8.00 |
| a. | | 2c deep brown ('64) | 325.00 | 32.50 |

---

| | | | | |
|---|---|---|---|---|
| 9 | A1 | 2c dull rose ('80) | 175.00 | 30.00 |
| a. | | 2c rose | 190.00 | 32.50 |
| 10 | A1 | 4c slate | 135.00 | 8.25 |
| a. | | 4c greenish grey | 350.00 | 55.00 |
| b. | | 4c bluish slate | 525.00 | 25.00 |
| 11 | A1 | 5c ultra ('80) | 550.00 | 50.00 |
| 12 | A1 | 6c lilac | 475.00 | 16.50 |
| a. | | 6c violet | 600.00 | 16.50 |
| 13 | A1 | 8c org buff ('65) | 575.00 | 12.50 |
| a. | | 8c bright orange | 450.00 | 13.00 |
| b. | | 8c brownish orange | 525.00 | 13.00 |
| 14 | A1 | 10c violet ('80) | 675.00 | 19.00 |
| 15 | A1 | 12c light blue | 37.50 | 7.00 |
| a. | | 12c light greenish blue | 1,100. | 37.50 |
| b. | | 12c deep blue | 275.00 | 14.00 |
| 16 | A1 | 16c yellow ('77) | 2,200. | 77.50 |
| 17 | A1 | 18c lilac ('66) | 7,750. | 350.00 |
| 18 | A1 | 24c green ('65) | 575.00 | 12.50 |
| a. | | 24c deep green | 1,000. | 32.50 |
| 19 | A1 | 30c vermilion | 850.00 | 17.50 |
| 20 | A1 | 30c violet ('71) | 300.00 | 7.00 |
| 21 | A1 | 48c rose carmine | 1,100. | 55.00 |
| 22 | A1 | 48c brown ('80) | 1,600. | 120.00 |
| 23 | A1 | 96c bister ('65) | 60,000. | 800.00 |
| 24 | A1 | 96c gray ('66) | 1,750. | 62.50 |

Imperfs. are plate proofs.

**1874    Perf. 12½**
25 A1 4c slate    13,500. 300.00

See #36-49. For surcharges or overprints on stamps of type A1 see #29-35B, 51-56, 61-66, 69-70.

A2

A3

A4

**1874    Engr.    Wmk. 1    Perf. 15½x15**

| | | | | |
|---|---|---|---|---|
| 26 | A2 | $2 sage green | 400.00 | 70.00 |
| 27 | A3 | $3 violet | 375.00 | 55.00 |
| 28 | A4 | $10 rose | 8,250. | 800.00 |

Nos. 26-28 are revenues which were used postally. Used values are for postally canceled stamps. Black "Paid All" cancels are fiscal usage.
See Nos. 57-59. For surcharges see Nos. 50, 60, 67.

Nos. 17 and 20 Surcharged in Black:

**1876    Perf. 14**

| | | | | |
|---|---|---|---|---|
| 29 | A1 | 16c on 18c lilac | 2,500. | 185.00 |
| 30 | A1 | 28c on 30c violet | 1,750. | 62.50 |

Stamps of 1863-80 Surcharged in Black

**1879-80**

| | | | | |
|---|---|---|---|---|
| 31 | A1 | 5c on 8c org ('80) | 1,100. | 110.00 |
| a. | | Inverted surcharge | | 18,500. |
| b. | | Double surcharge | | 20,000. |
| 32 | A1 | 5c on 18c lilac | 1,050. | 70.00 |
| 33 | A1 | 10c on 12c blue | 1,100. | 65.00 |
| 34 | A1 | 10c on 16c yellow | 4,750. | 175.00 |
| a. | | Inverted surcharge | | 85,000. |
| b. | | Double surcharge | | 85,000. |
| 35 | A1 | 10c on 24c green ('80) | 1,550. | 95.00 |

Most examples of No. 31a are damaged.

---

Nos. 16-17, 35B Surcharged in Black

A5

A6

**1879**

| | | | | |
|---|---|---|---|---|
| 35A | A5 | 3c on 16c on card | 425. | 2,200. |
| | | Stamp off card | | 475. |
| 35B | A5 | 5c on 18c on card | 425. | 2,600. |
| | | Stamp off card | | 550. |
| 35C | A6 | 3c on 5c on 18c on card | 8,000. | 9,500. |
| | | Stamp off card | 6,500. | 8,250. |

Nos. 35A-35C were sold affixed to postal cards. Most used stamps are found off card so values are given for these.

Type of 1862

**1882-1902    Wmk. 2    Perf. 14**

| | | | | |
|---|---|---|---|---|
| 36b | A1 | 2c carmine ('84) | 44.00 | 2.25 |
| 37 | A1 | 2c green ('00) | 32.50 | 1.10 |
| 38 | A1 | 4c slate ('96) | 16.00 | 2.00 |
| 39 | A1 | 4c car rose ('00) | 22.50 | 1.25 |
| 40 | A1 | 5c ultramarine | 32.50 | 1.25 |
| 41 | A1 | 5c yellow ('00) | 27.50 | 8.00 |
| 42 | A1 | 10c lilac | 875.00 | 18.00 |
| 43 | A1 | 10c green | 160.00 | 2.25 |
| a. | | 10c blue green | 2,000. | 45.00 |
| 44 | A1 | 10c vio, red ('91) | 29.00 | 2.25 |
| 45 | A1 | 10c ultra ('91) | 57.50 | 2.50 |
| 46 | A1 | 12c blue ('02) | 52.50 | 62.50 |
| 47 | A1 | 30c gray grn ('91) | 95.00 | 26.50 |
| a. | | 30c yellow green | 145.00 | 42.50 |
| 48 | A1 | 30c brown ('01) | 55.00 | 25.00 |
| | | Nos. 36b-48 (13) | 1,499. | 154.85 |

No. 47 has fugitive ink. Both colors will turn dull green upon soaking.
The 2c rose, perf 12, is most likely a proof.

No. 28 Surcharged in Black

**1880    Wmk. 1    Perf. 15½x15**
50 A4 12c on $10 rose    1,000. 375.00

Surcharged in Black

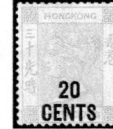

**1885-91    Wmk. 2    Perf. 14**

| | | | | |
|---|---|---|---|---|
| 51 | A1 | 20c on 30c ver | 155.00 | 7.00 |
| a. | | Double surcharge | | |
| 52 | A1 | 20c on 30c gray grn ('91) | 125.00 | 175.00 |
| a. | | 20c on 30c yellow green | 200.00 | 190.00 |
| 53 | A1 | 50c on 48c brown | 450.00 | 45.00 |
| 54 | A1 | 50c on 48c lil ('91) | 300.00 | 325.00 |
| 55 | A1 | $1 on 96c ol gray | 825.00 | 90.00 |
| 56 | A1 | $1 on 96c vio, red ('91) | 900.00 | 400.00 |

For overprints see Nos. 61-63.

Types of 1874 and

A7

**1890-1902    Wmk. 2    Perf. 14**
56A A7 2c dull purple    115.00 30.00

**Wmk. 1**

| | | | | |
|---|---|---|---|---|
| 57 | A2 | $2 gray green | 475.00 | 300.00 |
| 58 | A3 | $3 lilac ('02) | 625.00 | 525.00 |
| 59 | A4 | $10 gray grn ('92) | 12,000. | 12,000. |

Due to a shortage of 2c postage stamps, No. 56A was authorized for postal use December 24-30, 1890.
Fake postmarks are known on No. 59. Beware also of fiscal cancels altered to resemble postal cancels.
For surcharge see No. 68.

Type of 1874
Surcharged in
Black

**1891, Jan. 1** — Wmk. 2
60 A4 $5 on $10 vio, *red* 360.00 115.00

Nos. 36b, 44 Overprinted

a      b

**1891, Jan. 1**
60A A1 2c carmine (a) 1,100. 425.00
60B A1 2c carmine (b) 1,050. 425.00
  *a.* Inverted overprint 6,500.
60C A1 10c vio, *red* (a) 1,900. 475.00

Nos. 60A-60C were overprinted for use as
fiscal stamps, "S.O." denoting "Stamp Office"
and "S.D." denoting "Stamp Duty." They were
authorized for postal use Jan. 1, 1891-1893.
Examples of No. 60A with "O" changed to "D"
in manuscript are known.
Forged overprints are often encountered.
Expertization is required.

Nos. 52, 54 and 56 Handstamped with
Chinese characters

61 A1 (g) 20c on 30c gray
     green 45.00 8.50
  *a.* 20c on 30c dull green 62.50 11.00
  *b.* "20 CENTS" double 95.00 6.25
62 A1 (h) 50c on 48c lilac 95.00 6.25
63 A1 (i) $1 on 96c vio,
     red 525.00 27.50

No. 61 may be found with Chinese character
2, 2½ or 3mm high.
The handstamped Chinese surcharges on
Nos. 61-63 exist in several varieties including
inverted, double, triple, misplaced, omitted
and (on #63) on both front and back.

Nos. 43 and 20
Surcharged

**1891**
64 A1 7c on 10c green 82.50 9.00
  *a.* Double surcharge 6,500. 1,500.

— Wmk. 1
65 A1 14c on 30c violet 190.00 80.00

Beware of faked varieties.

No. 36 Overprinted in
Black

**1891, Jan. 22** — Wmk. 2
66 A1 2c rose 575.00 140.00
  *a.* Double overprint 17,500. 13,000.
  *b.* "U" of "JUBILEE" shorter 800.00 200.00
  *c.* "J" of "JUBILEE" shorter 800.00 200.00
  *d.* Tall "K" in "KONG" 1,300. 500.00

50th anniversary of the colony.
Beware of faked varieties.

No. 26 Surcharged
(Chinese
Handstamped)

**1897, Sept.** Wmk. 1 *Perf. 15½x15*
67 A2 $1 on $2 sage
     green 300.00 150.00
  *a.* Without Chinese
     surcharge 5,000. 4,500.

On No. 57
*Perf. 14*
68 A2 $1 on $2 gray
     green 300.00 150.00
  *a.* Without Chinese
     surcharge 2,100. 2,000.

Handstamp Surcharged
in Black

**1898** — Wmk. 2
69 A1 10c on 30c gray
     grn 60.00 87.50
  *a.* Large Chinese
     surcharge 1,250. 1,250.
  *b.* Without Chinese
     surcharge 600.00 1,100.
70 A1 $1 on 96c black 200.00 32.50
  *a.* Without Chinese
     surcharge 3,000. 4,000.

The Chinese surcharge is added separately.
See notes below Nos. 61-63. The small Chinese surcharge is illustrated.

King Edward VII — A10

**1903** — Wmk. 2
71 A10 1c brown & lilac 2.25 .55
72 A10 2c gray green 12.00 1.60
73 A10 4c violet, *red* 15.00 .45
74 A10 5c org & gray
     grn 13.00 10.00
75 A10 8c violet &
     black 12.00 1.75
76 A10 10c ultra & lil, *bl* 45.00 2.00
77 A10 12c red vio &
     gray grn,
     *yel* 10.00 5.25
78 A10 20c org brn &
     brnsh gray 52.50 4.00
79 A10 30c blk & gray
     grn 55.00 24.00
80 A10 50c red vio &
     gray green 50.00 50.00
81 A10 $1 olive grn &
     lil 100.00 25.00
82 A10 $2 scar & black 325.00 300.00
83 A10 $3 dp blue &
     blk 400.00 400.00
84 A10 $5 blue grn & lil 550.00 550.00
85 A10 $10 org & blk, *bl* 1,300. 500.00
     Nos. 71-85 (15) 2,941. 1,874.

**1904-11** — Wmk. 3
**Ordinary or Chalky Paper**
86 A10 1c brown ('10) 5.00 1.10
  *a.* Booklet pane of 4
87 A10 2c gray green 9.25 1.50
88 A10 2c deep green 25.00 1.90
  *a.* Booklet pane of 4
  *b.* Booklet pane of 12
89 A10 4c violet, *red* 21.00 .50
90 A10 4c carmine 10.00 .50
  *a.* Booklet pane of 4
  *b.* Booklet pane of 12
91 A10 5c org & gray grn 32.50 10.00
92 A10 6c red vio & org
     ('07) 27.50 5.25
93 A10 8c vio & blk ('07) 13.00 2.25
94 A10 10c ultra & lil, *bl* 22.50 1.50
95 A10 10c ultramarine 27.50 .50
96 A10 12c red vio &
     grn, *yel* ('07) 15.00 6.00
97 A10 20c org brn &
     brnsh gray 42.50 2.50
98 A10 20c ol grn & vio
     ('11) 50.00 50.00
99 A10 30c blk & gray grn 50.00 25.00
100 A10 30c org & vio ('11) 60.00 27.50
101 A10 50c red vio & gray
     green 90.00 10.00
102 A10 50c blk, *grn* ('11) 45.00 16.00
103 A10 $1 ol grn & lil 150.00 30.00
104 A10 $2 scar & black 275.00 130.00
105 A10 $2 blk & car ('10) 350.00 350.00
106 A10 $3 dp bl & blk 300.00 250.00
107 A10 $5 bl grn & lil 500.00 425.00
108 A10 $10 org & blk, *bl* 2,000. 1,200.
     Nos. 86-108 (23) 4,120. 2,547.

Nos. 86, 88, 90, 94 and 95 are on ordinary
paper only. Nos. 92, 93, 96, 98, 100, 102, 105,
106 and 107 are on chalky paper and the
others of the issue are on both papers.
The 4c, 5c, 8c, 12c 20c, 50c, $2 and $5
denominations of type A10 are expressed in
colored letters or numerals and letters on a
colorless background.

King George V
A11      A12

A13      A14

A15

**1912-14** — Ordinary Paper
109 A11 1c brown 3.00 .60
  *a.* Booklet pane of 12
110 A11 2c deep green 9.00 .40
  *a.* Booklet pane of 12
111 A12 4c carmine 5.00 .40
  *a.* Booklet pane of 12
  *b.* Booklet pane of 4
112 A13 6c orange 5.00 1.10
113 A12 8c gray 26.00 6.00
114 A11 10c ultramarine 37.50 .35
**Chalky Paper**
115 A14 12c vio, *yel* 6.00 8.00
116 A14 20c ol grn & vio 7.00 1.10
117 A15 25c red vio & dl
     violet 24.00 30.00
118 A13 30c org & violet 25.00 7.75
119 A14 50c black, *green* 16.00 2.00
  *b.* 50c black, *emerald* 27.50 10.00
  *c.* 50c black, *bl grn, ol*
     back 1,400. 32.50
  *d.* 50c black, *emer, ol back* 32.50 10.00
120 A11 $1 blue & vio,
     *bl* 50.00 4.00
121 A14 $2 black & red 150.00 60.00
122 A13 $3 vio & green 250.00 100.00
123 A14 $5 red & grn,
     *grn* 725.00 450.00
  *a.* $5 red & grn, *bl grn, ol*
     back 1,300. 375.00
124 A13 $10 blk & vio,
     *red* 675.00 95.00
     Nos. 109-124 (16) 2,013. 766.70

For overprints see British Offices in China
#1-27.

**1914, May** Surface-colored Paper
125 A14 12c violet, *yel* 8.00 16.00
126 A14 50c black, *green* 16.00 5.00
127 A14 $5 red & grn, *grn* 675.00 350.00
     Nos. 125-127 (3) 699.00 371.00

Stamp of 1912-14 Redrawn

至 instead of 弌 at upper left.

**1919, Sept.** Chalky Paper
128 A15 25c red vio & dl vio 175.00 65.00

Types of 1912-14 Issue

**1921-37** — Wmk. 4
**Ordinary Paper**
129 A11 1c brown 1.10 .50
130 A11 2c deep green 3.00 .55
131 A11 2c gray ('37) 21.00 8.00
132 A12 3c gray ('31) 8.00 1.10
133 A12 4c rose red 4.00 1.00
134 A12 5c violet ('31) 11.00 .40
135 A12 8c gray 15.00 40.00
136 A12 8c orange 4.75 2.00
137 A11 10c ultramarine 5.00 .45
**Chalky Paper**
138 A14 12c vio, *yel* ('33) 16.00 2.50
139 A14 20c ol grn & dl vio 6.00 .40
140 A15 25c red vio & dl
     vio, redrawn 5.50 .75
141 A13 30c yel & violet 12.00 1.75
142 A14 50c blk, *emerald* 16.00 .45
143 A11 $1 ultra & vio, *bl* 40.00 .60
144 A14 $2 black & red 140.00 6.50
145 A13 $3 dl vio & grn
     ('26) 200.00 70.00
146 A14 $5 red & grn, *em-*
     *er* ('25) 550.00 85.00
     Nos. 129-146 (18) 1,058. 221.95

Common Design Types
pictured following the introduction.

**Silver Jubilee Issue**
Common Design Type
**1935, May 6** Engr. *Perf. 11x12*
147 CD301 3c black & ultra 3.50 1.50
148 CD301 5c indigo & grn 11.00 1.75
149 CD301 10c ultra & brn 27.50 5.00
150 CD301 20c brn vio & ind 35.00 10.00
     Nos. 147-150 (4) 77.00 18.25
Set, never hinged 200.00

**Coronation Issue**
Common Design Type
**1937, May 12** *Perf. 11x11½*
151 CD302 4c deep green 4.00 3.00
152 CD302 15c dark carmine 8.75 3.00
153 CD302 25c deep ultra 11.25 2.50
     Nos. 151-153 (3) 24.00 8.50
Set, never hinged 40.00

King George VI — A16

**1938-48** Typo. *Perf. 14*
**Ordinary Paper**
154 A16 1c brown .75 .50
155 A16 2c gray 1.00 .20
156 A16 4c orange 2.00 1.50
157 A16 5c green 1.25 .20
157B A16 8c brown red
     ('41) 1.20 2.75
  *c.* Imperf., pair
158 A16 10c violet 3.00 .60
159 A16 15c carmine .90 .20
159A A16 20c gray ('46) .60 .20
159B A16 20c rose red
     ('48) 3.00 .35
160 A16 25c ultramarine 19.00 1.50
160A A16 25c gray ol ('46) 2.25 1.25
161 A16 30c olive bister 125.00 2.00
161B A16 30c lt ultra ('46) 3.00 .20
162 A16 50c red violet 3.25 .60
**Chalky Paper**
162B A16 80c lilac rose
     ('48) 2.25 .75
163 A16 $1 lilac & ultra 6.00 2.25
163B A16 $1 dp org &
     grn ('46) 8.50 .20
164 A16 $2 dp org &
     grn 60.00 15.00
164A A16 $2 vio & red
     ('46) 12.50 3.75
165 A16 $5 lilac & red 45.00 45.00
165A A16 $5 grn & vio
     ('46) 40.00 7.50
166 A16 $10 grn & vio 375.00 95.00
166A A16 $10 vio & ultra
     ('46) 100.00 35.00
     Nos. 154-166A (23) 815.45 216.50
Set, never hinged 1,250.

Coarse Impressions
Ordinary Paper
**1941-46** *Perf. 14½x14*
155a A16 2c gray 1.50 5.25
156a A16 4c orange ('46) 3.00 3.25
157a A16 5c green 1.75 5.25
158a A16 10c violet 6.00 .20
161a A16 30c dull olive bister 18.00 9.00
162a A16 50c red lilac 20.00 2.00
     Nos. 155a-162a (6) 50.25 24.95
Set, never hinged 85.00

A17

**1938, Jan. 11**                    **Wmk. 4**
167   A17  5c green            42.50  20.00
        Never hinged        85.00

No. 167 is a revenue stamp officially authorized to be sold and used for postal purposes. Used Jan. 11-20, 1938. The used price is for the stamp on cover. CTO covers exist.

Street
Scene — A18

Hong Kong
Bank — A22

Liner and
Junk — A19

University of
Hong
Kong — A20

Harbor — A21

China Clipper
and Seaplane
A23

**Perf. 13½x13, 13x13½**
**1941, Feb. 26    Engr.    Wmk. 4**
168   A18  2c sepia & org      4.00  2.00
169   A19  4c rose car & vio   4.00  2.00
170   A20  5c yel grn & blk    2.00   .35
171   A21  15c red & black     4.50  1.25
172   A22  25c dp blue & dk
              brn              10.00  4.00
173   A23  $1 brn org & brt bl 32.50 12.00
        Nos. 168-173 (6)       57.00 21.60
      Set, never hinged       100.00

Centenary of British rule.

---

**Catalogue values for unused stamps in this section, from this point to the end of the section, are for Never Hinged items.**

---

**Peace Issue**

Phoenix
Rising
from
Flames
A24

**1946, Aug. 29                Perf. 13x12½**
174   A24  30c car & dp blue   3.75  2.00
175   A24  $1 car & brown      5.75  1.00

Return to peace after WWII.

---

**Silver Wedding Issue**
**Common Design Types**
**Perf. 14x14½**
**1948, Dec. 22    Photo.    Wmk. 4**
178   CD304  10c purple        3.00  1.00

**Engr.; Name Typo.**
**Perf. 11½x11**
179   CD305  $10 rose car    450.00 110.00
        Set, hinged         300.00

**UPU Issue**
**Common Design Types**
**Engr.; Name Typo. on 20c & 30c**
**1949, Oct. 10    Perf. 13½, 11x11½**
180   CD306  10c violet        4.75  1.00
181   CD307  20c deep car     20.00  3.50
182   CD308  30c indigo       17.50  3.00
183   CD309  80c red violet   40.00 10.00
        Nos. 180-183 (4)      82.25 17.50
      Set, hinged            30.00

**Coronation Issue**
**Common Design Type**
**1953, June 2    Engr.    Perf. 13½x13**
184   CD312  10c purple & black 7.00  .35
        Hinged               2.50

Elizabeth II
A25

Arms of University
A26

**1954-60    Typo.    Perf. 13½x14**
185   A25  5c orange          1.75   .20
   a.    Imperf., pair     1,500.
186   A25  10c violet         3.00   .20
187   A25  15c green          5.00   .50
188   A25  20c brown          6.00   .25
189   A25  25c rose red       4.00  1.00
190   A25  30c gray           5.50   .20
191   A25  40c blue           5.00   .40
192   A25  50c red violet     5.75   .25
193   A25  65c lt gray ('60) 24.00  9.00
194   A25  $1 org & green     9.00   .20
195   A25  $1.30 bl & ver ('60) 30.00  .85
196   A25  $2 violet & red   15.00   .35
197   A25  $5 green & vio   100.00  2.25
198   A25  $10 violet & ultra 85.00  9.00
        Nos. 185-198 (14)   299.00 24.65
      Set, hinged          120.00

Nos. 185-187 are on ordinary paper; Nos. 188-198 on chalky paper.

**Perf. 11½x12**
**1961, Sept. 11    Photo.    Wmk. 314**
199   A26  $1 bl, blk, red, grn &
              gold             8.00  2.00
   a.    Gold omitted      1,750.

University of Hong Kong, 50th anniv.

Queen
Victoria
Statue,
Victoria
Park, Hong
Kong — A27

Queen Elizabeth
II — A28

**1962, May 4                Perf. 14**
200   A27  10c car rose & black  .65  .20
201   A27  20c blue & black    2.00  2.25
202   A27  50c bister & black  4.50   .45
        Nos. 200-202 (3)      7.15  2.90

1st postage stamps of Hong Kong, cent.

**Wmk. 314 Upright**
**1962, Oct. 4    Photo.    Perf. 14½x14**
**Size: 17x21mm**
203   A28  5c red orange        .60   .20
   a.    Booklet pane of 4    2.50
204   A28  10c purple          1.40   .20
   a.    Booklet pane of 4    5.00
205   A28  15c green           3.00   .20
206   A28  30c red brown       1.75   .20
   a.    Booklet pane of 4   11.00
207   A28  25c lilac rose      2.50   .20
208   A28  30c dark blue       2.50   .20

---

209   A28  40c Prus green      2.00   .20
210   A28  50c crimson         1.75   .20
   a.    Booklet pane of 4   25.00
211   A28  65c ultramarine    17.50  1.50
212   A28  $1 dark brown      17.50   .20

**Perf. 14x14½**
**Size: 25½x30½mm**
**Portrait in Natural Colors**
213   A28  $1.30 sky blue      5.00   .20
   a.    Ocher (sash) omitted 40.00
   b.    Yellow omitted      40.00
214   A28  $2 fawn             7.00   .20
   a.    Yellow and ocher (sash)
              omitted         75.00
   b.    Yellow omitted      40.00
215   A28  $5 orange          17.50   .95
   a.    Ocher (sash) omitted 50.00
216   A28  $10 green          30.00  1.90
217   A28  $20 violet blue   150.00 27.50
        Nos. 203-217 (15)    260.00 34.05

**1966-72    Wmk. 314 Sideways**
203b   A28  5c ('67)            .30   .20
204b   A28  10c ('67)           .75   .20
205a   A28  15c ('67)          2.00   .20
206b   A28  20c                1.50   .20
207a   A28  25c ('67)          3.00   .20
208a   A28  30c ('70)          7.50   .20
209a   A28  40c ('67)          3.00   .20
210b   A28  50c ('67)          3.00   .20
211a   A28  65c ('67)          8.00  2.75
212a   A28  $1 ('67)          17.50   .30
213c   A28  $1.30 ('72)       11.00   .90
214c   A28  $2 ('71)          16.00  2.50
215b   A28  $5 ('71)          75.00  5.50
217a   A28  $20 ('72)        200.00 60.00
        Nos. 203b-217a (14)  348.55 73.55

**Freedom from Hunger Issue**
**Common Design Type**
**Perf. 14x14½**
**1963, June 4    Photo.    Wmk. 314**
218   CD314  $1.30 green      55.00  8.50

**Red Cross Centenary Issue**
**Common Design Type**
**1963, Sept. 2    Litho.    Perf. 13**
219   CD315  10c black & red   4.00   .30
220   CD315  $1.30 ultra & red 32.50  8.25

**ITU Issue**
**Common Design Type**
**1965, May 17    Perf. 11x11½**
221   CD317  10c red lil & yel 4.00   .25
222   CD317  $1.30 apple grn &
              turq blue        25.00  4.00

**Intl. Cooperation Year Issue**
**Common Design Type**
**1965, Oct. 25              Perf. 14½**
223   CD318  10c blue grn & cl 3.00   .30
224   CD318  $1.30 lt violet & grn 21.00  3.50

**Churchill Memorial Issue**
**Common Design Type**
**1966, Jan. 24    Photo.    Perf. 14**
**Design in Black, Gold and Carmine Rose**
225   CD319  10c bright blue   2.75   .20
226   CD319  50c green         3.25   .35
227   CD319  $1.30 brown      22.50  3.25
228   CD319  $2 violet        35.00  7.50
        Nos. 225-228 (4)      63.50 11.30

**WHO Headquarters Issue**
**Common Design Type**
**1966, Sept. 20    Litho.    Perf. 14**
229   CD322  10c multicolored  3.00   .20
230   CD322  50c multicolored 10.00  1.75

**UNESCO Anniversary Issue**
**Common Design Type**
**1966, Dec. 1    Litho.    Perf. 14**
231   CD323  10c "Education"   3.75   .20
232   CD323  50c "Science"    13.00  1.00
233   CD323  $2 "Culture"     62.50 17.00
        Nos. 231-233 (3)      79.25 18.20

Three
Rams'
Heads
A29

Lunar New Year: $1.30, Three rams.

**1967, Jan. 17    Photo.    Perf. 14**
234   A29  10c red, citron &
              grn              2.25   .50
235   A29  $1.30 red, cit & brt
              grn             35.00 10.00

---

Outline of
Telephone
with Map of
South East
Asia and
Australia
A30

**1967, Mar. 30    Photo.    Perf. 12½**
236   A30  $1.30 dk red & blue 20.00  4.50

Completion of the Hong Kong-Malaysia link of the South East Asia Commonwealth Cable, SEACOM.

Monkeys
A31

Lunar New Year: $1.30, Two monkey families.

**1968, Jan. 23    Wmk. 314    Perf. 14**
237   A31  10c crim, blk & gold 2.00  .45
238   A31  $1.30 crim, blk & gold 35.00  8.00

Liner and
New Sea
Terminal
A32

Seacraft: 20c, Pleasure launch and sailing cruiser. 40c, Vehicle ferry. 50c, Passenger ferry. $1, Sampan. $1.30, Junk.

**Perf. 13x12½**
**1968, Apr. 24    Litho.    Unwmk.**
239   A32  10c multicolored    2.00   .20
240   A32  20c sky blue, bis &
              black            3.50   .75
241   A32  40c org, rose lil &
              black           10.00  8.00
242   A32  50c brt red, emer
              & black          7.00   .55
243   A32  $1 yel, cop red &
              black           16.00  5.00
244   A32  $1.30 dk bl, brt pink
              & black         45.00  4.00
        Nos. 239-244 (6)      83.50 18.50

Bauhinia
Blakeana — A33

**Perf. 14x14½**
**1968, Sept. 25    Photo.    Wmk. 314**
245   A33  65c shown          10.00   .50
   a.    Wmkd. sideways ('72) 52.50 16.00
246   A33  $1 Coat of Arms    10.00   .50
   a.    Wmkd. sideways ('71) 11.00  2.25

Human
Rights
Flame and
"Lamp of
Life"
A34

**1968, Nov. 20    Litho.    Perf. 13½**
247   A34  10c green, org & blk 2.00  .75
248   A34  50c magenta, yel & blk 6.00  2.25

International Human Rights Year.

Cock
A35

Design: $1.30, Cock, vert.

**Perf. 13x13½, 13½x13**

**1969, Feb. 11   Photo.   Unwmk.**
249 A35   10c brown, blk, org
    & red       8.00   1.00
   a.    Red omitted     250.00
250 A35   $1.30 ocher, blk, org
    & red      75.00 14.00

Lunar New Year, Feb. 17, 1969.

Chinese University Seal — A36

**1969, Aug. 26   Unwmk.   Perf. 13**
251 A36   40c multicolored     8.50   3.75

Chinese University of Hong Kong, founded 1963.

Radar, Globe and Satellite A37

**Perf. 14x14½**

**1969, Sept. 24   Photo.   Wmk. 314**
252 A37   $1 scar, blk, sil & bl    25.00   5.00

Opening of the satellite earth station (connected through the Indian Ocean satellite Intelsat III) on Stanley Peninsula, Hong Kong.

Chow — A38     Emblem — A39

Lunar New Year (Year of the Dog): $1.30, Chow, horiz.

**1970, Jan. 28   Perf. 14**
253 A38   10c black & multi     5.00   .50
254 A38   $1.30 green & multi    72.50 12.00

**Perf. 13½x13, 13x13½**

**1970, Mar. 14   Litho.   Wmk. 314**
25c, Emblem and Chinese junks, horiz.
255 A39   15c multicolored     .90   .90
256 A39   25c multicolored     1.90   1.90

EXPO '70 Intl. Exposition, Osaka, Japan, Mar. 15-Sept. 13.

"A Compassionate Ship on the Bitter Sea" — A40

**1970, Apr. 9   Photo.   Perf. 14**
257 A40   10c yel green & multi   1.00   .25
258 A40   50c scarlet & multi    4.25   1.50

Centenary of the Tung Wah Group of Hospitals (including schools and various charitable organizations).

A.P.Y. Emblem — A41

**1970, Aug. 5   Litho.   Wmk. 314**
259 A41   10c yellow & multi    1.40   .60

Issued for Asian Productivity Year.

Boar A42

**Perf. 13x13½**

**1971, Jan. 20   Photo.   Unwmk.**
260 A42   10c yel grn, gold &
    black       5.00   1.00
261 A42   $1.30 vio, gold & blk   37.50 11.00

Lunar New Year.

Scout Emblem and "60" — A43

**Perf. 14x14½**

**1971, July 23   Litho.   Wmk. 314**
262 A43   10c red, yellow & black   .75   .20
263 A43   50c blue, emer & black   4.00   1.00
264 A43   $2 vio, lil rose & blk   22.50   8.00
    Nos. 262-264 (3)     27.25   9.20

60th anniversary of Hong Kong Boy Scouts.

Festival Emblem A44     Symbolic Flower A45

Festival of Hong Kong: 50c, Dancers, horiz.

**1971, Nov. 2   Perf. 14**
265 A44   10c lilac & orange    1.60   .20

**Perf. 14½**
266 A45   50c lilac & multi     3.25   1.00
267 A45   $1 lilac & multi     9.50   7.50
    Nos. 265-267 (3)     14.35   8.70

Rats A46

**Perf. 13½x13**

**1972, Feb. 8   Photo.   Unwmk.**
268 A46   10c black, red &
    gold       4.00   .50
269 A46   $1.30 black, gold &
    red      40.00 12.50

Lunar New Year.

Cross Harbor Tunnel Entrance — A47

**Perf. 14x14½**

**1972, Oct. 20   Litho.   Wmk. 314**
270 A47   $1 multicolored    7.00   2.00

Inauguration of Cross Harbor Tunnel linking Victoria and Kowloon.

**Silver Wedding Issue, 1972**
Common Design Type

Design:   Queen Elizabeth II, Prince Philip, phoenix and dragon.

**1972, Nov. 20   Photo.   Perf. 14x14½**
271 CD324   10c citron & multi   1.30   .20
272 CD324   50c gray & multi   1.20   1.20

Ox A48

Lunar New Year: 10c, Ox, vert.

**1973, Feb. 3   Perf. 14**
273 A48   10c dk brown & red   3.00   .50
274 A48   '$1.30 dk brn, yel & org   9.00   7.50

Elizabeth II — A49

**Wmk. 314 Upright; Sideways (15c, 30c, 40c)**

**1973, June 12   Photo.   Perf. 14½x14**
**Size: 20x24mm**
275 A49   10c orange     .80   .20
   d.   Watermark sideways (coil)   1.75   1.25
276 A49   15c olive green    8.00   .20
277 A49   20c bright purple    .55   .20
278 A49   25c deep brown    12.50   .20
279 A49   30c ultramarine    1.10   .20
280 A49   40c blue green    2.75   .20
281 A49   50c red     1.50   .20
282 A49   65c dp bister    14.50   5.00
283 A49   $1 dk slate green   2.50   .55

**Perf. 14x14½**
**Wmk. 314 Sideways**
**Size: 28x32mm**
284 A49   $1.30 dk pur & yel   7.75   .75
285 A49   $2 dp brn & lt grn   9.00   .90
286 A49   $5 dk vio bl &
    rose     14.00   3.00

**Photo. & Embossed**
287 A49   $10 dk sl green &
    pink     20.00   9.00
288 A49   $20 black & rose   32.50 25.00
    Nos. 275-288 (14)   127.45 45.60

**1975-78   Wmk. 373   Perf. 14½x14**
**Size: 20x24mm**
275a A49   10c orange    .20   .20
   c.   Booklet pane of 4 ('76)   .80
276a A49   15c olive green    .25   .20
   c.   Booklet pane of 4   1.00
277a A49   20c bright purple    .25   .20
   c.   Booklet pane of 4 ('76)   1.10
278a A49   25c deep brown    .50   .20
279a A49   30c ultramarine    .70   .25
280a A49   40c blue green    .90   .30
281a A49   50c red    1.10   .45
   c.   Booklet pane of 4   4.50
282a A49   65c deep bister    1.60   .55
283a A49   $1 dark slate green   2.25   .70

**Perf. 14x14½**
**Size: 28x32mm**
284a A49   $1.30 dark purple &
    yel     3.00   .90
285a A49   $2 dp brn & lt grn   5.00   1.60
286a A49   $5 dk vio bl & rose
    ('78)     12.50   4.00
287a A49   $10 dk sl grn & pink
    ('78)     22.50   8.25
288a A49   $20 black & rose
    ('78)     45.00 19.00
    Nos. 275a-288a (14)   95.75 36.80

See Nos. 316-327.

**Princess Anne's Wedding Issue**
Common Design Type
**Wmk. 314**

**1973, Nov. 14   Litho.   Perf. 14**
289 CD325   50c ocher & multi   .75   .20
290 CD325   $2 lilac & multi   2.75   2.00

Chinese Character "Hong" — A50

Designs: 50c, "Kong." $1, "Festival."

**1973, Nov. 23   Litho.   Perf. 14½x14**
291 A50   10c red & green    .50   .20
292 A50   50c plum & red    2.25   .60
293 A50   $1 emerald & plum   5.25   1.60
    Nos. 291-293 (3)    8.00   2.40

Festival of Hong Kong 1973.

Tiger A51

Lunar New Year: $1.30, Tiger, vert.

**Perf. 14½x14, 14x14½**

**1974, Jan. 8   Wmk. 314**
294 A51   10c green & multi   2.50   .30
295 A51   $1.30 lilac & multi   12.00 10.00

Chinese Opera Mask — A52

Designs: Chinese opera masks.

**1974, Feb. 1   Photo.   Perf. 12x12½**
296 A52   10c black, red & org   .50   .25
297 A52   $1 multicolored    5.25   4.25
298 A52   $2 black, org & gold   11.00   9.00
   a.   Souvenir sheet of 3, #296-298,
    perf. 14x13    62.50 50.00
    Nos. 296-298 (3)    16.75 13.50

Hong Kong Arts Festival.

Carrier Pigeons A53

Cent. of UPU: 50c, Symbolic globe in envelope. $2, Hands holding letters.

**1974, Oct. 9   Litho.   Perf. 14**
299 A53   10c blue, grn & blk   .45   .20
   a.   Unwatermarked    30.00
300 A53   50c magenta & multi   2.10   .20
301 A53   $2 violet & multi   5.25   1.75
    Nos. 299-301 (3)    7.80   2.15

Rabbit A54

Lunar New Year: $1.30, Two rabbits.

**1975, Feb. 5    Wmk. 314    Perf. 14**

| | | | | |
|---|---|---|---|---|
| 302 | A54 | 10c silver & red | 1.00 | .40 |
| a. | | Unwatermarked | 1.00 | 1.00 |
| 303 | A54 | $1.30 gold & green | 7.50 | 7.50 |
| a. | | Unwatermarked | 7.50 | 7.50 |

Queen Elizabeth II, Prince Philip, Hong Kong Arms — A55

**Wmk. 373**

**1975, Apr. 30    Litho.    Perf. 13½**

| | | | | |
|---|---|---|---|---|
| 304 | A55 | $1.30 blue & multi | 3.25 | 1.50 |
| 305 | A55 | $2 yellow & multi | 4.50 | 4.50 |

Royal Visit 1975.

Mid-Autumn Festival — A56    Brown Laughing Thrush — A57

Abstract Designs: $1, Dragon Boat Festival (boats). $2, Tin Hau Festival (ships with flags).

**1975, July 31    Unwmk.    Perf. 14**

| | | | | |
|---|---|---|---|---|
| 306 | A56 | 50c rose lil & multi | 2.50 | .50 |
| 307 | A56 | $1 brt grn & multi | 10.00 | 2.50 |
| 308 | A56 | $2 orange & multi | 30.00 | 10.00 |
| a. | | Souv. sheet of 3, #306-308 | 120.00 | 50.00 |
| | | Nos. 306-308 (3) | 42.50 | 13.00 |

Hong Kong Festivals, 1975.

**1975, Oct. 29    Litho.    Wmk. 373**

Birds: $1.30, Chinese bulbul. $2, Black-capped kingfisher.

| | | | | |
|---|---|---|---|---|
| 309 | A57 | 50c lt blue & multi | 2.50 | .75 |
| 310 | A57 | $1.30 pink & multi | 10.00 | 6.00 |
| 311 | A57 | $2 yellow & multi | 18.00 | 12.50 |
| | | Nos. 309-311 (3) | 30.50 | 19.25 |

Dragon A58

Lunar New Year: $1.30, like 20c, pattern reversed.

**1976, Jan. 21    Litho.    Perf. 14½**

| | | | | |
|---|---|---|---|---|
| 312 | A58 | 20c gold, pur & lilac | 1.00 | .50 |
| 313 | A58 | $1.30 gold, red & grn | 7.50 | 3.25 |

**Queen Elizabeth Type of 1973**
**Wmk. 373 (#320-323), Unwmkd.**

**1976-81    Photo.    Perf. 14½x14**
**Size: 20x24mm**

| | | | | |
|---|---|---|---|---|
| 316 | A49 | 20c bright purple | 3.00 | 1.00 |
| 318 | A49 | 30c ultramarine | 6.00 | 1.75 |
| 320 | A49 | 60c lt violet ('77) | 1.75 | 1.25 |
| 321 | A49 | 70c yellow ('77) | 1.75 | .35 |
| 322 | A49 | 80c brt magenta ('77) | 2.00 | 1.50 |
| 323 | A49 | 90c sepia ('81) | 9.00 | 1.50 |

**Size: 28x32mm**
**Perf. 14x14½**

| | | | | |
|---|---|---|---|---|
| 324 | A49 | $2 dp brn & lt grn | 10.50 | 3.00 |
| 325 | A49 | $5 dk vio bl & rose | 12.00 | 5.75 |

**Photo. & Embossed**

| | | | | |
|---|---|---|---|---|
| 326 | A49 | $10 dk sl grn & pink | 90.00 | 35.00 |
| 327 | A49 | $20 black & rose | 175.00 | 47.50 |
| | | Nos. 316-327 (10) | 311.00 | 98.60 |

"60" and Girl Guides Emblem A59

$1.30, "60," tents and Girl Guides emblem.

**1976, Apr. 23    Wmk. 314    Perf. 14½**

| | | | | |
|---|---|---|---|---|
| 328 | A59 | 20c silver & multi | 1.00 | .25 |
| 329 | A59 | $1.30 silver & multi | 6.00 | 4.00 |

60th anniv. of Hong Kong Girl Guides.

"Postal Services" (in Chinese) — A60

Designs: $1.30, General Post Office, 1911-1976. $2, New G.P.O., 1976.

**1976, Aug. 11    Litho.    Wmk. 373**

| | | | | |
|---|---|---|---|---|
| 330 | A60 | 20c gray, green & black | .75 | .20 |
| 331 | A60 | $1.30 gray, red & black | 3.75 | 1.75 |
| 332 | A60 | $2 gray, yel & black | 6.50 | 3.50 |
| | | Nos. 330-332 (3) | 11.00 | 5.45 |

Opening of new GPO building.

Snake A61

Lunar New Year: $1.30, Snake & branch face left.

**1977, Jan. 6    Perf. 13½**

| | | | | |
|---|---|---|---|---|
| 333 | A61 | 20c multicolored | .80 | .25 |
| 334 | A61 | $1.30 multicolored | 5.50 | 3.25 |

Queen Dotting Eye of Dragon, 1975 Visit — A62

20c, Presentation of the orb. $2, Orb, vert.

**1977, Feb. 7    Litho.**

| | | | | |
|---|---|---|---|---|
| 335 | A62 | 20c multicolored | .50 | .25 |
| 336 | A62 | $1.30 multicolored | 1.40 | 1.00 |
| 337 | A62 | $2 multicolored | 1.75 | 1.25 |
| | | Nos. 335-337 (3) | 3.65 | 2.50 |

25th anniv. of the reign of Elizabeth II.

Streetcars — A63

Designs: 60c, Star ferryboat. $1.30, Funicular railway. $2, Junk and sampan.

**1977, June 30    Wmk. 373    Perf. 13½**

| | | | | |
|---|---|---|---|---|
| 338 | A63 | 20c multicolored | .65 | .20 |
| 339 | A63 | 60c multicolored | 1.50 | 1.25 |
| 340 | A63 | $1.30 multicolored | 3.00 | 2.00 |
| 341 | A63 | $2 multicolored | 3.50 | 3.00 |
| | | Nos. 338-341 (4) | 8.65 | 6.45 |

Tourist publicity.

Buttercup Orchid — A64

**1977, Oct. 12    Litho.    Perf. 14**

$1.30, Lady's-slipper. $2, Susan orchid.

| | | | | |
|---|---|---|---|---|
| 342 | A64 | 20c blue & multi | 1.25 | .25 |
| 343 | A64 | $1.30 yellow & multi | 4.25 | 1.50 |
| 344 | A64 | $2 green & multi | 6.50 | 3.25 |
| | | Nos. 342-344 (3) | 12.00 | 5.00 |

Horse and Chinese Character "Ma" — A65

**1978, Jan. 26    Litho.    Perf. 14½**

| | | | | |
|---|---|---|---|---|
| 345 | A65 | 20c multicolored | .65 | .20 |
| 346 | A65 | $1.30 multicolored | 4.75 | 4.00 |

Lunar New Year.

Elizabeth II — A66

**1978, June 2    Litho.    Perf. 14x14½**

| | | | | |
|---|---|---|---|---|
| 347 | A66 | 20c carmine & dk blue | .50 | .20 |
| 348 | A66 | $1.30 dk blue & carmine | 1.75 | 1.75 |

25th anniv. of coronation of Elizabeth II.

Boy and Girl A67

Design: $1.30, Ring-around-a-rosy.

**1978, Nov. 8    Wmk. 373    Perf. 14½**

| | | | | |
|---|---|---|---|---|
| 349 | A67 | 20c multicolored | .25 | .20 |
| 350 | A67 | $1.30 multicolored | 1.50 | .80 |

Centenary of Po Leung Kuk, society for help and education of orphans and poor children.

Electronics — A68

Industries: $1.30, Toy (bear and drum). $2, Garment (mannequins).

**1979, Jan. 9    Litho.    Perf. 14½**

| | | | | |
|---|---|---|---|---|
| 351 | A68 | 20c multicolored | .20 | .20 |
| 352 | A68 | $1.30 multicolored | 1.00 | .75 |
| 353 | A68 | $2 multicolored | 1.00 | 1.00 |
| | | Nos. 351-353 (3) | 2.20 | 1.95 |

Precis Orithya — A69

Butterflies: $1, Graphium sarpedon. $1.30, Heliophorus epicles phoenicoparyphus. $2, Danaus genutia.

**1979, June 20    Photo.    Unwmk.**

| | | | | |
|---|---|---|---|---|
| 354 | A69 | 20c multicolored | 1.00 | .20 |
| 355 | A69 | $1 multicolored | 1.75 | .75 |
| 356 | A69 | $1.30 multicolored | 2.00 | 1.75 |
| 357 | A69 | $2 multicolored | 2.25 | 2.25 |
| | | Nos. 354-357 (4) | 7.00 | 4.95 |

Cross Section of Station A70

Mass Transit Railroad: $1.30, Front, rear and side views of train. $2, Map of routes.

**1979, Oct. 1    Litho.    Perf. 13½**

| | | | | |
|---|---|---|---|---|
| 358 | A70 | 20c multicolored | .50 | .20 |
| 359 | A70 | $1.30 multicolored | 1.75 | .50 |
| 360 | A70 | $2 multicolored | 2.25 | 2.00 |
| | | Nos. 358-360 (3) | 4.50 | 2.70 |

Ching Chung Koon Temple, Tuen Mun — A71

Rural Architecture: 20c, Tsui Shing Lau Pagoda, Sheung Cheung Wai, vert. $1.30, Village house, Sai O.

**Perf. 13x13½, 13½x13**

**1980, May 14    Litho.    Wmk. 373**

| | | | | |
|---|---|---|---|---|
| 361 | A71 | 20c multicolored | .30 | .20 |
| 362 | A71 | $1.30 multicolored | 1.25 | 1.10 |
| 363 | A71 | $2 multicolored | 1.50 | 1.50 |
| | | Nos. 361-363 (3) | 3.05 | 2.80 |

**Queen Mother Elizabeth Birthday Issue**
**Common Design Type**

**1980, Aug. 4    Litho.    Perf. 14**

| | | | | |
|---|---|---|---|---|
| 364 | CD330 | $1.30 multicolored | 1.00 | .75 |

Botanical Gardens — A72

**1980, Nov. 12    Litho.    Perf. 13½**

| | | | | |
|---|---|---|---|---|
| 365 | A72 | 20c shown | .30 | .20 |
| 366 | A72 | $1 Ocean Park | .70 | .20 |
| 367 | A72 | $1.30 Kowloon Park | .80 | .75 |
| 368 | A72 | $2 Country Park | 1.40 | 1.25 |
| | | Nos. 365-368 (4) | 3.20 | 2.40 |

Epinephelus Akaara — A73

**1981, Jan. 28    Litho.    Perf. 13½**
369 A73   20c shown              .20   .20
370 A73   $1 Nemipterus vir-
               gatus              .60   .40
371 A73   $1.30 Choerodon azurio .75   .50
372 A73   $2 Scarus ghobban     1.20  1.20
     Nos. 369-372 (4)           2.75  2.30

**Royal Wedding Issue**
Common Design Type

**1981, July 29    Photo.    Perf. 14**
373 CD331   20c Bouquet          .20   .20
374 CD331   $1.30 Charles        .50   .30
375 CD331   $5 Couple           2.25  1.25
     Nos. 373-375 (3)           2.95  1.75

Public Housing Development A74

Various public housing developments.

**1981, Oct. 14    Litho.    Perf. 13½**
376 A74   20c multicolored       .20   .20
377 A74   $1 multicolored        .65   .35
378 A74   $1.30 multicolored     .95   .35
379 A74   $2 multicolored       1.10   .50
  a. Souvenir sheet of 4, #376-379  6.00  6.00
     Nos. 376-379 (4)           2.90  1.40

Port of Hong Kong A75

Various views of Port of Hong Kong.

**1982, Jan. 12    Litho.    Perf. 14½**
380 A75   20c multicolored       .50   .20
381 A75   $1 multicolored       1.50  1.00
382 A75   $1.30 multicolored    1.75  1.50
383 A75   $2 multicolored       2.50  2.00
     Nos. 380-383 (4)           6.25  4.70

Five-banded Civet — A76

**1982, May 4    Litho.    Perf. 14½**
384 A76   20c shown              .25   .20
385 A76   $1 Pangolin            .55   .40
386 A76   $1.30 Chinese porcu-
               pine             1.10   .80
387 A76   $5 Barking deer       3.25  2.25
     Nos. 384-387 (4)           5.15  3.65

Queen Elizabeth II
A77        A78

**Perf. 14½x14**
**1982, Aug. 30    Photo.    Wmk. 373**
388 A77   10c yellow & dk red    .75   .60
389 A77   20c blue vio & vio     .90   .70
390 A77   30c orange & pur      1.25   .30
391 A77   40c lt blue & red     1.25   .30
392 A77   50c pale grn & brn    1.25   .30
393 A77   60c gray & brt mag    2.75  1.50
394 A77   70c brt org & dk grn  2.75   .40
395 A77   80c gray ol & brn ol  2.75  1.50
396 A77   90c grnsh bl & grn    4.50   .30
397 A77   $1 brt pink & brn org 2.50   .30
398 A77   $1.30 rose vio & dk bl 4.00  .30
399 A77   $2 buff & blue        6.50  1.00

**Photo. & Embossed**
**Perf. 14x14½**
400 A78   $5 lemon & lake       8.00  2.50
401 A78   $10 brn & blk brn     9.00  5.00
402 A78   $20 lt blue & lake   15.00 15.00
403 A78   $50 gray & lake      36.00 30.00
     Nos. 388-403 (16)         99.15 60.00

Nos. 388 and 397 also issued in coils.

**1985-87    Unwmk.**
388a A77   10c                   .75   .20
389a A77   20c                 18.50  5.00
391a A77   40c                  1.00   .40
392a A77   50c                  1.00   .30
393a A77   60c                  1.60   .60
394a A77   70c                  1.90   .50
395a A77   80c                  2.25  1.00
396a A77   90c                  2.25   .50
397a A77   $1                   1.90   .40
398b A77   $1.30                2.50   .35
398A A77  $1.70 brt yel grn &
               dp bl            3.75   .75
399a A77   $2                   4.00   .75
400a A78   $5                   7.00  2.00
401a A78   $10                  8.25  3.00
402a A78   $20                 11.00  6.00
403a A78   $50                 32.50 20.00
     Nos. 388a-403a (16)      100.15 41.75

Issued: $1.30, 6/13/86; $1.70, 9/2/86; 20c, 6/87; others, 10/10/85.

3rd Far East and South Pacific Games for the Disabled A79

**Perf. 14x14½**
**1982, Oct. 31    Litho.    Wmk. 373**
404 A79   30c Table tennis      .40   .20
405 A79   $1 Racing            1.00   .90
406 A79   $1.30 Basketball     3.00  1.50
407 A79   $5 Archery           5.00  4.50
     Nos. 404-407 (4)          9.40  7.10

Performing Arts — A80

**1983, Jan. 26    Litho.    Perf. 14½x14**
408 A80   30c Dancing          .40   .20
409 A80   $1.30 Theater       2.00  1.50
410 A80   $5 Music            5.00  4.50
     Nos. 408-410 (3)         7.40  6.20

A81

**1983, Mar. 14    Perf. 14½x13½**
411 A81   30c Aerial view      .75   .20
412 A81   $1 Liverpool Bay    1.90   .80
413 A81   $1.30 Flag          1.90   .85
414 A81   $5 Queen Elizabeth
               II             3.75  2.00
     Nos. 411-414 (4)         8.30  3.85

Commonwealth Day.

Views by Night A82

**1983, Aug. 17    Litho.    Perf. 14½**
415 A82   30c Victoria Harbor  1.25   .65
416 A82   $1 Space Museum      3.75  2.10
417 A82   $1.30 Chinese New
               Year Fireworks  5.00  2.25
418 A82   $5 Jumbo Restau-
               rant           15.00  6.00
     Nos. 415-418 (4)         25.00 11.00

Royal Observatory Centenary — A83

**1983, Nov. 23    Litho.    Perf. 14½**
419 A83   40c Technical facili-
               ties            .75   .25
420 A83   $1 Wind measure-
               ment           2.25  1.25
421 A83   $1.30 Temperature
               measurement    2.50  1.50
422 A83   $5 Earthquake mea-
               surement       8.00  6.50
     Nos. 419-422 (4)        13.50  9.50

Training Plane, Dorado A84

**1984, Mar. 7    Wmk. 373    Perf. 13½**
423 A84   40c shown           1.25   .25
424 A84   $1 Hong Kong
               Clipper sea-
               plane          2.50  1.50
425 A84   $1.30 Jumbo jet, Kai
               Tak Airport    2.75  1.50
426 A84   $5 Baldwin Broth-
               ers balloon,
               vert.          8.00  7.00
     Nos. 423-426 (4)        14.50 10.25

Map of Hong Kong, 19th Cent. A85

Various maps.

**1984, June 21    Litho.    Perf. 14**
427 A85   40c multicolored    1.00   .35
428 A85   $1 multicolored     1.75  1.25
429 A85   $1.30 multicolored  3.00  1.75
430 A85   $5 multicolored    10.50  8.00
     Nos. 427-430 (4)        16.25 11.35

Chinese Lanterns A86

**1984, Sept. 6    Litho.    Perf. 13½x13**
431 A86   40c Rooster         1.00   .35
432 A86   $1 Bull             2.00  1.50
433 A86   $1.30 Butterfly     3.25  1.75
434 A86   $5 Fish             9.50  7.50
     Nos. 431-434 (4)        15.75 11.10

Jockey Club Centenary — A87

**1984, Nov. 21    Litho.    Perf. 14½**
435 A87   40c Supporting
               health care    1.25   .40
436 A87   $1 Supporting dis-
               abled          2.75  1.25
437 A87   $1.30 Supporting the
               arts           3.75  2.00
438 A87   $5 Supporting
               Ocean Park     8.50  7.50
  a. Souvenir sheet of 4, #435-438  27.50 27.50
     Nos. 435-438 (4)        16.25 11.15

Historic Buildings A88

**Perf. 13½**
**1985, Mar. 14    Unwmk.    Litho.**
439 A88   40c Hung Sing Tem-
               ple            .75   .30
440 A88   $1 St. John's Ca-
               thedral        1.75  1.50
441 A88   $1.30 Old Supreme
               Court Building 2.25  1.50
442 A88   $5 Wan Chai Post
               Office         6.75  5.50
     Nos. 439-442 (4)        11.50  9.05

Intl. Dragon Boat Festival A89

**Perf. 13½x13**
**1985, June 19    Wmk. 373    Litho.**
443 A89   40c multicolored    .60   .30
444 A89   $1 multicolored    2.00  1.25
445 A89   $1.30 multicolored 3.25  1.50
446 A89   $5 multicolored   10.00  7.50
  a. Strip of 4, #443-446        16.00 11.50
  b. Souvenir sheet of 4, #443-446,
       perf. 13x12½              27.50 27.50
     Nos. 443-446 (4)        15.85 10.55

Nos. 443-446 when placed together form a continuous design.

**Queen Mother 85th Birthday Issue**
Common Design Type

**1985, Aug. 7    Litho.    Perf. 14½x14**
447 CD336   40c At Glamis
               Castle, age
               9             .60   .25
448 CD336   $1 On balcony
               with Princes
               William and
               Charles      1.50  1.25
449 CD336   $1.30 Photograph
               by Cecil
               Beaton,1980  2.00  1.25
450 CD336   $5 Holding
               Prince Henry 5.50  4.00
     Nos. 447-450 (4)        9.60  6.75

Indigenous Flowers — A90

**1985, Sept. 25    Litho.    Perf. 13½**
451 A90   40c Melastoma      1.75   .60
452 A90   50c Chinese lily   2.00   .65
453 A90   60c Grantham's ca-
               mellia        2.50  1.50
454 A90   $1.30 Narcissus    3.50  1.50
455 A90   $1.70 Bauhinia     4.00  1.75
456 A90   $5 Chinese New
               Year flower   7.75  5.50
     Nos. 451-456 (6)       21.50 11.50

See No. 898.

Modern Architecture — A91

**1985, Nov. 27**      *Perf. 15*

| | | | | |
|---|---|---|---|---|
| 457 | A91 | 50c Hong Kong Academy for Performing Arts | .60 | .30 |
| 458 | A91 | $1.30 Exchange Square, vert. | 1.25 | .60 |
| 459 | A91 | $1.70 Hong Kong Bank Hdqtrs., vert. | 2.00 | .90 |
| 460 | A91 | $5 Hong Kong Coliseum | 7.25 | 2.60 |
| | | Nos. 457-460 (4) | 11.10 | 4.40 |

Halley's Comet A92

**1986, Feb. 26**    Litho.     *Perf. 13½x13*

| | | | | |
|---|---|---|---|---|
| 461 | A92 | 50c Comet, solar system | 1.40 | .20 |
| 462 | A92 | $1.30 Edmond Halley | 2.00 | 1.00 |
| 463 | A92 | $1.70 Hong Kong, trajectory | 3.25 | 1.25 |
| 464 | A92 | $5 Comet, Earth | 9.50 | 7.50 |
| a. | | Souvenir sheet of 4, #461-464 | 27.50 | 21.00 |
| | | Nos. 461-464 (4) | 16.15 | 9.95 |

**Queen Elizabeth II 60th Birthday**
**Common Design Type**

Designs: 50c, At the wedding of Cecillia Bowes-Lyon, Brompton Parish Church, 1939. $1, Most Noble Order of the Garter, service at St. George's Chapel, Windsor Castle, 1977. $1.30, State visit, 1975. $1.70, Queen Mother's 80th birthday celebration, Royal Lodge, Windsor, 1980. $5, Visiting Crown Agents' offices, 1983.

**1986, Apr. 21**      *Perf. 14½*

| | | | | |
|---|---|---|---|---|
| 465 | CD337 | 50c scar, blk & sil | .50 | .20 |
| 466 | CD337 | $1 ultra & multi | 1.10 | .35 |
| 467 | CD337 | $1.30 green & multi | 1.40 | .50 |
| 468 | CD337 | $1.70 violet & multi | 1.60 | .75 |
| 469 | CD337 | $5 rose vio & multi | 4.75 | 3.00 |
| | | Nos. 465-469 (5) | 9.35 | 4.80 |

EXPO '86, Vancouver — A93

**1986, July 18**    Litho.     *Perf. 13½*

| | | | | |
|---|---|---|---|---|
| 470 | A93 | 50c Transportation | .90 | .20 |
| 471 | A93 | $1.30 Finance | 1.50 | 1.00 |
| 472 | A93 | $1.70 Trade | 2.50 | 1.50 |
| 473 | A93 | $5 Communications | 7.00 | 5.00 |
| | | Nos. 470-473 (4) | 11.90 | 7.70 |

Fishing Vessels A94

**1986, Sept. 24**      Litho.

| | | | | |
|---|---|---|---|---|
| 474 | A94 | 50c Hand-liner sampan | .75 | .20 |
| 475 | A94 | $1.30 Stern trawler | 1.50 | 1.00 |
| 476 | A94 | $1.70 Long liner junk | 3.25 | 1.50 |
| 477 | A94 | $5 Junk trawler | 7.00 | 5.00 |
| | | Nos. 474-477 (4) | 12.50 | 7.95 |

19th Cent. Paintings — A95

50c, Possibly, Second puan khequa, by Spoilum. $1.30, Chinese woman, artist unknown. $1.70, Self-portrait at age 52, by Kwan Kiu Chin. $5, Possibly, Wife of a merchant, by George Chinnery.

**1986, Dec. 9**    Litho.     *Perf. 14*

| | | | | |
|---|---|---|---|---|
| 478 | A95 | 50c multicolored | .45 | .20 |
| 479 | A95 | $1.30 multicolored | 1.50 | 1.25 |
| 480 | A95 | $1.70 multicolored | 1.75 | 1.50 |
| 481 | A95 | $5 multicolored | 5.00 | 3.50 |
| | | Nos. 478-481 (4) | 8.70 | 6.45 |

New Year (Year of the Hare) A96

Embroideries of various rabbits.

**1987, Jan. 21**    Litho.     *Perf. 13½x14*

| | | | | |
|---|---|---|---|---|
| 482 | A96 | 50c multicolored | .75 | .30 |
| 483 | A96 | $1.30 multicolored | 1.50 | 1.25 |
| 484 | A96 | $1.70 multicolored | 1.75 | 1.25 |
| 485 | A96 | $5 multicolored | 6.75 | 4.50 |
| a. | | Souvenir sheet of 4, #482-485 | 40.00 | 30.00 |
| | | Nos. 482-485 (4) | 10.75 | 7.30 |

19th Century Paintings in the Hong Kong Museum of Art and Shanghai Banking Corp. A97

Scenes: 50c, A Village Square, Hong Kong Island, 1838, by Auguste Borget (1809-1877). $1.30, Boat Dwellers in Kowloon Bay, 1838, by Borget. $1.70, Flagstaff House, Lt. Governor D'Aguilar's Residence, 1846, by Murdoch Bruce. $5, A View of Wellington Street, late 19th century, by C. Andrasi.

**1987, Apr. 23**    Litho.     *Perf. 14*

| | | | | |
|---|---|---|---|---|
| 486 | A97 | 50c multicolored | .75 | .25 |
| 487 | A97 | $1.30 multicolored | 2.00 | 1.25 |
| 488 | A97 | $1.70 multicolored | 2.50 | 1.25 |
| 489 | A97 | $5 multicolored | 7.50 | 5.00 |
| | | Nos. 486-489 (4) | 12.75 | 7.75 |

Elizabeth II, Hong Kong Waterfront A98

Queen, Natl. Landmarks A99

Type I — Darker Shading Under Chin

Type II — Lighter Shading Under Chin

Designs: $5, Tsim Shah Tsui, Kowloon. $10, Victoria Harbor. $20, Legislative Council Building. $50, Government House.

**1987, July 13**    Litho.     *Perf. 14½x14*

| | | | | |
|---|---|---|---|---|
| 490 | A98 | 10c yel grn, gray & blk | .50 | .20 |
| 491 | A98 | 40c bluish grn, lt yel & blk | 1.25 | .20 |
| 492 | A98 | 50c brn org, buff & blk | 1.00 | .20 |
| 493 | A98 | 60c lt blue, pale rose & blk | 1.00 | .20 |
| 494 | A98 | 70c vio, pale rose & blk | 1.25 | .25 |
| 495 | A98 | 80c brt rose lil, lt blue & blk | 1.50 | 1.00 |
| 496 | A98 | 90c pink, pale beige & blk | 1.25 | 1.00 |
| 497 | A98 | $1 brt lem & blk | 1.25 | .40 |
| 498 | A98 | $1.30 rose claret, brt yel grn & blk | 1.25 | 1.25 |
| 499 | A98 | $1.70 lt blue & blk | 1.25 | .80 |
| 500 | A98 | $2 yel grn, cream & blk | 1.40 | .70 |

             *Perf. 14*

| | | | | |
|---|---|---|---|---|
| 501 | A99 | $5 grn, lt grn & blk | 3.50 | 2.00 |
| 502 | A99 | $10 brn, yel brn & blk | 8.00 | 5.00 |
| 503 | A99 | $20 rose vio, lil & blk | 17.50 | 10.00 |
| 504 | A99 | $50 sep, gray & blk | 42.50 | 32.50 |
| | | Nos. 490-504 (15) | 84.40 | 55.70 |

**1988, Sept. 1**          **Type II**

| | | | | |
|---|---|---|---|---|
| 490a | A98 | 10c | .60 | .20 |
| 491a | A98 | 40c | 1.25 | .20 |
| 492a | A98 | 50c | 1.25 | .25 |
| 493a | A98 | 60c | 1.25 | .25 |
| 494a | A98 | 70c | 1.50 | 1.00 |
| 495a | A98 | 80c | 1.50 | 1.00 |
| 496a | A98 | 90c | 1.50 | 1.00 |
| 497a | A98 | $1 | 1.50 | .45 |
| 498a | A98 | $1.30 | 2.25 | 1.50 |
| 499a | A98 | $1.70 | 1.50 | 1.00 |
| 500a | A99 | $5 | 1.75 | .75 |
| 501a | A99 | $10 | 5.50 | 2.25 |
| 502a | A99 | $10 | 10.00 | 6.00 |
| b. | | Souv. sheet of 1, inscribed "1990" | 110.00 | |
| c. | | As "b," inscribed "1990" | 50.00 | |
| d. | | As "b," inscribed "1991" | 20.00 | |
| 503a | A99 | $20 | 20.00 | 12.00 |
| 504a | A99 | $50 | 45.00 | 35.00 |
| | | Nos. 490a-504a (15) | 96.35 | 62.80 |

The selvage areas of Nos. 502b-502d are different: No. 502b for the New Zealand 1990 World Stamp Exhibition. No. 502c for Phila Nippon '91 Intl. Philatelic Exhibition. No. 502d for Hong Kong Post Office sponsorship of 1992 Olympic Games.

Issued: #502b, 8/24; #502c, 11/16/91; #502d, 12/4/91.

Nos. 490a-498a, 500a-504a reissued inscribed "1989," "1990." Nos. 490a, 492a-497a, 499a-504a, "1991."

See Nos. 532-533, 592-593, 629.

Nethersole Hospital, Cent. — A100

**1987, Sept. 8**      *Perf. 14½*

| | | | | |
|---|---|---|---|---|
| 505 | A100 | 50c Hospital, 1887 | 1.00 | .20 |
| 506 | A100 | $1.30 Patients, staff | 2.50 | 1.25 |
| 507 | A100 | $1.70 Technology, 1987 | 3.00 | 1.25 |
| 508 | A100 | $5 Treatment | 9.00 | 5.00 |
| | | Nos. 505-508 (4) | 15.50 | 7.70 |

Natl. Flag A101

Map of Hong Kong A101a

**Coil Stamps**

**1987, July 13**      *Perf. 15x14*

| | | | | |
|---|---|---|---|---|
| 509 | A101 | 10c shown | 1.60 | 1.60 |
| 510 | A101a | 50c olive green | 1.60 | 1.60 |

Nos. 509-510 reissued inscribed "1989," No. 509, "1990," "1991." See Nos. 611-614.

Folk Costumes — A102

**1987, Nov. 18**      *Perf. 13½*

| | | | | |
|---|---|---|---|---|
| 511 | A102 | 50c multicolored | .60 | .20 |
| 512 | A102 | $1.30 multi, diff. | 1.50 | 1.00 |
| 513 | A102 | $1.70 multi, diff. | 2.00 | 1.50 |
| 514 | A102 | $5 multi, diff. | 6.00 | 4.50 |
| | | Nos. 511-514 (4) | 10.10 | 7.20 |

New Year (Year of the Dragon) A103

**1988, Jan. 27**    Litho.     *Perf. 13½*

| | | | | |
|---|---|---|---|---|
| 515 | A103 | 50c multicolored | .75 | .30 |
| 516 | A103 | $1.30 multi, diff. | 2.00 | 1.00 |
| 517 | A103 | $1.70 multi, diff. | 2.25 | 1.50 |
| 518 | A103 | $5 multi, diff. | 4.50 | 4.00 |
| a. | | Souv. sheet of 4, #515-518 | 17.00 | 17.00 |
| | | Nos. 515-518 (4) | 9.50 | 6.80 |

See No. 838e.

Indigenous Birds — A104

Indigenous Trees — A105

**1988, Apr. 20**      *Perf. 13½x14*

| | | | | |
|---|---|---|---|---|
| 519 | A104 | 50c White-breasted kingfisher | 1.00 | .20 |
| 520 | A104 | $1.30 Fukien niltava | 2.25 | 1.25 |
| 521 | A104 | $1.70 Black kite | 2.75 | 1.50 |
| 522 | A104 | $5 Pied kingfisher | 6.00 | 5.00 |
| | | Nos. 519-522 (4) | 12.00 | 7.95 |

**1988, June 16**    Litho.     *Perf. 13½*

| | | | | |
|---|---|---|---|---|
| 523 | A105 | 50c Chinese banyan | .35 | .20 |
| 524 | A105 | $1.30 Bauhinia blakeana | 1.00 | .75 |
| 525 | A105 | $1.70 Cotton tree | 1.25 | .80 |
| 526 | A105 | $5 Schima | 3.50 | 2.50 |
| a. | | Souv. sheet of 4, #523-526 | 15.00 | 10.00 |
| | | Nos. 523-526 (4) | 6.10 | 4.25 |

See note after No. 940.

Peak Tramway, Victoria, Cent. — A106

Catholic Cathedral, Caine Road, Cent. — A107

Various views of Hong Kong and the tram line.

**1988, Aug. 4    Litho.    *Perf. 15***
527 A106   50c multicolored      .50    .20
528 A106  $1.30 multi, diff.     1.00    .85
529 A106  $1.70 multi, diff.     1.10   1.10
530 A106   $5 multi, diff.       3.50   3.50
   a.  Souvenir sheet of 4, #527-
       530                      10.00  10.00
       Nos. 527-530 (4)         6.10   5.65

**1988, Sept. 30    Litho.    *Perf. 14***
531 A107  60c multicolored       1.50   1.50

Queen and Waterfront Type of 1987
Type II

**1988, Sept. 1    Litho.    *Perf. 14½x14***
532 A98  $1.40 multicolored      2.25    .60
533 A98  $1.80 multicolored      3.75    .75

   Nos. 532-533 reissued inscribed "1989,"
"1990," No. 533, "1991."

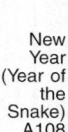

New
Year
(Year of
the
Snake)
A108

**1989, Jan. 18    Litho.    *Perf. 13½x14***
534 A108   60c multicolored      .50    .20
535 A108  $1.40 multi, diff.     1.25    .60
536 A108  $1.80 multi, diff.     1.50    .75
   a.  Bklt. pane, 5 each #534, 536  11.00
537 A108   $5 multi, diff.       5.00   3.50
   a.  Souv. sheet of 4, #534-537  15.00  10.00
       Nos. 534-537 (4)         8.25   5.05

See No. 838g.

Cheung Chau Bun
Festival — A109

**1989, May 4    Unwmk.    *Perf. 13½***
538 A109   60c Girl, doll        .60    .20
539 A109  $1.40 Girl            1.25    .60
540 A109  $1.80 Festival paper
              god               1.75    .75
541 A109   $5 Bun tower gate    4.50   3.00
       Nos. 538-541 (4)         8.10   4.55

Modern            Hong Kong
Art — A110        People — A111

60c, Twin, sculpture by Cheung Yee (b. 1936). $1.40, Figures, painted by Luis Chan (b. 1905). $1.80, Lotus, sculpture by Van Lau (b. 1933). $5, Zen, painted by Lui Shou-kwan (1919-1975).

**1989, July 19    *Perf. 12x13***
542 A110   60c multicolored      .60    .25
543 A110  $1.40 multicolored    1.40    .75
544 A110  $1.80 multicolored    1.75    .90
545 A110   $5 multicolored      3.75   2.50
       Nos. 542-545 (4)         7.50   4.40

**1989, Sept. 6    *Perf. 13x14½***

Designs: 60c, Youth holding autumn festival decoration, lunar year festival dragon. $1.40, Shadow boxer, horse racing. $1.80, Office and

construction workers. $5, Two women, two men (ethnic multiplicity).

546 A111   60c multicolored      .55    .25
547 A111  $1.40 multicolored    2.00    .75
548 A111  $1.80 multicolored    2.25    .75
549 A111   $5 multicolored      5.00   4.00
       Nos. 546-549 (4)         9.80   5.75

See No. 762.

Construction
Projects
A112

**1989, Oct. 5    Unwmk.    *Perf. 13***
550 A112   60c University of
              Science and
              Technology        .50    .20
551 A112   70c Cultural center  .55    .35
552 A112  $1.30 Eastern Harbor
              Crossing         1.00   1.00
553 A112  $1.40 Bank of China  1.00    .75
554 A112  $1.80 Convention
              center          1.25   1.00
555 A112   $5 Light rail transit  6.00   5.00
       Nos. 550-555 (6)        10.30   8.30

Visit of the Prince
and Princess of
Wales — A113

Portraits and view of Hong Kong: 60c, Charles and Diana. $1.40, Diana. $1.80, Charles. $5, Couple wearing formal attire.

**1989, Nov. 8    Wmk. 340    *Perf. 14½***
556 A113   60c multicolored     1.25    .30
557 A113  $1.40 multicolored    2.00   1.00
558 A113  $1.80 multicolored    1.75   1.00
559 A113   $5 multicolored      7.25   5.00
   a.  Souvenir sheet of 1     15.00  15.00
       Nos. 556-559 (4)        12.25   7.30

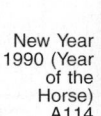

New Year
1990 (Year
of the
Horse)
A114

**    *Perf. 13½x12½***
**1990, Jan. 23    Unwmk.***
560 A114   60c multicolored      .85    .35
561 A114  $1.40 multi, diff.    1.75   1.25
562 A114  $1.80 multi, diff.    2.00   1.25
   a.  Bklt. pane, 3 each 60c, $1.80  15.00
       Complete booklet, 2 #562a  30.00
563 A114   $5 multi, diff.      5.50   4.50
   a.  Souvenir sheet of 4, #560-
       563                      10.00  12.50
       Nos. 560-563 (4)        10.10   7.35

Examples of No. 562a ovptd. with marginal inscription were released on May 3 to publicize Stamp World London '90.
See No. 838k.

Intl.              Pollutants — A116
Cuisine — A115

**1990, Apr. 26    Litho.    *Perf. 12½x13***
564 A115   60c Chinese          .60    .25
565 A115   70c Indian           .60    .40
566 A115  $1.30 Chinese, diff.  1.00    .90
567 A115  $1.40 Thai           1.00    .65

568 A115  $1.80 Japanese        1.50   1.00
569 A115   $5 French           4.50   3.50
       Nos. 564-569 (6)         9.20   6.70

**Wmk. 340**
**1990, June 5    Litho.    *Perf. 14½***
570 A116   60c Air              .40    .20
571 A116  $1.40 Noise           .90    .75
572 A116  $1.80 Water          1.50    .75
573 A116   $5 Land             3.25   2.50
       Nos. 570-573 (4)         6.05   4.20

World Environment Day.

Electrification of Hong Kong,
Cent. — A117

Views of Hong Kong and streetlights.

**1990, Oct. 2    Litho.    *Perf. 14½***
574 A117   60c 1890             .50    .20
575 A117  $1.40 1940           1.25   1.00
576 A117  $1.80 1960           1.40   1.00
577 A117   $5 1980             3.00   2.50
   a.  Souvenir sheet of 2, #575, 577  6.50   6.50
       Complete booklet, 4 #577a  26.00
       Nos. 574-577 (4)         6.15   4.70

Christmas — A118

**1990, Nov. 8**
578 A118   50c shown            .25    .20
579 A118   60c Dove, holly      .35    .20
580 A118  $1.40 Skyline, snow-
              man               .80    .40
581 A118  $1.80 Santa Claus'
              hat, skyscraper  1.00    .50
582 A118   $2 Children, Santa
              Claus            1.50   1.25
583 A118   $5 Candy cane,
              skyline          3.50   2.50
       Nos. 578-583 (6)         7.40   5.05

New Year
1991 (Year
of the
Sheep)
A119

Different embroidered rams.

**1991, Jan. 24    Litho.    *Perf. 13½x12½***
584 A119   60c multicolored     .35    .20
585 A119  $1.40 multicolored    .90    .50
586 A119  $1.80 multicolored   1.00    .75
   a.  Bklt. pane, 3 each #584, 586  5.00
       Complete booklet, 2 #586a  10.00
587 A119   $5 multicolored     3.25   2.50
   a.  Souv. sheet of 4, #584-587  8.00   7.00
       Nos. 584-587 (4)         5.50   3.95

See No. 838j.

Education — A120

**    *Perf. 13½x13***
**1991, Apr. 18    Litho.    Unwmk.***
588 A120   80c Kindergarten     .40    .25
589 A120  $1.80 Primary & sec-
              ondary           1.25    .80
590 A120  $2.30 Vocational     1.50   1.25
591 A120   $5 Tertiary         4.00   4.00
       Nos. 588-591 (4)         7.15   6.30

Queen and Waterfront Type of 1987
Type II

**1991, Apr. 2    Litho.    *Perf. 14½x14***
592 A98  $1.20 multicolored     .45    .30
593 A98  $2.30 multicolored     .90    .60

Transportation
A121

**1991, June 6    Unwmk.    *Perf. 14***
594 A121   80c Rickshaw         .55    .30
595 A121   90c Bus             .75    .60
596 A121  $1.70 Ferry          1.25   1.00
597 A121  $1.80 Tram           1.50    .80
598 A121  $2.30 Mass transit
              railway          2.25   2.00
599 A121   $5 Hydrofoil        4.25   3.75
       Nos. 594-599 (6)        10.55   8.45

A122

Historic
Landmarks
A123

Royal postboxes with contemporary envelopes: 80c, Stamp of Type A1, Queen Victoria. $1.70, Stamps of Type A10, King Edward VII. $1.80, #149, King George V. $2.30, Stamps of Type A16, King George VI. $5, $10, Stamp of Type A98, Queen Elizabeth II.

**1991, Aug. 25    Litho.    *Perf. 14***
600 A122   80c multicolored     .60    .30
601 A122  $1.70 multicolored   1.25   1.00
602 A122  $1.80 multicolored   1.75    .80
603 A122  $2.30 multicolored   1.50   1.25
604 A122   $5 multicolored     4.00   3.00
       Nos. 600-604 (5)         9.10   6.35

**Souvenir Sheet**
605 A122        15.00  15.00

Hong Kong Post Office, 150th anniv.
See No. 792.

**1991, Oct. 24**
606 A123   80c Bronze Buddha    .65    .25
607 A123  $1.70 Peak Pavilion  1.10    .55
608 A123  $1.80 Clock Tower    1.25    .60
609 A123  $2.30 Catholic Cathe-
              dral             1.75    .75
610 A123   $5 Wong Tai Sin
              Temple          4.25   1.75
       Nos. 606-610 (5)         9.00   3.90

Map of Hong Kong Type

**1992, Mar. 26    Photo.    *Perf. 14½x14***
**Coil Stamps**
**Color of Map**
611 A101a  80c red lilac        .50    .40
612 A101a  90c blue            .75    .60
613 A101a $1.80 brt yel grn    1.40   1.00
614 A101a $2.30 red brown      1.60   1.40
       Nos. 611-614 (4)         4.25   3.40

Inscribed 1991.

New
Year
1992
(Year of
the
Monkey)
A125

Various embroidery designs of monkeys.

| 1992, Jan. 22 | Litho. | | Perf. 14½ | |
|---|---|---|---|---|
| 615 | A125 | 80c multicolored | .40 | .25 |
| 616 | A125 | $1.80 multicolored | 1.00 | .50 |
| 617 | A125 | $2.30 multicolored | 1.75 | .75 |
| a. | | Bklt. pane, 3 ea #615, 617 | 7.00 | |
| | | Complete booklet, 2 #617a | 14.00 | |
| 618 | A125 | $5 multicolored | 4.00 | 3.00 |
| a. | | Sheet of 4, #615-618 | 12.00 | 12.00 |
| | | Nos. 615-618 (4) | 7.15 | 4.50 |

See No. 838i.

### Queen Elizabeth II's Accession to the Throne, 40th Anniv.
### Common Design Type
**Unwmk.**

| 1992, Feb. 11 | Litho. | | Perf. 14 | |
|---|---|---|---|---|
| 619 | CD349 | 80c multicolored | .35 | .20 |
| 620 | CD349 | $1.70 multicolored | .70 | .35 |
| 621 | CD349 | $1.80 multicolored | .75 | .40 |
| 622 | CD349 | $2.30 multicolored | 1.10 | .55 |
| 623 | CD349 | $5 multicolored | 2.75 | 1.10 |
| | | Nos. 619-623 (5) | 5.65 | 2.60 |

1992 Summer Olympics, Barcelona — A126

| 1992, Apr. 2 | Litho. | | Perf. 14½ | |
|---|---|---|---|---|
| | | **Black Inscription** | | |
| 624 | A126 | 80c Running | .40 | .20 |
| 625 | A126 | $1.80 Swimming and javelin | 1.00 | .80 |
| 626 | A126 | $2.30 Cycling | 1.50 | 1.25 |
| 627 | A126 | $5 High jump | 3.00 | 2.50 |
| | | Nos. 624-627 (4) | 5.90 | 4.75 |
| | | **Souvenir Sheet** | | |
| 628 | | Sheet of 4 | 7.50 | 7.50 |
| a. | A126 | 80c red inscription | .20 | .20 |
| b. | A126 | $1.80 green inscription | .60 | .60 |
| c. | A126 | $2.30 blue inscription | 1.00 | 1.00 |
| d. | A126 | $5 orange yellow inscription | 1.75 | 1.75 |
| e. | | Sheet of 4 with inscription in margin | 5.75 | 5.75 |

Issue date: No. 628e, July 25. New inscription on No. 628e sheet margin reads "To Commemorate the Opening of the 1992 Summer Olympic Games 25 July 1992" in English and Chinese.

### Queen and Landmarks Type of 1987
### Souvenir Sheet
**Perf. 14**

| 1992, May 22 | Litho. | | Type II | |
|---|---|---|---|---|
| 629 | A99 | $10 lt violet & black | 6.00 | 4.75 |

World Columbian Stamp Expo '92.

A127

**Perf. 15x14**

| 1992-97 | Photo. | | Unwmk. | |
|---|---|---|---|---|
| | | **Color of Chinese Inscription** | | |
| 630 | A127 | 10c pink | .30 | .30 |
| 630A | A127 | 20c black | 1.00 | 1.00 |
| 631 | A127 | 50c red orange | .30 | .25 |
| 632 | A127 | 60c blue | 1.50 | .40 |
| 633 | A127 | 70c red lilac | 1.50 | .55 |
| 634 | A127 | 80c rose | .30 | .20 |
| 635 | A127 | 90c gray green | .30 | .20 |
| 636 | A127 | $1 orange brown | .35 | .20 |
| 637 | A127 | $1.10 carmine | .35 | .20 |
| 638 | A127 | $1.20 violet | .35 | .20 |
| 639 | A127 | $1.30 dark blue | 1.50 | .65 |
| 640 | A127 | $1.40 apple green | 1.00 | .60 |
| 641 | A127 | $1.50 brown | 1.00 | .80 |
| 642 | A127 | $1.60 green | 1.00 | .45 |
| 643 | A127 | $1.70 ultramarine | .80 | .80 |
| 644 | A127 | $1.80 rose lilac | 1.50 | .55 |
| 645 | A127 | $1.90 green | .80 | .80 |
| 646 | A127 | $2 blue green | 1.00 | .50 |
| 647 | A127 | $2.10 claret | 1.50 | 1.10 |
| 648 | A127 | $2.30 gray | 1.50 | .65 |
| 649 | A127 | $2.40 dark blue | 2.50 | 1.25 |
| 650 | A127 | $2.50 olive green | 1.00 | .55 |
| a. | | Sheet of 6, 2 #647, 4 #650 | 9.00 | |
| d. | | Booklet pane, 2 #647, 4 #650 | 7.50 | |
| 651 | A127 | $2.60 dark brown | 1.50 | 1.50 |
| 651A | A127 | $3.10 salmon | 1.25 | .65 |
| l. | | Sheet of 6, 2 #642, 4 #651A | 8.00 | |

| o. | | Booklet pane, 2 #642, 4 #651A | 7.50 | |
|---|---|---|---|---|
| 651B | A127 | $5 bright green | 3.00 | 2.00 |
| k. | | Souvenir sheet of 1 | 7.00 | 2.00 |
| m. | | Sheet of 6, 4 #639, 2 #651B | 12.50 | |
| n. | | Booklet pane, 4 #639, 2 #651B | 18.00 | |
| p. | | Souvenir booklet of #650d, 651Ao, 651Bn | 35.00 | |

**Size: 25x30mm**
**Perf. 14½x14**

| 651C | A127 | $10 brown | 4.00 | 2.50 |
|---|---|---|---|---|
| h. | | Souvenir sheet of 1 | 6.00 | 2.50 |
| 651D | A127 | $20 orange red | 6.00 | 4.00 |
| 651E | A127 | $50 gray | 12.50 | 10.00 |
| | | Nos. 630-651E (28) | 50.25 | 32.75 |

Issued: 20c, $1.30, $1.90, $2.40, 11/1/93; #651Bk, 2/18/94; #651Ch, 8/16/94; $1.10, $1.50, $2.10, $2.60, 6/1/95; $1.40, $1.60, $2.50, $3.10, 9/2/96; #651Bp, 2/14/97; others, 6/16/92.

10c, 50c, 80c, 90c, $1, $1.20, $1.30, $1.50, $1.60, $1.80, $1.90, $2.10, 2.30, $2.40, $2.50, $2.60, $3.10 also issued in coils. These have numbers on the back of every fifth stamp.

No. 651Bk issued for Hong Kong '94; No. 651Ch for Conference of Commonwealth Postal Administrations.

Nos. 650a, 651Al, 651Bm are 130x85mm.
Nos. 650d, 651Ao, 651Bn are 180x130mm and are rouletted at left.
See Nos. 656, 677-678, 683, 688, 724, 729, 738, 743, 756-757.

| 1993-96 | Litho. | | Perf. 15x14 | |
|---|---|---|---|---|
| 636a | A127 | $1 Litho. | .75 | .75 |
| b. | | As "a," bklt. pane of 10 | 7.50 | |
| 638a | A127 | $1.20 Litho. | .75 | .75 |
| b. | | As "a," bklt. pane of 10 | 7.50 | |
| | | Complete booklet, #638b | 7.50 | |
| 639a | A127 | $1.30 Litho. | .50 | .50 |
| b. | | As "a," bklt. pane of 10 | 5.00 | |
| 645a | A127 | $1.90 Litho. | 1.00 | 1.00 |
| b. | | As "a," bklt. pane of 10 | 10.00 | |
| 647a | A127 | $2.10 Litho. | 1.00 | 1.00 |
| b. | | As "a," bklt. pane of 10 | 10.00 | |
| | | Complete booklet, #647b | 10.00 | |
| 649a | A127 | $2.40 Litho. | 1.00 | 1.00 |
| 650b | A127 | $2.50 Litho. | 1.00 | 1.00 |
| c. | | As "b," bklt. pane of 10 | 10.00 | |
| 651f | A127 | $2.60 Litho. | 1.00 | 1.00 |
| g. | | As "f," bklt. pane of 10 | 10.00 | |
| | | Complete booklet, #651g | 10.00 | |
| 651Ai | A127 | $3.10 Litho. | 1.00 | 1.00 |
| j. | | As "i," booklet pane of 10 | 10.00 | |
| | | Nos. 636a-651Ai (9) | 8.00 | 8.00 |

Chinese characters on Nos. 636a, 638a, 645a, 647a, 649a, 651f are lighter in shade and contrast less with the background color than characters on Nos. 636, 638, 645, 647, 649, 651.

Issued: #636a, 12/14/93; #645a, 649a, 12/28/93; #638a, 647a, 649a, 650a, 651Ai, 9/2/96.

Stamp Collecting — A128

Stamps and: 80c, Perforation gauge, #559, 586a. $1.80, Canceler, #66, stamp tongs. $2.30, Magnifying glass, #174, 180, 181. $5, Watermark detector, Type A1.

| 1992, July 15 | Litho. | | Perf. 14½ | |
|---|---|---|---|---|
| 652 | A128 | 80c multicolored | .35 | .20 |
| 653 | A128 | $1.80 multicolored | .75 | .40 |
| 654 | A128 | $2.30 multicolored | 1.10 | .90 |
| 655 | A128 | $5 multicolored | 2.25 | 1.75 |
| | | Nos. 652-655 (4) | 4.45 | 3.25 |

See note after No. 940.

### Queen Type of 1992
### Souvenir Sheet
**Perf. 14½x14**

| 1992, Sept. 1 | Photo. | | Unwmk. | |
|---|---|---|---|---|
| | | **Background Color** | | |
| 656 | A127 | $10 blue | 6.50 | 6.50 |

Kuala Lumpur Philatelic Exhibition '92.
Size of stamp: 25x30mm.

Chinese Opera — A129

| 1992, Sept. 24 | Litho. | | Perf. 13½ | |
|---|---|---|---|---|
| 657 | A129 | 80c Principal male role | 1.10 | .30 |
| 658 | A129 | $1.80 Martial role | 1.90 | 1.40 |
| 659 | A129 | $2.30 Principal female role | 2.25 | 1.60 |
| 660 | A129 | $5 Comic role | 4.25 | 3.25 |
| | | Nos. 657-660 (4) | 9.50 | 6.55 |

Greetings Stamps — A130

| 1992, Nov. 19 | Litho. | | Perf. 14½ | |
|---|---|---|---|---|
| 661 | A130 | 80c Hearts | .35 | .20 |
| 662 | A130 | $1.80 Stars | .70 | .35 |
| 663 | A130 | $2.30 Presents | .80 | .80 |
| 664 | A130 | $5 Balloons | 1.90 | 1.40 |
| a. | | Bklt. pane of 6, #662-664, 3 #661 | 6.00 | 5.00 |
| | | Complete booklet, 2 #664a | 12.00 | |
| | | Nos. 661-664 (4) | 3.75 | 2.75 |

New Year 1993 (Year of the Rooster) A131

Various embroidery designs of a rooster.

| 1993, Jan. 7 | Litho. | | Perf. 13½ | |
|---|---|---|---|---|
| 665 | A131 | 80c multicolored | .25 | .20 |
| 666 | A131 | $1.80 multicolored | .65 | .50 |
| 667 | A131 | $2.30 multicolored | 1.10 | 1.00 |
| a. | | Bklt. pane, 3 ea #665, 667 | 4.75 | |
| | | Complete booklet, 2 #667a | 9.50 | |
| 668 | A131 | $5 multicolored | 2.50 | 2.50 |
| a. | | Souvenir sheet of 4, #665-668 | 7.50 | 7.50 |
| | | Nos. 665-668 (4) | 4.50 | 4.20 |

See No. 838h.

Chinese String Instruments A132

| 1993, Apr. 14 | Litho. | | Perf. 14½ | |
|---|---|---|---|---|
| 669 | A132 | 80c Pipa | .40 | .20 |
| 670 | A132 | $1.80 Erhu | .75 | .70 |
| 671 | A132 | $2.30 Ruan | 1.10 | 1.00 |
| 672 | A132 | $5 Gehu | 2.25 | 2.00 |
| | | Nos. 669-672 (4) | 4.50 | 3.90 |

Coronation of Queen Elizabeth II, 40th Anniv. A133

Different views of Hong Kong with portraits of Queen that appear on Types A25, A28, A49 and A127.

| 1993, June 3 | Litho. | | Perf. 14 | |
|---|---|---|---|---|
| 673 | A133 | 80c multicolored | .40 | .20 |
| 674 | A133 | $1.80 multicolored | .80 | .75 |
| 675 | A133 | $2.30 multicolored | 1.25 | 1.10 |
| 676 | A133 | $5 multicolored | 3.00 | 2.50 |
| | | Nos. 673-676 (4) | 5.45 | 4.55 |

### Queen Type of 1992
### Souvenir Sheets

| 1993, July 6 | Litho. | | Perf. 14½x14 | |
|---|---|---|---|---|
| | | **Background Color** | | |
| 677 | A127 | $10 brown | 7.00 | 7.00 |

| 1993, Aug. 12 | | **Background Color** | | |
|---|---|---|---|---|
| 678 | A127 | $10 bright blue | 6.50 | 6.50 |

Hong Kong '94 Stamp Exhibition. Nos. 677-678 contain a 25x30mm stamp.

No. 678 exists with gold, silver or red overprints with the Hong Kong Philatelic Society emblem and Chinese characters. These sheets were sold only at various philatelic exhibitions.

Science and Technology — A134

Designs: 80c, Education, Hong Kong University of Science and Technology. $1.80, Public presentation, Hong Kong Science Museum. $2.30, Achievement recognition, Governor's Award. $5, World class telecommunications, telecommunications industry.

| 1993, Sept. 8 | Litho. | | Perf. 14½ | |
|---|---|---|---|---|
| 679 | A134 | 80c multicolored | .25 | .20 |
| 680 | A134 | $1.80 multicolored | .60 | .50 |
| 681 | A134 | $2.30 multicolored | .80 | .70 |
| 682 | A134 | $5 multicolored | 1.90 | 1.40 |
| | | Nos. 679-682 (4) | 3.55 | 2.80 |

### Queen Type of 1992
### Souvenir Sheet

| 1993, Oct. 5 | Litho. | | Perf. 14½x14 | |
|---|---|---|---|---|
| | | **Background Color** | | |
| 683 | A127 | $10 bright green | 4.50 | 4.50 |

Bangkok '93 Stamp Exhibition.
No. 683 contains one 25x30mm stamp.

Goldfish A135

| 1993, Nov. 17 | Litho. | | Perf. 14½ | |
|---|---|---|---|---|
| 684 | A135 | $1 Red calico egg-fish | .40 | .35 |
| 685 | A135 | $1.90 Red cap oranda | .80 | .50 |
| 686 | A135 | $2.40 Red & white fringetail | 1.25 | 1.10 |
| 687 | A135 | $5 Black & gold dragon-eye | 2.75 | 2.50 |
| a. | | Souvenir sheet of 4, #684-687 | 10.00 | 10.00 |
| | | Nos. 684-687 (4) | 5.20 | 4.45 |

### Queen Type of 1992
**Perf. 15x14**

| 1994, Jan. 27 | Photo. | | Wmk. 373 | |
|---|---|---|---|---|
| 688 | | Souvenir booklet | 20.00 | 20.00 |
| a. | A127 | Sheet of #630, 5 #646 | 6.50 | 6.50 |
| b. | A127 | Sheet of 5 #648 | 6.50 | 6.50 |
| c. | A127 | Sheet of 5 #636, #651B | 6.50 | 6.50 |

First Hong Kong stamps, 130th anniv. No. 688 sold for $38.

Year of the Dog A136

Various embroidery designs of dogs.

**1994, Jan. 27　　Litho.　　Perf. 14½**

| | | | |
|---|---|---|---|
| 689 | A136 | $1 multicolored | .35　.20 |
| 690 | A136 | $1.90 multicolored | .75　.50 |
| 691 | A136 | $2.40 multicolored | 1.00　.80 |
| a. | | Bklt. pane, 3 ea #689, 691 | 6.50 |
| | | Complete booklet, 2 #691a | 13.00 |
| 692 | A136 | $5 multicolored | 2.25　2.00 |
| a. | | Souvenir sheet of 4, #689-692 | 12.00　12.00 |
| | | Nos. 689-692 (4) | 4.35　3.50 |

See No. 838f.

Royal Hong Kong Police Force, 150th Anniv. — A137

Designs: $1, Traffic policeman, woman. $1.20, Marine policeman. $1.90, Male, female officers of 1950. $2, Policeman holding M-16. $2.40, Policemen, 1906, pre-1920. $5, Policemen, 1900.

**1994, May 4　　Litho.　　Perf. 13½**

| | | | |
|---|---|---|---|
| 693 | A137 | $1 multicolored | .35　.30 |
| 694 | A137 | $1.20 multicolored | .45　.35 |
| 695 | A137 | $1.90 multicolored | .65　.55 |
| 696 | A137 | $2 multicolored | 1.00　.60 |
| 697 | A137 | $2.40 multicolored | 1.50　1.25 |
| 698 | A137 | $5 multicolored | 3.25　3.00 |
| | | Nos. 693-698 (6) | 7.20　6.05 |

Traditional Chinese Festivals — A138

Designs: $1, Dragon Boat Festival. $1.90, Lunar New Year. $2.40, Seven Sisters Festival. $5, Mid-Autumn Festival.

**1994, June 8　　Litho.　　Perf. 14**

| | | | |
|---|---|---|---|
| 699 | A138 | $1 multicolored | .35　.25 |
| 700 | A138 | $1.90 multicolored | .75　.75 |
| 701 | A138 | $2.40 multicolored | 1.25　1.25 |
| 702 | A138 | $5 multicolored | 2.25　2.25 |
| | | Nos. 699-702 (4) | 4.60　4.50 |

XV Commonwealth Games, Victoria, BC, Canada — A139

**Unwmk.**

**1994, Aug. 25　　Litho.　　Perf. 14**

| | | | |
|---|---|---|---|
| 703 | A139 | $1 Swimming | .30　.25 |
| 704 | A139 | $1.90 Lawn bowling | 1.00　.50 |
| 705 | A139 | $2.40 Gymnastics | 1.25　.60 |
| 706 | A139 | $5 Weight lifting | 2.25　1.25 |
| | | Nos. 703-706 (4) | 4.80　2.60 |

Dr. James Legge (1815-97), Religious Leader, Translator — A140

**1994, Oct. 5　　Litho.　　Perf. 14**

| | | | |
|---|---|---|---|
| 707 | A140 | $1 multicolored | .75　.75 |

Corals — A141

**1994, Nov. 17　　Litho.　　Perf. 14**

| | | | |
|---|---|---|---|
| 708 | A141 | $1 Alcyonium | .35　.20 |
| 709 | A141 | $1.90 Zoanthus | .55　.45 |
| 710 | A141 | $2.40 Tubastrea | .75　.55 |
| 711 | A141 | $5 Platygyra | 1.75　1.10 |
| a. | | Souv. sheet of 4, #708-711 | 7.00　7.00 |
| | | Nos. 708-711 (4) | 3.40　2.30 |

New Year 1995 (Year of the Boar) A142

Various embroidery designs of pigs.

**1995, Jan. 17　　Litho.　　Perf. 14½**

| | | | |
|---|---|---|---|
| 712 | A142 | $1 multicolored | .40　.35 |
| 713 | A142 | $1.90 multicolored | .85　.65 |
| 714 | A142 | $2.40 multicolored | 1.10　.75 |
| a. | | Bklt. pane, 3 each #712, 714 | 6.00 |
| | | Complete booklet, 2 #714a | 12.00 |
| 715 | A142 | $5 multicolored | 2.10　1.50 |
| a. | | Souvenir sheet of 4, #712-715 | 7.00　7.00 |
| | | Nos. 712-715 (4) | 4.45　3.25 |

See No. 838d.

Intl. Sporting Events A143

Designs: $1, Hong Kong Rugby Sevens. $1.90, China Sea Race. $2.40, Intl. Dragon Boat Races. $5, Hong Kong Intl. Horse Races.

**1995, Mar. 22　　Litho.　　Perf. 14½**

| | | | |
|---|---|---|---|
| 716 | A143 | $1 multicolored | .50　.20 |
| 717 | A143 | $1.90 multicolored | .80　.80 |
| 718 | A143 | $2.40 multicolored | 1.25　1.25 |
| 719 | A143 | $5 multicolored | 2.50　2.50 |
| | | Nos. 716-719 (4) | 5.05　4.75 |

Traditional Buildings — A144

**Litho. & Engr.**

**1995, May 24　　　　Perf. 13½**

| | | | |
|---|---|---|---|
| 720 | A144 | $1 Tsui Shing Lau | .40　.20 |
| 721 | A144 | $1.90 Sam Tung UK | .75　.45 |
| 722 | A144 | $2.40 Lo Wai | .85　.50 |
| 723 | A144 | $5 Man Shek Tong | 2.00　1.10 |
| | | Nos. 720-723 (4) | 4.00　2.25 |

Queen Type of 1992
Souvenir Sheet

**1995, Aug. 25　　Litho.　　Perf. 14**

**Background Color**

| | | | |
|---|---|---|---|
| 724 | A127 | $10 carmine | 6.00　2.50 |

Singapore '95 World Stamp Exhibition. No. 724 contains one 25x30mm stamp.

Royal Hong Kong Regiment (1854-1995) — A145

$1.20, Modern Regimental Badge, vert. $2.10, Current flag. $2.60, Former flag. $5,

Royal Hong Kong Defense Force, 1951 soldier's badge, vert.

**1995, Aug. 16　　Litho.　　Perf. 14½**

| | | | |
|---|---|---|---|
| 725 | A145 | $1.20 multicolored | .30　.30 |
| 726 | A145 | $2.10 multicolored | .50　.50 |
| 727 | A145 | $2.60 multicolored | .80　.80 |
| 728 | A145 | $5 multicolored | 2.00　2.00 |
| | | Nos. 725-728 (4) | 3.60　3.60 |

Queen Type of 1992
Souvenir Sheet

**1995, Oct. 9　　Litho.　　Perf. 14**

**Background Color**

| | | | |
|---|---|---|---|
| 729 | A127 | $10 brown | 6.75　6.75 |

End of World War II, 50th anniv. No. 729 contains one 25x30mm stamp.

Hong Kong Movie Stars A146

**1995, Nov. 15　　Litho.　　Perf. 13½**

| | | | |
|---|---|---|---|
| 730 | A146 | $1.20 Bruce Lee | 2.00　1.00 |
| 731 | A146 | $2.10 Leung Sing-Por | .90　1.50 |
| 732 | A146 | $2.60 Yam Kim-Fai | 3.75　2.00 |
| 733 | A146 | $5 Lin Dai | 6.50　6.50 |
| | | Nos. 730-733 (4) | 15.25　11.00 |

New Year 1996 (Year of the Rat) A147

Various embroidery designs of rats.

**1996, Jan. 31　　Litho.　　Perf. 13½**

| | | | |
|---|---|---|---|
| 734 | A147 | $1.20 multicolored | .30　.30 |
| 735 | A147 | $2.10 multicolored | .55　.55 |
| 736 | A147 | $2.60 multicolored | .70　.70 |
| a. | | Bklt. pane, 3 ea #734, 736 | 3.75 |
| | | Complete booklet, 2 #736a | 7.50 |
| 737 | A147 | $5 multicolored | 1.25　1.25 |
| a. | | Souvenir sheet of 4, #734-737 | 5.00　5.00 |
| | | Nos. 734-737 (4) | 2.80　2.80 |

See No. 838a.

Queen Type of 1992
Souvenir Sheet

**Unwmk.**

**1996, Feb. 23　　Litho.　　Perf. 14**

| | | | |
|---|---|---|---|
| 738 | A127 | $10 org & grn | 7.00　7.00 |

Hong Kong '97 Stamp Exhibition. No. 738 contains one 25x30mm stamp.

1996 Summer Olympics, Atlanta — A148

**1996, Mar. 20　　Litho.　　Perf. 13½**

| | | | |
|---|---|---|---|
| 739 | A148 | $1.20 Gymnastics | .30　.30 |
| 740 | A148 | $2.10 Diving | .55　.55 |
| 741 | A148 | $2.60 Running | .70　.70 |
| 742 | A148 | $5 Basketball | 1.25　1.25 |
| | | Nos. 739-742 (4) | 2.80　2.80 |

**Souvenir Sheet**

| | | |
|---|---|---|
| 742A | Sheet of 4, #742b-742e | 4.00　4.00 |
| f. | As #742A, different sheet margin | 4.75　4.75 |

No. 742Af shows Olympic gold medal at top of sheet margin.
Nos. 748-751 have denominations in color and Olympic rings in gold. Nos. 739-742 have denominations in black, Olympic rings in different colors. No. 742Ab-742Ae have gold Olympic rings.
No. 742f issued 7/19/96.

Queen Type of 1992
Souvenir Sheet

**Unwmk.**

**1996, May 18　　Litho.　　Perf. 14**

| | | | |
|---|---|---|---|
| 743 | A127 | $10 brt grn & bl vio | 4.00　4.00 |

Hong Kong '97 Stamp Exhibition. No. 743 contains one 25x30mm stamp.

Archaeological Finds — A149

**1996, June 26　　Litho.　　Perf. 13½**

| | | | |
|---|---|---|---|
| 744 | A149 | $1.20 Painted pottery basin | .30　.30 |
| 745 | A149 | $2.10 Stone "Yue" | .55　.55 |
| 746 | A149 | $2.60 Stone "GE" | .80　.80 |
| 747 | A149 | $5 Pottery tripod | 1.50　1.50 |
| | | Nos. 744-747 (4) | 3.15　3.15 |

1996 Summer Olympic Games Type

**1996, July 19　　Litho.　　Perf. 14x14½**

**Color of Denomination**

| | | | |
|---|---|---|---|
| 748 | A148 | $1.20 like #739, red | .30　.20 |
| 749 | A148 | $2.10 like #740, blue | .40　.40 |
| 750 | A148 | $2.60 like #741, green | .75　.75 |
| 751 | A148 | $5 like #742, org | 1.50　1.50 |
| | | Nos. 748-751 (4) | 2.95　2.85 |

Nos. 748-751 have denominations in color and Olympic rings in gold. Nos. 739-742 have denominations in black, Olympic rings in different colors.

Mountains in Hong Kong — A150

**Unwmk.**

**1996, Sept. 24　　Litho.　　13½x14**

| | | | |
|---|---|---|---|
| 752 | A150 | $1.30 Pat Sing Leng | .50　.45 |

**Perf. 14x14½, 14½x14**

| | | | |
|---|---|---|---|
| 753 | A150 | $2.50 Ma On Shan | 1.00　1.00 |
| 754 | A150 | $3.10 Lion Rock, vert. | 1.25　1.25 |

**Perf. 14x13½**

| | | | |
|---|---|---|---|
| 755 | A150 | $5 Lantau Peak, vert. | 1.90　1.90 |
| | | Nos. 752-755 (4) | 4.65　4.60 |

No. 753 is 40x36mm, No. 754 36x40mm. See #899, 905.

Queen Type of 1992
Souvenir Sheets

**1996　　Photo.　　Unwmk.　　Perf. 14**

| | | | |
|---|---|---|---|
| 756 | A127 | $10 red & grn | 3.50　3.50 |
| 757 | A127 | $10 brn & dk brn | 4.00　4.00 |

Issued: No. 756, 10/16; No. 757, 10/29. Visit Hong Kong '97 Stamp Exhibition (#756). 1996 Summer Olympic Games, Atlanta (#757). Nos. 756-757 each contain one 25x30mm stamp.

Urban Heritage A151

Designs: $1.30, Main building, University of Hong Kong, 1912. $2.50, Western Market, 1906. $3.10, Old Pathological Institute, 1905. $5, Flagstaff House, 1846.

**Litho. & Engr.**

**1996, Nov. 20　　　　Perf. 13½**

| | | | |
|---|---|---|---|
| 758 | A151 | $1.30 multicolored | .45　.45 |
| 759 | A151 | $2.50 multicolored | .75　.75 |
| 760 | A151 | $3.10 multicolored | .90　.90 |
| 761 | A151 | $5 multicolored | 1.50　1.50 |
| | | Nos. 758-761 (4) | 3.60　3.60 |

## Hong Kong People Type of 1989
### Souvenir Sheet
**Perf. 13x13½**

**1997, Jan.**  **Photo.**  **Unwmk.**
762 A111 $5 like No. 549     1.50 1.50

No. 762 contains one 23x33mm stamp that has darker colors and a different perf. than No. 549.

Panoramic Views of Hong Kong Skyline — A152

#763-775: Various daytime views from harbor.
#776-778, Various nighttime views from harbor.

**Perf. 13½x13**

**1997, Jan. 26**  **Litho.**  **Unwmk.**
**Background Color**

| | | | | |
|---|---|---|---|---|
| 763 | A152 | 10c pink | .20 | .20 |
| 764 | A152 | 20c vermilion | .20 | .20 |
| 765 | A152 | 50c orange | .20 | .20 |
| 766 | A152 | $1 orange yellow | .25 | .25 |
| 767 | A152 | $1.20 olive | .30 | .30 |
| 768 | A152 | $1.30 apple green | .35 | .35 |
| a. | | Booklet pane of 10 | 3.50 | |
| | | Complete booklet, #768a | 3.50 | |
| 769 | A152 | $1.40 green | .35 | .35 |
| 770 | A152 | $1.60 blue green | .40 | .40 |
| 771 | A152 | $2 green blue | .55 | .55 |
| 772 | A152 | $2.10 blue | .55 | .55 |
| 773 | A152 | $2.50 purple | .65 | .65 |
| a. | | Booklet pane of 10 | 6.50 | |
| | | Complete booklet, #773a | 6.50 | |
| 774 | A152 | $3.10 rose | .80 | .80 |
| a. | | Booklet pane of 10 | 8.00 | |
| | | Complete booklet, #774a | 8.00 | |
| c. | | Sheet of 4, #771-774 | 2.50 | 2.50 |
| 775 | A152 | $5 orange | 1.25 | 1.25 |
| a. | | Sheet of 13, #763-775 | 5.75 | 5.75 |

**Size: 28x33mm**
**Perf. 14x13½**

| | | | | |
|---|---|---|---|---|
| 776 | A152 | $10 blue | 2.50 | 2.50 |
| a. | | Souv. sheet of 1 (Series #4) | 8.00 | |
| b. | | Souv. sheet of 1 (Series #5) | 8.00 | |
| c. | | Souv. Sheet of 1 (Sheet #12) | 3.00 | 3.00 |
| d. | | Souv. sheet of 1, perf14x13¼ (Sheet #14) | 2.60 | 2.60 |
| 777 | A152 | $20 bl, pur & rose | 5.25 | 5.25 |
| 778 | A152 | $50 purple & rose | 13.00 | 13.00 |
| a. | | Sheet of 3, #776-778 | 21.00 | |
| | | Nos. 763-778 (16) | 26.80 | 26.80 |

Hong Kong '97 (#776a-776b). 1996 Atlanta Paralympic Games (#776c). 13th Asian Games, Bangkok, Thailand (#774c). China 1999 World Philatelic Exhibition (#776d).
Perforations are alternating small and large holes.
Issued: #776a, 2/12; #776b, 2/16; #774c, 3/27/99; #776d, 8/21/99.
See note after No. 940.

#775a and 778a are continuous designs.

### Coil Stamps
**Photo.**  **Perf. 14½x14**

| | | | | |
|---|---|---|---|---|
| 763a | A152 | 10c | .25 | .25 |
| 765a | A152 | 50c | .25 | .25 |
| 768b | A152 | $1.30 | .45 | .45 |
| 770a | A152 | $1.60 | .50 | .50 |
| 773b | A152 | $2.50 | .80 | .80 |
| 774b | A152 | $3.10 | 1.00 | 1.00 |
| | | Nos. 763a-774b (6) | 3.25 | 3.25 |

These have numbers on back of every fifth stamp.
Perforations are the same size.

New Year 1997 (Year of the Ox) A153

Various designs of oxen.

**Perf. 14½**

**1997, Feb. 27**  **Litho.**  **Unwmk.**
**Background Color**

| | | | | |
|---|---|---|---|---|
| 780 | A153 | $1.30 pink | .30 | .30 |
| 781 | A153 | $2.50 orange yellow | .65 | .65 |
| 782 | A153 | $3.10 green | .80 | .80 |
| a. | | Booklet pane, 3 each #780a, 782b | 3.50 | |
| | | Complete booklet, 2 #782a | 7.00 | |
| 783 | A153 | $5 blue | 1.25 | 1.25 |
| a. | | Souvenir sheet of 4, #780-783 | 4.50 | 4.50 |
| | | Nos. 780-783 (4) | 3.00 | 3.00 |

See Nos. 838b, 838c.

---

**Perf. 13½**

| | | | | |
|---|---|---|---|---|
| 780a | A153 | $1.30 | .50 | .50 |
| 781a | A153 | $2.50 | .90 | .90 |
| 782b | A153 | $3.10 | 1.10 | 1.10 |
| 783b | A153 | $5 | 1.75 | 1.75 |
| c. | | Souvenir sheet of 4, #780a-781a, 782b-783b | 4.50 | 4.50 |

Migratory Birds — A154

$1.30, Yellow-breasted bunting. $2.50, Great knot. $3.10, Falcated teal. $5, Black-faced spoonbill.

**Perf. 13½**

**1997, Apr. 27**  **Unwmk.**  **Photo.**

| | | | | |
|---|---|---|---|---|
| 784 | A154 | $1.30 multicolored | .30 | .30 |
| 785 | A154 | $2.50 multicolored | .65 | .65 |
| 786 | A154 | $3.10 multicolored | .80 | .80 |
| 787 | A154 | $5 multicolored | 1.25 | 1.25 |
| | | Nos. 784-787 (4) | 3.00 | 3.00 |

Landmarks — A155

$1.30, Hong Kong Stadium. $2.50, The Peak Tower. $3.10, Hong Kong Convention & Exhibition Center. $5, The Lantau Link (bridge).

**1997, May 18**  **Perf. 13½**

| | | | | |
|---|---|---|---|---|
| 788 | A155 | $1.30 multicolored | .30 | .30 |
| 789 | A155 | $2.50 multicolored | .75 | .75 |
| 790 | A155 | $3.10 multicolored | 1.00 | 1.00 |
| 791 | A155 | $5 multicolored | 1.75 | 1.75 |
| a. | | Souvenir sheet of 1 | 2.25 | 2.25 |
| | | Nos. 788-791 (4) | 3.80 | 3.80 |

Opening of the Lantau Link (bridge) (#791a). Nos. 788-791 and 791a also exist perf 14x14½. Values are the same.

### Royal Postbox Type of 1991
### Souvenir Sheet

**1997, June 30**  **Litho.**  **Perf. 11½**
792 A122 $5 like No. 604     1.50 1.50

No. 792 contains one 19x29mm stamp.

## Special Administrative Region of People's Republic of China

First Issue Under Chinese Administration A156

Sights and symbols of Hong Kong: $1.30, Chinese architecture. $1.60, Modern buildings, methods of transportation. $2.50, Skyscrapers, Hong Kong Convention & Exhibition Center. $2.60, Cargo ship entering port. $3.10, Chinese junks, dolphins jumping in water. $5, Hibiscus flower.

**1997, July 1**  **Litho.**  **Perf. 12x12½**

| | | | | |
|---|---|---|---|---|
| 793 | A156 | $1.30 multicolored | .35 | .35 |
| 794 | A156 | $1.60 multicolored | .40 | .40 |
| 795 | A156 | $2.50 multicolored | .65 | .65 |
| 796 | A156 | $2.60 multicolored | .70 | .70 |
| 797 | A156 | $3.10 multicolored | .80 | .80 |
| 798 | A156 | $5 multicolored | 1.25 | 1.25 |
| a. | | Souvenir sheet of 1 | 1.25 | 1.25 |
| | | Nos. 793-798 (6) | 4.15 | 4.15 |

---

1997 World Bank Group/Intl. Monetary Fund Annual Meetings — A157

Designs: $1.30, Finance, banking. $2.50, Investment, stock exchange. $3.10, Trade, telecommunications. $5, Infrastructure, transport.

**Perf. 14½**

**1997, Sept. 21**  **Litho.**  **Unwmk.**

| | | | | |
|---|---|---|---|---|
| 799 | A157 | $1.30 multicolored | .30 | .30 |
| 800 | A157 | $2.50 multicolored | .65 | .65 |
| 801 | A157 | $3.10 multicolored | .80 | .80 |
| 802 | A157 | $5 multicolored | 1.25 | 1.25 |
| | | Nos. 799-802 (4) | 3.00 | 3.00 |

Shells — A158

**1997, Nov. 9**  **Photo.**  **Perf. 13½**

| | | | | |
|---|---|---|---|---|
| 803 | A158 | $1.30 Clam | .35 | .35 |
| 804 | A158 | $2.50 Cowrie | .65 | .65 |
| 805 | A158 | $3.10 Cone | .80 | .80 |
| 806 | A158 | $5 Murex | 1.25 | 1.25 |
| | | Nos. 803-806 (4) | 3.05 | 3.05 |

New Year 1998 (Year of the Tiger) A159

Various embroidery designs of tigers.

**1998, Jan. 4**  **Litho.**  **Perf. 13½**

| | | | | |
|---|---|---|---|---|
| 807 | A159 | $1.30 multicolored | .30 | .30 |
| 808 | A159 | $2.50 multicolored | .65 | .65 |
| 809 | A159 | $3.10 multicolored | .80 | .80 |
| a. | | Bklt. pane, 6 ea #807, 809 | 7.00 | |
| | | Complete booklet, #809a | 7.00 | |
| 810 | A159 | $5 multicolored | 1.25 | 1.25 |
| a. | | Souvenir sheet, #807-810 | 3.50 | 3.50 |
| | | Nos. 807-810 (4) | 3.00 | 3.00 |

See No. 838.

Star Ferry, Cent. A160

Star Ferry during: $1.30, 1900's. $2.50, 1910's-1920's. $3.10, 1920's-1950's. $5, Mid-1950's on.

**1998, Apr. 26**  **Photo.**  **Perf. 13½**

| | | | | |
|---|---|---|---|---|
| 811 | A160 | $1.30 multicolored | .30 | .30 |
| 812 | A160 | $2.50 multicolored | .65 | .65 |
| 813 | A160 | $3.10 multicolored | .80 | .80 |
| 814 | A160 | $5 multicolored | 1.25 | 1.25 |
| | | Nos. 811-814 (4) | 3.00 | 3.00 |

Nos. 811-814 also exist perf 14½ from a booklet of one each sold only at "Australia '99" International Stamp Exhibition for $25.

### Souvenir Sheet

The Closing of Kai Tak Airport — A161

---

Illustration reduced.

**1998, July 5**  **Photo.**  **Perf. 13½**
815 A161 $5 multicolored     1.50 1.50

New Hong Kong Airport A162

$1.30, Passengers on terminal's moving sidewalks. $1.60, Couple entering Automated People Mover. $2.50, Airport Railway, Tsing Ma Bridge. $2.60, Terminal building, Airmail Center. $3.10, Aircraft gates. $5, Terminal departure level.

**1998, July 5**  **Perf. 14**

| | | | | |
|---|---|---|---|---|
| 816 | A162 | $1.30 multicolored | .35 | .35 |
| 817 | A162 | $1.60 multicolored | .40 | .40 |
| 818 | A162 | $2.50 multicolored | .65 | .65 |
| 819 | A162 | $2.60 multicolored | .70 | .70 |
| 820 | A162 | $3.10 multicolored | .80 | .80 |
| 821 | A162 | $5 multicolored | 1.25 | 1.25 |
| a. | | Souvenir sheet of 1 | 1.50 | 1.50 |
| b. | | Block of 6, #816-821 | 4.75 | 4.75 |

See note after No. 940.

A163       A164

Scouting in Hong Kong: Rope tied in various knots, different scouting divisions: $1.30, Grasshopper Scouts, Cub Scouts. $2.50, Tower, tents, Boy Scouts, Girl Scouts. $3.10, Helicopter, sailboats, Venture Scouts. $5, City buildings, Rover Scouts, adult leaders.

**Unwmk.**

**1998, July 26**  **Litho.**  **Perf. 14**

| | | | | |
|---|---|---|---|---|
| 822 | A163 | $1.30 multicolored | .30 | .30 |
| 823 | A163 | $2.50 multicolored | .65 | .65 |
| 824 | A163 | $3.10 multicolored | .80 | .80 |
| 825 | A163 | $5 multicolored | 1.25 | 1.25 |
| | | Nos. 822-825 (4) | 3.00 | 3.00 |

**1998, Sept. 20**  **Litho.**  **Perf. 13½**

Hong Kong designs.

| | | | | |
|---|---|---|---|---|
| 826 | A164 | $1.30 Graphic | .35 | .35 |
| 827 | A164 | $2.50 Product | .65 | .65 |
| 828 | A164 | $3.10 Interior | .85 | .85 |
| 829 | A164 | $5 Fashion | 1.25 | 1.25 |
| | | Nos. 826-829 (4) | 3.10 | 3.10 |

Kites — A165

**1998, Nov. 15**  **Litho.**  **Perf. 13½**

| | | | | |
|---|---|---|---|---|
| 830 | A165 | $1.30 Dragonfly | .30 | .30 |
| 831 | A165 | $2.50 Dragon | .65 | .65 |
| 832 | A165 | $3.10 Butterfly | .80 | .80 |
| 833 | A165 | $5 Goldfish | 1.25 | 1.25 |
| a. | | Souvenir sheet, #830-833 | 3.00 | 3.00 |
| | | Nos. 830-833 (4) | 3.00 | 3.00 |

A166

**1999, Jan. 31   Photo.   Perf. 14x13½**

New Year 1999 (Year of the Rabbit): White rabbit with flower designs in various positions.

| 834 | A166 | $1.30 yel org & multi | .35 | .35 |
| | | Scratched panel | | .35 |
| | | Sheet of 10 | 3.50 | |
| 835 | A166 | $2.50 green & multi | .65 | .65 |
| | | Scratched panel | | .35 |
| | | Sheet of 10 | 6.50 | |
| 836 | A166 | $3.10 orange & multi | .80 | .80 |
| | | Scratched panel | | .35 |
| | | Sheet of 10 | 8.00 | |
| 837 | A166 | $5 red lilac & multi | 1.25 | 1.25 |
| | | Scratched panel | | .35 |
| | | Sheet of 10 | 12.50 | |
| | | Nos. 834-837 (4) | 3.05 | 3.05 |

Nos. 834-837 are printed with a layering of gold "scratch off" ink, which, when removed, reveals a Chinese greeting.

**New Year Types of 1987-98**

Designs: a, Like #734. b, Like #780. c, Like #783. d, Like #712. e Like 515. f, Like #691. g, Like #534. h, Like #668. i, Like #615. j, Like #584. k, Like #560. #a.-k. have 4 Chinese characters at UL instead of crown and ER.

**1999, Feb. 21   Litho.   Perf. 13½**
**Sheet of 12**

| 838 | $1.30 #a.-k., #807 + label | 6.00 6.00 |

Design in label and sheet selvage is engraved.

Intl. Year of Older Persons — A167

**Perf. 14½**
**1999, Mar. 14   Litho.   Unwmk.**

| 839 | A167 | $1.30 Calligraphy | .35 | .35 |
| 840 | A167 | $2.50 Bird raising | .65 | .65 |
| 841 | A167 | $3.10 Playing Go | .80 | .80 |
| 842 | A167 | $5 Voluntary services | 1.25 | 1.25 |
| | | Nos. 839-842 (4) | 3.05 | 3.05 |

**Souvenir Sheet**

Giant Pandas in Hong Kong — A168

Illustration reduced.

**1999, Apr. 25   Litho.   Perf. 14¼**
| 843 | A168 | $10 multicolored | 2.75 | 2.75 |

No. 843 contains one circular stamp 38mm in diameter.

Public Transport — A169

**1999, May 23**

| 844 | A169 | $1.30 Bus | .35 | .35 |
| 845 | A169 | $2.40 Minibus | .70 | .70 |
| 846 | A169 | $2.50 Tram | .75 | .75 |
| 847 | A169 | $2.60 Taxi | .80 | .80 |
| 848 | A169 | $3.10 Airport express | .90 | .90 |
| | | Nos. 844-848 (5) | 3.50 | 3.50 |

Hong Kong and Singapore Tourism — A170

Designs: $1.20, Hong Kong Harbor. $1.30, Singapore Skyline. $2.50, Giant Buddha, Hong Kong. $2.60, Merlion, Sentosa Island, Singapore. $3.10, Hong Kong street scene. $5, Bugis Junction, Singapore.

**Perf. 13¼**
**1999, July 1   Litho.   Unwmk.**

| 849 | A170 | $1.20 multicolored | .35 | .35 |
| 850 | A170 | $1.30 multicolored | .40 | .40 |
| 851 | A170 | $2.50 multicolored | .70 | .70 |
| 852 | A170 | $2.60 multicolored | .70 | .70 |
| 853 | A170 | $3.10 multicolored | .85 | .85 |
| 854 | A170 | $5 multicolored | 1.50 | 1.50 |
| a. | | Souvenir sheet, #849-854 | 4.50 | 4.50 |
| | | Nos. 849-854 (6) | 4.50 | 4.50 |

See Singapore Nos. 896-902.

People's Republic of China, 50th Anniv. — A171

Designs: $1.30, Flags of People's Republic and Hong Kong Special Administrative District. $2.50 Bauhinia blakeana flower, Hong Kong skyline. $3.10, Dragon dance. $5, Fireworks.

**Perf. 14¼ Syncopated**
**1999, Oct. 1   Photo.**
**Granite Paper**

| 855 | A171 | $1.30 multicolored | .40 | .40 |
| 856 | A171 | $2.50 multicolored | .75 | .75 |
| 857 | A171 | $3.10 multicolored | .85 | .85 |
| 858 | A171 | $5 multicolored | 1.50 | 1.50 |
| a. | | Block or strip of 4, #855-858 | 3.50 | 3.50 |

Issued in sheets of 4 blocks or strips and individually in sheets of 20.

Landmarks — A172

10c, Museum of Tea Ware. 20c, St. John's Cathedral. 50c, Legislative Council building. $1, Tai Fu Tai. $1.20, Wong Tai Sin Temple. $1.30, Victoria Harbor. $1.40, Hong Kong Railway Museum. $1.60, Tsim Sha Tsui Clock Tower. $2, Happy Valley Racecourse. $2.10, Kowloon-Canton Railway. $2.50, Chi Lin Nunnery. $3.10, Buddha at Po Lin Monastery. $5, Aw Boon Haw Gardens. $10, Tsing Ma Bridge. $20, Hong Kong Convention & Exhibition Center. $50, Hong Kong Intl. Airport.

**Perf. 13x13¾ Syncopated**
**1999, Oct. 18   Photo.**
**Granite Paper**

| 859 | A172 | 10c blue & multi | .20 | .20 |
| a. | | Booklet pane of 1 | .20 | |
| 860 | A172 | 20c blue & multi | .20 | .20 |
| a. | | Booklet pane of 1 | .25 | |
| 861 | A172 | 50c blue & multi | .20 | .20 |
| a. | | Booklet pane of 1 | .50 | |
| 862 | A172 | $1 blue & multi | .25 | .25 |
| a. | | Booklet pane of 1 | .60 | |
| 863 | A172 | $1.20 blue & multi | .30 | .30 |
| a. | | Booklet pane of 1 | .60 | |
| 864 | A172 | $1.30 blue & multi | .35 | .35 |
| a. | | Booklet pane of 1 | .70 | |
| 865 | A172 | $1.40 blue & multi | .35 | .35 |
| a. | | Booklet pane of 10 | 3.50 | — |
| b. | | Booklet, #865b | 3.50 | |
| 866 | A172 | $1.60 blue & multi | .40 | .40 |
| a. | | Booklet pane of 1 | .80 | |
| 867 | A172 | $2 blue & multi | .50 | .50 |
| a. | | Booklet pane of 1 | 1.00 | |

| 868 | A172 | $2.10 blue & multi | .55 | .55 |
| a. | | Booklet pane of 1 | 1.10 | |
| 869 | A172 | $2.50 blue & multi | .60 | .60 |
| a. | | Booklet pane of 1 | 1.25 | |
| 870 | A172 | $3.10 blue & multi | .75 | .75 |
| a. | | Booklet pane of 1 | 1.50 | |
| 871 | A172 | $5 blue & multi | 1.25 | 1.25 |
| a. | | Booklet pane of 1 | 2.50 | |
| | | Souv. booklet, #859a-871a | 12.00 | |
| b. | | Sheet of 13, #859-871 | 5.50 | 5.50 |
| c. | | Souvenir sheet of 1 (Definitive #4) | 1.25 | 1.25 |
| d. | | Souv. sheet of 1 (Definitive #6) | 1.25 | 1.25 |

**Size: 26x32mm**
**Perf. 13¼**

| 872 | A172 | $10 blue & multi | 2.50 | 2.50 |
| a. | | Souv. sheet of 1 (Definitive #1) | 2.50 | 2.50 |
| b. | | Souv. sheet of 1 (Exhibition #1) | 3.50 | 3.50 |
| c. | | Souv. sheet of 1 (Exhibition #2) | 2.50 | 2.50 |
| d. | | Souv. sheet of 1 (Definitive #2) | 2.50 | 2.50 |
| e. | | Souv. sheet of 1 (Definitive #5) | 2.50 | 2.50 |
| 873 | A172 | $20 blue & multi | 5.00 | 5.00 |
| 874 | A172 | $50 blue & multi | 12.50 | 12.50 |
| a. | | Sheet of 3, #872-874 | 20.00 | 20.00 |
| | | Nos. 859-874 (16) | 25.90 | 25.90 |

**Coil Stamps**
**Perf. 13¾x13¼ Syncopated**
**Size: 18x22mm**

| 874B | A172 | 10c blue & multi | .20 | .20 |
| 874C | A172 | 50c blue & multi | .20 | .20 |
| 874D | A172 | $1.30 blue & multi | .35 | .35 |
| 874E | A172 | $1.60 blue & multi | .40 | .40 |
| 874F | A172 | $2.50 blue & multi | .60 | .60 |
| 874G | A172 | $3.10 blue & multi | .75 | .75 |
| | | Nos. 874B-874G (6) | 2.50 | 2.50 |

#872a-872b are Syncopated perf 14x14¼. #872c is Syncopated perf 13¼x13. #872d is Syncopated perf 14x14½. No. 872e is Syncopated perf. 13¼x13.
Issued: #872a, 1/31/00; #872b, 2/10/00; #872c, 4/15/00; #872d, 12/2/00; #871c, 4/21/01; #872e, 8/1/01; #874B-874E, 874G, 10/18/99; #874F, 10/18/99; #871d, 1/19/02. #865b, 4/1/02.
See note after No. 940.
See also Nos. 991-993.

Chinese White Dolphin — A173

Various views of dolphin.

**1999, Nov. 14   Litho.   Perf. 14½**
**Granite Paper**

| 875 | A173 | $1.30 green & multi | .60 | .60 |
| 876 | A173 | $2.50 bl grn & multi | 1.00 | 1.00 |
| 877 | A173 | $3.10 blue & multi | 1.25 | 1.25 |
| 878 | A173 | $5 pur & multi | 1.75 | 1.75 |

**Souvenir Sheet**

| 879 | | Sheet of 4, #a.-d. | 3.25 | 3.25 |

Nos. 875-878 have Worldwide Fund for Nature (WWF) emblem; Nos. 879a-879d do not.
See No. 900.

**Souvenir Sheet**

Millennium — A174

No. 880: a, Dragon boat races, skyline. b, Bridge, birds.
Illustration reduced.

**Perf. 14¼ Syncopated**
**1999, Dec. 31   Photo.**
**Granite Paper**

| 880 | A174 | $5 Sheet of 2, #a.-b. | 3.00 | 3.00 |

New Millennium Children's Stamp Design Contest Winners — A175

Designs: $1.30, Scales. $2.50, Children planting tree on planet. $3.10, Planets. $5, Inhabited planets, space shuttle, rocket.

**2000, Jan. 1   Granite Paper**

| 881 | A175 | $1.30 multi | .40 | .30 |
| 882 | A175 | $2.50 multi | .75 | .75 |
| 883 | A175 | $3.10 multi | .85 | .85 |
| 884 | A175 | $5 multi | 1.50 | 1.50 |
| | | Nos. 881-884 (4) | 3.50 | 3.40 |

Victoria Harbor A176

**Litho. & Embossed with Foil Application**
**2000, Jan. 1   Perf. 13¼**

| 885 | A176 | $50 gold & multi | 16.00 | 16.00 |

New Year 2000 (Year of the Dragon) — A177

Various dragons.

**Perf. 14¼ Syncopated**
**2000, Jan. 23   Litho.**
**Granite Paper**

| 886 | A177 | $1.30 multi | .35 | .35 |
| 887 | A177 | $2.50 multi | .65 | .65 |
| 888 | A177 | $3.10 multi | .75 | .75 |
| 889 | A177 | $5 multi | 1.25 | 1.25 |
| a. | | Souvenir sheet of 1, imperf. | 13.50 | 13.50 |
| b. | | Souvenir sheet, #886-889 | 3.75 | 3.75 |
| | | Nos. 886-889 (4) | 3.00 | 3.00 |

Museums and Libraries — A178

Designs: $1.30, Heritage Museum. $2.50, Central Library. $3.10, Museum of Coastal Defense. $5 Museum of History.
Illustration reduced.

**Perf. 14½x14¼**
**2000, Mar. 26   Photo.**
**Granite Paper**

| 890 | A178 | $1.30 multi | .50 | .35 |
| 891 | A178 | $2.50 multi | .85 | .80 |
| 892 | A178 | $3.10 multi | .95 | .90 |
| 893 | A178 | $5 multi | 1.60 | 1.60 |
| a. | | Block, #890-893 | 4.00 | 4.00 |
| | | Nos. 890-893 (4) | 3.90 | 3.65 |

Nos. 890-893 issued in sheets of 24. No. 893a issued only in sheet containing 4 blocks.

Red Cross — A179

Designs: $1.30, Blood transfusion. $2.50, Special education. $3.10, Disaster relief. $5, Voluntary service.

### Perf. 14¼ Syncopated
**2000, May 7**     **Photo.**
**Granite Paper**

| | | | |
|---|---|---|---|
| 894 | A179 $1.30 multi | .40 | .30 |
| 895 | A179 $2.50 multi | .75 | .75 |
| 896 | A179 $3.10 multi | .85 | .85 |
| 897 | A179 $5 multi | 1.50 | 1.50 |
| a. | Souvenir sheet, #894-897 | 3.50 | 3.50 |
| | Nos. 894-897 (4) | 3.50 | 3.40 |

### Flower Type of 1989, Mountain Type of 1996 Inscribed "Hong Kong, China," and Dolphin Type of 1999
### Perf. 14¼ Syncopated
**2000, June 17**     **Photo.**
**Granite Paper**

| | | | |
|---|---|---|---|
| 898 | A90 $5 Booklet pane of 1, like #455 | 3.00 | 3.00 |
| 899 | A150 $5 Booklet pane of 1, like #755 | 3.00 | 3.00 |
| 900 | A173 $5 Booklet pane of 1, like #879d | 3.00 | 3.00 |
| | Booklet, #898-900 | 9.00 | |

Hong Kong 2001 Stamp Exhibition. Booklet sold for $35.

Insects — A180

Designs: $1.30, Pyrops candelarius. $2.50, Macromidia ellenae. $3.10, Troides helena spilotia. $5, Chiridopsis bowringi.

### Perf. 13½x13¼ Syncopated
**2000, July 16**     **Litho.**
**Granite Paper**

| | | | |
|---|---|---|---|
| 901-904 | A180   Set of 4 | 3.50 | 3.00 |
| 904a | Souvenir sheet, #901-904 | 3.50 | 3.50 |

### Mountain Type of 1996 Inscribed "Hong Kong, China"
### Souvenir Sheet
### Perf. 13¼ Syncopated
**2000, Aug. 12**     **Photo.**
**Granite Paper**

| | | | |
|---|---|---|---|
| 905 | A150 $10 Like #754 | 3.00 | 2.50 |

Hong Kong 2001 Stamp Exhibition.

2000 Summer Olympics, Sydney — A181

Designs: $1.30, Cycling, badminton. $2.50, Table tennis, running. $3.10, Judo, rowing. $5, Swimming, sailboarding.

### Perf. 14¼ Syncopated
**2000, Aug. 27**     **Litho.**
**Granite Paper**

| | | | |
|---|---|---|---|
| 906-909 | A181   Set of 4 | 3.75 | 3.00 |

Birds A182

**2000, Sept. 30**     **Photo.**
**Granite Paper**

| | | | |
|---|---|---|---|
| 910 | Booklet pane of 2 | 2.00 | |
| a. | A182 $1.30 Yellow-breasted bunting | .70 | .70 |
| b. | A182 $2.50 Great knot | 1.25 | 1.25 |
| 911 | Booklet pane of 2 | 4.25 | |
| a. | A182 $3.10 Falcated teal | 1.60 | 1.60 |
| b. | A182 $5 Black-faced spoonbill | 2.60 | 2.60 |
| | Booklet, #910-911 | 6.25 | |

Booklet containing Nos. 910-911 sold for $25.

Chinese General Chamber of Commerce, Cent. — A183

Designs: $1.30, Hong Kong in 1900. $2.50, Headquarters buildings. $3.10, People reading notice for distribution of relief funds. $5, Hand with computer mouse, currency symbols.

### Perf. 13¾ Syncopated
**2000, Oct. 22**     **Litho.**
**Granite Paper**

| | | | |
|---|---|---|---|
| 912-915 | A183   Set of 4 | 3.75 | 3.00 |

### Coral Type of 1994 Inscribed "Hong Kong, China"
### Souvenir Sheet
### Perf. 13¼ Syncopated
**2000, Nov. 25**     **Photo.**
**Granite Paper**

| | | | |
|---|---|---|---|
| 916 | A141 $10 Like #709 | 3.50 | 2.50 |

### Landmarks Type of 1999
### Souvenir Sheet
### Litho. & Holography
**2000, Dec. 31**

| | | | |
|---|---|---|---|
| 917 | A172 $20 Like #873 | 5.00 | 5.00 |

Soaking in water may affect hologram.

New Year 2001 (Year of the Snake) — A184

Various snakes. Denominations: $1.30, $2.50, $3.10, $5.

### Perf. 14½ Sync.
**2001, Jan. 1**     **Photo.**

| | | | |
|---|---|---|---|
| 918-921 | A184   Set of 4 | 3.50 | 3.00 |
| 921a | Souvenir sheet of 1, imperf. | 1.75 | 1.75 |
| 921b | Souvenir sheet, #918-921 | 4.00 | 4.00 |

### Souvenir Sheet

Opening of Hong Kong 2001 Stamp Exhibition — A185

No. 922: a, Year of the Dragon. b, Year of the Snake.

### Litho. & Embossed with Foil Application
**2001, Feb. 1**     **Perf. 13¼**

| | | | |
|---|---|---|---|
| 922 | A185 $50 Sheet of 2, #a-b | 30.00 | 30.00 |

### Indiginous Trees Type of 1988 Inscribed "Hong Kong, China"
**2001**     **Photo.**     **Perf. 14¼ Syncopated**
**Granite Paper**

| | | | |
|---|---|---|---|
| 923 | A105 $5 multi, sheetlet #5 | 1.75 | 1.75 |
| a. | Sheetlet #6 | 1.75 | 1.75 |
| b. | Sheetlet #7 | 1.75 | 1.75 |
| c. | Sheetlet #8 | 1.75 | 1.75 |

Issued: No. 923, 2/2; No. 923a, 2/3; No. 923b, 2/4; No. 923c, 2/5. No. 923b with gold overprint in margin reading "To commemorate the FIAP Day of HONG KONG 2001 Stamp Exhibition on 4th February, 2001" is a private emission.

See note after No. 940 for unsyncopated stamp.

Greetings — A186

Designs: $1.30, Maple leaves. $1.60, Swans. $2.50, Chicks. $2.60, Cherry blossoms. $3.10, Bamboo. $5, Snow-covered plant.

**2001, Feb. 1**     **Photo.**
**Granite Paper**
**Stamps + Labels**

| | | | |
|---|---|---|---|
| 924-929 | A186   Set of 6 | 5.00 | 4.00 |

See note after Nos. 934-937.

Hong Kong Water Supply, 150th Anniv. — A187

Designs: $1.30, Tai Tam Tuk Reservoir. $2.50, Plover Cove Reservoir. $3.10, Pipelines. $5, Beakers, chemical symbols.

**2001, Mar. 18**     **Litho. & Embossed**
**Granite Paper**

| | | | |
|---|---|---|---|
| 930-933 | A187   Set of 4 | 4.00 | 3.00 |
| a. | Block of 4, #930-933 | 4.00 | 4.00 |

Movie Stars A188

Designs: $1.30, Ng Cho-fan (1911-93) and Pak Yin (1920-87). $2.50, Sun Ma Si-tsang (1916-97) and Tang Bik-wan (1926-91). $3.10, Cheung Wood-yau (1910-85) and Wong Man-lei (1913-98). $5, Mak Bing-wing (1915-84) and Fung Wong-nui (1925-92).

**2001, Apr. 8**     **Litho.**
**Granite Paper**

| | | | |
|---|---|---|---|
| 934-937 | A188   Set of 4 | 4.00 | 3.00 |
| a. | Block of 4, #934-937 | 4.00 | 4.00 |

Values are for stamps with surrounding selvage.

On June 12, 2001 Hong Kong sold for $120 limited numbers of a sheet containing 18 examples of the $1.30 stamp, No. 924. The 18 labels to the right of the stamps on this sheet differ from those found on examples of No. 924 sold on the stamp's original date of issue, and the 18 labels to the left of the stamps depict Chinese celebrities.

Dragon Boat Races A189

Dragon boats and: No. 938, $5, Sydney Opera House. No. 939, Hong Kong Convention and Exhibition Center.

**2001, June 25**     **Litho.**     **Perf. 14x14½**
**Granite Paper**

| | | | |
|---|---|---|---|
| 938-939 | A189   Set of 2 | 3.50 | 2.50 |
| a. | Souvenir sheet, #938-939 | 3.50 | 3.50 |

See Australia Nos. 1977-1978.

Emblem of 2008 Summer Olympics, Beijing — A190

**2001, July 14**     **Photo.**     **Perf. 13x13¼**

| | | | |
|---|---|---|---|
| 940 | A190 $1.30 multi + label | .35 | .35 |

No. 940 printed in sheets of 12 stamp + label pairs with one large central label. See People's Republic of China No. 3119, Macao No. 1067. No. 940 with different label is from People's Republic of China No. 3119a.

On July 21, 2001 Hong Kong sold a booklet containing stamps with a face value of $12.40 for $30. The stamps are the Indigenous Trees type of 1988 with the inscription "Hong Kong, China." The first pane in the booklet contained $1.30 and $2.50 stamps, and those on the second pane contained $3.10 and $5 stamps.

On Aug. 25, 2001 Hong Kong sold a booklet containing stamps with a face value of $30 for $65. The first pane in the booklet contained four stamps with a face value of $1.80 of the Stamp Collecting type of 1992 with the inscription "Hong Kong, China." The second pane contained two $3.10 perf. 13½x13 stamps on granite paper of type A152, and two $3.10 perf. 13¾ syncopated stamps on granite paper of type A172. The third pane contained four $2.60 perf. 14¼ stamps on granite paper of type A162.

Tea Culture — A191

Various tea services and background colors of: $1.30, Lilac. $2.50, Orange brown. $3.10, Bright orange. $5, Green.

### Perf. 14¼x14½ Syncopated
**2001, Sept. 9**     **Litho.**

| | | | |
|---|---|---|---|
| 944-947 | A191   Set of 4 | 3.50 | 3.00 |

Herbs — A192

Designs: $1.30, Centella asiatica. $2.50, Lobelia chinensis. $3.10, Gardenia jasminoides. $5, Scutellaria indica.

### *Perf. 14½ Syncopated*
**2001, Oct. 7**     Litho.

**Granite Paper**

948-951 A192   Set of 4    3.75 3.00

Children's Stamp Coloring Contest — A193

Designs: $1.30, Bear. $2.50, Penguin. $3.10, Flower. $5, Bee.

### *Die Cut Perf. 13¾x13¼ Sync.*
**2001, Nov. 18**

**Granite Paper**
**Self-Adhesive**

952-955 A193   Set of 4    4.00 3.00
   a.    Souvenir sheet, #952-955   4.00 4.00

New Year 2002 (Year of the Horse) — A194

Various horses. Denominations: $1.30, $2.50, $3.10, $5.

**2002, Jan. 13**   *Perf. 14½ Syncopated*
**Granite Paper**

956-959 A194   Set of 4    3.50 3.00
   a.    Souvenir sheet of 1, imperf.   2.00 2.00
   b.    Souvenir sheet, #956-959   4.00 4.00

Souvenir Sheet

New Year 2002 (Year of the Horse) — A195

No. 960: a, Snake. b, Horse.

### Litho. & Embossed with Foil Application
**2002, Feb. 9**     *Perf. 13¼*
960 A195 $50 Sheet of 2, #a-b   30.00 30.00

Works of Art — A196

Details from: $1.30, Lines in Motion, by Chui Tze-hung. $2.50, Volume and Time, by Hon Chi-fun. $3.10, Bright Sun, by Aries Lee. $5, Midsummer, by Irene Chou.

---

### *Perf. 14½ Syncopated*
**2002, Feb. 24**     Litho.

**Granite Paper**

961-964 A196   Set of 4    4.00 3.00

### Landmarks Type of 1999

Designs: $1.40, Hong Kong Railway Museum. $1.80, Hong Kong Stadium. $1.90, Western Market. $2.40, Kwun Yam statue, Repulse Bay. $3, Peak Tower. $13, Hong Kong Cultural Center.

### *Perf. 13x13¾ Syncopated*
**2002, Apr. 1**     Photo.

**Granite Paper**

965 A172 $1.80 blue & multi   .45 .45
966 A172 $1.90 blue & multi   .50 .50
967 A172 $2.40 blue & multi   .60 .60
   a.    Booklet pane of 10   6.00
     Booklet, #967a   6.00
968 A172 $3 blue & multi   .75 .75
   a.    Booklet pane of 10   7.50
     Booklet, #968a   7.50

**Size: 26x32mm**
### *Perf. 13¼ Syncopated*
969 A172 $13 blue & multi   3.50 3.50
    Nos. 965-969 (5)   5.80 5.80

**Coil Stamps**
**Size: 18x22mm**
### *Perf. 14¾x13¼ Syncopated*
970 A172 $1.40 blue & multi   .35 .35
971 A172 $1.80 blue & multi   .45 .45
972 A172 $2.40 blue & multi   .60 .60
973 A172 $3 blue & multi   .75 .75
    Nos. 970-973 (4)   2.15 2.15

Cyberindustry in Hong Kong — A197

Designs: $1.40, Innovation. $2.40, Connectivity. $3, Trend. $5, Strength.

### *Perf. 13¾ Syncopated*
**2002, Apr. 14**     Litho.

**Granite Paper**

974-977 A197   Set of 4    3.50 3.00
   a.    Block of 4, #974-977   3.50 3.50

A booklet of two panes, one containing one each of Nos. 974 and 976, and another containing one each of Nos. 975 and 977, sold for $30. Value, $11.

2002 World Cup Soccer Championships, Japan and Korea — A198

No. 978: a, Goalie. b, Crowd and players.

### *Perf. 12 Syncopated*
**2002, May 16**     Photo.
978   Horiz. pair, with central label   1.00 1.00
   a.-b.    A198 $1.40 Either single   .50 .50

No. 978 was printed in sheets of 5 pairs and five different labels.
A souvenir sheet containing Nos. 978a-978b, People's Republic of China No. 3198, and Macao Nos. 1091a-1091b exists.

Corals A199

Designs: $1.40, North Atlantic pink tree, Pacific orange cup, and North Pacific horn corals. $2.40, North Atlantic giant orange tree, and Black corals. $3, Dendronepthea gigantea and Dendronepthea corals. $5, Tubastrea and Echinogorgia corals.

---

### *Perf. 13¾x14 Syncopated*
**2002, May 19**     Litho.

**Granite Paper**

979-982 A199   Set of 4    3.50 3.00
   a.    Souvenir sheet #979-982   3.50 3.50

On May 10, 2003, Hong Kong sold a booklet with a face value of $11.80 for $25. The first pane contains Nos. 979-980 perf 13¼x13. The second pane contains Nos. 981-982, perf 13¼x13.
See Canada Nos. 1948-1951.

Beijing — Kowloon Through Trains A200

Train and: $1.40, Hong Kong commercial buildings. $2.40, Wuhan-Changjiang Bridge, Wuchang. $3, Shaolin Monastery Pagodas, Zhengzhou. $5, Temple of Heaven, Beijing.

**2002, June 9**   *Perf. 14¼ Syncopated*
**Granite Paper**

983-986 A200   Set of 4    3.50 3.00
   a.    Horiz. strip of 4, #983-986   3.50 3.50

Hong Kong Special Administrative Region, 5th Anniv. — A201

Designs: $1.40, White dolphins, corals. $2.40, Students, bauhinia flowers. $3, Flying cranes, Hong Kong International Airport. $5, Flags of Hong Kong and People's Republic of China, fireworks over skyline.

**2002, July 1**     **Granite Paper**
987-990 A201   Set of 4    3.50 3.00
   a.    Souvenir sheet, #987-990   3.50 3.50

### Landmarks Type of 1999 with Pink Denomination and Country Name
**Souvenir Sheet**

Design: Tsing Ma Bridge.

### *Perf. 13¼ Syncopated*
**2002, July 27**     Photo.

**Granite Paper**

991 A172 $10 pink & multi   2.75 2.50

Philakorea 2002.

### Landmarks Type of 1999 With Olive Green Denomination and Country Name
**Souvenir Sheet**

Design: Tsing Ma Bridge.

### *Perf. 13¼ Syncopated*
**2002, Aug. 24**     Photo.

**Granite Paper**

992 A172 $10 ol green & multi   3.00 2.50

Amphilex 2002 Intl. Stamp Exhibition, Amsterdam.

### Landmarks Type of 1999 With Buff Background
**Souvenir Sheet**

Design: Tsing Ma Bridge.

**2002, Sept. 7**
993 A172 $10 blue, buff & multi   2.75 2.50

Rocks A202

Designs: $1.40, Ping Chau (siltstone). $2.40, Port Island (conglomerate). $3, Po Pin Chau (tuff). $5, Lamma Island (granite).

---

### *Perf. 13¼x12¾*
**2002, Sept. 15**     Litho.
994-997 A202   Set of 4    3.50 3.00
   a.    Souvenir sheet, #994-997   3.50 3.50

Portions of the designs were applied by a thermographic process, producing a shiny, raised effect.

Eastern and Western Cultures A203

Designs: 10c, Radar screen, luopan. 20c, Calculator, abacus. 50c, Incense coil, stained glass window. $1, Chair, Chinese bed. $1.40, Dim sum, loaves of bread. $1.80, Silverware, chopsticks and spoon. $1.90, Canned drinks, tea caddies. $2, Western and Eastern wedding cakes. $2.40, Erhu, violin. $2.50, Letter boxes, internet. $3, Sailboats, dragon boat. $5, Tiled roof, glass wall. $10, Ballet, Chinese opera. $13, Chess, Xiangqi. $20, Christmas decorations, lanterns. $50, Eastern and Western sculptures.

### *Perf. 13¼x13 Syncopated*
**2002, Oct. 14**     Photo.

**Granite Paper**

998 A203 10c multi   .20 .20
999 A203 20c multi   .20 .20
1000 A203 50c multi   .20 .20
1001 A203 $1 multi   .25 .25
1002 A203 $1.40 multi   .35 .25
   a.    Booklet pane of 10   3.50
     Booklet, #1002a   3.50
1003 A203 $1.80 multi   .45 .25
   a.    Booklet pane of 10 ('03)   4.75 —
     Complete booklet, #1003a   4.75
1004 A203 $1.90 multi   .50 .25
1005 A203 $2 multi   .50 .25
1006 A203 $2.40 multi   .60 .25
   a.    Booklet pane of 10   6.00
     Booklet, #1006a   6.00
1007 A203 $2.50 multi   .65 .30
1008 A203 $3 multi   .75 .35
   a.    Booklet pane of 10   7.50
     Booklet, #1008a   7.50
1009 A203 $5 multi   1.25 .40
   a.    Souvenir sheet, #998-1009   5.75 5.75
   b.    Booklet pane, #998-1009   5.75
     Booklet, #1009b   5.75

**Size: 40x24mm**
### *Perf. 14¾ Syncopated*
1010 A203 $10 multi   2.75 .25
1011 A203 $13 multi   3.50 .75
1012 A203 $20 multi   6.00 1.00
1013 A203 $50 multi   15.00 4.00
   a.    Souvenir sheet #1010-1013   27.50 27.50
    Nos. 998-1013 (16)   33.15 9.15

**Coil Stamps**
**Size: 22x19mm**
### *Perf. 13¼x14¾ Syncopated*
1014 A203 $1.40 multi   .35 .35
1015 A203 $1.80 multi   .45 .45
1016 A203 $2.40 multi   .60 .60
1017 A203 $3 multi   .75 .75
    Nos. 1014-1017 (4)   2.15 2.15

No. 1003a issued 10/7/04.

Christmas — A204

Designs: $1.40, Christmas tree. $2.40, Ornament. $3, Snowman. $5, Bell.

### Photo. with Hologram Applied
### *Perf. 13½ Syncopated*
**2002, Nov. 24**

**Granite Paper**

1018-1021 A204   Set of 4    3.50 3.00
   a.    Block or strip of 4, #1018-1021   3.50 3.50

Perforations within the stamp outline the designs.

Hong Kong
Disneyland
A205

Designs: $1.40, Main Street. $2.40,
Fantasyland. $3, Adventureland. $5,
Tomorrowland.

*Perf. 13¾ Syncopated*
2003, Jan. 12    Litho. & Embossed
**Granite Paper**

| 1022-1025 | A205 | Set of 4 | 3.50 | 3.00 |
| *a.* | Souvenir sheet, #1022-1025 | | 3.50 | 3.50 |

New Year 2003
(Year of the
Ram) — A206

Various rams: $1.40, $2.40, $3, $5.

*Perf. 14¼ Syncopated*
2003, Jan. 19                    Litho.
**Granite Paper**

| 1026-1029 | A206 | Set of 4 | 3.50 | 3.00 |
| *a.* | Souvenir sheet of 1, imperf. | | 2.00 | 2.00 |
| *b.* | Souvenir sheet, #1026-1029 | | 3.50 | 3.50 |

**New Year Types of 2000-03**
2003, Jan. 19  Litho.  *Perf. 12¾x13¼*
**Flocked Paper**

| 1030 | | Block of 4 | 10.50 | 10.50 |
| *a.* | A177 | $10 Like #888 | 2.60 | 2.60 |
| *b.* | A184 | $10 Like #920 | 2.60 | 2.60 |
| *c.* | A194 | $10 Like #957 | 2.60 | 2.60 |
| *d.* | A206 | $10 Like #1029 | 2.60 | 2.60 |

Souvenir Sheet

New Year 2003 (Year of the
Ram) — A207

No. 1031: a, Horse. b, Ram.

**Litho. & Embossed with Foil
Application**
2003, Jan. 19            *Perf. 13¼*

| 1031 | A207 | $50 Sheet of 2, #a-b | 27.50 | 27.50 |

Traditional Trades and
Handicrafts — A208

Designs: $1.40, Letter writing. $1.80, Bird
cage making, vert. $2.40, Qipao tailoring.
$2.50, Hairdressing, vert. $3, Dough figurine
making, vert. $5, Olive selling.

*Perf. 13½x14 Syncopated, 13½
Syncopated (vert. stamps)*
2003, Mar. 13                    Litho.
**Granite Paper**

| 1032-1037 | A208 | Set of 6 | 5.25 | 4.25 |
| *1037a* | Souvenir sheet, #1032-1037 | | 5.25 | 5.25 |

---

Souvenir Sheet

Hong Kong 2004 Stamp Expo — A209

2003, Apr. 8    *Perf. 13¼ Syncopated*
**Granite Paper**

| 1038 | A209 | $10 multi | 3.00 | 2.50 |

Souvenir Sheet

Master-of-Nets Garden,
Suzhou — A210

2003, June 27            **Granite Paper**

| 1039 | A210 | $10 multi | 3.50 | 3.00 |

Miniature Landscapes — A211

Plants: $1.40, Fukien tea. $2.40, Hedge
sageretia. $3, Fire-thorn, vert. $5, Chinese
hackberry, vert.

*Perf. 13¾x12¾ Syncopated,
12¾x13¾ Syncopated*
2003, July 17                    Photo.
**Granite Paper**

| 1040-1043 | A211 | Set of 4 | 3.50 | 3.00 |

Aquarium
Fish
A212

Various fish: $1.40, $2.40, $3, $5.

2003, Aug. 7    *Perf. 14¼ Syncopated*
**Granite Paper**
**With Fish-Shaped Holes in Paper**

| 1044-1047 | A212 | Set of 4 | 3.50 | 3.00 |
| *a.* | Block of 4, #1044-1047 | | 3.50 | 3.50 |

A213

Heartwarming
A214

---

*Perf. 13¾ Syncopated*
2003, Sept. 10                    Litho.
**Inscribed "Local Mail Postage"**
**Granite Paper**

| 1048 | A213 | ($1.40) multi | .40 | .35 |
| 1049 | A214 | ($1.40) multi | .40 | .35 |
| *a.* | Sheet of 16 + 17 labels ('04) | | 13.00 | 13.00 |

**Inscribed "Air Mail Postage"**

| 1050 | A213 | ($3) multi | 1.10 | .80 |
| 1051 | A214 | ($3) multi | 1.10 | .80 |
| *a.* | Sheet, 4 each #1048-1051, + 17 labels | | 12.00 | 12.00 |
| | *Nos. 1048-1051 (4)* | | 3.00 | 2.30 |

No. 1049a issued 10/7/04. No. 1049a sold
for $50 and has a 2004 Olympic Games theme
on the labels. A similar sheet issued in 2005
with labels having a Lions Club Convention
theme, sold for $108 in conjunction with other
items, and was not available separately.

Birds
A215

Designs: $1.40, Pied avocet. $2.40, Horned
grebe. $3, Black-throated diver. $5, Great
crested grebe.

*Perf. 12½ Syncopated*
2003, Oct. 4            Litho. & Engr.
**Granite Paper**

| 1052-1055 | A215 | Set of 4 | 3.50 | 3.00 |
| *1055a* | Booklet pane, #1052-1055 | 3.50 | — |
| | Complete booklet, 2 #1055a | 7.00 | |

See Sweden No. 2469.

Souvenir Sheet

Hong Kong 2004 Stamp Expo — A216

*Perf. 13¼ Syncopated*
2003, Oct. 14                    Litho.
**Granite Paper**

| 1056 | A216 | $10 multi | 3.00 | 2.00 |
| *1056a* | Sheet, 2 each #1038, 1056, + 2 labels | 21.00 | 21.00 |

No. 1056a was issued 1/30/04 and sold for
$80. Labels could be personalized.

Percussion
Instruments — A217

Designs: $1.40, Drum. $2.40, Clappers. $3,
Cymbals. $5, Gongs.
$13, Chimes.

*Perf. 13½x13¼ Syncopated*
2003, Nov. 6                    Photo.

| 1057-1060 | A217 | Set of 4 | 3.50 | 3.00 |

**Souvenir Sheet**
*Perf. 13¾x13¼ Syncopated*

| 1061 | A217 | $13 multi | 4.00 | 3.50 |

No. 1061 contains one 35x45mm stamp.

---

Launch of First Manned Chinese
Spacecraft — A218

No. 1062: a, Astronaut, Shenzhou spacecraft. b, Rocket lift-off.
Illustration reduced.

**2003, Oct. 16  Photo.  *Perf. 13x13¼***

| 1062 | A218 | $1.40 Pair, #a-b | 1.25 | .75 |

A booklet containing No. 1062, People's
Republic of China No. 3314 and Macao No.
1128a exists. The booklet sold for a premium
over face value.

UNESCO World Heritage Sites in
People's Republic of China — A219

Designs: $1.40, Potala Palace, vert.
(27x75mm). $1.80, Imperial Palace of the
Ming and Qing Dynasties. $2.40, Mausoleum
of the First Qin Emperor. $2.50, Mount Huang-
shan, vert. $3, Old Town of Lijiang, vert. $5,
Jiuzhaigou Valley (75x27mm).

*Perf. 13¼ Syncopated*
2003, Nov. 25                    Litho.
**Granite Paper**

| 1063 | A219 | $1.40 multi | .45 | .40 |
| *a.* | Perf. 13¼x13¼x13¼x13 Syncopated | | .45 | .40 |

*Perf. 13x13¼ Syncopated*

| 1064 | A219 | $1.80 multi | .55 | .50 |
| *a.* | Perf. 13x13¼x12½x13¼ Syncopated | | .55 | .50 |
| 1065 | A219 | $2.40 multi | .65 | .60 |
| *a.* | Perf. 12½x13¼ Syncopated | | .65 | .60 |

*Perf. 13 Syncopated*

| 1066 | A219 | $2.50 multi | .75 | .65 |
| *a.* | Perf. 13x13x13x13¼ Syncopated | | .75 | .65 |
| *b.* | Perf. 13¼x13x13x13 Syncopated | | .75 | .65 |
| *c.* | Perf. 13¼x13x13x13¼ Syncopated | | .75 | .65 |
| 1067 | A219 | $3 multi | .90 | .80 |
| *a.* | Perf. 12½x13x13x13¼ Syncopated | | .90 | .80 |

*Perf. 13x12¾ Syncopated*

| 1068 | A219 | $5 multi | 1.40 | 1.25 |
| *a.* | Perf. 13x12¾x13 and 13¼x13x13 Syncopated | | 1.40 | 1.25 |
| *b.* | Perf. 13 Syncopated | | 1.40 | 1.25 |
| *c.* | Miniature sheet (see note below) | | 14.00 | 14.00 |
| | *Nos. 1063-1068 (6)* | | 4.70 | 4.20 |

No. 1068c contains one each of Nos.
1063a, 1064, 1065, 1066a, 1066b, 1066c,
1067a, 1068b and two each of Nos. 1063,
1064a, 1065a, 1067 and 1068a. Perfs for the
minor varieties are for the measurement that
comprises the longest part of each side, as
the sides of some stamps have sections with
varying perf measurements. Approximately
one half of the bottom row of perfs on No.
1068a is perf. 13 while the other half is perf.
13¼.

Development of Public
Housing — A220

Various buildings.

*Perf. 13¼x13 Syncopated*
2003, Dec. 11                    Photo.
**Granite Paper**

| 1069 | A220 | $1.40 org & multi | .50 | .40 |
| *a.* | Tete-beche pair | | 1.00 | .80 |

| 1070 | A220 | $2.40 yel & multi | .75 | .60 |
|---|---|---|---|---|
| a. | | Tete-beche pair | 1.50 | 1.20 |
| 1071 | A220 | $3 pur & multi | 1.25 | .80 |
| a. | | Tete-beche pair | 2.50 | 1.60 |
| 1072 | A220 | $5 red & multi | 2.00 | 1.25 |
| a. | | Tete-beche pair | 4.00 | 2.50 |
| | | Nos. 1069-1072 (4) | 4.50 | 3.05 |

**New Year 2004 (Year of the Monkey) — A221**

Various monkeys: $1.40, $2.40, $3, $5.

***Perf. 13½x13¼ Syncopated***
**2004, Jan. 4**      **Litho.**
**Granite Paper**

| 1073-1076 | A221 | Set of 4 | 3.00 | 3.00 |
|---|---|---|---|---|
| 1076a | | Souvenir sheet of 1, imperf. | 1.50 | 1.50 |
| 1076b | | Souvenir sheet, #1073-1076 | 3.00 | 3.00 |

**Souvenir Sheet**

**New Year 2004 (Year of the Monkey) — A222**

No. 1077: a, Ram. b, Monkey.

**Litho. & Embossed with Foil Application**
**2004, Jan. 4**      **Perf. 13¼**

| 1077 | A222 | $50 Sheet of 2, #a-b | 26.00 | 26.00 |
|---|---|---|---|---|

**Souvenir Sheets**

**New Year Puddings and Greeting — A223**

**New Year Puddings With Two Greetings — A224**

**New Year Parade — A225**

**Jade — A226**

**Fire Dragon Dance — A227**

No. 1079: a, Same Chinese text as on No. 1078 when viewed from directly above (top character with long curved line at bottom). b, Text different from that on No. 1078 when viewed from directly above.

**2004**   **Litho.**   ***Perf. 13¼ Syncopated***
**Granite Paper**

| 1078 | A223 | $10 multi | 2.60 | 2.60 |
|---|---|---|---|---|
| 1079 | A224 | $10 Sheet of 2, | | |
| | | #a-b | 5.25 | 5.25 |
| 1080 | A225 | $10 multi | 2.60 | 2.60 |
| 1081 | A226 | $10 multi | 2.60 | 2.60 |
| 1082 | A227 | $10 multi | 2.60 | 2.60 |
| | | Nos. 1078-1082 (5) | 15.65 | 15.65 |

2004 Hong Kong Stamp Expo. Issued: Nos. 1078-1079, 1/30; No. 1080, 1/31; No. 1081, 2/1; No. 1082, 2/2.

Nos. 1079a and 1079b show the same two Chinese texts, but the texts appear different depending on the angle at which one views the stamps. Under magnification it can be seen that the two Chinese texts are printed differently to achieve this effect.

**Landmarks Type of 1999 With Red Violet Denomination and Country Name**

No. 1083: a, Museum of Tea Ware. b, St. John's Cathedral. c, Legislative Council Building. d, Tai Fu Tai. e, Wong Tai Sin Temple. f, Victoria Harbor. g, Hong Kong Railway Museum. h, Tsim Sha Tsui Clock Tower. i, Hong Kong Stadium. j, Western Market. k, Happy Valley Racecourse. l, Kowloon-Canton Railway. m, Repulse Bay. n, Chi Lin Nunnery. o, Peak Tower. p, Buddha at Po Lin Monastery. q, Aw Boon Haw Gardens. r, Tsing Ma Bridge. s, Hong Kong Cultural Center. t, Hong Kong Convention and Exhibition Center. u, Hong Kong Intl. Airport.

***Perf. 13x13¾ Syncopated***
**2004, Feb. 3**      **Photo.**
**Granite Paper**

| 1083 | | Sheet of 21 | 7.75 | 7.75 |
|---|---|---|---|---|
| a.-u. | | A172 $1.40 Any single, red vio & multi (23x27mm) | .35 | .35 |

2004 Hong Kong Stamp Expo.

**Rugby Sevens — A228**

Designs: $1.40, Hong Kong Sevens. $2.40, New Zealand Sevens. $3, Hong Kong Stadium. $5, Westpac Stadium, Wellington, New Zealand.

***Perf. 13¼x14¼ Syncopated***
**2004, Feb. 25**      **Litho.**
**Granite Paper**

| 1084-1087 | A228 | Set of 4 | 3.00 | 3.00 |
|---|---|---|---|---|
| 1087a | | Block of 4, #1084-1087 | 3.00 | 3.00 |

**Children's Games and Activities — A229**

Designs: $1.40, Scissors, Paper, Stone. $2.40, Chinese chess. $3, Blowing bubbles. $5, Hopscotch.

**2004, Apr. 7**      **Granite Paper**

| 1088-1091 | A229 | Set of 4 | 3.00 | 2.50 |
|---|---|---|---|---|
| 1091a | | Block of 4, #1088-1091 | 3.00 | 3.00 |

**Souvenir Sheet**

**Chen Clan Academy — A230**

***Perf. 13½x13¼ Syncopated***
**2004, May 6**

| 1092 | A230 | $10 multi | 3.00 | 2.50 |
|---|---|---|---|---|

**Trams in Hong Kong, Cent. — A231**

Various trams and tickets: $1.40, Green ticket. $2.40, Brown ticket. $3, Blue ticket. No. 1096, $5, Yellow ticket. No. 1097, Olive ticket.

**2004, May 27**      **Granite Paper**

| 1093-1096 | A231 | Set of 4 | 3.00 | 2.50 |
|---|---|---|---|---|
| 1096a | | Souvenir sheet, #1093-1096 | 3.00 | 3.00 |

**Souvenir Sheet**

| 1097 | A231 | $5 multi | 1.25 | 1.25 |
|---|---|---|---|---|

**People's Liberation Army Forces of Hong Kong — A232**

Inscriptions: $1.40, The Powerful and Civilized Military Force. $1.80, Social Services. $2.40, Open Day. $2.50, Army. $3, Navy. $5, Air Force.

***Perf. 13¼x14 Syncopated***
**2004, June 30**      **Litho.**
**Granite Paper**

| 1098 | A232 | $1.40 multi | .35 | .35 |
|---|---|---|---|---|
| a. | | Booklet pane of 4 | 2.00 | — |
| 1099 | A232 | $1.80 multi | .50 | .50 |
| a. | | Booklet pane of 4 | 2.50 | — |
| 1100 | A232 | $2.40 multi | .60 | .60 |
| a. | | Booklet pane of 4 | 3.25 | — |
| 1101 | A232 | $2.50 multi | .65 | .65 |
| a. | | Booklet pane of 4 | 3.50 | — |
| 1102 | A232 | $3 multi | .80 | .80 |
| a. | | Booklet pane of 4 | 4.25 | — |
| 1103 | A232 | $5 multi | 1.25 | 1.25 |
| a. | | Booklet pane of 4 | 6.50 | — |
| | | Complete booklet, #1098a-1103a | 22.00 | |
| | | Nos. 1098-1103 (6) | 4.15 | 4.15 |

Complete booklet sold for $85.

**Relay Race — A233**

**Diving — A234**

**Volleyball — A235**

**Cycling — A236**

**Badminton — A237**

No. 1104: a, Runners in blocks. b, Runners. c, Runner taking baton. d, Runner at finish.
No. 1105: a, Diver on board. b, Diver with legs tucked in. c, Diver with arms and legs extended. d, Diver entering water.
No. 1106: a, Player making save. b, Player leaping to get ball. c, Player striking ball above net. d, Player trying to block ball.
No. 1107: a, Cyclists, denomination at left. b, Cyclist at right, denomination at left. c, Cyclists, denomination at right. d, Cyclist with arms extended.
No. 1108: a, Bird above head, racquet at shoulder level. b, Bird at shoulder level, racquet at knee level. c, Bird and racquet above head. d, Player with face covered by arm.

Illustrations reduced.

***Perf. 13½x13¼ Syncopated***
**2004, July 20**
**Granite Paper**

| 1104 | A233 | $1.40 Horiz. strip of 4, #a-d | 1.50 | 1.50 |
|---|---|---|---|---|
| 1105 | A234 | $1.40 Horiz. strip of 4, #a-d | 1.50 | 1.50 |
| 1106 | A235 | $1.40 Horiz. strip of 4, #a-d | 1.50 | 1.50 |
| 1107 | A236 | $1.40 Horiz. strip of 4, #a-d | 1.50 | 1.50 |
| 1108 | A237 | $1.40 Horiz. strip of 4, #a-d | 1.50 | 1.50 |
| e. | | Miniature sheet, #1104-1108 | 7.50 | 7.50 |

**Souvenir Sheet**

**2004 Summer Olympics, Athens — A238**

No. 1109: a, Runner without clothes. b, Runner with clothes.

**2004, Aug. 13**      **Granite Paper**

| 1109 | A238 | $5 Sheet of 2, #a-b | 2.60 | 2.60 |
|---|---|---|---|---|

Deng Xiaoping (1904-97), Chinese Leader — A239

No. 1110: a, Saluting flags. b, Watching fireworks.
$10, Three photographs.
Illustration reduced.

**2004, Aug. 22**    **Perf. 13x13¼**
1110 A239 $1.40 Horiz. pair,
    #a-b    .75 .75

**Souvenir Sheet**
1111 A239 $10 multi    2.60 2.60

Hong Kong Currency — A240

Obverse and reverse of: $1.40, 1863 one mil bronze coin. $2.40, 1866 twenty cent silver coin. $3, 1935 one dollar banknotes. No. 1115, $5, 1997 one thousand dollar gold coin commemorating establishment of Special Administrative Region.
No. 1116, $5, 1993 ten dollar coin.

*Perf. 13¼x14 Syncopated*
**2004, Sept. 2**
**Granite Paper**
1112-1115 A240 Set of 4    3.00 3.00
*1115a*   Miniature sheet, #1112-1115   3.00 3.00
**Souvenir Sheet**
1116 A240 $5 multi    1.25 1.25

Pearl River Delta Region Development — A241

Designs: $1.40, Men and bridge. $2.40, Men and crane. $3, Tourist attractions. $5, Men and buildings.

**2004, Oct. 19**    **Granite Paper**
1117-1120 A241 Set of 4    3.00 3.00
*1120a*   Block of 4, #1117-1120   3.00 3.00
No. 1120a printed in sheets of 4 blocks.

Mushrooms
A242

Designs: $1.40, Straw mushrooms. $2.40, Red-orange mushrooms. $3, Violet marasmius. No. 1124, $5, Lingzhi mushrooms.
No. 1125, Hexagon fungi.

*Perf. 13½x13¼ Syncopated*
**2004, Nov. 23**
**Granite Paper**
1121-1124 A242 Set of 4    3.00 3.00
*1124a*   Souvenir sheet, #1121-1124   3.00 3.00
**Souvenir Sheet**
1125 A242 $5 multi    1.25 1.25

Letters of the Alphabet — A243

Nos. 1126 and 1127 — Upper half of letters made with common household items: a, Clothespin. b, Scissors. c, Lamp. d, Plastic cap for glue bottle. e, Steaming rack. f, Caliper with ruler. g, Bolt of padlock. h, Bamboo ladder. i, Flashlight. j, Toilet brush. k, Stapler. l, Sock. m, Draftsman's triangle. n, Nail clippers. o, Rubber band. p, Strainer. q, Link from chain. r, Sunglasses. s, Clothes hanger. t, Wooden broom. u, Sandals. v, Compass. w, Corkscrew. x, Faucet. y, Fork. z, Paint roller.

*Perf. 13¼x13 Syncopated*
**2005, Jan. 4**    **Litho.**
**Granite Paper (#1126)**
1126 A243 Sheet of 30 (see
    footnote)    11.00 11.00
*a.-z.*   $1.40 Any single    .35 .35
**Self-Adhesive**
*Serpentine Die Cut 12½ Syncopated*
1127 A243 Sheet of 30 (see
    footnote)    11.00
*a.-z.*   $1.40 Any single    .35 .35
Each sheet contains one of each letter and an additional example of a, e, i and o stamps. Covers were prepared in 2006 with se-tenant strips spelling "KUNG," "HEI," "FAT" and "CHOY," which are not found in No. 1126.

New Year 2004 (Year of the Rooster) — A244

Various roosters with background colors of: $1.40, Orange. $2.40, Green. $3, Dark red. $5, Blue.

**2005, Jan. 30**   *Perf. 14¼ Syncopated*
**Granite Paper**
1128-1131 A244 Set of 4    3.00 3.00
*1131a*   Souvenir sheet of 1, imperf.   1.50 1.50
*1131b*   Souvenir sheet, #1128-1131   3.00 3.00

Souvenir Sheet

New Year 2005 (Year of the Rooster) — A245

No. 1132: a, Monkey. b, Rooster.

**Litho. & Embossed With Foil Application**
**2005, Jan. 30**    **Perf. 13¼**
1132 A245 $50 Sheet of 2, #a-
    b    27.50 27.50

Fairy Tales by Hans Christian Andersen (1805-75) A246

Designs: $1.40, The Ugly Duckling. $2.40, The Little Mermaid. $3, The Little Match Girl. $5, The Emperor's New Clothes.

*Perf. 13¾ Syncopated*
**2005, Mar. 22**   **Litho. & Embossed**
**Granite Paper**
1133-1136 A246 Set of 4    4.00 4.00
*1133a*   Souvenir sheet of 4    1.75 1.75
*1134a*   Souvenir sheet of 4    3.00 3.00
*1135a*   Souvenir sheet of 4    4.00 4.00
*1136a*   Souvenir sheet of 4    6.50 6.50

Souvenir Sheet

Hong Kong Skyline, Sydney Opera House — A247

*Perf. 13½ Syncopated*
**2005, Apr. 21**    **Litho.**
**Granite Paper**
1137 A247 $10 multi    2.60 2.60
Pacific Explorer 2005 World Stamp Expo, Sydney.

Goldfish
A248

Designs: $1.40, Variegated pearl-scale. $2.40, Red and white swallow-tail. $3, Pale bronze egg-phoenix. No. 1141, $5, Blue wenyu.
No. 1142, $5, Red and white dragon-eye.

*Perf. 13¼x14 Syncopated*
**2005, May 12**
**Granite Paper**
1138-1141 A248 Set of 4    3.00 3.00
*1141a*   Souvenir sheet, #1138-1141   3.00 3.00
**Souvenir Sheet**
1142 A248 $5 multi    1.25 1.25
No. 1142 contains one 45x35mm stamp.

Maritime Expeditions of Zheng He, 600th Anniv. A249

No. 1143 — Ships and: a, Zheng He (1371-1433), explorer. b, Giraffe, ceramics. c, Compass wheel.
$10, Zheng He on ship.

**2005, June 28**    **Perf. 13x13¼**
1143   Horiz. strip of 3    1.10 1.10
*a.-c.*   A249 $1.40 Any single    .35 .35
**Souvenir Sheet**
**Perf. 13¼**
1144 A249 $10 multi    2.60 2.60
No. 1144 contains one 50x30mm stamp.

Creative Industries
A250

Designs: $1.40, Circles, squares and triangles (advertising). $2.40, Numerals, letters and symbols (computer and digital industries). $3, Vertical and horizontal lines (broadcasting industries). $5, Curved brushstrokes (arts and crafts).

*Perf. 14x14¼ Syncopated*
**2005, July 21**    **Litho.**
**Granite Paper**
1145-1148 A250 Set of 4    3.00 3.00
*1148a*   Block of 4 with selvage,
    #1145-1148    3.00 3.00
*1148b*   Booklet pane, 2 #1148a   6.00 —
    Complete booklet, 2 #1148b   12.00
Each block of 4 in the booklet has a different arrangement. Rouletting separates the blocks within each booklet pane.

Great Inventions of Ancient China — A251

Designs: $1.40, Compass. $2.40, Printing. $3, Gunpowder. $5, Papermaking.

*Perf. 13¼x14¼ Syncopated*
**2005, Aug. 18**
1149-1152 A251 Set of 4    3.00 3.00
*1152a*   Miniature sheet, 4 each
    #1149-1152    12.00 12.00

Opening of Hong Kong Disneyland A252

Designs: $1.40, Mickey and Minnie Mouse. $2.40, Dumbo. $3, Simba and Nala. No. 1156, $5, Pluto.
Nos. 1157, 1158, Mickey Mouse.

*Perf. 13¾x13½ Syncopated*
**2005, Sept. 12**    **Litho.**
**Granite Paper (#1153-1157)**
1153-1156 A252 Set of 4    3.00 3.00
*1156a*   Souvenir sheet, #1153-
    1156    3.00 3.00
**Souvenir Sheets**
1157 A252 $5 multi    1.25 1.25
**Litho. & Embossed with Foil Application**
1158 A252 $50 gold & multi    13.00 13.00

Souvenir Sheet

Qiantang Tidal Bore — A253

*Perf. 13¼ Syncopated*
**2005, Sept. 16**    **Litho.**
1159 A253 $10 multi    2.60 2.60

Fishing Villages A254

Designs: $1.40, Tai O, Hong Kong. $2.40, Aldeia da Carrasqueira, Portugal. $3, Tai O, diff. $5, Aldeia da Carrasqueira, diff.

**Perf. 14¼x14 Syncopated**
**2005, Oct. 18**
1160-1163 A254 Set of 4     3.00   3.00
*1163a*   Miniature sheet, 4 each
     #1160-1163     12.00   12.00

See Portugal Nos. 2767-2768.

Popular Singers — A255

Designs: $1.40, Wong Ka Kui. $1.80, Danny Chan. $2.40, Roman Tam. $3, Leslie Cheung. $5, Anita Mui.

**Perf. 13½x13¼ Syncopated**
**2005, Nov. 8**
**Granite Paper**
1164-1168 A255 Set of 5     3.50   3.50

Because of concerns about the licensing of the images of the singers in foreign countries, the philatelic bureau did not make Nos. 1164-1168 available by mail order to foreign customers. The stamps were freely available to any purchasers over the counter.

New Year 2006 (Year of the Dog) — A256

Designs: $1.40, Golden retriever. $2.40, Pekingese. $3, German shepherd. $5, Beagle.

**Perf. 13½x13¼ Syncopated**
**2006, Jan. 15**       Litho.
**Granite Paper**
1169-1172 A256 Set of 4     3.00   3.00
*1172a*   Souvenir sheet of #1172, imperf.
         1.25   1.25
*1172b*   Souvenir sheet, #1169-1172   3.00   3.00

Souvenir Sheet

New Year 2006 (Year of the Dog) — A257

No. 1173: a, Rooster. b, Dog.

**Litho. & Embossed with Foil Application**
**2006, Jan. 15**     Perf. 13½x13¼
1173 A257 $50 Sheet of 2, #a-
    b     26.00   26.00

Chinese Lanterns — A258

No. 1174: a, $1.40, Lotus Fairy lantern. $1.80, Narcissus lantern. $2.40, Peacock lantern. $5, Boys holding Dragon lantern.

**Perf. 12¾x13¼ Syncopated**
**2006, Feb. 12**       Litho.
**Granite Paper (#1174)**
1174 A258   Horiz. strip of 3, #a-
    c     1.50   1.50
**Souvenir Sheet**
**Perf. 13¼ Syncopated**
1175 A258 $5 multi     1.25   1.25
No. 1175 contains one 35x46mm stamp.

Teddy Bears in Costumes A259

Teddy bears in various costumes.

**Perf. 13¾ Syncopated**
**2006, Mar. 30**
**Granite Paper**
1176 A259 $1.40 multi     .35   .35
1177 A259 $1.80 multi     .50   .50
  *a.*   Booklet pane, #1176-1177   1.60   —
1178 A259 $2.40 multi     .60   .60
1179 A259 $2.50 multi     .65   .65
  *a.*   Booklet pane, #1178-1179   2.40   —
1180 A259 $3 multi     .80   .80
1181 A259 $5 multi     1.25   1.25
  *a.*   Booklet pane, #1180-1181   3.75   —
    Complete booklet, #1177a,
     1179a, 1181a     7.75
  *b.*   Souvenir sheet, #1176-1181, +
     central label     4.25   4.25

Complete booklet sold for $30.

Souvenir Sheet

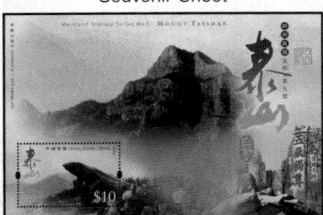

Gongbei Rock, Mount Taishan — A260

**2006, May 4**     Perf. 14¼ Syncopated
**Granite Paper**
1182 A260 $10 multi     2.60   2.60

Souvenir Sheet

Washington 2006 World Philatelic Exhibition — A261

**Perf. 13¼x12¾ Syncopated**
**2006, May 27**
**Granite Paper**
1183 A261 $10 multi     2.60   2.60

Chinese Idioms A262

Idioms: $1.40, Respect makes successful marriage. $2.40, Reading is always rewarding. $3, Prepare for success. $5, All in the same boat.

**Perf. 13¾ Syncopated**
**2006, June 15**
**Granite Paper**
1184-1187 A262 Set of 4     3.00   3.00
*1187a*   Souvenir sheet, #1184-1187   3.00   3.00

Attractions in Hong Kong's Districts — A263

Designs: No. 1188, $1.40, Central Police Station Historical Compound, Peak Tram, International Finance Center, Central and Western District. No. 1189, $1.40, Victoria Park, Island Eastern Corridor, Hong Kong Museum of Coastal Defense, Eastern District. No. 1190, $1.40, Floating restaurant, Murray House, Ocean Park, Southern District. No. 1191, $1.40, Hong Kong Convention and Exhibition Center, Old Wan Chai Post Office, Lovers' Rock, Wan Chai District. No. 1192, $1.40, Hong Kong Cultural Center, Temple Street, Yuen Po Bird Garden, Yau Tsim Mong District. No. 1193, $1.40, Wong Tai Sin Temple, Lion Rock, Chi Lin Nunnery, Wong Tai Sin District. No. 1194, $1.40, Lei Yue Mun Seafood Bazaar, buildings, Child-giving Rocks, Kwun Tong District. No. 1195, $1.40, Computer shopping center, Lingnan Garden, Festival Walk, Sham Shui Po District. No. 1196, $1.40, Kowloon Walled City Park, Wonderful Worlds of Whampoa, Sung Wong Toi, Kowloon City District. No. 1197, $1.40, Seafood Street, Tai Long Wan, Lions Nature Education Center Shell House, Sai Kung District. No. 1198, $1.40, Lantau Link View Point, Kwai Chung Container Terminals, Tsing Ma Bridge, Kwai Tsing District. No. 1199, $1.40, Lookout Tower, Lam Tsuen Wishing Tree, Tai Po Waterfront Park, Tai Po District. No. 1200, $1.40, Fung Ying Seen Koon, Chung Ying Street, Pak Hok Lam, North District. No. 1201, $1.40, Sam Tung Uk Museum, Yuen Yuen Institute, Tai Mo Shan Country Park, Tsuen Wan District. No. 1202, $1.40, Amah Rock, Shing Mun River Promenade, Che Kung Temple, Sha Tin District. No. 1203, $1.40, Hong Kong Gold Coast, Ching Chung Koon, Tsing Shan Monastery, Tuen Mun District. No. 1204, $1.40, Mai Po Nature Reserve, birds over farm, Chinese cakes, Yuen Long District. No. 1205, $1.40, Tian Tan Buddha, Cheung Chau Bun Festival, Tai O, Islands District.

**2006, July 18**    Perf. 13½ Syncopated
**Granite Paper**
1188-1205 A263 Set of 18     6.50   6.50
*1205a*   Souvenir sheet, #1188-1205   6.50   6.50

Fireworks A264

Designs: No. 1206, $5, No. 1208a, $50, Fireworks over Hong Kong Harbor. No. 1207, $5, No. 1208b, $50, Fireworks over Prater Ferris Wheel, Vienna, Austria.

**2006, Aug. 22**     Litho.     Perf. 14
1206-1207 A264 Set of 2     2.60   2.60
**Souvenir Sheet**
**Photo. With Glass Beads Affixed**
1208 A264 $50 Sheet of 2, #a-
    b     26.00   26.00

See Austria No. 2060.

Intl. Day of Peace — A265

Chinese characters and: $1.40, Flower and "Love." $1.80, Origami crane and "Peace." $2.40, Four-leaf clover and "Hope." $3, Tree and "Caring." $5, Earth and "Harmony."

**Perf. 13½x13¼ Syncopated**
**2006, Sept. 21**       Litho.
**Granite Paper**
1209-1213 A265 Set of 5     3.50   3.50
*1213a*   Souvenir sheet, #1209-1213   3.50   3.50

Government Vehicles — A266

Designs: $1.40, Correctional Services security bus. $1.80, Customs Department X-ray scanning vehicle. $2.40, Fire Department hydraulic platform pumper truck. $2.50, Government Flying Service Super Puma helicopter. $3, Police Department traffic patrol motorcycle. $5, Immigration Department launch.

**Perf. 13¼x14½ Syncopated**
**2006, Oct. 19**       Litho.
**Granite Paper**
1214-1219 A266 Set of 6     4.25   4.25
*1219a*   Sheet, 3 each #1214-1219   13.00   13.00

Dr. Sun Yat-sen (1866-1925), Republic of China President — A267

Photographs from: $1.40, 1883. $2.40, 1912. $3, 1916. No. 1223, $5, 1922. No. 1224, $5, 1924 (hands visible).

**Perf. 13¼x13 Syncopated**
**2006, Nov. 12**
**Granite Paper**
1220-1223 A267 Set of 4     3.00   3.00
**Souvenir Sheet**
1224 A267 $5 multi     1.25   1.25

A booklet containing two panes, one containing Nos. 1220-1221, and one containing Nos. 1222-1223 sold for $25.

Heartwarming A268

## Perf. 13½ Syncopated
### 2006, Nov. 28
### Granite Paper
### Inscribed "Local Mail Postage"

| | | | |
|---|---|---|---|
| 1225 | A268 ($1.40) Hearts | .35 | .35 |
| 1226 | A268 ($1.40) Bottles | .35 | .35 |
| a. | Sheet of 20 + 21 labels | 12.50 | 12.50 |

### Inscribed "Air Mail Postage"

| | | | |
|---|---|---|---|
| 1227 | A268 ($3) Flowers | .80 | .80 |
| 1228 | A268 ($3) Drink glass-es | .80 | .80 |
| a. | Sheet, 5 each #1225-1228, + 21 labels | 11.50 | 11.50 |
| b. | Sheet of 20 + 21 labels | 27.50 | 27.50 |
| | Nos. 1225-1228 (4) | 2.30 | 2.30 |

Nos. 1226a, 1228b issued 5/2/08. Labels on Nos. 1226a and 1228b could not be personalized. Nos. 1226a and 1228b sold as a set for $154.

Birds — A269

Designs: 10c, White-bellied sea eagle. 20c, Collared scops owl. 50c, Scarlet minivet. $1, Common kingfisher. $1.40, Fork-tailed sunbird. $1.80, Roseate tern. $1.90, Black-faced spoonbill. $2, Little egret. $2.40, Greater painted snipe. $2.50, Barn swallow. $3, Red-whiskered bulbul. $5, Long-tailed shrike. $10, White wagtail. $13, Northern shoveler. $20, Common magpie. $50, Dalmatian pelican.

## Perf. 13x13¾ Syncopated
### 2006, Dec. 31     Photo.
### Granite Paper
### Size: 22x26mm

| | | | |
|---|---|---|---|
| 1229 | A269 10c multi | .20 | .20 |
| 1230 | A269 20c multi | .20 | .20 |
| 1231 | A269 50c multi | .20 | .20 |
| 1232 | A269 $1 multi | .25 | .25 |
| 1233 | A269 $1.40 multi | .35 | .35 |
| a. | Booklet pane of 10 | 3.50 | |
| | Complete booklet, #1233a | 3.50 | |
| 1234 | A269 $1.80 multi | .45 | .45 |
| a. | Booklet pane of 10 | 4.50 | |
| | Complete booklet, #1234a | 4.50 | |
| 1235 | A269 $1.90 multi | .50 | .50 |
| 1236 | A269 $2 multi | .55 | .55 |
| 1237 | A269 $2.40 multi | .60 | .60 |
| a. | Booklet pane of 10 | 6.00 | |
| | Complete booklet, #1237a | 6.00 | |
| 1238 | A269 $2.50 multi | .65 | .65 |
| a. | Booklet pane of 10 | 8.00 | |
| | Complete booklet, #1239a | 8.00 | |
| 1239 | A269 $3 multi | .80 | .80 |
| a. | Booklet pane of 10 | 8.00 | |
| | Complete booklet, #1239a | 8.00 | |
| 1240 | A269 $5 multi | 1.40 | 1.40 |
| a. | Miniature sheet, #1229-1240 | 6.25 | 6.25 |
| b. | Booklet pane, #1229-1240 | 6.25 | — |
| | Complete booklet, #1240b | 6.25 | — |

### Size: 25x30mm
### Perf. 13½x13¼ Syncopated

| | | | |
|---|---|---|---|
| 1241 | A269 $10 multi | 2.60 | 2.60 |
| 1242 | A269 $13 multi | 3.50 | 3.50 |
| 1243 | A269 $20 multi | 5.25 | 5.25 |
| 1244 | A269 $50 multi | 13.00 | 13.00 |
| a. | Souvenir sheet, #1241-1244 | 25.00 | 25.00 |
| | Nos. 1229-1244 (16) | 30.50 | 30.50 |

### Coil Stamps
### Size: 17x21mm
### Perf. 14¾x13½ Syncopated

| | | | |
|---|---|---|---|
| 1245 | A269 $1.40 multi | .35 | .35 |
| 1246 | A269 $1.80 multi | .45 | .45 |
| 1247 | A269 $2.40 multi | .60 | .60 |
| 1248 | A269 $3 multi | .80 | .80 |
| | Nos. 1245-1248 (4) | 2.20 | 2.20 |

Nos. 1241-1244 have microperforations around denominations.

New Year 2007
(Year of the
Pig) — A270

Various pigs with background colors of:
$1.40, Brown. $2.40, Orange red. $3, Green.
$5, Rose.

## 2007, Feb. 4    Perf. 13½ Syncopated
### Granite Paper

| | | | |
|---|---|---|---|
| 1249-1252 | A270 Set of 4 | 3.00 | 3.00 |
| 1252a | Souvenir sheet of 1252, im-perf. | 1.25 | 1.25 |
| 1252b | Souvenir sheet, #1249-1252 | 3.00 | 3.00 |

### New Year Types of 2004
### 2007, Feb. 4    Litho.    Perf. 13x13½
### Flocked Paper

| | | | |
|---|---|---|---|
| 1253 | Block of 4 | 10.50 | 10.50 |
| a. | A221 $10 Like #1075 | 2.60 | 2.60 |
| b. | A244 $10 Like #1128 | 2.60 | 2.60 |
| c. | A256 $10 Like #1170 | 2.60 | 2.60 |
| d. | A270 $10 Like #1251 | 2.60 | 2.60 |

### Souvenir Sheet

New Year 2007 (Year of the
Pig) — A271

No. 1254: a, Beagle. b, Pig and piglet.

### Litho. & Embossed With Foil Application
### 2007, Feb. 4     Perf. 13¼

| | | | |
|---|---|---|---|
| 1254 | A271 $50 Sheet of 2, #a-b | 26.00 | 26.00 |

Scouting, Cent. — A272

Designs: $1.40, Campfire, Lord Robert Baden-Powell. $2.40, Hong Kong Scouting emblem, compass. $3, Backpack, knot. $5, Scouts, tent.

### Litho. With Foil Application
### Perf. 13¼x14¼ Syncopated
### 2007, Mar. 1
### Granite Paper

| | | | |
|---|---|---|---|
| 1255-1258 | A272 Set of 4 | 3.00 | 3.00 |
| 1258a | Souvenir sheet, #1255-1258 | 3.00 | 3.00 |

Children's
Games and
Puzzles
A273

Designs: $1.40, Find the difference between the two rabbits. $1.80, Color in the dotted areas. $2.40, Maze. $2.50, Follow lines to hunt for Easter Eggs. $3, Find the ten rabbits. $5, Look for a star.

## Perf. 13¾ Syncopated
### 2007, Mar. 22     Litho.
### Granite Paper

| | | | |
|---|---|---|---|
| 1259-1264 | A273 Set of 6 | 4.25 | 4.25 |
| 1264a | Souvenir sheet, #1259-1264 | 4.25 | 4.25 |

A booklet containing three panes, containing Nos. 1259-1260, 1261-1262, and 1263-1264 respectively, sold for $36.

### Souvenir Sheet

Stone Forest, Shilin — A274

## Perf. 13¼x14¼ Syncopated
### 2007, May 3
### Granite Paper

| | | | |
|---|---|---|---|
| 1265 | A274 $10 multi | 2.60 | 2.60 |

Chinese
Martial
Arts
A275

Designs: $1.40, Southern Lion Dance. $2.40, Nanquan. $3, Northern Lion Dance. $5, Beitui.

### Litho. with Foil Application
### 2007, May 22

| | | | |
|---|---|---|---|
| 1266-1269 | A275 Set of 4 | 3.00 | 3.00 |
| 1269a | Souvenir sheet, #1266-1269 | 3.00 | 3.00 |

Butterflies — A276

Designs: $1.40, Faunis eumeus. $1.80, Prioneris philonome. $2.40, Polyura nepenthes. $3, Tajuria maculata. $5, Acraea issoria.

## Perf. 13½ Syncopated
### 2007, June 14     Litho.
### Granite Paper

| | | | |
|---|---|---|---|
| 1270-1274 | A276 Set of 5 | 3.50 | 3.50 |

A booklet containing two panes, one containing Nos. 1270-1272 and the other containing Nos. 1273-1274, sold for $38.

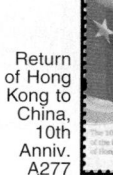

Return
of Hong
Kong to
China,
10th
Anniv.
A277

## Perf. 13x12¾ Syncopated
### 2007, July 1     Photo.

| | | | |
|---|---|---|---|
| 1275 | A277 $1.40 multi | .35 | .35 |

A souvenir sheet containing No. 1275 and People's Republic of China Nos. 3594-3596 sold for $12.95.

A278

Hong Kong Special Administrative
Region, 10th Anniv. — A279

Designs: $1.40, Ten children with joined hands. $1.80, Banner on Hong Kong Heritage Museum. $2.40, Vehicles on Tsing Ma Bridge. $2.50, Ten birds over Hong Kong Wetland Park. $3, Two International Finance Center Building and Moon. $5, Fireworks over Hong Kong.

No. 1282: a, "7" over Bank of China Tower, fireworks over Cheung Kong Center. b, Fireworks over smaller buildings. c, Fireworks over smaller buildings, Two International Finance Center Building at right.

## Perf. 13½x14¼ Syncopated
### 2007, July 1     Litho.
### Granite Paper

| | | | |
|---|---|---|---|
| 1276-1281 | A278 Set of 6 | 4.25 | 4.25 |

### Litho. With Foil Application and Hologram
### Perf. 13½

| | | | |
|---|---|---|---|
| 1282 | A279 $10 Sheet of 3, #a-c | 7.75 | 7.75 |

### Souvenir Sheet

Bangkok 2007 Asian International
Stamp Exhibition — A280

## Perf. 13½x14¼ Syncopated
### 2007, Aug. 3     Litho.
### Granite Paper

| | | | |
|---|---|---|---|
| 1283 | A280 $10 multi | 2.60 | 2.60 |

Civic
Education
A281

Designs: $1.40, Human rights. $2.40, Rule of law. $3, Social participation. $5, Corporate citizenship.

## 2007, Aug. 23    Perf. 13 Syncopated
### Granite Paper

| | | | |
|---|---|---|---|
| 1284-1287 | A281 Set of 4 | 3.00 | 3.00 |
| 1287a | Miniature sheet, 4 each #1284-1287 | 12.00 | 12.00 |

Declared Monuments — A282

Designs: $1.40, Tin Hau Temple, Causeway Bay. $1.80, Old Wan Chai Post Office. $2.40, Former Central Police Station Compound. $2.50, Former Yamen Building of Kowloon Walled City. $3, Kun Lung Gate Tower, Lung Yeuk Tau. $5, Tang Lung Chau Lighthouse.

### Litho. & Engr.
### 2007, Sept. 20    Perf. 14x13¼
### Granite Paper

| | | | |
|---|---|---|---|
| 1288-1293 | A282 Set of 6 | 4.25 | 4.25 |
| 1293a | Miniature sheet, #1288-1293 | 4.25 | 4.25 |

Christmas — A283

Designs: $1.40, Stocking. $2.40, Gingerbread man-shaped egg tart. $3, Bell decorated with neon lights. $5, Snowman with Chinese vest.

**2007, Oct. 11    Litho.    Perf. 13x13½**
**Granite Paper**
1294-1297 A283  Set of 4                3.00  3.00

Woodwork — A284

Designs: No. 1298, $5, Zitan armchair with dragon design, China, denomination at left. No. 1299, $5, Modern Finnish bowls, denomination at right.

**Perf. 13½x14¼ Syncopated**
**2007, Nov. 2**
**Granite Paper**
1298-1299 A284  Set of 2                2.60  2.60
1299a    Souvenir sheet, #1298-1299    2.60  2.60
         See Finland No. 1298.

Heartwarming
A285

Designs: No. 1300, Birds and flowers. No. 1301, Firecrackers. No. 1302, Gifts and balloons. No. 1303, Slippers.

**Perf. 13½ Syncopated**
**2007, Dec. 28                       Litho.**
**Granite Paper**
**Inscribed "Local Mail Postage"**
1300 A285 ($1.40) multi              .35   .35
1301 A285 ($1.40) multi              .35   .35
**Inscribed "Air Mail Postage"**
1302 A285   ($3) multi               .80   .80
1303 A285   ($3) multi               .80   .80
a.   Sheet, 5 each #1300-1303
     + 21 labels                   11.50 11.50

New Year 2008
(Year of the
Rat) — A286

Various rats with background colors of: $1.40, Blue. $2.40, Green. $3, Orange red. $5, Brown.

**Perf. 13½x13¼ Syncopated**
**2008, Jan. 26                      Litho.**
**Granite Paper**
1304-1307 A286  Set of 4             3.00  3.00
1307a    Souvenir sheet of #1307,
         imperf.                     1.25  1.25
1307b    Souvenir sheet of #1304-
         1307                        3.00  3.00

Souvenir Sheet

New Year 2008 (Year of the
Rat) — A287

No. 1308: a, Pig. b, Rat.

**Litho. & Embossed With Foil
Application**
**2008, Jan. 26              Perf. 13¼**
1308 A287 $50 Sheet of 2, #a-
         b                         26.00 26.00

Souvenir Sheet

Huanglong — A288

**Perf. 14¼ Syncopated**
**2008, Feb. 28                      Litho.**
**Granite Paper**
1309 A288 $10 multi                 2.60  2.60

Flowers
A289

Designs: $1.40, Chinese hibiscus. $1.80, Tree cotton. $2.40, Allamandas. $2.50, Azaleas. $3, Indian lotus. $5, Morning glories.

**Perf. 13½x13¼ Syncopated**
**2008, Mar. 14**
**Granite Paper**
1310-1315 A289  Set of 6             4.25  4.25
1315a    Souvenir sheet, #1310-1315  4.25  4.25

Paper Folding
Art — A290

Designs: $1.40, Bauhinia blossoms. $1.80, Bear, horiz. $2.40, Lunar New Year decorations. $2.50, Lotus flowers and rainbow, horiz. $3, Koalas, monkey with banana. $5, Christmas party scene, horiz.

**Perf. 14¼x13½, 13½x14¼
Syncopated**
**2008, May 22**
1316-1321 A290  Set of 6             4.25  4.25
1321a    Souvenir sheet, #1316-1321  4.25  4.25

Jellyfish — A291

Designs: $1.40, Flower hat jellyfish. $1.80, Octopus jellyfish, horiz. $2.40, Brown sea nettle. $2.50, Moon jellyfish, horiz. $3, Lion's mane jellyfish. $5, Pacific sea nettle.

**Perf. 14¼ Syncopated**
**2008, June 12                      Litho.**
**Granite Paper**
1322-1327 A291  Set of 6             4.25  4.25
1327a    Souvenir sheet, #1322-1327  4.25  4.25
Stamps have a glow-in-the-dark coating on the jellyfish illustrations. A booklet containing panes of Nos. 1322-1323, 1324-1325, and 1326-1327, sold for $36.

Giant Pandas
A292

Designs: $1.40, Ying Ying, Le Le, and hearts. $2.40, Ying Ying and leaves. $3, Le Le and panda heads. $5, Ying Ying, Le Le, and circles.

**2008, July 1     Perf. 13¾ Syncopated**
**Granite Paper**
1328-1331 A292  Set of 4             3.00  3.00
1331a    Sheet, 2 each # 1328-1331, +
         4 labels                    6.00  6.00

Hong Kong, Venue for 2008 Summer
Olympic Equestrian Events — A293

Designs: $1.40, Horse and rider jumping fence. $2.40, Dressage. $3, Horse and rider jumping over water obstacle. $5, Horse and rider at medal stand.

**Perf. 13¼x14 Syncopated**
**2008, Aug. 9**
**Granite Paper**
1332-1335 A293  Set of 4             3.00  3.00
1335a    Souvenir sheet, #1332-1335  3.00  3.00

Souvenir Sheet

Big Head
Buddha Mask,
Hong
Kong — A295

Chwibari Mask,
Korea — A296

**Perf. 13¼x14 Syncopated**
**2008, Nov. 6**
**Granite Paper**
1337 A295 $5 multi                   1.40  1.40
1338 A296 $5 multi                   1.40  1.40
a.   Souvenir sheet, #1337-1338      3.00  3.00
     See South Korea Nos.

The
Judiciary
A297

Designs: $1.40, Statue of Justice. $2.40, Court of Final Appeal. $3, Judicial robes for various courts. $5, Chief Justice's mace.

**Perf. 13¾ Syncopated**
**2008, Nov. 27**
**Granite Paper**
1339-1342 A297  Set of 4             3.00  3.00
1342a    Souvenir sheet, #1339-1342  3.00  3.00

New Year 2009
(Year of the
Ox) — A298

Various oxen with background colors of: $1.40, Purple. $2.40, Brown. $3, Green. $5, Blue.

**Perf. 13½x13¼ Syncopated**
**2009, Jan. 17                      Litho.**
**Granite Paper**
1343-1346 A298  Set of 4             3.00  3.00
1346a    Souvenir sheet of #1346, im-
         perf.                       1.25  1.25
1346b    Souvenir sheet, #1343-1346  3.00  3.00

Souvenir Sheet

New Year 2009 (Year of the
Ox) — A299

No. 1347: a, Rat. b, Ox.

Praga 2008 World Stamp
Exhibition — A294

**Perf. 13¼x14¼ Syncopated**
**2008, Sept. 12                     Litho.**
**Granite Paper**
1336 A294 $10 multi                 2.60  2.60

## Litho. & Embossed With Foil Application

**2009, Jan. 17**     *Perf. 13¼*
| | | | | |
|---|---|---|---|---|
| 1347 | A299 | $50 Sheet of 2, #a-b | | |
| | | | 26.00 | 26.00 |

## SEMI-POSTAL STAMPS

Catalogue values for unused stamps in this section are for Never Hinged items.

Community Chest of Hong Kong — SP1

**1988, Nov. 30**    **Litho.**    *Perf. 14½*
| | | | | |
|---|---|---|---|---|
| B1 | SP1 | 60c +10c Girl | .60 | .35 |
| B2 | SP1 | $1.40 +20c Elderly woman | .75 | .70 |
| B3 | SP1 | $1.80 +30c Blind youth | 1.75 | 1.00 |
| B4 | SP1 | $5 +$1 Mother and child | 4.25 | 2.75 |
| | | Nos. B1-B4 (4) | 7.35 | 4.80 |

Surtax for the social welfare organization.

## POSTAGE DUE STAMPS

Scales Showing Letter Overweight — D1

**1923, Dec.**   **Typo.**   **Wmk. 4**   *Perf. 14*
| | | | | |
|---|---|---|---|---|
| J1 | D1 | 1c brown | 2.75 | .70 |
| a. | | Chalky paper, wmkd. sideways | 1.60 | 3.50 |
| J2 | D1 | 2c green | 12.00 | 5.25 |
| J3 | D1 | 4c red | 30.00 | 7.50 |
| J4 | D1 | 6c orange | 29.00 | 15.00 |
| J5 | D1 | 10c ultramarine | 25.00 | 9.00 |
| | | Nos. J1-J5 (5) | 98.75 | 37.45 |
| | | Set, never hinged | 250.00 | |

No. J1a issued Mar. 21, 1956.

**1938-47**     *Perf. 14*
| | | | | |
|---|---|---|---|---|
| J6 | D1 | 2c gray | 1.40 | 10.00 |
| J7 | D1 | 4c orange yellow | 2.50 | 10.00 |
| J8 | D1 | 6c carmine | 10.00 | 6.00 |
| J9 | D1 | 8c fawn ('46) | 6.00 | 32.50 |
| J10 | D1 | 10c violet | 15.00 | 7.50 |
| J11 | D1 | 20c black ('46) | 10.00 | 3.50 |
| J12 | D1 | 50c blue ('47) | 35.00 | 16.00 |
| | | Nos. J6-J12 (7) | 79.90 | 85.50 |
| | | Set, never hinged | 175.00 | |

Nos. J6-J7 and J10 exist on both ordinary and chalky paper.

Catalogue values for unused stamps in this section, from this point to the end of the section, are for Never Hinged items.

### Wmk. 314 Sideways

**1965-69**     *Perf. 14*
| | | | | |
|---|---|---|---|---|
| J13 | D1 | 4c orange yellow | 9.00 | 25.00 |
| J14 | D1 | 5c orange ver ('69) | 3.75 | 5.25 |
| a. | | 5c carmine, wmk. upright ('67) | 4.00 | 5.00 |
| J15 | D1 | 10c purple ('67) | 4.75 | 3.00 |
| J16 | D1 | 20c black | 10.00 | 3.00 |
| J17 | D1 | 50c dark blue | 35.00 | 7.00 |
| a. | | Wmk. upright ('70) | 30.00 | 6.50 |
| | | Nos. J13-J17 (5) | 62.50 | 43.25 |

Size of 5c, 21x18mm.; others, 22x18mm.

### Wmk. 314 Upright

**1972-74**     *Perf. 13½x14*
| | | | | |
|---|---|---|---|---|
| J18 | D1 | 5c red brown ('74) | 3.00 | 3.50 |

*Perf. 14x14½*
| | | | | |
|---|---|---|---|---|
| J19 | D1 | 10c lilac | 7.00 | 3.00 |
| J20 | D1 | 20c black | 8.50 | 4.00 |
| J21 | D1 | 50c dull blue | 5.00 | 7.50 |
| | | Nos. J18-J21 (4) | 23.50 | 18.00 |

Nos. J18-J22 are on glazed paper.

**1976, Mar. 19**     **Wmk. 373**
| | | | | |
|---|---|---|---|---|
| J19a | D1 | 10c lilac | 1.00 | 2.50 |
| J20a | D1 | 20c black | 1.50 | 2.50 |
| J21a | D1 | 50c dull blue | 1.50 | 3.00 |
| b. | | Unwatermarked | 1.50 | 4.00 |
| J22 | D1 | $1 yellow | 5.00 | 4.00 |
| a. | | Unwatermarked | 5.00 | 4.00 |
| | | Nos. J19a-J22 (4) | 9.00 | 12.00 |

Size of $1, 20½x17mm; others, 22x18mm.
Issue date: No. J21b, J22, Jan. 11, 1986.

D2

*Perf. 14x15*

**1986, Mar. 25**    **Litho.**    **Unwmk.**
| | | | | |
|---|---|---|---|---|
| J23 | D2 | 10c light green | .20 | .20 |
| J24 | D2 | 20c dark red brown | .20 | .20 |
| J25 | D2 | 50c lilac | .20 | .20 |
| J26 | D2 | $1 light orange | .20 | .20 |
| J27 | D2 | $5 grayish blue | 1.00 | 1.50 |
| J28 | D2 | $10 rose red | 2.00 | 2.50 |
| | | Nos. J23-J28 (6) | 3.80 | 4.80 |

D3

*Perf. 14x14¾*

**2004, Sept. 23**    **Litho.**    **Unwmk.**
| | | | | |
|---|---|---|---|---|
| J29 | D3 | 10c dark blue | .20 | .20 |
| J30 | D3 | 20c blue | .20 | .20 |
| J31 | D3 | 50c orange | .20 | .20 |
| J32 | D3 | $1 pink | .25 | .25 |
| J33 | D3 | $5 olive green | 1.25 | 1.25 |
| J34 | D3 | $10 cerise | 2.60 | 2.60 |
| | | Nos. J29-J34 (6) | 4.70 | 4.70 |

## OCCUPATION STAMPS

### Issued under Japanese Occupation

War Factory Girl — A144

Gen. Maresuke Nogi — A84

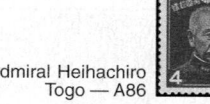

Admiral Heihachiro Togo — A86

Stamps of Japan, 1942-43 Surcharged in Black

### Wmk. 257

**1945, Apr.**    **Typo.**    *Perf. 13*
| | | | | |
|---|---|---|---|---|
| N1 | A144 | 1½y on 1s org brn | 35.00 | 30.00 |
| N2 | A84 | 3y on 2s ver | 14.00 | 25.00 |
| N3 | A86 | 5y on 5s brn lake | 975.00 | 175.00 |
| | | Nos. N1-N3 (3) | 1,024. | 230.00 |

No. N1 has eleven characters.

## HORTA

'hor-tə

LOCATION — An administrative district of the Azores, consisting of the islands of Pico, Fayal, Flores and Corvo
GOVT. — A district of the Republic of Portugal
AREA — 305 sq. mi.
POP. — 49,000 (approx.)
CAPITAL — Horta

1000 Reis = 1 Milreis

King Carlos
A1      A2
Chalk-surfaced Paper
*Perf. 11½, 12½, 13½*

**1892-93**    **Typo.**    **Unwmk.**
| | | | | |
|---|---|---|---|---|
| 1 | A1 | 5r yellow | 2.00 | 1.50 |
| 2 | A1 | 10r reddish violet | 2.00 | 1.75 |
| 3 | A1 | 15r chocolate | 2.00 | 2.00 |
| 4 | A1 | 20r lavender | 3.00 | 3.00 |
| 5 | A1 | 25r dp grn, perf. 11½ | 4.50 | 1.00 |
| a. | | Perf. 13½ | 5.00 | 3.75 |
| 6 | A1 | 50r blue | 6.25 | 3.00 |
| a. | | Perf. 13½ | 9.00 | 5.25 |
| 7 | A1 | 75r carmine | 6.50 | 4.00 |
| 8 | A1 | 80r yellow green | 9.00 | 6.00 |
| 9 | A1 | 100r brn, yel ('93) | 35.00 | 10.00 |
| a. | | Perf. 12½ | 125.00 | 90.00 |
| 10 | A1 | 150r car, rose ('93) | 45.00 | 32.50 |
| 11 | A1 | 200r dk bl, bl ('93) | 45.00 | 32.50 |
| 12 | A1 | 300r dark blue ('93) | 45.00 | 35.00 |
| | | Nos. 1-12 (12) | 205.25 | 132.25 |

Bisects of No. 1 were used in Aug. 1894. Value $16.
*The reprints have shiny white gum and clean-cut perforation 13½. The white paper is thinner than that of the originals. Value unused, $12 each.*

**1897-1905**     *Perf. 11½*
**Name and Value in Black Except 500r**
| | | | | |
|---|---|---|---|---|
| 13 | A2 | 2½r gray | .50 | .30 |
| 14 | A2 | 5r orange | .50 | .30 |
| 15 | A2 | 10r lt green | .50 | .30 |
| 16 | A2 | 15r brown | 5.25 | 3.00 |
| 17 | A2 | 15r gray grn ('99) | 1.25 | .80 |
| 18 | A2 | 20r gray violet | 1.75 | .85 |
| 19 | A2 | 25r sea green | 2.25 | .45 |
| 20 | A2 | 25r car rose ('99) | .90 | .50 |
| 21 | A2 | 50r blue | 3.00 | .70 |
| 22 | A2 | 50r ultra ('05) | 15.00 | 9.00 |
| 23 | A2 | 65r slate blue ('98) | .70 | .55 |
| 24 | A2 | 75r rose | 1.90 | .95 |
| 25 | A2 | 75r brn, yel ('05) | 20.00 | 12.50 |
| 26 | A2 | 80r violet | 1.25 | 1.10 |
| 27 | A2 | 100r dk blue, bl | 1.75 | .95 |
| 28 | A2 | 115r org brn, pink ('98) | 3.00 | 1.50 |
| 29 | A2 | 130r gray brn, buff ('98) | 3.00 | 1.50 |
| 30 | A2 | 150r lt brn, buff | 3.00 | 1.50 |
| 31 | A2 | 180r sl, pnksh ('98) | 3.00 | 1.75 |
| 32 | A2 | 200r red vio, pale lil | 5.50 | 4.00 |
| 33 | A2 | 300r dk blue, rose | 9.00 | 6.75 |
| 34 | A2 | 500r blk & red, bl | 12.00 | 8.50 |
| | | Nos. 13-34 (22) | 95.00 | 57.75 |

Stamps of Portugal replaced those of Horta.

# HUNGARY

ˈhəŋ-gə-ˌrē

LOCATION — Central Europe
GOVT. — Republic
AREA — 35,911 sq. mi.
POP. — 10,186,372 (1999 est.)
CAPITAL — Budapest

Prior to World War I, Hungary together with Austria comprised the Austro-Hungarian Empire. The Hungarian post became independent on May 1, 1867. During 1850-1871 stamps listed under Austria were also used in Hungary. Copies showing clear Hungarian cancels sell for substantially more.

100 Krajczár (Kreuzer) = 1 Forint 100 Fillér = 1 Korona (1900) 100 Fillér = 1 Pengö (1926) 100 Fillér = 1 Forint (1946)

> Catalogue values for unused stamps in this country are for Never Hinged items, beginning with Scott 503 in the regular postage section, Scott B92 in the semi-postal section, Scott C35 in the airpost section, Scott CB1 in the airpost semi-postal section, Scott F1 in the registrtation section, Scott J130 in the postage due section, and Scott Q9 in the parcel post section.

### Watermarks

Wmk. 91 — "ZEITUNGS-MARKEN" in Double-lined Capitals across the Sheet

Wmk. 106 — Multiple Star

Wmk. 132 — kr in Oval

Wmk. 133 — Four Double Crosses

Wmk. 135 — Crown in Oval or Circle, Sideways

Wmk. 136          Wmk. 136a

Wmk. 137 — Double Cross

Wmk. 210 — Double Cross on Pyramid

Wmk. 266 — Double Barred Cross, Wreath and Crown

Wmk. 283 — Double Barred Cross on Shield, Multiple

Watermarks 132, 135, 136 and 136a can be found normal, reversed, inverted, or reversed and inverted.

Values for unused stamps are for examples with original gum as defined in the catalogue introduction. Very fine examples of Nos. 1-12 will have perforations touching the framelines on one or two sides due to imperfect perforating methods. Stamps with perfs clear on all four sides are very scarce and will command substantial premiums.

### Issues of the Monarchy

Franz Josef I — A1

| 1871 | | Unwmk. | Litho. | Perf. 9½ |
|---|---|---|---|---|
| 1 | A1 | 2k orange | 225.00 | 90.00 |
| a. | | 2k yellow | 1,300. | 225.00 |
| 2 | A1 | 3k lt green | 725.00 | 550.00 |
| 3 | A1 | 5k rose | 300.00 | 20.00 |
| a. | | 5k brick red | 600.00 | 75.00 |
| 4 | A1 | 10k blue | 700.00 | 90.00 |
| a. | | 10k pale blue | 950.00 | 150.00 |
| 5 | A1 | 15k yellow brn | 750.00 | 100.00 |
| 6 | A1 | 25k violet | 750.00 | 175.00 |
| a. | | 25k bright violet | 850.00 | 275.00 |

The first printing of No. 1, in dark yellow, was not issued because of spots on the King's face. A few stamps were used at Pest in 1873. Value, $3,500.

| 1871-72 | | | | Engr. |
|---|---|---|---|---|
| 7 | A1 | 2k orange | 37.50 | 7.50 |
| a. | | 2k yellow | 150.00 | 17.00 |
| b. | | Bisect on cover | | |
| 8 | A1 | 3k green | 85.00 | 25.00 |
| a. | | 3k blue green | 110.00 | 30.00 |

| 9 | A1 | 5k rose | 50.00 | 1.75 |
|---|---|---|---|---|
| a. | | 5k brick red | 125.00 | 8.00 |
| 10 | A1 | 10k deep blue | 200.00 | 10.00 |
| 11 | A1 | 15k brown | 225.00 | 15.00 |
| a. | | 15k copper brown | — | 900.00 |
| b. | | 15k black brown | 875.00 | 85.00 |
| 12 | A1 | 25k lilac | 140.00 | 40.00 |
| | | Nos. 7-12 (6) | 737.50 | 99.25 |

*Reprints are perf. 11½ and watermarked "kr" in oval. Value, set $225.*

Crown of St. Stephen
A2          A3

Design A3 has an overall burelage of dots. Compare with design N3.

| 1874-76 | | | | Perf. 13 |
|---|---|---|---|---|
| 13 | A2 | 2k red violet | 50.00 | 4.00 |
| a. | | 2k violet | 60.00 | 5.00 |
| 14 | A2 | 3k yellow green | 50.00 | 4.00 |
| a. | | 3k blue green | 70.00 | 5.00 |
| 15 | A2 | 5k red | 15.00 | .80 |
| a. | | 5k brick red | 40.00 | 2.00 |
| b. | | 5k lilac red | 25.00 | 1.50 |
| c. | | 5k rose | 12.00 | .50 |
| 16 | A2 | 10k blue | 65.00 | 1.50 |
| 17 | A2 | 20k grnsh gray | 575.00 | 14.00 |
| a. | | 20k gray | 600.00 | 15.00 |
| | | Nos. 13-17 (5) | 755.00 | 24.30 |

| | | | | Perf. 11½ |
|---|---|---|---|---|
| 13b | A2 | 2k red violet | 70.00 | 10.00 |
| c. | | 2k violet | 75.00 | 12.00 |
| d. | | 2k rose lilac | 110.00 | 9.00 |
| e. | | 2k gray blue | 90.00 | 9.50 |
| 14b | A2 | 3k yellow green | 80.00 | 8.00 |
| c. | | 3k blue green | 90.00 | 10.00 |
| 15d | A2 | 5k red | 90.00 | 2.00 |
| e. | | 5k rose | 80.00 | 1.50 |
| 16a | A2 | 10k blue | 110.00 | 10.00 |
| 17b | A2 | 20k gray | 1,500. | 42.50 |

**Perf. 13x11½**

| | | | | |
|---|---|---|---|---|
| 13f | A2 | 2k red violet | 150.00 | 25.00 |
| g. | | 2k rose lilac | 165.00 | 30.00 |
| 14d | A2 | 3k yellow green | 100.00 | 4.25 |
| 15f | A2 | 5k lilac red | 125.00 | 12.00 |
| g. | | 5k rose | 150.00 | 15.00 |
| 16b | A2 | 10k blue | 200.00 | 5.75 |
| 17c | A2 | 20k gray | 600.00 | 47.50 |

**Perf. 11½x13**

| | | | | |
|---|---|---|---|---|
| 13h | A2 | 2k red violet | 100.00 | 4.75 |
| f. | | 2k rose lilac | 165.00 | 4.00 |
| g. | | 2k gray blue | 125.00 | 4.00 |
| 15h | A2 | 5k red | 125.00 | 1.00 |
| 17d | A2 | 20k gray | — | 95.00 |

**Perf. 9½**

| | | | | |
|---|---|---|---|---|
| 14e | A2 | 3k green | 3,000. | 2.000. |

All examples of the 5k perf 9½ are counterfeit.

**1881          Wmk. 132          Perf. 11½**

| | | | | |
|---|---|---|---|---|
| 18 | A2 | 2k lilac | 7.00 | .80 |
| a. | | 2k violet | 7.00 | .80 |
| b. | | 2k gray blue | 9.00 | 1.00 |
| 19 | A2 | 3k blue green | 7.00 | .80 |
| a. | | 3k yellow green | 9.00 | 1.20 |
| 20 | A2 | 5k rose | 5.00 | .30 |
| 21 | A2 | 10k blue | 12.00 | .80 |
| a. | | 10k pale blue | 14.00 | 1.20 |
| 22 | A2 | 20k gray | 9.00 | 1.25 |
| a. | | 20k greenish gray | 10.00 | 1.50 |
| | | Nos. 18-22 (5) | 40.00 | 3.95 |

**Perf. 13**

| | | | | |
|---|---|---|---|---|
| 18c | A2 | 2k violet | 150.00 | 18.00 |
| d. | | 2k gray blue | 120.00 | 9.50 |
| 19b | A2 | 3k blue green | 90.00 | 3.75 |
| c. | | 3k yellow green | 100.00 | 5.00 |
| 20a | A2 | 5k rose | 120.00 | 3.75 |
| 21b | A2 | 10k blue | 75.00 | 4.75 |
| 22b | A2 | 20k gray | 350.00 | 15.00 |

**Perf. 13x11½**

| | | | | |
|---|---|---|---|---|
| 18e | A2 | 2k violet | — | 40.00 |
| 19d | A2 | 3k blue green | 200.00 | 6.00 |
| e. | | 3k yellow green | | 8.00 |
| 20b | A2 | 5k rose | | 15.00 |
| 21c | A2 | 10k blue | | 8.00 |
| 22c | A2 | 20k gray | 600.00 | 40.00 |

**Perf. 11½x13**

| | | | | |
|---|---|---|---|---|
| 18f | A2 | 2k violet | 180.00 | 9.00 |
| 19f | A2 | 2k gray blue | 150.00 | 10.00 |
| g. | | 3k blue green | | 60.00 |
| | | | | 75.00 |
| 20c | A2 | 5k rose | 75.00 | 1.00 |
| 21d | A2 | 10k blue | 1,400. | 2.00 |
| 22d | A2 | 20k gray | | 40.00 |

**Perf. 12x11½**

| | | | | |
|---|---|---|---|---|
| 18h | A2 | 2k lilac | 1.00 | .25 |
| i. | | 2k violet | 12.50 | 1.20 |
| 19h | A2 | 3k blue green | 1.00 | .50 |
| 20d | A2 | 5k rose | 2.50 | .25 |
| 21e | A2 | 10k blue | 3.00 | .25 |
| 22e | A2 | 20k gray | 300.00 | 7.50 |

**1888-98   Typo.   Perf. 11½, 12x11½**
**Numerals in Black**

| | | | | |
|---|---|---|---|---|
| 22A | A3 | 1k black, one plate | .55 | .40 |
| c. | | "1" printed separately | 10.50 | .90 |
| 23 | A3 | 2k red violet | .80 | .35 |
| a. | | Perf. 11½ | 725.00 | 50.00 |
| 24 | A3 | 3k green | 2.00 | .50 |
| a. | | Perf. 11½ | 50.00 | 15.00 |
| 25 | A3 | 5k rose | 2.00 | .30 |
| a. | | Perf. 11½ | 65.00 | 1.75 |
| 26 | A3 | 8k orange | 7.00 | .80 |
| | | "8" double | 150.00 | |
| 27 | A3 | 10k blue | 5.50 | 1.40 |
| a. | | Perf. 11½ | 450.00 | 325.00 |
| 28 | A3 | 12k brown & green | 14.00 | 1.00 |
| 29 | A3 | 15k claret & blue | 11.00 | .40 |
| 30 | A3 | 20k gray | 8.50 | 2.25 |
| a. | | Perf. 11½ | 1,400. | 600.00 |
| 31 | A3 | 24k brn vio & red | 25.00 | 1.25 |
| 32 | A3 | 30k ol grn & brn | 27.50 | .45 |
| 33 | A3 | 50k red & org | 45.00 | 1.40 |

**Numerals in Red**

| | | | | |
|---|---|---|---|---|
| 34 | A3 | 1fo gray bl & sil | 185.00 | 2.50 |
| a. | | Perf. 11½ | 190.00 | 3.50 |
| 35 | A3 | 3fo lilac brn & gold | 18.00 | 11.00 |
| | | Nos. 22A-35 (14) | 351.85 | 24.00 |

**1898-99          Perf. 12x11½**
**Numerals in Black**
**Wmk. 135 (Oval)**

| | | | | |
|---|---|---|---|---|
| 35A | A3 | 1k black | 1.50 | .50 |
| 36 | A3 | 2k violet | 6.00 | .50 |
| 37 | A3 | 3k green | 4.00 | .60 |
| 38 | A3 | 5k rose | 5.00 | .40 |
| 39 | A3 | 8k orange | 17.50 | 4.00 |
| 40 | A3 | 10k blue | 5.00 | 1.00 |
| 41 | A3 | 12k red brn & grn | 75.00 | 9.00 |
| 42 | A3 | 15k rose & blue | 5.00 | .75 |
| 43 | A3 | 20k gray | 35.00 | 2.00 |
| 44 | A3 | 24k brn vio & red | 6.00 | 4.75 |
| 45 | A3 | 30k ol grn & brn | 40.00 | 1.50 |
| 46 | A3 | 50k dull red & org | 100.00 | 15.00 |
| | | Nos. 35A-46 (12) | 300.00 | 40.00 |

**Perf. 11½**

| | | | | |
|---|---|---|---|---|
| 35Ab | A3 | 1k black | 40.00 | 7.50 |
| 36a | A3 | 2k violet | 125.00 | 20.00 |
| 37a | A3 | 3k green | 100.00 | 15.00 |
| 38a | A3 | 5k rose | 140.00 | 15.00 |
| 39a | A3 | 8k orange | 250.00 | 120.00 |
| 40a | A3 | 10k blue | 150.00 | 40.00 |
| 41a | A3 | 12k red brn & grn | 300.00 | 75.00 |
| 42a | A3 | 15k rose & blue | 180.00 | 45.00 |
| 43a | A3 | 20k gray | 275.00 | 60.00 |
| 44a | A3 | 24k brn vio & red | 350.00 | 140.00 |
| 45a | A3 | 30k ol grn & brn | 200.00 | 50.00 |
| 46a | A3 | 50k dull red & org | 400.00 | 150.00 |

**Wmk. 135 (Circle)**
**Perf. 12x11½**

| | | | | |
|---|---|---|---|---|
| 35Ac | A3 | 1k black | 14.00 | 7.50 |
| 36b | A3 | 2k violet | 7.50 | .75 |
| 37b | A3 | 3k green | 8.50 | 1.25 |
| 38b | A3 | 5k rose | 10.00 | .50 |
| 39b | A3 | 8k orange | 50.00 | 15.00 |
| 40b | A3 | 10k blue | 75.00 | 3.00 |
| 41b | A3 | 12k red brn & grn | 60.00 | 22.50 |
| 42b | A3 | 15k rose & blue | 200.00 | 3.00 |
| 43b | A3 | 20k gray | 5.00 | 3.50 |
| 44b | A3 | 24k vio brn & red | 900.00 | 40.00 |
| 45b | A3 | 30k ol grn & brn | 5.00 | 4.00 |
| 46b | A3 | 50k dull red & org | 15.00 | 30.00 |

**Perf. 11½**

| | | | | |
|---|---|---|---|---|
| 35Ad | A3 | 1k black | 50.00 | 15.00 |
| 36c | A3 | 2k violet | 200.00 | 25.00 |
| 37c | A3 | 3k green | 200.00 | 40.00 |
| 38c | A3 | 5k rose | 100.00 | 15.00 |
| 39c | A3 | 8k orange | 80.00 | 12.50 |
| 40c | A3 | 10k blue | 350.00 | 80.00 |
| 41c | A3 | 12k red brn & grn | 550.00 | 300.00 |
| 42c | A3 | 15k rose & blue | 375.00 | 200.00 |
| 43c | A3 | 20k gray | 1,200. | 350.00 |
| 44c | A3 | 24k vio brn & red | 1,500. | 400.00 |
| 45c | A3 | 30k ol grn & brn | 600.00 | 150.00 |
| 46c | A3 | 50k dull red & org | 375.00 | 275.00 |

In the watermark with circles, a four-pointed star and "VI" appear four times in the sheet in the large spaces between the intersecting circles. The paper with the circular watermark is often yellowish and thinner than that with the oval watermark.

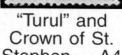

"Turul" and Crown of St. Stephen — A4

Franz Josef I Wearing Hungarian Crown — A5

**1900-04   Wmk. 135   Perf. 12x11½**
**Numerals in Black**

| | | | | |
|---|---|---|---|---|
| 47 | A4 | 1f gray | .60 | .40 |
| a. | | 1f dull lilac | .65 | .40 |
| 48 | A4 | 2f olive yel | .70 | .25 |
| 49 | A4 | 3f orange | .55 | .25 |
| 50 | A4 | 4f violet | .60 | .20 |
| a. | | Booklet pane of 6 | 60.00 | |
| 51 | A4 | 5f emerald | 2.75 | .20 |
| a. | | Booklet pane of 6 | 35.00 | |
| 52 | A4 | 6f claret | .95 | .60 |
| | | 6f violet brown | 1.75 | .60 |
| 53 | A4 | 6f bister ('01) | 12.00 | 1.20 |
| 54 | A4 | 6f olive grn ('02) | 4.00 | .60 |
| 55 | A4 | 10f carmine | 3.00 | .25 |
| a. | | Booklet pane of 6 | 35.00 | |
| 56 | A4 | 12f violet ('04) | 1.50 | 1.25 |
| 57 | A4 | 20f brown ('01) | 1.90 | .60 |
| 58 | A4 | 25f blue | 3.25 | .65 |
| a. | | Booklet pane of 6 | 60.00 | |
| 59 | A4 | 30f orange brn | 22.50 | .25 |
| 60 | A4 | 35f red vio ('01) | 12.50 | .40 |
| a. | | Booklet pane of 6 | 100.00 | |
| 61 | A4 | 50f lake | 13.00 | 1.25 |
| 62 | A4 | 60f green | 44.00 | .55 |
| 63 | A5 | 1k brown red | 45.00 | .70 |
| 64 | A5 | 2k gray blue ('01) | 275.00 | 22.50 |
| 65 | A5 | 3k sea green | 85.00 | 4.50 |
| 66 | A5 | 5k vio brown ('01) | 85.00 | 30.00 |
| | | Nos. 47-66 (20) | 613.80 | 66.60 |

The watermark on Nos. 47 to 66 is always the circular form of Wmk. 135 described in the note following No. 46.

Pairs imperf between of Nos. 47-49, 51 were favor prints made for an influential Budapest collector. Value, $90 each.

For overprints & surcharges see #B35-B52, 2N1-2N3, 6N1-6N6, 6NB127N1-7N6, 7NB1, 10N1.

**Perf. 11½**

| | | | | |
|---|---|---|---|---|
| 47b | A4 | 1f gray | 90.00 | 17.50 |
| 48a | A4 | 2f olive yel | 90.00 | 12.50 |
| 49a | A4 | 3f orange | 22.50 | 2.25 |
| 50b | A4 | 4f violet | 70.00 | 1.50 |
| 51b | A4 | 5f emerald | 5.50 | 1.40 |
| 52b | A4 | 6f claret | 110.00 | 12.50 |
| 53a | A4 | 6f bister ('01) | 80.00 | 22.50 |
| 54a | A4 | 6f olive grn ('02) | 160.00 | 90.00 |
| 55b | A4 | 10f carmine | 90.00 | 3.00 |
| 56a | A4 | 12f violet ('04) | 70.00 | 27.50 |
| 57a | A4 | 20f brown ('01) | 140.00 | 45.00 |
| 58b | A4 | 25f blue | 140.00 | 15.00 |
| 59a | A4 | 30f orange brn | 150.00 | 35.00 |
| 60b | A4 | 35f red vio ('01) | 190.00 | 80.00 |
| 61a | A4 | 50f lake | 190.00 | 80.00 |
| 62a | A4 | 60f green | 250.00 | 20.00 |
| 63a | A5 | 1k brown red | 45.00 | 3.25 |
| 64a | A5 | 2k gray blue ('01) | 550.00 | 120.00 |
| 65a | A5 | 3k sea green | — | 1,500. |
| 66a | A5 | 5k vio brown ('01) | 550.00 | 225.00 |

**1908-13          Wmk. 136          Perf. 15**

| | | | | |
|---|---|---|---|---|
| 67 | A4 | 1f slate | .35 | .20 |
| 68 | A4 | 2f olive yellow | .30 | .20 |
| 69 | A4 | 3f orange | .35 | .20 |
| 70 | A4 | 5f emerald | .35 | .20 |
| c. | | Booklet pane of 6 | 100.00 | |
| 71 | A4 | 6f olive green | .35 | .20 |
| 72 | A4 | 10f carmine | .45 | .20 |
| c. | | Booklet pane of 6 | 100.00 | |
| 73 | A4 | 12f violet | .40 | .20 |
| 74 | A4 | 16f gray green ('13) | .20 | .40 |

| | | | | |
|---|---|---|---|---|
| 75 | A4 | 20f dark brown | 3.50 | .20 |
| 76 | A4 | 25f blue | 2.25 | .20 |
| 77 | A4 | 30f orange brown | 2.50 | .20 |
| 78 | A4 | 35f red violet | 3.75 | .20 |
| 79 | A4 | 50f lake | 1.75 | .30 |
| 80 | A4 | 60f green | 4.00 | .20 |
| 81 | A5 | 1k brown red | 7.25 | .25 |
| 82 | A5 | 2k gray blue | 50.00 | .50 |
| 83 | A5 | 5k violet brown | 75.00 | 7.50 |
| | | Nos. 67-83 (17) | 152.75 | 11.40 |

Nos. 67-73, 75-83 exist imperf. Value, set $675.

**1904-05   Wmk. 136a   Perf. 12x11½**

| | | | | |
|---|---|---|---|---|
| 67a | A4 | 1f slate | 1.20 | 1.75 |
| 68a | A4 | 2f olive yellow | 3.50 | .40 |
| 69a | A4 | 3f orange | .90 | .25 |
| 70a | A4 | 5f emerald | 2.50 | .20 |
| 71a | A4 | 6f olive green | 1.25 | .45 |
| 72a | A4 | 10f carmine | 3.75 | .20 |
| 73a | A4 | 12f violet | 2.25 | 1.60 |
| 75a | A4 | 20f dark brown | 12.00 | .85 |
| 76a | A4 | 25f blue | 18.00 | .80 |
| 77a | A4 | 30f orange brown | 4.50 | .40 |
| 78a | A4 | 35f red violet | 14.00 | .80 |
| 79a | A4 | 50f lake | 10.50 | 2.50 |
| c. | | 50f magenta | .60 | 4.00 |
| 80a | A5 | 60f green | 200.00 | .75 |
| 81a | A5 | 1k brown red | 150.00 | 2.00 |
| 82a | A5 | 2k gray blue | 550.00 | 60.00 |
| c. | | Perf. 11½ | 575.00 | 87.50 |
| 83a | A5 | 5k violet brown | 175.00 | 80.00 |
| | | Nos. 67a-83a (16) | 1,149. | 152.95 |

**1906          Perf. 15**

| | | | | |
|---|---|---|---|---|
| 67b | A4 | 1f slate | .75 | .45 |
| 68b | A4 | 2f olive yellow | .40 | .20 |
| 69b | A4 | 3f orange | .70 | .20 |
| 70b | A4 | 5f emerald | .35 | .20 |
| 71b | A4 | 6f olive green | .90 | .20 |
| 72b | A4 | 10f carmine | .75 | .20 |
| 73b | A4 | 12f violet | 1.10 | .20 |
| 75b | A4 | 20f dark brown | 2.25 | .30 |
| 76b | A4 | 25f blue | 2.75 | .20 |
| 77b | A4 | 30f orange brown | 3.00 | .20 |
| 78b | A4 | 35f red violet | 13.00 | .20 |
| 79b | A4 | 50f lake | 2.25 | .50 |
| 80b | A4 | 60f green | 30.00 | .45 |
| 81b | A5 | 1k brown red | 30.00 | .65 |
| 82b | A5 | 2k gray blue | 100.00 | 8.00 |
| | | Nos. 67b-82b (15) | 188.20 | 12.15 |

**1913-16   Wmk. 137 Vert.   Perf. 15**

| | | | | |
|---|---|---|---|---|
| 84 | A4 | 1f slate | .30 | .20 |
| 85 | A4 | 2f olive yellow | .20 | .20 |
| 86 | A4 | 3f orange | .20 | .20 |
| 87 | A4 | 5f emerald | .50 | .20 |
| 88 | A4 | 6f olive green | .20 | .20 |
| 89 | A4 | 10f carmine | .20 | .20 |
| 90 | A4 | 12f violet, yel | .20 | .20 |
| 91 | A4 | 16f gray green | .35 | .50 |
| 92 | A4 | 20f dark brown | .75 | .20 |
| 93 | A4 | 25f ultra | .85 | .20 |
| 94 | A4 | 30f orange brown | .75 | .20 |
| 95 | A4 | 35f red violet | .75 | .20 |
| 96 | A4 | 50f lake, blue | .35 | .20 |
| | | Cliché of 35f in plate of 50f | 250.00 | — |
| 97 | A4 | 60f green | 4.25 | 2.25 |
| 98 | A4 | 60f green, salmon | .60 | .30 |
| 99 | A4 | 70f red brn, grn ('16) | .30 | .20 |
| 100 | A4 | 80f dull violet ('16) | .30 | .20 |
| 101 | A5 | 1k dull red | 1.25 | .20 |
| 102 | A5 | 2k dull blue | 2.75 | .30 |
| 103 | A5 | 5k violet brown | 9.00 | 2.00 |
| | | Nos. 84-103 (20) | 24.05 | 8.35 |

Nos. 89-97, 99-103 exist imperf. Value, set $800.

For overprints and surcharges see Nos. 2N1-2N3, 6N1-6N6, 6NB12, 7N1-7N6, 7NB1, 10N1.

**Wmk. 137 Horiz.**

| | | | | |
|---|---|---|---|---|
| 84a | A4 | 1f slate | .80 | 1.25 |
| 85a | A4 | 2f olive yellow | 2.10 | .60 |
| 87a | A4 | 5f emerald | .50 | .60 |
| 88a | A4 | 6f olive green | 1.00 | .60 |
| 89b | A4 | 10f carmine | 1.10 | .35 |
| 90a | A4 | 12f violet, yellow | 2.10 | .45 |
| 92a | A4 | 20f dark brown | 6.25 | .50 |
| 94a | A4 | 30f orange brown | 42.50 | .35 |
| 95a | A4 | 35f red violet | 150.00 | .50 |
| 96b | A4 | 50f lake, blue | 10.50 | 9.50 |
| 97a | A4 | 60f green | 3.75 | 2.50 |
| 98a | A4 | 60f green, salmon | 1.60 | .30 |
| 101a | A5 | 1k dull red | 16.00 | .50 |
| 102a | A5 | 2k dull blue | 75.00 | 2.50 |
| | | Nos. 84a-102a (14) | 313.20 | 20.50 |

A5a — 103A

**1916, July 1          Perf. 15**

| | | | | |
|---|---|---|---|---|
| 103A | A5a | 10f violet brown | .80 | .50 |

Although issued as a postal savings stamp, No. 103A was also valid for postage. Used value is for postal usage.

Exists imperf. Value $10.

For overprints and surcharges see Nos. 2N59, 5N23, 6N50, 8N13, 10N42.

Queen Zita — A6

Charles IV — A7

**1916, Dec. 30**

| | | | | |
|---|---|---|---|---|
| 104 | A6 | 10f violet | 1.00 | .85 |
| 105 | A7 | 15f red | 1.00 | .85 |

Coronation of King Charles IV and Queen Zita on Dec. 30, 1916.
Exist imperf. Value, set $20.

Harvesting (White Numerals) — A8

**1916**

| | | | | |
|---|---|---|---|---|
| 106 | A8 | 10f rose | .75 | .30 |
| 107 | A8 | 15f violet | .75 | .30 |

Exist imperf. Value, set $20.
For overprints and surcharges see Nos. B56-B57, 2N4-2N5, 5N1.

During 1921-24 the two center rows of panes of various stamps then current were punched with three holes forming a triangle. These were sold at post offices. Collectors and dealers who wanted the stamps unpunched would have to purchase them through the philatelic agency at a 10% advance over face value.

Harvesting Wheat — A9

Parliament Building at Budapest — A10

**1916-18          Perf. 15**

| | | | | |
|---|---|---|---|---|
| 108 | A9 | 2f brown orange | .20 | .20 |
| 109 | A9 | 3f red lilac | .20 | .20 |
| 110 | A9 | 4f slate gray ('18) | .20 | .20 |
| 111 | A9 | 5f green | .20 | .20 |
| 112 | A9 | 6f grnsh blue | .20 | .20 |
| 113 | A9 | 10f rose red | 1.75 | .20 |
| 114 | A9 | 15f violet | .20 | .20 |
| 115 | A9 | 20f gray brown | .20 | .20 |
| 116 | A9 | 25f dull blue | .50 | .20 |
| 117 | A9 | 35f brown | .20 | .20 |
| 118 | A9 | 40f olive green | .20 | .20 |

**Perf. 14**

| | | | | |
|---|---|---|---|---|
| 119 | A10 | 50f red vio & lil | .25 | .20 |
| 120 | A10 | 75f brt bl & pale bl | .25 | .20 |
| 121 | A10 | 80f grn & pale grn | .25 | .20 |
| 122 | A10 | 1k red brn & claret | .25 | .20 |
| 123 | A10 | 2k ol brn & bister | .25 | .20 |
| 124 | A10 | 3k dk vio & indigo | 1.50 | .20 |
| 125 | A10 | 5k dk brn & lt brn | 1.50 | .20 |
| 126 | A10 | 10k vio brn & vio | 2.75 | .20 |
| | | Nos. 108-126 (19) | 11.05 | 3.80 |

Exist imperf. Value, set $90.
See Nos. 335-377, 388-396. For overprints and surcharges see Nos. 153, 167, C1-C5, J76-J99, 1N1-1N21, 1N26-1N30, 1N33, 1N36-1N39, 2N6-2N27, 2N33-2N38, 2N41, 2N43-2N48, 4N1-4N4, 5N2-5N17, 6N7-6N24, 6N29-6N39, 7N7-7N30, 7N38, 7N41-7N42, 8N1-8N4, 9N1-9N2, 9N4, 10N2-10N16, 10N25-10N29, 10N31, 10N33-10N41, Szeged 1-15, 20-24, 27, 30, 32-33.

Charles
IV — A11

Queen
Zita — A12

**1918**       *Perf. 15*

| | | | | |
|---|---|---|---|---|
| 127 | A11 | 10f scarlet | .20 | .20 |
| 128 | A11 | 15f deep violet | .20 | .20 |
| 129 | A11 | 20f dark brown | .20 | .20 |
| 130 | A11 | 25f brt blue | .20 | .20 |
| 131 | A12 | 40f olive green | .20 | .20 |
| 132 | A12 | 50f lilac | .20 | .20 |
| | | *Nos. 127-132 (6)* | 1.20 | 1.20 |

Exist imperf. Value, set $27.50
For overprints see Nos. 168-173, 1N32, 1N34-1N35, 2N28-2N32, 2N39-2N40, 2N42, 2N49-2N51, 5N18-5N22, 6N25-6N28, 6N40-6N43, 7N31-7N37, 7N39-7N40, 8N5, 9N3, 10N17-10N21, 10N30, 10N32, Szeged 16-19, 25-26, 28-29, 31.

### Issues of the Republic

Hungarian Stamps of 1916-18 Overprinted in Black

**1918-19**    Wmk. 137    *Perf. 15, 14*
**On Stamps of 1916-18**

| | | | | |
|---|---|---|---|---|
| 153 | A9 | 2f brown orange | .20 | .20 |
| 154 | A9 | 3f red lilac | .20 | .20 |
| 155 | A9 | 4f slate gray | .20 | .20 |
| 156 | A9 | 5f green | .20 | .20 |
| 157 | A9 | 6f grnsh blue | .20 | .20 |
| 158 | A9 | 10f rose red | .20 | .20 |
| 159 | A9 | 20f gray brown | .25 | .20 |
| 162 | A9 | 40f olive green | .20 | .20 |
| 163 | A10 | 1k red brn & claret | .25 | .25 |
| 164 | A10 | 2k ol brn & bis | .25 | .25 |
| 165 | A10 | 3k dk violet & ind | .50 | .50 |
| 166 | A10 | 5k dk brn & lt brn | 1.50 | 1.50 |
| 167 | A10 | 10k vio brn & vio | .90 | .90 |

**On Stamps of 1918**

| | | | | |
|---|---|---|---|---|
| 168 | A11 | 10f scarlet | .20 | .20 |
| 169 | A11 | 15f deep violet | .20 | .20 |
| 170 | A11 | 20f dark brown | .20 | .20 |
| 171 | A11 | 25f brt blue | .25 | .20 |
| 172 | A12 | 40f olive green | .25 | .20 |
| 173 | A12 | 50f lilac | .25 | .20 |
| | | *Nos. 153-173 (19)* | 6.40 | 6.20 |

Nos. 153-164 exist imperf. Value, set $70.
Nos. 153-162, 168-173 exist with overprint inverted. Value, each $6.

A13        A14

**1919-20**       *Perf. 15*

| | | | | |
|---|---|---|---|---|
| 174 | A13 | 2f brown orange | .20 | .20 |
| 176 | A13 | 4f slate gray | .20 | .20 |
| 177 | A13 | 5f yellow grn | .20 | .20 |
| 178 | A13 | 6f grnsh blue | .20 | .20 |
| 179 | A13 | 10f red | .20 | .20 |
| 180 | A13 | 15f violet | .20 | .20 |
| 181 | A13 | 20f dark brown | .20 | .20 |
| 182 | A13 | 20f green ('20) | .20 | .20 |
| 183 | A13 | 25f dull blue | .20 | .20 |
| 184 | A13 | 40f olive green | .20 | .20 |
| 185 | A13 | 40f rose red ('20) | .20 | .20 |
| 186 | A13 | 45f orange | .20 | .20 |

           *Perf. 14*

| | | | | |
|---|---|---|---|---|
| 187 | A14 | 50f brn vio & pale vio | .25 | .25 |
| 188 | A14 | 60f brown & bl ('20) | .25 | .25 |
| 189 | A14 | 95f dk bl & bl | .25 | .25 |
| 190 | A14 | 1k red brn | .25 | .25 |
| 191 | A14 | 1k dk bl & dull bl ('20) | .25 | .25 |
| 192 | A14 | 1.20k dk grn & grn | .25 | .25 |
| 193 | A14 | 1.40k yellow green | .25 | .25 |
| 194 | A14 | 2k ol brn & bis | .25 | .25 |
| 195 | A14 | 3k dk vio & ind | .25 | .25 |
| 196 | A14 | 5k dk brn & brn | .25 | .25 |
| 197 | A14 | 10k vio brn & red vio | .75 | .75 |
| | | *Nos. 174-197 (23)* | 5.65 | 5.65 |

The 3f red lilac, type A13, was never regularly issued without overprint (Nos. 204 and 312). In 1923 a small quantity was sold by the Government at public auction. Value $4.00.

---

For overprints see Nos. 203-222, 306-330, 1N40, 2N52-2N58, 6N44-6N49, 8N6-8N12, 10N22-10N24, Szeged 34-35.
Nos. 174, 177-179, 181-197 exist imperf. Value set $55.

### Issues of the Soviet Republic

Karl Marx — A15

Sándor Petöfi — A16

Ignác Martinovics — A17

György Dózsa — A18

Friedrich Engels — A19

**Wmk. 137 Horiz.**
**1919, June 14   Litho.   *Perf. 12½x12***

| | | | | |
|---|---|---|---|---|
| 198 | A15 | 20f rose & brown | .75 | .75 |
| 199 | A16 | 45f brn org & dk grn | .75 | .75 |
| 200 | A17 | 60f blue gray & brn | 2.75 | 3.00 |
| 201 | A18 | 75f claret & vio brn | 2.75 | 3.00 |
| 202 | A19 | 80f olive db & blk brn | 2.75 | 3.00 |
| | | *Nos. 198-202 (5)* | 9.75 | 10.50 |

Used values are for favor cancels.
Exist imperf. Value, set $135.

**Wmk. Vertical**

| | | | |
|---|---|---|---|
| 198a | A15 | 20f | 10.00 |
| 199a | A16 | 45f | 10.00 |
| 200a | A17 | 60f | 10.00 |
| 201a | A18 | 75f | 10.00 |
| 202a | A19 | 80f | 20.00 |
| | | *Nos. 198a-202a (5)* | 60.00 |

Nos. 198a-202a were not used postally. "Canceled" examples exist. Same value.

Stamps of 1919 Overprinted in Red

**1919, July 21   Typo.   *Perf. 15***

| | | | | |
|---|---|---|---|---|
| 203 | A13 | 2f brown orange | .20 | .20 |
| 204 | A13 | 3f red lilac | .20 | .20 |
| 205 | A13 | 4f slate gray | .20 | .20 |
| 206 | A13 | 5f yellow green | .20 | .20 |
| 207 | A13 | 6f grnsh blue | .20 | .20 |
| 208 | A13 | 10f red | .20 | .20 |
| 209 | A13 | 15f violet | .20 | .20 |
| 210 | A13 | 20f dark brown | .20 | .20 |

---

| | | | | |
|---|---|---|---|---|
| 211 | A13 | 25f dull blue | .20 | .20 |
| 212 | A13 | 40f olive green | .20 | .20 |
| 213 | A13 | 45f orange | .20 | .20 |

Overprinted in Red

           *Perf. 14*

| | | | | |
|---|---|---|---|---|
| 214 | A14 | 50f brn vio & pale vio | .25 | .25 |
| 215 | A14 | 95f dk blue & blue | .25 | .25 |
| 216 | A14 | 1k red brown | .25 | .25 |
| 217 | A14 | 1.20k dk grn & grn | .25 | .25 |
| 218 | A14 | 1.40k yellow green | .25 | .25 |
| 219 | A14 | 2k ol brn & bister | .80 | .80 |
| 220 | A14 | 3k dk vio & ind | .65 | .65 |
| 221 | A14 | 5k dk brn & brn | .50 | .50 |
| 222 | A14 | 10k vio brn & red vio | 1.00 | 1.00 |
| | | *Nos. 203-222 (20)* | 6.40 | 6.40 |

"Magyar Tanacskösztarsasag" on Nos. 198 to 222 means "Hungarian Soviet Republic."
Nos. 203-218, 221-222 exist imperf. Value, set $115.

### Issues of the Kingdom

Stamps of 1919 Overprinted in Black

**1919, Nov. 16**

| | | | | |
|---|---|---|---|---|
| 306 | A13 | 5f green | .65 | .65 |
| 307 | A13 | 10f rose red | .65 | .65 |
| 308 | A13 | 15f violet | .65 | .65 |
| 309 | A13 | 20f gray brown | .65 | .65 |
| 310 | A13 | 25f dull blue | .65 | .65 |
| | | *Nos. 306-310 (5)* | 3.25 | 3.25 |

Issued to commemorate the Romanian evacuation. The overprint reads: "Entry of the National Army-November 16, 1919."
Forged overprints exist.

Nos. 203 to 213 Overprinted in Black

**1920, Jan. 26**      *Perf. 15*

| | | | | |
|---|---|---|---|---|
| 311 | A13 | 2f brown orange | 1.10 | 1.10 |
| 312 | A13 | 3f red lilac | .20 | .20 |
| 313 | A13 | 4f slate gray | 1.10 | 1.10 |
| 314 | A13 | 5f yellow green | .20 | .20 |
| 315 | A13 | 6f blue green | .30 | .30 |
| 316 | A13 | 10f red | .20 | .20 |
| 317 | A13 | 15f violet | .20 | .20 |
| 318 | A13 | 20f dark brown | .20 | .20 |
| 319 | A13 | 25f dull blue | 1.40 | 1.40 |
| 320 | A13 | 40f olive green | 1.40 | 1.40 |
| 321 | A13 | 45f orange | 1.40 | 1.40 |

---

Nos. 214 to 222 Overprinted in Black

           *Perf. 14*

| | | | | |
|---|---|---|---|---|
| 322 | A14 | 50f brn vio & pale vio | 1.50 | 1.50 |
| 323 | A14 | 95f dk bl & bl | 1.50 | 1.50 |
| 324 | A14 | 1k red brown | 1.50 | 1.50 |
| 325 | A14 | 1.20k dk grn & grn | 1.60 | 1.60 |
| 326 | A14 | 1.40k yellow green | 1.60 | 1.60 |
| 327 | A14 | 2k ol brn & bis | 7.50 | 7.50 |
| 328 | A14 | 3k dk vio & ind | 8.00 | 8.00 |
| 329 | A14 | 5k dk brn & brn | .40 | .40 |
| 330 | A14 | 10k vio brn & red vio | 9.00 | 9.00 |
| | | *Nos. 311-330 (20)* | 40.30 | 40.30 |

Counterfeit overprints exist.

**Types of 1916-18 Issue Denomination Tablets Without Inner Frame on Nos. 350 to 363**

**1920-24**    Wmk. 137    *Perf. 15*

| | | | | |
|---|---|---|---|---|
| 335 | A9 | 5f brown orange | .20 | .15 |
| 336 | A9 | 10f red violet | .20 | .20 |
| 337 | A9 | 40f rose red | .20 | .20 |
| 338 | A9 | 50f yellow green | .20 | .20 |
| 339 | A9 | 50f blue vio ('22) | .20 | .20 |
| 340 | A9 | 60f black | .20 | .20 |
| 341 | A9 | 1k green ('22) | .20 | .20 |
| 342 | A9 | 1½k brown vio ('22) | .20 | .20 |
| 343 | A9 | 2k grnsh blue ('22) | .20 | .20 |
| 344 | A9 | 2½k dp green ('22) | .20 | .20 |
| 345 | A9 | 3k brown org ('22) | .20 | .20 |
| 346 | A9 | 4k lt red ('22) | .20 | .20 |
| 347 | A9 | 4½k dull violet ('22) | .40 | .20 |
| 348 | A9 | 5k deep brown ('22) | .20 | .20 |
| 349 | A9 | 6k dark blue ('22) | .20 | .20 |
| 350 | A9 | 10k brown ('22) | .20 | .20 |
| 351 | A9 | 15k slate ('23) | .20 | .20 |
| 352 | A9 | 20k red vio ('23) | .20 | .20 |
| 353 | A9 | 25k orange ('23) | .20 | .20 |
| 354 | A9 | 40k gray grn ('23) | .20 | .20 |
| 355 | A9 | 50k dark blue ('23) | .20 | .20 |
| 356 | A9 | 100k claret ('23) | .25 | .20 |
| 357 | A9 | 150k dark green ('23) | .35 | .20 |
| 358 | A9 | 200k green ('23) | .35 | .20 |
| 359 | A9 | 300k rose red ('24) | .50 | .20 |
| 360 | A9 | 350k violet ('23) | 1.25 | .20 |
| 361 | A9 | 500k dark gray ('24) | 1.50 | .20 |
| 362 | A9 | 600k olive bis ('24) | 1.50 | .20 |
| 363 | A9 | 800k org yel ('24) | 2.10 | .20 |

           *Perf. 14*

| | | | | |
|---|---|---|---|---|
| 364 | A10 | 2.50k bl & gray bl | .25 | .20 |
| 365 | A10 | 3.50k gray | .25 | .20 |
| 366 | A10 | 10k brown ('22) | .60 | .20 |
| 367 | A10 | 15k dk gray ('22) | .25 | .20 |
| 368 | A10 | 20k red vio ('22) | .25 | .20 |
| 369 | A10 | 25k orange ('22) | .25 | .20 |
| 370 | A10 | 30k claret ('22) | .25 | .20 |
| 371 | A10 | 40k gray grn ('22) | .25 | .20 |
| 372 | A10 | 50k dp blue ('22) | .25 | .20 |
| 373 | A10 | 100k yel brn ('22) | .25 | .20 |
| 374 | A10 | 400k turq bl ('23) | .85 | .30 |
| 375 | A10 | 500k brt vio ('23) | .80 | .20 |
| 376 | A10 | 1000k lilac ('24) | .90 | .20 |
| 377 | A10 | 2000k car ('24) | 2.00 | .20 |
| | | *Nos. 335-377 (43)* | 19.60 | 8.70 |

Nos. 372 to 377 have colored numerals.
Nos. 335-338, 340, 350-365, 368, 370, 372-377 exist imperf. Value, set $170.

Madonna and Child — A23

**1921-25　　Typo.　　Perf. 12**

| | | | | |
|---|---|---|---|---|
| 378 | A23 | 50k dk brn & bl | .20 | .20 |
| 379 | A23 | 100k ol bis & yel brn | .30 | .20 |

**Wmk. 133**

| | | | | |
|---|---|---|---|---|
| 380 | A23 | 200k dk bl & ultra | .35 | .20 |
| 381 | A23 | 500k vio brn & vio | .65 | .25 |
| 382 | A23 | 1000k vio & red vio | .90 | .30 |
| 383 | A23 | 2000k grnsh bl & vio | 1.25 | .45 |
| 384 | A23 | 2500k ol brn & buff | 1.50 | .35 |
| 385 | A23 | 3000k brn red & vio | 1.50 | .35 |
| 386 | A23 | 5000k dk grn & yel grn | 1.50 | .35 |
| a. | | Center inverted | 15,000. | 8,000. |
| 387 | A23 | 10000k gray vio & pale bl | 1.50 | 1.25 |
| | | Nos. 378-387 (10) | 9.65 | 3.90 |

Nos. 380-387 exist imperf. Value, set of 8, $200.

Issue dates: 50k, 100k, Feb. 27, 1921; 2500k, 10,000k, 1925; others, 1923.

**Types of 1916-18 Denomination Tablets Without Inner Frame on Nos. 388-394**

**1924　　Wmk. 133　　Perf. 15**

| | | | | |
|---|---|---|---|---|
| 388 | A9 | 100k claret | .25 | .20 |
| 389 | A9 | 200k yellow grn | .20 | .20 |
| 390 | A9 | 300k rose red | .25 | .20 |
| 391 | A9 | 400k deep blue | .25 | .20 |
| 392 | A9 | 500k dark gray | .30 | .20 |
| 393 | A9 | 600k olive bister | .40 | .25 |
| a. | | "800" in upper right corner | 140.00 | 140.00 |
| 394 | A9 | 800k org yel | .45 | .20 |

**Perf. 14½x14**

| | | | | |
|---|---|---|---|---|
| 395 | A10 | 1000k lilac | 1.10 | .20 |
| 396 | A10 | 2000k carmine | 1.60 | .20 |
| | | Nos. 388-396 (9) | 4.80 | 1.85 |

Nos. 395 and 396 have colored numerals. Exist imperf. Value, set $35.

Maurus Jókai (1825-1904), Novelist A24

**1925, Feb. 1　　Unwmk.　　Perf. 12**

| | | | | |
|---|---|---|---|---|
| 400 | A24 | 1000k dp grn & blk brn | 5.50 | 5.50 |
| 401 | A24 | 2000k lt brn & blk brn | 2.50 | .65 |
| 402 | A24 | 2500k dk bl & blk brn | 5.50 | 5.50 |
| | | Nos. 400-402 (3) | 13.50 | 11.65 |

Exist imperf. Value, set $70.

Crown of St. Stephen A25

Matthias Cathedral A26

Palace at Budapest — A27

**1926-27　　Wmk. 133　　Litho.**

**Perf. 14, 15**

| | | | | |
|---|---|---|---|---|
| 403 | A25 | 1f dk gray | .45 | .20 |
| 404 | A25 | 2f lt blue | .50 | .20 |
| 405 | A25 | 3f orange | .50 | .20 |
| 406 | A25 | 4f violet | .60 | .20 |
| 407 | A25 | 6f lt green | .65 | .20 |
| 408 | A25 | 8f lilac rose | 1.40 | .20 |

**Typo.**

| | | | | |
|---|---|---|---|---|
| 409 | A26 | 10f deep blue | 1.75 | .20 |
| 410 | A26 | 16f dark violet | 1.75 | .20 |
| 411 | A26 | 20f carmine | 2.10 | .20 |
| 412 | A26 | 25f lt brown | 1.90 | .20 |

**Perf. 14½x14**

| | | | | |
|---|---|---|---|---|
| 413 | A27 | 32f dp vio & brt vio | 4.50 | .20 |
| 414 | A27 | 40f dk blue & blue | 5.75 | .20 |
| | | Nos. 403-414 (12) | 21.85 | 2.40 |

See Nos. 428-436. For surcharges see Nos. 450-456, 466-467.

Nos. 403-414, 418-421 exist imperf. Value, set $180.

Madonna and Child — A28

**1926-27　　Engr.　　Perf. 14**

| | | | | |
|---|---|---|---|---|
| 415 | A28 | 1p violet | 16.00 | .50 |
| 416 | A28 | 2p red | 16.00 | .75 |
| 417 | A28 | 5p blue ('27) | 16.00 | 2.75 |
| | | Nos. 415-417 (3) | 48.00 | 4.00 |

Exist imperf. Value, set $240.

Palace at Budapest A29　　St. Stephen A30

**1926-27　　Typo.**

| | | | | |
|---|---|---|---|---|
| 418 | A29 | 30f blue grn ('27) | 4.00 | .20 |
| 419 | A29 | 46f ultra ('27) | 5.25 | .30 |
| 420 | A29 | 50f brown blk ('27) | 6.00 | .20 |
| 421 | A29 | 70f scarlet | 9.75 | .20 |
| | | Nos. 418-421 (4) | 25.00 | .90 |

For surcharge see No. 480.

**1928-29　　Engr.　　Perf. 15**

| | | | | |
|---|---|---|---|---|
| 422 | A30 | 8f yellow grn | .65 | .30 |
| 423 | A30 | 8f rose lake ('29) | .65 | .30 |
| 424 | A30 | 16f orange red | .85 | .30 |
| 425 | A30 | 16f violet ('29) | .85 | .30 |
| 426 | A30 | 32f ultra | 2.25 | 1.10 |
| 427 | A30 | 32f bister ('29) | 2.25 | 1.10 |
| | | Nos. 422-427 (6) | 7.50 | 3.40 |

890th death anniversary of St. Stephen, the first king of Hungary.
Exist imperf. Value, set $160.

**Types of 1926-27 Issue**

**Perf. 14, 15**

**1928-30　　Typo.　　Wmk. 210**

| | | | | |
|---|---|---|---|---|
| 428 | A25 | 1f dk gray | .25 | .20 |
| 429 | A25 | 2f blue | .35 | .20 |
| 430 | A25 | 3f orange | .35 | .20 |
| 431 | A25 | 4f violet | .35 | .20 |
| 432 | A25 | 6f blue grn | .60 | .20 |
| 433 | A25 | 8f lilac rose | 1.10 | .20 |
| 434 | A26 | 10f dp blue ('30) | 4.50 | .20 |
| 435 | A26 | 16f violet | 1.75 | .20 |
| 436 | A26 | 20f dull red | 1.75 | .20 |
| | | Nos. 428-436 (9) | 11.00 | 1.80 |

On #428-433 the numerals have thicker strokes than on the same values of the 1926-27 issue.
Exist imperf. Value, set $55.

Palace at Budapest — A31

Type A31 resembles A27 but the steamer is nearer the right of the design.

**1928-31　　Perf. 14**

| | | | | |
|---|---|---|---|---|
| 437 | A31 | 30f emerald ('31) | 3.25 | .20 |
| 438 | A31 | 32f red violet | 4.00 | .30 |
| 439 | A31 | 40f deep blue | 4.75 | .20 |
| 440 | A31 | 46f apple green | 4.00 | .20 |
| 441 | A31 | 50f ocher ('31) | 4.00 | .20 |
| | | Nos. 437-441 (5) | 20.00 | 1.10 |

Exist imperf. Value, set $55.

Admiral Nicholas Horthy — A32

**1930, Mar. 1　　Litho.　　Perf. 15**

| | | | | |
|---|---|---|---|---|
| 445 | A32 | 8f myrtle green | 1.60 | .30 |
| 446 | A32 | 16f purple | 1.60 | .35 |
| 447 | A32 | 20f carmine | 4.00 | 1.10 |
| 448 | A32 | 32f olive brown | 4.00 | 3.75 |
| 449 | A32 | 40f dull blue | 7.75 | 1.65 |
| | | Nos. 445-449 (5) | 18.95 | 7.15 |

10th anniv. of the election of Adm. Nicholas Horthy as Regent, Mar. 1, 1920.
Exist imperf. Value, set $180.

**Stamps of 1926-28 Surcharged**

**1931, Jan. 1　　Perf. 14, 15**

| | | | | |
|---|---|---|---|---|
| 450 | A25 | 2f on 3f orange | 1.00 | .40 |
| 451 | A25 | 6f on 8f magenta | 1.00 | .20 |
| a. | | Perf. 14 | 25.00 | 25.00 |
| 452 | A26 | 10f on 16f violet | .90 | .20 |

**Wmk. 133**

| | | | | |
|---|---|---|---|---|
| 453 | A25 | 2f on 3f orange | 3.50 | 3.00 |
| 454 | A25 | 6f on 8f magenta | 2.75 | 3.00 |
| a. | | Perf. 14 | 65.00 | 65.00 |
| 455 | A26 | 10f on 16f dk vio | 2.25 | 1.50 |
| 456 | A26 | 20f on 25f lt brn | 2.25 | 1.25 |
| a. | | Perf. 14 | 1.50 | 1.50 |
| | | Nos. 450-456 (7) | 13.65 | 9.55 |

For surcharges see Nos. 466-467.

St. Elizabeth A33　　Ministering to Children A34

**Wmk. 210**

**1932, Apr. 21　　Photo.　　Perf. 15**

| | | | | |
|---|---|---|---|---|
| 458 | A33 | 10f ultra | 1.25 | .60 |
| 459 | A33 | 20f scarlet | 1.25 | .60 |

**Perf. 14**

| | | | | |
|---|---|---|---|---|
| 460 | A34 | 32f deep violet | 4.00 | 2.50 |
| 461 | A34 | 40f deep blue | 3.00 | 1.75 |
| | | Nos. 458-461 (4) | 9.50 | 5.45 |

700th anniv. of the death of St. Elizabeth of Hungary.
Exist imperf. Value, set $70.

Madonna, Patroness of Hungary — A35

**1932, June 1　　Perf. 12**

| | | | | |
|---|---|---|---|---|
| 462 | A35 | 1p yellow grn | 20.00 | .85 |
| 463 | A35 | 2p carmine | 22.50 | 1.50 |
| 464 | A35 | 5p deep blue | 85.00 | 5.00 |
| 465 | A35 | 10p olive bister | 125.00 | 30.00 |
| | | Nos. 462-465 (4) | 252.50 | 37.35 |

Exist imperf. Value, set $600.

**Nos. 451 and 454 Surcharged**

**1932, June 14　　Wmk. 210　　Perf. 15**

| | | | | |
|---|---|---|---|---|
| 466 | A25 | 2f on 6f on 8f mag | 1.50 | .40 |

**Wmk. 133**

| | | | | |
|---|---|---|---|---|
| 467 | A25 | 2f on 6f on 8f mag | 50.00 | 40.00 |

Imre Madách — A36

Designs: 2f, Janos Arany. 4f, Dr. Ignaz Semmelweis. 6f, Baron Roland Eotvos. 10f, Count Stephen Szechenyi. 16f, Ferenc Deak. 20f, Franz Liszt. 30f, Louis Kossuth. 32f, Stephen Tisza. 40f, Mihaly Munkacsy. 50f, Alexander Csoma. 70f, Farkas Bolyai.

**1932　　Wmk. 210　　Perf. 15**

| | | | | |
|---|---|---|---|---|
| 468 | A36 | 1f slate violet | .20 | .20 |
| 469 | A36 | 2f orange | .20 | .20 |
| 470 | A36 | 4f ultra | .20 | .20 |
| 471 | A36 | 6f yellow grn | .20 | .20 |
| 472 | A36 | 10f Prus green | .20 | .20 |
| 473 | A36 | 16f dull violet | .25 | .20 |
| 474 | A36 | 20f deep rose | .20 | .20 |
| 475 | A36 | 30f brown | .45 | .20 |
| 476 | A36 | 32f brown vio | .70 | .45 |
| 477 | A36 | 40f dull blue | .70 | .20 |
| 478 | A36 | 50f deep green | 1.10 | .20 |
| 479 | A36 | 70f cerise | 1.50 | .20 |
| | | Nos. 468-479 (12) | 5.90 | 2.65 |
| | | Set, never hinged | 11.50 | |

Issued in honor of famous Hungarians. Exist imperf. Value, set $70.
See Nos. 509-510.

No. 421 Surcharged

**1933, Apr. 15　　Wmk. 133　　Perf. 14**

| | | | | |
|---|---|---|---|---|
| 480 | A29 | 10f on 70f scarlet | 3.00 | .25 |
| | | Never hinged | 6.00 | |

Leaping Stag and Double Cross — A47

**Wmk. 210**

**1933, July 10　　Photo.　　Perf. 15**

| | | | | |
|---|---|---|---|---|
| 481 | A47 | 10f dk green | 1.00 | 1.25 |
| 482 | A47 | 16f violet brn | 1.50 | 2.50 |
| 483 | A47 | 20f car lake | 1.75 | 1.25 |
| 484 | A47 | 32f yellow | 3.75 | 4.00 |
| 485 | A47 | 40f deep blue | 4.25 | 4.00 |
| | | Nos. 481-485 (5) | 12.25 | 13.00 |
| | | Set, never hinged | 35.00 | |

Boy Scout Jamboree at Gödöllö, Hungary, July 20 - Aug. 20, 1933.
Exists imperf. Value, set $135.

**Souvenir Sheet**

Franz Liszt — A48

**1934, May 6　　Perf. 15**

| | | | | |
|---|---|---|---|---|
| 486 | A48 | 20f lake | 60.00 | 100.00 |
| | | Never hinged | 140.00 | |

2nd Hungarian Phil. Exhib., Budapest, and Jubilee of the 1st Hungarian Phil. Soc. Sold for 90f, including entrance fee. Size: 64x76mm.
Exists imperf. Value $1,500.

Francis II Rákóczy (1676-1735), Prince of Transylvania
A49

**1935, Apr. 8** — *Perf. 12*

| | | | | |
|---|---|---|---|---|
| 487 | A49 | 10f yellow green | .40 | .25 |
| 488 | A49 | 16f brt violet | 1.50 | 1.10 |
| 489 | A49 | 20f dark carmine | .50 | .25 |
| 490 | A49 | 32f brown lake | 2.25 | 1.00 |
| 491 | A49 | 40f blue | 3.00 | 2.00 |
| | | Nos. 487-491 (5) | 7.65 | 4.60 |
| | | Set, never hinged | 18.50 | |

Exists imperf. Value, set $375.

Cardinal Pázmány — A50

Signing the Charter — A51

**1935, Sept. 25**

| | | | | |
|---|---|---|---|---|
| 492 | A50 | 6f dull green | 1.10 | 1.00 |
| 493 | A51 | 10f dark green | .40 | .35 |
| 494 | A50 | 16f slate violet | 1.50 | 1.25 |
| 495 | A50 | 20f magenta | .45 | .40 |
| 496 | A51 | 32f deep claret | 3.50 | 1.60 |
| 497 | A51 | 40f dark blue | 3.00 | 1.60 |
| | | Nos. 492-497 (6) | 9.95 | 6.20 |
| | | Set, never hinged | 17.00 | |

Tercentenary of the founding of the University of Budapest by Peter Cardinal Pázmány. Exists imperf. Value, set $340.

Ancient City and Fortress of Buda — A52

Guardian Angel over Buda — A53

Shield of Buda, Cannon and Massed Flags — A54

First Hungarian Soldier to Enter Buda — A55

**1936, Sept. 2** — *Perf. 11½x12½*

| | | | | |
|---|---|---|---|---|
| 498 | A52 | 10f dark green | .75 | .45 |
| 499 | A53 | 16f deep violet | 2.00 | 3.00 |
| 500 | A54 | 20f car lake | .75 | .65 |
| 501 | A55 | 32f dark brown | 2.00 | 4.00 |
| 502 | A52 | 40f deep blue | 2.25 | 4.75 |
| | | Nos. 498-502 (5) | 7.75 | 12.85 |
| | | Set, never hinged | 20.00 | |

250th anniv. of the recapture of Budapest from the Turks.

---

Exists imperf. Value, set $375.

> **Catalogue values for unused stamps in this section, from this point to the end of the section, are for Never Hinged items.**

Budapest International Fair — A56

**1937, Feb. 22** — *Perf. 12*

| | | | | |
|---|---|---|---|---|
| 503 | A56 | 2f deep orange | .20 | .20 |
| 504 | A56 | 6f yellow green | .25 | .20 |
| 505 | A56 | 10f myrtle green | .30 | .20 |
| 506 | A56 | 20f deep cerise | .50 | .25 |
| 507 | A56 | 32f dark violet | 1.00 | .70 |
| 508 | A56 | 40f ultra | 1.25 | .70 |
| | | Nos. 503-508 (6) | 3.50 | 2.25 |

Exist imperf. Value, set $500.

**Portrait Type of 1932**

5f, Ferenc Kolcsey. 25f, Mihaly Vorosmarty.

**1937, May 5** — *Perf. 15*

| | | | | |
|---|---|---|---|---|
| 509 | A36 | 5f brown orange | .20 | .20 |
| 510 | A36 | 25f olive green | .45 | .20 |

Exist imperf. Value, set $250.

Pope Sylvester II, Archbishop Astrik — A59

Designs: 2f, 16f, Stephen the Church builder. 4f, 20f, St. Stephen enthroned. 5f, 25f, Sts. Gerhardt, Emerich, Stephen. 6f, 30f, St. Stephen offering holy crown to Virgin Mary. 10f, same as 1f. 32f, 50f, Portrait of St. Stephen. 40f, Madonna and Child. 70f, Crown of St. Stephen.

See designs A75-A77 for smaller stamps of designs similar Nos. 521-524, but with slanted "MAGYAR KIR POSTA."

**1938, Jan. 1** — *Perf. 12*

| | | | | |
|---|---|---|---|---|
| 511 | A59 | 1f deep violet | .20 | .20 |
| 512 | A59 | 2f olive brown | .20 | .20 |
| 513 | A59 | 4f brt blue | .20 | .20 |
| 514 | A59 | 5f magenta | .20 | .20 |
| 515 | A59 | 6f dp yel grn | .50 | .20 |
| 516 | A59 | 10f red orange | .60 | .20 |
| 517 | A59 | 16f gray violet | .60 | .25 |
| 518 | A59 | 20f car lake | .80 | .20 |
| 519 | A59 | 25f dark green | 1.10 | .50 |
| 520 | A59 | 30f olive bister | 2.50 | .20 |
| 521 | A59 | 32f dp claret, *buff* | 1.10 | .90 |
| 522 | A59 | 40f Prus green | 3.25 | .20 |
| 523 | A59 | 50f rose vio, *grnsh* | 4.75 | .20 |
| 524 | A59 | 70f ol grn, *bluish* | 6.00 | .20 |
| | | Nos. 511-524 (14) | 22.00 | 3.85 |

900th anniv. of the death of St. Stephen. Exists imperf. Value, set $550. For overprints see Nos. 535-536.

Admiral Horthy — A67

**1938, Jan. 1** — *Perf. 12½x12*

| | | | | |
|---|---|---|---|---|
| 525 | A67 | 1p peacock green | 4.00 | .20 |
| 526 | A67 | 2p brown | 4.00 | .25 |
| 527 | A67 | 5p sapphire blue | 8.00 | 1.10 |
| | | Nos. 525-527 (3) | 16.00 | 2.20 |

Exist imperf. Value, set $475.

---

Souvenir Sheet

St. Stephen — A68

**1938, May 22** — **Wmk. 210** — *Perf. 12*

| | | | | |
|---|---|---|---|---|
| 528 | A68 | 20f carmine lake | 25.00 | 17.50 |

3rd Hungarian Phil. Exhib., Budapest. Sheet sold only at exhibition with 1p ticket. Exists imperf. Value $3,500.

College of Debrecen
A69

Three Students — A71      George Marothy — A73

10f, 18th cent. view of College. 20f, 19th cent. view of College. 40f, Stephen Hatvani.

***Perf. 12x12½, 12½x12***

**1938, Sept. 24** — **Wmk. 210**

| | | | | |
|---|---|---|---|---|
| 529 | A69 | 6f deep green | .20 | .20 |
| 530 | A69 | 10f brown | .20 | .20 |
| 531 | A71 | 16f brown car | .30 | .20 |
| 532 | A69 | 20f crimson | .25 | .20 |
| 533 | A73 | 32f slate green | .80 | .45 |
| 534 | A73 | 40f brt blue | .90 | .30 |
| | | Nos. 529-534 (6) | 2.65 | 1.55 |

Founding of Debrecen College, 400th anniv. Exists imperf. Value $350.

**Types of 1938 Overprinted in Blue (#535) or Carmine (#536):**

a

b

**1938** — *Perf. 12*

| | | | | |
|---|---|---|---|---|
| 535 | A59(a) | 20f salmon pink | 1.25 | .50 |
| 536 | A59(b) | 70f brn, *grnsh* | 1.40 | .50 |
| *a.* | | Overprint omitted | 12,000. | 8,000. |

Restoration of the territory ceded by Czechoslovakia. Exists imperf. Value $135. Forgeries exist of No. 536a.

---

Crown of St. Stephen
A75

St. Stephen
A76

Madonna, Patroness of Hungary
A77

Coronation Church, Budapest
A78

Reformed Church, Debrecen
A79

Cathedral, Esztergom
A80

Deak Square Evangelical Church, Budapest — A81

Cathedral of Kassa — A82

**Wmk. 210**

**1939, June 1** — **Photo.** — *Perf. 15*

| | | | | |
|---|---|---|---|---|
| 537 | A75 | 1f brown car | .20 | .20 |
| 538 | A75 | 2f Prus green | .20 | .20 |
| 539 | A75 | 4f ocher | .20 | .20 |
| 540 | A75 | 5f brown violet | .20 | .20 |
| 541 | A75 | 6f yellow green | .20 | .20 |
| 542 | A75 | 10f bister brn | .20 | .20 |
| 543 | A75 | 16f rose violet | .20 | .20 |
| 544 | A75 | 20f rose red | .20 | .20 |
| 545 | A77 | 25f blue gray | .20 | .20 |

*Perf. 12*

| | | | | |
|---|---|---|---|---|
| 546 | A78 | 30f red violet | .50 | .20 |
| 547 | A79 | 32f brown | .40 | .20 |
| 548 | A80 | 40f greenish blue | .50 | .20 |
| 549 | A81 | 50f olive | .50 | .20 |
| 550 | A82 | 70f henna brown | .55 | .20 |
| | | Nos. 537-550 (14) | 4.25 | 2.80 |

See #578-596. For overprints see #559-560. Exist imperf. Value, set $350.

Girl Scout Sign and Olive Branch — A83

6f, Scout lily, Hungary's shield, Crown of St. Stephen. 10f, Girls in Scout hat & national headdress. 20f, Dove & Scout emblems.

**1939, July 20** — **Photo.** — *Perf. 12*

| | | | | |
|---|---|---|---|---|
| 551 | A83 | 2f brown orange | .40 | .35 |
| 552 | A83 | 6f green | .45 | .35 |
| 553 | A83 | 10f brown | .75 | .35 |
| 554 | A83 | 20f lilac rose | .90 | .70 |
| | | Nos. 551-554 (4) | 2.50 | 1.75 |

Girl Scout Jamboree at Gödöllö. Exist imperf. Value, set $400.

Admiral Horthy at Szeged, 1919 — A87

Admiral Nicholas Horthy A88

Cathedral of Kassa and Angel Ringing "Bell of Liberty" A89

**1940, Mar. 1**

| 555 | A87 | 6f green | .30 | .20 |
|-----|-----|----------|-----|-----|
| 556 | A88 | 10f ol blk & ol bis | .30 | .20 |
| 557 | A89 | 20f brt rose brown | .60 | .35 |
| | | Nos. 555-557 (3) | 1.20 | .75 |

20th anniversary of the election of Admiral Horthy as Regent of Hungary.
Exist imperf. Value, set $135.

Crown of St. Stephen A90

**1940, Sept. 5**

| 558 | A90 | 10f dk green & yellow | .20 | .20 |
|-----|-----|----------------------|-----|-----|

Issued in commemoration of the recovery of northeastern Transylvania from Romania.
Exists imperf. Value $35.

Nos. 542, 544 Overprinted in Red or Black

**1941, Apr. 21**     *Perf. 15*

| 559 | A75 | 10f bister brn (R) | .25 | .20 |
|-----|-----|--------------------|-----|-----|
| 560 | A76 | 20f rose red (Bk) | .25 | .20 |

Return of the Bacska territory from Yugoslavia.
Exist imperf. Value, set $70.

Admiral Nicholas Horthy — A92

**Wmk. 210**
**1941, June 18**   *Photo.*   *Perf. 12*

| 570 | A92 | 1p dk green & buff | .25 | .20 |
|-----|-----|--------------------|-----|-----|
| 571 | A92 | 2p dk brown & buff | .25 | .20 |
| 572 | A92 | 5p dk rose vio & buff | 2.00 | .40 |
| | | Nos. 570-572 (3) | 2.50 | .80 |

Exist imperf. Value, set $100.
See Nos. 597-599.

Count Stephen Széchenyi A93

Count Széchenyi and Royal Academy of Science A94

Representation of the Narrows of Kazán — A95

Chain Bridge, Budapest A96

Mercury, Train and Boat — A97

**1941, Sept. 21**

| 573 | A93 | 10f dk olive grn | .20 | .20 |
|-----|-----|-------------------|-----|-----|
| 574 | A94 | 16f olive brown | .20 | .20 |
| 575 | A95 | 20f carmine lake | .20 | .20 |
| 576 | A96 | 32f red orange | .30 | .20 |
| 577 | A97 | 40f royal blue | .30 | .20 |
| | | Nos. 573-577 (5) | 1.20 | 1.00 |

Count Stephen Szechenyi (1791-1860).
Exist imperf. Value, set $350.

Types of 1939
*Perf. 12x12½, 12½x12, 15*

**1941-43**     **Wmk. 266**

| 578 | A75 | 1f rose lake ('42) | .20 | .20 |
|-----|-----|---------------------|-----|-----|
| 579 | A75 | 3f dark brown | .20 | .20 |
| 580 | A75 | 5f violet gray ('42) | .20 | .20 |
| 581 | A75 | 6f lt green ('42) | .20 | .20 |
| 582 | A75 | 8f slate grn | .20 | .20 |
| 583 | A75 | 10f olive brn ('42) | .20 | .20 |
| 584 | A75 | 12f red orange | .20 | .20 |
| 585 | A76 | 20f rose red ('42) | .20 | .20 |
| 586 | A76 | 24f brown violet | .20 | .20 |
| 587 | A78 | 30f lilac ('42) | .20 | .20 |
| 588 | A82 | 30f rose red ('43) | .20 | .20 |
| 589 | A80 | 40f blue green ('42) | .20 | .20 |
| 590 | A79 | 40f gray black ('43) | .20 | .20 |
| 591 | A81 | 50f olive grn ('42) | .20 | .20 |
| 592 | A80 | 50f brt blue ('43) | .20 | .20 |
| 593 | A82 | 70f copper red ('42) | .20 | .20 |
| 594 | A81 | 70f gray green ('43) | .20 | .20 |
| 595 | A77 | 80f brown bister | .20 | .20 |
| 596 | A78 | 80f bister brn ('43) | .20 | .20 |
| | | Nos. 578-596 (19) | 3.80 | 3.80 |

Exist imperf. Value, set $350.

Horthy Type of 1941
*Perf. 12x12½*

**1941, Dec. 18**     **Wmk. 266**

| 597 | A92 | 1p dk green & buff | .60 | .20 |
|-----|-----|---------------------|-----|-----|
| 598 | A92 | 2p dk brown & buff | .30 | .20 |
| 599 | A92 | 5p dk rose vio & buff | .60 | .20 |
| | | Nos. 597-599 (3) | 1.50 | .60 |

Exist imperf. Value, set $60.

Stephen Horthy — A98

**1942, Oct. 15**     *Perf. 12*

| 600 | A98 | 20f black | .20 | .20 |
|-----|-----|-----------|-----|-----|

Death of Stephen Horthy (1904-42), son of Regent Nicholas Horthy, who died in a plane crash.
Exists imperf. Value $55.

Arpád — A99     A109

Portraits: 2f, King Ladislaus I. 3f, Miklós Toldi. 4f, János Hunyadi. 5f, Paul Kinizsi. 6f, Count Miklós Zrinyi. 8f, Francis II Rákóczy. 10f, Count Andrew Hadik. 12f, Arthur Görgei. 18f, 24f, Virgin Mary, Patroness of Hungary.

**1943-45**     *Perf. 15*

| 601 | A99 | 1f grnsh black | .20 | .20 |
|-----|-----|-----------------|-----|-----|
| 602 | A99 | 2f red orange | .20 | .20 |
| 603 | A99 | 3f ultra | .20 | .20 |
| 604 | A99 | 4f brown | .20 | .20 |
| 605 | A99 | 5f vermilion | .20 | .20 |
| 606 | A99 | 6f slate blue | .20 | .20 |
| 607 | A99 | 8f dk ol grn | .20 | .20 |
| 608 | A99 | 10f brown | .20 | .20 |
| 609 | A99 | 12f dp blue grn | .20 | .20 |
| 610 | A99 | 18f dk gray | .20 | .20 |
| 611 | A109 | 20f chestnut brn | .20 | .20 |
| 612 | A99 | 24f rose violet | .20 | .20 |
| 613 | A109 | 30f brt carmine | .20 | .20 |
| 614 | A109 | 50f blue | .20 | .20 |
| 615 | A109 | 80f yellow brn | .20 | .20 |
| 616 | A109 | 1p green | .30 | .20 |
| 616A | A109 | 2p brown ('45) | .50 | .60 |
| 616B | A109 | 5p dk red violet ('45) | .85 | 1.00 |
| | | Nos. 601-616B (18) | 4.65 | 4.80 |

Exist imperf. Value, set $175.
For overprints and surcharges see Nos. 631-658, 660-661, 664, 666-669, 671-672, 674-677, 679, 680, 682, 685-689, 691-698, 801-803, 805-806, 810-815, F2, Q2-Q3, Q7.

Message to the Shepherds A110

St. Margaret — A113

20f, Nativity. 30f, Adoration of the Magi.

**1943, Dec. 1**     *Perf. 12x12½*

| 617 | A110 | 4f dark green | .20 | .20 |
|-----|------|----------------|-----|-----|
| 618 | A110 | 20f dull blue | .20 | .20 |
| 619 | A110 | 30f brown orange | .20 | .20 |
| | | Nos. 617-619 (3) | .60 | .60 |

Exist imperf. Value, set $175.

**1944, Jan. 19**     *Perf. 15*

| 620 | A113 | 30f deep carmine | .20 | .20 |
|-----|------|-------------------|-----|-----|

Canonization of St. Margaret of Hungary.
Exists imperf. Value $55.
For surcharges see Nos. 662, 673A.

Kossuth with Family — A114     Lajos Kossuth — A117

Honvéd Drummer A115

Design: 30f, Kossuth orating.

**1944, Mar. 20**   *Perf. 12½x12, 12x12½*

| 621 | A114 | 4f yellow brown | .20 | .20 |
|-----|------|------------------|-----|-----|
| 622 | A115 | 20f dk olive grn | .20 | .20 |
| 623 | A115 | 30f henna brown | .20 | .20 |
| 624 | A117 | 50f slate blue | .20 | .20 |
| | | Nos. 621-624 (4) | .80 | .80 |

Louis (Lajos) Kossuth (1802-94).
Exist imperf. Value, set $175.
For surcharges see Nos. B175-B178.

St. Elizabeth — A118

Portraits: 24f, St. Margaret. 30f, Elizabeth Szilágyi. 50f, Dorothy Kanuizsai. 70f, Susanna Lórántffy. 80f, Ilona Zrinyi.

**1944, Aug. 1**     *Perf. 15*

| 625 | A118 | 20f olive | .20 | .20 |
|-----|------|-----------|-----|-----|
| 626 | A118 | 24f rose violet | .20 | .20 |
| 627 | A118 | 30f copper red | .20 | .20 |
| 628 | A118 | 50f dark blue | .20 | .20 |
| 629 | A118 | 70f orange red | .20 | .20 |
| 630 | A118 | 80f brown car | .20 | .20 |
| | | Nos. 625-630 (6) | 1.20 | 1.20 |

Exist imperf. Value, set $160.
For overprints and surcharges see Nos. 659, 663, 665, 670, 673, 678, 681, 683-684, 690, 804, 807-809, F1, F3, Q1, Q4-Q6, Q8.

**Issues of the Republic**

Types of Hungary, 1943 Surcharged in Carmine

**1945, May 1**     **Wmk. 266**
**Blue Surface-tinted Paper**

| 631 | A99 | 10f on 1f grnsh blk | 1.50 | 1.50 |
|-----|-----|----------------------|------|------|
| 632 | A99 | 20f on 3f ultra | 1.50 | 1.50 |
| 633 | A99 | 30f on 4f brown | 1.50 | 1.50 |
| 634 | A99 | 40f on 6f slate bl | 1.50 | 1.50 |
| 635 | A99 | 50f on 8f dk ol grn | 1.50 | 1.50 |
| 636 | A99 | 1p on 10f brown | 1.50 | 1.50 |
| 637 | A99 | 150f on 12f dp bl grn | 1.50 | 1.50 |
| 638 | A99 | 2p on 18f dk gray | 1.50 | 1.50 |
| 639 | A109 | 3p on 20f chnt brn | 1.50 | 1.50 |
| 640 | A99 | 5p on 24f rose vio | 1.50 | 1.50 |
| 641 | A109 | 6p on 50f blue | 1.50 | 1.50 |
| 642 | A109 | 10p on 80f yel brn | 1.50 | 1.50 |
| 643 | A109 | 20p on 1p green | 1.50 | 1.50 |

**Yellow Surface-tinted Paper**

| 644 | A99 | 10f on 1f grnsh blk | 1.50 | 1.50 |
|-----|-----|----------------------|------|------|
| 645 | A99 | 20f on 3f ultra | 1.50 | 1.50 |
| 646 | A99 | 30f on 4f brown | 1.50 | 1.50 |
| 647 | A99 | 40f on 6f slate bl | 1.50 | 1.50 |
| 648 | A99 | 50f on 8f dk ol grn | 1.50 | 1.50 |
| 649 | A99 | 1p on 10f brown | 1.50 | 1.50 |
| 650 | A99 | 150f on 12f dp bl grn | 1.50 | 1.50 |
| 651 | A99 | 2p on 18f dk gray | 1.50 | 1.50 |
| 652 | A109 | 3p on 20f chnt brn | 1.50 | 1.50 |
| 653 | A99 | 5p on 24f rose vio | 1.50 | 1.50 |
| 654 | A109 | 6p on 50f blue | 1.50 | 1.50 |
| 655 | A109 | 10p on 80f yel brn | 1.50 | 1.50 |
| 656 | A109 | 20p on 1p green | 1.50 | 1.50 |
| | | Nos. 631-656 (26) | 39.00 | 39.00 |

Hungary's liberation.

Types of Hungary, 1943-45, Surcharged in Carmine or Black

**1945**

**Blue Surface-tinted Paper**

| 657 | A99 | 10f on 4f brn (C) | .20 | .20 |
|-----|-----|---------------------|-----|-----|
| 658 | A99 | 10f on 10f brn (C) | .45 | .45 |
| 659 | A118 | 20f on 20f ol (C) | .20 | .20 |
| 660 | A99 | 28f on 5f ver | .20 | .20 |
| 661 | A109 | 30f on 30f brt car | .20 | .20 |
| 662 | A113 | 30f on 30f dp car | .20 | .20 |
| 663 | A118 | 30f on 30f cop red | .20 | .20 |
| 664 | A99 | 40f on 10f brown | .20 | .20 |
| 665 | A118 | 1p on 70f org red | .25 | .25 |
| 666 | A109 | 1p on 80f yel brn (C) | | |
| 667 | A99 | 2p on 4f brown | .20 | .20 |

| | | | | |
|---|---|---|---|---|
| 668 | A109 | 2p on 2p brn (C) | .20 | .20 |
| 669 | A109 | 4p on 30f brt car | .20 | .20 |
| 670 | A118 | 8p on 20f olive | .20 | .20 |
| 671 | A99 | 10p on 2f red org | 12.00 | 12.00 |
| 672 | A109 | 10p on 80f yel brn | .20 | .20 |
| 673 | A118 | 20p on 30f cop red | .20 | .20 |

**Same Surcharge with Thinner
Unshaded Numerals of Value**

| | | | | |
|---|---|---|---|---|
| 673A | A113 | 300p on 30f dp car | .20 | .20 |

**Surcharged as Nos. 657-673 Yellow
Surface-tinted Paper**

| | | | | |
|---|---|---|---|---|
| 674 | A99 | 10f on 12f dp bl grn (C) | .20 | .20 |
| 675 | A99 | 20f on 1f grnsh blk (C) | .20 | .20 |
| 676 | A99 | 20f on 18f dk gray (C) | .20 | .20 |
| a. | | Double surcharge | | |
| 677 | A99 | 40f on 24f rose vio (C) | .20 | .20 |
| 678 | A118 | 40f on 24f rose vio (C) | .20 | .20 |
| 679 | A109 | 42f on 20f chnt brn (C) | .20 | .20 |
| 680 | A109 | 50f on 50f bl (C) | .20 | .20 |
| 681 | A118 | 50f on 50f dk bl (C) | .20 | .20 |
| 682 | A99 | 60f on 8f dk ol grn (C) | .20 | .20 |
| 683 | A118 | 80f on 24f rose vio | .20 | .20 |
| 684 | A118 | 80f on 80f brn car (C) | .20 | .20 |
| 685 | A109 | 1p on 20f chnt brn | .20 | .20 |
| 686 | A109 | 1p on 1p grn (C) | .20 | .20 |
| 687 | A99 | 150f on 6f sl bl (C) | .90 | .90 |
| 688 | A99 | 1.60p on 12f dp bl grn | .20 | .20 |
| 689 | A99 | 3p on 3f ultra (C) | .30 | .30 |
| 690 | A118 | 3p on 50f dk bl | .20 | .20 |
| 691 | A99 | 5p on 8f dk ol grn | .20 | .20 |
| 692 | A109 | 5p on 5p dk red vio (C) | .25 | .25 |
| 693 | A109 | 6p on 50f blue | .20 | .20 |
| 694 | A109 | 7p on 1p grn | .20 | .20 |
| 695 | A99 | 9p on 1f grnsh blk | .20 | .20 |

**Same Surcharge with Thinner,
Unshaded Numerals of Value**

| | | | | |
|---|---|---|---|---|
| 696 | A99 | 40p on 8f dk ol grn | .20 | .20 |
| 697 | A99 | 60p on 18f dk gray | .20 | .20 |
| 698 | A99 | 100p on 12f dp bl grn | .20 | .20 |
| | | Nos. 657-698 (43) | 21.55 | 21.55 |

Various shades and errors of overprint exist on Nos. 657-698.
These surface-tinted stamps exist without surcharge, but were not so issued.

Construction
A124

Designs: 1.60p, Manufacturing. 2p, Railroading. 3p, Building. 5p, Agriculture. 8p, Communications. 10p, Architecture. 20p, Writing.

**1945, Sept. 11**     **Wmk. 266**
    **Photo.**     **Perf. 12**

| | | | | |
|---|---|---|---|---|
| 700 | A124 | 40f gray black | 7.00 | 7.00 |
| 701 | A124 | 1.60p olive bis | 7.00 | 7.00 |
| 702 | A124 | 2p slate green | 7.00 | 7.00 |
| 703 | A124 | 3p dark purple | 7.00 | 7.00 |
| 704 | A124 | 5p dark red | 7.00 | 7.00 |
| 705 | A124 | 8p brown | 7.00 | 7.00 |
| 706 | A124 | 10p deep claret | 7.00 | 7.00 |
| 707 | A124 | 20p slate blue | 7.00 | 7.00 |
| | | Nos. 700-707 (8) | 56.00 | 56.00 |

World Trade Union Conf., Paris, Sept. 25 to Oct. 10, 1945.
Exist imperf. Value, set $500.

"Reconstruction" — A132

**1945-46**

| | | | | |
|---|---|---|---|---|
| 708 | A132 | 12p brown olive | .25 | .25 |
| 709 | A132 | 20p brt green | .20 | .20 |
| 710 | A132 | 24p orange brn | .25 | .25 |
| 711 | A132 | 30p gray black | .20 | .20 |
| 712 | A132 | 40p olive green | .20 | .20 |
| 713 | A132 | 60p red orange | .20 | .20 |
| 714 | A132 | 100p orange yel | .20 | .20 |
| 715 | A132 | 120p brt ultra | .20 | .20 |
| 716 | A132 | 140p brt red | .40 | .40 |
| 717 | A132 | 200p olive brn | .20 | .20 |
| 718 | A132 | 240p brt blue | .20 | .20 |
| 719 | A132 | 300p dk carmine | .20 | .20 |
| 720 | A132 | 500p dull green | .20 | .20 |
| 721 | A132 | 1000p red violet | .20 | .20 |
| 722 | A132 | 3000p brt red ('46) | .20 | .20 |
| | | Nos. 708-722 (15) | 3.30 | 3.30 |

#708-721 exist tête bêche. Value: $12.50.
Exist imperf. Value, set $275.

"Liberation"
A133

**1946, Feb. 12**

| | | | | |
|---|---|---|---|---|
| 723 | A133 | 3ez p dark red | .20 | .20 |
| 724 | A133 | 15ez p ultra | .20 | .20 |

Exist imperf. Value, set $55.

Postrider — A134

**Photo.; Values Typo.**

**1946**     **Perf. 15**

| | | | | |
|---|---|---|---|---|
| 725 | A134 | 4ez p brown org | .20 | .20 |
| 726 | A134 | 10ez p brt red | .20 | .20 |
| 727 | A134 | 15ez p ultra | .20 | .20 |
| 728 | A134 | 20ez p dk brown | .20 | .20 |
| 729 | A134 | 30ez p red violet | .20 | .20 |
| 730 | A134 | 50ez p gray black | .20 | .20 |
| 731 | A134 | 80ez p brt ultra | .20 | .20 |
| 732 | A134 | 100ez p rose car | .20 | .20 |
| 733 | A134 | 160ez p gray green | .20 | .20 |
| 734 | A134 | 200ez p yellow grn | .20 | .20 |
| 735 | A134 | 500ez p red | .20 | .20 |
| 736 | A134 | 640ez p olive bis | .20 | .20 |
| 737 | A134 | 800ez p rose violet | .20 | .20 |
| | | Nos. 725-737 (13) | 2.60 | 2.60 |

Exist imperf. Value, set $80.

**Abbreviations:**
Ez (Ezer) = Thousand
Mil (Milpengo) = Million
Mlrd (Milliard) = Billion
Bil (Billio-pengo) = Trillion

Arms of
Hungary — A135

**1946**     **Wmk. 210**

| | | | | |
|---|---|---|---|---|
| 738 | A135 | 1mil p vermilion | .20 | .20 |
| a. | | "1" in center omitted | 600.00 | |
| 739 | A135 | 2mil p ultra | .20 | .20 |
| 740 | A135 | 3mil p brown | .20 | .20 |
| 741 | A135 | 4mil p slate gray | .20 | .20 |
| 742 | A135 | 5mil p rose violet | .20 | .20 |
| 743 | A135 | 10mil p green | .20 | .20 |
| 744 | A135 | 20mil p carmine | .20 | .20 |
| 745 | A135 | 50mil p olive | .20 | .20 |

Arms and Post Horn
A136      A137

| | | | | |
|---|---|---|---|---|
| 746 | A136 | 100mil p henna brn | .20 | .20 |
| 747 | A136 | 200mil p henna brn | .20 | .20 |
| 748 | A136 | 500mil p henna brn | .20 | .20 |
| 749 | A136 | 1000mil p henna brn | .20 | .20 |
| 750 | A136 | 2000mil p henna brn | .20 | .20 |
| 751 | A136 | 3000mil p henna brn | .20 | .20 |
| 752 | A136 | 5000mil p henna brn | .20 | .20 |
| 753 | A136 | 10,000mil p henna brn | .20 | .20 |
| 754 | A136 | 20,000mil p henna brn | .20 | .20 |
| 755 | A136 | 30,000mil p henna brn | .20 | .20 |
| 756 | A136 | 50,000mil p henna brn | .25 | .25 |

**Denomination in Carmine**

| | | | | |
|---|---|---|---|---|
| 757 | A137 | 100mlrd p olive | .20 | .20 |
| 758 | A137 | 200mlrd p olive | .20 | .20 |
| 759 | A137 | 500mlrd p olive | .20 | .20 |

Dove and
Letter — A138

**Denomination in Carmine**

| | | | | |
|---|---|---|---|---|
| 760 | A138 | 1bil p grnsh blk | .20 | .20 |
| 761 | A138 | 2bil p grnsh blk | .20 | .20 |
| 763 | A138 | 5bil p grnsh blk | .20 | .20 |

| | | | | |
|---|---|---|---|---|
| 764 | A138 | 10bil p grnsh blk | .20 | .20 |
| 765 | A138 | 20bil p grnsh blk | .20 | .20 |
| 766 | A138 | 50bil p grnsh blk | .20 | .20 |
| 767 | A138 | 100bil p grnsh blk | .20 | .20 |
| 768 | A138 | 200bil p grnsh blk | .20 | .20 |
| 769 | A138 | 500bil p grnsh blk | .20 | .20 |
| 770 | A138 | 1000bil p grnsh blk | .20 | .20 |
| 771 | A138 | 10,000bil p grnsh blk | .20 | .20 |
| 772 | A138 | 50,000bil p grnsh blk | .25 | .25 |
| 773 | A138 | 100,000bil p grnsh blk | .25 | .25 |
| 774 | A138 | 500,000bil p grnsh blk | .25 | .25 |

**Denomination in Black**

| | | | | |
|---|---|---|---|---|
| 775 | A137 | 5ez ap green | .20 | .20 |
| 776 | A137 | 10ez ap green | .20 | .20 |
| 777 | A137 | 20ez ap green | .20 | .20 |
| 778 | A137 | 50ez ap green | .20 | .20 |
| 779 | A137 | 80ez ap green | .20 | .20 |
| 780 | A137 | 100ez ap green | .20 | .20 |
| 781 | A137 | 200ez ap green | .20 | .20 |
| 782 | A137 | 500ez ap green | .20 | .20 |
| 783 | A137 | 1mil ap vermilion | .20 | .20 |
| 784 | A137 | 5mil ap vermilion | .20 | .20 |
| | | Nos. 738-784 (46) | 9.40 | 9.40 |

Denominations are expressed in "ado" or "tax" pengos.
Nos. 738-784 exist imperf. Value, set $500.

Early Steam
Locomotive
A139

Designs: 20,000ap, Recent steam locomotive. 30,000ap, Electric locomotive. 40,000ap, Diesel locomotive.

**1946, July 15**   **Wmk. 266**   **Perf. 12**

| | | | | |
|---|---|---|---|---|
| 785 | A139 | 10,000ap vio brn | 4.00 | 5.00 |
| 786 | A139 | 20,000ap dk blue | 4.00 | 5.00 |
| 787 | A139 | 30,000ap dp yel grn | 4.00 | 5.00 |
| 788 | A139 | 40,000ap rose car | 4.00 | 5.00 |
| b. | | "40,000 ap" omitted | 3,000. | |
| | | Nos. 785-788 (4) | 16.00 | 20.00 |

Centenary of Hungarian railways.
Exist imperf. Value, set $950.

Industry      Agriculture
A143      A144

**1946**   **Wmk. 210**   **Photo.**   **Perf. 15**

| | | | | |
|---|---|---|---|---|
| 788A | A143 | 8f henna brn | .20 | .20 |
| 789 | A143 | 10f henna brn | .30 | .20 |
| 790 | A143 | 12f henna brn | .25 | .20 |
| 791 | A143 | 20f henna brn | .30 | .20 |
| 792 | A143 | 30f henna brn | .40 | .20 |
| 793 | A143 | 40f henna brn | .40 | .20 |
| 794 | A143 | 60f henna brn | .40 | .20 |
| 795 | A144 | 1fo dp yel grn | .80 | .20 |
| 796 | A144 | 1.40fo dp yel grn | .80 | .20 |
| 797 | A144 | 2fo dp yel grn | 1.25 | .20 |
| 798 | A144 | 3fo dp yel grn | 5.50 | .20 |
| 799 | A144 | 5fo dp yel grn | 1.60 | .20 |
| 800 | A144 | 10fo dp yel grn | 2.75 | .35 |
| | | Nos. 788A-800 (13) | 14.95 | 2.75 |

For surcharges see Nos. Q9-Q11.
Exist imperf. Value, set $200.

**Stamps and Types of 1943-45
Overprinted in Carmine or Black to
Show Class of Postage for which Valid**

"Any." or "Nyomtatv." = Printed Matter.
"Hl" or "Helyi levél" = Local Letter.
"Hlp." or "Helyi lev.-lap" = Local Postcard.
"Tl." or "Távolsági levél" =Domestic Letter.
"Tlp." or "Távolsági lev.-lap" = Domestic Postcard.

a      b

**1946**     **Wmk. 266**

| | | | | |
|---|---|---|---|---|
| 801 | A99(a) | "Any 1." on 1f (#601;C) | .20 | .20 |
| 802 | A99(a) | "Any 2," on 1f (#601;C) | .20 | .20 |

| | | | | |
|---|---|---|---|---|
| 803 | A99(b) | "Nyomtatv. 20gr" on 60f on 8f (#682;Bk + C) | .20 | .20 |
| 804 | A118(a) | "Hl. 1" on 50f (#628;C) | .20 | .20 |
| 805 | A99(a) | "Hl. 2" on 40f on 10f (#664;C + Bk) | .20 | .20 |
| 806 | A99(b) | "Helyi levél" on 10f brn, bl (Bk) | .20 | .20 |
| 807 | A118(a) | "Hlp.1" on 8p on 20f (#670;C + Bk) | .20 | .20 |
| 808 | A118(a) | "Hlp.2" on 8p on 20f (#670;C + Bk) | .20 | .20 |
| 809 | A118(b) | "Helyi lev.-lap" on 20f ol, bl (C) | .20 | .20 |
| 810 | A99(a) | "Tl.1" on 10f (#608;Bk) | .20 | .20 |
| 811 | A99(a) | "Tl.2." on 10f on 4f (#657;Bk + C) | .20 | .20 |
| 812 | A99(b) | "Tavolsagi level" on 18f (#610;C) | .20 | .20 |
| 813 | A99(a) | "Tlp.1." on 4f (#604;Bk) | .20 | .20 |
| 814 | A99(a) | "Tlp.2." on 4f (#604;Bk) | .20 | .20 |
| 815 | A99(b) | "Tavolsagi lev.-lap" on 4f (#604;Bk) | .20 | .20 |
| | | Nos. 801-815 (15) | 3.00 | 3.00 |

Nos. 806, 809 not issued without overprint.

György
Dózsa — A145

Designs: 10f, Antal Budai-Nagy. 12f, Tamas Esze. 20f, Ignac Martinovics. 30f, Janos Batsanyi. 40f, Lajos Kossuth. 60f, Mihaly Tancsics. 1fo, Alexander Petőfi. 2fo, Andreas Ady. 4fo, Jozsef Attila.

**1947, Mar. 15**   **Photo.**   **Wmk. 210**

| | | | | |
|---|---|---|---|---|
| 816 | A145 | 8f rose brown | .40 | .20 |
| 817 | A145 | 10f deep ultra | .40 | .20 |
| 818 | A145 | 12f deep brown | .40 | .20 |
| 819 | A145 | 20f dk yel grn | .40 | .20 |
| 820 | A145 | 30f dk ol bis | .50 | .20 |
| 821 | A145 | 40f brown car | .50 | .20 |
| 822 | A145 | 60f cerise | .70 | .20 |
| 823 | A145 | 1fo dp grnsh bl | 1.00 | .20 |
| 824 | A145 | 2fo dk violet | 2.25 | .35 |
| 825 | A145 | 4fo grnsh black | 3.00 | .70 |
| | | Nos. 816-825 (10) | 9.55 | 2.65 |

Exist imperf. Value, set $200.

Peace and      Postal Savings
Agriculture      Emblem
A155      A156

**1947, Sept. 22**     **Perf. 12**

| | | | | |
|---|---|---|---|---|
| 826 | A155 | 60f bright red | 1.00 | .20 |
| a. | | "60f." omitted | 2,250. | |

Peace treaty.
Exists imperf. Value, set $100.

**1947, Oct. 31**

60f, Postal Savings Bank, Budapest.

| | | | | |
|---|---|---|---|---|
| 827 | A156 | 40f rose brown | .20 | .20 |
| 828 | A156 | 60f brt rose car | .80 | .20 |

Savings Day, Oct. 31, 1947.
Exist imperf. Value, set $70.

Hungarian
Flag — A157

1848 Printing
Press
A158

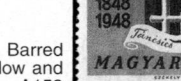

Barred
Window and
Dove — A159

1848 Shako,
Sword and
Trumpet
A160

"On your feet
Hungarian,
the Homeland
is Calling!"
A161

Arms of
Hungary — A162

### Perf. 12½x12, 12x12½

| 1948 | | Wmk. 283 | Photo. |
|---|---|---|---|
| 829 | A157 | 8f dk rose red | .40 | .20 |
| 830 | A158 | 10f ultra | .45 | .20 |
| 831 | A159 | 12f copper brn | .80 | .25 |
| 832 | A160 | 20f deep green | 1.60 | .20 |
| 833 | A161 | 30f olive brown | .80 | .20 |
| 834 | A157 | 40f dk vio brn | 1.10 | .20 |
| 835 | A161 | 60f carmine lake | 1.40 | .20 |
| a. | | Printed on both sides | 1,000. | |
| 836 | A162 | 1fo brt ultra | 1.60 | .20 |
| 837 | A162 | 2fo red brown | 2.75 | .25 |
| 838 | A162 | 3fo green | 4.50 | .60 |
| 839 | A162 | 4fo scarlet | 6.75 | .80 |
| | | Nos. 829-839 (11) | 22.15 | 3.30 |

Cent. of the beginning of Hungary's war for
independence.
#834 is inscribed "Kossuth," #835 "Petofi."
Exist imperf. Value, set $250.

Baron Roland
Eötvös
A163

### 1948, July 27
| 840 | A163 | 60f deep red | 1.50 | .25 |
|---|---|---|---|---|

Roland Eötvös, physicist, birth cent.
Exists imperf. Value $100.

Hungarian
Workers — A164

### 1948, Oct. 17          Wmk. 283      Perf. 12
| 841 | A164 | 30f dk carmine rose | 1.00 | .30 |
|---|---|---|---|---|
| a. | | Sheet of 4 | 22.00 | 20.00 |

The 17th Trade Union Congress, Budapest,
October 1948. No. 841a was sold for 2 forint.
Exist imperf. Value: single $40; sheet of 4
$2,000.

Marx Stamp of
1919 and
Crowd
Carrying
Flags — A165

Petöfi Stamp
of 1919 and
Flags — A166

### 1949, Mar. 19
#### Flags in Carmine
| 842 | A165 | 40f brown | .75 | .40 |
|---|---|---|---|---|
| 843 | A166 | 60f olive gray | .75 | .40 |

1st Hungarian Soviet Republic, 30th anniv.
Exist imperf. Value, set $30.

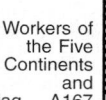

Workers of
the Five
Continents
and
Flag — A167

### 1949, June 29          Perf. 12x12½
#### Flag in Red
| 844 | A167 | 30f yellow brown | 3.25 | 3.00 |
|---|---|---|---|---|
| 845 | A167 | 40f brown violet | 3.25 | 3.00 |
| 846 | A167 | 60f lilac rose | 3.25 | 3.00 |
| 847 | A167 | 1fo violet blue | 3.25 | 3.00 |
| | | Nos. 844-847 (4) | 13.00 | 12.00 |

2nd Congress of the World Federation of
Trade Unions, Milan, 1949.
Exist imperf. Value, set $125.

Sándor
Petöfi — A168

Youth of Three
Races — A169

### Perf. 12½x12
### 1949, July 31          Engr.      Unwmk.
| 848 | A168 | 40f claret | .60 | .20 |
|---|---|---|---|---|
| 849 | A168 | 60f dark red | .30 | .20 |
| 850 | A168 | 1fo deep blue | .60 | .20 |
| | | Nos. 848-850 (3) | 1.50 | .60 |

Cent. of the death of Sándor Petöfi, poet.
Exist imperf. Value, set $30.
See Nos. 867-869.

### Perf. 12½x12
### 1949, Aug. 14      Photo.      Wmk. 283

Designs: 30f, Three fists. 40f, Soldier breaking chain. 60f, Soviet youths carrying flags.
1fo, Young workers displaying books.

| 851 | A169 | 20f dk violet brn | .75 | .70 |
|---|---|---|---|---|
| a. | | 20f blue green | 3.25 | 3.00 |
| 852 | A169 | 30f blue green | 1.00 | .80 |
| a. | | 30f violet brown | 3.25 | 3.00 |
| 853 | A169 | 40f olive bister | 1.25 | 1.00 |
| a. | | 40f ultramarine | 3.25 | 3.00 |
| 854 | A169 | 60f rose pink | 1.25 | 1.00 |
| a. | | 1fo olive bister | 3.75 | 3.50 |
| 855 | A169 | 1fo ultra | 2.00 | 1.50 |
| b. | | Souv. sheet of 5, #851a-<br>853a, 854, 855a | 30.00 | 25.00 |
| | | Nos. 851-855 (5) | 6.25 | 5.00 |

World Festival of Youth and Students, Budapest, Aug. 14-28, 1949.
Exist imperf. Value, set $110. No. 855b
imperf, $2,200.

Arms of
Hungarian
People's
Republic
A170

### 1949          Wmk. 283
#### Arms in Bister, Carmine, Blue and Green
| 856 | A170 | 20f green | 1.25 | .50 |
|---|---|---|---|---|
| a. | | Unwatermarked | 1.40 | .50 |
| 857 | A170 | 60f carmine | 1.25 | .25 |
| a. | | Unwatermarked | 1.10 | .25 |
| 858 | A170 | 1fo blue | 2.50 | .60 |
| a. | | Unwatermarked | 1.40 | .60 |
| | | Nos. 856-858 (3) | 5.00 | 1.35 |

Adoption of the Hungarian People's Republic constitution.
Nos. 856-858 exist imperf. Value, set $175.
Nos. 856-858 exist with papermaker's
watermark. These sell for more.

Symbols of
the
UPU — A171

### 1949, Nov. 1          Perf. 12x12½
| 859 | A171 | 60f rose red | .65 | .50 |
|---|---|---|---|---|
| a. | | Booklet pane of 6 | 9.75 | |
| 860 | A171 | 1fo blue | .65 | .50 |
| a. | | Booklet pane of 6 | 13.00 | |
| | | Nos. 859-860,C63 (3) | 2.55 | 2.00 |

75th anniv. of the UPU.
Nos. 859 and 860 exist imperf. and stamps
from 859a and 860a in horiz. pairs, imperf.
between. Values: set $3; pairs, imperf
between $10.
See No. C63, C81.

Chain Bridge
A172

### 1949, Nov. 20          Wmk. 283
| 861 | A172 | 40f blue green | .45 | .35 |
|---|---|---|---|---|
| 862 | A172 | 60f red brown | .45 | .20 |
| 863 | A172 | 1fo blue | .60 | .25 |
| | | Nos. 861-863,C64-C65 (5) | 4.00 | 3.30 |

Cent. of the opening of the Chain Bridge at
Budapest to traffic.
Exist imperf. Value, set $7.
For souvenir sheet see No. C66.

Joseph V.
Stalin — A173

### Perf. 12½x12
### 1949, Dec. 21          Engr.      Unwmk.
| 864 | A173 | 60f dark red | 1.00 | .20 |
|---|---|---|---|---|
| 865 | A173 | 1fo deep blue | 1.00 | .30 |
| 866 | A173 | 2fo brown | 2.75 | .50 |
| | | Nos. 864-866 (3) | 4.75 | 1.00 |

70th anniv. of the birth of Joseph V. Stalin.
Exist imperf. Value, set $20.
See Nos. 1034-1035.

Petöfi Type of 1949

### 1950, Feb. 5          Perf. 12½x12
| 867 | A168 | 40f brown | .75 | .20 |
|---|---|---|---|---|
| 868 | A168 | 60f dark carmine | .35 | .20 |
| 869 | A168 | 1fo dark green | .35 | .20 |
| | | Nos. 867-869 (3) | 1.45 | .60 |

Value, set $30.

Philatelic
Museum,
Budapest
A174

### Perf. 12x12½
### 1950, Mar. 12      Photo.      Wmk. 283
| 870 | A174 | 60f gray & brown | 7.50 | 7.50 |
|---|---|---|---|---|

20th anniv. of the establishment of the Hun-
garian PO Phil. Museum.
Exists imperf. Value $50.
See No. C68.

Coal Mining
A175

Designs: 10f, Heavy industry. 12f, Power
production. 20f, Textile industry. 30f, "Cultured
workers." 40f, Mechanized agriculture. 60f, Village cooperative. 1fo, Train. 1.70fo, "Holiday."
2fo, Defense. 3fo, Shipping. 4fo, Livestock.
5fo, Engineering. 10fo, Sports.

| 1950 | | Wmk. 283 | |
|---|---|---|---|
| 871 | A175 | 8f gray | .60 | .20 |
| 872 | A175 | 10f claret | .60 | .20 |
| 873 | A175 | 12f orange ver | 1.00 | .35 |
| 874 | A175 | 20f blue green | .60 | .20 |
| 875 | A175 | 30f rose violet | 1.00 | .20 |
| 876 | A175 | 40f sepia | 1.00 | .20 |
| 877 | A175 | 60f red | 1.25 | .20 |
| 878 | A175 | 1fo gray brn, yel<br>& lil | 3.50 | .25 |
| 879 | A175 | 1.70fo dk grn & yel | 6.00 | .40 |
| 880 | A175 | 2fo vio brn & cr | 3.25 | .20 |
| 881 | A175 | 3fo slate &<br>cream | 6.00 | .20 |
| 882 | A175 | 4fo blk brn & sal | 35.00 | 4.00 |
| 883 | A175 | 5fo rose vio &<br>yel | 15.00 | 1.90 |
| 884 | A175 | 10fo dk brn & yel | 70.00 | 11.00 |
| | | Nos. 871-884 (14) | 144.80 | 19.50 |
| | | Hinged set | 80.00 | |

Issued to publicize Hungary's Five Year Plan.
Exist imperf. Value, set $575.
See Nos. 945-958.

Citizens Welcoming Liberators — A176

### 1950, Apr. 4      Unwmk.      Perf. 12
| 885 | A176 | 40f gray black | 1.10 | .50 |
|---|---|---|---|---|
| 886 | A176 | 60f rose brown | .50 | .20 |
| 887 | A176 | 1fo deep blue | 1.00 | .20 |
| 888 | A176 | 2fo brown | 1.40 | .60 |
| | | Nos. 885-888 (4) | 4.00 | 1.50 |

Fifth anniversary of Hungary's liberation.
Exist imperf. Value, set $60.

Chess
Players
A177

Design: 1fo, Iron Workers Union building
and chess emblem.

### 1950, Apr. 9          Wmk. 106
| 889 | A177 | 60f deep magenta | 2.50 | .40 |
|---|---|---|---|---|
| 890 | A177 | 1fo deep blue | 3.00 | .85 |
| | | Nos. 889-890,C69 (3) | 11.00 | 2.25 |

World Chess Championship Matches,
Budapest.
Exist imperf. Value, set (3) $265.

Workers Symbolizing International
Proletariat — A178

Design: 60f, Blast furnace, tractor, workers holding Maypole.

**1950, May 1**

| | | | | |
|---|---|---|---|---|
| 891 | A178 | 40f orange brown | 2.00 | .35 |
| 892 | A178 | 60f rose carmine | 1.50 | .20 |
| 893 | A178 | 1fo deep blue | 1.50 | .45 |
| | | Nos. 891-893 (3) | 5.00 | 1.00 |

Issued to publicize Labor Day, May 1, 1950.
Exist imperf. Value, set $60.

Liberty, Cogwheel, Dove and Globes — A179

Inscribed: "1950. V. 10.-24."

Design: 60f, Three workers and flag.

**1950, May 10    Photo.    Perf. 12x12½**

| | | | | |
|---|---|---|---|---|
| 894 | A179 | 40f olive green | 1.50 | .35 |
| 895 | A179 | 60f dark carmine | 1.50 | .35 |
| | | Nos. 894-895,C70 (3) | 4.00 | 1.05 |

Meeting of the World Federation of Trade Unions, Budapest, May 1950.
Exist imperf. Value, set $60.

Doctor Inspecting Baby's Bath — A180

Children's Day: 30f, Physical Culture. 40f, Education. 60f, Boys' Camp. 1.70fo, Model plane building.

**1950, June 4    Wmk. 106**

| | | | | |
|---|---|---|---|---|
| 896 | A180 | 20f gray & brn | 2.00 | .75 |
| 897 | A180 | 30f brn & rose lake | .45 | .20 |
| 898 | A180 | 40f indigo & dk grn | .45 | .20 |
| 899 | A180 | 60f SZABAD | .70 | .20 |
| a. | A180 | UTANPOTLASUNK . . | 500.00 | 400.00 |
| 900 | A180 | 1.70fo dp grn & gray | 1.40 | .55 |
| | | Nos. 896-900 (5) | 5.00 | 1.90 |

Exist imperf. Value, set $60.

Youths Marching on Globe A181

Working Man and Woman — A182

30f, Foundry worker. 60f, Workers on Mt. Gellert. 1.70fo, Worker, peasant & student; flags.

Inscribed: Budapest 1950. VI. 17-18.

**Perf. 12x12½, 12½x12**

**1950, June 17**

| | | | | |
|---|---|---|---|---|
| 901 | A181 | 20f dark green | 1.40 | .40 |
| 902 | A181 | 30f deep red org | .40 | .20 |
| 903 | A182 | 40f dark brown | .40 | .20 |
| 904 | A181 | 60f deep claret | .70 | .20 |
| 905 | A182 | 1.70fo dark olive grn | 1.10 | .30 |
| | | Nos. 901-905 (5) | 4.00 | 1.30 |

Issued to publicize the First Congress of the Working Youth, Budapest, June 17-18, 1950.
Exist imperf. Value, set $60.

Peonies — A183

Designs: 40f, Anemones. 60f, Pheasant's-eye. 1fo, Geraniums. 1.70fo, Bluebells.

**Engraved and Lithographed
Perf. 12½x12**

**1950, Aug. 20    Unwmk.**

| | | | | |
|---|---|---|---|---|
| 906 | A183 | 30f rose brn, rose pink & grn | .95 | .20 |
| 907 | A183 | 40f dk green, lil & yel | 1.40 | .20 |
| 908 | A183 | 60f red brn, yel & grn | 1.90 | .35 |
| 909 | A183 | 1fo purple, red & grn | 4.50 | 1.25 |
| 910 | A183 | 1.70fo dk violet & grn | 3.75 | 1.00 |
| | | Nos. 906-910 (5) | 12.50 | 3.00 |

Exist imperf. Value, set $70.

Miner — A184

Designs: 60f, High speed lathe. 1fo, Prefabricated building construction.

**Perf. 12x12½**

**1950, Oct. 7    Photo.    Wmk. 106**

| | | | | |
|---|---|---|---|---|
| 911 | A184 | 40f brown | 1.75 | .20 |
| 912 | A184 | 60f carmine rose | 1.25 | .20 |
| 913 | A184 | 1fo brt blue | 1.50 | .45 |
| | | Nos. 911-913 (3) | 4.50 | .85 |

2nd National Exhibition of Inventions.
Exist imperf. Value, set $35.

Gen. Josef Bem and Battle at Piski A185

**Perf. 12½x12**

**1950, Dec. 10    Engr.    Unwmk.**

| | | | | |
|---|---|---|---|---|
| 914 | A185 | 40f dark brown | 1.25 | .60 |
| 915 | A185 | 60f deep carmine | 1.00 | .30 |
| 916 | A185 | 1fo deep blue | 1.50 | .65 |
| | | Nos. 914-916 (3) | 3.75 | 1.55 |

Gen. Josef Bem, death centenary.
Exist imperf. Value, set $35.
See No. C80.

Signing Petition A186

Peace Demonstrator Holding Dove — A187

1fo, Mother and Children with soldier.

**Wmk. 106**

**1950, Nov. 23    Photo.    Perf. 12**

| | | | | |
|---|---|---|---|---|
| 917 | A186 | 40f ultra & red brn | 8.75 | 6.50 |
| 918 | A187 | 60f red org & dk grn | 2.00 | 1.50 |
| 919 | A186 | 1fo ol grn & dk brn | 8.75 | 5.50 |
| | | Nos. 917-919 (3) | 19.50 | 13.50 |

Exist imperf. Value, set $80.

Women Swimmers A188

Designs: 20f, Vaulting. 1fo, Mountain climbing. 1.70fo, Basketball. 2fo, Motorcycling.

**1950, Dec. 2    Perf. 12x12½**

| | | | | |
|---|---|---|---|---|
| 920 | A188 | 10f blue & gray | .45 | .20 |
| 921 | A188 | 20f salmon & dk brn | .45 | .20 |
| 922 | A188 | 1fo olive & grn | .90 | .45 |
| 923 | A188 | 1.70fo ver & brn car | 1.50 | .55 |
| 924 | A188 | 2fo salmon & pur | 2.50 | 1.25 |
| | | Nos. 920-924,C82-C86 (10) | 15.55 | 6.30 |

Exist imperf. Value, set (10) $120.

**Canceled to Order**

The government stamp agency started about 1950 to sell canceled sets of new issues. Values in the second ("used") column are for these canceled-to-order stamps. Postally used stamps are worth more.

The practice was to end Apr. 1, 1991.

A189

Worker, Peasant, Soldier and Party Flag — A190

60f, Matthias Rakosi & allegory. 1fo, House of Parliament, columns of workers & banner.

Inscribed: "Budapest * 1951 * Februar 24."

**1951, Feb. 24    Perf. 12½x12, 12x12½**

| | | | | |
|---|---|---|---|---|
| 925 | A189 | 10f yellow green | .65 | .35 |
| 926 | A190 | 30f brown | .75 | .35 |
| 927 | A190 | 60f carmine rose | .75 | .35 |
| 928 | A189 | 1fo blue | .95 | .40 |
| | | Nos. 925-928 (4) | 3.10 | 1.45 |

2nd Congress of the Hungarian Workers' Party.
Exist imperf. Value, set $55.

Mare and Foal — A191

Designs: 30f, Sow and shoats. 40f, Ram and ewe. 60f, Cow and calf.

**1951, Apr. 5    Perf. 12x12½**

| | | | | |
|---|---|---|---|---|
| 929 | A191 | 10f ol bis & rose brn | 1.10 | .20 |
| 930 | A191 | 30f rose brn & ol bis | 1.25 | .30 |
| 931 | A191 | 40f dk green & brn | 1.25 | .25 |
| 932 | A191 | 60f brown org & brn | 1.50 | .30 |
| | | Nos. 929-932,C87-C90 (8) | 17.50 | 3.95 |

Issued to encourage increased livestock production.
Exist imperf. Value, set (8) $100.

Flags of Russia and Hungary — A192

Russian Technician Teaching Hungarians A193

**1951, Apr. 4    Perf. 12½x12, 12x12½**

| | | | | |
|---|---|---|---|---|
| 933 | A192 | 60f brnsh carmine | 1.25 | .20 |
| 934 | A193 | 1fo dull violet | 1.25 | .20 |

Issued to publicize the "Month of Friendship" between Hungary and Russia, 1951.
Exist imperf. Value, set $24.

Worker Holding Olive Branch and Mallet A194

Workers Carrying Flags — A195

1fo, Workers approaching Place of Heroes.

**Perf. 12x12½, 12½x12**

**1951, May 1    Photo.    Wmk. 106**

| | | | | |
|---|---|---|---|---|
| 935 | A194 | 40f brown | 1.00 | .40 |
| 936 | A195 | 60f scarlet | .75 | .20 |
| 937 | A194 | 1fo blue | .75 | .20 |
| | | Nos. 935-937 (3) | 2.50 | .80 |

Issued to publicize Labor Day, May 1, 1951.
Exist imperf. Value, set $30.

Leo Frankel — A196

Paris Street Fighting, 1871 — A197

**1951, May 20**

| | | | | |
|---|---|---|---|---|
| 938 | A196 | 60f dark brown | 1.00 | .20 |
| 939 | A197 | 1fo blue & red | 1.00 | .30 |

80th anniv. of the Commune of Paris.
Exist imperf. Value, set $20.

Children of Various Races — A198

## 1951, June 3 — Perf. 12½x12

Designs: 40f, Boy and girl at play. 50f, Street car and Girl Pioneer. 60f, Chemistry students. 1.70fo, Pioneer bugler.

**Inscribed:**
**"Nemzetkozi Gyermeknap 1951"**

| | | | | |
|---|---|---|---|---|
| 940 | A198 | 30f dark brown | .60 | .20 |
| 941 | A198 | 40f green | .60 | .20 |
| 942 | A198 | 50f brown red | .60 | .25 |
| 943 | A198 | 60f plum | .85 | .35 |
| 944 | A198 | 1.70fo blue | 1.10 | 1.00 |
| | | Nos. 940-944 (5) | 3.75 | 2.00 |

International Day of Children, 6/3/51. Exist imperf. Value, set $40.

### 5-Year-Plan Type of 1950

Designs as before.

| 1951-52 | | Wmk. 106 | Perf. 12x12½ | |
|---|---|---|---|---|
| 945 | A175 | 8f gray | .60 | .20 |
| 946 | A175 | 10f claret | .35 | .20 |
| 947 | A175 | 12f orange ver | .35 | .20 |
| 948 | A175 | 20f blue green | .35 | .20 |
| 949 | A175 | 30f rose violet | .35 | .20 |
| 950 | A175 | 40f sepia | .65 | .20 |
| 951 | A175 | 60f red | .75 | .20 |
| 952 | A175 | 1fo gray brn, yel & lil | .85 | .20 |
| 953 | A175 | 1.70fo dk grn & yel | 2.00 | .20 |
| 954 | A175 | 2fo vio brn & cr | 3.00 | .20 |
| 955 | A175 | 3fo slate & cream | 4.25 | .25 |
| 956 | A175 | 4fo blk brn & sal | 5.25 | .35 |
| 957 | A175 | 5fo rose vio & yel ('52) | 5.75 | .75 |
| 958 | A175 | 10fo dk brn & yel ('52) | 13.00 | 3.00 |
| | | Nos. 945-958 (14) | 37.50 | 6.35 |

Maxim Gorky — A199

### Perf. 12½x12

| 1951, June 17 | | Engr. | Unwmk. | |
|---|---|---|---|---|
| 959 | A199 | 60f copper red | .45 | .20 |
| 960 | A199 | 1fo deep blue | .80 | .25 |
| 961 | A199 | 2fo rose violet | 1.00 | .40 |
| | | Nos. 959-961 (3) | 2.25 | .85 |

15th anniversary of the death of Gorky. Exist imperf. Value, set $25.

### Budapest Buildings

Railroad Workshop
A200

Building in Lehel Street
A201

Suburban Bus Terminal
A202

Rakosi House of Culture
A203

George Kilian Street School
A204

Central Construction Headquarters
A205

### Design Size: 22x18mm

| 1951 | | Wmk. 106 Photo. | Perf. 15 | |
|---|---|---|---|---|
| 962 | A200 | 20f green | .50 | .20 |
| 963 | A201 | 30f red orange | .50 | .20 |
| 964 | A202 | 40f brown | .50 | .20 |
| 965 | A203 | 60f red | .75 | .20 |
| 966 | A204 | 1fo blue | 1.00 | .20 |
| 967 | A205 | 3fo deep plum | 3.00 | .20 |
| | | Nos. 962-967 (6) | 6.25 | 1.20 |

Exist imperf. Value, set $80.

---

See Nos. 1004-1011, 1048-1056C.

### Design Size: 21x17mm

| 1958 | | | | |
|---|---|---|---|---|
| 962a | A200 | 20f green | .60 | .20 |
| 963a | A201 | 30f red orange | 1.00 | .20 |
| 964a | A202 | 40f brown | .90 | .20 |
| 965a | A203 | 60f red | 1.25 | .20 |
| 966a | A204 | 1fo blue | 1.25 | .20 |
| 967a | A205 | 3fo deep plum | 3.00 | .20 |
| | | Nos. 962a-967a (6) | 8.00 | 1.20 |

Tractor Manufacture
A206

30f, Fluoroscope examination. 40f, Checking lathework. 60f, Woman tractor operator.

| 1951, Aug. 20 | | | Perf. 12x12½ | |
|---|---|---|---|---|
| 968 | A206 | 20f black brown | .20 | .20 |
| 969 | A206 | 30f deep blue | .20 | .20 |
| 970 | A206 | 40f crimson rose | .65 | .20 |
| 971 | A206 | 60f brown | .75 | .20 |
| | | Nos. 968-971,C91-C93 (7) | 5.00 | 1.80 |

The successful conclusion of the first year under Hungary's 5-year plan. Exist imperf. Value, set $55.

Soldiers of the People's Army — A207

| 1951, Sept. 29 | | | | |
|---|---|---|---|---|
| 972 | A207 | 1fo brown | 1.50 | .30 |

Issued to publicize Army Day, Sept. 29, 1951. See No. C94. Exist imperf. Value $15.

Stamp of 1871, Portrait Replaced by Postmark
A208

Cornflower
A209

### Perf. 12½x12

| 1951, Sept. 12 | | | Engr. | Unwmk. | |
|---|---|---|---|---|---|
| 973 | A208 | 60f olive green | 2.00 | 1.50 |
| | | Nos. 973,B207-B208 (3) | 22.00 | 20.00 |

80th anniv. of Hungary's 1st postage stamp. See Nos. C95, CB13-CB14. Exist imperf. Value, set (3) $70.

| 1951, Nov. 4 | | | Engr. & Litho. | |
|---|---|---|---|---|
| 974 | A209 | 30f shown | .75 | .20 |
| 975 | A209 | 40f Lily of the Valley | 3.00 | .75 |
| 976 | A209 | 60f Tulip | .75 | .20 |
| 977 | A209 | 1fo Poppy | 1.50 | .40 |
| 978 | A209 | 1.70fo Cowslip | 1.50 | 1.00 |
| | | Nos. 974-978 (5) | 7.50 | 2.55 |

Exist imperf. Value, set $70.

Storming of the Winter Palace
A210

Designs: 60f, Lenin speaking to soldiers. 1fo, Lenin and Stalin.

---

### Perf. 12x12½

| 1951, Nov. 7 | | Photo. | Wmk. 106 | |
|---|---|---|---|---|
| 979 | A210 | 40f gray green | 1.20 | .25 |
| 980 | A210 | 60f deep blue | .70 | .20 |
| 981 | A210 | 1fo rose lake | .70 | .40 |
| | | Nos. 979-981 (3) | 2.60 | .85 |

34th anniversary of the Russian Revolution. Exist imperf. Value, set $35.

Marchers Passing Stalin Monument — A211

| 1951, Dec. 16 | | | Wmk. 106 | |
|---|---|---|---|---|
| 982 | A211 | 60f henna brown | .90 | .20 |
| 983 | A211 | 1fo deep blue | .90 | .30 |

Joseph V. Stalin, 72nd birthday. Exist imperf. Value, set $30.

Grand Theater, Moscow
A212

Views of Moscow: 1fo, Lenin Mausoleum. 1.60fo, Kremlin.

| 1952, Feb. 20 | | | Perf. 12 | |
|---|---|---|---|---|
| 984 | A212 | 60f ol grn & rose brn | .60 | .20 |
| 985 | A212 | 1fo lil rose & ol brn | 1.00 | .30 |
| 986 | A212 | 1.60fo red brn & ol | 1.90 | .50 |
| | | Nos. 984-986 (3) | 3.50 | 1.00 |

Hungarian-Soviet Friendship Month. Exist imperf. Value, set $30.

Rakosi and Farmers
A213

Matyas Rakosi — A214

Design: 2fo, Rakosi and Workers.

### Perf. 12x12½, 12½x12

| 1952, Mar. 9 | | | Engr. | Unwmk. | |
|---|---|---|---|---|---|
| 987 | A213 | 60f deep plum | .80 | .20 |
| 988 | A214 | 1fo dk red brown | .95 | .25 |
| 989 | A213 | 2fo dp violet blue | 1.75 | .55 |
| | | Nos. 987-989 (3) | 3.50 | 1.00 |

60th anniv. of the birth of Matyas Rakosi, communist leader. Exist imperf. Value, set $35.

Lajos Kossuth and Speech at Debrecen
A215

Designs: 30f, Sándor Petöfi. 50f, Gen. Josef Bem. 60f, Mihaly Tancsics. 1fo, Gen. János Damjanich. 1.50fo, Gen. Alexander Nagy.

---

| 1952, Mar. 15 | | | Perf. 12x12½ | |
|---|---|---|---|---|
| 990 | A215 | 20f green | .20 | .20 |
| 991 | A215 | 30f rose violet | .20 | .20 |
| 992 | A215 | 50f grnsh blk | .40 | .20 |
| 993 | A215 | 60f brown car | .45 | .20 |
| 994 | A215 | 1fo blue | .75 | .20 |
| 995 | A215 | 1.50fo redsh brown | 1.00 | .50 |
| | | Nos. 990-995 (6) | 3.00 | 1.50 |

Heroes of the 1848 revolution. Exist imperf. Value, set $30. Nos. 990-995 also exist perf 12. Value, set $200.

### No. B204 Surcharged in Black with Bars Obliterating Inscription and Surtax

**Perf. 12½x12**

| 1952, Apr. 27 | | Photo. | Wmk. 283 | |
|---|---|---|---|---|
| 996 | SP121 | 60f magenta | 35.00 | 30.00 |

Budapest Philatelic Exhibition. Counterfeits exist.

Girl Drummer Leading Parade
A216

Designs: 60f, Workers and soldier. 1fo, Worker, flag-encircled globe and dove.

### Perf. 12½x12½

| 1952, May 1 | | Photo. | Wmk. 106 | |
|---|---|---|---|---|
| 997 | A216 | 40f dk grn & dull red | 1.75 | .45 |
| 998 | A216 | 60f dk red brn & dull red | .85 | .45 |
| 999 | A216 | 1fo sepia & dull red | 1.40 | .75 |
| | | Nos. 997-999 (3) | 4.00 | 1.65 |

Issued to publicize Labor Day, May 1, 1952. Exist imperf. Value, set $175.

Runner — A217

Designs: 40f, Swimmer. 60f, Fencer. 1fo, Woman gymnast.

| 1952, May 26 | | | Perf. 11 | |
|---|---|---|---|---|
| 1000 | A217 | 30f dark red brown | .65 | .20 |
| 1001 | A217 | 40f deep green | .65 | .20 |
| 1002 | A217 | 60f deep lilac rose | .80 | .25 |
| 1003 | A217 | 1fo deep blue | 1.40 | .50 |
| | | Nos. 1000-1003,C107-C108 (6) | 8.00 | 2.25 |

Issued to publicize Hungary's participation in the Olympic Games, Helsinki, 1952. Exist imperf. set (6) $100.

### Building Types of 1951

Buildings: 8f, School, Stalinvaros. 10f, Szekesfehervar Station. 12f, Building, Ujpest. 50f, Metal works, Inotai. 70f, Grain elevator, Hajdunanas. 80f, Tiszalok dam. 4fo, Miners' union headquarters. 5fo, Workers' apartments, Ujpest.

### Design Size: 22x18mm

| 1952 | | Wmk. 106 | Perf. 15 | |
|---|---|---|---|---|
| 1004 | A202 | 8f green | .45 | .20 |
| 1005 | A200 | 10f purple | .45 | .20 |
| 1006 | A202 | 12f carmine | .45 | .20 |
| 1007 | A202 | 50f gray blue | .65 | .20 |
| 1008 | A200 | 70f yellow brn | 1.00 | .20 |
| 1009 | A200 | 80f maroon | 1.25 | .20 |
| 1010 | A202 | 4fo olive grn | 2.75 | .20 |
| 1011 | A202 | 5fo gray black | 3.75 | .20 |
| | | Nos. 1004-1011 (8) | 10.75 | 1.60 |

Exist imperf. Value, set $105.

### Design Size: 21x17mm

| 1958 | | | | |
|---|---|---|---|---|
| 1004a | A202 | 8f green | .45 | .20 |
| 1005a | A200 | 10f purple | 2.00 | .20 |
| 1006a | A202 | 12f carmine | .50 | .20 |

| 1007a | A202 | 50f gray blue | .65 | .20 |
|---|---|---|---|---|
| 1008a | A202 | 70f yellow brn | .80 | .20 |
| 1009a | A200 | 80f maroon | 1.25 | .20 |
| 1010a | A202 | 4fo olive grn | 2.75 | .20 |
| 1011a | A202 | 5fo gray black | 4.00 | .20 |
| | *Nos. 1004a-1011a (8)* | | 12.40 | 1.60 |

Approaching Train — A218

Railroad Day: 1fo, Railroad Construction.

**1952, Aug. 10**     **Perf. 12x12½**

| 1012 | A218 | 60f red brown | 1.10 | .20 |
|---|---|---|---|---|
| 1013 | A218 | 1fo deep olive grn | 1.10 | .35 |

Exist imperf. Value, set $30.

Coal Excavator A219

Miners' Day: 1fo, Coal breaker.

**1952, Sept. 7**

| 1014 | A219 | 60f brown | .85 | .20 |
|---|---|---|---|---|
| 1015 | A219 | 1fo dark green | 1.40 | .25 |

Exist imperf. Value, set $30.

Lajos Kossuth — A220

Janos Hunyadi — A221

Design: 60f, Kossuth statue.

**1952, Sept. 19**     **Perf. 12½x12**

| 1016 | A220 | 40f ol brn, *pink* | .80 | .20 |
|---|---|---|---|---|
| 1017 | A220 | 60f black brn, *bl* | .80 | .20 |
| 1018 | A220 | 1fo purple, *citron* | .80 | .20 |
| | *Nos. 1016-1018 (3)* | | 2.40 | .65 |

150th anniv. of the birth of Lajos Kossuth.
Exist imperf. Value, set $30.

**1952, Sept. 28**     **Engr.**     **Unwmk.**

Portraits: 30f, Gyorgy Dozsa. 40f, Miklos Zrinyi. 60f, Ilona Zriuyi. 1fo, Bottyan Vak. 1.50fo, Aurel Stromfeld.

| 1019 | A221 | 20f purple | .20 | .20 |
|---|---|---|---|---|
| 1020 | A221 | 30f dark green | .20 | .20 |
| 1021 | A221 | 40f indigo | .20 | .20 |
| 1022 | A221 | 60f dk violet brn | .55 | .20 |
| 1023 | A221 | 1fo dk blue grn | .70 | .35 |
| 1024 | A221 | 1.50fo dark brown | 1.90 | .85 |
| | *Nos. 1019-1024 (6)* | | 3.75 | 2.00 |

Army Day, Sept. 28, 1952.
Exist imperf. Value, set $55.

Lenin and Conference at Smolny Palace A222

Designs: 60f, Stalin and Cavalry Attack. 1fo, Marx, Engels, Lenin and Stalin.

**1952, Nov. 7**     **Wmk. 106**
**Portraits in Olive Gray**

| 1025 | A222 | 40f deep claret | 2.10 | .70 |
|---|---|---|---|---|
| 1026 | A222 | 60f gray | .80 | .25 |
| 1027 | A222 | 1fo rose red | 2.10 | .40 |
| | *Nos. 1025-1027 (3)* | | 5.00 | 1.35 |

Russian Revolution, 35th anniversary.
Exist imperf. Value, set $50.

Peasant Woman Holding Wheat — A223

Peace Meeting A224

**Perf. 12½x12, 12x12½**
**1952, Nov. 22**

| 1028 | A223 | 60f brn red, *citron* | .90 | .20 |
|---|---|---|---|---|
| 1029 | A224 | 1fo brown, *blue* | 1.10 | .40 |

Third Hungarian Peace Congress, 1952.
Exist imperf. Value, set $30.

Subway Construction A225

Design: 1fo, Station and map.

**1953, Jan. 19**     **Photo.**     **Perf. 12x12½**

| 1030 | A225 | 60f dk slate green | .90 | .25 |
|---|---|---|---|---|
| 1031 | A225 | 1fo brown red | 1.60 | .45 |

Completion of the Budapest subway extension.
Exist imperf. Value, set $20.

Tank and Flag — A226

Stalin — A227

60f, Map of Central Europe and Soldier.

**1953, Feb. 18**

| 1032 | A226 | 40f dark car rose | 1.00 | .25 |
|---|---|---|---|---|
| 1033 | A226 | 60f chocolate | 1.00 | .20 |

Battle of Stalingrad, 10th anniversary.
Exist imperf. Value $20.

**Perf. 12x11½**

| 1953 | | **Engr.** | **Wmk. 106** |
|---|---|---|---|
| 1034 | A227 | 60f pur blk | 1.25 .20 |

**Souvenir Sheet**

| 1035 | A227 | 2fo purple black | 25.00 | 14.50 |
|---|---|---|---|---|

Death of Joseph Stalin (1879-1953).
Exist imperf. Values: 60f $20; 2fo $135.
Issue dates: #1034, Mar. 27; #1035, Mar. 9.

Workers' Rest Home, Galyateto A228

Designs: 40f, Home at Mecsek. 50f, Parad Mineral Baths. 60f, Home at Kekes. 70f, Balatonfured Mineral Baths.

**1953, Apr.**     **Photo.**     **Perf. 12x12½**

| 1036 | A228 | 30f fawn | .60 | .20 |
|---|---|---|---|---|
| 1037 | A228 | 40f deep blue | .60 | .20 |
| 1038 | A228 | 50f dk olive bis | .60 | .20 |
| 1039 | A228 | 60f dp yellow grn | .60 | .20 |
| 1040 | A228 | 70f scarlet | .60 | .25 |
| | *Nos. 1036-1040,C121-C122 (7)* | | 4.85 | 1.70 |

Exist imperf. Value, set (7) $70.

Young Workers with Red Flags — A229

Karl Marx — A230

**1953, May 1**     **Perf. 12½x12**

| 1041 | A229 | 60f brn & red, *yel* | 1.00 | .20 |
|---|---|---|---|---|

Issued to publicize Labor Day, May 1, 1953.
Exist imperf. Value $20.

**1953, May 1**     **Engr.**     **Perf. 11½x12**

| 1042 | A230 | 1fo black, *pink* | 1.50 | .20 |
|---|---|---|---|---|

70th anniv. of the death of Karl Marx. See No. 1898.
Exist imperf. Value $30.

Insurgents in the Forest — A231

30f, Drummer & fighters. 40f, Battle scene. 60f, Cavalry attack. 1fo, Francis Rákóczy II.

**1953, June 14**     **Photo.**     **Perf. 11**

| 1043 | A231 | 20f dk ol grn & org red, *grnsh* | .55 | .30 |
|---|---|---|---|---|
| 1044 | A231 | 30f vio brn & red org | .75 | .40 |
| 1045 | A231 | 40f gray bl & red org, *pink* | 1.10 | .40 |
| 1046 | A231 | 60f dk ol brn & org, *yel* | 2.10 | .75 |
| 1047 | A231 | 1fo dk red brn & org red, *yel* | 3.00 | 1.00 |
| | *Nos. 1043-1047 (5)* | | 7.50 | 2.85 |

250th anniv. of the insurrection of 1703.
Exist imperf. Value $55.

## Building Types of 1951

Buildings: 8f, Day Nursery, Ozd. 10f, Medical research institute, Szombathely. 12f, Apartments, Komlo. 20f, Department store, Ujpest. 30f, Brick factory, Maly. 40f, Metropolitan hospital. 50f, Sports building, Stalinvaros. 60f, Post office, Csepel. 70f, Blast furnace, Diosgyor. 1.20fo, Agricultural school, Ajkacsinger Valley. 1.70fo, Iron Works School, Csepel. 2fo, Optical works house of culture.

### Design Size: 22x18mm

| 1953 | | **Wmk. 106** | **Perf. 15** | |
|---|---|---|---|---|
| 1048 | A204 | 8f olive green | .35 | .20 |
| 1049 | A204 | 10f purple | .45 | .20 |
| 1050 | A205 | 12f rose carmine | .65 | .20 |
| 1051 | A204 | 20f dark green | .50 | .20 |
| 1052 | A204 | 30f orange | .80 | .20 |
| 1053 | A204 | 40f dark brown | 1.20 | .20 |
| 1054 | A205 | 50f blue violet | 1.50 | .20 |
| 1055 | A205 | 60f rose red | 1.20 | .20 |
| 1056 | A204 | 70f yellow brown | 1.60 | .20 |
| 1056A | A205 | 1.20fo red | 3.25 | .20 |
| 1056B | A204 | 1.70fo blue | 2.50 | .20 |
| 1056C | A204 | 2fo green | 4.00 | .20 |
| | *Nos. 1048-1056C (12)* | | 18.00 | 2.40 |

Exist imperf. Value, set $160.

### Design Size: 21x17mm

| 1958 | | | | |
|---|---|---|---|---|
| 1048a | A204 | 8f olive green | .70 | .20 |
| 1049a | A204 | 10f purple | | .45 |
| 1050a | A205 | 12f rose carmine | | |
| 1051a | A204 | 20f dark green | 1.20 | .20 |
| | | | 1.20 | .20 |

| 1052a | A204 | 30f orange | 1.10 | .20 |
|---|---|---|---|---|
| 1053a | A204 | 40f dark brown | 1.40 | .20 |
| 1054a | A205 | 50f blue violet | 1.40 | .20 |
| 1055a | A205 | 60f rose red | 1.40 | .20 |
| 1056Aa | A205 | 1.20fo yellow brown | 2.00 | .20 |
| 1056Aa | A205 | 1.20fo red | 2.75 | .20 |
| 1056Ba | A204 | 1.70fo blue | 1.80 | .20 |
| 1056Ca | A204 | 2fo green | 3.25 | .20 |
| | *Nos. 1048a-1056Ca (12)* | | 18.20 | 2.65 |

Exist imperf. Value, set $160.

Swimming — A232

**1953, Aug. 20**     **Perf. 11**

| 1057 | A232 | 20f shown | .40 | .25 |
|---|---|---|---|---|
| 1058 | A232 | 30f Swimming | .40 | .20 |
| 1059 | A232 | 40f Calisthenics | .40 | .20 |
| 1060 | A232 | 50f Discus | .60 | .20 |
| 1061 | A232 | 60f Wrestling | .75 | .20 |
| | *Nos. 1057-1061,C123-C127 (10)* | | 15.10 | 3.75 |

Opening of the People's Stadium, Budapest.
Exist imperf. Value, set (10) $120.

Kazar Costume A233

Lenin — A234

Provincial Costumes: 30f, Ersekcsanad. 40f, Kalocsa. 60f, Sioagard. 1fo, Sarkoz. 1.70fo, Boldog. 2fo, Orhalom. 2.50fo, Hosszuheteny.

**1953, Sept. 12**     **Engr.**     **Perf. 12**

| 1062 | A233 | 20f blue green | .95 | .30 |
|---|---|---|---|---|
| 1063 | A233 | 30f chocolate | .95 | .20 |
| 1064 | A233 | 40f ultra | 1.50 | .30 |
| 1065 | A233 | 60f red | 1.50 | .45 |
| 1066 | A233 | 1fo grnsh blue | 2.50 | .85 |
| 1067 | A233 | 1.70fo brt green | 3.50 | 1.25 |
| 1068 | A233 | 2fo carmine rose | 5.50 | 2.00 |
| 1069 | A233 | 2.50fo purple | 8.25 | 4.25 |
| | *Nos. 1062-1069 (8)* | | 24.65 | 9.60 |

Exist imperf. Value, set $135.
See No. 1189.

**1954, Jan. 21**     **Wmk. 106**     **Perf. 12**

Designs: 60f, Lenin and Stalin at meeting. 1fo, Lenin, facing left.

| 1073 | A234 | 40f dk blue grn | 2.00 | .75 |
|---|---|---|---|---|
| 1074 | A234 | 60f black brown | 1.00 | .25 |
| 1075 | A234 | 1fo dk car rose | 2.00 | .65 |
| | *Nos. 1073-1075 (3)* | | 5.00 | 1.65 |

30th anniversary, death of Lenin.
Exist imperf. Value, set $55.

Worker
Reading
A235

Revolutionary
and Red
Flag — A236

Design: 1fo, Soldier.

**Perf. 12x12½, 12½x12**

| 1954, Mar. 21 | | | Photo. | |
|---|---|---|---|---|
| 1076 | A235 | 40f gray blue & red | 4.00 | .60 |
| 1077 | A236 | 60f brown & red | 4.00 | .60 |
| 1078 | A235 | 1fo gray & red | 4.00 | .50 |
| | | Nos. 1076-1078 (3) | 12.00 | 1.70 |

35th anniversary of the "First Hungarian Communist Republic."
Exist imperf. Value, set $80.

Blood
Test — A237

Maypole — A238

Designs: 40f, Mother receiving newborn baby. 60f, Medical examination of baby.

| 1954, Mar. 8 | | | Perf. 12 | |
|---|---|---|---|---|
| 1079 | A237 | 30f brt blue | .20 | .20 |
| 1080 | A237 | 40f brown bister | .45 | .20 |
| 1081 | A237 | 60f purple | .45 | .20 |
| | | Nos. 1079-1081,C146-C148 (6) | 5.00 | 1.80 |

Exist imperf. Value, set $80.

| 1954, May 1 | | | Perf. 12½x12 | |
|---|---|---|---|---|

Design: 60f, Flag bearer.

| 1082 | A238 | 40f olive | .50 | .20 |
| 1083 | A238 | 60f orange red | .50 | .20 |

Issued to publicize Labor Day, May 1, 1954.
Exist imperf. Value, set $20.

Farm
Woman
with Fruit
A239

| 1954, May 24 | | | Perf. 12 | |
|---|---|---|---|---|
| 1084 | A239 | 60f red orange | .75 | .20 |

3rd Congress of the Hungarian Workers Party, Budapest, May 24, 1954.
Exists imperf. Value, set $15.

Natl. Museum,
Budapest — A240

Peppers
A241

Designs: 60f, Arms of People's Republic. 1fo, Dome of Parliament Building.

| 1954, Aug. 20 | | | Perf. 12½x12 | |
|---|---|---|---|---|
| 1085 | A240 | 40f brt blue | 1.50 | .20 |
| 1086 | A240 | 60f redsh brown | .50 | .20 |
| 1087 | A240 | 1fo dark brown | 1.50 | .25 |
| | | Nos. 1085-1087 (3) | 3.50 | .65 |

People's Republic Constitution, 5th anniv.
Exist imperf. Value, set $35.

| 1954, Sept. 11 | Engr., Fruit Litho. |
|---|---|

Fruit: 50f, Tomatoes. 60f, Grapes. 80f, Apricots. 1fo, Apples. 1.20fo, Plums. 1.50fo, Cherries. 2fo, Peaches.

**Fruit in Natural Colors**

| 1088 | A241 | 40f gray blue | .70 | .20 |
|---|---|---|---|---|
| 1089 | A241 | 50f plum | .70 | .20 |
| 1090 | A241 | 60f gray blue | .85 | .20 |
| 1091 | A241 | 80f chocolate | .90 | .20 |
| 1092 | A241 | 1fo rose violet | 1.25 | .25 |
| 1093 | A241 | 1.20fo dull blue | 1.60 | .35 |
| 1094 | A241 | 1.50fo plum | 1.25 | .65 |
| 1095 | A241 | 2fo gray blue | 2.75 | .45 |
| | | Nos. 1088-1095 (8) | 10.00 | 2.50 |

National agricultural fair.
Exist imperf. Value, set $70.

Maurus
Jokai — A242

| 1954, Oct. 17 | | | Engr. | |
|---|---|---|---|---|
| 1096 | A242 | 60f dk brown olive | 1.10 | .25 |
| 1097 | A242 | 1fo deep claret | 1.40 | .70 |

50th anniv. of the death of Maurus Jokai, writer.
Exist imperf. Value, set $30.
No. 1097 in violet blue is from the souvenir sheet, No. C157.

Janos Apacai
Csere
A243

| 1954, Dec. 5 | Photo. | Perf. 12x12½ |
|---|---|---|

Scientists: 10f, Csoma Sandor Korosi. 12f, Anyos Jedlik. 20f, Ignaz Semmelweis. 30f, Janos Irinyi. 40f, Frigyes Koranyi. 50f, Armin Vambery. 60f, Karoly Than. 1fo, Otto Herman. 1.70fo, Tivadar Puskas. 2fo, Endre Hogyes.

| 1098 | A243 | 8f dk vio brn, yel | .20 | .20 |
|---|---|---|---|---|
| 1099 | A243 | 10f brn, car, pink | .20 | .20 |
| 1100 | A243 | 12f gray, bl | .20 | .20 |
| 1101 | A243 | 20f brn, yel | .20 | .20 |
| 1102 | A243 | 30f vio bl, pink | .20 | .20 |
| 1103 | A243 | 40f dk grn, yel | .20 | .20 |
| 1104 | A243 | 50f red brn, pale grn | .20 | .20 |
| 1105 | A243 | 60f blue, pink | .20 | .20 |
| 1106 | A243 | 1fo olive | .50 | .20 |

| 1107 | A243 | 1.70fo rose brn, yel | .70 | .25 |
|---|---|---|---|---|
| 1108 | A243 | 2fo blue green | .95 | .40 |
| | | Nos. 1098-1108 (11) | 3.75 | 2.45 |

Exist imperf. Value, set $55.

Readers in Industrial
Library — A244

Industry
A245

1fo, Agriculture. 2fo, Liberation monument.

| 1955, Apr. 4 | Perf. 12½x12, 12x12½ |
|---|---|
| 1109 | A244 | 40f dk car & ol brn | .65 | .20 |
| 1110 | A245 | 60f dk green & red | .65 | .20 |
| 1111 | A245 | 1fo choc & grn | .95 | .20 |
| 1112 | A244 | 2fo blue grn & brn | 1.25 | .50 |
| | | Nos. 1109-1112 (4) | 3.50 | 1.10 |

10th anniversary of Hungary's liberation.
Exist imperf. Value, set $50.

Date, Flags,
Grain
Elevator and
Tractor
A246

| 1955, May 1 | | | Perf. 12x12½ | |
|---|---|---|---|---|
| 1113 | A246 | 1fo rose carmine | .80 | .20 |

Labor Day, May 1, 1955.
Exist imperf. Value, set $15.

Government
Printing
Plant — A247

| 1955, May 28 | | | Wmk. 106 | |
|---|---|---|---|---|
| 1114 | A247 | 60f gray grn & hn brn | .50 | .20 |

Centenary of the establishment of the government printing plant.
Exist imperf. Value, set $15.

Young Citizens and Hungarian
Flag — A248

| 1955, June 15 | | | Perf. 12 | |
|---|---|---|---|---|
| 1115 | A248 | 1fo red brown | .60 | .20 |

Issued to publicize the second national congress of the Hungarian Youth Organization.
Exist imperf. Value, set $20.

Truck Farmer
A249

10f, Fisherman. 12f, Bricklayer. 20f, Radio assembler. 30f, Woman potter. 40f, Railwayman & train. 50f, Clerk & scales. 60f, Postman emptying mail box. 70f, Cattle & herdsman. 80f, Textile worker. 1fo, Riveter.

1.20fo, Carpenter. 1.40fo, Streetcar conductor. 1.70fo, Herdsman & pigs. 2fo, Welder. 2.60fo, Woman tractor driver. 3fo, Herdsman in national costume & horse. 4fo, Bus driver. 5fo, Lineman. 10fo, Coal miner.

| 1955 | | Wmk. 106 | Perf. 12x12½ | |
|---|---|---|---|---|
| 1116 | A249 | 8f chestnut | .20 | .20 |
| 1117 | A249 | 10f Prus green | .25 | .20 |
| 1118 | A249 | 12f red orange | .25 | .20 |
| 1119 | A249 | 20f olive green | .40 | .20 |
| 1120 | A249 | 30f dark red | .35 | .20 |
| 1121 | A249 | 40f brown | .40 | .20 |
| 1122 | A249 | 50f violet bl | .40 | .20 |
| 1123 | A249 | 60f brown red | .50 | .20 |
| 1124 | A249 | 70f olive | .80 | .20 |
| 1125 | A249 | 80f purple | .50 | .20 |
| 1126 | A249 | 1fo blue | 1.00 | .20 |
| 1127 | A249 | 1.20fo olive bis | 1.20 | |
| 1128 | A249 | 1.40fo deep green | 1.00 | .20 |
| 1129 | A249 | 1.70fo purple | 1.00 | .20 |
| 1130 | A249 | 2fo rose brown | 1.00 | .20 |
| 1131 | A249 | 2.60fo vermilion | 1.25 | .20 |
| 1132 | A249 | 3fo green | 2.00 | .20 |
| 1133 | A249 | 4fo peacock blue | 1.75 | .20 |
| 1134 | A249 | 5fo orange brown | 1.75 | .25 |
| 1135 | A249 | 10fo violet | 1.50 | .55 |
| | | Nos. 1116-1135 (20) | 17.50 | 4.40 |

Exist imperf. Value, set $135.
For surcharges see Nos. B211-B216.

Postrider
Blowing
Horn — A250

| 1955, June 25 | | | Perf. 12½x12 | |
|---|---|---|---|---|
| 1136 | A250 | 1fo rose violet | .50 | .20 |

Hungarian Postal Museum, 25th anniv.
Exists tete-beche. Value: 2½ times the value of a single.
Exists imperf. Value $20.

Mihaly
Csokonai
Vitez
A251

1fo, Mihaly Vorosmarty. 2fo, Attila József.

| 1955, July 28 | | | Perf. 12 | |
|---|---|---|---|---|
| 1137 | A251 | 60f olive black | .90 | .30 |
| 1138 | A251 | 1fo dark blue | .90 | .25 |
| 1139 | A251 | 2fo rose brown | 1.90 | .65 |
| | | Nos. 1137-1139 (3) | 3.70 | 1.20 |

Issued to honor three Hungarian poets.
Exist imperf. Value $35.

Bela
Bartok — A252

| 1955, Oct. 9 | | | | |
|---|---|---|---|---|
| 1140 | A252 | 60f light brown | 1.25 | .50 |
| | | Nos. 1140,C168-C169 (3) | 6.00 | 3.10 |

10th anniversary of the death of Bela Bartok, composer.
Exist imperf. Value, set (3) $35.

Diesel
Train
A253

Designs: 60f, Bus. 80f, Motorcycle. 1fo, Truck. 1.20fo, Steam locomotive. 1.50fo, Dump truck. 2fo, Freighter.

**1955, Dec. 20**      **Perf. 14½**

| 1141 | A253 | 40f grn & vio brn | .20 | .20 |
|------|------|------------------|-----|-----|
| 1142 | A253 | 60f dp grn & ol | .20 | .20 |
| 1143 | A253 | 80f ol grn & brn | .35 | .20 |
| 1144 | A253 | 1fo ocher & grn | .70 | .30 |
| 1145 | A253 | 1.20fo salmon & blk | 1.25 | .35 |
| 1146 | A253 | 1.50fo grnsh blk & red brn | 1.40 | .50 |
| 1147 | A253 | 2fo aqua & brown | 1.90 | .75 |
| | | Nos. 1141-1147 (7) | 6.00 | 2.50 |

Exist imperf. Value, set $60.

Puli (Sheepdog) — A254

Puli and Steer A255

Hungarian Pointer — A256

Hungarian Dogs: 60f, Pumi (sheepdog). 1fo, Retriever with fowl. 1.20fo, Kuvasz (sheepdog). 1.50fo, Komondor (sheepdog) and cottage. 2fo, Komondor (head).

**Perf. 11x13 (A254), 12**

**1956, Mar. 17**      **Engr. & Litho.**

| 1148 | A254 | 40f yel, blk & red | .20 | .20 |
|------|------|------------------|-----|-----|
| 1149 | A255 | 50f blue, bis & blk | .20 | .20 |
| 1150 | A254 | 60f yel grn, blk & red | .35 | .20 |
| 1151 | A256 | 80f bluish grn, ocher & blk | .40 | .25 |
| 1152 | A256 | 1fo turq, ocher & blk | .45 | .30 |
| 1153 | A254 | 1.20fo salmon, blk & chnt | .75 | .35 |
| 1154 | A255 | 1.50fo ultra, blk & buff | 1.40 | .45 |
| 1155 | A254 | 2fo cerise, blk & chnt | 2.25 | .95 |
| | | Nos. 1148-1155 (8) | 6.00 | 2.90 |

Exist imperf. Value, set $55.

Pioneer Emblem A257

**Perf. 12x12½**

**1956, June 2**    **Photo.**    **Wmk. 106**

| 1156 | A257 | 1fo red | .50 | .20 |
|------|------|---------|-----|-----|
| 1157 | A257 | 1fo gray | .50 | .20 |

Pioneer movement, 10th anniversary. Exist imperf. Value, set $20.

Janos Hunyadi Statue — A258

Miner — A259

**1956, Aug. 12**      **Perf. 12**

1158 A258 1fo brown, *yelsh*   1.00 .35

500th anniv. of the defeat of the Turks at the battle of Pecs under Janos Hunyadi.

Printed in sheets of 50 with alternate vertical rows inverted and center row of perforation omitted, providing 25 tête bêche pairs, of which 5 are imperf. between. Values for tetebeche pairs: unused $1.25; used $.70. Values for tete-beche pairs, imperf between: unused $2; used $11.50.

Exists imperf. Value $10. Tête bêche pair also exists imperf. Value, $45.

**1956, Sept. 2**

1159 A259 1fo dark blue   .50 .20

Issued in honor of Miners' Day 1956. Exists imperf. Value $15.

Kayak Racer A260

Sports: 30f, Horse jumping hurdle. 40f, Fencing. 60f, Women hurdlers. 1fo, Soccer. 1.50fo, Weight lifting. 2fo, Gymnastics. 3fo, Basketball.

**1956, Sept. 25**   **Wmk. 106**   **Perf. 11**

**Figures in Brown Olive**

| 1160 | A260 | 20f lt blue | .20 | .20 |
|------|------|-------------|-----|-----|
| 1161 | A260 | 30f lt olive grn | .20 | .20 |
| 1162 | A260 | 40f deep orange | .20 | .20 |
| 1163 | A260 | 60f bluish grn | .20 | .20 |
| 1164 | A260 | 1fo vermilion | .35 | .20 |
| 1165 | A260 | 1.50fo blue violet | .65 | .25 |
| 1166 | A260 | 2fo emerald | .80 | .30 |
| 1167 | A260 | 3fo rose lilac | 1.40 | .40 |
| | | Nos. 1160-1167 (8) | 4.00 | 1.95 |

16th Olympic Games at Melbourne, Nov. 22-Dec. 8, 1956. Exist imperf. Value, set $100.

Franz Liszt A261

Portrait: 1fo, Frederic Chopin facing left.

**1956, Oct. 7**   **Photo.**   **Perf. 12x12½**

| 1168 | A261 | 1fo violet blue | 2.00 | 2.00 |
|------|------|----------------|------|------|
| 1169 | A261 | 1fo magenta | 2.00 | 2.00 |
| a. | | Pair, #1168-1169 | 6.00 | 6.00 |

29th Day of the Stamp. Sold only at the Philatelic Exhibition together with entrance ticket for 4fo. Exist imperf. Value, pair $30.

Janos Arany — A262

**1957, Sept. 15**   **Wmk. 106**   **Perf. 12**

1170 A262 2fo bright blue   .60 .20

75th anniv. of the death of Janos Arany, poet. Exists imperf. Value $10.

Arms of Hungary A263

**1957, Oct. 1**

| 1171 | A263 | 60f brt red | .75 | .20 |
|------|------|-------------|-----|-----|
| 1172 | A263 | 1fo dp yellow grn | .75 | .20 |

Exists imperf. Value, set $20.

Trade Union Congress Emblem A264

**1957, Oct. 4**

1173 A264 1fo dk carmine   .50 .20

4th Intl. Trade Union Cong., Leipzig, 10/4-15. Exists imperf. Value $10.

Dove and Colors of Communist Countries — A265

Design: 1fo, Lenin.

**1957, Nov. 7**   **Litho.**   **Perf. 12**

| 1174 | A265 | 60f gray, blk & multi | .50 | .20 |
|------|------|----------------------|-----|-----|
| 1175 | A265 | 1fo ol bis & indigo | .50 | .20 |

Russian Revolution, 40th anniversary. Exist imperf. Value, set $35.

Komarom Tumbler Pigeons A266

Pigeons: 40f, Two short-beaked Budapest pigeons. 60f, Giant domestic pigeon. 1fo, Three Szeged pigeons. 2fo, Two Hungarian fantails.

**Perf. 12x12½**

**1957-58**   **Photo.**   **Wmk. 106**

| 1176 | A266 | 30f yel grn, cl & ocher | .25 | .20 |
|------|------|------------------------|-----|-----|
| 1177 | A266 | 40f ocher & blk | .25 | .20 |
| 1178 | A266 | 60f blue & gray | .25 | .20 |
| 1179 | A266 | 1fo gray & red brn | .25 | .20 |
| 1180 | A266 | 2fo brt pink & gray | .60 | .40 |
| | | Nos. 1176-1180,C175 (6) | 2.50 | 1.70 |

Intl. Pigeon Exhibition, Budapest, 12/14-16. Exist imperf. Value, set (6) $35. Issued: 30f, 1/12/58; others, 12/14/57.

Television Station — A267

**1958, Feb. 22**   **Engr.**   **Perf. 11**

| 1181 | A267 | 2fo rose violet | 1.25 | .65 |
|------|------|----------------|------|-----|
| a. | | Perf. 12 | 7.50 | 7.50 |

**Souvenir Sheet**

1182 A267 2fo green   40.00 40.00

Issued to publicize the television industry. No. 1182 sold for 25fo. Exist imperf. Values: single $25; souvenir sheet $175.

Mother and Child A268

Designs: 30f, Old man feeding pigeons. 40f, School boys. 60f, "Working ants and fiddling grasshopper." 1fo, Honeycomb and bee. 2fo, Handing over money.

**1958, Mar. 9**   **Photo.**   **Perf. 12**

| 1183 | A268 | 20f yel grn & ol gray | .20 | .20 |
|------|------|----------------------|-----|-----|
| 1184 | A268 | 30f lt olive & mar | .20 | .20 |
| 1185 | A268 | 40f yel bis & brn | .20 | .20 |
| 1186 | A268 | 60f rose car & grnsh blk | .30 | .20 |
| 1187 | A268 | 1fo ol gray & dk brn | .60 | .35 |
| 1188 | A268 | 2fo org & ol gray | 1.50 | .50 |
| | | Nos. 1183-1188 (6) | 3.00 | 1.65 |

Issued to publicize the value of savings and insurance. Exist imperf. Value, set $40.

**Kazar Costume Type of 1953 Souvenir Sheet**

**1958, Apr. 17**   **Engr.**   **Perf. 12**

1189 A233 10fo magenta   25.00 25.00

Issued for the Universal and International Exposition at Brussels. Exists imperf. Value $80.

Arms of Hungary A269

**1958, May 23**   **Litho.**   **Wmk. 106**

**Arms in Original Colors**

| 1190 | A269 | 60f lt red brn & red | .20 | .20 |
|------|------|---------------------|-----|-----|
| 1191 | A269 | 1fo gray grn & grn | .50 | .20 |
| 1192 | A269 | 2fo gray & dk brn | .80 | .20 |
| | | Nos. 1190-1192 (3) | 1.50 | .60 |

1st anniv. of the law amending the constitution. Exist imperf. Value, set $20.

Youth Holding Book — A270

**1958, June 14**   **Photo.**   **Perf. 12½x12**

1193 A270 1fo brown carmine   .45 .20

5th Hungarian Youth Festival at Keszthely.

Printed with alternating label, inscribed: V. IFJUSAGI TALALKOZO KESZTHELY 1958. Exists imperf. Value, with label $10.

Post Horn and Town Hall, Prague — A271

**1958, June 30**

| 1194 | A271 | 60f green | .20 | .20 |
|---|---|---|---|---|
| a. | | Pair, #1194, C184 | .80 | .80 |

Conference of Postal Ministers of Communist Countries at Prague, June 30-July 8. Exists imperf. Value, $5. In pair with #C184 imperf, value $10.

Dolomite Flax — A272

Hungarian Thistles — A273

30f, Kitaibelia vitifolia. 60f, Crocuses. 1fo, Hellebore. 2fo, Lilies. 2.50fo, Pinks. 3fo, Dog roses.

*Perf. 11x13, 12½x12 (A273)*

**1958, Aug. 12    Photo.    Wmk. 106**

| 1195 | A272 | 20f red vio & yel | 1.00 | .20 |
|---|---|---|---|---|
| 1196 | A272 | 30f blue, yel & grn | .20 | .20 |
| 1197 | A273 | 40f brown & bis | .25 | .20 |
| 1198 | A273 | 60f bl grn & pink | .30 | .20 |
| 1199 | A273 | 1fo rose car & yel grn | .55 | .25 |
| 1200 | A272 | 2fo grn & yel | .95 | .20 |
| 1201 | A272 | 2.50fo vio bl & pink | 1.10 | .45 |
| 1202 | A272 | 3fo green & pink | 1.90 | .70 |
| a. | | Souv. sheet of 4, perf. 12 | 32.50 | 35.00 |
| | | Nos. 1195-1202 (8) | 6.25 | 2.40 |

No. 1202a and a similar imperf. sheet were issued for the International Philatelic Congress at Brussels, Sept. 15-17, 1958. They contain the triangular 20f, 30f, 2.50fo and 3fo stamps printed in different colors. Sheets measure 111x111mm. and are printed on unwatermarked, linen-finish paper. Background of stamps, marginal inscriptions and ornaments in green. No. 1202a also exists perf. 11; same value.

Exist imperf. Value, set $40. Value of 1202a imperf, $100.

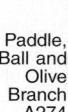

Paddle, Ball and Olive Branch A274

Designs: 30f, Table tennis player, vert. 40f, Wrestlers, vert. 60f, Wrestlers, horiz. 1fo, Water polo player, vert. 2.50fo, High dive, vert. 3fo, Swimmer.

**1958, Aug. 30    Wmk. 106    Perf. 12**

| 1203 | A274 | 20f rose red, pnksh | .20 | .20 |
|---|---|---|---|---|
| 1204 | A274 | 30f olive, grnsh | .20 | .20 |
| 1205 | A274 | 40f mag, yel | .25 | .20 |
| 1206 | A274 | 60f brown, bluish | .40 | .20 |
| 1207 | A274 | 1fo ultra, bluish | .45 | .20 |

| 1208 | A274 | 2.50fo dk red, yel | 1.10 | .30 |
|---|---|---|---|---|
| 1209 | A274 | 3fo grnsh bl, grnsh | 1.40 | .50 |
| | | Nos. 1203-1209 (7) | 4.00 | 1.80 |

Intl. Wrestling and European Swimming and Table Tennis Championships, held at Budapest.
Exist imperf. Value, set $32.50.

Red Flag — A275

Design: 2fo, Hand holding newspaper.

**1958, Nov. 21    Perf. 12½x12**

| 1210 | A275 | 1fo brown & red | .20 | .20 |
|---|---|---|---|---|
| 1211 | A275 | 2fo dk gray bl & red | .55 | .20 |

40th anniversary of the founding of the Hungarian Communist Party and newspaper.
Exist imperf. Value, set $15.

Satellite, Sputnik and American Rocket A276

Designs: 10f, Eötvös Torsion Balance and Globe. 20f, Deep sea exploration. 30f, Icebergs, penguins and polar light. 40f, Soviet Antarctic camp and map of Pole. 60f, "Rocket" approaching moon. 1fo, Sun and observatory.

**1959, Mar. 14    Perf. 12x12½**
**Size: 32x21mm**

| 1212 | A276 | 10f car rose & sepia | .35 | .20 |
|---|---|---|---|---|
| 1213 | A276 | 20f brt blue & gray | .25 | .20 |
| 1214 | A276 | 30f dk slate grn & bis | .40 | .20 |

*Perf. 12*
**Size: 35x26mm**

| 1215 | A276 | 40f slate bl & lt bl | .25 | .20 |
|---|---|---|---|---|

*Perf. 15*
**Size: 58x21mm**

| 1216 | A276 | 60f Prus bl & lemon | .45 | .20 |
|---|---|---|---|---|

*Perf. 12*
**Size: 35x26mm**

| 1217 | A276 | 1fo scarlet & yel | .70 | .30 |
|---|---|---|---|---|
| 1218 | A276 | 5fo brn & red brn | 1.60 | .80 |
| | | Nos. 1212-1218 (7) | 4.00 | 2.10 |

Intl. Geophysical Year. See No. 1262.
Exist imperf. Value, set $30.

"Revolution" — A277

**1959, Mar. 21    Perf. 12½x12**

| 1219 | A277 | 20f vio brn & red | .20 | .20 |
|---|---|---|---|---|
| 1220 | A277 | 60f blue & red | .20 | .20 |
| 1221 | A277 | 1fo brown & red | .45 | .20 |
| | | Nos. 1219-1221 (3) | .85 | .60 |

40th anniv. of the proclamation of the Hungarian Soviet Republic.
Exist imperf. Value, set $15.

Rose — A278

**1959, May 1    Photo.    Perf. 11**

| 1222 | A278 | 60f lilac, dp car & grn | .40 | .20 |
|---|---|---|---|---|
| 1223 | A278 | 1fo lt brn, dl red & grn | .60 | .20 |

Issued for Labor Day, May 1, 1959.
Exist imperf. Value, set $15.

Early Locomotive — A279

Designs: 30f, Diesel coach. 40f, Early semaphore, vert. 60f, Csonka automobile. 1fo, Icarus bus. 2fo, First Lake Balaton steamboat. 2.50fo, Stagecoach.

**1959, May 26    Litho.    Perf. 14½x15**

| 1224 | A279 | 20f multi | .20 | .20 |
|---|---|---|---|---|
| 1225 | A279 | 30f multi | .20 | .20 |
| 1226 | A279 | 40f multi | .20 | .20 |
| 1227 | A279 | 60f multi | .20 | .20 |
| 1228 | A279 | 1fo multi | .35 | .20 |
| 1229 | A279 | 2fo multi | .45 | .20 |
| 1230 | A279 | 2.50fo multi | .65 | .30 |
| | | Nos. 1224-1230,C201 (8) | 3.50 | 1.90 |

Transport Museum, Budapest.
Exist imperf. Value, set (8) $30.

*Perf. 10½x11½*

**1959, May 29    Wmk. 106**

| 1231 | A279 | 2.50fo multi | 2.00 | 2.00 |
|---|---|---|---|---|

Designer's name on No. 1231. Printed in sheets of four with four labels to commemorate the congress of the International Federation for Philately in Hamburg. Value $100.
Exist imperf. Values: paid with label $15; sheetlet $120.

Post Horn and World Map — A280

**1959, June 1    Photo.    Perf. 12**

| 1232 | A280 | 1fo cerise | .75 | .30 |
|---|---|---|---|---|

Postal Ministers Conference, Berlin.
Printed in sheets of 25 stamps with 25 alternating gray labels showing East Berlin Opera House.
Exists imperf. Value: in pair with label, $15.

Great Cormorant A281

Warrior, 10th Century — A282

Birds: 20f, Little egret and nest. 30f, Purple heron and nest. 40f, Great egret. 60f, White spoonbill. 1fo, Gray heron. 2fo, Squacco heron and nest. 3fo, Glossy ibis.

**1959, June 14**

| 1233 | A281 | 10f green & indigo | .20 | .20 |
|---|---|---|---|---|
| 1234 | A281 | 20f gray bl & ol grn | .20 | .20 |
| 1235 | A281 | 30f org, grnsh blk & vio | .20 | .20 |
| 1236 | A281 | 40f dark grn & gray | .20 | .20 |
| 1237 | A281 | 60f dp cl & pale rose | .35 | .20 |
| 1238 | A281 | 1fo dp bl grn & blk | .50 | .20 |
| 1239 | A281 | 2fo dp orange & gray | .85 | .30 |
| 1240 | A281 | 3fo bister & brn lake | 1.50 | .70 |
| | | Nos. 1233-1240 (8) | 4.00 | 2.20 |

Exist imperf. Value, set $40.

**1959, July 11**

Designs: 20f, Warrior, 15th century. 30f, Soldier, 18th century. 40f, Soldier, 19th century. 60f, Cavalry man, 19th century. 1fo, Fencer, assault. 1.40fo, Fencer on guard. 3fo, Swordsman saluting.

| 1241 | A282 | 10f gray & blue | .20 | .20 |
|---|---|---|---|---|
| 1242 | A282 | 20f gray & dull yel | .20 | .20 |
| 1243 | A282 | 30f gray & gray vio | .20 | .20 |
| 1244 | A282 | 40f gray & ver | .20 | .20 |
| 1245 | A282 | 60f gray & rose lil | .20 | .20 |
| 1246 | A282 | 1fo ind & lt bl grn | .30 | .20 |
| 1247 | A282 | 1.40fo orange & blk | .60 | .25 |
| 1248 | A282 | 3fo blk & ol grn | .90 | .70 |
| | | Nos. 1241-1248 (8) | 2.80 | 2.15 |

24th World Fencing Championships, Budapest.
Exist imperf. Value, set $35.

Sailboat, Lake Balaton — A283

40f, Vintager & lake, horiz. 60f, Bathers. 1.20fo, Fishermen. 2fo, Summer guests & ship.

**1959, July 11    Photo.    Wmk. 106**

| 1249 | A283 | 30f blue, yel | .20 | .20 |
|---|---|---|---|---|
| 1250 | A283 | 40f carmine rose | .20 | .20 |
| 1251 | A283 | 60f dp red brown | .20 | .20 |
| 1252 | A283 | 1.20fo violet | .30 | .20 |
| 1253 | A283 | 2fo red org, yel | .60 | .50 |
| | | Nos. 1249-1253,C202-C205 (9) | 2.60 | 2.20 |

Issued to publicize Lake Balaton and the opening of the Summer University.
Exist imperf. Value, set (9) $35.

Haydn's Monogram A284

Esterhazy Palace A285

Haydn and Schiller
Monograms — A286

Design: 1fo, Joseph Haydn and score.

**1959, Sept. 20    Wmk. 106    Perf. 12**
1254  A284  40f dp claret & yel      .20    .20
1255  A285  60f Prus bl, gray &
             yel                     .75    .75
1256  A284  1fo dk vio, lt brn &
             org                     .65    .60

Designs: 40f, Schiller's monogram. 60f, Pegasus rearing from flames. 1fo, Friedrich von Schiller.

1257  A284  40f olive grn & org      .20    .20
1258  A285  60f violet bl & lil      .40    .20
1259  A284  1fo dp cl & org brn      .80    .20
      Nos. 1254-1259 (6)            3.00   1.75

**Souvenir Sheet**
*Imperf*
1260  A286  Sheet of 2             16.00  16.00
  a.  3fo magenta                   3.25   3.25
  b.  3fo green                     3.25   3.25

150th anniv. of the death of Joseph Haydn, Austrian composer, Nos. 1254-1256; 200th anniv. of the birth of Friedrich von Schiller, German poet and dramatist, Nos. 1257-1259; No. 1260 honors both Haydn and Schiller. Nos. 1254-1260 exist imperf. Value, set $25. No. 1260 exists imperf. Value $22.

Shepherd — A287

**1959, Sept. 25    Engr.    Perf. 12**
1261  A287  2fo deep claret         1.50   1.50
  a.  With ticket                   1.75   1.75

Day of the Stamp and Natl. Stamp Exhib. Issued in sheets of 8 with alternating ticket. The 4fo sale price marked on the ticket was the admission fee to the Natl. Stamp Exhib. Exist imperf. Values: single $17; single with ticket $20.

Type of 1959 Overprinted in Red

**1959, Sept. 24    Photo.    Perf. 15**
1262  A276  60f dull bl & lem-
             on                      .50    .25
  a.  Overprint omitted            3,000.

Landing of Lunik 2 on moon, Sept. 14. Exists imperf. Value $12.

Handing over Letter A288

**1959, Oct. 4    Litho.    Perf. 12**
1263  A288  60f multicolored        .50    .20

Intl. Letter Writing Week, Oct. 4-10. Exists imperf. Value $7.

Szamuely and Lenin — A289

Designs: 40f, Aleksander Pushkin. 60pf, Vladimir V. Mayakovsky. 1fo, Hands holding peace flag.

**1959, Nov. 14    Photo.    Wmk. 106**
1264  A289  20f dk red & bister      .20    .20
1265  A289  40f brn & rose lil, blu-
             ish                     .20    .20
1266  A289  60f dk blue & bis        .20    .20
1267  A289  1fo bl, car, buff, red &
             grn                     .40    .30
      Nos. 1264-1267 (4)            1.00    .90

Soviet Stamp Exhibition, Budapest. Exists imperf. Value $20.

European Swallowtail A290

Butterflies: 30f, Arctia hebe, horiz. 40f, Lysandra hylas, horiz. 60f, Apatura ilia.

**Perf. 11½x12, 12x11½**
**1959, Nov. 20**
**Butterflies in Natural Colors**
1268  A290  20f blk & yel grn       .20    .20
1269  A290  30f lt blue & blk       .35    .20
1270  A290  40f dk gray & org brn   .35    .20
1271  A290  60f dk gray & dl yel    .45    .20
      Nos. 1268-1271,C206-C208 (7) 6.00   2.10

Exist imperf. Value, set (7) $40.

Worker with Banner — A291

Design: 1fo, Congress flag.

**1959, Nov. 30    Perf. 14½**
1272  A291  60f brown, grn & red    .25    .20
1273  A291  1fo brn, red, red &
             grn                     .25    .20

Issued to commemorate the 7th Congress of the Hungarian Socialist Workers' Party. Exist imperf. Value, set $12.

Teacher Reading Fairy Tales — A292

Fairy Tales: 30f, Sleeping Beauty. 40f, Matt, the Goose Boy. 60f, The Cricket and the Ant. 1fo, Mashenka and the Three Bears. 2fo, Hansel and Gretel. 2.50fo, Pied Piper. 3fo, Little Red Riding Hood.

**1959, Dec. 15    Litho.    Perf. 11½**
**Designs in Black**
1274  A292  20f gray & multi        .20    .20
1275  A292  30f brt pink            .20    .20
1276  A292  40f lt blue grn         .20    .20
1277  A292  60f lt blue             .20    .20
1278  A292  1fo yellow              .35    .25

1279  A292  2fo brt yellow grn      .55    .25
1280  A292  2.50fo orange           .70    .40
1281  A292  3fo crimson            1.10    .60
      Nos. 1274-1281 (8)           3.50   2.30

Exist imperf. Value, set $30.

Sumeg Castle — A293

Castles: 20fr, Tata. 30f, Diosgyor. 60f, Saros-Patak. 70f, Nagyvazsony. 1.40fo, Siklos. 1.70fo, Somlo. 3fo, Csesznek, vert. 5fo, Koszeg, vert. 10fo, Sarvar, vert.

**Wmk. 106**
**1960, Feb. 1    Photo.    Perf. 14½**
**Size: 21x17½mm**
1282  A293  8f purple               .20    .20
1283  A293  20f dk yel grn          .20    .20
1284  A293  30f orange brn          .20    .20
1285  A293  60f rose red            .20    .20
1286  A293  70f emerald             .20    .20

**Perf. 12x11½, 11½x12**
**Size: 28x21mm, 21x28mm**
1287  A293  1.40fo ultra            .20    .20
1288  A293  1.70fo dl vio,
             "Somlo"                .45    .20
  b.  "Somlyo"                      .65    .20
1289  A293  3fo red brown           .55    .20
  a.  Unwatermarked                1.00    .25
1290  A293  5fo yellow green       1.25    .20
  a.  Unwatermarked                2.25    .40
1291  A293  10fo carmine rose      2.50   2.15
      Nos. 1282-1291 (10)          5.95   2.15

Exist imperf. Value, set $80.

**Tinted Paper**
**Perf. 14½**
**Size: 21x17½mm**
1282a  A293  8f pur, bluish         .20    .20
1283a  A293  20f dk yel grn, grnsh  .20    .20
1284a  A293  30f org brn, yel       .30    .20
1285a  A293  60f rose red, pnksh    .20    .20
1286a  A293  70f emer, bluish       .60    .20

**Perf. 12x11½**
**Size: 28x21mm**
1287a  A293  1.40fo ultra, bluish   .65    .25
1288a  A293  1.70fo dl vio, bluish  .85    .25
      Nos. 1282a-1288a (7)         3.00   1.50

Exist imperf. Value, set $30.
See Nos. 1356-1365, 1644-1646.

Halas Lace — A294

Designs: Various Halas lace patterns.

**Wmk. 106**
**1960, Feb. 15    Litho.    Perf. 11½**
**Sizes: 20f, 60f, 1fo, 3fo: 27x37mm**
**30f, 40f, 1.50fo, 2fo: 37½x43½mm**
**Inscriptions in Orange**
1292  A294  20f brown black         .20    .20
1293  A294  30f violet              .20    .20
1294  A294  40f Prus blue           .40    .20
1295  A294  60f dark brown          .20    .20
1296  A294  1fo dark green          .25    .20
1297  A294  1.50fo green            .40    .20
1298  A294  2fo dark blue           .85    .25
1299  A294  3fo dk carmine         1.50    .55
      Nos. 1292-1299 (8)           4.00   2.00

Exist imperf. Value, set $30.
See Nos. 1570-1577.

Cross-country Skier — A295

**Souvenir Sheet**
Design as on No. 1299.

**1960, Sept. 3**
**Inscriptions in Orange**
1300  Sheet of 4 + 4 labels       15.00  15.00
  a.  3fo brown olive               3.00   3.00
  b.  3fo bright violet             3.00   3.00
  c.  3fo emerald                   3.00   3.00
  d.  3fo bright blue               3.00   3.00

Fédération Internationale de Philatélie Congress, Warsaw, Sept. 3-11. No. 1300 contains 4 stamps and 4 alternating labels, printed in colors of adjoining stamps. Exists imperf. Value $120.

**1960, Feb. 29    Photo.    Perf. 11½x12**

Sports: 40f, Ice hockey player. 60f, Ski jumper. 80f, Woman speed skater. 1fo, Downhill skier. 1.20fo, Woman figure skater.

**Inscriptions and Figures in Bister**
1301  A295  30f deep blue           .20    .20
1302  A295  40f brt green           .20    .20
1303  A295  60f scarlet             .20    .20
1304  A295  80f purple              .20    .20
1305  A295  1fo brt grnsh blue      .60    .20
1306  A295  1.20fo brown red        .70    .45
      Nos. 1301-1306,B217 (7)      3.00   1.80

8th Olympic Winter Games, Squaw Valley, Calif., Feb. 18-29, 1960. Exists imperf. Value $25.

Clara Zetkin — A296

Portraits: No. 1308, Kato Haman. No. 1309, Lajos Tüköry. No. 1310, Giuseppe Garibaldi. No. 1311, István Türr. No. 1312, Ottó Herman. No. 1313, Ludwig van Beethoven. No. 1314, Ferenc Mora. No. 1315, Istvan Toth Bucsoki. No. 1316, Donat Banki. No. 1317, Abraham G. Pattantyus. No. 1318, Ignaz Semmelweis. No. 1319, Frédéric Joliot-Curie. No. 1320, Ferenc Erkel. No. 1321, Janos Bolyai. No. 1322, Lenin.

**1960    Photo.    Perf. 10½**
1307  A296  60f lt red brn          .25    .20

**Engr.**
1308  A296  60f pale purple         .25    .20
1309  A296  60f rose red            .25    .20
1310  A296  60f violet              .25    .20
1311  A296  60f blue green          .25    .20
1312  A296  60f blue                .25    .20
1313  A296  60f gray brown          .25    .20
1314  A296  60f salmon pink         .25    .20
1315  A296  60f gray                .25    .20
1316  A296  60f rose lilac          .25    .20
1317  A296  60f green               .25    .20
1318  A296  60f violet blue         .25    .20
1319  A296  60f brown               .25    .20
1320  A296  60f rose brown          .25    .20
1321  A296  60f grnsh blue          .25    .20
1322  A296  60f dull red            .25    .20
      Nos. 1307-1322 (16)          4.00   3.20

Nos. 1307-1308 commemorate International Women's Day, Mar. 8. Exists imperf. Value $50.

Flower and Quill — A297

**Wmk. 106**
**1960, Apr. 2    Photo.    Perf. 12**
1323  A296  2fo brn, yel & grn     1.25   1.25
  a.  A297 With ticket             1.50   1.50

Issued for the stamp show of the National Federation of Hungarian Philatelists. The olive green 4fo ticket pictures the Federation's headquarters and served as entrance ticket to

the show. Printed in sheets of 35 stamps and 35 tickets.
Exists imperf. Value, stamp + ticket, $15.

Soviet Capt. Ostapenko Statue — A298

**Perf. 12½x11½, 11½x12½**
**1960, Apr. 4**

Designs: 60f, Youth holding flag, horiz.

| | | | | |
|---|---|---|---|---|
| 1324 | A298 | 40f dp carmine & brn | .20 | .20 |
| 1325 | A298 | 60f red brn, red & grn | .20 | .20 |

Hungary's liberation from the Nazis, 15th anniv.
Exist imperf. Value, set $10.

Boxers — A299

Sports: 10f, Rowers. 30f, Archer. 40f, Discus thrower. 50f, Girls playing ball. 60f, Javelin thrower. 1fo, Rider. 1.40fo, Wrestlers. 1.70fo, Swordsmen. 3fo, Hungarian Olympic emblem.

**1960, Aug. 21　　　　Perf. 11½x12**
**Designs in Ocher and Black**

| | | | | |
|---|---|---|---|---|
| 1326 | A299 | 10f blue | .20 | .20 |
| 1327 | A299 | 20f salmon | .20 | .20 |
| 1328 | A299 | 30f lt violet | .20 | .20 |
| 1329 | A299 | 40f yellow | .20 | .20 |
| 1330 | A299 | 50f deep pink | .20 | .20 |
| 1331 | A299 | 60f gray | .20 | .20 |
| 1332 | A299 | 1fo pale brn vio | .25 | .20 |
| 1333 | A299 | 1.40fo lt violet bl | .25 | .20 |
| 1334 | A299 | 1.70fo ocher | .45 | .20 |
| 1335 | A299 | 3fo multi | 1.00 | .50 |
| | | Nos. 1326-1335,B218 (11) | 3.90 | 2.60 |

17th Olympic Games, Rome, 8/25-9/11.
Exist imperf. Value, set $30.

**Souvenir Sheet**

Romulus and Remus Statue and Olympic Flame — A300

**1960, Aug. 21**

| | | | |
|---|---|---|---|
| 1336 | A300 | 10f multicolored | 17.50 16.00 |

Winter and Summer Olympic Games, 1960.
Exists imperf. Value $55.

Woman of Mezokovesd Writing Letter — A301

**Perf. 11½x12**
**1960, Oct. 15　　Photo.　　Wmk. 106**

| | | | | |
|---|---|---|---|---|
| 1337 | A301 | 2fo multicolored | 1.40 | 1.40 |
| a. | | With ticket | 1.75 | 1.75 |

Day of the Stamp and Natl. Stamp Exhib. Issued in sheets of 8 with alternating ticket. The 4fo sale price marked on the ticket was the admission fee to the Natl. Stamp Exhib.
Exists imperf. Value, stamp + ticket, $15.

The Turnip, Russian Fairy Tale — A302

Brown Bear — A303

Fairy Tales: 30f, Snow White and the Seven Dwarfs. 40f, The Miller, His Son and the Donkey. 60f, Puss in Boots. 80f, The Fox and the Raven. 1fo, The Maple-Wood Pipe. 1.70fo, The Fox and the Stork. 2fo, Momotaro (Japanese).

**1960, Dec. 1　　　　Perf. 11½x12**

| | | | | |
|---|---|---|---|---|
| 1338 | A302 | 20f multi | .20 | .20 |
| 1339 | A302 | 30f multi | .20 | .20 |
| 1340 | A302 | 40f multi | .20 | .20 |
| 1341 | A302 | 60f multi | .20 | .20 |
| 1342 | A302 | 80f multi | .20 | .20 |
| 1343 | A302 | 1fo multi | .35 | .20 |
| 1344 | A302 | 1.70fo multi | .65 | .35 |
| 1345 | A302 | 2fo multi | 1.00 | .50 |
| | | Nos. 1338-1345 (8) | 3.00 | 2.05 |

Exist imperf. Value, set $25.

**1961, Feb. 24　　　　Perf. 11½x12**

Animals: 20f, Kangaroo. 30f, Bison. 60f, Elephants. 80fr, Tiger with cubs. 1fo, Ibex. 1.40fo, Polar bear. 2fo, Zebra and young. 2.60fo, Bison cow with calf. 3fo, Main entrance to Budapest Zoological Gardens. 30f, 60f, 80f, 1.40fo, 2fo, 2.60fo are horizontal.

| | | | | |
|---|---|---|---|---|
| 1346 | A303 | 20f orange & blk | .20 | .20 |
| 1347 | A303 | 30f yel grn & blk brn | .20 | .20 |
| 1348 | A303 | 40f org brn & brn | .20 | .20 |
| 1349 | A303 | 60f lil rose & gray | .20 | .20 |
| 1350 | A303 | 80f gray & yel | .20 | .20 |
| 1351 | A303 | 1fo blue grn & brn | .20 | .20 |
| 1352 | A303 | 1.40fo grnsh bl, gray & blk | .35 | .20 |
| 1353 | A303 | 2fo pink & black | .50 | .25 |
| 1354 | A303 | 2.60fo brt vio & brn | .70 | .40 |
| 1355 | A303 | 3fo multicolored | 1.25 | .75 |
| | | Nos. 1346-1355 (10) | 4.00 | 2.80 |

Issued for the Budapest Zoo.
Exist imperf. Value, set $30.

**Castle Type of 1960**

10f, Kisvárda. 12f, Szigliget. 40f, Simon Tornya. 50f, Füzér. 80f, Egervár. 1fo, Vitány. 1.20fo, Sirok. 2fo, Boldogkö. 2.60fo, Hollókó. 4fo, Eger.

**1961, Mar. 3　　Photo.　　Perf. 14½**
**Size: 21x17½mm**

| | | | | |
|---|---|---|---|---|
| 1356 | A293 | 10f orange brn | .20 | .20 |
| 1357 | A293 | 12f violet blue | .20 | .20 |
| 1358 | A293 | 40f brt green | .20 | .20 |

| | | | | |
|---|---|---|---|---|
| 1359 | A293 | 50f brown | .20 | .20 |
| 1360 | A293 | 80f dull claret | .20 | .20 |

**Perf. 12x11½**
**Size: 28x21mm**

| | | | | |
|---|---|---|---|---|
| 1361 | A293 | 1fo brt blue | .20 | .20 |
| 1362 | A293 | 1.20fo rose violet | .25 | .20 |
| 1363 | A293 | 2fo olive bister | .40 | .20 |
| 1364 | A293 | 2.60fo dull blue | .60 | .20 |
| 1365 | A293 | 4fo brt violet | .75 | .20 |
| | | Nos. 1356-1365 (10) | 3.20 | 2.00 |

Exist imperf. Value, set $55.

Child Chasing Butterfly A304

Ferenc Rozsa, Journalist A305

40f, Man on operating table. 60f, Ambulance & stretcher. 1fo, Traffic light & scooter. 1.70fo, Syringe. 4fo, Emblem of Health Information Service (torch & serpent).

**1961, Mar. 17　　Litho.　　Perf. 10½**
**Cross in Red**
**Size: 18x18mm**

| | | | | |
|---|---|---|---|---|
| 1366 | A304 | 30f org brn & blk | .20 | .20 |
| 1367 | A304 | 40f bl grn, bl & sepia | .20 | .20 |

**Size: 25x30mm**

| | | | | |
|---|---|---|---|---|
| 1368 | A304 | 60f multi | .20 | .20 |
| 1369 | A304 | 1fo multi | .20 | .20 |
| 1370 | A304 | 1.70fo multi | .45 | .20 |
| 1371 | A304 | 4fo gray & yel grn | 1.25 | .50 |
| | | Nos. 1366-1371 (6) | 2.50 | 1.50 |

Health Information Service.
Exist imperf. Value, set $30.

**Wmk. 106, Unwmk.**
**1961　　　Photo.　　　Perf. 12**

Portraits: No. 1373, Gyorgy Kilian. No. 1374, Jozsef Rippl-Ronai. No. 1375, Sandor Latinka. No. 1376, Maté Zalka. No. 1377, Jozsef Katona.

| | | | | |
|---|---|---|---|---|
| 1372 | A305 | 1fo red brown | .25 | .20 |
| 1373 | A305 | 1fo greenish blue | .25 | .20 |
| 1374 | A305 | 1fo rose brown | .25 | .20 |
| 1375 | A305 | 1fo olive bister | .25 | .20 |
| 1376 | A305 | 1fo olive green | .25 | .20 |
| 1377 | A305 | 1fo maroon | .25 | .20 |
| | | Nos. 1372-1377 (6) | 1.50 | 1.20 |

Press Day (#1372); the inauguration of the Gyorgy Kilian Sports Movement (#1373); birth cent. of Jozsef Rippl-Ronai, painter (#1374); Sandor Latinka, revolutionary leader, 75th death anniv. (#1375); Mate Zalka, author and revolutionist (#1376); Jozsef Katona, dramatist (#1377).
Nos. 1374, 1375, 1377 are unwmkd. Others in this set have wmk. 106.
Exist imperf. Value, set $14.

Yuri A. Gagarin and Vostok 1 A306

Roses — A307

Design: 1fo, Launching Vostok 1.

**Perf. 11½x12**
**1961, Apr. 25　　　　Wmk. 106**

| | | | | |
|---|---|---|---|---|
| 1381 | A306 | 1fo dk bl & bis brn | .55 | .25 |
| 1382 | A306 | 2fo dp ultra & bis brn | 2.50 | 2.00 |

1st man in space, Yuri A. Gagarin, 4/12/61.
Exist imperf. Value, set $80.

**1961, Apr. 29　　　　Perf. 12½x11½**

Design: 2fo, as 1fo, design reversed.

| | | | | |
|---|---|---|---|---|
| 1383 | A307 | 1fo grn & dp car | .20 | .20 |
| 1384 | A307 | 2fo grn & dp car | .80 | .20 |
| a. | | Pair, #1383-1384 | 1.50 | .30 |

Issued for May Day, 1961.
Exist imperf. Value, No. 1384a $20.

"Venus" and Moon A308

Designs: Various Stages of Rocket.

**1961, May 24　　Wmk. 106　　Perf. 14½**

| | | | | |
|---|---|---|---|---|
| 1385 | A308 | 40f grnsh bl, bis & blk | .30 | .20 |
| 1386 | A308 | 60f brt bl, bis & blk | .40 | .20 |
| 1387 | A308 | 80f ultra & blk | .50 | .50 |
| 1388 | A308 | 2fo violet & yel | 1.25 | 1.25 |
| | | Nos. 1385-1388 (4) | 2.45 | 2.15 |

Soviet launching of the Venus space probe, Feb. 12, 1961. Exist imperf. Value, set $35. No. 1388 was also printed in sheets of four, perf. and imperf. Size: 130x76mm. Value: perf $10; imperf $275.

Warsaw Mermaid, Letter and Sea, Air and Land Transport — A309

Mermaid and: 60f, Television screen and antenna. 1fo, Radio.

**1961, June 19　　Photo.　　Perf. 13½**

| | | | | |
|---|---|---|---|---|
| 1389 | A309 | 40f red org & blk | .20 | .20 |
| 1390 | A309 | 60f lilac & blk | .20 | .20 |
| 1391 | A309 | 1fo brt blue & blk | .60 | .20 |
| | | Nos. 1389-1391 (3) | 1.00 | .60 |

Conference of Postal Ministers of Communist Countries held at Warsaw.
Exist imperf. Value, set $15.

Flag and Parliament — A310

Designs: 1.70fo, Orchid. 2.60fo, Small tortoise-shell butterfly. 3fo, Goldfinch.

**1961, June 23　　　　Perf. 11**
**Background in Silver**

| | | | | |
|---|---|---|---|---|
| 1392 | A310 | 1fo green, red & blk | .40 | .35 |
| 1393 | A310 | 1.70fo red & multi | .50 | .45 |
| 1394 | A310 | 2.60fo purple & multi | .75 | .75 |
| 1395 | A310 | 3fo blue & multi | 1.00 | 1.00 |

**1961, Aug. 19**
**Background in Gold**

| | | | | |
|---|---|---|---|---|
| 1396 | A310 | 1fo green & blk | .35 | .30 |
| 1397 | A310 | 1.70fo red & multi | .50 | .40 |
| 1398 | A310 | 2.60fo purple & multi | .75 | .75 |
| 1399 | A310 | 3fo blue & multi | 1.00 | 1.00 |
| | | Nos. 1392-1399 (8) | 5.25 | 5.00 |

Issued to publicize the International Stamp Exhibition, Budapest, Sept. 23-Oct. 3, 1961. #1392-1399 each printed in sheets of 4.
In gold background issue the top left inscription is changed on 1fo and 3fo.
Exist imperf. Values: set $50; sheetlet set $270.

George Stephenson A311

Winged Wheel, Steering Wheel and Road A312

Design: 2fo, Jenö Landler.

**Perf. 12½x11½**

| | | | **1961, July 4** | **Photo.** | **Wmk. 106** |
|---|---|---|---|---|---|
| 1400 | A311 | 60f yellow olive | | .20 | .20 |
| 1401 | A312 | 1fo blue & bister | | .25 | .20 |
| 1402 | A311 | 2fo yellow brown | | .25 | .20 |
| | | Nos. 1400-1402 (3) | | .70 | .60 |

Conference of Transport Ministers of Communist Countries held at Budapest.
Exist imperf. Value, set $20.

Soccer A313

| | | | **1961, July 8** | **Unwmk.** | **Perf. 14½** |
|---|---|---|---|---|---|
| 1403 | A313 | 40f shown | | .20 | .20 |
| 1404 | A313 | 60f Wrestlers | | .20 | .20 |
| 1405 | A313 | 1fo Gymnast | | .20 | .20 |
| | | Nos. 1403-1405 (3) | | .60 | .60 |

50th anniv. of the Steel Workers Sport Club (VASAS). See No. B219.
Exist imperf. Value, set of 4 (with B219) $16.

Galloping Horses — A314

40f, Hurdle Jump. 60f, Two trotters. 1fo, Three trotters. 1.70fo, Mares & foals. 2fo, Race horse "Baka." 3fo, Race horse "Kincsem."

**1961, July 22**

| | | | | |
|---|---|---|---|---|
| 1406 | A314 | 30f multi | .20 | .20 |
| 1407 | A314 | 40f multi | .20 | .20 |
| 1408 | A314 | 60f multi | .35 | .20 |
| 1409 | A314 | 1fo multi | .35 | .20 |
| 1410 | A314 | 1.70fo multi | .50 | .20 |
| 1411 | A314 | 2fo multi | .90 | .30 |
| 1412 | A314 | 3fo multi | 1.00 | .40 |
| | | Nos. 1406-1412 (7) | 3.50 | 1.70 |

Exist imperf. Value, set $35.

Keyboard, Music and Liszt Silhouette A315

Liszt Monument, Budapest A316

Designs: 2fo, Academy of Music, Budapest, and bar of music. 10fo, Franz Liszt.

**1961, Oct. 2     Unwmk.     Perf. 12**

| | | | | |
|---|---|---|---|---|
| 1413 | A315 | 60f gold & blk | .20 | .20 |
| 1414 | A315 | 1fo dark gray | .35 | .20 |
| 1415 | A315 | 2fo dk bl & gray grn | .50 | .40 |
| | | Nos. 1413-1415 (3) | 1.05 | .80 |

**Souvenir Sheet**

| | | | | |
|---|---|---|---|---|
| 1416 | A316 | 10fo multi | 8.50 | 7.00 |

150th anniv. of the birth, and the 75th anniv. of the death of Franz Liszt, composer.
Exist imperf. Value: set $25; souvenir sheet $40.

Lenin — A317

Monk's Hood — A318

**1961, Oct. 22     Perf. 11½**

| | | | | |
|---|---|---|---|---|
| 1417 | A317 | 1fo deep brown | .25 | .20 |

22nd Congress of the Communist Party of the USSR, Oct. 17-31.
Exist imperf. Value $5.

**Wmk. 106**

| | | | **1961, Nov. 4** | **Photo.** | **Perf. 12** |
|---|---|---|---|---|---|
| 1418 | A318 | 20f shown | | .20 | .20 |
| 1419 | A318 | 30f Centaury | | .20 | .20 |
| 1420 | A318 | 40f Blue iris | | .20 | .20 |
| 1421 | A318 | 60f Thorn apple | | .20 | .20 |
| 1422 | A318 | 1fo Purple holly-hock | | .30 | .20 |
| 1423 | A318 | 1.70fo Hop | | .40 | .20 |
| 1424 | A318 | 2fo Poppy | | .40 | .30 |
| 1425 | A318 | 3fo Mullein | | .60 | .50 |
| | | Nos. 1418-1425 (8) | | 2.50 | 2.00 |

Exist imperf. Value, set $30.

Nightingale A319

Mihaly Karolyi A320

Birds: 40f, Great titmouse. 60f, Chaffinch, horiz. 1fo, Eurasian jay. 1.20fo, Golden oriole, horiz. 1.50fo, European blackbird, horiz. 2fo, Yellowhammer, 3fo, Lapwing, horiz.

**1961, Dec. 18     Unwmk.     Perf. 12**

| | | | | |
|---|---|---|---|---|
| 1426 | A319 | 30f multi | .20 | .20 |
| 1427 | A319 | 40f multi | .20 | .20 |
| 1428 | A319 | 60f multi | .20 | .20 |
| 1429 | A319 | 1fo multi | .20 | .20 |
| 1430 | A319 | 1.20fo multi | .20 | .20 |
| 1431 | A319 | 1.50fo multi | .45 | .20 |
| 1432 | A319 | 2fo multi | .55 | .25 |
| 1433 | A319 | 3fo multi | .75 | .35 |
| | | Nos. 1426-1433 (8) | 2.75 | 1.80 |

Exist imperf. Value, set $30.

**1962, Mar. 18**

| | | | | |
|---|---|---|---|---|
| 1434 | A320 | 1fo black | .20 | .20 |

Mihaly Karolyi, (1875-1955), Prime Minister of Hungarian Republic (1918-19).
Exists imperf. Value $3.

**1962, Mar. 29**

Portrait: No. 1435, Ferenc Berkes.

| | | | | |
|---|---|---|---|---|
| 1435 | A320 | 1fo red brown | .20 | .20 |

Fifth Congress of the Hungarian Cooperative Movement, and to honor Ferenc Berkes, revolutionary. See Nos. 1457, 1459.
Exists imperf. Value $3.

Map of Europe, Train Signals and Emblem — A321

**1962, May 2     Photo.**

| | | | | |
|---|---|---|---|---|
| 1436 | A321 | 1fo blue green | .20 | .20 |

14th Intl. Esperanto Cong. of Railway Men.
Exists imperf. Value $3.

Xiphophorus Helleri A322

Tropical Fish: 30f, Macropodus opercularis. 40f, Lebistes reticulatus. 60f, Betta splendens. 80f, Puntius tetrazona. 1fo, Pterophyllum scalare. 1.20fo, Mesogonistius chaetodon. 1.50fo, Aphyosemion australe. 2fo, Hyphessobrycon innesi. 3fo, Symphysodon aequifasciata haraldi.

**1962, May 5     Perf. 11½x12**

**Fish in Natural Colors, Black Inscriptions**

| | | | | |
|---|---|---|---|---|
| 1437 | A322 | 20f blue | .20 | .20 |
| 1438 | A322 | 30f citron | .20 | .20 |
| 1439 | A322 | 40f lt blue | .20 | .20 |
| 1440 | A322 | 60f lt yellow grn | .20 | .20 |
| 1441 | A322 | 80f blue green | .30 | .20 |
| 1442 | A322 | 1fo brt bl grn | .20 | .20 |
| 1443 | A322 | 1.20fo blue green | .20 | .20 |
| 1444 | A322 | 1.50fo grnsh blue | .25 | .20 |
| a. | | "1962" twice in design | 2.00 | 2.00 |
| 1445 | A322 | 2fo green | .50 | .25 |
| 1446 | A322 | 3fo gray grn & yel | .75 | .50 |
| | | Nos. 1437-1446 (10) | 3.00 | 2.35 |

On No. 1444a, the year date appears both to the left and below the value inscription. On No. 14444, it appears only to the left of the value.
Exist imperf. Value, set $30.

Globe, Soccer Ball and Flags of Colombia and Uruguay — A323

Goalkeeper — A324

Flags of: 40f, USSR and Yugoslavia. 60f, Switzerland and Chile. 1fo, Germany and Italy. 1.70fo, Argentina and Bulgaria. 3fo, Brazil and Mexico.

**Unwmk.**

| | | | **1962, May 21** | **Photo.** | **Perf. 11** |
|---|---|---|---|---|---|
| | | **Flags in National Colors** | | | |
| 1447 | A323 | 30f rose & bis | | .20 | .20 |
| 1448 | A323 | 40f pale grn & bis | | .20 | .20 |
| 1449 | A323 | 60f pale lil & bis | | .20 | .20 |
| 1450 | A323 | 1fo blue & bis | | .75 | .20 |
| 1451 | A323 | 1.70fo ocher & bis | | .55 | .25 |
| 1452 | A323 | 3fo pink & blue bis | | 1.50 | .40 |
| | | Nos. 1447-1452,B224,C209A (8) | | 7.00 | 2.05 |

**Souvenir Sheet**

**Perf. 12**

| | | | | |
|---|---|---|---|---|
| 1453 | A324 | 10fo multicolored | 6.50 | 6.50 |

World Cup Soccer Championship, Chile, May 30-June 17.
Exist imperf. Value: set (8) $30; souvenir sheet $30.

Type of 1961 and

Johann Gutenberg A325

#1456, Miklós Misztófalusi Kis, Hungarian printer (1650-1702). #1457, Jozsef Pach. #1458, András Cházár. #1459, Dr. Ferenc Hutyra. #1460, Gábor Egressy & National Theater.

**1962     Unwmk.     Photo.     Perf. 12**

| | | | | |
|---|---|---|---|---|
| 1455 | A325 | 1fo blue black | .20 | .20 |
| 1456 | A325 | 1fo red brown | .20 | .20 |
| 1457 | A320 | 1fo blue | .20 | .20 |
| 1458 | A325 | 1fo violet | .20 | .20 |
| 1459 | A320 | 1fo deep blue | .30 | .20 |
| 1460 | A325 | 1fo rose red | .40 | .20 |
| | | Nos. 1455-1460 (6) | 1.50 | 1.20 |

Cent. of Printers' and Papermakers' Union (Nos. 1455-1456). 75th anniv. of founding, by Joszef Pech, of Hungarian Hydroelectric Service (No. 1457). András Cházár, founder of Hungarian deaf-mute education (No. 1458). Dr. Ferenc Hutyra, founder of Hungarian veterinary medicine (No. 1459). 125th anniv. of National Theater (No. 1460).
Exist imperf. Value, set $21.

Malaria Eradication Emblem — A327

**1962, June 25     Perf. 15**

| | | | | |
|---|---|---|---|---|
| 1461 | A327 | 2.50fo lemon & blk | .50 | .40 |
| a. | | 2.50fo grn & blk, sheet of 4, perf. 11 | 4.00 | 3.75 |

WHO drive to eradicate malaria.
Imperfs exist. Values: single (lemon) $4; single (green) $10; green sheetlet of 4 $50.
Imperf. sheets with control numbers exist.

Sword-into-Plowshare Statue, United
Nations, NY — A328

**1962, July 7**                          **Perf. 12**
1462  A328  1fo brown              .20   .20
World Congress for Peace and Disarmament, Moscow, July 9-14.
Exists imperf. Value $5.

 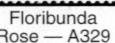

Floribunda                Festival
Rose — A329           Emblem — A330

**1962**                        **Perf. 12½x11½**
**Various Roses in Natural Colors**
1465  A329  20f orange brn       .20   .20
1466  A329  40f slate grn        .20   .20
1467  A329  50f violet           .20   .20
1468  A329  80f rose red         .20   .20
1469  A329  1fo dark green       .25   .20
1470  A329  1.20fo orange        .30   .20
1471  A329  2fo dk blue grn      .50   .45
1472  A330  3fo multi            .75   .35
        Nos. 1465-1472 (8)       2.60  2.00
No. 1472 was issued for the 8th World Youth
Festival, Helsinki, July 28-Aug. 6.
Exist imperf. Value, set $40.

Weight
Lifter — A331

Oil Derrick and
Primitive Oil
Well — A332

**1962, Sept. 16**                        **Perf. 12**
1473  A331  1fo copper red       .30   .20
European Weight Lifting Championships.
Exists imperf. Value $7.

**Perf. 12x11½**
**1962, Oct. 8    Photo.    Unwmk.**
1474  A332  1fo green            .20   .20
25th anniv. of the Hungarian oil industry.
Exists imperf. Value $7.

Racing Motorcyclist — A333

Designs: 30f, Stunt racing. 40f, Uphill race.
60f, Cyclist in curve. 1fo, Start. 1.20fo, Speed
racing. 1.70fo, Motorcyclist with sidecar. 2fo,
Motor scooter. 3fo, Racing car.

**1962, Dec. 28**                         **Perf. 11**
1475  A333  20f multi            .20   .20
1476  A333  30f multi            .20   .20
1477  A333  40f multi            .20   .20
1478  A333  60f multi            .20   .20
1479  A333  1fo multi            .20   .20
1480  A333  1.20fo multi         .20   .20
1481  A333  1.70fo multi         .35   .20
1482  A333  2fo multi            .50   .25
1483  A333  3fo multi            .75   .40
        Nos. 1475-1483 (9)       2.80  2.05
Exist imperf. Value, set $24.

Ice
Skater — A334

Designs: 20f-3fo, Various figure skating and
ice dancing positions. 20f, 3fo horiz. 10fo, Figure skater and flags of participating nations.

**Perf. 12x11½, 11½x12**
**1963, Feb. 5    Photo.    Unwmk.**
1484  A334  20f multi            .20   .20
1485  A334  40f multi            .20   .20
1486  A334  60f multi            .20   .20
1487  A334  1fo multi            .45   .20
1488  A334  1.40fo multi         .45   .20
1489  A334  2fo multi            .50   .25
1490  A334  3fo multi            1.00  .50
        Nos. 1484-1490 (7)       3.00  1.75

**Souvenir Sheet**
**Perf. 11½x12**
1491  A334  10fo multi           5.00  5.00
European Figure Skating and Ice Dancing
Championships, Budapest, Feb. 5-10.
Exist imperf. Value: set $24; souvenir sheet
$110.

János Batsányi (1763-1845) — A335

#1493, Helicon Monument. #1494, Actors
before Szeged Cathedral. #1495, Leo Weiner,
composer. #1496, Ferenc Entz,horticulturist.
#1497, Ivan Markovits, inventor of Hungarian
shorthand,1863. #1498, Dr. Frigyes Koranyi.
#1499, Ferenc Erkel (1810-93), composer.
#1500, Geza Gardonyi (1863-1922), writer of
Hungarian historical novels for youth. #1501,
Pierre de Coubertin, Frenchman, reviver of
Olympic Games. #1502, Jozsef Eötvös,

author, philosopher, educator. #1503, Budapest Industrial Fair emblem. #1504, Stagecoach and Arc de Triomphe, Paris. #1505,
Hungary map and power lines. #1506, Roses.

**1963          Unwmk.          Perf. 11**
1492  A335  40f dk car rose      .20   .20
1493  A335  40f blue             .20   .20
1494  A335  40f violet blue      .20   .20
1495  A335  40f olive            .20   .20
1496  A335  40f emerald          .20   .20
1497  A335  40f dark blue        .20   .20
1498  A335  60f dull violet      .20   .20
1499  A335  60f bister brn       .20   .20
1500  A335  60f gray green       .20   .20
1501  A335  60f red brown        .40   .20
1502  A335  60f lilac            .20   .20
1503  A335  1fo purple           .20   .20
1504  A335  1fo rose red         .25   .20
1505  A335  1fo gray             .25   .20
1506  A335  2fo multi            .50   .20
        Nos. 1492-1506 (15)      3.60  3.00
#1493, 10th Youth Festival, Keszthely.
#1494, Outdoor plays, Szeged. #1495, Buda-
pest Music Competition. #1496, Cent. of professional horticultural training. #1498, 50th
anniv. of the death of Prof. Koranyi, pioneer in
fight against tuberculosis. #1499, Erkel Memorial Festival, Gyula. #1501, 10th anniv. of the
People's Stadium, Budapest. #1502, 150th
anniv. of birth of Jozsef Eötvös, organizer of
modern public education in Hungary. #1504,
Paris Postal Conf., 1863. #1505, Rural electrification. #1506, 5th Natl. Rose Show.
Exist imperf. Value, set $80.

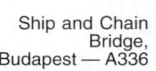

Ship and Chain
Bridge,
Budapest — A336

Bus and
Parliament
A337

20f, Trolley. 30f, Sightseeing bus & Natl.
Museum. 40f, Bus & trailer. 50f, Railroad tank
car. 60f, Trolley bus. 70f, Railroad mail car.
80f, Motorcycle messenger. #1516, Mail
plane, vert. #1517, Television transmitter, Miskolc, vert. 1.40fo, Mobile post office. 1.70fo,
Diesel locomotive. 2fo, Mobile radio transmitter & stadium. 2.50fo, Tourist bus. 2.60fo, Passenger train. 3fo, P.O. parcel conveyor. 4fo,
Television transmitters, Pecs, vert. 5fo,
Hydraulic lift truck & mail car. 6fo, Woman tele-
typist. 8fo, Map of Budapest & automatic dial
phone. 10fo, Girl pioneer &woman letter
carrier.

**1963-64        Photo.        Perf. 11**
1507  A336  10f brt blue         .20   .20
1508  A336  20f dp yellow grn    .20   .20
1509  A336  30f violet           .20   .20
1510  A336  40f orange           .20   .20
1511  A336  50f brown            .20   .20
1512  A336  60f crimson          .20   .20
1513  A336  70f olive gray       .20   .20
1514  A336  80f red brn ('64)    .25   .20

**Perf. 12x11½, 11½x12**
1515  A337  1fo rose claret      .20   .20
1516  A337  1.20fo orange brn    .80   .60
1517  A337  1.20fo dp vio ('64)  .20   .20
1518  A337  1.40fo dp yel grn    .20   .20
1519  A337  1.70fo maroon        .25   .20
1520  A337  2fo grnsh blue       .30   .20
1521  A337  2.50fo lilac         .35   .20
1522  A337  2.60fo olive         .35   .20
1523  A337  3fo dk blue ('64)    .25   .20
1524  A337  4fo blue ('64)       .35   .20
1525  A337  5fo ol brn ('64)     .45   .20
1526  A337  6fo dk ol bis ('64)  .55   .20
1527  A337  8fo red lilac ('64)  .80   .20
1528  A337  10fo emerald ('64)   .80   .40
        Nos. 1507-1528 (22)      7.50  5.00
Size of 20f, 60f: 20½-21x16¾-17mm.
Minute inscription in lower margin includes
year date, number of stamp in set and
designer's name (Bokros F. or Legrady S.).
Exist imperf. Value, set $35.
See Nos. 1983-1983B, 2196-2204.

**Coil Stamps**
**1965-67                        Perf. 14**
**Size: 21½x16½mm**
1508a  A336  20f deep yellow green  .30  .20
1512a  A336  60f crimson ('67)      .50  .20
Black control number on back of every 3rd
stamp.

Motorboat — A338

Girl, Steamer and Castle — A339

Design: 60f, Sailboat.

**1963, July 13**                        **Perf. 11**
1529  A338  20f sl grn, red & blk  .20  .20
1530  A339  40f multicolored       .20  .20
1531  A338  60f bl, blk, brn & org .60  .25
        Nos. 1529-1531 (3)         1.00  .65
Centenary of the summer resort Siofok.
Exist imperf. Value, set $15.

Child with Towel
and Toothbrush
A340

Karancsság
Woman
A341

Designs: 40f, Child with medicines. 60f,
Girls of 3 races. 1fo, Girl and heart. 1.40fo,
Boys of 3 races. 2fo, Medical examination of
child. 3fo, Hands shielding plants.

**1963, July 27**                        **Perf. 12x11½**
1532  A340  30f multi            .20   .20
1533  A340  40f multi            .20   .20
1534  A340  60f multi            .20   .20
1535  A340  1fo multi            .20   .20
1536  A340  1.40fo multi         .20   .20
1537  A340  2fo multi            .25   .25
1538  A340  3fo multi            .50   .40
        Nos. 1532-1538 (7)       1.75  1.65
Centenary of the International Red Cross.
Exist imperf. Value, set $20.

**1963, Aug. 18    Engr.    Perf. 11½**
Provincial Costumes: 30f, Kapuvár man.
40f, Debrecen woman. 60f, Hortobágy man.
1fo, Csököly woman. 1.70fo, Dunántúl man.
2fo, Buják woman. 2.50fo, Alföld man. 3fo,
Mezőkövesd bride.
1539  A341  20f claret           .20   .20
1540  A341  30f green            .20   .20
1541  A341  40f brown            .25   .20
1542  A341  60f brt blue         .25   .20
1543  A341  1fo brown red        .30   .20
1544  A341  1.70fo purple        .40   .20
1545  A341  2fo dk blue grn      .25   .20
1546  A341  2.50fo dk carmine    .55   .25
1547  A341  3fo violet blue      .85   .45
        Nos. 1539-1547 (9)       3.25  2.10
Popular Art Exhibition in Budapest.
Exist imperf. Value, set $50.

Slalom and 1964 Olympic
Emblem — A342

Sports: 60f, Downhill skiing. 70f, Ski jump.
80f, Rifle shooting on skis. 1fo, Figure skating
pair. 2fo, Ice hockey. 2.60fo, Speed ice skating. 10fo, Skier and mountains, vert.

## 1963-64          Photo.          Perf. 12
### 1964 Olympic Emblem in Black and Red

| | | | | |
|---|---|---|---|---|
| **1548** | A342 | 40f yel grn & bis | .20 | .20 |
| **1549** | A342 | 60f violet & bis | .20 | .20 |
| **1550** | A342 | 70f ultra & bis | .20 | .20 |
| **1551** | A342 | 80f emerald & bis | .20 | .20 |
| **1552** | A342 | 1fo brn org & bis | .20 | .20 |
| **1553** | A342 | 2fo brt blue & bis | .40 | .20 |
| **1554** | A342 | 2.60fo rose lake & bis | .60 | .40 |
| | *Nos. 1548-1554,B234 (8)* | | 2.70 | 1.90 |

### Souvenir Sheet
#### Perf. 11½x12

| | | | | |
|---|---|---|---|---|
| **1555** | A342 | 10fo grnsh bl, red & brn ('64) | 4.25 | 4.00 |

9th Winter Olympic Games, Innsbruck, Austria, Jan. 29-Feb. 9, 1964.
Exist imperf. Value: set (8) $25; souvenir sheet $30.

Four-Leaf Clover — A343

Good Luck Symbols: 20f, Calendar and mistletoe, horiz. 30f, Chimneysweep and clover. 60f, Top hat, pig and clover. 1fo, Clown with balloon and clover, horiz. 2fo, Lanterns, mask and clover.

#### Perf. 12x11½, 11½x12
### 1963, Dec. 12     Photo.     Unwmk.
Sizes: 28x22mm (20f, 1fo);
22x28mm (40f);
28x39mm (30f, 60f, 2fo)

| | | | | |
|---|---|---|---|---|
| **1556** | A343 | 20f multi | .20 | .20 |
| **1557** | A343 | 30f multi | .20 | .20 |
| **1558** | A343 | 40f multi | .20 | .20 |
| **1559** | A343 | 60f multi | .20 | .20 |
| **1560** | A343 | 1fo multi | .20 | .20 |
| **1561** | A343 | 2fo multi | .45 | .20 |
| | *Nos. 1556-1561,B235-B236 (8)* | | 2.65 | 1.80 |

New Year 1964.
Exist imperf. Value set $20.
The 20f and 40f issued in booklet panes of 10, perf. and imperf.; sold for 2 times and 1½ times face respectively.

Moon Rocket — A344

U.S. & USSR Spacecraft: 40f, Venus space probe. 60f, Vostok I, horiz. 1fo, Friendship 7. 1.70fo, Vostok III & IV. 2fo, Telstar 1 & 2, horiz. 2.60fo, Mars I. 3fo, Radar, rockets and satellites, horiz.

### 1964, Jan. 8     Perf. 11½x12, 12x11½

| | | | | |
|---|---|---|---|---|
| **1562** | A344 | 30f grn, yel & brnz | .20 | .20 |
| **1563** | A344 | 40f pur, bl & sil | .20 | .20 |
| **1564** | A344 | 60f bl, bk, yel, sil & red | .20 | .20 |
| **1565** | A344 | 1fo dk brn, red & sil | .20 | .20 |
| **1566** | A344 | 1.70fo vio bl, blk, tan & red | .30 | .20 |
| **1567** | A344 | 2fo sl grn, yel & sil | .40 | .20 |
| **1568** | A344 | 2.60fo dp bl, yel & brnz | .60 | .30 |
| **1569** | A344 | 3fo dp vio, lt bl & sil | .75 | .50 |
| | *Nos. 1562-1569 (8)* | | 2.85 | 2.00 |

Achievements in space research.
Exist imperf. Value, set $20.

### Lace Type of 1960

Various Halas Lace Designs.
Sizes: 20f, 2.60fo: 38x28mm. 30f, 40f, 60f, 1fo, 1.40fo, 2fo: 38x45mm.

---

## Engr. & Litho.
### 1964, Feb. 28                    Perf. 11½

| | | | | |
|---|---|---|---|---|
| **1570** | A294 | 20f emerald & blk | .20 | .20 |
| **1571** | A294 | 30f dull yel & blk | .20 | .20 |
| **1572** | A294 | 40f deep rose & blk | .20 | .20 |
| **1573** | A294 | 60f olive & blk | .20 | .20 |
| **1574** | A294 | 1fo red org & blk | .35 | .20 |
| **1575** | A294 | 1.40fo blue & blk | .45 | .20 |
| **1576** | A294 | 2fo bluish grn & blk | .55 | .25 |
| **1577** | A294 | 2.60fo lt vio & blk | .85 | .45 |
| | *Nos. 1570-1577 (8)* | | 3.00 | 1.90 |

Exist imperf. Value, set $30.

### Special Anniversaries-Events Issue

Imre Madach (1823-64) — A345

Shakespeare A346

Karl Marx and Membership Card of International Working Men's Association — A347

Michelangelo — A348

Lajos Kossuth and György Dózsa — A349

Budapest Fair Buildings — A350

#1579, Ervin Szabo. #1580, Writer Andras Fay (1786-1864). #1581, Aggtelek Cave scene. #1582, Excavating bauxite. #1584, Equestrian statue, Szekesfehervar. #1585, Bowler. #1586, Waterfall and forest. #1587, Architect Miklos Ybl (1814-91) and Budapest Opera. #1590, Armor, saber, sword & foil.

---

#1592, Galileo Galilei. #1593, Women basketball players. #1595, Two runners breaking tape.

### Perf. 11½x12, 12x11½, 11
### 1964     Photo.     Unwmk.
Inscribed: "ÉVFORDULÓK-ESEMÉNYEK"

| | | | | |
|---|---|---|---|---|
| **1578** | A345 | 60f brt purple | .20 | .20 |
| **1579** | A345 | 60f olive | .20 | .20 |
| **1580** | A345 | 60f olive grn | .20 | .20 |
| **1581** | A346 | 60f bluish grn | .20 | .20 |
| **1582** | A346 | 60f Prus blue | .20 | .20 |
| **1583** | A347 | 60f rose red | .20 | .20 |
| **1584** | A348 | 60f slate blue | .20 | .20 |
| **1585** | A345 | 1fo car rose | .20 | .20 |
| *a.* | | With Olympic rings bottom tab | 1.00 | 1.00 |
| **1586** | A346 | 1fo dull blue grn | .20 | .20 |
| **1587** | A348 | 1fo orange brn | .20 | .20 |
| **1588** | A349 | 1fo ultra | .20 | .20 |
| **1589** | A350 | 1fo brt green | .20 | .20 |
| **1590** | A345 | 2fo yellow brn | .20 | .20 |
| **1591** | A346 | 2fo magenta | .35 | .20 |
| **1592** | A346 | 2fo red brown | .25 | .20 |
| **1593** | A346 | 2fo brt blue | .25 | .20 |
| **1594** | A348 | 2fo gray brown | .30 | .20 |
| **1595** | A348 | 2fo brown red | .25 | .20 |
| | *Nos. 1578-1595 (18)* | | 4.00 | 3.60 |

No. 1579, Municipal libraries, 60th anniv., and librarian Szabo (1877-1918). No. 1582, Bauxite mining in Hungary, 30th year. No. 1583, Cent. of 1st Socialist Intl. No. 1584, King Alba Day in Székesfehérvár. No. 1585, 1st European Bowling Championship, Budapest. No. 1586, Cong. of Natl. Forestry Federation. No. 1588, City of Cegléd, 600th anniv. No. 1589, Opening of 1964 Budapest Intl. Fair. No. 1590, Hungarian Youth Fencing Association, 50th anniv. Nos. 1591-1592, Shakespeare and Galileo, 400th birth anniversaries. No. 1593, 9th European Women's Basketball Championship. No. 1594, Michelangelo's 400th death anniv. No. 1595, 50th anniv. of 1st Hungarian-Swedish athletic meet.
Exists imperf. Value, set $100. No. 1585a imperf value $350.

Eleanor Roosevelt — A351

Design, horiz.: a, d, Portrait at right. b, c, Portrait at left.

### 1964, Apr. 27                Perf. 12½

| | | | | |
|---|---|---|---|---|
| **1596** | A351 | 2fo gray, black & buff | .30 | .20 |

#### Miniature Sheet
#### Perf. 11

| | | | | |
|---|---|---|---|---|
| **1597** | | Sheet of 4 | 3.00 | 2.75 |
| *a.* | A351 | 2fo dp claret, brn & blk | .65 | .65 |
| *b.* | A351 | 2fo dk bl, brn & blk | .65 | .65 |
| *c.* | A351 | 2fo grn, brn & blk | .65 | .65 |
| *d.* | A351 | 2fo olive, brn & blk | .65 | .65 |

Exist imperf. Value: single $5; souvenir sheet $25.

Fencing — A352

Sport: 40f, Women's gymnastics. 60f, Soccer. 80f, Equestrian. 1fo, Running. 1.40fo, Weight lifting. 1.70fo, Gymnast on rings. 2fo, Hammer throw and javelin. 2.50fo, Boxing.

### 1964, June 12     Photo.     Perf. 11
#### Multicolored Design and Inscription

| | | | | |
|---|---|---|---|---|
| **1598** | A352 | 30f lt ver | .20 | .20 |
| **1599** | A352 | 40f blue | .20 | .20 |
| **1600** | A352 | 60f emerald | .20 | .20 |
| **1601** | A352 | 80f tan | .20 | .20 |
| **1602** | A352 | 1fo yellow | .20 | .20 |
| **1603** | A352 | 1.40fo bis brn | .20 | .20 |

---

| | | | | |
|---|---|---|---|---|
| **1604** | A352 | 1.70fo bluish gray | .30 | .20 |
| **1605** | A352 | 2fo gray grn | .35 | .20 |
| **1606** | A352 | 2.50fo vio gray | .55 | .40 |
| | *Nos. 1598-1606,B237 (10)* | | 3.00 | 2.75 |

18th Olympic Games, Tokyo, Oct. 10-25.
Exist imperf. Value, set (10) $25.

Elberta Peaches A353

Peaches: 40h, Blossoms (J. H. Hale). 60h, Magyar Kajszi. 1fo, Mandula Kajszi. 1.50fo, Borsi Rozsa. 1.70fo, Blossoms (Alexander). 2fo, Champion. 3fo, Mayflower.

### 1964, July 24               Perf. 11½

| | | | | |
|---|---|---|---|---|
| **1607** | A353 | 40f multi | .20 | .20 |
| **1608** | A353 | 60f multi | .20 | .20 |
| **1609** | A353 | 1fo multi | .20 | .20 |
| **1610** | A353 | 1.50fo multi | .20 | .20 |
| **1611** | A353 | 1.70fo multi | .25 | .20 |
| **1612** | A353 | 2fo multi | .35 | .20 |
| **1613** | A353 | 2.60fo multi | .45 | .30 |
| **1614** | A353 | 3fo multi | .65 | .50 |
| | *Nos. 1607-1614 (8)* | | 2.50 | 2.00 |

National Peach Exhibition, Szeged.
Exist imperf. Value, set $30.

Crossing Street in Safety Zone — A354

60f, "Watch out for Children" (child & ball). 1fo, "Look before Crossing" (mother & child).

### 1964, Sept. 27               Perf. 11

| | | | | |
|---|---|---|---|---|
| **1615** | A354 | 20f multicolored | .20 | .20 |
| **1616** | A354 | 60f multicolored | .20 | .20 |
| **1617** | A354 | 1fo lilac & multi | .60 | .60 |
| | *Nos. 1615-1617 (3)* | | 1.00 | .60 |

Issued to publicize traffic safety.
Exist imperf. Value, set $15.

### Souvenir Sheet

Voskhod 1 and Globe —- A355

### 1964, Nov. 6               Perf. 12x11½

| | | | | |
|---|---|---|---|---|
| **1618** | A355 | 10fo multicolored | 3.75 | 3.50 |

Russian space flight of Vladimir M. Komarov, Boris B. Yegorov and Konstantine Feoktistov.
Exists imperf. Value $45.

Arpad Bridge — A356

Danube Bridges, Budapest: 30f, Margaret Bridge. 60f, Chain Bridge. 1fo, Elizabeth Bridge. 1.50fo, Freedom Bridge. 2fo, Petöfi Bridge. 2.50fo, Railroad Bridge.

**1964, Nov. 21**   **Photo.**   *Perf. 11x11½*

| | | | | |
|---|---|---|---|---|
| **1619** | A356 | 20f multi | .20 | .20 |
| **1620** | A356 | 30f multi | .20 | .20 |
| **1621** | A356 | 60f multi | .20 | .20 |
| **1622** | A356 | 1fo multi | .25 | .20 |
| **1623** | A356 | 1.50fo multi | .30 | .20 |
| **1624** | A356 | 2fo multi | .50 | .20 |
| **1625** | A356 | 2.50fo multi | .85 | .40 |
| | | *Nos. 1619-1625 (7)* | 2.50 | 1.60 |

Opening of the reconstructed Elizabeth Bridge. See No. C250.

Exist imperf. Value, set $40.

Ring-necked Pheasant and Hunting Rifle — A357

Designs: 30f, Wild boar. 40f, Gray partridges. 60f, Varying hare. 80f, Fallow deer. 1fo, Mouflon. 1.70fo, Red deer. 2fo, Great bustard. 2.50fo, Roebuck and roe deer. 3fo, Emblem of National Federation of Hungarian Hunters (antlers).

**1964, Dec. 30**   **Photo.**   *Perf. 12x11½*

| | | | | |
|---|---|---|---|---|
| **1626** | A357 | 20f multi | .20 | .20 |
| **1627** | A357 | 30f multi | .20 | .20 |
| **1628** | A357 | 40f multi | .20 | .20 |
| **1629** | A357 | 60f multi | .20 | .20 |
| **1630** | A357 | 80f multi | .20 | .20 |
| **1631** | A357 | 1fo multi | .20 | .20 |
| **1632** | A357 | 1.70fo multi | .25 | .20 |
| **1633** | A357 | 2fo multi | .30 | .20 |
| **1634** | A357 | 2.50fo multi | .50 | .30 |
| **1635** | A357 | 3fo multi | .75 | .50 |
| | | *Nos. 1626-1635 (10)* | 3.00 | 2.40 |

Exist imperf. Value, set $40.

**Castle Type of 1960**

3fo, Czesznek, vert. 4fo, Eger. 5fo, Koszeg, vert.

**1964**   *Perf. 11½x12, 12x11½*
  **Size: 21x28mm, 28x21mm**

| | | | | |
|---|---|---|---|---|
| **1644** | A293 | 3fo red brown | 1.00 | .20 |
| **1645** | A293 | 4fo brt violet | 1.50 | .20 |
| **1646** | A293 | 5fo yellow grn | 1.50 | .20 |
| | | *Nos. 1644-1646 (3)* | 4.00 | .60 |

Equestrian, Gold and Bronze Medals — A358

Medals: 30f, Women's gymnastics, silver & bronze. 50f, Small-bore rifle, gold & bronze. 60f, Water polo, gold. 70f, Shot put, bronze. 80f, Soccer, gold. 1fo, Weight lifting, 1 bronze, 2 silver. 1.20fo, Canoeing, silver. 1.40fo, Hammer throw, silver. 1.50fo, Wrestling, 2 gold. 1.70fo, Javelin, 2 silver. 3fo, Fencing, 4 gold.

**1965, Feb. 20**   *Perf. 12*
  **Medals in Gold, Silver or Bronze**

| | | | | |
|---|---|---|---|---|
| **1647** | A358 | 20f lt ol grn & dk brn | .20 | .20 |
| **1648** | A358 | 30f violet & dk brn | .20 | .20 |
| **1649** | A358 | 50f olive & dk brn | .20 | .20 |
| **1650** | A358 | 60f lt bl & red brn | .20 | .20 |
| **1651** | A358 | 70f lt gray & red brn | .20 | .20 |
| **1652** | A358 | 80f yel grn & dk brn | .20 | .20 |
| **1653** | A358 | 1fo lil, vio & red brn | .20 | .20 |
| **1654** | A358 | 1.20fo lt bl, ultra & red brn | .20 | .20 |
| **1655** | A358 | 1.40fo gray & red brn | .20 | .20 |
| **1656** | A358 | 1.50fo tan, lt brn & red brn | .25 | .20 |
| **1657** | A358 | 1.70fo pink & red brn | .50 | .25 |
| **1658** | A358 | 3fo grnsh blue & brn | .70 | .55 |
| | | *Nos. 1647-1658 (12)* | 3.25 | 2.80 |

Victories by the Hungarian team in the 1964 Olympic Games, Tokyo, Oct. 10-25.

Exist imperf. Value, set $30.

Arctic Exploration A359

Chrysanthemums A360

Designs: 30f, Radar tracking rocket, ionosphere research. 60f, Rocket and earth with reflecting layer diagrams, atmospheric research. 80f, Telescope and map of Milky Way, radio astronomy. 1.50fo, Earth, compass rose and needle, earth magnetism. 1.70fo, Weather balloon and lightning, meteorology. 2fo, Aurora borealis and penguins, arctic research. 2.50fo, Satellite, earth and planets, space research. 3fo, IQSY emblem and world map. 10fo, Sun with flares and corona, snow crystals and rain.

**Perf. 11½x12**

**1965, Mar. 25**   **Photo.**   **Unwmk.**

| | | | | |
|---|---|---|---|---|
| **1659** | A359 | 20f blue, org & blk | .20 | .20 |
| **1660** | A359 | 30f gray, blk & emer | .20 | .20 |
| **1661** | A359 | 60f lilac, blk & yel | .20 | .20 |
| **1662** | A359 | 80f lt grn, yel & blk | .20 | .20 |
| **1663** | A359 | 1.50fo lemon, bl & blk | .20 | .20 |
| **1664** | A359 | 1.70fo blue, pink & blk | .20 | .20 |
| **1665** | A359 | 2fo ultra, sal & blk | .25 | .20 |
| **1666** | A359 | 2.50fo org brn, yel & blk | .40 | .20 |
| **1667** | A359 | 3fo lt bl, cit & blk | .70 | .40 |
| | | *Nos. 1659-1667 (9)* | 2.55 | 2.00 |

**Souvenir Sheet**

| | | | | |
|---|---|---|---|---|
| **1668** | A359 | 10fo ultra, org & blk | 2.50 | 2.50 |

Intl. Quiet Sun Year, 1964-65.

Exist imperf. Value: set $20; souvenir sheet $25.

**1965, Apr. 4**

30f, Peonies. 50f, Carnations. 60f, Roses. 1.40fo, Lilies. 1.70fo, Anemones. 2fo, Gladioli. 2.50fo, Tulips. 3fo, Mixed flower bouquet.

**Flowers in Natural Colors**

| | | | | |
|---|---|---|---|---|
| **1669** | A360 | 20f gold & gray | .20 | .20 |
| **1670** | A360 | 30f gold & gray | .20 | .20 |
| **1671** | A360 | 50f gold & gray | .20 | .20 |
| **1672** | A360 | 60f gold & gray | .20 | .20 |
| **1673** | A360 | 1.40fo gold & gray | .20 | .20 |
| **1674** | A360 | 1.70fo gold & gray | .20 | .20 |
| **1675** | A360 | 2fo gold & gray | .20 | .20 |
| **1676** | A360 | 2.50fo gold & gray | .30 | .20 |
| **1677** | A360 | 3fo gold & gray | .60 | .50 |
| | | *Nos. 1669-1677 (9)* | 2.30 | 2.10 |

20th anniversary of liberation from the Nazis.

Exist imperf. Value, set $20.

"Head of a Combatant" by Leonardo da Vinci — A361

**Perf. 11½x12**

**1965, May 4**   **Photo.**   **Unwmk.**

| | | | | |
|---|---|---|---|---|
| **1678** | A361 | 60f bister & org brn | .30 | .20 |

Issued to publicize the First International Renaissance Conference, Budapest.

Exists imperf. Value $9.

Nikolayev, Tereshkova and View of Budapest — A362

**1965, May 10**     *Perf. 11*

| | | | | |
|---|---|---|---|---|
| **1679** | A362 | 1fo dull blue & brn | .25 | .20 |

Visit of the Russian astronauts Andrian G. Nikolayev and Valentina Tereshkova (Mr. & Mrs. Nikolayev) to Budapest.

Exists imperf. Value $10.

ITU Emblem, Old and New Communication Equipment A363

**1965, May 17**

| | | | | |
|---|---|---|---|---|
| **1680** | A363 | 60f violet blue | .20 | .20 |

Cent. of the ITU.
Exists imperf. Value $7.

**Souvenir Sheet**

Austrian WIPA Stamp of 1933 — A363a

**1965, June 4**   **Photo.**   *Perf. 11*

| | | | | |
|---|---|---|---|---|
| **1681** | A363a | Sheet of 2 + 2 labels | 3.50 | 3.50 |
|   **a.** | | 2fo gray & deep ultra | 1.50 | 1.50 |

1965 Vienna Intl. Phil. Exhib. WIPA, 6/4-13.
Exists imperf. Value $30.

Marx and Lenin, Crowds with Flags — A364

ICY Emblem and Pulley — A365

**1965, June 15**     *Perf. 11½x12*

| | | | | |
|---|---|---|---|---|
| **1682** | A364 | 60f red, blk & yel | .20 | .20 |

6th Conference of Ministers of Post of Socialist Countries, Peking, June 21-July 15.
Exists imperf. Value $9.

**1965, June 25**

| | | | | |
|---|---|---|---|---|
| **1683** | A365 | 2fo dark red | .20 | .20 |
|   **a.** | | Min. sheet of 4, perf. 11 | 2.25 | 2.25 |

Intl. Cooperation Year, 1965. No. 1683a contains rose red, olive, Prussian green and violet stamps.

Exists imperf. Value: single $5; sheetlet of 4 $25.

Musical Clown — A366

Dr. Semmelweis A367

Circus Acts: 20f, Equestrians. 40f, Elephant. 50f, Seal balancing ball. 60f, Lions. 1fo, Wildcat jumping through burning hoops. 1.50fo, Black leopards. 2.50fo, Juggler. 3fo, Leopard and dogs. 4fo, Bear on bicycle.

**1965, July 26**   **Photo.**   *Perf. 11½x12*

| | | | | |
|---|---|---|---|---|
| **1684** | A366 | 20f multi | .20 | .20 |
| **1685** | A366 | 30f multi | .20 | .20 |
| **1686** | A366 | 40f multi | .20 | .20 |
| **1687** | A366 | 50f multi | .20 | .20 |
| **1688** | A366 | 60f multi | .20 | .20 |
| **1689** | A366 | 1fo multi | .20 | .20 |
| **1690** | A366 | 1.50fo multi | .25 | .20 |
| **1691** | A366 | 2.50fo multi | .35 | .20 |
| **1692** | A366 | 3fo multi | .40 | .20 |
| **1693** | A366 | 4fo multi | .50 | .40 |
| | | *Nos. 1684-1693 (10)* | 2.70 | 2.20 |

Exist imperf. Value, set $20.

**1965, Aug. 20**   **Photo.**   **Unwmk.**

| | | | | |
|---|---|---|---|---|
| **1694** | A367 | 60f red brown | .20 | .20 |

Dr. Ignaz Philipp Semmelweis (1818-1865), discoverer of the cause of puerperal fever and introduced antisepsis into obstetrics.
Exists imperf. Value $5.

Runner — A368

Sport: 30f, Swimmer at start. 50f, Woman diver. 60f, Modern dancing. 80f, Tennis. 1.70fo, Fencing. 2fo, Volleyball. 2.50fo, Basketball. 4fo, Water polo. 10fo, People's Stadium, Budapest, horiz.

**1965, Aug. 20**     *Perf. 11*
  **Size: 38x38mm**

| | | | | |
|---|---|---|---|---|
| **1695** | A368 | 20f multi | .20 | .20 |
| **1696** | A368 | 30f blue & red brn | .20 | .20 |
| **1697** | A368 | 50f bl grn, blk & red brn | .20 | .20 |
| **1698** | A368 | 60f vio, blk & red brn | .20 | .20 |
| **1699** | A368 | 80f tan, ol & red brn | .20 | .20 |
| **1700** | A368 | 1.70fo multi | .25 | .20 |
| **1701** | A368 | 2fo multi | .30 | .20 |
| **1702** | A368 | 2.50fo gray, blk & red brn | .45 | .25 |

| | | | | |
|---|---|---|---|---|
| **1703** | A368 | 4fo bl, red brn & blk | .75 | .45 |
| | | Nos. 1695-1703 (9) | 2.75 | 2.10 |

**Souvenir Sheet**
**Perf. 12x11½**

| | | | | |
|---|---|---|---|---|
| **1704** | A368 | 10fo bis, red brn & gray | 3.00 | 2.75 |

Intl. College Championships, "Universiade," Budapest. No. 1704 contains one 38x28mm stamp.
Exist imperf. Value: set $25; souvenir sheet $30.

Hemispheres and Warsaw Mermaid — A369

**1965, Oct. 8    Photo.    Perf. 12x11½**

| | | | | |
|---|---|---|---|---|
| **1705** | A369 | 60f brt blue | .20 | .20 |

Sixth Congress of the World Federation of Trade Unions, Warsaw.
Exists imperf. Value $5.

Phyllocactus Hybridus A370

Flowers from Botanical Gardens: 30f, Cattleya Warszewiczii (orchid). 60f, Rebutia calliantha. 70f, Paphiopedilum hybridium. 80f, Opuntia cactus. 1fo, Laelia elegans (orchid). 1.50fo, Christmas cactus. 2fo, Bird-of-paradise flower. 2.50fo, Lithops Weberi. 3fo, Victoria water lily.

**1965, Oct. 11    Perf. 11½x12**

| | | | | |
|---|---|---|---|---|
| **1706** | A370 | 20f gray & multi | .20 | .20 |
| **1707** | A370 | 30f gray & multi | .20 | .20 |
| **1708** | A370 | 60f gray & multi | .20 | .20 |
| **1709** | A370 | 70f gray & multi | .20 | .20 |
| **1710** | A370 | 80f gray & multi | .20 | .20 |
| **1711** | A370 | 1fo gray & multi | .20 | .20 |
| **1712** | A370 | 1.50fo gray & multi | .25 | .20 |
| **1713** | A370 | 2fo gray & multi | .25 | .20 |
| **1714** | A370 | 2.50fo gray & multi | .40 | .25 |
| **1715** | A370 | 3fo gray & multi | .60 | .35 |
| | | Nos. 1706-1715 (10) | 2.70 | 2.20 |

Exist imperf. Value: set $22.

"The Black Stallion" A371

Tales from the Arabian Nights: 30f, Shahriar and Scheherazade. 50f, Sinbad's Fifth Voyage (ship). 60f, Aladdin, or The Wonderful Lamp. 80f, Harun al-Rashid. 1fo, The Flying Carpet. 1.70fo, The Fisherman and the Genie. 2fo, Ali Baba and the Forty Thieves. 3fo, Sinbad's Second Voyage (flying bird).

**1965, Dec. 15    Litho.    Perf. 11½**

| | | | | |
|---|---|---|---|---|
| **1716** | A371 | 20f multi | .20 | .20 |
| **1717** | A371 | 30f multi | .20 | .20 |
| **1718** | A371 | 50f multi | .20 | .20 |
| **1719** | A371 | 60f multi | .20 | .20 |
| **1720** | A371 | 80f multi | .20 | .20 |
| **1721** | A371 | 1fo multi | .20 | .20 |
| **1722** | A371 | 1.70fo multi | .35 | .20 |
| **1723** | A371 | 2fo multi | .45 | .25 |
| **1724** | A371 | 3fo multi | .75 | .45 |
| | | Nos. 1716-1724 (9) | 2.75 | 2.10 |

Exist imperf. Value: set $25.

Congress Emblem A372

Callimorpha Dominula A373

**1965, Dec. 9    Photo.    Perf. 11½x12**

| | | | | |
|---|---|---|---|---|
| **1725** | A372 | 2fo dark blue | .30 | .20 |

Fifth Congress of the International Federation of Resistance Fighters (FIR), Budapest.
Exists imperf. Value $5.

**1966, Feb. 1    Photo.    Perf. 11½x12**
**Various Butterflies in Natural Colors;**
**Black Inscription**

| | | | | |
|---|---|---|---|---|
| **1726** | A373 | 20f lt aqua | .20 | .20 |
| **1727** | A373 | 60f pale violet | .20 | .20 |
| **1728** | A373 | 70f tan | .20 | .20 |
| **1729** | A373 | 80f lt ultra | .20 | .20 |
| **1730** | A373 | 1fo gray | .20 | .20 |
| **1731** | A373 | 1.50fo emerald | .40 | .20 |
| **1732** | A373 | 2fo dull rose | .30 | .20 |
| **1733** | A373 | 2.50fo bister | .45 | .30 |
| **1734** | A373 | 3fo blue | .70 | .50 |
| | | Nos. 1726-1734 (9) | 2.85 | 2.20 |

Exist imperf. Value: set $30.

Lal Bahadur Shastri A374

Designs: 60f, Bela Kun. 2fo, Istvan Széchenyi and Chain Bridge.

**Lithographed; Photogravure (#1736)**
**1966    Perf. 11½x12, 12x11½**

| | | | | |
|---|---|---|---|---|
| **1735** | A374 | 60f red & black | .20 | .20 |
| **1736** | A374 | 1fo brt violet | .20 | .20 |
| **1737** | A374 | 2fo dull yel, buff & sepia | .25 | .20 |
| | | Nos. 1735-1737 (3) | .65 | .60 |

Kun (1886-1939), communist labor leader; Shastri (1904-66), Indian Prime Minister; Count Istvan Széchenyi (1791-1860), statesman.
Exist imperf. Value: set $11.
See Nos. 1764-1765, 1769-1770.

Luna 9 — A375

Design: 3fo, Luna 9 sending signals from moon to earth, horiz.

**1966, Mar. 12    Photo.    Perf. 12**

| | | | | |
|---|---|---|---|---|
| **1738** | A375 | 2fo violet, blk & yel | .45 | .20 |
| **1739** | A375 | 3fo lt ultra, blk & yel | .85 | .60 |

1st soft landing on the moon by the Russian satellite Luna 9, Feb. 3, 1966.
Exist imperf. Value, set $12.

Crocus — A376

**1966, Mar. 12    Perf. 11**

Flowers: 30f, Cyclamen. 60f, Ligularia sibirica. 1.40fo, Lilium bulbiferum. 1.50fo, Snake's head. 3fo, Snapdragon and emblem of Hungarian Nature Preservation Society.

**Flowers in Natural Colors**

| | | | | |
|---|---|---|---|---|
| **1740** | A376 | 20f brown | .20 | .20 |
| **1741** | A376 | 30f aqua | .20 | .20 |
| **1742** | A376 | 60f rose claret | .20 | .20 |
| **1743** | A376 | 1.40fo gray | .30 | .20 |
| **1744** | A376 | 1.50fo ultra | .45 | .25 |
| **1745** | A376 | 3fo mag & sepia | .65 | .40 |
| | | Nos. 1740-1745 (6) | 2.00 | 1.45 |

Exist imperf. Value, set $25.

**1966, Apr. 16**

Designs: 20f, Barn swallows. 30f, Long-tailed tits. 60f, Red crossbill and pine cone. 1.40fo, Middle spotted woodpecker. 1.50fo, Hoopoe feeding young. 3fo, Forest preserve, lapwing and emblem of National Forest Preservation Society.

**Birds in Natural Colors**

| | | | | |
|---|---|---|---|---|
| **1746** | A376 | 20f brt green | .20 | .20 |
| **1747** | A376 | 30f vermilion | .20 | .20 |
| **1748** | A376 | 60f brt green | .20 | .20 |
| **1749** | A376 | 1.40fo vio blue | .25 | .20 |
| **1750** | A376 | 1.50fo blue | .65 | .35 |
| **1751** | A376 | 3fo brn, mag & grn | .75 | .50 |
| | | Nos. 1746-1751 (6) | 2.25 | 1.65 |

Nos. 1740-1751 issued to promote protection of wild flowers and birds.
Exist imperf. Value, set $30.

Locomotive, 1847; Monoplane, 1912; Autobus, 1911; Steamer, 1853, and Budapest Railroad Station, 1846 — A377

Designs: 2fo, Transportation, 1966: electric locomotive V.43; turboprop airliner IL-18; Ikarusz autobus; Diesel passenger ship; and Budapest South Railroad Station.

**1966, Apr. 2    Photo.    Perf. 12**

| | | | | |
|---|---|---|---|---|
| **1752** | A377 | 1fo yel, brn & grn | .20 | .20 |
| **1753** | A377 | 2fo pale grn, bl & brn | .35 | .20 |

Re-opening of the Transport Museum, Budapest.
Exist imperf. Value, set $12.

Bronze Order of Labor — A378

Decorations: 30f, Silver Order of Labor. 50f, Banner Order, third class. 60f, Gold Order of Labor. 70f, Banner Order, second class. 1fo, Red Banner Order of Labor. 1.20fo, Banner Order, first class. 2fo, Order of Merit. 2.50fo, Hero of Socialist Labor. Sizes: 20f, 30f, 60f, 1fo, 2fo, 2.50fo: 19½x38mm. 50f: 21x29mm. 70f, 25x31mm. 1.20fo: 28x38mm.

**1966, Apr. 2    Unwmk.    Perf. 11**
**Decorations in Original Colors**

| | | | | |
|---|---|---|---|---|
| **1754** | A378 | 20f dp ultra | .20 | .20 |
| **1755** | A378 | 30f lt brown | .20 | .20 |
| **1756** | A378 | 50f blue green | .20 | .20 |
| **1757** | A378 | 60f violet | .20 | .20 |
| **1758** | A378 | 70f carmine | .20 | .20 |
| **1759** | A378 | 1fo violet bl | .20 | .20 |
| **1760** | A378 | 1.20fo brt blue | .20 | .20 |
| **1761** | A378 | 2fo olive | .25 | .20 |
| **1762** | A378 | 2.50fo dull blue | .35 | .20 |
| | | Nos. 1754-1762 (9) | 2.00 | 1.80 |

Exist imperf. Value, set $20.

Portrait Type of 1966 and

Dubna Nuclear Research Institute — A379

WHO Headquarters, Geneva — A380

Designs: No. 1764, Pioneer girl. No. 1765, Tamás Esze (1666-1708), military hero. No. 1767, Old view of Buda and UNESCO emblem. No. 1768, Horse-drawn fire pump and emblem of Sopron Fire Brigade. No. 1769, Miklos Zrinyi (1508-66), hero of Turkish Wars. No. 1770, Sandor Koranyi (1866-1944), physician and scientist.

**1966    Litho.    Perf. 11½x12**

| | | | | |
|---|---|---|---|---|
| **1763** | A379 | 60f blue grn & blk | .20 | .20 |
| **1764** | A374 | 60f multicolored | .20 | .20 |
| **1765** | A374 | 60f brt bl & blk | .20 | .20 |
| **1766** | A380 | 2fo lt ultra & blk | .20 | .20 |
| **1767** | A380 | 2fo lt blue & pur | .25 | .20 |
| **1768** | A380 | 2fo orange & blk | .25 | .20 |
| **1769** | A374 | 2fo ol bis & brn | .20 | .20 |
| **1770** | A374 | 2fo multicolored | .20 | .20 |
| | | Nos. 1763-1770 (8) | 1.70 | 1.60 |

No. 1763, 10th anniv. of the United Institute for Nuclear Research, Dubna, USSR; No. 1764, 20th anniv. of Pioneer Movement; No. 1766, Inauguration of the WHO Headquarters, Geneva; No. 1767, 20th anniv. of UNESCO and 72nd session of Executive Council, Budapest, May 30-31; No. 1768, Cent. of Volunteer Fire Brigade.
Exist imperf. Value, set $42.

Hungarian Soccer Player and Soccer Field — A381

Jules Rimet, Cup and Soccer Ball — A382

Designs (Views of Soccer play): 30f, Montevideo 1930 (Uruguay 4, Argentina 2). 60f, Rome 1934 (Italy 2, Czechoslovakia 1). 1fo, Paris 1938 (Italy 4, Hungary 2). 1.40fo, Rio de Janeiro 1950 (Uruguay 2, Brazil 1). 1.70fo, Bern 1954 (Germany 3, Hungary 2). 2fo, Stockholm 1958 (Brazil 5, Sweden 2). 2.50fo, Santiago 1962 (Brazil 3, Czechoslovakia 1).

**Souvenir Sheet**

**1966, May 16    Photo.    Perf. 11½x12**
1771    A381    10fo multi                3.25    3.00

Exists imperf. Value $30.

**1966, June 6                Perf. 12x11½**
1772    A382    20f blue & multi          .25    .20
1773    A382    30f orange & multi        .25    .20
1774    A382    60f multi                 .20    .20
1775    A382    1fo multi                 .20    .20
1776    A382    1.40fo multi              .20    .20
1777    A382    1.70fo multi              .20    .20
1778    A382    2fo multi                 .25    .20
1779    A382    2.50fo multi              .60    .40
        Nos. 1772-1779,B258 (9)           2.75    2.30

World Cup Soccer Championship, Wembley, England, July 11-30.
Exist imperf. Value, set (9) $22.75.

European Red Fox — A383

Hunting Trophies: 60f, Wild boar. 70f, Wildcat. 80f, Roebuck. 1.50fo, Red deer. 2.50fo, Fallow deer. 3fo, Mouflon.

**1966, July 4    Photo.    Perf. 11½x12**
**Animals in Natural Colors**
1780    A383    20f gray & lt brn         .20    .20
1781    A383    60f buff & gray           .20    .20
1782    A383    70f lt bl & gray          .20    .20
1783    A383    80f pale grn & yel
                bis                       .25    .20
1784    A383    1.50fo pale lem & brn     .35    .20
1785    A383    2.50fo gray & brn         .60    .35
1786    A383    3fo pale pink &
                gray                      .95    .60
        Nos. 1780-1786 (7)                2.75    1.85

The 80f and 1.50fo were issued with and without alternating labels, which show date and place when trophy was taken; the 2.50fo was issued only with labels, 20f, 60f, 70f and 3fo without labels only.

---

Nos. 1780-1786 exist imperf. Value, set $30.

Discus Thrower and Matthias Cathedral A384

30f, High jump & Agriculture Museum. 40f, Javelin (women's) & Parliament. 50f, Hammer throw, Mt. Gellert & Liberty Bridge. 60f, Broad jump & view of Buda. 1fo, Shot put & Chain Bridge. 2fo, Pole vault & Stadium. 3fo, Long distance runners & Millenium Monument.

**1966, Aug. 30    Photo.    Perf. 12x11½**
1787    A384    20f grn, brn & org        .20    .20
1788    A384    30f multi                 .30    .20
1789    A384    40f multi                 .20    .20
1790    A384    50f multi                 .20    .20
1791    A384    60f multi                 .25    .20
1792    A384    1fo multi                 .25    .20
1793    A384    2fo multi                 .50    .20
1794    A384    3fo multi                 .75    .50
        Nos. 1787-1794 (8)                2.60    1.90

8th European Athletic Championships, Budapest, Aug. 30-Sept. 4. See No. C261.
Exist imperf. Value, set $20.

Girl in the Forest by Miklos Barabas A385

Paintings: 1fo, Mrs. Istvan Bitto by Miklos Barabas (1810-98). 1.50fo, Hunyadi's Farewell by Gyula Benczur (1844-1920). 1.70fo, Reading Woman by Gyula Benczur, horiz. 2fo, Woman with Fagots by Mihaly Munkacsi (1844-1900). 2.50fo, Yawning Boy by Mihaly Munkacsi. 3fo, Lady in Violet by Pal Szinyei Merse (1845-1920). 10fo, Picnic in May by Pal Szinyei Merse, horiz.

**1966, Dec. 9                Perf. 12½**
**Gold Frame**
1795    A385    60f multi                 .20    .20
1796    A385    1fo multi                 .25    .20
1797    A385    1.50fo multi              .40    .20
1798    A385    1.70fo multi              .40    .20
1799    A385    2fo multi                 .40    .20
1800    A385    2.50fo multi              .45    .20
1801    A385    3fo multi                 .90    .80
        Nos. 1795-1801 (7)                3.00    2.00

**Souvenir Sheet**
1802    A385    10fo multi                6.00    6.00

Issued to honor Hungarian painters. Size of stamp in No. 1802: 56x51mm.
Exist imperf. Value: set $20; souvenir sheet $30.

Vostoks 3 and 4 — A386

Space Craft: 60f, Gemini 6 and 7. 80f, Vostoks 5 and 6. 1fo, Gemini 9 and target rocket. 1.50fo, Alexei Leonov walking in space. 2fo, Edward White walking in space. 2.50fo, Voskhod. 3fo, Gemini 11 docking Agena target.

**1966, Dec. 29                Perf. 11**
1803    A386    20f multi                 .20    .20
1804    A386    60f multi                 .20    .20
1805    A386    80f multi                 .20    .20
1806    A386    1fo multi                 .20    .20
1807    A386    1.50fo multi              .30    .20
1808    A386    2fo multi                 .30    .20
1809    A386    2.50fo multi              .50    .30
1810    A386    3fo multi                 .75    .50
        Nos. 1803-1810 (8)                2.65    2.00

American and Russian twin space flights.

---

Exist imperf. Value, set $20.

Pal Kitaibel and Kitaibelia Vitifolia — A387

Flowers of the Carpathian Basin: 60f, Dentaria glandulosa. 1fo, Edraianthus tenuifolius. 1.50fo, Althaea pallida. 2fo, Centaurea mollis. 2.50fo, Sternbergia colchiciflora. 3fo, Iris Hungarica.

**1967, Feb. 7    Photo.    Perf. 11½x12**
**Flowers in Natural Colors**
1811    A387    20f rose, blk &
                gold                      .20    .20
1812    A387    60f green                 .20    .20
1813    A387    1fo violet gray           .20    .20
1814    A387    1.50fo blue               .20    .20
1815    A387    2fo light olive           .25    .20
1816    A387    2.50fo gray grn           .45    .30
1817    A387    3fo yellow grn            .75    .50
        Nos. 1811-1817 (7)                2.25    1.80

Pal Kitaibel (1757-1817), botanist, chemist and physician.
Exist imperf. Value, set $20.

Militiaman A388

**1967, Feb. 18    Photo.    Perf. 11½x12**
1818    A388    2fo blue gray             .40    .20

Workers' Militia, 10th anniversary.
Exists imperf. Value $4.

Mme. Du Barry and Louis XV, by Gyula Benczur (1844-1920) — A390

**Souvenir Sheet**

Painting: 10fo, Milton dictating "Paradise Lost" to his daughters, by Soma Orlai Petrics.

**1967, May 6    Photo.    Perf. 12½**
1819    A390    10fo multi                4.75    4.50

Exists imperf. Value $30.

**1967, June 22**

Paintings: 60f, Franz Liszt by Mihaly Munkacsi (1844-1900). 1fo, Samuel Lanyi, self-portrait, 1840. 1.50fo, Lady in Fur-lined Jacket by Jozsef Borsos (1821-83). 1.70fo, The Lovers, by Pal Szinyei Merse (1845-1920). 2fo, Portrait of Szidonia Deak, 1861, by Alajos Gyorgyi (1821-63). 2.50fo, National Guardsman, 1848, by Jozsef Borsos.

**Gold Frame**
1820    A390    60f multi                 .20    .20
1821    A390    1fo multi                 .20    .20
1822    A390    1.50fo multi              .20    .20
1823    A390    1.70fo multi, horiz.      .30    .20
1824    A390    2fo multi                 .35    .20

---

1825    A390    2.50fo multi              .45    .20
1826    A390    3fo multi                 .75    .70
        Nos. 1820-1826 (7)                2.45    1.90

Issued to honor Hungarian painters. No. 1819 commemorates AMPHILEX 67 and the F.I.P. Congress, Amsterdam, May 11-21. No. 1819 contains one 56x50mm stamp.
Exist imperf. Value, set $20.
See #1863-1870, 1900-1907, 1940-1947.

Map of Hungary, Tourist Year Emblem, Plane, Train, Car and Ship A391

**1967, May 6                Perf. 12x11½**
1827    A391    1fo brt blue & blk        .20    .20

International Tourist Year, 1967.
Exists imperf. Value $4.

S.S. Ferencz Deak, Schönbüchel Castle, Austrian Flag — A392

Designs: 60f, Diesel hydrobus, Bratislava Castle and Czechoslovak flag. 1fo, Diesel ship Hunyadi, Buda Castle and Hungarian flag. 1.50fo, Diesel tug Szekszard, Golubac Fortress and Yugoslav flag. 1.70fo, Towboat Miskolc, Vidin Fortress and Bulgarian flag. 2fo, Cargo ship Tihany, Galati shipyard and Romanian flag. 2.50fo, Hydrofoil Siraly I, Izmail Harbor and Russian flag.

**1967, June 1                Perf. 11½x12**
**Flags in National Colors**
1828    A392    30f lt blue grn           .35    .20
1829    A392    60f orange brn            .35    .20
1830    A392    1fo grnsh blue            .75    .25
1831    A392    1.50fo lt green           1.00    .30
1832    A392    1.70fo blue               1.25    .45
1833    A392    2fo rose lilac            2.25    .75
1834    A392    2.50fo lt olive grn       5.25    1.10
        Nos. 1828-1834 (7)               11.20    3.25

25th session of the Danube Commission.
Exists imperf. Value, set $375.

Poodle A393

Collie — A394

1fo, Hungarian pointer. 1.40fo, Fox terriers. 2fo, Pumi, Hungarian sheep dog. 3fo, German shepherd. 4fo, Puli, Hungarian sheep dog.

**1967, July 7    Litho.    Perf. 12**
1835    A393    30f multi                 .25    .20
1836    A394    60f multi                 .25    .20
1837    A393    1fo multi                 .20    .20
1838    A394    1.40fo multi              .25    .25
1839    A393    2fo multi                 .35    .20
1840    A394    3fo multi                 .60    .35
1841    A393    4fo multi                 .95    .60
        Nos. 1835-1841 (7)                2.85    2.00

Exist imperf. Value, set $30.

Sterlets
A395

Fish: 60f, Pike perch. 1fo, Carp. 1.70fo, European catfish. 2fo, Pike. 2.50fo, Rapfin.

**1967, Aug. 22   Photo.   Perf. 12x11½**
1842  A395   20f multi            .20   .20
1843  A395   60f bister & multi   .20   .20
1844  A395   1fo multi            .20   .20
1845  A395   1.70fo multi         .20   .20
1846  A395   2fo green & multi    .30   .20
1847  A395   2.50fo gray & multi  .75   .55
      Nos. 1842-1847,B263 (7)    2.75  2.00

14th Cong. of the Intl. Federation of Anglers (C.I.P.S.), Dunaujvaros, Aug. 20-28.
Exist imperf. Value, set $20.

Prince Igor, by Aleksandr Borodin — A396

Opera Scenes: 30f, Freischütz, by Karl Maria von Weber. 40f, The Magic Flute, by Mozart. 60f, Prince Bluebeard's Castle, by Bela Bartok. 80f, Carmen, by Bizet, vert. 1fo, Don Carlos, by Verdi, vert. 1.70fo, Tannhäuser, by Wagner, vert. 3fo. Laszlo Hunyadi, by Ferenc Erkel, vert.

**1967, Sept. 26   Photo.   Perf. 12**
1848  A396   20f multi     .20   .20
1849  A396   30f multi     .20   .20
1850  A396   40f multi     .20   .20
1851  A396   60f multi     .20   .20
1852  A396   80f multi     .20   .20
1853  A396   1fo multi     .20   .20
1854  A396   1.70fo multi  .45   .30
1855  A396   3fo multi    1.00   .70
      Nos. 1848-1855 (8)  2.65  2.20

Exist imperf. Value, set $20.

Teacher, Students and Stone from Pecs University, 14th Century
A397

**1967, Oct. 9   Photo.   Perf. 11½x12**
1856  A397   2fo gold & dp grn   .40   .20

600th anniv. of higher education in Hungary; University of Pecs was founded in 1367.
Exists imperf. Value $6.

Eötvös University, and Symbols of Law and Justice — A398

**1967, Oct. 12   Perf. 12x11½**
1857  A398   2fo slate   .40   .20

300th anniv. of the School of Political Science and Law at the Lorand Eötvös University, Budapest.
Exists imperf. Value $6.

Lenin as Teacher, by Sandor Legrady
A399

Paintings by Sandor Legrady: 1fo, Lenin. 3fo, Lenin on board the cruiser Aurora.

**1967, Oct. 31   Perf. 12½**
1858  A399   60f gold & multi   .20   .20
1859  A399   1fo gold & multi   .20   .20
1860  A399   3fo gold & multi   .60   .25
      Nos. 1858-1860 (3)       1.00   .65

50th anniv. of the Russian October Revolution.
Exist imperf. Value, set $17.50.

Venus 4 Landing on Venus — A400

**1967, Nov. 6   Perf. 12**
1861  A400   5fo gold & multi   1.25  1.10

Landing of the Russian automatic space station Venus 4 on the planet Venus.
Exists imperf. Value $10.

Souvenir Sheet

19th Century Mail Coach and Post Horn — A401

**Photogravure; Gold Impressed**
**1967, Nov. 21   Perf. 12½**
1862  A401   10fo multicolored   3.25  3.00

Hungarian Postal Administration, cent.
Exists imperf. Value $35.

Painting Type of 1967

Paintings: 60f, Brother and Sister by Adolf Fenyes (1867-1945). 1fo, Wrestling Boys by Oszkar Glatz (1872-1958). 1.50fo, "October" by Karoly Ferenczy (1862-1917). 1.70fo, Women at the River Bank by Istvan Szönyi (1894-1960), horiz. 2fo, Godfather's Breakfast by Istvan Csok (1865-1961). 2.50fo, "Eviction Notice" by Gyula Derkovits (1894-1934). 3fo, Self-portrait by M. T. Czontvary Kosztka (1853-1919). 10fo, The Apple Pickers by Bela Uitz (1887-).

**1967, Dec. 21   Photo.   Perf. 12½**
1863  A390   60f multi    .20   .20
1864  A390   1fo multi    .20   .20
1865  A390   1.50fo multi .20   .20
1866  A390   1.70fo multi .20   .20
1867  A390   2fo multi    .30   .20

1868  A390   2.50fo multi   .40   .25
1869  A390   3fo multi      .70   .45
      Nos. 1863-1869 (7)   2.20  1.70
**Miniature Sheet**
1870  A390   10fo multi    2.75  2.50

Issued to honor Hungarian painters.
Exists imperf. Value: set $20; souvenir sheet $22.

Biathlon — A402

Sport (Olympic Rings and): 60f, Figure skating, pair. 1fo, Bobsledding. 1.40fo, Slalom. 1.70fo, Women's figure skating. 2fo, Speed skating. 3fo, Ski jump. 10fo, Ice hockey.

**1967, Dec. 30   Photo.   Perf. 12½**
**Souvenir Sheet**
1871  A402   10fo lilac & multi   2.50  2.00

Exists imperf. Value $18.

**1968, Jan. 29   Perf. 11**
1872  A402   30f multi          .20   .20
1873  A402   60f multi          .20   .20
1874  A402   1fo multi          .20   .20
1875  A402   1.40fo rose & multi .20   .20
1876  A402   1.70fo multi       .20   .20
1877  A402   2fo multi          .30   .20
1878  A402   3fo ol & multi     .80   .30
      Nos. 1872-1878,B264 (8)  2.80  1.80

10th Winter Olympic Games, Grenoble, France, Feb. 6-18. No. 1871 contains one 43x43mm stamp.
Exist imperf. Value, set (8) $20.

Kando Statue, Miskolc, Kando Locomotive and Map of Hungary
A403

**1968, Mar. 30  Photo.  Perf. 11½x12**
1879  A403   2fo dark blue   .40   .20

Kalman Kando (1869-1931), engineer, inventor of Kando locomotive.
Exists imperf. Value $7.

Domestic Cat
A404

**1968, Mar. 30   Perf. 11**
1880  A404   20f shown            .20   .20
1881  A404   60f Cream Persian    .20   .20
1882  A404   1fo Smoky Persian    .20   .20
1883  A404   1.20fo Domestic kitten .20 .20
1884  A404   1.50fo White Persian  .30   .20
1885  A404   2fo Brown-striped
                    Persian        .30   .20
1886  A404   2.50fo Siamese        .60   .25
1887  A404   5fo Blue Persian     1.25   .55
      Nos. 1880-1887 (8)          3.25  2.00

Exist imperf. Value, set $30.

Zoltan Kodaly, by Sandor Légrády
A405

**1968, Apr. 17   Photo.   Perf. 12½**
1888  A405   5fo gold & multi   1.00   .75

Kodaly (1882-1967), composer & musicologist.
Exists imperf. Value $10.

White Storks
A406

Birds: 50f, Golden orioles. 60f, Imperial eagle. 1fo, Red-footed falcons. 1.20fo, Scops owl. 1.50fo, Great bustard. 2fo, European bee-eaters. 2.50fo, Graylag goose.

**1968, Apr. 25**
**Birds in Natural Colors**
1889  A406   20f ver & lt ultra   .20   .20
1890  A406   50f ver & gray       .20   .20
1891  A406   60f ver & lt bl      .20   .20
1892  A406   1fo ver & yel grn    .25   .20
1893  A406   1.20fo ver & brt grn .25   .20
1894  A406   1.50fo ver & lt vio  .25   .20
1895  A406   2fo ver & pale lil   .55   .30
1896  A406   2.50fo ver & bl grn 1.10   .50
      Nos. 1889-1896 (8)         3.00  2.00

International Bird Preservation Congress.
Exists imperf. Value $30.

City Hall, Kecskemét
A407

Student and Agricultural College
A408

**1968, Apr. 25   Perf. 12x11½**
1897  A407   2fo brown orange   .30   .20

600th anniversary of Kecskemét.
Exists imperf. Value $5.

Marx Type of 1953

**1968, May 5   Engr.   Perf. 12**
1898  A230   1fo claret   .20   .20

Karl Marx (1818-1883).
Exists imperf. Value $5.

**1968, May 24   Photo.   Perf. 12x11½**
1899  A408   2fo dk olive green   .30   .20

150th anniv. of the founding of the Agricultural College at Mosonmagyaróvár.
Exists imperf. Value $5.

Painting Type of 1967

Paintings: 40f, Girl with Pitcher, by Goya (1746-1828). 60f, Head of an Apostle, by El Greco (c. 1541-1614). 1fo, Boy with Apple Basket and Dogs, by Pedro Nunez (1639-1700), horiz. 1.50fo, Mary Magdalene, by El Greco. 2.50fo, The Breakfast, by Velazquez

(1599-1660), horiz. 4fo, The Virgin from The Holy Family, by El Greco. 5fo, The Knife Grinder, by Goya. 10fo, Portrait of a Girl, by Palma Vecchio (1480-1528).

| **1968, May 30** | | **Perf. 12½** | |
|---|---|---|---|
| **1900** | A390 | 40f multi | .20 .20 |
| **1901** | A390 | 60f multi | .20 .20 |
| **1902** | A390 | 1fo multi | .20 .20 |
| **1903** | A390 | 1.50fo multi | .20 .20 |
| **1904** | A390 | 2.50fo multi | .50 .20 |
| **1905** | A390 | 4fo multi | .70 .20 |
| **1906** | A390 | 5fo multi | 1.00 .35 |
| | *Nos. 1900-1906 (7)* | | 3.00 1.55 |

**Souvenir Sheet**

| **1907** | A390 | 10fo multi | 3.25 3.00 |
|---|---|---|---|

Issued to publicize art treasures in the Budapest Museum of Fine Arts and to publicize an art exhibition.

Exist imperf. Values: set of 7, $20; souvenir sheet $30.

Lake Balaton at Badacsony A409

Views on Lake Balaton: 40f like 20f. 60f, Tihanyi Peninsula. 1fo, Sailboats at Almadi. 2fo, Szigliget Bay.

| **1968-69** | | **Litho.** | **Perf. 12** | |
|---|---|---|---|---|
| **1908** | A409 | 20f multi | .20 .20 |
| **1908A** | A409 | 40f multi ('69) | .20 .20 |
| | **b.** | Bklt. pane, #1909, 1911, 2 each #1908A, 1910 | | .75 |
| | **c.** | Bklt. pane, #1909-1911, 3 #1908A | | .75 |
| | **d.** | Bklt. pane, #1911, 3 #1908A, 2 #1909 | | .75 |
| **1909** | A409 | 60f multi | .20 .20 |
| **1910** | A409 | 1fo multi | .20 .20 |
| **1911** | A409 | 2fo multi | .45 .20 |
| | *Nos. 1908-1911 (5)* | | 1.25 1.00 |

Exist imperf. Value, set $22.

Locomotive, Type 424 — A410

| **1968, July 14** | | **Photo.** | **Perf. 12x11½** | |
|---|---|---|---|---|
| **1912** | A410 | 2fo gold, lt bl & slate | .60 .20 |

Centenary of the Hungarian State Railroad. Exists imperf. Value $8.

Horses Grazing — A411

Designs: 40f, Horses in storm. 60f, Horse race on the steppe. 80f, Horsedrawn sleigh. 1fo, Four-in-hand and rainbow. 1.40fo, Farm wagon drawn by 7 horses. 2fo, One rider driving five horses. 2.50fo, Campfire on the range. 4fo, Coach with 5 horses.

| **1968, July 25** | | | **Perf. 11** | |
|---|---|---|---|---|
| **1913** | A411 | 30f multi | .20 .20 |
| **1914** | A411 | 40f multi | .20 .20 |
| **1915** | A411 | 60f multi | .20 .20 |
| **1916** | A411 | 80f multi | .20 .20 |
| **1917** | A411 | 1fo multi | .20 .20 |
| **1918** | A411 | 1.40fo multi | .30 .20 |
| **1919** | A411 | 2fo multi | .30 .20 |
| **1920** | A411 | 2.50fo multi | .40 .25 |
| **1921** | A411 | 4fo multi | .75 .45 |
| | *Nos. 1913-1921 (9)* | | 2.75 2.10 |

Horse breeding on the Hungarian steppe (Puszta). Exist imperf. Value, set $50.

Mihály Tompa (1817-68), Poet — A412

| **1968, July 30** | | **Photo.** | **Perf. 12x11½** | |
|---|---|---|---|---|
| **1922** | A412 | 60f blue black | .20 .20 |

Exists imperf. Value $5.

Festival Emblem, Bulgarian and Hungarian National Costumes — A413

| **1968, Aug. 3** | | **Litho.** | **Perf. 12** | |
|---|---|---|---|---|
| **1923** | A413 | 60f multicolored | .30 .20 |

Issued to publicize the 9th Youth Festival for Peace and Friendship, Sofia, Bulgaria. Exists imperf. Value $5.

**Souvenir Sheet**

Runners and Aztec Calendar Stone — A414

| **1968, Aug. 21** | | **Photo.** | **Perf. 12½** | |
|---|---|---|---|---|
| **1924** | A414 | 10fo multicolored | 2.50 2.25 |

19th Olympic Games, Mexico City, 10/12-27. Exists imperf. Value $30.

Scientific Society Emblem — A415

| | | **Perf. 12½x11½** | |
|---|---|---|---|
| **1968, Dec. 10** | | | **Photo.** |
| **1925** | A415 | 2fo brt blue & blk | .35 .20 |

Society for the Popularization of Scientific Knowledge. Exists imperf. Value $5.50.

Hesperis A416

Garden Flowers: 60f, Pansy. 80f, Zinnias. 1fo, Morning-glory. 1.40fo, Petunia. 1.50fo, Portulaca. 2fo, Michaelmas daisies. 2.50fo, Dahlia.

| **1968, Oct. 29** | | | **Perf. 11½x12** | |
|---|---|---|---|---|
| **Flowers in Natural Colors** | | | | |
| **1926** | A416 | 20f gray | .20 .20 |
| **1927** | A416 | 60f lt green | .20 .20 |
| **1928** | A416 | 80f bluish lilac | .25 .20 |
| **1929** | A416 | 1fo buff | .25 .20 |
| **1930** | A416 | 1.40fo lt grnsh bl | .20 .20 |
| **1931** | A416 | 1.50fo lt blue | .25 .20 |
| **1932** | A416 | 2fo pale pink | .30 .25 |
| **1933** | A416 | 2.50fo lt blue | .60 .40 |
| | *Nos. 1926-1933 (8)* | | 2.25 1.85 |

Exist imperf. Value, set $20.

Pioneers Saluting Communist Party — A417

Children's Paintings: 60f, Four pioneers holding banner saluting Communist Party. 1fo, Pioneer camp.

| **1968, Nov. 16** | | **Photo.** | **Perf. 12x11½** | |
|---|---|---|---|---|
| **1934** | A417 | 40f buff & multi | .20 .20 |
| **1935** | A417 | 60f buff & multi | .20 .20 |
| **1936** | A417 | 1fo buff & multi | .30 .20 |
| | *Nos. 1934-1936 (3)* | | .70 .60 |

50th anniv. of the Communist Party of Hungary. The designs are from a competition among elementary school children. Exist imperf. Value, set $12.

Workers, Monument by Z. Olcsai-Kiss — A418

Design: 1fo, "Workers of the World Unite!" poster by N. Por, vert.

| | | **Perf. 11½x12, 12x11½** | |
|---|---|---|---|
| **1968, Nov. 24** | | | **Photo.** |
| **1937** | A418 | 1fo gold, red, & blk | .20 .20 |
| **1938** | A418 | 2fo gold & multi | .20 .20 |

Communist Party of Hungary, 50th anniv. Exist imperf. Value, set $10.

Human Rights Flame — A419

| **1968, Dec. 10** | | | **Perf. 12½x11½** | |
|---|---|---|---|---|
| **1939** | A419 | 1fo dark red brown | .25 .20 |

International Human Rights Year. Exists imperf. Value $3.

**Painting Type of 1967**

Italian Paintings: 40f, Esterhazy Madonna, by Raphael. 60f, The Annunciation, by Bernardo Strozzi. 1fo, Portrait of a Young Man, by Raphael. 1.50fo, The Three Graces, by Battista Naldini. 2.50fo, Portrait of a Man, by Sebastiano del Piombo. 4fo, The Doge Marcantonio Trevisani, by Titian. 5fo, Venus, Cupid and Jealousy, by Angelo Bronzino. 10fo, Bathsheba Bathing, by Sebastiano Ricci, horiz.

| **1968, Dec. 10** | | **Photo.** | **Perf. 12½** | |
|---|---|---|---|---|
| **1940** | A390 | 40f multi | .20 .20 |
| **1941** | A390 | 60f multi | .20 .20 |
| **1942** | A390 | 1fo multi | .20 .20 |
| **1943** | A390 | 1.50fo multi | .20 .20 |
| **1944** | A390 | 2.50fo multi | .30 .20 |
| **1945** | A390 | 4fo multi | .60 .25 |
| **1946** | A390 | 5fo multi | .80 .35 |
| | *Nos. 1940-1946 (7)* | | 2.50 1.60 |

**Miniature Sheet**

**Perf. 11**

| **1947** | A390 | 10fo multi | 2.75 2.50 |
|---|---|---|---|

Issued to publicize art treasures in the Budapest Museum of Fine Arts. No. 1947 contains one stamp size of stamp: 62x45mm.

Exist imperf. Value: set $22; souvenir sheet $25.

1869 and 1969 Emblems of Athenaeum Press — A420

| **1969, Jan. 27** | | | **Perf. 12½x11½** | |
|---|---|---|---|---|
| **1948** | A420 | 2fo gold, gray, lt bl & blk | .30 .20 |

Centenary of Athenaeum Press, Budapest. Exists imperf. Value $4.50.

Endre Ady (1877-1919), Lyric Poet — A421

| **1969, Jan. 27** | | | **Perf. 11½x12** | |
|---|---|---|---|---|
| **1949** | A421 | 1fo multicolored | .20 .20 |

Exists imperf. Value $5.

Olympic Medal and Women's Javelin — A422

Olympic Medal and: 60f, Canadian singles (canoeing). 1fo, Soccer. 1.20fo, Hammer throw. 2fo, Fencing. 3fo, Greco-Roman Wrestling. 4fo, Kayak single. 5fo, Equestrian. 10fo, Head of Mercury by Praxiteles and Olympic torch.

| **1969, Mar. 7** | | **Photo.** | **Perf. 12** | |
|---|---|---|---|---|
| **1950** | A422 | 40f multi | .20 .20 |
| **1951** | A422 | 60f multi | .20 .20 |
| **1952** | A422 | 1fo multi | .20 .20 |
| **1953** | A422 | 1.20fo multi | .20 .20 |
| **1954** | A422 | 2fo multi | .20 .20 |
| **1955** | A422 | 3fo multi | .30 .20 |
| **1956** | A422 | 4fo multi | .70 .20 |
| **1957** | A422 | 5fo multi | .75 .45 |
| | *Nos. 1950-1957 (8)* | | 2.75 1.85 |

**Souvenir Sheet**

| | **Litho.** | **Perf. 11½** | |
|---|---|---|---|
| **1958** | A422 | 10fo multi | 2.75 2.75 |

Victories won by the Hungarian team in the 1968 Olympic Games, Mexico City, Oct. 12-

27, 1968. No. 1958 contains one 45x33mm stamp.
Exist imperf. Value: set $22; souvenir sheet $25.

1919 Revolutionary Poster — A423

Revolutionary Posters: 60f, Lenin. 1fo, Man breaking chains. 2fo, Industrial worker looking at family and farm. 3fo, Militia recruiter. 10fo, Shouting revolutionist with red banner, horiz.

**1969, Mar. 21    Photo.    Perf. 11½x12**
**Gold Frame**

| | | | | |
|---|---|---|---|---|
| 1960 | A423 | 40f red & black | .20 | .20 |
| 1961 | A423 | 60f red & black | .20 | .20 |
| 1962 | A423 | 1fo red & black | .20 | .20 |
| 1963 | A423 | 2fo black, gray & red | .25 | .20 |
| 1964 | A423 | 3fo multicolored | .35 | .20 |
| | *Nos. 1960-1964 (5)* | | 1.20 | 1.00 |

**Souvenir Sheet**
**Perf. 12½**

| | | | | |
|---|---|---|---|---|
| 1965 | A423 | 10fo red, gray & blk | 1.50 | 1.50 |

50th anniv. of the proclamation of the Hungarian Soviet Republic.
Exist imperf. Values: set $17.50; souvenir sheet $17.50.
The 60f red lilac with 4-line black printing on back was given away by the Hungarian PO. Value 75c, mint or cancelled.
No. 1965 contains one 51x38½mm stamp.

Jersey Tiger A424

Designs: Various Butterflies and Moths.

**1969, Apr. 15    Litho.    Perf. 12**

| | | | | |
|---|---|---|---|---|
| 1966 | A424 | 40f shown | .20 | .20 |
| 1967 | A424 | 60f Eyed hawk moth | .20 | .20 |
| 1968 | A424 | 80f Painted lady | .20 | .20 |
| 1969 | A424 | 1fo Tiger moth | .20 | .20 |
| 1970 | A424 | 1.20fo Small fire moth | .25 | .20 |
| 1971 | A424 | 2fo Large blue | .35 | |
| 1972 | A424 | 3fo Belted oak egger | .65 | .45 |
| 1973 | A424 | 4fo Peacock | .90 | .50 |
| | *Nos. 1966-1973 (8)* | | 2.95 | 2.15 |

Exist imperf. Value, set $30.

ILO Emblem A426

**1969, May 22    Photo.    Perf. 12x11½**

| | | | | |
|---|---|---|---|---|
| 1974 | A426 | 1fo car lake & lake | .20 | .20 |

50th anniv. of the ILO.
Exist imperf. Value $5.

Black Pigs, by Paul Gauguin A427

French Paintings: 60f, These Women, by Toulouse-Lautrec, horiz. 1fo, Venus in the Clouds, by Simon Vouet. 2fo, Lady with Fan, by Edouard Manet, horiz. 3fo, La Petra Camara (dancer), by Théodore Chassériau. 4fo, The Cowherd, by Constant Troyon, horiz. 5fo, The Wrestlers, by Gustave Courbet. 10fo, Pomona, by Nicolas Fouché.

**1969, May 28    Photo.    Perf. 12½**

| | | | | |
|---|---|---|---|---|
| 1975 | A427 | 40f multicolored | .20 | .20 |
| 1976 | A427 | 60f multicolored | .20 | .20 |
| 1977 | A427 | 1fo multicolored | .20 | .20 |
| 1978 | A427 | 2fo multicolored | .30 | .20 |
| 1979 | A427 | 3fo multicolored | .50 | .20 |
| 1980 | A427 | 4fo multicolored | .70 | .25 |
| 1981 | A427 | 5fo multicolored | 1.00 | .50 |
| | *Nos. 1975-1981 (7)* | | 3.10 | 1.75 |

**Miniature Sheet**

| | | | | |
|---|---|---|---|---|
| 1982 | A427 | 10fo multicolored | 3.25 | 3.00 |

Art treasures in the Budapest Museum of Fine Arts. No. 1982 contains one 40x62mm stamp.
Exist imperf. Value: set $20; souvenir sheet $25.

Hotel Budapest A428

Budapest Post Office 100 A429

**1969, May    Photo.    Perf. 11**

| | | | | |
|---|---|---|---|---|
| 1983 | A428 | 1fo brown | .20 | .20 |

Exists imperf. Value $15.

**Coil Stamps**

**1970, Aug. 3                Perf. 14**

| | | | | |
|---|---|---|---|---|
| 1983B | A429 | 40f gray | .30 | .20 |
| *1983a* | A428 | 1fo brown | .40 | .20 |

Yellow control number on back of every 5th stamp.

Arms and Buildings of Vac A430

Towns of the Danube Bend: 1fo, Szentendre. 1.20fo, Visegrad. 3fo, Esztergom.

**1969, June 9    Litho.    Perf. 12**

| | | | | |
|---|---|---|---|---|
| 1984 | A430 | 40f multi | .20 | .20 |
| *a.* | | Bklt. pane, #1985, 1987, 4 #1984 | 2.75 | |
| *b.* | | Bklt. pane, #1986, 3 #1984, 2 #1985 | 2.75 | |
| 1985 | A430 | 1fo multi | .20 | .20 |
| 1986 | A430 | 1.20fo multi | .20 | .20 |
| 1987 | A430 | 3fo multi | .30 | .25 |
| | *Nos. 1984-1987 (4)* | | .90 | .85 |

Stamps in booklet panes Nos. 1984a-1984b come in two arrangements.
Exist imperf. Value $17.50.

"PAX" and Men Holding Hands — A431

**1969, June 17    Photo.    Perf. 11½x12**

| | | | | |
|---|---|---|---|---|
| 1988 | A431 | 1fo lt bl, dk bl & gold | .20 | .20 |

20th anniversary of Peace Movement.
Exists imperf. Value $4.50.

The Scholar, by Rembrandt A432

**1969, Sept. 15                Perf. 11½x12**

| | | | | |
|---|---|---|---|---|
| 1989 | A432 | 1fo sepia | .20 | .20 |

Issued to publicize the 22nd International Congress of Art Historians, Budapest.
Exists imperf. Value $4.50.

Fossilized Zelkova Leaves — A433

Designs: 60f, Greenockit calcite sphalerite crystals. 1fo, Fossilized fish, clupea hungarica. 1.20fo, Quartz crystals. 2fo, Ammonite. 3fo, Copper. 4fo, Fossilized turtle, placochelys placodonta. 5fo, Cuprite crystals.

**1969, Sept. 21                Photo.**

| | | | | |
|---|---|---|---|---|
| 1990 | A433 | 40f red, gray & sep | .20 | .20 |
| 1991 | A433 | 60f violet, yel & blk | .20 | .20 |
| 1992 | A433 | 1fo blue, tan & brn | .20 | .20 |
| 1993 | A433 | 1.20fo emer, gray & lil | .20 | .20 |
| 1994 | A433 | 2fo olive, tan & brn | .20 | .20 |
| 1995 | A433 | 3fo orange, brt & dk grn | .30 | .20 |
| 1996 | A433 | 4fo dull blk grn, brn & blk | .55 | .30 |
| 1997 | A433 | 5fo multicolored | .90 | .40 |
| | *Nos. 1990-1997 (8)* | | 2.75 | 1.90 |

Centenary of the Hungarian State Institute of Geology.
Exists imperf. Value, set $20.

First Hungarian Postal Card — A435

**1969, Oct. 1**

| | | | | |
|---|---|---|---|---|
| 2004 | A435 | 60f ver & ocher | .20 | .20 |

Centenary of the postal card. Hungary and Austria both issued cards in 1869.
Exists imperf. Value $4.50.

Mahatma Gandhi — A436

**1969, Oct. 1                Perf. 11½x12**

| | | | | |
|---|---|---|---|---|
| 2005 | A436 | 5fo green & multi | 1.25 | .70 |

Mohandas K. Gandhi (1869-1948), leader in India's fight for independence.
Exists imperf. Value $8.

World Trade Union Emblem A437

**1969, Oct. 17    Photo.    Perf. 12x11½**

| | | | | |
|---|---|---|---|---|
| 2006 | A437 | 2fo fawn & dk blue | .30 | .20 |

Issued to publicize the 7th Congress of the World Federation of Trade Unions.
Exists imperf. Value $4.50.

Janos Balogh Nagy, Self-portrait A438

**1969, Oct. 17                Perf. 11½x12**

| | | | | |
|---|---|---|---|---|
| 2007 | A438 | 5fo gold & multi | 1.50 | .80 |

Janos Balogh Nagy (1874-1919), painter.
Exists imperf. Value $8.

St. John the Evangelist, by Anthony Van Dyck — A439

Dutch Paintings: 60f, Three Fruit Pickers (by Pieter de Molyn?). 1fo, Boy Lighting Pipe, by Hendrick Terbrugghen. 2fo, The Feast, by Jan Steen. 3fo, Woman Reading Letter, by Pieter de Hooch. 4fo, The Fiddler, by Dirk Hals. 5fo, Portrait of Jan Asselyn, by Frans Hals. 10fo,

Steeplechase — A434

Designs: 60f, Fencing. 1fo, Pistol shooting. 2fo, Swimmers at start. 3fo, Relay race. 5fo, Pentathlon.

**1969, Sept. 15    Photo.    Perf. 12x11½**

| | | | | |
|---|---|---|---|---|
| 1998 | A434 | 40f blue & multi | .20 | .20 |
| 1999 | A434 | 60f multi | .20 | .20 |
| 2000 | A434 | 1fo multi | .20 | .20 |
| 2001 | A434 | 2fo violet & multi | .30 | .20 |
| 2002 | A434 | 3fo lemon & multi | .50 | .30 |
| 2003 | A434 | 5fo bluish grn, gold & dk red | .75 | .50 |
| | *Nos. 1998-2003 (6)* | | 2.15 | 1.60 |

Hungarian Pentathlon Championships.
Exists imperf. Value, set $20.

Mucius Scaevola before Porsena, by Rubens and Van Dyck.

**1969-70**     **Photo.**     *Perf. 12½*
| | | | | |
|---|---|---|---|---|
| 2008 | A439 | 40f multi | .20 | .20 |
| 2009 | A439 | 60f multi | .20 | .20 |
| 2010 | A439 | 1fo multi | .20 | .20 |
| 2011 | A439 | 2fo multi | .25 | .20 |
| 2012 | A439 | 3fo multi | .40 | .20 |
| 2013 | A439 | 4fo multi | .50 | .30 |
| 2014 | A439 | 5fo multi | 1.00 | .50 |
| | *Nos. 2008-2014 (7)* | | 2.75 | 1.80 |

**Miniature Sheet**
| | | | | |
|---|---|---|---|---|
| 2015 | A439 | 10fo multi | 3.25 | 3.25 |

Treasures in the Museum of Fine Arts, Budapest and the Museum in Eger.
Exist imperf. Value: set $20; souvenir sheet $35.
Issued: 40f-5fo, 12/2/69; 10fo, 1/70.

Kiskunfelegyhaza Circling Pigeon — A440

**1969, Dec. 12**     **Photo.**     *Perf. 11½x12*
| | | | | |
|---|---|---|---|---|
| 2016 | A440 | 1fo multicolored | .20 | .20 |

Issued to publicize the International Pigeon Show, Budapest, Dec. 1969.
Exists imperf. Value $6.50.

Subway A441

**1970, Apr. 3**     **Photo.**     *Perf. 12*
| | | | | |
|---|---|---|---|---|
| 2017 | A441 | 1fo blk, lt grn & ultra | .30 | .20 |

Opening of new Budapest subway.
Exists imperf. Value $8.

**Souvenir Sheet**

Panoramic View of Budapest 1945 and 1970, and Soviet Cenotaph — A442

Illustration reduced.

**1970, Apr. 3**     *Perf. 12x11½*
| | | | | |
|---|---|---|---|---|
| 2018 | A442 | Sheet of 2 | 2.75 | 2.50 |
| a. | | 5fo "1945" | 1.00 | 1.00 |
| b. | | 5fo "1970" | 1.00 | 1.00 |

25th anniv. of the liberation of Budapest.
Exists imperf. Value $30.

Cloud Formation, Satellite, Earth and Receiving Station — A443

**1970, Apr. 8**     **Litho.**     *Perf. 12*
| | | | | |
|---|---|---|---|---|
| 2019 | A443 | 1fo dk bl, yel & blk | .20 | .20 |

Centenary of the Hungarian Meteorological Service.
Exists imperf. Value $5.

Lenin Statue, Budapest — A444

Design: 2fo, Lenin portrait.

**1970, Apr. 22**     **Photo.**     *Perf. 11*
| | | | | |
|---|---|---|---|---|
| 2020 | A444 | 1fo gold & multi | .25 | .20 |
| 2021 | A444 | 2fo gold & multi | .25 | .20 |

Lenin (1870-1924), Russian communist leader.
Exist imperf. Value, set $8.

Franz Lehar and "Giuditta" Music — A445

**1970, Apr. 30**     **Photo.**     *Perf. 12*
| | | | | |
|---|---|---|---|---|
| 2022 | A445 | 2fo multicolored | .50 | .20 |

Franz Lehar (1870-1948), composer.
Exists imperf. Value $7.

Samson and Delilah, by Michele Rocca A446

Paintings: 60f, Joseph Telling Dream, by Giovanni Battista Langetti. 1fo, Clio, by Pierre Mignard. 1.50fo, Venus and Satyr, by Sebastiano Ricci, horiz. 2.50fo, Andromeda, by Francesco Furini. 4fo, Venus, Adonis and Cupid, by Luca Giordano. 5fo, Allegorical Feast, by Corrado Giaquinto. 10fo, Diana and Callisto, by Abraham Janssens, horiz.

**1970, June 2**     **Photo.**     *Perf. 12½*
| | | | | |
|---|---|---|---|---|
| 2023 | A446 | 40f gold & multi | .20 | .20 |
| 2024 | A446 | 60f gold & multi | .20 | .20 |
| 2025 | A446 | 1fo gold & multi | .20 | .20 |
| 2026 | A446 | 1.50fo gold & multi | .25 | .20 |
| 2027 | A446 | 2.50fo gold & multi | .30 | .20 |
| 2028 | A446 | 4fo gold & multi | .60 | .30 |
| 2029 | A446 | 5fo gold & multi | .75 | .50 |
| | *Nos. 2023-2029 (7)* | | 2.50 | 1.80 |

**Miniature Sheet**
**Perf. 11**
| | | | | |
|---|---|---|---|---|
| 2030 | A446 | 10fo multi | 3.50 | 3.00 |

No. 2030 contains one 63x46mm horizontal stamp.
Exist imperf. Values: set $20; souvenir sheet $30.

Beethoven Statue, by Janos Pasztor, at Martonvasar A447

**1970, June 27**     **Litho.**     *Perf. 12*
| | | | | |
|---|---|---|---|---|
| 2031 | A447 | 1fo plum, gray grn & org yel | .75 | .20 |

Ludwig van Beethoven, composer. The music in the design is from his Sonatina No. 1.
Exists imperf. Value $10.

Foundryman A448

King Stephen I — A449

**1970, July 28**     **Litho.**     *Perf. 12*
| | | | | |
|---|---|---|---|---|
| 2032 | A448 | 1fo multicolored | .25 | .20 |

200th anniversary of the first Hungarian steel foundry at Diosgyor, now the Lenin Metallurgical Works.
Exists imperf. Value $4.

**1970, Aug. 19**     **Photo.**     *Perf. 11½x12*
| | | | | |
|---|---|---|---|---|
| 2033 | A449 | 3fo multicolored | 1.00 | .50 |

Millenary of the birth of Saint Stephen, first King of Hungary.
Exists imperf. Value $5.

Women's Four on Lake Tata and Tata Castle — A450

**1970, Aug. 19**     **Litho.**     *Perf. 12*
| | | | | |
|---|---|---|---|---|
| 2034 | A450 | 1fo multicolored | .35 | .20 |

17th European Women's Rowing Championships, Lake Tata.
Exists imperf. Value $6.

Mother Giving Bread to her Children, FAO Emblem — A451

**1970, Sept. 21**     **Litho.**     *Perf. 12*
| | | | | |
|---|---|---|---|---|
| 2035 | A451 | 1fo lt blue & multi | .20 | .20 |

7th European Regional Cong. of the UNFAO, Budapest, Sept. 21-25.
Exists imperf. Value $4.

Boxing and Olympic Rings A452

Designs (Olympic Rings and): 60f, Canoeing. 1fo, Fencing. 1.50fo, Water polo. 2fo, Woman gymnast. 2.50fo, Hammer throwing. 3fo, Wrestling. 5fo, Swimming, butterfly stroke.

**1970, Sept. 26**     **Photo.**     *Perf. 11*
| | | | | |
|---|---|---|---|---|
| 2036 | A452 | 40f lt violet & multi | .20 | .20 |
| 2037 | A452 | 60f sky blue & multi | .20 | .20 |
| 2038 | A452 | 1fo orange & multi | .20 | .20 |
| 2039 | A452 | 1.50fo multi | .25 | .20 |
| 2040 | A452 | 2fo multi | .30 | .20 |
| 2041 | A452 | 2.50fo multi | .30 | .20 |
| 2042 | A452 | 3fo multi | .40 | .25 |
| 2043 | A452 | 5fo multi | .60 | .40 |
| | *Nos. 2036-2043 (8)* | | 2.35 | 1.85 |

75th anniv. of the Hungarian Olympic Committee. The 5fo also publicizes the 1972 Olympic Games in Munich.
Exist imperf. Value, set $20.

Flame and Family A453

**1970, Sept. 28**     **Litho.**     *Perf. 12*
| | | | | |
|---|---|---|---|---|
| 2044 | A453 | 1fo ultra, org & emer | .20 | .20 |

5th Education Congress, Budapest.
Exists imperf. Value $4.

Chalice, by Benedek Suky, 1440 — A454

Hungarian Goldsmiths' Art: 60f, Altar burette, 1500. 1fo, Nadasdy goblet, 16th century. 1.50fo, Coconut goblet, 1600. 2fo, Silver tankard, by Mihaly Toldalaghy, 1623. 2.50fo, Communion cup of Gyorgy Rakoczy I, 1670. 3fo, Tankard, 1690. 4fo, Bell-flower cup, 1710.

**1970, Oct.**     **Photo.**     *Perf. 12*
| | | | | |
|---|---|---|---|---|
| 2045 | A454 | 40f gold & multi | .20 | .20 |
| 2046 | A454 | 60f gold & multi | .20 | .20 |
| 2047 | A454 | 1fo gold & multi | .20 | .20 |
| 2048 | A454 | 1.50fo gold & multi | .20 | .20 |
| 2049 | A454 | 2fo gold & multi | .20 | .20 |
| 2050 | A454 | 2.50fo gold & multi | .25 | .20 |
| 2051 | A454 | 3fo gold & multi | .40 | .30 |
| 2052 | A454 | 4fo gold & multi | .60 | .40 |
| | *Nos. 2045-2052 (8)* | | 2.25 | 1.90 |

Exist imperf. Value, set $20.

Virgin and Child, by
Giampietrino — A455

Paintings from Christian Museum, Esztergom: 60f, "Love" (woman with 3 children), by Gregorio Lazzarini. 1fo, Legend of St. Catherine, by Master of Bat. 1.50fo, Adoration of the Shepherds, by Francesco Fontebasso, horiz. 2.50fo, Adoration of the Kings, by Master of Aranyosmarot. 4fo, Temptation of St. Anthony the Hermit, by Jan de Cock. 5fo, St. Sebastian, by Marco Palmezzano. 10fo, Lady with the Unicorn, by Painter of Lombardy.

**1970, Dec. 7      Photo.      Perf. 12½**
| | | | | |
|---|---|---|---|---|
| 2053 | A455 | 40f silver & multi | .20 | .20 |
| 2054 | A455 | 60f silver & multi | .20 | .20 |
| 2055 | A455 | 1fo silver & multi | .20 | .20 |
| 2056 | A455 | 1.50fo silver & multi | .20 | .20 |
| 2057 | A455 | 2.50fo silver & multi | .40 | .20 |
| 2058 | A455 | 4fo silver & multi | .65 | .20 |
| 2059 | A455 | 5fo silver & multi | .90 | .40 |
| | *Nos. 2053-2059 (7)* | | 2.75 | 1.70 |

**Souvenir Sheet**
| | | | | |
|---|---|---|---|---|
| 2060 | A455 | 10fo silver & multi | 3.00 | 2.75 |

No. 2060 contains one 50½x56mm stamp.
Exist imperf. Values: set $20; souvenir sheet $20.

Monument to Hungarian Martyrs, by A. Makrisz — A456

**1970, Dec. 30   Photo.   Perf. 12x11½**
| | | | | |
|---|---|---|---|---|
| 2061 | A456 | 1fo ultra & sepia | .20 | .20 |

The 25th anniversary of the liberation of the concentration camps at Auschwitz, Mauthausen and Dachau.
Exists imperf. Value $4.

"Souvenir Sheets"
Beginning in 1971, the government stamp agency, as well as a number of other state sanctioned organizations, have created souvenir sheets that do not have postal validity. These are not listed in this catalogue.

Marseillaise, by Francois Rude — A457

**1971, Mar. 18    Litho.     Perf. 12**
| | | | | |
|---|---|---|---|---|
| 2062 | A457 | 3fo bister & green | .40 | .20 |

Centenary of the Paris Commune.
Exists imperf. Value $4.

Béla Bartók
(1881-1945),
Composer
A458

**1971**
Design: No. 2064, András L. Achim (1871-1911), peasant leader.
| | | | | |
|---|---|---|---|---|
| 2063 | A458 | 1fo gray & dk car | .55 | .20 |
| 2064 | A458 | 1fo gray & green | .20 | .20 |

Issued: #2063, Mar. 25; #2064, Apr. 17.
Exist imperf. Value, set $13.

Györ
Castle,
1594
A459

**1971, Mar. 27**
| | | | | |
|---|---|---|---|---|
| 2065 | A459 | 2fo lt blue & multi | .40 | .20 |

700th anniversary of Györ.
Exists imperf. Value $4.

Bison Hunt — A460

Designs: 60f, Wild boar hunt. 80f, Deer hunt. 1fo, Falconry. 1.20fo, Felled stag and dogs. 2fo, Bustards. 3fo, Net fishing. 4fo, Angling.

**1971, May       Photo.      Perf. 12**
| | | | | |
|---|---|---|---|---|
| 2066 | A460 | 40f ver & multi | .20 | .20 |
| 2067 | A460 | 60f plum & multi | .20 | .20 |
| 2068 | A460 | 80f multi | .20 | .20 |
| 2069 | A460 | 1fo lilac & multi | .20 | .20 |
| 2070 | A460 | 1.20fo multi | .25 | .20 |
| 2071 | A460 | 2fo multi | .25 | .20 |
| 2072 | A460 | 3fo multi | .40 | .30 |
| 2073 | A460 | 4fo green & multi | .55 | .40 |
| | *Nos. 2066-2073 (8)* | | 2.25 | 1.90 |

World Hunting Exhibition, Budapest, Aug. 27-30. See No. C313.
Exist imperf. Value, set $30.

Souvenir Sheet

Portrait of a Man, by Dürer — A461

**1971, May 21        Perf. 12½**
| | | | | |
|---|---|---|---|---|
| 2074 | A461 | 10fo gold & multi | 2.75 | 2.50 |

Albrecht Dürer (1471-1528), German painter and etcher.
Exists imperf. Value $25.

Carnation and Pioneers' Emblem — A462

**1971, June 2     Photo.      Perf. 12**
| | | | | |
|---|---|---|---|---|
| 2075 | A462 | 1fo dark red & multi | .20 | .20 |

Hungarian Pioneers' Organization, 25th anniv.
Exists imperf. Value $6.

FIR Emblem, Resistance Fighters — A463

**1971, July 3**
| | | | | |
|---|---|---|---|---|
| 2076 | A463 | 1fo brown & multi | .30 | .20 |

International Federation of Resistance Fighters (FIR), 20th anniversary.
Exists imperf. Value $5.50.

Walking in Garden, Tokyo School A464

Japanese Prints from Museum of East Asian Art, Budapest: 60f, Geisha in Boat, by Yeishi (1756-1829). 1fo, Woman with Scroll, by Yeishi. 1.50fo, Courtesans, by Kiyonaga (1752-1815). 2fo, Awabi Fisher Women, by Utamaro (1753-1806). 2.50fo, Seated Courtesan, by Harunobu (1725-1770). 3fo, Peasant Woman Carrying Fagots, by Hokusai (1760-1849). 4fo, Women and Girls Walking, by Yeishi.

**1971, July 9        Perf. 12½**
| | | | | |
|---|---|---|---|---|
| 2077 | A464 | 40f gold & multi | .20 | .20 |
| 2078 | A464 | 60f gold & multi | .20 | .20 |
| 2079 | A464 | 1fo gold & multi | .20 | .20 |
| 2080 | A464 | 1.50fo gold & multi | .20 | .20 |
| 2081 | A464 | 2fo gold & multi | .25 | .20 |
| 2082 | A464 | 2.50fo gold & multi | .30 | .20 |
| 2083 | A464 | 3fo gold & multi | .50 | .25 |
| 2084 | A464 | 4fo gold & multi | .75 | .45 |
| | *Nos. 2077-2084 (8)* | | 2.60 | 1.90 |

Exist imperf. Value, set $20.

Locomotive, Map of Rail System and Danube — A465

**1971, July 15    Litho.      Perf. 12**
| | | | | |
|---|---|---|---|---|
| 2086 | A465 | 1fo multi | .30 | .20 |

125th anniversary of first Hungarian railroad between Pest and Vac.
Exists imperf. Value $8.

Griffin Holding Ink Balls A466

**1971, Sept. 11  Photo.   Perf. 12x11½**
| | | | | |
|---|---|---|---|---|
| 2087 | A466 | 1fo multicolored | 1.00 | .75 |

Centenary of stamp printing in Hungary. Printed se-tenant with 2 labels showing printing presses of 1871 and 1971 and Hungary Nos. P1 and 1171. Value unused, $1.
Exists imperf. Value, strip $8.

OIJ Emblem and Printed Page — A467

**1971, Sept. 21       Perf. 11½x12**
| | | | | |
|---|---|---|---|---|
| 2088 | A467 | 1fo dk bl, bl & gold | .25 | .20 |

25th anniversary of the International Organization of Journalists (OIJ).
Exists imperf. Value $4.

Josef Jacob Winterl and Barren Strawberry — A468

Plants: 60f, Bromeliaceae. 80f, Titanopsis calcarea. 1fo, Periwinkle. 1.20fo, Gymnocalycium. 2fo, White water lily. 3fo, Iris arenaria. 5fo, Peony.

**1971, Oct. 29    Litho.      Perf. 12**
| | | | | |
|---|---|---|---|---|
| 2089 | A468 | 40f lt vio & multi | .20 | .20 |
| 2090 | A468 | 60f gray & multi | .20 | .20 |
| 2091 | A468 | 80f multi | .20 | .20 |
| 2092 | A468 | 1fo multi | .20 | .20 |
| 2093 | A468 | 1.20fo lilac & multi | .20 | .20 |
| 2094 | A468 | 2fo gray & multi | .30 | .20 |
| 2095 | A468 | 3fo multi | .50 | .25 |
| 2096 | A468 | 5fo multi | .75 | .40 |
| | *Nos. 2089-2096 (8)* | | 2.55 | 1.85 |

Bicentenary of Budapest Botanical Gardens.
Exist imperf. Value, set $25.

Galloping — A469

Equestrian Sports: 60f, Trotting. 80f, Horses fording river. 1fo, Jumping. 1.20fo, Start. 2fo, Polo. 3fo, Steeplechase. 5fo, Dressage.

**1971, Nov. 22    Photo.    Perf. 12**

| | | | | |
|---|---|---|---|---|
| 2097 | A469 | 40f blue & multi | .20 | .20 |
| 2098 | A469 | 60f ocher & multi | .20 | .20 |
| 2099 | A469 | 80f olive & multi | .20 | .20 |
| 2100 | A469 | 1fo red & multi | .20 | .20 |
| 2101 | A469 | 1.20fo multi | .25 | .20 |
| 2102 | A469 | 2fo multi | .30 | .20 |
| 2103 | A469 | 3fo violet & multi | .50 | .30 |
| 2104 | A469 | 5fo blue & multi | .75 | .50 |
| | | Nos. 2097-2104 (8) | 2.60 | 2.00 |

Exist imperf. Value, set $20.

Beheading of Heathen Chief Koppany A470

Designs: 60f, Samuel Aba pursuing King Peter. 1fo, Basarad's victory over King Charles Robert. 1.50fo, Strife between King Salomon and Prince Geza. 2.50fo, Founding of Obuda Church by King Stephen I and Queen Gisela. 4fo, Reconciliation of King Koloman and his brother Almos. 5fo, Oradea Church built by King Ladislas I. 10fo, Funeral of Prince Emeric and blinding of Vazul.

**1971, Dec. 10    Litho.**

| | | | | |
|---|---|---|---|---|
| 2105 | A470 | 40f buff & multi | .20 | .20 |
| 2106 | A470 | 60f buff & multi | .20 | .20 |
| 2107 | A470 | 1fo buff & multi | .20 | .20 |
| 2108 | A470 | 1.50fo buff & multi | .20 | .20 |
| 2109 | A470 | 2.50fo buff & multi | .25 | .20 |
| 2110 | A470 | 4fo buff & multi | .50 | .30 |
| 2111 | A470 | 5fo buff & multi | .75 | .50 |
| | | Nos. 2105-2111 (7) | 2.30 | 1.80 |

**Miniature Sheet**
**Perf. 11½**

| | | | | |
|---|---|---|---|---|
| 2112 | A470 | 10fo buff & multi | 3.00 | 2.75 |

History of Hungary, from miniatures from Illuminated Chronicle of King Louis the Great, c. 1370. No. 2112 contains one stamp (size 44½x52mm).
Exist imperf. Value: set $20; souvenir sheet $25.

Equality Year Emblem A471

**1971, Dec. 30    Litho.    Perf. 12**

| | | | | |
|---|---|---|---|---|
| 2113 | A471 | 1fo bister & multi | .30 | .20 |

Intl. Year Against Racial Discrimination.
Exists imperf. Value $4.

Ice Hockey and Sapporo '72 Emblem — A472

Sport and Sapporo '72 Emblem: 60f, Men's slalom. 80f, Women's figure skating. 1fo, Ski jump. 1.20fo, Long-distance skiing. 2fo, Men's figure skating. 3fo, Bobsledding. 4fo, Biathlon. 10fo, Buddha.

**1971, Dec. 30    Perf. 12**

| | | | | |
|---|---|---|---|---|
| 2114 | A472 | 40f black & multi | .20 | .20 |
| 2115 | A472 | 60f black & multi | .20 | .20 |
| 2116 | A472 | 80f black & multi | .20 | .20 |
| 2117 | A472 | 1fo black & multi | .20 | .20 |
| 2118 | A472 | 1.20fo black & multi | .25 | .20 |
| 2119 | A472 | 2fo black & multi | .35 | .20 |
| 2120 | A472 | 3fo black & multi | .50 | .30 |
| 2121 | A472 | 4fo black & multi | .75 | .50 |
| | | Nos. 2114-2121 (8) | 2.65 | 2.00 |

**Souvenir Sheet**
**Perf. 11½**

| | | | | |
|---|---|---|---|---|
| 2122 | A472 | 10fo gold & multi | 2.75 | 2.50 |

11th Winter Olympic Games, Sapporo, Japan, Feb. 3-13, 1972. No. 2122 contains one 86x48mm stamp.
Exist imperf. Value: set $20; souvenir sheet $25.

Hungarian Locomotive — A473

Locomotives: 60f, Germany. 80f, Italy. 1fo, Soviet Union. 1.20fo, Japan. 2fo, Great Britain. 4fo, Austria. 5fo, France.

**1972, Feb. 23    Photo.    Perf. 12x11½**

| | | | | |
|---|---|---|---|---|
| 2123 | A473 | 40f multi | .20 | .20 |
| 2124 | A473 | 60f ocher & multi | .20 | .20 |
| 2125 | A473 | 80f multi | .20 | .20 |
| 2126 | A473 | 1fo olive & multi | .20 | .20 |
| 2127 | A473 | 1.20fo ultra & multi | .35 | .30 |
| 2128 | A473 | 2fo ver & multi | .20 | .20 |
| 2129 | A473 | 3fo multi | .50 | .25 |
| 2130 | A473 | 5fo multi | .90 | .45 |
| | | Nos. 2123-2130 (8) | 2.75 | 2.00 |

Exist imperf. Value, set $30.

Janus Pannonius, by Andrea Mantegna A474

**1972, Mar. 27    Litho.    Perf. 12**

| | | | | |
|---|---|---|---|---|
| 2131 | A474 | 1fo gold & multi | .25 | .20 |

Janus Pannonius (Johannes Czezmiczei, 1434-1472), humanist and poet.
Exists imperf. Value $4.

Mariner 9 — A475

Design: No. 2133, Mars 2 and 3 spacecraft.

**1972, Mar. 30    Photo.    Perf. 11½x12**

| | | | | |
|---|---|---|---|---|
| 2132 | A475 | 2fo dk blue & multi | .45 | .45 |
| 2133 | A475 | 2fo multi | .45 | .45 |
| a. | | Strip #2132-2133 + label | 1.25 | 1.25 |

Exploration of Mars by Mariner 9 (US), and Mars 2 and 3 (USSR). Issued in sheets containing 4 each of Nos. 2132-2133 and 4 labels inscribed in Hungarian, Russian and English. Exist imperf. Values: strip $12, sheetlet $40.

13th Century Church Portal — A476

**1972, Apr. 11**

| | | | | |
|---|---|---|---|---|
| 2134 | A476 | 3fo greenish black | .40 | .20 |

Centenary of the Society for the Protection of Historic Monuments.
Exists imperf. Value $10.

Hungarian Greyhound — A477

Hounds: 60f, Afghan hound (head). 80f, Irish wolfhound. 1.20fo, Borzoi. 2fo, Running greyhound. 4fo, Whippet. 6fo, Afghan hound.

**1972, Apr. 14    Litho.    Perf. 12**

| | | | | |
|---|---|---|---|---|
| 2135 | A477 | 40f multi | .20 | .20 |
| 2136 | A477 | 60f brown & multi | .20 | .20 |
| 2137 | A477 | 80f multi | .20 | .20 |
| 2138 | A477 | 1.20fo multi | .20 | .20 |
| 2139 | A477 | 2fo multi | .30 | .20 |
| 2140 | A477 | 4fo multi | .70 | .20 |
| 2141 | A477 | 6fo multi | 1.10 | .60 |
| | | Nos. 2135-2141 (7) | 2.90 | 1.80 |

Exist imperf. Value, set $35.

József Imre, Emil Grósz, László Blaskovics (Ophthalmologists) — A478

Design: 2fo, Allvar Gullstrand, V. P. Filatov, Jules Gonin, ophthalmologists.

**1972, Apr. 17**

| | | | | |
|---|---|---|---|---|
| 2142 | A478 | 1fo red, brn & blk | .40 | .20 |
| 2143 | A478 | 2fo blue, brn & blk | .95 | .45 |

First European Ophthalmologists' Congress, Budapest.
Exist imperf. Value, set $20.

Girl Reading and UNESCO Emblem A479

Roses — A480

**1972, May 27    Photo.    Perf. 11½x12**

| | | | | |
|---|---|---|---|---|
| 2144 | A479 | 1fo multicolored | .40 | .20 |

International Book Year 1971.
Exists imperf. Value $5.

**1972, June 1**

| | | | | |
|---|---|---|---|---|
| 2145 | A480 | 1fo multicolored | .40 | .20 |

15th Rose Exhibition, Budapest.
Exists imperf. Value $5.

George Dimitrov A481

**1972, June 18    Litho.    Perf. 12**

| | | | | |
|---|---|---|---|---|
| 2146 | A481 | 3fo black & multi | .40 | .20 |

90th anniversary, birth of George Dimitrov (1882-1949), communist leader.
Exists imperf. Value $4.

**Souvenir Sheet**

St. Martin and the Beggar, Stained-glass Window — A482

**1972, June 20    Perf. 10½**

| | | | | |
|---|---|---|---|---|
| 2147 | A482 | 10fo multi | 2.75 | 2.50 |

Belgica 72, International Philatelic Exhibition, Brussels, June 24-July 9.
Exists imperf. Value $30.

Gyorgy Dozsa (1474-1514), Peasant Leader — A483

**1972, June 25    Photo.    Perf. 11½x12**

| | | | | |
|---|---|---|---|---|
| 2148 | A483 | 1fo red & multi | .20 | .20 |

Exists imperf. Value $4.

Olympic Rings, Soccer — A484

Designs (Olympic Rings and): 60f, Water polo. 80f, Javelin, women's. 1fo, Kayak, women's. 1.20fo, Boxing. 2fo, Gymnastics, women's. 5fo, Fencing.

**1972, July 15          Perf. 11**

| 2149 | A484 | 40f | multi | .20 | .20 |
|---|---|---|---|---|---|
| 2150 | A484 | 60f | multi | .20 | .20 |
| 2151 | A484 | 80f | multi | .20 | .20 |
| 2152 | A484 | 1fo | lilac & multi | .20 | .20 |
| 2153 | A484 | 1.20fo | blue & multi | .20 | .20 |
| 2154 | A484 | 2fo | multi | .40 | .25 |
| 2155 | A484 | 5fo | green & multi | .75 | .50 |

Nos. 2149-2155,B299 (8)   2.65   2.05

20th Olympic Games, Munich, Aug. 26-Sept. 11. See No. C325.
Exist imperf. Value, set $25.

Prince Geza Selecting Site of Székesfehérvár — A485

Designs: 60f, St. Stephen, first King of Hungary. 80f, Knights (country's defense). 1.20fo, King Stephen dictating to scribe (legal organization). 2fo, Sculptor at work (education). 4fo, Merchants before king (foreign relations). 6fo, View of castle and town of Székesfehérvár, 10th century. 10fo, King Andreas II presenting Golden Bull to noblemen.

**1972, Aug. 20     Photo.     Perf. 12**

| 2156 | A485 | 40f | slate & multi | .20 | .20 |
|---|---|---|---|---|---|
| 2157 | A485 | 60f | multi | .20 | .20 |
| 2158 | A485 | 80f | lilac & multi | .20 | .20 |
| 2159 | A485 | 1.20fo | multi | .20 | .20 |
| 2160 | A485 | 2fo | bister & multi | .40 | .20 |
| 2161 | A485 | 4fo | blue & multi | .55 | .25 |
| 2162 | A485 | 6fo | purple & multi | .75 | .50 |

Nos. 2156-2162 (7)   2.50   1.75

**Souvenir Sheet**
**Perf. 12½**

2163 A485 10fo black & multi   3.00   3.00

Millennium of the town of Székesfehérvár; 750th anniv. of the Golden Bull granting rights to lesser nobility. #2163 contains one 94x45mm stamp.
Exist imperf. Value: set $20; souvenir sheet $20.

Parliament,
Budapest
A486

Design: 6fo, Session room of Parliament.

**1972, Aug. 20               Litho.**

| 2164 | A486 | 5fo | dk blue & multi | .60 | .20 |
|---|---|---|---|---|---|
| 2165 | A486 | 6fo | multicolored | .75 | .30 |

Constitution of 1949.
Exist imperf. Value, set $15.

Eger, 17th Century View, and Bottle of
Bull's Blood — A487

Design: 2fo, Contemporary view of Tokay and bottle of Tokay Aszu.

**1972, Aug. 21     Litho.     Perf. 12**

| 2166 | A487 | 1fo | buff & multi | .30 | .20 |
|---|---|---|---|---|---|
| 2167 | A487 | 2fo | green & multi | .65 | .20 |

1st World Wine Exhibition, Budapest, Aug. 1972.
Exist imperf. Value, set $12.

Georgikon Emblems, Grain, Potato
Flower — A488

**1972, Sept. 3**

2168 A488 1fo multi   .20   .20

175th anniv. of the founding of the Georgikon at Keszthely, the 1st scientific agricultural academy.
Exists imperf. Value $5.

Covered
Candy Dish
A489

Herend Porcelain: 40f, Vase with bird. 80f, Vase with flowers and butterflies. 1fo, Plate with Mexican landscape. 1.20fo, Covered dish. 2fo, Teapot, cup and saucer. 4fo, Plate with flowers. 5fo, Baroque vase showing Herend factory.

**1972, Sept. 15**
**Sizes: 23x46mm (40f, 80f, 2fo, 5fo);**
**33x36mm, others**

| 2169 | A489 | 40f | gray & multi | .20 | .20 |
|---|---|---|---|---|---|
| 2170 | A489 | 60f | ocher & multi | .20 | .20 |
| 2171 | A489 | 80f | multi | .20 | .20 |
| 2172 | A489 | 1fo | multi | .20 | .20 |
| 2173 | A489 | 1.20fo | green & multi | .20 | .20 |
| 2174 | A489 | 2fo | multi | .30 | .20 |
| 2175 | A489 | 4fo | red & multi | .50 | .30 |
| 2176 | A489 | 5fo | multi | .70 | .50 |

Nos. 2169-2176 (8)   2.50   2.00

Herend china factory, founded 1839.
Exist imperf. Value, set $20.

UIC Emblem and M-62 Diesel
Locomotive — A490

**1972, Sept. 19  Photo.  Perf. 11½x12**

2177 A490 1fo dark red   .35   .20

50th anniversary of International Railroad Union Congress, Budapest, Sept. 19.
Exist imperf. Value $15.

"25" and
Graph — A491

**1972, Sept.          Perf. 11½x12**

2178 A491 1fo yellow & brown   .35   .20

Planned national economy, 25th anniv.
Exists imperf. Value $7.

Budapest, 1972 — A492

#2179, View of Obuda, 1872. #2181, Buda, 1872. #2183, Pest, 1872. #2182, 2184, Budapest, 1972.

**1972, Sept. 26          Perf. 12x11½**

| 2179 | A492 | 1fo | Prus bl & rose car | .20 | .20 |
|---|---|---|---|---|---|
| 2180 | A492 | 1fo | rose car & Prus bl | .20 | .20 |
| a. | | | Pair, #2179-2180 | .40 | .20 |
| 2181 | A492 | 2fo | ocher & olive | .30 | .20 |
| 2182 | A492 | 2fo | olive & ocher | .30 | .20 |
| a. | | | Pair, #2181-2182 | .75 | .35 |
| 2183 | A492 | 3fo | green & lt brn | .40 | .20 |
| 2184 | A492 | 3fo | lt brown & grn | .40 | .20 |
| a. | | | Pair, #2183-2184 | 1.25 | .50 |

Nos. 2179-2184 (6)   1.80   1.20

Centenary of unification of Obuda, Buda and Pest into Budapest.
Exist imperf. Value, set in pairs $30.

Ear and
Congress
Emblem
A493

**1972, Oct. 3          Perf. 11½x12**

2185 A493 1fo brown, yel & blk   .20   .20

11th Intl. Audiology Cong., Budapest.
Exists imperf. Value $8.

Muses, by
Jozsef Rippl-
Ronai
A495

Stained-glass Windows, 19th-20th Centuries: 60f, 16th century scribe, by Ferenc Sebesteny. 1fo, Flight into Egypt, by Karoly Lotz and Bertalan Székely. 1.50fo, Prince Arpad's Messenger, by Jenö Percz. 2.50fo, Nativity, by Lili Sztehlo. 4fo, Prince Arpad and Leaders, by Karoly Kernstock. 5fo, King Matthias and Jester, by Jenö Haranghy.

**1972, Nov. 15          Perf. 12**

| 2188 | A495 | 40f | multi | .20 | .20 |
|---|---|---|---|---|---|
| 2189 | A495 | 60f | multi | .20 | .20 |
| 2190 | A495 | 1fo | multi | .20 | .20 |
| 2191 | A495 | 1.50fo | multi | .20 | .20 |
| 2192 | A495 | 2.50fo | multi | .35 | .20 |
| 2193 | A495 | 4fo | multi | .65 | .30 |
| 2194 | A495 | 5fo | multi | 1.10 | .50 |

Nos. 2188-2194 (7)   2.90   1.80

Exist imperf. Value, set $20.

Weaver, Cloth and Cogwheel — A496

**1972, Nov. 27     Litho.     Perf. 12**

2195 A496 1fo silver & multi   .25   .20

Opening of Museum of Textile Techniques, Budapest.
Exists imperf. Value $7.

Main Square,
Szarvas — A497

Designs: 1fo, Modern buildings, Salgotarjan. 3fo, Tokay and vineyard. 4fo, Esztergom Cathedral. 7fo, Town Hall, Kaposvar. 20fo, Veszprem.

**1972               Litho.     Perf. 11**

| 2196 | A497 | 40f | brown & orange | .20 | .20 |
|---|---|---|---|---|---|
| 2197 | A497 | 1fo | dk & lt blue | .20 | .20 |

Exist imperf. Value, set $15.

Church and
City Hall,
Vac — A498

**1973               Perf. 12x11½**

| 2198 | A498 | 3fo | dk & lt green | .40 | .20 |
|---|---|---|---|---|---|
| 2199 | A498 | 4fo | red brn & org | .50 | .20 |
| 2200 | A498 | 7fo | blue vio & lil | 1.00 | .20 |
| 2200A | A498 | 20fo | multicolored | 2.50 | .40 |

Nos. 2196-2200A (6)   4.80   1.40

Exist imperf. Value, set $20.
See Nos. 2330-2335.

**Coil Stamps**
**Type of 1963-64**

Designs as before.

Flora
Martos — A494

**1972          Photo.          Perf. 11½x12**

Portrait: No. 2187, Miklós Radnóti.

| 2186 | A494 | 1fo | green & multi | .20 | .20 |
|---|---|---|---|---|---|
| 2187 | A494 | 1fo | brown & multi | .20 | .20 |

Flora Martos (1897-1938), Hungarian Labor Party leader, & Miklós Radnóti (1909-44), poet.
Exist imperf. Value, set $8.
Issued: #2186, Nov. 5; #2187, Nov. 11.

**1972, Nov.**    **Photo.**    *Perf. 14*
Size: 21½x17½mm, 17½x21½mm

| | | | | |
|---|---|---|---|---|
| 2201 | A336 | 2fo blue green | .40 | .20 |
| 2202 | A336 | 3fo dark blue | .55 | .20 |
| 2203 | A336 | 4fo blue, vert. | .75 | .25 |
| 2204 | A336 | 6fo bister | 1.10 | .35 |
| | | *Nos. 2201-2204 (4)* | 2.80 | 1.00 |

Black control number on back of every 5th stamp.
Minute inscription centered in lower margin: "Legrady Sandor."

Arms of Soviet Union — A498a

**1972, Dec. 30**    **Photo.**    *Perf. 11½x12*

| | | | | |
|---|---|---|---|---|
| 2205 | A498a | 1fo multicolored | .20 | .20 |

50th anniversary of Soviet Union.
Exists imperf. Value $15.

Petöfi Speaking at Pilvax Cafe A499

2fo, Portrait. 3fo, Petöfi on horseback, 1848-49.

**1972, Dec. 30**    **Engr.**    *Perf. 12*

| | | | | |
|---|---|---|---|---|
| 2206 | A499 | 1fo rose carmine | .20 | .20 |
| 2207 | A499 | 2fo violet | .35 | .20 |
| 2208 | A499 | 3fo Prus green | .45 | .25 |
| | | *Nos. 2206-2208 (3)* | 1.00 | .65 |

Sesquicentennial of the birth of Sandor Petöfi (1823-49), poet and revolutionary.
Exist imperf. Value, set $15.

Postal Zone Map of Hungary and Letter-carrying Crow — A500

**1973, Jan. 1**    **Litho.**    *Perf. 12*

| | | | | |
|---|---|---|---|---|
| 2209 | A500 | 1fo red & black | .20 | .20 |

Introduction of postal code system.
Exists imperf. Value $7.

Imre Madách (1823-64), Poet and Dramatist A501

**1973, Jan. 20**    **Photo.**    *Perf. 11½x12*

| | | | | |
|---|---|---|---|---|
| 2210 | A501 | 1fo multicolored | .20 | .20 |

Exists imperf. Value $8.

Busho Mask — A502

Designs: Various Busho masks.

**1973, Feb. 17**    **Litho.**    *Perf. 12*

| | | | | |
|---|---|---|---|---|
| 2211 | A502 | 40f tan & multi | .20 | .20 |
| 2212 | A502 | 60f dull grn & multi | .20 | .20 |
| 2213 | A502 | 80f lilac & multi | .20 | .20 |
| 2214 | A502 | 1.20fo multi | .20 | .20 |
| 2215 | A502 | 2fo tan & multi | .30 | .20 |
| 2216 | A502 | 4fo multi | .50 | .30 |
| 2217 | A502 | 6fo lilac & multi | .75 | .40 |
| | | *Nos. 2211-2217 (7)* | 2.35 | 1.70 |

Busho Walk at Mohacs, ancient ceremony to drive out winter.
Exist imperf. Value, set $20.

Nicolaus Copernicus A503

**1973, Feb. 19**    **Engr.**    *Perf. 12*

| | | | | |
|---|---|---|---|---|
| 2218 | A503 | 3fo bright ultra | .75 | .50 |

Printed with alternating label showing heliocentric system and view of Torun.
Exists imperf. Value $15.

Vascular System and WHO Emblem A504

**1973, Apr. 16**    **Photo.**    *Perf. 12*

| | | | | |
|---|---|---|---|---|
| 2219 | A504 | 1fo sl grn & brn red | .25 | .20 |

25th anniv. of WHO.
Exists imperf. Value $7.

Tank, Rocket, Radar, Plane, Ship and Soldier A505

**1973, May 9**    **Litho.**    *Perf. 12*

| | | | | |
|---|---|---|---|---|
| 2220 | A505 | 3fo blue & multi | .50 | .20 |

Philatelic Exhibition of Military Stamp Collectors of Warsaw Treaty Member States. No. 2220 was printed with alternating label showing flags of Warsaw Treaty members.
Exists imperf. Value $10.

Hungary No. 1396 and IBRA '73 Emblem — A506

**1973, May 11**    **Litho.**    *Perf. 12*

| | | | | |
|---|---|---|---|---|
| 2221 | A506 | 40f shown | .20 | .20 |
| 2222 | A506 | 60f No. 1397, POLSKA '73 | .20 | .20 |
| 2223 | A506 | 80f No. 1398, IBRA '73 | .20 | .20 |
| 2224 | A506 | 1fo No. 1399, POLSKA | .20 | .20 |
| 2225 | A506 | 1.20fo No. B293a, IBRA | .20 | .20 |
| 2226 | A506 | 2fo No. B293b, POLSKA | .25 | .20 |
| 2227 | A506 | 4fo No. B293c, IBRA | .50 | .30 |
| 2228 | A506 | 5fo No. B293d, POLSKA | .75 | .40 |
| | | *Nos. 2221-2228 (8)* | 2.50 | 1.90 |

Publicity for IBRA '73 International Philatelic Exhibition, Munich, May 11-20; and POLSKA '73, Poznan, Aug. 15-Sept. 2. See No. C345.
Exist imperf. Value, set $20.

Typesetting, from "Orbis Pictus," by Comenius A507

3fo, Printer & wooden screw press, woodcut from Hungarian translation of Gospels.

**1973, June 5**    **Photo.**    *Perf. 11½x12*

| | | | | |
|---|---|---|---|---|
| 2229 | A507 | 1fo black & gold | .20 | .20 |
| 2230 | A507 | 3fo black & gold | .40 | .20 |

500th anniv. of book printing in Hungary.
Exist imperf. Value, set $8.

Storm over Hortobagy Puszta, by Csontvary — A508

Paintings: 60f, Mary's Well, Nazareth. 1fo, Carriage Ride by Moonlight in Athens, vert. 1.50fo, Pilgrimage to Cedars of Lebanon, vert. 2.50fo, The Lonely Cedar. 4fo, Waterfall at Jajce. 5fo, Ruins of Greek Theater at Taormina. 10fo, Horseback Riders on Shore.

**1973, June 18**      *Perf. 12½*

| | | | | |
|---|---|---|---|---|
| 2231 | A508 | 40f gold & multi | .20 | .20 |
| 2232 | A508 | 60f gold & multi | .20 | .20 |
| 2233 | A508 | 1fo gold & multi | .20 | .20 |
| 2234 | A508 | 1.50fo gold & multi | .20 | .20 |
| 2235 | A508 | 2.50fo gold & multi | .40 | .20 |
| 2236 | A508 | 4fo gold & multi | .65 | .35 |
| 2237 | A508 | 5fo gold & multi | .80 | .50 |
| | | *Nos. 2231-2237 (7)* | 2.65 | 1.85 |

**Souvenir Sheet**

| | | | | |
|---|---|---|---|---|
| 2238 | A508 | 10fo gold & multi | 3.50 | 3.00 |

Paintings by Tividar Kosztka Csontvary (1853-1919). No. 2238 contains one stamp (size: 90x43mm).
Exist imperf. Value: set $20; souvenir sheet $30.

Hands Holding Map of Europe — A509

Flowers — A510

**1973, July 3**    **Photo.**    *Perf. 11½x12*

| | | | | |
|---|---|---|---|---|
| 2239 | A509 | 2.50fo blk & gldn brn | 3.00 | 3.00 |
| a. | | Sheetlet of 4 + 2 labels | 10.00 | 9.00 |

Conference for European Security and Cooperation, Helsinki, July 1973. No. 2239 was printed in a sheetlet of 4 stamps and 2 blue labels showing conference sites.
Exists imperf. Value, sheetlet $200.

**1973, Aug. 4**

| | | | | |
|---|---|---|---|---|
| 2240 | A510 | 40f Provence roses | .20 | .20 |
| 2241 | A510 | 60f Cyclamen | .20 | .20 |
| 2242 | A510 | 80f Lungwort | .20 | .20 |
| 2243 | A510 | 1.20fo English daisies | .20 | .20 |
| 2244 | A510 | 2fo Buttercups | .30 | .20 |
| 2245 | A510 | 4fo Violets | .70 | .30 |
| 2246 | A510 | 6fo Poppies | 1.00 | .50 |
| | | *Nos. 2240-2246 (7)* | 2.80 | 1.80 |

Exist imperf. Value, set $20.

"Let's be Friends in Traffic" — A511

Designs: 60f, "Not even one drink." 1fo, "Light your bicycle."

**1973, Aug. 18**    **Photo.**    *Perf. 12x11½*

| | | | | |
|---|---|---|---|---|
| 2247 | A511 | 40f green & orange | .20 | .20 |
| 2248 | A511 | 60f purple & orange | .20 | .20 |
| 2249 | A511 | 1fo indigo & orange | .20 | .20 |
| | | *Nos. 2247-2249 (3)* | .60 | .60 |

To publicize traffic rules.
Exist imperf. Value $3.50.

Adoration of the Kings A512

Paintings: 60f, Angels playing violin and lute. 1fo, Adoration of the Kings. 1.50fo, Annunciation. 2.50fo, Angels playing organ and harp. 4fo, Visitation of Mary. 5fo, Legend of St. Catherine of Alexandria. 10fo, Nativity.

**1973, Nov. 3**    **Photo.**    *Perf. 12½*

| | | | | |
|---|---|---|---|---|
| 2250 | A512 | 40f gold & multi | .20 | .20 |
| 2251 | A512 | 60f gold & multi | .20 | .20 |
| 2252 | A512 | 1fo gold & multi | .20 | .20 |
| 2253 | A512 | 1.50fo gold & multi | .25 | .20 |
| 2254 | A512 | 2.50fo gold & multi | .40 | .25 |
| 2255 | A512 | 4fo gold & multi | .60 | .30 |
| 2256 | A512 | 5fo gold & multi | .80 | .50 |
| | | *Nos. 2250-2256 (7)* | 2.65 | 1.85 |

## Souvenir Sheet
### Perf. 11

2257 A512  10fo gold & multi  3.00 2.75

Paintings by Hungarian anonymous early masters from the Christian Museum at Esztergom. No. 2257 contains one 49x74mm stamp.
Exist imperf. Value: set $20; souvenir sheet $20.

Mihaly Csokonai Vitez — A513

**1973, Nov. 17  Photo.  Perf. 11½x12**

2258 A513  2fo bister & multi  .35  .20

Mihaly Csokonai Vitez (1773-1805), poet.
Exists imperf. Value $5.

José Marti and Cuban Flag — A514

**1973, Nov. 30**

2259 A514  1fo dk brn, red & bl  .20  .20

Marti (1853-95), Cuban natl. hero and poet.
Exists imperf. Value $4.

Barnabas Pesti (1920-44), Member of Hungarian Underground Communist Party — A515

**1973, Nov. 30**

2260 A515  1fo blue, brn & buff  .20  .20

Exists imperf. Value $4.

Women's Double Kayak — A516

Designs: 60f, Water polo. 80f, Men's single kayak. 1.20fo, Butterfly stroke. 2fo, Men's fours kayak. 4fo, Men's single canoe. 6fo, Men's double canoe.

**1973, Dec. 29  Litho.  Perf. 12x11**

| | | | | |
|---|---|---|---|---|
| 2261 | A516 | 40f red & multi | .20 | .20 |
| 2262 | A516 | 60f blue & multi | .20 | .20 |
| 2263 | A516 | 80f multicolored | .20 | .20 |
| 2264 | A516 | 1.20fo green & multi | .25 | .20 |
| 2265 | A516 | 2fo car & multi | .35 | .20 |
| 2266 | A516 | 4fo violet & multi | .45 | .30 |
| 2267 | A516 | 6fo multicolored | .50 | .50 |
| | Nos. 2261-2267 (7) | | 2.15 | 1.80 |

Hungarian victories in water sports at Tampere and Belgrade.
Exist imperf. Value, set $25.

---

## Souvenir Sheet

Map of Europe — A517

**1974, Jan. 15  Photo.  Perf. 12x11½**

2268  Sheet of 2 + label  8.50  8.00
 a.  A517 5fo multicolored  2.25  2.25

European Peace Conference (Arab-Israeli War), Geneva, Jan. 1974.
Exists imperf. Value $150.

Lenin — A518

**1974, Jan. 21  Photo.  Perf. 11½x12**

2269 A518  2fo gold, dull bl & brn  .50  .20

50th anniv. of the death of Lenin (1870-1924).
Exists imperf. Value $6.

Jozsef Boczor, Imre Békés, Tamás Elek — A519

**1974, Feb. 21  Perf. 12½**

2270 A519  3fo brown & multi  .25  .20

30th anniversary of the death in France of Hungarian resistance fighters.
Exists imperf. Value $7.

Comecon Building, Moscow and Flags A520

**1974, Feb. 26  Photo.  Perf. 12x11½**

2271 A520  1fo multicolored  .25  .20

25th anniversary of the Council of Mutual Economic Assistance.
Exists imperf. Value $8.

Bank Emblem, Coins and Banknote A521

**1974, Mar. 1  Perf. 11½x12**

2272 A521  1fo lt green & multi  .25  .20

25th anniversary of the State Savings Bank.
Exists imperf. Value $4.

---

Spacecraft on Way to Mars — A522

Designs: 60f, Mars 2 over Mars. 80f, Mariner 4. 1fo, Mars and Mt. Palomar Observatory. 1.20fo, Soft landing of Mars 3. 5fo, Mariner 9 with Mars satellites Phobos and Deimos.

**1974, Mar. 11  Photo.  Perf. 12½**

| | | | | |
|---|---|---|---|---|
| 2273 | A522 | 40f & multi | .20 | .20 |
| 2274 | A522 | 60f silver & multi | .20 | .20 |
| 2275 | A522 | 80f gold & multi | .20 | .20 |
| 2276 | A522 | 1fo silver & multi | .20 | .20 |
| 2277 | A522 | 1.20fo gold & multi | .25 | .20 |
| 2278 | A522 | 5fo silver & multi | .75 | .40 |
| | Nos. 2273-2278,C347 (7) | | 2.55 | 1.90 |

Exploration of Mars. See No. C348.
Exist imperf. Value, set (7) $20.

Salvador Allende (1908-73), Pres. of Chile — A523

**1974, Mar. 27  Photo.  Perf. 11½x12**

2279 A523  1fo black & multi  .20  .20

Exists imperf. Value $4.

Mona Lisa, by Leonardo da Vinci A524

**1974, Apr. 19  Perf. 12½**

2280 A524  4fo gold & multi  6.25  6.00

Exists imperf. Value $20. Exhibition of the Mona Lisa in Asia.
Printed in sheets of 6 stamps and 6 labels with commemorative inscription. Value, $65.
Exist imperf. Value: single with labels $30; sheetlet $200.

## Souvenir Sheet

Issue of 1874 and Flowers — A525

a, Mallow. b, Aster. c, Daisy. d, Columbine.

**1974, May 11  Litho.  Perf. 11½**

2281 A525  Sheet of 4  2.75  2.75
 a.-d.  2.50fo any single  .50  .50

Centenary of the first issue inscribed "Magyar Posta" (Hungarian Post).
Exists imperf. Value, sheet of 4 $30.

---

Carrier Pigeon, World Map, UPU Emblem — A526

**1974, May 22  Litho.  Perf. 12**

| | | | | |
|---|---|---|---|---|
| 2282 | A526 | 40f shown | .20 | .20 |
| 2283 | A526 | 60f Mail coach | .20 | .20 |
| 2284 | A526 | 80f Old mail automobile | .25 | .20 |
| 2285 | A526 | 1.20fo Balloon post | .35 | .20 |
| 2286 | A526 | 2fo Mail train | .45 | .20 |
| 2287 | A526 | 4fo Mail bus | 1.00 | .40 |
| | Nos. 2282-2287,C349 (7) | | 3.20 | 2.00 |

Centenary of the Universal Postal Union.
Exist imperf. Value, set $25.

Dove of Basel, Switzerland No. 3L1, 1845 — A527

**1974, June 7  Photo.  Perf. 11½x12**

2288 A527  3fo gold & multi  1.25  1.25

INTERNABA 1974 Philatelic Exhibition, Basel, June 7-16. No. 2288 issued in sheets of 3 stamps and 3 labels showing Internaba 1974 emblem. Size: 104x125mm.
Exist imperf. Values: single $12; sheet $35.

Chess Players, from 13th Century Manuscript A528

Designs: 60f, Chess players, 15th century English woodcut. 80f, Royal chess party, 15th century Italian chess book. 1.20fo, Chess players, 17th century copper engraving by Selenus. 2fo, Farkas Kempelen's chess playing machine, 1769. 4fo, Hungarian Grand Master Geza Maroczy (1870-1951). 6fo, View of Nice and emblem of 1974 Chess Olympiad.

**1974, June 6  Litho.  Perf. 12**

| | | | | |
|---|---|---|---|---|
| 2289 | A528 | 40f multi | .20 | .20 |
| 2290 | A528 | 60f multi | .20 | .20 |
| 2291 | A528 | 80f multi | .25 | .20 |
| 2292 | A528 | 1.20fo multi | .30 | .20 |
| 2293 | A528 | 2fo multi | .45 | .20 |
| 2294 | A528 | 4fo multi | 1.10 | .30 |
| 2295 | A528 | 6fo multi | 1.75 | .50 |
| | Nos. 2289-2295 (7) | | 4.25 | 1.80 |

50th anniv. of Intl. Chess Federation and 21st Chess Olympiad, Nice, June 6-30.
Exist imperf. Value, set $170.

## Souvenir Sheet

Cogwheel Railroad — A529

Designs: a, Passenger train, 1874. b, Freight train, 1874. c, Electric train, 1929-73. d, Twin motor train, 1973.

**1974, June 25    Litho.    Perf. 12**
2296  A529  Sheet of 4              3.50  3.25
  a.-d.  2.50fo, any single       .50   .50
  Cent. of Budapest's cogwheel railroad.
  Exist imperf. Value, sheet $40.

Congress Emblem (Globe and Parliament) — A530

**1974, Aug. 18    Photo.    Perf. 12**
2297  A530  2fo silver, dk & lt bl     .35   .20
  4th World Congress of Economists, Budapest, Aug. 19-24.
  Exists imperf. Value $5.50.

Bathing Woman, by Károly Lotz A531

Paintings of Nudes: 60f, Awakening, by Károly Brocky. 1fo, Venus and Cupid, by Brocky, horiz. 1.50fo, After the Bath, by Lotz. 2.50fo, Resting Woman, by Istvan Csok, horiz. 4fo, After the Bath, by Bertalan Szekely. 5fo, "Devotion," by Erzsebet Korb. 10fo, Lark, by Pál Szinyei Merse.

**1974, Aug.                Perf. 12½**
2298  A531  40f gold & multi        .20   .20
2299  A531  60f gold & multi        .20   .20
2300  A531  1fo gold & multi        .20   .20
2301  A531  1.50fo gold & multi     .30   .20
2302  A531  2.50fo gold & multi     .35   .20
2303  A531  4fo gold & multi        .70   .25
2304  A531  5fo gold & multi        .90   .40
  Nos. 2298-2304 (7)             2.85  1.65
**Souvenir Sheet**
**Perf. 11**
2305  A531  10fo gold & multi       3.25  3.00
  No. 2305 contains one stamp (45x70mm).
  Exist imperf. Value: set $30; souvenir sheet $30.

Mimi, by Béla Czóbel A532

**1974, Sept. 4**
2306  A532  1fo multicolored        .50   .20
  91st birthday of Béla Czóbel, Hungarian painter.
  Exists imperf. Value $8.

Intersputnik Tracking Station — A533

High Voltage Line "Peace" and Pipe Line "Friendship" A534

**Perf. 11½x12, 12x11½**
**1974, Sept. 5               Litho.**
2307  A533  1fo blue & violet       .20   .20
2308  A534  3fo multicolored        .60   .20
  Technical assistance and cooperation between Hungary and USSR, 25th anniv.
  Exist imperf. Value, set $8.

Pablo Neruda — A535

**1974, Sept. 11    Photo.    Perf. 11½x12**
2309  A535  1fo multicolored        .20   .20
  Pablo Neruda (Neftali Ricar do Reyes, 1904-1973), Chilean poet.
  Exists imperf. Value $4.

Sweden No. 1 and Lion from Royal Palace, Stockholm A536

**1974, Sept. 21            Perf. 12x11½**
2310  A536  3fo ultra, yel grn & gold    1.50  1.50
  Stockholmia 74 Intl. Philatelic Exhibition, Stockholm, Sept. 21-29. No. 2310 issued in sheets of 3 stamps and 3 labels showing Stockholmia emblem. White margin inscribed "UPU" multiple in white. Size: 126x104mm. Value $6.50.
  Exists imperf. Value: single $10; sheetlet $30.

Tank Battle and Soldier with Anti-tank Grenade — A537

**1974, Sept. 28    Litho.    Perf. 12**
2311  A537  1fo gold, orange & blk   .20   .20
  Nos. 2311,C351-C352 (3)          .90   .60
  Army Day.
  Exist imperf. Value, set (3) $15.

Segner and Segner Crater on Moon A538

**1974, Oct. 5**
2312  A538  3fo multicolored        .75   .25
  270th anniversary of the birth of Janos Andras Segner, naturalist. No. 2312 printed se-tenant with label arranged checkerwise in sheet. Label shows Segner wheel.
  Exists imperf. Value, with label $10.

Rhyparia Purpurata — A539

Lepidoptera: 60f, Melanargia galathea. 80f, Parnassius Apollo. 1fo, Celerio euphorbia. 1.20fo, Catocala fraxini. 5fo, Apatura iris. 6fo, Palaeochrysophanus hypphothe.

**1974, Nov. 11    Photo.    Perf. 12½**
2313  A539  40f multicolored        .20   .20
2314  A539  60f violet & multi      .20   .20
2315  A539  80f multicolored        .20   .20
2316  A539  1fo brown & multi       .20   .20
2317  A539  1.20fo blue & multi     .25   .25
2318  A539  5fo purple & multi      .75   .30
2319  A539  6fo multicolored       1.00   .40
  Nos. 2313-2319 (7)             2.80  1.75
  Exist imperf. Value, set $25.

Motherhood A540

**1974, Dec. 24    Litho.    Perf. 12**
2320  A540  1fo lt blue, blk & yel   .25   .20
  Exists imperf. Value $4.

Robert Kreutz — A541

**1974, Dec. 24**
2321  A541  1fo shown               .30   .20
2322  A541  1fo István Pataki       .30   .20
  30th death anniv. of anti-fascist martyrs Kreutz (1923-44) and Pataki (1914-44).
  Exist imperf. Value, set $8.

Puppy A542

Young Animals: 60f, Siamese kittens, horiz. 80f, Rabbit. 1.20fo, Foal, horiz. 2fo, Lamb. 4fo, Calf, horiz. 6fo, Piglet.

**1974, Dec. 30**
2323  A542  40f lt blue & multi     .20   .20
2324  A542  60f multicolored        .20   .20
2325  A542  80f olive & multi       .20   .20
2326  A542  1.20fo green & multi    .20   .20
2327  A542  2fo brown & multi       .30   .20
2328  A542  4fo orange & multi      .70   .30
2329  A542  6fo violet & multi     1.10   .50
  Nos. 2323-2329 (7)             2.90  1.80

  Exist imperf. Value, set $20.
  See Nos. 2403-2409.

**Building Type of 1972**

4fo, Szentendre. 5fo, View of Szolnok across Tisza River. 6fo, Skyscraper, Dunaújváros. 8fo, Church and city hall, Vac. 10fo, City Hall, Kiskunfélegyháza. 50fo, Church (Turkish Mosque), Hunyadi Statue & TV tower, Pecs.

**1974-80    Litho.    Perf. 12x11½**
2330  A498  4fo red brn & pink      .60   .20
2331  A498  5fo dk blue & ultra     .75   .20
2332  A498  6fo dk brn & org        .90   .20
2333  A498  8fo dk & brt grn       1.25   .20
2334  A498  10fo brown & yel       1.75   .20
2335  A498  50fo multi             6.00  1.25
  Nos. 2330-2335 (6)            11.25  2.25

  Exist imperf. Value, set $75.

  Issued: 8fo, 12/7; 10fo, 50fo, 12/30; 5fo, 3/8/75; 6fo, 6/10/75; 4fo, 6/20/80.

Hospital, Lambarene — A544

60f, Dr. Schweitzer, patient & microscope. 80f, Patient arriving by boat. 1.20fo, Hospital supplies arriving by ship. 2fo, Globe, Red Cross, carrier pigeons. 4fo, Nobel Peace Prize medal. 6fo, Portrait & signature of Dr. Schweitzer, organ pipes & "J. S. Bach."

**1975, Jan. 14    Photo.    Perf. 12**
2340  A544  40f gold & multi        .20   .20
2341  A544  60f gold & multi        .20   .20
2342  A544  80f gold & multi        .20   .20
2343  A544  1.20fo gold & multi     .20   .20
2344  A544  2fo gold & multi        .25   .20
2345  A544  4fo gold & multi        .60   .30
2346  A544  6fo lil & multi         .80   .45
  Nos. 2340-2346 (7)             2.45  1.75
  Dr. Albert Schweitzer (1875-1965), medical missionary and musician, birth centenary.
  Exist imperf. Value, set $20.

Farkas Bolyai — A545

**1975, Feb. 7    Litho.    Perf. 11½x12**
2347  A545  1fo gray & red brown    .20   .20
  Bolyai (1775-1856), mathematician.
  Exists imperf. Value $8.

Mihály Károlyi
A546

**1975, Mar. 4     Litho.     Perf. 12**
2348  A546  1fo lt blue & brown      .20   .20
Birth centenary of Count Mihály Károlyi (1875-1955), prime minister, 1918-1919.
Exists imperf. Value $5.50.

Woman, IWY Emblem
A547

**1975, Mar. 8          Perf. 12x11½**
2349  A547  1fo aqua & black      .20   .20
International Women's Year 1975.
Exists imperf. Value $5.50.

"Let us Build up the Railroads" — A548

Posters: 60f, "Bread starts here." 2fo, "Hungarian Communist Party-a Party of Action." 4fo, "Heavy Industry-secure base of Three-year Plan." 5fo, "Our common interest-a developed socialist society."

**1975, Mar. 17     Photo.     Perf. 11**
2350  A548  40f red & multi      .20   .20
2351  A548  60f red & multi      .20   .20
2352  A548  2fo red & multi      .20   .20
2353  A548  4fo red & multi      .40   .20
2354  A548  5fo red & multi      .50   .30
       Nos. 2350-2354 (5)      1.50  1.10
Hungary's liberation from Fascism, 30th anniv.
Exist imperf. Value, set $20.

Arrow, 1915, Pagoda and Mt. Fuji — A549

Antique Cars: 60f, Swift, 1911, Big Ben and Tower of London. 80f, Model T Ford, 1908, Capitol and Statue of Liberty. 1fo, Mercedes, 1901, Towers of Stuttgart. 1.20fo, Panhard Levassor, 1912, Arc de Triomphe and Eiffel Tower. 5fo, Csonka, 1906, Fishermen's Bastion and Chain Bridge. 6fo, Emblems of Hungarian Automobile Club, Alliance Internationale de Tourisme and Federation Internationale de l'Automobile.

**1975, Mar. 27     Litho.     Perf. 12**
2355  A549  40f lt blue & multi      .20   .20
2356  A549  60f lt green & multi     .20   .20
2357  A549  80f pink & multi         .20   .20
2358  A549  1fo lilac & multi        .20   .20
2359  A549  1.20fo orange & multi    .20   .20
2360  A549  5fo ultra & multi        .65   .30
2361  A549  6fo lilac rose & multi   1.00  .50
       Nos. 2355-2361 (7)      2.65  1.80
Hungarian Automobile Club, 75th anniv.
Exist imperf. Value, set $25.

The Creation of Adam, by Michelangelo — A550

**1975, Apr. 23     Photo.     Perf. 12½**
2362  A550  10fo gold & multi      3.50  3.25
Michelangelo Buonarroti (1475-1564), Italian painter, sculptor and architect.
Exists imperf. Value $28.

Academy of Science
A551

Designs: 2fo, Dates "1975 1825." 3fo, Count Istvan Szechenyi.

**1975, May 5     Litho.     Perf. 12**
2363  A551  1fo green & multi      .20   .20
2364  A551  2fo green & multi      .30   .20
2365  A551  3fo green & multi      .50   .30
       Nos. 2363-2365 (3)      1.00   .70
Sesquicentennial of Academy of Science, Budapest, founded by Count Istvan Szechenyi.
Exists imperf. Value, set $15.

Emblem of 1980 Olympics and Proposed Moscow Stadium — A553

**1975, May 8     Photo.     Perf. 11½x12**
2366  A553  5fo lt blue & multi      1.50  1.25
Socfilex 75 Intl. Philatelic Exhibition, Moscow, 5/8-18. #2366 issued in sheets of 3 stamps and 3 labels showing Socfilex 75 emblem (War Memorial, Berlin-Treptow).
Exists imperf. Value: single with label $17.50; sheetlet $55.

France No. 1100 and Venus of Milo — A554

**1975, June 3     Photo.     Perf. 11½x12**
2367  A554  5fo lilac & multi      1.50  1.25
ARPHILA 75 International Philatelic Exhibition, Paris, June 6-16. No. 2367 issued in sheets of 3 stamps and 3 labels showing ARPHILA 75 emblem.
Exists imperf. Value: single with label $15; sheetlet $40.

Early Transformer, Kando Locomotive, 1902, Pylon — A555

**1975, June 10     Litho.     Perf. 12**
2368  A555  1fo multicolored      .30   .20
Hungarian Electrotechnical Association, 75th anniversary.
Exists imperf. Value $15.

Epée, Saber, Foil and Globe — A556

**1975, July 11**
2369  A556  1fo multicolored      .25   .20
32nd World Fencing Championships, Budapest, July 11-20.
Exists imperf. Value $12.

*Souvenir Sheet*

Whale Pavilion, Oceanexpo 75 — A557

**1975, July 21     Photo.     Perf. 12½**
2370  A557  10fo gold & multi      3.00  2.75
Oceanexpo 75, International Exhibition, Okinawa, July 20, 1975-Jan. 1976.
Exists imperf. Value $40.

Dr. Agoston Zimmermann (1875-1963), Veterinarian
A558

**1975, Sept. 4     Litho.     Perf. 12**
2371  A558  1fo brown & blue      .20   .20
Exists imperf. Value $7.

Symbolic of 14 Cognate Languages
A559

**1975, Sept. 9**
2372  A559  1fo gold & multi      .20   .20
International Finno-Ugrian Congress.

Exists imperf. Value $7.

Voters — A560

Design: No. 2374, Map of Hungary with electoral districts.

**1975, Oct. 1**
2373  A560  1fo multicolored      .30   .20
2374  A560  1fo multicolored      .30   .20
Hungarian Council System, 25th anniv.
Exist imperf. Value, set $8.

Fish and Waves (Ocean Pollution)
A561

Designs: 60f, Skeleton hand reaching for rose in water glass. 80f, Fish gasping for raindrop. 1fo, Carnation wilting in polluted soil. 1.20fo, Bird dying in polluted air. 5fo, Sick human lung and smokestack. 6fo, "Stop Pollution" (raised hand protecting globe from skeleton hand).

**1975, Oct. 16     Litho.     Perf. 11½**
2375  A561  40f multi       .20   .20
2376  A561  60f multi       .20   .20
2377  A561  80f multi       .20   .20
2378  A561  1fo multi       .20   .20
2379  A561  1.20fo multi    .25   .20
2380  A561  5fo multi       .60   .30
2381  A561  6fo multi       .85   .40
       Nos. 2375-2381 (7)   2.50  1.70
Environmental Protection.
Exist imperf. Value, set $20.

Mariska Gárdos (1885-1973)
A562

Portraits: No. 2383, Imre Mezö (1905-56). No. 2384, Imre Tarr (1900-37).

**1975, Nov. 4     Litho.     Perf. 12**
2382  A562  1fo black & red org      .25   .20
2383  A562  1fo black & red org      .25   .20
2384  A562  1fo black & red org      .25   .20
       Nos. 2382-2384 (3)      .75   .60
Famous Hungarians, birth anniversaries.
Exist imperf. Value, set $15.

Treble Clef, Organ and Orchestra — A563

**1975, Nov. 14**
2385  A563  1fo multicolored      .40   .20
Franz Liszt Musical Academy, centenary.
Exists imperf. Value $12.

Szigetcsep Icon — A564

Virgin and Child, 18th Century Icons: 60f, Graboc. 1fo, Esztergom. 1.50fo, Vatoped. 2.50fo, Tottos. 4fo, Gyor. 5fo, Kazan.

**1975, Nov. 25    Photo.    Perf. 12½**
| | | | | |
|---|---|---|---|---|
| 2386 | A564 | 40f gold & multi | .20 | .20 |
| 2387 | A564 | 60f gold & multi | .20 | .20 |
| 2388 | A564 | 1fo gold & multi | .20 | .20 |
| 2389 | A564 | 1.50fo gold & multi | .20 | .20 |
| 2390 | A564 | 2.50fo gold & multi | .35 | .20 |
| 2391 | A564 | 4fo gold & multi | .70 | .30 |
| 2392 | A564 | 5fo gold & multi | .90 | .60 |
| | | Nos. 2386-2392 (7) | 2.75 | 1.90 |

Exist imperf. Value, set $20.

Members' Flags, Radar, Mother and Child — A565

**1975, Dec. 15    Litho.    Perf. 12**
2393 A565 1fo multicolored .30 .20

20th anniversary of the signing of the Warsaw Treaty (Bulgaria, Czechoslovakia, German Democratic Rep., Hungary, Poland, Romania, USSR).
Exists imperf. Value $7.

Ice Hockey, Winter Olympics' Emblem — A566

Designs (Emblem and): 60f, Slalom. 80f, Ski race. 1.20fo, Ski jump. 2fo, Speed skating. 4fo, Cross-country skiing. 6fo, Bobsled. 10fo, Figure skating, pair.

**1975, Dec. 29    Photo.    Perf. 12x11½**
| | | | | |
|---|---|---|---|---|
| 2394 | A566 | 40f silver & multi | .20 | .20 |
| 2395 | A566 | 60f silver & multi | .20 | .20 |
| 2396 | A566 | 80f silver & multi | .20 | .20 |
| 2397 | A566 | 1.20fo silver & multi | .20 | .20 |
| 2398 | A566 | 2fo silver & multi | .35 | .20 |
| 2399 | A566 | 4fo silver & multi | .70 | .30 |
| 2400 | A566 | 6fo silver & multi | .90 | .50 |
| | | Nos. 2394-2400 (7) | 2.75 | 1.80 |

**Souvenir Sheet**
**Perf. 12½**
2401 A566 10fo silver & multi 3.25 3.00

12th Winter Olympic Games, Innsbruck, Austria, Feb. 4-15, 1976. No. 2401 contains one stamp (59x36mm).
Exist imperf. Value: set $20; souvenir sheet $20.

"P," 5-pengö and 500-pengö Notes — A567

**1976, Jan. 16    Litho.    Perf. 12**
2402 A567 1fo multicolored .25 .20

Hungarian Bank Note Co., 50th anniversary. Exists imperf. Value $10.

**Animal Type of 1974**

Young Animals: 40f, Wild boars, horiz. 60f, Squirrels. 80f, Lynx, horiz. 1.20fo, Wolves. 2fo, Foxes, horiz. 4fo, Bears. 6fo, Lions, horiz.

**1976, Jan. 26**
| | | | | |
|---|---|---|---|---|
| 2403 | A542 | 40f multi | .20 | .20 |
| 2404 | A542 | 60f blue & multi | .20 | .20 |
| 2405 | A542 | 80f multi | .20 | .20 |
| 2406 | A542 | 1.20fo multi | .20 | .20 |
| 2407 | A542 | 2fo violet & multi | .30 | .20 |
| 2408 | A542 | 4fo yellow & multi | .65 | .30 |
| 2409 | A542 | 6fo multi | .75 | .40 |
| | | Nos. 2403-2409 (7) | 2.50 | 1.70 |

Exist imperf. Value, set $20.

A.G. Bell, Telephone, Molniya I and Radar — A568

**1976, Mar. 10    Litho.    Perf. 11½x12**
2410 A568 3fo multicolored .75 .75

Centenary of first telephone call by Alexander Graham Bell, Mar. 10, 1876. Issued in sheets of 4.
Exists imperf. Value: single $5.50; sheetlet $20.

Battle of Kuruc-Labantz — A569

Paintings: 60f, Meeting of Rakoczi and Tamas Esze, by Endre Veszprem. 1fo, Diet of Onod, by Mor Than. 2fo, Camp of the Kurucs. 3fo, Ilona Zrinyi (Rakoczi's mother), vert. 4fo, Kuruc officers, vert. 5fo, Prince Francis II Rakoczy, by Adam Manyoki, vert. Painters of 40f, 2fo, 3fo, 4fo, are unknown.

**1976, Mar. 27    Photo.    Perf. 12½**
| | | | | |
|---|---|---|---|---|
| 2411 | A569 | 40f gold & multi | .20 | .20 |
| 2412 | A569 | 60f gold & multi | .20 | .20 |
| 2413 | A569 | 1fo gold & multi | .30 | .20 |
| 2414 | A569 | 2fo gold & multi | .60 | .20 |
| 2415 | A569 | 3fo gold & multi | .85 | .25 |
| 2416 | A569 | 4fo gold & multi | 1.25 | .30 |
| 2417 | A569 | 5fo gold & multi | 1.60 | .50 |
| | | Nos. 2411-2417 (7) | 5.00 | 1.85 |

Francis II Rakoczy (1676-1735), leader of Hungarian Protestant insurrection, 300th birth anniversary.
Exist imperf. Value, set $30.

Standard Meter, Hungarian Meter Act — A570

2fo, Istvan Krusper, his vacuum balance, standard kilogram. 3fo, Interferometer & rocket.

**1976, Apr. 5    Perf. 11½x12**
| | | | | |
|---|---|---|---|---|
| 2418 | A570 | 1fo multicolored | .20 | .20 |
| 2419 | A570 | 2fo multicolored | .30 | .20 |
| 2420 | A570 | 3fo multicolored | .50 | .30 |
| | | Nos. 2418-2420 (3) | 1.00 | .70 |

Introduction of metric system in Hungary, cent.
Exist imperf. Value, set $15.

US No. 1353 and Independence Hall, Philadelphia — A571

**Photogravure and Foil Embossed**
**1976, May 29    Perf. 11½x12**
2421 A571 5fo blue & multi 1.40 1.25

Interphil 76 International Philatelic Exhibition, Philadelphia, Pa., May 29-June 6. No. 2421 issued in sheets of 3 stamps and 3 labels showing bells. Size: 115x125mm.
Exists imperf. Value: single with label $10; sheetlet $35.

"30" and Various Pioneer Activities — A572

**1976, June 5    Litho.    Perf. 12**
2422 A572 1fo multicolored .30 .20

Hungarian Pioneers, 30th anniversary.
Exists imperf. Value $7.

Trucks, Safety Devices, Trade Union Emblem — A573

**1976, June    Perf. 12½**
2423 A573 1fo multicolored .20 .20

Labor safety.
Exists imperf. Value $7.

Intelstat 4, Montreal Olympic Emblem, Canadian Flag — A574

Designs: 60f, Equestrian. 1fo, Butterfly stroke. 2fo, One-man kayak. 3fo, Fencing. 4fo, Javelin. 5fo, Athlete on vaulting horse.

**1976, June 29    Photo.    Perf. 11½x12**
| | | | | |
|---|---|---|---|---|
| 2424 | A574 | 40f dk blue & multi | .20 | .20 |
| 2425 | A574 | 60f slate grn & multi | .20 | .20 |
| 2426 | A574 | 1fo blue & multi | .20 | .20 |
| 2427 | A574 | 2fo green & multi | .35 | .20 |
| 2428 | A574 | 3fo brown & multi | .45 | .20 |
| 2429 | A574 | 4fo bister & multi | .60 | .30 |
| 2430 | A574 | 5fo maroon & multi | .75 | .40 |
| | | Nos. 2424-2430 (7) | 2.75 | 1.70 |

21st Olympic Games, Montreal, Canada, July 17-Aug. 1. See No. C365.
Exist imperf. Value, set $30.

Denmark No. 2 and Mermaid, Copenhagen — A575

**1976, Aug. 19    Photo.    Perf. 11½x12**
2431 A575 3fo multicolored 1.25 1.25

HAFNIA 76 Intl. Phil. Exhib., Copenhagen, Aug. 20-29. No. 2431 issued in sheets of 3 stamps and 3 labels showing HAFNIA emblem.
Exists imperf. Value: single with label $7; sheetlet $25.

**Souvenir Sheet**

Discovery of Body of Lajos II, by Bertalan Székely — A576

**1976, Aug. 27    Photo.    Perf. 12½**
2432 A576 20fo multicolored 3.00 2.75

450th anniversary of the Battle of Mohacs against the Turks.
Exists imperf. Value $25.

Flora, by Titian A577

**1976, Aug. 27**
2433 A577 4fo gold & multi .75 .25
Titian (1477-1576), Venetian painter.
Exists imperf. Value $8.

Hussar, Herend China — A578

**1976, Sept. 28    Litho.    Perf. 12**
2434 A578 4fo multicolored .75 .25
Herend China manufacture, sesqui.
Exists imperf. Value $7.

Daniel Berzsenyi (1776-1836), Poet — A579

**1976, Sept. 28**
2435 A579 2fo black, gold & yel .25 .20
Exists imperf. Value $4.

Pal Gyulai (1826-1909), Poet and Historian A580

**1976, Sept. 28**
2436 A580 2fo orange & black .25 .20
Exists imperf. Value $4.

Tuscany No. 1 and Emblem — A581

**1976, Oct. 13   Photo.   Perf. 11½x12**
2437 A581 5fo orange & multi 1.75 1.75
ITALIA 76 International Philatelic Exhibition, Milan, Oct. 14-24. No. 2437 issued in sheets of 3 stamps and 3 labels showing Italia 76 emblem. Size: 106x127mm.

Exists imperf. Value: single with label $12; sheetlet $35.

Jozsef Madzsar, M.D. — A582

Labor leaders: No. 2439, Ignac Bogar (1876-1933), secretary of printers' union. No. 2440, Rudolf Golub (1901-44), miner.

**1976, Nov. 4    Litho.    Perf. 12**
2438 A582 1fo deep brown & red .20 .20
2439 A582 1fo deep brown & red .20 .20
2440 A582 1fo deep brown & red .20 .20
    Nos. 2438-2440 (3) .60 .60
Exist imperf. Value, set $15.

Science and Culture House, Georgian Dancer, Hungarian and USSR Flags A583

**1976, Nov. 4    Perf. 12½x12**
2441 A583 1fo multicolored .40 .20
House of Soviet Science and Culture, Budapest, 2nd anniversary.
Exists imperf. Value $4.

Koranyi Sanitarium and Statue — A584

**1976, Nov. 11    Perf. 12**
2442 A584 2fo multicolored .35 .20
Koranyi TB Sanitarium, founded by Dr. Frigyes Koranyi, 75th anniversary.
Exists imperf. Value $4.

Locomotive, 1875, Enese Station — A585

Designs: 60f, Steam engine No. 17, 1885, Rabatamasi Station. 1fo, Railbus, 1925, Fertoszentmiklos Station. 2fo, Express steam engine, Kapuvar Station. 3fo, Engine and trailer, 1926, Gyor Station. 4fo, Eight-wheel express engine, 1934, and Fertoboz Station. 5fo, Raba-Balaton engine, Sopron Station.

**1976, Nov. 26    Litho.    Perf. 12**
2443 A585 40f multicolored .20 .20
2444 A585 60f multicolored .20 .20
2445 A585 1fo multicolored .20 .20
2446 A585 2fo multicolored .30 .20
2447 A585 3fo multicolored .50 .20
2448 A585 4fo multicolored .70 .35
2449 A585 5fo multicolored .90 .50
    Nos. 2443-2449 (7) 3.00 1.85
Gyor-Sopron Railroad, centenary.
Exist imperf. Value, set $25.

Poplar, Oak, Pine and Map of Hungary A586

**1976, Dec. 14**
2450 A586 1fo multicolored .25 .20
Millionth hectare of reforestation.
Exists imperf. Value $8.

Weight Lifting and Wrestling, Silver Medals — A587

60f, Kayak, men's single & women's double. 1fo, Horse vaulting. 4fo, Women's fencing. 6fo, Javelin. 20fo, Water polo.

**1976, Dec. 14   Photo.   Perf. 11½x12**
2451 A587 40f multicolored .20 .20
2452 A587 60f multicolored .20 .20
2453 A587 1fo multicolored .20 .20
2454 A587 4fo multicolored .75 .50
2455 A587 6fo multicolored .90 .50
    Nos. 2451-2455 (5) 2.25 1.40
**Souvenir Sheet**
**Perf. 12½x11½**
2456 A587 20fo multicolored 3.25 3.25
Hungarian medalists in 21st Olympic Games.
Exist imperf. Value: set $20; souvenir sheet $20.

Spoonbills — A588

Birds: 60f, White storks. 1fo, Purple herons. 2fo, Great bustard. 3fo, Common cranes. 4fo, White wagtails. 5fo, Garganey teals.

**1977, Jan. 3    Litho.    Perf. 12**
2457 A588 40f multicolored .20 .20
2458 A588 60f multicolored .20 .20
2459 A588 1fo multicolored .25 .20
2460 A588 2fo multicolored .40 .20
2461 A588 3fo multicolored .45 .30
2462 A588 4fo multicolored .90 .40
2463 A588 5fo multicolored 1.10 .50
    Nos. 2457-2463 (7) 3.50 2.00
Birds from Hortobagy National Park.
Exist imperf. Value, set $25.

1976 World Champion Imre Abonyi Driving Four-in-hand — A589

Designs: 60f, Omnibus on Boulevard, 1870. 1fo, One-horse cab at Budapest Railroad Station, 1890. 2fo, Mail coach, Buda to Vienna route. 3fo, Covered wagon of Hajduszoboszlo. 4fo, Hungarian coach, by Jeremias Schemel, 1563. 5fo, Post chaise, from a Lübeck wood panel, 1430.

**1977, Jan. 31    Litho.    Perf. 12x11½**
2464 A589 40f multicolored .20 .20
2465 A589 60f multicolored .20 .20
2466 A589 1fo multicolored .20 .20
2467 A589 2fo multicolored .30 .20
2468 A589 3fo multicolored .30 .20
2469 A589 4fo multicolored .50 .35
2470 A589 5fo multicolored .70 .45
    Nos. 2464-2470 (7) 2.40 1.80
History of the coach.
Exist imperf. Value, set $25.

Peacock A590

Birds: 60f, Green peacock. 1fo, Congo peacock. 3fo, Argus pheasant. 4fo, Impeyan pheasant. 6fo, Peacock pheasant.

**1977, Feb. 22    Litho.    Perf. 12**
2471 A590 40f multicolored .20 .20
2472 A590 60f multicolored .20 .20
2473 A590 1fo multicolored .20 .20
2474 A590 3fo multicolored .40 .20
2475 A590 4fo multicolored .60 .30
2476 A590 6fo multicolored .90 .50
    Nos. 2471-2476 (6) 2.50 1.60
Exist imperf. Value, set $25.

Newspaper Front Page, Factories A591

**1977, Mar. 3    Litho.    Perf. 12**
2477 A591 1fo gold, black & ver .25 .20
Nepszava newspaper, centenary.
Exists imperf. Value $4.

Flowers, by Mihaly Munkacsy A592

Flowers, by Hungarian Painters: 60f, Jakab Bogdany. 1fo, Istvan Csok, horiz. 2fo, Janos Halapy. 3fo, Jozsef Rippl-Ronai, horiz. 4fo, Janos Tornyai. 5fo, Jozsef Koszta.

**1977, Mar. 18    Photo.    Perf. 12½**
2478 A592 40f gold & multi .20 .20
2479 A592 60f gold & multi .20 .20
2480 A592 1fo gold & multi .20 .20
2481 A592 2fo gold & multi .30 .20
2482 A592 3fo gold & multi .40 .20
2483 A592 4fo gold & multi .55 .30
2484 A592 5fo gold & multi .75 .50
    Nos. 2478-2484 (7) 2.60 1.80
Exist imperf. Value, set $17.

**Newton and Double Convex Lens A593**

**1977, Mar. 31    Litho.    Perf. 12**
2485  A593  3fo tan & multi          1.00    .80

Isaac Newton (1643-1727), natural philosopher and mathematician, 250th death anniversary. No. 2485 issued in sheets of 4 stamps and 4 blue and black labels showing illustration from Newton's "Principia Mathematica," and Soviet space rocket.
Exists imperf. Value: single with label $8; sheetlet $30.

**Janos Vajda (1827-97), Poet — A594**

**1977, May 2    Litho.    Perf. 12**
2486  A594  1fo green, cream & blk          .20    .20

Exists imperf. Value $4.

**Netherlands No. 1 and Tulips — A595**

**1977, May 23    Photo.    Perf. 11½x12**
2487  A595  3fo multicolored          1.25    1.25

AMPHILEX '77, Intl. Stamp Exhib., Amsterdam, May 26-June 5. Issued in sheets of 3 stamps + 3 labels showing Amphilex poster.
Exist imperf. Value: single with label $7; sheetlet $25.

**Scene from "Wedding at Nagyrede" A596**

**1977, June 14    Litho.    Perf. 12**
2488  A596  3fo multicolored          .50    .20

State Folk Ensemble, 25th anniversary.
Exists imperf. Value $7.

---

Souvenir Sheet

**Bath of Bathsheba, by Rubens — A597**

**1977, June 14    Photo.    Perf. 11**
2489  A597  20fo multicolored          3.75    3.50

Peter Paul Rubens (1577-1640), Flemish painter.
Exists imperf. Value $60.

**Medieval View of Sopron, Fidelity Tower, Arms A598**

**1977, June 25    Litho.    Perf. 12x11½**
2490  A598  1fo multicolored          1.40    1.40

700th anniv. of Sopron. Printed se-tenant with label showing European Architectural Heritage medal awarded Sopron in 1975.
Exists imperf. Value, single with label $20.

**Race Horse Kincsem A599**

**1977, July 16    Litho.    Perf. 12**
2491  A599  1fo multicolored          1.00    .90

Sesquicentennial of horse racing in Hungary. Printed se-tenant with label showing portrait of Count Istvan Szechenyi and vignette from his 1827 book "Rules of Horse Racing in Hungary."
Exists imperf. Value, single with label $16.

**Scythian Iron Bell, 6th Century B.C. — A601**

**Panel, Crown of Emperor Constantin Monomakhos — A602**

Designs: No. 2494, Bronze candlestick in shape of winged woman, 12th-13th centuries. No. 2495, Centaur carrying child, copper aquamanile, 12th century. No. 2496, Gold figure of Christ, from 11th century Crucifix. Designs show art treasures from Hungarian National Museum, founded 1802.

**1977, Sept. 3    Litho.    Perf. 12**
2493  A601  2fo multicolored          .75    .75
2494  A601  2fo multicolored          .75    .75
2495  A601  2fo multicolored          .75    .75
2496  A601  2fo multicolored          .75    .75
  a.    Horiz. strip of 4, #2493-2496   3.00   3.00

**Souvenir Sheet**
2497  A602  10fo multicolored          3.50    3.00

50th Stamp Day.
Exist imperf. Value: strip of 4 $20; souvenir sheet $22.

**Sputnik A603**

Spacecraft: 60f, Skylab. 1fo, Soyuz-Salyut 5. 3fo, Luna 24. 4fo, Mars 3. 6fo, Viking.

**1977, Sept. 20**
2498  A603  40f multicolored          .20    .20
2499  A603  60f multicolored          .20    .20
2500  A603  1fo multicolored          .20    .20
2501  A603  3fo multicolored          .40    .20
2502  A603  4fo multicolored          .65    .35
2503  A603  6fo multicolored          .90    .45
      Nos. 2498-2503 (6)              2.55   1.60

Space explorations, from Sputnik to Viking. See No. C375.
Exist imperf. Value, set $20.

**Janos Szanto Kovacs (1852-1908), Agrarian Movement Pioneer A604**

**Ervin Szabo (1877-1918), Revolutionary Workers' Movement Pioneer A605**

**1977, Nov. 4    Litho.    Perf. 12**
2504  A604  1fo red & black          .30    .20
2505  A605  1fo red & black          .30    .20

Exist imperf. Value, set $10.

**Monument to Hungarian October Revolutionists, Omsk — A606**

**1977, Nov. 4**
2506  A606  1fo black & red          .20    .20

60th anniv. of Russian October Revolution.
Exists imperf. Value $5.50.

**Hands and Feet Bathed in Thermal Spring — A607**

**1977, Nov. 1**
2507  A607  1fo multicolored          .25    .20

World Rheumatism Year.
Exists imperf. Value $4.

**Endre Ady — A608**

**1977, Nov. 22    Engr.    Perf. 12**
2508  A608  1fo violet blue          .35    .35

Endre Ady (1877-1919), lyric poet. Issued in sheets of 4.
Exists imperf. Value $7. Sheetlet $35.

**Lesser Panda — A609**

Designs: 60f, Giant panda. 1fo, Asiatic black bear. 4fo, Polar bear. 6fo, Brown bear.

**1977, Dec. 16    Litho.    Perf. 11½x12**
2509  A609  40f yellow & multi          .20    .20
2510  A609  60f yellow & multi          .20    .20
2511  A609  1fo yellow & multi          .35    .20

---

**German Democratic Republic No. 370 — A600**

**1977, Aug. 18    Photo.    Perf. 12x11½**
2492  A600  3fo multicolored          1.25    1.10

SOZPHILEX 77 Philatelic Exhibition, Berlin, Aug. 19-28. No. 2492 issued in sheets of 3 stamps and 3 labels showing SOZPHILEX emblem.
Exist imperf. Value: single with label $7; sheetlet $20.

2512 A609 4fo yellow & multi .75 .30
2513 A609 6fo yellow & multi 1.00 .50
Nos. 2509-2513 (5) 2.50 1.40
Exist imperf. Value $25.

### Souvenir Sheet

Flags and Ships along Intercontinental Waterway — A610

Flags: a, Austria. b, Bulgaria. c, Czechoslovakia. d, France. e, Luxembourg. f, Yugoslavia. g, Hungary. h, Fed. Rep. of Germany. i, Romania. j, Switzerland. k, USSR.

**1977, Dec. 28    Litho.    Perf. 12**
2514 A610 Sheet of 11 8.00 7.75
a.-k. 2fo, any single 1.00 1.00
European Intercontinental Waterway: Danube, Main and Rhine.
Exists imperf. Value $170.

Lancer, 17th Century A611

Hussars: 60f, Kuruts, 1710. 1fo, Baranya, 1762. 2fo, Palatine officer, 1809. 4fo, Sandor, 1848. 6fo, Trumpeter, 5th Honved Regiment, 1900.

**1978, Jan.    Litho.    Perf. 11½x12**
2515 A611 40f lilac & multi .20 .20
2516 A611 60f yel grn & multi .20 .20
2517 A611 1fo red & multi .20 .20
2518 A611 2fo dull bl & multi .35 .20
2519 A611 4fo olive bis & multi .70 .30
2520 A611 6fo gray & multi 1.10 .50
Nos. 2515-2520 (6) 2.75 1.60
Exist imperf. Value, set $20.

School of Arts and Crafts A612

**1978, Mar. 31    Litho.    Perf. 12**
2521 A612 1fo multicolored .20 .20
School of Arts and Crafts, 200th anniv.
Exists imperf. Value $7.

Soccer Players, Flags of West Germany and Poland — A613

Designs (Various Soccer Scenes and Flags): No. 2523, Hungary and Argentina. No. 2524, France and Italy. No. 2525, Tunisia and Mexico. No. 2526, Sweden and Brazil. No. 2527, Spain and Austria. No. 2528, Peru and Scotland. No. 2529, Iran and Netherlands.

Flags represent first round of contestants. 20fo, Argentina '78 emblem.

**1978, May 25    Litho.    Perf. 12**
2522 A613 2fo multicolored .20 .20
2523 A613 2fo multicolored .20 .20
2524 A613 2fo multicolored .20 .20
2525 A613 2fo multicolored .20 .20
2526 A613 2fo multicolored .25 .20
2527 A613 2fo multicolored .25 .20
2528 A613 2fo multicolored .55 .30
2529 A613 2fo multicolored .90 .40
Nos. 2522-2529 (8) 2.75 1.90
### Souvenir Sheet
**Perf. 11½**
2530 A613 20fo multicolored 3.75 3.75
Argentina '78 11th World Cup Soccer Championships, Argentina, June 2-25.
Exist imperf. Values: set $20; souvenir sheet $25.

Vase, Star and Glass Blower's Tube A614

**1978, May 20    Litho.    Perf. 12**
2531 A614 1fo multicolored .20 .20
Ajka Glass Works, centenary.
Exist imperf. Value $7.

Canada No. 1 and Trillium — A615

**1978, June 2**
2532 A615 3fo multicolored 1.00 .90
CAPEX '78, Canadian International Philatelic Exhibition, Toronto, Ont., June 9-18. Issued in sheets of 3 stamps and 3 labels showing CAPEX '78 emblem.
Exists imperf. Value: single with label $7; sheetlet $20.

### Souvenir Sheets

Leif Ericson and his Ship — A616

Explorers and their ships: #2533b, Columbus. c, Vasco da Gama. d, Magellan. #2534a, Drake. b, Hudson. c, Cook. d, Peary.

**1978, June 10    Litho.    Perf. 12x11½**
2533 Sheet of 4 3.25 3.00
a.-d. A616 2fo, any single .70 .70
2534 Sheet of 4 3.25 3.00
a.-d. A616 2fo, any single .70 .70
Exist imperf. Value: set of 2 sheets $100.

Diesel Train, Pioneer's Kerchief — A617

Congress Emblem as Flower — A618

**1978, June 10    Perf. 12**
2535 A617 1fo multicolored .20 .20
30th anniversary of Pioneer Railroad.
Exists imperf. Value $7.

**1978, June**
Design: No. 2537, Congress emblem, "Cuba" and map of Cuba.
2536 A618 1fo multi .25 .20
2537 A618 1fo multi .25 .20
a. Pair, #2536-2537 .50 .30
11th World Youth Festival, Havana.
Exist imperf. Value $10.

WHO Emblem, Stylized Body and Heart — A619

Clenched Fist, Dove and Olive Branch — A620

**1978, Aug. 21    Litho.    Perf. 12**
2538 A619 1fo multicolored .20 .20
Drive against hypertension.
Exists imperf. Value $4.

**1978, Sept. 1    Litho.    Perf. 12**
2539 A620 1fo gray, red & black .20 .20
Publication of review "Peace and Socialism," 20th anniversary.
Exists imperf. Value $4.

Train, Telephone, Space Communication — A621

**1978, Sept. 8    Litho.    Perf. 12**
2540 A621 1fo multicolored .25 .20
20th anniv. of Organization for Communication Cooperation of Socialist Countries.
Exists imperf. Value $4.

"Toshiba" Automatic Letter Sorting Machine — A622

**1978, Sept. 15    Litho.    Perf. 11½x12**
2541 A622 1fo multicolored .50 .20
Introduction of automatic letter sorting. No. 2541 printed with se-tenant label showing bird holding letter.
Exists imperf. Value: single with label $8.

Eros Offering Grapes, Villa Hercules A623

Roman Mosaics Found in Hungary: No. 2543, Tiger (Villa Hercules, Budapest). No. 2544, Bird eating berries (Balacapuszta). No. 2545, Dolphin (Aquincum). 10fo, Hercules aiming at Centaur fleeing with Deianeira (Villa Hercules).

### Photogravure and Engraved
**1978, Sept. 16    Perf. 11½**
2542 A623 2fo multicolored 1.50 1.25
2543 A623 2fo multicolored 1.50 1.25
2544 A623 2fo multicolored 1.50 1.25
2545 A623 2fo multicolored 1.50 1.25
Nos. 2542-2545 (4) 6.00 5.00
### Souvenir Sheet
2546 A623 10fo multicolored 9.00 8.50
Stamp Day. No. 2546 contains one stamp (52x35mm).
Exist imperf. Value: set $80; souvenir sheet $170.

Count Imre Thököly — A624

**1978, Oct. 1    Photo.    Perf. 12½**
2547 A624 1fo black & yellow .25 .20
300th anniv. of Hungary's independence movement, led by Imre Thököly (1657-1705).
Exists imperf. Value $4.

### Souvenir Sheet

Hungarian Crown Jewels — A625

**1978, Oct. 10**
2548 A625 20fo gold & multi 5.50 5.25
Return of Crown Jewels from US, 1/6/78.
Exists imperf. Value $40.

"The Red Coach" A626

**1978, Oct. 21    Litho.    Perf. 12**
2549  A626  3fo red & black        .50    .20
Gyula Krudy, 1878-1933, novelist.
Exists imperf. Value $7.

St. Ladislas I Reliquary, Györ Cathedral A627

**1978, Nov. 15    Perf. 11½x12½**
2550  A627  1fo multicolored        .20    .20
Ladislas I (1040-1095), 900th anniversary of accession to throne of Hungary.
Exists imperf. Value $4.

Miklos Jurisics Statue, Köszeg — A628

**1978, Nov. 15    Perf. 12**
2551  A628  1fo multicolored        .30    .20
650th anniversary of founding of Köszeg.
Exists imperf. Value $5.

Samu Czaban and Gizella Berzeviczy — A629

**Photogravure and Engraved**
**1978, Nov. 24    Perf. 11½x12**
2552  A629  1fo brown, buff & red    .50    .20
Samu Czaban (1878-1942) and Gizella Berzeviczy (1878-1954), Communist teachers during Soviet Republic (1918-1919).
Exists imperf. Value $3.50.

Communist Party Emblem A630

**1978, Nov. 24    Litho.    Perf. 12**
2553  A630  1fo gray, red & blk    .20    .20
Hungarian Communist Party, 60th anniv.
Exists imperf. Value $4.

Woman Cutting Bread A631

Ceramics by Margit Kovacs (1902-1976): 2fo, Woman with pitcher. 3fo, Potter.

**1978, Nov. 30    Litho.    Perf. 11½x12**
2554  A631  1fo multicolored        .20    .20
2555  A631  2fo multicolored        .30    .20
2556  A631  3fo multicolored        .70    .60
      Nos. 2554-2556 (3)          1.20   1.00

Exist imperf. Value, set $20.

Virgin and Child, by Dürer A632

Dürer Paintings: 60f, Adoration of the Kings, horiz. 1fo, Self-portrait, 1500. 2fo, St. George. 3fo, Nativity, horiz. 4fo, St. Eustatius. 5fo, The Four Apostles. 20fo, Dancing Peasant Couple, 1514 (etching).

**1979, Jan. 8    Photo.    Perf. 12½**
2557  A632  40f gold & multi        .20    .20
2558  A632  60f gold & multi        .20    .20
2559  A632  1fo gold & multi        .20    .20
2560  A632  2fo gold & multi        .30    .20
2561  A632  3fo gold & multi        .35    .20
2562  A632  4fo gold & multi        .70    .30
2563  A632  5fo gold & multi        .80    .60
      Nos. 2557-2563 (7)          2.75   1.90

**Souvenir Sheet**
**Litho.**
2564  A632  20fo buff & brown      3.50   3.25
Albrecht Dürer (1471-1528), German painter and engraver.
Exist imperf. Value: set $20; souvenir sheet $50.

Human Rights Flame — A633

**1979, Feb. 8    Litho.    Perf. 11½x12**
2565  A633  1fo dk & lt blue       1.25   1.25
Universal Declaration of Human Rights, 30th anniversary. No. 2565 issued in sheets of 12 stamps (3x4) and 4 labels. Alternating horizontal rows inverted.
Exists imperf. Value $12. Strip of 3 $30, Sheetlet $100.

Child at Play — A634

IYC Emblem and: No. 2567, Family. No. 2568, 3 children (international friendship).

**1979, Feb. 26    Perf. 12**
2566  A634  1fo multicolored        .75    .75
2567  A634  1fo multicolored        .75    .75
2568  A634  1fo multicolored       6.50   5.50
      Nos. 2566-2568 (3)          8.00   7.00

Exist imperf. Value, set $30.

Soldiers of the Red Army, by Bela Uitz A635

**1979, Mar. 21    Litho.    Perf. 12**
2569  A635  1fo silver, blk & red   .20    .20
60th anniv. of Hungarian Soviet Republic.
Exists imperf. Value $4.

Calvinist Church, Nyirbator — A636

**1979, Mar. 28    Perf. 11**
2570  A636  1fo brown & yellow      .20    .20
700th anniv. of Nyirbator. See No. 2601.
Exists imperf. Value $8.

Chessmen, Gold Cup, Flag — A637

**1979, Apr. 12    Litho.    Perf. 12**
2571  A637  3fo multicolored       1.00    .50
Hungarian victories in 23rd Chess Olympiad, Buenos Aires, 1978.
Exists imperf. Value $15.

Alexander Nevski Cathedral, Sofia, Bulgaria No. 1 — A638

**1979, May 18    Litho.    Perf. 11½x12**
2572  A638  3fo multicolored        .75    .75
Philaserdica '79 Philatelic Exhibition, Sofia, Bulgaria, May 18-27. No. 2572 issued in sheets of 3 stamps and 3 labels showing Philaserdica emblem and arms of Sofia.
Exist imperf. Value: single with label $7; sheetlet $25.

Stephenson's Rocket, 1829, IVA '79 Emblem — A639

Railroad Development: 60f, Siemens' first electric locomotive, 1879. 1fo, "Pioneer," Chicago & Northwestern Railroad, 1836. 2fo, Orient Express, 1883. 3fo, Trans-Siberian train, 1898. 4fo, Express train on Tokaido line, 1964. 5fo, Transrapid-O5 train, exhibited 1979. 20fo, Map of European railroad network.

**1979, June 8    Litho.    Perf. 12x11½**
2573  A639  40f multi              .20    .20
2574  A639  60f multi              .20    .20
2575  A639  1fo multi              .20    .20
2576  A639  2fo multi              .30    .20
2577  A639  3fo multi              .45    .25
2578  A639  4fo multi              .60    .45
2579  A639  5fo multi              .90    .50
      Nos. 2573-2579 (7)          2.85   2.00

**Souvenir Sheet**
**Perf. 12½x11½**
2580  A639  20fo multi            4.00   3.75
Intl. Transportation Exhibition (IVA '79), Hamburg. #2580 contains one 47x32mm stamp.
Exist imperf. Value: set $25; souvenir sheet $50.

Natural Gas Pipeline and Compressor A640

2fo, Lenin power station & dam, Dnieprepetrovsk & pylon. 3fo, Comecon Building, Moscow, & star symbolizing 10 member states.

**1979, June 26    Perf. 11½x12**
2581  A640  1fo multi              .20    .20
2582  A640  2fo multi              .25    .20
2583  A640  3fo multi              .40    .20
      Nos. 2581-2583 (3)           .85    .60

30th anniversary of the Council of Mutual Economic Assistance, Comecon.
Exist imperf. Value, set $15.

Zsigmond Moricz (1879-1942), Writer, by Jozsef Ripple-Ronai A641

**1979, June 29    Perf. 12**
2584  A641  1fo multi              .20    .20
Exists imperf. Value $4.

Town Hall, Helsinki, Finnish Flag, Moscow '80 Emblem A642

Designs (Moscow '80 Emblem and): 60f, Colosseum, Rome, Italian flag. 1fo, Asakusa Temple, Tokyo, Japanese flag. 2fo, Mexico City Cathedral, Mexican flag. 3fo, Our Lady's Church, Munich, German flag. 4fo, Skyscrapers, Montreal, Canadian flag. 5fo, Lomonosov University, Misha the bear and Soviet flag.

**1979, July 31**      *Perf. 12x11½*

| | | | | |
|---|---|---|---|---|
| 2585 | A642 | 40f multi | .20 | .20 |
| 2586 | A642 | 60f multi | .20 | .20 |
| 2587 | A642 | 1fo multi | .20 | .20 |
| 2588 | A642 | 2fo multi | .20 | .20 |
| 2589 | A642 | 3fo multi | .30 | .25 |
| 2590 | A642 | 4fo multi | .40 | .30 |
| 2591 | A642 | 5fo multi | .70 | .45 |

*Nos. 2585-2591 (7)*    2.20   1.80

Pre-Olympic Year.
Exist imperf. Value, set $24.

Boy with Horse and Greyhounds, by
Janos Vaszary — A643

Paintings of Horses: 60f, Coach and Five, by
Karoly Lotz. 1fo, Boys on Horseback, by
Celesztin Pallya. 2fo, Farewell, by Lotz. 3fo,
Horse Market, by Pallya. 4fo, Wanderer, by
Bela Ivanyi-Grunwald. 5fo, Ready for the Hunt,
by Karoly Sterio.

**1979, Aug. 11**    **Photo.**    *Perf. 12½*

| | | | | |
|---|---|---|---|---|
| 2592 | A643 | 40f multi | .20 | .20 |
| 2593 | A643 | 60f multi | .20 | .20 |
| 2594 | A643 | 1fo multi | .20 | .20 |
| 2595 | A643 | 2fo multi | .25 | .20 |
| 2596 | A643 | 3fo multi | .40 | .20 |
| 2597 | A643 | 4fo multi | .50 | .30 |
| 2598 | A643 | 5fo multi | .75 | .40 |

*Nos. 2592-2598 (7)*    2.50   1.70

Exist imperf. Value, set $30.

Sturgeons, Map of Danube,
"Calypso" — A644

**1979, Aug. 11**

| | | | | |
|---|---|---|---|---|
| 2599 | A644 | 3fo multi | .50 | .20 |

Environmental protection of rivers and seas.
Exists imperf. Value $7.

Pentathlon
A645

**1979, Aug. 12**    **Litho.**    *Perf. 12*

| | | | | |
|---|---|---|---|---|
| 2600 | A645 | 2fo multi | .50 | .20 |

Pentathlon World Championship, Budapest,
Aug. 12-18.
Exists imperf. Value $4.

### Architecture Type of 1979

Design: Vasvar Public Health Center.

**1979, Aug. 15**    **Litho.**    *Perf. 11*

| | | | | |
|---|---|---|---|---|
| 2601 | A636 | 40f multi | .20 | .20 |

700th anniversary of Vasvar.
Exists imperf. Value $8.

---

Denarius of
Stephen I,
1000-1038,
Reverse
A646

Hungarian Coins: 2fo, Copper coin of Bela
III, 1172-1196. 3fo, Golden groat of King Louis
the Great, 1342-1382. 4fo, Golden forint of
Matthias I, 1458-1490. 5fo, Silver gulden of
Wladislaw II, 1490-1516.

### Engraved and Photogravure

**1979, Sept. 3**    *Perf. 12x11½*

| | | | | |
|---|---|---|---|---|
| 2602 | A646 | 1fo multi | .20 | .20 |
| 2603 | A646 | 2fo multi | .25 | .20 |
| 2604 | A646 | 3fo multi | .35 | .25 |
| 2605 | A646 | 4fo multi | .50 | .40 |
| 2606 | A646 | 5fo multi | 1.00 | .70 |

*Nos. 2602-2606 (5)*    2.30   1.75

9th International Numismatic Congress,
Berne, Switzerland.
Exist imperf. Value $20.

### Souvenir Sheet

Unofficial Stamp, 1848 — A647

**1979, Sept. 15**    **Litho.**    *Perf. 12*

| | | | | |
|---|---|---|---|---|
| 2607 | A647 | 10fo dk brown, blk & red | 2.75 | 2.50 |

Stamp Day.
Exists imperf. Value $30.

### Souvenir Sheet

Gyor-Sopron-Ebenfurt rail service,
cent. — A648

Designs: a, Elbel Locomotive. b, Type 424
steam engine. c, "War Locomotive." d, Hydraulic diesel locomotive.

**1979, Oct. 19**    **Litho.**    *Perf. 12*

| | | | | |
|---|---|---|---|---|
| 2608 | A648 | Sheet of 4 | 3.25 | 3.00 |
| a.-d. | | A648 5fo any single | .65 | .65 |

Exists imperf. Value $37.50.

---

Vega-Chess,
by Victor
Vasarely
A649

**1979, Oct. 29**

| | | | | |
|---|---|---|---|---|
| 2609 | A649 | 1fo multi | .20 | .20 |

Exists imperf. Value $20.

International
Savings
Day — A650

**1979, Oct. 29**    **Litho.**    *Perf. 12*

| | | | | |
|---|---|---|---|---|
| 2610 | A650 | 1fo multi | .20 | .20 |

Exists imperf. Value $4.

Otter — A651

Wildlife Protection: 60f, Wild cat. 1fo, Pine
marten. 2fo, Eurasian badger. 4fo, Polecat.
6fo, Beech marten.

**1979, Nov. 20**

| | | | | |
|---|---|---|---|---|
| 2611 | A651 | 40f multi | .20 | .20 |
| 2612 | A651 | 60f multi | .20 | .20 |
| 2613 | A651 | 1fo multi | .20 | .20 |
| 2614 | A651 | 2fo multi | .30 | .20 |
| 2615 | A651 | 4fo multi | .60 | .25 |
| 2616 | A651 | 6fo multi | .90 | .60 |

*Nos. 2611-2616 (6)*    2.40   1.65

Exist imperf. Value, set $20.

Tom Thumb,
IYC Emblem
A652

IYC Emblem and Fairy Tale Scenes: 60f,
The Ugly Duckling. 1fo, The Fisherman and
the Goldfish. 2fo, Cinderella. 3fo, Gulliver's
Travels. 4fo, The Little Pigs and the Wolf. 5fo,
Janos the Knight. 20fo, The Fairy Ilona.

**1979, Dec. 29**    **Litho.**    *Perf. 12x11½*

| | | | | |
|---|---|---|---|---|
| 2617 | A652 | 40f multi | .20 | .20 |
| 2618 | A652 | 60f multi | .20 | .20 |
| 2619 | A652 | 1fo multi | .20 | .20 |
| 2620 | A652 | 2fo multi | .35 | .20 |
| 2621 | A652 | 3fo multi | .50 | .30 |
| 2622 | A652 | 4fo multi | .70 | .30 |
| 2623 | A652 | 5fo multi | 1.00 | .60 |

*Nos. 2617-2623 (7)*    3.15   2.00

### Souvenir Sheet

| | | | | |
|---|---|---|---|---|
| 2624 | A652 | 20fo multi | 3.75 | 3.50 |

Exist imperf. Value: set $25; souvenir sheet
$30.

---

Trichodes Apairius and Yarrow — A653

Insects Pollinating Flowers: 60f, Bumblebee
and blanketflower. 1fo, Red admiral butterfly
and daisy. 2fo, Cetonia aurata and rose. 4fo,
Graphosoma lineatum and petroselinum hor-
tense. 6fo, Chlorophorus varius and thistle.

**1980, Jan. 25**    **Litho.**    *Perf. 12*

| | | | | |
|---|---|---|---|---|
| 2625 | A653 | 40f multi | .20 | .20 |
| 2626 | A653 | 60f multi | .20 | .20 |
| 2627 | A653 | 1fo multi | .25 | .20 |
| 2628 | A653 | 2fo multi | .35 | .20 |
| 2629 | A653 | 4fo multi | .50 | .25 |
| 2630 | A653 | 6fo multi | .75 | .30 |

*Nos. 2625-2630 (6)*    2.25   1.35

Exist imperf. Value, set $20.

Hanging Gardens of Semiramis, 6th
Century B.C., Map showing
Babylon — A654

Seven Wonders of the Ancient World (and
Map): 60f, Temple of Artemis, Ephesus, 6th
century B.C. 1fo, Zeus, by Phidias, Olympia.
2fo, Tomb of Maussolos, Halikarnassos, 3rd
century B.C. 3fo, Colossos of Rhodes. 4fo,
Pharos Lighthouse, Alexandria, 3rd century
B.C. 5fo, Pyramids, 26th-24th centuries B.C.

**1980, Feb. 29**    **Litho.**    *Perf. 12x11½*

| | | | | |
|---|---|---|---|---|
| 2631 | A654 | 40f multi | .20 | .20 |
| 2632 | A654 | 60f multi | .20 | .20 |
| 2633 | A654 | 1fo multi | .20 | .20 |
| 2634 | A654 | 2fo multi | .30 | .20 |
| 2635 | A654 | 3fo multi | .40 | .25 |
| 2636 | A654 | 4fo multi | .60 | .35 |
| 2637 | A654 | 5fo multi | .85 | .60 |

*Nos. 2631-2637 (7)*    2.75   2.00

Exist imperf. Value, set $25.

Tihany Benedictine Abbey and
Deed — A655

**1980, Mar. 19**    **Litho.**    *Perf. 12*

| | | | | |
|---|---|---|---|---|
| 2638 | A655 | 1fo multi | .20 | .20 |

Benedictine Abbey, Tihany, 925th anniversary of deed (oldest document in Hungarian).
Exists imperf. Value $4.

Gabor
Bethlen,
Copperplate
Print — A656

**1980, Mar. 19**

| | | | | |
|---|---|---|---|---|
| 2639 | A656 | 1fo multi | .20 | .20 |

Gabor Bethlen (1580-1629), Prince of Transylvania (1613-29) and King of Hungary
(1620-29).
Exists imperf. Value $5.

Easter Casket of Garamszentbenedek, 15th Century (Restoration) — A657

**1980, Mar. 19**
| | | | | |
|---|---|---|---|---|
| 2640 | A657 | 1fo shown | .20 | .20 |
| 2641 | A657 | 2fo Three Marys | .25 | .25 |
| 2642 | A657 | 3fo Apostle James | .35 | .35 |
| 2643 | A657 | 4fo Thaddeus | .55 | .55 |
| 2644 | A657 | 5fo Andrew | .75 | .55 |
| | | *Nos. 2640-2644 (5)* | 2.10 | 1.90 |

Exist imperf. Value, set $20.

Liberation from Fascism, 35th Anniversary A658

**1980, Apr. 3    Litho.    Perf. 12**
| | | | | |
|---|---|---|---|---|
| 2645 | A658 | 1fr multi | .20 | .20 |

Exists imperf. Value $4.

Jozsef Attila, Poet and Lyricist — A659

**1980, Apr. 11**
| | | | | |
|---|---|---|---|---|
| 2646 | A659 | 1fo rose car & olive | .20 | .20 |

Exists imperf. Value $4.
See No. 2675.

Hungarian Postal Museum, 50th anniv. — A660

**1980, Apr. 28    Perf. 11½x12**
| | | | | |
|---|---|---|---|---|
| 2647 | A660 | 1fo multi | 1.90 | 1.50 |

Features Hungary No. 386a.
Exists imperf. Value $30.

Two Pence Blue, Mounted Guardsman, London 1980 Emblem — A661

**1980, Apr. 30    Perf. 11½x12**
| | | | | |
|---|---|---|---|---|
| 2648 | A661 | 3fo multi | 1.00 | 1.00 |

London 1980 International Stamp Exhibition, May 6-14. No. 2648 issued in sheets of 3 stamps and 3 labels showing London 1980 emblem and arms of city. Size: 104x125mm.
Exists imperf. Value: single with label $6; sheetlet $20.

Norway No. B51, Mother with Child, by Gustav Vigeland — A662

**1980, June 9    Litho.    Perf. 11½x12**
| | | | | |
|---|---|---|---|---|
| 2649 | A662 | 3fo multi | 1.00 | 1.00 |

NORWEX '80 Stamp Exhibition, Oslo, June 13-22. No. 2649 issued in sheets of 3 stamps and 3 labels showing NORWEX emblem. Size: 108x125mm.
Exists imperf. Value: single with label $6; sheetlet $19.

Margit Kaffka (1880-1918), Writer — A663

**1980, June 9    Perf. 12**
| | | | | |
|---|---|---|---|---|
| 2650 | A663 | 1fo blk & pur, *cr* | .25 | .20 |

Exists imperf. Value $4.

Zoltan Schönherz (1905-42), Anti-fascist Martyr — A664

**1980, July 25    Litho.**
| | | | | |
|---|---|---|---|---|
| 2652 | A664 | 1fo multi | .20 | .20 |

Exists imperf. Value $4.

Dr. Endre Hogyes and Congress Emblem A665

**1980, July 25**
| | | | | |
|---|---|---|---|---|
| 2653 | A665 | 1fo multi | .20 | .20 |

28th International Congress of Physiological Sciences, Budapest, Dr. Hogyes (1847-1906) first described equilibrium reflex-curve and modified Pasteur's rabies vaccine.
Exists imperf. Value $4.

Decanter, c. 1850 — A666

**1980, Sept.    Litho.    Perf. 12**
| | | | | |
|---|---|---|---|---|
| 2654 | A666 | 1fo shown | .25 | .25 |
| 2655 | A666 | 2fo Decorated glass | .35 | .35 |
| 2656 | A666 | 3fo Stem glass | .65 | .65 |
| | | *Nos. 2654-2656 (3)* | 1.25 | 1.25 |

**Souvenir Sheet**
| | | | | |
|---|---|---|---|---|
| 2657 | A666 | 10fo Pecs glass | 2.50 | 2.25 |

53rd Stamp Day.
Exist imperf. Value: set $15; souvenir sheet $20.

Bertalan Por, Self-portrait A667

**1980, Nov. 4    Litho.    Perf. 12**
| | | | | |
|---|---|---|---|---|
| 2658 | A667 | 1fo Artist (1880-1964) | .35 | .20 |

Exists imperf. Value $4.

Graylag Goose — A668

**1980, Nov. 11    Perf. 11½x12**
| | | | | |
|---|---|---|---|---|
| 2659 | A668 | 40f shown | .20 | .20 |
| 2660 | A668 | 60f Black-crowned night heron | .20 | .20 |
| 2661 | A668 | 1fo Shoveler | .20 | .20 |
| 2662 | A668 | 2fo Chlidonias leucopterus | .30 | .20 |
| 2663 | A668 | 4fo Great crested grebe | .60 | .30 |
| 2664 | A668 | 6fo Black-necked stilt | 1.00 | .50 |
| | | *Nos. 2659-2664 (6)* | 2.50 | 1.60 |

**Souvenir Sheet**
| | | | | |
|---|---|---|---|---|
| 2665 | A668 | 20fo Great white heron | 4.25 | 4.00 |

European Nature Protection Year. No. 2665 contains one stamp (37x59mm).
Exist imperf. Value: set $30; souvenir sheet $40.

Dove on Map of Europe — A669

**1980, Nov. 11    Perf. 12½x11½**
| | | | | |
|---|---|---|---|---|
| 2666 | A669 | 20fo multi | 4.50 | 4.00 |

European Security and Cooperation Conference, Madrid.
Exists imperf. Value $40.

Johannes Kepler and Model of his Theory — A670

**1980, Nov. 21    Litho.    Perf. 12**
| | | | | |
|---|---|---|---|---|
| 2667 | A670 | 1fo multi | .35 | .20 |

Johannes Kepler (1571-1630), German astronomer, 350th anniversary of death. No. 2667 printed se-tenant with label showing rocket and satellites orbiting earth.
Exists imperf. Value, single with label $10.

Karoly Kisfaludy (1788-1830), Poet and Dramatist A671

**1980, Nov. 21**
| | | | | |
|---|---|---|---|---|
| 2668 | A671 | 1fo brn red & dull brn | .20 | .20 |

Exists imperf. Value $4.

UN Headquarters, New York — A672

UN membership, 25th anniversary.

**Photogravure and Engraved**
**1980, Dec. 12    Perf. 11½x12**
| | | | | |
|---|---|---|---|---|
| 2669 | A672 | 40f shown | .20 | .20 |
| 2670 | A672 | 60f Geneva headquarters | .20 | .20 |
| 2671 | A672 | 1fo Vienna headquarters | .25 | .20 |
| 2672 | A672 | 2fo UN & Hungary flags | .30 | .20 |
| 2673 | A672 | 4fo UN, Hungary arms | .55 | .35 |
| 2674 | A672 | 6fo World map | .90 | .55 |
| | | *Nos. 2669-2674 (6)* | 2.40 | 1.70 |

Exist imperf. Value, set $30.

**Attila Type of 1980**

Ferenc Erdei (1910-71), economist & statesman.

**1980, Dec. 23    Litho.    Perf. 12**
| | | | | |
|---|---|---|---|---|
| 2675 | A659 | 1fo dk green & brown | .20 | .20 |

Exists imperf. Value $4.

Bela Szanto — A674

Count Lajos Batthyany A675

**1981, Jan. 31**    **Litho.**    **Perf. 12**
2676 A674 1fo multi    .20 .20

Bela Szanto (1881-1951), labor movement leader.
Exists imperf. Value $4.
See Nos. 2698, 2724, 2767.

**1981, Feb. 14**
2677 A675 1fo multi    .20 .20

Count Lajos Batthyany (1806-1849), prime minister, later executed.
Exists imperf. Value $4.

Bela Bartok (1881-1945), Composer A677

Design: b, Cantata Profana illustration.

**1981, Mar. 25**    **Litho.**    **Perf. 12½**
2685    Sheet of 2    2.50 2.50
   a.-b. A677 10fo any single    1.25 1.25

Exists imperf. Value $30.

Telephone Exchange System Cent. — A678

**1981, Apr. 29**    **Litho.**    **Perf. 12**
2686 A678 2fo multi    .25 .20

Exists imperf. Value $4.

Belling Stag — A679

**1981, Apr. 29**
2687 A679 2fo multi    .25 .20

Exists imperf. Value $4.

Flag of the House of Arpad, 11th Cent. A680

**1981, Apr. 29**
2688 A680 40f shown    .20 .20
2689 A680 60f Hunyadi family, 15th cent.    .20 .20
2690 A680 1fo Gabor Bethlen, 1600    .20 .20
2691 A680 2fo Ferenc Rakoczi II, 1716    .25 .20
2692 A680 4fo Honved, 1848    .60 .25
2693 A680 6fo Troop flag, 1919    .80 .35
   Nos. 2688-2693 (6)    2.25 1.40

Exist imperf. Value, set $20.

Red Cross and Ambulance Vehicles A681

Map of Europe and J. Henry Dunant (Red Cross Founder) — A682

**1981, May 4**
2694 A681 2fo multi    .25 .20
   **Souvenir Sheet**
   **Perf. 12½x11½**
2695 A682 20fo multi    2.50 2.50

Hungarian Red Cross cent. (2fo); 3rd European Red Cross Conf., Budapest, May 4-7 (20fo).
Exist imperf. Value: single $5; souvenir sheet $30.

   **Souvenir Sheet**

1933 WIPA Exhibition Seals — A683

**1981, May 15**    **Perf. 12x12½**
2696    Sheet of 4    2.75 2.75
   a.-d. A683 5fo any single    .65 .65

WIPA 1981 Phil. Exhib., Vienna, May 22-31.
Exists imperf. Value $30.

Stephenson and his Nonpareil — A684

**1981, June 12**    **Litho.**    **Perf. 12**
2697 A684 2fo multi    .25 .20

George Stephenson (1781-1848), British railroad engineer, birth bicentenary.
Exists imperf. Value $7.

**Famous Hungarians Type**
Bela Vago (1881-1939), anti-fascist martyr.

**1981, Aug. 7**    **Litho.**    **Perf. 12**
2698 A674 2fo ocher & brn ol    .25 .20

Exists imperf. Value $4.

Alexander Fleming (1881-1955), Discoverer of Penicillin — A686

**1981, Aug. 7**
2699 A686 2fo multi    .25 .20

Exists imperf. Value $7.

Bridal Chest A687

Designs: Bridal chests.

**1981, Sept. 12**    **Litho.**    **Perf. 12**
2700 A687 1fo Szentgal, 18th cent.    .20 .20
2701 A687 2fo Hodmezovasarhely, 19th cent.    .30 .20
   **Souvenir Sheet**
2702 A687 10fo Bacs County, 17th cent.    1.75 1.75

54th Stamp Day. No. 2702 contains one stamp (44x25mm).
Exist imperf. Values: Nos. 2700-2701 $8; No. 2702 $25.

Calvinist College, Papa, 450th Anniv. A688

**1981, Oct. 3**    **Litho.**    **Perf. 12**
2703 A688 2fo multi    .25 .20

Exists imperf. Value $4.

World Food Day — A689

**1981, Oct. 16**
2704 A689 2fo multi    .25 .20

Exists imperf. Value $7.

Passenger Ship Rakoczi, 1964, No. 1834 — A690

Sidewheelers and Hungarian stamps.

**1981, Nov. 25**    **Perf. 12x11½**
2705 A690 1fo Franz I, #1828    .20 .20
2706 A690 1fo Arpad, #1829    .20 .20
2707 A690 2fo Szechenyi, #1830    .30 .20
2708 A690 2fo Grof Szechenyi Istvan, #1831    .30 .20

2709 A690 4fo Sofia, #1832    .65 .30
2710 A690 6fo Felszabadulas, #1833    .95 .50
2711 A690 8fo shown    1.25 .65
   Nos. 2705-2711 (7)    3.85 2.25
   **Souvenir Sheet**
   **Perf. 13**
2712 A690 20fo Hydrofoil Solyom, #1830    3.00 3.00

European Danube Commission, 125th anniv.
Exist imperf. Value: set $30; souvenir sheet $35.

   **Souvenir Sheet**

Slovakian Natl. Costumes — A691

   **Perf. 12½x11½**
**1981, Nov. 18**    **Litho.**
2713    Sheet of 4    2.00 1.90
   a. A691 1fo shown    .20 .20
   b. A691 2fo German    .40 .35
   c. A691 3fo Croatian    .60 .60
   d. A691 4fo Romanian    .80 .75

Exists imperf. Value $30.

Christmas 1981 — A692

Sculptures: 1fo, Mary Nursing the Infant Jesus, by Margit Kovacs. 2fo, Madonna of Csurgo.

**1981, Dec. 4**    **Perf. 12½x11½**
2714 A692 1fo multi    .20 .20
2715 A692 2fo multi    .40 .20

Exist imperf. Value, set $8.

Pen Pals, by Norman Rockwell A693

**1981, Dec. 29**    **Perf. 11½x12**
Norman Rockwell Illustrations.
2716 A693 1fo shown    .20 .20
2717 A693 2fo Courting Under the Clock at Midnight    .20 .20
2718 A693 2fo Maiden Voyage    .20 .20
2719 A693 4fo Threading the Needle    .45 .25
   Nos. 2716-2719,C435-C437 (7)    3.10 2.50

Exist imperf. Value, set (7) $25.

## Souvenir Sheet

La Toilette, by Pablo Picasso (1881-1973) — A694

**1981, Dec. 29   Litho.   Perf. 11½**
2720  A694  20fo multicolored      3.50  3.50
　　　Exists imperf. Value $70.

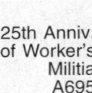

25th Anniv. of Worker's Militia A695

**1982, Jan. 26   Litho.   Perf. 12**
2721  A695  1fo Shooting practice      .20  .20
2722  A695  4fo Members, 3 generations      .50  .35
　　　Exist imperf. Value, set $8.

10th World Trade Union Congress — A696

**1982, Feb. 12   Litho.   Perf. 12x11½**
2723  A696  2fo multicolored      .25  .20
　　　Exists imperf. Value $4.

### Famous Hungarians Type
Gyula Alpri (1882-1944), anti-fascist martyr.

**1982, Mar. 24   Perf. 12**
2724  A674  2fo multicolored      .25  .20
　　　Exists imperf. Value $4.

Robert Koch — A698

**1982, Mar. 24   Litho.   Perf. 12**
2725  A698  2fo multicolored      .25  .20
　　　TB Bacillus centenary.
　　　Exists imperf. Value $4.

1982 World Cup — A699

Designs: Hungary in competition with other World Cup teams.
#2733: a, Barcelona Stadium. b, Madrid Stadium.

**1982, Apr. 16   Perf. 11**
2726  A699  1fo Egypt, 1934      .20  .20
2727  A699  1fo Italy, 1938      .20  .20
2728  A699  2fo Germany, 1954      .20  .20
2729  A699  2fo Mexico, 1958      .20  .20
2730  A699  4fo England, 1962      .45  .25
2731  A699  6fo Brazil, 1966      .70  .40
2732  A699  8fo Argentina, 1978      .90  .55
　　　Nos. 2726-2732 (7)      2.85  2.00

**Souvenir Sheet**
2733  　　　Sheet of 2      3.00  3.00
a.-b.  A699  10fo any single      1.40  1.40
　　　No. 2733 contains 44x44mm stamps.
　　　Exist imperf. Value: set $22.75; souvenir sheet $30.

European Table Tennis Championship, Budapest, Apr. 17-25 — A700

**1982, Apr. 16   Litho.   Perf. 11½x12**
2734  A700  2fo multi      .25  .20
　　　Exists imperf. Value $5.50.

Roses A701

25 Years of Space Travel — A702

**1982, Apr. 30   Perf. 12**
2735  A701  1fo Pascali      .20  .20
2736  A701  1fo Michele Meilland      .20  .20
2737  A701  2fo Diorama      .30  .20
2738  A701  2fo Wendy Cussons      .30  .20
2739  A701  3fo Blue Moon      .40  .25
2740  A701  3fo Invitation      .40  .25
2741  A701  4fo Tropicana      .60  .30
　　　Nos. 2735-2741 (7)      2.40  1.60

**Souvenir Sheet**
2742  A701  10fo Bouquet      2.50  2.50
　　　No. 2742 contains one stamp (34x59mm, perf. 11).
　　　Exist imperf. Value: set $25; souvenir sheet $40.

**1982, May 18   Photo.   Perf. 11½**
2743  A702  1fo Columbia shuttle, 1981      .20  .20
2744  A702  1fo Armstrong, Apollo 11, 1969      .20  .20
2745  A702  2fo A. Leonov, Voskhod 2, 1965      .30  .20
2746  A702  2fo Yuri Gagarin, Vostok      .30  .20
2747  A702  4fo Laika, Sputnik 2, 1957      .55  .35
2748  A702  4fo Sputnik I, 1957      .55  .35
2749  A702  6fo Space researcher K.E. Tsiolkovsky      .90  .50
　　　Nos. 2743-2749 (7)      3.00  2.00
　　　Exist imperf. Value, set $20.

A703

**1982, May 7   Litho.   Perf. 12**
2750  A703  2fo multi      .50  .20
　　　George Dimitrov (1882-1947), 1st prime minister of Bulgaria. SOZPHILEX '82 Stamp Exhib., Sofia, Bulgaria, May. No. 2750 se-tenant with label showing Bulgarian 1300th anniv. emblems.
　　　Exists imperf. Value, with label $10.

Diosgyor paper mill, bicent. — A704

**1982, May 27   Litho.   Perf. 12x11½**
2751  A704  2fo multi      .25  .20
　　　Exists imperf. Value $4.

First Rubik's Cube World Championship, Budapest, June 5 — A705

**1982, June 4   Perf. 11½x12**
2752  A705  2fo multi      .25  .20
　　　Exists imperf. Value $8.

## Souvenir Sheet

George Washington, by F. Kemmelmeyer — A706

Washington's 250th Birth Anniv.: a, Michael Kovats de Fabricy (1724-1779), Cavalry Commandant, by Sandor Finta.

**1982, July 2   Litho.   Perf. 11**
2753  A706  Sheet of 2      2.50  2.50
a.-b.  5fo any single      .75  .75
　　　Exists imperf. Value $25.

World Hematology Congress, Budapest — A707

Zirc Abbey, 800th Anniv. — A708

**1982, July 30   Perf. 12½x11½**
2754  A707  2fo multi      .25  .20
　　　Exists imperf. Value $4.

**1982, Aug. 19   Perf. 11½x12**
2755  A708  2fo multi      .25  .20
　　　Exists imperf. Value $4.

KNER Printing Office, Gyoma, Centenary — A709

**1982, Sept. 23   Litho.   Perf. 12x11½**
2756  A709  2fo Emblem      .25  .20
　　　Exists imperf. Value $4.

AGROFILA '82 Intl. Agricultural Stamp Exhibition, Godollo — A710

**1982, Sept. 24   Perf. 11½x12**
2757  A710  5fo Map      1.00  .95
　　　Issued in sheets of 3 stamps and 3 labels showing Godollo Agricultural University, emblem. Size: 109x127mm.
　　　Exist imperf. Value: single with label $6; sheetlet $20.

Public Transportation Sesquicentennial — A711

**1982, Oct. 5   Litho.   Perf. 12x11½**
2758  A711  2fo multi      .25  .20
　　　Exists imperf. Value $20.

Vuk and a Bird — A712

Scenes from Vuk the Fox Cub, Cartoon by Attila Dargay.

**1982, Nov. 11**     *Perf. 12½*
2759 A712 1fo shown    .20   .20
2760 A712 1fo Dogs    .20   .20
2761 A712 2fo Rooster    .25   .20
2762 A712 2fo Owl    .25   .20
2763 A712 4fo Geese    .50   .30
2764 A712 6fo Frog    .70   .55
2765 A712 8fo Master fox    1.00   .70
   *Nos. 2759-2765 (7)*    3.10   2.35
    Exist imperf. Value, set $22.

Engineering Education Bicentenary A713

**1982, Oct. 13**     *Perf. 12*
2766 A713 2fo Budapest Poly-
    technical Univ.    .25   .20
    Exists imperf. Value $4.

### Famous Hungarians Type

Gyorgy Boloni (1882-1959), writer and journalist.

**1982, Oct. 29**
2767 A674 2fo multi    .25   .20
    Exists imperf. Value $4.

October Revolution, 65th Anniv. — A715

Works of Art in Hungarian Chapel, Vatican — A716

**1982, Nov. 5**   *Litho.*   *Perf. 11½x12*
2768 A715 5fo Lenin    .75   .40
    Exists imperf. Value $7.

**1982, Nov. 30**     *Perf. 12x11½*
Designs: No. 2769, St. Stephen, first King of Hungary (1001-1038). No. 2770, Pope Sylvester II making donation to St. Stephen. No. 2771, Pope Callixtus III ordering noon victory bell ringing by St. John of Capistrano, 1456. No. 2772, Pope Paul VI showing Cardinal Lekai location of Hungarian Chapel. No. 2773, Pope John Paul II consecrating chapel, 1980. No. 2774, Madonna and Child. Nos. 2769, 2774 sculptures by Imre Varga; others by Amerigo Tot. Nos. 2770-2773, size 37x18mm,

in continuous design in block of 4 between Nos. 2769 and 2774.
2769 A716 2fo multi    .40   .40
2770 A716 2fo multi    .40   .40
2771 A716 2fo multi    .40   .40
2772 A716 2fo multi    .40   .40
2773 A716 2fo multi    .40   .40
2774 A716 2fo multi    .40   .40
   *a.*   Block of 6, #2769-2774   2.60   2.60
    Exist imperf. Value, block $20.

### Souvenir Sheet

Zoltan Kodaly (1882-1967), Composer — A717

**1982, Dec. 16**     *Perf. 11½*
2775 A717 20fo multi    2.75   2.75
    Exists imperf. Value $25.

A718

    *Perf. 12½x11½*
**1982, Dec. 16**     *Litho.*
2776 A718 2fo multi    .35   .20
    New Year 1983.
    Exists imperf. Value $4.

A719

**1982, Dec. 29**     *Perf. 11½x12½*
Design: Johann Wolfgang Goethe (1749-1832), German poet, by Heinrich Kolbe.

### Souvenir Sheet

2777 A719 20fo multi    2.75   2.75
    Exists imperf. Value $37.50.

10th Anniv. of Postal Code — A720

**1983, Jan. 24**     *Perf. 11½x12*
2778 A720 2fo multi    .25   .20
    Exists imperf. Value $4.

3rd Budapest Spring Festival, Mar. 18-27 A721

**1983, Mar. 18**   *Litho.*   *Perf. 12x11½*
2779 A721 2fo Ship of Peace, by
    Engre Szasz    .25   .20
    Exists imperf. Value $4.

Gyula Juhasz (1883-1937), Poet — A722

**1983, Apr. 15**     *Perf. 12*
2780 A722 2fo multi    .25   .20
    Exists imperf. Value $4.

City of Szentgotthard, 800th Anniv. — A723

**1983, May 4**   *Litho.*   *Perf. 11½*
2781 A723 2fo Monastery, seal,
    1489    .25   .20
    Exists imperf. Value $4.

Malomto Lake, Tapolca — A724

**1983, May 17**     *Perf. 11½x12*
2782 A724 5fo multi    .80   .80
    TEMBAL '83 Intl. Topical Stamp Exhibition, Basel, May 21-29. Issued in sheets of 3 stamps and 3 labels.
    Exists imperf. Value: single with label $5.50; sheetlet $20.

### Souvenir Sheet

5th Interparliamentary Union Conference on European Cooperation, Budapest, May 30-June 5 — A725

**1983, May 30**   *Litho.*   *Perf. 12½*
2783 A725 20fo Budapest Parlia-
    ment    3.50   3.25
    Exists imperf. Value $25.

Jeno Hamburger (1883-1936) A726

**1983, May 31**     *Perf. 12*
2784 A726 2fo multi    .45   .20
    Exists imperf. Value $4.

Lady with Unicorn, by Raphael (1483-1517) A727

Paintings: No. 2786, Joan of Aragon. No. 2787, Granduca Madonna. No. 2788, Madonna and Child with St. John. 4fo, La Muta. 6fo, La Valeta. 8fo, La Fornarina. 20fo, Esterhazy Madonna.

    *Perf. 11½x12½*
**1983, June 29**     *Litho.*
2785 A727 1fo multi    .20   .20
2786 A727 1fo multi    .20   .20
2787 A727 2fo multi    .25   .20
2788 A727 2fo multi    .25   .20
2789 A727 4fo multi    .45   .30
2790 A727 6fo multi    .65   .30
2791 A727 8fo multi    .75   .45
   *Nos. 2785-2791 (7)*    2.75   1.85
### Souvenir Sheet
2792 A727 20fo multi    3.00   3.00
    No. 2792 contains one stamp (24x37mm).
    Exist imperf. Value: set $25; souvenir sheet $25.

Simon Bolivar (1783-1830) A728

**1983, July 22**   *Litho.*   *Perf. 12*
2793 A728 2fo multi    .25   .20
    Exists imperf. Value $4.

Istvan Vagi (1883-1940), Anti-fascist Martyr A729

**1983, July 22**     **Perf. 11½x12½**
2794 A729 2fo multi    .45   .20

Exists imperf. Value $4.

68th World Esperanto Congress, Budapest, July 30-Aug. 6 — A730

**1983, July 29**     **Perf. 12**
2795 A730 2fo multi    .25   .20

Exists imperf. Value $5.

**Souvenir Sheet**

Martin Luther (1483-1546) — A731

**1983, Aug. 12**     **Perf. 12½**
2796 A731 20fo multi    2.75   2.50

Exists imperf. Value $25.

Birds — A732

Designs: Protected birds of prey and World Wildlife Fund emblem.

**1983, Aug. 18**     **Perf. 11½x12**
2797 A732 1fo Aquila heliaca   .20   .20
2798 A732 1fo Aquila pomarina   .20   .20
2799 A732 2fo Haliaetus albicilla   .25   .20
2800 A732 2fo Falco vespertinus   .25   .20
2801 A732 4fo Falco cherrug   .45   .30
2802 A732 6fo Buteo lagopus   .75   .35
2803 A732 8fo Buteo buteo   .90   .75
    Nos. 2797-2803 (7)   3.00   2.20

Exist imperf. Value, set $20.

29th Intl. Apicultural Congress, Budapest, Aug. 25-31 — A733

**1983, Aug. 25**     **Perf. 12**
2804 A733 1fo Bee collecting pollen   .20   .20

Exists imperf. Value $4.

Fruit, by Bela Czobel (1883-1976) — A734

**1983, Sept. 15**    **Litho.**    **Perf. 12x11½**
2805 A734 2fo multi    .25   .20

Exists imperf. Value $4.

World Communications Year — A735

No. 2806, Telecommunications, Earth Satellite. No. 2807, Intersputnik Earth Station. 2fo, TMM-81 Telephone Service. 3fo, Intelligent Terminal System. 5fo, OCR Optical Reading Instrument. 8fo, Teletext. 20fo, Molniya Communications Satellite.

**1983, Oct. 7**    **Litho.**    **Perf. 11½x12**
2806 A735 1fo multi   .20   .20
2807 A735 1fo multi   .20   .20
2808 A735 2fo multi   .25   .20
2809 A735 3fo multi   .40   .25
2810 A735 5fo multi   .70   .40
2811 A735 8fo multi   1.10   .65
    Nos. 2806-2811 (6)   2.85   1.90

**Souvenir Sheet**
**Perf. 12x12½**
2812 A735 20fo multi    3.00   3.00

Exist imperf. Value: set $20; souvenir sheet $25.

34th Intl. Astronautical Federation Congress — A736

**1983, Oct. 10**    **Photo.**    **Perf. 12**
2813 A736 2fo multi    .25   .20

Exists imperf. Value $4.

SOZPHILEX 83, Moscow — A737

**1983, Oct. 14**    **Litho.**    **Perf. 12**
2814 A737 2fo Kremlin    .50   .50

Issued in sheets of 3 stamps and 3 labels showing emblem. Size: 101x133mm.
Exists imperf. Value: single with label $6; sheetlet $20.

Mihaly Babits (1883-1941), Poet and Translator — A738

**1983, Nov. 25**
2815 A738 2fo multi    .25   .20

Exists imperf. Value $4.

**Souvenir Sheet**

European Security and Cooperation Conference, Madrid — A739

**Perf. 12½x11½**
**1983, Nov. 10**       **Litho.**
2816 A739 20fo multi    3.75   3.75

Exists imperf. Value $23.

1984 Winter Olympics, Sarajevo — A740

Designs: Ice dancers representing the seven phases of a figure cut.

**1983, Dec. 22**    **Litho.**    **Perf. 12x12½**
2817 A740 1fo Emblem upper right   .20   .20
2818 A740 1fo Emblem upper left   .20   .20
2819 A740 2fo Arms extended   .25   .20
2820 A740 2fo Arms bent   .25   .20
2821 A740 4fo Man looking down   .55   .30
2822 A740 4fo Girl looking up   .55   .30
2823 A740 6fo multi   .85   .45
   a.   Strip of 7, #2817-2823   3.00   2.00

**Souvenir Sheet**
**Perf. 12½**
2824 A740 20fo multi    3.00   3.00

No. 2824 contains one 49x39mm stamp.
Exist imperf. Value: strip $25; souvenir sheet $25.

Christmas A741

Resorts and Spas — A742

Designs: 1fo, Madonna with Rose, Kassa, 1500. 2fo, Altar piece, Csikmenasag, 1543.

**1983, Dec. 13**    **Litho.**    **Perf. 11½x12**
2825 A741 1fo multi   .20   .20
2826 A741 2fo multi   .30   .20

Exist imperf. Value, set $5.

**1983, Dec. 18**
2827 A742 1fo Zanka, Lake Balaton   .20   .20
2828 A742 2fo Hajduszoboszlo   .30   .20
2829 A742 5fo Heviz   .70   .35
    Nos. 2827-2829 (3)   1.20   .75

Exist imperf. Value, set $15.

Virgin with Six Saints, by Giovanni Battista Tiepolo — A743

Rest During Flight into Egypt, by Giovanni Domenico Tiepolo — A744

Paintings Stolen and Later Recovered, Museum of Fine Arts, Budapest: b, Esterhazy Madonna, by Raphael. c, Portrait of Giorgione, 16th cent. d, Portrait of a Woman, by Tintoretto. e, Pietro Bempo, by Raphael. f, Portrait of a Man, by Tintoretto.

**1984, Feb. 16**     **Perf. 12½x12**
2839   Sheet of 7   3.75   3.75
   a.-f.   A743 2fo multi   .35
   g.   A744 8fo multi   1.50

Exists imperf. Value $50.

Energy Conservation A745

**1984, Mar. 30**    **Litho.**    **Perf. 11½x12**
2840 A745 1fo multi    .25   .20

Exists imperf. Value $7.

Sandor Korosi Csoma (1784-1842), Master of Tibetan Philology A746

**1984, Mar. 30**     **Perf. 11½x12½**
2841 A746 2fo multi    .25   .20

Stamps with silver inscription and with back inscription "Gift of the Hungarian Post" issued to members of Natl. Fed. of Hungarian Philatelists. Value $1.50.
Exists imperf. Value $4.

## Miniature Sheet

No. 1900 — A747

Designs: b, No. 1346. c, No. 1259.

**1984, Apr. 20    Litho.    Perf. 12x11½**
2842    Sheet of 3 + 3 labels    2.75    2.75
a.-c.    A747 4fo multi    .70

Espana '84; Ausipex '84; Philatelia '84.
Exists imperf. Value $25.

Post-Roman Archaeological Discoveries — A748

#2843, Round gold disc hair ornaments, Rakamaz. #2844, Saber belt plates, Szolnok-Strazsahalom and Galgocz. #2845, Silver disc hair ornaments, Sarospatak. #2846, Swords. 4fo, Silver and gold bowl, Ketpo. 6fo, Bone walking stick handles, Hajdudorog and Szabadbattyan. 8fo, Ivory saddle bow, Izsak; bit, stirrups, Muszka.

**1984, May 15    Perf. 12**
2843    A748 1fo dk brn & tan    .20    .20
2844    A748 1fo dk brn & tan    .20    .20
2845    A748 2fo dk brn & tan    .25    .20
2846    A748 2fo dk brn & tan    .25    .20
2847    A748 4fo dk brn & tan    .50    .20
2848    A748 6fo dk brn & tan    .75    .30
2849    A748 8fo dk brn & tan    1.00    .40
    Nos. 2843-2849 (7)    3.15    1.70

Exist imperf. Value, set $20.

View of Cracow — A749

**1984, May 21    Litho.    Perf. 12½x11½**
2850    A749 2fo multi    .25    .20

Permanent Committee of Posts and Telecommunications, 25th Session, Cracow. Exists imperf. Value $4.

Butterflies A750

**1984, June 7    Perf. 11½x12**
2851    A750 1fo Epiphille dilecta    .20    .20
2852    A750 1fo Agra sara    .20    .20
2853    A750 2fo Morpho cypris    .25    .20
2854    A750 2fo Ancylusis formossissima    .25    .20
2855    A750 4fo Danaus chrysippus    .50    .20
2856    A750 6fo Catagramma cynosura    .75    .30

2857    A750 8fo Ornithoptera paradisea    1.00    .45
    Nos. 2851-2857 (7)    3.15    1.75
    Exist imperf. Value, set $25.

A751                    A752

Archer, by Kisfaludy Strobl (1884-1975).

**1984, July 26    Litho.    Perf. 12½x11½**
2858    A751 2fo multicolored    .25    .20
    Exists imperf. Value $4.

**1984, July 26**
2859    A752 2fo multicolored    .25    .20

Akos Hevesi (1884-1937), revolutionary. See Nos. 2884-2885, 2910, 2915, 2962. Exists imperf. Value $4.

Kepes Ujsag Peace Festival A753

Aerobatic Championship A754

**1984, Aug. 3    Litho.    Perf. 12½x11½**
2860    A753 2fo Map, building    .25    .20
    Exists imperf. Value $5.50.

**1984, Aug. 14**
2861    A754 2fo Plane, map    .25    .20
    Exists imperf. Value $4.

Horse Team World Championship, Szilvasvarad, Aug. 17-20 — A755

**1984, Aug. 17    Perf. 12**
2862    A755 2fo Horse-drawn wagon    .25    .20
    Exists imperf. Value $4. Exists imperf. Value $4.

Budapest Riverside Hotels — A756

**1984, Sept.**
2863    A756 1fo Atrium Hyatt    .20    .20
2864    A756 2fo Duna Intercontinental    .25    .20
2865    A756 4fo Forum    .50    .25
2866    A756 4fo Thermal Hotel, Margaret Isld.    .50    .25
2867    A756 5fo Hilton    .70    .35
2868    A756 8fo Gellert    1.00    .50
    Nos. 2863-2868 (6)    3.15    1.75

### Souvenir Sheet
2869    A756 20fo Hilton, diff.    2.75    2.75

Exist imperf. Value: set $20; souvenir sheet $25.

14th Conference of Postal Ministers, Budapest — A757

**1984, Sept. 10    Perf. 12½x11½**
2870    A757 2fo Building, post horn    .25    .20
    Exists imperf. Value $4.

57th Stamp Day A758

**1984, Sept. 21    Perf. 12**
2871    A758 1fo Four-handled vase, Zsolnay    .20    .20
2872    A758 2fo Platter, vert.    .80    .20

### Souvenir Sheet
2872A    A758 10fo #19 on cover    1.75    1.75

No. 2872A contains one stamp (44x27mm, perf. 11).
Exist imperf. Value: set $8; souvenir sheet $25.

Edible Mushrooms A759

### Photogravure and Engraved
**1984, Oct.    Perf. 12½x11½**
2873    A759 1fo Boletus edulis    .35    .20
2874    A759 1fo Marasmius oreades    .35    .20
2875    A759 2fo Morchella esculenta    .60    .20
2876    A759 2fo Agaricus campester    .60    .20
2877    A759 3fo Macrolepiota procera    .90    .25
2878    A759 3fo Cantharellus cibarius    .90    .25
2879    A759 4fo Armillariella mellea    1.25    .30
    Nos. 2873-2879 (7)    4.95    1.60
    Exist imperf. Value, set $20.

Budapest Opera House Centenary — A760

**1984, Sept. 27    Perf. 12x11½**
2880    A760 1fo Fresco by Mor Than    .20    .20
2881    A760 2fo Hallway    .25    .20
2882    A760 5fo Auditorium    .65    .30
    Nos. 2880-2882 (3)    1.10    .70

### Souvenir Sheet
2883    A760 20fo Building    2.75    2.75

No. 2883 contains one stamp (49x40mm, perf. 12½).
Exist imperf. Value: set $20; souvenir sheet $25.

### Famous Hungarians Type of 1984

#2884, Bela Balazs, writer (1884-1949); #2885, Kato Haman, labor leader (1884-1936).

**1984, Dec. 3    Litho.    Perf. 12½x11½**
2884    A752 2fo multi    .25    .20
2885    A752 2fo multi    .25    .20
    Exist imperf. Value, set $8.

Madonna and Child, Trensceny A763

**1984, Dec. 17    Litho.    Perf. 11½x12**
2886    A763 1fo multi    .20    .20
    Exists imperf. Value $4.

Owls — A764

### Photogravure and Engraved
**1984, Dec. 28    Perf. 12½x11½**
2887    A764 1fo Athene Noctua    .20    .20
2888    A764 1fo Tyto alba    .20    .20
2889    A764 2fo Strix aluco    .25    .20
2890    A764 2fo Asio otus    .25    .20
2891    A764 4fo Nyctea scadiaca    .45    .30
2892    A764 6fo Strix uralensis    .75    .40
2893    A764 8fo Bubo bubo    .90    .50
    Nos. 2887-2893 (7)    3.00    2.00
    Exist imperf. Value, set $20.

Torah Crown, Buda — A765

19th Cent. Art from Jewish Museum, Budapest.

**1984, Dec.    Litho.    Perf. 12**
2894    A765 1fo shown    .20    .20
2895    A765 1fo Chalice, Moscow    .20    .20
2896    A765 2fo Torah shield, Vienna    .25    .20
2897    A765 2fo Chalice, Warsaw    .25    .20
2898    A765 4fo Container, Augsburg    .55    .20
2899    A765 6fo Candlestick holder, Warsaw    .80    .35
2900    A765 8fo Money box, Pest    1.10    .45
    Nos. 2894-2900 (7)    3.35    1.80
    Exist imperf. Value, set $20.

## Souvenir Sheet

Hungarian Olympic Committee, 90th
Anniv. — A766

**1985, Jan. 2   Photo.   Perf. 12x12½**
2901 A766 20fo Long jump          2.75 2.75
Exists imperf. Value $25.

Novi Sad, Yugoslavia — A767

Danube Bridges: No. 2903, Baja. No. 2904, Arpad Bridge, Budapest. No. 2905, Bratislava, Czechoslovakia. 4fo, Reichsbrucke, Vienna. 6fo, Linz, Austria. 8fo, Regensburg, Federal Rep. of Germany. 20fo, Elizabeth Bridge, Budapest, and map.

**1985, Feb. 12   Litho.   Perf. 12x11½**
2902 A767 1fo multi          .20   .20
2903 A767 1fo multi          .20   .20
2904 A767 2fo multi          .25   .20
2905 A767 2fo multi          .25   .20
2906 A767 4fo multi          .50   .25
2907 A767 6fo multi          .75   .40
2908 A767 8fo multi         1.00   .45
  Nos. 2902-2908 (7)        3.15  1.90

### Souvenir Sheet
**Perf. 12½**
2909 A767 20fo multi        3.00  3.00
Exist imperf. Value: set $20; souvenir sheet $25.

### Famous Hungarians Type of 1984

Design: Laszlo Rudas (1885-1950), communist philosopher.

**1985, Feb. 21          Perf. 12½x11½**
2910 A752 2fo gold & brn     .25   .20
Exists imperf. Value $4.

Intl. Women's
Day, 75th
Anniv.
A769

**1985, Mar. 5   Photo.   Perf. 11½x12½**
2911 A769 2fo gold & multi   .25   .20
Exists imperf. Value $4.

OLYMPHILEX
'85, Lausanne
A770

**1985, Mar. 14   Litho.   Perf. 11½x12**
2912 A770 4fo No. B81        .50   .25
2913 A770 5fo No. B82        .65   .30
Exist imperf. Value, set $12.

## Souvenir Sheet

Liberation of Hungary From German
Occupation Forces, 40th
Anniv. — A771

Design: Liberty Bridge, Budapest and silhouette of the Liberation Monument on Gellert Hill illuminated by fireworks.

**1985, Mar. 28          Perf. 12½**
2914 A771 20fo multi        2.75  2.75
Exists imperf. Value $30.

### Famous Hungarians Type of 1984

Design: Gyorgy Lukacs (1885-1971) communist philosopher, educator.

**1985, Apr. 12          Perf. 12½x11½**
2915 A752 2fo gold & brn     .25   .20
Exists imperf. Value $4.

Totfalusi Bible,
300th
Anniv. — A773

**1985, Apr. 25          Perf. 12**
2916 A773 2fo gold & black   .25   .20
1st Bible printed in Hungarian by Nicolas Totfalusi Kis (1650-1702), publisher, in 1685. Exists imperf. Value $4.

Lorand Eotvos
Univ., 350th
Anniv. — A774

Design: Archbishop Peter Pazmany (1570-1637), founder.

**1985, May 14**
2917 A774 2fo magenta & gray   .50   .20
No. 2917 printed se-tenant with label picturing obverse and reverse of university commemorative medal.
Exists imperf. Value, with label $10.

26th European Boxing Championships,
Budapest — A775

**1985, May 25**
2918 A775 2fo multi          .25   .20
Exists imperf. Value $4.

Intl. Youth
Year — A776

**1985, May 29          Perf. 11½x12**
2919 A776 1fo Girl's soccer       .20   .20
2920 A776 2fo Windsurfing         .20   .20
2921 A776 2fo Aerobic exercise    .20   .20
2922 A776 4fo Karate              .45   .20
2923 A776 4fo Go-kart racing      .45   .20
2924 A776 5fo Hang gliding        .65   .25
2925 A776 6fo Skateboarding       .70   .35
  Nos. 2919-2925 (7)             2.85  1.60
Exist imperf. Value, set $20.

Electro-magnetic High-speed
Railway — A777

EXPO '85, Tsukuba, Japan: futuristic technology.

**1985, May 29          Perf. 12x11½**
2926 A777 2fo shown               .30   .20
2927 A777 4fo Fuyo (robot) Theater   .70   .20
Exist imperf. Value, set $10.

Audubon Birth
Bicentenary
A778

Audubon illustrations

**1985, June 19          Perf. 12**
2928 A778 2fo Colaptes cafer      .30   .20
2929 A778 2fo Bombycilla garrulus   .30   .20
2930 A778 2fo Dryocopus pileatus    .30   .20
2931 A778 4fo Icterus galbula       .55   .30
  Nos. 2928-2931,C446-C447 (6)    2.90  1.75
Exist imperf. Value, set (6) $25.

Mezohegyes Stud Farm,
Bicent. — A779

Horses: No. 2932, Nonius-36, 1883, a dark chestnut. No. 2933, Furioso-23, 1889, a light chestnut. No. 2934, Gidrian-1, 1935, a blond breed. No. 2935, Ramses-3, 1960, gray sporting horse. No. 2936, Krozus-1, 1970, chestnut sporting horse.

**1985, June 28**
2932 A779 1fo multi          .20   .20
2933 A779 2fo multi          .25   .20
2934 A779 4fo multi          .55   .20
2935 A779 4fo multi          .55   .20
2936 A779 6fo multi          .85   .35
  Nos. 2932-2936 (5)        2.40  1.15
Exist imperf. Value, set $20.

Prevention of
Nuclear
War — A780

Design: Illustration of a damaged globe and hands, by Imre Varga (b. 1923), 1973 Kossuth prize-winner.

**1985, June 28          Perf. 11½x12**
2937 A780 2fo multi          .25   .20
Intl. Physician's Movement for the Prevention of Nuclear War, 5th Congress.
Exists imperf. Value $7.

European Music
Year — A781

**1985, July 10          Perf. 11**

Composers and instruments: 1fo, George Frideric Handel (1685-1759), kettle drum, horn. 2fo, Johann Sebastian Bach (1685-1750), Thomas Church organ. No. 2940, Luigi Cherubini (1760-1842), harp, bass viol, baryton. No. 2941, Frederic Chopin (1810-1849), piano, 1817. 5fo, Gustav Mahler (1860-1911), pardessus de viole, kettle drum, double horn. 6fo, Erkel Ferenc (1810-1893), bass tuba, violin.

2938 A781 1fo multi          .20   .20
2939 A781 2fo multi          .25   .20
2940 A781 4fo multi          .50   .20
2941 A781 4fo multi          .50   .20
2942 A781 5fo multi          .65   .25
2943 A781 6fo multi          .75   .30
  Nos. 2938-2943 (6)        2.85  1.35
Exist imperf. Value, set $22.75.

Souvenir Sheet

12th World Youth Festival,
Moscow — A782

**1985, July 22**     **Perf. 12½**
2944 A782 20fo Emblem, Red
Square     2.75 2.50
Exists imperf. Value $37.50.

Souvenir Sheet

Helsinki Agreement, 10th
Anniv. — A783

**1985, Aug. 1**     **Perf. 11**
2945 A783 20fo Finlandia Hall,
Helsinki     3.00 3.00
Exists imperf. Value $37.50.

World Tourism
Day — A784

**Perf. 12½x11½**
**1985, Sept. 27**     **Litho.**
2946 A784 2fo Key, globe, heart   .25 .20
Exists imperf. Value $4.

COMNET
'85 — A785

**1985, Oct. 1**     **Perf. 11½**
2947 A785 4fo Computer terminal .60 .30
3rd Computer Sciences Conference, Budapest, Oct. 1-4.
Exists imperf. Value $4.

Souvenir Sheet

Danube River, Budapest
Bridges — A786

**1985, Oct. 15**     **Perf. 12**
2948 A786 20fo multi     3.25 3.25
European Security and Cooperation Confer-
ence and Cultural Forum, Budapest, Oct. 15-
Nov. 25. Exists inscribed "Kuturalis Forum
Resztvevoi Tiszteletere" in gold on front and
"Gift of the Hungarian Post" on back. Not valid
for postage.
Exists imperf. Value $40.

16-17th Century
Ceramics — A787

1fo, Faience water jar and dispenser, 1609.
2fo, Tankard, 1670. 10fo, Hexagonal medicine
jar, 1774.

**1985, Oct. 18**     **Perf. 12½x11½**
2949 A787 1fo multi     .20 .20
2950 A787 2fo multi     .80 .20
**Souvenir Sheet**
2951 A787 10fo multi     1.75 1.75
EUROPHILEX '85, Oct. 14-31.
Exist imperf. Value: set $10; souvenir sheet
$25.

Italy No. 799,
view of
Rome — A788

**1985, Oct. 21**     **Perf. 12x11½**
2952 A788 5fo multi     .90 .90
Italia '85, Rome, Oct. 25-Nov. 3.
Issued in sheets of 3 stamps and 3 labels
showing emblem.
Exists imperf. Value: single with label $7.50;
sheetlet $22.75.

UN, 40th
Anniv. — A789

**1985, Oct. 24**     **Perf. 11½x12**
2953 A789 4fo Dove, globe, emblem     .50 .30
Exists imperf. Value $4.

Indigenous
Lilies — A790

**Photogravure and Engraved**
**1985, Oct. 28**     **Perf. 12x11½**
2954 A790 1fo Lilium bulbiferum   .20 .20
2955 A790 2fo Lilium martagon   .25 .20
2956 A790 2fo Erythronium dens-
canis     .25 .20
2957 A790 4fo Fritillaria
meleagris     .55 .20
2958 A790 4fo Lilium tigrinum   .55 .20
2959 A790 5fo Hemerocallis lilio-
asphodelus     .70 .30
2960 A790 6fo Bulbocodium
vernum     .85 .35
Nos. 2954-2960 (7)     3.35 1.65
Exists imperf. Value, set $20.

Christmas 1985 — A791

**1985, Nov. 6**   **Litho.**   **Perf. 13½x13**
2961 A791 2fo Youths caroling   .25 .20
Exists imperf. Value $7.

Famous Hungarians Type of 1984
Design: Istvan Ries (1885-1950), Minister of
Justice (1949), labor movement.

**1985, Nov. 11**     **Perf. 12½x11½**
2962 A752 2fo gold & ol brn   .25 .20
Exists imperf. Value $4.

Motorcycle Centenary — A793

**Photogravure & Engraved**
**1985, Dec. 28**     **Perf. 11½x12**
2963 A793 1fo Fantic Sprinter,
1984     .20 .20
2964 A793 2fo Suzuki Katana
GSX, 1983     .20 .20
2965 A793 2fo Harley-Davidson
Duo-Glide, 1960     .20 .20
2966 A793 4fo Rudge-Whitworth,
1935     .45 .20
2967 A793 4fo BMW R47, 1927   .45 .20
2968 A793 5fo NSU, 1910     .60 .20
2969 A793 6fo Daimler, 1885   .70 .25
Nos. 2963-2969 (7)     2.80 1.45
Exist imperf. Value, set $20.

Bela Kun (1886-
1939), Communist
Party
Founder — A794

**Perf. 12½x11½**
**1986, Feb. 20**     **Litho.**
2970 A794 4fo multi     .50 .30
Exist imperf. Value $4.

Souvenir Sheet

US Shuttle Challenger — A795

**1986, Feb. 21**     **Perf. 11½**
2971 A795 20fo multi     3.25 3.25
Memorial to the US astronauts who died
when the Challenger exploded during takeoff,
Jan. 28.
Exist imperf. Value $25.

Halley's
Comet — A796

#2972, US Ice satellite, dinosaurs. #2973,
USSR Vega and Bayeaux tapestry detail,
1066, France. #2974, Japanese Suisei and
German engraving, 1507. #2975, European
Space Agency Giotto and The Three Magi,
tapestry by Giotto. #2976, USSR Astron and
Apianis constellation, 1531. #2977, US space
shuttle and Edmond Halley.

**Perf. 11½x13½**
**1986, Feb. 14**     **Litho.**
2972 A796 2fo multi     .25 .20
2973 A796 2fo multi     .25 .20
2974 A796 2fo multi     .25 .20
2975 A796 4fo multi     .45 .20
2976 A796 4fo multi     .45 .20
2977 A796 6fo multi     .80 .35
Nos. 2972-2977 (6)     2.45 1.35
Exist imperf. Value, set $19.

Seeing-eye Dog,
Red Cross
A797

Soccer
Players in
Blue and Red
Uniforms
A798

**Perf. 12½x11½**
**1986, Mar. 20**     **Litho.**
2978 A797 4fo multi     .50 .20
Assistance for the blind.
Exists imperf. Value $12.

**1986, Apr. 2**     **Perf. 11**
**Color of Uniforms**
2979 A798 2fo shown     .25 .20
2980 A798 2fo blue & green   .25 .20
2981 A798 4fo red & black     .55 .20
2982 A798 4fo yellow & red   .55 .20
2983 A798 4fo yellow & green   .55 .20
2984 A798 6fo orange & white   .75 .30
Nos. 2979-2984 (6)     2.90 1.30

## Souvenir Sheet
### Perf. 12½

**2985** A798 20fo Victors    3.50 3.50

1986 World Cup Soccer Championships, Mexico. No. 2979 contains one stamp (size: 41x32mm). Also exists with added inscription "In honor of the winner . . ." and red control number.
Exist imperf. Value: set $25; souvenir sheet $25.

Buda Castle Cable Railway Station Reopening — A799

**1986, Apr. 30**    **Perf. 11½x12**
**2986** A799 2fo org, brn & pale yel    .40 .20
Exists imperf. Value $4.

A800

A801

AMERIPEX '86, Chicago, May 22-June 1: a, Yankee doodle rose. b, America rose. c, George Washington, statue by Gyula Bezeredy (1858-1935), Budapest.

**1986, Apr. 30**    **Perf. 12½x11½**
**Souvenir Sheet**
**2987**    Sheet of 3    3.25 3.00
*a.-b.* A800 5fo any single    .75 .75
*c.* A800 10fo multi    1.50 1.50
Size of No. 2987c: 27x74mm.
Exists imperf. Value $35.

**1986, May 6**    **Perf. 11½x12**
**2988** A801 4fo Folk dolls    .50 .30
Hungary Days in Tokyo.
Exists imperf. Value $4.

Andras Fay (1786-1864), Author, Politician — A802

### Lithographed and Engraved
**1986, May 29**    **Perf. 12**
**2989** A802 4fo beige & fawn    .65 .30
Printed se-tenant with label picturing First Hungarian Savings Bank Union, founded by Fay.
Exists imperf. Value, with label $10.

Automobile, Cent. A803

#2990, 1961 Ferrari Tipo 156, 1985 race car. #2991, 1932 Alfa Romeo Tipo B, 1984 race car. #2992, 1936 Volkswagen, 1986 Porsche 959. #2993, 1902 Renault 14CV, 1985 Renault 5 GT Turbo. #2994, 1899 Fiat 3½, 1985 Fiat Ritmo. 6fo, 1886 Daimler, 1986 Mercedes-Benz 230SE.

**1986, July 24**    **Litho.**    **Perf. 12**
**2990** A803 2fo multi    .25 .20
**2991** A803 2fo multi    .25 .20
**2992** A803 2fo multi    .25 .20
**2993** A803 4fo multi    .55 .20
**2994** A803 4fo multi    .55 .20
**2995** A803 6fo multi    .85 .35
Nos. 2990-2995 (6)    2.70 1.35
Exists imperf. Value, set $22.

Wasa, 1628, Warship — A804

**1986, Aug. 15**    **Litho.**    **Perf. 11½x12**
**2996** A804 2fo multi    .50 .50
STOCKHOLMIA '86, 8/28-9/7. Printed se-tenant with label (size: 27x34mm) picturing exhibition emblem. Printed in sheets of 3.
Exists imperf. Value: single with label $7; sheetlet $25.

14th Intl. Cancer Congress, Budapest — A805

Design: Moritz Kaposi (1837-1902), Austrian cancer researcher.

**1986, Aug. 21**    **Perf. 12½x11½**
**2997** A805 4fo multicolored    .50 .30
Exists imperf. Value $7.

Recapture of Buda Castle, by Gyula Benzcur (1844-1920) — A806

**1986, Sept. 2**    **Perf. 12**
**2998** A806 4fo multicolored    .50 .30
Recapture of Buda from the Turks, 300th anniv.
Exists imperf. Value $5.50.

Tranquility — A807

Hope — A808

Stamp Day: Paintings by Endre Szasz.

**1986, Sept. 5**
**2999** A807 2fo shown    .40 .20
**3000** A807 2fo Confidence    .40 .20
**Souvenir Sheet**
**Perf. 11½**
**3001** A808 10fo shown    1.75 1.75
Exist imperf. Value: set $15; souvenir sheet $30.

5th Intl. Conference on Oriental Carpets, Vienna and Budapest A809

**1986, Sept. 17**    **Litho.**    **Perf. 11**
**3002** A809 4fo Anatolia crivelli, 15th cent.    .60 .30
Exists imperf. Value $5.50.

Franz Liszt, Composer A810

**1986, Oct. 21**    **Engr.**    **Perf. 12**
**3003** A810 4fo grayish green    .50 .30
Exists imperf. Value $5.

Intl. Peace Year — A811

**1986, Oct. 24**    **Litho.**
**3004** A811 4fo multicolored    .75 .30
No. 3004 printed se-tenant with label.
Exists imperf. Value, with label $20.

### Souvenir Sheet

Hofburg Palace, Vienna, and Map — A812

**1986, Nov. 4**    **Perf. 11**
**3005** A812 20fo multicolored    3.00 2.75
European Security and Cooperation Conference, Vienna.
Exists imperf. Value $35.

Fruits A813

### Photogravure & Engraved
**1986, Nov. 25**    **Perf. 12x11½**
**3006** A813 2fo Sour cherries    .25 .20
**3007** A813 2fo Apricots    .25 .20
**3008** A813 4fo Peaches    .50 .25
**3009** A813 4fo Raspberries    .50 .25
**3010** A813 4fo Apples    .50 .25
**3011** A813 6fo Grapes    .80 .35
Nos. 3006-3011 (6)    2.80 1.50
Exist imperf. Value, set $20.

Natl. Heroes — A814

Designs: No. 3012, Jozseph Pogany (1886-1939), journalist, martyr. No. 3013, Ferenc Munnich (1886-1967), prime minister, 1958-61.

**1986**    **Litho.**    **Perf. 12½x11½**
**3012** A814 4fo multi    .65 .30
**3013** A814 4fo multi    .65 .30
Issued: #3012, Nov. 6; #3013, Nov. 14.
Exist imperf. Value, set $6.

World Communist Youth Fed., 12th Congress A815

**1986, Nov. 21**    **Perf. 12**
**3014** A815 4fo multi    .50 .30
Exist imperf. Value $4.

Castles — A816

Festetics Castle, Keszthely A816a

2fo, Forgach, Szecseny. 3fo, Savoya, Rackeve. 4fo, Batthyany, Kormend. 5fo, Szechenyi, Nagycenk. 6fo, Rudnyanszky, Nagyteteny. 7fo, Esterhazy, Papa. 8fo, Szapary, Buk. 10fo, Festetics, Keszthely. 12fo, Dory Castle, Mihalyi. 20fo, Brunswick, Martonvasar. 30fo, De la Motte, Nosvaj. 40fo, L'Huillier-Coborg, Edeleny. 50fo, Teleki-Degenfeld, Szirak. 70fo, Magochy, Pacin. 100fo, Eszterhazy, Fertod.

**Perf. 12x11½, 11½x12½ (7fo)**

| 1986-91 | | | Litho. | |
|---|---|---|---|---|
| 3015 | A816 | 2fo multi | .20 | .20 |
| 3016 | A816 | 3fo multi | .20 | .20 |
| 3017 | A816 | 4fo multi | .20 | .20 |
| 3018 | A816 | 5fo multi | .30 | .20 |
| 3019 | A816 | 6fo multi | .35 | .20 |
| 3020 | A816 | 7fo multi | .50 | .30 |
| 3021 | A816 | 8fo multi | .50 | .30 |
| 3022 | A816 | 10fo multi | .85 | .40 |
| 3023 | A816 | 12fo multi | .90 | .50 |
| 3024 | A816 | 20fo multi | 1.75 | .75 |
| 3025 | A816 | 30fo multi | 2.25 | 1.10 |
| 3026 | A816 | 40fo multi | 3.00 | 1.60 |
| 3027 | A816 | 50fo multi | 4.00 | 1.90 |
| 3028 | A816 | 70fo multi | 5.00 | 2.75 |
| 3029 | A816 | 100fo multi | 8.00 | 4.00 |
| | Nos. 3015-3029 (15) | | 28.00 | 14.60 |

The 7fo, 12fo are inscribed "Magyarorszag." Issued: 2-6, 8fo, 11/28; 10, 20-30, 100fo, 5/28/87; 40-60fo, 7/30/87; 7fo, 6/27/91; 12fo, 9/6/91.
Exist imperf. Value, set $150.
For overprint see No. 3320.

**1989-92     Litho. & Engr.     Perf. 12**
| 3030 | A816a | 10fo multi | 1.50 | .85 |
|---|---|---|---|---|

**Litho.**
| 3031 | A816a | 15fo multi | 1.10 | .65 |
|---|---|---|---|---|

The 15fo is inscribed "Magyarorszag." Issued: 10fo, Feb. 28; 15fo, Mar. 27, 1992.
No. 3030 exist imperf. Value $8.

Wildlife Conservation A817

**1986, Dec. 15     Perf. 12**
| 3035 | A817 | 2fo Felis silvestris | .30 | .20 |
|---|---|---|---|---|
| 3036 | A817 | 2fo Lutra lutra | .30 | .20 |
| 3037 | A817 | 2fo Mustela erminea | .30 | .20 |
| 3038 | A817 | 4fo Sciurus vulgaris | .55 | .30 |
| 3039 | A817 | 4fo Erinaceus concolor | .55 | .30 |
| 3040 | A817 | 6fo Emys orbicularis | .80 | .40 |
| | Nos. 3035-3040 (6) | | 2.80 | 1.60 |

Exist imperf. Value, set $20.

Portraits of Hungarian Kings in the Historical Portrait Gallery — A818

King and reign: No. 3041, St. Steven, 997-1038. No. 3042, Geza I, 1074-1077. No. 3043, St. Ladislas, 1077-1095. No. 3044, Bela III, 1172-1196. No. 3045, Bela IV, 1235-1270.

**1986, Dec. 10     Perf. 11½x12**
| 3041 | A818 | 2fo multi | .30 | .20 |
|---|---|---|---|---|
| 3042 | A818 | 2fo multi | .30 | .20 |
| 3043 | A818 | 4fo multi | .60 | .30 |
| 3044 | A818 | 4fo multi | .60 | .30 |
| 3045 | A818 | 6fo multi | .90 | .45 |
| | Nos. 3041-3045 (5) | | 2.70 | 1.45 |

Exist imperf. Value, set $20.
See Nos. 3120-3122.

Fungi — A819

**Lithographed and Engraved**
**1986, Dec. 30     Perf. 11½**
| 3046 | A819 | 2fo Amanita phalloides | | .30 | .20 |
|---|---|---|---|---|---|
| 3047 | A819 | 2fo Inocybe patouillardi | | .30 | .20 |
| 3048 | A819 | 2fo Amanita muscaria | | .30 | .20 |
| 3049 | A819 | 4fo Omphalotus olearius | | .55 | .30 |
| 3050 | A819 | 4fo Amanita pantherina | | .55 | .30 |
| 3051 | A819 | 6fo Gyromitra esculenta | | .80 | .40 |
| | Nos. 3046-3051 (6) | | | 2.80 | 1.60 |

Exist imperf. Value, set $20.

Saltwater Fish — A820

**1987, Jan. 15     Photo.     Perf. 11½**
| 3052 | A820 | 2fo Colisa fasciata | .30 | .20 |
|---|---|---|---|---|
| 3053 | A820 | 2fo Pseudotropheus zebra | .30 | .20 |
| 3054 | A820 | 2fo Iriatherina werneri | .30 | .20 |
| 3055 | A820 | 4fo Aphyosemion multicolor | .55 | .30 |
| 3056 | A820 | 4fo Papiliochromis ramirezi | .55 | .30 |
| 3057 | A820 | 6fo Hyphessobrycon erythrostigma | .80 | .40 |
| | Nos. 3052-3057 (6) | | 2.80 | 1.60 |

Exist imperf. Value, set $25.

Seated Woman, 1918, by Bela Uitz (1887-1972), Painter A821

Abstract, 1960, by Lajos Kassak (1887-1967) A822

**1987, Mar. 6     Litho.     Perf. 12**
| 3058 | A821 | 4fo multicolored | .50 | .30 |
|---|---|---|---|---|

Exists imperf. Value $4.

**1987, Mar. 20**
| 3059 | A822 | 4fo black & red | .50 | .30 |
|---|---|---|---|---|

Exists imperf. Value $4.

Medical Pioneers — A823

Designs: 2fo, Hippocrates (460-377 B.C.), Greek physician. No. 3061, Avicenna or Ibn Sina (A.D. 980-1037), Islamic pharmacist, diagnostician. No. 3062, Ambroise Pare (1510-1590), French surgeon. No. 3063, William Harvey (1578-1657), English physician, anatomist. 6fo, Ignaz Semmelweis (1818-1865), Hungarian obstetrician.

**1987, Mar. 31**
| 3060 | A823 | 2fo black & dk red brn | .30 | .20 |
|---|---|---|---|---|
| 3061 | A823 | 4fo black & dk grn | .55 | .30 |
| 3062 | A823 | 4fo black & steel bl | .55 | .30 |
| 3063 | A823 | 4fo black & olive blk | .55 | .30 |
| 3064 | A823 | 6fo black & grn blk | .80 | .40 |
| | Nos. 3060-3064 (5) | | 2.75 | 1.50 |

Exists imperf. Value, set $20.

Neolithic and Copper Age Artifacts — A824

**1987, Apr. 15     Litho.     Perf. 12**
Designs: 2fo, Urn, Hodmezovasarhely. No. 3066, Altar, Szeged. No. 3067, Deity, Szegvar-Tuzkoves. 5fo, Vase, Center.

| 3065 | A824 | 2fo pale bl grn & sep | .25 | .20 |
|---|---|---|---|---|
| 3066 | A824 | 4fo buff & sepia | .55 | .30 |
| 3067 | A824 | 4fo pale org & sepia | .55 | .30 |
| 3068 | A824 | 5fo pale yel grn & sep | .80 | .40 |
| | Nos. 3065-3068 (4) | | 2.15 | 1.20 |

Exists imperf. Value, set $20.

**Souvenir Sheet**

Esztergom Cathedral Treasury Reopening — A825

**1987, Apr. 28     Perf. 11**
| 3069 | A825 | 20fo Calvary of King Matthias | 3.50 | 3.50 |
|---|---|---|---|---|

No. 3069 margin pictures the Horn Chalice of King Sigismund, Rhineland, 1408 (UL), Crozier of Archbishop Miklos Olah, Hungary, c. 1490 (UR), Monstrance of Imre Eszterhazy, by Gaspar Meichl, Vienna, 1728 (LL), and the Chalice of Matthias, Hungary, c. 1480.
Exists imperf. Value $30.

Hungarian First Aid Assoc., Cent. — A826

**1987, May 5     Perf. 11½x12**
| 3070 | A826 | 4fo Ambulances, 1887-1987 | .50 | .30 |
|---|---|---|---|---|

Exists imperf. Value $4.

**Souvenir Sheet**

CAPEX '87, Toronto A827

Stamp exhibitions: b, OLYMPHILEX '87, Rome. c, HAFNIA '87, Copenhagen.

**1987, May 20     Litho.     Perf. 11**
| 3071 | | Sheet of 3 + 3 labels | 3.50 | 2.75 |
|---|---|---|---|---|
| a.-c. | A827 | 5fo any single | 1.25 | .90 |

Exists imperf. Value $20.

Jozsef Marek (1886-1952), Veterinarian — A828

**1987, May 25     Perf. 12x11½**
| 3072 | A828 | 4fo multicolored | .50 | .30 |
|---|---|---|---|---|

Veterinary education, bicent.
Exists imperf. Value $4.

Teleki's African Expedition, Cent. — A829

**1987, June 10**
| 3073 | A829 | 4fo multicolored | .50 | .30 |
|---|---|---|---|---|

Samuel Teleki (1845-1916), explorer.
Exists imperf. Value $4.

Woodcut by Abraham von Werdt, 18th Cent. — A830

**Litho. & Engr.**
**1987, June 25     Perf. 12**
| 3074 | A830 | 4fo beige & sepia | .50 | .30 |
|---|---|---|---|---|

Hungarian Printing, Paper and Press Workers' Union, 125th anniv.
Exists imperf. Value $4.

Antarctic Research, 75th Anniv. — A831

Helicopter Landing, Mirnij Research Station — A832

**1987, June 30**       **Litho.**

Map, explorer and scene: No. 3075, James Cook (1728-1779) and ship. No. 3076, Fabian von Bellingshausen (1778-1852) and seals. No. 3077, Ernest H. Shackleton (1874-1922) and penguins. No. 3078, Roald Amundsen (1872-1928) discovering South Pole, dog team. No. 3079, Robert F. Scott (1868-1912) and ship. No. 3080, Richard E. Byrd (1888-1957) and Floyd Bennett monoplane.

| 3075 | A831 | 2fo multi | .30 | .20 |
|------|------|-----------|-----|-----|
| 3076 | A831 | 2fo multi | .30 | .20 |
| 3077 | A831 | 2fo multi | .30 | .20 |
| 3078 | A831 | 4fo multi | .55 | .30 |
| 3079 | A831 | 4fo multi | .55 | .30 |
| 3080 | A831 | 6fo multi | .80 | .40 |
| | | Nos. 3075-3080 (6) | 2.80 | 1.60 |

**Souvenir Sheet**
**Perf. 11½**

| 3081 | A832 | 20fo multi | 3.00 | 3.00 |
|------|------|-----------|------|------|

Exist imperf. Value: set $25; souvenir sheet $50.

Railway Officers Training Institute, Cent. — A833

**1987, Sept. 4**    **Litho.**    **Perf. 11½x12**

| 3082 | A833 | 4fo blue & black | .75 | .50 |
|------|------|------------------|-----|-----|

Exists imperf. Value $4.

Stamp Day, 60th Anniv. — A834

**Litho. & Engr.**
**1987, Sept. 18**      **Perf. 12**

Masonry of the medieval Buda Castle: 2fo, Flowers, dolphin. 4fo, Arms of King Matthias. 10fo, "ONDIDIT/GENEROSVM" inscribed on capital.

| 3083 | A834 | 2fo multi | .35 | .20 |
|------|------|-----------|-----|-----|
| 3084 | A834 | 4fo multi | .70 | .45 |

**Souvenir Sheet**
**Perf. 11**

| 3085 | A834 | 10fo multi | 1.75 | 1.75 |
|------|------|------------|------|------|

Exist imperf. Value: set $8; souvenir sheet $30.

A835

**1987, Sept. 30**    **Litho.**    **Perf. 12**

| 3086 | A835 | 4fo multi | .80 | .50 |
|------|------|-----------|-----|-----|
| a. | | Se-tenant with label | .80 | .50 |

No 3086 printed in sheet of 50 and in sheet of 25 plus 25 labels picturing 13th cent. church at Gyongyospata which houses the altar. Exists imperf. Value $9; with label $30.

A836

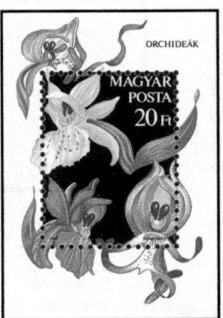

Orchids A837

**1987, Oct. 29**    **Litho.**    **Perf. 11**

| 3087 | A836 | 2fo Cypripedium calceolus | .35 | .25 |
|------|------|---------------------------|-----|-----|
| 3088 | A836 | 2fo Orchis purpurea | .35 | .25 |
| 3089 | A836 | 4fo Himantoglossum hircinum | .60 | .50 |
| 3090 | A836 | 4fo Ophrys scolopax cornuta | .65 | .50 |
| 3091 | A836 | 5fo Cephalanthera rubra | .75 | .60 |
| 3092 | A836 | 6fo Epipactis atrorubens | .80 | .75 |
| | | Nos. 3087-3092 (6) | 3.50 | 2.85 |

**Miniature Sheet**

| 3093 | A837 | 20fo shown | 3.50 | 3.25 |
|------|------|------------|------|------|

Exist imperf. Value: set $25; souvenir sheet $40.

1988 Winter Olympics, Calgary — A838

**1987, Nov. 24**

| 3094 | A838 | 2fo Speed skating | .35 | .25 |
|------|------|-------------------|-----|-----|
| 3095 | A838 | 2fo Cross-country skiing | .35 | .25 |
| 3096 | A838 | 4fo Biathlon | .65 | .40 |
| 3097 | A838 | 4fo Ice hockey | .65 | .40 |
| 3098 | A838 | 4fo 4-Man bobsled | .65 | .40 |
| 3099 | A838 | 6fo Ski-jumping | 1.00 | .65 |
| | | Nos. 3094-3099 (6) | 3.65 | 2.35 |

**Souvenir Sheet**

| 3100 | A838 | 20fo Slalom | 3.50 | 3.25 |
|------|------|-------------|------|------|

Exist imperf. Value: set $25; souvenir sheet $22.

Souvenir Sheet

U.S.-Soviet Summit, Dec. 7-10 — A839

**1987, Dec. 7**       **Perf. 12**

| 3101 | A839 | 20fo Shaking hands | 3.50 | 3.25 |
|------|------|--------------------|------|------|

Meeting of Gen. Secretary Gorbachev and Pres. Reagan to discuss and sign nuclear arms reduction treaty. Exists imperf. Value $22.

Fairy Tales — A840

Designs: No. 3102, The White Crane, from Japan. No. 3103, The Fox and the Crow, Aesop's Fables. No. 3104, The Tortoise and the Hare, Aesop's Fables. No. 3105, The Ugly Duckling, by Hans Christian Andersen. No. 3106, The Steadfast Tin Soldier, by Andersen.

**1987, Dec. 11**

| 3102 | A840 | 2fo multi | .40 | .25 |
|------|------|-----------|-----|-----|
| 3103 | A840 | 2fo multi | .40 | .25 |
| 3104 | A840 | 4fo multi | .75 | .50 |
| 3105 | A840 | 4fo multi | .75 | .50 |
| 3106 | A840 | 6fo multi | 1.00 | .75 |
| | | Nos. 3102-3106 (5) | 3.30 | 2.25 |

Exist imperf. Value, set $20.

Count Ferdinand von Zeppelin (1838-1917), Designer of Dirigibles — A841

**1988, Jan. 29**    **Litho.**    **Perf. 12**

| 3107 | A841 | 2fo LZ-2, 1905 | .40 | .25 |
|------|------|----------------|-----|-----|
| 3108 | A841 | 4fo LZ-4, 1908 | .80 | .45 |
| 3109 | A841 | 4fo LZ-10, Schwaben, 1911 | .90 | .45 |
| 3110 | A841 | 8fo LZ-127, Graf Zeppelin, 1928 | 1.50 | 1.00 |
| | | Nos. 3107-3110 (4) | 3.60 | 2.15 |

Exist imperf. Value, set $22.

1988 World Figure Skating Championships, Budapest — A842

Various athletes wearing period costumes.

**1988, Feb. 29**    **Photo.**    **Perf. 11½**

| 3111 | A842 | 2fo Male, 20th cent. | .35 | .25 |
|------|------|----------------------|-----|-----|
| 3112 | A842 | 2fo Male, (cap), 19th cent. | .35 | .25 |
| 3113 | A842 | 4fo Male (hat), 18th cent. | .60 | .40 |
| 3114 | A842 | 4fo Woman, c. 1930 | .60 | .40 |
| 3115 | A842 | 5fo Woman (contemporary) | .75 | .50 |
| 3116 | A842 | 6fo Pair | 1.00 | .65 |
| | | Nos. 3111-3116 (6) | 3.65 | 2.45 |

**Souvenir Sheet**
**Perf. 12x11½**

| 3117 | A842 | 20fo Death spiral | 3.50 | 3.25 |
|------|------|-------------------|------|------|

No. 3117 contains one 37x52mm stamp. Exist imperf. Value: set $20; souvenir sheet $25.

Illes Monus (1888-1944), Party Leader — A843

**1988, Mar. 11**    **Litho.**    **Perf. 11½x12**

| 3118 | A843 | 4fo multi | .75 | .50 |
|------|------|-----------|-----|-----|

Exists imperf. Value $4.
See Nos. 3152, 3160.

Miniature Sheet

Postmaster's Coat, Hat and Post Horn, 18th Cent. — A844

**1988, Mar. 18**    **Litho.**    **Perf. 13**

| 3119 | A844 | 4fo + 4 labels | 1.25 | 1.25 |
|------|------|----------------|------|------|

Intl. stamp exhibitions, 1988. No. 3119 contains 4 labels picturing exhibition emblems: JUVALUX '88, Luxembourg, Mar. 29-Apr. 4 (UL), SYDPEX '88, Sydney, Australia, July 30-Aug.7 (UR), FINLANDIA '88, Helsinki, Finland, June 1-12 (LR), and PRAGA '88, Prague, Czechoslovakia, Aug. 26-Sept. 4 (LL). Exists imperf. Value $30.

**King Type of 1986**

Portraits of Hungarian kings in the Historical Portrait Gallery. King and reign: 2fo, Charles Robert (1308-1342). 4fo, Louis I (1342-1382). 6fo, Sigismund (1387-1437).

**1988, Mar. 31**      **Perf. 11½x12**

| 3120 | A818 | 2fo pale grn, sep & red | .30 | .20 |
|------|------|-------------------------|-----|-----|
| 3121 | A818 | 4fo pale ultra, sep & red | .60 | .45 |
| 3122 | A818 | 6fo pale vio, sep & red | .90 | .65 |
| | | Nos. 3120-3122 (3) | 1.80 | 1.30 |

Exists imperf. Value, set $15.

1988 Summer Olympics, Seoul — A845

**1988, Apr. 20**    **Litho.**    **Perf. 13½x13**

| 3123 | A845 | 2fo Rowing | .30 | .20 |
|------|------|------------|-----|-----|
| 3124 | A845 | 4fo Hurdling | .60 | .45 |
| 3125 | A845 | 4fo Fencing | .60 | .45 |
| 3126 | A845 | 6fo Boxing | .90 | .65 |
| | | Nos. 3123-3126 (4) | 2.40 | 1.75 |

## Souvenir Sheet
### Perf. 12½
3127 A845 20fo Tennis    3.75 3.25
Exist imperf. Value: set $20; souvenir sheet $30.

Computer Animation A846

**1988, May 12**    **Perf. 12**

Design: Graphic from the computer-animated film *Dilemma*, 1972, by graphic artist Janos Kass (b. 1927) and cartoon film director John Halas (b. 1912).

3128 A846 4fo black, pur & ver    .75   .50
Exists imperf. Value $5.50.

Eurocheck Congress, June 10, Budapest — A847

**1988, June 10**   **Litho.**   **Perf. 12**
3129 A847 4fo multicolored    .75   .50
Eurocheck as legal tender, 20th anniv.
Exists imperf. Value $5.50.

*Sovereign of the Seas* — A848

**1988, June 30**
3130 A848 2fo shown    .35   .20
3131 A848 2fo *Santa Maria*    .35   .25
3132 A848 2fo *Mayflower*    .35   .25
3133 A848 4fo *Jylland*    .75   .50
3134 A848 6fo *St. Jupat*    1.10   .80
   Nos. 3130-3134 (5)    2.90 2.00
Exist imperf. Value, set $20.

Fight Drug Abuse — A849

**1988, July 7**   **Litho.**   **Perf. 12**
3135 A849 4fo multicolored    .75   .50
Exists imperf. Value $5.50.

Ducks A850

**1988, July 29**   **Litho.**   **Perf. 13x13½**
3136 A850 2fo Anas crecca    .30   .20
3137 A850 2fo Bucephala clangula    .30   .20

---

3138 A850 4fo Anas penelope    .65   .45
  a.   Pane of 10 #3136 + 10 #3138 with gutter btwn.    12.00
   Complete booklet, #3138a, with text and cover in either English or German    12.00
3139 A850 4fo Netta rufina    .65   .50
3140 A850 6fo Anas strepera    1.10   .65
   Nos. 3136-3140 (5)    3.00 2.00

### Souvenir Sheet
#### Perf. 12½x11½
3141 A850 20fo Anas platyrhynchos    4.75 3.50
No. 3141 contains one 52x37mm stamp.
Exist imperf. Value: set $25; souvenir sheet $40.
For surcharges see Nos. 3199-3200.

Antique Toys — A851

**1988, Aug. 12**    **Perf. 12**
3142 A851 2fo Train    .30   .25
3143 A851 2fo See-saw    .30   .25
3144 A851 4fo +2fo Pecking chickens    1.00   .65
3145 A851 5fo String-manipulated soldier    .85   .55
   Nos. 3142-3145 (4)    2.45 1.70
Surtax for youth philately programs.
Exist imperf. Value, set $20.

Calvinist College, Debrecen, 450th Anniv. — A852

**1988, Aug. 16**   **Litho.**   **Perf. 13½x13**
3146 A852 4fo multi    .75   .50
Exists imperf. Value $4.

58th American Society of Travel Agents World Congress, Oct. 23-29, Budapest A853

**1988, Aug. 30**    **Perf. 12**
3147 A853 4fo multi    .75   .50
Exists imperf. Value $4.

P.O. Officials Training School, Cent. — A854

**1988, Sept. 9**   **Litho.**   **Perf. 12**
3148 A854 4fo Badge on collar    .75   .50
Exists imperf. Value $4.

---

Gabor Baross (1848-1892), Minister of Commerce and Communication — A855

Portrait and: 2fo, Postal Savings Bank, Budapest, emblem and postal savings stamp. 4fo, Telephone and telegraph apparatus, registration label and cancellations. 10fo, East Railway Station, Budapest.

**1988, Sept. 16**
3149 A855 2fo multi    .30   .25
3150 A855 4fo multi    .65   .50

#### Souvenir Sheet
##### Perf. 11½
3151 A855 10fo multi    2.25 2.00
No. 3151 contains one 50x29mm stamp.
Exist imperf. Value: set $9; souvenir sheet $50.

### Famous Hungarians Type of 1988
Gyula Lengyel (1888-1941), political writer.

**1988, Oct. 7**    **Perf. 11½x12**
3152 A843 4fo multi    .75   .50
Exists imperf. Value $4.

Christmas — A857

#### Perf. 12½x11½
**1988, Nov. 10**    **Litho.**
3153 A857 2fo multi    .40   .25
Exists imperf. Value $5.

Nobel Prize Winners — A858

Designs: No. 3154, Richard Adolf Zsigmondy (1865-1929), Germany, chemistry (1925). No. 3155, Robert Barany (1876-1936), Austria, medicine (1914). No. 3156, Georg von Hevesy (1885-1966), Hungary, chemistry (1943). No. 3157, Albert Szent-Gyorgyi (1893-1986), Hungary-US, medicine (1937). No. 3158, Georg von Bekesy (1899-1972), US, medicine (1961). 6fo, Denis Gabor (1900-1979), Great Britain, physics (1971).

#### Litho. & Engr.
**1988, Nov. 30**    **Perf. 12**
3154 A858 2fo red brown    .35   .25
3155 A858 2fo green    .35   .25
3156 A858 2fo deep claret    .35   .25
3157 A858 4fo rose lake    .60   .40
3158 A858 4fo steel blue    .60   .40
3159 A858 6fo sepia    .75   .65
   Nos. 3154-3159 (6)    3.00 2.20
Exist imperf. Value, set $30.

### Famous Hungarians Type of 1988
Arpad Szakasits (1888-1965), party leader.

**1988, Dec. 6**    **Perf. 11½x12**
3160 A843 4fo multicolored    .75   .50
Exists imperf. Value $4.

---

### Souvenir Sheet

Medals Won by Hungarian Athletes at the 1988 Seoul Olympic Games — A860

**1988, Dec. 19**   **Litho.**   **Perf. 12**
3161 A860 20fo multicolored    3.75 3.50
Exists imperf. Value $30.

Silver and Cast Iron — A861

**1988, Dec. 28**    **Litho. & Engr.**
3162 A861 2fo Teapot, Pest, 1846    .35   .25
3163 A861 2fo Coffee pot, Buda, 18th cent.    .35   .25
3164 A861 4fo Sugar bowl, Pest, 1822    .65   .45
3165 A861 5fo Cast iron plate, Romania, 1850    .85   .55
   Nos. 3162-3165 (4)    2.20 1.50
Exist imperf. Value, set $20.

Postal Savings Bank Inauguration — A862

**1989, Jan. 20**   **Litho.**   **Perf. 12x11½**
3166 A862 5fo royal blue, blk & silver    .90   .55
Exists imperf. Value $4.

Kalman Wallisch (1889-1934), Labor Leader — A863

**1989, Feb. 28**   **Litho.**   **Perf. 12**
3167 A863 3fo dk red & brt bl    .55   .35
Exists imperf. Value $4.
See No. 3170.

World Indoor Sports Championships, Budapest, Mar. 3-5 — A864

**1989, Mar. 3**     **Perf. 13x13½**
3168 A864 3fo multicolored    .55   .35
    Exists imperf. Value $3.50.

Souvenir Sheet

Interparliamentary Union Cent. and 81st Session, Budapest, Mar. 13-18 — A865

a, Parliament, Big Ben & Tower Bridge, London. b, Parliament & Chain Bridge, Budapest.

**1989, Mar. 13**   **Litho.**   **Perf. 11**
3169 A865   Sheet of 2    3.75 3.50
a.-b.   10fo any single    1.75 1.60
    Exists with red inscriptions and control number. Value $75.
    Exists imperf. Value $25.

Famous Hungarians Type of 1989

    Janos Gyetvai (1889-1967), journalist, diplomat.

**1989, Apr. 7**   **Litho.**   **Perf. 12**
3170 A863 3fo dark red & brt grn   .55   .35
    Exists imperf. Value $4.

Stud Farm at Babolna, 200th Anniv. A867

    Horses: a, O Bajan. b, Meneskari Csikos. c, Gazal II.

**1989, May 18**   **Litho.**   **Perf. 12**
3171 A867   Strip of 3    1.75 1.10
a.-c.   A867 3fo any single    .55   .35
    Exists imperf. Value, strip $20.

ART '89, May 23-27, Budapest A868

**1989, May 23**     **Perf. 12x11½**
3172 A868 5fo multi    .90   .55
    Exhibition for disabled artists.
    Exists imperf. Value $4.

Flower Arrangements — A869

**1989, May 31**     **Perf. 12**
3173 A869 2fo multi, vert.    .35   .25
3174 A869 3fo multi, vert.    .40   .30
3175 A869 3fo shown    .40   .30
3176 A869 5fo multi, diff.    .85   .50
3177 A869 10fo multi, vert.    1.50 1.00
    Nos. 3173-3177 (5)    3.50 2.35
    Exist imperf. Value, set $20.

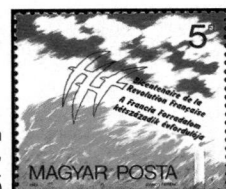

French Revolution, Bicent. A870

**1989, June 1**     **Perf. 12**
3178 A870 5fo brt blue, blk & red    .75   .50
    **Souvenir Sheet**
    **Perf. 11½**
3179 A870 20fo like 5fo    3.50 3.25
    No. 3179 contains one 50x30mm stamp.
    Exist imperf. Value: single $12; souvenir sheet $30.

Medieval Church of the Csolts Near Veszto — A871

Photography, 150th Anniv. — A872

**1989, June 15**   **Litho.**   **Perf. 12**
3180 A871 3fo multi    .50   .30
    Exists imperf. Value $4.

**1989, June 15**
3181 A872 5fo multi    .80   .50
    Exists imperf. Value $4.

Old Mills — A873

    Designs: 2fo, Water mill, Turistvandi, 18th cent. 3fo, Horse-driven mill, Szarvas, 1836. 5fo, Windmill, Kiskunhalas, 18th cent. 10fo, Water wheel on the Drava River.

**1989, June 20**
3182 A873 2fo multi    .30   .20
3183 A873 3fo multi    .45   .30
3184 A873 5fo multi    .75   .50
3185 A873 10fo multi    1.50 1.00
    Nos. 3182-3185 (4)    3.00 2.00
    Exist imperf. Value, set $20.

Souvenir Sheet

1st Moon Landing, 20th Anniv. — A874

**1989, July 12**   **Litho.**   **Perf. 12½**
3186 A874 20fo multi    3.75 3.50
    Exists imperf. Value $25.

Gliders — A875

**1989, July 20**     **Perf. 12**
3187 A875 3fo Futar    .45   .30
3188 A875 5fo Cimbora    .80   .60
    17th Intl. Old Timers Rally, Budakeszi Airport, and 60th anniv. of glider flying in Hungary.
    Exist imperf. Value, set $15.

Reptiles A876

**1989, July 26**     **Perf. 11**
3189 A876 2fo *Lacerta agilis*    .25   .20
3190 A876 3fo *Lacerta viridis*    .45   .25
3191 A876 5fo *Vipera rakosiensis*    .70   .40
3192 A876 5fo *Natrix natrix*    .70   .40
3193 A876 10fo *Emys orbicularis*    1.25   .75
    Nos. 3189-3193 (5)    3.35 2.00
    Exist imperf. Value, set $30.

31st Modern Pentathlon World Championships, Aug. 30-Sept. 4, Budapest — A877

**1989, July 31**     **Perf. 13½x13**
3194 A877 5fo multi    .80   .50
    Exists imperf. Value $4.

Caves — A878

    10th World Speleology Congress, Aug. 13-20, Sofia.

**1989, Aug. 14**   **Litho.**   **Perf. 11**
3195 A878 3fo Baradla    .30   .20
3196 A878 5fo Szemlohegy    .55   .40
3197 A878 10fo Anna    .90   .70
3198 A878 12fo Lake Cave of Tapolca    1.25   .80
    Nos. 3195-3198 (4)    3.00 2.10
    Exist imperf. Value, set $20.

Nos. 3136 and 3138 Surcharged

**1989, Aug. 14**     **Perf. 13x13½**
3199 A850 3fo on 2fo #3136    2.00 1.75
3200 A850 5fo on 4fo #3138    2.00 1.75
a.   Pane of 10 #3199 + pane of 10 #3200 with gutter between    20.00
    Complete booklet, #3200a, with text and cover in either English or German    35.00

A879

**1989, Aug. 24**     **Perf. 12**
3201 A879 5fo multi    .80   .45
    Third World Two-in-Hand Carriage-driving Championships, Balatonfenyves, Aug. 24-27.
    Exists imperf. Value $4.

A880

**1989, Sept. 8**   **Litho.**   **Perf. 12**
    Nurses: 5fo, Zsuzsanna Kossuth (1820-1854) and emblem. 10fo, Florence Nightingale (1820-1910) and medal awarded in her name by the Red Cross.
3202 A880 5fo multi    .65   .40
3203 A880 10fo multi    1.10   .75
    Stamp Day. See No. B341.
    Exist imperf. Value, set $15.

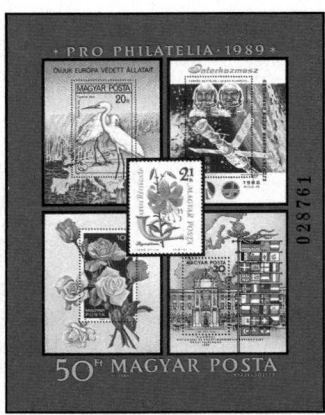

Pro-Philatelia 1989 — A881

**1989, Oct. 10**   **Litho.**   **Imperf.**
3204 A881 50fo #2665, C426, 2742, 3005, B233    6.25 5.75

Dismantling of the Electronic Surveillance System (Iron Curtain) on the Hungary-Austria Border — A882

**1989, Oct. 30**     **Perf. 11**
3205 A882 5fo multi    .75   .45
Exists imperf. Value $7.

Conquest of Hungary, by Mor Than — A883

**1989, Oct. 31**
3206 A883 5fo multi    .75   .45
Arpad, chief who founded the 1st Magyar dynasty of Hungary in 889.
Exists imperf. Value $4.

Christmas — A884

**1989, Nov. 10**   **Litho.**   **Perf. 11½x12**
3207 A884 3fo Flight to Egypt    .45   .25
Exists imperf. Value $4.

Jawaharlal Nehru — A885

**Litho. & Engr.**
**1989, Nov. 14**     **Perf. 12**
3208 A885 3fo buff & rose brn    .45   .25
Jawaharlal Nehru, 1st prime minister of independent India.
Exists imperf. Value $4.

Modern Art (Paintings) — A886

3fo, *Mike*, by Dezso Korniss. 5fo, *Sunrise*, by Lajos Kassak. 10fo, *Grotesque, Burial*, by Endre Balint. 12fo, *Memory of Toys*, by Tihamer Gyarmathy.

**1989, Dec. 18**   **Litho.**   **Perf. 12**
3209 A886 3fo multicolored    .35   .25
3210 A886 5fo multicolored    .65   .50
3211 A886 10fo multicolored    1.40   .95
3212 A886 12fo multicolored    1.60   1.10
   *Nos. 3209-3212 (4)*    4.00   2.80
Exist imperf. Value, set $30.

Medical Pioneers — A887

**1989, Dec. 29**   **Engr.**   **Perf. 12**
#3213, Galen (129-c.199), Greek physician. #3214, Paracelsus (1493-1541), German alchemist. 4fo, Andreas Vesalius (1514-64), Belgian anatomist. 6fo, Rudolf Virchow (1821-1902), German pathologist. 10fo, Ivan Petrovich Pavlov (1849-1936), Russian physiologist.
3213 A887 3fo olive gray    .40   .25
3214 A887 3fo brown    .40   .25
3215 A887 4fo black    .70   .45
3216 A887 6fo intense black    .85   .55
3217 A887 10fo brown violet    1.40   .80
   *Nos. 3213-3217 (5)*    3.75   2.30
Exist imperf. Value, set $25.

Hungarian Savings Bank, 150th Anniv. — A888

**1990, Jan. 11**     **Litho.**
3218 A888 5fo multicolored    .75   .45
Exists imperf. Value $7.

A889      A890

**1990, Jan. 15**     **Perf. 12**
3219 A889 5fo brown & sepia    .75   .45
Singer Sewing Machine, 25th anniv.
Exists imperf. Value $5.50.

**1990, Jan. 29**
3fo, Telephone, Budapest Exchange. 5fo, Mailbox and main p.o., Budapest, c. 1900.
3220 A890 3fo multicolored    .40   .20
3221 A890 5fo multicolored    .60   .30

**Coil Stamps**
**Size: 17x22mm**
**Perf. 14**
**Photo.**
3222 A890 3fo shown    .40   .20
3223 A890 5fo multi    .60   .30
   *Nos. 3220-3223 (4)*    2.00   1.00
Nos. 3220-3221 inscribed "Pj 1989." Nos. 3222-3223 inscribed "1989."
Nos. 3220-3221 exist imperf. Value, set $20.

A891

**Designs: Protected bird species.**

**1990, Feb. 20**   **Litho.**   **Perf. 11½x12**
3224 A891 3fo Alcedo atthis    .45   .30
3225 A891 3fo Pyrrhula pyrrhula    .45   .30
3226 A891 3fo Dendrocopos syriacus    .45   .30
3227 A891 5fo Upupa epops    .75   .50
3228 A891 5fo Merops apiaster    .75   .50
3229 A891 10fo Coracias garrulus    1.50   1.00
   *Nos. 3224-3229 (6)*    4.35   2.90
Exist imperf. Value, set $30.

A892

**1990, Mar. 14**    **Litho.**    **Perf. 12**
Flowers of the continents (Africa).
3230 A892 3fo Leucadendron    .40   .25
3231 A892 3fo Protea compacta    .40   .25
3232 A892 3fo Leucadendron spissifolium    .40   .25
3233 A892 5fo Protea barbigera    .70   .40
3234 A892 5fo Protea lepidocarpodendron    .70   .40
3235 A892 10fo Protea cynaroides    1.25   .85
   *Nos. 3230-3235 (6)*    3.85   2.40

**Souvenir Sheet**
**Perf. 12½x12**
3236 A892 20fo Montage of African flowers    3.75   3.75
No. 3236 contains one 27x38mm stamp. See Nos. 3278-3283, 3371-3375, 3377-3381, 3451-3455.
Exist imperf. Value: set $30; souvenir sheet $40.

A893

Portraits of Hungarian kings in the Historical Portrait Gallery. King and reign: No. 3237, Janos Hunyadi (c. 1407-1409). No. 3238, Matthias Hunyadi (1443-1490).

**1990, Apr. 6**   **Litho.**   **Perf. 11½x12**
3237 A893 5fo multicolored    .70   .40
3238 A893 5fo multicolored    .70   .40
   a.   Pair, #3237-3238    1.40   1.00
Exist imperf. Value, pair $10.

**Souvenir Sheet**

A894

**Litho. & Engr.**
**1990, Apr. 17**     **Perf. 12½x12**
3239 A894 20fo black & buff    3.75   3.25
Exist imperf. Value, pair $10. Penny Black 150th anniv., Stamp World London '90.
Exists imperf. Value $25.

Karoli Bible, 400th Anniv. — A895

**1990, Apr. 24**     **Litho.**
3240 A895 8fo Gaspar Karoli    1.00   .70
No. 3240 printed se-tenant with label picturing Bible frontispiece.
Exists imperf. Value, with label $10.

1990 World Cup Soccer Championships, Italy — A896

Various athletes.

**1990, Apr. 27**     **Perf. 11½x12**
3241 A896 3fo Dribble    .30   .20
3242 A896 5fo Heading the ball    .55   .35
3243 A896 5fo Kick    .55   .35
3244 A896 8fo Goal attempt    .80   .55
3245 A896 8fo Dribble, diff.    .80   .55
3246 A896 10fo Dribble, diff.    1.00   .75
   *Nos. 3241-3246 (6)*    4.00   2.75

**Souvenir Sheet**
**Perf. 12½**
3247 A896 20fo Dribble, diff.    3.50   3.50
No. 3247 contains one 32x42mm stamp.
Exist imperf. Value: set $30; souvenir sheet $25.

Kelemen Mikes (1690-1761), Writer — A897

**1990, May 31**   **Litho.**   **Perf. 13½x13**
3248 A897 8fo black & gold    1.10   .75
Exists imperf. Value $5.

Noemi and Beni Ferenczy, Birth Cent. — A898

Designs: 3fo, Painting by Noemi Ferenczy. 5fo, Sculpture by Beni Ferenczy.

**1990, June 18**   **Litho.**   **Perf. 12**
3249 A898 3fo multicolored    .30   .20
3250 A898 5fo multicolored    .50   .30
Exist imperf. Value, set $10.

Ferenc Kazinczy (1759-1831), Hungarian Language Reformer A899

**1990, July 18　Litho.　Perf. 12**
3251　A899　8fo multicolored　　.60　.40
　　Exists imperf. Value $10.

Ferenc Kolcsey (1790-1838), Poet — A900

**1990, Aug. 3**
3252　A900　8fo multicolored　　.60　.40
　　Exists imperf. Value $10.

New Coat of Arms A901

**1990, Aug. 17　Litho.　Perf. 13½x13**
3253　A901　8fo multicolored　　.60　.40

**Souvenir Sheet**
**Perf. 11**
3254　A901　20fo multicolored　　4.00　4.00
　　No. 3254 contains one 34x50mm stamp.
　　A souvenir sheet like No. 3254 was released with a hologram as the stamp. The sheet exists with black or red control numbers on the reverse. Values: with black numbers $175; with red numbers $300.
　　Exist imperf. Value: single $8; souvenir sheet $40.

Grapes and Wine Producing Areas — A902

　　Grapes and Growing Area: 3fo, Cabernet franc, Hajos-Vaskut. 5fo, Cabernet sauvignon, Villany-Siklos. No. 3257, Italian Riesling, Badacsony. No. 3258, Kadarka, Szekszard. No. 3259, Leanyka, Eger. 10fo, Furmint, Tokaj-Hegyalja.

**1990, Aug. 31　　　　Perf. 13x13½**
3255　A902　3fo multicolored　　.25　.20
3256　A902　5fo multicolored　　.45　.30
3257　A902　8fo multicolored　　.65　.45
3258　A902　8fo multicolored　　.65　.45
3259　A902　8fo multicolored　　.65　.45
3260　A902　10fo multicolored　　.85　.60
　　　Nos. 3255-3260 (6)　　3.50　2.45
　　Exist imperf. Value, set $30.
　　See Nos. 3580-3582, 3656-3657, 3704-3705.

Paintings by Endre Szasz A903

**1990, Oct. 12　Litho.　Perf. 12**
3261　A903　8fo Feast　　　.70　.45
3262　A903　12fo Message　　1.10　.65
　　Stamp Day. See No. B344.
　　Exist imperf. Value, set $20.

Prehistoric Animals A904

**1990, Nov. 16　Litho.　Perf. 12**
3263　A904　3fo Tarbosaurus　　.25　.20
3264　A904　5fo Brontosaurus　　.40　.25
3265　A904　5fo Stegosaurus　　.40　.25
3266　A904　5fo Dimorphodon　　.40　.25
3267　A904　8fo Platybelodon　　.70　.35
3268　A904　10fo Mammoth　　.85　.40
　　　Nos. 3263-3268 (6)　　3.00　1.70
　　Exist imperf. Value, set $30.

Intl. Literacy Year — A905

**1990, Nov. 21　　　　Perf. 13x13½**
3269　A905　10fo multicolored　　1.00　.65
　　Exist imperf. Value $5.

Budapest Stamp Museum, 60th Anniv. — A906

**1990, Nov. 23　　　　Perf. 12½**
3270　A906　5fo brn red & grn　　.50　.30
　　Exist imperf. Value $4.

**Souvenir Sheet**

Thurn & Taxis Postal System, 500th Anniv. — A907

Illustration reduced.

**1990, Nov. 30　Litho.　Perf. 12½x12**
3271　A907　50fo multicolored　　6.75　5.00

Antique Clocks — A908

**1990, Dec. 14　　　　Perf. 12**
3272　A908　3fo Travelling clock, 1576　　.25　.20
3273　A908　5fo Table clock, 1643　　.45　.30
3274　A908　5fo Mantel clock, 1790　　.45　.30
3275　A908　10fo Table clock, 1814　　.85　.60
　　　Nos. 3272-3275 (4)　　2.00　1.40
　　Exist imperf. Value, set $20.

Madonna with Child by Botticelli — A909

**1990, Dec. 14　　　Perf. 12½x11½**
3276　A909　5fo multicolored　　.45　.25
　　Exists imperf. Value $5.50.

Lorand Eotvos (1848-1919) and Torsion Pendulum A910

**1991, Jan. 31　Litho.　Perf. 11**
3277　A910　12fo multicolored　　1.10　.65
　　Exists imperf. Value $8.

**Flowers of the Continents Type**
　Flowers of the Americas.

**1991, Feb. 28　Litho.　Perf. 12**
3278　A892　5fo Mandevilla splendens　　.35　.20
3279　A892　7fo Lobelia cardinalis　　.45　.30
3280　A892　7fo Cobaea scandens　　.45　.30
3281　A892　12fo Steriphoma paradoxa　　.75　.50
3282　A892　15fo Beloperone guttata　　1.00　.70
　　　Nos. 3278-3282 (5)　　3.00　2.00
**Souvenir Sheet**
**Perf. 11**
3283　A892　20fo Flowers of the Americas　　3.50　1.75
　　No. 3283 contains one 27x44mm stamp.
　　Exist imperf. Value: set $20; souvenir sheet $60.

Post Office, Budapest A911

Designs: 7fo, Post Office, Pecs.

**Perf. 11½x12½**
**1991, Mar. 22　　　　Litho.**
3284　A911　5fo multicolored　　5.00　3.75
3285　A911　7fo multicolored　　6.00　4.00
　a.　Pair, #3284-3285　　12.00　10.00
　　Admission to CEPT.
　　Exist imperf. Value, pair $50.

Europa — A912

**1991, Apr.　Litho.　Perf. 12½**
3286　A912　12fo Ulysses probe　　4.00　2.00
3287　A912　30fo Cassini-Huygens probe　　8.00　6.00
　　Exist imperf. Value, set $50.

Budapest Zoological and Botanical Gardens, 125th Anniv. — A913

**1991, May 15　　　　Perf. 13½x13**
3288　A913　7fo Gorilla　　.60　.35
3289　A913　12fo Rhinoceros　　.85　.60
3290　A913　12fo Toucan　　.85　.60
3291　A913　12fo Polar bear　　.85　.60
3292　A913　20fo Orchid　　1.40　1.00
　　　Nos. 3288-3292 (5)　　4.55　3.15
　　Exist imperf. Value, set $22.

A914

A915

**1991, May 24　Litho.　Perf. 12**
3293　A914　12fo multi　　1.00　.60
　　Count Pal Teleki (1879-1941), politician.
　　Exists imperf. Value $5.50.

**1991, June 13　　　　Perf. 13x13½**
3294　A915　12fo multicolored　　1.00　.60
　　44th World Fencing Championships, Budapest.
　　Exists imperf. Value $5.50.

Images of the Virgin and Child in Hungarian Shrines A916

Designs: 7fo, Mariapocs. No. 3296, Mariagyud. No. 3297, Celldomolk. No. 3298, Mariaremete. 20fo, Esztergom.

**1991, June 17**     *Perf. 12½*
| | | | | |
|---|---|---|---|---|
| 3295 | A916 | 7fo multicolored | .55 | .35 |
| 3296 | A916 | 12fo multicolored | .85 | .60 |
| 3297 | A916 | 12fo multicolored | .85 | .60 |
| 3298 | A916 | 12fo multicolored | .85 | .60 |
| 3299 | A916 | 20fo multicolored | 1.40 | 1.00 |
| | *Nos. 3295-3299 (5)* | | 4.50 | 3.15 |

Compare with design A927.
Exist imperf. Value, set $20.

### Souvenir Sheet

Visit of Pope John Paul II, Aug. 16-20, 1991 — A917

**Litho. & Engr.**
**1991, July 15**     *Perf. 12*
| | | | | |
|---|---|---|---|---|
| 3300 | A917 | 50fo multicolored | 4.50 | 3.50 |

Exists imperf. Value $25.

Karoly Marko (1791-1860), Painter — A918

**1991, June 17**     *Perf. 12*
| | | | | |
|---|---|---|---|---|
| 3301 | A918 | 12fo multicolored | 1.25 | .75 |

Exists imperf. Value $5.50.

Basketball, Cent. — A919

**1991, June 27**    **Litho.**    *Perf. 12*
| | | | | |
|---|---|---|---|---|
| 3302 | A919 | 10fo multicolored | 1.25 | .75 |

Exists imperf. Value $8.

Otto Lilienthal's First Glider Flight, Cent. — A920

Aircraft of aviation pioneers.

**1991, June 27**
| | | | | |
|---|---|---|---|---|
| 3303 | A920 | 7fo Otto Lilienthal | .50 | .35 |
| 3304 | A920 | 12fo Wright Brothers | .80 | .65 |
| 3305 | A920 | 20fo Alberto Santos-Dumont | 1.40 | 1.00 |
| 3306 | A920 | 30fo Aladar Zselyi | 2.00 | 1.50 |
| | *Nos. 3303-3306 (4)* | | 4.70 | 3.50 |

Exist imperf. Value, set $25.

3rd Intl. Hungarian Philological Congress A921

**1991, Aug. 12**    **Litho.**    *Perf. 13½x13*
| | | | | |
|---|---|---|---|---|
| 3307 | A921 | 12fo multicolored | 1.10 | .65 |

Exists imperf. Value $5.

A922

A923

**1991, Sept. 6**    **Engr.**    *Perf. 12*
| | | | | |
|---|---|---|---|---|
| 3308 | A922 | 12fo dark red | .65 | .45 |

Count Istvan Szechenyi (1791-1860), founder of Academy of Sciences. Exists imperf. Value $5.

**1991, Sept. 6**     **Litho.**

Wolfgang Amadeus Mozart (1756-91).
| | | | | |
|---|---|---|---|---|
| 3309 | A923 | 12fo As child | 1.00 | .50 |
| 3310 | A923 | 20fo As adult | 2.00 | .80 |

### Souvenir Sheet
| | | | | |
|---|---|---|---|---|
| 3311 | A923 | 30fo +15fo, in red coat | 4.00 | 2.50 |

Stamp Day. No. 3311 contains one 30x40mm stamp.
Exist imperf. Value: set $30; souvenir sheet $60.

Telecom '91 — A924

**1991, Sept. 30**    **Litho.**    *Perf. 12*
| | | | | |
|---|---|---|---|---|
| 3312 | A924 | 12fo multicolored | .90 | .50 |

6th World Forum and Exposition on Telecommunications, Geneva, Switzerland. Exists imperf. Value $5.50.

A925

A926

**1991, Oct. 30**    **Litho.**    *Perf. 13½x13*
| | | | | |
|---|---|---|---|---|
| 3313 | A925 | 12fo multicolored | .90 | .50 |

Sovereign Order of the Knights of Malta. Exists imperf. Value, set $5.50.

**1991, Oct. 30**     *Perf. 12*

Early explorers and Discovery of America, 500th anniv. (in 1992): 7fo, Sebastian Cabot, Labrador Peninsula, Nova Scotia. No. 3315, Amerigo Vespucci, South American region. No. 3316, Hernando Cortez, Mexico. 15fo, Ferdinand Magellan, Straits of Magellan. 20fo, Francisco Pizarro, Peru, Andes Mountain region. 30fo, Christopher Columbus and coat of arms.

| | | | | |
|---|---|---|---|---|
| 3314 | A926 | 7fo multicolored | .50 | .25 |
| 3315 | A926 | 12fo multicolored | .80 | .45 |
| 3316 | A926 | 12fo multicolored | .80 | .45 |
| 3317 | A926 | 15fo multicolored | 1.00 | .60 |
| 3318 | A926 | 20fo multicolored | 1.40 | .75 |
| | *Nos. 3314-3318 (5)* | | 4.50 | 2.50 |

### Souvenir Sheet
| | | | | |
|---|---|---|---|---|
| 3319 | A926 | 30fo multicolored | 2.50 | 2.00 |

No. 3319 contains one 26x37mm stamp. Exist imperf. Value: set $22; souvenir sheet $60.

No. 3023 Overprinted in Brown

**1991, Oct. 22**    **Litho.**    *Perf. 12x11½*
| | | | | |
|---|---|---|---|---|
| 3320 | A816 | 12fo multi | 1.25 | .45 |

Anniversary of Hungarian revolution, 1956.

Christmas — A927

Images of the Virgin and Child from: 7fo, Mariapocs. 12fo, Mariaremete.

**1991, Nov. 20**     *Perf. 13½x13*
| | | | | |
|---|---|---|---|---|
| 3322 | A927 | 7fo multicolored | .65 | .25 |
| 3323 | A927 | 12fo multicolored | 1.10 | .45 |

Nos. 3322-3323 issued in sheets of 20 plus 20 labels.
Exist imperf. Value, set $16.

A928

**1991, Nov. 20**     *Perf. 12*
| | | | | |
|---|---|---|---|---|
| 3324 | A928 | 12fo multicolored | .90 | .45 |

Fight for human rights. Exist imperf. Value $20.

A929

**1991, Dec. 6**     *Perf. 13½x13*
| | | | | |
|---|---|---|---|---|
| 3325 | A929 | 7fo Cross-country skiing | .35 | .20 |
| 3326 | A929 | 12fo Slalom skiing | .70 | .30 |
| 3327 | A929 | 15fo Four-man bob-sled | .80 | .45 |
| 3328 | A929 | 20fo Ski jump | 1.10 | .60 |
| 3329 | A929 | 30fo Hockey | 1.60 | .85 |
| | *Nos. 3325-3329 (5)* | | 4.55 | 2.40 |

### Souvenir Sheet
*Perf. 12½x11½*
| | | | | |
|---|---|---|---|---|
| 3330 | A929 | 30fo Pairs figure skating | 2.50 | 2.00 |

1992 Winter Olympics, Albertville. Exist imperf. Value: set $30; souvenir sheet $22.

### Souvenir Sheet

First Hungarian Postage Stamp, 120th Anniv. — A930

**1991, Dec. 20**    **Litho.**    *Perf. 12x12½*
| | | | | |
|---|---|---|---|---|
| 3331 | A930 | 50fo No. 6 | 4.00 | 3.00 |

Piarist Order in Hungary, 350th Anniv. — A931

**1992, Jan. 22**     *Perf. 13½x13*
| | | | | |
|---|---|---|---|---|
| 3332 | A931 | 10fo multicolored | .85 | .40 |

World Heritage Village of Holloko
A932

**1992, Jan. 22**      **Perf. 12**
3333 A932 15fo multicolored    1.10   .60

1992 Summer Olympics, Barcelona — A933

**1992, Feb. 26**    **Litho.**    **Perf. 13½x13**
3334 A933 7fo Swimming    .55   .40
3335 A933 9fo Cycling    .75   .45
3336 A933 10fo Gymnastics    1.25   .50
3337 A933 15fo Running    2.50   1.25
    Nos. 3334-3337 (4)    5.05   2.60

Discovery of America, 500th Anniv. — A934

Expo '92, Seville: No. 3338, Map shaped as Indian, Columbus' fleet. No. 3339, Face-shaped map of ocean, sailing ship. No. 3340, Map shaped as European face, ship. No. 3341, Map, square, protractor, compass.

**1992, Mar. 27**    **Litho.**    **Perf. 12**
3338 A934 10fo multicolored    .60   .35
3339 A934 10fo multicolored    .60   .35
3340 A934 15fo multicolored    1.00   .55
3341 A934 15fo multicolored    1.00   .55
    Nos. 3338-3341 (4)    3.20   1.80

Jozsef Cardinal Mindszenty (1892-1975), Leader of Hungarian Catholic Church — A935

**1992, Mar. 27**      **Perf. 12½x11½**
3342 A935 15fo red, brn & buff    1.10   .60

A936

**1992, Mar. 27**      **Perf. 13½x13**
3343 A936 15fo multicolored    1.10   .60
Jan Amos Komensky (Comenius), writer, 400th birth anniv.

A937

**1992, Apr. 14**    **Litho.**    **Perf. 13½x13**
3344 A937 15fo Maya Indian
     sculpture    2.50   1.00
3345 A937 40fo Indian sculpture,
     diff.    7.25   3.00
   Europa. Discovery of America, 500th anniv..

European Gymnastics Championships, Budapest — A938

**1992, May 15**    **Litho.**    **Perf. 12**
3346 A938 15fo multicolored    1.10   .60

A939

**1992, June 26**    **Litho.**    **Perf. 13½x13**
3347 A939 15fo multicolored    1.00   .50
   St. Margaret, 750th Anniv. (in 1991). No. 3347 printed with se-tenant label.

A940

**1992, June 26**      **Perf. 13x13½**

Protected birds.

3348 A940 9fo Falco cherrug    .40   .20
3349 A940 10fo Hieraaetus pen-
     natus    .60   .20
3350 A940 15fo Circaetus gal-
     licus    .85   .50
3351 A940 40fo Milvus milvus    1.60   1.00
    Nos. 3348-3351 (4)    3.45   1.90

Raoul Wallenberg, Swedish Diplomat, 80th Anniv. of Birth — A941

**1992, July 30**    **Litho.**    **Perf. 12**
3352 A941 15fo gray & red    1.25   .45

Theodore von Karman (1881-1963), Physicist and Aeronautical Engineer — A942

Design: 40fo, John von Neumann (1903-1957), mathematician.

**1992, Aug. 3**    **Litho.**    **Perf. 12x11½**
3353 A942 15fo multicolored    .45   .25
3354 A942 40fo multicolored    1.90   .70

3rd World Congress of Hungarians A943

**1992, Aug. 3**      **Perf. 13½x13**
3355 A943 15fo multicolored    .80   .35

Telecom '92 — A945

**1992, Oct. 6**    **Litho.**    **Perf. 12½x11½**
3360 A945 15fo multicolored    .80   .35

Stamp Day — A946

**1992, Sept.4**      **Perf. 12**
3361 A946 10fo +5fo Coat of
     arms, vert.    .80   .80
3362 A946 15fo shown    .80   .35
3363 A946 15fo +5fo like #3362,
     inscribed "65.
     Belyegnap"    1.00   .80
    Nos. 3361-3363 (3)    2.60   1.95

**Souvenir Sheet**

3364 A946 50fo +20fo Postilion    4.50   3.25
   Eurofilex '92 (#3361, 3363-3364). Nos. 3361, 3363 printed with se-tenant label. No. 3364 contains one 40x30mm stamp.

Famous Men — A947

Postal Uniforms — A948

Designs: 10fo, Stephen Bathory (1533-1586), Prince of Transylvania and King of

Poland. 15fo, Stephen Bocskay (1557-1606), Prince of Transylvania. 40fo, Gabriel Bethlen (1580-1629), Prince of Transylvania and King of Hungary.

**1992, Oct. 28**    **Litho.**    **Perf. 12**
3365 A947 10fo multicolored    .40   .20
3366 A947 15fo multicolored    .70   .30
3367 A947 40fo multicolored    1.25   .85
    Nos. 3365-3367 (3)    2.35   1.35

**1992, Nov. 20**      **Perf. 13½x13**

Designs: 10fo, Postrider, 1703-1711. 15fo, Letter carrier, 1874.

3368 A948 10fo multicolored    .65   .30
3369 A948 15fo multicolored    1.00   .50

Christmas A949

**Litho. & Engr.**
**1992, Nov. 20**      **Perf. 12**
3370 A949 15fo blue & black    1.00   .50

**Flowers of the Continents Type of 1990**

Flowers of Australia: 9fo, Clianthus formosus. 10fo, Leschenaultia biloba. 15fo, Anigosanthos manglesii. 40fo, Comesperma ericinum. 50fo, Bouquet of flowers.

**1992, Nov. 20**      **Litho.**
3371 A892 9fo multicolored    .50   .25
3372 A892 10fo multicolored    .55   .40
3373 A892 15fo multicolored    .75   .50
3374 A892 40fo multicolored    1.75   1.25
    Nos. 3371-3374 (4)    3.55   2.40

**Souvenir Sheet**
**Perf. 12½**

3375 A892 50fo multicolored    5.00   3.75

No. 3375 contains one 32x41mm stamp.

1992 European Chess Championships A950

**1992, Oct. 28**      **Perf. 11**
3376 A950 15fo multicolored    1.10   .35

**Flowers of the Continents Type of 1990**

Flowers of Asia: No. 3377, Dendrobium densiflorum. No. 3378, Arachnis flos-aeris. No. 3379, Lilium speciosum. No. 3380, Meconopsis aculeata. 50fo, Bouquet of flowers.

**1993, Jan. 27**    **Litho.**    **Perf. 13½x13**
3377 A892 10fo multicolored    .45   .25
3378 A892 10fo multicolored    .45   .25
3379 A892 15fo multicolored    1.00   .50
3380 A892 15fo multicolored    1.00   .50
    Nos. 3377-3380 (4)    2.90   1.50

**Souvenir Sheet**
**Perf. 12½**

3381 A892 50fo multicolored    11.00   3.25

No. 3381 contains one 32x41mm stamp.

Scythian Archaeological Artifacts — A951

**1993, Feb. 25**    **Litho.**    **Perf. 13x13½**
3382 A951 10fo Horse standing    .50   .20
3383 A951 17fo Horse lying down   1.00   .25

Hungarian Rowing Association, Cent. — A952

**1993, Feb. 25    Litho.    Perf. 12**
3384  A952  17fo multicolored    .75  .20

Missale Romanum of Matthias Corvinus (Matyas Hunyadi, King of Hungary) — A953

Design: 40fo, Illuminated page.

**1993, Mar. 12    Litho.    Perf. 12**
3385  A953  15fo multicolored    .75  .25

**Souvenir Sheet**
3386  A953  40fo multicolored    5.00  4.00
Illustration reduced. No. 3386 contains one 60x38mm stamp.
See Belgium Nos. 1474, 1476.

Motocross World Championships A954

**1993, May 5    Litho.    Perf. 11½x12**
3387  A954  17fo multicolored    .60  .25

Europa — A955

Buildings designed by Imre Makovecz: 17fo, Roman Catholic Church, Paks. 45fo, Hungarian Pavilion, Expo '92, Seville.

**1993, May 5    Perf. 13x13½**
3388  A955  17fo multicolored    1.50  .50
3389  A955  45fo multicolored    2.75  1.25

Heliocentric Solar System, Copernicus — A956

**1993, May 5    Perf. 12**
3390  A956  17fo multicolored    .90  .25
Polska '93. No. 3390 issued in sheets of 8 + 4 labels.

Edible Mushrooms A957

**1993, June 18    Litho.    Perf. 13½x13**
3391  A957  10fo Ramaria botrytis    .40  .20
3392  A957  17fo Craterellus cornucopioides    .70  .25
3393  A957  45fo Amanita caesarea    2.25  .80
    Nos. 3391-3393 (3)    3.35  1.25

St. Christopher, by Albrecht Durer — A958

**1993, June 18    Perf. 12**
3394  A958  17fo sil, blk & buff    .65  .20
    Year of the Elderly.

City of Mohacs, 900th Anniv. — A959

**1993, June 18    Perf. 13½x13**
3395  A959  17fo buff, mar & red brn    .65  .20

Hungarian State Railways, 125th Anniv. A960

**1993, June 18    Perf. 13x13½**
3396  A960  17fo lt blue & blue    .65  .20

Comedians A961

**1993, July 28    Litho.    Perf. 12**
3397  A961  17fo Kalman Latabar    .70  .25
3398  A961  30fo Charlie Chaplin    1.10  .65

Butterflies A962

**1993, July 28    Perf. 13½x13**
3399  A962  10fo Limenitis populi    .30  .20
3400  A962  17fo Aricia artaxerxes    .70  .25
3401  A962  30fo Plebejides pylaon    1.25  .65
    Nos. 3399-3401 (3)    2.25  1.10

**Souvenir Sheet**

Helsinki Conference on European Security and Cooperation, 20th Anniv. — A963

**1993, July 28    Perf. 12**
3402  A963  50fo multicolored    2.75  2.50

Intl. Solar Energy Society Congress, Budapest — A964

**Perf. 12½x11½**
**1993, Aug. 23    Litho.**
3403  A964  17fo multicolored    .60  .20
No. 3403 printed se-tenant with label.

Writers — A965

**1993, Aug. 23    Perf. 12**
Designs: No. 3404, Laszlo Nemeth (1901-75). No. 3405, Dezso Szabo (1879-1945). No. 3406, Antal Szerb (1901-45).
3404  A965  17fo blue    .45  .20
3405  A965  17fo blue    .45  .20
3406  A965  17fo blue    .45  .20
    Nos. 3404-3406 (3)    1.35  .60

School of Agronomy, Pannon Agricultural Univ., 175th Anniv. — A966

**1993, Oct. 22    Litho.    Perf. 12**
3407  A966  17fo multicolored    .60  .30

Ships A967

**1993, Oct. 27    Perf. 13x13½**
3408  A967  10fo Steamer with sails    .35  .20
3409  A967  30fo Battleship    1.00  .50
    a.  Pair, #3408-3409    1.60  .70

Prehistoric Man — A968

**1993, Oct. 27    Perf. 13½x13**
3410  A968  17fo Skull fragment    .60  .30
3411  A968  30fo Stone tool    1.00  .50

**Souvenir Sheet**

Roman Roads — A969

**1993, Oct. 27    Perf. 11**
3412  A969  50fo multicolored    2.75  1.50

Christmas A970

Altarpiece: 10fo, Virgin and Christ Child, Cathedral of Szekesfehervar, by F. A. Hillebrant.

**1993, Nov. 24    Perf. 13½x13**
3413  A970  10fo multicolored    .35  .20

Sights of Budapest — A971

Designs: 17fo, Szechenyi Chain Bridge. 30fo, Opera House. 45fo, Matthias Church, vert. Illustration reduced.

**Photo. & Engr.**
**1993, Dec. 16    Perf. 12**
3414  A971  17fo lt grn & dk grn    1.00  .50
3415  A971  30fo lt mag & dk mag    1.50  .60
3416  A971  45fo lt brn & dk brn    2.50  1.40
    Nos. 3414-3416 (3)    5.00  2.50

    Expo '96.

Josef Antall (1932-93) — A972

**1993    Litho.    Perf. 11**
3417  A972  19fo multicolored    .80  .40
    a.  Souvenir sheet    1.50  1.50

ICAO, 50th
Anniv.
A973

**1994, Jan. 13        Perf. 13x13½**
3418  A973  56fo multicolored        1.90    .95

1994 Winter Olympics,
Lillehammer — A974

**1994, Jan. 13        Perf. 12**
3419  A974  12fo Downhill skiing     .40    .20
3420  A974  19fo Ice hockey          .70    .30

A975

Easter: 12fo, Golgotha, by Mihaly
Munkacsy.

**1994, Feb. 17  Litho.  Perf. 11½x12**
3421  A975  12fo multicolored        .40    .20

A976

**1994, Feb. 17**

Artists: 12fo, Gyula Benczur (1844-1920).
19fo, Mihaly Munkacsy (1844-1900).

3422  A976  12fo multicolored        .40    .20
3423  A976  19fo multicolored        .65    .30

Lajos Kossuth
(1802-94)
A977

**1994, Feb. 17**
3424  A977  19fo multicolored        .65    .30

Gen. Joseph
Bem (1794-
1850)
A978

**1994, Mar. 10        Perf. 12**
3425  A978  19fo multicolored        .65    .30

Otis
Tarda — A979

World Wildlife Fund: No. 3426, Female,
male with feathers ruffled in mating dance. No.
3427, Nestlings, female on nest. No. 3428,
Nestlings, female standing. No. 3429, Three
flying.

**1994, Mar. 14**
3426  A979  10fo multicolored        .75    .40
3427  A979  10fo multicolored        .75    .40
3428  A979  10fo multicolored        .75    .40
3429  A979  10fo multicolored        .75    .40
  a.    Block of 4, #3426-3429      3.50   3.00

A980

Europa: 19fo, Sailing steamer Tegetthoff,
Franz-Joseph Land, Julius Payer (1842-1915),
Austrian explorer. 50fo, Mark Aurel Stein
(1862-1943), explorer, archeologist, geographer,
Asian scenes.

**1994, Apr. 1  Litho.  Perf. 13x13½**
3430  A980  19fo multicolored       1.75    .50
3431  A980  50fo multicolored       2.75   1.25

Austro-Hungarian Arctic Expedition, 120th
anniv. (#3430).

A981

#3432, Baron Miklos Josika (1794-1865),
Novelist. #3433, Balint Balassi (1551-94),
poet.

**1994, May 19  Litho.  Perf. 12**
3432  A981  19fo gray               .65    .30
3433  A981  19fo rose lake          .65    .30

Creation of
Magyar Hungary,
1100th Anniv. (in
1996) — A982

Designs: No. 3434, Two soldiers on horseback. No. 3435, Soldier on white horse, others
in background with flags. No. 3436, Soldier on
black horse, others in background. No. 3437,
Man with staff, oxen pulling carts. No. 3438,
Oxen pulling royal cart. No. 3439, Man with
staff on shoulder, oxen with packs. No. 3440,

Minstrels, bard celebrating. No. 3441, Soldiers
preparing to sacrifice white horse. No. 3442,
Shaman before fire, headsman.

**1994-96**
3434  A982  19fo multicolored       .65    .30
3435  A982  19fo multicolored       .65    .30
3436  A982  19fo multicolored       .65    .30
  a.    Strip of 3, #3434-3436     2.00   2.00
3437  A982  22fo multicolored       .65    .30
3438  A982  22fo multicolored       .65    .30
3439  A982  22fo multicolored       .65    .30
  a.    Strip of 3, #3437-3439     2.00   2.00
3440  A982  24fo multicolored       .55    .30
3441  A982  24fo multicolored       .55    .30
3442  A982  24fo multicolored       .55    .30
  a.    Strip of 3, #3440-3442     1.65    .90
  Nos. 3434-3442 (9)               5.55   2.70

Nos. 3436a, 3439a, 3442a are continuous
design. #3436a sold for 59fo.
Nos. 3435, 3438, 3441 are 60x40mm.
Issued: #3434-3436, 5/19/94; #3437-3439,
2/23/95; #3440-3442, 2/29/96.

**Souvenir Sheet**

**1996, Apr. 18**
3442B  A982  195fo multicolored  20.00  16.00

Nos. 3436a, 3439a, 3442a are continuous
design. #3436a sold for 59fo. No. 3442B contains one each of Nos. 3436a, 3439a, 3442a.

Intl. Olympic Committee,
Cent. — A985

Designs: 12fo, 1896, 1992 medals. No.
3444, Flag, runners, Olympic flame. No. 3445,
Athens Stadium, 1896. 35fo, Pierre de
Coubertin (1863-1937), first president.

**1994, June 16  Litho.  Perf. 12½**
3443  A985  12fo multicolored       .45    .20
3444  A985  19fo multicolored       .65    .30
3445  A985  19fo multicolored       .65    .30
3446  A985  35fo multicolored      1.25    .60
  Nos. 3443-3446 (4)               3.00   1.40

1994 World Cup
Soccer
Championships,
US — A986

US flag, soccer players and: No. 3447, Elvis
Presley. No. 3448, Marilyn Monroe. No. 3449,
John Wayne.

**1994, June 16        Perf. 12**
3447  A986  19fo multicolored       .65    .30
3448  A986  19fo multicolored       .65    .30
3449  A986  35fo multicolored      1.25    .60
  Nos. 3447-3449 (3)               2.55   1.20

Intl. Year
of the
Family
A987

**1994, July 21  Litho.  Perf. 11**
3450  A987  19fo multicolored       .65    .30

**Flowers of the Continents Type of
1990**

Flowers of Europe: 12fo, Leucojum aes-
tivum. 19fo, Helianthemum nummularium.
35fo, Eryngium alpinum. 50fo, Thlaspi
rotundifolium. 100fo, Bouquet of European
flowers.

**1994, Aug. 18  Litho.  Perf. 11½x12**
3451  A892  12fo multicolored       .40    .20
3452  A892  19fo multicolored       .65    .35
3453  A892  35fo multicolored      1.25    .60
3454  A892  50fo multicolored      1.60    .85
  Nos. 3451-3454 (4)               3.90   2.00

**Souvenir Sheet**
**Perf. 12½**
3455  A892  100fo multicolored     4.00   2.50

No. 3455 contains one 32x41mm stamp.

UPU, 120th
Anniv.
A988

UPU emblem and: 19fo, Heinrich Von Stephan (1831-97). 35fo, Mihaly Gervay (1819-
96).
  #3458: a, Von Stephan, vert. b, Gervay,
vert.

**1994, Sept. 9  Litho.  Perf. 12**
3456  A988  19fo multicolored       .55    .30
3457  A988  35fo multicolored      1.00    .50

**Souvenir Sheet of 2**
3458  A988  50fo +25fo, #a.-b.     4.50   2.25

Stamp Day, 67th anniv.

Folk
Designs — A989

Various ornate designs.

**1994-96        Litho.  Perf. 11½x12**
3459   A989   1fo bl vio & blk      .20    .20
3460   A989   2fo multi             .20    .20
3461   A989   3fo multi             .20    .20
3461A  A989   9fo multi             .20    .20
3462   A989  11fo multi             .35    .20
3463   A989  12fo multi             .35    .20
3463A  A989  13fo grn, red &
                  blk               .20    .20
3464   A989  14fo multi             .25    .20
3465   A989  16fo bl, red & blk     .30    .20
3466   A989  17fo red & blk         .30    .20
3467   A989  19fo multi             .50    .25
3468   A989  22fo multi             .35    .20
3469   A989  24fo multi             .40    .20
3470   A989  32fo multi             .95    .50
3471   A989  35fo multi            1.00    .50
3472   A989  38fo multi             .65    .30
3473   A989  40fo multi            1.40    .55
3474   A989  50fo multi            1.75    .70
3475   A989  75fo multi            1.50    .65
3476   A989  80fo multi            1.75    .70
3477   A989  300fo multi           6.25   2.60
3478   A989  500fo multi          10.00   4.50
  Nos. 3459-3478 (22)             29.05  13.65

Issued: 11fo, 12fo, 19fo, 32fo, 35fo, 40fo,
50fo, 10/10/94; 1fo, 1/10/95; 2fo, 3fo, 9fo, 14fo,
22fo, 38fo, 4/3/95; 13fo, 16fo, 17fo, 24fo, 75fo,
80fo, 7/1/96.
See #3561, 3615, 3630, 3644-3646, 3649-
3650. For surcharge see #3583.

**Souvenir Sheet**

Summit Meeting of the Conference for
European Security &
Cooperation — A990

**1994, Sept. 10  Litho.  Perf. 12**
3479  A990  100fo Budapest         3.00   2.50

Holocaust, 50th Anniv. — A991

**1994, Oct. 20**
3480 A991 19fo multicolored .55 .30

Buildings in Budapest A992

#3481, Vajdahunyadvar Castle. #3482, Nemzeti Museum. #3483, Muszaki Palace.

**1994, Nov. 17                Engr.**
3481 A992 19fo violet .55 .30
3482 A992 19fo green .55 .30
3483 A992 19fo brown .55 .30
*Nos. 3481-3483 (3)* 1.65 .90

Christmas — A993

**1994, Nov. 17                Litho.**
3484 A993 12fo shown .40 .20
3485 A993 35fo Flight into Egypt 1.25 .60

Hungarian Shipping Co., Cent. — A994

Design: 22fo, Early steamer Francis Joseph I, cargo ship Baross.

**1995, Jan. 24    Litho.    Perf. 13**
3486 A994 22fo multicolored .65 .30

Easter — A995

**1995, Mar. 7                Perf. 12**
3487 A995 14fo black & lilac .45 .25

Hungarian Shipping — A996

Designs: 14fo, Tug-wheeled steamship, map of first navigable section of the Tisza, view of Szeged. 60fo, Pal Vasarhelyi, Tisza survey ship, surveyor.

**1995, Mar. 7                Perf. 13**
3488 A996 14fo multicolored .45 .25
3489 A996 60fo multicolored 2.00 1.00

Natl. Meteorological Service, 125th Anniv. — A997

**1995, Apr. 7                Perf. 12**
3490 A997 22fo multicolored .65 .30

FAO, 50th Anniv. — A998

**1995, Apr. 7**
3491 A998 22fo multicolored .65 .30

European Nature Conservation Year — A999

#3492, Crane, frog, flowers. #3493, Squirrel, insect. #3494, Bird, berries, flowers. #3495, Butterfly, hedgehog, flowers.

**1995, May 9    Litho.    Perf. 13½x13**
3492 A999 14fo multicolored .50 .20
3493 A999 14fo multicolored .50 .20
3494 A999 14fo multicolored .50 .20
3495 A999 14fo multicolored .50 .20
*a.* Strip of 4, #3492-3495 2.25 .75

Peace & Liberty — A1000

**1995, May 9**
3496 A1000 22fo multicolored 2.25 .40
Europa.

Hungarian Olympic Committee, Cent. — A1001

22fo, Diver, Pierre de Coubertin. 60fo, Javelin. 100fo, Fencing.

**1995, June 12    Litho.    Perf. 12**
3497 A1001 22fo multicolored .60 .30
3498 A1001 60fo multicolored 1.60 .80
3499 A1001 100fo multicolored 2.75 1.40
*Nos. 3497-3499 (3)* 4.95 2.50

St. Ladislas I (1040?-1095) A1002

**1995, June 12**
3500 A1002 22fo multicolored .60 .30

Laszlo Almasy, Sahara Researcher, Birth Cent. — A1003

**1995, Aug. 22    Litho.    Perf. 13x13½**
3501 A1003 22fo multicolored .75 .30

Odon Lechner, Architect, 150th Birth Anniv. — A1004

Design: 22fo, Museum of Applied Arts, Lechner. Illustration reduced.

**Litho. & Engr.**
**1995, Aug. 22                Perf. 12**
3502 A1004 22fo multicolored .75 .30

Contemporary Paintings A1005

No. 3503, Abstract, by Laszlo Moholy-Nagy (1895-1946). No. 3504, Woman with a violin, by Aurel Bernath (1895-1982).

**1995, Sept. 18                Litho.**
3503 A1005 22fo multicolored .75 .30
3504 A1005 22fo multicolored .75 .30

Eotvos College, Cent. — A1006

60fo, Eotvos College, Josef Eotvos (1813-71), statesman, writer, educational leader.

**1995, Sept. 18**
3505 A1006 60fo red brn, blk 1.60 .80

Stamp Day A1007

Designs: 22fo, Horse-drawn mail chaise. 40fo, Jet, map. 100fo + 30fo, Man, boys looking at stamp album, vert.

**1995, Sept. 29    Litho.    Perf. 13½x13**
3506 A1007 22fo multicolored .60 .30
3507 A1007 40fo multicolored 1.10 .55

**Souvenir Sheet**
**Perf. 12x12½**
3508 A1007 100fo +30fo multi 3.50 2.50

Buildings of Budapest A1008

#3509, Nyugati Palyaudvar. #3510, Vigado.

**1995                            Perf. 12**
3509 A1008 22fo dark olive brn 1.00 .30
3510 A1008 22fo deep claret 1.00 .30

UN, 50th Anniv. A1009

**1995, Oct. 24    Litho.    Perf. 11**
3511 A1009 60fo multicolored 1.60 .80

Christmas — A1010

**1995, Nov. 16                Perf. 12**
Children's designs: 14fo, Spark thrower. 60fo, The Three Magi.
3512 A1010 14fo multicolored .40 .20
3513 A1010 60fo multicolored 1.60 .80

Nobel Prize Fund Established, Cent. — A1011

**1995, Nov. 16**
3514 A1011 100fo Medals 2.75 1.40
No. 3514 is printed se-tenant with label.

St. Elizabeth of Hungary Bathing Lepers — A1012

**1995, Nov. 16                Perf. 13**
3515 A1012 22fo multicolored .60 .30
No. 3515 is printed se-tenant with label.

A1013

Archaeological Finds from Karos: a, Gold and silver saber. b, Badge.

**1996, Mar. 14    Litho.    Perf. 13½x13**
3516 A1013 24fo #a.-b. + 2 la-
          bels                          2.00  .55

**Souvenir Sheet**

Pannonhalma, Benedictine Monastery,
1000th Anniv. — A1014

**1996, Mar. 21    Engr.    Perf. 12**
3517 A1014 100fo deep violet        5.50 3.50
Sheet margin is litho. and multicolored.

1996 Summer
Olympics,
Atlanta
A1015

**1996, Apr. 18    Litho.    Perf. 11½x12**
3518 A1015 24fo Swimming            .55  .30
3519 A1015 50fo Tennis             1.10  .60
3520 A1015 75fo Kayak              1.75  .85
     Nos. 3518-3520 (3)            3.40 1.75

National
Productivity
A1016

**1996, Apr. 18    Litho.    Perf. 12**
3521 A1016 24fo multicolored        .55  .30

Natl. Writers
Assoc.,
Cent. — A1017

**1996, Apr. 18    Perf. 12x11½**
3522 A1017 50fo multicolored       1.10  .60

Budapest Subway, Cent. — A1018

**1996, May 2    Perf. 12**
3523 A1018 24fo multicolored        .80  .30

Famous
Women
A1019

Europa: 24fo, Queen Gizella. 75fo, Bavarian
Princess Elisabeth Wittelsbach.

**1996, May 2    Litho.    Perf. 12**
3524 A1019 24fo multicolored       1.00  .50
3525 A1019 75fo multicolored       3.00 1.25

Pannonhalma,
Benedictine
Monastery,
1000th Anniv.
A1020

Designs: 17fo, Entrance to cathedral. 24fo,
Monks in northern wing.

**1996, June 21    Engr.    Perf. 12**
3526 A1020 17fo red brown           .60  .20
3527 A1020 24fo dark blue           .90  .30
          See Nos. 3536-3537.

Intl. Anti-Drug
Day — A1021

**1996, June 21    Litho.    Perf. 14**
3528 A1021 24fo multicolored        .55  .30

Hungarian Developers of
Technolgy — A1022

Inventor, invention: 24fo, Denes Mihaly
(1894-1953), Telehor. 50fo, Jozsef Biro Laszlo
(1899-1985), mass-produced ball-point pen.
75fo, Zoltan Bay (1900-92), lunar radar set.

**1996, June 21    Perf. 12x11½**
3529 A1022 24fo multicolored        .55  .30
3530 A1022 50fo multicolored       1.10  .60
3531 A1022 75fo multicolored       1.75  .85
     Nos. 3529-3531 (3)            3.40 1.75

Hungarian Railways, 150th
Anniv. — A1023

Designs: 17fo, 303-Series steam tender
locomotive. No. 3533, 325-Series locomotive .
No. 3534, "Pest," steam locomotive made by
Cokerill and Co.

**1996, July 12    Perf. 13½x13**
3532 A1023 17fo multicolored        .55  .20
3533 A1023 24fo multicolored        .70  .30
3534 A1023 24fo multicolored       1.50  .30
     Nos. 3532-3534 (3)            2.75  .80

Second European
Congress of
Mathematicians
A1024

**1996, July 12    Perf. 12**
3535 A1024 24fo multicolored        .55  .30

Pannonhalma, Benedictine Monastery,
Type of 1996

Designs: 17fo, Refectory. 24fo, Main library.

**1996, Aug. 12    Engr.    Perf. 12**
3536 A1020 17fo dark brown          .60  .20
3537 A1020 24fo dark green          .90  .20

Nature
Expo '96
A1025

**1996, Aug. 12    Litho.    Perf. 12x11½**
3538 A1025 13fo Egretta alba        .20  .20
3539 A1025 13fo Iris sibirica       .20  .20
3540 A1025 13fo Lynx lynx           .20  .20
3541 A1025 13fo Ropalopus un-
              garicus              1.20 1.20
  a.    Block of 4, #3538-3541      2.00 2.00

A1026           A1027

**1996, Aug. 12    Perf. 12**
3542 A1026 24fo No. 4              1.00  .20
Hungarian postage stamps, 125th anniv.
Issued in miniature sheets of 6 stamps in
two columns of 3 separated by a column of
labels. Values, stamp plus label $1.50, minia-
ture sheet $7.50.

**1996, Aug. 21    Litho.    Perf. 11½x12**
Stamp Day, Budapest '96: 17fo, Prince
Arpad, people from 14th cent. "Vienna Picture
Chronicle," man stirring liquid in pot. 24fo,
Prince on horseback, archer.
  150fo+50fo, #601, first page from "The
Deeds of Hungarians."

3543 A1027  17fo multicolored       .60  .20
3544 A1027  24fo multicolored       .90  .20
**Souvenir Sheet**
**Perf. 12x12½**
3545 A1027 150fo +50fo multi       5.50 3.00

Steamships on Lake Balaton, 150th
Anniv. — A1028

Steamer Kisfaludy.

**1996, Sept. 17    Litho.    Perf. 12**
3548 A1028 17fo multicolored        .60  .20

Hungarian Revolution, 40th
Anniv. — A1029

Newspaper clippings and: 13fo, People
marching. 16fo, Troops on back of truck. 17fo,
Two men with guns. 24fo, Imre Nagy addressing people.
  40fo, Nagy Cabinet.

**1996, Oct. 23    Litho.    Perf. 12**
3549 A1029 13fo multicolored        .35  .20
3550 A1029 16fo multicolored        .40  .20
3551 A1029 17fo multicolored        .40  .20
3552 A1029 24fo multicolored        .60  .20
     Nos. 3549-3552 (4)            1.75  .80
**Souvenir Sheet**
3553 A1029 40fo multicolored       4.00 2.25

**Souvenir Sheet**

1996 Summer Olympic Games,
Atlanta — A1030

Illustration reduced.

**1996, Oct. 22**
3554 A1030 150fo multicolored      4.50 2.25

A1036

**1996, Nov. 14    Litho.    Perf. 11½x12**
3555 A1036 24fo multicolored        .40  .20
Miklos Wesselenyi (1796-1850), writer.

A1037

**1996, Nov. 14    Perf. 13½x13**
3556 A1037 24fo multicolored        .40  .20
UNICEF, 50th anniv.

Christmas
A1038

Paintings: 17fo, Mary with Infant Jesus and Two Angels, by Matteo di Giovanni. 24fo, Adoration of the Kings, by unknown painter of Salsburg.

**1996, Nov. 14**      *Perf. 12*
3557 A1038 17fo multicolored    .35   .20
3558 A1038 24fo multicolored    .65   .20

Hungarian Literature — A1039

Designs: No. 3559, Scenes from "The Umbrella of St. Peter," Kalman Mikszath (1847-1910). No. 3560, Scenes of men and dogs from "Abel in the Vast Trackless Forest" and "Matthias the Ice-breaker," Aron Tamasi (1897-1966).

**1997, Jan. 16**   Litho.   *Perf. 12x11½*
3559 A1039 27fo multicolored    .50   .25
3560 A1039 27fo multicolored    .50   .25

**Folk Art Type of 1994**

**1997, Mar. 26**      *Perf. 11½x12*
3561 A989 27fo multicolored     .50   .25

Coat of Arms of Budapest and Counties — A1040

No. 3562: a, Hajdú-Bihar. b, Baranya. c, Bács-Kiskun. d, Békés. e, Borsod-Abaúj-Zemplén.
No. 3563: a, Fejér. b, Györ-Moson-Sopron. c, Heves. d, Jász-Nagykun-Szolnok. e, Komárom-Esztergom. f, Nógrád.
No. 3564: a, Pest. b, Somogy. c, Toina. d, Vas. e, Veszprém. f, Zala.
No. 3565: a, Budapest. b, Csongrád. c, Szaboics-Szatmár-Bereg.

**1997, Mar. 26**      *Perf. 11½x12*
3562   A1040 27fo Sheet of 5,
       #a.-e. + label 4.25 3.00
3563   A1040 27fo Sheet of 6,
       #a.-f.      5.50 4.00
3564   A1040 27fo Sheet of 6,
       #a.-f.      5.50 4.00
3564G A1040 27fo Hajdu-Bihar   .50   .50
      **Size: 51x33mm**
3565   A1040 27fo Sheet of 3,
       #a.-c.      2.25 1.75

No. 3564G is 51x33mm and has the same design as No. 3562a which has a se-tenant label, but lacks the perforations separating these items. Nos. 3262a-3262e, 3563a-3563f, 3564a-3564f, 3565a-3565c were also printed

in individual sheets. Value, set of singles (20): mint $10; used $4.

Youth Stamps — A1042

Designs: 20fo, Scouting emblem, tents, sailboat, waterfall. 27fo+10fo, Knights on horseback from "Toldi," by Janos Arany.

**1997, Apr. 23**      *Perf. 12*
3566 A1041 20fo multicolored    .50   .20
3567 A1042 27fo +10fo multi   1.25   .35

A1043

**1997, Apr. 23**      *Perf. 13½x13*
3568 A1043 90fo multicolored   1.60   .80
World Meeting of Custom Directors.

A1044

**1997, Apr. 23**   Engr.   *Perf. 12*
3569 A1044 80fo deep violet   1.75   .70
St. Adalbert (956-997). See Germany No. 1964, Poland No. 3307, Czech Republic No. 3012, Vatican City No. 1040..

Stories and Legends A1045

Europa: 27fo, Hunters on horseback shooting bow and arrow at deer. 90fo, Preparing body in sarcophagus of Prince Geza.

**1997, May 5**   Litho.   *Perf. 13x13½*
3570 A1045 27fo multicolored   *1.00*   .40
3571 A1045 90fo multicolored   *2.25*   .90

African Animals A1046

16fo, Oryx gazella. #3573, Equus burchelli. #3574, Diceros bicornis. 27fo, Panthera leo. 90fo, Loxodonta africana.

**1997, May 5**      *Perf. 12*
3572 A1046 16fo multicolored    .25   .20
3573 A1046 20fo multicolored    .55   .20
3574 A1046 20fo multicolored    .55   .20
3575 A1046 27fo multicolored    .90   .30
    Nos. 3572-3575 (4)    2.25   .90
       **Souvenir Sheet**
3576 A1046 90fo multicolored   4.00 2.50

A1047

**1997, June 8**   Litho.   *Perf. 12*
3577 A1047 90fo multicolored   1.60   .70
Polish Queen Jadwiga (1373-99).

A1048

World Congress on Stress, Budapest: Janos (Hans) Selye (1907-82), founder of theory of stress, face of person under stress.

**1997, July 1**
3578 A1048 90fo multicolored   1.60   .70

Indigenous Fish A1049

Designs: a, Gymnocephalus schraetzer. b, Cottus gobio. c, Alburnoides bipunctatus. d, Cobitis taenia.

**1997, June 6**   Litho.   *Perf. 13x13½*
3579 A1049 20fo Strip of 4, #a.-
       d.      2.50 1.25

Grapes and Wine Producing Areas Type of 1990

Grapes and growing area: No. 3580, Nemes kadarka, Great Kiskoros. No. 3581, Teitfürtü ezerjo, Mor. No. 3582, Harslevelu, Gyongyos.

**1997, Aug. 12**   Litho.   *Perf. 13x13½*
3580 A902 27fo multicolored    .40   .20
3581 A902 27fo multicolored    .40   .20
3582 A902 27fo multicolored    .90   .20
    Nos. 3580-3582 (3)    1.70   .60

No. 3469 Surcharged in Red

**1997, July 10**   Litho.   *Perf. 11½x12*
3583 A989 60fo on 24fo multi    .90   .45

Christmas
A1050

20fo, Holy family. 27fo, Adoration of the Magi.

**1997, Oct. 31**   Litho.   *Perf. 13x13½*
3584 A1050 20fo multicolored    .40   .20
3585 A1050 27fo multicolored    .60   .20

World Weight Lifting Championships, Thailand A1051

**1997, Nov. 12**      *Perf. 12*
3586 A1051 90fo multicolored   1.60   .65

Zsigmond Szechenyi, African Explorer A1052

**1998, Jan. 22**   Litho.   *Perf. 12*
3587 A1052 60fo multicolored   1.60   .45

Natl. Anthem by Ferenc Kolcsey, 175th Anniv. A1053

**1998, Jan. 22**
3588 A1053 75fo multicolored   1.60   .55

1998 Winter Olympic Games, Nagano — A1054

**1998, Jan. 22**      *Perf. 13½x13*
3589 A1054 30fo Downhill skiing   .45   .25
3590 A1054 100fo Snowboarding 1.50   .75

Valentine's Day — A1055

**1998, Feb. 11**      *Perf. 11½x12*
3591 A1055 24fo multi      .55   .20

A1056          A1057

**1998, Feb. 11                        Perf. 12**
3592 A1056 50fo multicolored          1.50   .40
Leo Szilard (1898-1964), physicist.

**1998, Feb. 11                  Perf. 11½x12**
Balint Postas (Post Office Mascot) in front of
printed material: 23fo, Holding letter. 24fo,
Bowing. 30fo, Standing straight with arms outstretched. 65fo, Flying.

3593 A1057 23fo multicolored          .45   .20
3594 A1057 24fo multicolored          .45   .20
3595 A1057 30fo multicolored          .60   .25
3596 A1057 65fo multicolored         1.25   .50
    Nos. 3593-3596 (4)               2.75  1.15

Easter
A1058          A1059

**1998, Mar. 13    Litho.      Perf. 13½x13**
3597 A1058 24fo Stylized egg          .55   .20
                          **Perf. 11**
3598 A1059 30fo Christ's resur-
              rection                 .65   .20

1848-49 Revolution, War of
Independence, 150th Anniv. — A1060

23fo, Sandor Petofi (1823-49), poet, hand-
writing, tricolor. 24fo, Mihaly Tancsics, writer &
politician, ink well. 30fo, Lajos Kossuth (1802-
94), seal.

**1998, Mar. 13                        Perf. 12**
3599 A1060 23fo multicolored          .40   .20
3600 A1060 24fo multicolored          .50   .20
3601 A1060 30fo multicolored          .60   .20
    Nos. 3599-3601 (3)               1.50   .60

        See Nos. 3640-3643.

Art Nouveau — A1061

Ceramics: 20fo, Vase with relief design of
young girl picking flowers, 1899. 24fo, Flower
holder with peacock-eyed butterflies, 1901.
30fo, Vase with tulip stems, 1899. 95fo, Round
container with legs, 1912.

**1998, Mar. 31    Litho.               Perf. 12**
3602 A1061 20fo multi, vert.          .35   .20
        Complete booklet, 10 #3602   3.25
3603 A1061 24fo multi                 .40   .20
        Complete booklet, 10 #3603   3.75
3604 A1061 30fo multi, vert.          .50   .25
        Complete booklet, 10 #3604   4.75
3605 A1061 95fo multi                1.50   .70
    Nos. 3602-3605 (4)               2.75  1.35

Postal Regulation, 250th
Anniv. — A1062

Designs: 24fo+10fo, Courier of 1748, detail
of postal route connecting counties of Zala
and Gyor. 30fo+10fo, Mounted courier, blowing post horn, script of regulation.
150fo, Horse-drawn postal coach, detail of
postal route.

**1998, Apr. 10**
3606 A1062 24fo +10fo multi           .75   .45
3607 A1062 30fo +10fo multi          1.25   .60

            **Souvenir Sheet**
3608 A1062 150fo multicolored        5.00  2.50

            Stamp Day.

Animals of
the
Americas
A1063

23fo, Bison bison. #3610, Ursus horribilis.
#3611, Alligator mississippiensis. 30fo,
Leopardus pardalis.
150fo, Loddigesia mirabilis.

**1998, Apr. 30**
3609 A1063 23fo multicolored          .70   .35
3610 A1063 24fo multicolored          .70   .35
3611 A1063 24fo multicolored          .70   .35
3612 A1063 30fo multicolored          .90   .45
    Nos. 3609-3612 (4)               3.00  1.50

            **Souvenir Sheet**
3613 A1063 150fo multicolored        5.00  2.50

Gyorgy
Jendrassik,
Engineer,
Birth Cent.
A1064

**1998, May 4                          Engr.**
3614 A1064 100fo dark blue           1.50   .75

    Folk Designs Type of 1994
**1998, June 5    Litho.    Perf. 11½x12**
3615 A989 5fo multicolored            .20   .20

1998 Canoe-Kayak World
Championships, Szeged — A1065

**1998, June 5                         Perf. 12**
3616 A1065 30fo multicolored          .45   .20

1998 World Cup Soccer
Championships, France — A1066

Different soccer players.

**1998, June 5**
3617 A1066 30fo multicolored          .45   .20
3618 A1066 110fo multicolored        1.60   .80
    a.  Pair, 3617-3618              2.10  1.00

1998 European
Track & Field
Championships,
Budapest — A1067

**1998, June 5                       Perf. 12x11**
3619 A1067 24fo Hurdles               .35   .20
3620 A1067 65fo Pole vault            .95   .50
3621 A1067 80fo Hammer throw         1.25   .60
    Nos. 3619-3621 (3)               2.55  1.30

Gabor Baross
(1848-92),
Postal
Administrator
A1068

**1998, June 5                         Perf. 12**
3622 A1068 60fo multicolored          .90   .45

A1069

**1998, July 31    Litho.              Perf. 12**
3623 A1069 24fo multicolored          .60   .25
    Complete booklet, 10 #3623      10.00
Széchenyi Hill Children's Railway, 50th
anniv.

A1070

**1998, July 31                    Perf. 12x11½**
3624 A1070 65fo multicolored          .95   .50
World Congress of Computer Technology,
Budapest.

Natl.
Holidays — A1071

Europa: 50fo, Sculptures, Festival of the
1956 Revolution, Proclamation of the Republic, 1989, October 23. 60fo, Sheaf of grain,
Natl. arms, National Day, August 20.

**1998, Aug. 19    Litho.              Perf. 12**
3625 A1071 50fo multicolored         1.50   .65
3626 A1071 60fo multicolored         2.25   .85

A1072

**1998, Aug. 19**
3627 A1072 100fo multicolored        1.40   .70
World Federation of Hungarians, 60th Anniv.

National
Parks
A1073

Various flora, fauna, explorer of given
region: 24fo, Dr. Miklós Udvardy, Hortobágy
Natl. Park. 70fo, Adám Boros, Kiskunság Natl.
Park.

**1998, Oct. 6    Litho.               Perf. 12**
3628 A1073 24fo multicolored          .50   .20
3629 A1073 70fo multicolored         1.25   .50

    See Nos. 3654-3655, 3689-3690, 3745-
3747, 3689-3690, 4072.

    Folk Designs Type of 1994
**1998         Litho.       Perf. 11½x12**
3630 A989 200fo multicolored         5.00   .70

Christmas
A1074

Designs: 20fo, Painting, "Visit of the Shep-
herds," by Agnolo Bronzino (1503-72). 24fo,
Artwork, "Mary Upon the Throne with the
Infant," by Carlo Crivelli (1430?-94?), vert.

**1998, Oct. 30      Perf. 12x11½, 11½x12**
3631 A1074 20fo multicolored          .40   .20
        Complete booklet, 10 #3631   3.75
3632 A1074 24fo multicolored          .45   .20
        Complete booklet, 10 #3632   6.50

        See No. 3676.

Easter
A1075

**1999, Feb. 11    Litho.              Perf. 12**
3633 A1075 27fo Decorated eggs        .35   .20
3634 A1075 32fo Shroud of Turin       .75   .20

    No. 3634 is 38x53mm.

Intl. Year of the
Elderly
A1076

**1999, Feb. 11                    Perf. 12½x13½**
3635 A1076 32fo multicolored          .75   .20

Sailing Ships
A1077

**1999, Feb. 11**     *Perf. 12*
3636 A1077 32fo Novara .40 .20
3637 A1077 79fo Phoenix 1.00 .50
3638 A1077 110fo Galley, 15th
    cent. 1.40 .70
*Nos. 3636-3638 (3)* 2.80 1.40

**Souvenir Sheet**

Total Solar Eclipse, Aug. 11 — A1078

Illustration reduced.

**1999, Feb. 11**
3639 A1078 1999fo multi 22.00 22.00
No. 3639 contains a holographic image.
Soaking in water may affect the hologram.

**Revolution of 1848-49 Type of 1998**
24fo, Sword, Artúr Görgey (1818-1916),
general. 27fo, Military decoration, Lajos
Batthyány (1806-49), premier of 1st Hungarian
ministry. 32fo, Military decoration, Jósef Bem
(1794-1850), Polish General who joined Hungarian army.
100fo, Battle scene.

**1999, Mar. 12**
3640 A1060 24fo multicolored .45 .20
3641 A1060 27fo multicolored .55 .20
3642 A1060 32fo multicolored .60 .20
*Nos. 3640-3642 (3)* 1.60 .60

**Souvenir Sheet**
3643 A1060 100fo multicolored 4.00 2.00
No. 3643 contains one 45x28mm stamp.

**Folk Designs Type of 1994**
**1999**     Litho.     *Perf. 12½*
3644 A989 24fo multicolored .40 .20
3645 A989 65fo red & black 1.10 .30
3646 A989 90fo multicolored 2.00 .55
*Nos. 3644-3646 (3)* 3.50 1.05

Nos. 3644-3646 are inscribed "1999."

Entrance into
NATO — A1079

**1999, Mar. 12**   Litho.   *Perf. 12x11½*
3647 A1079 110fo multicolored 1.60 .55

**Souvenir Sheet**

1999 Modern Pentathlon World
Championships, Budapest — A1080

Illustration reduced.

**1999, Mar. 24**     *Perf. 12½*
3648 A1080 100fo multicolored 3.50 1.75

**Folk Designs Type of 1994**
Various ornate designs.

**1999, Apr. 19**   Litho.   *Perf. 11½x12*
3649 A989 79fo multicolored 1.60 .45
3650 A989 100fo multicolored 2.40 .60

A1081

A1082

**1999, May 3**     *Perf. 12*
3651 A1081 50fo slate & bister .85 .30
Ferenc Pápai Páriz (1649-1716).

**1999, May 3**
3652 A1082 100fo multicolored 1.50 .65
Ferencvárosi Torna Sport Club, cent.

World
Science
Conference
A1082a

**1999, May 3**   Litho.   *Perf. 11½x12½*
3652A A1082a 65fo multicolored 1.75 .50

Council
of
Europe,
50th
Anniv.
A1083

**1999, May 4**     *Perf. 13x13¼*
3653 A1083 50fo multicolored 1.75 .50

**National Parks Type of 1998**
Europa: 27fo, Aggteleki National Park. 32fo,
Bükki National Park.

**1999, May 6**     *Perf. 12*
3654 A1073 27fo multicolored 3.00 1.25
3655 A1073 32fo multicolored 4.50 2.00

**Grapes and Wine Producing Areas
Type of 1990**
Grapes, growing area and: 24fo, Castle
ruins, Somló region. 27fo, 17th cent. view of
Sopron.

**1999, May 6**   Litho.   *Perf. 12¼x12½*
3656 A902 24fo multi, horiz. .60 .20
3657 A902 27fo multi, horiz. .90 .25

Animals
of Asia
A1085

Designs: 27fo, Tigris regalis. 32fo, Ailuro-
podus melanoleucus. 52fo, Panthera pardus.
79fo, Pongo pygmaeus.
100fo, Áix galericulata.

**1999, May 6**     *Perf. 12*
3658 A1085 27fo multicolored .50 .25
3659 A1085 32fo multicolored .65 .30
3660 A1085 52fo multicolored .95 .40
3661 A1085 79fo multicolored 1.90 .50
*Nos. 3658-3661 (4)* 4.00 1.45

**Souvenir Sheet**
3662 A1085 100fo multicolored 6.00 4.25
No. 3662 contains one 50x30mm stamp.

Queen Maria
Theresa's
Introduction of
Mail Coach
Service, 250th
Anniv.
A1086

Stamp Day: 32fo+15fo, Decree by Maria
Theresa, coach, street. 52fo+20fo, People
entering coach, woman with letters, portion of
decree.
150fo, Horse-drawn coach arriving a station.

**1999, May 21**   Litho.   *Perf. 12½x12¼*
3663 A1086 32fo +15fo multi .80 .75
3664 A1086 52fo +20fo multi 1.40 1.00

**Souvenir Sheet**
3665 A1086 150fo multicolored 4.00 3.50
#3665 contains one 32x42mm stamp.

Red
Poppy — A1087

**1999, July 7**   Litho.   *Perf. 12x11½*
3666 A1087 27fo shown 1.00 .40
3667 A1087 32fo Stalkless gen-
    tian 1.50 .70

George Cukor
(1899-1983), Film
Director — A1088

**1999, July 7**   Litho.   *Perf. 12*
3668 A1088 50fo multicolored 1.00 .25

UPU, 125th
Anniv.
A1089

**1999, Aug. 13**   Litho.   *Perf. 12*
3669 A1089 32fo multicolored 1.00 .80
Issued in sheets of 3. Value $3.50.

Frankfurt Book Fair — A1090

**1999, Sept. 9**   Litho.   *Perf. 12*
3670 A1090 40fo multicolored 1.50 .20

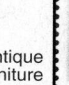

Antique
Furniture
A1091

Designs: 10fo, Chair, 17th cent, vert. 20fo,
Chair by Károly Lingel, 1915, vert. 50fo, Chair
by Pál Esterházy, vert. 70fo, Upholstered
chair, vert. 100fo, Couch by Lajos Kozma.

**Perf. 11½x12, 12x11½**
**1999, Oct. 7**     Litho.
3671 A1091 10fo bister & dk brn .20 .20
3672 A1091 20fo green & dk
    grn .35 .20
3673 A1091 50fo blue & dk bl .75 .25
3674 A1091 70fo red & dk red 1.10 .30
3675 A1091 100fo brown & dk
    brn 1.60 .45
*Nos. 3671-3675 (5)* 4.00 1.40

Nos. 3671-3673, 3675 exist dated "2001."
See Nos. 3711-3721.

**Bronzino Christmas Painting Type
of 1998 and**

Magi — A1092

Madonna and Child,
Stained Glass by
Miksa
Róth — A1093

**1999, Oct. 15**   *Perf. 12x11½, 11½x12*
3676 A1074 24fo multi .65 .20
   Complete booklet, 10 #3676 10.00
3677 A1092 27fo multi .85 .20
   Complete booklet, 10 #3677 9.50
3678 A1093 32fo multi 1.00 .20
   Complete booklet, 10 #3678 10.00
*Nos. 3676-3678 (3)* 2.50 .60

Jenö Wigner
(1902-95), Winner
of 1963 Nobel
Physics
Prize — A1094

**1999, Nov. 3**     *Perf. 12*
3679 A1094 32fo blue .50 .25

**Souvenir Sheet**

Chain Bridge, 150th Anniv. — A1095

Illustration reduced.

**1999, Nov. 3**
3680 A1095 150fo multi 3.00 2.00

Hungarian
Millennium
A1096

Designs: 28fo, 30fo, Coronation scepter. 34fo, 40fo, Millennium flag.

| 2000 | Litho. | Perf. 12x11½ | |
|---|---|---|---|
| 3681 | A1096 28fo multi | .75 | .20 |
| 3682 | A1096 30fo multi | .75 | .20 |
| 3683 | A1096 34fo multi | .75 | .20 |
| 3684 | A1096 40fo multi | 1.00 | .20 |
| | Nos. 3681-3684 (4) | 3.25 | .80 |

Coronation of Stephen I, Hungarian conversion to Christianity, 1000th anniv.
Issued: 30fo, 40fo, 1/1; 28fo, 24fo, 2/24.
No. 3681 exists dated 2001.

### Souvenir Sheet

Famous Hungarians
A1097

No. 3685: a, 30fo, Miklós Misztófalusi Kis (1650-1702), scientist. b, 40fo, Anyos Jedlik (1800-95), physicist. c, 50fo, Jeno Kvassay (1850-1919), engineer. d, 80fo, Jeno Barcsay (1900-88), painter.

| 2000, Jan. 11 | | Perf. 11½x12 | |
|---|---|---|---|
| 3685 | A1097 Sheet of 4, #a.-d. | 3.50 | 3.25 |

### Souvenir Sheet of 5

Literary and
Theatrical
Personalities
A1098

No. 3686: a, Mihály Vörösmarty (1800-55), dramatist. b, Mari Jászai (1850-1926), actress. c, Sándor Márai (1900-89), writer. d, Lujza Blaha (1850-1926), actress. e, Lorinc Szabó (1900-57), writer.

| 2000, Feb. 24 | | Perf. 12 | |
|---|---|---|---|
| 3686 | A1098 50fo #a.-e. | 3.50 | 3.00 |

A1099

Easter — A1100

| 2000, Mar. 20 | | | |
|---|---|---|---|
| 3687 | A1099 26fo multi | .40 | .20 |
| 3688 | A1100 28fo multi | .60 | .20 |

### National Parks Type of 1998

Designs: 29fo, Bluethroat, Siberian iris, ornithologist György Breuer (1887-1955), Ferto-Hanság Park. 34fo, Black stork, fritillary, scientist Pál Kitaibel (1757-1817), Duna-Dráva Park.

| 2000, Mar. 20 | Litho. | Perf. 12 | |
|---|---|---|---|
| 3689 | A1073 29fo multi | .60 | .20 |
| | Complete booklet, 10 #36892 | 5.50 | |
| 3690 | A1073 34fo multi | 1.00 | .35 |
| | Complete booklet, 10 #3690 | 7.50 | |

Ferihegy
Airport, 50th
Anniv. — A1101

| 2000, May 3 | | Perf. 12x11½ | |
|---|---|---|---|
| 3691 | A1101 136fo multi | 1.75 | .80 |

István Türr (1825-1908) and Canal
Boat — A1102

| 2000, May 9 | | Perf. 12 | |
|---|---|---|---|
| 3692 | A1102 80fo multi | 1.25 | .65 |

Expo 2000, Hanover.

Australian
Wildlife — A1103

| 2000, May 9 | | | |
|---|---|---|---|
| 3693 | A1103 26fo shown | .30 | .20 |
| 3694 | A1103 28fo Opossum | .35 | .20 |
| 3695 | A1103 83fo Koala | 1.10 | .30 |
| 3696 | A1103 90fo Red kangaroo | 1.00 | .35 |
| | Nos. 3693-3696 (4) | 2.75 | 1.05 |

### Souvenir Sheet

| 3697 | A1103 110fo Platypus | 3.50 | 2.00 |
|---|---|---|---|

### Souvenir Sheet

Millennium — A1104

### Litho., Hologram in Margin
2000, May 9

| 3698 | A1104 2000fo multi | 25.00 | 25.00 |
|---|---|---|---|

Soaking in water may affect the hologram.

### Europa, 2000
Common Design Type and

A1105

| 2000, May 9 | | Litho. | |
|---|---|---|---|
| 3699 | A1105 34fo multi | 2.75 | .75 |
| 3700 | CD17 54fo multi | 3.75 | 1.75 |

Stamp
Day — A1106

26fo, Queen Gisela in coronation gown. 28fo, King Stephen I in coronation gown.

| 2000, May 18 | | | |
|---|---|---|---|
| 3701 | A1106 26fo multi | .60 | .40 |
| 3702 | A1106 28fo multi | .90 | .60 |

Austria No.
4 and
Bisect
A1107

| 2000, May 18 | | | |
|---|---|---|---|
| 3703 | A1107 110fo multi | 1.75 | 1.75 |

WIPA 2000 Philatelic Exhibition, Vienna.

### Grapes and Wine Producing Areas Type of 1990

Grapes and: 29fo, Winery building, Balatonfüred-Csopak region, horiz. 34fo, Storage containers, Aszár-Neszmély region, horiz.

| 2000, May 25 | | Perf. 13¼x13 | |
|---|---|---|---|
| 3704 | A902 29fo multi | .60 | .35 |
| 3705 | A902 34fo multi | 1.00 | .40 |

Houses of
Worship
A1108

Designs: No. 3706, 30fo, Abbey Church, Ják. No. 3707, 30fo, Reformed Church, Tákos. No. 3708, 30fo, St. Antal's Church, Eger. No. 3709, 30fo, Deák Evangelical Church, Budapest. 120fo, Dohany Synagogue, Budapest.

| 2000 | Litho. | Perf. 12 | |
|---|---|---|---|
| 3706-3710 | A1108 Set of 5 | 3.00 | 3.00 |

Issued: 120fo, 9/19; others 6/30. See Israel No. 1416.

### Furniture Type of 1999

Designs: 2fo, Wooden chair, 1838, vert. 3fo, 19th cent. chair, vert. 4fo, Chair by Géza Maróti, 1900, vert. 5fo, Chair by Odon Farago, 1900, vert. 6fo, Chair by Márton Kovács, 1893, vert. 9fo, 18th cent. chair from Dunapataj, vert. 26fo, 1850 chair, vert. 29fo, 19th cent. chair with animal designs, vert. 30fo, Chair by Károly Nagy, 1935, vert. 80fo, 1840-50 chair, vert. 90fo, Chair by Lajos Kozma, 1928, vert.

| 2000 | | Perf. 11½x12 | |
|---|---|---|---|
| 3711-3721 | A1091 Set of 11 | 4.50 | 2.00 |

Issued: 2fo, 3fo, 9fo, 26fo, 29fo, 30fo, 6/30; others, 10/9.

Hungarian
Aviation, 90th
Anniv.
A1109

| 2000, Aug. 18 | | Perf. 12¾x12¼ | |
|---|---|---|---|
| 3722 | A1109 120fo multi | 1.75 | 1.50 |

### Souvenir Sheets

Hungarian
History
A1110

No. 3723: a, King with orb, knights. b, St. Laszlo with sword. c, St. Elizabeth, Mongol invasion. d, King Sigismund, knight on horseback. e, Janos Hunuyadi and Janos Kapisztran.

No. 3724: a, King Matthias. b, Crucifixion scene, Miklos Zrinyi. c, Trumpeter on horseback, battle scenes. d, Gabor Bethlen (in black hat). e, Peer Parmany, university.

| 2000, Aug. 18 | | Perf. 12 | |
|---|---|---|---|
| 3723 | Sheet of 5 | 5.00 | 3.50 |
| a.-e. | A1110 50fo Any single | .70 | .35 |
| 3724 | Sheet of 5 | 5.00 | 3.50 |
| a.-e. | A1110 50fo Any single | .70 | .35 |

A1111

A1112

Christmas
A1113

| 2000, Oct. 16 | | Perf. 12¼x11½ | |
|---|---|---|---|
| 3725 | A1111 26fo shown | .40 | .20 |
| | | Perf. 13¼x13 | |
| 3726 | A1112 28fo shown | .65 | .20 |
| | Booklet, 10 #3726 | 7.00 | |
| 3727 | A1112 29fo Christmas tree | .65 | .20 |
| | | Perf. 12 | |
| 3728 | A1113 34fo shown | .70 | .20 |
| | Booklet, 10 #3728 | 8.00 | |
| | Nos. 3725-3728 (4) | 2.40 | .80 |

European Convention on Human
Rights, 50th Anniv. — A1114

| 2000, Nov. 3 | | Perf. 12½ | |
|---|---|---|---|
| 3729 | A1114 50fo multicolored | .75 | .50 |

2000
Summer
Olympics,
Sydney
A1115

Sports and total of medals won: 30fo, Shooting, three bronzes. 40fo, Weight lifting, six silvers. 80fo, Men's rings, eight golds. 120fo, Rowing, total count.

| 2000, Nov. 22 | | Perf. 12 | |
|---|---|---|---|
| 3730-3732 | A1115 Set of 3 | 1.50 | 1.50 |
| | Souvenir Sheet | | |
| 3733 | A1115 120fo multi | 3.00 | 1.75 |

European Language Year A1116

**2001, Jan. 15    Litho.    Perf. 13x13¼**
3734 A1116 100fo multi                1.25 1.25

Souvenir Sheet

Greetings — A1117

No. 3735: a, Bugler on pig. b, Man, woman, flower. c, Baby in cradle. d, Clown. e, Mother and child.

**2001, Feb. 9    Perf. 11½x12**
3735 A1117 36fo Sheet of 5, #a-f    2.50 2.00

World Speed Skating Championships, Budapest — A1118

**2001, Feb. 9    Litho.    Perf. 13**
3736 A1118 140fo multi             1.75 1.75

**Furniture Type of 1999**

Designs: 1fo, Three-legged stool, by János Vincze, 1910, vert. 7fo, 1853 chair, vert. 8fo, 19th cent. chair, vert. 31fo, Like No. 3717, vert. 40fo, Armchair by Ignác Alpár, 1896, vert. 60fo, Armchair by Ferenc Steindl, 1840, vert. 200fo, Settee by Sebestyén Vogel, 1810.

**2001    Perf. 11½x12, 12x11½**
3737-3743 A1091   Set of 7         4.25 1.50
Issued: 31fo, 3/5; others, 2/9.

**Hungarian Millennium Type of 2000**
**2001, Mar. 5    Perf. 12x11½**
3744 A1096 36fo Millennium flag    1.00 .25

**National Parks Type of 1998**

Designs: 28fo, Balaton. 36fo, Körös-maros. 70fo, Duna-Ipoly.

**2001, Mar. 5    Perf. 12**
3745-3747 A1073   Set of 3          1.75 1.50

Easter A1119

**2001, Mar. 5    Perf. 13**
3748 A1119 28fo multi              .50 .20

Locomotives — A1120

Designs: 31fo, Mk. 48. 36fo, 490. 100fo, 394. 150fo, C50.

**2001, Apr. 13    Perf. 13¼x13**
3749-3752 A1120   Set of 4          3.25 3.25

Esztergom Archbishopric, 1000th Anniv. — A1121

**2001, Apr. 18    Perf. 12**
3753 A1121 124fo multi             1.50 1.25

Organizations — A1122

No. 3754: a, 70fo, Emblems of European and Mediterranean Plant Protection Organization and Intl. Plant Protection Convention. b, 80fo, UN High Commissioner for Refugees, 50th anniv.
Illustration reduced.

**2001, Apr. 18    Perf. 13¼x13**
3754 A1122   Horiz. pair, #a-b     1.75 1.50

Europa A1123

Designs: 36fo, Open chest with water. 90fo, Split globe with water.

**2001, May 9    Perf. 12**
3755-3756 A1123   Set of 2         3.25 1.75

Animals A1124

Designs: 28fo, Phoca hispida. 36fo, Canis lupus. 70fo, Testudo hermanni. 90fo, Alcedo atthis ispida.
200fo, Cervus elaphus.

**2001, May 9    Perf. 12**
3757-3760 A1124   Set of 4         2.50 2.50
**Souvenir Sheet**
3761 A1124 200fo multi             3.00 2.25

A1125

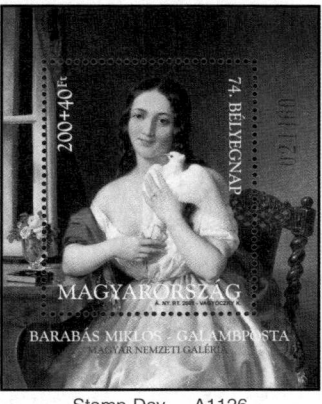

Stamp Day — A1126

Designs: 36fo, #N2. 90fo, #2. 200fo+40fo, Pigeon Post, by Miklos Barabás.

**2001, May 25    Perf. 12¼x11½**
3762-3763 A1125   Set of 2         1.75 1.50
a. Sheet, 6 each # 3762-3763      10.50 9.00
**Souvenir Sheet**
**Perf. 12½**
3764 A1126 200fo +40fo multi       3.50 2.75

European Water Polo Championships A1127

**2001, June 14    Perf. 13½x13**
3765 A1127 150fo multi             2.00 1.00

Intl. Scouting Conference — A1128

**2001, June 21    Perf. 12**
3766 A1128 150fo multi             2.00 1.00

World Youth Track and Field Championships, Debrecen — A1129

**2001, July 12    Litho.    Perf. 13x13¼**
3767 A1129 140fo multi             1.50 1.00

Artist's Colony, Gödöllö, Cent. — A1130

Fészek Arts Club, Cent. — A1131

**2001, July 12    Perf. 12**
3768 A1130 100fo multi             1.00 .50
3769 A1131 150fo blue & blk        1.50 .75

**Hungarian History Type of 2000**
**Souvenir Sheets**

No. 3770: a, Prince Francis II Rákóczy, swordsman on horseback, Ilona Zrinyi. b, Rider from Royal Horse Guard, Castle at Munkács, Queen Maria Theresa. c, Count Stephen Széchenyi, Chain Bridge. d, Lajos Kossuth, Artúr Görgey with sword on horseback, battle scene. e, Poet János Arany, Parliament building.

No. 3771: a, World War I soldier on horseback, outline map of Hungary and lost parts of empire, Hungarian people. b, Albert Szent-Gyorgi and chemistry equipment. c, Chain Bridge, World War II soldiers, Bishop Vilmos Apor. d, Pictures of 1956 revolution, Polish-Hungarian Solidarity banner. e, Barbed wire, children representing Hungary's future, Hungarian millennium flag.

**2001, Aug. 15**
3770     Sheet of 5               5.00 2.50
a.-e. A1110 50fo Any single        1.00 .35
3771     Sheet of 5               5.00 2.50
a.-e. A1110 50fo Any single        1.00 .35

Souvenir Sheet

Crown of St. Stephen — A1132

**Litho. & Embossed**
**2001, Aug. 15    Perf. 13x12¾**
3772 A1132 2001fo multi           22.00 22.00

**Grapes and Wine Producing Areas Type of 1990**

Grapes and: 60fo, Pannonhalma Abbey, Pannonhalma-Sokoróalja region, horiz. 70fo, Spherical observatory and Red Chapel, Balatonboglár, horiz.

**2001, Aug. 17    Litho.    Perf. 13¼x13**
3773-3774 A902   Set of 2         1.50 .75

Attempt To Create World's Largest Stamp Mosaic — A1133

**2001, Oct. 9    Perf. 12**
3775 A1133 10fo multi              .30 .20

Maria Valeria Bridge Reconstruction — A1134

**2001, Oct. 11    Perf. 13¼x13**
3776 A1134 36fo multi              .50 .50
See Slovakia No. 388.

Christmas A1135

**2001, Oct. 16    Perf. 12**
3777 A1135 36fo multi              .50 .20

State Printers, 150th Anniv. — A1136

| | | | | |
|---|---|---|---|---|
| **2001, Nov. 23** | **Litho.** | **Perf. 13¼x13** | | |
| 3778 | A1136 | 150fo multi | 1.75 | .75 |

2002 Winter Olympics, Salt Lake City — A1137

| | | | | |
|---|---|---|---|---|
| **2002, Feb. 8** | **Litho.** | **Perf. 12** | | |
| 3779 | A1137 | 160fo multi | 2.00 | .80 |

**Souvenir Sheet**

History of the Bicycle — A1138

No. 3780: a, Large-wheeled bicycle and rider, c. 1880. b, Tricycle, early 1900s. c, Károly Iszer (1860-1929), Budapest Sport Club chairman and bicycle. d, Tandem bicycle.

| | | | | |
|---|---|---|---|---|
| **2002, Feb. 20** | | **Perf. 11½x12¼** | | |
| 3780 | A1138 | 40fo Sheet of 4, #a-d | 2.25 | 1.60 |

**Souvenir Sheet**

Hungarian — Ottoman Battles of 1552 — A1139

No. 3781: a, 50fo, Siege of Eger Castle (25x30mm). b, 50fo, Battle of Temesvár (25x30mm). c, 100fo+50fo, Battle of Drégely Castle (40x30mm).

| | | | | |
|---|---|---|---|---|
| **2002, Feb. 20** | | **Perf. 12** | | |
| 3781 | A1139 | Sheet of 3, #a-c | 3.25 | 2.50 |

Easter — A1140

| | | | | |
|---|---|---|---|---|
| **2002, Mar. 14** | | **Perf. 11½x12¼** | | |
| 3782 | A1140 | 30fo multi | .50 | .20 |

Airplanes Designed by Hungarians — A1141

Designs: 180fo, Libelle, by János adorján, 1910. 190fo, Magyar Lloyd, by Tibor Melczer, 1914.

| | | | | |
|---|---|---|---|---|
| **2002, Mar. 14** | | **Perf. 12½** | | |
| 3783-3784 | A1141 | Set of 2 | 3.75 | 2.00 |

Famous Hungarians A1142

Designs: 33fo, Lajos Kossuth (1802-94), leader of Hungarian independence movement. 134fo, János Bolyai (1802-60), mathematician. 150fo, Gyula Illyés (1902-83), writer.

| | | | | |
|---|---|---|---|---|
| **2002, Mar. 14** | | **Perf. 13x13½** | | |
| 3785-3787 | A1142 | Set of 3 | 3.50 | 1.50 |

**Souvenir Sheet**

Parliament Building, Cent. — A1143

| | | | | |
|---|---|---|---|---|
| **2002, Mar. 14** | | **Perf. 11½x12¼** | | |
| 3788 | A1143 | 500fo multi | 6.00 | 5.00 |

**Souvenir Sheet**

Opening of National Theater — A1144

| | | | | |
|---|---|---|---|---|
| **2002, Mar. 14** | | | | |
| 3789 | A1144 | 500fo multi | 6.00 | 5.00 |

**Furniture Type of 1999**

Designs: 33fo, Chair, 1809, vert. 134fo, Theater armchair, 1900.

| | | | | |
|---|---|---|---|---|
| **2002, Mar. 28** | | **Perf. 11½x12, 12x11½** | | |
| 3790-3791 | A1091 | Set of 2 | 2.50 | 1.00 |

Environmental Protection — A1145

| | | | | |
|---|---|---|---|---|
| **2002, Mar. 28** | | **Perf. 12** | | |
| 3792 | A1145 | 158fo multi | 1.60 | .80 |

**Souvenir Sheet**

Founding of Hungarian National Museum and National Széchényi Library, Bicent. — A1146

No. 3793: a, Mihály Apafi psalter, 1686. b, Illuminated letter from Graduale Pars II. c, Standard of the Civil Guard of Pest, 1848. d, Basin for holy water, 12th cent.

| | | | | |
|---|---|---|---|---|
| **2002, Apr. 29** | | | | |
| 3793 | A1146 | 150fo Sheet of 4, #a-d | 7.50 | 7.50 |

Halas Lace, Cent. — A1147

Designs: 100fo, Tablecloth with Two Deer, by Mrs. Béla Bazala, 1916. 110fo, Swan Tablecloth, by Erno Stepanek, 1930. 140fo, Jancsi and Iluska, by Antal Tar, 1935.

**Litho. & Embossed**

| | | | | |
|---|---|---|---|---|
| **2002, May 3** | | **Perf. 12** | | |
| 3794-3796 | A1147 | Set of 3 | 4.00 | 1.75 |

Europa A1148

| | | | | |
|---|---|---|---|---|
| **2002, May 9** | | **Litho.** | **Perf. 11** | |
| 3797 | A1148 | 62fo multi | 1.50 | 1.50 |

2002 World Cup Soccer Championships, Japan and Korea — A1149

| | | | | |
|---|---|---|---|---|
| **2002, May 9** | | **Perf. 13x13½** | | |
| 3798 | A1149 | 160fo multi + label | 2.00 | 1.60 |

Fauna A1150

Designs: 30fo, Felis sylvestris. 38fo, Podarcis taurica. 110fo, Garrulus glandarius. 160fo, Rosalia alpina. 500fo, Acipenser ruthenus.

| | | | | |
|---|---|---|---|---|
| **2002, May 9** | | **Perf. 12** | | |
| 3799-3802 | A1150 | Set of 4 | 4.00 | 1.75 |
| **Souvenir Sheet** | | | | |
| 3803 | A1150 | 500fo multi | 6.00 | 5.00 |

Art — A1152

Designs: 62fo, Kodobálók, by Károly Ferenczy. 188fo, Táncosno, sculpture by Ferenc Megyessy, vert.

| | | | | |
|---|---|---|---|---|
| | | **Perf. 12¾x12¼, 12¼x12¾** | | |
| **2002, June 24** | | | | |
| 3807-3808 | A1152 | Set of 2 | 3.00 | 1.25 |

Greetings — A1151

No. 3804: a, Etesd meg! b, Megszülettem! c, Sok boldogságot! d, Ontözd meg! e, Ennyire szeretlek!

**Serpentine Die Cut 12¼x12¾**

| | | | | |
|---|---|---|---|---|
| **2002, May 29** | | | | |
| **Self-Adhesive** | | | | |
| 3804 | | Booklet pane of 5 | 2.50 | |
| a.-e. | A1151 | 38fo Any single | .50 | .20 |

**Flower Type of 1999**

Designs: 30fo, Red poppy. 38fo, Stalkless gentian.

| | | | | |
|---|---|---|---|---|
| **2002, June 24** | | **Perf. 12¼x11½** | | |
| 3805-3806 | A1087 | Set of 2 | 1.00 | .35 |

UNESCO World Heritage Sites — A1153

Designs: 100fo, Budapest. 150fo, Hollóko. 180fo, Caves of Aggtelek Karst, horiz.

| | | | | |
|---|---|---|---|---|
| **2002, June 24** | | **Perf. 12** | | |
| 3809-3811 | A1153 | Set of 3 | 4.50 | 2.25 |

See Nos. 3881-3882, 4073.

Kalocsa Archbishopric, 1000th Anniv. — A1154

| | | | | |
|---|---|---|---|---|
| **2002, Aug. 1** | **Litho.** | **Perf. 13¼x12½** | | |
| 3812 | A1154 | 150fo multi | 1.50 | .75 |

Medical Congresses A1155

No. 3813: a, 100fo, 38th European Diabetes Association Congress. b, 150fo, 16th European Arm and Shoulder Surgeons Congress.

| | | | | |
|---|---|---|---|---|
| **2002, Aug. 23** | | **Perf. 13x13¼** | | |
| 3813 | A1155 | Vert. pair, #a-b | 3.00 | 2.50 |

Printed in sheets of two pairs. Value $5.50.

Ceramics by Margit Kovács — A1156

No. 3814: a, 33fo, Madonna and Child, 1938. b, 38fo, Mother and Children, 1953. 400fo+200fo, St. George, 1936.

**2002, Oct. 3**      **Perf. 13¼x13**
3814 A1156   Pair, #a-b    1.00   .35

**Souvenir Sheet**
**Perf. 12¼x11½**
3815 A1156 400fo +200fo multi   6.00   6.00

Stamp Day. No. 3814 printed in sheets of two pairs. Value $1.75. No. 3815 contains one 25x36mm stamp.

Christmas
A1157

Designs: 30fo, Adoration of the Magi. 38fo, Bethlehem.

**Litho. with Foil Application**
**2002, Oct. 30**      **Perf. 12**
3816-3817 A1157   Set of 2   1.25   .35

World Gymnastics
Championships,
Debrecen — A1158

**2002, Nov. 20   Litho.   Perf. 13x13¼**
3818 A1158 160fo multi    1.60   .80

Hungarian and
Turkish
Buildings — A1159

Designs: 40fo, Rakoczi House, Tekirdag, Turkey. 110fo, Gazi Kassim Pasha Mosque, Pécs, Hungary.

**2002, Dec. 2   Litho.   Perf. 13½x13¼**
3819-3820 A1159   Set of 2   1.50   .75

See Turkey No. 2844.

**Furniture Type of 1999**
Designs: 32fo, Wooden chair with carved back, 19th cent., vert. 35fo, Armchair, 18th cent., vert. 65fo, Armchair with carved back, 1920, vert.

**2003, Jan. 30**      **Perf. 11½x12¼**
3821-3823 A1091   Set of 3   1.75   .70

Scientists
A1160

Designs: 32fo, John von Neumann (1903-57), mathematician, and computer pioneer. 40fo, Rezsö Soó (1903-80), botanist. 60fo, Károly Zipernowsky (1853-1942), electrical engineer.

**2003, Feb. 12**      **Perf. 13x13¼**
3824 A1160 32fo multicolored    .35   .25
3825 A1160 40fo multicolored    6.00   6.00
3826 A1160 60fo multicolored    .60   .60
   *Nos. 3824-3826 (3)*    6.95   6.85

**Souvenir Sheet**

Herend Porcelain — A1161

No. 3827: a, Platter with floral design, Frankenthal coffee set. b, Vase with floral design, coffee set. c, Vase with ram's head handles. d, Shell-shaped bowl, pitcher.

**2003, Feb. 12**      **Perf. 12**
3827 A1161 150fo Sheet of 4,
   #a-d    6.00   6.00

Defeat of Royal Hungarian Army, 60th
Anniv. — A1162

**2003, Feb. 15**      **Perf. 12¼x12½**
3828 A1162 40fo multi    .60   .25

Easter — A1163

**2003, Mar. 14**
3829 A1163 32fo multi    .50   .20

Nemzeti Sport, Cent. — A1164

*Illustration reduced.*

**2003, Mar. 14**      **Perf. 13x13¼**
3830 A1164 150fo multi + label   2.00   .75

**Airplanes Type of 2002**
Designs: 142fo, Gerle 13, by Antal Bánhidi, 1933. 160fo, L-2 Róma, by Árpád Lampich, 1925.

**2003, Mar. 20**      **Perf. 12½**
3831-3832 A1141   Set of 2   3.50   1.50

Hotels — A1165

Designs: 110fo, Rogner Hotel, Héviz. 120fo, Hélia Hotel, Budapest.

**2003, Mar. 20**
3833-3834 A1165   Set of 2   2.50   1.10

**Souvenir Sheet**

Extreme Sports — A1166

No. 3835: a, 100fo, BMX cycling. b, 100fo, Snowboarding. c, 100fo, Parachuting. d, 100fo+50fo, Kayaking.

**2003, Mar. 20**      **Perf. 12**
3835 A1166   Sheet of 4, #a-d   4.50   4.50

Greetings
A1167

No. 3836: a, Church. b, Two flowers. c, One flower. d, Easter eggs. e, Candles in window, Christmas tree.

***Serpentine Die Cut 12¾***
**2003, Mar. 20**
**Self-Adhesive**
3836   Booklet pane of 5    2.00
  *a.-e.*   A1167 40fo Any single   .40   .20

**Souvenir Sheet**

Space Shuttle Columbia — A1168

**2003, Apr. 9**      **Perf. 12**
3837 A1168 500fo multi    5.00   2.50

World Ice Hockey Championships,
Budapest — A1169

*Illustration reduced.*

**2003, Apr. 10**      **Perf. 13x13¼**
3838 A1169 110fo multi + label   1.10   .55

Budapest Sports Arena — A1170

*Illustration reduced.*

**2003, Apr. 10**
3839 A1170 120fo multi + label   1.25   .60

**Souvenir Sheet**

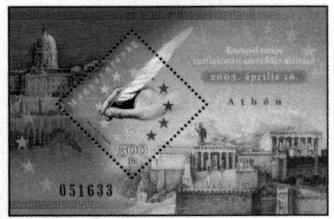

Ratification of European Union
Accession Treaty — A1171

**2003, Apr. 14**      **Perf. 12**
3840 A1171 500fo multi    7.50   7.50

Policeman
on
Motorcycle
and
Emergency
Phone
Number
A1172

**2003, Apr. 24**
3841 A1172 65fo multi    .65   .35

Stamp
Day — A1173

Designs: 35fo, Statue of woman with legs crossed. 40fo, Statue of woman with hand on chin.
400fo+100fo, Fountain.

**2003, May 6**      **Perf. 13¼x13**
3842-3843 A1173   Set of 2   .75   .40
**Souvenir Sheet**
**Perf. 12¾x13**
3844 A1173 400fo +100fo multi   7.00   5.00

No. 3844 contains one 31x40mm stamp.

**Souvenir Sheet**

Uprising Against Hapsburgs of Ferenc
Rákóczi II, 400th Anniv. — A1174

No. 3845: a, Swords and scabbards. b, Coins. c, Banner, pipes and drums. d, Guns.

**2003, May 6**      **Perf. 12**
3845 A1174 120fo Sheet of 4,
   #a-d    5.00   5.00

Europa — A1175

**2003, May 9**
3846 A1175 65fo multi    1.50   1.50

Fauna
A1176

Designs: 35fo, Mustela eversmanni. 40fo, Calandrella brachydactyla. 100fo, Hyla arborea. 110fo, Misgurnus fossilis. 500fo, Eresus cinnabarinus.

**2003, May 9**
3847-3850 A1176   Set of 4   2.90   1.50
**Souvenir Sheet**
3851 A1176 500fo multi    6.00   5.00

**Grapes and Wine Producing Areas**
**Type of 1990**
Grapes and: 60fo, Bükkalja region, horiz. 130fo, Balaton-felvidéki region, horiz.

**2003, June 6**      **Perf. 13¼x12½**
3852-3853 A902   Set of 2   2.50   1.00

## Souvenir Sheet

Robe of St. László — A1177

**2003, June 13**     **Perf. 12**
3854 A1177 300fo multi    4.25 3.00

Art
A1178

Designs: 32fo, Sculpture by Imre Varga, vert. 60fo, Mostar Bridge, by Tivadar Csontváry Kosztka.

**Perf. 12½x13¼, 13¼x12½**
**2003, July 18**
3855-3856 A1178   Set of 2    1.50 .50

## Souvenir Sheet

Sports History — A1179

No. 3857: a, Ferenc Puskás Stadium Budapest, 50th anniv. b, Hungary vs. England soccer match, 50th anniv.

**2003, July 18**     **Perf. 11½x12¼**
3857 A1179 250fo Sheet of 2,
   #a-b    5.75 5.00

European Union
Membership
A1180

**2003**    **Litho.**     **Perf. 12x11½**
3858 A1180 115fo shown    1.40 .60
3859 A1180 130fo Clock at 11:35 1.60 .70
Issued: 115fo, 9/16; 130fo, 10/18.

Nutrition
A1181

**2003, Sept. 16**     **Perf. 12**
3860 A1181 120fo multi    1.50 .60

European Automobile-free
Day — A1182

**2003, Sept. 16**
3861 A1182 150fo multi    1.50 .75

Reszo Soó
(1903-80),
Botanist
A1183

**2003, Sept. 23**
3862 A1183 44fo multi    .55 .25

Book Printing — A1184

Designs: No. 3863, 44fo, Hungarian Illuminated Chronicle, 1358. No. 3864, 44fo, Ritual of Zhou, China.

**2003, Sept. 30**
3863-3864 A1184   Set of 2    1.40 .45
See People's Republic of China Nos. 3309-3310.

## Souvenir Sheet

Ferenc Deák (1803-76),
Statesman — A1185

**2003, Oct. 18**
3865 A1185 500fo multi    6.00 5.00

Christmas — A1186

Designs: 35fo, Reindeer. 44fo, Angels, Christmas tree, houses.

**2003, Oct. 31**     **Perf. 11½x12**
3866-3867 A1186   Set of 2    1.00 .40

## Souvenir Sheet

World Science Forum,
Budapest — A1187

**2003, Nov. 7**    **Litho.**     **Perf. 12**
3868 A1187 500fo multi    6.00 5.00

### Locomotives Type of 2001

Designs: 120fo, Muki Diesel locomotive, Kemence Forest Railway. 150fo, Rezét steam locomotive, Gemenc Forest Railway.

**2004, Feb. 4**     **Perf. 13¼x13**
3869-3870 A1120   Set of 2    3.00 3.00

Famous
Men — A1188

Designs: 40fo, Bálint Balassi (1554-94), poet. 44fo, József Bajza (1804-58), poet. 80fo, János András Segner (1704-77), physicist.

**2004, Feb. 4**     **Perf. 13**
3871-3873 A1188   Set of 3    2.00 .80

## Souvenir Sheet

Dogs — A1189

No. 3874: a, 100fo, Puli. b, 100fo, Hungarian greyhound. c, 100fo, Mudi. d, 100fo+50fo, Vizsla.

**2004, Feb. 19**     **Perf. 12**
3874 A1189   Sheet of 4, #a-d   5.50 4.50
Surtax on No. 3874d for youth philately.

## Souvenir Sheet

Festivals — A1190

No. 3875: a, Busójárás Carnival. b, Virágkarnevál (Flower Carnival). c, Borfesztivál (Wine Festival). d, Fesztiválok Karnev-álok (Festivals and Carnivals).

**2004, Feb. 19**
3875 A1190 60fo Sheet of 4, #a-
   d    3.25 2.40

European Ministerial Conference on
the Information Society — A1191

No. 3876 — Color of panel and "e:" a, Red violet. b, Dark blue. c, Green. d, Orange. Illustration reduced.

**2004, Feb. 26**     **Perf. 13¼x13**
3876 A1191 40fo Block of 4, #a-d 3.00 2.25

### European Union Membership
### (Clock) Type of 2003

**2004**     **Perf. 12x11½**
3877 A1180 100fo Clock at 11:48 1.25 .50
3878 A1180 190fo Clock at 11:57 2.25 .90
Issued: 100fo, 3/5; 190fo, 4/19.

Tenth World
Indoor Track and
Field
Championships,
Budapest
A1192

**2004, Mar. 5**     **Perf. 13x13¼**
3879 A1192 120fo multi    1.50 .60

Easter — A1193

**2004, Mar. 18**     **Litho.**
3880 A1193 48fo multi    .50 .25

### World Heritage Sites Type of 2002

Designs: 150fo, Abbey of Pannonhalma. 170fo, Hortobágy National Park, horiz.

**2004, Mar. 18**     **Perf. 12**
3881-3882 A1153   Set of 2    3.75 1.60

### Hotels Type of 2003

Designs: 120fo, Bük Thermal and Sports Hotel, Bükfürdo. 150fo, Aqua-Sol Hotel, Hajdúszoboszló.

**2004, Mar. 18**
3883-3884 A1165   Set of 2    3.25 1.25

Holocaust,
60th Anniv.
A1194

**2004, Apr. 16**     **Perf. 13x13¼**
3885 A1194 160fo multi    1.90 .75

## Souvenir Sheet

Zsolnay Porcelain, 150th
Anniv. — A1195

No. 3886: a, Vase with handles. b, Small vase, vessel with horse and rider top. c, Vase. d, Mocha set.

**2004, Apr. 20**   **Litho.**    **Perf. 12**
3886 A1195 160fo Sheet of 4,
   #a-d    7.00 7.00

Police
Boat and
Emergency
Phone
Number
A1196

**2004, Apr. 23**   **Litho.**    **Perf. 13x13¼**
3887 A1196 48fo multi    .60 .35

## Souvenir Sheet

Admission to European
Union — A1197

**2004, Apr. 30**                    *Perf. 12*
3888  A1197  500fo multi              5.25  5.25

Expansion of the European
Union — A1198

No. 3889: a, 120fo, Stars and flowers. b,
150fo, Stars, map of Europe, flags of nations
entering European Union.
Illustration reduced.

**2004, May 1**                          *Litho.*
3889  A1198  Horiz. pair, #a-b        3.25  2.75

European
Parliament
Elections
A1199

**2004, May 7**                   *Perf. 12½x13½*
3890  A1199  150fo multi              1.75   .70

Europa
A1200

**2004, May 7**                       *Perf. 12*
3891  A1200  160fo multi              2.25  1.00

Fauna
A1201

Designs: 48fo, Nannospalax leucodon. 65fo,
Panurus biarmicus. 90fo, Ablepharus kitaibelii
fitzingeri. 120fo, Huso huso.
500fo, Anthaxia hungarica.

**2004, May 7**
3892-3895  A1201  Set of 4            4.00  1.50
**Souvenir Sheet**
3896  A1201  500fo multi              5.25  5.25

Stamp
Day — A1202

Designs: 48fo, Walls and Doors, sculpture
by Erzsébet Schaár. 65fo, Translucent Red
Circle, painting by Tihamér Gyarmathy.
400fo+200fo, The Wasp King, painting by
Béla Kondor.

**2004, May 7**  *Litho.*  *Perf. 12¼x12¾*
3897-3898  A1202  Set of 2     2.10  .55
**Souvenir Sheet**
*Perf. 12¾x12¼*
3899  A1202  400fo +200fo multi  7.25  5.75
No. 3899 contains one 41x31mm stamp.

FIFA (Fédération
Internationale de
Football
Association),
Cent. — A1203

**2004, May 21**  *Litho.*  *Perf. 13¼x13*
3900  A1203  100fo multi          1.25  .45

Central European Catholics'
Day — A1204

No. 3901: a, Basilica, Mariazell, Austria. b,
Statue of Madonna, Mariazell. c, Statue of
Madonna and Child, Mariazell. d, Statue of
Madonna, Celldömölk, Hungary. e, Framed
painting of Madonna and Child, Mariazell. f,
Statue of Mary of Kiscell, Obuda Parish,
Hungary.

**2004, May 21**  *Litho.*  *Perf. 11½x12*
3901  A1204  100fo  Sheet of 6,
               #a-f              6.50  5.75

Information
Technology
A1205

**2004, June 28**               *Perf. 13x13¼*
3902  A1205  120fo multi          1.25   .60

Theodor Herzl
(1860-1904),
Zionist Leader
A1206

**2004, July 6**  *Litho.*  *Perf. 12*
3903  A1206  150fo multi          2.25  .75
See Austria No. 1960, Israel No. 1566.

2004 Summer Olympics,
Athens — A1207

Designs: 90fo, Canoeing. 130fo, Volleyball.
150fo, Running.

**2004, July 13**
3904-3906  A1207  Set of 3        3.75  1.75

A1208

A1209

A1210

A1211

A1212

A1213

A1214

Folkloriada Festival — A1215

Illustrations reduced.

**2004, Aug. 12**
3907        Block of 10 + 10 la-
            bels              10.00  10.00
  a.  A1208 65fo dark blue      .75   .40
  b.  A1208 65fo orange         .75   .40
  c.  A1209 65fo orange brown   .75   .40
  d.  A1209 65fo purple         .75   .40
  e.  A1210 65fo carmine        .75   .40
  f.  A1211 65fo orange brown   .75   .40
  g.  A1212 65fo orange brown   .75   .40
  h.  A1213 65fo Prussian blue  .75   .40
  i.  A1214 65fo green          .75   .40
  j.  A1215 65fo orange brown   .75   .40
  k.  Sheet, #3907            32.00  32.00
No. 3907k has labels that could be personalized. The personalized sheet sold for 1600fo.

Chess
History — A1216

No. 3908 — Beginning of text, square color,
piece (if any): a, Á sakkjáték, tan, black rook.
b, A magyaroknak, brown. c, A magyar
történelem, tan, black bishop. d, A magyar
sakkirodalom, brown, black king. e, A XVIII.
században, tan, black queen. f, Az elso,
brown. g, Az 1839-ben, tan, black knight. h, A
XIX. század, brown, black rook. i, A magyar
sakkfeladványszerok, brown, black pawn. j,
Három, a XIX. század, tan, black pawn. k,
Maróczy Géza, brown, black pawn. l, Két
kiváló, tan, black pawn. m, A levelezási,
brown, black bishop. n, A sakkélet, tan, black
pawn. o, A férfi országos, brown, black pawn.
p, A II. világháború tan után sokáig, black
pawn. q, A nol sakkozás, tan. r, 1958-ban már,
brown. s, A sakkozók, tan, black knight. t,
1951-ben indult, brown. u, A XX. századnak,
tan. v, A II. világháború utá feladvány, brown.
w, A XX. században, tan. x, A XX. század
elején, brown. y, A világ sakkéletét, brown. z,
A két világháború között, tan. aa, A háború
után, brown. ab, A férfi sakkolimpián, tan. ac,
A nemzetek közti, brown, black pawn. ad,
1957-ben a hollandiai, tan. ae, A noi sak-
kolimpiákon, brown. af, A XIX. és XX.
században, tan. ag, Sakkirodalom nélkül, tan.
ah, A XX. század magyar, brown. ai, A széles
sakkozó, tan, white bishop. aj, A Magyar Sakk-
szövetség, brown. ak, Barcza Gedeon, tan,
white pawn. al, Szabo László, brown. am, Por-
tisch Lajos, tan. an, Adorján András, brown.
ao, Sax Gyula, brown. ap, Ribli Zoltán, tan. aq,
Lékó Péter, brown. ar, Álmási Zoltán, tan. as,
Bilek, István, brown. at, A két világháború
közti, tan, white knight. au, Az olimpiákon
többször, brown. av, Sok kiváló magyar, tan.
aw, Polgár Zsuzsa, tan, white pawn. ax, Polgár
Judit, brown, white pawn. ay, Polgár Zsófia,
tan, white pawn. az, Lángos Józsa, brown,
white pawn. ba, Veroci Zsuzsa, tan. bb, Ivánka
Mária, brown, white pawn. bc, Mádl Ildikó, tan,
white pawn. bd, Országos bajnoki, brown,
white pawn. be, Sakkozásunk a XXI.
századot, brown, white rook. bf, A sakkozás-
sal, tan, white knight. bg, A magyar sakkozás,
brown, white bishop. bh, Minden össz-
zefoglaló,tan, white king. bi, A jelen
munkában, brown, white queen. bj, Elek
Ferenc, tan. bk, Katkó (Regos) Imre, brown.
bl, Gróf Pongrácz Arnold, tan, white rook.

**2004, Sept. 24**
3908        Sheet of 64          42.50  42.50
  a.-bl.  A1216 50fo Any single    .60    .40

## Souvenir Sheet

Admission to European
Union — A1217

No. 3909 — Large stars and time of small
clock: a, 11:20. b, 11:35. c, 11:48. d, 11:57.

**2004, Oct. 8**                  *Perf. 12x11½*
3909  A1217  100fo  Sheet of 4,
               #a-d              5.50  4.00

Istvan Bocskay (1557-1606), Leader of
1604-06 Rebellion — A1218

**2004, Nov. 11**  *Litho.*  *Perf. 11½x12*
3910  A1218  120fo multi          1.25  .60

Intl. Organization of Supreme Audit Institutions, 18th Congress, Budapest A1219

**2004, Oct. 11**    *Perf. 11¼*
3911 A1219 150fo multi    1.50 .75

**Christmas Type of 2002 and**

A1220

A1221

A1222

A1223

A1224

A1225

A1226

A1227

A1228

A1229

A1230

A1231

A1232

A1233

A1234

Christmas — A1235

No. 3915: Various Christmas cookies. Illustration reduced.

**Litho. With Foil Application**
**2004**    *Perf. 12*
3912 A1157 48fo Bethlehem    .50 .25

**Litho.**
*Perf. 11¼*
3913   Sheet of 20 + 20 labels    30.00 16.50
   a. A1220 48fo multi + label   1.25 .40
   b. A1221 48fo multi + label   1.25 .40
   c. A1222 48fo multi + label   1.25 .40
   d. A1223 48fo multi + label   1.25 .40
   e. A1224 48fo multi + label   1.25 .40
   f. A1225 48fo multi + label   1.25 .40

3914   Sheet of 20 + 20 labels    30.00 16.50
   a. A1226 48fo multi + label   1.25 .40
   b. A1227 48fo multi + label   1.25 .40
   c. A1228 48fo multi + label   1.25 .40
   d. A1229 48fo multi + label   1.25 .40
   e. A1230 48fo multi + label   1.25 .40
   f. A1231 48fo multi + label   1.25 .40
   g. A1232 48fo multi + label   1.25 .40
   h. A1233 48fo multi + label   1.25 .40
   i. A1234 48fo multi + label   1.25 .40
3915 A1235 48fo Sheet of 20, #a-t, + 20 labels    30.00 16.50

Issued: No. 3912, 10/28; Nos. 3913-3915, 11/3.

No. 3913 contains 5 #3913b, 3 #3913c, 4 each #3913a, 3913e, 2 each #3913d, 3913f. Background colors on some stamps differ slightly.

No. 3914 contains #3914d, 3914e, 4 each #3914a, 3914b, 2 each #3914c, 3914f, 3914g, 3914h, 3914i.

Nos. 3913-3915 could be personalized, with each sheet selling for 2000fo.

Sándor Korösi Csoma (1784-1842), Philologist and Sir Marc Aurel Stein (1862-1943), Archaeologist A1236

**2004, Nov. 3**   **Litho.**   *Perf. 13x13¼*
3916 A1236 80fo multi    1.25 .40

Natura 2000 — A1237

**2004, Dec. 3**    *Perf. 11½x12*
3917 A1237 100fo multi    1.10 .55

Zodiac — A1238

No. 3918: a, Capricorn (goat). b, Aquarius (water bearer). c, Pisces (fish). d, Aries (ram). e, Taurus (bull). f, Gemini (twins). g, Cancer (crab). h, Leo (lion). i, Virgo (virgin). j, Libra (scales). k, Scorpio (scorpion). l, Sagittarius (archer).

**2005, Jan. 3**   **Litho.**   *Perf. 11¼*
3918 A1238 50fo Sheet of 12, #a-l    10.00 7.50
   m. Sheet of 20 #3918a + 20 labels   29.00 —
   n. Sheet of 20 #3918b + 20 labels   29.00 —
   o. Sheet of 20 #3918c + 20 labels   29.00 —
   p. Sheet of 20 #3918d + 20 labels   29.00 —
   q. Sheet of 20 #3918e + 20 labels   29.00 —
   r. Sheet of 20 #3918f + 20 labels   29.00 —
   s. Sheet of 20 #3918g + 20 labels   29.00 —
   t. Sheet of 20 #3918h + 20 labels   29.00 —
   u. Sheet of 20 #3918i + 20 labels   29.00 —
   v. Sheet of 20 #3918j + 20 labels   29.00 —
   w. Sheet of 20 #3918k + 20 labels   29.00 —
   x. Sheet of 20 #3918l + 20 labels   29.00 —

Nos. 3918m-3918x each sold for 2100fo and had labels that could be personalized.

Rotary International, Cent. — A1239

**2005, Feb. 4**    *Perf. 13¼x13*
3919 A1239 130fo multi    1.60 .70

**Souvenir Sheet**

Cats — A1240

No. 3920: a, 100fo, Siamese, silhouette of cat sitting. b, 100fo, Maine Coon cat, silhouette of cat with arched back and thin tail. c, 100fo, Persian, silhouette of cat with large tail. d, 100fo+50fo, Domestic cat, silhouette of cat walking.

**2005, Feb. 4**    *Perf. 12x11½*
3920 A1240   Sheet of 4, #a-d   4.75 4.75

Easter — A1241

**2005, Feb. 21**    *Perf. 12*
3921 A1241 50fo multi    .55 .25

Intl. Weight Lifting Federation, Cent. A1242

**2005, Mar. 3**    *Perf. 12¼x12½*
3922 A1242 170fo multi    1.90 .95

Sándor Iharos (1930-96), Runner A1243

**2005, Mar. 10**    *Perf. 13x13¼*
3923 A1243 90fo multi    1.00 .50

**Souvenir Sheet**

Opening of Palace of Arts, Budapest — A1244

**2005, Mar. 10**    *Perf. 12*
3924 A1244 500fo multi    5.50 5.50

World Theater Day — A1245

**2005, Mar. 21**     *Perf. 11¼*
3925 A1245 50fo multi     .80 .25

Compass and Map of Hungary — A1246

No. 3926: a, Compass at right, map of western Hungary. b, Compass at left, map of eastern Hungary.

**2005, Apr. 1**    **Litho.**    *Perf. 11¼*
3926 A1246 50fo Pair, #a-b, + 2 labels     2.00 1.10
    c.    Sheet of 20, 10 each
      #3926a-3926b, + 20 labels   40.00 —

No. 3926c sold for 2100fo. Labels on sheets of 3926 and 3926c could be personalized. Compare with No. 4054.

Writers A1247

Designs: 90fo, Jeno Rejto (1905-43), novelist, playwright. 140fo, Attila József (1905-37), poet.

**2005, Apr. 11**    **Litho.**    *Perf. 13x13¼*
3927-3928 A1247   Set of 2    2.75 1.25

Police Helicopter and Emergency Phone Number A1248

**2005, Apr. 22**     *Perf. 13x13¼*
3929 A1248 85fo multi     .90 .45

End of World War II, 60th Anniv. A1249

**2005, May 6**     *Perf. 13*
3930 A1249 150fo multi     1.60 .80

Farm Animals A1250

Designs: 50fo, Hungarian gray bull. 70fo, Hungarian spotted cow. 100fo, Hortobágy Racka sheep. 110fo, Cigája sheep. 500fo, Mangalica pigs.

**2005, May 9**     *Perf. 13x13¼*
3931-3934 A1250   Set of 4    3.75 1.60
**Souvenir Sheet**
3935 A1250 500fo multi     6.50 5.00
No. 3935 contains one 41x32mm stamp.

**Souvenir Sheet**

Europa — A1251

No. 3936 — Plate of Chicken Paprika and Dumplings with: a, Flowers at UR. b, Flowers at UL.

**2005, May 9**     *Perf. 12*
3936 A1251 160fo Sheet, 2 each
      #a-b     7.75 6.25
The top and bottom rows of stamps in the sheet are tete-beche.

**Souvenir Sheet**

Pope John Paul II (1920-2005) — A1252

**2005, May 18**
3937 A1252 500fo multi     6.00 5.00

**Grapes and Wine Producing Areas Type of 1990**

Designs: 120fo, Pintes grapes, Zala region, horiz. 140fo, Kunleány grapes, Csongrád region, horiz.

**2005, May 25**     *Perf. 13¼x12½*
3938-3939 A902   Set of 2    3.25 1.40

Church, Ják, and Ornament From Cluny Abbey, France A1253

**2005, May 25**     *Perf. 13x13¼*
3940 A1253 110fo multi     1.60 .55

**Souvenir Sheet**

Consecration of St. Stephen's Basilica, Budapest, Cent. — A1254

**2005, May 25**     *Perf. 12¾x13*
3941 A1254 500fo multi     6.00 5.00

Miniature Sheet

Budapest Tourist Attractions — A1255

No. 3942: a, Hallway and exhibits, Postal Museum. b, #386a and die of vignette, Stamp Museum, horiz. c, Agriculture Museum, Vajdahunyad Castle. d, Ethnographic Museum, horiz. e, Sándor Palace, horiz.

**Perf. 11½x12, 12x11½ (horiz. stamps)**
**2005, May 25**
3942 A1255 100fo Sheet of 5, #a-e, + 5 labels    6.50 5.00

First Hungarian in Space, 25th Anniv. — A1256

**2005, May 26**     *Perf. 12½*
3943 A1256 130fo multi     1.25 .65

A1257

Formula I Auto Racing in Hungary, 20th Anniv. (in 2006) A1258

Designs: Nos. 3944, 3947, Hungaroring Race Track. No. 3945, Car No. 12. No. 3946, Driver in red car.

**2005**    **Litho.**    *Perf. 11¼*
3944 A1257 50fo multi + label    .50 .25
      *Perf. 13x13¼*
3945 A1258 50fo multi     .75 .25
3946 A1258 90fo multi     1.25 .45
**Souvenir Sheet**
      *Perf. 13x12¾*
3947 A1258 500fo +200fo multi   7.75 7.00
78th Stamp Day (Nos. 3945-3947). Issued: Nos. 3944, 3947, 7/18; Nos. 3945-3946, 6/17. Labels on No. 3944 could be personalized.

Souvenir Sheet

Enameled Pictures on St. Stephen's Crown — A1259

No. 3948: a, 100fo, St. Thomas (20x26mm). b, 100fo, King Géza I (in square panel with black lettering) (20x26mm). c, 100fo, Byzantine Emperor Michael Ducas (in arched panel with red lettering) (20x26mm). d, 100fo, Byzantine Emperor Constantine (in square panel with red lettering) (20x26mm). e, 100fo, Jesus Christ (in arched panel with no lettering) (20x26mm). f, 500fo, St. Stephen's Crown (30x36mm).

**2005, Aug. 19**    **Litho.**    *Perf. 12x11½*
3948 A1259   Sheet of 6, #a-f   11.50 10.50

First Hungarian Mail Vehicle, Cent. A1260

**2005, Sept. 15**     *Perf. 11¼x11*
3949 A1260 50fo multi     .50 .25

Trash Recycling A1261

**2005, Sept. 15**     *Perf. 13x13¼*
3950 A1261 140fo multi     1.75 .70

World Wrestling Championships, Budapest — A1262

**2005, Sept. 26**     *Perf. 13*
3951 A1262 150fo multi     1.75 .75

Ferenc Farkas (1905-2000), Composer — A1263

**2005, Sept. 30**     *Perf. 13x13¼*
3952 A1263 100fo multi     1.75 .50

World Science Forum, Budapest A1264

**2005, Sept. 30**
3953 A1264 120fo multi 1.75 .60

Hungarian University of Craft and Design, 125th Anniv. A1265

**2005, Oct. 19** **Perf. 12**
3954 A1265 90fo multi 1.25 .45

The Three Magi — A1266

Christmas A1267

No. 3956: a, Candle. b, Apple. c, Heart-shaped ornament. d, Teddy bear.

**Litho. with Foil Application**
**2005, Oct. 19** **Perf. 12¾x12¼**
3955 A1266 50fo blue .75 .25
**Self-Adhesive**
**Litho.**
**Serpentine Die Cut 12¾**
3956 Booklet pane of 4 3.25
a.-d. A1267 50fo Any single .80 .25

House of the Future A1268

**2005, Dec. 16** **Litho.** **Perf. 12**
3957 A1268 100fo multi 1.25 .45

Hungarian News Agency, 125th Anniv. — A1269

**2006, Jan. 1** **Litho.** **Perf. 12x11½**
3958 A1269 90fo multi 1.10 .45

2006 Winter Olympics, Turin A1270

**2006, Feb. 10** **Perf. 13¼**
3959 A1270 200fo multi 3.00 .95

**Furniture Type of 1999**
Designs: 52fo, Like #3790, vert. 75fo, Chair with heart carved in back, 1893, vert. 212fo, Like #3791. 300fo, Settee, 18th cent. 500fo, Rococo settee, c. 1880. 1000fo, Vassily chair, by Marcel Breuer, 1925.

**2006** **Perf. 11½x12¼**
3960 A1091 52fo bl & dk bl .50 .25
3961 A1091 75fo org brn & brn .70 .35
**Perf. 12¼x11½**
3962 A1091 212fo grn & dk grn 2.00 1.00
**Perf. 12¾x12¼**
3963 A1091 300fo red & dk red 3.00 1.50
3964 A1091 500fo bl & dk bl 5.00 2.50
3965 A1091 1000fo ol & dk ol 10.00 5.00
Nos. 3960-3965 (6) 21.20 10.60
Issued: 52fo, 75fo, 212fo, 3/16; others, 5/19.

World Heritage Sites — A1271

Designs: 52fo, Early Christian Necropolis, Pecs. 90fo, Ferto-Neuseidler Lake Cultural Landscape, horiz.

**2006, Mar. 16** **Perf. 12**
3966-3967 A1271 Set of 2 1.40 .70

**Airplanes Type of 2002**
Designs: 120fo, Boeing 767-200ER. 140fo, Lockheed Sirius 8A.

**2006, Mar. 16**
3968-3969 A1141 Set of 2 3.00 1.25

Easter — A1272

**2006, Mar. 22**
3970 A1272 52fo multi .50 .25

Union of European Football Associations Congress, Budapest A1273

**2006, Mar. 22** **Perf. 13x13¼**
3971 A1273 170fo multi 2.00 .80

Sándor Légrády (1906-87), Stamp Designer, and Vignette of Unissued Stamp — A1274

**2006, Mar. 30** **Litho.** **Perf. 12x11½**
3972 A1274 75fo multi 1.00 .35

Ilona Sasváriné-Paulik (1954-99), Paralymic Athlete — A1275

**2006, Mar. 30** **Perf. 13x13¼**
3973 A1275 185fo multi 2.00 .85

László Detre (1906-74), Astronomer — A1276

**2006, Mar. 30** **Perf. 12**
3974 A1276 212fo multi 2.50 1.00

Wi-fi Technology A1277

**2006, Mar. 30** **Perf. 13x13¼**
3975 A1277 240fo multi 2.50 1.10

Orchid — A1278

Rose — A1279

Lily — A1280

Tulip — A1281

Gerbera Daisy — A1282

Rose — A1283

Rose — A1284

Rose — A1285

Butterfly and Wedding Rings — A1286

Butterfly and Rose — A1287

Daisy and Rubber Duck — A1288

Daisy and Blue Booties — A1289

Daisy and Pink Booties — A1290

Daisy and Rattle — A1291

Rose — A1292

Clematis — A1293

**2006**     **Litho.**     **Perf. 11¼**
3976    Vert. strip of 5 + 5 labels    2.60   2.60
   a.   A1278 52fo multi + label   .50   .25
   b.   A1279 52fo multi + label   .50   .25
   c.   A1280 52fo multi + label   .50   .25
   d.   A1281 52fo multi + label   .50   .25
   e.   A1282 52fo multi + label   .50   .25
   Sheet, 4 each #3976a-3976e   10.50
3977    Strip of 3 + 3 labels   1.50   1.50
   a.   A1283 52fo multi + label   .50   .25
   b.   A1284 52fo multi + label   .50   .25
   c.   A1285 52fo multi + label   .50   .25
   Sheet, 7 each #3977a-3977b, 6 #3977c   10.50   —
3978    Pair + 2 labels   1.00   1.00
   a.   A1286 52fo multi + label   .50   .25
   b.   A1287 52fo multi + label   .50   .25
   Sheet, 10 each #3978a-3978b   10.50   —
3979    Block or strip of 4 + 4 labels   2.10   2.10
   a.   A1288 52fo multi + label   .50   .25
   b.   A1289 52fo multi + label   .50   .25
   c.   A1290 52fo multi + label   .50   .25
   d.   A1291 52fo multi + label   .50   .25
   Sheet, 3 each #3979b-3979c, 7 each #3977a, 3977d   10.50   —
3980    Pair + 2 labels   1.75   1.75
   a.   A1292 90fo multi + label   .85   .45
   b.   A1293 90fo multi + label   .85   .45
   Sheet, 10 each #3980a-3980b   17.50   —
   *Nos. 3976-3980 (5)*   8.95   8.95

Issued: Nos. 3976, 3977, 5/4, others, 5/19. Background colors of stamps in full sheets varies. Labels could be personalized for an additional fee.
Compare with No. 4092.

Battle of Belgrade, 550th Anniv. — A1294

**2006, May 9**     **Perf. 13½x12½**
3981 A1294 120fo multi    1.50   .60

2006 World Cup Soccer Championships, Germany — A1295

**2006, May 9**     **Perf. 13x13¼**
3982 A1295 170fo multi    3.00   .85

Europa — A1296

**2006, May 9**     **Perf. 12**
3983 A1296 190fo multi    1.90   .95

Printed in sheets of 4, with each stamp rotated 90 degrees to create circle of faces. Value $9.

Horses A1297

Breeds: 75fo, Shagya Arab. 90fo, Furioso (Mezohegyes halfbreed). 140fo, Gidran. 160fo, Nonius.
No. 3988: a, Huçul. b, Lippizaner. c, Kisbér halfbreed.

**2006, May 9**
3984-3987 A1297   Set of 4   5.50   2.25
    **Souvenir Sheet**
3988 A1297 200fo Sheet of 3, #a-c   7.00   3.00

Margin of No. 3988 is embossed.

Composers — A1298

Designs: No. 3989, 90fo, George Enescu (1881-1955), and Romanian flag. No. 3990, 90fo, Béla Bartók (1881-1945) and Hungarian flag.

**2006, June 8**     **Perf. 13x13¼**
3989-3990 A1298   Set of 2   2.25   .85
See Romania No. 4838.

Miskolc Intl. Opera Festival A1299

**2006, June 15**     **Perf. 13¼x13**
3991 A1299 190fo multi    2.25   .85

    **Souvenir Sheet**

Budapest Museum of Fine Arts, Cent. — A1300

No. 3992: a, Esterházy Madonna, by Raphael. b, Mary Magdalene, by El Greco. c, Equestrian statue, by Leonardo da Vinci, horiz. d, Three Fishing Boats, by Claude Monet, horiz.

**2006, June 23**    **Litho.**    **Perf. 12**
3992 A1300 200fo Sheet of 4, #a-d   8.50   3.75

The Four Virtues, Frescoes From Castle Museum, Esztergom — A1301

Iconostasis, Szentendre Cathedral — A1302

No. 3993: a, Bölcsesség and Mértékletesség. b, Allhatatosság and Igazságosság.

**2006, June 23**     **Perf. 13¼x13**
3993 A1301 52fo Horiz. pair, #a-b   1.10   .45
    **Souvenir Sheet**
    **Perf. 12**
3994 A1302 400fo +200fo multi   6.50   5.50
Stamp Day.

Emblem of Border Guard and Falcon A1303

**2006, June 27**     **Perf. 12**
3995 A1303 170fo multi    1.75   .80

European Swimming Championships, Budapest — A1304

Designs: 90fo, Synchronized swimmers and diver. 180fo, Swimmers and fish.

**2006, July 27**     **Perf. 13x13¼**
3996-3997 A1304   Set of 2   2.75   1.25

Contemporary Art — A1305

Designs: 120fo, Child with Model Aircraft, by László Fehér. 140fo, Circle Dance, sculpture by István Haraszty, vert. 160fo, Aequilibrium, tapestry by Zsuzsa Péreli, vert.

**2006, July 27**    **Perf. 13x13¼, 13¼x13**
3998-4000 A1305   Set of 3   4.50   2.00

Hungaroring Race Track, 20th Anniv. — A1306

**2006, Aug. 3**     **Perf. 13x13¼**
4001 A1306 75fo multi    .75   .35

    Souvenir Sheet

Budapest Zoo, 140th Anniv. — A1307

**2006, Aug. 9**    **Litho.**    **Perf. 12**
4002 A1307 500fo multi    5.50   2.40

    Souvenir Sheet

Consecration of Esztergom Basilica, 150th Anniv. — A1308

**2006, Aug. 18**
4003 A1308 500fo multi    5.50   2.40

    Miniature Sheet

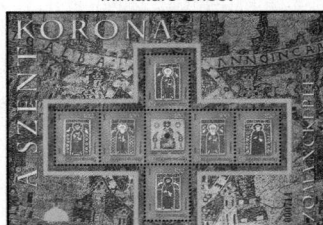

Enamel Paintings on St. Stephen's Crown — A1309

No. 4004: a, St. John (scsiohs inscription at top). b, St. Andrew (scsandreas) c, St. Peter (scspetrvs). d, God. e, St. Paul (scspavlus). f, St. Philip (scsphilipvs). g, St. Jacob (scsiacobvs).

**Litho. (Foil Application on Sheet Margin)**
**2006, Aug. 18**     **Perf. 12x11½**
4004 A1309 100fo Sheet of 7, #a-g   7.50   3.25

    Souvenir Sheet

1956 Revolution, 50th Anniv. — A1310

**2006, Oct. 20**    **Litho.**    **Perf. 13x12¾**
4005 A1310 500fo multi    5.00   2.50
No. 4005 has a die cut hole in the middle of the flag.

    **Christmas Type of 2002**
    **Litho. With Foil Application**
**2006, Oct. 27**     **Perf. 12**
4006 A1157 52fo Adoration of the Magi   .60   .25

## Souvenir Sheet

1956 Melbourne Summer Olympics, 50th Anniv. — A1311

**2006, Nov. 13  Litho.  Perf. 12**
4007 A1311 500fo László Papp    5.25  2.60

Hungarian Red Cross, 125th Anniv. A1312

**2006, Nov. 24  Perf. 12¼x11½**
4008 A1312 100fo multi    1.10  .55

Launch of Sputnik 1 and Sputnik 2, 50th Anniv. — A1313

**2007, Feb. 6  Litho.  Perf. 12**
4009 A1313 350fo multi    3.75  1.90

Easter — A1314

**2007, Feb. 9  Perf. 12¼x12¾**
4010 A1314 62fo multi    .65  .30

Famous Men — A1315

Designs: 107fo, János Ferencsik (1907-84), conductor. 135fo, Count Lajos Batthyány (1807-49), prime minister.

**2007, Feb. 9  Perf. 12**
4011-4012 A1315 Set of 2    2.50  1.25

Rural Life — A1316

Designs: 62fo, Man with bottle and woman with glass. 95fo, Girl with flowers and birds. 242fo, Man cooking fish over fire.

**2007, Feb. 9  Perf. 12¼x11½**
4013-4015 A1316 Set of 3    4.25  2.10

Customs and Finance Guards, 140th Anniv. A1317

**2007, Mar. 10  Perf. 12**
4016 A1317 180fo multi    2.00  1.00

Diets A1318

Designs: 210fo, Prince John Sigismund of Transylvania and Torda Church. 230fo, Prince Ferenc Rákóczi II and Marosvásárhely Castle

**2007, Apr. 10  Perf. 13¼x12½**
4017-4018 A1318 Set of 2    5.00  2.50

Diet of Torda, 450th anniv.; Diet of Marosvásárhely, 300th anniv.

## Souvenir Sheet

The Boys of Paul Street, Novel by Ferenc Molnár (1878-1952) — A1319

No. 4019: a, 160fo, Molnar. b, 160fo, Posted handbill. c, 160fo+30fo, Boy in red shirt. d, 160fo+30fo, Boy in green shirt.

**2007, Apr. 10  Perf. 12**
4019 A1319 Sheet of 4, #a-d    8.00  8.00

A1320

A1321

A1322

A1323

A1324

A1325

A1326

A1327

A1328

A1329

A1330

A1331

Graduation — A1332

No. 4020: a, Two hot air balloons. b, Graduate pulled by balloon, arch of books, diploma, hot air balloon. c, Graduation cap, hot air balloon, graduate. d, Three graduates, hot air balloon. e, Hot air balloon, graduate pulled by balloon, two graduates standing on books. f, Graduate on path, graduate holding portfolio. g, Diploma, two graduates standing on books. h, Diploma on path, bottom half of graduate at upper right. i, Three graduates on path. j, Arch of books, diploma, inkwell, quill pen, path. k, Two graduates on path. l, Inkwell, quill pen, three books. m, Graduate with magnifying glass, path. n, Graduate with magnifying glass.

o, Diploma on path, legs of two graduates, path. p, Graduate carrying portfolio, diploma on arch of books. q, Arch of books, diploma, inkwell, quill pen. r, Arch of books, diploma. s, Inkwell, quill pen, graduate. t, Diploma on path, graduate at right, legs of graduate at top.

**2007, Apr. 16  Litho.  Perf. 11¼**

| | | | | |
|---|---|---|---|---|
| 4020 | A1320 (62fo) Sheet of 20, #a-t, + 20 labels | | 20.00 | 14.00 |
| 4021 | Block of 8 + 8 labels | | 5.60 | 5.60 |
| a. | A1321 (62fo) multi + label | | .70 | .35 |
| b. | A1322 (62fo) multi + label | | .70 | .35 |
| c. | A1323 (62fo) multi + label | | .70 | .35 |
| d. | A1324 (62fo) multi + label | | .70 | .35 |
| e. | A1325 (62fo) multi + label | | .70 | .35 |
| f. | A1326 (62fo) multi + label | | .70 | .35 |
| g. | A1327 (62fo) multi + label | | .70 | .35 |
| h. | A1328 (62fo) multi + label | | .70 | .35 |
| | Sheet, 3 each #4021a-4021d, 2 each #4021e-4021h, + 20 labels | | 14.00 | 14.00 |
| 4022 | Pair + 2 labels | | 1.40 | 1.40 |
| a. | A1329 (62fo) multi + label | | .70 | .35 |
| b. | A1330 (62fo) multi + label | | .70 | .35 |
| | Sheet, 10 each #4022a-4022b, + 20 labels | | 14.00 | 14.00 |
| 4023 | Pair + 2 labels | | 2.10 | 2.10 |
| a. | A1331 (95fo) multi + label | | 1.00 | .50 |
| b. | A1332 (95fo) multi + label | | 1.00 | .50 |
| | Sheet, 10 each #4023a-4023b, + 20 labels | | 21.00 | 21.00 |

Labels on Nos. 4020-4023 could be personalized for an additional fee.

Stamp Day A1333

Designs: 62fo, St. Elizabeth of Hungary (1207-31) caring for the sick. 95fo, St. Elizabeth caring for poor. 500fo+200fo, St. Emeric (1007-31) praying.

**2007, Apr. 27  Litho.  Perf. 13**
4024-4025 A1333 Set of 2    1.75  .85

**Souvenir Sheet**
**Perf. 13x12¾**
4026 A1333 500fo +200fo multi    8.00  8.00

No. 4026 contains one 40x32mm stamp.

Television Broadcasting in Hungary, 50th Anniv. — A1334

**2007, May 9  Perf. 13x13½**
4027 A1334 160fo multi    1.75  .85

## Souvenir Sheet

Europa — A1335

No. 4028: a, Scouts in canoe. b, Scouts and Brownsea Island commemorative stone.

**2007, May 9  Perf. 12**
4028 A1335 210fo Sheet, 2 each #a-b    9.25  4.50

Scouting, cent.

Dogs A1336

Designs: 62fo, Komondor. 150fo, Transylvanian hound. 180fo, Kuvasz. 240fo, Pumis. 600fo, Hungarian vizsla.

**2007, May 9**      **Perf. 13x13½**
4029-4032 A1336 Set of 4    7.00 3.50
**Souvenir Sheet**
**Perf. 12**
4033 A1336 600fo multi    6.50 3.25

11th Intl. Cave Rescue Conference, Aggtelek-Jósvafo — A1337

**2007, May 15**   **Litho.**   **Perf. 12**
4034 A1337 200fo multi    2.25 1.10

Academy of Music Building, Budapest, Cent. — A1338

**2007, May 18**
4035 A1338 250fo multi    2.75 1.40

**Souvenir Sheet**

National Gallery, 50th Anniv. — A1339

No. 4036: a, The Mystical Betrothal of St. Catherine, c. 1490. b, View of Rome, by Károly Markó the Elder, 1835. c, October, by Károly Ferenczy, 1903. d, Picnic in May, by Pál Szinyei Merse, 1873, horiz.

**2007, May 23**      **Perf. 12**
4036 A1339 150fo Sheet of 4, #a-d    6.50 3.25

**Grapes and Wine Producing Areas Type of 1990**

Designs: 95fo, Cirfandli grapes, Pecs region. 140fo, Ezerfürtü grapes, Etyek-Buda region. 260fo, Zenit grapes, Tolna region.

**2007, May 25**      **Perf. 12½x13¼**
4037-4039 A902 Set of 3    5.50 2.75

Emblem of Border Guard and German Shepherd A1340

**2007, June 27**   **Litho.**   **Perf. 12**
4040 A1340 107fo multi    1.25 .60

**Personalized Stamp Types of 2004-05 Redrawn With "Belföld" Instead of Denomination and**

Pens — A1341

A1342

A1343

A1344

A1345

A1346

A1347

A1348

A1349

A1350

Doorknockers A1351

Chain Bridge, Budapest — A1352

Parliament, Budapest — A1353

Buda Castle, Budapest — A1354

Heroes Square, Budapest — A1355

Fisherman's Bastion, Budapest — A1356

No. 4043: a, Quill pen, open inkwell, ink spots, green background. b, Brown fountain pen with point on flourish of "M," brown background. c, Open and closed black and gold fountain pens, green background. d, Black and gold fountain pen with point on flourish of "M," green background. e, Ball-point pen, pen point at LL, pink background. f, Cap of black and gold pen, green background. g, Brown fountain head with flat circular tip on nib, open inkwell, brown background. h, Black and gold pen with pen point at UL, pink background. i, Black and gold fountain pen, pen point at LR, green background. j, Ball-point pen, pen point at LR, pink background. k, Fountain pen and quill, green background. l, Fountain pen, pen point at LR, brown background. m, Brown fountain pen, inkwell, brown background. n, Inkwell, quill, fountain pen, ink spots, green background. o, Plunger and clip of black ball-point pen, pink background. p, Quills, quill pen, ink spots, green background. q, Closed inkwell, pen nib, quill, ink spots, green background. r, Two fountain pens, brown background. s, Black and gold fountain pen and cap, green background. t, Tip of ball-point pen with point on flourish of "M," pink background. Illustration A1341 is reduced.

**2007**    **Litho.**    **Perf. 11¼**
| 4041 | Sheet of 20 + 20 labels | 14.00 | 14.00 |
|---|---|---|---|
| a. | A1220 (62fo) multi + label | .70 | .70 |
| b. | A1221 (62fo) multi + label | .70 | .70 |
| c. | A1222 (62fo) multi + label | .70 | .70 |
| d. | A1223 (62fo) multi + label | .70 | .70 |
| e. | A1224 (62fo) multi + label | .70 | .70 |
| f. | A1225 (62fo) multi + label | .70 | .70 |
| 4042 | Block or horiz. strip of 4 + 4 labels | 2.80 | 2.80 |
| a. | A1288 (62fo) multi + label | .70 | .70 |
| b. | A1289 (62fo) multi + label | .70 | .70 |
| c. | A1290 (62fo) multi + label | .70 | .70 |
| d. | A1291 (62fo) multi + label | .70 | .70 |
| | Sheet of 20, 7 each #4042a, 3 each #4042b, 4042c, + 20 labels | 14.00 | 14.00 |
| 4043 A1341 | Sheet of 20 + 20 labels | 14.00 | 14.00 |
| a.-t. | (62fo) Any single + label | .70 | .70 |
| 4044 | Block of 10 + 10 labels | 7.00 | 7.00 |
| a. | A1342 (62fo) multi + label | .70 | .70 |
| b. | A1343 (62fo) multi + label | .70 | .70 |
| c. | A1344 (62fo) multi + label | .70 | .70 |
| d. | A1345 (62fo) multi + label | .70 | .70 |
| e. | A1346 (62fo) multi + label | .70 | .70 |
| f. | A1347 (62fo) multi + label | .70 | .70 |
| g. | A1348 (62fo) multi + label | .70 | .70 |
| h. | A1349 (62fo) multi + label | .70 | .70 |
| i. | A1350 (62fo) multi + label | .70 | .70 |
| j. | A1351 (62fo) multi + label | .70 | .70 |
| | Sheet of 20, 2 each #4044a-4044j, + 20 labels | 14.00 | 14.00 |
| 4045 | Vert. strip of 5 + 5 labels | 3.50 | 3.50 |
| a. | A1352 (62fo) multi + label | .70 | .70 |
| b. | A1353 (62fo) multi + label | .70 | .70 |
| c. | A1354 (62fo) multi + label | .70 | .70 |
| d. | A1355 (62fo) multi + label | .70 | .70 |
| e. | A1356 (62fo) multi + label | .70 | .70 |
| | Sheet of 20, 4 each #4045a-4045e, + 20 labels | 14.00 | 14.00 |
| | Nos. 4041-4045 (5) | 41.30 | 41.30 |

Issued: No. 4041, 9/27; others, 7/16.
No. 4041 contains 4 each #4041a, 4041e, 2 each #4041d, 4041f, 5 #4041b and 3 #4041c. Background colors on some stamps differ slightly. Labels could be personalized for an additional fee.

Zoltán Kodály (1882-1967), Composer — A1357

**2007, July 16**      **Perf. 13x13¼**
4046 A1357 200fo multi    2.25 1.10

Hungarian University Sports Federation, Cent. — A1358

**2007, July 30**      **Perf. 11½x12**
4047 A1358 360fo multi    4.00 2.00

Dolomite Flax — A1359      Pasque Flower — A1360

***Serpentine Die Cut 10¾x10½***
**2007, Aug. 1**
**Self-Adhesive**
**Booklet Stamps**
| 4048 A1359 | 230fo multi | 2.50 | 1.25 |
|---|---|---|---|
| a. | Booklet pane of 4 + 4 etiquettes | 10.00 | |
| 4049 A1360 | 260fo multi | 3.00 | 1.50 |
| a. | Booklet pane of 4 + 4 etiquettes | 12.00 | |

## Souvenir Sheet

Enamel Paintings on St. Stephen's Crown — A1361

No. 4050: a, St. Cosmas (light blue robe). b, St. George (holding spear and shield). c, Archangel Michael (holding staff).

**Litho. (Litho. With Foil Application in Sheet Margin)**
**2007, Aug. 17**          **Perf. 12x11½**
4050 A1361 300fo Sheet of 3,
          #a-c                    9.50  4.75

János Selye (1907-82), Stress Researcher — A1362

**Perf. 13¼x12¾**
**2007, Aug. 23**          Litho.
4051 A1362 400fo multi         4.50  2.25
Second World Stress Conference, Budapest.

**World Science Forum Type of 2005 Redrawn**
**2007, Sept. 27**          **Perf. 13x13¼**
4052 A1264 230fo multi         2.60  1.25

Christmas — A1363

No. 4053: a, Annunciation. b, Holy Family and Shepherds. c, Adoration of the Magi. Illustration reduced.

**2007, Oct. 19**          **Perf. 12**
4053 A1363 62fo Horiz. strip of
          3, #a-c               2.25  1.10

**Compass and Map Type of 2005 Redrawn With "Belföld" Instead of Denomination**

No. 4054: a, Compass at right, map of western Hungary. b, Compass at left, map of eastern Hungary.

**2008, Feb. 8    Litho.    Perf. 11¼**
4054 A1246 (70fo) Pair, #a-b, + 2
          labels               1.60  1.60
      Sheet of 18 #4054a, 17
      #4054b, + 35 labels       28.00  —

Labels could be personalized.

Easter A1364

**2008, Feb. 27**          **Perf. 12**
4055 A1364 70fo multi          .80   .40

King Matthias, 550th Anniv. of Election — A1365

King Matthias, arms and: 70fo, Fountain. 100fo, Castle and horses. 600fo+200fo, King and Queen on throne.

**2008, Mar. 13**
4056-4057 A1365   Set of 2   2.10  1.10
**Souvenir Sheet**
4058 A1365 600fo +200fo multi 10.00 10.00
Stamp Day. No. 4058 contains one 40x30mm stamp.

General Károly Knezich (1808-49) A1366

**2008, Mar. 14**          **Perf. 13x12½**
4059 A1366 380fo multi         4.75  2.40

**Miniature Sheet**

Transportation — A1367

No. 4060: a, 150fo, Automobile. b, 150fo, Ship. c, 150fo+30fo, Train. d, 150fo+30fo, Airplane.

**2008, Mar. 14**          **Perf. 12**
4060 A1367   Sheet of 4, #a-d  8.25  8.25

Romany Dancer and Musicians A1368

German Dancer and Accordion A1369

**2008**               **Perf. 13½x13**
4061 A1368 260fo multi         3.25  1.60
4062 A1369 275fo multi         3.50  1.75
Hungarian ethnic minorities. Issued: 260fo, 4/8; 275fo, 5/9.

2008 Summer Olympics, Beijing A1370

Designs: 70fo, Water polo. 100fo, Wrestling. 170fo, Fencing.

**2008, Apr. 16**          **Perf. 13x13¼**
4063-4065 A1370   Set of 3    4.25  2.10

## Miniature Sheet

Europa — A1371

No. 4066: a, 100fo, Letter in envelope, capital "A." b, 230fo, Pen nib.

**2008, May 9**          **Perf. 12**
4066 A1371   Sheet, 2 each #a-
          b                    8.25  4.25
Stamps on bottom row are tete-beche in relation to the top row.

Indigenous Animals A1372

Designs: 145fo, Hungarian giant rabbit. 150fo, Hungarian domestic goat. 170fo, Cikta sheep. 310fo, Hungarian donkey. 600fo, Water buffalo.

**2008, May 9**
4067-4070 A1372   Set of 4    9.50  4.75
**Souvenir Sheet**
4071 A1372 600fo multi         7.50  3.75

**National Parks Type of 1998**
Design: Orség National Park.
**2008, May 16**
4072 A1073 220fo multi         3.00  1.50

**UNESCO World Heritage Sites Type of 2002**
Design: Tokaj Wine Region.
**2008, May 16**
4073 A1153 290fo multi         3.75  1.90

UEFA Euro 2008 Soccer Championships, Austria and Switzerland A1373

**2008, May 16**          **Perf. 13½x13**
4074 A1373 250fo multi         3.25  1.60

Vacation Vouchers, 10th Anniv. A1374

**2008, May 20**          **Perf. 12x11½**
4075 A1374 70fo multi          .90   .45

A1375

A1376

A1377

A1378

A1379

Philavillage A1380

**2008**     **Perf. 12, 13¼x13 (#4077)**
4076 A1375 100fo multi     1.40  .70
4077 A1376 100fo multi     1.40  .70
4078 A1377 100fo multi     1.40  .70
4079 A1378 100fo multi     1.40  .70
4080 A1379 100fo multi     1.40  .70
4081 A1380 100fo multi     1.40  .70
   Nos. 4076-4081 (6)      8.40  4.20

Issued: Nos. 4076-4077, 6/6; Nos. 4078-4079, 6/20; Nos. 4080-4081, 7/10. Stamps also served as game pieces for Philavillage board game.

A1381

A1382

A1383

A1384

A1385

Philavillage
A1386

| 2008 | | Litho. | **Perf. 12** | |
|---|---|---|---|---|
| 4082 | A1381 | 100fo multi | 1.25 | .60 |
| 4083 | A1382 | 100fo multi | 1.25 | .60 |

**Perf. 13x13¼, 13¼x13 (#4086)**

| 4084 | A1383 | 100fo multi | 1.10 | .55 |
|---|---|---|---|---|
| 4085 | A1384 | 100fo multi | 1.10 | .55 |
| 4086 | A1385 | 100fo multi | .95 | .50 |
| 4087 | A1386 | 100fo multi | .95 | .50 |
| | Nos. 4082-4087 (6) | | 6.60 | 3.30 |

Issued: Nos. 4082-4083, 9/2; Nos. 4084-4085, 10/9; Nos. 4086-4087, 11/5. Stamps also served as game pieces for Philavillage board game.

Hungarian
Illuminated
Chronicle, 650th
Anniv. — A1387

**Litho. & Embossed With Foil Application**
**2008, June 20**     **Perf. 12**
4088   A1387   400fo multi     5.50   2.75

Souvenir Sheet

Debrecen and Veszprém Zoos, 50th
Anniv. — A1388

No. 4089: a, Giraffes, cranes, hippopotamus, camel (Debrecen). b, Camel, crane, lion, zebra, rhinoceros, flamingo (Veszprém).

**2008, Aug. 14**     **Perf. 12**
4089   A1388   260fo Sheet of 2,
      #a-b      6.50   3.25

Souvenir Sheet

Enamel Paintings on St. Stephen's
Crown — A1389

No. 4090: a, Archangel Gabriel (holding staff). b, St. Demeter (with shield and spear). c, St. Damian (with beard).

**Litho. (Litho. With Foil Application in Sheet Margin)**
**2008, Aug. 19**     **Perf. 12x11½**
4090   A1389   300fo Sheet of 3,
      #a-c      11.50   5.75

Miklós
Zrinyi
(1508-66),
Military
Leader
A1390

**2008, Sept. 5**   **Litho.**   **Perf. 13x13¼**
4091   A1390   190fo multi     2.25   1.10

**Flowers Types of 2006 Redrawn With "Belföld" Instead of Denomination**

**2008, Sept. 2**    **Litho.**    **Perf. 11¼**
| 4092 | | Vert. strip of 5 + 5 labels | 4.25 | 4.25 |
|---|---|---|---|---|
| a. | A1278 | (70fo) multi + label | .85 | .85 |
| b. | A1279 | (70fo) multi + label | .85 | .85 |
| c. | A1280 | (70fo) multi + label | .85 | .85 |
| d. | A1281 | (70fo) multi + label | .85 | .85 |
| e. | A1282 | (70fo) multi + label | .85 | .85 |
| | | Sheet, 4 each #4092a-4092e, + 20 labels | 17.00 | |

Background colors of stamps in full sheets varies. Labels could be personalized for an additional fee.

Archangel
Gabriel,
Sculpture by
György Zala
(1858-1937)
A1391

**2008, Sept. 25**   **Litho.**   **Perf. 13¼x13**
4093   A1391   200fo multi     2.25   1.10

Synagogues
A1392

Designs: 200fo, Synagogue, Szeged. 250fo, Synagogue of the Jewish Theological Seminary, Budapest.

**2008, Sept. 25**     **Perf. 12½x13¼**
4094-4095   A1392   Set of 2     5.00   2.50

Cat — A1393

Bear — A1394

Rabbit — A1395

Lion — A1396

Giraffe — A1397

**2008, Oct. 9**     **Perf. 11¼**
| 4096 | | Vert. strip of 5 + 5 labels | 3.75 | 3.75 |
|---|---|---|---|---|
| a. | A1393 | (70fo) multi | .75 | .40 |
| b. | A1394 | (70fo) multi | .75 | .40 |
| c. | A1395 | (70fo) multi | .75 | .40 |
| d. | A1396 | (70fo) multi | .75 | .40 |
| e. | A1397 | (70fo) multi | .75 | .40 |
| | | Sheet, 4 each #4096a-4096e, + 20 labels | 15.00 | 15.00 |

Labels on No. 4096 could be personalized for an additional fee.

Souvenir Sheet

Ferenc Puskás (1927-2006), Player on
1952 Hungarian Olympic Soccer
Team — A1398

**2008, Oct. 28**     **Perf. 12**
4097   A1398   600fo multi     6.00   3.00

Christmas
A1399

Art by György Konecsni (1908-70): 70fo, Nativity. 100fo, Adoration of the Magi.

**2008, Oct. 28**     **Perf. 12¼x11½**
4098-4099   A1399   Set of 2     1.75   .85

Edward Teller (1908-2003), Nuclear
Physicist — A1400

**2008, Nov. 3**     **Perf. 13x13¼**
4100   A1400   250fo multi     2.40   1.25

Ludovika
Academy, 200th
Anniv. — A1401

**2008, Nov. 5**     **Perf. 13¼x13**
4101   A1401   300fo multi     3.00   1.50

## SEMI-POSTAL STAMPS

### Issues of the Monarchy

"Turul" and
St. Stephen's
Crown — SP1

Franz Josef I
Wearing
Hungarian
Crown — SP2

**Wmk. Double Cross (137)**
**1913, Nov. 20**    **Typo.**    **Perf. 14**
| B1 | SP1 | 1f | slate | .25 | .20 |
|---|---|---|---|---|---|
| B2 | SP1 | 2f | olive yellow | .25 | .20 |
| B3 | SP1 | 3f | orange | .25 | .20 |
| B4 | SP1 | 5f | emerald | .25 | .20 |
| B5 | SP1 | 6f | olive green | .25 | .20 |
| B6 | SP1 | 10f | carmine | .30 | .20 |
| B7 | SP1 | 12f | violet, *yellow* | .60 | .20 |
| B8 | SP1 | 16f | gray green | .90 | .20 |
| B9 | SP1 | 20f | dark brown | 2.40 | .40 |
| B10 | SP1 | 25f | ultra | 1.50 | .25 |
| B11 | SP1 | 30f | orange brown | 1.75 | .25 |
| B12 | SP1 | 35f | red violet | 1.75 | .25 |
| B13 | SP1 | 50f | lake, *blue* | 3.00 | .60 |
| B14 | SP1 | 60f | green, *salmon* | 3.00 | .50 |
| B15 | SP2 | 1k | dull red | 26.00 | 2.00 |
| B16 | SP2 | 2k | dull blue | 78.00 | 40.00 |
| B17 | SP2 | 5k | violet brown | 30.00 | 30.00 |
| | *Nos. B1-B17 (17)* | | | 150.45 | 75.85 |

Nos. B1-B17 were sold at an advance of 2f over face value, as indicated by the label at bottom. The surtax was to aid flood victims.
For overprints see Nos. 5NB1-5NB10, 6NB1-6NB11.
Exist imperf. Value, set $750.

Semi-Postal Stamps of 1913
Surcharged in Red, Green or Brown:

a                 b

**1914**
| B18 | SP1(a) | 1f | slate | .25 | .20 |
|---|---|---|---|---|---|
| B19 | SP1(a) | 2f | olive yel | .25 | .20 |
| B20 | SP1(a) | 3f | orange | .25 | .20 |
| B21 | SP1(a) | 5f | emerald | .25 | .20 |
| B22 | SP1(a) | 6f | olive green | .25 | .20 |
| B23 | SP1(a) | 10f | carmine (G) | .35 | .20 |
| B24 | SP1(a) | 12f | violet, *yel* | .25 | .20 |
| B25 | SP1(a) | 16f | gray green | .30 | .20 |
| B26 | SP1(a) | 20f | dark brown | 1.00 | .20 |
| B27 | SP1(a) | 25f | ultra | 1.00 | .20 |

| | | | |
|---|---|---|---|
| **B28** | SP1(a) | 30f orange brn | 1.40 | .25 |
| **B29** | SP1(a) | 35f red violet | 2.25 | .20 |
| **B30** | SP1(a) | 50f lake, *bl* | 1.75 | .50 |
| **B31** | SP1(a) | 60f green, *salmon* | 2.50 | .55 |
| **B32** | SP2(b) | 1k dull red (Br) | 55.00 | 25.00 |
| **B33** | SP2(b) | 2k dull blue | 40.00 | 26.00 |
| **B34** | SP2(b) | 5k violet brn | 30.00 | 21.00 |
| | *Nos. B18-B34 (17)* | | 137.05 | 75.50 |

Exist imperf. Value, set $600.

### Regular Issue of 1913 Surcharged in Red or Green:

c

d

### 1915, Jan. 1

| | | | | |
|---|---|---|---|---|
| **B35** | A4(c) | 1f slate | .20 | .20 |
| **B36** | A4(c) | 2f olive yel | .20 | .20 |
| **B37** | A4(c) | 3f orange | .20 | .20 |
| **B38** | A4(c) | 5f emerald | .20 | .20 |
| **B39** | A4(c) | 6f olive grn | .20 | .20 |
| **B40** | A4(c) | 10f carmine (G) | .20 | .20 |
| **B41** | A4(c) | 12f violet, *yel* | .20 | .20 |
| **B42** | A4(c) | 16f gray green | .25 | .25 |
| **B43** | A4(c) | 20f dark brown | .30 | .30 |
| **B44** | A4(c) | 25f ultra | .20 | .20 |
| **B45** | A4(c) | 30f orange brn | .40 | .20 |
| **B46** | A4(c) | 35f red violet | .45 | .20 |
| **B47** | A4(c) | 50f lake, *bl* | .65 | .25 |
| *a.* | On No. 96a | | 5,500. | |
| **B48** | A4(c) | 60f green, *salmon* | .85 | .30 |
| **B49** | A5(d) | 1k dull red | 1.25 | 3.00 |
| **B50** | A5(d) | 2k dull blue | 3.25 | 7.50 |
| **B51** | A5(d) | 5k violet brown | 9.00 | 17.50 |

### Surcharged as Type "c" but in Smaller Letters

| | | | | |
|---|---|---|---|---|
| **B52** | A4 | 60f green, *salmon* | 2.40 | 1.00 |
| | *Nos. B35-B52 (18)* | | 20.40 | 32.10 |

Nos. B18-B52 were sold at an advance of 2f over face value. The surtax to aid war widows and orphans.
Exist imperf. Value, set $180.

Soldiers Fighting
SP3    SP4

 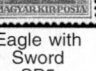

Eagle with Sword
SP5

Harvesting
SP6

### 1916-17    *Perf. 15*

| | | | | |
|---|---|---|---|---|
| **B53** | SP3 | 10f + 2f rose red | .20 | .20 |
| **B54** | SP4 | 15f + 2f dull violet | .20 | .20 |
| **B55** | SP5 | 40f + 2f brn car ('17) | .20 | .20 |
| | *Nos. B53-B55 (3)* | | .60 | .60 |

Exist imperf. Value, set $13.
For overprints and surcharge see Nos. B58-B60. 1NB1-1NB3, 2NB1-2NB6, 4NJ1, 5NB11-5NB13, 6NB13-6NB15, 7NB2-7NB3, 9NB1, 10NB1-10NB4, Szeged B1-B4.

### 1917, Sept. 15
### Surcharge in Red

| | | | | |
|---|---|---|---|---|
| **B56** | SP6 | 10f + 1k rose | .35 | .50 |
| **B57** | SP6 | 15f + 1k violet | .35 | .50 |

Nos. B56 and B57 were issued in connection with the War Exhibition of Archduke Josef.

### Issues of the Republic

Semi-Postal Stamps of 1916-17 Overprinted in Black

### 1918

| | | | | |
|---|---|---|---|---|
| **B58** | SP3 | 10f + 2f rose red | .20 | .20 |
| **B59** | SP4 | 15f + 2f dull violet | .20 | .20 |
| **B60** | SP5 | 40f + 2f brown car | .20 | .20 |
| | *Nos. B58-B60 (3)* | | .60 | .60 |

Nos. B58-B60 exist with inverted overprint.
Exist imperf. Value, set $12.

Postally used examples of Nos. B69-B174 sell for more.

### Issues of the Kingdom

Released Prisoner Walking Home — SP7

Prisoners of War — SP8

Homecoming of Soldier — SP9

### Wmk. 137 Vert. or Horiz.
### 1920, Mar. 10    *Perf. 12*

| | | | | |
|---|---|---|---|---|
| **B69** | SP7 | 40f + 1k dull red | 2.00 | 2.00 |
| **B70** | SP8 | 60f + 2k gray brown | 3.50 | 3.50 |
| **B71** | SP9 | 1k + 5k dk blue | 3.50 | 3.50 |
| | *Nos. B69-B71 (3)* | | 9.00 | 9.00 |
| | Set, never hinged | | 18.00 | |

The surtax was used to help prisoners of war return home from Siberia.
Exist imperf. Value, set $90.

Statue of Petöfi — SP10

Griffin — SP11

Sándor Petöfi — SP12

Petöfi Dying — SP13

Petöfi Addressing People — SP14

### 1923, Jan. 23    *Perf. 14 (10k, 40k), 12*

| | | | | |
|---|---|---|---|---|
| **B72** | SP10 | 10k slate green | .50 | 1.00 |
| **B73** | SP11 | 15k dull blue | 1.50 | 2.75 |
| **B74** | SP12 | 25k gray brown | .50 | 1.00 |
| **B75** | SP13 | 40k brown violet | 1.75 | 2.75 |
| **B76** | SP14 | 50k violet brown | 1.75 | 2.75 |
| | *Nos. B72-B76 (5)* | | 6.00 | 10.25 |
| | Set, never hinged | | 10.00 | |

Birth centenary of the Hungarian poet Sándor Petöfi. The stamps were on sale at double face value, for a limited time and in restricted quantities, after which the remainders were given to a charitable organization.
Exist imperf. Value, set $90.

Child with Symbols of Peace — SP15

Mother and Infant — SP16

Instruction in Archery — SP17

### Wmk. 133
### 1924, Apr. 8    *Engr.    Perf. 12*

| | | | | |
|---|---|---|---|---|
| **B77** | SP15 | 300k dark blue | 1.75 | 2.75 |
| *a.* | Perf. 11½ | | 35.00 | 30.00 |
| **B78** | SP16 | 500k black brown | 1.75 | 2.75 |
| **B79** | SP17 | 1000k black green | 2.00 | 4.00 |
| | *Nos. B77-B79 (3)* | | 5.50 | 9.50 |
| | Set, never hinged | | 12.00 | |

Each stamp has on the back an inscription stating that it was sold at a premium of 100 per cent over the face value.
Exist imperf. Value, set $80.

Parade of Athletes SP18

Skiing — SP19

Skating — SP20

Diving — SP21

Fencing SP22

Scouts Camping — SP23

Soccer SP24

Hurdling — SP25

### Perf. 12, 12½ and Compound
### 1925    Typo.    Unwmk.

| | | | | |
|---|---|---|---|---|
| **B80** | SP18 | 100k bl grn & brn | 3.50 | 4.00 |
| **B81** | SP19 | 200k lt brn & myr grn | 4.00 | 5.00 |
| **B82** | SP20 | 300k dark blue | 5.00 | 6.00 |
| **B83** | SP21 | 400k dp bl & dp grn | 5.75 | 8.00 |
| **B84** | SP22 | 500k purple brown | 7.50 | 10.00 |
| **B85** | SP23 | 1000k red brown | 8.50 | 11.00 |
| **B86** | SP24 | 2000k brown violet | 10.00 | 12.00 |
| **B87** | SP25 | 2500k olive brown | 12.00 | 14.00 |
| | *Nos. B80-B87 (8)* | | 56.25 | 70.00 |
| | Set, never hinged | | 100.00 | |

These stamps were sold at double face value, plus a premium of 10 per cent on orders sent by mail. They did not serve any postal need and were issued solely to raise funds to aid athletic associations. An inscription regarding the 100 per cent premium is printed on the back of each stamp.
Exist imperf. Value, set $270.

St. Emerich SP26

Sts. Stephen and Gisela SP27

St. Ladislaus SP28

Sts. Gerhardt and Emerich SP29

**1930, May 15    Wmk. 210    Perf. 14**

| B88 | SP26 | 8f + 2f deep green | .45 | .40 |
|---|---|---|---|---|
| B89 | SP27 | 16f + 4f brt violet | .50 | .70 |
| B90 | SP28 | 20f + 4f deep rose | 1.75 | 2.50 |
| B91 | SP29 | 32f + 8f ultra | 2.50 | 3.75 |
| | | Nos. B88-B91 (4) | 5.20 | 7.35 |
| | | Set, never hinged | 11.00 | |

900th anniv. of the death of St. Emerich, son of Stephen I, king, saint and martyr.
Exist imperf. Value, set $60.

> Catalogue values for unused stamps in this section, from this point to the end of the section, are for Never Hinged items.

St. Ladislaus — SP30

Holy Sacrament SP31

SP32

**1938 May 16    Photo.    Perf. 12**

| B92 | SP30 | 16f + 16f dull slate bl | 3.00 | 3.00 |
|---|---|---|---|---|
| B93 | SP31 | 20f + 20f dk car | 3.00 | 3.00 |

**Souvenir Sheet**

| B94 | SP32 | Sheet of 7 | 50.00 | 32.50 |
|---|---|---|---|---|
| a. | | 6f + 6f St. Stephen | 4.00 | 3.00 |
| b. | | 10f + 10f St. Emerich | 4.00 | 3.00 |
| c. | | 16f + 16f slate blue (B92) | 4.00 | 3.00 |
| d. | | 20f + 20f dark carmine (B93) | 4.00 | 3.00 |
| e. | | 32f + 32f St. Elizabeth | 4.00 | 3.00 |
| f. | | 40f + 40f St. Maurice | 4.00 | 3.00 |
| g. | | 50f + 50f St. Margaret | 4.00 | 3.00 |

Printed in sheets measuring 136½x155mm.
Nos. B94c and B94d are slightly smaller than B92 and B93.
Eucharistic Cong. in Budapest, May, 1938.
Exist imperf. Value: set $170; souvenir sheet $3,500.

St. Stephen, Victorious Warrior SP33

St. Stephen, Offering Crown SP34

SP35

**1938, Aug. 12    Perf. 12**

| B95 | SP33 | 10f + 10f violet brn | 3.00 | 3.00 |
|---|---|---|---|---|
| B96 | SP34 | 20f + 20f red org | 3.00 | 3.00 |

**Souvenir Sheet**

| B97 | SP35 | Sheet of 7 | 32.50 | 20.00 |
|---|---|---|---|---|
| a. | | 6f + 6f St. Stephen the Missionary | 3.25 | 2.00 |
| b. | | 10f + 10f violet brown (B95) | 3.25 | 2.00 |
| c. | | 16f + 16f Seated Upon Throne | 3.25 | 2.00 |
| d. | | 20f + 20f red orange (B96) | 3.25 | 2.00 |
| e. | | 32f + 32f Receives Bishops and Monks | 3.25 | 2.00 |
| f. | | 40f + 40f St. Gisela, St. Stephen and St. Emerich | 3.25 | 2.00 |
| g. | | 50f + 50f St. Stephen on Bier | 3.25 | 2.00 |

Death of St. Stephen, 900th anniversary.
No. B97 is on brownish paper, Nos. B95-B96 on white.
Nos. B95-B97 exist imperf. Value, Nos. B95-B96, $100; No. B97 $3,500.

Statue Symbolizing Recovered Territories SP36

Castle of Munkács SP37

Admiral Horthy Entering Komárom SP38

Cathedral of Kassa SP39

Girl Offering Flowers to Soldier — SP40

**1939, Jan. 16**

| B98 | SP36 | 6f + 3f myrtle grn | .60 | .35 |
|---|---|---|---|---|
| B99 | SP37 | 10f + 5f olive grn | .25 | .20 |
| B100 | SP38 | 20f + 10f dark red | .25 | .20 |
| B101 | SP39 | 30f + 15f grnsh blue | 1.10 | .60 |
| B102 | SP40 | 40f + 20f dk bl gray | 1.10 | .65 |
| | | Nos. B98-B102 (5) | 3.30 | 2.00 |

The surtax was for the aid of "Hungary for Hungarians" patriotic movement.
Exist imperf. Value, set $250.

Memorial Tablets SP41

Gáspár Károlyi, Translator of the Bible into Hungarian SP42

Albert Molnár de Szenci, Translator of the Psalms SP43

Prince Gabriel Bethlen — SP44

Susanna Lórántffy — SP45

**Perf. 12x12½, 12½x12**

**1939    Photo.    Wmk. 210**

| B103 | SP41 | 6f + 3f green | .70 | .55 |
|---|---|---|---|---|
| B104 | SP42 | 10f + 5f claret | .70 | .55 |
| B105 | SP43 | 20f + 10f copper red | .80 | .75 |
| B106 | SP44 | 32f + 16f bister | 1.25 | 1.00 |
| B107 | SP45 | 40f + 20f chalky blue | 1.40 | 1.00 |
| | | Nos. B103-B107 (5) | 4.85 | 3.85 |

**Souvenir Sheets**

**Perf. 12**

| B108 | SP44 | 32f olive & vio brn | 15.00 | 15.00 |
|---|---|---|---|---|

**Imperf**

| B109 | SP44 | 32f bl grn, cop red & gold | 15.00 | 15.00 |
|---|---|---|---|---|

National Protestant Day. The surtax was used to erect an Intl. Protestant Institute.
The souvenir sheets sold for 1.32p each.
Nos. B103-B108 exist imperf. Values: Nos. B103-B107 $350; No. B108 $3,500.
Issue dates: Nos. B103-B107, Oct. 2. Nos. B108-B109, Oct. 27.

Boy Scout Flying Kite — SP47

Allegory of Flight — SP48

Archangel Gabriel from Millennium Monument, Budapest, and Planes — SP49

**1940, Jan. 1    Perf. 12½x12**

| B110 | SP47 | 6f + 6f yellow grn | .85 | .90 |
|---|---|---|---|---|
| B111 | SP48 | 10f + 10f chocolate | .95 | 1.00 |
| B112 | SP49 | 20f + 20f copper red | 1.25 | 1.40 |
| | | Nos. B110-B112 (3) | 3.05 | 3.30 |

The surtax was used for the Horthy National Aviation Fund.
Exist imperf. Value, set $170.

SP50

Soldier Protecting Family from Floods SP51

**Souvenir Sheet**

**Wmk. 210**

**1940, May 6    Photo.    Perf. 12**

| B113 | SP50 | 20f + 1p dk blue grn | 5.00 | 5.00 |
|---|---|---|---|---|

Exist imperf. Value $3,500.

**1940, May**

| B114 | SP51 | 10f + 2f gray brown | .25 | .25 |
|---|---|---|---|---|
| B115 | SP51 | 20f + 4f orange red | .25 | .25 |
| B116 | SP51 | 20f + 50f red brown | .70 | .70 |
| | | Nos. B114-B116 (3) | 1.20 | 1.20 |

The surtax on Nos. B113-B116 was used to aid flood victims.
Exist imperf. Value, set $170.

Hunyadi Coat of Arms SP52

King Matthias SP54

Hunyadi Castle SP53

Equestrian Statue of King Matthias SP55

Corvin Codex — SP56

Equestrian Statue of King
Matthias — SP57

**1940**                    **Perf. 12½x12, 12x12½**
B117  SP52  6f + 3f blue grn          .30  .30
B118  SP53  10f + 5f gldn brn         .25  .25
B119  SP54  16f + 8f dk ol bis        .30  .30
B120  SP55  20f + 10f brick red       .50  .40
B121  SP56  32f + 16f dk gray        1.00  .70
      Nos. B117-B121 (5)             2.35 1.95

**Souvenir Sheet**
B122  SP57  20f + 1p dk bl grn &
                 pale grn            4.50 4.50
King Matthias (1440-1490) at Kolozsvar,
Transylvania. The surtax was used for war
relief.
   Nos. B117-B122 exist imperf. Values: Nos.
B117-B121 $220; No. B122 $3,500.
   Issued: #B117-B121, July 1. #B122. Nov. 7.

Hungarian
Soldier — SP58

20f+50f, Virgin Mary and Szekley, symbol-
izing the return of transylvania. 32f+50f,
Szekley Mother Offering Infant Son to the
Fatherland.

**1940, Dec. 2  Photo.   Perf. 12½x12**
B123  SP58  10f + 50f dk blue grn     .65  .50
B124  SP58  20f + 50f brown car       .65  .50
B125  SP58  32f + 50f yellow brn      .95  .75
      Nos. B123-B125 (3)             2.25 1.75

Occupation of Transylvania. The surtax was
for the Pro-Transylvania movement.
   Exist imperf. Value, set $200.

Symbol for
Drama
SP61

Symbol for
Sculpture — SP62

Symbols: 16f+16f, Art. 20f+20f, Literature.

**1940, Dec. 15  Perf. 12x12½, 12½x12**
B126  SP61  6f + 6f dark green       1.00 1.00
B127  SP62  10f + 10f olive bis      1.00 1.00
B128  SP62  16f + 16f dk violet      1.00 1.00
B129  SP61  20f + 20f fawn           1.00 1.00
      Nos. B126-B129 (4)             4.00 4.00

---

**Souvenir Sheet**

**1941, Jan. 5**                        **Imperf.**
B130      Sheet of 4                 5.50 5.50
   *a.*  SP61 6f + 6f olive brown    1.10 1.10
   *b.*  SP62 10f + 10f henna brown  1.10 1.10
   *c.*  SP62 16f + 16f dk blue green 1.10 1.10
   *d.*  SP61 20f + 20f rose violet  1.10 1.10

Surtax on #B126-B130 was used for the
Pension and Assistance Institution for Artists.
Nos. B126-B129 exist imperf. Value, set
$70.

Winged Head
of
Pilot — SP66

Designs: 10f+10f, Boy Scout with model
plane. 20f+20f, Glider in flight. 32f+32f, Our
Lady of Loreto, patroness of Hungarian pilots.

**1941, Mar. 24**              **Perf. 12x12½**
B131  SP66  6f + 6f grn olive         .50  .40
B132  SP66  10f + 10f dp claret       .50  .40
B133  SP66  20f + 20f org ver         .60  .50
B134  SP66  32f + 32f turq blue      1.50 1.25
      Nos. B131-B134 (4)             3.10 2.55

The surtax was used to finance civilian and
army pilot training through the Horthy National
Aviation Fund.
   Exist imperf. Value, set $270.

Infantry
SP70

12f+18f, Heavy artillery. 20f+30f, Plane and
tanks. 40f+60f, Cavalryman and cyclist.

**1941, Dec. 1   Photo.   Wmk. 266
Inscribed: "Honvedeink
Karacsonyara 1941"**
B135  SP70  8f + 12f dk green         .30  .30
B136  SP70  12f + 18f olive grn       .30  .30
B137  SP70  20f + 30f slate           .35  .35
B138  SP70  40f + 60f red brown       .55  .55
      Nos. B135-B138 (4)             1.50 1.50

The surtax was for the benefit of the Army.
Exist imperf. Value, set $175.

Soldier and
Emblem
SP74

**1941, Dec. 1**
B139  SP74  20f + 40f dark red       1.50 1.25

The surtax was for the soldiers' Christmas.
Exists imperf. Value $70.

Aviator and
Plane — SP75

Planes and
Ghostly Band
of Old Chiefs
SP76

Plane and
Archer
SP77

---

Aviators and
Plane — SP78

**1942, Mar. 15  Perf. 12½x12, 12x12½**
B140  SP75  8f + 8f dark green        .70  .70
B141  SP76  12f + 12f sapphire        .70  .70
B142  SP77  20f + 20f brown           .70  .70
B143  SP78  30f + 30f dark red        .70  .70
      Nos. B140-B143 (4)             2.80 2.80

The surtax aided the Horthy National Aviation Fund.
   Exist imperf. Value, set $270.

Blood
Transfusion — SP79

Designs: 8f+32f, Bandaging wounded soldier. 12f+50f, Radio and carrier pigeons.
20f+1p, Widows and orphans.

**1942, Sept. 1**             **Perf. 12½x12**
B144  SP79  3f + 18f dk ol & red      .80  .85
B145  SP79  8f + 32f dp brn &
                 red                  .80  .85
B146  SP79  12f + 50f dp cl & red     .80  .85
B147  SP79  20f + 1p slate bl &
                 red                  .80  .85
      Nos. B144-B147 (4)             3.20 3.40

The surtax aided the Hungarian Red Cross.
Sheets of 10. Value, set $85.
   Exist imperf. Value, set $300.

Widow of Stephen
Horthy — SP83

Red Cross
Nurse Aiding
Soldier
SP84

Magdalene
Horthy Mother of
Stephen
Horthy — SP85

**1942, Dec. 1**           **Perf. 13, Imperf.**
B148  SP83  6f + 1p vio bl &
                 red                 2.75 2.75
   *a.*     Sheet of 4              25.00 25.00
B149  SP84  8f + 1p dk ol grn
                 & red               2.75 2.75
   *a.*     Sheet of 4              25.00 25.00
B150  SP85  20f + 1p dk red
                 brn & red           2.75 2.75
   *a.*     Sheet of 4              25.00 25.00
      Nos. B148-B150 (3)             8.25 8.25

The surtax aided the Hungarian Red Cross.

---

King Ladislaus I
SP86           SP87

**1942, Dec. 21   Wmk. 266   Perf. 12**
B151  SP86  6f + 6f olive gray        .80 1.00
B152  SP87  8f + 8f green             .80 1.00
B153  SP87  12f + 12f dull violet     .80 1.00
B154  SP87  20f + 20f Prus green      .80 1.00
B155  SP86  24f + 24f brown           .80 1.00
B156  SP87  30f + 30f rose car        .80 1.00
      Nos. B151-B156 (6)             4.80 6.00

900th anniv. of the birth of St. Ladislaus
(1040-95), the 700th anniv. of the beginning of
the country's reconstruction by King Béla IV
(1206-70) and the 600th anniv. of the accession of King Lajos the Great (1326-82).
   The surtax aided war invalids and their
families.
   Exist imperf. Value, set $350.

Archer on
Horseback
SP92

Knight with Sword
and
Shield — SP93

Old Magyar
Arms — SP94

Designs: 3f+1f, 4f+1f, Warrior with shield
and battle ax. 12f+2f, Knight with lance,
20f+2f, Musketeer. 40f+4f, Hussar. 50f+6f,
Artilleryman.

**1943**
B157  SP92  1f + 1f dk gray           .20  .35
B158  SP93  3f + 1f dull violet       .30  .50
B159  SP93  4f + 1f lake              .20  .35
B160  SP93  8f + 2f green             .20  .35
B161  SP92  12f + 2f bister brn       .20  .35
B162  SP93  20f + 2f dp claret        .20  .35
B163  SP92  40f + 4f gray vio         .20  .35
B164  SP93  50f + 6f org brn          .25  .35
B165  SP94  70f + 8f slate blue       .25  .35
      Nos. B157-B165 (9)             2.00 3.30

The surtax aided war invalids.
   Exist imperf. Value, set $270.

Model
Glider — SP101          Gliders — SP102

White-tailed Sea Eagle and Planes — SP103

ME-109E Fighter and Gliders — SP104

**1943, July 17**
| | | | | |
|---|---|---|---|---|
| B166 | SP101 | 8f + 8f green | .75 | 1.00 |
| B167 | SP102 | 12f + 12f royal blue | .75 | 1.00 |
| B168 | SP103 | 20f + 20f chestnut | .75 | 1.00 |
| B169 | SP104 | 30f + 30f rose car | .75 | 1.00 |
| | Nos. B166-B169 (4) | | 3.00 | 4.00 |

The surtax aided the Horthy National Aviation Fund.
Exist imperf. Value, set $270.

Stephen Horthy SP105

**1943, Aug. 16**
| | | | | |
|---|---|---|---|---|
| B170 | SP105 | 30f + 20f dp rose vio | .30 | .25 |

The surtax aided the Horthy National Aviation Fund.
Exists imperf. Value $70.

Nurse and Soldier SP106

Designs: 30f+30f, Soldier, nurse, mother and child. 50f+50f, Nurse keeping lamp alight. 70f+70f, Wounded soldier and tree shoot.

**1944, Mar. 1**
**Cross in Red**
| | | | | |
|---|---|---|---|---|
| B171 | SP106 | 20f + 20f brown | .20 | .25 |
| B172 | SP106 | 30f + 30f henna | .20 | .25 |
| B173 | SP106 | 50f + 50f brown vio | .20 | .25 |
| B174 | SP106 | 70f + 70f Prus blue | .20 | .25 |
| | Nos. B171-B174 (4) | | .80 | 1.00 |

The surtax aided the Hungarian Red Cross.
Exist imperf. Value, set $270.

**Issues of the Republic**
Types of 1944 Surcharged in Red or Black:

a

b

**1945, July 23    Wmk. 266    Perf. 12**
| | | | | |
|---|---|---|---|---|
| B175 | A115(a) | 3p + 9p on 20f dk ol grn, yel | .25 | 1.00 |
| B176 | A114(b) | 4p + 12p on 4f yel brn, bl (Bk) | .25 | 1.00 |
| B177 | A117(b) | 8p + 24p on 50f sl bl, yel | .25 | 1.00 |
| B178 | A115(a) | 10p + 30p on 30f hn brn, bl (Bk) | .25 | 1.00 |
| | Nos. B175-B178 (4) | | 1.00 | 4.00 |

The surtax was for the Peoples Universities. "Béke" means "peace".

Imre Sallai and Sandor Fürst SP110

Designs: 3p+3p, L. Kabok and Illes Monus. 4p+4p, Ferenc Rozsa and Zoltan Schonerz. 6p+6p, Anna Koltai and Mrs. Paul Knurr. 10p+10p, George Sarkozi and Imre Nagy. 15p+15p, Vilmos Tartsay and Jeno Nagy. 20p+20p, Janos Kiss and Andreas Bajcsy-Zsilinszky. 40p+40p, Endre Sagvari and Otto Hoffmann.

**1945, Oct. 6    Photo.**
| | | | | |
|---|---|---|---|---|
| B179 | SP110 | 2p + 2p yel brn | 1.10 | 1.25 |
| B180 | SP110 | 3p + 3p deep red | 1.10 | 1.25 |
| B181 | SP110 | 4p + 4p dk pur | 1.10 | 1.25 |
| B182 | SP110 | 6p + 6p dk yel grn | 1.10 | 1.25 |
| B183 | SP110 | 10p + 10p dp car | 1.10 | 1.25 |
| B184 | SP110 | 15p + 15p dk sl grn | 1.10 | 1.25 |
| B185 | SP110 | 20p + 20p dk brn | 1.10 | 1.25 |
| B186 | SP110 | 40p + 40p dp bl | 1.10 | 1.25 |
| | Nos. B179-B186 (8) | | 8.80 | 10.00 |

The surtax was for child welfare.
Exist imperf. Value, set $150.

Andreas Bajcsy-Zsilinszky and Eagle — SP111

**1945, May 27**
| | | | | |
|---|---|---|---|---|
| B187 | SP111 | 1p + 1p dk brn vio | .40 | .80 |

1st anniv. of the death of Andreas Bajcsy-Zsilinszky, hanged by the Nazis for anti-fascist activities.
Exists imperf. Value $135.

Lion with Broken Shackles SP112

**1946, May 1**
| | | | | |
|---|---|---|---|---|
| B188 | SP112 | 500ez + 500ez p | 1.00 | 1.75 |
| B189 | SP112 | 1mil + 1mil p | 1.00 | 1.75 |
| B190 | SP112 | 1.5mil + 1.5mil p | 1.00 | 1.75 |
| B191 | SP112 | 2mil + 2mil p | 1.00 | 1.75 |
| | Nos. B188-B191 (4) | | 4.00 | 7.00 |

75th anniv. of Hungary's 1st postage stamp. The surtax was for the benefit of postal employees.
Exist imperf. Value, set $135.

"Agriculture" Holding Wheat — SP113

Physician with Syringe — SP114

**1946, Sept. 7    Photo.**
| | | | | |
|---|---|---|---|---|
| B192 | SP113 | 30f + 60f dp yel grn | 4.75 | 7.00 |
| B193 | SP113 | 60f + 1.20fo rose brn | 4.75 | 7.00 |
| B194 | SP113 | 1fo + 2fo dp brn | 4.75 | 7.00 |
| | Nos. B192-B194 (3) | | 14.25 | 21.00 |

1st Agricultural Congress and Exhibition.

Exist imperf. Value, set $280.

**1947, May 16    Wmk. 210**
Designs: 12f+50f, Physician examining X-ray picture. 20f+50f, Nurse and child. 60f+50f, Prisoner of war starting home.
| | | | | |
|---|---|---|---|---|
| B195 | SP114 | 8f + 50f ultra | 3.00 | 3.25 |
| B196 | SP114 | 12f + 50f choc | 3.00 | 3.25 |
| B197 | SP114 | 20f + 50f dk grn | 3.00 | 3.25 |
| B198 | SP114 | 60f + 50f dk red | 1.00 | 1.25 |
| | Nos. B195-B198 (4) | | 10.00 | 11.00 |

The surtax was for charitable purposes.
Exist imperf. Value, set $350.

Franklin D. Roosevelt and Freedom of Speech Allegory SP115

Pres. F. D. Roosevelt and Allegory: 12f+12f, Freedom of Religion. 20f+20f, Freedom from Want. 30f+30f, Freedom from Fear.

**1947, June 11    Photo.    Perf. 12x12½**
**Portrait in Sepia**
| | | | | |
|---|---|---|---|---|
| B198A | SP115 | 8f + 8f dark red | 3.75 | 5.00 |
| B198B | SP115 | 12f + 12f deep green | 3.75 | 5.00 |
| B198C | SP115 | 20f + 20f brown | 3.75 | 5.00 |
| B198D | SP115 | 30f + 30f blue | 3.75 | 5.00 |
| | Nos. B198A-B198D,CB1-CB1C (8) | | 29.00 | 40.00 |

Exist imperf. Value, set $225.
Nos. B198A-B198D and CB1-CB1C were also printed in sheets of 4 of each denomination (size: 117x96mm). Value, set of 8, $675. Exist imperf. Value $900.
A souvenir sheet exists, containing one each of Nos. B198A-B198D with border inscriptions and decorations in brown. Size: 161x122mm. Value $125. Exists imperf. Value $225.

Lenin — SP118

XVI Century Mail Coach SP119

Designs: 60f+60f, Soviet Cenotaph, Budapest. 1fo+1fo, Joseph V. Stalin.

**1947, Oct. 29    Photo.    Wmk. 283**
| | | | | |
|---|---|---|---|---|
| B199 | SP118 | 40f + 40f ol grn & org brn | 4.50 | 5.50 |
| B200 | SP118 | 60f + 60f red & sl bl | 1.00 | 1.00 |
| B201 | SP118 | 1fo + 1fo vio & brn blk | 4.50 | 5.50 |
| | Nos. B199-B201 (3) | | 10.00 | 12.00 |

The surtax was for the Hungarian-Soviet Cultural Association.
Exist imperf. Value, set $150.

**1947, Dec. 21    Perf. 12x12½**
| | | | | |
|---|---|---|---|---|
| B202 | SP119 | 30f (+ 50f) hn brn | 9.50 | 10.00 |
| | Sheet of 4 | | 42.50 | 42.50 |

Stamp Day. The surtax paid admission to a philatelic exhibition in any of eight Hungarian towns, where the stamps were sold.
Nos. B199-B202 exist imperf. Values: Nos. B199-B201 $475; No. B202 $675; No. B202 sheet of 4 $2,750.

Globe and Carrier Pigeon — SP120

Woman Worker — SP121

**1948, Oct. 17    Perf. 12½x12**
| | | | | |
|---|---|---|---|---|
| B203 | SP120 | 30f (+ 1fo) grnsh | 4.00 | 4.00 |
| | bl | | | |
| | Sheet of 4 | | 24.00 | 24.00 |

5th Natl. Hungarian Stamp Exhib., Budapest. Each stamp sold for 1.30 forint, which included admission to the exhibition.
Exists imperf. Value: single $450; sheetlet $2,250.

**1949, Mar. 8**
| | | | | |
|---|---|---|---|---|
| B204 | SP121 | 60f + 60f magenta | 2.50 | 2.50 |

Intl. Woman's Day, Mar. 8, 1949. The surtax was for the Democratic Alliance of Hungarian Women.
Exists imperf. Value $70.

Aleksander S. Pushkin — SP122

SP123

**1949, June 6    Photo.**
| | | | | |
|---|---|---|---|---|
| B205 | SP122 | 1fo + 1fo car lake | 7.50 | 7.50 |

**Souvenir Sheet**
**Perf. 12½x12,**
**Imperf**
| | | | | |
|---|---|---|---|---|
| B206 | SP123 | 1fo + 1fo red vio & car lake | 15.00 | 15.00 |

150th anniversary of the birth of Aleksander S. Pushkin. The surtax was for the Hungarian-Russian Culture Society.
No. B205 exists imperf. Value $220.

---

**IMPERFORATE STAMPS**
Through 1991, most semi-postal stamps were also issued imperforate. Where these items form part of a larger set with regular issues, values for imperfs will be included in that of the sets to which they belong, footnoted in the Regular Issues section. For Nos. B207-B345, values for imperfs will be given only for those items not included in sets with regular issues.

---

**1st Stamp Type**
**Perf. 12½x12**
**1951, Oct. 6    Engr.    Unwmk.**
| | | | | |
|---|---|---|---|---|
| B207 | A208 | 1fo + 1fo red | 7.50 | 7.00 |
| B208 | A208 | 2fo + 2fo blue | 12.50 | 11.50 |

Exists imperf.

Postwoman
Delivering
Mail — SP124

**1953, Nov. 1    Wmk. 106    *Perf. 12***
B209  SP124  1fo + 1fo blue grn      4.00  1.25
B210  SP124  2fo + 2fo rose vio      4.00  1.25
Stamp Day, Nov. 1, 1953.
Exist imperf. Value, set $60.

Stamps of
1955
Surcharged
in Red or
Lake

**1957, Jan. 31   Photo.   *Perf. 12x12½***
B211  A249  20f + 20f olive grn      .20   .20
B212  A249  30f + 30f dk red (L)     .25   .25
  a.   Red (cross) inverted               450.00
B213  A249  40f + 40f brown          .30   .25
B214  A249  60f + 60f brn red
            (L)                       .50   .30
B215  A249  1fo + 1fo blue           .75   .50
B216  A249  2fo + 2fo rose brn      1.00   .90
  Nos. B211-B216 (6)                3.00  2.40
The surtax was for the Hungarian Red
Cross.
Exist imperf. Value, set $135.

Winter Olympic Type of 1960
Design: Olympic Games emblem.

***Perf. 11½x12***
**1960, Feb. 29                     Wmk. 106**
B217  A295  2fo + 1fo multi          .90   .35
Exists imperf.

Olympic Type of 1960
Design: 2fo+1fo, Romulus and Remus.

***Perf. 11½x12***
**1960, Aug. 21   Photo.           Wmk. 106**
B218  A299  2fo + 1fo multi          .75   .30
Exists imperf.

Sport Club Type of 1961
Sport: 2fo+1fo, Sailboats.

**1961, July 8    Unwmk.    *Perf. 14½***
B219  A313  2fo + 1fo multi          .35   .20
Exists imperf.

St. Margaret's Island and
Danube — SP125

Views of Budapest: No. B221, Fishermen's
Bastion. No. B222, Coronation Church and
Chain Bridge. No. B223, Mount Gellert.

**Unwmk.**
**1961, Sept. 24  Photo.    *Perf. 12***
B220  SP125  2fo + 1fo multi         .70   .70
B221  SP125  2fo + 1fo multi         .70   .70
B222  SP125  2fo + 1fo multi         .70   .70
B223  SP125  2fo + 1fo multi         .70   .70
  a.   Horiz. strip of 4, #B220-B223 3.00  3.00
Stamp Day, 1961, and Budapest Intl. Stamp
Exhibition.
No. B223a has a continuous design.
Exist imperf. Value, strip $30.
Miniature presentation sheets, perf. and
imperf., contain one each of Nos. B220-B223;
size: 204x66½mm. Value for both sheets,
$1,300.

Soccer Type of Regular Issue, 1962
Design: Flags of Spain and Czechoslovakia.

**1962, May 21                     *Perf. 11***
**Flags in Original Colors**
B224  A323  4fo + 1fo lt grn & bis-
            ter                      2.50   .30
Exists imperf.

Austrian Stamp of
1850 with Pesth
Postmark
SP126

Stamps: No. B226, #201. No. B227, #C164.
No. B228, #C208.

**Lithographed and Engraved**
**1962, Sept. 22   Unwmk.    *Perf. 11***
**Design and Inscription
in Dark Brown**
B225  SP126  2fo + 1fo yellow        .55   .55
B226  SP126  2fo + 1fo pale
             pink                    .55   .55
B227  SP126  2fo + 1fo pale
             blue                    .55   .55
B228  SP126  2fo + 1fo pale yel
             grn                     .55   .55
  a.   Horiz. strip of 4, #B225-
       B228                         2.50  2.25
  b.   Souv. sheet of 4, #B225-
       B228                         6.00  6.00
35th Stamp Day and 10th anniv. of Mabeosz, the Hungarian Phil. Fed.
Exist imperf. Value: strip $23; souvenir
sheet $40.

Emblem, Cup
and Soccer
Ball — SP127

**1962, Nov. 18  Photo.  *Perf. 11½x12***
B229  SP127  2fo + 1fo multi         .60   .50
Winning of the "Coupe de l'Europe Centrale"
by the Steel Workers Sport Club (VASAS) in
the Central European Soccer Championships.
Exists imperf. Value $7.

Stamp
Day — SP128

**1963, Oct. 24                *Perf. 11½x12***
**Size: 32x43mm**
B230  SP128  2fo + 1fo Hyacinth      .50   .50
B231  SP128  2fo + 1fo Narcissus     .50   .50
B232  SP128  2fo + 1fo Chrysan-
             themum                  .50   .50
B233  SP128  2fo + 1fo Tiger lily    .50   .50
  a.   Horiz. strip of 4, #B230-B233 3.00  3.00
  b.   Min. sheet of 4, #B230-B233   3.50  3.50
#B233b contains 25x32mm stamps, perf. 11.
Exist imperf. Value: strip $25; miniature
sheet $40.

Winter Olympic Type of 1963
Design: 4fo+1fo, Bobsledding.

**1963, Nov. 11                    *Perf. 12***
B234  A342  4fo + 1fo grnsh bl &
            bis                      .70   .30
Exists imperf.

New Year Type of Regular Issue
Good Luck Symbols: 2.50fo+1.20fo, Horse-
shoe, mistletoe and clover. 3fo+1.50fo, Pigs,
clover and balloon, horiz.

***Perf. 12x11½, 11½x12***
**1963, Dec. 12   Photo.    Unwmk.**
**Sizes: 28x39mm (#B235); 28x22mm
(#B206)**
B235  A343  2.50fo + 1.20fo multi    .50   .25
B236  A343  3fo + 1.50fo multi       .70   .35
The surtax was for the modernization of the
Hungarian Postal and Philatelic Museum.
Exist imperf.

Olympic Type of Regular Issue
Design: 3fo+1fo, Water polo.

**1964, June 12                    *Perf. 11***
B237  A352  3fo + 1fo multi          .60   .75
Exists imperf.

Exhibition Hall — SP129

**1964, July 23                     Photo.**
B238  SP129  3fo + 1.50fo blk, red
             org & gray              .60   .35
Tennis Exhibition, Budapest Sports Museum.
Exists imperf. Value $10.

Twirling Woman
Gymnast
SP130

**1964, Sept. 4              *Perf. 11½x12***
**Size: 27x38mm**
B239  SP130  2fo + 1fo Lilac         .45   .45
B240  SP130  2fo + 1fo Mallards      .45   .45
B241  SP130  2fo + 1fo Gymnast       .45   .45
B242  SP130  2fo + 1fo Rocket &
             globe                   .45   .45
  a.   Horiz. strip of 4, #B239-B242 2.25  2.25
  b.   Souv. sheet of 4, #B239-B242  3.25  3.25
37th Stamp Day and Intl. Topical Stamp
Exhib., IMEX. No. B242b contains 4 20x28mm
stamps, perf. 11.
Exist imperf. Value: strip $20; souvenir
sheet $37.50.

13th
Century
Tennis
SP131

History of Tennis: 40f+10f, Indoor tennis,
16th century. 60f+10f, Tennis, 18th century.
70f+30f, Tennis court and castle. 80f+40f, Tennis court, Fontainebleau (buildings). 1fo+50f,
Tennis, 17th century. 1.50fo+50f, W. C.
Wingfield, Wimbledon champion 1877, and
Wimbledon Cup. 1.70fo+50f, Davis Cup, 1900.
2fo+1fo, Bela Kehrling (1891-1937), Hungarian champion.

**Lithographed and Engraved**
**1965, June 15   Unwmk.    *Perf. 12***
B243  SP131  30f + 10f mar, dl
             org                     .20   .20
B244  SP131  40f + 10f blk,
             pale lil                .20   .20
B245  SP131  60f + 10f grn, ol       .20   .20
B246  SP131  70f + 30f lil, brt
             grn                     .25   .20
B247  SP131  80f + 40f dk bl, lt
             vio                     .25   .20
B248  SP131  1fo + 50f grn, yel      .25   .20
B249  SP131  1.50fo + 50f sep, lt
             ol grn                  .30   .25
B250  SP131  1.70fo + 50f ind, lt
             bl                      .35   .25

B251  SP131  2fo + 1fo dk red,
             lt grn                  .50   .30
  Nos. B243-B251 (9)                2.50  2.00
Exist imperf. Value, set $25.

Flood
Scene
SP132

10fo+5fo, Relief commemorating 1838
flood.

**1965, Aug. 14  Photo.    *Perf. 12x11½***
B252  SP132  1fo + 50f org brn &
             bl                      .30   .30
**Souvenir Sheet**
B253  SP132  10fo + 5fo gldn brn
             & buff                 2.75  2.75
Surtax for aid to 1965 flood victims.
Exist imperf. Value: No. B252 $7; No. B253
$25.

Geranium
Stamp of
1950 (No.
909)
SP133

Stamp Day: No. B255, #120. No. B256,
#1489. No. B257, #1382.

***Perf. 12x11½***
**1965, Oct. 30   Photo.    Unwmk.**
**Stamps in Original Colors**
B254  SP133  2fo + 1fo gray & dk
             bl                      .65   .60
B255  SP133  2fo + 1fo gray & red    .65   .60
B256  SP133  2fo + 1fo gray &
             ocher                   .65   .60
B257  SP133  2fo + 1fo gray & vio    .65   .60
  a.   Horiz. strip of 4, #B254-B257 3.00  3.00
  b.   Souv. sheet of 4, #B254-B257  3.50  3.25
#B254b contains 32x23mm stamps, perf. 11.
Exist imperf. Value: No. B257a $20; No.
B257b $30.

Soccer Type of Regular Issue
Design: 3fo+1fo, Championship emblem
and map of Great Britain showing cities where
matches were held.

**1966, June 6   Photo.    *Perf. 12x11½***
B258  A382  3fo + 1fo multi          .60   .50
Exists imperf.

Woman
Archer
and
Danube
at
Visegrad
SP134

Stamp Day: No. B260, Gloria Hungariae
grapes and Lake Balaton. No. B261, Red poppies and ruins of Diosgyor Castle. No. B262,
Russian space dogs Ugolek and Veterok.

**1966, Sept. 16  Photo.   *Perf. 12x11½***
B259  SP134  2fo + 50f multi         .60   .60
B260  SP134  2fo + 50f multi         .60   .60
B261  SP134  2fo + 50f multi         .60   .60
B262  SP134  2fo + 50f multi         .60   .60
  a.   Horiz. strip of 4, #B259-B262 2.75  2.75
  b.   Souv. sheet of 4, #B259-B262  2.75  2.75
#B262b contains 4 29x21mm stamps, perf.
11.
Exist imperf. Value: B262a $20; B262b $35.

Anglers,
C.I.P.S.
Emblem
and View
of
Danube
SP135

**1967, Aug. 22  Photo.   Perf. 12x11½**
B263 SP135 3fo + 1fo multi        .90  .45
  See note after No. 1847.
  Exists imperf.

## Olympic Type of Regular Issue

Indoor stadium & Winter Olympics emblem.

**1968, Jan. 29  Photo.   Perf. 11**
B264 A402 4fo + 1fo multi        .70  .30
  Exists imperf.

Jug, Western
Hungary,
1618
SP136

Hungarian Earthenware: No. B266, Tiszafüred vase, 1847. No. B267, Toby jug, 1848. No. B268, Decorative Baja plate, 1870. No. B269a, Jug, Northern Hungary, 1672. No. B269b, Decorative Mezöcsat plate, 1843. No. B269c, Decorative Moragy plate, 1860. No. B269d, Pitcher, Debrecen, 1793.

**1968, Oct. 5   Litho.    Perf. 12**
B265 SP136 1fo + 50f ultra & multi      .50  .50
B266 SP136 1fo + 50f sky bl & multi      .50  .50
B267 SP136 1fo + 50f sepia & multi      .50  .50
B268 SP136 1fo + 50f yel brn & multi      .50  .50
  Nos. B265-B268 (4)       2.00 2.00

### Miniature Sheet
B269    Sheet of 4       2.75 2.50
  a.  SP136 2fo + 50f ultra & multi   .45  .40
  b.  SP136 2fo + 50f yel brn & multi   .45  .40
  c.  SP136 2fo + 50f olive & multi   .45  .40
  d.  SP136 2fo + 50f brt rose & multi   .45  .40

Issued for 41st Stamp Day. No. B269 contains 4 25x36mm stamps. See Nos. B271-B275.
  Exist imperf. Value: Nos. B265-B268 $20; No. B269 $20.

Suspension Bridge, Buda Castle and
Arms of Budapest — SP137

### Lithographed and Engraved
**1969, May 22    Perf. 12**
B270 SP137 5fo + 2fo sep, pale yel & gray    1.00 1.00
  Budapest 71 Philatelic Exposition.
  Exists imperf. Value $8.

## Folk Art Type of 1968

Hungarian Wood Carvings: No. B271, Stirrup cup from Okorag, 1880. No. B272, Jar with flower decorations from Felsötiszavidek, 1898. No. B273, Round jug, Somogyharsagy, 1935. No. B274, Two-legged jug, Alföld, 1740. No. B275a, Carved panel (farm couple), Csorna, 1879. No. B275b, Tankard, Okany, 1914. No. B275c, Round jar with soldiers, Sellye, 1899. No. B275d, Square box with 2 women, Lengyeltoti, 1880.

**1969, Sept. 13   Litho.    Perf. 12**
B271 SP136 1fo + 50f rose cl & multi      .60  .60
B272 SP136 1fo + 50f dp bis & multi      .60  .60
B273 SP136 1fo + 50f bl & multi      .60  .60

B274 SP136 1fo + 50f lt bl grn & multi      .60  .60
  Nos. B271-B274 (4)       2.40 2.40

### Miniature Sheet
B275    Sheet of 4       2.75 2.50
  a.  SP136 2fo + 50f ultra & multi   .50  .45
  b.  SP136 2fo + 50f brn org & multi   .50  .45
  c.  SP136 2fo + 50f lt brn & multi   .50  .45
  d.  SP136 2fo + 50f bl grn & multi   .50  .45

Issued for the 42nd Stamp Day. No. B275 contains 4 stamps (size: 25x36mm).
  Exists imperf. Value: B271-B274 $20; B275 $16.

Fishermen's Bastion,
Coronation Church
and Chain
Bridge — SP138

Designs: No. B277, Parliament and Elizabeth Bridge. No. B278, Castle and Margaret Bridge.

**1970, Mar. 7    Litho.    Perf. 12**
B276 SP138 2fo + 1fo gldn brn & multi      .60  .60
B277 SP138 2fo + 1fo bl & multi      .60  .60
B278 SP138 2fo + 1fo lt vio & multi      .60  .60
  Nos. B276-B278 (3)       1.80 1.80

Budapest 71 Philatelic Exhibition, commemorating the centenary of Hungarian postage stamps.
  Exist imperf. Value, set $12.

King Matthias I
Corvinus
SP139

Initials and Paintings from Bibliotheca Corvina: No. B280, Letter "A." No. B281, Letter "N." No. B282, Letter "O." No. B283a, Ransanus Speaking before King Matthias. No. B283b, Scholar and letter "Q." No. B283c, Portrait of Appianus and letter "C." No. B283d, King David and letter "A."

**1970, Aug. 22   Photo.   Perf. 11½x12**
B279 SP139 1fo + 50f multi      .40  .40
B280 SP139 1fo + 50f multi      .40  .40
B281 SP139 1fo + 50f multi      .40  .40
B282 SP139 1fo + 50f multi      .40  .40
  Nos. B279-B282 (4)       1.60 1.60

### Miniature Sheet
B283    Sheet of 4       2.75 2.50
  a.-d.  SP139 2fo + 50f, any single   .50  .45

Issued for the 43rd Stamp Day. No. B283 contains 4 stamps (size: 22½x32mm).
  Exist imperf. Value: B279-B282 $20; B283 $25.

View of Buda, 1470 — SP140

#B285, Buda, 1600. #B286, Buda and Pest, about 1638. #B287, Buda and Pest, 1770. #B288a, Buda, 1777. #B288b, Buda, 1850. #B288c, Buda, 1895. #B288d, Budapest, 1970.

**1971, Feb. 26   Litho.    Perf. 12**
B284 SP140 2fo + 1fo blk & yel      .60  .60
B285 SP140 2fo + 1fo blk & pink      .60  .60
B286 SP140 2fo + 1fo blk & pale grn      .60  .60

B287 SP140 2fo + 1fo blk & pale sal      .60  .60
  Nos. B284-B287 (4)       2.40 2.40

### Souvenir Sheet
**Perf. 10½**
B288    Sheet of 4       2.50 2.25
  a.  SP140 2fo + 1fo blk & pale sal   .50  .45
  b.  SP140 2fo + 1fo blk & pale grn   .50  .45
  c.  SP140 2fo + 1fo blk & lilac   .50  .45
  d.  SP140 2fo + 1fo blk & pink   .50  .45

Budapest 71 Intl. Stamp Exhib. for the cent. of Hungarian postage stamps, Budapest, Sept. 4-12. No. B288 contains 4 stamps, size: 39½x18mm.
  Exist imperf. Value: Nos. B284-B287 $17.50; No. B288 $20.

Iris and
#P1
SP141

Designs: No. B290, Daisy and #199. No. B291, Poppy and #391. No. B292, Rose and #B128. No. B293a, Carnations and #200. No. B293b, Dahlia and #1068. No. B293c, Tulips and #C196. No. B293d, Anenomes and #C251.

**1971, Sept. 4   Photo.   Perf. 12x11½**
B289 SP141 2fo + 1fo sil & multi      .70  .70
B290 SP141 2fo + 1fo sil & multi      .70  .70
B291 SP141 2fo + 1fo sil & multi      .70  .70
B292 SP141 2fo + 1fo sil & multi      .70  .70
  Nos. B289-B292 (4)       2.80 2.80

### Souvenir Sheet
**Perf. 11½**
B293    Sheet of 4       2.75 2.50
  a.-d.  SP141 2fo + 1fo, any single   .50  .45

Cent. of 1st Hungarian postage stamps and in connection with Budapest 71 Intl. Stamp Exhib., Sept. 4-12.
  Exist imperf. Value: Nos. B289-B292 $20; No. B293 $35.

Miskólcz Postmark, 1818-43 — SP142

Postmarks: No. B295, Szegedin, 1827-48. No. B296, Esztergom, 1848-51. No. B297, Budapest 1971 Exhibition. No. B298a, Paar family signet, 1593. No. B298b, Courier letter, 1708. No. B298c, First well-known Hungarian postmark "V. TOKAI," 1752. No. B298d, Letter, 1705.

**1972, May     Perf. 12x11½**
B294 SP142 2fo + 1fo blue & blk      .70  .70
B295 SP142 2fo + 1fo yel & blk      .70  .70
B296 SP142 2fo + 1fo yel grn & blk      .70  .70
B297 SP142 2fo + 1fo ver & multi      .70  .70
  Nos. B294-B297 (4)       2.80 2.80

### Souvenir Sheet
B298    Sheet of 4       2.50 2.25
  a.  SP142 2fo + 1fo yel grn & multi   .50  .45
  b.  SP142 2fo + 1fo brn & multi   .50  .45
  c.  SP142 2fo + 1fo ultra & multi   .50  .45
  d.  SP142 2fo + 1fo red & multi   .50  .45

9th Congress of National Federation of Hungarian Philatelists (Mabeosz). No. B298 contains 4 stamps (size: 32x23mm).
  Exist imperf. Value: Nos. B294-B297 $20; No. B298 $22.

## Olympic Type of Regular Issue

Design: Wrestling and Olympic rings.

**1972, July 15   Photo.    Perf. 11**
B299 A484 3fo + 1fo multi      .50  .30
  Exists imperf.

Historic Mail Box, Telephone and
Molnya Satellite — SP143

Design: No. B301, Post horn, Tokai postmark, and Nos. 183, 1802, 1809.

**1972, Oct. 27   Litho.    Perf. 12**
B300 SP143 4fo + 2fo grn & multi   .80  .70
B301 SP143 4fo + 2fo bl & multi   .80  .70
  Reopening of the Post and Philatelic Museums, Budapest.
  Exist imperf. Value, set $17.50.

Bird on
Silver Disk,
10th Century
SP144

Treasures from Hungarian Natl. Museum. No. B303, Ring with serpent's head, 11th cent. No. B304, Lovers, belt buckle, 12th cent. No. B305, Flower, belt buckle, 15th cent. No. B306a, Opal pendant, 16th cent. No. B306b, Jeweled belt buckle, 18th cent. No. B306c, Flower pin, 17th cent. No. B306d, Rosette pendant, 17th cent.

**1973, Sept. 22   Litho.    Perf. 12**
B302 SP144 2fo + 50f brn & multi      .65  .65
B303 SP144 2fo + 50f brt rose lil & multi      .65  .65
B304 SP144 2fo + 50f dk bl & multi      .65  .65
B305 SP144 2fo + 50f grn & multi      .65  .65
  Nos. B302-B305 (4)       2.60 2.60

### Souvenir Sheet
B306    Sheet of 4       2.50 2.50
  a.  SP144 2fo + 50f brown & multi   .35  .35
  b.  SP144 2fo + 50f car & multi   .35  .35
  c.  SP144 2fo + 50f ol grn & multi   .35  .35
  d.  SP144 2fo + 50f brt bl & multi   .35  .35

46th Stamp Day. No. B306 contains 4 stamps (size: 25x35mm).
  Exist imperf. Value: Nos. B302-B305 $20; No. B306 $25.

Gothic Wall
Fountain
SP145

Visegrad Castle and Bas-
reliefs — SP146

Designs: No. B308, Wellhead, Anjou period. No. B309, Twin lion-head wall fountain. B310, Fountain with Hercules riding dolphin. No. B311a, Raven panel. No. B311b, Visegrad Madonna. B311c, Lion panel. No. B311d, Visegrad Castle. Designs show artworks from Visegrad Palace of King Matthias Corvinus I, 15th century. Illustration SP146 is reduced.

**1975, Sept. 13 Litho. _Perf. 12_**
**Multicolored and:**

| | | | |
|---|---|---|---|
| B307 | SP145 | 2fo + 1fo green | 2.00 2.00 |
| B308 | SP145 | 2fo + 1fo ver | 2.00 2.00 |
| B309 | SP145 | 2fo + 1fo blue | 2.00 2.00 |
| B310 | SP145 | 2fo + 1fo lilac | 2.00 2.00 |
| a. | | Horizontal strip of 4 | 9.00 8.50 |

**Souvenir Sheet**

| | | | |
|---|---|---|---|
| B311 | SP146 | Sheet of 4 | 10.00 10.00 |
| a. | | 2fo + 1fo 21x32mm | 1.40 1.40 |
| b. | | 2fo + 1fo 47x32mm | 1.40 1.40 |
| c. | | 2fo + 1fo 21x32mm | 1.40 1.40 |
| d. | | 2fo + 1fo 99x32mm | 1.40 1.40 |

European Architectural Heritage Year 1975 and 48th Stamp Day.
Exist imperf. Value: Nos. B307-B310 $250; No. B311 $250.

Knight SP147

Gothic Sculptures, Buda Castle — SP148

Gothic sculptures from Buda Castle.

**1976 Photo. _Perf. 12_**

| | | | |
|---|---|---|---|
| B312 | SP147 | 2.50 + 1fo shown | .60 .60 |
| B313 | SP147 | 2.50 + 1fo Armor-bearer | .60 .60 |
| B314 | SP147 | 2.50 + 1fo Apostle | .60 .60 |
| B315 | SP147 | 2.50 + 1fo Bishop | .60 .60 |
| a. | | Horizontal strip of 4, #B312-B315 | 2.75 2.75 |

**Souvenir Sheet**

Designs: a, Man with hat. b, Woman with wimple. c, Man with cloth cap. d, Man with fur hat.

| | | | |
|---|---|---|---|
| B316 | | Sheet of 4 | 3.00 3.00 |
| a.-d. | SP148 | 2.50 + 1fo any single | .55 .55 |

49th Stamp Day.
No. B316 issued in connection with 10th Congress of National Federation of Hungarian Philatelists (Mabeosz).
Exist imperf. Value: Nos. B312-B315 $20; No. B316 $25.
Issued: #B316, May 22; #B312-B315, Sept. 4.

Young Runners SP149

**1977, Apr. 2 Litho. _Perf. 12_**
B317 SP149 3fo + 1.50fo multi .85 .85
Sports promotion among young people.
Exists imperf. Value $7.

Young Man and Woman, Profiles SP150

**1978, Apr. 1 Litho. _Perf. 12_**
B318 SP150 3fo + 1.50fo multi .90 .90
Hungarian Communist Youth Movement, 60th anniversary.
Exists imperf. Value $12.

"Generations," by Gyula Derkovits SP151

**1978, May 6 Litho. _Perf. 12_**
B319 SP151 3fo + 1.50fo multi .90 .90
Szocfilex '78, Szombathely. No. B319 printed in sheets of 3 stamps and 3 labels showing Szocfilex emblem.
Exists imperf. Value: single $7; sheetlet $22.50.

Girl Reading Book, by Ferenc Kovacs SP152

**1979, Mar. 31 Litho. _Perf. 12_**
B320 SP152 3fo + 1.50fo blk & ultra .45 .45
Surtax was for Junior Stamp Exhibition, Bekescsaba.
Exists imperf. Value $7.

Watch Symbolizing Environmental Protection SP153

**1980, Apr. 3 Litho. _Perf. 12_**
B321 SP153 3fo + 1.50fo multi .70 .70
Surtax was for Junior Stamp Exhibition, Dunaujvaros.
Exists imperf. Value $5.50.

International Year of the Disabled SP154    Youths and Factory SP155

**1981, May 15 Litho. _Perf. 12_**
B322 SP154 2fo + 1fo multi .45 .45
Exists imperf. Value $7.

**1981, May 29 _Perf. 12x11½_**
B323 SP155 4fo + 2fo multi .80 .80
Young Communist League, 10th Congress, Budapest, May 29-31.
Exists imperf. Value $9.

European Junior Tennis Cup, July 25-Aug. 1 — SP156

**1982, Apr. 2 Litho. _Perf. 12x11½_**
B324 SP156 4fo + 2fo multi .80 .80
Exists imperf. Value $8.

**Souvenir Sheet**

SP157

**_Perf. 12½x11½_**
**1982, June 11 Litho.**
B325 SP157 20fo + 10fo multi 4.00 4.00
PHILEXFRANCE '82 Stamp Exhibition, Paris, June 11-21.
Exists imperf. Value $20.

55th Stamp Day — SP158

Budapest Architecture and Statues: No. B326, Fishermen's Bastion, Janos Hunyadi (1403-1456). No. B327, Parliament, Ferenc Rakoczi the Second (1676-1735).

**1982, Sept. 10 Litho. _Perf. 12_**

| | | | |
|---|---|---|---|
| B326 | SP158 | 4fo + 2fo multi | .90 .90 |
| B327 | SP158 | 4fo + 2fo shown | .90 .90 |

Exist imperf. Value, set $17.50.

**Souvenir Sheet**

Parliament, Chain Bridge, Buda Castle, Budapest — SP159

Illustration reduced.

**1982, Sept. 10 _Perf. 11½_**
B328 SP159 20fo + 10fo multi 3.75 3.75
European Security and Cooperation Conference, 10th anniv.
Exists imperf. Value $24.

21st Junior Stamp Exhibition, Baja, Mar. 31-Apr. 9 — SP160

**1983, Mar. 31 Litho. _Perf. 12x11½_**
B329 SP160 4fo + 2fo multi .90 .90
Surtax was for show.
Exists imperf. Value $7.

56th Natl. Stamp Day SP161

Budapest Architecture (19th Cent. Engravings by): Rudolph Alt, H. Luders (No. B331).

**1983, Sept. 9 Litho. _Perf. 12_**

| | | | |
|---|---|---|---|
| B330 | SP161 | 4fo + 2fo Old Natl. Theater | .90 .90 |
| B331 | SP161 | 4fo + 2fo Municipal Concert Hall | .90 .90 |

**Souvenir Sheet**
**Lithographed and Engraved**
**_Perf. 11_**
B332 SP161 20fo + 10fo Holy Trinity Square 3.75 3.75
No. B332 contains one stamp (28x45mm).
Exist imperf. Value: Nos. B330-B331 $20; No. B332 $30.

SP162

**1984, Apr. 2 Litho. _Perf. 12½x11½_**
B333 SP162 4fo + 2fo Mother & Child .75 .75
Surtax was for children's foundation.
Exists imperf. Value $12.

SP163

Little Red Riding Hood, by the Brothers Grimm.

**1985, Apr. 2 Litho. _Perf. 11½x12_**
B334 SP163 4fo + 2fo multi .75 .75
Jacob (1785-1863) and Wilhelm (1786-1859) Grimm, fabulists and philologists.
Exists imperf. Value $10.

Natl. SOS Children's Village Assoc., 3rd Anniv. SP164

**1985, Dec. 10    Litho.    Perf. 11**
B335 SP164 4fo + 2fo multi        .75   .75
Surtax for natl. SOS Children's Village.
Exists imperf. Value $10.

Natl. Young Pioneers Org., 40th Anniv. SP165

**1986, May 30        Perf. 11½x12½**
B336 SP165 4fo + 2fo multi        .75   .60
Exists imperf. Value $8.

Souvenir Sheet

Budapest Natl. Theater — SP166

**Lithographed and Engraved**
**1986, Oct. 10        Perf. 11**
B337 SP166 20fo + 10fo tan, brn
& buff        4.00  4.00
Surtax benefited natl. theater construction.
Exists imperf. Value $30.

Natl. Communist Youth League, 30th Anniv. — SP167

**1987, Mar. 20        Perf. 13½x13**
B338 SP167 4fo + 2fo multi        .60   .60
Exists imperf. Value $8.

Souvenir Sheet

SOCFILEX '88, Aug. 12-21, Kecskemet — SP168

**1988, Mar. 10    Litho.    Perf. 11½**
B339 SP168 20fo +10fo multi        4.00  4.00
Surtax for SOCFILEX '88.
Exists imperf. Value $30.

*Sky High Tree,* a Tapestry by Erzsebet Szekeres SP169

**1989, Apr. 12    Litho.    Perf. 12**
B340 SP169 5fo +2fo multi        1.50  1.50
Surtax to promote youth philately.
Exist imperf. Value, set $10.

Souvenir Sheet

*Battle of Solferino,* by Carlo Bossoli — SP170

**1989, Sept. 8    Litho.    Perf. 10½**
B341 SP170 20fo +10fo multi        3.75  3.75
Stamp Day.
Exists imperf. Value $50.

Souvenir Sheet

*Martyrs of Arad,* Arad, Romania, 1849 — SP171

**1989, Oct. 6        Perf. 11½x12½**
B342 SP171 20fo +10fo multi        3.75  3.75
Surtax to fund production of another statue.
Exists imperf. Value $30.

Teacher's Training High School, Sarospatak Municipal Arms — SP172

**1990, Mar. 30    Litho.    Perf. 12x11½**
B343 SP172 8fo +4fo multi        1.75  1.75
28th Youth Stamp Exhib., Sarospatak, Apr. 6-22.
Exists imperf. Value $12.

Souvenir Sheet

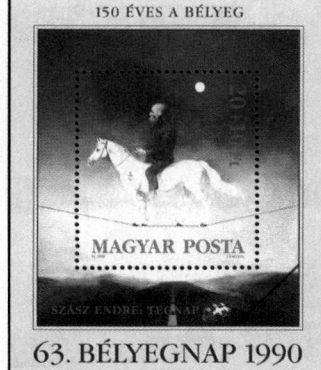

Yesterday, by Endre Szasz — SP173

**1990, Oct. 12    Litho.    Perf. 12**
B344 SP173 20fo +10fo multi        3.75  3.75
Stamp Day. Surtax for National Federation of Hungarian Philatelists.
Exists imperf. Value $37.50.

Tapestry, Peter and the Wolf, by Gabriella Hajnal — SP174

**1991, Apr. 30    Litho.    Perf. 12**
B345 SP174 12fo +6fo multi        1.50   .80
Surtax to promote youth philately.
Exists imperf. Value $7.

Children's Drawings SP175

Designs: 9fo + 4fo, Girl holding flower, vert. 10fo + 4fo, Child standing beneath sun. 15fo + 4fo, Boy wearing crown, vert.

**1992, May 15    Litho.    Perf. 12**
B346 SP175  9fo +4fo multi        1.10  1.10
B347 SP175 10fo +4fo multi        1.25  1.25
B348 SP175 15fo +4fo multi        1.65  1.65
Nos. B346-B348 (3)        4.00  4.00
Surtax for children's welfare.

Souvenir Sheet

1992 Summer Olympics, Barcelona — SP176

**1992, Sept. 4    Litho.    Perf. 12**
B349 SP176 50fo +20fo multi        3.00  3.00

Textile Art, by Erzsebet Szekeres SP177

**1993, Apr. 14    Litho.    Perf. 12**
B350 SP177 10fo +5fo Outdoor
scene        .60   .40
B351 SP177 17fo +8fo Tree of life 1.60  1.00

Stamp Day SP178

Stamp designers, stamps: 10fo + 5fo, Zoltan Nagy (1916-1987), #1062. 17fo + 5fo, Sandor Legrady (1906-1987), #523. 50fo + 20fo, Ferenc Helbing (1870-1959), #465.

**1993, Sept. 10    Litho.    Perf. 12**
B352 SP178 10fo +5fo multi        .60   .20
B353 SP178 17fo +5fo multi        .90   .25
**Souvenir Sheet**
B354 SP178 50fo +20fo multi        3.25  1.75
No. B354 contains one 35x27mm stamp.

The Little Prince, by Antoine de Saint-Exupery SP179

**1994, Apr. 1    Litho.    Perf. 13½x13**
B355 SP179 19fo +5fo multi        .80   .40
Surtax for children's welfare.

Poem, "John the Hero," 150th Anniv. SP180

**1995, Apr. 7    Litho.    Perf. 12**
B356  SP180  22fo +10fo multi    .90  .45
Surtax to promote youth philately.

Olympiafila '95, Budapest — SP181

**1995, June 12    Litho.    Perf. 11**
B357  SP181  22fo +11fo yellow
    rings    .90  .45
B358  SP181  22fo +11fo purple
    rings    .90  .45
   a.  Pair, #B357-B358    1.90  .90

No. B358a also sold in a strip of 3 pairs in a booklet.

World Festival of Puppet Players, Budapest SP182

Laszlo Vitez puppet and ghost puppet.

**1996, June 21    Litho.    Perf. 12**
B359  SP182  24fo +10fo multi    1.00  .40

Oder River Flood of 1997 SP183

**1997, Sept. 12    Litho.    Perf. 12**
B360  SP183  27fo +100fo flower
    in water    1.90  .95
Surtax is for aid to flood victims.

Stamp Day SP184

Early postman using: 27fo + 5fo, Motorized tricycle. 55fo + 5fo, Experimental registered letter-receiving machine, vert. 90fo + 30fo, Postal van.

**1997, Sept. 19**
B361  SP184  27fo +5fo multi    .75  .25
B362  SP184  55fo +5fo multi    1.50  .45
    **Souvenir Sheet**
B363  SP184  90fo +30fo multi    7.00  3.75

---

Souvenir Sheet

Revolution of 1848 — SP185

Design: Seven members of movement, newspaper *Nemzeti dal.* Illustration reduced.

**1998, Mar. 13    Litho.    Perf. 12**
B364  SP185  150fo +50fo multi    4.00  1.50
Surtax to promote youth philately.

Youth Stamp SP186

**1999, Mar. 12    Litho.    Perf. 12**
B365  SP186  52fo +25fo multi    1.25  .50

István Fekete (1900-70), Writer — SP187

**2000, Jan. 11    Litho.    Perf. 12**
B366  SP187  60fo +30fo multi    1.25  .70
Surtax for youth philately.

Hunphilex 2000 Stamp Exhibition, Budapest SP188

**2000, Jan. 11**
B367  SP188  200fo +100fo multi    3.50  2.60
Surtax to support stamp exhibition.

Souvenir Sheet

Hunphilex 2000 Stamp Exhibition, Budapest — SP189

**2000, Aug. 18    Litho.    Perf. 12**
B368  SP189  200fo +100fo Coro-
    nation robe    3.50  2.60
   a.  Sheet of 2    8.50  5.25

---

Star Over Eger, by Geza Gardonyi SP190

**2001, Jan. 15    Litho.    Perf. 13¼x13**
B369  SP190  60fo +30fo multi    1.50  .30
Surtax for youth philately.

Campaign Against Breast Cancer — SP191

**2005, Sept. 29    Litho.    Perf. 12**
B370  SP191  90fo +50fo multi    1.75  .70

Victory in First Grand Prix Race by Ferenc Szisz (1873-1944) — SP192

**2006, May 9    Litho.    Perf. 13x13¼**
B371  SP192  120fo +50fo multi    1.75  1.75

Smile, by Zita Zagyi SP193

**2008, May 20    Litho.    Perf. 13x13¼**
B372  SP193  100fo + 50fo multi    1.90  1.90

Design was a winner in a children's art contest. Surtax for Hungarian Ambulance Service.

---

### AIR POST STAMPS

**Issues of the Monarchy**

Nos. 120, 123 Surcharged in Red or Blue

**Wmk. 137**
**1918, July 4    Typo.    Perf. 14**
C1  A10  1k 50f on 75f (R)    25.00  27.50
C2  A10  4k 50f on 2k (Bl)    25.00  27.50
Counterfeits exist. Exist imperf. Value, set $170.

No. 126 Surcharged

**1920, Nov. 7**
C3  A10  3k on 10k (G)    1.25  1.25
C4  A10  8k on 10k (R)    1.25  1.25
C5  A10  12k on 10k (Bl)    1.25  1.25
    Nos. C3-C5 (3)    3.75  3.75
Set, never hinged    6.00

---

Icarus — AP3

**1924-25    Perf. 14**
C6  AP3  100k red brn & red    .60  1.00
C7  AP3  500k bl grn & yel grn    .60  1.00
C8  AP3  1000k bis brn & brn    .60  1.00
C9  AP3  2000k dk bl & lt bl    .60  1.00
    **Wmk. 133**
C10  AP3  5000k dl vio & brt vio    .85  1.50
C11  AP3  10000k red & dl vio    1.25  2.00
    Nos. C6-C11 (6)    4.50  7.50
Set, never hinged    9.00

Issued: 100k-2000k, 4/11; others, 4/20/25. Exist imperf. Value, set $70. Forgeries exist. For surcharges see Nos. J112-J116.

Mythical "Turul" — AP4

"Turul" Carrying Messenger
AP5    AP6

**1927-30    Engr.    Perf. 14**
C12  AP4  4f orange ('30)    .30  .30
C13  AP4  12f deep green    .30  .45
C14  AP4  16f red brown    .30  .55
C15  AP4  20f carmine    .30  .35
C16  AP4  32f brown vio    1.75  1.50
C17  AP4  40f dp ultra    1.75  .30
C18  AP5  50f claret    1.75  .40
C19  AP5  72f olive grn    2.00  .65
C20  AP5  80f dp violet    2.00  .65
C21  AP5  1p emerald ('30)    4.00  1.25
C22  AP5  2p red ('30)    5.00  3.50
C23  AP5  5p dk blue ('30)    8.00  25.00
    Nos. C12-C23 (12)    27.45  34.90
Set, never hinged    55.00

Exist imperf. Value, set $170.

**1931, Mar. 27**
    **Overprinted**
C24  AP6  1p orange (Bk)    40.00  42.50
C25  AP6  2p dull vio (G)    40.00  42.50
Set, never hinged    140.00

Exist imperf. Value, set $250.

Monoplane over Danube Valley — AP7

Worker Welcoming Plane, Double Cross and Sun Rays — AP8

Spirit of Flight on Plane Wing AP9

"Flight" Holding Propeller AP10

**Wmk. 210**
**1933, June 20    Photo.    Perf. 15**
C26  AP7  10f blue green    2.90  .20
C27  AP7  16f purple    2.00  .25

## Perf. 12½x12

| | | | | |
|---|---|---|---|---|
| C28 | AP8 | 20f carmine | 4.50 | .20 |
| C29 | AP8 | 40f blue | 4.00 | 1.25 |
| C30 | AP9 | 48f gray black | 4.50 | 1.50 |
| C31 | AP9 | 72f bister brn | 14.00 | 2.75 |
| C32 | AP10 | 1p yellow grn | 25.00 | 2.50 |
| C33 | AP10 | 2p violet brn | 77.50 | 17.50 |
| C34 | AP10 | 5p dk gray | 77.50 | 110.00 |
| | Nos. C26-C34 (9) | | 211.90 | 136.15 |
| | Set, never hinged | | 375.00 | |

Exist imperf. Value, set $1,500.

---

**Catalogue values for unused stamps in this section, from this point to the end of the section, are for Never Hinged items.**

---

Fokker F VII over Mail Coach AP11

Plane over Parliament AP12

Airplane AP13

### 1936, May 8          Perf. 12x12½

| | | | | |
|---|---|---|---|---|
| C35 | AP11 | 10f brt green | .50 | .20 |
| C36 | AP11 | 20f crimson | .50 | .20 |
| C37 | AP11 | 36f brown | .75 | .20 |
| C38 | AP12 | 40f brt blue | .75 | .20 |
| C39 | AP12 | 52f red org | 3.00 | .80 |
| C40 | AP12 | 60f brt violet | 17.50 | 1.50 |
| C41 | AP12 | 80f dk sl grn | 3.50 | .55 |
| C42 | AP13 | 1p dk yel grn | 4.50 | .35 |
| C43 | AP13 | 2p brown car | 7.00 | 1.75 |
| C44 | AP13 | 5p dark blue | 20.00 | 17.50 |
| | Nos. C35-C44 (10) | | 58.00 | 23.25 |

Exist imperf. Value, set $675.

### Issues of the Republic

Loyalty Tower, Sopron — AP14

Designs: 20f, Cathedral of Esztergom. 50f, Liberty Bridge, Budapest. 70f, Palace Hotel, Lillafüred. 1fo, Vajdahunyad Castle, Budapest. 1.40fo, Visegrád Fortress on the Danube. 3fo, Lake Balaton. 5fo, Parliament Building, Budapest.

### 1947, Mar. 5     Perf. 12½x12   Photo.   Wmk. 210

| | | | | |
|---|---|---|---|---|
| C45 | AP14 | 10f rose lake | 1.00 | .25 |
| C46 | AP14 | 20f gray green | .35 | .20 |
| C47 | AP14 | 50f copper brn | .40 | .20 |
| C48 | AP14 | 70f olive grn | .40 | .20 |
| C49 | AP14 | 1fo gray blue | .75 | .25 |
| C50 | AP14 | 1.40fo brown | .90 | .40 |
| C51 | AP14 | 3fo green | 2.00 | .25 |
| C52 | AP14 | 5fo rose violet | 4.25 | 1.00 |
| | Nos. C45-C52 (8) | | 10.05 | 2.75 |

Exist imperf. Value, set $280.

Johannes Gutenberg and Printing Press AP22

Designs: 2f, Columbus. 4f, Robert Fulton. 5f, George Stephenson. 6f, David Schwarz and Ferdinand von Zeppelin. 8f, Thomas A.

---

Edison. 10f, Louis Bleriot. 12f, Roald Amundsen. 30f, Kalman Kando. 40f, Alexander S. Popov.

### 1948, May 15       Perf. 12x12½       Wmk. 283

| | | | | |
|---|---|---|---|---|
| C53 | AP22 | 1f orange red | .20 | .20 |
| C54 | AP22 | 2f dp magenta | .20 | .20 |
| C55 | AP22 | 4f blue | .20 | .20 |
| C56 | AP22 | 5f orange brn | .20 | .20 |
| C57 | AP22 | 6f green | .25 | .20 |
| C58 | AP22 | 8f dp red vio | .25 | .20 |
| C59 | AP22 | 10f brown | .45 | .25 |
| C60 | AP22 | 12f blue grn | .45 | .30 |
| C61 | AP22 | 30f brown rose | 1.40 | .85 |
| C62 | AP22 | 40f blue violet | 1.40 | 1.00 |
| | Nos. C53-C62 (10) | | 5.00 | 3.60 |

Explorers and inventors.
Exist imperf. Value, set $70.
See Nos. CB3-CB12.

---

### IMPERFORATE STAMPS

Through 1991, most air post stamps stamps were also issued imperforate. Where these items form part of a larger set with regular issues, values for imperfs will be included in that of the sets to which they belong, footnoted in the Regular Issues section. For Nos. C63-C452, values for imperfs will be given only for those items not included in sets with regular issues.

### UPU Type

### 1949, Nov. 1

| | | | | |
|---|---|---|---|---|
| C63 | A171 | 2fo orange brn | 1.25 | 1.00 |
| a. | | Booklet pane of 6 | 35.00 | |

75th anniv. of the UPU. See No. C81.
Exists imperf.

### Chain Bridge Type and

Symbols of Labor — AP25

### 1949, Nov. 20

| | | | | |
|---|---|---|---|---|
| C64 | A172 | 1.60fo scarlet | 1.25 | 1.25 |
| C65 | A172 | 2fo olive | 1.25 | 1.25 |

### Souvenir Sheet
### Perf. 12½x12

| | | | | |
|---|---|---|---|---|
| C66 | AP25 | 50fo car lake | 325.00 | 300.00 |

Opening of the Chain Bridge, Budapest, cent.
No. C66 exists imperf. Value $3,500.

Postman and Mail Carrying Vehicles AP26

### 1949, Dec. 11                    Perf. 12

| | | | | |
|---|---|---|---|---|
| C67 | AP26 | 50f lilac gray | 5.00 | 4.00 |
| | | Sheet of 4 | 27.50 | 17.50 |

Stamp Day, 1949.
Exists imperf. Value: single $100; sheet $525.

---

Plane, Globe, Stamps and Stagecoach — AP27

### 1950, Mar. 12            Perf. 12x12½

| | | | | |
|---|---|---|---|---|
| C68 | AP27 | 2fo red brn & yel | 7.50 | 7.50 |

20th anniv. of the establishment of the Hungarian Post Office Philatelic Museum.
Exists imperf. Value $50.

Chess Emblem, Globe and Plane AP28

### 1950, Apr. 9       Wmk. 106       Perf. 12

| | | | | |
|---|---|---|---|---|
| C69 | AP28 | 1.60fo brown | 5.50 | 1.00 |

World Chess Championship Matches, Budapest.
Exists imperf.

Globes, Parliament Building and Chain Bridge — AP29

### 1950, May 16            Perf. 12x12½

| | | | | |
|---|---|---|---|---|
| C70 | AP29 | 1fo red brown | 1.00 | .35 |

Meeting of the World Federation of Trade Unions, Budapest, May 1950.
Exists imperf.

Statue of Liberty and View of Budapest — AP30

Designs: 30f, Crane and apartment house. 70f, Steel mill. 1fo, Stalinyec tractor. 1.60fo, Steamship. 2fo, Reaping-threshing machine. 3fo, Passenger train. 5fo, Matyas Rakosi Steel Mill, Csepel. 10fo, Budaörs Airport.

### Perf. 12½x12

| | | | | |
|---|---|---|---|---|
| 1950, Oct. 29 | | Engr. | Unwmk. | |
| C71 | AP30 | 20f claret | .65 | .25 |
| C72 | AP30 | 30f blue vio | .65 | .20 |
| C73 | AP30 | 70f violet brn | .25 | .20 |
| C74 | AP30 | 1f yellow brn | .25 | .20 |
| C75 | AP30 | 1.60fo ultra | .65 | .40 |
| C76 | AP30 | 2fo red org | .70 | .25 |
| C77 | AP30 | 3fo olive blk | .95 | .40 |
| C78 | AP30 | 5fo gray blue | 1.90 | 1.25 |
| C79 | AP30 | 10fo chestnut | 6.00 | 1.75 |
| | Nos. C71-C79 (9) | | 12.00 | 4.90 |

See Nos. C167 and C172.
Exist imperf. Value, set $85.

### Bem Type
### Souvenir Sheet

| | | | | |
|---|---|---|---|---|
| 1950, Dec. 10 | | Engr. | Imperf. | |
| C80 | A185 | 2fo deep plum | 40.00 | 40.00 |

Stamp Day and Budapest Stamp Exhibition.
Exists imperf. Value $55.

---

### UPU Type of 1949
### Perf. 12x12½, Imperf.

| | | | | |
|---|---|---|---|---|
| 1950, July 2 | | Photo. | Wmk. 106 | |
| C81 | A171 | 3fo dk car & dk brn | 20.00 | 20.00 |
| | | Sheet of 4 | 475.00 | 450.00 |

Exists imperf. Value: single $80; sheet of 4 $475.

### Sports Type

Designs: 30f, Volleyball. 40f, Javelin-throwing. 60f, Sports badge. 70f, Soccer. 3fo, Glider meet.

### 1950, Dec. 2

| | | | | |
|---|---|---|---|---|
| C82 | A188 | 30f lilac & magenta | .50 | .20 |
| C83 | A188 | 40f olive & indigo | .75 | .25 |
| C84 | A188 | 60f ol, dk brn & org red | 1.25 | .40 |
| C85 | A188 | 70f gray & dk brn | 2.75 | .55 |
| C86 | A188 | 3fo buff & dk brn | 4.50 | 2.25 |
| | Nos. C82-C86 (5) | | 9.75 | 3.65 |

Exist imperf.

### Livestock Type

| | | | | |
|---|---|---|---|---|
| 1951, Apr. 5 | | Photo. | Perf. 12x12½ | |
| C87 | A191 | 20f Mare & foal | 1.50 | .25 |
| C88 | A191 | 70f Sow & shoats | 1.90 | .35 |
| C89 | A191 | 1fo Ram & ewe | 3.75 | .90 |
| C90 | A191 | 1.60fo Cow & calf | 5.25 | 1.40 |
| | Nos. C87-C90 (4) | | 12.40 | 2.90 |

Exist imperf.

Telegraph Linemen AP34

Tank Column — AP35

Designs: 1fo, Workers on vacation. 2fo, Air view of Stalin Bridge.

### 1951, Aug. 20

| | | | | |
|---|---|---|---|---|
| C91 | AP34 | 70f henna brown | .55 | .25 |
| C92 | AP34 | 1fo blue green | .90 | .30 |
| C93 | AP34 | 2fo deep plum | 1.75 | .45 |
| | Nos. C91-C93 (3) | | 3.20 | 1.00 |

Successful conclusion of the 1st year under Hungary's 5-year plan.
Exist imperf.

### 1951, Sept. 29           Perf. 12½x12

| | | | | |
|---|---|---|---|---|
| C94 | AP35 | 60f deep blue | .50 | .20 |

Army Day, Sept. 29, 1951.
Exists imperf. Value $3.75.

### 1st Stamp Type
### Souvenir Sheet

| | | | | |
|---|---|---|---|---|
| 1951, Oct. 6 | | Engr. | Unwmk. | |
| C95 | A208 | 60f olive green | 75.00 | 65.00 |

Stamp exhibition to commemorate the 80th anniv. of Hungary's 1st postage stamp.
Exists imperf. Value $200.

Twelve hundred copies in rose lilac, perf. and imperf., were presented to exhibitors and members of the arranging committee of the exhibition. Value, each $1,600.

Avocet — AP37

Hungarian Birds: 30f, White stork. 40f, Golden oriole. 50f, Kentish plover. 60f, Black-winged stilt. 70f, Lesser gray shrike. 80f, Great bustard. 1fo, Redfooted falcon. 1.40fo, European bee-eater. 1.60fo, Glossy ibis. 2.50fo, Great white egret.

## Perf. 13x11
**1952, Mar. 16      Photo.      Wmk. 106**
### Birds in Natural Colors

| | | | | |
|---|---|---|---|---|
| C96 | AP37 | 20f emer, grnsh | .20 | .20 |
| C97 | AP37 | 30f sage grn, grysh | .20 | .20 |
| C98 | AP37 | 40f brown, cr | .30 | .20 |
| C99 | AP37 | 50f orange, cr | .35 | .20 |
| C100 | AP37 | 60f deep carmine | .35 | .20 |
| C101 | AP37 | 70f red org, cr | .40 | .20 |
| C102 | AP37 | 80f olive, cr | .55 | .20 |
| C103 | AP37 | 1fo dp blue, bluish | .75 | .25 |
| C104 | AP37 | 1.40fo gray, grysh | 2.00 | .50 |
| C105 | AP37 | 1.60fo org brn, cr | 2.50 | .55 |
| C106 | AP37 | 2.50fo rose vio, cr | 3.50 | .75 |
| | | Nos. C96-C106 (11) | 11.10 | 3.45 |

Exist imperf. Value, set $100.

### Olympic Games Type
Design: 2fo, Stadium, Budapest.

**1952, May 26      Perf. 11**

| | | | | |
|---|---|---|---|---|
| C107 | A217 | 1.70fo dp red orange | 2.10 | .60 |
| C108 | A217 | 2fo olive brown | 2.40 | .50 |

Issued to publicize Hungary's participation in the Olympic Games, Helsinki, 1952. Exist imperf.

Leonardo da Vinci — AP39

**1952, June 15      Perf. 12½x12**

| | | | | |
|---|---|---|---|---|
| C109 | AP39 | 1.60fo shown | 1.25 | .60 |
| C110 | AP39 | 2fo Victor Hugo | 1.25 | .70 |

Exist imperf. Value, set $35.

AP40

AP41

**1953, Mar. 4      Perf. 12x12½**

| | | | | |
|---|---|---|---|---|
| C111 | AP40 | 20f Red squirrel | .50 | .20 |
| C112 | AP41 | 30f Hedgehog | .65 | .20 |
| C113 | AP41 | 40f Hare | .65 | .20 |
| C114 | AP40 | 50f Beech marten | .80 | .20 |
| C115 | AP41 | 60f Otter | 1.00 | .20 |
| C116 | AP41 | 70f Red fox | 1.00 | .25 |
| C117 | AP40 | 80f Fallow deer | 1.25 | .40 |
| C118 | AP41 | 1fo Roe deer | 1.60 | .25 |
| C119 | AP41 | 1.50fo Boar | 4.00 | .85 |
| C120 | AP40 | 2fo Red deer | 4.50 | 1.00 |
| | | Nos. C111-C120 (10) | 15.95 | 3.75 |

Exist imperf. Value, set $50.

### Type of Regular Issue
Designs: 1fo, Children at Balaton Lake. 1.50fo, Workers' Home at Lillafured.

**1953, Apr. 19      Perf. 12**

| | | | | |
|---|---|---|---|---|
| C121 | A228 | 1fo brt grnsh blue | .60 | .25 |
| C122 | A228 | 1.50fo dp red lilac | 1.25 | .40 |

Exist imperf.

### People's Stadium Type
**1953, Aug. 20      Perf. 11**

| | | | | |
|---|---|---|---|---|
| C123 | A232 | 80f Water polo | .90 | .20 |
| C124 | A232 | 1fo Boxing | 1.90 | .20 |
| C125 | A232 | 2fo Soccer | 3.75 | .40 |
| C126 | A232 | 3fo Track | 2.25 | .90 |
| C127 | A232 | 5fo Stadium | 3.75 | 1.00 |
| | | Nos. C123-C127 (5) | 12.55 | 2.70 |

Exist imperf.

---

No. C125 Overprinted in Black

**1953, Dec. 3**

| | | | | |
|---|---|---|---|---|
| C128 | A232 | 2fo green & brown | 17.50 | 14.00 |

Hungary's success in the soccer matches at Wembley, England, Nov. 25, 1953. Counterfeits exist.
Exists imperf. Value $275.

Janos Bihari and Scene from Verbunkos AP44

Portraits: 40f, Ferenc Erkel. 60f, Franz Liszt. 70f, Mihaly Mosonyi. 80f, Karl Goldmark. 1fo, Bela Bartok. 2fo, Zoltan Kodaly.

**1953, Dec. 5      Photo.      Perf. 12**
### Frames and Portraits in Brown

| | | | | |
|---|---|---|---|---|
| C129 | AP44 | 30f blue gray | .35 | .20 |
| C130 | AP44 | 40f orange | .35 | .20 |
| C131 | AP44 | 60f green | .55 | .20 |
| C132 | AP44 | 70f red | .45 | .20 |
| C133 | AP44 | 80f gray blue | .45 | .25 |
| C134 | AP44 | 1fo olive bis | .95 | .30 |
| C135 | AP44 | 2fo violet | 1.40 | .65 |
| | | Nos. C129-C135 (7) | 4.50 | 2.00 |

Hungarian composers.
Exists imperf. Value, set $35.

Carrot Beetle — AP45

May (or June) Beetle AP46

Designs: Various beetles. 60f, Bee.

### Perf. 12½x12, 12x12½
**1954, Feb. 6      Wmk. 106**

| | | | | |
|---|---|---|---|---|
| C136 | AP45 | 30f dp org & dk brn | .50 | .20 |
| C137 | AP46 | 40f grn & dk brn | .60 | .20 |
| C138 | AP46 | 50f rose brn & blk | .85 | .30 |
| C139 | AP46 | 60f vio, dk brn & yel | .85 | .30 |
| C140 | AP45 | 80f grnsh gray, pur & rose | 1.25 | .30 |
| C141 | AP45 | 1fo ocher & blk | 1.75 | .25 |
| C142 | AP46 | 1.20fo dl grn & dk brn | 2.10 | .35 |
| C143 | AP46 | 1.50fo ol brn & dk brn | 3.25 | .40 |
| C144 | AP46 | 2fo hn brn & dk brn | 4.25 | .60 |
| C145 | AP45 | 3fo bl grn & dk brn | 5.50 | 1.00 |
| | | Nos. C136-C145 (10) | 20.90 | 3.90 |

Exists imperf. Value, set $110.

---

Lunchtime at the Nursery AP47

Designs: 1.50fo, Mother taking child from doctor. 2fo, Nurse and children.

**1954, Mar. 8      Perf. 12**

| | | | | |
|---|---|---|---|---|
| C146 | AP47 | 1fo olive green | .55 | .20 |
| C147 | AP47 | 1.50fo red brown | 1.25 | .35 |
| C148 | AP47 | 2fo blue green | 2.10 | .65 |
| | | Nos. C146-C148 (3) | 3.90 | 1.20 |

Exist imperf.

Model Glider Construction — AP48

Boy Flying Model Glider AP49

Designs: 60f, Gliders. 80f, Pilot leaving plane. 1fo, Parachutists. 1.20fo, Biplane. 1.50fo, Plane over Danube. 2fo, Jet planes.

**1954, June 25      Perf. 11**

| | | | | |
|---|---|---|---|---|
| C149 | AP48 | 40f brn, ol & dk bl gray | .30 | .20 |
| C150 | AP49 | 50f gray & red brn | .40 | .20 |
| C151 | AP48 | 60f red brn & dk bl gray | .40 | .20 |
| C152 | AP49 | 80f violet & sep | .45 | .20 |
| C153 | AP48 | 1fo brn & dk bl gray | .60 | .20 |
| C154 | AP49 | 1.20fo olive & sep | .90 | .25 |
| C155 | AP48 | 1.50fo cl & dk bl gray | 1.20 | .50 |
| C156 | AP49 | 2fo blue & dk brn | 1.75 | .50 |
| | | Nos. C149-C156 (8) | 6.00 | 2.25 |

Exist imperf. Value, set $75.

### Jokai Type
### Souvenir Sheet
**1954, Oct. 17      Engr.      Perf. 12½x12**

| | | | | |
|---|---|---|---|---|
| C157 | A242 | 1fo violet blue | 35.00 | 35.00 |

Stamp Day. Exists imperforate. Value $80.

Children on Sled — AP51

Skaters AP52

---

50f, Ski racer. 60f, Ice yacht. 80f, Ice hockey. 1fo, Ski jumper. 1.50fo, Downhill ski racer. 2fo, Man and woman exhibition-skating.

**1955      Photo.      Perf. 12**

| | | | | |
|---|---|---|---|---|
| C158 | AP51 | 40f multi | 1.25 | .20 |
| C159 | AP52 | 50f multi | .30 | .20 |
| C160 | AP51 | 60f multi | .30 | .20 |
| C161 | AP52 | 80f multi | .50 | .20 |
| C162 | AP51 | 1fo multi | 1.25 | .30 |
| C163 | AP52 | 1.20fo multi | 1.25 | .30 |
| C164 | AP51 | 1.50fo multi | 1.75 | .60 |
| C165 | AP52 | 2fo multi | 2.40 | .50 |
| | | Nos. C158-C165 (8) | 9.00 | 2.50 |

Exist imperf. Value, set $75.
Issued: 1.20fo, 2fo, Jan. 27; others Feb. 26.

### Government Printing Plant Type
### Souvenir Sheet
**1955, May 28      Perf. 12x12½**

| | | | | |
|---|---|---|---|---|
| C166 | A247 | 5fo hn brn & gray grn | 32.50 | 32.50 |

Cent. of the establishment of the government printing plant.
Exists imperf. Value $160.

### No. C78 Printed on Aluminum Foil
### Perf. 12½x12
**1955, Oct. 5      Engr.      Unwmk.**

| | | | | |
|---|---|---|---|---|
| C167 | AP30 | 5fo gray blue | 15.00 | 12.50 |

Intl. Cong. of the Light Metal Industry and for 20 years of aluminum production in Hungary.
Exists imperf. Value $100.

### Bartok Type
### Wmk. 106
**1955, Oct. 9      Photo.      Perf. 12**

| | | | | |
|---|---|---|---|---|
| C168 | A252 | 1fo gray green | 1.50 | .85 |
| C169 | A252 | 1fo violet brn | 3.25 | 1.75 |
| a. | | With ticket | 15.00 | 12.50 |

10th anniv. of the death of Bela Bartok, composer. No. C169a was issued for the Day of the Stamp, Oct. 16, 1955. The 5fo sales price, marked on the attached ticket, was the admission fee to any one of 14 simultaneous stamp shows.
Exist imperf. Value, set with ticket, $75.

"Esperanto" — AP55

Lazarus Ludwig Zamenhof AP56

**1957, June 8**

| | | | | |
|---|---|---|---|---|
| C170 | AP55 | 60f red brown | .50 | .25 |
| C171 | AP56 | 1fo dark green | .50 | .30 |

10th anniversary of the death of L. L. Zamenhof, inventor of Esperanto.
Exist imperf. Value $30.

### Type of 1950
Design: 20fo, Budaörs Airport.

### Perf. 12½x12
**1957, July 18      Engr.      Unwmk.**

| | | | | |
|---|---|---|---|---|
| C172 | AP30 | 20fo dk slate grn | 8.00 | 4.00 |
| | | Punched 3 holes | 9.25 | 4.50 |

A few days after issuance, stocks of No. C172 were punched with three holes and used on domestic surface mail.
Exist imperf. Value $70.

Courier and Fort Buda AP57

Design: No. C174, Plane over Budapest.

**Wmk. 106**
**1957, Oct. 13    Photo.    Perf. 12**
C173 AP57 1fo ol bis & brn, buff    .75    .75
C174 AP57 1fo ol bis & dp cl,
      buff    .75    .75
  a.   Strip of #C173-C174 + label    2.25    2.25

Stamp Day, Oct. 20th. The triptych sold for 6fo.
Exists imperf. Value, strip $30.

**Type of Regular Pigeon Issue**
Design: 3fo, Two carrier pigeons.

**1957, Dec. 14    Perf. 12x12½**
C175 A266 3fo red, grn, gray &
      blk    .90    .50

Exists imperf.

Hungarian Pavilion, Brussels — AP58

Designs: 40f, Map, lake and local products. 60f, Parliament. 1fo, Chain Bridge, Budapest. 1.40fo, Arms of Hungary and Belgium. 2fo, Fountain, Brussels, vert. 3fo, City Hall, Brussels vert. 5fo, Exposition emblem.

**Perf. 14½x15**
**1958, Apr. 17    Litho.    Wmk. 106**
C176 AP58 20f red org & red
      brn    .20    .20
C177 AP58 40f lt blue & brn    .20    .20
C178 AP58 60f crimson & sep    .20    .20
C179 AP58 1fo bis & red brn    .20    .20
C180 AP58 1.40fo dull vio & multi    .20    .20
C181 AP58 2fo gldn brn & dk
      brn    .35    .20
C182 AP58 3fo bl grn & sep    .80    .40
C183 AP58 5fo gray ol, blk,
      red, bl & yel    1.50    .60
  Nos. C176-C183 (8)    3.65    2.20

Universal and Intl. Exposition at Brussels.
Exist imperf. Value, set $30.

View of Prague and Morse Code AP59

**1958, June 30    Photo.    Perf. 12x12½**
C184 AP59 1fo rose brown    .35    .20

See No. 1194a for se-tenant pair.
Conference of Postal Ministers of Communist Countries at Prague, June 30-July 8.
Exists imperf.

Post Horn, Pigeon and Pen AP60

No. C185, Stamp under magnifying glass.

**1958, Oct. 25    Wmk. 106    Perf. 12**
C185 AP60 1fo dp car & bis    .55    .55
C186 AP60 1fo yel grn & bis    .55    .55
  a.   Strip, #C185-C186 + label    2.00    2.00

Natl. Stamp Exhib., Budapest, 10/25-11/2.
#C185 inscribed: "XXXI Belyegnap 1958."
Exist imperf. Value, strip $30.

**1958, Oct. 26**
Designs: 60f, as No. C186. 1fo, Ship, plane, locomotive and pen surrounding letter.

C187 AP60 60f dp plum & grysh
      buff    .40    .20
C188 AP60 1fo bl & grysh buff    .60    .20

Issued for Letter Writing Week.
Exist imperf. Value, set $10.

Plane over Heroes' Square Budapest — AP61

Design: 5fo, Plane over Tower of Sopron.

**Perf. 12½x12**
**1958, Nov. 3    Engr.    Wmk. 106**
C189 AP61 3fo gray, rose vio &
      red    1.25    .60
C190 AP61 5fo gray, dk bl & red    1.50    .90

40th anniv. of Hungarian air post stamps.
Exist imperf. Value, set $25.

**Same Without Commemorative Inscription**
Plane over: 20f, Szeged. 30f, Sarospatak. 70f, Gyor. 1fo, Budapest, Opera House. 1.60fo, Veszprém. 2fo, Budapest, Chain Bridge. 3fo, Sopron. 5fo, Heroes' Square, Budapest. 10fo, Budapest, Academy of Science and Parliament. 20fo, Budapest.

**1958, Dec. 31    Engr.    Wmk. 106**
**Yellow Paper**
**and Vermilion Inscriptions**
C191 AP61 20f green    .20    .20
C192 AP61 30f violet    .20    .20
C193 AP61 70f brown vio    .20    .20
C194 AP61 1fo blue    .35    .20
C195 AP61 1.60fo purple    .35    .20
C196 AP61 2fo Prus green    .40    .20
C197 AP61 3fo brown    .90    .20
C198 AP61 5fo olive green    1.40    .20
C199 AP61 10fo dark blue    2.00    .30
C200 AP61 20fo brown    3.50    .60
  Nos. C191-C200 (10)    9.50    2.50

Exist imperf. Value, set $70.

**Transport Type of Regular Issue**
Design: 3fo, Early plane.

**1959, May    Litho.    Perf. 14½x15**
C201 A279 3fo dl lil, blk, yel &
      brn    1.25    .40

Exist imperf.

Tihany — AP62

Designs: 70f, Ship. 1fo, Heviz and water lily. 1.70fo, Sailboat and fisherman statue.

**1959, July 15    Photo.    Perf. 11½x12**
C202 AP62 20f brt green    .20    .20
C203 AP62 70f brt blue    .20    .20
C204 AP62 1fo ultra & car
      rose    .20    .20
C205 AP62 1.70fo red brn, yel    .50    .30
  Nos. C202-C205 (4)    1.10    .90

Issued to publicize Lake Balaton and the opening of the Summer University.
Exist imperf.

**Moth-Butterfly Type of 1959**
Butterflies: 1fo, Lycaena virgaureae. 2fo, Acherontia atropos, horiz. 3fo, Red admiral.

**Perf. 11½x12, 12x11½**
**1959, Nov. 20    Wmk. 106**
**Butterflies in Natural Colors**
C206 A290 1fo black & lt bl grn    .90    .20
C207 A290 2fo black & lilac    1.50    .35
C208 A290 3fo dk gray & emer    2.25    .75
  Nos. C206-C208 (3)    4.65    1.30

Exist imperf.

**Souvenir Sheet**

Rockets in Orbit, Gagarin, Titov & Glenn — AP63

**Perf. 11, Imperf.**
**1962, Mar. 29    Unwmk.**
C209 AP63 10fo multi    9.50    7.50

Cosmonants Yuri A. Gagarin and Gherman Titov, USSR and astronaut John H. Glenn, Jr., US.
Exists imperf. Value $50.

**Soccer Type of 1962**
Flags of Hungary and Great Britain.

**1962, May 21    Photo.    Perf. 11**
**Flags in National Colors**
C209A A323 2fo greenish bister    1.10    .30

Exist imperf.

Glider and Lilienthal's 1898 Design — AP64

Designs: 30f, Icarus and Aero Club emblem. 60f, Light monoplane and 1912 aerobatic plane. 80f, Airship GZ-1 and Montgolfier balloon. 1fo, IL-18 Malev and Wright 1903 plane. 1.40fo, Stunt plane and Nyesterov's 1913 plane. 2fo, Helicopter and Asboth's 1929 helicopter. 3fo, Supersonic bomber and Zhukovski's turbomotor. 4fo, Space rocket and Tsiolkovsky's rocket.

**1962, July 19    Unwmk.    Perf. 15**
C210 AP64 30f blue & dull yel    .20    .20
C211 AP64 40f yel grn & ultra    .20    .20
C212 AP64 60f ultra & ver    .20    .20
C213 AP64 80f grnsh bl & sil    .20    .20
C214 AP64 1fo lilac, sil & bl    .20    .20
C215 AP64 1.40fo blue & org    .20    .20
C216 AP64 2fo bluish grn &
      brn    .25    .20
C217 AP64 3fo vio, sil & bl    .50    .25
C218 AP64 4fo grn, sil & blk    .80    .35
  Nos. C210-C218 (9)    2.75    2.00

Issued to show flight development: "From Icarus to the Space Rocket."
Exist imperf. Value, set $25.

Earth, TV Screens and Rockets — AP65

Design: 2fo, Andrian G. Nikolayev, Pavel R. Popovich and rockets.

**1962, Sept. 4    Perf. 12**
C219 AP65 1fo dk bl & org brn    .70    .35
C220 AP65 2fo dk bl & org brn    .80    .35
  a   Pair, #C219-C220    1.30    .90

First group space flight of Vostoks 3 and 4, Aug. 11-15, 1962. Printed in alternating horizontal rows.
Exist imperf. Value $20.

John H. Glenn, Jr. AP66

Astronauts: 40f, Yuri A. Gagarin. 60f, Gherman Titov. 1.40fo, Scott Carpenter. 1.70fo, Andrian G. Nikolayev. 2.60fo, Pavel R. Popovich. 3fo, Walter Schirra.

**1962, Oct. 27    Perf. 12x11½**
**Portraits in Bister**
C221 AP66 40f purple    .20    .20
C222 AP66 60f dark green    .20    .20
C223 AP66 1fo dark bl grn    .20    .20
C224 AP66 1.40fo dark brown    .20    .20
C225 AP66 1.70fo deep blue    .30    .25
C226 AP66 2.60fo violet    .65    .30
C227 AP66 3fo red brown    1.10    .45
  Nos. C221-C227 (7)    2.85    1.80

Issued to honor the first seven astronauts and in connection with the Astronautical Congress in Paris.
Exist imperf. Value, set $20.

Eagle Owl — AP67

Birds: 40f, Osprey. 60f, Marsh harrier. 80f, Booted eagle. 1fo, African fish eagle. 2fo, Lammergeier. 3fo, Golden eagle. 4fo, Kestrel.

**1962, Nov. 18    Litho.    Perf. 11½**
**Birds in Natural Colors**
C228 AP67 30f yel grn & blk    .20    .20
C229 AP67 40f org yel & blk    .20    .20
C230 AP67 60f bister & blk    .20    .20
C231 AP67 80f lt grn & blk    .20    .20
C232 AP67 1fo ol bis & blk    .20    .20
C233 AP67 2fo bluish grn & blk    .35    .20
C234 AP67 3fo lt vio & blk    .65    .30
C235 AP67 4fo dp org & blk    1.25    .50
  Nos. C228-C235 (8)    3.25    2.00

Exist imperf. Value, set $30.

Radio Mast and Albania No. 623 AP68

Designs (Communication symbols and rocket stamps of various countries): 30f, Bulgaria #C77, vert. 40f, Czechoslovakia #1108. 50f, Communist China #380. 60f, North Korea. 80f, Poland #875. 1fo, Hungary #1386. 1.20fo, Mongolia #189, vert. 1.40fo, DDR #580. 1.70fo, Romania #1200. 2fo, Russia #2456, vert. 2.60fo, North Viet Nam.

**Perf. 12x11½, 11½x12**
**1963, May 9    Photo.    Unwmk.**
**Stamp Reproductions in**
**Original Colors**
C236 AP68 20f olive green    .20    .20
C237 AP68 30f rose lake    .20    .20
C238 AP68 40f violet    .20    .20
C239 AP68 50f brt blue    .20    .20
C240 AP68 60f orange brn    .20    .20
C241 AP68 80f ultra    .20    .20
C242 AP68 1fo dull red brn    .20    .20
C243 AP68 1.20fo aqua    .20    .20
C244 AP68 1.40fo olive    .25    .20
C245 AP68 1.70fo brown olive    .25    .20
C246 AP68 2fo rose lilac    .30    .20
C247 AP68 2.60fo bluish green    .60    .40
  Nos. C236-C247 (12)    3.00    2.60

5th Conference of Postal Ministers of Communist Countries, Budapest.
Exist imperf. Value, set $30.

Souvenir Sheet

Globe and Spaceships — AP69

**Perf. 11½x12, Imperf.**

**1963, July 13**         **Unwmk.**
C248 AP69 10fo dk & lt blue    8.00   7.00

Space flights of Valeri Bykovski, June 14-19, and Valentina Tereshkova, 1st woman cosmonaut, June 16-19, 1963.
Exists imperf. Value $30.

Souvenir Sheet

Mt. Fuji and Stadium — AP70

**1964, Sept. 22 Photo.   Perf. 11½x12**
C249 AP70 10fo multi      4.00   3.50

18th Olympic Games, Tokyo, Oct. 10-24.
Exists imperf. Value $30.

Bridge Type of 1964
Souvenir Sheet

Design: Elizabeth Bridge.

**1964, Nov. 21   Photo.    Perf. 11**
C250 A356 10fo silver & dp grn   3.75   3.50

No. C250 contains one 59x20mm stamp.
Exists imperf. Value $100.

Lt. Col. Alexei
Leonov in
Space — AP71

Design: 2fo, Col. Pavel Belyayev, Lt. Col. Alexei Leonov and Voskhod 2.

---

**1965, Apr. 17   Photo.   Perf. 11½x12**
C251 AP71 1fo violet & gray    .45   .20
C252 AP71 2fo rose claret &
         ocher    1.10   .65

Space flight of Voskhod 2 and of Lt. Col. Alexei Leonov, the first man floating in space.
Exists imperf. Value, set $20.

Mariner IV
(USA) — AP72

New achievements in space research: 30f, San Marco satellite, Italy. 40f, Molniya satellite, USSR. 60f, Moon rocket, 1965, USSR. 1fo, Shapir rocket, France. 2.50fo, Zond III satellite, USSR. 3fo, Syncom III satellite, US. 10fo, Rocket sending off satellites, horiz.

**1965, Dec. 31   Photo.    Perf. 11**
C253 AP72 20f ultra, blk & org
         yel     .20   .20
C254 AP72 30f brn, vio & yel   .20   .20
C255 AP72 40f vio, brn & pink   .20   .20
C256 AP72 60f lt pur, blk &
         org yel   .20   .20
C257 AP72 1fo red lil, blk &
         buff    .30   .25
C258 AP72 2.50fo rose cl, blk &
         gray    .60   .35
C259 AP72 3fo bl grn, blk &
         bis    .75   .60
    Nos. C253-C259 (7)   2.45   2.00

Souvenir Sheet

**1965, Dec. 20**
C260 AP72 10fo brt bl, yel & dk
         ol    3.50   3.00

Exist imperf. Value: Nos. C253-C259 $20; No. C260 $30.

Sport Type of Regular Issue
Souvenir Sheet

10fo, Women hurdlers and Ferihegy airport.

**1966, Sept. 4   Photo.   Perf. 12x11½**
C261 A384 10fo brt bl, brn &
         red    4.00   3.75

Exists imperf. Value $30.

Plane over
Helsinki — AP73

Plane over Cities Served by Hungarian Airlines: 50f, Athens. 1fo, Beirut. 1.10fo, Frankfort on the Main. 1.20fo, Cairo. 1.50fo, Copenhagen. 2fo, London. 2.50fo, Moscow. 3fo, Paris. 4fo, Prague. 5fo, Rome. 10fo, Damascus. 20fo, Budapest.

**1966-67     Photo.    Perf. 12x11½**
C262 AP73 20f brown org   .20   .20
C263 AP73 50f brown    .20   .20
C264 AP73 1fo blue    .20   .20
C265 AP73 1.10fo black   .20   .20
C266 AP73 1.20fo orange   .20   .20
C267 AP73 1.50fo blue grn   .25   .20
C268 AP73 2fo brt blue   .30   .20
C269 AP73 2.50fo brt red   .30   .20
C270 AP73 3fo yel grn   .40   .20
C271 AP73 4fo brown red   1.10   1.00
C272 AP73 5fo brt pur   .55   .20
C273 AP73 10fo violet bl ('67)   .75   .20
C274 AP73 20fo gray ol ('67)   1.10   .35
    Nos. C262-C274 (13)   5.75   3.55

Exist imperf. Value, set $70.
See No. C276.

---

Souvenir Sheet

Icarus Falling — AP73a

**1968, May 11    Photo.    Perf. 11**
C275 AP73a 10fo multicolored   2.75   2.50

In memory of the astronauts Edward H. White, US, Vladimir M. Komarov and Yuri A. Gagarin, USSR.
Exists imperf. Value $25.

Type of 1966-67 without "Legiposta"
Inscription

Design: 2.60fo, Malev Airlines jet over St. Stephen's Cathedral, Vienna.

**1968, July 4    Photo.    Perf. 12x11½**
C276 AP73 2.60fo violet    .50   .20

50th anniv. of regular airmail service between Budapest and Vienna.
Exists imperf. Value $10.

Women Swimmers and Aztec
Calendar Stone — AP74

Aztec Calendar Stone, Olympic Rings and: 60f, Soccer. 80f, Wrestling. 1fo, Canoeing. 1.40fo, Gymnast on rings. 3fo, Fencing. 4fo, Javelin.

**1968, Aug. 21    Photo.    Perf. 12**
C277 AP74 20f brt bl & multi   .20   .20
C278 AP74 50f green & multi   .20   .20
C279 AP74 80f car rose &
         multi    .20   .20
C280 AP74 1fo grnsh bl &
         multi    .20   .20
C281 AP74 1.40fo violet & multi   .20   .20
C282 AP74 3fo brt lilac &
         multi    .65   .35
C283 AP74 4fo green & multi   1.00   .55
    Nos. C277-C283,CB31 (8)   3.00   2.25

Issued to publicize the 19th Olympic Games, Mexico City, Oct. 12-27.
Exist imperf. Value, set (8) $30.

Souvenir Sheet

Apollo 8 Trip Around the
Moon — AP75

**1969, Feb.    Photo.    Perf. 12½**
C284 AP75 10fo multi    3.50   3.50

Man's 1st flight around the moon, Dec. 21-27, 1968.
Exists imperf. Value $30.

---

Soyuz 4
and 5,
and Men
in Space
AP76

Design: No. C286, Soyuz 4 and 5.

**1969, Mar. 21   Photo.    Perf. 12x11½**
C285 AP76 2fo multi    .35   .35
C286 AP76 2fo dk bl, lt bl & red   .35   .35
   a.    Strip, # C285-C286 + label   .85

First team flights of Russian spacecraft Soyuz 4 and 5, Jan. 16, 1969.
Exist imperf. Value, strip $10.

Journey to the Moon, by Jules
Verne — AP77

Designs: 60f, Tsiolkovski's space station. 1fo, Luna 1. 1.50fo, Ranger 7. 2fo, Luna 9 landing on moon. 2.50fo, Apollo 8 in orbit around moon. 3fo, Soyuz 4 and 5 docking in space. 4fo, Lunar landing module landing on moon. 10fo, Apollo 11 astronauts on moon and lunar landing module.

**1969     Photo.    Perf. 12x11½**
C287 AP77 40f multi   .20   .20
C288 AP77 60f multi   .20   .20
C289 AP77 1fo multi   .20   .20
C290 AP77 1.50fo multi   .20   .20
C291 AP77 2fo multi   .20   .20
C292 AP77 2.50fo multi   .25   .20
C293 AP77 3fo multi   .50   .20
C294 AP77 4fo multi   .75   .40
    Nos. C287-C294 (8)   2.50   1.80

**Souvenir Sheet**
**Perf. 11**
C295 AP77 10fo multi   5.00   5.00

Moon landing issue. See note after Algeria No. 427.
No. C295 contains one 74x49mm stamp. Issued: #C287-C294, Nov. 1; #C295, Aug. 15.
Exist imperf. Value: Nos. C287-C294 $20; No. C295 $20.

Daimler, 1886 — AP78

Automobiles: 60f, Peugeot, 1894. 1fo, Benz, 1901. 1.50fo, Cudell mail truck, 1902. 2fo, Rolls Royce, 1908. 2.50fo, Model T Ford, 1908. 3fo, Vermorel, 1912. 4fo, Csonka mail car, 1912.

**1970, Mar.    Photo.    Perf. 12**
C296 AP78 40f ocher & multi   .20   .20
C297 AP78 60f multi   .20   .20
C298 AP78 1fo red & multi   .20   .20
C299 AP78 1.50fo bl & multi   .20   .20
C300 AP78 2fo multi   .25   .20
C301 AP78 2.50fo vio & multi   .30   .20
C302 AP78 3fo multi   .40   .30
C303 AP78 4fo multi   .70   .50
    Nos. C296-C303 (8)   2.45   2.00

Exist imperf. Value, set $20.

American Astronauts on
Moon — AP79

No. C305, Soyuz 6, 7 and 8 in space.

**1970, Mar. 20　Photo.　Perf. 11**
C304　AP79　3fo blue & multi　.75　.75
C305　AP79　3fo car rose & multi　.75　.75

Landing of Apollo 12 on the moon, Nov. 14, 1969, and group flight of Russian spacecraft Soyuz 6, 7 & 8, Oct. 11-13, 1969.
Nos. C304-C305 issued in sheets of 4. Size: 112½x78mm.
Exist imperf. Value: set $20; sheets of 4 $80.

"Rain at Foot of Fujiyama," by Hokusai, and Pavilion — AP80

3fo, Sun Tower, Peace Bell and globe.

**1970, Apr. 30　Photo.　Perf. 12½**
C306　AP80　2fo multi　.75　.75
C307　AP80　3fo multi　.75　.75

Issued to publicize EXPO '70 International Exhibition, Osaka, Japan, Mar. 15-Sept. 13.
Exist imperf. Value, set $10.

### Miniature Sheets

Phases of Apollo 13 Moon Flight — AP81

Vignettes of No. C308: Apollo 13 over moon; return to earth; capsule with parachutes; capsule floating, aircraft carrier and helicopter.
Vignettes of No. C309: Soyuz 9 on way to launching pad; launching of Soyuz 9 capsule in orbit; cosmonauts Andrian Nikolayev and Vitaly Sevastyanov.
Vignettes of No. C310: Luna 16 approaching moon; module on moon; landing; nose cone on ground.
Vignettes of No. C311: Lunokhod 1 on moon; trajectories of Luna 17 around earth and moon.

**1970-71　Litho.　Perf. 11½**
C308　AP81　Sheet of 4　2.25　2.25
**Photo.**
C309　AP81　Sheet of 4　2.25　2.25
C310　AP81　Sheet of 4 ('71)　2.25　2.25
C311　AP81　Sheet of 4 ('71)　2.25　2.25

Nos. C308-C311 were valid for postage only as full sheets. Each contains four 2.50fo vignettes.
No. C308 for the aborted moon flight and safe return of Apollo 13, 4/11-17/70.
No. C309 for the 424-hour flight of Soyuz 9, 6/1-9.
No. C310 for Luna 16, the unmanned, automated moon mission, 9/12-24/70.
No. C311 for Luna 17, unmanned, automated moon mission, 11/10-17/70.
Exist imperf. Value, set $80.
Issued: #C308, 6/10; #C309, 9/4; #C310, 1/15; #C311 3/8.

American Astronauts on Moon — AP82

**1971, Mar. 31　　Perf. 12½**
C312　AP82　10fo multi　2.50　2.50

Apollo 14 moon landing, 1/31-2/9/71.
Exists imperf. Value $25.
See Nos. C315, C326-C328.

### Hunting Type of Regular Issue Souvenir Sheet

Design: 10fo, Red deer group.

**1971, Aug. 27　Photo.　Perf. 11**
C313　A460　10fo multi　3.00　2.50

No. C313 contains one 70x45mm stamp.
Exists imperf. Value $50.

Astronauts Volkov, Dobrovolsky and Patsayev — AP83

### Souvenir Sheet

**1971, Oct. 4　Photo.　Perf. 12½**
C314　AP83　10fo multi　2.25　2.25

In memory of the Russian astronauts Vladislav N. Volkov, Lt. Col. Georgi T. Dobrovolsky and Victor I. Patsayev, who died during the Soyuz 11 space mission, June 6-30, 1971.
Exists imperf. Value $20.

### Apollo 14 Type of 1971 Souvenir Sheet

10fo, American Lunar Rover on moon.

**1972, Jan. 20　Photo.　Perf. 12½**
C315　AP82　10fo multi　3.00　3.00

Apollo 15 moon mission, 7/26-8/7/71.
Exist imperf. Value $20.

Soccer and Hungarian Flag — AP84

Various Scenes from Soccer and Natl. Flags of: 60f, Romania. 80f, DDR. 1fo, Great Britain. 1.20fo, Yugoslavia. 2fo, USSR. 4fo, Italy. 5fo, Belgium.

**1972, Apr. 29**
C316　AP84　40f gold & multi　.20　.20
C317　AP84　60f gold & multi　.20　.20
C318　AP84　80f gold & multi　.20　.20
C319　AP84　1fo gold & multi　.20　.20
C320　AP84　1.20fo gold & multi　.20　.20
C321　AP84　2fo gold & multi　.30　.20
C322　AP84　4fo gold & multi　.75　.40
C323　AP84　5fo gold & multi　1.10　.70
　*a.*　Sheet of 8, #C316-C323　3.00　2.50
　Nos. C316-C323 (8)　3.15　2.30

European Soccer Championships for the Henri Delaunay Cup.
Exist imperf. Value: set $55; sheet $55.
Nos. C316-C321 were later issued individually in sheets of 20 and in partly changed colors.

Olympic Rings and Globe — AP85

**1972, June 10　Photo.　Perf. 12½**
C324　AP85　10fo multi　6.00　5.75

20th Olympic Games, Munich, 8/26-9/11.
Exists imperf. Value $95.

### Olympic Type of Regular Issue Souvenir Sheet

Design: Equestrian and Olympic Rings.

**1972, July 15　Photo.　Perf. 12½**
C325　A484　10fo multi　2.50　2.50

20th Olympic Games, Munich, Aug. 26-Sept. 11. #C325 contains one 43x43mm stamp.
Exists imperf. Value $25.

### Apollo 14 Type of 1971 Souvenir Sheets

Design: 10fo, Astronaut in space, Apollo 16 capsule and badge.

**1972, Oct. 10　Photo.　Perf. 12½**
C326　AP82　10fo blue & multi　2.75　2.75

Apollo 16 US moon mission, 4/15-27/72.
Exists imperf. Value $30.

**1973, Jan. 15**

Design: Astronaut exploring moon, vert.

C327　AP82　10fo blue & multi　3.00　3.00

Apollo 17 US moon mission, Dec. 7-19, 1972. No. C327 contains one vertical stamp.
Exists imperf. Value $30.

**1973, Mar. 12　Photo.　Perf. 12½**
C328　AP82　10fo Venus 8　3.00　3.00

Venus 8 USSR space mission, Mar. 27-July 22, 1972.
Exists imperf. Value $17.50.

Equestrian (Pentathlon), Olympic Rings and Medal — AP86

Designs (Olympic Rings and Medals): 60f, Weight lifting. 1fo, Canoeing. 1.20fo, Swimming, women's. 1.80fo, Boxing. 4fo, Wrestling. 6fo, Fencing. 10fo, Allegorical figure lighting flame, vert.

**1973, Mar. 31**
C329　AP86　40f multi　.20　.20
C330　AP86　60f multi　.20　.20
C331　AP86　1fo blue & multi　.20　.20
C332　AP86　1.20fo multi　.20　.20
C333　AP86　1.80fo multi　.30　.20
C334　AP86　4fo multi　.65　.40
C335　AP86　6fo multi　1.00　.50
　Nos. C329-C335 (7)　2.75　1.80

### Souvenir Sheet
**Perf. 11**
C336　AP86　10fo blue & multi　3.75　3.75

Hungarian medalists at 20th Olympic Games. #C336 contains one 44x71mm stamp.
Exist imperf. Value: Nos. C329-C335 $20; No. C336 $80.

Wrens — AP87

**1973, Apr. 16　Litho.　Perf. 12**
C337　AP87　40f shown　.20　.20
C338　AP87　60f Rock thrush　.20　.20
C339　AP87　80f Robins　.20　.20
C340　AP87　1fo Firecrests　.20　.20
C341　AP87　1.20fo Linnets　.25　.20
C342　AP87　2fo Blue titmice　.35　.20
C343　AP87　4fo White-spotted　blue throat　.75　.25
C344　AP87　5fo Gray wagtails　1.10　.55
　Nos. C337-C344 (8)　3.25　2.00

Exist imperf. Value $25.

### Exhibition Type of Regular Issue Souvenir Sheet

10fo, Bavaria #1 with mill wheel cancellation; Munich City Hall, TV Tower and Olympic tent.

**1973, May 11　Litho.　Perf. 11**
C345　A506　10fo multi　2.75　2.75

No. C345 contains one 83x45mm stamp.
Exists imperf. Value $30.

### Souvenir Sheet

Skylab over Earth — AP88

**1973, Oct. 16　Photo.　Perf. 12½**
C346　AP88　10fo dk bl, lt bl & yel　2.75　2.75

First US manned space station.
Exists imperf. Value $20.

### Space Type of Regular Issue

Designs: 6fo, Mars "canals" and Giovanni V. Schiaparelli. 10fo, Mars 7 spacecraft.

**1974, Mar. 11　Photo.　Perf. 12½**
C347　A522　6fo gold & multi　.75　.50
### Souvenir Sheet
C348　A522　10fo gold & multi　2.75　2.50

Exist imperf. Value, souvenir sheet $22.

### UPU Type of 1974

Designs: a, Mail coach. b, Old mail automobile. c, Jet. d, Apollo 15.

**1974, May 22　Litho.　Perf. 12**
C349　A526　6fo UPU emblem and　TU-154 jet　.75　.60
### Souvenir Sheet
C350　　Sheet of 4　2.75　2.75
　*a.-d.*　A526 2.50fo, any single　.40　.40

No. C350 has bister UPU emblem in center where 4 stamps appear.
Exist imperf. Value, souvenir sheet $50.

### Army Day Type of 1974

Designs: 2fo, Ground-to-air missiles, vert. 3fo, Parachutist, helicopter, supersonic jets.

**1974, Sept. 28　Litho.　Perf. 12**
C351　A537　2fo gold, emer & blk　.25　.20
C352　A537　3fo gold, blue & blk　.45　.20

Exist imperf.

Carrier Pigeon, Elizabeth Bridge, Mt. Gellert — AP89

**1975, Feb. 7    Litho.    Perf. 12**
C353  AP89  3fo multi                    1.25  1.25
Carrier Pigeons' Olympics, Budapest, Feb. 7-9. No. C353 printed checkerwise with black and violet coupon showing Pigeon Olympics emblem.
Exists imperf. Value $10.

Sputnik 2, Apollo-Soyuz Emblem AP90

Spacecraft and Apollo-Soyuz Emblem: 60f, Mercury-Atlas 5. 80f, Lunokhod I on moon. 1.20fo, Lunar rover, Apollo 15 mission. 2fo, Soyuz take-off, Baikonur. 4fo, Apollo take-off, Cape Kennedy. 6fo, Apollo-Soyuz link-up. 10fo, Apollo, Soyuz, American and Russian flags over earth, horiz.

**1975, July 7    Photo.    Perf. 12x11½**
C354  AP90  40f silver & multi      .20   .20
C355  AP90  60f silver & multi      .20   .20
C356  AP90  80f silver & multi      .20   .20
C357  AP90  1.20fo silver & multi   .20   .20
C358  AP90  2fo silver & multi      .25   .20
C359  AP90  4fo silver & multi      .45   .30
C360  AP90  6fo silver & multi      .75   .45
    Nos. C354-C360 (7)              2.25  1.75
**Souvenir Sheet**
**Perf. 12½**
C361  AP90  10fo blue & multi       3.25  3.00
Apollo Soyuz space test project (Russo-American cooperation), launching July 15; link-up July 17. No. C361 contains one 59x38mm stamp.
Exist imperf. Value: Nos. C354-C360 $25; No. C361 $28.

**Souvenir Sheet**

Map of Europe and Cogwheels — AP91

**1975, July 30    Litho.    Perf. 12½**
C362  AP91  10fo multi              4.50  3.75
European Security and Cooperation Conference, Helsinki, July 30-Aug. 1.
Exists imperf. Value $70.

**Souvenir Sheet**

Hungary Nos. 1585, 1382, 2239, 2280, C81 — AP92

**1975, Sept. 9    Photo.    Perf. 12½**
C363  AP92  10fo multi              2.75  2.50
30 years of stamps.

Exists imperf. Value $25.
A similar souvenir sheet with blue margin, no denomination and no postal validity was released for the 25th anniversary of Filatelica Hungarica.

**Souvenir Sheet**

Paintings by Károly Lotz and János Halápi — AP93

**1976, Mar. 19    Photo.    Perf. 12½**
C364  AP93     Sheet of 2          3.25  2.50
  a.    5fo Horses in Storm        1.00  1.00
  b.    5fo Morning at Tihany      1.00  1.00
Tourist publicity. #C364a and C364b are imperf. between.
Exists imperf. Value $40.

**Souvenir Sheet**

Montreal Olympic Stadium — AP94

**1976, June 29    Litho.    Perf. 12½**
C365  AP94  20fo red, gray & blk   3.75  3.75
21st Olympic Games, Montreal, Canada, July 17-Aug. 1.
Exists imperf. Value $35.

US Mars Mission AP95

60f, Viking in space. 1fo, Viking on Mars. 2fo, Venus, rocket take-off. 3fo, Venyera 9 in space. 4fo, Venyera 10, separation in space. 5fo, Venyera on moon. 20fo, Viking 1 landing on Mars, vert.

**1976, Nov. 11    Photo.    Perf. 11**
C366  AP95  40f silver & multi     .20   .20
C367  AP95  60f silver & multi     .20   .20
C368  AP95  1fo silver & multi     .20   .20
C369  AP95  2fo silver & multi     .25   .20
C370  AP95  3fo silver & multi     .35   .20
C371  AP95  4fo silver & multi     .55   .30
C372  AP95  5fo silver & multi     .75   .40
    Nos. C366-C372 (7)             2.50  1.70
**Souvenir Sheet**
**Perf. 12½**
C373  AP95  20fo black & multi     3.00  2.75
US-USSR space missions. No. C373 contains one stamp (size: 41x64mm).
Exist imperf. Value: Nos. C366-C372 $20; No. C373 $25.

Hungary No. CB33 — AP96

**1977, Apr.    Litho.    Perf. 11½x12**
C374  AP96  3fo multi              1.50  1.50
European stamp exhibitions. Issued in sheets of 3 stamps and 3 labels. Labels show exhibition emblems respectively: 125th anniversary of Brunswick stamps, Brunswick, May 5-8; Regiofil XII, Lugano, June 17-19; centenary of San Marino Stamps, Riccione, Aug. 27-29.
Exists imperf. Value: single $9; sheetlet $30.

Space Type 1977
**Souvenir Sheet**
Design: 20fo, Viking on Mars.

**1977, Sept. 20    Litho.    Perf. 11½**
C375  A603  20fo multi             3.75  3.75
Exists imperf. Value $25.

**Souvenir Sheet**

"EUROPA," Map and Dove — AP97

**1977, Oct. 3              Perf. 12½**
C376  AP97  20fo multi             5.25  4.75
European Security Conference, Belgrade, Oct.-Nov.
Exists imperf. Value $35.

TU-154, Malev over Europe AP98

Planes, Airlines, Maps: 1.20fo, DC-8, Swissair, Southeast Asia. 2fo, IL-62, CSA, North Africa. 2.40fo, A 300B Airbus, Lufthansa, Northwest Europe. 4fo, Boeing 747, Pan Am, North America. 5fo, TU-144, Aeroflot, Northern Europe. 10fo, Concorde, Air France, South America. 20fo, IL-86, Aeroflot, Northeast Asia.

**1977, Oct. 26    Litho.    Perf. 11½x12**
**Size: 32x21mm**
C377  AP98  60f orange & blk      .20   .20
C378  AP98  1.20fo violet & blk   .35   .20
C379  AP98  2fo yellow & blk      .35   .20
C380  AP98  2.40fo bl grn & blk   .50   .20
C381  AP98  4fo ultra & blk       .50   .20
C382  AP98  5fo dp rose & blk     .70   .25
C383  AP98  10fo blue & blk       1.25  .40
**Perf. 12x11½**
**Size: 37½x29mm**
C384  AP98  20fo green & blk      1.40  .90
    Nos. C377-C384 (8)            5.25  2.55
Exist imperf. Value, set $35.

Montgolfier Brothers and Balloon, 1783 — AP99

Designs: 60f, David Schwarz and airship, 1850. 1fo, Alberto Santos-Dumont and airship flying around Eiffel Tower, 1901. 2fo, Konstantin E. Tsiolkovsky, airship and Kremlin, 1857. 3fo, Roald Amundsen, airship Norge, Polar

bears and map, 1872. 4fo, Hugo Eckener, Graf Zeppelin over Mt. Fuji, 1930. 5fo, Count Ferdinand von Zeppelin, Graf Zeppelin over Chicago, 1932. 20fo, Graf Zeppelin over Budapest, 1931.

**1977, Nov. 1    Photo.    Perf. 12x11½**
C385  AP99  40f gold & multi      .20   .20
C386  AP99  60f gold & multi      .20   .20
C387  AP99  1fo gold & multi      .20   .20
C388  AP99  2fo gold & multi      .25   .20
C389  AP99  3fo gold & multi      .40   .25
C390  AP99  4fo gold & multi      .50   .30
C391  AP99  5fo gold & multi      .75   .50
    Nos. C385-C391 (7)            2.50  1.85
**Souvenir Sheet**
**Perf. 12½**
C392  AP99  20fo silver & multi   3.25  3.00
History of airships. No. C392 contains one 60x36mm stamp.
Exist imperf. Value: Nos. C385-C391 $20; No. C392 $30.

Moon Station — AP100

Science Fiction Paintings by Pal Varga: 60f, Moon settlement. 1fo, Spaceship near Phobos. 2fo, Exploration of asteroids. 3fo, Spaceship in gravitational field of Mars. 4fo, Spaceship and rings of Saturn. 5fo, Spaceship landing on 3rd Jupiter moon.

**1978, Mar. 10    Litho.    Perf. 11**
C393  AP100  40f multi            .20   .20
C394  AP100  60f multi            .20   .20
C395  AP100  1fo multi            .20   .20
C396  AP100  2fo multi            .25   .20
C397  AP100  3fo multi            .40   .25
C398  AP100  4fo multi            .50   .30
C399  AP100  5fo multi            .75   .40
    Nos. C393-C399 (7)            2.50  1.75
Exist imperf. Value, set $20.

Louis Bleriot and La Manche AP101

60f, J. Alcock & R. W. Brown, Vickers Vimy, 1919. 1fo, A. C. Read, Navy Curtiss NC-4, 1919. 2fo, H. Köhl, G. Hünefeld, J. Fitzmaurice, Junkers W33, 1928. 3fo, A. Johnson, J. Mollison, Gipsy Moth, 1930. 4fo, G. Endresz, S. Magyar, Lockheed Sirius, 1931. 5fo, W. Gronau, Dornier WAL, 1932. 20fo, Wilbur & Orville Wright & their plane.

**1978, May 10    Litho.    Perf. 12**
C400  AP101  40f multi            .20   .20
C401  AP101  60f multi            .20   .20
C402  AP101  1fo multi            .20   .20
C403  AP101  2fo multi            .25   .20
C404  AP101  3fo multi            .40   .25
C405  AP101  4fo multi            .55   .30
C406  AP101  5fo multi            .85   .40
    Nos. C400-C406 (7)            2.65  1.75
**Souvenir Sheet**
C407  AP101  20fo multi           3.00  2.75
75th anniv. of 1st powered flight by Wright brothers. #C407 contains one 75x25mm stamp.
Exist imperf. Value: Nos. C400-C406 $20; No. C407 $35.

## Souvenir Sheet

Jules Verne and "Voyage from Earth to Moon" — AP102

**1978, Aug. 21    Perf. 12½x11½**
C408 AP102 20fo multi      3.00 2.75
Jules Verne (1828-1905), French science fiction writer.
Exists imperf. Value $35.

Vladimir Remek Postmarking Mail on Board Salyut 6 — AP103

**1978, Sept. 1    Photo.    Perf. 11½x12**
C409 AP103 3fo multi      .75  .75
PRAGA '78 International Philatelic Exhibition, Prague, Sept. 8-17. Issued in sheets of 3 stamps and 3 labels, showing PRAGA '78 emblem and Golden Tower, Prague. FISA emblems in margin.
Exists imperf. Value: single $6; sheetlet $20.

Ski Jump — AP104

Lake Placid '80 Emblem and: 60f, 20fo, Figure skating, diff. 1fo, Downhill skiing. 2fo, Ice hockey. 4fo, Bobsledding. 6fo, Cross-country skiing.

**1979, Dec. 15    Litho.    Perf. 12**
C410 AP104 40f multi      .20  .20
C411 AP104 60f multi      .20  .20
C412 AP104 1fo multi      .20  .20
C413 AP104 2fo multi      .30  .30
C414 AP104 4fo multi      .60  .30
C415 AP104 6fo multi     1.00  .55
    Nos. C410-C415 (6)   2.50 1.65

### Souvenir Sheet

C416 AP104 20fo multi      2.75 2.75
13th Winter Olympic Games, Lake Placid, NY, Feb. 12-24, 1980.
Exist imperf. Value: Nos. C410-C415 $30; No. C416 $35.

Soviet and Hungarian Cosmonauts AP105

**1980, May 27    Litho.    Perf. 11½x12**
C417 AP105 5fo multi      .60  .25
Intercosmos cooperative space program.
Exists imperf. Value $30.

---

Women's Handball, Moscow '80 Emblem, Olympic Rings — AP106

**1980, June 16    Photo.    Perf. 11½x12**
C418 AP106 40f shown      .20  .20
C419 AP106 60f Double kayak   .20  .20
C420 AP106 1fo Running    .20  .20
C421 AP106 2fo Gymnast    .25  .20
C422 AP106 3fo Equestrian   .40  .25
C423 AP106 4fo Wrestling    .55  .35
C424 AP106 5fo Water polo   .65  .50
    Nos. C418-C424 (7)   2.45 1.90

### Souvenir Sheet

C425 AP106 20fo Torch bearers  3.00 3.00
22nd Summer Olympic Games, Moscow, July 19-Aug. 3.
See No. C427.
Exist imperf. Value: Nos. C418-C424 $30; No. C425 $25.

### Souvenir Sheet

Cosmonauts Bertalan Farkes and Valery Kubasov, Salyut 6-Soyuz 35 and 36 — AP107

**1980, July 12    Litho.    Perf. 12½**
C426 AP107 20fo multi      3.25 3.00
Intercosmos cooperative space program (USSR-Hungary).
Exists imperf. Value $30.

### Olympic Type of 1980
### Souvenir Sheet

**1980, Sept. 26    Litho.    Perf. 12½**
C427 AP106 20fo Greek Frieze and gold medal    3.25 3.00
Olympic Champions.
Exists imperf. Value $30.

Kalman Kittenberger (1881-1958), Zoologist and Explorer — AP108

**1981, Mar. 6    Photo.    Perf. 11½**
C427A AP108 40f Cheetah    .20  .20
C427B AP108 60f Lion    .20  .20
C427C AP108 1fo Leopard    .20  .20
C427D AP108 2fo Rhinoceros   .35  .20
C427E AP108 3fo Antelope    .55  .25
C427F AP108 4fo African elephant    .65  .30
C427G AP108 5fo shown    .85  .40
    Nos. C427A-C427G (7)   3.00 1.75
Exist imperf. Value, set $25.

---

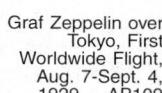

Graf Zeppelin over Tokyo, First Worldwide Flight, Aug. 7-Sept. 4, 1929 — AP109

Graf Zeppelin Flights (Zeppelin and): 2fo, Icebreaker Malygin, Polar flight, July 24-31, 1931. 3fo, Nine Arch Bridge, Hortobagy, Hungary, Mar. 28-30, 1931. 4fo, Holsten Tor, Lubeck, Baltic Sea, May 12-15, 1931. 5fo, Tower Bridge, England, Aug. 18-20, 1931. 6fo, Federal Palace, Chicago World's Fair, 50th crossing of Atlantic, Oct. 14-Nov. 2, 1933. 7fo, Lucerne, first flight across Switzerland, Sept. 26, 1929.

### Perf. 12½x11½

**1981, Mar. 16    Litho.**
C428 AP109 1fo multi      .20  .20
C429 AP109 2fo multi      .25  .20
C430 AP109 3fo multi      .40  .25
C431 AP109 4fo multi      .55  .35
C432 AP109 5fo multi      .65  .40
C433 AP109 6fo multi      .75  .55
C434 AP109 7fo multi      .85  .60
    Nos. C428-C434 (7)   3.65 2.55
LURABA '81, First Aviation and Space Philatelic Exhibition, Lucerne, Switzerland, Mar. 20-29. No. C434 se-tenant with label showing exhibition emblem.
Exist imperf. Value, set $20.

### Illustrator Type of 1981

Designs: Illustrations by A. Lesznai.

**1981, Dec. 29    Litho.    Perf. 11½x12**
C435 A693 4fo At the End of the Village    .55  .50
C436 A693 5fo Dance    .70  .55
C437 A693 6fo Sunday    .80  .60
    Nos. C435-C437 (3)   2.05 1.65
Exist imperf.

Manned Flight Bicentenary AP110

Various hot air balloons.

**1983, Apr. 5    Litho.    Perf. 12x11½**
C438 AP110 1fo 1811    .20  .20
C439 AP110 1fo 1896    .20  .20
C440 AP110 2fo 1904    .25  .20
C441 AP110 2fo 1977    .25  .20
C442 AP110 4fo 1981    .50  .25
C443 AP110 4fo 1982    .50  .25
C444 AP110 5fo 1981    .70  .35
    Nos. C438-C444 (7)   2.60 1.65

### Souvenir Sheet
### Perf. 12½

C445 AP110 20fo 1983      2.75 2.75
No. C445 contains one 39x49mm stamp.
Exist imperf. Value: Nos. C438-C444 $20; No. C445 $25.

### Audubon Type of 1985

**1985, June 19    Litho.    Perf. 12**
C446 A778 4fo Colaptes auratus  .60  .35
C447 A778 6fo Richmondena cardinalis    .85  .50
Exist imperf.

Aircraft — AP111

---

**1988, Aug. 31    Litho.    Perf. 11**
C448 AP111 1fo Lloyd CII    .20  .20
C449 AP111 2fo Brandenburg CI    .30  .20
C450 AP111 4fo UFAG CI    .50  .35
C451 AP111 10fo Gerle 13    1.40  .90
C452 AP111 12fo WM 13    1.60 1.10
    Nos. C448-C452 (5)   4.00 2.75
Exist imperf. Value, set $30.

---

## AIR POST SEMI-POSTAL STAMPS

> Catalogue values for unused stamps in this section are for Never Hinged items.

### Roosevelt Type of Semipostal Stamps, 1947

F. D. Roosevelt, Plane and Place: 10f+10f, Casablanca. 20f+20f, Tehran. 50f+50f, Yalta (map). 70f+70f, Hyde Park.

### Perf. 12x12½

**1947, June 11    Photo.    Wmk. 210**
### Portrait in Sepia

CB1  SP115 10f + 10f red vio   3.50 5.00
CB1A SP115 20f + 20f brn ol   3.50 5.00
CB1B SP115 50f + 50f vio    3.50 5.00
CB1C SP115 70f + 70f blk    3.50 5.00
    Nos. CB1-CB1C (4)   14.00 20.00
Exist imperf.
A souvenir sheet contains one each of Nos. CB1-CB1C with border inscriptions and decorations in gray. Size: 161x122mm. Value $350.
See note below Nos. B198A-B198D.

### Souvenir Sheet

Chain Bridge, Budapest — SPAP1

### Perf. 12x12½

**1948, May 15    Photo.    Wmk. 283**
CB1D SPAP1 2fo + 18fo brn car    110.00 110.00
Exists imperf. Value $2,400.

### Souvenir Sheet

Chain Bridge — SPAP2

**1948, Oct. 16**
CB2 SPAP2 3fo + 18fo dp grnsh bl    110.00 110.00
Exists imperf. Value $2,400.

### Type of Air Post Stamps of 1948
### Portraits at Right

Writers: 1f, William Shakespeare. 2f, Francois Voltaire. 4f, Johann Wolfgang von Goethe. 5f, Lord Byron. 6f, Victor Hugo. 8f, Edgar Allen Poe. 10f, Sandor Petőfi. 12f, Mark Twain. 30f, Count Leo Tolstoy. 40f, Maxim Gorky.

**1948, Oct. 16    Photo.**
CB3 AP22 1f dp ultra    .20  .20
CB4 AP22 2f rose carmine   .20  .20
CB5 AP22 4f dp yellow grn   .20  .20
CB6 AP22 5f dp rose lilac   .20  .20
CB7 AP22 6f deep blue    .20  .20

| | | | | |
|---|---|---|---|---|
| CB8 | AP22 | 8f olive brn | .20 | .20 |
| CB9 | AP22 | 10f red | .40 | .20 |
| CB10 | AP22 | 12f deep violet | .40 | .20 |
| CB11 | AP22 | 30f orange brn | 1.50 | .60 |
| CB12 | AP22 | 40f sepia | 1.50 | .90 |
| | | *Nos. CB3-CB12 (10)* | 5.00 | 3.10 |

Sold at a 50 per cent increase over face, half of which aided reconstruction of the Chain Bridge and the other half the hospital for postal employees.
Exist imperf. Value, set $115.

### 1st Stamp Type
### Souvenir Sheets
**Perf. 12½x12**

| | | | | |
|---|---|---|---|---|
| **1951, Sept. 12** | **Engr.** | | **Unwmk.** | |
| CB13 | A208 | 1fo + 1fo red | 75.00 | 65.00 |
| CB14 | A208 | 2fo + 2fo blue | 75.00 | 65.00 |

Exist imperf. Value, each $200.

Children Inspecting Stamp
Album — SPAP3

2fo+2fo, Children at stamp exhibition.

**Perf. 12x12½**

| | | | | |
|---|---|---|---|---|
| **1952, Oct. 12** | **Photo.** | | **Wmk. 106** | |
| CB15 | SPAP3 | 1fo + 1fo blue | 8.50 | 7.50 |
| CB16 | SPAP3 | 2fo + 2fo brn red | 8.50 | 7.50 |

Stamp week, Oct. 11-19, 1952.
Exist imperf. Value, set $100.

Globe and
Mailbox
SPAP4

Designs: 1fo+50f, Mobile post office. 2fo+1fo, Telegraph pole. 3fo+1.50fo, Radio. 5fo+2.50fo, Telephone. 10fo+5fo, Post horn.

| | | | | |
|---|---|---|---|---|
| **1957, June 20** | | **Perf. 12x12½, 12** | | |
| | | **Cross in Red** | | |
| | | **Size: 32x21mm** | | |
| CB17 | SPAP4 | 60f + 30f bister brn | .50 | .20 |
| CB18 | SPAP4 | 1fo + 50f lilac | .70 | .35 |
| CB19 | SPAP4 | 2fo + 1fo org ver | .95 | .45 |
| CB20 | SPAP4 | 3fo + 1.50fo blue | 1.25 | .70 |
| CB21 | SPAP4 | 5fo + 2.50fo gray | 1.90 | 1.75 |
| | | **Size: 46x31mm** | | |
| CB22 | SPAP4 | 10fo + 5fo pale grn | 4.00 | 4.00 |
| | | *Nos. CB17-CB22 (6)* | 9.30 | 7.45 |

The surtax was for the benefit of hospitals for postal and telegraph employees.
Exist imperf. Value, set $80.

Parachute of
Fausztusz
Verancsics,
1617
SPAP5

History of Hungarian Aviation: No. CB24, Balloon of David Schwarz, 1897. No. CB25, Monoplane of Ernő Horvath, 1911. No. CB26, PKZ-2 helicopter, 1918.

### Engraved and Lithographed

| | | | | |
|---|---|---|---|---|
| **1967, May 6** | | **Perf. 10½** | | |
| CB23 | SPAP5 | 2fo + 1fo sep & yel | .50 | .50 |
| CB24 | SPAP5 | 2fo + 1fo sep & lt bl | .50 | .50 |
| CB25 | SPAP5 | 2fo + 1fo sep & lt grn | .50 | .50 |
| CB26 | SPAP5 | 2fo + 1fo sep & pink | .50 | .50 |
| a. | | Horiz. strip of 4, #CB23-CB26 | 2.75 | 2.75 |
| b. | | Souv. sheet of 4, #CB23-CB26 | 3.00 | 2.75 |

"AEROFILA 67" International Airmail Exhibition, Budapest, Sept. 3-10.
Exist imperf. Value: strip $20; souvenir sheet $40.

| | | | | |
|---|---|---|---|---|
| **1967, Sept. 3** | | | | |

Aviation, 1967: No. CB27, Parachutist. No. CB28, Helicopter Mi-1. No. CB29, TU-154 jet. No. CB30, Space station Luna 12.

| | | | | |
|---|---|---|---|---|
| CB27 | SPAP5 | 2fo + 1fo slate & lt grn | .50 | .50 |
| CB28 | SPAP5 | 2fo + 1fo slate & buff | .50 | .50 |
| CB29 | SPAP5 | 2fo + 1fo slate & yel | .50 | .50 |
| CB30 | SPAP5 | 2fo + 1fo slate & pink | .50 | .50 |
| a. | | Horiz. strip of 4, #CB27-CB30 | 2.75 | 2.75 |
| b. | | Souv. sheet of 4, #CB27-CB30 | 3.75 | 3.75 |

Issued to commemorate (in connection with AEROFILA 67) the 7th Congress of FISA (Fédération Internationale des Sociétés Aérophilatéliques) and the 40th Stamp Day.
Exist imperf. Value: strip $20; souvenir sheet $35.

### Olympic Games Airmail Type

Design: 2fo+1fo, Equestrian.

| | | | | |
|---|---|---|---|---|
| **1968, Aug. 21** | **Photo.** | | **Perf. 12** | |
| CB31 | AP74 | 2fo + 1fo multi | .35 | .35 |

Exists imperf.

1st Hungarian Airmail Letter, 1918,
Plane — SPAP6

Designs: No. CB33, Letter, 1931, and Zeppelin. No. CB34, Balloon post letter, 1967, and balloon. No. CB35, Letter, 1969, and helicopter.
#CB36a, #C1. b, #C7. c, #C305. d, #C312.

| | | | | |
|---|---|---|---|---|
| **1974, Oct. 19** | **Litho.** | | **Perf. 12** | |
| CB32 | SPAP6 | 2fo + 1fo multi | .95 | .95 |
| CB33 | SPAP6 | 2fo + 1fo multi | .95 | .95 |
| a. | | Pair, #CB32-CB33 | 2.00 | 2.00 |
| CB34 | SPAP6 | 2fo + 1fo multi | .95 | .95 |
| CB35 | SPAP6 | 2fo + 1fo multi | .95 | .95 |
| a. | | Pair, #CB34-CB35 | 2.00 | 2.00 |
| | | *Nos. CB32-CB35 (4)* | 3.80 | 3.80 |
| | | **Souvenir Sheet** | | |
| CB36 | | Sheet of 4 | 3.50 | 3.50 |
| a. | | SPAP6 2fo+1fo any single | .50 | .50 |

AEROFILA, International Airmail Exhibition, Budapest, Oct. 19-27.
No. CB36 contains 4 35x25mm stamps.
Exist imperf. Value: set of 2 pairs $24; souvenir sheet $30.

---

### SPECIAL DELIVERY STAMPS

### Issue of the Monarchy

SD1                    SD2

| | | | | |
|---|---|---|---|---|
| **1916** | **Typo.** | **Wmk. 137** | **Perf. 15** | |
| E1 | SD1 | 2f gray green & red | .20 | .20 |

Exists imperf. Value $4.
For overprints and surcharges see Nos. 1NE1, 2NE1, 4N5, 5NE1, 6NE1, 7NE1, 8NE1, 10NE1, Szeged E1, J7-J8.

### Issue of the Republic

Special Delivery Stamp
of 1916 Overprinted

| | | | | |
|---|---|---|---|---|
| **1919** | | | | |
| E2 | SD1 | 2f gray green & red | .20 | .20 |

Exists imperf. Value $4.

### General Issue

| | | | | |
|---|---|---|---|---|
| **1919** | | | | |
| E3 | SD2 | 2f gray green & red | .20 | .20 |

Exists imperf. Value $5.

---

### REGISTRATION STAMPS

> Catalogue values for unused stamps in this section are for Never Hinged items.

Nos. 625, 609 and 626 Overprinted in Carmine

a                         b

"Ajl." or "Ajánlás" = Registered Letter.

| | | | | |
|---|---|---|---|---|
| **1946** | **Wmk. 266** | | **Perf. 15** | |
| F1 | A118(a) | "Ajl.1." on 20f | .20 | .20 |
| a. | | "Ajl.1." | 50.00 | |
| F2 | A99(a) | "Ajl.2." on 12f | .20 | .20 |
| F3 | A118(b) | "Ajánlás" on 24f | .20 | .20 |
| | | *Nos. F1-F3 (3)* | .60 | .60 |

### POSTAGE DUE STAMPS

### Issues of the Monarchy

D1

**Perf. 11½, 11½x12**

| | | | | |
|---|---|---|---|---|
| **1903** | **Typo.** | | **Wmk. 135** | |
| J1 | D1 | 1f green & blk | .40 | .20 |
| J2 | D1 | 2f green & blk | 1.00 | 1.00 |
| J3 | D1 | 5f green & blk | 3.25 | 4.00 |
| J4 | D1 | 6f green & blk | 2.25 | 3.50 |
| J5 | D1 | 10f green & blk | 25.00 | 2.25 |
| J6 | D1 | 12f green & blk | 1.00 | 1.50 |
| a. | | Perf. 11½ | 80.00 | 50.00 |
| J7 | D1 | 20f green & blk | 7.50 | 1.50 |
| a. | | Perf. 11½ | 100.00 | 24.00 |
| J8 | D1 | 50f green & blk | 8.00 | 9.50 |
| a. | | Perf. 11½ | 125.00 | 110.00 |
| J9 | D1 | 100f green & blk | .90 | .70 |
| | | *Nos. J1-J9 (9)* | 49.30 | 24.15 |

See Nos. J10-J26, J28-J43. For overprints and surcharges see Nos. J27, J44-J50, 1NJ1-1NJ5, 2NJ1-2NJ16, 4NJ2-4NJ3, 5NJ1-5NJ8, 6NJ1-6NJ9, 7NJ1-7NJ4, 9NJ1-9NJ3, 10NJ1-10NJ6, Szeged J1-J6.

| | | | | |
|---|---|---|---|---|
| **1908-09** | | **Wmk. 136** | **Perf. 15** | |
| J10 | D1 | 1f green & black | .45 | .45 |
| J11 | D1 | 2f green & black | .30 | .30 |
| J12 | D1 | 5f green & black | 2.50 | 1.10 |
| J13 | D1 | 6f green & black | .50 | .40 |
| J14 | D1 | 10f green & black | 1.50 | .40 |
| J15 | D1 | 12f green & black | .50 | .40 |
| J16 | D1 | 20f green & black | 10.00 | .45 |
| c. | | Center inverted | | 4,000. |
| J17 | D1 | 50f green & black | .95 | .95 |
| | | *Nos. J10-J17 (8)* | 16.70 | 4.45 |

| | | | | |
|---|---|---|---|---|
| **1905** | **Wmk. 136a** | | **Perf. 11½x12** | |
| J12a | D1 | 5f green & black | 75.00 | 50.00 |
| J13a | D1 | 6f green & black | 7.50 | 7.50 |
| J14a | D1 | 10f green & black | 75.00 | 5.00 |
| J15a | D1 | 12f green & black | 12.50 | 10.00 |
| J17a | D1 | 50f green & black | 7.50 | 5.00 |
| J18 | D1 | 100f green & black | 2.00 | |

| | | | | |
|---|---|---|---|---|
| **1906** | | | **Perf. 15** | |
| J11b | D1 | 2f green & black | 2.50 | 1.90 |
| J12b | D1 | 5f green & black | 2.00 | 1.75 |
| J13b | D1 | 6f green & black | 2.00 | 1.25 |
| J14b | D1 | 10f green & black | 10.00 | .60 |
| J15b | D1 | 12f green & black | .60 | .60 |
| J16b | D1 | 20f green & black | 15.00 | .60 |
| d. | | Center inverted | 3,000. | 3,000. |
| J17b | D1 | 50f green & black | 1.00 | .70 |
| | | *Nos. J11b-J17b (7)* | 33.10 | 7.40 |

| | | | | |
|---|---|---|---|---|
| **1914** | **Wmk. 137 Horiz.** | | **Perf. 15** | |
| J19 | D1 | 1f green & black | .20 | .20 |
| J20 | D1 | 2f green & black | .20 | .20 |
| J21 | D1 | 5f green & black | .40 | .40 |
| J22 | D1 | 6f green & black | .60 | .60 |
| J23 | D1 | 10f green & black | .70 | .70 |
| J24 | D1 | 12f green & black | .35 | .35 |

| | | | | |
|---|---|---|---|---|
| J25 | D1 | 20f green & black | .35 | .35 |
| J26 | D1 | 50f green & black | .40 | .40 |
| | | *Nos. J19-J26 (8)* | 3.20 | 3.20 |

| | | | | |
|---|---|---|---|---|
| **1914** | | **Wmk. 137 Vert.** | | |
| J20a | D1 | 2f green & black | 57.50 | 57.50 |
| J21a | D1 | 5f green & black | 7.50 | 6.25 |
| J22a | D1 | 6f green & black | 16.00 | 16.00 |
| J25a | D1 | 20f green & black | 2,750. | 900.00 |
| J26a | D1 | 50f green & black | 7.50 | 7.50 |

During 1921-24, a number of postage due stamps were punched with three holes prior to sale. See note following No. 105 in the Regular Postage section.

No. J9 Surcharged
in Red

| | | | | |
|---|---|---|---|---|
| **1915** | | | **Wmk. 135** | |
| J27 | D1 | 20f on 100f grn & blk | 1.25 | .90 |
| a. | | On No. J18, Wmk. 136a | 25.00 | 20.00 |

| | | | | |
|---|---|---|---|---|
| **1915-22** | | | **Wmk. 137** | |
| J28 | D1 | 1f green & red | .20 | .20 |
| J29 | D1 | 2f green & red | .20 | .20 |
| J30 | D1 | 5f green & red | .20 | .20 |
| J31 | D1 | 6f green & red | .20 | .20 |
| J32 | D1 | 10f green & red | .20 | .20 |
| J33 | D1 | 12f green & red | .20 | .20 |
| J34 | D1 | 15f green & red | .20 | .20 |
| J35 | D1 | 20f green & red | .20 | .20 |
| J36 | D1 | 30f green & red | .20 | .20 |
| J37 | D1 | 40f green & red ('20) | .20 | .20 |
| J38 | D1 | 50f green & red ('20) | .20 | .20 |
| a. | | Center inverted | 60.00 | |
| J39 | D1 | 120f green & red ('20) | .20 | .20 |
| J40 | D1 | 200f green & red ('20) | .20 | .20 |
| J41 | D1 | 2k green & red ('22) | .40 | .40 |
| J42 | D1 | 5k green & red ('22) | .20 | .20 |
| J43 | D1 | 50k green & red ('22) | .20 | .20 |
| | | *Nos. J28-J43 (16)* | 3.40 | 3.40 |

### Issues of the Republic

Postage Due Stamps
of 1914-18
Overprinted in Black

| | | | | |
|---|---|---|---|---|
| **1918-19** | | | | |
| | | **On Issue of 1914** | | |
| J44 | D1 | 50f green & black | .60 | .60 |
| | | **On Stamps and Type of 1915-18** | | |
| J45 | D1 | 2f green & red | .20 | .20 |
| J46 | D1 | 3f green & red | .20 | .20 |
| a. | | "KOZTARSASAG" omitted | 650.00 | |
| J47 | D1 | 10f green & red | .20 | .20 |
| J48 | D1 | 20f green & red | .20 | .20 |
| J49 | D1 | 40f green & red | .20 | .20 |
| a. | | Inverted overprint | 20.00 | 20.00 |
| J50 | D1 | 50f green & red | .20 | .20 |
| a. | | Center and overprint inverted | 25.00 | 25.00 |
| | | *Nos. J44-J50 (7)* | 1.80 | 1.80 |

### Issues of the Kingdom

D3

| | | | | |
|---|---|---|---|---|
| **1919-20** | | | **Typo.** | |
| J65 | D3 | 2f green & black | .20 | .20 |
| a. | | Inverted center | 1,000. | |
| J66 | D3 | 3f green & black | .20 | .20 |
| J67 | D3 | 20f green & black | .20 | .20 |
| J68 | D3 | 40f green & black | .20 | .20 |
| J69 | D3 | 50f green & black | .20 | .20 |
| | | *Nos. J65-J69 (5)* | 1.00 | 1.00 |

Postage Due Stamps of this type have been overprinted "Magyar Tancskztarsasag" but have not been reported as having been issued without the additional overprint "heads of wheat."
For overprints see Nos. J70-J75.

New Overprint in Black over "Magyar Tanacskoztarsasag"

## 1920

| | | | | |
|---|---|---|---|---|
| J70 | D3 | 2f green & black | .85 | 1.25 |
| J71 | D3 | 3f green & black | 1.25 | 1.25 |
| J72 | D3 | 10f green & black | 1.40 | 2.25 |
| J73 | D3 | 20f green & black | .85 | 1.25 |
| J74 | D3 | 40f green & black | .85 | 1.25 |
| J75 | D3 | 50f green & black | .85 | 1.25 |
| | | *Nos. J70-J75 (6)* | 6.05 | 8.50 |

Counterfeit overprints exist.

### Postage Issues Surcharged

## 1921-25

### Red Surcharge

| | | | | |
|---|---|---|---|---|
| J76 | A9 | 100f on 15f violet | .20 | .20 |
| J77 | A9 | 500f on 15f violet | .20 | .20 |
| J78 | A9 | 2½k on 10f red vio | .20 | .20 |
| J79 | A9 | 3k on 15f violet | .20 | .20 |
| J80 | A9 | 6k on 1½k violet | .20 | 1.50 |
| J81 | A9 | 9k on 40f ol grn | .20 | .20 |
| J82 | A9 | 10k on 2½k green | .20 | 1.25 |
| J83 | A9 | 12k on 60f blk brn | .20 | .20 |
| J84 | A9 | 15k on 1½k vio | .20 | .20 |
| J85 | A9 | 20k on 2½k grn | .20 | 1.10 |
| J86 | A9 | 25k on 1½k vio | .20 | .20 |
| J87 | A9 | 30k on 1½k vio | .20 | .20 |
| J88 | A9 | 40k on 2½k grn | .20 | 1.25 |
| J89 | A9 | 50k on 1½k vio | .20 | .20 |
| J90 | A9 | 100k on 4½k dl vio | .20 | .20 |
| J91 | A9 | 200k on 4½k dl vio | .20 | .20 |
| J92 | A9 | 300k on 4½k dl vio | .20 | .20 |
| J93 | A9 | 500k on 2k grnsh bl | .30 | .20 |
| J94 | A9 | 500k on 3k org brn | .30 | .30 |
| J95 | A9 | 1000k on 2k grnsh bl | .30 | .20 |
| J96 | A9 | 1000k on 3k org brn | .45 | .20 |
| J97 | A9 | 2000k on 2k grnsh bl | .35 | .40 |
| J98 | A9 | 2000k on 3k org brn | .70 | .35 |
| J99 | A9 | 5000k on 5k brown | .90 | 1.75 |
| | | *Nos. J76-J99 (24)* | 6.70 | 11.10 |

Year of issue: 6k, 15k, 25k, 30k, 50k, 1922. 10k, 20k, 40k, 100k — No. J93, Nos. J95, J97, 1923. 5,000k, 1924. Nos. J94, J96, J98, 1925. Others, 1921.

D6

## 1926 Wmk. 133 Litho. Perf. 14, 15

| | | | | |
|---|---|---|---|---|
| J100 | D6 | 1f rose red | .20 | .20 |
| J101 | D6 | 2f rose red | .20 | .20 |
| J102 | D6 | 3f rose red | .20 | .20 |
| J103 | D6 | 4f rose red | .20 | .20 |
| J104 | D6 | 5f rose red | .50 | .25 |
| a. | | Perf. 15 | 1.10 | .45 |
| J105 | D6 | 8f rose red | .20 | .20 |
| J106 | D6 | 10f rose red | .20 | .20 |
| J107 | D6 | 16f rose red | .35 | .20 |
| J108 | D6 | 32f rose red | .50 | .20 |
| J109 | D6 | 40f rose red | .50 | .20 |
| J110 | D6 | 50f rose red | .50 | .40 |
| J111 | D6 | 80f rose red | 1.75 | .65 |
| | | *Nos. J100-J111 (12)* | 5.30 | 3.10 |

Exist imperf. Value, set $100.

See Nos. J117-J123. For surcharges see Nos. J124-J129.

### Nos. C7-C11 Surcharged in Red or Green

## 1926 Wmk. 137 Perf. 14

| | | | | |
|---|---|---|---|---|
| J112 | AP3 | 1f on 500k (R) | .30 | .25 |
| J113 | AP3 | 2f on 1000k (G) | .30 | .20 |
| J114 | AP3 | 3f on 2000k (R) | .30 | .20 |
| | | **Wmk. 133** | | |
| J115 | AP3 | 5f on 5000k (G) | .65 | .55 |
| J116 | AP3 | 10f on 10000k (G) | .45 | .35 |
| | | *Nos. J112-J116 (5)* | 2.00 | 1.65 |

### Type of 1926 Issue

## 1928-32 Wmk. 210 Perf. 14, 15

| | | | | |
|---|---|---|---|---|
| J117 | D6 | 2f rose red | .20 | .20 |
| J118 | D6 | 4f rose red ('32) | .20 | .20 |
| J119 | D6 | 8f rose red | .20 | .20 |
| J120 | D6 | 10f rose red | .20 | .20 |
| J121 | D6 | 16f rose red | .20 | .20 |

| | | | | |
|---|---|---|---|---|
| J122 | D6 | 20f rose red | .30 | .20 |
| J123 | D6 | 40f rose red | .70 | .20 |
| | | *Nos. J117-J123 (7)* | 2.00 | 1.40 |

Exist imperf. Value, set $50.

### Postage Due Stamps of 1926 Surcharged in Black

## 1931-33 Wmk. 133

| | | | | |
|---|---|---|---|---|
| J124 | D6 | 4f on 5f rose red | .35 | .20 |
| J125 | D6 | 10f on 16f rose red | 1.00 | 3.75 |
| J126 | D6 | 10f on 80f rose red ('33) | .45 | .20 |
| J127 | D6 | 12f on 50f rose red ('33) | .45 | .20 |
| J128 | D6 | 20f on 32f rose red | .45 | .30 |
| | | *Nos. J124-J128 (5)* | 2.70 | 4.65 |

### Surcharged on No. J121

## 1931 Wmk. 210 Perf. 15

| | | | | |
|---|---|---|---|---|
| J129 | D6 | 10f on 16f rose red | .85 | 1.25 |

**Catalogue values for unused stamps in this section, from this point to the end of the section, are for Never Hinged items.**

### Figure of Value — D7

## 1934 Photo. Wmk. 210

| | | | | |
|---|---|---|---|---|
| J130 | D7 | 2f ultra | .25 | .20 |
| J131 | D7 | 4f ultra | .25 | .20 |
| J132 | D7 | 6f ultra | .25 | .20 |
| J133 | D7 | 8f ultra | .25 | .20 |
| J134 | D7 | 10f ultra | .25 | .20 |
| J135 | D7 | 12f ultra | .25 | .20 |
| J136 | D7 | 16f ultra | .25 | .20 |
| J137 | D7 | 20f ultra | .35 | .20 |
| J138 | D7 | 40f ultra | .75 | .20 |
| J139 | D7 | 80f ultra | 1.50 | .30 |
| | | *Nos. J130-J139 (10)* | 4.35 | 2.10 |

Exist imperf. Value, set $60.

### Coat of Arms and Post Horn — D8

## 1941

| | | | | |
|---|---|---|---|---|
| J140 | D8 | 2f brown red | .20 | .20 |
| J141 | D8 | 4f brown red | .20 | .20 |
| J142 | D8 | 6f brown red | .20 | .20 |
| J143 | D8 | 8f brown red | .20 | .20 |
| J144 | D8 | 10f brown red | .25 | .20 |
| J145 | D8 | 12f brown red | .30 | .20 |
| J146 | D8 | 16f brown red | .40 | .20 |
| J147 | D8 | 20f brown red | .50 | .20 |
| J148 | D8 | 40f brown red | .75 | .25 |
| | | *Nos. J140-J150 (9)* | 3.00 | 1.85 |

Exist imperf. Value, set $20.

## 1941-44 Wmk. 266

| | | | | |
|---|---|---|---|---|
| J151 | D8 | 2f brown red | .20 | .20 |
| J152 | D8 | 3f brown red | .20 | .20 |
| J153 | D8 | 4f brown red | .20 | .20 |
| J154 | D8 | 6f brown red | .20 | .20 |
| J155 | D8 | 8f brown red | .20 | .20 |
| J156 | D8 | 10f brown red | .20 | .20 |
| J157 | D8 | 12f brown red | .20 | .20 |
| J158 | D8 | 16f brown red | .20 | .20 |
| J159 | D8 | 18f brown red ('44) | .25 | .20 |
| J160 | D8 | 20f brown red | .20 | .20 |
| J161 | D8 | 24f brown red | .25 | .20 |
| J162 | D8 | 30f brown red ('44) | .20 | .20 |
| J163 | D8 | 36f brown red ('44) | .25 | .20 |
| J164 | D8 | 40f brown red | .20 | .20 |
| J165 | D8 | 50f brown red | .20 | .20 |
| J166 | D8 | 60f brown red ('44) | .30 | .20 |
| | | *Nos. J151-J166 (16)* | 3.40 | 3.20 |

Exist imperf. Value, set $25.
For surcharges see Nos. J167-J185.

### Issues of the Republic

### Types of Hungary Postage Due Stamps, 1941-44, Surcharged in Carmine

## 1945 Wmk. 266 Photo. Perf. 15

### Blue Surface-tinted Paper

| | | | | |
|---|---|---|---|---|
| J167 | D8 | 10f on 2f brn red | .20 | .20 |
| J168 | D8 | 10f on 3f brn red | .20 | .20 |
| J169 | D8 | 20f on 4f brn red | .20 | .20 |
| J170 | D8 | 20f on 6f brn red | 9.50 | 9.50 |
| J171 | D8 | 20f on 8f brn red | .20 | .20 |
| J172 | D8 | 40f on 12f brn red | .20 | .20 |
| J173 | D8 | 40f on 16f brn red | .20 | .20 |
| J174 | D8 | 40f on 18f brn red | .20 | .20 |
| J175 | D8 | 60f on 24f brn red | .20 | .20 |
| J176 | D8 | 80f on 30f brn red | .20 | .20 |
| J177 | D8 | 90f on 36f brn red | .20 | .20 |
| J178 | D8 | 1p on 10f brn red | .20 | .20 |
| J179 | D8 | 1p on 40f brn red | .20 | .20 |
| J180 | D8 | 2p on 12f brn red | .20 | .20 |
| J181 | D8 | 2p on 40f brn red | .20 | .20 |
| J182 | D8 | 2p on 60f brn red | .20 | .20 |

### Surcharged in Black, Thicker Type

| | | | | |
|---|---|---|---|---|
| J183 | D8 | 10p on 3f brn red | .20 | .20 |
| J184 | D8 | 12p on 36f brn red | .20 | .20 |
| J185 | D8 | 20p on 24f brn red | .20 | .20 |
| | | *Nos. J167-J185 (19)* | 13.10 | 13.10 |

D9

## 1946-50 Wmk. 210 Perf. 15

### Numerals in Deep Magenta

| | | | | |
|---|---|---|---|---|
| J186 | D9 | 4f magenta | .50 | .20 |
| J187 | D9 | 10f magenta | 1.25 | .20 |
| J188 | D9 | 20f magenta | .50 | .20 |
| J189 | D9 | 30f magenta | .50 | .20 |
| J190 | D9 | 40f magenta | .75 | .20 |
| J191 | D9 | 50f mag ('50) | 2.25 | .50 |
| J192 | D9 | 60f magenta | 1.50 | .20 |
| J193 | D9 | 1.20fo magenta | 2.25 | .25 |
| J194 | D9 | 2fo magenta | 3.75 | .30 |
| | | *Nos. J186-J194 (9)* | 13.25 | 2.25 |

## 1951 Wmk. 106

### Numerals in Deep Magenta

| | | | | |
|---|---|---|---|---|
| J194A | D9 | 4f magenta | .20 | .20 |
| J194B | D9 | 10f magenta | .20 | .20 |
| J194C | D9 | 20f magenta | 1.25 | .20 |
| j. | | "fiellr" | 35.00 | 7.50 |
| J194D | D9 | 30f magenta | 1.50 | .20 |
| J194E | D9 | 40f magenta | .50 | .20 |
| J194F | D9 | 50f magenta | 1.00 | .20 |
| J194G | D9 | 60f magenta | .85 | .20 |
| J194H | D9 | 1.20fo magenta | 3.50 | .20 |
| J194I | D9 | 2fo magenta | 3.00 | .20 |
| | | *Nos. J194A-J194I (9)* | 12.00 | 1.80 |

Nos. J194A-J194I are found in both large format (about 18x22mm) and small (about 17x21mm).

D10      D11

## 1951 Unwmk. Typo. Perf. 14½x15

### Paper with Vertical Lines in Green

### Revenue Stamps with Blue Surcharge

| | | | | |
|---|---|---|---|---|
| J195 | D10 | 8f dark brown | .20 | .20 |
| J196 | D10 | 10f dark brown | .20 | .20 |
| J197 | D10 | 12f dark brown | .40 | .40 |
| | | *Nos. J195-J197 (3)* | .80 | .80 |

## 1951 Wmk. 106 Photo. Perf. 14½

| | | | | |
|---|---|---|---|---|
| J198 | D11 | 4f brown | .20 | .20 |
| J199 | D11 | 6f brown | .20 | .20 |
| J200 | D11 | 8f brown | .20 | .20 |
| J201 | D11 | 10f brown | .20 | .20 |
| J202 | D11 | 14f brown | .35 | .25 |
| J203 | D11 | 20f brown | .20 | .20 |
| J204 | D11 | 30f brown | .20 | .20 |
| J205 | D11 | 40f brown | .20 | .20 |
| J206 | D11 | 50f brown | .25 | .20 |
| J207 | D11 | 60f brown | .30 | .20 |

| | | | | |
|---|---|---|---|---|
| J208 | D11 | 1.20fo brown | .30 | .20 |
| J209 | D11 | 2fo brown | .50 | .20 |
| | | *Nos. J198-J209 (12)* | 3.10 | 2.55 |

Exist imperf. Value, set $25.

D12      D13

### Photo., Numeral Typo. in Black

## 1953

### Numerals 3mm High

| | | | | |
|---|---|---|---|---|
| J210 | D12 | 4f dull green | .20 | .20 |
| J211 | D12 | 6f dull green | .20 | .20 |
| J212 | D12 | 8f dull green | .20 | .20 |
| J213 | D12 | 10f dull green | .20 | .20 |
| J214 | D12 | 12f dull green | .20 | .20 |
| J215 | D12 | 14f dull green | .20 | .20 |
| J216 | D12 | 16f dull green | .20 | .20 |
| J217 | D12 | 20f dull green | .20 | .20 |
| J218 | D12 | 24f dull green | .20 | .20 |
| J219 | D12 | 30f dull green | .20 | .20 |
| J220 | D12 | 36f dull green | .20 | .20 |
| J221 | D12 | 40f dull green | .20 | .20 |
| J222 | D12 | 50f dull green | .20 | .20 |
| J223 | D12 | 60f dull green | .20 | .20 |
| J224 | D12 | 70f dull green | .25 | .20 |
| J225 | D12 | 80f dull green | .30 | .20 |

### Numerals 4½mm High

| | | | | |
|---|---|---|---|---|
| J226 | D12 | 1.20fo dull green | .40 | .20 |
| J227 | D12 | 2fo dull green | .75 | .20 |
| a. | | Small "2" (3mm high) | 4.00 | 1.00 |
| | | *Nos. J210-J227 (18)* | 4.50 | 3.60 |

1st Hungarian postage due stamp, 50th anniv.

Exist imperf. Value, set $30.

### Photo., Numeral Typo. in Black on Nos. J228-J243

## 1958 Wmk. 106 Perf. 14½

### Size: 21x16½mm

| | | | | |
|---|---|---|---|---|
| J228 | D13 | 4f red | .20 | .20 |
| J229 | D13 | 6f red | .20 | .20 |
| J230 | D13 | 8f red | .20 | .20 |
| J231 | D13 | 10f red | .20 | .20 |
| J232 | D13 | 12f red | .20 | .20 |
| J233 | D13 | 14f red | .20 | .20 |
| J234 | D13 | 16f red | .20 | .20 |
| J235 | D13 | 20f red | .20 | .20 |
| J236 | D13 | 24f red | .20 | .20 |
| J237 | D13 | 30f red | .20 | .20 |
| J238 | D13 | 36f red | .20 | .20 |
| J239 | D13 | 40f red | .20 | .20 |
| J240 | D13 | 50f red | .20 | .20 |
| J241 | D13 | 60f red | .20 | .20 |
| J242 | D13 | 70f red | .20 | .20 |
| J243 | D13 | 80f red | .25 | .20 |

### Perf. 12

### Size: 31x21mm

| | | | | |
|---|---|---|---|---|
| J244 | D13 | 1.20fo dk red brn | .35 | .20 |
| J245 | D13 | 2fo dk red brn | .50 | .25 |
| | | *Nos. J228-J245 (18)* | 4.10 | 3.65 |

Exist imperf. Value, set $15.

### Photo., Numeral Typo. in Black on Nos. J246-J261

## 1965-69 Unwmk. Perf. 11½

### Size: 21x16½mm

| | | | | |
|---|---|---|---|---|
| J246 | D13 | 4f red | .20 | .20 |
| J247 | D13 | 6f red | .20 | .20 |
| J248 | D13 | 8f red | .20 | .20 |
| J249 | D13 | 10f red | .20 | .20 |
| J250 | D13 | 12f red | .20 | .20 |
| J251 | D13 | 14f red | .20 | .20 |
| J252 | D13 | 16f red | .20 | .20 |
| J253 | D13 | 20f red | .20 | .20 |
| J254 | D13 | 24f red | .20 | .20 |
| J255 | D13 | 30f red | .20 | .20 |
| J256 | D13 | 36f red | .20 | .20 |
| J257 | D13 | 40f red | .20 | .20 |
| J258 | D13 | 50f red | .20 | .20 |
| J259 | D13 | 60f red | .20 | .20 |
| J260 | D13 | 70f red | .20 | .20 |
| J261 | D13 | 80f red | .20 | .20 |

### Perf. 11½x12

### Size: 31x21mm

| | | | | |
|---|---|---|---|---|
| J262 | D13 | 1fo dk red brn ('69) | .20 | .20 |
| J263 | D13 | 1.20fo dk red brn | .25 | .20 |
| J264 | D13 | 2fo dk red brn | .30 | .20 |
| J265 | D13 | 4fo dk red brn ('69) | .50 | .20 |
| | | *Nos. J246-J265 (20)* | 4.45 | 4.00 |

Mail Plane and Truck — D14

## Postal History — D15

Designs: 20f, Money order canceling machine. 40f, Scales in self-service P.O. 80f, Automat for registering parcels. 1fo, Keypunch operator. 1.20fo, Mail plane and truck. 2fo, Diesel mail train. 3fo, Mailman on motorcycle with sidecar. 4fo, Rural mail delivery. 8fo, Automatic letter sorting machine. 10fo, Postman riding motorcycle.

| | | 1973-85 | Photo. | Perf. 11 |
|---|---|---|---|---|
| | | | Size: 21x18mm | |
| J266 | D14 | 20f brown & ver | .20 | .20 |
| J267 | D14 | 40f dl bl & ver | .20 | .20 |
| J268 | D14 | 80f violet & ver | .20 | .20 |
| J269 | D14 | 1fo ol grn & ver | .20 | .20 |
| | | | Perf. 12x11½ | |
| | | | Size: 28x22mm | |
| J270 | D14 | 1.20fo green & ver | .20 | .20 |
| J271 | D14 | 2fo lilac & ver | .20 | .20 |
| J272 | D14 | 3fo brt blue & ver | .25 | .20 |
| J273 | D14 | 4fo org brn & ver | .35 | .20 |
| J274 | D14 | 8fo deep mag & dark red | 1.10 | .30 |
| J275 | D14 | 10fo green & dark red | 1.25 | .35 |
| | | Nos. J266-J275 (10) | 4.15 | 2.25 |

Issued: 20f-4fo, 12/1973; 8fo, 10fo, 12/16/85.

| | | 1987, Dec. 10 | Litho. | Perf. 12 |
|---|---|---|---|---|

Designs: Excerpt from 18th cent. letter, innovations in letter carrying.

| J276 | D15 | 1fo Foot messenger, 16th cent. | .20 | .20 |
|---|---|---|---|---|
| J277 | D15 | 4fo Post rider, 17th cent. | .55 | .30 |
| J278 | D15 | 6fo Horse-drawn mail coach, 18th cent. | .75 | .45 |
| J279 | D15 | 8fo Railroad mail car, 19th cent. | 1.00 | .60 |
| J280 | D15 | 10fo Mail truck, 20th cent. | 1.25 | .65 |
| J281 | D15 | 20fo Airplane, 20th cent. | 2.25 | 1.25 |
| | | Nos. J276-J281 (6) | 6.00 | 3.45 |

## OFFICIAL STAMPS

During 1921-24, a number of Official stamps were punched with three holes prior to sale. See note following No. 105 in the Regular Postage section.

O1

| | | 1921-23 | Wmk. 137 | Typo. | Perf. 15 |
|---|---|---|---|---|---|
| O1 | O1 | 10f brn vio & blk | | .20 | .20 |
| O2 | O1 | 20f ol brn & blk | | .20 | .20 |
| a. | | "HIVATALOS" inverted | | | 10,000. |
| O3 | O1 | 60f blk brn & blk | | .20 | .20 |
| O4 | O1 | 100f dl rose & blk | | .20 | .20 |
| O5 | O1 | 250f bl & blk | | .20 | .20 |
| O6 | O1 | 350f gray & blk | | .25 | .20 |
| O7 | O1 | 500f lt brn & blk | | .25 | .20 |
| O8 | O1 | 1000f lil brn & blk | | .25 | .20 |
| O9 | O1 | 5k brn ('23) | | .20 | .20 |
| O10 | O1 | 10k choc ('23) | | .20 | .20 |
| O11 | O1 | 15k gray blk ('23) | | .20 | .20 |
| O12 | O1 | 25k org ('23) | | .20 | .20 |
| O13 | O1 | 50k brn & red ('22) | | .20 | .20 |
| O14 | O1 | 100k bis & red ('22) | | .20 | .20 |
| O15 | O1 | 150k grn & red ('23) | | .20 | .20 |
| O16 | O1 | 300k dl red & red ('23) | | .25 | .20 |
| O17 | O1 | 350k vio & red ('23) | | .30 | .20 |
| O18 | O1 | 500k org & red ('22) | | .30 | .20 |
| O19 | O1 | 600k ol bis & red ('23) | | .80 | .60 |
| O20 | O1 | 1000k bl & red ('22) | | 1.20 | .20 |
| | | Nos. O1-O20 (20) | | 6.00 | 4.40 |

Counterfeits of No. O2a exist.

---

Stamps of 1921 Surcharged in Red

| 1922 | | | | |
|---|---|---|---|---|
| O21 | O1 | 15k on 20f ol brn & blk | .20 | .20 |
| O22 | O1 | 25k on 60f blk brn & blk | .20 | .20 |

Stamps of 1921 Overprinted in Red

| 1923 | | | | |
|---|---|---|---|---|
| O23 | O1 | 350k gray & blk | .25 | .20 |

### With Additional Surcharge of New Value in Red

| O24 | O1 | 150k on 100f dl rose & blk | .30 | .20 |
|---|---|---|---|---|
| O25 | O1 | 2000k on 250f bl & blk | .60 | .40 |
| | | Nos. O23-O25 (3) | 1.15 | .80 |

| 1923-24 | Paper with Gray Moiré on Face | | | |
|---|---|---|---|---|
| O26 | O1 | 500k org & red ('23) | 2.10 | .25 |
| O27 | O1 | 1000k bl & red ('23) | 2.10 | .25 |
| O28 | O1 | 3000k vio & red ('24) | 2.10 | 1.25 |
| O29 | O1 | 5000k bl & red ('24) | 2.40 | 1.50 |
| | | Nos. O26-O29 (4) | 8.70 | 3.25 |

| 1924 | | Wmk. 133 | | |
|---|---|---|---|---|
| O30 | O1 | 500k orange & red | 1.40 | 1.00 |
| O31 | O1 | 1000k blue & red | 1.40 | 1.00 |

---

## NEWSPAPER STAMPS

### Issues of the Monarchy

St. Stephen's Crown and Post Horn
N1     N2

| 1871-72 | Litho. (#P1), Typo. (#P2) Unwmk. | | Imperf. |
|---|---|---|---|
| P1 | N1 | (1k) ver red | 50.00 20.00 |
| P2 | N2 | (1k) rose red ('72) | 10.00 2.00 |
| a. | | (1k) vermilion | 10.00 2.00 |
| b. | | Printed on both sides | |

Reprints of No. P2 are watermarked. Value, $450.

Letter with Crown and Post Horn — N3    N5

| 1874 | | | | |
|---|---|---|---|---|
| P3 | N3 | 1k orange | | 3.75 .35 |

| 1881 | | Wmk. "kr" in Oval (132) | | |
|---|---|---|---|---|
| P4 | N3 | 1k orange | 1.25 | .20 |
| a. | | 1k lemon yellow | 16.00 | 3.50 |
| b. | | Printed on both sides | | |

| 1898 | | | Wmk. 135 | |
|---|---|---|---|---|
| P5 | N3 | 1k orange | 1.25 | .20 |

See watermark note after No. 46.

| 1900 | | Wmk. Crown in Circle (135) | | |
|---|---|---|---|---|
| P6 | N5 | (2f) red orange | .75 | .20 |

| 1905 | | Wmk. Crown (136a) | | |
|---|---|---|---|---|
| P7 | N5 | (2f) red orange | 1.00 | .20 |
| a. | | Wmk. 136 ('08) | 1.00 | .20 |

| 1914-22 | | Wmk. Double Cross (137) | | |
|---|---|---|---|---|
| P8 | N5 | (2f) orange | .20 | .20 |
| a. | | Wmk. horiz. | 4.50 | 3.75 |

---

| P9 | N5 | (10f) deep blue ('20) | .20 | .20 |
|---|---|---|---|---|
| P10 | N5 | (20f) lilac ('22) | .20 | .20 |
| | | Nos. P8-P10 (3) | .60 | .60 |

For overprints and surcharges see Nos. 1NJ6-1NJ10, 1NP1, 2NP1, 5NP1, 6NP1, 8NP1, 10NP1, Szeged P1.

## NEWSPAPER TAX STAMPS

### Issues of the Monarchy

NT1     NT2

NT3

| | | Wmk. 91; Unwmk. from 1871 | | |
|---|---|---|---|---|
| 1868 | | Typo. | Imperf. | |
| PR1 | NT1 | 1k blue | 5.50 | 1.50 |
| a. | | Pair, one sideways | | |
| PR2 | NT2 | 2k brown | 17.50 | 15.00 |
| a. | | 2k red brown | 275.00 | 47.50 |
| 1868 | | | | |
| PR2B | NT3 | 1k blue | 9,500. | 6,000. |

No. PR2B was issued for the Military Border District only. All used stamps are precanceled (newspaper text printed on the stamp). A similar 2k was not issued.

| 1889-90 | | Wmk. "kr" in Oval (132) | | |
|---|---|---|---|---|
| PR3 | NT1 | 1k blue | 2.00 | .80 |
| PR4 | NT2 | 2k brown | 5.50 | 4.00 |

| 1898 | | Wmk. Crown in Oval (135) | | |
|---|---|---|---|---|
| PR5 | NT1 | 1k blue | 7.50 | 5.50 |

These stamps did not pay postage, but represented a fiscal tax collected by the postal authorities on newspapers.
Nos. PR3 and PR5 have a tall "k" in "kr."

## PARCEL POST STAMPS

Nos. 629, 613, 612, 615, 630, 667 and Type of 1943-45 Overprinted in Black or Carmine

a     b

"Cs." or "Csomag"=Parcel

| 1946 | | Wmk. 266 | Perf. 15 | |
|---|---|---|---|---|
| Q1 | A118 | "Cs. 5-1." on 70f | .20 | .20 |
| Q2 | A109 | "Cs. 5-1." on 30f | 22.50 | 20.00 |
| Q3 | A99 | "Cs. 5-2." on 24f | .20 | .20 |
| Q4 | A118 | "Cs. 10-1." on 70f | .20 | .20 |
| Q5 | A118 | "Cs. 10-1." on 80f | 27.50 | 26.00 |
| Q6 | A118 | "Cs. 10-2." on 80f | .20 | .20 |
| Q7 | A99 | "Csomag 5kg." on 2p on 4f (C+Bk) | .20 | .20 |
| Q8 | A118 | "Csomag 10kg." on 30f copper red, bl | .20 | .20 |
| | | Nos. Q1-Q8 (8) | 51.20 | 47.20 |

No. Q8 was not issued without overprint.

> Catalogue values for unused stamps in this section, from this point to the end of the section, are for Never Hinged items.

No. 796 Surcharged with New Value in Red or Black

| 1954 | | Wmk. 210 | | |
|---|---|---|---|---|
| Q9 | A144 | 1.70fo on 1.40fo | 1.40 | .20 |
| Q10 | A144 | 2fo on 1.40fo (Bk) | 1.60 | .30 |
| Q11 | A144 | 3fo on 1.40fo | 2.00 | .50 |
| | | Nos. Q9-Q11 (3) | 5.00 | 1.00 |
| | | Set, hinged | 1.80 | |

## OCCUPATION STAMPS

### Issued under French Occupation

### ARAD ISSUE

The overprints on this issue have been extensively forged. Even the inexpensive values are difficult to find with genuine overprints. Values are for genuine overprints. Collectors should be aware that stamps sold "as is" are likely to be forgeries, and unexpertized collections should be assumed to consist of mostly forged stamps. Education plus working with knowledgeable dealers is mandatory in this collecting area. More valuable stamps should be expertized.

Stamps of Hungary Overprinted in Red or Blue

On Issue of 1916-18

| 1919 | | Wmk. 137 | Perf. 15, 14 | |
|---|---|---|---|---|
| 1N1 | A9 | 2f brn org (R) | 1.60 | 1.60 |
| 1N2 | A9 | 3f red lil (R) | .75 | .75 |
| 1N3 | A9 | 5f green (R) | 20.00 | 20.00 |
| 1N4 | A9 | 6f grnsh bl (R) | 1.90 | 1.90 |
| a. | | Inverted overprint | 30.00 | 30.00 |
| 1N5 | A9 | 10f rose red | 4.00 | 4.00 |
| 1N6 | A9 | 15f violet (R) | 1.75 | 1.75 |
| a. | | Double overprint | 50.00 | 50.00 |
| 1N7 | A9 | 20f gray brn (R) | 50.00 | 50.00 |
| 1N8 | A9 | 35f brown (R) | 65.00 | 65.00 |
| 1N9 | A9 | 40f ol grn (R) | 37.50 | 37.50 |
| 1N10 | A10 | 50f red vio & lil | 6.00 | 6.00 |
| 1N11 | A10 | 75f brt bl & pale bl | 2.00 | 2.00 |
| 1N12 | A10 | 80f grn & pale grn | 2.75 | 2.75 |
| 1N13 | A10 | 1k red brn & cl | 15.00 | 15.00 |
| 1N14 | A10 | 2k ol brn & bis | 3.00 | 3.00 |
| a. | | Inverted overprint | 50.00 | 50.00 |
| 1N15 | A10 | 3k dk vio & ind | 17.50 | 17.50 |
| 1N16 | A10 | 5k dk brn & lt brn | 13.50 | 13.50 |
| 1N17 | A10 | 10k vio brn & vio | 70.00 | 70.00 |
| | | Nos. 1N1-1N17 (17) | 312.25 | 312.25 |

With Additional Surcharge:

a     b

c     d

| 1N18 | A9 (a) | 45f on 2f brn org | 8.00 | 8.00 |
|---|---|---|---|---|
| 1N19 | A9 (b) | 45f on 2f brn org | 8.00 | 8.00 |
| 1N20 | A9 (c) | 50f on 3f red lil | 8.00 | 8.00 |
| 1N21 | A9 (d) | 50f on 3f red lil | 8.00 | 8.00 |
| | | Nos. 1N18-1N21 (4) | 32.00 | 32.00 |

| | | Overprinted On Issue of 1918 | | |
|---|---|---|---|---|
| 1N22 | A11 | 10f scarlet (Bl) | 60.00 | 60.00 |
| 1N23 | A11 | 20f dk brn | .90 | .90 |
| 1N24 | A11 | 25f brt bl | 2.40 | 2.40 |
| a. | | Inverted overprint | 30.00 | 30.00 |
| 1N25 | A12 | 40f ol grn | 3.25 | 3.25 |
| | | Nos. 1N22-1N25 (4) | 66.55 | 66.55 |

| | | Ovptd. On Issue of 1918-19, Overprinted "Koztarsasag" | | |
|---|---|---|---|---|
| 1N26 | A9 | 2f brn org | 2.00 | 2.00 |
| a. | | Inverted overprint | 50.00 | 50.00 |
| 1N27 | A9 | 4f slate gray | 2.00 | 2.00 |
| 1N28 | A9 | 5f green | .60 | .60 |
| 1N29 | A9 | 6f grnsh bl | 12.00 | 12.00 |
| a. | | Inverted overprint | 30.00 | 30.00 |
| 1N30 | A9 | 10f rose red (Bl) | 60.00 | 60.00 |
| 1N31 | A9 | 20f gray brn | 15.00 | 15.00 |
| 1N32 | A11 | 25f brt bl | 2.75 | 2.75 |
| a. | | Inverted overprint | 30.00 | 30.00 |
| 1N33 | A9 | 40f ol grn | 2.00 | 2.00 |
| 1N34 | A12 | 40f ol grn | 60.00 | 60.00 |
| a. | | Inverted overprint | 125.00 | 125.00 |

| | | | | |
|---|---|---|---|---|
| 1N35 | A12 | 50f lilac | 8.00 | 8.00 |
| 1N36 | A10 | 1k red brn & cl (Bl) | 3.25 | 3.25 |
| 1N37 | A10 | 3k dk vio & ind (Bl) | 15.00 | 15.00 |
| | | *Nos. 1N26-1N37 (12)* | *182.60* | *182.60* |

**No. 1N36 With Additional Surcharge:**

e

f

| | | | | |
|---|---|---|---|---|
| 1N38 | A10 (e) | 10k on 1k | 13.50 | 13.50 |
| 1N39 | A10 (f) | 10k on 1k | 13.50 | 13.50 |

**On Issue of 1919**
**Inscribed "MAGYAR POSTA"**

| | | | | |
|---|---|---|---|---|
| 1N40 | A13 | 10f red (Bl) | 6.50 | 6.50 |

### SEMI-POSTAL STAMPS

Hungarian Semi-Postal Stamps of 1916-17 Overprinted "Occupation francaise" in Blue or Red

**1919** **Wmk. 137** **Perf. 15**

| | | | | |
|---|---|---|---|---|
| 1NB1 | SP3 | 10f + 2f rose red | 65.00 | 65.00 |
| 1NB2 | SP4 | 15f + 2f dl vio (R) | 9.50 | 9.50 |
| 1NB3 | SP5 | 40f + 2f brn car | 12.50 | 12.50 |
| | | *Nos. 1NB1-1NB3 (3)* | *87.00* | *87.00* |

### SPECIAL DELIVERY STAMP

Hungarian Special Delivery Stamp of 1916 Overprinted "Occupation francaise"

**1919** **Wmk. 137** **Perf. 15**

| | | | | |
|---|---|---|---|---|
| 1NE1 | SD1 | 2f gray green & red | .60 | .60 |

### POSTAGE DUE STAMPS

Hungarian Postage Due Stamps of 1915 Overprinted "Occupation francaise"

**1919** **Wmk. 137** **Perf. 15**

| | | | | |
|---|---|---|---|---|
| 1NJ1 | D1 | 2f green & red | 7.50 | 7.50 |
| 1NJ2 | D1 | 6f green & red | 4.00 | 4.00 |
| 1NJ3 | D1 | 12f green & red | 32.50 | 32.50 |
| 1NJ4 | D1 | 15f green & red | 42.50 | 42.50 |
| 1NJ5 | D1 | 20f green & red | 3.00 | 3.00 |

Hungarian Newspaper Stamp of 1914 Surcharged

| | | | | |
|---|---|---|---|---|
| 1NJ6 | N5 | 12f on 2f orange | 8.00 | 8.00 |
| 1NJ7 | N5 | 15f on 2f orange | 8.00 | 8.00 |
| 1NJ8 | N5 | 30f on 2f orange | 8.00 | 8.00 |
| a. | | Double surcharge | 50.00 | 50.00 |
| 1NJ9 | N5 | 50f on 2f orange | 8.00 | 8.00 |
| 1NJ10 | N5 | 100f on 2f orange | 8.00 | 8.00 |
| | | *Nos. 1NJ1-1NJ10 (10)* | *129.50* | *129.50* |

### NEWSPAPER STAMP

Hungarian Newspaper Stamp of 1914 Overprinted "Occupation francaise"

**1919** **Wmk. 137** **Imperf.**

| | | | | |
|---|---|---|---|---|
| 1NP1 | N5 | (2f) orange | 1.25 | 1.25 |

### ISSUED UNDER ROMANIAN OCCUPATION

### FIRST DEBRECEN ISSUE

The overprints on this issue have been extensively forged. Even the inexpensive values are difficult to find with genuine overprints. The more extensive note before No. 1N1 also applies to Nos. 2N1-2NP16.

Hungarian Stamps of 1913-19 Overprinted in Blue, Red or Black

**1919** **Wmk. 137** **Perf. 15, 14½x14**

**On Stamps of 1913**

| | | | | |
|---|---|---|---|---|
| 2N1 | A4 | 2f olive yellow | 90.00 | 90.00 |
| 2N2 | A4 | 3f orange | 125.00 | 125.00 |
| 2N3 | A4 | 6f olive grn (R) | 50.00 | 50.00 |

**On Stamps of 1916**

| | | | | |
|---|---|---|---|---|
| 2N4 | A8 | 10f rose | 75.00 | 75.00 |
| 2N5 | A8 | 15f violet (Bk) | 65.00 | 65.00 |

**On Stamps of 1916-18**

| | | | | |
|---|---|---|---|---|
| 2N6 | A9 | 2f brown org | 1.50 | 1.50 |
| 2N7 | A9 | 3f red lilac | .70 | .70 |
| 2N8 | A9 | 5f green | 4.75 | 4.75 |
| 2N9 | A9 | 6f grnsh bl (R) | 1.60 | 1.60 |
| 2N10 | A9 | 15f violet (Bk) | .80 | .80 |
| a. | | Red overprint | 75.00 | 75.00 |
| 2N11 | A9 | 20f gray brn | 125.00 | 125.00 |
| 2N12 | A9 | 25f dull bl (Bk) | 4.50 | 4.50 |
| 2N13 | A9 | 35f brown | 60.00 | 60.00 |
| 2N14 | A9 | 40f olive grn | 3.75 | 3.75 |
| 2N15 | A10 | 50f vio red & lil | 8.25 | 8.25 |
| 2N16 | A10 | 75f brt bl & pale bl (Bk) | 2.00 | 2.00 |
| 2N17 | A10 | 80f grn & pale grn (R) | 3.50 | 3.50 |
| 2N18 | A10 | 1k red brn & cl | 4.75 | 4.75 |
| 2N19 | A10 | 2k ol brn & bis (Bk) | 1.75 | 1.75 |
| 2N20 | A10 | 3k dk vio & ind (R) | 30.00 | 30.00 |
| a. | | Blue overprint | 65.00 | 65.00 |
| b. | | Black overprint | 250.00 | 250.00 |
| 2N21 | A10 | 5k dk brn & lt brn (Bk) | 27.50 | 27.50 |
| 2N22 | A10 | 10k vio brn & vio | 160.00 | 160.00 |

**With New Value Added**

| | | | | |
|---|---|---|---|---|
| 2N23 | A9 | 35f on 3f red lil | 2.00 | 2.00 |
| 2N24 | A9 | 45f on 2f brn org | 2.00 | 2.00 |
| 2N25 | A10 | 3k on 75f brt bl & pale bl (Bk) | 4.00 | 4.00 |
| 2N26 | A10 | 5k on 75f brt bl & pale bl (Bk) | 3.75 | 3.75 |
| 2N27 | A10 | 10k on 80f grn & pale grn (R) | 3.50 | 3.50 |

**On Stamps of 1918**

| | | | | |
|---|---|---|---|---|
| 2N28 | A11 | 10f scarlet | 60.00 | 60.00 |
| 2N28A | A11 | 15f violet (R) | 75.00 | 75.00 |
| b. | | Black overprint | 125.00 | 125.00 |
| 2N29 | A11 | 20f dk brown (R) | 6.25 | 6.25 |
| a. | | Black overprint | 30.00 | 30.00 |
| b. | | Blue overprint | 75.00 | 75.00 |
| 2N30 | A11 | 25f brt blue | 7.00 | 7.00 |
| a. | | Black overprint | 75.00 | 75.00 |
| 2N31 | A12 | 40f olive green | 3.00 | 3.00 |
| 2N32 | A12 | 50f lilac | 50.00 | 50.00 |

**On Stamps of 1918-19, Overprinted "Koztarsasag"**

| | | | | |
|---|---|---|---|---|
| 2N33 | A9 | 2f brn org | 3.00 | 3.00 |
| 2N34 | A9 | 3f red lilac | 65.00 | 65.00 |
| 2N35 | A9 | 4f sl gray (R) | 1.75 | 1.75 |
| 2N36 | A9 | 5f green | .65 | .65 |
| 2N37 | A9 | 6f grnsh bl (R) | 30.00 | 30.00 |
| 2N38 | A9 | 10f rose red | 37.50 | 37.50 |
| 2N39 | A11 | 10f scarlet | 25.00 | 25.00 |
| 2N40 | A11 | 15f dp vio (Bk) | 45.00 | 45.00 |
| a. | | Red overprint | 125.00 | 125.00 |

| | | | | |
|---|---|---|---|---|
| 2N41 | A9 | 20f gray brn | 3.25 | 3.25 |
| 2N42 | A11 | 20f dk brn (Bk) | 37.50 | 37.50 |
| b. | | Red overprint | 50.00 | 50.00 |
| 2N43 | A9 | 40f olive grn | 1.75 | 1.75 |
| 2N44 | A10 | 1k red brn & cl | 2.75 | 2.75 |
| 2N45 | A10 | 2k ol brn & bis (Bk) | 60.00 | 60.00 |
| a. | | Blue overprint | 125.00 | 125.00 |
| 2N46 | A10 | 3k dk vio & ind (R) | 9.75 | 9.75 |
| a. | | Blue overprint | 60.00 | 60.00 |
| b. | | Black overprint | 200.00 | 200.00 |
| 2N47 | A10 | 5k dk & lt brn (Bk) | 225.00 | 225.00 |
| 2N48 | A10 | 10k vio brn & vio | 500.00 | 500.00 |
| 2N49 | A11 | 25f brt bl (R) | 3.25 | 3.25 |
| a. | | Black overprint | 25.00 | 25.00 |
| 2N50 | A12 | 40f olive grn | 125.00 | 125.00 |
| 2N51 | A12 | 50f lilac | 2.25 | 2.25 |

**On Stamps of 1919**

| | | | | |
|---|---|---|---|---|
| 2N52 | A13 | 5f green | .50 | .50 |
| 2N53 | A13 | 6f grnsh bl (Bk) | 22.50 | 22.50 |
| 2N54 | A13 | 10f red | .20 | .20 |
| 2N55 | A13 | 20f dk brown | .20 | .20 |
| 2N56 | A13 | 25f dl bl (Bk) | 1.25 | 1.25 |
| 2N56A | A13 | 40f olive green | 125.00 | 125.00 |
| 2N57 | A13 | 45f orange | 15.00 | 15.00 |
| 2N57A | A14 | 95f dark blue & blue | 125.00 | 125.00 |
| 2N57B | A14 | 1.20k dark green & green | 125.00 | 125.00 |
| 2N57C | A14 | 1.40k yellow green | 125.00 | 125.00 |

No. 2N58

| | | | | |
|---|---|---|---|---|
| 2N58 | A14 | 5k dk brn & brn | 3,000. | 3,000. |

#2N58 is handstamped. Counterfeits exist. Expertization is required.

**On No. 103A**

| | | | | |
|---|---|---|---|---|
| 2N59 | A5a | 10f violet brn (R) | 50.00 | 50.00 |

**On No. 208**

| | | | | |
|---|---|---|---|---|
| 2N60 | A13 | 10f red | 75.00 | 75.00 |
| | | *Nos. 2N1-2N57,2N59-2N60 (61)* | *2,529.* | *2,529.* |

### SEMI-POSTAL STAMPS

Hungary Nos. B36, B37 Overprinted like Regular Issues in Blue

**1919** **Wmk. 137** **Perf. 14**

| | | | | |
|---|---|---|---|---|
| 2NB1 | A4(c) | 2f olive yellow | 125.00 | 125.00 |
| 2NB1A | A4(c) | 3f orange | 125.00 | 125.00 |

Same Overprint in Blue or Black on Hungary Nos. B53--B55

**1919** **Wmk. 137** **Perf. 15**

| | | | | |
|---|---|---|---|---|
| 2NB1B | SP3 | 10f + 2f rose red | 4.00 | 4.00 |
| 2NB2 | SP4 | 15f + 2f dl vio (Bk) | 17.00 | 17.00 |
| 2NB3 | SP5 | 40f + 2f brown car | 11.00 | 11.00 |
| | | *Nos. 2NB1B-2NB3 (3)* | *32.00* | *32.00* |

Same Overprint on Hungary Nos. B58-B60 (with "Köztarsasag")

**1919**

| | | | | |
|---|---|---|---|---|
| 2NB4 | SP3 | 10f + 2f rose red | 42.50 | 42.50 |
| 2NB5 | SP4 | 15f + 2f dl vio (Bk) | 75.00 | 75.00 |
| 2NB6 | SP5 | 40f + 2f brown car | 32.50 | 32.50 |
| | | *Nos. 2NB4-2NB6 (3)* | *150.00* | *150.00* |

### SPECIAL DELIVERY STAMP

Hungarian Special Delivery Stamp of 1916 Overprinted like Regular Issues

**1919** **Wmk. 137** **Perf. 15**

| | | | | |
|---|---|---|---|---|
| 2NE1 | SD1 | 2f gray grn & red (Bl) | 3.00 | 3.00 |

### POSTAGE DUE STAMPS

Hungarian Postage Due Stamps of 1914-19 Overprinted in Black like Regular Issues

**1919** **Wmk. 137** **Perf. 15**

**On Stamp of 1914**

| | | | | |
|---|---|---|---|---|
| 2NJ1 | D1 | 50f grn & blk | 125.00 | 125.00 |

**On Stamps of 1915**

| | | | | |
|---|---|---|---|---|
| 2NJ2 | D1 | 1f green & red | 62.50 | 62.50 |
| 2NJ3 | D1 | 2f green & red | 2.00 | 2.00 |
| 2NJ4 | D1 | 5f green & red | 225.00 | 225.00 |
| 2NJ5 | D1 | 6f green & red | 125.00 | 125.00 |
| 2NJ6 | D1 | 10f green & red | .80 | .80 |
| 2NJ7 | D1 | 12f green & red | 125.00 | 125.00 |
| 2NJ8 | D1 | 15f green & red | 20.00 | 20.00 |
| 2NJ9 | D1 | 20f green & red | 4.50 | 4.50 |
| 2NJ10 | D1 | 30f green & red | 13.50 | 13.50 |

**On Stamps of 1918-19, Overprinted "Koztarsasag"**

| | | | | |
|---|---|---|---|---|
| 2NJ11 | D1 | 2f green & red | 25.00 | 25.00 |
| 2NJ12 | D1 | 3f green & red | 30.00 | 30.00 |
| 2NJ13 | D1 | 10f green & red | 30.00 | 30.00 |
| 2NJ14 | D1 | 20f green & red | 30.00 | 30.00 |
| 2NJ15 | D1 | 40f green & red | 30.00 | 30.00 |
| 2NJ16 | D1 | 50f green & red | 30.00 | 30.00 |
| | | *Nos. 2NJ1-2NJ16 (16)* | *878.30* | |
| | | *Nos. 2NJ1-2NJ13,2NJ15-2NJ16 (15)* | | *848.30* |

### NEWSPAPER STAMP

Hungarian Newspaper Stamp of 1914 Overprinted like Regular Issues

**1919** **Wmk. 137** **Imperf.**

| | | | | |
|---|---|---|---|---|
| 2NP1 | N5 | (2f) orange (Bl) | .55 | .55 |
| a. | | Inverted overprint | 50.00 | 50.00 |
| b. | | Double overprint | 125.00 | 125.00 |

### SECOND DEBRECEN ISSUE

Complete forgeries exist of this issue and are often found in large multiples or even complete sheets. Values are for genuine stamps.

Mythical "Turul" — OS5

Throwing Lariat — OS6

Hungarian Peasant OS7

**1920** **Unwmk.** **Typo.** **Perf. 11½**

| | | | | |
|---|---|---|---|---|
| 3N1 | OS5 | 2f lt brown | 2.25 | 2.25 |
| 3N2 | OS5 | 3f red brown | 2.25 | 2.25 |
| 3N3 | OS5 | 4f gray | 2.25 | 2.25 |
| 3N4 | OS5 | 5f lt green | .50 | .50 |
| 3N5 | OS5 | 6f slate | 2.25 | 2.25 |
| 3N6 | OS5 | 10f scarlet | .50 | .50 |
| 3N7 | OS5 | 15f dk violet | 3.00 | 3.00 |
| 3N8 | OS5 | 20f dk brown | .60 | .60 |
| 3N9 | OS6 | 25f ultra | 1.25 | 1.25 |
| 3N10 | OS6 | 30f buff | .65 | .65 |
| 3N11 | OS6 | 35f claret | 1.25 | 1.25 |
| 3N12 | OS6 | 40f olive grn | .75 | .75 |
| 3N13 | OS6 | 45f salmon | 1.00 | 1.00 |
| 3N14 | OS6 | 50f pale vio | .75 | .75 |
| 3N15 | OS6 | 60f yellow grn | .90 | .90 |
| 3N16 | OS6 | 75f Prus blue | .75 | .75 |
| 3N17 | OS7 | 80f gray grn | .85 | .85 |
| 3N18 | OS7 | 1k brown red | 3.00 | 3.00 |
| 3N19 | OS7 | 2k chocolate | 3.00 | 3.00 |
| 3N20 | OS7 | 3k brown vio | 2.25 | 2.25 |

| 3N21 | OS7 | 5k bister brn | 2.25 | 2.25 |
|---|---|---|---|---|
| 3N22 | OS7 | 10k dull vio | 2.25 | 2.25 |
| | | Nos. 3N1-3N22 (22) | 34.50 | 34.50 |

**Thick, Glazed Paper**

| 3N23 | OS5 | 2f lt brown | 3.00 | 3.00 |
|---|---|---|---|---|
| 3N24 | OS5 | 3f red brown | 3.00 | 3.00 |
| 3N25 | OS5 | 4f gray | 3.00 | 3.00 |
| 3N26 | OS5 | 5f lt green | 3.00 | 3.00 |
| 3N27 | OS5 | 6f slate | 3.00 | 3.00 |
| 3N28 | OS5 | 10f scarlet | .75 | .75 |
| 3N29 | OS5 | 15f dk vio | 3.00 | 3.00 |
| 3N30 | OS7 | 20f dk brown | 1.00 | 1.00 |
| 3N31 | OS7 | 80f gray grn | 1.50 | 1.50 |
| 3N32 | OS7 | 1k brown red | 4.00 | 4.00 |
| 3N33 | OS7 | 1.20k orange | 8.00 | 8.00 |
| 3N34 | OS7 | 2k chocolate | 4.50 | 4.50 |
| | | Nos. 3N23-3N34 (12) | 37.75 | 37.75 |

## SEMI-POSTAL STAMPS

Carrying Wounded

**1920 Unwmk. Typo. Perf. 11½**

| 3NB1 | SP1 | 20f green | 1.25 | 1.25 |
|---|---|---|---|---|
| 3NB2 | SP1 | 50f gray brn | 2.25 | 2.25 |
| 3NB3 | SP1 | 1k blue green | 2.25 | 2.25 |
| 3NB4 | SP1 | 2k dk green | 2.25 | 2.25 |

**Colored Paper**

| 3NB5 | SP1 | 20f green, *bl* | 3.00 | 3.00 |
|---|---|---|---|---|
| 3NB6 | SP1 | 50f brn, *rose* | 3.00 | 3.00 |
| 3NB7 | SP1 | 1k dk grn, *grn* | 3.00 | 3.00 |
| | | Nos. 3NB1-3NB7 (7) | 17.00 | 17.00 |

## POSTAGE DUE STAMPS

D1

**1920 Typo. Perf. 15**

| 3NJ1 | D1 | 5f blue green | 1.50 | 1.50 |
|---|---|---|---|---|
| 3NJ2 | D1 | 10f blue green | 1.50 | 1.50 |
| 3NJ3 | D1 | 20f blue green | .75 | .75 |
| 3NJ4 | D1 | 30f blue green | .75 | .75 |
| 3NJ5 | D1 | 40f blue green | 1.25 | 1.25 |
| | | Nos. 3NJ1-3NJ5 (5) | 5.75 | 5.75 |

## TEMESVAR ISSUE

**Issued under Romanian Occupation**

Forgeries exist of the inverted and color error surcharges.

Hungary Nos. 108, 155, 109, 111, E1 Surcharged

**1919 Wmk. 137 Perf. 15**

| 4N1 | A9 | 30f on 2f brn org (Bl) | .40 | .40 |
|---|---|---|---|---|
| *a.* | | Red surcharge | 2.00 | 2.00 |
| *b.* | | Inverted surcharge (R) | 25.00 | 25.00 |
| 4N2 | A9 | 1k on 4f sl gray (R) | .30 | .30 |
| 4N3 | A9 | 150f on 3f red lil (Bk) | .20 | .20 |
| 4N4 | A9 | 150f on 5f grn (Bk) | .40 | .40 |
| 4N5 | SD1 | 3k on 2f gray grn & red (Bk) | .50 | .50 |
| *a.* | | Blue surcharge | 2.00 | 2.00 |
| | | Nos. 4N1-4N5 (5) | 1.80 | 1.80 |

## POSTAGE DUE STAMPS

D1    D2

**1919 Wmk. 137 Perf. 15**

| 4NJ1 | D1 | 40f on 15f + 2f vio (Bk) | .50 | .50 |
|---|---|---|---|---|
| *a.* | | Red surcharge | 2.00 | 2.00 |
| 4NJ2 | D2 | 60f on 2f grn & red (Bk) | 2.50 | 2.50 |
| *a.* | | Red surcharge | 8.00 | 8.00 |
| 4NJ3 | D2 | 60f on 10f grn & red (Bk) | 1.25 | 1.25 |
| *a.* | | Red surcharge | 4.00 | 4.00 |
| | | Nos. 4NJ1-4NJ3 (3) | 4.25 | 4.25 |

## FIRST TRANSYLVANIA ISSUE

**Issued under Romanian Occupation**

The scarcer values of this issue have been extensively forged. Genuine common values are more easily found.

Issued in Kolozsvar (Cluj)

Hungarian Stamps of 1916-18 Overprinted

**1919 Wmk. 137 Perf. 15, 14**

**On Stamp of 1916, White Numerals**

| 5N1 | A8 | 15b violet | 4.75 | 4.75 |
|---|---|---|---|---|

**On Stamps of 1916-18**

| 5N2 | A9 | 2b brown org | .20 | .25 |
|---|---|---|---|---|
| 5N3 | A9 | 3b red lilac | .20 | .25 |
| 5N4 | A9 | 5b green | .20 | .25 |
| 5N5 | A9 | 6b grnsh blue | .40 | .40 |
| 5N5A | A9 | 10b rose red | 60.00 | 60.00 |
| 5N6 | A9 | 15b violet | .20 | .25 |
| 5N7 | A9 | 25b dull blue | .20 | .25 |
| 5N8 | A9 | 35b brown | .20 | .25 |
| 5N9 | A9 | 40b olive grn | .50 | .50 |
| 5N10 | A10 | 50b red vio & lil | 1.00 | 1.00 |
| 5N11 | A10 | 75b brt bl & pale bl | .30 | .30 |
| 5N12 | A10 | 80b grn & pale grn | .20 | .25 |
| 5N13 | A10 | 1 l red brn & cl | .20 | .25 |
| 5N14 | A10 | 2 l ol brn & bis | .60 | .60 |
| 5N15 | A10 | 3 l dk vio & ind | 3.50 | 3.50 |
| 5N16 | A10 | 5 l dk brn & lt brn | 2.50 | 2.50 |
| 5N17 | A10 | 10 l vio brn & vio | 3.00 | 3.00 |

**On Stamps of 1918**

| 5N18 | A11 | 10b scarlet | 40.00 | 40.00 |
|---|---|---|---|---|
| 5N19 | A11 | 15b dp violet | 20.00 | 20.00 |
| 5N20 | A11 | 20b dk brown | .25 | .25 |
| *a.* | | Gold overprint | 75.00 | 75.00 |
| *b.* | | Silver overprint | 75.00 | 75.00 |
| 5N21 | A11 | 25b brt blue | .65 | .65 |
| 5N22 | A12 | 40b olive grn | .30 | .30 |

**On No. 103A**

| 5N23 | A5a | 10b violet brn | .35 | .35 |
|---|---|---|---|---|
| | | Nos. 5N1-5N23 (24) | 139.70 | 140.10 |

## SEMI-POSTAL STAMPS

Hungarian Semi-Postal Stamps of 1913-17 Overprinted like Regular Issues

On Issue of 1913

**1919 Wmk. 137 Perf. 14**

| 5NB1 | SP1 | 1 l on 1f slate | 27.50 | 27.50 |
|---|---|---|---|---|
| 5NB2 | SP1 | 1 l on 2f ol yel | 70.00 | 70.00 |
| 5NB3 | SP1 | 1 l on 3f org | 37.50 | 37.50 |
| 5NB4 | SP1 | 1 l on 5f emer | 3.25 | 3.25 |
| 5NB5 | SP1 | 1 l on 10f car | 4.50 | 4.50 |
| 5NB6 | SP1 | 1 l on 12f vio, *yel* | 16.00 | 16.00 |
| 5NB7 | SP1 | 1 l on 16f gray grn | 6.25 | 6.25 |
| 5NB8 | SP1 | 1 l on 25f ultra | 60.00 | 60.00 |
| 5NB9 | SP1 | 1 l on 35f red vio | 10.00 | 10.00 |
| 5NB10 | SP2 | 1 l on 1k dl red | 60.00 | 60.00 |

**On Issue of 1916-17**

**Perf. 15**

| 5NB11 | SP3 | 10b + 2b rose red | .20 | .25 |
|---|---|---|---|---|
| 5NB12 | SP4 | 15b + 2b dull vio | .20 | .25 |
| 5NB13 | SP5 | 40b + 2b brn car | .20 | .25 |
| | | Nos. 5NB1-5NB13 (13) | 295.60 | 295.75 |

## SPECIAL DELIVERY STAMP

Hungarian Special Delivery Stamp of 1916 Overprinted like Regular Issues

**1919 Wmk. 137 Perf. 15**

| 5NE1 | SD1 | 2b gray grn & red | .30 | .30 |
|---|---|---|---|---|

## POSTAGE DUE STAMPS

Hungarian Postage Due Stamps of 1914-18 Overprinted like Regular Issues

On Stamp of 1914

**1919 Wmk. 137 Perf. 15**

| 5NJ1 | D1 | 50b green & blk | 13.00 | 13.00 |
|---|---|---|---|---|

**On Stamps of 1915**

| 5NJ2 | D1 | 1b green & red | 350.00 | 350.00 |
|---|---|---|---|---|
| 5NJ3 | D1 | 2b green & red | .70 | .70 |
| 5NJ4 | D1 | 5b green & red | 60.00 | 60.00 |
| 5NJ5 | D1 | 10b green & red | .45 | .45 |
| 5NJ6 | D1 | 15b green & red | 20.00 | 20.00 |
| 5NJ7 | D1 | 20b green & red | .40 | .40 |
| 5NJ8 | D1 | 30b green & red | 30.00 | 30.00 |
| | | Nos. 5NJ1-5NJ8 (8) | 474.55 | 474.55 |

## NEWSPAPER STAMP

Hungarian Newspaper Stamp of 1914 Overprinted like Regular Issues

**1919 Wmk. 137 Imperf.**

| 5NP1 | N5 | 2b orange | 3.75 | 3.75 |
|---|---|---|---|---|

## SECOND TRANSYLVANIA ISSUE

The scarcer values of this issue have been extensively forged. Genuine common values are more easily found.

Issued in Nagyvarad (Oradea)

Hungarian Stamps of 1916-19 Overprinted

**1919 Wmk. 137 Perf. 15, 14**

**On Stamps of 1913-16**

| 6N1 | A4 | 2b olive yel | 7.00 | 7.00 |
|---|---|---|---|---|
| 6N2 | A4 | 3b orange | 13.00 | 13.00 |
| 6N3 | A4 | 6b olive grn | 1.75 | 1.75 |
| 6N4 | A4 | 16b gray grn | 37.50 | 37.50 |
| 6N5 | A4 | 50b lake, *bl* | 1.75 | 1.75 |
| 6N6 | A4 | 70b red brn & grn | 26.00 | 26.00 |

**On Stamp of 1916 (White Numerals)**

| 6N6A | A8 | 15b violet | 125.00 | 125.00 |
|---|---|---|---|---|

**On Stamps of 1916-18**

| 6N7 | A9 | 2b brown org | .20 | .25 |
|---|---|---|---|---|
| 6N8 | A9 | 3b red lilac | .20 | .25 |
| 6N9 | A9 | 5b green | .30 | .30 |
| 6N10 | A9 | 6b grnsh blue | 1.60 | 1.60 |
| 6N11 | A9 | 10b rose red | 2.10 | 2.10 |
| 6N12 | A9 | 15b violet | .20 | .25 |
| 6N13 | A9 | 20b gray brn | 20.00 | 20.00 |
| 6N14 | A9 | 25b dull blue | .30 | .30 |
| 6N15 | A9 | 35b brown | .45 | .45 |
| 6N16 | A9 | 40b olive grn | .30 | .30 |
| 6N17 | A10 | 50b red vio & lil | .60 | .60 |
| 6N18 | A10 | 75b brt bl & pale bl | .20 | .25 |
| 6N19 | A10 | 80b grn & pale grn | .30 | .30 |
| 6N20 | A10 | 1 l red brn & cl | .75 | .75 |
| 6N21 | A10 | 2 l ol brn & bis | .20 | .25 |
| 6N22 | A10 | 3 l dk vio & ind | 6.50 | 6.50 |
| 6N23 | A10 | 5 l dk brn & lt brn | 3.25 | 3.25 |
| 6N24 | A10 | 10 l vio brn & vio | 1.50 | 1.50 |

**On Stamps of 1918**

| 6N25 | A11 | 10b scarlet | 3.25 | 3.25 |
|---|---|---|---|---|
| 6N26 | A11 | 20b dk brown | .20 | .20 |
| 6N27 | A11 | 25b brt blue | .75 | .75 |
| 6N28 | A11 | 40b olive grn | 1.10 | 1.10 |

**On Stamps of 1918-19, Overprinted "Koztarsasag"**

| 6N29 | A9 | 2b brown org | 4.00 | 4.00 |
|---|---|---|---|---|
| 6N30 | A9 | 3b red lilac | .20 | .25 |
| 6N31 | A9 | 4b slate gray | .20 | .25 |
| 6N32 | A9 | 5b green | .50 | .50 |
| 6N33 | A9 | 6b grnsh bl | 3.00 | 3.00 |
| 6N34 | A9 | 10b rose red | 17.50 | 17.50 |
| 6N35 | A9 | 20b gray brn | 2.50 | 2.50 |
| 6N36 | A9 | 40b olive grn | .50 | .50 |
| 6N37 | A10 | 1 l red brn & cl | .20 | .25 |
| 6N38 | A10 | 3 l dk vio & ind | .75 | .75 |
| 6N39 | A10 | 5 l dk brn & lt brn | 4.50 | 4.50 |
| 6N40 | A11 | 10b scarlet | 75.00 | 75.00 |
| 6N41 | A11 | 20b dk brown | 4.50 | 4.50 |
| 6N42 | A11 | 25b brt blue | 1.25 | 1.25 |
| 6N43 | A12 | 50b lilac | .20 | .25 |

**On Stamps of 1919 Inscribed "MAGYAR POSTA"**

| 6N44 | A13 | 5b yellow brn | .20 | .25 |
|---|---|---|---|---|
| 6N45 | A13 | 10b red | .20 | .25 |
| 6N46 | A13 | 20b dk brown | .40 | .40 |
| 6N47 | A13 | 25b dull blue | 2.00 | 2.00 |
| 6N48 | A13 | 40b olive grn | .65 | .65 |
| 6N49 | A14 | 5 l dk brn & brn | 6.50 | 6.50 |

**On No. 103A**

| 6N50 | A5a | 10b violet brn | .85 | .85 |
|---|---|---|---|---|
| | | Nos. 6N1-6N50 (51) | 381.85 | 382.45 |

## SEMI-POSTAL STAMPS

Hungarian Semi-Postal Stamps of 1913-17 Overprinted like Regular Issues

On Stamps of 1913

**1919 Wmk. 137 Perf. 14**

| 6NB1 | SP1 | 1 l on 1f slate | 2.25 | 2.25 |
|---|---|---|---|---|
| 6NB2 | SP1 | 1 l on 2f olive yel | 8.50 | 8.50 |
| 6NB3 | SP1 | 1 l on 3f orange | 2.75 | 2.75 |
| 6NB4 | SP1 | 1 l on 5f emerald | .25 | .25 |
| 6NB5 | SP1 | 1 l on 6f olive grn | 2.25 | 2.25 |
| 6NB6 | SP1 | 1 l on 10f carmine | .30 | .30 |
| 6NB7 | SP1 | 1 l on 12f vio, *yel* | 60.00 | 60.00 |
| 6NB8 | SP1 | 1 l on 16f gray grn | 2.50 | 2.50 |
| 6NB9 | SP1 | 1 l on 20f dk brn | 11.00 | 11.00 |
| 6NB10 | SP1 | 1 l on 25f ultra | 7.50 | 7.50 |
| 6NB11 | SP1 | 1 l on 35f red vio | 7.75 | 7.75 |

**On Stamp of 1915**

**Wmk. 135 Perf. 11½**

| 6NB12 | A4 | 5b emerald | 20.00 | 20.00 |
|---|---|---|---|---|

**On Stamps of 1916-17**

**Wmk. 137 Perf. 15**

| 6NB13 | SP3 | 10b + 2b rose red | 1.25 | 1.25 |
|---|---|---|---|---|
| 6NB14 | SP4 | 15b + 2b dull vio | .45 | .45 |
| 6NB15 | SP5 | 40b + 2b brown car | .20 | .25 |
| | | Nos. 6NB1-6NB15 (15) | 126.95 | 127.00 |

## SPECIAL DELIVERY STAMP

Hungarian Special Delivery Stamp of 1916 Overprinted like Regular Issues

**1919 Wmk. 137 Perf. 15**

| 6NE1 | SD1 | 2b gray grn & red | .40 | .40 |
|---|---|---|---|---|

## POSTAGE DUE STAMPS

Hungarian Postage Due Stamps of 1915 Overprinted like Regular Issues

**1919 Wmk. 137 Perf. 15**

| 6NJ1 | D1 | 1b green & red | 30.00 | 30.00 |
|---|---|---|---|---|
| 6NJ2 | D1 | 2b green & red | .20 | .25 |
| 6NJ3 | D1 | 5b green & red | 9.75 | 9.75 |
| 6NJ4 | D1 | 6b green & red | 6.75 | 6.75 |
| 6NJ5 | D1 | 10b green & red | .20 | .25 |
| 6NJ6 | D1 | 12b green & red | 1.50 | 1.50 |
| 6NJ7 | D1 | 15b green & red | 1.50 | 1.50 |
| 6NJ8 | D1 | 20b green & red | .20 | .25 |
| 6NJ9 | D1 | 30b green & red | 1.60 | 1.60 |
| | | Nos. 6NJ1-6NJ9 (9) | 51.70 | 51.85 |

**On Hungary No. J27**

**Perf. 11½x12**
**Wmk. 135**
6NJ10 D1 20b on 100b grn & blk — 350.00 350.00

### NEWSPAPER STAMP

Hungarian Newspaper Stamp of 1914 Overprinted like Regular Issues
**1919   Wmk. 137   Imperf.**
6NP1 N5 2b orange — .45 .45

### FIRST BARANYA ISSUE

**Issued under Serbian Occupation**

The scarcer values of this issue have been extensively forged. Genuine common values are more easily found.

Hungarian Stamps of 1913-18 Overprinted in Black or Red:

On A4, A9, A11, A12   On A10

**1919   Wmk. 137   Perf. 15**
**On Issue of 1913-16**
7N1 A4 6f olive grn (R) .90 .90
7N2 A4 50f lake, *bl* .20 .20
7N3 A4 60f grn, *salmon* .75 .75
7N4 A4 70f red brn & grn (R) 2.00 2.00
7N5 A4 70f red brn & grn (Bk) .25 .25
7N6 A4 80f dl vio (R) 3.25 3.25
**On Issue of 1916-18**
7N7 A9 2f brown org (Bk) 4.25 4.25
7N8 A9 2f brown org .20 .20
7N9 A9 3f red lilac (Bk) .20 .20
7N10 A9 3f red lilac (R) .80 .80
7N11 A9 5f green (Bk) .80 .80
7N12 A9 5f green (R) .20 .20
7N13 A9 6f grnsh bl (Bk) 1.75 1.75
7N14 A9 6f grnsh bl (R) 2.00 2.00
7N15 A9 15f violet .35 .35
7N16 A9 20f gray brn 20.00 20.00
7N17 A9 25f dull blue 3.50 3.50
7N18 A9 35f brown 5.75 5.75
7N19 A9 40f olive grn 20.00 20.00
7N20 A10 50f red vio & lil 2.00 2.00
7N21 A10 75f brt bl & pale bl .40 .40
7N22 A10 80f grn & pale grn .65 .65
7N23 A10 1k red brn & cl .55 .55
7N24 A10 2k ol brn & bis .65 .65
7N25 A10 3k dk vio & ind .65 .65
7N26 A10 5k dk brn & lt brn 1.25 1.25
7N27 A10 10k vio brn & vio 4.00 *4.00*

7N28 A9 45f on 2f brn org .35 .35
7N29 A9 45f on 5f green .20 .20
7N30 A9 45f on 15f violet .20 .20
**On Issue of 1918**
7N31 A11 10f scarlet (Bk) .20 .20
7N32 A11 20f dk brn (Bk) .20 .20
7N34 A11 25f dp blue (Bk) 1.90 1.90
7N35 A11 25f dp blue (R) 1.10 1.10
7N36 A12 40f olive grn (Bk) 4.50 4.50
7N37 A12 40f olive grn (R) 30.00 30.00
**On Issue of 1918-19 (Koztarsasag)**
7N38 A9 2f brown org (Bk) 3.50 3.50
7N39 A12 40f ol grn (Bk) *125.00* *125.00*
7N40 A12 40f olive grn (R) 20.00 20.00

**With New Value Added**
7N41 A9 45f on 2f brn org (Bk) 2.00 2.00
7N42 A9 45f on 2f brn org (R) .45 .45

The overprints were set in groups of 25. In each group two stamps have the figures "1" of "1919" with serifs.

### SEMI-POSTAL STAMPS

Hungarian Semi-Postal Stamps Overprinted Regular Issue First Type On Stamp of 1915
**1919   Wmk. 137   Perf. 15**
7NB1 A4 50f + 2f lake, *bl* 16.00 16.00
**On Stamps of 1916**
7NB2 SP3 10f + 2f rose red .30 .30
7NB3 SP4 15f + 2f dull vio .40 .40
*Nos. 7NB1-7NB3 (3)* 16.70 16.70

### SPECIAL DELIVERY STAMP

SD1
**1919   Wmk. 137   Perf. 15**
7NE1 SD1 105f on 2f gray grn & red 1.25 1.25

### POSTAGE DUE STAMPS

Overprinted or Surcharged on Hungary Nos. J29, J32, J35

**1919   Wmk. 137   Perf. 15**
7NJ1 D1 2f green & red 3.75 3.75
7NJ2 D1 10f green & red 1.25 1.25
7NJ3 D1 20f green & red 1.60 1.60
**With New Value Added**
7NJ4 D1 40f on 2f grn & red 1.50 1.50
*Nos. 7NJ1-7NJ4 (4)* 8.10 8.10

### SECOND BARANYA ISSUE

The scarcer values of this issue have been extensively forged. Genuine common values are more easily found.

Hungarian Stamps of 1916-19 Surcharged in Black and Red

**1919   On Stamps of 1916-18**
8N1 A9 20f on 2f brn org 4.25 4.25
8N2 A9 50f on 5f green 2.00 2.00
8N3 A9 150f on 15f violet 2.00 2.00
8N4 A10 200f on 75f brt bl & pale bl .75 .75
**On Stamp of 1918-19, Overprinted "Koztarsasag"**
8N5 A11 150f on 15f dp vio .50 .50
**On Stamps of 1919**
8N6 A13 20f on 2f brn org .35 .35
8N7 A13 30f on 6f grnsh bl .70 .70
8N8 A13 50f on 5f yel grn .20 .20
8N9 A13 100f on 25f dull bl .25 .25
8N10 A13 100f on 40f ol grn .25 .25
8N11 A13 100f on 45f orange 1.10 1.10
8N12 A13 150f on 20f dk brn 1.40 1.40
**On No. 103A**
8N13 A5a 10f on 10f vio brn .75 .75
*Nos. 8N1-8N13 (13)* 14.50 14.50

### SPECIAL DELIVERY STAMP

Hungarian Special Delivery Stamp of 1916 Surcharged like Regular Issues
**1919   Wmk. 137   Perf. 15**
8NE1 SD1 10f on 2f gray grn & red .65 .65

### NEWSPAPER STAMP

Hungarian Newspaper Stamp of 1914 Surcharged like Regular Issues
**1919   Wmk. 137   Imperf.**
8NP1 N5 10f on 2f orange .80 .80

### TEMESVAR ISSUES

**Issued under Serbian Occupation**

Forgeries exist of the inverted and color error surcharges.

Hungarian Stamps of 1916-18 Surcharged in Black, Blue or Brown:

a   b

**1919**
9N1 A9(a) 10f on 2f brn org (Bl) .20 .25
  *a.* Black surcharge 15.00 15.00
9N2 A9(b) 30f on 2f brn org .20 .25
  *a.* Inverted surcharge 75.00 75.00
9N3 A11(b) 50f on 20f dk brn (Bl) .20 .25
  *a.* Inverted surcharge
9N4 A9(b) 1k 50f on 15f vio .30 .30
  *a.* Brown surcharge .75 .75
  *b.* Double surcharge (Bk) 50.00 50.00
*Nos. 9N1-9N4 (4)* .90 1.05

### SEMI-POSTAL STAMP

Hungarian Semi-Postal Stamp of 1916 Surcharged in Blue

**1919   Wmk. 137   Perf. 15**
9NB1 SP3 45f on 10f + 2f rose red .20 .25

### POSTAGE DUE STAMPS

Hungarian Postage Due Stamps of 1915 Surcharged

**1919   Wmk. 137   Perf. 15**
9NJ1 D1 40f on 2f grn & red .80 .80
9NJ2 D1 60f on 2f grn & red .80 .80
9NJ3 D1 100f on 2f grn & red .80 .80
*Nos. 9NJ1-9NJ3 (3)* 2.40 2.40

### BANAT, BACSKA ISSUE

**Issued under Serbian Occupation**

Postal authorities at Temesvar applied these overprints. The stamps were available for postage, but were chiefly used to pay postal employees' salaries.

The overprints on this issue have been extensively forged. Even the inexpensive values are difficult to find with genuine overprints. The more extensive note before 1N1 also applies to Nos. 10N1-10NP1.

Hungarian Stamps of 1913-19 Overprinted in Black or Red:

a   b

**1919**
**Type "a" on Stamp of 1913**
10N1 A4 50f lake, *blue* 4.00 4.00
**Type "a" on Stamps of 1916-18**
10N2 A9 2f brown org 4.00 4.00
10N3 A9 3f red lilac 4.00 4.00
10N4 A9 5f green 4.00 4.00
10N5 A9 6f grnsh blue 4.00 4.00
10N6 A9 15f violet 4.00 4.00
10N7 A9 35f brown 35.00 35.00
**Type "b"**
10N8 A10 50f red vio & lil (R) 30.00 30.00
10N9 A10 75f brt bl & pale bl 4.00 4.00
10N10 A10 80f grn & pale 4.00 4.00
  *a.* Red overprint 37.50 37.50
10N11 A10 1k red brn & cl 4.00 4.00
10N12 A10 2k ol brn & bis 4.00 4.00
  *a.* Red overprint 37.50 37.50
10N14 A10 3k dk vio & ind 65.00 65.00
10N15 A10 5k dk brn & lt brn 4.00 4.00
10N16 A10 10k vio brn & vio 4.00 4.00
**Type "a" on Stamps of 1918**
10N17 A11 10f scarlet 4.00 4.00
10N18 A11 20f dk brown 4.00 4.00
10N19 A11 25f brt blue 4.00 4.00
10N20 A12 40f olive grn 4.00 4.00
10N21 A12 50f lilac 4.00 4.00
**Type "a" on Stamps of 1919 Inscribed "Magyar Posta"**
10N22 A13 10f red 30.00 30.00
10N23 A13 20f dk brown 30.00 30.00
10N24 A13 25f dull blue 37.50 37.50
**Type "a" on Stamps of 1918-19 Overprinted "Koztarsasag"**
10N25 A9 4f slate gray 3.50 3.50
10N26 A9 4f sl gray (R) 42.50 42.50
10N27 A9 5f green 4.00 4.00
10N28 A9 6f grnsh blue 4.00 4.00
10N29 A9 10f rose red 30.00 30.00
10N30 A11 15f dp violet 30.00 30.00
10N31 A9 20f gray brn 30.00 30.00
10N32 A11 25f brt blue 30.00 30.00
10N33 A9 40f olive grn 3.50 3.50
10N34 A9 40f ol grn (R) 32.50 32.50
**Type "b"**
10N35 A10 1k red brn & cl 4.00 4.00
10N36 A10 2k ol brn & bis 30.00 30.00
10N37 A10 3k dk vio & ind 30.00 30.00
10N38 A10 5k dk brn & lt brn 30.00 30.00
10N39 A10 10k vio brn & vio 30.00 30.00
**Type "a" on Temesvár Issue**
10N40 A9 10f on 2f brn org (Bl & Bk) 4.00 4.00
10N41 A9 1k50f on 15f vio 4.00 4.00

10N42 A5a 50f on 10f vio brn 4.00 4.00
  *a.* Red overprint 75.00 75.00
*Nos. 10N1-10N42 (41)* 641.50 641.50

## SEMI-POSTAL STAMPS

Semi-Postal Stamps of 1916-17
Overprinted Type "a" in Black

**1919**

| | | | | |
|---|---|---|---|---|
| 10NB1 | SP3 | 10f + 2f rose red | 4.00 | 4.00 |
| 10NB2 | SP4 | 15f + 2f dull vio | 4.00 | 4.00 |
| 10NB3 | SP5 | 40f + 2f brn car | 4.00 | 4.00 |

### Same Overprint on Temesvar Issue

| | | | | |
|---|---|---|---|---|
| 10NB4 | SP3 | 45f on 10f + 2f rose red (Bl & Bk) | 4.00 | 4.00 |
| | | Nos. 10NB1-10NB4 (4) | 16.00 | 16.00 |

## SPECIAL DELIVERY STAMP

Hungary No. E1
Surcharged in Black

**1919**

| | | | | |
|---|---|---|---|---|
| 10NE1 | SD1 | 30f on 2f gray grn & red | 4.00 | 4.00 |
| a. | | Red overprint | 75.00 | 75.00 |

## POSTAGE DUE STAMPS

Postage Due Stamps of 1914-15
Overprinted Type "a" in Black

**1919**

| | | | | |
|---|---|---|---|---|
| 10NJ1 | D1 | 2f green & red | 4.00 | 4.00 |
| 10NJ2 | D1 | 10f green & red | 4.00 | 4.00 |
| 10NJ3 | D1 | 15f green & red | 32.50 | 32.50 |
| 10NJ4 | D1 | 20f green & red | 4.00 | 4.00 |
| 10NJ5 | D1 | 30f green & red | 30.00 | 30.00 |
| 10NJ6 | D1 | 50f green & blk | 30.00 | 30.00 |
| | | Nos. 10NJ1-10NJ6 (6) | 104.50 | 104.50 |

## NEWSPAPER STAMP

Stamp of 1914 Overprinted Type "a" in Black

**1919**

| | | | | |
|---|---|---|---|---|
| 10NP1 | N5 | (2f) orange | 4.00 | 4.00 |

## SZEGED ISSUE

The "Hungarian National Government, Szeged, 1919," as the overprint reads, was an anti-Bolshevist government which opposed the Soviet Republic then in control at Budapest.

The overprints on this issue have been extensively forged. Even the inexpensive stamps are difficult to find with genuine overprints. The more extensive note before No. 1N1 also applies to Szeged Nos. 1-P1.

## NEWSPAPER STAMP

Hungary Stamps of 1916-19 Overprinted in Green, Red and Blue

### On Stamps of 1916-18

**1919**       **Perf. 15, 14**

| | | | | |
|---|---|---|---|---|
| 1 | A9 | 2f brn org (G) | 2.25 | 2.25 |
| 2 | A9 | 3f red lilac (G) | .75 | .75 |
| 3 | A9 | 5f green | 2.75 | 2.75 |
| 4 | A9 | 6f grnsh blue | 32.50 | 32.50 |
| 5 | A9 | 15f violet | 3.50 | 3.50 |
| 6 | A10 | 50f red vio & lil | 19.00 | 19.00 |
| 7 | A10 | 75f brt bl & pale bl | 4.25 | 4.25 |
| 8 | A10 | 80f grn & pale grn | 18.00 | 18.00 |
| 9 | A10 | 1k red brn & cl (G) | 2.25 | 2.25 |
| 10 | A10 | 2k ol brn & bis | 4.75 | 4.75 |
| 11 | A10 | 3k dk vio & ind | 7.25 | 7.25 |
| 12 | A10 | 5k dk brn & lt brn | 60.00 | 60.00 |
| 13 | A10 | 10k vio brn & vio | 60.00 | 60.00 |

### With New Value Added

| | | | | |
|---|---|---|---|---|
| 14 | A9 | 45f on 3f red lil (R & G) | .80 | .80 |
| 15 | A10 | 10k on 1k red brn & cl (Bl & G) | 8.00 | 8.00 |

### On Stamps of 1918

| | | | | |
|---|---|---|---|---|
| 16 | A11 | 10f scarlet (G) | 2.50 | 2.50 |
| 17 | A11 | 20f dk brown | .60 | .60 |
| 18 | A11 | 25f brt blue | 22.50 | 22.50 |
| 19 | A12 | 40f olive grn | 11.00 | 11.00 |

### On Stamps of 1918-19
### Overprinted "Koztarsasag"

| | | | | |
|---|---|---|---|---|
| 20 | A9 | 3f red lil (G) | 42.50 | 42.50 |
| 21 | A9 | 4f slate gray | 11.00 | 11.00 |
| 22 | A9 | 5f green | 25.00 | 25.00 |
| 23 | A9 | 6f grnsh blue | 15.00 | 15.00 |
| 24 | A9 | 10f rose red (G) | 32.50 | 32.50 |
| 25 | A11 | 10f scarlet) | 30.00 | 30.00 |
| 26 | A11 | 15f dp violet | 10.00 | 10.00 |
| 27 | A9 | 20f gray brown | 50.00 | 50.00 |
| 28 | A11 | 20f dk brown | 65.00 | 65.00 |
| 29 | A11 | 25f brt blue | 20.00 | 20.00 |
| 30 | A9 | 40f olive | 2.25 | 2.25 |
| 31 | A12 | 50f lilac | 1.75 | 1.75 |
| 32 | A10 | 3k dk vio & ind | 37.50 | 37.50 |

### With New Value Added

| | | | | |
|---|---|---|---|---|
| 33 | A9 | 20f on 2f brn org (R & G) | .80 | .80 |

### On Stamps of 1919
### Inscribed "Magyar Posta"

| | | | | |
|---|---|---|---|---|
| 34 | A13 | 20f dk brown | 60.00 | 60.00 |
| 35 | A13 | 25f dull blue | 1.75 | 1.75 |
| | | Nos. 1-35 (35) | 667.70 | 667.70 |

## SEMI-POSTAL STAMPS

Szeged Overprint on Semi-Postal Stamps of 1916-17 in Green or Red

**1919**

| | | | | |
|---|---|---|---|---|
| B1 | SP3 | 10f + 2f rose red (G) | .85 | .85 |
| B2 | SP4 | 15f + 2f dl vio (R) | 3.75 | 3.75 |
| B3 | SP5 | 40f + 2f brn car (G) | 10.00 | 10.00 |

### With Additional Overprint "Koztarsasag"

| | | | | |
|---|---|---|---|---|
| B4 | SP5 | 40f + 2f brn car (Bk & G) | 15.00 | 15.00 |
| | | Nos. B1-B4 (4) | 29.60 | 29.60 |

## SPECIAL DELIVERY STAMP

Szeged Overprint on Special Delivery Stamp of 1916 in Red

**1919**

| | | | | |
|---|---|---|---|---|
| E1 | SD1 | 2f gray grn & red | 11.00 | 11.00 |

## POSTAGE DUE STAMPS

Szeged Overprint on Stamps of 1915-18 in Red

**1919**

| | | | | |
|---|---|---|---|---|
| J1 | D1 | 2f green & red | 3.00 | 3.00 |
| J2 | D1 | 6f green & red | 9.75 | 9.75 |
| J3 | D1 | 10f green & red | 3.75 | 3.75 |
| J4 | D1 | 12f green & red | 4.75 | 4.75 |
| J5 | D1 | 20f green & red | 6.00 | 6.00 |
| J6 | D1 | 30f green & red | 9.00 | 9.00 |

### Red Surcharge

| | | | | |
|---|---|---|---|---|
| J7 | SD1 | 50f on 2f gray grn & red | 2.75 | 2.75 |
| J8 | SD1 | 100f on 2f gray grn & red | 2.75 | 2.75 |
| | | Nos. J1-J8 (8) | 41.75 | 41.75 |

## NEWSPAPER STAMP

Szeged Overprint on Stamp of 1914 in Green

**1919**      **Wmk. 137**      **Imperf.**

| | | | | |
|---|---|---|---|---|
| P1 | N5 | (2f) orange | .85 | .85 |

## ICELAND

ˈīs-lənd

LOCATION — Island in the North Atlantic Ocean, east of Greenland
GOVT. — Republic
AREA — 39,758 sq. mi.
POP. — 272,069 (1997)
CAPITAL — Reykjavik

Iceland became a republic on June 17, 1944. Formerly this country was united with Denmark under the government of King Christian X who, as a ruling sovereign of both countries, was assigned the dual title of king of each. Although the two countries were temporarily united in certain affairs beyond the king's person, both were acknowledged as sovereign states.

96 Skillings = 1 Rigsdaler

100 Aurar (singular "Eyrir") = 1 Krona (1876)

> **Catalogue values for unused stamps in this country are for Never Hinged items, beginning with Scott 246 in the regular postage section, Scott B7 in the semipostal section and Scott C21 in the air post section.**

### Watermarks

Wmk. 112 — Crown     Wmk. 113 — Crown

Wmk. 47 — Multiple Rosette     Wmk. 114 — Multiple Crosses

Values for unused stamps are for examples with original gum as defined in the catalogue introduction. Very fine examples of Nos. 1-33A and O1-O12 will have centering with perforations clear of the framelines but with design noticeably off center, and Nos. 1-7 and O1-O3 additionally will have some irregular or shorter perforations. Well centered stamps are quite scarce and will command higher prices.

A1

### Perf. 14x13½

| | | 1873 | Typo. | | Wmk. 112 | |
|---|---|---|---|---|---|---|
| 1 | A1 | 2s ultra | | 1,250. | 3,000. |
| a. | | Imperf. | | 700. | |
| 2 | A1 | 4s dark carmine | | 225. | 1,250. |
| a. | | Imperf. | | 700. | |
| 3 | A1 | 8s brown | | 375. | 1,400. |
| a. | | Imperf. | | 400. | |
| 4 | A1 | 16s yellow | | 1,800. | 3,000. |
| a. | | Imperf. | | 450. | |

### Perf. 12½

| 5 | A1 | 3s gray | | 550. | 1,750. |
|---|---|---|---|---|---|
| a. | | Imperf. | | 825. | |
| 6 | A1 | 4s carmine | | 1,600. | 2,500. |
| 7 | A1 | 16s yellow | | 150. | 700. |

Fake and favor cancellations are often found on Nos. 1-7. Values are considerably less than those shown. The imperforate varieties lack gum.

A2

### 1876

| 8 | A2 | 5a blue | | 450.00 | 775.00 |
|---|---|---|---|---|---|

### Perf. 14x13½

| 9 | A2 | 5a blue | | 500.00 | 825.00 |
|---|---|---|---|---|---|
| a. | | Imperf. | | 2,250. | |
| 10 | A2 | 6a gray | | 160.00 | 35.00 |
| 11 | A2 | 10a carmine | | 250.00 | 8.50 |
| a. | | Imperf. | | 650.00 | 750.00 |
| 12 | A2 | 16a brown | | 125.00 | 57.50 |
| 13 | A2 | 20a dark violet | | 40.00 | 550.00 |
| 14 | A2 | 40a green | | 110.00 | 250.00 |

Fake and favor cancellations are often found on No. 13 and value is considerably less than that shown.

A3     A3a
Small "3"     Large "3"

### 1882-98

| 15 | A3 | 3a orange | | 70.00 | 25.00 |
|---|---|---|---|---|---|
| 16 | A2 | 5a green | | 57.50 | 15.00 |
| 17 | A2 | 20a blue | | 350.00 | 57.50 |
| a. | | 20a ultramarine | | 800.00 | 325.00 |
| 18 | A2 | 40a red violet | | 57.50 | 47.50 |
| a. | | Perf. 13 ('98) | | 5,750. | |
| 19 | A2 | 50a bl & car ('92) | | 100.00 | 110.00 |
| 20 | A2 | 100a brn & vio ('92) | | 95.00 | 160.00 |
| | | Nos. 15-20 (6) | | 730.00 | 415.00 |

See note after No. 68.

### 1896-1901 — Perf. 13

| 21 | A3 | 3a orange ('97) | | 110.00 | 13.00 |
|---|---|---|---|---|---|
| 22 | A3a | 3a yellow ('01) | | 7.50 | 25.00 |
| 23 | A2 | 4a rose & gray ('99) | | 21.00 | 25.00 |
| 24 | A2 | 5a green | | 4.50 | 3.25 |
| 25 | A2 | 6a gray ('97) | | 20.00 | 21.00 |
| 26 | A2 | 10a carmine ('97) | | 10.00 | 3.25 |
| 27 | A2 | 16a brown | | 80.00 | 110.00 |
| 28 | A2 | 20a dull blue ('98) | | 50.00 | 42.50 |
| a. | | 20a dull ultramarine | | 500.00 | 47.50 |
| 29 | A2 | 25a yel brown & blue ('00) | | 25.00 | 37.50 |
| 30 | A2 | 50a bl & car ('98) | | 450.00 | 700.00 |

See note after No. 68.
For surcharges see Nos. 31-33A, 45-68.

### Black and Red Surcharge

Surcharged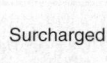

### 1897 — Perf. 13

| 31 | A2 | 3a on 5a green | | 800. | 600. |
|---|---|---|---|---|---|
| a. | | Perf. 14x13½ | | 26,500. | 4,750. |
| b. | | Inverted surcharge | | 1,500. | 1,250. |

Surcharged

| 32 | A2 | 3a on 5a green | | 650. | 525. |
|---|---|---|---|---|---|
| a. | | Inverted surcharge | | 1,300. | 1,000. |
| b. | | Perf. 14x13½ | | 12,500. | 2,750. |
| c. | | In vert. pair with #31 | | 1,650. | 1,300. |
| d. | | As "b," in vert. pair with #31a | | — | |

Unused value for #32b is for stamp without gum.

### Black Surcharge

Surcharged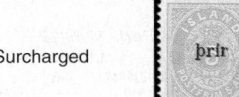

| 33 | A2 | 3a on 5a green | | 1,100. | 900. |
|---|---|---|---|---|---|
| b. | | Inverted surcharge | | 1,750. | 1,500. |

þrír
Surcharged

| 33A | A2 | 3a on 5a green | | 850. | 650. |
|---|---|---|---|---|---|
| c. | | Inverted surcharge | | 1,500. | 1,250. |

Excellent counterfeits are known.

King Christian IX — A4

### 1902-04 — Wmk. 113 — Perf. 13

| 34 | A4 | 3a orange | | 7.00 | 4.50 |
|---|---|---|---|---|---|
| 35 | A4 | 4a gray & rose | | 4.50 | 1.60 |
| 36 | A4 | 5a yel green | | 40.00 | 1.40 |
| 37 | A4 | 6a gray brown | | 24.00 | 13.00 |
| 38 | A4 | 10a car rose | | 7.00 | 1.40 |
| 39 | A4 | 16a chocolate | | 10.00 | 13.00 |
| 40 | A4 | 20a deep blue | | 3.50 | 5.50 |
| a. | | Inscribed "PJONUSTA" | | 75.00 | 110.00 |
| 41 | A4 | 25a brn & grn | | 5.00 | 8.25 |
| 42 | A4 | 40a violet | | 5.50 | 7.75 |
| 43 | A4 | 50a gray & bl blk | | 7.00 | 29.00 |
| 44 | A4 | 1k sl bl & yel brn | | 8.25 | 13.00 |
| 44A | A4 | 2k olive brn & brt blue ('04) | | 32.50 | 82.50 |
| 44B | A4 | 5k org brn & slate blue ('04) | | 175.00 | 275.00 |
| | | Nos. 34-44B (13) | | 329.25 | 455.90 |

For surcharge see No. 142.

Stamps of 1882-1901 Overprinted

### 1902-03 — Wmk. 112 — Perf. 13 — Red Overprint

| 45 | A2 | 5a green | | 1.10 | 9.50 |
|---|---|---|---|---|---|
| a. | | Inverted overprint | | 50.00 | 77.50 |
| b. | | "I" before Gildi omitted | | 175.00 | |
| c. | | '03-'03 | | 300.00 | |
| d. | | 02'-'03 | | 300.00 | |
| e. | | Pair, one without overprint | | 100.00 | |
| 46 | A2 | 6a gray | | 1.00 | 9.00 |
| a. | | Double overprint | | 60.00 | |
| b. | | Inverted overprint | | 47.50 | |
| c. | | '03-'03 | | 350.00 | |
| d. | | 02'-'03 | | 350.00 | |
| e. | | Pair, one with invtd. ovpt. | | 250.00 | |
| f. | | Pair, one without overprint | | 140.00 | |
| g. | | As "f", inverted | | 200.00 | |
| 47 | A2 | 20a dull blue | | .90 | 11.00 |
| a. | | Inverted overprint | | 35.00 | 55.00 |
| b. | | "I" before Gildi omitted | | 95.00 | |
| c. | | '03-'03 | | 300.00 | |
| 48 | A2 | 25a yel brn & bl | | 1.00 | 17.50 |
| a. | | Inverted overprint | | 47.50 | 60.00 |
| b. | | '03-'03 | | 300.00 | |
| c. | | 02'-'03 | | 300.00 | |
| d. | | Double overprint | | 125.00 | |

### Black Overprint

| 49 | A3 | 3a orange | | 210.00 | 550.00 |
|---|---|---|---|---|---|
| b. | | Inverted overprint | | 350.00 | 675.00 |
| c. | | "I" before Gildi omitted | | 450.00 | |
| d. | | '03-'03 | | 450.00 | |
| e. | | 02'-'03 | | 450.00 | |
| 50 | A3a | 3a yellow | | 1.40 | 2.25 |
| a. | | Double overprint | | 325.00 | |
| b. | | Inverted overprint | | 50.00 | 70.00 |
| c. | | "I" before Gildi omitted | | 300.00 | |
| d. | | 02'-'03 | | 375.00 | |
| 51 | A2 | 4a rose & gray | | 45.00 | 60.00 |
| a. | | Double overprint | | 200.00 | |
| b. | | Inverted overprint | | 110.00 | |
| c. | | Dbl. ovpt., one invtd. | | 275.00 | |
| d. | | "I" before Gildi omitted | | 250.00 | |
| e. | | '03-'03 | | 400.00 | |
| f. | | 02'-'03 | | 400.00 | |
| g. | | Pair, one with invtd. ovpt. | | 275.00 | |
| 52 | A2 | 5a green | | 400.00 | 675.00 |
| a. | | Inverted overprint | | 450.00 | |
| b. | | Pair, one without overprint | | 550.00 | |
| c. | | As "b", inverted | | 700.00 | |

| | | | | |
|---|---|---|---|---|
| 53 | A2 | 6a gray | 700.00 | 1,100. |
| a. | | Inverted overprint | 800.00 | |
| b. | | Pair, one without over- print | 800.00 | |
| c. | | Double overprint | 875.00 | |
| 54 | A2 | 10a carmine | 1.40 | 11.50 |
| a. | | Inverted overprint | 50.00 | 77.50 |
| b. | | Pair, one without over- print | 90.00 | |
| 55 | A2 | 16a brown | 30.00 | 45.00 |
| a. | | Inverted overprint | 140.00 | |
| b. | | "I" before Gildi omitted | 250.00 | |
| c. | | '03-'03 | 400.00 | |
| d. | | 02'-'03 | 400.00 | |
| 56 | A2 | 20a dull blue | 12,000. | |
| a. | | Inverted overprint | 12,500. | |
| 57 | A2 | 25a yel brn & bl | 12,750. | |
| a. | | Inverted overprint | 13,500. | |
| 58 | A2 | 40a red vio | 1.25 | 45.00 |
| a. | | Inverted overprint | 50.00 | |
| 59 | A2 | 50a bl & car | 3.75 | 75.00 |
| a. | | Double overprint | 250.00 | |
| b. | | 02'-'03 | 350.00 | |
| c. | | '03-'03 | 350.00 | |

### Perf. 14x13½
### Red Overprint

| | | | | |
|---|---|---|---|---|
| 60 | A2 | 5a green | 2,250. | — |
| a. | | '03-'03 | — | |
| 61 | A2 | 6a gray | 2,250. | — |
| 62 | A2 | 20a blue | 5,750. | — |
| a. | | 02'-'03 | 10,000. | |

### Black Overprint

| | | | | |
|---|---|---|---|---|
| 63 | A3 | 3a orange | 1,500. | 2,100. |
| a. | | Inverted overprint | 1,650. | |
| b. | | 02'-'03 | 2,000. | |
| c. | | '03-'03 | 2,000. | |
| 64 | A2 | 10a carmine | 9,000. | — |
| 65 | A2 | 16a brown | 1,650. | 2,000. |
| a. | | Inverted overprint | 1,750. | |
| b. | | 02'-'03 | 2,000. | |
| d. | | '03-'03 | 2,000. | |
| 65C | A2 | 20a dull blue | 7,750. | — |
| a. | | Inverted overprint | 10,000. | |
| 66 | A2 | 40a red vio | 25.00 | 110.00 |
| a. | | Inverted overprint | 450.00 | |
| b. | | '03-'03 | 350.00 | |
| c. | | 02'-'03 | 350.00 | |
| 67 | A2 | 50a bl & car | 45.00 | 140.00 |
| a. | | Inverted overprint | 200.00 | |
| b. | | '03-'03 | 400.00 | |
| c. | | 02'-'03 | 400.00 | |
| d. | | As "c," inverted | 400.00 | |
| 68 | A2 | 100a brn & vio | 55.00 | 90.00 |
| a. | | Inverted overprint | 160.00 | |
| b. | | 02'-'03 | 300.00 | |
| c. | | '03-'03 | 300.00 | |

"I GILDI" means "valid."

In 1904 Nos. 20, 22-30, 45-59 (except 49, 52, 53, 56 and 57) and No. 68 were reprinted for the Postal Union. The reprints are perforated 13 and have watermark type 113. Value $75 each. Without overprint, $125 each.

Kings Christian IX and Frederik VIII — A5

### Typo., Center Engr.

| | | 1907-08 | **Wmk. 113** | **Perf. 13** |
|---|---|---|---|---|
| 71 | A5 | 1e yel grn & red | 1.90 | 1.25 |
| 72 | A5 | 3a yel brn & ocher | 4.50 | 1.75 |
| 73 | A5 | 4a gray & red | 2.25 | 1.90 |
| 74 | A5 | 5a green | 92.50 | 1.40 |
| 75 | A5 | 6a gray & gray brn | 57.50 | 4.00 |
| 76 | A5 | 10a scarlet | 160.00 | 1.60 |
| 77 | A5 | 15a red & green | 8.25 | 1.40 |
| 78 | A5 | 16a brown | 9.50 | 47.50 |
| 79 | A5 | 20a blue | 8.75 | 6.75 |
| 80 | A5 | 25a bis brn & grn | 7.00 | 14.00 |
| 81 | A5 | 40a claret & vio | 6.75 | 17.00 |
| 82 | A5 | 50a gray & vio | 7.75 | 17.00 |
| 83 | A5 | 1k blue & brn | 30.00 | 72.50 |
| 84 | A5 | 2k dk brn & dk grn | 40.00 | 85.00 |
| 85 | A5 | 5k brn & slate | 225.00 | 425.00 |
| | | Nos. 71-85 (15) | 661.65 | 698.05 |

See Nos. 99-107.
For surcharges and overprints see Nos. 130-138, 143, C2, O69.

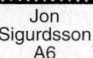

Jon Sigurdsson A6

Frederik VIII A7

### 1911     Typo. and Embossed

| | | | | |
|---|---|---|---|---|
| 86 | A6 | 1e olive green | 2.75 | 2.50 |
| 87 | A6 | 3a light brown | 5.25 | 16.00 |
| 88 | A6 | 4a ultramarine | 2.00 | 2.10 |
| 89 | A6 | 6a gray | 13.00 | 27.50 |

---

| | | | | |
|---|---|---|---|---|
| 90 | A6 | 15a violet | 16.00 | 2.10 |
| 91 | A6 | 25a orange | 29.00 | 52.50 |
| | | Nos. 86-91 (6) | 68.00 | 102.70 |

Sigurdsson (1811-79), statesman and author. For surcharge see No. 149.

### 1912, Feb. 17

| | | | | |
|---|---|---|---|---|
| 92 | A7 | 5a green | 35.00 | 13.00 |
| 93 | A7 | 10a red | 35.00 | 13.00 |
| 94 | A7 | 20a pale blue | 50.00 | 19.00 |
| 95 | A7 | 50a claret | 10.00 | 40.00 |
| 96 | A7 | 1k yellow | 32.50 | 80.00 |
| 97 | A7 | 2k rose | 30.00 | 80.00 |
| 98 | A7 | 5k brown | 175.00 | 250.00 |
| | | Nos. 92-98 (7) | 367.50 | 495.00 |

For surcharges and overprints see Nos. 140-141, O50-O51.

### Type of 1907-08
### Typo., Center Engr.

| | | 1915-18 | **Wmk. 114** | **Perf. 14x14½** |
|---|---|---|---|---|
| 99 | A5 | 1e yel grn & red | 9.50 | 20.00 |
| 100 | A5 | 3a bister brn | 4.75 | 3.25 |
| 101 | A5 | 4a gray & red | 4.75 | 10.50 |
| 102 | A5 | 5a green | 110.00 | 1.50 |
| 103 | A5 | 6a gray & gray brn | 22.50 | 150.00 |
| 104 | A5 | 10a scarlet | 4.25 | 1.40 |
| 107 | A5 | 20a blue | 250.00 | 26.00 |
| | | Nos. 99-107 (7) | 405.75 | 212.65 |

Revenue cancellations consisting of "TOLLUR" boxed in frame are found on stamps used to pay the tax on parcel post packages entering Iceland.

Christian X — A8

### 1920-22      Typo.

| | | | | |
|---|---|---|---|---|
| 108 | A8 | 1e yel grn & red | 1.00 | 1.25 |
| 109 | A8 | 3a bister brn | 9.00 | 17.50 |
| 110 | A8 | 4a gray & red | 5.25 | 2.75 |
| 111 | A8 | 5a green | 2.25 | 2.25 |
| 112 | A8 | 5a ol green ('22) | 5.25 | 1.75 |
| 113 | A8 | 6a dark gray | 15.00 | 9.00 |
| 114 | A8 | 8a dark brown | 9.00 | 2.50 |
| 115 | A8 | 10a red | 2.75 | 12.50 |
| 116 | A8 | 10a green ('21) | 3.75 | 2.00 |
| 117 | A8 | 15a violet | 45.00 | 1.60 |
| 118 | A8 | 20a deep blue | 3.00 | 19.00 |
| 119 | A8 | 20a choc ('22) | 65.00 | 1.75 |
| 120 | A8 | 25a brown & grn | 19.00 | 2.00 |
| 121 | A8 | 25a red ('21) | 19.00 | 62.50 |
| | | Revenue cancellation | | 4.25 |
| 122 | A8 | 30a red & green | 57.50 | 3.75 |
| | | Revenue cancellation | | 8.75 |
| 123 | A8 | 40a claret | 50.00 | 3.25 |
| | | Revenue cancellation | | 9.50 |
| 124 | A8 | 40a dk bl ('21) | 87.50 | 15.00 |
| | | Revenue cancellation | | 11.00 |
| 125 | A8 | 50a dk gray & cl | 200.00 | 12.50 |
| | | Revenue cancellation | | 13.50 |
| 126 | A8 | 1k dp bl & dk brn | 110.00 | 2.00 |
| | | Revenue cancellation | | 1.75 |
| 127 | A8 | 2k ol brn & myr green | 275.00 | 35.00 |
| | | Revenue cancellation | | 3.50 |
| 128 | A8 | 5k brn & ind | 62.50 | 19.00 |
| | | Revenue cancellation | | 3.50 |
| | | Nos. 108-128 (21) | 1,047. | 228.85 |

See Nos. 176-187, 202.
For surcharges and overprints see Nos. 139, 150, C1, C9-C14, O52, O70-O71.

A9    A10    A11

### 1921-25     Wmk. 113     Perf. 13

| | | | | |
|---|---|---|---|---|
| 130 | A4 | 5a on 16a brown | 4.75 | 32.50 |
| 131 | A4 | 5a on 16a brown | 2.75 | 9.75 |
| 132 | A4 | 20a on 25a brn & green | 9.25 | 9.25 |
| a. | | Double surcharge | 600.00 | |
| 133 | A5 | 20a on 25a bis brn & green | 5.25 | 9.25 |
| 134 | A4 | 20a on 40a violet | 9.75 | 25.00 |
| 135 | A5 | 20a on 40a cl & vio | 13.50 | 27.50 |
| 137 | A4 | 30a on 50a gray & bl blk ('25) | 40.00 | 40.00 |
| | | Revenue cancellation | | 17.50 |
| 138 | A4 | 50a on 5k org brn & sl bl ('25) | 62.50 | 60.00 |
| | | Revenue cancellation | | 35.00 |
| | | Nos. 130-138 (8) | 147.75 | 213.25 |

---

No. 111 Surcharged

### 1922     Wmk. 114     Perf. 14x14½

| | | | | |
|---|---|---|---|---|
| 139 | A8 | 10a on 5a green | 9.00 | 4.00 |

Nos. 95-96, 44A, 85 Surcharged

### 1924-30     Wmk. 113     Perf. 13

| | | | | |
|---|---|---|---|---|
| 140 | A7 | 10k on 50a ('25) | 325.00 | 475.00 |
| | | Revenue cancellation | | 40.00 |
| 141 | A7 | 10k on 1k | 400.00 | 650.00 |
| | | Revenue cancellation | | 75.00 |
| 142 | A4 | 10k on 2k ('29) | 80.00 | 35.00 |
| | | Revenue cancellation | | 8.75 |
| 143 | A5 | 10k on 5k ('30) | 475.00 | 600.00 |
| | | Revenue cancellation | | 35.00 |

"Tollur" is a revenue cancellation.

Landing the Mail — A12

Designs: 7a, 50a, Landing the mail. 10a, 35a, View of Reykjavik. 20a, Museum building.

### 1925, Sept. 12    Typo.    Wmk. 114    Perf. 14x15

| | | | | |
|---|---|---|---|---|
| 144 | A12 | 7a yel green | 40.00 | 7.50 |
| 145 | A12 | 10a dp bl & brn | 40.00 | .80 |
| 146 | A12 | 20a vermilion | 40.00 | .80 |
| 147 | A12 | 35a deep blue | 70.00 | 9.25 |
| 148 | A12 | 50a yel grn & brn | 70.00 | 1.60 |
| | | Nos. 144-148 (5) | 260.00 | 19.95 |

No. 91 Surcharged

### 1925     Wmk. 113     Perf. 13

| | | | | |
|---|---|---|---|---|
| 149 | A6 | 2k on 25a orange | 150.00 | 160.00 |
| | | Revenue cancellation | | 20.00 |

No. 124 Surcharged in Red

### 1926

| | | | | |
|---|---|---|---|---|
| 150 | A8 | 1k on 40a dark blue | 175.00 | 40.00 |
| | | Revenue cancellation | | 25.00 |

Parliament Building A15

Designs: 5a, Viking ship in storm. 7a, Parliament meeting place, 1690. 10a, Viking funeral. 15a, Vikings naming land. 20a, The dash for Thing. 25a, Gathering wood. 30a, Thingvalla Lake. 35a, Iceland woman in national costume. 40a, Iceland flag. 50a, First Althing, 930 A.D. 1k, Map of Iceland. 2k, Winter-bound home. 5k, Woman spinning. 10k, Viking Sacrifice to Thor.

### Perf. 12½x12

### 1930, Jan. 1    Litho.    Unwmk.

| | | | | |
|---|---|---|---|---|
| 152 | A15 | 3a dull vio & gray vio | 4.00 | 10.00 |
| 153 | A15 | 5a dk bl & sl grn | 4.00 | 10.00 |
| 154 | A15 | 7a grn & gray grn | 4.00 | 10.00 |
| 155 | A15 | 10a dk vio & lilac | 10.00 | 20.00 |
| 156 | A15 | 15a dp ultra & bl gray | 3.00 | 11.00 |

---

| | | | | |
|---|---|---|---|---|
| 157 | A15 | 20a rose red & sal | 47.50 | 90.00 |
| a. | | Double impression | 400.00 | |
| 158 | A15 | 25a dk brn & lt brown | 7.75 | 15.00 |
| 159 | A15 | 30a dk grn & sl grn | 6.50 | 14.00 |
| 160 | A15 | 35a ultra & bl gray | 7.25 | 13.50 |
| 161 | A15 | 40a dk ultra, red & slate grn | 6.50 | 14.00 |
| 162 | A15 | 50a red brn & cin- namon | 65.00 | 160.00 |
| 163 | A15 | 1k ol grn & gray green | 65.00 | 160.00 |
| 164 | A15 | 2k turq bl & gray green | 92.50 | 190.00 |
| 165 | A15 | 5k org & yellow | 52.50 | 150.00 |
| 166 | A15 | 10k mag & dl rose | 52.50 | 150.00 |
| | | Nos. 152-166 (15) | 428.00 | 1,017. |

Millenary of the "Althing," the Icelandic Parliament, oldest in the world.
Imperfs were privately printed.
For overprints see Nos. O53-O67.

Gullfoss (Golden Falls) — A30

### 1931-32    Unwmk.    Engr.    Perf. 14

| | | | | |
|---|---|---|---|---|
| 170 | A30 | 5a gray | 15.00 | 1.10 |
| 171 | A30 | 20a red | 12.50 | .25 |
| 172 | A30 | 35a ultramarine | 25.00 | 16.00 |
| | | Revenue cancellation | | 1.90 |
| 173 | A30 | 60a red lil ('32) | 15.00 | 1.25 |
| 174 | A30 | 65a red brn ('32) | 2.50 | 1.25 |
| 175 | A30 | 75a grnsh bl ('32) | 100.00 | 35.00 |
| | | Revenue cancellation | | 5.00 |
| | | Nos. 170-175 (6) | 170.00 | 54.85 |

Issued: 5a-35a, Dec. 15; 60a-75a, May 30.

### Type of 1920 Christian X Issue Redrawn

### Perf. 14x14½

### 1931-33    Typo.    Wmk. 114

| | | | | |
|---|---|---|---|---|
| 176 | A8 | 1e yel grn & red | 1.00 | 1.25 |
| 177 | A8 | 3a bister brown | 15.00 | 15.00 |
| | | Revenue cancellation | | 8.00 |
| 178 | A8 | 4a gray & red | 2.50 | 1.40 |
| 179 | A8 | 6a dark gray | 2.00 | 4.00 |
| 180 | A8 | 7a yel grn ('33) | .65 | 1.75 |
| 181 | A8 | 10a chocolate | 140.00 | 1.10 |
| 182 | A8 | 25a brn & green | 17.50 | 3.50 |
| | | Revenue cancellation | | 3.25 |
| 183 | A8 | 30a red & green | 29.00 | 5.75 |
| | | Revenue cancellation | | 7.75 |
| 184 | A8 | 40a claret | 225.00 | 21.00 |
| | | Revenue cancellation | | 11.50 |
| 185 | A8 | 1k dk bl & lt brn | 45.00 | 7.50 |
| | | Revenue cancellation | | 3.25 |
| 186 | A8 | 2k choc & dk grn | 275.00 | 80.00 |
| | | Revenue cancellation | | 8.00 |
| 187 | A8 | 10k yel grn & blk | 300.00 | 210.00 |
| | | Revenue cancellation | | 16.00 |
| | | Nos. 176-187 (12) | 1,052. | 352.25 |

On the redrawn stamps the horizontal lines of the portrait and the oval are closer together than on the 1920 stamps and are crossed by many fine vertical lines.
See No. 202.

Dynjandi Falls — A31

Mount Hekla — A32

### Perf. 12½

### 1935, June 28    Engr.    Unwmk.

| | | | | |
|---|---|---|---|---|
| 193 | A31 | 10a blue | 22.50 | .20 |
| | | Never hinged | 72.50 | |
| 194 | A32 | 1k greenish gray | 40.00 | .20 |
| | | Never hinged | 125.00 | |

Matthias Jochumsson — A33

### 1935, Nov. 11

| | | | | |
|---|---|---|---|---|
| 195 | A33 | 3a gray green | .70 | 4.00 |
| 196 | A33 | 5a gray | 14.00 | 1.25 |
| 197 | A33 | 7a yel green | 20.00 | 1.75 |
| 198 | A33 | 35a blue | .60 | 1.25 |
| | | Nos. 195-198 (4) | 35.30 | 8.25 |
| | | Set, never hinged | 100.00 | |

Birth cent. of Matthias Jochumsson, poet.
For surcharges see Nos. 212, 236.

King Christian X — A34

**1937, May 14** **Perf. 13x12½**
199 A34 10a green 2.30 22.50
200 A34 30a brown 2.30 10.00
201 A34 40a claret 2.30 10.00
Nos. 199-201 (3) 6.90 42.50
Set, never hinged 12.00

Reign of Christian X, 25th anniv.

Christian X Type of 1931-33
**1937 Unwmk. Typo. Perf. 11½**
202 A8 1e yel grn & red .80 2.25
Never hinged 2.00

Geyser
A35 A36

**1938-47 Engr. Perf. 14**
203 A35 15a dp rose vio 5.75 11.50
a. Imperf., pair 700.00
Never hinged 800.00
204 A35 20a rose red 25.00 .20
205 A35 35a ultra .70 1.10
206 A36 40a dk brn ('39) 15.00 32.50
207 A36 45a brt ultra ('40) .80 1.10
208 A36 50a dk slate grn 24.00 1.10
208A A36 60a brt ultra ('43) 5.75 1.10
c. Perf. 11½ ('47) 2.90 11.50
Never hinged (#208Ac) 5.75
208B A36 1k indigo ('45) 1.90 .35
d. Perf. 11½ ('47) 2.90 11.50
Never hinged (#208Bd) 5.75
Nos. 203-208B (8) 78.90 48.95
Set, never hinged 175.00

University
of Iceland
A37

**1938, Dec. 1** **Perf. 13½**
209 A37 25a dark grn 7.50 16.00
210 A37 30a brown 7.50 16.00
211 A37 40a brt red vio 7.50 16.00
Nos. 209-211 (3) 22.50 48.00
Set, never hinged 37.50

20th anniversary of independence.

No. 198 Surcharged with New Value
**1939, Mar. 17** **Perf. 12½**
212 A33 5a on 35a blue .90 1.75
Never hinged 2.00
a. Double surcharge 275.00
Never hinged 450.00

Trylon and
Perisphere
A38

Leif Ericsson's
Ship and Route
to America
A39

Statue of Thorfinn
Karlsefni — A40

**1939 Engr. Perf. 14**
213 A38 20a crimson 3.75 7.50
214 A39 35a bright ultra 4.25 9.00
215 A40 45a bright green 4.50 11.00
216 A40 2k dark gray 60.00 160.00
Nos. 213-216 (4) 72.50 187.50
Set, never hinged 110.00

New York World's Fair.
For overprints see Nos. 232-235.

Codfish — A41 Herring — A42

Flag of Iceland — A43

**1939-45 Engr. Perf. 14, 14x13½**
217 A41 1e Prussian blue .35 4.50
a. Perf. 14x13½ 1.60 5.50
218 A42 3a dark violet .35 .90
a. Perf. 14x13½ 2.25 8.50
219 A41 5a dark brown .35 .25
c. Perf. 14x13½ 2.75 1.40
220 A42 7a dark green 5.75 9.25
221 A42 10a green ('40) 40.00 .75
b. Perf. 14x13½ 62.50 1.60
Never hinged 180.00
222 A42 10a slate gray ('45) .35 .20
223 A42 12a dk grn ('43) .35 .55
224 A41 25a brt red ('40) 27.50 .20
b. Perf. 14x13½ 57.50 2.00
Never hinged (#224b) 170.00
225 A41 25a hn brn ('45) .35 .20
226 A42 35a carmine ('43) .50 .35
227 A41 50a dk bl grn ('43) .60 .20

**Typo.**
228 A43 10a car & ultra 2.25 1.25
Nos. 217-228 (12) 78.70 18.60
Set, never hinged 200.00

Statue of Thorfinn
Karlsefni — A44

**1939-45 Engr. Perf. 14**
229 A44 2k dark gray 3.50 .30
230 A44 5k dk brn ('43) 27.50 .55
231 A44 10k brn yel ('45) 13.50 2.10
Nos. 229-231 (3) 44.50 2.95
Set, never hinged 100.00

**1947 Perf. 11½**
229a A44 2k 9.25 1.90
230a A44 5k 35.00 2.40
231a A44 10k 13.50 55.00
Nos. 229a-231a (3) 57.75 59.30
Set, never hinged 175.00

New York World's Fair Issue of 1939
Overprinted "1940" in Black
**1940, May 11** **Perf. 14**
232 A38 20a crimson 10.00 32.50
233 A39 35a bright ultra 10.00 32.50
234 A40 45a bright green 10.00 32.50
235 A40 2k dark gray 125.00 450.00
Nos. 232-235 (4) 155.00 547.50
Set, never hinged 275.00

No. 195 Surcharged in Red
**1941, Mar. 6** **Perf. 12½**
236 A33 25a on 3a gray green .85 1.60
Never hinged 1.60

Statue of Snorri
Sturluson
A45

Jon Sigurdsson
A46

**1941, Nov. 17 Engr. Perf. 14**
237 A45 25a rose red 1.50 2.75
238 A45 50a deep ultra 2.10 6.25
239 A45 1k dk olive grn 2.10 6.25
Nos. 237-239 (3) 5.70 15.25
Set, never hinged 10.00

Snorri Sturluson, writer and historian, 700th
death anniv.

**Republic**

**1944, June 17** **Perf. 14x13½**
240 A46 10a gray black .45 1.00
241 A46 25a dk red brn .55 1.00
242 A46 50a slate grn .55 1.00
243 A46 1k blue black .95 1.00
244 A46 5k henna 3.00 13.00
245 A46 10k golden brn 47.50 110.00
Nos. 240-245 (6) 53.00 127.00
Set, never hinged 110.00

Founding of Republic of Iceland, June 17,
1944.

> **Catalogue values for unused
> stamps in this section, from this
> point to the end of the section, are
> for Never Hinged items.**

A47

A48

Eruption of Hekla Volcano: 35a, 60a, Close
view of Hekla.

**Unwmk.**
**1948, Dec. 3 Engr. Perf. 14**
246 A47 12a dark vio brn .25 .65
247 A48 25a green 2.00 .25
248 A47 35a carmine rose .55 .40
249 A47 50a brown 2.75 .25
250 A47 60a bright ultra 9.75 5.50
251 A48 1k orange brown 14.00 .25
252 A48 10k violet black 70.00 .55
Nos. 246-252 (7) 99.30 7.85
Set, hinged 47.50

For surcharge see No. 283.

Pack Train
and UPU
Monument,
Bern — A49

UPU, 75th Anniv.: 35a, Reykjavik. 60a,
Map. 2k, Thingvellir Road.

**1949, Oct. 9**
253 A49 25a dark green .40 .65
254 A49 35a deep carmine .40 .65
255 A49 60a blue .65 1.40
256 A49 2k orange red 1.60 1.50
Nos. 253-256 (4) 3.05 4.20

Trawler — A50

Jon
Arason — A51

Designs: 20a, 75a, 1k, Tractor plowing. 60a,
5k, Flock of sheep. 5a, 90a, 2k, Vestman-
naeyjar harbor.

**1950-54** **Perf. 13**
257 A50 5a dk brn ('54) .20 .20
258 A50 10a gray .20 .20
259 A50 20a brown .20 .20
260 A50 25a car ('54) .20 .20
261 A50 60a green 20.00 25.00
262 A50 75a red org ('52) .55 .20
263 A50 90a carmine .65 .40
264 A50 1k chocolate 7.50 .20
265 A50 1.25k red vio ('52) 25.00 .20
266 A50 1.50k deep ultra 18.00 .70
267 A50 2k purple 32.50 .35
268 A50 5k dark grn 45.00 1.25
Nos. 257-268 (12) 150.00 29.10
Set, hinged 45.00

For surcharges see Nos. B12-B13.

**1950, Nov. 7** **Perf. 14**
269 A51 1.80k carmine 3.50 3.75
270 A51 3.30k green 1.75 2.50

Bishop Jon Arason, 400th anniv. of death.

Mail Delivery,
1776 — A52

Design: 3k, Airmail, 1951.

**1951, May 13**
271 A52 2k deep ultra 2.75 2.75
272 A52 3k dark purple 4.00 3.25

175th anniv. of Iceland's postal service.

Parliament
Building — A53

**1952, Apr. 1** **Perf. 13x12½**
273 A53 25k gray black 210.00 19.00
Hinged 90.00

Sveinn
Björnsson
A54

Reykjabok
A55

**1952, Sept. 1** **Perf. 13½**
274 A54 1.25k deep blue 2.75 .20
275 A54 2.20k deep green .65 4.50
276 A54 5k indigo 9.50 1.60
277 A54 10k brown red 42.50 27.50
Nos. 274-277 (4) 55.40 33.80

Sveinn Björnsson, 1st President of Iceland.

**1953, Oct. 1** **Perf. 13½x13**

Designs: 70a, Lettering manuscript. 1k, Corner of 15th century manuscript, "Stjorn."
1.75k, Reykjabok. 10k, Corner from law
manuscript.

278 A55 10a black .20 .20
279 A55 70a green .30 .30
280 A55 1k carmine .40 .20
281 A55 1.75k blue 27.50 1.60
282 A55 10k orange brn 12.50 1.25
Nos. 278-282 (5) 40.90 3.55

No. 248 Surcharged With New Value
and Bars in Black
**1954, Mar. 31** **Perf. 14**
283 A47 5a on 35a car rose .35 .35
a. Bars omitted 90.00
b. Inverted surcharge 250.00

Hannes
Hafstein
A56

Icelandic
Wrestling
A57

Portraits: 2.45k, in oval. 5k, fullface.

**1954, June 1    Engr.    Perf. 13**
284 A56 1.25k deep blue       5.00    .70
285 A56 2.45k dark green     25.00   35.00
286 A56 5k carmine           27.50    3.25
   Nos. 284-286 (3)          57.50   38.95

Appointment of the first native minister to
Denmark, 50th anniv.

**1955, Aug. 9    Unwmk.    Perf. 14**
287 A57 75a shown             .20    .20
288 A57 1.25k Diving          .60    .30

See Nos. 300-301.

Skoga Falls — A58

Ellidaar
Power
Plant — A59

Waterfalls: 60a, Goda. 2kr, Detti. 5kr, Gull.
Electric Power Plants: 1.50kr, Sogs. 2.45kr,
Andakilsar. 3kr, Laxar.

**Perf. 11½, 13½x14 (A59)**
**1956, Apr. 4    Unwmk.**
289 A58 15a vio blue          .20    .20
290 A59 50a dull green        .30    .20
291 A59 60a brown            2.75    4.50
292 A59 1.50k violet         30.00    .20
293 A59 2k sepia             1.60    .45
294 A59 2.45k gray black     6.50    9.00
295 A59 3k dark blue         5.50    .90
296 A58 5k dark green        13.50    1.60
   Nos. 289-296 (8)          60.35   17.05

Telegraph-Telephone Emblem and
Map — A60

**1956, Sept. 29    Engr.    Perf. 13**
297 A60 2.30k ultramarine     .35    1.10

Telegraph and Telephone service in Iceland,
50th anniv.

### Northern Countries Issue

Whooper
Swans — A60a

**1956, Oct. 30    Perf. 12½**
298 A60a 1.50k rose red       .70    1.25
299 A60a 1.75k ultra         10.50   12.50

To emphasize the bonds among Denmark,
Finland, Iceland, Norway and Sweden.

### Sports Type of 1955

1.50k, Icelandic wrestling. 1.75k, Diving.

---

**1957, Apr. 1    Engr.    Perf. 14**
300 A57 1.50k carmine        1.10    .25
301 A57 1.75k ultramarine     .45    .25

### Type of 1952 Air Post Stamps
### Plane Omitted

Glaciers: 2k, Snaefellsjokull. 3k, Eiriksjokull.
10k, Oraefajokull.

**1957, May 8    Perf. 13½x14**
302 AP16 2k green            4.50    .30
303 AP16 3k dark blue        5.00    .30
304 AP16 10k reddish brn     6.75    .35
   Nos. 302-304 (3)         16.25    .95

Bessastadir,
President's
Residence
A61

**1957, Aug. 1    Engr.    Unwmk.**
305 A61 25k gray blk         25.00   4.50

Evergreen and
Volcanoes
A62

Jonas
Hallgrimsson
A63

**1957, Sept. 4    Perf. 13½x13**
306 A62 35a shown             .25    .20
307 A62 70a Birch             .25    .20

Issued to publicize a reforestation program.

**1957, Nov 16**
308 A63 5k grn & blk         1.75    .60

150th birth anniv. of Jonas Hallgrimsson,
poet.

Willow
Herb — A64

Icelandic
Pony — A65

**1958, July 8    Litho.    Unwmk.**
309 A64 1k shown              .20    .20
310 A64 2.50k Wild pansy      .45    .45

**1958, Sept. 27    Engr.**
311 A65 10a gray black        .20    .20
312 A65 2.25k brown           .70    .35

See No. 324.

Flag — A66

Old Icelandic
Government
Building — A67

**Perf. 13½x14**
**1958, Dec. 1    Litho.    Unwmk.**
   Size: 17½x21mm
313 A66 3.50k brt ultra & red  2.50   .70
   Size: 23x26½mm
314 A66 50k brt ultra & red    8.00   8.00

40th anniversary of Icelandic flag.

**1958, Dec. 9    Photo.    Perf. 11½**
315 A67 2k deep green         .55    .20
316 A67 4k deep brown         .65    .40

See Nos. 333-334.

---

Jon Thorkelsson
Teaching — A68

**1959, May 5    Engr.    Perf. 13½**
317 A68 2k green              .45    .55
318 A68 3k dull purple        .65    .75

Death bicentenary of Jon Thorkelsson,
headmaster of Skaholt.

Sockeye
Salmon
A69

Eider Ducks — A70

Design: 25k, Gyrfalcon.

**1959-60    Engr.    Perf. 14**
319 A69 25a dark blue         .20    .20
320 A70 90a chestnut & blk    .20    .20
321 A70 2k olive grn & blk    .45    .20
322 A69 5k gray green        10.50   1.10

**Litho.    Perf. 11½**
323 A70 25k dl pur, gray & yel 17.00 14.00
   Nos. 319-323 (5)          28.35  15.70

Issued: 25k, Mar. 1, 1960; others, Nov. 25.

### Pony Type of 1958

**1960, Apr. 7    Engr.    Perf. 13½x13**
324 A65 1k dark carmine       .50    .50

"The Outlaw" by
Einar Jonsson
A71

Wild Geranium
A72

**1960, Apr. 7    Perf. 14**
325 A71 2.50k reddish brn     .30    .30
326 A71 4.50k ultramarine     .85    .85

World Refugee Year, 7/1/59-6/30/60.

---

Common Design Types
pictured following the introduction.

### Europa Issue, 1960
Common Design Type
**1960, Sept. 18    Photo.    Perf. 11½**
   Size: 32½x22mm
327 CD3 3k grn & lt grn       .50    .50
328 CD3 5.50k dk bl & lt bl   .80    .80

**1960-62    Photo.    Perf. 11½**

Flowers: 50a, Bellflower. 2.50k, Dandelion.
3.50k, Buttercup.
329 A72 50a gray grn, grn & vi-
        olet ('62)            .20    .20
330 A72 1.20k sep, vio & grn  .20    .20
331 A72 2.50k brn, yel & grn  .20    .20
332 A72 3.50k dl bl, yel & green
        ('62)                 .65    .20
   Nos. 329-332 (4)          1.25    .80

See Nos. 363-366, 393-394.

---

### Building Type of 1958
**1961, Apr. 11    Unwmk.    Perf. 11½**
333 A67 1.50k deep blue       .30    .20
334 A67 3k dark carmine       .30    .20

Jon
Sigurdsson
A73

Reykjavik
A74

### Typographed and Embossed
**1961, June 17    Perf. 12½x14**
335 A73 50a crimson           .20    .20
336 A73 3k dark blue         1.50    1.00
337 A73 5k deep plum          .60    .55
   Nos. 335-337 (3)          2.30    1.75

Jon Sigurdsson (1811-1879), statesman
and scholar.

**1961, Aug. 18    Photo.    Perf. 11½**
338 A74 2.50k blue & grn      .65    .30
339 A74 4.50k lilac & vio bl 1.00    .50

Municipal charter of Reykjavik, 175th anniv.

### Europa Issue, 1961
Common Design Type
**1961, Sept. 18**
   Size: 32x22½mm
340 CD4 5.50k multicolored    .45    .45
341 CD4 6k multicolored       .45    .45

Benedikt
Sveinsson — A75

University of
Iceland — A76

Design: 1.40k, Björn M. Olsen.

**1961, Oct. 6    Photo.    Perf. 11½**
342 A75 1k red brown          .20    .20
343 A75 1.40k ultramarine     .20    .20
344 A76 10k green            1.40    .60
a.   Souv. sheet of 3, #342-344, im-
     perf.                    .90    1.60
   Nos. 342-344 (3)          1.80    1.00

50th anniv. of the University of Iceland;
Benedikt Sveinsson (1827-1899), statesman;
and Björn M. Olsen (1850-1919), first rector.

Production
Institute — A77

New Buildings: 4k, Fishing Research Institute. 6k, Farm Bureau.

**1962, July 6    Unwmk.    Perf. 11½**
345 A77 2.50k ultramarine     .40    .25
346 A77 4k dull green         .55    .25
347 A77 6k brown              .65    .30
   Nos. 345-347 (3)          1.60    .80

### Europa Issue, 1962
Common Design Type
**1962, Sept. 17    Perf. 11½**
   Size: 32½x22½mm
348 CD5 5.50k yel, lt grn & brn .20   .20
349 CD5 6.50k lt grn, grn & brn .60   .60

Map Showing Submarine Telephone Cable — A78

**1962, Nov. 20**
**Granite Paper**
350 A78 5k multicolored .... 1.10 .55
351 A78 7k grn, lt bl & red .... .55 .35

Inauguration of the submarine telephone cable from Newfoundland, via Greenland and Iceland to Scotland.

Sigurdur Gudmundsson, Self-portrait A79

Herring Boat A80

5.50k, Knight slaying dragon, Romanesque door from Valthjofsstad Church, ca. 1200 A.D.

**1963, Feb. 20    Photo.    Perf. 11½**
352 A79 4k bis brn & choc .... .50 .30
353 A79 5.50k gray ol & brn .... .50 .30

National Museum of Iceland, cent., and its first curator, Sigurdur Gudmundsson.

**1963, Mar. 21**
354 A80 5k multicolored .... .90 .30
355 A80 7.50k multicolored .... .25 .20

FAO "Freedom from Hunger" campaign.

View of Akureyri A81

**1963, July 2    Unwmk.    Perf. 11½**
356 A81 3k gray green .... .25 .20

**Europa Issue, 1963**
**Common Design Type**
**1963, Sept. 16**
**Size: 32½x23mm**
357 CD6 6k org brn & yel .... .75 .75
358 CD6 7k blue & yellow .... .75 .75

M.S. Gullfoss A82

**1964, Jan. 17    Photo.    Perf. 11½**
359 A82 10k ultra, blk & gray .... 2.25 1.60
  a.  Accent on 2nd "E" omitted .... 40.00 50.00

Iceland Steamship Company, 50th anniv.

Scout Emblem and "Be Prepared" A83

Icelandic Coat of Arms A84

**1964, Apr. 24**
360 A83 3.50k multicolored .... .55 .20
361 A83 4.50k multicolored .... .55 .30

Issued to honor the Boy Scouts.

**1964, June 17    Perf. 11½**
362 A84 25k multicolored .... 3.00 2.75

20th anniversary, Republic of Iceland.

**Flower Type of 1960-62**
Flowers: 50a, Eight-petal dryas. 1k, Crowfoot (Ranunculus glacialis). 1.50k, Buck bean. 2k, Clover (trifolium repens).

**1964, July 15**
**Flowers in Natural Colors**
363 A72  50a vio bl & lt vio bl .... .30 .20
364 A72   1k gray & dk gray .... .30 .20
365 A72  1.50k brn & pale brn .... .30 .20
366 A72   2k ol & pale olive .... .30 .20
     Nos. 363-366 (4) .... 1.20 .80

**Europa Issue, 1964**
**Common Design Type**
**1964, Sept. 14    Photo.    Perf. 11½**
**Granite Paper**
**Size: 22½x33mm**
367 CD7 4.50k golden brn, yel &
             Prus grn .... .75 .65
368 CD7  9k bl, yel & dk brn .... 1.25 1.00

Jumper — A85

**1964, Oct. 20    Unwmk.    Perf. 11½**
369 A85 10k lt grn & blk .... 1.25 1.00

18th Olympic Games, Tokyo, Oct. 10-25.

ITU Emblem A86

**1965, May 17    Photo.    Perf. 11½**
370 A86 4.50k green .... .90 .60
371 A86 7.50k bright ultra .... .20 .20

ITU, centenary.

Surtsey Island, April 1964 — A87

1.50k, Underwater volcanic eruption, Nov. 1963, vert. 3.50k, Surtsey, Sept. 1964.

**1965, June 23    Unwmk.    Perf. 11½**
372 A87 1.50k bl, bis & blk .... .65 .65
373 A87   2k multicolored .... .65 .65
374 A87 3.50k bl, blk & red .... .75 .65
     Nos. 372-374 (3) .... 2.05 1.95

Emergence of a new volcanic island off the southern coast of Iceland.

**Europa Issue, 1965**
**Common Design Type**
**1965, Sept. 27    Photo.    Perf. 11½**
**Size: 33x22½mm**
375 CD8 5k tan, brn & brt grn .... 1.50 1.00
376 CD8 8k brt grn, brn & yel
             green .... 1.00 .75

Einar Benediktsson A88

**Engr. & Litho.**
**1965, Nov. 16    Perf. 14**
377 A88 10k brt blue & brn .... 4.00 4.75

Einar Benediktsson, poet (1864-1940).

White-tailed Sea Eagle — A89

National Costume — A90

**1965-66    Photo.    Perf. 11½**
378 A89 50k multicolored .... 12.50 12.50
379 A90 100k multicolored .... 9.50 9.00

Issued: #378, 4/26/66; #379, 12/3/65.

West Iceland — A91

**1966, Aug. 4    Photo.    Perf. 11½**
380 A91 2.50k shown .... .35 .35
381 A91   4k North Iceland .... .55 .35
382 A91   5k East Iceland .... .90 .35
383 A91 6.50k South Iceland .... .70 .35
     Nos. 380-383 (4) .... 2.50 1.40

**Europa Issue, 1966**
**Common Design Type**
**1966, Sept. 26    Photo.    Perf. 11½**
**Size: 22½x33mm**
384 CD9 7k grnsh bl, lt bl & red .... 2.50 1.90
385 CD9 8k brn, buff & red .... 2.50 1.90

Literary Society Emblem A92

**1966, Nov. 18    Engr.    Perf. 11½**
386 A92 4k ultramarine .... .35 .30
387 A92 10k vermilion .... .80 .60

Icelandic Literary Society, 150th anniv.

Common Loon — A93

**1967, Mar. 16    Photo.    Perf. 11½**
388 A93 20k multicolored .... 5.50 5.50

**Europa Issue, 1967**
**Common Design Type**
**1967, May 2    Photo.    Perf. 11½**
**Size: 22½x33mm**
389 CD10 7k yel, brn & dk bl .... 1.50 1.00
390 CD10 8k emer, gray & dk bl .... 1.50 1.00

Old and New Maps of Iceland and North America A94

**1967, June 8    Photo.    Perf. 11½**
391 A94 10k blk, tan & lt bl .... .35 .30

EXPO '67 Intl. Exhibition, Montreal, Apr. 28-Oct. 27, 1967. The old map, drawn about 1590 by Sigurdur Stefansson, is at the Royal Library, Copenhagen.

Symbols of Trade, Fishing, Husbandry and Industry A95

**1967, Sept. 14    Photo.    Perf. 11½**
392 A95 5k dk bl, yel & emerald .... .35 .25

Icelandic Chamber of Commerce, 50th anniv.

**Flower Type of 1960-62**
Flowers: 50a, Saxifraga oppositifolia. 2.50k, Orchis maculata.

**1968, Jan. 17    Photo.    Perf. 11½**
**Flowers in Natural Colors**
393 A72  50a green & dk brn .... .25 .25
394 A72 2.50k dk brn, yel & grn .... .35 .35

**Europa Issue, 1968**
**Common Design Type**
**1968, Apr. 29    Photo.    Perf. 11½**
**Size: 33½x23mm**
395 CD11 9.50k dl yel, car rose
             & blk .... 1.75 1.50
396 CD11 10k brt yel grn, blk &
             org .... 1.25 1.00

Right-hand Driving — A96

**1968, May 21    Photo.    Perf. 11½**
397 A96 4k yellow & brn .... .35 .20
398 A96 5k lt reddish brn .... .35 .20

Introduction of right-hand driving in Iceland, May 26, 1968.

Fridrik Fridriksson, by Sigurjón Olafsson — A97

**1968, Sept. 5    Photo.    Perf. 11½**
399 A97 10k sky bl & dk gray .... .45 .55

Rev. Fridrik Fridriksson (1868-1961), founder of the YMCA in Reykjavik and writer.

Reading Room, National Library A98

Prime Minister Jon Magnusson (1859-1926) A99

**1968, Oct. 30    Photo.    Perf. 11½**
**Granite Paper**
400 A98 5k yellow & brn .... .25 .20
401 A98 20k lt bl & dp ultra .... .90 .90

Natl. Library, Reykjavik, sesquicentennial.

**1968, Dec. 12**
**Granite Paper**
402 A99 4k carmine lake .... .35 .25
403 A99 50k dark brown .... 3.75 4.25

50th anniversary of independence.

## Nordic Cooperation Issue

Five Ancient Ships — A99a

**1969, Feb. 28　Engr.　Perf. 12½**
404　A99a　6.50k vermilion　.55　.50
405　A99a　10k bright blue　.65　.60

50th anniv. of the Nordic Society and centenary of postal cooperation among the northern countries. The design is taken from a coin found at the site of Birka, an ancient Swedish town. See also Denmark Nos. 454-455, Finland No. 481, Norway Nos. 523-524, and Sweden Nos. 808-810.

### Europa Issue, 1969
#### Common Design Type
**1969, Apr. 28　Photo.　Perf. 11½**
**Size: 32½x23mm**
406　CD12　13k pink & multi　3.75　2.00
407　CD12　14.50k yel & multi　.45　.40

Flag of Iceland and Rising Sun — A100

**1969, June 17　Photo.　Perf. 11½**
408　A100　25k gray, gold, vio bl
　　　　　& red　.90　.55
409　A100　100k lt bl, gold, vio bl
　　　　　& red　5.75　5.75

25th anniversary, Republic of Iceland.

Boeing 727 A101

Design: 12k, Rolls Royce 400.

**1969, Sept. 3　Photo.　Perf. 11½**
410　A101　9.50k dk bl & sky bl　.55　.55
411　A101　12k dk bl & ultra　.55　.55

50th anniversary of Icelandic aviation.

Snaefellsjökull Mountain A102

**1970, Jan. 6　Photo.　Perf. 11½**
412　A102　1k shown　.20　.20
413　A102　4k Laxfoss　.35　.35
414　A102　5k Hattver, vert.　.40　.35
415　A102　20k Fjardargill, vert.　1.60　.55
　　　Nos. 412-415 (4)　2.55　1.45

First Meeting of Icelandic Supreme Court A103

**1970, Feb. 16　Photo.　Perf. 11½**
416　A103　6.50k multicolored　.30　.25

Icelandic Supreme Court, 50th anniv.

---

Column from "Skarosbók," 1363 (Law Book) — A104

Icelandic Manuscripts: 15k, Preface to "Flateyjarbók" (History of Norwegian Kings), 1387-1394. 30k, Initial from "Flateyjarbók" showing Harald Fairhair cutting fetters of Dofri.

**1970, Mar. 20　Photo.　Perf. 11½**
417　A104　5k multicolored　.25　.25
418　A104　15k multicolored　.65　.65
419　A104　30k multicolored　1.25　1.25
　　　Nos. 417-419 (3)　2.15　2.15

### Europa Issue, 1970
#### Common Design Type
**1970, May 4　Photo.　Perf. 11½**
**Size: 32x22mm**
420　CD13　9k brn & yellow　2.50　1.50
421　CD13　25k brt grn & bister　3.50　2.50

Nurse — A105　　Grimur Thomsen — A106

The Rest, by Thorarinn B. Thorlaksson A107

**1970, June 19　Photo.　Perf. 11½**
422　A105　7k ultra & lt bl　.35　.20
423　A106　10k ind & lt grnsh bl　.35　.45
424　A107　50k gold & multi　2.00　1.50
　　　Nos. 422-424 (3)　2.70　2.15

50th anniv. (in 1969) of the Icelandic Nursing Association (No. 422); 150th birth anniv. of Grimur Thomsen (1820-1896), poet (No. 423); Intl. Arts Festival, Reykjavik, June 1970 (No. 424).

Saxifraga Oppositifolia A108　　Lakagigar A109

**1970, Aug. 25　Photo.　Perf. 11½**
425　A108　3k multicolored　.30　.30
426　A109　15k multicolored　.90　.80

European Nature Conservation Year.

UN Emblem and Map of Iceland A110

**1970, Oct. 23　Photo.　Perf. 11½**
427　A110　12k multicolored　.55　.65

25th anniversary of United Nations.

---

"Flight," by Asgrimur Jonsson A111

**1971, Mar. 26　Photo.　Perf. 11½**
428　A111　10k multicolored　.80　.80

Joint northern campaign for the benefit of refugees.

### Europa Issue, 1971
#### Common Design Type
**1971, May 3　Photo.　Perf. 11½**
**Size: 33x22mm**
429　CD14　7k rose cl, yel & blk　2.50　1.75
430　CD14　15k ultra, yel & blk　3.00　2.00

Postal Checking Service Emblem A112

**1971, June 22　Photo.　Perf. 11½**
431　A112　5k vio bl & lt blue　.20　.25
432　A112　7k dk grn & yel grn　.30　.25

Introduction of Postal Checking Service, Apr. 30, 1971.

Tryggvi Gunnarsson A113　　Haddock Freezing Plant A114

Design: 30k, Patriotic Society emblem.

**1971, Aug. 19　Photo.　Perf. 11½**
433　A113　30k lt bl & vio blk　1.50　1.00
434　A113　100k gray & vio blk　6.00　5.75

Icelandic Patriotic Society, cent.; Tryggvi Gunnarsson (1835-1917), founder and president.

**1971, Nov. 18**
Fish Industry: 7k, Cod fishing. 20k, Shrimp canning plant.
435　A114　5k multicolored　.20　.20
436　A114　7k multicolored　.20　.20
437　A114　20k green & multi　1.10　.55
　　　Nos. 435-437 (3)　1.50　.95

Herdubreid Mountain — A115

**Engr. & Litho.**
**1972, Mar. 9　　Perf. 14**
438　A115　250k blue & multi　.70　.30

### Europa Issue 1972
#### Common Design Type
**1972, May 2　Photo.　Perf. 11½**
**Size: 22x32mm**
439　CD15　9k lt vio & multi　1.50　.90
440　CD15　13k yel grn & multi　2.75　1.75

---

"United Municipalities" — A116

**1972, June 14　Photo.　Perf. 11½**
441　A116　16k multicolored　.25　.20

Legislation for local government, cent.

Chessboard, World Map, Rook — A117

**1972, July 2　Litho.　Perf. 13**
442　A117　15k lt ol & multi　.45　.35

World Chess Championship, Reykjavik, July-Sept. 1972.

Hothouse Tomatoes A118

Designs: 12k, Steam valve and natural steam. 40k, Hothouse roses.

**1972, Aug. 23　Photo.　Perf. 11½**
443　A118　8k Prus bl & multi　.20　.20
444　A118　12k green & multi　.20　.20
445　A118　40k dk pur & multi　1.50　1.10
　　　Nos. 443-445 (3)　1.90　1.50

Hothouse gardening in Iceland, using natural steam and hot springs.

Iceland and the Continental Shelf — A119

**1972, Sept. 27　Litho.　Perf. 13**
446　A119　9k blue & multi　.25　.25

To publicize Iceland's offshore fishing rights.

### Europa Issue 1973
#### Common Design Type
**1973, Apr. 30　Photo.　Perf. 11½**
**Size: 32½x22mm**
447　CD16　13k vio & multi　6.00　3.25
448　CD16　25k olive & multi　1.00　.80

Iceland No. 1 and Messenger — A120

Designs (First Issue of Iceland and): 15k, No. 5 and pony train. 20k, No. 2 and mailboat "Esja." 40k, No. 3 and mail truck. 80k, No. 4 and Beech-18 mail plane.

**Litho. & Engr.**
**1973, May 23　　Perf. 13x13½**
449　A120　10k dl bl, blk & ultra　.30　.30
450　A120　15k grn, blk & gray　.20　.20
451　A120　20k maroon, blk & car　.20　.20
452　A120　40k vio, blk & brn　.20　.20
453　A120　80k olive, blk & yel　1.40　.90
　　　Nos. 449-453 (5)　2.30　1.80

Centenary of Iceland's first postage stamps.

## Nordic Cooperation Issue

Nordic House, Reykjavik
A120a

**1973, June 26    Engr.    Perf. 12½**
454  A120a  9k multicolored        .50   .20
455  A120a  10k multicolored      1.50  1.25

A century of postal cooperation among Denmark, Finland, Iceland, Norway and Sweden, and in connection with the Nordic Postal Conference, Reykjavik.

Ásgeir Ásgeirsson, (1894-1972),President of Iceland 1952-1968 — A121

**1973, Aug. 1    Engr.    Perf. 13x13½**
456  A121  13k carmine        .45   .35
457  A121  15k blue           .20   .35

Islandia 73 Emblem
A122

20k, Islandia 73 emblem; diff. arrangement.

**1973, Aug. 31    Photo.    Perf. 11½**
458  A122  17k gray & multi        .45   .45
459  A122  20k brn, ocher & yel    .35   .35

Islandia 73 Philatelic Exhibition, Reykjavik, Aug. 31-Sept. 9.

Man and WMO Emblem
A123

The Settlement, Tapestry by Vigdis Kristjansdottir
A124

**1973, Nov. 14    Photo.    Perf. 12½**
460  A123  50k silver & multi    .80   .65

Intl. meteorological cooperation, cent.

**1974    Photo.    Perf. 11½**

Designs: 13k, Establishment of Althing, painting by Johannes Johannesson, horiz. 15k, Gudbrandur Thorlakkson, Bishop of Holar 1571-1627. 17k, Age of Sturlungar (Fighting Vikings), drawing by Thorvaldur Skulason. 20k, Stained glass window honoring Hallgrimur Petursson (1614-74), hymn writer. 25k, Illumination from Book of Flatey, 14th century. 30k, Conversion to Christianity (altarpiece, Skalholt), mosaic by Nina Tryggvadottir. 40k, Wood carving (family and plants), 18th century. 60k, Curing the Catch, cement bas-relief. 70k, Age of Writing (Saemundur Riding Seal), sculpture by Asmundur Sveinsson. 100k, Virgin and Child with Angels, embroidered antependium, Stafafell Church, 14th century.

461  A124  10k multicolored    .20   .20
462  A124  13k multicolored    .20   .20
463  A124  15k multicolored    .20   .20
464  A124  17k multicolored    .35   .20
465  A124  20k multicolored    .35   .20
466  A124  25k multicolored    .20   .20
467  A124  30k multicolored    .90   .70
468  A124  40k multicolored   1.10   .85
469  A124  60k multicolored   1.10  1.10

470  A124  70k multicolored   1.10  1.00
471  A124  100k multicolored  1.60   .70
    Nos. 461-471 (11)         7.30  5.55

1100th anniv. of settlement of Iceland.
Issued: 10k, 13k, 30k, 70k, 3/12; 17k, 25k, 100k, 6/11; 15k, 20k, 40k, 60k, 7/16.

Horseback Rider, Wood, 17th Century — A125

Europa: 20k, "Through the Sound Barrier," contemporary bronze by Asmundur Sveinsson.

**1974, Apr. 29    Photo.    Perf. 11½**
472  A125  13k brn red & multi    .70   .40
473  A125  20k gray & multi      1.60  1.00

Clerk Selling Stamps, UPU Emblem
A126

Design: 20k, Mailman delivering mail.

**1974, Oct. 9    Photo.    Perf. 11½**
474  A126  17k ocher & multi    .35   .35
475  A126  20k olive & multi    .35   .35

Centenary of Universal Postal Union.

Volcanic Eruption, Heimaey, Jan. 23, 1973 — A127

Design: 25k, Volcanic eruption, night view.

**1975, Jan. 23    Photo.    Perf. 11½**
476  A127  20k multicolored    .65   .45
477  A127  25k multicolored    .35   .35

## Europa Issue 1975

Bird, by Thorvaldur Skulason
A128

Sun Queen, by Johannes S. Kjarval—A129

**1975, May 12    Photo.    Perf. 11½**
478  A128  18k multicolored    .50   .40
479  A129  23k gold & multi   1.50  1.00

Stephan G. Stephansson
A130

**1975, Aug. 1    Engr.    Perf. 13**
480  A130  27k green & brn        .55   .35

Stephan G. Stephansson (1853-1927), Icelandic poet and settler in North America; centenary of Icelandic emigration to North America.

Petursson, by Hjalti Thorsteinsson
A131

Einar Jonsson, Self-portrait
A132

23k, Arni Magnusson, by Hjalti Thorsteinsson. 30k, Jon Eiriksson, sculpture by Olafur Olafsson.

**1975, Sept. 18    Engr.    Perf. 13**
481  A131  18k slate green & indigo    .20   .20
482  A131  23k Prussian blue          .20   .20
483  A131  30k deep magenta           .20   .20
484  A132  50k indigo                 .50   .20
    Nos. 481-484 (4)                  1.10   .80

Famous Icelanders: Hallgrimur Petursson (1614-1674), minister and religious poet; Arni Magnusson (1663-1730), historian, registrar and manuscript collector; Jon Eiriksson (1728-1787), professor of law and cabinet member; Einar Jonsson (1874-1954), sculptor, painter and writer.

Red Cross A133

**1975, Oct. 15    Photo.    Perf. 11½x12**
485  A133  23k multicolored    .45   .20

Icelandic Red Cross, 50th anniversary.

Abstract Painting, by Nina Tryggvadottir
A134

**1975, Oct. 15    Perf. 12x12½**
486  A134  100k multicolored   1.40   .65

International Women's Year 1975.

Thorvaldsen Statue, by Thorvaldsen
A135

Saplings Growing in Bare Landscape
A136

**1975, Nov. 19    Photo.    Perf. 11½**
487  A135  27k lt vio & multi    .80   .45

Centenary of Thorvaldsen Society, a charity honoring Bertel Thorvaldsen (1768-1844), sculptor.

**1975, Nov. 19    Perf. 12x11½**
488  A136  35k multicolored    .60   .45

Reforestation.

Lang Glacier, by Asgrimur Jonsson
A137

**1976, Mar. 18    Photo.    Perf. 11½**
489  A137  150k gold & multi    2.00  1.50

Asgrimur Jonsson (1876-1958), painter.

Wooden Bowl — A138

Europa: 45k, Spinning wheel, vert.

**1976, May 3    Photo.    Perf. 11½**
490  A138  35k ver & multi     1.40  1.00
491  A138  45k blue & multi    1.40  1.40

No. 9 with First Day Cancel — A139

Decree Establishing Postal Service — A140

**1976, Sept. 22    Photo.    Perf. 11½
Granite Paper**
492  A139  30k bis, blk & gray bl    .35   .20

Centenary of aurar stamps.

**1976, Sept. 22    Engr.    Perf. 13**

45k, Conclusion of Decree with signatures.
493  A140  35k dark brown    .45   .35
494  A140  45k dark blue     .45   .35

Iceland's Postal Service, bicentenary.

Federation Emblem, People — A141

**1976, Dec. 2**    Photo.    *Perf. 12½*
**Granite Paper**
495 A141 100k multicolored    1.00   .70
Icelandic Federation of Labor, 60th anniv.

Five Water Lilies — A142

Ofaerufoss, Eldgja — A143

**Photo. & Engr.**
**1977, Feb. 2**      *Perf. 12½*
496 A142 35k brt grn & multi    .90   .65
497 A142 45k ultra & multi    .90   .65
Nordic countries cooperation for protection of the environment and 25th Session of Nordic Council, Helsinki, Feb. 19.

**1977, May 2**    Photo.    *Perf. 12*
Europa: 85k, Kirkjufell Mountain, seen from Grundarfjord.
498 A143 45k multicolored    3.00 1.00
499 A143 85k multicolored    2.00   .45

Harlequin Duck — A144

**1977, June 14**    Photo.    *Perf. 11½*
500 A144 40k multicolored    .55   .35
Wetlands conservation, European campaign.

Society Emblem — A145

**1977, June 14**
501 A145 60k vio bl & ultra    .75   .65
Federation of Icelandic Cooperative Societies, 75th anniversary.

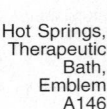

Hot Springs, Therapeutic Bath, Emblem A146

**1977, Nov. 16**    Photo.    *Perf. 11½*
502 A146 90k multicolored    .65   .55
World Rheumatism Year.

Stone Marker — A147

**1977, Dec. 12**    Engr.    *Perf. 11½*
503 A147 45k dark blue    .90   .65
Touring Club of Iceland, 50th anniversary.

Thorvaldur Thoroddsen, (1855-1921), Geologist, Scientist and Writer — A148

Design: 60k, Briet Bjarnhedinsdottir (1856-1940), Founder of Icelandic Women's Association and Reykjavik city councillor.

**1977, Dec. 12**    Engr.    *Perf. 11½*
504 A148 50k brn & slate grn    .20   .20
505 A148 60k grn & vio brn    .70   .60

Bailiff's Residence, Videy Island, 1752 — A149

Europa: 120k, Husavik Church, 1906.

**1978, May 2**    Photo.    *Perf. 11½*
506 A149 80k multicolored    2.25   .75
507 A149 120k multi, vert.    3.00 1.00

Alexander Johannesson, Junkers Planes — A150

100k, Fokker Friendship plane over mountains.

**1978, June 21**    Photo.    *Perf. 12½*
508 A150 60k multicolored    .55   .30
509 A150 100k multicolored    .55   .40
50th anniv. of domestic flights in Iceland.

Skeioara River Bridge A151

**1978, Aug. 17**    Photo.    *Perf. 11½*
510 A151 70k multicolored    .30   .30

Lava Near Mt. Hekla, by Jon Stefansson — A152

**1978, Nov. 16**    Photo.    *Perf. 12*
511 A152 1000k multicolored    5.00 4.25
Jon Stefansson (1881-1962), Icelandic painter.

Ship to Shore Rescue A153

**1978, Dec. 1**    Engr.    *Perf. 13*
512 A153 60k black    .30   .30
National Life Saving Assoc., 50th anniv.

Halldor Hermannsson (1878-1958), Historian, Librarian — A154

**1978, Dec. 1**
513 A154 150k indigo    .60   .50

Lighthouse A155      Telephone, c. 1900 A156

**1978, Dec. 1**    Photo.    *Perf. 11½*
514 A155 90k multicolored    .60   .50
Centenary of Icelandic lighthouses.

**1979, Apr. 30**    Photo.    *Perf. 11½*
Europa: 190k, Post horn and satchel.
515 A156 110k multicolored    3.75   .75
516 A156 190k multicolored    6.50 1.00

Jon Sigurdsson and Ingibjorg Einarsdottir A157

**1979, Nov. 1**    Engr.    *Perf. 13x12½*
517 A157 150k black    .60   .60
Jon Sigurdsson (1811-1879), Icelandic statesman and leader in independence movement.

Excerpt from Olafs Saga Helga — A158

**1979, Nov. 1**    Photo.    *Perf. 11½*
518 A158 200k multicolored    .80   .55
Snorri Sturluson (1178-1241), Icelandic historian and writer.

Children with Flowers ICY Emblem A159

**1979, Nov. 12**
519 A159 140k multicolored    .80   .55
International Year of the Child.

A160      A161

Icelandic Arms, before 1904 and 1904-1919.

**1979, Nov. 12**
520 A160 500k multicolored    1.50 1.00
Home rule, 75th anniversary.

**1979**    Engr.    *Perf. 13*
Designs: 80k, Ingibjorg H. Bjarnason (1867-1941). 100k, Bjarni Thorsteinsson (1861-1938), composer. 120k, Petur Gudjohnsen (1812-77), organist. 130k, Sveinbjorn Sveinbjornson (1847-1927), composer. 170k, Torfhildur Holm (1845-1918), poet.
521 A161 80k rose violet    .20   .20
522 A161 100k black    .20   .20
523 A161 120k rose carmine    .20   .20
524 A161 130k sepia    .45   .45
525 A161 170k carmine rose    .55   .40
    Nos. 521-525 (5)    1.60 1.45
Issued: 80k, 170k, Aug. 3; others, Dec. 12.

Canis Familiaris — A162

Design: 90k, Alopex lagopus.

**1980, Jan. 24**
526 A162 10k black    .25   .20
527 A162 90k sepia    .25   .20
See Nos. 534-536, 543-545, 552, 553, 556-558, 610-612.

Jon Sveinsson Nonni (1857-1944), Writer — A163

Europa: 250k, Gunnar Gunnarsson (1889-1975), writer.

**1980, Apr. 28**    Photo.    *Perf. 11½*
**Granite Paper**
528 A163 140k dl rose & blk    1.75   .75
529 A163 250k tan & blk    2.00   .90

Mountain Ash Branch and Berries — A164

**1980, July 8**    Photo.    *Perf. 12½*
530 A164 120k multicolored    .35   .35
Year of the Tree.

Laugardalur Sports Complex, Reykjavik A165

**1980, July 8**    Engr.    *Perf. 13x12½*
531 A165 300k slate green    .70   .55
1980 Olympic Games.

Carved and Painted Cabinet Door, 18th Cent. — A166      Radio Receiver, 1930 — A168

Nordic Cooperation: 180k, Embroidered cushion, 19th cent.

**1980, Sept. 9    Photo.    *Perf. 11½***
**Granite Paper**
532  A166  150k multicolored        .65   .50
533  A166  180k multicolored        .75   .60

**Animal Type of 1980**
**1980, Oct. 16    Engr.    *Perf. 13***
Designs: 160k, Sebastes marinus. 170k, Fratercula arctica. 190k, Phoca vitulina.
534  A162  160k rose violet         .90   .20
535  A162  170k black              1.00   .60
536  A162  190k dark brown          .20   .35
        *Nos. 534-536 (3)*         2.10  1.15

**1980, Nov. 20    Photo.    *Perf. 12½***
**Granite Paper**
537  A168  400k multicolored       1.10   .50
State Broadcasting Service, 50th anniv.

University Hospital, 50th Anniversary — A169

**1980, Nov. 20    *Perf. 11½***
538  A169  200k multicolored        .45   .45

A170

Design: 170a, Magnus Stephensen (1762-1833), Chief Justice. 190a, Finnur Magnusson (1781-1847), Privy Archives keeper.

**1981, Feb. 24    Engr.    *Perf. 13***
539  A170  170a bright ultra        .55   .35
540  A170  190a olive green         .55   .35

**Europa Issue 1981**

Europa — A171

**1981, May 4    Photo.    *Perf. 11½***
**Granite Paper**
541  A171  180a Luftur the Sorcerer  2.00  1.00
542  A171  220a Sea witch           2.00  1.00

**Animal Type of 1980**
**1981, Aug. 20    Engr.    *Perf. 13***
Designs: 50a, Troglodytes troglodytes. 100a, Pluvialis apricaria. 200a, Corvus corax.
543  A162  50a brown               .25   .20
544  A162  100a blue               .25   .20
545  A162  200a black              .25   .20
        *Nos. 543-545 (3)*         .75   .60

Intl. Year of the Disabled — A173

**1981, Sept. 29    Photo.    *Perf. 11½***
546  A173  200a multicolored        .30   .20

---

Skyggnir Earth Satellite Station, First Anniv. — A174

**1981, Sept. 29    Photo.    *Perf. 11½***
547  A174  500a multicolored       1.40   .70

Hauling the Line, by Gunnlaugur Scheving (1904-1972) A175

**1981, Oct. 21    Photo.    *Perf. 11½***
548  A175  5000a multi             7.00  3.75

Christian Missionary Work in Iceland Millennium A176

**1981, Nov. 24    Engr.    *Perf. 13***
549  A176  200a dark violet         .30   .30

Christmas A177

**1981, Nov. 24    Photo.    *Perf. 12½***
**Granite Paper**
550  A177  200a Leaf bread         1.00   .65
551  A177  250a Leaf bread, diff.  1.00   .55

**Animal Type of 1980**
**1982, Mar. 23    Engr.    *Perf. 13***
Designs: 20a, Buccinum undatum, vert. 600a, Chlamys islandica.
552  A162  20a copper brn          .25   .25
553  A162  600a vio brown         1.00   .50

**Europa Issue 1982**

First Norse Settlement, 874 — A179

**1982, May 3    Photo.    *Perf. 11½***
**Granite Paper**
554  A179  350a shown            10.00  1.50
555  A179  450a Discovery of North America, 1000   10.00  1.50

**Animal Type of 1980**
**1982, June 3    Engr.    *Perf. 13***
Designs: 300a, Ovis aries, vert. 400a, Bos taurus, vert. 500a, Felis catus, vert.
556  A162  300a brown              .90   .50
557  A162  400a lake               .65   .35
558  A162  500a gray               .20   .20
        *Nos. 556-558 (3)*        1.75  1.05

---

Kaupfelag Thingeyinga Cooperative Society Centenary — A181

**1982, June 3**
559  A181  1000a black & red        .90   .45

Man Riding Iceland Pony — A182

**1982, July 1    Photo.    *Perf. 11½***
**Granite Paper**
560  A182  700a multicolored        .80   .35

Centenary of School of Agriculture, Holar A183

**1982, July 1**
**Granite Paper**
561  A183  1500a multi            1.10   .65

Mount Herdubreid, by Isleifur Konradsson (1889-1972) A184

**1982, Sept. 8    Photo.    *Perf. 11½***
**Granite Paper**
562  A184  800a multicolored        .75   .65
UN World Assembly on Aging, 7/26-8/6.

Borbjorg Sveinsdottir (1828-1903) — A185

**1982, Sept. 8    Engr.    *Perf. 13***
563  A185  900a red brown          .70   .55
Borbjorg Sveinsdottir (1828-1903), midwife and Univ. founder.

**Souvenir Sheet**

NORDIA '84 — A186

**Photo. & Engr.**
**1982, Oct. 7    *Perf. 13½***
564      Sheet of 2               7.00  7.00
  **a.** A186 400a Reynistaour Monastery seal   3.50  3.50
  **b.** A186 800a Bingeyrar      3.50  3.50
NORDIA '84 Intl. Stamp Exhibition, Reykjavik, July 3-8, 1984. Sold for 18k.
See No. 581.

---

Christmas A187

Score from The Night was Such a Splendid One.

**1982, Nov. 16    Photo.    *Perf. 11½***
**Granite Paper**
565  A187  3k Birds                .90   .55
566  A187  3.50k Bells            1.00   .55

Caltha Palustris — A188

**1983, Feb. 10    Photo.**
**Granite Paper**
567  A188  7.50k shown             .55   .55
568  A188  8k Lychnis alpina       .90   .55
569  A188  10k Potentilla palustris  1.40   .55
570  A188  20k Myosotis scorpioides  2.50   .85
        *Nos. 567-570 (4)*        5.35  2.50
See #586-587, 593-594, 602-605, 663-664.

Nordic Cooperation A189

**1983, Mar. 24**
**Granite Paper**
571  A189  4.50k Mt. Sulur        1.20   .75
572  A189  5k Urrida Falls        1.20   .75

**Europa Issue, 1983**

Thermal Energy Projects — A190

**1983, May 5**
**Granite Paper**
573  A190  5k shown               7.50  2.00
574  A190  5.50k multi, diff.    25.00  2.50

Fishing Industry A191

**1983, June 8    Engr.    *Perf. 13x12½***
575  A191  11k Fishing boats       .40   .40
576  A191  13k Fishermen          1.40   .80

Bicentenary of Skaftareldar Volcanic Eruption A192

**1983, June 8      Photo.      Perf. 11½**
**Granite Paper**
577  A192  15k  Volcano, by Finnur
                Jonsson              .85   .75

Skiing — A193

**1983, Sept. 8     Photo.      Perf. 11½**
578  A193  12k  shown              .85   .65
579  A193  14k  Running          1.00   .75

World Communications Year — A194

**1983, Sept. 8                   Perf. 12½**
580  A194  30k  multi            2.75  1.25

NORDIA '84 Type of 1982
Souvenir Sheet

Bishops' Seals: 8k, Magnus Eyjolfsson of
Skalholt, 1477-90. 12k, Ogmundur Palsson of
Skalholt, 1521-40.

**Photo. & Engr.**
**1983, Oct. 6                    Perf. 13½**
581        Sheet of 2             9.25  9.25
  a.  A186  8k violet blue & black 4.50  4.50
  b.  A186  12k pale green & black 4.50  4.50

Sold for 30k.

Christmas        Pres. Kristjan
A195             Eldjarn (1916-82)
                 A196

**1983, Nov. 10    Photo.      Perf. 11½**
**Granite Paper**
582  A195  6k    Virgin and Child  .90   .55
583  A195  6.50k Angel             .90   .55

**1983, Dec. 6**
584  A196  6.50k brn carmine      1.10   .80
585  A196  7k    dark blue         .45   .25

Flower Type of 1983
**1984, Mar. 1     Photo.      Perf. 11½**
**Granite Paper**
586  A188  6k    Rosa pimpinellifolia 1.10 .55
587  A188  25k   Potentilla anserium 1.40 .55

Europa 1959-
84
A197

**1984, May 3**
588  A197  6.50k grnsh bl & blk   2.75   .75
589  A197  7.50k rose & black     1.50   .75

A198

---

Souvenir Sheet
Design: Abraham Ortelius' map of Northern
Europe, 1570.

**Photo. & Engr.**
**1984, June 6           Perf. 14x13½**
590  A198  40k  multi            18.00 18.00

NORDIA '84 Intl. Stamp Exhibition, Reykjavik, July 3-8. Sold for 60k.

A199

**1984, June 17    Photo.      Perf. 11½**
**Granite Paper**
591  A199  50k  Flags             6.00  3.25

40th Anniv. of Republic.

Good Templars Headquarters,
Akureyri — A200

**1984, July 18    Engr.        Perf. 13**
592  A200  10k  green             .70   .50

Order of the Good Templars, centenary in
Iceland, temperance org.

Flower Type of 1983
**1984, Sept. 11   Photo.      Perf. 11½**
**Granite Paper**
593  A188  6.50k Loiseleuria
                 procumbens       .55   .30
594  A188  7.50k Arctostaphylos
                 uva-ursi         .55   .30

Christmas        Gudbrand's Bible,
A201             400th Anniv.
                 A202

**1984, Nov. 29                     Photo.**
595  A201  600a Madonna and
                Child             .65   .30
596  A201  650a Angel, Christmas
                rose              .65   .45

**1984, Nov. 29    Engr.      Perf. 12½x13**
597  A202  6.50k Text             .55   .30
598  A202  7.50k Illustration     .35   .45

First Icelandic Bible.

Confederation of    Bjorn Bjarnarson
Employers, 50th     (1853-1918)
Anniv.              A204
A203

**1984, Nov. 9     Photo.    Perf. 12x12½**
**Granite Paper**
599  A203  30k  Building blocks  1.75  1.40

---

**1984, Nov. 9     Photo.      Perf. 11½**
**Granite Paper**
600  A204  12k  shown             .65   .65
601  A204  40k  New gallery build-
                ing, horiz.      2.10  1.50

Natl. Gallery centenary.

Flower Type of 1983
**1985, Mar. 20    Photo.      Perf. 11½**
**Granite Paper**
602  A188  8k   Rubus saxatilis   .90   .35
603  A188  9k   Veronica fruticans .90  .35
604  A188  16k  Lathyrus japonicus 2.50 .65
605  A188  17k  Draba alpina      .70   .60
       Nos. 602-605 (4)          5.00  1.95

Music Year Emblem,
Woman Playing the
Langspil — A205

Europa: 7.50k, Man playing the Icelandic
violin.

**1985, May 3      Photo.      Perf. 11½**
**Granite Paper**
606  A205  6.50k multicolored    3.50   .75
607  A205  7.50k multicolored    3.50   .95

Natl. Horticulture    Intl. Youth
Soc.,                 Year — A207
Cent. — A206

**1985, June 20    Photo.      Perf. 12**
608  A206  20k  Sorbus intermedia 1.10  .70

**1985, June 20    Photo.      Perf. 11½**
609  A207  25k  Icelandic girl   1.25   .95

Animal Type of 1980
**1985, Sept. 10   Engr.        Perf. 13**
Designs: 700a, Todarodes sagittatus. 800a,
Hyas araneus. 900a, Tealia felina.

610  A162  700a brn carmine      .20    .30
611  A162  800a dk brown         .35    .20
612  A162  900a carmine         1.10    .45
       Nos. 610-612 (3)         1.65    .95

Hannes Stephensen (1799-1856),
Cleric, Politician, Translator — A209

Famous men: 30k, Jon Gudmudsson (1807-
1875), editor, politician.

**1985, Sept. 10                    Engr.**
613  A209  13k  dp magenta       .65    .55
614  A209  30k  deep violet     1.50    .75

Yearning to
Fly, by
Johannes S.
Kjarval (1885-
1972),
Reykjavik Natl.
Museum
A210

**1985, Oct. 15    Photo.     Perf. 12x11½**
615  A210  100k multi           6.25  4.50

---

A211

Birds — A212

Abstract ice crystal paintings, by Snorri
Sveinn Fridriksson (b. 1934).

**1985, Nov. 14    Photo.      Perf. 11½**
616  A211  8k   Crucifix         .80    .35
617  A211  9k   Pine Trees       .80    .35

Christmas.

**1986, Mar. 19    Photo.      Perf. 11½**
**Granite Paper**
618  A212  6k   Motacilla alba   .20    .20
619  A212  10k  Anas acuta      1.75    .65
620  A212  12k  Falco columbarius 1.10  .65
621  A212  15k  Alca torda       .70    .45
       Nos. 618-621 (4)         3.75  1.95

See Nos. 642-645, 665-666, 671-672, 686-
687, 721, 725.

**Europa Issue 1986**

Natl.
Parks — A213

**1986, May 5**
622  A213  10k  Skaftafell      16.50  1.25
623  A213  12k  Jokulsargljufur  5.00  1.00

Nordic
Cooperation
Issue
A214

Sister towns.

**1986, May 27                  Perf. 11½**
624  A214  10k  Stykkisholmur   1.10    .75
625  A214  12k  Seydisfjordur   1.10    .75

Natl. Bank,
Cent.
A215

**1986, July 1     Engr.        Perf. 14**
626  A215  13k  Headquarters,
                Reykjavik       1.10    .80
627  A215  250k Banknote re-
                verse, 1928    11.00 10.00

Reykjavik
Bicent.
A216

**1986, Aug. 18    Engr.     Perf. 13½x14**
628  A216  10k  City seal, 1815  .85    .40
629  A216  12k  View from bank, il-
                lustration, 1856 .85    .40

630 A216 13k Laugardalur hot
water brook .85 .75
631 A216 40k City Theater 2.25 1.75
*Nos. 628-631 (4)* 4.80 3.30

Introduction of the
Telephone in
Iceland, 80th
Anniv. — A217

**1986, Sept. 29   Photo.   Perf. 11½**
**Granite Paper**
632 A217 10k Morse receiver,
1906 .55 .40
633 A217 20k Handset,
microchip, 1986 1.25 .70

Souvenir Sheet

Hvita River Crossing, Loa, 1836, by
Auguste Mayer — A218

**Photo. & Engr.**
**1986, Oct. 9   Perf. 14**
634 A218 20k bluish black 6.25 6.25
Stamp Day. Sold for 30k to benefit philatelic
organizations. See Nos. 646, 667.

Christmas — A219

Paintings by Bjoerg Thorsteinsdottir: 10k,
Christmas at Peace. 12k, Christmas Night.

**1986, Nov. 13   Photo.   Perf. 12**
635 A219 10k multicolored 1.00 .30
636 A219 12k multicolored .45 .30

Olafsvik
Trading
Station,
300th
Anniv.
A220

**1987, Mar. 26   Engr.   Perf. 14x13½**
637 A220 50k Merchantman
Svanur, 1777 3.00 1.10

Keflavik Intl. Airport Terminal
Inauguration — A221

**1987, Apr. 14   Photo.   Perf. 12x11½**
638 A221 100k multi 5.75 1.75

---

**Europa Issue 1987**

Stained Glass Windows by Leifur
Breidfjoerd, Fossvogur Cemetery
Chapel
A222

**1987, May 4   Photo.   Perf. 12x11½**
639 A222 12k Christ carrying the
cross 2.25 .75
640 A222 15k Soldiers, peace
dove 2.25 .95

Rasmus Christian
Rask (1787-
1832), Danish
Linguist — A223

**1987, June 10   Engr.   Perf. 13½**
641 A223 20k black 1.10 .80
Preservation of the Icelandic language.

Bird Type of 1986
**1987, Sept. 16   Photo.   Perf. 11½**
**Granite Paper**
642 A212 13k Asio flammeus 1.25 .50
643 A212 40k Turdus iliacus 2.25 .70
644 A212 70k Haematopus os-
tralegus 2.75 1.10
645 A212 90k Anas
platyrhynchos 5.00 1.50
*Nos. 642-645 (4)* 11.25 3.80

Stamp Day Type of 1986
Souvenir Sheet
**1987, Oct. 9   Engr.   Perf. 13½x14**
Trading Station of Djupivogur in 1836, by
Auguste Mayer.
646 A218 30k black 6.25 6.25
Stamp Day. Sold for 45k to benefit the
Stamp and Postal History Fund.

Dental
Protection — A226

**1987, Oct. 9   Photo.   Perf. 11½x12**
**Granite Paper**
647 A226 12k multi .55 .30

Vulture — A227

**Perf. 13 on 3 sides**
**1987, Oct. 9   Engr.**
Guardian Spirits of the North, East, South
and West.
**Booklet Stamps**
648 A227 13k shown .75 .50
649 A227 13k Dragon .75 .50
650 A227 13k Bull .75 .50
651 A227 13k Giant .75 .50
*a.* Block of 4, #648-651 3.00 3.00
*b.* Bklt. pane of 12, 3 #651a 9.00 —
Legend of Heimskringla, the story of the
Norse kings. Haraldur Gormsson, king of Denmark, deterred from invading Iceland after
hearing of the guardian spirits.
See Nos. 656-659, 677, 688-695.

---

Christmas — A228

**1987, Oct. 21   Photo.   Perf. 11½x12**
652 A228 13k Fir branch .65 .20
653 A228 17k Candle flame .65 .45

Steinn
Steinarr
(1908-1958)
A229

Poets: 21k, David Stefansson (1895-1964).

**1988, Feb. 25   Photo.   Perf. 12**
654 A229 16k multi .75 .35
655 A229 21k multi .90 .65

Guardian Spirit Type of 1987
**Perf. 13 on 3 sides**
**1988, May 2   Engr.**
**Booklet Stamps**
656 A227 16k Vulture .80 .55
657 A227 16k Dragon .80 .55
658 A227 16k Bull .80 .55
659 A227 16k Giant .80 .55
*a.* Block of 4, #656-659 3.25 3.25
*b.* Bklt. pane of 12, 3 #659a 9.75 —

**Europa Issue, 1988**

Modern Communication — A230

**1988, May 2   Photo.   Perf. 12x11½**
660 A230 16k Data transmission
system 1.25 .60
661 A230 21k Facsimile machine 5.00 2.00

1988
Summer
Olympics,
Seoul
A231

**1988, June 9   Photo.   Perf. 12**
**Granite Paper**
662 A231 18k Handball .80 .70

Flower Type of 1983
**1988, June 9   Perf. 11½**
**Granite Paper**
663 A188 10k Vicia cracca .55 .30
664 A188 50k Thymus praecox 3.00 .65

Bird Type of 1986
**1988, Sept. 21   Photo.   Perf. 11½**
**Granite Paper**
665 A212 5k Limosa limosa .45 .20
666 A212 30k Clangula hyemalis 1.75 .65

Stamp Day Type of 1986
Souvenir Sheet
**1988, Oct. 9   Engr.   Perf. 14**
Nupsstadur Farm, Fljotshverfi, 1836, by
Auguste Mayer.
667 A218 40k black 5.25 5.25
Stamp Day. Sold for 60k to benefit the
Stamp and Postal History Fund.

---

WHO, 40th
Anniv. — A234

**1988, Nov. 3   Photo.   Perf. 11½x12**
**Granite Paper**
668 A234 19k multicolored .80 .40

Christmas
A235

**1988, Nov. 3   Perf. 11½**
**Granite Paper**
669 A235 19k Fisherman at sea .90 .30
670 A235 24k Ship, buoy 1.10 .65

Bird Type of 1986
**1989, Feb. 2   Photo.**
671 A212 19k Phalaropus
lobatus 1.00 .40
672 A212 100k Plectrophenax
nivalis 6.00 1.25

Women's Folk
Costumes — A236

**1989, Apr. 20   Photo.   Perf. 11½x12**
**Granite Paper**
673 A236 21k Peysufot 1.75 .40
674 A236 26k Upphlutur 1.75 .65
Nordic cooperation.

Europa 1989
A237

Children's games.

**1989, May 30   Photo.   Perf. 11½**
**Granite Paper**
675 A237 21k Sailing toy boats 8.50 1.50
676 A237 26k Hoop, stick pony 8.50 1.50

Guardian Spirit Type of 1987
**1989, June 27   Engr.   Perf. 13**
677 A227 500k Dragon 19.00 8.50

Landscapes
A238

**1989, Sept. 20   Photo.   Perf. 11½**
**Granite Paper**
678 A238 35k Mt. Skeggi,
Arnarfjord 1.40 .55
679 A238 45k Thermal spring,
Namaskard 1.75 .55
See Nos. 713-714, 728, 737.

Agricultural College at Hvanneyri, Cent. A239

**1989, Sept. 20    Engr.    Perf. 14**
680  A239  50k multi                  2.00  1.25

Souvenir Sheet

NORDIA '91 — A240

Detail of *A Chart and Description of Northern Routes and Wonders to Be Found in the Nordic Countries,* 1539, by Olaus Magnus (1490-1557).

**1989, Oct. 9                    Perf. 12½**
681  A240  Sheet of 3          11.00  11.00
a.-c.  A240  any single          3.50   3.50

Stamp Day. Sold for 130k to benefit the exhibition.
See Nos. 715, 740.

Natural History Soc., Cent. A241

Flowers or fish and: 21k, Stefan Stefansson (1863-1921), botanist and founder. 26k, Bjarni Saemundsson (1867-1940), chairman.

**1989, Nov. 9    Photo.    Perf. 11½**
**Granite Paper**
682  A241  21k multi              .85   .85
683  A241  26k multi             1.00   .75

Christmas — A242

Paintings like stained-glass windows by Johannes Johannesson (b. 1921): 21k, Madonna and Child. 26k, Three Wise Men.

**1989, Nov. 9**
**Granite Paper**
684  A242  21k multi             1.10   .35
685  A242  26k multi             1.10   .65

Bird Type of 1986

**1990, Feb. 15**
**Granite Paper**
686  A212  21k *Anas penelope*   1.60   .55
687  A212  80k *Anser brachyrhynchus*  4.00  1.00

Guardian Spirit Type of 1987
*Perf. 13 on 3 Sides*

**1990, Feb. 15                   Engr.**
688  A227  5k Vulture             .25   .25
689  A227  5k Dragon              .25   .25
690  A227  5k Bull                .25   .25
691  A227  5k Giant               .25   .25
a.    Block of 4, #688-691       1.00  1.00
692  A227  21k Vulture            .75   .75
693  A227  21k Dragon             .75   .75
694  A227  21k Bull               .75   .75
695  A227  21k Giant              .75   .75
a.    Block of 4, #692-695       3.00  3.00
b.    Block of 8, #688-695       5.25  5.25
c.    Bklt. pane, 2 each #691a, 695a  9.00  9.00

Famous Women — A243

No. 696, Gudrun Larusdottir (1880-1938), author and politician, by Halldor Petursson. No. 697, Ragnhildur Petursdottir (1880-1961), educator, by Asgrimur Jonsson.

**1990, Mar. 22    Litho.    Perf. 13½x14**
696  A243  21k multicolored     .80   .60
697  A243  21k multicolored     .80   .60

Europa 1990 A244

Old and new post offices in Reykjavik and letter scales.

**1990, May 7    Photo.    Perf. 12x11½**
**Granite Paper**
698  A244  21k 1915            6.50   .90
699  A244  40k 1989            7.00  2.00

Sports — A245

**1990-94    Litho.    Perf. 13x14½**
700  A245  21k Archery         1.00   .45
701  A245  21k Soccer          1.00   .45
706  A245  26k Golf            1.00   .65
707  A245  26k Icelandic wrestling  1.00  .65
*Perf. 13½x14½*
**Photo.**
708  A245  30k Volleyball      1.25   .60
709  A245  30k Skiing          1.25   .60
710  A245  30k Running         1.25   .60
711  A245  30k Team handball   1.25   .60
**Litho.**
*Perf. 14x14½*
711A  A245  30k Swimming       1.10   .45
711B  A245  30k Weight lifting  1.10   .45
      Nos. 700-711B (10)      11.20  5.50

Issued: #700-701, 6/28; #706-707, 8/14/91; #708-709, 2/20/92; #710-711, 3/10/93; #711A-711B, 2/25/94.

European Tourism Year — A246

**1990, Sept. 6    Litho.    Perf. 13½**
712  A246  30k multicolored   1.10   .70

Landscape Type of 1989

**1990, Sept. 6    Photo.    Perf.**
713  A238  25k Hvitserkur     1.10   .55
714  A238  200k Lomagnupur    6.75  1.60

NORDIA '91 Map Type of 1989
Souvenir Sheet
Detail of 1539 Map by Olaus Magnus: a, Dania. b, Gothia. c, Gotlandia.

*Perf. 12x12½*
**1990, Oct. 9                Lith & Engr.**
715  A240  Sheet of 3         12.50  12.50
a.-c.    40k any single        4.00   4.00

Stamp Day. Sold for 170k to benefit the exhibition.

Christmas A247

**1990, Nov. 8              Perf. 13½x13**
716  A247  25k shown          1.40   .45
717  A247  30k Carolers       1.40   .55

Bird Type of 1986
**1991, Feb. 7    Photo.    Perf. 11½**
**Granite Paper**
721  A212  25k Podiceps auritus  1.20  .45
722  A212  100k Sula bassana   5.75  1.00

Landscape Type of 1989
**1991, Mar. 7    Photo.    Perf. 11½**
**Granite Paper**
728  A238  10k Vestrahorn      .55   .30
737  A238  300k Kverkfjoll    10.00  2.75

Europa A248

**1991, Apr. 29    Litho.    Perf. 14**
738  A248  26k Weather map    12.00  1.00
739  A248  47k Solar panels    7.00  2.00

NORDIA '91 Map Type of 1989
Souvenir Sheet
Detail of 1539 Map by Olaus Magnus: a, Iceland's west coast. b, Islandia. c, Mare Glacial.

**Litho. & Engr.**
**1991, May 23              Perf. 12½**
740  A240  Sheet of 3        15.00  15.00
a.-c.    50k any single       4.75   4.75

Sold for 215k to benefit the exhibition.

Jokulsarlon Lagoon A249

Design: 31k, Strokkur hot spring.

**1991, May 23    Litho.    Perf. 15x14**
741  A249  26k multicolored   1.75   .45
742  A249  31k multicolored   1.75   .55

Ragnar Jonsson (1904-1984), Patron of the Arts — A250

70k, Pall Isolfsson (1893-1974), musician, vert.

**1991, Aug. 14    Litho.    Perf. 14**
743  A250  60k multicolored   2.00  1.00
744  A250  70k multicolored   2.50  1.25

Ships A251

Designs: a, Soloven, schooner, 1840. b, Arcturus, steamer with sails, 1858. c, Gullfoss, steamer, 1915. d, Esja II, diesel ship, 1939.

**1991, Oct. 9    Litho.    Perf. 14**
745  Block or strip of 4     20.00  20.00
a.-d.  A251 30k any single     3.50   1.75
e.    A251 Bklt. pane, 2 #745  25.00

Issued in sheet of 8. No. 745e is distinguished from sheet of 8 by rouletted selvage at left.
See Nos. 803-806.

College of Navigation, Reykjavik, Cent. A252

**1991, Oct. 9                Perf. 13½**
746  A252  50k multicolored   1.75  1.25

Christmas — A253

Paintings by Eirikur Smith (b. 1925): 30k, Christmas star. 35k, Star over winter landscape.

**1991, Nov. 7    Litho.    Perf. 13½**
747  A253  30k multicolored   1.10   .30
748  A253  35k multicolored   1.10   .65

Europa A254

Map and: No. 749, Viking longboat of Leif Eriksson. No. 750, Sailing ship of Columbus.

**1992, Apr. 6    Litho.    Perf. 13½x14**
749  A254  55k multicolored   6.50  2.50
750  A254  55k multicolored   6.50  2.50
**Souvenir Sheet**
751  A254  Sheet of 2, #749-750  15.00  8.00

First landing in the Americas by Leif Erikson (#749). Discovery of America by Christopher Columbus, 500th anniv. (#750).
Stamps on #751 printed in continuous design. #749-751 have borders.

Export Trade and Commerce A255

Designs: 35k, Fishing boat, fish.

**1992, June 16    Litho.    Perf. 13½**
752  A255  30k multicolored   1.40   .75
753  A255  35k multicolored   1.40   .75

Bridges A256

**1992, Oct. 9    Litho.    Perf. 13½**
754  A256  5k Fnjoska, 1908    .20   .20
755  A256  250k Olfusa, 1891  9.50  4.00

See Nos. 766-767.

Mail Trucks A257

#756, Mail transport car RE 231, 1933. #757, Ford bus, 1946. #758, Ford TT, 1920-26. #759, Citroen snowmobile, 1929.

**1992, Oct. 9**      *Perf. 14*
| | | | | |
|---|---|---|---|---|
| 756 | A257 | 30k multicolored | 2.40 | .90 |
| 757 | A257 | 30k multicolored | 2.40 | .90 |
| 758 | A257 | 30k multicolored | 2.40 | .90 |
| 759 | A257 | 30k multicolored | 2.40 | .90 |
| a. | | Block or strip of 4, #756-759 | 9.75 | 9.75 |
| b. | | Bklt. pane, 2 ea #756-759 | 30.00 | |

Issued in sheets of 8. No. 759b has rouletted selvage at left.
See Nos. 820-823.

Christmas — A258

Paintings by Bragi Asgeirsson.

**1992, Nov. 9**    **Litho.**    *Perf. 13½x13*
| | | | | |
|---|---|---|---|---|
| 760 | A258 | 30k shown | 1.20 | .35 |
| 761 | A258 | 35k Sun over mountains | 1.20 | .65 |

Falco Rusticolus — A259

**1992, Dec. 3**    **Photo.**    *Perf. 11½*
**Granite Paper**
| | | | | |
|---|---|---|---|---|
| 762 | A259 | 5k Adult, two young | 2.30 | .55 |
| 763 | A259 | 10k Adult feeding | 2.90 | .90 |
| 764 | A259 | 20k Adult, head up | 2.90 | 1.00 |
| 765 | A259 | 35k Adult | 2.90 | 1.60 |
| | | Nos. 762-765 (4) | 11.00 | 4.05 |

Bridges Type of 1992

**1993, Mar. 10**    **Litho.**    *Perf. 13½x13*
| | | | | |
|---|---|---|---|---|
| 766 | A256 | 90k Hvita, 1928 | 2.75 | 1.60 |
| 767 | A256 | 150k Jokulsa a Fjollum, 1947 | 5.00 | 2.25 |

Nordica '93 — A260

Designs: 30k, The Blue Lagoon therapeutic bathing area, hot water plant, Svartsengi. 35k, Perlan hot water storage tanks, restaurant.

**1993, Apr. 26**    **Litho.**    *Perf. 13½x12*
| | | | | |
|---|---|---|---|---|
| 768 | A260 | 30k multicolored | 1.10 | .30 |
| 769 | A260 | 35k multicolored | 1.40 | .55 |

Sculptures — A261

Europa: 35k, Sailing, by Jon Gunnar Arnason. 55k, Hatching of the Jet, by Magnus Tomasson.

**1993, Apr. 26**      *Perf. 13x13½*
| | | | | |
|---|---|---|---|---|
| 770 | A261 | 35k multicolored | 2.00 | 1.25 |
| 771 | A261 | 55k multicolored | 2.75 | 1.50 |

Souvenir Sheet

Italian Group Flight, 60th Anniv. — A262

**1993, Oct. 9**    **Litho.**    *Perf. 13½*
| | | | | |
|---|---|---|---|---|
| 772 | A262 | Sheet of 3, #a.-c. | 8.00 | 8.00 |
| a. | | 10k #C12 | .65 | .65 |
| b. | | 50k #C13 | 2.50 | 2.50 |
| c. | | 100k #C14 | 4.50 | 4.50 |

No. 772 sold for 200k.

Seaplanes — A263

**1993, Oct. 9**      *Perf. 14*
| | | | | |
|---|---|---|---|---|
| 773 | A263 | 30k Junkers F-13 (D463) | 2.50 | 1.00 |
| 774 | A263 | 30k Waco YKS-7 (TF-ORN) | 2.50 | 1.00 |
| 775 | A263 | 30k Grumman G-21A/JRF-5 (RVK) | 2.50 | 1.00 |
| 776 | A263 | 30k PBY-5 Catalina (TF-ISP) | 2.50 | 1.00 |
| a. | | Block or strip of 4, #773-776 | 10.00 | 10.00 |
| b. | | Bklt. pane, 2 ea #773-776 | 22.50 | |

No. 776b is distinguished from sheet of 8 by rouletted selvage at left.
Issued in sheet of 8.
See Nos. 838-841.

Christmas A264

**1993, Nov. 8**    **Litho.**    *Perf. 12½*
| | | | | |
|---|---|---|---|---|
| 777 | A264 | 30k Adoration of the Magi | 1.25 | .45 |
| 778 | A264 | 35k Virgin and Child | 1.25 | 1.10 |

Intl. Year of the Family A265

**1994, Feb. 25**    **Litho.**    *Perf. 13½x13*
| | | | | |
|---|---|---|---|---|
| 779 | A265 | 40k multicolored | 1.25 | .65 |

Voyages of St. Brendan (484-577) A266

Europa: 35k, St. Brendan, Irish monks sailing past volcano. 55k, St. Brendan on island with sheep, monks in boat.

**1994, Apr. 18**    **Litho.**    *Perf. 14½x14*
| | | | | |
|---|---|---|---|---|
| 780 | A266 | 35k multicolored | 2.50 | 1.10 |
| | | Booklet, 10 #780 | 25.00 | |

| | | | | |
|---|---|---|---|---|
| 781 | A266 | 55k multicolored | 2.75 | 1.40 |
| | | Booklet, 10 #781 | 27.50 | |
| a. | | Miniature sheet of 2, #780-781 | 5.75 | 4.25 |

See Ireland Nos. 923-924; Faroe Islands Nos. 264-265.

Icelandic Art and Culture A267

**1994, May 25**    **Litho.**    *Perf. 13½x13*
| | | | | |
|---|---|---|---|---|
| 782 | A267 | 30k Music | 1.00 | .40 |
| 783 | A267 | 30k Crafts | 1.00 | .70 |
| 784 | A267 | 30k Film making | 1.00 | .70 |
| 785 | A267 | 30k Ballet, modern dance | 1.00 | .70 |
| 786 | A267 | 30k Theatre | 1.00 | .70 |
| | | Nos. 782-786 (5) | 5.00 | 3.20 |

Independence, 50th anniv.

Gisli Sveinsson (1880-1959), Politician — A268

**1994, June 14**      *Perf. 14*
| | | | | |
|---|---|---|---|---|
| 787 | A268 | 30k multicolored | 1.00 | .65 |

Proclamation of new constitution, 50th anniv.

Souvenir Sheet

Republic of Iceland, 50th Anniv. — A269

**1994, June 14**      

Presidents of Iceland: a, Sveinn Bjornsson (1881-1952). b, Asgeir Asgeirsson (1894-1972). c, Kristjan Eldjarn (1916-82). d, Vigdis Finnbogadottir (b. 1930).

**1994, June 17**    **Photo.**    *Perf. 11½*
**Granite Paper**
| | | | | |
|---|---|---|---|---|
| 788 | A269 | Sheet of 4, #a.-d. | 6.50 | 6.50 |
| a.-d. | | 50k any single | 1.60 | 1.60 |

Souvenir Sheet

Stamp Day — A270

Designs: a, Boy, girl with stamp album. b, Nos. 672, 713, portions of other Icelandic stamps. c, Girl, elderly man looking at globe.

**1994, Oct. 7**    **Litho.**    *Perf. 13½*
| | | | | |
|---|---|---|---|---|
| 789 | A270 | Sheet of 3 | 9.50 | 9.50 |
| a. | | 30k multicolored | 2.50 | 2.50 |
| b. | | 35k multicolored | 2.50 | 2.50 |
| c. | | 100k multicolored | 4.50 | 3.50 |

No. 789 sold for 200k for the benefit of the Stamp and Postal History Fund.

Christmas A271

**1994, Nov. 9**    **Litho.**    *Perf. 14½*
| | | | | |
|---|---|---|---|---|
| 790 | A271 | 30k Woman, stars | .95 | .30 |
| 791 | A271 | 35k Man, stars | 1.20 | .70 |

ICAO, 50th Anniv. A272

**1994, Nov. 9**      *Perf. 13½x14*
| | | | | |
|---|---|---|---|---|
| 792 | A272 | 100k multicolored | 3.50 | 1.40 |

A273        A274

**1995, Mar. 14**    **Litho.**    *Perf. 13*
| | | | | |
|---|---|---|---|---|
| 793 | A273 | 35k multicolored | 1.25 | .80 |

Salvation Army in Iceland, cent.

**1995, Mar. 14**
| | | | | |
|---|---|---|---|---|
| 794 | A274 | 90k multicolored | 4.00 | 1.40 |

Town of Seydisfjordur, cent.

1995 Men's Team Handball World Championships, Iceland — A275

Federation emblem, handball and: No. 795, Geyser, landscape. No. 796, Silhouette of building, landscape. No. 797, Volcano, lake. No. 798, Inlet, sunlight on water.

**1995, Mar. 14**    **Litho.**    *Perf. 14*
| | | | | |
|---|---|---|---|---|
| 795 | A275 | 35k multicolored | 1.75 | 1.10 |
| 796 | A275 | 35k multicolored | 1.75 | 1.10 |
| 797 | A275 | 35k multicolored | 1.75 | 1.10 |
| 798 | A275 | 35k multicolored | 1.75 | 1.10 |
| a. | | Block or strip of 4, #795-798 | 7.25 | 7.00 |
| b. | | Booklet pane, 2 #798a | 17.50 | |
| | | Complete booklet, #798b | 17.50 | |

Nos. 795-798 issued in sheets of 8 containing 2 each. No. 798b is separated from booklet by rouletted selvage at left, and sold for 480k in the complete booklet.

Norden 1995 — A276

Designs: 30k, Turf farmhouses, church. 35k, Volcano, Fjallsjokull glacier.

**1995, May 5**    **Litho.**    *Perf. 13½x13*
| | | | | |
|---|---|---|---|---|
| 799 | A276 | 30k multicolored | 1.00 | .55 |
| | | Booklet, 10 #799 | 10.00 | |
| 800 | A276 | 35k multicolored | 1.40 | .90 |

Spell-Broken, by Einar Jonsson (1874-1954) — A277

**1995, May 5** — *Perf. 13x13½*
801 A277 35k brown & multi 1.10 1.00
　　Booklet, 10 #801 12.60
802 A277 55k blue & multi 2.00 1.75
　　Booklet, 10 #802 20.00

Europa.

### Ship Type of 1991

**1995, June 30** — Litho. — *Perf. 14*
803 A251 30k SS Laura 1.20 .90
804 A251 30k MS Dronning
　　　　Alexandrine 1.20 .90
805 A251 30k MS Laxfoss 1.20 .90
806 A251 30k MS Godafoss III 1.20 .90
　a. Block or strip of 4, #803-806 5.00 4.50
　b. Bklt. pane, 2 ea #803-806 10.00
　　Prestige booklet, #806b 16.00

No. 806b is distinguished from sheet of 8 by
rouletted selvage at left.
Issued in sheets of 8.
Prestige booklet sold for 400k.

Luxembourg-Reykjavik, Iceland Air
Route, 40th Anniv. — A278

**1995, Sept. 18** — Litho. — *Perf. 13½*
807 A278 35k multicolored 1.50 1.10

See Luxembourg No. 936.

Birds
A279

**1995, Sept. 18** — *Perf. 13½*
808 A279 25k Acanthis flammea .80 .65
809 A279 250k Gallinago gal-
　　　linago 8.50 6.00

### Souvenir Sheet

Nordia '96, Reykjavik — A280

Design: Hraunfossar Waterfalls, Hvita River.
Illustration reduced.

**1995, Oct. 9** — *Perf. 13½x14*
810 A280 Sheet of 2, #a.-b. 9.00 9.00
　a. 10k multicolored 2.75 2.75
　b. 150k multicolored 5.75 5.75

See No. 830.

Christmas
A281

**1995, Nov. 8** — Litho. — *Perf. 13½*
811 A281 30k Snowman, woman 1.00 .75
812 A281 35k Three trees 1.10 .90

UN, 50th
Anniv. — A282

**1995, Nov. 8** — *Perf. 13x13½*
813 A282 100k multicolored 3.25 2.50

Water Birds
A283

Designs: 20k, Phalacrocorax carbo. 40k,
Bucephala islandica.

**1996, Feb. 7** — Litho. — *Perf. 13½*
814 A283 20k multicolored .65 .55
815 A283 40k multicolored 1.40 1.00

See Nos. 834-835.

Paintings
A284

100k, Seamen in a Boat, by Gunnlaugur
Scheving (1904-72). 200k, At the Washing
Springs, by Kristín Jónsdóttir (1888-1959).

**1996, Feb. 7**
816 A284 100k multicolored 3.50 2.75
817 A284 200k multicolored 6.00 5.25

Famous
Women
A285

Europa: 35k, Halldóra Bjarnadóttir (1873-
1981), educator. 55k, Olafía Jóhannsdóttir
(1863-1924), representative of women's
rights, temperance affairs.

**1996, Apr. 18** — Litho. — *Perf. 14½*
818 A285 35k multicolored 1.50 1.00
　　Booklet, 10 #818 15.00
819 A285 55k multicolored 1.75 1.25
　　Booklet, 10 #819 17.50

### Postal Vehicle Type of 1992

Designs: No. 820, 1931 Buick. No. 821,
1933 Studebaker, Reykjavík Municipal Bus
Service. No. 822, 1937 Ford, Iceland Motor
Coach Service. No. 823, 1946 REO, Post and
Telecommunications.

**1996, May 13** — Litho. — *Perf. 14*
820 A257 35k multicolored 1.25 .85
821 A257 35k multicolored 1.25 .85
822 A257 35k multicolored 1.25 .85
823 A257 35k multicolored 1.25 .85
　a. Block or strip of 4, #820-823 5.00 5.00
　b. Bklt. pane, 2 ea #820-823 10.00 10.00
　　Souvenir booklet, #823b 12.00

No. 823a issued in sheets of 8 stamps. No.
823b has rouletted selvage at left.

1996 Summer
Olympic
Games,
Atlanta
A286

**1996, June 25** — Litho. — *Perf. 12½*
824 A286 5k Running .20 .20
825 A286 25k Javelin .75 .40
826 A286 45k Long jump 1.40 1.10
827 A286 65k Shot put 2.10 1.50
　　Nos. 824-827 (4) 4.45 3.20

Order of the Sisters of St. Joseph in
Iceland, Cent. — A287

**1996, Sept. 17** — Litho. — *Perf. 14½x13*
828 A287 65k multicolored 2.00 1.60

Reykjavik
School,
150th
Anniv.
A288

**1996, Sept. 17** — *Perf. 12½x13*
829 A288 150k multicolored 4.75 3.75

### Nordia '96 Type of 1995

Design: Godafoss Waterfalls, Skjalfandafljot
River. Illustration reduced.

**1996, Oct. 9** — Litho. — *Perf. 13½x14*
830 A280 Sheet of 3, #a.-c. 11.50 11.50
　a. 45k multicolored 3.75 3.75
　b. 65k multicolored 3.75 3.75
　c. 90k multicolored 3.75 3.75

Reykjavik
Cathedral,
Bicent. — A289

**1996, Nov. 5** — *Perf. 14*
831 A289 45k multicolored 1.60 1.10

Christmas — A290

Artifacts from Natl. Museum of Iceland: 35k,
Figurine of Madonna and Child carved from
walrus tusk. 45k, Pax showing Nativity.

**1996, Nov. 5** — *Perf. 13½*
832 A290 35k multicolored 1.10 .75
　a. Booklet pane of 10 11.00
　　Booklet, #832a 11.00
833 A290 45k multicolored 1.40 1.00

### Bird Type of 1996

10k, Mergus serrator. 500k, Anas crecca.

**1997, Apr. 2** — Litho. — *Perf. 13½*
834 A283 10k multicolored .35 .20
835 A283 500k multicolored 15.00 13.50

Paintings
A291

150k, Song of Iceland, by Svavar
Guthnason. 200k, The Harbor, by Thorvaldur
Skúlason.

**1997, Mar. 6** — Litho. — *Perf. 14*
836 A291 150k multicolored 4.50 3.50
837 A291 200k multicolored 6.00 3.50

### Airplane Type of 1993

#838, De Havilland DH-89A (TF-ISM). #839,
Stinson SR 8B Reliant (TF-RVB). #840, Doug-
las DC-3 (TF-ISH). #841, De Havilland DHC-6
Twin Otter (TF-REG).

**1997, Apr. 15** — Litho. — *Perf. 14*
838 A263 35k multicolored 1.20 .90
839 A263 35k multicolored 1.20 .90
840 A263 35k multicolored 1.20 .90
841 A263 35k multicolored 1.20 .90
　a. Block or strip of 4, #838-841 5.00 5.00
　b. Booklet pane, 2 each #838-841 10.00
　　Booklet, #841b 10.00

Issued in sheet of 8.
No. 841b has rouletted selvage at left.

European
Games
A292

**1997, May 13** — Litho. — *Perf. 14½*
842 A292 35k Hurdles 1.10 .90
843 A292 45k Sailing 1.40 1.10

Europa
A293

Stories and legends by Asgrimur Jonsson:
45k, Couple on galloping horse. 65k, Old
woman reaching for children.

**1997, May 13** — *Perf. 13½*
844 A293 45k multicolored 2.00 1.50
　　Complete booklet of 10 20.00
845 A293 65k multicolored 2.50 1.75
　　Complete booklet of 10 25.00

Union of
Graphic
Workers,
Cent. — A294

**1997, Sept. 3** — Litho. — *Perf. 13½*
846 A294 90k multicolored 2.75 2.25

Reykjavik
Theater,
Cent. — A295

**1997, Sept. 3** — *Perf. 13½x14*
847 A295 100k multicolored 3.00 2.50

Stamp Day — A296

Icelandic row boats: a, Gideon, eight-oared
lugger, 1836. b, Breidafjördur double-ended
transport, 1904. c, Engey, six-oared craft,
1912.

**1997, Oct. 9** — Litho. — *Perf. 15*
848 A296 Sheet of 3 7.50 7.50
　a. 35k multicolored 1.60 1.60
　b. 100k multicolored 3.00 3.00
　c. 65k multicolored 2.40 2.40

Christmas
A297

**1997, Nov. 5   Litho.   Perf. 13½x13**
849 A297 35k Magi                          1.00   .70
a.  Booklet pane of 10                    10.00
    Booklet, #849a                        10.00
850 A297 45k Nativity                      1.40   .90

Rural Postman
A298

**Litho. & Engr.**
**1997, Nov. 5**                          **Perf. 13½**
851 A298 50k multicolored                  1.50  1.10

1998 Winter
Olympic
Games,
Nagano
A299

**1998, Jan. 22   Litho.   Perf. 13½**
852 A299 35k Downhill skier                1.00  1.00
853 A299 45k Cross country ski-
         er                                1.40  1.25

Nordic
Stamps
A300

**1998, Mar. 5   Litho.   Perf. 13½x13**
854 A300 35k Sailboats                     1.00  1.00
855 A300 45k Power boats                   1.40  1.00

Fish — A301

**1998, Apr. 16**
856 A301    5k Cyclopterus
             lumpus                         .20   .20
857 A301   10k Gadus morhua                 .30   .20
858 A301   60k Raja batis                  1.75  1.40
859 A301  300k Anarhicus lu-
             pus                           8.75  7.50
a.  Min. sheet of 4, #856-859            11.00 11.00
    Nos. 856-859 (4)                      11.00  9.30
Intl. Year of the Ocean (#859a).
See Nos. 915-916, 928-929.

National
Holidays and
Festivals
A302

Independence Day, June 17th: 45k, Children standing at attention, flag. 65k, Monument, parade.

**1998, May 12   Litho.   Perf. 14½**
860 A302 45k multicolored                  1.75  1.00
    Complete booklet, 10 #860            17.50
861 A302 65k multicolored                  2.25  1.50
    Complete booklet, 10 #861            22.50
        Europa.

Minerals — A303

**1998, Sept. 3   Litho.   Perf. 13½**
862 A303 35k Stilbite                      1.20   .90
863 A303 45k Scolecite                     1.40  1.10
        See Nos. 885-886.

Leprosy Hospital,
Laugarnes
A304

**1998, Sept. 3**                         **Perf. 13½x14**
864 A304 70k multicolored                  2.00  1.60

First Icelandic
Postage Stamp,
125th
Anniv. — A305

**1998, Oct. 9   Litho.   Perf. 13½**
865 A305 35k multicolored                  1.20   .80

Agricultural Tools — A306

**1998, Oct. 9**                          **Perf. 15**
866 A306   Sheet of 3                       7.50  7.50
a.  35k Turf scythe                         1.75  1.75
b.  65k Hay mower                           2.50  2.50
c.  100k Manure mincer                      3.25  3.25
        Stamp Day.

Christmas,
Children's
Drawings — A307

35k, Black cat, homes, mountains. 45k,
Angels, Christmas tree, moon and stars.

**1998, Nov. 5   Litho.   Perf. 13x13½**
867 A307 35k multicolored                  1.10   .90
a.  Booklet pane of 10                     11.00
    Complete booklet, #867a                11.00
868 A307 45k multicolored                  1.25  1.10

Universal Declaration of Human
Rights, 50th Anniv. — A308

**1998, Nov. 5**                          **Perf. 14½**
869 A308 50k multicolored                  1.50  1.50

Jón Leifs (1899-1968),
Composer — A309

**1999, Jan. 22   Litho.   Perf. 14½**
870 A309 35k multicolored                  1.10   .90

**Fish Type of 1998**
35k, Pleuronectez platessa. 55k, Clupea
harengus.

**1999, Jan. 22**                         **Perf. 14½x15**
871 A301 35k multicolored                  1.25   .90
872 A301 55k multicolored                  1.60  1.60

Marine Mammals — A311

Designs: 35k, Orcinus orca. 45k, Physeter
macrocephalus. 65k, Balaenoptera musculus.
85k, Phocoena phocoena.

**1999, Mar. 4   Litho.   Perf. 14½**
873 A311 35k multicolored                  1.00   .90
874 A311 45k multicolored                  1.25  1.10
875 A311 65k multicolored                  1.90  1.90
876 A311 85k multicolored                  2.40  2.40
a.  Sheet of 4, #873-876                    6.50  6.50
    Nos. 873-876 (4)                        6.55  6.30
        See Nos. 911-914, 945-948.

Locomotive
A312

**Perf. 13 on 2 or 3 Sides**
**1999, Apr. 15**
        **Booklet Stamps**
877 A312 25k green & multi                 7.00  7.00
878 A312 50k brown & multi                 2.50  2.50
a.  Booklet pane, 1 #877, 3 #878          14.50
    Complete booklet, #878a               14.50
879 A312 75k Ship                          3.50  3.50
a.  Booklet pane of 4                      14.00
    Complete booklet, #879a               14.00
    Nos. 877-879 (3)                      13.00 13.00
        See Nos. 908-909.

Council of
Europe,
50th Anniv.
A313

**1999, Apr.15**                          **Perf. 13x13½**
880 A313 35k multicolored                  1.20   .90

Mushrooms
A314

35k, Suillus grevillei. 75k, Agaricus
campestris.

**1999, May 20   Litho.   Perf. 14½**
881 A314 35k multicolored                  1.10  1.10
882 A314 75k multicolored                  2.25  2.25
    See Nos. 898-899, 957-958, 1021-1022,
1087-1088.

National
Parks — A315

**1999, May 20**                          **Perf. 13¼**
883 A315 50k Skutustadagigar               2.00  1.50
a.  Booklet pane of 10                     20.00
    Complete booklet, #883a                21.00
884 A315 75k Vid Arnarstapa                2.50  2.00
a.  Booklet pane of 10                     25.00
    Complete booklet, #884a                26.00
        Europa.

**Minerals Type of 1998**
**1999, Sept. 9   Litho.   Perf. 14¾**
885 A303 40k Calcite                       1.25  1.25
886 A303 50k Heulandite                    1.60  1.60

Nature
Conservation
A316

**1999, Sept. 9   Litho.   Perf. 14¼**
887 A316 35k "Hreinar"                     1.25  1.25
888 A316 35k "Markviss"                    1.25  1.25
889 A316 35k "Hreint"                      1.25  1.25
890 A316 35k "Endurheimt"                  1.25  1.25
891 A316 35k "Eflum"                       1.25  1.25
a.  Strip of 5, #887-891                    6.25  6.25

Reykjavik,
European
Cultural City
for 2000
A317

35k, Facescape, by Erro. 50k, Book, violin,
palette, masks, camera, computer.

**1999, Oct. 7   Litho.   Perf. 13¼**
892 A317 35k multi                         1.50  1.50
893 A317 50k multi                         2.00  2.00

        Souvenir Sheet

View of Skagafhordur, by Carl Emil
Baagoe — A318

Illustration reduced.

**1999, Oct. 7**                          **Perf. 13¼x13**
894 A318 200k olive & black                8.50  8.50
    Stamp Day. #894 sold for 250k.

Children's
Art — A319

**1999, Nov. 4   Litho.   Perf. 13**
895 A319 35k multi                         1.00  1.00

Christmas — A320

No. 896, Elf: a, With walking stick. b, Jumping over rock. c, Waving. d, Licking spoon. e, With hand in cauldron. f, With cup. g, At door. h, With ladle and barrel. i, With sausages. j, At window.

No. 897, Elf: a, Looking up. b, With ham. c, With candles.

**1999, Nov. 4**
| | | | | |
|---|---|---|---|---|
| 896 | | Strip of 10 | 15.00 | 15.00 |
| a.-j. | | A320 35k any single | 1.50 | 1.50 |
| k. | | Booklet pane, #896a-896j | 15.00 | |
| | | Complete booklet, #896k | 15.00 | |
| 897 | | Strip of 3 | 5.25 | 5.25 |
| a.-c. | | A320 50k any single | 1.75 | 1.75 |

See Nos. 924-926.

**Mushroom Type of 1999**

Designs: 40k, Cantharellus cibarius. 50k, Coprinus comatus.

**2000, Feb. 4    Litho.    Perf. 13**
| | | | | |
|---|---|---|---|---|
| 898 | A314 | 40k multi | 1.10 | 1.10 |
| a. | | Booklet pane of 10 | 11.00 | |
| | | Complete booklet, #898a | 11.00 | |
| 899 | A314 | 50k multi | 1.40 | 1.40 |

A321

Christianity in Iceland, 1000th Anniv. — A322

Illustration A322 reduced.

**2000, Feb. 4    Perf. 13¼x13¾**
| | | | | |
|---|---|---|---|---|
| 900 | A321 | 40k multi | 1.25 | 1.25 |

**Souvenir Sheet**
**Perf. 13¼x13**
| | | | | |
|---|---|---|---|---|
| 901 | A322 | 40k multi | 1.25 | 1.25 |

See Vatican City #1151.

Discovery of Vinland, 1000th Anniv. A323

Designs: 40k, Viking with shield, globe. 50k, Viking ship sailing. 75k, Viking ship at shore. 90k, Viking without shield, globe.

**Litho. & Engr.**
**2000, Mar. 16    Perf. 12½x13**
| | | | | |
|---|---|---|---|---|
| 902 | A323 | 40k multi | 1.40 | 1.40 |
| 903 | A323 | 50k multi | 1.60 | 1.60 |
| 904 | A323 | 75k multi | 2.25 | 2.25 |
| 905 | A323 | 90k multi | 2.75 | 2.75 |
| a. | | Souvenir sheet, #902-905 | 8.00 | 8.00 |
| | | Nos. 902-905 (4) | 8.00 | 8.00 |

Millennium
A324

Designs: 40k, Head, quill pen. 50k, Man, genealogical chart, circuit board.

**2000, Apr. 27    Litho.    Perf. 13x13¼**
| | | | | |
|---|---|---|---|---|
| 906 | A324 | 40k multi | 1.25 | 1.25 |
| 907 | A324 | 50k multi | 1.50 | 1.50 |

**Locomotive Type of 1999**
**Perf. 13 on 2 or 3 sides**
**2000, Apr. 27    Litho.**
**Booklet Stamps**
| | | | | |
|---|---|---|---|---|
| 908 | A312 | 50k Steam roller | 1.50 | 1.50 |
| a. | | Booklet pane of 4 | 6.00 | |
| | | Booklet, #908a | 6.00 | |
| 909 | A312 | 75k Fire pumper | 2.25 | 2.25 |
| a. | | Booklet pane of 4 | 9.00 | |
| | | Booklet, #909a | 9.00 | |

**Europa, 2000**
**Common Design Type**
**2000, May 18    Litho.    Perf. 13¼x13**
| | | | | |
|---|---|---|---|---|
| 910 | CD17 | 50k multi | 2.00 | 2.00 |
| a. | | Booklet pane of 10 | 20.00 | |
| | | Booklet, #910a | 21.00 | |

**Marine Mammals Type of 1999**

Designs: 5k, Hyperoodon ampullatus. 40k, Lagenorhynchus acutus. 50k, Megaptera novaeangliae. 75k, Balaenoptera acutorostrata.

**2000, May 18    Perf. 14½**
| | | | | |
|---|---|---|---|---|
| 911 | A311 | 5k multi | .20 | .20 |
| 912 | A311 | 40k multi | 1.10 | 1.10 |
| 913 | A311 | 50k multi | 1.40 | 1.40 |
| 914 | A311 | 75k multi | 2.00 | 2.00 |
| | | Nos. 911-914 (4) | 4.70 | 4.70 |

**Fish Type of 1998**

Designs: 10k, Melanogrammus aeglefinus. 250k, Mallotus villosus.

**2000, Sept. 14    Litho.    Perf. 13**
| | | | | |
|---|---|---|---|---|
| 915-916 | A301 | Set of 2 | 9.00 | 9.00 |

Flowers — A325

Designs: 40k, Viola x wittrockiana. 50k, Petunia x hybrida.

**2000, Sept. 14    Perf. 13**
| | | | | |
|---|---|---|---|---|
| 917-918 | A325 | Set of 2 | 2.75 | 2.50 |

See Nos. 931-932, 968-969, 982-983, 1005-1006.

Butterflies
A326

Designs: 40k, Chloroclysta citrata. 50k, Cerapteryx graminis.

**2000, Oct. 9    Perf. 14x14½**
| | | | | |
|---|---|---|---|---|
| 919-920 | A326 | Set of 2 | 2.75 | 2.50 |

**Souvenir Sheet**

Stamp Day — A327

Illustration reduced.

**Litho. & Engr.**
**2000, Oct. 9    Perf. 13¼**
| | | | | |
|---|---|---|---|---|
| 921 | A327 | 200k multi | 9.00 | 9.00 |

No. 921 sold for 250k.

Ancient Architecture — A328

Various buildings. Denominations: 45k, 75k.

**2000, Nov. 9    Litho.    Perf. 14**
| | | | | |
|---|---|---|---|---|
| 922-923 | A328 | Set of 2 | 4.00 | 3.50 |

**Christmas Type of 1999**

Designs: 40k, Elf grasping walking stick. 50k, Female elf carrying bag.

**2000, Nov. 9    Perf. 13**
| | | | | |
|---|---|---|---|---|
| 924 | A320 | 40k multi | 1.25 | 1.00 |
| a. | | Perf. 12¾x13¼ | 1.50 | 1.00 |
| b. | | Booklet pane, 4 #924a | 6.00 | |
| c. | | Booklet pane, 6 #924a | 9.00 | |
| | | Booklet, #924b, 924c | 15.00 | |
| 925 | A320 | 50k multi | 1.50 | 1.25 |

**Souvenir Sheet**
| | | | | |
|---|---|---|---|---|
| 926 | | Sheet of 2 | 2.75 | 2.25 |
| a. | | A320 40k As #924, 25x38mm | 1.25 | .95 |
| b. | | A320 50k As #925, 25x38mm | 1.50 | 1.25 |

Coast Guard, 75th Anniv.
A329

**2001, Jan. 18    Litho.    Perf. 13**
| | | | | |
|---|---|---|---|---|
| 927 | A329 | (40k) multi | 1.25 | 1.25 |
| a. | | Booklet pane of 10 | 12.50 | |
| | | Booklet, #927a | 12.50 | |

**Fish Type of 1998**

Designs: 55k, Reinhardtius hippoglossoides. 80k, Pollachius virens.

**2001, Jan. 18**
| | | | | |
|---|---|---|---|---|
| 928-929 | A301 | Set of 2 | 4.00 | 4.00 |

UN High Commissioner for Refugees, 50th Anniv. — A330

**2001, Mar. 8    Perf. 13¼x13**
| | | | | |
|---|---|---|---|---|
| 930 | A330 | 50k multi | 1.50 | 1.25 |

**Flower Type of 2000**

Designs: 55k, Calendula officinalis. 65k, Dorotheanthus bellidiformis.

**2001, Mar. 8    Perf. 13**
| | | | | |
|---|---|---|---|---|
| 931-932 | A325 | Set of 2 | 3.75 | 3.25 |

Icelandic Sheepdog
A331

Dog's coat: 40k, Brown. 80k, Black.

**2001, Apr. 18    Perf. 14¼**
| | | | | |
|---|---|---|---|---|
| 933-934 | A331 | Set of 2 | 4.00 | 3.25 |

Airplanes
A332

Designs: 55k: TF-OGN (biplane). 80k, Klemm TF-SUX (monoplane).

**Perf. 13½x12¾ on 2 or 3 Sides**
**2001, Apr. 18**
**Booklet Stamps**
| | | | | |
|---|---|---|---|---|
| 935 | A332 | 55k multi | 1.60 | 1.40 |
| a. | | Booklet pane of 4 | 6.50 | |
| | | Booklet, #935a | 6.50 | |
| 936 | A332 | 80k multi | 2.50 | 2.25 |
| a. | | Booklet pane of 4 | 10.00 | |
| | | Booklet, #936a | 10.00 | |

Europa
A333

Designs: 55k, Head, waterfall. 80k, Hand, wave.

**2001, May 17    Perf. 13**
| | | | | |
|---|---|---|---|---|
| 937 | A333 | 55k multi | 1.75 | 1.50 |
| a. | | Booklet pane of 10 | 17.50 | |
| | | Booklet, #937a | 19.00 | |
| 938 | A333 | 80k multi | 2.75 | 2.00 |
| a. | | Booklet pane of 10 | 27.50 | |
| | | Booklet, #938a | 29.00 | |

Horses
A334

Designs: 40k, Fet. 50k, Tölt. 55k, Brokk. 60k, Skeidh. 80k, Stökk.

**2001, May 17    Perf. 13x13¼**
| | | | | |
|---|---|---|---|---|
| 939-943 | A334 | Set of 5 | 8.50 | 7.50 |

**No. 873 Surcharged in Red**

**2001, July 10    Litho.    Perf. 14½**
| | | | | |
|---|---|---|---|---|
| 944 | A311 | (53k) on 35k multi | 1.75 | 1.75 |

**Marine Mammals Type of 1999**

Designs: 5k, Lagenorhynchus albirostris. 40k, Balaenoptera physalus. 80k, Balaenoptera borealis. 100k, Globicephala melas.

**2001, Sept. 6    Litho.    Perf. 14½**
| | | | | |
|---|---|---|---|---|
| 945 | A311 | 5k multi | .30 | .30 |
| 946 | A311 | 40k multi | 1.25 | 1.25 |
| 947 | A311 | 80k multi | 2.50 | 2.50 |
| 948 | A311 | 100k multi | 3.25 | 3.25 |
| | | Nos. 945-948 (4) | 7.30 | 7.30 |

Designs: 40k, Grimsey. 55k, Papey.

**2001, Oct. 9    Litho.    Perf. 13¼x13**
949-950  A335    Set of 2    3.00  2.50

See Nos. 975-976, 1001-1002, 1033-1034, 1158-1159.

### Souvenir Sheet

Esja Mountain — A336

**2001, Oct. 9            Perf. 13¼**
951  A336  250k multi    9.00  9.00

Stamp Day.

Birds — A337

Designs: 42k, Oenanthe oenanthe. 250k, Charadrius hiaticula.

**2001, Nov. 8            Perf. 13¼x13**
952-953  A337    Set of 2    10.00  10.00

Christmas A338

Churches: (42k), Brautarholt. 55k, Vidhmyri.

**2001, Nov. 8**
954  A338  (42k) multi    1.25  1.25
 a.   Booklet pane of 6    7.50  —
      Booklet, #954a, 4 #954    12.50
955  A338  55k multi    1.60  1.40

First Motorboat in Iceland, Cent. A339

**2002, Jan. 17    Litho.    Perf. 13x13½**
956  A339  60k multi    1.90  1.90

### Mushroom Type of 1999

Designs: (40k), Leccinum scabrum. 85k, Hydnum repandum.

**2002, Jan. 17            Perf. 13¼x12¾**
957-958  A314    Set of 2    3.75  3.75
      Booklet, 10 #957    12.50

No. 957 is inscribed "Bref 20g."

Intl. Year of Mountains A340

**2002, Mar. 7    Litho.    Perf. 13**
959  A340  (42k) multi    1.25  1.25

---

Halldór Laxness (1902-98), 1955 Nobel Literature Laureate A341

**2002, Mar. 7    Litho.    Perf. 13x13¼**
960  A341  100k multi    3.50  3.50
 a.   Souvenir sheet of 1    3.75  3.75

Examples of No. 960a with Nobel Prize medal in margin printed in gold foil and embossed sold for 1700k. Value, $75.

Lighthouses — A342

**Perf. 12¾x13¼ on 2 or 3 Sides**
**2002, Apr. 18**
### Booklet Stamps
961  A342  60k Grótta    1.75  1.60
 a.   Booklet pane of 4    7.00
      Booklet, #961a    7.00
962  A342  85k Kögur    2.50  2.25
 a.   Booklet pane of 4    10.00
      Booklet, #962a    10.00

Fyssa, by Rúrí — A343

Spenna, by Hafsteinn Austmann A344

**2002, Apr. 18    Litho.    Perf. 14½x14¾**
963  A343  (42k) multi    1.25  1.10
964  A344  60k multi    1.75  1.50

Nordic Council, 50th anniv. (No. 963).

Sesselja Sigmundsdóttir (1902-74), Advocate for Mentally Handicapped A345

**2002, May 9**
965  A345  45k multi    1.40  1.10

Europa A346

Designs: 60k, Acrobats, juggling clown. 85k, Head on stick, lion jumping through ring of fire.

**2002, May 9            Perf. 13**
966  A346  60k multi    1.75  1.25
 a.   Booklet pane of 10    17.50
      Booklet, #966a    19.00
967  A346  85k multi    2.50  1.50
 a.   Booklet pane of 10    25.00
      Booklet, #967a    26.00

### Flowers Type of 2000

Designs: 10k, Lobelia erinus. 200k, Centaurea cyanus.

**2002, Sept. 5    Litho.    Perf. 14¾x14½**
968-969  A325    Set of 2    6.75  6.75

---

Fish of Lake Thingvallavatn — A347

Designs: (45k), Salvelinus alpinus (Murta). (55k), Salmo trutta, vert. 60k, Salvelinus alpinus (Silableikja). 90k, Salvelinus alpinus (Kuthungableikja). 200k, Salvelinus alpinus (Dvergbleikja).

**Perf. 13¼x12¾, 12¾x13¼ (#971)**
**2002, Sept. 5**
970  A347  (45k) multi    1.50  1.50
 a.   Perf. 13¼x12½x13¼x13    1.50  1.50
971  A347  (55k) multi    2.50  2.50
 a.   Perf.
      13¼x12½:13x13¼x13:12½    2.50  2.50
972  A347  60k multi    2.00  2.00
 a.   Perf. 13¼x13    2.00  2.00
973  A347  90k multi    2.75  2.75
 a.   Perf. 13¼x13    2.75  2.75
974  A347  200k multi    6.00  6.00
 a.   Perf. 13¼x13    6.00  6.00
 b.   Booklet pane, #970a-974a    27.50
      Complete booklet, #974b    27.50
      Nos. 970-974 (5)    14.75  14.75

Nos. 970-974 were issued both in sheet format, perf 13¼x12¾ or 12¾x13¼ (#971), and in booklet pane format (#970a-974a), with small differences in the gauge of the stamps' perforations.

### Islands Type of 2001

Designs: 45k, Vigur. 55k, Flatey.

**2002, Oct. 9            Perf. 14**
975-976  A335    Set of 2    3.00  2.50

### Souvenir Sheet

Sudurgata, Reykjavik — A348

**2002, Oct. 9            Perf. 14½x14¾**
977  A348  250k multi    8.50  8.50

Stamp Day.

Birds A349

Christmas A350

Designs: 50k, Tringa totanus. 85k, Phalaropus fulicarius.

**2002, Nov. 7            Perf. 13¼x13**
978-979  A349    Set of 2    4.00  4.00

See Nos. 997-998, 1029-1030, 1059-1060.

**2002, Nov. 7            Perf. 13**
Designs: 45k, Gifts and ornaments. 60k, Gifts.

980  A350  45k multi    1.40  1.40
 a.   Booklet pane of 10    14.00
      Booklet, #980a    14.00
981  A350  60k multi    1.90  1.75

### Flower Type of 2000

Designs: 45k, Phlox drummondii. 60k, Gazania x hybrida.

**2003, Jan. 16            Perf. 13**
982  A325  45k multi    1.40  1.40
 a.   Booklet pane of 10    14.00
      Booklet, #982a    14.00
983  A325  60k multi    1.90  1.75

---

Icelandic Police Force, Bicent. — A351

Designs: 45k, Police officers, 2003. 55k, Policeman, 1803.

**2003, Jan. 16**
984-985  A351    Set of 2    3.00  3.00

Icelandic Cattle A352

Designs: 45k, Bull. 85k, Cow.

**2003, Mar. 13    Litho.    Perf. 13x13¼**
986-987  A352    Set of 2    4.00  4.00

### Souvenir Sheet

Nordia 2003 Philatelic Exhibition, Reykjavik — A353

**Litho. & Engr.**
**2003, Mar. 13            Perf. 14**
988  A353  250k multi    8.25  8.25

No. 988 sold for 300k.

Free Church, Reykjavik, Cent. — A354

**2003, Apr. 23    Litho.    Perf. 13**
989  A354  200k multi    6.25  6.25

Ferries A355

No. 990: a, Saefari. b, Saevar.
No. 991: a, Herjólfur. b, Baldur.

**Perf. 13 on 2 or 3 Sides**
**2003, Apr. 23**
### Booklet Stamps
990       Pair    2.75  2.75
 a.-b.  A355 45k Either single    1.35  1.35
   c.   Booklet pane, 2 #990    5.50
        Complete booklet, #990c    5.50
991       Pair    3.75  3.75
 a.-b.  A355 60k Either single    1.75  1.75
   c.   Booklet pane, 2 #991    7.50
        Complete booklet, #991c    7.50

Icelandic Chickens — A356

**2003, May 22**     *Perf. 13¼*
992 A356 45k multi     1.50 1.50

Europa — A357

Poster art.

**2003, May 22**     *Perf. 13½*
993 A357 60k red & multi     1.75 *1.25*
   *a.*   Booklet pane of 10, perf. 13½
      on 3 sides     17.50 —
      Complete booklet, #993a     19.00
994 A357 85k red & multi     2.50 *1.75*
   *a.*   Booklet pane of 10, perf. 13½
      on 3 sides     25.00 —
      Complete booklet, #994a     26.00

Friendship A358

**2003, Sept. 4**     *Perf. 14¼x14½*
995 A358 45k multi     1.40 1.40

First Census, 300th Anniv. — A359

**2003, Sept. 4**     *Perf. 13*
996 A359 60k multi     2.10 2.10

**Bird Type of 2002**

Designs: 70k, Anthus pratensis. 250k, Numenius phaeopus.

**2003, Sept. 4**     *Perf. 13¼x13*
997-998 A349   Set of 2     9.75 9.75

Rangifer Tarandus A360

**2003, Oct. 9**   Litho.    *Perf. 13*
999 A360 45k multi     1.50 1.50

**Souvenir Sheet**

Quonset Hut — A361

**2003, Oct. 9**
1000 A361 250k multi     7.75 7.75
    Stamp Day.

**Islands Type of 2001**

Designs: 85k, Heimaey. 200k, Hrísey.

**2003, Nov. 6**     *Perf. 13¼x13*
1001-1002 A335   Set of 2     9.00 9.00

Christmas — A362

Designs: 45k, Girl placing ornament on Christmas tree. 60k, Boy lighting candle.

**2003, Nov. 6**     *Perf. 14¼*
1003-1004 A362   Set of 2     3.25 3.25
   *a.*   Booklet pane of 10,
      #1003     14.00
      Booklet, #1003a     14.00

**Flowers Type of 2000**

Designs: 50k, Tagetes patula. 55k, Begonia x tuberhybrida.

**2004, Jan. 15**   Litho.    *Perf. 13*
1005-1006 A325   Set of 2     3.50 3.50

Hannes Hafstein (1861-1922), Politician, Poet — A363

**2004, Jan. 15**     *Perf. 13¼x13½*
1007 A363 150k multi     5.00 5.00
   *a.*   Souvenir sheet of 1     5.00 5.00
    Icelandic home rule, cent.

Trawler "Coot," Cent. A364

**2004, Mar. 11**   Litho.    *Perf. 13¼*
1008 A364 50k multi     1.50 1.50

Geothermal Energy — A365

Designs: 50k, Snorralaug hot water pool. 55k, Valve on geodesic dome, steam cloud, vert. (29x47mm). 60k, Steam pipes. 90k, Turbine. 250k, Map of Iceland showing geothermal zones, vert. (29x47mm).

    *Perf. 13x13¼, 13¼ (55k, 250k)*
**2004, Mar. 11**
1009 A365   50k multi     1.50 1.50
   *a.*   Perf. 13¼     4.00 4.00
1010 A365   55k multi     1.75 1.75
1011 A365   60k multi     2.00 2.00
   *a.*   Perf. 13¼     5.00 5.00
1012 A365   90k multi     2.75 2.75
   *a.*   Perf. 13¼     7.00 7.00
1013 A365   250k multi     7.50 7.50
   *a.*   Booklet pane, #1009a,
      1010, 1011a, 1012a, 1013   25.00 —
      Complete booklet, #1013a   25.00
      Nos. 1009-1013 (5)     15.50 15.50

Complete booklet sold for 750k.
Nos. 1009a, 1011a and 1012a only come from the booklet pane No. 1013a.

**Souvenir Sheet**

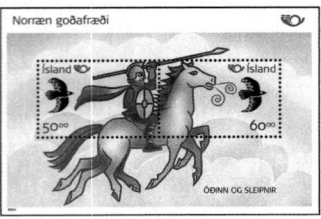

Norse Mythology — A366

No. 1014: a, God Odin and bird. b, Odin's horse, Sleipnir, and bird.

**2004, Mar. 26**     *Perf. 13*
1014 A366   Sheet of 2     3.50 3.50
   *a.*   50k multi     1.60 1.60
   *b.*   60k multi     1.90 1.90

Automobiles A367

No. 1015: a, 1956 Ford Fairlane Victoria. b, 1954 Pobeta.
No. 1016: a, 1955 Chevrolet Bel Air. b, 1952 Volkswagen.

    *Perf. 13 on 2 or 3 Sides*
**2004, Apr. 15**
    **Booklet Stamps**
1015   Pair     3.50 3.50
  *a.-b.*   A367 60k Either single   1.75 1.75
   *c.*   Booklet pane, 2 #1015   7.00
      Complete booklet, #1015c   7.00
1016   Pair     5.00 5.00
  *a.-b.*   A367 85k Either single   2.50 2.50
   *c.*   Booklet pane, 2 #1016   10.00
      Complete booklet, #1016c   10.00

Herring Industry, Cent. — A368

**2004, May 19**     *Perf. 13¼*
1017 A368 65k multi     2.00 2.00

Hringurin Women's Society, Cent. A369

**2004, May 19**     *Perf. 13x13¼*
1018 A369 100k violet blue     3.00 3.00

Europa A370

**2004, May 19**     *Perf. 13*
1019 A370 65k Cyclists     *2.00 2.00*
   *a.*   Booklet pane of 10     20.00
      Complete booklet, #1019a   20.00
1020 A370 90k Cars in snow     *2.75 2.75*
   *a.*   Booklet pane of 10     27.50
      Complete booklet, #1020a   27.50

**Mushrooms Type of 1999**

Designs: 50k, Amanita vaginata. 60k, Camarophyllus pratensis.

**2004, Sept. 2**   Litho.    *Perf. 13*
1021-1022 A314   Set of 2     3.50 3.50

Reykdal Power Station, Cent. — A371

**2004, Sept. 2**     *Perf. 13¼*
1023 A371 50k multi     1.50 1.50

First Automobile in Iceland, Cent. A372

**2004, Sept. 2**
1024 A372 100k multi     3.25 3.25

French Hospital, Fáskrúthsfirthi, Cent. — A373

    **Litho. & Engr.**
**2004, Oct. 8**     *Perf. 13¾*
1025 A373 60k multi     1.90 1.90

**Souvenir Sheet**

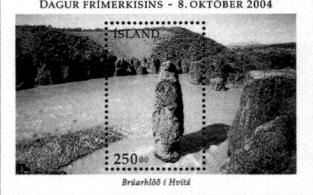

Brúarhlöth — A374

**2004, Oct. 8**   Litho.    *Perf. 13*
1026 A374 250k multi     7.75 7.75
    Stamp Day.

Insects A375

Designs: 50k, Nebria gyllenhali. 70k, Bombus lucorum.

**2004, Oct. 8**
1027-1028 A375   Set of 2     3.75 3.75
    See Nos. 1043-1044, 1089-1090, 1121-1122, 1161-1161.

**Bird Type of 2002**

Designs: 55k, Calidris maritima. 75k, Calidris alpina.

**2004, Nov. 4**   Litho.    *Perf. 13¼x13*
1029-1030 A349   Set of 2     4.00 4.00

Christmas — A376

Designs: 45k, Ptarmigan in snow. 65k, Reindeer in snow.

**2004, Nov. 4**
| | | | | |
|---|---|---|---|---|
| 1031-1032 | A376 | Set of 2 | 3.50 | 3.50 |
| 1031a | | Booklet pane of 10 #1031 | 14.00 | — |
| | | Complete booklet, #1031a | 14.00 | |

**Islands Type of 2001**

Designs: 5k, Vithey. 90k, Flatey.

**2005, Jan. 13**  Litho.  *Perf. 14*
| | | | | |
|---|---|---|---|---|
| 1033-1034 | A335 | Set of 2 | 3.25 | 3.25 |

Organized Forestation, Cent. A377

**2005, Jan. 13**
| | | | | |
|---|---|---|---|---|
| 1035 | A377 | 45k multi | 1.50 | 1.50 |

Souvenir Sheet

National Museum Artifacts — A378

No. 1036: a, Brooch, 11th cent. b, Statue of Thor, 10th cent.

**Litho. & Embossed**
**2005, Jan. 13**  *Perf. 13½x13*
| | | | | |
|---|---|---|---|---|
| 1036 | A378 | Sheet of 2 + central label | 8.50 | 8.50 |
| a. | | 100k multi | 3.50 | 3.50 |
| b. | | 150k multi | 5.00 | 5.00 |

Mice A379

Designs: 45k, Apodemus sylvaticus. 125k, Mus musculus.

*Perf. 13½x12¾*
**2005, Mar. 10**  Litho.
| | | | | |
|---|---|---|---|---|
| 1037-1038 | A379 | Set of 2 | 6.00 | 6.00 |

Flowers — A380

Designs: No. 1039, 50k, Roses. No. 1040, 50k, African daisies. No. 1041, 50k, Red calla lilies. 70k, Tulip.

---

**2005, Mar. 10**  *Perf. 13¼*
| | | | | |
|---|---|---|---|---|
| 1039-1042 | A380 | Set of 4 | 7.50 | 7.50 |
| 1042a | | Booklet pane, 2 each #1039-1042 | 15.00 | |

Nos. 1039-1042 each printed in sheets of 10, with each stamp in the sheet having a different background swirl pattern. Stamps of the same kind in the booklet pane have the same swirl pattern, which is the same as one found on the sheet.

**Insects Type of 2004**

Designs: 50k, Araneus diadematus (spider). 70k, Musca domestica.

**2005, Apr. 14**  *Perf. 13¼x13*
| | | | | |
|---|---|---|---|---|
| 1043-1044 | A375 | Set of 2 | 4.00 | 4.00 |

Fishing Boats A381

No. 1045: a, Vörthur ThH4. b, Karl VE47.
No. 1046: a, Saedís IS67. b, Guthbjörg NK74.

*Perf. 13 on 2 or 3 Sides*
**2005, Apr. 14**
**Booklet Stamps**
| | | | | |
|---|---|---|---|---|
| 1045 | | Pair | 4.50 | 4.50 |
| a.-b. | | A381 70k Either single | 2.25 | 2.25 |
| c. | | Booklet pane, 2 #1045 | 9.00 | |
| | | Complete booklet, #1045c | 9.00 | |
| 1046 | | Pair | 6.00 | 6.00 |
| a.-b. | | A381 95k Either single | 3.00 | 3.00 |
| c. | | Booklet pane, 2 #1045 | 12.00 | |
| | | Complete booklet, #1045c | 12.00 | |

Bridges, Cent. A382

Designs: 50k, Sogith Bridge. 95k, Lagarfljót Bridge. 165k, Jökulsá Bridge.

**2005, May 26**  Litho.  *Perf. 13¼x13½*
| | | | | |
|---|---|---|---|---|
| 1047-1049 | A382 | Set of 3 | 9.75 | 9.75 |

Europa A383

Fork, knife and: 70k, Fish dish, gutted fish, waterfall. 90k, Meat dish, hanging meat, flowers.

**2005, May 26**  *Perf. 13½*
| | | | | |
|---|---|---|---|---|
| 1050 | A383 | 70k multi | 2.10 | 2.10 |
| a. | | Booklet pane of 10 | 21.00 | |
| | | Complete booklet, #1050a | 21.00 | |
| 1051 | A383 | 90k multi | 2.75 | 2.75 |
| a. | | Booklet pane of 10 | 27.50 | |
| | | Complete booklet, #1050a | 27.50 | |

Salmon Fishermen and Fishing Flies — A384

Designs; 50k, Fisherman on Laxái Kjós River, Raud Frances fly. 60k, Fishermen in boat on Laxá í Athaldal River, Laxá Bla fly, vert.

*Perf. 13¾x13½, 13½x13¾*
**2005, Sept. 1**  Litho.
| | | | | |
|---|---|---|---|---|
| 1052-1053 | A384 | Set of 2 | 3.75 | 3.75 |

---

Berries — A385

Designs: 65k, Vaccinium uliginosum. 90k, Fragaria vesca.

**2005, Sept. 1**  *Perf. 14*
| | | | | |
|---|---|---|---|---|
| 1054 | A385 | 65k multi | 2.10 | 2.10 |
| a. | | Tete-beche pair | 4.25 | 4.25 |
| 1055 | A385 | 90k multi | 3.00 | 3.00 |
| a. | | Tete-beche pair | 6.00 | 6.00 |

See Nos. 1082-1083, 1116-1117.

Motorcycles — A386

**2005, Oct. 7**  *Perf. 13¼x13½*
| | | | | |
|---|---|---|---|---|
| 1056 | A386 | 50k multi | 1.75 | 1.75 |

First motorcycle in Iceland, cent.

Commercial College of Iceland, Cent. A387

**2005, Oct. 7**  *Perf. 13½x14¼*
| | | | | |
|---|---|---|---|---|
| 1057 | A387 | 70k multi | 2.25 | 2.25 |

Souvenir Sheet

Aerial View of Reykjavik Rooftops — A388

**2005, Oct. 7**  *Perf. 13¼*
| | | | | |
|---|---|---|---|---|
| 1058 | A388 | 200k multi | 7.00 | 7.00 |

Stamp Day.

**Birds Type of 2002**

Designs: 60k, Anser anser. 105k, Sturnus vulgaris.

**2005, Nov. 3**  *Perf. 14*
| | | | | |
|---|---|---|---|---|
| 1059-1060 | A349 | Set of 2 | 5.50 | 5.50 |

Christmas — A389

**2005, Nov. 3**  *Perf. 13½*
| | | | | |
|---|---|---|---|---|
| 1061 | A389 | 50k Apple | 1.75 | 1.75 |
| a. | | White border at top or bottom, perf. 13½ on 2 or 3 sides | 1.75 | 1.75 |
| b. | | Booklet pane of 10 #1061a | 17.50 | |
| | | Complete booklet, #1061b | 17.50 | |
| 1062 | A389 | 70k Christmas tree | 2.40 | 2.40 |

No. 1061 is impregnated with an apple and cinnamon scent; No. 1062 with a pine scent.

---

National Flower Dryas Octopetala — A390

**2006, Feb. 2**  Litho.  *Perf. 13¾*
| | | | | |
|---|---|---|---|---|
| 1063 | A390 | 50k multi | 1.60 | 1.60 |

Rock and Roll Music, 50th Anniv. — A391

**2006, Feb. 2**
| | | | | |
|---|---|---|---|---|
| 1064 | A391 | 60k multi | 1.90 | 1.90 |

Arrival in Iceland of Refugees of Hungarian Uprising, 50th Anniv. A392

**2006, Feb. 2**  *Perf. 13½x13¾*
| | | | | |
|---|---|---|---|---|
| 1065 | A392 | 70k multi | 2.25 | 2.25 |

Souvenir Sheet

Europa Stamps, 50th Anniv. — A393

No. 1066: a, #407. b, #395.

**2006, Feb. 2**  *Perf. 14¼x14*
| | | | | |
|---|---|---|---|---|
| 1066 | A393 | 150k Sheet of 2, #a-b | 9.50 | 9.50 |

Motion Pictures in Iceland, Cent. — A394

Designs: 50k, Early theater, projector and program. 95k, Projector reel, actor and actress. 160k, Actor in mask, clapboard, bag of popcorn, cameraman on location.

*Perf. 13¾x13½*
**2006, Mar. 29**  Litho.
| | | | | |
|---|---|---|---|---|
| 1067-1069 | A394 | Set of 3 | 8.50 | 8.50 |

Souvenir Sheet

Mythical Beings of Nordic Folklore — A395

**2006, Mar. 29**  *Perf. 13¼x13*
| | | | | |
|---|---|---|---|---|
| 1070 | A395 | 95k multi | 3.00 | 3.00 |

General Purpose Vehicles A396

No. 1071: a, 1951 Land Rover. b, 1946 Willys.
No. 1072: a, 1965 Austin Gypsy. b, 1955 GAZ-69.

**Perf. 13 on 2 or 3 Sides**

**2006, Mar. 29**

**Booklet Stamps**

| | | | |
|---|---|---|---|
| 1071 | Pair | 4.00 | 4.00 |
| a.-b. | A396 70k Either single | 2.00 | 2.00 |
| c. | Booklet pane, 2 #1071 | 8.00 | — |
| | Complete booklet, #1071c | 8.00 | |
| 1072 | Pair | 5.00 | 5.00 |
| a.-b. | A396 90k Either single | 2.50 | 2.50 |
| c. | Booklet pane, 2 #1072 | 10.00 | — |
| | Complete booklet, #1072c | 10.00 | |

A397

Europa A398

**2006, May 18**     **Perf. 13¼x13¾**
| 1073 | A397 75k blk & red | 2.40 | 2.40 |
|---|---|---|---|

**Perf. 13¾x13¼**
| 1074 | A398 95k blue & blk | 3.25 | 3.25 |
|---|---|---|---|

**Booklet Stamps**
**Self-Adhesive**
*Serpentine Die Cut 11¾x12¼*
| 1075 | A397 75k blk & red | 2.40 | 2.40 |
|---|---|---|---|
| a. | Booklet pane of 10 | 24.00 | |

*Serpentine Die Cut 12¼x11¾*
| 1076 | A398 95k blue & blk | 3.25 | 3.25 |
|---|---|---|---|
| a. | Booklet pane of 10 | 32.50 | |

Waterfalls — A399

Designs: 55k, Faxi. 65k, Oxaráfoss, vert. (29x47mm). 75k, Glymur, vert. (29x47mm). 95k, Hjálparfoss. 220k, Skeiðárfoss.

**2006, May 18**     **Perf. 13¼**
| 1077-1081 | A399 | Set of 5 | 14.50 | 14.50 |
|---|---|---|---|---|
| 1081a | Booklet pane, #1077-1081, perf. 13½ | 21.00 | — |
| | Complete booklet, #1081a | 21.00 | |

Booklet containing No. 1081a sold for 750k.

**Berries Type of 2005**

Designs: 75k, Empetrum nigrum. 130k, Rubus saxatilis.

**2006, Sept. 21**     **Perf. 13¼x13¾**
| 1082 | A385 75k multi | 2.25 | 2.25 |
|---|---|---|---|
| a. | Tete-beche pair | 4.50 | 4.50 |
| 1083 | A385 130k multi | 3.75 | 3.75 |
| a. | Tete-beche pair | 7.50 | 7.50 |

Iceland's First Olympic Medal, 50th Anniv. — A400

**Litho. & Embossed**

**2006, Sept. 21**     **Perf. 13¼**
| 1084 | A400 55k multi | 1.60 | 1.60 |
|---|---|---|---|

First Telephone Service in Iceland, Cent. — A401

**2006, Sept. 21**   **Litho.**   **Perf. 14**
| 1085 | A401 65k multi | 2.00 | 2.00 |
|---|---|---|---|

**Souvenir Sheet**

Icelandic Wrestling Tournament, Cent. — A402

**Litho. & Embossed**

**2006, Sept. 21**     **Perf. 13¼x14**
| 1086 | A402 200k multi | 6.50 | 6.50 |
|---|---|---|---|

Stamp Day.

**Mushrooms Type of 1999**

Designs: 70k, Xerocomus subtomentosus. 95k, Kuehneromyces mutabilis.

**2006, Nov. 2**   **Litho.**   **Perf. 13¾x13¼**
| 1087-1088 | A314 | Set of 2 | 5.00 | 5.00 |
|---|---|---|---|---|

**Insects Type of 2004**

Designs: 65k, Dolichovespula norwegica. 110k, Coccinella undecimpunctata.

**2006, Nov. 2**   **Litho.**   **Perf. 13¾x14¼**
| 1089-1090 | A375 | Set of 2 | 5.25 | 5.25 |
|---|---|---|---|---|

Christmas — A403

Designs: Nos. 1091, 1093, Angel, denomination at LL. 75k, Heart. No. 1094, Angel, denomination at LR.

**2006, Nov. 2**     **Perf. 13½x13¾**
| 1091 | A403 55k multi | 1.60 | 1.60 |
|---|---|---|---|
| 1092 | A403 75k multi | 2.25 | 2.25 |

**Self-Adhesive**
**Booklet Stamps**
*Serpentine Die Cut 9½x9¾*
| 1093 | A403 55k multi | 1.60 | 1.60 |
|---|---|---|---|
| 1094 | A403 55k multi | 1.60 | 1.60 |
| a. | Booklet pane, 5 each #1093-1094 | 16.00 | |
| | Nos. 1091-1094 (4) | 7.05 | 7.05 |

Women's Rights in Iceland, Cent. — A404

**Perf. 13½x13¼**
**2007, Feb. 15**     **Litho.**
| 1095 | A404 60k multi | 1.90 | 1.90 |
|---|---|---|---|

Fishing Trawler Jón Forseti, Cent. A405

**2007, Feb. 15**     **Perf. 13¾x13½**
| 1096 | A405 65k multi | 2.00 | 2.00 |
|---|---|---|---|

Geothermal Energy A406

**2007, Feb. 15**     **Perf. 14**
| 1097 | A406 75k multi | 2.25 | 2.25 |
|---|---|---|---|

West Nordic Council, 10th anniv.

**Souvenir Sheet**

Intl. Polar Year — A407

**2007, Feb. 15**     **Perf. 14x13½**
| 1098 | A407 Sheet of 2 | 5.25 | 5.25 |
|---|---|---|---|
| a. | 75k Volcano | 2.25 | 2.25 |
| b. | 95k Ice cap mapping equipment | 3.00 | 3.00 |

Youth Organization of Iceland, Cent. — A408

**2007, Apr. 20**     **Perf. 14**
| 1099 | A408 70k multi | 2.25 | 2.25 |
|---|---|---|---|

National Archives, 125th Anniv. — A409

**2007, Apr. 20**     **Perf. 12½**
| 1100 | A409 80k multi | 2.50 | 2.50 |
|---|---|---|---|
| a. | Tete-beche pair | 5.00 | 5.00 |

Organized Forestry in Iceland, Cent. — A410

Various tree branches with frame color of: 10k, Olive green. 60k, Rose carmine.

**2007, Apr. 20**     **Perf. 14**
| 1101-1102 | A410 | Set of 2 | 2.25 | 2.25 |
|---|---|---|---|---|
| 1101a | | Perf. 13½x14 | .25 | .25 |
| 1102a | | Perf. 13½x14 | 1.50 | 1.50 |

Issued: 1101a, 1102a, 11/6/08.

Cargo Boats A411

No. 1103: a, Hamrafell. b, Tröllafoss.
No. 1104: a, Langjökull. b, Akranes.

**Perf. 13 on 2 or 3 Sides**
**2007, Apr. 20**
**Booklet Stamps**
| 1103 | Pair | 5.00 | 5.00 |
|---|---|---|---|
| a.-b. | A411 80k Either single | 2.50 | 2.50 |
| c. | Booklet pane, 2 #1103 | 10.00 | |
| | Complete booklet, #1103c | 10.00 | |
| 1104 | Pair | 6.50 | 6.50 |
| a.-b. | A411 105k Either single | 3.25 | 3.25 |
| c. | Booklet pane, 2 #1104 | 13.00 | |
| | Complete booklet, #1104c | 13.00 | |

Glaciers A412

Designs: 5k, Breithamerkurjökull. 60k, Eystri Hagafellsjökull and Langjökull, vert. 80k, Mulajökull and Hofsjökull. 110k, Snaefellsjökull. 300k, Hvannadalshnúkur and Oraefajökull (70x30mm).

**2007, May 24**     **Perf. 14x13¼**
| 1105-1109 | A412 | Set of 5 | 18.00 | 18.00 |
|---|---|---|---|---|
| 1109a | Booklet pane, #1105-1109 | 25.00 | |
| | Complete booklet, #1109a | 25.00 | |

No. 1109a sold for 750k.

Europa — A413

Designs: 80k, Scouting fleur-de-lis. 105k, Scouting clover emblem.

**2007, May 24**     **Perf. 13¼**
| 1110 | A413 80k multi | 2.60 | 2.60 |
|---|---|---|---|
| 1111 | A413 105k multi | 3.50 | 3.50 |

**Booklet Stamps**
**Self-Adhesive**
*Die Cut*
| 1112 | A413 80k multi | 2.60 | 2.60 |
|---|---|---|---|
| a. | Booklet pane of 10 | 26.00 | |
| 1113 | A413 105k multi | 3.50 | 3.50 |
| a. | Booklet pane of 10 | 35.00 | |
| | Nos. 1110-1113 (4) | 12.20 | 12.20 |

Scouting, cent.

Soil Conservation Service, Cent. — A414

**Perf. 13¾x14¼**
**2007, May 24**     **Photo.**
| 1114 | A414 (60k) multi | 2.00 | 2.00 |
|---|---|---|---|

**Self-Adhesive**
*Serpentine Die Cut 12*
| 1115 | A414 (60k) multi | 2.00 | 2.00 |
|---|---|---|---|

No. 1114 was printed in a sheet of 10, No. 1115 was printed in a folded sheet of 50.

**Berries Type of 2005**

Designs: 120k, Vaccinium myrtillus. 145k, Cornus suecica.

**2007, Sept. 20**   **Litho.**   **Perf. 14**
| 1116 | A385 120k multi | 4.00 | 4.00 |
|---|---|---|---|
| a. | Tete-beche pair | 8.00 | 8.00 |
| 1117 | A385 145k multi | 4.75 | 4.75 |
| a. | Tete-beche pair | 9.50 | 9.50 |

New Bible Translation — A415

## Litho. With Foil Application
**2007, Sept. 20**      *Perf. 13½*
1118 A415 60k multi      2.00 2.00

### Souvenir Sheet

Royal Visit, Cent. — A416

## Litho. & Engr.
**2007, Sept. 20**      *Perf. 13x13¼*
1119 A416 250k multi      8.25 8.25

Jökulsá Canyon and Selfoss Waterfall — A417

No. 1120: a, Jökulsá Canyon (45x29mm). b, Selfoss Waterfall (30x29mm) Illustration reduced.

**2007, Oct. 1**   Litho.    *Perf. 13¼x13¾*
1120 A417   Horiz. pair     6.25 6.25
   a.    80k multi      2.75 2.75
   b.    105k multi      3.50 3.50

### Insects Type of 2004
Designs: 70k, Prionocera turcica. 190k, Euceraphis punctipennis.

**2007, Nov. 8**   Litho.    *Perf. 14*
1121-1122 A375   Set of 2      8.50 8.50

Jónas Hallgrímsson (1807-45), Poet — A418

**2007, Nov. 8**   Engr.    *Perf. 12¾x13*
1123 A418 65k brown      2.25 2.25

Kleppur Psychiatric Hospital, Cent. — A419

**2007, Nov. 8**   Litho.    *Perf. 13¼*
1124 A419 80k multi      2.60 2.60

Christmas A420

---

Various cut patterns in Icelandic leaf bread: 60k, 80k.

**2007, Nov. 8**    *Serpentine Die Cut*
**Self-Adhesive**
1125 A420 60k red & multi    2.00 2.00
   a.    Booklet pane of 10    20.00
1126 A420 80k grn & multi    2.60 2.60

Teachers' College of Iceland, Cent. — A421

**2008, Feb. 14**   Litho.    *Perf. 14x13¼*
1127 A421 85k multi      2.60 2.60

Kisses — A422

Lines from poem by Erla Thorsteindottir and people kissing with photograph colors in: No. 1128, 65k, Blue. No. 1129, 65k, Sepia. 75k, Green. 85k, Red violet.

**2008, Feb. 14**
1128-1131 A422   Set of 4      8.75 8.75

Agricultural Tools — A423

No. 1132: a, Ferguson tractor. b, International Harvester TD6 bulldozer.
No. 1133: a, Horse-drawn plow. b, Lanz turfkiller.

**2008, Mar. 27**   Litho.    *Perf. 13¼*
**Booklet Stamps**
1132     Pair      5.00 5.00
  a.-b.   A423 85k Either single   2.50 2.50
   c.    Booklet pane, 2 #1132   10.00
     Complete booklet, #1132c   10.00
1133     Pair      6.00 6.00
  a.-b.   A423 110k Either single   3.00 3.00
   c.    Booklet pane, 2 #1133   12.00
     Complete booklet, #1133c   12.00

Embroidery — A424

Designs: 65k, Refilsaumur. 85k, Augnsaumur. 110k, Krosssaumur.

**2008, Mar. 27**      *Perf. 14*
1134-1136 A424   Set of 3      7.25 7.25

### Souvenir Sheet

Snaefellsnes — A425

**2008, Mar. 27**      *Perf. 14x13¼*
1137 A425 120k multi      3.25 3.25

---

Personalized Stamp — A426

### Serpentine Die Cut 10 Syncopated
**2008, May 8**      Litho.
**Self-Adhesive**
1138 A426 (75k) multi      1.90 1.90

The vignette of the stamp shown above is the generic image for the issue, which was available at face value. Other images with the stamp frame shown are personalized stamps which sold for 3120k for a sheet of 24 stamps.

Geothermal Space Heating, Cent. — A427

**2008, May 8**      *Perf. 14x13½*
1139 A427 75k multi      1.90 1.90

Hafnarfjördhur, Cent. — A428

**2008, May 8**      *Perf. 13x12½*
1140 A428 80k multi      2.00 2.00

Icelandic Industrial Design A429

Designs: 65k, Proprio Foot prosthetic foot. 120k, Marel OptiCut volumetric portioning and meat cutting machine. 155k, Wish fly fishing reel. 200k, Gavia submarine.

**2008, May 8**      *Perf. 12½x13*
1141-1144 A429   Set of 4    14.00 14.00
  1141a    Tete beche pair    3.50 3.50
  1142a    Tete beche pair    6.25 6.25
  1143a    Tete beche pair    8.00 8.00

Europa — A430

Letter folded into: 85k, Boat. 110k, Airplane.

**2008, May 8**      *Perf. 14*
1145 A430 85k multi      2.25 2.25
1146 A430 110k multi      2.75 2.75

---

### Booklet Stamps
### Self-Adhesive
*Serpentine Die Cut 9½x10*
1147 A430   85k multi      2.25 2.25
   a.    Booklet pane of 10    22.50
1148 A430   110k multi      2.75 2.75
   a.    Booklet pane of 10    27.50

Knight and Final Position of 1958 Chess Match Between Fridhrik Olafsson and Bobby Fischer — A431

**2008, Sept. 18**   Litho.    *Perf. 13¼*
1149 A431 80k multi      1.90 1.90

First Cod War, 50th Anniv. A432

**2008, Sept. 18**      *Perf. 13¼x13*
1150 A432 90k multi      2.10 2.10

Aegagropila Linnaei — A433

**2008, Sept. 18**      *Perf. 13¼x13¾*
1151 A433 140k multi      3.25 3.25

### Souvenir Sheet

Intl. Year of Planet Earth — A434

**2008, Sept. 18**
1152 A434 215k multi      5.00 5.00

Stamp Day.

Peace Tower, Videy — A435

**2008, Oct. 9**   Litho.    *Perf. 13¼*
1153 A435 120k multi + label   2.50 2.50

Parts of the design were printed with a glow-in-the-dark ink.

### Forestry Type of 2005 Redrawn and

Forestry in Vaglaskógur, Cent. — A436

## 2008, Nov. 6    Litho.    Perf. 13½x14

| | | | |
|---|---|---|---|
| 1154 | A436 | 400k multi | 6.25 6.25 |
| 1155 | | Booklet pane of 4, #1101a, 1102a, 1154, 1155a | 12.50 — |
| a. | | A377 45k multi, denomination as "45" only | 1.10 1.10 |
| | | Complete booklet, #1155 | 12.50 |

No. 1155 sold for 800k.

Christmas
A437

Winning designs in children's stamp art contest: 70k, Christmas goblin Stiff-legs, by Heidhar Jökull Hafsteinsson. 90k, Christmas Cat, by Konrádh Kárason Thormar.

### *Serpentine Die Cut 12½*

## 2008, Nov. 6
### Self-Adhesive

| | | | |
|---|---|---|---|
| 1156 | A437 | 70k multi | 1.10 1.10 |
| a. | | Booket pane of 10 | 11.00 |
| 1157 | A437 | 90k multi | 1.40 1.40 |

Vertical pairs in booklet pane are tete-beche.

### Islands Type of 2001

Designs: 75k, Hjörsey. 90k, Málmey.

## 2009, Jan. 29    Litho.    Perf. 14

| | | | |
|---|---|---|---|
| 1158-1159 | A335 | Set of 2 | 3.00 3.00 |

### Insects Type of 2004

Designs: 80k, Psychodidae. 120k, Gnaphosidae (spider).

## 2009, Jan. 29

| | | | |
|---|---|---|---|
| 1160-1161 | A375 | Set of 2 | 3.50 3.50 |

### Souvenir Sheet

Intl. Polar Year — A438

No. 1162 — Map of ice cover of: a, 100k, North Pole, Northern Greenland. b, 130k, Iceland, Eastern Greenland.

### Litho. & Photo.

## 2009, Jan. 29    Perf. 13x13½

| | | | |
|---|---|---|---|
| 1162 | A438 | Sheet of 2, #a-b | 4.00 4.00 |

Parts of the design were printed with a thermographic ink that disappeared when warmed.

Civil Aviation in Iceland, 90th Anniv. A439

No. 1163: a, Avro 504K. b, Waco ZKS-7.
No. 1164: a, Boeing 757. b, Fokker 50.

---

### Perf. 14¼ Horiz.

## 2009, Mar. 19    Litho.
### Booklet Stamps

| | | | |
|---|---|---|---|
| 1163 | | Vert. pair | 3.25 3.25 |
| a.-b. | A439 | 90k Either single | 1.60 1.60 |
| c. | | Booklet pane, 2 #1163 | 6.50 — |
| | | Complete booklet, #1163c | 6.50 |
| 1164 | | Vert. pair | 4.25 4.25 |
| a.-b. | A439 | 120k Either single | 2.10 2.10 |
| c. | | Booklet pane, 2 #1164 | 8.50 — |
| | | Complete booklet, #1164c | 8.50 |

### Miniature Sheet

Legendary Creatures from Folktales — A440

No. 1165: a, Hrosshvalur. b, Skoffín. c, Múshveli. d, Raudhkembingur. e, Selamódhir. f, Ofuguggi. g, Saeneyti. h, Skeljaskrímsli. i, Urdharköt tur. j, Fjörulalli.

## 2009, Mar. 19    Perf. 13¼

| | | | |
|---|---|---|---|
| 1165 | A440 | 80k Sheet of 10, #a-j | 14.00 14.00 |

## SEMI-POSTAL STAMPS

Shipwreck and Rescue by Breeches Buoy SP1

Children Gathering Rock Plants SP2

Old Fisherman at Shore SP3

### Unwmk.

## 1933, Apr. 28    Engr.    Perf. 14

| | | | |
|---|---|---|---|
| B1 | SP1 | 10a + 10a red brown | 2.00 6.50 |
| B2 | SP2 | 20a + 20a org red | 2.00 6.50 |
| B3 | SP1 | 35a + 25a ultra | 2.00 6.50 |
| B4 | SP3 | 50a + 25a blue grn | 2.00 6.50 |
| | | *Nos. B1-B4 (4)* | 8.00 26.00 |
| | | Set, never hinged | 15.00 |

Receipts from the surtax were devoted to a special fund for use in various charitable works especially those indicated on the stamps: "Slysavarnir" (Rescue work), "Barnahaeli" (Asylum for scrofulous children), "Ellhaeli" (Asylum for the Aged).

---

### Souvenir Sheets

King Christian X — SP4

## 1937, May 15    Typo.

| | | | |
|---|---|---|---|
| B5 | SP4 | Sheet of 3 | 50.00 325.00 |
| | | Never hinged | 85.00 |
| a. | | 15a violet | 11.00 60.00 |
| b. | | 25a red | 11.00 60.00 |
| c. | | 50a blue | 11.00 60.00 |

Reign of Christian X, 25th anniv. Sheet sold for 2kr.

SP5

Designs: 30a, 40a, Ericsson statue, Reýkjavik. 60a, Iceland's position on globe.

## 1938, Oct. 9    Photo.    Perf. 12

| | | | |
|---|---|---|---|
| B6 | SP5 | Sheet of 3 | 6.00 32.50 |
| | | Never hinged | 10.00 |
| a. | | 30a scarlet | 1.40 13.00 |
| b. | | 40a purple | 1.40 13.00 |
| c. | | 60a deep green | 1.40 13.00 |

Leif Ericsson Day, Oct. 9, 1938.

> **Catalogue values for unused stamps in this section, from this point to the end of the section, are for Never Hinged items.**

Ill Child — SP6

Red Cross Nurse and Patient — SP7

Nurse Covering Patient — SP8

Elderly Couple — SP9

Rescue at Sea — SP10

---

### Unwmk.

## 1949, June 8    Engr.    Perf. 14

| | | | |
|---|---|---|---|
| B7 | SP6 | 10a + 10a olive grn | .65 1.40 |
| B8 | SP7 | 35a + 15a carmine | .90 1.40 |
| B9 | SP8 | 50a + 25a choc | .90 1.40 |
| B10 | SP9 | 60a + 25a brt ultra | .90 1.40 |
| B11 | SP10 | 75a + 25a slate gray | .90 1.40 |
| | | *Nos. B7-B11 (5)* | 4.25 7.00 |

The surtax was for charitable purposes.

Nos. 262 and 265 Surcharged in Black

## 1953, Feb. 12    Unwmk.    Perf. 13

| | | | |
|---|---|---|---|
| B12 | A50 | 75a + 25a red org | 1.50 5.50 |
| B13 | A50 | 1.25k + 25a red vio | 2.50 5.50 |

The surtax was for flood relief in the Netherlands.

St. Thorlacus — SP11

Cathedral at Skalholt SP12

1.75k+1.25k, Bishop Jon Thorkelsson Vidalin.

## 1956, Jan. 23    Perf. 11½

| | | | |
|---|---|---|---|
| B14 | SP11 | 75a + 25a car | .25 .30 |
| B15 | SP12 | 1.25k + 75a dk brn | .25 .65 |
| B16 | SP11 | 1.75k + 1.25k black | 1.00 2.00 |
| | | *Nos. B14-B16 (3)* | 1.50 2.95 |

Bishopric of Skalholt, 900th anniv.
The surtax was for the rebuilding of Skalholt, former cultural center of Iceland.

Ambulance SP13

## 1963, Nov. 15    Photo.    Unwmk.

| | | | |
|---|---|---|---|
| B17 | SP13 | 3k + 50a multi | .45 1.40 |
| B18 | SP13 | 3.50k + 50a multi | .45 1.40 |

Centenary of International Red Cross.

Rock Ptarmigan in Summer SP14

Design: #B20, Rock ptarmigan in winter.

## 1965, Jan. 27    Photo.    Perf. 12½
### Granite Paper

| | | | |
|---|---|---|---|
| B19 | SP14 | 3.50k + 50a multi | .80 2.25 |
| B20 | SP14 | 4.50k + 50a multi | .80 2.25 |

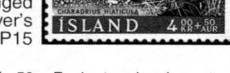

Ringed Plover's Nest — SP15

Design: 5k+50a, Rock ptarmigan's nest.

**1967, Nov. 22   Photo.   Perf. 11½**

| | | | |
|---|---|---|---|
| B21 | SP15 | 4k + 50a multi | .80   1.75 |
| B22 | SP15 | 5k + 50a multi | .80   1.75 |

ÍSLAND 7+1 KR
Arctic Terns — SP16

**1972, Nov. 22   Litho.   Perf. 13**

| | | | |
|---|---|---|---|
| B23 | SP16 | 7k + 1k multi | .55   1.10 |
| B24 | SP16 | 9k + 1k multi | .55   1.10 |

### AIR POST STAMPS

No. 115 Overprinted

**Perf. 14x14½**
**1928, May 31   Wmk. 114**

| | | | |
|---|---|---|---|
| C1 | A8 | 10a red | 1.10   14.00 |
| | | Never hinged | 1.75 |

**Same Overprint on No. 82**
**1929, June 29   Wmk. 113   Perf. 13**

| | | | |
|---|---|---|---|
| C2 | A5 | 50a gray & violet | 70.00   140.00 |
| | | Never hinged | 200.00 |

Gyrfalcon AP1

**Perf. 12½x12**
**1930, Jan. 1   Litho.   Unwmk.**

| | | | |
|---|---|---|---|
| C3 | AP1 | 10a dp ultra & gray blue | 25.00   72.50 |
| | | Never hinged | 50.00 |

Imperfs were privately printed.
For overprint see No. CO1.

Snaefellsjokull, Extinct Volcano — AP2

Parliament Millenary: 20a, Fishing boat. 35a, Iceland pony. 50a, Gullfoss (Golden Falls). 1k, Ingolfour Arnarson Statue.

**Wmk. 47**
**1930, June 1   Typo.   Perf. 14**

| | | | |
|---|---|---|---|
| C4 | AP2 | 15a org brn & dl bl | 30.00   60.00 |
| C5 | AP2 | 20a bis brn & sl bl | 30.00   60.00 |
| C6 | AP2 | 35a olive grn & brn | 55.00   125.00 |
| C7 | AP2 | 50a dp grn & dp bl | 55.00   125.00 |
| C8 | AP2 | 1k olive grn & dk red | 55.00   125.00 |
| | | Nos. C4-C8 (5) | 225.00   495.00 |
| | | Set, never hinged | 475.00 |

Regular Issue of 1920 Overprinted

**Perf. 14x14½**
**1931, May 25   Wmk. 114**

| | | | |
|---|---|---|---|
| C9 | A8 | 30a red & green | 50.00   175.00 |
| C10 | A8 | 1k dp bl & dk brn | 17.50   175.00 |
| C11 | A8 | 2k ol brn & myr grn | 70.00   175.00 |
| | | Nos. C9-C11 (3) | 137.50   525.00 |
| | | Set, never hinged | 275.00 |

Nos. 185, 128 and 187
Overprinted in Red

**1933, June 16**

| | | | |
|---|---|---|---|
| C12 | A8 | 1k dk bl & lt brn | 200.00   675.00 |
| | | Never hinged | 400.00 |
| C13 | A8 | 5k brn & indigo | 600.00   1,600. |
| | | Never hinged | 1,250. |
| C14 | A8 | 10k yel grn & blk | 1,300.   3,000. |
| | | Never hinged | 2,650. |

Excellent counterfeit overprints exist.
Visit of the Italian Flying Armada en route from Rome to Chicago; also for the payment of the charges on postal matter sent from Iceland to the US via the Italian seaplanes.

Plane over Thingvalla Lake — AP7

10a-20a, Plane over Thingvalla Lake. 25a-50a, Plane and Aurora Borealis. 1k-2k, Map of Iceland.

**Perf. 12½x14**
**1934, Sept. 1   Engr.   Unwmk.**

| | | | |
|---|---|---|---|
| C15 | AP7 | 10a blue | 2.30   2.75 |
| C16 | AP7 | 20a emerald | 4.50   6.50 |
| a. | | Perf. 14 | 22.50   19.00 |
| C17 | AP7 | 25a dark violet, perf. 14 | 11.50   17.50 |
| | | Revenue cancellation | 22.50 |
| a. | | Perf. 12½x14 | 22.50   30.00 |
| C18 | AP7 | 50a red vio, perf. 14 | 4.00   7.75 |
| | | Revenue cancellation | 22.50 |
| C19 | AP7 | 1k dark brown | 22.50   32.50 |
| | | Revenue cancellation | 22.50 |
| C20 | AP7 | 2k orange | 11.50   13.50 |
| | | Nos. C15-C20 (6) | 56.30   80.50 |
| | | Set, never hinged | 110.00 |

> Catalogue values for unused stamps in this section, from this point to the end of the section, are for Never Hinged items.

Thingvellir, Old Site of the Parliament AP10

Isafjörthur AP11

Eyjafjörthur AP12

Mt. Strandatindur AP13

Mt. Thyrill AP14

Aerial View of Reykjavik AP15

**1947, Aug. 18   Perf. 14**

| | | | |
|---|---|---|---|
| C21 | AP10 | 15a red orange | 1.00   1.75 |
| C22 | AP11 | 30a gray black | 1.00   1.75 |
| C23 | AP12 | 75a brown red | 1.00   1.40 |
| C24 | AP13 | 1k indigo | 1.00   1.40 |
| C25 | AP14 | 2k chocolate | 1.75   2.75 |
| C26 | AP15 | 3k dark green | 1.75   2.75 |
| | | Nos. C21-C26 (6) | 7.50   11.80 |

Snaefellsjokull AP16

Views: 2.50k, Eiriksjokull. 3.30k, Oraefajokull.

**1952, May 2   Unwmk.   Perf. 13½x14**

| | | | |
|---|---|---|---|
| C27 | AP16 | 1.80k slate blue | 21.00   16.00 |
| C28 | AP16 | 2.50k green | 37.50   1.40 |
| C29 | AP16 | 3.30k deep ultra | 8.50   10.50 |
| | | Nos. C27-C29 (3) | 67.00   27.90 |

See Nos. 302-304.

Vickers Viscount and Plane of 1919 AP17

4.05k, Skymaster and plane of 1919.

**1959, Sept. 3   Engr.   Perf. 13½**

| | | | |
|---|---|---|---|
| C30 | AP17 | 3.50k steel blue | .90   .75 |
| C31 | AP17 | 4.05k green | .55   .90 |

40th anniv. of air transportation in Iceland.

### AIR POST OFFICIAL STAMP

No. C3 Overprinted In Red

**1930, Jan. 1   Unwmk.   Perf. 12½x12**

| | | | |
|---|---|---|---|
| CO1 | AP1 | 10a dp ultra & gray blue | 22.50   125.00 |
| | | Never hinged | 55.00 |

Imperfs were privately printed.

### OFFICIAL STAMPS

O1

O2

O3

**Perf. 14x13½**
**1873   Typo.   Wmk. 112**

| | | | |
|---|---|---|---|
| O1 | O1 | 4s green | 8,500.   8,500. |
| a. | | Imperf. | 150. |
| O2 | O1 | 8s red lilac | 600.   750. |
| a. | | Imperf. | 700. |

**Perf. 12½**

| | | | |
|---|---|---|---|
| O3 | O1 | 4s green | 100.   450. |

The imperforate varieties lack gum.
No. O1 values are for copies with perfs just touching the design on at least one side.
Fake and favor cancellations are often found on Nos. O1-O3. Values are considerably less than those shown.

**1876-95   Perf. 14x13½**

| | | | |
|---|---|---|---|
| O4 | O2 | 3a yellow | 45.00   70.00 |
| O5 | O2 | 5a brown | 10.50   19.00 |
| a. | | Imperf. | 375.00 |
| O6 | O2 | 10a blue | 77.50   17.50 |
| a. | | 10a ultramarine | 500.00   70.00 |
| O7 | O2 | 16a carmine | 26.00   60.00 |
| O8 | O2 | 20a yellow green | 26.00   50.00 |
| O9 | O2 | 50a rose lilac ('95) | 77.50   97.50 |
| | | Nos. O4-O9 (6) | 262.50   314.00 |

**1898-1902   Perf. 13**

| | | | |
|---|---|---|---|
| O10 | O2 | 3a yellow | 15.00   40.00 |
| O11 | O2 | 4a gray ('01) | 40.00   50.00 |
| O12 | O2 | 10a ultra ('02) | 72.50   125.00 |
| | | Nos. O10-O12 (3) | 127.50   215.00 |

A 5a brown, perf. 13, Wmk. 112, exists. It was not regularly issued.
See note after No. O30.
For overprints see Nos. O20-O30.

**1902   Wmk. 113   Perf. 13**

| | | | |
|---|---|---|---|
| O13 | O3 | 3a buff & black | 4.75   3.25 |
| O14 | O3 | 4a dp grn & blk | 4.75   2.75 |
| O15 | O3 | 5a org brn & blk | 3.75   4.75 |
| O16 | O3 | 10a ultra & black | 4.25   4.75 |
| O17 | O3 | 16a carmine & blk | 3.75   17.00 |
| O18 | O3 | 20a green & blk | 19.00   8.75 |
| O19 | O3 | 50a violet & blk | 8.00   13.00 |
| | | Nos. O13-O19 (7) | 48.25   54.25 |

Stamps of 1876-1901 Overprinted in Black

**1902-03   Wmk. 112   Perf. 13**

| | | | |
|---|---|---|---|
| O20 | O2 | 3a yellow | 1.10   2.75 |
| a. | | "I" before Gildi omitted | 110.00 |
| b. | | Inverted overprint | 19.00   25.00 |
| c. | | As "a," invtd. | 250.00 |
| d. | | Pair, one with invtd. ovpt. | 110.00 |
| e. | | '03-'03 | 300.00 |
| f. | | 02'-'03 | 300.00 |
| O21 | O2 | 4a gray | 1.10   2.75 |
| a. | | "I" before Gildi omitted | 125.00 |
| b. | | Inverted overprint | 35.00   45.00 |
| e. | | '03-'03 | 300.00 |
| f. | | 02'-'03 | 300.00 |
| g. | | Pair, one without ovpt. | 110.00 |
| h. | | Pair, one with invtd. ovpt. | 125.00 |
| i. | | "L" only of "I GILDI" inverted | 200.00 |
| O22 | O2 | 5a brown | 1.00   2.75 |
| O23 | O2 | 10a ultramarine | 1.00   2.75 |
| a. | | "I" before Gildi omitted | 35.00 |
| b. | | Inverted overprint | 27.50   37.50 |
| c. | | '03-'03 | 300.00 |
| d. | | 02'-'03 | 300.00 |
| e. | | "L" only of "I GILDI" | 27.50 |
| f. | | As "e," inverted | 140.00 |
| g. | | "IL" only of "I GILDI" | 65.00 |
| O24 | O2 | 20a yel green | 1.00   27.50 |
| | | Nos. O20-O24 (5) | 5.20   38.50 |

**Perf. 14x13½**

| | | | |
|---|---|---|---|
| O25 | O2 | 3a yellow | 350.00   1,400. |
| a. | | "02'-'03 | 700.00 |
| b. | | '03-'03 | 700.00 |
| O26 | O2 | 5a brown | 9.00   160.00 |
| a. | | Inverted overprint | 70.00 |
| b. | | '03-'03 | 250.00 |
| c. | | 02'-'03 | 250.00 |
| d. | | "L" only of "I GILDI" inverted | 225.00 |
| O27 | O2 | 10a blue | 475.00   900.00 |
| a. | | "I" before Gildi omitted | 825.00 |
| b. | | Inverted overprint | 650.00   950.00 |
| c. | | '03-'03 | 900.00 |
| d. | | 02'-'03 | 900.00 |
| O28 | O2 | 16a carmine | 20.00   80.00 |
| a. | | "I" before Gildi omitted | 250.00 |
| b. | | Double overprint | 125.00 |
| c. | | Dbl. ovpt., one inverted | 400.00 |
| d. | | Inverted overprint | 125.00   175.00 |
| e. | | '03-'03 | 375.00 |
| O29 | O2 | 20a yel green | 26.00   100.00 |
| a. | | Inverted overprint | 125.00   175.00 |
| b. | | '03-'03 | 325.00 |
| c. | | 02'-'03 | 325.00 |
| O30 | O2 | 50a red lilac | 7.00   70.00 |
| a. | | "I" before Gildi omitted | 50.00 |
| b. | | Inverted overprint | 110.00 |
| | | Nos. O25-O30 (6) | 887.00   2,710. |

Nos. O10-O12, O20-O24, O28 and O30 were reprinted in 1904. They have the watermark of 1902 (type 113) and are perf. 13. Value $70 each. Without overprint $90 each.

Christian IX, Frederik VIII — O4

Christian X — O5

## Engraved Center

**1907-08**    **Wmk. 113**    **Perf. 13**

| | | | | |
|---|---|---|---|---|
| O31 | O4 | 3a yellow & gray | 7.50 | 8.75 |
| O32 | O4 | 4a green & gray | 4.00 | 9.25 |
| O33 | O4 | 5a brn org & gray | 11.50 | 4.50 |
| O34 | O4 | 10a deep bl & gray | 2.50 | 3.50 |
| O35 | O4 | 15a lt blue & gray | 5.00 | 9.25 |
| O36 | O4 | 16a carmine & gray | 5.00 | 32.50 |
| O37 | O4 | 20a yel grn & gray | 15.00 | 6.00 |
| O38 | O4 | 50a violet & gray | 8.00 | 11.50 |
| | | *Nos. O31-O38 (8)* | 58.50 | 85.25 |

**1918**    **Wmk. 114**    **Perf. 14x14½**

| | | | | |
|---|---|---|---|---|
| O39 | O4 | 15a lt bl & gray | 15.00 | 40.00 |

**1920-30**      **Typo.**

| | | | | |
|---|---|---|---|---|
| O40 | O5 | 3a yellow & gray | 5.00 | 4.00 |
| O41 | O5 | 4a dp grn & gray | 1.25 | 3.75 |
| O42 | O5 | 5a orange & gray | 1.25 | 1.25 |
| O43 | O5 | 10a dk bl & gray | 15.00 | 1.50 |
| O44 | O5 | 15a lt blue & gray | .75 | 1.25 |
| O45 | O5 | 20a yel grn & gray | 50.00 | 4.50 |
| O46 | O5 | 50a violet & gray | 45.00 | 2.25 |
| O47 | O5 | 1k car & gray | 45.00 | 3.00 |
| O48 | O5 | 2k bl & blk ('30) | 8.00 | 21.00 |
| O49 | O5 | 5k brn & blk ('30) | 40.00 | 57.50 |
| | | *Nos. O40-O49 (10)* | 211.25 | 100.00 |

See No. O68.

Nos. 97 and 98
Overprinted

**1922, May**    **Wmk. 113**    **Perf. 13**

| | | | | |
|---|---|---|---|---|
| O50 | A7 | 2k rose, larger letters, no period | 32.50 | 65.00 |
| a. | | Smaller letters, with period | 100.00 | 70.00 |
| O51 | A7 | 5k brown | 225.00 | 250.00 |

No. 115 Surcharged

**1923**    **Wmk. 114**    **Perf. 14x14½**

| | | | | |
|---|---|---|---|---|
| O52 | A8 | 20a on 10a red | 27.50 | 2.50 |

### Parliament Millenary Issue

#152-166
Overprinted
in Red or
Blue

**1930, Jan. 1**   **Unwmk.**   **Perf. 12½x12**

| | | | | |
|---|---|---|---|---|
| O53 | A15 | 3a (R) | 16.00 | 47.50 |
| O54 | A15 | 5a (R) | 16.00 | 47.50 |
| O55 | A15 | 7a (R) | 16.00 | 47.50 |
| O56 | A15 | 10a (Bl) | 16.00 | 47.50 |
| O57 | A15 | 15a (R) | 16.00 | 47.50 |
| O58 | A15 | 20a (Bl) | 16.00 | 47.50 |
| O59 | A15 | 25a (Bl) | 16.00 | 47.50 |
| O60 | A15 | 30a (R) | 16.00 | 47.50 |
| O61 | A15 | 35a (R) | 16.00 | 47.50 |
| O62 | A15 | 40a (Bl) | 16.00 | 47.50 |
| O63 | A15 | 50a (R) | 150.00 | 400.00 |
| O64 | A15 | 1k (R) | 150.00 | 400.00 |
| O65 | A15 | 2k (Bl) | 200.00 | 425.00 |
| O66 | A15 | 5k (Bl) | 200.00 | 425.00 |
| O67 | A15 | 10k (Bl) | 150.00 | 400.00 |
| | | *Nos. O53-O67 (15)* | 1,010. | 2,525. |

Type of 1920 Issue Redrawn

**1931**    **Wmk. 114**    **Typo.**

| | | | | |
|---|---|---|---|---|
| O68 | O5 | 20a yel grn & gray | 40.00 | 3.50 |

For differences in redrawing see note after No. 187.

No. 82 Overprinted in
Black

Overprint 15mm long

**1936, Dec. 7**    **Wmk. 113**    **Perf. 13**

| | | | | |
|---|---|---|---|---|
| O69 | A5 | 50a gray & vio | 25.00 | 30.00 |

---

### Same Overprint on Nos. 180 and 115
**Perf. 14x14½**
**Wmk. 114**

| | | | | |
|---|---|---|---|---|
| O70 | A8 | 7a yellow green | 3.25 | 32.50 |
| O71 | A8 | 10a red | 12.50 | 2.25 |
| | | *Nos. O69-O71 (3)* | 40.75 | 64.75 |

---

# IFNI

'if-nē

LOCATION — An enclave in southern Morocco on the Atlantic coast
GOVT. — Spanish possession
AREA — 580 sq. mi.
POP. — 51,517 (est. 1964)
CAPITAL — Sidi Ifni

Ifni was ceded to Spain by Morocco in 1860, but the Spanish did not occupy it until 1934. Sidi Ifni was also the administrative capital for Spanish West Africa. Spain turned Ifni back to Morocco June 30, 1969.

100 Centimos = 1 Peseta

Catalogue values for unused stamps in this country are for Never Hinged items, beginning with Scott 28 in the regular postage section, Scott B1 in the semi-postal section, and Scott C38 in the airpost section.

Stamps of Spain,
1936-40, Overprinted
in Red or Blue

**1941-42**    **Unwmk.**    **Imperf.**

| | | | | |
|---|---|---|---|---|
| 1 | A159 | 1c green | 8.50 | 6.00 |

**Perf. 10 to 11**

| | | | | |
|---|---|---|---|---|
| 2 | A160 | 2c org brn (Bl) | 8.50 | 6.00 |
| 3 | A161 | 5c gray brown | 1.25 | 1.10 |
| 5 | A161 | 10c dk car (Bl) | 5.00 | 2.25 |
| a. | | Red overprint | 17.50 | 8.25 |
| 6 | A161 | 15c lt green | 1.25 | 1.10 |
| 7 | A166 | 20c brt violet | 1.25 | 1.10 |
| 8 | A166 | 25c deep claret | 1.25 | 1.10 |
| 9 | A166 | 30c blue | 1.25 | 1.10 |
| 10 | A166 | 40c Prus green | 1.75 | 1.10 |
| 11 | A166 | 50c indigo | 9.25 | 2.00 |
| 12 | A166 | 70c blue | 9.25 | 5.00 |
| 13 | A166 | 1p gray black | 9.25 | 5.00 |
| 14 | A166 | 2p dull brown | 140.00 | 120.00 |
| 15 | A166 | 4p dl rose (Bl) | 500.00 | 210.00 |
| 16 | A166 | 10p light brn | 1,200. | 600.00 |
| | | *Nos. 1-16 (15)* | 1,897. | 962.85 |
| | | Set, never hinged | 2,500. | |

Counterfeit overprints exist.

Nomads — A1      Alcazaba
Fortress — A3

Designs: 2c, 20c, 45c, 3p, Marksman.

**1943**    **Litho.**    **Perf. 12½**

| | | | | |
|---|---|---|---|---|
| 17 | A1 | 1c brn & lil rose | .30 | .25 |
| 18 | A1 | 2c yel grn & sl lil | .30 | .25 |
| 19 | A3 | 5c magenta & vio | .30 | .25 |
| 20 | A1 | 15c sl grn & grn | .30 | .25 |
| 21 | A1 | 20c vio & red brn | .30 | .25 |
| 22 | A1 | 40c rose vio & vio | .35 | .30 |
| 23 | A1 | 45c brn vio & red | .40 | .35 |
| 24 | A3 | 75c indigo & bl | .40 | .35 |
| 25 | A1 | 1p red & brown | 2.00 | 1.75 |

---

| | | | | |
|---|---|---|---|---|
| 26 | A1 | 3p bl vio & sl grn | 2.50 | 2.25 |
| 27 | A3 | 10p blk brn & blk | 28.50 | 26.00 |
| | | *Nos. 17-27,E1 (12)* | 37.65 | 33.75 |
| | | Set, never hinged | 65.00 | |

Nos. 17-27 exist imperforate. Value, set $115.

Catalogue values for unused stamps in this section, from this point to the end of the section, are for Never Hinged items.

**1947, Feb.**      **Perf. 10**

| | | | | |
|---|---|---|---|---|
| 28 | A1 | 50c Nomad family | 13.50 | .75 |

Stamps of Spain,
1939-48,
Overprinted in
Carmine

**1948, Aug. 2**   **Perf. 9½x10½, 11, 13**

| | | | | |
|---|---|---|---|---|
| 29 | A161 | 5c gray brown (#664) | 4.50 | .65 |
| 30 | A194 | 15c gray green | 5.25 | .65 |
| 31 | A167 | 90c dark green (#714a) | 20.00 | 3.50 |
| 32 | A166 | 1p gray black | .55 | .25 |
| | | *Nos. 29-32 (4)* | 30.30 | 5.05 |

See Nos. 36 and 45.

Spain Nos. 769 and 770 Overprinted
in Violet Blue or Carmine

**1949, Oct. 9**    **Perf. 12½x13**

| | | | | |
|---|---|---|---|---|
| 33 | A202 | 50c red brown (VB) | 3.00 | 1.00 |
| 34 | A202 | 75c violet blue (C) | 3.00 | 1.00 |
| | | *Nos. 33-34,C40 (3)* | 9.25 | 3.10 |

75th anniv. of the UPU.

Stamps of Spain, 1938-48,
Overprinted in Blue or Carmine like
Nos. 29-32

**Perf. 13, 13½, 12½x13, 9½x10½**

**1949**      **Unwmk.**

| | | | | |
|---|---|---|---|---|
| 35 | A160 | 2c orange brn (Bl) | .25 | .25 |
| 36 | A161 | 5c gray brown (#664a) | .25 | .25 |
| 37 | A161 | 10c dk carmine | .25 | .25 |
| 38 | A161 | 15c dk green (II) | .25 | .25 |
| 39 | A166 | 25c brown violet | .25 | .25 |
| 40 | A166 | 30c blue | .30 | .25 |
| 41 | A195 | 40c red brown | .30 | .25 |
| 42 | A195 | 45c car rose (Bl) | .55 | .25 |
| 43 | A166 | 50c indigo | .50 | .25 |
| 44 | A195 | 75c dk vio bl | .75 | .35 |
| 45 | A167 | 90c dark green (#714) | .75 | .50 |
| 47 | A167 | 1.35p purple | 6.25 | 3.75 |
| 48 | A166 | 2p dl brn | 5.00 | 2.25 |
| 49 | A166 | 4p dl rose (Bl) | 17.00 | 6.75 |
| 50 | A166 | 10p lt brn | 40.00 | 20.00 |
| | | *Nos. 35-50 (15)* | 72.65 | 35.85 |

Gen. Francisco Franco and Desert Scene A4

**Perf. 12½x13**

**1951, July 18**   **Photo.**   **Unwmk.**

| | | | | |
|---|---|---|---|---|
| 51 | A4 | 50c dp org | .35 | .20 |
| 52 | A4 | 1p chocolate | 3.50 | 1.00 |
| 53 | A4 | 5p bl grn | 27.50 | 10.00 |
| | | *Nos. 51-53 (3)* | 31.35 | 11.20 |

Visit of Gen. Francisco Franco, 1950.

---

View of Granada and
Globe — A5

**1952, Dec. 10**    **Perf. 13x12½**

| | | | | |
|---|---|---|---|---|
| 54 | A5 | 5c red org | .25 | .20 |
| 55 | A5 | 35c dk ol grn | .30 | .20 |
| 56 | A5 | 60c brown | .30 | .20 |
| | | *Nos. 54-56 (3)* | .85 | .60 |

400th anniversary of the death of Leo Africanus (c. 1485-c. 1554), Arab traveler and scholar, author of "Descrittione dell' Africa."

Musician
A6

Design: 60c, Two musicians.

**1953, June 1**    **Perf. 12½x13**

| | | | | |
|---|---|---|---|---|
| 57 | A6 | 15c olive gray | .25 | .20 |
| 58 | A6 | 60c brown | .25 | .20 |
| | | *Nos. 57-58,B13-B14 (4)* | 1.00 | .80 |

Issued to promote child welfare.

Fish and
Branched
Sponges
A7

15c, Fish and jellyfish.

**1953, Nov. 23**

| | | | | |
|---|---|---|---|---|
| 59 | A7 | 15c dark green | .25 | .20 |
| 60 | A7 | 60c brown | .35 | .20 |
| | | *Nos. 59-60,B15-B16 (4)* | 1.10 | .80 |

Colonial Stamp Day, Nov. 23, 1953.

Sea
Gull — A8

Cactus — A9

25c, 60c, 2p, 5p, Salsola vermiculata.

**1954, Apr. 22**   **Perf. 12½x13, 13x12½**

| | | | | |
|---|---|---|---|---|
| 61 | A8 | 5c red org | .20 | .20 |
| 62 | A9 | 10c olive | .20 | .20 |
| 63 | A9 | 25c brn car | .20 | .20 |
| 64 | A9 | 35c olive gray | .20 | .20 |
| 65 | A9 | 40c rose lilac | .20 | .20 |
| 66 | A9 | 60c dk brn | .20 | .20 |
| 67 | A8 | 1p brown | 6.75 | .60 |
| 68 | A9 | 1.25p car rose | .25 | .20 |
| 69 | A9 | 2p darp blue | .30 | .20 |
| 70 | A9 | 4.50p olive grn | .40 | .35 |
| 71 | A9 | 5p olive blk | 32.50 | 9.50 |
| | | *Nos. 61-71 (11)* | 41.40 | 12.05 |

Mother and Child
A10   A11

**1954, June 1**   *Perf. 13x12½*
72   A10   15c dk gray grn   .25   .20
73   A11   60c dk brn   .25   .20
   *Nos. 72-73,B17-B18 (4)*   1.00   .80

Lobster
A12

Design: 60c, Hammerhead shark.

**1954, Nov. 23**   *Perf. 12½x13*
74   A12   15c olive green   .25   .20
75   A12   60c rose brown   .35   .25
   *Nos. 74-75,B19-B20 (4)*   1.10   .85

Issued to publicize Colonial Stamp Day.

Farmer Plowing and Statue of "Justice"
A13

**1955, June 1**   **Photo.**   **Unwmk.**
76   A13   50c gray olive   .25   .20
   *Nos. 76,B21-B22 (3)*   .75   .60

Squirrel
A14

**1955, Nov. 23**
77   A14   70c yellow green   .25   .20
   *Nos. 77,B23-B24 (3)*   .75   .60

Issued to publicize Colonial Stamp Day.

Senecio Antheuphorbium
A15

Design: 50c, Limoniastrum Ifniensis.

**1956, June 1**   *Perf. 13x12½*
78   A15   20c bluish green   .25   .20
79   A15   50c brown   .30   .25
   *Nos. 78-79,B25-B26 (4)*   1.05   .85

Arms of Sidi Ifni and Shepherd
A16

**1956, Nov. 23**   *Perf. 12½x13*
80   A16   70c light green   .25   .20

Issued for Colonial Stamp Day.

Rock Doves — A17

**1957, June 1**   **Photo.**   *Perf. 13x12½*
81   A17   70c yel grn & brn   .30   .25
   *Nos. 81,B29-B30 (3)*   .80   .65

See No. 86.

Jackal
A18

Design: 70c, Jackal's head, vert.

**Perf. 12½x13, 13x12½**
**1957, Nov. 23**
82   A18   20c emerald & lt grn   .25   .20
83   A18   70c green & brown   .35   .25
   *Nos. 82-83,B31-B32 (4)*   1.10   .85

Issued for the Day of the Stamp, 1957.
See Nos. 87, B41.

Basketball Players    Red-legged Partridges
A19    A20

Design: 70c, Cyclists.

**1958, June 1**   *Perf. 13x12½*
84   A19   20c bluish green   .25   .20
85   A19   70c olive green   .35   .25
   *Nos. 84-85,B36-B37 (4)*   1.10   .85

Types of 1957 inscribed "Pro-Infancia 1959"

Designs: 20c, Goat. 70c, Ewe and lamb.

**1959, June 1**   *Perf. 13x12½, 12½x13*
86   A17   20c dull green   .20   .20
87   A18   70c yellow green   .30   .25
   *Nos. 86-87,B41-B42 (4)*   1.00   .85

Issued to promote child welfare.

**1960, June 10**   *Perf. 13x12½*
88   A20   35c shown   .20   .20
89   A20   80c Camels   .30   .25
   *Nos. 88-89,B46-B47 (4)*   1.00   .85

White Stork
A21

Birds: 50c, 1.50p, 5p, European gold-finches. 75c, 2p, 10p, Skylarks, vert.

**1960**   **Unwmk.**   *Perf. 12½x13*
90   A21   25c violet   .20   .20
91   A21   50c olive black   .20   .20
92   A21   75c dull purple   .25   .20
93   A21   1p orange ver   .30   .20
94   A21   1.50p brt grnsh bl   .35   .20
95   A21   2p red lilac   .40   .25
96   A21   3p dark blue   .70   .25
97   A21   5p red brown   1.10   .45
98   A21   10p olive   4.50   1.40
   *Nos. 90-98 (9)*   8.00   3.35

Map of Ifni — A22

General Franco
A23

Design: 70c, Government palace.

**Perf. 13x12½, 12½x13**
**1961, Oct. 1**   **Photo.**
99   A22   25c gray violet   .20   .20
100   A23   50c olive brown   .20   .20
101   A23   70c brt green   .25   .20
102   A23   1p red orange   .30   .25
   *Nos. 99-102 (4)*   .95   .85

25th anniv. of the nomination of Gen. Francisco Franco as Head of State.

Admiral Jofre Tenoria — A24    Mailman — A25

Design: 50c, Cesareo Fernandez-Duro (1830-1908), writer.

**1962, July 10**   *Perf. 13x12½*
103   A24   25c dull violet   .20   .20
104   A24   50c deep blue grn   .25   .20
105   A24   1p orange brown   .25   .20
   *Nos. 103-105 (3)*   .70   .65

**1962, Nov. 23**   **Unwmk.**
Stamp Day: 35c, Hands, letter and winged wheel.
106   A25   15c dark blue   .20   .20
107   A25   35c lilac rose   .25   .20
108   A25   1p rose brown   .25   .25
   *Nos. 106-108 (3)*   .70   .65

Golden Tower, Seville    Butterflies
A26    A27

**1963, Jan. 29**   **Photo.**
109   A26   50c green   .25   .20
110   A26   1p brown orange   .30   .25

Issued for flood relief in Seville.

**1963, July 6**   *Perf. 13x12½*
Design: 50c, Butterfly and flower.
111   A27   25c deep blue   .25   .20
112   A27   50c light green   .25   .20
113   A27   1p carmine rose   .30   .25
   *Nos. 111-113 (3)*   .80   .65

Issued for child welfare.

Child with Flowers and Arms
A28

**1963, July 12**   *Perf. 12½x13*
114   A28   50c gray olive   .25   .20
115   A28   1p reddish brown   .30   .25

Issued for Barcelona flood relief.

Beetle (Steraspis Speciosa)    Mountain Gazelle
A29    A30

Stamp Day: 50c, Grasshopper.

**1964, Mar. 6**   *Perf. 13x12½*
116   A29   25c violet blue   .20   .20
117   A29   50c olive green   .25   .20
118   A29   1p red brown   .30   .25
   *Nos. 116-118 (3)*   .75   .65

**1964, June 1**   **Photo.**
Design: 50c, Head of roebuck.
119   A30   25c brt violet   .20   .20
120   A30   50c slate blk   .25   .20
121   A30   1p orange red   .30   .25
   *Nos. 119-121 (3)*   .75   .65

Issued for child welfare.

Bicycle Race
A31

Stamp Day: 1p, Motorcycle race.

**1964, Nov. 23**   *Perf. 12½x13*
122   A31   50c brown   .25   .20
123   A31   1p orange ver   .30   .25
124   A31   1.50p Prus green   .30   .25
   *Nos. 122-124 (3)*   .85   .70

Man — A32    Two Boys in School — A33

Cable Cars, Sidi Ifni — A34

**Perf. 13x12½, 12½x13**
**1965, Mar. 1**   **Photo.**   **Unwmk.**
125   A32   50c dark green   .25   .25
126   A33   1p orange ver   .25   .25
127   A34   1.50p dark blue   .30   .25
   *Nos. 125-127 (3)*   .80   .70

25 years of peace after the Spanish Civil War.

Eugaster
Fernandezi
A35

Insect: 1p, Halter halteratus.

**1965, June 1     Photo.     Unwmk.**
128 A35  50c purple          .25  .20
129 A35  1p rose red         .30  .25
130 A35  1.50p violet blue   .30  .25
   Nos. 128-130 (3)          .85  .70
   Issued for child welfare.

Eagle — A36

Arms of
Sidi
Ifni — A37

**Perf. 13x12½, 12½x13**
**1965, Nov. 23                  Photo.**
131 A36  50c dk red brown    .20  .20
132 A37  1p orange ver       .25  .25
133 A36  1.50p grnsh blue    .30  .25
   Nos. 131-133 (3)          .75  .70
   Issued for Stamp Day 1965.

Jetliner over Sidi
Ifni — A38

Design: 2.50p, Two 1934 biplanes, horiz.

**Perf. 13x12½, 12½x13**
**1966, June 1     Photo.     Unwmk.**
134 A38  1p orange brn       .25  .25
135 A38  1.50p brt blue      .30  .25
136 A38  2.50p dull violet   2.00 1.60
   Nos. 134-136 (3)          2.55 2.10
   Issued for child welfare.

Syntomis
Alicia — A39

**1966, Nov. 23     Photo.     Perf. 13**
40c, 4p, Danais chrysippus (butterfly).
137 A39  10c green & red      .35  .20
138 A39  40c dk brn & gldn brn .40 .25
139 A39  1.50p violet & yel   .45  .25
140 A39  4p dk pur & brt bl   .50  .25
   Nos. 137-140 (4)          1.70  .95
   Issued for Stamp Day, 1966.

Coconut
Palms — A40

---

Designs: 40c, 4p, Cactus.

**1967, June 1     Photo.     Perf. 13**
141 A40  10c dp grn & brn     .20  .20
142 A40  40c Prus grn & ocher .20  .20
143 A40  1.50p bl grn & sepia .25  .25
144 A40  4p sepia & ocher     .30  .20
   Nos. 141-144 (4)           .95  .85
   Issued for child welfare.

Sidi Ifni
Harbor
A41

**1967, Sept. 28  Photo.  Perf. 12½x13**
145 A41  1.50p grn & red brn  .25  .20
   Modernization of harbor installations.

Needlefish
(Skipper) — A42

Fish: 1.50p, John Dory, vert. 3.50p, Gurnard
(Trigla lucerna).

**1967, Nov. 23     Photo.     Perf. 13**
146 A42  1p blue & green      .25  .20
147 A42  1.50p vio blk & yel  .25  .20
148 A42  3.50p brt bl & scar  .35  .25
   Nos. 146-148 (3)           .85  .65
   Issued for Stamp Day 1967.

**Zodiac Issue**

Pisces — A43

Signs of the Zodiac:  1.50p, Capricorn.
2.50p, Sagittarius.

**1968, Apr. 25     Photo.     Perf. 13**
149 A43  1p brt mag, lt yel   .25  .20
150 A43  1.50p brown, pink    .25  .25
151 A43  2.50p dk vio, yel    .35  .25
   Nos. 149-151 (3)           .85  .70
   Issued for child welfare.

Mailing a
Letter
A44

Designs: 1.50p, Carrier pigeon carrying letter. 2.50p, Stamp under magnifying glass.

**1968, Nov. 23  Photo.  Perf. 12½x13**
152 A44  1p org yel & sl grn  .20  .20
153 A44  1.50p brt bl & vio blk .25 .25
154 A44  2.50p emer & vio blk .35  .25
   Nos. 152-154 (3)           .80  .70
   Issued for Stamp Day.

---

**SEMI-POSTAL STAMPS**

Catalogue values for unused
stamps in this section are for
Never Hinged items.

---

Gen. Francisco
Franco — SP1

Fennec — SP2

**Perf. 13x12½**
**1950, Oct. 19                Unwmk.**
B1 SP1  50c + 10c sepia      .55  .45
B2 SP1  1p + 25c blue       15.00 5.75
B3 SP1  6.50p + 1.65p dl grn 6.00 2.75
   Nos. B1-B3 (3)           21.55 8.95
   The surtax was for child welfare.

**1951, Nov. 30**
B4 SP2  5c + 5c brown        .25  .20
B5 SP2  10c + 5c red org     .25  .20
B6 SP2  60c + 15c olive brn  .45  .20
   Nos. B4-B6 (3)            .95  .60
   Colonial Stamp Day, Nov. 23, 1951.

Mother and
Child — SP3

Common
Shag — SP4

**1952, June 1**
B7 SP3  5c + 5c brn          .25  .20
B8 SP3  50c + 10c brn blk    .30  .20
B9 SP3  2p + 30c dp bl       1.75  .70
   Nos. B7-B9 (3)            2.30 1.10
   The surtax was for child welfare.

**1952, Nov. 23**
B10 SP4  5c + 5c brn         .25  .20
B11 SP4  10c + 5c brn car    .25  .20
B12 SP4  60c + 15c dk grn    .40  .25
   Nos. B10-B12 (3)          .90  .65
   Colonial Stamp Day, Nov. 23, 1952.

**Musician Type of Regular Issue**
**1953, June 1          Perf. 12½x13**
B13 A6  5c + 5c as No. 57    .25  .20
B14 A6  10c + 5c as No. 58   .25  .20
   The surtax was for child welfare.

**Fish Type of Regular Issue**
**1953, Nov. 23**
B15 A7  5c + 5c as No. 59    .25  .20
B16 A7  10c + 5c as No. 60   .25  .20
   Colonial Stamp Day, Nov. 23, 1953.

**Type of Regular Issue**
**1954, June 1          Perf. 13x12½**
B17 A10  5c + 5c org         .25  .20
B18 A11  10c + 5c rose vio   .25  .20
   The surtax was for child welfare.

**Type of Regular Issue**
**1954, Nov. 23         Perf. 12½x13**
B19 A12  5c + 5c as No. 74   .25  .20
B20 A12  10c + 5c as No. 75  .25  .20

"Dama de
Elche"
Protecting
Caravan
SP5

**1955, June 1     Photo.     Unwmk.**
B21 A13  10c + 5c rose lilac  .25  .20
B22 SP5  25c + 10c violet     .25  .20
   The surtax was to help Ifni people.

---

**Squirrel Type of Regular Issue**
Design: 15c+5c, Squirrel holding nut.

**1955, Nov. 23**
B23 A14  5c + 5c red brown    .25  .20
B24 A14  15c + 5c olive bister .25 .20

**Type of Regular Issue**
**1956, June 1          Perf. 13x12½**
B25 A15  5c + 5c as No. 78    .25  .20
B26 A15  15c + 5c as No. 79   .25  .20
   The tax was for child welfare.

Dorcas Gazelles and
Arms of
Spain — SP6

Design: 15c+5c, Arms of Sidi Ifni, boat and
woman with drum.

**1956, Nov. 23**
B27 SP6  5c + 5c dark brown   .25  .20
B28 SP6  15c + 5c golden brn  .25  .20
   Issued for Colonial Stamp Day.

**Dove Type of Regular Issue**
**1957, June 1  Photo.  Perf. 13x12½**
B29 A17  5c + 5c as No. 81    .25  .20
B30 A17  15c + 5c Stock doves .25  .20
   The surtax was for child welfare.

**Type of Regular Issue**
**Perf. 12½x13, 13x12½**
**1957, Nov. 23     Photo.     Unwmk.**
B31 A18  10c + 5c as No. 82   .25  .20
B32 A18  15c + 5c as No. 83   .25  .20

Swallows
and Arms
of Valencia
and Sidi
Ifni — SP7

**1958, Mar. 6          Perf. 12½x13**
B33 SP7  10c + 5c org brn     .25  .20
B34 SP7  15c + 10c bister     .25  .20
B35 SP7  50c + 10c brn olive  .30  .20
   Nos. B33-B35 (3)           .80  .60
   The surtax was to aid the victims of the
Valencia flood, Oct. 1957.

**Sport Type of Regular Issue, 1958**
**1958, June 1  Photo.  Perf. 13x12½**
B36 A19  10c + 5c as No. 84   .25  .20
B37 A19  15c + 5c as No. 85   .25  .20
   The surtax was for child welfare.

Guitarfish — SP8

Sailboats
SP9

Stamp Day: 10c+5c, Spotted dogfish.

**Perf. 13x12½, 12½x13**
**1958, Nov. 23**
B38 SP9  10c + 5c brn red     .25  .20
B39 SP8  25c + 10c dull vio   .25  .20
B40 SP9  50c + 10c olive      .30  .20
   Nos. B38-B40 (3)           .80  .60

Donkey and Man — SP10        Soccer — SP11

### Type of 1957 and SP10

Design: 10c+5c, Ewe and lamb.

**Perf. 12½x13, 13x12½**

**1959, June 1      Photo.      Unwmk.**
B41  A18  10c + 5c red brn           .25  .20
B42  SP10  15c + 5c golden brn       .25  .20

The surtax was for child welfare.

**1959, Nov. 23            Perf. 13x12½**

Designs: 20c+5c, Soccer players.
50c+20c, Javelin thrower.

B43  SP11  10c + 5c fawn             .25  .20
B44  SP11  20c + 5c slate green      .25  .20
B45  SP11  50c + 20c olive gray      .30  .25
        Nos. B43-B45 (3)             .80  .65

Issued for the day of the Stamp, 1959.
See Nos. B52-B54.

### Type of Regular Issue, 1960

**1960, June 10            Perf. 13x12½**
B46  A20  10c + 5c as No. 89         .25  .20
B47  A20  15c + 5c Wild boars        .25  .20

The surtax was for child welfare.

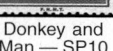

Santa Maria del Mar — SP12

Stamp Day: 20c+5c, 50c+20c, New school building, horiz.

**Perf. 13x12½, 12½x13**

**1960, Dec. 29                  Photo.**
B48  SP12  10c + 5c org brn          .25  .20
B49  SP12  20c + 5c dk sl grn        .25  .20
B50  SP12  30c + 10c red brn         .25  .20
B51  SP12  50c + 20c sepia           .25  .20
        Nos. B48-B51 (4)             1.00  .80

### Type of 1959 inscribed: "Pro-Infancia 1961"

Designs: 10c+5c, 80c+20c, Pole vaulting, horiz. 25c+10c, Soccer player.

**Perf. 12½x13, 13x12½**

**1961, June 21               Unwmk.**
B52  SP11  10c + 5c rose brn         .25  .20
B53  SP11  25c + 10c gray vio        .25  .20
B54  SP11  80c + 20c dk green        .25  .20
        Nos. B52-B54 (3)             .75  .60

The surtax was for child welfare.

Camel Rider and Truck SP13

Stamp Day: 25c+10c, 1p+10c, Ship in Sidi Ifni harbor.

**1961, Nov. 23            Perf. 12½x13**
B55  SP13  10c + 5c rose brn         .25  .20
B56  SP13  25c + 10c dk pur          .25  .20
B57  SP13  30c + 10c dk red brn      .25  .20
B58  SP13  1p + 10c red org          .25  .25
        Nos. B55-B58 (4)             1.00  .85

---

## AIR POST STAMPS

Stamps formerly listed as Nos. C1-C29 were privately overprinted. These include 1936 stamps of Spain overprinted "VIA AEREA" and plane, and 1939 stamps of Spain, type AP30, overprinted "IFNI" or "Territorio de Ifni."

Oasis        The Sanctuary
AP1                AP2

**1943    Unwmk.    Litho.    Perf. 12½**
C30  AP2  5c cer & vio brn           .35  .25
C31  AP1  25c yel grn & ol
           grn                       .35  .25
C32  AP2  50c ind & turq grn         .45  .35
C33  AP1  1p pur & grnsh bl          .50  .35
C34  AP2  1.40p gray grn & bl        .55  .35
C35  AP1  2p mag & org brn           1.50  1.25
C36  AP2  5p brn & pur               2.25  1.75
C37  AP1  6p brt bl & gray
           grn                       35.00  30.00
        Nos. C30-C37 (8)             40.95  34.55
Set, never hinged                    62.50

Nos. C30-C37 exist imperforate. Value, set $115.

> **Catalogue values for unused stamps in this section, from this point to the end of the section, are for Never Hinged items.**

Type of Spain, 1939-47, Overprinted in Carmine

**1947, Nov. 29**
C38  AP30  5c dull yellow            2.50  .75
C39  AP30  10c dk bl green           2.50  .75

Spain No. C126 Overprinted in Carmine like Nos. 33-34

**1949, Oct. 9            Perf. 12½x13**
C40  A202  4p dk olive grn           3.25  1.10

75th anniv. of the UPU.

Spain, Nos. C110 and C112 to C116, Overprinted in Blue or Carmine like Nos. 29-32

**1949                    Perf. 10**
C41  AP30  25c redsh brn (Bl)        .60  .20
C42  AP30  50c brown                 .70  .20
C43  AP30  1p chalky blue            .75  .20
C44  AP30  2p lt gray grn            4.50  .75
C45  AP30  4p gray blue              12.00  4.00
C46  AP30  10p brt purple            16.00  8.00
        Nos. C41-C46 (6)             34.55  13.35

---

Lope Sancho de        Woman Holding
Valenzuela and        Dove — AP4
Sheik — AP3

**1950, Nov. 23  Photo.   Perf. 13x12½**
C47  AP3  5p brown black             2.75  .70

Stamp Day, Nov. 23, 1950.

**1951, Apr. 22    Engr.    Perf. 10**
C48  AP4  5p red                     20.00  6.75

500th anniversary of the birth of Queen Isabella I of Spain.
The majority of this issue are poorly centered. Values are for very fine examples.

Ferdinand the Catholic — AP5

**1952, July 18    Photo.    Unwmk.**
C49  AP5  5p brown                   26.00  6.75

500th anniv. of the birth of Ferdinand the Catholic of Spain.

Plane and Mountain Gazelle — AP6

**1953, Apr. 1**
C50  AP6  60c light grn              .20  .20
C51  AP6  1.20p brn car              .25  .20
C52  AP6  1.60p lt brown             .30  .20
C53  AP6  2p deep blue               1.75  .20
C54  AP6  4p grnsh blk               1.00  .20
C55  AP6  10p brt red vio            6.00  1.40
        Nos. C50-C55 (6)             9.50  2.40

---

## SPECIAL DELIVERY STAMPS

Type A3 inscribed "URGENTE"

**1943                    Perf. 12½**
E1  A3  25c slate green & car        2.00  1.50

Spain, No. E20, Overprinted in Blue like Nos. 29-32

**1949      Unwmk.      Perf. 10**
E2  SD10  25c carmine                .30  .20

---

# INDIA

'in-dē-ə

LOCATION — Southern, central Asia
GOVT. — Republic
AREA — 1,266,732 sq. mi.
POP. — 1,000,848,550 (1999 est.)
CAPITAL — New Delhi

On August 15, 1947, India was divided into two self-governing dominions: Pakistan and India. India became a republic in 1950.

The stamps of pre-partition India fall into three groups:

1) Issues inscribed simply "East India" (to 1881) and "India" (from 1882), for use mainly in British India proper, but available and valid throughout the country;

2) Issues as above and overprinted with one of the names of the six "Convention" states (Chamba, Faridkot, Gwalior, Jind, Nabha and Patiala) which had a postal convention with British India, for use in these states.

3) Issues of the feudatory states, over which the British India government exercised little internal control, valid for use only within the states issuing them.

12 Pies = 1 Anna
16 Annas = 1 Rupee
100 Naye Paise = 1 Rupee (1957)
100 Paise = 1 Rupee (1964)

Catalogue values for unused stamps in this country are for Never Hinged items, beginning with Scott 168 in the regular postage section, Scott C7 in the air post section, Scott M44 in the military section, Scott O113 in the official section, Scott RA1 in the postal tax section, Scott 51 in Hyderabad regular issues, Scott O54 in Hyderabad officials, Scott 49 in Jaipur regular issues, Scott O30 in Jaipur officials, Scott 39 in Soruth regular issues and Scott O19 in Soruth official

All of the values are for Never Hinged for all of the items in the sections for the International Commission in Indo-China, Jasdan, Rajasthan, and Travancore-Cochin.

**Watermarks**

Wmk. 36 — Crown and INDIA

Wmk. 37 — Coat of Arms in Sheet. (Reduced illustration. Watermark covers a large section of the sheet.)

Wmk. 38 — Elephant's Head

Wmk. 39 — Star

Wmk. 40

Wmk. 41 — Small Umbrella

Wmk. 42 — Urdu Characters

Wmk. 43 — Shell

Wmk. 196 — Multiple Stars

Wmk. 211 — Urdu Characters

Wmk. 294 — Letters and Ornaments in Sheet (size reduced)

Wmk. 324 — Asoka Pillar, Multiple

Wmk. 360 — Star and GOVT INDIA

## SCINDE DISTRICT POST

A1

**1852, July 1      Embossed      Imperf.**

| | | | | |
|---|---|---|---|---|
| A1 | A1 | ½a white | 5,500. | 900.00 |
| A2 | A1 | ½a blue | 14,500. | 4,000. |
| A3 | A1 | ½a red | — | 10,000. |

Obsolete October, 1854.

Nos. A1-A3 were issued without gum. No. A3 is embossed on red wafer. It is usually found with cracks and these examples are worth somewhat less than the values given, depending on the degree of cracking.

## GENERAL ISSUES

Unused stamps of India are valued with original gum as defined in the catalogue introduction except for Nos. 1-7 which are valued without gum.

### East India Company

A1

A2

A3

A4

A5

### Queen Victoria
### Litho.; Typo. (#5)

| | | | | |
|---|---|---|---|---|
| **1854** | | **Wmk. 37** | | *Imperf.* |
| 1 | A1 | ½a red | 925.00 | |
| 2 | A2 | ½a blue | 75.00 | 17.50 |
| a. | | ½a deep blue | 85.00 | 22.50 |
| b. | | Printed on both sides | | 11,000. |
| 4 | A3 | 1a red | 70.00 | 40.00 |
| a. | | 1a scarlet | 160.00 | 45.00 |
| 5 | A4 | 2a green | 100.00 | 25.00 |
| a. | | Half used as 1a on cover | | 200,000. |
| 6 | A5 | 4a red & blue | 4,500. | 450.00 |
| a. | | 4a deep red & blue | 4,500. | 550.00 |
| | | Cut to shape | | 25.00 |
| c. | | Head inverted | | 100,000. |
| | | As "c," cut to shape | | 37,500. |
| e. | | Double impression of head | | 6,250. |

No. 1 was not placed in use.

Nos. 2, 4, 5 and 6 are known with unofficial perforation.

There are 3 dies of No. 2, and 2 dies of No. 4, showing slight differences.

There are 4 dies of the head and 2 dies of the frame of No. 6.

Beware of forgeries.

A6

**1855**

| | | | | |
|---|---|---|---|---|
| 7 | A6 | 1a red | 1,150. | 150.00 |

No. 7 was printed from a lithographic transfer made from the original die retouched. The lines of the bust at the lower left are nearly straight and meet in a point.
Beware of forgeries.

Nos. 9-35 are normally found with very heavy cancelations, and values are for stamps so canceled. Lightly canceled copies are seldom seen. The same holds true for Nos. O1-O26.

Diadem includes Maltese Crosses — A7

**1855-64 Unwmk. Typo. Perf. 14**
**Blue Glazed Paper**

| | | | | |
|---|---|---|---|---|
| 9 | A7 | 4a black | 575.00 | 18.50 |
| a. | | Imperf., pair | 3,750. | 3,750. |
| b. | | Half used as 2a on cover | | 8,000. |
| 10 | A7 | 8a rose | 475.00 | 16.50 |
| a. | | Imperf., pair | 2,200. | |
| b. | | Half used as 4a on cover | | 67,500. |

See #11-18, 20, 22-25, 31. For overprints see #O1-O5, O7-O9, O16-O19, O22-O24.

**1855-64 White Paper**

| | | | | |
|---|---|---|---|---|
| 11 | A7 | ½a blue | 70.00 | 2.25 |
| a. | | Imperf., pair | 365.00 | 1,200. |
| 12 | A7 | 1a brown | 55.00 | 3.00 |
| a. | | Imperf., pair | 800.00 | 1,500. |
| b. | | Vert. pair, imperf between | | |
| c. | | Half used as ½a on cover | | 75,000. |
| 13 | A7 | 2a dull rose | 575.00 | 32.50 |
| a. | | Imperf., pair | 2,000. | 2,000. |
| 14 | A7 | 2a yellow green | 725.00 | 825.00 |
| a. | | Imperf., pair | 2,000. | |
| 15 | A7 | 2a buff | 325.00 | 30.00 |
| a. | | 2a orange | 525.00 | 35.00 |
| b. | | Imperf., pair | 1,750. | — |
| 16 | A7 | 4a black | 325.00 | 9.50 |
| a. | | Imperf., pair | 2,200. | 2,200. |
| b. | | Diagonal half used as 2a on cover | | 27,500. |
| 17 | A7 | 4a green ('64) | 1,200. | 40.00 |
| 18 | A7 | 8a rose | 400.00 | 24.00 |
| a. | | Half used as 4a on cover | | 67,500. |

No. 14 was not regularly issued. See note after No. 25.

**Crown Colony**

Queen Victoria — A8

**1860-64 Unwmk. Perf. 14**

| | | | | |
|---|---|---|---|---|
| 19 | A8 | 8p lilac | 47.50 | 6.00 |
| a. | | Diagonal half used as 4p on cover | | 75,000. |
| b. | | Imperf., pair | 2,750. | 3,800. |
| 19C | A8 | 8p lilac, bluish | 210.00 | 90.00 |

See #21. For overprint See #O6 and footnote after #O4.

**1865-67 Wmk. 38**

| | | | | |
|---|---|---|---|---|
| 20 | A7 | ½a blue | 12.50 | 1.00 |
| a. | | Imperf., pair | | 1,600. |
| 21 | A8 | 8p lilac | 9.00 | 9.00 |
| 22 | A7 | 1a brown | 6.00 | .80 |
| 23 | A7 | 2a brownish orange | 27.50 | 1.75 |
| a. | | 2a yellow | 125.00 | 6.50 |
| b. | | Imperf., pair | | 3,250. |
| 24 | A7 | 4a green | 575.00 | 24.50 |
| 25 | A7 | 8a rose | 1,400. | 80.00 |

No. 21 was variously surcharged locally, "NINE" or "NINE PIE," to indicate that it was being sold for 9 pies (the soldier's letter rate had been raised from 8 to 9 pies). These surcharges were made without government authorization.

Stamps of types A7 and A9 overprinted with crown and surcharged with new values were for use in Straits Settlements.

A9

A10

Diadem: Rows of pearls & diamonds — A11

**FOUR ANNAS**
Type I — Slanting line at corner of mouth extends downward only. Shading about mouth and chin. Pointed chin.
Type II — Line at corner of mouth extends both up and down. Upper lip and chin are defined by a colored line. Rounded chin.

**1866-68**

| | | | | |
|---|---|---|---|---|
| 26 | A9 | 4a grn, type I | 75.00 | 4.25 |
| 26B | A9 | 4a bl grn, type II | 24.00 | 3.00 |
| 27 | A10 | 6a8p slate | 52.50 | 24.00 |
| a. | | Imperf., pair | 2,100. | |
| 28 | A11 | 8a rose ('68) | 37.50 | 6.50 |
| | | Nos. 26-28 (4) | 189.00 | 37.75 |

Type A11 is a redrawing of type A7. Type A7 has Maltese crosses in the diadem, while type A11 has shaded lozenges.
For overprints see #O10, O20-O21, O25-O26.

For designs A9-A85 overprinted CHAMBA, FARIDKOT, GWALIOR, JIND (JHIND, JEEND), NABHA, PATIALA (PUTTIALLA), see the various Convention States

A12

**SIX ANNAS**
Type I — "POSTAGE" 3½mm high
Type II — "POSTAGE" 2½mm high

**Blue Glazed Paper**
**Green Overprint**
**Perf. 14 Vert.**

**1866, June 28 Wmk. 36**

| | | | | |
|---|---|---|---|---|
| 29 | A12 | 6a violet, type I | 775.00 | 125.00 |
| a. | | Inverted overprint | | 10,000. |
| 30 | A12 | 6a violet, type II | 1,400. | 150.00 |

Nos. 29 and 30 were made from revenue stamps with the labels at top and bottom cut off. Most and sometimes all of the watermark was removed with the labels.
These stamps are often found with cracked surface or scuffs. Such examples sell for somewhat less.

A13

A14

A15

A16

**1873-76 Wmk. 38 Perf. 14**

| | | | | |
|---|---|---|---|---|
| 31 | A7 | ½a blue, redrawn | 5.50 | .85 |
| 32 | A13 | 9p lilac ('74) | 16.50 | 15.00 |
| 33 | A14 | 6a bister ('76) | 8.00 | 2.25 |
| 34 | A15 | 12a red brown ('76) | 10.00 | 22.50 |
| 35 | A16 | 1r slate ('74) | 60.00 | 27.50 |
| | | Nos. 31-35 (5) | 100.00 | 68.10 |

In the redrawn ½ anna the lines of the mouth are more deeply cut, making the lips appear fuller and more open, and the nostril is defined by a curved line.

Victorian and Edwardian stamps overprinted "Postal Service" and new denominations were customs fee due stamps, not postage stamps.

**Empire**

A17    A18

A19    A20

A21

A22

A23    A24

A25

A26

A27

**1882-87 Wmk. 39**

| | | | | |
|---|---|---|---|---|
| 36 | A17 | ½a green | 4.50 | .20 |
| a. | | Double impression | 525.00 | 675.00 |
| 37 | A18 | 9p rose | 1.10 | 2.25 |
| 38 | A19 | 1a maroon | 5.25 | .35 |
| a. | | 1a violet brown | 5.25 | .35 |
| 39 | A20 | 1a6p bister brown | 1.10 | 1.40 |
| 40 | A21 | 2a ultra | 4.00 | .35 |
| a. | | Double impression | 1,050. | 1,400. |
| 41 | A22 | 3a brown org | 9.50 | 1.75 |
| a. | | 3a orange | 14.00 | 6.25 |
| 42 | A23 | 4a olive green | 15.00 | 1.60 |
| 43 | A24 | 4a6p green | 22.50 | 5.50 |
| 44 | A25 | 8a rose violet | 27.50 | 2.25 |
| a. | | 8a red lilac | 25.00 | 2.25 |
| 45 | A26 | 12a violet, red | 7.50 | 3.50 |
| 46 | A27 | 1r gray | 20.00 | 5.50 |
| | | Nos. 36-46 (11) | 117.95 | 24.65 |

A 6a die essay was prepared, but no stamps were printed.
A postal counterfeit exists of No. 46. Examples are scarce.
No. 40a used value is for copy with postal cancellation.
See Nos. 56-58. For surcharges see Nos. 47, 53 and British East Africa No. 59. For overprints see Nos. M2-M4, M6-M9, O27-O31, O34-O36, Gwalior O1-O5.

Beginning with the 1882-87 issue, higher denomination stamps exist used for telegrams. The telegraph cancellation has concentric circles. These sell for 10-15% of the postally used values.

No. 43 Surcharged

2½ As.

**1891, Jan. 1**

| | | | | |
|---|---|---|---|---|
| 47 | A24 | 2½a on 4a6p green | 4.00 | .65 |

A28

A29

**1892**

| | | | | |
|---|---|---|---|---|
| 48 | A28 | 2a6p green | 3.25 | .45 |
| 49 | A29 | 1r car rose & grn | 15.00 | 2.25 |

See No. 59. For overprints see Nos. M5, M10, O32, Gwalior O6.

Queen Victoria
A30    A31

**1895, Sept. 1**

| | | | | |
|---|---|---|---|---|
| 50 | A30 | 2r brown & rose | 42.50 | 12.50 |
| 51 | A30 | 3r green & brown | 29.00 | 11.00 |
| 52 | A30 | 5r violet & ultra | 47.50 | 30.00 |
| | | Nos. 50-52 (3) | 119.00 | 53.50 |

Used high values such as Nos. 50-52, 71-76, 95-98, 124-125, as well as similar high value official issues are for postally used examples. Stamps bearing telegraph or revenue cancellations sell for much lower prices. Most telegraph cancellations on issues of Edward VII and George V can be recognized by the appearance of "T," "TEL" or "GTO" or if they contain the concentric circles of a target.

No. 36 Surcharged

¼

**1898**

| | | | | |
|---|---|---|---|---|
| 53 | A17 | ¼a on ½a green | .20 | .55 |
| a. | | Double surcharge | 250.00 | |
| b. | | Double impression of stamp | 260.00 | |

For #61, 81 with this overprint see #77, 105.

**1899**

| | | | | |
|---|---|---|---|---|
| 54 | A31 | 3p carmine rose | .45 | .20 |

See #55. For overprints see #M1, Gwalior O11.

**1900**

| | | | | |
|---|---|---|---|---|
| 55 | A31 | 3p gray | .80 | 1.40 |
| 56 | A17 | ½a light green | 1.75 | .50 |
| 57 | A19 | 1a carmine rose | 2.50 | .20 |
| 58 | A21 | 2a violet | 4.50 | 2.50 |
| 59 | A28 | 2a6p ultramarine | 3.75 | 4.25 |
| | | Nos. 55-59 (5) | 13.30 | 8.85 |

For overprints see #M11, Gwalior O7-O10.

Edward VII — A32

A33

A34   A35
A36   A37
A38   A39
A40   A41
A42   A43

## 1902-09

| | | | | |
|---|---|---|---|---|
| 60 | A32 | 3p gray | 1.10 | .20 |
| 61 | A33 | ½a green | 1.75 | .20 |
| a. | | Booklet pane of 6 ('04) | 32.50 | |
| 62 | A34 | 1a carmine rose | 1.60 | .20 |
| a. | | Booklet pane of 6 ('04) | 92.50 | |
| 63 | A35 | 2a violet | 4.25 | .45 |
| 64 | A36 | 2a6p ultra | 5.00 | .65 |
| 65 | A37 | 3a brown org | 5.00 | .65 |
| 66 | A38 | 4a olive green | 3.25 | .65 |
| 67 | A39 | 6a bister | 12.50 | 4.75 |
| 68 | A40 | 8a red violet | 8.75 | 1.10 |
| 69 | A41 | 12a violet, red | 9.50 | 2.25 |
| 70 | A42 | 1r car rose & grn | 6.75 | .75 |
| 71 | A43 | 2r brown & rose | 47.50 | 4.50 |
| 72 | A43 | 3r green & brn ('04) | 30.00 | 20.00 |
| 73 | A43 | 5r violet & ultra ('04) | 72.50 | 40.00 |
| 74 | A43 | 10r car rose & grn ('09) | 125.00 | 30.00 |
| 75 | A43 | 15r olive gray & ultra ('09) | 175.00 | 45.00 |
| 76 | A43 | 25r ultra & org brown | 925.00 | 925.00 |
| | | Telegraph cancel | | 300.00 |
| | | *Nos. 60-75 (16)* | 509.45 | 151.35 |

For overprints and surcharge see #M12-M20, O33, O37-O44, O47-O51, O67-O69, O73, Gwalior O12-O18.

### No. 61 Surcharged Like No. 53

## 1905

| | | | | |
|---|---|---|---|---|
| 77 | A33 | ¼a on ½a green | .60 | .20 |
| a. | | Inverted surcharge | 925.00 | |

A44   A45

## 1906

| | | | | |
|---|---|---|---|---|
| 78 | A44 | ½a green | 3.25 | .20 |
| a. | | Booklet pane of 4 | 17.50 | |
| 79 | A45 | 1a carmine rose | 1.90 | .20 |
| a. | | Booklet pane of 4 | 25.00 | |

For overprints see #O45-O46, Gwalior O19-O20.

A46   A47

A48   A49

A50   A51

A52   A53

A54   A55

George V — A56

## 1911-23    Wmk. 39

| | | | | |
|---|---|---|---|---|
| 80 | A46 | 3p gray | 1.50 | .20 |
| a. | | Booklet pane of 4 | 25.00 | |
| 81 | A47 | ½a green | 2.25 | .20 |
| a. | | Double impression | 175.00 | |
| b. | | Booklet pane of 4 | 21.00 | |
| 82 | A48 | 1a carmine rose | 2.75 | .20 |
| a. | | Printed on both sides | | |
| b. | | Booklet pane of 4 | 35.00 | |
| 83 | A48 | 1a dk brown ('22) | .85 | .20 |
| a. | | Booklet pane of 4 | 42.50 | |
| 84 | A49 | 2a dull violet | 3.50 | .40 |
| a. | | Booklet pane of 4 | 42.50 | |
| 85 | A50 | 2a6p ultramarine | 2.90 | 3.25 |
| 86 | A51 | 3a brown org | 4.25 | .20 |
| 87 | A51 | 3a ultra ('23) | 13.00 | .65 |
| 88 | A52 | 4a olive green | 8.00 | .55 |
| 89 | A53 | 6a yel bister | 4.25 | 1.50 |
| 90 | A53 | 6a bister ('15) | 4.25 | 1.10 |
| 91 | A54 | 8a red violet | 6.25 | 1.25 |
| 92 | A55 | 12a claret | 6.50 | 2.40 |
| 93 | A56 | 1r grn & red brn | 19.00 | 1.75 |
| 94 | A56 | 2r brn & car rose | 22.50 | 1.90 |
| 95 | A56 | 5r vio & ultra | 55.00 | 7.00 |
| 96 | A56 | 10r car rose & grn | 82.50 | 13.00 |
| 97 | A56 | 15r ol grn & ultra | 115.00 | 26.00 |
| 98 | A56 | 25r ultra & brn org | 190.00 | 37.50 |
| | | *Nos. 80-98 (19)* | 544.25 | 99.25 |

See #106-108, 110-111, 113-125. For surcharges and overprints see #104-105, M23-M25, M27, M29-M37, M39-M43, O52-O66, O70-O71, O74, O78-O81, O85, O87-O92, Gwalior O28-O29.

Nos. 93-98 also were used to pay for radio licenses, and stamps so used include "WIRELESS" in the cancel. Used values so canceled are worth 10-15% of the values shown, which are for postally used examples.

A57

## 1913-26

| | | | | |
|---|---|---|---|---|
| 99 | A57 | 2a6p ultramarine | 2.90 | .25 |
| 100 | A57 | 2a6p brown org ('26) | 6.00 | 6.00 |

See #112. For overprints and surcharge see #M28, M38, O77, O84.

"One and Half" — A58    "One and a Half" — A59

## 1919

| | | | | |
|---|---|---|---|---|
| 101 | A58 | 1½a chocolate | 3.75 | .45 |
| a. | | Booklet pane of 4 | 35.00 | |

For overprint and surcharge see #M26, O75.

## 1921-26

| | | | | |
|---|---|---|---|---|
| 102 | A59 | 1½a chocolate | 3.50 | 4.75 |
| 103 | A59 | 1½a rose ('26) | 3.25 | .35 |

See #109. For surcharge see #O76.

 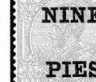

Type of 1911-26 Surcharged

## 1921

| | | | | |
|---|---|---|---|---|
| 104 | A48 | 9p on 1a rose | .90 | .35 |
| a. | | Surcharged "NINE-NINE" | 80.00 | 150.00 |
| b. | | Surcharged "PIES-PIES" | 80.00 | 150.00 |
| c. | | Double surcharge | 175.00 | 210.00 |
| e. | | Booklet pane of 4 | 27.50 | |

Forgeries exist of Nos. 104a-104c.

### No. 81 Surcharged Like No. 53

## 1922

| | | | | |
|---|---|---|---|---|
| 105 | A47 | ¼a on ½a green | .60 | .40 |
| a. | | Inverted surcharge | 10.00 | |
| b. | | Pair, one without surcharge | 240.00 | |

### Types of 1911-26 Issues

## 1926-36    Wmk. 196

| | | | | |
|---|---|---|---|---|
| 106 | A46 | 3p slate | .35 | .20 |
| 107 | A47 | ½a green | 1.40 | .20 |
| 108 | A48 | 1a dark brown | .55 | .20 |
| a. | | Tete beche pair | 1.50 | 11.00 |
| b. | | Booklet pane of 4 | 16.00 | |
| 109 | A59 | 1½a car rose ('29) | 3.50 | .20 |
| 110 | A49 | 2a dull violet | 2.00 | .20 |
| a. | | Booklet pane of 4 | 32.50 | |
| 111 | A49 | 2a ver ('34) | 4.00 | .55 |
| a. | | Small die ('36) | 5.00 | .35 |
| 112 | A57 | 2a6p buff | 2.50 | .20 |
| 113 | A51 | 3a ultramarine | 11.50 | 1.25 |
| 114 | A51 | 3a blue ('30) | 10.00 | .20 |
| 115 | A51 | 3a car rose ('32) | 9.75 | .20 |
| 116 | A52 | 4a olive green | 1.60 | .20 |
| 117 | A53 | 6a bister ('35) | 9.50 | 2.00 |
| 118 | A54 | 8a red violet | 4.25 | .20 |
| 119 | A55 | 12a claret | 5.25 | .35 |
| 120 | A56 | 1r grn & brn | 5.50 | .50 |
| 121 | A56 | 2r brn org & car rose | 15.00 | .85 |
| 122 | A56 | 5r dk vio & ultra | 30.00 | 1.40 |
| 123 | A56 | 10r car & grn | 62.50 | 3.50 |
| 124 | A56 | 15r ol grn & ultra | 28.00 | 32.50 |
| 125 | A56 | 25r blue & ocher | 115.00 | 40.00 |
| | | *Nos. 106-125 (20)* | 322.15 | 84.90 |

No. 111 measures 19x22½mm, while the small die, No. 111a, measures 18½x22mm.

For overprints see Gwalior #O30-O39, O44-O45.

A60   A61

## 1926-32    Typo.

| | | | | |
|---|---|---|---|---|
| 126 | A60 | 2a dull violet | .55 | .20 |
| a. | | Tete beche pair | 10.00 | 37.50 |
| b. | | 2a rose violet | .45 | .20 |
| c. | | Booklet pane of 4 | 19.00 | |
| 127 | A60 | 2a vermilion ('32) | 11.00 | 7.00 |
| 128 | A61 | 4a olive green | 6.25 | 7.00 |
| | | *Nos. 126-128 (3)* | 17.80 | 7.40 |

For overprints see #O82-O83, , O86, Gwalior O33-O34.

Fortress of Purana Qila — A62

George V Flanked by Dominion Columns A67

½a, War Memorial Arch. 1a, Council Building. 2a, Viceroy's House. 3a, Parliament Building.

### Wmk. 196 Sideways

## 1931, Feb. 9   Litho.   Perf. 13½x14

| | | | | |
|---|---|---|---|---|
| 129 | A62 | ¼a brown & ol grn | 3.00 | 4.50 |
| 130 | A62 | ½a green & violet | 1.75 | .60 |
| 131 | A62 | 1a choc & red vio | 1.75 | .30 |
| 132 | A62 | 2a blue & green | 2.25 | 1.50 |
| 133 | A62 | 3a car & choc | 5.25 | 3.00 |
| 134 | A67 | 1r violet & green | 13.50 | 30.00 |
| | | *Nos. 129-134 (6)* | 27.50 | 39.90 |
| | | Set, never hinged | 66.00 | |

Change of the seat of Government from Calcutta to New Delhi.

A68   A69

A70

### Wmk. 196

## 1932, Apr. 22   Litho.   Perf. 14

| | | | | |
|---|---|---|---|---|
| 135 | A68 | 9p dark green | 1.90 | .20 |
| 136 | A69 | 1a3p violet | .95 | .20 |
| 137 | A70 | 3a6p deep blue | 4.75 | .60 |
| | | *Nos. 135-137 (3)* | 7.60 | .60 |

No. 135 exists both litho. and typo.

For overprints and surcharge see #O94, O96, O104, Gwalior O41, O43.

A71   A72

## 1934    Typo.

| | | | | |
|---|---|---|---|---|
| 138 | A71 | ½a green | 5.75 | .20 |
| 139 | A72 | 1a dark brown | 4.00 | .20 |

For overprints see #O93, O95, Gwalior O40, O42.

### Silver Jubilee Issue

Gateway of India, Bombay A73

Designs: 9p, Victoria Memorial, Calcutta. 1a, Rameswaram Temple, Madras. 1¼a, Jain Temple, Calcutta. 2½a, Taj Mahal, Agra. 3½a, Golden Temple, Amritsar. 8a, Pagoda, Mandalay.

### Wmk. 196 Sideways

## 1935    Litho.   Perf. 13½x14

| | | | | |
|---|---|---|---|---|
| 142 | A73 | ½a lt green & black | 1.50 | .55 |
| 143 | A73 | 9p dull green & blk | 1.50 | .55 |
| 144 | A73 | 1a brown & black | 2.25 | .55 |
| 145 | A73 | 1¼a violet & black | 1.00 | .55 |
| 146 | A73 | 2½a brown org & blk | 3.25 | 1.10 |

| | | | | |
|---|---|---|---|---|
| 147 | A73 | 3½a blue & black | 6.50 | 2.50 |
| 148 | A73 | 8a rose lilac & blk | 7.25 | 6.00 |
| | | Nos. 142-148 (7) | 23.25 | 11.80 |
| | | Set, never hinged | 32.00 | |

25th anniv. of the reign of George V.

King George VI
A80      A82

Dak Runner A81

Mail transport: 2a6p, Dak bullock cart. 3a, Dak tonga. 3a6p, Dak camel. 4a, Mail train. 6a, Mail steamer. 8a, Mail truck. 12a, 14a, Mail plane.

### Perf. 13½x14 or 14x13½

| | | | Wmk. 196 | |
|---|---|---|---|---|
| **1937-40** | | **Typo.** | | |
| 150 | A80 | 3p slate | .40 | .20 |
| 151 | A80 | ½a brown | 1.10 | .20 |
| 152 | A80 | 9p green | 3.00 | .25 |
| 153 | A80 | 1a carmine | .35 | .30 |
| a. | | Tete beche pair | 3.50 | 2.10 |
| b. | | Booklet pane of 4 | 5.25 | |
| 154 | A81 | 2a scarlet | 2.10 | .35 |
| 155 | A81 | 2a6p purple | .65 | .30 |
| 156 | A81 | 3a yel grn | 3.75 | .35 |
| 157 | A81 | 3a6p ultramarine | 2.50 | .60 |
| 158 | A81 | 4a dark brown | 10.00 | .30 |
| 159 | A81 | 6a peacock blue | 10.00 | .95 |
| 160 | A81 | 8a blue violet | 6.00 | .60 |
| 161 | A81 | 12a car lake | 13.00 | 1.25 |
| 161A | A81 | 14a rose vio ('40) | 15.00 | 1.50 |
| 162 | A82 | 1r brn & slate | .90 | .20 |
| 163 | A82 | 2r dk brn & dk vio | 3.25 | .40 |
| 164 | A82 | 5r dp ultra & dk grn | 14.00 | .70 |
| 165 | A82 | 10r rose car & dk vio | 14.00 | 1.10 |
| 166 | A82 | 15r dk grn & dk brn | 70.00 | 90.00 |
| 167 | A82 | 25r dk vio & blue vio | 100.00 | 24.00 |
| | | Nos. 150-167 (19) | 270.00 | 123.55 |
| | | Set, never hinged | 580.00 | |

The King's portrait is larger on No. 161A than on other stamps of type A81.
For overprints see #O97-O103, Gwalior O48-O51.

> **Catalogue values for unused stamps in this section, from this point to the end of the section, are for Never Hinged items.**

A83      A84

A85

### Perf. 13½x14

| | | | Wmk. 196 | |
|---|---|---|---|---|
| **1941-43** | | **Typo.** | | |
| 168 | A83 | 3p slate ('42) | 1.00 | .20 |
| 169 | A83 | ½a rose vio ('42) | 3.50 | .20 |
| 170 | A83 | 9p light green | 3.50 | .20 |
| 171 | A83 | 1a car rose ('43) | 3.50 | .20 |
| 172 | A84 | 1a3p bister | 3.50 | .20 |
| 172A | A84 | 1½a dark pur ('42) | 4.00 | .20 |
| 173 | A84 | 2a scarlet | 5.00 | .20 |
| 174 | A84 | 3a violet | 10.00 | .20 |
| 175 | A84 | 3½a ultramarine | 3.50 | .65 |
| 176 | A85 | 4a chocolate | 2.50 | .20 |
| 177 | A85 | 6a peacock blue | 11.50 | .20 |

| | | | | |
|---|---|---|---|---|
| 178 | A85 | 8a blue violet | 5.00 | .65 |
| 179 | A85 | 12a carmine lake | 10.50 | 1.10 |
| | | Nos. 168-179 (13) | 67.00 | 4.40 |

Early printings of the 1½a and 3a were lithographed.
For surcharge see No. 199.

آل بوسعيد

For stamps with this overprint, or a smaller type, see Oman (Muscat).

Symbols of Victory A86

| | | | | |
|---|---|---|---|---|
| **1946, Jan. 2** | | **Litho.** | **Perf. 13** | |
| 195 | A86 | 9p green | .95 | 1.25 |
| 196 | A86 | 1½a dull purple | .55 | .45 |
| 197 | A86 | 3½a ultramarine | 1.25 | 1.25 |
| 198 | A86 | 12a brown lake | 3.25 | 1.40 |
| | | Nos. 195-198 (4) | 6.00 | 4.35 |

Victory of the Allied Nations in WWII.

### No. 172 Surcharged With New Value and Bars

| | | | | |
|---|---|---|---|---|
| **1946, Aug. 8** | | | **Perf. 13½x14** | |
| 199 | A84 | 3p on 1a3p bister | .20 | .20 |

### Dominion of India

Asoka Pillar — A87

National Flag A88

Four-Motor Plane A89

### Perf. 14x13½, 13½x14

| | | | Wmk. 196 | |
|---|---|---|---|---|
| **1947** | | **Litho.** | | |
| 200 | A87 | 1½a greenish gray | 1.50 | .45 |
| 201 | A88 | 3½a multicolored | 4.50 | 4.75 |
| 202 | A89 | 12a ultramarine | 6.00 | 4.75 |
| | | Nos. 200-202 (3) | 12.00 | 9.95 |

Elevation to dominion status, Aug. 15, 1947.

Mahatma Gandhi — A90

Design: 10r, Gandhi profile.

### Perf. 11½

| | | | | |
|---|---|---|---|---|
| **1948, Aug. 15** | | **Unwmk.** | **Photo.** | |
| | | Size: 22x32½mm | | |
| 203 | A90 | 1½a brown | 9.00 | 1.25 |
| 204 | A90 | 3½a violet | 17.50 | 5.00 |
| 205 | A90 | 12a dark gray green | 20.00 | 3.00 |

| | | | | |
|---|---|---|---|---|
| | | Size: 22x37mm | | |
| 206 | A90 | 10r rose brn & brn | 200.00 | 95.00 |
| | | Nos. 203-206 (4) | 246.50 | 104.25 |

Mohandas K. Gandhi, 1869-1948.
For overprints see #O112A-O112D.

Ajanta Panel — A91      Konarak Horse — A92

Bodhisattva A93      Tomb of Muhammad Adil Shah, Bijapur A95

Sanchi Stupa A94      Victory Tower, Chittorgarh A96

Red Fort, Delhi A97

Satrunjaya Temple, Palitana A98

9p, Trimurti. 2a, Nataraja. 3½a, Bodh Gaya Temple. 4a, Bhuvanesvara. 8a, Kandarya Mahadeva Temple. 12a, Golden Temple, Amritsar. 5r, Taj Mahal. 10r, Qutb Minar.

### Perf. 13½x14, 14x13½

| | | | Wmk. 196 | |
|---|---|---|---|---|
| **1949, Aug. 15** | | **Typo.** | | |
| 207 | A91 | 3p gray violet | .30 | .20 |
| 208 | A92 | 6p red brown | .35 | .20 |
| 209 | A93 | 9p green | .60 | .20 |
| 210 | A93 | 1a turquoise | .85 | .20 |
| 211 | A93 | 2a carmine | 1.25 | .20 |
| 212 | A94 | 3a red orange | 3.00 | .20 |
| 213 | A94 | 3½a ultramarine | 2.50 | 5.00 |
| 214 | A94 | 4a brown lake | 6.00 | .35 |
| 215 | A95 | 6a purple | 2.75 | .90 |
| 216 | A95 | 8a blue green | 2.25 | .20 |
| 217 | A95 | 12a blue | 3.00 | .35 |
| | | **Litho.** | | |
| 218 | A96 | 1r dk green & pur | 22.50 | .20 |
| 219 | A97 | 2r pur & rose red | 20.00 | .50 |
| 220 | A97 | 5r brn car & dk grn | 45.00 | 2.00 |
| 221 | A96 | 10r dp bl & brn car | 80.00 | 12.00 |
| | | **Perf. 13½x13** | | |
| 222 | A98 | 15r dp car & dk brn | 32.50 | 35.00 |
| | | Nos. 207-222 (16) | 222.85 | 57.70 |

See #231, 235-236. For overprints see #M44-M46, M48-M55 and Intl. Commission in Indo-china issues for Cambodia, #1, 3-5, Laos #1, 3-5 and Vietnam #1, 3-5.

Symbols of UPU and Asoka Pillar — A99

| | | | | |
|---|---|---|---|---|
| **1949, Oct.** | | **Litho.** | **Perf. 13½x13** | |
| 223 | A99 | 9p dull green | 2.75 | 1.75 |
| 224 | A99 | 2a carmine rose | 2.75 | 1.75 |
| 225 | A99 | 3½a ultramarine | 4.00 | 3.00 |
| 226 | A99 | 12a red brown | 5.00 | 4.00 |
| | | Nos. 223-226 (4) | 14.50 | 10.50 |

75th anniv. of the formation of the UPU.

### Republic of India

Rejoicing Crowds A100

Designs: 3½a, Quill pen, vert. 4a, Plow and wheat. 12a, Charkha and cloth.

### Perf. 13½x13

| | | | | |
|---|---|---|---|---|
| **1950, Jan. 26** | | | **Wmk. 196** | |
| 227 | A100 | 2a carmine | 2.75 | .75 |
| 228 | A100 | 3½a ultramarine | 4.00 | 6.25 |
| 229 | A100 | 4a purple | 4.00 | 1.50 |
| 230 | A100 | 12a claret | 9.00 | 4.75 |
| | | Nos. 227-230 (4) | 19.75 | 13.25 |

### Type of 1949 Redrawn

Bodhisattva — A101

| | | | | |
|---|---|---|---|---|
| **1950, July 15** | | **Typo.** | **Perf. 13½x14** | |
| 231 | A101 | 1a turquoise | 4.00 | .30 |

For overprints see No. M47, Intl. Commission in Indo-china issues for Cambodia, No. 2, Laos, No. 2, and Vietnam, No. 2.

Extinct Stegodon Ganesa A102

| | | | | |
|---|---|---|---|---|
| **1951, Jan. 13** | | | **Perf. 13** | |
| 232 | A102 | 2a deep carmine & black | 6.00 | 1.25 |

Geological Survey of India, cent.

Torch and Map — A103      Kabir — A104

| | | | | |
|---|---|---|---|---|
| **1951, Mar. 4** | | | **Typo.** | |
| 233 | A103 | 2a red vio & red org | 3.50 | .90 |
| 234 | A103 | 12a dark brown & ultra | 12.00 | 2.25 |

First Asian Games, New Delhi.

### Temple Type of 1949

2½a, Bodh Gaya Temple. 4a, Bhuvanesvara.

### Perf. 13½x14

| | | | | |
|---|---|---|---|---|
| **1951, Apr. 30** | | | **Wmk. 196** | |
| 235 | A94 | 2½a brown lake | 4.50 | 3.50 |
| 236 | A94 | 4a ultramarine | 10.00 | .40 |

| | | | | |
|---|---|---|---|---|
| **1952, Oct. 1** | | **Photo.** | **Perf. 14x13½** | |

1a, Tulsidas, poet & saint. 2a, Meera, Rajput princess. 4a, Surdas, blind poet and saint. 4½a, Ghalib, Urdu poet. 12a, Rabindranath Tagore.

| | | | | |
|---|---|---|---|---|
| 237 | A104 | 9p emerald | 1.00 | .75 |
| 238 | A104 | 1a crimson | 3.00 | .30 |
| 239 | A104 | 2a red orange | 4.00 | .30 |
| 240 | A104 | 4a ultramarine | 6.00 | 1.00 |

| 241 | A104 | 4½a red violet | 1.25 | 1.75 |
|---|---|---|---|---|
| 242 | A104 | 12a brown | 9.00 | 1.50 |
| | | Nos. 237-242 (6) | 22.25 | 5.60 |

First Locomotive and Streamliner A105

**1953, Apr. 16** — Perf. 14½x14

| 243 | A105 | 2a black | 3.00 | .50 |
|---|---|---|---|---|

Centenary of India's railroads.

Mt. Everest A106

**1953, Oct. 2**

| 244 | A106 | 2a violet | 2.25 | .35 |
|---|---|---|---|---|
| 245 | A106 | 14a brown | 6.50 | 1.50 |

Conquest of Mt. Everest, May 29, 1953.

Telegraph Poles of 1851 and 1951 A107

**1953, Nov. 1**

| 246 | A107 | 2a blue green | .75 | .35 |
|---|---|---|---|---|
| 247 | A107 | 12a blue | 6.25 | .85 |

Centenary of the telegraph in India.

Mail Transport, 1854 A108

Designs: 2a and 14a, Pigeon and plane. 4a, Mail transport, 1954.

**1954, Oct. 1**

| 248 | A108 | 1a rose lilac | .55 | .30 |
|---|---|---|---|---|
| 249 | A108 | 2a rose pink | .55 | .30 |
| 250 | A108 | 4a yellow brown | 5.00 | 1.25 |
| 251 | A108 | 14a blue | 3.00 | .40 |
| | | Nos. 248-251 (4) | 9.10 | 2.25 |

Centenary of India's postage stamps.

UN Emblem and Lotus Blossom A109

**1954, Oct. 24**

| 252 | A109 | 2a Prussian green | .60 | .45 |
|---|---|---|---|---|

United Nations Day.

Forest Research Institute, Dehra Dun A110

**1954, Dec. 11**

| 253 | A110 | 2a ultramarine | .40 | .30 |
|---|---|---|---|---|

4th World Forestry Cong., Dehra Dun.

Tractor A111

Charkha Operator A112

Symbols of Malaria Control A113

Designs: 6p, Power looms. 9p, Bullock irrigation pump. 1a, Damodar Valley dam. 3a, Naga woman at hand loom. 4a, Bullock team. 8a, Chittaranjan Locomotive Works. 10a, Plane over Marine Drive, Bombay. 12a, Hindustan aircraft factory. 14a, Plane over Kashmir valley. 1r, Telephone factory worker. 1r2a, Plane over Cape Comorin. 1r8a, Plane over Kanchenjunga Mountains. 2r, Rare earth factory. 5r, Sindri fertilizer factory. 10r, Steel mill.

***Perf. 14x14½, 14½x14***

**1955, Jan. 26** — Photo.

| 254 | A111 | 3p rose lilac | .40 | .20 |
|---|---|---|---|---|
| 255 | A111 | 6p deep violet | .40 | .20 |
| 256 | A111 | 9p orange brown | .55 | .20 |
| 257 | A111 | 1a dp blue green | .55 | .20 |
| 258 | A112 | 2a blue | .40 | .20 |
| 259 | A112 | 3a blue green | .60 | .20 |
| 260 | A111 | 4a rose red | .60 | .20 |
| 261 | A113 | 6a yellow brown | 1.75 | .20 |
| 262 | A111 | 8a deep blue | 8.75 | .20 |
| 263 | A113 | 10a aquamarine | 4.50 | 2.75 |
| 264 | A111 | 12a violet blue | 4.00 | .20 |
| 265 | A113 | 14a emerald | 6.50 | .40 |
| 266 | A111 | 1r greenish black | 5.00 | .20 |
| 267 | A113 | 1r2a gray | 2.75 | 5.75 |
| 268 | A113 | 1r8a claret | 10.00 | 6.00 |
| 269 | A111 | 2r carmine rose | 5.25 | .20 |
| 270 | A111 | 5r brown | 17.00 | .40 |
| 271 | A111 | 10r orange | 18.00 | 3.75 |
| | | Nos. 254-271 (18) | 87.00 | 21.45 |

See Nos. 316-319.

Bodhi Tree — A114

Ornament and Bodhi Tree A115

**1956, May 24** Wmk. 196 — Perf. 13

| 272 | A114 | 2a brown | 1.75 | .30 |
|---|---|---|---|---|
| 273 | A115 | 14a brick red | 7.00 | 4.00 |

2500th anniv. of the birth of Buddha.

Bal Gangadhar Tilak — A116

Map of India — A117

**1956, July 23** Wmk. 196 Photo.

| 274 | A116 | 2a orange brown | .50 | .50 |
|---|---|---|---|---|

Birth cent. of Bal Gangadhar Tilak, independence leader.

**1957-58** — Perf. 14x14½

| 275 | A117 | 1np blue green | .20 | .20 |
|---|---|---|---|---|
| 276 | A117 | 2np light brown | .20 | .20 |
| 277 | A117 | 3np brown | .20 | .20 |
| 278 | A117 | 5np emerald | 4.00 | .20 |
| 279 | A117 | 6np gray | .60 | .20 |
| 280 | A117 | 8np brt green ('58) | 6.50 | .50 |
| 281 | A117 | 10np dark green | 4.50 | .20 |
| 282 | A117 | 13np brt carmine | 1.10 | .20 |
| 283 | A117 | 15np violet ('58) | 4.00 | .20 |
| 284 | A117 | 20np bright blue | 1.25 | .20 |
| 285 | A117 | 25np ultramarine | .95 | .20 |
| 286 | A117 | 50np orange | 3.50 | .20 |
| 287 | A117 | 75np plum | 2.00 | .20 |
| 288 | A117 | 90np red lilac ('58) | 6.00 | 2.50 |
| | | Nos. 275-288 (14) | 35.00 | 5.40 |

Denominations of the 8np, 15np and 90np are inscribed nP.

See #302-315. For overprints see #M60 and Intl. Commission in Indo-China issues for Cambodia, #6-10, Laos, #6-10, and Vietnam, #6-10.

Laxmibai, Rani of Jhansi A118

Banyan Sapling, Arch and Flames — A119

***Perf. 14½x14, 13***

**1957, Aug. 15** Wmk. 196

| 289 | A118 | 15np brown | .50 | .50 |
|---|---|---|---|---|
| 290 | A119 | 90np bright red violet | 3.75 | 1.40 |

Centenary of the struggle for independence (Indian Mutiny).

Henri Dunant A120

**1957, Oct. 28** — Perf. 13½x13

| 291 | A120 | 15np car rose & black | .40 | .40 |
|---|---|---|---|---|

19th Intl. Red Cross Conf., New Delhi.

Boy Eating Banana A121

Bankura Horse — A122

Children's Day: 15np, Girl writing on tablet.

**1957, Nov. 14** — Perf. 13½

| 292 | A121 | 8np rose lilac | .35 | .35 |
|---|---|---|---|---|
| 293 | A121 | 15np aquamarine | .35 | .35 |
| 294 | A122 | 90np lt orange brown | .70 | .35 |
| | | Nos. 292-294 (3) | 1.40 | 1.05 |

Madras University A123

University Centenaries: No. 296, Calcutta. No. 297, Bombay, vert.

**1957, Dec. 31** Photo.
Size: 29½x25mm

| 295 | A123 | 10np light brown | .60 | .50 |
|---|---|---|---|---|
| 296 | A123 | 10np gray | .30 | .50 |

Size: 21½x38mm

| 297 | A123 | 10np violet | .30 | .50 |
|---|---|---|---|---|
| | | Nos. 295-297 (3) | 1.20 | 1.50 |

J. N. Tata and Steel Works, Jamshedpur — A124

**1958, Mar. 1** — Perf. 14½x14

| 298 | A124 | 15np red orange | .40 | .40 |
|---|---|---|---|---|

50th anniv. of Indian steel industry.

Dr. Dhondo Keshav Karve — A125

**1958, Apr. 18** — Perf. 14x13½

| 299 | A125 | 15np orange brown | .40 | .40 |
|---|---|---|---|---|

Cent. of the birth of Karve, educator and pioneer of women's education.

Wapiti and Hunter Planes A126

**1958, Apr. 30** — Perf. 14½x14

| 300 | A126 | 15np bright blue | 2.50 | .35 |
|---|---|---|---|---|
| 301 | A126 | 90np ultramarine | 2.75 | 2.50 |

25th anniv. of the Indian Air Force.

Map Type of 1957-58 and Industrial Type of 1955

1r, Telephone factory worker. 2r, Rare earth factory. 5r, Sindri fertilizer factory. 10r, Steel mill.

***Perf. 14x14½***

**1958-63** Photo. Wmk. 324

| 302 | A117 | 1np blue grn ('60) | 1.25 | .20 |
|---|---|---|---|---|
| a. | | Imperf., pair | 240.00 | |
| 303 | A117 | 2np light brown | .20 | .20 |
| 304 | A117 | 3np brown | .20 | .20 |
| 305 | A117 | 5np emerald | .20 | .20 |
| 306 | A117 | 6np gray ('63) | .20 | 4.00 |
| 307 | A117 | 8np bright green | .20 | .20 |
| 308 | A117 | 10np dark green | .20 | .20 |
| 309 | A117 | 13np bright car ('63) | 1.25 | 4.75 |
| 310 | A117 | 15np violet ('59) | .70 | .20 |
| 311 | A117 | 20np bright blue | .40 | .20 |
| 312 | A117 | 25np ultramarine | .40 | .20 |
| 313 | A117 | 50np orange ('59) | .40 | .20 |
| 314 | A117 | 75np plum ('59) | .75 | .20 |
| 315 | A117 | 90np red lilac ('60) | 6.75 | .20 |
| 316 | A111 | 1r dk grn ('59) | 4.75 | .20 |
| 317 | A111 | 2r lilac rose ('59) | 6.75 | .20 |
| 318 | A111 | 5r brown ('59) | 11.50 | .20 |
| 319 | A111 | 10r orange ('59) | 26.50 | 5.50 |
| | | Nos. 302-319 (18) | 62.60 | 17.25 |

For overprints see Nos. M56-M59, M61, Intl. Commission in Indo-china issues for Cambodia, No. 12, Laos, Nos. 12-16, and Vietnam Nos. 11-16.

Bipin Chandra Pal — A128

Nurse and Child — A129

**1958, Nov. 7**     *Perf. 13½*
320 A128 15np dull green    .50 .50
Birth cent. of Pal, early leader of India's freedom movement.

**1958, Nov. 30**
321 A128 15np brt greenish blue   .50 .50
Bose, physicist, plant physiologist, birth cent.

Portrait: Sir Jagadis Chandra Bose.

**1958, Nov. 14**     **Wmk. 324**
322 A129 15np violet    .50 .50
Children's Day, Nov. 14.

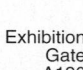

Exhibition Gate A130

**1958, Dec. 30**     *Perf. 14½x14*
323 A130 15np claret    .50 .50
India 1958 Exhibition at Kampur.

Sir Jamsetjee Jejeebhoy — A131

**1959, Apr. 13**     *Perf. 13½*
324 A131 15np brown    .50 .50
Cent. of the death of Jejeebhoy, philosopher and philanthropist.

"Triumph of Labor," by D. P. Roy Chowdhary — A132

**1959, June 15**     *Perf. 14½x14*
325 A132 15np dull green    .50 .50
40th anniv. of the ILO.

Children Arriving at Institution — A133

    *Perf. 14x14½*
**1959, Nov. 14**    **Photo.**    **Wmk. 324**
326 A133 15np dull green    .50 .50
   *a.*    Imperf., pair    500.00
Children's Day, Nov. 14.

Farmer Plowing with Bullocks A134

**1959, Dec. 30**     *Perf. 13*
327 A134 15np gray    .50 .40
World Agriculture Fair, New Delhi.

Thiruvalluvar Holding Stylus and Palmyra Leaf — A135

**1960, Feb. 15**     *Perf. 14*
328 A135 15np rose lilac    .50 .50
Honoring the ancient and saintly Tamil poet, Thiruvalluvar.

Scene from Meghduta — A136

Scene from Sakuntala A137

**1960, June 22**     *Perf. 13*
329 A136 15np gray    1.00 .40
330 A137 1.03r brown & bister    3.50 2.50
Honoring Kalidasa, 5th cent. poet and dramatist.
For surcharge see No. 371.

Subramania Bharati — A138

Dr. M. Visvesvaraya A139

**1960, Sept. 11**   **Photo.**   *Perf. 14x13½*
331 A138 15np bright blue    .50 .50
Honoring the poet and statesman Subramania Bharati (1882-1921).

**1960, Sept. 15**     *Perf. 13x13½*
332 A139 15np car rose & brown    .50 .50
Birth cent. of Visvesvaraya, engineer and statesman.

Children Playing and Studying A140

**1960, Nov. 14**     *Perf. 13½x13*
333 A140 15np green    .50 .50
Children's Day, Nov. 14.

Children and UN Emblem A141

**1960, Dec. 11**     **Wmk. 324**
334 A141 15np olive gray & org brn    .50 .50
UNICEF Day.

Tyagaraja, Indian Musician — A142

**1961, Jan. 6**    **Photo.**    *Perf. 14*
335 A142 15np bright blue    .50 .50
114th anniv. of Tyagaraja's death.

First Airmail Postmark — A143

Boeing 707 Jetliner — A144

Design: 1r, Humber-Sommer biplane.

    *Perf. 14, 13x13½*
**1961, Feb. 18**     **Wmk. 324**
336 A143 5np olive bister    2.25 .40
337 A144 15np gray & green    2.25 .40
338 A144 1r gray & claret    7.00 3.00
   Nos. 336-338 (3)    11.50 3.80
50th anniv. of the world's 1st airmail. The flight was from Allahabad to Naini, Feb. 18, 1911.

Chatrapati Sivaji Maharaj (1627-1680) A145

**1961, Apr. 17**     *Perf. 13x13½*
339 A145 15np gray green & brown    1.40 .65
Leader of the Marahattas in the fight against the Moguls.

Motilal Nehru — A146

Rabindranath Tagore — A147

**1961, May 6**     *Perf. 14x13½*
340 A146 15np orange & ol gray    .50 .40
Cent. of the birth of Motilal Nehru, leader in India's fight for freedom.

**1961, May 7**     *Perf. 13*
341 A147 15np blue grn & org    1.40 .60
Cent. of the birth of Tagore, poet.

Radio Masts and All India Radio Emblem A148

**1961, June 8**    **Photo.**    **Wmk. 324**
342 A148 15np ultramarine    .50 .50
25th anniv. of All India Radio.

Prafulla Chandra Ray — A149

Vishnu Narayan Bhatkhande A150

**1961, Aug. 2**     *Perf. 14x13½*
343 A149 15np gray    .50 .50
Cent. of the birth of Ray, scientist.

**1961, Sept. 1**     *Perf. 13*
344 A150 15np olive gray    .50 .50
Bhatkhande (1860-1936), musician.

Boy Making Pottery — A151

Gate at Fair — A152

**1961, Nov. 14**      **Perf. 13½**
345 A151 15np brown    .50   .50
Children's Day, Nov. 14.

**1961, Nov. 14**      **Perf. 14x14½**
346 A152 15np blue & carmine   .50   .50
Indian Industries Fair at New Delhi.

Forest and Himalayas — A153

**1961, Nov. 21**      **Perf. 13**
347 A153 15np brown & green   .80   .45
Cent. of the introduction of scientific forestry in India.

Yaksha, God of Fertility — A154

Kalibangan Seal — A155

**1961, Dec. 14**    **Photo.**    **Perf. 14**
348 A154 15np orange brown   .50   .40
349 A155 90np orange brn & olive   1.10   .40
Cent. of the Archaeological Survey of India.

Madan Mohan Malaviya — A156

**Nunmati Refinery, Gauhati — A157**

**1961, Dec. 25**      **Perf. 14x13½**
350 A156 15np slate    .50   .50
Cent. of the birth of Malaviya, Pres. of the Indian Natl. Cong. and Vice Chancellor of Benares University.

**1962, Jan. 1**    **Photo.**    **Perf. 13**
351 A157 15np blue    .70   .40
1st Indian oil refinery at Gauhati.

Bhikaiji Cama — A158

Village Council, Banyan Tree, Parliament and Map — A159

**1962, Jan. 26**      **Perf. 14**
352 A158 15np rose lilac    .50   .50
Cent. of the birth of Madame Cama, a leader in India's fight for independence.

**1962, Jan. 26**      **Perf. 13**
353 A159 15np red lilac    .50   .50
Panchayati Raj, the system of government by village council.

Dayananda Sarasvati — A160

Ganesh Shankar Vidyarthi — A161

**1962, Mar. 4**      **Perf. 14**
354 A160 15np brown orange   .50   .50
135th anniv. of the birth of Sarasvati, reformer of the Vedic religion and founder of the Arya Samaj educational institutions.

**1962, Mar. 25**
355 A161 15np reddish brown   .50   .50
Vidyarthi (1890-1931), reformer of community life.

Malaria Eradication Emblem — A162

Dr. Rajendra Prasad — A163

**1962, Apr. 7**      **Perf. 13**
356 A162 15np dk car rose & yel   .50   .50
WHO drive to eradicate malaria.

**1962, May 13**      **Perf. 13**
357 A163 15np bright red lilac   .50   .40
Prasad, President of India (1950-62).

High Court, Calcutta A164

**1962**    **Photo.**    **Perf. 13½x14**
358 A164 15np green    .90   .35
359 A164 15np Madras    .90   .35
360 A164 15np Bombay    .90   .35
    Nos. 358-360 (3)    2.70   1.05
Indian High Courts, cent. Issued: No. 358, July 1; No. 359, Aug. 8; No. 360, Aug. 14.

Ramabai Ranade — A165

Indian Rhinoceros A166

**1962, Aug. 15**      **Perf. 14**
361 A165 15np brown orange   .50   .50
Ramabai Ranade (1862-1924), woman social reformer.

**1962-63**    **Wmk. 324**    **Perf. 14**
10np, Gaur. No. 363, Lesser panda, vert. 30np, Elephant, vert. 50np, Tiger. 1r, Lion.

**Size: 30x26mm**
361A A166 10np yel org & blk ('63)   1.25   *1.50*
362 A166 15np Prus blue & brn   .75   .20

**Perf. 13x13½, 13½x13**
**Size: 25x36mm, 36x25mm**
363 A166 15np green & red brown ('63)   2.50   .55
364 A166 30np bister & slate ('63)   5.75   1.50
365 A166 50np dp grn, ocher & brown ('63)   4.50   .75
366 A166 1r brt bl & pale brown ('63)   4.25   .50
    Nos. 361A-366 (6)    19.00   5.00

Child Reaching for Flag A167

**1962, Nov. 14**      **Perf. 13**
367 A167 15np lt bluish grn & ver   .50   .50
Children's Day.

Eye within Lotus Blossom A168

**1962, Dec. 3**      **Photo.**
368 A168 15np olive gray    .50   .40
16th Intl. Cong. of Ophthalmology, New Delhi, Dec. 1962.

Srinivasa Ramanujan A169

Swami Vivekananda — A170

**1962, Dec. 22**      **Perf. 13½x14**
369 A169 15np olive gray   1.10   .55
75th anniv. of the birth of Ramanujan (1887-1920), mathematician.

**1963, Jan. 17**      **Perf. 14x14½**
370 A170 15np olive & orange brn   .50   .50
Cent. of the birth of Vivekananda (1863-1902), philosopher.

**No. 330 Surcharged with New Value and Two Bars**

**1963, Feb. 2**      **Perf. 13**
371 A137 1r on 1.03r brown & bis   .60   .45

Hands Reaching for "FAO" Emblem — A171

Henri Dunant and Centenary Emblem — A172

**1963, Mar. 21**                    **Photo.**
372 A171 15np chalky blue          3.00  .70
UNFAO Freedom from Hunger campaign.

**1963, May 8**                    **Perf. 13**
373 A172 15np gray & red           5.75  .60
Centenary of the International Red Cross.

Field Artillery and Helicopter A173

Design: 1r, Soldier guarding frontier and plane dropping supplies.

**1963, Aug. 15**            **Perf. 13½x14**
374 A173 15np dull green           1.00  .30
375 A173    1r red brown           1.60 1.25
Honoring the Armed Forces and the 16th anniv. of independence.

Dadabhoy Naoroji — A174

**1963, Sept. 4**                  **Perf. 13**
376 A174 15np gray green            .50  .50
Honoring Dadabhoy Naoroji (1825-1917), mathematician and statesman.

Annie Besant — A175

School Lunch — A176

**1963, Oct. 1     Photo.        Perf. 14**
377 A175 15np blue green            .50  .50
Besant (1847-1933), an English woman devoted to the cause of India's freedom, theosophist and writer. Stamp gives birth date as 1837.

**1963, Nov. 14   Wmk. 324    Perf. 14**
378 A176 15np olive bister          .50  .50
Children's Day.

Eleanor Roosevelt at Spinning Wheel A177

**1963, Dec. 10**                  **Perf. 13**
379 A177 15np rose violet           .50  .50
Honoring Eleanor Roosevelt on the 15th anniv. of the Universal Declaration of Human Rights.

Gopabandhu Das (1877-1928) A178

Lakshmi, Goddess of Wealth — A179

**1964, Jan. 4**                   **Perf. 13**
380 A178 15np dull purple           .50  .50
Gopabandhu Das, social reformer.

**1964, Jan. 4**                   **Photo.**
381 A179 15np dull violet blue      .50  .50
26th Intl. Cong. of Orientalists, New Delhi, Jan. 4-14.

Purandaradasa Holding Veena and Chipala — A180

**1964, Jan. 14**
382 A180 15np golden brown          .50  .50
400th anniv. of the death of Purandaradasa (1484-1564), musician.

Subhas Chandra Bose and INA Emblem A181

Design: 55np, Bose addressing troops.

**1964, Jan. 23**                  **Perf. 13**
383 A181 15np olive                1.10  .45
384 A181 55np red & black          1.10  .85
67th anniv. of the birth of Bose, organizer of the Indian Natl. Army.

Sarojini Naidu (1879-1949) A182

Kasturba Gandhi A183

**1964, Feb. 13**            **Perf. 14x13½**
385 A182 15np dull lilac & slate
                             grn    .50  .50
Mrs. Sarojini Naidu, poet, politician, governor of United Provinces.

**1964, Feb. 22    Photo.    Wmk. 324**
386 A183 15np brown orange          .50  .50
20th anniv. of the death of Kasturba Gandhi (1869-1944), wife of Mahatma Gandhi.

Dr. Waldemar M. Haffkine (1860-1930) A184

**1964, Mar. 16**                  **Perf. 13**
387 A184 15np violet brown, *buff*  .50  .50
Haffkine, bacteriologist, who as director of Haffkine Institute introduced inoculations against cholera and plague.

Jawaharlal Nehru (1889-1964) and People A185

**1964, June 12   Unwmk.     Perf. 13**
388 A185 15p grayish blue           .50  .50
Prime Minister Jawaharlal Nehru.

Asutosh Mookerjee and High Court, Calcutta A186

**1964, June 29             Wmk. 324**
389 A186 15p olive green & brn      .50  .50
Cent. of the birth of Asutosh Mookerjee (1864-1924), educator, lawyer and judge.

Sri Aurobindo Ghose (1872-1950), Writer and Philosopher A187

**1964, Aug. 15**                  **Photo.**
390 A187 15p violet brown           .50  .50

Raja Rammohun Roy — A188

**1964, Sept. 27**                 **Perf. 13**
391 A188 15p reddish brown          .50  .50
Roy (1772-1833), Hindu religious reformer.

Globe, Lotus, and Calipers — A189

Nehru Medal and Rose — A190

**1964, Nov. 9     Unwmk.     Photo.**
392 A189 15p carmine rose           .50  .50
6th gen. assembly of the Intl. Organization for Standardization.

**1964, Nov. 14**                 **Perf. 13½**
393 A190 15p blue gray              .50  .50
Children's Day. For overprints, see Nos. M62, Intl. Commission in Indo-china issues for Laos and Vietnam, No. 1.

St. Thomas Statue, Ortona, Italy — A191

Globe and Pickax — A192

**1964, Dec. 2    Unwmk.     Perf. 13½**
394 A191 15p rose violet            .50  .50
Visit of Pope Paul VI, Nov. 30-Dec. 2.

**1964, Dec. 14**                  **Wmk. 324**
395 A192 15p bright green           .80  .65
22nd Intl. Geological Cong., New Delhi.

Jamsetji N. Tata A193

**1965, Jan. 7    Unwmk.     Perf. 13**
396 A193 15p dk brown & orange      .50  .25
125th anniv. of the birth of Tata (1839-1904), founder of India's steel industry.

Lala Lajpatrai (1865-1928), a Leader in India's Fight for Independence A194

**1965, Jan. 28    Photo.    Perf. 13**
397 A194 15p brown                  .50  .50

ICC Emblem and Globe A195

**1965, Feb. 8**    **Litho.**
398 A195 15p dull green & car .50 .50
20th cong. of the Intl. Chamber of Commerce, New Delhi.

Freighter Jalausha at Visakhapatnam — A196

**Perf. 14½x14**
**1965, Apr. 5**   **Photo.**   **Wmk. 324**
399 A196 15p ultramarine .90 .90
National Maritime Day.

Death Centenary of Abraham Lincoln — A197

**1965, Apr. 15**    **Perf. 13**
400 A197 15p yellow & dk brown .60 .60

ITU Emblem, Old and New Communication Equipment — A198

**1965, May 17 Photo. Perf. 14½x14**
401 A198 15p rose violet 2.50 .75
Cent. of the ITU.

Torch and Rose — A199

**1965, May 27**   **Wmk. 324**   **Perf. 13**
402 A199 15p carmine & blue .40 .40
1st anniv. of the death of Jawaharlal Nehru.

ICY Emblem A200

**1965, June 26**   **Photo.**   **Unwmk.**
403 A200 15p bister & dk green 2.75 1.25
International Cooperation Year.

Indians Raising Flag on Everest — A201

**1965, Aug. 15**   **Unwmk.**   **Perf. 13**
404 A201 15p plum .75 .60
Success of the Indian Mt. Everest Expedition, May 20, 1965.

Elephant from Konarak Temple, Orissa A202

Tea Picking A203

Woman Writing Letter, Chandella Carving, 11th Century — A204

Trombay Atomic Center A205

Designs: 2p, Vase (bidri ware). 3p, Brass lamp. 4p, Coffee berries. 5p, Family (family planning). 8p, Axis deer (chital). 10p, Electric locomotive, 1961. 20p, Gnat plane. 30p, Male and female figurines. 40p, General Post Office, Calcutta, 1868. 50p, Mangoes. 60p, Somnath Temple. 70p, Stone chariot, Hampi, Mysore. 2r, Dal Lake, Kashmir. 5r, Bhakra Dam, Punjab.

**Perf. 14½x14, 14x14½**
**1965-68**    **Photo.**    **Wmk. 324**
405 A202 2p redsh brown
('67) .20 .55
406 A202 3p olive bis ('67) .40 2.40
407 A203 4p orange brn ('68) .20 2.10
408 A202 5p cerise ('67) .20 .20
409 A202 6p gray ('66) .20 3.25
410 A202 8p red brown ('67) .40 4.00
411 A203 10p brt blue ('66) .60 .20
412 A203 15p dk yel green 3.50 .20
413 A203 20p plum ('67) 8.00 .20
414 A203 30p brown ('67) .20 .20
415 A203 40p brown vio ('68) .20 .20
416 A202 50p green ('66) .35 .20
417 A202 60p dark gray ('67) .45 .20
418 A203 70p violet ('67) .95 .20
419 A204 1r deep claret &
red brown ('66) .95 .20
420 A205 2r vio & brt bl ('67) 3.25 .20
421 A205 5r brn & vio ('67) 3.50 1.60
422 A205 10r green & gray 24.00 1.10
Nos. 405-422 (18) 47.55 17.20

See Nos. 623, 666-670, 678, 680, 684-685. For overprints see Nos. RA1-RA2, Intl. Commission in Indo-china issues for Laos and Vietnam, Nos. 2-9.

**1975-76**   **Wmk. 360**   **Perf. 14½x14**
422A A202 2p redsh brown .90 .90
423 A202 5p cerise .75 .20
     **Unwmk.**
423A A202 5p cerise ('76) .50 .20

A206

A207

**1965, Sept. 10**   **Unwmk.**   **Perf. 13**
424 A206 15p dark green &
brown .50 .50
Govind Ballabh Pant (1887-1961), Home Minister of India.

**1965, Oct. 31**    **Perf. 14**
425 A207 15p gray .50 .50
Vallabhbhai Patel (1875-1950), Deputy Prime Minister of India.

Chittaranjan Das (1870-1925) A208

Vidyapati, 15th Cent. Poet A209

**1965, Nov. 5**   **Photo.**   **Perf. 13**
426 A208 15p brown .50 .50
Das, freedom fighter, pres. of Indian Natl. Cong., mayor of Calcutta.

**1965, Nov. 17**    **Perf. 14x14½**
427 A209 15p brown .50 .50

Tomb of Akbar the Great, Sikandra A210

**1966, Jan. 24**    **Perf. 14**
428 A210 15p dark gray .50 .50
Pacific Area Travel Assoc. Conf., New Delhi.

Soldier, Planes and Warships A211

**1966, Jan. 26**
429 A211 15p bright violet 2.50 .65
Honoring the Indian armed forces.

Lal Bahadur Shastri A212

Kambar A213

**1966, Jan. 26**    **Perf. 13**
430 A212 15p gray 1.10 .60
Prime Minister Shastri (1904-66).

**1966, Apr. 9**    **Perf. 14x14½**
431 A213 15p green .50 .50
Kambar, 9th century Tamil poet.

B. R. Ambedkar A214

Kunwar Singh A215

**1966, Apr. 14**   **Unwmk.**   **Perf. 14**
432 A214 15p violet brown .50 .50
10th anniv. of the death of Dr. Bhimrao R. Ambedkar (1891-1956), lawyer and leader in social reform.

**1966, Apr. 23**      **Photo.**
433 A215 15p orange brown .50 .50
Kunwar Singh (1777-1858), hero of 1857 War of Independence (1857 Mutiny).

Gopal Krishna Gokhale A216

**1966, May 9**   **Unwmk.**   **Perf. 13**
434 A216 15p violet brown & yel .50 .50
Cent. of the birth of Gokhale (1866-1915), professor of history and political economy and leader of the opposition party.

A. M. P. Dvivedi (1864-1938) A217

Ranjit Singh (1780-1839) — A218

**1966, May 15**    **Perf. 14**
435 A217 15p olive gray .50 .50
Acharya Mahavir Prasad Dvivedi, Hindi writer.

**1966, June 28**   **Unwmk.**   **Perf. 14**
436 A218 15p plum .50 .50
Maharaja Ranjit Singh, ruler of Punjab.

Homi Bhabha and Atomic Reactor
A219

**1966, Aug. 4          Perf. 14½x14**
437  A219  15p brown violet          1.25  1.25
Dr. Homi Bhabha (1909-1966), scientist.

Rama Tirtha
A220

**1966, Nov. 11    Unwmk.    Perf. 13**
438  A220  15p greenish blue          .50  .50
60th anniv. of the death of Swami Rama Tirtha (1873-1906).

A221

A222

**1966, Nov. 11    Photo.    Perf. 13½**
439  A221  15p dark violet blue          .50  .50
Abdul Kalam Azad (1888-1958), president of the All-India Congress.

**1966, Nov. 14          Perf. 13**
440  A222  15p Child and dove          1.40  .80
Children's Day.

Allahabad High Court, Cent.
A223

**1966, Nov. 25          Perf. 14½x14**
441  A223  15p violet brown          .50  .50

Family
A224

**1966, Dec. 12          Perf. 13½x13**
442  A224  15p brown          .50  .50
Intl. Conf. for Marriage Guidance, New Delhi, and Family Planning Week.

Hockey
A225

**1966, Dec. 31    Unwmk.    Perf. 13**
443  A225  15p bright blue          2.00  2.00
Victory of the Indian hockey team at the 5th Asian Games, Bangkok, Dec. 19.

Grain Harvest
A226

**1967, Jan. 11          Perf. 13½**
444  A226  15p yellow green          .75  .90
1st anniv. of the death of Prime Minister Lal Bahadur Shastri, who advocated self-sufficiency in food production.

Voters — A227

Guru Dwara Shrine, Patna — A228

**1967, Jan. 13          Photo.**
445  A227  15p light red brown          .50  .50
General elections, Feb. 1967.

**1967, Jan. 17          Perf. 14**
446  A228  15p violet          .90  .70
300th anniv. of the birth of Gobind Singh (1666-1708), religious leader.

Taj Mahal
A229

**1967, Mar. 19          Perf. 14½x14**
447  A229  15p brown & orange          .60  .60
International Tourist Year.

Nandalal Bose and Garuda — A230

**1967, Apr. 16          Perf. 13½**
448  A230  15p brown          .50  .50
Nandalal Bose (1882-1966), painter.

Survey of India Emblem
A231

**1967, May 1    Unwmk.    Perf. 13**
449  A231  15p lilac          1.10  .80
Bicentenary of Survey of India.

Basaveswara, 12th Cent. Statesman and Philosopher, at Work — A232

**1967, May 11          Perf. 13½x14**
450  A232  15p deep orange          .50  .50

Narsinha Mehta — A233

Maharana Pratap — A234

**1967, May 30          Perf. 13½**
451  A233  15p gray brown          .50  .50
Narsina Mehta, 15th cent. musician.

**1967, June 11          Perf. 14x14½**
452  A234  15p reddish brown          .50  .50
Pratap (1540-1597), Mewar ruler.

Narayana Guru
A235

Dr. Sarvepalli Radhakrishnan
A236

**1967, Aug. 21    Photo.    Perf. 14**
453  A235  15p brown          .60  .60
Narayana Guru (1855-1928), religious reformer.

**1967, Sept. 5    Unwmk.    Perf. 13**
454  A236  15p dull claret          1.00  .40
Radhakrishnan, Pres. of India 1962-67.

Martyrs' Memorial, Patna
A237

**1967, Oct. 1    Photo.    Perf. 14½x14**
455  A237  15p dark carmine          .50  .50
25th anniv. of the "Quit India" revolt led by Gandhi.

Map Showing Indo-European Telegraph
A238

**1967, Nov. 9    Photo.    Perf. 13½**
456  A238  15p blue & black          1.25  .80
Cent. of the laying of the Indo-European telegraph line.

Wrestlers
A239

**1967, Nov. 12**
457  A239  15p ocher & plum          1.00  .55
World Wrestling Championships, New Delhi, Nov. 1967.

Nehru and Naga Tribesmen — A240

Rashbehari Basu — A241

**1967, Dec. 4    Photo.    Perf. 13½**
458  A240  15p ultramarine          .50  .50

**1967, Dec. 26          Perf. 13½**
459  A241  15p dull purple          .50  .50
Basu (1886-1945), Bengali leader.

Bugle, Scout Emblem and Scout Sign
A242

**1967, Dec. 27          Perf. 14½x14**
460  A242  15p orange brown          2.00  .60
Boy Scout Movement, 60th anniv.

People Encircling the Globe and Human Rights Flame
A243

**1968, Jan. 1          Perf. 13**
461  A243  15p dark green          1.00  .75
Intl. Human Rights Year.

Conference Emblem and Gopuram Temple — A244

**1968, Jan. 3    Photo.    Unwmk.**
462  A244  15p purple          1.00  .55
2nd Intl. Conf. on Tamil Studies, Madras.

UN Emblem, Plane and Ship A245

**1968, Feb. 1**    Perf. 14½x14
463 A245 15p greenish blue    1.25 .55
UN Conference on Trade and Development, New Delhi, Feb. 1968.

Symbolic Bow and Quill Pen — A246

**1968, Feb. 20**    Perf. 13½x14
464 A246 15p ocher & sepia    .50 .50
Cent. of the newspaper Amrit Bazar Patrika, Calcutta.

Maxim Gorky (1868-1936), Russian Writer — A247

**1968, Mar. 28**    Photo.    Perf. 14
465 A247 15p brown violet    .50 .50

Exhibition Emblem — A248

**1968, Mar. 31**    Perf. 13
466 A248 15p dark blue & org    .60 .30
First Triennial Exhibition, New Delhi.

Symbolic Mail Box — A249

**1968, July 1**    Unwmk.    Perf. 13
467 A249 20p vermilion & blue    .80 .45
Opening of 100,000th Indian post office.

Wheat and Indian Agricultural Research Institute A250

**1968, July 15**    Photo.    Perf. 13
468 A250 20p brt grn & brn org    .60 .35
India's 1968 bumper wheat crop.

Gaganendranath Tagore (1867-1938), Self-portrait A251

**1968, Sept. 17**    Unwmk.    Perf. 13
469 A251 20p ocher & deep clar    1.00 .55

Lakshminath Bezbaruah (1868-1938), Writer — A252

**1968, Oct. 5**    Photo.    Perf. 13½
470 A252 20p sepia    .50 .40

19th Olympic Games, Mexico City A253

**1968, Oct. 12**    Perf. 14½x14
471 A253 20p blue gray & red brn    .40 .40
472 A253   1r olive gray & dk brn 1.00 .40

Bhagat Singh (1907-1931), Revolutionary — A254

**1968, Oct. 19**    Photo.    Perf. 13½x13
473 A254 20p orange brown    1.00 .80

Bose Reading Proclamation A255

Sister Nivedita A256

**1968, Oct. 21**    Perf. 14x14½
474 A255 20p dark blue    .80 .60
25th anniv. of the establishment of the Azad Hind (Free India) government by Subhas Chandra Bose (1897-1945), independence leader.

**1968, Oct. 27**
475 A256 20p blue green    .60 .50
Sister Nivedita (Margaret Noble, 1867-1911), Irish-born friend of India.

Marie Curie and Patient Receiving Radiation A257

**1968, Nov. 6**    Perf. 14½x14
476 A257 20p purple    2.50 .70
Marie Sklodowska Curie (1867-1934), discoverer of radium and polonium.

World Map — A258

Interior of Cochin Synagogue A259

**1968, Dec. 1**    Perf. 13
477 A258 20p blue    .60 .45
21st Intl. Geographical Congress.

**Perf. 13x13½**
**1968, Dec. 15**    Photo.    Unwmk.
478 A259 20p vio bl & car rose    1.75 .75
400th anniv. of Cochin Synagogue.

Frigate Nilgiri A260

**1968, Dec. 15**    Perf. 13½x13
479 A260 20p dull violet blue    3.50 .60
Navy Day. The Nilgiri, launched Oct. 23, 1968, was the 1st Indian warship.

Redbilled Blue Magpie A261

Birds: 50p, Brown-fronted pied woodpecker. 1r, Slaty-headed scimitar babbler, vert. 2r, Yellow-backed sunbirds.

**1968, Dec. 31**   Perf. 14½x14, 14x14½
480 A261 20p pink & multi    1.50 .70
481 A261 50p multicolored    2.00 2.25
482 A261   1r multicolored    3.50 1.40
483 A261   2r multicolored    3.00 2.00
   Nos. 480-483 (4)    10.00 6.35

Chatterjee (1838-94) A262

Dr. Bhagavan Das A263

**1969, Jan. 1**    Perf. 13½
484 A262 20p ultramarine    .50 .50
Bankim Chandra Chatterjee, writer.

**1969, Jan. 12**    Photo.    Perf. 13½
485 A263 20p red brown    .50 .50
Das (1869-1958), philosopher.

Martin Luther King, Jr. (1929-1968), American Civil Rights Leader — A264

**1969, Jan. 25**
486 A264 20p olive gray    .90 .35

Mirza Ghalib A265

**1969, Feb. 17**    Perf. 14½x14
487 A265 20p dk gray & salmon    .50 .50
Mirza Ghalib (Asad Ullah Beg Khan 1797-1869), poet who modernized the Urdu language.

Osmania University, Hyderabad, 50th Avviv. A266

**1969, Mar. 15**   Photo.   Perf. 14½x14
488 A266 20p green    .50 .50

Rafi Ahmed Kidwai A267

**1969, Apr. 1**    Perf. 13
489 A267 20p grayish blue    2.25 .75
Minister of communications and food, introduced around-the-clock airmail service.

ILO Emblems A268

**1969, Apr. 11**    Perf. 14½x14
490 A268 20p orange brown    .50 .50
50th anniv. of the ILO.

Memorial Monument and Hands Strewing Flowers — A269

**1969, Apr. 13**    Perf. 13½
491 A269 20p rose carmine    .50 .50
50th anniv. of Jallianwala Bagh, Amritsar, massacre.

Nageswara Rao (1867-1938), Journalist and Congressman A270

**1969, May 1**    Photo.    Perf. 13½x14
492 A270 20p brown    .50 .50

Ardaseer Cursetjee Wadia and Ships A271

**1969, May 27   Photo.   Perf. 14½x14**
493  A271  20p blue green          1.00   .75
Wadia (1808-1877), shipbuilder.

Serampore College, 150th Anniv. — A272

**1969, June 7   Photo.   Perf. 13½**
494  A272  20p violet brown         .50   .50

Dr. Zakir Husain (1897-1969), President of India 1967-1969 A273

**1969, June 11         Perf. 13**
495  A273  20p olive gray           .50   .50

Laxmanrao Kirloskar and Plow A274

**1969, June 20**
496  A274  20p gray                 .50   .50
Kirloskar (1869-1956), industrialist and social reformer, introduced the iron plow to India.

Mahatma Gandhi (1869-1948) A275

Gandhi on the Dandi March A276

20p, Gandhi and his wife Kasturba, horiz.
5r, Gandhi with spinning wheel, horiz.

**1969, Oct. 2   Photo.   Unwmk.**
**Size: 29x25mm**
**Perf. 13½**
497  A275  20p sepia               1.00   .80
**Size: 28x38mm**
**Perf. 13**
498  A275  75p ol gray, sal &
            brn                     2.40   .30
**Size: 20x38mm**
**Perf. 14x14½**
499  A276  1r bright blue          2.40  2.00
**Size: 35½x25½mm**
**Perf. 13**
500  A275  5r orange & sepia       8.00  7.00
      *Nos. 497-500 (4)*          13.80 10.10

Freighter and IMCO Emblem A277

**1969, Oct. 14         Perf. 13**
501  A277  20p ultramarine         3.50   .70
10th anniv. of the Intergovernmental Maritime Consultative Organization.

Globe and Parliament, New Delhi A278

**1969, Oct. 30   Photo.   Perf. 14½x14**
502  A278  20p bright blue          .50   .50
57th Interparliamentary Conf., New Delhi.

Astronaut on Moon — A279

Nanak Mausoleum, Talwandi, Punjab — A280

**1969, Nov. 19         Perf. 14x14½**
503  A279  20p olive brown         1.00   .60
See note after US No. C76.

**1969, Nov. 23   Photo.   Perf. 13½**
504  A280  20p gray violet          .50   .50
500th anniv. of the birth of the Guru Nanak, Sikh leader.

Tiger and Globe A281

**1969, Nov. 24         Perf. 14½x14**
505  A281  20p olive grn & red brn 1.10   .65
Intl. Union for the Conservation of Nature and Natural Resources.

T. L. Vaswani A282

Thakkar Bapa A283

**1969, Nov. 25         Perf. 14x14½**
506  A282  20p dark gray            .50   .50
T. L. Vaswani (1879-1966), writer and orator.

**1969, Nov. 29         Perf. 13½**
507  A283  20p dark brown           .50   .50
Thakkar Bapa (1869-1951), statesman who worked to help the untouchables.

Globe and Telecommunications Symbols — A284

**1970, Jan. 21         Perf. 13**
508  A284  20p Prussian blue        .50   .25
12th Plenary Assembly of the Intl. Radio Consultative Committee.

C. N. Annadurai (1909-1969), Journalist — A285

Munshi Newal Kishore and Printing Plant — A286

**1970, Feb. 2**
509  A285  20p dk blue & magenta   .50   .50

**1970, Feb. 19   Photo.   Perf. 13x13½**
510  A286  20p dark carmine        .50   .50
Kishore (1836-1895), publisher.

Cent. of Nalanda College A287

**1970, Mar. 27   Photo.   Perf. 14½x14**
511  A287  20p light red brown     .80   .45

Swami Shraddhanand (1856-1926), Patriot — A288

**1970, Mar. 30         Perf. 13½**
512  A288  20p orange brown       1.00   .50

Lenin A289

**1970, Apr. 22   Photo.   Perf. 13**
513  A289  20p multicolored        .80   .30

UPU Headquarters, Bern — A290

**1970, May 20**
514  A290  20p black & green        .50   .50
New UPU Headquarters in Bern.

Sher Shah Suri — A291

**1970, May 22   Photo.   Perf. 13**
515  A291  20p blue green           .50   .50
Suri, 15th cent. ruler of Delhi and postal service reformer.

Vir D. Savarkar and Prison at Port Blair, Andamans A292

**1970, May 28**
516  A292  20p orange brown        1.00  1.00
V. D. Savarkar (1883-1966), patriot.

"UN" and UN Emblem — A293

**1970, June 26   Photo.   Perf. 13**
517  A293  20p blue                .60   .35
25th anniv. of the UN.

Harvest, Crane, Factory and Emblem A294

**1970, Aug. 18         Perf. 14½x14**
518  A294  20p violet              .50   .40
Asian Productivity Year.

Dr. Maria Montessori and Education Symbol A295

**1970, Aug. 31         Perf. 13½x13**
519  A295  20p dull claret         .60   .50
Intl. Education Year and Maria Montessori (1870-1952), Italian educator and physician.

Jatindra Nath Mukherjee A296

**1970, Sept. 9**     **Perf. 14½x14**
520 A296 20p dark red brown   2.75   .80
Mukherjee (1879-1915), revolutionary leader.

Srinivasa Sastri (1869-1946) A297

Iswar Chandra Vidyasagar A298

**1970, Sept. 22**    **Photo.**    **Perf. 13**
521 A297 20p dk brown & ocher   .60   .50
V. S. Srinivasa Sastri, statesman.

**1970, Sept. 26**
522 A298 20p rose lilac & brown   .75   .65
Vidyasagar (1820-91), educator and writer.

Maharishi Valmiki (born c. 1400 B.C.), Poet A299

**1970, Oct. 14**    **Photo.**    **Perf. 13**
523 A299 20p plum      .80   .40

Calcutta Harbor A300

**1970, Oct. 17**
524 A300 20p blue     3.00 1.25
Cent. of Calcutta Port Commissioners.

Jamia Millia Islamia University, 50th Anniv. A301

**1970, Oct. 29**     **Perf. 14½x14**
525 A301 20p yellow green   1.10   .90

Jamnalal Bajai (1889-1942), Patriot — A302

**1970, Nov. 4**    **Wmk. 324**    **Perf. 13**
526 A302 20p sepia      .50   .40

Nurse and Patient — A303

Ludwig van Beethoven A305

Sant Namdeo (1270-1350), Holy Man — A304

**1970, Nov. 5**
527 A303 20p Prus. blue & red   1.25   .65
50th anniv. of the Indian Red Cross Soc.

**1970, Nov. 9**        **Photo.**
528 A304 20p orange     .50   .50

**1970, Dec. 16**    **Unwmk.**    **Perf. 13**
529 A305 20p dk brn & org   3.75   .90

Children with Stamp Album A306

Design: 1r, Hands holding magnifying glass over Gandhi stamp.

**1970, Dec. 23**    **Photo.**    **Perf. 13**
530 A306 20p dull green & lt brn   .75   .35
531 A306 1r ocher & brown   5.00 1.25
INPEX 1970, Indian Natl. Phil. Exhib., New Delhi, Dec. 23, 1970-Jan. 6, 1971.

Girl Guide and Sign — A307

Hands Shielding Flame — A308

**1970, Dec. 27**
532 A307 20p dark brown violet   1.00   .40
Girl Guides, 60th anniv.

**1971, Jan. 11**
533 A308 20p bis brn & dp clar   .50   .40
Centenary of Indian Life Insurance.

Kashi Vidyapith, 50th Anniv. A309

**1971, Feb. 10**     **Perf. 14½x14**
534 A309 20p black brown   .50   .40
Kashi Vidyapith University, Benares.

Charles Freer Andrews (1871-1940), British Publicist, Friend of Gandhi — A310

**1971, Feb. 12**     **Perf. 13x13½**
535 A310 20p orange brown   .60   .45

Ravidas, 15th Cent. Poet and Holy Man A311

**1971, Feb.**       **Perf. 13**
536 A311 20p rose carmine   1.10   .60

Acharya Narendra Deo (1889-1956), Educator, Patriot, Statesman A312

**1971, Feb. 18**    **Photo.**    **Perf. 13**
537 A312 20p olive bister   .50   .50

Cent. of Indian Census A313

**1971, Mar. 10**
538 A313 20p ultra & sepia    .50   .40

Ramana Maharshi (1879-1950), Holy Man — A314

**1971, Apr. 14**    **Photo.**    **Perf. 13½x14**
539 A314 20p ol gray & orange   .60   .50

Raja Ravi Varma (1848-1906) and His Painting, Damayanti and the Swan — A315

**1971, Apr. 29**     **Perf. 13x13½**
540 A315 20p deep yellow green   .80   .65

Dadasaheb Phalke, Movie Camera A316

**1971, Apr. 30**     **Perf. 13½x13**
541 A316 20p violet brown   1.25   .60
Dadasaheb Phalke (1870-1944), motion picture pioneer.

Abhisarika, by Abanindranath Tagore A317

Swami Virjanand A318

**1971, Aug. 7**   **Unwmk.**   **Perf. 14x14½**
542 A317 20p dark brn & ocher   .60   .50
Tagore (1871-1951), painter.

**1971, Sept. 14**     **Perf. 14x13½**
543 A318 20p orange brown   .60   .50
Virjanand (1778-1868), scholar and sage.

Scuptures and Stairway, Persepolis Palace A319

**1971, Oct. 12**       **Perf. 13**
544 A319 20p sepia     1.25   .70
2500th anniv. of the founding of the Persian empire by Cyrus the Great.

World Thrift Day A320

**1971, Oct. 31**     **Perf. 14½x14**
545 A320 20p dark violet blue   .50   .40

Bodhisatva Padampani, from Ajanta Cave — A321

Girls at Work, by Geeta Gupta — A322

**1971, Nov. 4**  *Perf. 13*
546 A321 20p brown   3.00 .90
25th anniv. of UNESCO.

**1971, Nov. 14**  *Perf. 14x14½*
547 A322 20p salmon pink   .50 .50
Chidren's Day.

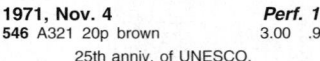

C. V. Raman A323

**1971, Nov. 21**  *Perf. 13*
548 A323 20p brown & dp org   1.00 .55
Sir Chandrasekhara Venkata Raman (1888-1970), physicist, Nobel Prize winner.

Rabindranath Tagore, Visva-Bharati Building — A324

**1971, Dec. 24**  *Perf. 14½x14*
549 A324 20p blk brn & org brn   1.00 .80
50th anniv. of Visva-Bharati, center for Eastern cultural studies.

Indian Cricket Victories A325

**1971, Dec. 24**
550 A325 20p green   4.50 1.10

Intelsat 3 over Map of Eastern Hemisphere A326

**1972, Feb. 26**  **Photo.**  *Perf. 13½*
551 A326 20p dark purple   .50 .40
Arvi Satellite Earth Station.

Plumb Line and Symbols — A327

Signal Panel and Route Diagram — A328

**1972, May 29**  **Photo.**  *Perf. 13*
552 A327 20p bluish gray & black   .50 .50
India's Bureau of Standards, 25th anniv.

**1972, June 30**
553 A328 20p black & multi   2.50 1.25
Intl. Railroad Union (UIC), 50th anniv.

Hockey, Olympic Rings A329

20th Olympic Games, Munich, Aug. 26-Sept. 11: 1.45r, "1972," Olympic rings, symbols for running, wrestling, shooting and hockey.

**1972, Aug. 10**  **Photo.**  *Perf. 13*
554 A329 20p dull violet   3.50 .35
555 A329 1.45r bl grn & dk red   4.00 3.00

Marchers with Flag, Parliament A330

**1972, Aug. 15**
556 A330 20p blue & multi   1.25 1.00
25th anniv. of Independence.

Armed Forces' Emblems — A331

**1972, Aug. 15**
557 A331 20p blue & multi   .75 .55
Honoring India's defense forces.

Symbol of Aurobindo and Sun — A332

**1972, Aug. 15**
558 A332 20p yellow & blue   .50 .50
Sri Aurobindo Ghose (1872-1950).

V.O. Chidambaram Pillai and Ship — A333

*Perf. 13½x13*
**1972, Sept. 5**  **Unwmk.**
559 A333 20p bl & dk red brn   1.50 .65
V.O. Chidambaram Pillai (1872-1936), founder of steamship company, trade union leader, resistance fighter.

Vemana, 17th-18th Cent. Poet — A334

Bertrand Russell — A335

**1972, Oct. 16**  **Wmk. 324**  *Perf. 14*
560 A334 20p black   .50 .50

**1972, Oct. 16**  **Unwmk.**
561 A335 1.45r black   6.25 4.00
British philosopher and pacifist (1872-1970).

Bhai Vir Singh — A336

T. Prakasam — A337

**1972, Oct. 16**  *Perf. 13½*
562 A336 20p dull purple   1.10 .45
Bhai Vir Singh (1872-1957), poet and scholar.

**1972, Oct. 16**
563 A337 20p yellow brown   .50 .40
T. Prakasam (1872-1957), national leader and lawyer.

Hand of Buddha, 9th Century Sculpture — A338

20p, Stylized Hand of Buddha as Fair emblem.

**1972, Nov. 3**  **Wmk. 324**  *Perf. 13*
564 A338 20p orange & black   .40 .40
565 A338 1.45r orange, blk & ind   1.00 *2.40*
3rd Asian Intl. Trade Fair, ASIA 72, New Delhi.

Vikram Ambalal Sarabhai, Rohini Rocket and Dove A339

**1972, Dec. 30**  **Unwmk.**
566 A339 20p slate grn & brn   .60 .60
1st anniv. of the death of Dr. Vikram Ambalal Sarabhai (1919-1971), chairman of Natl. Committee for Space Research.

Flag of USSR and Spasski Tower A340

**1972, Dec. 30**  *Perf. 13*
567 A340 20p red & yellow   .60 .60
50th anniv. of the Soviet Union.

INDIPEX 73 Emblem — A341

Wheel of Asoka, Naga (Serpent) — A342

India Gate, Gnat Planes, India's Colors A343

**1973, Jan. 8**  **Photo.**  *Perf. 13*
568 A341 1.45r black, pink & gold   .80 *1.40*
Intl. Phil. Exhib., New Delhi, 11/14-23/73. See Nos. 597-599.

**1973, Jan. 26**  *Perf. 13*
569 A342 20p orange & multi   .35 .35
*Perf. 14½x14*
570 A343 1.45r violet & multi   2.50 2.50
Republic Day, 25th year of Independence.

Ramakrishna Paramahamsa (1836-86) — A344

Army Postal
Service Corps
Emblem — A345

**1973, Feb. 18    Photo.    Perf. 13**
571  A344  20p yellow brown    .60    .50
  Hindu spiritual leader; Ramakrishna Mission founded by his followers.

**1973, Mar. 1**
572  A345  20p violet blue & red    .60    .60
  1st anniv. of establishment of Army Postal Service Corps.

Flower, Flag,
Map — A346

Kumaran
Asan — A347

**1973, Apr. 10    Unwmk.    Perf. 13**
573  A346  20p blue & multi    .60    .60
  1st anniv. of Bangladesh independence.

**1973, Apr. 12**
574  A347  20p brown    .50    .50
  Kumaran Asan (1873-1924), Kerala social reformer and writer.

Flame and Flag of
India — A348

**1973, Apr. 13**
575  A348  20p deep blue & multi    .50    .50
  In honor of the martyrs of the massacre of Jallianwala Bagh, Apr. 13, 1919.

B. R.
Ambedkar
and
Parliament
Building
A349

**1973, Apr. 14    Perf. 14½x14**
576  A349  20p olive & plum    .50    .50
  Bhimrao R. Ambedkar (1891-1956), lawyer, reformer of Hindu law and one of the writers of India's Constitution.

Radha-Kishangarh, by Nihal Chand,
1778 — A350

  Indian Miniatures: 50p, Dancing Couple, late 17th century. 1r, Lovers on a Camel, by Nasir-ud-Din, c. 1605. 2r, Chained Elephant, by Zain-al-Abidin, 16th century.

**1973, May 5    Photo.    Perf. 13½x13**
577  A350  20p gold & multi    .55    .55
578  A350  50p lilac & multi    1.25    2.00
579  A350  1r ocher & multi    1.60    1.60
580  A350  2r gold & multi    2.25    3.25
    Nos. 577-580 (4)    5.65    7.40

Himalayas
A351

**1973, May 15    Perf. 13½x13**
581  A351  20p blue    .80    .65
  15th anniv. of Indian Mountaineering Foundation.

Air India
Jet — A352

**1973, June 8    Photo.    Perf. 13**
582  A352  1.45r multicolored    7.00    5.50
  Air India, 25 years of intl. service.

Stone Cross on
St. Thomas's
Mount,
Madras — A353

Michael
Madhusudan
Dutt — A354

**1973, July 3**
583  A353  20p gray ol & blue gray    .50    .50
  1900th anniv. of the death of St. Thomas.

**1973, July 21    Photo.    Perf. 13**
584  A354  20p ocher & olive    1.60    .80
  Dutt (1824-1873), writer and poet.

Vishnu Dingambar Paluskar (1872-
1931), Musician — A355

**1973, July 21**
585  A355  30p red brown    2.00    2.00

Dr. Armauer
G. Hansen,
Microscope,
Petri Dish
with Bacilli
A356

**1973, July 21**
586  A356  50p deep brown    2.40    2.00
  Cent. of the discovery by Hansen of the Hansen bacillus, the cause of leprosy.

Nicolaus
Copernicus,
Heliocentric
System
A357

**1973, July 21**
587  A357  1r vio blue & red brown    2.40    2.00
  500th anniv. of the birth of Nicolaus Copernicus (1473-1543), Polish astronomer.

Allan Octavian
Hume (1829-1912)
A358

**1973, July 31**
588  A358  20p gray    .50    .50
  Hume, British civil servant and friend of India, on the 25th anniv. of independence.

Nehru and
Gandhi
A359

**1973, Aug. 15    Photo.    Perf. 13**
589  A359  20p blue vio & red
        brown    .50    .50
  25th anniv. of India's independence.

Romesh Chunder
Dutt — A360

Ranjit
Sinhji — A361

Vithalbhai Patel
(1873-1933),
National
Leader — A362

**1973, Sept. 27    Photo.    Perf. 13**
590  A360  20p brown    .50    .50
591  A361  30p dark green    6.25    6.25
592  A362  50p brown    .50    .50
    Nos. 590-592 (3)    7.25    7.25
  Birth anniv.: Dutt (1848-1909), economist and pres. of Natl. Cong. in 1890; Sinhji, Maharaja of Nawanagar (1872-1933), cricketer.

President's Body
Guard — A363

**1973, Sept. 30**
593  A363  20p multicolored    2.25    1.50
  Bicentenary of President's Body Guard.

INTERPOL
Emblem — A364

**1973, Oct. 9    Photo.    Perf. 13**
594  A364  20p brown    .70    .70
  50th anniv. of Intl. Criminal Police Org.

Syed
Ahmad
Khan,
Aligarh
University
A365

**1973, Oct. 17**
595  A365  20p olive gray    .50    1.00
  Khan (1817-1898), founder of Aligarh Muslim Univ.

Child's
Drawing
A366

**1973, Nov. 14    Photo.    Perf. 13**
596  A366  20p multicolored    .50    .50
  Children's Day.

Elephant with Howdah, and No. 200 — A367

**1973, Nov. 14**
| | | | | |
|---|---|---|---|---|
| 597 | A367 | 20p Emblem | .25 | .25 |
| 598 | A367 | 1r shown | 1.50 | 1.10 |
| 599 | A367 | 2r Peacock, vert. | 1.75 | 1.75 |
| *a.* | | Souvenir sheet of 4 | 7.50 | 7.50 |
| | | Nos. 597-599 (3) | 3.50 | 3.10 |

Intl. Phil. Exhib., INDIPEX 73, New Delhi, Nov. 14-23. No. 599a contains 4 imperf. stamps similar to Nos. 568, 597-599. The imperf. stamps from No. 599a were not valid individually.

NCC Emblem — A368

Rajagopalachari A369

**1973, Nov. 25**
| | | | | |
|---|---|---|---|---|
| 600 | A368 | 20p multicolored | .50 | .40 |

National Cadet Corps, 25th anniv.

**1973, Dec. 25**
| | | | | |
|---|---|---|---|---|
| 601 | A369 | 20p gray olive | .50 | .50 |

Chakravarti Rajagopalachari (1878-1972), statesman, governor general (1948-50).

Sun Mask — A370

Narasimha Mask — A371

Designs: Masks.

**1974, Apr. 15   Photo.   Perf. 13**
| | | | | |
|---|---|---|---|---|
| 602 | A370 | 20p shown | .30 | .30 |
| 603 | A370 | 50p Moon | .50 | .40 |
| 604 | A371 | 1r shown | .90 | .70 |
| 605 | A371 | 2r Ravana, horiz. | 1.10 | 1.40 |
| *a.* | | Souvenir sheet of 4, #602-605 | 3.75 | 3.75 |
| | | Nos. 602-605 (4) | 2.80 | 2.80 |

300th Anniv. of the Coronation of Chatrapati Sivaji Maharaj (1627-1680), Military Leader of the Maharattas and Enlightened Ruler — A372

**1974, June 2   Photo.   Perf. 13**
| | | | | |
|---|---|---|---|---|
| 606 | A372 | 25p gold & multi | 1.25 | .90 |

Maithili Sharan Gupta — A373

Utkal Gourab Madhusudan Das — A374

Kandukuri Veeresalingam A375

Tipu Sultan — A376

No. 608, Jainarain Vyas. 1r, Max Mueller.

**1974   Photo.   Perf. 13**
| | | | | |
|---|---|---|---|---|
| 607 | A373 | 25p red brown | .30 | .35 |
| 608 | A373 | 25p brown | .30 | .35 |
| 609 | A374 | 25p olive gray | .30 | .35 |
| 610 | A375 | 25p red brown | .45 | .50 |
| 611 | A376 | 50p violet brown | .95 | 1.25 |
| 612 | A376 | 1r brown | 1.10 | 1.25 |
| | | Nos. 607-612 (6) | 3.40 | 4.05 |

Gupta (1886-1964), poet and patriot; Vyas (1899-1963), writer and member of parliament; Das (1848-1934), writer and patriot. Veeresalingam (1848-1919), reformer; Sultan (1750-99), military leader and reformer; Mueller (1823-1900), German scholar of Sanskrit and Indian culture.
Issued: #607-609, 7/3; #610-612, 7/15.

Kamala Nehru — A377

**1974, Aug 1   Photo.   Perf. 14½x14**
| | | | | |
|---|---|---|---|---|
| 613 | A377 | 25p multicolored | 1.25 | 1.10 |

Kamala Nehru (1899-1936), champion of India's freedom, mother of Indira Gandhi.

WPY Emblem — A378

V. V. Giri — A379

**1974, Aug. 14   Unwmk.   Perf. 13½**
| | | | | |
|---|---|---|---|---|
| 614 | A378 | 25p buff & plum | .50 | .40 |

**1974, Aug. 24   Perf. 13x13½**
| | | | | |
|---|---|---|---|---|
| 615 | A379 | 25p green & multi | .50 | .50 |

Vaharagiri Venkata Giri, pres. of India, 1969-74.

Type of 1965-68 and

Tiger — A380

Veena A381

Design: 25p, Axis deer (chital).

**1974   Wmk. 324   Perf. 14½x14**
| | | | | |
|---|---|---|---|---|
| 622 | A380 | 15p dk brn (white "15") | 4.00 | .75 |
| 623 | A202 | 25p brown | 1.25 | 1.00 |
| 624 | A381 | 1r black & brown | 3.00 | .25 |
| | | Nos. 622-624 (3) | 8.25 | 2.00 |

Issue dates: 25p, Aug. 20; 15p, 1r, Oct. 1. See Nos. 671-682.

Madhubani Folk Design, UPU Emblem A384

Designs: 25p, UPU emblem. 2r, Arrows circling globe, UPU emblem, vert.

**1974, Oct. 3   Unwmk.   Perf. 13**
| | | | | |
|---|---|---|---|---|
| 634 | A384 | 25p brt blue & gray | .85 | .30 |
| 635 | A384 | 1r olive & multi | 1.25 | .85 |
| 636 | A384 | 2r ocher & multi | 2.00 | 1.90 |
| *a.* | | Souvenir sheet of 3, #634-636 | 10.00 | 10.00 |
| | | Nos. 634-636 (3) | 4.10 | 3.05 |

Cent. of UPU.

A385

**1974, Oct. 9   Photo.   Perf. 13½**
| | | | | |
|---|---|---|---|---|
| 637 | | 25p Flute player | .60 | .50 |
| 638 | | 25p Vidyadhara with garland | .60 | .50 |
| *a.* | A385 | Pair, #637-638 | 2.00 | 2.00 |

Cent. of Mathura Museum.

Nicholas Konstantin Roerich, by Henry Dropsy A387

**1974, Oct. 9   Perf. 13**
| | | | | |
|---|---|---|---|---|
| 639 | A387 | 1r dark gray & yellow | 1.00 | .80 |

Roerich (1874-1947), Russian painter and sponsor of Roerich Peace Pact.

Pavapuri Temple, Bihar A388

**1974, Nov. 13   Photo.   Perf. 13**
| | | | | |
|---|---|---|---|---|
| 640 | A388 | 25p slate | .80 | .25 |

2500th anniv. of attainment of Nirvana by Bhagwan Mahavira, leader and preacher of Jainism.

Dancers and Musician (Child's Drawing) A389

**1974, Nov. 14   Perf. 14½x14**
| | | | | |
|---|---|---|---|---|
| 641 | A389 | 25p multicolored | .80 | .55 |

UNICEF in India.

Cat (Child's Drawing) — A390

**1974, Nov. 14   Perf. 13**
| | | | | |
|---|---|---|---|---|
| 642 | A390 | 25p multicolored | .80 | .40 |

Children's Day.

Territorial Army Emblem — A391

**1974, Nov. 16** *Perf. 13*
643 A391 25p green, yel & black 1.10 .60
Territorial Army, 25th anniv.

Cows, from Handpainted Rajasthan Cloth — A392

**1974, Dec. 2** *Perf. 14*
644 A392 25p ocher & maroon .60 .35
19th Intl. Dairy Cong., New Delhi, Dec. 2-6.

Symbol of Retardates and Child A393

**1974, Dec. 8 Photo.** *Perf. 13½x13*
645 A393 25p black & vermilion .90 .65
Help the Retardates!

Guglielmo Marconi — A394

**1974, Dec. 12** *Perf. 13x13½*
646 A394 2r slate 4.50 3.00
Marconi (1874-1937), Italian electrical engineer and inventor.

St. Francis Xavier's Tomb and Statue A395

**1974, Dec. 24** *Perf. 13½x13*
647 A395 25p multicolored .50 .50
Showing of the body of St. Francis Xavier, Apostle to the Indies.

Saraswati, Goddess of Language and Learning, Inscription in Hindi — A396

**1975, Jan. 10 Photo.** *Perf. 14x14½*
648 A396 25p dark red & gray .70 .60
World Hindi Convention, Nagpur, Jan. 10-14. See No. 654.

Parliament House A397

**1975, Jan. 26** *Perf. 13*
649 A397 25p black, blue & silver 1.25 .95
Republic of India, 25th anniv.

Table Tennis Paddle and Ball — A398

**1975, Feb. 6** *Perf. 13½x13*
650 A398 25p black, red & olive 1.50 .55
33rd World Table Tennis Championship, Calcutta.

Woman's Hands Releasing Doves A399

**1975, Feb. 16**
651 A399 25p yellow & multi 1.10 .55
International Women's Year.

Bicentenary of Army Ordnance Corps — A400

**1975, Apr. 8 Photo.** *Perf. 13x13½*
652 A400 25p black & vermilion 2.25 1.10

Flame A401

**1975, Apr. 11** *Perf. 13½x13*
653 A401 25p orange & black .60 .50
Cent. of the founding of Arya Samaj, a movement dedicated to enlightenment and progress and to a revival of Vedic Law and Aryan culture.

**Saraswati Type of 1975**

25p, Saraswati and inscription in Telugu.

**1975, Apr. 12** *Perf. 14x14½*
654 A396 25p dp green & dk gray .80 .45
World Telugu Conf., Hyderabad, Apr. 12-18.

Aryabhata Satellite A402

**1975, Apr. 20** *Perf. 13½x13*
655 A402 25p multicolored 1.25 .85
Launching of 1st Indian satellite, Apr. 19, 1975.

Bluewinged Pitta A403

Birds: 50p, Black-headed oriole. 1r, Western tragopan, vert. 2r, Himalayan monal pheasant, vert.

**1975, Apr. 28** *Perf. 13½x13, 13x13½*
656 A403 25p multicolored .95 .30
657 A403 50p multicolored 2.25 2.25
658 A403 1r multicolored 3.25 3.25
659 A403 2r multicolored 4.50 4.50
Nos. 656-659 (4) 10.95 10.30

Quotation from Ram Charit Manas A404

**1975, May 24 Photo.** *Perf. 13½x13*
660 A404 25p red, orange & black 1.00 .25
Ram Charit Manas, Hindi poem by Goswami Tulsidas (1532-1623).

Women and YWCA Emblem — A405

**1975, June 20 Photo.** *Perf. 13x13½*
661 A405 25p gray & multi .60 .50
YWCA of India, cent.

Creation of Adam, by Michelangelo — A406

Design: Nos. 664-665, Creation of sun, moon and stars, by Michelangelo.

**1975, June 28** *Perf. 14x13½*
662 50p multicolored .65 .50
663 50p multicolored 1.25 1.00
a. A406 Pair #662-663 2.75 2.75
664 50p multicolored 1.25 1.00
665 50p multicolored 1.25 1.00
a. Block of 4, #662-665 4.50 4.50
b. A406 Pair #664-665 2.75 2.75
Michelangelo Buonarroti (1475-1564), Italian sculptor, painter and architect.

**Types of 1965-1974 Without Currency Designation and**

Flying Crane — A408

Jawaharlal Nehru — A409

Mahatma Gandhi — A410

Himalayas A411

Designs: 2p, Bidri vase. 5p, Family. 10p, Electric locomotive. 15p, Tiger. 20p, Wooden toy horse. 30p, Male and female figurines. 60p, Somnath Temple. 1r, Veena. 5r, Bhakra Dam, Punjab. 10r, Trombay Atomic Center.

*Perf. 14½x14, 14x14½, 14 (#674-676), 11½x12 (#681)*
Wmk. 324; 360 (# 666A, 667, 668, 670)

**1975-88** Photo.
Three types of 25p Nehru:
Type I: Size at top, 25mm. Character before NEHRU has 2 lower points.
Type II: Smaller portrait. Size at top, 23mm. Character has 3 points.
Type III: Portrait as in type I. Size at top, 25½mm. Character has 3 points.

666 A202 2(p) redsh brn, wmk. 324('76) 1.00 2.25
666A A202 2(p) redsh brn, wmk. 360('76) 1.00 2.25
667 A202 2(p) redsh brn, wmk. 360, litho ('79) 1.00 2.25
668 A202 5(p) cerise ('76) .60 .20
669 A203 10(p) brt blue ('76) .60 .20
670 A203 10(p) brt blue ('79) 3.25 .60
671 A380 15(p) dk brn (brown "15") 1.50 .20
672 A408 20(p) green .30 .20
673 A409 25(p) vio, I ('76) 8.00 .75
674 A409 25(p) vio, II ('76) 5.00 .75
675 A409 25(p) vio, III ('76) 4.00 .75
676 A410 25(p) red brn ('76) (23x29mm) 1.00 .30
677 A410 25(p) red brn ('78) (17x20mm) 6.50 2.25
678 A202 30(p) brown ('79) 3.25 .50
679 A408 50(p) violet blue 5.00 .30
680 A202 60(p) dk gray ('76) 1.50 1.00
681 A410 60(p) black ('88) .85 .25
682 A381 1(r) brown & blk 3.25 .25
683 A411 2(r) violet & brn 14.00 .50
684 A205 5(r) brn & vio ('76) 2.00 .90
685 A205 10(r) dl grn & sl ('76) 1.75 1.10
Nos. 666-685 (21) 65.35 17.75
No. 667 has a background of fine horizontal lines.
See #841-842, 844-845, 846A-846B, 916.
Size of No. 681, 17x20mm.

Irrigation Commission Emblem — A412

"Educational Television" A413

**Unwmk.**
**1975, July 28      Photo.      *Perf. 14***
686  A412  25p multicolored              .80   .30

9th Intl. Cong. on Irrigation and Drainage, Moscow, and 25th anniv. of the Intl. Commission on Irrigation and Drainage.

**1975, Aug. 1                 *Perf. 13x13½***
687  A413  25p multicolored              .80   .45

Inauguration of the Satellite Instructional Television Experiment (SITE).

Arunagirinathar
A414

**1975, Aug. 14     Photo.      *Perf. 13½***
688  A414  50p rose lilac               2.50  1.25

600th birth anniv. of Arunagirinathar, Advaita philosopher, saint and author of Tiruppugazh, a collection of songs.

A415

**1975, Aug. 26     Photo.      *Perf. 13½***
689  A415  25p rose & black             .80   .55

Namibia Day. See note after UN No. 241.

A416

**1975, Sept. 4**
690  A416  25p slate green              .50   .50

Mir Anees (1803-1874), Urdu poet.

Chhatri at
Maheshwar
A417

**1975, Sept. 4                *Perf. 13x13½***
691  A417  25p red brown               .50   .50

Queen Ahilyabai Holkar (1725-1795); building shown was place of last rites.

Bharata Natyam
Dance — A418

**1975, Oct. 20     Photo.      *Perf. 13x13½***

Designs: Indian traditional dances.

| 692 | A418 | 25p shown      | .95   | .65  |
|-----|------|----------------|-------|------|
| 693 | A418 | 50p Orissi     | 1.40  | .70  |
| 694 | A418 | 75p Kathak     | 1.90  | .90  |
| 695 | A418 | 1r Kathakali   | 2.25  | 1.10 |
| 696 | A418 | 1.50r Kuchipudi| 2.75  | 1.60 |
| 697 | A418 | 2r Manipuri    | 2.75  | 1.60 |
|     |      | *Nos. 692-697 (6)* | 12.00 | 6.55 |

Krishna
Menon — A419

Ameer
Khusrau — A420

Poem by
Bahadur
Shah Zafar
A421

Design: No. 699, Sardar Vallabhbhai Patel.

**1975                    *Perf. 13x13½, 13½x13***
| 698 | A419 | 25p olive            | 1.40 | .70  |
|-----|------|----------------------|------|------|
| 699 | A419 | 25p slate            | .50  | .50  |
| 700 | A420 | 50p yellow & brown   | 1.60 | .80  |
| 701 | A421 | 1r black, brn & buff | 2.00 | 1.00 |
|     |      | *Nos. 698-701 (4)*   | 5.50 | 3.00 |

Men of India: V. K. Krishna Menon (1896-1974), founder of India League and member of Parliament; Patel (1875-1950), statesman who unified India, birth cent.; Khusrau (1253-1325), poet; Zafar (1775-1862), last Mogul emperor and poet.
Issue dates: #699, Oct. 31; others Oct. 24.

Parliament
Annex,
New Delhi
A422

**1975, Oct. 28               *Perf. 14½x14***
702  A422  2r gray olive             3.00  1.60

21st Commonwealth Parliamentary Conf., New Delhi, Oct. 28-Nov. 4.

Karmavir Nabin
Chandra Bardoloi
(1875-1936),
Writer and Gandhi
Associate — A423

**1975, Nov. 3      Photo.      *Perf. 13***
703  A423  25p reddish brown          .50   .35

Cow, Child's
Painting
A424

**1975, Nov. 14**
704  A424  25p multicolored          1.00  .55

Children's Day.

Security
Press
Building
A425

**1975, Dec. 13     Photo.      *Perf. 13***
705  A425  25p multicolored          .70   .35

India Security Press, 50th anniv.

Gurdwara Sisganj,
Chandni
Chawk — A426

Theosophical
Society
Emblem — A427

**1975, Dec. 16**
706  A426  25p multicolored          .80   .50

300th anniv. of martyrdom of Tegh Bahadur (1621-75), 9th Sikh Guru; building shown was place of beheading.

**1975, Dec. 20**
707  A427  25p multicolored          .70   .35

Centenary of Theosophical Society.

Meteorological
Instruments
A428

Indian Bishop
Mark,
1775 — A430

**1975, Dec. 24     Photo.      *Perf. 13***
708  A428  25p blue vio, blk & grn  1.00  .55

Indian Meteorological Dept., cent.

Early Mail
Cart
A429

**1975, Dec. 25**
| 709 | A429 | 25p brown & black     | 1.00 | .40  |
|-----|------|-----------------------|------|------|
| 710 | A430 | 2r reddish brn & blk  | 3.25 | 1.75 |

INPEX 75, Indian Natl. Phil. Exhib., Calcutta, Dec. 25-31.

Lalit Narayan
Mishra — A431

**1975, Dec. 13      Photo.      *Perf. 13***

Tiger — A432

**1976, Jan. 3**
711  A431  25p sepia                .60   .30

Mishra (1923-75), Minister of Railroads.

**1976, Jan. 24**
712  A432  25p multicolored        1.75  .90

Jim Corbett (1875-1955), conservationist.

Painted
Storks
A433

**1976, Feb. 10     Photo.      *Perf. 13***
713  A433  25p sky blue & multi    1.75  .85

Keoladeo Ghana, Bharatpur Water Bird Sanctuary.

Tank
A434

**1976, Mar. 4      Photo.      *Perf. 13***
714  A434  25p multicolored        2.75  .55

16th Light Cavalry, senior regiment of Armoured Corps, bicentenary.

Alexander Graham
Bell — A435

**1976, Mar. 10  Photo.   *Perf. 13x13½***
715  A435  25p yellow & black      1.60  .90

Cent. of 1st telephone call by Bell, Mar. 10, 1876.

Muthuswami
Dikshitar — A436

**1976, Mar. 18               *Perf. 14x13½***
716  A436  25p dull violet        1.00  .55

Dikshitar (1775-1835), musician, composer.

Eye and
Red Cross
A437

**1976, Apr. 7**          *Perf. 13½x13*
717 A437 25p dark brown & red    1.40    .55
World Health Day: "Foresight prevents blindness."

"Industries"
A438

*Perf. 13x13½*
**1976, Apr. 30**          **Unwmk.**
718 A438 25p multicolored    .40    .25
Industrial development and progress.

1 F/I type,
Ajmer,
1895
A439

Locomotives: 25p, WDM 2 Diesel Locomotive, 1963. 1r, 1 WP./1, 4-6-2 Pacific type, 1963. 2r, 1 GIP No. 1, 1853.

**1976, May 15**          *Perf. 15x14*
719 A439 25p multicolored    1.10    .25
720 A439 50p multicolored    1.75    .80
721 A439 1r multicolored     4.00   1.90
722 A439 2r multicolored     4.75   2.10
    Nos. 719-722 (4)        11.60   5.05

Kumaraswamy
Kamaraj (1903-
1975),
Independence
Fighter — A440

**1976, July 15  Photo.  *Perf. 13½x13***
723 A440 25p sepia    .50    .50

Target, Olympic
Rings — A441

Hockey — A442

**1976, July 17**          *Perf. 14*
724 A441  25p dk blue & carmine    .40    .30
725 A441  1r "Team handball"    1.60    .80

726 A442 1.50r black & brt purple    2.75   1.60
727 A441 2.80r "Running"    2.75   2.75
    Nos. 724-727 (4)    7.50   5.45
21st Olympic Games, Montreal, Canada,
July 17-Aug. 1. .

Subhadra Kumari
Chauhan — A443

Param Vir Chakra
Medal — A444

**1976, Aug. 6  Photo.  *Perf. 13x13½***
728 A443 25p grayish blue    .50    .50
Chauhan (1904-1948), Hindi poetess and
member of Legislative Assembly.

**1976, Aug. 15**
729 A444 25p yellow & multi    .50    .50
Medal of Honor awarded for bravery to military men.

Women's
University,
Bombay
A445

**1976, Sept. 3  Photo.  *Perf. 13½x14***
730 A445 25p violet    .50    .30
Indian Women's Univ., 60th anniv.

Bharatendu
Harishchandra
A446

**1976, Sept. 9**          *Perf. 13*
731 A446 25p black brown    .50    .50
Harishchandra (1850-1885), writer, "Father
of Modern Hindi."

Sarat Chandra
Chatterji — A447

**1976, Sept. 15**          **Unwmk.**
732 A447 25p dull purple    .50    .50
Chatterji (1876-1938), writer.

Family
Planning — A448

**1976, Sept. 22  Photo.  *Perf. 14x14½***
733 A448 25p multicolored    .50    .50

Maharaja
Agrasen,
Coin and
Brick Wall
A449

**1976, Sept. 24**          *Perf. 13½x13*
734 A449 25p red brown    .50    .50
Maharaja Agrasen, legendary ruler of Agra.

India Blood
Donation
Day — A450

Wildlife
Protection
A451

**1976, Oct. 1**          *Perf. 13x13½*
735 A450 25p bister, car & black    1.40    .70

**1976, Oct. 1    *Perf. 14x14½, 14½x14***
736 A451  25p Swamp deer    .70    .35
737 A451  50p Lion    1.90    .95
738 A451  1r Leopard, horiz.    2.75   1.25
739 A451  2r Caracal, horiz.    3.00   1.50
    Nos. 736-739 (4)    8.35   4.05

Suryakant Tripathi
"Nirala" (1896-
1961), Hindi
poet — A452

**1976, Oct. 15**          *Perf. 13*
740 A452 25p dark violet    .50    .50

Children's
Day — A453

**1976, Nov. 14    Unwmk.    *Perf. 14***
741 A453 25p Mongoose and Woman    .60    .30

Hiralal
Shastri — A454

Hari Singh
Gour — A455

**1976, Nov. 24**          *Perf. 13*
742 A454 25p red brown    .50    .50
Hiralal Shastri (1899-1974), social worker
and political leader.

**1976, Nov. 26**
743 A455 25p plum    .50    .50
Hari Singh Gour (1870-1949), University
administrator, member Indian Legislative and
Constituent Assemblies.

Airbus
A456

**1976, Dec. 1**          *Perf. 14½x14*
744 A456 2r multicolored    4.00   2.10
Inauguration of Indian Airlines Airbus.

Hybrid Coconut
Palm — A457

**1976, Dec. 27  Photo.  *Perf. 13x13½***
745 A457 25p multicolored    .50    .40
75th anniv. of coconut research in India.

Vande
Mataram,
First Stanza
A458

**1976, Dec. 30**          *Perf. 13*
746 A458 25p multicolored    .50    .40
Vande Mataram, national song of India,
music by Bankim Chandra Chatterjee, 1896,
words by Rabindranath Tagore, 1911.

Film and
Globe
A459

**1977, Jan. 3**
747 A459 2r multicolored    2.50   1.25
6th Intl. Film Festival, New Delhi, Jan. 3-16.

Earth's Crust with Fault, Seismograph A460

**1977, Jan. 10**
748 A460 2r dull purple          1.75 1.40
6th World Conference on Earthquake Engineering, New Delhi, Jan. 10-14.

Tarun Ram Phookun — A461

**1977, Jan. 22   Photo.   Perf. 13x13½**
749 A461 25p sepia          .50 .50
Phookun (1877-1939), lawyer, Assam political leader.

Paramahansa Yogananda A462

**1977, Mar. 7   Photo.   Perf. 13½**
750 A462 25p deep orange          1.50 .80
Yogananda (1893-1952), religious leader, founder of Self-realization Society in America.

Red Cross Conference Emblem — A463

**1977, Mar. 9**
751 A463 2r multicolored          3.25 1.90
1st Asian Regional Red Cross Conference, New Delhi, Mar. 9-16.

**1977, Mar. 22   Photo.   Perf. 13½x13**
752 A464 25p multicolored          .60 .40
Ahmed, Pres. of India, 1974-77.

Asian-Oceanic Postal Union Emblem — A465

**1977, Apr. 1   Perf. 13**
753 A465 2r silver & multi          1.75 1.25
Asian-Oceanic Postal Union, 15th anniv.

"Loyalty" and Morarjee A466

**1977, Apr. 2   Perf. 13½x13**
754 A466 25p blue          1.25 .70
Narottam Morarjee (1877-1929), founder of Scindia Steam Ship Navigation Co.

Makhanlal Chaturvedi A467

**1977, Apr. 4   Perf. 13**
755 A467 25p orange brown          .50 .50
Chaturvedi (1889-1968), Hindi writer.

Mahaprabhu Vallabhacharya A468

**1977, Apr. 14**
756 A468 1r olive brown          .50 .50
Vallabhacharya (1479-1531), philosopher.

Federation Emblem A469

**1977, Apr. 23   Perf. 13½x13**
757 A469 25p ocher & purple          .50 .50
Federation of Indian Chambers of Commerce, 50th anniv.

Protection of Environment A470

**1977, June 5   Photo.   Perf. 13**
758 A470 2r multicolored          .80 .55

Council of States Chamber A471

**1977, June 21**
759 A471 25p multicolored          .50 .50
Council of States, Rajya Sabha (Parliament), 25th anniv.

Lotus A472

50p and 1r are vert.

**1977, July 1   Perf. 15x14, 14x15**
760 A472 25p shown          .40 .25
761 A472 50p Rhododendron          .70 .40
762 A472 1r Kadamba          .95 .65
763 A472 2r Gloriosa lily          1.50 .95
Nos. 760-763 (4)          3.55 2.25

Berliner Gramaphone — A473

**1977, July 20   Perf. 13½x13**
764 A473 2r black & brown          1.50 .90
Centenary of the phonograph.

Ananda Kentish Coomaraswamy (1877-1947) and Dancing Shiva — A474

**1977, Aug. 22   Photo.   Perf. 13x13½**
765 A474 25p multicolored          .60 .30
Coomaraswamy, art historian and critic.

Ganga Ram (1851-1927) and Hospital, New Delhi — A475

**1977, Sept. 4   Perf. 14½x14**
766 A475 25p rose carmine          .50 .35
Ram, social reformer and philanthropist.

Dr. Samuel Hahnemann and Cinchona — A476

19th Century Postman — A477

Lion and Palm Tree, East India Co. Essay — A478

**1977, Oct. 6   Photo.   Perf. 13**
767 A476 2r black & green          5.50 2.75
32nd Intl. Homeopathic Cong., New Delhi.

**1977, Oct. 12   Perf. 13**
768 A477 25p multicolored          1.00 .50

**Perf. 13½**
769 A478 2r mag & gray, buff          2.75 1.75
INPEX '77 Phil. Exhib., Bangalore, 10/12-16.

Ram Manohar Lohia (1910-67), Founder of Congress Socialist Party, Sec. of Foreign Dept. — A479

**1977, Oct. 12   Perf. 13x13½**
770 A479 25p red brown          1.60 1.10

Red Scinde Dawks, 1852 A480

Design: 3r, Foreign mail arriving at Ballard Pier, Bombay, 1927.

**1977, Oct. 19   Perf. 13½x13**
771 A480 1r orange & multi          2.50 1.10
772 A480 3r orange & multi          4.50 2.10
ASIANA 77, First Asian International Philatelic Exhibition, Bangalore, Oct. 19-23.

Statue of Rani Channamma — A481

**1977, Oct. 23**
773 A481 25p gray green          2.25 1.10
Rani Channamma of Kittue (1778-1829), who fought against British rule.

Mother and Child, Khajuraho Sculpture — A482

**1977, Oct. 23   Perf. 13x13½**
774 A482 2r gray & sepia          3.50 2.25
15th Intl. Pediatrics Congress.

Sun and National Colors — A483

Stylized Grain — A484

**1977, Nov. 8    Photo.    Perf. 13**
775  A483  25p multicolored    .60  .35
Union Public Service Commission, founded 1926.

**1977, Nov. 13**
776  A484  25p green    .60  .30
AGRIEXPO '77, Intl. Agriculture Exhib.

Cats A485

1r, Friends. Designs are from children's drawings.

**1977, Nov. 14**
777  A485  25p multicolored    .95  .45
778  A485  1r multicolored    3.50  2.25
Children's Day.

Jotirao Phooley — A486

**1977, Nov. 28    Wmk. 324**
779  A486  25p gray olive    .50  .40
Phooley (1827-1890), social reformer.

Senapati Bapat — A487

**1977, Nov. 28**
780  A487  25p brown orange    .50  .40
Senapati Bapat (Pandurang Mahadev Bapat, 1880-1967), scholar and fighter for India's independence.

Diagram of Population Growth — A488

**Perf. 13x13½**
**1977, Dec. 13    Unwmk.**
781  A488  2r carmine & blue grn    .80  .55
41st Session of Intl. Statistical Institute, New Delhi, Dec. 5-15.

Kamta Prasad (1875-1947) and Hindi Grammar A489

**1977, Dec. 25    Wmk. 324    Perf. 14**
782  A489  25p sepia    .50  .50
Prasad, compiler of Hindi Grammar.

Spasski Tower, Russian Flag — A490

**1977, Dec. 30    Unwmk.    Perf. 13**
783  A490  1r multicolored    .80  .55
60th anniv. of Russian October revolution.

Climber Crossing Crevasse — A491

Indian Flag near Summit A492

**Perf. 13½x13, 13x13½**
**1978, Jan. 15    Photo.**
784  A491  25p multicolored    .30  .30
785  A492  1r multicolored    .70  .55
Conquest of Kanchenjunga (Himalayas), by Indian team under Col. N. Kumar, May 31, 1977.

Tourists in Shikara on Dal Lake A493

**1978, Jan. 23    Perf. 13x13½**
786  A493  1r multicolored    3.50  1.75
27th Pacific Area Travel Assoc. Conf., New Delhi, Jan. 23-26.

Children in Library, Fair Emblem A494

**1978, Feb. 11    Photo.    Perf. 13**
787  A494  1r rose brown & indigo    .65  .40
3rd World Book Fair, New Delhi, Feb. 1978.

Mother of Pondicherry A495

**1978, Feb. 21**
788  A495  25p dark & light brown    .50  .40
Mother of the Sri Aurobindo Ashram, Pondicherry (Mira Richard, 1878-1973, born in Paris).

Wheat, Globe and Genetic Helix — A496

**1978, Feb. 23**
789  A496  25p yellow & blue green    .50  .40
5th Intl. Wheat Genetics Symposium.

Nanalal Dalpatram Kavi — A497

**Wmk. 324**
**1978, Mar. 16    Photo.    Perf. 13**
790  A497  25p rose brown    .50  .40
Kavi (1877-1946), Gujarati poet.

Surjya Sen (1894-1934), Patriot — A498

**1978, Mar. 22**
791  A498  25p ver, black & brown    .50  .40

Two Vaishnavas (Vishnu Worshippers) by Jaminy Roy — A499

Modern Indian Paintings: 50p, The Mosque, by Sailoz Mookherjea. 1r, Woman's Head, by Rabindranath Tagore. 2r, Hill Women, by Amrita Sher Gil.

**Perf. 13½x14**
**1978, Mar. 23    Unwmk.**
792  A499  25p black & multi    .30  .30
793  A499  50p black & multi    .60  .60
794  A499  1r black & multi    1.10  1.10
795  A499  2r black & multi    1.25  1.25
Nos. 792-795 (4)    3.25  3.25

Rubens, Self-portrait A500

**1978, Apr. 4    Photo.    Perf. 13½x13**
796  A500  2r multicolored    4.00  2.40

"The Little Tramp," Charlie Chaplin — A501

**1978, Apr. 16    Perf. 13**
797  A501  25p gold & indigo    2.75  1.25

Deendayal Upadhyaya (1916-68) — A502

**1978, May 5    Photo.    Perf. 13**
798  A502  25p multicolored    .50  .40
Upadhyaya, social and political reformer.

Syama Prasad Mookerjee (1901-1953) A503

"Airavat," 19th Century Wood Carving — A504

Kushan Gold Coin, 1st Century A505

**1978, July 6     Photo.     Perf. 13**
799  A503  25p gray olive          .50  .35
Dr. Mookerjee, educator, member of 1st natl. government.

**1978, July 27**
Designs: 50p, Wish-fulfilling tree, 2nd century B.C. 2r, Dagger and knife.

| | | | |
|---|---|---|---|
| 800 | A504 | 25p multicolored | .50 | .50 |
| 801 | A504 | 50p multicolored | .70 | .70 |
| 802 | A505 | 1r multicolored | 1.00 | 1.00 |
| 803 | A505 | 2r multicolored | 1.25 | 1.25 |
| | | Nos. 800-803 (4) | 3.45 | 3.45 |

Treasures from Indian museums.

Krishna and Arjuna on Battlefield, Quotation A506

**1978, Aug. 25     Unwmk.     Perf. 13**
804  A506  25p orange red & gold    .50  .40
Bhagavad Gita, part of Mahabharata Epic, the Divine Song of the Lord.

Bethune College for Women, Calcutta A507

**1978, Sept. 4**
805  A507  25p green & brown        .50  .40

E. V. Ramasami A508

**1978, Sept. 17**
806  A508  25p black               .50  .40
E. V. Ramasami (1879-1973), founder of Self-respect Movement, fighting caste system and social injustice.

Uday Shankar — A509

**1978, Sept. 26**
807  A509  25p buff & violet brown  .50  .40
Uday Shankar (1900-77), dancer.

Leo Tolstoi — A510

Vallathol Narayana Menon — A511

**1978, Oct. 2**
808  A510  1r multicolored         .75  .40
Tolstoi, novelist and philosopher.

**1978, Oct. 15     Photo.     Perf. 13**
809  A511  25p multicolored        .50  .50
Menon (1878-1958), poet.

"Two Friends" A512

**1978, Nov. 14     Photo.     Perf. 13**
810  A512  25p multicolored        .50  .40
Children's Day.

Worker at Lathe — A513

**1978, Nov. 17                Perf. 13½**
811  A513  25p green               .50  .40
Small Industries Fair.

Skinner's Horse Soldiers — A514

Chakravarti Rajagopalachari A515

**1978, Nov. 25                Perf. 13**
812  A514  25p multicolored       1.50  .80
175th anniv. of Skinner's Horse Regiment.

**1978, Dec. 10     Photo.     Perf. 13**
813  A515  25p maroon              .50  .40
Chakravarti Rajagopalachari (1878-1972), first post-independence Governor General.

A516

A517

**1978, Dec. 10**
814  A516  25p olive green         .50  .40
Mohammad Ali Jauhar (1878-1931), writer and patriot.

**1978, Dec. 23                Perf. 13x14**
815  A517  1r ocher & purple      1.25  .40
Wright Brothers, Flyer, 75th anniv. of 1st powered flight.

Ravenshaw College, Orissa, Centenary A518

**1978, Dec. 24                Perf. 14**
816  A518  25p green & maroon      .50  .40

Franz Schubert (1797-1828), Austrian Composer — A519

**1978, Dec. 25                Perf. 13**
817  A519  1r multicolored        2.25  .90

Punjab Regiment, Uniforms and Crest A520

**1979, Feb. 20     Photo.     Unwmk.**
818  A520  25p multicolored       2.50  1.00
Oldest Indian infantry unit.

Bhai Parmanand (1876-1947) A521

Gandhi and Child — A522

**1979, Feb. 24**
819  A521  25p violet blue         .50  .40
Parmanand, writer and educator.

**1979, Mar. 5     Photo.     Perf. 13**
Design: 1r, IYC emblem.
820  A522  25p dk brown & red      .50  .30
821  A522  1r dp org & dk brn      .75  .60

Albert Einstein (1879-1955), Theoretical Physicist — A523

**1979, Mar. 14**
822  A523  1r black               1.25  .65

Rajarshi Shahu Chhatrapati (1874-1922), Ruler of Kolhapur — A524

**1979, May 1     Photo.     Perf. 13x13½**
823  A524  25p dull purple         .50  .40

Lotus, India '80 Emblem A525

**1979, July 2     Photo.     Perf. 13**
824  A525  30p deep orange & green  .50  .40
India '80 Phil. Exhib., New Delhi, Jan. 25-Feb. 3, 1980.

Postal Cards, 1879 and 1979 — A526

Raja Mahendra
Pratap (1886-
1979),
Patriot — A527

**1979, July 2**
825 A526 50p multicolored          .50  .40

**1979, Aug. 15    Photo.    Perf. 13**
826 A527 30p olive gray            .50  .40

Jatindra Nath Das
(1904-1929)
A528

**1979, Sept. 13**
827 A528 30p dark brown           .50  .40

Das, political martyr.

Early and Modern
Light
Bulbs — A529

**1979, Oct. 21    Photo.    Perf. 13**
828 A529 1r rose magenta          .80  .65

Centenary of invention of electric light.

Buddhist
Text
A530

**1979, Oct. 23            Perf. 14½x14**
829 A530 30p brown & bister       .50  .40

National Archives.

Hirakud
Dam
A531

**Perf. 13½x13**
**1979, Oct. 29            Wmk. 324**
830 A531 30p brown red & dull
              grn                   .50  .40

13th Congress (Golden Jubilee) of the Intl.
Commission on Large Dams, New Delhi,
10/29-11/2.

Boy and
Alphabet
Book
A532

**1979, Nov. 10   Photo.   Perf. 14½x14**
831 A532 30p multicolored         .50  .40

Intl. Children's Book Fair, New Delhi, 11/10-
19.

Fair
Emblem — A533

**1979, Nov. 10            Perf. 13**
832 A533 1r black & orange        .50  .40

India Intl. Trade Fair, New Delhi, 11/10-12/9.

Dove,
Agency
Emblem
A534

**1979, Dec. 4            Perf. 13½x13**
833 A534 1r multicolored          .60  .45

23rd Intl. Atomic Energy Agency Conf., New
Delhi, Dec. 4-10.

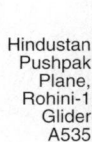

Hindustan
Pushpak
Plane,
Rohini-1
Glider
A535

**1979, Dec. 10           Perf. 13½x13**
834 A535 30p multicolored        2.75 1.40

Gurdwara Baoli
Shrine,
Goindwal — A536

**1979, Dec. 21           Perf. 13x13½**
835 A536 30p multicolored         .50  .40

Guru Amardas (1469-1574), Sikh spiritual
leader.

Types of 1975-79 and

Women in
Rice Field
A537

Family
Planning
A537a

Designs: 2p, Adult education. 5p, Fish. 15p,
Agricultural technology. 20p, Child nutrition.
No. 840, Poultry. No. 840B, Farm, wheat,
farmer plowing. 1r, Hybrid cotton. 2r, Weaving.
5r, Rubber tapping.

**Perf. 14x14½, 14½x14, 13 (#840B)**

| | | | Wmk. 324 | |
|---|---|---|---|---|
| **1979-85** | | **Photo.** | | |
| 836 | A537 | 2p violet | .65 | .65 |
| 837 | A537 | 5p blue | .65 | .65 |
| 838 | A537a | 15p blue grn ('80) | .65 | .65 |
| 839 | A537a | 20p henna brn ('81) | .65 | .65 |
| 840 | A537 | 25p brown | .65 | .65 |
| 840B | A537 | 25p brt green ('85) | .65 | .65 |
| 841 | A409 | 30p violet ('80) | 2.40 | .80 |
| 842 | A410 | 30p red brown ('80) | 1.60 | .80 |
| 843 | A537 | 30p yel green | .65 | .65 |
| 844 | A409 | 35p violet ('80) | 1.60 | .80 |
| 845 | A410 | 35p red brown ('80) | 1.10 | .80 |
| 846 | A537a | 35p cerise ('80) | .65 | .65 |
| 846A | A409 | 50p violet ('83) | .65 | .65 |
| 846B | A410 | 50p red brown ('83) | 1.60 | .80 |

**Size: 17x28mm**

| 847 | A537a | 1r brown ('80) | .65 | .65 |
|---|---|---|---|---|
| 848 | A537a | 2r rose violet ('80) | .95 | .65 |

**Size: 20x37mm**

| 849 | A537a | 5r multi ('80) | 1.40 | .80 |
|---|---|---|---|---|

Nos. 836-849 (17)          17.15 11.95
Size: #841-842, 844-845, 846A-846B,
17x20mm.
See Nos. 895-900A, 903-917.

| **1979-83** | | | **Perf. 13** | |
|---|---|---|---|---|
| 837a | A537 | 5p | .20 | .20 |
| 837b | A537 | 5p Litho. ('82) | .50 | .30 |
| 838a | A537a | 15p | .20 | .20 |
| 839a | A537a | 20p | .30 | .20 |
| 840a | A537 | 25p brown | .30 | .20 |
| 843a | A537 | 30p | .50 | .20 |
| 844a | A409 | 35p | .75 | .30 |
| 845a | A410 | 35p | .25 | .20 |
| 846c | A537a | 35p | .50 | .20 |
| 846d | A409 | 50p | .50 | .20 |
| 846e | A410 | 50p | .20 | .20 |

| | | | **Perf. 12½x13** | |
|---|---|---|---|---|
| 847a | A537a | 1r | .20 | .20 |

| | | | **Perf. 13x13½, 13½x13** | |
|---|---|---|---|---|
| 848a | A537a | 2r ('83) | .20 | .20 |
| 849a | A537a | 5r ('83) | .40 | .35 |

Nos. 837a-849a (14)       5.00 3.15

People Holding
Hands, UN
Emblem — A538

**1980, Jan. 21   Photo.   Perf. 13**
851 A538 1r multicolored          .50  .40

UN Industrial Development Org. (INIDO),
3rd Gen. Conf., New Delhi, Jan. 21-Feb. 8.

Field Post Office,
Cancels — A539

Money Order
Centenary — A540

2-Anna Copper
Coins,
1774 — A541

Rowland Hill,
Birthplace,
Kidderminster
A542

**Wmk. 360, Unwmkd. (1r)**
**1980, Jan. 25**
852 A539 30p gray olive           .55  .40
853 A540 50p brown & citron       .85  .85
854 A541 1r bronze               1.10 1.00
855 A542 2r dark gray            1.10 1.00
   Nos. 852-855 (4)              3.60 3.25

INDIA '80 Intl. Stamp Exhib., New Delhi,
Jan. 25-Feb. 3.

India Institution of
Engineers, 60th
Anniversary
A543

Uniforms, 1780
and 1980, Arms
and
Ribbon — A544

**Perf. 13x13½**
**1980, Feb. 17            Unwmk.**
856 A543 30p dark blue & gold     .50  .40

**1980, Feb. 26**
857 A544 30p multicolored        2.00 1.00

Madras Sappers bicentennial.

2nd Intl.
Apiculture
Conf., New
Delhi
A545

**1980, Feb. 29            Perf. 13½**
858 A545 1r multicolored         2.00 1.00

A546

A547

**1980, Feb. 29**      **Wmk. 360**
859 A546 30p bright blue    .60 .40
    4th World Book Fair, New Delhi.

**1980, Mar. 18**      *Perf. 13x13½*
860 A547 30p blue gray    .50 .35
    Welthy Fisher (b. 1879), educator, Literacy House, Lucknow.

Darul Uloom Islamic School, Deoband A548

**1980, Mar. 21**      *Perf. 13½*
861 A548 30p gray green    .50 .40

Keshub Chunder Sen — A549

**Perf. 13x13½**
**1980, Apr. 15**   **Photo.**   **Wmk. 360**
862 A549 30p brown    .50 .40
    Sen (1838-84), scholar, writer, journalist.

**1980, Apr. 21**      **Unwmk.**
863 A550 30p multicolored    .50 .40
    Sivaji (1627-80), Indian patriot.

Sivaji, Raigad Fort — A550

Narayan Malhar Joshi — A551

Ulloor S. Parameswara Iyer — A552

**Perf. 13x13½**
**1980, June 5**      **Wmk. 360**
864 A551 30p lilac rose    .80 .50
    Joshi (1879-1955), trade union pioneer.

**1980, June 6**
865 A552 30p dull purple    .80 .50
    Iyer (1877-1949), poet and scholar.

Syed Mohammad Zamin Ali — A553

**1980, June 25**
866 A553 30p dk yellow green    .50 .40
    Ali (1880-1955), linguist and educator.

Helen Keller (1880-1968) — A554

**1980, June 27**
867 A554 30p orange & black    1.60 .75
    Keller, blind and deaf writer and lecturer.

High Jump, Olympic Rings A555

Prem Chand (1880-1936) A556

**1980, July 19**   **Photo.**   *Perf. 13½x14*
868 A555 1r shown    1.00 .25
869 A555 2.80r Equestrian    2.50 1.50
    22nd Summer Olympic Games, Moscow, July 19-Aug. 3.

**1980, July 31**      *Perf. 13*
870 A556 30p red brown    .50 .40
    Pen name of Nawab Rai, writer.

Mother Teresa, Nobel Peace Prize Medallion A557

**Perf. 13½x13**
**1980, Aug. 27**   **Photo.**   **Wmk. 360**
871 A557 30p violet, *grayish*    2.50 1.25
    Mother Teresa, founder of Missionaries of Charity, 70th birthday.

Earl Mountbatten of Burma — A558

Asian Table Tennis Championship A559

**1980, Aug. 28**      *Perf. 13x13½*
872 A558 2.80r multicolored    5.00 2.50
    Mountbatten (1900-79), 1st governor gen. of India.

**1980, Sept.**   **Photo.**   *Perf. 13x13½*
873 A559 30p magenta    .80 .55

Scottish Church College, Calcutta, Sesquicentennial — A560

**1980, Sept. 27**   **Photo.**   *Perf. 13½*
874 A560 35p dull purple    .50 .40

Rajah Annamalai Chettiar (1881-1948), Banker, Founder of Annamalai University — A561

**1980, Sept. 30**   **Unwmk.**   *Perf. 14x15*
875 A561 35p dull purple    .50 .40

Gandhi A562

**1980, Oct. 2**      *Perf. 15x14*
876   35p Gandhi on Dandi March    .75 .50
877   35p Gandhi Defying Salt Law    .75 .50
  *a.*   A562 Pair, #876-877    3.00 3.00

Jayaprakash Narayan (1902-79), Writer — A564

**1980, Oct. 8**   **Wmk. 360**   *Perf. 14x15*
878 A564 35p red brown    .80 .55

Intl. Symposium on Bustards, Jaipur — A565

**1980, Nov. 1**   **Photo.**   *Perf. 13*
879 A565 2.30r Great Indian bustards    2.25 1.75

Hegira (Pilgrimage Year) A566

**1980, Nov. 3**      *Perf. 13x13½*
880 A566 35p multicolored    .50 .50

Children's Day — A567

**Perf. 13½x13**
**1980, Nov. 14**      **Unwmk.**
881 A567 35p multicolored    1.50 .90

Dhyan Chand — A568     Miner, Molten Gold — A569

**1980, Dec. 3**   **Wmk. 360**   *Perf. 14x15*
882 A568 35p dark rose brown    2.00 1.00
    Chand (1906-1979), field hockey player.

**Perf. 13x13½**
**1980, Dec. 20**      **Unwmk.**
883 A569 1r multicolored    3.50 .70
    Kolar gold fields centenary.

Mukhtar Ahmad Ansari (1880-1936), Surgeon — A570

**Perf. 14x15**
**1980, Dec. 25**      **Wmk. 360**
884 A570 35p olive gray    .60 .30

Government Mint, Bombay, Sesquicentennial — A571

*Perf. 13½x13*
**1980, Dec. 27**     **Unwmk.**
885 A571 35p multicolored .25 .20

Regional Bridal Outfits — A572     Mazharul Haque (1866-1930), Patriot — A573

**1980, Dec. 30**     *Perf. 13x13½*
886 A572 1r Kashmir 1.00 .60
887 A572 1r Bengal 1.00 .60
888 A572 1r Rajasthan 1.00 .60
889 A572 1r Tamilnada 1.00 .60
    Nos. 886-889 (4) 4.00 2.40

**1981, Jan. 2**   **Wmk. 360**   *Perf. 14x15*
890 A573 35p violet .50 .40

St. Stephen's College Centenary — A574

**1981, Feb. 1**   **Photo.**   *Perf. 14x14½*
891 A574 35p dull red .50 .40

Gommateshwara Statue, Shravanabelgola A575     Ganesh V. Mavalankar (1888-1956) A576

**1981, Feb. 9**     **Unwmk.**
892 A575 1r multicolored .50 .40

**1981, Feb. 27**
893 A576 35p light red brown .50 .40
Mavalankar, 1st speaker of parliament.

Type of 1979
*Perf. 14½x14*
**1981-86**   **Photo.**     **Wmk. 324**
**Size: 19½x37½mm**
895 A537 2.25r Cashew .75 .50
   a.   Perf. 14x14½ .30 .20
   b.   Perf. 13 .25 .20
896 A537 2.80r Apples 1.00 .60
   a.   Perf. 14x14½ .40 .20
897 A537 3.25r Oranges ('83) .60 .45
   a.   Perf. 13½x13 ('85) .30 .20
   b.   Perf. 13 .30 .20
900 A537 10r Trees on hillside ('84) .75 .40
   b.   Perf. 13x13½ 1.25 .60
*Perf. 13½x13*
**Size: 37½x19½mm**
900A A537 50r Windmill ('86) 2.00 1.25
    Nos. 895-900A (5) 5.10 3.20

Homage to Martyrs — A577

**1981, Mar. 23**   **Unwmk.**   *Perf. 14x15*
901 A577 35p multicolored .50 .40

Heinrich von Stephan and UPU Emblem A578

**1981, Apr. 8**     *Perf. 15x14*
902 A578 1r red brown & brt blue .50 .40

Types of 1979 and

Telecommunications A578a

Natural Gas A578b

*Perf. 14x14½, 14½x14, 13 (40p, 75p), 13x13½ (20r)*
**Wmk. 324, 360 (2p, 5p, 15p)**
**1981-90**     **Photo.**
903 A537 2p violet .20 .20
904 A537 5p blue .20 .20
905 A537 10p Irrigation .20 .20
   a.   Perf. 13 .20 .20
906 A537a 15p blue green .20 .20
912 A578a 40p dull red .20 .20
914 A537 50p Dairy industry .20 .20
   a.   Perf. 13 .20 .20
915 A537a 75p vermilion .20 .20
**Size: 17x20mm**
916 A410 1r orange brown .20 .20
917 A578b 20r sepia & dark blue 1.00 .60
    Nos. 903-917 (9) 2.60 2.20

Issued: 10p, 50p, 1/25/82; 40p, 10/15/88; 20r, 11/30/88; 75p, 1990; 1r, 1/30/91; others, 3/25/81.

Intl. Year of the Disabled A579

*Perf. 14½x14*
**1981, Apr. 20**   **Photo.**     **Unwmk.**
919 A579 1r blue & black .50 .40

Tribesman — A580

**1981, May 30**     *Perf. 14x14½*
920 A580 1r Khiamngan Naga .70 .50
921 A580 1r Toda .70 .50
922 A580 1r Bhil .70 .50
923 A580 1r Dandami Maria .70 .50
    Nos. 920-923 (4) 2.80 2.00

World Environment Day — A581

**1981, June 15**
924 A581 1r multicolored .50 .40

Nilmoni Phukan (1880-1978), Writer — A582

**1981, June 22**
925 A582 35p red brown .50 .40

Sanjay Gandhi (1946-1980), Politician — A583

**1981, June 23**     *Perf. 13x13½*
926 A583 35p multicolored .90 .60

SLV-3 Take-off — A584

**1981, July 18**   **Photo.**   *Perf. 14x15*
927 A584 1r multicolored .60 .40
Launching of India's 1st satellite, 1st anniv.

Mascot, Field Hockey A585

**1981, July 28**     *Perf. 13½x13*
928 A585 1r shown 1.60 .75
929 A585 1r Emblem 1.60 .75
9th Asian Games, New Delhi, 1982.

Flame of the Forest — A586

Designs: Flowering trees.

**1981, Sept. 1**   **Photo.**     *Perf. 13*
930 A586 35p shown 1.10 .35
931 A586 50p Crateva .65 .45
932 A586 1r Golden shower 1.50 .75
933 A586 2r Bauhinia 2.25 1.50
    Nos. 930-933 (4) 5.50 3.05

World Food Day — A587

**1981, Oct. 16**   **Photo.**   *Perf. 14x14½*
934 A587 1r multicolored .60 .45

Cyrestis Achates — A588

**1981, Oct. 20**     *Perf. 13*
935 A588 35p Stichophthalma camadeva, horiz. 1.50 .50
936 A588 50p Cethosia biblis, horiz. 2.50 1.50
937 A588 1r 3.25 1.00
938 A588 2r Treinopalpus imperialis 4.00 4.00
    Nos. 935-938 (4) 11.25 7.00

Bellary Raghava (1880-1946), Actor — A589

**1981, Oct. 31**     *Perf. 14½x14*
939 A589 35p olive gray 1.40 .60

40th Anniv. of Mahar Regiment — A590     Children's Day — A591

**1981, Nov. 9**     *Perf. 13*
940 A590 35p multicolored 1.75 .60

**1981, Nov. 14**     *Perf. 14x14½*
941 A591 35p multicolored 1.10 .45

Rajghat Stadium A591a

**1981**     *Perf. 13½x13*
942 A591a 1r shown 2.40 .45
943 A591a 1r Nehru Stadium .35 .25
Asian games. Issued: #942, 11/19; #943, 12/30.

Kashi Prasad Jayaswal (1881-1937), Historian — A592

**1981, Nov. 27**     *Perf. 14x14½*
944 A592 35p chalky blue     .80   .35

Intl. Palestinian Solidarity Day A593

**1981, Nov. 29**     *Perf. 14½x14*
945 A593 1r multicolored     4.25   .70

Naval Ship Taragiri A594

**1981, Dec. 4**
946 A594 35p multicolored     5.00 2.25

Henry Heras (1888-1955), Historian — A595

**1981, Dec. 14**   Photo.   *Perf. 14½x14*
947 A595 35p rose violet     .60   .35

Indian Ocean Commonwealth Submarine Telephone Cable — A596

**1981, Dec. 24**     *Perf. 13½*
948 A596 1r multicolored     4.00   .55

5th World Field Hockey Championship, Bombay — A597

**1981, Dec. 29**     *Perf. 13½x13*
949 A597 1r multicolored     2.25   .60

Telephone Service Centenary — A598

    *Perf. 13x13½*
**1982, Jan. 28**     Unwmk.
950 A598 2r multicolored     .75   .50

12th Intl. Soil Science Congress, New Delhi, Feb. 8-16 A599

**1982, Feb. 8**     *Perf. 13½x13*
951 A599 1r multicolored     .40   .25

Sir Jamsetjee Jejeebhoy School of Art, Bombay — A600

**1981, Mar. 2**   Photo.   *Perf. 14x14½*
952 A600 35p multicolored     .40   .30

Three Musicians, by Pablo Picasso (1881-1973) — A601

**1982, Mar. 15**   Photo.   *Perf. 14*
953 A601 2.85r multicolored     3.00 1.00

Deer, 5th Cent. Bas Relief — A602

Radio Telescope, Ooty A603

Festival of India, England: No. 955, Krishna, 9th cent. bronze sculpture.

**1982, Mar. 23**     *Perf. 14x15*
954 A602 2r multicolored     .90   .90
955 A602 3.05r multicolored     .60   .45
    *Perf. 13*
956 A603 3.05r multicolored     .60   .35
    Nos. 954-956 (3)     2.10 1.70

TB Bacillus Centenary A604

**1982, Mar. 24**     *Perf. 13*
957 A604 35p rose violet     3.50 1.60

Durgabai Deshmukh (1909-1981), Social Worker — A605

**1982, May 9**   Photo.   *Perf. 14½x14*
958 A605 35p blue     .80   .35

Himalayan Flowers — A606

**1982, May 29**     *Perf. 14x14½*
959 A606   35p Blue poppies    1.25   .60
960 A606   1r Showy inula    3.00   .60
961 A606   2r Cobra lily    3.50 2.50
962 A606   2.85r Brahma kamal    4.25 4.25
    Nos. 959-962 (4)     12.00 7.95

Ariana Passenger Payload Experimental (APPLE) Satellite, First Anniv. — A607

**1982, June 19**     *Perf. 13½x13*
963 A607 2r multicolored     1.00   .65

Bidhan Chandra Roy (1882-1962), Physician and Politician — A608

**1982, July 1**     *Perf. 14½x14*
964 A608 50p orange brown     1.40   .95

Sagar Samrat Drilling Rig — A609

**1982, Aug. 14**   Photo.   *Perf. 13*
985 A609 1r multicolored     3.00 1.25

Bindu (Cosmic Spirit), by Raza — A610

Kashmir Stag — A611

Paintings; 3.05r, Between the Spider and the Lamp, 1956, by M.F. Husain.

**1982, Sept. 17**     *Perf. 14x14½*
986 A610   2r multicolored    .90   .55
987 A610   3.05r multicolored    1.25 1.00

**1982, Oct. 1**     *Perf. 13x13½*
988 A611 2.85r multicolored     5.00 3.25

50th Anniv. of Indian Air Force A612

**1982, Oct. 8**     *Perf. 13⅛x13*
989 A612 1r Wapiti, MiG 25     9.50 2.00

50th Anniv. of Civil Aviation A613

**1982, Oct. 15**
990 A613 3.25r J.R.D. Tata and his Puss Moth, 1932     8.50 3.00

Police Memorial Day — A614

**1982, Oct. 21**
991 A614 50p Beat patrol     1.10   .55

Post Office Savings Bank Centenary A615

**1982, Oct. 23**
992 A615 50p brown     .50   .40

9th Asian Games A616

**1982**     *Perf. 13½x14*
993   A616 1r Wrestling, by Janaki, 17th cent.   1.60   .70
993A   A616 1r Archery    3.50   .60
    Issued: #993, Oct. 30; #993A, Nov. 6.

India-USSR Troposcatter Communications Link — A617

**1982, Nov. 2**     *Perf. 13½x13*
994 A617 3.05r multicolored     .70   .50

Children's Day — A618

**1982, Nov. 14** *Perf. 14x15*
995 A618 50p multicolored .60 .40

9th Asian Games A619

**1982** *Perf. 13*
996 A619 50p Cycling .25 .25
997 A619 2r Yachting .40 .30
998 A619 2r Javelin .45 .40
999 A619 2.85r Rowing .65 .45
1000 A619 2.85r Discus 2.00 .45
1001 A619 3.25r Soccer 2.50 .65
Nos. 996-1001 (6) 6.25 2.50

Issued: #997, 999, Nov. 25; others Nov. 19.

50th Anniv. of Indian Military Academy, Dehradun A620

**1982, Dec. 10** *Perf. 13½x13*
1002 A620 50p multicolored .70 .50

Purushottamdas Tandon (1882-1962), Politician — A621

**1982, Dec. 15** *Perf. 13*
1003 A621 50p bister .50 .40

Darjeeling Himalayan Railway Centenary A622

**1982, Dec. 18** *Perf. 13½x13*
1004 A622 2.85r multicolored 10.00 7.50

Indian Railway Car — A623

Nos. 2 and 201 — A624

**1982, Dec. 30 Photo.** *Perf. 13, 14*
1005 A623 50p multicolored 2.25 1.10
1006 A624 2r multicolored 3.75 3.00
INPEX '82 Stamp Exhibition.

First Anniv. of Antarctic Expedition A625

**1983, Jan. 9 Photo.** *Perf. 13½x13*
1007 A625 1r multicolored 7.50 3.50

Pres. Franklin D. Roosevelt (1882-1945) — A626

**1983, Jan. 30** *Perf. 13*
1008 A626 3.25r brown .90 .75

Siberian Cranes — A627

**1983, Feb. 7** *Perf. 13x13½*
1009 A627 2.85r multicolored 5.00 3.25

180th Anniv. of Jat Regiment A628

**1983, Feb. 16** *Perf. 13½x13*
1010 A628 50p Soldiers, emblem 3.25 2.10

7th Non-aligned Summit Conference A629

**1983, Mar. 7**
1011 A629 1r Emblem .35 .35
1012 A629 2r Jawaharlal Nehru .45 .45

Commonwealth Day — A630

**1983, Mar. 14** *Perf. 13*
1013 A630 1r Shore Temple, Mahabalipuram .25 .30
1014 A630 2r Mountains, Gomukh .45 .45

86th Session of Intl. Olympic Committee, New Delhi, Mar. 21-28 A631

**1983, Mar. 25 Litho.** *Perf. 13½x13*
1015 A631 1r Acropolis .60 .40

A632 A633

St. Francis of Assisi (1182-1226), by Giovanni Collina.

**1983, Apr. 4 Photo.** *Perf. 13*
1016 A632 1r brown 1.10 .55

**1983, May 5 Photo.** *Perf. 13x12½*
1017 A633 1r brown .70 .50
Karl Marx (1818-1883).

Charles Darwin (1809-1882) — A634

**1983, May 18** *Perf. 12½x13*
1018 A634 2r multicolored 6.00 2.50

50th Anniv. of Kanha Natl. Park A635

**1983, May 30** *Perf. 13½x13*
1019 A635 1r Barasinga stag 4.25 1.25

World Communications Year — A636

**1983, July 18 Photo.** *Perf. 13*
1020 A636 1r multicolored .60 .30

Simon Bolivar (1783-1830) — A637

**1983, July 24**
1021 A637 2r multicolored 4.00 2.50

Quit India Resolution, Aug. 8, 1942 — A638

Meera Behn (Madeleine Slade). Disciple of Gandhi, d. 1982 — A639

Design: No. 1024, Mahadev Desai (1892-1942).

**1983, Aug. 9 Photo.** *Perf. 14*
1022 A638 50p shown 1.40 1.10
*Perf. 13½x13*
1023 A639 50p shown 1.40 1.10
1024 A639 50p org, green & brn 1.40 1.10
a. Pair, #1023-1024 2.75 2.75

See Nos. 1033, 1035, 1042, 1052-1057, 1077, 1093-1094, 1103, 1107, 1109, 1122, 1137-1139, 1144, 1147-1149, 1163, 1167, 1198, 1202-1205, 1229-1231, 1238, 1243, 1257, 1268-1271, 1277.

Ram Nath Chopra (1882-1973), Pharma-cologist — A640

**1983, Aug. 17** *Perf. 13*
1025 A640 50p brown .80 .65

Indian Mountaineering Foundation, 25th Anniv. — A641

**1983, Aug. 27** *Perf. 13½*
1026 A641 2r Nanda Devi, Himalayas 4.00 2.25

Bombay Natural History Soc. — A642

**1983, Sept. 15** *Perf. 13x13½*
1027 A642 1r multicolored 6.00 1.60

Rock Garden, Chandigarh A643

**1983, Sept. 23**    *Perf. 13x13½*
1028 A643 1r multicolored    2.50 1.25

Wildlife A644

**1983, Oct. 1**    *Perf. 13½x13*
1029 A644 1r Golden langur    3.50 .75
1030 A644 2r Lion-tailed macaque    5.25 3.75

World Tourism, 5th General Assembly — A645

**1983, Oct. 3**    **Photo.**    *Perf. 14*
1031 A645 2r Ghats of Varanasi    1.00 .50

Krishna Kanta Handique, Linguist, Sanskritist, Educator and Scholar — A646

**1983, Oct. 7**    **Litho.**    *Perf. 13*
1032 A646 50p deep gray violet    .50 .35

Famous Indians Type of 1983
Design: Hemu Kalani, revolutionary patriot.

**1983, Oct. 18**    **Photo.**    *Perf. 13½x13*
1033 A639 50p org, grn & red brn    .50 .50

Children's Day — A648

Painting: Festival, by Kashyap Premswala

**1983, Nov. 14**    **Photo.**    *Perf. 13*
1034 A648 50p multicolored    .60 .45

Famous Indians Type of 1983
Design: Acharya Vinoba Bhave (1895-1982), freedom fighter.

**1983, Nov. 15**    **Photo.**    *Perf. 13½x13*
1035 A639 50p org, grn & dull brn    .50 .50

Manned Flight Bicent. — A650

Project Tiger — A651

**1983, Nov. 21**    **Photo.**    *Perf. 13*
1036 A650 1r 1st Indian Balloon    1.60 .55
1037 A650 2r Montgolfier Balloon    2.10 1.10

**1983, Nov. 22**    **Photo.**    *Perf. 13*
1038 A651 2r multicolored    6.00 4.25

Commonwealth Heads of Government Meeting, New Delhi — A652

Design: 2r, Goanese Couple, 19th century.

**1983, Nov. 23**    **Photo.**    *Perf. 13*
1039 A652 1r lt brnsh blue & multi    .70 .40
1040 A652 2r pink & multi    1.10 .50

Pratiksha — A653

**1983, Dec. 5**    **Photo.**    *Perf. 13*
1041 A653 1r multi    .40 .30

Nanda Lal Bose (1882-1966), artist.

Famous Indians Type of 1983
Design: Surendranath Banerjee, journalist.

**1983, Dec. 28**    **Photo.**    *Perf. 13½x13*
1042 A639 50p org, green & olive    .50 .50

7th Light Cavalry Bicent. A655

Deccan Horse Regiment, 194th Anniv. A656

**1984, Jan. 7**
1043 A655 1r Soldier, banner    6.00 2.25

**1984, Jan. 9**    *Perf. 13x13½*
1044 A656 1r multicolored    5.50 2.00

Asiatic Society Bicentenary — A657

Design: Society building, Calcutta; founder William Jones.

**1984, Jan. 15**    *Perf. 13*
1045 A657 1r brt green & dp lilac    .50 .35

Postal Life Insurance Centenary — A658

**1984, Feb. 1**    **Photo.**    *Perf. 13x13½*
1046 A658 1r Emblem    .50 .35

Presidential Review of Naval Fleet A659

**1984, Feb. 3**    *Perf. 13½x13*
1047 A659 1r Jet    2.50 1.50
1048 A659 1r Aircraft carrier    2.50 1.50
1049 A659 1r Submarine    2.50 1.50
1050 A659 1r Missile destroyer    2.50 1.50
   a.   Block of 4, #1047-1050    14.00 14.00

12th Intl. Leprosy Congress, New Delhi A660

**1984, Feb. 10**    *Perf. 13x13½*
1051 A660 1r Globe, emblem    .80 .60

Famous Indians Type of 1983
#1052, Vasudeo Balvant Phadke (d. 1884), freedom fighter. #1053, Baba Kanshi Ram. #1054, Begum Hazrat Mahal. #1055, Mangal Pandey. #1056, Nana Sahib. #1057, Tatya Tope.

**1984**    *Perf. 13½x13*
1052 A639 50p org, grn & dk ol    .55 .55
1053 A639 50p org, grn & brn    .55 .55
1054 A639 50p org, grn, red org & gray    1.25 .80
1055 A639 50p org, grn, brn & gray    1.25 .80
1056 A639 50p org, grn, vio & gray    1.25 .80
1057 A639 50p org, grn, dk ol & gray    1.25 .80
   Nos. 1052-1057 (6)    6.10 4.30

Issue dates: No. 1052, Feb. 23. No. 1053, Apr. 23. Nos. 1054-1057, May 10.

Indian-Russian Space Cooperation — A662

**1984, Apr. 3**    **Photo.**    *Perf. 14*
1058 A662 3r Spacecraft    1.50 .85

G. D. Birla (1894-1983), Industrialist — A663

Birla, Birla Institute of Technology, Pilani.

**1984, June 11**
1060 A663 50p sepia    .80 .45

1984 Summer Olympics — A664

*Perf. 13x12½, 12½x13*    **Photo.**
**1984, July 28**
1061 A664 50p Basketball    1.40 .65
1062 A664 1r High jump    1.10 .35
1063 A664 2r Gymnastics, horiz.    1.50 .95
1064 A664 2.50r Weight lifting, horiz.    1.75 1.50
   Nos. 1061-1064 (4)    5.75 3.45

Vellore Fort — A665

**1984, Aug. 3**    *Perf. 13½x13, 13x13½*
1065 A665 50p Gwalior, horiz.    1.00 .55
1066 A665 1r shown    1.50 .40
1067 A665 1.50r Simhagad    2.50 1.90
1068 A665 2r Jodhpur, horiz.    3.00 2.50
   Nos. 1065-1068 (4)    8.00 5.35

B.V. Paradkar, Editor — A665a

**1984, Sept. 14**    **Photo.**    *Perf. 13x13½*
1068A A665a 50p sepia    .80 .55

Dr. D.N. Wadia (1883-1969), Geologist — A665b

**1984, Oct. 23**    *Perf. 13*
1068B A665b 1r multicolored    2.50 .40

Indira Gandhi — A666

**1984, Nov. 19   Photo.   Perf. 15x14**
1069 A666 50p multicolored          4.00 4.00

Children's Day — A667

12th World Mining Congress — A668

**1984, Nov. 14   Photo.   Perf. 13**
1070 A667 50p Birds in trees          1.10 .70

**1984, Nov. 20   Photo.   Perf. 13**
1071 A668 1r Congress emblem          2.25 .45

Dr. Rajendra Prasad (1884-1963), 1st, Pres. — A669

**1984, Dec. 3   Photo.   Perf. 13**
1072 A669 50p multicolored          1.50 .90

Roses — A670

**1984, Dec. 23   Litho.   Perf. 13**
1073 A670 1.50r Mrinalini          4.00 2.25
1074 A670  2r Sugandha          4.25 2.50

Fergusson College Centenary A671

**1985, Jan. 2   Photo.   Perf. 13x13½**
1076 A671 100p multicolored          1.00 .50

---

Famous Indians Type of 1983

Design: Narhar Vishnu Gadgil (1896-1966), freedom fighter.

**1985, Jan. 10   Photo.   Perf. 13½x13**
1077 A639 50p org, grn & brn          6.00 4.00

Artillery Regiment, 50th Anniv. A673

**1985, Jan. 15   Perf. 13½x13**
1078 A673 1r Gunner, howitzer          7.00 2.25

Indira Gandhi (1917-1984) — A674

**1985, Jan. 31   Perf. 14**
1079 A674 2r Addressing UN
          General Assembly 6.50 4.25
          See Nos. 1098-1099.

Minicoy Lighthouse Cent. — A675

**1985, Feb. 2   Perf. 13**
1080 A675 1r multicolored          8.50 1.60

Bengal Medical College, 150th Anniv. A676

**1985, Feb. 20   Perf. 13½x13**
1081 A676 1r multicolored          4.50 .95

Madras Medical College, 150th Anniv. A677

**1985, Mar. 8   Perf. 13½x13**
1082 A677 1r multicolored          4.50 .95

Assam Rifles, North-East Sentinels, 150th Anniv. A679

**1985, Mar. 29**
1084 A679 1r multicolored          7.50 2.50

---

Potato Research, 50th Anniv. — A680

Baba Jassa Singh Ahluwalia, 1718-1783, Sikh Leader — A681

**1985, Apr. 1   Perf. 13**
1085. A680 50p brown & pale brown          2.75 1.60

**1985, Apr. 4**
1086 A681 50p rose violet          2.75 1.60

St. Xavier's College, 125th Anniv. A682

**1985, Apr. 12**
1087 A682 1r multicolored          2.50 .80

White-winged Wood Duck — A683

Bougainvillea A684

**1985, May 18   Perf. 14**
1088 A683 2r multicolored          11.50 5.50

**1985, June 5   Perf. 13**
1089 A684 50p multicolored          2.50 2.10
1090 A684  1r multicolored          3.00 1.75

Statue of Didarganj Yakshi, Indian Deity — A685

Yaudheya Tribal Republic Copper Coin, c. 200 B.C. — A686

**1985**
1091 A685 1r multicolored          4.00 2.10
1092 A686 2r multicolored          2.25 .50

Festival of India, festival in France and the US for cultural exchange.
Issue dates: 1r, June 7. 2r, June 13.

Famous Indians Type of 1983

Designs: No. 1093, Jairamdas Doulatram (1891-1979), journalist and politician. No. 1094, Nellie (1909-1973) & Jatindra Mohan (d. 1933) Sengupta, political activists, horiz.

---

**1985   Perf. 13½x13**
1093 A639 50p org, grn & dl red brn          .75 .50
    **Perf. 13x13½**
1094 A639 50p org, green & fawn .75 .50
    Issued: #1093, July 21; #1094, July 22.

Swami Haridas (1478-1573), Philosopher A689

**1985, Sept. 19   Photo.   Perf. 13½x13**
1095 A689 1r multicolored          2.50 1.50

Border Roads Org., 25th Anniv. — A690

**1985, Oct. 10   Perf. 13x14**
1096 A690 2r multicolored          4.00 2.75

Prime Minister Nehru at Podium A691

**1985, Oct. 24   Perf. 13x13½**
1097 A691 2r multicolored          1.75 1.10
    UN, 40th anniv.

Indira Gandhi Memorial Type of 1985

**1985   Perf. 14**
1098 A674 2r Gandhi addressing crowd          4.50 4.50
1099 A674 3r Portrait          4.50 4.50
    Issue dates: 2r, Oct. 31. 3r, Nov. 19.

Children's Day — A692

**1985, Nov. 14   Perf. 13½x13**
1100 A692 50p multicolored          1.40 .80

Halley's Comet — A693

**1985, Nov. 19   Perf. 13x13½**
1101 A693 1r multicolored          3.25 1.60
    Intl. Astronomical Union, 19th General Assembly, New Delhi, Nov. 19-28.

St. Stephen's Hospital, Delhi, Cent. A694

**1985, Nov. 25**     *Perf. 13*
1102 A694 1r multicolored    1.25 .55

**Famous Indians Type of 1983**
Design: Kakasaheb Kalelkar (1885-1981), author.

**1985, Dec. 2**     *Perf. 13½x13*
1103 A639 50p org, grn & ol brn   .75 .50

Map of South Asia A696

Flags of India, Pakistan, Bangladesh, Nepal, Bhutan, Sri Lanka and the Maldive Islands — A697

**1985, Dec. 8**    *Perf. 13½x13, 14*
1104 A696 1r multicolored    2.50 .50
1105 A697 3r multicolored    4.00 3.50
South Asian Regional Cooperation, SARC.

Shyama Shastri (1762-1827), Composer — A698

**1985, Dec. 21**     *Perf. 13½x13*
1106 A698 1r multicolored    4.00 1.60

**Famous Indians Type of 1983**
Master Tara Singh (1885-1967), Sikh leader.

**1985, Dec. 23**     *Perf. 13½x13*
1107 A639 50p org, green & blue   .75 .50

Intl. Youth Year A700

**1985, Dec. 24**
1108 A700 2r multicolored    4.25 2.25

**Famous Indians Type of 1983**
Design: Ravishankar Maharaj (1884-1984), freedom fighter, politician.

**1985, Dec. 24**     *Perf. 13½x13*
1109 A639 50p org, green & slate   .75 .50

Handel and Bach — A702

**1985, Dec. 27**     *Perf. 13x13½*
1110 A702 5r multicolored    8.50 4.75

Congress Presidents, 1924-1985 A703

**1985, Dec. 28**     *Perf. 14*
1111   Block of 4    13.00 13.00
   *a.-d.* A703 1r any single   2.50 2.25
Indian Natl. Congress, cent. Withdrawn on day of issue for a period of two weeks.

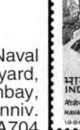

Naval Dockyard, Bombay, 250th Anniv. A704

**1986, Jan. 11**   Photo.   *Perf. 13½*
1112 A704 2.50r multicolored   7.50 4.50

INPEX '86, Jaipur, Feb. 14-19 A705

Designs: 50p, Hawa Mahal Palace, Jaipur. No. 3. 2r, Khar Desert mobile post office.

**1986, Feb. 14**     *Perf. 13½x13*
1113 A705 50p multicolored   2.50 .90
1114 A705 2r multicolored   3.75 2.10

Vikrant Aircraft Carrier, 25th Anniv. — A706

**1986, Feb. 16**     *Perf. 13x13½*
1115 A706 2r multicolored   11.50 8.00

Inaugural Airmail Flight, 75th Anniv. A707

**1986, Feb. 18**   *Perf. 13½x13, 13x13½*
1116 A707 50p Biplane    3.25 2.10
**Size: 41x28mm**
1117 A707   3r Jet    7.25 5.50

Sixth Triennale of the Arts, Lalit Kala Academy A708

Sri Chaitanya Mahaprabhu A709

**1986, Feb. 22**     *Perf. 13½x13*
1118 A708 1r multicolored   2.50 1.50

**1986, Mar. 3**     *Perf. 13*
1119 A709 2r multicolored   4.75 3.25

Mayo College, Ajmer, 111th Anniv. A710

**1986, Apr. 12**     *Perf. 13½x13*
1120 A710 1r multicolored   2.40 1.10

1986 World Cup Soccer Championships, Mexico — A711

**1986, May 31**   Photo.   *Perf. 13*
1121 A711 5r multicolored   8.00 4.25

**Famous Indians Type of 1983**
Bhim Sen Sachar (1894-1978), freedom fighter.

**1986, Aug. 14**   Photo.   *Perf. 13½x13*
1122 A639 50p org, green & sepia    8.25 4.50

Swami Sivananda (1887-1963), Religious Author — A713

**1986, Sept. 8**   Photo.   *Perf. 13½x13*
1123 A713 2r multicolored   5.00 3.00

10th Asian Games — A714

**1986, Sept. 16**     *Perf. 13½x13*
1124 A714 1.50r Women's volleyball    4.50 2.50
1125 A714   3r Hurdling   4.75 3.50

Madras Post Office, Bicent. A715

**1986, Oct. 9**   Photo.   *Perf. 13x13½*
1126 A715 5r black & brown orange    8.00 4.50

1st Battalion of Parachutists Regiment, 225th Anniv. — A716

Indian Police Force, 125th Anniv. — A717

**1986, Oct. 17**
1127 A716 3r multicolored   8.50 4.50

**1986, Oct. 21**     *Perf. 13½*
Uniforms, 1861-1986. No. 1129a has a continuous design.
1128 A717 1.50r multicolored   6.00 4.25
1129 A717   2r multicolored   6.00 4.25
   *a.*   Pair, #1129, 1128   14.00 14.00

Intl. Peace Year A718

**1986, Oct. 24**
1130 A718 5r sage grn, blue & rose    5.50 2.75

Children's Day — A719

**1986, Nov. 14**   Photo.   *Perf. 13½x13*
1131 A719 50p multicolored   4.00 2.10

UN, 40th Anniv. A720

**1986, Dec. 11**     *Perf. 13½x13*
1132 A720 50p Growth monitoring    3.25 2.25
1133 A720 5r Immunization   6.50 5.00
Child Survival Campaign.

Miyan Tansen, 17th Cent. Dhrupad Singer, Playing the Surbahar — A721

**1986, Dec. 12**
1134 A721 1r multicolored   3.50 1.00

Corbett Natl. Park, 50th Anniv. A722

**1986, Dec. 15**
1135 A722 1r Elephant 6.50 1.75
1136 A722 2r Gavial 7.50 5.25

**Famous Indians Type of 1983**
Designs: No. 1137, Alluri Seetarama Raju (b. 1897), freedom fighter. No. 1138, Sagarmal Gopa (b. 1900), freedom fighter. No. 1139, Veer Surendra Sai (b. 1809), freedom fighter.

**1986, Dec.** *Perf. 13½x13*
1137 A639 50p red, green & sepia 1.75 1.00
1138 A639 50p red, green & sl blue 1.75 1.00
1139 A639 50p red, green & dp red brn 1.75 1.00
Nos. 1137-1139 (3) 5.25 3.00
Issued: #1137, 26th; #1138, 29th; #1139, 30th.

St. Martha's Hospital, Bangalore, Cent. A724

**1986, Dec. 30** *Perf. 13½*
1140 A724 1r multicolored 4.00 2.25

Yacht Trishna A725

**1987, Jan. 10**
1141 A725 6.50r multicolored 8.00 4.25
1st Indian Army circumnavigation of the world, Sept. 28, 1985 to 1987.

Africa Fund — A726

**1987, Jan. 25 Photo.** *Perf. 14x14½*
1142 A726 6.50r black 8.25 4.50

ICC 29th Congress, New Delhi — A727

**1987, Feb. 11** *Perf. 13½*
1143 A727 5r multicolored 6.00 3.00

**Famous Indians Type of 1983**
Design: Hakim Ajmal Khan (1864-1927), physician, politician.

**1987, Feb. 13** *Perf. 13½x13*
1144 A639 60p org, grn & brn 2.75 .30

A729

Family Planning A730

**1987, Feb. 27** *Perf. 13, 13x13½*
1145 A729 35p dark red .20 .20
1146 A730 60p green & dark red .20 .20

**Famous Indians Type of 1983**
Designs: No. 1147, Lala Har Dayal (1884-1939). No. 1148, Manabendra Nath Roy (1887-1954). No. 1149, T. Ramaswamy Chowdary (1887-1943).

**1987 Photo.** *Perf. 13½x13*
1147 A639 60p org, green & purple .35 .25
1148 A639 60p org, green & red brn .35 .25
1149 A639 60p org, grn & brt blue .35 .25
Nos. 1147-1149 (3) 1.05 .75
Issued: #1147, 3/18; #1148, 3/21; #1149, 4/25.

SER Emblem, Blast Furnaces — A732

Electric Train Crossing Bridge — A734

Steam Locomotive No. 691 — A733

**1987, Mar. 28** *Perf. 13x13½, 13½x13*
1150 A732 1r shown .25 .25
1151 A733 1.50r shown .65 .35
1152 A734 2r shown 1.10 .45
1153 A733 4r Steam locomotive, c. 1890 1.50 .75
Nos. 1150-1153 (4) 3.50 1.80
Southeastern Railway, cent.

Kalia Bhomora Bridge, Assam A735

**1987, Apr. 14** *Perf. 13½*
1154 A735 2r multicolored .60 .30

Madras Christian College, 150th Anniv. A736

**1987, Apr. 16** *Perf. 13x13½*
1155 A736 1.50r black & rose lake .50 .40

A737

A738

**1987, May 1** *Perf. 13½*
1156 A737 1r dull brown .60 .30
Shree Shree Ma Anandamayee (1896-1982), spiritualist.

**1987, May 8** *Perf. 14*
1157 A738 2r multicolored .70 .35
Rabindranath Tagore (1861-1941), 1913 Nobel Laureate for literature.

A739

A740

**1987, May 10** *Perf. 13½*
1158 A739 1r multicolored 1.25 .50
Garhwal Rifles and Garhwal Scouts, cent.

**1987, May 11**
1159 A740 60p black brn & buff 1.10 .90
J. Krishnamurti (1895-1986), mystic.

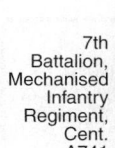

7th Battalion, Mechanised Infantry Regiment, Cent. A741

**1987, June 3** *Perf. 13½x13*
1160 A741 1r multicolored .90 .45

INDIA '89, New Delhi, Jan. 20-29, 1989 A742

**1987, June 15**
1161 A742 50p Swan emblem .25 .25
a. Bklt. pane of 4+inscribed margin ('89) .50
1162 A742 5r Hall of Nations, New Delhi 1.25 .45
a. Souv. sheet of 2, #1161-1162 2.50 2.50
b. Bklt. pane of 4+inscribed margin ('89) 6.00 6.00
Inscribed 1986. No. 1162a sold for 8r.

**Famous Indians Type of 1983**
Kailas Nath Katju (1887-1968), Chief Minister.

**1987, June 17** *Perf. 13½x13*
1163 A639 60p org, grn & yel brn .35 .25

Sadyah-Snata, Sanghol Sculpture, c. 2000 B.C. A744

**1987, July 3**
1164 A744 6.50r multicolored 1.75 .55
Festival of India in the USSR, July 3, 1987-88.

Natl. Independence, 40th Anniv. — A745

**1987, Aug. 15 Photo.** *Perf. 13x13½*
1165 A745 60p orange, brt blue & dk green .50 .40

Sant Harchand Singh Longowal (1932-1985), Social Reformer — A746

**1987, Aug. 20** *Perf. 13½*
1166 A746 1r multicolored 1.10 .40

**Famous Indians Type of 1983**
Design: S. Satyamurti (1887-1943), political reformer, martyr.

**1987, Aug. 22** *Perf. 13½x13*
1167 A639 60p org, green & brn .35 .25

Guru Ghasidas (1756-1837), Founder of the Saman Sect — A748

**1987, Sept. 1**
1168 A748 60p henna brown .50 .40

Sri Sri Thakur Anukul Chandra (1888-1969), Physician, Guru — A749

**1987, Sept. 2** *Perf. 13½*
1169 A749 1r multicolored 1.25 .60

University of Allahabad, Cent. A750

**1987, Sept. 23**     *Perf. 13½x13*
1170 A750 2r multicolored    .50 .30

Phoolwalon Ki Sair — A751

Maharaja Chhatrasal A752

**1987, Oct. 1**     *Perf. 13x13½*
1171 A751 2r Pankha (embroidered apron)    .50 .30
Festival of thanksgiving for fulfilled prayers.

**1987, Oct. 2**     *Perf. 14*
1172 A752 60p henna brown    .50 .35
Chhatrasal (1649-1731), military commander during the war against the Moguls.

Intl. Year of Shelter for the Homeless A753

**1987, Oct. 5**     *Perf. 13½x13*
1173 A753 5r multicolored    .80 .40

Asia Regional Conference of Rotary Intl. — A754

**1987, Oct. 14**
1174 A754 60p shown    .20 .20
1175 A754 6.50r Polio immunization    1.10 .50

Service to the Blind, Cent. A755

**1987, Oct. 15**
1176 A755 1r shown    .30 .30
1177 A755 2r Eye donation    .50 .35
World White Cane Day.

INDIA '89 — A756

Designs: 60p, The Iron Pillar, Quwwat-ul-Islam Mosque courtyard, 5th cent., Delhi.

1.50r, The India Gate, New Delhi, war memorial by Luytens, 1921. 5r, The Dewan-E-Khas, Hall of Private Audience, Red Fort, Delhi, c. 1648. 6.50r, Purana Qila, Old Fort, Delhi, c. 1540.

**1987, Oct. 17**
1178 A756 60p multicolored    .20 .20
   a.   Bklt. pane of 4 + inscribed margin ('89)    .60
1179 A756 1.50r multicolored    .40 .20
   a.   Bklt. pane of 4 + inscribed margin ('89)    1.60
1180 A756 5r multicolored    1.00 .40
   a.   Bklt. pane of 4 + inscribed margin ('89)    4.00
1181 A756 6.50r multicolored    1.50 .50
   a.   Souv. sheet of 4, #1178-1811    2.50 2.50
   b.   Bklt. pane of 4 + inscribed margin ('89)    6.00
    Nos. 1178-1181 (4)    3.10 1.30
No. 1181a sold for 15r.

Tyagmurti Goswami Ganeshdutt (1889-1959), Educator, Social Activist — A757

**1987, Nov. 2**     *Perf. 13½*
1182 A757 60p terra cotta    .50 .40

Children's Day — A758

**1987, Nov. 14**
1183 A758 60p multicolored    .50 .30

Trees A759

**1987, Nov. 19**     **Photo.**     *Perf. 13½*
1184 A759 60p Chinar, vert.    .25 .25
1185 A759 1.50r Pipal    .30 .25
1186 A759 5r Sal, vert.    .90 .55
1187 A759 6.50r Banyan    1.25 .80
    Nos. 1184-1187 (4)    2.70 1.85

Festival of the USSR in India — A760

Votive coin based on The Worker and the Peasant Woman, by Soviet sculptor Mukhina.

**1987, Nov. 21**     *Perf. 14*
1188 A760 5r multicolored    .80 .50

White Tiger — A761

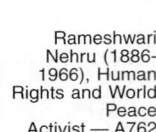

Rameshwari Nehru (1886-1966), Human Rights and World Peace Activist — A762

**1987, Nov. 29**     **Photo.**     *Perf. 13½*
1189 A761 1r shown    .75 .25
1190 A761 5r Snow leopard, horiz.    2.25 .90

**1987, Dec. 10**
1191 A762 60p red brown    .50 .40

Execution of Veer Narayan Singh (1795-1857), Sikh Uprising Leader — A763

**1987, Dec. 10**
1192 A763 60p dark brown    .50 .40

Father Kuriakose Elias Chavara (1806-1871), Theologian Beatified by Pope John Paul II Feb. 8, 1986 — A764

**1987, Dec. 20**
1193 A764 60p dark brown olive    .50 .40

Dr. Rajah Sir M.A. Muthiah Chettiar (1905-1984), Politician, Pro-chancellor of Annamalai University — A765

**1987, Dec. 21**     *Perf. 13*
1194 A765 60p chalky blue black    .50 .40

Sri Harmandir Sahib (Gold Temple), Amritsar, 400th Anniv. — A766

**1987, Dec. 26**     *Perf. 13½*
1195 A766 60p multicolored    1.25 .70

Rukmini Devi (1904-1986), Dancer, Choreographer — A767

**1987, Dec. 27**
1196 A767 60p dark red    .60 .35

Dr. Hiralal (1867-1934), Historian — A768

**1987, Dec. 31**
1197 A768 60p dark blue    .50 .40

Famous Indians Type of 1983

Design: Pandit Hriday Nath Kunzru (1887-1978), human rights activist, statesman.

**1987, Dec. 31**     *Perf. 13½x13*
1198 A639 60p org, grn & red brn    .35 .25

75th Session of the Indian Science Congress Assoc. A770

**1988, Jan. 1**
1199 A770 4r multicolored    .90 .55

Solar Energy A771

13th Asia Pacific Dental Congress, New Delhi, Jan. 28-Feb.2 A772

**Wmk. 324**
**1988, Jan. 1**     **Photo.**     *Perf. 13*
1200 A771 5r dp orange & sepia    .80 .40

**1988, Jan. 28**     **Unwmk.**     *Perf. 13*
1201 A772 4r multicolored    1.00 .50

Famous Indians Type of 1983

Designs: No. 1202, Mohan Lal Sukhadia (1916-1982). No. 1203, Dr. S.K. Sinha (1887-1961). No. 1204, Chandra Shekhar Azad (1906-1931). No. 1205, Govind Ballabh Pant (1887-1961).

**1988**     *Perf. 13½x13*
1202 A639 60p org, grn & bluish blk    .75 .60
1203 A639 60p org, grn & org brn    .75 .60
1204 A639 60p org, grn & rose red    .75 .60
1205 A639 60p org, grn & purple    .75 .60
    Nos. 1202-1205 (4)    3.00 2.40

Issue dates: Nos. 1202, Feb. 2; No. 1203, Feb. 4; No. 1204, Feb. 27; No. 1205, Mar. 7.

U. Tirot Sing (1800-1833), Patriot — A774

**1988, Feb. 3**
1206 A774 60p dull brown    .50 .40

Kumaon Regiment 4th Battalion, Bicent. — A775

Balgandharva (1888-1967), Musician — A776

**1988, Feb. 19**　　　　**Perf. 14**
1207　A775　1r Uniforms of 1788, 1947, 1988　　.60　.30

**1988, Feb. 22**　　　　**Perf. 13x13½**
1208　A776　60p brown　　.50　.40

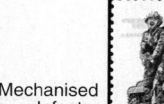

Mechanised Infantry Regiment A777

**1988, Feb. 24**　　　　**Perf. 13½x13**
1209　A777　1r multicolored　　.90　.45

A778

**1988, Feb. 26**　　　　**Perf. 13**
1210　A778　60p bluish black　　.50　.40
Sir B.N. Rau (1887-1953), constitutional advisor.

A779

**1988, Mar. 14　Photo.　Perf. 13x13½**
1211　A779　1r bright rose　　.50　.40
Mohindra College, Patiala, founded in 1875 by Maharaja Mohinder Singh, is now part of Punjabi University.

Dr. D.V. Gundappa (1887-1975), Journalist, and Gikhala Institute of Public Affairs — A780

**1988, Mar. 17**　　　　**Perf. 13½x13**
1212　A780　60p slate blue　　.50　.40

Woman Warrior Riding into Battle — A781

**1988, Mar. 20**　　　　**Perf. 13x13½**
1213　A781　60p bright rose　　.50　.40
Rani Avantibai (d. 1858), heroine of the 1857 independence war.

Malayala Manorama Newspaper, Cent. — A782

**1988, Mar. 23**
1214　A782　1r blue & black　　.50　.40
Malayala Manorama, published in Kottayam, is the largest circulated daily newspaper in India.

Maharshi Dadhichi, Vedic Period Saint Purported to Have Introduced Fire to Man — A783

**1988, Mar. 26**
1215　A783　60p deep orange　　.50　.40

Mohammad Iqbal (1877-1938), Poet — A784

**1988, Apr. 21**
1216　A784　60p carmine & gold　　.50　.40

Samarth Ramdas (1608-1682), Philosopher A785

**1988, May 1**　　　　**Perf. 13**
1217　A785　60p dk yellow green　　.50　.40

Swati Tirunal Rama Varma (1813-1846), Carnatic Composer — A786

**1988, May 2**　　　　**Perf. 13x13½**
1218　A786　60p brt violet　　.50　.40

1st War of Independence, the "Indian Mutiny of 1857" — A787
Painting: Rani Laxmi Bai transformed from a queen into a warrior fighting for justice, by M.F. Husain.

**1988, May 9　Photo.　Perf. 13x13½**
1219　A787　60p multicolored　　.50　.40

Bhaurao Patil (b. 1887), Educator A788

**1988, May 9**　　　　**Perf. 13½x13**
1220　A788　60p red brown　　.50　.40

Himalayan Peaks A789

**1988, May 19**
1221　A789　1.50r Broad Peak　　1.25　.30
1222　A789　4r Godwin Austin　　1.40　.40
1223　A789　5r Kanchenjunga　　1.40　.55
1224　A789　6.50r Nandadevi　　1.40　.70
　Nos. 1221-1224 (4)　　5.45　1.95

Care for the Elderly — A790

**1988, May 24**　　　　**Perf. 13x13½**
1225　A790　60p multicolored　　.50　.40

Victoria Terminal, Bombay, Cent. A791

**1988, May 30**　　　　**Perf. 13½x13**
1226　A791　1r multicolored　　.80　.30

Lawrence School, Lovedale, 130th Anniv. A792

**1988, May 31**　　　　**Perf. 13**
1227　A792　1r dk green & red brown　　.70　.40

World Environment Day — A793

**1988, June 5**　　　　**Perf. 14**
1228　A793　60p Khejri tree　　.50　.40

### Famous Indians Type of 1983

#1229, Dr. Anugrah Narain Singh (1887-1957), statesman. #1230, Kuladhor Chaliha (1886-1963), political and social reformer. #1231, Shivprasad Gupta (1883-1944), freedom fighter.

**1988**　　　　**Perf. 13½x13**
1229　A639　60p org, grn & rose vio　　.65　.40
1230　A639　60p org, grn & gray blk　　.65　.40
1231　A639　60p org, grn & dk vio　　.65　.40
　Nos. 1229-1231 (3)　　1.95　1.20
　Issued: #1229, 6/18; #1230, 6/19; #1231, 6/28.

Rani Durgawati (d. 1564), Ruler of Gondwana — A795

**1988, June 24**
1232　A795　60p red　　.50　.40

A796

A797

**1988, July 28　Photo.　Perf. 13x13½**
1233　A796　60p red brown　　.50　.40
Acharya Shanti Dev (687-765), Sanskrit and Pali scholar.

**1988, Aug. 4**
1234　A797　60p blue violet　　.50　.40
Yashwant Singh Parmar (1906-1981), administrator of Himachal Pradesh State.

Painting by M.F. Husain — A798

**1988, Aug. 16   Photo.   Perf. 13x13½**
1235  A798  60p India at upper left          .30   .30
1236          60p India at lower left          .30   .30
  *a.*  A798  Pair, #1235-1236               1.00  1.00

Natl. Independence 40th anniv.

Durgadas Rathore
(1638-1718),
Guardian of King
Ajit Singh — A799

**1988, Aug. 26                      Litho.**
1237  A799  60p dark red brown               .50   .40

Famous Indians Type of 1983

Design: Sarat Chandra Bose (1889-1950),
politician, lawyer, publisher.

**1988, Sept. 6   Photo.   Perf. 13½x13**
1238  A639  60p org, grn & dk
                 blue grn                       .50   .40

Gopinath Kaviraj
(1887-1976),
Scholar — A801

**1988, Sept. 7             Perf. 13x13½**
1239  A801  60p brown olive                   .50   .40

Hindi Language
Day, Sept. 14
A802

Indian Olympic
Assoc.
Emblem
A803

Glory of Sport, Independence 40th
Anniv. — A804

**1988, Sept. 14   Photo.   Perf. 13x13½**
1240  A802  60p ver & dk olive
                 green                           .50   .40

---

**1988, Sept. 17**
1241  A803  60p deep claret                   .80   .45
1242  A804   5r multicolored                  4.50  1.60

Famous Indians Type of 1983

Baba Kharak (1867-1963), nationalist.

**1988, Oct. 6                Perf. 13½x13**
1243  A639  60p org, green & org
                 brn                             .50   .40

Jerdon's
Courser — A806

**1988, Oct. 7                Perf. 13½**
1244  A806   1r multicolored                  5.00   .65

The Times of India, Newspaper, 150th
Anniv. — A807

**1988, Nov. 3              Perf. 13½x14**
1245  A807  1.50r black & gold                .50   .35

INDIA
'89 — A808

**Perf. 13½x13**
**1988, Oct. 9        Unwmk.        Photo.**
1246  A808   4r Bangalore P.O.                .75   .30
  *a.*    Bklt. pane of 6+inscribed mar-
           gin ('89)                          4.50
1247  A808   5r Bombay P.O.                   1.50   .35
  *a.*    Bklt. pane of 6+inscribed mar-
           gin ('89)                          9.00

Portrait of Azad
by K.K.
Hebbar — A809

**1988, Nov. 11**
1248  A809  60p multicolored                  .50   .40
  Maulana Abul Kalam Azad (1888-1958),
minister of education, natl. resources and scientific research.

Jawaharlal Nehru — A810

---

**1988, Nov. 14**
1249  A810  60p dk gray, dk or-
                 ange & dk grn              .65   .35
1250  A810   1r Portrait, vert.             .75   .35

Birsa,
Munda
Leader
A811

**1988, Nov. 15            Perf. 13½x13**
1251  A811  60p brown                        .50   .40

Bhakra Dam, 25th Anniv. — A812

**1988, Dec. 15            Perf. 14**
1252  A812  60p carmine rose               .70   .70

INDIA
'89 — A813

60p, Dead-letter cancellations, 1886. 6.50r,
Traveling p.o. cancellation, 1864-69.

**1988, Dec. 20           Perf. 13½x13**
1253  A813   60p multicolored               .75   .40
  *a.*    Bklt. pane of 6+inscribed
          margin ('89)                      5.00
1254  A813  6.50r multicolored             2.50  1.40
  *a.*    Bklt. pane of 6+inscribed
          margin ('89)                     15.00

K.M. Munshi (1887-1971),
Environmentalist, Statesmen — A814

**1988, Dec. 30**
1255  A814  60p dark olive green           .50   .40

Mannathu
Padmanabhan
(1878-1970),
Social
Reformer — A815

**1989, Jan. 2             Perf. 13½x13**
1256  A815  60p dull brown                 .50   .40

Famous Indians Type of 1983

Hare Krushna Mahtab (1899-1987), author.

**1989, Jan. 2             Perf. 13½x13**
1257  A639  60p orange, grn &
                 black                      .60   .40

---

Lok Sabha
Secretariat,
60th Anniv.
A817

**1989, Jan. 10           Perf. 13½x13**
1258  A817  60p dark olive green           .50   .40

State Museum,
Lucknow, 125th
Anniv. — A818

**1989, Jan. 11           Perf. 14**
1259  A818  60p Goddess Durga,
                 lion                       .50   .40

INDIA
'89 — A819

**1989, Jan. 20           Perf. 13½x13**
1260  A819   60p Youth collecting          .20   .20
  *a.*    Bklt. pane of 6 + inscribed
          margin                                 .60
1261  A819  1.50r Postal coach &
                 p.o., 1842                 .40   .20
  *a.*    Bklt. pane of 6 + inscribed
          margin                            2.40
1262  A819    5r Travancore #2             1.00   .40
  *a.*    Bklt. pane of 6 + inscribed
          margin                            6.00
1263  A819  6.50r Philatelic journal
                 mastheads                 1.50   .40
  *a.*    Bklt. pane of 6 + inscribed
          margin                            9.00
          Nos. 1260-1263 (4)               3.10  1.30

St. John Bosco
(1815-1888),
Educator — A820

**1989, Jan. 31           Perf. 13**
1264  A820  60p carmine rose               .50   .40

3rd Cavalry,
148th
Anniv.
A821

**1989, Feb. 8            Perf. 13½x13**
1265  A821  60p multicolored               1.00   .55

Dargah
Sharif Ajmer
A822

**1989, Feb. 13   Litho.   Perf. 13½x13**
1266  A822   1r multicolored               .50   .40

President's Review of the Naval Fleet — A823

**1989, Feb. 15**    *Perf. 14*
1267 A823 6.50r multicolored    3.50 1.90

**Famous Indians Type of 1983**

#1268, Sheikh Mohammad Abdullah. #1269, Balasaheb Gangadhar Kher (1888-1957), politician. #1270, Saiffuddin Kitchlew (1888-1963), lawyer, diplomat. #1271, Rajkumari Amrit Kaur (d. 1964), minister of health and welfare.

**1988-89**    **Photo.**    *Perf. 13½x13*
1268 A639 60p org, grn & lil rose   .50 .40
1269 A639 60p org, grn & dk vio   .50 .40
1270 A639 60p org, grn & blk brn   .50 .40
1271 A639 60p org, grn & grnsh blk   .50 .40
   Nos. 1268-1271 (4)   2.00 1.60

Issue dates: No. 1268, Dec. 5; No. 1269, Mar. 8, 1989; Nos. 1270-1271, Apr. 13, 1989.

Freedom Fighters — A825

#1272, Baldev Ramji Mirdha (1889-1956). #1273, Rao Gopal Singh (1899-1939).

**1989**    *Perf. 13½x13½*
1272 A825 60p slate   .50 .40
1273 A825 60p dark olive   .50 .40
Issue dates: #1272, Jan. 17; #1273, Mar. 30.

Freedom Fighters A826

Designs: No. 1274, Shaheed Laxman Nayak (1899-1943), protest leader. No. 1275, Bishu Ram Medhi (1888-1981), politician.

**1989**    *Perf. 13½x13*
1274 A826 60p org, sage grn & brn   .25 .20
   **Size: 24x37mm**
1275 A826 60p org, sage grn & dp yel grn   .35 .20
Issued: #1274, Mar. 29; #1275, Apr. 24.
See #1292, 1299-1300, 1317, 1429, 1487.

Sydenham College, Bombay A827

**1989, Apr. 19**    *Perf. 13½*
1276 A827 60p black   .50 .40

**Famous Indians Type of 1983**
Design: Asaf Ali (1888-1953), patriot.

**1989, May 11 Photo.**   *Perf. 13½x13*
1277 A639 60p org, green & sepia   .25 .20

N.S. Hardikar (1889-1975), Freedom Fighter — A829

**1989, May 13**    *Perf. 13x13½*
1278 A829 60p chestnut brown   .50 .40

Sankaracharya (b. 788), Philosopher — A830

**1989, May 17**    *Perf. 14x13½*
1279 A830 60p multicolored   .50 .40

Punjab University, Chandigarh A831

**1989, May 19**    *Perf. 13½x13*
1280 A831 1r blue green & brn   .50 .40

Film Industry, 75th Anniv. — A832

**1989, May 30**    **Photo.**    *Perf. 14*
1281 A832 60p dk olive bis & blk   .60 .45

Kirloskar Corporation, Cent. A833

**1989, June 20 Photo.**   *Perf. 13½x13*
1282 A833 1r multicolored   .50 .40

DAV Education Movement, Cent. A834

**1989, June 27 Photo.**   *Perf. 13½x13*
1283 A834 1r multicolored   .50 .40

Dakshin Gangotri Post Office in the Antarctic, 1988 A835

**1989, July 11**    *Perf. 14*
1284 A835 1r multicolored   2.50 .50

Allahabad Bank, 125th Anniv. A836

**1989, July 19**
1285 A836 60p multicolored   .50 .40

Central Reserve Police Force, 50th Anniv. A837

**1989, July 27**    *Perf. 13½x13*
1286 A837 60p golden brown   2.40 .80

Military Farms, Cent. A838

**1989, Aug. 18**
1287 A838 1r multicolored   1.20 4.50

Kemal Ataturk (1881-1938), 1st President of Turkey — A839

**1989, Aug. 30**    *Perf. 13x13½*
1288 A839 5r multicolored   2.40 .80

Sarvepalli Radhakrishnan, President of India, 1962-67 — A840

**1989, Sept. 11 Photo.**   *Perf. 13x13½*
1289 A840 60p black   .50 .40

P. Subbarayan (1889-1962), Lawyer, Political Reformer — A841

**1989, Sept. 30**    *Perf. 13x13½*
1290 A841 60p brown orange   .50 .40

Mohun Bagan Soccer Team, Cent. A842

**1989, Sept. 23 Photo.**   *Perf. 13½x13*
1291 A842 1r multicolored   2.40 1.00

**Freedom Fighter Type of 1989**
Shyamji Krishna Varma (1857-1930).

**1989, Oct. 4**    **Photo.**    *Perf. 13½x13*
1292 A826 60p org, sage grn & dk red brn   .50 .40

Sayaji Rao Gaekwad III (1863-1939), Maharaja of the Former State of Baroda — A843

**1989, Oct. 6**    *Perf. 13x13½*
1293 A843 60p black   .50 .40

Use Pin Code A844

**1989, Oct. 14**    *Perf. 14*
1294 A844 60p multicolored   .65 .25

Namakkal Kavignar (1888-1972), Poet Laureate — A845

**1989, Oct. 19 Photo.**   *Perf. 13x13½*
1295 A845 60p black   .50 .40

18th Intl. Epilepsy Congress and 14th World Neurology Congress, New Delhi A846

**1989, Oct. 21**    *Perf. 13½x13*
1296 A846 6.50r multicolored   4.25 1.10

Ramabai and Sharada Sadan School A847

**1989, Oct. 26**
1297 A847 60p brown   .50 .30

Pandita Ramabai (1858-1920), women's rights activist, founder of mission to help destitute women and children.

Pigeon Post A848

**1989, Nov. 3**
1298 A848 1r brown orange   .90 .35

**Freedom Fighter Type of 1989**

#1299, Acharya Narendra Deo (1889-1956), democratic socialist movement founder. #1300, Acharya Kripalani (1888-1982), politician.

**1989**                          **Perf. 13½x13**
1299 A826 60p org, sage grn &
      brn                           .50   .40
1300 A826 60p org, sage grn &
      dp gray                       .50   .40
Issue dates: #1299, Nov. 6; #1300, Nov. 11.

Jawaharlal Nehru, Birth Cent. — A849

**1989, Nov. 14**                 **Perf. 14x15**
1301 A849 1r buff, dk red brn &
      sepia                        1.00   .30

8th Asian Track and Field Meet,
Nov. 14-19, New Delhi — A850

**1989, Nov. 19**                 **Perf. 14x14½**
1302 A850 1r black, org & dp grn  .70   .40

A851

**1989, Nov. 20**                 **Perf. 13x13½**
1303 A851 60p deep brown          .60   .45
  Gurunath Bewoor (b. 1888), 1st Indian
appointed postmaster general.

A852

**1989, Dec. 8  Photo.   Perf. 13x13½**
1304 A852 60p black               .60   .45
  Balkrishna Sharma Navin (1897-1960), lit-
terateur, politician.

Bombay Art Soc., Cent. A853

**1989, Dec. 15**                 **Perf. 13½x13**
1305 A853 1r multicolored         .60   .45

Likh Florican — A854

Digboi Oil Field, 1889 — A855

**1989, Dec. 20**                 **Perf. 13x13½**
1306 A854 2r multicolored        3.00   .95

**1989, Dec. 29**                 **Perf. 14**
1307 A855 60p dark red brown      .80   .45
  Discovery of oil, Digboi, Assam, cent.

M.G. Ramachandran (1917-1987), Actor, Chief Minister — A856

**1990, Jan. 17**                 **Perf. 13x13½**
1308 A856 60p dark red brown      .80   .30

Extracting Silt from Sukhna Lake, Chandigarh A857

**1990, Jan. 29**                 **Perf. 13½x13**
1309 A857 1r multicolored         .60   .45
  Sukhna Shramda, society for the preservation of Sukhna Lake.

Presentation of Colors by Pres. Venkataraman to the Bombay Sappers (Corps of Engineers), Feb. 21 — A858

                              **Perf. 15x14x14**
**1990, Feb. 21**                 **Photo.**
1310 A858 60p multicolored       1.75  1.25

Asian Development Bank — A859

**1990, May 2**                   **Photo.    Perf. 14**
1311 A859 2r Seashell            1.40   .45

Great Britain No. 1, Simulated Cancel of India, Envelope A860

**1990, May 6**                   **Perf. 13x13½**
1312 A860 6r multicolored        2.25   .75
  Penny Black, 150th anniv.

Residence and Portrait A861

**1990, May 17  Photo.    Perf. 13½x13**
1313 A861 2r red brown & green    .60   .40
  Ho Chi Minh (1890-1969), Vietnamese
Communist Party leader.

A862                A863

**1990, May 29**
1314 A862 1r orange brown         .50   .45
  Prime Minister Chaudhary Charan Singh
(1902-1987).

**1990, July 30  Photo.   Perf. 13x13½**
1315 A863 2r multicolored         .80   .55
  Indian peace keeping force in Sri Lanka.

Indian Council of Agricultural Research — A864

**1990, July 31**                 **Perf. 14**
1316 A864 2r multicolored         .60   .40

Freedom Fighter Type of 1989
  Design: Khudiram Bose (1889-1908), vert.

**1990, Aug. 11  Photo.   Perf. 13x13½**
                              **Size: 26x35mm**
1317 A826 1r orange, grn & red
      brn                          .60   .45

Russian Child's Drawing of India — A865

6.50r, Indian child's drawing of Red Square.

**1990, Aug. 16  Photo.    Perf. 14**
1318 A865 1r multicolored        2.40  1.60
1319 A865 6.50r multicolored     2.40  1.60
  a.  Pair, #1318-1319            5.50  5.50
  See Russia Nos. 5925-5926.

A866

A867

**1990, Aug. 24**                 **Perf. 13**
1320 A866 1r lt red brown         .60   .45
  K. Kelappan (1889-1971), social
revolutionary.

**1990, Sept. 5**                 **Perf. 13x13½**
1321 A867 1r multicolored         .90   .50
  Care for young girls.

Intl. Literacy Year A868

**1990, Sept. 8**                 **Perf. 13½x13**
1322 A868 1r blue, brn & tan      .90   .50

A869

**1990, Sept. 10**                **Perf. 13x14**
1323 A869 4r blue grn & red      2.50  1.60
  Safe drinking water.

A870

**1990, Sept. 28  Photo.   Perf. 13x13½**
1324 A870 60p rose lake           .90   .50
  Sunder Lal Sharma (1881-1940), social
reformer.

11th Asian
Games,
Beijing — A871

**1990, Sept. 29**
1325 A871 1r Kabbadi .80 .35
1326 A871 4r Sprinting 2.40 1.75
1327 A871 4r Cycling 2.40 1.75
1328 A871 6.50r Archery 3.00 2.25
*Nos. 1325-1328 (4)* 8.60 6.10

A.K. Gopalan
(1904-1977),
Political and Social
Reformer — A872

**1990, Oct. 1**
1329 A872 1r red brown .90 .50

5th Gurkha Rifles,
3rd and 5th
Battalions — A873

**1990, Oct. 1**
1330 A873 2r yel brown & dk vio 3.00 1.75

Suryamall Mishran
(1815-1868),
Poet — A874

**1990, Oct. 19**
1331 A874 2r brown & yel brown 1.00 .60

Children's
Day — A875

*Perf. 13½x13*
**1990, Nov. 14 Photo. Unwmk.**
1332 A875 1r multicolored 1.25 .60

Border
Security
Force, 25th
Anniv.
A876

**1990, Nov. 30**
1333 A876 5r multicolored 3.25 1.60

Greetings — A877

4r, Two elephants carrying riders, horiz.

*Perf. 13x13½, 13½x13*
**1990, Dec. 17 Photo.**
1334 A877 1r multicolored .35 .30
1335 A877 4r multicolored 1.00 .50

Cities of
India
A878

**1990, Dec. 24 Photo. Perf. 13½x13**
1336 A878 4r Bikaner .80 .65
1337 A878 5r Hyderabad 1.25 .95
1338 A878 6.50r Cuttack 1.75 1.25
*Nos. 1336-1338 (3)* 3.80 2.85

Bhakta Kanakadas
(1488-1578),
Mystic — A879

**1990, Dec. 26 Perf. 14**
1339 A879 1r red orange .90 .45

Dnyaneshwari,
700th
Anniv. — A880

**1990, Dec. 31 Perf. 13½x13**
1340 A880 2r org red, red brown
& blk .60 .40

Calcutta, 300th
Anniv. — A881

**Unwmk.**
**1990, Dec. 28 Photo. Perf. 14**
Designs: 1r, Shaheed Minar. 6r, Sailing
ships on Ganges River.

1341 A881 1r multicolored .50 .30
**Size: 44x35mm**
1342 A881 6r multicolored 2.25 1.50

Pandit
Mohan
Malaviya,
Banaras
Hindu
University
A882

**1991, Jan. 20 Perf. 13½x13**
1343 A882 1r dk carmine rose .60 .35
Banaras Hindu University, 75th Anniv.

Intl.
Conference
on Traffic
Safety
A883

**1991, Jan. 30 Perf. 13½x13**
1344 A883 6.50r blue, red & blk 1.25 .80

7th Art
Triennial — A884

**1991, Feb. 12 Photo. Perf. 13x13½**
1345 A884 6.50r multicolored 1.00 .60

Jagannath
Sunkersett
A885

**1991, Feb. 15**
1346 A885 2r ultra & henna brn .80 .50
Jagannath Sunkersett (1803-1865), educator, reformer.

Tata
Memorial
Center,
50th Anniv.
A886

**1991, Feb. 28 Perf. 13½x13**
1347 A886 2r brown & buff .60 .35

River
Dolphin
A887

**1991, Mar. 4**
1348 A887 4r shown 2.75 1.75
1349 A887 6.50r Sea cow 3.75 2.40

Fight Against
Drugs — A888

World
Peace — A889

**1991, Mar. 5 Perf. 13x13½**
1350 A888 5r dp violet & red 3.00 1.90

**1991, Mar. 7 Photo. Perf. 13x13½**
1351 A889 6.50r black & tan 1.25 .75

Indian
Remote
Sensing
Satellite
1A — A890

**1991, Mar. 18 Perf. 14**
1352 A890 6.50r blue, red brn &
blk 1.00 .60

Babu Jagjivan
Ram (1908-1976),
Politician — A891

**1991, Apr. 5 Photo. Perf. 13½**
1353 A891 1r yellow & brown .60 .50

Dr. B.R. Ambedkar (1891-1956),
Social Reformer — A892

**1991, Apr. 14 Perf. 13½x13**
1354 A892 1r red brown & blue .60 .35

Tribal
Dances
A893

**1991, Apr. 30 Photo. Perf. 13½x13**
1355 A893 2.50r Valar .90 .50
1356 A893 4r Kayang 1.10 .60
1357 A893 5r Hozagiri 1.50 .70
1358 A893 6.50r Velakali 1.75 .85
*Nos. 1355-1358 (4)* 5.25 2.65

Ariyakudi Ramanuja Iyengar (1890-
1967), Musician — A894

**1991, May 18**
1359 A894 2r green & red brown 1.00 .60

Karpoori Thakur (1924-1988), Politician — A895

**1991, May 30**          *Perf. 13x13½*
1360  A895  1r red brown                    .60   .50

Antarctic Treaty, 30th Anniv. A896

**1991, June 23  Photo.  *Perf. 13½x13***
1361  A896  5r Penguins               3.50  2.10
1362  A896  6.50r Map, penguins       3.50  2.10
   *a.*   Pair, #1361-1362             7.50  7.50

No. 1362a printed in continuous design.

New Delhi, 60th Anniv. A897

Views of New Delhi architecture.

**1991, June 25**
1363  A897  5r multicolored           2.00  1.10
1364  A897  6.50r multicolored        2.00  1.10
   *a.*   Pair, #1363-1364            4.00  4.00

No. 1364a printed in continuous design.

Sri Ram Sharma Acharya (1911-1990), Social Reformer — A898

**1991, June 27**
1365  A898  1r red & blue green        .60   .50

K. Shankar Pillai (1902-1989), Cartoonist — A899

**1991, July 31  Photo.  *Perf. 13½x13***
1366  A899  4r shown                  1.75  1.25

**Perf. 13x13½**
1367  A899  6.50r The Big Show, vert.  2.50  1.90

Sriprakash (1890-1971), Politician — A900

**1991, Aug. 3**          *Perf. 13½x13*
1368  A900  2r yellow brown            .60   .40

Gopinath Bardoloi (1890-1950), Politician — A901

**1991, Aug. 5**          *Perf. 13x13½*
1369  A901  1r violet                  .60   .50

Rajiv Gandhi (1944-1991), Prime Minister — A902

**1991, Aug. 20**          *Perf. 13*
1370  A902  1r multicolored           1.50  1.00

Jain Muni Mishrimalji (1891-1984), Philospher — A903

**1991, Aug. 24  Photo.  *Perf. 13½***
1371  A903  1r brown                   .60   .35

Mahadevi Verma (1907-1987), Writer and Poet — A904

No. 1373: Jayshankar Prasad (1890-1937), poet and dramatist.

**1991, Sept. 16**
1372  A904  2r black & blue            .35   .25
1373  A904  2r black & blue            .35   .25
   *a.*   Pair, #1372-1373             .70   .70

37th Commonwealth Parliamentary Conference — A905

**1991, Sept. 27  Photo.  *Perf. 13½x13***
1374  A905  6.50r dk blue & brown    .80   .60

Greetings — A906

Orchids — A907

**1991, Sept. 30**          *Perf. 13x13½*
1375  A906  1r Frog                    .20   .20
1376  A906  6.50r Bird                 .90   .45
   *a.*   Pair, #1375-1376            1.10  1.00

**1991, Oct. 12**
1377  A907  1r Cymbidium
                  aloifolium           .25   .25
1378  A907  2.50r Paphiopedilum
                  venustum             .50   .30
1379  A907  3r Aerides crispum         .60   .40
1380  A907  4r Cymbidium bi-
                  colour               .90   .50
1381  A907  5r Vanda spathu-
                  lata                 1.00  .70
1382  A907  6.50r Cymbidium
                  devonianum           1.25  1.00
   Nos. 1377-1382 (6)                 4.50  3.15

2nd Battalion, Third Gurkha Rifles A908

**1991, Oct. 18**          *Perf. 13½x13*
1383  A908  4r multicolored           3.50  2.00

Kamaladevi Chattopadhyaya (1903-1988), Founder of All-India Handicrafts Board — A909

**1991, Oct. 29**          *Perf. 13x13½*
1384  A909  1r Horsemen               .70   .30
1385  A909  6.50r Puppet              1.90  1.10

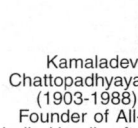

Chithira Tirunal Bala Rama Varma (1912-1991), Maharaja of Travancore — A910

**1991, Nov. 7  Photo.  *Perf. 13½x13***
1386  A910  2r violet                 1.25   .90

Children's Day — A911

**1991, Nov. 14**          *Perf. 13x13½*
1387  A911  1r multicolored           1.25   .50

18th Cavalry, Sesquicentennial (in 1992) — A912

**1991, Nov. 14**          *Perf. 13½x13*
1388  A912  6.50r multicolored        4.25  2.50

India Tourism Year A913

**1991, Nov. 15**
1389  A913  6.50r multicolored        1.25   .95

Intl. Conference on Youth Tourism — A914

Wolfgang Amadeus Mozart, Death Bicent. — A915

**1991, Nov. 18  Photo.  *Perf. 13x13½***
1390  A914  6.50r multicolored        2.00  1.25

**1991, Dec. 5**
1391  A915  6.50r multicolored        3.25  1.90

SAARC Year of Shelter A916

**1991, Dec. 7**          *Perf. 13½x13*
1392  A916  4r lake & bister          1.00   .75

Run for Your Heart A917

**1991, Dec. 11**
1393  A917  1r black, red & gray      .60   .50

Siddhartha With An Injured Bird — A918

**1991, Dec. 28** **Perf. 13x13½**
1394 A918 2r multicolored .60 .40
Asit Kumar Haldar (1890-1964), Painter

Yoga Exercises A919

**1991, Dec. 30 Photo. Perf. 13½x13**
1395 A919 2r Bhujangasana .25 .25
1396 A919 5r Dhanurasana .65 .30
1397 A919 6.50r Ustrasana .95 .45
1398 A919 10r Utthita
trikonasana 1.60 .65
Nos. 1395-1398 (4) 3.45 1.65

Intl. Assoc. for Bridge and Structural Engineering A920

#1399, Hooghly River Bridge, Madurai Temple. #1400, Sanchi Stupa gates, Hall of Nations.

**1992, Mar. 1 Photo. Perf. 13½x13**
1399 A920 2r sal, brn & blue 1.40 .85
1400 A920 2r sal, brn & blue 1.40 .85
a. Pair, #1399-1400 2.75 2.75

Fifth Intl. Conference on Goats — A921

Natl. Council of YMCAs, Cent. (in 1991) — A922

**1992, Mar. 2 Perf. 13½x13½**
1401 A921 6r dk blue & brown 5.00 2.75

**1992, Feb. 21**
1402 A922 1r blue & vermilion .60 .40

National Archives A923

**1992, Apr. 20 Photo. Perf. 13½x13**
1403 A923 6r multicolored .80 .55

Krushna Chandra Gajapathi — A924

Vijay Singh Pathik, Writer — A925

**1992, Apr. 29 Perf. 13x13½**
1404 A924 1r violet .60 .40
1405 A925 1r red brown .60 .40

Adventure Sports A926

**1992, Apr. 29 Perf. 13½x13**
1406 A926 2r Hang gliding .35 .35
1407 A926 4r Wind surfing 1.10 .60
1408 A926 5r River rafting 1.60 .95
1409 A926 11r Skiing 1.90 1.60
Nos. 1406-1409 (4) 4.95 3.50

Henry Gidney (1873-1942), Physician and Politician — A927

**1992, May 9 Perf. 13½x13**
1410 A927 1r blue & black 1.10 .55

Telecommunication Training Center, Jabalpur, 50th Anniv. — A928

**1992, May 30**
1411 A928 1r lemon .60 .50

A929

A930

**1992, July 31 Perf. 13x13½**
1412 A929 1r black & brown .60 .50
Sardar Udham Singh (1899-1940), freedom fighter.

**1992, Aug. 8**
1413 A930 1r Discus .50 .25
1414 A930 6r Gymnastics 1.40 .85
1415 A930 8r Field hockey 3.25 1.90
1416 A930 11r Boxing 3.25 2.25
Nos. 1413-1416 (4) 8.40 5.25
1992 Summer Olympics, Barcelona.

Quit India Movement, 50th Anniv. A931

Designs: 1r, Spinning wheel, inscription. 2r, Mahatma Gandhi, inscription.

**1992, Aug. 9 Perf. 13x13½**
1417 A931 1r pink, blk & pale
pink 3.75 .65
1418 A931 2r gray, black & claret 4.75 3.75

60th Parachute Field Ambulance, 50th Anniv. A932

**1992, Aug. 10**
1419 A932 1r multicolored 2.75 .90

Indian Air Force, 60th Anniv. A933

**1992, Oct. 8 Photo. Perf. 13½x13**
1420 A933 1r shown .95 .60
1421 A933 10r Biplane, jet fighter 1.90 1.10
a. Pair, #1420-1421 5.00 5.00

Phad Painting of Dev Narayan A934

**1992, Sept. 2 Photo. Perf. 13½x14**
1422 A934 5r multicolored 1.25 .95

Sisters of Jesus and Mary, 150th Anniv. — A935

**1992, Nov. 13 Photo. Perf. 13x13½**
1423 A935 1r gray & blue .60 .35

Children's Day A936

**1992, Nov. 14 Perf. 13½x13**
1424 A936 1r multicolored .60 .35

Shri Yogiji Maharaj, Religious Leader, Birth Cent. — A937

**1992, Dec. 2 Photo. Perf. 13½x13½**
1425 A937 1r blue 2.75 1.50

Army Service Corps 1760-1992 A938

**1992, Dec. 8 Photo. Perf. 13½x13**
1426 A938 1r multicolored 3.50 .80

Stephen Smith (1891-1951), Rocket Mail Pioneer — A939

**1992, Dec. 19 Photo. Perf. 13½x13**
1427 A939 11r multicolored 1.75 1.10

State of Haryana, 25th Anniv. A940

**1992, Dec. 20**
1428 A940 2r green & orange .60 .60

Freedom Fighter Type of 1989
Design: Madan Lal Dhingra, vert.

**1992, Dec. 28 Perf. 13x13½**
1429 A826 1r org, grn & brn .60 .35

Dr. Shri Shiyali Ramamrita Ranganathan (1892-1972), Writer and Librarian — A941

**1992, Aug. 30 Photo. Perf. 13½x13**
1430 A941 1r blue 2.75 .65

Hanuman Prasad Poddar — A942

Pandit Ravishankar Shukla — A943

**1992, Sept. 19   Photo.   Perf. 13x13½**
1431   A942   1r green                     .60   .30

**1992, Dec. 31**
1432   A943   1r rose lake                 .60   .30

Birds — A944

2r, Pandion haliaetus. 6r, Falco peregrinus. 8r, Gypaetus barbatus. 11r, Aquila chrysaetos.

**1992, Dec. 30**
1433   A944   2r multicolored     1.50   .85
1434   A944   6r multicolored     2.25   1.25
1435   A944   8r multicolored     2.50   1.40
1436   A944   11r multicolored    2.75   1.90
        Nos. 1433-1436 (4)         9.00   5.40

William Carey, Baptist Missionary to India, Bicent. of Appointment A945

**1993, Jan. 9   Photo.   Perf. 13½x13**
1437   A945   6r multicolored     2.00   1.10

Fakir Mohan Senapati, Writer — A946

**1993, Jan. 14   Perf. 13x13½**
1438   A946   1r orange brown     .75   .40

Council of Scientific and Industrial Research, 50th Anniv. — A947

**1993, Feb. 28   Perf. 13½x13**
1439   A947   1r violet brown     1.10   .45

Squadron No. 1, Indian Air Force, 60th Anniv. A948

**1993, Apr. 1**
1440   A948   1r shown            1.50   .35
1441   A948   1r Paratroopers,
              planes, artillery   1.50   .35
Parachute Field Regiment 9, 50th anniv. (#1441).

Rahul Sankrityayan (1893-1963), Politician — A949

**1993, Apr. 9**
1442   A949   1r multicolored     .75   .35

Mountain Locomotives A950

**1993, Apr. 16   Perf. 13½x13**
1443   A950   1r Neral Matheran   1.00   .30
1444   A950   6r DHR (Darjeeling) 2.00   1.00
1445   A950   8r Nilgiri Mountain
              Railway             2.25   1.25
1446   A950   11r Kalka-Simla     3.25   1.60
        Nos. 1443-1446 (4)        8.50   4.15

89th Inter-Parliamentary Union Conference, New Delhi — A951

**1993, Apr. 11   Photo.   Perf. 13x13½**
1447   A951   1r indigo           .75   .35

Meerut College, Cent. (in 1992) — A952

**1993, Apr. 25   Perf. 14**
1448   A952   1r indigo & red brown   .75   .60

P.C. Mahalanobis (b. 1893), Statistician — A953

**1993, June 29   Perf. 13x13½**
1449   A953   1r olive yellow     .60   .35

Dadabhai Naoroji's Election to House of Commons, Cent. — A957

**1993, Aug. 26   Photo.   Perf. 14**
1453   A957   6r blue & red brown   1.00   .70

A958

A959

**1993, Sept. 11   Perf. 13x13½**
1454   A958   2r gray, red brn & org   1.00   .55
Swami Vivekananda, Chicago address, cent.

**1993, Oct. 9   Photo.   Perf. 13x13½**
Trees: 1r, Lagerstroemia speciosa. 6r, Cochlospermum religiosum. 8r, Erythrina variegata. 11r, Thespesia populnea.
1455   A959   1r multicolored     .25   .25
1456   A959   6r multicolored     .75   .25
1457   A959   8r multicolored     1.00   .50
1458   A959   11r multicolored    1.50   .75
        Nos. 1455-1458 (4)        3.50   1.75

Dr. Dwarkanath Kotnis A960

**1993, Dec. 9   Photo.   Perf. 13½x13**
1459   A960   1r black & gray     .80   .40

A961

A962

**1993, Nov. 14   Perf. 14**
1460   A961   1r multicolored     .60   .35
Children's Day.

**1993, Nov. 8   Perf. 13x13½**
1461   A962   2r multicolored     .60   .35
College of Military Engineering, Pune, 50th anniv.

A963

A964

Design: Dr. Dwarm Venkataswamy Naidu.

**1993, Nov. 8**
1462   A963   1r orange brown     .60   .35

**1993, July 31**
1463   A964   2r multicolored     .60   .35
Bombay Municipal Corporation Building, cent.

India Tea A965

**1993, Dec. 11   Perf. 13**
1464   A965   6r green & red      1.10   .75

Papal Seminary, Pune, Cent. A966

**1993, Dec. 16   Perf. 13½x13**
1465   A966   6r multicolored     1.25   .85

Natl. Integration A967

**1993, Aug. 19**
1466   A967   1r orange & green   .60   .30

Khan Abdul Ghaffar Khan A968

**1993, Aug. 9**
1467   A968   1r multicolored     .60   .30

Heart Care Festival A969

**1993, Dec. 9**
1468   A969   6.50r multicolored  1.40   .75

Inpex '93 — A970

**1993**
1469 A970 1r shown .35 .35
1470 A970 2r Boats, beach .85 .35

Issued: 1r, Dec. 25; 2r, Dec. 27.

Meghnad Saha (1893-1956), Astrophysicist A971

**1993, Dec. 23  Photo.  Perf. 13x13½**
1471 A971 1r dark blue .75 .45

Dinanath Mageshkar, Musician A972

**1993, Dec. 29  Perf. 13½x13**
1472 A972 1r orange brown .60 .30

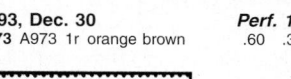

Nargis Dutt, Actress and Social Worker — A973

**1993, Dec. 30  Perf. 13**
1473 A973 1r orange brown .60 .30

Indian Natl. Army, 50th Anniv. A974

1r, Netaji Subhash Bose inspecting soldiers.

**1993, Dec. 31  Perf. 13½x13**
1474 A974 1r multicolored .80 .50

Satyendra Nath Bose (1894-1974), Mathematician and Physicist — A975

**1994, Jan. 1**
1475 A975 1r dark rose brown .80 .45

Satyajit Ray (1921-92) A976

6r, Scene from film, Pather Panchali.

**1994, Jan. 11  Perf. 13**
1476 A976 6r multicolored 2.40 1.60
1477 A976 11r multicolored 2.75 1.60
a. Pair, #1476-1477 5.25 5.25

No. 1476 is 68x30mm. No. 1477a is a continuous design.

Dr. Sampurnanand — A977

**1994, Jan. 10  Photo.  Perf. 13½x13**
1478 A977 1r multicolored .60 .60

Dr. Shanti Swarup Bhatnagar A978

**1994, Feb. 21**
1479 A978 1r dark blue .70 .70

Eighth Triennale A979

**1994, Mar. 14**
1480 A979 6r multicolored 1.00 .50

Prajapita Brahma (1876-1969), Religious Leader — A980

**1994, Mar. 7  Photo.  Perf. 13½x13**
1481 A980 1r multicolored .70 .70

Sanchi Stupa A981

**Wmk. 324**
**1994, Apr. 4  Photo.  Perf. 13**
1482 A981 5r blue green & brn .60 .40

ILO, 75th Anniv. A982

**1994, May 1  Unwmk.  Perf. 13½x13**
1483 A982 6r multicolored 1.00 .70

United Planters Assoc. of Southern India, Cent. — A983

**1994, Mar. 26  Photo.  Perf. 13x13½**
1484 A983 2r multicolored .70 .50

Rani Rashmoni (1793-1861), Philanthropist — A984

**1994, Apr. 9  Perf. 13½x13**
1485 A984 1r brown .70 .55

Jallianwala Bagh Martyrdom, 75th Anniv. A985

**1994, Apr. 13**
1486 A985 1r red & black .70 .70

Freedom Fighters Type of 1988
1r, Chandra Singh Garhwali (1891-1979).

**1994, Apr. 23**
1487 A826 1r org, sage grn & grn .70 .70

IPTA A986

Small Families A987

**1994, May 25  Perf. 13**
1488 A986 2r multi .70 .40

**1994  Perf. 13x12½**
1r, Family of 3 in front of house.
1489 A987 75c red brn & brn .30 .30
1490 A987 1r green & rose .30 .30

4th Battalion Madras Regiment, Bicent. — A988

**1994, Aug. 12**
1491 A988 6.50r multicolored 1.25 .85

Institute of Mental Health, Madras, Bicent. A989

**1994, Sept. 23  Photo.  Perf. 13½x13**
1492 A989 2r multicolored .70 .40

Mahatma Gandhi (1869-1948) A990

Design: 11r, Flag colors, Gandhi walking and at spinning wheel.

**1994, Oct. 2  Perf. 13**
1493 A990 6r multicolored 2.25 1.50
1494 A990 11r multicolored 3.00 2.50
a. Pair, #1493-1494 5.50 5.50

No. 1494 is 68x30mm.

16th Intl. Cancer Congress — A991

**1994, Oct. 30  Photo.  Perf. 13½**
1495 A991 6r multicolored 1.25 .70

World Conference on Human Resource Development — A992

**1994, Nov. 8  Perf. 13½x13**
1496 A992 6r multicolored 1.00 .65

Intl. Year of the Family — A993

**1994, Nov. 20  Perf. 13x12½**
1497 A993 2r multicolored .60 .35

Children's Day A994

**1994, Nov. 14  Perf. 13½x13**
1498 A994 1r multicolored .60 .50

J.R.D. Tata (1904-93) — A995

**1994, Nov. 29**       **Perf. 14**
1499 A995 2r multicolored      .60   .40

Calcutta School for the Blind, Cent. A996

**1994 Nov. 30**      **Perf. 13½x13**
1500 A996 2r brown & carmine    .60   .35

Endangered Waterbirds — A996A

Designs: 1r, Andaman teal. 6r, Eastern white stork. 8r, Black-necked crane. 11r, Pink-headed duck.

**1994, Nov. 23**      **Perf. 13**
| 1501 | A996A | 1r multicolored | 10.50 | 3.00 |
| 1502 | A996A | 6r multicolored | 15.00 | 6.00 |
| 1503 | A996A | 8r multicolored | 15.00 | 6.50 |
| 1504 | A996A | 11r multicolored | 16.00 | 9.00 |
| a. | | Block of 4, #1501-1504 | 60.00 | 60.00 |

This set was withdrawn shortly after issue, when it was discovered that it was printed with water soluble ink.

Begum Akhtar A996B

**1994, Dec 2**      **Perf. 13x13½**
1504B A996B 2r multicolored   10.00   7.50

No. 1504B was withdrawn shortly after issue, when it was discovered that it was printed with water soluble ink.

Remount Veterinary Corps, 215th Anniv. — A998

**1994, Dec. 14**    **Photo.**    **Perf. 13x13½**
1505 A998 6r multicolored     2.75   1.60

College of Engineering, Guindy, Madras, Bicent. — A999

**1994, Dec. 19**      **Perf. 14**
1506 A999 2r multicolored     .60   .35

Baroda Museum, Vadodara — A1000

Designs: 6r, Ancient artifact. 11r, Ancient artifact, man standing on pedestal.

**1994, Dec. 20**      **Perf. 14x13½**
| 1507 | | 6r black & bister | 4.50 | 2.25 |
| 1508 | | 11r black & bister | 4.50 | 2.25 |
| a. | | A1000 Pair, #1507-1508 | 9.50 | 9.50 |

Khuda Bakhsh Oriental Public Library A1001

**1994, Nov. 21**    **Photo.**    **Perf. 14**
1509 A1001 6r multicolored     8.50   1.60

A1002

A1003

**1995, Jan. 9**    **Photo.**    **Perf. 13x13½**
1510 A1002 1r Chhoturam     1.25   .30

**1995, Jan. 7**
1511 A1003 6r multicolored     .80   .55

India Natl. Science Academy, 30th Anniv.

St. Xavier's College, Bombay, 125th Anniv. A1005

**1994, Dec. 4**    **Photo.**    **Perf. 13½**
1513 A1005 2r multicolored     .35   .20

General Post Office, Bombay, Bicent. — A1006

Illustration reduced.

**1994, Dec. 28**    **Litho.**    **Perf. 13½**
1514 A1006 6r multicolored    9.00   3.00

Motion Pictures, Cent. A1007

Designs: 6r, Colored film, world map. 11r, Early camera, black & white film.

**1995, Jan. 11**    **Litho.**    **Perf. 13**
| 1515 | A1007 | 6r multicolored | 1.60 | 1.60 |
| 1516 | A1007 | 11r multicolored | 2.50 | 2.50 |
| a. | | Pair, #1515-1516 | 4.25 | 4.25 |

Oil Conservation A1008

Rafi Ahmed Kidwai A1009

**1995, Feb. 18**    **Photo.**    **Perf. 13**
1517 A1008 1r red brown & black   .20   .20

**1995, Feb. 18**
1518 A1009 1r red brown     .60   .60

K. L. Saigal A1010

**1995, Apr. 4**    **Photo.**    **Perf. 13½x13**
1519 A1010 5r black & brown    1.75   1.00

A1011

A1012

**1995, Jan. 5**    **Photo.**    **Perf. 13**
1520 A1011 2r King Rajaraja Chola     6.25   1.10

8th Intl. Conference of Tamil Studies.

**1995, Jan. 12**    **Photo.**    **Perf. 13½x13**
1521 A1012 2r multicolored     .60   .40

SAARC Youth Year.

A1013

A1014

**1995, Jan. 15**      
1522 A1013 2r multicolored    7.25   1.10

Prithvi Theater, 50th anniv.

**1995, Jan. 15**

Field Marshall K.M. Cariappa (1900-93).
1523 A1014 2r multicolored     .75   .45

A1015

A1017

**1995, Jan. 18**
1524 A1015 2r multicolored     .60   .40

Tex-Styles India '95, National Textile Fair, Bombay.

**1995, June 6**    **Photo.**    **Perf. 13**

UN, 50th Anniv.: 6r, Planting seedling, mother and child, child reading.
| 1526 | A1017 | 1r multicolored | .20 | .20 |
| 1527 | A1017 | 6r multicolored | .65 | .45 |

R.S. Ruikar — A1018

Bharti Bhavan Library, Allahabad A1019

**1995, May 1**    **Photo.**    **Perf. 13½**
1528 A1018 1r brown violet     .60   .60

**1995, Aug. 30**      **Perf. 14**
1529 A1019 6r multicolored     .75   .60

Asian Pacific Postal Training Center, Bangkok, 25th Anniv. A1020

**1995, Sept. 4    Litho.    Perf. 13½x13**
1530    A1020    10r multicolored    1.75    1.25

Headquarters Delhi Area — A1021

**1995, Sept. 26    Photo.    Perf. 13**
1531    A1021    2r multicolored    1.00    .55

Louis Pasteur (1822-95) A1022

**1995, Sept. 28**
1532    A1022    5r pale yel & black    3.00    1.50

La Martiniere College, Lucknow, 150th Anniv. A1023

**1995, Oct. 1**
1533    A1023    2r multicolored    .60    .40

Mahatma Gandhi (1869-1948) — A1024

**1995, Oct. 2**
1534        1r As young man    .65    .35
1535        2r As older man    .65    .35
  a.    A1024    Pair, #1534-1535    1.40    1.40
  b.    Souvenir sheet, #1535a    1.50    1.50
   See South Africa Nos. 918-919.

FAO, 50th Anniv. A1025

**1995, Oct. 16    Perf. 13½**
1536    A1025    5r multicolored    1.60    1.00

A1026

**1995, Oct. 30    Perf. 13**
1537    A1026    1r carmine    .60    .50
   P.M. Thevar (1908-63), politician.

A1027

**1995, Nov. 8    Photo.    Perf. 13x13½**
1538    A1027    6r multicolored    3.25    1.90
   Wilhelm Roentgen (1845-1923), discovery of the X-Ray, cent.

JAT Regiment, Bicent. A1028

**1995, Nov. 20    Perf. 13**
1539    A1028    5r multicolored    2.75    1.75

Radio Communication, Cent. — A1029

**1995, May 17    Litho.    Perf. 13½x13**
1540    A1029    5r multicolored    1.75    1.75

Dehli Development Authority — A1030

**1995, May 23**
1541    A1030    2r multicolored    .60    .60

Children's Day — A1031

**1995, Nov. 14    Photo.    Perf. 13x13½**
1542    A1031    1r multicolored    .60    .50

Rajputana Rifles, 175th Anniv. A1032

**1995, Nov. 28    Perf. 13½**
1543    A1032    5r multicolored    3.25    1.75

Communal Harmony — A1033

**1995, Nov. 19    Photo.    Perf. 13**
1544    A1033    2r multicolored    2.75    1.40

Sant Tukdoji Maharaj, Patriot, Social Worker A1034

**1995, Dec. 10**
1545    A1034    1r brown    .70    .55
   Dated 1993.

A1035          A1036

   Design: Yellapragada Subbarow (1895-1948), biochemist.

**1995, Dec. 19**
1546    A1035    1r yellow brown    .70    .55

**1995, Dec. 25**
   Giani Zail Singh (1916-94), Pres. of India.
1547    A1036    1r multicolored    .70    .55

Dome Barelvi's Mausoleum, Dargah — A1037

**1995, Dec. 31    Litho.**
1548    A1037    1r multicolored    .70    .55
   Ala Hazrat Barelvi (1856-1921), poet.

Cricket Players — A1038

**1996, Mar. 13    Photo.    Perf. 14**
1549    A1038    2r Deodhar    1.00    .75
1550    A1038    2r Vijay Merchant    1.00    .75
1551    A1038    2r Vinoo Mankad    1.00    .75
1552    A1038    2r C.K. Nayudu    1.00    .75
   Nos. 1549-1552 (4)    4.00    3.00
   Dated 1995.

Homi Bhabha and Tata Institute of Fundamental Research — A1039

**1996, Feb. 9    Photo.    Perf. 13**
1553    A1039    2r multicolored    .80    .50

Kasturba Trust — A1040

**1996, Feb. 22**
1554    A1040    1r multicolored    .60    .35

Cardiac Surgery, Cent. — A1041

**1996, Feb. 25    Litho.**
1555    A1041    5r multicolored    2.25    1.25

Miniature Paintings A1042

   #1556, Two women picking berries from trees. #1557, Woman, man embracing. #1558, Women looking upward, men, animals. #1559, Ceremony, black clouds.

**1996, Mar. 13    Perf. 13½**
1556    A1042    5r multicolored    1.50    .95
1557    A1042    5r multicolored    1.50    .95
1558    A1042    5r multicolored    1.50    .95
1559    A1042    5r multicolored    1.50    .95
   Nos. 1556-1559 (4)    6.00    3.80

Pt. Kunjilal Dubey — A1043

**1996, Mar. 18    Photo.    Perf. 13**
1560    A1043    1r brown    .60    .50

Himalayan Wildlife A1044

#1561, Saussurea simpsoniana. #1562, Capra falconeri. #1563, Ithaginis cruentus. #1564, Meconopsis horridula.

**1996, May 10**     **Litho.**
| | | | |
|---|---|---|---|
| 1561 | A1044 | 5r multicolored | 2.25 1.75 |
| 1562 | A1044 | 5r multicolored | 2.25 1.75 |
| 1563 | A1044 | 5r multicolored | 2.25 1.75 |
| 1564 | A1044 | 5r multicolored | 2.25 1.75 |
| a. | Souv. sheet of 4, #1561-1564 | | 9.00 9.00 |
| | Nos. 1561-1564 (4) | | 9.00 7.00 |

No. 1564a sold for 30r. Stamps in No. 1564a do not have "1996."

Morarji Desai — A1045

**1996, Apr. 10**   **Photo.**   **Perf. 13x13½**
1565 A1045 1r carmine     .60 .35

SKCG College A1047

**1996, May 25**     **Photo.**
1567 A1047 1r lt brn & dk brn    .80 .65

Muhammad Ismail Sahib — A1048

1996 Summer Olympic Games, Atlanta — A1049

**1996, June 5**     **Perf. 13x13½**
1568 A1048 1r claret     .80 .80

**1996, June 25**
1569 A1049 5r Olympic stadium   .90 .55
1570 A1049 5r Torch     .90 .55

A1050

A1051

**1996, July 19**     **Perf. 13x13½**
1571 A1050 1r blue & black   .80 .80
    Sister Alphonsa (1910-46).

**1996, Aug. 2**   **Litho.**   **Perf. 14**
1572 A1051 5r multicolored    2.25 1.40
    VSNL, 125th anniv.

A1052        A1053

1r, Chembai Vaidyanatha Bhagavathar. 2r, Ahilyabai Holkar.

**1996**    **Photo.**    **Perf. 13x13½**
1573 A1052 1r dk bl grn & brn   .80 .55
1574 A1052 2r rose brn & lt brn   .80 .65
    Issued: 1r, 8/28; 2r, 8/25.

**1996, Aug. 4**    **Photo.**   **Perf. 13**
1575 A1053 1r Sir Pherozsha Mehta    .80 .80

Poultry Production A1054

**1996, Sept. 2**
1576 A1054 5r Gallus gallus    4.00 3.00

Rani Gaidinliu — A1055

**1996, Sept. 12**
1577 A1055 1r dark blue green   .80 .80

Barrister Nath Pai — A1056

**1996, Sept. 25**
1578 A1056 1r blue     .80 .80

Indepex '97 World Philatelic Exhibition A1057

**1996, Oct. 5**   **Litho.**   **Perf. 13x13½**
1579 A1057 2r lake & bister   .80 .50

Children's Day A1058

**1996, Nov. 14**   **Photo.**   **Perf. 13½x13**
1580 A1058 8r multicolored   2.25 1.25

South Asian Assoc. for Regional Cooperation (SAARC), 10th Anniv. A1059

**1996, Dec. 8**     **Perf. 13**
1581 A1059 11r multicolored   2.40 1.60

Abai Konunbaev (1845-1904), Poet — A1060

2nd Intl. Crop Science Congress A1061

**1996, Dec. 9**     **Perf. 13x13½**
1582 A1060 5r red brown & lake   2.40 1.60
    Dated 1995.

**1996, Nov. 17**     **Perf. 13**
1583 A1061 2r multicolored   1.10 .70

Sikh Regiment, 150th Anniv. A1062

**1996, Oct. 19**
1584 A1062 5r multicolored    2.40 1.50

Natl. Rail Museum, 25th Anniv. — A1063

**1996, Oct. 7**   **Litho.**   **Perf. 13½**
1585 A1063 5r multicolored   3.75 2.10

Jananayak Debeswar Sarmah (1896-1993), Politician — A1064

**1996, Oct. 10**
1586 A1064 2r lt brn & red brn   .80 .50

Dr. Salim Ali, Birth Cent. — A1065

**1996, Nov. 12**   **Photo.**   **Perf. 13**
1587   8r Dr. Salim Ali   3.75 2.50
1588   11r Water fowl   3.75 2.50
  a.   A1065 Pair, #1587-1588   9.00 9.00

Second Battalion, The Grenadiers, Bicent. A1066

**1996, Dec. 4**     **Perf. 14**
1589 A1066 5r multicolored   2.40 1.25

Vijay Divas A1067

**1996, Dec. 16**
1590 A1067 2r multicolored   .35 .25

Vivekananda Rock Memorial, Kanyakumari — A1068

Illustration reduced.

**1996, Dec. 26**   **Litho.**   **Perf. 13**
1591 A1068 5r multicolored   3.25 1.90

Use of Anesthesia, 150th Anniv. — A1069

**1996, Dec. 27**
1592 A1069 5r multicolored     2.40 1.40

University of Roorkee, 150th Anniv. A1070

**1997, Jan. 1**    **Photo.**    *Perf. 13*
1593 A1070 8r multicolored     2.00 1.10

Vrindavan Lal Verma, Writer — A1071

**1997, Jan. 9**   **Photo.**   *Perf. 13x13½*
1594 A1071 2r red      .80 .50

Army Postal Service Corps. (APS), 25th Anniv. A1072

**1997, Jan. 22**     *Perf. 13½x13*
1595 A1072 5r multicolored     2.75 1.90

Jose Marti (1853-95), Cuban Revolutionary A1073

**1997, Jan. 28**     *Perf. 13x13½*
1596 A1073 11r multicolored     2.25 1.00

Inter-Parliamentary Specialized Conference, New Dehli — A1074

**1997, Feb. 15**    **Photo.**    *Perf. 13*
1597 A1074 5r multicolored     .80 .40

A1075

**1997, Mar. 4**    **Photo.**    *Perf. 13*
1598 A1075 1r lt brn & dk brn    .80 .50
   Shyam Lal Gupt (b. 1896), composer of song on natl. flag.

A1076

**1997, Mar. 8**     *Perf. 13x13½*
1599   5r Parijat Tree     1.25 .75
1600   6r Branch, flower    1.25 .75
   **a.** A1076 Pair, #1599-1600   2.50 2.50

Rashtriya Indian Military College, Dehra Dun, 75th Anniv. A1077

**1997, Mar. 13**     *Perf. 13½*
1601 A1077 2r multicolored    1.60 .60

Netaji Subhas Chandra Bose (1897-1945), Nationalist Leader — A1078

**1997, Jan. 23**     *Perf. 13*
1602 A1078 1r dk brn & lt brn    .80 .45

A1079

**1997, Feb. 25**   **Photo.**   *Perf. 13x13½*
1603 A1079 8r St. Andrews Church    1.60 .95

Morarji Desai, Prime Minister, 1977-79 — A1080

**1997, Feb. 28**    **Photo.**    *Perf. 13*
1604 A1080 1r brown & buff    .80 .45

Saint Dnyaneshwar (1274-95), Poet — A1081

**1997, Mar. 5**    **Photo.**    *Perf. 13*
1605 A1081 5r multicolored    1.40 .65

Ram Manohar Lohia (1910-67), Politician — A1082

**1997, Mar. 23**   **Litho.**   *Perf. 13x13½*
1606 A1082 1r multicolored    .60 .40

CENTIPEX '97 — A1083

**1997, Mar. 27**
   Philatelic Society of India, Cent.: No. 1608, #1, Front cover of "The Philatelic Journal of India," 1897.
1607   2r multicolored     1.25 1.00
1608   2r multicolored     1.25 1.00
   **a.** Pair, #1607-1608     2.50 2.50

Jnanpith Award Winners — A1084

   K.V. Puttappa, D.R. Bendre, Prof. V.K. Gokak, Dr. Masti V. Iyengar, writers.

**1997, Mar. 28**    **Photo.**    *Perf. 13*
1609 A1084 2r multi     .80 .50

Madhu Limaye (1922-95), Politician — A1085

**1997, May 1**
1610 A1085 2r green     .80 .50

A1086

**1997, June 24   Photo.   *Perf. 13x13½*
1611 A1086 2r Pandit Omkarnath Thakar     1.10 .65

A1087

**1997, Aug. 6**    **Photo.**    *Perf. 13*
1612 A1087 2r brown     1.75 1.25
   Thirumathi Rukmini Lakshmipathi (1892-1951), reformer.

Independence, 50th Anniv. — A1088

   Officers from Indian Natl. Army, Shah Nawaz Khan, G.S. Dhillon, P.K. Sahgal.

**1997, Aug. 15**
1613 A1088 2r multicolored     .40 .25

Newspaper Swantantra Bharat, 50th Anniv. A1089

**1997, Aug. 15**     *Perf. 13½x13*
1614 A1089 2r multicolored     .60 .40

A1090

A1091

**1997, Aug. 20** **Perf. 13**
1615 A1090 2r black & gray 1.75 .75
Sir Ronald Ross (1857-1932), physician, medical researcher.

**1997, Sept. 6**
1616 A1091 5r red brown 2.10 1.00
Swami Bhaktivedanta (b. 1896), humanitarian.

A1092

A1093

**1997, Sept. 14**
1617 A1092 2r black & gray .60 .40
Swami Brahmanand (1894-1984), social reformer.

**1997, Aug. 8**
1618 A1093 2r Sri Basaveswara .60 .40

Maratha Parachute Regiment, Bicent. A1094

**1997, Sept. 7** **Perf. 13½x13**
1619 A1094 2r multicolored .90 .45

Hazari Prasad Dwivedi — A1095

Firaq Gorakhpuri A1096

**1997, Dec. 13** **Photo.** **Perf. 13x13½**
1620 A1095 2r gray brown .60 .40

**1997, Aug. 28**
1621 A1096 2r brown .60 .40

Fossil Plants — A1097

Sir William Jones, 250th Birth Anniv. — A1098

No. 1622, Birbalsahnia divyadarshanii. No. 1623, Glossopteris. 6r, Pentoxylon. 10r, Williamsonia sewardiana.

**1997, Sept. 11**
1622 A1097 2r multicolored .50 .35
1623 A1097 2r multicolored .50 .35
1624 A1097 6r multicolored 1.50 .90
1625 A1097 10r multicolored 2.25 1.50
Nos. 1622-1625 (4) 4.75 3.10

**1997, Sept. 28**
1626 A1098 4r multicolored .70 .35

Lawrence School, Sanawar, 150th Anniv. A1099

**1997, Oct. 4** **Perf. 13½x13**
1627 A1099 2r multicolored .90 .55

Indepex '97 A1100

**1997, June 6** **Photo.** **Perf. 13½x13**
1628 A1100 2r Nalanda .50 .40
1629 A1100 6r Bodhgaya .80 .50
1630 A1100 10r Vaishali 1.25 .80
1631 A1100 11r Kushinagar 1.60 .80
a. Block of 4, #1628-1631 4.50 4.50

66th General Assembly Session of Interpol, 1997 A1101

**1997, Oct. 15** **Perf. 13½**
1632 A1101 4r multicolored 1.25 .80

V.K. Krishna Menon — A1102

**1997, Oct. 6** **Perf. 13**
1633 A1102 2r brown carmine 1.00 .75

Indepex '97 World Philatelic Exhibition A1103

Rural Indian women.

**1997, Oct. 15** **Photo.** **Perf. 13x13½**
1634 A1103 2r Arunachal
 Pradesh .50 .30
1635 A1103 6r Gujarat .95 .50
1636 A1103 10r Ladakh 1.25 .70
1637 A1103 11r Kerala 1.50 .95
a. Block of 4, #1634-1637 4.50 4.50

Scindia School, Cent. — A1104

Designs: No. 1638, Outdoor class. No. 1639, Founder, school building, aerial view.

**1997, Oct. 20** **Perf. 14**
1638 5r multicolored .70 .35
1639 5r multicolored .70 .35
a. A1104 Pair, #1638-1639 1.40 1.40

Medicinal Plants A1105

2r, Ocimum sanctum. 5r, Curcuma longa. 10r, Rauvolfia serpentina. 11r, Aloe barbadensis.

**1997, Oct. 28**
1640 A1105 2r multicolored .50 .30
1641 A1105 5r multicolored .95 .50
1642 A1105 10r multicolored 1.25 .95
1643 A1105 11r multicolored 1.50 .95
a. Block of 4, #1640-1643 4.50 3.75

A1106

A1107

**1997, July 2** **Litho.** **Perf. 13x13½**
1644 A1106 2r brown & sepia .60 .40
Ram Sewak Yadav (1926-74), politician, social reformer.

**1997, July 11**
1645 A1107 2r multicolored .60 .40
Sibnath Banerjee (1897-1982), politician, union leader.

Indepex '97 A1110

Indian beaches: 2r, Gopalpur on Sea, Orissa. 6r, Kovalam Beach, Thiruvananthapuram. 10r, Anjuna Beach, Goa. 11r, Bogmalo Beach, Goa.

**1997, Aug. 11** **Photo.** **Perf. 13½x13**
1648 A1110 2r multicolored .50 .25
1649 A1110 6r multicolored .70 .50
1650 A1110 10r multicolored 1.25 .70
1651 A1110 11r multicolored 1.75 .90
Nos. 1648-1651 (4) 4.20 2.35

Sant Kavi Sunderdas (1596-1689) A1111

Kotamaraju Rama Rao — A1112

**1997, Nov. 8** **Photo.** **Perf. 13x13½**
1652 A1111 2r lt brn & dk brn 1.00 .50

**1997, Nov. 9**
1653 A1112 2r dk brn & yel brn 1.40 .70

Children's Day A1113

**1997, Nov. 14** **Perf. 13½x13**
1654 A1113 2r Nehru with child .70 .40

A1114

A1115

**1997, Nov. 23** **Photo.** **Perf. 13**
1655 A1114 4r multicolored 1.75 1.10
World Convention on Reverence for All Life.

**1997, Dec. 15** **Photo.** **Perf. 13x13½**
1656 A1115 2r dk brn & lt brn .60 .40
Sardar Vallabhbhai Patel (1875-1950), politician.

Indepex '97
A1116

Designs: 2r, Post Office Heritage Building. 6r, Indian River Mail. 10r, Cancellations, Jal Cooper. 11r, Mail ship, SS Hindosthan.

**1997, Dec. 15   Photo.   Perf. 13½x13**
**1657**   A1116   2r multicolored   .50   .45
**1657A**  A1116   6r multicolored   1.00   .50
**1657B**  A1116   10r multicolored   1.25   1.00
**1657C**  A1116   11r multicolored   1.75   1.10
    *d.*   Block of 4, #1657-1657C   4.50   3.75

### Souvenir Sheet

Mother Teresa (1910-97) — A1117

Illustration reduced.

**1997, Dec. 15   Litho.   Perf. 13x13½**
**1658**   A1117   45r multicolored   4.50   4.50

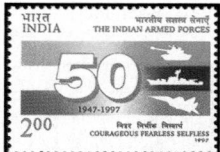

Indian Armed Forces, 50th Anniv. A1118

**1997, Dec. 16   Photo.   Perf. 13½x13**
**1659**   A1118   2r multicolored   .80   .40

Dr. B. Pattabhi Sitaramayya (1880-1959), Author, Politician — A1119

**1997, Dec. 17   Perf. 13x13½**
**1660**   A1119   2r dk brn & lt brn   1.10   .55

Fr. Jerome D'Souza (1897-1977) A1120

**1997, Dec. 18   Perf. 13½x13**
**1661**   A1120   2r red brown   .60   .40

Ashfaquallah Khan and Ram Prasad Bismil, Revolutionaries A1121

**1997, Dec. 19   Perf. 13**
**1662**   A1121   2r dk brn & brn   .60   .40

Cellular Jail Natl. Memorial, Port Blair A1122

**1997, Dec. 30**
**1663**   A1122   2r multicolored   .60   .40

A1123

**1998, Jan. 2**
**1664**   A1123   2r red brown   .40   .25
    Nanak Singh (1897-1971), novelist.

A1124

**1998, Jan. 9**
**1665**   A1124   2r plum   .40   .25
    Nahar Singh, minor leader of Great Mutiny.

Rotary Intl., 1998 Council on Legislation, New Delhi A1125

**1998, Jan. 12   Perf. 13½X13**
**1666**   A1125   8r multicolored   1.25   1.00

A1126

A1127

#1667, Maharana Pratap (1540-97), ruler, warrior. #1668, Vishnu S. Khandekar (b. 1898), writer.

**1998, Jan. 19   Perf. 13x13½**
**1667**   A1126   2r violet brown   .80   .50
**1668**   A1127   2r rose red & dull red   .80   .50

A1128            A1129

**1998, Jan. 25**
**1669**   A1128   10r multicolored   2.25   1.50
    Bharat Paryatan Diwas (India Tourism Day).

**1998, Jan. 2   Perf. 13½x13**
**1670**   A1129   4r multicolored   3.00   1.75
    11th Gurkha Rifles, 50th anniv.

A1130

Mahatma Gandhi, 50th Anniv. of Death: 2r, Peasants' welfare. 6r, Social upliftment. 10r, Salt Satyagraha. 11r, Communal harmony.

**1998, Jan. 30   Photo.   Perf. 14**
**1671**   A1130   2r multicolored   .60   .45
**1672**   A1130   6r multicolored   .90   .75
**1673**   A1130   10r multicolored   1.10   1.10
**1674**   A1130   11r multicolored   1.75   1.25
    *a.*   Block of 4, #1671-1674   4.75   4.25

A1131

**1998, Mar. 8   Photo.   Perf. 13x13½**
**1675**   A1131   6r multicolored   1.25   .60
    Universal Declaration of Human Rights, 50th anniv.

Savitribai Phule (1831-97), Educator, Women's Reformer A1132

**1998, Mar. 10   Perf. 13½x13**
**1676**   A1132   2r dk brn & lt brn   .80   .50

Jagdish Chandra Jain A1133

**1998, Jan. 28   Photo.   Perf. 13x13½**
**1677**   A1133   2r red brown   .80   .50

Syed Ahmad Khan (1817-98), Writer — A1134

Sardar A. Vedaratnam A1135

**1998, Mar. 27**
**1678**   A1134   2r brn & olive brn   .80   .50

**1998, Feb. 25**
**1679**   A1135   2r violet black   .80   .50

Global Environment Facility First Assembly Meeting — A1136

**1998, Apr. 1   Perf. 13**
**1680**   A1136   11r multicolored   1.75   1.10

A1137

A1138

**1998, Apr. 16   Photo.   Perf. 14**
**1681**   A1137   6r carmine   1.10   .70
    Defense Services Staff College.

**1998, May 3   Photo.   Perf. 13**
    Design: Pres. Zakir Husain (1897-1969).
**1682**   A1138   2r sepia   .60   .40

A1139            A1140

Jnanpith Literary Award winners, year: Shri Bishnu Dey (1909-82), 1971; Shri Tarashankar Bandopadhyay (1898-1971), 1966; Smt. Ashapurna Devi (1909-95), 1976.

**1998, June 5**
**1683**   A1139   2r olive brown   .60   .40

**1998, June 8   Photo.   Perf. 13**
    Designs: 5r, Parliament Clock Tower, London. 6r, Airplane, mascot, Gateway of India, Bombay.

**1684**   A1140   5r multicolored   .75   .40
    **Size: 56x35mm**
**1685**   A1140   6r multicolored   1.00   .50
    *a.*   Pair, #1684-1685   1.75   1.75
    Air India's 1st intl. flight, 50th anniv.

A1141

N.G. GORAY A1142

Design: Salem C. Vijiaraghavachariar (1852-1944), freedom fighter.

**1998, June 18**
1686 A1141 2r red brown .60 .35

**1998, May 1**
1687 A1142 2r N.G. Goray .60 .35

Sri Ramana Maharshi A1143

**1998, Apr. 14**
1688 A1143 2r violet black .60 .40

Konkan Railway — A1143a

Illustration reduced.

**1998, May 1    Photo.    Perf. 13**
1689 A1143a 8r multicolored 1.60 .95

A1144

A1145

Mohammed Abdurahiman Shahib.

**1998, May 15**
1690 A1144 2r red brown .60 .40

**1998, May 21    Photo.    Perf. 14**
1691 A1145 2r brown & sepia .60 .40
Lokanayak Omeo Kumar Das, freedom fighter.

Revolutionaries — A1146

Design: Satyendra Chandra Bardhan, Vakkom Abdul Khader, Fouja Singh.

**1998, May 25    Perf. 13**
1692 A1146 2r brn & red brn .60 .40

Natl. Savings Organization, 50th Anniv. — A1147

Design: 6r, Hand dropping coin into bank.

**1998, June 30**
1693 A1147 5r multicolored .65 .30
1694 A1147 6r multicolored .80 .50
a.    Pair, #1693-1694 1.50 1.25

Bhagwan Gopinathji, Spiritual Leader, Birth Cent. — A1148

**1998, July 3    Perf. 13½**
1695 A1148 3r brown & sepia .60 .40

Ardeshir (1868-1926) & Pirojsha (1882-1972) Godrej, Environmentalists — A1149

**1998, July 11    Perf. 13**
1696 A1149 3r green .60 .40

Aruna Asaf Ali, Revolutionay A1150

**1998, July 16**
1697 A1150 3r brown .60 .40

Vidyasagar College, 125th Anniv. A1151

**1998, July 29**
1698 A1151 2r dark gray .60 .30

Shivpujan Sahai (1893-1963), Writer — A1152

**1998, Aug. 9    Photo.    Perf. 13**
1699 A1152 2r brown .60 .30

Homage to Martyrs A1153

Designs: 3r, Minaret, silhouettes of soldiers standing in fort, flag of India. 8r, Symbols of industrial, scientific and technological developments.

**1998, Aug. 15    Perf. 14**
1700 A1153 3r multicolored .35 .25
1701 A1153 8r multicolored .75 .45
a.    Pair, #1700-1701 1.10 1.00

Gostha Behari Paul (1896-1976), Soccer Player — A1154

**1998, Aug. 20    Perf. 13**
1702 A1154 3r sepia .60 .40

Youth Hostels Assoc. of India, 50th Anniv. — A1155

**1998, Aug. 23    Perf. 14**
1703 A1155 5r multicolored .80 .45

Brigade of the Guards, Fourth Battalion, Bicent. A1156

**1998, Sept. 15    Photo.    Perf. 13½**
1704 A1156 6r multicolored 1.00 .55

Bhai Kanhaiyaji A1157

**1998, Sept. 18    Perf. 13**
1705 A1157 2r red .60 .30

20th Intl. Congress of Radiology A1158

**1998, Sept. 18    Perf. 13½x13**
1706 A1158 8r multicolored 1.75 .90

28th IBBY Congress A1159

**1998, Sept. 20    Perf. 13**
1707 A1159 11r multicolored 1.75 .85

Dr. Tristao Braganza Cunha — A1160

**1998, Sept. 26**
1708 A1160 3r dark brown .60 .40

Jananeta Hijam Irawat Singh — A1161

**1998, Sept. 30**
1709 A1161 3r brown .60 .40

Acharya Tulsi (1914-97) A1162

**1998, Oct. 20    Photo.    Perf. 13½x13**
1710 A1162 3r brown & orange .60 .40

Indian Women in
Aviation
A1163

Pulse Polio
Immunization
A1164

**1998, Oct. 15** *Perf. 13*
1711 A1163 8r blue 1.75 .85

**1998, Sept. 21**
1712 A1164 3r maroon .20 .20

2nd Battalion of the Rajput Regiment
(Kalichindi), Bicent. — A1165

**1998, Nov. 30**
1713 A1165 3r multicolored .60 .30

David Sassoon
Library & Reading
Room,
Mumbai — A1166

**1998, Nov. 30**
1714 A1166 3r lt blue & dk blue .60 .40

Army Postal
Service
Center,
Kamptee,
50th Anniv.
A1167

**1998, Dec. 2**
1715 A1167 3r multicolored 1.10 .55

Connemara
Public
Library,
Chennai
A1168

**1998, Dec. 5** *Perf. 13½x13*
1716 A1168 3r bister & brown .60 .40

A1169

A1170

**1998, Dec. 10** Litho. *Perf. 13½*
1717 A1169 3r multicolored 1.25 .60
Indian Pharmaceutical Cong. Assoc., 50th
anniv.

**1998, Dec. 12** Photo. *Perf. 13*
Design: Baba Raghv Das (1896-1958),
reformer, freedom fighter.
1718 A1170 2r deep gray violet .60 .30

Indra Lal Roy
(1898-1918),
World War I
Pilot — A1171

**1998, Dec. 19**
1719 A1171 3r multicolored .80 .40

Sant Gadge Baba (1876-1956),
Religious Philosopher — A1172

**1998, Dec. 20**
1720 A1172 3r multicolored .60 .40

Traditional
Musical
Instruments
A1173

Designs: 2r, Rudra veena (stringed instrument). 6r, Flute (wind insrument). 8r,
Pakhawaj (percussion instrument). 10r, Sarod
(stringed instrument).

**1998, Dec. 29**
1721 A1173 2r multicolored .35 .25
1722 A1173 6r multicolored .85 .55
1723 A1173 8r multicolored 1.10 .70
1724 A1173 10r multicolored 1.50 .90
Nos. 1721-1724 (4) 3.80 2.40

Children's
Day
A1174

**1998, Nov. 14** Photo. *Perf. 13½*
1725 A1174 3r multicolored .60 .40

INS Delhi
A1175

**1998, Nov. 15**
1726 A1175 3r multicolored 1.00 .60

President's
Bodyguard
A1176

**1998, Nov. 16**
1727 A1176 3r multicolored 1.25 .60

Shells
A1177

Designs: No. 1728, Cypraea staphylaea.
No. 1729, Cassis cornuta. No. 1730,
Chicoreus brunneus. 11r, Lambis lambis.

**1998, Dec. 30**
1728 A1177 3r multicolored .50 .70
1729 A1177 3r multicolored .70 .70
1730 A1177 3r multicolored 1.25 .70
1731 A1177 11r multicolored 1.75 1.40
Nos. 1728-1731 (4) 4.20 3.50

Indian
Police
Service,
50th Anniv.
A1178

**1999, Jan. 13** Litho. *Perf. 13½x13¼*
1732 A1178 3r multicolored 1.10 .55

Defense Research & Development
Organization — A1179

**1999, Jan. 26** Photo. *Perf. 13*
1733 A1179 10r multicolored 2.00 1.00

Newpapers in
Assam, 150th
Anniv. — A1180

**1999, Jan. 29** *Perf. 13x13½*
1734 A1180 3r multicolored 1.00 .70

Sanskrit
College,
Calcutta,
175th Anniv.
A1181

**1999, Feb. 25** *Perf. 13½x13*
1735 A1181 3r brown & yellow 1.00 .45

National
Defense
Academy,
50th Anniv.
A1182

*Perf. 13½x13¼*
**1999, Feb. 19** Litho.
1736 A1182 3r multicolored 1.00 .70

Hindu
College,
Delhi, Cent.
A1183

**1999, Feb. 17** Photo. *Perf. 13½x13*
1737 A1183 3r blue .60 .40

Biju Patnaik
(1916-97),
Politician
A1184

**1999, Mar. 5**
1738 A1184 3r multicolored 1.00 .50

A1185 A1186

**1999, Mar. 12** *Perf. 13*
1739 A1185 15r multicolored 1.75 1.00
Press Trust of India, 50th anniv.

**1999, Mar. 6**
1740 A1186 15r multicolored 1.75 1.00
Temple Complex of Khajuraho, 1000th anniv.

Dr. K.B. Hedgewar
(1889-1940)
A1187

**1999, Mar. 18**
1741 A1187 3r multicolored .60 .40

Bethune
Collegiate
School,
150th Anniv.
A1188

**1999** Photo. *Perf. 13*
1742 A1188 3r green .70 .50

Creation of
the Khalsa,
300th
Anniv.
A1189

**1999, Apr. 14**
1743 A1189 3r multicolored 1.00 .55

Maritime Heritage
A1190

**1999, Apr. 5  Litho.  Perf. 13½x13¼**
1744 A1190 3r Boat from 2200
B.C. .70 .50
1745 A1190 3r Ship from 1700 .70 .50

Technology Day
A1191

**1999, May 11  Litho.  Perf. 13½x13¼**
1746 A1191 3r multicolored .70 .50

Mumbai Port Trust, 125th Anniv.
A1192

**1999, June 26  Photo.  Perf. 12¾x13**
1747 A1192 3r blue gray .70 .50

A1193     A1194

**1999, June 30  Photo.  Perf. 13x12¾**
1748 A1193 3r multicolored .60 .40
Mizoram Accord.

**1999, July 4  Photo.  Perf. 13¼**
1749 A1194 3r multicolored .60 .40
Gulzari Lal Nanda (b. 1899), interim Prime Minister.

Jijabai, Mother of Shivaji — A1195

**1999, July 7  Photo.  Perf. 14x13½**
1750 A1195 3r claret .60 .40

P. S. Kumaraswamy Raja — A1196

**1999, July 8  Photo.  Perf. 13¼**
1751 A1196 3r sky blue & brown .60 .40

Balai Chand Mukhopadhyay (1879-1979), Writer — A1197

**1999, July 19  Photo.  Perf. 13¼**
1752 A1197 3r slate blue .60 .40

Sindh River Festival
A1198

**Perf. 13½x13¼**
**1999, July 28  Photo.**
1753 A1198 3r multicolored .60 .40

Geneva Conventions, 50th Anniv. — A1199

**1999, Aug. 12  Photo.  Perf. 13¾**
1754 A1199 15r black & red 2.25 1.60

Freedom Fighters
A1200

#1755, Swami Ramanand Teerth. #1756, Vishwambhar Dayalu Tripathi. #1757, Swami Keshawanand. #1758, Sardar Ajit Singh.

**Perf. 13½x13¼**
**1999, Aug. 15  Photo.**
1755 A1200 3r multicolored .55 .40
1756 A1200 3r multicolored .55 .40
1757 A1200 3r multicolored .55 .40
1758 A1200 3r multicolored .55 .40
Nos. 1755-1758 (4) 2.20 1.60

Kalki Krishnamurthy (1899-1954), Novelist — A1201

**1999, Sept. 9  Photo.  Perf. 13¾**
1759 A1201 3r black .60 .50

Qazi Nazrul Islam (1899-1976), Poet — A1202

Rambriksh Benipuri, Writer
A1203

Ramdhari Sinha "Dinkar," Poet
A1204

Jhaverchand Kalidas Meghani (b. 1896), Poet — A1205

**1999, Sept. 14  Photo.  Perf. 13x13¼**
1760 A1202 3r multicolored .60 .50
**Perf. 13¼**
1761 A1203 3r multicolored .60 .50
**Perf. 13¼x13**
1762 A1204 3r multicolored .60 .50
1763 A1205 3r multicolored .60 .50
Nos. 1760-1763 (4) 2.40 2.00

Arati Gupta, First Asian Woman to Swim Across English Channel
A1206

**1999, Sept. 29  Photo.  Perf. 13x13¼**
1764 A1206 3r multi .60 .50

Worldwide Fund for Nature
A1207

Asiatic lion: No. 1765, Male atop female. No. 1766, Two lions. No. 1767, Three lions. 15r, Two lions, diff.

**1999, Oct. 4  Perf. 13¼x13**
1765 A1207 3r multi 1.75 .50
1766 A1207 3r multi 1.75 .50
1767 A1207 3r multi 1.75 .50
1768 A1207 15r multi 3.00 1.50
Nos. 1765-1768 (4) 8.25 3.00

UPU, 125th Anniv.
A1208

#1769, Muria ritual object. #1770, Mask for Chhau dance. #1771, Rathva wall painting. 15r, Angami ornament.

**1999, Oct. 9  Perf. 13¼x13, 13x13¼**
1769 A1208 3r multi .55 .30
1770 A1208 3r multi .55 .30
1771 A1208 3r multi, vert. .55 .30
1772 A1208 15r multi, vert. 1.75 1.25
Nos. 1769-1772 (4) 3.40 2.15

Dr. T. M. A. Pai (1898-1979) — A1209

Chhaganlal K. Parekh (1894-1968) — A1209a

A. B. Walawalkar, Draftsman for Konkar Railway — A1209b

A. D. Shroff — A1209c

**1999, Oct. 9  Perf. 13x13¼**
1773 A1209 3r yel & brn .60 .60
**Perf. 12¾x13¼**
1774 A1209a 3r org brn & ind .60 .60
**Perf. 13¼**
1775 A1209b 3r lilac & maroon .60 .60
1776 A1209c 3r bister & olive .60 .60
Nos. 1773-1776 (4) 2.40 2.40

Veerapandia Kattabomman (1760-99), Freedom Fighter — A1210

**1999, Oct. 16  Photo.  Perf. 13x13¼**
1777 A1210 3r olive green .60 .50

Musicians
A1211

#1778, Ustad Allauddin Khan Saheb (1870-1972), sarod player. #1779, Musiri Subramania Iyer (1899-1975), music teacher.

**1999, Oct. 19  Photo.  Perf. 13¾**
1778 A1211 3r multicolored .75 .60
1779 A1211 3r multicolored .75 .60

A1212

A1213

**Perf. 13¼x13½**

**1999, Oct. 27**     **Photo.**
1780 A1212 3r violet brown    .70   .50

Brigadier Rajinder Singh (1899-1947).

**1999, Nov. 14**   **Photo.**   **Perf. 14**
1781 A1213 3r multi     .60   .40

Children's Day.

Sri Sathya Sai Water Supply Project A1214

**Perf. 12¾x13¼**

**1999, Nov. 23**     **Photo.**
1782 A1214 3r multi     .90   .50

Supreme Court, 50th Anniv. A1215

**Perf. 12¾x13¼**

**1999, Nov. 26**     **Photo.**
1783 A1215 3r multi     .60   .50

Dr. Punjabrao Deshmukh, Agriculture Minister A1215a

A. Vaidyanatha Iyer (d. 1955), Advocate of Untouchables — A1216

P. Kakkan, Politician A1217

Indulal Kanaiyalal Yagnik, Politician A1218

**1999, Dec. 9**     **Perf. 13¼**
1784 A1215a 3r brown & grn   .35   .25
1785 A1216 3r orange brown   .35   .25
1786 A1217 3r green & brn   .35   .25
1787 A1218 3r tan & black   .35   .25
   Nos. 1784-1787 (4)   1.40 1.00

Thermal Power, Cent. A1219

**1999, Dec. 14**   **Photo.**   **Perf. 13¼x13**
1788 A1219 3r bister & brn    .60   .50

Hindustan Times Newspaper, 75th Anniv. A1220

**1999, Dec. 16**   **Photo.**   **Perf. 13¼**
1789 A1220 15r multi    2.25 1.60

Family Planning Assoc. of India, 50th Anniv. — A1221

**1999, Dec. 18**     **Perf. 14x13¾**
1790 A1221 3r multi     .60   .50

Birth of Jesus Christ, 2000th Anniv. — A1222

**1999, Dec. 25**
1791 A1222 3r multi    1.00   .80

Tabo Monastery A1223

**1999, Dec. 31**     **Perf. 12¾x13¼**
1792 A1223 5r shown    .25   .25
1793 A1223 10r People    .45   .45
   a.   Pair, #1792-1793   .70   .70

First Sunrise of the Millennium A1224

**2000, Jan. 1**     **Perf. 13¼x13**
1794 A1224 3r multi    2.00 2.00

Agni II Missile A1225

**2000, Jan. 1**   **Litho.**   **Perf. 13x13¼**
1795 A1225 3r multi     .20   .20

Mahatma Gandhi — A1226

**2000, Jan. 27**     **Perf. 14x13¾**
1796 A1226 3r red & black   .60   .60

Republic of India, 50th anniv.

Gallantry Award Winners A1227

Designs: No. 1797, Karam Singh, regimental crest. No. 1798, Abdul Hamid, jeep-mounted artillery gun. No. 1799, Albert Ekka, grenades, knife. No. 1800, N. J. S. Sekhon, airplane. No. 1801, M. N. Mulla, ship.

**2000, Jan. 27**     **Perf. 13¼x13**
1797 A1227 3r multi     .60   .60
1798 A1227 3r multi     .60   .60
1799 A1227 3r multi     .60   .60
1800 A1227 3r multi     .60   .60
1801 A1227 3r multi     .60   .60
   a.   Strip of 5, #1797-1801   2.50 2.50

Republic of India, 50th anniv.

Millepex 2000 A1228

Endangered reptiles: No. 1802, Batagur terrapin. No. 1803, Olive ridley turtle.

**2000, Jan. 29**     **Perf. 13¼**
1802 A1228 3r multi     .50   .40
1803 A1228 3r multi     .50   .40
   a.   Pair, #1802-1803   2.00 1.75

Famous Men — A1229

Designs: No. 1804, Balwantrai Mehta. No. 1805, Arun Kumar Chanda. No. 1806, Dr. Harekrushna Mahatab, politician.

**2000, Feb. 17**   **Litho.**   **Perf. 13x13¼**
1804 A1229 3r multi     .60   .60
1805 A1229 3r multi     .60   .60
1806 A1229 3r multi     .60   .60
   Nos. 1804-1806 (3)   1.80 1.80

Patna Medical College, 75th Anniv. A1230

**2000, Feb. 26**     **Perf. 13¼x13**
1807 A1230 3r multi     .60   .60

Dr. Burgula Ramakrishna Rao, Politician — A1231

**2000, Mar. 13**     **Perf. 13x13¾**
1808 A1231 3r brn & ocher    .60   .60

Potti Sriramulu (1901-52), Advocate of Untouchables — A1232

**2000, Mar. 16**     **Perf. 13¼x13**
1809 A1232 3r red     .60   .60

Basawon Sinha (1909-89), Socialist Party Leader — A1233

**2000, Mar. 23**     **Perf. 13x13¼**
1810 A1233 3r multi     .60   .60

Indepex Asiana 2000 — A1234

**2000, Mar. 31**     **Perf. 13x13¼**
1811 A1234 3r Siroi lily    .50   .50
1812 A1234 3r Wild guava    .50   .50
1813 A1234 3r Sangai deer    .50   .50
1814 A1234 15r Slow loris   1.75 1.75
   a.   Souvenir sheet, #1811-1814   3.75 3.75
   Nos. 1811-1814 (4)   3.25 3.25

See Nos. 1831-1834.

Arya Samaj, 125th Anniv. — A1235

**Perf. 13x13¼**

**2000, Apr. 5**   **Litho.**   **Unwmk.**
1815 A1235 3r multi     .80   .80

Indigenous Cattle Breeds A1236

**Perf. 13¼x13**

**2000, Apr. 25**   **Litho.**   **Unwmk.**
1816 A1236 3r Gir     .55   .45
1817 A1236 3r Kangayam    .55   .45
1818 A1236 3r Kankrej    .55   .45
1819 A1236 15r Hallikar   2.00 1.50
   Nos. 1816-1819 (4)   3.65 2.85

Blackbuck A1237

Patel A1237a

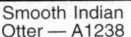

Smooth Indian Otter — A1238

Leopard Cat — A1239

Tiger A1240

Amaltaas — A1241

50p, Nilgiri tahr. 1r, Saras crane. 2r, Sardar Vallabhbhai Patel (1875-1950), Politician. 15r, Butterfly. 50r, Paradise flycatcher.

**Perf. 12¾x13, 13x12¾**

| | | | | |
|---|---|---|---|---|
| **2000** | | **Photo.** | **Wmk. 324** | |
| **1820** | A1237 | 25p olive brn | .20 | .20 |
| **1821** | A1237 | 50p yel brn | .20 | .20 |
| **1822** | A1237 | 1r blue | .20 | .20 |
| **1823** | A1237a | 2r black | .20 | .20 |
| **1824** | A1238 | 3r gray vio | .20 | .20 |
| **1825** | A1239 | 5r multi | .20 | .20 |
| **1826** | A1240 | 10r multi | .45 | .45 |
| **1827** | A1240 | 15r multi | .65 | .65 |
| **1828** | A1241 | 20r multi | .85 | .85 |
| **1829** | A1241 | 50r multi | 2.10 | 2.10 |
| | | Nos. 1820-1829 (10) | 5.25 | 5.25 |

Issued: 25p, 50p, 1r, 3r, 7/20; 2r, 10/31; 5r, 10r, 4/30; 15r, 20r, 11/20; 50r, 10/30.

Railways in Doon Valley, Cent. — A1244

**Perf. 13¼**

| | | | | |
|---|---|---|---|---|
| **2000, May 6** | | **Litho.** | **Unwmk.** | |
| **1830** | A1244 | 15r multi | 2.50 | 2.50 |

### Indepex Asiana Type of 2000

Birds: #1831, Rosy pastor. #1832, Garganey teal. #1833, Forest wagtail. #1834, White stork.

| | | | | |
|---|---|---|---|---|
| **2000, May 24** | | | **Perf. 13¼x13** | |
| **1831** | A1234 | 3r multi, horiz. | 1.10 | 1.10 |
| **1832** | A1234 | 3r multi, horiz. | 1.10 | 1.10 |
| **1833** | A1234 | 3r multi, horiz. | 1.10 | 1.10 |
| **1834** | A1234 | 3r multi, horiz. | 1.10 | 1.10 |
| *a.* | | Block of strip of 4, #1831-1834 | 3.50 | 3.50 |
| *b.* | | Souvenir sheet, #1831-1834 | 3.50 | 3.50 |

Dr. Nandamuri Taraka Rama Rao (1923-96), Actor, Politician A1245

| | | | | |
|---|---|---|---|---|
| **2000, May 28** | | | | |
| **1835** | A1245 | 3r multi | .60 | .60 |

Swami Sahajanand Saraswati (1889-1950), Freedom Fighter — A1246

| | | | | |
|---|---|---|---|---|
| **2000, June 26** | | | **Perf. 13x13¼** | |
| **1836** | A1246 | 3r multi | .60 | .60 |

Christian Medical College and Hospital, Vellore, Cent. A1247

| | | | | |
|---|---|---|---|---|
| **2000, Aug. 12** | | | **Perf. 13¼x13** | |
| **1837** | A1247 | 3r multi | .60 | .60 |

Social and Political Leaders — A1248

Designs: No. 1838, Radha Gobinda Baruah (1900-75), newspaper publisher. No. 1839, Vijaya Lakshmi Pandit (1900-90), President of UN General Assembly. No. 1840, Jaglal Choudhary (1895-1975), politician. No. 1841, R. Srinivasan (1859-1945), advocate of untouchables, newspaper founder.

| | | | | |
|---|---|---|---|---|
| **2000, Aug. 15** | | | **Perf. 13x13¼** | |
| **1838** | A1248 | 3r multi | .60 | .60 |
| **1839** | A1248 | 3r multi | .60 | .60 |
| **1840** | A1248 | 3r multi | .60 | .60 |
| **1841** | A1248 | 3r multi | .60 | .60 |
| | | Nos. 1838-1841 (4) | 2.40 | 2.40 |

Kodaikanal Intl. School, Cent. A1249

| | | | | |
|---|---|---|---|---|
| **2000, Aug. 26** | | **Litho.** | **Unwmk.** | |
| **1842** | A1249 | 15r multi | 1.75 | 1.75 |

2000 Summer Olympics, Sydney A1250

Designs: 3r, Discus. 6r, Tennis. 10r, Field hockey. 15r, Weight lifting.

| | | | | |
|---|---|---|---|---|
| **2000, Sept. 17** | | | **Perf. 13x13¼** | |
| **1843-1846** | A1250 | Set of 4 | 5.50 | 5.50 |

India in Space A1251

#1847, Oceansat 1. #1848, Insat 3B in orbit.

No. 1849, vert.: a, Astronaut on planet, spacecraft. b, Earth, spacecraft.

**Perf. 13¼x13, 13x13¼**

| | | | | |
|---|---|---|---|---|
| **2000, Sept. 29** | | | | |
| **1847-1848** | A1251 | 3r Set of 2 | 1.50 | 1.50 |
| **1849** | | Pair | 1.50 | 1.50 |
| *a.-b.* | A1251 | 3r Any single | 1.00 | 1.00 |

Madhubani-Mithila Painting — A1252

#1850, 3 figures. #1851, 2 figures and bird. #1852, 2 figures and cow, vert.
No. 1853, vert.: a, Red fish, palanquin. b, Yellow fish, elephant.

| | | | | |
|---|---|---|---|---|
| **2000, Oct. 15** | | | **Perf. 13¼** | |
| **1850-1852** | A1252 | 3r Set of 3 | 1.25 | 1.25 |
| **1853** | | Pair | 2.10 | 2.10 |
| *a.* | A1252 | 5r multi | .55 | .55 |
| *b.* | A1252 | 10r multi | 1.40 | 1.40 |

Raj Kumar Shukla (b. 1875), Farmer — A1253

| | | | | |
|---|---|---|---|---|
| **2000, Oct. 16** | | **Litho.** | **Perf. 13x13¼** | |
| **1854** | A1253 | 3r multi | .50 | .50 |

Pres. Shanker Dayal Sharma (1918-99) A1254

| | | | | |
|---|---|---|---|---|
| **2000, Oct. 29** | | | **Litho.** | |
| **1855** | A1254 | 3r multicolored | .60 | .60 |

Children's Day — A1255

| | | | | |
|---|---|---|---|---|
| **2000, Nov. 14** | | | | |
| **1856** | A1255 | 3r multicolored | .60 | .60 |

Maharaja Bijli Pasi A1256

| | | | | |
|---|---|---|---|---|
| **2000, Nov. 16** | | | **Perf. 13¼x13** | |
| **1857** | A1256 | 3r multicolored | .60 | .60 |

Gems and Jewelry — A1257

#1858, 3r, Ancient India. #1859, 3r, Sarpech. #1860, 3r, Taxila. #1861, 3r, Navratna. #1862, 3r, Temple. #1863, 3r, Bridal.

| | | | | |
|---|---|---|---|---|
| **2000, Dec. 7** | | | **Perf. 13¼** | |
| **1858-1863** | A1257 | Set of 6 | 6.50 | 6.50 |
| *a.* | | Block of 6, #1858-1863 | 7.50 | 7.50 |
| *b.* | | Souvenir sheet, #1858, 1860-1861, 1863 | 8.00 | 8.00 |

Issued: No. 1863b, 12/11. No. 1863b sold fo 15r.

Warship of Adm. Mohammed Kunjali Marakkar — A1258

| | | | | |
|---|---|---|---|---|
| **2000, Dec. 17** | | | **Perf. 13¼x13** | |
| **1864** | A1258 | 3r multi | 1.10 | 1.10 |

Ustad Hafiz Ali Khan (1888-1972), Musician — A1259

| | | | | |
|---|---|---|---|---|
| **2000, Dec. 28** | | | | |
| **1865** | A1259 | 3r multi | .60 | .60 |

Famous Men A1260

#1866, Gen. Zorawar Singh (1786-1841). #1867, Rajarshi Bhagyachandra (1740-98), King of Manipur, vert. #1868, Samrat Prithviraj Chauhan (1162-92), ruler of Delhi, vert. #1869, Raja Bhamashah (c. 1542-98), military leader, vert.

| | | | | |
|---|---|---|---|---|
| **2000, Dec. 31** | | **Perf. 13¼x13, 13x13¼** | | |
| **1866-1869** | A1260 | 3r Set of 4 | 2.40 | 2.40 |

St. Aloysius College Chapel Paintings, Cent. A1261

| | | | | |
|---|---|---|---|---|
| | | **Perf. 13¼** | | |
| **2001, Jan. 12** | | **Litho.** | **Unwmk.** | |
| **1870** | A1261 | 15r multi | 2.40 | 2.40 |

Subhas
Chandra
Bose
A1262

Dr. B. R.
Ambedkar
A1263

**Perf. 12¾x13**

**2001** **Photo.** **Wmk. 324**
1871 A1262 1r brown .20 .20
1872 A1263 3r blue green .20 .20
Issued: 1r, 1/23; 3r, 4/14.

Famous
Men — A1264

Designs: No. 1873, 3r, Sane Guruji (1899-
1950), social reformer. No. 1874, 3r, N. G.
Ranga (1900-95), politician. No. 1875, 3r, E.
M. S. Namboodiripad (1909-98), Marxist
leader. No. 1876, 3r, Giani Gurmukh Singh
Musafir (1899-1976), politician.

**Perf. 13x13¼**
**2001, Jan.** **Litho.** **Unwmk.**
1873-1876 A1264 Set of 4 2.40 2.40
Issued: No. 1873, 1/25; others, 1/27.

Famous
Men — A1265

Designs: No. 1877, 3r, Sheel Bhadra Yajee
(1906-96), freedom figher. No. 1878, 3r, Jubba
Sahni (1906-44), revolt leader. No. 1879, 3r,
Yogendra (1896-1966) and Baikunth (1907-
34) Shukla, freedom fighters.

**2001, Jan.**
1877-1879 A1265 Set of 3 1.75 1.75
Issued: No. 1877, 1/28; others, 1/29.

Western
Railways
Building,
Mumbai,
Cent. (in
1999)
A1266

**2001, Feb. 6** **Perf. 13¼x13**
1880 A1266 15r multi 3.75 3.75
Dated 1999.

2001
Census — A1267

**2001, Feb. 10** **Perf. 13x13¼**
1881 A1267 3r multi .60 .60

President's International Fleet
Review — A1268

Designs: No. 1882, 3r, Pal. No. 1883, 3r,
Galbat. No. 1884, 3r, Tarangini. 15r, Emblem.

**2001, Feb. 18** **Perf. 13¼x13**
1882-1885 A1268 Set of 4 3.50 3.50

Geological
Survey of
India,
150th
Anniv.
A1269

**2001, Mar. 4**
1886 A1269 3r multi .60 .60

4th Battalion of
Maratha Light
Infantry,
Bicent. — A1270

**2001, Mar. 6** **Perf. 13x13¼**
1887 A1270 3r multi .60 .60

Bhagwan
Mahavira, 2600th
Anniv. of
Birth — A1271

**2001, Apr. 6**
1888 A1271 3r multi .60 .60

First
Manned
Space
Flight, 40th
Anniv.
A1272

**2001, Apr. 12** **Perf. 13¼x13**
1889 A1272 15r multi 3.25 3.25

Frederic
Chopin
(1810-49),
Composer
A1273

**2001, May 4**
1890 A1273 15r multi 3.25 3.25

Suraj Narain
Singh (1908-73),
Politician
A1274

**2001, May 31** **Perf. 13x13¼**
1891 A1274 3r multi .60 .60

B. P. Mandal
(1918-82),
Politician
A1275

**2001, June 1**
1892 A1275 3r multi .60 .60

Samanta Chandra
Sekhar (1835-
1904), Astronomer
A1276

**2001, June 11**
1893 A1276 3r multi .60 .60

Sant Ravidas,
15th Cent
Religious
Leader — A1277

**2001, June 24**
1894 A1277 3r multi .60 .60

Famous
Men — A1278

Designs: No. 1895, 4r, Krishna Nath
Sarmah (1887-1947), social reformer. No.
1896, 4r, C. Sankaran Nair (1857-1934), President of Indian National Congress. No. 1897,
4r, Syama Prasad Mookerjee (1901-53), politician. No. 1898, 4r, U Kiang Nongbah (d.
1862), soldier.

**2001, July 6** **Litho.** **Perf. 13x13¼**
1895-1898 A1278 Set of 4 2.40 2.40

Chandragupta Maurya, Emperor, 3rd
Cent. B.C. — A1279

**2001, July 21** **Litho.** **Perf. 13¼**
1899 A1279 4r multi .60 .60

Jhalkari
Bai — A1280

**2001, July 22** **Litho.** **Perf. 13x13¼**
1900 A1280 4r multi .60 .60

Corals
A1281

Designs: No. 1901, 4r, Acropora digitifera.
No. 1902, 4r, Fungia horrida. 15r, Montipora
acquituberculata. 45r, Acropora formosa.

**2001, Aug. 2** **Perf. 13¼**
1901-1904 A1281 Set of 4 4.50 4.50

Dwarka Prasad
Mishra (1901-88),
Politician — A1282

**2001, Aug. 5** **Perf. 13x13¼**
1905 A1282 4r multi .60 .60

Chaudhary Brahm
Parkash (1918-93),
Government
Minister — A1283

**2001, Aug. 11**
1906 A1283 4r multi .80 .80

Ballia Revolution of
August
1942 — A1284

**2001, Aug. 19**
1907 A1284 4r multi    .80   .80

Jagdev Prasad
(1922-74), Socialist
Politician — A1285

**2001, Sept. 5**
1908 A1285 4r multi    .80   .80

Rani Avantibai (d.
1858), Queen of
Ramgarh — A1286

**2001, Sept. 19**
1909 A1286 4r multi    .80   .80

Painted Stork — A1287

***Perf. 12¾x13***
**2001, Sept. 20   Photo.   Wmk. 324**
1910 A1287 4r bister brown   .20   .20

Rao Tula Ram
(1825-63),
Chieftain — A1288

***Perf. 13x13¼***
**2001, Sept. 23   Litho.   Unwmk.**
1911 A1288 4r multi    .80   .80

Chaudhary Devi
Lal (1914-2001),
Deputy Prime
Minister — A1289

**2001, Sept. 25**
1912 A1289 4r multi    .80   .80

Satis Chandra
Samanta (1900-
83),
Politician — A1290

**2001, Sept. 29**
1913 A1290 4r multi    .80   .80

Sivaji Ganesan
(1928-2001),
Actor — A1291

**2001, Oct. 1**
1914 A1291 4r multi    .80   .80

Mahatma Gandhi, Man of the
Millennium — A1292

No. 1915: a, Gandhi and followers, birds. b,
Gandhi.
Type A Syncopation (1st stamp #1915): On
the two longer sides, an oval hole equal in
width to 3 holes is located in the center, with
an equal number of normal round holes to
either side.

***Perf. 13x13¼ Syncopated Type A***
**2001, Oct. 2**
1915 A1292 4r Horiz. pair, #a-b   2.50 2.50

Literary and
Performing
Arts
Personalities
A1293

Designs: No. 1916, 4r, Lachhu Maharaj
(1901-78), choreographer. No. 1917, 4r,
Master Mitrasen (1895-1946), playwright, theater founder. No. 1918, 4r, Bharathidasan
(1891-1964), Tamil poet.

**2001, Oct. 9    *Perf. 13¼x13***
1916-1918 A1293   Set of 3   2.40 2.40

Jayaprakash
Narayan
(1902-79),
Socialist
Politician
A1294

**2001, Oct. 11**
1919 A1294 4r multi    .80   .80

Panchatantra Fables — A1295

No. 1920 — The Monkey and the Crocodile,
4r: a, Monkey in tree. b, Monkey on crocodile's
back.

No. 1921 — The Lion and the Rabbit, 4r: a,
Lion and rabbit. b, Lion and rabbit on bridge.
No. 1922 — The Crows and the Snake, 4r:
a, Crows with necklace. b, Villagers pursuing
snake.
No. 1923 — The Tortoise and the Geese, 4r:
a, Tortoise in pond. b, Tortoise flying with
geese.
Sizes: Nos. 1920a-1923a, 58x39mm; Nos.
1920b-1923b, 29x39mm. Illustration reduced.

**2001, Oct. 17    *Perf. 13x13¼***
**Horiz. Pairs, #a-b**
1920-1923 A1295   Set of 4   6.00 6.00

Global Iodine
Deficiency
Disorders
Day — A1296

**2001, Oct. 21**
1924 A1296 4r multi    .80   .80

Thangal Kunju
Musaliar (1897-
1966), Industrialist
A1297

**2001, Oct. 26**
1925 A1297 4r multi    .80   .80

Children's
Day — A1298

**2001, Nov. 14   Litho.   *Perf. 13x13¼***
1926 A1298 4r multi    .80   .80

Dr. V.
Shantaram
(1901-90),
Movie
Producer
A1299

***Perf. 13¼x13 Syncopated***
**2001, Nov. 17**
1927 A1299 4r multi    .80   .80

Sobha Singh
(1901-86),
Artist — A1300

**2001, Nov. 29   Litho.   *Perf. 13x13¼***
1928 A1300 4r multi    .80   .80

Sun Temple, Konark — A1301

No. 1929: a, 4r, Carved wheel. b, 15r, Sun
Temple.

Illustration reduced.

***Perf. 13¼x13 Syncopated***
**2001, Dec. 1**
1929 A1301   Horiz. pair, #a-b   4.50 4.50

Intl.
Volunteers
Year
A1302

**2001, Dec. 5   Litho.   *Perf. 13¼x13***
1930 A1302 4r multi    .80   .80

Raj Kapoor
(1924-88),
Film Actor,
Director and
Producer
A1303

***Perf. 13¼x13 Syncopated***
**2001, Dec. 14    Litho.**
1931 A1303 4r multi    .80   .80

Greetings — A1304

Flowers and: 3r, Fireworks. 4r, Butterflies.

***Perf. 13x13¼ Syncopated***
**2001, Dec. 18    Litho.**
1932-1933 A1304   Set of 2   2.00 2.00

Digboi
Refinery,
Cent.
A1305

**2001, Dec. 18    *Perf. 13¼x13***
1934 A1305 4r multi    .80   .80

Vijaye Raje Scindia
(1919-2001),
Politician — A1306

***Perf. 13¼x13 Syncopated***
**2001, Dec. 20**
1935 A1306 4r multi    .80   .80

Temples
A1307

Designs: No. 1936, 4r, Kedarnath. No.
1937, 4r, Tryambakeshwar. No. 1938, 4r,
Aundha Nagnath. 15r, Rameswaram.

**2001, Dec. 22    *Perf. 13¼x13***
1936-1939 A1307   Set of 4   5.00 5.00

Cancer Awareness Day — A1308

**2001, Nov. 7**     *Perf. 13x13¼*
1940 A1308 4r multi     .80 .80

Maharaja Ranjit Singh (1780-1839), Founder of Sikh Kingdom of the Punjab — A1309

**2001, Nov. 9**
1941 A1309 4r multi     .80 .80

Directorate General of Mine Safety, Cent. — A1310

*Perf. 13x13¼ Syncopated*
**2002, Jan. 7**     Litho.
1942 A1310 4r multi     1.00 1.00

May 2001 Ascent of Mt. Everest by Indian Army Mountaineers A1311

**2002, Jan. 15**     *Perf. 13x13¼*
1943 A1311 4r multi     2.50 2.50

Bauddha Mahotsav Festival A1312

Designs: No. 1944, 4r, Dhamek Stupa, Sarnath. No. 1945, 4r, Gridhakuta Hills, Rajgir. 8r, Mahaparinirvana Temple, Kushinagar. 15r, Mahabodhi Temple, Bodhgaya.

*Perf. 13¼x13 Syncopated*
**2002, Jan. 21**
1944-1947 A1312   Set of 4    4.00 4.00

Book Year A1313

**2002, Jan. 28**     *Perf. 13¼x13*
1948 A1313 4r multi     1.00 1.00

Swami Ramanand A1314

**2002, Feb. 4**     *Perf. 13x13¼*
1949 A1314 4r multi     1.00 1.00

Indian Munitions Factories, 50th Anniv. A1315

*Perf. 13¼ Syncopated*
**2002, Mar. 18**     Litho.
1950 A1315 4r multi     1.00 1.00

Sido and Kanhu Murmu, 1855-57 Revolt Leaders A1316

**2002, Apr. 6**     *Perf. 13¼*
1951 A1316 4r multi     1.00 1.00

Indian Railways, 150th Anniv. — A1317

**2002, Apr. 16**     *Perf. 13¼x13*
1952 A1317 15r multi     5.00 5.00
a.   Souvenir sheet of 1    5.00 5.00

India — Japan Diplomatic Relations, 50th Anniv. — A1318

No. 1953: a, Kathakali actor, India. b, Kabuki actor, Japan.

**2002, Apr. 26**   Litho.   *Perf. 13x13¼*
1953 A1318 15r Horiz. pair, #a-b   6.00 6.00
c.   Souvenir sheet, #1953a-1953b   5.00 5.00

Parliament, 50th Anniv. A1319

**Litho. & Embossed**
**2002, May 13**     *Perf. 13¼*
1954 A1319 4r gold     1.00 1.00

Prabodhankar Thackeray (1885-1973), Writer — A1320

*Perf. 13x13¼ Syncopated*
**2002, May 19**     Litho.
1955 A1320 4r black     1.00 1.00

Cotton College, Guwahati A1321

**2002, May 26**   Photo.   *Perf. 13¼x13*
1956 A1321 4r grn & claret    1.00 1.00

P. L. Deshpande (1919-2000), Actor — A1322

**2002, June 16**   Litho.   *Perf. 13¼*
1957 A1322 4r multi     1.00 1.00

Brajlal Biyani (1896-1968), Politician and Writer — A1323

*Perf. 13x13¼ Syncopated*
**2002, June 22**
1958 A1323 4r multi     1.00 1.00

Writers — A1324

Designs: No. 1959, 5r, Babu Gulabrai (1888-1963). No. 1960, 5r, Pandit Suryanarayan Vyas (1902-76).

**2002, June 22**
1959-1960 A1324   Set of 2    2.00 2.00

Sree Thakur Satyananda (1902-69), Writer — A1325

**2002, July 23**   Litho.   *Perf. 13x13¼*
1961 A1325 5r multi     1.00 1.00

Anna Bhau Sathe (1920-69), Writer — A1326

*Perf. 13x13¼ Syncopated*
**2002, Aug. 1**     Litho.
1962 A1326 4r gray & black    1.00 1.00

Anand Rishiji Maharaj (1900-92), Humanitarian A1327

**2002, Aug. 9**     *Perf. 13¼*
1963 A1327 4r multi     1.00 1.00

Vithalrao Vikhe Patil (1901-80), Initiator of Cooperatives A1328

*Perf. 13x13¼ Syncopated*
**2002, Aug. 10**
1964 A1328 4r multi     1.00 1.00

Sant Tukaram (1608-50), Poet — A1329

**2002, Aug. 10**
1965 A1329 4r multi     1.00 1.00

Bhaurao Krishnaroao Gaikwad (1902-71), Politician — A1330

**2002, Aug. 26**
1966 A1330 4r multi     1.00 1.00

Social Reformers A1331

Designs: No. 1967, 5r, Ayyan Kali (1863-1941), advocate of rights for untouchables. No. 1968, 5r, Chandraprabha Saikiani (1901-72), women's rights advocate. No. 1969, 5r, Gora (1902-75), advocate of atheism.

*Perf. 13¼x13 Syncopated*
**2002, Sept. 12**
1967-1969 A1331   Set of 3    3.00 3.00

Ananda Nilayam Vimanam A1332

**2002, Oct. 11** *Perf. 13¼x13*
1970 A1332 15r multi 4.00 4.00

Kanika Bandopadhyay (1924-2000), Singer — A1333

**2002, Oct. 12 Photo.** *Perf. 13x13¼*
1971 A1333 5r multi 1.00 1.00

Arya Vaidya Sala Health Organization, Cent. — A1334

*Perf. 13¼x13 Syncopated*
**2002, Oct. 12 Litho.**
1972 A1334 5r multi 1.75 1.75

Bhagwan Baba (1896-1965), Religious Leader — A1335

*Perf. 13x13¼ Syncopated*
**2002, Oct. 15**
1973 A1335 5r multi 1.10 1.10

Bihar Chamber of Commerce, 75th Anniv. (in 2001) — A1336

**2002, Oct. 28**
1974 A1336 4r multi 1.75 1.75

UN Climate Change Convention A1337

Mangroves: No. 1975, 5r, Rhizophora mucronata. No. 1976, 5r, Nypa fruticans. No. 1977, 5r, Bruguiera gymnorrhiza. 15r, Sonneratia alba.

*Perf. 13¼x13 Syncopated*
**2002, Oct. 30**
1975-1978 A1337 Set of 4 5.00 5.00
1978a Souvenir sheet, #1975-1978 7.50 7.50

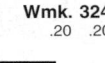

Rose — A1338

*Perf. 12¾x13*
**2002, Aug. 16 Photo. Wmk. 324**
1979 A1338 2r multi .20 .20

Swami Pranavananda (1896-1941), Religious Leader — A1339

*Perf. 12¾x13¼*
**2002, Nov. 3 Litho. Unwmk.**
1980 A1339 5r multi 1.50 1.50

Nagpur, 300th Anniv. — A1340

**2002, Nov. 11** *Perf. 13x13¼*
1981 A1340 5r multi 1.40 1.40

Children's Day A1341

**2002, Nov. 14** *Perf. 12¾x13¼*
1982 A1341 5r multi 1.40 1.40

Crafts — A1342

No. 1983: a, Cane and bamboo containers. b, Thewa. c, Patan's Patola. d, Dhokra.

**2002, Nov. 15** *Perf. 13¼*
1983 A1342 5r Block of 4, #a-d 3.50 3.50
e. Souvenir sheet of 1 #1983 3.50 3.50

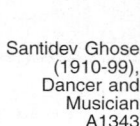

Santidev Ghose (1910-99), Dancer and Musician A1343

**2002, Dec. 1**
1984 A1343 5r multi 1.40 1.40

Formation of Tamralipta Jatiya Sarkar (National Government of Tamluk), 60th Anniv. — A1344

No. 1985: a, Ajoy Kumar Mukherjee (1901-86). b, Matangini Hazra (d. 1942). Illustration reduced.

**2002, Dec. 17** *Perf. 13¼x13*
1985 A1344 5r Horiz. pair, #a-b 1.00 1.00

Anglo-Bengali Inter College, Allahabad — A1345

*Perf. 13¼x13 Syncopated*
**2002, Dec. 23**
1986 A1345 5r multi 1.00 1.00

Gurukula Kangri Vishwavidyalaya, Hardwar — A1346

*Perf. 13x13¼ Syncopated*
**2002, Dec. 24**
1987 A1346 5r multi 1.00 1.00

Dhirubhai H. Ambani (1932-2002), Industrialist A1347

**2002, Dec. 28** *Perf. 13¼*
1988 A1347 5r multi 1.00 1.00

T. T. Krishnamachari (1899-1974), Finance Minister A1348

**2002, Dec. 31**
1989 A1348 5r multi 1.00 1.00

Forts in Andhra Pradesh — A1349

Designs: No. 1990, 5r, Goloconda Fort. No. 1991, 5r, Palace, Chandragiri Fort.

**2002, Dec. 31** *Perf. 13¼x13*
1990-1991 A1349 Set of 2 2.00 2.00

Aircraft A1350

Designs: No. 1992, 5r, HT-2 airplane. No. 1993, 5r, Marut airplane. No. 1994, 5r, LCA airplane. 15r, Dhruv helicopter.

**2003, Feb. 5** *Perf. 13¼*
1992-1995 A1350 Set of 4 5.00 5.00
1995a Souvenir sheet, #1992-1995 5.25 5.25

Ghantasala (1922-74), Singer — A1351

**2003, Feb. 11**
1996 A1351 5r multi 1.00 1.00

S. L. Kirloskar (1903-94), Industrialist A1352

**2003, Feb. 26**
1997 A1352 5r multi 1.00 1.00

Kusumagraj (V. V. Shirwadkar) (1912-99), Poet A1353

**2003, Mar. 14**
1998 A1353 5r multi 1.00 1.00

Sant Eknath (1533-99) — A1354

**2003, Mar. 23**
1999 A1354 5r multi 1.00 1.00

Frank Anthony (b. 1908), Philantropist A1355

**2003, Mar. 28** *Perf. 13x13¼*
2000 A1355 5r multi 1.00 1.00

Kakaji Maharaj (1918-86), Yogi — A1356

**2003, Mar. 30** *Perf. 13¼*
2001 A1356 5r multi 1.00 1.00

Medicinal Plants — A1357

No. 2002: a, Commiphora wightii. b, Bacopa monnieri. c, Withania somnifera. d, Emblica officinalis.

**2003, Apr. 7    Litho.    *Perf. 13x13¼***
2002    A1357    5r Block of 4, #a-d    4.00 4.00
    e.    Souvenir sheet, #2002a-2002d    4.50 4.50

Durga Das (1900-74), Journalist — A1358

**2003, May 2    Photo.    *Perf. 13x13¼***
2003    A1358    5r multi    1.00 1.00

Singers — A1359

Designs: No. 2004, 5r, Kishore Kumar (1929-87). No. 2005, 5r, Mukesh (1923-76). No. 2006, 5r, Mohammed Rafi (1924-80). No. 2007, 5r, Hemant Kumar (1920-89).

***Perf. 13x13¼ Syncopated***
**2003, May 15    Litho.**
2004-2007    A1359    Set of 4    3.25 3.25
    2007a    Souvenir sheet, #2004-2007    4.50 4.50

Ascent of Mt. Everest, 50th Anniv. — A1360

Muktabai (1279-99), Poet Saint — A1361

**2003, May 29    *Perf. 13x13¼***
2008    A1360    15r multi    2.50 2.50
    a.    Souvenir sheet of 1    4.50 4.50

**2003, May 30    *Perf. 13¼x12½***
2009    A1361    5r multi    1.00 1.00

Government Museum, Chennai — A1362

Designs: No. 2010, 5r, Sculpted medallion, Amravati, c. 150. No. 2011, 5r, Natesa, 12th cent. bronze sculpture. 15r, Museum Theater (58x28mm).

**2003, June 19    *Perf. 13x13¼***
2010-2012    A1362    Set of 3    3.00 3.00
    2012a    Souvenir sheet, #2010-2012    10.00 10.00

V. K. Rajwade (1863-1926), Historian — A1363

**2003, June 23    Photo.**
2013    A1363    5r multi    1.00 1.00

Bade Ghulam Ali Khan (1902-68), Singer — A1364

**2003, June 30    Litho.**
2014    A1364    5r multi    1.00 1.00

Temples — A1365

Designs: No.2015, Vishal Badri Temple, Badrinath. No.2016, Mallikarjunaswamy Temple, Srisailam. No.2017, Tripureswari Temple, Udaipur. No.2018, Jagannath Temple, Puri.

**2003, Sept. 15    Photo.    *Perf. 13¼x13***
2015    A1365    5r multicolored    .85 .85
2016    A1365    5r multicolored    .85 .85
2017    A1365    5r multicolored    .85 .85
2018    A1365    5r multicolored    .85 .85
    a.    Horiz. strip of 4, #2015-2018    3.50 3.50

Janardan Swami — A1366

**2003, Sept. 24    Photo.    *Perf. 13x13¼***
2019    A1366    5r brown    1.00 1.00

Intl. Autism Conference, Delhi A1367

**2003, Sept. 30    Litho.    *Perf. 13¼x13***
2020    A1367    5r multi    .25 .25

Waterfalls A1368

Designs: No. 2021, 5r, Kempty Falls, No. 2022, 5r, Athirapalli Falls. No. 2023, 5r, Kakolat Falls. 15r, Jog Falls.

**2003, Oct. 3    Litho.    *Perf. 13x13¼***
2021-2024    A1368    Set of 4    4.50 4.50
    2024a    Souvenir sheet, #2021-2024    6.00 6.00

Jnanpith Award Winners for Literature A1369

No. 2025: a, G. Sankara Kurup (1901-78), poet. b, S. K. Pottekkatt (1913-82), novelist. c, Thakazhi Sivasankara Pillai (1912-99), novelist.

**2003, Oct. 9    Photo.    *Perf. 13¼x13***
2025    Horiz. strip of 3    7.50 7.50
    a.-c.    A1369 5r Any single    1.00 1.00

Kota Shivarama Karanth (1902-97), Writer and Educator A1370

**2003, Oct. 10    *Perf. 13x13¼***
2026    A1370    5r multi    1.00 1.00

Narendra Mohan (1934-2002), Journalist A1371

**2003, Oct. 14    Litho.    *Perf. 13¼***
2027    A1371    5r brown    1.00 1.00

Govindrao Pansare (1913-46), Martyr A1372

**2003, Oct. 21    Photo.    *Perf. 13¾x14***
2028    A1372    5r multi    1.00 1.00

Greetings — A1373

No. 2029: a, Birds. b, Fish and starfish. c, Squirrels. d, Butterflies and flowers.

**2003, Oct. 30    Litho.    *Perf. 13¼x13***
2029    Horiz. strip of 4    3.75 3.75
    a.-b.    A1373 4r Either single    .80 .80
    c.-d.    A1373 5r Either single    1.00 1.00

First Telegraph Line in India, 150th Anniv. A1374

**2003, Nov. 1    *Perf. 13¼***
2030    A1374    5r multi    1.00 1.00

Bengal Sappers, Bicent. A1375

**2003, Nov. 7    Photo.    *Perf. 13¼x13***
2031    A1375    5r multi    1.00 1.00

Kalka-Shimla Railway, Cent. — A1376

**2003, Nov. 9    Litho.**
2032    A1376    5r multi    1.00 1.00

Snakes A1377

Designs: No. 2033, 5r, Python. No. 2034, 5r, Bamboo pit viper. No. 2035, 5r, King cobra. No. 2036, 5r, Gliding snake.

**2003, Nov. 12**
2033-2036    A1377    Set of 4    3.25 3.25
    2036a    Souvenir sheet, #2033-2036    4.00 4.00

Children's Day A1378

**2003, Nov. 14**
2037    A1378    5r multi    1.00 1.00

2nd Guards Batttalion (1st Grenadiers Battalion), 225th Anniv. — A1379

**2003, Nov. 22    Photo.    *Perf. 13***
2038    A1379    5r multi    1.00 1.00

Harivansh Rai Bachchan (1907-2003), Poet — A1380

**2003, Nov. 27    Litho.    *Perf. 13x13¼***
2039    A1380    5r sepia & blk    1.00 1.00

French and Indian Artisan's
Work — A1381

No. 2040: a, Illumination depicting rooster,
France, 15th cent. b, Jewelry design, India,
19th cent.

**2003, Nov. 29**
2040 A1381 22r Horiz. pair, #a-b    5.00 5.00
 c.      Souvenir sheet, #2040         9.00 9.00

See France Nos. 2986-2987.

Yashpal
(1903-76),
Writer
A1382

**2003, Dec. 3    Photo.    Perf. 13¼**
2041 A1382 5r multi                 1.00 1.00

India — South Korea Diplomatic
Relations, 30th Anniv. — A1383

No. 2042: a, Cheomsongdae Astronomical
Observatory, Gyeongju, Korea. b, Jantar
Mantar, Jaipur, India.

**2003, Dec. 10                      Litho.**
2042 A1383 15r Pair, #a-b          5.00 5.00

See South Korea No. 2136.
A privately-produced booklet containing two
strips of No. 2046 exists.

Rajya Sabha, 200th Session — A1384

**2003, Dec. 11**
2043 A1384 5r multi                 1.00 1.00

Mukut Behari Lal
Bhargava (b.
1903), Politician
A1385

**2003, Dec. 18              Photo.**
2044 A1385 5r multi                 1.00 1.00

Swami Swaroopanandji (1903-74),
Religious Leader — A1386

**2003, Dec. 20    Litho.    Perf. 13¼x13**
2045 A1386 5r multi                 1.00 1.00

Sangeet
Natak
Akademi,
50th Anniv.
A1387

No. 2046: a, Musicians. b, Actors. c,
Dancers.

**2003, Dec. 22**
2046    Strip of 3, #a-c            4.75 4.75
 a.-c.  A1387 5r Any single          1.10 1.10
 d.     Souvenir sheet, #2046        5.00 5.00

Folk Musicians
A1388

Designs: No. 2047, 5r, Allah Jilai Bai (1902-
92). No. 2048, 5r, Lalan Fakir (1774-1890).

**2003, Dec. 29**
2047-2048 A1388    Set of 2         2.00 2.00

Siddavanahalli
Nijalingappa
(1902-2000),
Politician
A1389

**2003, Dec. 31              Perf. 13x13¼**
2049 A1389 5r multi                 1.00 1.00

Major Somnath
Sharma (1923-47),
Military
Hero — A1390

**Perf. 13¼x12¾**
**2003, Dec. 31              Photo.**
2050 A1390 5r multi                 1.00 1.00

Chintaman D. Deshmukh (1896-1982),
Finance Minister — A1391

**2004, Jan. 14    Litho.    Perf. 13¼x13**
2051 A1391 5r multi                 1.00 1.00

Nani A. Palkhivala
(1920-2002),
Jurist — A1392

**2004, Jan. 16**
2052 A1392 5r multi                 1.00 1.00

A privately-produced booklet containing six
examples of No. 2052 exists.

Dr. Bhalchandra D.
Garware,
Businessman — A1393

**2004, Feb. 6**
2053 A1393 5r multi                 1.00 1.00

Annamacharya,
Mystic
Saint — A1394

**2004, Mar. 18    Photo.    Perf. 13¾**
2054 A1394 5r multi                 1.00 1.00

9th Battalion of Madras Regiment
(Travancore), 300th Anniv. — A1395

**2004, Apr. 1    Litho.    Perf. 13¼x13**
2055 A1395 5r multi                 1.00 1.00

V. Lakshminarayana,
Violinist — A1396

**2004, Apr. 14              Photo.**
2056 A1396 5r multi                 1.00 1.00

Indian Institute of
Social Welfare and
Business
Management, 51st
Anniv. — A1397

**2004, Apr. 25    Litho.    Perf. 13x13¼**
2057 A1397 5r multi                 1.00 1.00

Baji Rao Peshwa,
General,
Statesman
A1398

**2004, Apr. 25              Photo.**
2058 A1398 5r multi                 1.00 1.00

Circumnavigation of I.N.S.
Tarangini — A1399

**2004, Apr. 25    Litho.    Perf. 13¼x13**
2059 A1399 5r multi                 1.00 1.00
 a.      Souvenir sheet of 1        17.50 17.50

Siddhar Swamigal
(1904-64),
Spiritual
Leader — A1400

**2004, May 15              Perf. 13x13¼**
2060 A1400 5r multi                 1.00 1.00

Indra Chandra
Shastri (1912-86),
Philosopher
A1401

**2004, May 27              Photo.**
2061 A1401 5r black & green         1.00 1.00

Woodstock
School,
Mussoorie,
150th
Anniv.
A1402

**2004, June 2    Litho.    Perf. 12½x13¼**
2062 A1402 5r multi                 1.00 1.00

Jyotiprasad
Agarwalla (1903-
51), Musician,
Cinematographer
A1403

**2004, June 17  Photo.    Perf. 13x13¼**
2063 A1403 5r multi                 1.00 1.00

P. N. Panicker (1909-95), Educator A1404

**2004, June 19**
2064 A1404 5r multi          1.00 1.00

Great Trigonometrical Survey — A1405

Designs: No. 2065, 5r, Nain Singh (c. 1826-1882), Himalayan explorer. No. 2066, 5r, Radhanath Sikdan (1813-70), Surveyor who calculated height of Mt. Everest. No. 2067, 5r, Stylized map of India, triangles (38x28mm).

**2004, June 27   Litho.   Perf. 13¼**
2065-2067 A1405   Set of 3    2.50 2.50
2067a     Souvenir sheet, #2065-2067   8.00 8.00

A privately-produced booklet containing six examples of No. 2067 exists.

Aacharya Bhikshu, Founder of Jain Swetamber Terapanth Sect — A1406

**2004, June 30**                **Photo.**
2068 A1406 5r multi          .25 .25

2004 Summer Olympics, Athens — A1407

No. 2069: a, 5r, Wrestling. b, 5r, Women's long jump. c, 15r, Shooting. d, 15r, Field hockey.
Illustration reduced.

**Perf. 13¾x14¼**
**2004, Aug. 13**               **Photo.**
2069 A1407   Block of 4, #a-d  2.75 2.75

Poets — A1408

No. 2070: a, Kabir (1440-1518), Indian poet. b, Hafiz Shirazi (c. 1325-c. 1389), Persian poet.

---

Illustration reduced.

**2004, Aug. 16**              **Perf. 13¼**
2070 A1408 15r Horiz. pair, #a-b  2.00 2.00
   See Iran No. 2894.

Murasoli Maran (1934-2003), Politician, Film Maker, Journalist — A1409

**2004, Aug. 17**             **Perf. 12½x13¼**
2071 A1409 5r multi          .25 .25

Prime Minister Rajiv Gandhi (1944-91) and Windmills — A1410

**2004, Aug. 20   Litho.   Perf. 13¼**
2072 A1410 5r multi          .25 .25
Rajiv Gandhi Renewable Energy Day.

S. S. Vasan (1904-69), Film Producer, Magazine Publisher A1411

**2004, Aug. 28   Photo.   Perf. 13x13¼**
2073 A1411 5r multi          .25 .25

Panini (c. 520 B.C.-c. 460 B.C.), Grammarian — A1412

**2004, Aug. 30**            **Perf. 13¼x13**
2074 A1412 5r multi          .25 .25

K. Subrahmanyam (1904-71), Film Director and Producer — A1413

**2004, Sept. 10**
2075 A1413 5r multi          .25 .25

---

M. C. Chagla (1900-81), Judge, Diplomat A1414

**2004, Oct. 1**
2076 A1414 5r multi          .40 .40

Tirupur Kumaran (1904-32), Martyred Protester — A1415

**2004, Oct. 4**             **Perf. 13x13¼**
2077 A1415 5r multi          .25 .25

India Post, 150th Anniv. — A1416

No. 2078: a, Boat, #2, coach, train on bridge. b, Train on bridge, airplane, man with spear, frame of #C1. c, Mail box, building, #201. d, Computer, emblems for postal consumer services.

**2004, Oct. 4**             **Perf. 14¼x13¾**
2078     Horiz. strip of 4    2.00 2.00
a.-d.   A1416 5r Any single   .30 .30
e.      Souvenir sheet, #2078, perf.
        13¼                  10.00 10.00

Ashoka Chakra Winners — A1417

No. 2079: a, Neerja Bhanot (1963-86), airline purser killed in hijacking. b, Randhir Prasad Verma (1952-91), slain policeman.
Illustration reduced.

**2004, Oct. 8**             **Perf. 13¼x13**
2079 A1417 5r Horiz. pair, #a-b  .50 .50

Guru Dutt (1925-64), Film Actor, Director A1418

**2004, Oct. 10**
2080 A1418 5r multi          .25 .25

Indian Soldiers in UN Peacekeeping Forces — A1419

**2004, Oct. 24**            **Perf. 13¼**
2081 A1419 5r multi          .80 .80
a.    Souvenir sheet of 1    12.00 12.00

---

Periya (1748-1801) and Chinna (1753-1801) Marudhu, Rulers of Sivaganga, Rebellion Leaders A1420

**2004, Oct. 24**            **Perf. 13¾x14**
2082 A1420 5r multi          .25 .25

A privately-produced booklet containing six examples of No. 2082 exists.

Greetings — A1421

No. 2083: a, Kites. b, Dolls.

**2004, Oct. 25**            **Perf. 13½x13**
2083 A1421 4r Horiz. pair, #a-b  .35 .35

Dr. Svetoslav Roerich (1904-93), Painter A1422

**2004, Oct. 27**            **Perf. 13¼x13**
2084 A1422 5r multi          .25 .25

Tenneti Viswanatham (1895-1979), Politician — A1423

**2004, Nov. 10   Photo.   Perf. 13x13¼**
2085 A1423 5r multi          .25 .25

Children's Day — A1424

**2004, Nov. 14**
2086 A1424 5r multi          .25 .25

Walchand Hirachand (1882-1953), Industrialist A1425

**2004, Nov. 23**            **Perf. 13¾**
2087 A1425 5r multi          .25 .25

Dula Bhaya Kag (1903-77), Poet — A1426

**2004, Nov. 25**          *Perf. 13x13¼*
2088 A1426 5r multi          .25   .25

Aga Khan Award for Architecture — A1427

No. 2089: a, Khas Mahal (blue panel). b, Agra Fort (orange panel). Illustration reduced.

**2004, Nov. 28**          *Perf. 14x13¾*
2089          Horiz. pair          2.00   2.00
*a.-b.*   A1427 15r Either single   .75   .75
*c.*   Souvenir sheet, #2089a, 2089b, perf. 13¼   12.00   12.00

Bhagat Puran Singh (1904-92), Founder of Home for Poor — A1428

**2004, Dec. 10   Litho.   Perf. 13x13¼**
2090 A1428 5r multi          .25   .25

Women's Insurrections of 1904 and 1939 — A1429

**2004, Dec. 12   Photo.   Perf. 13¼x13**
2091 A1429 5r multi          .25   .25

Energy Conservation Day — A1430

**2004, Dec. 14**
2092 A1430 5r multi          .25   .25

Completion of Taj Mahal, 350th Anniv. — A1431

**2004, Dec. 16**          *Perf. 14x13¾*
2093 A1431 15r multi          1.25   1.25
*a.*   Souvenir sheet of 1, perf. 13¼   13.00   13.00

A privately produced booklet containing 3 #2093 exists.

Sahitya Academy, 50th Anniv. A1432

**2004, Dec. 21**          *Perf. 13¼x13*
2094 A1432 5r multi          .60   .60

Bhaskara Sethupathy (1868-1903), Ramanathapuram Ruler — A1433

**2004, Dec. 27**          *Perf. 13x13¼*
2095 A1433 5r multi          .25   .25

Dogs A1434

No. 2096: a, Himalayan sheepdog. b, Rampur hound. c, Mudhol hound. d, Rajapalayam.

**2005, Jan. 9**          *Perf. 13¼*
2096          Horiz. strip of 4          3.00   3.00
*a.-c.*   A1434 5r Any single   .30   .30
*d.*   A1434 15r multi   .70   .70

Padampat Singhania (1905-79), Industrialist A1435

**2005, Feb. 3**
2097 A1435 5r multi          .25   .25

Rotary International, Cent. — A1436

**2005, Feb. 23**          *Perf. 13¼x13*
2098 A1436 5r multi          .25   .25

Vice-President Krishan Kant (1927-2002) — A1437

**2005, Feb. 27   Photo.   Perf. 13¼**
2099 A1437 5r multi          .25   .25

Madhavrao Scindia (1945-2001), Government Minister — A1438

**2005, Mar. 10**
2100 A1438 5r multi          .25   .25

Flora and Fauna — A1439

No. 2101: a, Clouded leopard. b, Dillenia indica. c, Mishmi takin. d, Pitcher plant.

**2005, Mar. 24   Photo.   Perf. 13¼**
2101 A1439 5r Block of 4, #a-d   1.50   1.50
*e.*   Souvenir sheet, #2101   8.00   8.00

Intl. Year of Physics A1440

**Perf. 12¾x13**
**2005, Mar. 31**          **Wmk. 324**
2102 A1440 5r multi          .25   .25

Salt March to Dandi, 75th Anniv. — A1441

Mohandas Gandhi and: a, Marchers. b, Newspaper. c, Map of march. d, Text by Gandhi. Illustration reduced.

**Perf. 13¼**
**2005, Apr. 5   Photo.   Unwmk.**
2103 A1441 5r Block of 4, #a-d   2.00   2.00
*e.*   Souvenir sheet, #2103   10.00   10.00

15th Punjab (Patiala) Battalion, 300th Anniv. A1442

**2005, Apr. 13**
2104 A1442 5r multi          .25   .25

Bandung Conference, 50th Anniv. — A1443

**2005, Apr. 18**
2105 A1443 15r multi          1.00   1.00

Narayan Meghaji Lokhande (1848-1897), Labor Activist A1444

**2005, May 3**          *Perf. 13¾*
2106 A1444 5r multi          .25   .25

Cooperative Movement in India, Cent. — A1445

**2005, May 8**          *Perf. 13¼*
2107 A1445 5r multi          .25   .25

World Environment Day — A1446

**2005, June 5**
2108 A1446 5r multi          1.00   1.00

Guru Granth Sahib A1447

**2005, June 16   Photo.   Perf. 14x13¾**
2109 A1447 10r multi          45.00   —
*a.*   Souvenir sheet of 1   90.00   —

Because of a lack of an agreement with Indian postal officials and Sikh religious representatives, local post offices were alerted that the issuance of Nos. 2109 and 2109a was to be postponed and the stamps were not to be placed on sale on June 16. Examples were sold at several locations that apparently did not receive the message.

Abdul Qaiyum Ansari (1905-73), Nationalist Leader A1448

**2005, July 1   Photo.   Perf. 13¼**
2110 A1448 5r brown          .25   .25

Dheeran Chinnamalai (1765-1805), Freedom Fighter — A1449

**2005, July 31**
2111 A1449 5r multi .25 .25

State Bank of India, Bicent. — A1450

Illustration reduced.

**2005, Aug. 31**
2112 A1450 15r multi .70 .70

Intl. Day of Peace — A1451

**2005, Sept. 21 Photo. Perf. 13x13¼**
2113 A1451 5r multi .25 .25

A. M. M. Murugappa Chettiar (1902-65), Industrialist A1452

**2005, Oct. 1**
2114 A1452 5r multi .25 .25

Pratap Singh Kairon (1901-65), Government Minister — A1453

**2005, Oct. 1 Perf. 13¼x13**
2115 A1453 5r multi .25 .25

Dr. T. S. Soundram (1904-84), Founder of Gandhigram Development Program — A1454

**2005, Oct. 2**
2116 A1454 5r multi .90 .90

Mailboxes A1455

No. 2117: a, Victorian era box, horse-drawn carriage. b, Man inserting letter into Penfold box. c, Two cylindrical boxes. d, Two square letter boxes.

**2005, Oct. 18 Perf. 13x13¼**
2117 Horiz. strip of 4 3.50 3.50
a.-d. A1415 5r Any single .75 .30
e. Souvenir sheet, #2117a-
2117d, perf. 13¾ 15.00 15.00

V. Kalyanasundarnar (1883-1953), Union Leader — A1456

**2005, Oct. 21 Perf. 13¼**
2118 A1456 5r multi .25 .25

Ayothidhasa Pandithar (1845-1914), Social Reformer A1457

**2005, Oct. 21**
2119 A1457 5r multi .25 .25

Kavimani Desiga Vinayagam Pillai (1876-1954), Poet — A1458

**2005, Oct. 21 Perf. 13¼x13**
2120 A1458 5r multi .25 .25

Prabodh Chandra (1911-86), Writer — A1459

**2005, Oct. 24 Perf. 13x13¼**
2121 A1459 5r multi .25 .25

Children's Day — A1460

**2005, Nov. 14**
2122 A1460 5r multi .25 .25

Children's Film Society, 50th Anniv. A1461

**2005, Nov. 14**
2123 A1461 5r multi .25 .25

Progress, Harmony and Development Chamber of Commerce and Industry, Cent. — A1462

**2005, Nov. 16**
2124 A1462 5r multi .25 .25

World Summit on the Information Society, Tunis A1463

**2005, Nov. 17 Photo. Perf. 13¼x13**
2125 A1463 5r multi .25 .25

Calcutta Police Commissionerate, 150th Anniv. — A1464

**2005, Nov. 19 Perf. 13¾**
2126 A1464 5r multi .25 .25

Newborn Health — A1465

**2005, Nov. 24 Perf. 13¼**
2127 A1465 5r blue .25 .25

Jawaharlal Darda, Politician A1466

**2005, Dec. 2**
2128 A1466 5r multi .25 .25

Navy Ships Delhi, Kora and Udaygiri — A1467

**2005, Dec. 4 Perf. 13**
2129 A1467 5r multi .25 .25

M. S. Subbulakshmi (1916-2004), Singer — A1468

**2005, Dec. 18 Perf. 13¼x13**
2130 A1468 5r multi .25 .25

Integral Coach Factory, 50th Anniv. — A1469

**2005, Dec. 19 Perf. 13¾**
2131 A1469 5r multi .25 .25

Jadavpur University, 50th Anniv. — A1470

**2005, Dec. 21**
2132 A1470 5r multi .25 .25

16th Air Force Squadron, 55th Anniv. — A1471

**2005, Dec. 27 Perf. 14x13¾**
2133 A1471 5r multi .25 .25

De Facto Transfer of Pondicherry, 50th Anniv. (in 2006) — A1472

**2005, Dec. 30 Perf. 13¼x13**
2134 A1472 5r multi .25 .25

Pongal Festival A1473

**2006, Jan. 12**                  *Perf. 13¾*
2135 A1473 5r multi                    .25  .25

A. V. Meiyappan (1907-79), Film Producer and Director A1474

**2006, Jan. 22**                  *Perf. 13¼*
2136 A1474 5r multi                    .25  .25

N. M. R. Subbaraman, Politician, Cent. of Birth — A1475

**2006, Jan. 29**                  Photo.
2137 A1475 5r multi                    .25  .25
    Dated 2005.

Third Battalion of the Sikh Regiment, 150th Anniv. A1476

**2006, Feb. 1**                   *Perf. 13¼x13*
2138 A1476 5r multi                    .25  .25

President's Fleet Review, Visakhapatnam — A1477

No. 2139: a, Aircraft carrier and jet. b, Helicopter and two ships. c, Airplane and two ships. d, Two submarines.
Illustration reduced.

**2006, Feb. 12**                  *Perf. 13¾x13*
2139 A1477 5r Block of 4, #a-d  1.50  1.50

Thirumuruga Kirubananda Variyar (1906-93), Tamil Magazine Publisher A1478

Devaneya Pavanar (1902-81), Tamil Writer — A1479

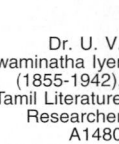

Dr. U. V. Swaminatha Iyer (1855-1942), Tamil Literature Researcher A1480

Tamilavel Umamaheswarar, Editor of Tamil Literary Magazine A1481

**2006, Feb. 18**                  *Perf. 13¼*
2140 A1478 5r red brown     .35  .35
2141 A1479 5r blue          .35  .35
2142 A1480 5r brown         .35  .35
2143 A1481 5r black         .35  .35
    Nos. 2140-2143 (4)     1.40  1.40

St. Bede's College, Shimla, 102nd Anniv. — A1482

**2006, Feb. 24**                  *Perf. 13x13¼*
2144 A1482 5r multi                    .25  .25

Gemini Ganesan (1920-2005), Actor — A1483

**2006, Feb. 25**                  *Perf. 13¼x13*
2145 A1483 5r black                    .25  .25

Salesians of Don Bosco in India, Cent. — A1484

**2006, Feb. 27**                  *Perf. 13x13¼*
2146 A1484 5r brown                    .25  .25

M. Singaravelar (1860-1946), Communist Politician A1485

**2006, Mar. 2**
2147 A1485 5r multi               .25  .25

World Consumer Rights Day A1486

**2006, Mar. 15**                  *Perf. 13¼x13*
2148 A1486 5r multi                    .25  .25

Indian Agricultural Research Institute, Delhi, Cent. A1487

**2006, Mar. 30**
2149 A1487 5r multi                    .25  .25

62nd Cavalry Armored Regiment, 50th Anniv. A1488

**2006, Apr. 1**
2150 A1488 5r multi                    .25  .25

Folk Dances — A1489

No. 2151 — Folk dances from: a, India. b, Cyprus.
Illustration reduced.

**2006, Apr. 12**                  *Perf. 13x13¾*
2151 A1489 15r Horiz. pair, #a-b  1.40  1.40
 c.    Souvenir sheet, #2151, perf.
       13¾x13¼                     4.25  4.25
    See Cyprus No. 1052.

Calcutta Girls' High School, 150th Anniv. A1490

**2006, Apr. 21**                  *Perf. 13¾x13*
2152 A1490 5r multi                    .25  .25

Pannalal Barupal (1913-83), Politician A1491

**2006, Apr. 28**                  *Perf. 13x13¼*
2153 A1491 5r multi                    .25  .25

Kurinji Flower A1492

**2006, Apr. 29**                  *Perf. 13x13¾*
2154 A1492 15r multi              .70  .70
 a.    Souvenir sheet of 1        3.25  3.25

Rainwater Harvesting A1493

**2006, June 5**                   *Perf. 13¼x13*
2155 A1493 5r multi                    .25  .25

Sri Pratap College, Srinigar, Cent. — A1494

**2006, June 15**                  *Perf. 13*
2156 A1494 5r multi                    .25  .25

Indraprastha Girls' School, New Delhi, 102nd Anniv. — A1495

**2006, July 8**                   *Perf. 13¾x13*
2157 A1495 5r multi                    .25  .25

Voorhees College, Vellore, 111th Anniv. A1496

**2006, July 10**                  *Perf. 13¼*
2158 A1496 5r multi                    .25  .25

Vellore Mutiny, Bicent. — A1497

**2006, July 10**   Litho.         *Perf. 13¼*
2159 A1497 5r multi                    .25  .25

High Court of Jammu and Kashmir — A1498

                   *Perf. 13¾x13¼*
**2006, July 29**                  Photo.
2160 A1498 5r multi                    .25  .25

Pankaj Kumar Mullick (1904-78), Composer A1499

**2006, Aug. 4**     *Perf. 13¼x13*
2161 A1499 5r multi     .25 .25

Oil and Natural Gas Corporation, Limited A1500

**2006, Aug. 14**
2162 A1500 5r multi     .25 .25

M. P. Sivagnanam, Tamil Politician, Cent. of Birth — A1501

**2006, Aug. 15**    *Litho.*    *Perf. 13¼*
2163 A1501 5r multi     .25 .25

University of Madras A1502

**2006, Sept. 4**     *Photo.*
2164 A1502 5r multi     .25 .25

L. V. Prasad (1908-94), Film Actor and Director A1503

**2006, Sept. 5**
2165 A1503 5r multi     .25 .25

Indian Merchants Chamber — A1504

**2006, Sept. 7**     *Perf. 13x13¼*
2166 A1504 5r multi     .25 .25

Horse Sculptures — A1505

No. 2167: a, Horse and rider. b, Horse only. Illustration reduced.

**2006, Sept. 11**     *Perf. 13¼x13¾*
2167 A1505 15r Horiz. pair, #a-b    1.40 1.40
   c.    Souvenir sheet, #2167    4.25 4.25

See Mongolia No. 2621.

---

Birds A1506

No. 2168: a, Greater adjutant stork. b, Nilgiri laughing thrush. c, Manipur bush-quail. d, Lesser florican.

**2006, Oct. 5**     *Perf. 13*
2168    Vert. strip of 4    1.00 1.00
   a.-d.    A1506 5r Any single    .25 .25
   e.    Souvenir sheet, #2168a-2168d    4.00 4.00

Madhya Pradesh Chamber of Commerce and Industry, Cent. A1507

**2006, Oct. 12**    *Photo.*    *Perf. 13¼*
2169 A1507 5r multi     .25 .25

Bishwanath Roy (1906-84), Politician A1508

**2007, Oct. 31**    *Litho.*    *Perf. 13¼x13*
2170 A1508 5r multi     .25 .25

G. Varadaraj, Industrialist (1936-90) A1509

**2006, Nov. 1**
2171 A1509 5r multi     .25 .25

Lakes — A1510

No. 2172: a, Roop Kund. b, Chandra Tal, vert. c, Tsomo Riri. d, Sela. e, Tsangu. Illustration reduced.

**2006, Nov. 6**    *Photo.*    *Perf. 13*
2172 A1510 5r Block of 5, #a-e    1.25 1.25

Lala Deen Dayal (1844-1905), Photographer A1511

**2006, Nov. 11**
2173 A1511 5r multi     .25 .25

---

Children's Day — A1512

No. 2174 — Various children's drawings: a, Denomination at LL. b, Denomination at UL. Illustration reduced.

**2006, Nov. 14**    *Litho.*    *Perf. 13*
2174 A1512 5r Horiz. pair, #a-b    .45 .45

The Tribune, 125th Anniv. A1513

**2006, Nov. 24**    *Photo.*    *Perf. 14*
2175 A1513 5r multi     .25 .25

World AIDS Day — A1514

**2006, Dec. 1**     *Perf. 13x13¼*
2176 A1514 5r multi     .25 .25

Bartholomaeus Ziegenbalg (1682-1719), First Lutheran Missionary to India — A1515

**2006, Dec. 8**     *Perf. 13¼*
2177 A1515 5r multi     .25 .25

Army Field Post Offices, 150th Anniv. — A1516

No. 2178: a, Soldier, cancel, ship, map of Bushire-Bombay route. b, Soldier writing letter, camel. c, Soldier reading letter, sign. d, Soldier reading letter, helicopter.

**2006, Dec. 10**    *Litho.*    *Perf. 13x13¼*
2178    Horiz. strip of 4    1.00 1.00
   a.-d.    A1516 5r Any single    .25 .25

Sandalwood Carving A1517

---

**2006, Dec. 18**    *Photo.*    *Perf. 13¼x13*
2179 A1517 15r multi     .70 .70
   a.    Souvenir sheet of 1, perf. 13    3.00 3.00

Stamps are impregnated with a sandalwood scent.

Stop Child Labor — A1518

No. 2180: a, Girl on tightrope. b, Boy with hoe. c, Boy pouring tea. d, Boy with large basket. Illustration reduced.

**2006, Dec. 28**     *Perf. 13¼x13*
2180 A1518 5r Block of 4, #a-d    1.00 1.00

Bimal Roy (1909-66), Film Director A1519

**2007, Jan. 8**    *Litho.*    *Perf. 13*
2181 A1519 5r multi     .25 .25

Tamil Nadu Cricket Association, 70th Anniv. — A1520

**2007, Jan. 26**     *Perf. 13x13¼*
2182 A1520 5r multi     .25 .25

Rose Varieties — A1521

No. 2183: a, 5r, Bhim. b, 5r, Neelam. c, 15r, Delhi Princess. d, 15r, Jawahar.

**2007, Feb. 7**    *Photo.*    *Perf. 13x13¼*
2183 A1521    Block of 4, #a-d    1.90 1.90
   e.    Souvenir sheet, #2183    5.00 5.00

Stamps are impregnated with a rose scent.

Manoharbhai Patel (1906-70), Politician A1522

**2007, Feb. 9**
2184 A1522 5r multi       .25   .25

Fairs — A1523

Designs: No. 2185, 5r, Sonepur Fair. No. 2186, 5r, Pushkar Fair. No. 2187, 5r, Goa Carnival. No. 2188, 5r, Baul Mela.

**2007, Feb. 27**      Litho.
2185-2188 A1523   Set of 4    1.00   1.00
2188a    Souvenir sheet, #2185-2188    3.00   3.00

Women's Day — A1524

No. 2189: a, Two women. b, Woman, three birds. c, Two women and birds. d, Woman and birds.

**2007, Mar. 8**   Photo.   *Perf. 13x13¼*
2189    Horiz. strip of 4    1.90   1.90
a.-b.   A1524 5r Either single   .25   .25
c.-d.   A1524 15r Either single   .70   .70
e.   Souvenir sheet, #2189   5.00   5.00

Raj Narain (1917-86), Politician A1525

**2007, Mar. 23**   Litho.   *Perf. 13¼*
2190 A1525 5r multi       .25   .25

Mehboob Khan (1907-64), Film Producer and Director — A1526

**2007, Mar. 30**
2191 A1526 5r multi       .25   .25

Dr. R. M. Alagappa Chettiar (1909-57), Industrialist and Philanthropist A1527

**2007, Apr. 6**   Photo.   *Perf. 13x13¼*
2192 A1527 5r multi       .25   .25

A1528

A1529

A1530

A1531

A1532

Mahaparinirvana of Buddha, 2550th Anniv. — A1533

**2007, May 2**       *Perf. 13¼*
2193 A1528 5r multi      .25   .25
2194 A1529 5r multi      .25   .25
2195 A1530 5r multi      .25   .25
2196 A1531 5r multi      .25   .25
2197 A1532 5r multi      .25   .25
2198 A1533 5r multi      .25   .25
a.   Miniature sheet, #2193-2198   3.50   3.50
   Nos. 2193-2198 (6)   1.50   1.50

Natl. Parks — A1534

No. 2199: a, Bandhavgarh Natl. Park. b, Bandipur Natl. Park. c, Kaziranga Natl. Park. d, Mudumalai Natl. Park. e, Periyar Natl. Park.

**2007, May 31**
2199    Vert. strip of 5    1.25   1.25
a.-e.   A1534 5r Any single   .25   .25

Saint Vallalar (1823-74) A1536

First War of Independence, 150th Anniv. — A1535

**2007, Aug. 9**       *Perf. 13¼x13*
2200 A1535   Vert. pair    1.00   1.00
a.   5r Battle of Lucknow   .25   .25
b.   15r Battle of Kanpur   .75   .75
c.   Souvenir sheet, #2200a-2200b   2.50   2.50

Maraimalai Adigal (1876-1950), Tamil Scholar A1537

V. G. Suryanarayana Sastriar (1870-1903), Tamil Writer — A1538

**2007, Aug. 18**   Litho.   *Perf. 13x13¼*
2201 A1536 5r multi      .25   .25
2202 A1537 5r multi      .25   .25
2203 A1538 5r multi      .25   .25
   Nos. 2201-2203 (3)   .75   .75

Bridges A1539

No. 2204: a, Howrah Bridge. b, Mahatma Gandhi Bridge. c, Pamban Bridge. d, Vidyasagar Bridge.

**2007, Aug. 17**       Photo.
2204   Vert. strip or block of 4   1.00   1.00
a.-d.   A1539 5r Any single   .25   .25
e.   Souvenir sheet, #2204a-2204d   2.50   2.50

J. P. Naik (1907-81), Education Reformer — A1540

**2007, Sept. 5**   Litho.   *Perf. 13¼x13*
2205 A1540 5r multi      .25   .25

53rd Commonwealth Parliamentary Conference, New Delhi — A1541

**2007, Sept. 23**   Litho.   *Perf. 13¼*
2206 A1541 15r multi      .80   .80

Sachin Deb Burman (1906-75), Composer A1542

**2007, Oct. 1**       *Perf. 13¼x13*
2207 A1542 15r multi      .80   .80

Satyagraha (Non-Violent Resistance), Cent. A1543

No. 2208 — Mohandas Gandhi and: a, Train. b, House, newspaper article. c, Crowd, building. d, People marching.

**2007, Oct. 2**   Photo.   *Perf. 13¼x13*
2208    Horiz. strip of 4    1.00   1.00
a.-d.   A1543 5r Any single   .25   .25
e.   Souvenir sheet, #2208a-2208d   3.00   3.00

Designs: No. 2209, 5r, DHRUV helicopter. No. 2210, 5r, Westland Wapiti biplane. No. 2211, 5r, AWACS airplane (84x32mm). 15r, IL-78 (84x32mm).

Indian Air Force, 75th Anniv. A1544

**2007, Oct. 8    Litho.    Perf. 13¼x13**
2209-2212  A1544  Set of 4          1.60  1.60
2212a    Souvenir sheet, #2209-2212   4.00  4.00

Fourth Military World Games, Hyderabad A1545

No. 2213: a, Parachutist. b, Soccer player. c, Swimmer.

**2007, Oct. 14    Perf. 13¼x13**
2213    Vert. strip of 3              .80  .80
a.-c.  A1545 5r Any single           .25  .25
d.    Souvenir sheet, #2213, perf. 13  3.00  3.00

Maharashtra Police Academy — A1546

**2007, Nov. 3    Photo.    Perf. 13¼**
2214  A1546 5r multi                 .25  .25

Children's Day A1547

Children's art: No. 2215, 5r, Children and stars. No. 2216, 5r, Fishermen and canoes at night.

**2007, Nov. 14    Litho.    Perf. 13¼x13**
2215-2216  A1547  Set of 2          .50  .50
2216a    Souvenir sheet, #2215-2216  2.00  2.00

Renewable Energy — A1548

Designs: No. 2217, 5r, Solar energy. No. 2218, 5r, Wind energy. No. 2219, 5r, Small hydroelectric power, vert. No. 2220, 5r, Biomass energy, vert.

**2007, Nov. 22    Photo.    Perf. 13**
2217-2220  A1548  Set of 4          1.00  1.00
2220a    Souvenir sheet, #2217-2220,
           perf. 13¾x13¼, 13¼x13¾    3.00  3.00
2220b    Miniature sheet, 6 each
           #2217-2218, 3 each #2219-
           2220                      4.50  4.50

First Battalion of the Fourth Gorkha Rifles, 150th Anniv. A1549

**2007, Nov. 27    Litho.    Perf. 13¼**
2221  A1549 5r multi                 .25  .25

Intl. Day of Disabled Persons — A1550

**Photo. & Embossed**
**2007, Dec. 3    Perf. 13**
2222  A1550 5r multi                 .25  .25

Daly College, Indore, 125th Anniv. — A1551

**2007, Dec. 8    Litho.    Perf. 13¼**
2223  A1551 5r multi                 .25  .25

Wilson College, Bombay, 175th Anniv. — A1552

**2007, Dec. 11    Photo.    Perf. 13**
2224  A1552 5r multi                 .25  .25

Greetings A1553

No. 2225: a, Sun, wheat, path. b, Fish, lotus flower. c, Bird. d, Man, flower, butterfly, deer. e, Flowers, stars and text, "Happy New Year," (58x29mm).

**2007, Dec. 15    Photo.    Perf. 13**
2225    Horiz. strip of 5            1.25  1.25
a.-e.  A1553 5r Any single           .25  .25

S. B. Chavan (1920-2004), Politician — A1554

**2007, Dec. 17    Litho.    Perf. 13¼x13**
2226  A1554 5r multi                 .25  .25

Snows Basilica, 425th Anniv. — A1555

**2007, Dec. 25    Perf. 13**
2227  A1555 5r multi                 .25  .25

Water Year — A1556

**2007, Dec. 28**
2228  A1556 5r multi                 .25  .25

Ritwik Ghatak (1925-76), Film Director A1557

**2007, Dec. 31    Photo.    Perf. 13¼x13**
2229  A1557 5r brown & black         .25  .25

Butterflies Of Andaman and Nicobar Islands — A1558

No. 2230: a, Male Papilio mayo. b, Female Papilio mayo. c, Female Pachliopta rhodifer. d, Male Pachliopta rhodifer.
Illustration reduced.

**2008, Jan. 2    Perf. 13**
2230  A1558 5r Block of 4, #a-d      1.00  1.00
e.    Souvenir sheet, #2230         3.00  3.00

Dr. Benjamin Peary Pal (1906-89), Rose Breeder and Plant Scientist A1559

**2008, Jan. 5    Litho.**
2231  A1559 5r multi                 .25  .25

Dr. Dhananjaya Ramachandra Gadgil (1901-71), Economist A1560

**2008, Feb. 8    Photo.**
2232  A1560 5r multi                 .25  .25

Damodaram Sanjeevaiah (1921-72), Politician — A1561

**2008, Feb. 14    Litho.**
2233  A1561 5r multi                 .25  .25

Maharshi Bulusu Sambamurthy (1886-1958), Lawyer — A1562

**2008, Mar. 4**
2234  A1562 5r multi                 .25  .25

Madhubala (1933-1969), Film Actress — A1563

**2008, Mar. 18    Photo.    Perf. 13**
2235  A1563 5r multi                 .25  .25
a.    Souvenir sheet of 1, perf.
        13x13¾                       1.50  1.50

Asrar Ul Haq (Majaaz) (1909-55), Urdu Poet A1564

**2008, Mar. 28    Litho.    Perf. 13**
2236  A1564 5r multi                 .25  .25

Civil Service A1565

**Photo. & Embossed**
**2008, Apr. 21**
2237  A1565 5r multi                 .25  .25

Tata Steel, Cent. — A1566

**2008, Apr. 22    Litho.**
2238  A1566 5r multi                 .25  .25

Jasmine Flowers — A1567

**2008, Apr. 26**                          **Photo.**
2239   A1567   5r shown                    .25    .25
2240   A1567   15r Flowers, horiz.         .75    .75
  a.      Souvenir sheet, #2239-2240      3.00   3.00

Nos. 2239-2240, 2240a are impregnated with a jasmine scent.

Aga Khan Foundation, 30th Anniv. — A1568

No. 2241: a, 5r, Heritage restoration (46x39mm). b, 15r, Social commitment (70x39mm).
Illustration reduced.

**2008, May 17**     **Photo.**     **Perf. 13**
2241   A1568   Horiz. pair, #a-b    .95    .95
  c.      Souvenir sheet, #2241a-2241b   3.00   3.00

Shri Shirdi Sai Baba (1835-1918), Hindu Saint — A1569

**2008, May 20**
2242   A1569   5r multi              .25    .25

Madhav Institute of Technology, Gwalior, 50th Anniv. — A1572

**2008, June 30**   **Litho.**   **Perf. 13¼**
2245   A1572   5r multi              .25    .25

Temples — A1573

No. 2246: a, Maha Bodhi Temple, India. b, White Horse Temple, China.

**2008, July 11**   **Photo.**   **Perf. 13**
2246   A1573   15r Horiz. pair, #a-b   1.40   1.40
  c.      Souvenir sheet, #2246        4.00   4.00

See People's Republic of China Nos. 3678-3679.

Punjab Regiment 14th Battalion, 250th Anniv. — A1574

**2008, July 21**   **Litho.**   **Perf. 13¼**
2247   A1574   5r multi              .25    .25

Damodar Dharmananda Kosambi (1907-66), Mathematician — A1575

**2008, July 31**
2248   A1575   5r multi              .25    .25

Aldabra Giant Tortoise A1576

Tortoise facing: 5r, Left. 15r, Forward.

**2008, Aug. 2**   **Photo.**   **Perf. 13**
2249-2250   A1576   Set of 2        .95    .95

2008 Summer Olympics, Beijing — A1577

No. 2251 — 2008 Summer Olympics emblem and: a, 5r, Olympic torch and mascot. b, 5r, Boxing. c, 15r, Shooting. d, 15r, Archery.
Illustration reduced.

**2008, Aug. 8**
2251   A1577   Block of 4, #a-d      1.90   1.90
  e.      Souvenir sheet, #2251a-2251d   3.00   3.00

Indian Coast Guard, 30th Anniv. — A1578

No. 2252: a, Airplane. b, Helicopter. c, Hovercraft (large wave at LL). d, Patrol boat (large wave at LR).
Illustration reduced.

**2008, Aug. 12**   **Litho.**   **Perf. 13¼**
2252   A1578   5r Block of 4, #a-d    .95    .95
  e.      Souvenir sheet, #2252a-2252d   3.00   3.00

Ustad Bismillah Khan (1916-2006), Musician — A1579

**2008, Aug. 21**
2253   A1579   5r multi              .25    .25

---

## AIR POST STAMPS

De Havilland Hercules over Lake AP1

### Wmk. 196 Sideways
**1929-30**      **Typo.**      **Perf. 14**
C1   AP1   2a dull green         .55    .30
C2   AP1   3a deep blue          .80    .55
C3   AP1   4a gray olive        2.25   1.10
  a.      4a olive green ('30)   2.75   1.10
C4   AP1   6a bister            2.75    .70
C5   AP1   8a red violet        3.25   3.25
C6   AP1   12a brown red        9.75   9.75
  Nos. C1-C6 (6)               19.35  15.65

> Catalogue values for unused stamps in this section, from this point to the end of the section, are for Never Hinged items.

### Dominion of India

Lockheed Constellation — AP2

**Perf. 13½x14**
**1948, May 29**   **Litho.**   **Wmk. 196**
C7   AP2   12a ultra & slate blk   2.25   2.25
Bombay-London flight of June 8, 1948.

### Republic of India

The Spirit of '76, by Archibald M. Willard — AP3

**1976, May 29**        **Perf. 13x13½**
C8   AP3   2.80r multicolored    4.00   4.00
American Bicentennial.

INDIA '80 Emblem, De Havilland Puss Moth AP4

**1979, Oct. 15   Photo.   Perf. 14½x14**
C9    AP4   30p shown           .80    .30
C10   AP4   50p Chetak helicopter   1.00   .50
C11   AP4   1r Boeing 737       1.25    .90
C12   AP4   2r Boeing 747       1.60   1.10
  Nos. C9-C12 (4)               4.65   2.80

INDIA '80 Intl. Stamp Exhib., New Delhi, Jan. 25-Feb. 3, 1980.

---

## MILITARY STAMPS

### China Expeditionary Force

Regular Issues of India, 1882-99, Overprinted

**1900**          **Wmk. 39**          **Perf. 14**
M1    A31   3p carmine rose      .70    2.10
M2    A17   ½a dark green       1.25    .45
M3    A19   1a maroon           7.00    2.50
M4    A21   2a ultra            5.25   15.00
M5    A28   2a6p green          4.75   21.00
M6    A22   3a orange           4.75   27.50
M7    A23   4a olive green      4.75   13.00
M8    A25   8a red violet       4.75   30.00
M9    A26   12a violet, red    30.00   30.00
M10   A29   1r car rose & grn  37.50   37.50
  a.      Double overprint
  Nos. M1-M10 (10)            100.70  179.05

The 1a6p of this set was overprinted, but not issued. Value $250.

Overprinted on 1900 Issue of India

**1904, Feb. 27**
M11   A19   1a carmine rose    55.00   15.00

Overprinted on 1902-09 Issue of India

**1904**
M12   A32   3p gray             8.00   10.00
M13   A34   1a carmine rose    12.00    1.10
M14   A35   2a violet          22.50    3.75
M15   A36   2a6p ultra          5.25    8.00
M16   A37   3a brown org        5.75    6.50
M17   A38   4a olive green     13.50   19.00
M18   A40   8a red violet      13.00   12.00
M19   A41   12a violet, red    18.00   30.00
M20   A42   1r car rose & grn  20.00   45.00
  Nos. M12-M20 (9)            118.00  135.35

Overprinted on 1906 Issue of India

**1909**
M21   A44   ½a green            2.10   1.90
M22   A45   1a carmine rose     2.75    .40

Overprinted on 1911-19 Issues of India

**1913-21**
M23   A46   3p gray             8.00   35.00
M24   A47   ½a green            6.25    7.50
M25   A48   1a car rose         7.25    4.75
M26   A58   1½a chocolate      40.00   95.00
M27   A49   2a violet          27.50   80.00
M28   A57   2a6p ultra         20.00   30.00
M29   A51   3a brown org       40.00  240.00
M30   A52   4a olive green     37.50  210.00
M31   A54   8a red violet      40.00  400.00
M32   A55   12a claret         37.50  140.00
M33   A56   1r grn & red brn  110.00  375.00
  Nos. M23-M33 (11)           374.00  1,617.

Issue dates: No. M23, 1913; others, 1921.

### Indian Expeditionary Force

Regular Issues of India, 1911-13, Overprinted

**1914**          **Wmk. 39**          **Perf. 14**
M34   A46   3p gray             .30    .55
  a.      Double overprint     70.00  55.00
M35   A47   ½a green            .80    .55
  a.      Double overprint    175.00 300.00
M36   A48   1a carmine rose    2.10    .55
M37   A49   2a violet          2.10    .55
M38   A57   2a6p ultra         2.50   4.00
M39   A51   3a brown org       1.75   2.75
M40   A52   4a olive green     1.75   2.75
M41   A54   8a red violet      2.10   4.25

| | | | | |
|---|---|---|---|---|
| M42 | A55 | 12a claret | 3.75 | 10.50 |
| M43 | A56 | 1r grn & red brn | 4.50 | 7.25 |
| | | Nos. M34-M43 (10) | 21.65 | 33.70 |

Catalogue values for unused stamps in this section, from this point to the end of the section, are for Never Hinged items.

### Korea Custodial Unit

Regular Issues of India Overprinted in Black

**Perf. 13½x14, 14x13½**

| 1953 | | | Wmk. 196 | |
|---|---|---|---|---|
| M44 | A91 | 3p gray violet | .35 | 2.50 |
| M45 | A92 | 6p red brown | .35 | 2.50 |
| M46 | A91 | 9p green | .35 | 2.50 |
| M47 | A101 | 1a turquoise | .50 | 3.00 |
| M48 | A93 | 2a carmine | .80 | 3.00 |
| M49 | A94 | 2½a brown lake | 1.50 | 3.50 |
| M50 | A94 | 3a red orange | 1.75 | 3.50 |
| M51 | A94 | 4a ultra | 2.10 | 3.50 |
| M52 | A95 | 6a purple | 8.00 | 8.25 |
| M53 | A95 | 8a blue green | 5.75 | 8.25 |
| M54 | A95 | 12a blue | 7.75 | 16.00 |
| M55 | A96 | 1r dk grn & pur | 12.50 | 16.00 |
| | | Nos. M44-M55 (12) | 41.70 | 72.50 |

Hindi overprint reads "Indian Custodial Unit, Korea."

### Indian UN Force in Congo

Nos. 302-303, 305, 307, 282 and 313 Overprinted: "U.N. FORCE (INDIA) CONGO"

**Wmk. 324, 196 (13np)**

| 1962, Jan. 15 | | Photo. | Perf. 14x13½ | |
|---|---|---|---|---|
| M56 | A117 | 1np blue green | .90 | .90 |
| M57 | A117 | 2np light brown | .90 | .90 |
| M58 | A117 | 5np emerald | .90 | .90 |
| M59 | A117 | 8np bright green | .90 | .90 |
| M60 | A117 | 13np brt carmine | 1.50 | 1.50 |
| M61 | A117 | 50np orange | 2.75 | 2.75 |
| | | Nos. M56-M61 (6) | 7.85 | 7.85 |

### Indian UN Force in Gaza

No. 393 Overprinted in Carmine

| 1965, Jan. 15 | | Unwmk. | Perf. 13½ | |
|---|---|---|---|---|
| M62 | A190 | 15p blue gray | 4.00 | 6.00 |

Overprint letters stand for "United Nations Emergency Force."

### INTERNATIONAL COMMISSION IN INDO-CHINA

Catalogue values for all unused stamps in this section are for Never Hinged items.

### Cambodia

India Nos. 207, 231, 211, 216 and 217 Overprinted in Black

**Perf. 13½x14**

| 1954, Dec. 1 | | | Wmk. 196 | |
|---|---|---|---|---|
| 1 | A91 | 3p gray violet | .50 | .50 |
| 2 | A101 | 1a turquoise | .60 | .60 |
| 3 | A93 | 2a carmine | 1.00 | 1.00 |
| 4 | A95 | 8a blue green | 4.00 | 4.25 |
| 5 | A95 | 12a blue | 5.50 | 6.25 |
| | | Nos. 1-5 (5) | 11.60 | 12.60 |

The overprint reads "International Commission Cambodia." Top line is 18mm on Nos. 4-5; 15½mm on Nos. 1-3, 6-12.

Same Overprint on India Nos. 276, 279, 282, 286 and 287

| 1957, Apr. 1 | | | Perf. 14x14½ | |
|---|---|---|---|---|
| 6 | A117 | 2np light brown | .40 | .40 |
| 7 | A117 | 6np gray | .40 | .40 |
| 8 | A117 | 13np bright carmine | 1.00 | .70 |
| 9 | A117 | 50np orange | 4.75 | 2.50 |
| 10 | A117 | 75np plum | 5.25 | 4.75 |
| | | Nos. 6-10 (5) | 11.80 | 8.75 |

Same Overprint on India No. 303

| 1962 | | | Wmk. 324 | |
|---|---|---|---|---|
| 12 | A117 | 2np light brown | .65 | .65 |

### Laos

India Nos. 207, 231, 211, 216 and 217 Overprinted in Black

**Perf. 13½x14**

| 1954, Dec. 1 | | | Wmk. 196 | |
|---|---|---|---|---|
| 1 | A91 | 3p gray violet | .50 | .50 |
| 2 | A101 | 1a turquoise | .60 | .60 |
| 3 | A93 | 2a carmine | 1.00 | 1.00 |
| 4 | A95 | 8a blue green | 4.00 | 4.25 |
| 5 | A95 | 12a blue | 5.50 | 6.25 |
| | | Nos. 1-5 (5) | 11.60 | 12.60 |

The overprint reads "International Commission Laos." Top line is 18mm on Nos. 4-5; 15½mm on Nos. 1-3, 6-16.

Same Overprint on India Nos. 276, 279, 282, 286 and 287

| 1957, Apr. 1 | | | Perf. 14x14½ | |
|---|---|---|---|---|
| 6 | A117 | 2np light brown | .40 | .40 |
| 7 | A117 | 6np gray | .40 | .40 |
| 8 | A117 | 13np brt carmine | 1.00 | .70 |
| 9 | A117 | 50np orange | 4.75 | 2.50 |
| 10 | A117 | 75np plum | 5.25 | 4.75 |
| | | Nos. 6-10 (5) | 11.80 | 8.75 |

Same Overprint on India Nos. 303-305, 313-314

| 1962-65 | | | Wmk. 324 | |
|---|---|---|---|---|
| 12 | A117 | 2np light brown | 2.50 | 3.00 |
| 13 | A117 | 3np brown ('63) | .60 | .60 |
| 14 | A117 | 5np emerald ('63) | .60 | .60 |
| 15 | A117 | 50np orange ('65) | 2.00 | 2.25 |
| 16 | A117 | 75np plum ('65) | 4.25 | 4.75 |
| | | Nos. 12-16 (5) | 9.95 | 11.20 |

### Laos and Viet Nam

No. 393 Overprinted in Carmine

| 1965, Jan. 15 | | Unwmk. | Perf. 13½ | |
|---|---|---|---|---|
| 1 | A190 | 15p blue gray | 4.00 | 4.00 |

Overprint letters stand for "International Control Commission."

Nos. 406-408, 411-412, 417 and 419-420 Overprinted in Carmine

**Perf. 14½x14, 14x14½**

| 1968, Oct. 2 | | Photo. | Wmk. 324 | |
|---|---|---|---|---|
| 2 | A202 | 2p reddish brown | .50 | .50 |
| 3 | A202 | 3p olive bister | .50 | .50 |
| 4 | A202 | 5p cerise | .50 | .50 |
| 5 | A203 | 10p bright blue | 2.50 | 2.50 |
| 6 | A203 | 15p green | 1.00 | 1.00 |
| 7 | A202 | 60p dark gray | 1.10 | 1.10 |
| 8 | A204 | 1r dp cl & red brn | 1.75 | 2.25 |
| 9 | A205 | 2r violet & brt blue | 4.00 | 5.50 |
| | | Nos. 2-9 (8) | 11.85 | 13.85 |

The arrangement of the lines of the overprint varies on each denomination.

### Viet Nam

India Nos. 207, 231, 211, 216 and 217 Overprinted in Black

**Perf. 13½x14**

| 1954, Dec. 1 | | | Wmk. 196 | |
|---|---|---|---|---|
| 1 | A91 | 3p gray violet | .50 | .50 |
| 2 | A101 | 1a turquoise | .60 | .60 |
| 3 | A93 | 2a carmine | 1.00 | 1.00 |
| 4 | A95 | 8a blue green | 4.00 | 4.25 |
| 5 | A95 | 12a blue | 5.50 | 5.50 |
| | | Nos. 1-5 (5) | 11.60 | 12.60 |

The overprint reads "International Commission Viet Nam." Top line of overprint is 18mm on Nos. 4-5; 15½mm on Nos. 1-3, 6-16.

Same Overprint on India Nos. 276, 279, 282, 286 and 287

| 1957, Apr. 1 | | | Perf. 14x14½ | |
|---|---|---|---|---|
| 6 | A117 | 2np light brown | .40 | .40 |
| 7 | A117 | 6np gray | .40 | .40 |
| 8 | A117 | 13np bright carmine | 1.00 | .70 |
| 9 | A117 | 50np orange | 4.75 | 2.10 |
| 10 | A117 | 75np plum | 5.25 | 4.75 |
| | | Nos. 6-10 (5) | 11.80 | 8.35 |

Same Overprint on India Nos. 302-305, 313-314

| 1961-65 | | | Wmk. 324 | |
|---|---|---|---|---|
| 11 | A117 | 1np blue green | 1.40 | 1.40 |
| 12 | A117 | 2np light brown ('62) | 2.75 | 2.75 |
| 13 | A117 | 3np brown ('63) | 1.00 | 1.00 |
| 14 | A117 | 5np emerald ('63) | .65 | .80 |
| 15 | A117 | 50np orange ('65) | 2.25 | 2.75 |
| 16 | A117 | 75np plum ('65) | 4.25 | 4.75 |
| | | Nos. 11-16 (6) | 12.30 | 13.45 |

### OFFICIAL STAMPS

Nos. O1-O26 are normally found with very heavy cancellations, and values are for stamps so canceled. Lightly canceled copies are seldom seen.

Nos. 11-12, 18, 20-22, 23a, 24, 26 Overprinted in Black

| 1866, Aug. 1 | | Unwmk. | Perf. 14 | |
|---|---|---|---|---|
| O1 | A7 | ½a blue | 1,100. | 140.00 |
| a. | | Inverted overprint | | |
| O3 | A7 | 1a brown | | 140.00 |
| O4 | A7 | 8a rose | 22.50 | 50.00 |

The 8p lilac unwatermarked (No. 19) with "Service" overprint was not officially issued.

| | | | Wmk. 38 | |
|---|---|---|---|---|
| O5 | A7 | ½a blue | 225.00 | 12.50 |
| a. | | Inverted overprint | | |
| b. | | Without period | | 210.00 |
| O6 | A8 | 8p lilac | 20.00 | 52.50 |
| O7 | A7 | 1a brown | 190.00 | 15.00 |
| O8 | A7 | 2a yellow | 175.00 | 85.00 |
| a. | | Imperf. | | |
| b. | | Inverted overprint | | |
| O9 | A7 | 4a green | 200.00 | 80.00 |
| a. | | Inverted overprint | | |
| O10 | A9 | 4a green (I) | 1,000. | 250.00 |

Reprints were made of #O5, O7, O10 (type II).

Revenue Stamps Surcharged or Overprinted

Queen Victoria — O1

Blue Glazed Paper
Black Surcharge

| 1866 | | Wmk. 36 | Perf. 14 Vertically | |
|---|---|---|---|---|
| O11 | O1 | 2a violet | 350.00 | 250.00 |

The note after No. 30 will apply here also.

No. O10 is often found with cracked surface or scuffs. Such examples sell for somewhat less.

Reprints of No. O11 are surcharged in either black or green, and have the word "SERVICE" 16½x2½mm, instead of 16½x2¾mm and "TWO ANNAS" 18x3mm, instead of 20x3¼mm.

O2

O3

O4

**1866**

### Green Overprint

| O12 | O2 | 2a violet | 825. | 325. |
|---|---|---|---|---|
| O13 | O3 | 4a violet | 4,500. | 1,250. |
| O14 | O4 | 8a violet | 5,000. | 5,000. |

The note after No. 30 will apply here also. These stamps are often found with cracked surface or scuffs. Such examples sell for somewhat less.

Reprints of No. O12 have the overprint in sans-serif letters 2¼mm high, instead of Roman letters 2½mm high. On the reprints of No. O13 "SERVICE" measures 16½x2¼mm, instead of 20¼x3mm and "POSTAGE" 18x2¼mm, instead of 22x3mm. On No. O14 "SERVICE" is 20½mm long, instead of 20mm and "POSTAGE" is 23mm long, instead of 22mm. All three overprints are in a darker green than on the original stamps.

O5

### Green Overprint

| 1866 | Wmk. 40 | Perf. 15½x15 | | |
|---|---|---|---|---|
| | | Lilac Paper | | |
| O15 | O5 | ½a violet | 425.00 | 85.00 |
| a. | | Double overprint | | 3,000. |

Nos. 20, 31, 22-23, 23a, 26, 28 Overprinted in Black

| 1866-73 | | Wmk. 38 | Perf. 14 | |
|---|---|---|---|---|
| O16 | A7 | ½a blue | 30.00 | .35 |
| O17 | A7 | ½a bl, re-engraved | 140.00 | 67.50 |
| a. | | Double overprint | | |
| O18 | A7 | 1a brown | 32.50 | .40 |
| O19 | A7 | 2a orange | 4.50 | 2.00 |
| a. | | 2a yellow | 20.00 | 2.25 |
| O20 | A9 | 4a green (I) | 2.75 | 1.50 |
| O21 | A11 | 8a rose | 3.00 | 1.50 |
| | | Nos. O16-O21 (6) | 212.75 | 73.25 |

The 6a8p with this overprint was not issued. Value $25.

Nos. 31, 22-23, 26, 28 Overprinted in Black

**1874-82**

| O22 | A7 | ½a blue, re-engraved | 8.00 | .20 |
|---|---|---|---|---|
| a. | | Blue overprint | 350.00 | 45.00 |
| O23 | A7 | 1a brown | 12.50 | .20 |
| a. | | Blue overprint | 550.00 | 120.00 |
| O24 | A7 | 2a orange | 40.00 | 17.50 |
| O25 | A9 | 4a green (I) | 12.50 | 2.75 |
| O26 | A11 | 8a rose | 4.25 | 4.00 |
| | | Nos. O22-O26 (5) | 77.25 | 24.65 |

**Same Overprint on Nos. 36, 38, 40, 42, 44, 49**

**1883-97** Wmk. 39

| O27 | A17 | ½a green | .40 | .20 |
|---|---|---|---|---|
| a. | | Pair, one without overprint | | — |
| b. | | Double overprint | | 1,150. |
| O28 | A19 | 1a maroon | .35 | .20 |
| a. | | Inverted overprint | 350.00 | 475.00 |
| b. | | Double overprint | | 1,150. |
| c. | | 1a violet brown | 2.25 | .35 |
| O29 | A21 | 2a ultramarine | 4.50 | .50 |
| O30 | A23 | 4a olive green | 15.00 | .40 |
| O31 | A25 | 8a red violet | 7.00 | .40 |
| O32 | A29 | 1r car rose & grn | 11.00 | .40 |
| | | Nos. O27-O32 (6) | 38.25 | 2.10 |

**Same Overprint on No. 54**

**1899**

| O33 | A31 | 3p carmine rose | .20 | .20 |
|---|---|---|---|---|

**Same Overprint on Nos. 56-58**

**1900**

| O34 | A17 | ½a light green | 1.25 | .30 |
|---|---|---|---|---|
| O35 | A19 | 1a carmine rose | 2.50 | .20 |
| a. | | Double overprint | | 1,350. |
| b. | | Inverted overprint | | 1,400. |
| O36 | A21 | 2a violet | 27.50 | .50 |
| | | Nos. O34-O36 (3) | 31.25 | 1.00 |

**Same Overprint on Nos. 60-63, 66-68, 70**

**1902-09**

| O37 | A32 | 3p gray | .85 | .20 |
|---|---|---|---|---|
| O38 | A33 | ½a green | 1.00 | .20 |
| O39 | A34 | 1a carmine rose | .85 | .20 |
| O40 | A35 | 2a violet | 2.50 | .20 |
| O41 | A38 | 4a olive green | 4.25 | .20 |
| O42 | A39 | 6a bister | 2.25 | .20 |
| O43 | A40 | 8a red lilac | 5.25 | .50 |
| O44 | A42 | 1r car rose & green ('05) | 4.50 | .20 |
| | | Nos. O37-O44 (8) | 21.45 | 1.90 |

For surcharge see No. O73.

**Same Overprint on Nos. 78-79**

**1906-07**

| O45 | A44 | ½a green | 1.00 | .20 |
|---|---|---|---|---|
| O46 | A45 | 1a carmine rose | 1.75 | .20 |
| a. | | Pair, one without overprint | | — |
| b. | | Overprint on back | | — |

**Same Overprint on Nos. 71, 73-76**

**1909**

| O47 | A43 | 2r brown & rose | 6.50 | .90 |
|---|---|---|---|---|
| O48 | A43 | 5r violet & ultra | 11.00 | 1.00 |
| O49 | A43 | 10r car rose & grn | 21.00 | 8.50 |
| a. | | 10r red & green | 52.50 | 6.00 |
| O50 | A43 | 15r ol gray & ultra | 52.50 | 30.00 |
| O51 | A43 | 25r ultra & org brn | 130.00 | 50.00 |
| | | Nos. O47-O51 (5) | 221.00 | 90.40 |

For surcharges see Nos. O67-O69.

Nos. 80-84, 88, 90-91 Overprinted in Black

**1912-22**

| O52 | A46 | 3p gray | .25 | .20 |
|---|---|---|---|---|
| O53 | A47 | ½a green | .25 | .20 |
| a. | | Double overprint | 110.00 | |
| O54 | A48 | 1a carmine rose | .75 | .20 |
| a. | | Double overprint | 950.00 | |
| O55 | A48 | 1a dark brown ('22) | 1.00 | .20 |
| a. | | Imperf, pair | 75.00 | |
| O56 | A49 | 2a violet | .50 | .20 |
| O57 | A52 | 4a olive green | .75 | .20 |
| O58 | A53 | 6a bister | 1.25 | 1.75 |
| O59 | A54 | 8a red violet | 1.75 | .75 |

Nos. 93-98 Overprinted in Black

| O60 | A56 | 1r grn & red brn | 2.00 | .80 |
|---|---|---|---|---|
| O61 | A56 | 2r yel brn & car rose | 2.50 | 3.50 |
| O62 | A56 | 5r violet & ultra | 10.50 | 13.50 |
| O63 | A56 | 10r car rose & grn | 35.00 | 32.50 |
| O64 | A56 | 15r ol grn & ultra | 80.00 | 95.00 |
| O65 | A56 | 25r ultra & brn org | 180.00 | 150.00 |
| | | Nos. O52-O65 (14) | 316.50 | 299.00 |

For surcharges see Nos. O69b, O70-O71.

O6        O7

**Black Surcharge on No. 82**

**1921** Black Surcharge

| O66 | O6 | 9p on 1a rose | .75 | .60 |
|---|---|---|---|---|

For overprint see Gwalior No. O28.

Nos. O49-O51 Surcharged

**1925**

| O67 | A43 | 1r on 15r | 4.00 | 3.00 |
|---|---|---|---|---|
| O68 | A43 | 1r on 25r | 20.00 | 60.00 |
| O69 | A43 | 2r on 10r red & grn | 3.50 | 3.50 |
| a. | | 2r on 10r carmine rose & green | 210.00 | 55.00 |
| b. | | Surcharge on #O63 (error) | 800.00 | |

Nos. O64-O65 Surcharged

| O70 | A56 | 1r on 15r | 19.00 | 65.00 |
|---|---|---|---|---|
| a. | | Inverted surcharge | | — |
| O71 | A56 | 1r on 25r | 5.00 | 9.00 |
| a. | | Inverted surcharge | 600.00 | |
| | | Nos. O67-O71 (5) | 51.50 | 140.50 |

**Black Surcharge on No. O42**

**1926**

| O73 | O7 | 1a on 6a bister | .40 | .40 |
|---|---|---|---|---|

Nos. 83, 101, 102, 99 Surcharged

| O74 | A48 | 1a on 1a dk brn (error) | 180.00 | 180.00 |
|---|---|---|---|---|
| O75 | A58 | 1a on 1½a choc | .20 | .20 |
| O76 | A59 | 1a on 1½a choc | 1.75 | 4.00 |
| b. | | Double surcharge | 30.00 | |
| O77 | A57 | 1a on 2a6p ultra | .50 | .50 |
| | | Nos. O73-O77 (5) | 182.85 | 185.10 |

Nos. O74, O75 and O76 have short bars over the numerals in the upper corners.

Nos. 106-108, 111, 126-127, 112, 116, 128, 118-119 Overprinted

a

**1926-35** Wmk. 196

| O78 | A46 | 3p slate ('29) | .20 | .20 |
|---|---|---|---|---|
| O79 | A47 | ½a green ('31) | 5.00 | .40 |
| O80 | A48 | 1a dark brown | .20 | .20 |
| a. | | Overprint as on No. O55 | 100.00 | 4.75 |
| O81 | A49 | 2a vermilion ('35) | 1.00 | 1.00 |
| a. | | Small die | .85 | .20 |
| O82 | A60 | 2a dull violet | .20 | .20 |
| O83 | A60 | 2a vermilion ('32) | .90 | 2.00 |
| O84 | A57 | 2a6p buff ('32) | .25 | .20 |
| O85 | A52 | 4a olive green ('35) | 1.00 | .20 |
| O86 | A61 | 4a olive green | .35 | .20 |
| O87 | A53 | 6a bister ('35) | 18.00 | 9.00 |
| O88 | A54 | 8a red violet | .50 | .20 |
| O89 | A55 | 12a claret | .50 | 1.75 |

Nos. 120-121, 123 Overprinted

b

| O90 | A56 | 1r green & brn ('30) | 2.25 | .90 |
|---|---|---|---|---|
| O91 | A56 | 2r brn org & car rose ('30) | 6.00 | 6.00 |
| O92 | A56 | 10r car & green ('31) | 70.00 | 50.00 |
| | | Nos. O78-O92 (15) | 106.35 | 72.45 |

**#138, 135, 139, 136 Overprinted Type "a"**

**1932-35**

| O93 | A71 | ½a green ('35) | .60 | .20 |
|---|---|---|---|---|
| O94 | A68 | 9p dark green | .25 | .20 |
| O95 | A72 | 1a dark brown ('35) | 1.90 | .20 |
| O96 | A69 | 1a3p violet | .25 | .20 |
| | | Nos. O93-O96 (4) | 3.00 | .80 |

**Nos. 151-153, 162-165 Overprinted Type "a"**

**1937-39** Perf. 13½x14

| O97 | A80 | ½a brown ('38) | 18.00 | .45 |
|---|---|---|---|---|
| O98 | A80 | 9p green | 20.00 | .60 |
| O99 | A80 | 1a carmine | 3.75 | .35 |

**Type "b" Overprint**

| O100 | A82 | 1r brn & sl ('38) | .55 | .55 |
|---|---|---|---|---|
| O101 | A82 | 2r dk brown & dk vio ('38) | 1.50 | 3.25 |
| O102 | A82 | 5r dp ultra & dk green ('38) | 2.50 | 7.50 |
| O103 | A82 | 10r rose car & dark violet ('39) | 15.00 | 6.75 |
| | | Nos. O97-O103 (7) | 61.30 | 19.45 |

**No. 136 Surcharged in Black**

**1939, May** Wmk. 196 Perf. 14

| O104 | A69 | 1a on 1a3p violet | 17.00 | 3.00 |
|---|---|---|---|---|

King George VI — O8

| **1939-43** | | Typo. | Perf. 13½x14 | |
|---|---|---|---|---|
| O105 | O8 | 3p slate | .40 | .40 |
| O106 | O8 | ½a brown | 8.00 | .40 |
| O106A | O8 | ½a dk rose vio ('43) | .40 | .40 |
| O107 | O8 | 9p green | .40 | .40 |
| O108 | O8 | 1a car rose | .40 | .40 |
| O108A | O8 | 1a3p bister ('41) | 7.00 | 1.25 |
| O108B | O8 | 1½a dull pur ('43) | .40 | .40 |
| O109 | O8 | 2a scarlet | .40 | .40 |
| O110 | O8 | 2½a purple | .40 | .40 |
| O111 | O8 | 4a dark brown | .40 | .40 |
| O112 | O8 | 8a blue violet | .60 | .40 |
| | | Nos. O105-O112 (11) | 18.80 | 5.25 |

For overprints see Gwalior Nos. O52-O61. Stamps overprinted "Postal Service" or "I. P. N." were not used as postage stamps.

> Catalogue values for unused stamps in this section, from this point to the end of the section, are for Never Hinged items.

Nos. 203-206 (Gandhi Issue) Overprinted Type "a"

*Perf. 11½*

| **1948, Aug.** | | Unwmk. | Photo. | |
|---|---|---|---|---|
| O112A | A90 | 1½a brown | 65.00 | 45.00 |
| O112B | A90 | 3½a violet | 1,200. | 650.00 |
| O112C | A90 | 12a dk gray green | 3,500. | 2,200. |
| O112D | A90 | 10r rose brn & brown | 20,000. | |

Overprint forgeries exist.

Capital of Asoka Pillar

O9        O10

*Perf. 13½x14*

| **1950** | | Wmk. 196 | Typo. | |
|---|---|---|---|---|
| O113 | O9 | 3p violet blue | .40 | .40 |
| O114 | O9 | 6p chocolate | .40 | .40 |
| O115 | O9 | 9p green | .65 | .40 |
| O116 | O9 | 1a turquoise | .95 | .40 |
| O117 | O9 | 2a red | .40 | .40 |
| O118 | O9 | 3a vermilion | 4.75 | 2.75 |
| O119 | O9 | 4a brown car | 7.00 | .40 |
| O120 | O9 | 6a purple | 5.75 | .40 |
| O121 | O9 | 8a orange brn | 2.75 | .40 |

Litho.

*Perf. 14x13½*

| O122 | O10 | 1r dark purple | 3.75 | .40 |
|---|---|---|---|---|
| O123 | O10 | 2r brown red | 1.50 | .40 |
| O124 | O10 | 5r dark green | 2.75 | 2.25 |
| O125 | O10 | 10r rose brown | 8.50 | 22.50 |
| | | Nos. O113-O125 (13) | 39.55 | 31.50 |

Issue dates: 1r-10r, Jan. 2, others, July 1.

| **1951, Oct. 1** | | | Typo. | |
|---|---|---|---|---|
| O126 | O9 | 4a violet blue | .20 | .20 |

Type of 1950 Redrawn; Denomination in Naye Paise

**Typo. or Litho.**

| **1957-58** | | | Perf. 13½x14 | |
|---|---|---|---|---|
| O127 | O9 | 1np slate blue | .55 | .55 |
| O128 | O9 | 2np blue violet | .55 | .55 |
| O129 | O9 | 3np chocolate | .55 | .55 |
| O130 | O9 | 5np yellow green | .55 | .55 |
| O131 | O9 | 6np turquoise | .55 | .55 |
| O132 | O9 | 13np red | .55 | .55 |
| O133 | O9 | 15np dk purple ('58) | .55 | .55 |
| O134 | O9 | 20np vermilion | .55 | .55 |
| O135 | O9 | 25np violet blue | .55 | .55 |
| O136 | O9 | 50np reddish brown | 1.00 | .55 |
| | | Nos. O127-O136 (10) | 5.95 | 5.50 |

Issue dates: 15np, June; others, Apr. 1.

Redrawn Type of 1957-58

**Typo. or Litho.**

| **1958-71** | | Wmk. 324 | Perf. 13½x14 | |
|---|---|---|---|---|
| O137 | O9 | 1np slate blue ('59) | .30 | .30 |
| O138 | O9 | 2np blue violet ('59) | .30 | .30 |
| O139 | O9 | 3np chocolate | .30 | .30 |
| O140 | O9 | 5np yel green | .30 | .30 |
| O141 | O9 | 6np turquoise ('59) | .30 | .30 |
| O142 | O9 | 10np dk green ('63) | .30 | .30 |
| O142A | O9 | 13np red ('63) | .30 | .30 |
| O143 | O9 | 15np dk purple | .30 | .30 |
| O144 | O9 | 20np ver ('59) | .30 | .30 |
| O145 | O9 | 25np vio blue ('59) | .30 | .30 |
| O146 | O9 | 50np redsh brown ('59) | .30 | .30 |

Litho.

*Perf. 14*

| O147 | O10 | 1r rose vio ('59) | .30 | .30 |
|---|---|---|---|---|
| O148 | O10 | 2r rose red ('60) | .50 | .30 |
| a. | | Watermark sideways ('69) | .50 | .60 |
| O149 | O10 | 5r green ('59) | 1.40 | 1.40 |
| a. | | Watermark sideways ('69) | .90 | .30 |
| O150 | O10 | 10r rose lake ('59) | 2.50 | 1.10 |
| a. | | Watermark sideways ('71) | 3.75 | 3.75 |
| | | Nos. O137-O150 (15) | 8.00 | 6.40 |

Capital of Asoka Pillar
O11    O12

*Perf. 14½x14*

**1967-76    Photo.    Wmk. 360**
**Without Gum**

| | | | | |
|---|---|---|---|---|
| O151 | O11 | 2p violet black | .85 | .85 |
| O152 | O11 | 3p dk red brown | .85 | .85 |
| O153 | O11 | 5p bright green | .85 | .85 |
| O154 | O11 | 6p Prussian blue | 3.25 | 3.25 |
| O155 | O11 | 15p slate green | .85 | .85 |
| O156 | O11 | 15p purple | .85 | .85 |
| O157 | O11 | 20p orange ver | .85 | .85 |
| O158 | O11 | 25p deep car ('76) | 26.00 | 11.00 |
| O159 | O11 | 30p violet blue | .85 | .85 |
| O160 | O11 | 50p red brown | .85 | .85 |
| | | Nos. O151-O160 (10) | 36.05 | 21.05 |

No. O153 Overprinted

**1971, Nov. 15    Wmk. 360**
**Without Gum**

| | | | | |
|---|---|---|---|---|
| O161 | O11 | 5p green | .40 | .40 |

**No. O153 Overprinted "Refugee /
Relief"**

| | | | | |
|---|---|---|---|---|
| O162 | O11 | 5p green | 1.00 | 1.00 |

No. O162 was used in Maharashtra state.

**1971, Dec. 1(?)**
**Without Gum**

| | | | | |
|---|---|---|---|---|
| O163 | O12 | 5p green | .20 | .20 |

Nos. O161-O163 were obligatory on all official mail as a postal tax to benefit refugees from East Pakistan. The tax was paid out of the various governmental departments' budgets.

Type of 1968

**1967-74    Wmk. 324    Perf. 14½x14**

| | | | | |
|---|---|---|---|---|
| O164 | O11 | 2p violet | .80 | 1.00 |
| O165 | O11 | 5p brt green ('74) | .80 | .20 |
| O166 | O11 | 10p slate green ('74) | 1.25 | .20 |
| O167 | O11 | 15p purple ('73) | 1.60 | .40 |
| O168 | O11 | 20p dp orange ('74) | 5.25 | 5.00 |
| O169 | O11 | 30p ultramarine | 3.50 | 1.00 |
| O170 | O11 | 50p red brown ('73) | 2.75 | 2.00 |
| O171 | O11 | 1r dull purple | .55 | .20 |
| | | Nos. O164-O171 (8) | 16.50 | 10.00 |

Without Currency Designation
O13    O14

*Perf. 14½x14*

**1976-80    Litho.    Wmk. 360**
**Without Gum**

| | | | | |
|---|---|---|---|---|
| O172 | O13 | 2p violet black | .35 | .35 |
| O173 | O13 | 5p bright green | .35 | .35 |
| O174 | O13 | 10p slate green | .35 | .35 |
| O175 | O13 | 15p purple | .35 | .35 |
| O176 | O13 | 20p brown orange | .35 | .35 |
| O177 | O13 | 25p carmine rose | .80 | .80 |
| O178 | O13 | 30p blue ('79) | 2.50 | 2.50 |
| O179 | O13 | 35p violet ('80) | .75 | .35 |
| O180 | O13 | 50p red brown | 3.50 | 1.75 |
| O181 | O13 | 1r dull purple ('80) | 4.00 | .90 |

**Wmk. 324**

| | | | | |
|---|---|---|---|---|
| O182 | O13 | 1r dull purple | .90 | .90 |

*Perf. 14x13½*

| | | | | |
|---|---|---|---|---|
| O183 | O14 | 2r salmon rose | 3.50 | 3.50 |
| O184 | O14 | 5r deep green | 3.50 | 3.50 |
| O185 | O14 | 10r red brown | 1.25 | 1.25 |
| | | Nos. O172-O185 (14) | 22.45 | 17.20 |

 O15

*Perf. 15x14*

**1981, Feb.    Wmk. 360**
**Without Gum**

| | | | | |
|---|---|---|---|---|
| O186 | O15 | 2r orange vermilion | 1.00 | .60 |
| O187 | O15 | 5r dark green | 3.00 | 1.40 |
| O188 | O15 | 10r dark red brown | 6.00 | 3.00 |
| | | Nos. O186-O188 (3) | 10.00 | 5.00 |

**Unwmk.**

**1981, Dec. 10    Litho.    Imperf.**
**Cream Paper**

| | | | | |
|---|---|---|---|---|
| O189 | O13 | 5p bright green | .90 | 1.25 |
| O190 | O13 | 10p slate green | 1.00 | 1.25 |
| O191 | O13 | 15p purple | 1.00 | 1.25 |
| O192 | O13 | 20p brown orange | 1.00 | 1.25 |
| O193 | O13 | 25p carmine rose | 2.25 | 2.75 |
| O194 | O13 | 35p violet | 1.25 | .90 |
| O195 | O13 | 50p brown | 2.25 | 2.25 |
| O196 | O13 | 1r dull purple | 2.50 | 2.25 |
| O197 | O15 | 2r salmon rose | 2.50 | 2.25 |
| O198 | O15 | 5r deep green | 2.75 | 7.25 |
| O199 | O15 | 10r red brown | 3.75 | 9.75 |
| | | Nos. O189-O199 (11) | 21.15 | 35.40 |

*Perf. 12½x13*

**1982, Nov. 22    Photo.    Wmk. 360**
**Without Gum**

| | | | | |
|---|---|---|---|---|
| O200 | O13 | 5p bright green | .80 | 1.10 |
| O201 | O13 | 10p slate green | 1.00 | 1.25 |
| O202 | O13 | 15p purple | 1.10 | 1.25 |
| O203 | O13 | 20p fawn | 1.25 | 1.25 |
| O204 | O13 | 25p car rose | 1.60 | 2.50 |
| O205 | O13 | 30p dark blue | 1.60 | 2.50 |
| O206 | O13 | 35p violet | 1.60 | .70 |
| O207 | O13 | 50p light brown | 2.50 | 2.50 |
| O208 | O13 | 1r dull purple | 2.50 | 2.50 |
| O209 | O15 | 2r salmon rose | 2.75 | 3.75 |
| O210 | O15 | 5r deep green | 3.25 | 6.50 |
| O211 | O15 | 10r red brown | 4.00 | 9.00 |
| | | Nos. O200-O211 (12) | 23.95 | 34.80 |

*Perf. 12½x13*

**1984-99    Photo.    Wmk. 324**
**Without Gum**

| | | | | |
|---|---|---|---|---|
| O212 | O13 | 5p green | .20 | .20 |
| O213 | O13 | 10p dark green | .20 | .20 |
| O214 | O13 | 15p rose lake | .20 | .20 |
| O215 | O13 | 20p fawn | .20 | .20 |
| O216 | O13 | 25p deep carmine | .20 | .20 |
| O217 | O13 | 30p blue | .20 | .20 |
| O218 | O13 | 35p purple | .20 | .20 |
| O219 | O13 | 40p violet | .20 | .20 |
| O220 | O13 | 50p brown | .20 | .20 |
| O221 | O13 | 60p brown | .20 | .20 |
| O222 | O15 | 1r violet brown | .20 | .20 |
| O223 | O15 | 2r orange ver | .40 | .20 |
| O223A | O15 | 3r orange | 1.00 | |
| O224 | O15 | 5r gray green | 1.00 | .50 |
| O225 | O15 | 10r red brown | 2.00 | 1.00 |
| | | Nos. O213-O225 (14) | 5.60 | 3.90 |

Issued: 25p, 1986. 60p, 4/15/88; 40p, 10/15/88; 3r, 3/22/99; others, 4/16/84. This is an expanding set. Numbers may change again.

**POSTAL TAX STAMPS**

> Catalogue values for unused stamps in this section are for Never Hinged items.

No. 408 Overprinted

*Perf. 14½x14*

**1971, Nov. 15    Photo.    Wmk. 324**

| | | | | |
|---|---|---|---|---|
| RA1 | A202 | 5p cerise | .20 | .20 |

**No. 408 Overprinted
"Refugee/Relief"**

| | | | | |
|---|---|---|---|---|
| RA2 | A202 | 5p cerise | .20 | .20 |

No. RA2 was used in Maharashtra. In order to make the obligatory tax stamps available immediately throughout India postmasters were authorized to overprint locally No. 408. This resulted in a great variety of mostly hand-stamped overprints of various types and sizes.

Refugees — PT1

*Perf. 14x14½*

**1971, Dec. 1    Photo.    Wmk. 324**

| | | | | |
|---|---|---|---|---|
| RA3 | PT1 | 5p cerise | .20 | .20 |

Nos. RA1-RA3 were obligatory on all mail. The tax was for refugees from East Pakistan. See Nos. O161-O163.

---

# CONVENTION STATES

**CONVENTION STATES OF THE
BRITISH EMPIRE IN INDIA**
Stamps of British India overprinted for use in the States of Chamba, Faridkot, Gwalior, Jhind, Nabha and Patiala.
These stamps had franking power throughout all British India.

**Forgeries**
Numerous forgeries exist of the high valued Convention States stamps, unused and used. Most cancelled examples of those stamps whose value used is far greater than unused bear favor or counterfeit cancels. Such stamps are worth far less than the values below, which are for postally used examples. More valuable Indian States stamps should be expertized.

## CHAMBA

'chəm-bə

LOCATION — A State of India located in the north Punjab, south of Kashmir.
AREA — 3,127 sq. mi.
POP. — 168,908 (1941)
CAPITAL — Chamba

The varieties with small letters in the overprint are not listed as the letters are merely broken and not from another font of type.

Indian Stamps
Overprinted in Black

**1886-95    Wmk. 39    Perf. 14**

| | | | | |
|---|---|---|---|---|
| 1 | A17 | ½a green | 1.50 | 1.75 |
| a. | | "CHMABA" | 600.00 | 950.00 |
| c. | | Double overprint | 950.00 | |
| 2 | A19 | 1a violet brown | 3.75 | 3.75 |
| a. | | "CHMABA" | 900.00 | 950.00 |
| 3 | A20 | 1a6p bis brown ('95) | 4.50 | 21.00 |
| 4 | A21 | 2a ultramarine | 2.00 | 3.25 |
| a. | | "CHMABA" | 2,750. | 4,000. |
| 5 | A28 | 2a6p green ('95) | 52.50 | 150.00 |
| 6 | A22 | 3a brn org | 4.50 | 9.00 |
| a. | | 3a orange | 16.00 | 35.00 |
| b. | | Inverted overprint | | |
| c. | | "CHMABA" | 7,500. | 11,000. |
| 7 | A23 | 4a olive green | 8.25 | 14.00 |
| a. | | "CHMABA" | 2,400. | 4,000. |
| 8 | A25 | 8a red violet | 13.50 | 18.00 |
| a. | | "CHMABA" | 6,000. | 6,250. |
| 9 | A26 | 12a vio, red ('90) | 10.50 | 24.00 |
| a. | | "CHMABA" | 12,500. | |
| b. | | 1st "T" of "STATE" invtd. | 12,500. | |
| 10 | A27 | 1r gray | 72.50 | 225.00 |
| a. | | "CHMABA" | 21,000. | |
| 11 | A29 | 1r car rose & grn ('95) | 14.00 | 25.00 |
| 12 | A30 | 2r brown & rose ('95) | 150.00 | 600.00 |
| 13 | A30 | 3r grn & brown ('95) | 175.00 | 525.00 |
| 14 | A30 | 5r vio & bl ('95) | 190.00 | 825.00 |

**Wmk. 38**

| | | | | |
|---|---|---|---|---|
| 15 | A14 | 6a bister ('90) | 8.25 | 32.50 |
| | | Nos. 1-15 (15) | 710.75 | 2,477. |

**1900    Wmk. 39**

| | | | | |
|---|---|---|---|---|
| 15B | A31 | 3p carmine rose | .90 | 1.40 |

**1902-04**

| | | | | |
|---|---|---|---|---|
| 16 | A31 | 3p gray ('04) | .90 | 3.25 |
| a. | | Inverted overprint | 120.00 | |
| 17 | A17 | ½a light green | 1.00 | 2.50 |
| 18 | A19 | 1a carmine rose | 1.00 | .60 |
| 19 | A21 | 2a violet ('03) | 16.00 | 52.50 |
| | | Nos. 16-19 (4) | 18.90 | 58.85 |

**1903-05**

| | | | | |
|---|---|---|---|---|
| 20 | A32 | 3p gray | .35 | 2.40 |
| 21 | A33 | ½a green | 1.20 | .90 |
| 22 | A34 | 1a carmine rose | 2.40 | 1.40 |
| 23 | A35 | 2a violet | 2.75 | 5.25 |
| 24 | A37 | 3a brown org ('05) | 7.00 | 9.00 |
| 25 | A38 | 4a olive green ('04) | 10.50 | 32.50 |
| 26 | A39 | 6a bister ('05) | 6.50 | 35.00 |
| 27 | A40 | 8a red violet ('04) | 9.00 | 35.00 |
| 28 | A41 | 12a violet, red | 12.00 | 47.50 |
| 29 | A42 | 1r car rose & grn ('05) | 11.00 | 35.00 |
| | | Nos. 20-29 (10) | 62.70 | 203.95 |

**1907**

| | | | | |
|---|---|---|---|---|
| 30 | A44 | ½a green | 3.75 | 6.00 |
| 31 | A45 | 1a carmine rose | 3.75 | 6.00 |

**1913-24**

| | | | | |
|---|---|---|---|---|
| 32 | A46 | 3p gray | .60 | 1.90 |
| 33 | A47 | ½a green | 1.50 | 1.90 |
| 34 | A48 | 1a carmine rose | 15.00 | 17.50 |
| 35 | A48 | 1a dark brown ('22) | 5.25 | 8.25 |
| 36 | A49 | 2a violet | 6.00 | 17.50 |
| 37 | A51 | 3a brown orange | 7.00 | 13.00 |
| 38 | A51 | 3a ultra ('24) | 6.25 | 35.00 |
| 39 | A52 | 4a olive green | 6.00 | 8.25 |
| 40 | A53 | 6a bister | 6.50 | 11.00 |
| 41 | A54 | 8a red violet | 9.00 | 24.00 |
| 42 | A55 | 12a claret | 8.50 | 19.00 |
| 43 | A56 | 1r green & red brown | 27.50 | 47.50 |
| | | Nos. 32-43 (12) | 99.10 | 204.80 |

India No. 104 Overprinted

**1921**

| | | | | |
|---|---|---|---|---|
| 44 | A48 | 9p on 1a rose | 1.50 | 27.50 |

India Stamps of 1913-26 Overprinted

**1922-27**

| | | | | |
|---|---|---|---|---|
| 45 | A58 | 1½a chocolate | 40.00 | 190.00 |
| 46 | A59 | 1½a chocolate | 3.75 | 9.50 |
| 47 | A59 | 1½a rose | 1.40 | 35.00 |
| 48 | A57 | 2a6p ultramarine | .90 | 6.50 |
| 49 | A57 | 2a6p brown orange | 4.00 | 35.00 |
| | | Nos. 45-49 (5) | 50.05 | 276.00 |

India Stamps of 1926 Overprinted

**1927-28    Wmk. 196**

| | | | | |
|---|---|---|---|---|
| 50 | A46 | 3p slate | .30 | 2.50 |
| 51 | A47 | ½a green | .45 | 3.75 |
| 52 | A48 | 1a dark brown | 2.50 | 2.25 |
| 53 | A60 | 2a dull violet | 3.25 | 6.00 |
| 54 | A51 | 3a ultramarine | 1.90 | 32.50 |
| 55 | A61 | 4a olive green | 1.90 | 10.00 |
| 57 | A54 | 8a red violet | 2.40 | 17.50 |
| 58 | A55 | 12a claret | 2.40 | 24.00 |

Overprinted

| | | | | |
|---|---|---|---|---|
| 59 | A56 | 1r green & brown | 17.50 | 45.00 |
| | | Nos. 50-55,57-59 (9) | 32.60 | 143.50 |

**India Stamps of 1926-35 Overprinted**

**1932-37**
| | | | | |
|---|---|---|---|---|
| 60 | A71 | ½a green | 1.60 | 16.00 |
| 61 | A68 | 9p dark green | 7.50 | 32.50 |
| 62 | A72 | 1a dark brown | 2.50 | 2.25 |
| 63 | A69 | 1a3p violet | 2.10 | 9.50 |
| 64 | A59 | 1½a carmine rose | 9.50 | 11.00 |
| 65 | A49 | 2a vermilion | 1.90 | 37.50 |
| a. | | Small die | 175.00 | 210.00 |
| 66 | A57 | 2a6p buff | 5.00 | 30.00 |
| 67 | A51 | 3a carmine rose | 3.25 | 17.50 |
| 68 | A52 | 4a olive green ('36) | 8.25 | 25.00 |
| 69 | A53 | 6a bister ('37) | 45.00 | 250.00 |
| | | Nos. 60-69 (10) | 86.60 | 431.25 |

**Same Overprint on India Stamps of 1937**

**1938**  Wmk. 196  Perf. 13½x14
| | | | | |
|---|---|---|---|---|
| 70 | A80 | 3p slate | 14.00 | 32.50 |
| 71 | A80 | ½a brown | 2.00 | 21.00 |
| 72 | A80 | 9p green | 12.50 | 57.50 |
| 73 | A80 | 1a carmine | 2.50 | 5.50 |

**Overprinted**
| | | | | |
|---|---|---|---|---|
| 74 | A81 | 2a scarlet | 10.00 | 24.00 |
| 75 | A81 | 2a6p purple | 11.00 | 47.50 |
| 76 | A81 | 3a yellow green | 11.50 | 42.50 |
| 77 | A81 | 3a6p ultra | 11.50 | 45.00 |
| 78 | A81 | 4a dark brown | 30.00 | 45.00 |
| 79 | A81 | 6a peacock blue | 32.50 | 100.00 |
| 80 | A81 | 8a blue violet | 30.00 | 97.50 |
| 81 | A81 | 12a carmine lake | 22.50 | 97.50 |

**Overprinted**
| | | | | |
|---|---|---|---|---|
| 82 | A82 | 1r brown & slate | 45.00 | 110.00 |
| 83 | A82 | 2r dk brn & dk vio | 75.00 | 525.00 |
| 84 | A82 | 5r dp ultra & dk green | 120.00 | 700.00 |
| 85 | A82 | 10r rose car & dk violet | 190.00 | 1,100.00 |
| 86 | A82 | 15r dk grn & dk brown | 200.00 | 1,500.00 |
| 87 | A82 | 25r dk vio & bl vio | 290.00 | 1,600.00 |
| | | Nos. 70-87 (18) | 1,110.00 | 6,150.00 |
| | | Set, never hinged | 1,300. | |

**India Nos. 151 and 153 Overprinted**

**1942**
| | | | | |
|---|---|---|---|---|
| 87B | A80 | ½a brown | 62.50 | 67.50 |
| | | Never hinged | 75.00 | |
| 88 | A80 | 1a carmine | 95.00 | 90.00 |
| | | Never hinged | 110.00 | |

**Same Ovpt. on India Stamps of 1941-42**

**1942-44**
| | | | | |
|---|---|---|---|---|
| 89 | A83 | 3p slate | 1.50 | 8.25 |
| 90 | A83 | ½a rose violet ('43) | .85 | 9.50 |
| 91 | A83 | 9p lt green ('43) | 1.40 | 30.00 |
| 92 | A83 | 1a carmine rose ('43) | 2.10 | 8.25 |
| 93 | A84 | 1½a dk purple ('44) | 2.50 | 21.00 |
| 94 | A84 | 2a scarlet ('43) | 10.00 | 24.00 |
| 95 | A84 | 3a violet ('43) | 26.00 | 72.50 |
| 96 | A84 | 3½a ultra ('43) | 14.00 | 67.50 |
| 97 | A85 | 4a chocolate ('43) | 19.00 | 75.00 |
| 98 | A85 | 6a pck blue ('43) | 21.00 | 62.50 |

| | | | | |
|---|---|---|---|---|
| 99 | A85 | 8a blue violet ('43) | 22.50 | 75.00 |
| 100 | A85 | 12a car lake ('43) | 30.00 | 97.50 |
| | | Nos. 89-100 (12) | 150.85 | 551.00 |
| | | Set, never hinged | 200.00 | |

**India Nos. 162-167 Overprinted**

**1943**  Wmk. 196  Perf. 13½x14
| | | | | |
|---|---|---|---|---|
| 101 | A82 | 1r brown & slate | 26.00 | 97.50 |
| 102 | A82 | 2r dk brown & dk vio | 30.00 | 400.00 |
| 103 | A82 | 5r dp ultra & dk grn | 55.00 | 450.00 |
| 104 | A82 | 10r rose car & dk vio | 85.00 | 700.00 |
| 105 | A82 | 15r dk grn & dk brn | 190.00 | 1,250.00 |
| 106 | A82 | 25r dk vio & bl vio | 175.00 | 1,250.00 |
| | | Nos. 101-106 (6) | 561.00 | 4,147. |
| | | Set, never hinged | 850.00 | |

**India No. 161A Overprinted**

**1948**
| | | | | |
|---|---|---|---|---|
| 107 | A81 | 14a rose violet | 17.50 | 4.50 |

### OFFICIAL STAMPS

**Indian Stamps Overprinted in Black**

**1886-98**  Wmk. 39  Perf. 14
| | | | | |
|---|---|---|---|---|
| O1 | A17 | ½a green | 1.10 | .20 |
| a. | | "CHMABA" | 375.00 | 375.00 |
| c. | | "SERV CE" | | |
| O2 | A19 | 1a violet brown | 3.75 | 2.25 |
| a. | | "CHMABA" | 600.00 | 600.00 |
| c. | | "SERV CE" | 5,250. | |
| d. | | "SERVICE" double | 3,000. | 1,600. |
| O3 | A21 | 2a ultra | 4.50 | 3.00 |
| a. | | "CHMABA" | 1,500. | 3,250. |
| O4 | A22 | 3a brown orange | 3.75 | 19.00 |
| a. | | 3a orange | — | |
| b. | | "CHMABA" | 4,500. | 5,250. |
| O5 | A23 | 4a olive green | 5.50 | 12.00 |
| a. | | "CHMABA" | 1,600. | 3,250. |
| c. | | "SERV CE" | 6,000. | |
| O6 | A25 | 8a red violet | 5.50 | 4.50 |
| a. | | "CHMABA" | 12,000. | 12,000. |
| O7 | A26 | 12a vio, *red* ('90) | 15.00 | 72.50 |
| a. | | "CHMABA" | 11,000. | |
| b. | | 1st "T" of "STATE" invtd. | | |
| O8 | A27 | 1r gray ('90) | 22.50 | 225.00 |
| a. | | "CHMABA" | 7,500. | |
| O9 | A29 | 1r car rose & grn ('98) | 9.00 | 62.50 |

**Wmk. 38**
| | | | | |
|---|---|---|---|---|
| O10 | A14 | 6a bister | 7.50 | 22.50 |
| | | Nos. O1-O10 (10) | 78.10 | 423.45 |

**1902-04**  Wmk. 39
| | | | | |
|---|---|---|---|---|
| O11 | A31 | 3p gray ('04) | .90 | 1.20 |
| O12 | A17 | ½a light green | 1.90 | 6.00 |
| O13 | A19 | 1a carmine rose | 2.25 | .90 |
| O14 | A21 | 2a violet | 17.50 | 52.50 |
| | | Nos. O11-O14 (4) | 22.55 | 60.60 |

**1903-05**
| | | | | |
|---|---|---|---|---|
| O15 | A32 | 3p gray | .50 | .20 |
| O16 | A33 | ½a green | .30 | .20 |
| O17 | A34 | 1a carmine rose | 1.90 | .45 |
| O18 | A35 | 2a violet | 1.90 | 2.25 |
| O19 | A38 | 4a olive green ('05) | 5.25 | 30.00 |
| O20 | A40 | 8a red violet ('05) | 12.50 | 30.00 |
| O21 | A42 | 1r car rose & grn ('05) | 2.50 | 21.00 |
| | | Nos. O15-O21 (7) | 24.85 | 84.10 |

**1907**
| | | | | |
|---|---|---|---|---|
| O22 | A44 | ½a green | .60 | 1.10 |
| a. | | Inverted overprint | 6,750. | 8,250. |
| O23 | A45 | 1a carmine rose | 3.25 | 3.75 |

**1913**
| | | | | |
|---|---|---|---|---|
| O24 | A49 | 2a violet | 22.50 | |
| O25 | A52 | 4a olive green | 20.00 | |

**India No. 63 Overprinted**

**1907**
| | | | | |
|---|---|---|---|---|
| O26 | A35 | 2a violet | 60.00 | |

No. O26 was never placed in use.

**India Stamps of 1911-29 Overprinted:**

a          b

**1913-25**
| | | | | |
|---|---|---|---|---|
| O27 | A46 (a) | 3p gray | .30 | .60 |
| O28 | A47 (a) | ½a green | .30 | .90 |
| O29 | A48 (a) | 1a carmine rose | .30 | .20 |
| O30 | A48 (a) | 1a dk brown ('25) | 6.50 | 1.00 |
| O31 | A49 (a) | 2a violet ('14) | 1.60 | 22.50 |
| O32 | A52 (a) | 4a olive green | 1.60 | 30.00 |
| O33 | A54 (a) | 8a red violet | 2.50 | 30.00 |
| O34 | A56 (b) | 1r grn & red brn | 8.25 | 47.50 |
| | | Nos. O27-O34 (8) | 21.35 | 132.70 |

**India No. O66 Overprinted**

**1921**
| | | | | |
|---|---|---|---|---|
| O35 | O6 | 9p on 1a rose | .20 | 12.50 |

**India Stamps of 1926-35 Overprinted**

**1927-39**  Wmk. 196
| | | | | |
|---|---|---|---|---|
| O36 | A46 | 3p slate | .75 | .60 |
| O37 | A47 | ½a green | .50 | .20 |
| O38 | A68 | 9p dark green ('32) | 6.00 | 16.00 |
| O39 | A48 | 1a dark brown | .30 | .20 |
| O40 | A69 | 1a3p violet ('32) | 9.00 | 1.50 |
| O41 | A60 | 2a dull violet | 3.75 | .90 |
| O42 | A61 | 4a olive green | 2.25 | 4.00 |
| O43 | A54 | 8a red violet | 12.00 | 16.00 |
| O44 | A55 | 12a claret | 7.50 | 37.50 |

**Overprinted**
| | | | | |
|---|---|---|---|---|
| O45 | A56 | 1r green & brown | 22.50 | 72.50 |
| O45A | A56 | 2r brn org & car rose ('39) | 35.00 | 375.00 |
| O45B | A56 | 5r dk vio & ultra ('39) | 62.50 | 450.00 |
| O45C | A56 | 10r car & grn ('39) | 97.50 | 450.00 |
| | | Nos. O36-O45C (13) | 259.55 | 1,424. |

**India Stamps of 1926-35 Overprinted**

**1935-36**
| | | | | |
|---|---|---|---|---|
| O46 | A71 | ½a green | 8.25 | .75 |
| O47 | A72 | 1a dark brown | 8.00 | .65 |
| O48 | A49 | 2a vermilion | 8.25 | 1.90 |
| a. | | Small die | 11.00 | 30.00 |
| O49 | A52 | 4a olive grn ('36) | 12.00 | 11.00 |
| | | Nos. O46-O49 (4) | 36.50 | 14.30 |

**Same Overprint on India Stamps of 1937**

**1938**  Perf. 13½x14
| | | | | |
|---|---|---|---|---|
| O50 | A80 | 9p green | 30.00 | 100.00 |
| | | Never hinged | 8.25 | |
| O51 | A80 | 1a carmine | 37.50 | 9.00 |
| | | Never hinged | 45.00 | |

**India Stamps of 1937 Overprinted**

**1940-41**
| | | | | |
|---|---|---|---|---|
| O51A | A82 | 1r brn & sl ('41) | 300.00 | 1,100. |
| O52 | A82 | 2r dk brn & dk vio | 52.50 | 600.00 |
| O53 | A82 | 5r dp ultra & dk grn | 75.00 | 650.00 |
| O54 | A82 | 10r rose car & dk vio | 105.00 | 1,200. |
| | | Set, never hinged | 625.00 | |

**India Official Stamps of 1939-43 Overprinted**

**1941-46**  Wmk. 196
| | | | | |
|---|---|---|---|---|
| O55 | O8 | 3p slate ('44) | .85 | 1.90 |
| O56 | O8 | ½a brown | 37.50 | 5.50 |
| O57 | O8 | ½a dk rose vio ('44) | .85 | 5.50 |
| O58 | O8 | 9p green | 8.75 | 17.50 |
| O59 | O8 | 1a carmine rose | 1.25 | 4.50 |
| O60 | O8 | 1a3p bister ('46) | 105.00 | 32.50 |
| O61 | O8 | 1½a dull pur ('46) | 9.50 | 12.50 |
| O62 | O8 | 2a scarlet ('44) | 9.50 | 12.50 |
| O63 | O8 | 2½a purple ('44) | 5.50 | 35.00 |
| O64 | O8 | 4a dark brown ('44) | 9.50 | 27.50 |
| O65 | O8 | 8a blue vio ('41) | 21.00 | 100.00 |
| | | Nos. O55-O65 (11) | 209.20 | 254.90 |
| | | Set, never hinged | 250.00 | |

**India Nos. 162-165 Overprinted**

**1944**
| | | | | |
|---|---|---|---|---|
| O66 | A82 | 1r brown & slate | 27.50 | 325.00 |
| O67 | A82 | 2r dk brn & dk vio | 42.50 | 450.00 |
| O68 | A82 | 5r dp ultra & dk grn | 80.00 | 650.00 |
| O69 | A82 | 10r rose car & dk vio | 95.00 | 1,100. |
| | | Nos. O66-O69 (4) | 245.00 | 2,525. |
| | | Set, never hinged | 295.00 | |

## FARIDKOT

fe-'rēd-ˌkōt

LOCATION — A State of India lying northeast of Nabha in the central Punjab.

AREA — 638 sq. mi.

POP. — 164,364

CAPITAL — Faridkot

Previous stamp issues are listed under Feudatory States. Stamps of Faridkot were superseded by those of India in 1901.

The varieties with small letters in the overprint are not listed as the letters are merely broken and not from another font.

India Stamps Overprinted in Black

| 1887-93 | | Wmk. 39 | | Perf. 14 |
|---|---|---|---|---|
| 4 | A17 | ½a green | 3.75 | 2.50 |
| | a. | "ARIDKOT" | | |
| 5 | A19 | 1a violet brown | 2.25 | 3.75 |
| 6 | A21 | 2a ultramarine | 4.75 | 10.50 |
| 7 | A22 | 3a orange | 5.50 | 9.00 |
| 8 | A23 | 4a olive green | 12.50 | 27.50 |
| | a. | "ARIDKOT" | 2,100. | |
| 9 | A25 | 8a red violet | 22.50 | 67.50 |
| | a. | "ARIDKOT" | 4,500. | |
| 10 | A27 | 1r gray | 67.50 | 550.00 |
| | a. | "ARIDKOT" | 5,250. | |
| 11 | A29 | 1r car rose & grn ('93) | 60.00 | 175.00 |
| | | Wmk. 38 | | |
| 12 | A14 | 6a bister | 3.00 | 27.50 |
| | a. | "ARIDKOT" | 2,750. | |
| | | Nos. 4-12 (9) | 181.75 | 873.25 |

| 1900 | | Wmk. Star. (39) | | |
|---|---|---|---|---|
| 13 | A31 | 3p car rose | 2.25 | 67.50 |
| 14 | A26 | 12a violet, red | 67.50 | 625.00 |

### OFFICIAL STAMPS

India Stamps Overprinted in Black

| 1886 | | Wmk. 39 | | Perf. 14 |
|---|---|---|---|---|
| O1 | A17 | ½a green | .90 | 1.10 |
| | a. | "SERV CE" | 3,750. | |
| O2 | A19 | 1a violet brown | 1.50 | 3.00 |
| | a. | "SERV CE" | 5,500. | |
| O3 | A21 | 2a ultramarine | 3.00 | 16.00 |
| | a. | "SERV CE" | 5,500. | |
| O4 | A22 | 3a orange | 6.00 | 57.50 |
| O5 | A23 | 4a olive green | 7.00 | 45.00 |
| | a. | "SERV CE" | 4,750. | |
| O6 | A25 | 8a red lilac | 15.00 | 45.00 |
| | a. | "SERV CE" | 4,500. | |
| O7 | A27 | 1r gray | 82.50 | 400.00 |
| | | Wmk. 38 | | |
| O8 | A14 | 6a bister | 37.50 | 42.50 |
| | a. | "ARIDKOT" | 2,100. | |
| | b. | "SERVIC" | 4,500. | |
| | | Nos. O1-O8 (8) | 153.40 | 610.10 |

| 1896 | | Wmk. 39 | | |
|---|---|---|---|---|
| O9 | A29 | 1r car rose & green | 140.00 | 1,000. |

Obsolete March 31, 1901.

## GWALIOR

ˈgwäl-ē-ˌȯȯˌr

LOCATION — One of the Central Provinces of India
AREA — 26,008 sq. mi.
POP. — 4,006,159 (1941)
CAPITAL — Lashkar

The varieties with small letters in the overprint are not listed as the letters are merely broken and not from another font.

India Stamps Overprinted in Black

Lines Spaced 16-17mm

| 1885 | | Wmk. 39 | Perf. 14 |
|---|---|---|---|
| 1 | A17 | ½a green | 90.00 |
| 2 | A19 | 1a violet brown | 97.50 |
| 3 | A20 | 1a6p bister brown | 125.00 |
| 4 | A21 | 2a ultramarine | 100.00 |
| 5 | A25 | 8a red lilac | 110.00 |
| 6 | A27 | 1r gray | 110.00 |
| | | Wmk. 38 | |
| 7 | A9 | 4a green | 140.00 |
| 8 | A14 | 6a bister | 140.00 |
| | | Nos. 1-8 (8) | 912.50 |

The Hindi overprint measures 13½-14x2mm and 15-15½x2½mm.
The two sizes are found in the same sheet in the proportion of one of the smaller to three of the larger.
The ½a, 1a, 2a, also exist with lines 13mm apart and the short Hindi overprint.
*Reprints of the ½a and 1a have the 13mm spacing, the short Hindi overprint and usually carry the overprint "Specimen."*

India Stamps Overprinted

### Red Overprint

| 1885 | | Wmk. 39 | | |
|---|---|---|---|---|
| 9 | A17 | ½a green | 1.90 | .20 |
| 10 | A21 | 2a ultramarine | 35.00 | 27.50 |
| 11 | A27 | 1r gray | 12.50 | 37.50 |
| | | Wmk. 38 | | |
| 12 | A9 | 4a green | 42.50 | 24.00 |
| | | Nos. 9-12 (4) | 91.90 | 89.25 |

*Nos. 9-12 have been reprinted. They have the short Hindi overprint. Most stamps bear the word "Reprint." Those without it cannot be distinguished from the originals.*

### Black Overprint

| 1885-91 | | Wmk. 39 | | |
|---|---|---|---|---|
| 13 | A17 | ½a green | .75 | .20 |
| | a. | "GWALICR" | 125.00 | 150.00 |
| | b. | Double overprint | 1,250. | |
| 14 | A18 | 9p rose | 47.50 | 82.50 |
| 15 | A19 | 1a violet brown | 3.00 | .25 |
| 16 | A20 | 1a6p bister brown | 3.25 | 1.20 |
| 17 | A21 | 2a ultramarine | 4.00 | .20 |
| 18 | A22 | 3a orange | 6.25 | .20 |
| 19 | A23 | 4a olive green | 7.50 | 1.90 |
| 20 | A25 | 8a red violet | 7.50 | 1.90 |
| 21 | A26 | 12a violet, red | 5.00 | 1.00 |
| 22 | A27 | 1r gray | 6.50 | 3.75 |
| | | Wmk. 38 | | |
| 23 | A14 | 6a bister | 5.25 | 12.50 |
| | | Nos. 13-23 (11) | 96.50 | 105.60 |

The Hindi overprint measures 13½-14x2mm and 15-15½x2½mm as in the preceding issue.

| 1896 | | Wmk. 39 | | |
|---|---|---|---|---|
| 24 | A28 | 2a6p green | 13.50 | 30.00 |
| | a. | "GWALICR" | 1,000. | |
| 25 | A29 | 1r car rose & grn | 9.50 | 8.25 |
| | a. | "GWALICR" | 1,350. | 2,100. |
| 26 | A30 | 2r bis brn & rose | 8.25 | 4.50 |
| 27 | A30 | 3r green & brown | 11.00 | 5.25 |
| 28 | A30 | 5r violet & blue | 21.00 | 9.50 |
| | | Nos. 24-28 (5) | 63.25 | 57.50 |

The Hindi inscription varies from 13 to 15½mm long.

| 1899 | | | | |
|---|---|---|---|---|
| 29 | A31 | 3p carmine rose | .75 | .20 |
| | a. | Inverted overprint | 1,650. | 825.00 |

| 1901-04 | | | | |
|---|---|---|---|---|
| 30 | A31 | 3p gray ('04) | 11.00 | 90.00 |
| 31 | A17 | ½a light green | 2.10 | 2.40 |
| 32 | A19 | 1a carmine rose | 1.90 | .50 |
| 33 | A21 | 2a violet | 4.00 | 8.25 |
| 34 | A28 | 2a6p ultra ('03) | 2.25 | 9.50 |
| | | Nos. 30-34 (5) | 21.25 | 110.65 |

| 1903-08 | | | | |
|---|---|---|---|---|
| 35 | A32 | 3p gray | 2.10 | .25 |
| 36 | A33 | ½a green | 2.25 | .45 |
| 37 | A34 | 1a carmine rose | .30 | .20 |
| 38 | A35 | 2a violet | 3.00 | 1.50 |
| 39 | A36 | 2a6p ultra ('05) | 37.50 | 120.00 |
| 40 | A37 | 3a brown org ('04) | 3.00 | .50 |
| 41 | A38 | 4a olive green | 3.75 | .60 |
| 42 | A39 | 6a bister ('06) | 9.00 | 2.10 |
| 43 | A40 | 8a red violet | 7.50 | 2.40 |
| 44 | A41 | 12a vio, red ('05) | 4.50 | 30.00 |
| 45 | A42 | 1r car rose & grn ('05) | 4.50 | 2.50 |
| 46 | A43 | 2r brown & rose | 13.50 | 16.50 |
| 47 | A43 | 3r grn & brn ('08) | 42.50 | 75.00 |
| 48 | A43 | 5r vio & bl ('08) | 27.50 | 40.00 |
| | | Nos. 35-48 (14) | 160.90 | 292.00 |

There are two settings of the overprint on Nos. 35, 37-46. In the first (1903), "GWALIOR" is 14mm long and lines are spaced 1¾mm. In the second (1908), "GWALIOR" is 13mm long and lines are 2¾mm apart. No. 36 exists only with first overprint, Nos. 47-48 only with second.

| 1907 | | | | |
|---|---|---|---|---|
| 49 | A44 | ½a green | .30 | 1.00 |
| 50 | A45 | 1a carmine rose | 2.25 | .25 |

No. 49 exists with both settings of overprint. See note below No. 48.

| 1912-23 | | | | |
|---|---|---|---|---|
| 51 | A46 | 3p gray | .30 | .20 |
| 52 | A47 | ½a green | .30 | .20 |
| | a. | Inverted overprint | 600.00 | |
| 53 | A48 | 1a car rose | .35 | .20 |
| | a. | Double overprint | 37.50 | |
| 54 | A48 | 1a dk brown ('23) | 1.60 | .20 |
| 55 | A49 | 2a violet | 1.20 | .20 |
| 56 | A51 | 3a brown orange | 1.00 | .20 |
| 57 | A52 | 4a olive grn ('13) | .90 | .90 |
| 58 | A53 | 6a bister | 1.90 | 2.10 |
| 59 | A54 | 8a red vio ('13) | 3.25 | 1.20 |
| 60 | A55 | 12a claret ('14) | 2.10 | 6.00 |
| 61 | A56 | 1r green & red brn | 13.50 | .65 |
| 62 | A56 | 2r brn & car rose | 7.50 | 6.50 |
| 63 | A56 | 5r violet & ultra | 35.00 | 9.50 |
| | | Nos. 51-63 (13) | 68.90 | 28.05 |

### India No. 104 Overprinted

| 1921 | | | | |
|---|---|---|---|---|
| 64 | A48 | 9p on 1a rose | .20 | .75 |
| | a. | Inverted overprint | | |

### India Stamps of 1911-26 Overprinted

### Hindi Overprint 15mm Long

| 1923-27 | | | | |
|---|---|---|---|---|
| 66 | A59 | 1½a choc ('25) | 3.25 | .75 |
| 67 | A59 | 1½a rose ('27) | .30 | .25 |
| | a. | Inverted overprint | | |
| 68 | A57 | 2a6p ultra ('25) | 3.25 | 2.50 |
| 69 | A57 | 2a6p brown org ('27) | .50 | .75 |
| 70 | A51 | 3a ultra ('24) | 3.75 | .90 |
| | | Nos. 66-70 (5) | 11.05 | 5.15 |

### Similar Ovpt. on India Stamps of 1926-35
### Hindi Overprint 13½mm Long

| 1928-32 | | Wmk. 196 | | |
|---|---|---|---|---|
| 71 | A46 | 3p slate ('32) | 1.50 | .20 |
| 72 | A47 | ½a green ('30) | 2.25 | .20 |
| 73 | A48 | 1a dark brown | 1.25 | .20 |
| 74 | A60 | 2a dull violet | .80 | .45 |
| 75 | A51 | 3a ultramarine | 1.50 | .60 |
| 76 | A61 | 4a olive green | 1.90 | 1.50 |
| 77 | A54 | 8a red violet | 1.90 | 1.60 |
| 78 | A55 | 12a claret | 3.25 | 5.25 |

Overprinted

| 79 | A56 | 1r green & brown | 4.50 | 6.00 |
|---|---|---|---|---|
| 80 | A56 | 2r brn org & car rose | 8.00 | 6.50 |
| 81 | A56 | 5r dk vio & ultra ('29) | 27.50 | 37.50 |
| 82 | A56 | 10r car & grn ('30) | 97.50 | 62.50 |
| 83 | A56 | 15r olive green & ultra ('30) | 150.00 | 100.00 |
| 84 | A56 | 25r bl & ocher ('30) | 325.00 | 472.50 |
| | | Nos. 71-84 (14) | 626.85 | 472.50 |

### India Stamps of 1932-35 Overprinted in Black

### Hindi Overprint 13½mm Long

| 1933-36 | | | | |
|---|---|---|---|---|
| 85 | A71 | ½a green ('36) | .75 | .25 |
| 86 | A68 | 9p dk green ('33) | 4.50 | .45 |
| 87 | A72 | 1a dk brown ('36) | .30 | .20 |
| 88 | A69 | 1a3p violet ('36) | .75 | .20 |
| 89 | A49 | 2a vermilion ('36) | 4.50 | 5.50 |
| | | Nos. 85-89 (5) | 10.80 | 6.60 |

### Same Ovpt. on India Stamps of 1937

| 1938-40 | | Perf. 13½x14 | | |
|---|---|---|---|---|
| 90 | A80 | 3p slate ('40) | 12.00 | .25 |
| 91 | A80 | ½a brown | 13.50 | .20 |
| 92 | A80 | 9p green ('40) | 72.50 | 6.00 |
| 93 | A80 | 1a carmine | 12.50 | .20 |
| 94 | A81 | 3a yel green ('39) | 42.50 | 7.50 |
| 95 | A81 | 4a dark brown | 67.50 | 5.25 |
| 96 | A81 | 6a pck blue ('39) | 6.00 | 16.50 |
| | | Nos. 90-96 (7) | 226.50 | 35.90 |
| | | Set, never hinged | 225.00 | |

### Same Overprinted on India Stamps of 1941-43

| 1942-49 | | | | |
|---|---|---|---|---|
| 100 | A83 | 3p slate ('44) | .55 | .20 |
| 101 | A83 | ½a rose vio ('46) | 1.25 | .20 |
| 102 | A83 | 9p light green | .55 | .20 |
| 103 | A83 | 1a car rose ('44) | 1.25 | .20 |
| 104 | A84 | 1½a dk purple ('44) | 8.75 | .25 |
| 105 | A84 | 2a scarlet ('44) | 1.90 | .25 |
| 106 | A84 | 3a violet ('44) | 20.00 | 2.50 |
| 108 | A85 | 4a choc ('44) | 4.00 | .25 |
| 109 | A85 | 6a pck blue ('48) | 17.50 | 40.00 |
| 110 | A85 | 8a blue violet | 4.75 | 4.00 |
| 111 | A85 | 12a carmine lake | 7.00 | 35.00 |

### India Nos. 162-167 Overprinted

| | | Perf. 13½x14 | | |
|---|---|---|---|---|
| 112 | A82 | 1r brn & slate ('45) | 15.00 | 2.50 |
| 113 | A82 | 2r dk brn & dk vio ('49) | 62.50 | 14.00 |
| 114 | A82 | 5r dp ultra & dk grn ('49) | 40.00 | 60.00 |
| 115 | A82 | 10r rose car & dk vio ('49) | 40.00 | 62.50 |
| 116 | A82 | 15r dk grn & dk brn ('48) | 110.00 | 250.00 |
| 117 | A82 | 25r dk vio & blue vio ('48) | 110.00 | 190.00 |
| | | Nos. 100-106,108-117 (17) | 445.00 | 662.05 |
| | | Set, never hinged | 525.00 | |

### India Stamps of 1941-43 Overprinted

| 1949 | | | | |
|---|---|---|---|---|
| 118 | A83 | 3p slate | 2.50 | .75 |
| 119 | A83 | ½a rose violet | 2.50 | .75 |
| 120 | A83 | 1a carmine rose | 2.25 | .90 |
| 121 | A84 | 2a scarlet | 32.50 | 3.25 |
| 122 | A84 | 3a violet | 80.00 | 45.00 |
| 123 | A85 | 4a chocolate | 9.25 | 5.00 |
| 124 | A85 | 6a pck blue | 67.50 | 97.50 |
| 125 | A85 | 8a blue violet | 140.00 | 82.50 |
| 126 | A85 | 12a carmine lake | 525.00 | 225.00 |
| | | Nos. 118-126 (9) | 861.50 | 460.65 |
| | | Set, never hinged | 1,050. | |

### OFFICIAL STAMPS

India Stamps Overprinted in Black

| 1895 | | Wmk. 39 | | Perf. 14 |
|---|---|---|---|---|
| O1 | A17 | ½a green | .75 | .20 |
| | a. | Double overprint | 1,400. | |
| O2 | A19 | 1a maroon | 18.00 | 2.10 |
| O3 | A21 | 2a ultramarine | 5.00 | .60 |
| O4 | A23 | 4a olive green | 5.25 | 2.25 |

| O5 | A25 | 8a red violet | 6.50 | 5.00 |
|---|---|---|---|---|
| O6 | A29 | 1r car rose & grn | 12.50 | 4.50 |
| | | Nos. O1-O6 (6) | 48.00 | 14.65 |

Nos. O1 to O6 inclusive are known with the last two characters of the lower word transposed.

**1901-04**

| O7 | A31 | 3p gray ('04) | 3.75 | 5.25 |
|---|---|---|---|---|
| O8 | A17 | ½a light green | 1.10 | .20 |
| O9 | A19 | 1a carmine rose | 9.00 | .20 |
| O10 | A21 | 2a violet ('03) | 2.50 | 2.25 |
| | | Nos. O7-O10 (4) | 16.35 | 7.90 |

**1902**

| O11 | A31 | 3p carmine rose | 1.90 | .35 |
|---|---|---|---|---|

**1903-05**

| O12 | A32 | 3p gray | 1.00 | .20 |
|---|---|---|---|---|
| O13 | A33 | ½a green | 4.50 | .20 |
| O14 | A34 | 1a carmine rose | 1.60 | .20 |
| O15 | A35 | 2a violet | 2.50 | .45 |
| O16 | A38 | 4a olive grn ('05) | 25.00 | 2.50 |
| O17 | A40 | 8a red violet | 11.00 | 1.00 |
| O18 | A42 | 1r car rose & grn ('05) | 4.00 | 3.00 |
| | | Nos. O12-O18 (7) | 49.60 | 7.55 |

**1907**

| O19 | A44 | ½a green | 2.50 | .20 |
|---|---|---|---|---|
| O20 | A45 | 1a carmine rose | 10.00 | .20 |

Two spacings of the overprint lines, 10mm and 8mm, are found on Nos. O12-O20.

**1913**

| O21 | A46 | 3p gray | .35 | .20 |
|---|---|---|---|---|
| O22 | A47 | ½a green | .30 | .20 |
| O23 | A48 | 1a carmine rose | .45 | .20 |
| a. | | Double overprint | 97.50 | |
| O24 | A49 | 2a violet | 2.25 | .25 |
| O25 | A52 | 4a olive green | .90 | 2.25 |
| O26 | A54 | 8a red violet | 1.90 | 1.50 |
| O27 | A56 | 1r grn & red brn | 40.00 | 35.00 |
| | | Nos. O21-O27 (7) | 46.15 | 39.60 |

India No. O66 Overprinted

**1921**

| O28 | O6 | 9p on 1a rose | .20 | .45 |
|---|---|---|---|---|

India No. 83
Overprinted

**1923**

| O29 | A48 | 1a dark brown | 5.50 | .20 |
|---|---|---|---|---|

Similar Ovpt. on India Stamps of
1926-35

**1927-35          Wmk. 196**

| O30 | A46 | 3p slate | .30 | .20 |
|---|---|---|---|---|
| O31 | A47 | ½a green | .30 | .20 |
| O32 | A48 | 1a dark brown | .30 | .20 |
| O33 | A60 | 2a dull violet | .30 | .20 |
| O34 | A61 | 4a olive green | 1.00 | .45 |
| O35 | A54 | 8a red violet | .90 | 1.60 |

Overprinted

| O36 | A56 | 1r green & brown | 1.50 | 2.50 |
|---|---|---|---|---|
| O37 | A56 | 2r brn org & car rose ('35) | 29.00 | 30.00 |
| O38 | A56 | 5r dk vio & ultra ('32) | 35.00 | 250.00 |
| O39 | A56 | 10r car & grn ('32) | 240.00 | 650.00 |
| | | Nos. O30-O39 (10) | 308.60 | 935.35 |

India Stamps of 1926-
35 Overprinted

**1933-37          Perf. 13½x14, 14**

| O40 | A71 | ½a green ('36) | .35 | .25 |
|---|---|---|---|---|
| O41 | A68 | 9p dk green ('35) | .30 | .25 |
| O42 | A72 | 1a dk brown ('36) | .30 | .20 |
| O43 | A69 | 1a3p violet ('33) | .75 | .20 |

| O44 | A49 | 2a ver ('36) | .30 | .60 |
|---|---|---|---|---|
| a. | | Small die ('36) | 3.75 | 1.90 |
| O45 | A52 | 4a olive green ('37) | .90 | 1.10 |
| | | Nos. O40-O45 (6) | 2.90 | 2.60 |

For surcharge see No. O62.

Same Overprint on India Stamps

**1938                 Perf. 13½x14**

| O46 | A80 | ½a brown | 8.00 | .45 |
|---|---|---|---|---|
| | | Never hinged | 9.50 | |
| O47 | A80 | 1a carmine | 2.00 | .20 |
| | | Never hinged | 2.25 | |

India Nos. 162-
165 Overprinted

**1945-48   Wmk. 196   Perf. 13½x14**

| O48 | A82 | 1r brown & slate | 12.50 | 32.50 |
|---|---|---|---|---|
| O49 | A82 | 2r dk brn & dk vio | 22.50 | 140.00 |
| O50 | A82 | 5r dp ultra & dk grn ('46) | 37.50 | 825.00 |
| O51 | A82 | 10r rose car & dk vio ('48) | 100.00 | 1,650. |
| | | Nos. O48-O51 (4) | 172.50 | 2,647. |
| | | Set, never hinged | 200.00 | |

India Official Stamps of 1939-43
Overprinted

**1940-44   Wmk. 196   Perf. 13½x14**

| O52 | O8 | 3p slate | .65 | .20 |
|---|---|---|---|---|
| O53 | O8 | ½a brown | 5.50 | .35 |
| O54 | O8 | ½a dk rose vio ('43) | .75 | .20 |
| O55 | O8 | 9p green ('43) | .85 | 1.00 |
| O56 | O8 | 1a car rose ('41) | 2.75 | .20 |
| O57 | O8 | 1a3p bister ('42) | 55.00 | 2.50 |
| O58 | O8 | 1 ½a dull purple ('43) | 1.50 | .45 |
| O59 | O8 | 2a scarlet ('41) | 1.50 | .45 |
| O60 | O8 | 4a dark brown ('44) | 1.50 | 5.00 |
| O61 | O8 | 8a blue vio ('44) | 6.00 | 14.00 |
| | | Nos. O52-O61 (10) | 76.00 | 24.35 |
| | | Set, never hinged | 25.00 | |

Gwalior No. O43 with
Additional Surcharge in
Black

**1942**

| O62 | A69 | 1a on 1a3p violet | 30.00 | 4.50 |
|---|---|---|---|---|
| | | Never hinged | 37.50 | |

**JIND**

'jind

**(Jhind)**

LOCATION — A State of India in the north Punjab.
AREA — 1,299 sq. mi.
POP. — 361,812 (1941)
CAPITAL — Sangrur

Previous stamp issues are listed under Feudatory States.
The varieties with small letters are not listed as the letters are merely broken and not from another font.

India Stamps
Overprinted in Black

**1885         Wmk. 39         Perf. 14**

| 33 | A17 | ½a green | 7.00 | 8.25 |
|---|---|---|---|---|
| a. | | Inverted overprint | 140.00 | 160.00 |

| 34 | A19 | 1a violet brown | 62.50 | 90.00 |
|---|---|---|---|---|
| 35 | A21 | 2a ultra | 29.00 | 32.50 |
| a. | | Inverted overprint | 1,000. | 1,200. |
| 36 | A25 | 8a red lilac | 625.00 | |
| a. | | Inverted overprint | 18,000. | |
| 37 | A27 | 1r gray | 700.00 | |
| a. | | Inverted overprint | 21,000. | |

**Wmk. 38**

| 38 | A9 | 4a green | 97.50 | 140.00 |
|---|---|---|---|---|
| | | Nos. 33-38 (6) | 1,521. | 270.75 |

On the reprints of Nos. 33 to 38 "Jhind" measures 8mm instead of 9mm and "State" 9mm instead of 9½mm.
Examples of "inverted overprints" exist of the ½a, 1a and 2a with the lines much less curved. These are thought to come from a trial printing.

India Stamps Overprinted in J E E N D
Red or Black              STATE

**1885              Wmk. 39**

| 39 | A17 | ½a green (R) | 210.00 | |
|---|---|---|---|---|
| 40 | A19 | 1a violet brown | 210.00 | |
| 41 | A21 | 2a ultra (R) | 210.00 | |
| 42 | A25 | 8a red lilac | 290.00 | |
| 43 | A27 | 1r gray (R) | 290.00 | |

**Wmk. 38**

| 44 | A9 | 4a green (R) | 290.00 | |
|---|---|---|---|---|
| | | Nos. 39-44 (6) | 1,500. | |

India Stamps Overprinted   J H I N D
                               STATE

Red Overprint

**1886              Wmk. 39**

| 45 | A17 | ½a green | 52.50 | |
|---|---|---|---|---|
| a. | | "JEIND" | 1,800. | |
| 46 | A21 | 2a ultramarine | 57.50 | |
| a. | | "JEIND" | 1,800. | |
| 47 | A27 | 1r gray | 90.00 | |
| a. | | "JEIND" | 2,750. | |

**Wmk. 38**

| 48 | A9 | 4a green | 90.00 | |
|---|---|---|---|---|
| | | Nos. 45-48 (4) | 290.00 | |

Nos. 46, 47 and 48 were not placed in use.

Black Overprint

**1886-98              Wmk. 39**

| 49 | A17 | ½a green ('88) | 1.20 | .20 |
|---|---|---|---|---|
| a. | | Inverted overprint | 300.00 | |
| 50 | A19 | 1a violet brown | 3.75 | .25 |
| a. | | "JEIND" | 750.00 | |
| 51 | A20 | 1a6p bister brn ('97) | 3.75 | 5.50 |
| 52 | A21 | 2a ultra | 3.75 | .60 |
| 53 | A22 | 3a orange | 5.00 | 1.00 |
| 54 | A23 | 4a olive green | 6.00 | 3.25 |
| 55 | A25 | 8a red violet | 12.50 | 30.00 |
| a. | | "JEIND" | 2,400. | |
| 56 | A26 | 12a vio, red ('97) | 10.00 | 37.50 |
| 57 | A27 | 1r gray ('91) | 17.50 | 82.50 |
| 58 | A29 | 1r car rose & green ('98) | 16.50 | 90.00 |
| 59 | A30 | 2r brn & rose ('97) | 525.00 | 1,500. |
| 60 | A30 | 3r grn & brn ('97) | 750.00 | 1,350. |
| 61 | A30 | 5r vio & bl ('97) | 750.00 | 1,250. |

**Wmk. 38**

| 62 | A14 | 6a bister | 6.50 | 21.00 |
|---|---|---|---|---|
| | | Nos. 49-62 (14) | 2,111. | 4,371. |

**1900              Wmk. 39**

| 63 | A31 | 3p carmine rose | 1.60 | 2.50 |
|---|---|---|---|---|

**1902-04**

| 64 | A31 | 3p gray ('04) | .60 | 6.00 |
|---|---|---|---|---|
| 65 | A17 | ½a light green | 7.00 | 10.00 |
| 66 | A19 | 1a carmine rose | 1.90 | 10.00 |
| | | Nos. 64-66 (3) | 9.50 | 26.00 |

**1903-09**

| 67 | A32 | 3p gray | .35 | .20 |
|---|---|---|---|---|
| 68 | A33 | ½a green | 3.00 | 2.50 |
| 69 | A34 | 1a car rose ('09) | 3.25 | 2.40 |
| 70 | A35 | 2a violet ('06) | 5.00 | 3.25 |
| 70A | A36 | 2a6p ultra ('09) | 1.00 | 10.00 |
| 71 | A37 | 3a brown orange | 3.75 | .60 |
| a. | | Double overprint | 175.00 | 325.00 |
| 72 | A38 | 4a olive green | 13.50 | 14.00 |
| 73 | A39 | 6a bister ('05) | 11.00 | 32.50 |
| 74 | A40 | 8a red violet | 4.50 | 32.50 |
| 75 | A41 | 12a vio, red ('05) | 5.00 | 17.50 |
| 76 | A42 | 1r car rose & grn ('05) | 5.50 | 32.50 |
| | | Nos. 67-76 (11) | 55.85 | 147.95 |

**1907**

| 77 | A44 | ½a green | .60 | .25 |
|---|---|---|---|---|
| 78 | A45 | 1a carmine rose | 2.25 | 1.00 |

**1913**

| 80 | A46 | 3p gray | .30 | 3.50 |
|---|---|---|---|---|
| 81 | A47 | ½a green | .30 | 1.10 |
| 82 | A48 | 1a carmine rose | .30 | .65 |
| 83 | A49 | 2a violet | .30 | 6.25 |
| 84 | A51 | 3a brown orange | 2.25 | 21.00 |
| 85 | A53 | 6a bister | 12.50 | 42.50 |
| | | Nos. 80-85 (6) | 15.95 | 75.00 |

India Stamps of 1911-
26 Overprinted

**1913-14**

| 88 | A46 | 3p gray | 1.50 | .20 |
|---|---|---|---|---|
| 89 | A47 | ½a green | 3.75 | .20 |
| 90 | A48 | 1a carmine rose | 2.40 | .20 |
| 91 | A49 | 2a violet | 6.50 | 1.90 |
| 92 | A51 | 3a brown orange | .75 | 6.00 |
| 93 | A52 | 4a olive green | 3.00 | 14.00 |
| 94 | A53 | 6a bister | 6.00 | 24.00 |
| 95 | A54 | 8a red violet | 8.25 | 24.00 |
| 96 | A55 | 12a claret | 7.50 | 30.00 |
| 97 | A56 | 1r grn & red brn | 17.50 | 35.00 |
| | | Nos. 88-97 (10) | 57.15 | 135.50 |

India No. 104 Overprinted

**1921**

| 98 | A48 | 9p on 1a rose | 1.90 | 22.50 |
|---|---|---|---|---|

India Stamps of 1913-
19 Overprinted

**1922**

| 99 | A58 | 1 ½a chocolate | 5.00 | 9.00 |
|---|---|---|---|---|
| 100 | A57 | 2a6p ultramarine | .75 | 7.00 |

Same Overprint on India Stamps of
1911-26

**1924**

| 101 | A48 | 1a dark brown | 9.00 | 4.50 |
|---|---|---|---|---|
| 102 | A59 | 1 ½a chocolate | .75 | 2.25 |

Same Overprint on India No. 87

**1925**

| 103 | A51 | 3a ultramarine | 3.00 | 7.50 |
|---|---|---|---|---|

Same Overprint on India Stamps of
1911-26

**1927**

| 104 | A59 | 1 ½a rose | .30 | 2.25 |
|---|---|---|---|---|
| 105 | A57 | 2a6p brown orange | 1.90 | 12.00 |
| 106 | A56 | 2r yel brn & car rose | 9.50 | 225.00 |
| 107 | A56 | 5r violet & ultra | 67.50 | 450.00 |
| | | Nos. 104-107 (4) | 79.20 | 689.25 |

India Stamps of 1926-
35 Overprinted

**1927-32              Wmk. 196**

| 108 | A46 | 3p slate | .30 | .20 |
|---|---|---|---|---|
| 109 | A47 | ½a green | .30 | .50 |
| 110 | A68 | 9p dark green ('32) | 3.25 | .60 |
| 111 | A48 | 1a dark brown | .30 | .20 |
| 112 | A69 | 1a3p violet ('32) | .35 | .45 |
| 113 | A59 | 1 ½a carmine rose | .90 | 5.50 |
| 114 | A60 | 2a dull violet | 5.00 | .60 |
| 115 | A57 | 2a6p buff | 2.40 | 16.00 |
| 116 | A51 | 3a ultramarine | 9.50 | 27.50 |
| 117 | A61 | 4a olive green | 2.50 | 5.25 |
| 118 | A54 | 8a red violet | 9.00 | 3.25 |
| 119 | A55 | 12a claret | 12.00 | 32.50 |

Overprinted

| 120 | A56 | 1r green & brown | 7.50 | 9.00 |
|---|---|---|---|---|
| 121 | A56 | 2r buff & car rose | 62.50 | 225.00 |

| | | | | |
|---|---|---|---|---|
| 122 | A56 | 5r dk vio & ultra | 19.00 | 62.50 |
| 123 | A56 | 10r car rose & grn | 22.50 | 27.50 |
| 124 | A56 | 15r ol grn & blue | 140.00 | 1,050. |
| 125 | A56 | 25r blue & ocher | 225.00 | 1,250. |
| | | Nos. 108-125 (18) | 522.30 | 2,716. |

### India Stamps of 1926-35 Overprinted

**1934-37**

| | | | | |
|---|---|---|---|---|
| 126 | A71 | ½a green | .45 | .35 |
| 127 | A72 | 1a dark brown | 3.00 | .45 |
| 128 | A49 | 2a vermilion | 5.50 | .90 |
| 129 | A51 | 3a carmine rose | 5.00 | .60 |
| 130 | A70 | 3a6p deep blue ('37) | .90 | 30.00 |
| 131 | A52 | 4a olive green | 5.00 | 2.25 |
| 132 | A53 | 6a bister ('37) | 1.00 | 32.50 |
| | | Nos. 126-132 (7) | 20.85 | 67.05 |

### Same Overprint on India Stamps of 1937

**1937-38     Wmk. 196     Perf. 13½x14**

| | | | | |
|---|---|---|---|---|
| 133 | A80 | 3p slate ('38) | 12.50 | 3.75 |
| 134 | A80 | ½a brown ('38) | .95 | 7.50 |
| 135 | A80 | 9p green ('38) | .95 | 6.00 |
| 136 | A80 | 1a carmine ('38) | .95 | .90 |
| 137 | A81 | 2a scarlet ('38) | 2.10 | 27.50 |
| 138 | A81 | 2a6p purple ('38) | 1.60 | 35.00 |
| 139 | A81 | 3a yel grn ('38) | 8.00 | 30.00 |
| 140 | A81 | 3a6p ultra ('38) | 4.00 | 35.00 |
| 141 | A81 | 4a dk brown ('38) | 12.00 | 27.50 |
| 142 | A81 | 6a pck blue ('38) | 7.50 | 42.50 |
| 143 | A81 | 8a blue vio ('38) | 6.25 | 35.00 |
| 144 | A81 | 12a car lake ('38) | 3.50 | 45.00 |

### Overprinted

**1938**

| | | | | |
|---|---|---|---|---|
| 145 | A82 | 1r brown & slate | 15.00 | 62.50 |
| 146 | A82 | 2r dk brn & dk violet | 19.00 | 190.00 |
| 147 | A82 | 5r dp ultra & dk green | 32.50 | 125.00 |
| 148 | A82 | 10r rose car & dk violet | 60.00 | 120.00 |
| 149 | A82 | 15r dk grn & dk brown | 125.00 | 1,200. |
| 150 | A82 | 25r dk vio & bl vio | 690.00 | 1,400. |
| | | Nos. 133-150 (18) | 1,001. | 3,393. |
| | | Set, never hinged | 1,200. | |

### India Stamps of 1937 Overprinted

**1942-43     Wmk. 196     Perf. 13½x14**

| | | | | |
|---|---|---|---|---|
| 155 | A80 | 3p slate | 17.50 | 32.50 |
| 156 | A80 | ½a brown | 1.25 | 3.75 |
| 157 | A80 | 9p green | 16.00 | 30.00 |
| 158 | A80 | 1a carmine | 1.25 | 9.00 |
| 159 | A82 | 1r brn & slate | 11.00 | 40.00 |
| 160 | A82 | 2r dk brn & dk violet | 22.50 | 52.50 |
| 161 | A82 | 5r dp ultra & dk green | 50.00 | 140.00 |
| 162 | A82 | 10r rose car & dk vio ('43) | 75.00 | 140.00 |
| 163 | A82 | 15r dk grn & dk brn ('43) | 160.00 | 250.00 |
| 164 | A82 | 25r dk vio & bl vio | 75.00 | 525.00 |
| | | Nos. 155-164 (10) | 429.50 | 1,222. |
| | | Set, never hinged | 510.00 | |

### Same Overprint on India Stamps of 1941-43

| | | | | |
|---|---|---|---|---|
| 165 | A83 | 3p slate | .60 | 2.10 |
| 166 | A83 | ½a rose vio ('43) | .60 | 3.25 |
| 167 | A83 | 9p light green | .95 | 6.50 |
| 168 | A83 | 1a car rose ('43) | 1.25 | 2.25 |
| 169 | A84 | 1a3p bister ('43) | 1.25 | 7.50 |
| 170 | A84 | 1½a dark purple | 10.00 | 7.50 |
| 171 | A84 | 2a scarlet | 2.25 | 7.50 |
| 172 | A84 | 3a violet ('43) | 30.00 | 9.00 |
| 173 | A84 | 3½a ultramarine | 11.00 | 17.50 |
| 174 | A85 | 4a chocolate | 7.50 | 9.00 |
| 175 | A85 | 6a peacock blue | 8.00 | 25.00 |

---

| | | | | |
|---|---|---|---|---|
| 176 | A85 | 8a blue violet | 5.25 | 22.50 |
| 177 | A85 | 12a carmine lake | 17.50 | 27.50 |
| | | Nos. 165-177 (13) | 96.15 | 147.10 |
| | | Set, never hinged | 115.00 | |

---

## OFFICIAL STAMPS

### India Stamps Overprinted in Black

**1885     Wmk. 39     Perf. 14**

| | | | | |
|---|---|---|---|---|
| O1 | A17 | ½a green | 3.00 | .60 |
| a. | | Inverted overprint | 150.00 | 90.00 |
| O2 | A19 | 1a violet brown | 1.00 | .20 |
| a. | | Inverted overprint | 17.50 | 11.00 |
| O3 | A21 | 2a ultra | 60.00 | 72.50 |
| a. | | Inverted overprint | 1,500. | 1,750. |
| | | Nos. O1-O3 (3) | 64.00 | 73.30 |

*The reprints may be distinguished by the same measurements as the reprints of the corresponding regular issue.*

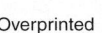

### India Stamps Overprinted in Red or Black

**1885**

| | | | |
|---|---|---|---|
| O4 | A17 | ½a green (R) | 150.00 |
| O5 | A19 | 1a violet brown | 125.00 |
| O6 | A21 | 2a ultra (R) | 140.00 |
| | | Nos. O4-O6 (3) | 415.00 |

### India Stamps Overprinted

**1886**

### Red Overprint

| | | | |
|---|---|---|---|
| O7 | A17 | ½a green | 42.50 |
| a. | | "JEIND" | 1,050. |
| b. | | "ERVICE" | 6,000. |
| O8 | A21 | 2a ultramarine | 47.50 |
| a. | | "JEIND" | 1,750. |
| b. | | "ERVICE" | 3,750. |

No. O8 was not placed in use.

**1886-96**

### Black Overprint

| | | | | |
|---|---|---|---|---|
| O9 | A17 | ½a green ('88) | 3.00 | .25 |
| O10 | A19 | 1a violet brown | 19.00 | 2.25 |
| a. | | "JEIND" | 750.00 | |
| b. | | "ERVICE" | | |
| O11 | A21 | 2a ultramarine | 5.00 | 1.50 |
| O12 | A23 | 4a olive green | 5.25 | 3.00 |
| O13 | A25 | 8a red violet | 8.25 | 12.50 |
| O14 | A29 | 1r car rose & grn ('96) | 9.50 | 75.00 |
| | | Nos. O9-O14 (6) | 50.00 | 94.50 |

**1902**

| | | | | |
|---|---|---|---|---|
| O15 | A17 | ½a light green | 3.75 | .45 |

**1903-06**

| | | | | |
|---|---|---|---|---|
| O16 | A32 | 3p gray | 1.00 | .20 |
| O17 | A33 | ½a green | 5.25 | .20 |
| a. | | "HIND" | 4,500. | 450.00 |
| O18 | A34 | 1a carmine rose | 4.50 | .20 |
| a. | | "HIND" | 5,250. | 400.00 |
| O19 | A35 | 2a violet | 3.00 | .20 |
| O20 | A38 | 4a olive green | 2.50 | .65 |
| O21 | A40 | 8a red violet | 9.00 | 2.25 |
| O22 | A42 | 1r car rose & grn ('06) | 3.75 | 3.25 |
| | | Nos. O16-O22 (7) | 29.00 | 6.95 |

**1907**

| | | | | |
|---|---|---|---|---|
| O23 | A44 | ½a green | 1.50 | .20 |
| O24 | A45 | 1a carmine rose | 2.50 | .20 |

---

### Indian Stamps of 1911-26 Overprinted

a                    b

**1914-27**

| | | | | |
|---|---|---|---|---|
| O25 | A46(a) | 3p gray | .30 | .20 |
| O26 | A47(a) | ½a green | .40 | .20 |
| O27 | A48(a) | 1a car rose | 1.00 | .20 |
| O28 | A49(a) | 2a violet | .35 | .45 |
| O29 | A52(a) | 4a olive green | 1.90 | .25 |
| O30 | A54(a) | 8a red violet | 1.00 | 1.50 |
| O31 | A56(b) | 1r grn & red brn | 3.75 | 2.50 |
| O32 | A56(b) | 2r yel brn & car rose ('27) | 27.50 | 100.00 |
| O33 | A56(b) | 5r vio & ultra ('27) | 35.00 | 375.00 |
| | | Nos. O25-O33 (9) | 71.20 | 480.30 |

### India Nos. 83 and 89 Overprinted Type "a"

**1924-27**

| | | | | |
|---|---|---|---|---|
| O34 | A48 | 1a dark brown | .90 | .20 |
| O35 | A53 | 6a bister ('27) | 2.50 | 3.25 |

### India Stamps of 1926-35 Overprinted

c

**1927-32**

| | | | | |
|---|---|---|---|---|
| O36 | A46 | 3p slate | .20 | .20 |
| O37 | A47 | ½a green | .20 | 1.50 |
| O38 | A68 | 9p dark green ('32) | .90 | .20 |
| O39 | A48 | 1a dark brown | .20 | .20 |
| O40 | A69 | 1a3p violet ('32) | .60 | .25 |
| O41 | A60 | 2a dull violet | .35 | .20 |
| O42 | A61 | 4a olive green | .50 | .35 |
| O43 | A54 | 8a red violet | .90 | 2.50 |
| O44 | A55 | 12a claret | 3.25 | 27.50 |

### Overprinted

d

| | | | | |
|---|---|---|---|---|
| O45 | A56 | 1r green & brown | 7.50 | 8.25 |
| O46 | A56 | 2r buff & car rose | 75.00 | 62.50 |
| O47 | A56 | 5r dk vio & ultra | 19.00 | 400.00 |
| O48 | A56 | 10r car rose & grn | 57.50 | 225.00 |
| | | Nos. O36-O48 (13) | 166.10 | 728.65 |

### India Stamps of 1926-35 Overprinted Type "c"

**1934-37**

| | | | | |
|---|---|---|---|---|
| O49 | A71 | ½a green | .30 | .20 |
| O50 | A72 | 1a dark brown | .30 | .20 |
| O51 | A49 | 2a vermilion | .45 | .20 |
| O52 | A57 | 2a6p buff ('37) | 1.90 | 30.00 |
| O53 | A52 | 4a olive green | 9.00 | .45 |
| O54 | A53 | 6a bister ('37) | 5.50 | 25.00 |
| | | Nos. O49-O54 (6) | 17.45 | 56.05 |

### India Nos. 151-153 Overprinted Type "c"

**1937-42     Perf. 13½x14**

| | | | | |
|---|---|---|---|---|
| O55 | A80 | ½a brown ('42) | 80.00 | .45 |
| O56 | A80 | 9p green | 3.00 | 24.00 |
| O57 | A80 | 1a carmine | 2.25 | .45 |

### India Nos. 162-165 Overprinted Type "d"

| | | | | |
|---|---|---|---|---|
| O58 | A82 | 1r brn & sl ('40) | 52.50 | 67.50 |
| O59 | A82 | 2r dk brn & dk vio ('40) | 55.00 | 375.00 |
| O60 | A82 | 5r dp ultra & dk grn ('40) | 120.00 | 600.00 |
| O61 | A82 | 10r rose car & dk vio ('40) | 525.00 | 1,500. |
| | | Nos. O55-O61 (7) | 837.75 | 2,567. |
| | | Set, never hinged | 875.00 | |

---

### India Official Stamps of 1939-43 Overprinted

**1940-43**

| | | | | |
|---|---|---|---|---|
| O62 | O8 | 3p slate | .75 | 3.00 |
| O63 | O8 | ½a brown | 2.50 | 1.90 |
| O64 | O8 | ½a dk rose vio ('43) | .75 | .45 |
| O65 | O8 | 9p green | 3.75 | 19.00 |
| O66 | O8 | 1a car rose | 4.50 | .20 |
| O67 | O8 | 1½a dull pur ('43) | 11.00 | 2.40 |
| O68 | O8 | 2a scarlet | 10.00 | .45 |
| O69 | O8 | 2½a purple | 6.25 | 14.00 |
| O70 | O8 | 4a dark brown | 11.00 | 7.00 |
| O71 | O8 | 8a blue violet | 11.00 | 12.00 |

### India Nos. 162-165 Overprinted

**1942     Wmk. 196     Perf. 13½x14**

| | | | | |
|---|---|---|---|---|
| O72 | A82 | 1r brown & slate | 22.50 | 82.50 |
| O73 | A82 | 2r dk brn & dk vio | 52.50 | 250.00 |
| O74 | A82 | 5r dp ultra & dk green | 87.50 | 625.00 |
| O75 | A82 | 10r rose car & dk violet | 175.00 | 825.00 |
| | | Nos. O62-O75 (14) | 399.00 | 1,842. |
| | | Set, never hinged | 500.00 | |

## NABHA

'näb-hə

LOCATION — A State of India in the eastern and southeastern Punjab
AREA — 966 sq. mi.
POP. — 340,044 (1941)
CAPITAL — Nabha

The varieties with small letters in the overprint are not listed as the letters are merely broken and not from another font.

### Indian Stamps Overprinted in Black

**1885     Wmk. 39     Perf. 14**

| | | | | |
|---|---|---|---|---|
| 1 | A17 | ½a green | 6.25 | 9.00 |
| 2 | A19 | 1a violet brown | 82.50 | 290.00 |
| 3 | A21 | 2a ultramarine | 37.50 | 97.50 |
| 4 | A25 | 8a red lilac | 475.00 | |
| 5 | A27 | 1r gray | 550.00 | |
| | | **Wmk. 38** | | |
| 6 | A9 | 4a green | 125.00 | 375.00 |

*On the reprints "Nabha" and "State" each measure 9½mm. On the originals they measure 11 and 10mm respectively.*

### Indian Stamps Overprinted

### Red Overprint

**1885     Wmk. 39**

| | | | | |
|---|---|---|---|---|
| 7 | A17 | ½a green | 1.90 | 1.50 |
| 8 | A21 | 2a ultramarine | 3.75 | 3.25 |
| 9 | A27 | 1r gray | 190.00 | 450.00 |
| | | **Wmk. 38** | | |
| 10 | A9 | 4a green | 67.50 | 325.00 |

### Black Overprint

**1885-97     Wmk. 39**

| | | | | |
|---|---|---|---|---|
| 11 | A17 | ½a green | .90 | .20 |
| 12 | A18 | 9p rose ('92) | 3.00 | 5.25 |
| 13 | A19 | 1a violet brown | 4.50 | 1.50 |

| 14 | A20 | 1a6p bister brn | 2.50 | 6.00 |
|---|---|---|---|---|
| a. | | "ABHA" | 450.00 | |
| 15 | A21 | 2a ultramarine | 4.50 | 3.00 |
| 16 | A22 | 3a orange | 16.00 | 32.50 |
| 17 | A23 | 4a olive green | 9.00 | 5.00 |
| 18 | A25 | 8a red lilac | 6.00 | 5.25 |
| 19 | A26 | 12a vio, *red* ('89) | 7.00 | 8.25 |
| 20 | A27 | 1r gray | 22.50 | 90.00 |
| 21 | A29 | 1r car rose & grn ('93) | 21.00 | 10.50 |
| a. | | "N BHA" | | |
| 22 | A30 | 2r brn & rose ('97) | 210.00 | 450.00 |
| 23 | A30 | 3r grn & brn ('97) | 210.00 | 550.00 |
| 24 | A30 | 5r vio & blk ('97) | 225.00 | 825.00 |

**Wmk. 38**

| 25 | A14 | 6a bister ('89) | 5.50 | 6.50 |
|---|---|---|---|---|
| | | Nos. 11-25 (15) | 747.40 | 1,998. |

*Nos. 7, 8, 9, 10, 13, and 18 have been reprinted. They usually bear the overprint "Specimen."*

**1900** — **Wmk. 39**

| 26 | A31 | 3p carmine rose | .45 | .20 |
|---|---|---|---|---|

**1903-09**

| 27 | A32 | 3p gray | 1.10 | .20 |
|---|---|---|---|---|
| 28 | A33 | ½a green | 1.60 | 1.00 |
| a. | | "NABH" | 1,650. | |
| 29 | A34 | 1a car rose | 2.50 | 2.25 |
| 30 | A35 | 2a violet | 3.75 | 5.25 |
| 30A | A36 | 2a6p ultra | 29.00 | 130.00 |
| 31 | A37 | 3a brown orange | 2.40 | .60 |
| 32 | A38 | 4a olive green | 7.00 | 2.50 |
| 33 | A39 | 6a bister | 6.00 | 30.00 |
| 34 | A40 | 8a red violet | 15.00 | 40.00 |
| 35 | A41 | 12a violet, *red* | 6.50 | 40.00 |
| 36 | A42 | 1r car rose & grn | 14.00 | 27.50 |
| | | Nos. 27-36 (11) | 88.85 | 279.30 |

**1907**

| 37 | A44 | ½a green | 2.25 | 1.90 |
|---|---|---|---|---|
| 38 | A45 | 1a carmine rose | 2.25 | 1.00 |

**1913**

| 40 | A46 | 3p gray | .75 | .75 |
|---|---|---|---|---|
| 41 | A47 | ½a green | .75 | .45 |
| 42 | A48 | 1a carmine rose | 1.60 | .20 |
| 43 | A49 | 2a violet | 1.50 | 1.50 |
| 44 | A51 | 3a brown orange | .75 | .45 |
| 45 | A52 | 4a olive green | 1.00 | 3.00 |
| 46 | A53 | 6a bister | 1.90 | 9.50 |
| 47 | A54 | 8a red violet | 9.50 | 9.00 |
| 48 | A55 | 12a claret | 4.50 | 35.00 |
| 49 | A56 | 1r green & red brn | 15.00 | 11.00 |
| | | Nos. 40-49 (10) | 37.25 | 70.85 |

**1924**

| 50 | A48 | 1a dark brown | 10.00 | 6.00 |
|---|---|---|---|---|

**India Stamps of 1926-35 Overprinted**

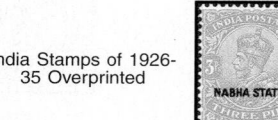

**1927-32** — **Wmk. 196**

| 51 | A46 | 3p slate ('32) | 2.50 | .20 |
|---|---|---|---|---|
| 52 | A47 | ½a green | 1.50 | .45 |
| 53 | A48 | 1a dark brown | 2.25 | .20 |
| 54 | A60 | 2a dull violet ('32) | 3.75 | .50 |
| 55 | A57 | 2a6p buff ('32) | 1.75 | 14.00 |
| 56 | A51 | 3a blue ('30) | 4.50 | 2.10 |
| 57 | A61 | 4a olive green ('32) | 6.75 | 3.75 |

**Overprinted**

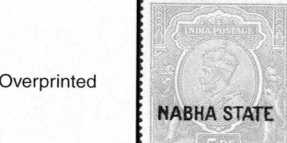

| 58 | A56 | 2r brown org & car rose ('32) | 47.50 | 210.00 |
|---|---|---|---|---|
| 59 | A56 | 5r dk violet & ultra ('32) | 110.00 | 600.00 |
| | | Nos. 51-59 (9) | 180.50 | 831.20 |

**India Stamps of 1926-35 Overprinted**

---

**1936-37**

| 63 | A71 | ½a green | .75 | .60 |
|---|---|---|---|---|
| 64 | A68 | 9p dark green ('37) | 3.00 | 1.60 |
| 65 | A72 | 1a dark brown | .75 | .45 |
| 66 | A69 | 1a3p violet ('37) | 3.50 | 11.00 |
| 67 | A51 | 3a car rose ('37) | 5.00 | 25.00 |
| 68 | A52 | 4a olive green ('37) | 7.50 | 7.50 |
| | | Nos. 63-68 (6) | 20.50 | 46.15 |
| | | Set, never hinged | 25.00 | |

**Same Overprint in Black on 1937 Stamps of India**

**1938-39** — **Perf. 13½x14**

| 69 | A80 | 3p slate | 11.00 | 2.25 |
|---|---|---|---|---|
| 70 | A80 | ½a brown | 8.75 | 2.50 |
| 71 | A80 | 9p green | 25.00 | 7.50 |
| 72 | A80 | 1a carmine | 3.75 | 1.50 |
| 73 | A81 | 2a scarlet | 1.50 | 12.00 |
| 74 | A81 | 2a6p purple | 1.50 | 17.50 |
| 75 | A81 | 3a yel green | 1.75 | 9.00 |
| 76 | A81 | 3a6p ultramarine | 2.00 | 37.50 |
| 77 | A81 | 4a dark brown | 9.50 | 10.50 |
| 78 | A81 | 6a peacock blue | 4.00 | 40.00 |
| 79 | A81 | 8a blue violet | 2.75 | 37.50 |
| 80 | A81 | 12a car lake | 3.00 | 37.50 |

**Overprinted**

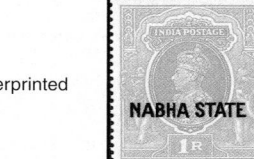

| 81 | A82 | 1r brown & slate | 15.00 | 52.50 |
|---|---|---|---|---|
| 82 | A82 | 2r dk brn & dk vio | 37.50 | 175.00 |
| 83 | A82 | 5r dp ultra & dk green | 50.00 | 300.00 |
| 84 | A82 | 10r rose car & dk vio ('39) | 75.00 | 600.00 |
| 85 | A82 | 15r dk grn & dk brn ('39) | 240.00 | 1,250. |
| 86 | A82 | 25r dk vio & blue vio ('39) | 175.00 | 1,250. |
| | | Nos. 69-86 (18) | 667.00 | 3,842. |
| | | Set, never hinged | 1,200. | |

**India Stamps of 1937 Overprinted in Black**

**1942** — **Perf. 13½x14**

| 87 | A80 | 3p slate | 50.00 | 9.00 |
|---|---|---|---|---|
| 88 | A80 | ½a brown | 100.00 | 10.50 |
| 89 | A80 | 9p green | 14.00 | 24.00 |
| 90 | A80 | 1a carmine | 15.00 | 6.50 |
| | | Nos. 87-90 (4) | 179.00 | 50.00 |
| | | Set, never hinged | 210.00 | |

**Same on India Nos. 168-179**

**1942-46** — **Wmk. 196**

| 100 | A83 | 3p slate | 1.50 | 1.50 |
|---|---|---|---|---|
| 101 | A83 | ½a rose vio ('43) | 3.75 | 2.50 |
| 102 | A83 | 9p lt green ('43) | 3.00 | 2.50 |
| 103 | A83 | 1a car rose ('46) | 1.25 | 6.50 |
| 104 | A84 | 1a3p bister ('44) | 1.25 | 5.50 |
| 105 | A84 | 1½a dark pur ('43) | 3.00 | 4.50 |
| 106 | A84 | 2a scarlet ('44) | 1.40 | 6.50 |
| 107 | A84 | 3a violet ('44) | 8.00 | 8.00 |
| 108 | A84 | 3½a ultramarine ('43) | 21.00 | 100.00 |
| 109 | A85 | 4a choc ('43) | 2.25 | 1.50 |
| 110 | A85 | 6a pck blue ('44) | 17.50 | 82.50 |
| 111 | A85 | 8a blue vio ('44) | 16.00 | 62.50 |
| 112 | A85 | 12a car lake ('44) | 14.00 | 100.00 |
| | | Nos. 100-112 (13) | 93.90 | 384.00 |
| | | Set, never hinged | 110.00 | |

---

**OFFICIAL STAMPS**

**Indian Stamps Overprinted in Black**

**1885** — **Wmk. 39** — **Perf. 14**

| O1 | A17 | ½a green | 7.50 | 2.25 |
|---|---|---|---|---|
| O2 | A19 | 1a violet brown | 1.00 | .30 |
| O3 | A21 | 2a ultra | 125.00 | 250.00 |
| | | Nos. O1-O3 (3) | 133.50 | 252.55 |

*The reprints have the same measurements as the reprints of the regular issue of the same date.*

---

**Indian Stamps Overprinted**

**1885** — **Red Overprint**

| O4 | A17 | ½a green | 11.00 | 8.25 |
|---|---|---|---|---|
| O5 | A21 | 2a ultramarine | 2.40 | .80 |

**1885-97** — **Black Overprint**

| O6 | A17 | ½a green | .60 | .20 |
|---|---|---|---|---|
| a. | | Period after "SERVICE" | 190.00 | 3.25 |
| O7 | A19 | 1a violet brown | 3.00 | .35 |
| a. | | "NABHA STATE" double | 2,750. | 375.00 |
| b. | | Period after "SERVICE" | 13.50 | 1.10 |
| O8 | A21 | 2a ultra | 5.00 | 2.50 |
| O9 | A22 | 3a orange | 37.50 | 140.00 |
| O10 | A23 | 4a olive green | 5.25 | 2.25 |
| O11 | A25 | 8a red vio ('89) | 4.00 | 2.25 |
| O12 | A26 | 12a vio, *red* ('89) | 9.50 | 32.50 |
| O13 | A27 | 1r gray ('89) | 62.50 | 525.00 |
| O14 | A29 | 1r car rose & grn ('97) | 24.00 | 35.00 |

**Wmk. 38**

| O15 | A14 | 6a bister ('89) | 32.50 | 52.50 |
|---|---|---|---|---|
| | | Nos. O6-O15 (10) | 183.85 | 792.55 |

*Nos. O4, O5, and O7 have been reprinted. They usually bear the overprint "Specimen."*

**1903-06** — **Wmk. 39**

| O16 | A32 | 3p gray ('06) | 3.75 | 25.00 |
|---|---|---|---|---|
| O17 | A33 | ½a green | 1.20 | .50 |
| O18 | A34 | 1a carmine rose | 1.20 | .20 |
| O19 | A35 | 2a violet | 5.00 | 2.10 |
| O20 | A38 | 4a olive green | 2.40 | .75 |
| O21 | A40 | 8a red violet | 2.50 | 2.25 |
| O22 | A42 | 1r car rose & grn | 2.50 | 3.75 |
| | | Nos. O16-O22 (7) | 18.55 | 34.55 |

**1907**

| O23 | A44 | ½a green | 2.50 | .75 |
|---|---|---|---|---|
| O24 | A45 | 1a carmine rose | 1.00 | .40 |

**1913**

| O25 | A52 | 4a olive green | 17.50 | 100.00 |
|---|---|---|---|---|
| O26 | A56 | 1r grn & red brn | 92.50 | 750.00 |

**India Stamps of 1911-26 Overprinted:**

a      b

**1913**

| O27 | A46(a) | 3p gray | 1.60 | 15.00 |
|---|---|---|---|---|
| O28 | A47(a) | ½a green | 1.00 | .20 |
| O29 | A48(a) | 1a carmine rose | .90 | .20 |
| O30 | A49(a) | 2a violet | 1.90 | .20 |
| O31 | A52(a) | 4a olive green | 1.50 | .90 |
| O32 | A54(a) | 8a red violet | 2.50 | 3.00 |
| O33 | A56(b) | 1r grn & red brn | 10.00 | 6.50 |
| | | Nos. O27-O33 (7) | 19.40 | 26.00 |

**India Stamps of 1926-35 Overprinted**

**Perf. 13½x14, 14**

**1932-45** — **Wmk. 196**

| O34 | A46 | 3p slate | .30 | .20 |
|---|---|---|---|---|
| O35 | A72 | 1a dark brown ('35) | .30 | .20 |
| O36 | A52 | 4a olive green ('45) | 35.00 | 3.75 |
| O37 | A54 | 8a red violet ('37) | 1.50 | 4.00 |
| | | Nos. O34-O37 (4) | 37.10 | 8.15 |

**Same Overprint in Black on India Stamps of 1937**

**1938**

| O38 | A80 | 9p green | 6.00 | 6.00 |
|---|---|---|---|---|
| | | Mever hinged | 7.00 | |
| O39 | A80 | 1a carmine | 22.50 | 1.60 |
| | | Mever hinged | 27.50 | |

---

**Official Stamps of India 1939-43 Overprinted in Black**

**1942-44** — **Perf. 13½x14**

| O40 | O8 | 3p slate | 1.50 | 3.00 |
|---|---|---|---|---|
| O41 | O8 | ½a brown ('43) | 1.40 | .45 |
| O42 | O8 | ½a dk rose vio ('44) | 5.50 | 2.25 |
| O43 | O8 | 9p green ('43) | 1.50 | .45 |
| O44 | O8 | 1a car rose ('43) | .75 | .25 |
| O45 | O8 | 1 ½a dull purple ('43) | .85 | .60 |
| O46 | O8 | 2a scarlet ('43) | 2.75 | 2.25 |
| O47 | O8 | 4a dark brown ('43) | 4.25 | 5.25 |
| O48 | O8 | 8a blue violet ('43) | 6.75 | 30.00 |

**India Nos. 162-164 Overprinted in Black**

| O49 | A82 | 1r brown & slate | 10.50 | 62.50 |
|---|---|---|---|---|
| O50 | A82 | 2r dk brn & dk vio | 37.50 | 275.00 |
| O51 | A82 | 5r dp ultra & dk green | 210.00 | 825.00 |
| | | Nos. O40-O51 (12) | 283.25 | 1,207. |
| | | Set, never hinged | 350.00 | |

---

# PATIALA

ˌpət-ē-ˈäl-ə

LOCATION — A State of India in the central Punjab
AREA — 5,942 sq. mi.
POP. — 1,936,259 (1941)
CAPITAL — Patiala

The varieties with small letters in the overprint are not listed as the letters are merely broken and not from another font.

**Indian Stamps Overprinted in Red**

**1884** — **Wmk. 39** — **Perf. 14**

| 1 | A17 | ½a green | 6.00 | 7.00 |
|---|---|---|---|---|
| a. | | Double ovpt., one horiz. | 4,750. | 1,200. |
| 2 | A19 | 1a violet brown | 75.00 | 110.00 |
| a. | | Double overprint | | |
| b. | | Double ovpt., one in black | 1,050. | |
| c. | | Pair, one as "b," one without overprint | | |
| 3 | A21 | 2a ultra | 19.00 | 24.00 |
| 4 | A25 | 8a red lilac | 650.00 | 1,600. |
| a. | | Double ovpt., one in black | 190.00 | 650.00 |
| c. | | Overprint reversed | | |
| d. | | Pair like "a," one with overprint reversed | | |
| 5 | A27 | 1r gray | 225.00 | 950.00 |

**Wmk. 38**

| 6 | A9 | 4a green | 140.00 | 150.00 |
|---|---|---|---|---|
| | | Nos. 1-6 (6) | 1,115. | 2,841. |

**Indian Stamps Overprinted in Red**

**1885** — **Wmk. 39**

| 7 | A17 | ½a green | 3.25 | .45 |
|---|---|---|---|---|
| a. | | "AUTTIALLA" | 24.00 | 52.50 |
| c. | | "STATE" only | | |
| 8 | A21 | 2a ultra | 9.00 | 2.50 |
| a. | | "AUTTIALLA" | 62.50 | |
| 9 | A27 | 1r gray | 24.00 | 125.00 |
| a. | | "AUTTIALLA" | 650.00 | |

**Wmk. 38**

| 10 | A9 | 4a green | 6.00 | 6.25 |
|---|---|---|---|---|
| a. | | Double overprint, one in black | 375.00 | |

**b.** Pair, one as "a," one with black overprint

## Same, Overprinted in Black
### Wmk. 39

| | | | | |
|---|---|---|---|---|
| 11 | A19 | 1a violet brown | .90 | .45 |
| **a.** | | "AUTTIALLA" | 100.00 | |
| **c.** | | Double overprint, one in red | 17.50 | 140.00 |
| **d.** | | Pair, one as "c," one without overprint | | |
| 12 | A25 | 8a red lilac | 35.00 | 82.50 |
| **a.** | | "AUTTIALLA" | 550.00 | |
| | | Nos. 7-12 (6) | 78.15 | 217.15 |

Nos. 7-12 have been reprinted. Most of them bear the word "Reprint." The few stamps that escaped the overprint cannot be distinguished from the originals.

The error "AUTTIALLA" has been reprinted in entire sheets, in red on the ½, 2, 4a and 1r and in black on the ½, 1, 2, 4, 8a and 1r. "STATE" is 7¾mm long, instead of 8½mm. Most stamps are overprinted "Reprint."

## Same, Overprinted in Black

### 1891-96

| | | | | |
|---|---|---|---|---|
| 13 | A17 | ½a green | .75 | .20 |
| 14 | A18 | 9p rose | 1.50 | 3.25 |
| 15 | A19 | 1a violet brown | 2.10 | .45 |
| **a.** | | "STATE" only | 300.00 | 625.00 |
| 16 | A20 | 1a6p bister brown | 2.10 | 3.00 |
| 17 | A21 | 2a ultra | 3.25 | 1.50 |
| 18 | A22 | 3a orange | 3.75 | 1.10 |
| 19 | A23 | 4a olive grn ('96) | 3.75 | 1.10 |
| **a.** | | "STATE" only | 750.00 | 375.00 |
| 20 | A25 | 8a red violet ('96) | 5.50 | 24.00 |
| 21 | A26 | 12a violet, red | 3.75 | 24.00 |
| 22 | A29 | 1r car rose & grn ('96) | 6.50 | 82.50 |
| 23 | A30 | 3r brn & rose ('95) | 210.00 | 1,250. |
| 24 | A30 | 3r grn & brn ('95) | 290.00 | 1,350. |
| 25 | A30 | 5r vio & bl ('95) | 325.00 | 1,400. |

### Wmk. 38

| | | | | |
|---|---|---|---|---|
| 26 | A14 | 6a bister | 3.75 | 22.50 |
| | | Nos. 13-26 (14) | 861.70 | 4,163. |

### 1899
### Wmk. 39

| | | | | |
|---|---|---|---|---|
| 27 | A31 | 3p carmine rose | .45 | .20 |
| **a.** | | Pair, one without overprint | 6,000. | |

### 1902

| | | | | |
|---|---|---|---|---|
| 28 | A17 | ½a light green | 1.50 | .90 |
| 29 | A19 | 1a carmine rose | 3.75 | 2.50 |

### 1903-06

| | | | | |
|---|---|---|---|---|
| 31 | A32 | 3p gray | .60 | .20 |
| 32 | A33 | ½a green | 1.60 | .20 |
| 33 | A34 | 1a carmine rose | 2.10 | .20 |
| **a.** | | Pair, one without overprint | 1,500. | |
| 34 | A35 | 2a violet | 2.40 | 1.00 |
| 35 | A37 | 3a brown orange | 2.40 | .60 |
| 36 | A38 | 4a olive green ('06) | 4.00 | 2.25 |
| 37 | A39 | 6a bister ('05) | 5.00 | 15.00 |
| 38 | A40 | 8a red violet ('06) | 5.50 | 4.50 |
| 39 | A41 | 12a vio, red ('06) | 11.00 | 40.00 |
| 40 | A42 | 1r car rose & grn ('05) | 6.50 | 9.00 |
| | | Nos. 31-40 (10) | 41.10 | 72.85 |

### 1908

| | | | | |
|---|---|---|---|---|
| 41 | A44 | ½a green | .60 | .35 |
| 42 | A45 | 1a carmine rose | 2.50 | 1.50 |

### 1912-14

| | | | | |
|---|---|---|---|---|
| 43 | A46 | 3p gray | .35 | .20 |
| 44 | A47 | ½a green | 1.00 | .25 |
| 45 | A48 | 1a carmine rose | 2.40 | .25 |
| 46 | A49 | 2a violet | 2.25 | 2.25 |
| 47 | A51 | 3a brown orange | 3.75 | 2.50 |
| 48 | A52 | 4a olive green | 5.25 | 5.25 |
| 49 | A53 | 6a bister | 3.00 | 6.50 |
| 50 | A54 | 8a red violet | 4.50 | 4.50 |
| 51 | A55 | 12a claret | 5.50 | 15.00 |
| 52 | A56 | 1r green & red brn | 14.00 | 22.50 |
| | | Nos. 43-52 (10) | 42.00 | 59.20 |

### 1922-26

| | | | | |
|---|---|---|---|---|
| 53 | A48 | 1a dk brown ('23) | 4.00 | .75 |
| 54 | A58 | 1½a chocolate | .45 | .80 |
| 55 | A51 | 3a ultra ('26) | 5.00 | 14.00 |
| 56 | A56 | 2r yel brn & car rose ('26) | 21.00 | 225.00 |
| 57 | A56 | 5r vio & ultra ('26) | 52.50 | 300.00 |
| | | Nos. 53-57 (5) | 82.95 | 540.55 |

## India Stamps of 1926-35 Overprinted

### 1928-34
### Wmk. 196

| | | | | |
|---|---|---|---|---|
| 60 | A46 | 3p slate | 3.00 | .20 |
| 61 | A47 | ½a green | .35 | .20 |
| 62 | A68 | 9p dark green | 3.25 | 1.50 |
| 63 | A48 | 1a dark brown | 1.10 | .35 |
| 64 | A69 | 1a3p violet | 4.50 | .20 |
| 65 | A60 | 2a dull violet | 2.50 | .60 |
| 66 | A57 | 2a6p buff | 7.00 | 4.00 |
| 67 | A51 | 3a blue | 4.50 | 4.00 |
| 68 | A61 | 4a olive green | 7.50 | 3.00 |
| 69 | A54 | 8a red violet | 10.50 | 6.00 |

## Overprinted

| | | | | |
|---|---|---|---|---|
| 70 | A56 | 1r green & brown | 10.50 | 15.00 |
| 71 | A56 | 2r buff & car rose | 16.00 | 82.50 |
| | | Nos. 60-71 (12) | 70.70 | 117.55 |

## India Stamps of 1926-35 Overprinted Like Nos. 60-69

### 1935-37
### Perf. 14

| | | | | |
|---|---|---|---|---|
| 75 | A71 | ½a green ('37) | 1.00 | .45 |
| 76 | A72 | 1a dk brown ('36) | 1.40 | .25 |
| 77 | A49 | 2a ver ('36) | .50 | 2.25 |
| 78 | A51 | 3a car rose ('37) | 7.00 | 8.00 |
| 79 | A52 | 4a olive green | 2.25 | 3.50 |
| | | Nos. 75-79 (5) | 12.15 | 14.45 |
| | | Set, never hinged | 29.00 | |

## Same Overprint in Black on Stamps of India, 1937

### 1937-38
### Perf. 13½x14

| | | | | |
|---|---|---|---|---|
| 80 | A80 | 3p slate ('38) | 25.00 | .50 |
| 81 | A80 | ½a brown ('38) | 10.00 | .75 |
| 82 | A80 | 9p green | 6.25 | 1.50 |
| 83 | A80 | 1a carmine | 3.50 | .25 |
| 84 | A81 | 2a scarlet ('38) | 1.90 | 14.00 |
| 85 | A81 | 2a6p purple ('38) | 7.00 | 30.00 |
| 86 | A81 | 3a yel green ('38) | 7.50 | 13.50 |
| 87 | A81 | 3a6p ultra ('38) | 8.00 | 37.50 |
| 88 | A81 | 4a dark brown ('38) | 29.00 | 25.00 |
| 89 | A81 | 6a pck blue ('38) | 30.00 | 90.00 |
| 90 | A81 | 8a blue violet ('38) | 32.50 | 62.50 |
| 91 | A81 | 12a car lake ('38) | 30.00 | 105.00 |

## Overprinted Like Nos. 70-71

### 1938

| | | | | |
|---|---|---|---|---|
| 92 | A82 | 1r brown & slate | 35.00 | 62.50 |
| 93 | A82 | 2r dk brn & dk vio | 35.00 | 160.00 |
| 94 | A82 | 5r dp ultra & dk green | 47.50 | 375.00 |
| 95 | A82 | 10r rose car & dk vio | 62.50 | 600.00 |
| 96 | A82 | 15r dk grn & dk brn | 150.00 | 950.00 |
| 97 | A82 | 25r dk vio & bl vio | 175.00 | 950.00 |
| | | Nos. 80-97 (18) | 695.65 | 3,478. |
| | | Set, never hinged | 850.00 | |

## India Nos. 150-153 Overprinted in Black

### 1942-43
### Perf. 13½x14

| | | | | |
|---|---|---|---|---|
| 98 | A80 | 3p slate | 13.50 | 4.00 |
| 99 | A80 | ½a brown ('43) | 8.00 | 3.25 |
| 100 | A80 | 9p green ('43) | 375.00 | 12.00 |
| 101 | A80 | 1a carmine | 30.00 | 3.75 |
| | | Nos. 98-101 (4) | 426.50 | 23.00 |
| | | Set, never hinged | 515.00 | |

## India Stamps of 1941-43 with same Overprint in Black

### 1942-47
### Perf. 13½x14

| | | | | |
|---|---|---|---|---|
| 102 | A83 | 3p slate | 5.00 | .20 |
| 103 | A83 | ½a rose violet ('43) | 5.00 | .20 |
| 104 | A83 | 9p lt green ('43) | 1.90 | .20 |
| **a.** | | Pair, one without overprint | 4,750. | |
| 105 | A83 | 1a car rose ('46) | 1.25 | .20 |
| 106 | A84 | 1a3p bister ('43) | 2.00 | 5.25 |
| 107 | A84 | 1½a dk purple ('43) | 16.00 | 5.50 |
| 108 | A84 | 2a scarlet ('46) | 11.00 | .75 |
| 109 | A84 | 3a violet ('46) | 10.00 | 3.75 |
| 110 | A84 | 3½a ultra ('46) | 24.00 | 57.50 |
| 111 | A85 | 4a choc ('46) | 11.00 | 6.50 |
| 112 | A85 | 6a pck blue ('46) | 4.25 | 45.00 |
| 113 | A85 | 8a blue vio ('46) | 3.75 | 22.50 |
| 114 | A85 | 12a car lake ('45) | 30.00 | 125.00 |

## India No. 162 Overprinted in Black

| | | | | |
|---|---|---|---|---|
| 115 | A82 | 1r brown & slate ('47) | 19.00 | 120.00 |
| | | Nos. 102-115 (14) | 144.15 | 392.55 |
| | | Set, never hinged | 170.00 | |

## OFFICIAL STAMPS

### Indian Stamps Overprinted in Black and Red

### 1884
### Wmk. 39
### Perf. 14

| | | | | |
|---|---|---|---|---|
| O1 | A17 | ½a green | 27.50 | .60 |
| O2 | A19 | 1a vio brown | 1.50 | .20 |
| **a.** | | "SERVICE" double | 3,000. | 950.00 |
| **b.** | | "SERVICE" inverted | | 2,500. |
| **c.** | | "PUTTIALLA STATE" dbl. | | 175.00 |
| **d.** | | "PUTTIALLA STATE" invtd. | 3,000. | 400.00 |
| O3 | A21 | 2a ultra | 7,500. | 175.00 |

## Same, Overprinted in Red or Black:

a     b

### 1885-90

| | | | | |
|---|---|---|---|---|
| O4 | A17(a) | ½a green (R & Bk) | 2.25 | .35 |
| **a.** | | "AUTTIALLA" | 80.00 | 25.00 |
| **d.** | | "SERVICE" double | | 1,050. |
| O5 | A17(b) | ½a green (Bk) | 2.25 | .20 |
| O6 | A19(a) | 1a vio brn (Bk) | 2.25 | .20 |
| **a.** | | "AUTTIALLA" | 1,050. | 72.50 |
| **c.** | | "SERVICE" dble., one invtd. | | 900.00 |
| **d.** | | "SERVICE" double | 3,000. | |
| O7 | A21(b) | 2a ultra (R) | 1.10 | .60 |
| **a.** | | "SERVICE" dbl., one invtd. | 45.00 | 290.00 |
| | | Nos. O4-O7 (4) | 7.85 | 1.35 |

There are reprints of Nos. O4, O6 and O7. That of No. O4 has "SERVICE" overprinted in red in large letters and that of No. O6 has the same overprint in black. The originals have the word in small black letters. The reprints of No. O7, except those overprinted "Reprint," cannot be distinguished from the originals. These three reprints also exist with the error "AUTTIALLA."

## Same, Overprinted in Black

### 1891-1900

| | | | | |
|---|---|---|---|---|
| O8 | A17 | ½a green ('95) | .75 | .20 |
| **b.** | | "SERVICE" inverted | 90.00 | |
| O9 | A19 | 1a vio brown ('00) | 9.00 | .20 |
| **a.** | | "SERVICE" inverted | 90.00 | |
| O10 | A21 | 2a ultramarine | 5.00 | 3.25 |
| **a.** | | "SERVICE" inverted | 90.00 | 300.00 |
| O11 | A22 | 3a orange | 3.75 | 5.00 |
| O12 | A23 | 4a olive green | 3.00 | .45 |
| O13 | A25 | 8a red violet | 5.25 | 2.50 |
| O14 | A26 | 12a violet, red | 3.50 | .80 |
| O15 | A27 | 1r gray | 3.75 | 1.00 |

### Wmk. 38

| | | | | |
|---|---|---|---|---|
| O16 | A14 | 6a bister | 2.40 | .50 |
| | | Nos. O8-O16 (9) | 36.40 | 13.90 |

### 1902
### Wmk. 39

| | | | | |
|---|---|---|---|---|
| O17 | A19 | 1a carmine rose | 1.40 | .20 |

### 1903

| | | | | |
|---|---|---|---|---|
| O18 | A29 | 1r car rose & green | 9.00 | 15.00 |

### 1903-09

| | | | | |
|---|---|---|---|---|
| O19 | A32 | 3p gray | .60 | .20 |
| O20 | A33 | ½a green | 1.50 | .20 |
| O21 | A34 | 1a carmine rose | .90 | .20 |
| O22 | A35 | 2a violet | 1.20 | .20 |
| O23 | A37 | 3a brown orange | 6.00 | 5.25 |
| O24 | A38 | 4a olive green ('05) | 4.00 | .25 |
| O25 | A40 | 8a red violet | 2.50 | 1.10 |
| O26 | A42 | 1r car rose & grn ('06) | 3.00 | 1.20 |
| | | Nos. O19-O26 (8) | 19.70 | 8.60 |

### 1907

| | | | | |
|---|---|---|---|---|
| O27 | A44 | ½a green | .75 | .25 |
| O28 | A45 | 1a carmine rose | .90 | .20 |

### India Stamps of 1911-26 Overprinted:

a     b

### 1913-26

| | | | | |
|---|---|---|---|---|
| O29 | A46(a) | 3p gray | .25 | .20 |
| O30 | A47(a) | ½a green | .20 | .20 |
| O31 | A48(a) | 1a car rose | .20 | .20 |
| O32 | A49(a) | 2a violet | 1.40 | 1.10 |
| O33 | A52(a) | 4a olive green | .75 | .50 |
| O34 | A54(a) | 8a red violet | .80 | 1.00 |
| O35 | A56(b) | 1r grn & red brn | 2.10 | 2.10 |
| O36 | A56(b) | 2r yel brn & car rose ('26) | 27.50 | 75.00 |
| O37 | A56(b) | 5r vio & ultra ('26) | 17.50 | 35.00 |
| | | Nos. O29-O37 (9) | 50.70 | 115.30 |

### Same Overprint on India Nos. 83 and 89

### 1925-26

| | | | | |
|---|---|---|---|---|
| O38 | A48(a) | 1a dark brown | 11.00 | 1.50 |
| O39 | A53(a) | 6a bister ('26) | 2.50 | 3.75 |

### India Stamps of 1926-35 Overprinted

### 1927-36
### Wmk. 196

| | | | | |
|---|---|---|---|---|
| O40 | A46 | 3p slate | .20 | .20 |
| O41 | A47 | ½a green | 1.50 | .80 |
| O42 | A48 | 1a dark brown | .20 | .20 |
| O43 | A69 | 1a3p violet | .60 | .20 |
| O44 | A60 | 2a dull violet | .25 | .45 |
| O45 | A60 | 2a vermilion | .45 | .50 |
| O46 | A57 | 2a6p buff | 4.50 | .50 |
| O47 | A61 | 4a olive green | .75 | .45 |
| O48 | A54 | 8a red violet | 1.90 | 1.00 |

### Overprinted

| | | | | |
|---|---|---|---|---|
| O49 | A56 | 1r green & brown | 7.50 | 5.00 |
| O50 | A56 | 2r brn org & car rose ('36) | 24.00 | 62.50 |
| | | Nos. O40-O50 (11) | 41.85 | 71.80 |

### India Stamps of 1926-34 Overprinted

## 1935-36

| | | | | |
|---|---|---|---|---|
| O51 | A71 | ½a green ('36) | .20 | .20 |
| O52 | A72 | 1a dark brown ('36) | .45 | .45 |
| O53 | A49 | 2a vermilion | .30 | .45 |
| a. | | Small die | 21.00 | 7.50 |
| O54 | A52 | 4a olive green ('36) | 3.50 | 2.50 |
| | | Nos. O51-O54 (4) | 4.45 | 3.60 |
| | | Set, never hinged | 5.00 | |

Same Overprint on India #151-153

## 1938-39      Perf. 13½x14

| | | | | |
|---|---|---|---|---|
| O55 | A80 | ½a brown ('39) | .95 | .30 |
| O56 | A80 | 9p green ('39) | 16.00 | 95.00 |
| O57 | A80 | 1a carmine | .95 | .60 |
| | | Nos. O55-O57 (3) | 17.90 | 95.90 |
| | | Set, never hinged | 22.00 | |

India No. 136
Surcharged in Black

## 1939      Perf. 14

| | | | | |
|---|---|---|---|---|
| O58 | A69 | 1a on 1a3p violet | 15.00 | 5.25 |
| | | Never hinged | 18.00 | |

"SERVICE" measures 9¼mm.

No. 64 Surcharged in
Black     **1ᴬ SERVICE 1ᴬ**

## 1940

| | | | | |
|---|---|---|---|---|
| O59 | A69 | 1a on 1a3p violet | 12.50 | 5.00 |
| | | Never hinged | 15.00 | |

"SERVICE" measures 8½mm.

India Nos. 162-
164 Overprinted

**PATIALA STATE**
**SERVICE**

## Perf. 13½x14

| | | | | |
|---|---|---|---|---|
| O60 | A82 | 1r brown & slate | 1.25 | 10.50 |
| O61 | A82 | 2r dk brn & dk vio | 7.50 | 7.50 |
| O62 | A82 | 5r dp ultra & dk grn | 21.00 | 95.00 |
| | | Set, never hinged | 36.00 | |

India Official Stamps of
1939-43 Overprinted

## 1940-45

| | | | | |
|---|---|---|---|---|
| O63 | O8 | 3p slate ('41) | 2.25 | .20 |
| O64 | O8 | ½a brown | 6.25 | .20 |
| O65 | O8 | ½a dk rose vio ('43) | 1.25 | .20 |
| O66 | O8 | 9p green | 1.25 | .75 |
| O67 | O8 | 1a carmine rose | 4.00 | .20 |
| O68 | O8 | 1a3p bister ('41) | 1.50 | .35 |
| O69 | O8 | 1½a dull purple ('45) | 8.00 | 1.90 |
| O70 | O8 | 2a scarlet ('41) | 12.50 | .50 |
| O71 | O8 | 2½a purple ('41) | 4.75 | 1.50 |
| O72 | O8 | 4a dk brown ('45) | 2.25 | 3.75 |
| O73 | O8 | 8a blue violet ('45) | 6.25 | 9.00 |

India Nos. 162-
164 Overprinted
in Black

**PATIALA**
**SERVICE**

| | | | | |
|---|---|---|---|---|
| O74 | A82 | 1r brn & slate ('43) | 6.25 | 16.00 |
| O75 | A82 | 2r dk brn & dk vio ('45) | 16.00 | 95.00 |
| O76 | A82 | 5r dp ultra & dk grn ('45) | 26.00 | 125.00 |
| | | Nos. O63-O76 (14) | 98.50 | 254.55 |
| | | Set, never hinged | 145.00 | |

---

# NATIVE FEUDATORY STATES

**NATIVE FEUDATORY STATES**
These stamps had franking power solely in the states in which they were issued, except for Cochin and Travancore which had a reciprocal postal agreement.

---

## ALWAR

'əl-wər

LOCATION — A Feudatory State of India, lying southwest of Delhi in the Jaipur Residency.
AREA — 3,158 sq. mi.
POP. — 749,751.
CAPITAL — Alwar

Katar (Indian Dagger) — A1

## 1877   Unwmk.   Litho.   Rouletted

| | | | | |
|---|---|---|---|---|
| 1 | A1 | ¼a ultramarine | 7.00 | 1.60 |
| a. | | ¼a blue | 7.00 | 1.60 |
| 2 | A1 | 1a brown | 5.25 | 1.90 |
| a. | | 1a yellow brown | 16.00 | 8.25 |
| b. | | 1a red brown | 5.00 | 2.25 |

### Redrawn

## 1899-1901     Pin-perf. 12

| | | | | |
|---|---|---|---|---|
| 3 | A1 | ¼a sl blue, wide margins | 12.50 | 4.50 |
| a. | | Horiz. pair, imperf. btwn. | 600.00 | 750.00 |
| b. | | Vert. pair, imperf. btwn. | 1,200. | 1,250. |
| 4 | A1 | ¼a yel grn, narrow margins ('01) | 11.00 | 4.00 |
| a. | | Horiz. pair, imperf. btwn. | | 950.00 |
| b. | | Imperf, pair | 950.00 | |
| c. | | ¼a emer, wide margins ('99) | 600.00 | |
| d. | | ¼a emer, narrow margins | 5.25 | 4.75 |
| e. | | As "d," imperf, pair | 550.00 | |
| f. | | As "d," vert. pair, imperf between | 500.00 | |
| g. | | As "d," horiz. pair, imperf between | 450.00 | 525.00 |
| h. | | As "d," vert. pair, imperf horiz. | 450.00 | 525.00 |

Nos. 3 and 4b are printed farther apart in the sheet.
On Nos. 3 and 4, the shading of the left border line is missing.
Nos. 1 to 4 occasionally show portions of the papermaker's watermark, W. T. & Co.
Alwar stamps became obsolete in 1902.

---

## BAMRA

'bäm-rə

LOCATION — A Feudatory State in the Eastern States, Orissa States Agency, Bengal.
AREA — 1,988 sq. mi.
POP. — 151,259
CAPITAL — Deogarh

Stamps of Bamra were issued without gum.

A1

A2

## 1888   Unwmk.   Typeset   Imperf.

| | | | | |
|---|---|---|---|---|
| 1 | A1 | ¼a black, yellow | 700.00 | |
| a. | | "g" inverted | 7,000. | |
| 2 | A1 | ¼a black, rose | 125.00 | |
| a. | | "g" inverted | 2,400. | |
| 3 | A1 | 1a black, blue | 100.00 | |
| a. | | "g" inverted | 2,100. | |
| 4 | A1 | 2a black, green | 140.00 | 550.00 |
| a. | | "postge" | 2,400. | |
| 5 | A1 | 4a black, yellow | 120.00 | 550.00 |
| a. | | "postge" | 2,250. | |
| 6 | A1 | 8a black, rose | 72.50 | |
| a. | | "postge" | 1,900. | |
| | | Nos. 1-6 (6) | 1,257. | |

All values may be found with the scroll inverted, and with the long end of the scroll pointing to the right or left.
On No. 5 the last character on the 3rd line is a vertical line. On No. 1 it is not vertical.
On No. 2 the last character on the 3rd line looks like a backwards "R" with a bent leg. On No. 6 it looks like an apostrophe.
*Nos. 1 and 2 have been reprinted in blocks of 8 and Nos. 1-6 in blocks of 20. In the reprints the 4th character of the native inscription often has the curved upper line broken at the left, but in many instances comparison with photographic reproductions of the original settings is the only certain test.*

## 1890

| | | | | |
|---|---|---|---|---|
| 7 | A2 | ¼a black, rose lilac | 7.00 | 9.00 |
| a. | | "Quarter" | 32.50 | 57.50 |
| b. | | "e" of "Postage" inverted | 32.50 | 57.50 |
| c. | | "Eeudatory" | 32.50 | 57.50 |
| 8 | A2 | ½a black, green | 5.25 | 5.25 |
| a. | | "Eeudatory" | 90.00 | 110.00 |
| b. | | "postage" with small "p" | 5.25 | 5.25 |
| 9 | A2 | 1a black, yellow | 6.50 | 5.00 |
| a. | | "Eeudatory" | 195.00 | 225.00 |
| b. | | "postage" with small "p" | 6.50 | 5.00 |
| c. | | "annas" | 300.00 | 325.00 |
| 10 | A2 | 2a black, rose lilac | 30.00 | 57.50 |
| a. | | "Eeudatory" | 275.00 | 550.00 |
| 11 | A2 | 4a black, bright rose | 9.50 | 12.50 |
| a. | | "Eeudatory" | 6,750. | |
| 12 | A2 | 8a black, rose lilac | 40.00 | 100.00 |
| a. | | "BAMBA" | 375.00 | 550.00 |
| b. | | "Foudatory" & "Postage" | 375.00 | 550.00 |
| c. | | "postage" with small "p" | 40.00 | 100.00 |
| 13 | A2 | 1r black, rose lilac | 100.00 | 160.00 |
| a. | | "BAMBA" | 650.00 | 825.00 |
| b. | | "Eeudatory" | 825.00 | 1,050. |
| c. | | "postage" with small "p" | 100.00 | 160.00 |
| | | Nos. 7-13 (7) | 198.25 | 349.25 |

## 1893

| | | | | |
|---|---|---|---|---|
| 14 | A2 | ¼a black, rose | 3.00 | 4.50 |
| a. | | "postage" with small "p" | 3.00 | 4.50 |
| 15 | A2 | ¼a black, magenta | 3.00 | 4.00 |
| a. | | "postage" with small "p" | 3.00 | 4.00 |
| d. | | "AMRA" of "BAMRA" inverted | 100.00 | 100.00 |
| e. | | "M" and 2nd "A" of "BAMRA" inverted | 140.00 | 140.00 |
| f. | | First "a" of "anna" inverted | 72.50 | 82.50 |
| 16 | A2 | 2a black, rose | 21.00 | 12.00 |
| a. | | "postage" with small "p" | 21.00 | 12.00 |
| 17 | A2 | 4a black, rose | 16.00 | 12.00 |
| a. | | "postage" with small "p" | 16.00 | 12.00 |
| b. | | "BAMBA" | 1,600. | 1,800. |
| 18 | A2 | 8a black, rose | 42.50 | 29.00 |
| a. | | "postage" with small "p" | 42.50 | 29.00 |
| 19 | A2 | 1r black, rose | 35.00 | 35.00 |
| a. | | "postage" with small "p" | 35.00 | 35.00 |
| | | Nos. 14-19 (6) | 120.50 | 96.50 |

The central ornament varies in size and may be found in various positions.
Bamra stamps became obsolete Dec. 31, 1894.

---

## BARWANI

bər-'wän-ē

LOCATION — A Feudatory State of Central India, in the Malwa Agency.
AREA — 1,178 sq. mi.
POP. — 141,110
CAPITAL — Barwani

The stamps of Barwani were all typographed and normally issued in booklets containing panes of four. Exceptions are noted (Nos. 14-15, 20-25). The majority were completely perforated, but some of the earlier printings were perforated only between the stamps, leaving one or two sides imperf. Nos. 1-25 were issued without gum. Many shades exist.

Rana Ranjit Singh
A1      A2

## 1921, April (?) Unwmk.   Pin-Perf 7
### Toned Medium Wove Paper
#### Clear Impression

| | | | | |
|---|---|---|---|---|
| 1 | A1 | ¼a dull Prus grn | 225.00 | 625.00 |
| 2 | A1 | ½a dull blue | 500.00 | 950.00 |

## 1921    Coarse Perf. 7 x Imperf.
### White Thin Wove Paper
#### Blurred Impression

| | | | | |
|---|---|---|---|---|
| 3 | A1 | ¼a dull green | 37.50 | 190.00 |
| 4 | A1 | ½a pale blue | 25.00 | 275.00 |

## 1921   Toned Laid Paper    Imperf.

| | | | | |
|---|---|---|---|---|
| 5 | A1 | ¼a light green | 30.00 | 125.00 |
| 6 | A1 | ½a light green | 8.25 | |
| a. | | Perf. 11, top or bottom only | 7.00 | |

## 1921    Coarse Perf. 7, 7 x Imperf.
### Thick Wove Paper
#### Very Blurred Impression

| | | | | |
|---|---|---|---|---|
| 7 | A1 | ¼a dull blue | 25.00 | |
| 8 | A1 | ½a dull green | 22.50 | |

In 1927 #7-8 were printed on thin hard paper.

## 1922      Perf. 7 x Imperf.
### Thick Glazed Paper

| | | | | |
|---|---|---|---|---|
| 9 | A1 | ¼a dull ultra | 160.00 | |

### Rough Perf. 11 x Imperf.

| | | | | |
|---|---|---|---|---|
| 10 | A2 | 1a vermilion | 3.75 | 30.00 |
| 11 | A2 | 2a violet | 3.25 | 37.50 |
| a. | | Double impression | 450.00 | |
| | | Nos. 9-11 (3) | 167.00 | 67.50 |

Shades of No. 11 include purple. No. 11 was also printed on thick dark toned paper.

## 1923-26      Perf.
### Wove, Laid Paper

| | | | | |
|---|---|---|---|---|
| 12 | A1 | ¼a grayish ultra, perf. 8½ | 2.40 | 72.50 |
| 13 | A1 | ¼a black, perf. 7 x imperf. | 110.00 | 550.00 |
| 14 | A1 | ¼a dull rose, perf. 11½-12 | 3.75 | 21.00 |
| 15 | A1 | ¼a dk bl, perf. 11 ('26) | 2.25 | 16.00 |
| 16 | A1 | ½a grn, perf. 11 x imperf. | 1.90 | 30.00 |
| | | Nos. 12-16 (5) | 120.30 | 689.50 |

No. 12 was also printed on pale gray thin toned paper.
No. 14 was printed on horizontally laid paper in horizontal sheets of 12 containing three panes of 4.
No. 15 was printed on vertically laid paper in horizontal sheets of 8.

Rana Ranjit Singh — A3

## 1927-28      Perf. 7
### Thin Wove Paper

| | | | | |
|---|---|---|---|---|
| 17 | A3 | 4a dull orange | 140.00 | 675.00 |

No. 17 was also printed in light brown on thick paper, pin-perf. 6, and in orange brown on thick paper, rough perf. 7.

## 1928      Coarse Perf. 7
### Thick Glazed Paper

| | | | | |
|---|---|---|---|---|
| 18 | A1 | ¼a bright brown | 16.00 | |
| 19 | A1 | ½a bright yel green | 37.50 | |

## 1928, Nov.     Rough Perf. 10½

| | | | | |
|---|---|---|---|---|
| 20 | A1 | ¼a deep ultra | 9.50 | |
| a. | | Tête bêche pair | 19.00 | |
| 21 | A1 | ½a yellow green | 7.00 | |
| a. | | Tête bêche pair | 14.00 | |

## 1929-31      Perf. 11

| | | | | |
|---|---|---|---|---|
| 22 | A1 | ¼a blue | 3.25 | 21.00 |
| a. | | ¼a ultramarine | 3.00 | 21.00 |
| 23 | A1 | ½a emerald green | 4.00 | 24.00 |
| 24 | A2 | 1a car pink ('31) | 24.00 | 67.50 |
| 25 | A3 | 4a salmon | 120.00 | 325.00 |
| | | Nos. 22-25 (4) | 151.25 | 437.50 |

Nos. 20-25 were printed in sheets of 8 (4x2).
No. 22 had five printings in various shades (bright to deep blue) in horizontal or vertical format.
No. 23 also printed in dark myrtle green.

Rana Ranjit Singh
A1      A2

Rana Devi Singh
A4          A5

| 1932-48 | | | Perf. 11, 12 | |
|---|---|---|---|---|
| | | **Glazed Paper** | | |
| 26 | A4 | ¼a dark gray | 3.75 | 35.00 |
| 27 | A4 | ½a blue green | 6.00 | 35.00 |
| 28 | A4 | 1a brown | 6.00 | 32.50 |
| a. | | 1a chocolate, perf. 8½ ('48) | 21.00 | 75.00 |
| 29 | A4 | 2a deep red violet | 5.50 | 62.50 |
| b. | | Perf. 12x11 | 12.50 | |
| | | 2a red lilac | | |
| 30 | A4 | 4a olive green | 9.00 | 62.50 |
| | | Nos. 26-30 (5) | 30.25 | 227.50 |

Types of 1921-27

| 1934-48 | | | Perf. 11 | |
|---|---|---|---|---|
| 31 | A1 | ¼a slate gray | 6.00 | 47.50 |
| 32 | A1 | ½a green | 6.50 | 60.00 |
| 33 | A2 | 1a dark brown | 16.00 | 29.00 |
| a. | | 1a brown, perf. 8½ ('48) | 15.00 | 75.00 |
| 34 | A2 | 2a brt purple ('38) | 125.00 | 490.00 |
| 35 | A2 | 2a rose car ('46) | 35.00 | 190.00 |
| 36 | A3 | 4a olive green | 20.00 | 67.50 |
| | | Nos. 31-36 (6) | 208.50 | 884.00 |

In the nine printings of Nos. 26-36, several plate settings spaced the cliches from 2 to 9mm apart. Hence the stamps come in different overall sizes. Not all values were in each printing. Values are for the commonest varieties.

No. 36 was also printed in pale sage green.

| 1938 | | | | |
|---|---|---|---|---|
| 37 | A5 | 1a dark brown | 50.00 | 110.00 |
| a. | | Booklet pane of 4 | — | |

Stamps of type A5 in red are revenues. Barwani stamps became obsolete 7/1/48.

---

## BHOPAL

bō-'päl

LOCATION — A Feudatory State of Central India, in the Bhopal Agency.
AREA — 6,924 sq. mi.
POP. — 995,745
CAPITAL — Bhopal

Inscription in Urdu in an octagon embossed on Nos. 1-83, in a circle embossed on Nos. 84-90. On designs A1-A3, A7, A11-A12, A14-A15, A19-A21 the embossing makes up the central part of the design.

The embossing may be found inverted or sideways.

Expect irregular perfs on the perforated stamps, Nos. 19-77, due to a combination of imperfect perforating methods and the fragility of the papers. Nos. 1-90 issued without gum.

A1          A2

Double Lined Frame

| 1876 | | Unwmk. | Litho. | Imperf. |
|---|---|---|---|---|
| 1 | A1 | ¼a black | 950.00 | 700.00 |
| a. | | "EGAM" | 2,750. | 2,400. |
| b. | | "BFGAM" | 2,750. | 2,400. |
| c. | | "BEGAN" | 1,500. | 1,250. |
| 2 | A1 | ½a red | 30.00 | 72.50 |
| a. | | "EGAM" | 110.00 | 250.00 |
| b. | | "BFGAM" | 110.00 | 250.00 |
| c. | | "BEGAN" | 72.50 | 160.00 |

Single Lined Frame

| 1877 | | | | |
|---|---|---|---|---|
| 3 | A2 | ¼a black | | 9,000. |
| 4 | A2 | ½a red | 52.50 | 110.00 |
| a. | | "NWAB" | 250.00 | 490.00 |

A3          A4

| 1878 | | | | |
|---|---|---|---|---|
| 5 | A3 | ¼a black | 12.00 | 24.00 |
| a. | | "J" diagonal, plate II | 13.50 | 27.50 |

All stamps of type A3 are lettered "EEGAM" for "BEGAM."

| 1878 | | | | |
|---|---|---|---|---|
| 6 | A4 | ½a pale red | 10.50 | 24.00 |
| a. | | ½a brown red | 42.50 | 67.50 |
| b. | | "NWAB" | 35.00 | |
| c. | | "JAHN" | 57.50 | |
| d. | | "EECAM" | 57.50 | |

A5          A6

| 1879-80 | | | | |
|---|---|---|---|---|
| 7 | A5 | ¼a green | 21.00 | 40.00 |
| 8 | A5 | ½a red | 27.50 | 35.00 |
| | | **Perf.** | | |
| 9 | A5 | ¼a green | 16.00 | 27.50 |
| 10 | A5 | ½a red | 160.00 | |
| | | Nos. 7-10 (4) | 224.50 | 102.50 |

Nos. 7 and 9 have the value in parenthesis; Nos. 8 and 10 are without parenthesis.

| 1881 | | | | Imperf. |
|---|---|---|---|---|
| 11 | A6 | ¼a green | | 13.50 |
| a. | | "NAWA" | | 42.50 |
| b. | | "CHAH" | | 120.00 |
| | | **Perf.** | | |
| 12 | A6 | ¼a green | | 18.00 |
| a. | | "NAWA" | | 67.50 |
| b. | | "CHAH" | | 160.00 |

A7

| 1881-89 | | | | Imperf. |
|---|---|---|---|---|
| 13 | A7 | ¼a black | 9.00 | 35.00 |
| a. | | "NWAB" | 22.50 | |
| 14 | A7 | ½a red | 7.50 | 25.00 |
| a. | | "NWAB" | 18.00 | |
| 15 | A7 | 1a brown | 6.50 | 29.00 |
| a. | | "NWAB" | 14.00 | |
| 16 | A7 | 2a blue | 5.00 | 29.00 |
| a. | | | 9.50 | |
| 17 | A7 | 4a yellow | 30.00 | 100.00 |
| a. | | "NWAB" | 82.50 | |
| | | Nos. 13-17 (5) | 58.00 | 218.00 |

A8          A9

| 1884 | | | | Perf. |
|---|---|---|---|---|
| 19 | A8 | ¼a green | 225.00 | 275.00 |
| a. | | "JAN" | 225.00 | 275.00 |
| b. | | "BEGM" | 450.00 | 625.00 |
| c. | | "NWAB" | 950.00 | |
| d. | | "SHAHAN" | 950.00 | |
| f. | | "JAHA" | 450.00 | |
| 20 | A9 | ¼a green | 8.25 | 27.50 |

On type A9 there is a dash at the left of "JA" of "JAHAN" instead of a character like a comma as on types A5 and A6. Imitations of No. 19 were printed about 1904 in black on wove paper and in red on laid paper, both imperf. and pin-perf.

A10

| 1884 | | **Laid Paper** | | Imperf. |
|---|---|---|---|---|
| 21 | A10 | ¼a blue green | 240.00 | 275.00 |
| a. | | "NWAB" | 675.00 | |
| b. | | "NAWAJANAN" | 675.00 | |
| c. | | "SAH" | 675.00 | |
| 22 | A10 | ½a black | 3.25 | 3.75 |
| a. | | "NWAB" | 15.00 | 18.00 |
| b. | | "NAWAJANAN" | 15.00 | 18.00 |
| c. | | "SAH" | 15.00 | 18.00 |
| | | **Perf.** | | |
| 23 | A10 | ¼a blue green | 1.50 | 6.00 |
| a. | | "NWAB" | 6.00 | |
| b. | | "NAWAJANAN" | 6.00 | |
| c. | | "SAH" | 6.00 | |
| 24 | A10 | ½a black | 1.40 | 5.00 |
| a. | | "NWAB" | 5.50 | 12.50 |
| b. | | "NAWAJANAN" | 5.50 | 12.50 |
| c. | | "SAH" | 5.50 | 12.50 |
| | | Nos. 21-24 (4) | 246.15 | 289.75 |

Type Redrawn

| 1886 | | **Wove Paper** | | Imperf. |
|---|---|---|---|---|
| 25 | A10 | ¼a grayish green | .80 | 5.00 |
| a. | | ¼a green | .80 | 5.00 |
| b. | | "NWAB" | 3.00 | 10.00 |
| c. | | "NAWA" | 4.50 | 13.50 |
| d. | | "NAWAA" | 4.50 | 13.50 |
| e. | | "NAWABABEGAAM" | 4.50 | 13.50 |
| f. | | "NWABA" | 4.50 | 13.50 |
| 26 | A10 | ½a red | 1.00 | 2.50 |
| a. | | "SAH" | 6.00 | 9.50 |
| b. | | "NAWABA" | 4.50 | 7.50 |
| | | **Perf.** | | |
| 27 | A10 | ¼a green | 3.75 | 6.00 |
| a. | | "NWAB" | 20.00 | |
| b. | | "NAWA" | 12.00 | |
| c. | | "NAWAA" | 20.00 | |
| d. | | "NAWABABEGAAM" | 20.00 | |
| e. | | "NWABA" | 20.00 | |
| 28 | A10 | ½a red | 1.20 | 3.00 |
| a. | | "SAH" | 9.00 | |
| b. | | "NAWABA" | 12.00 | |
| | | Nos. 25-28 (4) | 6.75 | 16.50 |

On Nos. 25-28 the inscriptions are closer to the value than on Nos. 21-24.

A11

A12

| 1886 | | | | Imperf. |
|---|---|---|---|---|
| 29 | A11 | ½a red | 4.00 | 15.00 |
| a. | | "BEGAM" | 18.00 | 47.50 |
| b. | | "NWAB" | 18.00 | |
| | | **Laid Paper** | | |
| 30 | A12 | 4a yellow | 18.00 | 57.50 |
| a. | | "EEGAM" | 24.00 | |
| b. | | Wove paper | 1,500. | |
| c. | | As "a," wove paper | 1,900. | |
| | | **Perf.** | | |
| 31 | A12 | 4a yellow | 6.50 | 30.00 |
| a. | | "EEGAM" | 9.50 | 42.50 |
| | | Nos. 29-31 (3) | 28.50 | |

A13          A14

| 1889 | | **Wove Paper** | | Imperf. |
|---|---|---|---|---|
| 32 | A13 | ¼a green | 1.50 | 3.00 |
| a. | | "SAH" | 6.50 | 10.50 |
| b. | | "NAWA" | 6.50 | 10.50 |
| 33 | A14 | ¼a black | 3.25 | 8.25 |
| a. | | "EEGAN" | 27.50 | 47.50 |
| | | **Perf.** | | |
| 34 | A13 | ¼a green | 3.00 | 4.00 |
| a. | | "SAH" | 11.00 | 13.50 |
| b. | | "NAWA" | 11.00 | 13.50 |
| c. | | Vert. pair, imperf between | 325.00 | |
| 35 | A14 | ¼a black | 2.50 | 8.25 |
| a. | | "EEGAN" | 22.50 | 47.50 |
| b. | | Horiz. pair, imperf. between | 400.00 | |
| | | Nos. 32-35 (4) | 10.25 | 23.50 |

Type A13 has smaller letters in the upper corners than Type A10.

A15          A16

| 1890 | | | | Imperf. |
|---|---|---|---|---|
| 36 | A15 | ¼a black | 3.25 | 3.00 |
| 37 | A15 | 1a brown | 3.25 | 7.00 |
| a. | | "EEGAM" | 21.00 | 40.00 |
| b. | | "BBGAM" | 21.00 | 40.00 |
| 38 | A7 | 2a greenish blue | 3.00 | 3.25 |
| a. | | "BBEGAM" | 12.50 | 21.00 |
| b. | | "NAWAH" | 12.50 | 21.00 |
| 39 | A7 | 4a yellow | 3.75 | 5.50 |
| 40 | A16 | 8a blue | 100.00 | 180.00 |
| a. | | "HAH" | 110.00 | 190.00 |
| b. | | "JABAN" | 120.00 | |
| | | Nos. 36-40 (5) | 113.25 | 198.75 |

An imperf. imitation of Nos. 36 and 41 was printed about 1904 in black on wove paper.

| | | | **Perf.** | |
|---|---|---|---|---|
| 41 | A15 | ¼a black | 4.50 | 6.25 |
| a. | | Pair, imperf. between | 500.00 | |
| 42 | A15 | 1a brown | 6.50 | 11.00 |
| a. | | "EECAM" | 37.50 | 52.50 |
| b. | | "BBGAM" | 37.50 | 52.50 |
| 43 | A7 | 2a greenish blue | 3.75 | 5.50 |
| a. | | "BBEGAM" | 14.00 | 27.50 |
| b. | | "NAWAH" | 14.00 | 27.50 |
| 44 | A7 | 4a yellow | 4.50 | 12.00 |
| 45 | A16 | 8a blue | 100.00 | 180.00 |
| a. | | "HAH" | 110.00 | |
| b. | | "JABAN" | 120.00 | |
| | | Nos. 41-45 (5) | 119.25 | 214.75 |

Nos. 40 and 45 have a frame line around each stamp.

| | | | **Imperf** | |
|---|---|---|---|---|
| 46 | A12 | ½a red (BECAM) | 3.00 | 5.50 |
| 47 | A13 | ½a red (NWAB) | 3.00 | 2.25 |
| a. | | Inverted "N" | | |
| b. | | "SAH" | 9.00 | |
| | | | **Perf.** | |
| 48 | A12 | ½a red (BECAM) | 2.50 | 7.00 |
| a. | | Without embossing | | |
| 49 | A13 | ½a red (NWAB) | 1.20 | 3.00 |
| a. | | Inverted "N" | | |
| b. | | "SAH" | 7.50 | |
| | | Nos. 46-49 (4) | 9.70 | 17.75 |

| 1891-93 | | **Laid Paper** | | Imperf. |
|---|---|---|---|---|
| 50 | A16 | 8a deep green | 110.00 | 225.00 |
| a. | | "HAH" | 125.00 | |
| b. | | "JABAN" | 140.00 | |
| | | | **Perf.** | |
| 51 | A16 | 8a deep green | 110.00 | 225.00 |
| a. | | "HAH" | 125.00 | |
| b. | | "JABAN" | 140.00 | |

For overprint, see No. 83.

| 1894 | | **Redrawn** | | Imperf. |
|---|---|---|---|---|
| 53 | A10 | ¼a green | 2.25 | 2.50 |
| a. | | "NAWAH" | 11.00 | 12.00 |
| 54 | A11 | ½a brick red | 3.25 | 3.25 |
| 55 | A16 | 8a blue black | 32.50 | 32.50 |
| a. | | Laid paper | 300.00 | 450.00 |
| | | | **Perf.** | |
| 56 | A10 | ¼a green | 4.50 | 3.25 |
| a. | | "NAWAH" | 19.00 | 16.00 |
| 57 | A11 | ½a brick red | 1.20 | 3.00 |
| 58 | A16 | 8a blue black | 45.00 | 60.00 |
| | | Nos. 53-58 (6) | 88.70 | 104.50 |

The ¼a redrawn has letters in corners larger; value in very small characters. The 8a redrawn has no frame to each stamp but a frame to the sheet.

| 1898 | | | | Imperf. |
|---|---|---|---|---|
| 60 | A16 | 8a black | 62.50 | 82.50 |
| b. | | "E" of "BEGAM" inverted | 140.00 | 150.00 |

A17

A18

A19

A20

A21

**1895**

**Laid Paper**

| 61 | A17 | ¼a green | 2.25 | 2.50 |
|----|-----|----------|------|------|
| 62 | A18 | ¼a red | 10.50 | 5.00 |
| 63 | A19 | ¼a black | 5.25 | 4.50 |
| a. | "A" inserted in "NAW B" | | 12.50 | 10.00 |
| 64 | A20 | ½a black | 2.25 | 2.50 |
| 65 | A21 | ½a red | 3.25 | 3.25 |

**Perf.**

| 66 | A17 | ¼a green | 4.50 | 3.25 |
|----|-----|----------|------|------|
| 67 | A18 | ¼a red | | 1,250. |
| | Nos. 61-67 (7) | | 1,278. | 1,271. |

On No. 63a, the second "A" in "NAWAB" has been inserted by hand and varies somewhat in size.

Imperf. imitations of No. 65 were printed about 1904 in deep red on laid paper and in black on wove paper.

Stamps of types A16 and A19-A21 with a circular embossed seal and perforated, were prepared but not issued.

A22

A23

**1898** **Imperf.**

| 72 | A22 | ¼a black | .75 | .75 |
|----|-----|----------|-----|-----|
| a. | "SHAN" | | 5.00 | 5.00 |
| 73 | A22 | ¼a green | 1.10 | 1.20 |
| a. | "SHAN" | | 5.25 | 5.25 |
| 74 | A23 | ¼a black | 2.10 | 2.10 |
| | Nos. 72-74 (3) | | 3.95 | 4.05 |

**1899**

| 75 | A13 | ½a black ("NWAB") | 6.50 | 9.50 |
|----|-----|-------------------|------|------|
| b. | "NWASBAHJAHNJ" | | 32.50 | 42.50 |
| d. | "SBAH" | | 15.00 | 22.50 |
| e. | "SBAN" | | 32.50 | 42.50 |
| f. | "NWIB" | | 32.50 | 42.50 |
| g. | "BEIAM" | | 32.50 | 42.50 |

A24

Coat of Arms — A25

**1902**

| 76 | A24 | ¼a red | 5.50 | 9.00 |
|----|-----|--------|------|------|
| 77 | A24 | ½a black | 6.00 | 10.00 |
| a. | Printed on both sides | | 1,100. | |
| 78 | A24 | 1a brown | 10.00 | 25.00 |
| 79 | A24 | 2a blue | 12.50 | 22.50 |
| 80 | A24 | 4a orange | 110.00 | 160.00 |
| 81 | A24 | 8a violet | 150.00 | 290.00 |
| 82 | A24 | 1r rose | 400.00 | 600.00 |
| | Nos. 76-82 (7) | | 694.00 | 1,116. |

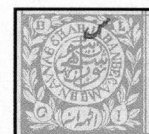

No. 50 Overprinted in Red

**1903**

| 83 | A16 | 8a deep green | 210.00 | 225.00 |
|----|-----|---------------|--------|--------|
| a. | Inverted overprint | | 550.00 | 600.00 |

There are two types of the overprint which is the Arabic S, initial of the Begum.

**Inscription in Circle Embossed on Each Stamp**

**1903** **Wove Paper**

| 84 | A24 | ¼a red | 2.25 | 7.50 |
|----|-----|--------|------|------|
| 85 | A24 | ½a black | 1.90 | 7.50 |
| 86 | A24 | 1a brown | 4.50 | 11.00 |
| 87 | A24 | 2a blue | 10.00 | 37.50 |
| 88 | A24 | 4a orange | 27.50 | 75.00 |
| 89 | A24 | 8a violet | 82.50 | 190.00 |
| 90 | A24 | 1r rose | 125.00 | 290.00 |
| | Nos. 84-90 (7) | | 253.65 | 618.50 |

**Laid Paper**

| 84a | A24 | ¼a red | 1.50 | 12.00 |
|-----|-----|--------|------|-------|
| 85a | A24 | ½a black | 1.50 | 12.50 |
| 86a | A24 | 1a brown | 10.00 | |
| 87a | A24 | 2a blue | 250.00 | 325.00 |
| 88a | A24 | 4a orange | 500.00 | 500.00 |
| 89a | A24 | 8a violet | 2,400. | |
| 90a | A24 | 1r rose | 1,900. | |
| | Nos. 84a-90a (7) | | 5,063. | 849.50 |

The embossing in a circle, which was first used in 1903, has been applied to many early stamps and impressions from redrawn plates of early issues. So far as is now known, these should be classed as reprints.

**1908** **Engr.** **Perf. 13½**

| 99 | A25 | 1a yellow green | 5.50 | 6.75 |
|----|-----|-----------------|------|------|
| a. | Printed on both sides | | 180.00 | |

## OFFICIAL STAMPS

O1

Size: 20½x25mm

Overprinted

**1908** **Unwmk.** **Engr.** **Perf. 13½**

| O1 | O1 | ½a yellow green | 3.25 | .20 |
|----|----|-----------------|------|-----|
| a. | Pair, one without ovpt. | | 950.00 | |
| b. | Inverted overprint | | 275.00 | 225.00 |
| c. | Double ovpt., one invtd. | | 160.00 | |
| O2 | O1 | 1a carmine | 6.25 | .60 |
| a. | Inverted overprint | | 180.00 | 150.00 |
| O3 | O1 | 2a blue | 36.00 | .20 |
| O4 | O1 | 4a red brown | 21.00 | .80 |
| | Nos. O1-O4 (4) | | 66.50 | 1.80 |

Overprinted

| O5 | O1 | ½a yellow green | 11.00 | 1.90 |
|----|----|-----------------|-------|------|
| O6 | O1 | 1a carmine | 14.00 | 1.40 |
| O7 | O1 | 2a blue | 6.00 | .90 |
| a. | Inverted overprint | | 37.50 | |
| O8 | O1 | 4a red brown | 120.00 | 2.25 |
| a. | Inverted overprint | | 30.00 | 100.00 |
| | Nos. O5-O8 (4) | | 151.00 | 6.45 |

The difference in the two overprints is in the shape of the letters, most noticeable in the "R."

Type of 1908 Issue
Size: 25½x30½mm

Overprinted

**1930-31** **Litho.** **Perf. 14**

| O9 | O1 | ½a gray green ('31) | 18.00 | 2.50 |
|----|----|---------------------|-------|------|
| O10 | O1 | 1a carmine | 16.00 | .20 |
| O11 | O1 | 2a blue | 14.00 | .65 |
| O12 | O1 | 4a brown | 15.00 | 1.40 |
| | Nos. O9-O12 (4) | | 63.00 | 4.75 |

½a, 2a, 4a are inscribed "POSTAGE" on the left side; 1a "POSTAGE AND REVENUE."

Similar to Type O1
Size: 21x25mm
"POSTAGE" at left
"BHOPAL STATE" at right

**1932-33** **Perf. 11½, 13, 13½, 14**

| O13 | O1 | ¼a orange yellow | 3.75 | .75 |
|-----|----|------------------|------|-----|
| a. | Pair, one without overprint | | 180.00 | |
| b. | Perf. 13½ | | 16.00 | .45 |
| c. | Perf. 14 | | 18.00 | .45 |

**"BHOPAL GOVT." at right**
**Perf. 13½**

| O14 | O1 | ½a yellow green | 11.00 | .20 |
|-----|----|-----------------|-------|-----|
| O15 | O1 | 1a brown red | 16.00 | .20 |
| O16 | O1 | 2a blue | 16.00 | .65 |
| O17 | O1 | 4a brown | 16.00 | 1.50 |
| a. | Perf 14 ('34) | | 24.00 | .60 |
| | Nos. O13-O17 (5) | | 62.75 | 3.30 |

No. O14, O16-O17 Surcharged in Red, Violet, Black or Blue:

a

b

c

**1935-36** **Perf. 13½**

| O18 | O1(a) | ¼a on ½a (R) | 47.50 | 21.00 |
|-----|-------|--------------|-------|-------|
| a. | Inverted surcharge | | 300.00 | 125.00 |
| O19 | O1(b) | 3p on ½a (R) | 5.50 | 5.25 |
| O20 | O1(a) | ¼a on 2a (R) | 42.50 | 30.00 |
| a. | Inverted surcharge | | 300.00 | 110.00 |
| O21 | O1(b) | 3p on 2a (R) | 6.75 | 6.75 |
| a. | Inverted surcharge | | 120.00 | 60.00 |
| O22 | O1(a) | ¼a on 4a (R) | 1,500. | 500.00 |
| O23 | O1(a) | ¼a on 4a (Bk) | | |
| | ('36) | | 120.00 | 40.00 |
| O24 | O1(b) | 3p on 4a (R) | 210.00 | 100.00 |
| O25 | O1(b) | 3p on 4a (Bk) | | |
| | ('36) | | 3.75 | 5.00 |
| O26 | O1(c) | 1a on ½a (V) | 7.50 | 2.25 |
| a. | Inverted surcharge | | 100.00 | 67.50 |
| O27 | O1(c) | 1a on 2a (R) | 3.25 | 3.00 |
| a. | Inverted surcharge | | 140.00 | 140.00 |
| O28 | O1(c) | 1a on 2a (Bk) | | |
| | ('36) | | 1.00 | 3.75 |
| O29 | O1(c) | 1a on 4a (Bl) | 10.50 | 7.50 |
| | Nos. O18-O29 (12) | | 1,958. | 724.50 |

Nos. O18-O25 are arranged in composite sheets of 100. The 2 top horizontal rows of each value are surcharged "a" and the next 5 rows as "b." The next 3 rows as "b" but in a narrower setting.

Various errors of spelling or inverted letters are found on Nos. O18-O29.

Arms of Bhopal — O2

**1935** **Litho.**

| O30 | O2 | 1a3p claret & blue | 5.25 | 2.25 |
|-----|----|--------------------|------|------|

Inscribed: "Bhopal State Postage"
Ovptd. "SERVICE" 11mm long

**1937** **Perf. 12**

| O31 | O2 | 1a6p dk claret & blue | 3.75 | 1.50 |
|-----|----|------------------------|------|------|
| a. | Overprint omitted | | 275.00 | 210.00 |
| b. | Double overprint, one inverted | | 750.00 | 750.00 |
| c. | Blue printing double | | | 250.00 |
| d. | Imperf, pair | | | 275.00 |
| e. | Pair, imperf between | | 300.00 | 325.00 |

See Nos. O42, O45.

Arms of Bhopal — O3

**Brown or Black Overprint**

**1936-38** **Typo.**

| O32 | O3 | ¼a orange (Br) | 1.40 | .90 |
|-----|----|----------------|------|-----|
| a. | Inverted overprint | | 525.00 | 400.00 |
| b. | Vert. pair, imperf between | | 250.00 | |
| c. | Horiz. pair, imperf between | | | 450.00 |
| d. | Black overprint | | 12.50 | 1.10 |
| e. | As "d," inverted ovpt. | | | 600.00 |
| f. | As "d," double ovpt. | | | 450.00 |
| O32B | O3 | ¼a yellow (Br) | | |
| | ('38) | | 5.25 | 2.25 |
| O33 | O3 | 1a carmine | 1.90 | .20 |
| a. | Horiz. pair, imperf vert. | | 250.00 | |
| b. | Vert. pair, imperf between | | 490.00 | |
| c. | Horiz. pair, imperf between | | 200.00 | 225.00 |
| d. | Block of 4, imperf between | | 625.00 | 625.00 |
| | Nos. O32-O33 (3) | | 8.55 | 3.35 |

Moti Mahal O4

**Overprinted "SERVICE"**

**1936** **Perf. 11½**

| O34 | O4 | ½a green & chocolate | .85 | 1.20 |
|-----|----|----------------------|-----|------|
| a. | Double impression of stamp | | 150.00 | 22.50 |
| b. | Double overprint | | 350.00 | 250.00 |
| c. | Vert. pair, imperf between | | | 325.00 |
| d. | Horiz. pair, imperf between | | | 325.00 |

Moti Masjid — O5

4a, Taj Mahal and Be-Nazir Palaces.

**Overprinted "SERVICE"**

**1937** **Perf. 11½**

| O35 | O5 | 2a dk blue & brown | 2.50 | 1.40 |
|-----|----|--------------------|------|------|
| a. | Inverted overprint | | 375.00 | 550.00 |
| b. | Vert. pair, imperf between | | | 525.00 |
| c. | Horiz. pair, imperf between | | | 375.00 |
| O36 | O5 | 4a bister brn & blue | 4.50 | .75 |
| a. | Double overprint | | 240.00 | |
| b. | Center double | | 600.00 | |
| c. | Horiz. pair, imperf between | | | 1,000. |
| d. | Overprint omitted | | | 490.00 |

## Types of 1937
### Overprinted "SERVICE" in Black or Brown

**1938-44**

Designs: 4a, Taj Mahal. 8a, Ahmadabad Palace. 1r, Rait-Ghat.

| | | | |
|---|---|---|---|
| O37 | O4 | ½a dp grn & brn | .90 | .60 |
| O38 | O5 | 2a violet & dp grn | 15.00 | .45 |
| O39 | O5 | 4a red brn & brt bl | 4.25 | .80 |
| a. | Frame double | | 450.00 |
| O40 | O5 | 8a red vio & blue | 7.00 | 3.25 |
| a. | "SERAICE" | | 550.00 | 825.00 |
| b. | Overprint omitted | | 250.00 |
| c. | Double overprint | | 240.00 |
| d. | Vert. pair, imperf between | | 625.00 |
| e. | "1" for "I" in "SERVICE" | | 550.00 | 825.00 |
| O41 | O5 | 1r bl & red vio (Br) | 27.50 | 12.50 |
| a. | Black overprint ('44) | | 21.00 | 6.50 |
| b. | "SREVICE" | | 160.00 | 375.00 |
| c. | Overprint omitted | | 1,100. |
| d. | Vert. pair, imperf horiz. | | | 2,250. |
| | Nos. O37-O41 (5) | | 54.65 | 17.60 |

#O39 measures 36½x22½mm, #O40 39x24mm, #O41 45½x27¾mm.

### Type of 1935

**1939**       *Perf. 12*

| | | | | |
|---|---|---|---|---|
| O42 | O2 | 1a6p dark claret | 7.50 | 2.50 |
| a. | Overprint omitted | | 625.00 |
| b. | Double overprint | | 625.00 |
| c. | Double overprint, one inverted | | 625.00 |
| d. | Pair, imperf between | | 250.00 | 325.00 |

Tiger — O6

Design: 1a, Deer.

**1940**    Typo.    *Perf. 11½*

| | | | | |
|---|---|---|---|---|
| O43 | O6 | ¼a ultramarine | 6.00 | 2.50 |
| O44 | O6 | 1a red violet | 35.00 | 4.50 |

### Type of 1935
Inscribed: "Bhopal State Postage"

**1941**

| | | | | |
|---|---|---|---|---|
| O45 | O2 | 1a3p emerald | 2.50 | 3.25 |
| a. | Pair, imperf between | | 550.00 | 700.00 |

Moti Palace — O7     Coat of Arms — O8

2a, Moti Mosque. 4a, Be-Nazir Palaces.

**1944-46**   Unwmk.   Typo.   *Perf. 11½, 12*

| | | | | |
|---|---|---|---|---|
| O46 | O8 | 3p ultramarine | 1.25 | 1.25 |
| O47 | O7 | ½a light green | 1.10 | 1.50 |
| O48 | O8 | 9p orange brn ('46) | 12.00 | 5.00 |
| a. | Imperf., pair | | | 290.00 |
| O49 | O8 | 1a brt red vio ('45) | 6.25 | 2.60 |
| O50 | O8 | 1½a deep plum | 1.90 | 1.90 |
| O51 | O7 | 2a red violet ('45) | 13.50 | 6.00 |
| O52 | O8 | 3a yellow ('46) | 16.00 | 21.00 |
| a. | Imperf., pair | | | 290.00 |
| O53 | O7 | 4a brown ('45) | 8.75 | 3.25 |
| O54 | O8 | 6a brt rose ('46) | 24.00 | 75.00 |
| a. | Imperf., pair | | | 400.00 |
| | Nos. O46-O54 (9) | | 84.75 | 117.50 |

For surcharges see Nos. O58-O59.

**1946-47**   Unwmk.   *Perf. 11½*

| | | | | |
|---|---|---|---|---|
| O55 | O8 | 1a violet | 11.00 | 4.75 |
| O56 | O7 | 2a violet ('47) | 13.50 | 22.50 |
| O57 | O8 | 3a deep orange | 125.00 | 160.00 |
| a. | Imperf., pair | | — | 275.00 |
| | Nos. O55-O57 (3) | | 149.50 | 187.25 |

#### No. O50 Surcharged "2 As." and Bars

**1949**        *Perf. 12*

| | | | | |
|---|---|---|---|---|
| O58 | O8 | 2a on 1½a dp plum | 3.00 | 11.00 |
| c. | Imperf., pair | | 300.00 | 450.00 |

---

### Same Surcharged "2 As." and Rosettes

**1949**        *Imperf.*

| | | | | |
|---|---|---|---|---|
| O59 | O8 | 2a on 1½a dp plum | 1,250. | 1,500. |
| a. | Perf 12 | | 1,350. | 1,600. |

Three or more types of "2" in surcharge. Bhopal stamps became obsolete in 1950.

---

## BHOR

ˈbōˌər

LOCATION — A Feudatory State in the Kolhapur Residency and Deccan States Agency.
AREA — 910 sq. mi.
POP. — 141,546
CAPITAL — Bhor

A1

A2

### Handstamped
**1879**   Unwmk.   Imperf.   Without Gum

| | | | | |
|---|---|---|---|---|
| 1 | A1 | ½a carmine | 5.50 | 7.50 |
| 2 | A2 | 1a carmine | 8.25 | 12.00 |

Pant Sachiv Shankarrao — A3

**1901**      Without Gum     Typo.

| | | | | |
|---|---|---|---|---|
| 3 | A3 | ½a red | 24.00 | 60.00 |

---

## BIJAWAR

bi-ˈjä-wər

LOCATION — A Feudatory State in the Bundelkhand Agency of Central India.
AREA — 973 sq. mi.
POP. — 115,852
CAPITAL — Bijawar

A1

Maharaja Sir Sawant Singh — A2

---

### 1935-36   Typo.   Unwmk.   *Perf. 10½*

| | | | | |
|---|---|---|---|---|
| 1 | A1 | 3p brown | 11.00 | 8.25 |
| b. | Imperf., pair | | 13.50 |
| b. | Rouletted 7 ('36) | | 9.00 | 9.00 |
| 2 | A1 | 6p carmine | 9.50 | 8.25 |
| a. | Rouletted 7 ('36) | | 12.00 | 32.50 |
| 3 | A1 | 9p purple | 12.50 | 7.50 |
| a. | Rouletted 7 ('36) | | 9.00 | 160.00 |
| 4 | A1 | 1a dark blue | 14.00 | 8.25 |
| a. | Rouletted 7 ('36) | | 15.00 | 180.00 |
| 5 | A1 | 2a slate green | 13.50 | 7.50 |
| a. | Rouletted 7 ('36) | | 19.00 | 190.00 |

**1937**        *Perf. 9*

| | | | | |
|---|---|---|---|---|
| 6 | A2 | 4a red orange | 22.50 | 120.00 |
| 7 | A2 | 6a yellow | 22.50 | 120.00 |
| 8 | A2 | 8a emerald | 24.00 | 160.00 |
| 9 | A2 | 12a turquoise blue | 24.00 | 160.00 |
| 10 | A2 | 1r purple | 62.50 | 250.00 |
| a. | "1Rs" instead of "1R" | | 75.00 | 500.00 |
| | Nos. 1-10 (10) | | 216.00 | 849.75 |

Bijawar stamps became obsolete in 1939.

---

## BUNDI

ˈbün-dē

LOCATION — A Feudatory State in the Rajputana Agency of India.
AREA — 2,220 sq. mi.
POP. — 216,722
CAPITAL — Bundi

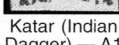

Katar (Indian Dagger) — A1

A2

A3

### Laid Paper
**1894**   Unwmk.   Litho.   Imperf.   Without Gum
#### Gutters between Stamps

| | | | | |
|---|---|---|---|---|
| 1 | A1 | ½a slate | 19,000. | 3,250. |

#### Redrawn; Blade Does Not Touch Oval
#### No Gutters between Stamps
#### Wove Paper

| | | | | |
|---|---|---|---|---|
| 1A | A1 | ½a slate | 67.50 | 72.50 |
| b. | Value above, name below | | 400.00 | 525.00 |
| c. | Top right ornament omitted | | 3,750. | 4,000. |

On No. 1A, the dagger is thinner and its point does not touch the oval inner frame.

**1896**

#### Laid Paper
#### Without Gum

| | | | | |
|---|---|---|---|---|
| 2 | A2 | ½a slate | 9.00 | 14.00 |

**1897-98**       **Without Gum**

| | | | | |
|---|---|---|---|---|
| 3 | A3 | 1a red | 18.00 | 27.50 |
| 4 | A3 | 2a yellow green | 21.00 | 40.00 |
| 5 | A3 | 4a yellow green | 100.00 | 140.00 |
| 6 | A3 | 8a red | 160.00 | 160.00 |
| 7 | A3 | 1r yellow, *blue* | 500.00 | 825.00 |
| | Nos. 3-7 (5) | | 799.00 | 1,482. |

A4

A5

#### Redrawn; Blade Wider and Diamond-shaped

**1898-1900**      **Without Gum**

| | | | | |
|---|---|---|---|---|
| 8 | A3 | ½a slate | 7.00 | 7.00 |
| 9 | A3 | 1a red | 5.50 | 5.50 |
| 10 | A3 | 2a emerald | 19.00 | 25.00 |
| a. | 1st 2 characters of value omitted | | 3,000. | 3,000. |

| | | | | |
|---|---|---|---|---|
| 11 | A3 | 4a yel grn | 42.50 | 100.00 |
| 12 | A4 | 8a red | 21.00 | 27.50 |
| 13 | A5 | 1r yellow, *blue* | 47.50 | 82.50 |
| a. | Wove paper | | 24.00 | 40.00 |
| | Nos. 8-13 (6) | | 142.50 | 247.50 |

On Nos. 9-10, the blade is wider and nearly diamond-shaped.

#### Point of Dagger to Left

| | | | | |
|---|---|---|---|---|
| 14 | A3 | 4a green | 5.00 | 5.00 |

Maharao Rajah with Symbols of Spiritual and Temporal Power — A6

### Rouletted 11 to 13 in Color

**1915**        Typo.
#### Without Gum
#### "Bundi" in 3 Characters (word at top right)

| | | | | |
|---|---|---|---|---|
| 15 | A6 | ¼a blue | 2.90 | 6.25 |
| a. | Laid paper | | 6.75 | 35.00 |
| 16 | A6 | ½a black | 4.00 | 9.00 |
| 17 | A6 | 1a vermilion | 5.50 | 18.00 |
| a. | Laid paper | | 15.00 | 45.00 |
| 18 | A6 | 2a emerald | 11.00 | 35.00 |
| 19 | A6 | 2½a yellow | 11.00 | 40.00 |
| 20 | A6 | 3a brown | 12.50 | 67.50 |
| 21 | A6 | 4a yel green | 5.25 | 62.50 |
| 23 | A6 | 6a ultramarine | 21.00 | 160.00 |
| a. | 6a deep blue | | 11.00 | 180.00 |
| 24 | A6 | 8a orange | 11.00 | 160.00 |
| 25 | A6 | 10a olive | 24.00 | 150.00 |
| 26 | A6 | 12a dark green | 19.00 | 140.00 |
| 27 | A6 | 1r violet | 40.00 | 250.00 |
| 28 | A6 | 2r car brn & blk | 125.00 | 325.00 |
| 29 | A6 | 3r blue & brown | 200.00 | 450.00 |
| 30 | A6 | 4r pale grn & red brown | 400.00 | 550.00 |
| 31 | A6 | 5r ver & pale grn | 400.00 | 550.00 |
| | Nos. 15-31 (16) | | 1,292. | 2,973. |

Minor differences in lettering in top and bottom panels may be divided into 8 types, but not all values come in each type. In one subtype the top appears as one word. Nos. 30-31 have an ornamental frame around the design. For overprints see Nos. O1-O39.

**1941**        *Perf. 11*
#### "Bundi" in 4 Characters (word at top right)

| | | | | |
|---|---|---|---|---|
| 32 | A6 | ¼a light blue | 2.25 | 62.50 |
| 33 | A6 | ½a black | 40.00 | 47.50 |
| 34 | A6 | 1a carmine | 15.00 | 75.00 |
| 35 | A6 | 2a yellow green | 20.00 | 110.00 |
| | Nos. 32-35 (4) | | 77.25 |

The 4-character spelling of "Bundi" is found also on stamps rouletted in color: on ½a and 4a in small characters, and on ¼a, 1a, 4a, 4r and 5r in large characters like those on Nos. 32-35.

For overprints see Nos. O41-O48.

Arms of Bundi — A7

**1941-45**      Typo.      *Perf. 11*

| | | | | |
|---|---|---|---|---|
| 36 | A7 | 3p bright ultra | 3.50 | 7.50 |
| 37 | A7 | 6p indigo | 5.25 | 12.50 |
| 38 | A7 | 1a red orange | 8.00 | 15.00 |
| 39 | A7 | 2a fawn | 10.50 | 27.50 |
| a. | 2a brown ('45) | | 19.00 | 30.00 |
| 40 | A7 | 4a brt yel green | 19.00 | 82.50 |
| 41 | A7 | 8a dull green | 25.00 | 300.00 |
| 42 | A7 | 1r royal blue | 52.50 | 450.00 |
| | Nos. 36-42 (7) | | 123.75 | 895.00 |

The 1st printing of Nos. 36-42 was gummed. All later printings were without gum. **Values are for stamps without gum.**

For overprints see Nos. O49-O55.

A8

Maj. Maharao
Rajah Bahadur
Singh — A9

View of
Bundi — A10

| 1947 | | | Perf. 11 | |
|---|---|---|---|---|
| 43 | A8 | ¼a deep green | 2.75 | 57.50 |
| 44 | A8 | ½a purple | 2.50 | 47.50 |
| 45 | A8 | 1a yellow green | 2.50 | 47.50 |
| 46 | A9 | 2a red | 2.40 | 97.50 |
| 47 | A9 | 4a deep orange | 2.75 | 140.00 |
| 48 | A10 | 8a violet blue | 3.75 | |
| 49 | A10 | 1r chocolate | 19.00 | |
| | | Nos. 43-49 (7) | 35.65 | 390.00 |

For overprints see Rajasthan Nos. 1-14.

### OFFICIAL STAMPS

Regular Issue of 1915 Handstamped
in Black, Red or Green

 a

*Rouletted 11 to 13 in Color*

| 1918 | | | Unwmk. |
|---|---|---|---|
| | | | *Without Gum* |
| O1 | A6 | ¼a dark blue | 1.90 |
| O2 | A6 | ½a black | 1.10 |
| O3 | A6 | 1a vermilion | 1.90 |
| O4 | A6 | 2a emerald | 9.50 |
| O5 | A6 | 2½a yellow | 6.00 |
| O6 | A6 | 3a brown | 5.50 |
| O7 | A6 | 4a yel green | 18.00 |
| O8 | A6 | 6a blue | 22.50 |
| O9 | A6 | 8a orange | 22.50 |
| O10 | A6 | 10a olive green | 75.00 |
| O11 | A6 | 12a dark green | 75.00 |
| O12 | A6 | 1r violet | 90.00 |
| O13 | A6 | 2r car brn & blk | 600.00 |
| O14 | A6 | 3r blue & brown | 525.00 |
| O15 | A6 | 4r pale grn & red brn | 450.00 |
| O16 | A6 | 5r ver & pale grn | 490.00 |
| | | Nos. O1-O16 (16) | 2,393. |

All values come with black handstamp and most exist in red. The overprint is found in various positions, double, inverted, etc.
Several denominations exist in two or more types. See notes following Nos. 31 and 35.

Regular Issue of 1915 Handstamped
in Black, Red or Green

 b

| 1919 | | | Without Gum |
|---|---|---|---|
| O17 | A6 | ¼a dark blue | 2.60 |
| O18 | A6 | ½a black | 4.50 |
| O19 | A6 | 1a vermilion | 16.00 |
| O20 | A6 | 2a emerald | 29.00 |
| O21 | A6 | 2½a yellow | 30.00 |
| O22 | A6 | 3a brown | 35.00 |
| O23 | A6 | 4a yel green | 120.00 |
| O24 | A6 | 6a blue | 45.00 |
| O25 | A6 | 8a orange | 52.50 |
| O26 | A6 | 10a olive green | 140.00 |
| O27 | A6 | 12a dark green | 120.00 |
| O28 | A6 | 1r violet | 82.50 |
| O29 | A6 | 2r car brn & blk | 275.00 |
| O30 | A6 | 3r blue & brown | 325.00 |
| O31 | A6 | 4r pale grn & red brn | 450.00 |
| O32 | A6 | 5r ver & pale grn | 490.00 |
| | | Nos. O17-O32 (16) | 2,217. |

Note following No. O16 applies to this issue.

Regular Issue of 1915 Handstamped
in Carmine or Black

 c

| 1919 | | | *Rouletted in Color* |
|---|---|---|---|
| | | | *Without Gum* |
| O33 | A6 | ¼a blue | 11.00 |
| O34 | A6 | ½a black | 18.00 |
| O35 | A6 | 1a vermilion | 35.00 |
| O36 | A6 | 2a yel green | 140.00 |
| O37 | A6 | 8a orange | 450.00 |
| O38 | A6 | 10a olive | 700.00 |
| O39 | A6 | 12a dark green | 900.00 |
| | | Nos. O33-O39 (7) | 2,254. |

Nos. 33 and 35 Handstamped Type
"a" in Black or Carmine

| 1941 | | | Perf. 11 |
|---|---|---|---|
| O41 | A6 | ½a black | 240.00 |
| O42 | A6 | 2a yellow green | 825.00 |

Nos. 32 and 35 Handstamped Type
"b" in Black or Carmine

| O43 | A6 | ¼a light blue | 90.00 |
|---|---|---|---|
| O44 | A6 | 2a yellow green | 210.00 |

Nos. 32-35 Handstamped Type "c" in
Black or Carmine

| 1941 | | | |
|---|---|---|---|
| O45 | A6 | ¼a light blue | 190.00 |
| O46 | A6 | ½a black | 375.00 |
| O47 | A6 | 1a carmine | 700.00 |
| O48 | A6 | 2a yellow green | 625.00 |
| | | Nos. O45-O48 (4) | 1,890. |

Nos. 36 to 42
Overprinted in Black or
Carmine

| 1941 | | | Perf. 11 | |
|---|---|---|---|---|
| O49 | A7 | 3p brt ultra (C) | 7.50 | 24.00 |
| O50 | A7 | 6p indigo (C) | 20.00 | 24.00 |
| O51 | A7 | 1a red orange | 19.00 | 16.00 |
| O52 | A7 | 2a fawn | 20.00 | 19.00 |
| O53 | A7 | 4a brt yel green | 72.50 | 160.00 |
| O54 | A7 | 8a dull green | 225.00 | 950.00 |
| O55 | A7 | 1r royal blue (C) | 310.00 | 950.00 |
| | | Nos. O49-O55 (7) | 674.00 | 2,143. |

### BUSSAHIR

ˈbus-ə-ˌhi͜ə r

### (Bashahr)

LOCATION — A Feudatory State in the Punjab Hill States Agency
AREA — 3,439 sq. mi.
POP. — 100,192
CAPITAL — Bashahr

Tiger
A1     A2

A3     A4

A5     A6

A7     A8

Overprinted "R S" in Violet, Rose, or
Blue Green (BG)

Laid Paper

| 1895 | | Unwmk. | Litho. | *Imperf.* | |
|---|---|---|---|---|---|
| 1 | A1 | ¼a pink (V) | 3,750. | |
| 2 | A2 | ½a slate (R) | 750.00 | 1,000. |
| 3 | A3 | 1a red (V) | 300.00 | |
| 4 | A4 | 2a yellow (V,R) | 110.00 | 300.00 |
| 5 | A5 | 4a violet (V,R) | 190.00 | |
| 6 | A6 | 8a brown (V,BG) | 210.00 | 375.00 |
| a. | | Without overprint | 400.00 | |
| 7 | A7 | 12a green (V,R) | 450.00 | |
| 8 | A8 | 1r ultra (R) | 190.00 | |
| | | Nos. 1-8 (8) | 5,950. | |

| | | | *Perf. 7 to 14* | |
|---|---|---|---|---|
| 9 | A1 | ¼a pink (V,BG) | 100.00 | 150.00 |
| 10 | A2 | ½a slate (R) | 35.00 | 210.00 |
| 11 | A3 | 1a red (V) | 35.00 | 140.00 |
| a. | | Pin-perf. | 275.00 | 300.00 |
| 12 | A4 | 2a yel (V,R,BG) | 47.50 | 140.00 |
| a. | | Pin-perf. (V,R) | 100.00 | 240.00 |
| 13 | A5 | 4a violet (V,R,BG) | 37.50 | 140.00 |
| a. | | Pin-perf. | 450.00 | |
| 14 | A6 | 8a brown (V,BG) | 35.00 | 160.00 |
| 15 | A7 | 12a green (V,R) | 120.00 | 200.00 |
| a. | | Pin-perf. (R) | 650.00 | 825.00 |
| b. | | Without overprint | 325.00 | |
| 16 | A8 | 1r ultra (V,R) | 65.00 | 180.00 |
| a. | | Pin-perf. (R) | 700.00 | |
| | | Nos. 9-16 (8) | 475.00 | 1,320. |

"R. S." are the initials of Tika Raghunath Singh, son of the Raja.

A9     A10

A11     A12

A13     A14

Overprinted "R S" Like Nos. 1-16
Wove Paper

| 1896 | | | Engr. | *Pin-perf.* | |
|---|---|---|---|---|---|
| 17 | A9 | ¼a dk gray vio (R) | — | 1,500. |
| 18 | A10 | ½a blue gray (R) | 1,200. | 450.00 |

| 1900 | | | Litho. | *Imperf.* | |
|---|---|---|---|---|---|
| 19 | A9 | ¼a red (V,BG) | 7.50 | 16.00 |
| 20 | A9 | ¼a violet (V,R) | 12.50 | |
| 21 | A10 | ½a blue (V,R) | 15.00 | 40.00 |
| 22 | A11 | 1a olive (V,R) | 27.50 | 65.00 |
| 23 | A11 | 1a red (V,BG) | 7.00 | 24.00 |
| 24 | A12 | 2a yellow (V) | 75.00 | |
| a. | | 2a ocher (R) | 75.00 | |
| 25 | A13 | 2a yellow (V) | 90.00 | |
| 26 | A14 | 4a brn vio (V,R,BG) | 82.50 | 180.00 |
| | | Nos. 19-26 (8) | 317.00 | |

| | | | *Pin-perf.* | |
|---|---|---|---|---|
| 27 | A9 | ¼a red (V,BG) | 6.25 | 16.00 |
| 28 | A9 | ¼a violet (R) | 30.00 | 27.50 |
| 29 | A10 | ½a blue (V,R) | 90.00 | 140.00 |
| 30 | A11 | 1a olive (V,R) | 40.00 | |
| 31 | A11 | 1a red (V) | — | 300.00 |
| 32 | A11 | 1a vermilion (BG) | 11.00 | 22.50 |
| 33 | A12 | 2a yellow (BG) | 1,250. | 1,350. |
| 34 | A13 | 2a yellow (V,R) | 75.00 | 120.00 |
| a. | | 2a ocher (V) | 100.00 | |
| 35 | A14 | 4a brn vio (V,R,BG) | 120.00 | |
| | | Nos. 27-35 (8) | 1,622. | |

Obsolete March 31, 1901.

Stamps overprinted with the monogram above (RNS) or with the monogram "PS" were never issued for postal purposes. They are either reprints or remainders to which this overprint has been applied. Many other varieties have appeared since the stamps became obsolete. It is probable that all or nearly all of them are reprints.

### CHARKHARI

chər-ˈkär-ē

LOCATION — A Feudatory State in the Bundelkhand Agency in Central India.
AREA — 880 sq. mi.
POP. — 120,351
CAPITAL — Maharajnagar

A1

Thin White or Blue Wove Paper

| 1894 | | Unwmk. | Typo. | *Imperf.* | |
|---|---|---|---|---|---|
| | | | Value in the Plural | |
| | | | *Without Gum* | |
| 1 | A1 | 1a green | 2,750. | 3,750. |
| 2 | A1 | 2a green | 3,250. | |
| 3 | A1 | 4a green | 2,100. | |

| 1897 | | | | | |
|---|---|---|---|---|---|
| | | Value in the Singular | | |
| | | *Without Gum* | | |
| 3A | A1 | ¼a rose | 1,800. | 1,100. |
| 4 | A1 | ¼a purple | 5.50 | 5.50 |
| 5 | A1 | ½a purple | 3.75 | 4.50 |
| 6 | A1 | 1a green | 6.50 | 9.50 |

| 7 | A1 | 2a green | 11.00 | 12.50 |
| 8 | A1 | 4a green | 17.50 | 27.50 |
| | | Nos. 4-8 (5) | 44.25 | 59.50 |

In a later printing, the numerals of Nos. 4-8 are smaller or of different shape.

Proofs are known on paper of various colors.

A2                          A3

Size: 19½x23mm

| **1909** | | **Litho.** | **Perf. 11** | |
| 9 | A2 | 1p red brown | 7.00 | 57.50 |
| 10 | A2 | 1p pale blue | .90 | .65 |
| 11 | A2 | ½a scarlet | 1.50 | 1.90 |
| 12 | A2 | 1a light green | 3.75 | 2.40 |
| 13 | A2 | 2a ultra | 4.50 | 5.25 |
| 14 | A2 | 4a deep green | 6.25 | 8.25 |
| 15 | A2 | 8a brick red | 11.00 | 30.00 |
| 16 | A2 | 1r red brown | 19.00 | 62.50 |
| | | Nos. 9-16 (8) | 53.90 | 168.45 |

See #22-27, 39-43. For surcharges see #37-38A.

| **1912-17** | **Handstamped** | | **Imperf.** |
| | **Without Gum** | | |
| 21 | A3 | 1p violet ('17) | 10.50 | 7.50 |
| c. | | Double frameline | 1,050. | 125.00 |

The 1p black, type A3, is a proof.

A3a

Wove Paper

| **1922** | | | **Imperf.** |
| | **Without Gum** | | |
| 21A | A3a | 1a violet | 120.00 | 125.00 |
| b. | | Perf. 11, laid paper | 110.00 | 210.00 |

Type of 1909 Issue Redrawn
Size: 20x23½mm

| **1930-40** | | | **Typo.** |
| | **Without Gum** | | |
| 22 | A2 | 1p dark blue | .90 | 21.00 |
| 23 | A2 | ½a olive green | 3.75 | 21.00 |
| 23A | A2 | ½a cop brown ('40) | 9.00 | 37.50 |
| 24 | A2 | 1a light green | 3.75 | 24.00 |
| 25 | A2 | 1a chocolate | 19.00 | 40.00 |
| 25A | A2 | 1a dull red ('40) | 190.00 | 100.00 |
| 26 | A2 | 2a light blue | 1.90 | 25.00 |
| a. | | Tête bêche pair | 14.00 | |
| 27 | A2 | 4a carmine | 4.50 | 30.00 |
| a. | | Tête bêche pair | 21.00 | |
| | | Nos. 22-27 (8) | 232.80 | 298.50 |

Guesthouse of Raja at Charkhari Reservoir — A4

Imlia Palace — A5

Industrial School — A6

---

View of City — A7

Maharajnagar Fort, Charkhari City — A8

Guesthouse A9

Palace Gate — A10

Temples at Rampur — A11

Govordhan Temple — A12

| **1931** | | | **Perf. 11, 11½, 12** | |
| 28 | A4 | ½a dull green | 3.25 | .20 |
| 29 | A5 | 1a black brown | 2.40 | .20 |
| 30 | A6 | 2a purple | 2.50 | .20 |
| 31 | A7 | 4a olive green | 2.25 | .20 |
| 32 | A8 | 8a magenta | 3.00 | .20 |
| 33 | A9 | 1r rose & green | 4.00 | .30 |
| 34 | A10 | 2r brown & red | 6.00 | .35 |
| 35 | A11 | 3r bl grn & choc | 22.50 | .60 |
| 36 | A12 | 5r violet & blue | 14.00 | .75 |
| | | Nos. 28-36 (9) | 59.90 | 3.00 |

Size range of A4-A12: 30-31x19½-24mm.
Many errors of perforation and printing exist.
Used values are for canceled to order stamps.

Nos. 15-16 Surcharged in Black

½ As.

| **1940** | | | **Perf. 11** | |
| 37 | A2 | ½a on 8a brick red | 52.50 | 200.00 |
| a. | | Surcharge inverted | 450.00 | 600.00 |
| b. | | "1" of "½" inverted | 400.00 | |
| 38 | A2 | 1a on 1r red brown | 175.00 | 625.00 |
| b. | | Surcharge inverted | 490.00 | |
| 38A | A2 | "1 ANNA" on 1r red brown | 400.00 | 450.00 |

Type of 1930

| **1943** | | **Unwmk.** | **Typo.** | **Imperf.** |
| | | **Size: 20x23½mm** | | |
| 39 | A2 | 1p violet | 32.50 | 240.00 |
| a. | | Tête bêche pair | 82.50 | |
| 40 | A2 | 1p apple green | 90.00 | 325.00 |
| 41 | A2 | ½a orange red | 30.00 | 62.50 |
| 42 | A2 | ½a black | 90.00 | 290.00 |
| 43 | A2 | 2a grayish green | 140.00 | 290.00 |
| a. | | Tête bêche pair | 180.00 | |
| | | Nos. 39-43 (5) | 382.50 | 1,207. |

---

## COCHIN

kō-'chin

LOCATION — A Feudatory State in the Madras States Agency in Southern India.
AREA — 1,480 sq. mi.
POP. — 1,422,875 (1941)
CAPITAL — Ernakulam

See the United State of Travancore and Cochin.

6 Puttans = 5 Annas
12 Pies = 1 Anna
16 Annas = 1 Rupee

A1                  State Seal — A1a

| **1892** | | **Unwmk.** | **Typo.** | **Perf. 12** | |
| 1 | A1 | ½p yellow | 3.75 | 4.50 |
| a. | | Imperf., pair | | |
| b. | | Laid paper | 700.00 | 200.00 |
| 2 | A1 | 1p red violet | 4.50 | 4.00 |
| a. | | 1p purple (error) | 175.00 | 125.00 |
| 3 | A1 | 2p purple | 3.00 | 3.25 |
| a. | | Imperf. | | |
| | | Nos. 1-3 (3) | 11.25 | 11.75 |

Nos. 1 to 3 sometimes have watermark large umbrella in the sheet.

### Wmk. Coat of Arms and Inscription in Sheet

| **1896** | | | | |
| 4 | A1a | 1p violet | 140.00 | 140.00 |

**Wmk. 43**

| 4A | A1a | 1p violet | 27.50 | 47.50 |

Originally intended for revenue use, Nos. 4-4A were later authorized for postal use. Beware of fraudulently removed fiscal markings.

| **1894** | | | **Wmk. 41** | |
| | | **Thin Paper** | | |
| 5 | A1 | ½p orange | 3.75 | 2.25 |
| a. | | Imperf., pair | | |
| 6 | A1 | 1p magenta | 10.50 | 10.50 |
| 7 | A1 | 2p purple | 6.25 | 6.75 |
| a. | | Imperf., pair | | |
| | | Nos. 5-7 (3) | 20.50 | 19.50 |

A2

A3                  A4

A5

Thin Paper

| **1898** | | | | |
| 8 | A2 | 3p ultra | 2.10 | 1.60 |
| a. | | Double impression | 950.00 | |
| 9 | A3 | ½p gray green | 2.50 | 2.25 |
| a. | | Pair, one sideways | | 3,750. |
| 10 | A4 | 1p rose | 5.50 | 2.50 |
| a. | | Laid paper | | 2,400. |
| b. | | Tete beche pair | 5,250. | 3,250. |
| c. | | As "a," tete beche pair | | 12,000. |
| 11 | A5 | 2p purple | 5.00 | 3.25 |
| | | Nos. 8-11 (4) | 15.10 | 9.60 |

---

Thick Paper

| **1903** | | | | |
| 12 | A2 | 3p ultra | 1.80 | .20 |
| d. | | Double impression | | 450.00 |
| 12A | A3 | ½p gray green | 1.90 | .60 |
| e. | | Double impression | | 450.00 |
| f. | | Pair, one sideways | 1,250. | 1,250. |
| 12B | A4 | 1p rose | 2.50 | .20 |
| g. | | Tete beche pair | | 5,250. |
| 12C | A5 | 2p purple | 3.75 | .75 |
| h. | | Double impression | 1,250. | 450.00 |
| | | Nos. 8-11 (4) | 15.10 | 9.60 |

> Beware of fake overprint surcharge varieties, such as double, inverted, etc. This applies also to early official varieties. Such varieties require expertization.

Type of 1898 Surcharged

| **1909** | | | | |
| 13 | A2 | 2p on 3p red violet | .20 | .75 |
| a. | | Inverted surcharge | 15.00 | 150.00 |
| b. | | Pair, stamps tete beche | 250.00 | 290.00 |
| c. | | Pair, stamps & surch. tete beche | 300.00 | 375.00 |

The surcharge is also known in a thin "2" measuring 5½x7mm, with curving foot. Values: unused $1,200; used $600.

Sri Rama Varma I — A6

| **1911-13** | | **Engr.** | **Perf. 14** | |
| 14 | A6 | 2p brown | .45 | .20 |
| a. | | Imperf., pair | | |
| 15 | A6 | 3p blue | 2.25 | .20 |
| a. | | Perf. 14x12½ | 40.00 | 3.00 |
| 16 | A6 | 4p yel green | 2.50 | .20 |
| 17 | A6 | 9p car rose | 2.10 | .20 |
| 18 | A6 | 1a orange buff | 4.50 | .20 |
| 19 | A6 | 1½a lilac | 11.00 | .65 |
| 20 | A6 | 2a gray | 11.00 | .60 |
| 21 | A6 | 3a vermilion | 57.50 | 57.50 |
| | | Nos. 14-21 (8) | 91.30 | 59.75 |

For surcharge and overprints see Nos. 34, O2-O9, O23-O24, O27.

Sri Rama Varma II
A7                  A8

| **1918-23** | | **Engr.** | **Perf. 14** | |
| 23 | A7 | 2p brown | 12.00 | .20 |
| 24 | A7 | 4p green | 1.50 | .20 |
| 25 | A7 | 6p red brown ('22) | 3.75 | .20 |
| 26 | A7 | 8p black brown ('23) | 2.50 | .20 |
| 27 | A7 | 9p carmine rose | 30.00 | .50 |
| 28 | A7 | 10p deep blue | 9.00 | .20 |
| 29 | A8 | 1a brown orange | 27.50 | 4.50 |
| 30 | A7 | 1½a red violet ('21) | 5.50 | .30 |
| 31 | A7 | 2a gray | 6.25 | .20 |
| 32 | A7 | 2¼a yel green ('22) | 10.50 | 4.75 |
| 33 | A7 | 3a vermilion | 17.50 | .50 |
| | | Nos. 23-33 (11) | 126.00 | 11.75 |

The 2p and 1a are found in two types, the difference lying in the first of the three characters directly above the maharaja's head.

For surcharges and overprints see Nos. 36-40, 52-53, O10-O22, O25-O26, O28-O36, O71A.

No. 15 Surcharged

Type I — Numeral 8mm high. Curved foot. Top begins with a ball. (As illustrated.)
Type II — Numeral 9mm high. Curved foot. Top begins with a curved line.
Type III — Numeral 6mm high. Straight foot. "Two pies" 15mm wide.
Type IV — "2" as in type III. Capital "P" in "Pies." "Two Pies" 13mm wide.
Type V — Heavy gothic numeral. Capital "P" in "Pies."

**1922-29**

| | | | |
|---|---|---|---|
| 34 | A6 2p on 3p blue (Type I) | .60 | .45 |
| a. | Type II | 5.00 | 1.50 |
| b. | Type III | 10.50 | .50 |
| c. | Type IV | 16.00 | 16.00 |
| d. | Type V | 110.00 | 200.00 |
| e. | Double surcharge, I | 500.00 | 500.00 |
| f. | Double surcharge II | 1,100. | |

Types II and III exist with a capital "P" in "Pies." It occurs once in each sheet of the second and third settings. There are four settings.

Type V is the first stamp, fourth row, of the fourth setting.

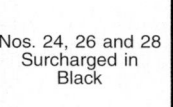

No. 32 Surcharged

**1928**

| | | | |
|---|---|---|---|
| 36 | A7 1a on 2¼a yel green | 9.00 | 18.00 |
| a. | Double surcharge | | |

Nos. 24, 26 and 28 Surcharged in Black

**1932-33**

| | | | |
|---|---|---|---|
| 38 | A7 3p on 4p green | 1.90 | 2.10 |
| 39 | A7 3p on 8p black brown | 3.25 | 4.00 |
| 40 | A7 9p on 10p deep blue | 2.25 | 5.00 |
| | Nos. 38-40 (3) | 7.40 | 11.10 |

Sri Rama Varma III
A9                    A10

**1933-38** | **Engr.** | **Perf. 13x13½** |

| | | | |
|---|---|---|---|
| 41 | A9 2p brown ('36) | 1.25 | .75 |
| 42 | A9 4p green | .90 | .20 |
| 43 | A9 6p red brown | 1.00 | .20 |
| 44 | A10 1a brown org ('34) | 1.25 | .30 |
| 45 | A9 1a8p rose red | 4.50 | 9.50 |
| 46 | A9 2a gray black ('38) | 9.00 | 2.40 |
| 47 | A9 2¼a yellow green | 2.50 | .45 |
| 48 | A9 3a red org ('38) | 8.25 | 2.40 |
| 49 | A9 3a4p violet | 2.50 | 2.10 |
| 50 | A9 6a8p black brown | 2.50 | 22.50 |
| 51 | A9 10a deep blue | 4.50 | 25.00 |
| | Nos. 41-51 (11) | 38.15 | 65.80 |

See Nos. 55-58. For overprints and surcharges see Nos. 54, 59-62, 73A-74, 76-77, 89, O37-O57, O70-O71, O72-O77A, O89.

Nos. 26 and 28 Surcharged in Red

**1934** | **Perf. 13½** |

| | | | |
|---|---|---|---|
| 52 | A7 6p on 8p black brown | 1.10 | .90 |
| 53 | A7 6p on 10p dark blue | 2.50 | 3.00 |

No. 44 Overprinted in Black

a

**1939** | **Engr.** |

| | | | |
|---|---|---|---|
| 54 | A10 1a brown orange | 6.25 | 2.50 |

Types of 1933-38

**1938-41** | **Litho.** | **Perf. 11, 13** |

| | | | |
|---|---|---|---|
| 55 | A9 2p dull brown | 1.25 | .60 |
| 56 | A9 4p dull green ('41) | 1.25 | .50 |
| 57 | A9 6p red brown | 4.50 | .20 |
| c. | Perf. 13 | | 4,750. |
| 57A | A10 1a brown orange | 95.00 | 140.00 |
| 58 | A10 2¼a yellow green | 7.50 | .35 |
| | Nos. 55-58 (5) | 109.50 | 141.65 |

Type of 1934 Overprinted in Black
Type "a" or

b

**1941-42** | **Perf. 11 (#59), 13 (#60)** |

| | | | |
|---|---|---|---|
| 59 | A10(a) 1a brown orange | 425.00 | 2.50 |
| a. | Perf. 13 | | 525.00 |
| 60 | A10(b) 1a brown org ('42) | 16.00 | .90 |
| a. | Perf. 11 | 1.00 | 2.50 |

No. 45 Surcharged in Black

c

**1943-44** | **Engr.** | **Perf. 13x13½** |

| | | | |
|---|---|---|---|
| 61 | A9 3p on 1a8p rose red ('44) | 4.25 | 30.00 |
| 62 | A9 1a3p on 1a8p rose red | 1.25 | .75 |

Maharaja Sri Kerala Varma
A11                    A12

**1943** | **Litho.** | **Wmk. 294** | **Perf. 11, 13** |

| | | | |
|---|---|---|---|
| 63 | A11 2p dull gray brn, wmk. 41 | 4.25 | 6.75 |
| a. | Wmk. 294 | 37.50 | 5.50 |
| 64 | A11 4p gray green | 4.50 | 8.25 |
| a. | Wmk. 41 | 1,100. | 550.00 |
| 65 | A11 6p red brown | 4.75 | .20 |
| 66 | A11 9p ultramarine | 55.00 | 1.90 |

| | | | |
|---|---|---|---|
| 67 | A12 1a brown orange | 29.00 | 80.00 |
| a. | Wmk. 41 | 120.00 | 175.00 |
| 68 | A11 2¼a lt ol green | 32.50 | 3.75 |
| | Nos. 63-68 (6) | 130.00 | 100.85 |

For surcharges and overprints see Nos. 69-73, 75, 78, 78B, O58-O69.

No. 64 Surcharged Type "c"

| | | | |
|---|---|---|---|
| 69 | A11 3p on 4p gray green | 8.75 | .20 |
| a. | Wmk. 41 | 110.00 | 35.00 |

Nos. 64, 64a and 65 Surcharged in Black

d

**1944-48** | **Wmk. 294** |

| | | | |
|---|---|---|---|
| 70 | A11 2p on 6p red brown | .95 | 6.00 |
| 71 | A11 3p on 4p gray green | 8.75 | .20 |
| 72 | A11 3p on 6p red brown | 1.00 | .20 |
| 73 | A11 4p on 6p red brown | 6.25 | 18.00 |
| | Nos. 70-73 (4) | 16.95 | 24.40 |

Nos. 57A, 67a Surcharged in Black

**1944** | **Litho.** | **Wmk. 41** |

| | | | |
|---|---|---|---|
| 73A | A10 6p on 1a brown org | 300.00 | 225.00 |
| 74 | A10 9p on 1a brown org | 450.00 | 60.00 |
| 75 | A12 9p on 1a brown org | 8.00 | 5.50 |
| | Nos. 73A-75 (3) | 758.00 | 290.50 |

No. 56 Surcharged Type "c" in Black

| | | | |
|---|---|---|---|
| 76 | A9 3p on 4p dull green | 8.75 | 6.00 |

Nos. 57A, 67a Surcharged in Black

**1944**

| | | | |
|---|---|---|---|
| 77 | A10 9p on 1a brown orange | 30.00 | 12.00 |
| 78 | A12 9p on 1a brown orange | 9.50 | 3.25 |

No. 67a Surcharged Type "c"

**1944** | **Wmk. 41** |

| | | | |
|---|---|---|---|
| 78B | A12 1a3p on 1a brn org | | 5,600. |

Maharaja Ravi Varma
A13                    A15

**1944-46** | **Wmk. 294** | **Perf. 13** |

| | | | |
|---|---|---|---|
| 79 | A13 9p ultra ('46) | 20.00 | 27.50 |
| a. | Perf. 11 | 20.00 | 6.00 |
| 80 | A13 1a3p magenta | 10.00 | 12.50 |
| 81 | A13 1a9p ultra ('46) | 12.00 | 24.00 |
| | Nos. 79-81 (3) | 42.00 | 64.00 |

For overprints and surcharges see Nos. O78-O80, Travancore 12, 14, O10.

**1946-50** | **Litho.** | **Perf. 13** |

| | | | |
|---|---|---|---|
| 82 | A15 2p dull brown | 3.25 | .25 |
| a. | Perf. 11 | 10.00 | .90 |
| b. | Perf. 11x13 | 450.00 | 210.00 |
| 83 | A15 3p carmine rose | .60 | .45 |
| 83A | A15 4p gray green ('50) | 3,100. | 120.00 |

| | | | |
|---|---|---|---|
| 84 | A15 6p red brown ('47) | 30.00 | 9.50 |
| a. | Perf. 11 | 210.00 | 8.25 |
| 85 | A15 9p ultramarine | 1.90 | .20 |
| 86 | A15 1a dp orange ('47) | 11.00 | 47.50 |
| a. | Perf. 11 | 625.00 | |
| 87 | A15 2a gray ('47) | 150.00 | 12.50 |
| a. | Perf. 11 | 190.00 | 10.00 |
| 88 | A15 3a vermilion | 100.00 | 225.00 |
| | Nos. 82-83,84-88 (7) | 296.75 | 295.40 |

For surcharges and overprints see Nos. 98-99, O81-O88, Travancore 8, 13, 15-15A, O11.

No. 45 Surcharged Type "d"
**Perf. 13x13½**

**1947-48** | **Wmk. 41** | **Engr.** |

| | | | |
|---|---|---|---|
| 89 | A9 6p on 1a8p rose red | 4.25 | 30.00 |

Maharaja Sri Kerala Varma II — A16

Die I                    Die II

Two dies on 2p: Die I, back of headdress almost touches value tablet; Die II, back of headdress further away from value tablet.

**1948-49** | **Wmk. 294** | **Perf. 11** |

| | | | |
|---|---|---|---|
| 90 | A16 2p olive brown | 2.25 | .20 |
| a. | Die II | 190.00 | 3.25 |
| 91 | A16 3p car ('49) | 1.90 | .20 |
| 92 | A16 4p gray green | 21.00 | 5.25 |
| a. | Horiz. pair, imperf. vert. | 350.00 | 500.00 |
| 93 | A16 6p red brown | 22.50 | .35 |
| 94 | A16 9p ultra ('49) | 3.00 | .75 |
| 95 | A16 2a black | 80.00 | 3.75 |
| 96 | A16 3a ver ('49) | 87.50 | 1.50 |
| 97 | A16 3a4p violet ('49) | 87.50 | 525.00 |
| | Nos. 90-97 (8) | 305.65 | 537.00 |

For overprints see Nos. O90-O97, Travancore 9-11, O8-O9.

No. 86 Surcharged Type "d" in Black

**1949**

| | | | |
|---|---|---|---|
| 98 | A15 6p on 1a dp orange | 80.00 | 225.00 |
| 99 | A15 9p on 1a dp orange | 120.00 | 225.00 |

Dutch Palace
A17

Design: 2a, Chinese fishing net.

**1949** | **Unwmk.** | **Perf. 11** |

| | | | |
|---|---|---|---|
| 100 | A17 2a gray | 6.25 | 12.50 |
| a. | Imperf. vert., horiz. pair | 600.00 | |
| 101 | A17 2¼a gray green | 3.50 | 14.00 |
| a. | Imperf. vert., horiz. pair | 600.00 | 600.00 |

See Travancore-Cochin for succeeding issues.

---

**OFFICIAL STAMPS**

See note above No. 13.

Stamps and Type of 1911-14 Overprinted

h

**1913-14** | **Wmk. 41** | **Engr.** | **Perf. 14** |

| | | | |
|---|---|---|---|
| O2 | A6 4p yel green | 13.50 | .20 |
| a. | Inverted overprint | — | 450.00 |

| O3 | A6 | 9p car rose | 160.00 | .20 |
|---|---|---|---|---|
| O4 | A6 | 1½a red violet | 72.50 | .20 |
| a. | | Double overprint | — | 1,000. |
| O5 | A6 | 2a gray | 19.00 | .20 |
| O6 | A6 | 3a vermilion | 82.50 | .65 |
| O7 | A6 | 6a violet | 90.00 | 3.00 |
| O8 | A6 | 12a blue | 60.00 | 10.00 |
| O9 | A6 | 1½r deep green | 52.50 | 110.00 |
| | | Nos. O2-O9 (8) | 550.00 | 124.45 |

### Stamps and Type of 1918-23 Overprinted

h

**1918-34**

| O10 | A7 | 4p green | 6.00 | .20 |
|---|---|---|---|---|
| a. | | Double overprint | — | 750.00 |
| O11 | A7 | 6p red brn ('22) | 18.00 | .20 |
| a. | | Double overprint | — | 650.00 |
| O12 | A7 | 8p blk brn ('26) | 16.00 | .20 |
| O13 | A7 | 9p carmine rose | 97.50 | .20 |
| O14 | A7 | 10p dp blue ('23) | 21.00 | .20 |
| O16 | A7 | 1½a red vio ('21) | 8.25 | .20 |
| a. | | Double overprint | — | 1,000. |
| O17 | A7 | 2a gray | 62.50 | .45 |
| O18 | A7 | 2¼a yel grn ('22) | 19.00 | .20 |
| b. | | Double overprint | — | 625.00 |
| O19 | A7 | 3a ver ('22) | 27.50 | .35 |
| a. | | Double overprint | — | 650.00 |
| O20 | A7 | 6a violet ('22) | 57.50 | .75 |
| O21 | A7 | 12a blue ('29) | 25.00 | 7.50 |
| O22 | A7 | 1½r dk green ('34) | 37.50 | 175.00 |
| | | Nos. O10-O22 (12) | 395.75 | 185.45 |

On Nos. O2-O22, width of overprint varies from 14¾mm to 16½mm.

### No. 15 Overprinted in Red

j

**1921**

| O23 | A6 | 3p blue | 175.00 | .20 |
|---|---|---|---|---|

### Nos. O3 and O13 Surcharged with New Values

**1923-29**

| O24 | A6 | 8p on 9p car rose | 525.00 | 2.50 |
|---|---|---|---|---|
| O25 | A7 | 8p on 9p car rose | 100.00 | .20 |
| a. | | Double surcharge | — | 400.00 |
| O26 | A7 | 10p on 9p car rose ('25) | 120.00 | 1.50 |
| a. | | Double surcharge | — | 450.00 |
| O27 | A6 | 10p on 9p car rose ('29) | 1,750. | 27.50 |
| | | Nos. O24-O27 (4) | 2,495. | 31.70 |

### Regular Issue of 1918-23 Overprinted

k

**1933-34**

| O28 | A7 | 4p green | 32.50 | 2.50 |
|---|---|---|---|---|
| O29 | A7 | 6p red brown ('34) | 21.00 | .20 |
| O30 | A7 | 8p black brown | 10.00 | .20 |
| O31 | A7 | 10p deep blue | 9.00 | .20 |
| O32 | A7 | 2a gray ('34) | 60.00 | .35 |
| O33 | A7 | 3a vermilion | 12.50 | .30 |
| O34 | A7 | 6a dk violet ('34) | 150.00 | 4.50 |
| | | Nos. O28-O34 (7) | 295.00 | 8.25 |

Same with Additional Surcharge on Type of Regular Issue of 1918-23 in Red

| O35 | A7 | 6p on 8p black brown | 3.75 | .20 |
|---|---|---|---|---|
| O36 | A7 | 6p on 10p dk blue ('34) | 6.00 | .20 |

### Regular Issue of 1933 Overprinted Type "k" in Black as in 1933-34

**1933-35**    *Perf. 13x13½*

| O37 | A9 | 4p green | 6.25 | .20 |
|---|---|---|---|---|
| O38 | A9 | 6p red brown | 5.50 | .20 |
| O39 | A10 | 1a brown orange | 24.00 | .20 |
| O40 | A9 | 1a8p rose red | 2.25 | .45 |
| O41 | A9 | 2a gray | 27.50 | .20 |
| O42 | A9 | 2¼a yellow green | 9.00 | .20 |
| O43 | A9 | 3a vermilion | 67.50 | .20 |
| O44 | A9 | 3a4p violet | 2.25 | .20 |
| O45 | A9 | 6a8p black brown | 2.25 | .30 |
| O46 | A9 | 10a deep blue | 2.25 | 1.50 |
| | | Nos. O37-O46 (10) | 148.75 | 3.65 |

### Regular Stamps of 1934-38 Overprinted in Black

m

**1939-41**    *Perf. 11, 13x13½*

| O47 | A10 | 1a brown orange | 50.00 | .90 |
|---|---|---|---|---|
| O48 | A9 | 2a gray black | 27.50 | 3.00 |
| O49 | A9 | 3a red orange | 13.50 | 3.75 |
| | | Nos. O47-O49 (3) | 91.00 | 7.65 |

### Similar Overprint on Types of 1933-36

*Perf. 11, 13x13½*

**1939-41**    **Wmk. 294**

| O50 | A9 | 4p dull green ('41) | 92.50 | 24.00 |
|---|---|---|---|---|

**Wmk. 41**

| O51 | A9 | 6p red brown ('41) | 14.00 | 6.50 |
|---|---|---|---|---|
| a. | | Wmk. 294 | 25.00 | 1.50 |
| O52 | A10 | 1a brown orange | 1.25 | .20 |
| a. | | Wmk. 294 | 2.25 | 6.50 |
| O53 | A9 | 3a orange ('40) | 3.75 | 2.50 |
| b. | | Wmk. 294 | 24.00 | 11.00 |
| | | Nos. O50-O53 (4) | 111.50 | 33.20 |

O53A — Similar Overprint in Narrow Serifed Capitals on No. 57

**Wmk. 41**    *Perf. 11*

| O53A | A9 | 6p red brown | 1,050. | 600.00 |
|---|---|---|---|---|

### Type of 1933-36 Overprinted in Black

o

*Perf. 10½, 11, 13x13½*

| O54 | A9 | 4p dull green ('41) | 35.00 | 4.00 |
|---|---|---|---|---|
| O55 | A9 | 6p red brown ('41) | 32.50 | .60 |
| O56 | A9 | 2a gray black | 25.00 | 1.50 |
| | | Nos. O54-O56 (3) | 92.50 | 6.10 |

### Type of 1934 Overprinted in Black

p

**1941**    *Perf. 11*

| O57 | A10 | 1a brown orange | 375.00 | 3.75 |
|---|---|---|---|---|

### Stamps and Types of 1944 Overprinted in Black

q

*Perf. 11, 13x13½*

**1944-48**    **Wmk. 294**

| O58 | A11 | 4p gray green | 50.00 | 10.00 |
|---|---|---|---|---|
| a. | | Perf. 11 | 175.00 | 8.25 |
| O59 | A11 | 6p red brown | 3.50 | .20 |
| O60 | A11 | 2a gray black | 8.75 | 1.50 |
| O61 | A11 | 2¼a dull yel green | 5.25 | 1.60 |
| a. | | Additional ovpt. on back | — | 160.00 |
| O62 | A11 | 3a red orange | 12.50 | 2.50 |
| | | Nos. O58-O62 (5) | 80.00 | 15.80 |

### Same Overprint with Additional Surcharge

| O63 | A11 | 3p on 4p gray green | 4.25 | .20 |
|---|---|---|---|---|
| a. | | Additional overprint on back | — | 210.00 |
| O64 | A12 | 3p on 1a brown org | 32.50 | 11.00 |
| O65 | A11 | 9p on 6p red brown | 16.00 | 5.25 |
| O66 | A12 | 1a3p on 1a brown org | 16.00 | 4.00 |
| | | Nos. O63-O66 (4) | 68.75 | 20.45 |

### Same Overprint in Black on Types of 1944 Surcharged Type "c"

| O67 | A11 | 3p on 4p gray green | 6.25 | .60 |
|---|---|---|---|---|
| O68 | A11 | 9p on 6p red brown | 5.50 | .60 |
| O69 | A12 | 1a3p on 1a brown org | 4.50 | .20 |
| | | Nos. O67-O69 (3) | 16.25 | 1.40 |

### Nos. O52 and O16 Surcharged Type "d"

**1944**   **Wmk. 41**   *Perf. 11, 13x13½, 14*

| O70 | A10 | 3p on 1a brn org | 2.75 | 5.00 |
|---|---|---|---|---|
| O71 | A10 | 9p on 1a brn org | 325.00 | 82.50 |

**Engr.**

| O71A | A7 | 9p on 1½a red vio | 800.00 | 40.00 |
|---|---|---|---|---|

### No. O52 Surcharged Type "c"

| O72 | A10 | 1a3p on 1a brn org | 375.00 | 150.00 |
|---|---|---|---|---|

### No. 76 Overprinted in Black

*Perf. 13*

| O72A | A9 | 3p on 4p dull green | 210.00 | 90.00 |
|---|---|---|---|---|

### No. 45 Overprinted Type "k" and Surcharged Type "d"

**1944-48**   **Wmk. 41**   *Perf. 13x13½*

| O73 | A9 | 9p on 1a8p rose red | 160.00 | 50.00 |
|---|---|---|---|---|
| O74 | A9 | 1a9p on 1a8p rose red | 3.50 | 4.00 |

### No. 45 Overprinted Type "k" and Surcharged Type "c"

**1944-48**

| O75 | A9 | 3p on 1a8p rose red | 7.00 | 4.50 |
|---|---|---|---|---|
| O76 | A9 | 1a9p on 1a8p rose red | 1.90 | .60 |

Type of 1939-41 Overprinted in Black

**1946**    **Wmk. 294**    *Perf. 11*

| O77 | A9 | 2a gray | 92.50 | 1.20 |
|---|---|---|---|---|
| O77A | A9 | 2¼a yellow green | 2,000. | 10.00 |

### Same Overprint in Black on #79-81

**1946**    **Litho.**    *Perf. 13*

| O78 | A13 | 9p ultramarine | 3.75 | .20 |
|---|---|---|---|---|
| O79 | A13 | 1a3p magenta | 2.00 | .20 |
| a. | | Double overprint | 25.00 | 18.00 |
| O80 | A13 | 1a9p ultramarine | .50 | 1.50 |
| | | Nos. O78-O80 (3) | 6.25 | 1.90 |

### Types and Stamps of 1946-48 Overprinted Type "h"

**1946-48**

| O81 | A15 | 3p car rose | 1.50 | .20 |
|---|---|---|---|---|
| O82 | A15 | 4p gray green | 37.50 | 10.00 |
| O83 | A15 | 6p red brown | 17.50 | 2.50 |
| O84 | A15 | 9p ultra | .95 | .20 |
| O85 | A15 | 1a3p magenta | 5.00 | 2.10 |
| O86 | A15 | 1a9p ultra | 6.00 | .60 |
| O87 | A15 | 2a gray black | 19.00 | 4.50 |
| O88 | A15 | 2¼a olive green | 29.00 | 7.50 |
| | | Nos. O81-O88 (8) | 116.45 | 27.60 |

### No. 56 Overprinted Type "q" and Surcharged Type "d"

**1947**   **Wmk. 41**   **Engr.**   *Perf. 13x13½*

| O89 | A9 | 3p on 4p dull green | 32.50 | 11.00 |
|---|---|---|---|---|

### Stamps and Type of 1948-49 Overprinted Type "o"

**1948-49**   **Wmk. 294**   **Litho.**   *Perf. 11*

| O90 | A16 | 3p carmine ('49) | 1.50 | .20 |
|---|---|---|---|---|
| O91 | A16 | 4p gray green | 1.90 | .60 |
| O92 | A16 | 6p red brown | 3.50 | .45 |
| O93 | A16 | 9p ultramarine | 4.00 | .20 |
| O94 | A16 | 2a black ('49) | 3.50 | .20 |
| O95 | A16 | 2¼a lt ol green ('49) | 4.00 | 9.50 |
| O96 | A16 | 3a vermilion ('49) | 1.40 | 1.50 |
| O97 | A16 | 3a4p deep pur ('49) | 55.00 | 67.50 |
| | | Nos. O90-O97 (8) | 74.80 | 80.15 |

See Travancore-Cochin for succeeding issues.

---

## DHAR

'där

LOCATION — A Feudatory State in the Malwa Agency in Central India.
AREA — 1,800 sq. mi.
POP. — 243,521
CAPITAL — Dhar

A1      Arms of Dhar — A2

The stamps of type A1 have an oval control mark handstamped in black.

**Unwmk.**

**1897-1900**   **Typeset**   *Imperf.* **Without Gum**

| 1 | A1 | ½p black, *red* | 4.50 | 5.00 |
|---|---|---|---|---|
| a. | | Characters for "pice" transposed | 100.00 | |
| b. | | Four characters in first word | 4.00 | 6.00 |
| c. | | Without control mark | 500.00 | |
| 2 | A1 | ¼a black, *org red* ('00) | 5.50 | 7.50 |
| a. | | Without control mark | 375.00 | |
| 3 | A1 | ½a black, *lil rose* | 6.75 | 8.25 |
| 4 | A1 | 1a black, *bl grn* | 12.50 | 25.00 |
| 5 | A1 | 2a black, *yel* ('00) | 42.50 | 75.00 |
| | | Nos. 1-5 (5) | 71.75 | 120.75 |

**1898-1900**   **Typo.**   *Perf. 11½*

| 6 | A2 | ½a red | 7.00 | 9.50 |
|---|---|---|---|---|
| 7 | A2 | ½a rose ('00) | 6.25 | 9.00 |
| a. | | Imperf., pair | 60.00 | |
| 8 | A2 | 1a maroon | 6.25 | 12.00 |
| 9 | A2 | 1a violet ('00) | 6.25 | 22.50 |
| 10 | A2 | 1a claret ('00) | 6.25 | 12.00 |
| 11 | A2 | 2a dark green ('00) | 11.00 | 37.50 |
| | | Nos. 6-11 (6) | 43.00 | 102.50 |

Obsolete Mar. 31, 1901.

## DUNGARPUR

LOCATION — A princely state in Rajasthan, in northwestern India.
AREA — 1,447 sq. mi.
POP. — 100,103 (1901)
CAPITAL — Dungarpur

Arms of
Dungarpur — A1

**1933-1947 Unwmk. Litho. Perf. 11**

| | | | | |
|---|---|---|---|---|
| 1 | A1 | ¼a bister yellow | 2,000. | 400.00 |
| | | On cover | | 1,000. |
| a. | | ¼a lemon yellow ('34) | 2,500. | 500.00 |
| | | On cover | | 1,250. |
| 2 | A1 | ¼a salmon ('35) | 5,000. | 1,000. |
| | | On cover | | 2,500. |
| a. | | ¼a red brown ('36) | 3,750. | 750.00 |
| | | On cover | | 1,900. |
| b. | | ¼a orange red ('38) | 6,250. | 1,250. |
| | | On cover | | 3,100. |
| 3 | A1 | 1a pale turquoise blue | 1,500. | 300.00 |
| | | On cover | | 750.00 |
| a. | | 1a turquoise blue | 2,000. | 400.00 |
| | | On cover | | 1,000. |
| 4 | A1 | 1a3p deep red violet ('35) | 3,000. | 600.00 |
| | | On cover | | 2,400. |
| 5 | A1 | 2a deep dull green ('47) | 3,750. | 750.00 |
| | | On cover | | 2,400. |
| 6 | A1 | 4a dull rose red | 6,250. | 1,250. |
| | | On cover | | 5,000. |
| a. | | 4a rose red ('34) | 7,000. | 1,400. |
| | | On cover | | 5,500. |

A2      A3

A4      A5

A6      A7

A8      A9

A10

Maharawal Lakshman Singh

**1934-38 Typo. Perf. 12**

| | | | | |
|---|---|---|---|---|
| 7 | A2 | ¼a org buff ('36) | 1,750. | 200.00 |
| | | On cover | | 450.00 |
| 8 | A3 | ½a vermilion, Die I | 500.00 | 125.00 |
| | | On cover | | 350.00 |

| | | | | |
|---|---|---|---|---|
| 9 | A4 | 1a blue | | |
| a. | | Perf 11½ ('38) | 750.00 | 125.00 |
| | | | | 350.00 |
| 10 | A5 | 4a gray brown | 2,000. | 650.00 |
| | | | | 2,000. |

There are three dies of the ½ anna: Die I measures 21x25½mm, and width of turban is 7½mm; Die II measures 20x20½mm; Die III measures 21x25½mm, and width of turban is 6½mm. There are 4 distinct cliches of Die III, printed in a block of 4, differing in the space between the top of the turban and the frame: Pos. 1 = 2mm; Pos. 2 = 2.5mm; Pos. 3 = 1mm; Pos. 4 = 1.5mm.

**1940-41 Perf. 11, 11½ (#15)**

| | | | | |
|---|---|---|---|---|
| 11 | A2 | ¼a dull org('41) | 1,500. | 150.00 |
| | | On cover | | 300.00 |
| 12 | A3 | ½a carmine, Die I | 500.00 | 150.00 |
| | | On cover | | 450.00 |
| 13 | A4 | 1a blue | 500.00 | 100.00 |
| | | On cover | | 250.00 |
| 14 | A6 | 2a bright green | 2,500. | 900.00 |
| | | On cover | | 2,500. |
| 15 | A5 | 4a gray brown | 1,800. | 450.00 |
| | | On cover | | 1,350. |

**1943 Pin-Perf 11½**

| | | | | |
|---|---|---|---|---|
| 16 | A6 | 2a bright green | 2,500. | 900.00 |
| | | On cover | | 2,500. |

**1943-44 Perf. 10½**

| | | | | |
|---|---|---|---|---|
| 17 | A2 | ¼a dull org('44) | 1,500. | 150.00 |
| | | On cover | | 300.00 |
| 18 | A3 | ½a vermilion, Die I ('44) | 600.00 | 175.00 |
| | | On cover | | 550.00 |
| 19 | A7 | ½a vermilion, Die II ('44) | 600.00 | 175.00 |
| | | On cover | | 550.00 |
| a. | | Horiz. pair, #18 + #19 | 1,300. | 450. |
| | | On cover | | 1,000. |
| b. | | Vert. pair, imperf between | | 5,000. |
| 20 | A4 | 1a blue ('44) | 500.00 | 100.00 |
| | | On cover | | 250.00 |
| 21 | A8 | 1a3p mauve | 2,000. | 450.00 |
| | | | | 1,500. |
| 22 | A5 | 4a pale brown ('44) | 2,400. | 650.00 |
| | | | | 2,000. |

**1945 Perf. 10**

| | | | | |
|---|---|---|---|---|
| 23 | A2 | ¼a orange | 2,000. | 150.00 |
| | | On cover | | 300.00 |
| 24 | A9 | ½a vermilion, Die III ('44) | 800.00 | 100.00 |
| | | On cover | | 250.00 |
| 25 | A4 | 1a blue | 500.00 | 100.00 |
| | | On cover | | 250.00 |
| 26 | A8 | 1a3p bright mauve | 2,000. | 450.00 |
| | | On cover | | 1,500. |
| 27 | A10 | 1½a deep violet | 2,000. | 450.00 |
| | | | | 1,350. |
| 28 | A5 | 4a brown | 1,600. | 450.00 |
| | | On cover | | 1,000. |

The stamps of Dungarpur became obsolete in Sept. 1949.

## DUTTIA

'dət-ē-ə

## (Datia)

LOCATION — A Feudatory State in the Bundelkhand Agency in Central India.
AREA — 912 sq. mi.
POP. — 158,834
CAPITAL — Datia

Ganesh, Elephant-headed
God

A1      A2

All Duttia stamps have a circular control mark, about 23mm in diameter, handstamped in blue or black. All were issued without gum.

**1893 Typeset Unwmk. Imperf.**

| | | | | |
|---|---|---|---|---|
| 1 | A1 | ¼a black, org red | 6,250. | |
| 2 | A1 | ½a blk, grysh grn | 24,000. | |
| 3 | A2 | 1a black, red | 4,750. | 7,500. |
| 4 | A1 | 2a black, yellow | 5,250. | |
| 5 | A1 | 4a black, rose | 1,900. | |

Type A2 with Frameline around God,
Rosettes in Lower Corners

**1896 (?)**

| | | | | |
|---|---|---|---|---|
| 5A | A2 | ½ black, green | 15,000. | |
| 5C | A2 | 2a dk blue, lemon | 3,750. | |

A 1a in this revised type has been reported.

**1897**

| | | | | |
|---|---|---|---|---|
| 6 | A2 | ½a black, green | 100.00 | 675.00 |
| 7 | A2 | 1a black | 150.00 | 525.00 |
| a. | | Laid paper | | 32.50 |
| 8 | A2 | 2a black, yellow | 42.50 | 500.00 |
| 9 | A2 | 4a black, rose | 40.00 | 325.00 |
| | | Nos. 6-9 (4) | 332.50 | 2,025. |

A3      A4

| | | | | |
|---|---|---|---|---|
| 10 | A3 | ½a black, green | 150.00 | 825.00 |
| 11 | A3 | 1a black | 290.00 | |
| 12 | A3 | 2a black, yellow | 175.00 | 825.00 |
| 13 | A3 | 4a black, rose | 175.00 | 825.00 |
| | | Nos. 10-13 (4) | 790.00 | 2,475. |

**1899-1900**
**Rouletted in Colored Lines on 2 or 3 Sides**

| | | | | |
|---|---|---|---|---|
| 14 | A4 | ¼a red (shades) | 5.00 | 32.50 |
| b. | | Tete beche pair | | 4,900. |
| 15 | A4 | ½a black, green | 4.00 | 30.00 |
| 16 | A4 | 1a black | 4.50 | 30.00 |
| 17 | A4 | 2a black, yellow | 5.25 | 35.00 |
| 18 | A4 | 4a black, rose red | 5.00 | 32.50 |
| a. | | Tete beche pair | | |
| | | Nos. 14-18 (5) | 23.75 | 160.00 |

**1904 Imperf.**

| | | | | |
|---|---|---|---|---|
| 22 | A4 | ¼a carmine | 5.50 | 47.50 |
| 23 | A4 | ½a black, green | 27.50 | |
| 24 | A4 | 1a black | 21.00 | 75.00 |
| | | Nos. 22-24 (3) | 54.00 | 122.50 |

**1911 Perf. 13½**

| | | | | |
|---|---|---|---|---|
| 25 | A4 | ¼a carmine | 9.50 | 75.00 |

**1916 Imperf.**

| | | | | |
|---|---|---|---|---|
| 26 | A4 | ¼a dull blue | 8.25 | 40.00 |
| 27 | A4 | ½a green | 8.25 | 40.00 |
| 28 | A4 | 1a violet | 10.00 | 42.50 |
| | | Tete beche pair | | 35.00 |
| 29 | A4 | 2a brown | 22.50 | 52.50 |
| 29A | A4 | 4a brick red | 110.00 | |
| | | Nos. 26-29A (5) | 159.00 | 175.00 |

**1918**

| | | | | |
|---|---|---|---|---|
| 31 | A4 | ½a ultramarine | 5.25 | 27.50 |
| 32 | A4 | 1a rose | 5.25 | 27.50 |
| 33 | A4 | 2a violet | 11.00 | 40.00 |

**Perf. 12**

| | | | | |
|---|---|---|---|---|
| 34 | A4 | ¼a black | 7.50 | 37.50 |
| | | Nos. 31-34 (4) | 29.00 | 132.50 |

**1920 Rouletted**

| | | | | |
|---|---|---|---|---|
| 35 | A4 | ¼a blue | 4.00 | 21.00 |
| 36 | A4 | ½a rose | 5.25 | 24.00 |

**Perf. 7**

| | | | | |
|---|---|---|---|---|
| 37 | A4 | ½a dull red | 24.00 | 62.50 |
| | | Nos. 35-37 (3) | 33.25 | 107.50 |

Duttia stamps became obsolete in 1921.

## FARIDKOT

fe-'rēd-ˌkōt

LOCATION — A Feudatory State in the Punjab Agency of India.
AREA — 638 sq. mi.
POP. — 164,364
CAPITAL — Faridkot

4 Folus or Paisas = 1 Anna

A1      A2

A3

Handstamped

**1879-86 Unwmk. Imperf.**
**Without Gum**

| | | | | |
|---|---|---|---|---|
| 1 | A1 | 1f ultramarine | 4.00 | 6.00 |
| a. | | Laid paper | 21.00 | 24.00 |
| b. | | Tete beche pair | 400.00 | |
| 2 | A2 | 1p ultramarine | 7.50 | 16.00 |
| a. | | Laid paper | 125.00 | 150.00 |
| 3 | A3 | 1p ultramarine | 2.25 | |
| a. | | Tete beche pair | 340.00 | |
| | | Nos. 1-3 (3) | 13.75 | |

Several other varieties exist, but it is believed that only the stamps listed here were issued for postal use. They became obsolete Dec. 31, 1886. See Faridkot under Convention States for issues of 1887-1900.

## HYDERABAD (DECCAN)

'hīd-ə-ˌrə-ˌbad

LOCATION — Central India
AREA — 82,313 sq. mi.
POP. — 16,338,534 (1941)
CAPITAL — Hyderabad

This independent princely state was occupied and annexed by India in 1948.

> **Catalogue values for unused stamps in this State are for Never Hinged items, beginning with Scott 51 in the regular postage section, and Scott O54 in the officials section.**

Expect irregular perfs on the Nos. 1-14 and O1-O20 due to the nature of the paper.

A1      A2

**1869-71 Engr. Unwmk. Perf. 11½**

| | | | | |
|---|---|---|---|---|
| 1 | A1 | ½a brown ('71) | 6.00 | 6.50 |
| 2 | A2 | 1a olive green | 27.50 | 11.00 |
| a. | | Imperf. horiz., pair | 900.00 | 175.00 |
| 3 | A1 | 2a green ('71) | 90.00 | 72.50 |
| | | Nos. 1-3 (3) | 123.50 | 90.00 |

For overprints see Nos. O1-O3, O11-O13.
*The reprints are perforated 12½.*

A3      A4

Wove Paper

**1871-1909 Perf. 12½**

| | | | | |
|---|---|---|---|---|
| 4 | A3 | ½a orange brown | 4.00 | .20 |
| a. | | ½a red brown | 4.00 | .20 |
| b. | | ½a magenta (error) | 75.00 | 12.00 |
| c. | | Perf. 11½ | 27.50 | 30.00 |
| d. | | ½a rose | 4.00 | .30 |
| e. | | ½a bright vermilion | 4.00 | .20 |
| 5 | A3 | 1a dark brown | 1.90 | .20 |
| a. | | Imperf., pair | | 550.00 |
| b. | | Horiz. blk, imperf. vert. | | 1,350. |
| c. | | Vert. pair, imperf. horiz. | | 1,350. |
| d. | | Perf. 11½ | 180.00 | 200.00 |
| 6 | A3 | 1a black ('09) | 3.50 | .20 |
| 7 | A3 | 2a green | 5.50 | .20 |
| a. | | 2a olive green ('09) | 5.50 | .50 |
| b. | | Perf. 11½ | 1,900. | |
| 8 | A3 | 3a yellow brown | 4.50 | 2.25 |
| a. | | Perf. 11½ | 60.00 | 82.50 |
| 9 | A3 | 4a slate | 11.00 | 5.25 |
| a. | | Imperf. horiz., pair | 1,350. | 1,350. |
| b. | | Perf. 11½ | 225.00 | 225.00 |

| 10 | A3 | 4a deep green | 8.25 | 5.00 |
|---|---|---|---|---|
| a. | | 4a olive green | 9.00 | 3.75 |
| 11 | A3 | 8a bister brown | 5.25 | 6.50 |
| a. | | Perf. 11½ | | |
| 12 | A3 | 12a blue | 7.00 | 12.00 |
| a. | | Perf. 11½ | 500.00 | |
| b. | | 12a slate green | 7.50 | 7.50 |
| | | Nos. 4-12 (9) | 50.90 | 31.80 |

For overprints see Nos. 13, O4-O10, O14-O20, O25-O26.

Surcharged

**1900**

| 13 | A3 | ¼a on ½a brt ver | .75 | 1.25 |
|---|---|---|---|---|
| a. | | Inverted surcharge | 57.50 | 35.00 |

**1902**

| 14 | A4 | ¼a blue | 8.25 | 5.25 |
|---|---|---|---|---|

Seal of the Nizam
A5　　　　A6

**Engraved by A. G. Wyon**

**1905**　　　　**Wmk. 42**

| 17 | A5 | ¼a blue | 3.75 | .90 |
|---|---|---|---|---|
| 18 | A5 | ½a red | 6.00 | .35 |
| 19 | A5 | ½a orange | 9.00 | .50 |
| | | Nos. 17-19 (3) | 18.75 | 1.75 |

For overprints see Nos. O21-O23.

**Perf. 11, 11½, 12½, 13½ and Compound**

**1908-11**

| 20 | A5 | ¼a gray | 1.50 | .20 |
|---|---|---|---|---|
| 21 | A5 | ½a green | 7.00 | .20 |
| 22 | A5 | 1a carmine | 5.25 | .20 |
| 23 | A5 | 2a lilac | 2.40 | .20 |
| 24 | A5 | 3a brn orange ('09) | 4.00 | 1.50 |
| 25 | A5 | 4a olive green ('09) | 4.50 | 1.90 |
| 26 | A5 | 8a violet ('11) | 1.90 | 1.20 |
| 27 | A5 | 12a blue green ('11) | 10.50 | 6.00 |
| | | Nos. 20-27 (8) | 37.05 | 11.40 |

For overprints see Nos. O24, O27-O38.

**Engr. by Bradbury, Wilkinson & Co.**

**1912**

| 28 | A5 | ¼a brown violet | 1.20 | .20 |
|---|---|---|---|---|
| 29 | A5 | ½a deep green | 2.50 | .20 |
| a. | | Imperf., pair | 550.00 | |

The frame of type A5 differs slightly in each denomination.
Nos. 20-21 measure 19½x20½mm.
Nos. 28-29 measure 20x21½mm.
For overprints see Nos 37, O39-O40, O44.

**1915-16**

| 30 | A6 | ½a green | 1.50 | .20 |
|---|---|---|---|---|
| 31 | A6 | 1a carmine rose | 3.75 | .20 |
| 32 | A6 | 1a red | 2.50 | .20 |
| | | Nos. 30-32 (3) | 7.75 | .60 |

Unless used, imperf. stamps of types A5 and A6 are from plate proof sheets.
See #58. For overprints see #38, O41-O43, O45.

A7

**1927**　**Wmk. 211**　**Perf. 13½**

| 36 | A7 | 1r yellow | 13.50 | 18.00 |
|---|---|---|---|---|

Stamps of 1912-16 Surcharged in Red

(4 pies)　　　　(8 pies)

---

**1930**

| 37 | A5 | 4p on ¼a brn vio | .45 | .20 |
|---|---|---|---|---|
| a. | | Perf. 11 | 675.00 | |
| b. | | Double surcharge | 350.00 | |
| 38 | A6 | 8p on ½a green | .60 | .20 |
| a. | | Perf. 11 | 400.00 | 210.00 |

For overprints see Nos. O44-O45.

Seal of
Nizam — A8

Char Minar — A9

High Court of
Justice
A10

Reservoir for
City of
Hyderabad
A11

Bidar College — A13

Entrance to
Ajanta Caves
A12

Victory Tower at
Daulatabad
A14

**Wmk. 211**
**Engr.**　　**Perf. 13½**

**1931-48**

| 39 | A8 | 4p black | .45 | .20 |
|---|---|---|---|---|
| a. | | Laid paper ('47) | 3.75 | 8.25 |
| 39B | A8 | 6p car lake ('48) | 15.00 | 12.50 |
| 40 | A8 | 8p green | .75 | .20 |
| a. | | 8p yel grn, laid paper ('47) | 4.50 | 6.75 |
| b. | | Imperf., pair | 90.00 | 180.00 |
| 41 | A9 | 1a dark brown | .75 | .20 |
| 42 | A10 | 2a dark violet | 4.50 | .20 |
| a. | | Imperf., pair | 195.00 | 400.00 |
| 43 | A11 | 4a ultramarine | 2.40 | 1.00 |
| a. | | Imperf., pair | 210.00 | 500.00 |
| 44 | A12 | 8a deep orange | 10.50 | 6.00 |
| 45 | A13 | 12a scarlet | 11.00 | 18.00 |
| 46 | A14 | 1r yellow | 7.50 | 7.50 |
| | | Nos. 39-46 (9) | 52.85 | 45.80 |

On No. 39B, "POSTAGE" has been moved to ribbon at bottom of design.
Nos. 39a and 40a are printed from worn plates. The background of the design is unshaded.
See #59. For overprints see #O46-O53, O56.

Unani
General
Hospital
A15

Osmania
General
Hospital
A16

---

Osmania
University
A17

Osmania
Jubilee
Hall — A18

**Perf. 13½x14**

**1937, Feb. 13**　**Litho.**　**Unwmk.**

| 47 | A15 | 4p violet & black | .75 | 3.25 |
|---|---|---|---|---|
| 48 | A16 | 8p brown & black | 1.25 | 3.25 |
| 49 | A17 | 1a dull orange & gray | 1.75 | 2.10 |
| 50 | A18 | 2a dull green & gray | 2.25 | 6.75 |
| | | Nos. 47-50 (4) | 6.00 | 15.35 |

The Nizam's Silver Jubilee.

Catalogue values for unused stamps in this section, from this point to the end of the section, are for Never Hinged items.

Returning
Soldier — A19

**1946**　**Typo.**　**Perf. 13½**

| 51 | A19 | 1a dark blue | .20 | .20 |
|---|---|---|---|---|

**Wmk. 211**

| 52 | A19 | 1a blue | .20 | .20 |
|---|---|---|---|---|

**Wmk. Nizam's Seal in Sheet
Laid Paper**

| 53 | A19 | 1a dark blue | 1.00 | 1.20 |
|---|---|---|---|---|
| | | Nos. 51-53 (3) | 1.40 | 1.60 |

Victory of the Allied Nations in WW II.

Town Hall,
Hyderabad
A20

**1947, Feb. 17**　**Litho.**　**Wove Paper**

| 54 | A20 | 1a black | 2.00 | 2.90 |
|---|---|---|---|---|

Inauguration of the Reformed Legislature, Feb. 17th, 1947.

Power House,
Hyderabad
A21

Designs: 3a, Kaktyai Arch, Warangal Fort. 6a, Golkunda Fort.

**Perf. 13½x14**

**1947-49**　**Typo.**　**Wmk. 211**

| 55 | A21 | 1a4p dark green | 1.50 | 3.25 |
|---|---|---|---|---|
| 56 | A21 | 3a blue | 2.50 | 6.50 |
| 57 | A21 | 6a olive brown | 5.50 | 27.50 |
| a. | | 6a red brown ('49) | 25.00 | 47.50 |
| b. | | Imperf., pair | 190.00 | |
| | | Nos. 55-57 (3) | 9.50 | 37.25 |

**Seal Type of 1915**

**1947**　**Engr.**　**Perf. 13½**

| 58 | A6 | ½a rose lake | 3.75 | 1.10 |
|---|---|---|---|---|

For overprint see No. O54.

---

**Seal Type of 1931**

**1949**　　　　**Litho.**

| 59 | A8 | 2p brown | 3.00 | 3.50 |
|---|---|---|---|---|

For overprint see No. O55.

**OFFICIAL STAMPS**

Regular Issues of
1869-71 Overprinted

**1873**　　**Unwmk.**　**Perf. 11½, 12½**
**Red Overprint**

| O1 | A1 | ½a brown | 195.00 | 125.00 |
|---|---|---|---|---|
| O2 | A2 | 1a olive green | 35.00 | 35.00 |
| O3 | A1 | 2a green | 72.50 | 57.50 |
| O4 | A3 | ½a red brown | 27.50 | 9.00 |
| O5 | A3 | 1a dark brown | 195.00 | 125.00 |
| O6 | A3 | 2a green | 72.50 | 57.50 |
| O7 | A3 | 3a yel brown | 250.00 | 250.00 |
| O8 | A3 | 4a slate | 120.00 | 72.50 |
| O9 | A3 | 8a bister | 125.00 | 225.00 |
| O10 | A3 | 12a blue | 195.00 | 240.00 |

**Black Overprint**

| O11 | A1 | ½a brown | | 52.50 |
|---|---|---|---|---|
| O12 | A2 | 1a olive green | 4.50 | 3.75 |
| O13 | A1 | 2a green | 7.50 | 9.00 |
| O14 | A3 | ½a red brown | 16.00 | 5.25 |
| O15 | A3 | 1a dark brown | — | 52.50 |
| O16 | A3 | 2a green | 7.50 | 9.00 |
| O17 | A3 | 3a yel brown | 62.50 | 52.50 |
| O18 | A3 | 4a slate | 32.50 | 30.00 |
| O19 | A3 | 8a bister | 75.00 | 62.50 |
| O20 | A3 | 12a blue | 90.00 | 120.00 |

The above official stamps became obsolete in August, 1878. Since that date the "Official" overprint has been applied to the reprints and probably to original stamps. Two new varieties of the overprint have also appeared, both on the reprints and on the current stamps. These are overprinted in various colors, positions and combinations.

**Same Ovpt. On Regular Issues of 1905-11**

**1908**　　　　**Wmk. 42**

| O21 | A5 | ½a green | 30.00 | .20 |
|---|---|---|---|---|
| O22 | A5 | 1a carmine | 97.50 | .20 |
| O23 | A5 | 2a lilac | 97.50 | .20 |
| | | Nos. O21-O23 (3) | 225.00 | .60 |

**Perf. 11, 11½, 12½, 13½ and Compound**

**1909-11**

| O24 | A5 | ½a red | 210.00 | .20 |
|---|---|---|---|---|
| O25 | A3 | 1a black | 140.00 | .75 |
| O26 | A5 | 2a olive green | 150.00 | .50 |
| O27 | A5 | 3a brown orange | 11.00 | 9.00 |
| O28 | A5 | 4a olive green ('11) | 45.00 | 1.90 |
| O29 | A5 | 8a violet ('11) | 19.00 | 5.25 |
| O30 | A5 | 12a blue green ('11) | 15.00 | 18.00 |
| | | Nos. O24-O30 (7) | 590.00 | 18.60 |

Regular Issue of 1908-
11 Overprinted

**1911-12**

| O31 | A5 | ¼a gray | 6.75 | 1.10 |
|---|---|---|---|---|
| O32 | A5 | ½a green | 5.25 | .20 |
| O33 | A5 | 1a carmine | 3.00 | .20 |
| O34 | A5 | 2a lilac | 2.50 | 1.90 |
| O35 | A5 | 3a brown orange | 27.50 | 1.10 |
| O36 | A5 | 4a olive green | 7.00 | .20 |
| O37 | A5 | 8a violet | 11.00 | .30 |
| O38 | A5 | 12a blue green | 36.00 | 3.75 |
| | | Nos. O31-O38 (8) | 99.00 | 8.75 |

**Same Overprint on Regular Issue of 1912**

**1912**

| O39 | A5 | ¼a brown violet | 5.50 | .20 |
|---|---|---|---|---|
| a. | | ¼a gray blue | 5.50 | .20 |
| O40 | A5 | ½a deep green | 5.25 | .20 |

**Same Ovpt. On Regular Issue of 1915-16**

**1917**

| O41 | A6 | ½a green | 5.25 | .20 |
|---|---|---|---|---|
| O42 | A6 | 1a carmine rose | 7.00 | .20 |
| O43 | A6 | 1a red | 4.00 | .20 |
| | | Nos. O41-O43 (3) | 16.25 | .60 |

Same Overprint on Nos. 37 and 38

**1930**
| | | | | |
|---|---|---|---|---|
| O44 | A5 | 4p on ¼a brown violet | 3.25 | .20 |
| O45 | A6 | 8p on ½a green | 2.25 | .20 |

Same Overprint on Regular Issue of 1931

**1934-47    Wmk. 211    Perf. 13½**
| | | | | |
|---|---|---|---|---|
| O46 | A8 | 4p black | 4.00 | .20 |
| a. | | Laid paper ('47) | | 7.50 |
| b. | | Imperf., pair | 120.00 | |
| O47 | A8 | 8p green | 1.90 | .20 |
| a. | | 8p yel grn, laid paper ('47) | 10.00 | 7.50 |
| b. | | Inverted overprint | | 240.00 |
| O48 | A9 | 1a dark brown | 3.00 | .20 |
| O49 | A10 | 2a dark violet | 11.00 | .20 |
| O50 | A11 | 4a ultramarine | 6.00 | .35 |
| O51 | A12 | 8a deep orange | 21.00 | .90 |
| O52 | A13 | 12a scarlet | 19.00 | 2.50 |
| O53 | A14 | 1r yellow | 30.00 | 3.75 |
| | | Nos. O46-O53 (8) | 95.90 | 8.30 |

> Catalogue values for unused stamps in this section, from this point to the end of the section, are for Never Hinged items.

Same Overprint on Nos. 58-59, 39B

**1947-50    Perf. 13½**
| | | | | |
|---|---|---|---|---|
| O54 | A6 | ½a rose lake | 9.00 | 10.50 |
| O55 | A8 | 2p brown ('49) | 9.00 | 15.00 |
| O56 | A8 | 6p car lake ('50) | 11.00 | 35.00 |
| | | Nos. O54-O56 (3) | 29.00 | 60.50 |

## IDAR

ˈē-dər

**LOCATION** — A Feudatory State in the Western India States Agency.
**AREA** — 1,669 sq. mi.
**POP.** — 262,660
**CAPITAL** — Himmatnagar

Stamps of Idar are in booklet panes of four. All stamps have one or two straight edges.

Maharaja Shri Himatsinhji
A1          A2

**1939    Unwmk.    Typo.    Perf. 11**
| | | | | |
|---|---|---|---|---|
| 1 | A1 | ½a light green | 21.00 | 37.50 |

**1941    Same Redrawn**
| | | | | |
|---|---|---|---|---|
| 2 | A1 | ½a green | 17.50 | 40.00 |

The panels containing denomination and name of state are shaded.

**1944    Unwmk.    Perf. 12**
| | | | | |
|---|---|---|---|---|
| 3 | A2 | ½a green | 4.00 | 110.00 |
| 4 | A2 | 1a purple | 4.00 | 100.00 |
| a. | | Imperf., pair | 250.00 | |
| 5 | A2 | 2a blue | 4.50 | 150.00 |
| 6 | A2 | 4a red | 4.75 | 160.00 |
| | | Nos. 3-6 (4) | 17.25 | |

## INDORE

in-ˈdō̞ə̞r

### (Holkar)

**LOCATION** — A Feudatory State in the Indore Agency in Central India.
**AREA** — 9,902 sq. mi.
**POP.** — 1,513,966
**CAPITAL** — Indore

Maharaja Tukoji
Rao II — A1

A2

**1886    Unwmk.    Litho.    Perf. 15**
| | | | | |
|---|---|---|---|---|
| 1 | A1 | ½a lilac | 5.50 | 3.25 |

**1889    Handstamped    Imperf.**
| | | | | |
|---|---|---|---|---|
| 3 | A2 | ¼a black, rose | 5.25 | 5.50 |

No. 3 exists in two types.
*The originals of this stamp are printed in water color. The reprints are in oil color and on paper of a deeper shade of rose.*

Maharaja Shivaji
Rao — A3

**1889-92    Engr.    Perf. 15**
| | | | | |
|---|---|---|---|---|
| 4 | A3 | ¼a orange | 2.25 | 1.20 |
| 5 | A3 | ½a brown violet | 3.75 | .20 |
| 6 | A3 | 1a green | 4.50 | 1.90 |
| 7 | A3 | 2a vermilion | 10.50 | 3.00 |
| | | Nos. 4-7 (4) | 21.00 | 6.30 |

For overprint see No. 14.

Maharaja Tukoji Rao III
A4          A5

**1904-08    Perf. 13½, 14**
| | | | | |
|---|---|---|---|---|
| 8 | A4 | ¼a orange | .90 | .20 |
| 9 | A5 | ½a lake ('08) | 13.50 | .20 |
| a. | | Imperf., pair | 35.00 | |
| 10 | A5 | 1a green ('07) | 3.75 | .20 |
| a. | | Imperf., pair | 175.00 | |
| 11 | A5 | 2a brown ('05) | 22.50 | 1.50 |
| a. | | Imperf., pair | 120.00 | |
| 12 | A5 | 3a violet | 35.00 | 10.50 |
| 13 | A5 | 4a ultramarine | 7.50 | 2.10 |
| | | Nos. 8-13 (6) | 83.15 | 14.70 |

For overprints see Nos. O1-O7.

No. 5 Surcharged

**1905    Perf. 15**
| | | | | |
|---|---|---|---|---|
| 14 | A3 | ¼a on ½a brown violet | 9.00 | 30.00 |

Maharaja Yeshwant Rao II
A6          A7

**1928-38    Engr.    Perf. 13½**
| | | | | |
|---|---|---|---|---|
| 15 | A6 | ¼a orange | .90 | .30 |
| 16 | A6 | ½a claret | 3.25 | .20 |
| 17 | A6 | 1a green | 4.00 | .20 |
| 18 | A6 | 1¼a green ('33) | 6.00 | 1.25 |
| 19 | A6 | 2a dark brown | 19.00 | 3.25 |
| 20 | A6 | 2a Prus blue ('36) | 19.00 | 3.25 |
| a. | | Imperf., pair | 37.50 | 275.00 |
| 21 | A6 | 3a dull violet | 3.00 | 14.00 |
| 22 | A6 | 3½a dull violet ('34) | 10.50 | 15.00 |
| a. | | Imperf., pair | 100.00 | 650.00 |
| 23 | A6 | 4a ultramarine | 10.50 | 7.50 |
| 24 | A6 | 4a bister ('38) | 52.50 | 2.50 |
| a. | | Imperf., pair | 45.00 | 500.00 |
| 25 | A6 | 8a gray | 9.50 | 6.50 |
| 26 | A6 | 8a red orange ('38) | 40.00 | 35.00 |
| 27 | A6 | 12a rose red ('34) | 7.50 | 15.00 |

**Perf. 14**
| | | | | |
|---|---|---|---|---|
| 28 | A7 | 1r lt blue & black | 12.50 | 22.50 |
| 29 | A7 | 2r car lake & blk | 82.50 | 90.00 |
| 30 | A7 | 5r org brn & black | 140.00 | 140.00 |
| | | Nos. 15-30 (16) | 420.65 | 356.45 |

Imperforates of types A6 and A7 were used with official sanction at Indore City during a stamp shortage in 1938. They were from sheets placed by the printers (Perkins, Bacon) on top of packets of 100 perforated sheets as identification.

Stamps of 1929-33 Surcharged in Black

**1940    Perf. 13, 14**
| | | | | |
|---|---|---|---|---|
| 31 | A7 | ¼a on 5r org brn & blk | 19.00 | 2.50 |
| a. | | Dbl. surch., black over green | 700.00 | |
| 32 | A7 | ½a on 2r car lake & blk | 32.50 | 5.00 |
| 33 | A6 | 1a on 1¼a green | 32.50 | 1.20 |
| a. | | Inverted surcharge | 110.00 | |
| | | Nos. 31-33 (3) | 84.00 | 8.70 |

Stamps with green surcharge only are proofs.

A8

**1941-47    Typo.    Perf. 11**
| | | | | |
|---|---|---|---|---|
| 34 | A8 | ¼a orange | 2.50 | .20 |
| 35 | A8 | ½a rose lilac | 4.75 | .20 |
| 36 | A8 | 1a dk olive green | 12.50 | .20 |
| 37 | A8 | 1¼a yellow green | 20.00 | 20.00 |
| a. | | Imperf., pair | 275.00 | |
| 38 | A8 | 2a turquoise blue | 14.00 | 1.75 |
| 39 | A8 | 4a bister ('47) | 20.00 | 20.00 |

**Size: 23x28¼mm**
| | | | | |
|---|---|---|---|---|
| 40 | A8 | 2r car lake & blk ('47) | 16.00 | 250.00 |
| 41 | A8 | 5r brn org & blk | 15.00 | 325.00 |
| | | Nos. 34-41 (8) | 104.75 | 617.35 |

## OFFICIAL STAMPS

Stamps and Type of 1904-08 Overprinted

**1904-06    Perf. 13½, 14**
| | | | | |
|---|---|---|---|---|
| O1 | A5 | ½a lake | 1.10 | 1.90 |
| a. | | Inverted overprint | 35.00 | 62.50 |
| b. | | Double overprint | 35.00 | |
| c. | | Imperf., pair | 110.00 | |
| O2 | A5 | 1a green | .20 | .20 |
| O3 | A5 | 2a brown ('05) | .45 | .45 |
| O4 | A5 | 3a violet ('06) | 2.50 | 5.50 |
| a. | | Imperf., pair | 425.00 | |
| O5 | A5 | 4a ultra ('05) | 7.50 | 2.25 |
| | | Nos. O1-O5 (5) | 11.75 | 10.30 |

Same Overprint on No. 8

**1907**
| | | | | |
|---|---|---|---|---|
| O6 | A4 | ¼a orange | 1.10 | 1.90 |

No. 9 Overprinted

| | | | | |
|---|---|---|---|---|
| O7 | A5 | ½a lake | .20 | 1.75 |

#O1, O7 differ mainly in the shape of the "R."

## JAIPUR

ˈjī-ˌpu̇ə̞r

**LOCATION** — A Feudatory State in the Jaipur Residency of India.
**AREA** — 15,610 sq. mi.
**POP.** — 3,040,876
**CAPITAL** — Jaipur

> Catalogue values for unused stamps in this State are for Never Hinged items, beginning with Scott 49 in the regular postage section, and Scott O30 in the officials section.

A1          Chariot of Surya, Sun God — A1a

**Pin-perf. 14x14½**
**1904    Typo.    Unwmk.**
| | | | | |
|---|---|---|---|---|
| 1 | A1 | ½a ultramarine | 290.00 | 275.00 |
| a. | | ½a pale blue | 210.00 | 275.00 |
| b. | | ½a gray blue | 3,250. | 300.00 |
| c. | | As "b," imperf. | 525.00 | 900.00 |
| 1D | A1a | ½a blue | 5.00 | 10.00 |
| e. | | ½a ultramarine | 5.50 | 10.00 |
| f. | | Imperf. | 5.50 | 10.00 |
| 2 | A1 | 1a dull red | 8.25 | 21.00 |
| a. | | 1a chestnut | 8.25 | 21.00 |
| 3 | A1 | 2a pale green | 8.25 | 21.00 |
| a. | | 2a emerald | 9.00 | |
| | | Nos. 1-3 (4) | 311.50 | 327.00 |

No. 1 has 36 varieties (on 2 plates), differing in minor details. Nos. 1b and 1c are from plate II. No. 1D has 24 varieties (one plate).

Chariot of Surya — A2

**Perf. 12½x12 and 13½**
**1904-06    Engr.**
| | | | | |
|---|---|---|---|---|
| 4 | A2 | ¼a olive green ('06) | 1.25 | 1.60 |
| 5 | A2 | ½a deep blue | 2.25 | .75 |
| 6 | A2 | 1a carmine | 3.75 | 6.75 |
| 7 | A2 | 2a dark green | 5.25 | 2.25 |
| 8 | A2 | 4a red brown | 11.00 | 3.25 |
| 9 | A2 | 8a violet | 6.00 | 4.00 |
| 10 | A2 | 1r yellow | 35.00 | 24.00 |
| | | Nos. 4-10 (7) | 64.50 | 42.60 |

For overprints see Nos. 21-22.

A3

A4

**1911 Typo. Imperf.**
**Without Gum**

| | | | | |
|---|---|---|---|---|
| 11 | A3 | ¼a yellow green | 3.75 | 5.00 |
| a. | | ¼a olive green | 3.75 | 5.00 |
| b. | | "¼" inverted | 9.00 | |
| 12 | A3 | ¼a olive yellow | .45 | 1.50 |
| b. | | ¼a blue (error) | | |
| 13 | A3 | ½a ultramarine | .45 | 1.50 |
| a. | | ½a dull blue | 4.00 | 4.00 |
| b. | | "½" for "½" | 7.00 | |
| 14 | A3 | 1a carmine | .75 | 1.00 |
| 15 | A3 | 2a deep green | 3.00 | 9.50 |
| a. | | 2a gray green | 4.00 | 8.25 |
| | | Nos. 11-15 (5) | 8.40 | 18.50 |

There are six types for each value and several settings of the ¼a and ½a in the 1911 issue.

**Wmk. "Dorling & Co., London" in Sheet**

**1913-18 Perf. 11**

| | | | | |
|---|---|---|---|---|
| 16 | A4 | ¼a olive bister | 1.00 | 2.25 |
| a. | | Vert. pair, imperf. between | 300.00 | 300.00 |
| b. | | Horiz. pair, imperf. between | — | 240.00 |
| 17 | A4 | ½a ultramarine | 2.25 | 1.90 |
| 18 | A4 | 1a carmine ('18) | 8.25 | 8.25 |
| a. | | 1a scarlet | 6.00 | 5.50 |
| b. | | Vert. pair, imperf. btwn. | 1,250. | 1,250. |
| c. | | Vert. pair, imperf. horiz. | | 1,250. |
| 19 | A4 | 2a green ('18) | 6.00 | 7.50 |
| 20 | A4 | 4a red brown | 10.50 | 15.00 |
| | | Nos. 16-20 (5) | 28.00 | 34.90 |

For overprints see Nos. O1-O6, O9-O10.

**Stamps of 1904-06 Surcharged**

**1926 Unwmk. Engr. Perf. 13½**

| | | | | |
|---|---|---|---|---|
| 21 | A2 | 3a on 8a violet | 3.00 | 5.25 |
| a. | | Inverted surcharge | 275.00 | 210.00 |
| 22 | A2 | 3a on 1r yellow | 4.00 | 9.50 |
| a. | | Inverted surcharge | 825.00 | 275.00 |

**Wmk. "Overland Bank" in Sheet**

**1928 Typo. Perf. 12**

| | | | | |
|---|---|---|---|---|
| 17a | A4 | ½a ultramarine | 4.75 | 6.00 |
| 18c | A4 | 1a rose red | 40.00 | 25.00 |
| 18d | A4 | 1a scarlet | 62.50 | 17.50 |
| 19a | A4 | 2a green | 140.00 | 45.00 |
| 20a | A4 | 4a pale brown | | |
| 23 | A4 | 1r red orange | 600.00 | 825.00 |

**Durbar Commemorative Issue**

Chariot of Surya, Sun God — A5

Maharaja Man Singh II — A6

Elephant with Standard — A7

Sowar in Armor — A8

Blue Peafowl — A9

Royal Bullock Carriage — A10

Royal Elephant Carriage — A11

Albert Museum — A12

Sireh-Deorhi Gate — A13

Chandra Palace — A14

Amber Palace — A15

Rajas Jai Singh II and Man Singh II — A16

**Perf. 13½x14, 14, 14x13½**

**1931, Mar. 14 Typo. Unwmk.**

| | | | | |
|---|---|---|---|---|
| 24 | A5 | ¼a red brn & blk | 4.50 | 4.00 |
| 25 | A6 | ½a dull vio & blk | .75 | .30 |
| 26 | A7 | 1a blue & black | 13.50 | 14.00 |
| 27 | A8 | 2a ocher & black | 13.50 | 14.00 |
| 28 | A9 | 2½a rose & black | 47.50 | 90.00 |
| 29 | A10 | 3a dk grn & blk | 27.50 | 67.50 |
| 30 | A11 | 4a dull grn & blk | 27.50 | 82.50 |
| 31 | A12 | 6a dk blue & blk | 9.00 | 82.50 |
| 32 | A13 | 8a brown & black | 30.00 | 140.00 |
| 33 | A14 | 1r olive & black | 60.00 | 500.00 |
| 34 | A15 | 2r lt green & blk | 62.50 | 550.00 |
| 35 | A16 | 5r violet & black | 82.50 | 600.00 |
| | | Nos. 24-35 (12) | 378.75 | 2,144. |

Investiture of the Maharaja Man Singh II with full ruling powers.

Eighteen sets of this issue were overprinted in red "INVESTITURE — MARCH 14, 1931" for presentation to distinguished personages.

For surcharges see Nos. 47, 48, 58. For overprints see Nos. O12-O16, Rajasthan 16.

Man Singh II Type of 1931 and
Raja Man Singh II — A18

**1932-46 Perf. 14**

| | | | | |
|---|---|---|---|---|
| 36 | A6 | ¼a red brn & blk | .75 | .75 |
| 36A | A6 | ¾a brn orange & black ('43) | 12.00 | 6.25 |
| 37 | A18 | 1a blue & black | 5.00 | 2.50 |
| 37A | A6 | 1a blue & black | 14.00 | 6.75 |
| 38 | A18 | 2a ocher & black | 6.75 | 4.00 |
| 38A | A6 | 2a ocher & blk ('45) | 19.00 | 7.50 |
| 39 | A6 | 2½a dk car & blk | 6.75 | 5.00 |
| 40 | A6 | 3a green & black | 6.00 | 1.00 |
| 41 | A18 | 4a gray grn & blk | 6.75 | 17.50 |
| 41A | A6 | 4a gray green & blk ('45) | 72.50 | 2.40 |
| 42 | A6 | 6a blue & black | 9.00 | 45.00 |
| 43 | A18 | 8a choc & black | 9.00 | 22.50 |
| 43A | A6 | 8a choc & blk ('45) | 42.50 | 190.00 |
| 44 | A18 | 1r bis & gray blk | 40.00 | 175.00 |
| 44A | A6 | 1r bis & gray blk ('46) | 30.00 | 240.00 |
| 45 | A18 | 2r yel grn & blk | 140.00 | 700.00 |
| | | Nos. 36-45 (16) | 420.00 | 1,426. |

For overprints see Nos. O17-O30, Rajasthan Nos. 15, 17-25.

**Stamps of 1931-32 Surcharged in Red or Black**

**1936 Perf. 14x13½, 13½x14**

| | | | | |
|---|---|---|---|---|
| 46 | A18 | 1r on 2r yel grn & blk (R) | 15.00 | 160.00 |
| 47 | A16 | 1r on 5r violet & blk | 15.00 | 125.00 |

**No. 25 Surcharged in Red**

**1938 Perf. 14x13½**

| | | | | |
|---|---|---|---|---|
| 48 | A6 | ¼a on ½a dull vio & blk | 17.50 | 25.00 |

> **Catalogue values for unused stamps in this section, from this point to the end of the section, are for Never Hinged items.**

Amber Palace A19

Designs: ¼a, Palace gate. ¾a, Map of Jaipur. 1a, Observatory. 2a, Palace of the Winds. 3a, Arms of the Raja. 4a, Gate of Amber Fort. 8a, Chariot of the Sun. 1r, Raja Man Singh II.

**1947-48 Unwmk. Engr. Perf. 14**

| | | | | |
|---|---|---|---|---|
| 49 | A19 | ¼a dk green & red brn ('48) | 2.25 | 7.50 |
| 50 | A19 | ½a blue vio & dp grn | .75 | 6.75 |
| 51 | A19 | ¾a dk car & blk ('48) | 2.25 | 9.00 |
| 52 | A19 | 1a dp ultra & choc | 1.50 | 7.00 |
| 53 | A19 | 2a car & blue vio | 1.50 | 7.50 |
| 54 | A19 | 3a dk gray & grn ('48) | 2.50 | 9.50 |
| 55 | A19 | 4a choc & dp ultra | 1.50 | 7.50 |
| 56 | A19 | 8a dk brown & red | 1.50 | 9.00 |

| | | | | |
|---|---|---|---|---|
| 57 | A19 | 1r dk red vio & bl grn ('48) | 4.00 | 67.50 |
| | | Nos. 49-57 (9) | 17.75 | 131.25 |

25th anniv. of the enthronement of Raja Man Singh II.

**No. 25 Surcharged in Carmine with New Value and Bars**

**1947**

| | | | | |
|---|---|---|---|---|
| 58 | A6 | 3p on ½a | 25.00 | 40.00 |
| a. | | "3 PIE" | 75.00 | 160.00 |
| b. | | Inverted surcharge | 72.50 | 62.50 |
| c. | | Double surch., one inverted | 110.00 | 82.50 |
| d. | | As "a," inverted surcharge | 375.00 | 325.00 |

For overprint see No. O31.

---

### OFFICIAL STAMPS

**Regular Issue of 1913-22 Overprinted in Black or Red**

**1929 Unwmk. Perf. 12½x12, 11**

| | | | | |
|---|---|---|---|---|
| O1 | A4 | ¼a olive green | 3.75 | 4.00 |
| O2 | A4 | ½a ultramarine | 1.90 | .30 |
| a. | | Inverted overprint | | 675.00 |
| O3 | A4 | ½a ultra (R) | 4.00 | .45 |
| O4 | A4 | 1a red | 2.25 | .45 |
| O5 | A4 | 2a green | 2.25 | .60 |
| O6 | A4 | 4a red brown | 3.00 | 2.50 |
| O7 | A4 | 8a purple (R) | 25.00 | 82.50 |
| O8 | A4 | 1r red orange | 57.50 | 550.00 |
| | | Nos. O1-O8 (8) | 99.65 | 640.80 |

The 8a and 1r not issued without overprint. For overprint see No. O11.

**Regular Issue of 1913-22 Overprinted in Black or Red**

b

**1931 Perf. 11, 12½x12**

| | | | | |
|---|---|---|---|---|
| O9 | A4 | ½a ultra | 575.00 | .20 |
| O10 | A4 | ½a ultra (R) | 300.00 | .20 |
| O10A | A4 | 8a purple | 675.00 | 300.00 |
| O10B | A4 | 1r red orange | 700.00 | 400.00 |
| | | Nos. O9-O10B (4) | 2,250. | 700.40 |

**No. O5 Surcharged**

**1932**

| | | | | |
|---|---|---|---|---|
| O11 | A4 | ½a on 2a green | 225.00 | 3.00 |

**Regular Issue of 1931 Overprinted in Red**

**1931-37 Perf. 13½x14, 14**

| | | | | |
|---|---|---|---|---|
| O12 | A6 | ¼a red brn & blk ('36) | .60 | .20 |
| O13 | A6 | ½a dull vio & blk | .45 | .20 |
| O14 | A7 | 1a blue & black | 400.00 | 4.50 |
| O15 | A8 | 2a ocher & blk ('36) | 6.75 | 8.25 |
| O16 | A11 | 4a dl grn & blk ('37) | 72.50 | 60.00 |

For overprint see No. O32.

**Same on Regular Issue of 1932 in Red**

**1932-37 Perf. 14**

| | | | | |
|---|---|---|---|---|
| O17 | A18 | 1a blue & black | 6.75 | .30 |
| O18 | A18 | 2a ocher & black | 8.25 | .30 |
| O19 | A18 | 4a gray grn & blk ('37) | 550.00 | 16.00 |
| O20 | A18 | 8a choc & black | 17.50 | 1.60 |
| O21 | A18 | 1r bis & gray blk | 45.00 | 40.00 |
| | | Nos. O17-O21 (5) | 627.50 | 58.20 |

No. 36 Overprinted Type "b" in Black

**1939** **Perf. 14**
O22 A6 ¼a red brown & blk 140.00 110.00

Nos. 36A, 38A, 39, 41A, 43A, 44A and Type of 1931 Overprinted in Carmine

**1941-46** **Unwmk.** **Perf. 13½, 14**
O23 A6 ¾a brn org & blk ('43) 2.25 .75
O24 A6 1a blue & blk ('41) 6.75 .45
O25 A6 2a ocher & black 6.00 5.00
O26 A6 2½a dk car & blk ('46) 16.00 160.00
O27 A6 4a gray grn & blk ('46) 9.00 11.00
O28 A6 8a choc & black 6.00 12.50
O29 A6 1r bis & gray blk 60.00
  Nos. O23-O28 (6) 46.00 189.70

Catalogue values for unused stamps in this section, from this point to the end of the section, are for Never Hinged items.

No. O24 Surcharged with New Value and Bars in Carmine

**1947** **Perf. 13½**
O30 A6 9p on 1a blue & blk 5.50 5.50

**No. 58 Overprinted in Red "SERVICE"**
**Perf. 14**
O31 A6 3p on ½a 9.00 21.00
  a. Inverted surcharge — 2,250.
  b. Double surch., one inverted 72.50 72.50
  c. "3 PIE" 400.00 450.00

No. O13 Surcharged "Three-quarter Anna" in Devanagari, similar to surcharge on No. 48, and Bars in Carmine

**1949** **Perf. 14x13½**
O32 A6 ¾a on ½a dl vio & blk 27.50 10.00

For later issues see Rajasthan.

---

**JAMMU AND KASHMIR**

ˈjəm-ˌü and ˈkash-ˌmiˌər

LOCATION — A Feudatory State in the Kashmir Residency in the extreme north of India.
AREA — 82,258 sq. mi.
POP. — 4,021,616 (1941)
CAPITAL — Srinagar

All stamps of Jammu and Kashmir were issued without gum.

½ Anna — A1          1 Anna — A2

4 Annas (¼ Rupee) — A3

Native Grayish Laid Paper
**Handstamped**
**1866-67** **Unwmk.** **Imperf.**
**Printed in Water Colors**
1 A1 ½a gray black 375.00 150.00
  Cut to shape 75.00 30.00

2 A2 1a dull blue 900.00 180.00
  a. 1a ultramarine 900.00 180.00
  b. 1a royal blue — 750.00
  Cut to shape — 150.00
3 A2 1a gray black 2,400. 2,100.
  Cut to shape 475.00 425.00
4 A3 4a dull blue 4,500. 4,500.
  a. 4a ultramarine 4,500. 4,500.
  b. 4a indigo 4,500. 4,500.
  Cut to shape 900.00 900.00
5 A3 4a gray black 3,000.
  Cut to shape 1,600. —
  Nos. 1-5 (5) 11,175. 6,930.

It has now been proved by the leading authorities on Indian stamps that all stamps of ½ anna and 1 anna printed from the so-called Die A are forgeries and that no such die was ever in use.
See Nos. 24-59.

---

**JAMMU**

A part of the Feudatory State of Jammu & Kashmir, both being ruled by the same sovereign.

½ Anna — A4          1 Anna — A5

Printed in blocks of four, three types of the ½a and one of the 1a.

Native Grayish Laid Paper
**Printed in Water Colors**
**1867-77** **Unwmk.** **Imperf.**
6 A4 ½a black 1,800. 625.00
7 A4 ½a indigo 625.00 490.00
  a. ½a deep ultramarine 490.00 290.00
  b. ½a deep violet blue 325.00 160.00
8 A4 ½a red 12.50 6.75
  a. ½a orange red 375.00 120.00
  b. ½a orange 195.00 225.00
9 A5 1a black 3,750. 2,600.
10 A5 1a indigo 1,350. 625.00
  a. 1a deep ultramarine 1,200. 625.00
  b. 1a deep violet blue 1,250. 625.00
11 A5 1a red 30.00 19.00
  a. 1a orange red 1,250. 525.00
  b. 1a orange 4,500. 2,750.

**1876**
12 A4 ½a emerald 3,750. 1,900.
13 A4 ½a bright blue 2,400. 550.00
14 A5 1a emerald 5,250. 3,000.
15 A5 1a bright blue 700.00 750.00

Native Grayish Laid Paper
**1877** **Printed in Oil Colors**
16 A4 ½a red 18.00 13.50
  a. ½a brown red — 67.50
17 A4 ½a black — 1,800.
18 A5 1a red 57.50 40.00
  a. 1a brown red — 225.00
19 A5 1a black 3,750. 2,750.

The formerly listed ½a dark blue, ½a dark green, 1a dark blue and 1a dark green are believed to be reprints.

**European White Laid Paper**
20 A4 ½a red — 1,600.
  a. Thin laid bâtonné paper — 2,750.
21 A5 1a red —
  a. Thin laid bâtonné paper 6,750.

**European White Wove Paper**
22 A4 ½a red — 675.00
23 A5 1a red —

**RE-ISSUES**
**For Jammu Only**
Native Grayish Laid Paper
**Printed in Water Colors**
**1869-76** **Imperf.**
24 A1 ½a deep black 500.00
25 A1 ½a bright blue 550.00 675.00
26 A1 ½a orange red 1,000. 1,100.
  a. ½a orange to salmon 400.00
  b. ½a red 150.00 525.00
27 A1 ½a emerald 175.00 450.00
28 A1 ½a yellow 1,100. 1,400.
29 A2 1a deep black 500.00
30 A2 1a bright blue 195.00 550.00
31 A2 1a orange red 1,000. 1,100.
  b. 1a red 300.00 500.00
32 A2 1a emerald 195.00 450.00
33 A2 1a yellow 1,400.
34 A3 4a deep black 450.00 —
35 A3 4a bright blue 325.00 —
  a. 4a indigo —
36 A3 4a orange red 325.00 425.00
  a. 4a orange —
  b. 4a red 325.00 425.00
37 A3 4a emerald 450.00 1,000.
38 A3 4a yellow 900.00

Native Grayish Laid Paper
**1877** **Printed in Oil Colors**
39 A1 ½a red 52.50 90.00
40 A1 ½a black 57.50 97.50
41 A1 ½a slate blue 240.00 400.00
42 A1 ½a sage green 210.00
43 A2 1a red 72.50 290.00
45 A2 1a slate blue 57.50 450.00
46 A2 1a sage green 225.00
47 A3 4a red 475.00 825.00
50 A3 4a sage green 225.00

**European White Laid Paper**
51 A1 ½a red — 1,800.
52 A1 ½a black 47.50 97.50
53 A1 ½a slate blue 82.50 450.00
54 A1 ½a yellow 240.00
56 A2 1a slate blue 90.00 600.00
57 A3 4a red 650.00 750.00
58 A3 4a sage green 2,250.

**European Brownish Wove Paper**
59 A1 ½a red — 1,400.

It is probable that the issues of 1876, 1877 and the re-issues of the circular stamps were made to supply the demands of philatelists more than for postal needs. They were, however, available for postage.

There exist also reprints, printed in a variety of colors, on native and European thin wove paper. Collectors are warned against official imitations, which are very numerous. They are printed on several kinds of paper and in a great variety of colors.

A5a

**Handstamped in Oil Color**
**1877, Nov.**
60 A5a (½a) red 1,900.

This provisional, made with a canceling device, was used only in Nov. 1877, at Jammu city.

---

**KASHMIR**

A part of the Feudatory State of Jammu & Kashmir, both being ruled by the same sovereign.

½ Anna — A6

Printed in Water Colors
Native Grayish Laid Paper
Printed from a Single Die
**1866** **Unwmk.** **Imperf.**
62 A6 ½a black 5,250. 675.00

¼ Anna — A7          ½ Anna — A8

1 Anna          2 Annas
A9          A10

4          8
Annas — A11          Annas — A12

The ¼a, 1a and 2a are printed in strips of five varieties, the ½a in sheets of twenty varieties and the 4a and 8a from single dies.

**1866-70**
63 A7 ¼a black 6.75 7.00
64 A8 ½a black 2,250. 300.00
65 A8 ½a ultra 7.50 2.50
  a. ½a blue 13.50 6.75
66 A9 1a black 4,000. 750.00
67 A9 1a red orange 22.50 17.50
68 A9 1a Venetian red 27.50 19.00
69 A9 1a orange brown 22.50 17.50
70 A9 1a ultra 6,500. 2,500.
71 A10 2a olive yellow 30.00 32.50
72 A11 4a emerald 75.00 72.50
73 A12 8a red 75.00 72.50

All the stamps printed in oil colors are reprints.

As in Jammu, official imitations are numerous and are found in many colors and on various papers.

---

**JAMMU & KASHMIR**

¼          ½
Anna — A13          Anna — A14

1          2
Anna — A15          Annas — A16

4          8
Annas — A17          Annas — A18

Laid Paper
**Printed in Oil Colors**
**1878** **Rough Perf. 10-14**
74 A13 ¼a red
75 A14 ½a red 21.00 25.00
  a. Wove paper 500.00
76 A14 ½a slate blue 110.00 110.00
77 A15 1a red 1,900.
78 A15 1a bright violet —

**1878-80** **Imperf.**
79 A13 ¼a red 35.00 30.00
80 A14 ½a red 15.00 16.00
81 A14 ½a slate 27.50 24.00
82 A15 1a red 4.00 17.50
83 A15 1a violet 40.00 42.50
  a. 1a dull purple 67.50 62.50
84 A16 2a red 140.00 140.00
85 A16 2a bright violet 60.00 57.50
86 A16 2a dull ultra 175.00 175.00
87 A17 4a red 340.00 290.00

**Thick Wove Paper**
88 A14 ½a red 47.50 90.00
89 A15 1a red 75.00 37.50
90 A16 2a red 32.50 40.00

Thin Toned Wove Paper
**1879-80**
91 A13 ¼a red 5.50 6.75
92 A14 ½a red 1.50 1.50
93 A15 1a red 3.75 5.25
94 A16 2a red 5.00 7.00
95 A17 4a red 16.00 16.00
96 A18 8a red 17.50 20.00
  Nos. 91-96 (6) 49.25 56.50

Thin Laid Bâtonné Paper
**1880** **Printed in Water Color**
97 A13 ¼a ultramarine 1,350. 900.00

Thin Toned Wove Paper
**1881** **Printed in Oil Colors**
98 A13 ½a orange 17.50 17.50
99 A14 ½a orange 35.00 25.00
100 A15 1a orange 37.50 21.00
101 A16 2a orange 27.50 21.00

| | | | | |
|---|---|---|---|---|
| 102 | A17 | 4a orange | 67.50 | *82.50* |
| 103 | A18 | 8a orange | 110.00 | *120.00* |
| | | Nos. 98-103 (6) | 295.00 | 293.50 |

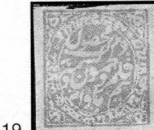

⅛ Anna — A19

**Thin White or Yellowish Wove Paper**
**1883-94**

| | | | | |
|---|---|---|---|---|
| 104 | A19 | ⅛a yellow brown | 2.25 | 3.00 |
| a. | | ⅛a yellow | 2.25 | 3.00 |
| 105 | A13 | ¼a brown | 1.90 | 1.50 |
| a. | | Double impression | 1,800. | |
| 106 | A14 | ½a red | 1.90 | 1.25 |
| a. | | ½a rose | 2.40 | 1.50 |
| 106B | A19 | ½a bright blue | 82.50 | |
| c. | | ½a dull blue | 12.00 | |
| 107 | A15 | 1a bronze green | 1.50 | 1.50 |
| 108 | A15 | 1a yel green | 1.50 | 1.50 |
| 109 | A15 | 1a blue green | 3.00 | — |
| 110 | A15 | 1a bister | | — |
| 111 | A17 | 4a green | 6.50 | 6.00 |
| 112 | A17 | 4a olive green | 6.00 | 7.00 |
| 113 | A18 | 8a deep blue | 19.00 | 22.50 |
| 114 | A18 | 8a dark ultra | 18.00 | 21.00 |
| 115 | A18 | 8a gray violet | 15.00 | 32.50 |

**Printed in Water Color**

| | | | | |
|---|---|---|---|---|
| 116 | A18 | 8a gray blue | 225.00 | 225.00 |

**Printed in Oil Colors**
**Yellow Pelure Paper**

| | | | | |
|---|---|---|---|---|
| 117 | A16 | 2a red | 4.00 | 1.90 |

**Yellow Green Pelure Paper**

| | | | | |
|---|---|---|---|---|
| 118 | A16 | 2a red | 5.50 | 6.00 |

**Deep Green Pelure Paper**

| | | | | |
|---|---|---|---|---|
| 119 | A16 | 2a red | 27.50 | 27.50 |

**Coarse Yellow Wove Paper**

| | | | | |
|---|---|---|---|---|
| 120 | A16 | 2a red | 4.00 | 1.90 |
| | | Nos. 104-120 (17) | 425.05 | 360.05 |

**Thin Creamy Laid Paper**
**1886-94**

| | | | | |
|---|---|---|---|---|
| 121 | A19 | ⅛a yellow | 90.00 | 100.00 |
| 122 | A13 | ¼a brown | 13.50 | 10.00 |
| 123 | A14 | ½a vermilion | 15.00 | 9.50 |
| 124 | A14 | ½a rose red | | 110.00 |
| 125 | A15 | 1a green | 150.00 | 150.00 |
| 126 | A17 | 4a green | — | — |

**Printed in Water Color**

| | | | | |
|---|---|---|---|---|
| 127 | A18 | 8a gray blue | 160.00 | 150.00 |
| | | Nos. 121-127 (6) | 428.50 | 529.50 |

Impressions of types A13 to A19 in colors other than the issued stamps are proofs. Forgeries to defraud the post exist, and some are common.

¼ Anna

Stamps of the above type, printed in red or black, were never placed in use.

**OFFICIAL STAMPS**

Same Types as Regular Issues
White Laid Paper

| | | | | |
|---|---|---|---|---|
| **1878** | | **Unwmk.** | **Rough Perf. 10-14** | |
| O1 | A14 | ½a black | | 3,000. |

**Imperf**

| | | | | |
|---|---|---|---|---|
| O3 | A14 | ½a black | 150.00 | 140.00 |
| O4 | A15 | 1a black | 100.00 | 100.00 |
| O5 | A16 | 2a black | 82.50 | 90.00 |
| | | Nos. O3-O5 (3) | 332.50 | 330.00 |

**Thin White or Yellowish Wove Paper**
**1880**

| | | | | |
|---|---|---|---|---|
| O6 | A13 | ¼a black | 2.50 | 3.00 |
| O7 | A14 | ½a black | .20 | 1.10 |
| O8 | A15 | 1a black | .30 | 1.50 |
| O9 | A16 | 2a black | .45 | .65 |
| O10 | A17 | 4a black | 1.90 | 2.50 |
| O11 | A18 | 8a black | 3.75 | 1.60 |
| | | Nos. O6-O11 (6) | 9.10 | 10.35 |

---

**Thin Creamy Laid Paper**
**1890-91**

| | | | | |
|---|---|---|---|---|
| O12 | A13 | ¼a black | 12.50 | 13.50 |
| O13 | A14 | ½a black | 7.00 | 7.00 |
| O14 | A15 | 1a black | 4.00 | 5.25 |
| O15 | A16 | 2a black | 22.50 | |
| O16 | A17 | 4a black | 82.50 | 97.50 |
| O17 | A18 | 8a black | 42.50 | 75.00 |
| | | Nos. O12-O17 (6) | 171.00 | 198.25 |

Obsolete October 31, 1894.

---

### JASDAN

LOCATION — A Feudatory State in the Kathiawar Agency in Western India.
AREA — 296 sq. mi.
POP. — 34,056 (1931)
CAPITAL — Jasdan

In 1948 Jasdan was incorporated in the United State of Saurashtra (see Soruth).

> **Catalogue values for all unused stamps in this state are for Never Hinged items.**

Sun — A1

| | | | | |
|---|---|---|---|---|
| **1942** | | **Unwmk.** | **Typo.** | |
| 1 | A1 | 1a green | 30.00 | 240.00 |

Issued in booklet panes of 4 and 8. The 1a carmine is a revenue stamp. Jasdan's stamp became obsolete Feb. 15, 1948.

---

### JHALAWAR

ˈjäl-ə-ˌwär

LOCATION — A Feudatory State in the Rajputana Agency of India.
AREA — 813 sq. mi.
POP. — 107,890
CAPITAL — Jhalrapatan

Apsaras, Hindu Nymph
A1            A2
Laid Paper

| | | | | |
|---|---|---|---|---|
| **1887-90** | | **Unwmk.** | **Imperf.** | |
| | | **Without Gum** | | |
| 1 | A1 | 1p yellow green | 7.00 | 22.50 |
| 2 | A2 | ¼a green | 1.90 | 3.75 |

Obsolete October 31, 1900.

---

### JIND

ˈjind

(Jhind)

LOCATION — A State of India in the north Punjab.
AREA — 1,299 sq. mi.
POP. — 361,812 (1941)
CAPITAL — Sangrur

---

A1

A2

A3                A4

A5

| | | | | |
|---|---|---|---|---|
| **1874** | | **Unwmk.  Litho.** | **Imperf.** | |
| | | **Thin White Wove Paper** | | |
| | | **Without Gum** | | |
| 1 | A1 | ½a blue | 10.00 | 6.25 |
| 2 | A2 | 1a lilac | 10.00 | 9.50 |
| 3 | A3 | 2a yellow | 1.50 | 6.75 |
| 4 | A4 | 4a green | 37.50 | 9.00 |
| 5 | A5 | 8a dark violet | 340.00 | 140.00 |
| | | Nos. 1-5 (5) | 399.00 | 171.50 |

| | | | | |
|---|---|---|---|---|
| **1875** | | | | |
| | | **Thick Blue Laid Paper** | | |
| | | **Without Gum** | | |
| 6 | A1 | ½a blue | 1.50 | 7.00 |
| 7 | A2 | 1a red violet | 4.00 | 16.00 |
| 8 | A3 | 2a brown orange | 6.50 | 22.50 |
| 9 | A4 | 4a green | 5.50 | 22.50 |
| 10 | A5 | 8a purple | 13.50 | 32.50 |
| | | Nos. 6-10 (5) | 31.00 | 100.50 |

Nos. 3 and 6 were perforated 12 in 1885 for use as fiscal stamps.

A6                A7

A8                A9

A10               A11

| | | | | |
|---|---|---|---|---|
| **1882-84** | | **Without Gum** | **Imperf.** | |
| | | **Thin Yellowish Wove Paper** | | |
| 12 | A6 | ¼a buff | .45 | 2.25 |
| a. | | Double impression | 75.00 | |
| 13 | A7 | ½a yellow | 3.75 | 2.50 |
| 14 | A8 | 1a brown | 2.50 | 5.00 |
| 15 | A9 | 2a blue | 3.00 | 13.50 |
| 16 | A10 | 4a green | 2.25 | 1.50 |
| 17 | A11 | 8a red | 9.50 | 6.75 |
| | | Nos. 12-17 (6) | 21.45 | 31.50 |

**Perf. 12**

| | | | | |
|---|---|---|---|---|
| 18 | A6 | ¼a buff | 1.50 | 4.00 |
| 19 | A7 | ½a yellow | 240.00 | 240.00 |
| 20 | A8 | 1a brown | 3.75 | 8.25 |
| 21 | A9 | 2a blue | 5.50 | 15.00 |
| 22 | A10 | 4a green | 7.50 | 16.00 |
| 23 | A11 | 8a red | 18.00 | |
| a. | | Thick white paper | 15.00 | |
| | | Nos. 18-23 (6) | 276.25 | 283.25 |

**Laid Paper**
**Imperf**

| | | | | |
|---|---|---|---|---|
| 24 | A6 | ¼a buff | 1.90 | |
| 25 | A7 | ½a yellow | 1.90 | |
| 26 | A8 | 1a brown | 1.90 | 3.75 |
| 27 | A9 | 2a blue | 27.50 | 30.00 |
| 28 | A11 | 8a red | 3.75 | 16.00 |
| | | Nos. 24-28 (5) | 36.95 | 49.75 |

---

**Perf. 12**

| | | | | |
|---|---|---|---|---|
| 29 | A6 | ¼a buff | 12.50 | |
| 30 | A7 | ½a yellow | 190.00 | 40.00 |
| 31 | A8 | 1a brown | 2.25 | |
| 32 | A11 | 8a red | 3.75 | 15.00 |
| | | Nos. 29-32 (4) | 208.50 | 55.00 |

As postage stamps these issues became obsolete in July, 1885, but some possibly remained in use as revenue stamps.

For later issues see Jind under Convention States.

---

### KISHANGARH

ˈkish-ən-ˌgär

LOCATION — A Feudatory State in the Jaipur Residency of India.
AREA — 858 sq. mi.
POP. — 85,744
CAPITAL — Kishangarh

Kishangarh was incorporated in Rajasthan in 1947-49.
Stamps were issued without gum except Nos. 27-35.

Coat of Arms — A1

| | | | | |
|---|---|---|---|---|
| **1899-1900** | | **Unwmk.  Typo.** | **Imperf.** | |
| | | **Soft Porous Paper** | | |
| 1 | A1 | 1a green | 32.50 | 90.00 |
| 2 | A1 | 1a blue ('00) | *600.00* | |

**Pin-perf**

| | | | | |
|---|---|---|---|---|
| 3 | A1 | 1a green | | 110.00 |

A2                A3

Coat of
Arms — A4

Maharaja
Sardul
Singh — A5

A6                A7

Coat of Arms — A9
A8

**Thin Wove Paper**

| | | | | |
|---|---|---|---|---|
| **1899-1900** | | **Handstamped** | **Imperf.** | |
| 4 | A2 | ¼a rose pink | 1.90 | 4.00 |
| a. | | ¼a carmine | 12.50 | |
| 5 | A2 | ¼a green | 825.00 | *1,200.* |
| 6 | A3 | ½a light blue | 1.90 | 2.50 |
| 7 | A3 | ½a green | 57.50 | 62.50 |
| 8 | A3 | ½a carmine | 3,750. | *1,900.* |
| 9 | A3 | ½a violet | 240.00 | *490.00* |
| 10 | A4 | 1a gray violet | 1.60 | 1.50 |
| a. | | 1a gray | 7.50 | 7.50 |

| | | | | |
|---|---|---|---|---|
| 11 | A4 | 1a rose | 110.00 | 300.00 |
| 11A | A5 | 2a orange | 7.50 | 6.75 |
| 12 | A6 | 4a chocolate | 9.00 | 15.00 |
| a. | | Laid paper | 125.00 | 125.00 |
| 13 | A7 | 1r dull green | 35.00 | 52.50 |
| 13A | A7 | 1r light brown | 30.00 | 37.50 |
| 14 | A8 | 2r brown red | 125.00 | 190.00 |
| a. | | Laid paper | 100.00 | |
| 15 | A9 | 5r violet | 120.00 | 150.00 |
| a. | | Laid paper | 120.00 | |

**Pin-perf**

| | | | | |
|---|---|---|---|---|
| 16 | A2 | ¼a magenta | 7.50 | 10.00 |
| a. | | ¼a rose | .35 | .60 |
| 17 | A2 | ¼a green | 400.00 | 700.00 |
| a. | | Imperf. vertically, pair | 1,900. | |
| 18 | A3 | ½a blue | 1.50 | .75 |
| a. | | ½a dark blue | 3.75 | 5.00 |
| 19 | A3 | ½a green | 27.50 | 40.00 |
| a. | | Imperf. vert., pair | 275.00 | |
| 20 | A4 | 1a gray violet | 1.10 | 1.50 |
| a. | | 1a gray | 8.25 | 5.25 |
| b. | | 1a red lilac | 2.25 | 3.00 |
| d. | | As "b," laid paper | 62.50 | 19.00 |
| 20E | A4 | 1a rose | 125.00 | 375.00 |
| 21 | A5 | 2a orange | 6.00 | 7.50 |
| 21B | A6 | 4a pale red brown | 5.25 | 9.00 |
| c. | | 4a chocolate | 3.50 | 9.00 |
| 22 | A7 | 1r dull green | 16.00 | 22.50 |
| b. | | Laid paper | 140.00 | |
| 23 | A8 | 2r brown red | 52.50 | 82.50 |
| b. | | Laid paper | 67.50 | |
| 24 | A9 | 5r red violet | 52.50 | 82.50 |
| d. | | Laid paper | 110.00 | |

Nos. 4-24 exist tête bêche and sell for a slight premium.
For overprints see #O1-O11, Rajasthan #26-28, 30-32.

A9a     A9b

**Soft Porous Paper**

| | | | | |
|---|---|---|---|---|
| **1901** | | | **Typo.** | |
| 24A | A9a | ½a rose | 12.00 | 9.00 |
| 24B | A9b | 1a dull violet | 72.50 | 40.00 |

For overprint see No. O12.

A10     A11

| | | | | |
|---|---|---|---|---|
| **1903** | | **Stout Hard Paper** | **Imperf.** | |
| 25 | A10 | 1a pink | 20.00 | 5.25 |
| a. | | Printed on both sides | 2,100. | |
| **1904** | | **Thin Wove Paper** | **Pin-perf.** | |
| 25B | A11 | 8a gray | 7.50 | 11.00 |
| c. | | tête bêche pair | 40.00 | |

For overprints see #O13, O33, Rajasthan #29.

A11a     Maharaja Sardul Singh — A12

| | | | | |
|---|---|---|---|---|
| 25D | A11a | 1r green | 27.50 | 27.50 |

For overprint see No. O13A.

| | | | | |
|---|---|---|---|---|
| **1903** | | | **Imperf.** | |
| | | **Stout Hard Paper** | | |
| 26 | A12 | 2a yellow | 4.50 | 9.00 |

For overprints see Nos. O14, O34.

Maharaja Madan Singh
A13     A14

| | | | | |
|---|---|---|---|---|
| **1904-05** | | **Engr.** | **Perf. 12½, 13½** | |
| 27 | A13 | ¼a carmine | .65 | 1.10 |
| 28 | A13 | ½a chestnut | 1.90 | .45 |
| 29 | A13 | 1a deep blue | 3.75 | 4.00 |
| 30 | A13 | 2a orange | 22.50 | 10.00 |
| 31 | A13 | 4a dark brown | 22.50 | 25.00 |
| 32 | A13 | 8a purple ('05) | 19.00 | 37.50 |
| 33 | A13 | 1r dark green | 42.50 | 67.50 |
| 34 | A13 | 2r lemon yellow | 42.50 | 250.00 |
| 35 | A13 | 5r purple brown | 35.00 | 300.00 |
| | | Nos. 27-35 (9) | 190.30 | 695.55 |

For overprints see Nos. O15-O22, Rajasthan Nos. 33-39.

**Thin Wove Paper**

| | | | | |
|---|---|---|---|---|
| **1913** | | **Typo.** | **Rouletted 9½** | |
| 37 | A14 | 2 "ANNA" violet | 8.25 | 13.50 |
| a. | | tête bêche pair | 18.00 | 60.00 |

See #40-50. For overprint see Rajasthan #43.

Maharaja Madan Singh
A15     A16

**Thick, Chalk-surfaced Paper**

| | | | | |
|---|---|---|---|---|
| **1913** | | | **Rouletted 6½, 12** | |
| 38 | A15 | ¼a pale blue | .45 | 1.40 |
| a. | | "Kishangahr" | 7.50 | 10.00 |
| b. | | Imperf., pair | 11.00 | |
| 39 | A16 | 2a purple | 12.50 | 27.50 |
| a. | | "Kishangahr" | 75.00 | 140.00 |

For overprint see No. O23.

| | | | | |
|---|---|---|---|---|
| **1913-16** | | | **Rouletted 12, 14½** | |
| 40 | A14 | ¼a pale blue | .30 | .65 |
| 41 | A14 | ½a green ('15) | .30 | 1.50 |
| a. | | Printed on both sides | 350.00 | |
| 42 | A14 | 1a carmine | 1.90 | 3.75 |
| 43 | A14 | 2 "ANNAS" pur | 9.00 | 12.00 |
| 44 | A14 | 4a ultramarine | 9.00 | 12.00 |
| 45 | A14 | 8a brown | 10.00 | 60.00 |
| 46 | A14 | 1r rose lilac | 24.00 | 190.00 |
| 47 | A14 | 2r dark green | 150.00 | 525.00 |
| 48 | A14 | 5r brown | 60.00 | 675.00 |
| | | Nos. 40-48 (9) | 264.50 | 1,479. |

On Nos. 40-48 the halftone screen covers the entire design.
Nos. 41-48 have ornaments on both sides of value in top panel.
For overprints see Nos. O24-O30, O39-O43, Rajasthan Nos. 40-42, 44-48.

**Type of 1913-16 Redrawn**

| | | | | |
|---|---|---|---|---|
| **1918** | | | **Rouletted** | |
| 50 | A14 | 1a rose red | 2.25 | 8.25 |

The redrawn stamp is 24¾mm wide instead of 26mm. There is a white oval around the portrait with only traces of the red line. There is less shading outside the wreath.
For overprint see No. O44.

Maharaja Jagjanarajan Singh
A17     A18

**Thick Glazed Paper**

| | | | | |
|---|---|---|---|---|
| **1928-29** | | | **Pin-perf. 14½ to 16** | |
| 52 | A17 | ¼a light brown | 1.90 | 3.00 |
| 53 | A17 | ½a lt yellow green | 6.00 | 3.50 |
| a. | | Imperf., pair | 180.00 | 180.00 |
| 54 | A18 | 1a carmine rose | 1.10 | 2.25 |
| 55 | A18 | 2a red violet | 5.00 | 12.00 |
| 56 | A17 | 4a yellow brown | 2.50 | 2.50 |
| 57 | A17 | 8a purple | 8.25 | 42.50 |
| 58 | A17 | 1r green | 30.00 | 95.00 |
| 59 | A17 | 2r lemon | 42.50 | 340.00 |
| 60 | A17 | 5r red brown | 67.50 | 400.00 |
| a. | | Imperf., pair | 190.00 | |
| | | Nos. 52-60 (9) | 164.75 | 901.25 |

**Thick Soft Unglazed Paper**

| | | | | |
|---|---|---|---|---|
| **1945-47** | | | | |
| 52a | A17 | ¼a gray blue | 6.25 | 19.00 |
| b. | | ¼a greenish blue ('47) | 4.00 | 15.00 |
| 53b | A17 | ½a deep green | 2.25 | 4.00 |
| 54a | A18 | 1a dull carmine | 12.50 | 6.50 |
| 55a | A18 | 2a deep red violet | 16.00 | 19.00 |
| b. | | 2a violet brown, imperf. | 125.00 | 30.00 |
| 56a | A17 | 4a brown | 35.00 | 30.00 |
| 57a | A17 | 8a violet | 60.00 | 240.00 |
| 58a | A17 | 1r deep brown | 75.00 | 250.00 |
| 59a | A17 | 2r lemon | | |
| 60b | A17 | 5r red brown | 875.00 | 1,100. |

For overprints see Rajasthan Nos. 49-58.
For later issues see Rajasthan.

## OFFICIAL STAMPS

Used values are for CTO stamps.

Regular Issues of 1899-1916 Handstamped

**Black Handstamp**
**On Issue of 1899-1900**

| | | | | |
|---|---|---|---|---|
| **1918** | | **Unwmk.** | **Imperf.** | |
| O1 | A2 | ¼a carmine | | 12.00 |
| O2 | A4 | 1a gray violet | 82.50 | 8.25 |
| O3 | A6 | 4a chocolate | | 190.00 |
| | | **Pin-perf** | | |
| O4 | A2 | ¼a carmine | 3.25 | .90 |
| O4A | A2 | ¼a green | | 175.00 |
| O4B | A3 | ½a blue | 640.00 | 67.50 |
| O6 | A4 | 1a gray violet | 67.50 | 2.25 |
| O7 | A5 | 2a orange | | 225.00 |
| O8 | A6 | 4a chocolate | 100.00 | 24.00 |
| O9 | A7 | 1r dull green | 250.00 | 180.00 |
| O10 | A8 | 2r brown red | | 1,400. |
| O11 | A9 | 5r red violet | | 3,000. |

See tete beche note after No. 24.

**On Issue of 1901**

| | | | | |
|---|---|---|---|---|
| O12 | A9b | 1a dull violet | 75.00 | 2.25 |

**On Issue of 1904**

| | | | | |
|---|---|---|---|---|
| O13 | A11 | 8a gray | 140.00 | 35.00 |
| O13A | A11a | 1r green | | 1,350. |
| | | **Imperf.** | | |
| O14 | A12 | 2a yellow | 125.00 | 7.50 |

**On Issue of 1904-05**
**Perf. 12½, 13**

| | | | | |
|---|---|---|---|---|
| O15 | A13 | ¼a carmine | | 450.00 |
| O16 | A13 | ½a chestnut | .60 | 1.50 |
| O17 | A13 | 1a deep blue | 16.00 | 6.00 |
| O18 | A13 | 2a orange | | 1,500. |
| O19 | A13 | 4a dark brown | 90.00 | 27.50 |
| O20 | A13 | 8a purple | 600.00 | 375.00 |
| O21 | A13 | 1r dark green | 1,200. | 1,100. |
| O22 | A13 | 5r purple brn | | |

**On Issue of 1913**
**Rouletted**

| | | | | |
|---|---|---|---|---|
| O23 | A15 | ¼a pale blue | 11.00 | |

**On Issue of 1913-16**

| | | | | |
|---|---|---|---|---|
| O24 | A14 | ¼a pale blue | .90 | .75 |
| O25 | A14 | ½a green | 1.50 | 1.10 |
| O26 | A14 | 1a carmine | 24.00 | 13.50 |
| O27 | A14 | 2a purple | 12.50 | 6.00 |
| O28 | A14 | 4a ultra | 42.50 | 22.50 |
| O29 | A14 | 8a brown | 190.00 | 67.50 |
| O30 | A14 | 1r rose lilac | 525.00 | 500.00 |
| O31 | A14 | 2r dark green | | |
| O32 | A14 | 5r brown | | 2,750. |

**Red Handstamp**
**On Issue of 1904**
**Pin-perf**

| | | | | |
|---|---|---|---|---|
| O33 | A11 | 8a gray | | 450.00 |
| | | **Imperf** | | |
| O34 | A12 | 2a yellow | 675.00 | 400.00 |

**On Issue of 1904-05**
**Perf. 12½, 13**

| | | | | |
|---|---|---|---|---|
| O35 | A13 | 1a deep blue | 35.00 | 10.00 |
| O36 | A13 | 4a dark brown | 140.00 | 62.50 |
| O37 | A13 | 8a purple | | 400.00 |
| O38 | A13 | 1r dark green | | 1,000. |

**On Issue of 1913-16**
**Rouletted**

| | | | | |
|---|---|---|---|---|
| O39 | A14 | ¼a pale blue | 3.00 | 2.50 |
| O40 | A14 | ½a green | 6.50 | 2.40 |
| O41 | A14 | 2a purple | 210.00 | 100.00 |
| O42 | A14 | 4a ultra | | 52.50 |
| O43 | A14 | 8a brown | | 140.00 |

**On Issue of 1918**
**Redrawn**

| | | | | |
|---|---|---|---|---|
| O44 | A14 | 1a rose red | | |

The overprint on Nos. O1 to O44 is hand-stamped and, as usual with that style of overprint, is found inverted, double, etc. In this instance there is evidence that many of the varieties were deliberately made.

## LAS BELA

ləs ˈbāl-ə

LOCATION — A Feudatory State in the Baluchistan District.
AREA — 7,132 sq. mi.
POP. — 63,008
CAPITAL — Bela

A1

A2

| | | | | |
|---|---|---|---|---|
| **1897-98** | | **Unwmk.** | **Typo.** | **Perf. 12** |
| 1 | A1 | ½a black, *white* | 45.00 | 25.00 |
| 2 | A1 | ½a black, *gray* | 25.00 | 16.00 |
| 3 | A1 | ½a blk, *blue* ('98) | 30.00 | 16.00 |
| | | Nos. 1-3 (3) | 100.00 | 57.00 |

| | | | | |
|---|---|---|---|---|
| **1901** | | | | |
| 4 | A2 | 1a black, *red orange* | 35.00 | 40.00 |

| | | | | |
|---|---|---|---|---|
| **1904** | | | **Pin-perf** | |
| 5 | A1 | ½a black, *lt blue* | 24.00 | 13.50 |
| | | **Granite Paper** | | |
| 6 | A1 | ½a black, *greenish gray* | 24.00 | 13.50 |

Las Bela stamps became obsolete in Mar. 1907.

## MORVI

ˈmor-vē

LOCATION — A Feudatory State in the Kathiawar Agency, Western India.
AREA — 822 sq. mi.
POP. — 113,023
CAPITAL — Morvi

In 1948 Morvi was incorporated in the United State of Saurashtra (see Soruth).

Sir Lakhdhirji Waghji The Thakur Sahib of Morvi — A1

| | | | | |
|---|---|---|---|---|
| **1931** | | **Unwmk.** | **Typo.** | **Perf. 12** |
| | | **Size: 21½x26½mm** | | |
| 1 | A1 | 3p red | 4.50 | 22.50 |
| a. | | 3p deep blue (error) | 6.50 | 35.00 |

| | | | | |
|---|---|---|---|---|
| 2 | A1 | ½a deep blue | 40.00 | 67.50 |
| 3 | A1 | 1a red brown | 5.00 | 25.00 |
| 4 | A1 | 2a yellow brown | 6.00 | 60.00 |
| | | *Nos. 1-4 (4)* | 55.50 | *175.00* |

Nos. 1-4 and 1a were printed in two blocks of four, with stamps 5½mm apart, and perforated on four sides. Nos. 1 and 2 were also printed in blocks of four, with stamps 10mm apart, and perforated on two or three sides.

A2      A3

**1932   Size: 21x25½mm   Perf. 11**

| | | | | |
|---|---|---|---|---|
| 5 | A2 | 3p rose | 7.50 | 21.00 |
| 6 | A2 | 6p gray green | 12.00 | 25.00 |
| 7 | A2 | 6p emerald | 9.50 | 21.00 |
| 8 | A2 | 1a ultramarine | 6.50 | 21.00 |
| 9 | A2 | 2a violet | 16.00 | 60.00 |
| | | *Nos. 5-9 (5)* | 51.50 | *148.00* |

**1934-48   Perf. 14, Rough Perf. 11**

| | | | | |
|---|---|---|---|---|
| 10 | A3 | 3p carmine rose | 3.75 | 5.25 |
| a. | | 3p red | 2.50 | 6.50 |
| 11 | A3 | 6p emerald | 2.50 | 10.00 |
| a. | | 6p green | 10.00 | 25.00 |
| 12 | A3 | 1a red brown | 2.75 | 21.00 |
| a. | | 1a brown | 15.00 | 25.00 |
| 13 | A3 | 2a violet | 3.75 | 30.00 |
| | | *Nos. 10-13 (4)* | 12.75 | *66.25* |

The 1934 London printing of Nos. 10-13 is perf. 14; the later Morvi Press printing is rough perf. 11.

Morvi stamps became obsolete Feb. 15, 1948.

## NANDGAON

'nän,d,-,gaun

LOCATION — A Feudatory State in the Chhattisgarh States Agency in Central India.
AREA — 871 sq. mi.
POP. — 182,380
CAPITAL — Rajnandgaon

A1

White Paper
**1892, Feb.   Unwmk. Typo.   Imperf.**
**Without Gum**

| | | | | |
|---|---|---|---|---|
| 1 | A1 | ½a blue | 10.00 | 275.00 |
| 2 | A1 | 2a rose | 40.00 | 825.00 |

Some authorities claim that No. 2 was a revenue stamp.
For overprints see Nos. O1-O2.

A2

**1893     Without Gum**

| | | | | |
|---|---|---|---|---|
| 4 | A2 | ½a green | 19.00 | 140.00 |
| 5 | A2 | 2a rose | 19.00 | 140.00 |

For overprint see No. O5.

**Same Redrawn**
**1894     Without Gum**

| | | | | |
|---|---|---|---|---|
| 6 | A2 | ½a yellow green | 37.50 | 140.00 |
| 7 | A2 | 1a rose | 82.50 | 175.00 |
| a. | | Laid paper | 375.00 | |

The redrawn stamps have smaller value characters and wavy lines between the stamps.

---

For overprints see Nos. O3-O4.

### OFFICIAL STAMPS

Regular Issues Handstamped in Violet

**1893-94   Unwmk.   Imperf.**
**Without Gum**

| | | | | |
|---|---|---|---|---|
| O1 | A1 | ½a blue | *550.00* | |
| O2 | A1 | 2a red | *1,350.* | |
| O3 | A2 | ½a yellow green | 9.50 | 17.50 |
| O4 | A2 | 1a rose | 16.00 | 37.50 |
| a. | | Laid paper | 16.00 | 125.00 |
| O5 | A2 | 2a rose | 3.00 | 3.00 |

Some authorities believe that this handstamp was used as a control mark, rather than to indicate a stamp for official mail.
*The 1 anna has been reprinted in brown and in blue.*
Nandgaon stamps became obsolete in July, 1895.

---

### NOWANUGGUR

,nau-ə-'nəg-ər

## (Navanagar)

LOCATION — A Feudatory State in the Kathiawar Agency, Western India.
AREA — 3,791 sq. mi.
POP. — 402,192
CAPITAL — Navanagar

Stamps of Nowanuggur were superseded by those of India.

6 Dokra = 1 Anna
16 Annas = 1 Rupee

Kandjar (Indian Dagger) — A1

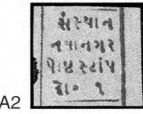

A2

**1877   Unwmk. Typo.   Imperf.**
**Without Gum**
**Laid Paper**

| | | | | |
|---|---|---|---|---|
| 1 | A1 | 1d dull blue | 1.00 | 37.50 |
| a. | | 1d ultramarine | 1.00 | 37.50 |
| b. | | Tete beche pair | 1,900. | |

**Perf. 12½**

| | | | | |
|---|---|---|---|---|
| 2 | A1 | 1d slate | 120.00 | 175.00 |
| a. | | Tete beche pair | 2,400. | |

No. 2 on wove paper is of private origin.

**1877-88     Imperf.**
**Without Gum**
**Wove Paper**

| | | | | |
|---|---|---|---|---|
| 3 | A2 | 1d black, *red violet* | 5.25 | 16.00 |
| a. | | 1d black, *rose* | 5.25 | |
| b. | | Characters at beginning of 3rd line read "4102" instead of "418" | | |
| 4 | A2 | 2d black, *green* | 8.25 | 21.00 |
| a. | | 2d black, *blue green* | 12.50 | |
| b. | | "4102" instead of "418" | | |
| 5 | A2 | 3d black, *yellow* | 9.00 | 30.00 |
| a. | | 3d black, *orange yellow* | 19.00 | |
| b. | | "4102" instead of "418" | | |
| c. | | Laid paper | 160.00 | |
| d. | | 2d black, *yellow* (error in sheet of 3d) | 600.00 | |
| | | *Nos. 3-5 (3)* | 22.50 | *67.00* |

Nos. 3-5 range in width from 14 to 19mm.

---

Seal of the State — A3

**1893   Thick Paper   Imperf.**
**Without Gum**

| | | | |
|---|---|---|---|
| 6 | A3 | 1d black | 450.00 |

**Perf. 12**

| | | | |
|---|---|---|---|
| 7 | A3 | 1d black | 6.50 |
| 8 | A3 | 3d orange | 7.50 |

**Imperf**
**Thin Paper**

| | | | |
|---|---|---|---|
| 9 | A3 | 1d black | 350.00 |
| 10 | A3 | 2d dark green | 450.00 |
| 11 | A3 | 3d orange | 400.00 |
| | | *Nos. 9-11 (3)* | 1,200. |

**Perf. 12**

| | | | | |
|---|---|---|---|---|
| 12 | A3 | 1d black | 2.50 | 9.00 |
| 13 | A3 | 2d green | 3.40 | 12.00 |
| 14 | A3 | 3d orange | 3.40 | 17.50 |
| a. | | Imperf. vert., pair | | |
| | | *Nos. 12-14 (3)* | 9.30 | *38.50* |

Obsolete at end of 1895.

---

### ORCHHA

'or-chə

## (Orcha)

LOCATION — A Feudatory State in the Bundelkhand Agency in Central India.
AREA — 2,080 sq. mi.
POP. — 314,661
CAPITAL — Tikamgarh

Seal of Orchha — A1

**1913-17   Unwmk.   Litho.   Imperf.**
**Without Gum**

| | | | | |
|---|---|---|---|---|
| 1 | A1 | ¼a ultra ('15) | 3.00 | 7.50 |
| 2 | A1 | ½a emerald ('14) | .85 | 9.50 |
| a. | | Background of arms unshaded | 52.50 | 150.00 |
| 3 | A1 | 1a carmine ('14) | 3.75 | 10.00 |
| a. | | Background of arms unshaded | 30.00 | 275.00 |
| 4 | A1 | 2a brown ('17) | 6.75 | 35.00 |
| 5 | A1 | 4a orange ('14) | 12.00 | 57.50 |
| | | *Nos. 1-5 (5)* | 26.35 | *119.50* |

Essays similar to Nos. 2-5 are in different colors.

A2      Maharaja Singh Dev — A3

**1939-40     Perf. 13½, 13½x14**

| | | | | |
|---|---|---|---|---|
| 6 | A2 | ¼a chocolate | 5.00 | 120.00 |
| 7 | A2 | ½a yellow green | 4.50 | 100.00 |
| 8 | A2 | ¾a ultramarine | 7.00 | 150.00 |
| 9 | A2 | 1a rose red | 4.50 | 30.00 |
| 10 | A2 | 1¼a deep blue | 5.50 | 150.00 |
| 11 | A2 | 1½a lilac | 6.00 | 190.00 |
| 12 | A2 | 2a vermilion | 4.50 | 120.00 |
| 13 | A2 | 2½a turq green | 7.50 | 340.00 |
| 14 | A2 | 3a dull violet | 8.00 | 180.00 |
| 15 | A2 | 4a blue gray | 9.00 | 42.50 |
| 16 | A2 | 8a rose lilac | 15.00 | 340.00 |
| 17 | A3 | 1r sage green | 200.00 | 750.00 |
| 18 | A3 | 2r lt violet ('40) | 60.00 | 1,000. |
| 19 | A3 | 5r yel org ('40) | 200.00 | 2,750. |
| 20 | A3 | 10r blue | 700.00 | 4,500. |
| | | *Nos. 6-20 (15)* | 1,296. | *10,762.* |

---

### POONCH

'pünch

LOCATION — A Feudatory State in the Kashmir Residency in India.
AREA — 1,627 sq. mi.
POP. — 287,000 (estimated)
CAPITAL — Poonch

Poonch was feudatory to Jammu and Kashmir. Cancellations of Jammu and Kashmir are found on Poonch stamps, which became obsolete in 1894. The stamps are all printed in watercolor and handstamped from single dies. They may be found on various papers, including wove, laid, wove batonne, laid batonne and ribbed, in various colors and tones. Nearly all Poonch stamps exist tete beche and impressed sideways. Issued without gum.

A1

White Paper
**Handstamped**
**1876   Unwmk.   Imperf.**
**Size: 22x21mm**

| | | | | |
|---|---|---|---|---|
| 1 | A1 | 6p red | 18,000. | 240.00 |

**1877**
**Size: 19x17mm**

| | | | | |
|---|---|---|---|---|
| 1A | A1 | ½a red | 22,500. | *7,500.* |

**1879**
**Size: 21x19mm**

| | | | | |
|---|---|---|---|---|
| 1B | A1 | ½a red | — | *7,500.* |

A2      A3

A4      A5

A6

**1880-88**
**White Paper**

| | | | | |
|---|---|---|---|---|
| 2 | A2 | 1p red ('84) | 40.00 | 40.00 |
| 3 | A3 | ½a red | 4.00 | 5.25 |
| 4 | A4 | 1a red | 6.75 | |
| 5 | A5 | 2a red | 16.00 | 19.00 |
| 6 | A6 | 4a red | 25.00 | |

**Yellow Paper**

| | | | | |
|---|---|---|---|---|
| 7 | A2 | 1p red | 5.50 | 5.50 |
| 8 | A3 | ½a red | 9.50 | 9.50 |
| 9 | A4 | 1a red | 82.50 | |
| 10 | A5 | 2a red | 15.00 | 17.50 |
| 11 | A6 | 4a red | 7.50 | 7.50 |

**Blue Paper**

| | | | | |
|---|---|---|---|---|
| 12 | A2 | 1p red | 4.00 | 3.75 |
| 13 | A4 | 1a red | 6.00 | 625.00 |

**Orange Paper**

| | | | | |
|---|---|---|---|---|
| 14 | A2 | 1p red | 5.50 | 5.50 |
| 15 | A3 | ½a red | 42.50 | |
| 16 | A5 | 2a red | 150.00 | |
| 17 | A6 | 4a red | 37.50 | |

**Green Paper**

| | | | | |
|---|---|---|---|---|
| 18 | A3 | ½a red | 67.50 | |
| 19 | A4 | 1a red | 5.00 | 7.50 |
| 20 | A5 | 2a red | 67.50 | |
| 21 | A6 | 4a red | 100.00 | |

## Lavender Paper

| | | | | |
|---|---|---|---|---|
| 22 | A2 | 1p red | 75.00 | 82.50 |
| 23 | A4 | 1a red | 125.00 | 160.00 |
| 24 | A5 | 2a red | 5.00 | 5.50 |

## OFFICIAL STAMPS

### White Paper
#### Handstamped

| 1888 | | Unwmk. | | *Imperf.* |
|---|---|---|---|---|
| O1 | A2 | 1p black | 4.00 | 4.50 |
| O2 | A3 | ½a black | 4.50 | 6.00 |
| O3 | A4 | 1a black | 4.00 | 4.50 |
| O4 | A5 | 2a black | 7.50 | 7.50 |
| O5 | A6 | 4a black | 12.00 | 16.00 |
| | | Nos. O1-O5 (5) | 32.00 | 38.50 |

### 1890
#### Yellowish Paper

| | | | | |
|---|---|---|---|---|
| O6 | A2 | 1p black | 3.75 | |
| O7 | A3 | ½a black | 4.50 | 5.25 |
| O8 | A4 | 1a black | 22.50 | 21.00 |
| O9 | A5 | 2a black | 9.50 | 9.50 |
| O10 | A6 | 4a black | 15.00 | |
| | | Nos. O6-O10 (5) | 55.25 | 35.75 |

Obsolete since 1894.

---

## RAJASTHAN

'rä-jə-ˌstän

## (Greater Rajasthan Union)

AREA — 128,424 sq. miles
POP. — 13,085,000

The Rajasthan Union was formed in 1947-49 by 14 Indian States, including the stamp-issuing States of Bundi, Jaipur and Kishangarh.

Catalogue values for all unused stamps in this state are for Never Hinged items.

Bundi Nos. 43 to 49 Overprinted

a

| 1948 | | Unwmk. | | *Perf. 11* |
|---|---|---|---|---|
| | | **Handstamped in Black** | | |
| 1 | A8 | ¼a dp grn | 8.25 | 50.00 |
| a. | | Pair, one without overprint | 550.00 | |
| 2 | A8 | ½a purple | 8.25 | 50.00 |
| a. | | Pair, one without overprint | 600.00 | |
| 3 | A8 | 1a yel green | 7.00 | 42.50 |
| 4 | A9 | 2a red | 21.00 | 125.00 |
| 5 | A9 | 4a dp orange | 72.50 | 450.00 |
| 6 | A10 | 8a vio blue | 13.50 | 80.00 |
| | | Nos. 1-6 (6) | 130.50 | 797.50 |
| | | **Handstamped in Violet** | | |
| 1b | A8 | ¼a dp grn | 9.00 | 55.00 |
| 2b | A8 | ½a purple | 9.00 | 55.00 |
| c. | | Pair, one without overprint | 550.00 | |
| 3a | A8 | 1a yel green | 24.00 | 140.00 |
| b. | | Pair, one without overprint | 550.00 | |
| 4a | A9 | 2a red | 47.50 | 275.00 |
| 5a | A9 | 4a dp orange | 47.50 | 275.00 |
| 6a | A10 | 8a vio blue | 14.00 | 80.00 |
| 7 | A10 | 1r chocolate | 400.00 | 2,400. |
| | | Nos. 1b-7 (7) | 551.00 | 3,280. |
| | | **Handstamped in Blue** | | |
| 1c | A8 | ¼a dp grn | 52.50 | 300.00 |
| 2d | A8 | ½a purple | 72.50 | 450.00 |
| 3c | A8 | 1a yel green | 67.50 | 400.00 |
| 5b | A9 | 4a dp orange | 190.00 | 1,100. |
| 6b | A10 | 8a vio blue | 120.00 | 725.00 |
| 7a | A10 | 1r chocolate | 140.00 | 825.00 |
| | | Nos. 1c-7a (6) | 642.50 | 3,800. |
| | | **Typo. in Black** | | |
| 11 | A9 | 2a red | 15.00 | 100.00 |
| a. | | Inverted overprint | 450.00 | |
| 12 | A9 | 4a deep orange | 6.00 | 100.00 |
| a. | | Double overprint | 400.00 | |
| 13 | A10 | 8a violet blue | 27.50 | |
| a. | | Inverted overprint | 950.00 | |
| b. | | Double overprint | 600.00 | |
| 14 | A10 | 1r chocolate | 11.00 | |
| | | Nos. 11-14 (4) | 59.50 | |

Stamps of Jaipur, 1931-47, Overprinted in Blue or Carmine

| 1949 | | Center in Black | | *Perf. 14* |
|---|---|---|---|---|
| 15 | A6 | ¼a red brown (Bl) | 12.00 | 32.50 |
| 16 | A6 | ½a dull violet | 9.50 | 35.00 |
| 17 | A6 | ¾a brown org (Bl) | 15.00 | 40.00 |
| 18 | A6 | 1a blue | 11.00 | 72.50 |
| 19 | A6 | 2a ocher | 12.50 | 100.00 |
| 20 | A6 | 2½a rose (Bl) | 13.50 | 45.00 |
| 21 | A6 | 3a green | 16.00 | 110.00 |
| 22 | A6 | 4a gray green | 14.00 | 125.00 |
| 23 | A6 | 6a blue | 14.00 | 180.00 |
| 24 | A6 | 8a chocolate | 24.00 | 250.00 |
| 25 | A6 | 1r bister | 35.00 | 375.00 |
| | | Nos. 15-25 (11) | 176.50 | 1,365. |

Kishangarh Stamps and Types of 1899-1904 Handstamped Type "a" in Rose

| 1949 | | *Pin-perf., Rouletted* | | |
|---|---|---|---|---|
| 26 | A3 | ½a blue (#18) | 900.00 | |
| 27 | A4 | 1a dull lilac (#20) | 21.00 | 62.50 |
| 28 | A6 | 4a pale red brown (#21B) | 125.00 | 160.00 |
| 29 | A11 | 8a gray (#25B) | 160.00 | 275.00 |
| 30 | A7 | 1r dull green (#22) | 450.00 | 500.00 |
| 31 | A8 | 2r brown red (#23) | 550.00 | |
| 32 | A9 | 5r red violet (#24) | 525.00 | 525.00 |
| | | Nos. 26-32 (7) | 2,731. | |

Kishangarh Nos. 28, 31-36 Handstamped Type "a" in Rose or Green

| 1949 | | Engr. | | *Perf. 13½, 12½* |
|---|---|---|---|---|
| 33 | A13 | ½a chestnut (R) | 300.00 | |
| 34 | A13 | 4a dark brown (G) | 375.00 | |
| 35 | A13 | 4a dark brown (R) | 20.00 | |
| 36 | A13 | 8a purple (R) | 16.00 | |
| 37 | A13 | 1r dark green (R) | 21.00 | |
| 38 | A13 | 2r lemon yellow (R) | 27.50 | |
| 39 | A13 | 5r purple brown (R) | 47.50 | |
| | | Nos. 33-39 (7) | 807.00 | |

Kishangarh Nos. 40-42, 37, 43, 46-48 Handstamped Type "a" in Rose

| 1949 | | Typo. | | *Rouletted* |
|---|---|---|---|---|
| 40 | A14 | ¼a pale blue | 8.00 | 8.00 |
| 41 | A14 | ½a green | 675.00 | 375.00 |
| 42 | A14 | 1a carmine | — | 450.00 |
| 43 | A14 | 2 "anna" violet | 825.00 | |
| 44 | A14 | 2 "annas" purple | 4.50 | 12.50 |
| 45 | A14 | 8a brown | 7.50 | |
| 46 | A14 | 1r rose lilac | 15.00 | |
| 47 | A14 | 2r dark green | 15.00 | |
| 48 | A14 | 5r brown | 675.00 | |
| | | Nos. 40-48 (8) | 2,225. | 845.50 |

Kishangarh Stamps and Types of 1928-29 Handstamped Type "a" in Rose

| 1949 | | | | *Pin-perf* |
|---|---|---|---|---|
| 49 | A17 | ¼a greenish blue | 75.00 | 75.00 |
| 50 | A17 | ½a yel green | 60.00 | 60.00 |
| 51 | A18 | 1a car rose | 110.00 | 110.00 |
| 52 | A18 | 2a red violet | 325.00 | 325.00 |
| 53 | A17 | 4a yel brown | 4.00 | 12.50 |
| 54 | A18 | 8a purple | 21.00 | 90.00 |
| 55 | A17 | 1r deep green | 10.00 | |
| 56 | A17 | 2r lemon | 140.00 | |
| 57 | A17 | 5r red brown | 75.00 | |
| | | Nos. 49-57 (9) | 820.00 | 672.50 |

Type of Kishangarh 1928-29, Handstamped Type "a" in Rose

| 1949 | | | | *Pin-perf* |
|---|---|---|---|---|
| 58 | A18 | 1a dark violet blue | 140.00 | |

No. 58 exists imperf.
Rajasthan stamps became obsolete Apr. 1, 1950.

---

## RAJPEEPLA

räj-'pē-plə

## (Rajpipla)

LOCATION — A Feudatory State near Bombay in the Gujarat States Agency in India.
AREA — 1,517 sq. mi.
POP. — 206,086
CAPITAL — Nandod

4 Paisas = 1 Anna

Kandjar (Indian Daggers) — A1

A2     A3

| 1880 | | Unwmk. Litho. | *Perf. 11, 12½* | |
|---|---|---|---|---|
| | | **Without Gum** | | |
| 1 | A1 | 1pa ultramarine | 5.25 | 57.50 |
| 2 | A2 | 2a green | 45.00 | 160.00 |
| a. | | Horiz. pair, imperf. btwn. | 900.00 | 900.00 |
| 3 | A3 | 4a red | 24.00 | 100.00 |
| | | Nos. 1-3 (3) | 74.25 | 317.50 |

The stamps of Rajpeepla have been obsolete since 1886.

---

## SIRMOOR

sir-'muˌə,r

## (Sirmur)

LOCATION — A Feudatory State in the Punjab District of India.
AREA — 1,046 sq. mi.
POP. — 148,568
CAPITAL — Nahan

A1    Raja Sir Shamsher Prakash — A2

| 1879 | | Unwmk. | *Perf. 11½* | |
|---|---|---|---|---|
| | | **Wove Paper** | | |
| 1 | A1 | 1p green | 24.00 | 500.00 |
| a. | | Imperf., pair | | |
| | | **Laid Paper** | | |
| 2 | A1 | 1p blue | 6.75 | 250.00 |
| a. | | Imperf., pair | | |

| 1885-88 | | Litho. | *Perf. 14 and 14½.* | |
|---|---|---|---|---|
| 3 | A2 | 3p brown | 1.00 | .60 |
| 4 | A2 | 3p orange | 2.50 | .45 |
| 5 | A2 | 6p green | 6.50 | 6.00 |
| 6 | A2 | 1a blue | 4.00 | 5.50 |
| 7 | A2 | 2a carmine | 6.25 | 21.00 |
| | | Nos. 3-7 (5) | 20.25 | 33.55 |

There are several printings, dies and minor variations of this issue.
For overprints see Nos. O1-O16.

A3    Elephant — A4

| 1893 | | | *Perf. 11½* | |
|---|---|---|---|---|
| 9 | A3 | 1p yellow green | 1.60 | 1.60 |
| a. | | 1pa dark blue green | 1.10 | 1.10 |
| 10 | A3 | 1p ultramarine | 1.90 | 1.20 |
| a. | | Imperf., pair | 110.00 | |

Nos. 9 and 10 are re-issues, which were available for postage.
The printed perforation, which is a part of the design, is in addition to the regular perforation.

| 1895-99 | | Engr. | *Perf. 14* | |
|---|---|---|---|---|
| 11 | A4 | 3p orange | 5.45 | .45 |
| 12 | A4 | 6p green | 1.10 | .45 |
| a. | | Vert. pair, imperf between | 15,000. | |
| 13 | A4 | 1a dull blue | 6.50 | 5.25 |
| 14 | A4 | 2a dull red | 5.25 | 2.25 |
| 15 | A4 | 3a yellow green | 35.00 | 67.50 |
| 16 | A4 | 4a dark green | 24.00 | 35.00 |
| 17 | A4 | 8a deep blue | 27.50 | 42.50 |
| 18 | A4 | 1r vermilion | 57.50 | 110.00 |
| | | Nos. 11-18 (8) | 162.30 | 263.40 |

No. 12a is unique.

Sir Surendar Bikram Prakash — A5

| 1899 | | | | |
|---|---|---|---|---|
| 19 | A5 | 3a yellow green | 6.25 | 32.50 |
| 20 | A5 | 4a dark green | 8.25 | 35.00 |
| 21 | A5 | 8a blue | 11.00 | 30.00 |
| 22 | A5 | 1r vermilion | 18.00 | 75.00 |
| | | Nos. 19-22 (4) | 43.50 | 172.50 |

---

## OFFICIAL STAMPS

Regular Stamps Overprinted

### Black Overprint

| 1890-91 | | Unwmk. | *Perf. 14, 14½* | |
|---|---|---|---|---|
| O1 | A2 | 3p orange | 4.50 | 52.50 |
| O2 | A2 | 6p green | 2.25 | 2.25 |
| a. | | Double overprint | 275.00 | |
| b. | | Double ovpt., one in red | 1,250. | |
| O3 | A2 | 1a blue | 600.00 | 700.00 |
| O4 | A2 | 2a carmine | 27.50 | 100.00 |
| | | Nos. O1-O4 (4) | 634.25 | |

### 1890-92
#### Red Overprint

| | | | | |
|---|---|---|---|---|
| O5 | A2 | 6p green | 42.50 | 3.50 |
| O6 | A2 | 1a blue | 37.50 | 47.50 |

| | | | | |
|---|---|---|---|---|
| O7 | A2 | 6p green | 8.25 | .75 |
| b. | | Inverted overprint | 210.00 | 150.00 |
| O8 | A2 | 1a blue | 27.50 | 6.25 |
| a. | | Inverted overprint | 500.00 | 300.00 |
| b. | | Double overprint | 500.00 | |

### 1892
#### Black Overprint

| | | | | |
|---|---|---|---|---|
| O9 | A2 | 3p orange | .90 | .75 |
| a. | | Inverted overprint | 375.00 | |
| O10 | A2 | 6p green | 12.00 | 3.25 |
| O11 | A2 | 1a blue | 18.00 | 1.50 |
| a. | | Double overprint | 600.00 | |
| O12 | A2 | 2a carmine | 10.00 | 10.00 |
| a. | | Inverted overprint | 1,350. | 1,350. |
| | | Nos. O9-O12 (4) | 40.90 | 15.50 |

### Black Overprint

| | | | | |
|---|---|---|---|---|
| O13 | A2 | 3p orange | 19.00 | 1.90 |
| a. | | Inverted overprint | | 1,000. |
| O14 | A2 | 6p green | 8.25 | .90 |
| O15 | A2 | 1a blue | 11.00 | 1.90 |
| O16 | A2 | 2a carmine | 25.00 | 21.00 |
| | | Nos. O13-O16 (4) | 63.25 | 25.70 |

There are several settings of some of these overprints, differing in the sizes and shapes of the letters, the presence or absence of the periods, etc.

The overprints on Nos. O1-O16 are press printed. In addition, nine varieties of hand-stamped overprints were applied in 1894-96. Most of the handstamps are very similar to the press printed overprints.

Obsolete Mar. 31, 1901.

---

## SORUTH

### (Sorath)
### (Junagarh)
### (Saurashtra)

LOCATION — A Feudatory State near Bombay in the Western India States Agency in India.
AREA — 3,337 sq. mi.
POP. — 670,719
CAPITAL — Junagarh

The United State of Saurashtra (area 31,885 sq. mi.; population 2,900,000) was formed in 1948 by 217 States, including the stamp-issuing States of Jasdan, Morvi, Nowanuggur and Wadhwan.

Nos. 1-27 were issued without gum.

> **Catalogue values for unused stamps in this State are for Never Hinged items, beginning with Scott 39 in the regular postage section, and Scott O19 in the officials section.**

### Junagarh

A1              A2

**Handstamped in Watercolor**

| | | | | |
|---|---|---|---|---|
| **1864** | | **Unwmk.** | | **Imperf.** |
| | | **Laid Paper** | | |
| 1 | A1 | (1a) black, *bluish* | 950.00 | 125.00 |
| *a.* | Wove paper | | | 275.00 |
| 1B | A1 | (1a) black, *gray* | 950.00 | 125.00 |
| | | **Wove Paper** | | |
| 2 | A1 | (1a) black, *cream* | | 1,500. |

| | | | | |
|---|---|---|---|---|
| **1868** | | **Typo.** | | **Imperf.** |
| | | **Wove Paper** | | |
| 3 | A2 | 1a black, *yellowish* | | 37,500. |
| 4 | A2 | 1a red, *green* | | 16,000. |
| 5 | A2 | 1a red, *blue* | | 12,500. |
| 6 | A2 | 1a black, *pink* | 825.00 | 110.00 |
| 7 | A2 | 2a black, *yellow* | | 16,000. |
| | | **Laid Paper** | | |
| 8 | A2 | 1a black, *blue* | 140.00 | 13.50 |
| *a.* | Left character, 3rd line, omitted | | | |
| 9 | A2 | 1a red | 32.50 | 37.50 |
| *a.* | Left character, 3rd line, omitted | | | |
| 10 | A2 | 4a black | 400.00 | *675.00* |
| *a.* | Left character, 3rd line, omitted | | | |

A 1a black on white laid paper exists in type A2. Value, used $9,500.

*In 1890 official imitations of 1a and 4a stamps, type A2, were printed in sheets of 16 and 4. Original sheets have 20 stamps. Four of these imitations are perf. 12, six are imperf.*

A3              A4

| | | | | |
|---|---|---|---|---|
| **1877-86** | | **Laid Paper** | | **Imperf.** |
| 11 | A3 | 1a green | 1.50 | .75 |
| *a.* | Printed on both sides | 750.00 | 825.00 |
| 12 | A4 | 4a vermilion | 4.00 | 2.50 |
| *a.* | Printed on both sides | 950.00 | |
| 13 | A4 | 4a scarlet, *bluish* | 5.50 | 5.00 |
| | | Nos. 11-13 (3) | 11.00 | 8.25 |

| | | | | |
|---|---|---|---|---|
| | | | | **Perf. 12** |
| 14 | A3 | 1a green | .60 | .20 |
| *a.* | 1a blue (error) | 900.00 | 900.00 |
| *c.* | Wove paper | 5.25 | 5.25 |
| *d.* | Imperf., pair | 120.00 | 160.00 |
| *e.* | As "a," wove paper | | 900.00 |

---

| | | | | |
|---|---|---|---|---|
| *f.* | As "c," vert. pair, imperf horiz. | | 240.00 |
| 15 | A3 | 1a green, *bluish* | 5.25 | *6.75* |
| *a.* | Vert. pair, imperf horiz. | | 525.00 |
| *b.* | Horiz. pair, imperf vert. | | 210.00 |
| 16 | A4 | 4a red | 4.00 | 1.90 |
| *a.* | 4a carmine | 6.50 | 5.25 |
| *c.* | Wove paper | 7.50 | 18.00 |
| *d.* | As "c," imperf., pair | 340.00 | 450.00 |
| 17 | A4 | 4a scarlet, *bluish* | 16.00 | *25.00* |
| | | Nos. 14-17 (4) | 25.85 | 33.85 |

### Nos. 14d and 16c Surcharged

| | | | | |
|---|---|---|---|---|
| **1913-14** | | | | **Perf. 12** |
| 18 | A3 | 3p on 1a green | .20 | .45 |
| *a.* | Laid paper | 110.00 | 45.00 |
| *b.* | Inverted surcharge | 52.50 | 30.00 |
| *c.* | Imperf., pair | 52.50 | |
| 19 | A4 | 1a on 4a red | 3.75 | 10.00 |
| *a.* | Laid paper | 11.00 | *82.50* |
| *b.* | Imperf., pair | 950.00 | |
| *c.* | Double surcharge | 1,000. | |

A5              A6

| | | | | |
|---|---|---|---|---|
| **1914** | | | | **Perf. 12** |
| 20 | A5 | 3p green | 2.10 | .50 |
| *a.* | Imperf., pair | 12.50 | 40.00 |
| 21 | A6 | 1a rose carmine | 2.25 | *3.25* |
| *a.* | Imperf., pair | 30.00 | 140.00 |
| *b.* | Laid paper | 375.00 | 160.00 |

### Nawab Mahabat Khan III
A7              A8

| | | | | |
|---|---|---|---|---|
| **1923-29** | | **Wove Paper** | | **Perf. 12** |
| 22 | A7 | 3p violet | .50 | .65 |
| *a.* | Laid paper | 450.00 | |
| *b.* | Laid paper ('29) | 7.50 | 6.50 |
| *c.* | As "b," imperf, pair ('29) | 5.25 | *52.50* |
| *d.* | As "b," horiz. pair, imperf btwn. | 4.50 | *37.50* |
| 23 | A8 | 1a red | 4.50 | 14.00 |
| *b.* | Laid paper | 4.50 | 14.00 |

Single examples of Nos. 23 and 23b cannot usually be distinguished.

### Surcharged with New Value

| | | | | |
|---|---|---|---|---|
| 27 | A8 | 3p on 1a red | 7.50 | 10.00 |

Two types of surcharge.

Junagarh City and The Girnar
A9

Gir Lion — A10

Nawab Mahabat Khan III — A11

---

Kathi Horse
A12

| | | | | |
|---|---|---|---|---|
| **1929** | | | | **Perf. 14** |
| 30 | A9 | 3p dk green & blk | 1.50 | .20 |
| 31 | A10 | ½a dk blue & blk | 9.00 | .20 |
| 32 | A11 | 1a claret & blk | 7.50 | 1.50 |
| 33 | A12 | 2a org buff & blk | 19.00 | 3.00 |
| 34 | A9 | 3a car rose & blk | 9.00 | 19.00 |
| 35 | A10 | 4a dull vio & blk | 19.00 | *42.50* |
| 36 | A12 | 8a apple grn & blk | 25.00 | 35.00 |
| 37 | A11 | 1r dull blue & blk | 21.00 | 45.00 |
| | | Nos. 30-37 (8) | 111.00 | 146.40 |

For surcharges see Nos. 40-42, O20-O25.
For overprints see Nos. O1-O14.

### Type of 1929 Inscribed "Postage and Revenue"

| | | | | |
|---|---|---|---|---|
| **1937** | | | | |
| 38 | A11 | 1a claret & black | 15.00 | 1.50 |

For overprint see No. O15.

> **Catalogue values for unused stamps in this section, from this point to the end of the section, are for Never Hinged items.**

### United State of Saurashtra

A13

### Bhavnagar Court Fee Stamp Overprinted in Black "U.S.S. Revenue & Postage Saurashtra"

| | | | | |
|---|---|---|---|---|
| **1949** | | **Unwmk.** | **Typo.** | **Perf. 11** |
| 39 | A13 | 1a deep claret | 16.00 | 15.00 |
| *a.* | "POSTAGE" omitted | 525.00 | 375.00 |
| *b.* | Double overprint | 525.00 | 600.00 |

### Nos. 30, 31 Surcharged in Black or Carmine "POSTAGE & REVENUE ONE ANNA"

| | | | | |
|---|---|---|---|---|
| **1949-50** | | | | **Perf. 14** |
| 40 | A9 | 1a on 3p dk grn & blk (bl) ('50) | 60.00 | *82.50* |
| *a.* | "OSTAGE" | 750.00 | 900.00 |
| 41 | A10 | 1a on ½a dk bl & blk (C) | 14.00 | 7.50 |
| *a.* | Double surcharge | 825.00 | |

For overprint see No. O19.

### No. 33 Surcharged in Green "Postage & Revenue ONE ANNA"

| | | | | |
|---|---|---|---|---|
| **1949** | | | | |
| 42 | A12 | 1a on 2a org buff & blk | 24.00 | 40.00 |
| *a.* | "EVENUE" omitted | 1,100. | |

For overprint see No. O26.

---

### OFFICIAL STAMPS

### Regular Issue of 1929 Overprinted in Red

a

| | | | | |
|---|---|---|---|---|
| **1929** | | **Unwmk.** | | **Perf. 14** |
| O1 | A9 | 3p dk green & black | 2.50 | .20 |
| O2 | A10 | ½a dk blue & black | 6.00 | .20 |
| O3 | A11 | 1a claret & black | 6.00 | .20 |
| O4 | A12 | 2a org buff & black | 3.75 | .90 |
| O5 | A9 | 3a car rose & black | 1.10 | .75 |
| O6 | A10 | 4a dull violet & blk | 6.25 | .65 |

---

| | | | | |
|---|---|---|---|---|
| O7 | A12 | 8a apple green & blk | 5.50 | 4.50 |
| O8 | A11 | 1r dull blue & blk | 5.50 | 35.00 |
| | | Nos. O1-O8 (8) | 36.60 | 42.40 |

For surcharges see Nos. O20-O24.

### Regular Issue of 1929 Overprinted in Red

b

| | | | | |
|---|---|---|---|---|
| **1933-49** | | | | |
| O9 | A9 | 3p dk grn & black ('49) | 375.00 | 25.00 |
| O10 | A10 | ½a dk bl & black ('49) | 900.00 | 22.50 |
| O11 | A9 | 3a car rose & blk | 32.50 | 27.50 |
| O12 | A10 | 4a dull vio & blk | 42.50 | 24.00 |
| O13 | A12 | 8a apple grn & blk | 47.50 | 27.50 |
| O14 | A11 | 1r dull blue & blk | 52.50 | 140.00 |

The 3p is also known with ms. "SARKARI" overprint in carmine.
For surcharge see No. O25.

### No. 38 Overprinted Type "a" in Red

| | | | | |
|---|---|---|---|---|
| **1938** | | | | |
| O15 | A11 | 1a claret & black | 21.00 | 2.25 |

> **Catalogue values for unused stamps in this section, from this point to the end of the section, are for Never Hinged items.**

### United State of Saurashtra
### No. 41 with Manuscript "Service" in Carmine

| | | | | |
|---|---|---|---|---|
| **1949** | | | | |
| O19 | A10 | 1a on ½a dk bl & blk (C) | 225.00 | |

Used value for No. O19 is for an example used on piece, cancelled at Gadhda or Una between June and December, 1949.
No. 42 is also known with carmine ms. "Service" overprint in English or Gujarati.

### Nos. O4-O8 and O14 Surcharged "ONE ANNA" in Blue or Black

| | | | | |
|---|---|---|---|---|
| **1949** | | | | |
| | | **Surcharge 2¼mm high** | | |
| O20 | A12 | 1a on 2a (Bl) | 21,000. | 40.00 |
| O21 | A9 | 1a on 3a | 5,250. | 100.00 |
| O22 | A10 | 1a on 4a | 600.00 | 100.00 |
| O23 | A12 | 1a on 8a | 525.00 | 72.50 |
| | | **Surcharge 4mm High, Handstamped** | | |
| O24 | A11 | 1a on 1r (#O8) | 3,250. | 72.50 |
| O25 | A11 | 1a on 1r (#O14) | 1,350. | 75.00 |
| | | Nos. O20-O25 (6) | 31,975. | 460.00 |

### No. 42 Overprinted Type "b" in Carmine

| | | | | |
|---|---|---|---|---|
| **1949** | | **Unwmk.** | | **Perf. 14** |
| O26 | A12 | 1a on 2a | 125.00 | 35.00 |

---

## TRAVANCORE

ˈtrav-ən-ˌkō͝ə͟r

LOCATION — A Feudatory State in the Madras States Agency, on the extreme southwest coast of India.
AREA — 7,662 sq. mi.
POP. — 6,070,018 (1941)
CAPITAL — Trivandrum

16 Cash = 1 Chuckram
2 Chuckrams = 1 Anna

Conch Shell (State Seal)
A1              A2

**1888 Unwmk. Typo. Perf. 12**
**Laid Paper**

| | | | | |
|---|---|---|---|---|
| 1 | A1 | 1ch ultramarine | 7.00 | 6.50 |
| 2 | A1 | 2ch orange red | 9.00 | 16.00 |
| 3 | A1 | 4ch green | 30.00 | 25.00 |
| | | Nos. 1-3 (3) | 46.00 | 47.50 |

The frame and details of the central medallion differ slightly on each denomination of type A1.

Laid paper printings of Nos. 1-3, 5-7 in completely different colors are essays.

**1889-99 Wove Paper Wmk. 43**

| | | | | |
|---|---|---|---|---|
| 4 | A1 | ½ch violet | .90 | .35 |
| 5 | A1 | 1ch ultramarine | 2.25 | .20 |
| a. | | Vertical pair, imperf. between | | 675.00 |
| 6 | A1 | 2ch scarlet | 4.50 | .20 |
| a. | | Horizontal pair, imperf. between | 550.00 | 550.00 |
| 7 | A1 | 4ch dark green | 5.00 | 1.00 |
| | | Nos. 4-7 (4) | 12.65 | 1.75 |

Shades exist for each denomination.
For surcharges see #10-11. For type surcharged see #20. For overprints see #O1-O2, O4, O6, O18, O24-O25, O27B, O32-O33, O42.

**1901-32**

| | | | | |
|---|---|---|---|---|
| 8 | A2 | ¾ch black | 4.50 | 2.10 |
| 9 | A2 | ¾ch brt violet ('32) | .50 | .20 |
| a. | | Horizontal pair, imperf. between | | |

For overprints see Nos. O26-O27, O44, O52.

No. 4 Surcharged

**1906**

| | | | | |
|---|---|---|---|---|
| 10 | A1 | ¼ch on ½ch violet | 1.10 | .45 |
| a. | | Inverted surcharge | 90.00 | 52.50 |
| 11 | A1 | ⅜ch on ½ch violet | .60 | .50 |
| a. | | Pair, one without surcharge | | 75.00 |
| b. | | Inverted surcharge | | |
| c. | | Double surcharge | | |

A3 · A4

**1908-11**

| | | | | |
|---|---|---|---|---|
| 12 | A3 | 4ca rose | .45 | .20 |
| 13 | A1 | 6ca red brown ('10) | .45 | .20 |
| a. | | Printed on both sides | | 75.00 |
| 14 | A4 | 3ch purple ('11) | 4.00 | .30 |
| | | Nos. 12-14 (3) | 4.90 | .70 |

For surcharge & overprints see #19, O3, O5, O8, O13, O15, O20, O22, O30-O31, O53.

A5 · A6

**1916**

| | | | | |
|---|---|---|---|---|
| 15 | A5 | 7ch red violet | 3.50 | .75 |
| 16 | A6 | 14ch orange | 4.00 | 3.75 |

For overprints see Nos. O11-O12, O34-O35.

A7 · A8

**1920-33**

| | | | | |
|---|---|---|---|---|
| 17 | A7 | 1¼ch claret | .80 | .80 |
| 18 | A7 | 1½ch light red ('33) | 4.00 | .20 |

For surcharges see Nos. 27-28. For overprints see Nos. O7, O17, O28-O29, O38, O56.

No. 12 and Type of 1888 Surcharged

**1921**

| | | | | |
|---|---|---|---|---|
| 19 | A3 | 1ca on 4ca rose | .20 | .20 |
| a. | | Inverted surcharge | 37.50 | 16.00 |
| 20 | A1 | 5ca on 1ch dull bl (R) | 1.50 | .20 |
| a. | | Inverted surcharge | 19.00 | 12.00 |
| b. | | Double surcharge | 100.00 | 67.50 |

**1921-32**

| | | | | |
|---|---|---|---|---|
| 21 | A8 | 5ca bister | 1.20 | .20 |
| 22 | A8 | 5ca brown ('32) | 4.00 | .20 |
| 23 | A8 | 10ca rose | .60 | .20 |
| | | Nos. 21-23 (3) | 5.80 | .60 |

For surcharges & overprints see #29-30, O9-O10, O14, O16, O19, O21, O23, O36-O37.

Sri Padmanabha Shrine at Trivandrum — A9

State Chariot — A10

Maharaja Sir Bala Rama Varma — A11

**1931, Nov. 6**

| | | | | |
|---|---|---|---|---|
| 24 | A9 | 6ca emerald & black | 2.40 | 2.40 |
| 25 | A10 | 10ca ultra & black | 1.90 | 1.00 |
| 26 | A11 | 3ch violet & black | 4.00 | 4.50 |
| | | Nos. 24-26 (3) | 8.30 | 7.90 |

Investiture of Sir Bala Rama Varma with full ruling powers.

No. 17 Surcharged

**1932, Jan. 14**

| | | | | |
|---|---|---|---|---|
| 27 | A7 | 1ca on 1¼ch claret | .20 | .75 |
| a. | | Inverted surcharge | 6.50 | 10.00 |
| b. | | Double surcharge | 47.50 | 47.50 |
| 28 | A7 | 2ca on 1¼ch claret | .20 | .20 |
| a. | | Inverted surcharge | 6.50 | 10.00 |
| b. | | Double surcharge | 42.50 | |
| c. | | Pair, one without surcharge | 180.00 | 190.00 |

Type of 1932 and No. 23 Surcharged like Nos. 19-20

**1932, Mar. 5**

| | | | | |
|---|---|---|---|---|
| 29 | A8 | 1ca on 5ca vio brown | .20 | .20 |
| a. | | Inverted surcharge | 11.00 | 15.00 |
| b. | | Double surcharge | | |
| c. | | Pair, one without surcharge | | 180.00 |
| 30 | A8 | 2ca on 10ca rose | .20 | .20 |
| a. | | Inverted surcharge | 7.50 | 12.00 |
| b. | | Double surcharge | 32.50 | 35.00 |

Untouchables Entering Temple and Maharaja — A12

Designs: Different temples and frames.

**Perf. 11½, 12½**

**1937, Mar. 29 Litho.**

| | | | | |
|---|---|---|---|---|
| 32 | A12 | 6ca carmine | 3.75 | 1.90 |
| 33 | A12 | 12ca ultramarine | 5.25 | .60 |
| 34 | A12 | 1½ch light green | 2.25 | 3.00 |
| 35 | A12 | 3ch purple | 6.50 | 3.50 |
| | | Nos. 32-35 (4) | 17.75 | 9.00 |

Temple Entry Bill.

Lake Ashtamudi A13

A14 · A15

Sir Bala Rama Varma — A16

Sri Padmanabha Shrine — A17

View of Cape Comerin A18

Pachipara Reservoir A19

**Perf. 11, 12, 12½ or Compound**

**1939, May 9 Litho.**

| | | | | |
|---|---|---|---|---|
| 36 | A13 | 1ch yellow green | 8.25 | .20 |
| 37 | A14 | 1½ch carmine | 5.25 | 6.75 |
| a. | | Perf. 13½ | 27.50 | 100.00 |
| 38 | A15 | 2ch orange | 10.00 | 3.50 |
| 39 | A16 | 3ch chocolate | 9.50 | .20 |
| 40 | A17 | 4ch henna brown | 12.50 | .60 |
| 41 | A18 | 7ch light blue | 16.00 | 30.00 |
| 42 | A19 | 14ch turq green | 10.00 | 100.00 |
| | | Nos. 36-42 (7) | 71.50 | 141.25 |

27th birthday of Maharaja Sir Bala Rama Varma.

For surcharges and overprints see Nos. 45, O45-O51, Travancore-Cochin 3-7, O3-O7.

Maharaja Sir Bala Rama Varma and Aruvikara Falls A20

Maharaja and Marthanda Varma Bridge, Alwaye A21

**1941, Oct. 20 Typo.**

| | | | | |
|---|---|---|---|---|
| 43 | A20 | 6ca violet black | 11.00 | .20 |
| 44 | A21 | ¾ch dull brown | 12.50 | .30 |

29th birthday of the Maharaja, Oct. 20, 1941.
For overprints & surcharges see #46-47, 49, O54-O55, Travancore-Cochin 1, O1.

Stamps and Types of 1939-41 Surcharged in Black

**Perf. 11, 12½**

**1943, Sept. 17 Wmk. 43**

| | | | | |
|---|---|---|---|---|
| 45 | A14 | 2ca on 1½ch carmine | 2.25 | 1.90 |
| 46 | A21 | 4ca on ¾ch dull brown | 6.00 | .45 |
| 47 | A20 | 8ca on 6ca red | 7.00 | .20 |
| | | Nos. 45-47 (3) | 15.25 | 2.55 |

For overprints see Nos. O57-O59.

Maharaja Sir Bala Rama Varma — A22

**1946, Oct. 24 Typo. Perf. 11, 12**

| | | | | |
|---|---|---|---|---|
| 48 | A22 | 8ca rose red | 1.90 | 3.00 |

For overprint see No. O60. For surcharges see Travancore-Cochin Nos. 2, O2.

No. O54 Overprinted "SPECIAL" Vertically in Orange

**1946 Perf. 12½**

| | | | | |
|---|---|---|---|---|
| 49 | A20 | 6ca violet black | 9.50 | 4.50 |

**OFFICIAL STAMPS**

Nos. O1-O60 were issued without gum.

Regular Issues of 1889-1911 Overprinted in Red or Black

**Perf. 12, 12½**

**1911, Aug. 16 Wmk. 43**

| | | | | |
|---|---|---|---|---|
| O1 | A1 | 1ch indigo (R) | 1.10 | .20 |
| a. | | Inverted overprint | 10.00 | 6.50 |
| b. | | "nO" for "On" | 120.00 | 120.00 |
| c. | | Double overprint | 100.00 | .75 |
| O2 | A1 | 2ch scarlet | .50 | .20 |
| a. | | Inverted overprint | 12.00 | 12.00 |
| O3 | A4 | 3ch purple | .50 | .20 |
| a. | | Inverted overprint | 15.00 | 15.00 |
| b. | | Double overprint | 120.00 | 100.00 |
| O4 | A1 | 4ch dark green | .80 | .20 |
| a. | | Inverted overprint | 82.50 | 19.00 |
| b. | | Double overprint | 190.00 | 140.00 |
| | | Nos. O1-O4 (4) | 2.90 | .80 |

Same Ovpt. on Regular Issues of 1889-1920

**1918-20**

| | | | | |
|---|---|---|---|---|
| O5 | A3 | 4ca rose | .20 | .20 |
| a. | | Imperf., pair | 450.00 | 450.00 |
| b. | | Inverted overprint | | 120.00 |
| c. | | Double overprint | 180.00 | 140.00 |
| O6 | A1 | ½ch violet (R) | 3.75 | .35 |
| a. | | Inverted overprint | 19.00 | 5.25 |
| O7 | A7 | 1¼ch claret | .60 | .20 |
| a. | | Inverted overprint | 14.00 | 12.00 |
| b. | | Double overprint | 67.50 | |
| | | Nos. O5-O7 (3) | 4.55 | .75 |

Same Ovpt. on Regular Issues of
1909-21

**1921**

| | | | | |
|---|---|---|---|---|
| O8 | A1 | 6ca red brown | .45 | .20 |
| a. | | Inverted overprint | 200.00 | 180.00 |
| O9 | A8 | 10ca rose | 1.00 | .20 |
| a. | | Inverted overprint | | 27.50 |
| b. | | Double overprint | 140.00 | 110.00 |

Same Overprint on Regular Issue of
1921

**1922**

| | | | | |
|---|---|---|---|---|
| O10 | A8 | 5ca bister | 1.40 | .20 |
| a. | | Inverted overprint | 21.00 | 13.50 |

For surcharge see No. O39B.

Same Overprint on Regular Issue of
1916

**1925**

| | | | | |
|---|---|---|---|---|
| O11 | A5 | 7ch plum | 2.50 | .45 |
| O12 | A6 | 14ch orange | 3.25 | .60 |

Same Overprint in Blue on Regular
Issues of 1889-1921

| | | | | |
|---|---|---|---|---|
| O13 | A3 | 4ca rose | 80.00 | 1.00 |
| O14 | A8 | 5ca bister | .90 | .20 |
| O15 | A1 | 6ca red brown | 19.00 | 2.50 |
| O16 | A8 | 10ca rose | 120.00 | 32.50 |
| O17 | A7 | 1¼ch claret | — | 120.00 |
| O18 | A4 | 4ch dark green | — | 100.00 |

Some authorities question the authenticity
of No. O14.

**1930**

**Black Overprint**

| | | | | |
|---|---|---|---|---|
| O19 | A8 | 5ca brown | | .35　.90 |

Regular Issues of
1889-1932
Overprinted in Black
or Red

**1930-34**

| | | | | |
|---|---|---|---|---|
| O20 | A3 | 4ca rose | 18.00 | 60.00 |
| O21 | A8 | 5ca brown | 35.00 | 14.00 |
| a. | | Inverted overprint | 100.00 | 100.00 |
| O22 | A1 | 6ca org brown | .20 | .20 |
| O23 | A8 | 10ca rose | 6.50 | 4.50 |
| O24 | A1 | ½ch violet ('34) | .75 | .20 |
| O25 | A1 | ½ch purple (R) | .20 | .20 |
| O26 | A2 | ¾ch black (R) ('32) | .60 | .45 |
| O27 | A2 | ¾ch brt vio ('33) | .45 | .20 |
| O27B | A1 | 1ch gray blue (R) ('33) | 1.50 | .35 |
| O28 | A7 | 1¼ch claret | 2.10 | 2.40 |
| O29 | A7 | 1½ch dull red ('32) | .60 | .20 |
| O30 | A4 | 3ch purple ('33) | 1.90 | .90 |
| O31 | A4 | 3ch purple (R) | 1.20 | .20 |
| O32 | A1 | 4ch dp grn (R) | 2.25 | .20 |
| O33 | A1 | 4ch deep green | 2.75 | 1.40 |
| O34 | A5 | 7ch maroon | 1.90 | .45 |
| O35 | A6 | 14ch orange ('31) | 2.50 | .60 |
| | | Nos. O20-O35 (17) | 78.40 | 86.45 |

The overprint on Nos. O22, O26 and O28 is
smaller than the illustration. There are two
sizes of the overprint on No. O27.
For surcharges see Nos. O39, O40-O41.

Type of 1921-32 and
No. 17 Surcharged
and Overprinted

**1932**

| | | | | |
|---|---|---|---|---|
| O36 | A8 | 6ca on 5ca dk brown | .20 | .45 |
| O36A | A8 | 6ca on 5ca bister | 2.50 | 3.00 |
| O37 | A8 | 12ca on 10a rose | .20 | .20 |
| a. | | New value inverted | 9.00 | 11.00 |
| O38 | A7 | 1ch8ca on 1¼ch cl | .50 | .30 |
| | | Nos. O36-O38 (4) | 3.40 | 3.95 |

Nos. O21, O10, O23 and O28
Surcharged in Black

| | | | | |
|---|---|---|---|---|
| O39 | A8 | 6ca on 5ca dk brown | .30 | .45 |
| a. | | New value inverted | 16.00 | 19.00 |
| O39B | A8 | 6ca on 5ca bis | .60 | .20 |
| O40 | A8 | 12ca on 10ca rose | 3.00 | 2.25 |
| a. | | New value inverted | 10.00 | 10.00 |
| b. | | "On S S" inverted | 24.00 | 27.50 |
| c. | | Ovpt. & surch. inverted | 60.00 | 62.50 |
| O41 | A7 | 1ch8ca on 1¼ch cl | 4.50 | 1.90 |
| a. | | New value inverted | | 150.00 |
| | | Nos. O39-O41 (4) | 8.40 | 4.80 |

Regular Issue of
1889-94 Overprinted

**1933**

| | | | | |
|---|---|---|---|---|
| O42 | A1 | ½ch violet | 1.75 | 1.25 |

Regular Issue of 1901
Overprinted in Red

**1933**

| | | | | |
|---|---|---|---|---|
| O44 | A2 | ¾ch black | .50 | .20 |

Regular Issue of 1939 Overprinted in
Black

a

**1939** 　　　　**Perf. 11, 12, 12½**

| | | | | |
|---|---|---|---|---|
| O45 | A13 | 1ch yellow green | 10.00 | .50 |
| a. | | Inverted overprint | 15.00 | 15.00 |
| b. | | Double overprint | 15.00 | 15.00 |
| O46 | A14 | 1½ch carmine | 11.00 | 1.90 |
| a. | | "SESVICE" | | 250.00 |
| O47 | A15 | 2ch orange | 11.00 | 11.00 |
| a. | | "SESVICE" | 190.00 | 210.00 |
| O48 | A16 | 3ch chocolate | 9.50 | .30 |
| a. | | "SESVICE" | 150.00 | 30.00 |
| O49 | A17 | 4ch henna brown | 22.50 | 7.50 |
| O50 | A18 | 7ch light blue | 24.00 | 5.50 |
| O51 | A19 | 14ch turq green | 30.00 | 8.25 |
| | | Nos. O45-O51 (7) | 118.00 | 34.95 |

27th birthday of Maharaja Sir Bala Rama
Varma.

No. 9 Overprinted

b

**1939**　　**Wmk. 43**　　**Perf. 12.**

| | | | | |
|---|---|---|---|---|
| O52 | A2 | ¾ch violet | 27.50 | .30 |

No. 13 Overprinted Type "b"

**1941**

| | | | | |
|---|---|---|---|---|
| O53 | A1 | 6ca red brown | 1.20 | .45 |

Nos. 43-44 Overprinted Type "a"

**1941**　　　　　**Perf. 12½**

| | | | | |
|---|---|---|---|---|
| O54 | A20 | 6ca violet black | .90 | .75 |
| O55 | A21 | ¾ch dull brown | 9.50 | .20 |

29th birthday of the Maharaja, Oct. 20, 1941.
For overprint see No. 49.

No. 18 Overprinted Type "b"

**1945**　　　　　**Perf. 12**

| | | | | |
|---|---|---|---|---|
| O56 | A7 | 1½ch light red | 21.00 | 12.00 |

Nos. 45-48 Overprinted Type "a"

**1945-49**　　　　**Perf. 11, 12**

| | | | | |
|---|---|---|---|---|
| O57 | A14 | 2ca on 1½ch car | .90 | 1.50 |
| O58 | A21 | 4ca on ¾ch dull brn | 6.00 | .60 |
| O59 | A20 | 8ca on 6ca red | 5.25 | .45 |
| O60 | A22 | 8ca rose red ('49) | 3.75 | 1.25 |
| a. | | Double impression of stamp | 47.50 | |
| | | Nos. O57-O60 (4) | 15.90 | 3.80 |

Travancore stamps became obsolete June
30, 1949.

### TRAVANCORE-COCHIN

ˈtrav-ən-ˌkō͝ə͡r kō-ˈchin

LOCATION — Southern India
AREA — 9,155 sq. mi.
POP. — 7,492,000

The United State of Travancore-
Cochin was established July 1, 1949.

> Catalogue values for all unused
> stamps in this state are for Never
> Hinged items.

Travancore Stamps of 1939-47
Surcharged in Red or Black

a

**Perf. 11, 12, 12½**

**1949, July 1**　　　　**Wmk. 43**

| | | | | |
|---|---|---|---|---|
| 1 | A20 | 2p on 6ca vio blk (R) | .75 | .30 |
| 2 | A22 | 4p on 8ca rose red | 2.25 | .45 |
| 3 | A13 | ½a on 1ch yel grn | 5.25 | .45 |
| a. | | Inverted surcharge | 7.50 | |
| b. | | "NANA" | 300.00 | 180.00 |
| 4 | A15 | 1a on 2ch orange | 1.10 | .45 |
| 5 | A17 | 2a on 4ch hn brn | 5.00 | .80 |
| a. | | Inverted surcharge | | 450.00 |
| 6 | A18 | 3a on 7ch lt blue | 9.00 | 5.50 |
| 7 | A19 | 6a on 14ch turq grn | 27.50 | 45.00 |
| | | Nos. 1-7 (7) | 50.85 | 52.95 |

For overprints see Nos. O1-O7, O12-O17.
For types overprinted see Nos. O18-O23.

Cochin Nos. 80, 91 and Types of
1944-46 Surcharged in Black or
Carmine

b

**1949-50**　　**Wmk. 294**　　**Perf. 11, 13**

| | | | | |
|---|---|---|---|---|
| 8 | A15 | 3p on 9p ultra | 18.00 | 35.00 |
| 9 | A16 | 3p on 9p ultra | 4.00 | 3.00 |
| 10 | A16 | 3p on 9p ultra (C) | 8.25 | 4.00 |
| 11 | A16 | 6p on 9p ultra (C) | 2.50 | .60 |
| 12 | A13 | 6p on 1a3p mag ('50) | 8.25 | 6.75 |
| 13 | A15 | 6p on 1a3p magenta | 24.00 | 22.50 |
| 14 | A13 | 1a on 1a9p ultra (C) | 3.50 | 2.10 |
| 15 | A15 | 1a on 1a9p ultra (C) | 5.25 | 3.50 |
| | | Nos. 8-15 (8) | 73.75 | 77.45 |

The surcharge exists with line of Hindi characters varying from 16½ to 23mm wide.
For overprints see Nos. O10-O11, O24.

Cochin No. 86
Overprinted

**1949**

| | | | | |
|---|---|---|---|---|
| 15A | A15 | 1a deep orange | 9.00 | 100.00 |

| Conch | View of |
|---|---|
| Shell — A23 | River — A24 |

**Wmk. 196**

**1950, Oct.**　　**Litho.**　　**Perf. 14**

| | | | | |
|---|---|---|---|---|
| 16 | A23 | 2p rose red | 4.50 | 5.00 |
| 17 | A24 | 4p ultramarine | 5.50 | 24.00 |

Cochin No. 86 and
Type of 1948-50
Overprinted
in Black

**1950, Apr. 1**　**Wmk. 294**　**Perf. 13, 11**

| | | | | |
|---|---|---|---|---|
| 18 | A15 | 1a deep orange | 11.00 | 100.00 |

No. 18 Surcharged
in Black

| | | | | |
|---|---|---|---|---|
| 20 | A15 | 6p on 1a deep orange | 6.75 | 82.50 |
| 21 | A15 | 9p on 1a deep orange | 6.50 | 72.50 |

### OFFICIAL STAMPS

Travancore Stamps of 1939-46
Surcharged Type "a" in Red or Black
and Overprinted

c

**1949**　　**Wmk. 43**　　**Perf. 11, 12, 12½**

| | | | | |
|---|---|---|---|---|
| O1 | A20 | 2p on 6ca vio blk (R) | .90 | .70 |
| O2 | A22 | 4p on 8ca rose red | 5.50 | .50 |
| O3 | A13 | ½a on 1ch yel grn | 1.50 | .35 |
| O4 | A15 | 1a on 2ch orange | 24.00 | 11.00 |
| O5 | A17 | 2a on 4ch hn brn | 3.50 | .90 |
| O6 | A18 | 3a on 7ch lt blue | 5.50 | 1.50 |
| O7 | A19 | 6a on 14ch turq grn | 24.00 | 16.00 |
| | | Nos. O1-O7 (7) | 64.90 | 30.95 |

Cochin Nos. O90-O91 Surcharged
Type "b" in Black

**1950**　　**Wmk. 294**　　**Perf. 11**

| | | | | |
|---|---|---|---|---|
| O8 | A16 | 6p on 3p carmine | 1.90 | 1.10 |
| a. | | Double surcharge | — | 526.00 |
| O9 | A16 | 9p on 4p gray grn | 1.60 | 1.60 |

No. O9 exists with Hindi characters varying
from 18 to 22mm wide.

Travancore-Cochin Nos. 14-15
Overprinted "ON C G S"
**Perf. 13**

| | | | |
|---|---|---|---|
| O10 | A13 1a on 1a9p ultra | .90 | 1.00 |
| O11 | A15 1a on 1a9p ultra | 35.00 | 25.00 |

Nos. 2-7 Overprinted in Black

d

**1949-51    Wmk. 43    Perf. 11, 12½**

| | | | |
|---|---|---|---|
| O12 | A22 4p on 8ca rose red | .75 | .30 |
| O13 | A13 ½a on 1ch yel green | 1.50 | .30 |
| O14 | A15 1a on 2ch orange | .60 | .30 |
| O15 | A17 2a on 4ch hn brn | 2.25 | 1.60 |
| O16 | A18 3a on 7ch lt blue | 2.25 | 1.60 |
| O17 | A19 6a on 14ch turq grn | 2.25 | *6.50* |
| | *Nos. O12-O17 (6)* | 9.60 | 10.60 |

Types of 1949 Overprinted Type "d"

**1951                        Wmk. 294**

| | | | |
|---|---|---|---|
| O18 | A13 ½a on 1ch yel green | .60 | .60 |
| O19 | A15 1a on 2ch orange | .75 | .60 |

Type of 1949 Overprinted Type "c"
**Unwmk.**

| | | | |
|---|---|---|---|
| O20 | A22 4p on 8ca rose red | 1.40 | 1.10 |

No. O20 is not from an unwatermarked part of sheet with wmk. 294 but is printed on paper entirely without watermark.

Nos. 1, 3 and 5 Overprinted Type "c"
**Wmk. 294**

| | | | |
|---|---|---|---|
| O21 | A13 ½a on 1ch yel green | 1.10 | .50 |
| O22 | A20 2p on 6ca violet black | .20 | *1.00* |
| O23 | A17 2a on 4ch henna brown | 1.10 | .75 |
| | *Nos. O21-O23 (3)* | 2.40 | 2.25 |

No. 9 Overprinted
in Black

**1951**

| | | | |
|---|---|---|---|
| O24 | A16 3p on 9p ultra | .90 | *1.20* |

---

### WADHWAN

wə-'dwän

LOCATION — A Feudatory State in Kathiawar Agency, Western India.
AREA — 242 sq. mi.
POP. — 44,259
CAPITAL — Wadhwan

Coat of
Arms — A1

**1888    Litho.    Unwmk.    Pin-perf.**
**Thin Paper**

| | | | |
|---|---|---|---|
| 1 | A1 ½p black | 160.00 | |

**Perf. 12½**

| | | | |
|---|---|---|---|
| 2 | A1 ½p black | 30.00 | *100.00* |

**1889                 Perf. 12 and 12½**
**Thick Paper**

| | | | |
|---|---|---|---|
| 3 | A1 ½p black | 12.50 | *14.00* |
| | *Nos. 1-3 (3)* | 202.50 | |

---

# hagner
## stocksheets

The original
Hagner Stock
sheets are made from archival
quality pH board and feature pure polyester
film pockets that are glued to each page with special
chemically inert glue. For more than 40 years, collectors all over the world
have come to rely on Hagner stock sheets for their long-term stamp protection. Single-sided stock sheets are available in black or white. Double-sided sheets available in black only. **Sold in packages of 5.**

| | Retail | AA* |
|---|---|---|
| Single Sided Sheets | $6.35 | **$5.50** |
| Double Sided Sheets | $10.95 | **$8.50** |

| 1 Pocket 242 mm | | 4 Pockets 58 mm | | 7 Pockets 31 mm | |
|---|---|---|---|---|---|
| HGB01 | Black | HGB04 | Black | HGB07 | Black |
| HGB11* | Black | HGB44* | Black | HGB77* | Black |
| HGW01 | White | HGW04 | White | HGW07 | White |
| **2 Pockets 119 mm** | | **5 Pockets 45 mm** | | **8 Pockets 27 mm** | |
| HGB02 | Black | HGB05 | Black | HGB08 | Black |
| HGB22* | Black | HGB55* | Black | HGB88* | Black |
| HGW02 | White | HGW05 | White | HGW08 | White |
| **3 Pockets 79 mm** | | **6 Pockets 37 mm** | | **Mult-Pockets** | |
| HGB03 | Black | HGB06 | Black | HGB03 | Black |
| HGB33* | Black | HGB66* | Black | HGB33* | Black |
| HGW03 | White | HGW66 | White | HGW03 | White |

**STOCK PAGE BINDER AND SLPCASE**
Keep all your stock pages neat and tidy with binder and matching slipcase. Available in two colors.

| Item | | Retail | AA* |
|---|---|---|---|
| SSBSBR | Burgundy | $20.99 | **$17.99** |
| SSBSBL | Blue | $20.99 | **$17.99** |

**SCOTT**
1-800-572-6885
P.O. Box 828,
Sidney OH 45365
**www.amosadvantage.com**
*AA prices apply to paid subscribers to Amos Hobby titles*

**AMOS**
PUBLISHING

# INDO-CHINA

,in-ˌdō-'chī-nə

LOCATION — French possessions on the Cambodian Peninsula in southeastern Asia, bordering on the South China Sea and the Gulf of Siam
GOVT. — French Colony and Protectorate
AREA — 280,849 sq. mi.
POP. — 27,030,000 (estimated 1949)
CAPITAL — Hanoi

In 1949, Indo-China was divided into Cambodia, Laos and Viet Nam each issuing its own stamps.

100 Centimes = 1 Franc
100 Cents = 1 Piaster (1918)

Stamps of French Colonies
Surcharged in Black or Red:

a      b

**1889**   **Unwmk.**   **Perf. 14x13½**
| | | | | | |
|---|---|---|---|---|---|
| 1 | A9(a) | 5c on 35c dp vio, org | | 14.00 | 12.00 |
| a. | | Without date | | 240.00 | 225.00 |
| 2 | A9(b) | 5c on 35c dp vio, org (R) | | 100.00 | 95.00 |
| a. | | Date in smaller type | | 200.00 | 200.00 |
| b. | | Inverted surcharge, #2 | | 1,900. | 1,900. |
| c. | | Inverted surcharge, #2a | | 2,600. | 2,600. |

Issue dates: No. 1, Jan. 8; No. 2, Jan. 10.
"R" is the Colonial Governor, P. Richaud, "D" is the Saigon P.M. General P. Demars.

For other overprints on designs A3-A27a see various issues of French Offices in China.

Navigation & Commerce A3      France A4

Name of Colony in Blue or Carmine
**1892-1900**   **Typo.**   **Perf. 14x13½**
| | | | | |
|---|---|---|---|---|
| 3 | A3 | 1c blk, lil bl | 1.25 | 1.25 |
| 4 | A3 | 2c brn, buff | 1.60 | 1.60 |
| 5 | A3 | 4c claret, lav | 1.60 | 1.60 |
| 6 | A3 | 5c grn, grnsh | 2.40 | 2.40 |
| 7 | A3 | 5c yel grn ('00) | 2.00 | 1.25 |
| 8 | A3 | 10c blk, lavender | 7.50 | 2.00 |
| 9 | A3 | 10c red ('00) | 3.50 | 2.00 |
| 10 | A3 | 15c blue, quadrille paper | 37.50 | 2.00 |
| 11 | A3 | 15c gray ('00) | 9.00 | 2.40 |
| 12 | A3 | 20c red, grn | 10.00 | 7.00 |
| 13 | A3 | 25c blk, rose | 19.00 | 3.75 |
| a. | | "INDO-CHINE" omitted | 7,200. | 7,200. |
| 14 | A3 | 25c blue ('00) | 22.00 | 5.00 |
| 15 | A3 | 30c brn, bis | 26.00 | 7.50 |
| 16 | A3 | 40c red, straw | 26.00 | 13.50 |
| 17 | A3 | 50c car, rose | 42.00 | 16.00 |
| 18 | A3 | 50c brn, az ('00) | 29.00 | 9.50 |
| 19 | A3 | 75c dp vio, org | 23.00 | 17.00 |
| a. | | "INDO-CHINE" inverted | 7,200. | 7,200. |
| 20 | A3 | 1fr brnz grn, straw | 55.00 | 36.00 |
| a. | | "INDO-CHINE" double | 1,100. | 1,300. |
| 21 | A3 | 5fr red lil, lav ('96) | 125.00 | 110.00 |
| | | Nos. 3-21 (19) | 443.35 | 241.75 |

Perf. 13½x14 stamps are counterfeits.
For surcharges and overprints see Nos. 22-23, Q2-Q4.

Nos. 11 and 14 Surcharged in Black

**1903**
| | | | | |
|---|---|---|---|---|
| 22 | A3 | 5c on 15c gray | 2.00 | 1.25 |
| 23 | A3 | 15c on 25c blue | 2.50 | 1.60 |

Issue dates: No. 22, Dec. 4; No. 23, Aug. 8.

**1904-06**
| | | | | |
|---|---|---|---|---|
| 24 | A4 | 1c olive grn | .80 | .80 |
| 25 | A4 | 2c vio brn, buff | 1.25 | .80 |
| 26 | A4 | 4c claret, bluish | .80 | .80 |
| 27 | A4 | 5c deep green | 1.25 | .50 |
| 28 | A4 | 10c carmine | 1.60 | .75 |
| 29 | A4 | 15c org brn, bl | 1.60 | 1.00 |
| 30 | A4 | 20c red, grn | 3.50 | 1.60 |
| 31 | A4 | 25c deep blue | 14.00 | 1.60 |
| 32 | A4 | 30c pale brn | 6.00 | 3.00 |
| 33 | A4 | 35c blk, yel ('06) | 21.50 | 3.25 |
| 34 | A4 | 40c blk, bluish | 5.50 | 1.60 |
| 35 | A4 | 50c bister brn | 10.50 | 3.00 |
| 36 | A4 | 75c red, org | 45.00 | 29.00 |
| 37 | A4 | 1fr brn, org | 21.50 | 8.25 |
| 38 | A4 | 2fr brn, org | 52.50 | 40.00 |
| 39 | A4 | 5fr dp vio, lil | 220.00 | 180.00 |
| 40 | A4 | 10fr org brn, grn | 220.00 | 180.00 |
| | | Nos. 24-40 (17) | 627.30 | 455.95 |

For surcharges see Nos. 59-64.

Annamite Girl — A5

Cambodian Girl — A6

Cambodian Woman — A7

Annamite Women — A8

Hmong Woman — A9      Laotian Woman — A10

Cambodian Woman — A11

**1907**      **Perf. 14x13½**
| | | | | |
|---|---|---|---|---|
| 41 | A5 | 1c ol brn & blk | .40 | .40 |
| 42 | A5 | 2c yel brn & blk | .40 | .40 |
| 43 | A5 | 4c blue & blk | 1.25 | 1.25 |
| 44 | A5 | 5c grn & blk | 1.60 | .80 |
| 45 | A5 | 10c red & blk | 1.60 | .55 |
| 46 | A5 | 15c vio & blk | 1.40 | 1.25 |
| 47 | A6 | 20c vio & blk | 3.00 | 1.60 |
| 48 | A6 | 25c bl & blk | 7.25 | 1.25 |
| 49 | A6 | 30c brn & blk | 12.00 | 6.50 |
| 50 | A6 | 35c ol grn & blk | 2.75 | 2.25 |
| 51 | A6 | 40c yel brn & blk | 4.50 | 2.00 |
| 52 | A6 | 45c org & blk | 10.50 | 6.50 |
| 53 | A6 | 50c car & blk | 15.00 | 5.75 |

     **Perf. 13½x14**
| | | | | |
|---|---|---|---|---|
| 54 | A7 | 75c ver & blk | 12.00 | 7.75 |
| 55 | A8 | 1fr car & blk | 55.00 | 20.00 |
| 56 | A9 | 2fr grn & blk | 17.00 | 16.00 |
| 57 | A10 | 5fr blue & blk | 42.50 | 42.50 |
| 58 | A11 | 10fr pur & blk | 92.50 | 92.50 |
| | | Nos. 41-58 (18) | 280.65 | 209.25 |

For surcharges see Nos. 65-93, B1-B7.

Stamps of 1904-06 Surcharged in Black or Carmine

a      b

**1912, Nov.**      **Perf. 14x13½**
| | | | | |
|---|---|---|---|---|
| 59 | A4 | 5c on 4c cl, bluish | 6.00 | 6.00 |
| 60 | A4 | 5c on 15c org brn, bl (C) | 1.25 | 1.25 |
| 61 | A4 | 5c on 30c pale brn | 1.60 | 1.60 |
| 62 | A4 | 10c on 40c blk, bluish (C) | 1.60 | 1.60 |
| 63 | A4 | 10c on 50c bis brn (C) | 2.00 | 2.00 |
| 64 | A4 | 10c on 75c red, org | 5.25 | 5.25 |
| | | Nos. 59-64 (6) | 17.70 | 17.70 |

Two spacings between the surcharged numerals are found on Nos. 59-64.

Nos. 41-58 Surcharged with New Values in Cents or Piasters in Black, Red or Blue

**1919, Jan.**
| | | | | |
|---|---|---|---|---|
| 65 | A5 | ⅖c on 1c | .80 | .55 |
| 66 | A5 | ⅘c on 2c | 1.25 | .90 |
| 67 | A5 | 1⅗c on 4c (R) | 2.00 | .80 |
| 68 | A5 | 2c on 5c | 1.60 | .30 |
| a. | | Inverted surcharge | 135.00 | |
| 69 | A5 | 4c on 10c (Bl) | 1.60 | .55 |
| a. | | Closed "4" | 9.00 | 3.25 |
| b. | | Double surcharge | 130.00 | |
| 70 | A5 | 6c on 15c | 6.50 | 1.25 |
| a. | | Inverted surcharge | 130.00 | |
| 71 | A6 | 8c on 20c | 5.25 | 1.90 |
| 72 | A6 | 10c on 25c | 5.00 | .55 |
| 73 | A6 | 12c on 30c | 6.75 | 1.10 |
| 74 | A6 | 14c on 35c | 3.25 | .75 |
| a. | | Closed "4" | 12.00 | 5.75 |
| 75 | A6 | 16c on 40c | 6.50 | 2.00 |
| 76 | A6 | 18c on 45c | 8.00 | 2.75 |
| 77 | A6 | 20c on 50c (Bl) | 12.00 | 1.25 |
| 78 | A7 | 30c on 75c (Bl) | 16.00 | 2.75 |
| 79 | A8 | 40c on 1fr (Bl) | 24.00 | 2.75 |
| 80 | A9 | 80c on 2fr (R) | 27.50 | 8.50 |
| a. | | Double surcharge | 350.00 | 275.00 |
| 81 | A10 | 2pi on 5fr (R) | 105.00 | 105.00 |
| 82 | A11 | 4pi on 10fr (R) | 150.00 | 150.00 |
| | | Nos. 65-82 (18) | 383.00 | 284.10 |

Types of 1907 Issue Surcharged with New Values in Black or Red

Nos. 88-92      No. 93

**1922**
| | | | | |
|---|---|---|---|---|
| 88 | A5 | 1c on 5c ocher & blk | 1.60 | |
| 89 | A5 | 2c on 10c gray grn & blk | 2.40 | |
| 90 | A6 | 6c on 30c lt red & blk | 2.75 | |
| 91 | A6 | 10c on 50c lt bl & blk | 2.75 | |
| 92 | A6 | 11c on 55c vio & blk, bluish | 2.90 | |
| 93 | A6 | 12c on 60c lt bl & blk, pnksh (R) | 2.75 | |
| | | Nos. 88-93 (6) | 15.15 | |

Nos. 88-93 were sold officially in Paris but were never placed in use in the colony.

Nos. 88-93 exist without surcharge but were not regularly issued in that condition. Value, Nos. 88-89, each $190; Nos. 90-91, each $140; Nos. 92-93, each $100.

A12      A13

"CENTS" below Numerals
**1922-23**      **Perf. 14x13½**
| | | | | |
|---|---|---|---|---|
| 94 | A12 | ¹⁄₁₀c blk & sal ('23) | .25 | .25 |
| a. | | Double impression of frame | | |
| 95 | A12 | ⅕c blue & blk | .25 | .25 |
| 96 | A12 | ⅖c ol brn & blk | .25 | .25 |
| a. | | Head and value doubled | 260.00 | 260.00 |
| 97 | A12 | ⅘c rose & blk, lav | .40 | .35 |
| 98 | A12 | 1c yel brn & blk | .75 | .25 |
| 99 | A12 | 2c gray grn & blk | .75 | .55 |
| 100 | A12 | 3c vio & blk | .50 | .35 |
| 101 | A12 | 4c org & blk | .35 | .35 |
| 102 | A12 | 5c car & blk | .65 | .65 |
| a. | | Head and value doubled | 290.00 | 290.00 |
| 103 | A13 | 6c dl red & blk | .50 | .30 |
| 104 | A13 | 7c grn & blk | .75 | .65 |
| 105 | A13 | 8c blk, lav | 2.00 | 1.25 |
| 106 | A13 | 9c ocher & blk, grnsh | 1.50 | .90 |
| 107 | A13 | 10c bl & blk | .80 | .75 |
| 108 | A13 | 11c vio & blk | .75 | .75 |
| 109 | A13 | 12c brn & blk | .55 | .55 |
| a. | | Head and value double (11c+12c) | 450.00 | 450.00 |
| 110 | A13 | 15c org & blk | 1.00 | .80 |
| 111 | A13 | 20c bl & blk, straw | 1.60 | .80 |
| 112 | A13 | 40c ver & blk, bluish | 2.75 | 1.40 |
| 113 | A13 | 1pi bl grn & blk, grnsh | 7.00 | 5.25 |
| 114 | A13 | 2pi vio brn & blk, pnksh | 13.00 | 13.00 |
| | | Nos. 94-114 (21) | 36.35 | 29.65 |

For overprints see Nos. O17-O32.

Plowing near Tower of Confucius A14      Bay of Along A15

Angkor Wat, Cambodia A16

Carving Wood A17

That Luang Temple, Laos A18

Founding of Saigon A19

**1927, Sept. 26**
| | | | | |
|---|---|---|---|---|
| 115 | A14 | ¹⁄₁₀c lt olive grn | .25 | .25 |
| 116 | A14 | ⅕c yellow | .25 | .25 |
| 117 | A14 | ⅖c light blue | .55 | .55 |
| 118 | A14 | ⅘c dp brn | .55 | .55 |
| 119 | A14 | 1c orange | .65 | .30 |
| 120 | A14 | 2c blue grn | 1.10 | .50 |
| 121 | A14 | 3c indigo | 1.00 | .30 |
| 122 | A14 | 4c lil rose | 1.60 | 1.25 |
| 123 | A14 | 5c dp vio | .80 | .30 |
| a. | | Booklet pane of 10 | 200.00 | |
| 124 | A14 | 6c deep red | 2.10 | .80 |
| a. | | Booklet pane of 10 | 200.00 | |
| 125 | A15 | 7c lt brn | 1.50 | .80 |
| 126 | A15 | 8c gray green | 2.10 | 1.00 |
| 127 | A15 | 9c red vio | 1.50 | 1.00 |
| 128 | A15 | 10c light blue | 2.00 | 1.25 |
| 129 | A15 | 11c orange | 2.00 | 1.25 |
| 130 | A15 | 12c myrtle grn | 1.50 | 1.00 |
| 131 | A16 | 15c dl rose & ol brn | 7.50 | 7.50 |
| 132 | A16 | 20c vio & slate | 4.00 | 2.40 |
| 133 | A17 | 25c org brn & lil rose | 8.00 | 6.50 |
| 134 | A17 | 30c dp bl & ol gray | 5.00 | 4.00 |
| 135 | A18 | 40c ver & lt bl | 7.50 | 3.25 |
| 136 | A18 | 50c lt grn & slate | 10.00 | 3.25 |

| | | | |
|---|---|---|---|
| **137** | A19 | 1pi dk bl, blk & yel | 22.00  9.50 |
| *a.* | | Yellow omitted | 275.00 |
| **138** | A19 | 2pi red, dp bl & org | 27.50 16.50 |
| | | *Nos. 115-138 (24)* | 110.65 63.95 |

Common Design Types
pictured following the introduction.

### Colonial Exposition Issue
Common Design Types
Surcharged with New Values

| | | | |
|---|---|---|---|
| **1931, Apr. 13** | | **Engr.** | **Perf. 12½** |
| | | Name of Country in Black | |
| **140** | CD71 | 4c on 50c violet | 3.25  3.25 |
| **141** | CD72 | 6c on 90c red org | 3.25  3.25 |
| **142** | CD73 | 10c on 1.50fr dl bl | 4.00  4.00 |
| | | *Nos. 140-142 (3)* | 10.50 10.50 |

Junk — A20

Tower at Ruins of Angkor Thom — A21

Planting Rice — A22

Apsaras, Celestial Dancer A23

| | | | |
|---|---|---|---|
| **1931-41** | | **Photo.** | **Perf. 13½x13** |
| **143** | A20 | ⅒c Prus blue | .25  .25 |
| **144** | A20 | ⅕c lake | .25  .25 |
| **145** | A20 | ⅖c org red | .25  .25 |
| **146** | A20 | ½c red brn | .25  .25 |
| **147** | A20 | ⅘c dk vio | .25  .25 |
| **148** | A20 | 1c blk brn | .25  .25 |
| **149** | A20 | 2c dk grn | .25  .25 |
| **150** | A21 | 3c dp brn | .25  .25 |
| **151** | A21 | 3c dk grn ('34) | 5.75  1.60 |
| **152** | A21 | 4c dk bl | 1.25  .50 |
| **153** | A21 | 4c dk grn ('38) | .80  .55 |
| **153A** | A21 | 4c yel org ('40) | .40  .40 |
| **154** | A21 | 5c dp vio | .30  .30 |
| **154A** | A21 | 5c dp grn ('41) | .40  .40 |
| **155** | A21 | 6c org red | .25  .25 |
| *a.* | | Bklt. pane 5 + 1 label | 100.00 |
| **156** | A21 | 7c blk ('38) | .30  .30 |
| **157** | A21 | 8c rose lake ('38) | .30  .30 |
| **157A** | A21 | 9c blk, yel ('41) | .75  .75 |
| **158** | A22 | 10c dark blue | .65  .50 |
| **158A** | A22 | 10c ultra, pink ('41) | .55  .55 |
| **159** | A22 | 15c dk brn | 5.75  1.40 |
| **160** | A22 | 15c dk bl ('33) | .25  .25 |
| **161** | A22 | 18c blue ('38) | .75  .50 |
| **162** | A22 | 20c rose | .30  .25 |
| **163** | A22 | 21c olive grn | .30  .30 |
| **164** | A22 | 22c dk grn ('38) | .55  .55 |
| **165** | A22 | 25c dp vio | 3.25  1.60 |
| **165A** | A22 | 25c dk bl ('41) | .55  .55 |
| **166** | A22 | 30c org brn ('32) | .50  .30 |
| | | **Perf. 13½** | |
| **167** | A23 | 50c dk brn | .75  .25 |
| **168** | A23 | 60c dl vio ('32) | .90  .65 |
| **168A** | A23 | 70c lt bl ('41) | .55  .55 |
| **169** | A23 | 1pi yel grn | .90  .65 |
| **170** | A23 | 2pi red | 1.10  .75 |
| | | *Nos. 143-170 (34)* | 30.10 16.95 |

Without "RF," see Nos. 226A-226D.
For surcharge & overprints see #214A, O1-O16.

Emperor Bao-Dai A24

King Sisowath Monivong A25

### For Use in Annam

| | | | |
|---|---|---|---|
| **1936, Nov. 20** | | **Engr.** | **Perf. 13** |
| **171** | A24 | 1c brown | 1.00  1.00 |
| **172** | A24 | 2c green | 1.00  1.00 |
| **173** | A24 | 4c violet | 1.00  1.00 |
| **174** | A24 | 5c red brn | 1.50  1.50 |
| **175** | A24 | 10c lil rose | 2.00  2.00 |
| **176** | A24 | 15c ultra | 2.75  2.75 |
| **177** | A24 | 20c scarlet | 2.75  2.75 |
| **178** | A24 | 30c plum | 3.50  3.50 |
| **179** | A24 | 50c slate grn | 3.50  3.50 |
| **180** | A24 | 1pi rose vio | 4.50  4.50 |
| **181** | A24 | 2pi black | 5.25  5.25 |
| | | *Nos. 171-181 (11)* | 28.75 28.75 |

### For Use in Cambodia

| | | | |
|---|---|---|---|
| **182** | A25 | 1c brown | 1.00  1.00 |
| **183** | A25 | 2c green | 1.00  1.00 |
| **184** | A25 | 4c violet | 1.10  1.10 |
| **185** | A25 | 5c red brn | 1.10  1.10 |
| **186** | A25 | 10c lil rose | 2.40  2.40 |
| **187** | A25 | 15c ultra | 3.25  3.25 |
| **188** | A25 | 20c scarlet | 2.75  2.75 |
| **189** | A25 | 30c plum | 3.25  3.25 |
| **190** | A25 | 50c slate grn | 3.25  3.25 |
| **191** | A25 | 1pi rose vio | 4.00  4.00 |
| **192** | A25 | 2pi black | 5.25  5.25 |
| | | *Nos. 182-192 (11)* | 28.35 28.35 |

### Paris International Exposition Issue
Common Design Types

| | | | |
|---|---|---|---|
| **1937, Apr. 15** | | | |
| **193** | CD74 | 2c dp vio | 1.60  1.60 |
| **194** | CD75 | 3c dk grn | 1.10  1.10 |
| **195** | CD76 | 4c car rose | 1.10  1.10 |
| **196** | CD77 | 6c dk brn | 1.10  1.10 |
| **197** | CD78 | 9c red | 1.10  1.10 |
| **198** | CD79 | 15c ultra | 1.25  1.25 |
| | | *Nos. 193-198 (6)* | 7.25  7.25 |

### Colonial Arts Exhibition Issue
Souvenir Sheet
Common Design Type

| | | | |
|---|---|---|---|
| **1937, Apr. 15** | | | **Imperf.** |
| **199** | CD79 | 30c dull violet | 9.00 12.00 |

Governor-General Paul Doumer — A26

| | | | |
|---|---|---|---|
| **1938, June 8** | | **Photo.** | **Perf. 13½x13** |
| **200** | A26 | 5c rose car | 1.00  .65 |
| **201** | A26 | 6c brown | 1.10  1.10 |
| **202** | A26 | 18c brt bl | 1.10  1.10 |
| | | *Nos. 200-202,C18 (4)* | 3.95  3.10 |

Trans-Indo-Chinese Railway, 35th anniv.

### New York World's Fair Issue
Common Design Type

| | | | |
|---|---|---|---|
| **1939, May 10** | | **Engr.** | **Perf. 12½x12** |
| **203** | CD82 | 13c car lake | .80  .80 |
| **204** | CD82 | 23c ultra | 1.25  1.25 |

Mot Cot Pagoda, Hanoi — A27

| | | | |
|---|---|---|---|
| **1939, June 12** | | | **Perf. 13** |
| **205** | A27 | 6c blk brn | 1.10  1.10 |
| **206** | A27 | 9c vermilion | 1.10  1.10 |
| **207** | A27 | 23c ultra | 1.10  1.10 |
| **208** | A27 | 39c rose vio | 1.50  1.50 |
| | | *Nos. 205-208 (4)* | 4.80  4.80 |

Golden Gate International Exposition.

Angkor Wat and Marshal Pétain A27a

| | | | |
|---|---|---|---|
| **1941** | | **Engr.** | **Perf. 12½x12** |
| **209** | A27a | 10c dk car | .80 |
| **209A** | A27a | 25c blue | .80 |

Nos. 209-209A were issued by the Vichy government in France, but were not placed on sale in Indo-China.
For overprints, see Nos. 262-263. For surcharges, see B21A-B21B.

Gum
#210-261 issued without gum.

### Imperfs

Many issues between Nos. 209-263, B19A-B26 and C1-C28, plus some postage dues and official stamps, exist imperf.

King Norodom Sihanouk of Cambodia A28

Harnessed Elephant on Parade A29

| | | | |
|---|---|---|---|
| | | **Pin-perf. 12½** | |
| **1941, Oct. 15** | | **Unwmk.** | **Litho.** |
| **210** | A28 | 1c red org | 1.60  1.60 |
| **211** | A28 | 6c violet | 3.25  3.25 |
| **212** | A28 | 25c dp ultra | 21.00 21.00 |
| | | *Nos. 210-212 (3)* | 25.85 25.85 |

Coronation of Norodom Sihanouk, King of Cambodia, October, 1941.

| | | | |
|---|---|---|---|
| **1942, Mar. 29** | | | |
| **213** | A29 | 3c reddish brown | 2.00  1.60 |
| **214** | A29 | 6c crimson | 2.00  1.60 |

Fête of Nam-Giao in Annam.

No. 165 Surcharged in Black

| | | | |
|---|---|---|---|
| **1942** | | | **Perf. 13** |
| **214A** | A22 | 10c on 25c dp vio | .50  .30 |

View of Saigon Fair — A30

| | | | |
|---|---|---|---|
| **1942, Dec. 20** | | | **Perf. 13½** |
| **215** | A30 | 6c carmine rose | .80  .80 |

Saigon Fair of 1942.

Nam-Phuong, Empress of Annam — A31

Marshal Pétain — A32

| | | | |
|---|---|---|---|
| **1942, Sept. 1** | | | **Pin-perf. 11½** |
| **216** | A31 | 6c carmine rose | 1.25  .80 |

| | | | |
|---|---|---|---|
| **1942-44** | | | **Perf. 12, 13½** |
| **217** | A32 | 1c blk brn | .35  .35 |
| **218** | A32 | 3c olive brn ('43) | .35  .35 |
| **219** | A32 | 6c rose red | .55  .55 |
| **220** | A32 | 10c dull grn ('43) | 1.20  1.20 |
| **221** | A32 | 40c dk blue ('43) | 1.60  1.60 |
| **222** | A32 | 40c slate bl ('44) | .80  1.25 |
| | | *Nos. 217-222 (6)* | 4.85  5.30 |

Bao-Dai, Emperor of Annam A33

Norodom Sihanouk, King of Cambodia A34

| | | | |
|---|---|---|---|
| **1942** | | | **Perf. 13½** |
| **223** | A33 | ½c brown | 1.25  1.60 |
| **224** | A33 | 6c carmine rose | 1.25  1.25 |

Issue dates: ½c, Nov. 1; 6c, Sept. 1.

| | | | |
|---|---|---|---|
| **1943** | | | **Perf. 11½** |
| **225** | A34 | 1c brown | 1.25  .80 |
| **226** | A34 | 6c red | 1.00  .55 |

Issue dates: 1c, Mar. 10; 6c, May 10.

Types of 1931-32 Without "RF"

| | | | |
|---|---|---|---|
| **1943** | | **Photo.** | **Perf. 13½x13** |
| **226A** | A22 | 30c orange brown | 1.60 |
| **226B** | A23 | 50c dark brown | 1.60 |
| **226C** | A23 | 1pi yellow green | 2.75 |
| **226D** | A23 | 2pi red | 3.50 |
| | | *Nos. 226A-226D (4)* | 9.45 |

Nos. 226A-226D were issued by the Vichy government in France, but were not placed on sale in Indo-China.

Sisavang-Vong, King of Laos — A35

Family, Country and Labor — A36

| | | | |
|---|---|---|---|
| **1943** | | | |
| **227** | A35 | 1c bister brown | .55  1.25 |
| **228** | A35 | 6c carmine rose | 1.25  .65 |

Issue dates: 1c, Mar. 10; 6c, June 1.

| | | | |
|---|---|---|---|
| **1943, Nov. 5** | | | **Perf. 12** |
| **229** | A36 | 6c carmine rose | .65  .50 |

National revolution, 3rd anniversary.

Admiral Rigault de Genouilly A37

François Chasseloup-Laubat A38

Admiral André A. P. Courbet A39

## 1943     Perf. 11½, 12, 12x11½

| | | | |
|---|---|---|---|
| **230** | A37 | 6c carmine rose | .50 1.40 |
| **231** | A38 | 6c carmine rose | .50 .35 |
| **232** | A39 | 6c carmine rose | 1.40 .25 |
| | | *Nos. 230-232 (3)* | 2.40 2.00 |

Issued: #230, 232, Sept. 1; #231, Oct. 5.
A 5c dull brown, type A37, was not regularly issued without the Viet Nam overprint. Value, $10.
A 3c light brown, type A39, was prepared but not issued. Value, $10.

Pigneau de Behaine, Bishop of Adran — A40

Alexandre Yersin — A41

## 1943, June 10     Perf. 12

| | | | |
|---|---|---|---|
| **233** | A40 | 20c dull red | 1.50 *1.75* |

## 1943-45     Perf. 12x11½

| | | | |
|---|---|---|---|
| **234** | A41 | 6c carmine rose | 1.50 1.50 |
| **235** | A41 | 15c vio brn ('44) | .55 .55 |
| **236** | A41 | 1pi yel grn ('45) | .75 .75 |
| | | *Nos. 234-236 (3)* | 2.80 2.80 |

Issued to honor Dr. Alexandre Yersin (1863-1943), the Swiss bacteriologist who introduced rubber culture into Indo-China.
Issued: 6c, 10/5; 15c, 12/10; 1pi, 1/10.

Lt. M. J. François Garnier A42

## 1943, Sept.     Perf. 12

| | | | |
|---|---|---|---|
| **237** | A42 | 1c dull olive bister | .90 *1.25* |

A 15c brown violet was prepared but not issued. Value, $16.

Alexandre de Rhodes A43

## 1943-45     Pin-perf., Perf. 12

| | | | |
|---|---|---|---|
| **238** | A43 | 15c dk vio brn ('45) | .40 .40 |
| **239** | A43 | 30c org brn | .80 .80 |
| | *a.* | 30c yellow brown, perf. 13½ | .80 .80 |

Nos. 239, 239a carry the monogram "EF."
Issue dates: 15c, Mar. 10; 30c, June 15.

Athlete Giving Olympic Salute A44

## 1944, July 10     Perf. 12

| | | | |
|---|---|---|---|
| **241** | A44 | 10c dk vio brn & yel | 2.40 2.40 |
| **242** | A44 | 50c dl red | 2.75 2.75 |

Adm. Pierre de La Grandière A45

## 1943-45

| | | | |
|---|---|---|---|
| **243** | A45 | 1c dull brn | .25 *1.25* |
| **244** | A45 | 5c dark brn ('45) | .30 .30 |

The upper left corner of No. 244 contains the denomination "5c" instead of "EF" monogram.
Issue dates: 1c, Aug.; 5c, Jan. 10.

Auguste Pavie A46

## 1944     Perf. 12

| | | | |
|---|---|---|---|
| **245** | A46 | 4c org yel | .50 .30 |
| **246** | A46 | 10c dl grn | .30 .65 |

Issue dates: 4c, Feb. 10; 10c, Jan. 5.
A 20c dark red, type A46, was not regularly issued without the Viet Nam overprint. Value without overprint, $10.

Governor-General Pierre Pasquier — A47

## 1944

| | | | |
|---|---|---|---|
| **247** | A47 | 5c brn vio | .65 .65 |
| **248** | A47 | 10c dl grn | .30 *1.25* |

Issue dates: 5c, Nov. 1; 10c, Sept.

Joost Van Vollenhoven — A48

## 1944, Oct. 10

| | | | |
|---|---|---|---|
| **249** | A48 | 1c olive brown | .35 .35 |
| **250** | A48 | 10c green | .75 .90 |

Governor-General J. M. A. de Lanessan — A49

## 1944

| | | | |
|---|---|---|---|
| **251** | A49 | 1c dl gray brn | .65 .50 |
| **252** | A49 | 15c dl rose vio | 1.90 1.60 |

Issued: 1c, Dec. 10; 15c, Oct. 16.

Governor-General Paul Doumer — A50

## 1944

| | | | |
|---|---|---|---|
| **253** | A50 | 2c red vio | .30 .30 |
| **254** | A50 | 4c lt brn | .30 .30 |
| **255** | A50 | 10c yel grn | .30 .30 |
| | | *Nos. 253-255 (3)* | .90 .90 |

Issue dates: 2c, May 15; 4c, June 15; 10c, Jan. 5.

Admiral Charner — A51

Doudart de Lagrée — A52

## 1944

| | | | |
|---|---|---|---|
| **256** | A51 | 10c green | .50 *1.40* |
| **257** | A51 | 20c brn red | .65 *1.40* |
| **258** | A51 | 1pi pale yel grn | 1.00 1.00 |
| | | *Nos. 256-258 (3)* | 2.15 3.80 |

Issue dates: 10c, 20c, Aug. 10; 1pi, July.

## 1944-45

| | | | |
|---|---|---|---|
| **259** | A52 | 1c dl gray brn ('45) | .25 .25 |
| **260** | A52 | 15c dl rose vio | .50 .55 |
| **261** | A52 | 40c brt bl | .65 1.00 |
| | | *Nos. 259-261 (3)* | 1.40 1.80 |

Issue dates: 1c, Jan. 10; 15c, 40c, Nov.

Nos. 209-209A Overprinted in Black

## 1946     Unwmk.     Perf. 12½x12

| | | | |
|---|---|---|---|
| **262** | A27a | 10c dk car | 1.10 *1.60* |
| **263** | A27a | 25c blue | 2.75 3.25 |

---

## SEMI-POSTAL STAMPS

No. 45 Surcharged

## 1914, Oct. 28     Perf. 14x13½     Unwmk.

| | | | |
|---|---|---|---|
| **B1** | A5 | 10c +5c red & blk | 1.60 1.60 |

Nos. 44-46 Surcharged

## 1915-17

| | | | |
|---|---|---|---|
| **B2** | A5 | 5c + 5c grn & blk ('17) | 1.60 1.60 |
| | *a.* | Double surcharge | 210.00 210.00 |
| **B3** | A5 | 10c + 5c red & blk | 2.40 2.00 |
| **B4** | A5 | 15c + 5c vio & blk ('17) | 2.40 2.00 |
| | *a.* | Triple surcharge | 190.00 |
| | *b.* | Quadruple surcharge | 190.00 |
| | | *Nos. B2-B4 (3)* | 6.40 5.60 |

Nos. B2-B4 Surcharged with New Values in Blue or Black

## 1918-19

| | | | |
|---|---|---|---|
| **B5** | A5 | 4c on 5c + 5c (Bl) | 4.00 4.00 |
| | *a.* | Closed "4" | 220.00 |
| **B6** | A5 | 6c on 10c + 5c | 3.75 *4.00* |
| **B7** | A5 | 8c on 15c + 5c ('19) | 13.00 13.00 |
| | *a.* | Double surcharge | 220.00 |
| | | *Nos. B5-B7 (3)* | 20.75 21.00 |

France Nos. B5-B10 Surcharged

## 1919

| | | | |
|---|---|---|---|
| **B8** | SP5 | 10c on 15c + 10c | 1.60 1.60 |
| **B9** | SP5 | 16c on 25c + 15c | 4.00 4.00 |
| **B10** | SP6 | 24c on 35c + 25c | 6.50 6.50 |
| | *a.* | Double surcharge | 800.00 800.00 |

| | | | |
|---|---|---|---|
| **B11** | SP7 | 40c on 50c + 50c | 12.50 12.50 |
| **B12** | SP8 | 80c on 1fr + 1fr | 27.50 27.50 |
| **B13** | SP8 | 4pi on 5fr + 5fr | 220.00 220.00 |
| | | *Nos. B8-B13 (6)* | 272.10 272.10 |

### Curie Issue
Common Design Type
Inscription and Date in Upper Margin

## 1938, Oct. 24     Engr.     Perf. 13

| | | | |
|---|---|---|---|
| **B14** | CD80 | 18c + 5c brt ultra | 11.00 11.00 |

### French Revolution Issue
Common Design Type
Name and Value Typo. in Black

## 1939, July 5     Photo.

| | | | |
|---|---|---|---|
| **B15** | CD83 | 6c + 2c green | 12.00 12.00 |
| **B16** | CD83 | 7c + 3c brown | 12.00 12.00 |
| **B17** | CD83 | 9c + 4c red org | 12.00 12.00 |
| **B18** | CD83 | 13c + 10c rose pink | 12.00 12.00 |
| **B19** | CD83 | 23c + 20c blue | 12.00 12.00 |
| | | *Nos. B15-B19 (5)* | 60.00 60.00 |

Common Design Type and

Tonkinese Sharpshooter SP1

Legionary SP2

## 1941     Photo.     Perf. 13½

| | | | |
|---|---|---|---|
| **B19A** | SP1 | 10c + 10c red | 1.60 |
| **B19B** | CD86 | 15c + 30c maroon | 1.60 |
| **B19C** | SP2 | 25c + 10c blue | 1.60 |
| | | *Nos. B19A-B19C (3)* | 4.80 |

Nos. B19A-B19C were issued by the Vichy government in France, but were not placed on sale in Indo-China.

Portal and Flags, City University, Hanoi — SP3

Coat of Arms and Sword — SP4

## 1942, June 1     Unwmk.     Perf. 11½     Litho.

| | | | |
|---|---|---|---|
| **B20** | SP3 | 6c + 2c car rose | 1.25 1.25 |
| **B21** | SP3 | 15c + 5c brn vio | 1.25 1.25 |

Nos. 209-209A Surcharged in Black or Red

## 1944     Engr.     Perf. 12½x12

| | | | |
|---|---|---|---|
| **B21A** | | 5c + 15c on 25c blue (R) | .95 |
| **B21B** | | + 25c on 10c dk car | 1.00 |

Colonial Development Fund.
Nos. B21A-B21B were issued by the Vichy government in France, but were not placed on sale in Indo-China.

No. B20
Surcharged in Black

**1944, June 10**

| B22 | SP3 | 10c + 2c on 6c + 2c | .65 | .65 |

**1942, Aug. 1**      **Perf. 12**

| B23 | SP4 | 6c + 2c red & blue | .80 | .80 |
| B24 | SP4 | 15c + 5c vio blk, red & bl | .80 | .80 |

#B23 Surcharged in Black Like #B22

**1944, Mar. 15**

| B25 | SP4 | 10c + 2c on 6c + 2c | .75 | .75 |

Aviator Do-
Huu-Vi
SP5

**1943, Aug. 1**

| B26 | SP5 | 6c + 2c car rose | .65 | 1.60 |

#B26 Surcharged in Black Like #B22

**1944, Feb. 10**

| B27 | SP5 | 10c + 2c on 6c + 2c | .80 | .80 |

Surcharge arranged to fit size of stamp.

Aviator Roland
Garros — SP6

**1943, Nov. 15**

| B28 | SP6 | 6c + 2c rose car | .80 | .80 |

#B28 Surcharged in Black Like #B22

**1944, Feb. 10**

| B29 | SP6 | 10c + 2c on 6c + 2c | .80 | .80 |

Cathedral
of Orléans
SP7

**1944, Dec. 20**

| B30 | SP7 | 15c + 60c brn vio | 1.60 | 1.60 |
| B31 | SP7 | 40c + 1.10pi blue | 1.60 | 2.75 |

Type of
France,
1945,
Surcharged
in Black

**1945**    **Unwmk.**    **Engr.**    **Perf. 13**

| B32 | A152 | 50c + 50c on 2fr green | .65 | .65 |
| B33 | A152 | 1pi + 1pi on 2fr brn | .65 | .65 |
| B34 | A152 | 2pi + 2pi on 2fr Prus grn | 1.00 | 1.00 |
| | | *Nos. B32-B34 (3)* | 2.30 | 2.30 |

## AIR POST STAMPS

Airplane
AP1

**1933-41**   **Unwmk.**   **Photo.**   **Perf. 13½**

| C1 | AP1 | 1c ol brn | .25 | .25 |
| C2 | AP1 | 2c dk grn | .30 | .25 |
| C3 | AP1 | 5c yel grn | .30 | .25 |
| C4 | AP1 | 10c red brn | .65 | .30 |
| C5 | AP1 | 11c rose car ('38) | .80 | .30 |
| C6 | AP1 | 15c dp bl | .50 | .25 |
| C6A | AP1 | 16c brt pink ('41) | .35 | .35 |
| C7 | AP1 | 20c grnsh gray | .50 | .50 |
| C8 | AP1 | 30c org brn | .30 | .25 |
| C9 | AP1 | 36c car rose | 1.90 | .35 |
| C10 | AP1 | 37c ol grn ('38) | .80 | .30 |
| C10A | AP1 | 39c dk ol grn ('41) | .35 | .35 |
| C11 | AP1 | 60c dk vio | 1.90 | .35 |
| C12 | AP1 | 66c olive grn | .55 | .25 |
| C13 | AP1 | 67c brt bl ('38) | 1.75 | 1.00 |
| C13A | AP1 | 69c brt ultra ('41) | .65 | .65 |
| C14 | AP1 | 1pi black | .90 | .25 |
| C15 | AP1 | 2pi yel org | 1.00 | .35 |
| C16 | AP1 | 5pi purple | 1.90 | .50 |
| C17 | AP1 | 10pi deep red | 3.75 | .90 |
| | | *Nos. C1-C17 (20)* | 19.40 | 7.95 |

Issue dates: 11c, 37c, June 8; 67c, Oct. 5; 16c, 39c, 69c, Feb. 5; others, June 1, 1933.
See Nos. C18A-C18O, C27-C28.

Trans-Indo-Chinese Railway Type

**1938, June 8**      **Perf. 13½x13**

| C18 | A26 | 37c red orange | .75 | .25 |

Type of 1933-38 Without "RF"

**1942-44**      **Perf. 13½**

| C18A | AP1 | 5c yellow green | | .25 |
| C18B | AP1 | 10c red brown | | .25 |
| C18C | AP1 | 11c rose carmine | | .30 |
| C18D | AP1 | 15c deep blue | | .40 |
| C18E | AP1 | 20c greenish gray | | .40 |
| C18F | AP1 | 36c carmine rose | | .40 |
| C18G | AP1 | 37c olive green | | .65 |
| C18H | AP1 | 60c dark violet | | .65 |
| C18I | AP1 | 66c brown olive | | .65 |
| C18J | AP1 | 67c bright blue | | .80 |
| C18K | AP1 | 69c br ultramarine | | .90 |
| C18L | AP1 | 1pi black | | 1.25 |
| C18M | AP1 | 2pi yellow orange | | 1.25 |
| C18N | AP1 | 5pi purple | | 1.75 |
| C18O | AP1 | 10pi deep red | | 3.50 |
| | | *Nos. C18A-C18O (15)* | | 13.40 |

Nos. C18A-C18O were issued by the Vichy government in France, but were not placed on sale in Indo-China.

### Victory Issue
Common Design Type
**Perf. 12½**

**1946, May 8**   **Unwmk.**   **Engr.**

| C19 | CD92 | 80c red org | 1.00 | .55 |

### Chad to Rhine Issue
Common Design Types

**1946, June 6**

| C20 | CD93 | 50c yel grn | .90 | .90 |
| C21 | CD94 | 1pi violet | .90 | .90 |
| C22 | CD95 | 1.50pi carmine | 1.10 | 1.10 |
| C23 | CD96 | 2pi vio brn | 1.10 | 1.10 |
| C24 | CD97 | 2.50pi dp bl | 1.10 | 1.10 |
| C25 | CD98 | 5pi org red | 1.30 | 1.30 |
| | | *Nos. C20-C25 (6)* | 6.40 | 6.40 |

### UPU Issue
Common Design Type

**1949, July 4**      **Perf. 13**

| C26 | CD99 | 3pi dp bl, dk vio, grn & red | 4.75 | 4.00 |

Plane Type of 1933-41

**1949, June 13**   **Photo.**   **Perf. 13½**

| C27 | AP1 | 20pi dk bl grn | 11.50 | 6.50 |
| C28 | AP1 | 30pi brown | 13.00 | 6.50 |

## AIR POST SEMI-POSTAL STAMPS

### French Revolution Issue
Common Design Type
**Unwmk.**

**1939, July 5**   **Photo.**   **Perf. 13**
Name and Value Typo. in Orange

| CB1 | CD83 | 39c + 40c brn blk | 25.00 | 25.00 |

Poor Family — SPAP1

Orphans
SPAP2

Caring for Children — SPAP3

**Perf. 13½x12½, 13 (#CB4)**
Photo., Engr. (#CB4)

**1942, June 22**

| CB2 | SPAP1 | 15c + 35c green | 1.00 | |
| CB3 | SPAP2 | 20c + 60c brown | 1.00 | |
| CB4 | SPAP3 | 30c + 90c car red | 1.05 | |
| | | *Nos. CB2-CB4 (3)* | 3.05 | |

Native children's welfare fund. Nos. CB2-CB4 were issued by the Vichy government in France, but were not placed on sale in Indo-China.

### Colonial Education Fund
Common Design Type
**Perf. 12½x13½**

**1942, June 22**      **Engr.**

| CB5 | CD86a | 12c + 18c blue & red | 1.10 | |

No. CB5 was issued by the Vichy government in France, but was not placed on sale in Indo-China.

---

## POSTAGE DUE STAMPS

French Colonies No. J21 Surcharged

**1904, June 26**   **Unwmk.**   **Imperf.**

| J1 | D1 | 5c on 60c brn, *buff* | 14.00 | 14.00 |

French Colonies Nos. J10-J11
Surcharged in Carmine

**1905, July 22**

| J2 | D1 | 5c on 40c black | 32.00 | 16.00 |
| J3 | D1 | 10c on 60c black | 32.00 | 20.00 |
| J4 | D1 | 30c on 60c black | 32.00 | 20.00 |
| | | *Nos. J2-J4 (3)* | 96.00 | 56.00 |

Dragon from Steps of
Angkor Wat

| | D1 | D2 |

**1908**   **Typo.**   **Perf. 14x13½**

| J5 | D1 | 2c black | 1.25 | 1.00 |
| J6 | D1 | 4c dp bl | 1.25 | 1.00 |
| J7 | D1 | 5c bl grn | 1.60 | 1.10 |
| J8 | D1 | 10c carmine | 2.90 | 1.10 |
| J9 | D1 | 15c violet | 3.50 | 2.50 |
| J10 | D1 | 20c chocolate | 1.75 | 1.40 |
| J11 | D1 | 30c ol grn | 1.75 | 1.40 |
| J12 | D1 | 40c claret | 8.25 | 6.50 |
| J13 | D1 | 50c grnsh bl | 7.00 | 1.60 |
| J14 | D1 | 60c orange | 11.00 | 9.50 |
| J15 | D1 | 1fr gray | 24.00 | 18.50 |
| J16 | D1 | 2fr yel brn | 24.00 | 18.50 |
| J17 | D1 | 5fr red | 40.00 | 37.50 |
| | | *Nos. J5-J17 (13)* | 128.25 | 101.60 |

Surcharged with New Values in Cents or Piasters

**1919**

| J18 | D1 | ⅘c on 2c blk | 1.60 | 1.25 |
| J19 | D1 | 1⅘c on 4c dp bl | 1.60 | 1.25 |
| J20 | D1 | 2c on 5c bl grn | 2.90 | 1.60 |
| J21 | D1 | 4c on 10c car | 4.00 | 1.25 |
| J22 | D1 | 6c on 15c vio | 9.00 | 2.75 |
| J23 | D1 | 8c on 20c choc | 6.50 | 2.40 |
| J24 | D1 | 12c on 30c ol grn | 9.25 | 2.40 |
| J25 | D1 | 16c on 40c cl | 9.25 | 2.00 |
| J26 | D1 | 20c on 50c grnsh bl | 12.00 | 6.50 |
| J27 | D1 | 24c on 60c org | 3.25 | 2.00 |
| a. | | Closed "4" | 20.00 | 16.00 |
| J28 | D1 | 40c on 1fr gray | 5.25 | 1.60 |
| a. | | Closed "4" | 20.00 | 16.00 |
| J29 | D1 | 80c on 2fr yel brn | 40.00 | 19.00 |
| J30 | D1 | 2pi on 5fr red | 57.50 | 40.00 |
| a. | | Double surcharge | 220.00 | 175.00 |
| b. | | Triple surcharge | 220.00 | 175.00 |
| | | *Nos. J18-J30 (13)* | 162.10 | 84.00 |

"CENTS" below Numerals

**1922, Oct.**

| J31 | D2 | ⅖c black | .25 | .25 |
| J32 | D2 | ⅘c red | .30 | .30 |
| J33 | D2 | 1c buff | .50 | .40 |
| J34 | D2 | 2c gray grn | .65 | .50 |
| J35 | D2 | 3c violet | .75 | .75 |
| J36 | D2 | 4c orange | .75 | .40 |
| a. | | "4 CENTS" omitted | 675.00 | |
| b. | | "4 CENTS" double | 105.00 | 105.00 |
| J37 | D2 | 6c ol grn | 1.60 | .65 |
| J38 | D2 | 8c blk, *lav* | 1.25 | .65 |
| J39 | D2 | 10c dp bl | 2.00 | .65 |
| J40 | D2 | 12c ocher, *grnsh* | 1.60 | 1.10 |
| J41 | D2 | 20c dp bl, *straw* | 2.00 | .90 |
| J42 | D2 | 40c red, *bluish* | 2.00 | 1.10 |
| J43 | D2 | 1pi brn vio, *pnksh* | 6.50 | 3.50 |
| | | *Nos. J31-J43 (13)* | 20.15 | 11.15 |

Pagoda of
Mot Cot,
Hanoi — D3

Dragon of
Annam — D4

**Perf. 14x13½, 13½x14**

**1927, Sept. 26**

| J44 | D3 | ⅖c vio brn & org | .25 | .25 |
| J45 | D3 | ⅘c vio & blk | .25 | .25 |
| J46 | D3 | 1c brn red & sl | .90 | .90 |
| J47 | D3 | 2c grn & brn ol | 1.00 | 1.00 |
| J48 | D3 | 3c red brn & bl | 1.60 | 1.60 |
| J49 | D3 | 4c ind & brn | 1.60 | 1.60 |
| J50 | D3 | 6c dp red & ver | 2.00 | 1.60 |
| J51 | D3 | 8c ol brn & vio | 1.60 | 1.25 |
| J52 | D4 | 10c dp bl | 2.40 | 1.25 |
| J53 | D4 | 12c olive | 5.25 | 4.50 |
| J54 | D4 | 20c rose | 3.50 | 2.00 |
| J55 | D4 | 40c bl grn | 3.50 | 3.25 |
| J56 | D4 | 1pi red org | 17.50 | 17.50 |
| | | *Nos. J44-J56 (13)* | 41.35 | 36.95 |

D5

Value Surcharged in Black or Blue

**1931-41**      **Perf. 13**

| J57 | D5 | ⅕c red, *org* ('38) | .25 | .25 |
| J58 | D5 | ⅖c red, *org* | .25 | .25 |
| J59 | D5 | ⅘c red, *org* | .25 | .25 |
| J60 | D5 | 1c red, *org* | .25 | .25 |
| J61 | D5 | 2c red, *org* | .25 | .25 |
| J62 | D5 | 2.5c red, *org* ('40) | .25 | .25 |
| J63 | D5 | 3c red, *org* ('38) | .30 | .25 |
| J64 | D5 | 4c red, *org* | .30 | .30 |
| J65 | D5 | 5c red, *org* ('38) | .30 | .30 |
| J66 | D5 | 6c red, *org* | .30 | .30 |
| J67 | D5 | 10c red, *org* | .30 | .30 |
| J68 | D5 | 12c red, *org* | .50 | .30 |
| J69 | D5 | 14c red, *org* ('38) | .50 | .30 |
| J70 | D5 | 18c red, *org* ('41) | .50 | .50 |
| J71 | D5 | 20c red, *org* | .50 | .50 |
| J72 | D5 | 50c red, *org* | .75 | .50 |
| J72A | D5 | 1pi red, *org* | 9.50 | 8.50 |
| J73 | D5 | 1pi red, *org* (Bl) | 2.25 | 1.25 |
| | | *Nos. J57-J73 (18)* | 17.50 | 14.80 |

D6

D7

### Perf. 12, 13½ and Compound

| | | 1943-44 Litho. | Unwmk. | |
|---|---|---|---|---|
| J74 | D6 | 1c red, *org* | .25 | .25 |
| J75 | D6 | 2c red, *org* | .25 | .25 |
| J76 | D6 | 3c red, *org* | .30 | .30 |
| J77 | D6 | 4c red, *org* | .30 | .30 |
| J78 | D6 | 6c red, *org* | .40 | .40 |
| J79 | D6 | 10c red, *org* | .40 | .40 |
| J80 | D7 | 12c blue, *pnksh* | .50 | .50 |
| J81 | D7 | 20c blue, *pnksh* | .50 | .50 |
| J82 | D7 | 30c blue, *pnksh* | .50 | .50 |
| | | Nos. J74-J82 (9) | 3.40 | 3.40 |

Issued: 2c, 3c, 7/15/43; 6c-30c, 8/43; 1c, 4c, 6/10/44.

---

## OFFICIAL STAMPS

Regular Issues of 1931-32 Overprinted in Blue or Red

Overprinted

### Perf. 13, 13½

| | | 1933, Feb. 27 | Unwmk. | |
|---|---|---|---|---|
| O1 | A20 | 1c black brown (Bl) | .80 | .75 |
| O2 | A20 | 2c dark green (Bl) | .90 | .50 |

Overprinted

| | | | | |
|---|---|---|---|---|
| O3 | A21 | 3c deep brown (Bl) | 1.25 | .65 |
| a. | | Inverted overprint | 150.00 | |
| O4 | A21 | 4c dark blue (R) | 1.50 | .90 |
| a. | | Inverted overprint | 150.00 | |
| O5 | A21 | 5c deep violet (Bl) | 2.40 | .90 |
| O6 | A21 | 6c orange red (Bl) | 2.40 | 1.25 |

Overprinted

| | | | | |
|---|---|---|---|---|
| O7 | A22 | 10c dk blue (R) | 1.25 | .90 |
| O8 | A22 | 15c dk brown (Bl) | 2.75 | 1.60 |
| O9 | A22 | 20c rose (Bl) | 3.25 | .75 |
| O10 | A22 | 21c olive grn (Bl) | 2.75 | 1.50 |
| O11 | A22 | 25c dp violet (Bl) | 1.60 | .50 |
| O12 | A22 | 30c orange brn (Bl) | 3.25 | .80 |

Overprinted

| | | | | |
|---|---|---|---|---|
| O13 | A23 | 50c dark brown (Bl) | 11.50 | 3.50 |
| O14 | A23 | 60c dull violet (Bl) | 2.75 | 2.40 |
| O15 | A23 | 1pi yellow green (Bl) | 28.00 | 10.50 |
| O16 | A23 | 2pi red (Bl) | 10.00 | 9.00 |
| | | Nos. O1-O16 (16) | 76.35 | 36.40 |

Type of Regular Issue, 1922-23 Overprinted diagonally in Black or Red "SERVICE"

| | | 1934, Oct. 4 | Perf. 14x13 | |
|---|---|---|---|---|
| O17 | A13 | 1c olive green | 1.00 | .75 |
| O18 | A13 | 2c brown orange | 1.00 | .75 |
| O19 | A13 | 3c yellow green | 1.25 | .65 |
| O20 | A13 | 4c cerise | 2.25 | 1.30 |
| O21 | A13 | 5c yellow | 1.25 | .75 |
| O22 | A13 | 6c orange red | 5.25 | 5.00 |
| O23 | A13 | 10c gray grn (R) | 3.00 | 2.25 |
| O24 | A13 | 15c ultra | 2.10 | 1.50 |
| O25 | A13 | 20c gray black (R) | 1.80 | 1.50 |
| O26 | A13 | 21c light violet | 10.00 | 8.25 |
| O27 | A13 | 25c rose lake | 11.50 | 10.00 |
| O28 | A13 | 30c lilac gray | 1.50 | 1.30 |
| O29 | A13 | 50c brt violet | 7.50 | 6.25 |
| O30 | A13 | 60c gray | 14.00 | 10.50 |

| | | | | |
|---|---|---|---|---|
| O31 | A13 | 1pi blue (R) | 27.50 | 23.00 |
| O32 | A13 | 2pi deep red | 45.00 | 32.50 |
| | | Nos. O17-O32 (16) | 135.90 | 106.25 |

The value tablet has colorless numeral and letters on solid background.

---

## PARCEL POST STAMPS

French Colonies No. 50 Overprinted

| | 1891 Unwmk. | Perf. 14x13½ | |
|---|---|---|---|
| Q1 | A9 10c black, *lavender* | 24.00 | 10.50 |

The overprint on No. Q1 was also handstamped in shiny ink. Value unused, $750.

Indo-China No. 8 Overprinted

**1898**

| | | | |
|---|---|---|---|
| Q2 | A3 10c black, *lavender* | 28.00 | 28.00 |

Nos. 8 and 9 Overprinted

**1902**

| | | | |
|---|---|---|---|
| Q3 | A3 10c black, *lavender* | 52.50 | 32.50 |
| a. | Inverted overprint | 110.00 | 48.00 |
| Q4 | A3 10c red | 52.50 | 32.50 |
| a. | Inverted overprint | 80.00 | 48.00 |
| b. | Double overprint | 80.00 | 48.00 |

---

# INDONESIA

ˌin-də-ˈnē-zhə

LOCATION — In the East Indies
GOVT. — Republic
AREA — 741,101 sq. mi.
POP. — 195,280,000 (1995 est.)
CAPITAL — Jakarta

Formerly Netherlands Indies, Indonesia achieved independence late in 1949 as the United States of Indonesia and became the Republic of Indonesia August 15, 1950. See Netherlands Indies for earlier issues.

100 Sen = 1 Rupiah

> **Catalogue values for all unused stamps in this country are for Never Hinged items.**

Watermarks

Wmk. 404

---

Wmk. 228

---

## REVOLUTIONARY ISSUES

Following the surrender of Japan to the Allies in 1945, Indonesian nationalists declared independence and formed the Republic of Indonesia. On Sept. 27, the Djawan PTT (now PT Pos Indonesia) was established and assumed reponsibility for the postal system. Within days, civil war had broken out between the nationalists and the returning Dutch, who sought to reestablish control over their East Indies colony. During the hostilities, which continued until Dec. 1949, a Dutch blockade of the rebel strongholds in Java and Sumatra made regular communications between the two islands impossible, and the Djawan PTT was forced to organize separate postal services, using locally produced stamps, on Java and Sumatra.

## JAVA ISSUES

Netherlands Indies Nos. 168, 200, 201 Overprinted "Repoeblik Indonesia" and 3 bars in Black or Red (R)

| | 1945, Nov. | Perf. 11½ | |
|---|---|---|---|
| 1L1 | A17 1c lilac gray (R) | 2.25 | 2.75 |
| 1L2 | A17 2c plum | 4.50 | 6.25 |
| 1L3 | A17 3½c dark gray (R) | 60.00 | 60.00 |
| | Nos. 1L1-1L3 (3) | 66.75 | 69.00 |

Forgeries of Nos. 1L1-1L3 exist.

Netherlands Indies Nos. 228-231 Overprinted "Repoeblik Indonesia" and 2 bars in Black or Red (R)

| | 1945, Nov. | Perf. 12½ | |
|---|---|---|---|
| 1L4 | A23 2½c rose violet | 1.60 | 2.75 |
| 1L5 | A24 3c green (R) | 1.60 | 2.75 |
| 1L6 | A25 4c olive green (R) | 1.75 | 3.00 |
| 1L7 | A26 5c blue (R) | 75.00 | 65.00 |
| | Nos. 1L4-1L7 (4) | 79.95 | 73.50 |

Forgeries of Nos. 1L4-1L7 exist.

Netherlands Indies Nos. N2, N3 Overprinted "Repoeblik Indonesia" and 2 bars in Black or Red (R)

---

| | 1945, Nov. | Perf. 12½ | |
|---|---|---|---|
| 1L8 | OS2 3½s carmine | 325.00 | 325.00 |
| 1L9 | OS3 5s green (R) | 22.50 | 15.00 |

Forgeries of Nos. 1L8-1L9 exist.

Netherlands Indies Nos. N5-N11 Overprinted "Repoeblik Indonesia" and 2 bars in Black or Red (R)

| | 1945, Nov. | Perf. 12½ | |
|---|---|---|---|
| 1L10 | OS5 3½s rose red | 50.00 | 50.00 |
| 1L11 | OS6 5s yel green (R) | .65 | 1.40 |
| 1L12 | OS7 10s dk blue (R) | .65 | 1.40 |
| a. | Perf 12 | 1.75 | 2.25 |
| 1L13 | OS8 20s gray olive (R) | .65 | 1.40 |
| 1L14 | OS9 40s rose lilac (R) | .70 | 1.40 |
| 1L15 | OS10 60s red orange | .90 | 1.20 |
| 1L16 | OS11 80s fawn | 20.00 | 20.00 |
| | Nos. 1L10-1L16 (7) | 73.55 | 76.80 |

Forgeries of Nos. 1L10-1L16 exist.

Netherlands Indies Nos. 200, 201, 228-230, N38 Overprinted "Repoeblik Indonesia" and a thick Red or Brown (Br) bar

### Perf. 12½, 12x12½ (#A18, A19)

| | 1945, Nov. | | |
|---|---|---|---|
| 1L17 | A17 1s lilac gray | 2.25 | 2.90 |
| 1L18 | A17 1s lilac gray (Br) | 10.00 | 12.00 |
| 1L19 | OS21 2s carmine | 1.40 | 2.25 |
| 1L20 | A23 2½s rose violet | 20.00 | 20.00 |
| 1L21 | A24 3s green | 3.50 | 3.50 |
| 1L22 | A25 4s olive green | 3.50 | 3.50 |
| | Nos. 1L17-1L22 (6) | 40.65 | 44.15 |

Forgeries of Nos. 1L17-1L22 exist.

A large number of proofs, both perf and imperf, in original and in different colors, exist for Nos. 1L23-1L50. All are scarce.

Bull — A1

Bull & Flag — A2

### Perf. 11½

| | 1945, Dec. 1 Typo. | Unwmk. | |
|---|---|---|---|
| | With Gum | | |
| 1L23 | A1 10s chocolate | 8.50 | 8.50 |
| a. | Imperf | 95.00 | 150.00 |
| 1L24 | A2 20s choc & carmine red | 7.50 | 7.50 |

Issued to celebrate the first half-year of Indonesian independence.

Nos. 1L25-1L50 were issued without gum.

Road & Mountains — A3

Sentry — A4

Boat in
Storm — A5

Wayang
Puppet — A6

Kris &
Flag — A7

Temple — A8

### 1946-47 Various perfs
| | | | | |
|---|---|---|---|---|
| 1L25 | A3 | 5s pale gray blue | .75 | .95 |
| 1L26 | A4 | 20s lt red brown | .75 | .95 |
| 1L27 | A5 | 30s carmine red | .80 | 1.00 |
| 1L28 | A6 | 50s deep blue | 17.50 | 16.00 |
| 1L29 | A7 | 60s deep rose | 6.50 | 300.00 |
| 1L30 | A8 | 80s dp red vio ('47) | 65.00 | 600.00 |
| | | Nos. 1L25-1L30 (6) | 91.30 | 918.90 |

Issued: 5s, 20s, 6/1/46. 30s, 50s, 7/1/46. 60s, 9/1/46. 80s, 7/1/47.

Buffalo Breaking
Chains — A9

Bandung,
March
1946 — A10

Bombing of
Soerabaya,
Nov.
1945 — A11

Anti-aircraft
Crew — A12

Quai at Tandjong
Priok — A13

Pilot — A14

Ambarawa
A15

Meeting,
Jakarta — A17

Mounted
Soldier — A18

### 1946-47 Various perfs
| | | | | |
|---|---|---|---|---|
| 1L31 | A9 | 3s dull carmine | .35 | 1.75 |
| a. | | Imperf | .20 | .20 |
| 1L32 | A10 | 5s gray blue | .60 | .95 |
| a. | | Imperf | .35 | .50 |
| 1L33 | A11 | 10s blue black | 11.50 | 6.25 |
| a. | | Imperf | 11.50 | 11.50 |
| 1L34 | A11 | 15s dark purple | .95 | 1.25 |
| a. | | Imperf | .95 | .95 |
| 1L35 | A12 | 30s green | 2.40 | 5.75 |
| a. | | Imperf | 1.75 | 2.40 |
| 1L36 | A13 | 40s dk blue vio | .95 | 2.40 |
| a. | | Imperf | 1.00 | 1.00 |
| 1L37 | A9 | 50s violet black | 1.75 | 2.90 |
| a. | | Imperf | 1.20 | 1.20 |
| 1L38 | A10 | 60s dp red vio | 3.50 | 4.50 |
| a. | | Imperf | 1.75 | 1.75 |
| 1L39 | A14 | 80s br rose red | 1.20 | 7.00 |
| a. | | Imperf | 150.00 | |
| 1L40 | A15 | 100s dull brn red | 1.75 | 3.50 |
| a. | | Imperf | 1.20 | 1.20 |
| 1L41 | A16 | 200s dull lilac | 2.90 | 3.50 |
| a. | | Imperf | 1.50 | 2.40 |
| 1L42 | A17 | 500s car red | 14.00 | 24.00 |
| a. | | Imperf | 9.00 | 9.00 |
| 1L43 | A18 | 1000s lt blue green | 14.00 | 30.00 |
| a. | | Imperf | 7.00 | 7.00 |
| | | Nos. 1L31-1L43 (13) | 55.85 | 93.75 |

First anniv. of independence.
Issued: 3s, 10s-200s, 8/17/46. 5s, 500s, 1000s, 2/1/47.

Worker & Ship — A19

### 1948, Aug. 17 Imperf.
| | | | | |
|---|---|---|---|---|
| 1L44 | A19 | 50s dull blue | 3.50 | 4.50 |
| a. | | Perf 11 | 11.50 | |
| 1L45 | A19 | 100s dull scarlet | 4.00 | 5.00 |
| a. | | Perf 11 | 11.50 | |

Nos. 1L44 and 1L45 were printed on paper with papermaker's watermark. Nos. A45a and A46a were printed on unwatermarked paper.

Flag Over Waves — A20

### 1949, July 20 Imperf.
| | | | | |
|---|---|---|---|---|
| 1L46 | A20 | 100s car rose | 5.25 | 6.75 |
| a. | | Perf 11 | 175.00 | 290.00 |
| 1L47 | A20 | 150s car rose | 7.50 | 17.00 |
| a. | | Perf 11 | 47.50 | 180.00 |

Return of the Indonesian government to Jakarta.
Nos. 1L46-1L47 were printed on paper bearing papermaker's watermark "MADE IN U.S.A." once in each sheet, and a few stamps within each sheet bear portions of the watermark.

Nos. 1L46a, 1L47a overprinted
"Republik Indonesia Serikat 27 Des
'49"

No. A49

### 1949, Dec. 27 Perf. 11
| | | | |
|---|---|---|---|
| 1L48 | A20 | 100s car rose | 17.00 |
| 1L49 | A20 | 150s car rose | 19.00 |

Return of the Indonesian government to Jakarta.

### POSTAGE DUE STAMPS
Netherlands Indies Nos. J29, J32a overprinted "SEGEL, 25 sen, PORTO"

No. AJ1

### 1948 Perf. 12½
| | | | | |
|---|---|---|---|---|
| 1LJ1 | D5 | 25s on 7½c salmon | 24.00 | 35.00 |
| 1LJ2 | D5 | 25s on 15c salmon | 12.50 | 30.00 |

### MILITARY STAMP

M1

### 1949, Aug. Imperf.
Without Gum
| | | | | |
|---|---|---|---|---|
| 1LM1 | M1 | 15r ultramarine | 6,750. | 5,250. |

No. 1LM1 was issued for provisional use at Surakarta, a Dutch stronghold in central Java, occupied by Indonesian forces in August, 1949.

---

### SUMATRA ISSUES

Netherlands Indies Nos. 231, 201
Overprinted "Repoeblik Indonesia,"
New Value and Thick Bar

### 1946
| | | | | |
|---|---|---|---|---|
| 2L1 | A26 | 15s on 5c blue | .75 | 1.00 |
| 2L2 | A17 | 40s on 2c plum | .40 | 1.00 |

Netherlands Indies Nos. 168//201
Overprinted "Repoeblik Indonesia,"
New Value and 5mm Thick Bar

### 1946
| | | | | |
|---|---|---|---|---|
| 2L3 | A17 | 20s on 3½c dk gray | 24.00 | 24.00 |
| 2L4 | A17 | 30s on 1c lilac gray | 12.00 | 12.00 |
| 2L5 | A17 | 40s on 2c plum | 1.00 | 1.50 |
| 2L6 | A17 | 60s on 2½c bister | 175.00 | 175.00 |
| 2L7 | A17 | 80s on 3c yel grn | 12.50 | 12.50 |
| | | Nos. 2L3-2L7 (5) | 224.50 | 225.00 |

Netherlands Indies Nos. 234, 236
Overprinted "Repoeblik Indonesia,"
New Value and Two Bars

### 1946
| | | | | |
|---|---|---|---|---|
| 2L8 | A28 | 50s on 17½c orange | 90.00 | 90.00 |
| 2L9 | A28 | 1r on 10c red orange | 15.00 | 15.00 |

Some examples of Nos. 2L8 and 2L9 bear handstamps previously applied by local authorities during and after the Japanese occupation. Such multiply-overprinted stamps command prices that may be more or less than the values shown, which are for examples without other overprints.

Nos. 2L10-2L84 were issued without gum.

Farmer &
Oxen in Rice
Paddy — A23

Sentry &
Flag — A24

Airplane over
City — A25

### 1946, May 17 Perf. 11½x10
| | | | | |
|---|---|---|---|---|
| 2L10 | A23 | 5s (+25s) yel grn | 1.40 | 2.00 |
| 2L11 | A24 | 15s (+35s) deep red | 3.00 | 3.00 |
| 2L12 | A25 | 40s (+60s) orange | 1.40 | 2.00 |
| | | Nos. 2L10-2L12 (3) | 5.80 | 7.00 |

Nos. 2L10-2L12 were sold at a premium over face value, not indicated on the stamps themselves, to benefit the Freedom Fund ("Fonds Kemerdekkan").

Pres.
Soekarno — A26

### 1946, June 1 Perf. 10¾
| | | | | |
|---|---|---|---|---|
| 2L13 | A26 | 40s (+60s) red | 2.25 | 10.00 |
| 2L14 | A26 | 40s (+60s) deep red | 15.00 | 15.00 |

Nos. 2L13-2L14 were sold at a premium over face value, not indicated on the stamps themselves, to benefit the Freedom Fund ("Fonds Kemerdekkan").

As Nos. 2L10-2L12, in different
colors on thicker paper

Wonokroma
Dam,
Soerabaya
A16

## 1946, Aug. 17      Perf. 11½x10

| | | | | |
|---|---|---|---|---|
| 2L15 | A23 | 5s (+25s) turquoise | .75 | 2.40 |
| 2L16 | A24 | 15s (+35s) purple | .75 | 2.40 |
| 2L17 | A25 | 40s (+60s) deep red | 6.25 | 7.00 |
| 2L18 | A25 | 40s (+60s) bister | 13.00 | 32.50 |
| | | Nos. 2L15-2L18 (4) | 20.75 | 44.30 |

Nos. 2L15-2L18 were sold at a premium over face value, not indicated on the stamps themselves, to benefit the Freedom Fund ("Fonds Kemerdekkan").

Nos. 2L15-2L17, One- or two-bar overprint over "FONDS KEMERDEKAAN"

## 1946      Perf. 11½x10¾

| | | | | |
|---|---|---|---|---|
| 2L19 | A23 | 5s turquoise | 100.00 | 175.00 |
| 2L20 | A24 | 15s purple | 100.00 | 175.00 |
| 2L21 | A25 | 40s deep red | 100.00 | 87.50 |
| | | Nos. 2L19-2L21 (3) | 300.00 | 437.50 |

As Nos. 2L10-2L12, 2L15-18 without "FONDS KEMERDEKAAN" inscription

## 1946-47      Perf. 11¾x10½

### First Issue

| | | | | |
|---|---|---|---|---|
| 2L22 | A23 | 2s red | .75 | 4.00 |
| 2L23 | A23 | 3s green | 1.20 | 7.00 |
| 2L24 | A23 | 5s turquoise | .40 | 7.00 |
| 2L25 | A24 | 15s purple | .40 | 2.40 |
| 2L26 | A25 | 40s brown | .50 | 25.00 |
| | | Nos. 2L22-2L26 (5) | 3.25 | 45.40 |

### Second Issue

| | | | | |
|---|---|---|---|---|
| 2L27 | A23 | 2s chocolate | 4.00 | 5.50 |
| 2L28 | A23 | 3s orange | 4.75 | 4.50 |
| 2L29 | A24 | 15s green | 4.75 | 5.00 |
| 2L30 | A25 | 40s blue | 24.00 | 40.00 |
| | | Nos. 2L27-2L30 (4) | 37.50 | 55.00 |

Japanese Occupation of Sumatra Revenue Stamps Overprinted "prangko," "N.R.I." and new value

A27

## 1947, May 12      Various Rough Perfs

| | | | | |
|---|---|---|---|---|
| 2L31 | A27 | 50s light red | 30.00 | 30.00 |
| 2L32 | A27 | 1f light red | 30.00 | 40.00 |
| 2L33 | A27 | 2f light red | 25.00 | 30.00 |
| 2L34 | A27 | 2.50f light red | 22.50 | 30.00 |
| | | Nos. 2L31-2L34 (4) | 107.50 | 170.00 |

No. 2L13 Surcharged with New Values

## 1947, May 12

| | | | | |
|---|---|---|---|---|
| 2L35 | A26 | 50s on 40s red | 7.75 | 7.75 |
| 2L36 | A26 | 1f on 40s red | 14.50 | 14.50 |
| 2L37 | A26 | 1.50f on 40s red | 9.00 | 9.00 |
| 2L38 | A26 | 2.50f on 40s red | 1.20 | 3.75 |
| 2L39 | A26 | 3.50f on 40s red | 1.75 | 4.00 |
| 2L40 | A26 | 5f on 40s red | 1.20 | 3.75 |
| | | Nos. 2L35-2L40 (6) | 35.40 | 42.75 |

Nos. 2L24, 2L26 Surcharged, with Small Ornament covering Original Value

## 1947

| | | | | |
|---|---|---|---|---|
| 2L41 | A23 | 50s on 5s turq | 9.50 | 9.50 |
| 2L42 | A23 | 1f on 5s turq | 8.25 | 8.25 |
| 2L43 | A23 | 1.50f on 5s turq | 9.75 | 9.75 |
| 2L44 | A25 | 1r on 40s purple | .85 | 4.50 |
| 2L45 | A23 | 2r on 5s turq | 1.00 | 4.50 |
| | | Nos. 2L41-2L45 (5) | 29.35 | 36.50 |

Types of 2L22-2L30, Surcharged in Black or Red (R), with Large Ornament covering Original Value

## 1947

| | | | | |
|---|---|---|---|---|
| 2L46 | A24 | 1s on 15s violet (R) | .80 | 3.00 |
| 2L47 | A23 | 5s on 3s slate blue (R) | .75 | 3.00 |
| 2L48 | A24 | 10s on 15s orange | .85 | 3.00 |
| 2L49 | A23 | 50s on 3s br red | 25.00 | 35.00 |
| | | Nos. 2L46-2L49 (4) | 27.40 | 44.00 |

Nos. 2L48 and 2L49 were not issued without ovpt.

No. 2L15 Surcharged with New Values

## 1947

| | | | | |
|---|---|---|---|---|
| 2L50 | A25 | 30s on 40s dp red | 1.00 | 2.50 |
| 2L51 | A25 | 50s on 40s dp red | 18.50 | 25.00 |
| 2L52 | A25 | 1f on 40s dp red | 3.50 | 2.50 |
| 2L53 | A25 | 1.50f on 40s dp red | 5.00 | 8.50 |
| 2L54 | A25 | 2.50s on 40s dp red | .75 | 2.50 |
| | | Nos. 2L50-2L54 (5) | 28.75 | 41.00 |

Nos. 2L23-2L26, Surcharged in Black or Red, with Rectangle covering Original Value, New Value 2.8mm High

## 1948

| | | | | |
|---|---|---|---|---|
| 2L55 | A23 | .50f on 5s turq. | 900.00 | 850.00 |
| 2L56 | A24 | .50f on 15s purple | 900.00 | 850.00 |
| 2L57 | A23 | 1f on 5s turq. | 175.00 | 175.00 |
| 2L58 | A24 | 1f on 15s purple | 350.00 | 350.00 |
| 2L59 | A25 | 1f on 40s brown | 575.00 | |
| 2L60 | A23 | 2.50f on 5s turq. | 900.00 | 850.00 |
| 2L61 | A24 | 2.50f on 15s purple | 575.00 | 475.00 |
| 2L62 | A24 | 5f on 15s purple | 900.00 | 900.00 |
| 2L63 | A25 | 5f on 40s brown | 400.00 | 400.00 |
| 2L64 | A23 | 50s on 5s turq. | 1,000. | 1,000. |
| 2L65 | A24 | 50s on 15s purple | 400.00 | 450.00 |
| | | Nos. 2L55-2L65 (11) | 7,075. | 6,300. |

### New Currency
Values 3.2mm High

## 1949

| | | | | |
|---|---|---|---|---|
| 2L66 | A23 | 2.50r on 3s green | 25.00 | 30.00 |
| a. | | Red overprint | 25.00 | 30.00 |
| 2L67 | A24 | 5r on 15s purple | 10.00 | 30.00 |
| a. | | Red overprint | 10.00 | 30.00 |
| 2L68 | A23 | 10r on 3s green | 110.00 | 110.00 |
| a. | | Red overprint | 110.00 | 110.00 |
| | | Nos. 2L66-2L68 (3) | 145.00 | 170.00 |

Emergency provisional issue for Aceh Province.

Nos. 2L15, 2L22, 2L23, 2L25 Surcharged in Black or Red, with Rectangle covering Original Value, New Value 4.5mm High

## 1949

| | | | | |
|---|---|---|---|---|
| 2L69 | A23 | 2r on 3s green | 42.50 | 80.00 |
| a. | | Red overprint | 42.50 | 80.00 |
| 2L70 | A23 | 2.50r on 3s green | 24.00 | 60.00 |
| a. | | Red overprint | 24.00 | 60.00 |
| 2L71 | A24 | 5r on 15s purple | 10.00 | 16.00 |
| a. | | Red overprint | 10.00 | 16.00 |
| 2L72 | A23 | 10r on 3s green | 18.00 | 40.00 |
| a. | | Red overprint | 18.00 | 40.00 |
| 2L73 | A23 | 20r on 2s red | 300.00 | 600.00 |
| a. | | Red overprint | 350.00 | 600.00 |
| 2L74 | A24 | 50r on 15s purple | 400.00 | 575.00 |
| a. | | Red overprint | 400.00 | 575.00 |
| 2L75 | A24 | 100r on 15s purple | 150.00 | 150.00 |
| a. | | Red overprint | 150.00 | 150.00 |
| 2L76 | A25 | 200r on 40s brown | 175.00 | 175.00 |
| a. | | Red overprint | 175.00 | 175.00 |
| | | Nos. 2L69-2L76 (8) | 1,119. | 1,696. |

Nos. 2L22, 2L25, 2L26 Surcharged in Black, with Rectangle covering Original Value, New Value 7.2mm High

## 1949

| | | | | |
|---|---|---|---|---|
| 2L77 | A24 | 10s on 15s purple | 18.00 | 18.00 |
| 2L78 | A24 | 20s on 15s purple | 18.00 | 18.00 |
| 2L79 | A24 | 30s on 15s purple | 18.00 | 8.50 |
| 2L80 | A23 | 1r on 2s red | 60.00 | 125.00 |
| 2L81 | A24 | 1.50f on 15s purple | | 500.00 |
| 2L82 | A24 | 2.50f on 15s purple | 22.50 | 50.00 |
| 2L83 | A25 | 5r on 40s brown | 290.00 | 210.00 |
| | | Nos. 2L77-2L83 (7) | 426.50 | 929.50 |

Nos. 1L46-1L47 Surcharged with New Values

## 1949

| | | | | |
|---|---|---|---|---|
| 2L84 | A20 | 15r on 100s car rose | 27.50 | 70.00 |
| 2L85 | A20 | 15r on 150s car rose | 27.50 | 70.00 |

## AIR POST STAMPS

Nos. 66, 75 overprinted "POS UDARA" and New Values

## 1947

| | | | | |
|---|---|---|---|---|
| 2LC1 | A26 | 10r on 40s br red | 3.00 | 4.50 |
| 2LC2 | A26 | 20r on 5s turq | 1.80 | 4.50 |

### REPUBLIC OF INDONESIA

Nos. 1-119, C1-C61, CE1-CE4, CO1-CO16, E1-E1G, J1-J39 and O1-O24 were authorized by the Indonesia PTT and were produced in Vienna and Philadelphia. Because most were printed by the Austrian State Printing Office (Staatsdruckerei), they are usually described as the "Vienna" issues. The first issue was released in Dec. 1948, but supplies did not reach republican-held areas of Java and Sumatra until mid-Jan., 1949. Through 1949, small supplies of these issues were sent to some 20 post offices in Java and Sumatra, where they were used both for local mail and for mail to foreign destinations, which was carried through the Dutch blockade by overseas (largely Indian) air carriers.

Following independence, the Vienna issues continued to be valid for postage for several years. While most covers on the market are philatelic in nature, commercial covers dated 1949-53 exist.

The Vienna issues were produced and heavily marketed by a U.S. stamp dealer. Proofs, deluxe sheetlets of one, and various overprints exist for these issues, as well as several unissued sets.

Values for the Vienna Issues are for mint never hinged stamps. Hinged examples are generally offered at 50-75% of these values. Used stamps are scarce, though generally not rare, and pricing information on values for used stamps is not presently available.

Map, Indonesian Archipelago A28

Farmer — A29

Red Cross Airplane A30

Balinese Dancer — A31

Military Officer, Flag of Republic A32

Designs: 1s, Map of Indonesian Archipelago. 2s, Republican sentry and Toba Lake, Sumatra. 2½, Military review, Gen. Soedirmari. 3s, Farmer working field with pitchfork. 3½s, Sultan Sjahrir and Thomas Jefferson. 4s, Buffalo Canyon, Sumatra. 5s, Policemen on motorcycles, Sastroamidjojo.

7½s, Red Cross nurse with wounded soldier. 10s, Dr. Maramis, Minister of Finance, and Abraham Hamilton. 15s, Construction of Great Postal Road, Java. 17½s, Hadji Agoes Salim, philosopher, and Benjamin Franklin. 20s, Djanger dancer, Bali. 35s, Planting rice. 40s, Vice Pres. Mohammed Hatta and Abraham Lincoln. 50s, Mountain, Sumatra. 60s, Rice fields, Java. 80s, Boy holding pineapple. 1r, Pres. Soekarno and George Washington. 2r, Mosque, Medan, Sumatra. 2½r, Fish ponds, Tjipanas. 5r, Officer presenting flag. 10r, Vice Pres. Hatta. 25r, Pres. Soekarno.

*Perf. 14x13¾, 13¼x14 (#6), 13½x14¼ (#12, 14-16, 19, 20), 14¼x13½ (#13, 17, 17, 21), 12½ (#22-24)*

**Photo, Engr. (#22-24)**

| 1948, Dec. 15 | | | Unwmk. | |
|---|---|---|---|---|
| 1 | A28 | 1s dk turq grn & brn | .45 | — |
| 2 | A28 | 2s dp brn & dp blue | .20 | — |
| 3 | A28 | 2½s dk brn & org red | .35 | — |
| 4 | A29 | 3s dk lil & dp red brn | .20 | — |
| 5 | A28 | 3½s dk bl vio & br grn | .20 | — |
| 6 | A29 | 4s dk bl vio & dp ol grn | .30 | — |
| 7 | A28 | 5s turq & dull blue | .20 | — |
| 8 | A28 | 7½s dp brn & dk lil | .35 | — |
| 9 | A28 | 10s dp blue & brn rose | .50 | — |
| 10 | A28 | 15s brown & dk grn | .60 | — |
| 11 | A28 | 17½s ultra & org brn | .30 | — |
| 12 | A30 | 20s Prus grn & dp bis brn | .45 | — |
| 13 | A31 | 30s dk brn & dull vio | .30 | — |
| 14 | A30 | 35s dk lilac & brn | .30 | — |
| 15 | A30 | 40s dk brn & blue | .30 | — |
| 16 | A30 | 50s dk brn & turq | .30 | — |
| 17 | A31 | 60s dk brn & lt red brn | .50 | — |
| 18 | A31 | 80s dk lilac & slate | .45 | — |
| 19 | A30 | 1r br blue & pur brn | .35 | — |
| 20 | A30 | 2r dk brn & dk grn | .55 | — |
| 21 | A31 | 2½r dk lilac & blue | .65 | — |
| 22 | A32 | 5r yel brn & black | 3.50 | — |
| 23 | A32 | 10r emerald & black | 5.00 | — |
| 24 | A32 | 25r rose red & blk | 7.00 | — |
| | | *Nos. 1-24 (24)* | 23.30 | |

See Nos. C1-C13.
For overprints, see Nos. 70-90, O1-O6.

A33

Designs: 10s, 25s, Map, ships. 15s, 60s, Dockworkers loading ship, vert. 1r, Ships. Illustration reduced.

| 1949, Aug. 17 | | Photo. | Perf. 12½ | |
|---|---|---|---|---|
| 25 | A33 | 10s gray & green | .75 | — |
| 26 | A33 | 15s gray & maroon | .75 | — |
| 27 | A33 | 25s gray & blue | .75 | — |
| 28 | A33 | 60s maroon & gray | 2.75 | — |
| 29 | A33 | 1r org & dull blue | 7.50 | — |
| | | *Nos. 25-29 (5)* | 12.50 | |

Failure of Dutch blockade.
See Nos. C14-C18.

Soekarno Decorating Soldier — A35

Planting Rice — A36

Boy Holding Pineapple — A37

Military Officer, Flag of Republic A38

Designs: 1s, Republican sentry and Toba Lake, Sumatra. 2s, Soekarno decorating soldier. 2½s, Woman weaving batik. 3s, Metalcraft worker. 3½s, Construction of Great Postal Road, Java. 4s, Farmer working field with pitchfork. 5s, Javanese Wajang Wong dancer. 7½s, Planting rice on the sawah. 10s, Red Cross nurse with wounded soldier. 15s, Buffalo Canyon, Sumatra. 17½s, Plowing with oxen. 20s, Planting rice. 30s, Mountain, Sumatra. 35s, Boy holding pineapple. 40s, Fish ponds, Tjipanas. 50s, Djanger dancer, Bali. 60s, Javanese Serimpi court dancer. 80s, Mosque, Medan, Sumatra. 1r, Overcoming illiteracy. 2r, Idol. 2½r, Map of Indonesian Archipelago. 5r, Officer presenting flag. 10r, Vice Pres. Mohammed Hatta. 25r, Pres. Soekarno.

Country name inscription has been changed from "Repoeblik" to "Republik," to make spelling more American and less Dutch. This spelling change also officially changed Pres. Soekarno's name to Sukarno.

*Perf. 14x13¾, 13¾x14 (#31-33, 35, 36, 39), 13½x14¼ (#41, 42, 47, 50), 14¼x13½ (#43-46), 12½ (#51-53)*

**Photo, Engr. (#51-53)**

| 1949, Aug. 17 | | | | |
|---|---|---|---|---|
| 30 | A34 | 1s dp brn & dp blue | .30 | — |
| 31 | A35 | 2s dk red vio & dp grn | .40 | — |
| 32 | A35 | 2½s dk brn & br scarlet | .35 | — |
| 33 | A35 | 3s dp turq & org ver | .45 | — |
| 34 | A34 | 3½s dp brn & dp grn | .40 | — |
| 35 | A35 | 4s dull vio & dk yel brn | .50 | — |
| 36 | A34 | 5s turq & dull blue | .35 | — |
| 37 | A34 | 7½s dp brn & dk lil | .40 | — |
| 38 | A34 | 10s dk brn & dp vio | .50 | — |
| 39 | A35 | 15s dk vio & dp dull grn | .65 | — |
| 40 | A34 | 17½s dk brn & red org | .55 | — |
| 41 | A36 | 20s dull vio & dp brn | .25 | — |
| 42 | A36 | 30s dp brn & dk blue vio | .45 | — |
| 43 | A37 | 35s sl vio & dk yel brn | .25 | — |
| 44 | A37 | 40s dull vio & dk yel brn | .45 | — |
| 45 | A37 | 50s dk brn & Prus grn | .40 | — |
| 46 | A37 | 60s br blue & dk yel brn | .55 | — |
| 47 | A36 | 80s dull vio & dull bl | .50 | — |
| 48 | A36 | 1r dp blue & dp choc | .50 | — |
| 49 | A37 | 2r dp brn & org ver | .30 | — |
| 50 | A36 | 2½r dp brn & br blue | 1.00 | — |
| 51 | A38 | 5r red vio & black | 6.50 | — |
| 52 | A38 | 10r green & black | 4.25 | — |
| 53 | A38 | 25r red & blk | 6.50 | — |
| | | *Nos. 30-53 (24)* | 26.75 | |

For overprints, see Nos. 89-109, O7-O12.

A39

A40

Designs: 10s, 25s, Map, ships. 15s, 60s, Dockworkers loading ship, vert. 1r, Ships. Illustrations reduced.

| 1948, Dec. 15 | | Photo. | Perf. 14½ | |
|---|---|---|---|---|
| 54 | A39 | 10s gray & red | 1.25 | — |
| 55 | A39 | 15s gray & dp blue | 1.25 | — |
| 56 | A39 | 25s gray & red brn | 1.10 | — |
| 57 | A39 | 60s gray & maroon | 2.00 | — |
| 58 | A39 | 1r gray & maroon | 4.50 | — |
| | | *Nos. 54-58 (5)* | 10.10 | |

**Souvenir Sheets**

| 59 | A40 | 10s, 15s, 25s, 60s | 50.00 | — |
| a. | | Imperf | 400.00 | |
| 60 | A40 | 30s, 50s, 1r, 2½r | 25.00 | — |
| a. | | Imperf | 175.00 | |
| b. | A39 | 2½r gray & maroon | | |
| | | As "b," imperf | | |
| 61 | A40 | 1r, 4½r | 40.00 | — |
| a. | | Imperf | 75.00 | |
| b. | A39 | 4½r maroon | | |
| c. | | As "b," imperf | | |

Failure of Dutch blockade, second issue.
The stamps contained in No. 60 and the 4½r stamp contained in No. 61 are air post stamps and are inscribed "POS UDARA."
See Nos. C32-C36.
For overprints, see Nos. 112-119.

Map, UPU Emblem & *Banteng* (Nationalist Symbol) — A41

| 1949, Dec. 1 | | Photo. | Wmk. 404 | Perf. 14 | |
|---|---|---|---|---|---|
| 62 | A41 | 10s multicolored | | .55 | — |
| a. | | Imperf | | .60 | |
| 63 | A41 | 20s multicolored | | .55 | — |
| a. | | Imperf | | .60 | |
| 64 | A41 | 50s multicolored | | .60 | — |
| a. | | Imperf | | .70 | |
| 65 | A41 | 1r multicolored | | .60 | — |
| a. | | Imperf | | .75 | |
| b. | | Souvenir Sheet of 4, #62-65 | | 22.50 | — |
| c. | | As "b," imperf | | 25.00 | |
| | | *Nos. 62-65 (4)* | | 2.30 | |

**Unwatermarked**

| 66 | A41 | 10s multicolored | .45 | — |
| a. | | Imperf | .45 | |
| 67 | A41 | 20s multicolored | .45 | — |
| a. | | Imperf | .45 | |
| 68 | A41 | 50s multicolored | .45 | — |
| a. | | Imperf | .45 | |
| 69 | A41 | 1r multicolored | .45 | — |
| a. | | Imperf | .45 | |
| | | *Nos. 66-69 (4)* | 1.80 | |

Nos. 64, 65, 68 and 69 are air post stamps and are inscribed "POS UDARA."
Souvenir sheets of 4, as No. 65c, without watermark, are proofs.
Most varieties of Nos. 1-69 exist overprinted "RIS," "RIS Merdeka" and "RIS Djakarta." These were not issued in Indonesia.

**Liberation of Jakarta**

**Nos. 1-61 overprinted "Merdeka Djojakarta 6 Djuli 1949"**

70ovpt

| 1949, Dec. 7 | | | | |
|---|---|---|---|---|
| 70 | A28 | 1s dk turq grn & brn | .25 | — |
| 71 | A28 | 2s dp brn & dp blue | .90 | — |
| 72 | A28 | 2½s dk brn & org red | .25 | — |
| 73 | A29 | 3s dk lil & dp red | .45 | — |
| 74 | A28 | 3½s dk bl vio & br grn | .25 | — |
| 75 | A29 | 4s dk bl vio & dp ol grn | .55 | — |
| 76 | A28 | 5s turq & dull blue | .25 | — |
| 77 | A28 | 7½s dp brn & dk lil | .45 | — |
| 78 | A28 | 10s dp blue & brn rose | .25 | — |
| 79 | A28 | 15s brown & dk grn | 1.25 | — |
| 80 | A28 | 17½s ultra & org brn | 2.00 | — |
| 81 | A30 | 20s Prus grn & dp bis brn | 1.00 | — |
| 82 | A31 | 30s dk brn & dull vio | 3.50 | — |
| 83 | A30 | 35s dk lilac & brn | 5.75 | — |
| 84 | A30 | 40s dk brn & blue | .85 | — |
| 85 | A30 | 50s dk brn & turq | 4.50 | — |
| 86 | A31 | 60s dk brn & lt red brn | 6.75 | — |
| 87 | A31 | 80s dk lilac & slate | 1.75 | — |
| 88 | A30 | 1r br blue & pur brn | 3.50 | — |
| 89 | A30 | 2r dk brn & dk grn | 1.00 | — |
| 90 | A31 | 2½r dk lilac & blue | 7.50 | — |
| | | *Nos. 70-90 (21)* | 42.95 | |

Nos. 30-50 overprinted

93ovpt

| 91 | A34 | 1s dp brn & dp blue | .20 | — |
| 92 | A35 | 2s dk red vio & dp grn | 1.25 | — |
| 93 | A35 | 2½s dk brn & br scarlet | .20 | — |
| 94 | A35 | 3s dp turq & org ver | .20 | — |
| 95 | A34 | 3½s dp brn & dp grn | .20 | — |
| 96 | A35 | 4s dull vio & dk yel brn | .25 | — |
| 97 | A35 | 5s turq & dull blue | .50 | — |
| 98 | A34 | 7½s dp brn & dk lil | .60 | — |
| 99 | A34 | 10s dk brn & dp vio | .75 | — |
| 100 | A35 | 15s dk vio & dp dull grn | 1.25 | — |
| 101 | A34 | 17½s dk brn & red org | 1.25 | — |
| 102 | A36 | 20s dull vio & dp brn | 3.25 | — |
| 103 | A36 | 30s dp brn & dk blue vio | 2.75 | — |
| 104 | A37 | 35s sl vio & dk yel brn | 2.75 | — |
| 105 | A37 | 40s dull vio & dk yel brn | 2.75 | — |
| 106 | A37 | 50s dk brn & Prus grn | 5.00 | — |
| 107 | A37 | 60s br blue & dk yel brn | 5.00 | — |
| 108 | A36 | 80s dull vio & dull bl | 5.00 | — |
| 109 | A36 | 1r dp blue & dp choc | 2.75 | — |
| 110 | A37 | 2r dp brn & org ver | 2.75 | — |
| 111 | A36 | 2½r dp brn & br blue | 6.00 | — |
| | | *Nos. 91-111 (21)* | 44.65 | |

Nos. 54-61 overprinted

| 112 | A39 | 10s gray & red | .40 | — |
| 113 | A39 | 15s gray & dp blue | .40 | — |

| | | | | |
|---|---|---|---|---|
| 114 | A39 | 25s gray & red brn | 1.25 | — |
| 115 | A39 | 60s gray & maroon | 1.25 | — |
| 116 | A39 | 1r gray & maroon | 2.40 | — |
| | | Nos. 54-58 (5) | 10.10 | |

### Souvenir Sheets

| | | | | |
|---|---|---|---|---|
| 117 | A40 | 10s, 15s, 25s, 60s | 750.00 | — |
| a. | | Imperf | 2,250. | |
| 118 | A40 | 30s, 50s, 1r, 2½r | 50.00 | — |
| a. | | Imperf | 150.00 | |
| b. | A39 | 2½r gray & maroon | | — |
| c. | | As "b," imperf | | — |
| 119 | A40 | 1r, 4½r | 40.00 | — |
| a. | | Imperf | 55.00 | |
| b. | A39 | 4½r maroon | | — |
| c. | | As "b," imperf | | — |

The stamps contained in No. 118 and the 4½r stamp contained in No. 119 are air post stamps and are inscribed "POS UDARA."

### United States of Indonesia

Mountain, Palms and Flag of Republic — A49

**Perf. 12½x12**

**1950, Jan. 17**   **Photo.**   **Unwmk.**
**Size: 20½x26mm**

| | | | | |
|---|---|---|---|---|
| 333 | A49 | 15s red | 1.00 | .25 |

Exists imperf, without gum. Value $70.

**1950, June**   **Perf. 11½**
**Size: 18x23mm**

| | | | | |
|---|---|---|---|---|
| 334 | A49 | 15s red | 6.25 | 2.00 |

Exists imperf, without gum. Value $50.

Netherlands Indies
Nos. 307-315
Overprinted in Black

**1950**     **Perf. 11½, 12½**

| | | | | |
|---|---|---|---|---|
| 335 | A42 | 1s gray | 1.00 | .75 |
| 336 | A42 | 2s claret | 1.25 | 3.50 |
| a. | | Perf 11½ | 1.60 | 2.10 |
| 337 | A42 | 2½s olive brown | 1.00 | .75 |
| a. | | Perf 12½ | 1.25 | .70 |
| 338 | A42 | 3s rose pink | 1.00 | .45 |
| a. | | Perf 12½ | 1.00 | .60 |
| 339 | A42 | 4s green | 1.00 | .75 |
| a. | | Perf 12½ | 1.60 | 1.00 |
| 340 | A42 | 5s blue | .50 | .20 |
| 341 | A42 | 7½s dark green | .50 | .50 |
| 342 | A42 | 10s violet | 1.00 | .75 |
| a. | | Perf 12½ | 1.75 | 1.75 |
| 343 | A42 | 12½s bright red | .75 | .30 |

Netherlands Indies Nos. 317-330
Overprinted in Black

**Perf. 11½, 12½**

| | | | | |
|---|---|---|---|---|
| 345 | A43 | 20s gray black | 30.00 | 27.50 |
| 346 | A43 | 25s ultra | 1.00 | .75 |
| a. | | Perf 12½ | 1.75 | .75 |
| 347 | A44 | 30s bright red | 10.00 | 20.00 |
| a. | | Perf 12½ | 50.00 | 70.00 |
| 348 | A44 | 40s gray green | 1.00 | .45 |
| a. | | Perf 12½ | 1.00 | .45 |
| 349 | A45 | 45s claret | 1.75 | .50 |
| 350 | A45 | 50s orange brown | 1.75 | .50 |
| 351 | A45 | 60s brown | 8.50 | 13.00 |
| a. | | Perf 12½ | — | 35.00 |
| 352 | A45 | 80s scarlet | 3.25 | 1.00 |
| a. | | Perf 12½ | 3.75 | 1.25 |

Perf. 11½, 20s, 45s, 50s. Others, both perfs.

### Overprint 12mm High

**Perf. 12½**

| | | | | |
|---|---|---|---|---|
| 353 | A46 | 1r purple | 2.75 | .75 |
| 354 | A46 | 2r olive green | 325.00 | 160.00 |
| 355 | A46 | 3r red violet | 140.00 | 55.00 |
| 356 | A46 | 5r dark brown | 50.00 | 24.00 |
| 357 | A46 | 10r gray | 85.00 | 35.00 |
| 358 | A46 | 25r orange brown | 30.00 | 15.00 |
| | | Nos. 335-358 (23) | 698.00 | 361.40 |
| | | Set, hinged | 325.00 | |

For overprints see Riau Archipelago #17-22.

---

### Republic of Indonesia

Arms of the Republic A50     Doves in Flight A51

**Perf. 12½x12**

**1950, Aug. 17**   **Photo.**   **Unwmk.**

| | | | | |
|---|---|---|---|---|
| 359 | A50 | 15s red | 2.50 | .50 |
| 360 | A50 | 25s dull green | 3.50 | 2.00 |
| 361 | A50 | 1r sepia | 10.00 | 2.50 |
| | | Nos. 359-361 (3) | 16.00 | 5.00 |

5th anniv. of Indonesia's proclamation of independence.

**1951, Oct. 24**   **Engr.**   **Perf. 12**

| | | | | |
|---|---|---|---|---|
| 362 | A51 | 7½s blue green | 5.75 | .70 |
| 363 | A51 | 10s violet | 1.25 | .20 |
| 364 | A51 | 20s red | 1.25 | .20 |
| 365 | A51 | 30s carmine rose | 1.25 | .50 |
| 366 | A51 | 35s ultra | 1.25 | .90 |
| 367 | A51 | 1r sepia | 20.00 | 2.25 |
| | | Nos. 362-367 (6) | 30.75 | 4.75 |

6th anniv. of the UN and the 1st anniv. of the Republic of Indonesia as a member.

A52     Post Office — A53

Mythological Hero — A54     Pres. Sukarno — A55

**1951-53**    **Photo.**    **Perf. 12½**

| | | | | |
|---|---|---|---|---|
| 368 | A52 | 1s gray | .30 | .50 |
| 369 | A52 | 2s plum | .30 | .50 |
| 370 | A52 | 2½s brown | 5.50 | .75 |
| 371 | A52 | 5s car rose | .40 | .20 |
| 372 | A52 | 7½s green | .40 | .60 |
| 373 | A52 | 10s blue | 1.60 | .20 |
| a. | | Perf 11½ | 8.50 | 8.50 |
| 374 | A52 | 15s purple | 1.10 | .40 |
| 375 | A52 | 20s rose red | .50 | .40 |
| 376 | A52 | 25s deep green | .30 | .20 |
| 377 | A53 | 30s red orange | .20 | .20 |
| 378 | A53 | 35s purple | .50 | .20 |
| 379 | A53 | 40s dull green | .20 | .20 |
| 380 | A53 | 45s deep claret | .20 | .40 |
| 381 | A53 | 50s brown | 5.75 | .20 |
| 382 | A54 | 60s dark brown | .20 | .20 |
| 383 | A54 | 70s gray | .20 | .20 |
| 384 | A54 | 75s ultra | .20 | .20 |
| 385 | A54 | 80s claret | .20 | .20 |
| 386 | A54 | 90s gray green | .20 | .20 |
| | | Nos. 368-386 (19) | 18.25 | 5.95 |

**Perf. 12½x12**

| | | | | |
|---|---|---|---|---|
| 387 | A55 | 1r purple | .20 | .20 |
| 388 | A55 | 1.25r dp orange | 1.40 | .20 |
| 389 | A55 | 1.50r brown | .20 | .20 |
| 390 | A55 | 2r green | .20 | .20 |
| 391 | A55 | 2.50r rose brown | .20 | .20 |
| 392 | A55 | 3r blue | .20 | .20 |
| 392A | A55 | 4r apple green | .20 | .20 |
| 393 | A55 | 5r brown | .20 | .20 |
| 394 | A55 | 6r rose lilac | .20 | .20 |
| 395 | A55 | 10r slate | .20 | .20 |
| 396 | A55 | 15r yellow | .20 | .20 |
| 397 | A55 | 20r sepia | .20 | .20 |
| 398 | A55 | 25r scarlet | .60 | .20 |
| 399 | A55 | 40r yellow green | .60 | 1.00 |
| 400 | A55 | 50r violet | .95 | 1.00 |
| | | Nos. 387-400 (15) | 5.75 | 4.60 |

Nos. 368-376, 387, 390, 392, 393, 395, 398 were issued in 1951; Nos. 377-386, 388-389, 391, 392A, 394, 396-397, 399-400 in 1953.
Values are for the later Djakarta printings which have thicker numerals and a darker over-all impression. Earlier printings by Joh. Enschede and Sons, Haarlem, Netherlands, sell for more.
For surcharge see No. B68. For overprints see Riau Archipelago Nos. 1-16, 32-40.

---

Melati Flowers — A56     Crowd Releasing Doves — A57

**1953, Dec. 22**   **Perf. 12½**

| | | | | |
|---|---|---|---|---|
| 401 | A56 | 50s blue green | 10.50 | .50 |

25th anniv. of the formation of the Indonesian Women's Congress.

**1955, Apr. 18**   **Perf. 13x12½**

| | | | | |
|---|---|---|---|---|
| 402 | A57 | 15s gray | .90 | .20 |
| 403 | A57 | 35s brown | .90 | .20 |
| 404 | A57 | 50s deep magenta | 1.90 | .20 |
| 405 | A57 | 75s blue green | .75 | .20 |
| | | Nos. 402-405 (4) | 4.45 | .80 |

Asian-African Conf., Bandung, April 18-24.

Proclamation of Independence A58

**1955, Aug. 17**   **Photo.**   **Perf. 12½**

| | | | | |
|---|---|---|---|---|
| 406 | A58 | 15s green | .75 | 1.00 |
| 407 | A58 | 35s ultra | 1.25 | 1.00 |
| 408 | A58 | 50s brown | 8.00 | .90 |
| 409 | A58 | 75s magenta | 1.25 | .60 |
| | | Nos. 406-409 (4) | 11.25 | 3.50 |

Ten years of independence.

Voters — A59

**1955, Sept. 29**   **Perf. 12**
**Without gum**

| | | | | |
|---|---|---|---|---|
| 410 | A59 | 15s rose violet | .60 | .60 |
| 411 | A59 | 35s green | .60 | .60 |
| 412 | A59 | 50s carmine rose | 1.90 | .40 |
| 413 | A59 | 75s lt ultra | .85 | .40 |
| | | Nos. 410-413 (4) | 3.95 | 2.00 |

First free elections in Indonesia.

Mas Soeharto Postmaster General A60     Helmet, Wreath and Monument A61

**1955, Sept. 27**   **Perf. 12½**

| | | | | |
|---|---|---|---|---|
| 414 | A60 | 15s brown | 1.25 | .45 |
| 415 | A60 | 35s dark carmine | 1.25 | .45 |
| 416 | A60 | 50s ultra | 6.75 | 2.25 |
| 417 | A60 | 75s dull green | 1.25 | .35 |
| | | Nos. 414-417 (4) | 10.50 | 3.50 |

Issued to mark 10 years of Indonesia's Postal, Telegraph and Telephone system.

**1955, Nov. 10**

| | | | | |
|---|---|---|---|---|
| 418 | A61 | 25s bluish green | 1.25 | .60 |
| 419 | A61 | 50s ultra | 1.25 | .35 |
| 420 | A61 | 1r dk car rose | 10.00 | .40 |
| | | Nos. 418-420 (3) | 12.50 | 1.35 |

Issued in honor of the soldiers killed in the war of liberation from the Netherlands.

---

Torch, Book and Map A62     Lesser Malay Chevrotain A63

**1956, May 26**   **Photo.**

| | | | | |
|---|---|---|---|---|
| 421 | A62 | 25s ultra | 1.40 | .75 |
| 422 | A62 | 50s carmine rose | 7.00 | .40 |
| 423 | A62 | 1r dark green | 1.60 | .40 |
| | | Nos. 421-423 (3) | 10.00 | 1.55 |

Asia-Africa Student Conf., Bandung, May, 1956.

**1956**    **Unwmk.**    **Perf. 12½x13½**

Animals: 5s, 10s, Lesser Malay chevrotain. 20s, 25s, Otter. 35s, Malayan pangolin. 50s, Banteng. 75s, Asiatic two-horned rhinoceros.

| | | | | |
|---|---|---|---|---|
| 424 | A63 | 5s deep ultra | .25 | .20 |
| 425 | A63 | 10s yellow brown | .25 | .20 |
| 426 | A63 | 15s rose violet | .40 | .20 |
| 427 | A63 | 20s dull green | .40 | .20 |
| 428 | A63 | 25s deep claret | .40 | .20 |
| 429 | A63 | 35s brt violet blue | .40 | .20 |
| 430 | A63 | 50s brown | .75 | .20 |
| 431 | A63 | 75s dark brown | .40 | .20 |
| | | Nos. 424-431 (8) | 3.25 | 1.60 |

See Nos. 450-456. For overprints see Riau Archipelago Nos. 23-31.

Dancing Girl and Gate — A64     Telegraph Key — A65

**1956, Oct. 7**   **Perf. 12½x12**

| | | | | |
|---|---|---|---|---|
| 432 | A64 | 15s slate green | 1.25 | .50 |
| 433 | A64 | 35s brown violet | 1.25 | .50 |
| 434 | A64 | 50s blue black | 2.50 | 2.50 |
| 435 | A64 | 75s deep claret | 2.50 | .80 |
| | | Nos. 432-435 (4) | 7.50 | 4.30 |

Founding of the city of Jogjakarta, 200th anniv.

**1957, May 10**   **Unwmk.**

| | | | | |
|---|---|---|---|---|
| 436 | A65 | 10s lt crimson | 2.10 | .50 |
| 437 | A65 | 15s brt blue | .50 | .45 |
| 438 | A65 | 25s gray | .50 | .20 |
| 439 | A65 | 50s brown red | .65 | .20 |
| 440 | A65 | 75s lt blue green | .80 | .20 |
| | | Nos. 436-440 (5) | 4.55 | 1.55 |

Indonesian telegraph system centenary.

Thrift Symbolism A66     Douglas DC-3 A67

Design: 15s, 1r, People and hands holding wreath of rice and cotton.

**1957, July 12**   **Photo.**   **Perf. 12½**

| | | | | |
|---|---|---|---|---|
| 441 | A66 | 10s blue | .50 | .45 |
| 442 | A66 | 15s rose carmine | .65 | .45 |
| 443 | A66 | 50s green | 1.25 | .95 |
| 444 | A66 | 1r brt violet | 1.25 | .50 |
| | | Nos. 441-444 (4) | 3.65 | 2.35 |

Cooperation Day, July 12.

**1958, Apr. 9**   **Perf. 12½x12**

Aircraft: 15s, Helicopter. 30s, Miles Magister. 50s, Two-motor plane of Indonesian Airways. 75s, De Havilland Vampire.

| | | | | |
|---|---|---|---|---|
| 445 | A67 | 10s reddish brown | .45 | .20 |
| 446 | A67 | 15s blue | .45 | .20 |
| 447 | A67 | 35s orange | .45 | .20 |

**448** A67 50s bright green .45 .20
**449** A67 75s gray .45 .20
Nos. 445-449 (5) 2.25 1.00

Issued for National Aviation Day, April 9.

### Animal Type of 1956

Animals: 30s, Otter. 40s, 45s, Malayan pangolin. 60s, 70s, Banteng. 80s, 90s, Asiatic two-horned rhinoceros.

**1958** **Photo.** *Perf. 12½x13½*
**450** A63 30s orange .25 .20
**451** A63 40s brt yellow grn .30 .20
**452** A63 45s rose lilac .30 .20
**453** A63 60s dark blue .45 .20
**454** A63 70s orange ver .45 .20
**455** A63 80s red .60 .20
**456** A63 90s yellow green .60 .20
Nos. 450-456 (7) 2.95 1.40

Thomas Cup A68

**1958, Aug. 15** *Perf. 13½x13*
**457** A68 25s rose carmine .20 .20
**458** A68 50s orange .25 .20
**459** A68 1r brown .25 .20
Nos. 457-459 (3) .70 .60

Indonesia's victory in the 1958 Thomas Cup World Badminton Championship.

Satellite Circling Globe — A69

**1958, Oct. 15** **Litho.** *Perf. 12½x12*
**460** A69 10s dk grn, pink & lt bl .90 .20
**461** A69 15s vio, gray & pale bluish grn .30 .20
**462** A69 35s brown, blue & pink .30 .20
**463** A69 50s bl, redsh brn & gray .30 .20
**464** A69 75s black, vio & buff .30 .20
Nos. 460-464 (5) 2.10 1.00

International Geophysical Year, 1957-58.

Bicyclist and Map A70

**1958, Nov. 15** **Photo.** *Perf. 13½x13*
**465** A70 25s bright blue .30 .20
**466** A70 50s brown carmine .65 .20
**467** A70 1r gray .30 .20
Nos. 465-467 (3) 1.25 .60

Bicycle Tour of Java, Aug. 15-30.

Man Looking into Light A71

Wild Boar (Babirusa) A72

Designs: 15s, Hands and flame. 35s, Woman holding candle. 50s, Family hailing torch. 75s, Torch and "10."

**1958, Dec. 10** *Perf. 12½x12*
**468** A71 10s gray brown .20 .20
**469** A71 15s dull red brn .20 .20
**470** A71 35s ultra .20 .20
**471** A71 50s pale brown .25 .20
**472** A71 75s lt blue grn .30 .20
Nos. 468-472 (5) 1.15 1.00

10th anniv. of the signing of the Universal Declaration of Human Rights.

---

**1959, June 1** **Photo.** *Perf. 12*
Animals: 15s, Anoa (smallest buffalo). 20s, Orangutan. 50s, Javan rhinoceros. 75s, Komodo dragon (lizard). 1r, Malayan tapir.
**473** A72 10s olive bis & sepia .20 .20
**474** A72 15s org brn & sepia .20 .20
**475** A72 20s lt ol grn & sepia .20 .20
**476** A72 50s bister brn & sepia .60 .20
**477** A72 75s dp rose & sepia .80 .20
**478** A72 1r blue grn & blk 1.00 1.00
Nos. 473-478 (6) 3.00 1.20

Issued to publicize wildlife preservation.

A73

Factories — A74

**1959, Aug. 17** **Litho.** *Perf. 12*
**479** A73 20s blue & red .20 .20
**480** A73 50s rose red & blk .20 .20
**481** A73 75s brown & red .20 .20
**482** A73 1.50r lt green & blk .40 .40
Nos. 479-482 (4) 1.00 1.00

Introduction of the constitution of 1945 embodying "guided democracy."

**1959, Oct. 26** **Photo.** *Perf. 12*
Designs: 20s, 75s, Cogwheel and train. 1.15r, Means of transportation.
**483** A74 15s brt green & blk .20 .20
**484** A74 20s dull org & blk .20 .20
**485** A74 50s red & black .20 .20
**486** A74 75s brt grnsh bl & blk .20 .20
**487** A74 1.15r magenta & blk .20 .20
Nos. 483-487 (5) 1.00 1.00

11th Colombo Plan Conference, Jakarta.

Mother & Child, WRY Emblem — A75

15s, 75s, Destroyed town & fleeing family. 20s, 1.15r, World Refugee Year emblem.

**1960, Apr. 7** **Unwmk.** *Perf. 12½x12*
**488** A75 10s claret & blk .20 .20
**489** A75 15s bister & blk .20 .20
**490** A75 20s org brn & blk .20 .20
**491** A75 50s green & blk .20 .20
**492** A75 75s dk blue & blk .20 .20
**493** A75 1.15r scarlet & blk .20 .20
Nos. 488-493 (6) 1.20 1.20

World Refugee Year, 7/1/59-6/3/60.

Tea Plantation — A76

5s, Oil palms. 10s, Sugar cane and railroad. 15s, Coffee. 20s, Tobacco. 50s, Coconut palms. 75s, Rubber plantation. 1.15r, Rice.

**1960** *Perf. 12x12½*
**494** A76 5s gray .20 .20
**495** A76 10s red brown .20 .20
**496** A76 15s plum .20 .20
**497** A76 20s ocher .20 .20
**498** A76 25s brt blue grn .20 .20
**499** A76 50s deep blue .20 .20
**500** A76 75s scarlet .20 .20
**501** A76 1.15r plum .20 .20
Nos. 494-501 (8) 1.60 1.60

For surcharges see Nos. B132-B134.

---

Anopheles Mosquito — A77

**1960, Nov. 12** **Photo.** *Perf. 12x12½*
**502** A77 25s carmine rose .20 .20
**503** A77 50s orange brown .20 .20
**504** A77 75s brt green .20 .20
**505** A77 3r orange .30 .30
Nos. 502-505 (4) .90 .90

World Health Day, Nov. 12, 1960, and to promote malaria control.

Pres. Sukarno with Hoe — A78

**1961, Feb. 15** *Perf. 12½x12*
**506** A78 75s gray .70 .20

Planned National Development.

Dayak Dancer of Borneo A79

Designs: 10s, Ambonese boat. 15s, Tangkubanperahu crater. 20s, Bull races. 50s, Toradja houses. 75s, Balinese temple. 1r, Lake Toba. 1.50r, Balinese dancer and musicians. 2r, Buffalo hole, view. 3r, Borobudur Temple, Java.

**1961** *Perf. 13½x13*
**507** A79 10s rose lilac .65 .20
**508** A79 15s gray .65 .20
**509** A79 20s orange .65 .20
**510** A79 25s orange ver .65 .20
**511** A79 50s carmine rose .65 .20
**512** A79 75s red brown .65 .20
**513** A79 1r brt green 1.25 .20
**514** A79 1.50r bister brn 1.25 .20
**515** A79 2r grnsh blue 1.60 .30
**516** A79 3r gray 1.75 .30
Set of 4 souvenir sheets 22.50 2.50
Nos. 507-516 (10) 9.75 2.20

Issued for tourist publicity.
The four souvenir sheets among them contain one each of Nos. 507-516 imperf., with two or three stamps to a sheet and English marginal inscriptions: "Visit Indonesia" and "Visit the Orient Year." Size: 139x105mm or 105x139mm.

Sports Hall and Thomas Cup A80

*Perf. 13½x12½*
**1961, June 1** **Photo.**
**517** A80 75s pale violet & blue .20 .20
**518** A80 1r citron & dk grn .20 .20
**519** A80 3r salmon pink & dk bl .20 .20
Nos. 517-519 (3) .60 .60

1961 Thomas Cup World Badminton Championship.

New Buildings and Workers A81

**1961, July 6** **Unwmk.**
**520** A81 75s violet & grnsh bl .20 .20
**521** A81 1.50r emerald & buff .20 .20
**522** A81 3r dk red & salmon .20 .20
Nos. 520-522 (3) .60 .60

16th anniversary of independence.

---

Sultan Hasanuddin — A82

Portraits: 20s, Abdul Muis. 30s, Surjopranoto. 40s, Tengku Tjhik Di Tiro. 50s, Teuku Umar. 60s, K. H. Samanhudi. 75s, Captain Pattimura. 1r, Raden Adjeng Kartini. 1.25r, K. H. Achmad Dahlan. 1.50r, Tuanku Imam Bondjol. 2r, Si Singamangaradja XII. 2.50r, Mohammad Husni Thamrin. 3r, Ki Hadjar Dewantoro. 4r, Djenderal Sudirman. 4.50r, Dr. G. S. S. J. Ratulangie. 5r, Pangeran Diponegoro. 6r, Dr. Setyabudi. 7.50r, H. O. S. Tjokroaminoto. 10r, K. H. Agus Salim. 15r, Dr. Soetomo.

*Perf. 13½x12½*
**1961-62** **Unwmk.** **Photo.**
**Black Inscriptions; Portraits in Sepia**
**523** A82 20s olive .20 .20
**524** A82 25s gray olive .20 .20
**525** A82 30s brt lilac .20 .20
**526** A82 40s brown orange .50 .20
**527** A82 50s bluish green .50 .20
**528** A82 60s green ('62) .20 .20
**529** A82 75s lt red brown .50 .20
**530** A82 1r lt blue .55 .20
**531** A82 1.25r lt ol grn ('62) .20 .20
**532** A82 1.50r emerald .50 .20
**533** A82 2r org red ('62) .20 .20
**534** A82 2.50r rose claret .50 .20
**535** A82 3r gray blue .70 .20
**536** A82 4r olive green .90 .20
**537** A82 4.50r red lilac ('62) .55 .20
**538** A82 5r brick red 1.10 .20
**539** A82 6r bister ('62) .55 .20
**540** A82 7.50r violet bl ('62) .70 .20
**541** A82 10r green ('62) .90 .20
**542** A82 15r dp org ('62) 1.10 .20
Nos. 523-542 (20) 10.75 4.00

National heroes. The 25s, 75s, 1.50r, 5r issued on 8/17, Independence Day; 40s, 50s, 4r on 10/5, Army Day; 20s, 30s, 1r, 2.50r, 3r on 11/10, Republic Day; 60s, 2r, 7.50r, 15r on 10/5/62; 1.25r, 4.50r, 6r, 10r on 11/10/62.

Symbols of Census A83

**1961, Sept. 15** *Perf. 13½x12½*
**543** A83 75s rose violet .60 .20

First census in Indonesia.

Djataju — A84

Scenes from Ramayana Ballet: 40s, Hanuman. 1r, Dasamuka. 1.50r, Kidang Kentiana. 3r, Dewi Sinta. 5r, Rama.

*Perf. 12x12½*
**1962, Jan. 15** **Unwmk.**
**544** A84 30s ocher & red brn .20 .20
**545** A84 40s rose lilac & vio .30 .20
**546** A84 1r green & claret .60 .20
**547** A84 1.50r sal pink & dk grn .75 .20
**548** A84 3r pale grn & dp bl 1.10 .20
**549** A84 5r brn org & dk brn 1.60 .20
Nos. 544-549 (6) 4.55 1.20

Asian Games Emblem — A85

Main Stadium — A86

Designs: 10s, Basketball. 15s, Main Stadium, Jakarta. 20s, Weight lifter. 25s, Hotel Indonesia. 30s, Cloverleaf intersection. 40s, Discus thrower. 50s, Woman diver. 60s, Soccer. 70s, Press House. 75s, Boxers. 1r, Volleyball. 1.25r, 2r, 3r, 5r, Asian Games emblem. 1.50r, Badminton. 1.75r, Wrestlers. 2.50r, Woman rifle shooter. 4.50r, Hockey. 6r, Water polo. 7.50r, Tennis. 10r, Table tennis. 15r, Bicyclist. 20r, Welcome Monument.

| 1962 | Photo. | | Perf. 12½ | |
|---|---|---|---|---|
| 550 | A85 | 10s green & yel | .20 | .20 |
| 551 | A85 | 15s grnsh blk & bis | .20 | .20 |
| 552 | A85 | 20s red lil & lt grn | .20 | .20 |
| 553 | A86 | 25s car & lt grn | .20 | .20 |
| 554 | A86 | 30s bl grn & yel | .35 | .20 |
| 555 | A85 | 40s ultra & pale bl | .35 | .20 |
| 556 | A85 | 50s choc & gray | .35 | .20 |
| 557 | A85 | 60s lil rose & vio gray | .35 | .20 |
| 558 | A85 | 70s dk brn & rose | .35 | .20 |
| 559 | A85 | 75s choc & org | .35 | .20 |
| 560 | A85 | 1r purple & lt bl | .35 | .20 |
| 561 | A85 | 1.25r dk bl & rose car | .35 | .20 |
| 562 | A85 | 1.50r red org & lil | .35 | .20 |
| 563 | A85 | 1.75r dk car & rose | .40 | .20 |
| 564 | A85 | 2r brn & yel grn | .40 | .20 |
| 565 | A85 | 2.50r dp bl & lt brn | .40 | .20 |
| 566 | A85 | 3r black & dk red | .70 | .20 |
| 567 | A85 | 4.50r dk grn & red | .70 | .20 |
| 568 | A85 | 5r gray grn & lem | .70 | .20 |
| 569 | A85 | 6r brn red & dp yel | .75 | .20 |
| 570 | A85 | 7.50r red brn & sal | .75 | .20 |
| 571 | A85 | 10r dk blue & blue | .75 | .20 |
| 572 | A85 | 15r dl vio & pale vio | 1.00 | .20 |
| 573 | A85 | 20r dk grn & ol bis | 1.60 | .20 |
| | | Nos. 550-573 (24) | 12.10 | 4.80 |

4th Asian Games, Jakarta.

Malaria Eradication Emblem — A87

| 1962, Apr. 7 | | | Perf. 12½x12 | |
|---|---|---|---|---|
| 574 | A87 | 40s dull bl & vio bl | .20 | .20 |
| 575 | A87 | 1.50r yel org & brn | .20 | .20 |
| 576 | A87 | 3r green & indigo | .20 | .20 |
| 577 | A87 | 6r lilac & blk | .20 | .20 |
| | | Nos. 574-577 (4) | .80 | .80 |

WHO drive to eradicate malaria. The 1.50r and 6r have Indonesian inscription on top.

Atom Diagram — A88

| 1962, Sept. 24 | Photo. | Perf. 12x12½ | |
|---|---|---|---|---|
| 578 | A88 | 1.50r dk blue & yel | .20 | .20 |
| 579 | A88 | 4.50r brick red & yel | .20 | .20 |
| 580 | A88 | 6r green & blk | .20 | .20 |
| | | Nos. 578-580 (3) | .60 | .60 |

Development through science.

Pacific Travel Association Emblem — A89

Mechanized Plow — A90

1.50r, Prambanan Temple and Mount Merapi. 6r, Balinese Meru (Buildings), Pura Taman Ajun.

| 1963, Mar. 14 | | | Unwmk. | |
|---|---|---|---|---|
| 581 | A89 | 1r grn & indigo | .20 | .20 |
| 582 | A89 | 1.50r olive & indigo | .20 | .20 |
| 583 | A89 | 3r ocher & indigo | .20 | .20 |
| 584 | A89 | 6r dp org & indigo | .40 | .20 |
| | | Nos. 581-584 (4) | 1.00 | .80 |

12th conf. of the Pacific Area Travel Assoc., Bandung.

**1963, Mar. 21** *Perf. 12½x12, 12x12½*

1r, 3r, Hand holding rice stalks, vert.

| 585 | A90 | 1r blue & yel | .20 | .20 |
|---|---|---|---|---|
| 586 | A90 | 1.50r brt grn & indigo | .20 | .20 |
| 587 | A90 | 3r rose car & org | .20 | .20 |
| 588 | A90 | 6r orange & blk | .20 | .20 |
| | | Nos. 585-588 (4) | .80 | .80 |

FAO "Freedom from Hunger" campaign. English inscription on 3r and 6r.

Long-Armed Lobster — A91

Fish: 1.50r, Little tuna. 3r, River roman. 6r, Chinese pompano.

| 1963, Apr. 6 | | | Perf. 12½x12 | |
|---|---|---|---|---|
| 589 | A91 | 1r ver, blk & yel | .45 | .20 |
| 590 | A91 | 1.50r ultra, blk & yel | .45 | .20 |
| 591 | A91 | 3r Prus bl, bis & car | .60 | .20 |
| 592 | A91 | 6r ol grn, blk & ocher | .60 | .20 |
| | | Nos. 589-592 (4) | 2.10 | .80 |

Pen and Conference Emblem — A92

Designs: 1.50r, Pen, Emblem and map of Africa and Southeast Asia. 3r, Globe, pen and broken chain, vert. 6r, Globe, hand holding pen and broken chain, vert.

**Perf. 12½x12, 12x12½**

| 1963, Apr. 24 | Photo. | | Unwmk. | |
|---|---|---|---|---|
| 593 | A92 | 1r lt bl & dp org | .25 | .20 |
| 594 | A92 | 1.50r pale vio & mar | .25 | .20 |
| 595 | A92 | 3r olive, bl & blk | .25 | .20 |
| 596 | A92 | 6r brick red & blk | .40 | .20 |
| | | Nos. 593-596 (4) | 1.15 | .80 |

Asian-African Journalists' Conference.

"Indonesia's Flag from Sabang to Merauke" — A93

4.50r, Parachutist landing in New Guinea. 6r, Bird of paradise & map of New Guinea.

| 1963, May 1 | | | Perf. 12½x12 | |
|---|---|---|---|---|
| 597 | A93 | 1.50r org brn, blk & red | .20 | .20 |
| 598 | A93 | 4.50r multicolored | .20 | .20 |
| 599 | A93 | 6r multicolored | .20 | .20 |
| | | Nos. 597-599 (3) | .60 | .60 |

Issued to mark the acquisition of Netherlands New Guinea (West Irian).

Centenary Emblem — A94

Design: 1.50r, 6r, Red Cross.

| 1963, May 8 | | | Perf. 12 | |
|---|---|---|---|---|
| 600 | A94 | 1r brt grn & red | .20 | .20 |
| 601 | A94 | 1.50r lt bl & red | .20 | .20 |
| 602 | A94 | 3r gray & red | .20 | .20 |
| 603 | A94 | 6r lt bis & red | .20 | .20 |
| | | Nos. 600-603 (4) | .80 | .80 |

Centenary of the International Red Cross.

Bank of Indonesia, Djalan A95

Daneswara, God of Prosperity A96

| 1963, July 5 | Photo. | | Perf. 12 | |
|---|---|---|---|---|
| 604 | A95 | 1.75r lt bl & pur | .20 | .20 |
| 605 | A96 | 4r citron & sl grn | .20 | .20 |
| 606 | A95 | 6r lt green & brn | .20 | .20 |
| 607 | A96 | 12r org & dk red brn | .20 | .20 |
| | | Nos. 604-607 (4) | .80 | .80 |

Issued for National Banking Day.

Standard Bearers — A97

Designs: 1.75r, "Pendet" dance. 4r, GANEFO building, Senajan, Jakarta. 6r, Archery. 10r, Badminton. 12r, Javelin. 25r, Sailing. 50r, Torch.

| 1963, Nov. 10 | | Unwmk. | Perf. 12½ | |
|---|---|---|---|---|
| 608 | A97 | 1.25r gray vio & dk brn | .20 | .20 |
| 609 | A97 | 1.75r org & ol grn | .20 | .20 |
| 610 | A97 | 4r emer & dk brn | .20 | .20 |
| 611 | A97 | 6r rose brn & blk | .20 | .20 |
| 612 | A97 | 10r lt ol grn & dk brn | .20 | .20 |
| 613 | A97 | 12r rose car & grnsh blk | .25 | .20 |
| 614 | A97 | 25r blue & dk blue | .35 | .20 |
| 615 | A97 | 50r red & black | .40 | .20 |
| | | Nos. 608-615 (8) | 2.00 | 1.60 |

1st Games of the New Emerging Forces, GANEFO, Jakarta, Nov. 10-22.

Pres. Sukarno — A98

| 1964 | Photo. | | Perf. 12½x12 | |
|---|---|---|---|---|
| 616 | A98 | 6r brown & dk bl | .20 | .20 |
| 617 | A98 | 12r bister & plum | .20 | .20 |
| 618 | A98 | 20r blue & org | .20 | .20 |
| 619 | A98 | 30r red org & bl | .20 | .20 |
| 620 | A98 | 40r green & brn | .20 | .20 |
| 621 | A98 | 50r red & dp grn | .20 | .20 |
| 622 | A98 | 75r vio & red org | .20 | .20 |
| 623 | A98 | 100r sil & red brn | .20 | .20 |
| 624 | A98 | 250r dk blue & sil | .20 | .20 |
| 625 | A98 | 500r red & gold | .20 | .20 |
| | | Nos. 616-625 (10) | 2.00 | 2.00 |

See Nos. B165-B179. For surcharges see Nos. 661, 663-667.

Trailer Truck — A99

Designs: 1r, Oxcart. 1.75r, Freighter. 2r, Lockheed Electra plane. 2.50r, Buginese sailboat, vert. 4r, Mailman with bicycle. 5r, Dakota plane. 7.50r, Teletype operator. 10r, Diesel train. 15r, Passenger ship. 25r, Convair Coronado Plane. 35r, Telephone switchboard operator.

| 1964 | | Perf. 12x12½, 12½x12 | | |
|---|---|---|---|---|
| 626 | A99 | 1r dull claret | .20 | .20 |
| 627 | A99 | 1.25r red brown | .20 | .20 |
| 628 | A99 | 1.75r Prus blue | .20 | .20 |
| 629 | A99 | 2r red orange | .20 | .20 |
| 630 | A99 | 2.50r brt blue | .20 | .20 |
| 631 | A99 | 4r bluish grn | .20 | .20 |
| 632 | A99 | 5r olive bister | .20 | .20 |
| 633 | A99 | 7.50r brt green | .20 | .20 |
| 634 | A99 | 10r orange | .20 | .20 |
| 635 | A99 | 15r dark blue | .20 | .20 |
| 636 | A99 | 25r violet blue | .20 | .20 |
| 637 | A99 | 35r red brown | .20 | .20 |
| | | Nos. 626-637 (12) | 2.40 | 2.40 |

For surcharges see Nos. 659-660, 662.

Ramses II — A100

Design: 6r, 18r, Kiosk of Trajan, Philae.

| 1964, Mar. 8 | | | Perf. 12½x12 | |
|---|---|---|---|---|
| 638 | A100 | 4r ol bis & ol grn | .20 | .20 |
| 639 | A100 | 6r grnsh bl & ol grn | .20 | .20 |
| 640 | A100 | 12r rose & ol grn | .35 | .20 |
| 641 | A100 | 18r emer & ol grn | .45 | .20 |
| | | Nos. 638-641 (4) | 1.20 | .80 |

UNESCO world campaign to save historic monuments in Nubia.

Stamps of Netherlands Indies and Indonesia — A101

| 1964, Apr. 1 | | | Perf. 12½ | |
|---|---|---|---|---|
| 642 | A101 | 10r gold, dk bl & red org | .90 | .50 |

Centenary of postage stamps in Indonesia.

Indonesian Pavilion — A102

**1964, May 16**      **Perf. 12½x12**
643 A102 25r sil, blk, red & dk bl .40 .30
644 A102 50r gold, Prus bl, red &
        grn .70 .30
New York World's Fair, 1964-65.

Thomas
Cup — A103

**1964, Aug. 15**      **Perf. 12½x13½**
645 A103 25r brt grn, gold & red .20 .20
646 A103 50r ultra, gold & red .30 .20
647 A103 75r purple, gold & red .55 .80
    Nos. 645-647 (3) 1.05 1.20
Thomas Cup Badminton World Championship, 1964.

Cruisers and Map of West
Irian — A104

30r, Submarine. 40r, Torpedo boat.

**Perf. 12½x12**
**1964, Oct. 5**      **Photo.**      **Unwmk.**
648 A104 20r yellow & brn .30 .20
649 A104 30r rose & blk .35 .20
650 A104 40r brt grn & ultra .35 .80
    Nos. 648-650 (3) 1.00 1.20
Issued to honor the Indonesian Navy.

Map of Africa
and Asia and
Mosque — A105

15r, 50r, Mosque and clasped hands.

**1965, Mar. 6**      **Photo.**      **Perf. 12½**
651 A105 10r lt blue & pur .20 .20
652 A105 15r org & red brn .25 .20
653 A105 25r brt grn & brn .45 .20
654 A105 50r brn red & blk .45 .70
    Nos. 651-654 (4) 1.35 1.30
Afro-Asian Islamic Conf., Bandung, Mar. 1965.

---

Hand Holding
Scroll — A106

Design: 25r, 75r, Conference emblem (globe, cotton and grain).

**1965, Apr. 18**      **Unwmk.**      **Perf. 12½**
655 A106 15r silver & dp car .25 .20
656 A106 25r aqua, gold & red .25 .20
657 A106 50r gold & dp ultra .35 .20
658 A106 75r pale vio, gold &
        red .35 .80
    Nos. 655-658 (4) 1.20 1.40
10th anniv. of the First Afro-Asian Conf.

### Nos. 618-623 and Nos. 634-636 Surcharged in Revalued Currency in Orange or Black

**1965, Dec.**      **Perf. 12x12½, 12½x12**
659 A99 10s on 10r (B) .20 .20
660 A99 15s on 15r .20 .20
661 A99 20s on 20r .20 .20
662 A99 25s on 25r (B) .20 .20
663 A98 30s on 30r .20 .20
664 A98 40s on 40r .20 .20
665 A98 50s on 50r .20 .20
666 A98 75s on 75r .20 .20
667 A98 100s on 100r .20 .20
    Nos. 659-667 (9) 1.80 1.80
The surcharge on Nos. 659-660 and No. 662 is in two lines and larger.

Pres.
Sukarno — A107

**1966-67**      **Photo.**      **Perf. 12½x12**
668 A107 1s sep & Prus grn .20 .20
669 A107 3s sep & lt ol grn .20 .20
670 A107 5s sep & dp car .20 .20
671 A107 8s sep & Prus grn .20 .20
672 A107 10s sep & vio bl .20 .20
673 A107 15s sep & blk .20 .20
674 A107 20s sep & dp grn .20 .20
675 A107 25s sep & dk red
        brn .20 .20
676 A107 30s sep & dp bl .20 .20
677 A107 40s sep & red brn .20 .20
678 A107 50s sep & brt vio .20 .20
679 A107 80s sep & org .20 .20
680 A107 1r sep & emer .20 .20
681 A107 1.25r sep & dk gray
        ol .20 .20
682 A107 1.50r sep & emer .20 .20
683 A107 2r sep & mag .20 .20
684 A107 2.50r sep & gray .20 .20
685 A107 5r sep & ocher .20 .20
686 A107 10r sep & ol grn .20 .20
686A A107 12r grn & org ('67) .20 .20
686B A107 25r grn & brt pur
        ('67) .20 .20
    Nos. 668-686B (21) 4.20 4.20
The 12r is inscribed "1967" instead of "1966."

---

Dockyard      Gen. Ahmad
Workers — A108     Yani — A109

Designs: 40s, Lighthouse. 50s, Fishermen. 1r, Maritime emblem (wheel and eagle). 1.50r, Sailboat. 2r, Loading dock. 2.50r, Diver emerging from water. 3r, Liner at pier.

**1966**      **Photo.**      **Perf. 12x12½**
687 A108 20s lt ultra & grn .20 .20
688 A108 40s pink & dk bl .20 .20
689 A108 50s green & brn .20 .20
690 A108 1r salmon, bl & yel .20 .20
691 A108 1.50r dull lil & dl grn .20 .20
692 A108 2r gray & dp org .20 .20
693 A108 2.50r rose lil & dk red .20 .20
694 A108 3r brt green & blk .20 .20
    a. Souvenir sheet 9.50 3.50
    Nos. 687-694 (8) 1.60 1.60
Maritime Day. Issued: #687-690, Sept. 23; #691-694, Oct. 23.
No. 694a contains one imperf. stamp similar to No. 694.

**1966, Nov. 10**

Heroes of the Revolution: #696, Lt. Gen. R. Suprapto. #697, Lt. General Harjono. #698, Lt. Gen. S. Parman. #699, Maj. Gen. D. I. Pandjaitan. #700, Maj. Gen. Sutojo Siswomihardjo. #701, Brig. General Katamso. #702, Colonel Soegijono. #703, Capt. Pierre Andreas Tendean. #704, Adj. Insp. Karel Satsuit Tubun.

#### Deep Blue Frame

695 A109 5r org brn .30 .30
696 A109 5r brt grn .30 .30
697 A109 5r gray brn .30 .30
698 A109 5r olive .30 .30
699 A109 5r gray .30 .30
700 A109 5r brt purple .30 .30
701 A109 5r red lilac .30 .30
702 A109 5r slate green .30 .30
703 A109 5r dull rose lil .30 .30
704 A109 5r orange .30 .30
    Nos. 695-704 (10) 3.00 3.00
Issued to honor military men killed during the Communist uprising, October, 1965.

Tjlempung,
Java — A110

Musical Instruments and Maps: 1r, Sasando, Timor. 1.25r, Foi doa, Flores. 1.50r, Kultjapi, Sumatra. 2r, Arababu, Sangihe and Talaud Islands. 2.50r, Drums, West New Guinea. 3r, Katjapi, Celebes. 4r, Hape, Borneo. 5r, Gangsa, Bali. 6r, Serunai, Sumatra. 8r, Rebab, Java. 10r, Trompet, West New Guinea. 12r, Totobuang, Moluccas. 15r, Drums, Nias. 20r, Kulintang, Celebes. 25r, Keledi, Borneo.

**1967 Unwmk. Photo. Perf. 12½x12**
705 A110 50s red & gray .20 .20
706 A110 1r brn & dp org .20 .20
707 A110 1.25r mar & ultra .20 .20
708 A110 1.50r grn & lt vio .20 .20
709 A110 2r vio bl & yel bis .20 .20
710 A110 2.50r ol grn & dl red .20 .20
711 A110 3r brt grn & dl cl .20 .20
712 A110 4r vio bl & org .20 .20
713 A110 5r dull red & bl .20 .20
714 A110 6r blk & brt pink .20 .20
715 A110 8r red brn & brt
        grn .30 .20
716 A110 10r lilac & red .40 .20
717 A110 12r ol grn & lil .45 .20
718 A110 15r vio & lt ol grn .65 .20
719 A110 20r gray & sepia .90 .20
720 A110 25r black & green 1.10 .20
    Nos. 705-720 (16) 5.80 3.20
Issued: 1.25r, 10r, 12r, 15r, 20r, 25r, Mar. 1; others Feb. 1.
For surcharges see Nos. J118-J137.

---

Aviator and MiG-
21 — A111

**1967, Apr. 9**      **Perf. 12½**
Aviation Day: 4r, Traffic control tower and 990A Convair jetliner. 5r, Hercules transport plane.
721 A111 2.50r multicolored .50 .30
722 A111 4r multicolored .50 .30
723 A111 5r multicolored .80 .25
    Nos. 721-723 (3) 1.80 .85

Thomas Cup
with Victory
Dates — A112

Design: 12r, Thomas Cup and globe.

**1967, May 31**      **Perf. 12x12½**
724 A112 5r multicolored .20 .20
725 A112 12r multicolored .50 .20
Issued to commemorate the Thomas Cup Badminton World Championship of 1967.

Balinese Girl in
Front of Temple
Gate — A113

**1967, July 1**      **Photo.**      **Perf. 12½**
726 A113 12r multicolored 1.25 1.00
    a. Souv. sheet of 1, imperf. 4.50 4.50
Intl. Tourist Year, 1967. See No. 739.

Heroes of the
Revolution
Monument,
Lubang
Buaja — A114

Designs: 5r, Full view of monument, horiz. 7.50r, Shrine at monument.

INDONESIA

*Perf. 12x12½, 12½x12*

**1967, Aug. 17**       **Photo.**
727 A114 2.50r pale grn & dk brn .25 .20
728 A114 5r brt rose lil & pale brn .50 .30
729 A114 7.50r pink & Prus grn .50 .30
    Nos. 727-729 (3) 1.25 .80

Issued to publicize the "Heroes of the Revolution" Monument in Lubang Buaja.

Forest Fire, by Raden Saleh A115

50r, Fight to Death, by Raden Saleh.

**1967, Oct. 30**    **Photo.**    *Perf. 12½*
730 A115 25r org & gray grn .30 .30
 a.    Souvenir sheet of 1 4.00 4.00
731 A115 50r vio brn & org .60 .45

Indonesian painter Raden Saleh (1813-80).

Human Rights Flame — A116

**1968, Jan. 1**    **Photo.**    *Perf. 12½*
732 A116 5r grn, lt vio bl & red .20 .20
733 A116 12r grn, ol bis & red .35 .20

International Human Rights Year 1968.

Armed Forces College Emblem — A117

**1968, Jan. 29**    **Litho.**    *Perf. 12½*
734 A117 10r lt blue, yel & brn .45 .20

Integration of the Armed Forces College.

WHO Emblem and "20" — A118

20th anniv. of WHO: 20r, WHO emblem.

**1968, Apr. 7**    **Photo.**    *Perf. 12½*
735 A118 2r dp yel, pale yel & dk brn .20 .20
736 A118 20r emerald & blk .40 .20

Trains of 1867 and 1967 and Railroad's Emblem — A119

**1968, May 15**    **Photo.**    *Perf. 12½x12*
737 A119 20r multicolored .35 .30
738 A119 30r multicolored .35 .30

Indonesian railroad centenary (in 1967).

Tourist Type of 1967

Tourist Publicity: 30r, Butterfly dancer from West Java.

**1968, July 1**      *Perf. 12½*
739 A113 30r gray & multi 1.25 1.00
 a.    Souv. sheet of 1 + label 5.00 5.00

Bosscha Observatory and Andromeda Nebula — A120

30r, Observatory, globe and sky, vert.

**1968, Sept. 20 Photo.**   *Perf. 12½x12*
740 A120 15r ultra & yellow .50 .30
741 A120 30r violet & orange .75 .30

Bosscha Observatory, 40th anniversary.

Weight Lifting — A121

Designs: 7.50r+7.50r, Sailing, horiz. 12r, Basketball. 30r, Dove, Olympic flame and emblem, horiz.

**1968, Oct. 12**      *Perf. 12½*
742 A121 5r ocher, blk & grn .25 .20
743 A121 Pair .40 .40
 a.    7.50r Left half .20 .20
 b.    7.50r Right half .20 .20
 c.    Souvenir sheet 5.50 5.50
744 A121 12r blue & multi .30 .40
745 A121 30r blue grn & multi .80 .25
    Nos. 742-745 (4) 1.75 1.25

19th Olympic Games, Mexico City, Oct. 12-27. No. 743 is perforated vertically in the center, dividing it into two separate stamps, each inscribed "Republic Indonesia" and "7.50r."· There is no gutter along the center perforation; and the design is continous over the two stamps.

No. 743c contains one No. 743 with track design surrounding the stamps.

Eugenia Aquea Burm. f. — A122

Fruits: 15r, Papaya. 30r, Durian, vert.

*Perf. 12½x12, 12x12½*

**1968, Dec. 20**      **Photo.**
746 A122 7.50r multicolored .40 .35
747 A122 15r multicolored .55 .45
 a.    Souvenir sheet of 1 4.25 4.25
748 A122 30r multicolored .85 .85
 a.    Souvenir sheet of 1 4.25 4.25
    Nos. 746-748 (3) 1.80 1.65

Issued for the 11th Social Day.

Globe, ILO and UN Emblems — A123

Designs: 7.50r, 25r, ILO and UN emblems.

**1969, Feb. 1**    **Photo.**    *Perf. 12½*
749 A123 5r yel grn & scar .20 .20
750 A123 7.50r org & dk grn .20 .20
751 A123 15r lilac & org .20 .20
752 A123 25r bl grn & dull red .30 .20
    Nos. 749-752 (4) .90 .80

50th anniv. of the ILO.

R. Dewi Sartika A124      Red Crosses A125

#754, Tjoet Nja Din. #755, Tjoet Nja Meuthia. #756, General Gatot Subroto. #757, Sutan Sjahrir. #758, Dr. F. L. Tobing. #753-755 show portraits of women.

**1969, Mar. 1**    **Photo.**    *Perf. 12½x12*
753 A124 15r green & pur .30 .20
754 A124 15r red lilac & grn .30 .20
755 A124 15r dk blue & ver .30 .20
756 A124 15r lilac & dk blue .30 .20
757 A124 15r lemon & red .30 .20
758 A124 15r pale brn & blue .30 .20
    Nos. 753-758 (6) 1.80 1.20

Heroes of Indonesian independence.

**1969, May 5**    **Photo.**    *Perf. 12*

20r, Red Cross surrounded by arms.

759 A125 15r green & dp red .30 .20
760 A125 20r org yel & red .50 .20

50th anniversary of the League of Red Cross Societies.

"Family Planning Leads to National Development and Prosperity" — A126

Design: 10r, Family, birds and factories.

**1969, June 2**    **Photo.**    *Perf. 12½*
761 A126 10r blue grn & org .30 .20
762 A126 20r gray & magenta .50 .20

Planned Parenthood Conference of Southeast Asia and Oceania, Bandung, June 1-7.

Map of Bali and Mask A127

Designs: 15r, Map of Bali and woman carrying basket with offerings on head. 30r, Map of Bali and cremation ceremony.

**1969, July 1**    **Litho.**    *Perf. 12½x12*
763 A127 12r gray & multi .55 .55
764 A127 15r lilac & multi 1.00 1.00
765 A127 30r multicolored 1.00 .65
 a.    Souvenir sheet of 1 4.75 4.75
    Nos. 763-765 (3) 2.55 2.20

Issued for tourist publicity.

Agriculture A128

Designs: 5r, Religious coexistence (roofs of mosques and churches). 10r, Social welfare (house and family). 12r, Import-export (cargo and ship). 15r, Clothing industry (cloth and spindles). 20r, Education (school children). 25r, Research (laboratory). 30r, Health care

(people and syringe). 40r, Fishing (fish and net). 50r, Statistics (charts).

Radar, Djatiluhur Station — A129

**1969**    **Photo.**    *Perf. 12x12½*
766 A128 5r yel grn & bl .20 .20
767 A128 7.50r rose brn & yel .20 .20
768 A128 10r slate & red .30 .20
769 A128 12r blue & dp org .40 .20
770 A128 15r slate grn & org .55 .20
771 A128 20r purple & yel .60 .20
772 A128 25r orange & blk .65 .20
773 A128 30r car rose & gray .70 .20
774 A128 40r green & org .95 .20
775 A128 50r sepia & org 1.00 .20
    Nos. 766-775 (10) 5.55 2.00

Five-year Development Plan. See No. 968a.

**1969, Sept. 29**      *Perf. 12½*

30r, Communications satellite and earth.

776 A129 15r multicolored .35 .20
777 A129 30r multicolored .70 .20

Vickers Vimy and Borobudur Temple A130

100r, Vickers Vimy and map of Indonesia.

**1969, Nov. 1**      *Perf. 13½x12½*
778 A130 75r dp org & dull pur .60 .60
779 A130 100r yellow & green .90 .60

50th anniv. of the 1st flight from England to Australia (via Java).

EXPO '70, Indonesian Pavilion — A131

Designs: 15r, Garuda, symbol of Indonesian EXPO '70 committee. 30r, like 5r.

**1970, Feb. 15**    **Photo.**    *Perf. 12x12½*
780 A131 5r brown, yel & grn .50 .25
781 A131 15r dk bl, yel grn & red .80 .30
782 A131 30r red, yel & dk bl 1.40 .60
    Nos. 780-782 (3) 2.70 1.15

Issued to publicize EXPO '70 International Exposition, Osaka, Japan, Mar. 15-Sept. 13.

Upraised Hands, Bars and Scales of Justice — A132

**1970, Mar. 15**    **Photo.**    *Perf. 12½*
783 A132 10r red orange & pur .65 .20
784 A132 15r brt green & pur .80 .20

Rule of law and justice in Indonesia.

UPU Monument, Bern — A133

Dancers — A134

Design: 30r, UPU Headquarters, Bern.

**1970, May 20   Photo.   Perf. 12x12½**
785 A133 15r emer & copper red   .75   .20
786 A133 30r ocher & blue   1.25   .20
Inauguration of the new UPU Headquarters in Bern, Switzerland.

**1970, July 1   Photo.   Perf. 12**
787 A134 20r Timor dancers   1.00   .60
788 A134 45r Bali dancers   2.25   .75
a.   Souvenir sheet of 1   7.75   8.25
Tourist publicity. No. 788a sold for 60r.

Asian Productivity Year — A135

Independence Proclamation Monument — A136

**1970, Aug. 1   Photo.   Perf. 12**
789 A135 5r emerald, org & red   .45   .25
790 A135 30r violet, org & red   1.25   .75

**1970, Aug. 17**
791 A136 40r lt ultra & magenta   13.50 3.50
The 25th anniversary of independence.

Post and Telecommunications Emblems — A137

Postal Worker and Telephone Dial — A138

**Perf. 12x12½, 12½x12**
**1970, Sept. 27   Photo.**
792 A137 10r green, ocher & yel   5.75 1.60
793 A138 25r pink, blk & yel   7.75   .80
25th anniversary of the postal service.

UN Emblem A139

Education Year and UNESCO Emblems A140

**1970, Oct. 10   Photo.   Perf. 12½**
794 A139 40r pur, red & yel grn   13.50 1.40
25th anniversary of the United Nations.

**1970, Nov. 16   Photo.   Perf. 12½**
Design: 50r, similar to 25r, but without oval background.
795 A140 25r yel, dk red & brn   10.50 1.25
796 A140 50r lt blue, blk & red   15.00 1.90
International Education Year.

Batik Worker — A141

50r, Woman with bamboo musical instrument (angklung). 75r, Menangkabau house & family in traditional costumes.

**1971, May 26   Litho.   Perf. 12½**
797 A141 20r multi   3.75 1.00
798 A141 50r multi, vert.   5.75 2.75
a.   Souvenir sheet of 1   50.00 42.50
799 A141 75r multi   8.00 3.75
Nos. 797-799 (3)   17.50 7.50
"Visit Asian lands." No. 798a sold for 70r.

Fatahillah Park, Djakarta — A142

30f, City Hall. 65r, Lenong Theater performance. 80r, Ismail Marzuki Cultural Center.

**1971, June 19   Photo.   Perf. 12½**
800 A142 15r yel grn, brn & bl   2.75 1.00
801 A142 65r org brn, dk brn & lt grn   5.50 3.50
802 A142 80r olive, bl & mag   9.50 3.75
Nos. 800-802 (3)   17.75 8.25

**Souvenir Sheet**
803 A142 30r bl, yel & lil rose   25.00 19.00
444th anniv. of Djakarta. #803 sold for 60r.

Rama and Sita — A143

Design: 100r, Rama with bow.

**1971, Aug. 31**
804 A143 30r yellow, grn & blk   1.75   .50
805 A143 100r blue, red & blk   4.50   .75
International Ramayana Festival.

Carrier Pigeon and Conference Emblem — A144

**1971, Sept. 20**
806 A144 50r ocher & dp brown   1.75   .50
5th Asian Regional Postal Conference.

Globes and UPU Monument, Berne — A145

**1971, Oct. 4   Photo.   Perf. 13½x13**
807 A145 40r blue & dull vio   2.00   .50
Universal Postal Union Day.

Boy Writing, UNICEF Emblem — A146

40r, Boy with sheaf of rice, emblem.

**1971, Dec. 11   Perf. 12½**
808 A146 20r orange & multi   2.50   .40
809 A146 40r blue & multi   3.00   .75
25th anniv. UNICEF.

Lined Tang A147

Fish: 30r, Moorish goddess. 40r, Imperial angelfish.

**1971, Dec. 27   Litho.   Perf. 12½**
810 A147 15r lilac & multi   4.75 1.00
811 A147 30r dull grn & multi   11.00 2.50
812 A147 40r blue & multi   13.00 4.00
Nos. 810-812 (3)   28.75 7.50
See #834-836, 859-861, 926-928, 959-961.

UN Emblem A148

Radio Tower A149

Design: 100r, Road and dam.

**1972, Mar. 28   Photo.   Perf. 12½**
813 A149 40r lt grnsh bl & bl   3.00   .85
814 A149 75r dk car, yel & grnsh bl   3.50   .85
815 A148 100r green, yel & blk   6.00 1.75
Nos. 813-815 (3)   12.50 3.45
UN Economic Commission for Asia and the Far East (ECAFE), 25th anniv.

"Your Heart is your Health" — A150

Woman Weaver, Factories — A151

**1972, Apr. 7**
816 A150 50r multicolored   2.00   .55
World Health Day.

**1972, Apr. 22**
817 A151 35r orange, yel & pur   2.00   .50
Textile Technology Institute, 50th anniv.

Book Readers A152

**1972, May 15   Perf. 13½x12½**
818 A152 75r blue & multi   3.00   .55
International Book Year 1972.

Weather Satellite — A153

**1972, July 20   Photo.   Perf. 12½**
819 A153 35r shown   2.50   .20
820 A153 50r Astronaut on moon   3.50 2.00
821 A153 60r Indonesian rocket Kartika 1   6.00   .75
Nos. 819-821 (3)   12.00 2.95
Space achievements.

Hotel Indonesia — A154

**1972, Aug. 5**
822 A154 50r grn, lt bl & car   2.60   .55
Hotel Indonesia, 10th anniversary.

Silat (Self Defense) A155

Family, Houses of Worship A156

Olympic Emblems and: 35r, Running. 50r, Diving. 75r, Badminton. 100r, Olympic Stadium.

**1972, Aug. 26   Photo.**
823 A155 20r lt blue & multi   1.50   .25
824 A155 35r multicolored   1.50   .30
825 A155 50r yel grn & multi   2.75   .50
826 A155 75r multicolored   3.00 1.25
827 A155 100r multicolored   4.75 2.00
Nos. 823-827 (5)   13.50 4.30
20th Olympic Games, Munich, 8/26-9/11.

**1972, Sept. 27   Perf. 12½x13½**
Family planning: 75r, Healthy family. 80r, Working family (national prosperity).
828 A156 30r lemon & multi   1.75   .40
829 A156 75r lilac & multi   3.25 1.00
830 A156 80r multicolored   5.50 1.40
Nos. 828-830 (3)   10.50 2.80

Moluccas Dancer A157

Thomas Cup, Shuttlecock A158

60r, Man, woman and Toradja house, Celebes. 100fr, West Irian house, horiz.

**Perf. 12½x13½, 13½x12½**
**1972, Oct. 28   Photo.**
831 A157 30r olive pink & brn   1.90   .40
832 A157 60r multicolored   4.25 1.10
833 A157 100r lt bl, brn & dl yel   6.25 1.25
Nos. 831-833 (3)   12.40 2.75

## Fish Type of 1971

Fish: 30r, Butterflyfish. 50r, Regal angelfish. 100r, Spotted triggerfish.

**1972, Dec. 4      Litho.      Perf. 12½**
834  A147  30r blue & multi        6.00  1.60
835  A147  50r blue & multi       10.50  2.40
836  A147  100r blue & multi      13.50  3.75
      Nos. 834-836 (3)            30.00  7.75

**1973, Jan. 2      Litho.      Perf. 12½**
Thomas Cup, Shuttlecock and: 75r, National monument & Istora Sports Hall. 80r, Indonesian flag & badminton player.

837  A158  30r emerald & brt bl     .60   .25
838  A158  75r dull grn & dk car   2.00   .35
839  A158  80r gold & red          2.75   .65
      Nos. 837-839 (3)            5.35  1.25

Thomas Cup Badminton World Championship 1973.

WMO Emblem, Anemometer, Wayang Figure — A159

**Perf. 13½x12½**
**1973, Feb. 15                  Litho.**
840  A159  80r blue, grn & claret  2.00   .40
Cent. of intl. meteorological cooperation.

"Health Begins at Home" — A160

**1973, Apr. 7      Photo.      Perf. 12½**
841  A160  80r dk grn, org & ultra  2.00   .40
25th anniv. of WHO.

Ceremonial Mask, Java — A161

**1973, June 1      Photo.      Perf. 12½**
842  A161  30r shown               4.50   .75
843  A161  60r Mask, Kalimantan    8.00  2.50
844  A161  100r Mask, Bali        12.50  1.60
      Nos. 842-844 (3)            25.00  4.85
Tourist publicity.

Hand Putting Coin into Bank — A162

**1973, July 2      Photo.      Perf. 12½**
30r, Symbolic coin bank and hand, horiz.
845  A162  25r yellow, lt brn & blk  1.10   .50
846  A162  30r green, yel & gold    1.60   .50
National savings movement.

Chess — A163          INTERPOL Emblem and Policemen — A164

8th National Sports Week: 60r, Karate. 75r, Hurdling, horiz.

**1973, Aug. 4      Photo.      Perf. 12½**
847  A163  30r red, yellow & blk    2.00   .50
848  A163  60r black, ocher & lt grn  2.50   .50
849  A163  75r black, lt bl & rose  4.00   .55
      Nos. 847-849 (3)            8.50  1.55

**1973, Sept. 3**
Design: 50r, INTERPOL emblem and guard statue from Sewu Prambanan Temple, vert.
850  A164  30r yellow, grn & blk    1.40   .40
851  A164  50r yellow, brn & blk    2.00   .60
50th anniv. of Intl. Police Organization.

Batik Worker and Parang Rusak Pattern A165

Batik designs: 80r, Man and Pagi Sore pattern. 100r, Man and Merak Ngigel pattern.

**1973, Oct. 9      Photo.      Perf. 12½**
852  A165  60r multicolored        4.00   .85
853  A165  80r multicolored        4.75  1.10
854  A165  100r multicolored       7.25  2.00
      Nos. 852-854 (3)           16.00  3.95

Farmer, Grain, UN and FAO Emblems — A166

**1973, Oct. 24      Photo.      Perf. 12½**
855  A166  30r lilac & multi        2.50   .50
World Food Program, 10th anniversary.

Houses of Worship — A167

Family planning: 30r, Classroom. 60r, Family and home.

**1973, Nov. 10**
856  A167  20r dk bl, lt bl & ver   1.10   .35
857  A167  30r ocher, blk & yel     1.40   .50
858  A167  60r lt grn, yel & blk    3.75   .40
      Nos. 856-858 (3)            6.25  1.25

## Fish Type of 1971

Fish: 40r, Acanthurus leucosternon. 65r, Chaetodon trifasciatus. 100r, Pomacanthus annularis.

**1973, Dec. 10      Litho.      Perf. 12½**
859  A147  40r multicolored        3.00  1.10
860  A147  65r multicolored        7.75  1.90
861  A147  100r multicolored      11.00  3.00
      Nos. 859-861 (3)           21.75  6.00

Adm. Sudarso and Battle of Arafuru — A168

**1974, Jan. 15**
862  A168  40r brt blue & multi     2.50   .75
12th Navy Day.

Bengkulu Costume A169

Designs: Regional Costumes.

**1974, Mar. 28      Litho.      Perf. 12½**
863  A169  5r shown               14.00  1.10
864  A169  7.50r Kalimantan, Timor  8.00  1.10
865  A169  10r Kalimantan, Tengah  4.75   .80
866  A169  15r Jambi               1.25   .80
867  A169  20r Sulawesi, Tenggara  1.25   .80
868  A169  25r Nusatenggara, Timor  1.40   .80
869  A169  27.50r Maluku           1.40  2.50
870  A169  30r Lampung             1.40  1.50
871  A169  35r Sumatra, Barat      1.40   .80
872  A169  40r Aceh                1.40   .80
873  A169  45r Nusatenggara, Barat  3.50   .80
874  A169  50r Riouw               2.75  2.00
875  A169  55r Kalimantan, Barat   2.75   .80
876  A169  60r Sulawesi, Utara     2.75   .80
877  A169  65r Sulawesi, Tengah    2.75   .80
878  A169  70r Sumatra, Selatan    2.75   .80
879  A169  75r Java, Barat         2.75   .80
880  A169  80r Sumatra, Utara      2.75   .80
881  A169  90r Yogyakarta          2.75  5.00
882  A169  95r Kalimantan, Selatan  2.75   .80
883  A169  100r Java, Timor        2.75  1.60
884  A169  120r Irian, Java        7.00  1.10
885  A169  130r Java, Tengah       7.00   .80
886  A169  135r Sulawesi, Selatan  6.25   .80
887  A169  150r Bali               6.25   .80
888  A169  160r Djakarta           6.25  1.60
      Nos. 863-888 (26)          100.00 31.10

Baladewa A170

Designs (Figures from Shadow Plays): 80r, Kresna. 100r, Bima.

**1974, June 1      Photo.      Perf. 12½**
889  A170  40r lt violet & multi    3.25   .85
890  A170  80r salmon & multi       5.75  1.50
891  A170  100r rose               7.00  1.50
      Nos. 889-891 (3)           16.00  3.85

Pres. Suharto      Family and WPY
A171              Emblem A172

**1974-76      Photo.      Perf. 12½**
**Portrait in Dark Brown**
901  A171  40r lt green & blk       .40   .20
903  A171  50r ultra & blk          .80   .20
906  A171  65r brt pink & blk      1.10   .20
908  A171  75r yellow & blk        1.40   .20
912  A171  100r buff & blk         1.90   .20
913  A171  150r citron & blk       2.75   .30
914  A171  200r green & blue       3.25   .40
915  A171  300r brn org & car      5.50   .55
916  A171  400r green & yellow     7.50   .75
917  A171  500r lilac & car        9.25  1.00
      Nos. 901-917 (10)          33.85  4.00

#914-917 have wavy lines in background.
Issued: #901-913, 8/17/74; #914-917, 8/17/76.

**1974, Aug. 19**
918  A172  65r ultra, gray & ocher  1.60   .40
World Population Year 1974.

"Welfare" A173

"Development" A174

"Religion" A175

**1974, Sept. 9**
919  A173  25r green & multi        .80   .20
920  A174  40r yellow grn & multi  1.60   .20
921  A175  65r dk vio brn & multi  2.25   .20
      Nos. 919-921 (3)           4.65   .60
Family planning.

Mailmen with Bicycles, UPU Emblem — A176

UPU cent.: 40r, Horse-drawn mail cart. 65r, Mailman on horseback. 100r, Sailing ship, 18th century.

**1974, Oct. 9**
922  A176  20r dk green & multi     2.40   .35
923  A176  40r dull blue & multi    2.40   .50
924  A176  65r black brn & yel      2.40   .50
925  A176  100r maroon & multi      2.40  1.25
      Nos. 922-925 (4)            9.60  2.60

## Fish Type of 1971

Fish: 40fr, Zebrasoma veliferum. 80r, Euxiphipops navarchus. 100r, Synchiropus splendidus.

**1974, Oct. 30      Photo.      Perf. 12½**
926  A147  40r blue & multi         4.00   .40
927  A147  80r blue & multi         6.00  1.10
928  A147  100r blue & multi        6.00  1.40
      Nos. 926-928 (3)            16.00  2.90

Drill Team Searching for Oil — A177

Designs (Pertamina Emblem and): 75r, Oil refinery. 95r, Pertamina telecommunications and computer center. 100r, Gasoline truck and station. 120r, Plane over storage tanks. 130r, Pipes and tanker. 150r, Petro-chemical storage tanks. 200r, Off-shore drilling platform. 95r, 100r, 120r, 130r, vertical.

**1974, Dec. 10**     **Perf. 13½**
| | | | | |
|---|---|---|---|---|
| 929 | A177 | 40r black & multi | .25 | .45 |
| 930 | A177 | 75r black & multi | .45 | .45 |
| 931 | A177 | 95r black & multi | .70 | .45 |
| 932 | A177 | 100r black & multi | .70 | .45 |
| 933 | A177 | 120r black & multi | .85 | .45 |
| 934 | A177 | 130r black & multi | .90 | .45 |
| 935 | A177 | 150r black & multi | 1.10 | .45 |
| 936 | A177 | 200r black & multi | 1.50 | .45 |
| | | Nos. 929-936 (8) | 6.45 | 3.60 |

Pertamina State Oil Enterprise, 17th anniv.

Spittoon, Sumatra A178

Artistic Metalware: 75r, Condiment dish, Sumatra. 100r, Condiment dish, Kalimantan.

**1975, Feb. 24**    **Photo.**     **Perf. 12½**
| | | | | |
|---|---|---|---|---|
| 937 | A178 | 50r red & black | 1.90 | .75 |
| 938 | A178 | 75r green & black | 2.25 | .75 |
| 939 | A178 | 100r brt blue & multi | 3.75 | .75 |
| | | Nos. 937-939 (3) | 7.90 | 2.25 |

Blood Donors' Emblem A179

Globe, Standard Meter and Kilogram A180

**1975, Apr. 7**
940   A179   40r yellow, red & grn    1.40   .20

"Give blood, save lives."

**1975, May 20**
941   A180   65r blue, red & yel    2.50   .20

Cent. of Intl. Meter Convention, Paris, 1875.

Farmer, Teacher, Mother, Policewoman and Nurse — A181

IWY Emblem — A182

---

**1975, June 26**    **Photo.**     **Perf. 12½**
| | | | | |
|---|---|---|---|---|
| 942 | A181 | 40r multicolored | 1.50 | .55 |
| 943 | A182 | 100r multicolored | 2.25 | .55 |

International Women's Year 1975.

Dendrobium Pakarena A183

Stupas and Damaged Temple — A184

Orchids: 70r, Aeridachnis bogor. 85r, Vanda genta.

**1975, July 21**
| | | | | |
|---|---|---|---|---|
| 944 | A183 | 40r multicolored | 4.00 | .85 |
| 945 | A183 | 70r multicolored | 6.00 | 1.50 |
| 946 | A183 | 85r multicolored | 10.00 | 2.10 |
| | | Nos. 944-946 (3) | 20.00 | 4.45 |

See Nos. 1010-1012, 1036-1038.

**1975, Aug. 10**      **Perf. 12½**

Designs (UNESCO Emblem and): 40r, Buddha statues, stupas and damaged wall. 65r, Stupas and damaged wall, horiz. 100r, Buddha statue and stupas, horiz.

| | | | | |
|---|---|---|---|---|
| 947 | A184 | 25r yellow, brn & org | 2.60 | .50 |
| 948 | A184 | 40r black, grn & yel | 4.25 | .75 |
| 949 | A184 | 65r lemon, cl & grn | 8.50 | 2.50 |
| 950 | A184 | 100r bister, brn & sl bl | 12.50 | 2.25 |
| | | Nos. 947-950 (4) | 27.85 | 6.00 |

UNESCO campaign to save Borobudur Temple, Java.

Banjarmasin Battle — A185

Battle Scenes: 40r, Batua, 9/8/46. 75r, Margarana, 11/20/46. 100r, Palembang, 1/1/47.

**1975, Aug. 17**
| | | | | |
|---|---|---|---|---|
| 951 | A185 | 25r yellow & blk | .55 | .30 |
| 952 | A185 | 40r org ver & red | .95 | .30 |
| 953 | A185 | 75r vermilion & blk | 1.75 | .60 |
| 954 | A185 | 100r orange & blk | 2.75 | .50 |
| | | Nos. 951-954 (4) | 6.00 | 1.70 |

Indonesian independence, 30th anniversary.

"Education" A186

Heroes' Monument, Surabaya A187

Family plannings: 25r, "Religion." 40r, "Prosperity."

---

**1975, Oct. 20**    **Photo.**     **Perf. 12½**
| | | | | |
|---|---|---|---|---|
| 955 | A186 | 20r blue, salmon & blk | 1.00 | .25 |
| 956 | A186 | 25r emerald, sal & blk | 1.25 | .40 |
| 957 | A186 | 40r dp org, blue & blk | 1.50 | .50 |
| | | Nos. 955-957 (3) | 3.75 | 1.15 |

**1975, Nov. 10**
958   A187   100r maroon & green    3.00   .60

War of independence, 30th anniversary.

**Fish Type of 1971**

Fish: 40r, Coris angulata. 75r, Chaetodon ephippium. 150r, Platax pinnatus, vert.

**1975, Dec. 15**    **Litho.**     **Perf. 12½**
| | | | | |
|---|---|---|---|---|
| 959 | A147 | 40r multicolored | 2.25 | .40 |
| 960 | A147 | 75r multicolored | 4.25 | 1.00 |
| 961 | A147 | 150r multicolored | 8.50 | 2.00 |
| | | Nos. 959-961 (3) | 15.00 | 3.40 |

Thomas Cup — A188

40r, Uber Cup. 100r, Thomas & Uber Cups.

**1976, Jan. 31**    **Photo.**     **Perf. 12½**
| | | | | |
|---|---|---|---|---|
| 962 | A188 | 20r blue & multi | .75 | .35 |
| 963 | A188 | 40r multicolored | 1.10 | .50 |
| 964 | A188 | 100r green & multi | 2.75 | .50 |
| | | Nos. 962-964 (3) | 4.60 | 1.35 |

Indonesia, Badminton World Champions.

Refugees on Truck and New Village — A189

Designs: 50r, Neglected and restored village streets. 100r, Derelict and rebuilt houses.

**1976, Feb. 28**    **Photo.**     **Perf. 12½**
| | | | | |
|---|---|---|---|---|
| 965 | A189 | 30r yellow & multi | .75 | .25 |
| 966 | A189 | 50r blue & multi | 1.25 | .40 |
| 967 | A189 | 100r ocher & multi | 2.25 | .50 |
| | | Nos. 965-967 (3) | 4.25 | 1.15 |

World Human Settlements Day.

Telephones, 1876 and 1976 — A190

**1976, Mar. 10**    **Photo.**     **Perf. 12½**
| | | | | |
|---|---|---|---|---|
| 968 | A190 | 100r yel, org & brn | 1.60 | .40 |
| a. | | Bkt. pane of 8, 4 #968, 4 #775 + 2 labels ('78) | 7.75 | |

Centenary of first telephone call by Alexander Graham Bell, Mar. 10, 1876. Stamps from #968a have straight edges.

Eye and WHO Emblem — A191

Design: 40r, Blind man, eye and World Health Organization emblem.

**1976, Apr. 7**    **Photo.**     **Perf. 12½**
| | | | | |
|---|---|---|---|---|
| 969 | A191 | 20r yel, lt grn & blk | .75 | .35 |
| 970 | A191 | 40r yel, blue & blk | .95 | .50 |

Foresight prevents blindness.

---

Montreal Stadium — A192

**1976, May 17**
971   A192   100r ultra    1.60   .50

21st Olympic Games, Montreal, Canada, July 17-Aug. 1.

Lake Tondano, Celebes — A193

Tourist publicity: 40r, Lake Kelimutu, Flores. 75r, Lake Maninjau, Sumatra.

**1976, June 1**
| | | | | |
|---|---|---|---|---|
| 972 | A193 | 35r lt green & blk | .90 | .35 |
| 973 | A193 | 40r gray, rose & lt grn | 1.10 | .35 |
| 974 | A193 | 75r blue & sl grn | 2.00 | .35 |
| a. | | Bklt. pane of 8 (7 #974, #998, 2 labels) ('78) | 7.75 | |
| | | Nos. 972-974 (3) | 4.00 | 1.05 |

Stamps from #974a have straight edges.

Radar Station — A194

Designs: 50r, Master control radar station. 100r, Apalata satellite.

**1976, July 8**    **Photo.**     **Perf. 12½**
| | | | | |
|---|---|---|---|---|
| 975 | A194 | 20r multicolored | .65 | .35 |
| 976 | A194 | 50r green & blk | 1.25 | .35 |
| 977 | A194 | 100r multicolored | 2.25 | .75 |
| a. | | Bklt. pane of 9 (4 #977, 5 #987, label) ('78) | 13.50 | |
| | | Nos. 975-977 (3) | 4.15 | 1.45 |

Inauguration of domestic satellite system. Stamps from #977a have straight edges.

Arachnis Flos-aeris — A195

Orchids: 40r, Vanda putri serang. 100r, Coelogyne pandurata.

**1976, Sept. 7**
| | | | | |
|---|---|---|---|---|
| 978 | A195 | 25r multicolored | 1.40 | .60 |
| a. | | Souvenir sheet of 1 | 72.50 | |
| 979 | A195 | 40r multicolored | 2.00 | .60 |
| 980 | A195 | 100r multicolored | 6.00 | 1.40 |
| | | Nos. 978-980 (3) | 9.40 | 2.60 |

Tree and Mountain — A196

**1976, Oct. 4**
981   A196   20r green, blue & brn    1.10   .35

16th National Reforestation Week.

Dagger and Sheath from
Timor — A197

Historic Daggers and Sheaths: 40r, from
Borneo. 100r, from Aceh.

**1976, Nov. 1** **Perf. 12½**
| | | | | |
|---|---|---|---|---|
| 982 | A197 | 25r multicolored | 1.25 | .40 |
| 983 | A197 | 40r multicolored | 2.00 | .60 |
| a. | | Souvenir sheet of 1, imperf | 12.50 | 12.50 |
| 984 | A197 | 100r green & multi | 4.00 | 1.60 |
| | | Nos. 982-984 (3) | 7.25 | 2.60 |

No. 983a exists perf. Value $25.

Open Book
A198

Children
Reading
A199

**1976, Dec. 8** **Photo.** **Perf. 12½**
| | | | | |
|---|---|---|---|---|
| 985 | A198 | 20r multicolored | .80 | .20 |
| 986 | A199 | 40r multicolored | 1.50 | .20 |

Better books for children.

UNICEF
Emblem
A200

Ballot Box
A201

**1976, Dec. 11**
| | | | | |
|---|---|---|---|---|
| 987 | A200 | 40r multicolored | 1.75 | .50 |

UNICEF, 30th anniv.

**1977, Jan. 5** **Photo.** **Perf. 12½**

1977 elections: 75r, Ballot box, grain and
factory. 100r, Coat of arms.

| | | | | |
|---|---|---|---|---|
| 988 | A201 | 40r multicolored | 2.25 | .25 |
| 989 | A201 | 75r multicolored | 2.50 | .35 |
| 990 | A201 | 100r multicolored | 4.00 | .75 |
| | | Nos. 988-990 (3) | 8.75 | 1.35 |

Camp and Flags
Scout Emblems,
A202

Designs: 30r, Tent, emblems and trees. 40r,
Boy and Girl Scout flags and emblems.

**1977, Feb. 28**
| | | | | |
|---|---|---|---|---|
| 991 | A202 | 25r multicolored | 1.60 | .40 |
| 992 | A202 | 30r multicolored | 1.75 | .40 |
| 993 | A202 | 40r multicolored | 2.00 | .75 |
| | | Nos. 991-993 (3) | 5.35 | 1.55 |

11th National Scout Jamboree.

Letter with
"AOPU" — A203

Anniversary
Emblem,
Djakarta
Arms — A204

Design: 100r, Stylized bird and letter.

**1977, Apr. 1** **Photo.** **Perf. 12½**
| | | | | |
|---|---|---|---|---|
| 994 | A203 | 65r multicolored | 1.00 | .35 |
| 995 | A203 | 100r multicolored | 1.50 | .50 |

Asian-Oceanic Postal Union, 15th
convention.

**1977, May 23** **Photo.** **Perf. 12½**

Designs: Anniversary emblem and arms of
Djakarta in different arrangements.

| | | | | |
|---|---|---|---|---|
| 996 | A204 | 20r orange & blue | .75 | .35 |
| 997 | A204 | 40r emerald & blue | 1.00 | .50 |
| 998 | A204 | 100r slate & blue | 2.00 | .60 |
| a. | | Souvenir sheet of 1 | 8.00 | 8.00 |
| | | Nos. 996-998 (3) | 3.75 | 1.45 |

450th anniversary of Djakarta. No. 998a
also issued imperf. Value $20.

Rose — A205

Various Sports
Emblems — A206

**1977, May 26** **Photo.** **Perf. 12½**
| | | | | |
|---|---|---|---|---|
| 999 | A205 | 100r shown | 2.00 | .60 |
| a. | | Souvenir sheet | 8.00 | 6.25 |
| 1000 | A205 | 100r Envelope | 2.00 | .60 |
| a. | | Souvenir sheet of 4 | 9.50 | 7.50 |
| b. | | Pair, Nos. 999-1000 | 4.00 | 3.00 |

Amphilex 77 Phil. Exhib., Amsterdam, May
26-June 5. No. 999a contains one stamp similar to No. 999 with blue background. No.
1000a contains 2 each of Nos. 999-1000.
Nos. 999a, 1000a exist imperf. Values: No.
999a, $8.50; No. 1000a, $20.
See No. 1013a.

**1977, June 22**

9th Natl. Sports Week: 50r, 100r, Different
sports emblems.

| | | | | |
|---|---|---|---|---|
| 1001 | A206 | 40r silver & multi | 2.25 | 1.25 |
| 1002 | A206 | 50r silver & multi | 3.25 | 1.25 |
| 1003 | A206 | 100r gold & multi | 8.00 | 2.50 |
| | | Nos. 1001-1003 (3) | 13.50 | 5.00 |

Contest Trophy
A207

Emblem
A208

**1977, July 20**
| | | | | |
|---|---|---|---|---|
| 1004 | A207 | 40r green & multi | 1.90 | .20 |
| 1005 | A208 | 100r yellow & multi | 3.75 | .30 |

10th Natl. Koran Reading Contest, 7/20-27.

Map of ASEAN
Countries,
Satellite — A209

35r, Map of ASEAN countries. 50r, Flags of
founding members: Indonesia, Malaysia, Philippines, Singapore & Thailand; ship, plane &
train.

**1977, Aug. 8**
| | | | | |
|---|---|---|---|---|
| 1006 | A209 | 25r multicolored | 1.50 | .20 |
| 1007 | A209 | 35r multicolored | 1.90 | .20 |
| 1008 | A209 | 50r multicolored | 2.50 | .20 |
| | | Nos. 1006-1008 (3) | 5.90 | .60 |

Association of South East Asian Nations
(ASEAN), 10th anniversary.

Uniform, Jakarta
Regiment
A210

**1977, Aug. 19**
| | | | | |
|---|---|---|---|---|
| 1009 | A210 | 25r green, gold & brn | .75 | .20 |

Indonesia-Pakistan Economic and Cultural
Organization, 1968-1977.

Orchid Type of 1975

Orchids: 25r, Taeniophyllum. 40r, Phalaenopsis violacea. 100r, Dendrobium spectabile.

**1977, Oct. 28** **Photo.** **Perf. 12½**
| | | | | |
|---|---|---|---|---|
| 1010 | A183 | 25r orange & multi | 1.75 | .75 |
| 1011 | A183 | 40r blue & multi | 2.75 | 1.40 |
| 1012 | A183 | 100r yel grn & multi | 5.75 | 2.00 |
| a. | | Souvenir sheet of 1, imperf | 12.00 | 12.00 |
| | | Nos. 1010-1012 (3) | 10.25 | 4.15 |

No. 1012a contains one stamp similar to No.
1012 with blue background. No. 1012a exists
perf. Value $16.

Child and
Mosquito
A211

**1977, Nov. 7** **Perf. 12½**
| | | | | |
|---|---|---|---|---|
| 1013 | A211 | 40r brt grn, red & blk | .75 | .35 |
| a. | | Bklt. pane of 9+label (4 #999, 5 #1013) ('78) | | 7.75 |

Natl. Health campaign to eradicate malaria.
Stamps from #1013a have straight edges.
Issue date: No. 1013a, Sept. 27, 1978.

Proboscis Monkey — A212

Designs: 40r, Indian elephant. 100r, Tiger.

**1977, Dec. 22**
| | | | | |
|---|---|---|---|---|
| 1014 | A212 | 20r multicolored | 1.60 | .70 |
| 1015 | A212 | 40r multicolored | 2.25 | 1.25 |
| 1016 | A212 | 100r multicolored | 6.00 | 3.00 |
| a. | | Souvenir sheet of 1 | 7.00 | 7.00 |
| | | Nos. 1014-1016 (3) | 9.85 | 4.95 |

Wildlife protection. #1016a exists imperf.
Value $7.

Conference
Emblem
A213

Mother and
Child
A214

**1978, Mar. 27** **Photo.** **Perf. 12½**
| | | | | |
|---|---|---|---|---|
| 1017 | A213 | 100r lt blue & ultra | 1.25 | .25 |

United Nations Conference on Technical
Cooperation among Developing Countries.

**1978, Apr. 7** **Photo.** **Perf. 12½**

75r, Mother and child, symbolic design.

| | | | | |
|---|---|---|---|---|
| 1018 | A214 | 40r lt green & blue | .75 | .35 |
| 1019 | A214 | 75r orange red & brn | 1.10 | .65 |

Promotion of breast feeding.

Dome of The Rock,
Jerusalem — A215

**1978, May 15** **Photo.** **Perf. 12½**
| | | | | |
|---|---|---|---|---|
| 1020 | A215 | 100r multicolored | 1.75 | .60 |

Palestinian fighters and their families.

Argentina '78
Emblem
A216

Head and "Blood
Circulation"
A217

**1978, June 1**
| | | | | |
|---|---|---|---|---|
| 1021 | A216 | 40r multicolored | .55 | .20 |
| 1022 | A216 | 100r multicolored | 1.40 | .20 |

11th World Cup Soccer Championships,
Argentina, June 1-25.

**1978, June 17** **Photo.** **Perf. 12½**
| | | | | |
|---|---|---|---|---|
| 1023 | A217 | 100r black, blue & red | 1.25 | .20 |

World Health Day and drive against
hypertension.

Leather Puppets — A218

Art from Wayang Museum, Djakarta: 75r,
Wooden puppets. 100r, Actors with puppet
masks.

**1978, July 22** **Litho.** **Perf. 12½**
| | | | | |
|---|---|---|---|---|
| 1024 | A218 | 40r multicolored | 2.40 | .60 |
| 1025 | A218 | 75r multicolored | 3.50 | 1.25 |
| 1026 | A218 | 100r multicolored | 5.25 | 1.75 |
| | | Nos. 1024-1026 (3) | 11.15 | 3.60 |

Congress
Emblem
A219

IAAY Emblem
A220

**1978, Aug. 1**
| | | | | |
|---|---|---|---|---|
| 1027 | A219 | 100r slate | 1.25 | .20 |

27th Congress of World Confederation of
Organizations of Teachers (WCOTP),
Djakarta, June 26-Aug. 2.

**1978, Aug. 16** **Photo.** **Perf. 12½**
| | | | | |
|---|---|---|---|---|
| 1028 | A220 | 100r org & dk blue | 1.50 | .20 |

International Anti-Apartheid Year.

Congress
Emblem
A221

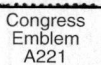

Youth Pledge
Emblem
A222

Design: 100r, People and trees.

**1978, Oct. 16     Photo.     Perf. 12½**
1029  A221  40r emerald & blue      .60   .35
1030  A221  100r emerald & blk      1.10   .75

8th World Forestry Congress, Djakarta.

**1978, Oct. 28**
1031  A222  40r dk brown & red      .85   .50
1032  A222  100r salmon, brn &
                  red              1.40   .75

50th anniv. of Youth Pledge. See #1044a.

Wildlife Protection — A223

**1978, Nov. 1**
1033  A223  40r Porcupine ant-
                  eater             1.60   .50
1034  A223  75r Deer               2.75  1.40
   a.  Souv. sheet of 5, #1034, 4
          #1035 + label           14.00  14.00
1035  A223  100r Clouded tiger     4.50  1.60
   a.  Souvenir sheet of 1         4.75  4.75
       Nos. 1033-1035 (3)          8.85  3.50

Stamps in No. 1034a are in changed colors.
Souvenir sheets inscribed for Essen 2nd Intl.
Stamp Fair.

### Orchid Type of 1975

Orchids: 40r, Phalaenopsis sri rejeki. 75r,
Dendrobium macrophilium. 100r, Cymbidium
fynlaysonianum.

**1978, Dec. 22     Photo.     Perf. 12½**
1036  A183  40r multicolored       1.50   .50
1037  A183  75r multicolored       2.25   .85
1038  A183  100r multicolored      3.75  1.10
   a.  Souvenir sheet of 1         4.75  4.75
       Nos. 1036-1038 (3)          7.50  2.45

Douglas DC-3, 1949, over
Volcano — A224

Designs: 75r, Douglas DC-9 over village.
100r, Douglas DC-10 over temple.

**1979, Jan. 26     Photo.     Perf. 12½**
1039  A224  40r multicolored       1.00   .40
1040  A224  75r multicolored       1.25   .40
1041  A224  100r multicolored      2.10  1.00
       Nos. 1039-1041 (3)          4.35  1.80

Garuda Indonesian Airways, 30th anniv.

A225

40r, Thomas Cup and badminton player.

**1979, Feb. 24     Photo.     Perf. 12½**
1042  A225  40r Thomas Cup&
                  player           .50   .20
1043  A225  100r Player hitting ball  1.10   .20
1044  A225  100r Player facing left   1.40   .20
   a.  Pair, #1043-1044            2.50
   b.  Blkt. pane, 3 each #1032,
          1043-1044 + label        7.75
       Nos. 1042-1044 (3)          3.00   .60

11th Thomas Cup, Djakarta, May 24-June 2.
#1044a forms a continuous design.
Stamps from #1044b have straight edges.

Paphiopedilum
Lowii — A227

Orchids: 100r, 300r, Vanda limbata. 125r,
Phalaenopsis gigantea. 250r, as 60r.

**1979, Mar. 22     Photo.     Perf. 12½**
1045  A227  60r multi              1.40   .40
1046  A227  100r multi             2.00   .60
1047  A227  125r multi             2.75  1.00
   a.  Souvenir sheet of 1         4.25  4.25
   b.  Souv. sheet of 2 (250r,
          300r)                   10.00 10.00
       Nos. 1045-1047 (3)          6.15  2.00

No. 1047b, issued for Asian Phil. Exhib.,
Dortmund, West Germany, May 24-27. Sold
for 650r.

Family and
Houses — A228

Third Five-year Plan: 60r, Pylon and fields.
100r, School and clinic. 125r, Factories and
trucks. 150r, Motorized mail delivery.

**1979-82**
1047C  A228  12.50r Plane, food
                  ('80)            .20   .20
1047D  A228  17.50r Bridge ('82)   .20   .20
1048   A228  35r green & olive     .20   .20
1049   A228  60r blue & olive      .35   .20
1050   A228  100r blue & dk brn    .60   .20
1051   A228  125r red brn & ol     .85   .25
1052   A228  150r carmine &
                  yel              .90   .20
       Nos. 1047C-1052 (7)         3.30  1.55

See No. 1058a.

R. A.
Kartini
and
Girls'
School
A229

**1979, Apr. 21     Photo.     Perf. 12½**
1053  A229  100r Kartini           1.00   .30
1054  A229  100r School            1.00   .30
   a.  Pair, #1053-1054            2.00   .75

Mrs. R. A. Kartini, educator, birth centenary.

Bureau of Education,
UNESCO
Emblems — A231

**1979, May 25     Photo.     Perf. 12½**
1055  A231  150r multicolored      1.90   .20

50th anniversary of the statutes of the International Bureau of Education.

Self Defense
A232

Cooperation
Emblem
A233

Designs: 125r, Games' emblem. 150r,
Senayan Main Stadium.

**1979, June 21     Photo.     Perf. 12½**
1056  A232  60r multicolored       .60   .20
1057  A232  125r multicolored      1.10   .25
1058  A232  150r multicolored      1.50   .30
   a.  Bklt. pane of 6+4 labels
          (#1052, 5 #1058)         7.75
       Nos. 1056-1058 (3)          3.20   .75

10th So. East Asia Games, Djakarta, Sept.
21-30.
Stamps from #1058a have straight edges.
Issue date: No. 1058a, Sept. 27.

**1979, July 12     Photo.     Perf. 12½**
1059  A233  150r multicolored      1.25   .25

32nd Indonesian Cooperative Day.

A234

Designs: 60r, IYC and natl. IYC emblems.
150r, IYC emblem.

**1979, Aug. 4     Photo.     Perf. 12½**
1060  A234  60r emerald & blk      .55   .20
1061  A234  150r blue & blk        1.00   .25

International Year of the Child.

A235

**1979, Sept. 20     Photo.     Perf. 12½**
1062  A235  150r TELECOM 79        1.25   .25

3rd World Telecommunications Exhibition,
Geneva, Sept. 20-26.

Fight Drug
Abuse — A236

**1979, Oct. 17     Photo.     Perf. 12½**
1063  A236  150r deep rose & blk   1.25   .30

Dolphin — A237

Wildlife Protection: 125r, Freshwater
dolphin. 150r, Leatherback turtle.

**1979, Nov. 24     Photo.     Perf. 12½**
1064  A237  60r multi              1.50   .75
1065  A237  125r multi             2.75   .85
1066  A237  150r multi             5.25  1.10
       Nos. 1064-1066 (3)          9.50  2.70

**Souvenir Sheet**
1066A  A237  200r like #1066       7.50   .50

Ship Made of
Cloves — A238

Spice Race, Jakarta-Amsterdam (Sailing
Ships): 60r, Penisi, vert. 150r, Madurese boat,
vert.

**1980, Mar. 12     Photo.     Perf. 12½**
1067  A238  60r bright blue        .50   .20
1068  A238  125r red brown         1.00   .20
1069  A238  150r red lilac         1.50   .25
       Nos. 1067-1069 (3)          3.00   .65

**1980**

**Souvenir Sheets**
1069A  A238  300r like #1068       5.50  2.10
1069B  A238  500r like #1067       7.50  2.75

Issue dates: 300r, Mar. 12. 500r, May 6.
500r for London 1980 Intl. Stamp Exhib.

Rubber
Raft in
Rapids
A239

**Perf. 13½x13, 13x13½**
**1980, Mar. 21                    Photo.**
1070  A239  60r shown              .40   .20
1071  A239  125r Mountain
                  climbing, vert.  1.10   .20
1072  A239  150r Hang gliding,
                  vert.            1.50   .25
       Nos. 1070-1072 (3)          3.00   .65

**Souvenir Sheet**
1072A  A239  300r like #1070       5.00  3.25

A240                A241

**1980, Apr. 15                    Perf. 12½**
1073  A240  150r multicolored      1.25   .30

Anti-smoking Campaign.

**1980, Apr. 21     Photo.     Perf. 12½**
1074  A241  125r Flowers In vase   1.10   .20
1075  A241  150r Bouquet           1.60   .25

2nd Flower Festival, Jakarta, Apr. 19-21.
See No. 1080a-1080b.

A242                A243

**1980, Apr. 24                    Perf. 13x13½**

Conference building.

1076  A242  150r gold & lil rose   1.50   .25

**Souvenir Sheet**
1076A  A242  300r multicolored     4.50  3.25

1st Asian-African Conf., 25th anniv.

**1980, May 2                      Perf. 12½**

Designs: 60r, Male figure. 125r, Elephant
stone. 150r, Taman Bali Stone Sarcophagus,
2000 B.C.

1077  A243  60r multicolored       .65   .20
1078  A243  125r multicolored      1.25   .20
1079  A243  150r multicolored      1.75   .25
       Nos. 1077-1079 (3)          3.65   .65

## Flower and Sculpture Types of 1980
### Souvenir Sheet

| 1980 | **Photo.** | | **Perf. 12½** | |
|---|---|---|---|---|
| **1080** | Sheet of 8 | | 17.00 | 3.00 |
| a. | A241 100r like #1074 | | 1.10 | .20 |
| b. | A241 100r like #1075 | | 1.10 | .20 |
| c. | A243 200r like #1077 | | 2.00 | .45 |
| d. | A243 200r like #1079 | | 2.00 | .45 |

London 1980 Intl. Stamp Exhib., May 6-14. No. 1080 contains 2 stamps of each design (4x2).

Draftsman in Wheelchair A244

Discus Thrower A245

**1980, May 18    Photo.    Perf. 12½**

| 1081 | A244 | 100r multicolored | 1.00 | .20 |
|---|---|---|---|---|

Disabled Veterans Corp, 30th anniversary.

**1980, May 18**

| 1082 | A245 | 75r dp orange & sep | 1.00 | .20 |
|---|---|---|---|---|

Olympics for the Disabled, Arnhem, Netherlands, June 21-July 5.

Pres. Suharto — A246

A246a

A246b

**Perf. 13½x12½, 12½**

| 1980-83 | | | **Photo.** | |
|---|---|---|---|---|
| **1083** | A246 | 12.50r lt grn & grn | .50 | .25 |
| **1084** | A246 | 50r lt grn & bl | .50 | .20 |
| **1084A** | A246 | 55r red rose & red lil | .50 | .20 |
| **1085** | A246 | 75r lem & gldn brn | .75 | .20 |
| **1086** | A246 | 100r brt pink & bl | 1.25 | .20 |
| a. | | Bklt pane of 8 + 2 labels (6 #1086, 2 #1088, Inscribed 1981) | 8.00 | |
| **1087** | A246a | 110r dull org & dp red lil | .50 | .20 |
| **1088** | A246 | 200r dull org & brn | 1.25 | 1.25 |
| **1088A** | A246a | 250r dull org & brn | 2.25 | .50 |
| **1089** | A246a | 275r lt ap grn & dk grn | 1.25 | .20 |
| **1090** | A246 | 300r rose lil & gold | 3.25 | .60 |
| **1091** | A246 | 400r multicolored | 3.50 | .80 |

**Engr.**
**Perf. 12½x13**

| 1092 | A246b | 500r dk red brown | 3.75 | 1.00 |
|---|---|---|---|---|
| | Nos. 1083-1092 (12) | | 19.25 | 5.60 |

Issued: 12.50r, 50r, 75r, 100r, 200r, 6/8; 300r, 400r, 8/8/81; 250r, 9/82; 500r, 3/11/83; 55r, 7/83; 110r, 275r, 9/27/83.

See Nos. 1257-1261, 1265, 1268. For surcharge see No. 1527.

Map of Indonesia, People — A247

**1980, July 17    Perf. 12½**

| 1093 | A247 | 75r blue & pink | .45 | .20 |
|---|---|---|---|---|
| 1094 | A247 | 200r blue & dull yel | 1.50 | .40 |

1980 population census.

Ship Laying Cable — A248

**1980, Aug. 8    Photo.    Perf. 12½**

| 1095 | A248 | 75r multicolored | .45 | .20 |
|---|---|---|---|---|
| 1096 | A248 | 200r multicolored | 1.50 | .40 |

Singapore-Indonesia submarine cable opening.

50s Stamp of 1946 — A249

100r, 15s Battle of Surabaya stamp, 1946, horiz. 200r, 15s Independence Fund stamp, 1946.

**1980, Aug. 17**

| 1097 | A249 | 75r dk brn & dp org | .60 | .35 |
|---|---|---|---|---|
| 1098 | A249 | 100r gold & purple | 1.25 | .50 |
| 1099 | A249 | 200r multicolored | 1.90 | .80 |
| | Nos. 1097-1099 (3) | | 3.75 | 1.65 |

Independence, 35th anniversary.

 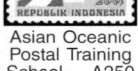

Asian Oceanic Postal Training School — A250

OPEC Anniv. Emblem — A251

**1980, Sept. 10    Photo.    Perf. 12½**

| 1100 | A250 | 200r multicolored | 1.50 | .40 |
|---|---|---|---|---|

**1980, Sept. 14**

| 1101 | A251 | 200r multicolored | 1.60 | .40 |
|---|---|---|---|---|

Organization of Petroleum Exporting Countries, 20th anniversary.

Armed Forces, 35th Anniversary — A252

**1980, Oct. 5    Photo.    Perf. 13½x13**

| 1102 | A252 | 75r shown | .80 | .50 |
|---|---|---|---|---|
| 1103 | A252 | 200r Service men and emblem | 1.40 | .75 |

Vulturine Parrot — A253

One Day Beauty Orchid — A254

Designs: Parrots.

**1980, Nov. 25    Photo.    Perf. 13x12½**

| 1104 | A253 | 75r shown | 1.90 | .60 |
|---|---|---|---|---|
| 1105 | A253 | 100r Yellow-backed lory | 3.50 | .90 |
| 1106 | A253 | 200r Red lory | 6.50 | 1.10 |
| | Nos. 1104-1106 (3) | | 11.90 | 2.60 |

### Souvenir Sheet
**Perf. 12½**

| 1106A | | Sheet of 3 | 25.00 | 22.50 |
|---|---|---|---|---|
| b. | A253 | 250r like #1105 | 4.50 | 3.50 |
| c. | A253 | 350r like #1104 | 7.00 | 6.00 |
| d. | A253 | 400r like #1106 | 8.00 | 7.00 |

**1980, Dec. 10    Perf. 13x13½**

Designs: Orchids.

| 1107 | A254 | 75r shown | 1.25 | .35 |
|---|---|---|---|---|
| 1108 | A254 | 100r Dendrobium discolor | 2.50 | .85 |
| 1109 | A254 | 200r Dendrobium lasianthera | 4.50 | .85 |
| | Nos. 1107-1109 (3) | | 8.25 | 2.05 |

### Souvenir Sheet

| 1980 | | | **Perf. 13x13½** | |
|---|---|---|---|---|
| **1110** | | Sheet of 2 | 19.00 | 12.50 |
| a. | A254 | 250r like #1109 | 8.00 | 5.00 |
| b. | A254 | 350r like #1108 | 10.50 | 7.00 |

Heinrich von Stephan (1831-1897), UPU Founder — A255

**1981, Jan. 7    Perf. 13½x12½**

| 1111 | A255 | 200r brt bl & dk bl | 1.60 | .80 |
|---|---|---|---|---|

6th Asian Pacific Scout Jamboree A256

**1981    Perf. 13½x12½, 12½x13½**

| 1112 | A256 | 75r Emblems | .65 | .50 |
|---|---|---|---|---|
| 1113 | A256 | 100r Scouts, vert. | 1.00 | .50 |
| 1114 | A256 | 200r Emblems, diff. | 1.60 | .80 |
| | Nos. 1112-1114 (3) | | 3.25 | 1.80 |

### Souvenir Sheet

| 1115 | A256 | 150r like #1113 | 5.50 | .60 |
|---|---|---|---|---|

Issued: #1112-1114, 2/22; #1115, 8/14.

4th Asian-Oceanian Postal Union Congress A257

Blood Donor Campaign A258

**1981, Mar. 18    Perf. 12½**

| 1116 | A257 | 200r multicolored | 1.75 | .40 |
|---|---|---|---|---|

**1981, Apr. 22**

| 1117 | A258 | 75r Girl holding blood drop | .50 | .20 |
|---|---|---|---|---|
| 1118 | A258 | 100r Hands holding blood drop | .90 | .20 |
| 1119 | A258 | 200r Hands, blood, diff. | 1.60 | .40 |
| | Nos. 1117-1119 (3) | | 3.00 | .80 |

Intl. Family Planning Conference — A259

**1981, Apr. 26**

| 1120 | A259 | 200r multicolored | 1.50 | .80 |
|---|---|---|---|---|

Natl. Education Day — A260

Traditional Bali Paintings: Nos. 1121-1122, Song of Sritanjung. No. 1123, Birth of the Eagle.

**1981, May 2**

| 1121 | A260 | 100r multicolored | 1.10 | .20 |
|---|---|---|---|---|
| 1122 | A260 | 200r multicolored | 2.10 | .40 |
| a. | A260 | Pair #1121-1122 | 3.20 | .60 |

### Souvenir Sheet

| 1123 | | Sheet of 2 | 12.00 | 3.00 |
|---|---|---|---|---|
| a. | A260 | 400r multicolored | 3.50 | .75 |
| b. | A261 | 600r multicolored | 6.00 | 1.25 |

No. 1123 has margin showing WIPA '81 emblem. Sheets exist with marginal inscription "Indonesien grusst WIPA."

A262

A263

**1981, May 9**

| 1124 | A262 | 200r multicolored | 1.75 | .40 |
|---|---|---|---|---|

ASEAN Building Jakarta, opening.

**1981, May 22**

| 1125 | A263 | 200r multicolored | 3.00 | .40 |
|---|---|---|---|---|

Uber Cup '81 Badminton Championship, Tokyo.

World Environment Day — A264

Bas-reliefs, Candhi Merut Buddhist Temple, Central Java: 75r, Tree of Life. 200r, Reclining Buddha.

**1981, June 5**

| 1126 | A264 | 75r multicolored | .50 | .20 |
|---|---|---|---|---|
| 1127 | A264 | 200r multicolored | 1.50 | .40 |

12th Koran Reading Competition, June 7-14 — A265

**1981, June 7    Perf. 13½x12½**

| 1128 | A265 | 200r multicolored | 1.25 | .40 |
|---|---|---|---|---|

Intl. Year of the Disabled A266

**1981, July 31    Perf. 12½**

| 1129 | A266 | 75r Blind man | .55 | .20 |
|---|---|---|---|---|
| 1130 | A266 | 200r Speech, hearing disabilities | 1.25 | .45 |

Soekarno-Hatta Independence
Monument, Jakarta — A267

**1981, Aug. 17**
1131 A267 200r multicolored 1.75 .40

Natl. Sports
Week, Sept.
19-30 — A268

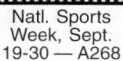

World Food
Day — A268a

**1981, Sept. 19**
1132 A268 75r Skydiving .50 .20
1133 A268 100r Skin diving,
horiz. .90 .20
1134 A268 200r Equestrian 1.60 .40
Nos. 1132-1134 (3) 3.00 .80

The horse on No. 1134 is brown black, See
Nos. 1374-1375 for souvenir sheets containing
No. 1134 in different colors.

**1981, Oct. 16**
1135 A268a 200r multicolored 3.50 .40

Provincial
Arms — A269

Natl.
Arms
A270

**1981-83**
1136 A269 100r Aceh 1.75 .30
1137 A269 100r Bali 1.75 .30
1138 A269 100r Bengkulu 1.75 .30
1139 A269 100r Jakarta 1.75 .30
1140 A269 100r West Irian 1.75 .30
1141 A269 100r West Java 1.75 .30
1142 A269 100r Jambi 1.75 .30
1143 A269 100r Central Java 1.75 .30
1144 A269 100r East Java 1.75 .30
1145 A269 100r South Kalimantan 1.75 .30
1146 A269 100r East Kali-
mantan 1.75 .30
1147 A269 100r West Kali-
mantan 1.75 .30
1148 A269 100r Lampung 1.75 .30
1149 A269 100r Central Kalimantan 1.75 .30
1150 A269 100r Moluccas 1.75 .30
1151 A269 100r West Nusa
Tenggara 1.75 .30
1152 A269 100r East Nusa
Tenggara 1.75 .30
1153 A269 100r Southeast Celebes 1.75 .30
1154 A269 100r Central Celebes 1.75 .30
1155 A269 100r West Sumatra 1.75 .30
1156 A269 100r North Celebes 1.75 .30
1157 A269 100r North Sumatra 1.75 .30
1158 A269 100r South Sumatra 1.75 .30
1159 A269 100r Riau 1.75 .30
1160 A269 100r South Sulawesi 1.75 .30
1161 A269 100r Yogyakarta 1.75 .30
1161A A269 100r Timor .50 .20
1162 A270 250r shown 4.00 .75
Nos. 1136-1162 (28) 50.00 8.75

Issued: Nos. 1136-1140, 1981; Nos. 1141-
1161, 1162, 1982; No. 1161A, 1983.

Pink-crested
Cockatoo — A271

**1981, Dec. 10**
1163 A271 75r shown 2.50 .20
1164 A271 100r Sulphur-crested
cockatoo 3.25 .20
1165 A271 200r King cockatoo 6.75 .40
Nos. 1163-1165 (3) 12.50 .80

**Souvenir Sheet**
1166 Sheet of 2 21.00 1.25
a. A271 150r like #1164 4.75 .30
b. A271 350r like #1165 15.00 .70

Bumiputra Mutual Life Insurance Co.,
70th Anniv. — A272

**1982, Feb. 12**
1167 A272 75r Family .50 .20
1168 A272 100r Family, diff. .85 .20
1169 A272 200r Hands holding
symbols 1.40 .40
Nos. 1167-1169 (3) 2.75 .80

Search and
Rescue Institute,
10th
Anniv. — A273

General
Election — A274

**1982, Feb. 28** *Perf. 12½x13½*
1170 A273 250r multicolored 1.75 .50

**1982, Mar. 1** *Perf. 12½*
1171 A274 75r Ballot, houses .50 .20
1172 A274 100r Farm .85 .20
1173 A274 200r Arms 1.40 .40
Nos. 1171-1173 (3) 2.75 .80

2nd UN Conference
on Exploration and
Peaceful Uses of
Outer Space,
Vienna, Aug. 9-
21 — A275

**1982, Apr. 19** *Perf. 13x13½*
1174 A275 150r Couple 1.10 .30
1175 A275 250r Emblem 2.50 .30

12th Thomas Badminton Cup, London,
May — A276

**1982, May 19**
1176 A276 250r multicolored 2.50 .50
a. Souvenir sheet of 2 9.50

No. 1176a also exists overprinted
"INDONESIE SALUE PHILEXFRANCE" in red
or black. Value, each $50.

1982 World
Cup — A277

**1982, June 14**
1177 A277 250r multi 3.25 .50
a. Souvenir sheet of 2 10.00
b.-c. Souvenir sheets of 2, each 200.00 80.00

#1177b overprinted in black; #1177c in red.
Fake overprints exist.

60th Anniv. of
Taman Siswa
Educational
System — A278

**1982, July 3**
1178 A278 250r multicolored 1.10 .50

15th Anniv. of Assoc. of South East
Asian Nations (ASEAN) — A279

**1982, Aug. 8** *Photo.* *Perf. 12½*
1179 A279 150r Members' flags 2.50 .30

Balinese
Starling
A280

Red Birds of
Paradise
A281

**1982, Oct. 11** *Photo.* *Perf. 13x13½*
1180 A280 100r shown 2.50 .20
1181 A280 250r King birds of
paradise 4.75 .55

**Souvenir Sheet**
1181A A280 500r like 100r 15.00 1.25

3rd World Natl. Park Cong., Denpasar Bali.

**1982, Dec. 20** *Perf. 12½x13½*
1182 A281 100r Lawe's six-
wired parotia 2.75 .20
1183 A281 150r Twelve-wired
birds of par-
adise 4.50 .30
1184 A281 250r shown 6.25 .50
Nos. 1182-1184 (3) 13.50 1.00

**Souvenir Sheet**
*Perf. 12½x13½*
1184A Sheet of 2 22.50 1.10
b. A281 200r like 100r 7.75 .45
c. A281 300r like 250r 12.50 .65

Scouting
Year
A282

**1983, Feb. 22** *Photo.* *Perf. 13½x13*
1185 A282 250r multi 2.50 .50

Restoration of Borobudur
Temple — A283

**1983, Feb. 23** *Perf. 12½*
1186 A283 100r Scaffolding,
crane, vert. 1.75 .20
1187 A283 150r Buddha statue,
stupas, vert. 2.75 .20
1188 A283 250r Statue, temple 4.50 .35
Nos. 1186-1188 (3) 9.00 .75

**Souvenir Sheet**
1189 A283 500r Temple 17.50 1.10

Gas Plant — A284

World Commun-
ications
Year — A285

**1983, May 16** *Photo.* *Perf. 12½*
1190 A284 275r multi 1.75 .40

7th Intl. Liquefied Natural Gas Conference
and Exhibition, Jakarta, May 16-19.

**1983, May 17** *Perf. 12½x13½*
1191 A285 75r Dove, ships .55 .20
1192 A285 110r Satellite .70 .20
1193 A285 175r Dish antenna, jet 1.10 .30
1194 A285 275r Airmail envelope,
globe 1.40 .40
Nos. 1191-1194 (4) 3.75 1.10

See Nos. 1215-1216.

13th Natl. Koran Reading Competition,
Padang, May 23-31 — A286

**1983, May 23** *Perf. 13½x13*
1195 A286 275r multi 1.75 .35

Total Solar Eclipse, June 11 — A287

**1983, June 11** *Perf. 12½*
1196 A287 110r Map, eclipse 1.10 .20
1197 A287 275r Map 2.25 .40

**Souvenir Sheet**
1198 A287 500r like 275r 15.00 1.10

Launch of
Palapa B
Satellite — A288

Agricultural
Census — A289

**1983, June 18          Perf. 12½x13½**
1199  A288  275r  multi                    1.75   .25

**1983, July 1     Photo.     Perf. 12½**
1200  A289  110r  Produce          .80   .20
1201  A289  275r  Farmer          1.60   .20

15th Anniv. of Indonesia-Pakistan
Economic and Cultural Cooperation
Org. — A290

Weavings.

**1983, Aug. 19**
1202  A290  275r  Indonesian,
                  Lombok           2.00   .20
1203  A290  275r  Pakistani, Balu-
                  chistan          2.00   .20

Krakatoa
Eruption
Centenary
A291

**1983, Aug. 26**
1204  A291  110r  Volcano         1.00   .20
1205  A291  275r  Map             2.00   .20

CN-235, Light Air Transport — A292

**1983, Sept. 10   Photo.    Perf. 12½**
1206  A292  275r  multi           1.75   .20

Tropical Fish — A293

**1983, Oct. 17     Photo.     Perf. 12½**
1207  A293  110r  Puntius te-
                  trazona          2.50   .20
1208  A293  175r  Rasbora
                  einthoveni       4.00   .20
1209  A293  275r  Toxotes jacu-
                  lator            7.00   .20
      Nos. 1207-1209 (3)         13.50   .60

Canderawasih
Birds — A294

**1983, Nov. 30   Photo.     Perf. 12½**
1210  A294  110r  Diphyllodes re-
                  spublica         1.60   .20
1211  A294  175r  Epimachus fas-
                  tuosus           2.25   .20
1212  A294  275r  Drepanornis al-
                  bertisi          4.25   .20
1213  A294  500r  like #1212       6.75   .40
      a.    Souvenir sheet of 1   24.00   .95
      Nos. 1210-1213 (4)         14.85  1.00

Inalienable
Rights of
the
Palestinian
People
A295

**1983, Dec. 20          Perf. 13½x13**
1214  A295  275r  multi           1.75   .20

WCY Type of 1983
Souvenir Sheets

**1983       Photo.    Perf. 12½x13½**
1215  A285  400r  like No. 1192  11.00   .60
1216  A285  500r  like No. 1194  11.00   .60

Telecom '83 exhib., Geneva, Oct. 26-Nov. 1
(400r). Philatelic Museum opening, Jakarta
(500r). Issued: 400r, Oct. 26; 500r, Sept. 29.

Fight Against
Polio — A296

4th Five-Year
Development
Plan — A297

**1984, Feb. 17    Photo.     Perf. 12½**
1217  A296  110r  Emblem          .65   .20
1218  A296  275r  Stylized person 1.50   .20

**1984, Apr. 1     Photo.     Perf. 12½**
1219  A297   55r  Fertilizer industry  .25   .20
1220  A297   75r  Aviation         .35   .20
1221  A297  110r  Shipping         .50   .20
1222  A297  275r  Communications  1.25   .20
      Nos. 1219-1222 (4)          2.35   .80

Forestry
Resources
A298

**1984, May 17    Photo.     Perf. 12½**
1223  A298   75r  Forest, paper
                  mill             .65   .20
1224  A298  110r  Seedling        1.10   .20
1225  A298  175r  Tree cutting    1.50   .20
1226  A298  275r  Logs            2.75   .20
      a.    Souv. sheet of 2, #1225-1226  20.00  .55
      Nos. 1223-1226 (4)          6.00   .80

17th Annual Meeting of ASEAN
Foreign Ministers — A299

**1984, July 9    Photo.     Perf. 12½**
1227  A299  275r  Flags           2.75   .20

1984 Summer
Olympics
A300

Horse Dancers,
Central Java — A301

**1984, July 28    Photo.     Perf. 12½**
1228  A300   75r  Pole vault      .75   .20
1229  A300  110r  Archery         .75   .20
1230  A300  175r  Boxing         1.25   .20
1231  A300  250r  Shooting       2.25   .25
1232  A300  275r  Weight lifting 2.50   .25
1233  A300  325r  Swimming       2.50   .30
      Nos. 1228-1233 (6)        10.00  1.40

**1984, Aug. 17          Perf. 12½x13½**

Processions.

1234  A301   75r  shown           .75   .20
1235  A301  110r  Reyog Po-
                  norogo, East
                  Java            1.25   .20
1236  A301  275r  Lion Dance,
                  West Java       3.00   .20
1237  A301  325r  Barong of Bali  3.50   .25
      Nos. 1234-1237 (4)          8.50   .85

Natl.
Sports
Day
A302

**1984, Sept. 9   Photo.    Perf. 13½x13**
1238  A302  110r  Thomas Cup vic-
                  tory            .75   .20
1239  A302  275r  Gymnastics     2.00   .20

Postcode
System
Inauguration
A303

**1984, Sept. 27   Photo.     Perf. 12½**
1240  A303  110r  multi          .55   .20
1241  A303  275r  multi         1.25   .20

Birds of Irian
Jaya — A304

Oath of the
Youth — A305

**1984, Oct. 15          Perf. 12½x13½**
1242  A304   75r  Chlamydera
                  lauterbachi     1.60   .20
1243  A304  110r  Sericulus aure-
                  us              2.50   .20
1244  A304  275r  Astrapia nigra  6.00   .25
1245  A304  325r  Lophorhina su-
                  perba           6.50   .30
      a.    Souv. sheet of 2, #1242,
           1245                  29.00  5.50
      Nos. 1242-1245 (4)         16.60   .95

No. 1245a for PHILAKOREA '84.

**1984, Oct. 28          Perf. 12½**
1246  A305  275r  Emblem          1.60   .20

ICAO, 40th Anniversary — A306

**1984, Dec. 7   Photo.   Perf. 13½x12½**
1247  A306  275r  Airplane, Em-
                  blem            1.75   .20

Indonesia
Netherlands
Marine Exped.,
1984-85 — A307

75th Intl.
Women's
Day — A308

Survey ship Snellius II and: 50r, Marine geological and geophysical exploration. 100r,
Mapping ocean currents. 275r, Studying
marine flora and fauna.

**1985, Feb. 27   Photo.   Perf. 13x13½**
1248  A307   50r  multi          .50   .20
1249  A307  100r  multi         1.00   .20
1250  A307  275r  multi         3.00   .25
      Nos. 1248-1250 (3)        4.50   .65

**1985, Mar. 8**
1251  A308  100r  Emblem         2.25   .20
1252  A308  275r  Silhouettes, em-
                  blem           6.75   .20

Five Year
Plan
A309

**1985, Apr. 1          Perf. 13½x13**
1254  A309   75r  Mecca pilgrim-
                  age program     .40   .20
1255  A309  140r  Compulsory edu-
                  cation          .75   .20
1256  A309  350r  Cement industry,
                  Padang works   1.90   .35
      Nos. 1254-1256 (3)         3.05   .75

Suharto Type of 1980-83 and

A310

A310a

A310b

A310c

**Perf. 13½x12½, 12½ (A310, A310a, A310b, A310c)**

**1983-93** Photo.

| | | | | |
|---|---|---|---|---|
| 1257 | A246 | 10r pale grn & dk grn | .20 | .20 |
| 1258 | A246 | 25r pale org & dk cop red | .30 | .20 |
| 1259 | A246 | 50r beige & dk brn | .20 | .20 |
| 1260 | A246 | 55r sal rose & rose | .25 | .20 |
| 1261 | A246 | 100r lt blue green & ultra | .40 | .20 |
| 1262 | A310 | 140r rose & dp brn | .65 | .20 |
| 1263 | A310c | 150r yel grn & multi | .55 | .20 |
| 1264 | A310b | 200r pink, bl & red | .55 | .20 |
| 1265 | A246 | 300r lt dull grn, bl grn & gold | 1.50 | .20 |
| 1266 | A310c | 300r multicolored | 1.25 | .20 |
| 1267 | A310 | 350r red & brt lil | 1.90 | .35 |
| 1268 | A246 | 400r blue grn, int blue & gold | 2.00 | .30 |
| 1268A | A310b | 700r pale grn, rose lil & grn | 2.10 | .35 |
| 1268B | A310c | 700r red & multi | 3.00 | 1.10 |
| 1269 | A310a | 1000r multi | 5.00 | .75 |
| | | Nos. 1257-1269 (15) | 19.85 | 4.85 |

Issued: 10r, 25r, 3/11; 140r, 350r, 4/10/85; 50r, 100r, #1265, 12/24/86; 55r, 400r, 12/87; 200r, 12/89; 700r, 3/90; 1000r, 8/17/88; 150r, #1266, 1268B, 8/17/93.

For surcharge see No. 1527.

Asia-Africa Conference, 30th Anniv. — A311

**1985, Apr. 24** Perf. 12½
1270 A311 350r Emblem, inscription 2.50 .30

Intl. Youth Year — A312

UN Decade for Women — A313

**1985, July 12** Perf. 12½x13½
1271 A312 75r Three youths, globe 1.00 .20
1272 A312 140r Youths supporting globe 2.00 .20

**1985, July 26**
1273 A313 55r Profiles of women, emblem .55 .20
1274 A313 140r Globe, emblem 1.25 .20

Indonesian Trade Fair — A314

**1985, Aug. 1**
1275 A314 140r Hydro-electric plant 1.00 .20
1276 A314 350r Farmer, industrial plant 2.50 .25

Republic of Indonesia, 40th anniv.

11th Natl. Sports Week, Jakarta, Sept. 9-20 A315

**Perf. 13½x12½, 12½x13½**

**1985, Sept. 9** Photo.
1277 A315 55r Sky diving .40 .20
1278 A315 100r Combat sports .75 .20
1279 A315 140r High jump 1.00 .20
1280 A315 350r Wind surfing, vert. 2.50 .25
Nos. 1277-1280 (4) 4.65 .85

Org. of Petroleum Exporting Countries, OPEC, 25th Anniv. — A316

**1985, Sept. 14** Perf. 12½
1281 A316 140r multi 1.50 .20

Natl. Oil Industry, Cent. A317

**1985, Oct. 8** Perf. 13½x13
1282 A317 140r Oil tankers .80 .20
1283 A317 250r Refinery 1.40 .20
1284 A317 350r Offshore oil rig 2.00 .25
Nos. 1282-1284 (3) 4.20 .65

UN, 40th Anniv. — A318

Design: 140r, Doves, 40, emblem. 300r, Bombs transformed into plants.

**1985, Oct. 24** Perf. 12½
1285 A318 140r multicolored .85 .20
1286 A318 300r multicolored 1.60 .20

Wildlife A318a

**1985, Dec. 27 Photo. Perf. 14½x13**
1286A A318a 75r Rhinoceros sondaicus 1.25 .20
1286B A318a 150r Anoa depressicornis 2.50 .20
1286C A318a 300r Varanus komodoensis 5.00 .20
Nos. 1286A-1286C (3) 8.75 .60

1986 Industrial Census — A319

**1986, Feb. 8 Photo. Perf. 12½**
1287 A319 Pair 1.75 .40
a. 175r Census emblem .85 .20
b. 175r Symbols of industry .85 .20

UN Child Survival Campaign A320

**1986, Mar. 15 Photo. Perf. 12½**
1288 A320 75r Breastfeeding .80 .20
1289 A320 140r Immunization 1.40 .20

UNICEF, 40th anniv.

4th 5-year Development Plan — A321

14th Thomas Cup, 13th Uber Cup, Jakarta — A322

**1986, Apr. 1 Photo. Perf. 12½**
1290 A321 140r Construction .30 .20
1291 A321 500r Agriculture 1.25 .30

**1986, Apr. 22**
1292 A322 55r Cup, racket .90 .20
1293 A322 150r Cups, horiz. 2.00 .20

EXPO '86, Vancouver — A323

**1986, May 2 Perf. 12½x14½**
1294 A323 75r Pinisi junk .65 .20
1295 A323 150r Kentongan, satellite 1.25 .20
1296 A323 300r Pavilion emblem 2.25 .30
Nos. 1294-1296 (3) 4.15 .70

Natl. Scout Jamboree, JAMNAS '86, Cibubur Jakarta East A324

**Perf. 13½x12½, 12½x13½**

**1986, June 21** Photo.
1297 A324 100r Saluting flag 1.25 .20
1298 A324 140r Cookout 1.75 .20
1299 A324 210r Map-reading, vert. 2.50 .25
Nos. 1297-1299 (3) 5.50 .65

Air Show '86, Jakarta, June 22-July 1 A325

**1986, June 23** Perf. 13½x12½
1300 A325 350r multi 2.25 .25

Folk Dances — A326

**1986, July 30 Photo. Perf. 12½**
1301 A326 140r Legong Kraton 1.25 .20
1302 A326 350r Barong 3.25 .35
1303 A326 500r Kecak 4.50 .45
Nos. 1301-1303 (3) 9.00 1.00

19th Congress of Intl. Society of Sugar Cane Technologists, Jakarta — A327

**1986, Aug. 5** Perf. 12½x13½
1304 A327 150r Planting .90 .20
1305 A327 300r Sugar 1.75 .30

Sea-Me-We Submarine Cable Inauguration — A328

**1986, Sept. 8** Perf. 12½
1306 A328 140r shown .75 .20
1307 A328 350r Map, diff. 2.25 .35

Southeast Asia, Middle East, Western Europe Submarine Cable.

Intl. Peace Year — A329

1987 General Election — A330

**1986, Dec. 17 Photo. Perf. 12½**
1308 A329 350r shown 1.25 .20
1309 A329 500r Dove circling Earth 2.50 .35

**1987, Jan. 19**

75r, Tourism, party emblems, industry. 350r, Emblems, natl. eagle, ballot box.

1310 A330 75r multi .35 .20
1311 A330 140r multi .70 .20
1312 A330 350r multi 1.60 .35
Nos. 1310-1312 (3) 2.65 .75

A331

A332

**1987, Mar. 21    Photo.    Perf. 12½**
1313  A331  350r  Satellite, horiz.  1.00  .20
1314  A331  500r  shown  2.25  .35
Launch of Palapa B-2P, Cape Canaveral.

**1987, Apr. 1**
1315  A332  140r  Boy carving figurines, horiz.  .40  .20
1316  A332  350r  shown  1.00  .35
4th 5-Year Development Plan.

Folk Costumes — A333

**1987, May 25    Perf. 13x13½**
1317  A333  140r  Kalimantan Timur  4.75  .20
1318  A333  350r  Daerah Aceh  11.00  .35
1319  A333  400r  Timor Timur  12.50  .45
Nos. 1317-1319 (3)  28.25  1.00
See Nos. 1358-1363, 1412-1417, 1448-1453, 1464-1469.

14th Southeast Asia Games, Jakarta, Sept. 9-20 A334

Anniv. Emblems A335

**1987, June 10    Perf. 12½**
1320  A334  140r  Weight lifting  .70  .20
1321  A334  250r  Swimming  1.40  .25
1322  A334  350r  Running  1.90  .35
Nos. 1320-1322 (3)  4.00  .80

**1987, June 20**
1323  A335  75r  multi, horiz.  1.75  .20
1324  A335  100r  shown  2.25  .20
City of Jakarta, 460th anniv.; Jakarta Fair, 20th anniv.

Children's Day — A336

ASEAN Headquarters, Jakarta — A337

**1987, July 23**
1325  A336  100r  Education, horiz.  .60  .20
1326  A336  250r  Universal immunization  1.40  .25

**1987, Aug. 8**
1327  A337  350r  multi  2.00  .25
ASEAN, 20th anniv.

Assoc. of Physicians Specializing in Internal Diseases, 30th Anniv. — A338

**1987, Aug. 23    Photo.**
1328  A338  300r  Stylized man, caduceus  1.40  .25

Sand Craters, Mt. Bromo, Timur A339

**1987, Oct. 20    Perf. 13½x12½**
1329  A339  140r  shown  .75  .20
1330  A339  350r  Bratan (Bedugul) Lake, Bali  2.75  .35
1331  A339  500r  Sea gardens, Bunaken Is.  4.00  .45
Nos. 1329-1331 (3)  7.50  1.00
Tourism. See Nos. 1367-1370A, 1408-1410, 1420-1422.

Role of Women in the Fight for Independence A340

**1987, Nov. 10    Perf. 12½**
1332  A340  75r  Veteran  .65  .20
1333  A340  100r  Soldiers, barbed wire (Laskar Wanita)  .85  .20

Fish — A341

**1987, Dec. 30**
1334  A341  150r  Osphronemus goramy  1.50  .20
1335  A341  200r  Cyprinus carpio  2.00  .20
1336  A341  500r  Clarias batrachus  5.00  .55
Nos. 1334-1336 (3)  8.50  .95

Natl. Veteran's League, 31st Anniv. — A342

**1988, Jan. 2**
1337  A342  250r  blue grn & org  1.40  .25

Occupational Health and Safety for Greater Efficiency and Productivity — A343

**1988, Jan. 12    Perf. 13½x12½**
1338  A343  350r  Worker using safety equipment  1.75  .35
See No. 1419.

Natl. Craft Council, 8th Anniv. — A344

Crafts: 120r, Carved wood snake and frog. 350r, Cane rocking chair. 500r, Ornate carved bamboo containers and fan.

**1988, Mar. 3    Photo.    Perf. 12½**
1339  A344  120r  ultra & dark brn  .65  .20
1340  A344  350r  lt blue & dark brn  1.60  .30
1341  A344  500r  yel grn & dark brn  2.25  .40
Nos. 1339-1341 (3)  4.50  .90

Pelita IV (Five-Year Development Plan) — A345

**1988, Apr. 1**
1342  A345  140r  Oil rig, refinery  .30  .20
1343  A345  400r  Crayfish, trawler  .95  .20

World Expo '88, Brisbane, Australia A346

Intl. Red Cross and Red Crescent Organizations, 125th Annivs. A347

Designs: 200r, Two children, Borobudur Temple in silhouette. 350r, Boy wearing armor and headdress. 350r, Girl, boy and a Tongkonan house, Toraja, South Sulawesi.

**1988, Apr. 30    Photo.    Perf. 12½**
1344  A346  200r  multi  .90  .20
1345  A346  300r  multi  1.40  .25
1346  A346  350r  multi  1.90  .35
a.    Souv. sheet of 3, #1344-1346  15.00  4.00
Nos. 1344-1346 (3)  4.20  .80
No. 1346a exists imperf. Value: $40 unused, $30 used.

**1988, May 8**
1347  A347  350r  black & red  1.60  .30

Orchids — A348

**1988, May 17    Perf. 13x13½**
1348  A348  400r  Dendrobium none  1.75  .30
1349  A348  500r  Dendrobium abang  2.25  .35

1988 Summer Olympics, Seoul — A349

Intl. Council of Women, Cent. — A350

**1988, June 15    Photo.    Perf. 12½**
1350  A349  75r  Running  .50  .20
1351  A349  100r  Weight lifting  .55  .20
1352  A349  200r  Archery  1.10  .20
1353  A349  300r  Table tennis  1.60  .20
1354  A349  400r  Swimming  2.25  .30
a.    Souv. sheet of 3 + label, #1351-1352, 1354, imperf  22.50  3.25

1355  A349  500r  Tennis  2.75  .35
a.    Souv. sheet of 3 + label, #1350, 1353, 1355, imperf  22.50  3.50
Nos. 1350-1355 (6)  8.75  1.45
Sheets exist perf. Value, each $30.

**1988, June 26**
1356  A350  140r  brt blue & blk  1.00  .20

7th Natl. Farmers' Week — A351

**1988, July 9**
1357  A351  350r  lake & bister  1.75  .25

Folk Costumes Type of 1987

Traditional wedding attire from: 55r, West Sumatra. 75p, Jambi. 100r, Bengkulu. 120r, Lampung. 200r, Moluccas. 250r, East Nusa.

**1988, July 15    Perf. 12½x14½**
1358  A333  55r  multicolored  .55  .20
**Perf. 12½x13½**
1359  A333  75r  multicolored  .80  .20
1360  A333  100r  multicolored  1.00  .20
1361  A333  120r  multicolored  1.25  .20
**Perf. 12½x14½**
1362  A333  200r  multicolored  1.90  .20
1363  A333  250r  multicolored  2.50  .20
Nos. 1358-1363 (6)  8.00  1.20

A352

A353

**1988, Sept. 29    Photo.    Perf. 12½**
1364  A352  500r  multicolored  2.00  .25
13th Congress of the Non-Aligned News Agencies Pool, Jakarta, Sept. 29-Oct. 1.

**1988, Oct. 9**
1365  A353  140r  multi  1.10  .20
Intl. Letter Writing Week.

Transportion and Communications Decade for Asia and the Pacific (1985-1995) A354

**1988, Oct. 24**
1366  A354  350r  blk & lt blue  2.00  .30

Tourism Type of 1987

Architecture: 250r, Al Mashun Mosque, Medan. 300r, Pagaruyung Palace, Batusangkar. 500r, 1000r, Keong Emas Taman Theater, Jakarta.

**1988-89    Photo.    Perf. 13½x13**
1367  A339  250r  multi  1.25  .20
1368  A339  300r  multi  1.50  .20
1369  A339  500r  multi  2.50  .35
Nos. 1367-1369 (3)  5.25  .75

**Souvenir Sheets**
**Imperf**
1370  A339  1000r  multi  14.00  1.40
**Perf. 14½x13**
1370A    Sheet of 2  19.00  4.75
b.    A339 1500r like No. 1367  7.25  1.60
c.    A339 2500r like No. 1368  11.50  2.75
No. 1370 exists perf 14½x12½. Value $18.
Issue dates: No. 1370A, Nov. 1989; others, Nov. 25, 1988. World Stamp Expo '89, Washington, DC.

Butterflies
A356

Flora
A357

**1988, Dec. 20**     **Perf. 12½x13½**
| | | | | |
|---|---|---|---|---|
| 1371 | A356 | 400r | *Papilio gigon* | 2.75 | .30 |
| 1372 | A356 | 500r | *Graphium androcles* | 3.75 | .35 |

**Souvenir Sheet**
**Imperf**
| | | | | |
|---|---|---|---|---|
| 1373 | A356 | 1000r | like 500r | 11.00 | .75 |

No. 1373 exists perf. 12½x14½. Value *$26.*

**Equestrian Type of 1981**
**Souvenir Sheets**
**1988**     **Imperf.**
| | | | |
|---|---|---|---|
| 1374 | | Sheet of 4 | 12.50 | .65 |
| a. | | A268 200r blk, dark red & grn | .50 | .20 |
| 1375 | | Sheet of 1 + label, dk bl, dark red & deep org | 12.50 | .20 |

FILACEPT '88, The Hague, Oct. 18-23, 1988. Nos. 1374-1375 exist perf. 12½. Value, each *$17.*

**1989, Jan. 7**   **Photo.**   **Perf. 13½x13**
| | | | | |
|---|---|---|---|---|
| 1376 | A357 | 200r | *Rafflesia* | .90 | .20 |
| 1377 | A357 | 1000r | *Amorphophallus titanum* | 4.50 | .70 |

**Souvenir Sheet**
**Perf. 13½x14½**
| | | | | |
|---|---|---|---|---|
| 1378 | A357 | 1000r | like No. 1377, value in blk | 35.00 | .70 |

Garuda Indonesia Airlines, 40th Anniv. — A358

**1989, Jan. 26**     **Perf. 12½**
| | | | | |
|---|---|---|---|---|
| 1379 | A358 | 350r | bl grn & brt bl | 2.00 | .25 |

World Wildlife Fund — A359

Orangutans, *Pongo pygmaeus.*

**1989, Mar. 6**   **Photo.**   **Perf. 12½**
| | | | | |
|---|---|---|---|---|
| 1380 | A359 | 75r | Adult and young | 4.00 | .85 |
| 1381 | A359 | 100r | Adult hanging in tree | 4.00 | .45 |
| a. | | Souv. sheet of 2, #1380-1381 | 67.50 | 60.00 |
| 1382 | A359 | 140r | Adult, young in tree | 4.00 | .55 |
| 1383 | A359 | 500r | Adult's head | 11.00 | 3.00 |
| a. | | Souv. sheet of 2, #1382-1383 | 67.50 | 60.00 |
| | | Nos. 1380-1383 (4) | 23.00 | 4.85 |

Use of Postage Stamps in Indonesia, 125th Anniv. — A360

**1989, Apr. 1**
| | | | | |
|---|---|---|---|---|
| 1384 | A360 | 1000r | grn, rose lilac & deep blue | 2.75 | .70 |

5th Five-year Development Plan — A361

Industries.

**1989, Apr. 1**
| | | | | |
|---|---|---|---|---|
| 1385 | A361 | 55r | Fertilizer | .20 | .20 |
| 1386 | A361 | 150r | Cilegon Iron and Steel Mill | .30 | .20 |
| 1387 | A361 | 350r | Petroleum | .80 | .25 |
| | | Nos. 1385-1387 (3) | 1.30 | .65 |

See Nos. 1427-1428, 1461-1462, 1488-1489, 1530-1532.

Natl. Education Day — A362

Ki Hadjar Dewantara (b. 1889), founder of Taman Siswa school and: 140r, Graduate. 300r, Pencil, globe and books.

**1989, May 2**
| | | | | |
|---|---|---|---|---|
| 1388 | A362 | 140r | ver, lake & brt rose lil | .60 | .20 |
| 1389 | A362 | 300r | vio & pale grn | 1.40 | .20 |

Terbuka University (140r) and freedom from illiteracy (300r).

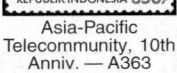

Asia-Pacific Telecommunity, 10th Anniv. — A363

Sudirman Cup, Flag — A364

**1989, July 1**   **Photo.**   **Perf. 12½**
| | | | | |
|---|---|---|---|---|
| 1390 | A363 | 350r | green & vio | 1.50 | .30 |

**1989, July 3**
| | | | | |
|---|---|---|---|---|
| 1391 | A364 | 100r | scar, gold & dark red brn | 1.75 | .20 |

Sudirman Cup world badminton mixed team championships, Jakarta, May 24-28.

Natl. Children's Day — A365

CIRDAP, 10th Anniv. — A366

**1989, July 23**
| | | | | |
|---|---|---|---|---|
| 1392 | A365 | 100r | Literacy | .50 | .20 |
| 1393 | A365 | 250r | Physical fitness | 1.25 | .20 |

**1989, July 29**
| | | | | |
|---|---|---|---|---|
| 1394 | A366 | 140r | blue & dark red brn | 1.10 | .20 |

Center on Integrated Rural Development for Asia and the Pacific.

A367

A368

Paleoanthropological Discoveries in Indonesia: Fossils of *Homo erectus* and *Homo sapiens* men.

**1989, Aug. 31**
| | | | | |
|---|---|---|---|---|
| 1395 | A367 | 100r | Sangiran 17 | .80 | .20 |
| 1396 | A367 | 150r | Perning 1 | 1.10 | .20 |
| 1397 | A367 | 200r | Sangiran 10 | 1.60 | .20 |
| 1398 | A367 | 250r | Wajak 1 | 1.90 | .20 |
| 1399 | A367 | 300r | Sambungmacan 1 | 2.25 | .20 |
| 1400 | A367 | 350r | Ngandong 7 | 2.75 | .30 |
| | | Nos. 1395-1400 (6) | 10.40 | 1.30 |

Nos. 1398-1400 vert.

**1989, Sept. 4**
| | | | | |
|---|---|---|---|---|
| 1401 | A368 | 350r | deep blue & yel grn | 1.50 | .25 |

Interparliamentary Union, Cent.

12th Natl. Sports Week — A369

**1989, Sept. 18**
| | | | | |
|---|---|---|---|---|
| 1402 | A369 | 75r | Tae kwando | .35 | .20 |
| 1403 | A369 | 100r | Tennis | .45 | .20 |
| 1404 | A369 | 140r | Judo | .65 | .20 |
| 1405 | A369 | 350r | Volleyball | 1.60 | .25 |
| 1406 | A369 | 500r | Boxing | 2.25 | .35 |
| 1407 | A369 | 1000r | Archery | 4.50 | .70 |
| | | Nos. 1402-1407 (6) | 9.80 | 1.90 |

**Tourism Type of 1987**

Structures in Miniature Park: 120r, Taman Burung. 350r, Natl. Philatelic Museum. 500r, Istana Anak-Anak, vert.

**Perf. 13½x12½, 12½x13½**
**1989, Oct. 9**
| | | | | |
|---|---|---|---|---|
| 1408 | A339 | 120r | multicolored | .65 | .20 |
| 1409 | A339 | 350r | multicolored | 1.75 | .30 |
| 1410 | A339 | 500r | multicolored | 2.50 | .50 |
| | | Nos. 1408-1410 (3) | 4.90 | 1.00 |

Film Festival — A370

**1989, Nov. 11**   **Photo.**   **Perf. 12½**
| | | | | |
|---|---|---|---|---|
| 1411 | A370 | 150r | yel bister & blk | 1.50 | .20 |

**Folk Costumes Type of 1987**

Traditional wedding attire from: 50r, North Sumatra. 75r, South Sumatra. 100r, Jakarta. 140r, North Sulawesi. 350r, Mid Sulawesi. 500r, South Sulawesi. 1500r, North Sulawesi.

**1989, Dec. 11**     **Perf. 13x13½**
| | | | | |
|---|---|---|---|---|
| 1412 | A333 | 50r | multicolored | .25 | .20 |
| 1413 | A333 | 75r | multicolored | .35 | .20 |
| 1414 | A333 | 100r | multicolored | .50 | .20 |
| 1415 | A333 | 140r | multicolored | .65 | .20 |
| 1416 | A333 | 350r | multicolored | 2.00 | .20 |
| 1417 | A333 | 500r | multicolored | 2.75 | .30 |
| | | Nos. 1412-1417 (6) | 6.50 | 1.30 |

**Souvenir Sheet**
**Imperf**
| | | | | |
|---|---|---|---|---|
| 1418 | A333 | 1500r | multicolored | 9.50 | .85 |

No. 1418 exists perf. 12½x13½. Value *$12.*

**Health and Safety Type of 1988**
**1990, Jan. 12**     **Perf. 13x12½**
**Size: 29x21mm**
| | | | | |
|---|---|---|---|---|
| 1419 | A343 | 200r | Lineman, power lines | 1.25 | .20 |

**Tourism Type of 1987**

Architecture: 200r, Fort Marlborough, Bengkulu. 400r, 1000r, National Museum, Jakarta. 500r, 1500r, Mosque of Baiturrahman, Banda Aceh.

**1990, Feb. 1**     **Perf. 13½x13**
| | | | | |
|---|---|---|---|---|
| 1420 | A339 | 200r | multicolored | .75 | .20 |
| 1421 | A339 | 400r | multicolored | 1.60 | .20 |
| 1422 | A339 | 500r | multicolored | 2.00 | .30 |
| | | Nos. 1420-1422 (3) | 4.35 | .70 |

**Souvenir Sheet**
| | | | | |
|---|---|---|---|---|
| 1423 | | Sheet of 2 | 12.00 | 1.25 |
| a. | A339 | 1000r multicolored | 4.75 | .50 |
| b. | A339 | 1500r multicolored | 7.25 | .75 |

Flora
A371

**1990, Mar. 1**
| | | | | |
|---|---|---|---|---|
| 1424 | A371 | 75r | Mammilaria fragilis | .20 | .20 |
| 1425 | A371 | 1000r | Gmelina ellipitca | 3.00 | 1.00 |

**Souvenir Sheet**
| | | | | |
|---|---|---|---|---|
| 1426 | A371 | 1500r | like #1425 | 15.00 | 3.00 |

**5th Five-year Development Plan Type of 1989**
**1990, Apr. 1**     **Perf. 12½**
| | | | | |
|---|---|---|---|---|
| 1427 | A361 | 200r | Road construction | .35 | .20 |
| 1428 | A361 | 1000r | Lighthouse, ship | 1.90 | .50 |

Visit Indonesia Year, 1991 A372

**Perf. 13½x12½, 12½x13½**
**1990, May 1**
| | | | | |
|---|---|---|---|---|
| 1429 | A372 | 100r | shown | .35 | .20 |
| 1430 | A372 | 500r | Steps, ruin | 1.90 | .25 |

**Souvenir Sheet**
**Perf. 14½x12½**
| | | | | |
|---|---|---|---|---|
| 1430A | A372 | 5000r | like #1429 | 20.00 | 2.75 |

No. 1430A, Stamp World London '90.

A373

A374

**1990, May 18**     **Perf. 12½**
| | | | | |
|---|---|---|---|---|
| 1431 | A373 | 1000r | gray grn & brn org | 2.25 | .50 |

Disabled Veterans Corps, 40th anniv.

**1990, June 8**     **Perf. 12½**
| | | | | |
|---|---|---|---|---|
| 1432 | A374 | 75r | shown | .45 | .20 |
| 1433 | A374 | 150r | multi, diff. | .90 | .20 |
| 1434 | A374 | 400r | multi, diff. | 2.25 | .25 |
| | | Nos. 1432-1434 (3) | 3.60 | .65 |

**Souvenir Sheet**
| | | | | |
|---|---|---|---|---|
| 1435 | A374 | 1500r | multi | 12.00 | .75 |

World Cup Soccer Championships, Italy.

Family Planning in Indonesia, 20th Anniv. — A375

**1990, June 29**
| | | | | |
|---|---|---|---|---|
| 1436 | A375 | 60r | brown & red | .85 | .20 |

Natl. Census — A376

**1990, July 1**
| | | | | |
|---|---|---|---|---|
| 1437 | A376 | 90r | yel grn & dk grn | 1.00 | .20 |

Natl. Children's
Day — A377

**1990, July 23**
1438  A377  500r multicolored        1.60   .30

Souvenir Sheet

Traditional Lampung Wedding
Costumes — A378

*Perf. 12½x14½*

**1990, June 10**                    **Photo.**
1439  A378  2000r multicolored       9.00  1.00
  Natl. Philatelic Exhibition, Stamp World
London '90 and New Zealand '90.

Independence, 45th
Anniv. — A379

**1990, Aug. 17**          *Perf. 12½x13½*
1440  A379  200r  Soldier raising
                    flag               .65   .20
1441  A379  500r  Skyscraper,
                    highway           1.50   .40

**Souvenir Sheet**
1442  A379  1000r like #1441         9.00   .85

Indonesia-Pakistan Economic &
Cultural Cooperation
Organization — A380

Designs: 400r, Woman dancing in traditional
costume, vert.

*Perf. 13½x12½, 12½x13½*
**1990, Aug. 19**                    **Litho.**
1443  A380  75r multicolored         .40   .20
1444  A380  400r multicolored       1.75   .55

Asian Pacific
Postal Training
Center, 20th
Anniv. — A381

**1990, Sept. 10**       **Photo.**   *Perf. 12½*
1445  A381  500r vio bl, bl & ultra  1.40   .40

A382                          A383

**1990, Sept. 14**
1446  A382  200r gray, blk & org     1.25   .20
  Organization of Petroleum Exporting Countries (OPEC), 30th anniv.

**1990, Oct. 24**
1447  A383  1000r multicolored       2.75   .85
  Environmental Protection Laws, 40th anniv.

Folk Costumes Type of 1987
  Traditional wedding attire from: 75r, West
Java. 100r, Central Java. 150r, Yogyakarta.
200r, East Java. 400r, Bali. 500r, West Nusa
Tenggara.

**1990, Nov. 1**            *Perf. 13x13½*
1448  A333  75r multicolored         .30   .20
1449  A333  100r multicolored        .40   .20
1450  A333  150r multicolored        .65   .20
1451  A333  200r multicolored        .80   .20
1452  A333  400r multicolored       1.60   .40
1453  A333  500r multicolored       1.90   .55
       Nos. 1448-1453 (6)           5.65  1.75

A385                          A386

Visit Indonesia Year 1991: Women in traditional costumes.

**1991, Jan. 1**   **Photo.**   *Perf. 12½x13½*
1454  A385  200r multicolored        .60   .20
1455  A385  500r multicolored       1.75   .30
1456  A385  1000r multicolored      3.00   .50
       Nos. 1454-1456 (3)           5.35  1.00
**Souvenir Sheet**
1456A  A385  1500r As No.
                    1454           16.00  16.00

**1991, Feb. 4**               *Perf. 12½*
1457  A386  200r yel, grn & bl grn  1.40   .20
  16th natl. Koran reading competition,
Jogjakarta.

Palace of
Sultan
Ternate,
the
Moluccas
A387

  Design: 1000r, 2500r, Bari House, Palembang, South Sumatra.

**1991, Mar. 1**            *Perf. 13½x12½*
1458  A387  500r multicolored       1.10   .25
1459  A387  1000r multicolored      2.25   .55
**Souvenir Sheet**
1460  A387  2500r multicolored      9.00  1.25

5th Five Year Development Plan Type
of 1989

**1991, Apr. 1**               *Perf. 12½*
1461  A361  75r  Steel mill, vert.   .30   .20
1462  A361  200r  Computers          .75   .20

Danger of
Smoking — A388

**1991, May 31**    **Photo.**   *Perf. 12½*
1463  A388  90r multicolored        1.10   .20

Folk Costumes Type of 1987
  Traditional wedding attire from: 100r, West
Kalimantan. 200r, Mid Kalimantan. 300r,
South Kalimantan. 400r, Southeast Sulawesi.
500r, Riau. 1000r, Irian Jaya.

**1991, June 15**           *Perf. 13x13½*
1464  A333  100r multicolored        .20   .20
1465  A333  200r multicolored        .50   .20
1466  A333  300r multicolored        .75   .20
1467  A333  400r multicolored       1.00   .20
1468  A333  500r multicolored       1.25   .30
1469  A333  1000r multicolored      2.50   .65
       Nos. 1464-1469 (6)           6.20  1.75

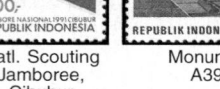

Natl. Scouting          Monument
Jamboree,                 A390
Cibubur
A389

**1991, June 15**              *Perf. 12½*
1470  A389  200r multicolored       1.40   .20

**1991, July 6**
1471  A390  200r multicolored       1.40   .20

Natl. Farmers'     Indonesian Chemical
Week — A391         Society, 4th Natl.
                    Congress — A392

**1991, July 15**
1472  A391  500r brt bl, yel & grn  1.75   .25

**1991, July 28**
1473  A392  400r grn, ver & dull
                    grn            1.75   .25
  Chemindo '91.

A393                          A394

**1991, Aug. 24**  **Photo.**   *Perf. 12½*
1474  A393  300r blk, red & gray   1.60   .35
  5th Junior Men's and 4th Women's Asian
Weightlifting Championships.

**1991, Aug. 30**
1475  A394  500r lilac & sky blue  1.40   .45
  World Cup Parachuting Championships.

A395                          A396

**1991, Sept. 17**
1476  A395  200r multicolored      1.50   .20
  Indonesian Red Cross, 46th aAnniv.

**1991, Oct. 6**
1477  A396  300r yellow & blue     1.60   .35
  Intl. Amateur Radio Union, 8th regional
conf., Bandung.

Istiqlal
(Independence)
Festival,
Jakarta — A397

**1991, Oct. 15**
1478  A397  200r gray, blk & ver   1.50   .20

Intl. Conference on
the Great
Apes — A398

  Pongo pygmaeus: 200r, Sitting in tree. 500r,
Walking. 1000r, 2500r, Sitting on ground.

**1991, Dec. 18**          *Perf. 12½x13½*
1479  A398  200r multicolored        .75   .20
1480  A398  500r multicolored       1.75   .55
1481  A398  1000r multicolored      3.50  1.00
       Nos. 1479-1481 (3)           6.00  1.75
**Souvenir Sheet**
1481A  A398  2500r multicolored    11.00  1.25

Intl. Convention on Quality Control
Circles, Bali — A399

**1991, Oct. 22**              *Perf. 12½*
1482  A399  500r multicolored      2.00   .50

Automation of the Post Office — A400

  200r, P.O. 500r, Mail sorting equipment.

**1992, Jan. 9**   **Photo.**   *Perf. 13½x13*
1483  A400  200r multicolored        .40   .20
1484  A400  500r multicolored        .95   .30

National
Elections
A401

**1992, Feb. 10**     **Perf. 12½**
1485 A401   75r shown     .20   .20
1486 A401 100r Ballot boxes,
    globe     .20   .20
1487 A401 500r Hands dropping
    ballots in ballot
    boxes     1.25   .35
    Nos. 1485-1487 (3)     1.65   .75

5th Five-year Development Plan Type
of 1989

**1992, Apr. 1**     **Perf. 12½**
1488 A361 150r Construction
    worker     .30   .20
1489 A361 300r Aviation technol-
    ogy     .65   .20

Visit Asia
Year, 1992
A402

**1992, Mar. 1**     **Perf. 13½x13**
1490 A402 300r Lembah
    Baliem, Irian
    Jaya     .75   .20
1491 A402 500r Tanah Lot, Bali   1.25   .35
1492 A402 1000r Lombah Anai,
    Sumatra Barat   2.75   .60
    Nos. 1490-1492 (3)     4.75   1.15

**Souvenir Sheet**
1493 A402 3000r like #1491     9.00   2.10

Birds — A403

**1992, July 1**   **Photo.**   **Perf. 12½x13½**
1494 A403 100r Garrulax
    leucolophus   .25   .20
1495 A403 200r Dinopium
    javanense   .50   .20
1496 A403 400r Buceros rhi-
    noceros   1.00   .25
1497 A403 500r Alisterus
    amboinensis   1.25   .35
    Nos. 1494-1497 (4)     3.00   1.00

**Souvenir Sheet**
1498 A403 3000r like #1494     10.00   1.90

Children's Day — A404

75r, Street scene. 100r, Children with balloons. 200r, Boating scene. 500r, Girl feeding
bird.

**1992, July 23**     **Perf. 12½**
1499 A404   75r multicolored   .20   .20
1500 A404 100r multicolored   .25   .20
1501 A404 200r multicolored   .55   .20
1502 A404 500r multicolored   1.40   .30
    Nos. 1499-1502 (4)     2.40   .90

1992 Summer
Olympics,
Barcelona — A405

Designs: No. 1508a, 2000r, like #1504. b,
3000r, like #1507.

**1992, June 1**     **Perf. 12½x13½**
1503 A405   75r Weight lifting   .20   .20
1504 A405 200r Badminton   .40   .20
1505 A405 300r Symbols of
    events   .65   .20
1506 A405 500r Women's ten-
    nis   1.10   .35
1507 A405 1000r Archery   2.10   .65
    Nos. 1503-1507 (5)     4.45   1.60

**Souvenir Sheet**
1508 A405   Sheet of 2, #a.-b.     12.00   3.75

ASEAN,
25th
Anniv.
A406

**1992, Aug. 8**     **Perf. 13½x12½**
1509 A406 200r shown   .55   .20
1510 A406 500r Flags, map   1.25   .35
1511 A406 1000r Flags on poles   2.50   .65
    Nos. 1509-1511 (3)     4.30   1.20

Flowers
A407

Designs: 200r, Phalaenopsis ambilis. 500r,
Rafflesia arnoldii. 1000r, 2000r, Jasminum
sambae.

**Perf. 13½x12½**
**1992, Jan. 20**     **Photo.**
1512 A407 200r multicolored   .50   .20
1513 A407 500r multicolored   1.25   .35
1514 A407 1000r multicolored   2.25   .65
    Nos. 1512-1514 (3)     4.00   1.20

**Souvenir Sheet**
**Perf. 13½x13**
1515 A407 2000r multicolored     10.00   2.25

A408

A409

**Perf. 12½x13½**
**1992, Sept. 6**     **Photo.**
1516 A408 200r shown   .50   .20
1517 A408 500r Flags, emblem   1.25   .35

10th Non-Aligned Summit, Jakarta.

**1992, Nov. 29**   **Photo.**   **Perf. 12½**
1518 A409 200r green & blue   .85   .20

Intl. Planned Parenthood Federation, 40th
anniv.

A410         A411

**Perf. 12½x13½**
**1992, Aug. 16**     **Photo.**
1519 A410 200r Globe, satellite   .45   .20
1520 A410 500r Palapa satellite   1.10   .35
1521 A410 1000r Old, new tele-
    phones   2.10   .65
    Nos. 1519-1521 (3)     3.65   1.20

Satellite Communications in Indonesia, 16th
anniv.

**1992, Oct. 1**     **Perf. 12½x13½**
Traditional Dances: 200r, 3000r, Tari
Ngremo, Timor. 500r, Tari Gending Sriwijaya,
Sumatra.

1522 A411 200r multicolored   .65   .20
1523 A411 500r multicolored   1.40   .35

**Souvenir Sheet**
1524 A411 3000r like #1518     9.00   4.50

No. 1523 was withdrawn from sale on 10/5.
See Nos. 1564-1567, 1596-1600, 1628-
1632, 1688-1692, 1747-1751, 1815-1820.

Antara News
Agency, 55th
Anniv. — A412

**1992, Dec. 13**   **Photo.**   **Perf. 12½**
1525 A412 500r blue & black   1.25   .20

Natl. Afforestation Campaign — A413

**Perf. 13½x12½**
**1992, Dec. 24**     **Photo.**
1526 A413 500r multicolored   1.25   .30

No. 1260 Surcharged

**1993, Feb. 1**   **Photo.**   **Perf. 13½x12½**
1527 A246 50r on 55r #1260   .75   .20

1993 General Session of the People's
Consultative Assembly — A414

**1993, Mar. 1**   **Photo.**   **Perf. 13½x12½**
1528 A414 300r Building exterior   .50   .20
1529 A414 700r Building interior   1.25   .55

5th Five Year Development Plan Type
of 1989

300r, Soldier's silhouettes over city. 700r,
Immunizing children. 1000r, Runners.

**1993, Apr. 1**     **Perf. 12½**
1530 A361 300r multicolored   .40   .20
1531 A361 700r multicolored   .85   .50
1532 A361 1000r multicolored   1.25   .70
    Nos. 1530-1532 (3)     2.50   1.40

Ornithoptera Goliath — A415

**1993, Apr. 20**   **Photo.**   **Perf. 12½**
1533 A415 1000r multicolored   2.00   .95

For overprint see No. 1540.

Surabaja,
700th
Anniv.
A416

Designs: 300r, Siege of Yamato Hotel. 700r,
World Habitat Award, Surabaya skyline. 1000r,
Candi Bajang Ratu, natl. monument.

**Perf. 13½x12½**
**1993, May 29**     **Photo.**
1534 A416 300r multicolored   .45   .20
1535 A416 700r multicolored   1.00   .40
1536 A416 1000r multicolored   1.60   .65
    Nos. 1534-1536 (3)     3.05   1.25

For overprints see Nos. 1538-1539, 1541.

Nos.
1533-1536
Ovptd. in
Red

and

Indopex '93 — A417

**1993**     **Perfs. as Before**
1538 A416 300r on #1534   .45   .20
1539 A416 700r on #1535   1.10   .40
1540 A415 1000r on #1533   1.50   .60
1541 A416 1000r on #1536   1.50   .60
    Nos. 1538-1541 (4)     4.55   1.80

**Souvenir Sheet**
**Perf. 13½x12½**
1542 A417 3500r multicolored     5.00   3.00

Location of overprint varies. Issued: No.
1540, Apr. 20; others, May 29.

Environmental Protection — A418

Flowers: Nos. 1543a, 1545a, Jasminum
sambac. No. 1543b, Phalaenopsis amabilis.
No. 1543c, Rafflesia arnoldi.
Wildlife: Nos. 1544a, 1545b, Varanus
komodoensis. No. 1544b, Scleropages
formasus. No. 1544c, Spizaetus bartelsi.

**Perf. 12½x13½**
**1993, June 5**     **Photo.**
1543 A418 300r Tripytych, #a.-c.   2.25   .85
1544 A418 700r Tripytych, #a.-c.   5.25   1.90

**Souvenir Sheet of 2**
1545 A418 1500r #a.-b.     8.00   1.90

1st World Community Development
Camp — A419

Designs: 300r, Boy scouts working on road.
700r, Pres. Suharto shaking hands with scout.

**Perf. 13½x12½**

| | | | |
|---|---|---|---|
| **1993, July 27** | | **Photo.** | |
| 1546 | A419 | 300r multicolored | .45 .20 |
| 1547 | A419 | 700r multicolored | 1.10 .45 |

Papilio
Blumei — A420

Armed Forces
Day — A421

**Perf. 12½x13½**

| | | | |
|---|---|---|---|
| **1993, Aug. 24** | | **Photo.** | |
| 1548 | A420 | 700r multicolored | 1.50 .60 |
| **Souvenir Sheets** | | | |
| 1549 | A420 | 3000r multicolored | 7.50 1.90 |
| 1550 | A420 | 3000r multicolored | 7.50 1.90 |

Inscription at top of No. 1549 is like that on
No. 1548. No. 1550 contains a stamp
inscribed "1993," a se-tenant label and Bangkok '93 Philatelic Exhibition inscription in sheet
margin.

| | | | |
|---|---|---|---|
| **1993, Oct. 5** | | **Perf. 12½** | |
| 1551 | A421 | 300r Soedirman | .50 .20 |
| 1552 | A421 | 300r Oerip | | |
| | | Soemohardjo | .50 .20 |
| a. | | Pair, #1551-1552 | 1.00 .45 |

Tourism — A422

13th Natl.
Sports
Week — A423

300r, 3000r, Waterfall. 700r, Cave formations. 1000r, Dormant volcanic crater, horiz.

**Perf. 12½x13½, 13½x12½**

| | | | |
|---|---|---|---|
| **1993, Oct. 4** | | | |
| 1553 | A422 | 300r multicolored | .45 .20 |
| 1554 | A422 | 700r multicolored | .95 .50 |
| 1555 | A422 | 1000r multicolored | 1.60 .75 |
| | | Nos. 1553-1555 (3) | 3.00 1.45 |
| **Souvenir Sheet** | | | |
| 1556 | A422 | 3000r multicolored | 5.00 1.90 |

| | | | |
|---|---|---|---|
| **1993, Sept. 9** | | **Perf. 12½x13½** | |
| 1557 | A423 | 150r Swimming | .20 .20 |
| 1558 | A423 | 300r Cycling | .45 .20 |
| 1559 | A423 | 700r Mascot | 1.00 .50 |
| 1560 | A423 | 1000r High jump | 1.40 .70 |
| | | Nos. 1557-1560 (4) | 3.05 1.60 |
| **Souvenir Sheet** | | | |
| 1561 | A423 | 3500r like No. 1560 | 6.00 2.40 |

Flora and
Fauna — A424

Designs: a, Michelia champaca. b, Cananga
odorata. c, Copsychus pyrropygus. d, Gracula
religiosa robusta.

| | | | |
|---|---|---|---|
| **1993, Nov. 5** | **Photo.** | **Perf. 12½x13½** | |
| 1562 | A424 | 300r Block of 4, #a.-d. | 4.50 .80 |

Migratory Farm
Workers — A425

| | | | |
|---|---|---|---|
| **1993, Dec. 4** | | **Perf. 12½** | |
| 1563 | A425 | 700r Field workers | .90 .40 |

Traditional Dance Type of 1992

Dance and region: 300r, Gending Sriwijaya,
South Sumatra. 700r, Tempayan, West Kalimantan. 1000r, 3500r, Tifa, Irian Jaya.

| | | | |
|---|---|---|---|
| **1993, Dec. 22** | | **Perf. 12½x13½** | |
| 1564 | A411 | 300r multicolored | .50 .20 |
| 1565 | A411 | 700r multicolored | 1.00 .40 |
| 1566 | A411 | 1000r multicolored | 1.50 .55 |
| | | Nos. 1564-1566 (3) | 3.00 1.15 |
| **Souvenir Sheet** | | | |
| 1567 | A411 | 3500r multicolored | 5.50 1.90 |

Intl. Year
of the
Family
A426

| | | | |
|---|---|---|---|
| **1994, Mar. 1** | **Photo.** | **Perf. 13½x12½** | |
| 1568 | A426 | 300r multicolored | .75 .20 |

Indonesian Postage Stamps, 130th
Anniv. — A427

Design: 700r, Netherlands Indies #B7, #N7,
Indonesia #B214.

| | | | |
|---|---|---|---|
| **1994, Apr. 1** | | **Perf. 12½** | |
| 1569 | A427 | 700r multicolored | 1.10 .55 |
| **Souvenir Sheet** | | | |
| **Imperf** | | | |
| 1569A | A427 | 3500r like #1569 | 6.00 2.75 |

PHILAKOREA '94 (#1569A).

6th Five Year
Development
Plan — A428

Buddhist dieties and: 100r, Professional
women. 700r, Education. 2000r, Medical care
for children.

| | | | |
|---|---|---|---|
| **1994, Apr. 1** | | **Perf. 12½** | |
| 1570 | A428 | 100r multicolored | .20 .20 |
| 1571 | A428 | 700r multicolored | .85 .45 |
| 1572 | A428 | 2000r multicolored | 2.10 1.00 |
| | | Nos. 1570-1572 (3) | 3.15 1.65 |

Tropical
Fish
A429

Designs: 300r, Telmatherina ladigesi. 700r,
3500r, Melanotaenia boesemani.

| | | | |
|---|---|---|---|
| **1994, Apr. 20** | **Photo.** | **Perf. 13** | |
| 1573 | A429 | 300r multicolored | .70 .20 |
| 1574 | A429 | 700r multicolored | 1.50 .70 |
| **Souvenir Sheet** | | | |
| 1575 | A429 | 3500r multicolored | 6.50 3.25 |

No. 1575 has continuous design.

Intl. Federation of
Red Cross & Red
Crescent Societies,
75th Anniv. —
A429a

| | | | |
|---|---|---|---|
| **1994, May 5** | | **Perf. 12½x13** | |
| 1575A | A429a | 300r multicolored | .75 .20 |

Second Asian and Pacific Ministerial
Conference on Women,
Jakarta — A430

| | | | |
|---|---|---|---|
| **1994, June 13** | | **Perf. 13½x12½** | |
| 1576 | A430 | 700r multicolored | 1.10 .45 |

A431

1994 World Cup Soccer Championships,
US: 150r, Player dribbling ball, vert. 300r,
Mascot chasing ball, vert. 700r, 1994 Tournament emblem. 1000r, Ball in net. 3500r, Soccer ball in net.

| | | | |
|---|---|---|---|
| **1994, June 17** | | **Perf. 12½x13½** | |
| 1577 | A431 | 150r multicolored | .20 .20 |
| 1578 | A431 | 300r multicolored | .50 .20 |
| **Perf. 13½x12½** | | | |
| 1579 | A431 | 700r multicolored | 1.10 .50 |
| 1580 | A431 | 1000r multicolored | 1.50 .65 |
| | | Nos. 1577-1580 (4) | 3.30 1.55 |
| **Souvenir Sheet** | | | |
| 1581 | A431 | 3500r multicolored | 6.00 2.10 |

Thomas & Uber Cups — A432

Designs: a, Uber Cup. b, Thomas Cup.

| | | | |
|---|---|---|---|
| **1994, June 22** | | **Perf. 12½** | |
| 1582 | A432 | 300r Pair, #a.-b. | 1.10 .45 |
| **Souvenir Sheet of 2** | | | |
| 1583 | A432 | 1750r #a.-b. | 5.25 2.40 |

A433

A434

**Perf. 12½x13½**

| | | | |
|---|---|---|---|
| **1994, July 27** | | **Photo.** | |
| 1584 | A433 | 700r multicolored | 1.25 .55 |

Human Rights Day.

**Perf. 13]x13½**

| | | | |
|---|---|---|---|
| **1994, Aug. 19** | | **Photo.** | |
| 1585 | A434 | 300r Brown pottery vase | .55 .20 |
| 1586 | A434 | 700r Blue & white vase | 1.25 .55 |

Indonesia-Pakistan Econiomic & Cultural
Cooperation Organization.
See Pakistan Nos. 822-823.

Bogoriense Zoological Museum,
Cent. — A435

700r, Skeleton of Javan rhinoceros. 1000r,
3500r, Skeleton of blue whale.

| | | | |
|---|---|---|---|
| **1994, Aug. 20** | | **Perf. 13½x13** | |
| 1587 | A435 | 700r multicolored | 1.25 .55 |
| **Size: 80x22mm** | | | |
| 1588 | A435 | 1000r multicolored | 2.50 1.20 |
| **Souvenir Sheet** | | | |
| **Perf. 13x13½** | | | |
| 1588A | A435 | 3500r multicolored | 6.50 3.50 |

12th
Asian
Games,
Hiroshima
1994
A436

| | | | |
|---|---|---|---|
| **1994, Oct. 2** | **Litho.** | **Perf. 13½x13** | |
| 1589 | A436 | 300r Mascots | .65 .20 |
| 1590 | A436 | 700r Hurdlers | 1.40 .70 |

Bakosurtanal, 25th Anniv. — A437

| | | | |
|---|---|---|---|
| **1994, Oct. 17** | **Litho.** | **Perf. 13½x13** | |
| 1591 | A437 | 700r multicolored | 1.25 .50 |

Flora &
Fauna — A438

Designs: a, Morus macroura. b, Oncosperma tigillaria. c, Eucalyptus urophylla. d,
Phalaenopsis amabilis. e, Pometia pinnata. f,
Argusianus argus. g, Loriculus pusillus. h,
Philemon buceroides. i, Alisterus amboinensis. j, Seleucidis melanoleuca.
3500r, Philemon buceroides, diff.

**1994, Nov. 5  Photo.  Perf. 12½x13½**
1592  A438  150r  Block or strip
of 10, #a.-j.  9.00  .90

**Souvenir Sheet**
1593  A438  3500r  multicolored  6.00  2.50
a.  With added inscription in blue  12.00

Inscription in sheet margin of No. 1593a contains emblem and "PRIMERA '95." Issued: No. 1593a, 8/21/95.
See Nos. 1622, 1680-1682, 1737-1738, 1812-1814.

Asian-Pacific Economic Cooperation Summit (APEC '94) — A439

Design: 700r, Presidential retreat, Bogor.

**1994, Nov. 15  Perf. 13½X13**
1594  A439  700r  multicolored  1.25  .50
For overprint see No. 1616A.

ICAO, 50th Anniv. A440

**1994, Dec. 7**
1595  A440  700r  multicolored  1.25  .50

Traditional Dance Type of 1992
Dance, region: 150r, Mengaup, Jambi. 300r, Mask, West Java. 700r, Anging Mamiri, South Sulawesi. 1000r, Pisok, North Sulawesi. 2000r, Bidu, East Nusa Tenggara. 3500r, Mask dance, West Java.

**1994, Dec. 27  Perf. 12½x13½**
1596  A411  150r  multicolored  .20  .20
1597  A411  300r  multicolored  .50  .20
1598  A411  700r  multicolored  1.25  .50
1599  A411  1000r  multicolored  1.75  .70
1600  A411  2000r  multicolored  3.75  1.50
a.  Bklt. pane, 2 ea #1596-1600  17.50
Complete booklet, #1600a  17.50
Nos. 1596-1600 (5)  7.45  3.10

**Souvenir Sheet**
1601  A411  3500r  multicolored  6.50  5.75

World Tourism Organization, 20th Anniv. — A441

Designs: 300r, Yogyakarta Palace. 700r, Floating market. 1000r, Pasola Sumba ritual.

**1995, Jan. 2  Perf. 13½x12½**
1602  A441  300r  multicolored  .50  .20
1603  A441  700r  multicolored  1.25  .50
1604  A441  1000r  multicolored  1.40  .60
Nos. 1602-1604 (3)  3.15  1.30

Indonesian Children, First Lady & Pres. Suharto A442

**Perf. 13½x12½**

**1995, Mar. 11  Photo.**
1605  A442  700r  multicolored  1.25  .50

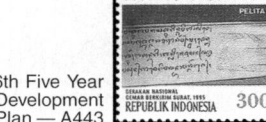

6th Five Year Development Plan — A443

Designs: 300r, Letter from King of Klunglung, 18th-19th cent. 700r, Carrier pigeon mascot of natl. letter writing campaign.

**1995, Apr. 1  Photo.  Perf. 12½**
1606  A443  300r  multicolored  .50  .20
1607  A443  700r  multicolored  1.25  .50

4th Intl. Bamboo Conference — A444

Designs: 300r, Schizostachyum brachycladum. 700r, Dendrocalamus asper.

**Perf. 12½x13½**

**1995, June 19  Photo.**
1608  A444  300r  multicolored  .50  .20
1609  A444  700r  multicolored  1.25  .50

First Flight of N250 Turboprop Commuter Airplane A445

**1995, Aug. 10  Perf. 13½x12½**
1610  A445  700r  multicolored  1.25  .50

Independence, 50th Anniv. — A446

**1995, Aug. 17**
1611  A446  300r  Anniv. emblem  .45  .20
1612  A446  700r  Boy, natl. flag  1.25  .50

**Souvenir Sheet**
1612A  A446  2500r  like No. 1612  5.00  1.60

JAKARTA '95, 8th Asian Intl. Philatelic Exhibition A447

Scenes in Jakarta: 300r, Kota Intan Drawbridge. 700r, Fatahillah Historical Museum.

**1995, Aug. 19**
1613  A447  300r  multicolored  .45  .20
1614  A447  700r  multicolored  1.25  .50

No. 1613 exists in 7 souvenir sheets of 1, each with different color margins. Sold at the 2nd International Stamp Exhibition in Jakarta. Value, $75.

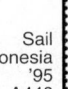

Sail Indonesia '95 A448

**1995, Aug. 19**
1615  A448  700r  multicolored  1.10  .40

**Souvenir Sheet**
1616  A448  2500r  multicolored  5.00  1.60

No. 1594 Overprinted "PRIMERA '95" in Blue

**1995, Aug. 21  Photo.  Perf. 13½x13**
1616A  A439  700r  on #1594  3.00  3.00

Istiqlal (Independence) Festival II 1995, Jakarta — A449

**1995, Sept. 23  Perf. 12½x13½**
1617  A449  700r  multicolored  1.25  .50

Takeover of Post, Telegraph, & Telephone Headquarters, 50th Anniv. — A450

**1995, Sept. 27  Perf. 13½x12½**
1618  A450  700r  multicolored  1.25  .50

FAO, 50th Anniv. — A451      UN, 50th Anniv. — A452

**1995, Oct. 16  Perf. 12½x13½**
1619  A451  700r  multicolored  1.25  .50

**1995, Oct. 24  Perf. 12½**
UN emblem, "50," and: 300r, Flags of nations. 700r, Rainbow over earth.
1620  A452  300r  multicolored  .45  .20
1621  A452  700r  multicolored  1.25  .50

Flora and Fauna Type of 1994
Designs: a, Cyrtostachys renda. b, Panthera tigris sumatrae. c, Bouea macrophylla. d, Rhinoceros sondaicus. e, Santalum album. f, Varanus komodoensis. g, Diospyros celebica. h, Macrocephalon maleo. i, Nephleium ramboutan-ake.  j,  Polyplectron schleiermacheri.
2500r, Panthera tigris sumatrae.

**1995, Nov. 5  Photo.  Perf. 12½x13½**
1622  A438  150r  Block of 10, #a.-j.  3.00  1.40

**Souvenir Sheet**
1623  A438  2500r  multicolored  10.00  1.50

1995 Aga Khan Award for Architecture — A453

Designs: 300r, Masjid Agung, Kraton Yogyakarta. 700r, Kraton Surakarta.

**1995, Nov. 23  Perf. 13½x13**
1624  A453  300r  multicolored  .45  .20
1625  A453  700r  multicolored  1.25  .50

Sir Rowland Hill (1795-1879) — A454

300r, Hill, letter carriers on motorcycles. 700r, Hill, Indonesian postal service logo.

**1995, Dec. 3  Perf. 13½x12½**
1626  A454  300r  multicolored  .45  .20
1627  A454  700r  multicolored  1.25  .50

Traditional Dance Type of 1992
Dance and region: 150r, Nguri, West Nusa Tenggara. 300r, Muli Betanggai, Lampung. 700r, Mutiara, Maluku. 1000r, Gantar, East Kalimantan. 2500r, Tari Nguri, Nusa Tenggara Barat.

**1995, Dec. 27  Perf. 12½x13½**
1628  A411  150r  multicolored  .20  .20
1629  A411  300r  multicolored  .50  .20
1630  A411  700r  multicolored  1.25  .50
1631  A411  1000r  multicolored  1.60  .60
Nos. 1628-1631 (4)  3.55  1.50

**Souvenir Sheet**
1632  A411  2500r  multicolored  4.25  1.50

1996 Economic Census — A455

Design: 300r, Economic sectors, vert.

**1996, Jan. 2  Perf. 12½**
1633  A455  300r  multicolored  .45  .20
1634  A455  700r  multicolored  1.25  .50

Greetings Stamps — A456

Various flowers.

**1996, Feb. 1  Photo.  Perf. 12½**
1635  A456  150r  multicolored  .25  .20
1636  A456  300r  multicolored  .50  .20
1637  A456  700r  multicolored  1.25  .50
Nos. 1635-1637 (3)  2.00  .90

See Nos. 1657-1659.

PWI Journalists' Assoc., 50th Anniv. — A457

Designs: 300r, RM Soemanang Soeriowinoto. 700r, Djamaluddin Adinegoro.

**1996, Feb. 9**
1638  A457  300r  multicolored  .45  .20
1639  A457  700r  multicolored  1.25  .50

Australian Spotted Cuscus — A458

Design: Nos. 1640, 1642a, shown. Nos. 1641, 1642b, Indonesian bear cuscus.

**1996, Mar.22  Photo.  Perf. 13x13½**
1640  A458  300r  multicolored  .50  .20
1641  A458  300r  multicolored  .50  .20
a.  Pair, Nos. 1640-1641  1.00  .40
b.  Sheet of 5 #1641a  21.00  10.50

**Souvenir Sheet**
1642  A458  1250r  Sheet of 2, #a.-b.  4.00  1.60
c.  #1642 with added inscription, ovpt.  6.00  1.60

Indonesia '96 (#1641b).
No. 1642c has black CHINA '96 exhibition emblem in upper right corner. The bottom sheet margin contains gold overprint: "CHINA '96 - 9th Asian International Philatelic Exhibition" in both Chinese and English.
No. 1641b exists folded and affixed to a booklet cover. Value, $12.50.
See Australia Nos. 1489-1490.

A459

Launching of Palapa C
Satellite — A460

**1996, Jan. 31**                    *Perf. 13*
1643  A459  300r multicolored        .50   .20
                    *Perf. 12½*
1644  A460  700r multicolored       1.25   .50

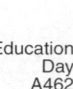

Indonesia
'96, World
Junior
Philatelic
Exhibition
A461

Designs: 300r, No. 1647a, Building. 700r,
No. 1647b, Decorated sun umbrellas.

**1996, Mar. 21**            *Perf. 13½x13*
1645  A461  300r multicolored        .40   .20
1646  A461  700r multicolored       1.10   .45

**Souvenir Sheet of 2**
1647  A461  1250r #a.-b.            6.00  1.50
No. 1647 exists imperf with different color
margins. A souvenir sheet containing No.
1645-1646 and progressive color proofs of No.
1646 exists.

Education
Day
A462

Children's drawings: 150r, Teachers, students with outstretched arms. 300r, Children
carrying books to school. 700r, Classroom
instruction.

**1996, May 2   Photo.   *Perf. 13½x13***
1648  A462  150r multicolored        .20   .20
1649  A462  300r multicolored        .45   .20
1650  A462  700r multicolored       1.25   .50
        *Nos. 1648-1650 (3)*        1.90   .90

Natl. Youth
Kirab
A463

**1996, June 8**
1651  A463  300r shown               .45   .20
1652  A463  700r Holding flag, em-
                    blem              1.25   .50

1996
Summer
Olympics,
Atlanta
A464

**1996, May 15**
1653  A464  300r Archery             .50   .20
1654  A464  700r Weight lifting     1.25   .50
1655  A464  1000r Badminton         1.60   .70
        *Nos. 1653-1655 (3)*        3.35  1.40

**Souvenir Sheet**
1656  A464  2500r like #1653        4.00  1.60
No. 1656 is a continuous design.

---

Greetings Type of 1996
**1996, Apr. 15   Photo.   *Perf. 12½***
1657  A456  150r Roses               .20   .20
1658  A456  300r Orchids             .45   .20
1659  A456  700r Chrysanthe-
                    mums             1.25   .50
        *Nos. 1657-1659 (3)*        1.90   .90

Maritime and
Aviation
Year — A465

300r, N-2130 aircraft, control tower at
Soekarno-Hatta Airport. 700r, Inter-island passenger ship.

**1996, June 22**
1660  A465  300r multicolored        .50   .20
1661  A465  700r multicolored       1.25   .90

1996 Natl. Scout
Jamboree
A466

Designs: a, Climbing rope. b, Sliding down
rope. c, Girls at bottom of ropes. d, Girls
assembling wood and rope ladder. e, Riding
unicycle, eagle emblem, boys building scaffolding. f, Girls building scaffolding, campground. g, Two boys with project. h, Woman
seated at control center.
    No. 1662I, like #1662a-1662d. No. 1662J,
like #1662e-1662h.

**1996, June 26**
1662  A466  150r Block of 8,
                    #a.-h.          2.00   .90

**Souvenir Sheets**
1662I  A466  1250d multicolored     3.00  1.50
1662J  A466  1250d multicolored     3.00  1.50
Istanbul '96 (#1662I-1662J). Nos. 1662I-
1662J each contain one 64x48mm stamp.
Nos. 1662a-1662d, 1663e-1662h are continuous designs.

Bank
BNI,
50th
Anniv.
A467

**1996, July 5**
1663  A467  300r shown               .40   .20
1664  A467  700r Sailing ship       1.10   .45

UNICEF,
50th
Anniv.
A468

**1996, July 23**            *Perf. 13½x13*
1665  A468  300r Child reading       .45   .20
1666  A468  700r Two children       1.10   .40
1667  A468  1000r Three children    1.50   .70
        *Nos. 1665-1667 (3)*        3.05  1.30

Ibu Tien Suharto
(1923-96) First
Lady — A469

**1996, Aug. 5**            *Perf. 12½x13½*
1668  A469  700r multicolored       1.25   .50

**Souvenir Sheet**
1669  A469  2500r like #1668        3.75  1.60
No. 1669 is a continuous design.

---

14th Natl.
Sports
Week,
Jakarta
A470

**Perf. 13½x12½**
**1996, Sept. 2**                   **Photo.**
1670  A470  300r Softball            .45   .20
1671  A470  700r Field hockey       1.10   .40
1672  A470  1000r Basketball        1.50   .70
        *Nos. 1670-1672 (3)*        3.05  1.30

World
Wildlife
Fund
A471

Rhinoceros sondaicus: a, #1674a, Adult. b,
Adult with young. Dicerorhinus sumatrensis: c,
Up close. d, #1674b, Adult.

**1996, Oct. 2   Photo.   *Perf. 13½x13***
1673  A471  300r Block of 4, #a.-
                    d.              2.75  1.75
  e.    Souvenir sheet, 2 #1673    7.25  4.00
  f.    As "e," ovptd. in sheet margin  5.75  3.75
Overprint in margin of No. 1673f reads:
"Bursa Filateli SEA Games XIX / Jakarta, 11-
19 Oktober 1997" in gold.
1674  A471  1500r Sheet of 2, #a.-
                    b.              6.75  4.00

Greetings
Stamps — A472

Bouquets of various flowers.

**1996, Oct. 15   Photo.   *Perf. 12½***
**Background Colors**
1675  A472  150r yellow & blue       .20   .20
1676  A472  300r yellow & green      .45   .20
1677  A472  700r pink & blue        1.10   .45
        *Nos. 1675-1677 (3)*        1.75   .85

Financial
Day, 50th
Anniv.
A473

**1996, Oct. 30**            *Perf. 13½x12½*
1678  A473  700r multicolored       1.25   .50

Flora & Fauna Type of 1994
Fauna: No. 1680: a, Aceros cassidix. b,
Orcaella brevirostris. c, Oriolus chinensis. d,
Helarctos    malayanus.    e,    Leucopsar
rothschildi.
    Flora: f, Borassus flabellifer. g, Coelogyne
pandurata. h, Michelia alba. i, Amorphophallus
titanum. j, Dysoxyleum densiflorium.
    No. 1681, Like #1680e. No. 1682, Like
#1680g.

**1996, Nov. 5   Litho.   *Perf. 12½x13½***
1680  A438  300r Block or strip
                    of 10, #a.-j.   5.00  2.50
  a.-j.  Any single                  .50   .25

**Souvenir Sheets**
1681  A438  1250r multicolored      3.50  1.10
1682  A438  1250r multicolored      3.50  1.10

---

Souvenir Sheet

Aceros Cassidix — A474

                    *Perf. 12½x13½*
**1996, Dec. 14**                   **Photo.**
1683  A474  2000r multicolored    15.00 15.00
        ASEANPEX '96.

Scenes
from Timor
A475

Designs: 300r, Deep sea diving. 700r, Sailing ships entering harbor, 18th cent.

**1996-97**                  *Perf. 13½x12½*
1684  A475  300r multicolored        .50   .20
1685  A475  700r multicolored       1.50   .50

**Souvenir Sheet**
1685A  A475  2000d like #1685       4.00  2.00
        Hong Kong '97 (#1685A).
    Issued: #1686-1687, 12/18/96; #1685A,
2/12/97.

Foster
Parents
A476

150r, Children at playground, vert. 300r,
Children, adult's hand holding picture of girl.

**Perf. 12½x13½, 13½x12½**
**1996, Dec. 20**
1686  A476  150r multicolored        .25   .20
1687  A476  300r multicolored        .50   .20

Traditional Dance Type of 1992
Dance, region: 150r, Tari Baksa Kembang,
Kalimantan Selatan. 300r, 2000r, Tari
Ngarojeng, Jakarta. 700r, Tari Rampai, Aceh.
1000r, Tari Boituka, Timor.

**1996, Dec. 27**            *Perf. 12½x13½*
1688  A411  150r multicolored        .40   .20
1689  A411  300r multicolored        .40   .20
1690  A411  700r multicolored        .90   .25
1691  A411  1000r multicolored      1.40   .35
        *Nos. 1688-1691 (4)*        3.10  1.00

**Souvenir Sheet**
1692  A411  2000r multicolored      3.50  1.75

Telecommunications Year — A477

Designs: 300r, Satellite dish, men at computers, map. 700r, Telephone keypad, woman
using telephone, satellite in earth orbit.

**1997, Jan. 1**     **Perf. 13½x12½**
1693 A477 300r multicolored .40 .20
1694 A477 700r multicolored 1.25 .50

Greetings
Stamps — A478

Designs: No. 1695, Heart, ribbon. No. 1696, Children, "Happy Birthday."

**1997, Jan. 15**     **Perf. 12½**
1695 A478 600r multicolored .85 .35
1696 A478 600r multicolored .85 .35

1997
General
Election
A479

Ballot box and: 300r, Means of transportation. 700r, Indonesian Archipelago, House of Representatives Building. 1000r, Map, symbols of development.

**1997, Feb. 3**     **Perf. 13½x13**
1697 A479 300r multicolored .40 .20
1698 A479 700r multicolored 1.25 .50
1699 A479 1000r multicolored 1.60 .70
   Nos. 1697-1699 (3) 3.25 1.40

Birth of Indonesia's 200-millionth
Citizen — A480

**Perf. 13½x12½**
**1997, Mar. 24**     **Litho.**
1700 A480 700r Pres. Suharto,
     baby 1.25 .50

A481         A482

Indonesian Philatelists Assoc., 75th Anniv.: 300r, Youth examining stamps, #1672. 700r, Magnifying glass, #1660, #1592h, #1580.

**1997, Mar. 29**     **Perf. 12½x13½**
1701 A481 300r multicolored .45 .20
1702 A481 700r multicolored 1.25 .50

**1997, Apr. 30**    **Litho.**    **Perf. 13x13½**
Indonesian Artists: 300r, Wage Rudolf Soepratman (1903-38), composer, violinist. 700r, Usmar Ismail (1921-71), film pioneer, director. 1000r, Affandi (1907-90), painter.
1703 A482 300r multicolored .45 .20
1704 A482 700r multicolored 1.10 .50
1705 A482 1000r multicolored 1.50 .60
  b.   Sheet, 3 each #1703-1705
      + label 10.00 4.75
    Nos. 1703-1705 (3) 3.05 1.30

**Souvenir Sheet**
1705A A482 2000r like #1705 3.00 1.50

Indonesia
2000
A483

Gemstones: 300r, Picture jasper. 700r, Chrysocolla. 1000r, Geode. 2000r, Banded agate.

**1997, May 20**    **Litho.**    **Perf. 13½x13**
1706 A483 300r multicolored .45 .20
1707 A483 700r multicolored 1.10 .50
1708 A483 1000r multicolored 1.50 .60
  a.   Sheet, 3 each, #1706-1708 +
      label 10.00 4.75
  b.   As "a," control No. in margin 17.50 8.75
    Nos. 1706-1708 (3) 3.05 1.30

**Souvenir Sheet**
1709 A483 2000r multicolored 3.00 .85
  a.   Control No. in margin 4.75 2.50

Nos. 1708b, 1709a promote INDONESIA 2000, Jakarta, Aug. 15-21, 2000. Nos. 1708a-1709 and 1708b-1709a were issued in presentation packs with certificate of authenticity. See Nos. 1764-1767A, 1848-1851.

A484

**1997, May 31**    **Photo.**    **Perf. 12½**
1710 A484 1000r multicolored 1.50 .60

World Day to Stop Smoking.

World Environment
Day — A485

**1997, June 5**    **Litho.**    **Perf. 13x13½**
Various marine life of the coral reefs.
1711 A485 150r multicolored .40 .20
1712 A485 300r multicolored .50 .20
1713 A485 700r multicolored 1.10 .50
    Nos. 1711-1713 (3) 2.00 .90

**Souvenir Sheet**
1714 A485 2000r multicolored 4.50 2.00

ASEAN,
30th
Anniv.
A486

300r, Hands reaching out to each other. 700r, Rice stalks arranged to form number 30, globe.

**1997, Aug. 8**    **Litho.**    **Perf. 13½x13**
1715 A486 300r multicolored .40 .20
1716 A486 700r multicolored 1.10 .50

19th Southeast
Asia Games,
Jakarta — A487

#1717, Logo, "Hanoman" mascot. #1718, Runner carrying torch, flags of participating nations, logo. #1719, Runner, track, discus thrower. #1720, Hurdler, runners.

**1997, Sept. 9**    **Litho.**    **Perf. 12½**
1717 A487 300r multicolored .40 .20
1718 A487 300r multicolored .40 .20
  a.   Pair, #1717-1718 .80 .20
1719 A487 700r multicolored 1.10 .40
1720 A487 700r multicolored 1.10 .40
  a.   Pair, #1719-1720 2.25 .80
  b.   Bklt. pane, 2 ea #1717-1720 6.50
     Complete booklet, 1 #1720b 6.50
    Nos. 1717-1720 (4) 3.00 1.20

Transportation — A488

**1997, Sept. 17**
1721 A488 300r Buses, ox cart .40 .20
1722 A488 300r Trains .40 .20
  a.   Pair, #1721-1722 .80 .20
1723 A488 700r Ships 1.10 .40
1724 A488 700r Airplanes 1.10 .40
  a.   Pair, #1723-1724 2.25 .80
    Nos. 1721-1724 (4) 3.00 1.20

**Souvenir Sheet**

Oriolus Chinensis — A489

**1997, May 29**     **Perf. 12½x13½**
1725 A489 2000r multicolored 5.00 2.50

PACIFIC 97.

Nusantara
Royal
Palace
Festival
A490

Royal carriages: 300r, Singa Baraong wooden carriage, 1549, with carving of mythical animal. 700r, Paksi Naga Liman carriage, phoenix-like bird.

**1997, July 1**    **Litho.**    **Perf. 13½x12½**
1726 A490 300r multicolored .40 .20
1727 A490 700r multicolored 1.10 .45

18th Natl. Koran Reading
Contest — A491

Designs: 300r, Decorated roof peaks, windows. 700r, Al-Ikhsaniah Mosque.

**1997, July 9**     **Perf. 12½**
1728 A491 300r multicolored .40 .20
1729 A491 700r multicolored 1.10 .45

Indonesian Membership in UPU, 50th
Anniv. — A492

Emblem of UPU and: 300r, Mas Soeharto. 700r, Heinrich von Stephan.

**1997, Sept. 27**    **Litho.**    **Perf. 13½x13**
1730 A492 300r multicolored .40 .20
1731 A492 700r multicolored 1.10 .45

1997-98 General Session of People's
Consultative Assembly — A493

**1997, Oct. 1**     **Perf. 12½**
1732 A493 700r multicolored .90 .20

Indonesian
Armed
Forces
Day
A494

Designs: a, ABRI Village Program. b, Jalesveva Jayamahe Monument. c, Blue Falcon Flight Demonstration Team. d, Police Fast Reaction Unit.

**1997, Oct. 5**     **Perf. 13½x12½**
1733 A494 300r Block of 4, #a.-d. 1.50 .20

**Flora and Fauna Type of 1994**

Fauna: No. 1737: a, Chitala lopis. b, Haliastur indus. c, Rhinoplax vigil. d, Cervus timorensis. e, Bubalus depressicornis.
Flora: f, Lansium domesticum. g, Salacca zalacca. h, Shorea stenoptera. i, Diospyros macrophylla. j, Diplocaulobium utile.
#1738: a, Shorea stenoptera. b, Haliastur indus.

**1997, Nov. 5**     **Perf. 12½x13½**
1737 A438 300r Block of 10 4.00 2.00
  a.-j.   Any single .40 .20

**Souvenir Sheet**
1738 A438 1250r Sheet of 2, #a.-
     b. 3.00 1.50

A495

Indonesian
Cooperatives
Day — A496

Designs: No. 1739, Cooperatives Monument, Tasikmalaya. No. 1740, Cooperatives Monument, Jakarta. No. 1741, Adult taking child's hand. No. 1742, Globe, movement towards globalization. No. 1743, Dr. Mohammad Hatta, Pres. Suharto.

**1997, July 12**   **Litho.**   **Perf. 12½x13½**
1739 A495 150r multicolored .35 .20
1740 A495 150r multicolored .35 .20
  a.   Pair, #1739-1740 .70 .20
1741 A495 300r multicolored .40 .20
1742 A495 300r multicolored .40 .20
  a.   Pair, #1741-1742 .80 .35

**Perf. 12½**
1743 A496 700r multicolored 1.25 .50
    Nos. 1739-1743 (5) 2.75 1.30

ASCOPE
'97 (Asian
Council on
Petroleum)
A497

a, LNG tanker. b, Petroleum trucks. c, Drilling rig, pumping wells. d, Refinery.

**1997, Nov. 24**    **Perf. 13½x12½**
1744 A497 300r Block of 4, #a.-d. 1.50 .60

Foster Parents Natl. Movement A498

**1997, Dec. 20**    **Photo.**
1745 A498 700r multicolored .80 .35

Family Welfare Movement, 25th Anniv. A499

**1997, Dec. 27**    **Litho.**
1746 A499 700r multicolored .80 .35

Traditional Dance Type of 1992

Dance, region: 150r, Mopuputi Cengke (clove picking), Central Sulawesi. 300r, Mandau Talawang Nyai Balau, Central Kalimantan. 600r, 2000r, Gambyong, Central Java. 700r, Cawan (bowl,) North Sumatra. 1000r, Legong Keraton, Bali.

**1997, Dec. 27**
1747 A411 150r multicolored .30 .20
1748 A411 300r multicolored .30 .20
1749 A411 600r multicolored .60 .35
1750 A411 700r multicolored .75 .40
1751 A411 1000r multicolored 1.00 .55
   Nos. 1747-1751 (5) 2.95 1.70

**Souvenir Sheet**
**Perf. 12½x13½**
1752 A411 2000r multicolored 2.75 1.40
No. 1752 is a continuous design.

Souvenir Sheet

Sulawesi Selatan — A500

Illustration reduced.

**1997, Oct. 11 Litho. Perf. 13½x12½**
1753 A500 2000r multicolored 3.00 1.50
Makasser '97 National Philatelic Exhibition.

Year of Art and Culture 1998 — A501

Designs: 300r, Erau Festival, East Kalimantan. 700r, Tabot Festival, Bengkulu.

**1998, Jan. 1 Litho. Perf. 12½**
1754 A501 300r multicolored .30 .20
1755 A501 700r multicolored .75 .20

Indonesian Folktales A502

Folktale, region — No. 1759; a-e, Malin Kundang, West Sumatra. f-j: Sangkuriang, West Java. k-o, Roro Jonggrang, Central Java. p-t: Tengger, East Java. Each horizontal strip of 5 has continuous design.
2500r, Kasodo Ceremony, Tenegger, East Java.

**1998, Feb. 2**    **Perf. 13½x12½**
1759   Sheet of 20 7.50 4.00
a.-t.   A502 300r Any single .35 .20

**Souvenir Sheet**
1760 A502 2500r like #1759e 2.75 1.50
See Nos. 1828-1829, 1886-1887.

Presidential Palaces — A503

Designs: a, Jakarta. b, Bogor. c, Cipanas. d, Yogyakarta. e, Tampak Siring.

**1998, Apr. 1**
1761 A503 300r Strip of 5, #a.-e. 1.25 .65

World Health Organization, 50th Anniv. — A504

Designs: 300r, Pregnant woman, man, vert. 700r, Woman holding baby.

**1998, Apr. 7 Litho. Perf. 12½**
1762 A504 300r multicolored .30 .20
1763 A504 700r multicolored .75 .40

Indonesia 2000 Type of 1997

Gemstones: 300r, Chrysopal. 700r, Tektite. 1000r, Amethyst. #1767, Petrified wood. #1767A, opal.

**1998, May 20**    **Perf. 13½x12½**
1764 A483 300r multicolored .35 .20
1765 A483 700r multicolored .35 .20
1766 A483 1000r multicolored .35 .20
a.   Sheet, 3 each #1764-1766
   + label 2.50 1.25
   Nos. 1764-1766 (3) 1.05 .60

**Souvenir Sheets**
1767 A483 2500r multicolored 1.50 .75

**Perf. 13½x14**
1767A A483 2500r multicolored 3.50 2.00
b.   Sheet, 2 each #1764-1766,
   1 each #1767, 1767A 10.00 9.00

Nos. 1767A, 1764b were issued in presentation packs with control numbers printed in margin and certificate of authenticity.
No. 1767A sold for 10,000r. No. 1767Ab sold for 25,000r.

1998 World Cup Soccer Championships, France — A505

Young boys playing soccer in Indonesia: 300r, Outside school, boy on bicycle. 700r, In neighborhood lot. 1000r, 2500r, In rural area.

**1998, June 1**
1768 A505 300r multicolored .30 .20
1769 A505 700r multicolored .70 .35
1770 A505 1000r multicolored 1.00 .45
   Nos. 1768-1770 (3) 2.00 1.00

**Souvenir Sheet**
1771 A505 2500r multicolored 2.50 2.50

World Environment Day — A506

Trees along river bank, denomination at: No. 1772, lower right. No. 1773, lower left.

**1998, June 5**
1772 A506 700r multicolored .70 .35
1773 A506 700r multicolored .70 .35
a.   Pair, #1772-1773 1.40 .70

**Souvenir Sheet**

Juvalux '98, World Philatelic Exhibition, Luxembourg — A507

**1998, June 18**    **Perf. 12½x13½**
1774 A507 5000r Felis viverrina 6.00 3.00

World Day to Fight Drug Abuse and Illicit Drug Trafficking — A508

Cartoons depicting how to say no to drugs.

**1998, June 26**
1775 A508 700r red & multi .70 .35
1776 A508 700r yellow & multi .70 .35
a.   Pair, #1775-1776 1.40 .70
b.   Tete beche pair, #1775-1776 1.40 .70

Tourism — A509

Temples, shrines in Bali: Nos. 1777, 1779, Pura Besakih. No. 1778, Pura Taman Ayun.

**1998, July 1**    **Perf. 12½**
1777 A509 700r multicolored .70 .35
1778 A509 700r shown .70 .35
a.   Pair, #1777-1778 1.40 .70

**Souvenir Sheet**
**Perf. 13½x13**
1779 A509 2500r multicolored 3.75 1.75
No. 1777 is 64x24mm. No. 1779 contains one 41x25mm stamp.

Souvenir Sheet

Panthera Tigris — A510

Illustration reduced.

**1998, July 23 Litho. Perf. 13½x12½**
1780 A510 5000r multicolored 2.50 1.25
Singpex '98.

Trains A511

Train going right: a, Cattle, freight cars. b, Freight, box cars. c, Passenger cars. d, Passenger car, tender. e, Locomotive 850.
Train going left: f, Locomotive D52. g, Coal tender. h, Car with 2 doors. i, Dining car with large windows. j, Car with two windows.
2500r, Locomotive.

**1998, Aug. 10**
1781 A511 300r Block of 10,
   #a.-j. 2.50 1.25

**Souvenir Sheet**
1782 A511 2500r multicolored 1.75 .80

No. 1781 issued in sheets of 20 stamps consisting of two tete-beche blocks of 10. No. 1782 contains one 41x25mm stamp.

Pres. H.B.J. Habibie — A512

**1998, Aug. 17**    **Perf. 12½x13½**
1783 A512 300r pink & multi .35 .20
1784 A512 700r blue & multi .35 .20
1785 A512 4500r green & multi 1.90 .90
1786 A512 5000r yellow & multi 2.00 1.00
   Nos. 1783-1786 (4) 4.60 2.30

13th Asian Games A513

**1998, Sept. 9**    **Perf. 13½x12½**
1787 A513 300r Fencing .35 .20
1788 A513 700r Taekwondo .35 .20
1789 A513 4000r Wushu 1.75 .40
a.   Souvenir sheet of #1787-1789 2.50 1.25
   Nos. 1787-1789 (3) 2.45 .80

Intl. Year of the Ocean A514

**Perf. 13½x12½**
**1998, Sept. 26**    **Litho.**
1790 A514 700r multicolored .75 .20

Souvenir Sheets

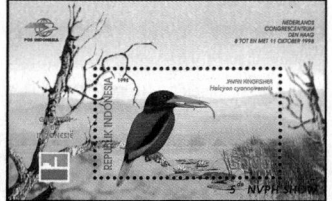

5th NVPH (Netherlands Philatelic Congress) Exhibition, The Hague — A514a

Birds: 5000r, Halcyon cyannoventris. 35,000r, Vannelus macropterus, vert. Illustration reduced.

**1998, Oct. 8 Litho. Perf. 13½x12½**
1790A A514a 5000r multi 2.00 1.00
1790B A514a 35,000r multi 10.00 5.50

A515

A516

**1998, Oct. 9**     *Perf. 12½x13½*
| | | | | |
|---|---|---|---|---|
| 1791 | A515 | 700r #922 | .50 | .20 |
| 1792 | A515 | 700r #414 | .50 | .20 |
| a. | | Pair, #1791-1792 | 1.00 | .20 |

World Stamp Day.

**Litho. (#1793-1799, 1805)**
**1998**     *Perf. 12½*

Ducks and Geese: 250r, #1805, Aythya australis. 500r, Anas superciliosa. 700r, Anas gibberifrons. 1000r, Nettapus coromandelianus. 1500r, Nettapus pulchelus. 2500r, Dendrocygna javanica. 3500r, Dendrocygna arcuata. 4000r, Anseranas semipalmata. #1801, Dendrocygna guttata. 10,000r, Anas waigiuensis. 15,000r, Tadorna radjah. 20,000r, Cairina scutulata.

| | | | | |
|---|---|---|---|---|
| 1793 | A516 | 250r multi | .40 | .20 |
| 1794 | A516 | 500r multi | .40 | .20 |
| 1795 | A516 | 700r multi | .40 | .20 |
| 1796 | A516 | 1000r multi | .50 | .20 |
| 1797 | A516 | 1500r multi | .75 | .20 |
| 1798 | A516 | 2500r multi | 1.25 | .50 |
| 1799 | A516 | 3500r multi | 1.60 | .75 |

**Litho. With Hologram**
**Perf. 13½x12½**
**Size: 42x25mm**

| | | | | |
|---|---|---|---|---|
| 1800 | A516 | 4000r horiz. | 1.25 | .60 |
| 1801 | A516 | 5000r horiz. | 1.50 | .70 |
| 1802 | A516 | 10,000r horiz. | 3.25 | 1.50 |
| 1803 | A516 | 15,000r horiz. | 5.00 | 2.50 |
| 1804 | A516 | 20,000r horiz. | 6.00 | 3.25 |
| a. | | Sheet of 5, #1800-1804, + 4 labels | 20.00 | 10.00 |
| | | Nos. 1793-1804 (12) | 22.30 | 10.80 |

**Souvenir Sheet**
**Perf. 12½**

| | | | | |
|---|---|---|---|---|
| 1805 | A516 | 5000r lt blue sky | 2.50 | 1.10 |

Soaking in water may affect the hologram on #1800-1804.
Issued: #1793-1799, 1805, 12/1; others 10/19.

Souvenir Sheet

Italia '98 — A516a

Illustration reduced.

**1998, Oct. 23**     *Perf. 12½x13½*
| | | | | |
|---|---|---|---|---|
| 1805A | A516a | 5000r Jakarta Cathedral | 2.75 | 1.25 |

National Flag — A517

Mountains and: #1806, Flagpole at right. #1807, Flagpole at left.

**1998, Oct. 28 Litho.**    *Perf. 12½x13½*
| | | | | |
|---|---|---|---|---|
| 1806 | A517 | 700r multicolored | .50 | .20 |
| 1807 | A517 | 700r multicolored | .50 | .20 |
| a. | | Pair, #1806-1807 | 1.00 | .20 |

Reform Movement
A518

No. 1809, Dove, national flag. No. 1810, Students, Parliament Building.

**1998, Oct. 28**     *Perf. 13½x12½*
| | | | | |
|---|---|---|---|---|
| 1808 | A518 | 700r shown | .50 | .20 |
| 1809 | A518 | 700r multicolored | .50 | .20 |
| a. | | Pair, #1808-1809 | 1.00 | .20 |

**Size: 83x25mm**
| | | | | |
|---|---|---|---|---|
| 1810 | A518 | 1000r multicolored | .55 | .20 |

**Flora and Fauna Type of 1994**

Flora — #1812: a, Stelechocarpus burahol. b, Polianthes tuberosa. c, Mirabilis jalapa. d, Mangifera casturi. e, Ficus minahassae.
Fauna — f, Geopelia striata. g, Gallus varius. h, Elephas maximus. i, Nasalis larvatus. j, Tarsius spectrum.
No. 1813, like #1812b. No. 1814, like #1812i.

**1998, Nov. 5**     *Perf. 12½x13½*
| | | | | |
|---|---|---|---|---|
| 1812 | A438 | 500r Block of 10 | 2.50 | 1.25 |
| a.-j. | | Any single | .25 | .20 |

**Souvenir Sheets**
| | | | | |
|---|---|---|---|---|
| 1813 | A438 | 2500r multicolored | 2.00 | .75 |
| 1814 | A438 | 2500r multicolored | 2.00 | .75 |

**Traditional Dance Type of 1992**

Dance, region: 300r, Oreng-oreng Gae, Southeast Sulawesi. 500r, Tribute dance, Bengkulu. 700r, Fan dance, Riau. 1000r, Srimpi, Yogyakarta. 2000r, 5000r, Tribute dance, West Sumatra.

**1998, Dec. 27**
| | | | | |
|---|---|---|---|---|
| 1815 | A411 | 300r multicolored | .40 | .20 |
| 1816 | A411 | 500r multicolored | .40 | .20 |
| 1817 | A411 | 700r multicolored | .40 | .20 |
| 1818 | A411 | 1000r multicolored | .50 | .20 |
| 1819 | A411 | 2000r multicolored | 1.10 | .20 |
| | | Nos. 1815-1819 (5) | 2.80 | 1.00 |

**Souvenir Sheet**
| | | | | |
|---|---|---|---|---|
| 1820 | A411 | 5000r multicolored | 2.75 | 1.25 |

Creation and Engineering Year — A519

Designs: 500r, Hydroelectric turbine, power lines. 700r, Plumbing fixture, water pipes.

**1999, Jan. 1 Litho.**    *Perf. 12½*
| | | | | |
|---|---|---|---|---|
| 1821 | A519 | 500r multicolored | .35 | .20 |
| 1822 | A519 | 700r multicolored | .45 | .20 |

7th Far East & South Pacific Games for Disabled
A520

Garuda Indonesia Airways, 50th Anniv.
A521

**1999, Jan. 10**     *Perf. 12½x13½*
| | | | | |
|---|---|---|---|---|
| 1823 | A520 | 500r Throwing shotput | .35 | .20 |
| 1824 | A520 | 500r Medals, wheelchair | .35 | .20 |
| a. | | Pair, #1823-1824 | .70 | .20 |

**1999, Jan. 26**     *Perf. 13x13½*
| | | | | |
|---|---|---|---|---|
| 1825 | A521 | 500r Logo | .40 | .20 |
| 1826 | A521 | 700r Aircraft maintenance | .40 | .20 |
| 1827 | A521 | 2000r Pilot, attendant | 1.00 | .50 |
| | | Nos. 1825-1827 (3) | 1.80 | .90 |

**Indonesian Folktales Type of 1998**

Folktale, region — #1828: a-e, Danau Toba, North Sumatra. f-j, Banjarmasin, South Kalimantan. k-o, Buleleng, Bali. p-t, Woiram, Irian Jaya.
5000r, like #1828e.

**1999, Feb. 15**     *Perf. 13½x12½*
| | | | | |
|---|---|---|---|---|
| 1828 | | Sheet of 20 | 6.00 | 3.00 |
| a.-e. | A502 | 500r Strip of 5 | 1.50 | .75 |
| f.-j. | A502 | 500r Strip of 5 | 1.50 | .75 |
| k.-o. | A502 | 500r Strip of 5 | 1.50 | .75 |
| p.-t. | A502 | 500r Strip of 5 | 1.50 | .75 |

**Souvenir Sheet**
| | | | | |
|---|---|---|---|---|
| 1829 | A502 | 5000r multicolored | 2.50 | 1.25 |

Nos. 1829 is a continuous design.

Souvenir Sheet

Surabaya '99, Natl. Philatelic Exhibition — A522

Illustration reduced.

**1999, Mar. 4 Litho.**    *Perf. 13½x12½*
| | | | | |
|---|---|---|---|---|
| 1830 | A522 | 5000r Apples | 2.50 | 1.25 |
| a. | | Ovptd. in sheet margin | 2.50 | 1.25 |

No. 1830a Overprinted in Gold in Sheet Margin with "APPI SHOW '99 / SURABAYA, 10-18 JULI 1999" and Emblem. Issued, 7/10.

Souvenir Sheet

Australia '99, World Stamp Expo — A523

Illustration reduced.

**1999, Mar. 19**     *Perf. 12½x13½*
| | | | | |
|---|---|---|---|---|
| 1831 | A523 | 5000r Tarsius spectrum | 2.50 | 1.25 |
| a. | | Ovptd. in sheet margin | 2.50 | 1.25 |

No. 1831a Overprinted in Gold in Sheet Margin with "The 13th / Thaipex / China / Stamp Exhibition / Bangkok '99 / 4 -15. 8. 99" and Emblem. Issued, 8/15.

Mushrooms — A524

No. 1832: a, Mutinus bambusinus. b, Ascosparassis heinricherii. c, Mycena sp.
No. 1833: a, Microporus xanthopus. b, Gloeophyllum imponens. c, Termitomyces eurrhizus.
No. 1834: a, Aseroe rubra. b, Calostoma orirubra. c, Boedijnopeziza insititia.
5000r, Termitomyces eurrhizus.

**1999, Apr. 1**     *Perf. 12½*
| | | | | |
|---|---|---|---|---|
| 1832 | A524 | 500r Triptych, #a.-c. | .80 | .20 |
| 1833 | A524 | 700r Triptych, #a.-c. | 1.10 | .50 |
| 1834 | A524 | 1000r Triptych, #a.-c. | 1.50 | .70 |
| d. | | Souvenir sheet #1832-1834 | 3.50 | 1.75 |

**Souvenir Sheet**
| | | | | |
|---|---|---|---|---|
| 1835 | A524 | 5000r multicolored | 2.50 | 1.25 |

**Booklet Stamps**
**Size:32x24mm**

| | | | | |
|---|---|---|---|---|
| 1836 | A524 | 500r Like #1832a | .40 | .20 |
| 1837 | A524 | 500r Like #1832b | .40 | .20 |
| 1838 | A524 | 500r Like #1832c | .40 | .20 |
| a. | | Booklet pane, 3 each #1836-1838, + label | 3.75 | |
| | | Complete booklet, #1838a | 3.75 | |
| | | Nos. 1836-1838 (3) | 1.20 | .60 |

No. 1835 contains one 25x41mm stamp. Numbers have been reserved for additional values in this set.

Public Health Care Insurance
A525

**1999, Apr. 7**     *Perf. 13½x12½*
| | | | | |
|---|---|---|---|---|
| 1845 | A525 | 700r multicolored | .70 | .20 |

Souvenir Sheet

IBRA '99, Intl. Philatelic Exhibition, Nuremberg — A526

Illustration reduced.

**1999, Apr. 27**     *Perf. 12½x13½*
| | | | | |
|---|---|---|---|---|
| 1846 | A526 | 5000r Dendrobium abang betawi | 2.50 | 1.25 |

Y2K Millennium Bug — A527

Designs: a, "Bug." b, Circuit, android.

**1999, May 2**     *Perf. 13½x12½*
| | | | | |
|---|---|---|---|---|
| 1847 | A527 | 500r Pair, #a.-b. | .75 | .20 |

**Indonesia 2000 Type of 1997**
**1999, May 20 Litho.**    *Perf. 13½x12¾*
| | | | | |
|---|---|---|---|---|
| 1848 | A483 | 500r Chrysoprase | .40 | .20 |
| 1849 | A483 | 1000r Smoky quartz | .60 | .20 |

| | | | |
|---|---|---|---|
| 1850 | A483 | 2000r Opal blue | 1.25 .60 |
| a. | | Sheet, 3 ea #1848-1850 + label | 7.00 7.00 |
| | | Nos. 1848-1850 (3) | 2.25 1.00 |

**Souvenir Sheet**

| | | | |
|---|---|---|---|
| 1851 | A483 | 4000r Silicified coral | 3.00 1.25 |
| 1851A | A483 | 4000r Javan jade | 6.00 6.00 |
| b. | | Sheet, #1851-1851A, 2 ea # 1849-1850, 4 #1848 | 18.00 18.00 |

Nos. 1851A, 1851Ab were issued in presentation packs with certificate of authenticity. Control numbers and silver overpint "1 Tahun/ Lagi / 1 Year / to Go" printed in margin. No. 1851A sold for 10,000r; No. 1851b for 30,000r.

Environmental Care — A528

Winning designs of 1999 Ecophila Stamp Design Contest: 500r, Girl wrapped in blanket, people walking through water. 1000r, 3000r, Boy swimming with duck, plant, cherry. 2000r, Elderly woman drinking water from pitcher, outdoor scene.

**1999, June 5**

| | | | |
|---|---|---|---|
| 1852 | A528 | 500r multicolored | .40 .20 |
| 1853 | A528 | 1000r multicolored | .60 .20 |
| 1854 | A528 | 2000r multicolored | 1.25 .30 |
| | | Nos. 1852-1854 (3) | 2.25 .70 |

**Souvenir Sheet**

| | | | |
|---|---|---|---|
| 1855 | A528 | 3000r multicolored | 2.00 .90 |

1999 General Election — A529

Designs: a, "48," Banner, people standing in line to vote. b, People waiting turn to enter election booth, map.

**1999, June 4**

| | | | |
|---|---|---|---|
| 1856 | A529 | 1000r Pair, #a.-b. | 1.25 .50 |

**Souvenir Sheet**

PhilexFrance '99 — A530

**1999, July 2  Litho.  Perf. 12¾x13½**

| | | | |
|---|---|---|---|
| 1858 | A530 | 5000r multi | 3.00 1.40 |

Red Cross / Red Crescent Millennium Year Campaign — A531

**Photo. & Litho.**

**1999, Aug. 12  Perf. 12½**

| | | | |
|---|---|---|---|
| 1859 | A531 | 1000r multicolored | .60 .20 |

National Heroes — A532

No. 1860: a, Dr. W. Z. Johannes (1895-1924). b, Martha Christina Tijahahu (1800-18), freedom fighter. c, Frans Kaisiepo (1921-79), politician. d, Maria Walanda Maramis (1872-1924), educator.

**Litho. & Engr.**

**1999, Aug. 17  Perf. 12½**

| | | | |
|---|---|---|---|
| 1860 | | Strip of 4 | 1.25 .50 |
| a.-d. | A532 | 500r any single | .30 .20 |
| e. | | Booklet pane of 4, #1860a | 1.50 |
| f. | | Booklet pane of 4, #1860b | 1.50 |
| g. | | Booklet pane of 4, #1860c | 1.50 |
| h. | | Booklet pane of 4, #1860d | 1.50 |
| | | Complete bklt., #1860e-1860h | 6.00 |

Complete booklet sold for 10,000r.

**Souvenir Sheet**

China 1999 World Philatelic Exhibition — A533

Illustration reduced.

**Perf. 13½x12¾**

**1999, Aug. 21  Litho.**

| | | | |
|---|---|---|---|
| 1861 | A533 | 5000r multi | 3.00 1.40 |

Gadjah Mada University, 50th Anniv. — A534

**1999, Sept. 19  Perf. 12½**

| | | | |
|---|---|---|---|
| 1862 | A534 | 500r shown | .40 .20 |
| 1863 | A534 | 1000r Building, diff. | .50 .20 |

Intl. Year of Older Persons A535

**1999, Oct. 1  Perf. 13½x12¾**

| | | | |
|---|---|---|---|
| 1864 | A535 | 500r multi | .40 .20 |

UPU, 125th Anniv. — A536

**1999, Oct. 9  Perf. 12½**

| | | | |
|---|---|---|---|
| 1865 | A536 | 500r Postman on horse | .30 .20 |
| 1866 | A536 | 500r Postman on motorcycle | .30 .20 |
| a. | | Pair, #1865-1866 + label | .60 .20 |

| | | | |
|---|---|---|---|
| 1866B | | Pair + 2 labels | 5.00 2.50 |
| c. | A536 | 1000r Like #1865, 30x32mm | 2.50 1.25 |
| d. | A536 | 1000r Like #1866, 30x32mm | 2.50 1.25 |

No. 1866B issued in sheets of 5 pairs. As the labels could be personalized, sheets were available only through special orders with Indonesia Post and sold for 20,000r.

Batik Designs — A537

**1999, Oct. 1**

| | | | |
|---|---|---|---|
| 1867 | A537 | 500r Cirebon | .40 .20 |
| 1868 | A537 | 500r Madura | .40 .20 |
| 1869 | A537 | 500r Jambi | .40 .20 |
| 1870 | A537 | 500r Yogyakarta | .40 .20 |
| | | Nos. 1867-1870 (4) | 1.60 .80 |

Domesticated Animals — A538

**1999, Nov. 5  Perf. 13½x12¾**

| | | | |
|---|---|---|---|
| 1871 | A538 | 500r Dogs | .40 .20 |
| 1872 | A538 | 500r Chickens | .40 .20 |
| a. | | Pair, #1871-1872 | .80 .20 |
| 1873 | A538 | 500r Cat | .40 .20 |
| 1874 | A538 | 500r Rabbits | .40 .20 |
| a. | | Pair, #1873-1874 | .80 .20 |
| 1875 | A538 | 1000r Pigeon | .50 .20 |
| 1876 | A538 | 1000r Geese | .50 .20 |
| a. | | Pair, #1875-1876 | 1.00 .50 |
| b. | | Sheet of 6, #1871-1876 | 2.75 1.25 |
| | | Nos. 1871-1876 (6) | 2.60 1.20 |

**Souvenir Sheet**

| | | | |
|---|---|---|---|
| 1877 | A538 | 4000r Like #1874 | 2.75 1.25 |

Millennium — A539

Designs: No. 1878, 1000r, No. 1880, 20,000r, 1999 agenda book. No. 1879, 1000r, No. 1881, 20,000r, Clock, child.

**Litho. & Photo.**

**1999-2000  Perf. 13½x12¾**

| | | | |
|---|---|---|---|
| 1878-1879 | A539 | Set of 2 | 1.00 .50 |
| a. | | Sheet of 20 + 20 labels | 14.00 14.00 |

**Souvenir Sheets**

| | | | |
|---|---|---|---|
| 1880-1881 | A539 | Set of 2 | 20.00 8.00 |

Labels on No. 1879a could be personalized. The sheet sold for 38,000r.
Issued: Nos. 1878, 1880, 12/31/99; Nos. 1879, 1879a, 1881, 1/1/00.

Visit Indonesia Decade — A540

Designs: 500r, Satellite, fish. 1000r, Hydroponic agriculture.

**2000, Jan. 1  Perf. 12¾x13½**

| | | | |
|---|---|---|---|
| 1882-1883 | A540 | Set of 2 | .80 .20 |

University of Indonesia, 50th Anniv. — A541

Designs: 500r, Salemba campus. 1000r, University building, Depok.

**2000, Feb. 2  Perf. 12½**

| | | | |
|---|---|---|---|
| 1884-1885 | A541 | Set of 2 | .80 .20 |

**Indonesian Folktales Type of 1998**

Folktale, region — #1886: a-e, Tapak Tuan, Aceh. f-j, Batu Ballah, West Kalimantan. k-o, Sawerigading, South Sulawesi. p-t, 7 Putri kahyangan, Moluccas. 5000r, Like #1886e

**2000, Feb. 5  Perf. 13½x12¾**

| | | | |
|---|---|---|---|
| 1886 | | Sheet of 20 | 9.00 5.00 |
| a.-e. | | 500r Strip of 5 | 2.25 1.25 |
| f.-j. | | 500r Strip of 5 | 2.25 1.25 |
| k.-o. | | 500r Strip of 5 | 2.25 1.25 |
| p.-t. | | 500r Strip of 5 | 2.25 1.25 |

**Souvenir Sheet**

| | | | |
|---|---|---|---|
| 1887 | A502 | 5000r multi | 3.00 1.50 |

**Indonesia 2000 Type of 1997**

Designs: 500r, Prehnite. 1000r, Chalcedony. 2000r, Volcanic obsidian.

**2000, Mar. 1**

| | | | |
|---|---|---|---|
| 1888-1890 | A483 | Set of 3 | 2.00 1.00 |
| 1890a | | Souvenir sheet, 3 each #1888-1890 + label | 6.00 3.00 |

**Souvenir Sheet**

| | | | |
|---|---|---|---|
| 1891 | A483 | 5000r Jasperized limestone | 2.75 1.25 |
| a. | | Sheet, #1891, 14 #1888, 2 #1889, 3 #1890 + 20 labels | 11.00 — |

No. 1891a sold for 41,000r with labels personalized.

Comic Strip Characters — A542

Designs: No. 1892, 500r, I Brewok, by Gungun. No. 1893, 500r, Pak Tuntung, by Basuki. No. 1894, Pak Bei, by Masdi Sunardi. No. 1895, 500r, Mang Ohle, by Didin D. Basuni. No. 1896, 500r, Panji Koming, by Dwi Koendoro.

**Perf. 12¾x13½**

**2000, Mar. 13  Photo.**

| | | | |
|---|---|---|---|
| 1892-1896 | A542 | Set of 5 | 1.75 .85 |
| 1896a | | Souvenir sheet, 3 each #1892-1896 + label | 5.25 2.50 |

World Meteorological Organization, 50th Anniv. — A543

**Litho. & Photo.**

**2000, Mar. 23  Perf. 12½**

| | | | |
|---|---|---|---|
| 1897 | A543 | 500r multi | .40 .20 |

Souvenir Sheet

Bangkok 2000 Stamp
Exhibition — A544

Illustration reduced.

**2000, Mar. 23**     **Perf. 13½x12¾**
1898 A544 5000r multi    3.00 1.40

15th
Natl.
Sports
Week
A545

Designs: 500r, Cycling. 1000r, Canoeing.
2000r, High jump.

**2000, Apr. 1**
1899-1901 A545 Set of 3    1.75 .80

Souvenir Sheet

The Stamp Show 2000,
London — A546

Illustration reduced.

**2000, May 22**
1902 A546 5000r multi    2.75 1.50

Environmental Care — A547

Designs; 500r, Birds in nest. 1000r,
Monkeys. 2000r, Fish.

**2000, June 5**
1903-1905 A547 Set of 3    1.60 .80
**Souvenir Sheet**
1906 A547 4000r Like #1904    2.25 1.00

2000 Summer Olympics,
Sydney — A548

No. 1907, 500r: a, Boxing. b, Judo.
No. 1908, 1000r: a, Badminton. b, Weight
lifting.
No. 1909, 2000r: a, Swimming. b, Running.
Illustration reduced.

**2000, July 1**
    **Pairs, #a-b**
1907-1909 A548 Set of 3    3.00 1.50
**Souvenir Sheet**
1910 A548 5000r Like #1908b    2.50 1.10

Worldwide Fund for Nature
(WWF) — A549

Komodo dragon: No. 1911, 500r, No.
1915a, 2500r, With tongue extended. No.
1912, 500r, On log. No. 1913, 500r, Pair walking. No. 1914, 500r, No. 1915b, 2500r, Pair
fighting.

**2000, Aug. 13**
1911-1914 A549 Set of 4    2.75 1.75
   a.    Souvenir sheet, 2
      each #1911-1914    9.00 6.00
    **Souvenir Sheet**
1915 A549 2500r Sheet of 2,
    #a-b    6.50 4.00

Souvenir Sheet

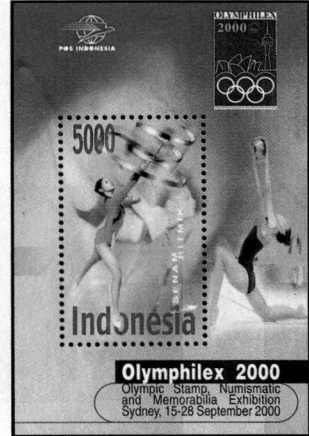

Olymphilex 2000 Stamp
Exhibition — A550

**2000, Sept. 15**     **Perf. 12¾x13½**
1916 A550 5000r multi    2.75 1.25

A551

No. 1917: a, Pres. Abdurrahman Wahid. b,
Vice Pres. Megawati Soekarnoputri
Illustration reduced.

    **Photo. & Engr.**
**2000, Sept. 27**     **Perf. 12½**
1917 A551 1000r Pair, #a-b    1.00 .20

   **Ducks and Geese Type of 1998**
**2000, Sept. 27**   **Photo.**   **Perf. 12½**
1918 A516 800r Like #1798    .50 .20
1919 A516 900r Like #1793    .50 .20

Traditional
Costumes
A552

Provinces and regions: a, Aceh. b, Jambi. c,
Banten. d, Yogyakarta. e, Central Kalimantan
(Kalimantan Tengah). f, Southeast Sulawesi
(Sulawesi Tenggara). g, East Nusa Tenggara
(Nusa Tenggara Timur). h, North Sumatra
(Sumatera Utara). i, Bengkulu. j, Jakarta. k,
East Java (Jawa Timur). l, East Kalimantan
(Kalimantan Timur). m, South Sulawesi
(Sulawesi Selatan). n, Maluku. o, West Suma-
tra (Sumatera Barat). p, South Sumatra
(Sumatera Selatan). q, West Java (Jawa
Barat). r, West Kalimantan (Kalimantan Barat).
s, North Sulawesi (Sulawesi Utara). t, Bali. u,
North Maluku (Maluku Utara). v, Riau. w,
Lampung. x, Central Java (Jawa Tengah). y,
South Kalimantan (Kalimantan Selatan). z,
Central Sulawesi (Sulawesi Tengah). aa, West
Nusa Tenggara (Nusa Tenggara Barat). ab,
Irian Jaya.

    **Litho. & Photo.**
**2000, Oct. 28**     **Perf. 12½**
1920    Sheet of 28 + 7 la-
    bels    14.00
  a.-ab.   A552 900r Any single    .50 .20

Artists and Entertainers — A553

No. 1921, horiz.: a, Bing Slamet (1927-74),
singer, comedian. b, S. Sudjojono (1913-86),
painter. c, I Ketut Maria (1897-1968), dancer.
d, Chairil Anwar (1922-49), poet. e, Ibu Sud
(1908-93), musician.

**2000, Nov. 1**     **Perf. 13½x12¾**
1921    Horiz. strip of 5    2.25 1.10
  a.-e.   A553 900r Any single    .45 .20
    **Souvenir Sheet**
1922 A553 4000r Chairil Anwar    2.00 1.00

Indonesia Post in the
21st Century — A554

Designs: 800r, Philately, vert. 900r, Business communications. 1000r, Business financial services, vert. 4000r, Business logistics,
vert.

    **Litho. & Photo.**
**2000, Dec. 20**     **Perf. 12½**
1923 A554    800r multi    .40 .20
1924 A554    900r multi    .40 .20
1925 A554   1000r multi    .40 .20
1926 A554   4000r multi    1.75 .75
    Nos. 1923-1926 (4)    2.95 1.35

Solar System — A555

No. 1927: a, Sun. b, Mercury. c, Venus. d,
Earth. e, Mars. f, Jupiter. g, Saturn. h, Uranus.
i, Neptune. j, Pluto.
Illustration reduced.

**2001, Jan. 1**   **Litho.**   **Perf. 13½x12¾**
1927    Block of 10 + 5 la-
    bels    3.75
  a.-j.   A555 900r Any single    .35 .20
  k.   Sheet of 10 + 5 labels    3.75
  l.   Sheet of 20 + 20 labels    10.00 10.00
    **Souvenir Sheet**
1928 A555 5000r Sun    2.50 1.25

Labels on No. 1927l could be personalized.
The sheet sold for 36,000r.

   **Indonesian Folktales Type of 1998**

Folktale, region — No. 1929: a-e, Batang
Tuaka, Riau. f-j, Si Pitung, Jakarta. k-o,
Terusan Nusa, Central Kalimantan. p-t, Ile
Mauraja, East Nusa Tenggara.
5000r, Like No. 1929h.

    **Litho. & Photo.**
**2001, Feb. 2**     **Perf. 13½x12¾**
1929    Sheet of 20    10.00 5.00
  a.-e.   A502 900r Strip of 5    2.50 1.25
  f.-j.   A502 900r Strip of 5    2.50 1.25
  k.-o.   A502 900r Strip of 5    2.50 1.25
  p.-t.   A502 900r Strip of 5    2.50 1.25
    **Souvenir Sheet**
1930 A502 5000r multi    2.75 1.25

Masks — A556

No. 1931, 500r — Arsa Wijaya, Bali: a,
Denomination at L. b, Denomination at R.
No. 1932, 800r — Asmat, Irian Jaya: a,
Denomination at L. b, Denomination at R.
No. 1933, 800r — Cirebon, West Java: a,
Denomination at L. b, Denomination at R.
No. 1934, 900r — Hudoq, East Kalimantan:
a, Denomination at L. b, Denomination at R.
No. 1935, 900r — Wayang Wong, Yogy-
akarta: a, Denomination at L. b, Denomination
at R.
5000r, Like No. 1934b.

**2001, Mar. 2**     **Perf. 12¾x13½**
    **Pairs, #a-b**
1931-1935 A556   Set of 5    4.00 1.50
  c.   Sheet, #1931-1935 +2
    labels    4.00
    **Souvenir Sheet**
1936 A556 5000r multi    2.50 1.25
  a.   Ovptd. in margin in silver    3.00 1.50

Issued: No. 1936a, 10/16/01. No. 1936
overprinted with "HAFNIA '01 / World Philatelic
Exhibition / Copenhagen / 16-21 October
2001," show emblem and new price of 7500r.

Traditional Communication
Instruments — A557

No. 1937: a, Beduk. b, Bendé. c, Kentongan. d, Nafiri.

**2001, Mar. 10**      *Perf. 12½*
1937    Vert. strip of 4    1.60   .80
 a.-d.   A557 900r Any single   .40   .20
 e.   Sheet, 2 each #1937a-1937d   3.00

Greetings —
A558

Various flowers. Denominations: 800, 900, 1000, 1500, 2000, 4000, 5000, 10000r.

**Litho. & Typo.**      *Perf. 12½*
**2001, Apr. 21**
1938-1945 A558   Set of 8    10.00 5.00

A558a

Greetings — A558b

Illustration A558a reduced.

*Perf. 13½x12¾*
1945A A558a 900r multi + label   1.50 1.50
*Perf. 12½*
1945B A558b 900r multi + label   1.50 1.50

No. 1945A was issued in sheets of 20 + 20 labels that could be personalized. The sheet sold for 36,000r. No. 1945B was issued in sheets of 10 + 10 labels that could be personalized. The sheet sold for 20,000r.

Environmental Care — A559

Children and: 800r, Fish. 900r, 5000r, Deer. 100r, Sea turtle.

**Litho. & Photo.**
**2001, June 5**     *Perf. 13½x12¾*
1946 A559   800r multi    .80   .20
 a.   Tete-beche pair   1.60 1.60
1947 A559   900r multi    .80   .20
 a.   Tete-beche pair   1.60 1.60
1948 A559   1000r multi    .80   .20
 a.   Tete-beche pair   1.60 1.60
   Nos. 1946-1948 (3)   2.40   .60
**Souvenir Sheet**
1949 A559 3000r multi    2.00 1.50

No. 1949 exists imperf. Value $3.

Pres. Sukarno (1901-70) — A560

Various portraits: 500, 800, 900, 1000r. 5000r, Sukarno at microphone.

**2001, June 6**      *Perf. 12½*
1950-1953 A560   Set of 4    1.25   .60
 a.   Sheet, 2 each #1950-
     1953   2.50

**Souvenir Sheet**
*Perf. 13½x12¾*
1954 A560 5000r multi    2.00 1.00

No. 1954 contains one 41x25mm stamp

National Police — A561

Police and: a, Children. b, Helicopter. Illustration reduced.

**2001, July 1   Photo.   Perf. 13½x12¾**
1955 A561 1000r Horiz. pair,   
   #a-b   1.00   .20

National Scouting Jamboree — A562

Scouts: a, Raising flag. b, Pitching tent. Illustration reduced.

**2001, July 3**
1956 A562 1000r Horiz. pair,
   #a-b   1.25   .20

Children's Games A563

Designs: 800r, Kaki Siapa. 900r, Egrang Bambu. 1000r, Dakon. 2000r, Kuda Pelepah Pisang.

**Litho. & Photo.**
**2001, July 23**     *Perf. 13½x12¾*
1957-1960 A564   Set of 4    2.25 1.10
 a.   Sheet, 2 each #1957-
     1960   4.50

**Souvenir Sheet**

Phila Nippon '01, Japan — A564

**2001, Aug. 1**      **Photo.**
1961 A564 10,000r multi    4.50 2.25

Dr. R. Soeharso Orthopedic Hospital, Surakarta, 50th Anniv. A565

**Litho. & Photo.**
**2001, Aug. 28**     *Perf. 13½x12¾*
1962 A565 1000r multi    .60   .20

Traditional Transportation — A566

Designs: No. 1963, 1000r, Rowboat. No. 1964, 1000r, Trishaw. No. 1965, Horse-drawn carriage.

**2001, Sept. 17**
1963-1965 A566   Set of 3    2.00   .60
 a.   Sheet, 3 each #1963-
     1965 +label   6.00 6.00

Post Offices A567

Buildings in: 800r, Makassar. 900r, Bandung. 1000r, Balikpapan. 2000r, Padang.

**2001, Sept. 27**
1966-1969 A567   Set of 4    2.00   .90

Gemstones — A568

Designs: 800r, Rose quartz. 900r, Brecciated jasper. 1000r, Malachite. 5000r, Diamond.

**2001, Oct. 1**
1970-1972 A568   Set of 3    1.25   .55
 a.   Sheet, 3 each #1970-
     1972 + label   4.00 2.75

**Souvenir Sheet**
1973 A568 5000r multi    2.25 1.10

Year of Dialogue Among Civilizations — A569

**2001, Oct. 9   Litho.   Perf. 12¾x13½**
1974 A569 1000r multi    .80   .20

Beetles — A570

Designs: 800r, Agestrata dehaan. 900r, Mormolyce phyllodes. No. 1977, 1000r, Batocera rosenbergi. No. 1978, 1000r, Chrysochroa buqueti. 2000r, 5000r, Chalcosoma caucasus.

**2001, Nov. 5**      **Litho. & Photo.**
1975-1979 A570   Set of 5    3.00 1.50
 a.   Booklet pane, #1975-
     1979 + label   3.00   —
   Booklet, 2 #1979a   6.00

**Souvenir Sheet**
1980 A570 5000r multi    2.25 1.10

Folktales — A571

No. 1981, 1000r — Pulau Kembara, South Sumatra: a, Four people, lanterns. b, Two men, woman, boat. c, Man and woman standing in boat. d, Man and woman in water. e, Boat, snake, fish.
No. 1982, 1000r — Nyi Koro Kidul, Yogyakarta: a, Woman at tight pointing. b, Woman at foreground with hand at mouth. c, Two men with hats at right. d, Woman in sea. e, Sea and island.
No. 1983, 1000r — Aji Tatin, East Kalimantan: a, Bird in tree, woman, man with hand outstretched. b, Woman, bird boat. c, Sinking boat. d, Woman and tree. e, Bird in tree.
No. 1984, 1000r — Danau Tondano, North Sulawesi: a, Woman with long hair in foreground. b, Man holding spear. c, Man at left

with arm to head. d, Man and woman embracing. e, Sea and island.
5000r, Like No. 1981e.
Illustration reduced.

**Litho. & Photo.**
**2002, Feb. 2**     *Perf. 13½x12¾*
**Blocks of 5, #a-e**
1981-1984 A571   Set of 4    6.50 3.25
**Souvenir Sheet**
1985 A571 5000r multi    2.50 1.25

Nos. 1981-1984 are printed in sheets of four blocks of five. Stamp "e" is always adjacent to the LL stamp in the block of the remaining four stamps, and is found tete beche to both stamps "a" and "e" from adjacent blocks of five.

2002 World Cup Soccer Championships, Japan and Korea — A572

Celebrations: 1000r, Player lifting shirt over face. 1500r, Four players with fists raised, horiz. 2000r, 5000r, Player with arms outstretched.

*Perf. 12¾x13½, 13½x12¾*
**2002, Apr. 1**      **Litho. & Photo.**
1986-1988 A572   Set of 3    2.25 1.00
**Souvenir Sheet**
1989 A572 5000r multi    2.50 1.25

Indonesian Cancer Foundation, 25th Anniv. — A573

**2002, Apr. 17**     *Perf. 12¾x13½*
1990 A573 1000r multi    .50   .20
 a.   Tete-beche pair   1.00   .50

Telecommunications — A574

No. 1991: a, Woman using telephone (2/4). b, Man using cellular phone (1/4). c, Satellite above Earth (4/4). d, Satellite, world map, computer, satellite dish (3/4).

**2002, May 17**
1991 A574 1000r Block of 4,
    #a-d   2.00 1.00
 e.   Sheet, 2 each #1991a-
     1991d   4.00 2.00
 f.   Booklet pane, 4 #1991a   2.00
 g.   Booklet pane, 4 #1991b   2.00
 h.   Booklet pane, 4 #1991c   2.00
 i.   Booklet pane, 4 #1991d   2.00
   Booklet, #1991f-1991i   8.00

Marine Life — A575

No. 1992, 1000r: a, Charonia tritonis. b, Symphyllia radians.
No. 1993, 1500r: a, Cromileptes altivelis. b, Acanthaster planci.
No. 1994, 2000r, horiz.: a, Paracanthurus hepatus. b, Tridacna gigas.
5000r, Acanthaster planci.

**2002, June 5**
**Horiz. Pairs, #a-b**
| | | | | |
|---|---|---|---|---|
| 1992-1994 | A575 | Set of 3 | 4.00 | 2.00 |
| *c.* | | Sheet, #1992, 1993, 1994a, 1994b | 4.00 | 2.00 |

**Souvenir Sheet**
| | | | | |
|---|---|---|---|---|
| 1995 | A575 | 5000r multi | 2.50 | 1.25 |

Aceh Province — A576

Designs: 1500r, Student, Aceh dance, map of Aceh. 3500r, Masjid Raya Banda Aceh, map of Indonesia.

**2002, June 15** **Perf. 12½**
| | | | | |
|---|---|---|---|---|
| 1996-1997 | A576 | Set of 2 | 2.50 | 1.25 |

Natl. Family Day A577

**Perf. 13½x12¾**
**2002, June 29** **Litho. & Typo.**
| | | | | |
|---|---|---|---|---|
| 1998 | A577 | 1000r multi | .50 | .20 |

33rd Intl. Physics Olympiad, Bali — A578

No. 1999: a, Eclipse (1/2). b, Spectrum colors and Balinese symbols (2/2).

**2002, July 14** **Perf. 12¾x13½**
| | | | | |
|---|---|---|---|---|
| 1999 | A578 | Horiz. pair, #a-b | 1.00 | .20 |

Kites A579

No. 2000: a, Popotengan (bird-shaped) (1/5). b, Barong (dragon head) (2/5). c, Fighting (3/5). d, Bebean (4/5). e, Modern (box and wing) (5/5).
5000r, Popotengan.

**Litho. & Photo.**
**2002, July 15** **Perf. 13½x12¾**
| | | | | |
|---|---|---|---|---|
| 2000 | | Horiz. strip of 5 | 2.50 | 1.25 |
| *a.-e.* | A579 | 1000r Any single | .50 | .20 |

**Souvenir Sheet**
| | | | | |
|---|---|---|---|---|
| 2001 | A579 | 5000r multi | 2.50 | 1.25 |

Fruit — A580

Designs: 300r, Morinda citrifolia. 500r, Mangifera indica. 1500r, Averrhoa carambola. 3000r, Durio zibethinus.

**2002, Aug. 1 Photo.** **Perf. 13½x12¾**
| | | | | |
|---|---|---|---|---|
| 2002 | A580 | 300r multi | .40 | .20 |
| 2003 | A580 | 500r multi | .40 | .20 |
| 2004 | A580 | 1500r multi | .60 | .20 |
| 2005 | A580 | 3000r multi | 1.40 | .60 |
| | | Nos. 2002-2005 (4) | 2.80 | 1.20 |

Souvenir Sheet

Philakorea 2002 World Stamp Exhibition, Seoul — A581

**2002, Aug. 2 Litho.** **Perf. 12¾x13½**
| | | | | |
|---|---|---|---|---|
| 2006 | A581 | 7000r multi | 3.25 | 1.60 |

Mohammad Hatta (1902-80), Prime Minister — A582

No. 2007, 1000r: a, Denomination at left. b, Denomination at right.
No. 2008, 1500r: a, Denomination at left. b, Denomination at right.
5000r, Hatta standing.

**Litho. & Photo.**
**2002, Aug. 12** **Perf. 12½**
**Pairs, #a-b**
| | | | | |
|---|---|---|---|---|
| 2007-2008 | A582 | Set of 2 | 2.25 | 1.10 |
| *c.* | | Sheet, 2 each #2007-2008 + 2 labels | 4.50 | 2.25 |

**Souvenir Sheet**
**Perf. 12¾x13½**
| | | | | |
|---|---|---|---|---|
| 2009 | A582 | 5000r multi | 2.25 | 1.10 |

No. 2009 contains one 25x41mm stamp.

President and Vice-President — A583

No. 2010: a, Pres. Megawati Soekarnoputri. b, Vice-president Hamzah Haz.
Illustration reduced.

**Photo. with Foil Application**
**2002, Aug. 17** **Perf. 12½**
| | | | | |
|---|---|---|---|---|
| 2010 | A583 | 1500r Horiz. pair, #a-b, + central label | 1.60 | 1.60 |

**Souvenir Sheet**

Amphilex 2002 Intl. Stamp Exhibition, Amsterdam — A584

**Perf. 13½x12¾**
**2002, Aug. 30** **Photo.**
| | | | | |
|---|---|---|---|---|
| 2011 | A584 | 7000r multi | 3.50 | 1.75 |

**Souvenir Sheet**

Panfila 2002 Philatelic Exhibition, Yogyakarta — A585

**2002, Sept. 19** **Perf. 12¾x13½**
| | | | | |
|---|---|---|---|---|
| 2012 | A585 | 6000r multi | 3.00 | 1.50 |

Paintings — A586

No. 2013, 1000r: a, Seko, Guerrilla Vanguard, by S. Sudjojono. b, Cat, by Popo Iskandar.
No. 2014, 1500r, vert.: a, Catching Lice, by Hendra Gunawan. b, Gatut Kaca with Prigiwa and Prigiwati, by R. Basuki Abdullah.

**Litho. & Photo.**
**2002, Sept. 27** **Perf. 12½**
**Pairs, #a-b**
| | | | | |
|---|---|---|---|---|
| 2013-2014 | A586 | Set of 2 | 2.25 | 1.10 |
| *c.* | | Sheet, 2 each #2013-2014 | 4.50 | 2.25 |

Souvenir Sheet

España 2002 Youth Philatelic Exhibition, Salamanca — A587

**2002, Oct. 4 Photo.** **Perf. 13½x12¾**
| | | | | |
|---|---|---|---|---|
| 2015 | A587 | 7000r multi | 3.00 | 1.50 |

Flora and Fauna A588

No. 2016, 1000r: a, Trimeresurus hageni. b, Rafflesia micropylora.
No. 2017, 1500r: a, Panthera pardus. b, Terminalia catappa.
No. 2018, 2000r: a, Papilionanthe hookeriana. b, Varanus salvator.
3500r, Panthera pardus.

**Litho. & Photo.**
**2002, Nov. 5** **Perf. 12¾x13½**
**Horiz. Pairs, #a-b**
| | | | | |
|---|---|---|---|---|
| 2016-2018 | A588 | Set of 3 | 4.00 | 2.00 |

**Souvenir Sheet**
| | | | | |
|---|---|---|---|---|
| 2019 | A588 | 3500r multi | 2.00 | 1.00 |

No. 2019 exists imperf. Value $3.

Antara, Indonesian News Agency — A589

**Litho. & Typo.**
**2002, Dec. 13** **Perf. 12½**
| | | | | |
|---|---|---|---|---|
| 2020 | A589 | 1500r multi | .80 | .40 |

Happy Birthday — A590

No. 2021: a, Food platter. b, Birthday cake.

**2003 Photo.** **Perf. 12½**
| | | | | |
|---|---|---|---|---|
| 2021 | | Strip of 2 stamps and 2 alternating labels | 2.00 | 1.00 |
| *a.-b.* | A590 | 1500r Any single | 1.00 | .50 |
| *c.* | | Sheet of 5 #2021 | 7.50 | |

No. 2021 was printed in sheets containing 10 strips with labels that could be personalized. The sheet sold for 45,000r. The labels on No. 2021c could also be personalized, and that sheet sold for 30,000r.

Folklore — A591

No. 2022 — Scenes from Danau Ranau, Lampung (#a.-e.), Kongga Owose, Southeast Sulawesi (#f.-j.), Putri Gading Cempaka, Bengkulu (#k.-o.), Putri Mandalika Nyale,

West Nusa Tenggara (#p.-t.) and stamp numbers: a, 01/20. b, 02/20. c, 03/20. d, 04/20. e, 05/20. f, 06/20. g, 07/20. h, 08/20. i, 09/20. j, 10/20. k, 11/20. l, 12/20. m, 13/20. n, 14/20. o, 15/20. p, 16/20. q, 17/20. r, 18/20. s, 19/20. t, 20/20.
5000r, Like #2022e.

**Litho. & Photo.**

| | | | | Perf. 13½x12¾ | |
|---|---|---|---|---|---|
| **2003, Feb. 2** | | | | Perf. 13½x12¾ | |
| **2022** | A591 | 1500r | Sheet of 20, #a-t | 11.00 | 5.00 |

**Souvenir Sheet**

| **2023** | A591 | 5000r multi | | 2.25 | .80 |

22nd South East Asia Games, Hanoi, Viet Nam A592

Designs: 1000r, Billiards. 1500r, Rowing. 2500r, Rhythmic gymnastics.

**Litho. & Photo.**

| **2003, May 12** | | | | Perf. 14 | |
|---|---|---|---|---|---|
| **2024-2026** | A592 | Set of 3 | | 2.00 | 1.00 |

Values are for stamps with surrounding selvage.

Volcanoes — A593

Designs: 500r, Kerinci. No. 2028, 1000r, Krakatoa. No. 2029, 1000r, Merapi. No. 2030, 1000r, Tambora. 2000r, Ruang. Illustration reduced.

| **2003, June 5** | | | | Perf. 12½ | |
|---|---|---|---|---|---|
| **2027-2031** | A593 | Set of 5 | | 2.25 | 1.10 |
| *2031a* | | Sheet, 2 each #2027-2031 + 2 labels | | 4.75 | 3.00 |

Astronomy — A594

No. 2032: a, Andromeda Galaxy (1/5). b, Earth and Mars (2/5). c, Moon (3/5).
No. 2033: a, External view of observatory (4/5). b, Zeiss telescope (5/5). 5000r, Like No. 2033a.

| **2003, June 7** | | | Perf. 12½ | |
|---|---|---|---|---|
| **2032** | | Strip of 3 | 1.25 | .65 |
| *a.-c.* | A594 | 1000r Any single | .40 | .20 |
| **2033** | | Pair | 1.25 | .65 |
| *a.-b.* | A594 | 1500r Either single | .60 | .20 |
| *c.* | | Sheet, 2 each #2032a-2032c, 2033a-2033b | 7.00 | 3.50 |

**Souvenir Sheet**

| | | | Perf. 13½x12¾ | |
|---|---|---|---|---|
| **2034** | A594 | 5000r multi | 3.00 | 1.75 |

Stamps in No. 2033c are tete-beche. No. 2034 contains one 41x25mm stamp.

Bank Indonesia, 50th Anniv. — A595

Designs: 1000r, Tower and flowers. 1500r, People at graduation ceremony, books. Illustration reduced.

**Perf. 13½x13¼ Syncopated**

| **2003, July 1** | | | | | |
|---|---|---|---|---|---|
| **2035-2036** | A595 | Set of 2 | | 1.00 | .50 |

Sri Sultan Hamengku Buwono IX and Lord Robert Baden-Powell — A596

Illustration reduced.

**Perf. 13½x12¾**

| **2003, Aug. 14** | | | Photo. | |
|---|---|---|---|---|
| **2037** | A596 | 1500r multi | 1.00 | .50 |

Independence Day Games — A597

No. 2038, 1000r: a, Panjat Pinang (1/4). b, Pukul Bantal (2/4).
No. 2039, 1500r, horiz.: a, Balap Kelom (3/4). b, Balap Karung (4/4).

**Perf. 12¾x13½, 13½x12¾**

| **2003, Aug. 17** | | | **Litho. & Photo.** | | |
|---|---|---|---|---|---|
| | | | Pairs, #a-b | | |
| **2038-2039** | A597 | Set of 2 | | 2.25 | 1.10 |
| *2039c* | | Sheet, 2 each #2038a-2038b, 2039a-2039b | | 6.75 | 3.25 |

**Souvenir Sheet**

Paintings of Srihadi Soedarsono — A598

No. 2040: a, Pendet, Dinamika Remaja. b, Borobudur-Purnama dalam Keheningan.

| **2003** | | | Perf. 13½ Syncopated | |
|---|---|---|---|---|
| **2040** | A598 | 3000r Sheet of 2, #a-b | 4.00 | 4.00 |
| *c.* | | Sheet with margin design in cyan only | 4.00 | 4.00 |
| *d.* | | As "c," with magenta added to margin design | 4.00 | 4.00 |
| *e.* | | As "d," with yellow added to margin design | 4.00 | 4.00 |
| *f.* | | As "e," with black added to margin design, but lacking artist's face and signature | 4.00 | 4.00 |
| *g.* | | Sheet, 2 each #2040a-2040b | 7.50 | 7.50 |

Emmitan-Philex 2003, Surabaya (#2040, 2040c, 2040d, 2040e, 2040f), 10th ASEAN Postal Business Meeting (#2040g).
Issued: No. 2040, 9/4; No. 2040c, 8/29; No. 2040d, 8/30; No. 2040e, 8/31; No. 2040f, 9/1; No. 2040g, 9/3. No. 2040 exists imperf, issued 9/2.

Tourism — A599

No. 2041, 1000r: a, Jou Uci Sabea, North Maluku (1/4). b, Mome'ati, Gorontalo (2/4).

No. 2042, 1500r: a, Muang Jong, Bangka Belitung (3/4). b, Seba Baduy, Banten (4/4).
5000r, Like No. 2042a.

| **2003, Sept. 27** | | | Perf. 12½ | |
|---|---|---|---|---|
| | | | Vert. Pairs, #a-b | |
| **2041-2042** | A599 | Set of 2 | 2.00 | 1.00 |

**Souvenir Sheet**

| **2043** | A599 | 5000r multi | 3.00 | 1.75 |

**Souvenir Sheet**

Bangkok 2003 World Philatelic Exhibition — A600

| **2003, Oct. 4** | | | Perf. 13½x12¾ | |
|---|---|---|---|---|
| **2044** | A600 | 8000r multi | 3.00 | 1.75 |

Handshake — A601

Fish and Water Lily — A602

Birds — A603

Handshake and Flag — A604

Flower — A605

Illustrations reduced.

| **2003, Oct. 27** | | | Litho. | Perf. 12½ | |
|---|---|---|---|---|---|
| **2045** | A601 | 1000r multi + label | | 1.00 | 1.00 |
| **2046** | A602 | 1500r multi + label | | 1.25 | 1.25 |
| **2047** | A603 | 1500r multi + label | | 1.25 | 1.25 |
| **2048** | A604 | 1500r multi + label | | 1.25 | 1.25 |
| **2049** | A605 | 1500r multi + label | | 1.25 | 1.25 |
| | | Nos. 2045-2049 (5) | | 6.00 | 6.00 |

Nos. 2045-2049 were each issued in sheets of 20 stamps + 20 labels that could be personalized. Sheets of No. 2045 sold for 35,000r, while sheets of Nos. 2046-2049 each sold for 45,000r.

Indonesian Youth Pledge, 75th Anniv. — A606

| **2003, Oct. 28** | | | Litho. | Perf. 12¾x13¼ | |
|---|---|---|---|---|---|
| **2050** | A606 | 1500r | Nos. 1031-1032, 1246 | .60 | .20 |

Flowers and Insects — A607

No. 2051: a, Paphiopedilum mastersianum (9/12). b, Platylomia flavida (8/12). c, Osmoxylon palmatum (7/12). d, Apis dorsata (12/12). e, Freycinetia pseudoinsignis (11/12). f, Sia ferox (10/12). g, Aularches miliaris (3/12). h, Butea monosperma (2/12). i, Orthetrum testaceum (1/12). j, Anaphalis javanica (6/12). k, Hierodula vitrea (5/12). l, Saraca declinata (4/12).
No. 2052: a, Like #2051j. b, Like #2051i.

**Litho. & Photo.**

| **2003, Nov. 5** | | | Perf. 12½ | |
|---|---|---|---|---|
| **2051** | A607 | 1500r Block of 12, #a-l | 8.50 | 4.25 |
| *m.* | | Booklet pane, #2051a, 2051c, 2051e, 2051h, 2051j, 2051l | 4.25 | — |
| *n.* | | Booklet pane, #2051b, 2051d, 2051f, 2051g, 2051i, 2051k | 4.25 | — |
| | | Complete booklet, #2051m, 2051n | 8.50 | |

**Souvenir Sheet**

| **2052** | A607 | 3000r Sheet of 2, #a-b, + label | 3.00 | 1.75 |

Famous Men A608

No. 2053: a, Prof. Roosseno (1908-96) (3/4). b, Prof. Sutami (1928-80) (4/4). c, Nurtanio Pringgoadisuryo (1923-66) (1/4). d, Martinus Putuhena (1901-82) (2/4).

**Litho. & Engr.**

| **2003, Nov. 10** | | | Perf. 13¼x13 | |
|---|---|---|---|---|
| **2053** | | Strip of 4 | 3.00 | 1.50 |
| *a.-d.* | A608 | 2000r Any single | .70 | .40 |

Flowers — A609

No. 2054: a, Styrax benzoin (1/30). b, Kopsia fruticosa (2/30). c, Impatiens tujuhensis (3/30). d, Hoya diversifolia (4/30). e, Etlingera elatior (5/30). f, Dillenia suffruticosa (6/30). g, Papilionanthe hookerianum (7/30). h, Medinilla speciosa (8/30). i, Costus speciosus (9/30). j, Melastoma sylvaticum (10/30). k, Nelumbo nucifera (11/30). l, Begonia robusta (12/30). m, Anaphalis longifolia (13/30). n, Pisonia grandis (14/30). o, Ixora javanica (15/30). p, Plumeria acuminata (16/30). q, Cassia fistula (17/30). r, Calotropis gigantea (18/30). s, Dimorphorchis lowii (19/30). t, Aeschynanthus radicans (20/30). u, Sonneratia caseolaris (21/30). v, Rhododendron orbiculatum (22/30). w, Passiflora edulis (23/30). x, Pterospermum celebicum (24/30). y, Quisqualis indica (25/30). z, Spathiphyllum commutatum (26/30). aa, Lilium longiflorum (27/30). ab, Clitoria ternatea (28/30). ac, Pecteilis susannae (29/30). ad, Grammatophyllum speciosum (30/30).

## Litho. & Photo.

**2004, Jan. 5**     **Perf. 12½**
2054     Sheet of 30     15.00 7.50
   a.-ad.   A609 1500r Any single    .50 .20

Folktales — A610

No. 2055 — Scenes from Putri Selaras Pinang Masak, Jambi (#a.-e.), Tanjung Lesung, Banten (#f.-j.), Patung Palindo, Central Sulawesi (#k.-o.), Danau Tolire, North Maluku (#p.-t.) and stamp number: a, 01/20. b, 02/20. c, 03/20. d, 04/20. e, 05/20. f, 06/20. g, 07/20. h, 08/20. i, 09/20. j, 10/20. k, 11/20. l, 12/20. m, 13/20. n, 14/20. o, 15/20. p, 16/20. q, 17/20. r, 18/20. s, 19/20. t, 20/20.
   6000r, Like # 2055j.

## Litho. & Photo.

**2004, Feb. 20**     **Perf. 13½x12¾**
2055   A610 1500r Sheet of 20,
     #a-t     10.00 4.75

### Souvenir Sheet

2056   A610 6000r multi     3.00 1.75

Museums — A611

No. 2057: a, Sri Baduga Museum, Bandung (3/4). b, Bahari Museum, Jakarta (1/4). c, Telecommunications Museum, Jakarta (4/4). d, Geology Museum, Bandung (2/4).

**2004, Feb. 29**     **Perf. 13¼x12¾**
2057     Vert. strip of 4     2.25 1.10
   a.-d.   A611 1500r Any single    .55 .20

General Elections — A612

No. 2058: a, Man and woman pointing at people holding flags (1/2). b, Man and woman casting ballots (2/2).

**2004, Apr. 5**   **Litho.**    **Perf. 12¾x13¼**
2058   A612 1500r Horiz. pair,
     #a-b     1.10 .55

Famous
Women — A613

No. 2059: a, Gedong Bagoes Oka (1921-2002), social worker, religious leader (2/4). b, Ani Idrus (1918-99), journalist (1/4). c, Nyonya Meneer (1895-1978), founder of herbal medicine factory (3/4). d, Sandiah (Ibu Kasur) (1926-2002), composer of children's songs, television personality (4/4).

### Perf. 13¼x13½ Syncopated

**2004, Apr. 21**     **Litho. & Engr.**
2059     Horiz. strip of 4     3.00 1.50
   a.-d.   A613 2500r Any single    .75 .35

2004
Summer
Olympics,
Athens
A614

No. 2060: a, Swimming (1/3). b, Women's high jump (2/3). c, Hurdling (3/3).

## Litho. & Photo.

**2004, May 5**     **Perf. 14**
2060     Horiz. strip of 3     2.50 1.25
   a.-c.   A614 2500r Any single    .80 .40

Environmental Protection — A615

Designs: Nos. 2061a, 2062a, Bird, killer whale (1/2). Nos. 2061b, 2062b, Shark, turtle (2/2).

**2004, June 5**     **Perf. 13¼x12¾**
2061   A615 1500r Vert. pair,
     #a-b     1.40 .70

### Souvenir Sheet

2062   A615 2500r Sheet of 2,
     #a-b     3.00 1.75

Indonesian Cuisine — A616

No. 2063: a, Gajebo, West Sumatra (1/4). b, Sambal Udang Terung Pipit, West Kalimantan (3/4). c, Kare Rajungan, East Java (2/4). d, Tinotuan, North Sulawesi (4/4).
Illustration reduced.

**2004, July 6**   **Litho.**    **Perf. 13¼x12¾**
2063   A616 1500r Block of 4, #a-d   2.25 1.10

Presidential Limousines — A617

No. 2064: a, 1939 Buick with REP-1 license plate (1/2). b, 1942 DeSoto with REP-2 license plate (2/2).

**2004, Aug. 17**
2064   A617 2500r Vert. pair, #a-b   2.00 1.25
   c.      Souvenir sheet #2064a-2064b   2.00 1.25

16th National Games — A618

No. 2065: a, Volleyball (1/2). b, Sepak takraw (2/2).
Illustration reduced.

## Litho. & Photo.

**2004, Sept. 2**     **Perf. 14**
2065   A618 1500r Pair, #a-b     1.10 .55

## Flowers and Insects Type of 2003

No. 2066: a, Gryllotalpa hirsuta (4/6). b, Alstonia scholaris (5/6). c, Scolopendra subspinipes (6/6). d, Cinnamomun sintok (3/6). e, Heterometrus cyaneus (2/6). f, Parkia roxburghii (1/6).
No. 2067: a, Like #2066e. b, Like #2066f.

**2004, Nov. 5**     **Perf. 12½**
2066   A607 1500r Block of 6, #a-f   3.00 1.75

### Souvenir Sheet

2067   A607 3000r Sheet of 2, #a-
     b, + label     2.25 1.10

National Teacher's Day — A619

No. 2068: a, Teacher, students with microscope and book (1/2). b, Teacher students with pen and book (2/2).

**2004, Nov. 25**     **Perf. 12¾x13¼**
2068   A619 1500r Horiz. pair, #a-
     b     1.10 .55

### Souvenir Sheet

National Philatelic Exhibition,
Surabaya — A620

No. 2069 — Paintings by Sunaryo: a, Setagen Rhythm. b, Sebelum Pentas. c, Bercinta.

**2004, Dec. 16**   **Litho.**    **Perf. 12½**
2069   A620 5000r Sheet of 3, #a-
     c     5.00 2.50
   d.    Souvenir sheet of 1, #2069a   2.00 1.00
   e.    Souvenir sheet of 1, #2069b   2.00 1.00
   f.    Souvenir sheet of 1, #2069c   2.00 1.00
   g.    Souvenir sheet of 1, #2069a,
       imperf.     2.00 1.00
   h.    Souvenir sheet of 1, #2069b,
       imperf.     2.00 1.00
   i.    Souvenir sheet of 1, #2069c,
       imperf.     2.00 1.00

Folktales — A621

No. 2070 — Scenes from Lahilote, Gorontalo (#a.-e.), Kolam Putri, Riau Islands (#f.-j.), Batu Balai, Bangka Belitung (#k.-o.), Bulan & Sagu di Ibuanari, Papua (#p.-t.) and stamp number: a, 1/20. b, 2/20. c, 3/20. d, 4/20. e, 5/20. f, 6/20. g, 7/20. h, 8/20. i, 9/20. j, 10/20. k, 11/20. l, 12/20. m, 13/20. n, 14/20. o, 15/20. p, 16/20. q, 17/20. r, 18/20. s, 19/20. t, 20/20.
   6000r, Like #2070j.

**2005, Feb. 2**     **Perf. 13½x12¾**
2070   A621 1500r Sheet of 20,
     #a-t     8.50 4.25

### Souvenir Sheet

2071   A621 6000r multi     2.25 1.10

Asian-African Summit, 50th
Anniv. — A622

No. 2072: a, Dove and "50." b, Dove, world map and people.

### Perf. 13½x13¼ Syncopated

**2005, Apr. 18**     **Litho. & Photo.**
2072     Horiz. pair + central la-
     bel     1.25 .60
   a.-b.   A622 2500r Either single    .60 .25
   c.      Souvenir sheet, #2072b    .60 .25

Mangrove Forest Protection — A623

No. 2073 — Mangroves and: a, Bird. b, Fish.

**2005, June 5**   **Litho.**    **Perf. 12¾x13¼**
2073   A623 1500r Horiz. pair, #a-
     b     1.25 .60
   c.      Souvenir sheet, #2073    1.25 .60

Voyages
of
Admiral
Zheng
He, 600th
Anniv.
A624

### Litho. & Photo.

**2005, June 28**     **Perf. 13½x12¾**
2074   A624 2500r multi     .75 .35
   a.      Souvenir sheet of 1     .75 .35

Traditional Food — A625

No. 2075: a, Sayur Tauco (North Sumatra) (1/4). b, Soto Banjar (South Kalimantan) (3/4). c, Nasi Timbel (West Java) (2/4). d, Langga Roko (South Sulawesi) (4/4).

**2005, July 6**     **Litho.**
2075     Vert. strip of 4     2.00 1.00
   a.-d.   A625 1500r Any single    .50 .20

Energy Conservation
A626

Designs: 1500r, Bus, electric plug (1/3).
2000r, Electric plugs and outlet (2/3). 2500r,
Automobile (3/3).

**2005, Aug. 17                  Perf. 12½**
2076-2078 A626    Set of 3         2.00  1.00

Indonesian
Leaders
A627

Designs: Nos. 2079a, 2080a, Pres. Susilo
Banbang Yudhoyono. Nos. 2079b, 2080b,
Vice-president Muhammad Jusuf Kalla.

**2005, Aug. 17                          Litho.**
2079    Horiz. pair with central
          label                         1.25   .60
  a.-b.  A627 1500r Either single        .60   .20

**Litho. With Foil Application**
2080    Horiz. pair with central
          label                         2.00  1.00
  a.-b.  A627 2500r Either single       1.00   .50
  c.     Souvenir sheet, #2080a, 2080b  2.00  1.00

Borobudur Ship Expedition — A628

No. 2081: a, Ship, head of Buddha (2/2). b,
Carving of ship (1/2).
Illustration reduced.

**2005, Sept. 17**
2081  A628 1500r Pair, #a-b          1.25   .60
  c.    As "a," with "2/2" removed     .70   .20
  d.    As "b," with "1/2" removed     .70   .20
  e.    Souvenir sheet, #2081c, 2081d
          + central label             1.25   .60

Souvenir Sheet

National Philatelic Exhibition,
Cilegon — A629

No. 2082 — Paintings by Sudjana Kerton: a,
Nyawer. b, Makan Siang. c, Wayang Golek. d,
Tanah Air Indonesia.

**2005, Sept. 23                  Perf. 12½**
2082  A629    Sheet of 4             6.00  3.00
  a.-c.  5000r Any single            1.25   .60
  d.     8000r multi                 2.25  1.10
  e.     Souvenir sheet, #2082a, im-
           perf.                     1.25   .60
  f.     Souvenir sheet, #2082b, im-
           perf.                     1.25   .60
  g.     Souvenir sheet, #2082c, im-
           perf.                     1.25   .60
  h.     Souvenir sheet, #2082d, im-
           perf.                     2.25  1.10

Sea Mammals and Plants — A630

No. 2083: a, Neophocaena phocaenoides
(1/4). b, Dugong dugon (2/4). c, Gelidium
latifolium (3/4). d, Halimeda opuntia (4/4).
Illustration reduced.

**2005, Nov. 5                    Perf. 12½**
2083  A630 1500r Block of 4, #a-d 2.50 1.25
  e.    As "a," with "1/4" removed    .70   .20
  f.    As "b," with "3/4" removed    .70   .20
  g.    Souvenir sheet, #2083e, 2083f
          + central label            1.25   .60

Folktales — A631

No. 2084: a, Bawang Merah & Bawang
Putih (1/4). b, Keong Emas (2/4). c, Si Kancil
(3/4). d, Timun Emas (4/4).

**2006, Feb. 6    Litho.    Perf. 12¾x13½**
2084     Block or strip of 4         2.50  1.25
  a.-d.  A631 1500r Any single        .60   .20
  e.     Souvenir sheet, #2084a-2084d,
           imperf.                   2.50  1.25

Miniature Sheets

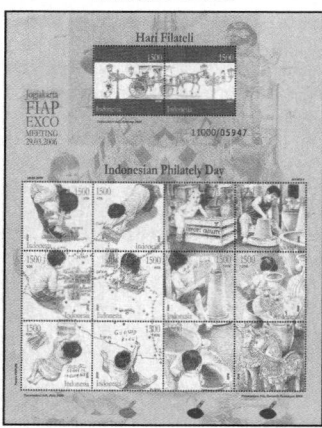

Philately Day — A632

No. 2085, 1500r — Illustrations in brown: a,
Family in coach (1/28). b, Horse pulling coach
(2/28). c, Girl, standing, with three photographs (3/28). d, Boy with one photograph
(4/28). e, Boy with three photographs (5/28). f,
Girl, wearing sandals, holding photograph
(6/28). g, Barefoot girl touching photograph
(7/28). h, Boy drawing map (8/28). i, Boy and
crate (9/28). j, Boy at potter's wheel, finished
pottery (10/28). k, Boy at potter's wheel
(11/28). l, Girl pointing (12/28). m, Boy touching pottery (13/28). n, Caparisoned pottery
horses (14/28).
No. 2086, 1500r — Illustrations in color: a,
Like #2085a (15/28). b, Like #2085b (16/28).
c, Like #2085c (17/28). d, Like #2085d (18/28).
e, Like #2085e (19/28). f, Like #2085f (20/28).
g, Like #2085g (21/28). h, Like #2085h
(22/28). i, Like #2085i (23/28). j, Like #2085j
(24/28). k, Like #2085k (25/28). l, Like #2085l
(26/28). m, Like #2085m (27/28). n, Like
#2085n (28/28).

**2006, Mar. 29    Litho.    Perf. 14**
**Sheets of 14, #a-n**
2085-2086 A632    Set of 2           9.25  4.75

2006 World Cup Soccer
Championships, Germany — A633

No. 2087: a, World Cup emblem, goal, soccer ball (1/4). b, World Cup emblem, soccer
ball (2/4). c, World Cup trophy at right, soccer
ball at bottom (3/4). d, World Cup trophy at left,
soccer ball at right (4/4).
Illustration reduced.

**Die Cut, With Perf. 14 Selvage
Between Stamps**
**2006, May 6**
**Self-Adhesive**
2087  A633 2500r Block of 4, #a-d 2.40 1.25
  e.    Booklet pane, #2087a-2087d,
          die cut, imperf. selvage be-
          tween stamps               2.40   —
          Complete booklet, #2087e   2.40

Individual stamps have various die cut soccer players in center. Values are for unused
stamps with surrounding selvage. Used
stamps may or may not have the die cut soccer players.

Environmental Care — A634

No. 2088: a, Village, flowers, butterfly (1/2).
b, Girl (2/2).

**2006, June 5  Litho.   Perf. 13¼x12¾**
2088  A634 1500r Pair, #a-b          1.00   .45
  c.    Souvenir sheet, #2088a-2088b 1.00   .45

Local
Foods
A635

No. 2089: a, Pempek (South Sumatra, 1/4).
b, Gudeg (Yogyakarta, 2/4). c, Ayam Betutu
(Bali, 3/4). d, Aunu Senebre (Papua, 4/4).

**2006, July 6**
2089     Block or strip of 4         2.00  1.00
  a.-d.  A635 1500r Any single        .50   .20

National Scout Jamboree — A636

No. 2090: a, Kak Mashudi and scouts
around campfire (1/2). b, Jigsaw puzzle of
scouts (2/2).
Illustration reduced.

**Litho. & Photo.**
**2006, July 16                  Perf. 12½**
2090  A636 1500r Pair, #a-b          1.00   .50

Sultans
A637

No. 2091d Overprinted in Red Foil

No. 2091: a, Sultan Ma'moen Al Rasyid
Perkasa Alamsyah Sultan Deli IX (1873-1924)
(1/4). b, Sultan Agung Sultan Mataram III
(1613-45) (2/4). c, Sultan Adji Mohamad
Parikesit Sultan Kutai Kertanegara XX (1920-
60) (3/4). d, Sultan Hasanuddin Sultan Gowa
XVI (1653-69) (4/4).

**Litho., Litho. with Foil Application
(#2091e)**
**Perf. 13½ Syncopated**
**2006, Aug. 17**
2091     Block or strip of 4         2.00  1.00
  a.-d.  A637 1500r Any single        .50   .20
  e.     As "d," overprinted in red foil .50 .20
  f.     Block or strip of 4, #2091a-
           2091c, 2091e              2.00  1.00

Puppets — A638

No. 2092: a, Indonesian puppet (1/2). b,
Slovakian marionette (2/2).

**Litho. & Photo.**
**2006, Sept. 27          Perf. 13x13¼**
2092  A638 2500r Horiz. pair, #a-
          b                          1.50   .75
  c.    Souvenir sheet, #2092       1.50   .75

See Slovakia Nos. 506-507.

Miniature Sheet

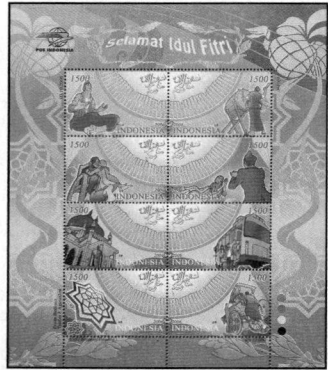

Eid ul-Fitr — A639

No. 2093: a, Man sitting with crossed legs in
prayer (1/8). b, Drummer (5/8). c, Older
woman hugging young woman (2/8). d,
Woman and man with hands in prayer (6/8). e,
Mosque (3/8). f, People getting on bus (7/8). g,
Geometric design (4/8). h, People and horse
cart (8/8).

**2006, Oct. 3     Litho.     Perf. 12½**
2093  A639 1500r Sheet of 8, #a-
          h                          3.25  1.60

Flora and Fauna — A640

No. 2094: a, Licuala arbuscula (3/4). b, Livistona mamberamoensis (4/4). c, Melipotes carolae (1/4). d, Amblyornis flavifrons (2/4). Illustration reduced.

**2006, Nov. 5**      *Perf. 12½*
| | | | | |
|---|---|---|---|---|
| 2094 | A640 1500r Block of 4, #a-d | 2.00 | 1.00 |
| e. | As "a," with "3/4" removed | .50 | .20 |
| f. | As "d," with "2/4" removed | .50 | .20 |
| g. | Souvenir sheet, #2094e-2094f + label | 1.00 | .50 |

**Souvenir Sheet**

Bandung '06 Natl. Philatelic Exhibition — A641

No. 2095: a, Panthera pardus (1/2). b, Bouea macrophylla (2/2).

*Perf. 13½x12¾*
**2006, Nov. 30**      Litho.
| | | | | |
|---|---|---|---|---|
| 2095 | A641 2500r Sheet of 2, #a-b | 1.50 | .75 |
| c. | Like #2095, with margin illustration in blue and black | 1.50 | .75 |
| d. | Like #2095, with margin illustration in red and black | 1.50 | .75 |
| e. | Like #2095, with margin illustration in yellow and black | 1.50 | .75 |
| f. | Like #2095, with margin illustration in black | 1.50 | .75 |

On No. 2095, the code number at lower left of sheet ends with "5," that of Nos. 2095c-2095f end in "1" to "4" respectively. Margin illustrations show progressive color printing.

Containers — A642

No. 2096: a, Container from Bali (2/2). b, Lidded basket from East Kalimantan (1/2). Illustration reduced.

**2006, Dec. 23**      *Perf. 13½x12¾*
| | | | |
|---|---|---|---|
| 2096 | A642 1500r Horiz. pair, #a-b | 1.00 | .50 |

New Year 2007 (Year of the Pig) A643

No. 2097: a, Chinese zodiac animals and lanterns (1/2). b, Chinese zodiac animals, people and temple (2/2).
No. 2098: a, Rat (1/13). b, Ox (2/13). c, Tiger (3/13). d, Rabbit (4/13). e, Dragon (5/13). f, Snake (6/13). g, Horse (7/13). h, Goat (8/13). i, Monkey (9/13). j, Rooster (10/13). k, Dog (11/13). l, Pig (12/13). m, Like #2097b (96x64mm, 13/13).
No. 2099, Like #2097b.

**Litho., Litho. With Foil Application**
**(#2098m, 2099)**
**2007, Feb. 1**      *Perf. 12½*
| | | | | |
|---|---|---|---|---|
| 2097 | | Pair | .70 | .35 |
| a.-b. | A643 1500r Either single | .35 | .20 |
| 2098 | | Sheet of 13 | 7.00 | 7.00 |
| a.-l. | A643 2000r Any single | .45 | .20 |
| m. | A643 6000r multi | 1.40 | .70 |

**Souvenir Sheet**
| | | | |
|---|---|---|---|
| 2099 | A643 2000r multi | 1.40 | .70 |

Dances — A644

No. 2100: a, Lion dance (1/2). b, Dragon dance (2/2).

*Perf. 13¼x13½ Syncopated*
**2007, Apr. 13**      Litho.
| | | | | |
|---|---|---|---|---|
| 2100 | A644 2500r Pair, #a-b | 1.10 | .55 |
| c. | Souvenir sheet, #2100a-2100b | 1.10 | .55 |

See People's Republic of China Nos. 3581-3582.

Reading and Writing A645

No. 2101: a, Boy writing in book, mother reading (2/2). b, Boy looking at girl writing in book (1/2).

**2007, May 2**    Litho.    *Perf. 13½x12¾*
| | | | |
|---|---|---|---|
| 2101 | A645 1500r Pair, #a-b | .70 | .35 |

A646

Environmental Care — A647

Nos. 2102, 2104: a, Iceberg, top of polar bear's head (1/4). b, Crying polar bear (2/4). No. 2103: a, Forest fire (3/4). b, Burnt forest (4/4).

**2007, June 5**
| | | | |
|---|---|---|---|
| 2102 | A646 1500r Vert. pair, #a-b | .70 | .35 |
| 2103 | A647 1500r Vert. pair, #a-b | .70 | .35 |

**Souvenir Sheet**
| | | | |
|---|---|---|---|
| 2104 | A646 2500r Sheet of 2, #a-b | 1.10 | .55 |

Nos. 2102 and 2103 were each printed in sheets containing 10 pairs with the bottom stamp in the pair tete-beche with the same stamp.

Campaign Against Drug Abuse — A648

No. 2105: a, Guitarist, Indonesian inscription (1/2). b, Basketball player, English inscription (2/2).

**2007, June 26**      *Perf. 12¾x13½*
| | | | |
|---|---|---|---|
| 2105 | A648 1500r Pair, #a-b | .70 | .35 |

Traditional Foods — A649

No. 2106: a, Roti Cane and Kari Kambing (Aceh, 1/4). b, Gecok (West Nusa Tenggara, 3/4). c, Soto Kudus (Central Java, 2/4). d, Ikan Air Garam (Maluku, 4/4).

**2007, July 6**      *Perf. 13½x12¾*
| | | | | |
|---|---|---|---|---|
| 2106 | | Strip of 4 | 1.40 | .70 |
| a.-d. | A649 1500r Any single | .35 | .20 |

Fireworks — A654

Guitar and G Clef A655

Paint Brushes — A656

Film and Reel A657

*Perf. 12½x12½x12½x4*
**2007, July 21**      Litho.
| | | | | |
|---|---|---|---|---|
| 2111 | A654 1500r multi + label | .40 | .40 |
| 2112 | A655 1500r multi + label | .40 | .40 |
| 2113 | A656 1500r multi + label | .40 | .40 |
| 2114 | A657 1500r multi + label | .40 | .40 |
| | Nos. 2111-2114 (4) | 1.60 | 1.60 |

Nos. 2111-2114 were each printed in sheets of 8 stamps + 8 labels that sold for 15,000r face. No. 2111 also was printed in four different sheets of 12 stamps + 12 labels that each sold for 30,000r. Labels could not be personalized.

Scouting, Cent. — A658

No. 2115: a, Centenary emblem, full color background (1/4). b, Scout, full color (2/4).
No. 2116: a, Centenary emblem, blue background (3/4). b, Scout in blue (4/4).

**2007, Aug. 1**      *Perf. 13½ Syncopated*
| | | | | |
|---|---|---|---|---|
| 2115 | A658 2500r Horiz. pair, #a-b | 1.10 | .55 |

**Booklet Stamps**
| | | | | |
|---|---|---|---|---|
| 2116 | A658 1500r Horiz. pair, #a-b | .65 | .30 |
| c. | Booklet pane, 5 #2116 | 3.25 | — |
| | Complete booklet, #2116c | 3.25 | |

Nepenthes Mirabilis — A659

Nepenthes Ampuliaria — A660

**2007, Aug. 3**      *Perf. 13½x12¾*
| | | | |
|---|---|---|---|
| 2117 | A659 1500r multi | .35 | .20 |

*Perf. 12¾x13½*
| | | | |
|---|---|---|---|
| 2118 | A660 1500r multi | .35 | .20 |

**Souvenir Sheet**
*Perf. 13½x12¾*
| | | | | |
|---|---|---|---|---|
| 2119 | | Sheet of 2 | 1.10 | .55 |
| a. | A659 2500r multi | .55 | .25 |
| b. | A660 2500r multi | .55 | .25 |

Bangkok 2007 Intl. Stamp Exhibition.

Association of South East Asian Nations (ASEAN), 40th Anniv. A661

Designs: 1500r, Fatahillah Museum, Jakarta.
No. 2121: a, Secretariat Building, Bandar Seri Begawan, Brunei (1/10). b, National Museum of Cambodia (2/10). c, Fatahillah Museum, Jakarta (3/10). d, Typical house, Laos (4/10). e, Malayan Railway Headquarters Building, Kuala Lumpur, Malaysia (5/10). f, Yangon Post Office, Myanmar (6/10). g, Malacañang Palace, Philippines (7/10). h, National Museum of Singapore (8/10). i, Vimanmek Mansion, Bangkok, Thailand (9/10). j, Presidential Palace, Hanoi, Viet Nam (10/10).

**2007, Aug. 8  Perf. 13½ Syncopated**
2120  A661  1500r multi  .35  .20
2121  Sheet of 10  5.50  2.75
a.-j.  A661 2500r Any single  .55  .25

See Brunei No. 607, Burma No. 370, Cambodia No. 2339, Laos Nos. , Malaysia No. 1170, Philippines Nos. 3103-3105, Singapore No. 1265, Thailand No. 2315, and Viet Nam Nos. 3302-3311.

Lighthouses — A662

No. 2122: a, Semarang Lighthouse (1/2). b, Cikoneng Lighthouse (2/2).

**2007, Aug. 17  Perf. 12¾x13½**
2122  A662  1500r Horiz. pair, #a-
b  .65  .30

Padjadjaran University, 50th Anniv. — A663

No. 2123: a, Tiger and ram (1/4). b, Men and dancers (2/4). c, Building (3/4). d, Symbols and globe (4/4).

**2007, Sept. 5  Perf. 13½x12¾**
2123  Horiz. strip of 4 + central label  1.25  .65
a.-d.  A663 1500r Any single  .30  .20

Butterflies — A664

No. 2124: a, Delias kristianiae (1/4). b, Ornithoptera aesacus (2/4). c, Ornithoptera croesus (3/4). d, Troides hypolitus (4/4).
No. 2125: a, Like #2124a. b, Like #2124c.

**2007, Nov. 5  Perf. 12½**
2124  Block of 4  1.25  .60
a.-d.  A664 1500r Any single  .30  .20
**Souvenir Sheet**
2125  Sheet of 2 + central label  1.10  .55
a.-b.  A664 2500r Either single  .55  .25

**No. 2125 Surcharged in Gold**

**2007, Nov. 21  Litho.  Perf. 12½**
2126  Sheet of 2 + central label  2.25  1.10
a.-b.  A664 5000r on 2500r Either single  1.10  .55

No. 2126 also is overprinted in gold in margin and label with emblem and text for

Bandungfilex 2007 and Jakarta 2008 Intl. Stamp Exhibition.

24th South East Asian Games, Nakhon Ratchasima, Thailand — A665

No. 2127: a, Bowling (1/4). b, Indoor soccer (2/4). c, Kempo (3/4). d, Hammer throw (4/4).

**2007, Dec. 6  Perf. 14**
2127  Horiz. strip of 4  2.25  1.10
a.-d.  A665 2500r Any single  .55  .25

Djuanda Declaration, 50th Anniv. — A666

No. 2128: a, Map of Indonesia, children (1/3). b, Prime Minister Djuanda Kartawidjaja, eagle, and procession (2/3). c, Djuanda Kartawidjaja and map of Indonesia (3/3).

**2007, Dec. 13  Perf. 13½x12¾**
2128  Vert. strip of 3  .95  .50
a.-c.  A666 1500r Any single  .30  .20

**Miniature Sheet**

Jakarta 2008 Intl. Stamp Exhibition — A667

No. 2129: a, Prasasti Tugu (2/7). b, Arca Dewa Visnu (statue of Vishnu) (3/7). c, Prasasti Padrao (4/7). d, Peta Nusantara Zaman Portugis (5/7). e, Naskah Perjanjian Sunda Kelapa (6/7). f, Kapal Bangsa Portugis (7/7). g, Bendera Singa Ali and Fatahillah (1/7). Nos. 2129a-2129f are 41x25mm; No. 2129g, 83x25mm.

**2008, Jan. 20  Litho.  Perf. 13½x12¾**
2129  A667  Sheet of 7  5.50  2.75
a.-f.  2500r Any single  .55  .25
g.  10,000r multi  2.10  1.10

A668

New Year 2008 (Year of the Rat) — A669

No. 2130: a, Rat facing right (1/3). b, Rat facing left (2/3). c, Rat on hind legs (3/3).

**2008, Jan. 26  Perf. 13½x12¾**
2130  Vert. strip of 3 + label  1.40  .70
a.-c.  A668 2000r Any single  .45  .20
**Souvenir Sheet**
**Perf. 12½**
2131  A669  5000r black & gray  1.10  .55

**Souvenir Sheet**

Flora and Fauna — A670

No. 2132: a, Casuarius casuarius (1/2). b, Crinum asiaticum (2/2).

**2008, Mar. 7  Perf. 12¾x13½**
2132  A670  5000r Sheet of 2, #a-
b  2.25  1.10

Jakarta 2008 Intl. Stamp Exhibition, Taipei 2008 Intl. Stamp Exhibition, Stamp Passion '08 Stamp Exhibition, Netherlands.

2008 Summer Olympics, Beijing — A671

No. 2133: a, Sailboarding (1/4). b, Soccer (2/4). c, Badminton (3/4). d, Weight lifting (4/4).
Illustration reduced.

**2008, Mar. 18  Perf. 14**
2133  A671  2500r Block of 4, #a-
d  2.25  1.10

**Miniature Sheet**

Jakarta 2008 Intl. Stamp Exhibition — A672

No. 2134: a, Istana Pemerintahan Batavia (2/7). b, Gedung Keuangan (3/7). c, Penyerangan Batavia oleh Sultan Agung, denomination at LR (4/7). d, Penyerangan Batavia oleh Sultan Agung, denomination at LL (5/7). e, Perubahan Batavia Menjadi Jakarta (6/7). f, Penyerahan Kekuasaan Indonesia (7/7). g, Penangkapan Pangeran Jayawikarta oleh Pasukan Banten (1/7). Nos. 2134a-2134f are 41x25mm; No. 2134g, 83x25mm.

**Perf. 13½x12¾**
**2008, Mar. 29  Litho.**
2134  A672  Sheet of 7  5.50  2.75
a.-f.  2500r Any single  .55  .25
g.  10,000r multi  2.10  1.10

Diplomatic Relations Between Indonesia and Japan, 50th Anniv. — A673

No. 2135, 2500r: a, Kelimutu Volcano, Indonesia (1/10). b, Mt. Fuji, Japan (2/10).
No. 2136, 2500r: a, Borobudur, Indonesia (3/10). b, Toji Temple, Japan (4/10).
No. 2137, 2500r: a, Rafflesia arnoldi (5/10). b, Cherry blossoms (6/10).
No. 2138, 2500r: a, Angklung (7/10). b, Gaku biwa (8/10).
No. 2139, 2500r, horiz: a, Scleropages formosus (9/10). b, Nishiki-goi (10/10).
Illustration reduced.

**2008, Apr. 15  Perf. 12½**
**Horiz. Pairs, #a-b**
2135-2139  A673  Set of 5  5.50  2.75
2139c  Miniature sheet, #2135-2139  5.50  2.75

Nos. 2135-2139 were each printed in sheets of 4 pairs. See Japan No. 3018.

Special Needs Education A674

No. 2140: a, Boy in wheelchair waving flags (1/3). b, Man in racing wheelchair (2/3). c, Handicapped children playing anklungs (3/3).

**Litho. & Embossed**
**2008, May 2  Perf. 13½x12¾**
2140  Strip of 3  1.00  .50
a.-c.  A674 1500r Any single  .30  .20

National Awakening, Cent. — A675

No. 2141: a, People with fists raised, flag. b, Flag, people, satellite.

**2008, May 20 Litho. Perf. 12¾x13½**
2141 A675 1500r Horiz. pair, #a-
b .65 .30

Environmental Care — A676

Nos. 2142 and 2143: a, Cyclists, motor vehicles (1/2). b, Seedling, forest (2/2). Stamps from No. 2143 lack stamp numbers.

**2008, June 5 Perf. 13½x12¾**
2142 A676 1500r Pair, #a-b .65 .30
**Souvenir Sheet**
2143 A676 2500r Sheet of 2, #a-
b 1.10 .55

**Miniature Sheet**

Jakarta 2008 Intl. Stamp
Exhibition — A677

No. 2144: a, Jakarta Philatelic Center (Kantor Filateli Jakarta) (2/7). b, National Museum (3/7). c, Dunia Fantasi (4/7). d, Taman Mini Indonesia (5/7). e, Wisana Seni and Budaya (6/7). f, Wisata Bihari (7/7). g, Warna Warni Jakarta (1/7). Nos. 2144a-2144f are 41x25mm; No. 2144g, 83x25mm.

**2008, June 22 Perf. 13½x12¾**
2144 A677 Sheet of 7 5.50 2.75
*a.-f.* 2500r Any single .55 .25
*g.* 10,000r multi 2.10 1.10

17th National Games — A678

No. 2145: a, Mountain biking (1/4). b, Bodybuilding (2/4). c, Steeplechase (3/4). d, Palaran Main Stadium, Samarinda (4/4). Illustration reduced.

**2008, July 5 Perf. 14**
2145 A678 1500r Block of 4, #a-d 1.40 .70

**Traditional Foods Type of 2007**

No. 2146: a, Nasi Lemak (Riau, 1/4). b, Sate Bandeng (Banten, 2/4). c, Ayem Cincane (East Kalimantan, 3/4). d, Kaledo (Central Sulawesi, 4/4).

**2008, July 6 Perf. 13½x12¾**
2146 Block of 4 1.40 .70
*a.-d.* A649 1500r Any single .35 .20

Printed in sheets containing four of each stamp + four labels.

Provincial Arms and
Architecture — A679

Arms of: Nos. 2147, 1500r, 2158a, 2500r, Bali (1/33). Nos. 2148, 1500r, 2158b, 2500r, Gorontalo (2/33). Nos. 2149, 1500r, 2158c, 2500r, Jawa Barat (West Java) (3/33). Nos. 2150, 1500r, 2158d, 2500r, Jawa Tengah (Central Java) (4/33). Nos. 2151, 1500r, 2158e, 2500r, Kalimantan Barat (West Kalimantan) (5/33). Nos. 2152, 1500r, 2158f, 2500r, Maluku (Moluccas) (6/33). Nos. 2153, 1500r, 2158g, 2500r, Aceh (7/33). Nos. 2154, 1500r, 2158h, 2500r, Papua (8/33). Nos. 2155, 1500r, 2158i, 2500r, Riau (9/33). Nos. 2156, 1500r, 2158j, 2500r, Sulawesi Barat (West Sulawesi) (10/33). Nos. 2157, 1500r, 2158k, 2500r, Sumatera Barat (West Sumatra) (11/33).

**2008, Aug. 17 Perf. 12½**
2147-2157 A679 Set of 11 3.75 1.90
2158 Sheet of 11 + label 6.25 3.25
*a.-k.* A679 2500r Any single .55 .25

Nos. 2147-2157 each were printed in sheets of 10.

Great
Post
Road of
Java
A680

No. 2159: a, Lighthouse, map of western part of road (1/4). b, Building, map of central part of road (2/4). c, Lighthouse, map of eastern part of road (3/4). d, Letter from Governor General Herman Daendels (4/4).
10,000r, Map of entire road.

**2008, Sept. 27 Perf. 13½x12¾**
2159 Horiz. strip of 4 2.25 1.10
*a.-d.* A680 2500r Any single .55 .25
**Souvenir Sheet**
2160 A680 10,000r multi 2.25 1.10

No. 2160 contains one 125x25mm stamp.

**Souvenir Sheets**

A681

A682

A683

A684

A685

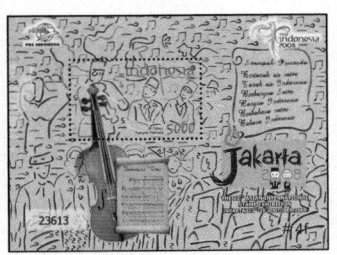

Jakarta 2008 Intl. Stamp
Exhibition — A686

**2008 Perf. 13½x12¾**
2161 A681 5000r multi .95 .45
2162 A682 5000r multi .95 .45
2163 A683 5000r multi .95 .45
2164 A684 5000r multi .95 .45
2165 A685 5000r multi .95 .45
2166 A686 5000r multi .95 .45
*Nos. 2161-2166 (6)* 5.70 2.70

Issued: No. 2161, 10/23; No. 2162, 10/24; No. 2163, 10/25; No. 2164, 10/26; No. 2165, 10/27; No. 2166, 10/28.

**Miniature Sheet**

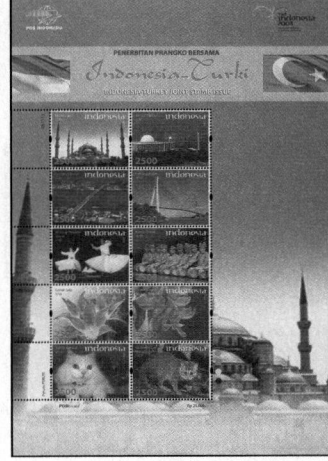

Friendship Between Indonesia and
Turkey — A687

No. 2167: a, Blue Mosque, Turkey (1/10). b, Istiqlal Mosque, Indonesia (2/10). c, Bosporus Bridge, Turkey (3/10). d, Barelang Bridge, Indonesia (4/10). e, Whirling dervishes (5/10). f, Saman dance (6/10). g, Turkish tulip (7/10). h, Flame of Irian (8/10). i, Turkish Van cat (9/10). j, Flat-headed cat (10/10).

**2008, Oct. 24 Perf. 13½ Syncopated**
2167 A687 2500r Sheet of 10,
#a-j 4.75 2.40

**Miniature Sheet**

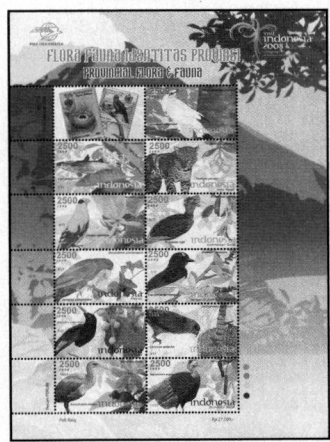

Flora and Fauna of the
Provinces — A688

No. 2168: a, Leucopsar rothschildi, Dysoxylum densiflorum, Bali (1/11). b, Liza dussumieri, Vitex cofassus, Gorontalo (2/11). c, Panthera pardus, Bouea macrophylla, Jawa Barat (West Java) (3/11). d, Oriolus chinensis, Michelia alba, Jawa Tengah (Central Java) (4/11). e, Rhinoplax vigil, Shorea stenoptera, Kalimantan Barat (West Kalimantan) (5/11). f, Alisterus amboinensis, Dendrobium phalaenopsis, Maluku (Moluccas) (6/11). g, Copsychus pyrropygus, Michelia champaca, Aceh (7/11). h, Seleucidis melanoleuca, Pometia pinnata, Papua (8/11). i, Loriculus galgulus, Oncosperma tigillarium, Riau (9/11). j, Aramidopsis plateni, Elmerrillia ovalis, Sulawesi Barat (West Sulawesi) (10/11). k, Argusianus argus, Morus macroura, Sumatera Barat (West Sumatra) (11/11).

**2008, Nov. 5 Perf. 13½x12¾**
2168 A688 2500r Sheet of 11,
#a-k, + label 5.25 2.60

Cut Nyak Dhien (1848-1908), Leader
of Aceh Resistance to Dutch
Rule — A689

No. 2169: a, House (1/2). b, Cut Nyak Dhien
(2/2).

**2008, Nov. 5**
2169 A689 1500r Horiz. pair, #a-
b .55 .25

Islands
A690

No. 2170: a, Damar Island (1/4). b, Sebatik
Island (2/4). c, Batubawaikang Island (3/4). d,
Bras Island (4/4).

**2008, Dec. 3**
2170 Block or strip of 4 1.10 .55
*a.-d.* A690 1500r multi .25 .20
*e.* Miniature sheet, 4 each #2170a-
2170d 4.50 2.25

## SEMI-POSTAL STAMPS

Symbols of
Olympic
Games
SP43

Wings and
Flame
SP44

*Perf. 12½x12*

**1951, Jan. 2 Photo. Unwmk.**
B58 SP43 5s + 3s gray grn .20 .20
B59 SP43 10s + 5s dk vio bl .20 .20
B60 SP43 20s + 5s org red .20 .20
B61 SP43 30s + 10s dk brn .65 .20
B62 SP43 35s + 10s ultra 2.25 1.00
Nos. B58-B62 (5) 3.50 1.85

Issued to publicize the Asiatic Olympic
Games of 1951 at New Delhi, India.

**1951, Oct. 15**
B63 SP44 5s + 3s olive green .20 .20
B64 SP44 10s + 5s dull blue .20 .20
B65 SP44 20s + 5s red .25 .20
B66 SP44 30s + 10s brown .35 .20
B67 SP44 35s + 10s ultra .70 .20
Nos. B63-B67 (5) 1.70 1.00

2nd Natl. Games, Djakarta, 10/21-28/51.

No. 378 Surcharged
in Black

**1953, May 8 Perf. 12½**
B68 A53 35s + 10s purple .35 .20

The surcharge reads "Natural Disaster."
Surtax was for emergency relief following volcanic eruption and floods.

Merapi Erupting
SP45

Young
Musicians
SP46

---

**1954, Apr. 15 Litho. Perf. 12½x12**
B69 SP45 15s + 10s bl grn .20 .20
B70 SP45 35s + 15s pur .20 .20
B71 SP45 50s + 25s red .20 .20
B72 SP45 75s + 25s vio bl .25 .20
B73 SP45 1r + 25s car .40 .20
B74 SP45 2r + 50s blk brn 1.10 .50
B75 SP45 3r + 1r gray grn 13.00 3.50
B76 SP45 5r + 2.50r org brn 17.50 4.50
Nos. B69-B76 (8) 32.85 9.50

The surtax was for victims of the Merapi
volcano eruption.

**1954, Dec. 22 Photo. Perf. 12½**

15s+10s, Parasol dance. 35s+15s, Girls
playing dakon. 50s+15s, Boy on stilts.
75s+25s, Bamboo flute players. 1r+25s, Javanese dancer.

B77 SP46 10s + 10s dk pur .20 .20
B78 SP46 15s + 10s dk grn .20 .20
B79 SP46 35s + 15s car rose .20 .20
B80 SP46 50s + 15s rose brn .30 .20
B81 SP46 75s + 25s ultra .40 .20
B82 SP46 1r + 25s brt org .70 .20
Nos. B77-B82 (6) 2.00 1.20

The surtax was for child welfare.

Scout Emblem
SP47

Scout Signaling
SP48

Designs: 50s+25s, Campfire. 75s+25s,
Scout feeding fawn. 1r+50s, Scout saluting.

**1955, June 27 Unwmk. Perf. 12½**
B83 SP47 15s + 10s bl grn .20 .20
B84 SP48 35s + 15s ultra .20 .20
B85 SP48 50s + 25s scar .40 .20
B86 SP48 75s + 25s brn .45 .20
B87 SP48 1r + 50s vio .75 .20
Nos. B83-B87 (5) 2.00 1.00

First National Boy Scout Jamboree.

Blind Weaver
SP49

Red Cross and
Heart
SP50

35s+15s, Basket weaver. 50s+25s, Boy
studying map. 75s+50s, Woman reading
Braille.

**1956, Jan. 4**
B88 SP49 15s + 10s dp grn .20 .20
B89 SP49 35s + 15s yel brn .30 .20
B90 SP49 50s + 25s rose car 2.25 .20
B91 SP49 75s + 50s ultra 1.25 .20
Nos. B88-B91 (4) 4.00 .80

The surtax was for the benefit of the blind.

**1956, July 26 Litho.**

Designs: 35s+15s, 50s+15s, Transfusion
bottle. 75s+25s, 1r+25s, Outstretched hands.

### Cross in Red

B92 SP50 10s + 10s ultra .20 .20
B93 SP50 15s + 10s carmine .20 .20
B94 SP50 35s + 15s lt brn .20 .20
B95 SP50 50s + 15s bl grn .45 .20
B96 SP50 75s + 25s orange .45 .20
B97 SP50 1r + 25s brt pur .45 .20
Nos. B92-B97 (6) 1.95 1.20

Surtax for the Indonesian Red Cross.

Invalids Doing Batik
Work — SP51

Designs: 15s+10s, Amputee painting.
35s+15s, Lathe operator. 50s+15s, Crippled

---

child learning to walk. 75s+25s, Treating
amputee. 1r+25s, Painting with artificial hand.

**1957, Mar. 26 Photo. Perf. 12½**
B98 SP51 10s + 10s dp blue .20 .20
B99 SP51 15s + 10s brown .30 .20
B100 SP51 35s + 15s red .30 .20
B101 SP51 50s + 15s dp vio .30 .20
B102 SP51 75s + 25s green .45 .20
B103 SP51 1r + 25s dk car
rose .45 .20
Nos. B98-B103 (6) 2.00 1.20

The surtax was for rehabilitation of invalids.

Kembodja
Flower
SP52

Designs: 15s+10s, Michelia. 35s+15s, Sunflower. 50s+15s, Jasmine. 75s+50s, Orchid.

**1957, Dec. 23 Perf. 13½x12½**
**Flowers in Natural Colors**
B104 SP52 10s + 10s blue 2.00 .20
B105 SP52 15s + 10s dp yel grn 1.40 .20
B106 SP52 35s + 15s dk red brn .90 .20
B107 SP52 50s + 15s ol & dk
brn .70 .20
B108 SP52 75s + 60s rose brn .70 .20
Nos. B104-B108 (5) 5.70 1.00

Children
SP53

Indonesian
Scout Emblem
SP54

15s+10s, 50s+25s, 1r+50s, Girl and boy.

**1958, July 1 Photo. Perf. 12½x12**
B109 SP53 10s + 10s blue .20 .20
B110 SP53 15s + 10s rose brn .20 .20
B111 SP53 35s + 15s gray green .20 .20
B112 SP53 50s + 25s gray olive .20 .20
B113 SP53 75s + 50s brn car .20 .20
B114 SP53 1r + 50s brown .25 .20
Nos. B109-B114 (6) 1.25 1.20

The surtax was for orphans.

**1959, July 17 Photo. Unwmk.**

Design: 15s + 10s, 50s + 25s, 1r + 50s,
Scout emblem and compass.

### Emblem in Red

B115 SP54 10s + 5s bister .20 .20
B116 SP54 15s + 10s bluish grn .20 .20
B117 SP54 20s + 10s lilac gray .20 .20
B118 SP54 50s + 25s olive .20 .20
B119 SP54 75s + 35s yel brn .50 .20
B120 SP54 1r + 50s dark gray .60 .20
Nos. B115-B120 (6) 1.90 1.20

10th World Scout Jamboree, Makiling
National Park near Manila, July 17-26.

Palm-leaf Ribs,
Gong and 5
Rings
SP55

Young Couple
Holding
Sharpened
Bamboo
Weapon
SP56

Design: 20s+10s, 75s+35s, Bamboo musical instrument and 5-ring emblem.

**1960, Feb. 14 Perf. 12½x12**
B121 SP55 15s + 5s bis & dk
brn .20 .20
B122 SP55 20s + 10s grn & blk .20 .20
B123 SP55 50s + 25s bl & pur .20 .20

---

B124 SP55 75s + 35s ol & dk
grn .20 .20
B125 SP56 1.15r + 50s car & blk .35 .20
Nos. B121-B125 (5) 1.15 1.00

All-Indonesian Youth Cong., Bandung, 2/14-
21/60.

Social Emblem
SP57

Pineapple
SP58

Designs: 15s+15s, Rice, lotus and cotton.
20s+20s, Lotus blossom and tree. 50s+25s,
Girl and boy. 75s+25s, Watering of plant in
man's hand. 3r+50s, Woman nursing infant.

*Perf. 12½x12*
**1960, Dec. 20 Photo. Unwmk.**
**Inscribed: "Hari Sosial Ke III"**
B126 SP57 10s + 10s ocher &
blk .20 .20
B127 SP57 15s + 15s dp cl & blk .20 .20
B128 SP57 20s + 20s bl & blk .20 .20
B129 SP57 50s + 25s bis brn &
blk .20 .20
B130 SP57 75s + 25s emer & blk .20 .20
B131 SP57 3r + 50s red & blk .30 .20
Nos. B126-B131 (6) 1.30 1.20

3rd Social Day, Dec. 20.

Type of 1960 Surcharges: "BENTJANA
ALAM 1961"

**1961, Feb. 17 Perf. 12x12½**
B132 A76 15s + 10s plum .20 .20
B133 A76 20s + 15s ocher .20 .20
B134 A76 75s + 25s scarlet .20 .20
Nos. B132-B134 (3) .60 .60

The surtax was for flood relief.

**1961, Dec. 20 Perf. 12½x13½**

4th Social Day: 75s+25s, Mangosteen.
3r+1r, Rambutan.

B135 SP58 20s + 10s bl, yel &
red .35 .20
B136 SP58 75s + 25s gray, grn
& dp claret .40 .20
B137 SP58 3r + 1r grn, yel &
red 1.25 .20
Nos. B135-B137 (3) 2.00 .60

Istiqlal Mosque, Djakarta — SP59

40s+20s, 3r+1r, Different view of mosque.

**1962, Feb. 22 Perf. 12½x12**
B138 SP59 30s + 20s Prus grn
& yel .20 .20
B139 SP59 40s + 20s dk red &
yel .20 .20
B140 SP59 1.50r + 50s brn & bl .50 .20
B141 SP59 3r + 1r grn & yel .55 .20
Nos. B138-B141 (4) 1.45 .80

Issued for the benefit of the new Istiqlal
Mosque.

National
Monument,
Djakarta — SP60

1.50r+50s, 6r+1.50r, Aerial view of monument.

**1962, May 20 Photo. Perf. 12x12½**
B142 SP60 1r + 50s org brn & blk .20 .20
B143 SP60 1.50r + 50s ol grn & ultra .20 .20
B144 SP60 3r + 1r lil rose & dk grn .30 .20
B145 SP60 6r + 1.50r vio bl & red .45 .20
*Nos. B142-B145 (4)* 1.15 .80

Vanda
Tricolor
SP61

Orchids: 1.50r+50s, Phalaenopsis amabilis, vert. 3r+1r, Dendrobium phalaenopsis, vert. 6r+1.50r, Paphiopedilum praestans.

**Perf. 13½x12½, 12½x13½**
**1962, Dec. 20 Unwmk.**
**Orchids in Natural Colors**
B146 SP61 1r + 50s ultra & yel .40 .20
B147 SP61 1.50r + 50s grnsh bl & ver .40 .20
B148 SP61 3r + 1r dp bl & ocher .40 .20
B149 SP61 6r + 1.50r org & dl vio .40 .20
*Nos. B146-B149 (4)* 1.60 .80

Issued for the 5th Social Day.

West Irian
Monument,
Djakarta — SP62

**1963, Feb. 15 Perf. 12½x13½**
B150 SP62 1r + 50s rose red & blk .20 .20
B151 SP62 1.50r + 50s mag & dk brn .20 .20
B152 SP62 3r + 1r bl & dk brn .20 .20
B153 SP62 6r + 1.50r grn & brn .25 .20
*Nos. B150-B153 (4)* .85 .80

The surtax was for the construction of the West Irian Monument in Djakarta.

Erupting
Volcano
SP63

**1963, June 29 Photo. Perf. 13½x13**
B154 SP63 4r + 2r rose red .20 .20
B155 SP63 6r + 3r grnsh bl .20 .20

The surtax was for victims of national natural disasters.

Papilio Blumei,
Celebes — SP64

Butterflies: 4r+1r, Charaxes dehaani, Java. 6r+1.50r, Graphium, West Irian. 12r+3r, Troides amphrysus, Sumatra.

**1963, Dec. 20 Perf. 12x12½**
B156 SP64 1.75r + 50s multi .35 .20
B157 SP64 4r + 1r multi .35 .20
B158 SP64 6r + 1.50r multi .35 .20
B159 SP64 12r + 3r multi .70 .20
*Nos. B156-B159 (4)* 1.75 .80

Issued for the 6th Social Day.

Malaysian
Fantails — SP65

Birds: 6r+1.50r, Zebra doves. 12r+3r, Black drongos. 20r+5r, Black-naped orioles. 30r+7.50r, Javanese sparrows.

**Perf. 12½x13½**
**1965, Jan. 25 Photo. Unwmk.**
B160 SP65 4r + 1r dl yel, lil & blk .50 .20
B161 SP65 6r + 1.50 grn, blk & pink .50 .20
B162 SP65 12r + 3r ol & blk .50 .20
B163 SP65 20r + 5r gray, yel & red .50 .20
B164 SP65 30r + 7.50r car rose, sl bl & blk .50 .20
*Nos. B160-B164 (5)* 2.50 1.00

Issued for the 7th Social Day.

Type of Regular Issue, 1964, Inscribed Vertically "Confo"
**1965 Perf. 12½x12**
B165 A98 1r + 1r org red & brn .20 .20
B166 A98 1.25r + 1.25r org red & brn .20 .20
B167 A98 1.75r + 1.75r org, red & brn blk .20 .20
B168 A98 2r + 2r org red & sl grn .20 .20
B169 A98 2.50r + 2.50r org red & red brn .20 .20
B170 A98 4r + 3.50r org red & dp bl .20 .20
B171 A98 6r + 4r org red & emer .20 .20
B172 A98 10r + 5r org red & yel grn .20 .20
B173 A98 12r + 5.50r org red & org .20 .20
B174 A98 15r + 7.50r org red & bl grn .20 .20
B175 A98 20r + 10r org red & dk gray .20 .20
B176 A98 25r + 10r org red & pur .20 .20
B177 A98 40r + 15r ver & plum .20 .20
B178 A98 50r + 15r org red & dp vio .20 .20
B179 A98 100r + 25r org red & dk ol gray .20 .20
*Nos. B165-B179 (15)* 3.00 3.00

Conference of New Emerging Forces.

Makara Mask
and Magic
Rays — SP66

**1965, July 17 Perf. 12**
B180 SP66 20r + 10r red & dk bl .35 .20
B181 SP66 30r + 15r bl & dk red .35 .20

Issued to publicize the fight against cancer.

Family and
Produce
SP67

State Principles: 20r+10r, Humanitarianism; clasped hands, globe, flags and chain. 25r+10r, Nationalism; map of Indonesia and tree. 40r+15r, Democracy; conference and bull's head. 50r+15r, Belief in God; houses of worship and star.

**1965, Aug. 17 Photo. Perf. 12½**
B182 SP67 10r + 5r fawn, yel & blk .30 .20
B183 SP67 20r + 10r dp yel, red & blk .30 .20
B184 SP67 25r + 10r rose red, red, grn & blk .30 .20
B185 SP67 40r + 15r bl, red & blk .30 .20
B186 SP67 50r + 15r lil, yel & blk .30 .20
*Nos. B182-B186 (5)* 1.50 1.00

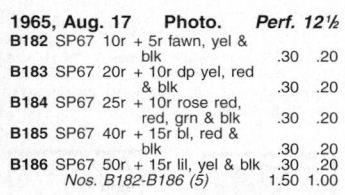

Samudra Beach Hotel and Pres.
Sukarno — SP68

Designs: 25r+10r, 80r+20r, Ambarrukmo Palace Hotel and Pres. Sukarno.

**1965, Dec. 1 Photo. Perf. 12½**
B187 SP68 10r + 5r dk bl & lt bl grn .25 .30
B188 SP68 25r + 10r vio blk & yel grn .30 .30
B189 SP68 40r + 15r dk brn & vio bl .40 .40
B190 SP68 80r + 20r dk pur & org .60 .40
*Nos. B187-B190 (4)* 1.55 1.40

Issued for tourist publicity.

Gloriosa — SP69

40r+15r, Magaguabush. 80r+20r, Balsam. 100r+25r, Crape myrtle.

**1965, Dec. 20 Photo. Perf. 12**
**Flowers in Natural Colors**
B191 SP69 30r + 10r deep blue .20 .20
B192 SP69 40r + 15r deep blue .35 .20
B193 SP69 80r + 20r deep blue .50 .20
B194 SP69 100r + 25r deep blue .70 .20
*Nos. B191-B194 (4)* 1.75 .80

Dated "1966"
10s+5s, Senna. 20s+5s, Crested barleria. 30s+10s, Scarlet ixora. 40s+10s, Rose of China (hibiscus).

**1966, Feb. 10**
**Flowers in Natural Colors**
B195 SP69 10s + 5s Prus bl .35 .20
B196 SP69 20s + 5s grn .35 .20
B197 SP69 30s + 10s grn .35 .20
B198 SP69 40s + 10s Prus bl .55 .20
*Nos. B195-B198 (4)* 1.60 .80

Nos. B191-B198 issued for the 8th Social Day, Dec. 20, 1965. An imperf. souvenir sheet contains one No. B198. Size: 58x78mm.

Type of 1965 Inscribed: "BENTJANA ALAM / NASIONAL 1966"
15s+5s, Gloriosa. 25s+5s, Magaguabush. 30s+10s, Balsam. 80s+20s, Crape myrtle.

**1966, May 2**
**Flowers in Natural Colors**
B199 SP69 15s + 5s blue .30 .20
B200 SP69 25s + 5s dk bl .30 .20
B201 SP69 30s + 10s dk bl .35 .20
B202 SP69 80s + 20s lt bl .80 .20
*Nos. B199-B202 (4)* 1.75 .80

The surtax was for victims of national natural disasters.

Reticulated Python — SP70

Reptiles: 3r+50s, Bloodsucker. 4r+75s. Saltwater crocodile. 6r+1r, Hawksbill turtle (incorrectly inscribed *chelonia mydas*, "green turtle").

**1966, Dec. 20 Photo. Perf. 12½x12**
B203 SP70 2r + 25s multi .30 .30
B204 SP70 3r + 50s multi .30 .30
B205 SP70 4r + 75s multi .55 .30
B206 SP70 6r + 1r multi .60 .30
*Nos. B203-B206 (4)* 1.75 1.20

Flooded Village
SP71

Buddha &
Stupa,
Borobudur
Temple
SP72

2.50r+25s, Landslide. 4r+40s, Fire destroying village. 5r+50s, Erupting volcano.

**1967, Dec. 20 Photo. Perf. 12½**
B207 SP71 1.25r + 10s dl vio bl & yel .20 .20
B208 SP71 2.50r + 25s dl vio bl & yel .20 .20
B209 SP71 4r + 40s dp org & blk .35 .20
B210 SP71 5r + 50s dp org & blk .50 .20
a. Souv. sheet of 2, #B209-B210 27.50 17.00
*Nos. B207-B210 (4)* 1.25 .80

Surtax for victims of natl. natural disasters.

**1968, Mar. 1 Photo. Perf. 12½**
Designs: No. B211, Musicians. No. B212, Sudhana and Princess Manohara. No. B213, Procession with elephant and horses.
B211 SP72 2.50r + 25s brt grn & gray ol .55 .20
B212 SP72 2.50r + 25s brt grn & gray ol .55 .20
B213 SP72 2.50r + 25s brt grn & gray ol .55 .20
a. Souv. sheet of 3, #B211-B213 25.00 11.50
b. Strip of 3, #B211-B213 1.60 .35
B214 SP72 7.50r + 75s org & gray ol .55 .20
*Nos. B211-B214 (4)* 2.20 .80

The surtax was to help save Borobudur Temple in Central Java, c. 800 A.D.
No. B213b has continuous design showing a frieze from Borobudur.

Scout with
Pickax — SP73

Designs: 10r+1r, Bugler. 30r+3r, Scouts singing around campfire, horiz.

**1968, June 1 Photo. Perf. 12½**
**Size: 28½x44½mm**
B215 SP73 5r + 50 dp org & brn .50 .50
B216 SP73 10r + 1r brn & gray ol .60 .75

**Size: 68x28½mm**

B217 SP73 30r + 3r ol gray & grn  1.00  .65
*Nos. B215-B217 (3)*  2.10  1.90
Surtax for Wirakarya Scout Camp.

Woman with Flower — SP74

**1969, Apr. 21　　　Perf. 13½x12½**
B218 SP74 20r + 2r emer, red &
yel  .75  .20
Emancipation of Indonesian women.

Noble Voluta — SP75

Sea shells: 7.50r+50s, Common hairy triton. 10r+1r, Spider conch. 15r+1.50r, Murex ternispina.

**1969, Dec. 20　Photo.　Perf. 12½**
B219 SP75 5r + 50s multi  .30  .20
B220 SP75 7.50r + 50s multi  .40  .20
B221 SP75 10r + 1r multi  .65  .20
B222 SP75 15r + 1.50r multi  .90  .20
*Nos. B219-B222 (4)*  2.25  .80
Issued for the 12th Social Day, Dec. 20.

Chrysocoris Javanus SP76

Insects: 15r+1.50r, Dragonfly. 20r+2r, Carpenter bee.

**1970, Dec. 21　Photo.　Perf. 12½**
B223 SP76 7.50r + 50c multi  6.00  .20
B224 SP76 15r + 1.50r multi  15.00  .20
B225 SP76 20r + 2r multi  19.00  .20
*Nos. B223-B225 (3)*  40.00  .60
The 13th Social Day, Dec. 20.

Fight Against Cancer — SP77

Patient receiving radiation treatment, Jakarta Hospital.

**1983, July 1　Photo.　Perf. 12½**
B226 SP77 55r + 20r multi  .75  .20
B227 SP77 75r + 25r multi  1.25  .20

Children's Day SP78

Children's Drawings. Surtax was for Children's Palace building fund.

**1984, June 17　Photo.　Perf. 13½x13**
B228 SP78 75r + 25r multi  .95  .20
B229 SP78 110r + 25r multi  1.25  .20
B230 SP78 175r + 25r multi  1.75  .20

B231 SP78 275r + 25r multi  3.00  .20
a. Souv. sheet of 2, #B230-
B231  30.00  .65
b. Souv. sheet of 4 + 2 labels  25.00  1.25
*Nos. B228-B231 (4)*  6.95  .80
AUSIPEX '84. No. B231b for FILACENTO '84, Netherlands, Sept. 6-9.

SP79　　　　　　SP80

**1987, May 12　Photo.　Perf. 12½**
B232 SP79 350r +25r dark ultra &
yel  1.75  .30
Yayasan Cancer Medical Assoc., 10th anniv.

**1991, June 1　Photo.　Perf. 12½**
B233 SP80 200r +25r multi  1.25  .30
Natl. Fed. for Welfare of Mentally Handicapped, 24th anniv.

Yayasan Cancer Medical Assoc., 15th Anniv. — SP81

**1992, May 12　Photo.　Perf. 12½**
B234 SP81 200r +25r brown & mag  .35  .20
B235 SP81 500r +50r blue & mag  .90  .35

Natl. Kidney Foundation — SP82

**Perf. 13½x12½**
**1994, Apr. 30　　　　　Photo.**
B236 SP82 300r +30r multi  .85  .20

Rehibilitation Intl., 10th Asia & Pacific Regional Conference — SP83

Design: 700r+100r, Painting, Mother's Love, by disabled artist Patricia Saerang.

**Perf. 13½x12½**
**1995, Sept. 12　　　　　Photo.**
B238 SP83 700r +100r multi  1.25  .65

March 1, 1949, Day of Total Attack SP84

Designs: No. B239, Natl. flag, tanks, map. No. B240, Soldiers fighting, soldiers standing at attention, natl. flag.

**1996, Mar. 1　Photo.　Perf. 13½x12½**
B239 SP84 700r +100r multi  1.00  .50
B240 SP84 700r +100r multi  1.00  .50
a. Pair, #B239-B240  2.00  1.00

World AIDS Day SP85

**1997, Dec. 1　Photo.　Perf. 13½x12½**
B241 SP85 700r +100r multi  1.00  .55

PETA (Pembela Tanah Air) Volunteer Army — SP86

**Perf. 12½x13½**
**1998, Nov. 10　　　　　Litho.**
B242 SP86 700r Statue, museum  .70  .20

National Disaster Fund — SP87

**2005, May 20　Litho.　Perf. 12½**
B243 SP87 1500r +300r multi +
label  1.00  1.00
Surtax for victims of Dec. 26, 2004 tsunami.

---

## AIR POST STAMPS

Airplane, Marshal Surydarma AP1

Airplane Over Buffalo Canyon AP2

Designs: 10s, Airplane, Air Chief Marshal Suryadi Surydarma. 20s, Sentry and aircraft, Lake Toba, Sumatra. 30s, Pilots. 40c, Indian Red Cross plane, Sumatra. 50s, Red Cross plane. 75s, Airplane over Buffalo Canyon. 1r, Crew studying flight plan. 1½r, Aircraft over Tjipanas Fish Ponds, Java. 4½r, DC-3 over rice fields. 7½r, DC-4 over Indonesian Archipelago.
Nos. C10, C12 and C13 are overprinted ("POS UDARA" and Airplane) on Nos. 22-24.

**Perf. 14½, 12½ (#C10, C12, C13)**
**1948, Dec. 15　　　　　Photo.**
C1 AP1 10s dk lilac & brn  .35  —
C2 AP1 20s Pruss grn & org
red  .40  —
C3 AP1 30s dp blue & dull lil  .45  —
C4 AP1 40s red brn & blue
emerald  .25  —
C5 AP1 50s dp vio & dull bl  .25  —
C6 AP2 75s dp brn & org brn  .75  —
C7 AP2 1r dp choc & purple brown  .90  —
C8 AP2 1½r dk viol & dp yel
brown  2.25  —
C9 AP2 4½r Pruss grn & dull
purple  2.25  —

C10 A32 5r yel brn & black  7.50  —
C11 AP1 7½r brn & slate vio  3.75  —
C12 A32 10r emerald & black  9.00  —
C13 A32 25r rose red & black  12.00  —
*Nos. C1-C13 (13)*  40.10

AP3

Designs: 30s, 1r, Map, ships. 50s, Harbor scene, vert. 2½r, 4½r, Ships. Illustration reduced.

**1949, Aug. 17　Photo.　Perf. 12½**
C14 AP3 30s blue & orange  1.75  —
C15 AP3 50s green & orange  3.00  —
C16 AP3 1r brn & green  1.90  —
C17 AP3 2½r blk & dull grn  6.00  —
C18 AP3 4½r blue & rose red  15.00  —
*Nos. C14-C18 (5)*  27.65
Failure of Dutch blockade.

Airplane, Indonesian Archipelago — AP4

Hot Spring, Java — AP5

Designs: 10s, DC-4 over Indonesian Archipelago. 20s, Aircraft mechanics working on plane. 30s, Servicing plane on runway. 40c, Pilots. 50s, Briefing pilots. 75s, Sentry and aircraft, Lake Toba, Sumatra. 1r, Plane, mountain in Sumatra. 1½r, DC-3 over rice fields. 4½r, DC-3 over rice fields. 7½r, Aircraft over Tjipanas Fish Ponds, Java.
Nos. C28, C30 and C31 are overprinted ("POS UDARA" and Airplane) on Nos. 51-53.

**Perf. 14½, 12½ (#C10, C12, C13)**
**1949, Aug. 17　　　　　Photo.**
C19 AP4 10s pur & lt blue  .50  —
C20 AP5 20s brn & sl blue  1.00  —
C21 AP4 30s red brn & bl grn  2.00  —
C22 AP4 40s dk brn & pur  1.50  —
C23 AP4 50s dp bl grn & red
brn  2.25  —
C24 AP4 75s bl grn & brn  .95  —
C25 AP4 1r pur & dk grn  1.25  —
C26 AP4 1½r blk bl & org  3.00  —
C27 AP5 4½r pur & chestnut  3.50  —
C28 A38 5r red vio & black  3.50  —
C29 AP5 7½r dk grn & vio brn  3.50  —
C30 A38 10r grn & black  6.00  —
C31 A38 25r red & black  14.00  —
*Nos. C19-C31 (13)*  42.95

AP6

Designs: 50s, Map, airplanes, horiz. 30s, 1r, Harbor scene. 2½r, Airplane on runway, horiz. 4½r, Airplane landing, horiz.

| 1949 | | Photo. | | Perf. 14½ |
|---|---|---|---|---|
| C32 | AP6 | 30s multicolored | 1.75 | |
| C33 | AP6 | 50s multicolored | 2.00 | — |
| C34 | AP6 | 1r multicolored | 1.25 | — |
| C35 | A39 | 2½r multicolored | 2.00 | — |
| C36 | A39 | 4½r multicolored | 3.50 | — |
| | | Nos. C32-C36 (5) | 10.50 | |

### Liberation of Jakarta

**Nos. C1//C31 overprinted "Merdeka Djojakarta 6 Djuli 1949"**

Nos. C1-C9, C11, C12 Overprinted

| 1949, Dec. 7 | | | |
|---|---|---|---|
| C37 | AP1 | 10s dk lilac & brn | .25 |
| C38 | AP1 | 20s Pruss grn & org red | .25 |
| C39 | AP1 | 30s dp blue & dull lil | .25 |
| C40 | AP1 | 40s red brn & blue emerald | 12.00 — |
| C41 | AP1 | 50s dp vio & dull bl | .55 — |
| C42 | AP2 | 75s dp brn & org brn | .55 — |
| C43 | AP2 | 1r dp choc & purple brown | 1.25 |
| C44 | AP2 | 1½r dk viol & dp yel brown | 1.40 |
| C45 | AP2 | 4½r Pruss grn & dull purple | 2.00 — |
| C46 | AP7 | 7½r brn & slate vio | 12.50 — |
| | | Nos. C37-C46 (10) | 31.00 |

Nos. C19-C27, C29 Overprinted

| C47 | AP4 | 10s pur & lt blue | .25 | — |
|---|---|---|---|---|
| C48 | AP5 | 20s brn & sl blue | 1.25 | — |
| C49 | AP4 | 30s red brn & bl grn | .30 | — |
| C50 | AP4 | 40s dk brn & pur | 1.10 | — |
| C51 | AP4 | 50s dp bl grn & red brn | .30 | — |
| C52 | AP4 | 75s bl grn & brn | .30 | — |
| C53 | AP4 | 1r pur & dk grn | 1.50 | — |
| C54 | AP4 | 1½r blk bl & org | 2.00 | — |
| C55 | AP5 | 4½r pur & chestnut | 2.50 | — |
| C56 | AP5 | 7½r dk grn & vio brn | 2.75 | — |
| | | Nos. C47-C56 (10) | 12.25 | |

Nos. C32-C36 Overprinted

| C57 | AP6 | 30s multicolored | 5.00 | — |
|---|---|---|---|---|
| C58 | AP6 | 50s multicolored | 3.00 | — |
| C59 | AP6 | 1r multicolored | 3.00 | — |
| C60 | A39 | 2½r multicolored | 4.50 | — |
| C61 | A39 | 4½r multicolored | 6.50 | — |
| | | Nos. C57-C61 (5) | 22.00 | |

### AIR POST SPECIAL DELIVERY STAMPS

Aircraft Over Beach APSD1

**Perf. 14½**

| 1948, Dec. 15 | | Photo. | Unwmk. |
|---|---|---|---|
| CE1 | APSD1 | 40s dk brn & blue emerald | 1.00 — |

Type APSD1, inscribed "REPUBLIK"

| 1948, Dec. 15 | | Perf. 13½x14 |
|---|---|---|
| CE2 | APSD1 | 40s brn & blue emer | .75 — |

No. CE1, Overprinted "Merdeka Djojakarta 6 Djuli 1949"

| 1949, Dec. 7 | | | |
|---|---|---|---|
| CE3 | APSD1 | 40s brn & blue emer | .75 — |

No. CE2, Overprinted "Merdeka Djojakarta 6 Djuli 1949"

| 1949, Dec. 7 | | | |
|---|---|---|---|
| CE4 | APSD1 | 40s brn & blue emer | 7.00 — |

### AIR POST OFFICIAL STAMPS

Nos. C1//C7 Overprinted "RESMI"

| 1948, Dec. 15 | | | |
|---|---|---|---|
| CO1 | AP1 | 10s dk lilac & brn | 1.25 — |
| CO2 | AP1 | 30s dk lilac & brn | 2.00 — |
| CO3 | AP1 | 50s dk lilac & brn | 2.25 — |
| CO4 | AP2 | 1r dp choc & purle brown | 5.00 — |
| | | Nos. CO1-CO4 (4) | 10.50 |

Nos. C19//C25 Overprinted "RESMI"

| 1949, Aug. 17 | | | |
|---|---|---|---|
| CO5 | AP4 | 10s pur & lt blue | 3.50 — |
| CO6 | AP4 | 30s red brn & bl grn | 2.00 — |
| CO7 | AP4 | 50s dp bl grn & red brn | 4.50 — |
| CO8 | AP4 | 1r pur & dk grn | 3.25 — |
| | | Nos. CO5-CO8 (4) | 13.25 |

Nos. CO1-CO4 Overprinted "Merdeka Djojakarta 6 Djuli 1949"

| 1949, Dec. 7 | | | |
|---|---|---|---|
| CO9 | AP1 | 10s dk lilac & brn | 2.50 — |
| CO10 | AP1 | 30s dk lilac & brn | 5.00 — |
| CO11 | AP1 | 50s dk lilac & brn | 2.50 — |
| CO12 | AP2 | 1r dp choc & purle brown | 2.00 — |
| | | Nos. CO9-CO12 (4) | 12.00 |

Nos. CO5-CO8 Overprinted "Merdeka Djojakarta 6 Djuli 1949"

| 1949, Dec. 7 | | | |
|---|---|---|---|
| CO13 | AP4 | 10s pur & lt blue | 2.00 — |
| CO14 | AP4 | 30s red brn & bl grn | 6.00 — |
| CO15 | AP4 | 50s dp bl grn & red brn | 1.25 — |
| CO16 | AP4 | 1r pur & dk grn | 3.50 — |
| | | Nos. CO9-CO12 (4) | 12.00 |

### SPECIAL DELIVERY STAMPS

Train & Minangkabau House — SD1

**Perf. 13½x14¼**

| 1948, Dec. 15 | | Unwmk. | Photo. |
|---|---|---|---|
| E1 | SD1 | 10s dp bluish grn & chestnut | .20 — |
| E1A | SD1 | 15s ches & steel bl | .45 — |

Type SD1, Inscribed "REPUBLIK"

| 1949, Aug. 17 | | | |
|---|---|---|---|
| E1B | SD1 | 10s red brn & dp blue | .50 — |
| E1C | SD1 | 15s turq & dk yel brn | .35 — |

Nos. E1-E1A Overprinted "Merdeka Djojakarta 6 Djuli 1949"

| 1949, Dec. 7 | | | |
|---|---|---|---|
| E1D | SD1 | 10s dp bluish grn & chestnut | .30 — |
| E1E | SD1 | 15s ches & steel bl | .75 — |

Nos. E1B-E1C Overprinted "Merdeka Djojakarta 6 Djuli 1949"

| 1949, Dec. 7 | | | |
|---|---|---|---|
| E1F | SD1 | 10s red brn & dp blue | .30 — |
| E1G | SD1 | 15s urq & dk yel brn | .60 — |

Garuda SD2

| 1967 | | Unwmk. | Photo. |
|---|---|---|---|
| E1H | SD2 | 10r lt ultra & dl pur | .40 .20 |
| E2 | SD2 | 15r org & dl pur | 1.10 .20 |
| | | Nos. E1-E2 (10) | 4.95 .40 |

Inscribed "1968"

| 1968 | | | |
|---|---|---|---|
| E3 | SD2 | 10r lt ultra & dl pur | .50 .20 |
| E4 | SD2 | 15r org & dl pur | .70 .20 |
| E5 | SD2 | 20r yel & dl pur | .80 .20 |
| E6 | SD2 | 30r brt grn & dl pur | 1.10 .20 |
| E7 | SD2 | 40r lil & dl pur | 1.50 .35 |
| | | Nos. E3-E7 (5) | 4.60 1.20 |

Same Inscribed "1969"

| 1969 | | | |
|---|---|---|---|
| E8 | SD2 | 20r yel & dl pur | .50 .20 |
| E9 | SD2 | 30r brt grn & dl pur | .75 .20 |
| E10 | SD2 | 40r lil & dl pur | .85 .25 |
| | | Nos. E8-E10 (3) | 2.10 .65 |

### POSTAGE DUE STAMPS

D1

| 1948 | | Perf. 13¾x14, 14½ (#J8-J13) | |
|---|---|---|---|
| J1 | D1 | 1s blue & brn | .30 |
| J2 | D1 | 2½s dk brn & dk pur | .45 — |
| J3 | D1 | 3½s pur & lt grn | .20 — |
| J4 | D1 | 5s dk grn & brn | .40 — |
| J5 | D1 | 7½s dk brn & dk grn | .50 — |
| J6 | D1 | 10s dk pur & brn | .45 — |
| J7 | D1 | 20s brn & org yel | 1.25 — |
| J8 | D1 | 25s dk pur & dk brn | 1.50 — |
| J9 | D1 | 30s blue & car red | 1.25 — |
| J10 | D1 | 40s blue & org yel | .95 — |
| J11 | D1 | 50s lt brn & pur | 2.00 — |
| J12 | D1 | 75s dk bl & dk grn | 2.75 — |
| J13 | D1 | 1r brn & green | 4.00 — |
| | | Nos. J1-J13 (13) | 16.00 |

As Type D1, inscribed "REPUBLIK"

| 1949, Aug. 17 | | Perf. 13¾x14, 14½ (#J8-J13) | Unwmk. |
|---|---|---|---|
| J14 | D1 | 1s dk blue & brn | 35.00 — |
| J15 | D1 | 2½s brn & pur | 35.00 — |
| J16 | D1 | 3½s pur & grn | 35.00 — |
| J17 | D1 | 5s dk grn & brn | 35.00 — |
| J18 | D1 | 7½s dk brn & dk grn | 35.00 — |
| J19 | D1 | 10s pur & brn | 35.00 — |
| J20 | D1 | 20s dk brn & yel | 35.00 — |
| J21 | D1 | 25s vio & dk pur | 35.00 — |
| J22 | D1 | 30s blue & red | 35.00 — |
| J23 | D1 | 40s blue & yel | 35.00 — |
| J24 | D1 | 50s brn & pur | 35.00 — |
| J25 | D1 | 75s dk bl & dk grn | 35.00 — |
| J26 | D1 | 1r dk brn & green | 35.00 — |
| | | Nos. J14-J26 (13) | 455.00 |

Nos. J1-J13 Overprinted "Merdeka Djojakarta 6 Djuli 1949"

| 1949, Dec. 7 | | | |
|---|---|---|---|
| J27 | D1 | 1s blue & brn | 1.25 — |
| J28 | D1 | 2½s dk brn & dk pur | .65 — |
| J29 | D1 | 3½s pur & lt grn | .75 — |
| J30 | D1 | 5s dk grn & brn | .75 — |
| J31 | D1 | 7½s dk brn & dk grn | 1.25 — |
| J32 | D1 | 10s dk pur & brn | .35 — |
| J33 | D1 | 20s brn & org yel | 9.00 — |
| J34 | D1 | 25s dk pur & dk brn | 4.50 — |
| J35 | D1 | 30s blue & car red | 12.50 — |
| J36 | D1 | 40s blue & org yel | 15.00 — |
| J37 | D1 | 50s lt brn & pur | 7.50 — |
| J38 | D1 | 75s dk bl & dk grn | 22.50 — |
| J39 | D1 | 1r brn & green | 15.00 — |
| | | Nos. J27-J39 (13) | 91.00 |

Netherlands Indies Nos. J57 to J59 Surcharged in Black

| 1950 | | Wmk. 228 | Perf. 14½x14 |
|---|---|---|---|
| J60 | D7 | 2½s on 50c yellow | 1.25 .50 |
| J61 | D7 | 5s on 100c apple grn | 3.50 .85 |
| J62 | D7 | 10s on 75c aqua | 6.00 1.25 |
| | | Nos. J60-J62 (3) | 10.75 2.60 |

D8     "1966" — D9

**Wmk. 228**

| **1951-52** | | **Litho.** | | **Perf. 12½** |
|---|---|---|---|---|
| J63 | D8 | 2½s vermilion | .20 | .20 |
| J64 | D8 | 5s vermilion | .20 | .20 |
| J65 | D8 | 10s vermilion | .20 | .20 |
| J66 | D8 | 20s blue ('52) | .20 | .20 |
| J67 | D8 | 25s olive bister ('52) | .85 | .50 |
| J68 | D8 | 50s vermilion | 10.00 | 10.00 |
| J69 | D8 | 1r citron | 3.00 | 5.50 |
| | | Nos. J63-J69 (7) | 14.65 | 11.30 |

| **1953-55** | | | | **Unwmk.** |
|---|---|---|---|---|
| J70 | D8 | 15s lt magenta ('55) | .60 | .25 |
| J71 | D8 | 30s red brown | .20 | .20 |
| J72 | D8 | 40s green | .50 | .25 |
| | | Nos. J70-J72 (3) | 1.30 | .70 |

| **1958-61** | | | | **Perf. 13½x12½** |
|---|---|---|---|---|
| J73 | D8 | 10s orange | .20 | .20 |
| J74 | D8 | 15s orange ('59) | .20 | .20 |
| J74A | D8 | 20s orange ('61) | .20 | .20 |
| J75 | D8 | 25s orange | .20 | .20 |
| J76 | D8 | 30s orange ('60) | .20 | .20 |
| J77 | D8 | 50s orange | 1.75 | .50 |
| J78 | D8 | 100s orange ('60) | .60 | .20 |
| | | Nos. J73-J78 (7) | 3.35 | 1.70 |

| **1962-65** | | | | **Perf. 13½x12½** |
|---|---|---|---|---|
| J79 | D8 | 50s light bluish green | .20 | .20 |
| J80 | D8 | 100s bister | .20 | .20 |
| J81 | D8 | 250s blue | .20 | .20 |
| J82 | D8 | 500s dull yellow | .20 | .20 |
| J83 | D8 | 750s pale lilac | .25 | .20 |
| J84 | D8 | 1000s salmon | .50 | .25 |
| J85 | D8 | 50r red ('65) | .20 | .20 |
| J86 | D8 | 100r maroon ('65) | .45 | .25 |
| | | Nos. J79-J86 (8) | 2.20 | 1.70 |

| **1966-67** | | | **Unwmk.** | **Photo.** |
|---|---|---|---|---|
| J91 | D9 | 5s dl grn & dl yel | .20 | .20 |
| J92 | D9 | 10s red & lt bl | .20 | .20 |
| J93 | D9 | 20s dk bl & pink | .20 | .20 |
| J94 | D9 | 30s brn & rose | .20 | .20 |
| J95 | D9 | 40s plum & bis | .20 | .20 |
| J96 | D9 | 50s ol grn & pale lil | .20 | .20 |
| J97 | D9 | 100s dk red & yel grn | .40 | .20 |
| J98 | D9 | 200s brt grn & pink ('67) | .30 | .20 |
| J99 | D9 | 500s yel & lt bl ('67) | .40 | .25 |
| J100 | D9 | 1000s rose lil & yel ('67) | .65 | .20 |
| | | Nos. J91-J100 (10) | 2.95 | 2.15 |

**Dated "1967"**

| **1967** | | | | |
|---|---|---|---|---|
| J101 | D9 | 50s ol grn & pale lil | .20 | .20 |
| J102 | D9 | 100s dk red & yel grn | .25 | .20 |
| J103 | D9 | 200s brt grn & pink | .35 | .20 |
| J104 | D9 | 500s yel & lt bl | .60 | .20 |
| J105 | D9 | 1000s rose lil & yel | 1.00 | .20 |
| J106 | D9 | 15r org & gray | .80 | .20 |
| J107 | D9 | 25r lil & citron | 1.40 | .25 |
| | | Nos. J101-J107 (7) | 4.60 | 1.45 |

Similar stamps inscribed "Bajar" or "Bayar", year date and "Sumbangan Ongkos Tjetak" or ". . . Cetak" are revenues.

**Dated "1973"**
Inscribed "BAYAR PORTO"

| **1973** | | | | |
|---|---|---|---|---|
| J108 | D9 | 25r lilac & citron | 1.10 | |

**Dated "1974"**
Inscribed "BAYAR PORTO"

| **1974** | | | | |
|---|---|---|---|---|
| J109 | D9 | 65r olive grn & bister | 2.50 | 1.25 |
| J110 | D9 | 125r lil & pale pink | 9.00 | 2.50 |

**Dated "1975"**

| **1975** | | **Photo.** | | **Perf. 13½x12½** |
|---|---|---|---|---|
| J111 | D9 | 25r lilac & citron | 1.75 | .40 |

"1976" — D10

| **1976** | | | | |
|---|---|---|---|---|
| J112 | D10 | 125r lil & pale pur | 3.25 | .50 |

---

**Dated "1977"**

| **1977** | | | | |
|---|---|---|---|---|
| J113 | D10 | 100r dp vio & pale pink | .65 | .50 |
| J114 | D10 | 200r brt bl & lt lil | .85 | .85 |
| J115 | D10 | 300r choc & lt sal | 1.25 | 1.25 |
| J116 | D10 | 400r brt grn & tan | 2.00 | 2.00 |
| J117 | D10 | 500r red & tan | 2.50 | 2.50 |
| | | Nos. J113-J117 (5) | 7.25 | 7.10 |

See Nos. J138, J139, J142.

Nos. 706, 709, 712-713, 716, 718 Surcharged in Red

| **1978** | | **Photo.** | | **Perf. 12½x12** |
|---|---|---|---|---|
| J118 | A110 | 25r on 1r | | .25 |
| J119 | A110 | 50r on 2r | | .50 |
| J120 | A110 | 100r on 4r | | 1.50 |
| J121 | A110 | 200r on 5r | | 3.00 |
| J122 | A110 | 300r on 10r | | 4.00 |
| J123 | A110 | 400r on 15r | | 5.75 |
| | | Nos. J118-J123 (6) | | 15.00 |

**Surcharged in Black**

| J124 | A110 | 25r on 1r | | .25 |
|---|---|---|---|---|
| J125 | A110 | 50r on 2r | | .55 |
| J126 | A110 | 100r on 4r | | 1.60 |
| J127 | A110 | 200r on 5r | | 4.00 |
| J128 | A110 | 300r on 10r | | 5.00 |
| J129 | A110 | 400r on 15r | | 6.75 |
| | | Nos. J124-J129 (6) | | 18.15 |

Nos. 710, 717 Surcharged

| **1978** | | **Photo.** | | **Perf. 12½x12** |
|---|---|---|---|---|
| J130 | A110 | 40r on 2.50r | | .95 |
| J131 | A110 | 40r on 12r | | .95 |
| J132 | A110 | 65r on 2.50r | | 1.50 |
| J133 | A110 | 65r on 12r | | 1.50 |
| J134 | A110 | 125r on 2.50r | | 3.50 |
| J135 | A110 | 125r on 12r | | 3.50 |
| J136 | A110 | 150r on 2.50r | | 5.00 |
| J137 | A110 | 150r on 12r | | 4.25 |
| | | Nos. J130-J137 (8) | | 21.15 |

**Type of 1976 Dated "1979"**

| **1979** | | | | **Perf. 13½x12½** |
|---|---|---|---|---|
| J138 | D10 | 25r lilac & citron | .50 | .20 |

**Type of 1976 and**

D11

**Perf. 13½x12½, 13½x13 (#J144-J148, J150-J153), 14½x13 (#J154-J156A)**

| **1980-90** | | | | **Photo.** |
|---|---|---|---|---|
| | | **Dated "1980"** | | |
| J139 | D10 | 25r dk lil & beige | .20 | .20 |
| J140 | D11 | 50r multi | .40 | .20 |
| J141 | D11 | 75r rose lake & rose | .60 | .20 |
| J142 | D10 | 125r rose lil & lt pink | .60 | .25 |
| | | Nos. J139-J142 (4) | 1.80 | .85 |
| | | **Dated "1981"** | | |
| J144 | D11 | 25r brt vio & pale yel grn | .20 | .20 |
| J145 | D11 | 50r sl grn & lt vio | .25 | .20 |
| J146 | D11 | 75r rose vio & pink | .40 | .20 |
| J147 | D11 | 125r pur & yel grn | .70 | .25 |
| | | Nos. J144-J147 (4) | 1.55 | .85 |
| | | **Dated "1982"** | | |
| J148 | D11 | 125r dp rose lil & pink | .65 | .25 |
| | | **Dated "1983"** | | |
| J149 | D11 | 125r dp rose & lil pink | .60 | .40 |
| J150 | D11 | 200r dp vio & lt bl | 1.25 | .55 |
| J151 | D11 | 300r dk grn & cit | 1.40 | .75 |
| J152 | D11 | 400r ol grn & brn ol | 1.75 | .95 |

---

| J153 | D11 | 500r sepia & beige | 2.25 | 1.10 |
|---|---|---|---|---|
| | | Nos. J149-J153 (5) | 7.25 | 3.75 |
| | | **Dated "1984"** | | |
| J154 | D11 | 25r brt vio & pale yel grn | 1.25 | .35 |
| J155 | D11 | 50r sl grn & lt vio | 1.25 | .40 |
| J156 | D11 | 125r rose lil & lt pink | 3.50 | .35 |
| J156A | D11 | 500r sepia & beige | 14.00 | 1.25 |
| | | Nos. J154-J156A (4) | 20.00 | 2.35 |
| | | **Dated "1988"** | | |
| J157 | D11 | 1000r dp vio & gray | 1.40 | .60 |
| J158 | D11 | 2000r red & dp rose lil | 2.75 | 1.10 |
| J159 | D11 | 3000r brn & dl org | 4.50 | 1.75 |
| J160 | D11 | 5000r grn & bl grn | 8.75 | 2.25 |
| | | Nos. J157-J160 (4) | 17.40 | 5.70 |
| | | **Dated "1990"** | | |
| J161 | D11 | 2000r emer & brt yel | 4.50 | 2.10 |
| J162 | D11 | 3000r dk bl grn & rose lil | 6.75 | 3.25 |
| J163 | D11 | 4000r brn vio & brt yel grn | 13.50 | 7.00 |
| | | Nos. J161-J163 (3) | 24.75 | 12.35 |

---

## OFFICIAL STAMPS

Nos. 2//16 Overprinted "RESMI"

| **1948, Dec. 15** | | | | |
|---|---|---|---|---|
| O1 | A28 | 2s dp brn & dp blue | .20 | — |
| O2 | A28 | 5s turq & dull blue | .50 | — |
| O3 | A28 | 10s dp blue & brn rose | .45 | — |
| O4 | A28 | 15s brown & dk grn | .20 | — |
| O5 | A31 | 30s dk brn & dull vio | 1.50 | — |
| O6 | A30 | 50s dk brn & turq | .60 | — |
| | | Nos. O1-O6 (6) | 3.45 | |

Nos. 31//45 Overprinted "RESMI"

| **1949, Aug. 17** | | | | |
|---|---|---|---|---|
| O7 | A35 | 2s dk red vio & dp grn | .30 | — |
| O8 | A35 | 5s turq & dull blue | .30 | — |
| O9 | A34 | 10s dk brn & dp vio | 1.00 | — |
| O10 | A35 | 15s dk vio & dp dull grn | 1.50 | — |
| O11 | A36 | 30s brn & dk blue vio | .75 | — |
| O12 | A37 | 50s dk brn & Prus grn | 2.00 | — |
| | | Nos. O7-O12 (6) | 5.85 | |

Nos. O1-O6 Overprinted "Merdeka Djojakarta 6 Djuli 1949"

| **1948, Dec. 15** | | | | |
|---|---|---|---|---|
| O13 | A28 | 2s dp brn & dp blue | .75 | — |
| O14 | A28 | 5s turq & dull blue | 1.60 | — |
| O15 | A28 | 10s dp blue & brn rose | 1.60 | — |
| O16 | A28 | 15s brown & dk grn | 1.60 | — |
| O17 | A31 | 30s dk brn & dull vio | 3.00 | — |
| O18 | A30 | 50s dk brn & turq | 3.00 | — |
| | | Nos. O13-O18 (6) | 11.55 | |

Nos. O7-O12 Overprinted "Merdeka Djojakarta 6 Djuli 1949"

---

| **1948, Dec. 15** | | | | |
|---|---|---|---|---|
| O19 | A28 | 2s dp brn & dp blue | 1.00 | — |
| O20 | A28 | 5s turq & dull blue | .45 | — |
| O21 | A28 | 10s dp blue & brn rose | .45 | — |
| O22 | A28 | 15s brown & dk grn | 1.00 | — |
| O23 | A31 | 30s dk brn & dull vio | 2.50 | — |
| O24 | A30 | 50s dk brn & turq | 3.00 | — |
| | | Nos. O13-O18 (6) | 11.55 | |

---

## RIAU ARCHIPELAGO

(Riouw Archipelago)
100 Sen = 1 Rupiah
(1 rupiah = 1 Malayan dollar)

Indonesia Nos. 371-386 Overprinted in Black

a        b

**Overprint "a"**

| **1954** | | | **Unwmk.** | **Perf. 12½** |
|---|---|---|---|---|
| 1 | A52 | 5s car rose | 57.50 | 57.50 |
| 2 | A52 | 7½s green | .55 | .55 |
| 3 | A52 | 10s blue | 67.50 | 80.00 |
| 4 | A52 | 15s purple | 1.40 | 1.40 |
| 5 | A52 | 20s rose red | 1.40 | 1.40 |
| 6 | A52 | 25s dp green | 67.50 | 32.50 |
| | | **Overprint "b"** | | |
| 7 | A53 | 30s red orange | 2.75 | 2.75 |
| 8 | A53 | 35s purple | .55 | .55 |
| 9 | A53 | 40s dull green | .55 | .55 |
| 10 | A53 | 45s dp claret | .55 | .55 |
| 11 | A54 | 50s brown | 475.00 | 100.00 |
| 12 | A54 | 60s dk brown | .55 | .55 |
| 13 | A54 | 70s gray | 1.40 | 1.40 |
| 14 | A54 | 75s ultra | 4.75 | 3.25 |
| 15 | A54 | 80s claret | .95 | .95 |
| 16 | A54 | 90s gray green | .95 | .95 |

Netherlands Indies Nos. 325-330 Overprinted Type "a" in Black

| | | | **Perf. 12½x12** | |
|---|---|---|---|---|
| 17 | A46 | 1r purple | 6.50 | 4.00 |
| 18 | A46 | 2r olive grn | 1.40 | 1.40 |
| 19 | A46 | 3r red violet | 2.00 | 2.00 |
| 20 | A46 | 5r dk brown | 2.00 | 2.00 |
| 21 | A46 | 10r gray | 2.75 | 2.75 |
| 22 | A46 | 25r orange brn | 2.75 | 2.75 |
| | | Nos. 1-22 (22) | 701.25 | 299.75 |

Mint values are for stamps with somewhat tropicalized gum (stained brown and cracked). Stamps with clean, clear gum sell for about twice as much.

Indonesia Nos. 424-428, 450 and 430 Overprinted Type "b" or

| **1957-64** | | **Photo.** | | **Perf. 12½x13½** |
|---|---|---|---|---|
| 23 | A63(b) | 5s dp ultra | .50 | .50 |
| 24 | A63 | 10s yellow brn | 13.00 | 10.00 |
| 25 | A63(b) | 10s yellow brn | .50 | .50 |
| 26 | A63(b) | 15s rose vio ('64) | .50 | .50 |
| 27 | A63(b) | 20s dull grn ('60) | .50 | .50 |
| 27A | A63 | 25s dp claret | 40.00 | 40.00 |
| 28 | A63(b) | 25s dp claret | .50 | .50 |
| 29 | A63(b) | 30s orange | .50 | .50 |
| 30 | A63 | 50s brown | 13.00 | 10.00 |
| 31 | A63(b) | 50s brown | .50 | .50 |

The "b" overprint measures 12mm in this set.

Sukarno Type of Indonesia Overprinted Type "a"

| **1960** | | | | **Perf. 12½x12** |
|---|---|---|---|---|
| 32 | A55 | 1.25r dp orange | 4.00 | 4.00 |
| 33 | A55 | 1.50r brown | 4.00 | 4.00 |
| 34 | A55 | 2.50r rose brown | 5.50 | 5.50 |
| 35 | A55 | 4r apple green | 1.00 | .50 |
| 36 | A55 | 6r rose lilac | 1.00 | .50 |
| 37 | A55 | 15r yellow | 1.00 | .50 |
| 38 | A55 | 20r sepia | 1.00 | .50 |
| 39 | A55 | 40r yellow grn | 1.00 | .50 |
| 40 | A55 | 50r violet | 3.00 | .50 |
| | | Nos. 23-40 (19) | 91.00 | 80.00 |

Nos. 26, 35-37, 39-40 are valued CTO with Bandung cancels. Postally used sell for much more.

## WEST IRIAN

'west ˌir-ē-'än

(Irian Barat)
(West New Guinea)
LOCATION — Western half of New Guinea, southwest Pacific Ocean
GOVT. — Province of Indonesia
AREA — 162,927 sq. mi.
POP. — 923,440 (1973)
CAPITAL — Djajapura (formerly Hollandia)

The former Netherlands New Guinea became a territory under the administration of the United Nations Temporary Executive Authority on Oct. 1, 1962.
The territory came under Indonesian administration on May 1, 1963.

100 Sen = 1 Rupiah
(1 rupiah = 1 former Netherlands New Guinea gulden)

**Catalogue values for all unused stamps in this country are for Never Hinged items.**

Netherlands New Guinea Stamps of 1950-60 Overprinted

### Type 2 Overprint
#### Perf. 12½x12, 12½x13½

| | | | Photo. | Unwmk. | |
|---|---|---|---|---|---|
| 1962-63 | | | | | |
| 1a | A4 | 1c vermilion & yel | | .20 | .20 |
| 2a | A1 | 2c deep orange | | .25 | .20 |
| 3a | A4 | 5c choc & yel | | .25 | .20 |
| 4a | A5 | 7c org red, bl & brn vio | | .25 | .20 |
| 5a | A4 | 10c aqua & red brn | | .25 | .20 |
| 6a | A5 | 12c grn, bl & brn vio | | .25 | .20 |
| 7a | A4 | 15c dp yel & red brn | | .50 | .25 |
| 8a | A5 | 17c brn vio & bl | | .60 | .35 |
| 9a | A4 | 20c lt bl grn & red brn | | .60 | .35 |
| 10a | A6 | 25c red | | .35 | .30 |
| 11a | A6 | 30c deep blue | | .80 | .35 |
| 12a | A6 | 40c deep orange | | .80 | .35 |
| 13a | A6 | 45c dark olive | | 1.40 | .75 |
| 14a | A6 | 55c slate blue | | 1.25 | .55 |
| 15a | A6 | 80c dl gray vio | | 5.75 | 5.75 |
| 16a | A6 | 85c dk vio brn | | 3.00 | 3.00 |
| 17a | A6 | 1g plum | | 3.50 | 1.90 |

#### Engr.
| 18a | A3 | 2g reddish brn | | 12.00 | 15.00 |
|---|---|---|---|---|---|
| 19a | A3 | 5g green | | 6.75 | 5.00 |
| | | Nos. 1a-19a (19) | | 38.75 | 35.10 |

The overprint exists in four types:
1) Size 17½mm. Applied locally and sold in 1962 in West New Guinea. Top of "N" is slightly lower than the "U," and the base of the "T" is straight, or nearly so. This set sells for about $20 more than Nos. 1a-19a.
2) Size 17½mm. Applied in the Netherlands and sold in 1963 by the UN in New York. Top of the "N" is slightly higher than the "U," and the base of the "T" is concave. This is the set listed above.
3) Size 14mm. Exists on eight values. Set value, $150.
4) Size 19mm. Exists on 1c and 10c. Set value, $150.
Types 3 and 4 were applied in West New Guinea and it is doubtful whether they were regularly issued.
See the *U.S. Specialized Catalogue* for complete listings and values of the UNTEA overprints.

Indonesia Nos. 454, 456, 494-501, 387, 390, 392 and 393 Surcharged or Overprinted: "IRIAN BARAT"
#### Perf. 12½x13½

| | | | Photo. | Unwmk. | |
|---|---|---|---|---|---|
| 1963, May 1 | | | | | |
| 20 | A63 | 1s on 70s org ver | | .20 | .20 |
| 21 | A63 | 2s on 90s yel grn | | .20 | .20 |

#### Perf. 12x12½
| 22 | A76 | 5s gray | .20 | .20 |
|---|---|---|---|---|
| 23 | A76 | 6s on 20s ocher | .20 | .20 |
| 24 | A76 | 7s on 50s dp bl | .20 | .20 |
| 25 | A76 | 10s red brn | .20 | .20 |
| 26 | A76 | 15s plum | .20 | .20 |
| 27 | A76 | 25s brt bl grn | .20 | .20 |
| 28 | A76 | 30s on 75s scar | .20 | .25 |
| 29 | A76 | 40s on 1.15r plum | .20 | .30 |

#### Perf. 12½x12
| 30 | A55 | 1r purple | .45 | .55 |
|---|---|---|---|---|
| 31 | A55 | 2r green | .80 | .90 |
| 32 | A55 | 3r dk bl | 1.40 | 1.50 |
| 33 | A55 | 5r brown | 2.25 | 3.00 |
| | | Nos. 20-33 (14) | 6.90 | 8.10 |

"Indonesia's Flag from Sabang to Merauke" — A1

20s, 50s, Parachutist landing in New Guinea. 60s, 75s, Bird of paradise and map of New Guinea.

| 1963, May 1 | | | | |
|---|---|---|---|---|
| 34 | A1 | 12s org brn, blk & red | .20 | .25 |
| 35 | A1 | 17s org brn, blk & red | .20 | .35 |
| 36 | A1 | 20s multi | .25 | .50 |
| 37 | A1 | 50s multi | .25 | .85 |
| 38 | A1 | 60s multi | .60 | .95 |
| 39 | A1 | 75s multi | .80 | 1.75 |
| | | Nos. 34-39 (6) | 2.30 | 4.65 |

Liberation of West New Guinea.

Maniltoa Gemmipara — A2

15s, Dendrobium lancifolium (orchid). 30s, Gardenia gjellerupii. 40s, Maniltoa flower. 50s, Phalanger. 75s, Cassowary. 1r, Kangaroo. 3r, Crowned pigeons.

| 1968, Aug. 17 | | Photo. | Perf. 12½x12 | |
|---|---|---|---|---|
| 40 | A2 | 5s dl grn & vio blk | .40 | .40 |
| 41 | A2 | 15s emer & dk pur | .75 | .75 |
| 42 | A2 | 30s org & dp grn | 1.75 | 1.75 |
| 43 | A2 | 40s lemon & brt pur | 1.75 | 1.75 |
| 44 | A2 | 50s rose car & blk | 1.75 | 1.75 |
| 45 | A2 | 75s dl bl & blk | 2.10 | 2.10 |
| 46 | A2 | 1r brn org & blk | 4.50 | 4.50 |
| 47 | A2 | 3r apple grn & blk | 7.00 | 7.00 |
| | | Nos. 40-47 (8) | 20.00 | 20.00 |

Man, Map of Indonesia and Torches — A3

| 1968, Aug. 17 | | | | |
|---|---|---|---|---|
| 48 | A3 | 10s ultra & gold | 3.00 | 2.00 |
| 49 | A3 | 25s crimson & gold | 4.75 | 2.75 |

Issued to publicize the pledge of the people of West Irian to remain unified and integrated with the Republic of Indonesia.

Carving, Mother and Child — A4    Black-capped Lory — A5

West Irian Wood Carvings: 6s, Shield with 3 human figures. 7s, Child atop filigree carving.

10s, Drum. 25s, Seated man. 30s, Drum (3-tiered base). 50s, Carved bamboo. 75s, Man-shaped ornament. 1r, Shield. 2r, Seated man (hands raised).

| 1970 | | Photo. | Perf. 12½x12 | |
|---|---|---|---|---|
| 50 | A4 | 5s multi | .40 | .40 |
| 51 | A4 | 6s multi | .40 | .40 |
| 52 | A4 | 7s multi | .40 | 1.50 |
| 53 | A4 | 10s multi | .40 | 1.50 |
| 54 | A4 | 25s multi | .40 | .40 |
| 55 | A4 | 30s multi | .60 | .40 |
| 56 | A4 | 50s multi | .70 | .40 |
| 57 | A4 | 75s multi | .70 | .40 |
| 58 | A4 | 1r multi | .90 | .40 |
| 59 | A4 | 2r multi | 1.25 | .85 |
| | | Nos. 50-59 (10) | 6.15 | 6.65 |

Issued: #50-54, 4/30; #55-59, 4/15.

| 1970, Oct. 26 | | Photo. | Perf. 12x12½ | |
|---|---|---|---|---|
| 60 | A5 | 5r shown | 1.50 | 3.00 |
| 61 | A5 | 10r Bird of paradise | 1.50 | 5.25 |

### POSTAGE DUE STAMPS
Type of Indonesia Overprinted: "IRIAN BARAT"
#### Perf. 13½x12½

| | | | Litho. | Unwmk. | |
|---|---|---|---|---|---|
| 1963, May 1 | | | | | |
| J1 | D8 | 1s light brown | | .20 | .45 |
| J2 | D8 | 5s light gray olive | | .20 | .50 |
| J3 | D8 | 10s light blue | | .20 | .50 |
| J4 | D8 | 25s gray | | .25 | .90 |
| J5 | D8 | 40s salmon | | .45 | 1.40 |
| J6 | D8 | 100s bister | | 1.00 | 2.00 |
| | | Nos. J1-J6 (6) | | 2.30 | 6.25 |

Type of Indonesia Dated "1968" and Overprinted: "IRIAN BARAT"

| 1968 | | Photo. | Perf. 13½x12½ | |
|---|---|---|---|---|
| J7 | D9 | 1s blue & lt grn | .20 | .55 |
| J8 | D9 | 5s grn & pink | .20 | .65 |
| J9 | D9 | 10s red & gray | .20 | .65 |
| J10 | D9 | 25s grn & yel | .25 | .90 |
| J11 | D9 | 40s vio brn & pale grn | .55 | 1.40 |
| J12 | D9 | 100s org & bister | 1.10 | 3.00 |
| | | Nos. J7-J12 (6) | 2.50 | 7.15 |

---

## INHAMBANE

ˌin-yəm-'ban-ə

LOCATION — East Africa
GOVT. — A district of Mozambique, former Portuguese colony
AREA — 21,000 sq. mi. (approx.)
POP. — 248,000 (approx.)
CAPITAL — Inhambane

1000 Reis = 1 Milreis
100 Centavos = 1 Escudo (1913)

Stamps of Mozambique Overprinted

### On 1886 Issue
| 1895, July 1 | | Unwmk. | Perf. 12½ | |
|---|---|---|---|---|
| | | Without Gum | | |
| 1 | A2 | 5r black | 37.50 | 30.00 |
| 2 | A2 | 10r green | 35.00 | 25.00 |
| a. | | Perf. 13½ | 80.00 | 75.00 |
| 3 | A2 | 20r rose | 60.00 | 30.00 |
| 4 | A2 | 25r lilac | 500.00 | 250.00 |
| 5 | A2 | 40r chocolate | 55.00 | 40.00 |
| 6 | A2 | 50r blue | 55.00 | 32.50 |
| a. | | Perf. 13½ | 50.00 | 50.00 |
| 7 | A2 | 100r yellow brown | 750.00 | 400.00 |
| 8 | A2 | 200r gray violet | 50.00 | 40.00 |
| 9 | A2 | 300r orange | 50.00 | 40.00 |
| | | Nos. 1-9 (9) | 1,592. | 887.50 |

### On 1894 Issue
#### Perf. 11½
| 10 | A3 | 50r lt blue | 42.50 | 35.00 |
|---|---|---|---|---|
| a. | | Perf. 12½ | 55.00 | 42.50 |
| 11 | A3 | 75r rose | 55.00 | 40.00 |
| 12 | A3 | 80r yellow green | 45.00 | 37.50 |
| 13 | A3 | 100r brown, *buff* | 140.00 | 60.00 |
| 14 | A3 | 150r carmine, *rose* | 50.00 | 45.00 |
| | | Nos. 10-14 (5) | 332.50 | 217.50 |

700th anniv. of the birth of St. Anthony of Padua.
The status of Nos. 4 and 7 is questionable. No. 3 is always discolored.
Forged overprints exist. Genuine overprints are 21mm high.

---

King Carlos — A1

### 1903, Jan. 1   Typo.   Perf. 11½
#### Name and Value in Black except 500r

| 15 | A1 | 2½r gray | .30 | .30 |
|---|---|---|---|---|
| 16 | A1 | 5r orange | .30 | .30 |
| 17 | A1 | 10r lt green | .60 | .40 |
| 18 | A1 | 15r gray green | 1.00 | .75 |
| 19 | A1 | 20r gray violet | .85 | .55 |
| 20 | A1 | 25r carmine | .70 | .55 |
| 21 | A1 | 50r brown | 1.75 | 1.25 |
| 22 | A1 | 65r dull blue | 20.00 | 15.00 |
| 23 | A1 | 75r lilac | 2.00 | 1.40 |
| 24 | A1 | 100r dk blue, *blue* | 2.75 | 1.25 |
| 25 | A1 | 115r org brn, *pink* | 5.00 | 5.00 |
| 26 | A1 | 130r brown, *straw* | 5.00 | 5.00 |
| 27 | A1 | 200r red vio, *pink* | 5.00 | 4.25 |
| 28 | A1 | 400r dull bl, *straw* | 8.25 | 7.50 |
| 29 | A1 | 500r blk & red, *bl* | 18.00 | 12.00 |
| 30 | A1 | 700r gray blk, *straw* | 20.00 | 13.00 |
| | | Nos. 15-30 (16) | 91.50 | 68.50 |

For surcharge & overprints see #31-47, 88-101.

No. 22 Surcharged in Black

### 1905
| 31 | A1 | 50r on 65r dull blue | 2.75 | 2.00 |
|---|---|---|---|---|

Nos. 15-21, 23-30 Overprinted in Carmine or Green

### 1911
| 32 | A1 | 2½r gray | .20 | .20 |
|---|---|---|---|---|
| 33 | A1 | 5r orange | .20 | .20 |
| 34 | A1 | 10r lt green | .20 | .20 |
| 35 | A1 | 15r gray green | .30 | .30 |
| 36 | A1 | 20r gray violet | .30 | .30 |
| 37 | A1 | 25r carmine (G) | .70 | .50 |
| 38 | A1 | 50r brown | .50 | .50 |
| 39 | A1 | 75r lilac | .50 | .50 |
| 40 | A1 | 100r dk blue, *bl* | .50 | .50 |
| 41 | A1 | 115r org brn, *pink* | 1.00 | .95 |
| 42 | A1 | 130r brown, *straw* | 1.00 | .95 |
| 43 | A1 | 200r red vio, *pink* | 1.00 | .95 |
| 44 | A1 | 400r dull bl, *straw* | 1.25 | 1.00 |
| 45 | A1 | 500r blk & red, *bl* | 1.50 | 1.00 |
| 46 | A1 | 700r gray blk, *straw* | 1.75 | 1.50 |
| | | Nos. 32-46 (15) | 10.90 | 9.55 |

No. 31 Overprinted in Red

### 1914
| 47 | A1 | 50r on 65r dull blue | 1.75 | 1.25 |
|---|---|---|---|---|
| a. | | "Republica" inverted | 25.00 | 25.00 |

### Vasco da Gama Issue of Various Portuguese Colonies

Common Design Types CD20-CD27 Surcharged

### 1913
#### On Stamps of Macao
| 48 | CD20 | ¼c on ½a bl grn | 1.25 | 1.25 |
|---|---|---|---|---|
| 49 | CD21 | ¼c on 1a red | 1.25 | 1.25 |
| 50 | CD22 | 1c on 2a red vio | 1.25 | 1.25 |
| a. | | Inverted surcharge | 35.00 | 35.00 |
| 51 | CD23 | 2½c on 4a yel grn | 1.25 | 1.25 |
| 52 | CD24 | 5c on 8a dk bl | 1.25 | 1.25 |
| 53 | CD25 | 7½c on 12a vio brn | 2.25 | 2.25 |

| | | | | |
|---|---|---|---|---|
| 54 | CD26 | 10c on 16a bis brn | 1.75 | 1.75 |
| 55 | CD27 | 15c on 24a bis | 1.75 | 1.75 |
| | | *Nos. 48-55 (8)* | 12.00 | 12.00 |

**On Stamps of Portuguese Africa**

| | | | | |
|---|---|---|---|---|
| 56 | CD20 | ¼c on 2½r bl grn | 1.00 | 1.00 |
| 57 | CD21 | ½c on 5r red | 1.00 | 1.00 |
| 58 | CD22 | 1c on 10r red vio | 1.00 | 1.00 |
| 59 | CD23 | 2½c on 25r yel grn | 1.00 | 1.00 |
| 60 | CD24 | 5c on 50r dk bl | 1.00 | 1.00 |
| 61 | CD25 | 7½c on 75r vio brn | 2.00 | 2.00 |
| 62 | CD26 | 10c on 100r bis brn | 1.50 | 1.50 |
| 63 | CD27 | 15c on 150r bis | 1.50 | 1.50 |
| | | *Nos. 56-63 (8)* | 10.00 | 10.00 |

**On Stamps of Timor**

| | | | | |
|---|---|---|---|---|
| 64 | CD20 | ¼c on ½a bl grn | 1.25 | 1.25 |
| a. | | Inverted surcharge | 35.00 | 35.00 |
| 65 | CD21 | ½c on 1a red | 1.25 | 1.25 |
| 66 | CD22 | 1c on 2a red vio | 1.25 | 1.25 |
| 67 | CD23 | 2½c on 4a yel grn | 1.25 | 1.25 |
| 68 | CD24 | 5c on 8a dk bl | 1.25 | 1.25 |
| 69 | CD25 | 7½c on 12a vio brn | 2.50 | 2.50 |
| 70 | CD26 | 10c on 16a bis brn | 1.75 | 1.75 |
| 71 | CD27 | 15c on 24a bis | 1.75 | 1.75 |
| | | *Nos. 64-71 (8)* | 12.25 | 12.25 |
| | | *Nos. 48-71 (24)* | 34.25 | 34.25 |

Ceres — A2

**1914**      **Typo.**      *Perf. 15x14*
**Name and Value in Black**

| | | | | |
|---|---|---|---|---|
| 72 | A2 | ¼c olive brown | .50 | .50 |
| 73 | A2 | ½c black | .50 | .50 |
| a. | | Imperf. | | |
| 74 | A2 | 1c blue green | .50 | .50 |
| 75 | A2 | 1½c lilac brown | .50 | .50 |
| 76 | A2 | 2c carmine | .50 | .50 |
| 77 | A2 | 2½c lt violet | .35 | .35 |
| 78 | A2 | 5c deep blue | .80 | .80 |
| 79 | A2 | 7½c yellow brown | 1.25 | 1.25 |
| 80 | A2 | 8c slate | 1.25 | 1.25 |
| 81 | A2 | 10c orange brown | 1.10 | 1.10 |
| 82 | A2 | 15c plum | 2.00 | 1.60 |
| 83 | A2 | 20c yellow green | 2.00 | 1.60 |
| 84 | A2 | 30c brown, *grn* | 3.00 | 2.50 |
| 85 | A2 | 40c brown, *pink* | 3.00 | 2.75 |
| 86 | A2 | 50c orange, *sal* | 5.00 | 4.50 |
| 87 | A2 | 1e green, *blue* | 6.00 | 5.00 |
| | | *Nos. 72-87 (16)* | 28.25 | 25.20 |

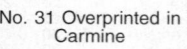

No. 31 Overprinted in Carmine

**1915**      *Perf. 11½*

| | | | | |
|---|---|---|---|---|
| 88 | A1 | 50c on 65r dull blue | 8.00 | 6.00 |

Nos. 15-21, 23-30 Overprinted Locally

**1917**

| | | | | |
|---|---|---|---|---|
| 89 | A1 | 2½r gray | 25.00 | 25.00 |
| 90 | A1 | 5r orange | 25.00 | 25.00 |
| 91 | A1 | 15r gray green | 2.50 | 2.50 |
| 92 | A1 | 20r gray violet | 2.00 | 2.00 |
| 93 | A1 | 50r brown | 2.00 | 2.00 |
| 94 | A1 | 75r lilac | 2.00 | 2.00 |
| 95 | A1 | 100r blue, *blue* | 3.00 | 2.50 |
| 96 | A1 | 115r org brn, *pink* | 3.00 | 2.50 |
| 97 | A1 | 130r brn, *straw* | 3.00 | 2.50 |
| 98 | A1 | 200r red vio, *pink* | 3.00 | 2.50 |
| 99 | A1 | 400r dull bl, *straw* | 6.00 | 3.00 |
| 100 | A1 | 500r blk & red, *bl* | 5.00 | 3.00 |
| 101 | A1 | 700r gray blk, *straw* | 14.00 | 8.00 |
| | | *Nos. 89-101 (13)* | 95.50 | 82.50 |

The stamps of Inhambane have been superseded by those of Mozambique.

---

## ININI

ē-ni-'nē

LOCATION — In northeastern South America, adjoining French Guiana
GOVT. — Territory of French Guiana
AREA — 30,301 sq. mi.

POP. — 5,024 (1946)
CAPITAL — St. Elie

Inini was separated from French Guiana in 1930 and reunited with it in when the colony became an integral part of the Republic, acquiring the same status as the departments of Metropolitan France, under a law effective Jan. 1, 1947.

100 Centimes = 1 Franc

Used values are for canceled-to-order copies.

Stamps of French Guiana, 1929-40, Overprinted in Black, Red or Blue:

Nos. 1-9

Nos. 10-26

Nos. 27-40

**1932-40**    **Unwmk.**    *Perf. 13½x14*

| | | | | |
|---|---|---|---|---|
| 1 | A16 | 1c gray lil & grnsh bl | .40 | .55 |
| 2 | A16 | 2c dk red & bl grn | .40 | .55 |
| 3 | A16 | 3c gray lil & grnsh bl ('40) | .55 | .65 |
| 4 | A16 | 4c ol brn & red vio ('38) | .55 | .75 |
| 5 | A16 | 5c Prus bl & red org | .55 | .75 |
| 6 | A16 | 10c magenta & brn | .40 | .55 |
| 7 | A16 | 15c yel brn & red org | .40 | .55 |
| 8 | A16 | 20c dk bl & ol grn | .40 | .55 |
| 9 | A16 | 25c dk red & dk brn | .90 | 1.00 |

**Perf. 14x13½**

| | | | | |
|---|---|---|---|---|
| 10 | A17 | 30c dl grn & lt grn | 1.90 | 2.00 |
| 11 | A17 | 30c grn & brn ('40) | .55 | .65 |
| 12 | A17 | 35c Prus grn & ol ('38) | 1.00 | 1.05 |
| 13 | A17 | 40c org brn & ol gray | .80 | 1.00 |
| 14 | A17 | 45c ol grn & lt grn ('40) | 1.30 | 1.50 |
| 15 | A17 | 50c dk bl & ol gray | .65 | .75 |
| 16 | A17 | 55c vio bl & car ('38) | 4.25 | 4.75 |
| 17 | A17 | 60c sal & grn ('40) | .65 | .75 |
| 18 | A17 | 65c sal & grn ('38) | 1.50 | 1.60 |
| 19 | A17 | 70c ind & sl bl ('40) | .75 | .80 |
| 20 | A17 | 75c ind & sl bl (Bl) | 2.50 | 2.90 |
| 21 | A17 | 80c blk & vio bl (R) ('38) | .90 | 1.00 |
| 22 | A17 | 90c dk red & ver | 1.50 | 1.60 |
| 23 | A17 | 90c red vio & brn ('39) | .75 | .80 |
| 24 | A17 | 1fr lt vio & brn | 15.00 | 16.50 |
| 25 | A17 | 1fr car & lt red ('38) | 1.30 | 1.50 |
| 26 | A17 | 1fr blk & vio bl ('40) | .80 | 1.10 |
| 27 | A18 | 1.25fr blk brn & bl grn ('33) | 1.00 | 1.10 |
| 28 | A18 | 1.25fr rose & lt red ('39) | .90 | 1.00 |
| 29 | A18 | 1.40fr ol brn & red vio ('40) | .80 | 1.10 |
| 30 | A18 | 1.50fr dk bl & lt bl | .90 | 1.00 |
| 31 | A18 | 1.60fr ol brn & bl grn ('40) | .90 | 1.10 |
| 32 | A18 | 1.75fr brn, red & blk brn ('33) | 18.00 | 18.00 |
| 33 | A18 | 1.75fr vio bl ('38) | 1.50 | 1.60 |
| 34 | A18 | 2fr dk grn & rose red | 1.10 | 1.25 |
| 35 | A18 | 2.25fr vio bl ('39) | .90 | 1.00 |
| 36 | A18 | 2.50fr cop red & brn ('40) | .90 | 1.10 |
| 37 | A18 | 3fr brn red & red vio | 1.00 | 1.25 |
| 38 | A18 | 5fr dl vio & yel grn | 1.00 | 1.25 |

| | | | | |
|---|---|---|---|---|
| 39 | A18 | 10fr ol gray & dp ultra (R) | 1.30 | 1.50 |
| 40 | A18 | 20fr indigo & ver | 1.30 | 1.50 |
| | | *Nos. 1-40 (40)* | 72.15 | 79.90 |

Without "RF," see Nos. 46-49.

Common Design Types pictured following the introduction.

**Colonial Arts Exhibition Issue**
Souvenir Sheet
Common Design Type

**1937**      *Imperf.*

| | | | | |
|---|---|---|---|---|
| 41 | CD75 | 3fr red brown | 16.00 | 20.00 |

**New York World's Fair Issue**
Common Design Type

**1939, May 10**   **Engr.**   *Perf. 12½x12*

| | | | | |
|---|---|---|---|---|
| 42 | CD82 | 1.25fr car lake | 3.75 | 4.00 |
| 43 | CD82 | 2.25fr ultra | 3.75 | 4.00 |

French Guiana Nos. 170A-170B Overprinted "ININI" in Green or Red

**1941**    **Engr.**    *Perf. 12½x12*

| | | | | |
|---|---|---|---|---|
| 44 | A21a | 1fr deep lilac | 1.00 | |
| 45 | A21a | 2.50fr blue (R) | 1.00 | |

Nos. 44-45 were issued by the Vichy government in France, but were not placed on sale in Inini.
For surcharges, see Nos. B9-B10.

Types of 1932-40 Without "RF"
**Methods and Perfs as Before**

**1942**

| | | | | |
|---|---|---|---|---|
| 46 | A16 | 20c dk bl & ol grn | 1.10 | |
| 47 | A17 | 1fr black & ultra | 1.00 | |
| 48 | A18 | 10fr ol gr & dp ultra (R) | 1.30 | |
| 49 | A18 | 20fr indigo & ver | 2.25 | |
| | | *Nos. 46-49 (4)* | 5.65 | |

Nos. 46-49 were issued by the Vichy government in France, but were not placed on sale in Inini.

---

## SEMI-POSTAL STAMPS

Common Design Type
Photo.; Name & Value Typo. in Black

**1939, July 5**   **Unwmk.**   *Perf. 13*

| | | | | |
|---|---|---|---|---|
| B1 | CD83 | 45c + 25c green | 14.00 | 15.00 |
| B2 | CD83 | 70c + 30c brown | 14.00 | 15.00 |
| B3 | CD83 | 90c + 35c red org | 14.00 | 15.00 |
| B4 | CD83 | 1.25fr + 1fr rose pink | 14.00 | 15.00 |
| B5 | CD83 | 2.25fr + 2fr blue | 14.00 | 15.00 |
| | | *Nos. B1-B5 (5)* | 70.00 | 75.00 |

Common Design Type and French Guiana Nos. B9 and B11 Overprinted "ININI" in Blue or Red

**1941**    **Photo.**    *Perf. 13½*

| | | | | |
|---|---|---|---|---|
| B6 | SP1 | 1fr + 1fr red (B) | 1.60 | |
| B7 | CD86 | 1.50fr + 3fr maroon | 1.60 | |
| B8 | SP2 | 2.50fr + 1fr blue (R) | 1.60 | |
| | | *Nos. B6-B8 (3)* | 4.80 | |

Nos. B6-B8 were issued by the Vichy government in France, but were not placed on sale in Inini.

Nos. 44-45 Surcharged in Black or Red

**1944**    **Engr.**    *Perf. 12½x12*

| | | | | |
|---|---|---|---|---|
| B9 | | 50c + 1.50fr on 2.50fr deep blue (R) | 1.00 | |
| B10 | | + 2.50fr on 1fr dp lilac | 1.00 | |

Colonial Development Fund.
Nos. B9-B10 were issued by the Vichy government in France, but were not placed on sale in Inini.

---

## AIR POST SEMI-POSTAL STAMPS

Nurse with Mother & Child — SPAP1

**Unwmk.**
**1942, June 22**   **Engr.**   *Perf. 13*

| | | | | |
|---|---|---|---|---|
| CB1 | SPAP1 | 1.50fr + 50c green | 1.10 | |
| CB2 | SPAP1 | 2fr + 6fr brn & red | 1.10 | |

Native children's welfare fund.
Nos. CB1-CB2 were issued by the Vichy government in France, but were not placed on sale in Inini.

**Colonial Education Fund**
Common Design Type

**1942, June 22**

| | | | | |
|---|---|---|---|---|
| CB3 | CD86a | 1.20fr + 1.80fr blue & red | 1.10 | |

No. CB3 was issued by the Vichy government in France, but was not placed on sale in Inini.

---

## POSTAGE DUE STAMPS

Postage Due Stamps of French Guiana, 1929, Overprinted in Black

**1932, Apr. 7**   **Unwmk.**   *Perf. 13½x14*

| | | | | |
|---|---|---|---|---|
| J1 | D3 | 5c indigo & Prus bl | .25 | .40 |
| J2 | D3 | 10c bis brn & Prus grn | .65 | .80 |
| J3 | D3 | 20c grn & rose red | .65 | .80 |
| J4 | D3 | 30c ol brn & rose red | .65 | .80 |
| J5 | D3 | 50c vio & ol brn | 1.00 | 1.30 |
| J6 | D3 | 60c brn red & ol brn | 1.10 | 1.40 |

Overprinted in Black or Red

| | | | | |
|---|---|---|---|---|
| J7 | D4 | 1fr dp bl & org brn | 1.10 | 1.40 |
| J8 | D4 | 2fr brn red & bluish grn | 1.40 | 1.80 |
| J9 | D4 | 3fr vio & blk (R) | 7.00 | 9.00 |
| J10 | D4 | 3fr vio & blk | 3.00 | 3.50 |
| | | *Nos. J1-J10 (10)* | 16.80 | 21.20 |

# IONIAN ISLANDS

ī-'ō-nē-ən 'ī-lənds

LOCATION — Seven Islands, of which six-Corfu, Paxos, Lefkas (Santa Maura), Cephalonia, Ithaca and Zante-are in the Ionian Sea west of Greece, and a seventh-Cerigo (Kithyra)-is in the Mediterranean south of Greece

GOVT. — Integral part of Kingdom of Greece

AREA — 752 sq. miles

POP. — 231,510 (1938)

These islands were acquired by Great Britain in 1815 but in 1864 were ceded to Greece on request of the inhabitants.

In 1941 the islands were occupied by Italian forces. The Italians withdrew in 1943 and German forces continued the occupation, using current Greek stamps without overprinting, except for Zante.

For stamps of the Italian occupation of Corfu, see Corfu.

10 Oboli = 1 Penny
12 Pence = 1 Shilling
100 Lepta = 1 Drachma
100 Centesimi = 1 Lira

## Watermarks

Wmk. 138 — "2"    Wmk. 139 — "1"

Queen Victoria — A1

**1859    Unwmk.    Engr.    Imperf.**
1  A1  (½p) orange          110.00  575.00
**Wmk. 138**
2  A1  (1p) blue            26.50  210.00
**Wmk. 139**
3  A1  (2p) lake            20.00  210.00
Nos. 1-3 (3)               156.50  995.00

Forged cancellations are plentiful.

---

## ISSUED UNDER ITALIAN OCCUPATION

Values of stamps overprinted by letterpress in pairs are for unsevered pairs. Single stamps, unused, sell for one third the price of a pair; used, one half the price of a pair.

Handstamped overprints were also applied to pairs, with "isola" instead of "isole."

## Issue for Cephalonia and Ithaca

Stamps of Greece, 1937-38, Overprinted in Pairs Vertically, Reading Down, or Horizontally (H) in Black

**Perf. 12½x12, 13½x12, 12x13½**
**1941          Wmk. 252, Unwmk.**

| No. | Type | Denom | | Un | Us |
|---|---|---|---|---|---|
| N1 | A69 | 5 l brn red & bl | | 40.00 | 40.00 |
| N2 | A70 | 10 l bl & red brn (#413) (H) | | 40.00 | 40.00 |
| a. | | On No. 397 (H) | | 160.00 | 160.00 |
| N3 | A71 | 20 l blk & grn (H) | | 40.00 | 40.00 |
| a. | | Overprint inverted | | 250.00 | |
| N4 | A72 | 40 l green & blk | | 40.00 | 40.00 |
| N5 | A73 | 50 l brown & blk | | 40.00 | 40.00 |
| N6 | A74 | 80 l ind & yel brn (H) | | 55.00 | 55.00 |
| a. | | Overprint inverted | | 325.00 | 250.00 |
| N7 | A67 | 1d green (H) | | 250.00 | 160.00 |
| N8 | A84 | 1.50d green (H) | | 175.00 | 95.00 |
| a. | | Overprint inverted | | 275.00 | 200.00 |
| N9 | A75 | 2d ultra | | 40.00 | 40.00 |
| N10 | A76 | 5d red | | 140.00 | 52.50 |
| N11 | A77 | 6d olive brown | | 140.00 | 52.50 |
| N12 | A78 | 7d dark brown | | 140.00 | 52.50 |
| N13 | A67 | 8d dp blue (H) | | 225.00 | 110.00 |
| N14 | A79 | 10d red brn | | 140.00 | 52.50 |
| N15 | A80 | 15d green | | 240.00 | 95.00 |
| N16 | A81 | 25d dk blue (H) | | 275.00 | 130.00 |
| a. | | Overprint inverted | | 525.00 | 450.00 |
| N17 | A84 | 30d org brn (H) | | 1,200. | 675.00 |
| a. | | Overprint inverted | | 1,300. | 800.00 |
| | | Nos. N1-N17 (17) | | 3,220. | 1,770. |

A variety with wrong font "C" in "Cephalonia" is found in several positions in each sheet of all denominations except those overprinted on single stamps. It sells for about three times the price of a normal pair.

Several other minor spelling errors in the overprint occur on several denominations in one of the printings.

Forgeries exist of many of the higher valued stamps and minor varieties of Nos. N1-N17, NC1-NC11 and NRA1-NRA5.

### Overprint Reading Up

| No. | Type | Denom | Un | Us |
|---|---|---|---|---|
| N1a | A69 | 5 l | 40.00 | 40.00 |
| N4a | A72 | 40 l | 40.00 | 40.00 |
| N5a | A73 | 50 l | 40.00 | 40.00 |
| N9a | A75 | 2d | 55.00 | 46.00 |
| N10a | A76 | 5d | 140.00 | 52.50 |
| N11a | A77 | 6d | 140.00 | 52.50 |
| N12a | A78 | 7d | 140.00 | 52.50 |
| N14a | A79 | 10d | 140.00 | 55.00 |
| N15a | A80 | 15d | 240.00 | 95.00 |
| | | Nos. N1a-N15a (9) | 975.00 | 480.00 |

### General Issue

Stamps of Italy, 1929, Overprinted in Red or Black

**1941          Wmk. 140          Perf. 14**

| No. | Type | Denom | Un | Us |
|---|---|---|---|---|
| N18 | A90 | 5c olive brn (R) | .65 | 2.40 |
| N19 | A92 | 10c dk brown (R) | .65 | 2.40 |
| N20 | A91 | 20c rose red | .65 | 2.40 |
| N21 | A94 | 25c deep green | .65 | 2.40 |
| N22 | A95 | 30c olive brn (R) | .65 | 2.40 |
| a. | | "SOLE" for "ISOLE" | 65.00 | |
| N23 | A95 | 50c purple (R) | .65 | 2.40 |
| N24 | A94 | 75c rose red | .65 | 2.40 |
| N25 | A94 | 1.25 l dp blue (R) | .65 | 2.40 |
| | | Nos. N18-N25 (8) | 5.20 | 19.20 |

The stamps overprinted "Isole Jonie" were issued for all the Ionian Islands except Cerigo which used regular postage stamps of Greece.

---

## ISSUED UNDER GERMAN OCCUPATION

### Zante Issue

Nos. N21 and N23 with Additional Handstamped Overprint in Black

**1943          Wmk. 140          Perf. 14**

| No. | Type | Denom | Un | Us |
|---|---|---|---|---|
| N26 | A94 | 25c deep green | 20.00 | 45.00 |
| a. | | Carmine overprint | 30.00 | 75.00 |
| N27 | A95 | 50c purple | 20.00 | 45.00 |
| a. | | Carmine overprint | 30.00 | 75.00 |

No. N19 with this overprint is a proof. Value, black $70; carmine $375.

Nos. N26-N27 were in use 8 days, then were succeeded by stamps of Greece.

Forgeries of Nos. N26-N27, NC13 and their cancellations are plentiful.

---

Greek stamps with Italian overprints for the islands of Cerigo (Kithyra), Paxos and Lefkas (Santa Maura) are fraudulent.

---

## OCCUPATION AIR POST STAMPS

### Issued under Italian Occupation

### Issue for Cephalonia and Ithaca

Stamps of Greece Overprinted in Pairs Vertically, Reading Down, or Horizontally (H) in Black Like Nos. N1-N17

**Perf. 13x12½, 12½x13**
**1941          Unwmk.**
**On Greece Nos. C22, C23, C25 and C27 to C30**
**Grayish Paper**

| No. | Type | Denom | Un | Us |
|---|---|---|---|---|
| NC1 | AP16 | 1d dp red | 120.00 | 95.00 |
| NC1A | AP17 | 2d dl bl | 55.00 | 47.50 |
| NC2 | AP19 | 7d bl vio (H) | 120.00 | 190.00 |
| NC3 | AP21 | 25d rose (H) | 450.00 | 350.00 |
| a. | | Overprint inverted | 800.00 | 450.00 |
| NC4 | AP22 | 30d dk grn | 725.00 | 450.00 |
| a. | | Overprint reading up | 725.00 | 450.00 |
| b. | | Horizontal overprint on single stamp | — | — |
| c. | | As "b," inverted | — | |
| NC5 | AP23 | 50d vio (H) | 3,600. | 2,500. |
| NC6 | AP24 | 100d brown | 1,900. | 1,900. |
| a. | | Overprint reading up | 1,600. | 1,200. |

No. NC1A is known only with overprint reading up.

**On Greece Nos. C31-C34**
**Reengraved; White Paper**

| No. | Type | Denom | Un | Us |
|---|---|---|---|---|
| NC7 | AP16 | 1d red | 120.00 | 95.00 |
| NC8 | AP17 | 2d gray bl | 40.00 | 25.00 |
| a. | | Overprint reading up | 40.00 | 25.00 |
| b. | | Horiz. ovpt. on pair | 800.00 | 425.00 |
| c. | | Horizontal overprint on single stamp | | |
| NC9 | AP18 | 5d vio (H) | 95.00 | 72.50 |
| a. | | Overprint inverted | 800.00 | 425.00 |
| b. | | Vert. ovpt. on single stamp, up or down | 800.00 | 450.00 |
| NC10 | AP19 | 7d dp ultra (H) | 275.00 | 200.00 |
| a. | | Overprint inverted | 800.00 | 300.00 |

**Overprinted Horizontally on No. C36**
**Rouletted 13½**

| No. | Type | Denom | Un | Us |
|---|---|---|---|---|
| NC11 | D3 | 50 l vio brn | 1,200. | 900.00 |
| a. | | Pair, one without ovpt. | 2,000. | |
| b. | | On No. C36a | | |

See footnote following No. N17.

### General Issue

Italy No. C13 Overprinted in Red Like Nos. N18-N25

**1941          Wmk. 140          Perf. 14**

| No. | Type | Denom | Un | Us |
|---|---|---|---|---|
| NC12 | AP3 | 50c olive brown | .80 | 3.25 |
| a. | | "SOLE" for "ISOLE" | 65.00 | |

Used in all the Ionian Islands except Cerigo which used air post stamps of Greece.

No. NC12 with additional overprint "BOLLO" is a revenue stamp.

---

## Issued under German Occupation
### ZANTE ISSUE

No. NC12 with Additional Handstamped Overprint in Black Like Nos. N26-N27

**1943          Wmk. 140          Perf. 14**

| No. | Type | Denom | Un | Us |
|---|---|---|---|---|
| NC13 | AP3 | 50c olive brown | 25.00 | 50.00 |
| a. | | "SOLE" for "ISOLE" | 300.00 | |
| b. | | Carmine overprint | 135.00 | 260.00 |

See note after No. N27.

---

## OCCUPATION POSTAGE DUE STAMPS

### General Issue

Postage Due Stamps of Italy, 1934, Overprinted in Black Like Nos. N18-N25

**1941          Wmk. 140          Perf. 14**

| No. | Type | Denom | Un | Us |
|---|---|---|---|---|
| NJ1 | D6 | 10c blue | 3.25 | 6.50 |
| NJ2 | D6 | 20c rose red | 3.25 | 6.50 |
| NJ3 | D6 | 30c red orange | 3.25 | 6.50 |
| NJ4 | D7 | 1 l red orange | 3.25 | 6.50 |
| | | Nos. NJ1-NJ4 (4) | 13.00 | 26.00 |

See footnote after No. N25.

---

## OCCUPATION POSTAL TAX STAMPS

### Issued under Italian Occupation

### Issue for Cephalonia and Ithaca

Greece No. RA56 with Additional Overprint on Horizontal Pair in Black Like Nos. N1-N17

**Serrate Roulette 13½**
**1941          Unwmk.**

| No. | Type | Denom | Un | Us |
|---|---|---|---|---|
| NRA1 | D3 | 10 l car (Bl+Bk) | 24.00 | 24.00 |
| a. | | Blue overprint double | 95.00 | 95.00 |
| b. | | Inverted overprint | 275.00 | 275.00 |

**Same Overprint Reading Down on Vertical Pairs of Nos. RA61-RA63**
**Perf. 13½x12**

| No. | Type | Denom | Un | Us |
|---|---|---|---|---|
| NRA2 | PT7 | 10 l brt rose, pale rose | 32.50 | 24.00 |
| a. | | Overprint on horiz. pair | 100.00 | 40.00 |
| b. | | Horizontal overprint on single stamp | 950.00 | |
| c. | | Overprint reading up | 15.00 | 12.50 |
| NRA3 | PT7 | 50 l gray grn, pale grn | 32.50 | 24.00 |
| a. | | Overprint reading up | 32.50 | 24.00 |
| b. | | Ovpt. on horiz. pair | 24.00 | 24.00 |
| c. | | Horizontal overprint on single stamp | 300.00 | |
| NRA4 | PT7 | 1d dl bl, lt bl | 65.00 | 45.00 |
| a. | | Overprint reading up | 65.00 | 45.00 |

**Same Overprint Reading Down on Vertical Pair of No. RA65**

| No. | Type | Denom | Un | Us |
|---|---|---|---|---|
| NRA5 | PT7 | 50 l gray grn, pale grn | 800.00 | 650.00 |
| a. | | Overprint reading up | 800.00 | 650.00 |

Nos. NRA5 and NRA5a were not placed in use on any compulsory day.

See footnote following No. N17.

## IRAN

i-'rän

### (Persia)

LOCATION — Western Asia, bordering on the Persian Gulf and the Gulf of Oman
GOVT. — Islamic republic
AREA — 636,000 sq. mi.
POP. — 65,179,752 (1999 est.)
CAPITAL — Tehran

20 Shahis (or Chahis) = 1 Kran
10 Krans = 1 Toman
100 Centimes = 1 Franc = 1 Kran (1881)
100 Dinars = 1 Rial (1933)
100 Rials = 1 Pahlavi
100 Rials = 1 Toman

**Catalogue values for unused stamps in this country are for Never Hinged items, beginning with Scott 1054 in the regular postage section, Scott B36 in the semi-postal section, Scott C83 in the airpost section, Scott O72 in the officials section, Scott Q36 in the parcel post section, and Scott RA4 in the postal tax section.**

Values of early stamps vary according to condition. Quotations for Nos. 1-20, 33-40 are for fine copies. Very fine to superb specimens sell at much higher prices, and inferior or poor copies sell at reduced prices, depending on the condition of the individual specimen.
Cracked gum on unused stamps does not detract from the value.

Beware of forgeries and/or reprints of most Iran stamps between the years 1870-1925. Scott values are for genuine stamps. Collectors should be aware that forgeries of many issues outnumber genuine examples by factors of 10 or 20 to one. Failing specialized knowledge on the part of the collector, these stamps should be examined or authenticated by acknowledged experts before purchase.

### Watermarks

Wmk. 161 — Lion

Wmk. 306 — Arms of Iran

Wmk. 316 — Persian Inscription

Wmk. 349 — Persian Inscription and Crown in Circle

Illustration of Wmk. 349 shown sideways. Circles in Wmk. 349 are 95mm apart.

Wmk. 353 — Persian Inscription and Coat of Arms in Circle

Wmk. 381 — "Islamic Republic of Iran" in Persian (Partial Illustration)

Many issues have handstamped surcharges. As usual with such surcharges there are numerous inverted, double and similar varieties.

Coat of Arms
A1     A2

Design A2 has value numeral below lion.

| 1870 | | Unwmk. | Typo. | Imperf. |
|---|---|---|---|---|
| 1 | A1 | 1s dull violet | 200.00 | |
| 2 | A1 | 2s green | 125.00 | |
| 3 | A1 | 4s greenish blue | 125.00 | |
| 4 | A1 | 8s red | 125.00 | |
| | | Nos. 1-4 (4) | 575.00 | |

Values for used examples of Nos. 1-4 are omitted, since this issue was only pen canceled. After 1875, postmarked remainders were sold to collectors. Values same as unused.
Printed in blocks of 4. Many shades exist. Forgeries exist.

**Printed on Both Sides**

| 1a | A1 | 1s | | 1,300. |
|---|---|---|---|---|
| 2a | A1 | 2s | | 900. |
| 3a | A1 | 4s | | 2,000. |
| 4a | A1 | 8s | | 1,200. |

**Vertically Rouletted 10½ on 1 or 2 Sides**

| 1875 | | | Thick Wove Paper | |
|---|---|---|---|---|
| 11 | A2 | 1s black | 150.00 | 50.00 |
| a. | | Imperf., pair | 400.00 | 400.00 |
| 12 | A2 | 2s blue | 125.00 | 50.00 |
| a. | | Tête bêche pair | 10,000. | |
| b. | | Imperf., pair | 575.00 | 575.00 |
| 13 | A2 | 4s vermilion | 200.00 | 60.00 |
| a. | | Imperf., pair | 625.00 | 625.00 |
| b. | | 4s bright red, thin paper, imperf. | 525.00 | |
| 14 | A2 | 8s yellow green | 100.00 | 60.00 |
| a. | | Tête bêche pair | 12,500. | 7,500. |
| b. | | Imperf., pair | 70.00 | 70.00 |
| | | Nos. 11-14 (4) | 575.00 | 220.00 |

Four varieties of each.

Nos. 11-14 were printed in horizontal strips of 4 with 3-10mm spacing between stamps. The strips were then cut very close all around (generally touching or cutting the outer framelines). Then they were hand-rouletted between the stamps. Values are for stamps with rouletting on both sides and margins clear at top and bottom. Stamps showing the rouletting on only one side sell for considerably less.
Nos. 11 to 14 also exist pin-perforated and percé en scie.
No. 13b has spacing of 2-3mm.
See Nos. 15-20, 33-40.

**Medium to Thin White or Grayish Paper**

| 1876 | | | | Imperf. |
|---|---|---|---|---|
| 14A | A2 | 1s black | 200.00 | 300.00 |
| 15 | A2 | 1s gray black | 37.50 | 75.00 |
| a. | | Printed on both sides | 1,000. | |
| b. | | Laid paper | 500.00 | |
| 16 | A2 | 2s gray blue | 375.00 | 450.00 |
| a. | | Printed on both sides | — | |
| 17 | A2 | 2s black | 600.00 | |
| a. | | Tête bêche pair | 5,750. | |
| 18 | A2 | 4s vermilion | 200.00 | 60.00 |
| a. | | Printed on both sides | 800.00 | 450.00 |
| 19 | A2 | 1k rose | 600.00 | 50.00 |
| a. | | Printed on both sides | | 350.00 |
| b. | | Laid paper | 2,000. | 225.00 |
| c. | | 1k yellow (error) | 9,500. | |
| d. | | Tête bêche pair | | 15,000. |
| 20 | A2 | 4k yellow | 1,000. | 70.00 |
| a. | | Printed on both sides | | 825.00 |
| b. | | Laid paper | 1,000. | 110.00 |
| c. | | Tête bêche pair | | 18,000. |

Nos. 15-16, 18-20 were printed in blocks of 4, and Nos. 14A and 17 in vertical strips of 4, with spacing of 2mm or less.
Nos. 14A and 17 are on medium to thick grayish wove paper. Forgeries exist.
*Official reprints of the 1s and 4s are on thick coarse white paper without gum. Value, each $350.*

*Unofficial Reprints:*
*1875 and 1876 issues.*
The reprints of the 1s and 1k stamps are readily told; the pearls of the circle are heavier, the borders of the circles containing the Persian numeral of value are wider and the figure "1" below the lion is always Roman.
The reprints of the 2s have the outer line of the frame at the left and at the bottom broken and on some specimens entirely missing.
A distinguishing mark by which to tell the 4s and 4k stamps is the frame, the outer line of which is of the same thickness as the inner line, while on the originals the inner line is very thin and the outer line thick; another feature of most of the reprints is a gash in the lower part of the circle below the figure "4."
In the reprints of the 8s stamps the small scroll nearest to the circles with Persian numerals at the bottom of the stamp touches the frame below it; the inner and outer lines of the frame are of equal thickness, while in the originals the outer line is much heavier than the inner one.
All reprints are found canceled to order.

Nasser-eddin Shah Qajar — A3

**Perf. 10½, 11, 12, 13, and Compounds**

| 1876 | | | | Litho. |
|---|---|---|---|---|
| 27 | A3 | 1s lilac & blk | 20.00 | 6.00 |
| 28 | A3 | 2s green & blk | 25.00 | 7.50 |
| 29 | A3 | 5s rose & blk | 25.00 | 4.00 |
| 30 | A3 | 10s blue & blk | 40.00 | 8.00 |
| | | Nos. 27-30 (4) | 110.00 | 25.50 |

Bisects of the 5s and 1s, the latter used with 2s stamps, were used to make up the 2½ shahis postcard rate. Bisects of the 10s were used in the absence of 5s stamps to make up the letter rate.

The 10s was bisected and surcharged "5 Shahi" or "5 Shahy" for local use in Azerbaijan province and Khoy in 1877.

"Imperfs" of the 5s are envelope cutouts.

Forgeries and official reprints exist.

Very fine examples will have perforations cutting the background net on one side. Genuine stamps withs perfs clear of net on all four sides are very scarce.

| 1878 | | Typo. | | Imperf. | |
|---|---|---|---|---|---|
| 33 | A2 | 1k car rose | | 300.00 | 90.00 |
| 34 | A2 | 1k red, *yellow* | | 2,000. | 90.00 |
| a. | | Tête bêche pair | | | 5,250. |
| 35 | A2 | 4k ultramarine | | 275.00 | 100.00 |
| 36 | A2 | 5k violet | | 850.00 | 200.00 |
| 37 | A2 | 5k gold | | *3,500.* | *450.00* |
| 38 | A2 | 5k red bronze | | 7,500. | 1,750. |
| 39 | A2 | 5k vio bronze | | 25,000. | 2,250. |
| 40 | A2 | 1t bronze, *bl* | | 55,000. | 5,500. |

Four varieties of each except for 4k which has 3.

Nos. 33 and 34 are printed from redrawn clichés. They have wide colorless circles around the corner numerals.

Nasser-eddin Shah Qajar — A6

Sun — A7

### Perf. 10½, 12, 13, and Compounds

| 1879 | | | Litho. | |
|---|---|---|---|---|
| 41 | A6 | 1k brown & blk | 300.00 | 7.00 |
| a. | | Imperf., pair | — | |
| b. | | Inverted center | | 3,500. |
| 42 | A6 | 5k blue & blk | 400.00 | 5.00 |
| a. | | Imperf., pair | | 450.00 |
| b. | | Inverted center | | 1,350. |
| c. | | Inverted center, imperf | | 1,350. |

| 1880 | | | | |
|---|---|---|---|---|
| 43 | A6 | 1s red & black | 50.00 | 15.00 |
| b. | | Pair, imperf between | | 2,750. |
| 44 | A6 | 2s yellow & blk | 85.00 | 10.00 |
| 45 | A6 | 5s green & blk | 350.00 | 2.00 |
| 46 | A6 | 10s violet & blk | 550.00 | 25.00 |
| | | *Nos. 43-46 (4)* | 1,035. | 52.00 |

Forgeries and official reprints exist.

*The 2, 5 and 10sh of this issue and the 1 and 5kr of the 1879 issue have been reprinted from a new die which resembles the 5 shahi envelope. The aigrette is shorter than on the original stamps and touches the circle above it.*

### Imperf., Pair

| 43a | A6 | 1s | 1,500. | |
|---|---|---|---|---|
| 44a | A6 | 2s | — | 750.00 |
| 46a | A6 | 10s | — | 600.00 |

| 1881 | | Litho. | Perf. 12, 13, 12x13 | |
|---|---|---|---|---|
| 47 | A7 | 5c dull violet | 35.00 | 10.00 |
| 48 | A7 | 10c rose | 35.00 | 10.00 |
| 49 | A7 | 25c green | 5,500. | 75.00 |
| | | *Nos. 47-49 (3)* | 5,570. | 95.00 |

| 1882 | | Engr., Border Litho. | | |
|---|---|---|---|---|
| 50 | A7 | 5c blue vio & vio | 40.00 | 40.00 |
| 51 | A7 | 10c dp pink & rose | 40.00 | 40.00 |
| 52 | A7 | 25c deep grn & grn | 700.00 | 20.00 |
| | | *Nos. 50-52 (3)* | 780.00 | 100.00 |

Very fine examples of Nos. 50-52 will have perforations cutting the outer colored border but clear of the inner framelines.

Counterfeits of Nos. 50-52, 53, 53a are plentiful and have been used to create forgeries of Nos. 66, 66a, 70 and 70a. They usually have a strong, complete inner frameline at right. On genuine stamps that line is weak or missing.

A8

---

Shah Nasr-ed-Din
A9    A10

A11     Type I

Type II (error)

Type I: Three dots at right end of scroll.
Type II: Two dots at right end of scroll.

| 1882-84 | | | Engr. | |
|---|---|---|---|---|
| 53 | A8 | 5s green, type I | 35.00 | 1.50 |
| a. | | 5s green, type II | 75.00 | 10.00 |
| 54 | A9 | 10s buff, org & blk | 75.00 | 10.00 |
| 55 | A10 | 50c buff, org & blk | 400.00 | 55.00 |
| 56 | A10 | 50c gray & blk ('84) | 125.00 | 65.00 |
| 57 | A10 | 1fr blue & black | 150.00 | 10.00 |
| 58 | A10 | 5fr rose red & blk | 125.00 | 10.00 |
| 59 | A11 | 10fr buff, red & blk | 150.00 | 30.00 |
| | | *Nos. 53-59 (7)* | 1,060. | 181.50 |

Crude forgeries of Nos. 58-59 exist. Halves of the 10s, 50c and 1fr surcharged with Farsi characters in red or black are frauds. The 50c and 1fr surcharged with a large "5" surrounded by rays are also frauds.

No. 59 used is valued for c-t-o.

For overprints and surcharges see #66-72.

Very fine examples of Nos. 53-59 will have perforations cutting the outer colored border but clear of the inner framelines.

A12    A13

### Perf. 12-12½, 13

| 1885, March-May | | | | Litho. |
|---|---|---|---|---|
| 59A | A12 | 5c blue | 400.00 | 35.00 |
| a. | | 5c violet blue | 400.00 | 50.00 |
| b. | | 5c ultramarine | 400.00 | 50.00 |
| c. | | 5c dp reddish lilac | 650.00 | 100.00 |
| d. | | As "a," imperf | 3,000. | |

No. 59A was issued because of an urgent need for 5c stamps, pending the arrival of No. 62 in July. No. 59A has 88 sunrays instead of the 124 sunrays on the typographed stamp, No. 62.

| 1885-86 | | | | Typo. |
|---|---|---|---|---|
| 60 | A12 | 1c green | 15.00 | 1.50 |
| 61 | A12 | 2c rose | 15.00 | 1.50 |
| 62 | A12 | 5c dull blue | 40.00 | .75 |
| 63 | A13 | 10c brown | 15.00 | 1.50 |
| 64 | A13 | 1k slate | 40.00 | 2.00 |
| 65 | A13 | 5k dull vio ('86) | 700.00 | 35.00 |
| | | *Nos. 60-65 (6)* | 825.00 | 42.25 |

Nos. 53, 54, 56 and 58 Surcharged in Black:

a      b

---

c    d

e    f

| 1885 | | | | |
|---|---|---|---|---|
| 66 | (a) | 6c on 5s grn, type I | 125.00 | 30.00 |
| a. | | 6c on 5s green, type II | 200.00 | 100.00 |
| 67 | (b) | 12c on 50c gray & blk | 125.00 | 30.00 |
| 68 | (c) | 18c on 10s buff, org & black | 125.00 | 30.00 |
| 69 | (d) | 1t on 5fr rose red & black | 125.00 | 30.00 |
| | | *Nos. 66-69 (4)* | 500.00 | 120.00 |

| 1887 | | | | |
|---|---|---|---|---|
| 70 | (e) | 3c on 5s grn, type I | 125.00 | 30.00 |
| a. | | 3c on 5s green, type II | 200.00 | 100.00 |
| 71 | (a) | 6c on 10s buff, org & black | 125.00 | 30.00 |
| 72 | (f) | 8c on 50c gray & blk | 125.00 | 30.00 |
| | | *Nos. 70-72 (3)* | 375.00 | 90.00 |

The word "OFFICIEL" indicated that the surcharged stamps were officially authorized.

Surcharges on the same basic stamps of values other than those listed are believed to be bogus.

Counterfeits of Nos. 66-72 abound.

Very fine examples of Nos. 66-72 will have perforations cutting the outer colored border but clear of the inner framelines.

> Beware of forgeries and/or reprints of most Iran stamps between the years 1870-1925. Scott values are for genuine stamps. Collectors should be aware that forgeries of many issues outnumber genuine examples by factors of 10 or 20 to one. Failing specialized knowledge on the part of the collector, these stamps should be examined or authenticated by acknowledged experts before purchase.

A14    A15

---

| 1889 | Typo. | Perf. 11, 13½, 11x13½ | | |
|---|---|---|---|---|
| 73 | A14 | 1c pale rose | 2.50 | .75 |
| 74 | A14 | 2c pale blue | 2.50 | .75 |
| 75 | A14 | 5c lilac | 1.50 | .50 |
| 76 | A14 | 7c brown | 7.50 | 1.50 |
| 77 | A15 | 10c black | 2.50 | .75 |
| 78 | A15 | 1k red orange | 4.50 | .75 |
| 79 | A15 | 2k rose | 40.00 | 6.00 |
| 80 | A15 | 5k green | 25.00 | 6.00 |
| | | *Nos. 73-80 (8)* | 86.00 | 17.00 |

All values exist imperforate.

Canceled to order stamps of No. 76 abound.

For surcharges see Nos. 622-625.

Nos. 73-80 with average centering, faded colors and/or toned paper sell for much less.

A16    A17

| 1891 | | | Perf. 10½, 11½ | |
|---|---|---|---|---|
| 81 | A16 | 1c black | 2.50 | 1.00 |
| 82 | A16 | 2c brown | 2.50 | 1.00 |
| 83 | A16 | 5c deep blue | 2.50 | .20 |
| 84 | A16 | 7c gray | 350.00 | 12.00 |
| 85 | A16 | 10c rose | 2.50 | .50 |
| 86 | A16 | 14c orange | 2.50 | 1.50 |
| 87 | A17 | 1k green | 25.00 | 2.00 |
| 88 | A17 | 2k orange | 700.00 | 25.00 |
| 89 | A17 | 5k ocher yellow | 8.00 | 30.00 |
| | | *Nos. 81-89 (9)* | 1,095. | 73.20 |

For surcharges see Nos. 626-629.

A18    Nasser-eddin Shah — A19

| 1894 | | | Perf. 12½ | |
|---|---|---|---|---|
| 90 | A18 | 1c lilac | 1.00 | .20 |
| 91 | A18 | 2c blue green | 1.00 | .20 |
| 92 | A18 | 5c ultramarine | 1.00 | .20 |
| 93 | A18 | 8c brown | 1.00 | .20 |

| | | | Perf. 11½x11 | |
|---|---|---|---|---|
| 94 | A19 | 10c orange | 1.25 | .75 |
| 95 | A19 | 16c rose | 25.00 | 50.00 |
| 96 | A19 | 1k red & yellow | 3.00 | .75 |
| 97 | A19 | 2k brn org & pale bl | 4.00 | 1.00 |
| 98 | A19 | 5k violet & silver | 5.00 | 1.50 |
| 99 | A19 | 10k red & gold | 15.00 | 10.00 |
| 100 | A19 | 50k green & gold | 30.00 | 10.00 |
| | | *Nos. 90-100 (11)* | 87.25 | 74.80 |

Canceled to order stamps sell for much less than listed values, which are for postally used. *Reprints exist. They are hard to distinguish from the originals. Value, set $15.*

See Nos. 104-112, 136-144. For overprints see Nos. 120-128, 152-167, 173-181. For surcharges see Nos. 101-103, 168, 206, 211.

## Nos. 93, 98 With Violet or Magenta Surcharge

a

b

| 1897 | | Perf. 12½, 11½x11 | |
|---|---|---|---|
| 101 | A18(a) | 5c on 8c brown (V) | 25.00 4.00 |
| 102 | A19(b) | 1k on 5k vio & sil (V) | 35.00 16.00 |
| 103 | A19(b) | 2k on 5k vio & sil (M) | 50.00 30.00 |
| | | Nos. 101-103 (3) | 110.00 50.00 |

Forgeries exist.

## Lion Type of 1894 and

Shah Muzaffar-ed-Din
A22

| 1898 | | Typo. | Perf. 12½ |
|---|---|---|---|
| 104 | A18 | 1c gray | 5.00 .35 |
| 105 | A18 | 2c pale brown | 5.00 .35 |
| 106 | A18 | 3c dull violet | 10.00 3.00 |
| 107 | A18 | 4c vermilion | 10.00 3.00 |
| 108 | A18 | 5c yellow | 5.00 .25 |
| 109 | A18 | 8c orange | 20.00 7.00 |
| 110 | A18 | 10c light blue | 5.00 .50 |
| 111 | A18 | 12c rose | 15.00 1.00 |
| 112 | A18 | 16c green | 20.00 7.00 |
| 113 | A22 | 1k ultramarine | 10.00 1.00 |
| 114 | A22 | 2k pink | 10.00 2.00 |
| 115 | A22 | 3k yellow | 10.00 3.00 |
| 116 | A22 | 4k gray | 10.00 5.00 |
| 117 | A22 | 5k emerald | 10.00 6.00 |
| 118 | A22 | 10k orange | 30.00 15.00 |
| 119 | A22 | 50k bright vio | 50.00 25.00 |
| | | Nos. 104-119 (16) | 225.00 79.45 |

*Unauthorized reprints of Nos. 104-119 were made from original clichés. Paper shows a vertical mesh. These abound unused and canceled to order. Value unused, hinged, $20.*

See Nos. 145-151. For overprints see Nos. 129-135, 182-188. For surcharges see Nos. 169, 171, 207, 209, 215.

Reprints have been used to make counterfeits of Nos. 120-135, 152-167.

## Stamps of 1898 Handstamped in Violet:

a

b

c

---

d

e

f

g

h

| 1899 | | | | |
|---|---|---|---|---|
| 120 | (a) | 1c gray | 5.00 | 5.00 |
| 121 | (b) | 2c pale brown | 5.00 | 8.00 |
| 122 | (b) | 3c dull violet | 12.00 | 15.00 |
| 123 | (c) | 4c vermilion | 18.00 | 30.00 |
| 124 | (c) | 5c yellow | 10.00 | 3.00 |
| 125 | (d) | 8c orange | 15.00 | 40.00 |
| 126 | (d) | 10c light blue | 6.50 | 8.00 |
| a. | | Type "b" handstamp | 350.00 | 350.00 |
| 127 | (d) | 12c rose | 15.00 | 8.00 |
| 128 | (d) | 16c green | 25.00 | 30.00 |
| 129 | (e) | 1k ultramarine | 25.00 | 10.00 |
| 130 | (f) | 2k pink | 30.00 | 25.00 |
| 131 | (f) | 3k yellow | 80.00 | 200.00 |
| 132 | (g) | 4k gray | 100.00 | 200.00 |
| 133 | (g) | 5k emerald | 30.00 | 40.00 |
| 134 | (h) | 10k orange | 60.00 | 60.00 |
| 135 | (h) | 50k brt violet | 120.00 | 150.00 |
| | | Nos. 120-135 (16) | 556.50 | 832.00 |

The handstamped control marks on Nos. 120-135 exist sideways, inverted and double. Counterfeits are plentiful.

### Types of 1894-98

| 1899 | | Typo. | Perf. 12½ |
|---|---|---|---|
| 136 | A18 | 1c gray, *green* | 7.50 .75 |
| 137 | A18 | 2c brown, *green* | 7.50 .75 |
| 138 | A18 | 3c violet, *green* | 20.00 5.00 |
| 139 | A18 | 4c red, *green* | 12.00 5.00 |
| 140 | A18 | 5c yellow, *green* | 5.00 .30 |
| 141 | A18 | 8c orange, *green* | 15.00 5.00 |
| 142 | A18 | 10c pale blue, *grn* | 5.00 .50 |
| 143 | A18 | 12c lake, *green* | 15.00 1.25 |
| 144 | A18 | 16c green, *green* | 25.00 5.00 |
| 145 | A22 | 1k red | 30.00 1.25 |
| 146 | A22 | 2k deep green | 30.00 8.50 |
| 147 | A22 | 3k lilac brown | 30.00 17.00 |
| 148 | A22 | 4k orange red | 30.00 17.00 |
| 149 | A22 | 5k gray brown | 30.00 17.00 |
| 150 | A22 | 10k deep blue | 400.00 100.00 |
| 151 | A22 | 50k brown | 75.00 30.00 |
| | | Nos. 136-151 (16) | 737.00 214.30 |

Canceled to order stamps abound.
*Unauthorized reprints of Nos. 136-151 were made from original clichés. Paper is chalky and has white gum. The design can be seen through the back of the reprints. Value unused, hinged, set $30.*

For surcharges and overprints see Nos. 171, 173-188, 206-207, 209, 211, 215.

---

## Nos. 104-111 Handstamped in Violet

(Struck once on every two stamps.)

| 1900 | | | |
|---|---|---|---|
| 152 | A18 | 1c gray | 35.00 15.00 |
| 153 | A18 | 2c pale brown | 45.00 20.00 |
| 154 | A18 | 3c dull violet | 70.00 50.00 |
| 155 | A18 | 4c vermilion | 80.00 50.00 |
| 156 | A18 | 5c yellow | 20.00 10.00 |
| 158 | A18 | 10c light blue | — — |
| 159 | A18 | 12c rose | 80.00 50.00 |
| | | Nos. 152-159 (6) | 330.00 195.00 |

Values are for single authenticated stamps. Pairs sell for much more.
This control mark, in genuine state, was not applied to the 8c orange (Nos. 109, 125).

### Same Overprint Handstamped on Nos. 120-127 in Violet

(Struck once on each block of 4.)

| 160 | A18 | 1c gray | 100.00 50.00 |
|---|---|---|---|
| 163 | A18 | 4c vermilion | 250.00 140.00 |
| 164 | A18 | 5c yellow | 50.00 20.00 |
| 166 | A18 | 10c light blue, type "d" hand- stamp | 500.00 |
| a. | | Type "b" handstamp | 250.00 100.00 |
| 167 | A18 | 12c rose | 110.00 50.00 |
| | | Nos. 160-167 (5) | 510.00 760.00 |

Values are for single authenticated stamps. Blocks are rare and worth much more.
Counterfeits exist of Nos. 152-167.

## No. 93 Surcharged in Violet

| 1900 | | | |
|---|---|---|---|
| 168 | A18 | 5c on 8c brown | 35.00 2.50 |

## No. 145 Surcharged in Violet

| 1901 | | | |
|---|---|---|---|
| 169 | A22 | 12c on 1k red | 100.00 100.00 |
| a. | | Blue surcharge | 125.00 125.00 |

Counterfeits exist.
Some specialists state that No. 169 with black surcharge was made for collectors.

A23

| 1902 | | | Violet Surcharge |
|---|---|---|---|
| 171 | A23 | 5k on 50k brown | 200.00 80.00 |
| a. | | Blue surcharge | 200.00 90.00 |

Counterfeits exist. See No. 207.

## Nos. 136-151 Overprinted in Black

| 1902 | | | |
|---|---|---|---|
| 173 | A18 | 1c gray, *green* | 50.00 20.00 |
| 174 | A18 | 2c brown, *green* | 50.00 20.00 |
| 175 | A18 | 3c violet, *green* | 75.00 45.00 |
| 176 | A18 | 4c red, *green* | 125.00 150.00 |
| 177 | A18 | 5c yellow, *green* | 20.00 5.00 |
| 178 | A18 | 8c orange, *green* | 125.00 150.00 |

---

| 179 | A18 | 10c pale blue, *grn* | 35.00 15.00 |
|---|---|---|---|
| 180 | A18 | 12c lake, *green* | 75.00 25.00 |
| 181 | A18 | 16c green, *green* | 200.00 200.00 |
| 182 | A22 | 1k red | 100.00 25.00 |
| 183 | A22 | 2k deep green | 250.00 50.00 |
| 188 | A22 | 50k brown | 300.00 125.00 |

### Overprinted on No. 168

| 206 | A18 | 5c on 8c brown | 100.00 50.00 |
|---|---|---|---|

### Overprinted on Nos. 171 and 171a

| 207 | A23 | 5k on 50k brown | 200.00 100.00 |
|---|---|---|---|
| a. | | On #171a | 250.00 100.00 |

### Overprinted on Nos. 169 and 169a

| 209 | A22 | 12c on 1k red | 100.00 50.00 |
|---|---|---|---|
| a. | | On #169a | 100.00 50.00 |

Counterfeits of the overprint of Nos. 173-183, 188, 206-207, 209 are plentiful. Practically all examples with overprint sideways, inverted, double and double with one inverted are frauds.

## Nos. 142 and 145 Surcharged in Violet

| 1902 | | | |
|---|---|---|---|
| 211 | A18 | 5c on 10c pale bl, *grn* | 50.00 20.00 |

Surcharges in different colors were made for collectors.

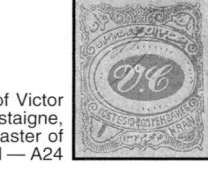

Initials of Victor Castaigne, Postmaster of Meshed — A24

| 1902 | | Typo. | Imperf. | |
|---|---|---|---|---|
| 222 | A24 | 1c black | 1,500. | 450. |
| a. | | Inverted frame | | |
| b. | | Inverted center | — | 3,000. |
| 223 | A24 | 2c black | 1,250. | 450. |
| a. | | Inverted frame | | |
| b. | | "2" in right upper corner | 3,000. | 1,750. |
| c. | | Frame printed on both sides | — | |
| 224 | A24 | 3c black | 3,250. | 1,000. |
| 225 | A24 | 5c violet | 750. | 200. |
| a. | | "5" in right upper corner | | |
| b. | | Frame printed on both sides | 2,250. | 1,000. |
| c. | | Inverted center | | |
| 226 | A24 | 5c black | 900. | 350. |
| a. | | Persian "5" in lower left cor- ner | | |
| b. | | Inverted center | | |
| 227 | A24 | 12c dull blue | 4,000. | 1,500. |
| a. | | Inverted frame | | |
| b. | | Inverted center | | |
| 228 | A24 | 1k rose | 30,000. | 3,500. |

Used values for Nos. 222-228 canceled to order are about ⅓ to ½ the values shown, which are for postally used stamps.
The design of No. 228 differs slightly from the illustration.
Nos. 222-228 were printed in three operations. Inverted centers have frames and numerals upright. Inverted frames have centers and numerals upright.

### Pin-perforated

| 234 | A24 | 12c dull blue | 3,000. 1,500. |
|---|---|---|---|

The post office at Meshed having exhausted its stock of stamps, the postmaster issued the above series provisionally. The center of the design is the seal of the postmaster who also wrote his initials upon the upper part, using violet ink for the 1k and red for the others.
Unauthorized reprints, including pinperforated examples of Nos. 222-226, and forgeries exist.
Expert knowledge or certificates of authenticity are required.

A25

TWO TYPES:
Type I — "CHAHI" or "KRANS" are in capital letters.
Type II — Only "C" of "Chahi" or "K" of "Krans" is a capital.
The 3c and 5c sometimes have a tall narrow figure in the upper left corner. The 5c is also

found with the cross at the upper left broken or missing. These varieties are known with many of the overprints.

Stamps of Design A25 have a faint fancy background in the color of the stamp. All issued stamps have handstamped controls as listed.

### Handstamp Overprinted in Black

**1902**       **Typeset**       *Imperf.*
**Type I**

| | | | | |
|---|---|---|---|---|
| 235 | A25 | 1c gray & buff | *300.00* | 100.00 |
| 236 | A25 | 2c brown & buff | *300.00* | 100.00 |
| 237 | A25 | 3c green & buff | *300.00* | 110.00 |
| 238 | A25 | 5c red & buff | *200.00* | 75.00 |
| 239 | A25 | 12c ultra & buff | *500.00* | 150.00 |
| | | Nos. 235-239 (5) | *1,600.* | 535.00 |

Counterfeits abound. Type II stamps with this overprint are forgeries.

The 3c with violet overprint is believed not to have been regularly issued.

### Handstamp Overprinted in Rose

**1902**       **Type I**

| | | | | |
|---|---|---|---|---|
| 247 | A25 | 1c gray & buff | 25.00 | 2.00 |
| a. | | With Persian numerals "2" | 100.00 | 100.00 |
| 248 | A25 | 2c brown & buff | 25.00 | 2.00 |
| 249 | A25 | 3c dp grn & buff | 25.00 | 2.00 |
| 250 | A25 | 5c red & buff | 25.00 | .75 |
| 251 | A25 | 10c ol yel & buff | 50.00 | 3.00 |
| 252 | A25 | 12c ultra & buff | 75.00 | 5.00 |
| 253 | A25 | 1k violet & bl | 60.00 | 6.00 |
| 254 | A25 | 2k ol grn & bl | 100.00 | 12.50 |
| 256 | A25 | 10k dk bl & bl | 150.00 | 30.00 |
| 257 | A25 | 50k red & blue | 1,500. | 600.00 |
| | | Nos. 247-257 (10) | 2,035. | 663.25 |

A 5k exists but its' status is doubtful.

Nos. 247-257 and the 12c on brown paper and on blue paper with blue quadrille lines are known without overprint but are not believed to have been regularly issued in this condition.

The 1c to 10k, A25 type I, with violet overprint are believed not to have been regularly issued. Five denominations also exist with overprint in blue, black or green.

**Type II**

| | | | | |
|---|---|---|---|---|
| 280 | A25 | 1c gray & yellow | 150.00 | 100.00 |
| 281 | A25 | 2c brown & yel | 150.00 | 100.00 |
| 282 | A25 | 3c dk grn & yel | 750.00 | 500.00 |
| 283 | A25 | 5c red & yellow | 50.00 | 15.00 |
| 284 | A25 | 10c ol yel & yel | 100.00 | 15.00 |
| 285 | A25 | 12c blue & yel | 125.00 | 25.00 |
| 290 | A25 | 50k org red & bl | 1,250. | 280.00 |

The 3c, inscribed "Persans," is not believed to have been regularly issued.

The same overprint in violet was applied to nine denominations of the Type II stamps, but these, too, are believed not to have been regularly issued. The overprint also exists in blue, black and green.

Reprints, counterfeits, counterfeit overprints, with or without cancellations, are plentiful for Nos. 247-257, 280-290.

Five stamps of type A25, type II, in high denominations (10, 20, 25, 50 and 100 tomans), with "Postes 1319" lion overprint in blue, were used only on money orders, not for postage. They are usually numbered on the back in red, blue or black.

Beware of forgeries and/or reprints of most Iran stamps between the years 1870-1925. Scott values are for genuine stamps. Collectors should be aware that forgeries of many issues outnumber genuine examples by factors of 10 or 20 to one. Failing specialized knowledge on the part of the collector, these stamps should be examined or authenticated by acknowledged experts before purchase.

### Handstamp Surcharged in Black

**1902**       **Type I**

| | | | | |
|---|---|---|---|---|
| 308 | A25 | 5k on 5k ocher & bl | *175.00* | 50.00 |

Counterfeits of No. 308 abound.
This surcharge in rose, violet, blue or green is considered bogus.
This surcharge on 50k orange red and blue, and on 5k ocher and blue, type II, is considered bogus.

### Handstamp Overprinted Diagonally in Black

**1902**       **Type I**

| | | | | |
|---|---|---|---|---|
| 315 | A25 | 2c brown & buff | 175.00 | 60.00 |
| a. | | Rose overprint | 500.00 | 500.00 |

**Type II**

| | | | | |
|---|---|---|---|---|
| 316 | A25 | 2c brown & yel | — | — |
| a. | | Rose overprint | — | — |

"P. L." stands for "Poste Locale."
Counterfeits of Nos. 315-316 exist.
Some specialists believe that Type II stamps were not used officially for this overprint.

### Handstamp Overprinted in Black or Rose

**1902**       **Type II**

| | | | | |
|---|---|---|---|---|
| 317 | A25 | 2c brn & yellow | 175.00 | 60.00 |
| 318 | A25 | 2c brown & yel (R) | 500.00 | 500.00 |

Counterfeits of Nos. 317-318 exist.

### Overprinted in Blue

**1903**       **Type I**

| | | | | |
|---|---|---|---|---|
| 321 | A25 | 1k violet & blue | 60.00 | 60.00 |

**Type II**

| | | | | |
|---|---|---|---|---|
| 336 | A25 | 1c gray & yellow | 40.00 | 40.00 |
| 337 | A25 | 2c brown & yellow | 40.00 | 40.00 |
| 338 | A25 | 5c red & yellow | 35.00 | 35.00 |
| 339 | A25 | 10c olive yel & yel | 50.00 | 50.00 |
| 340 | A25 | 12c blue & yellow | 55.00 | 55.00 |
| | | Nos. 321-340 (6) | 280.00 | 280.00 |

The overprint also exists in violet and black, but it is doubtful whether such items were regularly issued.
Forgeries of Nos. 321, 336-340 abound. Genuine unused examples are seldom found.

Arms of Persia
A26

Shah Muzaffar-ed-Din
A27

**1902 (Dec.)-1904**       **Typo.**       **Perf. 12½**

| | | | | |
|---|---|---|---|---|
| 351 | A26 | 1c violet | 2.00 | .20 |
| 352 | A26 | 2c gray | 2.00 | .20 |
| 353 | A26 | 3c green | 2.00 | .20 |
| 354 | A26 | 5c rose | 2.00 | .20 |
| 355 | A26 | 10c yellow brn | 3.00 | 1.50 |
| 356 | A26 | 12c blue | 4.00 | .50 |

**Engr.**
**Perf. 11½x11**

| | | | | |
|---|---|---|---|---|
| 357 | A27 | 1k violet | 12.00 | .50 |
| 358 | A27 | 2k ultramarine | 20.00 | 1.25 |
| 359 | A27 | 5k orange brn | 30.00 | 2.00 |
| 360 | A27 | 10k rose red | 30.00 | 4.00 |
| 361 | A27 | 20k orange ('04) | 35.00 | 5.00 |
| 362 | A27 | 30k green ('04) | 60.00 | 12.50 |
| 363 | A27 | 50k green | 400.00 | 100.00 |
| | | Nos. 351-363 (13) | 602.00 | 128.05 |

Nos. 351-363 used are valued canceled to order.

No. 355 exists with blue diagonal surcharge "1 CHAHI"; its status is questioned.

A government decree in November, 1903, required that all picture postcards be censored by the Central Post Office, which would apply a control mark on each card to show that the 2c tax for this service had been paid. No. 352 was overprinted "Controle" in several styles, for this purpose. Value: unused $100; used, from $25.

See Nos. 428-433. For surcharges and overprints see #364-420, 446-447, 464-469, O8-O28, P1.

### No. 353 Surcharged in Violet or Blue

**1903**

| | | | | |
|---|---|---|---|---|
| 364 | A26 | 1c on 3c green (V) | 25.00 | 12.50 |
| 365 | A26 | 2c on 3c green (Bl) | 25.00 | 12.50 |

A 2c surcharge on No. 354 exists, but its status is dubious.

### No. 360 Surcharged in Blue

| | | | | |
|---|---|---|---|---|
| 366 | A27 | 12c on 10k rose red | 75.00 | 40.00 |
| a. | | Black surcharge | | 40.00 |
| b. | | Violet surcharge | | 40.00 |
| | | Nos. 364-366 (3) | 125.00 | 65.00 |

Nos. 366, 366a and 366b used are valued canceled to order.

### No. 363 Surcharged in Blue or Black

**1903**

| | | | | |
|---|---|---|---|---|
| 368 | A27 | 2t on 50k grn (Bl) | 175.00 | 55.00 |
| a. | | Rose surcharge | 200.00 | 100.00 |
| b. | | Black surcharge | 200.00 | 100.00 |
| 370 | A27 | 3t on 50k grn (Bk) | 175.00 | 55.00 |
| a. | | Violet surcharge | 200.00 | 55.00 |
| b. | | Rose surcharge | 225.00 | 125.00 |

### No. 363 Surcharged in Blue or Black

**1904**

| | | | | |
|---|---|---|---|---|
| 372 | A27 | 2t on 50k grn (Bl) | 175.00 | 55.00 |
| 375 | A27 | 3t on 50k grn (Bk) | 175.00 | 55.00 |

The 2t on 50k also exists with surcharge in rose, violet, black and magenta; the 3t on 50k in rose, violet and blue. Values about the same unused; about 50 percent higher used.

### No. 352 Overprinted in Violet

**1904**       **Perf. 12½**

| | | | | |
|---|---|---|---|---|
| 393 | A26 | 2c gray | 50.00 | 25.00 |
| a. | | Black overprint | 50.00 | 25.00 |
| b. | | Rose overprint | 50.00 | 25.00 |

This overprint also exists in blue, violet blue, maroon and gray, but these were not regularly issued.

**Stamps of 1903 Surcharged in Black:**

a            b

c

**1904**

| | | | | |
|---|---|---|---|---|
| 400 | A26(a) | 3c on 5c rose | 30.00 | .75 |
| 401 | A26(b) | 6c on 10c brown | 30.00 | .75 |
| 402 | A27(c) | 9c on 1k violet | 50.00 | 3.50 |
| | | Nos. 400-402 (3) | 110.00 | 5.00 |

**Stamps of 1903 Surcharged in Black, Magenta or Violet:**

**1905-06**

| | | | | |
|---|---|---|---|---|
| 404 | A26 | 1c on 3c green ('06) | 35.00 | 15.00 |
| 405 | A27 | 1c on 1k violet | 35.00 | 15.00 |
| 406 | A27 | 2c on 5k orange brn | 40.00 | 25.00 |
| 407 | A26 | 1c on 3c grn (M) ('06) | 15.00 | 5.00 |
| 408 | A27 | 1c on 1k violet (M) | 20.00 | 10.00 |
| 409 | A27 | 2c on 5k org brn (V) | 30.00 | 15.00 |
| | | Nos. 404-409 (6) | 175.00 | 85.00 |

### Nos. 355 and 358 Surcharged in Violet

**1906**

| | | | | |
|---|---|---|---|---|
| 419 | A26 | 1c on 10c brown | *150.00* | 300.00 |
| 420 | A27 | 2c on 2k ultra | *250.00* | 500.00 |

Forgeries of Nos. 419-420 are common. Forgeries of No. 420, especially, are hard to distinguish since the original handstamp was used. Genuine used stamps may, in some cases, be identified by the cancellation.

A28

## Typeset; "Provisoire" Overprint Handstamped in Black

**1906** — **Imperf.**

| | | | | |
|---|---|---|---|---|
| 422 | A28 | 1c violet | 10.00 | 1.00 |
| a. | | Irregular pin perf. or perf. 10½ | 40.00 | 15.00 |
| 423 | A28 | 2c gray | 15.00 | 5.00 |
| 424 | A28 | 3c green | 10.00 | 1.00 |
| 425 | A28 | 6c red | 10.00 | .75 |
| 426 | A28 | 10c brown | 60.00 | 75.00 |
| 427 | A28 | 13c blue | 40.00 | 10.00 |
| | | Nos. 422-427 (6) | 145.00 | 92.75 |

Stamps of type A28 have a faint background pattern of tiny squares within squares, an ornamental frame and open rectangles for the value corners.

The 3c and 6c also exist perforated.

Nos. 422-427 are known without overprint but were probably not issued in that condition. Nearly all values are known with overprint inverted and double.

Forgeries are plentiful.

### Lion Type of 1903 and

| Mohammad-Ali Shah Qajar | |
|---|---|
| A29 | A30 |

**1907-09** — **Typo.** — **Perf. 12½**

| | | | | |
|---|---|---|---|---|
| 428 | A26 | 1c vio, *blue* | 5.00 | .25 |
| 429 | A26 | 2c gray, *blue* | 5.00 | .25 |
| 430 | A26 | 3c green, *blue* | 5.00 | .25 |
| 431 | A26 | 6c rose, *blue* | 5.00 | .25 |
| 432 | A26 | 9c org, *blue* | 5.00 | .30 |
| 433 | A26 | 10c brown, *blue* | 6.00 | 1.00 |

**Engr.** — **Perf. 11, 11½**

| | | | | |
|---|---|---|---|---|
| 434 | A29 | 13c dark blue | 5.00 | 2.00 |
| 435 | A29 | 1k red | 7.00 | 1.50 |
| 436 | A29 | 26c red brown | 7.00 | 2.00 |
| 437 | A29 | 2k deep grn | 20.00 | 1.50 |
| 438 | A29 | 3k pale blu | 20.00 | 1.00 |
| 439 | A29 | 4k brt yellow | 350.00 | 10.00 |
| 440 | A29 | 4k bister | 20.00 | 3.00 |
| 441 | A29 | 5k dark brown | 20.00 | 3.00 |
| 442 | A29 | 10k pink | 25.00 | 3.00 |
| 443 | A29 | 20k gray black | 25.00 | 10.00 |
| 444 | A29 | 30k dark violet | 25.00 | 15.00 |
| 445 | A30 | 50k gold, ver & black ('09) | 100.00 | 25.00 |
| | | Nos. 428-445 (18) | 655.00 | 79.30 |

Frame of No. 445 lithographed. Nos. 434-444 were issued in 1908.

Remainders canceled to order abound. Used values for Nos. 437-445 are for c-t-os.

### Nos. 428-429 Overprinted in Black

**1909** — **Perf. 12½**

| | | | | |
|---|---|---|---|---|
| 446 | A26 | 1c violet, *blue* | 60.00 | 30.00 |
| 447 | A26 | 2c gray, *blue* | 60.00 | 30.00 |

Counterfeits of Nos. 446-447 exist.

### Coat of Arms — A31

**1909** — **Typo.** — **Perf. 12½x12**

| | | | | |
|---|---|---|---|---|
| 448 | A31 | 1c org & maroon | .50 | .35 |
| 449 | A31 | 2c vio & maroon | .50 | .35 |
| 450 | A31 | 3c yel grn & mar | .50 | .35 |
| 451 | A31 | 6c red & maroon | .50 | .35 |
| 452 | A31 | 9c gray & maroon | .50 | .35 |
| 453 | A31 | 10c red vio & mar | .50 | .35 |
| 454 | A31 | 13c dk blue & mar | .50 | 2.00 |
| 455 | A31 | 1k sil, vio & bis brown | 1.00 | 2.00 |
| 456 | A31 | 26c dk grn & mar | 1.00 | 3.00 |
| 457 | A31 | 2k sil, dk grn & bis brown | 1.00 | 2.00 |
| 458 | A31 | 3k sil, gray & bis brown | 1.00 | 3.50 |

---

| | | | | |
|---|---|---|---|---|
| 459 | A31 | 4k sil, by & bis brn | 1.00 | 3.50 |
| 460 | A31 | 5k gold, brn & bis brown | 2.50 | 3.50 |
| 461 | A31 | 10k gold, org & bis brown | 5.00 | 10.00 |
| 462 | A31 | 20k gold, ol grn & bister brn | 7.00 | 20.00 |
| 463 | A31 | 30k gold, car & bis brown | 12.00 | 20.00 |
| | | Nos. 448-463 (16) | 35.00 | 71.60 |

Unauthorized reprints of Nos. 448-463 abound. Originals have clean, bright colors, centers stand out clearly, and paper is much thinner. Nos. 460-463 originals have gleaming gold margins; reprint margins appear as blackish yellow. Centers of reprints of Nos. 448-454, 456 are brown.

Values above are for unused reprints and for authenticated used stamps. Original unused stamps sell for much higher prices.

For surcharges & overprints see #516-519, 541-549. 582-585, 588-594, 597, 601-606, 707-722, C1-C16, O31-O40.

### Nos. 428-444, Imperf., Surcharged in Red or Black:

**1910** — **Blue Paper** — **Imperf.**

| | | | | |
|---|---|---|---|---|
| 464 | A26 | 1c on 1c violet | 175.00 | 125.00 |
| 465 | A26 | 1c on 2c gray | 175.00 | 125.00 |
| 466 | A26 | 1c on 3c green | 175.00 | 125.00 |
| 467 | A26 | 1c on 6c rose (Bk) | 175.00 | 125.00 |
| 468 | A26 | 1c on 9c orange | 175.00 | 125.00 |
| 469 | A26 | 1c on 10c brown | 175.00 | 125.00 |

**White Paper**

| | | | | |
|---|---|---|---|---|
| 470 | A29 | 2c on 13c dp bl | 175.00 | 125.00 |
| 471 | A29 | 2c on 26c red brown (Bk) | 175.00 | 125.00 |
| 472 | A29 | 2c on 1k red (Bk) | 175.00 | 125.00 |
| 473 | A29 | 2c on 2k dp grn | 175.00 | 125.00 |
| 474 | A29 | 2c on 3k pale bl | 175.00 | 125.00 |
| 475 | A29 | 2c on 4k brt yel | 175.00 | 125.00 |
| 476 | A29 | 2c on 4k bister | 175.00 | 125.00 |
| 477 | A29 | 2c on 5k dk brn | 175.00 | 125.00 |
| 478 | A29 | 2c on 10k pink (Bk) | 175.00 | 125.00 |
| 479 | A29 | 2c on 20k gray blk | 175.00 | 125.00 |
| 480 | A29 | 2c on 30k dk vio | 175.00 | 125.00 |
| | | Nos. 464-480 (17) | 2,975. | 2,125. |

Nos. 464-480 were prepared for use on newspapers, but nearly the entire printing was sold to stamp dealers. The issue is generally considered speculative. Counterfeit surcharges exist on trimmed stamps.

Used values are for c-t-o.

### Ahmad Shah Qajar — A32

**Perf. 11½, 11½x11, 11½x12**

**Engr. center, Typo. frame**

**1911-13**

| | | | | |
|---|---|---|---|---|
| 481 | A32 | 1c green & org | .50 | .20 |
| 482 | A32 | 2c red & sepia | .50 | .20 |
| 483 | A32 | 3c gray brn & grn | .50 | .20 |
| a. | | 3c bister brown & green | .50 | 1.00 |
| 484 | A32 | 5c brn & car ('13) | .50 | .75 |
| 485 | A32 | 6c gray & car | .50 | .20 |
| 486 | A32 | 6c grn & red brown ('13) | .50 | .20 |
| 487 | A32 | 9c yel brn & vio | .75 | .20 |
| 488 | A32 | 10c red & org brn | .75 | .20 |
| 489 | A32 | 12c grn & ultra ('13) | .50 | .50 |
| 490 | A32 | 13c violet & ultra | 1.00 | 2.00 |
| 491 | A32 | 1k ultra & car | 1.00 | .50 |
| 492 | A32 | 24c vio & grn ('13) | 1.00 | 1.00 |
| 493 | A32 | 26c ultra & green | 1.00 | 5.00 |
| 494 | A32 | 2k grn & red vio | 2.00 | 1.00 |
| 495 | A32 | 3k violet & blk | 2.00 | 1.50 |
| 496 | A32 | 4k ultramarine & gray ('13) | 2.00 | 20.00 |
| 497 | A32 | 5k red & ultra | 3.00 | 3.00 |
| 498 | A32 | 10k ol bis & cl | 5.00 | 3.00 |
| 499 | A32 | 20k vio brn & bis | 6.00 | 4.00 |
| 500 | A32 | 30k red & green | 7.00 | 5.00 |
| | | Nos. 481-500 (20) | 36.00 | 47.65 |

Values for Nos. 481-500 unused are for reprints, which cannot be distinguished from

---

the late printings of the stamps. These are perf 11½ (11½x12 for the 4k) with the distance between the inner lines of the inscription tablets at top and bottom of the portrait being 19mm. Unused stamps with other perfs or a shorter vignette sell for much higher prices.

The reprints include inverted centers for some denominations.

For surcharges and overprints see Nos. 501-515, 520-540, 586-587, 595, 598, 600, 607-609, 630-634, 646-666.

### Stamps of 1911 Overprinted in Black

**1911**

| | | | | |
|---|---|---|---|---|
| 501 | A32 | 1c grn & orange | 35.00 | 5.00 |
| 502 | A32 | 2c red & sepia | 35.00 | 5.00 |
| 503 | A32 | 3c gray brn & grn | 35.00 | 5.00 |
| 504 | A32 | 6c gray & carmine | 35.00 | 5.00 |
| 505 | A32 | 9c yel brn & vio | 35.00 | 5.00 |
| 506 | A32 | 10c red & org brn | 60.00 | 5.00 |
| 507 | A32 | 13c vio & ultra | 85.00 | 7.00 |
| 508 | A32 | 1k ultra & car | 120.00 | 10.00 |
| 509 | A32 | 26c ultra & green | 120.00 | 12.00 |
| 510 | A32 | 2k grn & red vio | 150.00 | 15.00 |
| 511 | A32 | 3k vio & black | 200.00 | 15.00 |
| 512 | A32 | 5k red & ultra | 225.00 | 20.00 |
| 513 | A32 | 10k ol bis & claret | 850.00 | 40.00 |
| 514 | A32 | 20k vio brn & bis | 750.00 | 50.00 |
| 515 | A32 | 30k red & green | 750.00 | 50.00 |
| | | Nos. 501-515 (15) | 3,485. | 249.00 |

The "Officiel" overprint does not signify that the stamps were intended for use on official correspondence but that they were issued by authority. It was applied to the stocks in Tabriz and all post offices in the Tabriz region after a large quantity of stamps had been stolen during the Russian occupation of Tabriz.

The "Officiel" overprint has been counterfeited.

### Stamps of 1909-11 Overprinted in Black

### On #449-451, 454

**1911, Oct.**

| | | | | |
|---|---|---|---|---|
| 516 | A31 | 2c vio & maroon | 200.00 | 100.00 |
| 517 | A31 | 3c yel grn & mar | 200.00 | 100.00 |
| 518 | A31 | 6c red & maroon | 200.00 | 100.00 |
| 519 | A31 | 13c dk blue & mar | 200.00 | 100.00 |

### On #482-483, 485, 490

| | | | | |
|---|---|---|---|---|
| 520 | A32 | 2c red & sepia | 300.00 | 150.00 |
| 521 | A32 | 3c gray brn & grn | 300.00 | 150.00 |
| 522 | A32 | 6c gray & car | 300.00 | 150.00 |
| 523 | A32 | 13c violet & ultra | 300.00 | 150.00 |

Stamps were sold at a 10% discount to stagecoach station keepers on the Tehran-Recht route. To prevent speculation, these stamps were overprinted "Stagecoach Stations" in French and Farsi.

Forgeries exist, usually overprinted on reprints of the 1909 issue and used examples of the 1911 issue. Values are for authenticated stamps.

---

In 1912 this overprint, reading "Sultan Mohammad Ali Shah Kajar," was handstamped on outgoing mail in the Persian Kurdistan region occupied by the forces of the former Shah Mohammad Ali. It was applied after the stamps were on cover and is found on 8 of the Shah Ahmed stamps of 1911 (1c, 2c, 3c, 6c, 9c, 13c, 1k and 26c). Some specialists add the 10c. Forgeries are abundant.

### Nos. 490 and 493 Surcharged:

| a | b |
|---|---|

**1914**

| | | | | |
|---|---|---|---|---|
| 535 | A32(a) | 1c on 13c | 17.50 | 2.00 |
| 536 | A32(b) | 3c on 26c | 17.50 | 4.00 |

In 1914 a set of 19 stamps was prepared as a coronation issue. The 10 lower values each carry a different portrait; the 9 higher values show buildings and scenes. The same set printed with black centers was overprinted in red "SERVICE." The stamps were never placed in use, but were sold to stamp dealers in 1923.

### Nos. 484 and 489 Surcharged in Black or Violet:

| c | d |
|---|---|

**1915**

| | | | | |
|---|---|---|---|---|
| 537 | A32(c) | 1c on 5c | 15.00 | 2.00 |
| 538 | A32(c) | 2c on 5c (V) | 15.00 | 2.00 |
| 539 | A32(c) | 2c on 5c | 125.00 | 40.00 |
| 540 | A32(d) | 6c on 12c | 20.00 | 2.00 |
| | | Nos. 537-540 (4) | 175.00 | 46.00 |

### Nos. 455, 454 Surcharged:

| e | f |
|---|---|

**1915** — **Perf. 12½x12**

| | | | | |
|---|---|---|---|---|
| 541 | A31(e) | 5c on 1k multi | 27.50 | 5.00 |
| 542 | A31(f) | 12c on 13c multi | 32.50 | 7.00 |

Counterfeit surcharges on reprints abound.

### Nos. 448-453, 455 Overprinted

**1915**

| | | | | |
|---|---|---|---|---|
| 543 | A31 | 1c org & maroon | 15.00 | 2.00 |
| 544 | A31 | 2c vio & maroon | 15.00 | 2.00 |
| 545 | A31 | 3c grn & maroon | 15.00 | 2.00 |
| 546 | A31 | 6c red & maroon | 15.00 | 2.00 |
| 547 | A31 | 9c gray & maroon | 15.00 | 3.00 |
| 548 | A31 | 10c red vio & mar | 50.00 | 5.00 |
| 549 | A31 | 1k sil, vio & bis brn | 75.00 | 5.00 |
| | | Nos. 543-549 (7) | 200.00 | 21.00 |

This overprint ("1333") also exists on the 2k, 10k, 20k and 30k, but they were not issued.

Counterfeit overprints, usually on reprints, abound.

Beware of forgeries and/or reprints of most Iran stamps between the years 1870-1925. Scott values are for genuine stamps. Collectors should be aware that forgeries of many issues outnumber genuine examples by factors of 10 or 20 to one. Failing specialized knowledge on the part of the collector, these stamps should be examined or authenticated by acknowledged experts before purchase.

Imperial Crown — A33

King Darius, Farohar overhead — A34

Ruins of Persepolis — A35

**Perf. 11½ or Compound 11x11½**
**Engr., Typo.**

| 1915, Mar. | | | Wmk. 161 | | |
|---|---|---|---|---|---|
| 560 | A33 | 1c car & indigo | | .20 | 2.00 |
| 561 | A33 | 2c bl & carmine | | .20 | 2.00 |
| 562 | A33 | 3c dark green | | .20 | 2.00 |
| a. | | Inverted center | | | |
| 564 | A33 | 5c red | | .20 | 2.50 |
| 565 | A33 | 6c olive grn & car | | .20 | 2.00 |
| a. | | Inverted center | | | — |
| 566 | A33 | 9c yel brn & vio | | .20 | 2.00 |
| 567 | A33 | 10c bl grn & yel brn | | .20 | 2.00 |
| 568 | A33 | 12c ultramarine | | .20 | 2.00 |
| 569 | A34 | 1k sil, yel brn & gray | | .65 | 5.00 |
| 570 | A33 | 24c yel brn & dk brn | | .25 | 5.00 |
| 571 | A34 | 2k silver, bl & rose | | .65 | 5.00 |
| 572 | A34 | 3k sil, vio & brn | | .65 | 5.00 |
| 573 | A34 | 5k sil, brn & green | | .65 | 7.00 |
| 574 | A35 | 1t gold, pur & blk | | .65 | 10.00 |
| 575 | A35 | 2t gold, grn & brn | | 1.00 | 10.00 |
| 576 | A35 | 3t gold, cl & red brn | | 1.00 | 10.00 |
| 577 | A35 | 5t gold, blue & ind | | 1.00 | 10.00 |
| | | Nos. 560-577 (17) | | 8.10 | 83.50 |

Coronation of Shah Ahmed.

Nos. 560-568, 570 are engraved. Nos. 569, 571-573 are engraved except for silver margins. Nos. 574-577 have centers engraved, frames typographed.

The 3c and 6c with inverted centers are considered genuine errors. Unauthorized reprints exist of these varieties and of other denominations with inverted centers. **Values unused for Nos. 560-577 are for reprints.**

For surcharges and overprints see Nos. 610-616, 635-646, O41-O57, Q19-Q35.

Nos. 455, 461-463 Overprinted

| 1915 | | Unwmk. Typo. | Perf. 12½x12 | |
|---|---|---|---|---|
| 582 | A31 | 1k sil, vio & bis brn | 2.00 | 20.00 |
| 583 | A31 | 10k multicolored | 5.00 | 30.00 |
| 584 | A31 | 20k multicolored | 7.00 | 100.00 |
| 585 | A31 | 30k multicolored | 12.00 | 60.00 |
| | | Nos. 582-585 (4) | 26.00 | 210.00 |

Genuine unused examples are rare. Most unused stamps offered in the marketplace are reprints, and the unused values above are for reprints. Used values for for authenticated stamps.

Forgeries abound of Nos. 582-585.

No. 491 Surcharged

| 1917 | | | Perf. 11½ | |
|---|---|---|---|---|
| 586 | A32 | 12c on 1k multi | 2,250. | 2,500. |
| 587 | A32 | 24c on 1k multi | 1,200. | 1,500. |

Issued during the Turkish occupation of Kermanshah. Forgeries exist.

Values for unused stamps are for reprints. Unused examples of the original stamps are rare, and most stamps offered in the marketplace are reprints.

No. 448 Overprinted "1335" in Persian Numerals

| 1917 | | | Perf. 12½x12 | |
|---|---|---|---|---|
| 588 | A31 | 1c org & maroon | 350.00 | 250.00 |

Overprint on No. 588 is similar to date in "k" and "l" surcharges. Forgeries exist.

Nos. 449, 452-453, 456 Surcharged:

k        l

| 1917 | | | | |
|---|---|---|---|---|
| 589 | A31(k) | 1c on 2c | 20.00 | 3.00 |
| 590 | A31(k) | 1c on 9c | 25.00 | 4.00 |
| 591 | A31(k) | 1c on 10c | 20.00 | 3.00 |
| 592 | A31(l) | 3c on 9c | 25.00 | 4.00 |
| 593 | A31(l) | 3c on 10c | 20.00 | 3.00 |
| 594 | A31(l) | 3c on 26c | 30.00 | 5.00 |

**Same Surcharge on No. 488**

| 595 | A32(k) | 1c on 10c | 37.50 | 1.50 |
|---|---|---|---|---|
| 596 | A32(l) | 3c on 10c | 37.50 | 1.50 |

**Nos. 454 & 491 Surcharged Type "e"**

| 597 | A31 | 5c on 13c | 25.00 | 5.00 |
|---|---|---|---|---|
| 598 | A32 | 5c on 1k | 20.00 | 2.00 |

Counterfeit surcharges on "canceled" reprints of Nos. 449, 452-454, 456 abound.

No. 489 Surcharged

| 600 | A32 | 6c on 12c grn & ultra | 65.00 | 15.00 |
|---|---|---|---|---|

No. 457 Overprinted

| 1918 | | | | |
|---|---|---|---|---|
| 601 | A31 | 2k multi | 55.00 | 10.00 |

Nos. 459-460 Surcharged:

| 1918 | | | | |
|---|---|---|---|---|
| 602 | A31 | 24c on 4k multi | 62.50 | 10.00 |
| 603 | A31 | 10k on 5k multi | 100.00 | 15.00 |

The surcharges of Nos. 602-603 have been counterfeited.

Nos. 457-463 Overprinted

| 1918 | | | | |
|---|---|---|---|---|
| 603A | A31 | 2k multicolored | 3.00 | 65.00 |
| 604 | A31 | 3k multicolored | 3.00 | 15.00 |
| 604A | A31 | 4k multicolored | 5.00 | 150.00 |
| 604B | A31 | 5k multicolored | 5.00 | 75.00 |
| 605 | A31 | 10k multicolored | 8.00 | 50.00 |
| 605A | A31 | 20k multicolored | 20.00 | 200.00 |
| 606 | A31 | 30k multicolored | 15.00 | 100.00 |
| | | Nos. 603A-606 (7) | 59.00 | 655.00 |

Genuine unused examples are rare. Most unused stamps offered in the marketplace are reprints, and the unused values above are for reprints. Used values for for authenticated stamps.

Forgeries abound of Nos. 603A-606.

Nos. 489, 488 and 491 Surcharged:

m        n

| 607 | A32(m) | 3c on 12c | 50.00 | 1.50 |
|---|---|---|---|---|
| 608 | A32(n) | 6c on 10c | 35.00 | 1.50 |
| 609 | A32(m) | 6c on 1k | 35.00 | 1.50 |
| | | Nos. 607-609 (3) | 120.00 | 4.50 |

Genuine unused examples are rare. Most unused stamps offered in the marketplace are reprints, and the unused values above are for reprints.

Nos. 571-577 Overprinted in Black or Red

| 1918 | | | Wmk. 161 | |
|---|---|---|---|---|
| 610 | A34 | 2k sil, blue & rose | 10.00 | 10.00 |
| 611 | A34 | 3k sil, vio & brn (R) | 10.00 | 10.00 |
| 612 | A34 | 5k sil, brn & grn (R) | 10.00 | 10.00 |
| 613 | A35 | 1t gold, pur & black (R) | 15.00 | 15.00 |
| 614 | A35 | 2t gold, grn & brn | 15.00 | 15.00 |
| 615 | A35 | 3t gold, cl & red brn | 15.00 | 15.00 |
| 616 | A35 | 5t gold, bl & ind (R) | 15.00 | 20.00 |
| | | Nos. 610-616 (7) | 90.00 | 95.00 |

The overprint commemorates the end of World War I. Counterfeits of this overprint are plentiful.

A36

**Color Litho., Black Typo.**

| 1919 | | Unwmk. | Perf. 11½ | |
|---|---|---|---|---|
| 617 | A36 | 1c yel & black | 20.00 | 1.00 |
| 618 | A36 | 3c green & black | 20.00 | 1.00 |
| 619 | A36 | 5c rose & black | 45.00 | 3.00 |
| 620 | A36 | 6c vio & black | 35.00 | 1.00 |
| 621 | A36 | 12c blue & black | 100.00 | 10.00 |
| | | Nos. 617-621 (5) | 220.00 | 16.00 |

Nos. 617-621 exist imperf., in colors other than the originals, with centers inverted and double impressions. Some specialists call them fraudulent, others call them reprints.

This issue has been extensively counterfeited, and most examples in the marketplace are forgeries.

Counterfeits having double line over "POSTES" abound.

Nos. 75, 85-86 Surcharged in Various Colors

| 1919 | | | Perf. 10½, 11, 11½, 13½ | |
|---|---|---|---|---|
| 622 | A14 | 2k on 5c lilac (Bk) | 7.50 | 7.50 |
| 623 | A14 | 3k on 5c lilac (Br) | 7.50 | 7.50 |
| 624 | A14 | 4k on 5c lilac (G) | 7.50 | 7.50 |
| 625 | A14 | 5k on 5c lilac (V) | 7.50 | 7.50 |
| 626 | A16 | 10k on 10c rose (Bl) | 20.00 | 20.00 |
| 627 | A16 | 20k on 10c rose (G) | 20.00 | 20.00 |
| 628 | A16 | 30k on 10c rose (Br) | 20.00 | 20.00 |
| 629 | A16 | 50k on 14c org (V) | 20.00 | 20.00 |
| | | Nos. 622-629 (8) | 110.00 | 110.00 |

Nos. 622-629 exist with inverted and double surcharge. Some specialists consider these fraudulent.

Nos. 486, 489 Handstamp Surcharged

| 1921 | | | Perf. 11½, 11½x11 | |
|---|---|---|---|---|
| 630 | A32 | 10c on 6c | 75.00 | 15.00 |
| 631 | A32 | 1k on 12c | 75.00 | 15.00 |

Counterfeits exist.

No. 489 Surcharged

| 632 | A32 | 6c on 12c | 250.00 | 15.00 |
|---|---|---|---|---|

Nos. 486, 489 Surcharged in Violet:

| 1921 | | | | |
|---|---|---|---|---|
| 633 | A32 | 10c on 6c | 120.00 | 40.00 |
| a. | | Surcharge handstamped in black | 350.00 | 350.00 |
| 634 | A32 | 1k on 12c | 120.00 | 40.00 |
| a. | | Surcharge handstamped in black | 350.00 | 350.00 |

Counterfeits exist.

Coronation Issue of 1915 Overprinted

| 1921, May | | Wmk. 161 | Perf. 11, 11½ | |
|---|---|---|---|---|
| 635 | A33 | 3c dark grn | 15.00 | |
| a. | | Center and overprint inverted | | |
| 636 | A33 | 5c red | 15.00 | |
| 637 | A33 | 6c olive grn & car | 15.00 | |
| 638 | A33 | 10c bl grn & yel brn | 15.00 | |
| 639 | A33 | 12c ultramarine | 15.00 | |
| 640 | A34 | 1k sil, yel brn & gray | 20.00 | |
| 641 | A34 | 2k sil, blue & rose | 20.00 | |
| 642 | A34 | 5k sil, brn & green | 20.00 | |
| 643 | A35 | 2t gold, grn & brn | 25.00 | |

| | | | | |
|---|---|---|---|---|
| 644 | A35 | 3t gold, cl & red | | |
| | | brn | 30.00 | |
| 645 | A35 | 5t gold, blue & ind | 30.00 | |
| | | *Nos. 635-645 (11)* | 220.00 | |

Counterfeits of this Feb. 21, 1921, overprint are plentiful. Inverted overprints exist on all values; some specialists consider them fraudulent.

Stamps of 1911-13
Overprinted

**1922**     **Unwmk.**     **Perf. 11½, 11½x11**

| | | | | |
|---|---|---|---|---|
| 646 | A32 | 1c grn & orange | 10.00 | .20 |
| a. | | Inverted overprint | | |
| 647 | A32 | 2c red & sepia | 10.00 | .20 |
| 648 | A32 | 3c gray brn & green | 15.00 | .20 |
| a. | | 3c bister brown & green | 10.00 | .20 |
| 649 | A32 | 5c brown & car | 85.00 | 25.00 |
| 650 | A32 | 6c grn & red brn | 10.00 | .20 |
| 651 | A32 | 9c yel brn & vio | 10.00 | .20 |
| 652 | A32 | 10c red & org brn | 10.00 | .20 |
| a. | | Double ovpt., one inverted | | |
| 653 | A32 | 12c green & ultra | 15.00 | .50 |
| 654 | A32 | 1k ultra & car | 20.00 | 1.00 |
| 655 | A32 | 24c vio & green | 20.00 | 1.00 |
| 656 | A32 | 2k grn & red vio | 60.00 | 1.00 |
| 657 | A32 | 3k vio & black | 60.00 | 1.50 |
| 658 | A32 | 4k ultra & gray | 150.00 | 20.00 |
| 659 | A32 | 5k red & ultra | 75.00 | 2.00 |
| 660 | A32 | 10k ol bis & cl | 400.00 | 5.00 |
| 661 | A32 | 20k vio brn & bis | 400.00 | 7.00 |
| 662 | A32 | 30k red & green | 500.00 | 10.00 |
| | | *Nos. 646-662 (17)* | 1,850. | 75.20 |

The status of inverted overprints on 5c and 12c is dubious. Unlisted inverts on other denominations are generally considered fraudulent. Counterfeits of this overprint exist.

Nos. 653, 655
Surcharged

**1922**

| | | | | |
|---|---|---|---|---|
| 663 | A32 | 3c on 12c | 75.00 | 1.00 |
| 664 | A32 | 6c on 24c | 110.00 | 2.00 |

Nos. 661-662 Surcharged:

**1923**

| | | | | |
|---|---|---|---|---|
| 665 | A32 | 10c on 20k | 120.00 | 10.00 |
| 666 | A32 | 1k on 30k | 145.00 | 15.00 |

Ahmed Shah
Qajar — A37

**Perf. 11½, 11x11½, 11½x11**

**1924-25**         **Engr.**

| | | | | |
|---|---|---|---|---|
| 667 | A37 | 1c magenta | 2.50 | .20 |
| 668 | A37 | 2c magenta | 2.50 | .20 |
| 669 | A37 | 3c orange brown | 2.50 | .20 |
| 670 | A37 | 6c black brown | 2.50 | .20 |
| 671 | A37 | 9c dark green | 5.00 | .75 |
| 672 | A37 | 10c dark violet | 2.00 | .30 |
| 673 | A37 | 12c red | 2.00 | .30 |
| 674 | A37 | 1k dark blue | 2.00 | .35 |
| 675 | A37 | 2k indigo & red | 5.00 | 1.00 |
| a. | | Center inverted | 10,000. | 3,000. |

| | | | | |
|---|---|---|---|---|
| 676 | A37 | 3k dk vio & red brown | 17.00 | 2.00 |
| 677 | A37 | 5k red & brown | 20.00 | 30.00 |
| 678 | A37 | 10k choc & lilac | 25.00 | 30.00 |
| 679 | A37 | 20k dk grn & brn | 30.00 | 30.00 |
| 680 | A37 | 30k org & blk brn | 40.00 | 40.00 |
| | | *Nos. 667-680 (14)* | 158.00 | 135.50 |

For overprints see Nos. 703-706.

A38

SIX CHAHIS

Type I            Type II

Dated 1924
Color Litho., Black Typo.

**1924**         **Perf. 11**

| | | | | |
|---|---|---|---|---|
| 681 | A38 | 1c yel brn & blk | 15.00 | 1.00 |
| 682 | A38 | 2c gray & blk | 15.00 | 1.00 |
| 683 | A38 | 3c dp rose & blk | 15.00 | 1.00 |
| 684 | A38 | 6c orange & blk (I) | 25.00 | 1.50 |
| a. | | 6c orange & blk (II) | 25.00 | 2.00 |
| | | *Nos. 681-684 (4)* | 70.00 | 4.50 |

The 1c was surcharged "Chahis" by error. Later the "s" was blocked out in black. Counterfeits having double line over "POSTES" are plentiful.

Dated 1925

**1925**

| | | | | |
|---|---|---|---|---|
| 686 | A38 | 2c yel grn & blk | 10.00 | 1.00 |
| 687 | A38 | 3c red & blk | 10.00 | 1.00 |
| 689 | A38 | 6c chalky bl & blk | 10.00 | 1.00 |
| 690 | A38 | 9c lt brn & blk | 30.00 | 2.00 |
| 691 | A38 | 10c gray & blk | 50.00 | 5.00 |
| 694 | A38 | 1k emer & blk | 65.00 | 10.00 |
| 695 | A38 | 2k lilac & blk | 150.00 | 40.00 |
| | | *Nos. 686-695 (7)* | 325.00 | 60.00 |

Counterfeits having double line over "POSTES" are plentiful.

A39

Gold Overprint on Treasury
Department Stamps

**1925**

| | | | | |
|---|---|---|---|---|
| 697 | A39 | 1c red | 7.00 | 4.00 |
| 698 | A39 | 2c yellow | 7.00 | 4.00 |
| 699 | A39 | 3c yellow green | 7.00 | 4.00 |
| 700 | A39 | 5c dark gray | 30.00 | 20.00 |
| 701 | A39 | 10c deep orange | 15.00 | 5.00 |
| 702 | A39 | 1k ultramarine | 15.00 | 10.00 |
| | | *Nos. 697-702 (6)* | 81.00 | 47.00 |

Deposition of Ahmad Shah Qajar and establishment of provisional government of Reza Shah Pahlavi.

#697-702 have same center (Persian lion in sunburst) with 6 different frames. Overprint reads: "Post / Provisional Government / of Pahlavi / 9th Abanmah / 1304 / 1925."

Nos. 667-670
Overprinted

**1926**        **Perf. 11½, 11x11½, 11½x11**

| | | | | |
|---|---|---|---|---|
| 703 | A37 | 1c orange | 3.00 | 1.50 |
| 704 | A37 | 2c magenta | 3.00 | 2.00 |
| 705 | A37 | 3c orange brown | 3.00 | 1.50 |
| 706 | A37 | 6c black brown | 75.00 | 75.00 |
| | | *Nos. 703-706 (4)* | 84.00 | 80.00 |

Overprinted to commemorate the Pahlavi dynasty, dated 16 December 1925. Counterfeits exist.

Nos. 448-463
Overprinted

**1926**        **Perf. 11½, 12½x12**

| | | | | |
|---|---|---|---|---|
| 707 | A31 | 1c org & maroon | 7.00 | .25 |
| a. | | Inverted overprint | 625.00 | |
| 708 | A31 | 2c vio & maroon | 7.00 | .25 |
| 709 | A31 | 3c yel grn & mar | 7.00 | .25 |
| a. | | Inverted overprint | 625.00 | |
| 710 | A31 | 6c red & maroon | 7.00 | .25 |
| 711 | A31 | 9c gray & maroon | 7.00 | .25 |
| 712 | A31 | 10c red vio & mar | 7.00 | .35 |
| 713 | A31 | 13c dk bl & mar | 15.00 | .35 |
| 714 | A31 | 1k multi | 30.00 | .35 |
| 715 | A31 | 26c dk grn & mar | 15.00 | .35 |
| 716 | A31 | 2k multi | 30.00 | .50 |
| 717 | A31 | 3k multi | 70.00 | .50 |
| 718 | A31 | 4k sil, bl & bis brn | 500.00 | 10.00 |
| 719 | A31 | 5k multi | 150.00 | 8.00 |
| 720 | A31 | 10k multi | 500.00 | 8.50 |
| 721 | A31 | 20k multi | 600.00 | 10.00 |
| 722 | A31 | 30k multi | 600.00 | 12.00 |
| | | *Nos. 707-722 (16)* | 2,552. | 52.15 |

Provisional issue, overprinted to denote Reign of the Pahlavi dynaty.

Values for Nos. 707-722 are for stamps perf. 11½, on thick paper. Stamps perf. 12½x12 on thin paper are worth substantially more.

Forgeries exist perf. 12½x12, with either machine overprints or handstamps. Most of these fakes can be identified by the absence of the top serif of the "1" in "1926."

Reza Shah Pahlavi
A40            A41

**1926-29**     **Typo.**     **Perf. 11**

| | | | | |
|---|---|---|---|---|
| 723 | A40 | 1c yellow green | 4.00 | .20 |
| 724 | A40 | 2c gray violet | 4.00 | .20 |
| 725 | A40 | 3c emerald | 4.00 | .20 |
| 727 | A40 | 6c magenta | 5.00 | .25 |
| 728 | A40 | 9c rose | 10.00 | .50 |
| 729 | A40 | 10c bister brown | 20.00 | 5.00 |
| 730 | A40 | 12c deep orange | 25.00 | 3.00 |
| 731 | A40 | 15c pale ultra | 30.00 | 2.00 |
| 733 | A41 | 1k dull bl ('27) | 50.00 | 10.00 |
| 734 | A41 | 2k brt vio ('29) | 150.00 | 50.00 |
| | | *Nos. 723-734 (10)* | 302.00 | 71.35 |

**1928**          **Redrawn**

| | | | | |
|---|---|---|---|---|
| 740 | A40 | 1c yellow green | 25.00 | .25 |
| 741 | A40 | 2c gray violet | 25.00 | .25 |
| 742 | A40 | 3c emerald | 25.00 | .25 |
| 743 | A40 | 6c rose | 25.00 | .50 |
| | | *Nos. 740-743 (4)* | 100.00 | 1.25 |

On the redrawn stamps much of the shading of the face, throat, collar, etc., has been removed.

The letters of "Postes Persanes" and those in the circle at upper right are smaller. The redrawn stamps measure 20¼x25¾mm instead of 19¾x25¼mm.

A42

Reza Shah
Pahlavi — A43

**Perf. 11½, 12, 12½, Compound**

**1929**           **Photo.**

| | | | | |
|---|---|---|---|---|
| 744 | A42 | 1c yel grn & cer | 2.00 | .25 |
| 745 | A42 | 2c scar & brt blue | 1.50 | .25 |
| 746 | A42 | 3c mag & myr grn | 1.50 | .25 |
| 747 | A42 | 6c yel brn & ol grn | 2.00 | .25 |
| 748 | A42 | 9c Prus bl & ver | 3.00 | .25 |
| 749 | A42 | 10c bl grn & choc | 4.00 | .25 |
| 750 | A42 | 12c gray blk & pur | 6.00 | .30 |
| 751 | A42 | 15c citron & ultra | 7.00 | .30 |
| 752 | A42 | 1k dull bl & blk | 10.00 | .30 |
| 753 | A42 | 24c ol grn & red brn | 7.00 | .50 |

**Engr.**

**Perf. 11½**

| | | | | |
|---|---|---|---|---|
| 754 | A42 | 2k brn org & dk vio | 100.00 | 1.50 |
| 755 | A42 | 3k dark grn & dp rose | 150.00 | 2.00 |
| 756 | A42 | 5k red brn & dp green | 50.00 | 2.00 |
| 757 | A42 | 1t ultra & dp rose | 50.00 | 5.00 |
| 758 | A42 | 2t carmine & blk | 75.00 | 15.00 |

**Engr. and Typo.**

| | | | | |
|---|---|---|---|---|
| 759 | A43 | 3t gold & dp vio | 150.00 | 25.00 |
| | | *Nos. 744-759 (16)* | 619.00 | 53.60 |

For overprints see Nos. 810-817.

Reza Shah
Pahlavi — A44

**1931-32**     **Litho.**     **Perf. 11**

| | | | | |
|---|---|---|---|---|
| 760 | A44 | 1c ol brn & ultra | 3.00 | .20 |
| 761 | A44 | 2c red brn & blk | 3.00 | .20 |
| 762 | A44 | 3c lilac rose & ol | 3.00 | .20 |
| 763 | A44 | 6c red org & vio | 3.00 | .20 |
| 764 | A44 | 9c ultra & red org | 10.00 | .40 |
| 765 | A44 | 10c ver & gray | 20.00 | 1.00 |
| 766 | A44 | 11c bl & dull red | 30.00 | 20.00 |
| 767 | A44 | 12c turq blue & lil rose | 40.00 | .70 |
| 768 | A44 | 16c black & red | 40.00 | 1.75 |
| 769 | A44 | 1k car & turq bl | 80.00 | 1.75 |
| 770 | A44 | 27c dk gray & dl bl | 70.00 | 1.75 |
| | | *Nos. 760-770 (11)* | 302.00 | 28.15 |

For overprints see Nos. 818-826.

A45            Reza Shah
Pahlavi — A46

**1933-34**

| | | | | |
|---|---|---|---|---|
| 771 | A45 | 5d olive brown | 1.50 | .25 |
| 772 | A45 | 10d blue | 1.50 | .25 |
| 773 | A45 | 15d gray | 1.50 | .25 |
| 774 | A45 | 30d emerald | 1.50 | .25 |
| 775 | A45 | 45d turq blue | 2.00 | .50 |
| 776 | A45 | 50d magenta | 3.00 | .50 |
| 777 | A45 | 60d green | 4.00 | .50 |
| 778 | A45 | 75d brown | 7.00 | 1.00 |
| 779 | A45 | 90d red | 8.00 | 1.50 |
| 780 | A46 | 1r dk rose & blk | 20.00 | 1.00 |
| 781 | A46 | 1.20r gray blk & rose | 25.00 | 1.00 |

| | | | | | |
|---|---|---|---|---|---|
| 782 | A46 | 1.50 citron & bl | | 30.00 | 1.00 |
| 783 | A46 | 2r lt bl & choc | | 40.00 | 1.00 |
| 784 | A46 | 3r mag & green | | 55.00 | 2.00 |
| 785 | A46 | 5r dk brn & red org | | 200.00 | 35.00 |
| | | *Nos. 771-785 (15)* | | 400.00 | 46.00 |

For overprints see Nos. 795-809.

"Justice" A47

"Education" A49

Ruins of Persepolis A48

Tehran Airport A50

Sanatorium at Sakhtessar — A51

Cement Factory, Chah-Abdul-Azim — A52

Gunboat "Palang" A53

Railway Bridge over Karun River A54

Post Office and Customs Building, Tehran A55

**1935, Feb. 21      Photo.      Perf. 12½**

| | | | | | |
|---|---|---|---|---|---|
| 786 | A47 | 5d red brn & grn | | 1.00 | .75 |
| 787 | A48 | 10d red org & gray black | | 1.00 | .75 |
| 788 | A49 | 15d mag & Prus bl | | 1.50 | .75 |
| 789 | A50 | 30d black & green | | 1.50 | .75 |
| 790 | A51 | 45d ol grn & red brn | | 2.00 | .75 |
| 791 | A52 | 75d grn & dark brn | | 6.00 | 1.25 |
| 792 | A53 | 90d blue & car rose | | 20.00 | 5.00 |
| 793 | A54 | 1r red brn & pur | | 60.00 | 20.00 |
| 794 | A55 | 1½r violet & ultra | | 25.00 | 10.00 |
| | | *Nos. 786-794 (9)* | | 118.00 | 40.00 |

Reign of Riza Shah Pahlavi, 10th anniv.

Stamps of 1933-34 Overprinted in Black

**1935                                    Perf. 11**

| | | | | | |
|---|---|---|---|---|---|
| 795 | A45 | 5d olive brown | | 1.50 | .50 |
| 796 | A45 | 10d blue | | 1.50 | .50 |
| 797 | A45 | 15d gray | | 2.00 | .50 |
| 798 | A45 | 30d emerald | | 2.00 | .50 |
| 799 | A45 | 45d turq blue | | 7.00 | 1.75 |
| 800 | A45 | 50d magenta | | 4.00 | .50 |
| 801 | A45 | 60d green | | 4.00 | .50 |
| 802 | A45 | 75d brown | | 7.50 | 5.00 |
| 803 | A45 | 90d red | | 25.00 | 25.00 |
| 804 | A46 | 1r dk rose & blk | | 75.00 | 100.00 |
| 805 | A46 | 1.20r gray black & rose | | 10.00 | 1.50 |
| 806 | A46 | 1.50r citron & bl | | 10.00 | 1.50 |
| 807 | A46 | 2r lt bl & choc | | 30.00 | 1.50 |
| 808 | A46 | 3r mag & green | | 50.00 | 7.00 |
| 809 | A46 | 5r dk brn & red org | | 250.00 | 250.00 |
| | | *Nos. 795-809 (15)* | | 479.50 | 396.25 |

Same Overprint on Stamps of 1929

**1935                          Perf. 12, 12x12½**

| | | | | | |
|---|---|---|---|---|---|
| 810 | A42 | 1c yel green & cer | | 425.00 | 600.00 |
| 811 | A42 | 2c scar & brt blue | | 275.00 | 400.00 |
| 812 | A42 | 3c mag & myr grn | | 175.00 | 200.00 |
| 813 | A42 | 6c yel brn & ol grn | | 140.00 | 150.00 |
| 814 | A42 | 9c Prus bl & ver | | 85.00 | 80.00 |

**Perf. 11½**

| | | | | | |
|---|---|---|---|---|---|
| 815 | A42 | 1t ultra & dp rose | | 42.50 | 30.00 |
| 816 | A42 | 2t carmine & blk | | 50.00 | 40.00 |
| 817 | A43 | 3t gold & dp vio | | 70.00 | 50.00 |
| | | *Nos. 810-817 (8)* | | 1,262. | 1,550. |

No. 817 is overprinted vertically.
Forged overprints exist.

Same Ovpt. on Stamps of 1931-32

**1935                                    Perf. 11**

| | | | | | |
|---|---|---|---|---|---|
| 818 | A44 | 1c ol brn & ultra | | 340.00 | 325.00 |
| 819 | A44 | 2c red brn & blk | | 125.00 | 125.00 |
| 820 | A44 | 3c lilac rose & ol | | 90.00 | 100.00 |
| 821 | A44 | 6c red org & vio | | 175.00 | 175.00 |
| 822 | A44 | 9c ultra & red org | | 200.00 | 225.00 |
| 823 | A44 | 11c blue & dull red | | 12.50 | 3.50 |
| 824 | A44 | 12c turq bl & lil rose | | 375.00 | 500.00 |
| 825 | A44 | 16c black & red | | 15.00 | 5.00 |
| 826 | A44 | 27c dk gray & dull bl | | 19.00 | 5.00 |
| | | *Nos. 818-826 (9)* | | 1,351. | 1,463. |

Forged overprints exist.

Reza Shah Pahlavi — A56

**1935          Photo.          Perf. 11**
**Size: 19x27mm**

| | | | | | |
|---|---|---|---|---|---|
| 827 | A56 | 5d violet | | 2.00 | .20 |
| 828 | A56 | 10d lilac rose | | 2.00 | .20 |
| 829 | A56 | 15d turquoise bl | | 2.00 | .20 |
| 830 | A56 | 30d emerald | | 2.00 | .20 |
| 831 | A56 | 45d orange | | 2.00 | .20 |
| 832 | A56 | 50d dull lt brn | | 2.75 | .20 |
| 833 | A56 | 60d ultramarine | | 10.00 | .65 |
| 834 | A56 | 75d red orange | | 10.00 | .75 |
| 835 | A56 | 90d rose | | 12.50 | .75 |

**Size: 21½x31mm**

| | | | | | |
|---|---|---|---|---|---|
| 836 | A56 | 1r dull lilac | | 25.00 | .50 |
| 837 | A56 | 1.50r blue | | 25.00 | 2.00 |
| 838 | A56 | 2r dk olive grn | | 40.00 | .75 |
| 839 | A56 | 3r dark brown | | 45.00 | 2.00 |
| 840 | A56 | 5r slate black | | 250.00 | 15.00 |
| | | *Nos. 827-840 (14)* | | 430.25 | 23.70 |

Reza Shah Pahlavi
A57          A58

**1936-37          Litho.          Perf. 11**
**Size: 20x27mm**

| | | | | | |
|---|---|---|---|---|---|
| 841 | A57 | 5d bright vio | | 2.00 | .20 |
| 842 | A57 | 10d magenta | | 2.00 | .20 |
| 843 | A57 | 15d bright ultra | | 2.00 | .20 |
| 844 | A57 | 30d yellow green | | 2.00 | .20 |
| 845 | A57 | 45d vermilion | | 3.00 | .20 |
| 846 | A57 | 50d black brn ('37) | | 3.00 | .20 |
| 847 | A57 | 60d brown orange | | 3.00 | .20 |
| 848 | A57 | 75d rose lake | | 3.00 | .25 |
| 849 | A57 | 90d rose red | | 5.00 | .35 |

**Size: 23x31mm**

| | | | | | |
|---|---|---|---|---|---|
| 850 | A57 | 1r turq green | | 15.00 | .25 |
| 851 | A57 | 1.50r deep blue | | 15.00 | .35 |
| 852 | A57 | 2r bright blue | | 20.00 | .35 |
| 853 | A57 | 3r violet brown | | 25.00 | .80 |
| 854 | A57 | 5r slate green | | 40.00 | 1.25 |
| 855 | A57 | 10r dark brown & ultra ('37) | | 200.00 | 20.00 |
| | | *Nos. 841-855 (15)* | | 340.00 | 25.00 |

**1938-39                                    Perf. 11**
**Size: 20x27mm**

| | | | | | |
|---|---|---|---|---|---|
| 856 | A58 | 5d light violet | | 2.00 | .20 |
| 857 | A58 | 10d magenta | | 2.00 | .20 |
| 858 | A58 | 15d violet blue | | 2.00 | .20 |
| 859 | A58 | 30d bright green | | 2.00 | .20 |
| 860 | A58 | 45d vermilion | | 3.00 | .20 |
| 861 | A58 | 50d black brown | | 3.00 | .20 |
| 862 | A58 | 60d brown orange | | 3.00 | .20 |
| 863 | A58 | 75d rose lake | | 3.00 | .20 |
| 864 | A58 | 90d rose red ('39) | | 5.00 | .25 |

**Size: 22½x30mm**

| | | | | | |
|---|---|---|---|---|---|
| 865 | A58 | 1r turq green | | 10.00 | .25 |
| 866 | A58 | 1.50r deep blue | | 15.00 | .30 |
| 867 | A58 | 2r lt blue ('39) | | 20.00 | .30 |
| 868 | A58 | 3r violet brown | | 30.00 | .70 |
| 869 | A58 | 5r gray grn ('39) | | 50.00 | 1.25 |
| 870 | A58 | 10r dark brown & ultra ('39) | | 150.00 | 7.50 |
| | | *Nos. 856-870 (15)* | | 300.00 | 12.15 |

Reza Shah Pahlavi — A58a

**1939, Mar. 15                          Perf. 13**

| | | | | | |
|---|---|---|---|---|---|
| 870A | A58a | 5d gray blue | | 2.00 | 2.00 |
| 870B | A58a | 10d brown | | 2.00 | 2.00 |
| 870C | A58a | 30d green | | 2.00 | 2.00 |
| 870D | A58a | 60d dark brown | | 2.00 | 2.00 |
| 870E | A58a | 90d red | | 4.00 | 4.00 |
| 870F | A58a | 1.50r blue | | 15.00 | 10.00 |
| 870G | A58a | 5r lilac | | 25.00 | 25.00 |
| 870H | A58a | 10r carmine | | 45.00 | 45.00 |
| | | *Nos. 870A-870H (8)* | | 97.00 | 92.00 |

60th birthday of Riza Shah Pahlavi. Printed in sheets of 4, perf. 13 and imperf. The imperf. sell for 50% more. The 1r violet and 2r orange were not available to the public. Value unused $15 each.

Crown Prince and Princess Fawziya A59

**1939, Apr. 25          Photo.          Perf. 11½**

| | | | | | |
|---|---|---|---|---|---|
| 871 | A59 | 5d red brown | | .50 | .30 |
| 872 | A59 | 10d bright violet | | .50 | .30 |
| 873 | A59 | 30d emerald | | 1.50 | .35 |
| 874 | A59 | 90d red | | 12.00 | .00 |
| 875 | A59 | 1.50r bright blue | | 20.00 | 4.00 |
| | | *Nos. 871-875 (5)* | | 34.50 | 6.95 |

Wedding of Crown Prince Mohammad Reza Pahlavi to Princess Fawziya of Egypt.

Bridge over Karun River A60

Veresk Bridge, North Iran — A61

Granary, Ahwaz A62

Train and Bridge A63

Museum, Side View
A64          A67

Ministry of Justice A65

School Building A66

Mohammad Reza Shah Pahlavi
A68          A69

**1942-46     Unwmk.     Litho.     Perf. 11**

| | | | | | |
|---|---|---|---|---|---|
| 876 | A60 | 5d violet | | 2.00 | .20 |
| 877 | A60 | 5d red org ('44) | | .75 | .20 |
| 878 | A61 | 10d magenta | | 2.00 | .20 |
| 879 | A61 | 10d pck grn ('44) | | .75 | .20 |
| 880 | A62 | 20d lt red violet | | 2.50 | .25 |
| 881 | A62 | 20d mag ('44) | | 1.00 | .20 |
| 882 | A63 | 25d rose carmine | | 25.00 | 5.00 |
| 883 | A63 | 25d violet ('44) | | 5.00 | .50 |
| 884 | A64 | 35d emerald | | 1.50 | .30 |
| 885 | A65 | 50d ultramarine | | 2.50 | .30 |
| 886 | A65 | 50d emerald ('44) | | 1.75 | .20 |
| 887 | A66 | 70d dull vio brn | | 1.50 | .35 |
| 888 | A67 | 75d rose lake | | 12.50 | .35 |
| 889 | A67 | 75d rose car ('46) | | 10.00 | .35 |
| 890 | A68 | 1r carmine | | 10.00 | .25 |
| 891 | A68 | 1r maroon ('45) | | 10.00 | .25 |
| 892 | A68 | 1.50r red | | 10.00 | .25 |
| 893 | A68 | 2r light blue | | 15.00 | .25 |
| 894 | A68 | 2r sage grn ('44) | | 12.00 | .30 |
| 895 | A68 | 2.50r dark blue | | 15.00 | .30 |
| 896 | A68 | 3r peacock grn | | 85.00 | 1.00 |
| 897 | A68 | 3r brt vio ('44) | | 35.00 | .35 |
| 898 | A68 | 5r sage green | | 200.00 | 10.00 |
| 899 | A68 | 5r lt blue ('44) | | 25.00 | .50 |

| | | | | |
|---|---|---|---|---|
| **900** | A69 | 10r brn org & blk | 50.00 | 3.00 |
| **901** | A69 | 10r dk org brn & black ('44) | 20.00 | 1.00 |
| **902** | A69 | 20r choc & vio | 650.00 | 50.00 |
| **903** | A69 | 20r orange & black ('44) | 120.00 | 4.00 |
| **904** | A69 | 30r gray blk & emerald | 1,200. | 50.00 |
| **905** | A69 | 30r emer & black ('44) | 45.00 | 5.00 |
| **906** | A69 | 50r dl bl & brn red | 150.00 | 25.00 |
| **907** | A69 | 50r brt vio & black ('45) | 50.00 | 10.00 |
| **908** | A69 | 100r rose red & blk ('45) | 400.00 | 50.00 |
| **909** | A69 | 200r bl & blk ('45) | 375.00 | 50.00 |
| | | *Nos. 876-909 (34)* | 3,545. | 270.05 |

Sixteen denominations of this issue were handstamped at Tabriz in 1945-46 in Persian characters: "Azerbaijan National Government, Dec. 12, 1945." A rebel group did this overprinting while the Russian army held that area.

Flag of Iran A70

Designs: 50d, Docks at Bandar Shapur. 1.50r, Motor convoy. 2.50r, Gorge and railway viaduct. 5r, Map and Mohammad Reza Shah Pahlavi.

Inscribed: "En souvenir des efforts de l'Iran pour la Victoire"

**Engr. & Litho.**

**1949, Apr. 28**       *Perf. 12½*

| | | | | |
|---|---|---|---|---|
| **910** | A70 | 25d multicolored | 4.00 | 2.00 |

**Engr.**

| | | | | |
|---|---|---|---|---|
| **911** | A70 | 50d purple | 4.00 | 2.00 |
| **912** | A70 | 1.50r carmine rose | 10.00 | 2.00 |
| **913** | A70 | 2.50r deep blue | 15.00 | 2.50 |
| **914** | A70 | 5r green | 40.00 | 3.00 |
| | | *Nos. 910-914 (5)* | 73.00 | 11.50 |

Iran's contribution toward the victory of the Allied Nations in World War II.

Bridge over Zaindeh River A71

National Bank A72

Former Ministry of P.T.T. — A73

Mohammad Reza Shah Pahlavi — A74

5d-20r, Various views and buildings.

**1949-50**    **Unwmk.**    **Litho.**    *Perf. 10½*

| | | | | |
|---|---|---|---|---|
| **915** | A71 | 5d rose & dk grn | .50 | .20 |
| **916** | A71 | 10d ultra & brown | .50 | .20 |
| **917** | A71 | 20d vio & ultra | .50 | .25 |
| **918** | A71 | 25d blk brn & dp blue | .60 | .20 |
| **919** | A71 | 50d grn & ultra | 1.00 | .20 |
| **920** | A71 | 75d dk brn & red | 2.00 | .25 |
| **921** | A72 | 1r vio & green | 2.00 | .20 |
| **922** | A72 | 1.50r dk grn & ver | 2.00 | .20 |
| **923** | A72 | 2r dp car & blk brn | 4.00 | .25 |
| **924** | A72 | 2.50r chlky bl & bl | 6.00 | .25 |
| **925** | A72 | 3r vio bl & red orange | 6.00 | .20 |
| **926** | A72 | 5r dp car & vio | 10.00 | .20 |
| **927** | A73 | 10r car & blue green ('50) | 35.00 | .50 |
| *a.* | | Inverted center | 2,750. | |
| **928** | A73 | 20r brown black & red ('50) | 350.00 | 20.00 |
| **929** | A74 | 30r choc & deep blue ('50) | 75.00 | 15.00 |
| **930** | A74 | 50r red & deep blue ('50) | 75.00 | 15.00 |
| | | *Nos. 915-930 (16)* | 570.10 | 53.10 |

Globes and Pigeons A75

Symbols of UPU — A76

**1950, Mar. 16**       **Photo.**

| | | | | |
|---|---|---|---|---|
| **931** | A75 | 50d brn carmine | 25.00 | 25.00 |
| **932** | A76 | 2.50r deep blue | 32.50 | 32.50 |

UPU, 75th anniv. (in 1949).

Riza Shah Pahlavi and his Tomb — A77

**1950, May 8**

| | | | | |
|---|---|---|---|---|
| **933** | A77 | 50d brown | 15.00 | 6.50 |
| **934** | A77 | 2r sepia | 25.00 | 10.00 |

Re-burial of Riza Shah Pahlavi, May 12, 1950.

Mohammad Reza Shah Pahlavi, 31st Birthday — A78

Various portraits.

**1950, Oct. 26**    **Engr.**    *Perf. 12½*
**Center in Black**

| | | | | |
|---|---|---|---|---|
| **935** | A78 | 25d carmine | 7.50 | 2.00 |
| **936** | A78 | 50d orange | 7.50 | 2.00 |
| **937** | A78 | 75d brown | 25.00 | 12.00 |
| **938** | A78 | 1r green | 20.00 | 10.00 |
| **939** | A78 | 2.50r deep blue | 20.00 | 10.00 |
| **940** | A78 | 5r brown lake | 35.00 | 10.00 |
| | | *Nos. 935-940 (6)* | 115.00 | 46.00 |

Shah and Queen Soraya A79

A80

**1951, Feb. 12**    **Litho.**    *Perf. 10½*

| | | | | |
|---|---|---|---|---|
| **941** | A79 | 5d rose violet | 2.00 | 1.00 |
| **942** | A79 | 25d orange red | 3.00 | 1.00 |
| **943** | A79 | 50d emerald | 5.00 | 2.00 |
| **944** | A80 | 1r brown | 9.00 | 2.00 |
| **945** | A80 | 1.50r carmine | 12.50 | 2.00 |
| **946** | A80 | 2.50r blue | 20.00 | 2.50 |
| | | *Nos. 941-946 (6)* | 51.50 | 10.50 |

Wedding of Mohammad Reza Shah Pahlavi to Soraya Esfandiari.

Farabi — A81

**1951, Feb. 20**

| | | | | |
|---|---|---|---|---|
| **947** | A81 | 50d red | 10.00 | 1.50 |
| **948** | A81 | 2.50r blue | 15.00 | 2.50 |

Death millenary of Farabi, Persian philosopher.

Mohammad Reza Shah Pahlavi
A82      A83

**1951-52**   **Unwmk.**   **Photo.**   *Perf. 10½*

| | | | | |
|---|---|---|---|---|
| **950** | A82 | 5d brown orange | .50 | .20 |
| **951** | A82 | 10d violet | .50 | .20 |
| **952** | A82 | 20d choc ('52) | 1.10 | .35 |
| **953** | A82 | 25d blue ('52) | .90 | .20 |
| **954** | A82 | 50d green | 1.50 | .20 |
| **955** | A82 | 75d rose | 1.50 | .30 |
| **956** | A83 | 1r gray green | 1.50 | .20 |
| **957** | A83 | 1.50r cerise | 1.50 | .45 |
| **958** | A83 | 2r chocolate | 5.00 | .20 |
| **959** | A83 | 2.50r deep blue | 5.00 | .25 |
| **960** | A83 | 3r red orange | 6.00 | .20 |
| **961** | A83 | 5r dark green | 12.00 | .20 |
| **962** | A83 | 10r olive ('52) | 35.00 | .50 |
| **963** | A83 | 20r org brn ('52) | 20.00 | 3.00 |
| **964** | A83 | 30r vio bl ('52) | 15.00 | 2.00 |
| **965** | A83 | 50r blk brn ('52) | 40.00 | 7.50 |
| | | *Nos. 950-965 (16)* | 147.00 | 15.95 |

See Nos. 975-977.

Oil Well and Mosque — A84

Oil Well, Mosque and Monument A85

**1953, Feb. 20**       **Litho.**

| | | | | |
|---|---|---|---|---|
| **966** | A84 | 50d green & yel | 2.00 | .50 |
| **967** | A85 | 1r lil rose & yel | 2.00 | .50 |
| **968** | A84 | 2.50r blue & yellow | 3.00 | 1.00 |
| **969** | A85 | 5r blk brn & yel | 6.00 | 2.50 |
| | | *Nos. 966-969 (4)* | 13.00 | 4.50 |

Discovery of oil at Qum.

Abadan Oil Refinery A86

Super Fractionators — A87

Designs: 1r, Storage tanks. 5r, Pipe lines. 10r, Abadan refinery.

**1953, Mar. 20**       **Photo.**

| | | | | |
|---|---|---|---|---|
| **970** | A86 | 50d blue green | 1.00 | .50 |
| **971** | A86 | 1r rose | 2.00 | .50 |
| **972** | A87 | 2.50r bright ultra | 6.00 | 1.50 |
| **973** | A86 | 5r red orange | 7.00 | 1.50 |
| **974** | A86 | 10r dark violet | 11.00 | 2.00 |
| | | *Nos. 970-974 (5)* | 27.00 | 6.00 |

Nationalization of oil industry, 2nd anniv.

**Shah Types of 1951-52**

**1953-54**    **Photo.**    *Perf. 10½*

| | | | | |
|---|---|---|---|---|
| **975** | A82 | 50d dark gray grn | 15.00 | .35 |
| **976** | A83 | 1r dk blue green | 1.50 | .20 |
| **977** | A83 | 1.50r cerise ('54) | 1.50 | .20 |
| | | *Nos. 975-977 (3)* | 18.00 | .75 |

The background has been highlighted on the 1r and 1.50r.

Gymnast — A88

Archery A89

Designs: 3r, Climbing Mt. Demavend. 5r, Ancient polo. 10r, Lion hunting.

**1953, Oct. 26**

| | | | | |
|---|---|---|---|---|
| **978** | A88 | 1r deep green | 3.00 | 1.50 |
| **979** | A89 | 2.50fr brt grnsh bl | 15.00 | 3.50 |
| **980** | A89 | 3r gray | 20.00 | 4.00 |
| **981** | A88 | 5r bister | 17.00 | 9.00 |
| **982** | A88 | 10r rose lilac | 50.00 | 12.00 |
| | | *Nos. 978-982 (5)* | 105.00 | 30.00 |

Mother with Children and UN Emblem A90

## 1953, Oct. 24
| | | | | |
|---|---|---|---|---|
| 983 | A90 | 1r bl grn & dk grn | 1.50 | .30 |
| 984 | A90 | 2.50r lt bl & indigo | 2.00 | .70 |

United Nations Day, Oct. 24.

Herring A91

Refrigeration Compressor — A92

Processing Equipment, National Fisheries — A93

Designs: 2.50r, Sardines. 10r, Sturgeon.

## 1954, Jan. 31
| | | | | |
|---|---|---|---|---|
| 985 | A91 | 1r multi | 4.00 | 1.00 |
| 986 | A91 | 2.50r multi | 30.00 | 5.00 |
| 987 | A92 | 3r vermilion | 12.00 | 5.00 |
| 988 | A93 | 5r deep bl grn | 14.00 | 8.00 |
| 989 | A91 | 10r multi | 40.00 | 15.00 |
| | | Nos. 985-989 (5) | 100.00 | 34.00 |

Nationalization of fishing industry.

Broken Shackles — A94

Mother Feeding Baby — A95

3r, Torch flag. 5r, Citizen holding flag of Iran.

## 1954, Aug. 19    Litho.
| | | | | |
|---|---|---|---|---|
| 990 | A94 | 2r multicolored | 5.00 | 1.00 |
| 991 | A94 | 3r multicolored | 8.00 | 2.00 |
| 992 | A94 | 5r multicolored | 12.00 | 3.00 |
| | | Nos. 990-992 (3) | 25.00 | 6.00 |

Return of the royalist government, 1st anniv.

## 1954, Oct. 24    Photo.
| | | | | |
|---|---|---|---|---|
| 993 | A95 | 2r red lil & org | 2.00 | .75 |
| 994 | A95 | 3r vio bl & org | 2.50 | 1.25 |

Issued to honor the United Nations.

Woodsman Felling Tree — A96

Designs: 2.50r, Laborer carrying firewood. 5r, Worker operating saw. 10r, Wooden galley.

## 1954, Dec. 11
| | | | | |
|---|---|---|---|---|
| 995 | A96 | 1r brn & grnsh black | 20.00 | 15.00 |
| 996 | A96 | 2.50r grnsh blk & bl | 25.00 | 20.00 |
| 997 | A96 | 5r lil & dk brn | 45.00 | 30.00 |
| 998 | A96 | 10r bl & claret | 60.00 | 40.00 |
| | | Nos. 995-998 (4) | 150.00 | 105.00 |

4th World Forestry Congress, Dehra Dun, India, 1954.

Mohammad Reza Shah Pahlavi
A97    A98

## 1954-55    Unwmk.
| | | | | |
|---|---|---|---|---|
| 999 | A97 | 5d yellow brn | .50 | .25 |
| 1000 | A97 | 10d violet | .50 | .25 |
| 1001 | A97 | 25d scarlet | .50 | .20 |
| 1002 | A97 | 50d black brn | .50 | .20 |
| 1003 | A98 | 1r blue green | .50 | .20 |
| 1004 | A98 | 1.50r cerise | .50 | .25 |
| 1005 | A98 | 2r ocher | 1.50 | .25 |
| 1006 | A98 | 2.50r blue | 1.75 | .20 |
| 1007 | A98 | 3r olive | 6.50 | .25 |
| 1008 | A98 | 5r dk sl grn | 6.50 | 1.50 |
| 1009 | A98 | 10r lilac rose | 20.00 | 1.50 |
| 1010 | A98 | 20r indigo | 30.00 | 6.00 |
| 1011 | A98 | 30r dp yel brn | 150.00 | 7.50 |
| 1012 | A98 | 50r dp orange | 30.00 | 5.00 |
| 1013 | A98 | 100r light vio | 375.00 | 50.00 |
| 1014 | A98 | 200r yellow | 125.00 | 20.00 |
| | | Nos. 999-1014 (16) | 749.25 | 93.55 |

See Nos. 1023-1036.

Regional Costume — A99

Regional Costumes: 1r, 2r, Men's costumes. 2.50r, 3r, 5r, Women's costumes.

## 1955, June 26    Photo.    Perf. 11
| | | | | |
|---|---|---|---|---|
| 1015 | A99 | 1r bluish gray & multi | 5.00 | 2.00 |
| 1016 | A99 | 2r dl rose & multi | 6.00 | 2.50 |
| 1017 | A99 | 2.50r buff & multi | 15.00 | 3.00 |
| 1018 | A99 | 3r rose lil & multi | 9.00 | 3.50 |
| 1019 | A99 | 5r gray brn & multi | 15.00 | 6.50 |
| | | Nos. 1015-1019 (5) | 50.00 | 17.50 |

Parliament Gate — A100

Designs: 3r, Statue of Liberty, vert. 5r, Old Gate of Parliament.

## 1955, Aug. 6    Wmk. 306    Perf. 11
| | | | | |
|---|---|---|---|---|
| 1020 | A100 | 2r red vio & grn | 3.00 | 1.00 |
| 1021 | A100 | 3r dk bl & aqua | 9.50 | 1.75 |
| 1022 | A100 | 5r Prus grn & red org | 7.50 | 4.25 |
| | | Nos. 1020-1022 (3) | 20.00 | 7.00 |

50th anniversary of constitution.

### Shah Types of 1954-55
## 1955-56    Wmk. 306    Perf. 11
| | | | | |
|---|---|---|---|---|
| 1023 | A97 | 5d violet ('56) | 3.00 | 1.50 |
| 1024 | A97 | 10d carmine ('56) | .50 | .20 |
| 1025 | A97 | 25d brown | .50 | .20 |
| 1026 | A97 | 50d dk carmine | .50 | .20 |
| 1027 | A98 | 1r dark bl grn | .50 | .20 |
| 1028 | A98 | 1.50r red brn ('56) | 35.00 | 3.00 |
| 1029 | A98 | 2r ol grn ('56) | 20.00 | .25 |
| 1030 | A98 | 2.50r blue ('56) | 2.50 | .30 |
| 1031 | A98 | 3r bister | 3.25 | .20 |
| 1032 | A98 | 5r red lilac | 5.00 | .20 |
| 1033 | A98 | 10r brt grnsh bl | 8.00 | .35 |
| 1034 | A98 | 20r slate green | 17.50 | 2.00 |

| | | | | |
|---|---|---|---|---|
| 1035 | A98 | 30r red org ('56) | 125.00 | 17.50 |
| 1036 | A98 | 50r red brn ('56) | 100.00 | 20.00 |
| | | Nos. 1023-1036 (14) | 321.25 | 46.10 |

UN Emblem and Globes A101

## 1955, Oct. 24    Perf. 11x12½
| | | | | |
|---|---|---|---|---|
| 1039 | A101 | 1r dp car & org | 1.25 | .50 |
| 1040 | A101 | 2.50r dk bl & grnsh blue | 1.75 | 1.25 |

UN, 10th anniv.Nations, Oct. 24, 1955.

Wrestlers A102

## 1955, Oct. 26    Wmk. 306    Perf. 11
| | | | | |
|---|---|---|---|---|
| 1041 | A102 | 2.50r multi | 10.00 | 4.00 |

Victory in intl. wrestling competitions.

Garden, Namazi Hospital A103    Immortal Guardsman A105

Nemazi Hospital, Shiraz A104

5r, Gate of the Koran. 10r, Ha'fez of Shiraz.

## 1956, Mar. 21    Perf. 11x12½
| | | | | |
|---|---|---|---|---|
| 1042 | A103 | 50d multi | 3.00 | .75 |
| 1043 | A104 | 1r multi | 4.00 | 1.00 |
| 1044 | A105 | 2.50r multi | 6.00 | 6.00 |
| 1045 | A104 | 5r multi | 11.00 | 4.00 |
| 1046 | A105 | 10r multi | 20.00 | 7.00 |
| | | Nos. 1042-1046 (5) | 44.00 | 18.75 |

Opening of Nemazi Hospital, Shiraz.

Arms of Iran and Olympic Rings — A106

Tomb at Maragheh A107

## 1956, May 15    Wmk. 306
| | | | | |
|---|---|---|---|---|
| 1047 | A106 | 5r rose lilac | 30.00 | 20.00 |

National Olympic Committee, 10th anniv.

## 1956, May 26   Photo.   Perf. 11x12½

2.50r, Astrolabe. 5r, Nasr-ud-Din of Tus.
| | | | | |
|---|---|---|---|---|
| 1048 | A107 | 1r orange | 3.50 | 1.00 |
| 1049 | A107 | 2.50r deep ultra | 6.00 | 1.50 |
| 1050 | A107 | 5r sepia & pur | 8.00 | 2.00 |
| | | Nos. 1048-1050 (3) | 17.50 | 4.50 |

700th death anniv. of Nasr-up-Din of Tus, mathematician and astronomer.

WHO Emblem — A108

### Perf. 11x12½
## 1956, Sept. 19    Wmk. 306
| | | | | |
|---|---|---|---|---|
| 1051 | A108 | 6r cerise | 3.00 | 1.00 |

6th Regional Congress of the WHO.

Scout Bugler and Camp A109

5r, Scout badge and Shah in scout uniform.

## 1956, Aug. 5    Perf. 12½x11
| | | | | |
|---|---|---|---|---|
| 1052 | A109 | 2.50r ultra & blue | 10.50 | 5.00 |
| 1053 | A109 | 5r lil & red lil | 14.00 | 7.50 |

National Boy Scout Jamboree.

> Catalogue values for unused stamps in this section, from this point to the end of the section, are for Never Hinged items.

Former Telegraph Office, Tehran A110

6r, Telegraph lines & ancient monument.

## 1956, Oct. 26
| | | | | |
|---|---|---|---|---|
| 1054 | A110 | 2.50r brt bl & grn, bluish | 8.50 | 3.50 |
| 1055 | A110 | 6r rose car & lil | 11.00 | 5.00 |

Centenary of Persian telegraph system.

UN Emblem and People of the World A111

Design: 2.50r, UN Emblem and scales.

**1956, Oct. 24**
| 1056 | A111 | 1r bluish green | 1.50 | .40 |
| 1057 | A111 | 2.50r blue & green | 3.00 | .60 |

United Nations Day, Oct. 24.

Shah and Pres. Iskander Mirza of Pakistan
A112

**1956, Oct. 31**
| 1058 | A112 | 1r multicolored | 5.00 | 1.00 |

Visit of Pres. General Iskander Mirza of Pakistan to Tehran, Oct. 31-Nov. 10.

Mohammad Reza Shah Pahlavi
A113          A114

**Perf. 13½x11**

**1956-57      Wmk. 306      Photo.**
| 1058A | A113 | 5d brt car & red | .45 | 1.00 |
| 1058B | A113 | 10d vio bl & dl vio | .45 | 1.00 |
| 1059 | A113 | 25d dk brn & brn | .65 | .35 |
| 1059A | A113 | 50d brn & ol brn | .70 | .20 |
| b. | | Inverted center | 3,750. | |
| 1060 | A113 | 1r brn & brt grn | .70 | .20 |
| 1061 | A113 | 1.50r brt lil & brown | .70 | .20 |
| 1062 | A113 | 2r red vio & red | .70 | .20 |
| 1063 | A113 | 2.50r ultra & blue | 1.00 | .20 |
| 1064 | A113 | 3r brn & dk ol bis | 1.00 | .20 |
| 1065 | A113 | 5r ver & mar | 1.00 | .20 |
| 1066 | A114 | 6r dk vio & brn lil | 6.00 | .25 |
| 1067 | A114 | 10r lt blue & grn | 12.00 | .20 |
| 1068 | A114 | 20r green & blue | 25.00 | 3.00 |
| 1069 | A114 | 30r rose red & org | 30.00 | 5.00 |
| 1070 | A114 | 50r dk grn & ol grn | 25.00 | 5.00 |
| 1071 | A114 | 100r lilac & cer | 300.00 | 27.50 |
| 1072 | A114 | 200r dp plum & vio bl | 175.00 | 15.00 |
| | | *Nos. 1058A-1072 (17)* | 580.35 | 59.70 |

Issued: 1.50r, 2r, 3r, 5r, 6r, 1956; others, 1957.
See Nos. 1082-1098.

Lord Baden-Powell
A115

Train and Map
A117

**1957, Feb. 22          Perf. 12½**
| 1073 | A115 | 10r dk grn & brn | 8.50 | 4.00 |

Birth cent. of Robert Baden-Powell, founder of the Boy Scout movement.

Railroad Tracks — A116

**1957, May 2 · Perf. 11x12½, 12½x11**

Design: 10r, Train and mosque.
| 1074 | A116 | 2.50r grnsh blk, bl & ocher | 10.00 | 1.50 |
| 1075 | A117 | 5r multi | 12.00 | 5.00 |
| 1076 | A116 | 10r blk, yel & bl | 25.00 | 9.00 |
| | | *Nos. 1074-1076 (3)* | 47.00 | 15.50 |

Opening of the Tehran Meshed-Railway.

Pres. Giovanni Gronchi of Italy and Shah — A118

Design: 6r, Ruins of Persepolis and Colosseum in Rome and flags.

**Wmk. 316**

**1957, Sept. 7      Photo.      Perf. 11**
| 1077 | A118 | 2r slate bl, grn & red | 3.25 | 1.00 |
| 1078 | A118 | 6r slate bl, grn & red | 6.75 | 2.00 |

Visit of Pres. Giovanni Gronchi of Italy to Iran, Sept. 7.

Queen Soraya and Hospital
A119

**1957, Sept. 29    Wmk. 316    Perf. 11**
| 1079 | A119 | 2r lt bl & grn | 7.50 | 2.00 |

Sixth Medical Congress, Ramsar.

Globes Showing Location of Iran — A120

**1957, Oct. 22    Litho.    Perf. 12½x11**
| 1080 | A120 | 10r blk, lt bl, yel & red | 7.50 | 2.00 |

Intl. Cartographic Conference, Tehran.

Shah and King Faisal II — A121

**1957, Oct. 18                    Photo.**
| 1081 | A121 | 2r slate bl, grn & red | 7.50 | 2.00 |

Visit of King Faisal of Iraq, Oct. 19.

**Shah Types of 1956-57**

**1957-58      Wmk. 316      Perf. 11**
| 1082 | A114 | 5d violet & pur | .25 | 2.00 |
| 1083 | A114 | 10d claret & rose car | .25 | 2.00 |

| 1084 | A114 | 25d rose car & brick red | .50 | .35 |
| 1085 | A114 | 50d grn & olive grn | .40 | .20 |
| 1086 | A114 | 1r dark green | .40 | .20 |
| 1087 | A114 | 1.50r claret & red lil | .50 | .25 |
| 1088 | A114 | 2r bl & grnsh blue | 1.60 | .20 |
| 1089 | A114 | 2.50r dk bl & blue | 1.60 | .25 |
| 1090 | A114 | 3r rose car & ver | 1.60 | .20 |
| 1091 | A114 | 5r violet blue | 1.60 | .20 |
| 1092 | A113 | 6r bright blue | 1.60 | .20 |
| 1093 | A113 | 10r deep green | 3.00 | .30 |
| 1094 | A113 | 20r grn & olive grn | 10.00 | .45 |
| 1095 | A113 | 30r vio bl & dk brn | 20.00 | 4.00 |
| 1096 | A113 | 50r dk brn & lt brn | 25.00 | 5.00 |
| 1097 | A113 | 100r rose lil & car rose | 140.00 | 25.00 |
| 1098 | A113 | 200r vio & yel brn | 100.00 | 30.00 |
| | | *Nos. 1082-1098 (17)* | 308.30 | 70.80 |

Issued: 1.50r, 2r, 3r, 1957; others, 1958.

Weight Lifter — A122

Modern and Old Houses, Radio Transmitter
A123

**1957, Nov. 8          Perf. 11x14½**
| 1099 | A122 | 10r bl, grn & red | 6.75 | 2.00 |

Iran's victories in weight lifting.

**1958, Feb. 22                  Litho.**
| 1100 | A123 | 10r brn, ocher & bl | 7.00 | 2.00 |

30th anniversary of radio in Iran.

Oil Derrick and Symbolic Flame — A124

Train on Viaduct — A125

**Wmk. 316**

**1958, Mar. 10    Photo.    Perf. 11**
| 1101 | A124 | 2r gray & multi | 5.00 | 1.00 |
| 1102 | A124 | 10r multicolored | 10.00 | 2.00 |

Drilling of Iran's 1st oil well, 50th anniv.

**1958, Apr. 24    Wmk. 306    Perf. 11**

Design: 8r, Train and map.
| 1103 | A125 | 6r dull purple | 20.00 | 5.00 |
| 1104 | A125 | 8r green | 25.00 | 10.00 |

Opening of Tehran-Tabriz railway line.

Exposition Emblem
A126

**1958, Apr. 17                Perf. 12½x11**
| 1105 | A126 | 2.50r bl & light bl | 1.00 | .20 |
| 1106 | A126 | 6r car & salmon | 1.75 | .20 |

World's Fair, Brussels, Apr. 17-Oct. 19.

Mohammad Reza Shah Pahlavi — A127       UN Emblem and Map of Iran — A128

**1958-59    Wmk. 316    Photo.    Perf. 11**
| 1107 | A127 | 5d blue violet | .50 | .25 |
| 1108 | A127 | 10d lt vermilion | .50 | .25 |
| 1109 | A127 | 25d crimson | .50 | .25 |
| 1110 | A127 | 50d brt blue | .50 | .25 |
| 1111 | A127 | 1r dark green | 1.00 | .20 |
| 1113 | A127 | 2r dark brown | 8.00 | .25 |
| 1115 | A127 | 3r dk red brown | 15.00 | .20 |
| 1117 | A127 | 6r bright blue | 6.00 | .45 |
| 1118 | A127 | 8r magenta | 5.00 | .35 |
| 1120 | A127 | 14r blue violet | 12.00 | 1.75 |
| 1121 | A127 | 20r green | 20.00 | .45 |
| a. | | Wmk. 306 | 25.00 | 10.00 |
| 1122 | A127 | 30r brt car rose | 17.00 | 1.75 |
| 1123 | A127 | 50r rose violet | 55.00 | 6.00 |
| 1124 | A127 | 100r red orange | 20.00 | 4.50 |
| 1125 | A127 | 200r slate green | 60.00 | 9.00 |
| | | *Nos. 1107-1125 (15)* | 221.00 | 25.90 |

See Nos. 1138-1151, 1173-1179.

**1958, Oct. 24**
| 1126 | A128 | 6r bright blue | 1.25 | .75 |
| 1127 | A128 | 10r dk violet & grn | 2.25 | 1.00 |

Issued for United Nations Day, Oct. 24.

Globe and Hands
A129

**1958, Dec. 10**
| 1128 | A129 | 6r dk red brn & brn | 1.00 | .45 |
| 1129 | A129 | 8r dk grn & gray grn | 1.75 | .65 |

Universal Declaration of Human Rights, 10th anniv.

Rudaki — A130

Wrestlers, Flag and Globe — A131

Flag
A130a

Design: 5r, Rudaki, different pose.

**1958, Dec. 24    Photo.    Wmk. 306**
1130  A130  2.50r bluish black    6.50    .90
1131  A130  5r violet    12.50    1.50
1132  A130  10r dark brown    21.00    2.75
  Nos. 1130-1132 (3)    40.00    5.15

1100th birth anniv. of Rudaki, blind Persian poet.

Design: Red Lion & Sun flag (Iranian Red Cross Organization).

**Perf. 14½x11**
**1959, May 8    Wmk. 316**
1132A  A130a  1r multicolored    2.00    .75
1132B  A130a  6r multicolored    3.50    1.00
  Centenary of the Red Cross.

**1959    Litho.    Perf. 11x12½**
1133  A131  6r multicolored    20.00    7.50
  World Wrestling Championships, Tehran.

Globe, UN Building and Hand Holding Torch of Freedom
A132

**1959, Oct. 24    Photo.    Perf. 11**
1134  A132  6r gray brn, red & bister    1.50    .50
  Issued for United Nations Day, Oct. 24.

Shah and Pres. Ayub Khan of Pakistan — A133

**1959, Nov. 9    Litho.    Perf. 11x16**
1135  A133  6r multicolored    7.50    1.00
  Visit of Pres. Khan to Iran.

ILO Emblem — A134

**1959, Nov. 12    Perf. 16**
1136  A134  1r blue    1.10    .30
1137  A134  5r brown    1.90    .45
  ILO, 40th anniversary.

Shah Type of 1958-59

**1959-63  Wmk. 316  Photo.  Perf. 11**
1138    A127  5d red brn ('60)    .35    .30
1139    A127  10d Prus grn ('60)    .35    .30
  a.    10d Prussian blue ('63)    .50    .50
1140    A127  25d orange    1.00    .20
  a.    Perf. 12x11½    50.00    20.00
1141    A127  50d scarlet    1.00    .25
1142    A127  1r deep violet    1.00    .20
1142A   A127  2r brown    8.00    .20
1143    A127  3r olive    3.00    .20
1143A   A127  6r cobalt blue    6.00    .20
1144    A127  8r brown olive    1.50    .20
1145    A127  10r ol blk ('60)    1.50    .20

1146    A127  14r yel green    1.75    .25
  a.    14r emerald green    3.00    .50
1147    A127  20r sl grn ('60)    6.00    .35
1148    A127  30r choc ('60)    6.50    .65
1149    A127  50r dp blue ('60)    6.50    .60
1150    A127  100r green ('60)    110.00    10.00
1151    A127  200r cer ('60)    225.00    15.00
  Nos. 1138-1151 (16)    379.45    29.10

Pahlavi Foundation Bridge, Karun River — A135

Design: 5r, Bridge, different view.

**1960, Feb. 29    Litho.    Perf. 16x11**
1152  A135  1r dk brn & brt bl    1.50    .20
1153  A135  5r blue & emerald    2.50    .50
  Opening of Pahlavi Foundation Bridge at Khorramshahr on the Karun River.

Uprooted Oak Emblem A136

Design: 6r, Arched frame.

**1960, Apr. 7    Perf. 11**
1154  A136  1r brt ultra    .65    .20
1155  A136  6r gray olive    .75    .20
  World Refugee Year, 7/1/59-6/30/60.

Mosquito — A137

Man with Spray Gun — A138

Design: 3r, Mosquito on water.

**1960, Apr. 7    Wmk. 316**
1156  A137  1r blk & red, yel    1.50    .25
1157  A138  2r lt bl, ultra & blk    2.00    .35
1158  A137  3r blk & red, yel grn    4.00    .75
  Nos. 1156-1158 (3)    7.50    1.35
  Issued to publicize malaria control.

Polo Player — A139

Design: 6r, Persian archer.

**1960, June 9    Litho.    Wmk. 316**
1159  A139  1r deep claret    2.00    .30
1160  A139  6r dk blue & lt blue    3.50    .75
  17th Olympic Games, Rome, 8/25-9/11.

Shah and King Hussein of Jordan — A140

**1960, July 6    Perf. 11**
1161  A140  6r multicolored    7.50    1.50
  Visit of King Hussein of Jordan to Tehran.

Iranian Scout Emblem in Flower — A141

Tents and Pillars of Persepolis A142

**1960, July 18**
1162  A141  1r green    .75    .35
1163  A142  6r brn, brt bl & buff    1.50    .65
  3rd National Boy Scout Jamboree.

Shah and Queen Farah — A143

**1960, Sept. 9    Litho.    Perf. 11**
1164  A143  1r green    3.50    1.50
1165  A143  5r blue    7.50    1.00
  Marriage of Shah Mohammad Reza Shah Pahlavi and Farah Diba.

UN Emblem and Globe — A144

**1960, Oct. 24    Wmk. 316**
1166  A144  6r bl, blk & lt brn    1.00    .20
  15th anniversary of the United Nations.

Shah and Queen Elizabeth II A145

**1961, Mar. 2    Litho.    Perf. 11**
1167  A145  1r lt red brown    2.00    .45
1168  A145  6r bright ultra    3.50    .90
  Visit of Queen Elizabeth II to Tehran, Feb. 1961.

Girl Playing Arganoon — A146

Safiaddin Amavi — A147

**1961, Apr. 10    Wmk. 316    Perf. 11**
1169  A146  1r dk brown & buff    1.00    .50
1170  A147  6r greenish gray    2.00    .65
  International Congress of Music, Tehran.

Shah Type of 1958-59 Redrawn

**1961-62    Litho.    Perf. 11**
1173  A127  25d orange    1.50    .50
1174  A127  50d scarlet    1.50    .40
1175  A127  1r deep violet    3.00    .20
1176  A127  2r chocolate    4.00    .20
1177  A127  3r olive brown    5.00    .50
1178  A127  6r brt blue ('62)    50.00    3.50
1179  A127  8r brown ol ('62)    20.00    2.25
  Nos. 1173-1179 (7)    85.00    7.55

On Nos. 1173-1179 (lithographed), a single white line separates the lower panel from the shah's portrait. On Nos. 1107-1125, 1138-1151 (photogravure), two lines, one in color and one in white, separate panel from portrait. Other minor differences exist.

Shah and Queen Farah Holding Crown Prince — A148

**1961, June 2    Litho.**
1186  A148  1r bright pink    2.50    1.25
1187  A148  6r light blue    6.50    3.00
  Birth of Crown Prince Reza Kourosh Pahlavi, Oct. 31, 1960.

Swallows and UN Emblem — A149

Planting
Tree — A150

**1961, Oct. 24**     *Perf. 11*
1188 A149 2r blue & car rose   1.00 .20
1189 A149 6r blue & violet   1.50 .30

Issued for United Nations Day, Oct. 24.

**1962, Jan. 11**
1190 A150 2r ol grn, citron & dk
    bl   1.00 .20
1191 A150 6r ultra, grn & pale bl   1.50 .30

Tree Planting Day.

Worker and
Symbols of
Labor and
Agriculture
A151

Map, Family and
Cogwheel
A152

**1962, Mar. 15**     *Litho.*
1192 A151 2r bl grn, brn & blk   1.00 .20
1193 A151 6r lt ultra, brn & blk   1.50 .30

Issued for Workers' Day.

**1962, Mar. 20**     *Perf. 11*
1194 A152 2r black, yel & lil   1.50 .25
1195 A152 6r black, bl & ultra   2.00 .40

Social Insurance Week.

Sugar Refinery, Khuzistan — A153

**1962, Apr. 14**     *Wmk. 316*
1196 A153 2r dk & lt blue & grn   1.50 .25
1197 A153 6r ultra, buff & blue   2.00 .50

Opening of sugar refinery in Khuzistan.

Karaj
Dam — A154

**1962, May 15**
1198 A154 2r dk brn & gray grn   1.50 .25
1199 A154 6r vio bl & lt blue   2.00 .50

Inauguration of Karaj Dam, renamed Amir
Kabir Dam.

Sefid
Rud
Dam
A155

**1962, May 19**     *Litho.*
1200 A155 2r dk grn, lt bl & buff   1.50 .25
1201 A155 6r red brn, sl grn & lt
    blue   2.00 .65

Inauguration of Sefid Rud Dam.

"UNESCO" and
UN
Emblem — A156

**1962, June 2**   *Wmk. 316*   *Perf. 11*
1202 A156 2r black, emer & red   1.00 .25
1203 A156 6r blue, emer & red   2.00 .45

15th anniv. of UNESCO.

Malaria
Eradication
Emblem and
Sprayer
A157

2r, Emblem & arrow piercing mosquito,
horiz. 10r, Emblem & globe, horiz. Sizes: 2r,
10r, 40x25mm; 6r, 29½x34½mm.

**1962, June 20**
1204 A157 2r black & bluish grn   1.00 .30
1205 A157 6r pink & vio blue   1.50 .30
1206 A157 10r lt blue & ultra   2.50 .50
    Nos. 1204-1206 (3)   5.00 1.10

WHO drive to eradicate malaria.

Oil Field and
UN Emblem
A158

**1962, Sept. 1**     *Photo.*
1207 A158 6r grnsh blue & brn   2.00 .30
1208 A158 14r gray & sepia   3.50 .70

2nd Petroleum Symposium of ECAFE (UN
Economic Commission for Asia and the Far
East).

Mohammad Reza
Shah Pahlavi — A159

Palace of
Darius,
Persepolis
A160

**1962**     *Photo.*     *Wmk. 316*
1209 A159 5d green   1.00 .25
1210 A159 10d chestnut   1.00 .50
1211 A159 25d dark blue   1.00 .35
1212 A159 50d Prus green   1.00 .20
1213 A159 1r orange   3.00 .20
1214 A159 2r violet blue   2.00 .20
1215 A159 5r dark brown   3.00 .20
1216 A160 6r blue   12.00 2.50
1217 A160 8r yellow grn   5.00 1.00
1218 A160 10r grnsh blue   8.00 .50
1219 A160 11r slate green   4.50 .65
1220 A160 14r purple   10.00 .65
1221 A160 20r red brown   11.00 1.50
1222 A160 50r vermilion   15.00 1.50
    Nos. 1209-1222 (14)   77.50 10.20

See Nos. 1331-1344.

*Perf. 11, 10½x11*

Hippocrates and Avicenna — A161

**1962, Oct. 7**     *Litho.*
1226 A161 2r brown, buff & ultra   2.50 .35
1227 A161 6r grn, pale grn & ul-
    tra   3.00 .60

Near and Middle East Medical Congress.

Hands
Laying
Bricks
A162

Design: 6r, Houses and UN emblem, vert.

**1962, Oct. 24**
1228 A162 6r dk blue & ultra   2.00 .35
1229 A162 14r dk blue & emer   3.00 .60

Issued for United Nations Day, Oct. 24.

Crown Prince Receiving
Flowers — A163

**1962, Oct. 31**
1230 A163 6r blue gray   5.00 1.00
1231 A163 14r dull green   10.00 1.90

Children's Day, Oct. 31; 2nd birthday of
Crown Prince Riza.

Map of Iran and
Persian
Gulf — A164

Hilton Hotel,
Tehran — A165

**1962, Dec. 12**   *Wmk. 316*   *Perf. 11*
1232 A164 6r dk & lt bl, vio bl &
    rose   2.00 .35
1233 A164 14r dk & lt bl, pink &
    rose   3.00 .60

The Persian Gulf Seminar.

**1963, Jan. 21**     *Photo.*
1234 A165 6r deep blue   3.00 .45
1235 A165 14r dark red brown   5.00 .60

Opening of the Royal Tehran Hilton Hotel.

Mohammad
Riza Shah
Dam
A166

**1963, Mar. 14**     *Litho.*
**Center Multicolored**
1236 A166 6r violet blue   3.50 .40
1237 A166 14r dark brown   6.00 .75

Mohammad Riza Shah Dam inauguration
(later Dez Dam).

Worker with
Pickax — A167

Stylized Bird
over
Globe — A168

**1963, Mar. 15**
1238 A167 2r cream & black   1.10 .20
1239 A167 6r lt blue & blk   2.00 .30

Issued for Labor Day.

**1963, Mar. 21**     *Perf. 11*

Designs: 6r, Stylized globe and "FAO." 14r,
Globe in space and wheat emblem.

1240 A168 2r ultra, lt bl & bis   1.50 .20
1241 A168 6r ultra, ocher &
    blk   2.25 .30
1242 A168 14r slate bl & ocher   3.75 .85
    Nos. 1240-1242 (3)   7.50 1.35

FAO "Freedom from Hunger" campaign.

Shah and List of Bills — A169

**1963, Mar. 21**     *Wmk. 316*
1243 A169 6r green & lt blue   6.00 2.00
1244 A169 14r green & dull yel   9.00 3.00

Signing of six socioeconomic bills by Shah,
1st anniv.

Shah and King of Denmark — A170

**1963, May 3**     **Litho.**     *Perf. 11*
1245 A170   6r indigo & dk ultra   3.50   .55
1246 A170   14r dk brn & red brn   5.00   1.00

Visit of King Frederik IX of Denmark.

Flags, Shah Mosque, Isfahan, and Taj Mahal, Agra A171

**1963, May 19**
1247 A171   6r blue, yel grn & red   3.50   .55
1248 A171   14r multicolored   5.00   1.00

Visit of Dr. Sarvepalli Radhakrishnan, president of India.

Chahnaz Dam — A172

Cent. Emblem with Red Lion and Sun — A173

**1963, June 8**     **Wmk. 316**     *Perf. 11*
1249 A172   6r ultra, bl & grn   3.50   .45
1250 A172   14r dk grn, bl & buff   3.50   .75

Inauguration of Chahnaz Dam (later Hamadan Dam).

**1963, June 10**
1251 A173   6r blue, gray & red   3.50   .65
1252 A173   14r buff, gray & red   5.50   .90

Centenary of International Red Cross.

Shah and Queen Juliana A174

*Perf. 11x10½*
**1963, Oct. 3**     **Wmk. 349**
1253 A174   6r ultra & blue   4.00   .50
1254 A174   14r sl grn & dull grn   6.00   .75

Visit of Queen Juliana of the Netherlands.

Literacy Corps Emblem and Soldier Teaching Village Class — A175

**1963, Oct. 15**     **Litho.**     *Perf. 10½*
1255 A175   6r multicolored   4.50   1.00
1256 A175   14r multicolored   6.50   1.00

Issued to publicize the Literacy Corps.

Gen. Charles de Gaulle and View of Persepolis — A176

**1963, Oct. 16**
1257 A176   6r ultra & blue   4.50   1.00
1258 A176   14r brn & pale brn   5.50   1.00

Visit of General de Gaulle of France.

Fertilizer Plant, Oil Company Emblem and Map — A177

Design: 14r, Factory and Iranian Oil Company emblem, horiz.

*Perf. 10½x11, 11x10½*
**1963, Oct. 18**     **Wmk. 316**
1259 A177   6r black, yel & red   4.50   .50
1260 A177   14r black, bl & yel   5.50   1.50

Opening of Shiraz Chemical Factory.

Pres. Heinrich Lübke of Germany and Mosque in Tehran A178

**1963, Oct. 23**     **Wmk. 349**     *Perf. 10½*
1261 A178   6r ultra & dk blue   4.50   .65
1262 A178   14r gray & brown   5.50   1.60

Visit of Pres. Lubke of Germany.

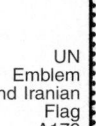

UN Emblem and Iranian Flag A179

**1963, Oct. 24**
1263 A179   8r multicolored   2.75   .50

Issued for United Nations Day.

UN Emblem and Jets A180

**1963, Oct. 24**
1264 A180   6r multicolored   2.75   .50

Iranian jet fighters with UN Force in the Congo.

Crown Prince Rzza — A181

**1963, Oct. 31**
1265 A181   2r brown   1.75   .25
1266 A181   6r blue   4.50   .50

Children's Day; Crown Prince Riza's 3rd birthday.

Pres. Brezhnev of USSR — A182

**1963, Nov. 16**     **Wmk. 349**     *Perf. 10½*
1267 A182   6r dk brn, yel & bl   3.25   .35
1268 A182   11r dk brn, yel & red   6.00   .75

Visit of Pres. Leonid I. Brezhnev.

Atatürk's Mausoleum, Ankara — A183

**1963, Nov. 28**     **Litho.**
1269 A183   4r shown   3.25   .30
1270 A183   5r Kemal Ataturk   3.25   .30

25th death anniv. of Kemal Atatürk, president of Turkey.

Scales and Globe — A184

**1963, Dec. 10**
1271 A184   6r brt yel grn, blk & ultra   2.75   .35
1272 A184   14r org brn, blk & buff   3.50   .45

Universal Declaration of Human Rights, 15th anniv.

Mother and Child — A185

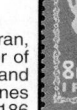

Map of Iran, Chamber of Industry and Mines Emblem — A186

**1963, Dec. 16**
1273 A185   2r multicolored   2.25   .25
1274 A185   4r multicolored   3.25   .50

Issued for Mother's Day.

**1963, Dec. 17**     **Litho.**
1275 A186   8r bl grn, buff & dk bl   4.00   .40

Chamber of Industry and Mines.

Factories and Hand Holding Bill — A187

Designs: 4r, Factories and bills on scale. 6r, Man on globe carrying torch of education. 8r, Tractor, map and yardstick. 10r, Forest. 12r, Gate of Parliament and heads of man and woman.

**1964, Jan. 26**     **Wmk. 349**     *Perf. 10½*
1276 A187   2r multicolored   3.00   .75
1277 A187   4r brown & gray   4.00   .75
1278 A187   6r multicolored   5.00   .75
1279 A187   8r multicolored   6.00   1.00
1280 A187   10r multicolored   7.00   1.25
1281 A187   12r red org & brn   8.00   1.50
    *Nos. 1276-1281 (6)*   33.00   6.00

2nd anniv. of six socioeconomic bills: 2r, Shareholding for factory workers. 4r, Sale of shares in government factories. 6r, Creation of Army of Education. 8r, Land reforms. 10r, Nationalization of forests. 12r, Reforms in parliamentary elections.

"ECAFE" and UN Emblem A188

**1964, Mar. 2**     **Wmk. 349**
1282 A188   14r brt green & blk   3.00   .45

20th session of ECAFE (Economic Commission for Asia and the Far East), Mar. 2-17.

Flowering Branch — A189

**1964, Mar. 5**     *Perf. 10½*
1283 A189   50d emerald, blk & org   .45   .25
1284 A189   1r brt blue, blk & org   .55   .25

Novrooz, Iranian New Year, Mar. 21.

Anemometer A190

Mosque and Arches, Isfahan — A191

**1964, Mar. 23**      **Litho.**
1285 A190 6r brt blue & vio bl   1.50   .25
4th World Meteorological Day.

**1964, Apr. 7**      *Perf. 10½*
11r, Griffon & winged bull, Persepolis.
1286 A191 6r lilac, grn & blk   3.00   .40
1287 A191 11r orange, brn & blk   4.00   .55
Issued for tourist publicity.

Rudaki and Harp — A192

**1964, May 16**   **Photo.**   **Wmk. 349**
1288 A192 6r blue   2.50   .45
1289 A192 8r red brown   4.50   .55
Opening of an institute for the blind. The inscription translates: "Wisdom is better than eye and sight."

Sculpture, Persepolis A193

Designs: 4r, Achaemenian horse-drawn mail cart, map of Iran, horiz. 6r, Vessel with sculptured animals. 10r, Head of King Shapur, sculpture.

**1964, June 5**   **Wmk. 349**   **Litho.**
1290 A193 2r gray & blue   4.50   1.75
1291 A193 4r vio bl, lt bl & bl   8.50   2.00
1292 A193 6r brown & yellow   9.00   2.50
1293 A193 10r yel & ol grn   12.00   3.50
Nos. 1290-1293 (4)   34.00   9.75
Opening of the "7000 Years of Persian Art" exhibition in Washington, D.C.

Shah and Emperor Haile Selassie A194

**1964, Sept. 14**   **Wmk. 349**   *Perf. 10½*
1294 A194 6r ultra & lt blue   3.50   .60
Visit of Emperor Haile Selassie of Ethiopia.

Tooth and Dentists' Assoc. Emblem A195

"2 I.D.A." A196

**1964, Sept. 14**      **Litho.**
1295 A195 2r blue, red & dk blue   2.00   .30
1296 A196 4r ultra, bl & pale brn   2.50   .35
Iranian Dentists' Association, 2nd congress.

Research Institute, Microscope, Wheat and Locust — A197

Beetle under Magnifying Glass — A198

**1964, Sept. 23**   **Wmk. 349**   *Perf. 10½*
1297 A197 2r red, orange & brn   3.50   .40
1298 A198 6r blue, brn & indigo   4.50   .60
Fight against plant diseases and damages.

Mithras (Mehr) on Ancient Seal — A199

Eleanor Roosevelt (1884-1962) A200

**1964, Oct. 8**      **Litho.**
**Size: 26x34mm**
1299 A199 8r org & brn org   2.50   1.00
Mehragan celebration. See No. 1406.

**1964, Oct. 11**
1300 A200 10r vio bl & rose vio   4.00   .35

Clasped Hands and UN Emblem — A201

Symbolic Airplane and UN Emblem — A202

**1964, Oct. 24**   **Wmk. 349**   *Perf. 10½*
1301 A201 6r ultra, yel, red & blk   1.50   .30
1302 A202 14r org, ultra & red   2.25   .50
Issued for United Nations Day.

Persian Gymnast — A203

Polo Player A204

**1964, Oct. 26**
1303 A203 4r tan, sep & Prus bl   2.00   .35
1304 A204 6r red & black   2.50   .40
18th Olympic Games, Tokyo, Oct. 10-25.

Crown Prince Riza — A205

**1964, Oct. 31**      **Litho.**
1305 A205 1r dull green & brn   1.40   .30
1306 A205 2r deep rose & ultra   2.75   .50
1307 A205 6r ultra & red   4.00   .65
Nos. 1305-1307 (3)   8.15   1.45
Children's Day; Crown Prince Riza's 4th birthday.

UN Emblem, Flame and Smokestack — A206

**1964, Nov. 16**   **Wmk. 349**   *Perf. 10½*
1308 A206 6r black, lt bl & car   1.50   .35
1309 A206 8r black, emer & car   2.50   .40
Petro-Chemical Conference and Gas Seminar, Nov.-Dec. 1964.

Shah and King Baudouin — A207

**1964, Nov. 17**
1310 A207 6r black, org & yel   1.75   .35
1311 A207 8r black, org & emer   3.00   .75
Visit of King Baudouin of Belgium.

Rhazes A208

**1964, Dec. 27**   **Wmk. 349**   *Perf. 10½*
1312 A208 2r multicolored   2.50   .35
1313 A208 6r multicolored   3.50   .60
1100th birth anniv. of Rhazes (abu-Bakr Mohammad Zakariya Razi), Persian physician.

Shah and King Olav V A209

**1965, Jan. 7**      **Litho.**
1314 A209 2r dk brown & lilac   2.50   .35
1315 A209 4r brown & green   3.50   .75
Visit of King Olav V of Norway.

Map of Iran and Six-pointed Star — A210

**1965, Jan. 26**   **Wmk. 349**   *Perf. 10½*
1316 A210 2r black, brt bl & org   1.50   .20
Shah's six socioeconomic bills, 3rd anniv.

Woman and UN Emblem — A211

Green Wheat and Tulip — A212

**1965, Mar. 1**   **Wmk. 349**   *Perf. 10½*
1317 A211 6r black & blue   .85   .20
1318 A211 8r ultra & red   1.25   .20
18th session of the UN commission on the status of women.

**1965, Mar. 6**
1319 A212 50d multicolored .30 .20
1320 A212 1r multicolored .30 .20
Novrooz, Iranian New Year, Mar. 21.

Pres. Habib Bourguiba and Minarets of Tunis Mosque — A213

**1965, Mar. 14 Litho. Perf. 10½**
1321 A213 4r multicolored 1.50 .35
Visit of Pres. Habib Bourguiba of Tunisia.

Map of Iran and Trade Mark of Iranian Oil Co. A214

**1965, Mar. 20 Litho.**
1322 A214 6r multicolored 2.50 .25
1323 A214 14r multicolored 3.50 .55
Oil industry nationalization, 14th anniv.

ITU Emblem, Old and New Communication Equipment — A215

**1965, May 17 Wmk. 349 Perf. 10½**
1324 A215 14r dp car rose & gray 1.25 .25
ITU, centenary.

ICY Emblem A216

**1965, June 22 Litho. Perf. 10½**
1325 A216 10r sl grn & gray bl 2.25 .35
International Cooperation Year, 1965.

Iran Airways Emblem A217

**1965, July 17 Wmk. 349 Perf. 10½**
1326 A217 14r multicolored 2.25 .45
Tenth anniversary of Iran Airways.

Hands Holding Book A218

---

Map and Flags of Turkey, Iran and Pakistan A219

**1965, July 21 Litho.**
1327 A218 2r dk brn, org brn & buff .75 .20
1328 A219 4r multicolored 1.25 .20
Signing of the Regional Cooperation for Development Pact by Turkey, Iran and Pakistan, 1st anniv.

Iranian Scout Emblem and Ornament A220

**1965, July 23**
1329 A220 2r multicolored 1.00 .20
a. Vert. pair, imperf. horiz. 75.00
Middle East Rover Moot (senior Boy Scout assembly).

Majlis Gate A221

**1965, Aug. 5 Wmk. 349 Perf. 10½**
1330 A221 2r lilac rose & brn .75 .20
60th anniversary of Iranian constitution.

**Types of Regular Issue, 1962**
**Wmk. 349**

| | | | | Perf. 10½ | |
|---|---|---|---|---|---|
| **1964-65** | | **Photo.** | | | |
| 1331 | A159 | 5d dk sl grn ('65) | | .35 | .30 |
| a. | | Wmk. 353 | | .35 | .30 |
| 1332 | A159 | 10d chestnut | | .35 | .30 |
| 1333 | A159 | 25d dk blue ('65) | | .50 | .25 |
| 1334 | A159 | 50d Prus green | | .75 | .20 |
| 1335 | A159 | 1r orange | | .75 | .20 |
| 1336 | A159 | 2r violet blue | | .50 | .20 |
| 1337 | A159 | 5r dark brown | | 3.00 | .50 |
| 1338 | A160 | 6r blue ('65) | | 11.00 | 1.00 |
| 1339 | A160 | 8r yel grn ('65) | | 3.50 | .25 |
| 1340 | A160 | 10r grnsh bl ('65) | | 3.00 | .25 |
| 1341 | A160 | 11r sl grn ('65) | | 10.00 | 1.50 |
| 1342 | A160 | 14r purple ('65) | | 7.00 | 1.40 |
| 1343 | A160 | 20r red brn ('65) | | 6.00 | 2.00 |
| 1344 | A160 | 50r org ver ('65) | | 7.50 | 2.00 |
| | | Nos. 1331-1344 (14) | | 54.20 | 10.35 |

| | | | | Perf. 11x10½ | |
|---|---|---|---|---|---|
| 1331b | A159 | 5d Wmk. 353 | | 4.00 | 1.00 |
| 1332a | A159 | 10d | | .55 | .50 |
| 1333a | A159 | 25d | | .80 | .25 |
| 1334a | A159 | 50d | | 3.00 | 2.00 |
| 1335a | A159 | 1r | | 3.00 | 2.00 |
| 1337a | A159 | 5r | | 6.00 | .50 |
| | | Nos. 1331b-1337a (6) | | 17.35 | 6.25 |

Dental Congress Emblem — A222

**1965, Sept. 7 Litho. Perf. 10½**
1345 A222 6r gray, ultra, & car .60 .25
Iranian Dentists' Association, 3rd congress.

---

Classroom and Literacy Corps Emblem A223

Alphabets on Globe — A224

Designs: 6r, UNESCO emblem and open book (diamond shape). 8r, UNESCO emblem and inscription, horiz. 14r, Mohammad Reza Shah Pahlavi and inscription in six languages.

**1965, Sept. 8**
1346 A223 2r multi .35 .20
1347 A224 5r multi .40 .25
**Size: 30x30mm**
1348 A223 6r multi .80 .30
**Size: 35x23mm**
1349 A223 8r dk bl, car emer & buff .80 .25
**Size: 34x46mm**
1350 A223 14r cit, dk bl & brn 2.00 .30
Nos. 1346-1350 (5) 4.35 1.30
World Congress Against Illiteracy, Tehran, Sept. 8-19.

Mohammad Reza Pahlavi — A225

**1965, Sept. 16 Litho. Perf. 10½**
1351 A225 1r crim, rose red & gray 2.00 .40
1352 A225 2r dk red, rose red & yel 2.00 .60
Reign of Shah, 25th anniv.

Emblem of Persian Medical Society A226

**1965, Sept. 21 Wmk. 349**
1353 A226 5r ultra, dp ultra & gold .50 .25
14th Medical Congress, Ramsar.

Pres. Jonas of Austria A227

**1965, Sept. 30**
1354 A227 6r bl, brt bl & gray 1.50 .25
Visit of President Franz Jonas of Austria.

---

Mithras (Mehr) on Ancient Seal — A228

**1965, Oct. 8 Litho. Wmk. 353**
1355 A228 4r brt grn, gold, brn & blk 1.00 .20
Mehragan celebration during month of Mehr, Sept. 23-Oct. 22. Persian inscription of watermark vertical on No. 1355.

UN Emblem — A229

**1965, Oct. 24 Wmk. 353 Perf. 10½**
1356 A229 5r bl, grn & rose car .55 .20
20th anniversary of the United Nations.

Symbolic Arches A230

**1965, Oct. 26**
1357 A230 3r vio bl, blk, yel & red .55 .20
Exhibition of Iranian Commodities.

Crown Prince Reza A231

**1965, Oct. 31**
1358 A231 2r brown & yellow 1.10 .45
Children's Day; Crown Prince Reza's 5th birthday.

Weight Lifters — A232

**1965, Nov. 1**
1359 A232 10r brt bl, vio & brt pink .60 .20
World Weight Lifting Championships, Tehran.

Open Book
A233

**1965, Dec. 1    Wmk. 353    Perf. 10½**
1360  A233  8r bl, brt pink & blk    .60   .20
Issued for Book Week.

Shah
and King
Faisal
A234

**1965, Dec. 8    Litho.**
1361  A234  4r olive bister & brn    3.00   .50
Visit of King Faisal of Saudi Arabia.

Scales and
Olive Branch
A235

**1965, Dec. 12**
1362  A235  14r multicolored    .60   .20
Human Rights Day (Dec. 10).

Tractor,
"Land
Reform"
A236

Symbols of Reform Bills: 2r, Trees, nationalization of forests. 3r, Factory and gear wheel,
sale of shares in government factories. 4r,
Wheels, shareholding for factory workers. 5r,
Parliament gate, women's suffrage. 6r, Children before blackboard, Army of Education.
7r, Caduceus, Army of Hygiene. 8r, Scales,
creation of rural courts. 9r, Two girders, creation of Army of Progress.

**1966, Jan. 26    Wmk. 353    Perf. 10½**
1363  A236  1r orange & brown    .30   .30
1364  A236  2r dl grn & green    .30   .30
1365  A236  3r silver & gray    .30   .30
1366  A236  4r light & dk vio    .40   .30
1367  A236  5r rose & brown    .60   .30
1368  A236  6r olive & brown    .90   .30
1369  A236  7r bl & vio blue    1.00   .30
1370  A236  8r ultra & dp ultra    1.40   .30
1371  A236  9r brn org & dk brn    1.40   .30
     Nos. 1363-1371 (9)    6.60  2.70
Parliamentary approval of the Shah's reform
plan.

Shah — A237

Ruins of
Persepolis
A238

**Wmk. 353**
**1966-71    Photo.    Perf. 10½**
1372  A237  5d green    .30   .25
1373  A237  10d chestnut    .30   .25
1374  A237  25d dark blue    .30   .25

---

1375  A237  50d Prussian
                green    .50   .25
  a.  50d blue green ('71)    .50   .30
1376  A237  1r orange    .50   .20
1377  A237  2r violet    .50   .20
1377A  A237  4r cl brn ('68)    6.00  1.00
1378  A237  5r dark brn    1.00   .25
1379  A237  6r deep blue    1.50   .25
1380  A238  8r yellow grn    1.50   .25
  a.  8r dull green ('71)    1.00   .25
1381  A238  10r Prus bl    1.50   .20
1382  A238  11r slate grn    1.50   .20
1383  A238  14r purple    2.00   .25
1384  A238  20r brown    17.00   .50
1385  A238  50r cop red    7.50  1.50
1386  A238  100r brt blue    17.00  2.50
1387  A238  200r chnt brn    12.50  4.50
     Nos. 1372-1387 (17)    71.40 12.80
Set, except 4r, issued Feb. 22, 1966.

Student Nurse          Narcissus
Taking Oath              A240
A239

**1966, Feb. 24    Litho.**
1388  A239  5r brt pink & mag    1.50   .25
1389  A239  5r lt bl & brt bl    1.50   .25
  a.  Se-tenant pair, #1388-1389    3.50  2.00
Nurses' Day.  Nos. 1388-1389 printed in
sheets of 50 arranged checkerwise.

**1966, Mar. 7**
1390  A240  50d ultra, yel & emer    .50   .20
1391  A240  1r lilac, yel & emer    .50   .20
Novrooz, Iranian New Year, Mar. 21.

Oil Derricks in Persian Gulf — A241

**1966, Mar. 20    Perf. 10½**
1392  A241  14r blk, brt bl & brt
                rose lil    2.00   .40
Formation of six offshore oil companies.

Radio
Tower — A242

2r, Radar, horiz. 6r, Emblem & waves. 8r,
Compass rose & waves. 10r, Tower & waves.

**1966, Apr. 27    Litho.    Wmk. 349**
1393  A242  2r dark grn    .30   .30
1394  A242  4r ultra & dp org    .30   .30
1395  A242  6r gray ol & plum    .35   .30
1396  A242  8r brt bl & dk bl    .45   .35
1397  A242  10r brn & bister    .65   .35
     Nos. 1393-1397 (5)    2.05  1.60
Inauguration of the radio telecommunication
system of the Central Treaty Organization of
the Middle East (CENTO).

---

WHO Headquarters, Geneva — A243

**1966, May 3    Wmk. 353**
1398  A243  10r brt bl, yel & blk    .75   .30
Opening of the WHO Headquarters, Geneva.

World Map — A244

**1966, May 14    Litho.**
1399  A244  6r bl & multi    .65   .30
1400  A244  8r multicolored    .75   .30
Intl. Council of Women, 18th Conf., Tehran,
May 1966.

Globe, Map of Iran and Ruins of
Persepolis — A245

**1966, Sept. 5    Wmk. 353    Perf. 10½**
1401  A245  14r multicolored    1.25   .40
International Iranology Congress, Tehran.

Emblem of
Iranian
Medical
Society
A246

**1966, Sept. 21**
1402  A246  4r ultra, grnsh bl & bis    .50   .30
15th Medical Congress, held at Ramsar.

Gate of Parliament, Mt. Demavend
and Congress Emblem — A247

8r, Senate building, Mt. Demavend &
emblem.

**1966, Oct. 2    Wmk. 353    Perf. 10½**
1403  A247  6r brick red, ultra &
                dk grn    .65   .30
1404  A247  8r lt lil, ultra & dk grn    .75   .30
55th Interparliamentary Union Conf., Tehran.

---

Visit of President Cevdet Sunay of
Turkey — A248

**1966, Oct. 2    Litho.**
1405  A248  6r vio & dk brn    .50   .20

Mithras Type of 1964
**1966, Oct. 8    Size: 30x40mm**
1406  A199  6r olive bister & brn    .50   .30
Mehragan celebration.

Farmers — A249

**1966, Oct. 13**
1407  A249  5r olive bister & brn    2.50  1.00
Establishment of rural courts of justice.

UN Emblem — A250

**1966, Oct. 24    Wmk. 353    Perf. 10½**
1408  A250  6r brn org & blk    .50   .30
21st anniversary of United Nations.

Crown Prince
Reza — A251

**1966, Oct. 31    Litho.**
1409  A251  1r ultramarine    1.00   .75
1410  A251  2r violet    1.50   .75
  a.  Pair, #1409-1410    3.00  2.50
Children's Day; Crown Prince Reza's 6th
birthday.

Symbolic Woman's
Face — A252

**1966, Nov. 6**
1411  A252  5r gold, blk & ultra    .50   .20
Founding of the Iranian Women's Org.

Film Strip and Song Bird A253

**1966, Nov. 6**
1412 A253 4r blk, red lil & vio .65 .25
First Iranian children's film festival.

"Census Count" — A254

**1966, Nov. 11**
1413 A254 6r dk brn & gray .50 .20
National census.

Book Cover — A255

**1966, Nov. 15**
1414 A255 8r tan, brn & ultra .50 .20
Issued to publicize Book Week.

Reza Shah Pahlavi A256

Design: 2r, Reza Shah Pahlavi without kepi.

**1966, Nov. 16**     **Litho.**
1415 A256 1r slate blue 3.00 1.00
1416 A256 1r brown 3.00 1.00
  a.   Pair, #1415-1416 7.50 3.00
1417 A256 2r gray green 3.00 1.00
1418 A256 2r violet blue 3.00 1.00
  a.   Pair, #1417-1418 7.50 3.00
    Nos. 1415-1418 (4) 12.00 4.00
Reza Shah Pahlavi (1877-1944), founder of modern Iran.

EROPA Emblem and Map of Persia A257

**1966, Dec. 4**   **Wmk. 353**   **Perf. 10½**
1419 A257 8r dk brn & emerald 1.00 .25
4th General Assembly of the Org. of Public Administrators, EROPA.

Shah Giving Deeds to Farmers A258

**1967, Jan. 9**   **Wmk. 353**   **Perf. 10½**
1420 A258 6r ol bis, yel & brn 2.00 .20
Approval of land reform laws, 5th anniv.

Shah and 9-Star Crescent — A259

Design: 2r, Torch and 9-star crescent.

**1967, Jan. 26**   **Wmk. 353**   **Litho.**
1421 A259 2r multicolored 1.75 .50
1422 A259 6r multicolored 2.50 .50
5th anniv. of Shah's reforms, the "White Revolution."

Ancient Sculpture of Bull — A260

Designs: 5r, Sculptured mythical animals. 8r, Pillar from Persepolis.

**1967, Feb. 25**   **Wmk. 353**   **Perf. 10½**
1423 A260 3r dk brn & ocher 1.00 .35
1424 A260 5r Prus grn, brn & ocher 1.25 .45
1425 A260 8r vio, blk & sil 1.75 .65
    Nos. 1423-1425 (3) 4.00 1.45
Issued to publicize Museum Week.

Planting Tree — A261

**1967, Mar. 6**
1426 A261 8r brn org & grn .50 .20
Tree Planting Day.

Goldfish — A262

**1967, Mar. 11**
    **Size: 26x20mm**
1427 A262 1r shown .35 .20
    **Size: 35x27mm**
1428 A262 8r Swallows 1.00 .30
Issued for Novrooz, Iranian New Year.

Microscope, Animals and Emblem — A263

**1967, Mar. 11**     **Perf. 10½**
1429 A263 5r blk, gray & mag .50 .20
Second Iranian Veterinary Congress.

Pres. Arif of Iraq, Mosque — A264

**1967, Mar. 14**   **Litho.**   **Wmk. 353**
1430 A264 6r brt bl & grn .50 .30
Visit of Pres. Abdul Salam Mohammad Arif.

Fireworks A265

**1967, Mar. 17**
1431 A265 5r vio bl & multi 1.50 .50
Issued for United Nations Stamp Day.

Map of Iran and Oil Company Emblem — A266

**1967, Mar. 20**
1432 A266 6r multicolored 2.00 .45
Nationalization of Iranian Oil Industry.

Fencers A267

**1967, Mar. 23**
1433 A267 5r vio & bister 1.00 .50
Intl. Youth Fencing Championships, Tehran.

Shah and King of Thailand A268

**1967, Apr. 23**   **Wmk. 353**   **Perf. 10½**
1434 A268 6r brn org & dk brn 1.75 .45
Visit of King Bhumibol Adulyadej.

Old and Young Couples A269

**1967, Apr. 24**     **Litho.**
1435 A269 5r ol bis & vio bl .50 .20
15th anniversary of Social Insurance.

Skier and Iranian Olympic Emblem A270

Designs: 6r, Assyrian soldiers, Olympic rings and tablet inscribed "I.O.C." 8r, Wrestlers and Iranian Olympic emblem.

**1967, May 5**
1436 A270 3r brown & black .75 .25
1437 A270 6r multicolored 1.00 .45
1438 A270 8r ultra & brown 1.25 .75
    Nos. 1436-1438 (3) 3.00 1.45
65th Intl. Olympic Cong., Tehran, May 2-11.

Lions International — A271

**1967, May 11**
    **Size: 41½x30½mm**
1439 A271 3r shown .90 .50
    **Size: 36x42mm**
1440 A271 7r Emblem, vert. 1.40 .75
50th anniversary of Lions International.

Visit of Pres. Chivu Stoica of Romania — A272

**1967, May 13**
1441 A272 6r orange & dk bl .50 .20

International Tourist Year
Emblem — A273

**1967, June 6   Wmk. 353   *Perf. 10½***
1442   A273   3r brick red & ultra    .50   .20

Iranian
Pavilion and
Ornament
A274

**1967, June 7           Litho.**
1443   A274   4r dk brn, red & gold   .50   .20
1444   A274   10r red, dk brn & gold   .90   .20

EXPO '67, Montreal, Apr. 28-Oct. 27.

Stamp of
1870,
No. 1
A275

**1967, July 23   Wmk. 353   *Perf. 10½***
1445   A275   6r multi          .60   .30
1446   A275   8r multi          .90   .30

Centenary of first Persian postage stamp.

World Map and
School
Children — A276

**1967, Sept. 8    Litho.    Wmk. 353**
1447   A276   3r ultra & brt & brt bl   .40   .20
1448   A276   5r brown & yellow    .60   .20

World campaign against illiteracy.

Globe and
Oriental
Musician — A277

**1967, Sept. 10         *Perf. 10½***
1449   A277   14r brn org & dk brn   .75   .50

Intl. Conf. on Music Education in Oriental
Countries, Sept. 1967.

---

Child's Hand
Holding
Adult's — A278

**1967, Sept. 14    Litho.    Wmk. 353**
1450   A278   8r dk brn & yel    6.00   3.00

Introduction of Children's Villages in Iran.
(Modelled after Austrian SOS Villages for
homeless children).

Winged Wild
Goat — A279

**1967, Sept. 19**
1451   A279   8r dk brn & lemon    .60   .25
Festival of Arts, Persepolis.

UN
Emblem
A280

**1967, Oct. 17**
1452   A280   6r olive bister & vio bl   .35   .20
Issued for United Nations Day.

Shah and
Empress
Farah — A281

**1967, Oct. 26   Wmk. 353   *Perf. 10½***
**Various Frames**
1453   A281   2r sil, bl & brn      1.00   .40
1454   A281   10r sil, bl & vio     1.25   .60
1455   A281   14r lt bl, bl, gold & vio   2.75   1.50
      *Nos. 1453-1455 (3)*     5.00   2.50

Coronation of Shah Mohammad Reza Pahlavi and Empress Farah, Oct. 26, 1967.
Nos. 1453-1455 exist in imperf between
pairs, with top sheet margin, and in imperf
between blocks of 4, ungummed. Fake imperf
between pairs, lacking the top sheet margin,
have been manufactured by fraudulently perforating imperf-between blocks.

**1967, Oct. 31            Litho.**
Design: Crown Prince Reza.
1456   A281   2r silver & violet    1.00   .35
1457   A281   8r sil & red brown   1.50   .45
Children's Day; Crown Prince Reza's 7th
birthday.

---

Visit of Pres. Georgi
Traikov of
Bulgaria — A283

**1967, Nov. 20**
1458   A283   10r lilac & dk brn    .50   .20

Persian
Boy
Scout
Emblem
A284

**1967, Dec. 3   Wmk. 353   *Perf. 10½***
1459   A284   8r olive & red brn   1.50   .50

Cooperation Week of the Iranian Boy
Scouts, Dec. 5-12.

Hands
Holding
Chain
Link
A285

**1967, Dec. 6           Litho.**
1460   A285   6r multicolored    .50   .20
Issued to publicize Cooperation Year.

Visit of Sheik
Sabah of
Kuwait — A286

**1968, Jan. 10   Wmk. 353   *Perf. 10½***
1461   A286   10r lt bl & slate grn   .60   .20

List of Shah's 12 Reform Laws
4 — A287

**1968, Jan. 27    Litho.    Wmk. 353**
1462   A287   2r sl grn, brn & sal   .60   .30
1463   A287   8r vio, dk grn & lt      1.40   .35
            grn
1464   A287   14r brn, pink & lt lil   2.00   .50
      *Nos. 1462-1464 (3)*     4.00   1.15

"White Revolution of King and People."

Almond
Blossoms
A288

Haji Firooz
(New Year
Singer)
A289

Design: 2r, Tulips.

---

**1968, Mar. 12   Wmk. 353   *Perf. 10½***
1465   A288   1r multi          .40   .25
1466   A288   2r bluish gray & multi   .40   .25
1467   A288   2r brt rose lil & multi   .40   .25
1468   A289   6r multi         1.25   .45
      *Nos. 1465-1468 (4)*     2.45   1.20

Issued for Novrooz, Iranian New Year.

Oil Worker and
Derrick
A290

**1968, Mar. 20           Litho.**
1469   A290   14r grn, blk & org yel   1.50   .50
Oil industry nationalization, 17th anniv.

WHO Emblem
A291

**1968, Apr. 7   Wmk. 353   *Perf. 10½***
1470   A291   14r brn, bl & org    .85   .30
WHO, 20th anniversary.

Marlik Chariot,
Ancient
Sculpture
A292

**1968, Apr. 13**
1471   A292   8r blue, brn & buff   .50   .20

Fifth World Congress of Persian Archaeology and Art, Tehran.

Shah
and
King
Hassan
II
A293

**1968, Apr. 16**
1472   A293   6r bright vio & buff   1.10   .25
Visit of King Hassan II of Morocco.

Human Rights
Flame — A294

Soccer
Player — A295

Design: 14r, Frameline inscription reads, "International Conference on Human Rights Tehran 1968"; "Iran" at left.

**1968, May 5    Wmk. 353    Perf. 10½**
1473  A294  8r red & dk grn        .45   .25
1474  A294  14r vio bl & bl        .75   .30

Intl. Human Rights Year. The 8r commemorates the Iranian Human Rights Committee; the 14r, the Intl. Conference on Human Rights, Tehran, 1968.

**1968, May 10    Litho.**
1475  A295  8r multicolored       .45   .30
1476  A295  10r multicolored      .75   .30

Asian Soccer Cup Finals, Tehran.

Tehran Oil Refinery A296

**1968, May 21    Wmk. 353    Perf. 10½**
1477  A296  14r brt bl & multi    1.25   .35

Opening of the Tehran Oil Refinery.

Queen Farah as Girl Guide — A297

**1968, June 24    Litho.    Perf. 10½**
1478  A297  4r brt rose lil & bl
                green             2.00   .75
1479  A297  6r car & brn         2.50  1.00

Great Camp of Iranian Girl Guides.

Anopheles Mosquito, Congress Emblem — A298

Winged Figure with Banner, and Globe — A299

**1968, Sept. 7    Wmk. 353    Perf. 10½**
1480  A298  6r brt pur & blk      .65   .35
1481  A298  14r dk grn & mag     1.00   .40

8th Intl. Congress on Tropical Medicine and Malaria, Tehran, Sept. 7-15.

**1968, Sept. 8    Litho.**
1482  A299  6r lt vio, bis & bl   .50   .25
1483  A299  14r dl yel, sl grn &
                brn               .80   .30

World campaign against illiteracy.

Oramental Horse and Flower — A300

**1968, Sept. 11**
1484  A300  14r sl grn, org & yel
                grn               .75   .20

2nd Festival of Arts, Shiraz-Persepolis.

INTERPOL Emblem and Globe — A301

**1968, Oct. 6    Wmk. 353    Perf. 10½**
1485  A301  10r dk brn & bl       .75   .20

37th General Assembly of the Intl. Police Org. (INTERPOL) in Tehran.

Police Emblem on Iran Map in Flag Colors — A302

Peace Dove and UN Emblem — A303

**1968, Oct. 7    Litho.**
1486  A302  14r multicolored     1.25   .30

Issued for Police Day.

**1968, Oct. 24**
1487  A303  14r bl & vio bl      1.00   .25

Issued for United Nations Day.

Empress Farah — A304

Designs: 8r, Mohammad Reza Shah Pahlavi. 10fr, Shah, Empress and Crown Prince.

**1968, Oct. 26**
1488  A304  6r multi            7.00   3.50
1489  A304  8r multi            8.00   5.00
1490  A304  10r multi          10.00   6.00
      Nos. 1488-1490 (3)       25.00  14.50

Coronation of Mohammad Reza Shah Pahlavi and Empress Farah, 1st anniv.

Shah's Crown and Bull's Head Capital — A305

UNICEF Emblem and Child's Drawing — A306

**1968, Oct. 30**
1491  A305  14r ultra, gold, sil &
                red               .75   .20

Festival of Arts and Culture.

**1968, Oct. 31    Litho.**
Children's Drawings and UNICEF Emblem: 3r, Boat on lake, house and trees, horiz. 5r, Flowers, horiz.

1492  A306  2r dk brn & multi    .30   .25
1493  A306  3r dk grn & multi    .40   .30
1494  A306  5r multicolored      .65   .40
      Nos. 1492-1494 (3)        1.35   .95

Issued for Children's Day.

Labor Union Emblem A307

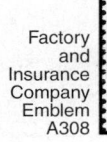

Factory and Insurance Company Emblem A308

Designs: 8r, Members of Army of Hygiene, and Insurance Company emblem. 10r, Map of Persia, Insurance Company emblem, car, train, ship and plane.

**1968, Nov. 6    Wmk. 353    Perf. 10½**
1495  A307  4r sil & vio bl      .40   .30
1496  A308  5r multicolored      .55   .30
1497  A308  8r ultra, gray & yel .70   .30
1498  A308  10r multicolored     .80   .35
      Nos. 1495-1498 (4)        2.45  1.25

Issued to publicize Insurance Day.

Human Rights Flame, Man and Woman — A309

**1968, Dec. 10    Litho.    Perf. 10½**
1499  A309  8r lt bl, vio bl & car .60  .20

International Human Rights Year.

Symbols of Shah's Reform Plan — A310

Design: Each stamp shows symbols of 3 of the Shah's reforms. No. 1503a shows the 12 symbols in a circle with a medallion in the center picturing 3 heads and a torch.

**1969, Jan. 26    Wmk. 353    Perf. 10½**
1500  2r ocher, grn & lil        1.50   .50
1501  4r lil, ocher & grn        1.50   .60
1502  6r lil, ocher & grn        1.75   .75
1503  8r lil, ocher & grn        2.75  1.10
   a. A310 Block of 4, #1500-1503 10.00  4.50
      Nos. 1500-1503 (4)         7.50  2.95

Declaration of the Shah's Reform Plan.

Shah and Crowd A311

**1969, Feb. 1    Litho.**
1504  A311  6r red, bl & brn     2.00   .35

10,000th day of the reign of the Shah.

European Goldfinch A312

2r, Ring-necked pheasant. 8r, Roses.

**1969, Mar. 6    Wmk. 353    Perf. 10½**
1505  A312  1r multicolored      .30   .20
1506  A312  2r multicolored      .35   .20
1507  A312  8r multicolored     1.00   .20
      Nos. 1505-1507 (3)        1.65   .60

Issued for Novrooz, Iranian New Year.

"Woman Lawyer" Holding Scales of Justice — A313

Workers, ILO and UN Emblems — A314

**1969, Apr. 8    Litho.    Perf. 10½**
1508  A313  6r blk & brt bl          .50  .20
15th General Assembly of Women Lawyers, Tehran, Apr. 8-14.

**1969, Apr. 30    Wmk. 353    Perf. 10½**
1509  A314  10r bl & vio bl          .65  .20
ILO, 50th anniversary.

Freestyle Wrestlers and Aryamehr Cup — A315

**1969, May 6    Litho.**
1510  A315  10r lilac & multi          2.00  .75
Intl. Freestyle Wrestling Championships, 3rd round.

Birds and Flower A316

**1969, June 10    Wmk. 353    Perf. 10½**
1511  A316  10r vio bl & multi         .75  .20
Issued to publicize Handicrafts Day.

Boy Scout Symbols A317

**1969, July 9    Wmk. 353    Perf. 10½**
1512  A317  6r lt bl & multi          1.25  .30
Philia 1969, an outdoor training course for Boy Scout patrol leaders.

Lady Serving Wine, Safavi Miniature, Iran — A318

#1514, Lady on Balcony, Mogul miniature, Pakistan. #1515, Sultan Suleiman Receiving Sheik Abdul Latif, 16th cent. miniature, Turkey.

**1969, July 21    Litho.**
1513  A318  25r multi          2.50  .65
1514  A318  25r multi          2.50  .65
1515  A318  25r multi          2.50  .70
       Nos. 1513-1515 (3)    7.50  2.00
Signing of the Regional Cooperation for Development Pact by Turkey, Iran and Pakistan, 5th anniv.

Neil A. Armstrong and Col. Edwin E. Aldrin on Moon — A319

**1969, July 26**
1516  A319  24r bister, bl & brn          7.50  3.00
See note after Algeria No. 427.

Quotation from Shah's Declaration on Education and Art — A320

**1969, Aug. 6    Wmk. 353    Perf. 10½**
1517  A320  10r car, cream & emer   .75  .20
Anniv. of educational and art reforms.

Offshore Oil Rig in Persian Gulf — A321

**1969, Sept. 1    Litho.**
1518  A321  8r multicolored          1.40  .35
Marine drillings by the Iran-Italia Oil Co., 10th anniv.

Dancers Forming Flower — A322

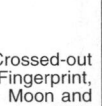

Crossed-out Fingerprint, Moon and Rocket — A323

**1969, Sept. 6    Wmk. 353    Perf. 10½**
1519  A322  6r multicolored          .45  .25
1520  A322  8r multicolored          .65  .25
3rd Festival of Arts, Shiraz and Persepolis, Aug. 30-Sept. 9.

**1969, Sept. 8    Litho.**
1521  A323  4r multicolored          .40  .20
World campaign against illiteracy.

Persepolis, Simulated Stamp with UPU Emblem, and Shah — A324

**1969, Sept. 28**
1522  A324  10r lt bl & multi          3.00  1.00
1523  A324  14r multicolored          4.00  1.50
16th Congress of the UPU, Tokyo.

Fair Emblem — A325

14r, like 8r, inscribed "ASIA 69." 20r, Fair emblem, world map and "ASIA 69," horiz.

**1969, Oct. 5    Wmk. 353    Perf. 10½**
1524  A325  8r rose & multi          .60  .30
1525  A325  14r blue & multi          .75  .30
1526  A325  20r tan & multi          1.25  .40
       Nos. 1524-1526 (3)    2.60  1.00
2nd Asian Trade Fair, Tehran.

Justice — A326

**1969, Oct. 13    Litho.**
1527  A326  8r bl grn & dk brn          .60  .20
Rural Courts of Justice Day.

UN Emblem A327

**1969, Oct. 24**
1528  A327  2r lt bl & dp bl          .40  .20
25th anniversary of the United Nations.

Emblem and Column Capital, Persepolis — A328

**1969, Oct. 28**
1529  A328  2r deep blue & multi          .60  .25
2nd Festival of Arts and Culture.  See Nos. 1577, 1681, 1735.

Child's Drawing and UNICEF Emblem A329

Children's Drawings and UNICEF Emblem: 1r, Boy and birds, vert. 5r, Dinner.

**1969, Oct. 31    Wmk. 353    Perf. 10½**
**Size: 28x40mm, 40x28mm**
1530  A329  1r lt blue & multi          .30  .20
1531  A329  2r lt grn & multi          .40  .20
1532  A329  5r lt lil & multi          .75  .25
       Nos. 1530-1532 (3)    1.45  .65
Children's Week.  See Nos. 1578-1580.

Globe Emblem A330

**1969, Nov. 6**
1533  A330  8r dk brn & bl          .60  .20
Meeting of the Natl. Society of Parents and Educators, Tehran.

Satellite Communications Station — A331

**1969, Nov. 19    Litho.**
1534  A331  6r blk brn & bis          1.00  .30
1st Iranian Satellite Communications Earth Station, Hamadan.

Mahatma Gandhi (1869-1948) A332

**1969, Dec. 29    Wmk. 353    Perf. 10½**
1535  A332  14r gray & dk rose
                       brn          8.00  3.00

Globe, Flags and Emblems A333

Design: 6r, Globe and Red Cross, Red Lion and Sun, and Red Crescent Emblems.

**1969, Dec. 31**
1536 A333 2r red & multi .75 .30
1537 A333 6r red & multi 1.25 .40

League of Red Cross Societies, 50th anniv.

Symbols of Reform Laws and Shah A334

**1970, Jan. 26 Litho. Wmk. 353**
1538 A334 1r bister & multi 1.25 .40
1539 A334 2r multicolored 1.50 .60

Declaration of the Shah's Reform Plan.

Pansies A335

New Year's Table A336

**1970, Mar. 6 Wmk. 353 Perf. 10½**
1540 A335 1r multicolored .35 .20
1541 A336 8r multicolored 1.75 .30

Issued for the Iranian New Year.

Chemical Plant, Kharg Island, and Iranian Oil Company Emblem — A337

Designs (Iranian Oil Company Emblem and): 2r, Shah's portrait and quotation. 4r, Laying of gas pipe line and tractor. 8r, Tankers at pier of Kharg Island, vert. 10r, Tehran refinery.

**1970, Mar. 20 Wmk. 353 Perf. 10½**
1542 A337 2r gray & multi 1.50 .50
1543 A337 4r multicolored 1.75 .75
1544 A337 6r lt bl & multi 2.00 .95
1545 A337 8r multicolored 2.50 1.00
1546 A337 10r multicolored 3.00 1.25
Nos. 1542-1546 (5) 10.75 4.45

Nationalization of the oil industry, 20th anniv.

EXPO '70 Emblem — A338

Radar, Satellite and Congress Emblem — A339

**1970, Mar. 27 Litho.**
1547 A338 4r brt rose lil & vio bl .40 .20
1548 A338 10r lt bl & pur .75 .20

EXPO '70, Osaka, Japan, Mar. 15-Sept. 13.

**1970, Apr. 20 Wmk. 353 Perf. 10½**
1549 A339 14r multicolored 1.25 .35

Asia-Australia Telecommunications Congress, Tehran.

UPU Headquarters, Bern — A340

**1970, May 10**
1550 A340 2r gray, brn & lil rose .50 .25
1551 A340 4r lil, brn & lil rose .75 .25

Inauguration of the new UPU Headquarters, Bern.

Asia Productivity Year Emblem — A341

**1970, May 19 Wmk. 353 Perf. 10½**
1552 A341 8r gray & multi .55 .20

Asian Productivity Year, 1970.

Bird Bringing Baby A342

**1970, June 15 Litho.**
1553 A342 8r brn & dk blue .65 .25

Iranian School for Midwives, 50th anniv.

Tomb of Cyrus the Great, Meshed-Morghab in Fars — A343

Designs: 8r, Pillars of Apadana Palace, Persepolis, vert. 10r, Bas-relief from a Mede tomb, Iraq. 14r, Achaemenian officers, bas-relief, Persepolis.

**1970, June 21 Photo. Perf. 13**
1554 A343 6r gray, red & vio 1.75 .25
1555 A343 8r pale rose, blk & bl grn 2.00 .50
1556 A343 10r yel, red & brn 2.25 .65
1557 A343 14r bl, blk & red brn 2.50 1.00
Nos. 1554-1557 (4) 8.50 2.40

2500th anniversary of the founding of the Persian Empire by Cyrus the Great. See #1561-1571, 1589-1596, 1605-1612.

Seeyo-Se-Pol Bridge, Isfahan — A344

#1559, Saiful Malook Lake, Pakistan, vert. #1560, View of Fethiye, Turkey, vert.

**Wmk. 353**
**1970, July 21 Litho. Perf. 10½**
1558 A344 2r multicolored 1.00 .25
1559 A344 2r multicolored 1.00 .25
1560 A344 2r multicolored 1.00 .25
Nos. 1558-1560 (3) 3.00 .75

Signing of the Regional Cooperation for Development Pact by Iran, Turkey and Pakistan, 6th anniv.

Queen Buran, Dirhem Coin A345

Wine Goblet with Lion's Head — A346

Designs: No. 1562, Achaemenian eagle amulet. No. 1563, Mithridates I, dirhem coin. No. 1564, Sassanidae art (arch, coin, jugs). No. 1566, Shapur I, dirhem coin. No. 1567, Achaemenian courier. No. 1568, Winged deer. No. 1569, Ardashir I, dirhem coin. No. 1570, Seal of Darius I (chariot, palms, lion). 14r, Achaemenian tapestry.

**1970 Wmk. 353 Photo. Perf. 13**
1561 A345 1r gold & multi 1.25 .25
1562 A346 2r gold & multi 1.50 .40
1563 A345 2r gold & multi 1.50 .50
1564 A346 2r lilac & multi 1.50 .50
1565 A346 6r lilac & multi 1.75 .40
1566 A345 6r lilac & multi 1.75 .60
1567 A346 8r lilac & multi 2.00 .60
1568 A346 8r lilac & multi 2.00 .50
1569 A345 8r lilac & multi 2.00 .75
1570 A345 8r lilac & multi 2.25 .75
1571 A345 14r lt bl & multi 2.50 1.10
Nos. 1561-1571 (11) 20.00 6.60

2500th anniversary of the founding of the Persian Empire by Cyrus the Great.
Issued: 1r, #1563, 1566, 1569, 8/22; #1562, 1565, 1568, 14r, 8/6; others, 9/22.

Candle and Globe — A347

Persian Decoration A348

**1970, Sept. 8 Litho. Perf. 10½**
1572 A347 1r lt bl & multi .25 .20
1573 A347 2r pale sal & multi .30 .20

Issued to publicize World Literacy Day.

**1970, Sept. 14**
1574 A348 6r multi .45 .20

Isfahan Intl. Cong. of Architects, Sept. 1970.

Emblem — A349

UN Emblem, Dove and Scales — A350

**1970, Sept. 28 Perf. 10½**
1575 A349 2r lt bl & pur .30 .20

Congress of Election Committees of Persian States and Tehran.

**1970, Oct. 24 Litho. Wmk. 353**
1576 A350 2r lt bl, mag & dk bl .30 .20

Issued for United Nations Day.

Festival Type of 1969

**1970, Oct. 28 Perf. 10½**
1577 A328 2r org & multi .40 .20

3rd Festival of Arts and Culture.

UNICEF Type of 1969

Children's Drawings and UNICEF Emblem: 50d, Herdsman and goats. 1r, Family picnic. 2r, Mosque.

**1970, Oct. 31**
**Size: 43½x31mm**
1578 A329 50d black & multi .25 .20
1579 A329 1r black & multi .30 .20
1580 A329 2r black & multi .45 .20
Nos. 1578-1580 (3) 1.00 .60

Issued for Children's Week.

Mohammad
Reza Shah
Pahlavi
A351

**1971, Jan. 26**    **Wmk. 353**    *Perf. 10½*
1581 A351 2r lt bl & multi      3.00 .75
Publicizing the "White Revolution of King
and People" and the 12 reform laws.

Sheldrake — A352

2r, Ruddy shelduck. 8r, Flamingo, vert.

**1971, Jan. 30**          **Litho.**
1582 A352 1r multicolored    1.50 .50
1583 A352 2r multicolored    1.75 .75
1584 A352 8r multicolored    3.00 1.00
     Nos. 1582-1584 (3)    6.25 2.25
· Intl. Wetland and Waterfowl Conf., Ramsar.

Reza Shah
Pahlavi — A353

**1971, Feb. 22**    **Wmk. 353**    *Perf. 10½*
1585 A353 6r multicolored    6.00 2.50
50th anniversary of the Pahlavi dynasty's
accession to power.

Rooster
A354

2r, Barn swallow and nest. 6r, Hoopoe.

**1971, Mar. 6**    **Photo.**    *Perf. 13½x13*
1586 A354 1r multicolored    1.25 .45
1587 A354 2r multicolored    1.75 .75
1588 A354 6r multicolored    3.00 1.00
     Nos. 1586-1588 (3)    6.00 2.20
Novrooz, Iranian New Year.

Shapur II Hunting — A355

Bull's Head,
Persepolis
A356

1r, Harpist, mosaic. #1591, Investiture of
Ardashir I, bas-relief. 5r Winged lion ornament. 6r, Persian archer, bas-relief. 8r, Royal
audience, bas-relief. 10r, Bronze head of Parthian prince.

**1971**      **Litho.**      *Perf. 10½*
1589 A356 1r multicolored    1.50 .45
1590 A355 2r blk & brn org    1.75 .45
1591 A355 2r lil, gldn brn & blk    1.75 .45
1592 A356 4r pur & multi    1.75 .45
1593 A356 5r multicolored    2.00 .55
1594 A356 6r multicolored    2.00 .55
1595 A356 8r lt bl & multi    2.75 .80
1596 A356 10r dp bis, blk &
             slate    2.75 .90
     Nos. 1589-1596 (8)    16.25 4.60
2500th anniversary of the founding of the
Persian Empire by Cyrus the Great.
   Issued: 4r, 5r, 6r, 8r, 5/15; others, 6/15.

Prisoners Leaving Jail — A357

**1971, May 20**    **Litho.**    **Wmk. 353**
1597 A357 6r multicolored    1.75 .20
1598 A357 8r multicolored    3.00 .20
Rehabilitation of Prisoners Week.

Religious
School,
Chaharbagh,
Ispahan
A358

#1600, Mosque of Selim, Edirne, Turkey.
#1601, Badshahi Mosque, Lahore, Pakistan,
horiz.

**1971, July 21**    **Litho.**    *Perf. 10½*
1599 A358 2r multicolored    .40 .20
1600 A358 2r multicolored    .40 .20
1601 A358 2r multicolored    .40 .20
     Nos. 1599-1601 (3)    1.20 .60
7th anniversary of Regional Cooperation
among Iran, Pakistan and Turkey.

"Fifth Festival of
Arts" — A359

**1971, Aug. 26**      **Litho. & Typo.**
1602 A359 2r lt & dk grn, red &
             gold    .85 .30
5th Festival of Arts, Shiraz-Persepolis.

"Fight Against Illiteracy" — A360

**1971, Sept. 8**          **Litho.**
1603 A360 2r grn & multi    .65 .30
International Literacy Day, Sept. 8.

Kings
Abdullah
and
Hussein
II of
Jordan
A361

**1971, Sept. 11**
1604 A361 2r yel grn, blk & red    .75 .35
Hashemite Kingdom of Jordan, 50th anniv.

Shahyad Aryamehr Monument — A362

Designs: 1r, Aryamehr steel mill, near Isfahan. 3r, Senate Building, Tehran. 11r, Shah
Abbas Kabir Dam, Zayandeh River.

**1971, Sept. 22**
1605 A362 1r blue & multi    1.50 .45
1606 A362 2r multicolored    1.75 .45
1607 A362 3r brt pink & multi    1.75 .45
1608 A362 11r org & multi    2.50 .90
     Nos. 1605-1608 (4)    7.50 2.25
2500th anniversary of the founding of the
Persian empire by Cyrus the Great.

Mohammad Reza Shah
Pahlavi — A363

Designs: 2r, Riza Shah Pahlavi. 5r, Stone
tablet with proclamation of Cyrus the Great,
horiz. 10r, Crown of present empire (erroneously inscribed Le Couronne).

**1971, Oct. 12**
1609 A363 1r gold & multi    4.00 2.00
1610 A363 2r gold & multi    4.00 2.00
1611 A363 5r gold & multi    5.00 2.50
1612 A363 10r gold & multi    6.00 3.00
     Nos. 1609-1612 (4)    19.00 9.50
2500th anniversary of the founding of the
Persian empire by Cyrus the Great.

Ghatour Railroad Bridge — A364

**1971, Oct. 7**
1613 A364 2r multicolored    2.00 .75
Iran-Turkey railroad.

Racial Equality
Emblem
A365

**1971, Oct. 24**
1614 A365 2r lt blue & multi    .25 .20
Intl. Year Against Racial Discrimination.

Mohammad Riza
Pahlavi — A366

           *Perf. 13½x13*
**1971, Oct. 26**    **Photo.**    **Wmk. 353**
       **Size: 20½x28mm**
1615 A366 5d lilac    .20 .20
1616 A366 10d henna brown    .20 .20
1617 A366 50d brt bl grn    .25 .20
1618 A366 1r dp yel grn    .30 .20
1619 A366 2r brown    .30 .20
       **Size: 27x36½mm**
1620 A366 6r slate green    1.10 .20
1621 A366 8r violet blue    1.60 1.10
1622 A366 10r red lilac    1.40 .30
1623 A366 11r blue green    5.00 1.10
1624 A366 14r brt blue    8.50 .50
1625 A366 20r car rose    8.00 .65
1626 A366 50r yellow bis    6.75 1.25
     Nos. 1615-1626 (12)    33.60 6.10
See Nos. 1650-1661B, 1768-1772.

Child's Drawing and Emblem — A367

Designs: No. 1631, Ruins of Persepolis,
vert. No. 1632, Warrior, mosaic, vert.

**1971, Oct. 31**    **Litho.**    *Perf. 10½*
1630 A367 2r multicolored    .40 .20
1631 A367 2r multicolored    .40 .20
1632 A367 2r multicolored    .40 .20
     Nos. 1630-1632 (3)    1.20 .60
Children's Week.

UNESCO Emblem and "25" A368

**1971, Nov. 4**
1633 A368 6r ultra & rose claret .50 .20
25th anniversary of UNESCO.

Domestic Animals and Emblem A369

**1971, Nov. 22**
1634 A369 2r gray, blk & car .40 .20
4th Iranian Veterinarians' Congress.

ILO Emblem, Cog Wheels and Globe A370

**1971, Dec. 4**
1635 A370 2r black, org & bl .40 .20
7th ILO Conference for the Asian Region.

UNICEF Emblem, Bird Feeding Young A371

**1971, Dec. 16       Perf. 13x13½**
1636 A371 2r lt bl, mag & blk .40 .20
25th anniversary of UNICEF.

Mohammad Reza Shah Pahlavi A372

**1972, Jan. 26   Wmk. 353   Perf. 10½**
1637 A372 2r lt green & multi 4.00 2.00
a.   20r Souvenir sheet 15.00 10.00
"White Revolution of King and People" and the 12 reform laws. No. 1637a contains one stamp with simulated perforations.

Pintailed Sandgrouse — A373

#1639, Rock ptarmigan. 2r, Yellow-billed waxbill and red-cheeked cordon-bleu.

**1972, Mar. 6   Litho.   Perf. 13x13½**
1638 A373 1r lt green & multi 1.00 .50
1639 A373 1r lt blue & multi 1.00 .50
1640 A373 2r yellow & multi 1.75 .60
Nos. 1638-1640 (3) 3.75 1.60
Iranian New Year.

"Your Heart is your Health" — A374

Film Strip and Winged Antelope A375

**1972, Apr. 4                   Perf. 10½**
1641 A374 10r lemon & multi 2.00 .30
World Health Day; Iranian Society of Cardiology.

**1972, Apr. 16          Litho. & Engr.**
8r, Film strips and winged antelope.
1642 A375 6r ultra & gold 1.00 .30
1643 A375 8r yellow & multi 1.75 .35
Tehran International Film Festival.

Rose and Bud — A376

**1972, May 5                    Litho.**
1644 A376 1r shown .40 .30
1645 A376 2r Yellow roses .70 .35
1646 A376 5r Red rose .85 .40
Nos. 1644-1646 (3) 1.95 1.05
See Nos. 1711-1713.

Persian Woman, by Behzad A377

Paintings: No. 1648, Fisherman, by Cevat Dereli (Turkey). No. 1649, Young Man, by Abdur Rehman Chughtai (Pakistan).

**1972, July 21                Wmk. 353**
1647 A377 5r gray & multi 1.40 .30
1648 A377 5r gray & multi 1.40 .30
1649 A377 5r gray & multi 1.40 .30
Nos. 1647-1649 (3) 4.20 .90
Regional Cooperation for Development Pact among Iran, Turkey and Pakistan, 8th anniv.

Shah Type of 1971
**1972-73   Photo.   Perf. 13½x13**
**Bister Frame & Crown**
**Size: 20½x28mm**
1650 A366 5d lilac .20 .20
1651 A366 10d henna brown .20 .20
1652 A366 50d brt blue grn .25 .20
1653 A366 1r dp yel grn .30 .20
a.   Brn frame & crown ('73) .55 .20
1654 A366 2r brown .50 .20
**Size: 27x36½mm**
1655 A366 6r slate grn .75 .20
1656 A366 8r violet blue .75 .20
1657 A366 10r red lilac 1.00 .20
1658 A366 11r blue green 1.40 .80
1659 A366 14r dull blue 5.50 .60
1660 A366 20r car rose 8.50 .50
1661 A366 50r grnsh blue 3.75 1.00
1661A A366 100r violet ('73) 5.00 2.00
1661B A366 200r slate ('73) 11.00 3.50
Nos. 1650-1661B (14) 39.10 10.00

Festival Emblem A378

**1972, Aug. 31   Litho.   Perf. 10½**
1662 A378 6r emerald, red & blk 1.10 .20
1663 A378 8r brt mag, blk & grn 1.60 .25
6th Festival of Arts, Shiraz-Persepolis, Aug. 31-Sept. 8.

Pens and Emblem A379

"10" and Emblems A380

**1972, Sept. 8**
1664 A379 1r lt blue & multi .25 .20
1665 A379 2r yellow & multi .40 .20
World Literacy Day, Sept. 8.

**1972, Sept. 18**
1666 A380 1r lilac & multi .25 .20
1667 A380 2r dull yel & multi .45 .25
10th Congress of Iranian Dentists' Assoc., Sept. 18-22.

Asian Broadcasting Union Emblem — A381

No. 450 on Cover — A382

**1972, Oct. 1**
1668 A381 6r lt green & multi .75 .20
1669 A381 8r gray & multi 1.50 .20
9th General Assembly of Asian Broadcasting Union, Tehran, Oct. 1972.

**1972, Oct. 9**
1670 A382 10r lt blue & multi 2.25 .25
International Stamp Day.

Chess and Olympic Rings — A383

Olympic Rings and: 2r, Hunter. 3r, Archer. 5r, Equestrians. 6r, Polo. 8r, Wrestling.

**1972, Oct. 17**
1671 A383 1r brown & multi 3.00 1.50
1672 A383 2r blue & multi 2.50 .50
1673 A383 3r lilac & multi 2.50 .50
1674 A383 5r bl grn & multi 3.00 .75
1675 A383 6r red & multi 4.00 .75
1676 A383 8r yel grn & multi 6.00 1.00
a.   Souv. sheet of 6, #1671-
1676, imperf. 25.00 15.00
Nos. 1671-1676 (6) 21.00 5.00
20th Olympic Games, Munich, 8/26-9/11.

Communications Symbol, UN Emblem — A384

Children and Flowers — A385

**1972, Oct. 24**
1677 A384 10r multicolored 2.00 .20
United Nations Day.

**1972, Oct. 31   Litho.   Wmk. 353**
Children's Drawings and Emblem: No. 1679, Puppet show. 6r, Boys cutting wood, horiz.
1678 A385 2r gray & multi .35 .20
1679 A385 2r bister & multi .70 .20
1680 A385 6r pink & multi 1.40 .20
Nos. 1678-1680 (3) 2.45 .60
Children's Week.

## Festival Type of 1969

Design: 10r, Crown, emblems and column capital, Persepolis.

**1972, Nov. 11**
1681 A328 10r dp blue & multi    6.00 1.00

10th anniv. of White Revolution; Festival of Culture and Art.

Family Planning Emblem A386

**1972, Dec. 5**
1682 A386 1r blue & multi    .30 .20
1683 A386 2r brt pink & multi    .40 .20

To promote family planning.

Iranian Scout Organization, 20th anniv. — A387

**1972, Dec. 9**
1684 A387 2r multicolored    .50 .20

Ancient Seal A388

Designs: Various ancient seals.

**1973, Jan. 5**    *Perf. 10½*
1685 A388 1r blue, red & brn    .60 .20
1686 A388 1r yellow & multi    .60 .20
1687 A388 1r pink & multi    .60 .20
1688 A388 2r lt brick red & multi    .60 .20
1689 A388 2r dull org & multi    .60 .20
1690 A388 2r olive & multi    .60 .20
    Nos. 1685-1690 (6)    3.60 1.20

Development of writing.

Books and Book Year Emblem A389

Design: 6r, Illuminated page, 10th century, from Shahnameh, by Firdousi.

**1973, Jan. 10**
1691 A389 2r black & multi    .75 .20
1692 A389 6r yellow & multi    1.10 .20

International Book Year.

"12 Improvements by the King" — A390

Designs: 2r, 10r, 12 circles symbolizing 12 improvements. 6r, like 1r.

**1973, Jan. 26**    **Litho.**
**Size: 29x43mm**
1693 A390 1r gold, ultra, red & yel    .30 .20
1694 A390 2r sil, plum, ol & yel    .35 .20
**Size: 65x84mm**
1695 A390 6r gold, ultra, red & yel    2.00 1.00
    Nos. 1693-1695 (3)    2.65 1.40
**Souvenir Sheet**
*Imperf*
1696 A390 10r sil, plum, ol & yel    3.25 1.50

Introduction of the King's socioeconomic reforms, 10th anniv.

Blue Surgeonfish A391

Fish: No. 1698, Gilthead. No. 1699, Banded sergeant major. No. 1700, Porkfish. No. 1701, Black-spot snapper.

**1973, Mar. 6    Wmk. 353    Perf. 10½**
1697 A391 1r multicolored    .75 .30
1698 A391 1r multicolored    .75 .30
1699 A391 2r multicolored    1.25 .45
1700 A391 2r multicolored    1.25 .45
1701 A391 2r multicolored    1.25 .45
    Nos. 1697-1701 (5)    5.25 1.95

Iranian New Year.

WHO Emblem A392

**1973, Apr. 7    Litho.    Wmk. 353**
1702 A392 10r brn, grn & red    1.25 .20

25th anniversary of the WHO.

Soccer — A393       Tracks and Globe — A394

**1973, Apr. 13**
1703 A393 14r orange & multi    1.40 .25

15th Asian Youth Football (soccer) Tournament.

**1973, May 10    Wmk. 353    *Perf. 10½***
1704 A394 10r dk grn, lil & vio bl    2.00 .60

13th International Railroad Conference.

Clay Tablet with Aryan Script — A395

Designs: Clay tablets with various scripts.

**1973, June 5**    *Perf. 10½*
1705 A395 1r shown    .50 .20
1706 A395 1r Kharoshthi    .50 .20
1707 A395 1r Achaemenian    .50 .20
1708 A395 2r Parthian (Mianeh)    .90 .20
1709 A395 2r Parthian (Arsacide)    .90 .20
1710 A395 2r Gachtak (Dabireh)    .90 .20
    Nos. 1705-1710 (6)    4.20 1.20

Development of writing.

## Flower Type of 1972

**1973, June 20**
1711 A376 1r Orchid    .20 .20
1712 A376 2r Hyacinth    .55 .20
1713 A376 6r Columbine    1.25 .20
    Nos. 1711-1713 (3)    2.00 .60

Regional Cooperation for Development Pact Among Iran, Turkey and Pakistan, 9th Anniv. — A396

Designs: No. 1714, Head from mausoleum of King Antiochus I (69-34 B.C.), Turkey. No. 1715, Statue, Shahdad Kerman, Persia, 4000 B.C. No. 1716, Street, Mohenjo-Daro, Pakistan.

**1973, July 21**
1714 A396 2r brown & multi    .35 .20
1715 A396 2r green & multi    .35 .20
1716 A396 2r blue & multi    .35 .20
    a.    Strip of 3, #1714-1716    1.25 .75

Shah, Oil Pump, Refinery and Tanker A397

**1973, Aug. 4**
1717 A397 5r blue & black    2.50 .75

Nationalization of oil industry.

Soldiers and Rising Sun — A398

**1973, Aug. 19    Litho.    Wmk. 353**
1718 A398 2r ultra & multi    .45 .20

20th anniversary of return of monarchy.

Gymnasts and Globe — A399

**1973, Aug. 23**    *Perf. 10½*
1719 A399 2r olive & multi    .30 .20
1720 A399 2r violet bl & multi    .30 .20

7th Intl. Congress of Physical Education and Sports for Girls and Women, Tehran, Aug. 19-25.

Shahyad Monument (later Azadi Monument), Rainbow and WMO Emblem — A400

**1973, Sept. 4**
1721 A400 5r multicolored    .75 .20

Intl. meteorological cooperation, centenary.

Festival Emblem — A401

**1973, Aug. 31**
1722 A401 1r silver & multi    .30 .20
1723 A401 5r gold & multi    .50 .20

7th Festival of Arts, Shiraz-Persepolis.

Wrestlers A402

**1973, Sept. 6    Litho.    Wmk. 353**
1724 A402 6r lt green & multi    1.50 .50

World Wrestling Championships, Tehran, Sept. 6-14.

"Literacy as Light" — A403

**1973, Sept. 8**
1725 A403 2r multicolored    .30 .20

World Literacy Day, Sept. 8.

Audio-Visual Equipment A404

**1973, Sept. 11**
1726 A404 10r yellow & multi   1.00   .35
Tehran Intl. Audio-Visual Exhib., Sept. 11-24.

Warrior Taming Winged Bull A405

**1973, Sept. 16**
1727 A405 8r blue gray & multi   .75   .20
Intl. Council of Military Sports, 25th anniv.

Abu Rayhan Biruni (973-1048), Philosopher and Mathematician A406

**1973, Sept. 16**
1728 A406 10r brown & black   1.10   .35

Soccer Cup — A407

**1973, Oct. 2   Wmk. 353   Perf. 10½**
1729 A407 2r lilac, blk & buff   .35   .20
Soccer Games for the Crown Prince's Cup.

INTERPOL Emblem — A408

**1973, Oct. 7**
1730 A408 2r multicolored   .35   .20
50th anniversary of INTERPOL.

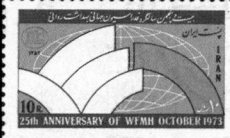

Symbolic Arches and Globe A409

**1973, Oct. 8**
1731 A409 10r orange & multi   .55   .25
World Federation for Mental Health, 25th anniv.

UPU Emblem, Letter, Post Horn — A410

**1973, Oct. 9**
1732 A410 6r blue & orange   .50   .20
World Post Day, Oct. 9.

Honeycomb A411

**1973, Oct. 24**
1733 A411 2r lt brown & multi   .30   .20
1734 A411 2r gray olive & multi   .30   .20
UN Volunteer Program, 5th anniv.

**Festival Type of 1969**
2r, Crown & column capital, Persepolis.

**1973, Oct. 26**
1735 A328 2r yellow & multi   .40   .20
Festival of Culture and Art.

Turkish Bosporus Bridge, Flag A412

8r, Kemal Ataturk & Reza Shah Pahlavi.

**1973, Oct. 29   Litho.   Perf. 10½**
1736 A412 2r multicolored   .75   .20
1737 A412 8r multicolored   1.25   .25
50th anniversary of the Turkish Republic.

Mother and Child, Emblem — A413

Children's Drawings and Emblem: No. 1739, Wagon, horiz. No. 1740, House and garden with birds.

**1973, Oct. 31**
1738 A413 2r multicolored   .30   .20
1739 A413 2r multicolored   .30   .20
1740 A413 2r multicolored   .30   .20
Nos. 1738-1740 (3)   .90   .60
Children's Week.

Cow, Wheat and FAO Emblem A414

**1973, Nov. 4**
1741 A414 10r multicolored   1.00   .20
10th anniversary of World Food Program.

Proclamation of Cyrus the Great; Red Cross, Lion and Crescent Emblems A415

**1973, Nov. 8**
1742 A415 6r lt blue & multi   .75   .20
22nd Intl. Red Cross Conf., Tehran, 1972.

"Film Festival" — A416

**1973, Nov. 26   Wmk. 353   Perf. 10½**
1743 A416 2r black & multi   .35   .20
2nd International Tehran Film Festival.

Globe and Travelers — A417

**1973, Nov. 26   Litho.**
1744 A417 10r orange & multi   .60   .20
12th annual Congress of Intl. Assoc. of Tour Managers.

Human Rights Flame A418

**1973, Dec. 10**
1745 A418 8r lt blue & multi   .75   .20
Universal Declaration of Human Rights, 25th anniv.

Score and Emblem — A419

**1973, Dec. 21**
Design: No. 1747, Score and emblem, diff.
1746 A419 10r yel grn, red & blk   .75   .25
1747 A419 10r lt bl, ultra & red   .75   .25
Dedicated to the art of music.

Forestry, Printing, Education — A420

Designs (Symbols of Reforms): No. 1749, Land reform, sales of shares, women's suffrage. No. 1750, Army of progress, irrigation, women's education. No. 1751, Hygiene, rural courts, housing.

**1974, Jan. 26   Litho.   Perf. 10½**
1748   1r lt blue & multi   .20   .20
1749   1r lt blue & multi   .20   .20
1750   2r lt blue & multi   .25   .20
1751   2r lt blue & multi   .25   .20
  a. A420 Block of 4, #1748-1751   1.25   .90
**Imperf**
**Size: 76½x102mm**
1752 A420 20r multicolored   4.00   2.00
"White Revolution of King and People" and 12 reform laws.

Pir Amooz Ketabaty Script — A421

Various Scripts: No. 1754, Mo Eghely Ketabaty. No. 1755, Din Dabireh, Avesta script. No. 1756, Pir Amooz, Naskh style. No. 1757, Pir Amooz, decorative style. No. 1758, Decorative and architectural style.

**1974, Feb. 14   Wmk. 353   Perf. 10½**
1753 A421 1r silver, ocher & multi   .75   .30
1754 A421 1r gold, gray & multi   .75   .30
1755 A421 1r silver, yel & multi   .75   .30
1756 A421 2r gold, gray & multi   .75   .30
1757 A421 2r gold, slate & multi   .75   .30
1758 A421 2r gold, claret & multi   .75   .30
Nos. 1753-1758 (6)   4.50   1.80
Development of writing.

Fowl, Syringe and Emblem A422

**1974, Feb. 23**
1759 A422 6r red brown & multi   .60   .20
5th Iranian Veterinary Congress.

Monarch
Butterfly
A423

Designs: Various butterflies.

**1974, Mar. 6      Litho.      Perf. 10½**
| | | | | |
|---|---|---|---|---|
| 1760 | A423 | 1r rose lilac & multi | 1.00 | .35 |
| 1761 | A423 | 1r brt rose & multi | 1.00 | .35 |
| 1762 | A423 | 2r lt blue & multi | 1.50 | .45 |
| 1763 | A423 | 2r green & multi | 1.50 | .45 |
| 1764 | A423 | 2r bister & multi | 1.50 | .45 |
| | | Nos. 1760-1764 (5) | 6.50 | 2.05 |

Novrooz, Iranian New Year.

Jalaludin
Mevlana (1207-
1273),
Poet — A424

**1974, Mar. 12      Perf. 13**
| | | | | |
|---|---|---|---|---|
| 1765 | A424 | 2r pale violet & multi | .50 | .25 |

Shah Type of 1971

**1974      Photo.      Perf. 13½x13**
**Size: 20½x28mm**
| | | | | |
|---|---|---|---|---|
| 1768 | A366 | 50d orange & bl | .45 | .20 |
| 1769 | A366 | 1r emerald & bl | .50 | .20 |
| 1770 | A366 | 2r red & blue | .80 | .20 |

**Size: 27x36½mm**
| | | | | |
|---|---|---|---|---|
| 1771 | A366 | 10r lt green & bl | 7.00 | .20 |
| 1772 | A366 | 20r lilac & bl | 4.25 | .20 |
| | | Nos. 1768-1772 (5) | 13.00 | 1.00 |

Palace of the Forty Columns,
Hippocrates, Avicenna — A425

**1974, Apr. 11      Litho.      Perf. 10½**
| | | | | |
|---|---|---|---|---|
| 1773 | A425 | 10r multicolored | .75 | .20 |

9th Medical Congress of the Near and Middle East, Isfahan.

Onager — A426

Athlete and
Games
Emblem — A427

**1974, Apr. 13**
| | | | | |
|---|---|---|---|---|
| 1774 | A426 | 1r shown | .50 | .20 |
| 1775 | A426 | 2r Great bustard | .75 | .20 |
| 1776 | A426 | 6r Fawn and deer | 1.50 | .35 |
| 1777 | A426 | 8r Caucasian black | | |
| | | grouse | 2.25 | .40 |
| a. | | Strip of 4, #1774-1777 | 6.00 | 3.00 |
| | | Nos. 1774-1777 (4) | 5.00 | 1.15 |

Intl. Council for Game and Wildlife
Preservation.

**1974, Apr. 30**
| | | | | |
|---|---|---|---|---|
| 1778 | A427 | 1r shown | .55 | .20 |
| 1779 | A427 | 1r Table tennis | .55 | .20 |
| 1780 | A427 | 2r Boxing | 1.00 | .20 |
| 1781 | A427 | 2r Hurdles | 1.00 | .20 |
| 1782 | A427 | 6r Weight lifting | 1.60 | .20 |
| 1783 | A427 | 8r Basketball | 2.50 | .20 |
| | | Nos. 1778-1783 (6) | 7.20 | 1.20 |

7th Asian Games, Tehran; first issue.

Lion of Venice — A428

Painting: 8r, Audience with the Doge of
Venice.

**1974, May 5**
| | | | | |
|---|---|---|---|---|
| 1784 | A428 | 6r multicolored | .55 | .25 |
| 1785 | A428 | 8r multicolored | 1.00 | .35 |

Safeguarding Venice..

Links and
Grain — A429

**1974, May 13      Litho.      Perf. 10½**
| | | | | |
|---|---|---|---|---|
| 1786 | A429 | 2r multicolored | .30 | .20 |

Cooperation Day.

Military
Plane,
1924
A430

**1974, June 1**
| | | | | |
|---|---|---|---|---|
| 1787 | A430 | 10r shown | 2.00 | .40 |
| 1788 | A430 | 10r Jet, 1974 | 2.00 | .40 |

50th anniversary of Iranian Air Force.

Swimmer and
Games Emblem
A431

Bicyclists and
Games Emblem
A432

**1974, July 1      Wmk. 353      Perf. 10½**
| | | | | |
|---|---|---|---|---|
| 1789 | A431 | 1r shown | .65 | .20 |
| 1790 | A431 | 1r Tennis, men's | | |
| | | doubles | .65 | .20 |
| 1791 | A431 | 2r Wrestling | .80 | .20 |
| 1792 | A431 | 2r Hockey | .80 | .20 |
| 1793 | A431 | 4r Volleyball | 1.25 | .40 |
| 1794 | A431 | 10r Tennis, women's | | |
| | | singles | 2.50 | .50 |
| | | Nos. 1789-1794 (6) | 6.65 | 1.70 |

7th Asian Games, Tehran; second issue.

**1974, Aug. 1**
| | | | | |
|---|---|---|---|---|
| 1795 | A432 | 2r shown | .90 | .20 |
| 1796 | A432 | 2r Soccer | .90 | .20 |
| 1797 | A432 | 2r Fencing | .90 | .20 |
| 1798 | A432 | 2r Small-bore rifle | | |
| | | shooting | .90 | .20 |
| | | Nos. 1795-1798 (4) | 3.60 | .80 |

7th Asian Games, Tehran; third issue.

Ghaskai
Costume — A433

Gold Winged
Lion
Cup — A434

Regional Costumes: No. 1800, Kurdistan,
Kermanshah District. No. 1801, Kurdistan,
Sanandaj District. No. 1802, Mazandaran. No.
1803, Bakhtiari. No. 1804, Torkaman.

**1974, July 6**
| | | | | |
|---|---|---|---|---|
| 1799 | A433 | 2r lt ultra & multi | 1.40 | .75 |
| 1800 | A433 | 2r buff & multi | 1.40 | .75 |
| 1801 | A433 | 2r green & multi | 1.40 | .75 |
| 1802 | A433 | 2r lt blue & multi | 1.40 | .75 |
| 1803 | A433 | 2r gray & multi | 1.40 | .75 |
| 1804 | A433 | 2r dull grn & multi | 1.40 | .75 |
| a. | | Block of 6, #1799-1804 | 8.50 | 4.50 |

**1974, July 13**
| | | | | |
|---|---|---|---|---|
| 1805 | A434 | 2r dull green & multi | .30 | .20 |

Iranian Soccer Cup.

Tabriz Rug, Late
16th
Century — A435

King Carrying Vases,
Bas-relief — A436

Designs: No. 1807, Anatolian rug, 15th century. No. 1808, Kashan rug, Lahore.

**1974, July 21**
| | | | | |
|---|---|---|---|---|
| 1806 | A435 | 2r brown & multi | .45 | .20 |
| 1807 | A435 | 2r blue & multi | .45 | .20 |
| 1808 | A435 | 2r red & multi | .45 | .20 |
| a. | | Strip of 3, #1806-1808 | 1.40 | .30 |

Regional Cooperation for Development Pact
among Iran, Turkey and Pakistan, 10th anniv.

**1974, Aug. 15      Litho.      Perf. 10½**
| | | | | |
|---|---|---|---|---|
| 1809 | A436 | 2r black & multi | .30 | .20 |

8th Iranian Arts Festival, Shiraz-Persepolis.

Aryamehr Stadium, Tehran — A437

#1811, Games' emblem and inscription.
#1812, Aerial view of games' site.

**1974**
| | | | | |
|---|---|---|---|---|
| 1810 | A437 | 6r multicolored | 1.00 | .20 |

**Souvenir Sheets**
| | | | | |
|---|---|---|---|---|
| 1811 | A437 | 10r multicolored | 3.00 | 1.50 |
| 1812 | A437 | 10r multicolored | 3.00 | 1.50 |

7th Asian Games, Tehran; fourth and fifth
issues. Nos. 1811-1812 contain one imperf
51x38mm stamp each.
Issued: #1811-1812, 9/1; #1810, 9/16.

"Welfare" — A438

"Education"
A439

**1974, Sept. 11**
| | | | | |
|---|---|---|---|---|
| 1813 | A438 | 2r orange & multi | .30 | .20 |
| 1814 | A439 | 2r blue & multi | .30 | .20 |

Welfare and free education.

Map of
Hasanlu, 1000-
800
B.C. — A440

**1974, Sept. 24**
| | | | | |
|---|---|---|---|---|
| 1815 | A440 | 8r multicolored | .70 | .20 |

2nd Intl. Congress of Architecture, Shiraz-
Persepolis, Sept. 1974.

Achaemenian Mail Cart and UPU Emblem — A441

Design: 14r, UPU emblem and letters.

**1974, Oct. 9  Wmk. 353  Perf. 10½**
| | | | | |
|---|---|---|---|---|
| 1816 | A441 | 6r orange, grn & blk | 1.00 | .40 |
| 1817 | A441 | 14r multicolored | 1.50 | .50 |

Centenary of Universal Postal Union.

Road Through Farahabad Park — A442

**1974, Oct. 16**
| | | | | |
|---|---|---|---|---|
| 1818 | A442 | 1r shown | .30 | .20 |
| 1819 | A442 | 2r Recreation Bldg. | .35 | .20 |

Inauguration of Farahabad Park, Tehran.

Farahnaz Dam and Mohammad Reza Shah Pahlavi — A443

Designs: 5d, Kharg Island petro-chemical plant. 10d, Ghatour Railroad Bridge. 1r, Tehran oil refinery. 2r, Satellite communication station, Hamadan, and Mt. Alvand. 6r, Aryamehr steel mill, Isfahan. 8r, University of Tabriz. 10r, Shah Abbas Kabir Dam. 14r, Rudagi (later Vahdat) Music Hall. 20r, Shayad Monument. 50r, Aryamehr Stadium.

**1974-75  Photo.  Perf. 13x13½**
**Size: 28x21mm**
**Frame & Shah in Brown**
| | | | | |
|---|---|---|---|---|
| 1820 | A443 | 5d slate green | .30 | .20 |
| 1821 | A443 | 10d orange | .30 | .20 |
| 1822 | A443 | 50d blue green | .30 | .20 |
| 1823 | A443 | 1r ultra | .30 | .20 |
| 1824 | A443 | 2r deep lilac | .30 | .20 |

**Size: 36x26½mm**
**Frame & Shah in Dark Blue**
| | | | | |
|---|---|---|---|---|
| 1825 | A443 | 6r brown | .50 | .30 |
| 1826 | A443 | 8r grnsh blue | .50 | .40 |
| 1827 | A443 | 10r deep lilac | .80 | .20 |
| a. | | Value in Farsi omitted | 30.00 | 30.00 |
| 1828 | A443 | 14r deep green | 17.00 | .60 |
| 1829 | A443 | 20r magenta | 3.50 | .50 |
| 1830 | A443 | 50r violet | 4.50 | 1.40 |
| | | Nos. 1820-1830 (11) | 28.30 | 4.50 |

Issued: 50d, 1r, 2r, 10/16/74; 14r, 11/1974; others 3/6/75.
See Nos. 1831-1841. For overprints see Nos. 2008, 2010.

**1975-77**
**Size: 28x21mm**
**Frame & Shah in Green**
| | | | | |
|---|---|---|---|---|
| 1831 | A443 | 5d orange ('77) | .30 | .20 |
| 1832 | A443 | 10d rose mag ('77) | .30 | .20 |
| 1833 | A443 | 50d lilac | .30 | .20 |
| 1834 | A443 | 1r dark blue | .30 | .20 |
| 1835 | A443 | 2r brown | .30 | .20 |

**Size: 36x26½mm**
**Frame & Shah in Brown**
| | | | | |
|---|---|---|---|---|
| 1836 | A443 | 6r vio bl ('76) | .40 | .35 |
| 1837 | A443 | 8r deep org ('77) | 2.00 | .30 |
| 1838 | A443 | 10r dp yel grn ('76) | 1.75 | .20 |
| 1839 | A443 | 14r lilac | 8.00 | .20 |
| 1840 | A443 | 20r brt green ('76) | 3.50 | .40 |
| 1841 | A443 | 50r dp blue ('76) | 3.00 | .90 |
| | | Nos. 1831-1841 (11) | 20.15 | 3.35 |

Festival Emblem, Crown and Column Capital, Persepolis — A444

**1974, Oct. 26  Litho.  Perf. 10½**
| | | | | |
|---|---|---|---|---|
| 1842 | A444 | 2r multicolored | .40 | .20 |

Festival of Culture and Art.

Destroyer "Palang" and Flag — A445

**1974, Nov. 5**
| | | | | |
|---|---|---|---|---|
| 1843 | A445 | 10r multicolored | 1.50 | .35 |

Navy Day.

Girl at Spinning Wheel A446

Designs: Children's drawings.

**1974, Nov. 7  Perf. 10½**
| | | | | |
|---|---|---|---|---|
| 1844 | A446 | 2r shown | .35 | .20 |
| 1845 | A446 | 2r Scarecrow, vert. | .35 | .20 |
| 1846 | A446 | 2r Picnic | .35 | .20 |
| | | Nos. 1844-1846 (3) | 1.05 | .60 |

Children's Week.

Winged Ibex — A447

**1974, Nov. 25  Litho.  Wmk. 353**
| | | | | |
|---|---|---|---|---|
| 1847 | A447 | 2r vio, org & blk | .35 | .20 |

Third Tehran International Film Festival.

WPY Emblem A448

**1974, Dec. 1**
| | | | | |
|---|---|---|---|---|
| 1848 | A448 | 8r orange & multi | .60 | .20 |

World Population Year.

Gold Bee A449

Design: 8r, Gold crown, gift of French people to Empress Farah. Bee pin was gift of the Italian people.

**1974, Dec. 20**
| | | | | |
|---|---|---|---|---|
| 1849 | A449 | 6r multicolored | .70 | .30 |
| 1850 | A449 | 8r multicolored | .90 | .35 |

14th wedding anniv. of Shah and Empress Farah.

Angel with Banner — A450

**1975, Jan. 7  Litho.  Perf. 10½**
| | | | | |
|---|---|---|---|---|
| 1851 | A450 | 2r org & vio bl | .30 | .20 |

International Women's Year.

Symbols of Agriculture, Industry and the Arts — A451

**1975, Jan. 26  Wmk. 353**
| | | | | |
|---|---|---|---|---|
| 1852 | A451 | 2r multicolored | .30 | .20 |

"White Revolution of King and People."

Tourism Year 75 Emblem — A452

**1975, Feb. 17**
| | | | | |
|---|---|---|---|---|
| 1853 | A452 | 6r multicolored | .30 | .20 |

South Asia Tourism Year.

"Farabi" in Shape of Musical Instrument or Alembic — A453

**1975, Mar. 1**
| | | | | |
|---|---|---|---|---|
| 1854 | A453 | 2r brn red & multi | .30 | .20 |

Abu-Nasr al-Farabi (870?-950), physician, musician and philosopher, 1100th birth anniversary.

Ornament, Rug Pattern — A454

**1975, Mar. 6**
| | | | | |
|---|---|---|---|---|
| 1855 | A454 | 1r shown | .25 | .20 |
| 1856 | A454 | 1r Blossoms and cypress trees | .25 | .20 |
| 1857 | A454 | 1r Shah Abbasi flower | .25 | .20 |
| a. | | Strip of 3, #1855-1857 | 1.00 | .60 |

Novrooz, Iranian New Year. Nos. 1855-1857 printed in sheets of 45 stamps + 5 labels.

Nasser Khosrov, Poet, Birth Millenary — A455

Formula — A456

**1975, Mar. 11**
| | | | | |
|---|---|---|---|---|
| 1858 | A455 | 2r blk, gold & red | .30 | .20 |

**1975, May 5  Litho.  Perf. 10½**
| | | | | |
|---|---|---|---|---|
| 1859 | A456 | 2r buff & multi | .40 | .20 |

5th Biennial Symposium of Iranian Biochemical Society.

Charioteer, Bas-relief, Persepolis — A457

Design: 2r, Heads of Persian warriors, bas-relief from Persepolis, vert.

**1975, May 5**
| | | | | |
|---|---|---|---|---|
| 1860 | A457 | 2r lt brn & multi | 2.00 | .75 |
| 1861 | A457 | 10r blue & multi | 4.00 | 1.25 |

Rotary International, 70th anniversary.

Signal Fire, Persian Castle A458

Design: 8r, Communications satellite.

**1975, May 17**
| | | | | |
|---|---|---|---|---|
| 1862 | A458 | 6r multicolored | .75 | .45 |
| 1863 | A458 | 8r lil & multi | .85 | .55 |

7th World Telecommunications Day.

Cooperation Day — A459

**1975, May 13**
1864 A459 2r multicolored          .30   .20

Jet, Shayad Monument, Statue of Liberty — A460

**1975, May 29    Litho.    Wmk. 353**
1865 A460 10r org & multi          1.00   .50
Iran Air's 1st flight to New York, May 1975.

Emblem — A461

**1975, June 5**
1866 A461 6r blue & multi          .45   .20
World Environment Day.

Dam A462

**1975, June 10**
1867 A462 10r multicolored          .70   .20
9th Intl. Congress on Irrigation & Drainage.

Resurgence Party Emblem — A463

Girl Scout Symbols A464

**1975, July 1    Wmk. 353    Perf. 10½**
1868 A463 2r multicolored          .30   .20
Organization of Resurgence Party.

**1975, July 16**
1869 A464 2r multicolored          .50   .25
2nd Natl Girl Scout Camp, Tehran, July 1976.

Festival of Tus — A465

**1975, July 17**
1870 A465 2r gray, lil & vio          .30   .20
Festival of Tus in honor of Firdausi (940-1020), Persian poet born near Tus in Khorasan.

Ceramic Plate, Iran A466

#1872, Camel leather vase, Pakistan, vert.
#1873, Porcelain vase, Turkey, vert.

**1975, July 21**
1871 A466 2r bister & multi          .35   .20
1872 A466 2r bister & multi          .35   .20
1873 A466 2r bister & multi          .35   .20
    Nos. 1871-1873 (3)          1.05   .60
Regional Cooperation for Development Pact among Iran, Pakistan and Turkey.

Majlis Gate A467

**1975, Aug. 5    Litho.    Perf. 10½**
1874 A467 10r multi          .75   .20
Iranian Constitution, 70th anniversary.

Column with Stylized Branches — A468

**1975, Aug. 21    Litho.    Wmk. 353**
1875 A468 8r red & multi          .60   .20
9th Iranian Arts Festival, Shiraz-Persepolis.

Flags over Globe — A469

**1975, Sept. 8**
1876 A469 2r vio bl & multi          .30   .20
Intl. Literacy Symposium, Persepolis.

Stylized Globe — A470

World Map and Envelope — A471

**1975, Sept. 13**
1877 A470 2r vio & multi          .30   .20
3rd Tehran International Trade Fair.

**1975, Oct. 9    Litho.    Perf. 10½**
1878 A471 14r ultra & multi          1.00   .20
World Post Day, Oct. 9.

Crown, Column Capital, Persepolis — A472

**1975, Oct. 26    Litho.    Wmk. 353**
1879 A472 2r ultra & multi          .35   .20
Festival of Culture and Art. See No. 1954.

Face and Film — A473

**1975, Nov. 2**
1880 A473 6r multicolored          .65   .20
Tehran Intl. Festival of Children's Films.

"Mother's Face" — A474

Girl — A475

Design: No. 1882, 2r, "Our House," horiz. All designs after children's drawings.

**1975, Nov. 5**
1881 A474 2r multicolored          .35   .20
1882 A475 2r multicolored          .35   .20
1883 A475 2r multicolored          .35   .20
    Nos. 1881-1883 (3)          1.05   .60
Children's Week.

"Film" — A476

**1975, Dec. 4    Wmk. 353    Perf. 10½**
1884 A476 8r multicolored          .60   .20
4th Tehran International Film Festival.

Symbols of Reforms — A477

People — A478

**1976, Jan. 26    Litho.    Perf. 10½**
1885 A477 2r shown          .35   .20
1886 A478 2r shown          .35   .20
1887 A477 2r Five reform sym-
              bols          .35   .20
    Nos. 1885-1887 (3)          1.05   .60
"White Revolution of King and People."

Motorcycle Policeman A479

Police Helicopter — A480

**1976, Feb. 16**
1888 A479 2r multicolored 1.25 .75
1889 A480 6r multicolored 2.00 1.00
Highway Police Day.

Soccer Cup — A481

Candlestick A482

**1976, Feb. 24 Litho. Wmk. 353**
1890 A481 2r org & multi .30 .20
3rd Intl. Youth Soccer Cup, Shiraz and Ahvaz.

**1976, Mar. 6**
Designs: No. 1892, Incense burner. No. 1893, Rose water container.

1891 A482 1r olive & multi .30 .20
1892 A482 1r claret & multi .30 .20
1893 A482 1r Prus bl & multi .30 .20
  a. Strip of 3, #1891-1893 1.00 .60
Novrooz, Iranian New Year.

Telephones, 1876 and 1976 — A483

Eye Within Square — A484

**1976, Mar. 10**
1894 A483 10r multicolored .75 .20
Centenary of first telephone call by Alexander Graham Bell, Mar. 10, 1876.

**1976, Apr. 29 Litho. Perf. 10½**
1895 A484 6r blk & multi 2.00 .20
  a. Perf. 12½ 9.50 7.50
World Health Day: "Foresight prevents blindness."

Nurse with Infant A485

Young Man Holding Old Man's Hand — A486

**1976, May 10**
1896 A485 2r shown .50 .20
1897 A485 2r Engineering apprentices .50 .20
1898 A486 2r shown .50 .20
  Nos. 1896-1898 (3) 1.50 .60
Royal Org. of Social Services, 30th anniv.

Map of Iran, Men Linking Hands — A487

Waves and Ear Phones — A488

**1976, May 13 Wmk. 353**
1899 A487 2r yel & multi .30 .20
Iranian Cooperatives, 10th anniversary.

**1976, May 17**
1900 A488 14r gray & multi .75 .20
World Telecommunications Day.

Emblem, Woman with Flag, Man with Gun — A489

**1976, June 6**
1901 A489 2r bister & multi .35 .20
To publicize the power of stability.

Map of Iran, Columns of Persepolis, Nasser Khosrow — A490

**1976, July 6 Litho. Perf. 10½**
1902 A490 6r yel & multi .50 .20
Tourist publicity.

Reza Shah Pahlavi — A491

**1976, July 21 Litho. Wmk. 353**
6r, Mohammad Ali Jinnah. 8r, Kemal Ataturk.

1903 A491 2r gray & multi .50 .20
1904 A491 6r gray & multi .60 .20
1905 A491 8r gray & multi .75 .25
  Nos. 1903-1905 (3) 1.85 .65
Regional Cooperation for Development Pact among Iran, Turkey and Pakistan, 12th anniversary.

Torch, Montreal and Iranian Olympic Emblems A492

**1976, Aug. 1**
1906 A492 14r multicolored 1.00 .25
21st Olympic Games, Montreal, Canada, July 17-Aug. 1.

Reza Shah Pahlavi in Coronation Robe — A493

Festival Emblem — A494

Designs: 2r, Reza Shah and Mohammad Reza Shah Pahlavi, horiz. 14r, 20r, Mohammad Reza Shah Pahlavi in coronation robe and crown.

**1976, Aug. 19 Wmk. 353 Perf. 10½**
1907 A493 2r lilac & multi 1.00 .50
1908 A493 6r blue & multi 2.00 .75
1909 A493 14r grn & multi 3.00 1.00
  Nos. 1907-1909 (3) 6.00 2.25

Souvenir Sheet
**1976, Oct. 8 Imperf.**
1910 A493 20r multi 10.00 6.00
50th anniv. of Pahlavi dynasty; 35th anniv. of reign of Mohammad Reza Shah Pahlavi. No. 1910 contains one stamp 43x62mm.

**1976, Aug. 29 Litho. Perf. 10½**
1911 A494 10r multicolored .65 .20
10th Iranian Arts Festival, Shiraz-Persepolis.

Iranian Scout Emblem — A495

**1976, Oct. 2 Litho. Perf. 10½**
1912 A495 2r lt bl & multi .30 .20
10th Asia Pacific Conference, Tehran 1976.

Cancer Radiation Treatment — A496

**1976, Oct. 6**
1913 A496 2r black & multi .30 .20
Fight against cancer.

Target, Police Woman Receiving Decoration A497

**1976, Oct. 7**
1914 A497 2r lt bl & multi .30 .20
Police Day.

UPU Emblem, No. 1907 on Cover A498

**1976, Oct. 9**
1915 A498 10r multicolored 1.00 .20
International Post Day.

Crown Prince Riza with Cup — A499

**1976, Oct. 10**
1916 A499 6r multicolored .50 .20
Natl. Soc. of Village Culture Houses, anniv.

Riza Shah and Mohammad Reza Shah Pahlavi, Railroad A500

**1976, Oct. 15**
1917 A500 8r black & multi .......... 4.00 1.50
Railroad Day.

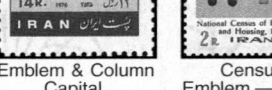

Emblem & Column Capital, Persepolis — A501

Census Emblem — A502

**1976, Oct. 26**
1918 A501 14r blue & multi .......... 1.00 .30
Festival of Culture and Art.

**1976, Oct. 30**
1919 A502 2r gray & multi .......... .30 .20
Natl. Population & Housing Census, 1976.

Flowers and Birds — A503

Mohammad Ali Jinnah — A504

Designs: No. 1921, Flowers and bird. No. 1922, Flowers and butterfly. Designs are from covers of children's books.

**1976, Oct. 31**        *Perf. 10½*
1920 A503 2r multicolored .......... .35 .20
1921 A503 2r multicolored .......... .35 .20
1922 A503 2r multicolored .......... .35 .20
    Nos. 1920-1922 (3) .......... 1.05 .60
Children's Week.

**1976, Dec. 25**    Litho.    Wmk. 353
1923 A504 10r multicolored .......... .60 .20
Jinnah (1876-1948), 1st Governor General of Pakistan.

Development and Agriculture Corps — A505

17-Point Reform Law: 5d, Land reform. 10d, Nationalization of forests. 50d, Sale of shares of state-owned industries. 1r, Profit sharing for factory workers. 2r, Parliament Gate, Woman suffrage. 3r, Education Corps formation. 5r, Health Corps. 8r, Establishment of village courts. 10r, Nationalization of water resources. 12r, Reconstruction program, urban and rural. 14r, Administrative and educational reorganization. 20r, Sale of factory shares. 30r, Commodity pricing. 50r, Free education. 100r, Child care. 200r, Care of the aged (social security).

**1977, Jan. 26**   Photo.   *Perf. 13x13½*
**Frame and Shah's Head in Gold**
**Size: 28x21mm**
1924 A505   5d rose & green .......... .20 .20
1925 A505   10d lt grn & brn .......... .20 .20
1926 A505   50d yel & vio bl .......... .20 .20
1927 A505   1r lil & vio bl .......... .20 .20
1928 A505   2r org & green .......... .20 .20
1929 A505   3r lt bl & red .......... .40 .20
1930 A505   5r bl grn & mag .......... .40 .20
**Size: 37x27mm**
1931 A505   6r brn, mar & black .......... .55 .20
1932 A505   8r ultra, mar & blk .......... .55 .20
1933 A505   10r lt grn, bl & black .......... 1.50 .20
1934 A505   12r vio, mar & black .......... 1.10 .20
1935 A505   14r org, red & blk .......... 1.60 .75
1936 A505   20r gray, ocher & black .......... 3.25 .50
1937 A505   30r bl, grn & blk .......... 3.25 .65
1938 A505   50r yel, brn & blk .......... 5.50 .60
1939 A505   100r multi .......... 5.00 1.25
1940 A505   200r multi .......... 11.00 2.50
    Nos. 1924-1940 (17) .......... 35.10 8.45
"White Revolution of King and People" reform laws.

Man in Guilan Costume — A506

Electronic Tree — A507

2r, Woman in Guilan costume (Northern Iran).

**1977, Mar. 6**    Wmk. 353    *Perf. 13*
1941 A506 1r multicolored .......... .30 .20
1942 A506 2r multicolored .......... .35 .20
Novrooz, Iranian New Year.

**1977, May 17**   Photo.   *Perf. 13*
1943 A507 20r multicolored .......... 1.25 .35
World Telecommunications Day.

Reza Shah Dam A508

**1977, May 31**        *Perf. 13x13½*
1944 A508 5r multicolored .......... .40 .20
Inauguration of Reza Shah Dam.

Olympic Rings A509

**1977, June 23**   Litho.   *Perf. 10½*
1945 A509 14r multicolored .......... .90 .20
Olympic Day.

Terra-cotta Jug, Iran — A510

#1947, Terra-cotta bullock cart, Pakistan. #1948, Terra-cotta pot with human face, Turkey.

*Perf. 13x13½*
**1977, July 21**   Photo.   Wmk. 353
1946 A510 5r violet & multi .......... .40 .20
1947 A510 5r emer & multi .......... .40 .20
1948 A510 5r green & multi .......... .40 .20
    Nos. 1946-1948 (3) .......... 1.20 .60
Regional Cooperation for Development Pact among Iran, Turkey and Pakistan, 13th anniv.

Flowers with Scout Emblems, Map of Asia — A511

**1977, Aug. 5**   Litho.   *Perf. 13*
1949 A511 10r multicolored .......... 1.00 .25
2nd Asia-Pacific Jamboree, Nishapur.

Map of Eastern Hemisphere with Iran — A512

Tree of Learning, Symbolic Letters — A513

**1977, Sept. 20**   Photo.   Wmk. 353
1950 A512 3r multicolored .......... .35 .20
9th Asian Electronics Conference, Tehran.

**1977, Oct. 8**    Wmk. 353    *Perf. 13*
1951 A513 10r multicolored .......... .60 .20
Honoring the teachers.

Globe, Envelope, UPU Emblem A514

**1977, Oct. 9**           Photo.
1952 A514 14r multicolored .......... 1.00 .20
Iran's admission to the UPU, cent.

Folk Art — A515

**1977, Oct. 16**
1953 A515 5r multicolored .......... .40 .20
Festival of Folk Art.

**Festival Type of 1975**
Design: 20r, similar to 1975 issue, but with small crown within star.

**1977, Oct. 26**        *Perf. 10½*
1954 A472 20r bis, grn, car & blk 1.25 .20
Festival of Culture and Art.

Joust — A516

Emblem — A517

#1956, Rapunzel. #1957, Little princess with attendants.

**1977, Oct. 31**        Photo.
1955 A516 3r multicolored .......... .30 .20
1956 A516 3r multicolored .......... .30 .20
1957 A516 3r multicolored .......... .30 .20
  a.    Strip of 3, #1955-1957 1.25 .60
Children's Week.

**1977, Nov. 7**    Wmk. 353    *Perf. 13*
1958 A517 5r multicolored .......... .40 .20
First Regional Seminar on the Education and Welfare of the Deaf.

Mohammad Iqbal A518

African Sculpture A519

**1977, Nov. 9**    Litho.    *Perf. 10½*
1959 A518 5r multicolored .......... .45 .20
Iqbal (1877-1938) of Pakistan, poet and philosopher.

**1977, Dec. 14**
1960 A519 20r multicolored .......... 3.25 .55
African art.

Shah Mosque, Isfahan — A520

Designs: 1r, Ruins, Persepolis. 2r, Khajou Bridge, Isfahan. 5r, Imam Riza Shrine, Meshed. 9r, Warrior frieze, Persepolis. 10r, Djameh Mosque, Isfahan. 20r, King on throne, bas-relief. 25r, Sheik Lotfollah Mosque. 30r, Ruins, Persepolis, diff. view. 50r, Ali Ghapou Palace, Isfahan. 100r, Bas-relief, Tagh Bastan. 200r, Horseman and prisoners, bas-relief, Naqsh Rostam.

**1978-79**   Photo.   *Perf. 13x13½*
**"Iran" and Head in Gold**
**Size: 28x21mm**
1961 A520 1r deep brn .......... .30 .25
1962 A520 2r emerald .......... .30 .25
1963 A520 3r magenta .......... .50 .25
1964 A520 5r Prus blue .......... .70 .25
**Size: 36x27mm**
1965 A520 9r sepia ('79) .......... 1.75 .75
1966 A520 10r brt bl ('79) .......... 5.75 .85
1967 A520 20r rose .......... 1.75 .55
1968 A520 25r ultra ('79) .......... 25.00 9.75
1969 A520 30r magenta .......... 2.75 .55
1970 A520 50r deep yel grn ('79) .......... 4.50 3.50
1971 A520 100r dk bl ('79) .......... 14.00 9.75
1972 A520 200r vio bl ('79) .......... 19.00 19.00
    Nos. 1961-1972 (12) .......... 76.30 45.70
For overprints see Nos. 2009, 2011-2018.

Persian Rug — A521

Designs: Persian rugs.

**1978, Feb. 11    Litho.    Perf. 10½**
1973 A521  3r sil & multi    .35  .25
1974 A521  5r sil & multi    .45  .25
1975 A521  10r sil & multi   .75  .35
   Nos. 1973-1975 (3)        1.55  .85
   Opening of Carpet Museum.

Mazanderan Man — A522

Design: 5r, Mazanderan woman.

**1978, Mar. 6              Perf. 13**
1976 A522  3r yel & multi    .35  .20
1977 A522  5r lt bl & multi  .55  .20
   Novrooz, Iranian New Year.

Mohammad Reza Shah Pahlavi — A523

**1978, Jan. 26**
1978 A523  20r multicolored  4.00  1.25
   Shah's White Revolution, 15th anniv.

Reza Shah Pahlavi and Crown Prince Inspecting Girls' School — A524

Designs (Reza Shah Pahlavi and Crown Prince Mohammad Reza Shah Pahlavi): 5r, Inauguration of Trans-Iranian railroad. 10r, At stairs of Palace, Persepolis. 14r, Shah handing Crown Prince (later Shah) officer's diploma at Tehran Officers' Academy.

**1978, Mar. 15**
1979 A524  3r multicolored   .50  .25
1980 A524  5r multicolored   .75  .35
1981 A524  10r multicolored  1.25  .40
1982 A524  14r multicolored  1.75  .70
   Nos. 1979-1982 (4)        4.25  1.70
   Reza Shah Pahlavi (1877-1944), founder of Pahlavi dynasty.

Communications Satellite over Map of Iran — A525

**1978, Apr. 19    Litho.    Perf. 10½**
1983 A525  20r multicolored  1.25  .30
   ITU, 7th meeting, Tehran; 10th anniv. of Iran's membership.

Antenna, ITU Emblem A526

**1978, May 17    Litho.    Perf. 10½**
1984 A526  15r multicolored  .90  .30
   10th World Telecommunications Day.

Welfare Legion Emblem — A527

**1978, June 13    Photo.    Perf. 13x13½**
1985 A527  10r multicolored  .60  .30
   Universal Welfare Legion, 10th anniversary.

Pink Roses, Iran — A528

Designs: 10r, Yellow rose, Turkey. 15r, Red roses, Pakistan.

**                         Perf. 13½x13**
**1978, July 21            Wmk. 353**
1986 A528  5r multicolored   .60  .25
1987 A528  10r multicolored  .90  .25
1988 A528  15r multicolored  1.00  .40
   Nos. 1986-1988 (3)        2.50  .90
   Regional Cooperation for Development Pact among Iran, Turkey and Pakistan, 14th anniversary.

Rhazes, Pharmaceutical Tools — A529

**1978, Aug. 26    Wmk. 353    Perf. 13**
1989 A529  5r multicolored   .60  .25
   Pharmacists' Day. Rhazes (850-923), chief physician of Great Hospital in Baghdad.

Girl Scouts, Aryamehr Arch A530

**1978, Sept. 2             Perf. 10½**
1990 A530  5r multicolored   1.00  .35
   23rd World Girl Scouts Conference, Tehran, Sept. 1978.

Reza Shah Pahlavi A531

Design: 5r, Mohammad Reza Shah Pahlavi.

**1978, Sept. 11    Litho.    Perf. 10½**
1991 A531  3r multicolored   1.50  .40
1992 A531  5r multicolored   1.75  .50
   Bank Melli Iran, 50th anniversary.

Girl and Bird A532

**1978, Oct. 31    Photo.    Perf. 13**
1993 A532  3r multicolored   .75  .30
   Children's Week.

Envelope, Map of Iran, UPU Emblem A533

**1978, Nov. 22            Perf. 13x13½**
1994 A533  14r gold & multi  1.50  .40
   World Post Day, Oct. 22.

Communications Symbols and Classroom — A534

**1978, Nov. 22            Perf. 10½**
1995 A534  10r multicolored  1.25  .40
   Faculty of Communications, 50th anniv.

Human Rights Flame A535

**1978, Dec. 17    Photo.    Perf. 13**
1996 A535  20r bl, blk & gold  3.50  .50
   Universal Declaration of Human Rights, 30th anniv.

Kurdistani Man — A536

Design: 5r, Kurdistani woman.

**1979, Mar. 17**
1997 A536  3r multicolored   .90  .25
1998 A536  5r multicolored   1.25  .25

Rose — A537

**1979, Mar. 17**
1999 A537  2r multicolored   .25  .20
   Novrooz, Iranian New Year.
   See No. 2310i.

### Islamic Republic

Demonstrators — A538

Islamic revolution: 3r, Demonstrators. 5r, Hands holding rose, gun and torch breaking through newspaper. 20r, Hands breaking prison bars, and dove, vert.

**1979, Apr. 20            Perf. 10½**
2000 A538  3r multicolored   2.00  .35
2001 A538  5r multicolored   1.40  .35
2002 A538  10r multicolored  1.40  .65
2003 A538  20r multicolored  3.00  .75
   Nos. 2000-2003 (4)        7.80  2.10

Nos. 1837-1838, 1966, 1970 and Type A520 Overprinted

Designs: 15r, Warriors on horseback, bas-relief, Naqsh-Rostam. 19r, Chehel Sotoon Palace, Isfahan.

**1979        Wmk. 353    Perf. 13x13½**
2008 A443  8r org & brown    3.00  1.00
2009 A520  9r gold & dp brn  1.50  1.50
2010 A443  10r dp yel grn    50.00  10.00
2011 A520  10r gold & brt bl  1.75  1.00
2012 A520  15r gold & red lil  1.75  1.00
2013 A520  19r gold & slate
                      grn     1.75  1.00
2016 A520  50r gold & dp yel
                      grn     5.00  2.00
2017 A520  100r gold & vio bl  10.00  4.00
2018 A520  200r gold & vio bl  12.50  8.50
   Nos. 2008-2018 (9)        87.25  30.00
   Overprint means Islamic revolution.
   Forgeries of No. 2010 exist.

Symbolic
Tulip — A539

**1979, June 5    Photo.    *Perf. 13***
2019  A539  5r multicolored          1.50    .40

Potters,
by
Kamalel
Molk
A540

#2021, at the Well, by Allah Baksh, Pakistan. #2022, Plowing, by Namik Ismail, Turkey.

**1979, July 21    Litho.    *Perf. 10½***
2020  A540  5r multicolored          3.75    .35
2021  A540  5r multicolored          2.75    .35
2022  A540  5r multicolored          2.75    .35
       *Nos. 2020-2022 (3)*           9.25   1.05

Regional Cooperation for Development Pact among Iran, Turkey and Pakistan, 15th anniv.

"TELECOM
79" — A541

**1979, Sept. 20          *Perf. 10½***
2023  A541  20r multicolored         12.50    .30

3rd World Telecommunications Exhibition, Geneva, Sept. 20-26.

Greeting the          Persian Rug
Sunrise — A542      Design — A543

Children's Drawings and IYC Emblem: 2r, Tulip over wounded man. 2r, Children with banners.

**1979, Sept. 23**
2024  A542  2r multicolored          2.00    .50
2025  A542  3r multicolored          2.00    .50
2026  A542  5r multicolored          3.50    .50
       *Nos. 2024-2026 (3)*           7.50   1.50

International Year of the Child.

**1979-80    Photo.    *Perf. 13½x13***
2027  A543  50d brn & pale sal       .20    .20
2028  A543  1r dark & lt bl          .20    .20
2029  A543  2r red & yellow          .20    .20
2030  A543  3r dk bl & lt lil        .20    .20
2031  A543  5r slate grn & lt
            grn                        .20    .20
2032  A543  10r blk & salmon
            pink ('80)                .30    .20
2033  A543  20r brn & gray
            ('80)                     .55    .20

**Size: 27x37½mm**

2034  A543  50r dp violet &
            gray ('80)               1.40    .50
2035  A543  100r blk & slate grn
            ('80)                     5.00   1.40
2036  A543  200r dk bl & cr ('80)    5.50   2.75
       *Nos. 2027-2036 (10)*         13.75   6.05

Globe in
Envelope — A544

**1979, Oct. 9    Litho.    *Perf. 10½***
2041  A544  10r multicolored         3.00    .40

World Post Day.

Ghyath-al-din
Kashani,
Astrolabe
A545

**1979, Dec. 5    Litho.    *Perf. 10½***
2042  A545  5r ocher & blk           1.50    .40

Kashani, mathematician, 550th death anniv.

Ka'aba,
Flame
and
Mosque
A546

Hegira (Pilgrimage Year): 5r, Koran open over globe, vert. 10r, Salman Farsi (follower of Mohammad), map of Iran.

**1980, Jan. 19**
2043  A546  3r multicolored          .20    .20
2044  A546  5r multicolored          .25    .20
2045  A546  10r multicolored         .55    .25
       *Nos. 2043-2045 (3)*          1.00    .65

Reissued in May-June, 1980, with shiny gum and watermark position changed.

People, Map
and Flag of
Iran — A547

Islamic Revolution, 1st Anniversary: 3r, Blood dripping on broken sword. 5r, Window open on sun of Islam, people.

**1980, Feb. 11**
2046  A547  1r multicolored          .20    .20
2047  A547  3r multicolored          .35    .25
2048  A547  5r multicolored          .65    .30
       *Nos. 2046-2048 (3)*          1.20    .75

For similar stamps measuring 24x36mm see Nos. 2310a, 2310b, 2310d.

Dehkhoda,
Dictionary Editor,
Birth
Cent. — A548

**1980, Feb. 26**
2049  A548  10r multicolored         .30    .20

East Azerbaijani      Mohammad
Woman                 Mossadegh
A549                  A550

Novrooz (Iranian New Year): 5r, East Azerbaijani man.

**1980, Mar. 5**
2050  A549  3r multicolored          .20    .20
2051  A549  5r multicolored          .25    .20

**1980, Mar. 19    Photo.    *Perf. 13x13½***
2052  A550  20r multi                .60    .20

Oil industry nationalization, 29th anniv.; Mohammad Mossadegh, prime minister who initiated nationalization, birth cent.

Professor Morteza
Motahhari, 1st Death
Anniversary — A551

**1980, May 1    Litho.    *Perf. 10½***
2053  A551  10r black & red          .50    .20

World Telecommunications
Day — A552

**1980, May 17    Photo.    *Perf. 13x13½***
2054  A552  20r multicolored         .50    .20

Interior of
Mosque
A553

**1980, June 11    Litho.    *Perf. 10½***
2055  A553  50d shown                .20    .20
2056  A553  1r Demonstration         .20    .20
2057  A553  3r Avicenna, al-
            Biruni, Farabi           .40    .20
2058  A553  5r Hegira emblem         .30    .20
       *Nos. 2055-2058 (4)*          1.10    .80

Hegira, 1400th anniv.

Ali Sharyati,
Educator
A554

**1980, June 15    Photo.    *Perf. 13x13½***
2059  A554  5r multicolored          .30    .20

Holy Ka'aba and
Hand Waving
Banner — A555

**1980, June 28**
2060  A555  5r multicolored          .30    .20

Hazrat Mehdi, 12th Imam's birth anniv.

A556              OPEC
                  Emblem — A557

**1980, Sept. 10          *Perf. 13½x13***
2061  A556  5r multicolored          .30    .20

Ayatollah Seyed Mahmood Talegani, death anniv. Compare with design A829.

**1980, Sept. 15**
2062  A557  5r shown                 .30    .20
2063  A557  10r Men holding
            OPEC emblem              .60    .20

20th anniversary of OPEC.

"Let Us Liberate       Tulip and
Jerusalem"             Fayziyye Mosque,
A558                   Qum
                       A559

**1980, Oct. 9          *Perf. 13x13½***
2064  A558  5r multicolored          .25    .20
2065  A558  20r multicolored         .85    .20

**1981, Feb. 11          *Perf. 13***
2066  A559  3r shown                 .20    .20
2067  A559  5r Blood spilling on
            tulip                     .20    .20
2068  A559  20r Tulip, Republic
            emblem                    .50    .20
       *Nos. 2066-2068 (3)*          .90    .60

Islamic Revolution, 2nd anniversary.
See Nos. 2310c, 2310e, 2310j, watermark 381 (3r, unserifed "R" in denomination. 5r, bright yellow background; 20r, light blue background behind flower.)

Lorestani Man — A560

Telecom- munications Day — A561

Novrooz (Iranian New Year): 10r, Lorestani woman.

**1981, Mar. 11**
2069 A560 5r multicolored .20 .20
2070 A560 10r multicolored .30 .20

*Perf. 13½x13*
**1981, May 17 Photo. Wmk. 353**
2071 A561 5r dk grn & org .20 .20

Ayatollah Kashani Birth Centenary — A562

Adult Education A563

*Perf. 13x13½*
**1981, July 21 Wmk. 381**
2072 A562 15r dk grn & dl pur .40 .20

*Perf. 13x13½, 13½x13 (5r, 10r, 200r)*
**1981, Aug.**
50d, Citizens bearing arms. 2r, Irrigation. 3r, Friday prayer service. 5r, Paasdaar emblem and members. 10r, Koran text. 20r, Hejaab (women's veil). 50r, Industrial development. 100r, Religious ceremony, Mecca. 200r, Mosque interior. 5r, 10r, 200r vert.

2073 A563 50d blk & dp bister .20 .20
2074 A563 1r dl pur & grn .20 .20
2075 A563 2r brn & grnsh bl .20 .20
**Size: 38x28mm, 28x38mm**
2076 A563 3r brt yel grn & black .20 .20
2077 A563 5r dk bl & brn org .20 .20
2078 A563 10r dk bl & grnsh blue .25 .20
2079 A563 20r red & black .60 .20
2080 A563 50r lilac & black 1.40 .30
2081 A563 100r org brn & blk 3.00 .60
2082 A563 200r blk & bl grn 5.75 1.25
Nos. 2073-2082 (10) 12.00 3.55

Islamic Iranian Army A564

**1981, Sept. 21 Photo. Perf. 13**
2087 A564 5r multicolored .20 .20

World Post Day and 12th UPU Day — A565

*Perf. 13x13½*
**1981, Oct. 9 Wmk. 381**
2088 A565 20r black & blue .50 .25

Millennium of Nahjul Balaghah (Sacred Book) A566

**1981, Oct. 17 Perf. 13**
2089 A566 25r multicolored .60 .20

Martyrs' Memorial — A567

**1981, Nov. 9 Photo. Perf. 13**
2090 A567 3r June 28, 1981 victims .20 .20
2091 A567 5r Pres. Rajai, Prime Minister Bahonar .20 .20
2092 A567 10r Gen. Chamran .25 .20
Nos. 2090-2092 (3) .65 .60

Ayatollah M. H. Tabatabaee, Scholar — A568

**1981, Dec. 25 Photo. Perf. 13**
2093 A568 5r multicolored .20 .20

Literacy Campaign A569

Islamic Revolution, 3rd Anniv. — A570

**1982, Jan. 20 Photo. Perf. 13x13½**
2094 A569 5r blue & gold .20 .20

**1982, Feb. 11 Wmk. 381 Perf. 13**
2095 A570 5r Map .20 .20
2096 A570 10r Tulip .25 .20
2097 A570 20r Globe .50 .20
a. Strip of 3, #2095-2097 .90 .40

See Nos. 2310f, 2310g, 2310k (5r, orange background, Arabian "5" 6mm above black panel. 10r, dark green background, gray dove with thick black lines around it. 20r, pink background, bright blue globe, faint latitude and longitude lines.)

Unity Week — A571

Khuzestan Man — A573

Koran Verse Relative to Christ A572

**1982, Feb. 20 Photo. Perf. 13**
2098 A571 25r multicolored 1.00 .20

**1982, Mar. 11 Photo. Wmk. 381**
2099 A572 20r multicolored .50 .20

**1982, Mar. 13**
2100 A573 3r shown .20 .20
2101 A573 5r Khuzestan woman .20 .20
a. Pair, #2100-2101 .20 .20
Novrooz (New Year).

3rd Anniv. of Islamic Revolution A574

**1982, Apr. 1**
2102 A574 30r multicolored .90 .25

Seyed Mohammad Bagher Sadr — A575

**1982, Apr. 8 Photo. Perf. 13½x13**
2103 A575 50r multicolored 1.00 .40

Martyrs of Altar (Ayatollahs Madani and Dastgeyb) — A576

**1982, Apr. 21 Perf. 13**
2104 A576 50r multicolored 1.00 .40

A577

A578

**1982, May 1 Photo. Perf. 13½x13**
2105 A577 100r multi 2.25 .80
Intl. Workers' Solidarity Day.

**1982, May 17 Perf. 13x13½**
2106 A578 100r multi 2.25 .80
14th World Telecommunications Day.

Mab'as Day (Mohammad's Appointment as Prophet) — A579

1963 Islamic Rising, 19th Anniv. — A580

**1982, May 21 Perf. 13½x13**
2107 A579 32r multicolored .90 .30

**1982, June 5 Wmk. 381 Perf. 13**
2108 A580 28r multicolored .60 .30

Lt. Islambuli, Assassin of Anwar Sadat — A581

1st Death Anniv. of Ayatollah Beheshti — A582

**1982, June 17**
2109 A581 2r multicolored .40 .20

**1982, June 28**
2110 A582 10r multicolored .40 .20
a. Missing dot in Arabic numeral 1.00 1.00

Iran-Iraq War A583

**1982, July 7 Perf. 13x13½**
2111 A583 5r multicolored .20 .20

Universal Jerusalem Day A584

**1982, July 15 Perf. 13**
2112 A584 1r Dome of the Rock .20 .20

Pilgrimage to Mecca — A585

13th World UPU
Day — A586

**1982, Sept. 28**
2113 A585 10r multicolored      .30   .20

**1982, Oct. 9**      **Perf. 13½x13**
2114 A586 30r multicolored      .75   .25

4th Anniv. of
Islamic
Revolution — A587

**1983, Feb. 11**   **Photo.**   **Perf. 13**
2115 A587 30r multicolored      .75   .25

See No. 2310n for stamp with orange or
orange red crowd and thick sharp lettering in
black panels.

4th Anniv. of
Islamic
Republic — A588

**1983, Apr. 1**   **Photo.**   **Perf. 13**
2116 A588 10r multicolored      .30   .20

Teachers'
Day — A589

World Com-
munications
Year — A590

**Perf. 13½x13**
**1983, May 1**      **Wmk. 381**
2117 A589 5r multicolored      .25   .20

**1983, May 17**
2118 A590 20r multicolored      .60   .20

First Session of Islamic Consultative
Assembly — A591

**1983, May 28**      **Perf. 13**
2119 A591 5r multicolored      .20   .20

20th Anniv. of
Islamic
Movement — A592

**1983, June 5**   **Photo.**   **Perf. 13**
2120 A592 10r multicolored      .30   .20

Iraqi MiG
Bombing
Now Rooz
Oil Well
A593

**1983, June 11**      **Perf. 13x13½**
2121 A593 5r multicolored      .50   .20
Ecology week.

Ayatollah Mohammad
Sadooghi — A594

**1983, July 2**   **Photo.**   **Perf. 13½**
2122 A594 20r blk & dl red      .60   .20

Universal Day of
Jerusalem — A595

Government Week — A596

**1983, July 8**
2123 A595 5r Dome of the Rock    .20   .20

**1983, Aug. 30**   **Wmk. 381**   **Perf. 13**
2124 A596 3r multicolored      .20   .20
Death of Pres. Rajai and Prime Minister
Bahonar, 2nd anniv.

Iran-Iraq War, 3rd
Anniv. — A597

**1983, Sept. 28**   **Photo.**   **Perf. 13**
2125 A597 5r rose red & blk      .20   .20

Ayatollah Ashrafi
Esphahani,
Martyr of
Altar — A598

Mirza Kuchik
Khan — A599

**1983, Oct. 15**   **Photo.**   **Perf. 13**
2126 A598 5r multicolored      .20   .20

**1983-84**      **Photo.**      **Perf. 13**
Religious and Political Figures: 1r, Sheikh
Mohammad Khiabani. 3r, Seyd Majtaba
Navab Safavi. 5r, Seyd Jamal-ed-Din
Assadabadi. 10r, Seyd Hassan Modaress.
20r, Sheikh Fazel Assad Nouri. 30r, Mirza
Mohammad Hossein Naiyni. 50r, Sheikh
Mohammad Hossein Kashef. 100r, Seyd Has-
san Shirazi. 200r, Mirza Reza Kermani.

| 2128 | A599 | 1r black & pink | .20 | .20 |
|---|---|---|---|---|
| 2129 | A599 | 2r org & black | .20 | .20 |
| 2130 | A599 | 3r brt bl & blk | .20 | .20 |
| 2131 | A599 | 5r rose red & blk | .20 | .20 |
| 2132 | A599 | 10r yel grn & blk | .30 | .20 |
| 2133 | A599 | 20r lilac & blk | .60 | .20 |
| 2134 | A599 | 30r gldn brn & blk | .90 | .30 |
| 2135 | A599 | 50r blk & lt bl | 1.50 | .50 |
| 2136 | A599 | 100r blk & org | 3.00 | 1.00 |
| 2137 | A599 | 200r blk & bluish grn | 6.00 | 2.00 |
| | | *Nos. 2128-2137 (10)* | 13.10 | 5.00 |

Issue dates: 1r, 50r-200r, Feb. 1984.
Others, Oct. 23, 1983.

UPU Day
A600

**1983, Oct. 9**   **Photo.**   **Wmk. 381**
2138 A600 10r multi      .25   .20

Takeover of the US
Embassy, 4th
Anniv. — A601

**1983, Nov. 4**   **Photo.**   **Perf. 13**
2139 A601 28r multicolored      .50   .50

UN Day
A602

**1983, Oct. 24**      **Perf. 13½**
2140 A602 32r multicolored      .90   .25
Protest of veto by US, Russia, People's
Rep. of China, France and Great Britain.

Intl. Medical
Seminar,
Tehran — A603

**1983, Nov. 20**
2141 A603 3r Avicenna      .20   .20

People's Forces Preparation
Day — A604

**1983, Nov. 26**      **Perf. 13**
2142 A604 20r multicolored      .60   .20

Conference on Crimes of Iraqi Pres.
Saddam Hussein — A605

**1983, Nov. 28**      **Perf. 13½x13**
2143 A605 5r multicolored      .20   .20

Mohammad Mofatteh — A606

**1983, Dec. 18**   **Photo.**   **Perf. 13**
2144 A606 10r multicolored      .30   .20

Birth Anniversary of
the Prophet
Mohammad
A607

**1983, Dec. 22**   **Photo.**   **Perf. 13**
2145 A607 5r multicolored      .45   .20

Approximately 700,000 examples of No.
2145 were issued before a spelling error was
discovered, and the remainder of the issue
was then withdrawn from sale.

5th Anniv. of
Islamic
Revolution — A608

**1984, Feb. 11**   **Photo.**   **Perf. 13x13½**
2146 A608 10r multicolored      .75   .20

See No. 2310h for stamp with splotchy colors in blue background and denomination,
flag colors and darker, thicker black lines
around tulips. Background and denominations
on No. 2146 have a screened appearance.

Nurses'
Day
A609

**1984, Feb. 24**      **Perf. 13**
2147 A609 20r Attending wounded
          soldiers      .45   .20

Invalids'
Day — A610

Local
Flowers — A611

**1984, Feb. 29**
2148 A610 5r Man in wheelchair .20 .20

**1984, Mar. 10** *Perf. 13½x13*
2149 A611 3r Lotus gebelia .20 .20
2150 A611 5r Tulipa chrysantha .20 .20
2151 A611 10r Glycyrhiza glabra .25 .20
2152 A611 20r Matthiola alyssifolia .45 .20
  a. Block of 4, #2149-2152 1.00 .75
Novrooz (New Year).

Islamic Republic,
5th
Anniv. — A612

Sheik Ragheb
Harb, Lebanese
Religious
Leader — A614

World
Health Day
A613

**1984, Apr. 1** *Photo.* *Perf. 13*
2153 A612 5r Flag, globe, map .20 .20

**1984, Apr. 7**
2154 A613 10r Children .30 .20

**1984, Apr. 18**
2155 A614 5r multicolored .20 .20

World Red Cross
Day — A615

16th World Telecom-
munications
Day — A616

**1984, May 8** *Photo.* *Perf. 13½x13*
2156 A615 5r multicolored .20 .20

**1984, May 17**
2157 A616 20r multicolored .45 .20

Martyrdom of
Seyyed
Ghotb — A617

**1984, May 28** *Perf. 13*
2158 A617 10r multicolored .30 .20

Struggle Against
Discrimination — A618

**1984, Mar. 21** *Photo.* *Perf. 13*
2159 A618 5r Malcolm X 1.00 .20

Conquest
of Mecca
Anniv.
A619

**1984, June 20**
2160 A619 5r Holy Ka'aba, idol
  destruction .20 .20

Universal Day of
Jerusalem
A620

Id Al-fitr Feast
A621

**1984, June 29**
2161 A620 5r Map, Koran .20 .20
2162 A621 10r Moon, praying
  crowd, mosque .25 .20
  a. Pair, #2161-2162 .40 .20

Tchogha Zanbil Excavation,
Susa — A622

Cultural Heritage Preservation: b,
Emamzadeh Hossein Shrine, Kazvin. c,
Emam Mosque, Isfahan. d, Ark Fortress,
Tabriz. e, Mausoleum of Daniel Nabi, Susa.

**1984, Aug. 20** *Perf. 13½*
2163 Strip of 5 .75 .25
  a.-e. A622 5r, any single .20 .20

"Eid Ul-
Adha"
A623

*Perf. 13x13½*
**1984, Sept. 6** *Photo.* *Wmk. 381*
2164 A623 10r Holy Ka'aba .30 .20
Feast of Sacrifices (end of pilgrimage to
Mecca).

10th Tehran Intl.
Trade
Fair — A624

Iraq-Iran War, 4th
Anniv. — A625

**1984, Sept. 11**
2165 A624 10r multicolored .30 .20

**1984, Sept. 22** *Photo.* *Perf. 13½x13*
2166 A625 5r Flower, bullets .20 .20

UPU Day
A626

**1984, Oct. 9** *Perf. 13½*
2167 A626 20r Dove, UPU emblems .50 .20

Haj
Seyyed
Mostafa
Khomeini
Memorial
A627

**1984, Oct. 23**
2168 A627 5r multicolored .20 .20

Ghazi Tabatabaie
Memorial — A628

Mohammad's
Birthday, Unity
Week — A630

Intl. Saadi
Congress
A629

**1984, Nov. 1** *Perf. 13x13½*
2169 A628 5r Portrait .20 .20

**1984, Nov. 25** *Perf. 13½*
2170 A629 10r Portrait, mausoleum, emblem .50 .20
Saadi (c. 1213-1292), Persian poet.

**1984, Dec. 6** *Photo.* *Perf. 13x13½*
2171 A630 5r Koran, mosque .25 .20

Islamic
Revolution, 6th
Anniv. — A631

Arbor
Day — A632

**1985, Feb. 11** *Perf. 13x13½*
2172 A631 40r multicolored .90 .40
See No. 2310o for stamp with bright pink
denomination and dove tail.

**1985, Mar. 6** *Perf. 13*
2173 A632 3r Sapling, deciduous
  trees .20 .20
2174 A632 5r Maturing trees .20 .20
  a. Pair, #2173-2174 .30 .20

Local
Flowers — A633

**1985, Mar. 9** *Perf. 13½x13*
2175 A633 5r Fritillaria imperialis .20 .20
2176 A633 5r Ranunculus fi-
  carioides .20 .20
2177 A633 5r Crocus sativus .20 .20
2178 A633 5r Primula heter-
  ochroma stapf .20 .20
  a. Block of 4, #2175-2178 .50 .30
Novrooz (New Year).

Women's
Day — A634

Republic of Iran,
6th
Anniv. — A635

**1985, Mar. 13** *Perf. 13x13½*
2179 A634 10r Procession of women .30 .20
Birth anniv. of Mohammad's daughter,
Fatima.

**1985, Apr. 1**
2180 A635 20r Tulip, ballot box .45 .20

Mab'as
Festival
A636

**1985, Apr. 18**
2181 A636 10r Holy Koran .30 .20
Religious festival celebrating the recognition
of Mohammad as the true prophet.

Day of the Oppressed
A637

World Telecommunications Day
A638

**1985, May 6**

2182 A637 5r Koran, flag, globe .20 .20

Birthday of the 12th Imam.

**1985, May 17**     *Perf. 13½x13*

2183 A638 20r ITU emblem .45 .20

Liberation of Khorramshahr, 1st Anniv. — A639

**1985, May 24**

2184 A639 5r Soldier, bridge .20 .20

Fist, Theological Seminary, Qum — A640

Day of Jerusalem
A642

World Handicrafts Day
A641

**1985, June 5**     *Perf. 13x13½*

2185 A640 10r multicolored .50 .20

1963 Uprising, 22nd Anniv.

**1985, June 10**     *Perf. 13½*

2186 A641 20r Plates, flasks .45 .20

**1985, June 14**

2187 A642 5r multicolored .20 .20

Id Al-fitr Feast — A643

Founding of the Islamic Propagation Org. — A644

**1985, June 20**

2188 A643 5r multicolored .20 .20

**1985, June 22**

2189 A644 5r tan & emerald .20 .20

Ayatollah Sheikh Abdolhossein Amini — A645

**1985, July 3**     **Photo.**     *Perf. 13*

2190 A645 5r multicolored .25 .20

Pilgrimage to Mecca — A646

Goharshad Mosque Uprising, 50th Anniv. — A648

Cultural Heritage Preservation — A647

**1985, July 20**     **Photo.**     *Perf. 13½*

2191 A646 10r multicolored .30 .20

**1985, Aug. 20**

Ceramic plates from Nishabur: a, Swords. b, Farsi script. c, Peacock. d, Four leaves.

2192     Block of 4 .60 .20
    *a.-d.*   A647 5r, any single .20 .20

**1985, Aug. 21**     *Perf. 13x13½*

2193 A648 10r multicolored .20 .20

Week of Government
A649

Bleeding Tulips
A650

Designs: a, Industry and communications. b, Industry and agriculture. c, Health care, red crescent. d, Education.

**1985, Aug. 30**    **Photo.**    *Perf. 13x13½*

2194     Block of 4 .60 .20
    *a.-d.*   A649 5r, any single .20 .20

**1985, Sept. 8**

2195 A650 10r multicolored .30 .20

17th Shahrivar, Bloody Friday memorial.

OPEC, 25th Anniv. — A651

Design: No. 2196b, OPEC emblem and 25.

**1985, Sept. 14**     *Perf. 13½*

2196     Pair .50 .20
    *a.-b.*   A651 5r, any single .25 .20

Iran-Iraq War, 5th Anniv. — A652

Designs: a, Dead militiaman. b, Mosque and Ashura in Persian. c, Rockets descending on doves. d, Palm grove, rifle shot exploding rocket.

**1985, Sept. 22**

2197     Block of 4 .60 .20
    *a.-d.*   A652 5r any single .20 .20

Ashura mourning.

Ash-Sharif Ar-Radi — A653

**1985, Sept. 26**    **Photo.**    *Perf. 13x13½*

2198 A653 20r brt bl, lt bl & gold .60 .20

Ash-Sharif Ar-Radi, writer, death millennium.

UPU Day
A654

**1985, Oct. 9**     *Perf. 13½*

2199 A654 20r multicolored .60 .20

World Standards Day
A655

**1985, Oct. 14**

2200 A655 20r Natl. Standards Office emblem .60 .20

Agricultural Training and Development Year — A656

Takeover of US Embassy, 6th Anniv. — A657

**1985, Oct. 19**     *Perf. 13x13½*

2201 A656 5r Hand, wheat .20 .20

**1985, Nov. 4**     *Perf. 13*

2202 A657 40r multicolored .60 .40

Moslem Unity Week
A658

High Council of the Cultural Revolution
A659

**1985, Nov. 25**     *Perf. 13x13½*

2203 A658 10r Holy Ka'aba .30 .20

Birth of prophet Mohammad, 1015th anniv.

**1985, Dec. 10**

2204 A659 5r Roses .20 .20

Intl. Youth Year — A660

Designs: a, Education. b, Defense. c, Construction. d, Sports.

**1985, Dec. 18**    **Photo.**    *Perf. 13x13½*

2205     Block of 4 .60 .20
    *a.-d.*   A660 5r, any single .20 .20

Ezzeddin al-Qassam, 50th Death Anniv. — A661

**1985, Dec. 20**      *Perf. 13½*
2206 A661 20r sil, sep & hn brn    .60   .20

Map, Fists, Bayonets
A662

**1985, Dec. 25**      *Wmk. 381*
2207 A662 40r multi      1.25   .40

Occupation of Afghanistan and Moslem resistance, 6th anniv.

Mirza Taqi Khan Amir Kabir (d. 1851) — A663

**1986, Jan. 8**    **Litho.**    *Perf. 13*
2208 A663 5r multicolored    1.25   .20

Students Destroying Statue of the Shah, Tulips — A664

Women's Day — A666

Sulayman Khater, 40th Death Anniv. — A665

**1986, Feb. 11**    **Photo.**    *Perf. 13½*
2209 A664 20r multicolored    .60   .20

Iranian Revolution, 7th anniv.

---

See No. 2310l for 24x36mm stamp with yellow Arabic script.

**1986, Feb. 15**      *Perf. 13*
2210 A665 10r multicolored    .30   .20

**1986, Mar. 3**      *Perf. 13½*
2211 A666 10r multicolored    .30   .20

Birth anniv. of Mohammad's daughter, Fatima.

Flowers — A667

a, Papaver orientale. b, Anemone coronaria. c, Papaver bracteatum. d, Anemone biflora.

**1986, Mar. 11**   **Photo.**   *Perf. 13½*
2212    Block of 4    .60   .20
   *a.* A667 5r any single    .20   .20

Novrooz (New Year).

2000th Day of Sacred Defense
A668

Intl. Day Against Racial Discrimination
A669

**1986, Mar. 14**   **Photo.**   *Perf. 13x13½*
2213 A668 5r scarlet & grn    .20   .20

**1986, Mar. 21**      *Perf. 13½*
2214 A669 5r multicolored    .20   .20

Islamic Republic of Iran, 7th Anniv. — A670

**1986, Apr. 1**      *Perf. 13*
2215 A670 10r Flag, map    .30   .20

Mab'as Festival
A671

**1986, Apr. 7**
2216 A671 40r multicolored    .60   .20

---

Army Day — A672

Day of the Oppressed — A673

**1986, Apr. 18**      *Perf. 13½*
2217 A672 5r multicolored    .20   .20

**1986, Apr. 25**      *Perf. 13x13½*
2218 A673 10r blk, gold & dk red   .20   .20

Helicopter Crash — A674

Teacher's Day — A675

**1986, Apr. 25**      *Wmk. 381*
2219 A674 40r multicolored    1.25   .40

US air landing at Tabass Air Base, 6th anniv.

**1986, May 2**   **Photo.**   *Perf. 13x13½*
2220 A675 5r multicolored    .20   .20

World Telecommunications Day — A676

**1986, May 17**      *Perf. 13½x13*
2221 A676 20r blk, sil & ultra    .60   .20

Universal Day of the Child — A677

**1986, June 1**      *Perf. 13*
2222 A677 15r Child's war drawing   .45   .20
2223 A677 15r Hosein Fahmide, Iran-Iraq war hero   .45   .20
   *a.* Pair, #2222-2223    .90   .30

1963 Uprising, 23rd Anniv. — A678

---

**1986, June 5**      *Perf. 13x13½*
2224 A678 10r Qum Theological Seminary    .30   .20

Day of Jerusalem — A679

**1986, June 6**
2225 A679 10r multicolored    .30   .20

Id Al-Fitr Feast
A680

**1986, June 9**      *Perf. 13*
2226 A680 10r Moslems praying    .75   .20

World Handicrafts Day
A681

a, Baluchi cross-hatched rug. b, Craftsman. c, Qalamkar flower rug. d, Copper repousse vase.

**1986, June 10**      *Perf. 13½*
2227    Block of 4    1.25   .40
   *a.-d.* A681 10r, any single    .30   .20

Intl. Day for Solidarity with Black So. Africans — A682

Ayatollah Beheshti — A683

**1986, June 26**
2228 A682 10r multicolored    .30   .20

**1986, June 28**      *Perf. 13x13½*
2229 A683 10r multicolored    .30   .20

Death of Beheshti and Islamic Party workers, Tehran headquarters bombing, 5th anniv.

Ayatollah Mohammad Taqi Shirazi, Map of Iraq — A684

Shrine of Imam Reza — A685

**1986, June 30   Photo.   Wmk. 381**
2230 A684 20r multicolored    .60   .20
Iraqi Moslem uprising against the British.

**1986, July 19     Perf. 13½**
2231 A685 10r multicolored    .30   .20

Eid Ul-Adha, Feast of Sacrifice — A686    Eid Ul-Ghadir Feast — A688

Cultural Heritage Preservation — A687

**1986, Aug. 17     Perf. 13x13½**
2232 A686 10r multicolored    .30   .20

**1986, Aug. 20**
Designs: No. 2233, Bam Fortress. No. 2234, Kabud (Blue) Mosque, Tabriz. No. 2235, Mausoleum of Sohel Ben Ali at Astenah, Arak. No. 2236, Soltanieh Mosque, Zendjan Province.

2233 A687 5r Hilltop    .25   .20
2234 A687 5r shown    .25   .20
2235 A687 5r Intact roof    .25   .20
2236 A687 5r Damaged roof    .25   .20
    Nos. 2233-2236 (4)    1.00   .80

**1986, Aug. 25**
2237 A688 20r multicolored    .60   .20

Population and Housing Census — A689

Iran-Iraq War, 6th Year — A690

**1986, Sept. 9     Perf. 13½x13**
2238 A689 20r multicolored    .40   .20

**1986, Sept. 22     Perf. 13**
2239 A690 10r Battleship Paykan    .30   .20
2240 A690 10r Susangerd    .30   .20
2241 A690 10r Khorramshahr    .30   .20
2242 A690 10r Howeizeh    .30   .20
2243 A690 10r Siege of Abadan    .30   .20
    Nos. 2239-2243 (5)    1.50   1.00

10th Asian Games, Seoul A691

**1986, Oct. 2   Photo.   Wmk. 381**
2244 A691 15r Wrestling    .40   .20
2245 A691 15r Rifle shooting    .40   .20

World Post Day A692

**1986, Oct. 9**
2246 A692 20r multicolored    .60   .20

UNESCO, 40th Anniv. — A693

**1986, Nov. 4   Photo.   Perf. 13x13½**
2247 A693 45r blk, sky bl & brt rose    1.25   .45

Ayatollah Tabatabaie (d. 1981) — A694

**1986, Nov. 15   Photo.   Perf. 13½x13**
2248 A694 10r multicolored    .30   .20

Unity Week — A695

**1986, Nov. 20**
2249 A695 10r multicolored    .30   .20
Birth anniv. of Mohammad.

People's Militia — A696

**1986, Nov. 26     Perf. 13**
2250 A696 5r multicolored    .20   .20
Mobilization of the Oppressed Week.

Afghan Resistance Movement, 7th Anniv. — A697

**1986, Dec. 27**
2251 A697 40r multicolored    1.25   .40

Nurses' Day — A698

**1987, Jan. 12   Photo.   Perf. 13**
2252 A698 20r multicolored    .60   .20
Hazrat Zainab birth anniv.

Fifth Islamic Theology Conference, Tehran — A699

**Wmk. 381**
**1987, Jan. 29   Photo.   Perf. 13**
2253 A699 20r multicolored    .60   .20

Islamic Revolution, 8th Anniv. — A700

**1987, Feb. 11**
2254 A700 20r multicolored    .60   .20
    See No. 2310m for 24x36mm stamp.

Islamic Revolutionary Committees, 8th Anniv. — A701

**1987, Feb. 12**
2255 A701 10r brt bl, scar & yel    .30   .20

Women's Day — A702

**1987, Feb. 19**
2256 A702 10r multicolored    .30   .20
Birthday of Fatima, daughter of Mohammad.

Iran Air, 25th Anniv. A703

**1987, Feb. 24**
2257 A703 30r multicolored    .90   .30

Ayatollah Mirza Mohammad Hossein Naeini, 50th Death Anniv. — A704

**1987, Mar. 6   Photo.   Perf. 13**
2258 A704 10r multicolored    .30   .20

New Year — A705

Mab'as Festival A706

Flowers: a, Iris persica. b, Rosa damascena. c, Iris paradoxa. d, Tulipa clusiana.

**1987, Mar. 11     Perf. 13½x13**
2259   Block of 4    2.00   .50
a.-d. A705 5r, any single    .50   .20
    See Nos. 2313, 2361, 2411, 2443.

**1987, Mar. 28     Perf. 13**
2260 A706 45r gold, dk grn & grn   1.40   .45

Universal Day of the Oppressed A707

**1987, Apr. 14**
2261 A707 20r multicolored .60 .20
Savior Mahdi's birthday.

Memorial to Lebanese Hizbollah Martyrs — A708

**1987, Apr. 5**
2262 A708 10r grn, gray & brt car .30 .20

Revolutionary Guards Day — A709

**1987, Apr. 2**
2263 A709 5r multi .20 .20
Imam Hossein's birthday.

8th Anniv. of Islamic Republic A710

**1987, Apr. 1**
2264 A710 20r multicolored .60 .20

World Health Day — A711

Child survival through immunization: 3r, Intravenous. 5r, Oral.

**1987, Apr. 7** Perf. 13x13½
2265 A711 3r multicolored .20 .20
2266 A711 5r multicolored .30 .20
a. Pair, #2265-2266 .50 .25

Int'l. Labor Day — A712

**1987, May 1** Photo. Perf. 13
2267 A712 5r multicolored .20 .20

Teachers' Day — A713

**1987, May 2** Wmk. 381
2268 A713 5r Ayatollah Mottahari .20 .20

A714

**1987, May 17** Perf. 13½x13
2269 A714 20r multicolored .70 .20
World Telecommunications Day.

A715

**1987, May 18** Perf. 13
2270 A715 20r Sassanian silver gilt vase .60 .20
2271 A715 20r Bisque pot, Rey, 12th cent. .60 .20
Intl. Museum Day.

Universal Day of Jerusalem A716

1963 Uprising, 24th Anniv. A718

World Crafts Day A717

**1987, May 22** Perf. 13½x13
2272 A716 20r multicolored .60 .20

Tax Reform Week — A719

**1987, June 10** Perf. 13x13½
a, Blown glass tea service. b, Stained glass window. c, Ceramic plate. d, Potter.
2273 Block of 4 .75 .20
a.-d. A717 5r any single .20 .20

**1987, June 5** Photo. Perf. 13½
2274 A718 20r multicolored .60 .20

**1987, July 10** Perf. 13
2275 A719 10r black, sil & gold .30 .20

Welfare Week — A720

**1987, July 17**
2276 A720 15r multicolored .45 .20

Eid Ul-adha, Feast of Sacrifice — A721

**1987, Aug. 6**
2277 A721 12r sil, blk & Prus grn .45 .20

Eid Ul-Ghadir Festival A722

Banking Week — A723

**1987, Aug. 14**
2278 A722 18r black, green & gold .55 .20

**1987, Aug. 17** Perf. 13½x13
2279 A723 15r red brn, gold & pale grnsh bl .45 .20

1st Cultural and Artistic Congress of Iranian Calligraphers A724

**1987, Aug. 21** Photo. Perf. 13x13½
2280 A724 20r multicolored .60 .20

Memorial to Iranian Pilgrims Killed in Mecca — A725

**1987, Aug. 26** Wmk. 381 Perf. 13
2281 A725 8r multicolored .30 .20

Assoc. of Iranian Dentists, 25th Anniv. — A726

Intl. Peace Day — A727

**1987, Aug. 27** Photo. Perf. 13½x13
2282 A726 10r multicolored .30 .20

**1987, Sept. 1** Perf. 13
2283 A727 20r gold & lt ultra .60 .20

Iran-Iraq War, 7th Anniv. — A728

Police Day — A729

**1987, Sept. 22** Perf. 13½x13
2284 A728 25r shown .75 .25
2285 A728 25r Soldier, battle scene .75 .25
a. Pair, #2284-2285

**1987, Sept. 28**
2286 A729 10r multicolored .30 .20

Intl. Social Security Week, Oct. 4-10 — A730

World Post
Day — A731

**1987, Oct. 4**          **Wmk. 381**
2287 A730 15r blk, gold & brt blue   .45   .20

**1987, Oct. 9**          *Perf. 13x13½*
   UPU emblem and: No. 2288, M. Ghandi, minister of the Post and Telecommunications Bureau. No. 2289, Globe, dove.
2288 A731 15r multicolored    .45   .20
2289 A731 15r multicolored    .45   .20

> Importation Prohibited
> Importation of stamps was prohibited effective Oct. 29, 1987.

A732

A733

**Wmk. 381**
**1987, Nov. 4**    **Photo.**      *Perf. 13*
2290 A732 40r multicolored      1.25
   Takeover of US Embassy, 8th anniv.

**1987, Nov. 5**
2291 A733 20r multicolored      .90
   1st Intl. Tehran Book Fair.

Mohammad's
Birthday, Unity
Week — A734

**1987, Nov. 10**
2292 A734 25r multicolored      .60

---

Ayatollah
Modarres
Martyrdom,
50th
Anniv. — A735

**1987, Dec. 1**
2293 A735 10r brn & bister      .40

Agricultural Training and Extension
Week — A736

**1987, Dec. 6**
2294 A736 10r multicolored      .50

Afghan Resistance, 8th Anniv. — A737

**1987, Dec. 27**
2295 A737 40r multicolored      1.25

Main Mosques
A738

**1987-92**     *Perf. 13x13½, 13½x13*
**Silver Background**
2295A A738   1r Shoushtar
2296 A738   2r Ouroumieh
2296A A738   3r Kerman
2297 A738   5r Kazvin
2298 A738   10r Varamin
    *a.*   Unwatermarked ('91)
2299 A738   20r Saveh
    *a.*   Unwatermarked ('91)
2300 A738   30r Natanz, vert.
2301 A738   40r Shiraz
    *a.*   Unwatermarked ('92)
2302 A738   50r Isfahan, vert.
    *a.*   Unwatermarked ('91)
2303 A738   100r Hamadan
    *a.*   Unwatermarked ('91)
2304 A738   200r Dezfoul, vert.
    *a.*   Unwatermarked ('91)
2305 A738   500r Yazd, vert.
    *a.*   Unwatermarked ('91)

   Issued: 10r, 12/1; 5r, 12/30; 500r, 1/10/88; 20r, 1/14/88; 2r, 1/24/88; 50r, 1/24/89; 100r, 10/21/89; 200r, 10/28/89; 30r, 40r, 3/17/90; 1r, 3r, 3/92.
   For surcharges see #2750-2751.
   Watermarks on this issue can be difficult to discern. The paper of the unwatermarked stamps show fluoresence under long wave ultraviolet light.

Qum Uprising, 10th
Anniversary — A739

**1988, Jan. 9**       *Perf. 13*
2306 A739 20r multicolored      .50

---

Bombing of Schools
by Iraq — A740

**1988, Feb. 1**       *Perf. 13x13½*
2307 A740 10r multicolored      .80

Gholamreza Takhti, World Wrestling
Champion — A741

**1988, Feb. 4**       *Perf. 13½*
2308 A741 15r multicolored      .30

Women's
Day — A742

**1988, Feb. 9**       *Perf. 13*
2309 A742 20r multicolored      .40
   Birth anniv. of Mohammad's daughter, Fatima.

Souvenir Sheet
Types of 1979-88 and

Islamic Revolution,
9th Anniv. — A743

**Perf. 13, Imperf**
**1988, Feb. 11**       **Wmk. 381**
2310    Sheet of 16       7.00
   *a.* A547   1r like #2046
   *b.* A547   3r like #2047
   *c.* A559   3r like #2066
   *d.* A547   5r like #2048
   *e.* A559   5r like #2067
   *f.* A570   5r like #2095
   *g.* A570   10r like #2096
   *h.* A608   10r like #2146
   *i.* A537   18r like #1999
   *j.* A559   20r like #2068
   *k.* A570   20r like #2097
   *l.* A664   20r like #2209
   *m.* A700   20r like #2254
   *n.* A587   30r like #2115
   *o.* A631   40r like #2172
   *p.* A743   40r shown

   Nos. 2310a, 2310b, 2310d, 2310l, 2310m are smaller than the original issues. See original issues for distinguishing features on other stamps.

Tabriz Uprising, 10th Anniv. — A744

**1988, Feb. 18**       *Perf. 13*
2311 A744 25r multicolored      .50

---

Arbor
Day — A745

**1988, Mar. 5**
2312 A745 15r multicolored      .70

   New Year Festival Type of 1987

   Flowers: a, Anthemis hyalina. b, Malva silvestria. c, Viola odorata. d, Echium amaenum.

**1988, Mar. 10**       *Perf. 13½x13*
2313    Block of 4
   *a.-d.* A705 10r any single

Islamic
Republic, 9th
Anniv. — A746

**1988, Apr. 1**       *Perf. 13*
2314 A746 20r multicolored      .40

Universal Day
of the
Oppressed
— A747

**1988, Apr. 3**
2314A A747 20r multicolored      .30
   Savior Mahdi's Birthday.

Cultural Heritage — A748

**1988, Apr. 18**
2315 A748 10r Mosque
2316 A748 10r Courtyard
    *a.*   Pair, #2315-2316
2317 A748 10r Minarets, vert.
2318 A748 10r Corridor, vert.
    *a.*   Pair, #2317-2318

Chemical
Bombardment
of Halabja,
Iraq — A749

**1988, Apr. 26**
2319 A749 20r multicolored      .90

A750

A750a

Palestinian
Uprising
A750b

**1988, May 13**
2320    Strip of 5    2.50
  *a.*  A750 10r multi
  *b.*  A750a 10r multi
  *c.*  A750b 10r multi
  *d.*  A750b 10r multi, diff.
  *e.*  A750b 10r Rock in hand, rioters

World Telecommunications
Day — A751

**1988, May 17**    *Perf. 13x13½*
2321  A751 20r green & blue  .80

Intl. Museum
Day — A752

Designs: a, Ceramic vase, 1982. b, Bastan
Museum, entranceway. c, Tabriz silk rug, 14th
cent. d, Gold ring, 7th cent. B.C.

**1988, May 18**    *Perf. 13*
2322    Block of 4    1.50
  *a.-d.*  A752 10r any single  .30

Mining
Day — A753

**1988, May 22**    Photo.    Wmk. 381
2323  A753 20r multicolored  1.25

Intl. Day of the
Child — A754

**1988, June 1**
2324  A754 10r multicolored  .50

June 5th
Uprising, 25th
Anniv. — A755

**1988, June 5**
2325  A755 10r multicolored  .40

World
Crafts Day
A756

**1988, June 10**    *Perf. 13x13½*
2326  A756 10r Straw basket  .30
2327  A756 10r Weaver  .30
  *a.*  Pair, #2326-2327  .75
2328  A756 10r Tapestry, vert.  .30
2329  A756 10r Miniature, vert.  .30
  *a.*  Pair, #2328-2329  .75

Child Health
Campaign
A757

**1988, July 6**    *Perf. 13*
2330  A757 20r blk, blue & green  .40

Tax Reform
Week — A758

**1988, July 10**
2331  A758 20r multicolored  .40

A759

**1988, July 15**    *Perf. 13½x13*
2332  A759 20r Allameh Balkhi  .40

A760

**1988, July 21**    *Perf. 13*
2333  A760 10r Holy Ka'aba,
    dove, stars  .25
2334  A760 10r shown  .25
Massacre of Muslim Pilgrims at Mecca.
Nos. 2333-2334 were printed together in
one sheet, with alternating placement.

Destruction of
Iranian
Airliner — A761

**1988, Aug. 11**
2335  A761 45r multicolored  1.25

A762

A763

**1988, Aug. 13**
2336  A762 20r Seyyed Ali
    Andarzgou  .50

**1988, Sept. 1**    *Perf. 13½x13*
2337  A763 20r multicolored  .50

    Islamic Banking Week.

Divine Day of
17 Shahrivar,
10th
Anniv. — A764

**1988, Sept. 8**
2338  A764 25r multicolored  .70

1988 Summer
Olympics,
Seoul — A765

Designs: a, Weightlifting. b, Pommel horse.
c, Judo. d, Soccer. e, Wrestling.

**1988, Sept. 10**
2339    Strip of 5    2.00
  *a.-e.*  A765 10r any single  .35

A766        A767

**1988, Sept. 17**    *Perf. 13½x13*
2340  A766 30r blk, grn & yel  .60

    Agricultural census.

**1988, Sept. 22**    *Perf. 13x13½*
2341  A767 20r multicolored  .50

    Iran-Iraq War, 8th anniv.

World
Post
Day
A768

**1988, Oct. 9**    *Perf. 13*
2342  A768 20r blk, ultra & grn  .80

Parents and Teachers Cooperation Week — A769

**1988, Oct. 16**
2343 A769 20r multicolored .70

Mohammad's Birthday, Unity Week — A770

**1988, Oct. 29**
2344 A770 10r multicolored .50

A771

A772

**1988, Nov. 4**
2345 A771 45r multicolored 1.10
Takeover of US embassy, 9th anniv.

**1988, Nov. 6**         *Perf. 13½x13*
2346 A772 10r multicolored .80
Insurance Day.

Intl. Congress on the Writings of Hafiz — A773

Illustration reduced.

**1988, Nov. 19**       *Perf. 13x13½*
2347 A773 20r blue, gold & pink .50

Agricultural Training and Extension Week — A774

**1988, Dec. 6**         *Perf. 13*
2348 A774 15r multicolored .60

Scientists, Artists and Writers A775

**1988, Dec. 18**      *Perf. 13x13½*
2349 A775 10r Parvin E'Tessami .35
2350 A775 10r Jalal Al-Ahmad .35
2351 A775 10r Muhammad Mo'in .35
  a.   Pair, #2350-2351 .75
2352 A775 10r Qaem Maqam
           Farahani .35
2353 A775 10r Kamal Al-Molk .35
  a.   Pair, #2352-2353 .75
       See Nos. 2398-2402.

Afghan Resistance, 9th Anniv. — A776

**1988, Dec. 27**       *Perf. 13*
2354 A776 40r multicolored .45

Transportion and Communication Decade — A777

                        *Perf. 13x13½*
**1989, Jan. 16**       Wmk. 381
2355 A777 20r Satellite, enve-
           lopes, microwave
           dish .70
2356 A777 20r Cargo planes .70
  a.   Pair, #2355-2356 1.50
2357 A777 20r Train, trucks .70
2358 A777 20r Ships .70
  a.   Pair, #2357-2358 1.50

Prophethood of Mohammad A778

**1989, Mar. 6**        *Perf. 13*
2359 A778 20r multicolored .50
       Mab'as festival.

Arbor Day — A779

**1989, Mar. 6**
2360 A779 20r multicolored .70

**New Year Festival Type of 1987**
  Flowers: a, Cephalanthera kurdica.
b, Dactylorhiza romana. c, Comperia comperi-
ana. d, Orchis mascula.

**1989, Mar. 11**      *Perf. 13½x13*
2361   Block of 4 1.25
  a.-d. A705 10r any single .25

A780

A781

**1989, Mar. 23**
2362 A780 20r shown .60
2363 A780 30r Meteorological
           devices, ship .60
  a.   Pair, #2362-2363 1.25
       World Meteorology Day.

**1989, Apr. 1**        *Perf. 13*
2364 A781 20r multicolored .40
       Islamic Republic, 10th anniv.

Reconstruction of Abadan Refinery A782

**1989, Apr. 1**
2365 A782 20r multicolored .70

Ayatollah Morteza Motahhari, 10th Death Anniv. — A783

**1989, May 2**
2366 A783 20r multi .40
       Teachers' Day.

A784

**1989, May 5**
2367 A784 30r multicolored .75
       Universal Day of Jerusalem.

A785

**1989, May 17**       *Perf. 13½x13*
2368 A785 20r multicolored .70
       World Telecommunications Day.

A786

**1989, Mar. 23** 

A787

Intl. Museum Day: Gurgan pottery, 6th cent.

**1989, May 18**       *Perf. 13x13½*
2369 A786 20r Jar .50
2370 A786 20r Bottle .50
  a.   Pair, #2369-2370 1.10

**1989, June 4**        *Perf. 13*
2371 A787 20r multicolored .40
       Nomads' Day.

World Crafts Day A788

**1989, July 5**        *Perf. 13x13½*
2372 A788 20r Engraver .40
2373 A788 20r Copper vase .40
  a.   Pair, #2372-2373 1.00
2374 A788 20r Copper plate,
           vert. .40
2375 A788 20r Copper wall hang-
           ing, vert. .40
  a.   Pair, #2374-2375 1.00

Ayatollah
Khomeini
(1900-89)
A789

**1989, July 6**　　　*Perf. 13*
2376 A789 20r multicolored　.50

Pasteur and
Avicenna
A790

**1989, July 7**
2377 A790 30r multicolored　.70
2378 A790 50r multicolored　1.00
　a.　Pair, #2377-2378　1.75

PHILEXFRANCE.

Asia-Pacific Telecommunity, 10th
Anniv. — A791

**1989, July 25**
2379 A791 30r blk, org brn & bl　.80

Mehdi Araghi,
10th Death
Anniv. — A792

**1989, Aug. 30**
2380 A792 20r brn org & org brn　.40

M.H. Shahryar, Poet — A793

**1989, Sept. 17**
2381 A793 20r multicolored　.50

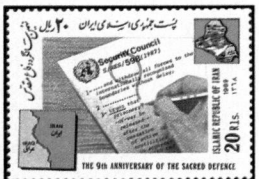

Iran-Iraq War, 9th Anniv. — A794

**1989, Sept. 22**
2382 A794 20r UN Security
　　　Council res. 598　.60

Ayatollah Khomeini — A795

Designs: 1r, Khomeini's birthplace, flower.
2r, Portrait as youth. 3r, Giving speech. 5r,
Map, rifles, exile. 10r, Khomeini returns to
Iran, Feb. 1, 1979. 20r, Khomeini seated
before microphone. 30r, Khomeini with grand-
son.40r, Other mullahs. 50r, Khomeini ges-
turing with hands. 70r, On balcony before
crowd. 100r, Slogan. 200r, Empty lectern.
500r, Mausoleum. 1000r, Sun rays.

**1989-92　Litho.　Unwmk.　Perf. 13½**
2382A A795　1r green & multi
2382B A795　2r green & multi
2383 A795　3r green & multi
2384 A795　5r brt vio & mul-
　　　　　　ti
2385 A795　10r brt bl & multi
2386 A795　20r blue & multi
2387 A795　30r pink & multi
2388 A795　40r red & multi
2389 A795　50r gray & multi
2390 A795　70r brt grn &
　　　　　　multi
2391 A795　100r ultra & multi
2392 A795　200r red brn &
　　　　　　multi
2393 A795　500r black & multi
2393A A795 1000r multicolored

Issued: 1r, 1/3/91; 3r, 3/16/90; 5r, 12/13;
10r, 10/22; 20r, 30r, 50r, 9/23/90; 40r, 2/9/90;
100, 200r, 9/26/90; 70r, 500r, 6/4/91; 2r,
1000r, 3/16/92.

World
Post
Day
A796

**Wmk. 381**
**1989, Oct. 9　Photo.　Perf. 13**
2394 A796 20r multicolored　.85

Mohammad's
Birthday, Unity
Week — A797

**1989, Oct. 18**
2395 A797 10r multi　.80

Takeover of US
Embassy, 10th
Anniv. — A798

**1989, Nov. 4**　　　*Perf. 13½x13*
2396 A798 40r multicolored　.40

Bassij of the
Oppressed
(Militia), 10th
Anniv. — A799

**1989, Nov. 27**　　　*Perf. 13*
2397 A799 10r multicolored

Scientists, Artists and Writers Type of
1988

**1989, Dec. 18**　　　*Perf. 13x13½*
2398 A775 10r Mehdi Elahi
　　　　　　Ghomshei　.30
2399 A775 10r Dr. Abdulazim
　　　　　　Gharib　.30
2400 A775 10r Seyyed Hossein
　　　　　　Mirkhani　.30
　a.　Pair, #2399-2400　.75
2401 A775 10r Ayatollah Seyyed
　　　　　　Hossein
　　　　　　Boroujerdi　.30
2402 A775 10r Ayatollah Sheikh
　　　　　　Abdulkarim Haeri　.30
　a.　Pair, #2401-2402　.75

Intl. Literacy
Year — A800

**Wmk. 381**
**1990, Jan. 1　Photo.　Perf. 13½**
2403 A800 20r multicolored　.70

Cultural
Heritage
A801

Designs: No. 2404, Drinking vessel, 1980.
No. 2405, Footed vase, 1979.

**1990, Jan. 21**　　　*Perf. 13*
2404 A801 20r blk & deep org　.50
2405 A801 20r blk & yel grn　.50
　a.　Pair, #2404-2405　1.25

New
Identification
Card
System — A802

**1990, Feb. 9**
2406 A802 10r multicolored　.25

Islamic
Revolution,
11th
Anniv. — A803

**1990, Feb. 11**
2407 A803 50r multicolored　1.00

Intl. Koran
Recitation
Competition
A804

**1990, Feb. 23**
2408 A804 10r blk, bl & grn　.70

A805

A806

**1990, Mar. 2**　　　*Perf. 13½x13*
2409 A805 10r multicolored　.70

Invalids of Islamic Revolution.

**1990, Mar. 6**　　　*Perf. 13*
2410 A806 20r multicolored　.40

Arbor Day.

New Year Festival Type of 1987

Flowers: a, Coronilla varia. b, Astragalus
cornu-caprae. c, Astragalus obtusifolius. d,
Astragalus straussii.

**1990, Mar. 11**　　　*Perf. 13½x13*
2411　Block of 4　1.00
　a.-d.　A705 10r any single　.25

Islamic
Republic, 11th
Anniv. — A807

**1990, Apr. 1**　　　*Perf. 13*
2412 A807 30r multicolored　.70

World Health
Day — A808

**1990, Apr. 7**
2413 A808 40r multicolored .90

A809

**1990, June 4 Unwmk. *Perf. 11x10½***
2414 A809 50r multicolored .70
Ayatollah Khomeini, 1st death anniv.

A810

**1990, Dec. 15 Litho. *Perf. 10½***
2415 A810 100r multicolored 2.00
Jerusalem Day.

A811

**1990, Oct. 20 *Perf. 13***
2416 A811 20r Turkoman jewelry .40
2417 A811 50r Gilded steel bird 1.00
  a. Pair, #2416-2417 1.75
World Crafts Day.

**1990, Nov. 17 *Perf. 10½***
2418 A812 20r multicolored
Intl. Day of the Child.

Aid to Earthquake Victims — A813

**1990, Nov. 19 *Perf. 13x13½***
2419 A813 100r multicolored .45

Return and
Tribute to
Former
Prisoners of
Iran-Iraq
War — A814

**1990, Nov. 21 *Perf. 13***
2420 A814 250r multicolored 3.00

Ferdowsi Intl. Congress — A815

Illustration reduced.

**1990, Dec. 22 Litho. *Imperf.***
**Size: 60x75mm**

2421 A815 100r Portrait 2.00
2422 A815 100r Statue 2.00
2423 A815 100r Monument 2.00
2424 A815 100r Slogan, diamond
cartouche 2.00
2425 A815 100r Rectangular slogan 2.00
2426 A815 100r Slogan, diff. 2.00
2427 A815 200r Two riders embracing 4.00
2428 A815 200r Archer, birds 4.00
2429 A815 200r Six men 4.00
2430 A815 200r White elephant 4.00
2431 A815 200r Warrior, genie,
horse 4.00
2432 A815 200r Hunting scene 4.00
2433 A815 200r Riding through
fire 4.00
2434 A815 200r Four slogan tablets 4.00
2435 A815 200r Man with feet
shackled 4.00
2436 A815 200r Palace scene 4.00

Conference on epic poem "Book of Kings"
by Ferdowsi.
In 1991 some imperf between blocks of 4
were released.

"Victory Over
Iraq" — A816

**1991, Feb. 25 *Perf. 13***
2437 A816 100r multicolored 1.25

Intl. Museum Day — A817

Designs: No. 2438, Gold jug with Kufric
inscription, 10th cent. A.D. No. 2439, Silver-
inlaid brass basin, 14th cent. A.D.

**1991, Feb. 25**
2438 A817 50r multicolored 1.10
2439 A817 50r multicolored 1.10
  a. Pair, #2438-2439 2.25

A818

A819

**1991, Mar. 12 *Perf. 10½***
2440 A818 50r multicolored 1.00
World Telecommunications Day.

**1991, Feb. 25 *Perf. 13***
2441 A819 200r org brn & blk 3.00
Opening of Postal Museum.

Islamic Revolution, 12th
Anniv. — A820

**1991, Feb. 11 Photo. *Perf. 13***
2442 A820 100r multicolored 2.50

**New Year Festival Type of 1987**

Designs: No. 2443a, Iris spuria. b, Iris
lycotis. c, Iris demawendica. d, Iris meda.

**1991, Mar. 11 *Perf. 13½x13***
2443 A705 20r Block of 4, #a.-d. 2.00

Saleh Hosseini,
10th Death
Anniv. — A821

**1991, Mar. 19 *Perf. 13½x13***
2444 A821 30r red & black .90

Mab'as
Festival
A822

**1991, Mar. 19 *Perf. 13x13½***
2445 A822 100r multicolored 1.50

Universal Day
of the
Oppressed
A823

**1991, Mar. 25 *Perf. 13***
2446 A823 50r multicolored 1.00
Savior Mahdi's Birthday.

Revolutionaries, 25th Death Anniv. — A824

**1990, June 16**
2447 A824 50r maroon & red org .80
Dated 1990.

Islamic Republic, 12th Anniv. — A825

**Unwmk.**
**1991, Apr. 1     Photo.     Perf. 13**
2448 A825 20r blk, slate, grn & red
                                        .60

World Health Day — A826

**1991, Apr. 7     Perf. 13½x13**
2449 A826 100r multicolored 1.50

Day of Jerusalem A827

**1991, Apr. 12     Perf. 13**
2450 A827 100r bl, blk & brn 1.60

A828                    A829

**1991, Apr. 12     Litho.     Perf. 10½**
2451 A828 50r multicolored .80
Women's Day. Birth anniv. of Mohammad's daughter, Fatima.

**Perf. 13½x13**
**1991, Apr. 28     Photo.     Unwmk.**
2452 A829 200r bl grn & blk 4.00
Ayatollah Borujerdi, 30th death anniv.

Teachers' Day — A830

Illustration reduced.

**1991, May 2     Perf. 13x13½**
2453 A830 50r multicolored 1.10

Decade for Natural Disaster Reduction A831

**1991, May 11     Litho.     Perf. 10½**
2454 A831 100r multicolored 1.75

World Telecommunications Day — A832

**Perf. 13½x13**
**1991, May 17     Photo.     Unwmk.**
2455 A832 100r multicolored 1.50

Intl. Museum Day — A833

**1991, May 18     Perf. 13**
2456 A833 20r multicolored .50
2457 A833 40r multicolored 1.00
a.     Pair, #2456-2457 2.00

**1991, May 24     Perf. 13x13½**
2458 A834 30r multicolored .85
Liberation of Khorramshahr, 7th anniv.

Flags — A834

Ewers, Kashan, 13th cent.: 20r, With spout. 40r, Baluster.

**1991, May 18     Perf. 13**
2456 A833 20r multicolored .50
2457 A833 40r multicolored 1.00
a.     Pair, #2456-2457 2.00

**1991, May 24     Perf. 13x13½**
2458 A834 30r multicolored .85
Liberation of Khorramshahr, 7th anniv.

Abol-Hassan Ali-ebne-Mosa Reza, Birth Anniv. — A835

Views of shrine, Meshed.

**1991, May 26     Perf. 13**
2459     10r Mausoleum .25
2460     30r Gravestone .75
a.     A835 Pair, #2459-2460 1.25

First Intl. Conf. on Seismology and Earthquake Engineering A836

**1991, May 27     Perf. 13½x13**
2461 A836 100r multicolored 2.00

World Child Day — A837

**1991, June 1     Photo.     Perf. 13½**
2462 A837 50r multicolored 1.00

Holy Shrine at Karbola, Iraq Destroyed by Invasion — A838

**Unwmk.**
**1991, June 3     Photo.     Perf. 13**
2463 A838 70r multicolored 1.10

Ayatollah Khomeini, 2nd Death Anniv. — A839

**1991, June 4**
2464 A839 100r multicolored 2.50

World Handicrafts Day — A840

Designs: No. 2465, Engraved brass wares. No. 2466, Gilded samovar set.

**1991, June 10     Perf. 13½x13**
2465 A840 40r multicolored 1.00
2466 A840 40r multicolored 1.00
a.     Pair #2465-2466 2.50

Intl. Congress on Poet Nezami — A841

**1991, June 22     Perf. 13**
2467 A841 50r multicolored 1.10

A842

A843

**1991, July 15     Photo.     Perf. 13**
2468 A842 50r multicolored .80
Ali Ibn Abi Talib, 1330th death anniv.

**Unwmk.**
**1991, July 29     Photo.     Perf. 13**
2469 A843 50r multicolored 1.00
Blood Transfusion Week.

Return of Prisoners of War, First Anniv. — A844

Illustration reduced.

**1991, Aug. 27     Perf. 13x13½**
2470 A844 100r multicolored 1.75

Ayatollah Marashi, Death
Anniv. — A845

Illustration reduced.

**1991, Aug. 29**          *Perf. 13½x13*
2471 A845 30r multicolored          1.25

Ayatollah-ol-Ozma Seyyed Abdol-
Hossein Lary, Revolutionary — A846

Design includes 1909 stamp issued by Lary.

**1991, Sept. 9**          *Perf. 13x13½*
2472 A846 30r multicolored          .70

Start of Iran-Iraq
War, 11th
Anniv. — A847

**1991, Sept. 22**          *Perf. 13½x13*
2473 A847 20r multicolored          .50

Mosque,
Kaaba, Unity
Week — A848

**1991, Sept. 22**          *Perf. 13*
2474 A848 30r multicolored          .70

World
Tourism
Day
A849

**1991, Sept. 27**   Photo.   *Perf. 13½*
2475 A849 200r multicolored          4.50

Dr. Mohammad
Gharib,
Pediatrician
A849a

**1991, Sept. 29**   Photo.   *Perf. 13*
**2475A**  A849a 100r bl & blk          1.50
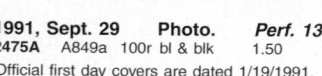
Official first day covers are dated 1/19/1991.

World Post
Day
A850

**Unwmk.**
**1991, Oct. 9**   Photo.   *Perf. 13*
2476 A850 70r #2071 on cover          1.00

Khaju-ye Kermani Intl.
Congress — A851

**1991, Oct. 15**
2477 A851 30r multicolored          1.00

A852

A853

**1991, Oct. 16**
2478 A852 80r multicolored          .90
World Food Day.

**1991, Oct. 19**          *Perf. 13½x13*
2479 A853 40r bl vio & gold          .70
Intl. Conference Supporting Palestinians.

Illustrators of
Children's
Books, 1st
Asian Biennial
A854

**1991, Oct. 25**          *Perf. 13*
2480 A854 100r Hoopoe          1.75
"Children" misspelled.

World Standards
Day — A855

**1991, Oct. 14**          *Perf. 13½*
2481 A855 100r multicolored          2.00

1st Seminar on
Adolescent and
Children's
Literature
A856

**1991, Nov. 3**          *Perf. 13*
2482 A856 20r multicolored          .70

Roshid Intl.
Educational
Film Festival
A857

**1991, Nov. 6**
2483 A857 50r multicolored          1.20

7th Ministerial
Meeting of the
Group of
77 — A858

**1991, Nov. 16**
2484 A858 30r vio & bl grn          .70

Bassij of the Oppressed (Militia), 12th
Anniv. — A859

**1991, Nov. 25**
2485 A859 30r multicolored          .65

Ayatollah Aref
Hosseini — A860

**1991, Dec. 18**          *Perf. 13½*
2486 A860 50r multicolored          1.10

Sadek
Ghanji
A861

**1991, Dec. 20**
2487 A861 50r multicolored          1.10

Agricultural
Training and
Extension
Week — A862

**1991, Dec. 22**          *Perf. 13*
2488 A862 70r multicolored          1.25

World Telecommunications
Day — A863

#2489: a, 20r, Telegraph key. b, 20r, Phone
lines. c, 20r, Early telephones. d, 40r, Satellite
dishes. e, 40r, Telecommunications satellite.

**1992, May 17**   Photo.   *Perf. 13*
2489 A863  Strip of 5, #a.-e.          3.50

New Year — A863a

Flora of Iran: Nos. 2490a, 2490d, 20r. Nos.
2490b, 2490c, 40r.

**1992, Apr. 18**          *Perf. 13½x13*
2490 A863a  Block of 4, #a.-d. 3.00

Mosque of
Jerusalem
A864

**1992, Mar. 27**          *Perf. 13x13½*
2491 A864 200r multicolored          2.50
Day of Jerusalem and honoring A. Mousavi,
the Shiva leader of Lebanon, with Sheikh
Ragheb Harb in background.

Reunification of Yemen — A865

**1992, May 22**     *Perf. 13½x13*
2492 A865 50r multicolored    .90

World Child Day A866

**1992, June 1**     *Perf. 13x13½*
2493 A866 50r multicolored    .90

Intl. Conference of Surveying and Mapping A867

**1992, May 25**     *Perf. 13*
2494 A867 40r multicolored    .70

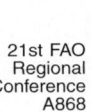

21st FAO Regional Conference A868

**1992, May 17**     *Perf. 13x13½*
2495 A868 40r blk, bl & grn    .50

South and West Asia Postal Union — A869

Mosques: No. 2496, Imam's Mosque, Isfahan. No. 2497, Lahore Mosque, Pakistan. No. 2498, St. Sophia Mosque, Turkey.

**1992, Mar. 27**     *Perf. 13½x13*
2496 A869 50r multicolored    .90
2497 A869 50r multicolored    .90
2498 A869 50r multicolored    .90

Economic Cooperation Organization Summit — A870

Design: 20r, Flags, emblem, vert.

**1992**     *Perf. 13½x13, 13x13½*
2499 A870 20r multicolored    .75
2500 A870 200r multicolored    4.50
    Issued: 20r, Apr. 25; 200r, Feb. 17.

Natural Resources A871

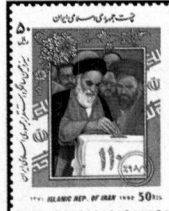

Islamic Republic, 13th Anniv. — A872

**1992, Apr. 15**    Litho.    *Perf. 13½x13*
2501 A871 100r multicolored    2.00

**1992, Apr. 1**     *Perf. 13½x13*
2502 A872 50r multicolored    .70

Establishment of Postal Airline — A873

**1992, Apr. 1**     *Perf. 13x13½*
2503 A873 60r multicolored    1.25

Islamic Revolution, 13th Anniv. — A874

    **Unwmk.**
**1992, Feb. 11**    Photo.    *Perf. 13*
2504   30r multicolored    1.00
2505   50r multicolored    1.25
  a.   A874 Pair, #2504-2505    2.50

A875

A876

**1992, Mar. 23**   Photo.   *Perf. 13½x13*
2506 A875 100r multicolored    1.10
    World Meteorological Day.

**1991-92**     *Perf. 13x13½*
    Famous Men: No. 2507, Mohammad Bagher Madjlessi. No. 2508, Hadi Sabzevari, wearing turban. No. 2509, Omman Samani, wearing fez. No. 2510, Chapter of praise from Koran (Arabic script), by Ostad Mir Emad.

2507 A876 50r shown    .70
2508 A876 50r brown & multi    .70
2509 A876 50r multicolored    .70
2510 A876 50r multicolored    .70
    Issued: #2510, 12/18/91; others, 5/17/92. First day covers of #2507-2509 may be dated 12/18/91.

Intl. Museum Day A877

#2511, Gray ceramic ware, 1st millennium B.C. #2512, Painted ceramic bowl.

**1992, May 18**
2511 A877 40r multicolored    .90
2512 A877 40r multicolored    .90

Ayatollah Khomeini, 3rd Anniv. of Death — A878

**1992, June 4**     *Perf. 13*
2513 A878 100r multicolored    1.40

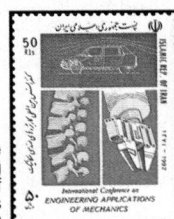

Intl. Conference on Engineering Applications of Mechanics A879

**1992, June 9**     *Perf. 13½x13*
2514 A879 50r multicolored    .80

A880

**1992, June 13**     *Perf. 13x13½*
2515 A880 20r multicolored    .60
    In memory of clergy-lady Amini.

Sixth Conference of Nonaligned News Agencies — A881

**1992, June 15**
2516 A881 100r multicolored    1.10

A882

A883

**1992, June 23**     *Perf. 13x13½*
2517 A882 100r grn, blk & gold    1.25
    Meeting of Ministers of Industry and Technology.

**1992, June 26**     *Perf. 13½x13*
2518 A883 100r multicolored    1.75
    World Anti-narcotics Day.

Holy Ka'aba — A884

Prayer Calligraphy A885

Designs: No. 2520, Ayatollah Khomeini in prayer. No. 2521, Khomeini holding prayer beads. No. 2522, Khomeini unwrapping turban. Nos. 2523-2524, Islamic prayers.

**1992**    Photo.    *Perf. 13½x13*
2519 A884 50r multicolored    .70
2520 A884 50r multicolored    .70
2521 A884 50r multicolored    .70
2522 A884 50r multicolored    .70
    *Perf. 13x13½*
2523 A885 50r dk green & lt green    .70
2524 A885 50r dk blue & lt blue    .70
    Issue dates: July 27, Aug. 24.

Iran Shipping Line, 25th Anniv. A886

**1992, Aug. 24**   Photo.   *Perf. 13x13½*
2525 A886 200r multicolored    2.00

A887

A888

**1992, Sept. 15**     **Perf. 13½x13**
2526 A887 40r multicolored    .60

Mohammad's Birthday, Unity Week.

**Perf. 13½x13, 13x13½**
**1992, Sept. 22**

Iranian Defense Forces: 20r, Soldiers on patrol. 40r, Soldier seated at water's edge, horiz.

2527 A888 20r multicolored    .50
2528 A888 40r multicolored    .50

Intl. Congress on the History of Islamic Medicine — A889

**1992, Sept. 23**   **Litho.**   **Perf. 13**
2529 A889 20r Avicenna, child    .50
2530 A889 40r Physician's instruments    .65
   a.   Pair, #2529-2530    1.25

Mobarake Steel Plant — A890

**1992, Sept. 26**   **Photo.**   **Perf. 13x13½**
2531   20r Inside plant    .40
2532   70r Outside plant    .70
   a.   A890 Pair, #2531-2532    1.25

Intl. Tourism Day A891

**1992, Sept. 27**     **Perf. 13x13½**
2533 A891 20r Mazandaran    .45
2534 A891 20r Isfahan    .45
2535 A891 30r Bushehr (Bushire)    .65
2536 A891 30r Hormozgan    .65

Intl. Trade Fair — A892

**1992, Oct. 2**     **Perf. 13½x13**
2537 A892 200r multicolored    2.25

World Post Day A893

**1992, Oct. 9**     **Perf. 13x13½**
2538 A893 30r Early post office    .80

World Food Day A894

**1992, Oct. 16**     **Perf. 13**
2539 A894 100r blk, bl & yel    1.10

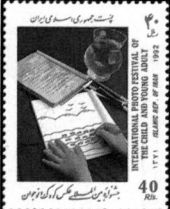

Intl. Youth Photo Festival — A895

**1992, Nov. 1**   **Photo.**   **Perf. 13½x13**
2540 A895 40r multicolored    1.00

A896

**1992, Nov. 4**     **Perf. 13**

a, Seizure of US embassy, 12th anniv. b, Student's day (Eagles flying over dead doves). c, Khomeini's exile (Eagles, dove).

2541 A896 100r Strip of 3, #a.-c.    4.50

Fighting in Bosnia and Herzegovina A897

Islamic Development Bank — A898

**1992, Nov. 4**     **Perf. 13½x13**
2542 A897 40r multicolored    .90

**1992, Nov. 10**   **Litho.**   **Perf. 13½x13**
2543 A898 20r multicolored    .50

Iran-Azerbaijan Telecommunications — A899

**1992, Nov. 21**   **Photo.**   **Perf. 13x13½**
2544 A899 40r multicolored    .90

Azad (Open) University, 10th Anniv. — A900

**1992, Nov. 23**     **Perf. 13½x13**
2545 A900 200r dark grn & emer 1.75

Week of the Basij (Militia) A901

**1992, Nov. 26**     **Perf. 13x13½**
2546 A901 40r multicolored    .60

Seyed Mohammad Hosseyn Shahrian, Poet — A902

**1992, Dec. 1**
2547 A902 80r multicolored    .70

Women's Day — A903

**1992, Dec. 15**
2548 A903 70r multicolored    .70

Birth anniv. of Fatima.

Famous Iranians — A904

Scientists and writers: No. 2551a, Ayatollah Mirza Abolhassan Shar'rani (in turban). b, Prof. Mahmoud Hessabi, U=o formula. c,

Mohiyt Tabatabaiy, books on shelves. d, Mehrdad Avesta, calligraphy.

**1992, Dec. 18**
2549 A904 20r Block of 4, #a.-d.    2.00

Natl. Iranian Oil Drilling Co. A905

**1992, Dec. 22**
2550 A905 100r shown    1.50
2551 A905 100r Ocean drilling platform    1.50

A906       A907

**1992, Dec. 28**     **Perf. 13½x13**
2552 A906 80r multicolored    .70
Promotion of literacy.

**1993-95**   **Photo.**   **Perf. 13½x13**
2553 A907   20r Narcissus
2554 A907   30r Iris
2555 A907   35r Tulips
2556 A907   40r Tuberose
2557 A907   50r White jasmine
2558 A907   60r Guelder rose
2559 A907   70r Pansies
2560 A907   75r Snapdragons
2561 A907   100r Lily
2562 A907   120r Petunia
2563 A907   150r Hyacinth
2564 A907   200r Damascus rose
2565 A907   500r Morning glory
2566 A907   1000r Corn rose
   Nos. 2553-2566 (14)    15.00 5.00

The 60r exists with inverted flowers. Value $9.

Issued: 20r, 1/12/93; 40r, 2/22/93; 100r, 4/21/93; 200r, 4/29/93; 500r, 6/27/93; 1000r, 7/19/93; 30r, 60r, 10/93; 50r, 8/93; 120r, 5/94; 35r, 75r, 3/95; 70r, 150r, 5/95.

For surcharges see Nos. 2759-2760, 2792-2794.

Prophethood of Mohammad — A908

**1993, Jan. 21**   **Photo.**   **Perf. 13x13½**
2567 A908 200r multicolored    1.75
Mab'as Festival.

Day of the Disabled — A909

Designs: 40r, Player wearing medal, team members with hands raised.

**1993, Jan. 27**
2568   20r multicolored    .50
2569   40r multicolored    .50
   a.   A909 Pair, #2568-2569    1.25

Cultural Heritage
Preservation
A910

Planning
Day — A911

**1993, Jan. 31**     *Perf. 13½x13*
2570 A910 40r Mosque, exterior   1.00
2571 A910 40r Mosque, interior   1.00
   a.   Pair, #2570-2571    2.50

**1993, Jan. 31**     *Perf. 13*
2572 A911 100r multicolored   2.00

Universal
Day of the
Oppressed
A912

**1993, Feb. 8**   Litho.   *Perf. 13*
2573 A912 60r multicolored    .80
Savior Mahdi's Birthday.

Islamic
Revolution,
14th Anniv.
A913

a, Iranian flag. b, Flag, soldiers. c, Soldiers,
shellbursts. d, Oil derricks, storage tanks, people harvesting. e, Crowd, car, Ayatollah
Khomeini.

**1993, Feb. 11**   Photo.   *Perf. 13x13½*
2574 A913 20r Strip of 5, #a.-e.   5.00

A914

1st Islamic Women's Games: a, Volleyball.
b, Basketball. c, Medal. d, Swimming. e,
Running.

**1993, Feb. 13**     *Perf. 13*
2575 A914 40r Strip of 5, #a.-e.   6.00

A915

**1993, Feb. 16**     *Perf. 13½*
2576 A915 40r Morteza Ansari    .80

Arbor Day
A916

**1993, Mar. 6**
2577 A916 70r multicolored   1.10

New
Year
A917

a, 20r, Butterfly, tulip. b, 20r, Butterfly, lily. c,
40r, Butterfly, flowers. d, 40r, Butterfly, 3
roses.

**1993, Mar. 11**     *Perf. 13½x13*
2578 A917   Block of 4, #a.-d.   5.00 1.50

World Jerusalem
Day — A918

End of Ramadan
A919

**1993, Mar. 14**     *Perf. 13½x13*
2579 A918 20r multicolored    .90

**1993, Mar. 26**     *Perf. 13½x13*
2580 A919 100r multicolored   3.00

Islamic
Republic,
14th Anniv.
A920

**1993, Apr. 1**     *Perf. 13x13½*
2581 A920 40r Natl. anthem    .90

Intl. Congress on the Millennium of
Sheik Mofeed — A921

**1993, Apr. 17**     *Perf. 13*
2582 A921 80r multicolored   1.10

A922

**1993, Apr. 21**     *Perf. 13½x13*
2583 A922 100r multicolored   1.10
13th Conference of Asian and Pacific Labor
Ministers.

A924

**1993, May 17**     *Perf. 13½x13*
2585 A924 50r multicolored   1.20
Intl. Congress for Advancement of Science
and Technology in Islamic World.

A925

A928

**1993, May 1**
2586 A925 40r multicolored   1.00
Intl. Museum Day.

**1993, June 1**   Photo.   *Perf. 13½x13*
2589 A928 50r multicolored   1.00
Intl. Child Day.

Ayatollah
Khomeini, 4th
Death
Anniv. — A929

**1993, June 4**     *Perf. 13*
2590 A929 20r multicolored    .70

World
Crafts Day
A930

World Population
Day — A931

**1993, June 10**     *Perf. 13½x13*
2591 A930 70r multicolored   1.50

**1993, July 11**     *Perf. 13*
2592 A931 30r multicolored    .90

1st Cultural-Athletic Olympiad of Iran
University Students — A932

Various sports.

**1993, July 22**     *Perf. 13x13½*
**Background Colors**
2593 A932 20r blue    1.00   .35
2594 A932 40r henna brown   2.50   .75
2595 A932 40r ocher   2.50   .75

Intl. Festival of Films for Children and
Young Adults, Isfahan — A935

**1993, Sept. 11**   Photo.   *Perf. 13*
2598 A935 60r multicolored   1.25

World Post
Day — A937

**1993, Oct. 9**   Photo.   *Perf. 13*
2600 A937 60r multicolored   1.25

A939

World of water with fish and: a, Birds. b, Girl.
c, Angel with trumpet. d, Trees.

**1993, Nov. 5**   Photo.   *Perf. 13½x13*
2602 A939 30r Block of 4, #a.-d.   3.50
Illustrators of Children's Books, Intl. Biennial.

A940

**1993, Nov. 16     Photo.     *Perf. 13***
2603  A940  30r multicolored                    .80
   Khaje Nassireddin Tussy, scientist and astronomer.

Week of the Bassij (Militia) A941

   Designs: No. 2604, Woman tying bandana around militiman's head. No. 2605, Militiaman facing line of tanks.

**1993, Dec. 1          *Perf. 13½***
2604  A941  50r multicolored                   1.00
2605  A941  50r multicolored                   1.00

Death of Grand Ayatollah Mohammad Reza Golpaigani A942

**1993, Dec. 20         *Perf. 13***
2606  A942  300r multicolored                  4.00

Support for Bosnia and Herzegovina A943

   #2607, Children playing hopscotch. #2608, Soldier, minaret. #2609, Woman, mosque.

**1993, Dec. 27**
2607  A943  40r multicolored                   1.00
2608  A943  40r multicolored                   1.00
2609  A943  40r multicolored                   1.00
   *a.*       Strip of 3, #2607-2609           3.25

Day of Invalids — A944

**1994, Jan. 18**
2610  A944  80r multicolored                    .90

Agriculture Week — A945

**1994, Jan. 23**
2611  A945  60r multicolored                    .80

Conf. on Islamic Law — A946

**1994, Feb. 20**
2612  A946  60r multicolored                   1.00

Islamic Revolution, 15th Anniv. — A947

   Designs: a, Town, farm, telephone lines. b, Flag, Ayatollah Khomeini, revolutionaries. c, Fisherman, bridge. d, Women working.

**1994, Feb. 11**
2613  A947  40r Block of 4, #a.-d.   3.50

Youth Welfare A948

**1994, Mar. 1**
2614  A948  30r multicolored                    .90

A949

A951

**1994, Mar. 28    Photo.    *Perf. 13½x13***
2615  A949  30r multicolored                    .90
   25th Iranian Mathematics Conference, Shareef Industrial University.

**1994, Mar. 11                *Perf. 13***
2616  A950  50r multicolored                    .90
   World Jerusalem Day.

**1994, Mar. 16    *Perf. 13x13½, 13½x13***
2617  A951  40r Partridges, horiz.   3.50  1.25
2618  A951  40r Heron                3.50  1.25
2619  A951  40r Bustard              3.50  1.25
2620  A951  40r Pheasants, horiz.    3.50  1.25
   New year.

Islamic Republic, 15th Anniv. — A952

**1994, Apr. 1     Photo.     *Perf. 13***
2621  A952  40r multicolored                    .90

A953

**1994, Apr. 7**
2622  A953  100r multicolored                  1.50
   Intl. congress of Dentist's Assoc. and World Health Day.

Re-els Ali Delvary, 80th Anniv. of Death A954

**1994, Apr. 9          *Perf. 13x13½***
2623  A954  50r multicolored                   1.00

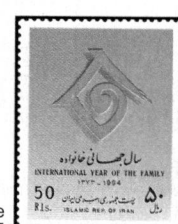

Intl. Year of the Family — A955

**1994, May 10   Photo.   *Perf. 13½x13***
2624  A955  50r multicolored                    .75

World Telecommunications Day — A956

**1994, May 17         *Perf. 13x13½***
2625  A956  50r multicolored         6.50  2.00

A957

A958

**1994, May 18         *Perf. 13***
2626  A957  40r Marlik gold cup            .90
   World Museum Day.

**1994, May 21**
   Cultural Preservation: 40r, Enameled pot with Kufic inscription, 13th cent.
2627  A958  40r multicolored           .80   .25

Ayatollah Khomeini, 5th Death Anniv. — A959

**1994, June 4**
2628  A959  30r multicolored           .50   .20

Ayatollah Motahari, 15th Anniv. of Death — A961

**1994, June 10**
2630  A961  30r multicolored           .60   .20

World Crafts Day — A962

**1994, June 10**    **Photo.**    *Perf. 13*
2631   A962   60r Weaver    2.50   1.00
2632   A962   60r Glass pitcher    2.50   1.00

Islamic University Students' Solidarity Games — A963

**1994, July 18**
2633   A963   60r multicolored    .90   .30

Mohammad's Birthday, Unity Week — A964

**1994, Aug. 26**
2634   A964   30r multicolored    .80   .25

Seyed Mortaza Avini, Sacred Defense Week A965

**1994, Sept. 22**    *Perf. 13x13½*
2635   A965   70r multicolored    .80

World Post Day A966

**1994, Oct. 9**
2636   A966   50r multicolored    .75

Women's Day — A967

A968

**1994, Nov. 24**    *Perf. 13*
2637   A967   70r multicolored    .90
   Birth anniv. of Fatima.

**1994, Nov. 26**
2638   A968   30r multicolored    .45
   Week of the Bassij (Militia).

Book Week — A969

**1994, Dec. 10**
2639   A969   40r multicolored    .60

Support for Moslems of Bosnia & Herzegovina A970

**1994, Dec. 27**
2640   A970   80r Moslem family    1.25
2641   A970   80r Map, arms, homes    1.25

Grand Ayatollah Araky — A971

**1995, Jan. 5**
2642   A971   100r multicolored    1.25

Universal Day of the Oppressed A972

**1995, Jan. 17**
2643   A972   50r multicolored    .75
   Savior Mahdi's birthday.

Major General Mehdi Zin-el-Din A973

Major General Mehdi Bakeri — A974

Major General Hasan Bagheri A975

Martyred commanders: #2647, Major General Hosein Kherazi.

**1995, Feb. 2**
2644   A973   50r multicolored    .55   .20
2645   A974   50r multicolored    .55   .20
2646   A975   50r multicolored    .55   .20
2647   A975   50r multi, diff.    .55   .20

A976

A977

**1995, Feb. 11**
2648   A976   100r multicolored    1.50   .50
   Islamic Revolution, 16th anniv.

**1995, Feb. 24**
2649   A977   100r multicolored    2.25   .75
   World Jerusalem Day.

Arbor Day — A978

New Year — A979

**1995, Mar. 6**
2650   A978   50r multicolored    .70

**1995, Mar. 16**    *Perf. 13½x13*
2651   A979   50r shown    1.50   .55
2652   A979   50r Pansies    1.50   .55
2653   A979   50r Hyacinths    1.50   .55
2654   A979   50r Tulips, fish bowl    1.50   .55

Opening of Bafq-Bandar Abbas Railway Line — A980

**1995, Mar. 17**
2655   A980   100r multicolored    1.75   1.00

Islamic Republic of Iran, 16th Anniv. — A981

**1995, Apr. 1**    **Photo.**    *Perf. 13*
2656   A981   100r multicolored    1.10

Second Press Fesitval A982

**1995, Apr. 26**
2657   A982   100r multicolored    .90

Ayatollah Ahmad Khomeini A983

**1995, Apr. 27**
2658 A983 50r multicolored          .70

Day of Invalids — A984

**1995, June 1**
2659 A984 80r Arabic script          .80

Ayatollah Ali Vaziri — A985

**1995, May 4**
2660 A985 100r multicolored          .80

World Telecommunications Day — A986

**1995, May 17**
2661 A986 100r multicolored          1.10

Ayatollah Khomeini, 6th Death Anniv. — A987

**1995, June 4**
2662 A987 100r multicolored          1.25

UN, 50th Anniv. — A988

a, Infant, hand holding vaccination (WHO). b, Child laughing (UNICEF). c, Shafts of grain, world map (FAO). d, Woman reading (UNESCO).

**1995, June 10**          **Perf. 13x13½**
2663 A988 100r Block of 4, #a.-d. 3.50

Iqbal Ashtiany, Writer — A989

**1995, Aug. 14**          **Perf. 13**
2664 A989 100r multicolored          1.10

Government Week — A990

**1995, Aug. 28**          **Perf. 13x13½**
2665 A990 100r Workers, dam          1.10
Construction of the Karun dam and hydo-electric power station.

Sacred Defense Week — A991

**1995, Sept. 22**          **Perf. 13**
2666 A991 100r Gun, Koran          1.25

World Post Day — A992

**1995, Oct. 9**          **Perf. 13½x13**
2667 A992 100r Globe, enve-
          lopes          1.25

M.J. Tondgooyan, Oil Minister A993

**1995, Dec. 20**          **Perf. 13**
2668 A993 100r multicolored          1.10

Prophet Mohammad A994

**1995, Dec. 20**
2669 A994 100r Arabic calligra-
          phy          1.25

Fathi Shaghaghi, Islamic Jihad Secretary General A995

**1995, Dec. 31**
2670 A995 100r multicolored          1.25

Islamic Revolution, 17th Anniv. — A996

**1996, Feb. 11**
2671 A996 100r multicolored          1.40

World Jerusalem Day — A997

**1996, Feb. 17**
2672 A997 100r Dome of the
          Rock          1.25

Birds A998

**1996, Mar. 15**
2673 A998 100r shown          2.00
2674 A998 100r Crested head          2.00
2675 A998 100r blue & multi          2.00
2676 A998 100r yel, grn & multi          2.00
          New year.

Air Force Maj. Gen. Abbas Babai — A999

Major Ali Akbar Shiroody A1000

Maj. Gen. Mahammed Ebrahim Hemmat A1001

Maj. Gen. Mohammad Broujerdi A1002

**1996, Mar. 18**
2677 A999 100r multicolored     2.25 1.00
2678 A1000 100r multicolored    2.25 1.00
2679 A1001 100r multicolored    2.25 1.00
2680 A1002 100r multicolored    2.25 1.00
          See Nos. 2700-2707 for similar stamps dated 1997.

Islamic Republic of Iran, 17th Anniv. — A1003

**1996, Mar. 31**     **Photo.**     **Perf. 13**
2681 A1003 200r multicolored    2.25 1.00

Intl. Book Fair, Tehran A1004

**1996, May 8**
2682 A1004 85r multicolored     1.25  .50
          For surcharge see No. 2759A.

Mashhad-Sarakhs-Tajan Intl.
Railway — A1005

**1996, May 13**
2683 A1005 200r multicolored          2.00 1.00
Turkmenistan intl. railway link,

Prisoners of
War — A1006

**1996, May 29**
2684 A1006  200r multicolored          2.25 1.00
Captives and Missing Day.

Ayatollah
Khomeini, 7th
Death
Anniv. — A1007

**1996, June 3**
2685 A1007 200r multicolored          2.00 1.00

World Crafts
Day — A1008

**1996, June 24     Photo.     Perf. 13**
2686 A1008 200r multicolored          2.00 1.00

Third PTT
Ministerial
Conference,
Tehran
A1009

**1996, July 8**
2687 A1009 200f multicolored              1.60

Prophet
Mohammad's
Birthday, Unity
Week — A1010

Designs: a, Zouqeblateyne Mosque. b,
Tomb of Imam Hossein (red flag on top of
dome). c, Mohammad's Mosque (dome without flag). d, Tomb of Imam Riza (green flag on
top of dome). e, Qaba Mosque (four minarets).

**1996, Aug. 3**
2688 A1010 200r Strip of 5, #a.-
         e.                       12.50

Government
Week — A1011

Flag colors and: a, Tehran Subway. b, Iron
works, Isfahan. c, Merchant fleet. d, Oil refinery, Bandar-e-Imam (clouds in sky). e, Satellite dish, Boumehen.

**1996, Aug. 23**
2689 A1011 200r Strip of 5, #a.-
         e.                       13.00

Ayatollah
Moqddas
Ardebily
A1012

**1996, Sept. 12     Photo.     Perf. 13**
2690 A1012 200r multicolored              1.60

Sacred Defense Week — A1013

**1996, Sept. 21**
2691 A1013 200r multicolored              1.60

World Standards Day — A1014

**1996, Oct. 13**
2692 A1014 200r multicolored              1.60

World Food
Day — A1015

**1996, Oct. 16**
2693 A1015 200r multicolored              1.60

Natl. Census
A1016

**1996, Oct. 22**
2694 A1016 200r multicolored         1.50 .65

2nd World University Wrestling
Championships, Tehran — A1017

**1996, Dec. 10**
2695 A1017 500r multicolored         5.00 2.00

Islamic Revolution,
18th
Anniv. — A1018

a, Ayatollah Khomeini holding man to his
chest. b, Martyrs. c, Khomeini waving. d,
Khomeini, leaders, airplane. e, Soldiers wearing helmets.

**1997, Feb. 10**
2696 A1018 200r Strip of 5, #a.-
         e.                    16.00 7.50

Arbor
Day — A1019

**1997, Mar. 5**
2697 A1019 200r multicolored         2.00 .80

Islamic
Republic, 18th
Anniv. — A1020

**1997, Apr. 1**
2698 A1020 200r multicolored              1.60

8th Intl.
Conference on
Rainwater
Catchment
Systems
A1021

**1997, Apr. 21**
2699 A1021 200r multicolored

Sheikh
Fazlollah
Mahallati
A1022

Brig. Gen.
Abbas Karimi
A1023

Brig. Gen.
Alireza
Movahed
Danesh
A1024

Sheikh
Abdollah
Mishmi
A1025

Brig. Gen.
Naser Kazemi
A1026

Gen.
Mohammad
Reza Vasture
A1027

Maj. Gen.
Yousef
Kolahdooz
A1028

Brig. Gen.
Yadollah Kalhor
A1029

**1997, May 4**
2700 A1022 100r multicolored  1.25
2701 A1023 100r multicolored  1.25
2702 A1024 100r multicolored  1.25
2703 A1025 100r multicolored  1.25
2704 A1026 100r multicolored  1.25
2705 A1027 100r multicolored  1.25
2706 A1028 100r multicolored  1.25
2707 A1029 100r multicolored  1.25

Martyred commanders. See Nos. 2677-2680 for similar stamps.

Post, Telecommunications — A1030

**1997, May 22**
2708 A1030 200r multicolored  1.75

Ayatollah
Khomeini, 8th
Death
Anniv. — A1031

**1997, June 4**
2709 A1031 200r multicolored  1.60

Montreal
Protocol on
Substances
that Deplete
Ozone Layer,
10th
Anniv. — A1032

**1997, Sept. 16   Photo.   *Perf. 13***
2710 A1032 200r multicolored  1.50

Tehran
Subway — A1033

Designs: 50r, Grain elevator. 65r, Medals, Students' Science Olympiad. 70r, Mobarake Steel Plant. 100r, Telecommunications. 130r, Port facilities. 150r, Bandar Abbas Oil Refinery. 200r, Rajai Dam. 350r, Rajai power station. 400r, Front of Foreign Affairs office. 500r, Child receiving oral polio vaccine. 650r, Printing house for Koran. 1000r, Imam Khomeini Intl. Airport. 2000r, Prayer place and tomb of Ayatollah Khomeini, Teheran.

**1997   Photo.   *Perf. 13½x13***
2711 A1033 40r multicolored
2712 A1033 50r multicolored
2713 A1033 65r multicolored
2714 A1033 70r multicolored
2715 A1033 100r multicolored
2716 A1033 130r multicolored
2717 A1033 150r multicolored
2718 A1033 200r multicolored
2719 A1033 350r multicolored
2720 A1033 400r multicolored
2721 A1033 500r multicolored
2722 A1033 650r multicolored
2723 A1033 1000r multicolored
2724 A1033 2000r multicolored
  *Nos. 2711-2724 (14)*    30.00 18.50

Issued: 2000r, 10/22; others, Sept.

Sacred Defense
Week — A1034

**1997, Sept. 28   Photo.   *Perf. 13***
2725 A1034 200r multicolored  1.50

Poets — A1035

#2726, Maitre Eqbal Lahouri. #2727, Molana Djalaleddin Mohammad Molavi.

**1997, Oct. 15**
2726 A1035 200r green & multi  1.50
2727 A1035 200r salmon & multi  1.50

World Post
Day — A1036

**1997, Oct. 15**
2728 A1036 200r multicolored  1.50

Naim Frasheri (1846-1900), Albanian
Moslem Poet — A1037

**1997, Nov. 5**
2729 A1037 200r multicolored  1.50

Eighth Islamic
Summit
A1038

Various ornate designs, Islamic texts: a, Seven ornaments. b, Ornament at bottom. c, Ornament at right. d, Ornament at upper left. e, Ornament above crescent.

**1997, Dec. 9**
2730 A1038 300r Strip of 5, #a.-
  e.    20.00 7.50

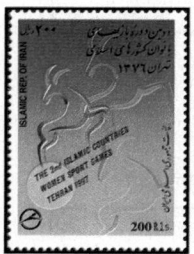

2nd Islamic
Countries
Women's
Sports Games,
Tehran
A1039

**1997, Dec. 12**
2731 A1039 200r multicolored  1.50

Islamic
Revolution,
19th Anniv.
A1040

a, Natl. flags. b, Harvesting grain, factory. c, Soldiers carrying flags. d, Crowd cheering, picture of Ayatollah Khomeini. e, Ayatollah Khomeini.

**1998, Feb. 11**
2732 A1040 200r Strip of 5, #a.-
  e.    12.50 5.00

World
Jerusalem
Day — A1041

**1998, Feb. 17**
2733 A1041 250r multicolored  3.00 1.25

New
Year — A1042

**1998, Mar. 5**
2734 A1042 200r Still life  1.60

Arbor
Day
A1043

**1998, Mar. 11**
2735 A1043 200r multicolored  1.60 .90

Islamic Republic, 19th Anniv. — A1044

**1998, Apr. 1   Photo.   *Perf. 13***
2736 A1044 250r multicolored  4.00 1.50

A1045

A1046

**1998, May 17**          **Perf. 13½x13**
2737  A1045  200r multicolored          2.25  1.00
World Telecommunications Day.

**1998, May 23**   **Photo.**   **Perf. 13**
2738  A1046  200r multicolored          2.25  1.00
Election day.

War Martyrs

A1047

A1048

A1049

A1050

**1998, May 24**   **Photo.**   **Perf. 13**
2739  A1047  100r multicolored      2.50   .90
2740  A1048  100r multicolored      2.50   .90
2741  A1049  100r multicolored      2.50   .90
2742  A1050  100r multicolored      2.50   .90

Shahriyar,
Poet — A1051

**1998, May 27**
2743  A1051  200r multicolored      2.25  1.00

Ayatollah
Khomeini, 9th
Death
Anniv. — A1052

**1998, June 4**          **Perf. 13**
2744  A1052  200r multicolored      2.50  1.25

2nd Congress
of the South
West Asia
Postal Union,
Tehran
A1053

**1998, June 8**
2745  A1053  250r multicolored          1.75

1998 World Cup Soccer
Championships, France — A1054

**1998, June 10**
2746  A1054  500r multicolored          3.50

A1055

A1056

**1998, June 10**
2747  A1055  200r multicolored      2.25  1.25
World Handicrafts Day.

**1998, Sept. 4**
2748  A1056  250r Union Day         2.50  1.50

1000th Friday
of Public Prayer
A1057

**1998, Oct. 30**   **Litho.**   **Perf. 13**
2749  A1057  250r multicolored      2.50  1.50

Nos. 2295A & 2296A Surcharged in
Black or Green

**1998, Nov. 11**          **Perf. 13x13½**
2750  A738  200r on 1r Shoustar     5.50  3.00
2751  A738  200r on 3r Kerman
          (G)                       5.50  3.00

Intl. Year of the
Ocean
A1058

**1998, Nov. 14**          **Perf. 13**
2752  A1058  250r multicolored      3.00  1.75

Sacred Defense Week — A1059

**1998, Nov. 23**
2753  A1059  250r multicolored      2.50  1.00

World
Post
Day
A1060

**1998, Dec. 2**
2754  A1060  200r multicolored      2.00   .75

1998 World Wrestling Championships,
Tehran — A1061

**1998, Dec. 8**
2755  A1061  250r multicolored      5.00  2.75

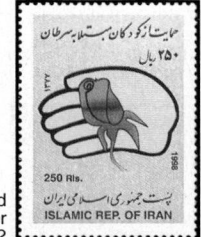

Children and
Cancer
A1062

**1998, Dec. 13**
2756  A1062  250r multicolored      2.00   .75

Cultural
Development
A1063

**1998, Dec. 16**   **Photo.**   **Perf. 13**
2757  A1063  250r multicolored      2.25  1.00

Islamic
Revolution,
20th
Anniv. — A1064

**1999, Feb. 11**   **Photo.**   **Perf. 13**
2758  A1064  250r multicolored      2.00   .75

#2554, 2682, 2555 Surcharged in
Black or Red

#2759, 2760

#2759A

**1999, Feb. Photo. Perf. 13, 13½x13**
2759 A907 200r on 35r
(#2555) 10.00 —
2759A A1004 250r on 85r (R,
#2682) 20.00 —
2760 A907 900r on 30r
(#2554) 10.00 —

Establishment of Islamic Republic,
20th Anniv. — A1065

**1999, Apr. 1 Photo. Perf. 13**
2761 A1065 250r multicolored 2.00 1.00

Ghadir Khom
Religious
Feast — A1066

**1999, Apr. 5 Photo. Perf. 13**
2762 A1066 250r multicolored 2.00 1.00

Ayatollah Khomieni's Charity
Account — A1067

**1999, Apr. 10 Photo. Perf. 13**
2763 A1067 250r Houses 2.25 1.00
2764 A1067 250r Village, palm
trees 2.25 1.00

Army
Day
A1068

**1999, Apr. 18**
2765 A1068 250r multicolored 2.50 1.25

Mullah
Sadra — A1069

**1999, May 22**
2766 A1069 250r multicolored 2.00 1.00

Ayatollah
Khomeini, 10th
Anniv. of
Death — A1070

**1999, May 25**
2767 A1070 250r multicolored 4.00 2.00

Islamic Parliament, 20th
Anniv. — A1071

**1999, May 28 Photo. Perf. 13**
2768 A1071 250r multicolored 2.00 1.00

Islamic Inter-parliamentary
Conference — A1072

**1999, June 15 Photo. Perf. 13**
2769 A1072 250r multicolored 2.00 1.25

Unity
Week
A1073

**1999, July 1 Photo. Perf. 13**
2770 A1073 250r multicolored 2.00 1.25

Handicrafts
Day — A1074

**1999, July 25 Photo. Perf. 13**
2771 A1074 250r multicolored 3.00 1.25

Total Solar
Eclipse, Aug.
11 — A1075

Designs: a, Moon over right portion of sun.
b, Baily's beads at top. c, Totality. d, Baily's
beads at right. e, Moon over left portion of sun.

**1999, Feb. 11 Photo. Perf. 13**
2772 A1075 250r Strip of 5,
#a.-e. 25.00 20.00

Birds — A1076

**1999-2002 Photo. Perf. 13x13½**
2776 A1076 100r Hoopoe .70
2778 A1076 150r Kingfisher .80
2779 A1076 200r Robin 1.00
2780 A1076 250r Lark 1.25
2781 A1076 300r Red-backed
shrike 1.50
2782 A1076 350r Eurasian
roller 1.75
2782A A1076 400r Blue tit 2.00
2783 A1076 500r Eurasian
bee-eater 2.50
2784 A1076 1000r Redwing 2.75
2785 A1076 2000r Twite 4.00
2786 A1076 3000r White throat 6.00
2786A A1076 4500r Turtle dove 8.00

Numbers have been reserved for additional
values in this set.
Issued: 150r, 8/6; 250r, 8/4; 100r, 6/17/00;
300r, 5/31/00; 500r, 8/30/00; 1000r, 10/30/00;
2000r, 1/13/01; 3000r, 1/23/01. 200r, 4/24/02;
400r, 5/18/02; 4500r, 7/16/02; 350r, 4/17/01.

UPU,
125th
Anniv.
A1077

**1999, Oct. 2 Photo. Perf. 13**
2787 A1077 250r multicolored 2.25 1.00

Children's
Day — A1078

a, Iranian girl. b, Latin American boy. c,
Eskimo boy. d, African girl. e, Russian boy. f,

French girl. g, Chinese girl. h, Asian Indian
girl. i, American Indian girl. j, Arabian boy.

**1999, Oct. 8**
2788 A1078 150r Strip of 10,
#a.-j. 20.00 15.00
Order of stamps in strip varies.

Intl. Exhibition
of Children's
Book
Illustrators
A1079

Background colors: a, Blue. b, Yellow. c,
Red. d, Green.

**1999, Nov. 15**
2789 A1079 250r Block of 4,
#a.-d. 17.50 10.00

Ayatollah
Mohammad
Taghi
Jafari — A1080

**1999, Nov. 16**
2790 A1080 250r multicolored 2.00 1.00

Islamic
Revolution, 21st
Anniv. — A1081

**2000, Feb. 11 Photo. Perf. 13**
2791 A1081 300r multi 2.25 1.25

**Nos. 2558, 2560, 2562 Surcharged
Like No. 2759**

**Methods and Perfs. as Before**
**2000, Feb.**
2792 250r on 60r 3.25 3.25
2793 A907 250r on 75r 3.25 3.25
2794 A907 250r on 120r 3.25 3.25

The 60r stamp with the inverted flowers footnoted after No. 2566 is known with the 250r
surcharge. Value $15.

New
Year — A1082

**2000, Mar. 13 Photo. Perf. 13**
2795 A1082 300r multi 2.75 1.50

Science & Technology University, 70th
Anniv. — A1083

**2000, July 9     Photo.     Perf. 13**
2796  A1083  300r multi              8.00  5.00
Dated 1999.

Dr. Mohammad Mofatteh (1928-79),
Martyr — A1084

**2000, July 22**
2797  A1084  300r multi              2.00

A1085

A1086

A1087

A1088

A1089

A1090

A1091

Martyrs
A1092

**2000**
2798  A1085  150r multi              2.00
2799  A1086  150r multi              2.00
2800  A1087  150r multi              2.00
2801  A1088  150r multi              2.00
2802  A1089  150r multi              1.25
2803  A1090  150r multi              1.25
2804  A1091  150r multi              1.25
2805  A1092  150r multi              1.25

Issued: Nos. 2798-2801, 8/6/00; Nos. 2802-
2805, 7/30/01.

National
Archives
Day — A1093

**2000, May 5     Photo.     Perf. 13**
2806  A1093  300r multi              2.25  1.50

University
Jihad
Movement
A1094

**2000, Aug. 6**
2807  A1094  300r multi              2.00  1.25

8th Asia-Pacific Postal Union
Congress, Tehran — A1095

**2000, Sept. 12**
2808  A1095  300r multi              2.00  1.25

World Space
Week
A1096

Satellite and: No. 2809, 500r, Dish at R. No.
2810, 500r, Dish at L.

**2000, Oct. 4**
2809-2810  A1096   Set of 2         6.00  4.00

World
Breastfeeding
Week
A1097

**2000, Oct.**
2811  A1097  300r multi              2.00  1.25

Ghadir Khom
Festival
A1098

**2001, Mar. 14**
2812  A1098  500r multi              2.25  1.25

Year of H. H.
Ali — A1099

**2001, Mar. 14**
2813  A1099  500r multi              2.25  1.00

New
Year — A1100

Birds: No. 2814, 300r, shown. No. 2815,
300r, Bird, diff., vert.

**2001, Mar. 18   Perf. 13x13½, 13½x13**
2814-2815  A1100   Set of 2         6.50  3.00

Palestinian Intifada — A1100a

**2001, Apr. 24     Photo.     Perf. 13**
2815A  A1100a  350r multi           7.00  5.00

Belgica 2001 Intl Stamp Exhibition,
Brussels — A1101

Designs: No. 2816, 350r, Chaffinch
(shown). No. 2817, 350r, Waxwing. No. 2818,
350r, National Garden, vert.

**2001, June 9                    Perf. 13**
2816-2818  A1101   Set of 3   12.00  8.00

Phila
Nippon
'01,
Japan
A1102

Emblem and: No. 2819, 250r, Mount Fuji,
Japan. No. 2820, 250r, Mount Damavand,
Iran.

**2001, Aug. 1     Photo.     Perf. 13**
2819-2820  A1102   Set of 2         4.00  2.50

World Tourism Day — A1103

**2001, Sept. 22**
2821 A1103 500r multi      2.00 1.25

Police Week — A1104

No. 2822: a, Helicopters, parachutists, police cars, motorcycle police. b, Parachutists, officer saluting flag, motorcycle police, naval patrol.
Illustration reduced.

**2001, Sept. 29**     **Perf. 13x13½**
2822 A1104 250r Horiz. pair,
      #a-b      2.75 2.00

Year of Dialogue Among Civilizations A1105

Designs: No. 2823, 250r, Shown. No. 2824, 250r, Cubist and Oriental art, horiz.

**2001, Oct. 9**     **Perf. 13**
2823-2824 A1105   Set of 2     4.50 2.50

Third Moslem Women's Games, Tehran — A1106

**2001, Oct. 24**
2825 A1106 250r multi      2.00 1.25

Spring of the Holy Koran — A1107

**2001, Nov. 26**
2826 A1107 500r multi      2.50 1.50

---

Honeybee — A1108

**2001, Dec. 3**
2827 A1108 500r multi      2.75 1.75

UN High Commissioner for Refugees, 50th Anniv. — A1109

**2001, Dec. 10**
2828 A1109 500r multi      2.00

Transportation Day — A1110

No. 2829: a, Truck on road. b, Truck on bridge, truck on road, gate.
Illustration reduced.

**2001, Dec. 17**     **Perf. 13x13½**
2829 A1110 350r Horiz. pair,
      #a-b      5.00 3.00

Navy Day A1111

No. 2830, 500r: a, Ship heading right. b, Ship heading left.
No. 2831, 500r: a, Helicopter, hovercraft. b, Submarine.

**2001, Nov. 28**    **Photo.**    **Perf. 13**
      **Vert. Pairs, #a-b**
2830-2831 A1111   Set of 2     8.50 8.50

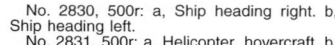

Tehran Subway A1112

---

No. 2832: a, Train headed right. b, Train headed left.

**2001, Dec. 13**
2832 A1112 500r Vert. pair, #a-b   4.00 3.00

Iranian-made Automobiles — A1113

Designs: No. 2833, 500r, shown. No. 2834, 500r, Automobile, vert.

**2002, Jan. 15**
2833-2834 A1113   Set of 2     4.00 2.50

Arbor Day — A1114

**2002, Mar. 6**
2835 A1114 500r multi      1.75 1.25

A1115

New Year's Day — A1116

No. 2836: a, Bird with yellow breast. b, Parrot.
No. 2837: a, Stork facing left. b, Hoopoe facing right.
Illustration reduced.

**2002, Mar. 16**
2836 A1115 500r Horiz. pair,
      #a-b      3.75 3.00
2837 A1116 500r Horiz. pair,
      #a-b      3.75 3.00

Imam Hossein — A1117

Illustration reduced.

**2002, July 8**    **Photo.**    **Imperf.**
2838 A1117 400r multi      1.50 1.50

---

Butterflies — A1118

No. 2839: a, Danaus sita. b, Polygonia c-album. c, Precis orithya. d, Vanessa cardui. e, Papilio maacki.

**2002, July 29**     **Perf. 13**
2839   Horiz. strip of 5    6.50 6.50
 **a.-e.**   A1118 400r Any single   1.10 .90

A1119

PhilaKorea 2002 World Stamp Exhibition, Seoul — A1120

No. 2840 — Flowers: a, Hyoscyamus muticus. b, Frittilaria. c, Calotropis procera. d, Ranuculus.
No. 2841 — Horse breeds: a, Caspian. b, Kurd. c, Turkoman. d, Arab.
Illustrations reduced.

**2002, Aug. 2**
2840 A1119 400r Block of 4, #a-
      d, + 2 labels     6.00 6.00
2841 A1120 400r Block of 4, #a-
      d, + 2 labels     6.00 6.00

Ayatollah Khomeini (1900-89) A1121

**2002, Aug. 20**
2842 A1121 400r multi      2.00 1.00

Jerusalem Day — A1122

**2002, Nov. 29**
2843 A1122 400r multi      2.00 1.00

Iran — Brazil Diplomatic Relations, Cent. — A1123

No. 2844: a, Iranian ceramics. b, Brazilian ceramics.

**2002, Dec. 15**
2844    Horiz. pair + label    5.00 5.00
*a.-b.* A1123 400r Either single    2.00 1.00

See Brazil Nos. 2868-2869.

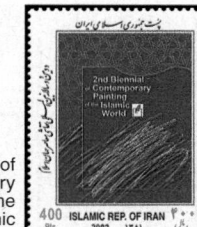

2nd Biennial of
Contemporary
Painting of the
Islamic
World — A1124

**2002, Dec. 25**
2845 A1124 400r multi    2.00 1.00

Esco Production Line, 30th
Anniv. — A1125

Illustration reduced.

**2003, Jan. 13**    *Perf. 13x13½*
2846 A1125 400r multi    2.50 1.50

Air
Force
Day
A1126

Various aircraft: 300r, 400r, 500r, 600r,
700r.

**2003, Feb. 8**    Photo.    *Perf. 13*
2847-2851 A1126    Set of 5    7.50 7.50

New
Year
2003
A1127

Mammals: No. 2852, 1000r, Goitered
gazelle without horns. No. 2853, 1000r,
Goitered gazelle with horns. No. 2854, 1000r,
Red deer. No. 2855, 1000r, Urial.

**2003, Mar. 15**
2852-2855 A1127    Set of 4    9.00 9.00

Iranian and
Chinese
Buildings
A1128

No. 2856: a, Mosque, Isfahan. b, Bell Tower,
Xian, People's Republic of China.

**2003, Apr. 15**    *Perf. 13x13½*
2856    Horiz. pair + label    6.00 6.00
*a.-b.* A1128 400r Either single    1.50 1.25

See China (People's Republic) Nos. 3271-
3272.

---

Book, Children
and
Family — A1129

**2003, May 4**    Photo.    *Perf. 13*
2857 A1129 500r multi    1.75 1.25

Butterflies
A1130

**2003-05**    Photo.    *Perf. 13x13½*
2858 A1130 100r Zygaena sp.    .25 —
2859 A1130 200r Issoria
     lathonia    .40 —
2859A A1130 250r Utethesia
     pulchella    .50 —
2860 A1130 300r Argynnis
     paphia    .60 —
  *a.*   Longer "Rls." + label ('04)    1.50 —
2862 A1130 500r Polygonia
     egea    1.00 —
2863 A1130 600r Papilio
     machaon    1.25 ·
  *a.*   Longer "Rls." + label ('04)    2.50 —
2864 A1130 650r Colias
     aurorina
     ('04)    1.25 —
2866 A1130 1000r Inachis io
     ('04)    1.40 —
2867 A1130 2000r Papilio
     demoleus
     ('04)    4.00 —
2867A A1130 2100r Papilio
     domoleus
     ('05)    2.25 —
2868 A1130 3000r Euphydryas
     aurinia ('04)    3.75 —
2868A A1130 4400r Danaus me-
     lanippus    4.25 —
2869 A1130 5500r Colias
     aurorina    5.50 —

Issued: 100r, 7/14; 200r, 5/12; 300r, 5/14;
500r, 8/25; 600r, 6/10; 250r, 12/17; 1000r,
1/6/04; Nos. 2860a, 2863a, 1/21/04; 1000r,
2/22/04; 3000r, 3/10/04, 650r, 2004. 2100r,
4/18/05; 4400r, 3/15/05; 5500r, 4/13/05.
The period in "Rls." is under the second
zero on Nos. 2860a and 2863a. It is under the
first zero on Nos. 2860 and 2863.

Social Security
Organization,
50th
Anniv. — A1131

**2003, Aug. 16**    Photo.    *Perf. 13*
2870 A1131 600r multi    1.75 1.00

Government Martyrs — A1132

Illustration reduced.

**2003, Aug. 24**
2871 A1132 600r multi + label    2.00 2.00

---

Government
Week — A1133

**2003, Aug. 25**
2872 A1133 600r multi    1.50 1.00

Caspian
Sea
Fauna
A1134

No. 2873: a, Caspian seal. b, Beluga.

**2003, Sept. 9**
2873    Horiz. pair + label    7.50 7.50
*a.-b.* A1134 600r Either single    1.50 1.50
  *c.*   Souvenir sheet, 2 each #2873a-
     2873b    9.50 9.50

See Russia No. 6795.

World
Post
Day
A1135

No. 2874: a, Computer, UPU emblem, satellite. b, Post office loading dock, mail box, airplanes. c, Postal clerk at desk, truck. d, Post
rider, ruins and statues.

**2003, Oct. 9**
2874    Horiz. strip of 4    8.00 8.00
*a.-d.* A1135 600r Any single    1.00 .75

Shared
Functions of
the Police and
Post
Office — A1136

**2003, Oct. 5**    Photo.    *Perf. 13*
2875 A1136 500r multi    1.00 .75

Worldwide Fund for Nature
(WWF) — A1137

No. 2876 — Cheetah: a, Cub. b, Two adults
lying in grass. c, Two adults standing. d, Head
of adult.

**2003, Nov. 18**
2876 A1137 500r Block of 4, #a-
     d    4.75 4.75

---

Eid ul-Fitr
A1138

**2003, Nov. 26**
2877 A1138 600r multi    1.75 1.25

Miniature Sheet

Bam Earthquake, Dec. 26,
2003 — A1139

No. 2878: a, Landmarks in Bam before
earthquake. b, Earthquake devastation. c,
Doctors treating injured people. d, Rescue
personnel, map of world.

**2004, Feb. 4**
2878 A1139 500r Sheet of 4,
     #a-d    3.25 3.25

Islamic
Revolution,
25th Anniv.
A1140

**2004, Feb. 11**
2879 A1140 600r multi    1.00 1.00

Hossein Rezazadeh,
Weightlifter — A1141

Illustration reduced.

**2004, Feb. 15**
2880 A1141 1200r multi    2.00 2.00

Dated 2003.

ISO 9001-2000
Certification
A1142

**2004, Feb. 29**
2881 A1142 600r multi    1.00 1.00

Freshwater Fish — A1143

Designs: Nos. 2882, 2888a, 100r, Carassius auratus. Nos. 2883, 2888b, 200r, Carassius auratus, diff. Nos. 2884, 2888c, 300r, Poecilia reticulate. Nos. 2885, 2888d, 400r, Betta splendens. Nos. 2886, 2888e, 500r, Carassius auratus, diff. Nos. 2887, 2888f, 600r, Carassius auratus, diff.

**2004, Mar. 6**
**Stamps With White Frames**
2882-2887 A1143  Set of 6  4.00 4.00
**Miniature Sheet**
**Stamps Without White Frames**
2888 A1143  Sheet of 6, #a-f  5.00 5.00

FIFA (Fédération Internationale de Football Association), Cent. — A1144

Illustration reduced.

**2004, May 21**  **Perf. 13**
2889 A1144 600r multi  1.00 1.00

**Miniature Sheet**

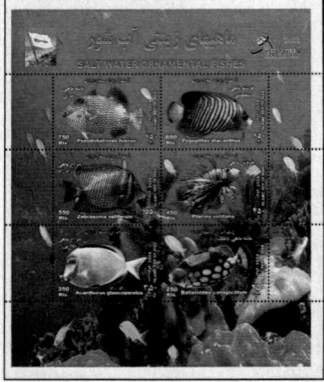

Saltwater Fish — A1145

No. 2890: a, 250r, Balistoides conspicillum. b, 350r, Acanthurus glaucopareius. c, 450r, Pterois volitans. d, 550r, Zebrasoma veliferum. e, 650r, Pygoplites diacanthus. f, 750r, Pseudobalistes fuscus.

**2004, May 22**  **Perf. 13**
2890 A1145  Sheet of 6, #a-f  4.25 4.25
España 2004 Intl. Philatelic Exhibition, Riccione Philatelic Exhibition.

Reporter's Day — A1147

**2004, Aug. 7**
2892 A1147 650r multi  .80 .80

2004 Summer Olympics, Athens — A1148

No. 2893: a, Taekwondo. b, Weight lifting. c, Wrestling. d, Judo.
Illustration reduced.

**2004, Aug. 12**
2893 A1148 650r Block of 4, #a-d  3.50 3.50

Poets — A1149

No. 2894: a, Kabir (1440-1518), Indian poet. b, Hafiz Shirazi (c. 1325-c. 1389), Persian poet.
Illustration reduced.

**2004, Aug. 16**  **Perf. 13**
2894 A1149 600r Horiz. pair, #a-b  1.50 1.50
See India No. 2070.

International Avicenna Congress — A1150

No. 2895: a, Memorial. b, Avicenna (980-1037), scientist, philosopher.
Illustration reduced.

**2004, Aug. 22**
2895 A1150 650r Horiz. pair, #a-b  1.60 1.60

**Miniature Sheet**

Primates — A1151

No. 2896: a, Chacma baboons. b, Chimpanzee. c, Chimpanzees. d, Mandrill.

**2004, Aug. 28**
2896 A1151 500r Sheet of 4, #a-d  5.00 5.00
World Stamp Championship 2004, Singapore.

**Miniature Sheet**

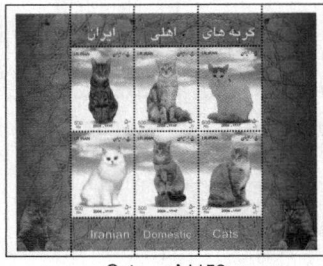

Cats — A1152

No. 2897: a, Gray cat, no tail visible. b, Gray cat, tail at right. c, Brown and white cat. d, White cat. e, Gray cat on rock. f, Gray cat, tail at left.

**2004, Aug. 31**
2897 A1152 500r Sheet of 6, #a-f  6.00 6.00

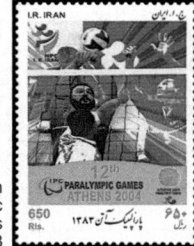

12th Paralympic Games, Athens A1153

**2004, Sept. 17**
2898 A1153 650r multi  .80

Iran - Iraq War, 24th Anniv. A1154

**2004, Sept. 21**
2899 A1154 650r multi  .80

Tehran University, 70th Anniv. A1155

**2004, Oct. 22**
2900 A1155 650r multi  .80

Poets — A1156

No. 2901: a, Dr. Jalal-eddin Ashtiani (wearing turban). b, Mahmoud Farschian (with hand on chin). c, Dr. Jafar Shahidi (looking right). d, Dr. Hosain Mirshamsi (looking left).
Illustration reduced.

**2004, Nov. 9**  **Photo.**  **Perf. 13**
2901 A1156 500r Block of 4, #a-d 2.50

Mountains — A1157

No. 2902: a, Damavand Mountain, Iran. b, Bolivar Peak, Venezuela.
Illustration reduced.

**2004, Nov. 28**  **Photo.**  **Perf. 13**
2902 A1157 650r Horiz. pair, #a-b  1.50

First Intl. Biennale of Islamic Poster Art — A1158

No. 2903: a, Hand. b, Dove in nest. c, Slingshot. d, Crescent.

**2004, Nov. 29**
2903 A1158 500r Block of 4, #a-d  2.50

Imam Reza's Birthday — A1159

No. 2904: a, Corner of mosque. b, Dome. c, Facade. d, Archway.

Illustration reduced.

**2004, Dec. 24  Photo.  Perf. 13x13¼**
2904 A1159 500r Block of 4, #a-d 2.50

Ali Daei,
Soccer Player
A1160

**2005, Feb. 2  Photo.  Perf. 13**
2905 A1160 650r multi          .75

Iran Film Museum — A1161

No. 2906: a, Scene from *Where is the Friend's Home?* b, Scene from *The Children of Heaven.* c, Museum building. d, Scene from *The Cow.*
Illustration reduced.

**2005, Feb. 10**
2906 A1161 500r Block of 4, #a-d 2.00

Airplanes — A1162

No. 2907: a, AN-140. b, IR-140.
Illustration reduced.

**2005, Mar. 6  Perf. 13x13½**
2907  Horiz. pair with central
       label                    2.00
a.-b. A1162 850r Either single
       See Ukraine No. 568.

Souvenir Sheet

Expo 2005, Aichi, Japan — A1163

No. 2908: a, Persepolis. b, Yazd air ventilation towers. c, Iranian flag, typical Iranian desert architecture. d, Clay tablet with inscriptions.

**2005, Mar. 24  Perf. 13**
2908 A1163 650r Sheet of 4, #a-
       d                         2.50

Tehran University of Medical Sciences,
70th Anniv. — A1164

**2005, May 2**
2909 A1164 650r multi          .75

Police
Week — A1165

**2005, Oct. 29**
2910 A1165 650r multi          .75

Mevlana Jalal
ad-Din ar-Rumi
(1207-73),
Islamic
Philosopher
A1166

**2005, Dec. 3**
2911 A1166 650r multi          1.50
       See Afghanistan No. , Syria No. 1574, Turkey No. 2971.

Gardens — A1167

No. 2912: a, Gardens of Royal Palace of La Granja de San Ildefonso, Segovia, Spain. b, Bagh-e-Shahzadeh, Kerman, Iran.
Illustration reduced.

**2005, Dec. 17**
2912 A1167 650r Horiz. pair, #a-
       b                         1.50
       See Spain No. 3374.

Self-Sufficiency
in Wheat
Production
A1168

**2006, Jan. 4**
2913 A1168 650r multi          .75

Souvenir Sheet

Maps of the Persian Gulf — A1169

No. 2914: a, German map, 16th cent. b, Egyptian Ministry of Culture map, 1966. c, Saudi Arabian map, 1952. d, Map by Scoteri Motthaei, 18th cent.

**2006, June 7**
2914 A1169 650r Sheet of 4, #a-
       d                         5.00

2006 World Cup Soccer
Championships, Germany — A1170

Illustration reduced.

**2006, June 10**
2915 A1170 650r multi          .90

Abbas
Shafi — A1171

Alama
Mohammed
Reza Hakimi
A1172

Mohamed
Hossein Gandji
A1173

Alama
Mohammed
Hassan
Amoli — A1174

**2006, Sept. 18  Litho.  Perf. 13**
2916     Block of 4
a.  A1171 650r multi
b.  A1172 650r multi
c.  A1173 650r multi
d.  A1174 650r multi

       Dated 2005.

Third Meeting of Economic
Cooperation Organization Postal
Authorities, Tehran — A1175

Illustration reduced.

**2006, Sept. 20**
2917 A1175 650r multi
       Compare with Pakistan No. 1101.

Basij, 27th
Anniv.
A1176

**2006, Nov. 26**
2918 A1176 650r multi

Souvenir Sheet

Isfahan, 2006 Islamic Cultural
Capital — A1177

No. 2919: a, Chehel Sotun Palace. b, Emam Mosque. c, Aliqapu Palace. d, Khajo Bridge.

**2006, Dec. 30**
2919 A1177 650r Sheet of 4, #a-
       d

Martyrs — A1178

No. 2920: a, Man and flags. b, Ten men.

**2007, Jan. 7**
2920 A1178 650r Horiz. pair, #a-
b

Dated 2006.

**Souvenir Sheet**

Iranian Constitution, Cent. — A1179

No. 2921: a, Man, gate. b, Parliament. c,
Three men, gate. d, Two men, gate.

**2006, May 8**    **Litho.**    *Perf. 13*
2921 A1179 650r Sheet of 4, #a-
d

**Souvenir Sheet**

Seventh General Assembly of
Association of Asian Parliaments for
Peace, Tehran — A1180

No. 2922: a, Emblem of Association of
Asian Parliaments for Peace. b, Dove, colors
of Iranian flag. c, Gate and flags. d, Emblem of
Islamic Consultative Assembly.

**2006, Nov. 14**
2922 A1180 650r Sheet of 4, #a-
d

Peaceful Nuclear Energy — A1181

Illustration reduced.

**2007, Feb. 11**
2923 A1181 650r multi

Iranian-built
Engine
A1182

**2007, Feb. 26**
2924 A1182 650r multi

---

Shrine of
Fatima,
Qom — A1183

**2007, Mar. 18**
2925 A1183 650r multi

New Year — A1184

No. 2926: a, Flowers, man with drum. b,
Trumpeters, fishbowl, Koran, apples, grass.
Illustration reduced.

**2007, Mar. 19**
2926 A1184 650r Horiz. pair, #a-
b

Map of Persian
Gulf — A1185

**2007**    **Litho.**    *Perf. 13x13½*
**Side Panel Color**

2927 A1185  200r brown
2928 A1185  300r yellow
2929 A1185  650r orange
2930 A1185 2100r blue
2931 A1185 4400r blue

Issued: 200r, 9/9; 300r, 5/23; 4400r, 7/25.
650r, 10/30; 2100r, 11/24.
See Nos. 2943-2945.

Chemical Weapons Convention, 10th
Anniv. — A1186

**2007, June 29**    *Perf. 13*
2932 A1186 650r multi

38th Intl. Physics Olympiad,
Isfahan — A1187

**2007, July 3**
2933 A1187 650r multi

---

K. K. Sarughy
A1188

**2007, Aug. 22**
2934 A1188 650r multi

Imam Moussa
Sadr, Shiite
Leader Who
Disappeared in
1978 — A1189

**2007, Aug. 31**
2935 A1189 650r multi

Worldwide Fund for Nature
(WWF) — A1190

No. 2936 — Grus leucogranus: a, Pair, one
with head raised, other with head lowered. b,
Pair, facing each other. c, Pair, both standing
on one leg. d, Running with wings extended.
Illustration reduced.

**2007, Sept. 9**
2936 A1190 650r Block of 4, #a-d

**Miniature Sheet**

Great Messenger Year — A1191

No. 2937 — Arabic text and: a, Arch. b,
Arabic text in diamond. c, Roman Colosseum.
d, Pyramids.

**2007, Jan. 6**    **Litho.**    *Perf. 13*
2937 A1191 650r Sheet of 4, #a-
d

---

Communications and Public Relations
Day — A1192

**2007, May 17**
2938 A1192 650r multi

**Miniature Sheet**

Return of Prisoners of War — A1193

No. 2939 — Flowers and: a, Geese. b, Iranian man, hand symbol. c, Prisoners of war on
bus. d, People on motorcycles greeting prisoners of war.

**2007, Aug. 17**
2939 A1193 650r Sheet of 4, #a-
d

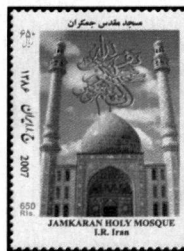

Jamkaran
Mosque
A1194

**2007, Aug. 29**
2940 A1194 650r multi

World Post
Day — A1195

**2007, Sept. 10**
2941 A1195 650r multi

Mevlana Jalal
ad-Din ar-Rumi
(1207-73),
Islamic
Philosopher
A1196

**2007, Oct. 28**
2942 A1196 650r multi

## Map of Persian Gulf Type of 2007
**2008** *Perf. 13x13½*
**Side Panel Color**
2943 A1185 1000r green
2944 A1185 2000r lilac
2945 A1185 5500r red

Issued: 1000r, 1/16; 2000r, 2/5; 5500r, 1/5.

Information
Technology
Infrastructure
Development
A1197

**2008, Jan. 16** *Perf. 13*
2946 A1197 650r multi

Navvab Safavi
(1924-55),
Founder of
Islamic
Fedayeen
A1198

**2008, Jan. 17**
2947 A1198 650r multi

Falsafi, Preacher, 100th Anniv. of
Birth — A1199

**2008, Feb. 27**
2948 A1199 650r multi

Death of Emad Moghnie, Hezbollah
Leader — A1200

Illustration reduced.

**2008, Mar. 10**
2949 A1200 650r multi

---

New
Year
A1201

**2008, Mar. 15**
2950 A1201 650r multi

Abdulazim Shrine — A1202

Illustration reduced.

**2008, Apr. 11** *Perf. 13x13½*
2951 A1202 650r multi

Children and
Youth Water
Festival
A1203

**2008, Apr. 21** *Perf. 13*
2952 A1203 650r multi

Islamic City
Councils, 10th
Anniv.
A1204

**2008, Apr. 28**
2953 A1204 650r multi

Thiqat al-Islam
Kulayni, Islamic
Legal Scholar,
1100th Anniv.
of
Death — A1205

**2008, May 8**
2954 A1205 650r multi

Buildings in Morocco and
Iran — A1206

No. 2955: a, Kasbah, Oudayas, Morocco. b,
Falak-Ol-Aflak Castle, Iran.
Illustration reduced.

---

**2008, May 12** *Litho.* *Perf. 13*
2955 A1206 650r Horiz. pair, #a-
b, + label

See Morocco No. 1061.

## Map of Persian Gulf Type of 2007
**2008** *Litho.* *Perf. 13x13½*
**Side Panel Color**
2956 A1185 100r blue
2959 A1185 400r red

Issued: 100r, 9/8; 400r, 9/13.

Handicrafts Day — A1207

No. 2962: a, Engraved copper cup. b, Mina
vase.
Illustration reduced.

**2008, June 10** *Litho.* *Perf. 13*
2962 A1207 650r Horiz. pair, #a-
b

Javid-al-Asar
Haj Ahmed
Motevasselian,
Diplomat
A1208

**2008, July 3**
2963 A1208 650r multi

Mountains in Kyrgyzstan and
Iran — A1209

No. 2964: a, Khan-Tengri, Kyrgyzstan. b,
Sabalan Peak, Iran.
Illustration reduced.

**2008, Aug. 15**
2964 A1209 650r Horiz. pair, #a-
b, + central la-
bel

See Kyrgyzstan No. 313.

Ancient Jewelry From Iran and
Kazakhstan — A1210

No. 2965: a, Gold medal depicting lions, 7th
cent. B.C., Iran. b, Buckle depicting snow leopard and mountains, 4th-5th cent. B.C.,
Kazakhstan.
Illustration reduced.

**2008, Sept. 7**
2965 A1210 650r Horiz. pair, #a-
b

See Kazakhstan No. 578.

---

Iran Post Corporation, 20th
Anniv. — A1211

Illustration reduced.

**2008, Oct. 8** *Perf. 13x13½*
2966 A1211 1200r multi

---

## SEMI-POSTAL STAMPS

Lion and Bull,
Persepolis
SP1

Persian Soldier,
Persepolis — SP2

Palace of
Darius the
Great — SP3

Tomb of Cyrus
the Great,
Pasargadae
SP4

King Darius
on his
Throne — SP5

*Perf. 13x13½, 13½x13*
**1948, Jan. 30** *Engr.* *Unwmk.*
B1 SP1 50d + 25d emer 1.75 1.75
B2 SP2 1r + 50d red 1.75 1.75
B3 SP3 2½r + 1¼r blue 1.75 1.75
B4 SP4 5r + 2½r pur 2.75 2.75
B5 SP5 10r + 5r vio brn 2.75 2.75
　Nos. B1-B5 (5) 10.75 10.75

The surtax was for reconstruction of the
tomb of Avicenna (980-1037), Persian physician and philosopher, at Hamadan.

Ardashir II — SP6

Shapur I and
Valerian
SP7

Designs: 1r+50d, King Narses, Naqsh-i-
Rustam. 5r+2½r, Taq-i-Kisra, Ctesiphon.
10r+5r, Ardashir I and Ahura Mazda.

**1949, June 11**

| | | | | |
|---|---|---|---|---|
| B6 | SP6 | 50d + 25d green | 1.50 | 1.50 |
| B7 | SP6 | 1r + 50d ver | 1.50 | 1.50 |
| B8 | SP7 | 2½r + 1½r blue | 1.50 | 1.50 |
| B9 | SP7 | 5r + 2½r magenta | 3.00 | 3.00 |
| B10 | SP7 | 10r + 5r grnsh gray | 2.40 | 2.40 |
| | *Nos. B6-B10 (5)* | | 10.50 | 10.50 |

The surtax was for reconstruction of Avicenna's tomb at Hamadan.

Gunbad-i-Ali — SP8

Alaviyan, Hamadan SP9

Seldjukide Coin — SP10

Designs: 1r+½r, Masjid-i-Jami, Isfahan. 5r+2½r, Masjid-i-Jami, Ardistan.

**1949, Dec. 22**

| | | | | |
|---|---|---|---|---|
| B11 | SP8 | 50d + 25d bl grn | 1.25 | 1.25 |
| B12 | SP8 | 1r + ½r dk brn | 1.25 | 1.25 |
| B13 | SP9 | 2½r + 1¼r blue | 1.25 | 1.25 |
| B14 | SP9 | 5r + 2½r red | 2.25 | 2.25 |
| B15 | SP10 | 10r + 5r olive gray | 2.40 | 2.40 |
| | *Nos. B11-B15 (5)* | | 8.40 | 8.40 |

The surtax was for reconstruction of Avicenna's tomb at Hamadan.

Koran, Crescent and Flag — SP11

**1950, Oct. 2    Litho.    Perf. 11**

| | | | | |
|---|---|---|---|---|
| B16 | SP11 | 1.50r + 1r multi | 25.00 | 15.00 |

Economic Conference of the Islamic States.

Tomb of Baba Afzal at Kashan SP12

Gorgan Vase — SP13

Designs: 2½r+1¼r, Tower of Ghazan. 5r+2½r, Masjid-i Gawhar. 10r+5r, Mihrab of the Mosque at Rezaieh.

**Perf. 13x13½, 13½x13**

**1950, Aug. 23    Engr.**

| | | | | |
|---|---|---|---|---|
| B17 | SP12 | 50d + 25d dk grn | 1.25 | *1.25* |
| B18 | SP13 | 1r + ½r blue | 1.25 | *1.25* |
| B19 | SP13 | 2½r + 1¼r choc | 1.25 | *1.25* |

| | | | | |
|---|---|---|---|---|
| B20 | SP12 | 5r + 2½r red | 2.25 | *2.25* |
| B21 | SP12 | 10r + 5r gray | 2.40 | *2.40* |
| | *Nos. B17-B21 (5)* | | 8.40 | 8.40 |

The surtax was for reconstruction of Avicenna's tomb at Hamadan.

Mohammad Reza Shah Pahlavi and Map — SP14

Monument to Fallen Liberators of Azerbaijan SP15

Designs: 1r+50d, Marching troops. 1.50r+75d, Running advance with flag. 2.50r+1.25r, Mohammad Reza Shah Pahlavi. 3r+1.50r, Parade of victors.

**1950, Dec. 12    Litho.**

| | | | | |
|---|---|---|---|---|
| B22 | SP14 | 10d + 5d blk brn | 10.00 | 3.50 |
| B23 | SP15 | 50d + 25d blk brn | 10.00 | 3.50 |
| B24 | SP15 | 1r + 50d brown lake | 15.00 | 4.50 |
| B25 | SP14 | 1.50r + 75d org ver | 15.00 | 9.00 |
| B26 | SP14 | 2.50r + 1.25r blue | 25.00 | 11.00 |
| B27 | SP15 | 3r + 1.50r ultra | 25.00 | 8.50 |
| | *Nos. B22-B27 (6)* | | 100.00 | 40.00 |

Liberation of Azerbaijan Province from communists, 4th anniv.
The surtax was for families of Persian soldiers who died in the struggle.

Koran Gate at Shiraz SP16

Saadi — SP17

Design: 50d+50d, Tomb of Saadi, Shiraz.

**Perf. 11x10½, 10½x11**

**1952, Apr. 30    Photo.    Unwmk.**

| | | | | |
|---|---|---|---|---|
| B28 | SP16 | 25d + 25d dl bl grn | 3.75 | 2.00 |
| B29 | SP16 | 50d + 50d brn ol | 4.25 | 2.25 |
| B30 | SP17 | 1.50r + 50d vio bl | 25.00 | 6.00 |
| | *Nos. B28-B30 (3)* | | 33.00 | 10.25 |

770th birthday of Saadi, Persian poet. The surtax was to help complete Saadi's tomb at Shiraz.
Three stamps of same denominations and colors, with values enclosed in tablets, were prepared but not officially issued.

View of Hamadan SP18

Avicenna — SP19

Designs: 2½r+1¼r, Gonbad Qabus (tower of tomb). 5r+2½r, Old tomb of Avicenna. 10r+5r, New tomb.

**Perf. 13x13½, 13½x13**

**1954, Apr. 21    Engr.    Unwmk.**

| | | | | |
|---|---|---|---|---|
| B31 | SP18 | 50d + 25d dp grn | 1.25 | 1.25 |
| B32 | SP19 | 1r + ½r vio brn | 1.25 | 1.25 |
| B33 | SP19 | 2½r + 1¼r blue | 1.25 | 1.25 |
| B34 | SP18 | 5r + 2½r ver | 2.00 | 2.00 |
| B35 | SP18 | 10r + 5r ol gray | 3.00 | 3.00 |
| | *Nos. B31-B35 (5)* | | 8.75 | 8.75 |

The surtax was for reconstruction of Avicenna's tomb at Hamadan.

> **Catalogue values for unused stamps in this section, from this point to the end of the section, are for Never Hinged items.**

Mother with Children and Ruins — SP20

**Wmk. 316**

**1963, Feb. 4    Litho.    Perf. 10½**

| | | | | |
|---|---|---|---|---|
| B36 | SP20 | 14r + 6r dk bl grn & lt brn | 2.00 | .50 |

The surtax was for the benefit of survivors of the Kazvin earthquake.
For overprints see Nos. C86-C88.

---

**AIR POST STAMPS**

Type of 1909 Overprinted

**1927    Unwmk.    Typo.    Perf. 11½**

| | | | | |
|---|---|---|---|---|
| C1 | A31 | 1c org & maroon | 2.50 | 1.00 |
| C2 | A31 | 2c vio & maroon | 2.50 | 1.00 |
| C3 | A31 | 3c grn & maroon | 2.50 | 1.00 |
| C4 | A31 | 6c red & maroon | 2.50 | 1.00 |
| C5 | A31 | 9c gray & maroon | 4.00 | 1.00 |
| C6 | A31 | 10c red vio & mar | 6.00 | 1.00 |
| C7 | A31 | 13c dk bl & mar | 8.00 | 2.50 |
| C8 | A31 | 1k sil, vio & bis brown | 8.00 | 2.50 |
| C9 | A31 | 26c dk grn & mar | 8.00 | 2.50 |
| C10 | A31 | 2k sil, dk grn & bis brown | 15.00 | 3.00 |
| C11 | A31 | 3k sil, gray & bis brown | 25.00 | 6.00 |
| C12 | A31 | 4k sil, bl & bis brown | 40.00 | 15.00 |
| C13 | A31 | 5k gold, brn & bis brown | 40.00 | 10.00 |
| C14 | A31 | 10k gold, org & bis brown | 250.00 | 250.00 |
| C15 | A31 | 20k gold, ol grn & bis brn | 250.00 | 250.00 |
| C16 | A31 | 30k gold, car & bis brown | 250.00 | 250.00 |
| | *Nos. C1-C16 (16)* | | 914.00 | 797.50 |

Counterfeit overprints are plentiful. They are found on Nos. 448-463, perf. 12½x12 instead of 11½.
Exist without overprint. Value, set $4,000.

AP1

AP2

AP3

AP4

AP5

Airplane, Value and "Poste aérièn" Surcharged on Revenue Stamps

**1928    Perf. 11**

| | | | | |
|---|---|---|---|---|
| C17 | AP1 | 3k yellow brn | 125.00 | 40.00 |
| C18 | AP2 | 5k dark brown | 30.00 | 10.00 |
| C19 | AP3 | 1t gray vio | 30.00 | 10.00 |
| C20 | AP4 | 2t olive bister | 30.00 | 10.00 |
| C21 | AP5 | 3t deep green | 35.00 | 15.00 |
| | *Nos. C17-C21 (5)* | | 250.00 | 85.00 |

AP6

AP7

"Poste aerienne"

**1928-29**

| | | | | |
|---|---|---|---|---|
| C22 | AP6 | 1c emerald | 1.00 | .50 |
| a. | | 1c yellow green | 1.00 | .50 |
| b. | | Double overprint | 35.00 | |
| C23 | AP6 | 2c light blue | 1.00 | .20 |
| C24 | AP6 | 3c bright rose | 1.00 | .20 |
| C25 | AP6 | 5c olive brn | 1.00 | .20 |
| a. | | "5" omitted | 750.00 | 850.00 |
| b. | | Horiz. pair, imperf. btwn. | 250.00 | |
| C26 | AP6 | 10c dark green | 1.00 | .20 |
| a. | | "10" omitted | 30.00 | |
| b. | | "1" inverted | 50.00 | |
| C27 | AP7 | 1k dull vio | 2.00 | 1.00 |
| a. | | "1" inverted | 65.00 | |
| C28 | AP7 | 2k orange | 5.00 | 2.00 |
| a. | | "S" for "s" in "Krs" | 100.00 | |
| | *Nos. C22-C28 (7)* | | 12.00 | 4.30 |

Counterfeits exist.

Revenue Stamps Similar to Nos. C17 to C21, Overprinted like Nos. C22 to C28: "Poste aerienne"

**1929**

| | | | | |
|---|---|---|---|---|
| C29 | AP1 | 3k yellow brn | 100.00 | 25.00 |
| C30 | AP2 | 5k dark brn | 20.00 | 5.00 |
| C31 | AP3 | 10k violet | 25.00 | 10.00 |
| C32 | AP4 | 20k olive grn | 30.00 | 10.00 |
| C33 | AP5 | 30k deep grn | 40.00 | 15.00 |
| | *Nos. C29-C33 (5)* | | 215.00 | 65.00 |

Reza Shah Pahlavi and Eagle — AP8

**1930, July 6    Photo.    Perf. 12½x11½**

| | | | | |
|---|---|---|---|---|
| C34 | AP8 | 1c ol bis & brt bl | .50 | .50 |
| C35 | AP8 | 2c blue & gray blk | .50 | .50 |
| C36 | AP8 | 3c ol grn & dk vio | .50 | .50 |
| C37 | AP8 | 4c dk vio & pck bl | .50 | .50 |
| C38 | AP8 | 5c lt grn & mag | .50 | .50 |

| | | | | |
|---|---|---|---|---|
| C39 | AP8 | 6c mag & bl grn | .50 | .50 |
| C40 | AP8 | 8c dk gray & dp violet | .50 | .50 |
| C41 | AP8 | 10c dp ultra & ver | .50 | .50 |
| C42 | AP8 | 12c slate & org | .50 | .50 |
| C43 | AP8 | 15c org brn & ol green | .50 | .50 |
| C44 | AP8 | 1k Prus bl & scar | 5.00 | 2.50 |

**Engr.**

| | | | | |
|---|---|---|---|---|
| C45 | AP8 | 2k black & ultra | 5.00 | 2.50 |
| C46 | AP8 | 3k dk brn & gray green | 6.50 | 3.00 |
| C47 | AP8 | 5k dp red & gray black | 6.50 | 4.00 |
| C48 | AP8 | 1t orange & vio | 25.00 | 8.00 |
| C49 | AP8 | 2t dk grn & red brown | 25.00 | 10.00 |
| C50 | AP8 | 3t brn vio & sl bl | 175.00 | 50.00 |
| | | Nos. C34-C50 (17) | 253.00 | 85.00 |

Same Overprinted in Black

**1935**     **Photo.**

| | | | | |
|---|---|---|---|---|
| C51 | AP8 | 1c ol bis & brt bl | .50 | .50 |
| C52 | AP8 | 2c blue & gray blk | .50 | .50 |
| C53 | AP8 | 3c ol grn & dk vio | .50 | .50 |
| C54 | AP8 | 4c dk vio & pck bl | .50 | .50 |
| C55 | AP8 | 5c lt grn & mag | .50 | .50 |
| C56 | AP8 | 6c mag & bl grn | .50 | .50 |
| C57 | AP8 | 8c dk gray & dp violet | .50 | .50 |
| C58 | AP8 | 10c dp ultra & ver | .50 | .50 |
| C59 | AP8 | 12c slate & org | .50 | .50 |
| C60 | AP8 | 15c org brn & ol green | .50 | .50 |
| C61 | AP8 | 1k Prus bl & scar | 25.00 | 30.00 |

**Engr.**

| | | | | |
|---|---|---|---|---|
| C62 | AP8 | 2k blk & ultra | 20.00 | 25.00 |
| C63 | AP8 | 3k dk brn & gray green | 25.00 | 15.00 |
| C64 | AP8 | 5k dp red & gray black | 10.00 | 10.00 |
| C65 | AP8 | 1t orange & vio | 225.00 | 175.00 |
| C66 | AP8 | 2t dk grn & red brown | 25.00 | 20.00 |
| C67 | AP8 | 3t brn vio & sl bl | 35.00 | 20.00 |
| | | Nos. C51-C67 (17) | 370.00 | 300.00 |

Plane Over Mt. Demavend AP9

Plane above Mosque AP10

**Unwmk.**

**1953, Jan. 21**    **Photo.**    *Perf. 11*

| | | | | |
|---|---|---|---|---|
| C68 | AP9 | 50d bl green | 1.00 | .20 |
| C69 | AP10 | 1r car rose | 1.00 | .20 |
| C70 | AP10 | 2r dark blue | 1.00 | .20 |
| C71 | AP10 | 3r dark brn | 1.00 | .20 |
| C72 | AP10 | 5r purple | 3.00 | .20 |
| C73 | AP10 | 10r org ver | 3.00 | .30 |
| C74 | AP10 | 20r vio blue | 3.00 | .50 |
| C75 | AP10 | 30r olive | 7.00 | 1.00 |
| C76 | AP10 | 50r brown | 15.00 | 2.50 |
| C77 | AP10 | 100r black brn | 60.00 | 12.00 |
| C78 | AP10 | 200r dk bl grn | 35.00 | 14.00 |
| | | Nos. C68-C78 (11) | 130.00 | 31.30 |

AP11

Golden Dome Mosque and Oil Well AP12

**1953, May 4**    **Litho.**    *Perf. 10½*
Mosque in Deep Yellow

| | | | | |
|---|---|---|---|---|
| C79 | AP11 | 3r violet | 10.00 | 7.00 |
| C80 | AP12 | 5r chocolate | 17.00 | 10.00 |
| C81 | AP11 | 10r bl green | 45.00 | 20.00 |
| C82 | AP12 | 20r red vio | 90.00 | 40.00 |
| | | Nos. C79-C82 (4) | 162.00 | 77.00 |

Discovery of oil at Qum.

---

**Catalogue values for unused stamps in this section, from this point to the end of the section, are for Never Hinged items.**

---

Globe and UN Emblem AP13

*Perf. 10½x12½*

**1957, Oct. 24**    **Photo.**    **Wmk. 316**

| | | | | |
|---|---|---|---|---|
| C83 | AP13 | 10r brt red lil & rose | 3.00 | .90 |
| C84 | AP13 | 20r dl vio & rose vio | 6.00 | 1.25 |

United Nations Day, Oct. 24, 1957.

UNESCO Emblem AP14

**Wmk. 353**
**1966, June 20**    **Litho.**    *Perf. 10½*

| | | | | |
|---|---|---|---|---|
| C85 | AP14 | 14r multi | 1.10 | .30 |

20th anniversary of UNESCO.

No. B36 Surcharged in Maroon, Brown or Red

**1969, Dec. 4**    **Wmk. 316**    *Perf. 10½*

| | | | | |
|---|---|---|---|---|
| C86 | SP20 | 4r on 14r + 6r (M) | 2.75 | .75 |
| C87 | SP20 | 10r on 14r + 6r (B) | 2.75 | .75 |
| C88 | SP20 | 14r on 14r + 6r (R) | 2.75 | .75 |
| | | Nos. C86-C88 (3) | 8.25 | 2.25 |

1st England-Australia flight, via Iran, made by Capt. Ross Smith and Lt. Keith Smith, 50th anniv.

IATA Emblem and Persepolis AP15

---

*Perf. 13x13½*
**1970, Oct. 27**    **Photo.**    **Wmk. 353**

| | | | | |
|---|---|---|---|---|
| C89 | AP15 | 14r multi | 5.50 | .60 |

26th meeting of the Intl. Air Transport Assoc. (IATA), Tehran.

"UIT" AP16

**1972, May 17**    **Litho.**    *Perf. 10½*

| | | | | |
|---|---|---|---|---|
| C90 | AP16 | 14r multicolored | 2.50 | .50 |

4th World Telecommunications Day.

Shah and Jet AP17

**1974, June 1**    **Photo.**    *Perf. 13*

| | | | | |
|---|---|---|---|---|
| C91 | AP17 | 4r org & black | .50 | .20 |
| C92 | AP17 | 10r blue & black | 1.75 | .20 |
| C93 | AP17 | 12r dull yel & blk | 1.75 | .35 |
| C94 | AP17 | 14r lt green & blk | 1.90 | .35 |
| C95 | AP17 | 20r red lilac & blk | 2.50 | .50 |
| C96 | AP17 | 50r dull bl & blk | 6.75 | 1.40 |
| | | Nos. C91-C96 (6) | 15.15 | 3.00 |

Crown Prince at Controls of Light Aircraft — AP18

**1974, Oct. 31**    **Litho.**    *Perf. 10½*

| | | | | |
|---|---|---|---|---|
| C97 | AP18 | 14r gold & multi | 1.50 | .50 |

Crown Prince Reza's 14th birthday.

---

**Importation Prohibited**
Importation of stamps was prohibited effective Oct. 29, 1987.

---

Islamic Revolution, 10th Anniv. — AP19

**1989, Feb. 11**    *Perf. 13x13½*

| | | | | |
|---|---|---|---|---|
| C98 | AP19 | 40r red vio, blk & gold | .75 | .50 |
| C99 | AP19 | 50r bl vio, blk & gold | .75 | .50 |
| a. | | Pair, #C98-C99 | 1.75 | 1.50 |

Ayatollah Khomeini — AP20

**1989, July 11**    *Perf. 13*

| | | | | |
|---|---|---|---|---|
| C100 | AP20 | 70r multicolored | 1.00 | .50 |

---

## OFFICIAL STAMPS

Four bicolored stamps of this design (1s, 2s, 5s, 10s), with centers embossed, exist, but were never issued or used in Iran. Value $40. They are known imperforate and in many trial colors.

Mozaffar-eddin Shah Qajar — O1

No. 145 Surcharged in Black

**1902**      *Perf. 12½*

| | | | | |
|---|---|---|---|---|
| O5 | O1 | 5c on 1k red | 30.00 | 30.00 |
| O6 | O1 | 10con 1k red | 30.00 | 30.00 |
| O7 | O1 | 12con 1k red | 40.00 | 40.00 |
| | | Nos. O5-O7 (3) | 100.00 | 100.00 |

Nos. 351-363 Overprinted in Black

**1903-06**

| | | | | |
|---|---|---|---|---|
| O8 | A26 | 1c violet | 2.50 | .20 |
| O9 | A26 | 2c gray | 2.50 | .20 |
| O10 | A26 | 3c green | 2.50 | .20 |
| O11 | A26 | 5c rose | 2.50 | .20 |
| O12 | A26 | 10c yel brown | 5.00 | .20 |
| O13 | A26 | 12c blue | 7.00 | .20 |

*Perf. 11½x11*

| | | | | |
|---|---|---|---|---|
| O14 | A27 | 1k violet | 8.00 | 1.50 |
| O15 | A27 | 2k ultra | 8.00 | 2.00 |
| a. | | Violet overprint | 50.00 | |
| O16 | A27 | 5k org brown | 22.50 | 2.50 |
| O17 | A27 | 10k rose red | 22.50 | 3.50 |
| a. | | Violet overprint | 50.00 | |
| O18 | A27 | 20k orange ('06) | 100.00 | 7.00 |
| O19 | A27 | 30k green ('06) | 150.00 | 20.00 |
| O20 | A27 | 50k green | 250.00 | 100.00 |
| | | Nos. O8-O20 (13) | 583.00 | 137.70 |

**Overprinted on Nos. 368, 370a**

| | | | | |
|---|---|---|---|---|
| O21 | A27 | 2t on 50k grn (Bl) | 175.00 | 75.00 |
| O22 | A27 | 3t on 50k grn (V) | 175.00 | 75.00 |

Overprinted on Nos. 372, 375, New Value Surcharged in Blue or Black

**1905**

| | | | | |
|---|---|---|---|---|
| O23 | A27 | 2t on 50k grn (Bl) | 175.00 | 75.00 |
| O28 | A27 | 3t on 50k grn (Bk) | 175.00 | 75.00 |

The 2t on 50k also exists with surcharge in black and magenta; the 3t on 50k in violet and magenta. Values about the same.

Regular Issue of 1909 Overprinted

There is a space between the word "Service" and the Persian characters.

**1911**      *Perf. 12½x12*

| | | | | |
|---|---|---|---|---|
| O31 | A31 | 1c org & maroon | 8.00 | 6.00 |
| O32 | A31 | 2c vio & maroon | 8.00 | 6.00 |
| O33 | A31 | 3c yel grn & mar | 8.00 | 6.00 |
| O34 | A31 | 6c red & maroon | 8.00 | 6.00 |
| O35 | A31 | 9c gray & maroon | 17.50 | 11.00 |
| O36 | A31 | 10c multicolored | 17.50 | 12.00 |
| O38 | A31 | 1k multicolored | 45.00 | 35.00 |
| O40 | A31 | 2k multicolored | 125.00 | 80.00 |
| | | Nos. O31-O40 (8) | 237.00 | 162.00 |

The 13c, 26c and 3k to 30k denominations were not regularly issued with this overprint. Dangerous counterfeits exist, usually on reprints.

Regular Issue of
1915 Overprinted

**1915**    **Wmk. 161**    **Perf. 11, 11½**

| | | | |
|---|---|---|---|
| O41 | A33 | 1c car & indigo | 2.50 2.50 |
| O42 | A33 | 2c bl & carmine | 2.50 2.50 |
| O43 | A33 | 3c dark green | 2.50 2.50 |
| O44 | A33 | 5c red | 2.50 2.50 |
| O45 | A33 | 6c ol grn & car | 2.50 2.50 |
| O46 | A33 | 9c yel brn & vio | 2.50 2.50 |
| O47 | A33 | 10c multicolored | 2.50 2.50 |
| O48 | A33 | 12c ultramarine | 3.00 3.00 |
| O49 | A34 | 1k multicolored | 7.00 7.00 |
| O50 | A34 | 24c multicolored | 3.50 3.50 |
| O51 | A34 | 2k sil, bl & rose | 7.00 7.00 |
| O52 | A34 | 3k sil, vio & brn | 7.00 7.00 |
| O53 | A34 | 5k multicolored | 7.50 7.50 |
| O54 | A35 | 1t gold, pur & blk | 10.00 10.00 |
| O55 | A35 | 2t gold, grn & brn | 10.00 10.00 |
| O56 | A35 | 3t multicolored | 12.50 12.50 |
| O57 | A35 | 5t gold, bl & ind | 15.00 15.00 |
| | | Nos. O41-O57 (17) | 100.00 *100.00* |

Coronation of Shah Ahmed.
*Reprints have dull rather than shiny overprint. Value, set, $17.50.*

Coat of Arms
O2     O3

**1941**    **Unwmk.**    **Litho.**    **Perf. 11**
**For Internal Postage**

| | | | |
|---|---|---|---|
| O58 | O2 | 5d violet | 5.00 .20 |
| O59 | O2 | 10d magenta | 5.00 .20 |
| O60 | O2 | 25d carmine | 5.00 .20 |
| O61 | O2 | 50d brown black | 5.00 .20 |
| O62 | O2 | 75d claret | 7.50 .45 |

**Size: 22½x30mm**

| | | | |
|---|---|---|---|
| O63 | O2 | 1r peacock grn | 10.00 .45 |
| O64 | O2 | 1½r deep blue | 12.00 1.50 |
| O65 | O2 | 2r light blue | 15.00 1.50 |
| O66 | O2 | 3r vio brown | 17.50 1.50 |
| O67 | O2 | 5r gray green | 35.00 2.00 |
| O68 | O2 | 10r dk brn & bl | 350.00 5.00 |
| O69 | O2 | 20r chlky bl & brt pink | 450.00 20.00 |
| O70 | O2 | 30r vio & brt grn | 600.00 150.00 |
| O71 | O2 | 50r turq grn & dk brown | 1,200. 250.00 |
| | | Nos. O58-O71 (14) | 2,717. 433.20 |

> Catalogue values for unused stamps in this section, from this point to the end of the section, are for Never Hinged items.

**Perf. 13½x13**
**1974, Feb. 25**   **Photo.**   **Wmk. 353**
**Size: 20x28mm**

| | | | |
|---|---|---|---|
| O72 | O3 | 5d vio & lilac | .30 .25 |
| O73 | O3 | 10d mag & grnsh bl | .30 .25 |
| O74 | O3 | 50d org & lt green | .30 .20 |
| O75 | O3 | 1r green & gold | .40 .20 |
| O76 | O3 | 2r emerald & org | .70 .20 |

**Perf. 13**
**Size: 23x37mm**

| | | | |
|---|---|---|---|
| O77 | O3 | 6r slate grn & org | .75 .20 |
| O78 | O3 | 8r ultra & yellow | 1.00 .20 |
| O79 | O3 | 10r dk bl & lilac | 4.25 .25 |
| O80 | O3 | 11r pur & light bl | 1.75 .25 |
| O81 | O3 | 14r red & lt ultra | 1.75 .60 |
| O82 | O3 | 20r vio blue & org | 3.50 .90 |
| O83 | O3 | 50r dk brn & brt grn | 9.00 1.75 |
| | | Nos. O72-O83 (12) | 24.00 4.85 |

**1977-79**   **Wmk. 353**   **Perf. 13½x13**
**Size: 20x28mm**

| | | | |
|---|---|---|---|
| O87 | O3 | 1r black & lt grn | .35 .20 |
| O88 | O3 | 2r brown & gray | .40 .20 |
| O89 | O3 | 3r ultra & orange | .50 .20 |
| O90 | O3 | 5r green & rose | .65 .20 |

**Perf. 13**
**Size: 23x37mm**

| | | | |
|---|---|---|---|
| O91 | O3 | 6r dk bl & lt bl ('78) | .75 .45 |
| O92 | O3 | 8r red & bl grn ('78) | .80 .50 |
| O93 | O3 | 10r dk grn & yel grn | .80 .25 |
| O94 | O3 | 11r dk blue & brt yellow ('79) | 1.75 .50 |

| | | | |
|---|---|---|---|
| O95 | O3 | 14r dl grn & gray | 1.75 .50 |
| O96 | O3 | 15r bl & rose lil ('78) | 3.25 1.00 |
| O97 | O3 | 20r purple & yel | 3.25 .40 |
| O98 | O3 | 30r brn & ocher ('78) | 3.75 1.25 |
| O99 | O3 | 50r blk & gold ('78) | 10.00 1.25 |
| | | Nos. O87-O99 (13) | 28.00 6.90 |

## NEWSPAPER STAMP

No. 429 Overprinted

**1909**   **Typo.**   **Unwmk.**   **Perf. 12½**
| | | | |
|---|---|---|---|
| P1 | A26 | 2c gray, *blue* | 45.00 20.00 |

## PARCEL POST STAMPS

Regular issues of 1907-08 (types A26, A29) with the handstamp above in blue, black or green are of questionable status as issued stamps. The handstamp probably is a cancellation.

No. 436 Overprinted
in Black

**1909**   **Engr.**   **Perf. 11½**
| | | | |
|---|---|---|---|
| Q18 | A29 | 26c red brown | 20.00 15.00 |

The overprint is printed.

Regular Issue of
1915 Overprinted in
Black

**1915**   **Wmk. 161**   **Perf. 11, 11½**

| | | | |
|---|---|---|---|
| Q19 | A33 | 1c car & indigo | *2.50 2.50* |
| Q20 | A33 | 2c bl & carmine | *2.50 2.50* |
| Q21 | A33 | 3c dark green | *2.50 2.50* |
| Q22 | A33 | 5c red | *2.50 2.50* |
| Q23 | A33 | 6c ol green & car | *2.50 2.50* |
| Q24 | A33 | 9c yel brn & vio | *2.50 2.50* |
| Q25 | A33 | 10c bl grn & yel brn | *2.50 2.50* |
| Q26 | A33 | 12c ultramarine | *3.00 3.00* |
| Q27 | A34 | 1k multicolored | *7.00 7.00* |
| Q28 | A34 | 24c multicolored | *3.50 3.50* |
| Q29 | A34 | 2k multicolored | *7.00 7.00* |
| Q30 | A34 | 3k multicolored | *7.00 7.00* |
| Q31 | A34 | 5k multicolored | *7.50 7.50* |
| Q32 | A35 | 1t multicolored | *10.00 10.00* |
| Q33 | A35 | 2t gold, grn & brn | *10.00 10.00* |
| Q34 | A35 | 3t multicolored | *12.50 12.50* |
| Q35 | A35 | 5t multicolored | *15.00 15.00* |
| | | Nos. Q19-Q35 (17) | *100.00 100.00* |

Coronation of Shah Ahmed.
*Reprints have dull rather than shiny overprint. Value, set, $16.*

> Catalogue values for unused stamps in this section, from this point to the end of the section, are for Never Hinged items.

Post Horn — PP1

Black frame and "IRAN" (reversed) are printed on back of Nos. Q36-Q65, to show through when stamp is attached to parcel.

**1958**   **Wmk. 306**   **Typo.**   **Perf. 12½**

| | | | |
|---|---|---|---|
| Q36 | PP1 | 50d olive bis | .75 .25 |
| Q37 | PP1 | 1r carmine | 1.00 .25 |
| Q38 | PP1 | 2r blue | 1.00 .25 |
| a. | | Imperf., pair | 100.00 |
| Q39 | PP1 | 3r green | 1.00 .25 |
| Q40 | PP1 | 5r purple | 1.00 .25 |
| Q41 | PP1 | 10r orange brn | 3.75 .25 |
| Q42 | PP1 | 20r dp orange | 10.00 .35 |
| Q43 | PP1 | 30r lilac | 12.50 1.60 |
| Q44 | PP1 | 50r dk carmine | 19.00 2.50 |
| Q45 | PP1 | 100r yellow | 40.00 5.00 |
| Q46 | PP1 | 200r light grn | 60.00 9.00 |
| | | Nos. Q36-Q46 (11) | 150.00 19.95 |

**1961-66**   **Wmk. 316**

| | | | |
|---|---|---|---|
| Q51 | PP1 | 5r purple ('66) | 12.50 5.00 |
| Q52 | PP1 | 10r org brn ('62) | 12.50 5.00 |
| Q53 | PP1 | 20r orange | 17.50 7.00 |
| Q54 | PP1 | 30r red lil ('63) | 17.50 8.00 |
| Q55 | PP1 | 50r dk car ('63) | 25.00 10.00 |
| Q56 | PP1 | 100r yellow ('64) | 65.00 30.00 |
| Q57 | PP1 | 200r emer ('64) | 80.00 30.00 |
| | | Nos. Q51-Q57 (7) | 230.00 95.00 |

**1967-74**   **Wmk. 353**
**Shiny Gum**

| | | | |
|---|---|---|---|
| Q58 | PP1 | 2r blue ('74) | 5.00 — |
| Q59 | PP1 | 5r dk pur ('69) | 5.00 — |
| Q60 | PP1 | 10r orange brn | 5.00 — |
| Q61 | PP1 | 20r orange ('69) | 10.00 — |
| Q62 | PP1 | 30r red lilac | 12.00 — |
| Q63 | PP1 | 50r red brn ('68) | 15.00 — |
| Q64 | PP1 | 100r yellow | 50.00 — |
| Q65 | PP1 | 200r emerald ('69) | 80.00 — |
| | | Nos. Q58-Q65 (8) | 182.00 |

**1977**   **Wmk. 353**
**White Dry Gum**

| | | | |
|---|---|---|---|
| Q58a | PP1 | 2r blue | 1.00 .20 |
| Q59a | PP1 | 5r dk pur | 1.00 .20 |
| Q60a | PP1 | 10r orange brn | 1.00 .20 |
| Q61a | PP1 | 20r orange | 1.50 .20 |
| Q62a | PP1 | 30r pink | 2.00 .25 |
| Q63a | PP1 | 50r red brn | 2.50 .50 |
| Q64a | PP1 | 100r yellow | 3.50 1.00 |
| Q65a | PP1 | 200r emerald | 6.00 3.00 |
| | | Nos. Q58a-Q65a (8) | 18.50 5.55 |

**Perf. 13½x13, 10½ (#100r)**
**1981**   **Typo.**   **Wmk. 353**
**Without Black Frame and IRAN on Back**

| | | | |
|---|---|---|---|
| Q67 | PP1 | 50r orange brown | 25.00 25.00 |
| Q68 | PP1 | 100r yellow | 100.00 100.00 |
| a. | | 100r dull orange | |
| Q69 | PP1 | 200r green | *25.00 25.00* |

Nos. Q67, Q69 printed from new dies. Numerals are larger and higher in the value tablet on No. Q67. Numerals read down from upper left to lower right in value tablet on No. Q69.

## POSTAL TAX STAMPS

Iranian Red
Cross Lion
and Sun
Emblem
PT1

**1950**   **Unwmk.**   **Litho.**   **Perf. 11**
| | | | |
|---|---|---|---|
| RA1 | PT1 | 50d grn & car rose | 10.00 .90 |
| RA2 | PT1 | 2r vio & lil rose | 4.00 1.50 |

**1955**   **Wmk. 306**
| | | | |
|---|---|---|---|
| RA3 | PT1 | 50d emer & car rose | 75.00 5.00 |

> Catalogue values for unused stamps in this section, from this point to the end of the section, are for Never Hinged items.

**1957-58**   **Wmk. 316**
| | | | |
|---|---|---|---|
| RA4 | PT1 | 50d emer & rose lil | 4.00 .90 |
| RA5 | PT1 | 2r vio & car rose ('58) | 2.50 1.00 |

**1965**   **Wmk. 349**   **Perf. 10½**
| | | | |
|---|---|---|---|
| RA6 | PT1 | 50d emer & car rose | 2.00 .50 |
| RA7 | PT1 | 2r vio & lil rose | 2.50 .65 |

**1965-66**   **Wmk. 353**
| | | | |
|---|---|---|---|
| RA8 | PT1 | 50d emer & car rose (I) | 1.00 .20 |
| a. | | Type II | 3.00 .20 |
| RA9 | PT1 | 2r vio & car rose ('66) | 3.00 .35 |

No. RA8 was printed in two types: I. Without diagonal line before Persian "50." II. With line.

**1976, Sept.-78**   **Photo.**   **Perf. 13x13½**
| | | | |
|---|---|---|---|
| RA10 | PT1 | 50d emerald & red | 2.50 .30 |
| RA11 | PT1 | 2r slate & red ('78) | 2.50 2.50 |

Nos. RA10-RA11 are redrawn and have vertical watermark.

Nos. RA1-RA11 were obligatory on all mail. 50d stamps were for registered mail, 2r stamps for parcel post. The tax was for hospitals.

The 2.25r and 2.50r of type PT1 were used only on telegrams.

# IRAQ

i-räk

LOCATION — In western Asia, bounded on the north by Syria and Turkey, on the east by Iran, on the south by Saudi Arabia and Kuwait, and on the west by Jordan

GOVT. — Republic
AREA — 167,925 sq. mi.
POP. — 22,427,150 (1999 est.)
CAPITAL — Baghdad

Iraq, formerly Mesopotamia, a province of Turkey, was mandated to Great Britain in 1920. The mandate was terminated in 1932. For earlier issues, see Mesopotamia.

16 Annas = 1 Rupee
1000 Fils = 1 Dinar (1932)

Catalogue values for unused stamps in this country are for Never Hinged items, beginning with Scott 79 in the regular postage section, Scott C1 in the air post section, Scott CO1 in the air post official section, Scott O90 in the officials section, Scott RA1 in the postal tax section, and Scott RAC1 in the air post postal tax section.

### Issues under British Mandate

Sunni Mosque — A1

Gufas on the Tigris — A2

Assyrian Winged Bull — A4

Motif of Assyrian Origin — A3

Ctesiphon Arch — A5

Colors of the Dulaim Camel Corps — A6

Golden Shiah Mosque of Kadhimain — A7

Conventionalized Date Palm or "Tree of Life" — A8

**1923-25    Engr.    Wmk. 4    Perf. 12**

| | | | | |
|---|---|---|---|---|
| 1 | A1 | ½a olive grn | 1.00 | .25 |
| 2 | A2 | 1a brown | 1.75 | .25 |
| 3 | A3 | 1½a car lake | .95 | .25 |
| 4 | A4 | 2a brown org | .95 | .25 |
| 5 | A5 | 3a dp blue | 2.00 | .25 |
| 6 | A6 | 4a dull vio | 3.50 | .35 |
| 7 | A7 | 6a blue grn | 2.75 | .35 |
| 8 | A6 | 8a olive bis | 4.00 | .75 |
| 9 | A8 | 1r grn & brn | 6.00 | .90 |
| 10 | A1 | 2r black | 21.00 | 8.50 |
| 11 | A1 | 2r bister ('25) | 57.50 | 4.00 |
| 12 | A6 | 5r orange | 52.50 | 17.50 |
| 13 | A7 | 10r carmine | 67.50 | 25.00 |
| | | Nos. 1-13 (13) | 221.40 | 58.60 |

For overprints see Nos. O1-O24, O42, O47, O51-O53.

King Faisal I — A9

**1927**

| | | | | |
|---|---|---|---|---|
| 14 | A9 | 1r red brown | 11.00 | 1.25 |

See No. 27. For overprint and surcharges see Nos. 43, O25, O54.

King Faisal I
A10        A11

**1931**

| | | | | |
|---|---|---|---|---|
| 15 | A10 | ½a green | 1.00 | .30 |
| 16 | A10 | 1a chestnut | 1.00 | .30 |
| 17 | A10 | 1½a carmine | 1.50 | .45 |
| 18 | A10 | 2a orange | 1.25 | .20 |
| 19 | A10 | 3a light blue | 1.50 | .20 |
| 20 | A10 | 4a pur brown | 2.00 | 1.75 |
| 21 | A10 | 6a Prus blue | 2.50 | .80 |
| 22 | A10 | 8a dark green | 3.00 | 2.00 |
| 23 | A11 | 1r dark brown | 5.50 | 1.75 |
| 24 | A11 | 2r yel brown | 7.75 | 5.00 |
| 25 | A11 | 5r dp orange | 27.50 | 35.00 |
| 26 | A11 | 10r red | 82.50 | 85.00 |
| 27 | A9 | 25r violet | 700.00 | 800.00 |
| | | Nos. 15-27 (13) | 837.00 | 932.75 |

See Nos. 44-60. For overprints see Nos. O26-O41, O43-O46, O48-O50, O54-O71.

### Issues of the Kingdom
Nos. 6, 15-27 Surcharged in "Fils" or "Dinars" in Red, Black or Green:

a

b

c

d

**1932, Apr. 1**

| | | | | |
|---|---|---|---|---|
| 28 | A10(a) | 2f on ½a (R) | .50 | .20 |
| 29 | A10(a) | 3f on ½a | .50 | .20 |
| a. | | Double surcharge | 160.00 | |
| b. | | Inverted surcharge | 160.00 | |
| 30 | A10(a) | 4f on 1a (G) | 1.75 | .35 |
| 31 | A10(a) | 5f on 1a | .65 | .20 |
| a. | | Double surcharge | 275.00 | |
| b. | | Inverted Arabic "5" | 35.00 | 40.00 |
| 32 | A10(a) | 8f on 1½a | .75 | .50 |
| a. | | Inverted surcharge | 160.00 | |
| 33 | A10(a) | 10f on 2a | .80 | .20 |
| 34 | A10(a) | 15f on 3a | 1.75 | 1.50 |
| 35 | A10(a) | 20f on 4a | 2.75 | 1.50 |
| 36 | A6(b) | 25f on 4a | 4.50 | 3.75 |
| a. | | "Flis" for "Fils" | 350.00 | 425.00 |
| b. | | Inverted Arabic "5" | 425.00 | 550.00 |
| 37 | A10(a) | 30f on 6a | 3.25 | .75 |
| 38 | A10(a) | 40f on 8a | 4.25 | 2.75 |
| 39 | A11(c) | 75f on 1r | 4.00 | 2.75 |
| 40 | A11(c) | 100f on 2r | 10.00 | 4.75 |
| 41 | A11(c) | 200f on 5r | 22.50 | 24.00 |
| 42 | A11(c) | ½d on 10r | 82.50 | 95.00 |
| a. | | Bar in "½" omitted | 800.00 | 925.00 |
| 43 | A9(d) | 1d on 25r | 175.00 | 200.00 |
| | | Nos. 28-43 (16) | 315.45 | 338.40 |

King Faisal I
A12        A13

A14

Values in "Fils" and "Dinars"

**1932, May 9    Engr.**

| | | | | |
|---|---|---|---|---|
| 44 | A12 | 2f ultra | .50 | .20 |
| 45 | A12 | 3f green | .50 | .20 |
| 46 | A12 | 4f vio brown | .50 | .20 |
| 47 | A12 | 5f gray green | .60 | .20 |
| 48 | A12 | 8f deep red | .80 | .20 |
| 49 | A12 | 10f yellow | 1.00 | .20 |
| 50 | A12 | 15f deep blue | 1.50 | .20 |
| 51 | A12 | 20f orange | 1.75 | .55 |
| 52 | A12 | 25f rose lilac | 1.75 | .55 |
| 53 | A12 | 30f olive grn | 3.00 | .20 |
| 54 | A12 | 40f dark violet | 2.25 | 1.00 |
| 55 | A12 | 50f deep brown | 2.25 | .30 |
| 56 | A13 | 75f lt ultra | 3.75 | 2.00 |
| 57 | A13 | 100f deep green | 5.50 | 1.25 |
| 58 | A13 | 200f dark red | 17.50 | 7.00 |
| 59 | A14 | ½d gray blue | 55.00 | 40.00 |
| 60 | A14 | 1d claret | 125.00 | 100.00 |
| | | Nos. 44-60 (17) | 223.15 | 154.25 |

For overprints see Nos. O55-O71.

A15        A16

King Ghazi — A17

**1934-38    Unwmk.**

| | | | | |
|---|---|---|---|---|
| 61 | A15 | 1f purple ('38) | .75 | .25 |
| 62 | A15 | 2f ultra | .45 | .25 |
| 63 | A15 | 3f green | .45 | .25 |
| 64 | A15 | 4f pur brown | .45 | .25 |
| 65 | A15 | 5f gray green | .45 | .25 |
| 66 | A15 | 8f deep red | .75 | .25 |
| 67 | A15 | 10f yellow | .95 | .25 |
| 68 | A15 | 15f deep blue | .95 | .25 |
| 69 | A15 | 20f orange | .95 | .25 |
| 70 | A15 | 25f brown vio | 1.75 | .35 |
| 71 | A15 | 30f olive grn | 1.50 | .25 |
| 72 | A15 | 40f dark vio | 1.75 | .25 |
| 73 | A16 | 50f deep brown | 3.50 | .25 |
| 74 | A16 | 75f ultra | 3.25 | .40 |
| 75 | A16 | 100f deep green | 3.75 | .50 |
| 76 | A16 | 200f dark red | 5.75 | 1.00 |

| | | | | |
|---|---|---|---|---|
| 77 | A17 | ½d gray blue | 17.50 | 10.00 |
| 78 | A17 | 1d claret | 60.00 | 16.00 |
| | | Nos. 61-78 (18) | 104.90 | 31.25 |

For overprints see Nos. 226, O72-O89.

Catalogue values for unused stamps in this section, from this point to the end of the section, are for Never Hinged items.

Sitt Zubaidah Mosque — A18

Mausoleum of King Faisal I — A19

Lion of Babylon — A20

Malwiye of Samarra (Spiral Tower) — A21

Oil Wells — A22

Mosque of the Golden Dome, Samarra — A23

**Perf. 14, 13½, 12½, 12x13½, 13½x12, 14x13½**

**1941-42    Engr.**

| | | | | |
|---|---|---|---|---|
| 79 | A18 | 1f dark violet ('42) | .40 | .20 |
| 80 | A18 | 2f chocolate ('42) | .40 | .20 |
| 81 | A19 | 3f brt green ('42) | .40 | .20 |
| 82 | A19 | 4f purple ('42) | .40 | .20 |
| 83 | A19 | 5f dk car rose ('42) | .40 | .20 |
| 84 | A20 | 8f carmine | .70 | .25 |
| 85 | A20 | 8f ocher ('42) | .55 | .20 |
| 86 | A20 | 10f ocher | 16.00 | 3.25 |
| 87 | A20 | 10f carmine ('42) | 1.25 | .20 |
| 88 | A20 | 15f dull blue | 2.10 | .20 |
| 89 | A20 | 15f black ('42) | 2.50 | .20 |
| 90 | A20 | 20f black | 4.25 | .60 |
| 91 | A20 | 20f dull blue ('42) | 1.00 | .20 |
| 92 | A21 | 25f dark violet | .45 | .30 |
| 93 | A21 | 30f deep orange | .45 | .30 |
| 94 | A21 | 40f brn orange | 1.75 | .50 |
| 95 | A21 | 40f chestnut ('42) | 1.75 | .45 |
| 96 | A21 | 50f ultra | 3.00 | .60 |
| 97 | A21 | 75f rose violet | 2.50 | .60 |
| 98 | A22 | 100f olive green ('42) | 2.25 | 1.00 |
| 99 | A22 | 200f dp orange ('42) | 8.00 | 1.00 |
| 100 | A23 | ½d lt bl, perf. 12x13½ ('42) | 27.50 | 5.50 |
| a. | | Perf. 14 | 32.50 | 9.00 |
| 101 | A23 | 1d grnsh bl ('42) | 40.00 | 11.00 |
| | | Nos. 79-101 (23) | 118.00 | 27.35 |

Nos. 92-95 measure 17¾x21½mm, Nos. 96-97 measure 21x24mm.
For overprints see #O90-O114, O165, RA5.

King Faisal II
A24        A25

**Photo.; Frame Litho.**

**1942    Perf. 13 x 13½**

| | | | | |
|---|---|---|---|---|
| 102 | A24 | 1f violet & brown | .40 | .40 |
| 103 | A24 | 2f dk blue & brown | .40 | .40 |
| 104 | A24 | 3f lt green & brown | .40 | .40 |
| 105 | A24 | 4f dull brown & brn | .40 | .40 |
| 106 | A24 | 5f sage green & brn | .40 | .40 |
| 107 | A24 | 6f red orange & brn | .40 | .40 |

| | | | | |
|---|---|---|---|---|
| 108 | A24 | 10f dl rose red & lt brn | .40 | .40 |
| 109 | A24 | 12f yel green & brown | .40 | .40 |
| | | *Nos. 102-109 (8)* | 3.20 | 3.20 |

For overprints see Nos. O115-O122.

**Perf. 11½x12**

**1948, Jan. 15    Engr.    Unwmk.**

**Size: 17¾x20½mm**

| | | | | |
|---|---|---|---|---|
| 110 | A25 | 1f slate | .60 | .20 |
| 111 | A25 | 2f sepia | .35 | .20 |
| 112 | A25 | 3f emerald | .35 | .20 |
| 113 | A25 | 4f purple | .35 | .20 |
| 114 | A25 | 5f rose lake | .35 | .20 |
| 115 | A25 | 6f plum | 2.00 | .25 |
| 116 | A25 | 8f ocher | 4.50 | .75 |
| 117 | A25 | 10f rose red | .45 | .20 |
| 118 | A25 | 12f dark olive | .45 | .20 |
| 119 | A25 | 15f black | 8.00 | 2.00 |
| 120 | A25 | 20f blue | 1.00 | .20 |
| 121 | A25 | 25f rose violet | 1.10 | .20 |
| 122 | A25 | 30f red orange | 1.10 | .20 |
| 123 | A25 | 40f orange brn | 2.25 | .75 |

**Perf. 12x11½**

**Size: 22x27½mm**

| | | | | |
|---|---|---|---|---|
| 124 | A25 | 60f deep blue | 1.50 | .70 |
| 125 | A25 | 75f lilac rose | 1.50 | .70 |
| 126 | A25 | 100f olive green | 7.00 | 1.50 |
| 127 | A25 | 200f deep orange | 5.75 | 1.50 |
| 128 | A25 | ½d blue | 15.00 | 15.00 |
| 129 | A25 | 1d green | 50.00 | 17.50 |
| | | *Nos. 110-129 (20)* | 103.60 | 32.65 |

Sheets of 6 exist, perforated and imperforate, containing Nos. 112, 117, 120 and 125-127, with arms and Arabic inscription in blue green in upper and lower margins. Value perf or imperf, unused $100 each, used $160 each.
See Nos. 133-138. For overprints see Nos. 188-194, O123-O142, O166-O177, O257, O258, O272-O282, RA1-RA4, RA6.

Post Rider and King Ghazi — A26

Designs: 40f, Equestrian statue & Faisal I. 50f, UPU symbols & Faisal II.

**1949, Nov. 1    Perf. 13x13½**

| | | | | |
|---|---|---|---|---|
| 130 | A26 | 20f blue | 2.00 | 1.50 |
| 131 | A26 | 40f red orange | 2.25 | 1.50 |
| 132 | A26 | 50f purple | 7.00 | 5.25 |
| | | *Nos. 130-132 (3)* | 11.25 | 8.25 |

75th anniv. of the UPU.

**Type of 1948**

**1950-51    Unwmk.    Perf. 11½x12**

**Size: 17¾x20½mm**

| | | | | |
|---|---|---|---|---|
| 133 | A25 | 3f rose lake | 8.00 | 2.00 |
| 134 | A25 | 5f emerald | 8.50 | 4.00 |
| 135 | A25 | 14f dk olive ('50) | 2.10 | .75 |
| 136 | A25 | 16f rose red | 2.00 | .75 |
| 137 | A25 | 28f blue | 2.10 | .45 |

**Perf. 12x11½**

**Size: 22x27½mm**

| | | | | |
|---|---|---|---|---|
| 138 | A25 | 50f deep blue ('50) | 6.50 | 1.50 |
| | | *Nos. 133-138 (6)* | 29.20 | 9.45 |

For overprints see Nos. 160, O143-O148, O258, O273, O275-O276.

King Faisal II

A27    A28

**1953, May 2    Engr.    Perf. 12**

| | | | | |
|---|---|---|---|---|
| 139 | A27 | 3f deep rose car | 1.25 | 1.25 |
| 140 | A27 | 14f olive | 2.50 | 1.25 |
| 141 | A27 | 28f blue | 7.00 | 1.75 |
| b. | | Souv. sheet of 3, #139-141 | 100.00 | 150.00 |
| | | *Nos. 139-141 (3)* | 10.75 | 4.25 |

Coronation of King Faisal II, May 2, 1953.

**1954-57    Perf. 11½x12**

**Size: 18x20½mm**

| | | | | |
|---|---|---|---|---|
| 141A | A28 | 1f blue ('56) | .55 | .20 |
| 142 | A28 | 2f chocolate | .20 | .20 |
| 143 | A28 | 3f rose lake | .20 | .20 |
| 144 | A28 | 4f violet | .20 | .20 |
| 145 | A28 | 5f emerald | .20 | .20 |
| 146 | A28 | 6f plum | .25 | .20 |

| | | | | |
|---|---|---|---|---|
| 147 | A28 | 8f ocher | .25 | .20 |
| 148 | A28 | 10f blue | .30 | .20 |
| 149 | A28 | 15f black | 1.50 | 1.10 |
| 149A | A28 | 16f brt rose ('57) | 2.40 | 2.00 |
| 150 | A28 | 20f olive | 1.10 | .20 |
| 151 | A28 | 25f rose vio ('55) | 1.10 | .20 |
| 152 | A28 | 30f ver ('55) | 1.10 | .20 |
| 153 | A28 | 40f orange brn | 1.40 | .45 |

**Size: 22x27½mm**

| | | | | |
|---|---|---|---|---|
| 154 | A28 | 50f blue | 1.75 | .70 |
| 155 | A28 | 75f pink | 3.00 | .75 |
| 156 | A28 | 100f olive green | 5.25 | .80 |
| 157 | A28 | 200f orange | 8.25 | 1.60 |
| | | *Nos. 141A-157 (18)* | 29.05 | 9.60 |

For overprints see Nos. 158-159, 195-209, 674, 676, 678, O148A-O161A, O178-O191, O259-O260, O263, O266, O268, O270, O283-O291.

No. 143, 148 and 137 Overprinted in Black

**1955, Apr. 6    Perf. 11½x12**

| | | | | |
|---|---|---|---|---|
| 158 | A28 | 3f rose lake | 1.10 | .45 |
| 159 | A28 | 10f blue | 1.25 | .45 |
| 160 | A25 | 28f blue | 2.10 | 1.00 |
| | | *Nos. 158-160 (3)* | 4.45 | 1.90 |

Abrogation of Anglo-Iraq treaty of 1930.

King Faisal II — A29

**1955, Nov. 26    Perf. 13½x13**

| | | | | |
|---|---|---|---|---|
| 161 | A29 | 3f rose lake | .90 | .40 |
| 162 | A29 | 10f light ultra | 1.60 | .60 |
| 163 | A29 | 28f blue | 2.25 | 1.50 |
| | | *Nos. 161-163 (3)* | 4.75 | 2.50 |

6th Arab Engineers' Conf., Baghdad, 1955. For surcharge see No. 227.

Faisal II and Globe — A30

**1956, Mar. 3    Perf. 13x13½**

| | | | | |
|---|---|---|---|---|
| 164 | A30 | 3f rose lake | 1.25 | .60 |
| 165 | A30 | 10f light ultra | 1.60 | .60 |
| 166 | A30 | 28f blue | 2.25 | 1.25 |
| | | *Nos. 164-166 (3)* | 5.10 | 2.45 |

Arab Postal Conf., Baghdad, Mar. 3. For overprint see #173. For surcharge see #251.

Mechanical Loom A31

Designs: 3f, Dam. 5f, Modern city development. 10f, Pipeline. 40f, Tigris Bridge.

**1957, Apr. 8    Photo.    Perf. 11½**
**Granite Paper**

| | | | | |
|---|---|---|---|---|
| 167 | A31 | 1f Prus bl & org yel | .45 | .20 |
| 168 | A31 | 3f multicolored | .45 | .20 |
| 169 | A31 | 5f multicolored | .50 | .20 |
| 170 | A31 | 10f lt bl, ocher & red | .80 | .20 |
| 171 | A31 | 40f lt bl, blk & ocher | 1.60 | .70 |
| | | *Nos. 167-171 (5)* | 3.80 | 1.50 |

Development Week, 1957. See #185-187.

Fair Emblem — A32

**1957, June 1    Unwmk.**
**Granite Paper**

| | | | | |
|---|---|---|---|---|
| 172 | A32 | 10f brown & buff | .95 | .80 |

Agricultural and Industrial Exhibition, Baghdad, June 1.

No. 166 Overprinted in Red

**1957, Nov. 14    Perf. 13x13½**

| | | | | |
|---|---|---|---|---|
| 173 | A30 | 28f blue | 5.00 | 2.25 |
| a. | | Double overprint | 200.00 | 225.00 |

Iraqi Red Crescent Soc., 25th anniv.

King Faisal II — A33

**Perf. 11½x12**

**1957-58    Unwmk.    Engr.**

| | | | | |
|---|---|---|---|---|
| 174 | A33 | 1f blue | .30 | .35 |
| 175 | A33 | 2f chocolate | .30 | .35 |
| 176 | A33 | 3f dark car ('57) | .30 | .35 |
| 177 | A33 | 4f dull violet | .30 | .35 |
| 177A | A33 | 5f emerald | .70 | .65 |
| 178 | A33 | 6f plum | .70 | .65 |
| 179 | A33 | 8f ocher | 1.40 | 1.00 |
| 180 | A33 | 10f blue | 1.40 | 1.00 |
| | | *Nos. 174-180 (8)* | 5.40 | 4.70 |

Higher denominations exist without Republic overprint. They were probably not regularly issued.
See note below No. 225.
For overprints see Nos. 210-225, 675, O162-O164, O192-O199, O269, O292-O294. For types overprinted see #677, 679, O261, O264, O267, O271, O295.

Tanks — A34

King Faisal II — A35

Army Day, Jan. 6:  10f, Marching soldiers. 20f, Artillery and planes.

**1958, Jan. 6    Perf. 13x13½**

| | | | | |
|---|---|---|---|---|
| 181 | A34 | 8f green & black | 1.00 | .85 |
| 182 | A34 | 10f brown & black | 1.25 | 1.10 |
| 183 | A34 | 20f blue & red brown | 1.25 | 1.10 |
| 184 | A35 | 30f car & purple | 2.00 | 1.50 |
| | | *Nos. 181-184 (4)* | 5.50 | 4.55 |

**Type of 1957**

3f, Sugar beet, bag & refining machinery, vert. 5f, Farm. 10f, Dervendi Khan dam.

**1958, Apr. 26    Photo.    Perf. 11½**
**Granite Paper**

| | | | | |
|---|---|---|---|---|
| 185 | A31 | 3f gray vio, grn & lt gray | .45 | .30 |
| 186 | A31 | 5f multicolored | .60 | .60 |
| 187 | A31 | 10f multicolored | 1.75 | 1.00 |
| | | *Nos. 185-187 (3)* | 2.80 | 1.80 |

Development Week, 1958.

**Republic**

Stamps of 1948-51 Overprinted

**Perf. 11½x12, 12x11½**

**1958    Engr.    Unwmk.**

**Size: 17¾x20½mm**

| | | | | |
|---|---|---|---|---|
| 188 | A25 | 12f dark olive | .80 | .25 |
| 189 | A25 | 14f olive | 1.00 | .25 |
| 190 | A25 | 16f rose red | 12.50 | 4.00 |
| 191 | A25 | 28f blue | 1.25 | .65 |

**Size: 22x27½mm**

| | | | | |
|---|---|---|---|---|
| 192 | A25 | 60f deep blue | 4.00 | .75 |
| 193 | A25 | ½d blue | 20.00 | 5.25 |
| 194 | A25 | 1d green | 40.00 | 19.00 |
| | | *Nos. 188-194 (7)* | 79.55 | 30.15 |

Other denominations of type A25 exist with this overprint, but these were probably not regularly issued.

**Same Overprint on Stamps of 1954-57**

**Size: 18x20½mm**

| | | | | |
|---|---|---|---|---|
| 195 | A28 | 1f blue | .65 | .20 |
| 196 | A28 | 2f chocolate | .65 | .20 |
| 196A | A28 | 4f violet | .65 | .20 |
| 196B | A28 | 5f emerald | .65 | .20 |
| 197 | A28 | 6f plum | .65 | .20 |
| 198 | A28 | 8f ocher | .65 | .20 |
| 199 | A28 | 10f blue | .75 | .20 |
| 200 | A28 | 15f black | .95 | .20 |
| 201 | A28 | 16f bright rose | 2.40 | .35 |
| 202 | A28 | 20f olive | 1.10 | .55 |
| 203 | A28 | 25f rose violet | .75 | .65 |
| 204 | A28 | 30f vermilion | 1.10 | .20 |
| 205 | A28 | 40f orange brn | 1.10 | .35 |

**Size: 22½x27½mm**

| | | | | |
|---|---|---|---|---|
| 206 | A28 | 50f blue | 5.25 | 3.00 |
| 207 | A28 | 75f pink | 4.00 | 1.50 |
| 208 | A28 | 100f olive green | 4.50 | 3.00 |
| 209 | A28 | 200f orange | 13.00 | 5.50 |
| | | *Nos. 195-209 (17)* | 38.80 | 16.85 |

The lines of this overprint are found transposed on Nos. 195, 196 and 199.

**Same Overprint on Stamps and Type of 1957-58**

**Size: 18x20mm**

| | | | | |
|---|---|---|---|---|
| 210 | A33 | 1f blue | 3.25 | .70 |
| 211 | A33 | 2f chocolate | .60 | .25 |
| 212 | A33 | 3f dark carmine | .60 | .25 |
| 213 | A33 | 4f dull violet | .70 | .25 |
| 214 | A33 | 5f emerald | .60 | .25 |
| 215 | A33 | 6f plum | .60 | .25 |
| 216 | A33 | 8f ocher | .60 | .25 |
| 217 | A33 | 10f blue | .60 | .25 |
| 218 | A33 | 20f olive | .60 | .25 |
| 219 | A33 | 25f rose violet | 1.25 | .80 |
| 220 | A33 | 30f vermilion | 1.50 | .25 |
| 221 | A33 | 40f orange brn | 4.25 | 1.50 |

**Size: 22x27½mm**

| | | | | |
|---|---|---|---|---|
| 222 | A33 | 50f rose violet | 3.00 | .70 |
| 223 | A33 | 75f olive | 3.00 | 1.25 |
| 224 | A33 | 100f orange | 4.00 | 1.25 |
| 225 | A33 | 200f blue | 10.50 | 2.25 |
| | | *Nos. 210-225 (16)* | 35.65 | 10.70 |

#218-225 were not issued without overprint.
The lines of this overprint are found transposed on Nos. 210 and 214.
Many errors of overprint exist of #188-226.
For overprint see No. O198.

**Same Overprint on No. 78**
**Perf. 12**

| | | | | |
|---|---|---|---|---|
| 226 | A17 | 1d claret | 27.50 | 27.50 |

## No. 163 Surcharged in Red

### 1958, Nov. 26     Perf. 13x13½
227 A29 10f on 28f blue     1.75   1.00

Arab Lawyers' Conf., Baghdad, Nov. 26.

Soldier and Flag A36

### 1959, Jan. 6    Photo.    Perf. 11½
| | | | | |
|---|---|---|---|---|
| 228 | A36 | 3f bright blue | .40 | .20 |
| 229 | A36 | 10f olive green | .75 | .35 |
| 230 | A36 | 40f purple | 1.40 | .70 |
| | | Nos. 228-230 (3) | 2.55 | 1.25 |

Issued for Army Day, Jan. 6.

Orange Tree — A37

Emblem of Republic — A38

### 1959, Mar. 21    Unwmk.    Perf. 11½
231 A37 10f green, dk grn & org    .90   .25

Issued for Arbor Day.

### 1959-60    Litho. & Photo.    Perf. 11½
#### Granite Paper
#### Emblem in Gold, Red and Blue; Blue Inscriptions
| | | | | |
|---|---|---|---|---|
| 232 | A38 | 1f gray | .20 | .20 |
| 233 | A38 | 2f salmon | .20 | .20 |
| 234 | A38 | 3f pale violet | .20 | .20 |
| 235 | A38 | 4f bright yel | .20 | .20 |
| 236 | A38 | 5f light blue | .20 | .20 |
| 237 | A38 | 10f bright pink | .20 | .20 |
| 238 | A38 | 15f light green | .55 | .20 |
| 239 | A38 | 20f bister brn | .55 | .20 |
| 240 | A38 | 30f light gray | .55 | .20 |
| 241 | A38 | 40f orange yel | 1.00 | .35 |
| 242 | A38 | 50f yel green | 3.75 | .90 |
| 243 | A38 | 75f pale grn ('60) | 1.50 | .45 |
| 244 | A38 | 100f orange ('60) | 3.00 | .90 |
| 245 | A38 | 200f lilac ('60) | 5.00 | .90 |
| 246 | A38 | 500f bister ('60) | 8.00 | 3.00 |
| 247 | A38 | 1d brt grn ('60) | 18.00 | 7.25 |
| | | Nos. 232-247 (16) | 43.10 | 15.55 |

See Nos. 305A-305B. For overprints see Nos. 252, 293-295, O200-O221.

Worker and Buildings — A39

Victorious Fighters A40

---

### Perf. 12½x13, 13x12½
### 1959, July 14     Photo.
| | | | | |
|---|---|---|---|---|
| 248 | A39 | 10f ocher & blue | .60 | .55 |
| 249 | A40 | 30f ocher & emerald | 1.10 | .70 |

1st anniv. of the Revolution of July 14 (1958), which overthrew the kingdom.

Harvest — A41

### 1959, July 14     Perf. 11½
250 A41 10f lt grn & dk grn    .65   .20

### No. 166 Surcharged in Dark Red

### 1959, June 1    Engr.    Perf. 13x13½
251 A30 10f on 28f blue     1.25   .65

Issued for Children's Day, 1959.

### No. 237 Overprinted

### Litho. and Photo.
### 1959, Oct. 23     Perf. 11½
252 A38 10f multicolored     1.00   .55

Health and Sanitation Week.

Abdul Karim Kassem and Army Band — A42

Abdul Karim Kassem and: 16f, Field maneuvers, horiz. 30f, Antiaircraft. 40f, Troops at attention, flag and bugler. 60f, Fighters and flag, horiz.

### 1960, Jan. 6    Photo.    Perf. 11½
| | | | | |
|---|---|---|---|---|
| 253 | A42 | 10f blue, grn & mar | .80 | .55 |
| 254 | A42 | 16f brt blue & red | 1.25 | .70 |
| 255 | A42 | 30f ol grn, yel & brn | 1.25 | .70 |
| 256 | A42 | 40f deep vio & buff | 1.90 | .90 |
| 257 | A42 | 60f dk brown & buff | 2.50 | 1.00 |
| | | Nos. 253-257 (5) | 7.70 | 3.85 |

Issued for Army Day, Jan. 6.

Prime Minister Abdul Karim Kassem — A43

Maroof el Rasafi — A44

---

### 1960, Feb. 1    Engr.    Perf. 12½
| | | | | |
|---|---|---|---|---|
| 258 | A43 | 10f lilac | .60 | .35 |
| 259 | A43 | 30f emerald | 1.10 | .55 |

Issued to honor Prime Minister Kassem on his recovery from an assassination attempt.

### 1960, May 10    Photo.    Perf. 13½x13
| | | | | |
|---|---|---|---|---|
| 260 | A44 | 10f maroon & blk | 4.00 | 1.40 |
| a. | | Inverted overprint | 115.00 | 100.00 |

Exists without overprint. Value $11.

Symbol of the Republic — A45

Unknown Soldier's Tomb and Kassem with Freedom Torch — A46

### 1960, July 14     Perf. 11½
| | | | | |
|---|---|---|---|---|
| 261 | A45 | 6f ol grn, red & gold | .90 | .55 |
| 262 | A46 | 10f green, blue & red | .95 | .55 |
| 263 | A46 | 16f vio, blue & red | 1.00 | .80 |
| 264 | A45 | 18f ultra, red & gold | 1.00 | .80 |
| 265 | A45 | 30f brown, red & gold | 1.50 | 1.00 |
| 266 | A46 | 60f dk brn, bl & red | 2.50 | 1.50 |
| | | Nos. 261-266 (6) | 7.85 | 5.20 |

2nd anniv. of the July 14, 1958 revolution.

Gen. Kassem and Marching Troops — A47

Gen. Kassem and Arch — A48

### 1961, Jan. 6     Perf. 11½
#### Granite Paper
| | | | | |
|---|---|---|---|---|
| 267 | A47 | 3f gray ol, emer, yel & gold | .65 | .20 |
| 268 | A47 | 6f pur, emer, yel & gold | .70 | .20 |
| 269 | A47 | 10f sl, emer, yel & gold | .85 | .20 |
| 270 | A48 | 20f bl grn, blk & buff | 1.00 | .25 |
| 271 | A48 | 30f bis brn, blk & buff | 1.10 | .35 |
| 272 | A48 | 40f ultra, black & buff | 1.50 | .65 |
| | | Nos. 267-272 (6) | 5.80 | 1.85 |

Issued for Army Day, Jan. 6.

Gen. Kassem and Children A49

### 1961, June 1    Photo.    Unwmk.
#### Granite Paper
| | | | | |
|---|---|---|---|---|
| 273 | A49 | 3f yellow & brown | .80 | .45 |
| 274 | A49 | 6f blue & brown | 1.10 | .45 |
| 275 | A49 | 10f pink & brown | 1.50 | .45 |
| 276 | A49 | 30f yellow & brown | 1.75 | .45 |
| 277 | A49 | 50f lt grn & brown | 2.75 | .70 |
| | | Nos. 273-277 (5) | 7.90 | 2.50 |

Issued for World Children's Day.

Gen. Kassem and Flag — A50

---

5f, 30f, 40f, Gen. Kassem saluting and flags.

### 1961, July 14     Perf. 11½
#### Granite Paper
| | | | | |
|---|---|---|---|---|
| 278 | A50 | 1f multicolored | .50 | .20 |
| 279 | A50 | 3f multicolored | .50 | .20 |
| 280 | A50 | 5f multicolored | .50 | .20 |
| 281 | A50 | 6f multicolored | .50 | .20 |
| 282 | A50 | 10f multicolored | .50 | .20 |
| 283 | A50 | 30f multicolored | .75 | .55 |
| 284 | A50 | 40f multicolored | 1.00 | .55 |
| 285 | A50 | 50f multicolored | 1.75 | 1.00 |
| 286 | A50 | 100f multicolored | 4.50 | 1.75 |
| | | Nos. 278-286 (9) | 10.50 | 4.85 |

3rd anniv. of the July 14, 1958 revolution.

Gen. Kassem and Flag — A51

Gen. Kassem and Symbol of Republic A52

### Perf. 11½
### 1962, Jan. 6    Unwmk.    Photo.
#### Granite Paper
| | | | | |
|---|---|---|---|---|
| 287 | A51 | 1f multicolored | .65 | .20 |
| 288 | A51 | 3f multicolored | .65 | .20 |
| 289 | A51 | 6f multicolored | .75 | .20 |
| 290 | A52 | 10f blk, lilac & gold | 1.00 | .20 |
| 291 | A52 | 30f black, org & gold | 1.25 | .30 |
| 292 | A52 | 50f blk, pale grn & gold | 2.00 | .50 |
| | | Nos. 287-292 (6) | 6.30 | 1.60 |

Issued for Army Day, Jan. 6.

### Nos. 234, 237 and 240 Overprinted

### Litho. & Photo.
### 1962, May 29     Perf. 11½
| | | | | |
|---|---|---|---|---|
| 293 | A38 | 3f multicolored | .50 | .20 |
| 294 | A38 | 10f multicolored | .50 | .20 |
| 295 | A38 | 30f multicolored | 1.25 | .35 |
| | | Nos. 293-295 (3) | 2.25 | .75 |

Fifth Islamic Congress.

Hands Across Map of Arabia and North Africa — A53

### 1962, July 14     Photo.
| | | | | |
|---|---|---|---|---|
| 296 | A53 | 1f brn, org, grn & gold | .65 | .20 |
| 297 | A53 | 3f brn, yel grn, grn & gold | .65 | .20 |
| 298 | A53 | 6f blk, lt brn, grn & gold | .75 | .20 |
| 299 | A53 | 10f brn, lil, grn & gold | 1.00 | .20 |
| 300 | A53 | 30f brn, rose, grn & gold | 1.25 | .30 |
| 301 | A53 | 50f brn, gray, grn & gold | 2.00 | .45 |
| | | Nos. 296-301 (6) | 6.30 | 1.55 |

Revolution of July 14, 1958, 4th anniv.

al-Kindi — A54    Emblem of Republic — A54a

Designs: 3f, Horsemen with standards and trumpets. 10f, Old map of Baghdad and Tigris. 40f, Gen. Kassem, modern building and flag.

**Perf. 14x13½**

| | | | | |
|---|---|---|---|---|
| **1962, Dec. 1** | | **Litho.** | **Unwmk.** | |
| 302 | A54 | 3f multicolored | .65 | .20 |
| 303 | A54 | 6f multicolored | .65 | .20 |
| 304 | A54 | 10f multicolored | .75 | .35 |
| 305 | A54 | 40f multicolored | 2.00 | 1.00 |
| | | Nos. 302-305 (4) | 4.05 | 1.75 |

9th century Arab philosopher al-Kindi; millenary of the Round City of Baghdad.

| | | | | |
|---|---|---|---|---|
| **1962, Dec. 20** | | | **Perf. 13½x14** | |
| 305A | A54a | 14f brt green & blk | 2.25 | .50 |
| 305B | A54a | 35f ver & black | 2.75 | .75 |

Nos. 305A-305B were originally sold affixed to air letter sheets, obliterating the portrait of King Faisal II. They were issued in sheets for general use in 1966.
For overprints see Nos. RA15-RA16.

Tanks on Parade and Gen. Kassem — A55    Malaria Eradication Emblem — A56

| | | | | |
|---|---|---|---|---|
| **1963, Jan. 6** | | **Photo.** | **Perf. 11½** | |
| 306 | A55 | 3f black & yellow | .60 | .20 |
| 307 | A55 | 5f brown & plum | .65 | .20 |
| 308 | A55 | 6f blk & lt green | .75 | .20 |
| 309 | A55 | 10f blk & lt blue | .80 | .20 |
| 310 | A55 | 10f black & pink | .85 | .20 |
| 311 | A55 | 20f black & ultra | 1.00 | .20 |
| 312 | A55 | 40f blk & rose lilac | 1.25 | .25 |
| 313 | A55 | 50f brn & brt ultra | 1.75 | .40 |
| | | Nos. 306-313 (8) | 7.65 | 1.85 |

Issued for Army Day, Jan. 6.

| | | | | |
|---|---|---|---|---|
| **1962, Dec. 31** | | | **Perf. 14** | |
| **Republic Emblem in Red, Blue & Gold** | | | | |
| 314 | A56 | 3f yel grn, blk & dk grn | .50 | .20 |
| 315 | A56 | 10f org, blk & dark blue | .75 | .20 |
| 316 | A56 | 40f lilac, black & blue | 1.00 | .30 |
| | | Nos. 314-316 (3) | 2.25 | .70 |

WHO drive to eradicate malaria.

Gufas on the Tigris — A57

Shepherd and Sheep A58

Designs: 2f, 500f, Spiral tower, Samarra. 4f, 15f, Ram's head harp, Ur. 5f, 75f, Map and Republic emblem. 10f, 50f, Lion of Babylon. 20f, 40f, Baghdad University. 30f, 200f, Kadhimain mosque. 100f, 1d, Winged bull, Khorsabad.

---

**Engr.; Engr. and Photo. (bicolored)**

| | | | | |
|---|---|---|---|---|
| **1963, Feb. 16** | | **Unwmk.** | **Perf. 12x11** | |
| 317 | A57 | 1f green | .65 | .20 |
| 318 | A57 | 2f purple | .65 | .20 |
| 319 | A57 | 3f black | .65 | .20 |
| 320 | A57 | 4f black & yel | .65 | .20 |
| 321 | A57 | 5f lilac & lt grn | .70 | .20 |
| 322 | A57 | 10f rose red | 1.00 | .20 |
| 323 | A57 | 15f brn & buff | 1.50 | .20 |
| 324 | A57 | 20f violet blue | 1.60 | .20 |
| 325 | A57 | 30f orange | 1.00 | .35 |
| 326 | A57 | 40f brt green | 1.75 | .20 |
| 327 | A57 | 50f dark brown | 7.50 | .65 |
| 328 | A57 | 75f blk & lt grn | 3.75 | .45 |
| 329 | A57 | 100f brt lilac | 4.00 | .20 |
| 330 | A57 | 200f brown | 7.50 | .50 |
| 331 | A57 | 500f blue | 10.00 | 2.25 |
| 332 | A57 | 1d deep claret | 13.50 | 4.50 |
| | | Nos. 317-332 (16) | 56.40 | 10.75 |

For overprints see Nos. O314-O317, RA7-RA12.

| | | | | |
|---|---|---|---|---|
| **1963, Mar. 21** | | **Litho.** | **Perf. 13½x14** | |

10f, Man holding sheaf. 20f, Date palm grove.

| | | | | |
|---|---|---|---|---|
| 333 | A58 | 3f emerald & gray | .40 | .20 |
| 334 | A58 | 10f dp brn & lil rose | .65 | .20 |
| 335 | A58 | 20f dk bl & red brn | 1.10 | .35 |
| a. | | Souv. sheet of 3, #333-335 | 5.75 | |
| | | Nos. 333-335 (3) | 2.15 | .75 |

FAO "Freedom from Hunger" campaign. No. 335a sold for 50f.
No. 335a was overprinted in 1970 in black to commemorate the UN 25th anniv. Denominations on the 3 stamps were obliterated, leaving "Price 50 Fils" in the margin.

Cent. Emblem — A59    Rifle, Helmet and Flag — A60

Design: 30f, Iraqi Red Crescent Society Headquarters, horiz.

| | | | | |
|---|---|---|---|---|
| **Perf. 11x11½, 11½x11** | | | | |
| **1963, Dec. 30** | | | **Photo.** | |
| 336 | A59 | 3f violet & red | .40 | .20 |
| 337 | A59 | 10f gray & red | .45 | .20 |
| 338 | A59 | 30f blue & red | .90 | .20 |
| | | Nos. 336-338 (3) | 1.75 | .60 |

Centenary of International Red Cross.

| | | | | |
|---|---|---|---|---|
| **1964, Jan. 6** | | **Unwmk.** | **Perf. 11½** | |
| **Granite Paper** | | | | |
| 339 | A60 | 3f brn, blue & emer | .40 | .20 |
| 340 | A60 | 10f brn, pink & emer | .60 | .20 |
| 341 | A60 | 30f brown, yel & emer | 1.10 | .65 |
| | | Nos. 339-341 (3) | 2.10 | 1.05 |

Issued for Army Day, Jan. 6.

Flag and Soldiers Storming Government Palace — A61

| | | | | |
|---|---|---|---|---|
| **1964, Feb. 8** | | | **Perf. 11½** | |
| **Granite Paper** | | | | |
| 342 | A61 | 10f pur, red, grn & blk | .55 | .20 |
| 343 | A61 | 30f red brn, red, grn & blk | 1.00 | .25 |
| a. | | Souv. sheet of 2, imperf | 6.25 | 2.75 |
| b. | | Souv. sheet of 2 (4th anniv.) ('67) | 7.25 | 2.75 |

Revolution of Ramadan 14, 1st anniv. #343a contains stamps similar to #342-343 in changed colors (10f olive, red, green & black; 30f ultra, red, green & black). Sold for 50f.
No. 343b consists of various block-outs and overprints on No. 343a. It commemorates the 4th anniv. of the Revolution of Ramadan 14. Sold for 70f. Issued Feb. 8, 1967.

---

Hammurabi and a God from Stele in Louvre — A62

Design: 10f, UN emblem and scales.

| | | | | |
|---|---|---|---|---|
| **1964, June 10** | | **Litho.** | **Perf. 13½** | |
| 344 | A62 | 6f lilac & pale grn | .55 | .45 |
| 345 | A62 | 10f org & vio blue | 1.00 | .45 |
| 346 | A62 | 30f blue & pale grn | 1.50 | .70 |
| | | Nos. 344-346 (3) | 3.05 | 1.60 |

15th anniv. (in 1963) of the Universal Declaration of Human Rights.

"Industrialization of Iraq" — A63

Soldier Planting New Flag — A64

| | | | | |
|---|---|---|---|---|
| **1964, July 14** | | | **Perf. 11** | |
| 347 | A63 | 3f gray, org & black | .40 | .20 |
| 348 | A64 | 10f rose red, blk & emer | .40 | .20 |
| 349 | A64 | 20f rose red, blk & emer | .50 | .20 |
| 350 | A63 | 30f gray, org & black | .75 | .20 |
| | | Nos. 347-350 (4) | 2.05 | .80 |

6th anniv. of the July 14, 1958 revolution.

Star and Fighters A65

| | | | | |
|---|---|---|---|---|
| **1964, Nov. 18** | | **Photo.** | **Perf. 11½** | |
| 351 | A65 | 5f sepia & orange | .40 | .20 |
| 352 | A65 | 10f lt bl & orange | .40 | .20 |
| 353 | A65 | 50f vio & red orange | 1.00 | .30 |
| | | Nos. 351-353 (3) | 1.80 | .70 |

Revolution of Nov. 18, 1963, 1st anniv.

Musician with Lute — A66

| | | | | |
|---|---|---|---|---|
| **Perf. 13x13½** | | | | |
| **1964, Nov. 28** | | **Litho.** | **Unwmk.** | |
| 354 | A66 | 3f bister & multi | 1.00 | .20 |
| 355 | A66 | 10f dl grn & multi | 1.00 | .20 |
| 356 | A66 | 30f dl rose & multi | 1.25 | .60 |
| | | Nos. 354-356 (3) | 3.25 | 1.00 |

International Arab Music Conference.

---

Map of Arab Countries and Emblem A67

| | | | | |
|---|---|---|---|---|
| **1964, Dec. 13** | | | **Perf. 12½x14** | |
| 357 | A67 | 10f lt grn & rose lilac | .75 | .20 |

9th Arab Engineers' Conference, Baghdad.

Arab Postal Union Emblem — A67a    Soldier, Flag and Rising Sun — A68

| | | | | |
|---|---|---|---|---|
| **1964, Dec. 21** | | **Photo.** | **Perf. 11** | |
| 358 | A67a | 3f sal pink & blue | .40 | .20 |
| 359 | A67a | 10f brt red lil & brn | .50 | .20 |
| 360 | A67a | 30f orange & blue | 1.00 | .20 |
| | | Nos. 358-360 (3) | 1.90 | .65 |

10th anniv. of Permanent Office of APU
For overprint see No. 707.

| | | | | |
|---|---|---|---|---|
| **Perf. 14x12½** | | | | |
| **1965, Jan. 6** | | **Litho.** | **Unwmk.** | |
| 361 | A68 | 5f dull green & multi | .40 | .20 |
| 362 | A68 | 15f henna brn & multi | .40 | .20 |
| 363 | A68 | 30f black brn & multi | 1.00 | .20 |
| | | Nos. 361-363 (3) | 1.80 | .60 |

Issued for Army Day, Jan. 6.
An imperf. souvenir sheet carries a revised No. 363 with "30 FILS" omitted, and a portrait of Pres. Abdul Salam Arif. Violet inscriptions including "PRICE 60 FILS." Value $7.50.

Symbols of Agriculture and Industry A69

| | | | | |
|---|---|---|---|---|
| **1965, Jan. 8** | | | **Perf. 12½x14** | |
| 364 | A69 | 10f ultra, brn & blk | .50 | .20 |

Arab Labor Ministers' Conference.

Tanker A70

| | | | | |
|---|---|---|---|---|
| **1965, Jan. 30** | | | **Perf. 14** | |
| 365 | A70 | 10f multicolored | 1.00 | .45 |

Inauguration (in 1962) of the deep sea terminal for oil tankers.

Soldier with Flag and Rifle — A71

Tree
Week — A72

**1965, Feb. 8    Litho.    Perf. 13½**
366 A71 10f multicolored   .75  .20
Revolution of Ramadan 14, 2nd anniv.

**1965, Mar. 6    Unwmk.    Perf. 13**
367 A72 6f multicolored   .40  .20
368 A72 20f multicolored   1.00  .20

Federation
Emblem — A73

Dagger in Map
of
Palestine — A74

**1965, Mar. 24    Unwmk.    Perf. 14**
369 A73 3f lt bl, vio bl & gold   .40  .20
370 A73 10f gray, black & gold   .40  .20
371 A73 30f rose, car & gold   1.00  .30
   Nos. 369-371 (3)   1.80  .70
Arab Federation of Insurance.

**1965, Apr. 9    Litho.    Perf. 14x12½**
372 A74 10f gray & black   1.75  .35
373 A74 20f lt brn & dk blue   2.25  .55
Deir Yassin massacre, Apr. 9, 1948.
See Jordan No. 499 and Kuwait Nos. 281-282.

Smallpox Attacking People — A75

**1965, Apr. 30    Litho.    Perf. 14**
374 A75 3f multicolored   .45  .20
375 A75 10f multicolored   .55  .20
376 A75 20f multicolored   1.25  .70
   Nos. 374-376 (3)   2.25 1.10
WHO's fight against smallpox. Exist imperf.
Value $5.50.

ITU Emblem, Old and New
Telecommunication Equipment — A76

**1965, May 17    Perf. 14, Imperf.**
377 A76 10f multicolored   .70  .20
378 A76 20f multicolored   1.50  .55
   *a.* Souv. sheet of 2, #377-378   16.00 6.50
ITU, centenary. No. 378a sold for 40f and
exists imperf. Value for imperf $16.

Map of Arab
Countries and
Banner — A77

**1965, May 26    Litho.    Perf. 14x12½**
379 A77 10f multicolored   .50  .20
Anniversary of the treaty with the UAR.

Library
Aflame
and Lamp
A78

**1965, June    Photo.    Perf. 11**
380 A78 5f black, grn & red   .50  .20
381 A78 10f blk, green & red   .60  .20
Burning of the Library of Algiers, 6/7/62.

Revolutionist
with Torch,
Cannon and
Flames — A79

**1965, June 30    Litho.    Perf. 13**
382 A79 5f multicolored   .40  .20
383 A79 10f multicolored   .45  .20
45th anniversary, Revolution of 1920.

Mosque — A80

**1965, July 12    Photo.    Perf. 12**
384 A80 10f multicolored   .90  .60
Prophet Mohammed's birthday. A souvenir
sheet contains one imperf. stamp similar to
No. 384. Sold for 50f. Value $6.

Factories and
Grain — A81

Arab Fair
Emblem — A82

**1965, July 14    Litho.    Perf. 13**
385 A81 10f multicolored   .55  .20
7th anniv. of the July 14, 1958 Revolution.

**1965, Oct. 22    Unwmk.    Perf. 13**
386 A82 10f multicolored   .55  .20
Second Arab Fair, Baghdad.

Pres. Abdul Salam
Mohammed
Arif — A83

**1965, Nov. 18    Photo.    Perf. 11½**
**Granite Paper**
387 A83 5f org, buff & dk blue   .65  .20
388 A83 10f lt ultra, gray & dk brn   .90  .20
389 A83 50f lil, pale pink & sl blk   2.50  .90
   Nos. 387-389 (3)   4.05 1.30
Revolution of Nov. 18, 1963, 2nd anniv.

Census Chart and Adding
Machine — A84

**1965, Nov. 29    Litho.    Perf. 13**
390 A84 3f gray & plum   .50  .20
391 A84 5f brown red & brn   .60  .20
392 A84 15f olive bis & dl bl   1.00  .20
   Nos. 390-392 (3)   2.10  .60
Issued to publicize the 1965 census.

Date
Palms — A85

Soldiers'
Monument
A86

**1965, Dec. 27    Litho.    Perf. 13½x14**
393 A85 3f olive bis & multi   .40  .20
394 A85 10f car rose & multi   .90  .20
395 A85 15f blue & multi   1.60  .80
   Nos. 393-395 (3)   2.90 1.20
2nd FAO Intl. Dates Conference, Baghdad,
Dec. 1965.
For surcharges see Nos. 694-695.

**1966, Jan. 6    Photo.    Perf. 12**
396 A86 2f car rose & multi   .45  .20
397 A86 5f multicolored   .45  .20
398 A86 40f yel grn & multi   1.75  .75
   Nos. 396-398 (3)   2.65 1.15
Issued for Army Day.

Eagle and Flag of
Iraq — A87

**Perf. 12½**
**1966, Feb. 8    Photo.    Unwmk.**
399 A87 5f dl bl & multi   .40  .20
400 A87 10f orange & multi   .75  .20
3rd anniv. of the Revolution of Ramadan 14,
which overthrew the Kassem government.

Arab League
Emblem — A88

Soccer
Players — A89

**1966, Mar. 22    Perf. 11x11½**
401 A88 5f org, brn & brt grn   .40  .20
402 A88 15f ol, rose lil & ultra   .75  .20
Arab Publicity Week.

**1966, Apr. 1    Perf. 12**
5f, Player and goal post. 15f, As 2f. 50f,
Legs of player, ball and emblem, horiz.
403 A89 2f multicolored   .75  .20
404 A89 5f multicolored   .50  .20
405 A89 15f multicolored   1.50  .45
   Nos. 403-405 (3)   2.75  .85

**Miniature Sheet**
**Imperf**
406 A89 50f vio & multi   6.75 10.50
3rd Arab Soccer Cup, Baghdad, Apr. 1-10.
For overprint, see No. O296.

Steam
Shovel
Within
Cogwheel
A90

**1966, May 1   Litho.   Perf. 13½**
407 A90 15f multicolored   .40   .20
408 A90 25f red, blk, & sil   .50   .20
   Issued for Labor Day, May 1, 1966.

Queen
Nefertari — A91

Facade
of Abu
Simbel
A92

**Perf. 12½x13, 13½**
**1966, May 20        Litho.**
409 A91 5f olive, yel & blk   .40   .20
410 A91 15f blue, yel & brn   .40   .20
411 A92 40f bis brn, red & blk   1.90   1.30
   Nos. 409-411 (3)   2.70   1.70
   UNESCO world campaign to save historic monuments in Nubia.

President Arif and Flag — A93

**1966, July 14    Photo.    Perf. 11½**
412 A93 5f multicolored   .40   .20
413 A93 15f multicolored   .50   .20
414 A93 50f multicolored   1.75   1.00
   Nos. 412-414 (3)   2.65   1.40
   8th anniv. of the July 14, 1958 revolution.

A94

**1966, July 22    Litho.    Perf. 12**
**Multicolored Vignette**
415 A94 5f lt olive green   .40   .20
416 A94 15f lt greenish blue   .40   .20
417 A94 30f lt yellow green   1.00   .75
   Nos. 415-417 (3)   1.80   1.15
   Mohammed's 1,396th birthday.

Iraqi
Museum,
Baghdad
A95

   Designs: 50f, Golden headdress, Ur. 80f, Carved Sumerian head, vert.

**1966, Nov. 9    Litho.    Perf. 14**
418 A95 15f multicolored   .50   .20
419 A95 50f lt bl, blk, gold & pink   1.50   .80
420 A95 80f crim, blk, bl & gold   3.25   1.00
   Nos. 418-420 (3)   5.25   2.00
   Opening of New Iraqi Museum, Baghdad.

UNESCO
Emblem — A96

Iraqi
Citizens — A97

**1966, Dec.        Perf. 13½**
421 A96 5f blue, black & tan   .40   .20
422 A96 15f brt org brn, blk & gray   .40   .20
   20th anniv. of UNESCO.

**1966, Nov. 18      Perf. 13½x13**
423 A97 15f multicolored   .60   .35
424 A97 25f multicolored   1.00   .85
   3rd anniv. of the Revolution of 11/18/63.

Rocket
Launchers
and
Soldier
A98

**1967, Jan. 6    Photo.    Perf. 11½**
425 A98 15f citron, dk brn & dp bis   .40   .20
426 A98 20f brt lil, dk brn & dp bis   .60   .20
   Issued for Army Day, Jan. 6.

Oil Derrick, Pipeline,
Emblem — A99

   15f, 50f, Refinery and emblem, horiz.

**1967, Mar. 6    Litho.    Perf. 14**
427 A99 5f ol grn, pale yel & blk   .40   .20
428 A99 15f multicolored   .40   .20
429 A99 40f vio, yel & blk   .80   .70
430 A99 50f multicolored   1.75   1.00
   Nos. 427-430 (4)   3.35   2.10
   6th Arab Petroleum Cong., Baghdad, Mar. 1967.

New
Year's
Emblem
and
Spider's
Web
A100

**1967, Apr. 11    Litho.    Perf. 13½**
431 A100 5f multicolored   .40   .20
432 A100 15f multicolored   .40   .20
   Issued for the Hajeer Year (New Year).

Worker Holding
Cogwheel and Map
of Arab
Countries — A101

**1967, May 1      Perf. 12½x13**
433 A101 10f gray & multi   .40   .20
434 A101 15f lt ultra & multi   .40   .20
   Issued for Labor Day.

A102

**1967, June 20    Litho.    Perf. 14**
435 A102 5f multicolored   .40   .20
436 A102 15f blue & multi   .50   .20
   Mohammed's 1,397th birthday.

Flag, Hands
with
Clubs — A103

**1967, July 7      Perf. 13x13½**
437 A103 5f multicolored   .40   .20
438 A103 15f multicolored   .40   .20
   47th anniversary of Revolution of 1920.

Um Qasr
Harbor
A104

   10f, 15f, Freighter loading in Um Qasr harbor.

**1967, July 14    Litho.    Perf. 14x13½**
439 A104 5f multicolored   .40   .20
440 A104 10f multicolored   .60   .20
441 A104 15f multicolored   1.00   .20
442 A104 40f multicolored   2.00   1.00
   Nos. 439-442 (4)   4.00   1.60
   9th anniv. of the July 14, 1958 revolution and the inauguration of the port of Um Qasr.

Iraqi
Man — A105

President
Arif — A106

   Iraqi Costumes: 5f, 15f, 25f, Women's costumes. 10f, 20f, 30f, Men's costumes.

**1967, Nov. 10    Litho.    Perf. 13**
443 A105 2f pale brn & multi   .40   .20
444 A105 5f ver & multi   .40   .20
445 A105 10f multicolored   .70   .20
446 A105 15f ultra & multi   .90   .50
447 A105 20f lilac & multi   1.10   .50
448 A105 25f lemon & multi   1.10   .60
449 A105 30f fawn & multi   1.25   .60
   Nos. 443-449,C19-C21 (10)   11.85   5.50
   For overprints see Nos. 597-599, O228-O231, RA17.

**Perf. 11x11½, 11½x11**
**1967, Nov. 18**
   15f, Pres. Arif and map of Iraq, horiz.
450 A106 5f bl, vio blk & yel   .40   .20
451 A106 15f rose & multi   .75   .25
   4th anniversary of Nov. 18th revolution.

Ziggurat of
Ur — A107

   Designs: 5f, Gate with Nimrod statues. 10f, Gate, Babylon. 15f, Minaret of Mosul, vert. 25f, Arch and ruins of Ctesiphon.

**1967, Dec. 1    Litho.    Perf. 13**
452 A107 2f orange & multi   .40   .20
453 A107 5f lilac & multi   .40   .20
454 A107 10f orange & multi   .40   .20
455 A107 15f rose red & multi   .60   .20
456 A107 25f vio bl & multi   .80   .20
   Nos. 452-456,C22-C26 (10)   51.60   24.10
   International Tourist Year.
   For overprints see Nos. 593, 680, O225-O227, O308, RA18.

Iraqi Girl
Scout
Emblem and
Sign — A108

   5f, Girl Scouts at campfire & Girl Scout emblem. 10f, Boy Scout emblem & Boy Scout sign. 15f, Boy Scouts pitching tent & Boy Scout sign.

**1967, Dec. 15**
457 A108 2f orange & multi   1.00   .20
458 A108 5f blue & multi   1.25   .25
459 A108 10f green & multi   1.40   .40
460 A108 15f blue & multi   1.50   .50
   a.   Souv. sheet of 4   9.00   9.00
   Nos. 457-460 (4)   5.15   1.35
   Issued to honor the Scout movement.
   No. 460a contains 4 stamps similar to Nos. 457-460 with simulated perforations. Sold for 50f.
   For overprint see No. RA19.

Soldiers on
Maneuvers
A109

**1968, Jan. 6    Photo.    Perf. 11½**
461 A109 5f lt bl, brn & brt grn   .40   .20
462 A109 15f lt bl, ind & olive   .60   .20
   Issued for Army Day 1968.

White-cheeked
Bulbul — A110

   Birds: 10f, Hoopoe. 15f, Eurasian jay. 25f, Peregrine falcon. 30f, White stork. 40f, Black partridge. 50f, Marbled teal.

**1968, Jan.    Litho.    Perf. 14**
463 A110 5f org & black   .70   .25
464 A110 10f blue, blk & brn   .90   .25
465 A110 15f pink & multi   1.40   .25
466 A110 25f dl org & multi   2.00   .50
467 A110 30f emer, blk & brn   2.50   .50
468 A110 40f rose lil & multi   3.25   .75
469 A110 50f multicolored   4.75   1.25
   Nos. 463-469 (7)   15.50   3.75
   For overprint, see No. O311.

Fighting
Soldiers
A111

**1968, Feb. 8** *Perf. 11½*
470 A111 15f blk, org & brt bl 3.00 .90
Revolution of Ramadan 14, 5th anniv.

Factories, Tractor and Grain — A112

**1968, May 1** **Litho.** *Perf. 13*
471 A112 15f lt bl & multi .40 .20
472 A112 25f multicolored .60 .20
Issued for Labor Day.

Soccer
A113

5f, 25f, Goalkeeper holding ball, vert.

**1968, June 14** *Perf. 13½*
473 A113 2f multicolored .40 .20
474 A113 5f multicolored .40 .20
475 A113 15f multicolored .50 .20
476 A113 25f multicolored 2.25 .75
*a.* Souv. sheet, 70f, imperf. 9.00 10.00
Nos. 473-476 (4) 3.55 1.35

23rd C.I.S.M. (Conseil Internationale du
Sports Militaire) Soccer Championships.
No. 476a shows badge of Military Soccer
League.

Soldier, Flag,
Chain and
Rising
Sun — A114

**1968, July 14** **Photo.** *Perf. 13½x14*
478 A114 15f multicolored .50 .20
10th anniv. of the July 14, 1958 revolution.

World Health Organization
Emblem — A115

5f, 10f, Staff of Aesculapius over emblem,
vert.

**1968, Nov. 29** **Litho.** *Perf. 13½*
479 A115 5f multicolored .40 .20
480 A115 10f multicolored .40 .20
481 A115 15f blue, red & black .50 .20
482 A115 25f yel grn, red & blk .75 .20
Nos. 479-482 (4) 2.05 .80

WHO, 20th anniv. Exist imperf. Value $5.
For overprints, see Nos. O222-O224.

Human Rights
Flame — A116

Mother and
Children — A117

**1968, Dec. 22** **Litho.** *Perf. 13½*
483 A116 10f lt bl, yel & car .40 .20
484 A116 25f lt yel grn, yel & car .50 .20
*a.* Souv. sheet, 100f, imperf. 5.00 5.00
International Human Rights Year.
For overprint, see No. O232.

**1968, Dec. 31** **Litho.** *Perf. 13½*
485 A117 15f multi .50 .20
486 A117 25f bl & multi 1.25 .20
*a.* Souv. sheet, 100f, imperf 8.00 5.25

UNICEF. For overprints see Nos. 624-625,
O234-O235.

Tanks
A118

**1969, Jan. 6** **Photo.**
487 A118 25f vio, car & brn 3.50 1.00
Issued for Army Day, Jan. 6.
For overprint, see No. O244.

Harvester
A119

**1969, Feb.** **Photo.** *Perf. 13½*
488 A119 15f yel brn & multi .50 .20
6th anniv. of the Revolution of Ramadan 14.

Mosque
A119a

**1969, Mar. 19** **Photo.** *Perf. 13x13½*
488A A119a 15f multicolored .50 .20
Issued for Hajeer (pilgrimage) Year.

Emblem
A120

**1969, Apr. 12** **Litho.** *Perf. 12½x12*
489 A120 10f yel grn & multi .60 .20
490 A120 15f orange & multi 1.00 .20
1st conference of the Arab Veterinary Union,
Baghdad, Apr. 1969.

Barbus
Grypus
A121

Fish: 3f, Barbus puntius sharpeyi. 10f,
Pampus argenteus. 100f, Barbus esocinus.

**1969, May 9** *Perf. 14*
491 A121 2f multicolored 1.75 .45
492 A121 3f multicolored 1.90 .45
493 A121 10f multicolored 2.00 .45
494 A121 100f multicolored 6.00 3.75
Nos. 491-494 (4) 11.65 5.10
For overprints, see Nos. O312-313.

Holy Kaaba,
Mecca
A122

**1969, May 28** **Photo.** *Perf. 12*
495 A122 15f blue & multi .65 .20
Mohammed's 1,399th birthday.

ILO Emblem
A123

**1969, June 6** **Litho.** *Perf. 13x12½*
496 A123 5f lt vio, yel & blk .40 .20
497 A123 15f grnsh gray, yel &
black .40 .20
498 A123 50f rose, yel & blk 1.00 .50
*a.* Souv. sheet, 100f, imperf. 6.00 7.00
Nos. 496-498 (3) 1.80 .90
ILO, 50th anniv.
For overprint, see No. O297.

Weight
Lifting — A124

Design: 5f, 35f, High jump.

**1969, June 20** *Perf. 13½x13*
500 A124 3f org yel & multi .55 .20
501 A124 5f blue & multi .55 .20
502 A124 10f rose pink & multi .65 .20
503 A124 35f yellow & multi 1.25 1.00
*a.* Souv. sheet of 4, #500-503,
imperf. 12.00 12.00
Nos. 500-503 (4) 3.00 1.60
19th Olympic Games, Mexico City, Oct. 12-
27, 1968. No. 503a sold for 100f.

Coat of Arms,
Symbols of
Industry — A125

**1969, July 14** **Photo.** *Perf. 13*
504 A125 10f brn org & multi .40 .20
505 A125 15f multicolored .60 .20
11th anniv. of the July 14, 1958 revolution.

Street
Fighting
A126

Pres. Ahmed
Hassan al-
Bakr — A127

Wheat and Fair
Emblem — A128

Design: 20f, Baghdad International Airport.

**1969, July 17** *Perf. 13½*
506 A126 10f yel & multi .50 .20
507 A126 15f blue & multi .50 .20
508 A126 20f blue & multi 1.60 .45
509 A127 200f gold & multi 20.00 9.00
Nos. 506-509 (4) 22.60 9.85

Coup of July 17, 1968, 1st anniv. #508 also
for the inauguration of Baghdad Intl. Airport.
No. 509 exists imperf. Value $27.50.

**1969, Oct. 1** **Photo.** *Perf. 13½*
510 A128 10f brt grn, gold & dl
red .65 .20
511 A128 15f ultra, gold & red .80 .35
6th International Fair, Baghdad.
For overprints see Nos. 567A-567B.

Motor Ship
Al-Waleed
A129

Designs: 15f, Floating crane Antara. 30f,
Pilot ship Al-Rasheed. 35f, Suction dredge
Hillah. 50f, Survey ship Al-Fao.

**1969, Oct. 8** **Litho.** *Perf. 12½*
512 A129 15f black & multi .50 .25
513 A129 20f black & multi .70 .45
514 A129 30f black & multi 1.10 .55
515 A129 35f black & multi 1.75 1.00
516 A129 50f black & multi 5.25 2.25
Nos. 512-516 (5) 9.30 4.50
50th anniversary of Basrah Harbor.

Radio Tower and
Map of Palestine
A130

"Search for
Knowledge"
A131

**1969, Nov. 9** **Litho.** *Perf. 12½x13*
517 A130 15f multicolored 1.25 .20
518 A130 50f multicolored 3.25 .80
10th anniversary of Iraqi News Agency.
For overprints see Nos. 698-699.

**1969, Nov. 21** **Photo.** *Perf. 13*
519 A131 15f blue & multi .40 .20
520 A131 20f green & multi .40 .20
Campaign against illiteracy.

Front Page of First Baghdad Newspaper A132

**1969, Dec. 26   Litho.   Perf. 13½**
521  A132  15f yel, org & black   .70   .30
Centenary of the Iraqi press.
For overprint see No. 552.

Soldier, Map of Iraq and Plane — A133

**1970, Jan. 6   Photo.   Perf. 13**
522  A133  15f lt vio & multi   .70   .30
523  A133  20f yellow & multi   1.40   .65
Issued for Army Day 1970.

Soldier, Farmer and Worker Shoring up Wall in Iraqi Colors — A134

Poppies — A135

**1970, Feb. 8   Photo.   Perf. 13**
524  A134  10f multicolored   .20   .20
525  A134  15f brick red & multi   .40   .20
7th anniv. of the Revolution of Ramadan 14.

**1970, June 12   Litho.   Perf. 13**
Flowers: 3f, Poet's narcissus. 5f, Tulip. 10f, 50f, Carnations. 15f, Rose.
526  A135  2f emer & multi   .40   .20
527  A135  3f blue & multi   .40   .20
528  A135  5f multicolored   .40   .20
529  A135  10f lt grn & multi   .60   .35
530  A135  15f pale sal & multi   1.10   .55
531  A135  50f lt grn & multi   3.25   1.25
   Nos. 526-531 (6)   6.15   2.75

The overprinted sets Nos. 532-543 were released before Nos. 526-531.
For overprints see Nos. 621-623, RA20. For surcharge see No. 726.

Nos. 526-531 Overprinted in Ultramarine

**1970, Mar. 21**
532  A135  2f emer & multi   .40   .20
533  A135  3f lt bl & multi   .40   .20
534  A135  5f multicolored   .40   .20
535  A135  10f lt grn & multi   .60   .20
536  A135  15f pale sal & multi   1.00   .20
537  A135  50f lt grn & multi   4.00   1.50
   Nos. 532-537 (6)   6.80   2.50

Issued for Novrooz (New Year).

Nos. 526-531 Overprinted in Black

**1970, Apr. 18**
538  A135  2f emer & multi   .40   .20
539  A135  3f lt bl & multi   .40   .20
540  A135  5f multicolored   .40   .20
541  A135  10f lt grn & multi   .50   .20
542  A135  15f pale sal & multi   .70   .20
543  A135  50f lt grn & multi   3.00   .75
   Nos. 538-543 (6)   5.40   1.75

Issued for the Spring Festival, Mosul.

Map of Arab Countries, Slogans — A136

50f, 150f, People, flag, sun and map of Iraq.

**1970, Apr. 7   Perf. 13x12½**
544  A136  15f gold & multi   .40   .20
545  A136  35f sil & multi   .60   .50
546  A136  50f red & multi   1.75   .70
a.  Souv. sheet, 150f, imperf.   11.00   11.00
   Nos. 544-546 (3)   2.75   1.40

23rd anniversary of Al-Baath Party.

Workers and Cogwheel — A137

**1970, May 1**
547  A137  10f silver & multi   .40   .20
548  A137  15f silver & multi   .50   .30
549  A137  35f silver & multi   1.40   .65
   Nos. 547-549 (3)   2.30   1.15

Issued for Labor Day.

Kaaba, Mecca, and Koran A138

**1970, May 17   Photo.   Perf. 13**
550  A138  15f brt bl & multi   .40   .20
551  A138  20f orange & multi   .40   .20
Mohammed's 1,400th birthday.

No. 521 Overprinted "1970" and Arabic Inscription in Prussian Blue

**1970, June 15   Litho.   Perf. 13½**
552  A132  15f yel, org & black   .55   .55
Day of Iraqi press.

Revolutionists and Guns — A139

Designs: 35f, Revolutionist and rising sun.

**1970, June 30   Litho.   Perf. 13**
553  A139  10f blk & apple grn   .40   .20
554  A139  15f black & gold   .40   .20
555  A139  35f blk & red org   .75   .45
a.  Souv. sheet, 100f, imperf.   5.50   5.50
   Nos. 553-555 (3)   1.55   .85

50th anniversary, Revolution of 1920.

Broken Chain and New Dawn — A140

**1970, July 14   Perf. 13x13½**
557  A140  15f multicolored   .40   .20
558  A140  20f multicolored   .40   .20
12th anniv. of the July 14, 1958 revolution.

Map of Arab Countries and Hands — A141

**1970, July 17   Perf. 13**
559  A141  15f gold & multi   .40   .20
560  A141  25f gold & multi   .40   .20
2nd anniversary of coup of July 17, 1968.

Pomegranates A142

**1970, Aug. 21   Perf. 14**
561  A142  3f shown   .40   .20
562  A142  5f Grapefruit   .40   .20
563  A142  10f Grapes   .40   .20
564  A142  15f Oranges   1.10   .35
565  A142  35f Dates   3.50   1.90
   Nos. 561-565 (5)   5.80   2.85

The Latin inscriptions on the 5f and 10f have been erroneously transposed.
For overprints & surcharge see #613-615, 725, O240-O245.

Kaaba, Mecca, Moon over Mountain and Spider Web — A143

**1970, Sept. 4   Photo.   Perf. 13**
566  A143  15f multicolored   .40   .20
567  A143  25f multicolored   .40   .20
Issued for Hajeer (Pilgrimage) Year.

Nos. 510-511 Overprinted in Red

**1970, Sept.   Photo.   Perf. 13½**
567A  A128  10f multi   3.50   2.00
567B  A128  15f multi   3.50   2.00
7th International Fair, Baghdad.

Intl. Education Year Emblem A144

**1970, Nov. 13   Photo.   Perf. 13**
568  A144  5f yel green & multi   .40   .20
569  A144  15f brick red & multi   .40   .20

Flag and Map of Arab League Countries A145

**1970   Perf. 11**
570  A145  15f olive & multi   .40   .20
571  A145  35f gray & multi   .50   .20
25th anniversary of the Arab League.

Baghdad Hospital and Emblem A146

**1970, Dec. 7   Litho.   Perf. 12**
572  A146  15f yellow & multi   .40   .20
573  A146  40f lt green & multi   1.10   .60
Iraqi Medical Society, 50th anniv.

Sugar Beet — A147

15f, Sugar factory, horiz. 30f, like 5f.

**Perf. 13x13½, 13½x13**
**1970, Dec. 25   Photo.**
574  A147  5f ocher, grn & blk   .40   .20
575  A147  15f black & multi   .45   .20
576  A147  30f org ver, grn & blk   1.50   .75
   Nos. 574-576 (3)   2.35   1.15

Publicity for Mosul sugar factory.

OPEC Emblem A148

**1970, Dec. 30   Litho.   Perf. 13x13½**
577  A148  10f rose claret, bis & bl   .75   .20
578  A148  40f emer, bis & blue   3.25   1.25
OPEC, 10th anniversary.

Soldiers — A149

Soldiers, Maps of Arab Countries and Israel — A150

**Perf. 13½x14, 11½x12½**
**1971, Jan. 6**
| 579 | A149 | 15f multicolored | .55 | .20 |
| 580 | A150 | 40f red org & multi | 3.00 | .90 |
| a. | | Souv. sheet of 2, #579-580, imperf. | 10.00 | 10.00 |

Army Day, 50th anniversary.
No. 580a sold for 100f.

Marchers and Map of Arab Countries — A151

**1971, Feb. 8 Litho. Perf. 11½x12½**
| 581 | A151 | 15f yellow & multi | .45 | .20 |
| 582 | A151 | 40f pink & multi | 1.25 | .50 |

Revolution of Ramadan 14, 8th anniversary.

Spider Web, Pilgrims A152

**1971, Feb. 26 Photo. Perf. 13**
| 583 | A152 | 10f pink & multi | .25 | .20 |
| 584 | A152 | 15f buff & multi | .45 | .20 |

Hajeer (New) Year.

President al-Bakr A153

**1971, Mar. 11 Litho. Perf. 14**
| 585 | A153 | 15f orange & multi | .70 | .40 |
| 586 | A153 | 100f emer & multi | 3.25 | 1.50 |

First anniversary of Mar. 11th Manifesto.

Marshland A154

Tourist Publicity: 10f, Stork flying over Baghdad. 15f, "Summer Resorts." 100f, Return of Sindbad the Sailor.

**1971, Mar. 15 Perf. 13**
| 587 | A154 | 5f multicolored | .45 | .20 |
| 588 | A154 | 10f lt grn & multi | .80 | .20 |
| 589 | A154 | 15f pink & multi | 1.00 | .50 |
| 590 | A154 | 100f multicolored | 5.25 | 3.00 |
| | | Nos. 587-590 (4) | 7.50 | 3.90 |

Blacksmith Taming Serpent — A155

**1971, Mar. 21 Perf. 11½x12**
| 591 | A155 | 15f multicolored | .85 | .20 |
| 592 | A155 | 25f yel & multi | 1.60 | .65 |

Novrooz Festival.

No. 455 Overprinted

**1971, Mar. 23 Litho. Perf. 13**
| 593 | A107 | 15f rose red & multi | 3.00 | 1.00 |

World Meteorological Day. See No. C39.

Workers, Soldier, Map of Arab Countries — A156

**1971, Apr. 7**
| 594 | A156 | 15f yel & multi | .75 | .40 |
| 595 | A156 | 35f multicolored | 1.25 | .75 |
| 596 | A156 | 250f multicolored | 10.00 | 7.50 |
| | | Nos. 594-596 (3) | 12.00 | 8.65 |

24th anniv. of the Al Baath Party. No. 596 has circular perforation around vignette set within a white square of paper, perforated on 4 sides. The design of No. 596 is similar to Nos. 594-595, but with denomination within the circle and no inscriptions in margin.

Nos. 443-444, 448 Overprinted

**1971, Apr. 14**
| 597 | A105 | 2f pale brn & multi | .50 | .20 |
| 598 | A105 | 5f ver & multi | .70 | .20 |
| 599 | A105 | 25f lemon & multi | 2.25 | 1.00 |
| | | Nos. 597-599 (3) | 3.45 | 1.40 |

Mosul Festival.

Worker, Farm Woman with Torch A157

**1971, May 1 Litho. Perf. 13**
| 600 | A157 | 15f ocher & multi | .35 | .20 |
| 601 | A157 | 40f olive & multi | 1.25 | .30 |

Labor Day.

Muslim Praying in Mecca A158

**1971, May 7**
| 602 | A158 | 15f yellow & multi | .25 | .20 |
| 603 | A158 | 100f pink & multi | 2.75 | 1.00 |

Mohammed's 1,401st birthday.

People, Fists, Map of Iraq A159

**1971, July 14 Photo. Perf. 14**
| 604 | A159 | 25f green & multi | .55 | .20 |
| 605 | A159 | 50f lt bl & multi | 1.25 | .60 |

13th anniv. of the July 14, 1958 revolution.

Surveyor, Preacher, Rising Sun A160

**1971, July 17 Perf. 13**
| 606 | A160 | 25f multicolored | .60 | .30 |
| 607 | A160 | 70f orange & multi | 1.90 | .75 |

3rd anniversary of July 17, 1968, coup.

Rafidain Bank Emblem A161

**1971, Sept. 24 Photo. Perf. 13½**
**Diameter: 27mm**
| 608 | A161 | 10f multicolored | .45 | .85 |
| 609 | A161 | 15f multicolored | .85 | .85 |
| 610 | A161 | 25f multicolored | 1.60 | 2.75 |

**Diameter: 32mm**
| 611 | A161 | 65f multicolored | 8.50 | 4.25 |
| 612 | A161 | 100f multicolored | 21.00 | 12.50 |
| | | Nos. 608-612 (5) | 32.40 | 21.20 |

30th anniversary of Rafidain Bank. Nos. 608-612 have circular perforation around design within a white square of paper, perforated on 4 sides.

Nos. 561, 564-565 Overprinted

**1971, Oct. 15 Litho. Perf. 14**
| 613 | A142 | 3f bl grn & multi | 2.25 | 2.25 |
| 614 | A142 | 15f red & multi | 2.75 | 2.25 |
| 615 | A142 | 35f orange & multi | 4.00 | 2.25 |
| | | Nos. 613-615 (3) | 9.00 | 6.75 |

Agricultural census, Oct. 15, 1971.

Soccer A162

Designs: 25f, Track and field. 35f, Table tennis. 75f, Gymnastics. 95f, Volleyball and basketball.

**1971, Nov. 17 Litho. Perf. 13½**
| 616 | A162 | 15f green & multi | .30 | .20 |
| 617 | A162 | 25f pink & multi | .80 | .30 |
| 618 | A162 | 35f lt bl & multi | 1.00 | .90 |
| 619 | A162 | 70f lt grn & multi | 4.25 | 1.50 |
| 620 | A162 | 95f yel grn & multi | 7.50 | 2.50 |
| a. | | Souvenir sheet of 5 | 22.50 | 22.50 |
| | | Nos. 616-620 (5) | 13.85 | 5.40 |

4th Pan-Arab Schoolboys Sports Games, Baghdad. No. 620a contains 5 stamps similar to Nos. 616-620 with simulated perforations. Sold for 200f.

Nos. 527-528, 530 Overprinted and Surcharged

**1971, Nov. 23 Litho. Perf. 13**
| 621 | A135 | 15f multicolored | 1.75 | .30 |
| 622 | A135 | 25f on 5f multi | 2.00 | 1.00 |
| 623 | A135 | 70f on 3f multi | 9.50 | 3.00 |
| | | Nos. 621-623 (3) | 13.25 | 4.30 |

Students' Day. The 15f has only first 3 lines of Arabic overprint.

Nos. 485-486 Overprinted

**1971, Dec. 11 Litho. Perf. 13½**
| 624 | A117 | 15f multicolored | 2.75 | 1.00 |
| 625 | A117 | 25f blue & multi | 7.25 | 3.25 |

25th anniv. of UNICEF.

Children Crossing Street — A162a

**1971, Dec. 17 Litho. Perf. 13x12½**
| 625A | A162a | 15f yel & multi | 1.50 | .80 |
| 625B | A162a | 25f brt rose & multi | 3.00 | 1.50 |

2nd Traffic Week. For overprints see #668-669.

Arab Postal Union Emblem A163

**1971, Dec. 24   Photo.   Perf. 11½**
626 A163 25f emer, yel & brn   .45   .20
627 A163 70f vio bl, yel & red   1.75   .65
25th anniv. of the Conf. of Sofar, Lebanon, establishing Arab Postal Union.

Racial Equality Emblem — A164

**1971, Dec. 31   Perf. 13½x14**
628 A164 25f brt grn & multi   .25   .20
629 A164 70f orange & multi   1.00   .90
Intl. Year Against Racial Discrimination.

Soldiers with Flag and Torch — A165

Workers A166

**1972, Jan. 6   Photo.   Perf. 14x13½**
630 A165 25f blue & multi   .90   .45
631 A165 70f brt grn & multi   3.75   2.00
Army Day, Jan. 6.

**1972, Feb. 8**
632 A166 25f brt grn & multi   2.25   .60
633 A166 95f lilac & multi   4.50   2.25
Revolution of Ramadan 14, 9th anniv.

Mosque, Minaret, Crescent and Caravan A167

**1972, Feb. 26   Litho.   Perf. 12½x13**
634 A167 25f bl grn & multi   .35   .20
635 A167 35f purple & multi   .70   .40
Hegira (Pilgrimage) Year.

Peace Symbols and "11" — A168

**1972, Mar. 11   Photo.   Perf. 11x12½**
636 A168 25f lt blue & blk   1.50   .25
637 A168 70f brt lilac & blk   4.25   1.25
2nd anniversary of Mar. 11 Manifesto.

Mountain Range and Flowers — A169

**1972, Mar. 21   Perf. 11½x11**
638 A169 25f vio blue & multi   1.25   .20
639 A169 70f vio blue & multi   4.25   1.50
Novrooz, New Year Festival.

Party Emblem A170

Symbolic Design — A171

***Perf. 14 (A170), 13 (A171)***
**1972**   **Litho.**
640 A170 10f brn org & multi   .35   .20
641 A171 25f bister & multi   .80   .40
642 A170 35f brn org & multi   .90   .50
643 A171 70f red & multi   2.75   2.10
　　Nos. 640-643 (4)   4.80   3.20
Iraqi Arab Baath Socialist Party, 25th anniv.
Issued: 25f, 70f, Mar. 23; 10f, 35f, Apr. 7.

Emblem, Map, Weather Balloons and Chart — A172

**1972, May 1   Photo.   Perf. 11½**
654 A177 25f yel grn & multi   .45   .20
655 A177 35f orange & multi   .80   .40
Labor Day.

Cogwheel and Ship — A173

**1972, Mar. 23   Photo.   Perf. 14x13½**
644 A172 25f multicolored   1.75   .50
645 A172 35f yel & multi   3.00   1.40
12th World Meteorological Day.

**1972, Mar. 25   Perf. 11x11½**
646 A173 25f ocher & multi   .50   .20
647 A173 35f pink & multi   1.00   .40
Arab Chamber of Commerce.

Derrick and Flame A174　　Quill Pens, Map of Arab Countries A175

**1972, Apr. 7   Perf. 13x13½**
648 A174 25f multicolored   1.25   .25
649 A174 35f multicolored   1.75   .90
Opening of North Rumaila (INOC, North Iraq Oil Fields).

**1972, Apr. 17   Photo.   Perf. 11x11½**
650 A175 25f orange & multi   .55   .20
651 A175 35f blue & multi   1.75   1.00
3rd Congress of Arab Journalists.

Women's Federation Emblem A176

**1972, Apr. 22   Litho.   Perf. 13½**
652 A176 25f green & multi   .55   .20
653 A176 35f lilac & multi   1.75   1.10
Iraqi Women's Federation, 4th anniversary.

Hand Holding Globe-shaped Wrench — A177

Kaaba, Mecca, and Crescent — A178

**1972, May 26**
656 A178 25f green & multi   .55   .20
657 A178 35f purple & multi   1.75   1.10
Mohammed's 1,402nd birthday.

Soldier, Civilian and Guns — A179

**1972, July 14   Photo.   Perf. 13½x14**
658 A179 35f multicolored   .90   .25
659 A179 70f lilac & multi   2.75   1.00
14th anniv. of July 14, 1958, revolution.

Dome of the Rock, Arab Countries' Map, Fists A180

**1972, July 17   Perf. 13**
660 A180 25f citron & multi   1.10   .60
661 A180 95f blue & multi   3.25   2.50
4th anniv. of July 17, 1968 coup.

Congress Emblem, Scout Saluting Iraqi Flag — A182

**1972, Aug. 12   Photo.   Perf. 13½x14**
664 A182 20f multicolored   2.25   1.00
665 A182 25f lilac & multi   3.25   1.10
10th Arab Boy Scouts Jamboree and Conference, Mosul, Aug. 10-19.

**1972, Aug. 24**
Congress emblem and Girl Guide in camp.
666 A182 10f yellow & multi   1.50   .65
667 A182 45f multicolored   4.50   1.10
4th Arab Guides Camp & Conf., Mosul, Aug. 24-30.

No. 625A Overprinted and Surcharged, No. 625B Overprinted with New Date:

**1972, Oct. 4   Photo.   Perf. 13x12½**
668 A162a 25f brt rose & multi   6.75   3.00
669 A162a 70f on 15f multi   8.50   7.00
Third Traffic Week.

Central
Bank of
Iraq
A183

**1972, Nov. 16    Photo.    Perf. 13**
670  A183  25f lt blue & multi          .80    .40
671  A183  70f lt green & multi         2.25   .90
25th anniversary, Central Bank of Iraq.

UIC
Emblem
A184

**1972, Dec. 29**
672  A184  25f dp rose & multi          1.50   .60
673  A184  45f brt vio & multi          5.00   3.00
50th anniv., Intl. Railroad Union (UIC).

Nos. 148-149, 151, 180 and Type of
1957-58 Overprinted with 3 Bars

**1973, Jan. 29    Engr.    Perf. 11½x12**
674  A28  10f blue                      3.50   1.25
675  A33  10f blue                      3.50   1.25
676  A28  15f black                     3.50   1.25
677  A33  15f black                     3.50   1.25
678  A28  25f rose violet               3.50   1.25
679  A33  25f rose violet               3.50   1.25
     Nos. 674-679 (6)                  21.00   7.50
The size and position of the bottom bar of
overprint differs; the bar can be same size as 2
top bars, short and centered or moved to the
right.

No. 455
Overprinted

**1973, Mar. 25    Litho.    Perf. 13**
680  A107  15f rose red & multi        10.00   3.25
Intl. History Cong. See Nos. C52-C53.

Workers
and Oil
Wells
A185

Ram's-head
Harp — A186

**1973, June 1    Litho.    Perf. 13**
681  A185  25f yel & multi              2.00   .90
682  A185  70f rose & multi             9.50   3.00
1st anniv. of nationalization of oil industry.
For overprint, see No. O298.

**1973, June    Litho.    Perf. 13x12½**
Designs: 25f, 35f, 45f, Minaret, Mosul, 50f,
70f, 95f, Statue of goddess. 10f, 20f, like 5f.
683  A186  5f orange & blk             .20    .20
684  A186  10f bister & blk            .20    .20
685  A186  20f brt rose & blk          .20    .20
686  A186  25f ultra & blk             .20    .20
687  A186  35f emer & blk              .45    .20
688  A186  45f blue & black            .55    .25
689  A186  50f olive & yel             .80    .25
690  A186  70f violet & yel            1.00   .50
691  A186  95f brown & yel             1.75   .75
     Nos. 683-691 (9)                  5.35   2.75
For overprints see Nos. O299-O307, RA21.

People with
Flags,
Grain
A187

**1973, July 14**
692  A187  25f multicolored            .70    .30
693  A187  35f multicolored            1.40   .40
July Festivals.

Nos. 393 and
395 Surcharged

**1973    Litho.    Perf. 13½x14**
694  A85  25f on 3f multi              4.00   2.25
695  A85  70f on 15f multi            10.00   5.00
Festival of Date Trees.

INTERPOL Headquarters — A188

**1973, Sept. 20    Litho.    Perf. 12**
696  A188  25f multicolored            1.00   .60
697  A188  70f brt bl & multi          5.00   3.00
50th anniv. of Intl. Criminal Police Org.

Nos. 517-518
Overprinted in
Silver

**1973, Sept. 29    Litho.    Perf. 12½x13**
698  A130  15f multicolored            3.50   1.00
699  A130  50f multicolored            6.00   3.00
Meeting of Intl. Org. of Journalists' Executive Committee, Sept. 26-29.

Flags and Fair
Emblem — A189

WMO
Emblem — A190

**1973, Oct. 10    Photo.    Perf. 11**
700  A189  10f brt grn & dk brn        .45    .20
701  A189  20f ocher & multi           .80    .30
702  A189  65f blue & multi            1.75   .90
     Nos. 700-702 (3)                  3.00   1.40
10th International Baghdad Fair, Oct. 1-21.

**1973, Nov. 15    Litho.    Perf. 12**
703  A190  25f org, blk & green        .70    .20
704  A190  35f brt rose, blk & grn     2.25   1.00
Intl. meteorological cooperation, cent.

Flags of
Arab
League
and Iraq,
Maghreb
Emblem
A191

**1973, Dec. 1    Photo.    Perf. 14**
705  A191  20f dl org & multi          .40    .20
706  A191  35f blue & multi            1.40   .90
11th session of Civil Aviation Council of
Arab States, Baghdad, Dec. 1973.

No. 360 Overprinted

**1973, Dec. 12    Photo.    Perf. 11**
707  A67a  30f orange & blue           5.00   2.75
6th Executive Council Meeting of APU.

Human Rights
Flame — A192

**1973, Dec. 25    Perf. 11½**
708  A192  25f multicolored            .20    .20
709  A192  70f ultra & multi           .90    .50
Universal Declaration of Human Rights,
25th anniv.

Military
College
Crest
and
Cadets
A193

**1974, Jan. 6    Perf. 12x11½**
710  A193  25f ocher & multi           .45    .20
711  A193  35f ultra & multi           1.50   .90
50th anniversary of the Military College.

UPU and Arab
Postal Union
Emblems
A194

**1974, May 28    Photo.    Perf. 11½x12**
712  A194  25f gold & multi            .90    .20
713  A194  35f gold & multi            .90    .40
714  A194  70f gold & multi            1.60   .90
     Nos. 712-714 (3)                  3.40   1.50
Centenary of the Universal Postal Union.

Symbols of Ancient Mesopotamia and
Oil Industry — A195

**1974, June 1    Litho.    Perf. 12½**
715  A195  10f blue & multi            .40    .20
716  A195  25f ocher & multi           .85    .25
717  A195  70f rose & multi            2.75   2.00
     Nos. 715-717 (3)                  4.00   2.45
Nationalization of the oil industry, 2nd anniv.

Festival
A196

**1974, July 17    Perf. 11½x12**
718  A196  20f lilac & multi           .35    .20
719  A196  35f dull org & multi        1.00   .50
July Festivals.

National
Front
Emblem
and
People
A197

**1974, July 17    Perf. 12x11½**
720  A197  25f blue & multi            .65    .20
721  A197  70f brt grn & multi         1.50   .75
1st anniv. of Progressive National Front.

Cement Plant
and Brick
Wall — A198

**1974, Oct. 19    Perf. 11½x12**
722  A198  20f gray bl & multi         .45    .20
723  A198  25f red & multi             .65    .30
724  A198  70f emerald & multi         1.40   1.00
     Nos. 722-724 (3)                  2.50   1.50
25th anniversary of Iraqi Cement Plant.

Nos. 561 and 527 Surcharged

a

b

**1975, Jan. 9    Litho.    Perf. 13, 14**
725  A142 (a) 10f on 3f multi          3.50  2.25
726  A135 (b) 25f on 3f multi         11.00  7.25

Globe and WPY
Emblem
A199

**1975, Jan. 30                  Perf. 11½x12**
727  A199 25f dull bl & blk            .60   .20
728  A199 35f brt pink & ind          1.25   .65
729  A199 70f yel grn & vio           3.50  1.40
     Nos. 727-729 (3)                  5.35  2.25

World Population Year 1974.

Festival Symbols — A200

**1975, July 17    Litho.    Perf. 12x11½**
730  A200  5f lt brn & multi           .20   .20
731  A200 10f lt brn & multi           .20   .20
732  A200 35f lt brn & multi          1.75   .75
     Nos. 730-732 (3)                  2.15  1.15

Festivals, July 1975.

Map of
Arab
Countries
A201

**1975, Aug. 5    Photo.    Perf. 13**
733  A201 25f rose & multi             .50   .20
734  A201 35f multicolored            .90   .60
735  A201 45f multicolored           1.00   .65
     Nos. 733-735 (3)                  2.40  1.45

Arab Working Org., 10th anniv.

Symbols of
Women, Oil
Industry and
Agriculture
A202

**1975, Aug. 15                  Perf. 14**
736  A202 10f lilac & multi            .50   .30
737  A202 35f multicolored           1.00   .85
738  A202 70f bl & multi              4.25  1.50
  a.   Souv. sheet, 100f, imperf.    10.00 10.00
     Nos. 736-738 (3)                  5.75  2.65

International Women's Year.

Euphrates Dam and
Causeway — A203

**1975, Sept. 5    Litho.    Perf. 12x11½**
739  A203  3f orange & multi          .20   .20
740  A203 25f purple & multi          .70   .20
741  A203 70f rose red & multi       2.75  1.25
     Nos. 739-741 (3)                  3.65  1.65

Intl. Commission on Irrigation and Drainage,
25th anniv.

National
Insurance
Co. Seal
A204

**1975, Oct. 11    Photo.    Perf. 13**
742  A204 20f brt bl & multi          .80   .20
743  A204 25f crim & multi           1.00   .40
  a.   Souv. sheet, 100f, imperf.     7.00  8.50

Natl. Insurance Co., Baghdad, 25th anniv.

Musician
Entertaining
King — A205

**1975, Nov. 21                  Perf. 14**
744  A205 25f silver & multi          .65   .20
745  A205 45f gold & multi           1.50   .90

Baghdad Intl. Music Conf., Nov. 1975.

Telecommunications Center — A206

**1975, Dec. 22    Litho.    Perf. 12½**
746  A206  5f lil rose & multi         .20   .20
747  A206 10f blue & multi            .20   .20
748  A206 60f green & multi          1.75  1.00
     Nos. 746-748 (3)                  2.15  1.40

Inauguration of Telecommunications Center
Building during July 1975 Festival.

Diesel Locomotive — A207

Conference Emblem and: 30f, Diesel passenger locomotive #511. 35f, 0-3-0 steam tank
locomotive with passenger train. 50f, 2-3-0
German steam locomotive, c. 1914.

**1975, Dec. 22    Photo.    Perf. 14**
749  A207 25f tan & multi            5.50  1.00
750  A207 30f tan & multi            8.50   .20
751  A207 35f yel grn & multi       11.00  3.50
752  A207 50f yel grn & multi       16.00  9.50
     Nos. 749-752 (4)                 41.00 16.00

15th Taurus Railway Conference, Baghdad.

A208

A209

Design: Soldier on guard.

**1976, Jan. 6                    Perf. 13**
753  A208  5f silver & multi          .20   .20
754  A208 25f silver & multi          .55   .20
755  A208 50f gold & multi           1.50   .60
     Nos. 753-755 (3)                  2.25  1.00

55th Army Day.

**1976, Jan. 8    Photo.    Perf. 13½x13**
Fingerprint crossed out, Arab world.
756  A209  5f violet & multi          .20   .20
757  A209 15f blue & multi            .45   .20
758  A209 35f green & multi          1.50   .90
     Nos. 756-758 (3)                  2.15  1.30

Statue of
Goddess — A210

20f-30f, Two female figures forming column.
35f-75f, Head of bearded man.

**1976, Jan. 1    Litho.    Perf. 13x12½**
759  A210  5f lilac & multi           .20   .20
760  A210 10f rose & multi           .20   .20
761  A210 15f yellow & multi         .20   .20
762  A210 20f bister & multi         .20   .20
763  A210 25f lt grn & multi         .45   .20
764  A210 30f blue & multi           .65   .20
765  A210 35f lil rose & multi       .80   .20
766  A210 50f citron & multi        1.10   .25
767  A210 75f violet & multi        1.60   .60
     Nos. 759-767 (9)                 5.40  2.25

Iraq Earth
Station
A211

**1976, Feb. 8                    Perf. 13x13½**
768  A211 10f silver & multi          .40   .25
769  A211 25f silver & multi         1.25   .45
770  A211 75f gold & multi           4.50  2.00
     Nos. 768-770 (3)                  6.15  2.70

Revolution of Ramadan 14, 13th anniv.

Telephones
1876 and
1976 — A212

Map of Maghreb,
ICATU
Emblem — A213

**1976, Mar. 17    Litho.    Perf. 12x12½**
771  A212 35f multicolored          1.25   .45
772  A212 50f multicolored          2.50   .70
773  A212 75f multicolored          4.00  1.00
     Nos. 771-773 (3)                  7.75  2.15

Centenary of first telephone call by Alexander Graham Bell, Mar. 10, 1876.

**1976, Mar. 24    Photo.    Perf. 13½**
774  A213  5f green & multi          .35   .20
775  A213 10f green & multi          .35   .20
     Nos. 774-775,C54 (3)            4.70  2.40

20th Intl. Conf. of Arab Trade Unions.

Map of Iraq, Family,
Torch and
Wreath — A214

**1976, Apr. 1                    Perf. 12½**
776  A214  5f multicolored           .20   .20
777  A214 15f lilac & multi          .45   .20
778  A214 35f multicolored          2.25   .90
     Nos. 776-778 (3)                  2.90  1.30

Police Day.

Pipeline, Map of
Iraq — A215

Pres. A. H. al-Bakr Embracing Vice
Pres. Saddam Hussein — A216

**1976, June 1    Photo.    Perf. 13**
779  A215 25f multicolored          1.50   .75
780  A215 75f multicolored          4.50  2.00

**Souvenir Sheet**
*Imperf*
781  A216 150f multicolored        32.50 32.50

4th anniversary of oil nationalization.

"Festival" — A217

**1976, July 17**      *Perf. 14*
782 A217 15f orange & multi     .35   .20
783 A217 35f orange & multi    1.00   .70

Festivals, July 1976.

Archbishop Capucci, Map of Palestine
A218

**1976, Aug. 18**    Litho.    *Perf. 12*
784 A218 25f multicolored     .70   .25
785 A218 35f multicolored    1.00   .40
786 A218 75f multicolored    2.75 1.25
    Nos. 784-786 (3)    4.45 1.90

Detention of Archbishop Hilarion Capucci in Israel, Aug. 18, 1974.

Common Kingfisher — A219

"15" — A220

10f, Turtle dove. 15f, Pin-tailed sandgrouse. 25f, Blue rock thrush. 50f, Purple and gray herons.

**1976, Sept. 15**    Litho.    *Perf. 13½x14*
787 A219   5f multicolored    2.75   .85
788 A219 10f multicolored    2.75   .85
789 A219 15f multicolored    3.75   .85
790 A219 25f multicolored    7.25 1.10
791 A219 50f multicolored   11.00 1.50
    Nos. 787-791 (5)    27.50 5.15

**1976, Nov. 23**    Photo.    *Perf. 13½*
792 A220 30f multicolored    1.00   .50
793 A220 70f multicolored    2.50   .75

15th anniv. of National Students Union.

Oil Tanker and Emblems
A221

25f, 50f, Pier, refinery, pipeline.

**1976, Dec. 25**      *Perf. 12½x12*
794 A221 10f multicolored    .70   .25
795 A221 15f multicolored    .90   .40
796 A221 25f multicolored   2.10   .75
797 A221 50f multicolored   3.00 1.25
    Nos. 794-797 (4)    6.70 2.65

1st Iraqi oil tanker (10f, 15f) and Nationalization of Basrah Petroleum Co. Ltd., 1st anniv. (25f, 50f).

Happy Children — A222

Ornament A223

UNESCO Emblem and: 25f, Children with flowers and butterflies. 75f, Children planting flowers around flagpole.

**1976, Dec. 25**      *Perf. 12x12½*
798 A222 10f multicolored    .25   .20
799 A222 25f multicolored   2.00   .40
800 A222 75f multicolored   3.50 1.10
    Nos. 798-800 (3)    5.75 1.70

30th anniv. of UNESCO, and Books for Children Campaign.

**1977, Mar. 2**    Photo.    *Perf. 13½*
801 A223 25f gold & multi    .70   .20
802 A223 35f gold & multi   1.00   .30
    Nos. 801-802 (2) 

Birthday of Mohammed (570-632).

Peace Dove — A224

Dahlia — A225

**1977, Mar. 11**      *Perf. 14x13½*
803 A224 25f lt bl & multi    .35   .20
804 A224 30f buff & multi    .65   .30

Peace Day.

**1977, Mar. 21**    Litho.    *Perf. 12½*
Flowers: 10f, Sweet peas. 35f, Chrysanthemums. 50f, Verbena.

805 A225   5f multicolored    .20   .20
806 A225 10f multicolored    .45   .20
807 A225 35f multicolored   1.10   .30
808 A225 50f multicolored   2.25   .65
    Nos. 805-808 (4)    4.00 1.35

Spring Festivals, Baghdad.

Emblem with Doves A226

Designs: 75f, Emblem with flame. 100f, Dove with olive branch.

**1977, Apr. 7**    Photo.    *Perf. 13*
809 A226 25f yel & multi    .60   .20
810 A226 75f yel & multi   2.25   .40

**Souvenir Sheet**
*Imperf*
811 A226 100f multicolored    6.00 6.00

Al Baath Party, 30th anniversary. No. 811 contains one 49x35mm stamp.

APU Emblem, Members' Flags
A227

**1977, Apr. 12**    Litho.    *Perf. 14*
812 A227 25f orange & multi    .35   .20
813 A227 35f gray & multi    .70   .40

25th anniversary of Arab Postal Union.

Cogwheel, Globe and "1" — A228

**1977, May 1**    Litho.    *Perf. 14½x14*
814 A228 10f multicolored    .20   .20
815 A228 30f multicolored    .55   .20
816 A228 35f multicolored    .70   .60
    Nos. 814-816 (3)    1.45 1.00

Labor Day.

Weight Lifting A229

75f, Weight lifter, standing up. 100f, Symbolic weight lifter with Iraqi coat of arms, laurel wreath.

**1977, May 8**    Photo.    *Perf. 14*
817 A229 25f multicolored    .90   .60
818 A229 75f multicolored   2.50 1.10

**Souvenir Sheet**
*Imperf*
819 A229 100f multicolored    8.50 8.50

8th Asian Weight Lifting Championship, Baghdad, May 1977. No. 819 contains one 42x52mm stamp.

Arabian Garden A230

Grain and Dove — A231

Arab Tourist Year: 10f, View of town with minarets, horiz. 30f, Landscape with bridge and waterfall. 50f, Hosts welcoming tourists, and drum, horiz.

*Perf. 11½x12, 12x11½*
**1977, June 15**      Litho.
820 A230   5f multicolored    .25   .25
821 A230 10f multicolored    .25   .25
822 A230 30f multicolored    .95   .25
823 A230 50f multicolored   2.75 1.75
    Nos. 820-823 (4)    4.20 2.50

**1977, July 17**    Photo.    *Perf. 14*
824 A231 25f multicolored    .55   .20
825 A231 30f multicolored    .70   .30

Festivals, July 1977.

Map of Arab Countries
A232

**1977, Sept. 9**   Photo.   *Perf. 13½x14*
826 A232 30f multicolored    .80   .45
827 A232 70f multicolored   2.40   .90

UN Conference on Desertification, Nairobi, Kenya, Aug. 29-Sept. 9.

Census Emblem — A233      Festival Emblem — A234

**1977, Oct. 17**    Litho.    *Perf. 14x14½*
828 A233 20f ultra & multi    .25   .20
829 A233 30f brown & multi    .70   .20
830 A233 70f gray & multi   1.25   .75
    Nos. 828-830 (3)    2.20 1.15

Population Census Day, Oct. 17.

**1977, Nov. 1**    Photo.    *Perf. 14*
831 A234 25f silver & multi    .30   .20
832 A234 50f gold & multi    .65   .40

Al Mutanabby Festival, Nov. 1977.

A235           A236

Junblatt, caricatures of Britain, US, Israel.

**1977, Nov. 16**    Photo.    *Perf. 14*
833 A235 20f multicolored    .35   .20
834 A235 30f multicolored    .55   .20
835 A235 70f multicolored   1.10   .60
    Nos. 833-835 (3)    2.00 1.00

Kemal Junblatt, Druse leader, killed in Lebanese war.

**1977, Dec. 12**    Photo.    *Perf. 14*
836 A236 30f gold & multi    .40   .20
837 A236 35f silver & multi    .50   .20

Hegira (Pilgrimage) Year.

Young People and Flags — A237

Coins and Coin Bank — A238

**1978, Apr. 7    Photo.    Perf. 11½x11**
838  A237  10f multicolored            .20    .20
839  A237  15f multicolored            .25    .20
840  A237  35f multicolored            .55    .20
    Nos. 838-840 (3)                   1.00    .60
                Youth Day.

**1978, Apr. 15**
841  A238  15f multicolored            .30    .20
842  A238  25f multicolored            .50    .20
843  A238  35f multicolored           1.00    .40
    Nos. 841-843 (3)                   1.80    .80

6th anniversary of postal savings law.

Microwave Transmission and Receiving A239

Emblems and Flags of Participants — A240

**1978, May 17    Photo.    Perf. 14**
844  A239  25f org & multi             .40    .20
845  A239  35f lilac & multi           .40    .20
846  A239  75f emer & multi           1.00    .60
    Nos. 844-846 (3)                   1.80   1.00

10th World Telecommunications Day and 1st anniversary of commissioning of national microwave network.

**Perf. 12½x11½**
**1978, June 19                        Litho.**
847  A240  25f multicolored            .55    .20
848  A240  35f multicolored            .85    .20

Conference of Postal Ministers of Arabian Gulf Countries, Baghdad (Saudi Arabia, United Arab Emirates, Qatar, Bahrain, Kuwait, Oman, People's Republic of Yemen).

Ancient Coin — A241

Designs: Ancient Iraqi coins. 75f vertical.

**Perf. 11½x12½**
**1978, June 25                        Photo.**
849  A241  1f citron & multi           .20    .20
850  A241  2f blue & multi             .20    .20
851  A241  3f salmon & multi           .20    .20
852  A241  4f salmon & multi           .20    .20
853  A241  75f bl grn & multi         2.40   1.30
    Nos. 849-853 (5)                   3.20   1.30

Festival Emblem — A242

Festival Poster — A243

**1978, July 17            Perf. 13½x13**
854  A242  25f multicolored            .35    .20
855  A242  35f multicolored            .55    .20
            **Souvenir Sheet**
              **Perf. 13x13½**
856  A243  100f multicolored          6.50   6.50
            Festivals, July 1978.

WHO Emblem, Nurse, Hospital, Sick Child A244

**1978, Aug. 18    Photo.    Perf. 14**
857  A244  25f multicolored            .25    .20
858  A244  35f multicolored            .65    .20
859  A244  75f multicolored           1.75    .95
    Nos. 857-859 (3)                   2.65   1.35
            Eradication of smallpox.

Maritime Union Emblem A245

**1978, Aug. 30    Photo.    Perf. 11½x12**
860  A245  25f multicolored            .55    .20
861  A245  75f multicolored           1.25    .50
            1st World Maritime Day.

Workers A246

**1978, Sept. 12            Perf. 14**
862  A246  10f multicolored            .20    .20
863  A246  25f multicolored            .55    .20
864  A246  35f multicolored           1.00    .65
    Nos. 862-864 (3)                   1.75   1.05
        10th anniv. of People's Work Groups.

Fair Emblem with Atom Symbol — A247          Map of Iraq, Ruler and Globe — A248

**1978, Oct. 1**
865  A247  25f multicolored            .25    .20
866  A247  35f multicolored            .30    .20
867  A247  75f multicolored           1.40    .85
    Nos. 865-867 (3)                   1.95   1.25

15th International Fair, Baghdad, Oct. 1-15.

**1978, Oct. 14**
868  A248  25f multicolored            .25    .20
869  A248  35f multicolored            .30    .20
870  A248  75f multicolored           1.40    .85
    Nos. 868-870 (3)                   1.95   1.25

            World Standards Day.

Altharthar-Euphrates Dam — A249

**1978            Photo.            Perf. 11½**
871  A249  5f multicolored             .20    .20
872  A249  10f multicolored            .20    .20
873  A249  15f multicolored            .20    .20
874  A249  25f multicolored            .30    .20
875  A249  35f multicolored            .40    .20
876  A249  50f multicolored            .60    .25
    Nos. 871-876 (6)                   1.90   1.25

Arab Summit Conference A250

Surgeons' Conference Emblem — A251

**1978, Nov. 2    Photo.    Perf. 14**
890  A250  25f multicolored            .25    .20
891  A250  35f multicolored            .45    .25
892  A250  75f multicolored           1.10    .85
    Nos. 890-892 (3)                   1.80   1.30

9th Arab Summit Conference, Baghdad, Nov. 2-5.

**1978, Nov. 8    Litho.    Perf. 12x11½**
893  A251  25f multicolored            .35    .20
894  A251  75f multicolored           1.00    .65

4th Cong. of the Assoc. of Thoracic & Cardiovascular Surgeons of Asia, Baghdad, Nov. 6-10.

Pilgrims at Mt. Arafat and Holy Ka'aba A252

**1978, Nov. 9    Photo.    Perf. 14**
895  A252  25f multicolored            .35    .20
896  A252  35f multicolored            .55    .20

            Pilgrimage to Mecea.

Atom Symbol, Map of South America, Africa, Arabia A253

Hands Holding Emblem — A254

**1978, Nov. 11            Perf. 13½**
897  A253  25f multicolored            .65    .20
898  A253  50f multicolored            .55    .25
899  A253  75f multicolored            .80    .35
    Nos. 897-899 (3)                   2.00    .70

Technical Cooperation Among Developing Countries Conf., Buenos Aires, Argentina, Sept. 1978.

Globe and Flame Emblem — A255

**1978, Nov. 30    Litho.    Perf. 13½x13**
900  A254  25f multicolored            .30    .20
901  A254  50f multicolored            .70    .25
902  A254  75f multicolored           2.00    .65
    Nos. 900-902 (3)                   3.00   1.10

            Anti-Apartheid Year.

**1978, Dec. 20            Perf. 14**
903  A255  25f multicolored            .50    .20
904  A255  75f multicolored           1.50   1.00

Declaration of Human Rights, 30th anniv.

Candle and Emblem — A256

Book, Pencil and Flame — A257

**1979, Jan. 9    Photo.    Perf. 14**
905  A256  10f multicolored            .35    .20
906  A256  25f multicolored            .35    .20
907  A256  35f multicolored            .65    .20
    Nos. 905-907 (3)                   1.35    .60
                Police Day.

**1979, Feb. 15    Photo.    Perf. 14**
908  A257  15f multicolored            .25    .20
909  A257  25f multicolored            .35    .20
910  A257  35f multicolored            .90    .20
    Nos. 908-910 (3)                   1.50    .60

Application of Compulsory Education Law, anniversary.

Pupils, School and Teacher — A258

**1979, Mar. 1** *Perf. 13*
911 A258 10f multicolored .20 .20
912 A258 15f multicolored .20 .20
913 A258 50f multicolored .80 .50
Nos. 911-913 (3) 1.20 .90
Teacher's Day.

Pupils, Flag, Pencil — A259

**1979, Mar. 10** *Perf. 13½x13*
914 A259 15f multicolored .25 .20
915 A259 25f multicolored .45 .20
916 A259 35f multicolored .70 .20
Nos. 914-916 (3) 1.40 .60
National Comprehensive Compulsory Literacy Campaign.

Book, World Map, Arab Achievements A260

**1979, Mar. 22** *Perf. 13*
917 A260 35f multicolored .50 .20
918 A260 75f multicolored 1.50 .65
Achievements of the Arabs.

Girl Playing Flute — A261

**1979, Apr. 15** *Litho.* *Perf. 13½*
919 A261 15f multicolored .35 .20
920 A261 25f multicolored .55 .20
921 A261 35f multicolored 1.00 .40
Nos. 919-921 (3) 1.90 .80
Mosul Spring Festival.

Iraqi Flag, Globe, UPU Emblem A262

**1979, Apr. 22** *Photo.* *Perf. 13x13½*
922 A262 25f multicolored .60 .20
923 A262 35f multicolored .60 .20
924 A262 75f multicolored 1.50 .65
Nos. 922-924 (3) 2.70 1.05
50th anniv. of Iraq's admission to the UPU.

Soccer Tournament Emblem A263

**1979, May 4** *Photo.* *Perf. 13*
925 A263 10f multicolored .20 .20
926 A263 15f multicolored .30 .20
927 A263 50f multicolored 1.00 .50
Nos. 925-927 (3) 1.50 .90
5th Arabian Gulf Soccer Championship.

Child With Globe and Candle A264

Design: 100f, IYC emblem, boy and girl reaching for UN emblem, vert.

**1979, June 1 Photo.** *Perf. 13x13½*
928 A264 25f multicolored .70 .30
929 A264 75f multicolored 1.75 1.00

**Souvenir Sheet**
930 A264 100f multicolored 30.00 27.50
International Year of the Child.
No. 930 contains one 30x42mm stamp.

Leaf and Flower — A265

**1979, July 17** *Litho.* *Perf. 12½*
931 A265 15f multicolored .20 .20
932 A265 25f multicolored .35 .20
933 A265 35f multicolored .35 .20
Nos. 931-933 (3) .90 .60
July festivals.

Students Holding Globe, UNESCO Emblem A266

**1979, July 25**
934 A266 25f multicolored .40 .20
935 A266 40f multicolored .70 .30
936 A266 100f multicolored 2.00 .50
Nos. 934-936 (3) 3.10 1.00
Intl. Bureau of Education, Geneva, 50th anniv.

S. al Hosari, Philosopher A267

Designs: No. 938, Mustapha Jawad, historian. No. 939, Jawad Selim, sculptor.

**1979, Oct. 15** *Litho.* *Perf. 12½*
937 A267 25f multicolored .45 .20
938 A267 25f multicolored .45 .20
939 A267 25f multicolored .45 .20
Nos. 937-939 (3) 1.35 .60

Pilgrimage to Mecca A268

**1979, Oct. 25** *Litho.* *Perf. 12½*
940 A268 25f multicolored .45 .20
941 A268 50f multicolored .80 .35

Iraqi News Agency, 20th Anniversary A269

**1979, Nov. 9 Photo.** *Perf. 11½*
942 A269 25f multicolored .45 .20
943 A269 50f multicolored 1.00 .25
944 A269 75f multicolored 1.25 .40
Nos. 942-944 (3) 2.70 .85

Telecom 79 — A270

**1979, Nov. 20 Litho.** *Perf. 11½*
945 A270 25f multicolored .45 .20
946 A270 50f multicolored .70 .30
947 A270 75f multicolored 1.25 .65
Nos. 945-947 (3) 2.40 1.15
3rd World Telecommunications Exhibition, Geneva, Sept. 20-26.

International Palestinian Solidarity Day — A271

**1979, Nov. 29 Photo.** *Perf. 11½x12*
948 A271 25f multicolored .90 .25
949 A271 50f multicolored 1.75 .45
950 A271 75f multicolored 2.40 .85
Nos. 948-950 (3) 5.05 1.55

A272 A273

Designs: 25f, 75f, Ahmad Hassan Al-Bakr. 35f, 100f, Pres. Saddam Hussein.

**1979, Dec. 1 Photo.** *Perf. 13x13½*
951 A272 25f multicolored .30 .20
952 A272 35f multicolored .50 .20
953 A272 75f multicolored 1.00 .40
954 A272 100f multicolored 4.00 2.25
Nos. 951-954 (4) 5.80 3.05

**1979, Dec. 10** *Perf. 14*
Vanguard Emblem and: 10f, Boy and violin. 15f, Children, map of Iraq. 25f, Youths. 35f, Vanguard emblem alone.
955 A273 10f multicolored .25 .20
956 A273 15f multicolored .25 .20
957 A273 25f multicolored .40 .20
958 A273 35f multicolored .50 .20
Nos. 955-958 (4) 1.40 .80

World Meteorological Day — A274

World Health Day — A275

**1980, Mar. 23 Photo.** *Perf. 14*
959 A274 15f multicolored .20 .20
960 A274 25f multicolored .30 .20
961 A274 35f multicolored .70 .25
Nos. 959-961 (3) 1.20 .65

**1980, Apr. 7 Photo.** *Perf. 14*
962 A275 25f multicolored .35 .20
963 A275 35f multicolored .50 .20
964 A275 75f multicolored 1.90 .50
Nos. 962-964 (3) 2.75 .90

Festivals Emblem — A276

Pres. Hussein — A277

**1980, July 17 Photo.** *Perf. 13½x13*
965 A276 25f multicolored .35 .20
966 A276 35f multicolored .45 .20

**Souvenir Sheet**
967 A277 100f multicolored 8.00 8.00
July Festivals.

Hurdles, Moscow '80 Emblem A278

**1980, July 30 Photo.** *Perf. 14*
968 A278 15f shown .25 .20
969 A278 20f Weight lifting, vert. .45 .30

970 A278 30f Boxing .85 .40
971 A278 35f Soccer, vert. 1.75 .75
Nos. 968-971 (4) 3.30 1.65

**Souvenir Sheet**

972 A278 100f Wrestling 10.50 10.50

22nd Summer Olympic Games, Moscow, July 19-Aug. 3.

Fruits — A279

**1980, Aug. 15**
973 A279 5f Blackberries .25 .20
974 A279 15f Apricots .50 .20
975 A279 20f Pears .70 .20
976 A279 25f Apples .85 .20
977 A279 35f Plums 1.10 .30
Nos. 973-977 (5) 3.40 1.10

World Tourism Conference, Manila, Sept. 27 — A279a

**1980, Aug. 30    Litho.    Perf. 12½**
978 A279a 25f multicolored .35 .20
979 A279a 50f multicolored .85 .25
980 A279a 100f multicolored 1.75 .85
Nos. 978-980 (3) 2.95 1.30

Postal Union Emblem, Posthorn, Map of Arab States — A280

**1980, Sept. 8    Perf. 12**
981 A280 10f multicolored .25 .20
982 A280 30f multicolored .35 .20
983 A280 35f multicolored .70 .20
Nos. 981-983 (3) 1.30 .60

Arab Postal Union, 11th Congress, Baghdad.

20th Anniversary of OPEC — A281

**1980, Sept. 30**
984 A281 30f multicolored 1.00 .25
985 A281 75f multicolored 1.60 .50

Papilio Machaon A282

**1980, Oct. 20    Photo.    Perf. 13½x14**
987 A282 10f shown 2.00 .35
988 A282 15f Danaus chrysippus 2.25 .65

989 A282 20f Vanessa atalanta 3.25 .80
990 A282 30f Colias croceus 5.25 1.25
Nos. 987-990 (4) 12.75 3.05

Hegira, 1,500th Anniv. A283

**1980, Nov. 9    Litho.    Perf. 11½x12**
991 A283 15f multicolored .25 .20
992 A283 25f multicolored .60 .20
993 A283 35f multicolored .70 .30
Nos. 991-993 (3) 1.55 .70

International Palestinian Solidarity Day — A284

**1980, Nov. 29**
994 A284 25f multicolored .60 .20
995 A284 35f multicolored .85 .20
996 A284 75f multicolored 1.75 .75
Nos. 994-996 (3) 3.20 1.15

Army Day — A285

**1981, Jan. 6    Photo.    Perf. 14x13½**
997 A285 5f multicolored .25 .20
998 A285 30f multicolored .55 .20
999 A285 75f multicolored 1.50 .65
Nos. 997-999 (3) 2.30 1.05

**1981, Feb. 8    Perf. 12**
1000 A286 15f multicolored .25 .20
1001 A286 30f multicolored .45 .20
1002 A286 35f multicolored .70 .20
Nos. 1000-1002 (3) 1.40 .60

Map of Arab Countries A287

**1981, Mar. 22    Litho.    Perf. 12½**
1003 A287 5f multicolored .20 .20
1004 A287 25f multicolored .50 .20
1005 A287 35f multicolored .70 .20
Nos. 1003-1005 (3) 1.40 .60

February Revolution, 18th Anniversary A286

Battle of Qadisiya — A288

**1981, Apr. 7    Photo.    Perf. 13½x13**
1006 A288 30f multicolored .45 .20
1007 A288 35f multicolored .60 .20
1008 A288 75f multicolored 1.10 .50
Nos. 1006-1008 (3) 2.15 .90

**Souvenir Sheet**

1009 A288 100f multicolored 6.50 6.50

No. 1009 contains one horiz. stamp.

Helicopters and Tank A289

**1981, June 1    Photo.**
1010 A289 5f shown .20 .20
1011 A289 10f Plane .35 .20
1012 A289 15f Rocket .50 .20
Nos. 1010-1012,C66 (4) 5.05 3.10

Air Force, 50th anniv.

Natl. Assembly Election, First Anniv. — A290

**1981, June 20    Perf. 12½**
1013 A290 30f multicolored .45 .20
1014 A290 35f multicolored .60 .20
1015 A290 45f multicolored .95 .35
Nos. 1013-1015 (3) 2.00 .75

July Festivals A291

**1981, July 17    Photo.**
1016 A291 15f multicolored .25 .20
1017 A291 25f multicolored .40 .20
1018 A291 35f multicolored .70 .20
Nos. 1016-1018 (3) 1.35 .60

Pottery Maker — A292

Designs: Popular industries.

**1981, Aug. 15    Perf. 14**
1019 A292 5f Straw weaver .20 .20
1020 A292 30f Metal worker .55 .20
1021 A292 35f shown .75 .20
1022 A292 50f Rug maker, horiz. 1.00 .35
Nos. 1019-1022 (4) 2.50 .95

Islamic Pilgrimage — A293

**1981, Oct. 7    Photo.    Perf. 12x11½**
1023 A293 25f multicolored .55 .20
1024 A293 45f multicolored 1.00 .30
1025 A293 50f multicolored 1.00 .30
Nos. 1023-1025 (3) 2.55 .80

World Food Day A294

**1981, Oct. 16    Photo.    Perf. 14**
1026 A294 30f multicolored .55 .20
1027 A294 45f multicolored 1.00 .40
1028 A294 75f multicolored 1.50 .75
Nos. 1026-1028 (3) 3.05 1.35

Intl. Year of the Disabled — A295

**1981, Nov. 15**
1029 A295 30f multicolored .45 .20
1030 A295 45f multicolored .75 .30
1031 A295 75f multicolored 1.10 .60
Nos. 1029-1031 (3) 2.30 1.10

5th Anniv. of United Arab Shipping Co. A296

**1981, Dec. 2    Perf. 13x13½**
1032 A296 50f multicolored 1.40 .60
1033 A296 120f multicolored 4.00 1.75

Saddam Hussein Gymnasium A297

**1981, Sept. 26    Litho.    Perf. 12x12½**
1034 A297 45f shown .70 .25
1035 A297 50f Palace of Conferences .70 .30
1036 A297 120f like #1035 2.10 1.25
1037 A297 150f like #1034 2.75 1.50
Nos. 1034-1037 (4) 6.25 3.30

For surcharges see Nos. 1097-1099.

35th Anniv. of Al Baath Party — A298

Mosul Spring Festival — A299

**1982, Apr. 7    Photo.    Perf. 13½x13**
1038 A298 25f Pres. Hussein, flowers .45 .20
1039 A298 30f "7 7 7" .45 .20
1040 A298 45f like 25f .75 .40
1041 A298 50f like 30f .75 .40
Nos. 1038-1041 (4) 2.40 1.20

## Souvenir Sheet
### Imperf
1042 A298 150f multicolored    5.75 5.75

**1982, Apr. 15   Litho.   Perf. 11½x12**
1043 A299 25f Birds    1.10 .20
1044 A299 30f Girl    .70 .20
1045 A299 45f like 25f    1.10 .50
1046 A299 50f like 30f    1.10 .40
    Nos. 1043-1046 (4)    4.00 1.30

Intl. Workers' Day A300

**1982, May 1    Perf. 12½**
1047 A300 25f multicolored    .45 .20
1048 A300 45f multicolored    .70 .30
1049 A300 50f multicolored    .75 .40
    Nos. 1047-1049 (3)    1.90 .90

14th World Telecommunications Day — A301

**1982, May 17   Photo.   Perf. 13x13½**
1050 A301 5f multicolored    .20 .20
1051 A301 50f multicolored    .70 .35
1052 A301 100f multicolored    1.60 .90
    Nos. 1050-1052 (3)    2.50 1.45

10th Anniv. of Oil Nationalization A302

**1982, June 1   Litho.   Perf. 12½**
1053 A302 5f Oil gusher    .25 .20
1054 A302 25f like 5f    .60 .20
1055 A302 45f Statue    1.25 .25
1056 A302 50f like 45f    1.50 .35
    Nos. 1053-1056 (4)    3.60 1.00

Martyrs' Day — A303

Women's Day — A304

**1981, Dec. 1   Photo.   Perf. 14**
1057 A303 45f multicolored    .45 .35
1058 A303 50f multicolored    .55 .45
1059 A303 120f multicolored    1.50 1.00
    Nos. 1057-1059,O339A-O339C (6) 8.50 3.80

**1982, Mar. 4   Litho.   Perf. 12½x13**
1060 A304 25f multicolored    .55 .20
1061 A304 45f multicolored    .90 .40
1062 A304 50f multicolored    .90 .50
    Nos. 1060-1062 (3)    2.35 1.10

A305

A305a

**1982, Apr. 12    Perf. 12½**
1063 A305 25f multicolored    .55 .20
1064 A305 45f multicolored    .90 .30
1065 A305 50f multicolored    .90 .30
    Nos. 1063-1065 (3)    2.35 .80

Arab Postal Union, 30th anniv.

**1982, June 7   Photo.   Perf. 14**
1065A A305a 30f Nuclear power
         emblem, lion    .60 .30
1065B A305a 45f shown    1.00 .35
1065C A305a 50f like 30f    1.10 .50
1065D A305a 120f like 45f    2.40 1.50
    Nos. 1065A-1065D (4)    5.10 2.65

First anniv. of attack on nuclear power reactor.

July Festivals — A306

**1982, July 17   Photo.   Perf. 14½x14**
1066 A306 25f multicolored    .40 .20
1067 A306 45f multicolored    .60 .25
1068 A306 50f multicolored    .65 .30
    Nos. 1066-1068 (3)    1.65 .75

Lacerta Viridis A307

**1982, Aug. 20   Litho.   Perf. 12½**
1069 A307 25f shown    2.25 .75
1070 A307 30f Vipera aspis    2.25 .75
1071 A307 45f Lacerta virdis,
        diff.    3.00 1.10
1072 A307 50f Natrix tessellata    3.50 1.50
    Nos. 1069-1072 (4)    11.00 4.10

7th Non-aligned Countries Conference, Baghdad, Sept. — A308

#1073, Tito. #1074, Nehru. #1075, Nasser. #1076, Kwame Nkrumah. #1077, Hussein.

**1982, Sept. 6   Photo.   Perf. 13x13½**
1073 A308 50f multicolored    .85 .40
1074 A308 50f multicolored    .85 .40
1075 A308 50f multicolored    .85 .40
1076 A308 50f multicolored    .85 .40
1077 A308 100f multicolored    1.90 .55
    Nos. 1073-1077 (5)    5.30 2.15

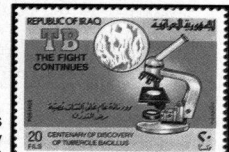

TB Bacillus Centenary A309

**1982, Oct. 1    Perf. 14x14½**
1078 A309 20f multicolored    .65 .20
1079 A309 50f multicolored    1.10 .30
1080 A309 100f multicolored    2.10 .85
    Nos. 1078-1080 (3)    3.85 1.35

1982 World Cup — A310

Designs: Various soccer players. 150f horiz.

**1982, July 1   Litho.   Perf. 11½x12**
1081 A310 5f multicolored    .50 .25
1082 A310 45f multicolored    1.00 .45
1083 A310 50f multicolored    1.10 .50
1084 A310 100f multicolored    2.00 1.00
    Nos. 1081-1084 (4)    4.60 2.20

## Souvenir Sheet
### Perf. 12½
1085 A310 150f multicolored    3.50 3.50

13th UPU Day A311

**1982, Oct. 9    Perf. 12x11½**
1086 A311 5f multicolored    .20 .20
1087 A311 45f multicolored    .70 .30
1088 A311 100f multicolored    1.60 .85
    Nos. 1086-1088 (3)    2.50 1.35

Musical Instruments A312

**1982, Nov. 15    Perf. 12½x13**
1089 A312 5f Drums    .25 .20
1090 A312 10f Zither    .25 .20
1091 A312 35f Stringed instru-
        ment    .85 .35
1092 A312 100f Lute    2.75 .95
    Nos. 1089-1092 (4)    4.10 1.70

Birth Anniv. of Mohammed — A313

Mecca Mosque views.

**1982, Dec. 27   Litho.   Perf. 12x11½**
1093 A313 25f multicolored    .25 .20
1094 A313 30f multicolored    .40 .25
1095 A313 45f multicolored    .55 .25
1096 A313 50f multicolored    .70 .35
    Nos. 1093-1096 (4)    1.90 1.05

Nos. 1034-1036 Surcharged

**1983, May 15   Litho.   Perf. 12x12½**
1097 A297 60f on 50f multi    1.25 .50
1098 A297 70f on 45f multi    1.75 .60
1099 A297 160f on 120f multi    4.50 2.00
    Nos. 1097-1099 (3)    7.50 3.10

July Festivals A314

**1983, July 17   Litho.   Perf. 14½x14**
1100 A314 30f multicolored    .45 .20
1101 A314 60f multicolored    1.00 .35
1102 A314 70f multicolored    1.40 .45
    Nos. 1100-1102 (3)    2.85 1.00

Local Flowers — A315

**1983, June 15   Photo.   Perf. 15x14**
### Border Color
1103 A315 10f shown, light blue    .25 .20
1104 A315 20f Flowers, diff.,
        pale yellow    .45 .20
1105 A315 30f like 10f, yellow    .55 .20
1106 A315 40f like 20f, gray    .95 .40
1107 A315 50f like 10f, pale
        green    1.10 .50
1108 A315 100f like 20f, pink    2.25 1.00
   a.   Bklt. pane of 6, #1103-1108    9.75
    Nos. 1103-1108 (6)    5.55 2.50

Nos. 1103-1108 issued in booklets only. For surcharges see Nos. 1501-1506.

A316

Battle of Thi Qar — A317

**1983, Oct. 30   Photo.   Perf. 12½x13**
1109 A316 20f silver & multi    .25 .20
1110 A317 50f silver & multi    .75 .30
1111 A316 60f gold & multi    1.00 .35
1112 A317 70f gold & multi    1.10 .40
    Nos. 1109-1112 (4)    3.10 1.25

World Communications Year — A318

25f, 70f show emblem and hexagons.

**1983, Oct. 20 Photo.** *Perf. 11½x12*
| | | | | |
|---|---|---|---|---|
| 1113 | A318 | 5f brt yel grn & multi | .20 | .20 |
| 1114 | A318 | 25f rose lil & multi | .30 | .20 |
| 1115 | A318 | 60f brt org yel & multi | .90 | .35 |
| 1116 | A318 | 70f brt bl vio & multi | 1.10 | .40 |
| | | Nos. 1113-1116 (4) | 2.50 | 1.15 |

**Souvenir Sheet**
| | | | | |
|---|---|---|---|---|
| 1117 | A318 | 200f apple grn & multi | 4.25 | 4.25 |

Baghdad Intl. Fair — A319

Symbolic "9" — A320

**1983, Nov. 1 Photo.** *Perf. 12½*
| | | | | |
|---|---|---|---|---|
| 1118 | A319 | 60f multicolored | .75 | .40 |
| 1119 | A319 | 70f multicolored | .95 | .50 |
| 1120 | A319 | 160f multicolored | 2.10 | 1.25 |
| | | Nos. 1118-1120 (3) | 3.80 | 2.15 |

**1983, Nov. 10 Photo.** *Perf. 14*

9th Natl. Congress of Arab Baath Socialist Party: 30f, 70f, Symbols of development. 60f, 100f, Torch, eagle, globe, open book.
| | | | | |
|---|---|---|---|---|
| 1121 | A320 | 30f multicolored | .35 | .20 |
| 1122 | A320 | 60f multicolored | .75 | .40 |
| 1123 | A320 | 70f multicolored | .95 | .50 |
| 1124 | A320 | 100f multicolored | 1.40 | .70 |
| | | Nos. 1121-1124 (4) | 3.45 | 1.80 |

Festival Crowd — A321

Various Paintings.

**1983, Nov. 20 Litho.** *Perf. 12½*
| | | | | |
|---|---|---|---|---|
| 1125 | A321 | 60f shown | 1.50 | .60 |
| 1126 | A321 | 60f Men hauling boat, vert. | 1.50 | .60 |
| 1127 | A321 | 60f Decorations | 1.50 | .60 |
| 1128 | A321 | 70f Village | 2.00 | .85 |
| 1129 | A321 | 70f Crowd | 2.00 | .85 |
| | | Nos. 1125-1129 (5) | 8.50 | 3.50 |

Sabra and Shattela Palestinian Refugee Camp Massacre A322

Various Victims.

**1983, Nov. 29** *Perf. 11½x12*
| | | | | |
|---|---|---|---|---|
| 1130 | A322 | 10f multicolored | .25 | .20 |
| 1131 | A322 | 60f multicolored | 1.00 | .40 |
| 1132 | A322 | 70f multicolored | 1.25 | .50 |
| 1133 | A322 | 160f multicolored | 2.75 | 1.25 |
| | | Nos. 1130-1133 (4) | 5.25 | 2.35 |

Pres. Hussein, Map — A323

**1983 Photo.** *Perf. 13½x13*
| | | | | |
|---|---|---|---|---|
| 1134 | A323 | 60f multicolored | .75 | .30 |
| 1135 | A323 | 70f multicolored | 1.00 | .50 |
| 1136 | A323 | 250f multicolored | 3.50 | 2.00 |
| | | Nos. 1134-1136 (3) | 5.25 | 2.80 |

Hussein as head of Al Baath Party, 4th anniv.

Modern Building — A324

Various buildings.

**1983, Dec. 31 Litho.** *Perf. 14*
| | | | | |
|---|---|---|---|---|
| 1137 | A324 | 60f multicolored | .70 | .40 |
| 1138 | A324 | 70f multicolored | .90 | .50 |
| 1139 | A324 | 160f multicolored | 2.25 | 1.10 |
| 1140 | A324 | 200f multicolored | 2.75 | 1.40 |
| | | Nos. 1137-1140,O340-O341 (6) | 8.50 | 4.55 |

Medical Congress Emblem A325

**1984, Mar. 10** *Perf. 13x12½*
| | | | | |
|---|---|---|---|---|
| 1141 | A325 | 60f multicolored | .80 | .40 |
| 1142 | A325 | 70f multicolored | 1.00 | .50 |
| 1143 | A325 | 200f multicolored | 3.00 | 1.40 |
| | | Nos. 1141-1143 (3) | 4.80 | 2.30 |

25th Intl. Congress of Military Medicine and Pharmacy, Baghdad, Mar. 10-15.

Pres. Hussein's Birthday — A326

Various portraits of Hussein.

**1984, Apr. 28 Litho.** *Perf. 12½x13*
| | | | | |
|---|---|---|---|---|
| 1144 | A326 | 60f multicolored | .65 | .30 |
| 1145 | A326 | 70f multicolored | .70 | .40 |
| 1146 | A326 | 160f multicolored | 2.10 | 1.25 |
| 1147 | A326 | 200f multicolored | 2.50 | 1.60 |
| | | Nos. 1144-1147 (4) | 5.95 | 3.55 |

**Souvenir Sheet**
**Imperf**
| | | | | |
|---|---|---|---|---|
| 1148 | A326 | 250f multicolored | 5.00 | 5.00 |

Gold ink on Nos. 1144-1147 and dark green ink in "margin" of No. 1148 was applied by a thermographic process, producing a raised effect. No. 1148 has perf. 12½x13 label picturing Pres. Hussein.

1984 Summer Olympics, Los Angeles — A327

**1984, Aug. 12 Litho.** *Perf. 12x11½*
| | | | | |
|---|---|---|---|---|
| 1149 | A327 | 50f Boxing | .70 | .50 |
| 1150 | A327 | 60f Weight lifting | .90 | .50 |
| 1151 | A327 | 70f like 50f | 1.10 | .60 |
| 1152 | A327 | 100f like 60f | 1.60 | .90 |

**Size: 80x60mm**
**Imperf**
| | | | | |
|---|---|---|---|---|
| 1153 | A327 | 200f Soccer | 5.00 | 5.00 |
| | | Nos. 1149-1153 (5) | 9.30 | 7.50 |

Nos. 1153 contains one 32x41mm perf. 12½ label within the stamp.

A328

A329

50f, 70f, Pres. Hussein, flaming horses heads, map. 60f, 100f, Abstract of woman, sapling, rifle. 200f, Shield, heraldic eagle.

**1984, Sept. 22** *Perf. 11½x12*
| | | | | |
|---|---|---|---|---|
| 1154 | A328 | 50f multicolored | .55 | .30 |
| 1155 | A328 | 60f multicolored | .70 | .40 |
| 1156 | A328 | 70f multicolored | .85 | .50 |
| 1157 | A328 | 100f multicolored | 1.25 | .65 |

**Size: 80x60mm**
**Imperf**
| | | | | |
|---|---|---|---|---|
| 1158 | A328 | 200f multicolored | 3.50 | 3.50 |
| | | Nos. 1154-1158 (5) | 6.85 | 5.35 |

Battle of Qadisiya. No. 1158 contains one 32x41mm perf. 12½ label within the stamp.

**1984, Dec. 1** *Perf. 13½*

Martyrs' Day: 50f, 70f, Natl. flag as flame. 60f, 100f, Woman holding rifle, medal.
| | | | | |
|---|---|---|---|---|
| 1159 | A329 | 50f multicolored | .45 | .35 |
| 1160 | A329 | 60f multicolored | .65 | .35 |
| 1161 | A329 | 70f multicolored | .75 | .40 |
| 1162 | A329 | 100f multicolored | 1.00 | .65 |
| | | Nos. 1159-1162 (4) | 2.85 | 1.75 |

Pres. Hussein's Visit to Al-Mustansiriyah University, 5th Anniv. — A330

**1985, Apr. 2 Photo.** *Perf. 12x11½*
| | | | | |
|---|---|---|---|---|
| 1163 | A330 | 60f dk bl gray & dk pink | .55 | .35 |
| 1164 | A330 | 70f myr grn & dk pink | .65 | .40 |
| 1165 | A330 | 250f blk & dk pink | 2.50 | 1.40 |
| | | Nos. 1163-1165 (3) | 3.70 | 2.15 |

Iraqi Air Force, 54th Anniv. — A331

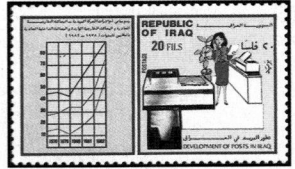

Pres. Hussein, 48th Birthday — A332

10f, 160f, Pres. Hussein, fighter planes, pilot's wings. 60f, 70f, 200f, Planes, flag, "54," horiz.

**Perf. 13x12½, 13½ (60f, 70f)**
**1985, Apr. 22** Litho.
| | | | | |
|---|---|---|---|---|
| 1166 | A331 | 10f multicolored | .30 | .20 |
| 1167 | A331 | 60f multicolored | 1.50 | .75 |
| 1168 | A331 | 70f multicolored | 1.60 | .75 |
| 1169 | A331 | 160f multicolored | 4.00 | 2.00 |
| | | Nos. 1166-1169 (4) | 7.40 | 3.70 |

**Souvenir Sheet**
**Perf. 12½**
| | | | | |
|---|---|---|---|---|
| 1170 | A331 | 200f multicolored | 6.75 | 6.75 |

**1985, Apr. 28** *Perf. 13½*

30f, 70f, Pres. Hussein, sunflower. 60f, 100f, Pres., candle & flowers. 200f, Flowers & text.
| | | | | |
|---|---|---|---|---|
| 1171 | A332 | 30f multicolored | .35 | .20 |
| 1172 | A332 | 60f multicolored | .65 | .30 |
| 1173 | A332 | 70f multicolored | .75 | .40 |
| 1174 | A332 | 100f multicolored | 1.10 | .60 |
| | | Nos. 1171-1174 (4) | 2.85 | 1.50 |

**Souvenir Sheet**
**Perf. 13x12½**
| | | | | |
|---|---|---|---|---|
| 1175 | A332 | 200f multicolored | 3.75 | 3.75 |

Posts and Telecommunications Development Program — A333

Designs: 20f, 60f, Graph, woman in modern office. 50f, 70f, Satellite dish and graphs.

**1985, June 30** *Perf. 12½*
| | | | | |
|---|---|---|---|---|
| 1176 | A333 | 20f multicolored | .35 | .20 |
| 1177 | A333 | 50f multicolored | .70 | .30 |
| 1178 | A333 | 60f multicolored | .70 | .30 |
| 1179 | A333 | 70f multicolored | .95 | .50 |
| | | Nos. 1176-1179 (4) | 2.70 | 1.30 |

Battle of Qadisiya A334

Designs: 10f, 60f, Shown. 20f, 70f, Pres. Hussein, Al-Baath Party emblem. 200f, Dove, natl. flag as shield, soldier.

**1985, Sept. 4** *Perf. 11½x12*
| | | | | |
|---|---|---|---|---|
| 1180 | A334 | 10f multicolored | .20 | .20 |
| 1181 | A334 | 20f multicolored | .25 | .20 |
| 1182 | A334 | 60f multicolored | .90 | .40 |
| 1183 | A334 | 70f multicolored | 1.10 | .65 |
| | | Nos. 1180-1183 (4) | 2.45 | 1.45 |

**Souvenir Sheet**
**Perf. 12x12½**
| | | | | |
|---|---|---|---|---|
| 1184 | A334 | 200f multicolored | 3.25 | 3.25 |

No. 1184 contains one stamp 30x45mm.

Solar Energy Research Center A335

## 1985, Sept. 19 — Perf. 13½
1185 A335 10f multicolored .20 .20
1186 A335 50f multicolored .95 .40
1187 A335 100f multicolored 1.90 .95
Nos. 1185-1187 (3) 3.05 1.55

UN Child Survival
Campaign
A336

Al Sharif, Poet,
Death Millennium
A337

Designs: 10f, 50f, Stop Polio Campaign.
15f, 100f, Girl, infant.

## 1985, Oct. 10
1188 A336 10f multicolored .20 .20
1189 A336 15f multicolored .20 .20
1190 A336 50f multicolored .75 .30
1191 A336 100f multicolored 1.50 .85
Nos. 1188-1191 (4) 2.65 1.55

## 1985, Oct. 20
1192 A337 10f multicolored .25 .20
1193 A337 50f multicolored .55 .30
1194 A337 100f multicolored 1.25 .80
Nos. 1192-1194 (3) 2.05 1.30

UN, 40th
Anniv.
A338

## 1985, Oct. 24
1195 A338 10f multicolored .20 .20
1196 A338 40f multicolored .55 .20
1197 A338 100f multicolored 1.40 .75
Nos. 1195-1197 (3) 2.15 1.15

Death of Iraqi
Prisoners of War
in Iran — A339

30f, 100f, Knife, Geneva Convention declaration, red crescent, red cross. 70f, 200f,
POWs, gun shell, natl. flag, cherub & dove.

## 1985, Nov. 10 — Perf. 14
1198 A339 30f multicolored .35 .20
1199 A339 70f multicolored .75 .40
1200 A339 100f multicolored 1.10 .65
1201 A339 200f multicolored 2.50 1.25

### Size: 110x80mm
#### Imperf
1202 A339 250f multicolored 5.00 5.00
Nos. 1198-1202 (5) 9.70 7.50

No. 1202 contains 2 perf. 14 labels similar
to 100f and 200f designs within the stamp.

Intl.
Palestinian
Solidarity
Day
A341

## 1985, Nov. 29 Litho. — Perf. 13½
1207 A341 10f multicolored .25 .20
1208 A341 50f multicolored .95 .40
1209 A341 100f multicolored 2.10 .95
Nos. 1207-1209 (3) 3.30 1.55

Martyrs'
Day — A342

## 1985, Dec. 1 — Perf. 11½x12
1210 A342 10f multicolored .20 .20
1211 A342 40f multicolored .45 .20
1212 A342 100f multicolored 1.40 .75
Nos. 1210-1212 (3) 2.05 1.15

Intl. Youth
Year — A343

## 1985, Dec. 12 Litho. — Perf. 11½x12
IYY emblem and: 40f, 100f, Soldier holding
flag. 50f, 200f, Youths, flag. 250f, Flag, cogwheel, rifle muzzle, symbols of industry.

1213 A343 40f multicolored .45 .20
1214 A343 50f multicolored .65 .30
1215 A343 100f multicolored 1.40 .75
1216 A343 200f multicolored 2.75 2.00
Nos. 1213-1216 (4) 5.25 3.25

### Souvenir Sheet
#### Perf. 12x12½
1217 A343 250f multicolored 5.00 5.00
No. 1217 contains one stamp 30x45mm.
Exists imperf.

Army Day
A344

Pres. Hussein, "6" and: 10f, 50f, Soldier,
flowers, vert. 40f, 100f, Flag, cogwheel, rockets. 200f, Al-Baath Party emblem, rifle,
waves.

## 1986, Jan. 6 — Perf. 11½x12, 12x11½
1218 A344 10f multicolored .20 .20
1219 A344 40f multicolored .65 .20
1220 A344 50f multicolored .85 .30
1221 A344 100f multicolored 1.75 .95
Nos. 1218-1221 (4) 3.45 1.65

### Miniature Sheet
#### Perf. 12½x11½
1222 A344 200f multicolored 5.00 5.00
No. 1222 contains one stamp 52x37mm.

Women's
Day
A345

Designs: 30f, 100f, Women in traditional
and modern occupations, vert. 50f, 150f,
Emblem, green flag, battle scene, grapes.

## 1986, Mar. 8 — Litho.
## Perf. 11½x12, 12x11½
1223 A345 30f multicolored .45 .20
1224 A345 50f multicolored .65 .20
1225 A345 100f multicolored 1.40 .75
1226 A345 150f multicolored 2.25 1.00
Nos. 1223-1226 (4) 4.75 2.25

Pres. Hussein,
49th Birthday
A346

Designs: 30f, 100f, Children greeting Pres.
50f, 150f, Portrait. 250f, Portrait, flag, flowers.

## 1986, Apr. 28 Litho. — Perf. 11½x12
1227 A346 30f multicolored .45 .20
1228 A346 50f multicolored .75 .25
1229 A346 100f multicolored 1.50 .45
1230 A346 150f multicolored 2.10 .65

### Size: 80x60mm
#### Imperf
1231 A346 250f multicolored 5.00 5.00
Nos. 1227-1231 (5) 9.80 6.55

Oil
Nationalization
Day,
June 1 — A347

Labor
Day — A348

Designs: 10f, 100f, Symbols of industry,
horiz. 40f, 150f, Oil well, pipeline to refinery.

## Perf. 12x11½, 11½x12
## 1986, July 25 — Litho.
1232 A347 10f multicolored .20 .20
1233 A347 40f multicolored .55 .20
1234 A347 100f multicolored 1.50 .75
1235 A347 150f multicolored 2.10 1.25
Nos. 1232-1235 (4) 4.35 2.40

## 1986, July 28 — Perf. 11½x12
Designs: 10f, 100f, Laborer, cog wheel.
40f, 150f, May Day emblem.

1236 A348 10f multicolored .25 .20
1237 A348 40f multicolored .75 .20
1238 A348 100f multicolored 1.40 .65
1239 A348 150f multicolored 2.10 .95
Nos. 1236-1239 (4) 4.50 2.00

Iraqi Air
Force,
55th
Anniv.
A349

Designs: 30f, 100f, Fighter plane, pilot's
wings, natl. flag. 50f, 150f, Fighter planes.
250f, Medal, aircraft in flight.

## 1986, July 28 — Perf. 12x11½
1240 A349 30f multicolored .70 .20
1241 A349 50f multicolored 1.40 .30
1242 A349 100f multicolored 2.75 1.40
1243 A349 150f multicolored 4.25 1.90

### Size: 81x61mm
#### Imperf
1244 A349 250f multicolored 5.00 5.00
Nos. 1240-1244 (5) 14.10 8.80

No. 1244 also exists perf.

July Festivals
A350

Pres. Hussein and: 20f, 100f, Flag. 30f,
150f, "17." 250f, Inscription, portrait inside
medal of honor.

## 1986, July 29 — Perf. 11½x12
1245 A350 20f multicolored .30 .20
1246 A350 30f multicolored .40 .20
1247 A350 100f multicolored 1.50 .75
1248 A350 150f multicolored 2.25 1.25

### Size: 81x61mm
#### Imperf
1249 A350 250f multicolored 4.00 4.00
Nos. 1245-1249 (5) 8.45 6.40

1st Qadisiya
Battle — A351

Designs: 20f, 70f, Warrior, shield, vert. 60f,
100f, Pres. Hussein, star, battle scene.

### Perf. 13x13½, 13½x13
## 1986, Sept. 4 — Litho.
1250 A351 20f multicolored .35 .20
1251 A351 60f multicolored .80 .40
1252 A351 70f multicolored .95 .50
1253 A351 100f multicolored 1.60 .65
Nos. 1250-1253 (4) 3.70 1.75

Battle between the Arabs and Persian
Empire.

Hussein's Battle of Qadisiya — A352

30f, 100f, Pres. Hussein, soldiers saluting
peace, vert. 40f, 150f, Pres., armed forces.
250f, Pres., soldiers, flags, military scenes.

### Perf. 11½x12½, 12½x11½
## 1986, Sept. 4
1254 A352 30f multicolored .90 .20
1255 A352 40f multicolored 1.25 .20
1256 A352 100f multicolored 2.50 .50
1257 A352 150f multicolored 4.25 .70

### Size: 80x60mm
#### Imperf
1258 A352 250f multicolored 4.75 4.75
Nos. 1254-1258 (5) 13.65 6.35

Intl. Peace
Year — A353

**1986, Nov. 15    Litho.    Perf. 11½x12**
| | | | | |
|---|---|---|---|---|
|1259|A353|50f Dove, flag, G clef|.65|.25|
|1260|A353|100f Globe, dove, rifle|1.10|.60|
|1261|A353|150f like 50f|1.75|1.00|
|1262|A353|250f like 100f|2.50|1.40|

**Size: 80x69mm**
*Imperf*
| | | | | |
|---|---|---|---|---|
|1263|A353|200f Emblem, flag, map, fist|2.75|2.75|

*Nos. 1259-1263 (5)*    8.75    6.00

Pres. Hussein
A354          A355

**1986**          **Perf. 12½x12**
| | | | | |
|---|---|---|---|---|
|1264|A354|30f multicolored|.70|.20|
|1265|A354|30f multicolored|.70|.20|
|1266|A354|50f multicolored|.90|.25|
|1267|A355|50f multicolored|.90|.25|
|1268|A354|100f multicolored|1.90|.65|
|1269|A355|100f multicolored|1.90|.65|
|1270|A354|150f multicolored|2.40|.85|
|1271|A355|150f multicolored|2.60|.85|
|1272|A354|250f multicolored|4.75|1.40|
|1273|A355|350f multicolored|6.25|1.90|

*Nos. 1264-1273 (10)*    23.00    7.20

For overprints & surcharges see #1347-1348, 1455, 1480-1481, 1484, 1499-1500, 1518-1519.

Army Day — A356

**1987, Jan. 6    Litho.    Perf. 12x12½**
| | | | | |
|---|---|---|---|---|
|1274|A356|20f shown|.25|.20|
|1275|A356|40f Hussein, armed forces|.35|.30|
|1276|A356|90f like 20f|.95|.90|
|1277|A356|100f like 40f|1.00|1.00|

*Nos. 1274-1277 (4)*    2.55    2.40

United Arab Shipping Co., 10th Anniv. (in 1986) A357

**1987, Apr. 3    Litho.    Perf. 12½**
| | | | | |
|---|---|---|---|---|
|1278|A357|50f Cargo ship|.55|.25|
|1279|A357|100f Container ship Chaleb Ibn Al Waleeb|1.10|.60|
|1280|A357|150f like 50f|1.75|.85|
|1281|A357|250f like 100f|3.00|1.40|

**Size: 102x91mm**
*Imperf*
| | | | | |
|---|---|---|---|---|
|1282|A357|200f Loading cargo aboard the Waleeb|3.75|3.75|

*Nos. 1278-1282 (5)*    10.15    6.85

Arab Baath Socialist Party, 40th Anniv. — A358

**1987, Apr. 7    Litho.    Perf. 12x12½**
| | | | | |
|---|---|---|---|---|
|1283|A358|20f shown|.25|.20|
|1284|A358|40f Hussein, "7," map|.35|.30|
|1285|A358|90f like 20f|.95|.90|
|1286|A358|100f like 40f|1.00|1.00|

*Nos. 1283-1286 (4)*    2.55    2.40

Pres. Hussein's 50th Birthday A359

**1987, Apr. 28          Perf. 12½x12**
| | | | | |
|---|---|---|---|---|
|1287|A359|20f shown|.25|.20|
|1288|A359|40f Portrait|.35|.30|
|1289|A359|90f like 20f|.95|.90|
|1290|A359|100f like 40f|1.10|1.00|

*Nos. 1287-1290 (4)*    2.65    2.40

July Festivals — A360

**1987, July 17    Perf. 12½x12, 12x12½**
| | | | | |
|---|---|---|---|---|
|1291|A360|20f Hussein, star, flag, horiz.|.25|.20|
|1292|A360|40f shown|.35|.30|
|1293|A360|90f like 20f, horiz.|.95|.90|
|1294|A360|100f like 40f|1.00|1.00|

*Nos. 1291-1294 (4)*    2.55    2.40

**1987, Oct. 4    Perf. 12x12½, 12½x12**
| | | | | |
|---|---|---|---|---|
|1295|A361|20f shown|.25|.20|
|1296|A361|40f "40," horiz.|.35|.30|
|1297|A361|90f like 20f|.95|.90|
|1298|A361|100f like 40f, horiz.|1.00|1.00|

*Nos. 1295-1298 (4)*    2.55    2.40

UNICEF, 40th Anniv. — A361

Census Day A362

**1987, Nov. 1          Perf. 12x11½**
| | | | | |
|---|---|---|---|---|
|1299|A362|20f shown|.25|.20|
|1300|A362|30f Graph, Arabs, diff.|.35|.30|
|1301|A362|50f like 30f|.55|.35|
|1302|A362|500f like 20f|5.25|4.00|

*Nos. 1299-1302 (4)*    6.40    4.75

Army Day A363

**Perf. 11½x12, 12x11½**
**1988, Jan. 6                      Litho.**
| | | | | |
|---|---|---|---|---|
|1303|A363|20f "6," Hussein, troops, vert.|.25|.20|
|1304|A363|30f shown|.25|.20|
|1305|A363|50f like 20f, vert.|.55|.20|
|1306|A363|150f like 30f|1.60|.60|

*Nos. 1303-1306 (4)*    2.65    1.20

Art Day — A364

A365

**1988, Jan. 8    Litho.    Perf. 11½x12**
| | | | | |
|---|---|---|---|---|
|1307|A364|20f shown|.35|.20|
|1308|A364|30f Hussein, rainbow, gun barrel, music|.50|.30|
|1309|A364|50f like 20f|.70|.35|
|1310|A364|100f like 30f|1.25|.40|

**Size: 60x80mm**
*Imperf*
| | | | | |
|---|---|---|---|---|
|1311|A364|150f Notes, instruments, floral ornament|2.50|2.50|

*Nos. 1307-1311 (5)*    5.30    3.75

**1988, Feb. 8    Perf. 11½x12, 12x11½**
| | | | | |
|---|---|---|---|---|
|1312|A365|20f "8," troops, Hussein, horiz.|.35|.20|
|1313|A365|30f "8," Hussein, eagle|.45|.20|
|1314|A365|50f like 20f, horiz.|.65|.35|
|1315|A365|150f like 30f|2.10|.65|

*Nos. 1312-1315 (4)*    3.55    1.40

Popular Army, 18th anniv. (20f, 50f); Feb. 8th Revolution, 25th anniv. (30f, 150f).

Al-Baath Arab Socialist Party, 50th Anniv. — A366

President Hussein's 41st Birthday — A367

**1988, Apr. 7    Perf. 12x12½, 12½x12**
| | | | | |
|---|---|---|---|---|
|1316|A366|20f Flag, grain, convention, horiz.|.35|.20|
|1317|A366|30f shown|.45|.30|
|1318|A366|50f like 20f, horiz.|.65|.30|
|1319|A366|150f like 30f|2.10|.60|

*Nos. 1316-1319 (4)*    3.55    1.40

**1988, Apr. 28          Perf. 12x12½**
| | | | | |
|---|---|---|---|---|
|1320|A367|20f shown|.40|.30|
|1321|A367|30f Hussein, 3 hands, flowers|.50|.40|
|1322|A367|50f like 20f|.75|.40|
|1323|A367|150f like 30f|1.50|.60|

**Size: 90x99mm**
*Imperf*
| | | | | |
|---|---|---|---|---|
|1324|A367|150f Sun, Hussein, heart, flowers|4.25|4.25|

*Nos. 1320-1324 (5)*    7.40    5.95

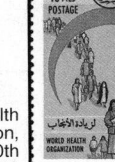

World Health Organization, 40th Anniv. — A368

Regional Marine Environment Day, Apr. 4 — A369

**1988, June 1    Perf. 12x12½, 12x12½**
| | | | | |
|---|---|---|---|---|
|1325|A368|20f WHO anniv. emblem, horiz.|.35|.20|
|1326|A368|40f shown|.45|.30|
|1327|A368|90f like 20f, horiz.|1.25|.40|
|1328|A368|100f like 40f|1.40|.40|

*Nos. 1325-1328 (4)*    3.45    1.30

**1988, Apr. 24    Perf. 12x12½, 12½x12**
| | | | | |
|---|---|---|---|---|
|1329|A369|20f shown|.45|.20|
|1330|A369|40f Flag in map, fish, horiz.|.45|.30|
|1331|A369|90f like 20f|1.25|.40|
|1332|A369|100f like 40f, horiz.|1.25|.40|

*Nos. 1329-1332 (4)*    3.40    1.30

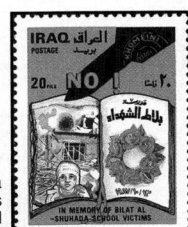

Shuhada School Victims Memorial A370

A371

**1988, June 1    Perf. 11½x12, 12x11½**
| | | | | |
|---|---|---|---|---|
|1333|A370|20f shown|.35|.20|
|1334|A370|40f Girl caught in explosion, horiz.|.45|.30|
|1335|A370|90f like 20f|1.25|.40|
|1336|A370|100f like 40f, horiz.|1.40|.40|

*Nos. 1333-1336 (4)*    3.45    1.30

**Souvenir Sheet**
**Perf. 12½**
| | | | | |
|---|---|---|---|---|
|1337|A371|150f red, blk & brt grn|2.10|2.10|

Pilgrimage to Mecca — A372

**1988, July 24    Litho.    Perf. 13½**
| | | | | |
|---|---|---|---|---|
|1338|A372|90f multicolored|1.25|.40|
|1339|A372|100f multicolored|1.50|.60|
|1340|A372|150f multicolored|2.25|.70|

*Nos. 1338-1340 (3)*    5.00    1.70

Basra,
1350th
Anniv.
A373

**1988, Oct. 22**          **Perf. 12x11½**
1341 A373 100f multicolored          1.40 .60

Natl. Flag, Grip
on Lightning — A374

Pres. Hussein, Natl. Flag — A375

**1988, July 17**          **Perf. 12x12½**
1342 A374 50f shown          .75 .40
1343 A374 90f Map, Hussein,
          desert          1.40 .50
1344 A374 100f like 50f          1.50 .50
1345 A374 150f like 90f          2.00 .60
          **Size: 90x70mm**
          **Imperf**
1346 A375 250f shown          6.00 4.50
     Nos. 1342-1346 (5)          11.65 6.50

July Festivals and 9th anniv. of Pres. Hussein's assumption of office.

Nos. 1272-1273
Overprinted

**1988, Aug. 7   Litho.   Perf. 12½x12**
1347 A354 250f multicolored          6.00 2.00
1348 A354 350f multicolored          8.50 4.00
          Victory.

Navy Day — A376

**1988, Aug. 12**          **Perf. 12x12½**
1349 A376 50f shown          1.10 .40
1350 A376 90f Map, boats          2.00 .60
1351 A376 100f like 50f          2.25 .85
1352 A376 150f like 90f          3.50 1.00
          **Size: 91x70mm**
          **Imperf**
1353 A376 250f Emblem, Pres.
          Hussein dec-
          orating of-
          ficers          9.00 9.00
     Nos. 1349-1353 (5)          17.85 11.85

1988 Summer
Olympics,
Seoul — A377

**1988, Sept. 19**          **Perf. 12x12½**
1354 A377 100f Boxing, char-
          acter trade-
          mark          2.25 .80
1355 A377 150f Flag, emblems          3.50 1.10
          **Size: 101x91mm**
          **Imperf**
1356 A377 500f Emblem,
          trademark,
          Hussein, tro-
          phy          17.00 17.00
     Nos. 1354-1356 (3)          22.75 18.90

Liberation of Fao — A378

**1988, Sept. 1**          **Perf. 12x11½**
1357 A378 100f multicolored          2.00 .60
1358 A378 150f multicolored          3.00 .95
          **Size: 60x80mm**
          **Imperf**
1359 A378 500f Hussein, text          16.50 16.50
     Nos. 1357-1359 (3)          21.50 18.05

Mosul
A379

Baghdad
A380

Ancient cities.

**1988, Oct. 22   Perf. 12x11½, 11½x12**
1360 A379 50f Fortress          .95 .20
1361 A380 150f Astrolabe, mod-
          ern architecture          3.00 .95

Al-Hussein
Missile — A381

**1988, Sept. 10**          **Perf. 11½x12**
1362 A381 100f multicolored          1.40 .50
1363 A381 150f multicolored          2.25 .70
          **Size: 80x60mm**
          **Imperf**
1364 A381 500f Hussein, map,
          missile          10.00 10.00
     Nos. 1362-1364 (3)          13.65 11.20

2nd Intl.
Festival,
Babylon
A382

**1988, Sept. 30**          **Perf. 11½x12**
1365 A382 100f multicolored          1.40 .60
1366 A382 150f multicolored          2.00 .70
          **Size: 60x80mm**
          **Imperf**
1367 A382 500f Medallions          8.50 8.50
     Nos. 1365-1367 (3)          11.90 9.80

Victorious
Iraq
A383

**1988, Aug. 8   Litho.   Perf. 12x11½**
1368 A383 50f multicolored          6.00 6.00
1369 A383 100f multicolored          10.00 10.00
1370 A383 150f multicolored          14.50 14.50
     Nos. 1368-1370 (3)          30.50 30.50

Birthday of
Mohammed
A384

**1988, Oct. 23   Litho.   Perf. 11½x12**
1371 A384 100f multicolored          1.50 .60
1372 A384 150f multicolored          2.00 .90
1373 A384 1d multicolored          14.00 5.25
     Nos. 1371-1373 (3)          17.50 6.75

Martyrs'
Day
A385

**1988, Dec. 1   Litho.   Perf. 13½**
1374 A385 100f multicolored          1.00 .40
1375 A385 150f multicolored          1.90 .70
1376 A385 500f multicolored          6.50 2.00
     Nos. 1374-1376 (3)          9.40 3.15

Police
Day
A386

**1989, Jan. 9   Litho.   Perf. 12x11½**
1377 A386 50f multicolored          .60 .40
1378 A386 100f multicolored          1.40 .45
1379 A386 150f multicolored          2.00 .90
     Nos. 1377-1379 (3)          4.00 1.75

Postal Savings
Bank — A387

a

**1988          Litho.          Perf. 11½x12**
1380 A387     50f shown          1.60 .80
          **Size: 23½x25mm**
          **Perf. 13½x13**
1381 A387(a) 100f multi          6.25 3.00
1382 A387(a) 150f multi          6.75 3.25
     Nos. 1380-1382 (3)          14.60 7.05

#1381-1382 have a line of Arabic at the top.
 #1381-1382 without overprint are postal savings stamps.
 For surcharges see #1507-1510, 1512-1514.

Arab Cooperation Council — A388

**1989, Feb. 12   Litho.   Perf. 12x11½**
1383 A388 100f shown          1.40 .40
1384 A388 150f Statesmen, diff.          2.00 .70

52nd
Birthday
of Pres.
Hussein
A392

**1989, Apr. 28   Litho.   Perf. 12x11½**
1392 A392 100f multicolored          1.25 .50
1393 A392 150f multicolored          1.75 .50
          **Size: 60x81mm**
          **Imperf**
1394 A392 250f Hussein, diff.          6.00 6.00
     Nos. 1392-1394 (3)          9.00 7.00

Fao Liberation, 1st Anniv. — A393

**1989, Apr. 18**          **Perf. 12x11½**
1395 A393 100f multi          1.25 .50
1396 A393 150f multi          2.00 .50
          **Size: 60x81mm**
          **Imperf**
1397 A393 250f Calendar          3.00 3.00
     Nos. 1395-1397 (3)          6.25 4.00

Gen. Adnan
Khairalla — A394

Reconstruction of
Basra — A395

**1989, May 6    Litho.    Perf. 13½**
1398 A394 50f gold & multi          .80    .30
1399 A394 100f copper & multi      1.60    .40
1400 A394 150f silver & multi      2.40    .75
    Nos. 1398-1400 (3)             4.80   1.45

Gen. Adnan Khairalla (1940-1989), deputy
commander-in-chief of the armed forces and
minister of defense.

**1989, June 14**
1401 A395 100f multi               1.60    .40
1402 A395 150f multi               2.40    .75

Reconstruction of          Women — A397
Fao — A396

**1989, June 25**
1403 A396 100f multi               1.60    .40
1404 A396 150f multi               2.40    .75

**1989, June 25    Litho.    Perf. 11½x12**
1405 A397 100f yel & multi         1.25    .35
1406 A397 150f brt pink &
                multi              1.40    .55
1407 A397 1d brt blue &
                multi             12.00   3.75
1408 A397 5d white & multi        50.00  16.00
    Nos. 1405-1408 (4)            64.65  20.65

For surcharges see Nos. 1485-1486, 1511,
1522.

July
Festivals — A398

**1989, July 17    Litho.    Perf. 12x12½**
1409 A398 50f multicolored         .65    .30
1410 A398 100f multicolored       1.25    .40
1411 A398 150f multicolored       2.10    .65
    Nos. 1409-1411 (3)            4.00   1.35

Election of Pres. Hussein, 10th anniv.

Family
A399

**1989, July 19    Perf. 13½**
1412 A399 50f multicolored        1.00    .45
1413 A399 100f multicolored       1.75    .75
1414 A399 150f multicolored       4.75   1.25
    Nos. 1412-1414 (3)            7.50   2.45

A400

Victory Day — A401

**1989, Aug. 8    Perf. 12x12½**
1415 A400 100f multicolored       1.25    .40
1416 A400 150f multicolored       2.10    .65

**Size: 71x91mm**
*Imperf*
1417 A401 250f multicolored       4.25   4.25
    Nos. 1415-1417 (3)            7.60   5.30

Interparliamentary Union,
Cent. — A402

**1989, Sept. 15    Perf. 12½x12**
1418 A402 25f multicolored        .35    .20
1419 A402 100f multicolored      1.25    .40
1420 A402 150f multicolored      2.10    .65
    Nos. 1418-1420 (3)           3.70   1.25

Ancient Cities
A403

**1989, Oct. 15    Perf. 11½x12½**
1421 A403 100f Dhi Qar-ur        1.75    .55
1422 A403 100f Erbil             1.75    .55
1423 A403 100f An Najaf          1.75    .55
    Nos. 1421-1423 (3)           5.25   1.65

5th Session of the Arab Ministers of
Transport Council, Baghdad, Oct. 21
A404

Designs: 100f, Land, air and sea transport,
diff. 150f, Modes of transport, flags, vert.

**1989, Oct. 21    Perf. 12x11½, 11½x12**
1424 A404 50f shown              1.25    .55
1425 A404 100f multicolored      2.60    .75
1426 A404 150f multicolored      4.00   1.10
    Nos. 1424-1426 (3)           7.85   2.40

Iraqi News
Agency,
30th Anniv.
A405

**1989, Nov. 9    Perf. 13½**
1427 A405 50f multicolored       .55    .30
1428 A405 100f multicolored     1.10    .40
1429 A405 150f multicolored     1.75    .65
    Nos. 1427-1429 (3)          3.40   1.35

Declaration of
Palestinian State,
1st
Anniv. — A406

Flowers — A407

**1989, Nov. 15    Perf. 12x12½**
1430 A406 25f shown             .25    .20
1431 A406 50f Palestinian upris-
                ing             .65    .30
1432 A406 100f like 25f        1.25    .40
1433 A406 150f like 50f        2.10    .60
    Nos. 1430-1433 (4)         4.25   1.50

**1989, Nov. 20    Perf. 13½x13**
1434 A407 25f *Viola sp.*       .35    .35
1435 A407 50f *Antirrhinum
                majus*          .75    .35
1436 A407 100f *Hibiscus trionum* 1.50  .45
1437 A407 150f *Mesembryanthe-
                mum sparkles*   2.40    .45
    Nos. 1434-1437 (3)         5.00   1.60

**Miniature Sheet**
**Perf. 12½x11½**
1438        Sheet of 4         9.25   9.25
  a.  A407 25f like No. 1434   2.10   2.10
  b.  A407 50f like No. 1435   2.10   2.10
  c.  A407 100f like No. 1436  2.10   2.10
  d.  A407 150f like No. 1437  2.10   2.10

No. 1438 has a continuous design. No.
1438 sold for 500f.
For overprints and surcharges see Nos.
1450-1451, 1456, 1516, 1524.

A408

A409

**1989, Oct. 25    Litho.    Perf. 13½**
1439 A408 100f multicolored     1.40    .40
1440 A408 150f multicolored     2.10    .65

Reconstruction of Fao.

**1989, Dec. 4    Litho.    Perf. 13½**
1441 A409 50f multicolored      .65    .30
1442 A409 100f multicolored    1.25    .40
1443 A409 150f multicolored    1.75    .65
    Nos. 1441-1443 (3)         3.65   1.35

Martyrs' Day.

Iraqi Red
Crescent
Soc. — A410

**1989, Dec. 10    Litho.    Perf. 13½**
1444 A410 100f multicolored     .70    .35
1445 A410 150f multicolored    2.00    .80
1446 A410 500f multicolored    6.75   2.50
    Nos. 1444-1446 (3)         9.45   3.65

Arab Cooperation Council, 1st
Anniv. — A411

**1990, Feb. 16    Litho.    Perf. 13x13½**
1447 A411 50f yellow & multi    1.00    .50
1448 A411 100f orange & multi   2.75    .90

**Size: 80x62mm**
*Imperf*
1449 A411 250f blue & multi     7.50   7.50
    Nos. 1447-1449 (3)         11.25   8.90

For surcharge see No. 1523.

Nos. 1435, 1437
Ovptd.

**1990, May 28    Litho.    Perf. 13½x13**
1450 A407 50f multicolored     1.10    .85
1451 A407 150f multicolored    3.75   2.50

Arab League Summit Conf., Baghdad.

End of Iran-Iraq
War, 2nd
Anniv. — A412

**1990, Aug. 30    Litho.    Perf. 13½x13**
1452 A412 50f purple & multi          .75
1453 A412 100f blue & multi          1.50

*Imperf*
**Size: 59x81mm**
1454 A412 250f Saddam Hussein, dove 5.00

For surcharge see No. 1525.

The surcharged issues of 1992-97 have been extensively forged. Collectors are urged to purchase these stamps with certificates of authenticity or from expert sellers who can attest to their authenticity

No. 1269 Surcharged
**1992(?)** Litho. *Perf. 12½x12*
1455 A355 1d on 100f #1269 8.50

No. 1434 Surcharged

Type I

Type II

**1993, Aug. 1** Litho. *Perf. 13½x13*
1456 A407 10d on 25f Type I 30.00
a. Type II 40.00

No. RA23
Surcharged

**1992** Photo. *Perf. 14*
1457 PT3 100f on 5f multi 3.00

Reconstruction of Iraq — A413

Designs: 250f, Satellite dish. 500f, Bridges. 750f, Power plant, horiz. 1d, Factory.

**1993, Sept.** Photo. *Perf. 14*
1459 A413 250f red & multi .85
1460 A413 500f blue & multi 1.50
1461 A413 750f yellow & multi 2.25
1462 A413 1d multicolored 3.00
Nos. 1459-1462 (4) 7.60

Stamps of this issue may be poorly centered or have perforations running through the design.
For surcharge see No. 1526.

Peace Ship
A414

**1993** Photo. *Perf. 14*
1463 A414 2d red & multi 2.50
1464 A414 5d green & multi 6.50

No. RA23 Surcharged

b    c

d    e

f    g

h    i

j    k

l    m

n    o

p    q

r

✳ ٢٥ دينار ✳

s

t

**1994, Feb. 5** Photo. *Perf. 14*
1465 PT3(b) 500f on 5f multi, ovpt. 17mm wide 15.00
a. Overprint 14½mm wide 40.00
1466 PT3(c) 1d on 5f multi 2.00
1467 PT3(d) 1d on 5f multi 3.50
a. PT3(e) 1d on 5f multi 6.00
b. PT3(f) 1d on 5f multi 3.00
c. PT3(g) 1d on 5f multi 3.00
1468 PT3(h) 2d on 5f multi 7.00
1469 PT3(i) 2d on 5f multi 3.50
1470 PT3(j) 3d on 5f multi 2.00
1471 PT3(k) 3d on 5f multi 2.00
1472 PT3(l) 5d on 5f multi 3.00
a. PT3(m) 5d on 5f multi 2.00
b. PT3(n) 5d on 5f multi 4.50
1473 PT3(o) 5d on 5f multi 4.25
1474 PT3(p) 10d on 5f multi 4.25
1475 PT3(q) 25d on 5f multi 8.50
a. PT3(r) 25d on 5f multi 14.00
1476 PT3(s) 25d on 10d on 5f 5.00
1477 PT3(t) 50d on 5f multi 28.00

No. 1273 Surcharged

u    v

**1994, Apr. 28** Litho. *Perf. 12½x12*
1480 A354(u) 5d on 350f #1273 7.00
1481 A354(v) 5d on 350f #1273 7.00
a. Pair, #1480-1481 22.50

Alqa'id Two-Deck Bridge A415

**1994, July 17** *Perf. 14*
1482 A415 1d pink & multi 3.50
1483 A415 3d blue & multi 3.50
a. Pair, #1482-1483 8.50

No. 1273
Surcharged

عيد النصر
٩٩٤/٨/٨
✳ ٥ دينار ✳

**1994, Aug. 8** *Perf. 12½x12*
1484 A354 5d on 350f #1273 4.75

No. 1406 Surcharged

w

x

**1995, Jan. 2** *Perf. 11½x12*
1485 A397(w) 5d on 150f #1406 5.00
1486 A397(x) 5d on 150f #1406 5.00
a. Pair 20.00

Baghdad Clock — A416    Saddam Tower — A417

**1995, Feb. 28** *Perf. 11*
1487 A416 7d blue & black 2.50
**Size: 76x98mm**
*Imperf*
1488 A416 25d multicolored 14.00

**1995, Mar. 12** *Perf. 14*
1489 A417 2d multicolored 1.00
1490 A417 5d multicolored 3.25
a. Vert. pair, #1489-1490 4.50

Honoring Dead From Battle of Um Almariq (Mother of All Battles) — A418

Illustration reduced.

**1995** *Imperf.*
1491 A418 100d multicolored 14.00

Saddam Hussein, 58th
Birthday — A419

Design: No. 1492, Saddam seated, flowers
& flag behind him, vert.
Illustration reduced.

**1995, Apr. 28**      *Imperf.*
1492 A419 25d multicolored    16.00
1493 A419 25d multicolored    16.00

Saddam River
Canal Project
A420

**1995, July 17**      *Perf. 11*
1494 A420   4d olive yellow &
        blue    4.00
1495 A420   4d red & blue    4.00
     **Size: 97x57mm**
     *Imperf*
1496 A420 25d multicolored,
        denom. in
        black    13.50
  a.   Denomination in red    13.50

Embargo of
Iraq — A421

**1995, Aug. 6**      *Perf. 11*
1497 A421 10d blue green &
        rose lilac    3.00
     **Size: 77x100mm**
     *Imperf*
1498 A421 25d multicolored    14.00

No. 1273 Surcharged

y

z

**1995, Oct. 15**   Litho.   *Perf. 12½x12*
1499 A354(y) 25d on 350f
          #1273    3.00
1500 A354(z) 25d on 350f
          #1273    3.00
  a.   Pair    20.00

---

Nos. 1103-1108 Surcharged

aa          ab

**1995(?)**    Photo.    *Perf. 15x14*
1501 A315(aa) 25d on 10f
          #1103    2.00
1502 A315(ab) 25d on 20f
          #1104    2.00
1503 A315(aa) 25d on 30f
          #1105    2.00
1504 A315(ab) 25d on 40f
          #1106    8.00
1505 A315(aa) 25d on 50f
          #1107    8.00
1506 A315(ab) 25d on 100f
          #1108    8.00
  a.   Bklt. pane of 6, #1501-
       1506    32.00

No. 1380, Postal Savings Stamps
Similar to Type A387 Surcharged in
Red or Black

ac          ad

ae

**1995(?)**    Litho.    *Perf. 11½x12*
     **Size: 23½x25mm**
1507 A387(ac) 25d on 100f multi    2.00
1508 A387(ac) 25d on 150f blue
           & multi    2.00
1509 A387(ad) 50d on 250f yel &
           multi (R)    4.00
1510 A387(ae) 50d on 50f #1380    4.00

   The 250f postal savings stamp was also
overprinted in denominations of 500f, 2500f
and 5000f. These were not issued and were
demonitized Feb. 1, 1996. They were subsequently surcharged with new values and with a
bar obliterating the original overprint. See Nos.
1512-1514.

No. 1406
Surcharged

**1995(?)**
1511 A397 100d on 150f multi    5.00

Postal Savings Stamps Similar to Type
A387 Surcharged in Red

af

ag

---

ah

**1996**    Litho.    *Perf. 11½x12*
     **Size: 23½x25mm**
     **On 250f Yellow & Multi**
1512 A387(af) 25d on 500d    6.00
1513 A387(ag) 25d on 5000d    5.00
1514 A387(ah) 50d on 2500d    10.00
     Nos. 1512-1514 (3)    21.00

A421a

A421b

Children, Bank —
A421c

**1996**    Litho.    *Perf. 13½*
1514A A421a 25d on 10f grn
            & multi    35.00
1514B A421b 25d on 25f bl &
            multi    2.00
1514C A421c 50d on 10f grn &
            multi    110.00

Children,
Bank — A422

**1996**    Litho.    *Perf. 13½*
1515 A422 50d on 50f multi    3.00
   No. 1515 without surcharge is a postal savings stamp.

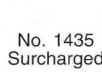

No. 1435
Surcharged

**1996**      *Perf. 13½x13*
1516 A407 100d on 50f multi    6.50

No. O341
Surcharged

**1996**      *Perf. 14*
1517 A324 100d on 70f #O341    5.00

---

No. 1273 Surcharged

ak          al

**1996**    Litho.    *Perf. 12½x12*
1517A A354(ak) 25d on 350f    1.25
1519A A354(al) 1000d on 350f    42.50

No. 1273 Surcharged in Blue or Black

ai          aj

**1996**      *Perf. 12½x12*
1518 A354(ai) 250d on 350f
            (Bl)    7.50
1519 A354(aj) 350d on 350f    18.00

No. O345
Surcharged

**1996**    Litho.    *Perf. 13½*
1519B A329 100d on 60f    5.00

Battle of Um Al
Maarik — A423

**1997, Feb. 13**   Photo.   *Perf. 11*
1520 A423   25d blk, red &
          green    1.00
1521 A423 100d blue, red & grn    5.00
  a.   Arabic word at right center re-
       versed    20.00

No. 1406
Surcharged

**1997, Apr. 22**   Litho.   *Perf. 11½x12*
1522 A397 25d on 150f #1406    4.25
     Post Day.

No. 1448 Surcharged

**1997**          *Perf. 13x13½*
1523 A411 25d on 100f #1448   2.00
Baath Party, 50th anniv.

No. 1450 Surcharged like No. 1516
**1997**    Litho.    *Perf. 13½*
1524 A407 100d on 50f multi   45.00

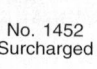

No. 1452
Surcharged

**1997**        *Perf. 13½x13*
1525 A412 100d on 50f multi   8.00

No. 1459
Surcharged

**1997**        *Perf. 14*
1526 A413 25d on 250f multi   1.25

A424

A425

Referendum Day: 250d, Saddam Hussein, map of Arab nations.

**1997**        *Perf. 14*
1527 A424 25d shown   1.50
1527A A424 100d multicolored   6.00
     *Imperf*
     **Size: 91x77mm**
1528 A424 250d multicolored   10.00

**1997, Dec. 19**      *Perf. 14*
Saddam Hussein and: 25d, 100d, #1531, Water irrigating trees, grain. #1532, Water pipeline, flowers, grain.
   **Self-Adhesive (#1530)**
1529 A425 25d multicolored   1.00
1530 A425 100d multicolored   3.00

---

     *Imperf*
     **Size: 68x81mm**
1531 A425 250d multicolored   6.00
     **Size: 64x82mm**
1532 A425 250d multicolored   6.00
     Wafa'a Alqa'id project.

Saladin (1169-1250), Founder of Ayyubid Dynasty, Saddam Hussein — A426

**1998, Feb.**    Litho.    *Perf. 14*
     **Self-Adhesive**
1533 A426 25d multicolored   1.00
1534 A426 100d multicolored   3.00
     **Size: 79x67mm**
     *Imperf*
1535 A426 250d multicolored   18.00
Nos. 1533-1534 exist imperf. No. 1535 has water-activated gum.

New Year — A427

Illustration reduced.

**1998, Mar. 21**      *Imperf.*
1536 A427 250d Zinnias   9.00
1537 A427 250d Irises   9.00

1998 World Cup Soccer Championship, France — A428

Illustration reduced.

**1998, June**      *Imperf.*
1538 A428 250d shown   7.00
     **Size: 63x76mm**
1539 A428 250d Two players, vert.   6.00

---

Souvenir Sheet

Arab Police & Security Leaders Conf., 25th Anniv. — A429

Illustration reduced.

**1998, July 12**    Litho.    *Imperf.*
1540 A429 250d multicolored   6.00

A430

"Zad" Day (Arabic Alphabet) — A431

**1998, Oct. 25**      *Perf. 14*
1541 A430 25d multicolored   .50
1542 A431 100d multicolored   2.00

Flowers — A432

Designs: 25d, Chamomilla recutita. 50d, Helianthus annuus. 1000d, Carduus nutans.

**1998, Oct. 27**
1543 A432   25d multicolored   .40
1544 A432   50d brown leaves   .75
1545 A432   50d green leaves   —
1546 A432   1000d multicolored   8.50
     **Self-Adhesive**
1547 A432   25d like #1543   7.50
No. 1547 is printed on glossy paper.

A433

Martyr's Day — A434

---

**1998, Dec. 1**
1548 A433 25d multicolored   .50
1549 A434 100d multicolored   1.75
Nos. 1548-1549 exist imperf.

Martyr's Day — A434a

Illustration reduced.

**1998, Dec. 1**      Litho.
     *Imperf*
1550 A434a 250d multicolored   4.50

Anthocharis Euphome — A435

**1998, Dec. 20**
1551 A435 100d Precis orithya   3.00
1552 A435 150d shown   4.50
Exist imperf. Value, set $15.

Intl. Conference on Tower of Babel and Ziggurat of Borsippa — A436

**1999, Jan. 23**    Litho.    *Perf. 14*
1553 A436 25d multicolored   1.00
1554 A436 50d multicolored   2.00
     *Imperf*
     **Size: 71x89mm**
1555 A436 250d multicolored   9.00

Great Dam — A437

Saddam Hussein, 62nd Birthday — A439

Saddam Theater — A438

**1999, Apr. 28** *Perf. 14*
1556 A437 25d Dam 1.00
1557 A437 100d Dam, Saddam
Hussein 2.50
*Imperf*
**Size: 70x92mm**
1558 A437 250d Like #1557 9.00

**1999, May 7** *Perf. 14*
1559 A438 25d Saddam Hussein,
emblem 1.00
1560 A438 100d Al-Saddamiyah
City 2.00
*Imperf*
**Size: 92x70mm**
1561 A438 250d Clock tower 9.00

**1999, May 17** *Perf. 14*
1562 A439 25d multicolored .25
1563 A439 50d multicolored .50
1564 A439 150d multicolored 1.75
1565 A439 500d multicolored 6.00
1566 A439 1000d multicolored 14.00
1567 A439 5000d multi, horiz. 55.00
Nos. 1562-1567 (6) 77.50

1998 World Cup,
France — A440

Honey
Bees — A441

**1999, July 17**
1568 A440 25d Two players 1.75
1569 A440 100d Goalie save, horiz. 4.00

**1999, Sept. 18**
1570 A441 25d brown & multi 2.00
1571 A441 50d black & multi 3.00

Al Fat'h
Day
A442

Saddam Hussein and: 25d, Eagle, flowers.
50d, People. 250d, Eagle, flag.

**1999, Dec. 12** *Litho.* *Perf. 14*
1572-1573 A442 Set of 2 2.00
*Imperf*
**Size: 93x71mm**
1574 A442 250d multi 6.75

A443

A444

A445

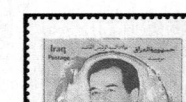

Jerusalem
Day
A446

**2000, Feb.** *Perf. 14*
1575 A443 25d multi .50
1576 A444 50d multi .75
1577 A445 100d multi 1.50
1578 A446 150d multi 2.75
Nos. 1575-1578 (4) 5.50
*Imperf*
**Size: 93x71mm**
1579 A446 250d multi 6.75

A447

Saddam
Hussein's
Birthday
A448

**2000, May 17** *Perf. 14*
1580 A447 25d multi .50
1581 A448 50d multi .75
*Imperf*
**Size: 92x71mm**
1582 A448 500d Saddam Hussein, stars 9.00

Sculpture
A449

Text "July Festivals 2000": a, At right. b, At
left. c, At bottom center on two lines. d, At
lower left. e, At bottom center on 3 lines.

**2000, July 12** *Perf. 14*
1583 Horiz. strip of 5 2.00
a.-e. A449 25d Any single .35
Exists imperf. Value, strip $10.

Victory
Day — A450

Designs: 25d, 250d, Saddam Hussein. 50d,
Saddam Hussein, flag.

**2000, Aug. 8** *Perf. 14*
1584-1585 A450 Set of 2 2.50
*Imperf*
**Size: 71x91mm**
1586 A450 250d multi 4.50

Birds
A451

Designs: 25d, Anas platyrhynchos. 50d,
Passer domesticus. 150d, Porphyrio
poliocephalus.

**2000, Aug. 28** *Perf. 14*
1587-1589 A451 Set of 3 5.00
*Imperf*
**Size: 93x71mm**
1590 A451 500d Carduelis
carduelis 10.00

Prophet
Mohammad's
Birthday — A452

Designs: 25d, Green background. 50d, Tan
background.

**2000, Oct. 11** *Perf. 14*
1591-1592 A452 Set of 2 2.00

A453

Referendum Day — A454

**2000, Oct. 15** *Perf. 14*
1593 A453 25d multi .35
1594 A454 50d multi .75
*Imperf*
**Size: 93x72mm**
1595 A453 250d Saddam Hussein, crowd 4.50

Baytol Hikma,
1200th
Anniv. — A455

**2001, Jan.** *Perf. 14*
1596-1597 A455 Set of 2 1.50
1597a Pair 4.50

A456

A457

Writing, 5th
Millennium
A458

**2001, Mar.** *Litho.* *Perf. 14*
1598 A456 25d multi .30
1599 A457 50d multi .55
1600 A456 75d multi .80
1601 A457 100d multi 1.10
1602 A458 150d multi 1.75
1603 A458 250d multi 2.75
Nos. 1598-1603 (6) 7.25

Bombing of
Al Amiriya
Shelter,
10th Anniv.
A459

Designs: 25d, 150d, Mother, injured child,
rescue workers. 50d, Doves, wreath, picture
frames, vert.

**2001, Mar.** *Perf. 14*
1604-1605 A459 Set of 2 1.50
*Imperf*
**Size: 91x71mm**
**Without Gum**
1606 A459 150d multi 4.00

Al Baath
Party, 54th
Anniv.
A460

Designs: 25d, People, torch. 50d, Presidents Hassan al-Bakr, Saddam Hussein.
100d, Map of Middle East.

**2001, Apr. 7** *Perf. 14*
1607-1609 A460 Set of 3 2.00

Saddam Hussein's 64th Birthday A461

Saddam Hussein: 25d, Seated, with flowers, vert. 50d, Seated. 100d, Seated, with people. 250d, Standing, with crowd.

**2001, Apr. 28**     **Perf. 14**
1610-1612 A461   Set of 3    1.50
     *Imperf*
    **Size: 89x69mm**
    **Without Gum**
1613 A461 250d multi     4.50

Fish A462

Designs: 25d, Barbus sharpeyi. 50d, Barbus esocinus. 100d, Barbus xanthopterus. 150d, Pampus argenteus.

**2001, Aug. 4**     **Perf. 14**
1614-1617 A462   Set of 4    5.00

Battle of Um Al Maarik, 10th Anniv. — A463

Frame color: 25d, Red. 100d, Black.

**2001, Aug.**
1618-1619 A463   Set of 2    1.25

Mammals A464

Designs: 100d, Gazella subgutturosa. 250d, Lepus europaeus. 500d, Camelus dromedarius. 1000d, Various mammals.

**2001, Aug.**     **Perf. 14**
1620-1622 A464   Set of 3    7.50
     *Imperf*
    **Size: 92x70mm**
    **Without Gum**
1623 A464 1000d multi     9.00

Nationalization of Oil Industries, 29th Anniv. — A465

Designs: 25d, Oil rig, workers, soldier, Iraqi flag. 50d, Oil rig, refinery, pipeline.

**2001, Sept. 15**   **Litho.**   **Perf. 14**
1624-1625 A465   Set of 2    1.00

Support for Palestinians A466

Designs: No. 1626, 25d, Saddam Hussein, map of Israel and Iraq. No. 1627, 25d, Dome of the Rock, Palestinian flag, gunman, vert. 50d, Dome of the Rock, Palestinian flag, gunman with arms raised, vert.
   No. 1629, 250d, Dome of the Rock, Israeli tank and Palestinian rock-thrower. No. 1630, 250d, Dome of the Rock, doves, Palestinian flag and Mohammad J. Durra and father.

**2001, Sept. 20**
1626-1628 A466   Set of 3    1.25
     *Imperf*
    **Size: 88x67mm**
    **Without Gum**
1629-1630 A466   Set of 2    5.00

2001 Youth Soccer World Cup A467

Designs: 25d, Players, map of world. 50d, Map of Asia, player, trophy, vert.

**2001, Oct. 7**     **Perf. 14**
1631-1632 A467   Set of 2    1.00

Iraqi Claim of Depleted Uranium US Bombs Dropped on Iraqi Citizens — A468

Falling bombs and: No. 1633, 25d, Woman and children. No. 1634, 25d, No. 1636, 250d, Disfigured people. 50d, People, Iraqi flag, horiz.

**2001, Nov.**
1633-1635 A468   Set of 3    4.00
     *Imperf*
    **Size: 70x91mm**
    **Without Gum**
1636 A468 250d multi     7.00

Army Day — A469

Designs: 25d, Iraqi flag, soldiers, airplanes, ship and tank. No. 1638, 50d, No. 1640, 250d, Monument, vert. 100d, Soldier, Iraqi flag, tank, vert.

**2002, Jan. 6**     **Perf. 14**
1637-1639 A469   Set of 3    3.50
     *Imperf*
    **Size: 73x91mm**
    **Without Gum**
1640 A469 250d multi     3.50

Liberation of Fao — A470

Saddam Hussein and : 25d, Mosque. 100d, Soldier, map of Iraq, horiz.

**2002, Apr. 17**     **Perf. 14**
1641-1642 A470   Set of 2    1.50

February 8 Revolution, 39th Anniv. — A470a

February 8 Revolution, 39th Anniv. — A470b

**2002, Feb. 8**   **Litho.**   **Perf. 14**
1642A A470a 50d multi    8.00   —
1642B A470b 100d multi   12.00   —

Jerusalem Day — A471

Frame color: 25d, Blue. 50d, Yellow. 100d, Pink.

**2002, Apr.**
1643-1645 A471   Set of 3    2.00

Hegira, Year 1423 A472

Designs: 25d, Mosques, Holy Kaaba. 50d, Minaret and mosque, vert. 75d, Bird, spider web.

**2002, Apr.**
1646-1648 A472   Set of 3    1.75

Bombardment of Al Amirya Shelter, 11th Anniv. — A473

Frame color: 25d, Black. 50d, Red.

**2002, Apr.**
1649-1650 A473   Set of 2    1.00

War Against Iraq, 11th Anniv. — A474

**2002, Apr.**
1651 A474 100d multi     1.75

Flowers — A475

Designs: 25d, Roses. 50d, Roses, diff. 150d, Poppies, carnations. 250d, Roses, diff.

**2002, Apr.**     **Perf. 14**
1652-1654 A475   Set of 3    3.50
     *Imperf*
    **Size: 73x91mm**
    **Without Gum**
1655 A475 250d multi     5.00

Saddam Hussein's 65th Birthday — A476

Color of vignette frame and country name: 25d, Red. 50d, Purple. 75d, Green. 100d, Dark blue.
   No. 1660, 250d, Saddam Huseein, hearts and flowers. No. 1661, 250d, Saddam Hussein with headdress.

**2002, Apr. 28**     **Perf. 14**
1656-1659 A476   Set of 4    2.75
     *Imperf*
    **Size: 74x91mm**
    **Without Gum**
1660-1661 A476   Set of 2    6.00

Palestinian Unity — A477

**2002**     **Litho.**     **Perf. 14**
1662 A477 5000d multi     35.00

Mosques — A478

Designs: 25d, Sheikh Maroof Mosque. 50d, Al-Mouiz Mosque. 75d, Um Al Marik Mosque.

**2002**
1663-1665 A478   Set of 3    2.00

Post Day — A479

Air mail envelope and: 50d, Stamp with dove. 100d, Airplane, ship, train, map of world. 250d, Globe and dove.

**2002**
1666-1667 A479   Set of 2    2.00

*Imperf*
**Size: 70x91mm**
**Without Gum**
1668 A479 250d multi .................. 4.50

**2002 World Cup Soccer Championships, Japan and Korea — A480**

World Cup, various players and background color of: 50d, Blue. 100d, Yellow. 150d, Red violet.
250d, Purple.

| 2002 | | | Perf. 14 |
|---|---|---|---|
| 1669-1671 | A480 | Set of 3 | 3.00 |

*Imperf*
**Size: 70x92mm**
**Without Gum**
1672 A480 250d multi .................. 4.00

Ancient Ships A481

Various ships: 150d, 250d, 500d.

| 2002 | | | Perf. 14 |
|---|---|---|---|
| 1673-1675 | A481 | Set of 3 | 9.00 |

Victory Day — A482

Frame color: 25d, Blue. 50d, Pink. 150d, Eagle, vert.

| 2002 | | | Perf. 14 |
|---|---|---|---|
| 1676-1677 | A482 | Set of 2 | 1.75 |

*Imperf*
**Size: 71x90mm**
**Without Gum**
1678 A482 150d multi .................. 4.00

A483

A484

A485

A486

**Poets — A487**

Illustration A487 reduced.

| 2002 | | Litho. | Perf. 14 |
|---|---|---|---|
| 1679 | A483 | 25d multi | .35 |
| 1680 | A484 | 50d multi | .50 |
| 1681 | A485 | 75d multi | 1.00 |
| 1682 | A486 | 100d multi | 1.25 |
| | Nos. 1679-1682 (4) | | 3.10 |

*Imperf*
**Size: 70x92mm**
**Without Gum**
1683 A487 150d multi .................. 4.00

A488

A489

A490

**Baghdad Day — A491**

Illustration A491 reduced.

| 2002 | | | Perf. 14 |
|---|---|---|---|
| 1684 | A488 | 25d multi | .35 |
| 1685 | A489 | 50d multi | .50 |
| 1686 | A490 | 75d multi | 1.00 |
| | Nos. 1684-1686 (3) | | 1.85 |

*Imperf*
**Size: 91x70mm**
**Without Gum**
1687 A491 250d multi .................. 5.00

Referendum Day — A492

Designs: 100d, 250d, Saddam Hussein, people, hands, heart and flowers. 150d, Fist, ballot box.

| 2002 | | | Perf. 14 |
|---|---|---|---|
| 1688-1689 | A492 | Set of 2 | 2.50 |

*Imperf*
**Size: 71x92mm**
**Without Gum**
1690 A492 250d multi .................. 2.75

Mammals A493

Designs: 25d, Oryx leucoryx. 50d, Acionyx jubatus, vert. 75d, 250d, Panthera leo persica, vert. 100d, Castor fiber. 150d, Equus hemionus hemippus.

| 2002 | | | Perf. 14 |
|---|---|---|---|
| 1691-1695 | A493 | Set of 5 | 7.00 |

*Imperf*
**Size: 70x93mm**
**Without Gum**
1696 A493 250d multi .................. 8.00

Saddam University A494

Background colors: 50d, Brown. 100d, Blue.

| 2002 | | | Perf. 14 |
|---|---|---|---|
| 1697-1698 | A494 | Set of 2 | 2.00 |

Iraqi Coalition Provisional Authority postal officials have declared as illegal 13 Iraqi stamps of the Saddam Hussein regime with various overprints and surcharges that read "Iraq / In Coalition / Occupation."

**Issues of the Coalition Provisional Authority**

Transportation — A495

Designs: 50d, Raft. 100d, Horse-drawn carriage. 250d, Horse-drawn rail car. 500d, Boat. 5000d, Camel caravan.

| 2004, Jan. 15 | | Litho. | Perf. 14 |
|---|---|---|---|
| 1699-1703 | A495 | Set of 5 | 9.75 9.75 |
| | Dated 2003. | | |

New Year — A496

| 2006, Mar. 16 | | Litho. | Perf. 13 |
|---|---|---|---|
| 1704 | A496 | 250d multi | 1.00 1.00 |

A497

June 30, 2004 Installation of Iraqi Interim Government A498

| 2006, Sept. 7 | | Litho. | Perf. 14½ |
|---|---|---|---|
| 1705 | A497 | 100d multi | .35 .35 |
| 1706 | A498 | 250d multi | .90 .90 |

Iraq Civilization A499

Designs: 100d, Mannequin with headdress. 150d, Golden bull. 200d, Stone carving. 250d, Paintings of horses on walls.

| 2006, Sept. 11 | | Litho. | Perf. 14½ |
|---|---|---|---|
| 1707-1709 | A499 | Set of 3 | 1.75 1.75 |

*Imperf*
**Size: 80x61mm**
1710 A499 250d multi .................. 2.00 2.00

2004 Summer Olympics,
Athens — A500

Designs: 100d, Soccer players. 150d,
Runners.
500d, Various athletes.

**2006, Sept. 24**     **Perf. 14¼**
1711-1712 A500   Set of 2    1.25 1.25
**Imperf**
**Size: 100x70mm**
1713 A500 500d multi     2.50 2.50

Paintings — A501

Unnamed paintings by: 100d, Akram Shukri.
150d, Hafidh Al Duroubi. 200d, Faiq Hassan.
250d, Atheer M. G.

**2006, Oct. 9**     **Perf. 14¼**
1714-1716 A501   Set of 3    1.75 1.75
**Imperf**
**Size: 88x70mm**
1717 A501 250d multi     2.00 2.00

Flowers — A502

Designs: 250d, Anemone. 750d, Viola mam-
mola. 1000d, Atropa belladonna.

**2007**     **Litho.**    **Die Cut**
**Self-Adhesive**
1718-1720 A502   Set of 3    3.25 3.25
1720a    Souvenir sheet, #1718-1720    3.25 3.25
Issued: Nos. 1718-1720, 4/11; No. 1720a,
5/7.

Singers and
Cat — A503

**2007, Apr. 23**     **Perf. 13½x13¼**
1721 A503 5000d multi     12.00 12.00
Dated 2006.

Butterflies
A504

Designs: 100d, Papilio demodocus. 250d,
Precis orithua. 500d, Coitas croceus.
1000d, Papilio demodocus, diff.

**2007, Apr. 23**     **Perf. 13½x13¼**
1722-1724 A504   Set of 3    2.10 2.10
**Size: 80x61mm**
**Imperf**
1725 A504 1000d multi     2.40 2.40

Artisans — A505

Designs: 250d, Rug maker. 350d, Blanket
maker. 500d, Basket maker.

**2007, May 22**     **Litho.**    **Die Cut**
**Self-Adhesive**
1726-1728 A505   Set of 3    3.00 3.00
1728a    Miniature sheet, #1726-1728    3.00

Folklore — A506

Illustration reduced.

**2007, June 7**     **Imperf.**
1729 A506 1000d multi     2.40 2.40
Dated 2006.

Rafidain Bank,
65th Anniv. (in
2006) — A507

Background colors: 100d, Light blue. 150d,
Orange red. 250d, Brown. 500d, Lilac.

**2007, July 10**     **Perf. 14**
1730-1733 A507   Set of 4    2.40 2.40
Dated 2006.

Birds
A508

Designs: 150d, Anser anser. 250d, Merops
superciliosus. 500d, Pterocles alchata.
1500d, Ducks in flight.

**2007, Sept.**     **Perf. 14**
1734-1736 A508   Set of 3    2.10 2.10
**Imperf**
**Size: 80x80mm**
1737 A508 1500d multi     3.50 3.50

A509

Musicians
and Actors
A510

Designs: 250d, Mohammad al-Qubanchi,
singer. 500d, Haqi al-Shibly, actor, horiz.
750d, Nazem al-Ghazaly, singer, horiz. 1000d,
Munir Bashir, musician.

**2007, Oct. 1**     **Die Cut**
**Self-Adhesive**
1738 A509   250d multi    1.00 1.00
1739 A509   500d multi    2.00 2.00
1740 A509   750d multi    3.00 3.00
1741 A509   1000d multi    4.00 4.00
a.    Miniature sheet, #1738-1741    10.00
Nos. 1738-1741 (4)    10.00 10.00

## AIR POST STAMPS

> Catalogue values for unused
> stamps in this section are for
> Never Hinged items.

Basra Airport — AP1

Diyala Railway
Bridge — AP2

Vickers Viking over: 4f, 20f, Kut Dam. 5f,
35f, Faisal II Bridge.

**Perf. 11½, 11½x12**
**1949, Feb. 1**    **Engr.**    **Unwmk.**
C1   AP1   3f blue green    .40   .20
C2   AP1   4f red violet    .40   .20
C3   AP1   5f red brown    .45   .20
C4   AP1   10f carmine    3.75   1.00
C5   AP1   20f blue    2.25   .60
C6   AP1   35f red orange    2.50   .60
C7   AP2   50f olive    3.25   .95
C8   AP2   100f violet    7.50   2.00
   Nos. C1-C8 (8)    20.50   5.75

Sheets exist, perf. and imperf., containing
one each of Nos. C1-C8, with arms and Arabic
inscription in blue green in upper and lower
margin. Value (2 sheets), each $80.

**Republic**

ICY Emblem — AP3

**1965, Aug. 13**    **Litho.**    **Perf. 13½**
C9   AP3   5f brn org & black    .60   .20
C10   AP3   10f citron & dk brn    1.10   .20
C11   AP3   30f ultra & black    2.75   .95
   Nos. C9-C11 (3)    4.45   1.35
International Cooperation Year.

Trident
1E Jet
Plane
AP4

**1965, Dec. 1**    **Photo.**    **Perf. 11½**
**Granite Paper**
C12   AP4   5f multicolored    .40   .20
C13   AP4   10f multicolored    .40   .20
C14   AP4   40f multicolored    4.25   .80
   Nos. C12-C14 (3)    5.05   1.20
Introduction by Iraqi Airways of Trident 1E
jet planes.

Arab
International
Tourist Union
Emblem — AP5

Travelers
on Magic
Carpet
AP6

**1966, Dec. 3**    **Litho.**    **Perf. 13½, 14**
C15   AP5   2f multicolored    .65   .20
C16   AP6   5f yellow & multi    .90   .20
C17   AP5   15f blue & multi    1.10   .20
C18   AP6   50f multicolored    2.00   .50
   Nos. C15-C18 (4)    4.65   1.10
Meeting of the Arab Intl. Tourist Union,
Baghdad.
For overprint see No. RAC1.

Costume Type of Regular Issue

Iraqi Costumes: 40f, Woman's head. 50f,
Woman's costume. 80f, Man's costume.

**1967, Nov. 10**    **Litho.**    **Perf. 13**
C19   A105   40f multicolored    1.25   .65
C20   A105   50f blue & multi    2.00   .95
C21   A105   80f green & multi    2.75   1.10
   Nos. C19-C21 (3)    6.00   2.70
For overprints, see CO1-CO3.

International Tourist Year Type of
Regular Issue

Designs: 50f, Female statue, Temples of
Hatra. 80f, Spiral Tower (Malwiye of Samarra).
100f, Adam's Tree. 200f, Aladdin's Cave.
500f, Golden Shiah Mosque of Kadhimain.
50f, 80f, 100f and 200f are vert.

**1967, Dec. 1**       **Litho.**
C22   A107   50f multicolored    3.00   .40
C23   A107   80f multicolored    3.25   .65
C24   A107   100f multicolored    3.25   .80
C25   A107   200f ver & multi    7.00   3.25
C26   A107   500f brn & multi    32.50   18.00
   Nos. C22-C26 (5)    49.00   23.10
For overprints see Nos. C39, C52, C53,
CO4.

Arabian
AP7

Animals: 2f, Striped hyena. 3f, Leopard.
5f, Mountain gazelle. 200f, Arabian stallion.

**1969, Sept. 1**    **Litho.**    **Perf. 14**
C27   AP7   2f multicolored    .50   .20
C28   AP7   3f multicolored    .50   .20
C29   AP7   5f multicolored    .50   .20
C30   AP7   10f multicolored    .75   .20
C31   AP7   200f multicolored    11.50   6.00
   Nos. C27-C31 (5)    13.75   6.80
For overprints, see Nos. CO5-CO7.

Ross Smith's Vickers Vimy AP8

**1969, Dec. 4    Litho.    Perf. 14**
C32 AP8 15f dk bl & multi    2.50  1.00
C33 AP8 35f multicolored    4.00  2.50
  a.  Souv. sheet of 2, #C32-C33, imperf.    15.00 13.00

50th anniv. of the first England to Australia flight of Capt. Ross Smith and Lt. Keith Smith. No. C33a sold for 100f.

View Across Euphrates — AP9

Iraqi Banknotes and Pres. Hassan al-Bakr AP10

**1970, Oct. 30    Litho.    Perf. 13**
C34 AP9 10f brt bl & multi    1.75  .50
C35 AP9 15f multicolored    2.75  1.10
C36 AP10 1d multicolored    65.00 24.00
  Nos. C34-C36 (3)    69.50 25.60

National Development Plan. For overprints see Nos. C42-C43.

Telecommunications Emblem — AP11

**1970, Dec. 15    Litho.    Perf. 14x13½**
C37 AP11 15f gray & multi    .50  .20
C38 AP11 25f lt bl & multi    .75  .35

10th Conf. of Arab Telecommunications Union.

No. C23 Overprinted

**1971, Apr. 23    Perf. 13**
C39 A107 80f multicolored    6.00  4.25

World Meteorological Day.

Iraqi Philatelic Society Emblem — AP12

**1972, Feb. 25    Litho.    Perf. 13**
C40 AP12 25f multicolored    1.10  .95
C41 AP12 70f pink & multi    3.75  2.10

Iraqi Philatelic Society, 20th anniversary.

Nos. C34-C35 Overprinted

**1972, Feb. 25**
C42 AP9 10f brt bl & multi    2.40  2.40
C43 AP9 15f multicolored    2.40  2.40

9th Cong. of Natl. Union of Iraqi Students.

Soccer and C.I.S.M. Emblem AP13

20f, 35f, Players, soccer ball, C.I.S.M. emblem. 100f, Winged lion, Olympic & C.I.S.M. emblems.

**1972, June 9    Litho.    Perf. 13½**
C46 AP13 10f lt bl & multi    .55  .30
C47 AP13 20f dp bl & multi    1.25  .30
C48 AP13 25f green & multi    1.25  .30
C49 AP13 35f brt bl & multi    4.25  .80
  a.  Souv. sheet, 100f, imperf.    22.50 22.50
  Nos. C46-C49 (4)    7.30  1.70

25th Military Soccer Championships (C.I.S.M.), Baghdad, June 9-19.

Statue of Athlete — AP14

Design: 70f, Mesopotamian archer on horseback, ancient and modern athletes.

**1972, Nov. 15    Photo.    Perf. 14x13½**
C50 AP14 25f multicolored    1.25  .65
C51 AP14 70f multicolored    3.50  2.10

Cong. of Asian and World Body Building Championships, Baghdad, Nov. 15-23, 1972.

Nos. C23, C26 Overprinted

**1973, Mar. 25    Litho.    Perf. 13**
C52 A107 80f multi    21.00  7.25
C53 A107 500f multi    75.00 75.00

International History Congress.

**ICATU Type of 1976**

**1976, Mar. 24    Photo.    Perf. 13½**
C54 A213 75f blue & multi    4.00  2.00

Symbolic Eye AP15

Basketball AP16

**1976, June 20    Photo.    Perf. 14**
C55 AP15 25f ultra & dk brn    .30  .20
C56 AP15 35f brt grn & dk brn    .50  .20
C57 AP15 50f orange & multi    1.00  .60
  Nos. C55-C57 (3)    1.80  1.00

World Health Day: Foresight prevents blindness.

**1976, July 30    Litho.    Perf. 12x12½**

Montreal Olympic Games Emblem and: 35f, Volleyball. 50f, Wrestling. 75f, Boxing. 100f, Target shooting, horiz.

C58 AP16 25f yel & multi    .50  .20
C59 AP16 35f blue & multi    .75  .50
C60 AP16 50f ver & multi    1.00  .95
C61 AP16 75f yel grn & multi    2.00  1.25
  Nos. C58-C61 (4)    4.25  2.90

**Souvenir Sheet**
**Imperf**

C62 AP16 100f grn & multi    6.00  6.00

21st Olympic Games, Montreal, Canada, July 17-Aug. 1.

13th World Telecommunications Day — AP17

**1981, May 17    Photo.    Perf. 12½**
C63 AP17 25f multicolored    .50  .20
C64 AP17 50f multicolored    1.00  .40
C65 AP17 75f multicolored    1.75  .85
  Nos. C63-C65 (3)    3.25  1.45

**Air Force Type of 1981**

**1981, June 1    Photo.    Perf. 14x13½**
C66 A289 120f Planes, vert.    4.00  2.50

**AIR POST OFFICIAL STAMP**

**Catalogue values for all unused stamps in this section are for Never Hinged items.**

Nos. C19-C22 Overprinted

**1971    Litho.    Perf. 13**
CO1 A105 40f multicolored    4.75  1.40
CO2 A105 50f multicolored    6.00  1.40
CO3 A105 80f multicolored    5.50  1.40

**"Official" Reading Down**
CO4 A107 50f multicolored    5.25  3.25
  Nos. CO1-CO4 (4)    21.50  7.45

Nos. C27-C28, C30 Overprinted or Surcharged

**1971    Perf. 14**
CO5 AP7 10f multicolored    7.50  5.00
CO6 AP7 15f on 3f multi    7.50  5.00
CO7 AP7 25f on 2f multi    7.50  5.00
  Nos. CO5-CO7 (3)    22.50 15.00

No bar and surcharge on No. CO5.

---

**OFFICIAL STAMPS**

**British Mandate**
Regular Issue of 1923 Overprinted:

k                            l

**1923    Wmk. 4    Perf. 12**
O1 A1(k) ½a olive grn    .90  .50
O2 A2(k) 1a brown    1.00  .20
O3 A3(l) 1½a car lake    2.75  .75
O4 A4(k) 2a brown org    1.75  .30
O5 A5(k) 3a deep blue    3.50  .75
O6 A6(l) 4a dull violet    3.50  .50
O7 A7(k) 6a blue green    5.25  1.40
O8 A6(l) 8a olive bister    5.75  1.30
O9 A8(l) 1r green & brn    6.50  1.40
O10 A1(k) 2r black (R)    20.00  9.00
O11 A6(l) 5r orange    60.00 27.50
O12 A7(k) 10r carmine    85.00 60.00
  Nos. O1-O12 (12)    195.90 103.60

Regular Issue of 1923-25 Overprinted:

m

n

**1924-25**
O13 A1(m) ½a olive green    1.25  .30
O14 A2(m) 1a brown    1.00  .30
O15 A3(n) 1½a car lake    1.00  .30
O16 A4(m) 2a brown org    1.75  .30
O17 A5(m) 3a deep blue    2.25  .30
O18 A6(n) 4a dull violet    5.00  .30
O19 A6(n) 6a blue green    2.10  .30
O20 A6(n) 8a olive bister    5.00  .40
O21 A8(n) 1r green & brn    11.00  1.00
O22 A1(m) 2r bister ('25)    37.50  4.50
O23 A6(n) 5r orange    60.00 50.00
O24 A7(m) 10r brown red    85.00 52.50
  Nos. O13-O24 (12)    212.85 110.50

For overprint see Nos. O42, O47, O51-O53.

No. 14 Overprinted Type "n"
**1927**
O25 A9 1r red brown    8.00  2.00

### Regular Issue of 1931 Overprinted Vertically

o

**1931**

| O26 | A10 | ½a green | .20 | 3.00 |
|---|---|---|---|---|
| O27 | A10 | 1a chestnut | .20 | .20 |
| O28 | A10 | 1½a carmine | 7.50 | 16.00 |
| O29 | A10 | 2a orange | .70 | .20 |
| O30 | A10 | 3a light blue | 1.25 | .70 |
| O31 | A10 | 4a purple brown | 1.40 | .90 |
| O32 | A10 | 6a Pruss blue | 5.00 | 12.50 |
| O33 | A10 | 8a dark green | 5.00 | 12.50 |

### Overprinted Horizontally

p

| O34 | A11 | 1r dark brown | 9.50 | 12.50 |
|---|---|---|---|---|
| O35 | A11 | 2r yellow brown | 20.00 | 45.00 |
| O36 | A11 | 5r deep orange | 47.50 | 85.00 |
| O37 | A11 | 10r red | 85.00 | 140.00 |
| | | Nos. O26-O37 (12) | 183.25 | 328.50 |

### Overprinted Vertically Reading Up

| O38 | A9(p) | 25r violet | 900.00 | 1,200. |

For overprints see Nos. O39-O41, O43-O46, O48-O50, O54.

### Kingdom

Nos. O15, O19, O22-O24, O26-O31, O33-O35, O38 Surcharged with New Values in Fils and Dinars, like Nos. 28-43

**1932, Apr. 1**

| O39 | A10 | 3f on ½a | 4.00 | 4.00 |
|---|---|---|---|---|
| O40 | A10 | 4f on 1a (G) | 2.75 | .20 |
| O41 | A10 | 5f on 1a | 2.75 | .20 |
| a. | | Inverted Arabic "5" | 52.50 | 35.00 |
| O42 | A3 | 8f on 1½a | 6.25 | .60 |
| O43 | A10 | 10f on 2a | 3.50 | .20 |
| O44 | A10 | 15f on 3a | 4.75 | 2.75 |
| O45 | A10 | 20f on 4a | 4.75 | 2.75 |
| O46 | A10 | 25f on 4a | 5.00 | 2.25 |
| O47 | A7 | 30f on 6a | 5.25 | 2.00 |
| O48 | A10 | 40f on 8a | 4.50 | 4.00 |
| a. | | "Flis" for "Fils" | 300.00 | 450.00 |
| O49 | A11 | 50f on 1r | 6.25 | 4.00 |
| O50 | A11 | 75f on 1r | 7.00 | 7.00 |
| O51 | A1 | 100f on 2r | 20.00 | 4.00 |
| O52 | A6 | 200f on 5r | 26.00 | 26.00 |
| O53 | A7 | ½d on 10r | 75.00 | 100.00 |
| a. | | Bar in "½" omitted | 850.00 | 975.00 |
| O54 | A9 | 1d on 25r | 140.00 | 210.00 |
| | | Nos. O39-O54 (16) | 317.75 | 369.95 |

### Regular Issue of 1932 Overprinted Vertically like Nos. O26-O33

**1932, May 9**

| O55 | A12 | 2f ultramarine | 1.00 | .20 |
|---|---|---|---|---|
| O56 | A12 | 3f green | 1.00 | .20 |
| O57 | A12 | 4f violet brn | 1.25 | .20 |
| O58 | A12 | 5f gray | 1.25 | .20 |
| O59 | A12 | 8f deep red | 1.25 | .20 |
| O60 | A12 | 10f yellow | 2.25 | .20 |
| O61 | A12 | 15f deep blue | 2.75 | .20 |
| O62 | A12 | 20f orange | 2.75 | .20 |
| O63 | A12 | 25f rose lilac | 2.75 | .40 |
| O64 | A12 | 30f olive grn | 4.00 | .40 |
| O65 | A12 | 40f dark violet | 5.75 | .40 |

### Overprinted Horizontally Like Nos. O34 to O37

| O66 | A13 | 50f deep brown | 3.75 | .50 |
|---|---|---|---|---|
| O67 | A13 | 75f lt ultra | 2.75 | 1.00 |
| O68 | A13 | 100f deep green | 12.50 | 1.50 |
| O69 | A13 | 200f dark red | 20.00 | 8.75 |

### Overprinted Vertically like No. O38

| O70 | A14 | ½d gray blue | 15.00 | 22.50 |
|---|---|---|---|---|
| O71 | A14 | 1d claret | 70.00 | 100.00 |
| | | Nos. O55-O71 (17) | 152.50 | 137.05 |

### Regular Issue of 1934-38 Overprinted Type "o" Vertically Reading up in Black

**1934-38**      Unwmk.

| O72 | A15 | 1f purple ('38) | 1.10 | .50 |
|---|---|---|---|---|
| O73 | A15 | 2f ultramarine | 1.10 | .20 |
| O74 | A15 | 3f green | .65 | .20 |
| O75 | A15 | 4f purple brn | 1.10 | .20 |
| O76 | A15 | 5f gray green | 1.00 | .20 |
| O77 | A15 | 8f deep red | 4.50 | .20 |
| O78 | A15 | 10f yellow | .45 | .20 |
| O79 | A15 | 15f deep blue | 10.00 | 1.50 |
| O80 | A15 | 20f orange | 1.00 | .20 |

| O81 | A15 | 25f brown violet | 20.00 | 6.25 |
|---|---|---|---|---|
| O82 | A15 | 30f olive green | 4.50 | .20 |
| O83 | A15 | 40f dark violet | 5.75 | .40 |

### Overprinted Type "p"

| O84 | A16 | 50f deep brown | | .65 |
|---|---|---|---|---|
| O85 | A16 | 75f ultramarine | 6.75 | .90 |
| O86 | A16 | 100f deep green | 1.75 | 1.00 |
| O87 | A16 | 200f dark red | 4.50 | 2.75 |

### Overprinted Type "p" Vertically Reading Up

| O88 | A17 | ½d gray blue | 11.00 | 18.00 |
|---|---|---|---|---|
| O89 | A17 | 1d claret | 45.00 | 55.00 |
| | | Nos. O72-O89 (18) | 121.15 | 88.55 |

> **Catalogue values for unused stamps in this section, from this point to the end of the section, are for Never Hinged items.**

### Stamps of 1941-42 Overprinted in Black or Red:

r

s

*Perf. 11½x13½, 13 to 14 and Compound*

**1941-42**

| O90 | A18(r) | 1f dk vio ('42) | .50 | .20 |
|---|---|---|---|---|
| O91 | A18(r) | 2f choc ('42) | .50 | .20 |
| O92 | A19(r) | 3f brt grn ('42) | .50 | .20 |
| O93 | A19(r) | 4f pur (R) ('42) | .50 | .20 |
| O94 | A19(r) | 5f car rose ('42) | .50 | .20 |
| O95 | A20(s) | 8f carmine | 1.75 | .20 |
| O96 | A20(s) | 8f ocher ('42) | .50 | .20 |
| O97 | A20(s) | 10f ocher | 12.75 | .85 |
| O98 | A20(s) | 10f car ('42) | 1.40 | .20 |
| O99 | A20(s) | 15f dull blue | 12.75 | 1.50 |
| O100 | A20(s) | 15f blk (R) ('42) | 2.25 | .65 |
| O101 | A20(s) | 20f black (R) | 3.75 | .65 |
| O102 | A20(s) | 20f dl bl ('42) | 1.25 | .20 |
| O103 | A21(r) | 25f dark vio | 1.75 | .65 |
| O104 | A21(r) | 25f dk vio ('42) | 2.00 | .65 |
| O105 | A21(s) | 30f dp orange | 1.75 | .65 |
| O106 | A21(r) | 30f dk org ('42) | 1.75 | .65 |
| O107 | A21(s) | 40f brown org | 1.10 | .25 |
| O108 | A21(r) | 40f chnt ('42) | 1.75 | .65 |
| O109 | A21(s) | 50f ultra | 3.25 | .25 |
| O110 | A21(r) | 75f rose vio | 2.00 | .85 |
| O111 | A22(s) | 100f ol grn ('42) | 4.50 | .65 |
| O112 | A22(s) | 200f dp org ('42) | 6.00 | 1.75 |
| O113 | A23(r) | ½d blue ('42) | 20.00 | 20.00 |
| O114 | A23(r) | 1d grnsh bl ('42) | 32.50 | 29.00 |
| | | Nos. O90-O114 (25) | 117.25 | 61.45 |

The space between the English and Arabic on overprints "r" and "s" varies with the size of the stamps.

For overprints see Nos. O165, RA5.

### Stamps of 1942 Overprinted in Black

**1942**    Unwmk.    *Perf. 13x13½*

| O115 | A24 | 1f violet & brown | .65 | .65 |
|---|---|---|---|---|
| O116 | A24 | 2f dark blue & brn | .65 | .65 |
| O117 | A24 | 3f lt green & brn | .65 | .65 |
| O118 | A24 | 4f dl brown & brn | .65 | .65 |
| O119 | A24 | 5f sage green & brn | .85 | .85 |
| O120 | A24 | 6f red orange & brn | .85 | .85 |
| O121 | A24 | 10f dl rose red & brn | 1.10 | 1.10 |
| O122 | A24 | 12f yel green & brn | 1.50 | 1.50 |
| | | Nos. O115-O122 (8) | 6.90 | 6.90 |

### Stamps of 1948 Overprinted in Black

**1948, Jan. 15**    *Perf. 11½x12*
**Size: 17¾x20½mm**

| O123 | A25 | 1f slate | .20 | .35 |
|---|---|---|---|---|
| O124 | A25 | 2f sepia | .20 | .45 |
| O125 | A25 | 3f emerald | .20 | .45 |
| O126 | A25 | 4f purple | .20 | .35 |
| O127 | A25 | 5f rose lake | .20 | .25 |
| O128 | A25 | 6f plum | .20 | .45 |
| O129 | A25 | 8f ocher | .20 | .45 |
| O130 | A25 | 10f rose red | .20 | .35 |
| O131 | A25 | 12f dark olive | .20 | .35 |
| O132 | A25 | 15f black | 4.00 | 6.75 |
| O133 | A25 | 20f blue | .25 | .20 |
| O134 | A25 | 25f rose violet | .25 | .20 |
| O135 | A25 | 30f red orange | .25 | .25 |
| O136 | A25 | 40f orange brn | .55 | .45 |

*Perf. 12x11½*
**Size: 22x27½mm**

| O137 | A25 | 60f deep blue | .80 | .25 |
|---|---|---|---|---|
| O138 | A25 | 75f lilac rose | 1.40 | .40 |
| O139 | A25 | 100f olive grn | 1.40 | 1.00 |
| O140 | A25 | 200f dp orange | 2.25 | 1.00 |
| O141 | A25 | ½d blue | 19.00 | 16.00 |
| O142 | A25 | 1d green | 27.50 | 35.00 |
| | | Nos. O123-O142 (20) | 59.45 | 64.95 |

For overprints see Nos. O166-O177, O257, O272, O274, O277, O282, RA1, RA3, RA4.

### Same Overprint on Nos. 133-138

**1949-51**    *Perf. 11½x12*
**Size: 17¾x20½mm**

| O143 | A25 | 3f rose lake ('51) | 3.25 | 1.00 |
|---|---|---|---|---|
| O144 | A25 | 5f emerald ('51) | 3.50 | 1.00 |
| O145 | A25 | 14f dk olive ('50) | 1.75 | .35 |
| O146 | A25 | 16f rose red ('51) | 3.25 | .35 |
| O147 | A25 | 28f blue ('51) | 1.00 | .35 |

*Perf. 12x11½*
**Size: 22x27½mm**

| O148 | A25 | 50f deep blue | 1.25 | .50 |
|---|---|---|---|---|
| | | Nos. O143-O148 (6) | 14.00 | 3.55 |

For overprints see #O258, O273, O275, O276.

### Same Overprint in Black on Stamps and Type of 1954-57

**1955-59**    *Perf. 11½x12*

| O148A | A28 | 1f blue ('56) | .20 | .20 |
|---|---|---|---|---|
| O149 | A28 | 2f chocolate | .20 | .20 |
| O150 | A28 | 3f rose lake | .20 | .20 |
| O151 | A28 | 4f violet | .25 | .20 |
| O152 | A28 | 5f emerald | .25 | .20 |
| O153 | A28 | 6f plum ('56) | .25 | .20 |
| O154 | A28 | 8f ocher ('56) | .25 | .20 |
| O155 | A28 | 10f blue | .25 | .20 |
| O155A | A28 | 16f brt rose ('57) | 22.50 | 22.50 |
| O156 | A28 | 20f olive | .45 | .25 |
| O157 | A28 | 25f rose violet | 2.25 | 1.00 |
| O158 | A28 | 30f vermilion | 1.00 | .20 |
| O159 | A28 | 40f orange brn | .45 | .20 |

**Size: 22½x27½mm**

| O160 | A28 | 50f blue | 2.25 | .75 |
|---|---|---|---|---|
| O161 | A28 | 60f pale purple | 14.00 | 5.75 |
| O161A | A28 | 100f ol grn ('59) | 32.50 | 16.00 |
| | | Nos. O148A-O161A (16) | 77.25 | 48.25 |

Dates of issue for Nos. O155A and O161A are suppositional.

For overprints see Nos. O178-O191, O259-O260, O283-O291.

### Same Ovpt. on Stamps of 1957-58

| O162 | A33 | 1f blue | 4.25 | 1.75 |
|---|---|---|---|---|
| O162A | A33 | 2f chocolate | 5.00 | 3.75 |
| O162B | A33 | 3f dk carmine | 6.50 | 2.75 |
| O162C | A33 | 4f dull violet | 7.75 | 1.75 |
| O162D | A33 | 5f emerald | 4.25 | 1.75 |
| O163 | A33 | 6f plum | 4.25 | 2.75 |
| O164 | A33 | 10f blue | 4.25 | 1.40 |
| | | Nos. O162-O164 (7) | 36.25 | 15.90 |

For overprints see #O192-O199, O292-O293.

### Republic

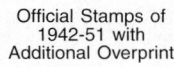

### Official Stamps of 1942-51 with Additional Overprint

*Perf. 13½x14*

**1958-59**    **Engr.**    **Unwmk.**

| O165 | A22 | 200f dp orange | 10.00 | 5.75 |

*Perf. 11½x12, 12x11½*

| O166 | A25 | 12f dk olive | 1.00 | .75 |
|---|---|---|---|---|
| O167 | A25 | 14f olive | 1.10 | .95 |
| O168 | A25 | 15f black | .95 | .50 |
| O169 | A25 | 16f rose red | 3.75 | 2.10 |
| O170 | A25 | 25f rose vio | 3.50 | 2.00 |
| O171 | A25 | 28f blue | 2.00 | 1.60 |
| O172 | A25 | 40f orange brn | 1.25 | .95 |
| O173 | A25 | 60f deep blue | 5.00 | 2.50 |
| O174 | A25 | 75f lilac rose | 2.25 | 1.90 |
| O175 | A25 | 200f dp orange | 2.75 | 2.40 |
| O176 | A25 | ½d blue | 17.00 | 6.25 |
| O177 | A25 | 1d green | 27.50 | 12.50 |
| | | Nos. O166-O177 (12) | 68.05 | 34.40 |

Other denominations of types A22 and A25 exist with this overprint, but these were probably not regularly issued.

### Same Ovpt. on Nos. O148A-O161A

| O178 | A28 | 1f blue | .60 | .20 |
|---|---|---|---|---|
| O179 | A28 | 2f chocolate | .60 | .20 |
| O180 | A28 | 3f rose lake | .60 | .20 |
| O181 | A28 | 4f violet | .60 | .20 |
| O181A | A28 | 5f emerald | .65 | .40 |
| O182 | A28 | 6f plum | .60 | .20 |
| O183 | A28 | 8f ocher | .55 | .20 |
| O183A | A28 | 10f blue | .80 | .25 |
| O184 | A28 | 16f bright rose | 7.50 | 7.00 |
| O185 | A28 | 20f olive | .65 | .20 |
| O186 | A28 | 25f rose violet | .65 | .40 |
| O187 | A28 | 30f vermilion | .70 | .40 |
| O188 | A28 | 40f orange brn | 1.00 | .40 |
| O189 | A28 | 50f blue | 1.00 | .50 |
| O190 | A28 | 60f pale purple | 1.00 | .60 |
| O191 | A28 | 100f olive grn | 2.10 | .60 |
| | | Nos. O178-O191 (16) | 19.60 | 11.75 |

### Same Ovpt. on #O162-O164, 216

| O192 | A33 | 1f blue | .20 | .20 |
|---|---|---|---|---|
| O193 | A33 | 2f chocolate | .20 | .20 |
| O194 | A33 | 3f dark carmine | .45 | .20 |
| O195 | A33 | 4f dull violet | .20 | .20 |
| O196 | A33 | 5f emerald | .20 | .20 |
| O197 | A33 | 6f plum | .65 | .20 |
| O198 | A33 | 8f ocher | .65 | .20 |
| O199 | A33 | 10f blue | .70 | .20 |
| | | Nos. O192-O199 (8) | 2.80 | 1.60 |

### Nos. 232-233, 235-237, 242 Overprinted

**Litho. & Photo.**

**1961, Apr. 1**    Unwmk.    *Perf. 11½*

| O200 | A38 | 1f multi | .40 | .30 |
|---|---|---|---|---|
| O201 | A38 | 2f multi | .40 | .30 |
| O202 | A38 | 4f multi | .40 | .30 |
| O203 | A38 | 5f multi | .50 | .30 |
| O204 | A38 | 10f multi | .80 | .60 |
| O205 | A38 | 50f multi | 13.50 | 10.50 |
| | | Nos. O200-O205 (6) | 16.00 | 12.30 |

### Nos. 232-247 Overprinted

**1961**

### Emblem in Gold, Red and Blue; Blue Inscriptions

| O206 | A38 | 1f gray | .40 | .30 |
|---|---|---|---|---|
| O207 | A38 | 2f salmon | .40 | .30 |
| O208 | A38 | 3f pale violet | .40 | .30 |
| O209 | A38 | 4f bright yel | .40 | .30 |
| O210 | A38 | 5f light blue | .40 | .30 |
| O211 | A38 | 10f bright pink | .40 | .30 |
| O212 | A38 | 15f lt green | .40 | .30 |
| O213 | A38 | 20f bister brn | .40 | .30 |
| O214 | A38 | 30f light gray | .50 | .30 |
| O215 | A38 | 40f orange yel | .50 | .30 |
| O216 | A38 | 50f yel green | .60 | .30 |
| O217 | A38 | 75f pale green | .80 | .40 |
| O218 | A38 | 100f orange | .90 | .65 |
| O219 | A38 | 200f dull lilac | 3.25 | 1.40 |
| O220 | A38 | 500f bister | 11.50 | 5.50 |
| O221 | A38 | 1d brt green | 22.50 | 11.50 |
| | | Nos. O206-O221 (16) | 43.75 | 22.75 |

Nos. 480-482 Overprinted

| | | | | |
|---|---|---|---|---|
| **1971** | | **Litho.** | **Perf. 13½** | |
| O222 | A115 | 10f multicolored | .80 | 1.50 |
| O223 | A115 | 15f blue & multi | 8.00 | 1.50 |
| O224 | A115 | 25f multicolored | 8.00 | 3.00 |
| | | *Nos. O222-O224 (3)* | 16.80 | 6.00 |

Overprint lines are spaced 16mm on No. O222, 32½mm on Nos. O223-O224.

Same Overprint on Nos. 453, 455-456

| | | | | |
|---|---|---|---|---|
| **1971** | | | **Perf. 13** | |
| O225 | A107 | 5f lilac & multi | 6.00 | .30 |
| O226 | A107 | 15f rose red & multi | 6.00 | .50 |
| O227 | A107 | 25f vio bl & multi | 8.50 | 1.50 |
| | | *Nos. O225-O227 (3)* | 20.50 | 2.30 |

Overprint horizontal on Nos. O225 and O227; vertical, reading down on No. O226. Distance between English and Arabic words: 8mm.

Nos. 446, 448-449
Overprinted

| | | | | |
|---|---|---|---|---|
| **1971** | | **Litho.** | **Perf. 13** | |
| O228 | A105 | 15f multicolored | 1.50 | .65 |
| O229 | A105 | 15f multi, wide ovpt. setting | 62.50 | 7.50 |
| a. | | Narrow setting | | 47.50 |
| O230 | A105 | 25f multicolored | 10.50 | 3.00 |
| O231 | A105 | 30f multicolored | 10.50 | 3.00 |
| | | *Nos. O228-O231 (4)* | 85.00 | 14.15 |

No. O229 overprinted "Official" horizontally. Two overprint settings on O229: wide, 6.5mm between English and Arab inscriptions; narrow, 2mm between inscriptions.

Same Overprint on Nos. 483-486

| | | | | |
|---|---|---|---|---|
| **1972** | | | **Perf. 13½** | |
| O232 | A116 | 10f multicolored | 5.00 | .50 |
| O233 | A116 | 25f multicolored | 5.00 | 1.00 |

| | | | | |
|---|---|---|---|---|
| **1972** | | | | |
| O234 | A117 | 15f multicolored | 5.00 | .50 |
| O235 | A117 | 25f multicolored | 5.00 | 1.00 |

Same Overprint, "Official" Reading Down on Nos. 562-565

| | | | | |
|---|---|---|---|---|
| **1972** | | | | |
| O240 | A142 | 5f multicolored | 5.00 | 3.75 |
| O241 | A142 | 10f multicolored | 5.00 | 3.75 |
| O242 | A142 | 15f multicolored | 5.00 | 3.75 |
| O243 | A142 | 35f multicolored | 5.00 | 3.75 |
| | | *Nos. O240-O243 (4)* | 20.00 | 15.00 |

Latin inscription on Nos. O240-O241 obliterated with heavy bar.

No. 487 Overprinted "Official" like No. CO5

| | | | | |
|---|---|---|---|---|
| **1972** | | **Photo.** | **Perf. 13½** | |
| O244 | A118 | 25f multicolored | 10.50 | 3.00 |

#134, O148 Ovptd. with 3 Bars
**Perf. 11½x12, 12x11½**

| | | | | |
|---|---|---|---|---|
| **1973, Jan. 29** | | | **Engr.** | |
| O257 | | 25f rose violet | 6.00 | 1.50 |
| O258 | A25 | 50f deep blue | 6.00 | 5.50 |

Same on Nos. O157 and O160

| | | | | |
|---|---|---|---|---|
| O259 | A28 | 25f rose violet | 6.00 | 1.50 |
| O260 | A28 | 50f blue | 6.00 | 1.50 |

Type of 1957
Overprinted

---

**Size: 22x27½mm**

| | | | | |
|---|---|---|---|---|
| O261 | A33 | 50f rose violet | 6.00 | 1.50 |
| | | *Nos. O257-O261 (5)* | 30.00 | 11.50 |

See note after No. 679. No. O261 not issued without overprints.

King Faisal Issues
Overprinted

Two sizes of overprint: Arabic 6½mm or 9mm.

| | | | | |
|---|---|---|---|---|
| **1973** | | | | |
| O263 | A28 | 15f black (#149) | 4.00 | 3.75 |
| O264 | A33 | 15f black | 4.00 | 1.00 |
| O265 | A25 | 25f rose vio (#121) | 15.00 | 6.00 |
| O266 | A28 | 25f rose vio (#151) | 4.00 | 1.00 |
| O267 | A33 | 25f rose violet | 4.00 | 1.00 |

Same Overprint on Nos. 674-677

| | | | | |
|---|---|---|---|---|
| O268 | A28 | 10f blue | 3.75 | 3.75 |
| O269 | A28 | 10f blue | 52.50 | 60.00 |
| O270 | A28 | 15f black | 67.50 | 75.00 |
| O271 | A33 | 15f black | 2.50 | 2.00 |
| | | *Nos. O263-O271 (9)* | 157.25 | 153.50 |

Official Stamps of 1948-51 Overprinted

Overprint design faces left or right.

| | | | | |
|---|---|---|---|---|
| **1973** | | | | |
| O272 | A25 | 12f (#O131) | 1.75 | .30 |
| O273 | A25 | 14f (#O145) | 1.75 | .50 |
| O274 | A25 | 15f (#O132) | 1.75 | .50 |
| O275 | A25 | 16f (#O146) | 3.25 | .85 |
| O276 | A25 | 28f (#O147) | 6.75 | 1.10 |
| O277 | A25 | 30f (#O135) | 6.75 | .95 |
| O278 | A25 | 40f (#O136) | 6.75 | 1.40 |
| O279 | A25 | 60f (#O137) | 6.75 | 5.25 |
| O280 | A25 | 100f (#O139) | 22.50 | 8.50 |
| O281 | A25 | ½d (#O141) | 57.50 | 22.50 |
| O282 | A25 | 1d (#O142) | 110.00 | 110.00 |
| | | *Nos. O272-O282 (11)* | 225.50 | 151.85 |

Same Overprint on Official Stamps of 1955-59

| | | | | |
|---|---|---|---|---|
| O283 | A28 | 3f (#O150) | 1.75 | .60 |
| O284 | A28 | 6f (#O153) | 1.75 | .60 |
| O285 | A28 | 8f (#O154) | 1.75 | .60 |
| O286 | A28 | 16f (#O155A) | 15.00 | 15.00 |
| O287 | A28 | 20f (#O156) | 1.75 | .60 |
| O288 | A28 | 30f (#O158) | 1.75 | .95 |
| O289 | A28 | 40f (#O159) | 1.75 | 1.60 |
| O290 | A28 | 60f (#O161) | 8.75 | 2.00 |
| O291 | A28 | 100f (#O161A) | 27.50 | 8.00 |
| | | *Nos. O283-O291 (9)* | 61.75 | 29.95 |

Same Overprint on 1957-58 Issues

| | | | | |
|---|---|---|---|---|
| O292 | A33 | 3f dk car (#O162B) | 5.00 | 1.25 |
| O293 | A33 | 6f plum (#O163) | 5.00 | 1.25 |
| O294 | A33 | 8f ocher (#179) | 5.00 | 1.25 |
| O295 | A33 | 30f red orange | 5.00 | 1.25 |
| | | *Nos. O292-O295 (4)* | 20.00 | 5.00 |

The overprint on Nos. O294-O295 includes the "On State Service" overprint; No. O295 was not issued without overprints. The overprint leaf design faces left or right and varies in size.

Nos. 403, 497, 681
Overprinted

**Perf. 12½, 13x12½, 13½**

| | | | | |
|---|---|---|---|---|
| **1974 (?)** | | | **Photo., Litho.** | |
| O296 | A89 | 2f multicolored | 5.00 | |
| O297 | A123 | 15f multicolored | 6.00 | .50 |
| O298 | A185 | 25f multicolored | 3.75 | 1.00 |
| | | *Nos. O296-O298 (3)* | 14.75 | |

Size of "Official" on Nos. O297-O298 9mm.

---

Nos. 683-691
Overprinted

| | | | | |
|---|---|---|---|---|
| **1974** | | **Litho.** | **Perf. 13x12½** | |
| O299 | A186 | 5f orange & blk | .30 | .30 |
| O300 | A186 | 10f bister & blk | .30 | .30 |
| O301 | A186 | 20f brt rose & blk | .65 | .30 |
| O302 | A186 | 25f ultra & blk | 1.25 | 1.25 |
| O303 | A186 | 35f emerald & blk | 1.25 | .50 |
| O304 | A186 | 45f blue & black | 1.25 | .60 |
| O305 | A186 | 50f olive & yel | 1.75 | .65 |
| O306 | A186 | 70f violet & yel | 1.75 | .95 |
| O307 | A186 | 95f brown & yel | 2.50 | 1.10 |
| | | *Nos. O299-O307 (9)* | 11.00 | 5.95 |

Nos. 455 and 467
Overprinted

| | | | | |
|---|---|---|---|---|
| **1975** | | **Litho.** | **Perf. 13, 14** | |
| O308 | A107 | 15f multicolored | 3.50 | 3.50 |
| O311 | A107 | 30f multicolored | 6.25 | 4.25 |

Space between Arabic and English lines of overprint is 4mm on No. O308, 13mm on No. O311.

Nos. 491-493 Overprinted or Surcharged like Nos. CO5-CO7

| | | | | |
|---|---|---|---|---|
| **1975** | | | **Perf. 14** | |
| O312 | A121 | 10f multicolored | 6.50 | 4.00 |
| O312A | A121 | 15f on 3f multi | 6.50 | 4.00 |
| O313 | A121 | 25f on 2f multi | 6.50 | 4.00 |
| | | *Nos. O312-O313 (3)* | 19.50 | 12.00 |

Nos. 322-325
Overprinted

**Engr.; Engr. & Photo.**

| | | | | |
|---|---|---|---|---|
| **1975** | | | **Perf. 12x11** | |
| O314 | A57 | 10f rose red | 8.00 | .60 |
| O315 | A57 | 15f brown & buff | 8.00 | .75 |
| O316 | A57 | 20f violet blue | 8.00 | .75 |
| O317 | A57 | 30f orange | 15.00 | .80 |
| | | *Nos. O314-O317 (4)* | 39.00 | 2.90 |

Arms of
Iraq — O1

Altharthar -
Euphrates
Canal — O2

| | | | | |
|---|---|---|---|---|
| **1975** | | **Photo.** | **Perf. 14** | |
| O318 | O1 | 5f multicolored | .30 | .30 |
| O319 | O1 | 10f blue & multi | .30 | .30 |
| O320 | O1 | 15f yel & multi | .40 | .40 |
| O321 | O1 | 20f ultra & multi | .65 | .65 |
| O322 | O1 | 25f org & multi | .90 | .90 |
| O323 | O1 | 30f rose & multi | 1.00 | 1.00 |
| O324 | O1 | 50f multicolored | 1.75 | 1.75 |
| O325 | O1 | 100f multicolored | 3.25 | 3.25 |
| | | *Nos. O318-O325 (8)* | 8.55 | 8.55 |

Nos. 787-791 Overprinted "OFFICIAL" in English and Arabic

| | | | | |
|---|---|---|---|---|
| **1976, Sept. 15** | | **Litho.** | **Perf. 13½x14** | |
| O327 | A219 | 5f multicolored | 1.25 | .75 |
| O328 | A219 | 10f multicolored | 1.25 | .95 |
| O329 | A219 | 15f multicolored | 1.40 | .95 |
| O330 | A219 | 25f multicolored | 3.75 | 1.25 |
| O331 | A219 | 50f multicolored | 6.25 | 2.25 |
| | | *Nos. O327-O331 (5)* | 13.90 | 6.15 |

| | | | | |
|---|---|---|---|---|
| **1978** | | **Photo.** | **Perf. 11½** | |
| O332 | O2 | 5f multicolored | .30 | .30 |
| O333 | O2 | 10f multicolored | .30 | .30 |
| O334 | O2 | 15f multicolored | .45 | .30 |
| O335 | O2 | 25f multicolored | .90 | .30 |
| | | *Nos. O332-O335 (4)* | 1.95 | 1.20 |

---

Baghdad
University
Entrance — O3

| | | | | |
|---|---|---|---|---|
| **1981, Oct. 21** | | **Litho.** | **Perf. 12x12½** | |
| O336 | O3 | 45f multicolored | .65 | .40 |
| O337 | O3 | 50f multicolored | .70 | .50 |

Nos. O336-O337 Surcharged

| | | | | |
|---|---|---|---|---|
| **1983, May 15** | | **Litho.** | **Perf. 12x12½** | |
| O338 | O3 | 60f on 45f multi | 2.50 | .50 |
| O339 | O3 | 70f on 50f multi | 3.00 | .75 |

Martyrs Type of 1981

| | | | | |
|---|---|---|---|---|
| **1981** | | **Photo.** | **Perf. 14** | |
| O339A | A303 | 45f silver border | 1.25 | .40 |
| O339B | A303 | 50f gold border | 1.25 | .50 |
| O339C | A303 | 120f metallic bl border | 3.50 | 1.10 |
| | | *Nos. O339A-O339C (3)* | 6.00 | 2.00 |

Building Type of 1983

| | | | | |
|---|---|---|---|---|
| **1982, Dec. 31** | | **Litho.** | **Perf. 14** | |
| O340 | A324 | 60f multicolored | .90 | .50 |
| O341 | A324 | 70f multicolored | 1.00 | .65 |

For surcharge see No. 1517.

Martyr Type of 1984

| | | | | |
|---|---|---|---|---|
| **1984, Dec. 1** | | | **Perf. 13½** | |
| O342 | A329 | 20f multicolored | .30 | .30 |
| O343 | A329 | 30f multicolored | .30 | .30 |
| O344 | A329 | 50f multicolored | .55 | .40 |
| O345 | A329 | 60f multicolored | .70 | .40 |
| | | *Nos. O342-O345 (4)* | 1.85 | 1.40 |

No. RA22 Overprinted

| | | | | |
|---|---|---|---|---|
| **1985 (?)** | | **Litho.** | **Perf. 13x12½** | |
| O346 | PT2 | 5f bister, blk & yel | 3.25 | 1.00 |

## POSTAL TAX STAMPS

Catalogue values for unused stamps in this section are for Never Hinged items.

Nos. O125 and 115
Surcharged in Carmine
or Black

| | | | | |
|---|---|---|---|---|
| **1949** | | **Unwmk.** | **Perf. 11½x12** | |
| RA1 | A25 | 2f on 3f emer (C) | 25.00 | 15.00 |
| RA2 | A25 | 2f on 6f plum | 32.50 | 14.00 |

Similar Overprint in Carmine or Black
on Nos. O124, O127 and O94
Middle Arabic Line Omitted

**Perf. 11½x12**

| | | | | |
|---|---|---|---|---|
| RA3 | A25 | 2f sepia (C) | 20.00 | 9.00 |
| RA4 | A25 | 5f rose lake | 40.00 | 20.00 |

**Perf. 12x13½, 14**

| | | | | |
|---|---|---|---|---|
| RA5 | A19 | 5f dark car rose | 20.00 | 10.50 |

Larger overprint on #RA5, 20½mm wide. Value $22.50.

No. 115 Surcharged in
Black

**Perf. 11½x12**

| | | | | |
|---|---|---|---|---|
| RA6 | A25 | 5f on 6f plum | 45.00 | 17.00 |

The tax on Nos. RA1-RA6 was to aid the war in Palestine.

Nos. 317, 322-326 Surcharged

**Engr.; Engr. & Photo.**

| 1963 | | | **Perf. 12x11** |
|---|---|---|---|
| RA7 | A57 5f on 1f green | 3.75 | 4.50 |
| RA8 | A57 5f on 10f rose red | 3.75 | 4.50 |
| RA9 | A57 5f on 15f brn & buff | 3.75 | 4.50 |
| RA10 | A57 5f on 20f vio blue | 3.75 | 4.50 |
| RA11 | A57 5f on 30f orange | 3.75 | 4.50 |
| RA12 | A57 5f on 40f brt green | 3.75 | 4.50 |
| | Nos. RA7-RA12 (6) | 22.50 | 27.00 |

Surtax was for the Defense Fund.

PT1      b

**1967, Aug.   Photo.   Perf. 13½**
RA13 PT1 5f brown     .45   .20

Surtax was for flood victims.

Same Overprinted "b"

**1967, Nov.**
RA14 PT1 5f brown     .45   .45

Surtax was for Defense Fund.

Nos. 305A-305B with Surcharge
Similar to Nos. RA7-RA12

**1972   Litho.   Perf. 13½x14**
RA15 A54a 5f on 14f    7.00   7.00
RA16 A54a 5f on 35f    7.00   7.00

Surtax was for the Defense Fund. The 2 disks obliterating old denominations are on one line at the bottom. Size of Arabic inscription: 17x12mm.

No. 452 with Surcharge Similar to Nos. RA7-RA12, and Nos. 443, 457 and 526 Surcharged:

**1973   Litho.   Perf. 13**
RA17 A105 5f on 2f multi   8.50   8.50
RA18 A107 5f on 2f multi   8.50   8.50
RA19 A108 5f on 2f multi   8.50   8.50
RA20 A135 5f on 2f multi   8.50   8.50
Nos. RA17-RA20 (4)   34.00   34.00

Surtax was for the Defense Fund. Surcharges on Nos. RA17-RA20 are adjusted to fit shape of stamps and to obliterate old denominations.

No 683 Overprinted

**1974   Litho.   Perf. 13x12½**
RA21 A186 5f orange & blk   6.00   4.00

Soldier      Dome of the
PT2        Rock, Jerusalem
           PT3

**1974**
RA22 PT2 5f bister, blk & yel   2.50   3.00

Surtax of Nos. RA21-RA22 was for the Defense Fund.
For overprint see No. O346.

**1977   Photo.   Perf. 14**
RA23 PT3 5f multicolored   2.75   1.50

Surtax was for families of Palestinians.
For surcharges see Nos. 1457, 1465-1477.

---

**AIR POST POSTAL TAX STAMPS**

Catalogue values for unused stamps in this section are for Never Hinged items.

#C15 Surcharged Like #RA17-RA20

**1973     Perf. 13½**
RAC1 AP5 5f on 2f multi   8.50   8.50

Surtax was for the Defense Fund.

---

# IRELAND

ˈīr-lənd

(Eire)

LOCATION — Comprises the entire island of Ireland, except 5,237 square miles at the extreme north
GOVT. — Republic
AREA — 27,136 sq. mi.
POP. — 3,626,087 (1996)
CAPITAL — Dublin

12 Pence = 1 Shilling
100 Pence = 1 Pound (Punt) (1971)
100 Cents = 1 Euro (2002)

Catalogue values for unused stamps in this country are for Never Hinged items, beginning with Scott 99 in the regular postage section, Scott C1 in the air post section, and Scott J5 in the postage due section.

**Watermarks**

Wmk. 44 — SE in Monogram

The letters "SE" are the initials of "Saorstat Eireann" (Irish Free State).

Wmk. 262 — Multiple "e"

**Overprinted by Dollard, Ltd.**
Great Britain Nos. 159-167, 170-172, 179-181 Overprinted

Overprint measures 15x17½mm

This overprint means "Provisional Government of Ireland."

Black or Gray Black Overprint

| **1922, Feb. 17   Wmk. 33   Perf. 15x14** | | |
|---|---|---|
| 1   A82   ½p green | .90 | 1.00 |
|   Never hinged | 1.50 | |
| a.   Inverted overprint | 500.00 | 700.00 |
|   Never hinged | 750.00 | |
| 2   A83   1p scarlet | 1.00 | 1.00 |
|   Never hinged | 1.75 | |
| a.   Inverted overprint | 300.00 | 550.00 |
| b.   Double overprint | | |
| 3   A86   2½p ultra | 1.75 | 6.50 |
|   Never hinged | 4.25 | |
| 4   A87   3p violet | 7.00 | 10.00 |
|   Never hinged | 12.50 | |
| 5   A88   4p slate green | 4.50 | 15.00 |
|   Never hinged | 10.00 | |
| 6   A89   5p yel brown | 5.50 | 16.00 |
|   Never hinged | 13.00 | |
| 7   A90   9p black brown | 16.00 | 30.00 |
|   Never hinged | 40.00 | |
| 8   A90   10p light blue | 11.00 | 25.00 |
|   Never hinged | 20.00 | |
|   Nos. 1-8 (8) | 47.65 | 104.50 |

The ½p with red overprint is a proof.

Red or Carmine Overprint

| **1922, Apr.-July** | | |
|---|---|---|
| 9   A86   2½p ultra | 1.90 | 7.00 |
|   Never hinged | 3.75 | |
| 10   A88   4p slate green (R) | 12.50 | 21.00 |
|   Never hinged | 25.00 | |
| 10A   A88   4p slate green (C) | 65.00 | 90.00 |
|   Never hinged | 125.00 | |
| 11   A90   9p black brown | 20.00 | 30.00 |
|   Never hinged | 50.00 | |
|   Nos. 9-11 (4) | 99.40 | 148.00 |

Overprinted in Black

Overprint measures 21½x14mm

There is a variation that is 21x14mm. The "h" and "é" are 1mm apart. See Nos. 36-38.

| **1922, Feb. 17   Wmk. 34   Perf. 11x12** | | |
|---|---|---|
| 12   A91   2sh6p brown | 40.00 | 90.00 |
|   Never hinged | 100.00 | |
| 13   A91   5sh car rose | 85.00 | 160.00 |
|   Never hinged | 200.00 | |
| 14   A91   10sh gray blue | 175.00 | 350.00 |
|   Never hinged | 375.00 | |
|   Nos. 12-14 (3) | 300.00 | 600.00 |

**Overprinted by Alex. Thom & Co.**

Overprinted in Black

Overprint measures 14½x16mm

TWO PENCE
Die I — Four horizontal lines above the head. Heavy colored lines above and below the bottom tablet. The inner frame line is closer to the central design than it is to the outer frame line.
Die II — Three lines above the head. Thinner lines above and below the bottom tablet. The inner frame line is midway between the central design and the outer frame line.

| **1922, Feb. 17   Wmk. 33   Perf. 15x14** | | |
|---|---|---|
| 15   A84   1½p red brown | 1.50 | 1.75 |
|   Never hinged | 4.00 | |
| a.   "PENCF" | 400.00 | 350.00 |
| 16   A85   2p orange (II) | 2.75 | 1.25 |
|   Never hinged | 6.00 | |
| a.   Inverted overprint (II) | 400.00 | 500.00 |
| b.   2p orange (I) | 2.75 | 1.25 |
|   As "b," never hinged | 6.00 | |
| c.   Inverted overprint (I) | 210.00 | 300.00 |
| 17   A89   6p red violet | 11.00 | 8.00 |
|   Never hinged | 25.00 | |

| 18   A90   1sh bister | 19.00 | 17.50 |
|---|---|---|
|   Never hinged | 40.00 | |
|   Nos. 15-18 (4) | 34.25 | 28.50 |

Important: see Nos. 25-26, 31, 35.

**Overprinted by Harrison & Sons**
Coil Stamps

Overprinted in Black in Glossy Black Ink

Overprint measures 15¼x17mm

| **1922, June** | | |
|---|---|---|
| 19   A82   ½p green | 3.50 | 8.00 |
|   Never hinged | 6.50 | |
| 20   A83   1p scarlet | 3.50 | 6.50 |
|   Never hinged | 5.00 | |
| 21   A84   1½p red brown | 6.50 | 45.00 |
|   Never hinged | 10.00 | |
| 22   A85   2p orange (I) | 20.00 | 37.50 |
|   Never hinged | 35.00 | |
| a.   2p orange (II) | 18.00 | 42.50 |
|   Never hinged | 40.00 | |
|   Nos. 19-22 (4) | 33.50 | 97.00 |

In Harrison overprint, "i" of "Rialtas" extends below the base of the other letters.
The Harrison stamps were issued in coils, either horizontal or vertical. The paper is double where the ends of the strips were overlapped. Mint pairs with the overlap sell for about three times the price of a single. The perforations are often clipped.

**Overprinted by Alex. Thom & Co.**
Stamps of Great Britain, 1912-22
Overprinted as Nos. 15 to 18, in Shiny to Dull Blue Black, or Red
Overprint measures 14½x16mm

Note: The blue black overprints can be distinguished from the black by use of 50-power magnification with a light source behind the stamp.

| **1922, July-Nov.** | | **Perf. 15x14** |
|---|---|---|
| 23   A82   ½p green | 2.00 | 1.35 |
|   Never hinged | 4.50 | |
| 24   A83   1p scarlet | 1.00 | 1.75 |
|   Never hinged | 3.00 | |
| 25   A84   1½p red brown | 6.00 | 7.00 |
|   Never hinged | 11.00 | |
| 26   A85   2p orange (II) | 3.00 | 1.00 |
|   Never hinged | 4.75 | |
| a.   Inverted overprint (II) | 275.00 | 500.00 |
| b.   2p orange (I) | 20.00 | 2.00 |
|   Never hinged | 40.00 | |
| 27   A86   2½p ultra (R) | 10.00 | 24.00 |
|   Never hinged | 15.00 | |
| 28   A87   3p violet | 2.50 | 4.00 |
|   Never hinged | 5.00 | |
| 29   A88   4p slate green (R) | 4.00 | 4.75 |
|   Never hinged | 7.00 | |
| 30   A89   5p yellow brown | 8.50 | 12.00 |
|   Never hinged | 14.00 | |
| 31   A89   6p red violet | 8.00 | 5.00 |
|   Never hinged | 15.00 | |
| 32   A90   9p blk brn (R) | 14.00 | 17.00 |
|   Never hinged | 30.00 | |
| 33   A90   9p ol grn (R) | 7.50 | 32.50 |
|   Never hinged | 15.00 | |
| 34   A90   10p light blue | 26.00 | 50.00 |
|   Never hinged | 50.00 | |
| 35   A90   1sh bister | 12.50 | 11.00 |
|   Never hinged | 25.00 | |
|   Nos. 23-35 (13) | 105.00 | 171.35 |

Nos. 23, 24, 28, 34 overprinted in dull black, rather than the normal blue-black, are believed to be proofs, pressed into use when supplies of the issued values ran low.

Overprinted as Nos. 12 to 14 in Blue Black (Shiny to Dull)
Overprint measures 21x13½mm

The "h" and "é" are ½mm apart.

| **1922   Wmk. 34** | | **Perf. 11x12** |
|---|---|---|
| 36   A91   2sh6p gray brown | 200. | 325. |
|   Never hinged | 400. | |
| 37   A91   5sh car rose | 225. | 375. |
|   Never hinged | 450. | |
| 38   A91   10sh gray blue | 1,500. | 1,800. |
|   Never hinged | 2,500. | |
|   Nos. 36-38 (3) | 1,925. | 2,500. |

Overprinted in Blue
Black

Overprint measures 15¾x16mm

| 1922, Dec. | | | Wmk. 33 | Perf. 15x14 |
|---|---|---|---|---|
| 39 | A82 | ½p green | 1.50 | 2.00 |
| | | Never hinged | 2.25 | |
| 40 | A83 | 1p scarlet | 1.50 | 4.00 |
| | | Never hinged | 6.00 | |
| 41 | A84 | 1½p red brown | 2.75 | 12.50 |
| | | Never hinged | 6.00 | |
| 42 | A85 | 2p orange (II) | 10.00 | 10.00 |
| | | Never hinged | 17.50 | |
| 43 | A90 | 1sh bister | 35.00 | 47.50 |
| | | Never hinged | 55.00 | |
| | | Nos. 39-43 (5) | 50.75 | 76.00 |

Stamps of Great Britain,
1912-22, Overprinted in
Shiny to Dull Blue Black
or Red

This overprint means "Irish Free State"

Overprint measures 15x8½mm
"1922" is 6¼mm long

The inner loop of the "9" is an upright oval. The measurement of "1922" is made across the bottom of the numerals and does not include the serif at the top of the "1."

There were 5 plates for printing the overprint on Nos. 44-55. In the impressions from plate I the 12th stamp in the 15th row has no accent on the 2nd "A" of "SAORSTAT." To correct this an accent was inserted by hand, sometimes this was in a reversed position.

On Nos. 56-58 the accent was omitted on the 2nd stamp in the 3rd and 8th rows. Damage to the plate makes the accent look reversed on the 4th stamp in the 7th row. The top of the "t" slants down in a line with the so-called accent.

| 1922-23 | | | Wmk. 33 | Perf. 15x14 |
|---|---|---|---|---|
| 44 | A82 | ½p green | .60 | .75 |
| | | Never hinged | 1.25 | |
| a. | | Accent omitted | 1,300. | 1,000. |
| b. | | Accent added | 125.00 | 150.00 |
| 45 | A83 | 1p scarlet | .60 | .75 |
| | | Never hinged | 1.25 | |
| a. | | Accent omitted | 8,750. | 6,500. |
| b. | | Accent added | 150.00 | 175.00 |
| c. | | Accent and final "t" omitted | 7,750. | 5,500. |
| d. | | Accent and final "t" added | 250.00 | 300.00 |
| 46 | A84 | 1½p red brown | 3.00 | 12.50 |
| | | Never hinged | 7.00 | |
| 47 | A85 | 2p orange (II) | 1.75 | 3.00 |
| | | Never hinged | 5.00 | |
| 48 | A86 | 2½p ultra (R) | 2.75 | 7.50 |
| | | Never hinged | 6.00 | |
| a. | | Accent omitted | 160.00 | 200.00 |
| 49 | A87 | 3p violet | 8.00 | 10.00 |
| | | Never hinged | 15.00 | |
| a. | | Accent omitted | 325.00 | 350.00 |
| 50 | A88 | 4p sl green (R) | 3.75 | 6.00 |
| | | Never hinged | 7.00 | |
| a. | | Accent omitted | 225.00 | 300.00 |
| 51 | A89 | 5p yel brown | 3.00 | 7.00 |
| | | Never hinged | 7.00 | |
| 52 | A89 | 6p dull violet | 2.75 | 2.25 |
| | | Never hinged | 6.00 | |
| a. | | Accent added | 900.00 | 900.00 |
| 53 | A90 | 9p ol green (R) | 3.50 | 9.00 |
| | | Never hinged | 8.50 | |
| a. | | Accent omitted | 275.00 | 350.00 |
| 54 | A90 | 10p lt blue | 20.00 | 40.00 |
| | | Never hinged | 40.00 | |
| 55 | A90 | 1sh bister | 12.50 | 11.00 |
| | | Never hinged | 32.50 | |
| a. | | Accent omitted | 7,000. | 8,000. |
| b. | | Accent added | 825.00 | 900.00 |

| | | Perf. 11x12 Wmk. 34 | | |
|---|---|---|---|---|
| 56 | A91 | 2sh6p lt brown | 45.00 | 80.00 |
| | | Never hinged | 95.00 | |
| a. | | Accent omitted | 450.00 | 500.00 |
| 57 | A91 | 5sh car rose | 90.00 | 160.00 |
| | | Never hinged | 175.00 | |
| a. | | Accent omitted | 550.00 | 650.00 |
| 58 | A91 | 10sh gray blue | 190.00 | 375.00 |
| | | Never hinged | 400.00 | |
| a. | | Accent omitted | 2,750. | 3,250. |
| | | Nos. 44-58 (15) | 387.20 | 724.75 |

**Overprinted by Harrison & Sons**
Coil Stamps
Same Ovpt. in Black or Blue Black

| 1923 | | | Wmk. 33 | Perf. 15x14 |
|---|---|---|---|---|
| 59 | A82 | ½p green | 2.00 | 12.00 |
| | | Never hinged | 4.00 | |
| a. | | Tall "1" | 8.00 | 45.00 |
| | | Never hinged | 20.00 | |
| 60 | A83 | 1p scarlet | 4.50 | 16.00 |
| | | Never hinged | 10.00 | |
| a. | | Tall "1" | 35.00 | 140.00 |
| | | Never hinged | 80.00 | |

| 61 | A84 | 1½p red brown | 5.00 | 40.00 |
|---|---|---|---|---|
| | | Never hinged | 15.00 | |
| a. | | Tall "1" | 80.00 | 200.00 |
| | | Never hinged | 150.00 | |
| 62 | A85 | 2p orange (II) | 6.00 | 12.00 |
| | | Never hinged | 11.00 | |
| a. | | Tall "1" | 10.00 | 45.00 |
| | | Never hinged | 25.00 | |
| | | Nos. 59-62 (4) | 17.50 | 80.00 |

These stamps were issued in coils, made by joining horizontal or vertical strips of the stamps. See 2nd paragraph after #22. In some strips there were two stamps with the "1" of "1922" 2½mm high and with serif at foot. In this setting the middle "e" of "eireann" is a trifle above the line of the other letters, making the word appear slightly curved. The lower end of the "1" of "1922" is rounded on #59-62 instead of flat as on #44-47.

The inner loop of the "9" is round.

See Nos. 77b, 78b and 79b.

---

### Booklet Panes

For very fine the perforation holes at top or bottom of the pane should be visible, though not necessarily perfect half circles.

"Sword of Light" — A1     Map of Ireland — A2

Coat of Arms — A3     Celtic Cross — A4

**Perf. 15x14**

| 1922-23 | | Typo. | Wmk. 44 | |
|---|---|---|---|---|
| 65 | A1 | ½p emerald | .40 | .40 |
| | | Never hinged | .85 | |
| a. | | Booklet pane of 6 | 300.00 | |
| 66 | A2 | 1p car rose | .40 | .40 |
| | | Never hinged | 1.50 | |
| a. | | Booklet pane of 6 | 350.00 | |
| b. | | Booklet pane of 3 + 3 labels | 250.00 | |
| 67 | A2 | 1½p claret | 1.50 | 2.25 |
| | | Never hinged | 5.00 | |
| 68 | A2 | 2p deep green | .40 | .40 |
| | | Never hinged | 1.00 | |
| a. | | Booklet pane of 6 | 275.00 | |
| b. | | Perf. 15 horiz. ('35) | 12,500. | 1,500. |

No. 68b is valued in the grade of fine.

| 69 | A3 | 2½p chocolate | 1.50 | 4.50 |
|---|---|---|---|---|
| | | Never hinged | 6.00 | |
| 70 | A4 | 3p ultra | 1.50 | 2.00 |
| | | Never hinged | 6.00 | |
| 71 | A3 | 4p slate | 2.25 | 3.50 |
| | | Never hinged | 7.50 | |
| 72 | A1 | 5p deep violet | 11.00 | 10.00 |
| | | Never hinged | 45.00 | |
| 73 | A1 | 6p red violet | 4.00 | 4.00 |
| | | Never hinged | 10.00 | |
| 74 | A3 | 9p violet | 18.00 | 17.50 |
| | | Never hinged | 100.00 | |
| 75 | A4 | 10p brown | 9.00 | 20.00 |
| | | Never hinged | 42.50 | |
| 76 | A1 | 1sh light blue | 22.50 | 12.50 |
| | | Never hinged | 90.00 | |
| | | Nos. 65-76 (12) | 72.45 | 77.45 |

The 2p was issued in 1922; other denominations in 1923.

No. 68b is a vertical coil stamp.

See Nos. 87, 91-92, 105-117, 137-138, 225-226, 326. For types overprinted see Nos. 118-119.

---

**Overprinted by the Government Printing Office, Dublin Castle and British Board of Inland Revenue at Somerset House, London**

Great Britain Nos. 179-181 Ovptd. in Black or Gray Black

"1922" is 5½mm long

The measurement of "1922" is made across the bottom of the numerals and does not include the serif at the top of the "1."

| 1925 | | | Wmk. 34 | Perf. 11x12 |
|---|---|---|---|---|
| 77 | A91 | 2sh6p gray brown | 50.00 | 120.00 |
| | | Never hinged | 100.00 | |
| 78 | A91 | 5sh rose red | 60.00 | 210.00 |
| | | Never hinged | 125.00 | |
| 79 | A91 | 10sh gray blue | 160.00 | 425.00 |
| | | Never hinged | 375.00 | |
| | | Nos. 77-79 (3) | 270.00 | 755.00 |

In 1927 the 2sh6p, 5sh and 10sh stamps were overprinted from a plate in which the Thom and Castle clichés were combined, thus including wide and narrow "1922" in the same setting.

**Overprinted by British Board of Inland Revenue at Somerset House, London**
Pair with "1922" Wide and Narrow

| 1927 | | | | |
|---|---|---|---|---|
| 77a | A91 | 2sh6p | 325.00 | |
| | | Never hinged | 500.00 | |
| 78a | A91 | 5sh | 500.00 | |
| | | Never hinged | 850.00 | |
| 79a | A91 | 10sh | 1,500. | |
| | | Never hinged | 2,250. | |
| | | Nos. 77a-79a (3) | 2,325. | |

Wide "1922"
"1922" is 6¼mm long

| 1927-28 | | | | |
|---|---|---|---|---|
| 77b | A91 | 2sh6p | 50.00 | 50.00 |
| | | Never hinged | 90.00 | |
| 78b | A91 | 5sh ('28) | 90.00 | 100.00 |
| | | Never hinged | 175.00 | |
| 79b | A91 | 10sh ('28) | 225.00 | 325.00 |
| | | Never hinged | 400.00 | |
| | | Nos. 77b-79b (3) | 365.00 | 475.00 |

Daniel O'Connell — A5

**Perf. 15x14**

| 1929, June 22 | | | Wmk. 44 | |
|---|---|---|---|---|
| 80 | A5 | 2p dark green | .50 | .40 |
| | | Never hinged | .75 | |
| 81 | A5 | 3p dark blue | 5.00 | 10.00 |
| | | Never hinged | 14.00 | |
| 82 | A5 | 9p dark violet | 6.00 | 9.50 |
| | | Never hinged | 15.00 | |
| | | Nos. 80-82 (3) | 11.50 | 19.90 |

Catholic Emancipation in Ireland, centenary.

Shannon River Hydroelectric Station — A6

| 1930, Oct. 15 | | | | |
|---|---|---|---|---|
| 83 | A6 | 2p black brown | .65 | 1.00 |
| | | Never hinged | 5.00 | |

Opening of the hydroelectric development of the River Shannon.

Farmer with Scythe — A7     Cross of Cong and Chalice — A8

| 1931, June 12 | | | | |
|---|---|---|---|---|
| 84 | A7 | 2p pale blue | .70 | .50 |
| | | Never hinged | 2.00 | |

Bicentenary of Royal Dublin Society.

| 1932, May 12 | | | | |
|---|---|---|---|---|
| 85 | A8 | 2p dark green | .80 | .50 |
| | | Never hinged | 3.00 | |
| 86 | A8 | 3p bright blue | 2.00 | 4.75 |
| | | Never hinged | 7.50 | |

International Eucharistic Congress.

Coil Stamp
Type of 1922-23 Issue

| 1933-34 | | | Perf. 15 Horizontally | |
|---|---|---|---|---|
| 87 | A2 | 1p rose ('34) | 25.00 | 30.00 |
| | | Never hinged | 45.00 | |
| a. | | 1p carmine rose | 125.00 | 175.00 |
| | | Never hinged | 200.00 | |

No. 87a has a single perforation at each side near the top, while No. 87 is perforated top and bottom only.

See No. 68b.

Adoration of the Cross A9     Hurling A10

| 1933, Sept. 18 | | | Perf. 15x14 | |
|---|---|---|---|---|
| 88 | A9 | 2p slate green | .40 | .40 |
| | | Never hinged | 1.50 | |
| 89 | A9 | 3p deep blue | 2.25 | 5.00 |
| | | Never hinged | 8.50 | |

Holy Year.

| 1934, July 27 | | | | |
|---|---|---|---|---|
| 90 | A10 | 2p green | .90 | .75 |
| | | Never hinged | 2.00 | |

50th anniv. of the Gaelic Athletic Assoc.

Coil Stamps
Types of 1922-23

| 1934 | | | Wmk. 44 Sideways | Perf. 14 Vertically |
|---|---|---|---|---|
| 91 | A1 | ½p green | 32.50 | 37.50 |
| | | Never hinged | 50.00 | |
| 92 | A2 | 2p gray green | 55.00 | 70.00 |
| | | Never hinged | 100.00 | |

**Overprinted by Harrison & Sons**

Great Britain Nos. 222-224 Overprinted in Black

| 1935 | | | Wmk. 44 | Perf. 11x12 |
|---|---|---|---|---|
| 93 | A91 | 2sh6p brown | 50.00 | 62.50 |
| | | Never hinged | 125.00 | |
| 94 | A91 | 5sh carmine | 175.00 | 210.00 |
| | | Never hinged | 375.00 | |
| 95 | A91 | 10sh dark blue | 500.00 | 650.00 |
| | | Never hinged | 1,300. | |
| | | Nos. 93-95 (3) | 725.00 | 922.50 |

Waterlow printing can be distinguished by the crossed lines in the background of portrait. Previous issues have horizontal lines only.

St. Patrick and Paschal Fire — A11

| 1937, Sept. 8 | | Wmk. 44 | Perf. 14x15 | |
|---|---|---|---|---|
| 96 | A11 | 2sh6p bright green | 70.00 | 60.00 |
| | | Never hinged | 225.00 | |
| 97 | A11 | 5sh brown violet | 120.00 | 100.00 |
| | | Never hinged | 275.00 | |
| 98 | A11 | 10sh dark blue | 70.00 | 70.00 |
| | | Never hinged | 225.00 | |
| | | Nos. 96-98 (3) | 260.00 | 230.00 |

See Nos. 121-123.

Allegory of Ireland and Constitution
A12

**1937, Dec. 29**     **Perf. 15x14**
99 A12 2p plum     1.25 .50
100 A12 3p deep blue     6.50 6.00
Constitution Day.
See Nos. 169-170.

Father Theobald Mathew
A13

**1938, July 1**
101 A13 2p black brown     1.50 .25
102 A13 3p ultramarine     10.50 6.50
Temperance Crusade by Father Mathew, centenary.

Washington, US Eagle and Harp — A14

**1939, Mar. 1**
103 A14 2p bright carmine     1.00 .30
104 A14 3p deep blue     11.00 9.50
US Constitution, 150th anniv.

Coil Stamp
Type of 1922-23
**1940-46**   **Wmk. 262**   **Perf. 15 Horiz.**
105 A2 1p car rose ('46)     50.00 15.00
a.   Perf. 14 horiz.     45.00 50.00

Types of 1922-23
**1940-42**     **Perf. 15x14**
**Size: 18x22mm**
106 A1 ½p emerald ('41)     1.50 .50
a.   Booklet pane of 6     350.00
107 A2 1p car rose ('41)     .40 .40
a.   Booklet pane of 6     6.00
b.   Bkt. pane of 3 + 3 labels     1,250.
108 A2 1½p claret ('41)     12.00 .75
a.   Booklet pane of 6     140.00
109 A2 2p deep green     .40 .40
a.   Booklet pane of 6     12.50
110 A3 2½p choc ('41)     12.00 .75
a.   Booklet pane of 6     95.00
111 A4 3p dull blue ('41)     .40 .40
a.   Booklet pane of 6     40.00
112 A3 4p slate     .40 .40
a.   Booklet pane of 6     65.00
113 A1 5p deep violet     .40 .40
114 A1 6p red violet ('42)     .75 .40
115 A3 9p violet     .75 .90
116 A4 10p olive brown     1.00 .90
117 A1 1sh blue     120.00 20.00
Nos. 106-117 (12)     150.00 26.20

Types of 1922-23
Overprinted in Green or Violet

Overprint reads: "In memory of the Rebellion of 1916."

**1941, Apr. 12**     **Perf. 15x14**
118 A2 2p yellow orange     2.75 .50
119 A4 3p blue (V)     40.00 20.00

Volunteer Soldier and Dublin Post Office
A15

**1941, Oct. 27**
120 A15 2½p bluish black     1.50 .60
Nos. 118-120 commemorate the 25th anniv. of the Easter Rebellion.

---

St. Patrick Type of 1937
**1943-45**   **Wmk. 262**   **Perf. 14x15**
121 A11 2sh6p bright green     6.00 1.50
122 A11 5sh brown violet     9.00 3.50
123 A11 10sh dark blue ('45)     16.00 7.50
Nos. 121-123 (3)     31.00 12.50

Dr. Douglas Hyde     Sir Rowan Hamilton
A16     A17

**1943, July 31**     **Perf. 15x14**
124 A16 ½p green     .50 .60
125 A16 2½p red lilac     1.25 .50
50th anniv. of the Gaelic League.

**1943, Nov. 13**   **Typo.**   **Wmk. 262**
126 A17 ½p deep green     .75 .60
127 A17 2½p dk red brown     3.50 .40
Centenary of discovery of the mathematical formula of Quaternions by William Rowan Hamilton.

Brother Michael O'Clery — A18

**1944, June 30**     **Perf. 14x15**
128 A18 ½p emerald     .25 .25
a.   Booklet pane of 6     25.00
129 A18 1sh reddish brown     1.25 .25
300th anniv. of the death of Michael O'Clery, Irish historian.

Edmund Rice — A19     Sower — A20

**1944, Aug. 29**     **Perf. 15x14**
130 A19 2½p slate     1.00 .40
Death centenary of Edmund Ignatius Rice, founder of the Christian Brothers of Ireland.

**1945, Sept. 15**
131 A20 2½p ultramarine     1.50 .20
132 A20 6p red violet     9.00 6.00
Commemorates the work of the Young Irelanders and the death centenary of Thomas Davis, Sept. 16, 1845.

Plowman A21

**1946, Sept. 16**     **Typo.**
133 A21 2½p red     1.50 .20
134 A21 3p dark blue     6.00 4.50
Birth centenary of Charles Stewart Parnell and Michael Davitt, leaders in the struggle for Irish political independence.

Theobald Wolfe Tone A22

**Perf. 15x14**
**1948, Nov. 19**     **Wmk. 262**
135 A22 2½p deep plum     2.00 .20
136 A22 3p deep violet     7.00 5.00
Insurrection of 1798, 150th anniversary.

---

Types of 1922-23
**1949**
137 A1 8p bright red     1.60 .50
138 A4 11p carmine rose     2.50 1.50

Leinster House, Dublin
A23

**1949, Nov. 21**
139 A23 2½p red brown     1.50 .40
140 A23 3p violet blue     7.25 4.25
International recognition of the Republic, Easter Monday, 1949.

James Clarence Mangan     Statue of St. Peter
A24     A25

**1949, Dec. 5**
141 A24 1p dark green     4.00 .75
Mangan (1803-1849), poet.

**Wmk. 262**
**1950, Sept. 11**   **Engr.**   **Perf. 12½**
142 A25 2½p violet     1.25 .30
143 A25 3p blue     11.50 9.00
144 A25 9p brown     11.50 10.00
Nos. 142-144 (3)     24.25 19.30
Holy Year, 1950.

Thomas Moore — A26     Irish Harp — A27

**1952, Nov. 10**     **Perf. 13**
145 A26 2½p deep plum     .20 .20
146 A26 3½p dk olive green     4.00 3.50
Death centenary of Thomas Moore (1779-1852), poet.

**1953, Feb. 9**   **Typo.**   **Perf. 14x15**
147 A27 2½p bright green     1.00 .20
148 A27 1sh4p bright blue     27.50 25.00
Ireland's National festival "An Tostal."

Robert Emmet — A28     Madonna by della Robbia — A29

**1953, Sept. 21**   **Engr.**   **Perf. 12½x13**
149 A28 3p deep green     3.25 .25
150 A28 1sh3p carmine rose     52.50 17.50
150th anniv. of the execution of Robert Emmet (1778-1803), Irish nationalist.

---

**1954, May 24**     **Perf. 15**
151 A29 3p blue     1.50 .20
152 A29 5p deep green     10.00 5.00
Marian Year, 1953-54.

John Henry Cardinal Newman     Statue of John Barry
A30     A31

**1954, July 19**   **Typo.**   **Perf. 15x14**
153 A30 2p rose lilac     3.00 .20
154 A30 1sh3p blue     19.00 9.00
Opening of the Catholic University of Ireland, centenary.

**1956, Sept. 16**   **Engr.**   **Perf. 15**
155 A31 3p dull purple     1.00 .20
156 A31 1sh3p blue     15.00 10.00
John Barry (1745-1803), "Father of the American Navy," on the occasion of the unveiling of a statue in Wexford, Ireland, his birthplace.

Redmond     O'Crohan
A32     A33

**Perf. 14x15**
**1957, June 11**     **Wmk. 262**
157 A32 3p dark blue     1.50 .20
158 A32 1sh3p rose lake     16.50 10.00
Birth cent. of John Edward Redmond (1856-1918), Irish political leader.

**1957, July 1**
159 A33 2p dull purple     2.00 .20
160 A33 5p violet     8.00 6.00
Birth cent. of Thomas O'Crohan (Tomas O'Criomhthain) (1856-1937), fisherman and author.

Brown     Father Luke Wadding
A34     A35

**1957, Sept. 23**   **Typo.**   **Perf. 15x14**
161 A34 3p blue     3.50 .20
162 A34 1sh3p carmine rose     42.50 20.00
Adm. William (Guillermo) Brown (1777-1857), founder of the Argentine Navy.

**1957, Nov. 25**   **Engr.**   **Perf. 15**
163 A35 3p dark blue     2.00 .50
164 A35 1sh3p deep claret     22.00 9.00
Luke Wadding (1588-1657), Irish Franciscan friar and historian.

Clarke     Aikenhead
A36     A37

**1958, July 28**     **Wmk. 262**
165 A36   3p deep green   1.00 .20
166 A36   1sh3p red brown   16.50 9.50

Thomas J. Clarke (1858-1916), patriot.

**1958, Oct. 20**     **Perf. 15x14**
167 A37   3p blue   1.50 .20
168 A37   1sh3p carmine   22.50 10.50

Mother Mary Aikenhead (1787-1858), founder of the Irish Sisters of Charity.

Constitution Type of 1937

**1958, Dec. 29**   **Typo.**    **Wmk. 262**
169 A12   3p brown   .75 .20
170 A12   5p bright green   6.00 5.00

21st anniv. of the constitution.

Arthur Guinness — A38

**1959, July 20**   **Engr.**    **Perf. 15**
171 A38   3p rose lake   2.50 .20
172 A38   1sh3p dark blue   20.00 7.50

Bicentenary of Guinness Brewery.

Flight of the Holy Family A39

**1960, June 20**     **Perf. 15**
173 A39   3p rose violet   .25 .20
174 A39   1sh3p sepia   1.00 2.00

World Refugee Year, 7/1/59-6/30/60.

**Europa Issue**

Symbolic Wheel CD3

**1960, Sept. 19**   **Engr.**    **Perf. 15**
175 CD3   6p orange brown   30.00 2.00
176 CD3   1sh3p violet   70.00 12.00

No. 176 has fugitive ink.

De Havilland Dragon, Boeing 707 Jet and Dublin Airport A41

**1961, June 26**     **Perf. 15**
177 A41   6p dull blue   2.25 2.00
178 A41   1sh3p green   5.50 3.50

25th anniv. of the founding of Aer Lingus, Irish International Airlines.

St. Patrick — A42

**1961, Sept. 25**     **Perf. 14½**
179 A42   3p blue   .80 .20
180 A42   8p pale purple   2.25 5.00
181 A42   1sh3p green   2.50 1.40
     Nos. 179-181 (3)   5.55 6.60

1,500th anniv. of St. Patrick's death.

John O'Donovan and Eugene O'Curry A43

**1962, Mar. 26**     **Perf. 15**
182 A43   3p crimson   .40 .20
183 A43   1sh3p purple   4.75 4.00

Death centenaries of John O'Donovan (1806-1861) and Eugene O'Curry (1794-1862), Gaelic scholars and translators.

**Europa Issue**

19 Leaves on Young Tree CD5

**1962, Sept. 17**   **Engr.**    **Wmk. 262**
184 CD5   6p pink & dark red   .75 .50
185 CD5   1sh3p bluish grn & dk blue grn   1.50 1.00

Wheat Emblem and Globe A45

**1963, Mar. 21**     **Wmk. 262**
186 A45   4p violet   .40 .20
187 A45   1sh3p red   2.50 2.50

FAO "Freedom from Hunger" campaign.

**Europa Issue**

Stylized Links, Symbolizing Unity CD6

**1963, Sept. 16**     **Perf. 15**
188 CD6   6p rose carmine   1.75 1.25
189 CD6   1sh3p dark blue   3.50 2.00

Centenary Emblem A47

**1963, Dec. 2**   **Photo.**    **Perf. 14½x14**
190 A47   4p gray & red   .50 .20
191 A47   1sh3p brt green, gray & red   1.50 2.00

Centenary of the International Red Cross.

Wolfe Tone A48

**1964, Apr. 13**   **Engr.**    **Perf. 15**
192 A48   4p black   .75 .20
193 A48   1sh3p dark blue   5.25 5.50

Birth bicentenary of Theobald Wolfe Tone (1763-1798), Irish revolutionist.

Irish Pavilion A49

**1964, July 20**   **Photo.**    **Perf. 14½x14**
194 A49   5p multicolored   1.00 .20
   a.   Brown omitted   3,000.
195 A49   1sh5p multicolored   5.00 5.00

New York World's Fair, 1964-65.

**Europa Issue**

CEPT Daisy (22 Petals) — CD7

       **Perf. 14x14½**
**1964, Sept. 14**   **Litho.**    **Wmk. 262**
196 CD7   8p dull grn & ultra   3.00 1.00
197 CD7   1sh5p red brown & org   13.00 2.50

ITU Emblem, Globe and Communication Waves — A51

**1965, May 17**   **Photo.**    **Perf. 14½x14**
198 A51   3p dp blue & emerald   .75 .20
199 A51   8p black & emerald   3.25 4.00

ITU, cent.

William Butler Yeats — A52

**1965, June 14**     **Perf. 15**
200 A52   5p orange brn & blk   .50 .25
201 A52   1sh5p gray green, brn & black   5.00 5.00

Birth centenary of William Butler Yeats (1865-1939), poet and dramatist.

ICY Emblem A53

**1965, Aug. 16**   **Photo.**    **Perf. 15**
202 A53   3p brt blue & vio bl   1.00 .50
203 A53   10p redsh brn & dk brn   4.50 5.00

International Cooperation Year.

**Europa Issue**

Leaves and Fruit — CD8

**1965, Sept. 27**     **Perf. 15**
204 CD8   8p brick red & blk   7.50 .60
205 CD8   1sh5p lt blue & claret   18.50 2.75

James Connolly A55

Designs: No. 207, Thomas J. Clarke. No. 208, Patrick Henry Pearse. No. 209, Symbolic of lives lost in fight for independence, and of Ireland marching into freedom. No. 210, Eamonn Ceannt. No. 211, Sean MacDiarmada. No. 212, Thomas MacDonagh. No. 213, Joseph Plunkett.

**1966, Apr. 12**   **Wmk. 262**    **Perf. 15**
206 A55   3p blue & black   1.10 .35
207 A55   3p olive green   1.10 .35
   a.   Pair, #206-207   3.00 1.50
208 A55   5p olive & black   1.25 .35
209 A55   5p brt grn, blk & orange   1.25 .35
   a.   Pair, #208-209   3.25 1.75
210 A55   7p dull org & blk   1.25 2.50
211 A55   7p blue grn & blk   1.25 2.50
   a.   Pair, #210-211   3.75 7.50
212 A55   1sh5p grnsh bl & blk   1.25 2.00
213 A55   1sh5p emerald & blk   1.25 2.00
   a.   Pair, #212-213   5.00 10.00
     Nos. 206-213 (8)   9.70 10.40

50th anniv. of the Easter Week Rebellion, and to honor the signers of the Proclamation of the Irish Republic.

Roger Casement A56

Symbolic Sailboat CD9

**1966, Aug. 3**     **Perf. 15**
214 A56   5p black   .20 .20
215 A56   1sh dark red brown   1.10 .80

50th death anniv. of Roger Casement (1864-1916), British consular agent and Irish rebel who was executed for treason.

**Europa Issue**

**1966, Sept. 26**   **Photo.**    **Perf. 15**
216 CD9   7p orange & green   1.75 .30
217 CD9   1sh5p gray & green   4.50 1.25

Ballintubber Abbey A58

**1966, Nov. 8**     **Perf. 15**
218 A58   5p red brown   .25 .20
219 A58   1sh black   .65 .65

750th anniversary of Ballintubber Abbey.

Cross and Sword Types of 1922

**1966-67**   **Photo.**    **Perf. 15**
     **Size: 17x20½mm**
225 A4 3p blue ('67)   .50 .50
226 A1 5p brt vio, type II ('68)   .50 .50
   a.   Booklet pane of 6, No. 226b   37.50
   b.   Type I ('66)   6.00 6.00

Type I has irregularly spaced lines in shading behind sword.

**Europa Issue**

Cogwheels — CD10

**1967, May 2**
232 CD10   7p green & gold   2.00 .40
233 CD10   1sh5p dk red & gold   4.50 .90

Maple Leaves A60

**1967, Aug. 28**     **Photo.**
234 A60   5p multicolored   .20 .20
235 A60   1sh5p multicolored   .75 .80

Centenary of the Canadian Confederation.

Rock of
Cashel
A61

**1967, Sept. 25    Wmk. 262    Perf. 15**
236 A61  7p sepia          .20  .30
237 A61  10p Prussian blue  .75  .75
International Tourist Year.

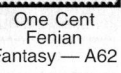

One Cent
Fenian
Fantasy — A62

Swift's Bust
and St.
Patrick's
Cathedral,
Dublin — A63

Design: 1sh, 24c Fenian fantasy.

**1967, Oct. 23    Photo.    Perf. 15**
238 A62  5p lt green & slate grn  .20  .20
239 A62  1sh pale pink & gray    .40  .50
Fenian Rising, centenary. The Fenian fantasy was created by S. Allan Taylor.

**1967, Nov. 30    Perf. 15**
Design: 1sh5p, Gulliver, Lilliputian army.
240 A63  3p gray & sepia      .20  .20
241 A63  1sh5p lt blue & sepia  .60  .50
Birth tercentenary of Jonathan Swift (1667-1745), author of Gulliver's Travels.

### Europa Issue

Golden Key
with CEPT
Emblem
CD11

**1968, Apr. 29    Photo.    Wmk. 262**
242 CD11  7p multicolored    .80  .55
243 CD11  1sh5p multicolored  2.25  1.00

St. Mary's
Cathedral,
Limerick
A65

**1968, Aug. 26    Engr.    Perf. 15**
244 A65  5p dull blue  .20  .20
245 A65  10p olive    .40  .80
800th anniv. of the founding of St. Mary's Cathedral by Donal Mor O'Brien, last King of Munster.

Countess
Markievicz
A66

**1968, Sept. 23    Photo.    Wmk. 262**
246 A66  3p black      .20  .20
247 A66  1sh5p dark blue  .35  .80
Birth centenary of Countess Constance Markievicz (1868-1927), champion of Irish Independence and first Minister of Labor.

James
Connolly — A67

**1968, Sept. 23    Perf. 15**
248 A67  6p brown, dk brn & blk    .20  .45
249 A67  1sh dull grn, grn & blk   .30  .45
Birth centenary of James Connolly (1868-1916), founder of the Irish Socialist Party, editor of "Workers' Republic" and Commander of the Irish Citizen Army.

Dog from Ancient
Brooch, County
Kilkenny — A68

Winged Ox
from
Lichfield
Gospel
Book
A69

Designs: ½p, 1p, 2p, 3p, 4p, 5p, 6p, Dog. 7p, 8p, 9p, 10p, 1sh, 1sh9p, Stag from ancient bowl, Kent. 2sh6p, 5sh, Winged ox. 10sh, Eagle, from ancient manuscript.

**1968-70    Photo.    Wmk. 262    Perf. 15**
250 A68  ½p orange            .25   .30
251 A68  1p yellow green      .25   .20
252 A68  2p ocher             .25   .20
253 A68  3p bright blue       .25   .20
254 A68  4p dark red          .40   .45
255 A68  5p deep green        .45   .45
256 A68  6p brown             .40   .25
  a.   Booklet pane of 6 ('70)  25.00
257 A68  7p yel & brown       .95  3.25
258 A68  8p red org & blk     .95  1.40
259 A68  9p ol grn & dk bl    .95   .80
260 A68  10p violet & dk brn  1.00  2.00
261 A68  1sh dk red brn &
            brown             .85   .80
262 A68  1sh9p grnsh bl & dk
            brown             .90  2.50
263 A69  2sh6p red org, bl, ol
            & dull yel        5.00   .90
264 A69  5sh ol, gray, bis &
            yel               6.00  1.40
265 A69  10sh dk red brn, yel
            & dp org         12.50  2.50
  Nos. 250-265 (16)          31.35 17.40

Issued: 2p, 8p, 2sh6p, 10sh, 10/14/68; 6p, 9p, 1sh9p, 5sh, 2/24/69; 4p, 5p, 10p, 1sh, 3/31/69; ½p, 1p, 3p, 7p, 6/9/69.
See #290-304, 343-359, 395-402, 466-475.

### Coil Stamps
**1970    Perf. 14x15**
251a A68  1p yellow green  1.25  3.00
252a A68  2p ocher        1.25  3.00
253a A68  3p bright blue  1.25  3.00
  Nos. 251a-253a (3)      3.75  9.00

Human Rights
Flame — A70

**1968, Nov. 4    Wmk. 262    Perf. 15**
266 A70  5p black, ocher & gold   .20  .20
267 A70  7p crim, ocher & gold    .35  .45
International Human Rights Year.

First
Meeting of
Irish
Parliament
A71

**1969, Jan. 21    Perf. 15x14½**
268 A71  6p dark slate green  .20  .20
269 A71  9p dark blue gray    .35  .45
50th anniv. of the first meeting of the Dail Eireann at the Mansion House, Dublin, Jan. 21, 1919.

"EUROPA"
and "CEPT"
CD12

**1969, Apr. 28    Photo.    Perf. 15**
270 CD12    9p ultra, gray &
              ocher           1.50  .50
271 CD12  1sh9p car, gray & gold  2.50  .80
Europa and CEPT, 10th anniv.

ILO Emblem — A73

**1969, July 14    Perf. 15**
272 A73  6p gray & black    .25  .20
273 A73  9p yellow & black  .75  .75
ILO, 50th anniv.

Last
Supper
and
Crucifixion,
by Evie
Hone
A74

**Perf. 15x14½**
**1969, Sept. 1    Photo.    Wmk. 262**
274 A74  1sh multicolored  .75  1.50
The design is after a stained-glass window by Evie Hone (1894-1955) in the Eton College Chapel.

Mahatma
Gandhi
A75

**1969, Oct. 2    Perf. 15**
275 A75    6p dk yel grn & blk    .25  .20
276 A75  1sh9p yel, grn & black   .65  .75
Mohandas K. Gandhi (1869-1948), leader in India's fight for independence.

Stylized
Bird, Tree
and
Shamrock
A76

**1970, Feb. 23    Perf. 15**
277 A76  6p olive bister & black  .25  .20
278 A76  9p violet & black       1.10  .75
Nature Conservation Year.

### Europa Issue

Interwoven
Threads
CD13

**1970, May 4    Photo.    Perf. 15**
279 CD13  6p purple & silver      1.50  .20
280 CD13  9p yel brn & silver     2.25  .85
281 CD13  1sh9p dk gray & sil     3.50 1.25
  Nos. 279-281 (3)                7.25 2.30

Sailing
Boats, by
Peter
Monamy
(1670-1749)
A78

**1970, July 13    Perf. 15**
282 A78  4p gold & multi  .35  .20
250th anniv. of the Royal Cork Yacht Club.

Madonna of
Eire, by Mainie
Jellett (1896-
1943)
A79

Tomás
MacCurtain
A80

**1970, Sept. 1    Photo.    Perf. 15**
283 A79  1sh violet blue & multi  .50  .50

**1970, Oct. 26    Perf. 15**
Nos. 285, 287, Terence MacSwiney.
284 A80    9p violet & black     1.10  .90
285 A80    9p violet & black     1.10  .90
  a.   Pair, #284-285           4.00  4.50
286 A80  2sh9p brt blue & blk    3.00  2.75
287 A80  2sh9p brt blue & blk    3.00  2.75
  a.   Pair, #286-287           8.00 12.00
50th anniv. of the deaths of Tomás MacCurtain (1884-1920) and Terence MacSwiney (1879-1920), lord mayors of Cork, who died during the Irish war of independence.

Kevin Barry
A81

**1970, Nov. 2**
288 A81  6p olive green    .30  .20
289 A81  1sh2p violet blue  .80 1.00
50th anniv. of the death of Kevin Barry (1902-1920), who was hanged during the Irish war of independence.

### Decimal Currency Issue
Types of 1968-69 (Numerals only)
Designs: ½p, 1p, 1½p, 2p, 2½p, 3p, 3½p, 4p, 5p, Dog. No. 298A, 6p, 7p, 7½p, 9p, Stag. 10p, 12p, 20p, Winged ox. 50p, Eagle.

Two types of 10p:
I — Ox outlined in lilac
II — Outlined in brown

**1971-75    Wmk. 262    Photo.    Perf. 15**
290 A68  ½p yellow green     .25   .20
  a.   Booklet pane of 6    40.00
291 A68  1p bright blue     1.00   .45
  a.   Booklet pane of 6     4.50
  c.   Bklt. pane of 5 + label ('74)  1.50
292 A68  1½p brown red       .30   .30
293 A68  2p dark green       .40   .40
  b.   Booklet pane of 5 + label
          ('75)              1.50
294 A68  2½p sepia           .50   .50
  a.   Booklet pane of 6     9.00
295 A68  3p yel orange       .40   .40
296 A68  3½p deep orange     .50   .50
297 A68  4p violet           .35   .35
298 A68  5p ap grn & brn    1.50  1.00

| | | | | |
|---|---|---|---|---|
| 298A | A68 | 5p apple grn ('74) | 2.25 | 1.00 |
| c. | | Booklet pane of 6 ('74) | 10.00 | |
| d. | | Bklt. pane of 5 + label ('74) | 2.00 | |
| 299 | A68 | 6p blue gray & dk brown | 1.50 | .90 |
| 299A | A68 | 7p ol green & ind ('74) | 4.00 | 4.00 |
| 300 | A68 | 7½p rose vio & dk brown | .65 | .85 |
| 301 | A68 | 9p bl grn & blk | 2.00 | 1.00 |
| 302 | A69 | 10p lil & multi (I) | 17.50 | 7.50 |
| b. | | Type II | 19.00 | 1.00 |
| 302A | A69 | 12p multi ('74) | 1.25 | 1.40 |
| 303 | A69 | 20p slate & multi | 4.25 | 1.00 |
| 304 | A69 | 50p rose brn & multi | 12.00 | 1.40 |
| | | Nos. 290-304 (18) | 50.60 | 23.15 |

Booklet panes have watermark sideways.
Issued: #298A, 7p, 12p, 1/29/74; others, 2/15/71.
See Nos. 343-359, 395-402, 466-475.

### Coil Stamps

| **1971-74** | | | **Perf. 14x15** | |
|---|---|---|---|---|
| 291b | A68 | 1p bright blue | .90 | .50 |
| 292a | A68 | 1½p brown red | .25 | .50 |
| 293a | A68 | 2p dark green ('72) | .30 | .40 |
| 294b | A68 | 2½p sepia | .30 | .75 |
| c. | | Strip of 3 (1p, 1½p, 2½p) | 2.50 | 1.50 |
| 297a | A68 | 4p violet ('72) | 1.25 | 1.00 |
| b. | | Strip of 4 (1½p, 2p, 2½p, 4p) ('72) | 2.50 | 2.00 |
| 298b | A68 | 5p apple green ('74) | 1.25 | 1.00 |
| e. | | Strip of 4 (2x1½p, 2p, 5p) ('74) | 2.50 | 2.00 |

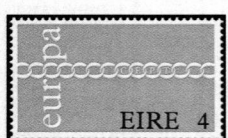

Europa Issue, 1971 — CD14

### Common Design Type

| **1971, May 3** | | **Wmk. 262** | **Perf. 15** | |
|---|---|---|---|---|
| 305 | CD14 | 4p apple green & blk | 1.50 | .20 |
| 306 | CD14 | 6p blue & black | 4.00 | 1.25 |

John M. Synge — A82

An Island Man, by Jack B. Yeats — A83

| **1971, July 19** | | **Photo.** | **Perf. 15** | |
|---|---|---|---|---|
| 307 | A82 | 4p gray, black & gold | .25 | .25 |
| 308 | A82 | 10p org, black & gold | 1.10 | 1.10 |

Birth cent. of John Millington Synge (1871-1909), poet and dramatist.

| **1971, Aug. 30** | | | **Perf. 15** | |
|---|---|---|---|---|
| 309 | A83 | 6p multicolored | .80 | .80 |

Jack Butler Yeats (1871-1957), painter.

Racial Equality Emblem A84

Madonna, by John Hughes, Loughrea Cathedral A85

### Perf. 14x14½

| **1971, Oct. 18** | | **Litho.** | **Unwmk.** | |
|---|---|---|---|---|
| 310 | A84 | 4p red | .20 | .20 |
| 311 | A84 | 10p black | .80 | .80 |

Intl. Year Against Racial Discrimination.

| **1971, Nov. 15** | | **Photo.** | **Perf. 15** | |
|---|---|---|---|---|
| 312 | A85 | 2½p dp bl grn, gold & slate | .20 | .20 |
| 313 | A85 | 6p ultra, gold & slate | .80 | .70 |

Christmas.

---

"Your Heart is your Health" A86

| **1972, Apr. 7** | | **Photo.** | **Wmk. 262** | |
|---|---|---|---|---|
| 314 | A86 | 2½p gold & brown | .25 | .25 |
| 315 | A86 | 12p silver & black | 3.00 | 2.50 |

World Health Day.

### Europa Issue

Sparkles, Symbolic of Communications — CD15

| **1972, May 1** | | | **Perf. 15** | |
|---|---|---|---|---|
| 316 | CD15 | 4p red, black & sil | 4.50 | .50 |
| 317 | CD15 | 6p blue, black & sil | 12.50 | 4.00 |

Dove Soaring Past Rising Moon — A88

| **1972, June 1** | | | **Photo.** | |
|---|---|---|---|---|
| 318 | A88 | 4p gray blue, org & dk bl | .25 | .25 |
| 319 | A88 | 6p olive, yel & dk green | .85 | .75 |

The patriot dead of 1922-23.

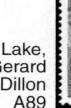

Black Lake, by Gerard Dillon A89

| **1972, July 10** | | | **Perf. 15** | |
|---|---|---|---|---|
| 320 | A89 | 3p indigo & multi | .55 | .75 |

Rider from Clonmacnoise Slab and Olympic Rings — A90

| **1972, Aug. 28** | | **Photo.** | **Wmk. 262** | |
|---|---|---|---|---|
| 321 | A90 | 3p yellow, black & gold | .25 | .25 |
| 322 | A90 | 6p salmon, black & gold | .75 | .75 |

20th Olympic Games, Munich, Aug. 26-Sept. 11, and 50th anniversary of the Olympic Council of Ireland.

Madonna and Child — A91

Ireland No. 68 — A92

---

| **1972, Oct. 16** | | **Unwmk.** | **Perf. 15** | |
|---|---|---|---|---|
| 323 | A91 | 2½p dk green & multi | .25 | .20 |
| 324 | A91 | 4p tan & multi | .50 | .30 |
| 325 | A91 | 12p multicolored | 2.00 | 1.00 |
| | | Nos. 323-325 (3) | 2.75 | 1.50 |

Christmas. The design is after a miniature in the Book of Kells, 9th century.

| **1972, Dec. 6** | | | **Photo.** | |
|---|---|---|---|---|
| 326 | A92 | 6p blue gray & dp grn | .75 | 1.10 |
| a. | | Souvenir sheet of 4 | 10.00 | 12.00 |

50th anniv. of 1st Irish postage stamp.

Recurrent Celtic Head Motif — A93

| **1973, Jan. 1** | | | **Unwmk.** | |
|---|---|---|---|---|
| 327 | A93 | 6p orange & multi | .40 | .50 |
| 328 | A93 | 12p green & multi | 1.60 | 1.50 |

Ireland's entry into the European Community.

### Europa Issue

Post Horn of Arrows CD16

| **1973, Apr. 30** | | | | |
|---|---|---|---|---|
| 329 | CD16 | 4p bright ultra | 1.50 | .20 |
| 330 | CD16 | 6p black | 5.00 | 1.75 |

"Berlin Blues I," by William Scott A95

### Perf. 15x14½

| **1973, Aug. 9** | | **Photo.** | **Unwmk.** | |
|---|---|---|---|---|
| 331 | A95 | 5p lt blue, blue & dk brn | .55 | .45 |

Weather Map of Northwest Europe — A96

| **1973, Sept. 4** | | | **Perf. 14½x15** | |
|---|---|---|---|---|
| 332 | A96 | 3½p ultra & multi | .25 | .20 |
| 333 | A96 | 12p lilac & multi | 1.75 | 1.50 |

Intl. meteorological cooperation, cent.

Tractor Plowing and Birds A97

| **1973, Oct. 5** | | | **Perf. 15x14½** | |
|---|---|---|---|---|
| 334 | A97 | 5p emerald & multi | .25 | .25 |
| 335 | A97 | 7p emerald & multi | 1.50 | .75 |

World Plowing Championships, Wellington Bridge, County Wexford, Oct. 1-7.

---

Flight into Egypt, by Jan de Cock — A98

| **1973, Nov. 1** | | | **Perf. 15** | |
|---|---|---|---|---|
| 336 | A98 | 3½p black & multi | .20 | .20 |
| 337 | A98 | 12p gold & multi | 1.40 | 1.40 |

Christmas.

Rescue, by Bernard Gribble A99

Design: Ballycotton lifeboat rescuing crew of Daunt Rock Lightship, 1936.

| **1974, Mar. 28** | | **Photo.** | **Wmk. 262** | |
|---|---|---|---|---|
| 338 | A99 | 5p multicolored | .60 | .50 |

Sesquicentennial of the founding of the Royal National Lifeboat Institution.

Edmund Burke, by John Henry Foley — A100

Oliver Goldsmith, by John Henry Foley — A101

### Europa Issue
### Perf. 14½x15

| **1974, Apr. 29** | | | **Unwmk.** | |
|---|---|---|---|---|
| 339 | A100 | 5p lt ultra & black | 2.00 | .20 |
| 340 | A100 | 7p lt green & black | 11.00 | 1.25 |

| **1974, June 24** | | | **Photo.** | |
|---|---|---|---|---|
| 341 | A101 | 3½p brt citron & blk | .25 | .20 |
| 342 | A101 | 12p emerald & black | 2.50 | 1.50 |

Oliver Goldsmith (1728-1774), writer.

### Types of 1968-69

½p, 1p, 2p, 3p, 3½p, 5p, #350, 352, Dog. #349, 351, 8p, 9p, Stag. 10p, 15p, 20p, Winged ox. 50p, £1, Eagle.
Two types of 50p: I, fine screen. II, coarse screen.

| **1974-78** | | | **Unwmk.** | **Perf. 15** |
|---|---|---|---|---|
| 343 | A68 | ½p yel green ('78) | .20 | .20 |
| 344 | A68 | 1p brt blue ('75) | .20 | .20 |
| 345 | A68 | 2p dark green ('76) | .20 | .20 |
| 346 | A68 | 3p ocher ('75) | .20 | .20 |
| 347 | A68 | 3½p deep orange | 4.00 | 4.00 |
| 348 | A68 | 5p apple green | .50 | .20 |
| 349 | A68 | 6p bl gray & dk brn | 2.00 | 2.25 |
| 350 | A68 | 6p blue gray ('75) | .45 | .40 |
| 351 | A68 | 7p lt ol grn & indigo | 2.75 | 2.75 |
| 352 | A68 | 7p olive green ('75) | .60 | .60 |
| a. | | Bklt. pane of 5 + label ('77) | 14.00 | |
| 353 | A68 | 8p brown & dk brn ('75) | 1.25 | 1.00 |
| 354 | A68 | 9p lt bl grn & black ('75) | 1.85 | .60 |
| 355 | A69 | 10p lil & multi ('75) | 2.75 | .85 |
| 356 | A69 | 15p multi ('75) | 2.25 | 1.10 |
| 357 | A69 | 20p slate & multi | 1.40 | .35 |

358  A69  50p rose brown &
           multi, type I
           ('74)                           1.75    .60
  a.   Type II ('83)                        2.75    2.75
359  A69  £1 multi ('75)                    4.00    1.50
     Nos. 343-359 (17)                     26.35   17.00

## Coil Stamps

**1977, Mar. 21           Perf. 14x15**
344b  A68  1p bright blue                          .75    .85
345b  A68  2p dark green                           .50    .60
348b  A68  5p apple green                         1.25    1.50
  c.   Strip of 4 (1p, 2x2p, 5p)                  2.50    2.75

Kitchen Table, by
Norah
McGuinness
A102

**1974, Aug. 19    Photo.    Perf. 14x15**
360  A102  5p multicolored                         .75    .75

Rugby
A103

**1974, Sept. 2    Engr.    Perf. 15x14**
361  A103  3½p slate green                         .75    .50
  a.   3½ deep slate green                         9.00    9.00
362  A103  12p multicolored                        3.00    3.00

Centenary of Irish Rugby Union.
No. 361a was printed from a reengraved
plate with more deeply engraved lines. The
original printing (No. 361) was considered to
be of unsatisfactory quality.

UPU "Postmark"
A104

Virgin and Child,
by Bellini — A105

**1974, Oct. 9    Photo.    Perf. 14½x15**
363  A104  5p emerald & black                      .30    .20
364  A104  7p ultra & black                        .80    1.00

Centenary of Universal Postal Union.

**1974, Nov. 14**
365  A105  5p multicolored                         .50    .20
366  A105  15p multicolored                        2.00    2.00

Christmas.

"Peace" — A106

**1975, Mar. 25    Photo.    Perf. 14½x15**
367  A106  8p dp rose lil & ultra                  .30    .20
368  A106  15p ultra & emerald                    1.60    1.40

International Women's Year.

### Europa Issue

Castletown
Hunt
(detail), by
Robert
Healy
A107

**1975, Apr. 28    Photo.    Perf. 15x14½**
369  A107  7p black                               4.00    —
370  A107  9p green                               9.50    2.00

Chipping
from the
Fringe
A108

**1975, June 26    Photo.    Perf. 15x14½**
371  A108  6p shown                                .50    .25
372  A108  9p Putting                             2.50    1.50

9th European Amateur Golf Team Championships, Killarney.

Bird of
Prey, by
Oisín Kelly
A109

**1975, July 28**
373  A109  15p ocher                               .90    1.10

Nano Nagle and
Pupils, Engraving
by Charles
Turner — A110

Clock Tower, St.
Ann's Church,
Shandon — A111

**1975, Sept. 1    Photo.    Perf. 14½x15**
374  A110  5p light blue & black                   .20    .20
375  A110  7p buff & black                         .75    .75

Presentation Order of Nuns, bicentenary.

**1975, Oct. 6    Photo.    Perf. 12½**
Designs: 7p, 9p, Holycross Abbey.

376  A111  5p sepia                                .30    .20
377  A111  6p ultra & multi                        .50    1.00
378  A111  7p sapphire                             .75    .30
379  A111  9p multicolored                        1.00    1.00
     Nos. 376-379 (4)                             2.55    2.50

European Architectural Heritage Year.

St. Oliver Plunkett,
by Imogen
Stuart — A112

Madonna and
Child, by Fra
Filippo
Lippi — A113

**1975, Oct. 13    Engr.    Perf. 14x14½**
380  A112  7p black                                .30    .20
381  A112  15p dull red                           1.10    1.25

Canonization of Oliver Plunkett (1625-
1681), Primate of Ireland.

**1975, Nov. 13    Photo.    Perf. 15**
382  A113  5p multicolored                         .20    .20
383  A113  7p multicolored                         .50    .20
384  A113  10p gold & multi                       1.00    1.00
     Nos. 382-384 (3)                             1.70    1.40

Christmas.

James
Larkin — A114

Bell Making First
Call — A115

**1976 Jan. 21    Photo.    Perf. 14½x15**
385  A114  7p gray & slate grn                     .20    .20
386  A114  11p ocher & brown                      1.25    .80

James Larkin (1876-1947), trade union
leader.

**1976, Mar. 10    Photo.    Perf. 14½x15**
387  A115  9p multicolored                         .30    .25
388  A115  15p multicolored                       1.40    1.00

Centenary of first telephone call by Alexander Graham Bell, March 10, 1876.

13 Stars
and Stripes
A116

Designs: 8p, 50 stars, and stripes. 9p, 15p,
Benjamin Franklin on Albany essay of 1847.

**1976, May 17    Litho.    Perf. 15x14**
389  A116  7p ultra, sil & red                     .25    .20
  a.   Silver (inscription) omitted                      275.00
390  A116  8p ultra, sil & red                     .40    .80
391  A116  9p bl, sil & ocher                      .70    .40
392  A116  15p red, sil & bl                       .80    .80
  a.   Souvenir sheet of 4, #389-
       392                                         8.00    10.00
  b.   Silver (inscription) omitted,
       #392                                      950.00   900.00
     Nos. 389-392 (4)                             2.15    2.20

American Bicentennial. No. 392a exists with
silver omitted.

Irish Delft
Spirit Barrel
A117

Europa: 11p, Bowl, Irish Delft. Designs
show mark of Henry Delamain's Factory, Dublin, both pieces c. 1756.

**1976, July 1    Photo.    Perf. 15x14½**
393  A117  9p gray & magenta                      2.50    .25
394  A117  11p gray & blue                        5.00    1.00

### Types of 1968

Designs: 8p, 9p, 9½p, No. 399, Dog. No.
398, 11p, 12p, Stag. 17p, Winged ox.

**1976-79    Photo.    Unwmk.    Perf. 15**
395  A68  8p brown                                 .35    .20
396  A68  9p blue green                            .40    .20
397  A68  9½p red ('79)                            .50    .20
398  A68  10p lilac & black                       1.50    .50
399  A68  10p purple ('77)                         .40    .20
400  A68  11p carmine & black                      .75    .50
401  A68  12p emer & black ('77)                   .85    .20
402  A69  17p ol, bl & ocher ('77)                1.25    .75
     Nos. 395-402 (8)                             6.00    2.75

The
Lobster
Pots, by
Paul Henry
A118

**1976, Aug. 30    Photo.    Perf. 15**
405  A118  15p gold & multi                       1.00    1.00

Paul Henry (1876-1958), birth centenary.

Radio
Waves
A119

Radio Tower and
Waves,
Globe — A120

**Perf. 14½x14, 14x14½**
**1976, Oct. 5                            Litho.**
406  A119  9p brt blue & black                     .20    .20
407  A120  11p black & multi                      1.10    1.25

Irish broadcasting, 50th anniversary.

Nativity, by
Lorenzo
Monaco
A121

**1976, Nov. 11                        Perf. 15x14½**
408  A121  7p multicolored                         .25    .20
409  A121  9p multicolored                         .50    .25
410  A121  15p multicolored                       1.00    .80
     Nos. 408-410 (3)                             1.75    1.25

Christmas.

Irish
Manuscript,
16th
Century
A122

Stone from Newgrange Burial Mound A123

**1977, May 9   Photo.   *Perf. 15x14½***
411 A122 8p multicolored .30 .20
412 A123 10p multicolored .65 .60
Centenaries of National Library (8p) and National Museum (10p).

**Europa Issue**

View of Ballynahinch A124

Lugalla Lake — A125

**1977, June 27   Litho.   *Perf. 14x14½***
413 A124 10p multicolored 3.50 .25
414 A125 12p multicolored 12.50 1.40

Head, by Louis le Brocquy, 1973 — A126

**1977, Aug. 8   *Perf. 14x14½***
415 A126 17p multicolored 1.00 1.00

Girl Guide and Tents A127

Design: 17p, Boy Scout and tents.

**1977, Aug. 22   Photo.   *Perf. 15x14½***
416 A127 8p multicolored .50 .25
417 A127 17p multicolored 1.25 1.25
European Scout and Guide Conference, Ireland, and 50th anniversary of Catholic Boy Scouts of Ireland.

The Shanachie, by Jack B. Yeats — A128

Eriugena A129

**Perf. 14x14½, 14½x14**
**1977, Sept. 12   Litho.**
418 A128 10p black .40 .30
419 A129 12p black 1.10 1.25
Folklore of Ireland Society, 50th anniv. and 1100th death anniv. of Johannes Scottus Eriugena, philospher, poet and mystic.

"Electricity," Mural by Robert Ballagh — A130

Bulls, from Contemporary Coin — A131

Greyhound A132

**Litho. (10p, 17p); Photo. (12p)**
***Perf. 14½x14; 15x14½ (12p)***
**1977, Oct. 10**
420 A130 10p multicolored .30 .20
421 A131 12p multicolored .60 .60
422 A132 17p multicolored 1.00 .80
Nos. 420-422 (3) 1.90 1.60

50th anniversaries of: Electricity Supply Board (10p); Agricultural Credit Act (12p); introduction of greyhound racing (17p).

Holy Family, by Giorgione — A133

Bremen, Junkers Monoplane A134

**1977, Nov. 3   Photo.   *Perf. 14½x15***
423 A133 8p multicolored .35 .20
424 A133 10p multicolored .60 .60
425 A133 17p multicolored 1.00 1.00
Nos. 423-425 (3) 1.95 1.80
Christmas.

**1978, Apr. 13   Litho.   *Perf. 14***
426 A134 10p ultra & black .35 .35
427 A134 17p lt brown & black .90 .90
50th anniversary of first East-West transatlantic flight from Baldonnel, County Dublin, to Greenly Island, Gulf of St. Lawrence.

Spring Gentian — A135

Wild flowers: 10p, Strawberry tree. 11p, Large-flowered butterwort. 17p, St. Daboec's heath.

**1978, June 12   Litho.   *Perf. 14x14½***
428 A135 8p multicolored .25 .25
429 A135 10p multicolored .50 .50
430 A135 11p multicolored .65 .95
431 A135 17p multicolored .85 1.25
Nos. 428-431 (4) 2.25 2.95

Catherine McAuley — A136

William Orpen, Self-portrait A138

Vaccination, lithograph by Manigaud — A137

**1978, Sept. 18   Litho.   *Perf. 14***
432 A136 10p multicolored .30 .20
433 A137 11p multicolored .50 .50
434 A138 17p multicolored 1.00 .80
Nos. 432-434 (3) 1.80 1.50
Catherine McAuley (1778-1841), founder of Sisters of Mercy (10p); eradication of smallpox (11p); William Orpen (1878-1931), painter (17p).

Offshore Oil Well — A139

Woodcock on Farthing A140

Virgin and Child, by Guercino — A141

**1978, Oct. 18   Litho.   *Perf. 14***
435 A139 10p multicolored .50 .35
First natural gas coming in off the Irish Coast at Kinsale.

**1978, Oct. 26   Photo.   *Perf. 15x14½***
Coins: 10p, Salmon on florin. 11p, Hen and chicks on penny. 17p, Horse on half crown.
436 A140 8p multicolored .40 .20
437 A140 10p multicolored .50 .25
438 A140 11p multicolored .60 .60
439 A140 17p multicolored 1.00 1.00
Nos. 436-439 (4) 2.50 2.05
Irish currency, 50th anniversary.

**1978, Nov. 16   Photo.   *Perf. 14½x15***
440 A141 8p multicolored .30 .20
441 A141 10p multicolored .40 .25
442 A141 17p multicolored .75 .65
Nos. 440-442 (3) 1.45 1.10
Christmas.

Conolly Folly, Castletown A142

Europa: 11p, Belvedere on Tower Hill at Dromoland.

**1978, Dec. 6   *Perf. 15x14½***
443 A142 10p brown 3.00 .25
444 A142 11p dull green 9.00 1.00

Cross-country Runners — A143

**1979, Aug. 20   Litho.   *Perf. 14½x14***
445 A143 8p multicolored .30 .30
7th World Cross-country Championships, Greenpark Racecourse, Limerick, March 25.

Rowland Hill, Bronze Statue — A144

"European Communities" (7 Languages) A145

**1979, Aug. 20   *Perf. 14x14½***
446 A144 17p multicolored .60 .60
Sir Rowland Hill (1795-1879), originator of penny postage.

**1979, Aug. 20  Photo.  Perf. 14½x15**
447 A145 10p lt greenish gray .40 .40
448 A145 11p rose lilac .45 .45
European Parliament, first direct elections, June 7-10.

Wren
A146

Birds: 10p, Great crested grebe. 11p, Greenland white-fronted geese. 17p, Peregrine falcon.

**1979, Aug. 30  Litho.  Perf. 14½x14**
449 A146 8p multicolored .35 .20
450 A146 10p multicolored .50 .50
451 A146 11p multicolored .60 .60
452 A146 17p multicolored 1.00 1.00
Nos. 449-452 (4) 2.45 2.30

A Happy Flower
A147

Children's Drawings: 11p, "Me and my skipping rope," vert. 17p, "Swans on a lake."

**Perf. 14½x14, 14x14½**
**1979, Sept. 13  Litho.**
453 A147 10p multicolored .30 .30
454 A147 11p multicolored .75 .45
455 A147 17p multicolored 1.00 .60
Nos. 453-455 (3) 2.05 1.35

International Year of the Child.

Pope John Paul II
A148

**1979, Sept. 29  Litho.  Perf. 14½x14**
456 A148 12p multicolored .50 .50
Visit of Pope John Paul II to Ireland.

Hospitaller Brother Teaching Child
A149

**1979, Oct. 4**
457 A149 9½p rose & black .50 .30
Hospitaller Order of St. John of God, centenary in Ireland.

Windmill and Sun — A150

**1979, Oct. 4  Photo.  Perf. 14½x15**
458 A150 11p multicolored .50 .40
Energy conservation.

"Seated Figure," by F.E. McWilliam
A151

**1979, Oct. 4  Litho.  Perf. 14½x14**
459 A151 20p multicolored 1.00 .70

Patrick Pearse
A152

**1979, Nov. 10  Photo.  Perf. 15x14½**
460 A152 12p multicolored .45 .30
Patrick Henry Pearse (1879-1916), Irish writer and leader of Easter Rebellion.

Mother and Child, Panel, Domnach Argid Shrine — A153

**1979, Nov. 15  Photo.  Perf. 14½x15**
461 A153 9½p multicolored .50 .20
462 A153 20p multicolored 1.00 .75
Christmas.

**Europa Issue**

Bianconi Long Car, 1836
A154

Laying Transatlantic Cable, Steamer William Cory, 1866 — A155

**1979, Dec. 6  Litho.  Perf. 15x14**
463 A154 12p multicolored 1.50 .40
464 A155 13p multicolored 9.50 .85

**Type of 1968**
Designs: 13p, 16p, Stag; others, Dog.

**1980-82  Photo.  Perf. 15**
466 A68 12p green .50 .30
467 A68 13p red brown & dk brn 1.00 .30
468 A68 15p ultra .90 .50
469 A68 16p olive green & blk 1.00 .50

**Litho.**
**Perf. 14x15**
470 A68 18p dull red brn ('81) .95 .60
471 A68 19p dull blue ('81) 1.00 .55
472 A68 22p gray blue ('81) .95 .20
473 A68 24p brown olive ('81) 1.25 .40
474 A68 26p bluish green ('82) 1.25 .65
475 A68 29p dp rose lilac ('82) 1.50 .80
Nos. 466-475 (10) 10.30 4.80

Issued: 12p, 13p, 3/26/80; 15p, 16p, 7/10/80; 18p, 19p, 4/27/81; 22p, 9/1/81; 24p, 10/29/81; 26p, 29p, 4/1/82.

St. Jean Baptiste de la Salle — A156

**1980, Mar. 19  Litho.  Perf. 14x15**
477 A156 12p multicolored .45 .30
The Brothers of the Christian School (founded by St. Jean Baptiste), centenary in Ireland.

**Europa Issue**

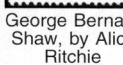

George Bernard Shaw, by Alick Ritchie
A157

Oscar Wilde, by Toulouse-Lautrec
A158

**1980, May 7  Litho.  Perf. 14x15**
478 A157 12p multicolored 3.50 .30
479 A158 13p multicolored 3.50 .65

Irish Ermine — A159

Bodhran Drum and Whistle Players — A160

**1980, July 30  Litho.  Perf. 14x15**
480 A159 12p shown .30 .25
481 A159 15p Irish hare .50 .30
482 A159 16p Fox .50 .40
483 A159 25p Red deer 1.00 1.00
a.  Miniature sheet of 4, #480-483 3.00 4.25
Nos. 480-483 (4) 2.30 1.95

**1980, Sept. 25  Photo.  Perf. 14x15**
484 A160 12p shown .45 .25
485 A160 15p Piper, Uilleann pipes .60 .60
486 A160 25p Irish jig .85 .85
Nos. 484-486 (3) 1.90 1.70

Sean O'Casey (1880-1964), Playwright
A161

Gold Painting No. 57, by Patrick Scott — A162

**1980, Oct. 23  Litho.  Perf. 14x14½**
487 A161 12p multicolored .45 .35

**1980, Oct. 23  Perf. 14x15**
488 A162 25p multicolored .85 .65

A163

A164

**1980, Dec. 4  Photo.  Perf. 15x14½**
489 A163 12p multicolored .30 .20
490 A163 15p multicolored .60 .35
491 A163 25p multicolored 1.00 .60
Nos. 489-491 (3) 1.90 1.15
Christmas.

**1981, Mar. 12  Litho.  Perf. 14x14½**
Scientists and Inventions: 12p, Robert Boyle (1627-1691), and Air Pump, 1659. 15p, Harry Ferguson (1884-1960), hydraulic tractor, 1936. 16p, Charles Parsons (1854-1931), Parsons' turbine, 1884. 25p, John Holland (1841-1914), Holland submarine, 1878.

492 A164 12p multicolored .25 .20
493 A164 15p multicolored .40 .25
494 A164 16p multicolored .50 .35
495 A164 25p multicolored 1.00 .75
Nos. 492-495 (4) 2.15 1.55

The Cock and the Pot, Rubbing, 1841 — A165

Europa: 19p, The Scales of Judgment, rubbing, 1827.

**1981, May 4  Litho.  Perf. 14½x15**
496 A165 18p multicolored 4.00 .30
497 A165 19p multicolored 7.00 .50

Hiking
A166

**Perf. 14x15, 15x14**
**1981, June 24  Litho.**
498 A166 15p Bicycling, vert. .40 .20
499 A166 18p shown .60 .35
500 A166 19p Mountain climbing .75 .60

501 A166 30p Rock climbing,
vert.                              1.25    .75
Nos. 498-501 (4)              3.00   1.90
Youth Hostel Assn., 50th anniv.

Jeremiah
O'Donovan Rossa
(1831-1915),
Journalist — A167

Railway Embankment, by William John
Leech (1881-1968) — A168

**Perf. 14½x15, 15x14½**
**1981, Aug. 31**
502 A167 15p multicolored          .35    .45
503 A168 30p multicolored         1.25   1.25

James Hoban (1762-1831), White
House Architect — A169

**1981, Sept. 29          Perf. 15x14**
504 A169 18p multicolored          .75    .60
Same design used for US Nos. 1935-1936.

Draft Horse
King of
Diamonds
A170

Famous Horses: No. 505, Show-jumper
Boomerang. No. 506, Steeplechaser Arkle.
24p, Flat racer Ballymoss. 36p, Connemara
pony Coosheen Finn.

**1981, Oct. 23     Litho.     Perf. 15x14**
505 A170 18p multicolored          .80    .40
506 A170 18p multicolored          .80    .40
  a.    Pair, #505-506             1.75   1.75
507 A170 22p multicolored         1.00    .60
508 A170 24p multicolored          .80   1.00
509 A170 36p multicolored         1.60   1.60
Nos. 505-509 (5)              5.00   4.00

Nativity, by
Federico
Barocci — A171

A172

**1981, Nov. 19     Litho.     Perf. 14x15**
510 A171 18p multicolored          .50    .20
511 A171 22p multicolored          .65    .25
512 A171 36p multicolored         1.25    .55
Nos. 510-512 (3)              2.40   1.00
Christmas 1981.

**1981, Dec. 10    Litho.     Perf. 14x14½**
513 A172 18p multicolored          .65    .50
Land Law Act centenary.

250th
Anniv. of
Royal
Dublin
Society
A173

**1981, Dec. 10               Perf. 14½x14**
514 A173 22p multicolored          .80    .55

50th Anniv.
of Killarney
Natl. Park
A174

**1982, Feb. 26    Litho.     Perf. 14½x14**
515 A174 18p Upper Lake            .75    .30
516 A174 36p Eagle's Nest         1.25   1.10

The
Stigmatization of
St. Francis, by
Sassetta — A175

Francis Makemie, Old Presbyterian
Church, Ramelton — A176

**1982, Apr. 2      Perf. 14x15, 15x14**
517 A175 22p multicolored          .75    .50
518 A176 24p brown                1.10    .90
800th birth anniv. of St. Francis of Assisi;
300th anniv. of Francis Makemie's ordination
(father of American Presbyterianism).

**Europa Issue**

Great Famine of
1845-50 — A177

Conversion of Ireland to Christianity
(St. Patrick and his Followers, by
Vincenzo Valdre)
A178

**1982, May 4**
519 A177 26p tan & brown         11.00    .75
520 A178 29p multicolored        15.00   4.00

Padraic
O'Connaire
(1882-1928),
Writer — A179

Designs: 26p, James Joyce (1882-1941),
writer and poet, by Brancusi. 29p, John Field
(1782-1837), Composer and pianist, Nocturne
score. 44p, Charles Joseph Kickham (1828-
1882), journalist and writer. 29p, 44p by Colin
Harrison.

**1982, June 16    Litho.     Perf. 14x15**
521 A179 22p blue & black          .50    .30
522 A179 26p black & brown         .75    .60
523 A179 29p black & blue         1.10   1.10
524 A179 44p gray green & black   1.75   1.75
Nos. 521-524 (4)              4.10   3.75

Porbeagle
Shark
A180

**1982, July 29              Perf. 15x14**
525 A180 22p shown                 .75    .50
526 A180 22p Oyster                .75    .50
527 A180 26p Salmon               1.25    .50
528 A180 29p Dublin Bay prawn     1.50   1.50
Nos. 525-528 (4)              4.25   3.00

Currach
A181

**1982, Sept. 21     Perf. 15x14, 14x15**
529 A181 22p shown                 .70    .35
530 A181 22p Galway hooker,
vert.                              .70    .35
531 A181 26p Asgard II training
ship                              1.10    .60
532 A181 29p Howth 17-footer,
vert.                             1.50   1.50
Nos. 529-532 (4)              4.00   2.80

The Irish
House of
Commons,
by Francis
Wheatley
A182

**1982, Oct. 14    Litho.     Perf. 14½x14**
533 A182 22p multicolored          .60    .40
Bicentenary of Grattan's Parliament.

A183

A183a

Eamon de Valera (1882-1975), President,
by Robert Ballagh.

**1982, Oct. 14               Perf. 14x14½**
534 A183 26p multicolored          .75    .75

**1982, Nov. 11    Litho.     Perf. 14½x15**
Madonna and Child, by Andrea della Robbia
(1435-1525)
535 A183a 22p lt violet & multi    .60    .40
536 A183a 26p gray & multi         .75    .50
Christmas.

A184                     A185

Killarney Cathedral,
1855 — A186

Designs: 1p-5p, Central Pavilion, Dublin
Botanical Gardens. 6p, 7p, 10p, 12p, Dr.
Steeven's Hospital, Dublin. 15p, 20p, 22p,
Aughnanure Castle, Oughterard, 16th cent.
23p, 26p, Cormac's Chapel, 1134. 29p, 30p,
St. Mac Dara's Church. 50p, Casino, Marino.
£1, Cahir Castle, 15th century. £5 Central Bus
Station, Dublin, 1953.
50p, £1, £5 horiz.

**1982-90     Litho.     Perf. 14x15, 15x14**
537 A184  1p dull blue             .20    .20
538 A184  2p gray green            .20    .20
539 A184  3p black                 .20    .20
540 A184  4p rose lake             .20    .20
  a.   Perf. 13½ on 3 or 4 sides  1.00    .20
541 A184  5p brown                 .50    .50
542 A184  6p dull blue             .50    .50
543 A184  7p gray green            .90    .75
544 A184 10p black                 .90    .75
545 A184 12p rose lake             .90    .75
546 A185 15p gray green           1.25    .90
547 A185 20p rose lake            1.25    .90
548 A185 22p dull blue            1.25    .90
  a.   Bklt. pane of 7+label (3 4p, 4
       22p) ('88)                  6.00
549 A185 23p gray green           1.75   1.50
550 A185 26p black                2.00   1.50
  a.   Bklt. pane, 2 ea 2p, 22p, 26p     7.00
  b.   Bklt. pane, 4 ea 2p, 22p, 26p    14.00
  c.   Bklt. pane, 3 4p, 5 22p, 4 26p
       ('88)                      15.00
  d.   Perf. 13½ on 3 sides       3.00   2.00
551 A184 29p gray green           2.25   2.00
552 A184 30p black                1.50   1.00
  a.   Perf. 13½ on 3 or 4 sides  2.50   1.00

**Perf. 14x15, 15x14**
553 A186 44p gray & black         2.25   2.00
554 A186 50p gray & dull blue     2.25   1.25
555 A186 £1 gray & brown          8.00   4.00
556 A186 £5 gray & rose lake     21.00  15.00
Nos. 537-556 (20)           49.25  35.00

Stamps from #550c imprinted "Booklet
Stamp" in green on reverse side. #550c sold
for £2.
Issued: 4p, 6p-7p, 20p, 23p, 30p, 50p,
3/16/83; 1p-3p, 5p, 10p-15p, 7/6/83; #540a,
550d, 552a, 5/3/90; others, 12/15/82.
See Nos. 638-645, 803a, 804b.

Dublin Chamber
of Commerce
Bicentenary
A187

Bank of Ireland Bicentenary — A188

**1983, Feb. 23**        **Litho.**
557 A187 22p Ouzel Galley goblet     .55  .50
558 A188 26p Bank     .85  .65

Padraig
Siochfhradha
(1883-1964),
Writer — A189

Boys' Brigade
Centenary
A190

**1983, Apr. 7**    **Litho.**    **Perf. 14x14½**
559 A189 26p multicolored    .75  .35
560 A190 29p multicolored    1.25 1.00

Europa
A191

Design: 26p, Newgrange Winter Solstice,
Neolithic Pattern Drawing by Louis le Brocquy.
29p, Quaternion formula, by William Rowan
Hamilton (1805-1865).

**1983, May 4**    **Litho.**    **Perf. 14½x14**
561 A191 26p black & gold    7.00  .65
562 A191 29p multicolored    19.00 6.00

Kerry Blue
Terrier
A192

Drawings of dogs by Wendy Walsh.

**1983, June 23**
563 A192 22p shown    .70  .70
564 A192 26p Irish wolfhound    .80  .80
565 A192 26p Irish water spaniel    .80  .80
566 A192 29p Irish terrier    1.00 1.00
567 A192 44p Irish setters    1.50 1.50
   a.   Miniature sheet of 5, #563-567    8.50 8.50
     Nos. 563-567 (5)    4.80 4.80

Sean
Mac Diarmada
(1883-1916),
Nationalist
A193

Society for
the
Prevention
of Cruelty
to Animals
A194

Society of St.
Vincent de Paul
Sesquicentennial
A195

Industrial
Credit Co.,
50th Anniv.
A196

US Pres. Andrew
Jackson (1767-
1845)
A197

**Perf. 14x14½, 14½x14**
**1983, Aug. 11**
568 A193 22p multicolored    .85  .85
569 A194 22p multicolored    .85  .85
570 A195 26p multicolored    1.10 1.10
571 A196 26p multicolored    1.10 1.10
572 A197 44p gray    2.25 2.25
     Nos. 568-572 (5)    6.15 6.15

WCY — A198

Handicrafts
A199

**1983, Sept. 15**    **Litho.**    **Perf. 14x15**
573 A198 22p Mailman    1.00 1.00
574 A198 29p Dish antenna    1.25 1.25

**1983, Oct. 13**    **Litho.**    **Perf. 14x15**
575 A199 22p Weaving    .75  .45
576 A199 26p Basketweaving    1.00  .75
577 A199 29p Irish crochet    1.25 1.00
578 A199 44p Harpmaking    2.50 1.75
     Nos. 575-578 (4)    5.50 3.95

La Natividad by
Rogier van der
Weyden — A200

**1983, Nov. 30**    **Litho.**    **Perf. 14x14½**
579 A200 22p multicolored    .60  .35
580 A200 26p multicolored    1.25 1.25
     Christmas.

Irish Railways
Sesquicentenary — A201

Locomotives: 23p, Princess, Dublin and
Kingstown Railway. 26p, Macha, Great South-
ern Railways. 29p, Kestrel, Great Northern
Railway. 44p, Link-Hoffman railcar, Coras
Iompair Eireann.

**1984, Jan. 30**        **Perf. 14½x14**
581 A201 23p multicolored    1.10 1.10
582 A201 26p multicolored    .65  .65
583 A201 29p multicolored    1.25 1.25
584 A201 44p multicolored    2.00 2.00
   a.   Souvenir sheet of 4, #581-584    7.00 7.50
     Nos. 581-584 (4)    5.00 5.00

**Private Overprints**
Nos. 584a, 684a, 708a, 708b, 803a,
804a, 811a, 826a, 847a, 855a, 876b,
and others, exist with privately applied
show overprints.

Local Trees
A202

**1984, Mar. 1**    **Litho.**    **Perf. 15x14**
585 A202 22p Irish whitebeam    .65  .55
586 A202 26p Irish yew    .85  .75
587 A202 29p Irish willow    1.25 1.00
588 A202 44p Birch    1.75 1.75
     Nos. 585-588 (4)    4.50 4.05

St. Vincent's Hospital, Dublin,
Sesquicentenary — A203

Royal College of Surgeons in Ireland
Bicentenary — A204

**1984, Apr. 12**        **Litho.**
589 A203 26p multicolored    1.00  .75
590 A204 44p multicolored    1.75 1.50

2nd
European
Parliament
Election
A205

**1984, May 10**    **Litho.**    **Perf. 15x14**
591 A205 26p multicolored    1.40  .85

Europa
(1959-84)
A206

**1984, May 10**
592 A206 26p multicolored    7.00 3.00
593 A206 29p multicolored    15.00 3.75

John McCormack
(1884-1945),
Singer — A207

**1984, June 6**    **Litho.**    **Perf. 14x14½**
594 A207 22p multicolored    1.25  .75
     See US No. 2090.

1984
Summer
Olympics
A208

**1984, June 21**    **Litho.**    **Perf. 14½x14**
595 A208 22p Hammer throw    .70  .50
596 A208 26p Hurdles    .90  .75
597 A208 29p Running    1.10 1.00
     Nos. 595-597 (3)    2.70 2.25

Gaelic
Athletic
Assoc.
Centenary
A209

**1984, Aug. 23**    **Litho.**    **Perf. 14x15**
598 A209 22p Hurlers    .65  .45
599 A209 26p Soccer, vert.    1.00  .85

Mayoral City of
Galway, 500th
Anniv. — A210

St.
Brendan
(484-577)
A211

**1984, Sept. 18**        **Perf. 14x15, 15x14**
600 A210 26p Medal    .75  .75
601 A211 44p Portrait, manuscript    1.50 1.50

Post Office Bicentenary — A212

**1984, Oct. 19**　　　　　*Perf. 15x14*
602　A212　26p　Handing sealed
　　　　　　　letter　　　　　1.10　.75

A213

Virgin And Child
by Sassoferrato
A214

*Perf. 14½x14, 14x14½*
**1984, Nov. 26**　　　　　　Litho.
603　A213　17p multicolored　　.45　.20
604　A214　22p multicolored　　.75　.45
605　A214　26p multicolored　1.25　.65
　　　Nos. 603-605 (3)　　　2.45　1.30
　　　　　　Christmas.

Love
A215

A216

**1985, Jan. 31　Litho.　　*Perf. 15x14***
606　A215　22p　Heart-shaped bal-
　　　　　　　loon　　　　　.75　.50
607　A216　26p　Bouquet of hearts　1.50　1.25

Dunsink
Observatory,
200th
Anniv. — A217

Cork City
Charter,
800th
Anniv.
A218

---

Royal Irish
Academy, 200th
Anniv. — A219

1st Manned Flight
in Ireland, 200th
Anniv. — A220

**1985, Mar. 14**　　　　　Litho.
608　A217　22p black　　　　.60　.60
609　A218　26p multicolored　　.80　.80
610　A219　37p multicolored　1.25　1.25
611　A220　44p multicolored　1.50　1.50
　　　Nos. 608-611 (4)　　　4.15　4.15

Butterflies
A221

**1985, Apr. 11　Litho.　*Perf. 14x15***
612　A221　22p　Common blue　1.25　1.10
613　A221　26p　Red admiral　1.40　1.25
614　A221　28p　Brimstone　　1.60　1.25
615　A221　44p　Marsh fritillary　2.25　2.00
　　　Nos. 612-615 (4)　　　6.50　5.60

Europa
A222

26p, Charles Villiers Stanford (1852-1924),
composer. 37p, Turlough O'Carolan (1670-
1738), Composer.

**1985, May 16　Litho.　*Perf. 15x14***
616　A222　26p multicolored　3.75　.75
617　A222　37p multicolored　9.50　6.50

European Music
Year — A223

Composers: No. 618, Giuseppe Domenico
Scarlatti (1685-1757). No. 619, George
Frideric Handel (1685-1759). No. 620, Johann
Sebastian Bach (1685-1750).

**1985, May 16　Litho.　*Perf. 14x15***
618　A223　22p multicolored　1.60　*1.90*
619　A223　22p multicolored　1.60　*1.90*
　a.　　Pair, #618-619　　3.50　4.00
620　A223　26p multicolored　1.60　*1.90*
　　　Nos. 618-620 (3)　　　4.80　5.70

---

Irish UN
Defense
Forces in
the Congo,
1960
A224

Thomas Ashe
(1885-1917),
Patriot and
Educator — A225

Bishop George
Berkeley (1685-
1753),
Philosopher and
Educator — A226

*Perf. 15x14, 14x15*
**1985, June 20**　　　　　Litho.
621　A224　22p multicolored　　.90　.60
622　A225　26p multicolored　1.00　1.00
623　A226　44p multicolored　1.75　1.75
　　　Nos. 621-623 (3)　　　3.65　3.35
Irish forces as part of the UN Defense
Forces, 25th anniv. (22p).

Intl. Youth
Year — A227

**1985, Aug. 1**　　　　　Litho.
624　A227　22p multi, horiz.　　.85　.65
625　A227　26p multicolored　1.00　.75

**Architecture Type of 1982**

Designs: 24p, 39p, Cormac's Chapel. 28p,
32p, 37p, St. Mac Dara's Church. 46p, Cahir
Castle. £1, Killarney Cathedral. £2, Casino,
Marino. 46p, £2, horiz.

*Perf. 15x14, 14x15 (A184, No. 644)*
**1985-88**　　　　　　　Litho.
638　A185　24p brown　　　　1.00　.50
639　A184　28p rose lake　　1.25　.30
　a.　Bklt. pane, 4 2p, 2 24p, 1 4p,
　　　5 28p ('88)　　　　5.75
　c.　Bklt. pane, 2 2p, 3 4p, 3 24p,
　　　4 28p ('88)　　　　6.00
640　A184　32p brown　　　　1.50　.75
641　A184　37p dull blue　　2.50　2.50
642　A185　39p rose lake　　2.50　1.75
643　A186　46p gray & gray grn　2.75　2.00
644　A184　£1 gray & dull bl　5.00　1.50
645　A186　£2 gray & gray grn　11.50　4.50
　　　Nos. 638-645 (8)　　28.00　13.80

Issued: 24p, 28p, 37p, £1, June 27, 1985;
32p, 39p, 46p, May 1, 1986; £2, July 26, 1988.

Industrial
Innovations
A228

---

Institution
of
Engineers,
150th
Anniv.
A229

**1985, Oct. 3　　Litho.　　*Perf. 15x14***
646　A228　22p　Computer technol-
　　　　　　　ogy　　　　　.75　.50
647　A228　26p　Peat production　1.00　1.00
648　A229　44p　The Key Man, by
　　　　　　　Sean Keating　2.00　1.50
　　　Nos. 646-648 (3)　　　3.75　3.00

Candle,
Holly — A230

Virgin and Child in
a Landscape, by
Adrian van
Ijsenbrandt
A231

Christmas: No. 651, The Holy Family, by
Murillo. 26p, Adoration of the Shepherds, by
Louis Le Nain, horiz.

*Perf. 14x15, 15x14*
**1985, Nov. 26**　　　　　Litho.
649　A230　22p shown　　　1.00　.75
650　A231　22p shown　　　1.00　.75
651　A231　22p multicolored　1.00　.75
　a.　　Pair, #650-651　　2.00　2.00
652　A231　26p multicolored　1.50　1.50
　　　Nos. 649-652 (4)　　　4.50　3.75

#649 was issued in discount sheets of 16
that sold for £3. Value $16.

Love — A232

**1986, Jan. 30**　　　　*Perf. 14x15*
653　A232　22p shown　　　1.00　.60
654　A232　26p　Heart-shaped
　　　　　　　mailbox　　　1.25　1.10

Ferns — A233

Europa — A234

**1986, Mar. 20    Litho.    Perf. 14½x15**
655 A233 24p Hart's tongue ..... .80 .30
656 A233 28p Rusty-back ..... 1.00 .75
657 A233 46p Killarney ..... 1.75 1.75
　　Nos. 655-657 (3) ..... 3.55 2.80

**1986, May 1    Perf. 14x15, 15x14**
658 A234 28p Industry and na-
　　ture ..... 10.00 1.25
659 A234 39p Hedgerows,
　　horiz. ..... 35.00 6.00

Aer Lingus, 50th Anniv. A235

**1986, May 27    Perf. 15x14**
660 A235 28p Jet, 1986 ..... 1.40 1.00
661 A235 46p The Eagle, 1936 ..... 2.25 2.00

Inland Waterways A236

**1986, May 27    Perf. 15x14, 14x15**
662 A236 24p Robertstown
　　Grand Canal ..... 1.00 .60
663 A236 28p Fishing, County
　　Mayo, vert. ..... 1.25 1.00
664 A236 30p Yachting, River
　　Shannon ..... 1.50 1.50
　　Nos. 662-664 (3) ..... 3.75 3.10

British & Irish Steam Packet Co., 150th Anniv. A237

**1986, July 10    Perf. 15x14**
665 A237 24p Steamer Severn,
　　1836 ..... 1.00 .75
666 A237 28p M.V. Leinster,
　　1986 ..... 1.50 1.25

Lighthouses A238

**1986, July 10    Perf. 14½x15**
667 A238 24p Kish, helicopter ..... 1.50 1.25
668 A238 30p Fastnet ..... 2.25 1.75

Dublin Council of Trade Unions, Cent. — A239

Arthur Griffith (1871-1922), Statesman A240

Women in Society, Construction Surveyor — A241

A242

Intl. Peace Year A242a

**Perf. 14½x15, 14x15 (#670, 672), 15x14½, 15x14**

**1986, Aug. 21**
669 A239 24p multicolored ..... .85 .65
670 A240 28p multicolored ..... 1.10 .70
671 A241 28p multicolored ..... 1.10 .70
672 A242 30p multi, vert. ..... 1.25 .90
673 A242a 46p shown ..... 1.75 1.40
　　Nos. 669-673 (5) ..... 6.05 4.35

　　See Nos. 699, 711, 749, 807, 836.

William Mulready (1786-1863), Letter Sheet Designer — A243

Carriages by Charles Bianconi (1786-1875) — A244

**Perf. 15x14, 14x15**
**1986, Oct. 2    Litho.**
674 A243 24p multicolored ..... .75 .60
675 A244 28p multi, vert. ..... 1.25 1.00
676 A244 39p shown ..... 1.75 1.50
　　Nos. 674-676 (3) ..... 3.75 3.10

Adoration of the Shepherds, by Francesco Pascucci A245

Adoration of the Magi, by Frans Francken III (1542-1616) A246

**1986, Nov. 20    Perf. 15x14, 14½x15**
677 A245 21p multicolored ..... 1.00 .70
678 A246 28p multicolored ..... 1.50 1.25

　　Christmas. #677 was issued in discount sheets of 12 that sold for £2.50. Value $25.

Love A247

**Perf. 15x14, 14x15**
**1987, Jan. 27    Litho.**
679 A247 24p Flowers, butterfly ..... 1.00 .75
680 A247 28p Postman, vert. ..... 1.40 1.00

Trolleys A248

**1987, Mar. 4    Litho.    Perf. 15x14**
681 A248 24p Cork Electric ..... 1.00 .60
682 A248 28p Dublin Standard ..... 1.10 .70
683 A248 30p Howth (G.N.R.) ..... 1.25 1.00
684 A248 46p Galway Horse ..... 2.00 1.75
　a.　Miniature sheet of 4, #681-684 ..... 7.50 7.50
　　Nos. 681-684 (4) ..... 5.35 4.10

　　See note following No. 584.

Waterford Chamber of Commerce, 200th Anniv. A249

Muintir Na Tire, 50th Anniv. A250

Trinity College Botanical Gardens, Dublin, 300th Anniv. — A251

Medical Missionaries of Mary, 50th Anniv. — A252

　　Anniversaries and events: 24p, Three ships, Chamber crest. 28p, Canon Hayes (1887-1957), founder, and symbols of Muintir Na Tire

activities. 30p, College crest, Calceolaria burbidgei. 39p, Intl. Missionary Training Hospital, Drogheda, and Mother Mary Martin.

**Perf. 15x14, 14x15**
**1987, Apr. 9    Litho.**
685 A249 24p vio bl, blk & dk grn ..... .90 .90
686 A250 28p multicolored ..... 1.10 1.10
687 A251 30p multicolored ..... 1.25 1.25
688 A252 39p multicolored ..... 1.50 1.50
　　Nos. 685-688 (4) ..... 4.75 4.75

Europa A253

　　Modern architecture, art: 28p, Borda na Mona headquarters, Dublin, and The Turf Cutter, by sculptor John Behan. 39p, St. Mary's Church and ruins of Romanesque monastery at Cong.

**1987, May 14    Perf. 15x14**
689 A253 28p multicolored ..... 6.00 2.00
690 A253 39p multicolored ..... 9.00 5.00

Cattle A254

**1987, July 2**
691 A254 24p Kerry ..... 1.00 .45
692 A254 28p Friesian ..... 1.25 1.25
693 A254 30p Hereford ..... 1.25 1.25
694 A254 39p Shorthorn ..... 1.75 1.75
　　Nos. 691-694 (4) ..... 5.25 4.70

Festivals A255

**1987, Aug. 27    Perf. 14x15**
695 A255 24p Fleadh Nua, Ennis ..... .75 .75
696 A255 28p Festival Queen,
　　Tralee ..... 1.00 1.00
697 A255 30p Wexford opera fes-
　　tival ..... 1.25 1.25
698 A255 46p Ballinasloe horse
　　fair ..... 2.00 2.00
　　Nos. 695-698 (4) ..... 5.00 5.00

　　Nos. 695-696 vert.

Statesmen Type of 1986 and

Ewer and Chalice, Company Crest A256

Harp in Shield, Preamble Excerpt A257

Woman Leading Board Meeting — A258

Design: No. 699, Cathal Brugha, vert.

**Perf. 14x15, 15x14**

**1987, Oct. 1**      **Litho.**
699 A240 24p black    .80   .80
700 A256 24p multicolored    .80   .80
701 A257 28p multicolored    .90   .90
702 A258 46p multicolored   1.50 1.50
   Nos. 699-702 (4)   4.00 4.00

Company of Goldsmiths of Dublin, 350th anniv. (No. 700); Irish Constitution, 50th anniv. (28p); Women in Society, (46p).

A259

Christmas
A260

21p, 12 Days of Christmas (1st 3 days). 24p, Embroidery (detail), Waterford Vestments, 15th cent. 28p, Neapolitan creche (detail), 1850.

**Perf. 15x14, 14x15**

**1987, Nov. 17**      **Litho.**
703 A259 21p multicolored    .75   .35
704 A260 24p multicolored   1.00   .75
705 A260 28p multicolored   1.25 1.00
   Nos. 703-705 (3)   3.00 2.10

No. 703 issued in discount sheets of 14 + center label; sheet sold for £2.90. Value $15.

Love
A261

**Perf. 15x14½, 14½x15**

**1988, Jan. 27**      **Litho.**
706 A261 24p shown   1.10 1.10
707 A261 28p Pillar box, vert.   1.25 1.25

Dublin
Millennium
A262

**1988, Mar. 1**      **Perf. 15x14**
708 A262 28p multicolored   1.10 1.00
   a.   Booklet pane of 4, Gaelic   4.50
   b.   Booklet pane of 4, English   4.50

Nos. 708a, 708b consist of two vert. pairs separated by a history in Gaelic or English. See note following No. 584.

A263

Impact of
the Irish
Abroad
A264

Designs: No. 709, Robert O'Hara Burke (1820-1861), by Sir Sidney Nolan; 19th cent. map of Australia with Burke & Wills expedition route. 46p, Mural (detail) of the Eureka Stockade by Nolan.

**1988, Mar. 1**
709 A263 24p multicolored   1.25 1.25
710 A264 46p multicolored   1.75 1.75

Statesmen Type of 1986 and

1988
Summer
Olympics,
Seoul
A265

Order of
Malta
Ambulance
Corps,
50th Anniv.
A266

Barry Fitzgerald
(1888-1961),
Actor — A267

Designs: 24p, William T. Cosgrave (1880-1965), president of the United Ireland and Fine Gael party. No. 713, Cycling.

**Perf. 14x15, 15x14**

**1988, Apr. 7**      **Litho.**
711 A240 24p black    .75   .75
712 A265 24p multicolored   1.00 1.00
713 A265 28p multicolored   1.00 1.00
   a.   Pair, #712-713   2.00 2.00
714 A266 30p multicolored   1.25 1.25
715 A267 50p multicolored   1.50 1.50
   Nos. 711-715 (5)   5.50 5.50

Nos. 712-713 printed in sheets of 5 each plus two labels.

Sirius
Sailing
from
Passage
West,
County
Cork
A268

**1988, May 12**    **Litho.**    **Perf. 15x14**
716 A268 24p multicolored   1.00 1.00

1st scheduled transatlantic crossing by steamship, sesquicentennial.

Europa
A269

28p, Air traffic controllers and A320 Airbus. 39p, Europe on globe, letters.

**1988, May 12**    **Litho.**    **Perf. 15x14**
717 A269 28p multicolored   4.00 1.00
718 A269 39p multicolored   7.00 3.00

Maia and
Mercury
Flying
Boats in
Foynes
Harbor
A269a

**1988, May 12**    **Litho.**    **Perf. 15x14**
719 A269a 46p multicolored   1.75 1.75

1st east-west transatlantic crossing by seaplane, 50th anniv.

Conservation of
Flora — A270

**1988, June 21**    **Litho.**    **Perf. 14x15**
720 A270 24p Otanthus maritimus    .80   .80
721 A270 28p Saxifraga hartii   1.00 1.00
722 A270 46p Astragalus danicus   1.50 1.50
   Nos. 720-722 (3)   3.30 3.30

Irish
Security
Forces
A271

**1988, Aug. 23**    **Litho.**    **Perf. 15x14**
723 A271 28p Garda Siochana (police)   2.00 1.00
724 A271 28p Army   2.00 1.00
725 A271 28p Navy, air corps   2.00 1.00
726 A271 28p FCA, Slua Muiri   2.00 1.00
   a.   Strip of 4, #723-726   8.00 8.00

Institute of
Chartered
Accountants,
Cent. — A272

Defeat of
the
Spanish
Armada,
400th
Anniv.
A273

**Perf. 14x15, 15x14**

**1988, Oct. 6**      **Litho.**
727 A272 24p multicolored   1.25   .50
728 A273 46p Duquesa Santa Ana off Donegal Coast   2.00 2.00

John F.
Kennedy,
Portrait by
James
Wyeth
A274

**1988, Nov. 24**    **Litho.**    **Perf. 15x14**
729 A274 28p multicolored   1.60   .90

A275

Christmas
A276

**1988, Nov. 24**      **Perf. 14x15**
730 A275 21p St. Kevin's Church, Glendalough    .60   .30
731 A276 24p Adoration of the Magi    .75   .50
732 A276 28p Flight into Egypt   1.25 1.25
733 A276 46p Holy Family   2.00 2.00
   Nos. 730-733 (4)   4.60 4.05

No. 730 issued only in discount sheets of 14. Sheet sold for £2.90. Value $15.

Love
A277

The Sonnet, by
William Mulready
(1786-1863)
A278

**Perf. 15x14, 14x15**

**1989, Jan. 24**      **Litho.**
734 A277 24p multicolored   1.00 1.00
735 A278 28p multicolored   1.25 1.25

Mulready, designer of Rowland Hill's first stamped envelope.

Classic Automobiles — A279

**1989, Apr. 11**    **Litho.**    **Perf. 15x14**
736 A279 24p Silver Stream    .75   .75
737 A279 28p Benz Comfortable   1.00 1.00
   a.   Booklet pane, 2 each 24p, 28p   4.00
738 A279 39p Thomond Car   1.25 1.25
739 A279 46p Chambers Car   1.50 1.50
   a.   Booklet pane of 4, #736-739   5.50
   Nos. 736-739 (4)   4.50 4.50

Parks and
Gardens
A280

**1989, Apr. 11**
740 A280 24p Garinish Is.    .75   .75
741 A280 28p Glenveagh   1.00 1.00
742 A280 32p Connemara Natl. Park   1.25 1.25

743 A280 50p St. Stephen's
Green 2.00 2.00
*Nos. 740-743 (4)* 5.00 5.00

Europa
A281

**1989, May 11**
744 A281 28p Ring-a-ring-a-rosie 1.00 .90
745 A281 39p Hopscotch 1.75 1.50

Irish Red Cross
Soc., 50th
Anniv. — A282

**1989, May 11** **Perf. 14x15**
746 A282 24p multicolored 1.00 1.00

European
Parliament 3rd
Elections — A283

**1989, May 11**
747 A283 28p Stars from flag 1.00 1.00

Sts. Kilian, Colman and Totnan (d.
689), Martyred Missionaries, and
Shamrock — A284

**1989, June 15** **Litho.** **Perf. 13½**
748 A284 28p multicolored 1.00 1.00
*a.* Booklet pane of 4, English 5.00
*b.* Booklet pane of 4, Gaelic 5.00
*c.* Booklet pane of 4, German 5.00
*d.* Booklet pane of 4, Latin 5.00
See Federal Republic of Germany No. 1580.

Statesmen Type of 1986 and

RIAI
Emblem — A285

Dublin-Cork Coach, 1789 — A286

Singer,
Scene from
La Boheme
A287

Nehru — A288

Design: 24p, Sean Thomas O'Kelly (1883-
1966), 2nd president.

**Perf. 14x15, 15x14**
**1989, July 25** **Litho.**
749 A240 24p black .85 .85
750 A285 28p multicolored .85 .85
751 A286 28p multicolored .85 .85
752 A287 30p multicolored 1.00 1.00
753 A288 46p red brown 1.50 1.50
*Nos. 749-753 (5)* 5.05 5.05
Royal Institute of Architects, 150th anniv.;
Mail coach in Ireland, bicent.; Margaret Burke
Sheridan (1889-1958), soprano; Jawaharlal
Nehru, 1st prime minister of independent
India.

Flags and
*Sail Ireland
Yacht
Rounding
Cape Horn,*
by Des
Fallon
A289

**1989, Aug. 31** **Litho.** **Perf. 15x14**
754 A289 28p multicolored 1.25 1.00
Whitbread round of the World Yacht Race
1989-90.

Wildlife:
Game
Birds — A290

**1989, Oct. 5** **Litho.** **Perf. 13½**
755 A290 24p *Lagopus lagopus* .95 .40
756 A290 28p *Vanellus vanellus* 1.10 1.10
757 A290 39p *Scolopax rusticola* 1.50 1.50
758 A290 46p *Phasianus
colchicus* 1.90 1.90
*a.* Miniature sheet of 4, #755-758 8.00 8.00
*Nos. 755-758 (4)* 5.45 4.90

Children and
Creche — A291

Miniatures from a
Flemish Psalter,
13th
Cent. — A292

**1989, Nov. 14** **Litho.** **Perf. 14x15**
759 A291 21p multicolored .75 .75
760 A292 24p Annunciation .75 .75
761 A292 28p Nativity 1.00 1.00
762 A292 46p Adoration of the
Magi 1.50 1.50
*Nos. 759-762 (4)* 4.00 4.00
No. 759 issued only in discount sheets of
14. Sheet sold for £2.90. Value $15.

Ireland's Presidency of the European
Communities — A293

European
Tourism
Year
A294

**1990, Jan. 9** **Litho.** **Perf. 15x14**
763 A293 30p multicolored 1.00 1.00
764 A294 50p multicolored 2.00 1.75

Love
Issue — A295

Love
Issue — A296

**1990, Jan. 30** **Litho.** **Perf. 14x15**
765 A295 26p shown 1.25 1.25
766 A296 30p "Love!" 1.25 1.25

Enamel Latchet
Brooch — A297

Ardagh
Chalice
A298

Art treasures of Ireland: 1p, 2p, Silver Kite
Brooch, vert. 4p, 5p, Dunamase Food Vessel,
vert. 10p, Derrinboy Armlets. 20p, Gold Dress
Fastener. 26p, 28p, Lismore Crosier, vert.
32p, Brighter Collar. 34p, 37p, 38p, 40p,
Gleninsheen Collar, vert. 41p, 44p, 45p, Silver
thistle brooch, vert. 50p, 52p, Brighter boat,
vert. £2, Tara Brooch. £5, St. Patrick's Bell
Shrine, vert.

**1990-95** **Litho.** **Perf. 15x14, 14x15**
767 A297 1p blue & blk .20 .20
768 A297 2p orange & blk .20 .20
770 A297 4p violet & blk .30 .30
*a.* Perf. 13x13½ .30 .30
*b.* Photo. .30 .30
771 A297 5p green & blk .35 .35
774 A297 10p orange & blk .60 .60
777 A297 20p yel & blk (I) .90 .90
778 A297 26p violet & blk 1.50 1.50
*a.* Perf. 13½ on 3 or 4 sides 2.50 2.50

779 A297 28p org & blk (I) 1.50 .65
*a.* Bklt. pane, 3 #770, 4 #779
+ label 3.00
*b.* Photo. 2.00 2.00
780 A297 30p brt blue & blk 1.50 .70
*a.* Perf. 13½ 2.50 2.50
*b.* Bklt. pane, 3 #540a, 1
#550d, 2 #778a, 2 #780a 5.50
*c.* Bklt. pane, #768, 3 #770,
#778, 2 #780 + label 4.00
781 A297 32p green & blk 1.50 .75
*a.* Bklt. pane, 2 #770b, #779b,
2 #781d 3.25
*b.* Perf. 13½x13 1.25 1.25
*c.* Bklt. pane, #770a, 3 #781b 3.75
*d.* Photo. 1.00 1.00
*e.* Booklet pane, 1 #770, 3
#781 3.75
782 A297 34p yellow & blk 2.00 1.40
783 A297 37p green & blk 2.50 1.75
784 A297 38p purple & blk 2.50 1.75
785 A297 40p blue & black 2.00 1.75
786 A297 41p orange & blk 2.00 1.75
787 A297 44p yellow & blk 2.50 1.75
788 A297 45p violet & black 2.50 1.75
789 A297 50p yellow & blk 2.50 1.40
790 A297 52p blue & blk (I) 2.50 2.00
791 A298 £1 yellow & blk 4.25 2.10
792 A298 £2 green & blk 7.50 4.25
793 A298 £5 blue & blk 20.00 10.50

**Self-Adhesive**
*Die cut perf 11*
**Size: 27x21mm**
794 A297 32p like #781 2.00 .90
*a.* Die cut perf. 11½ 3.00 .90
*b.* Die cut perf. 9½x9 2.00 .90
*Nos. 767-794 (23)* 62.80 38.30

Issued: 26p, 30p, 32p, 41p, 50p, £1, 3/8;
#780b, 5/3; 1p, 2p, 4p, 10p, 34p, £2, 7/26;
#780c, 11/15; 5p, 20p, £5, 1/26/91; #781a,
5/14/91; 28p, 37p, 38p, 44p, 52p, 4/3/91;
#779a, 10/17/91; #794, 10/31/91; 40p, 45p,
5/14/92; #770a, 781b, 9/24/93; #781e,
11/16/95; No. 794b, 6/8/95.

£1
#791-793

£1
Type IV

*Nos. 777a-790a (type II):*
Type I — Coarse background dot structure.
Type II — Fine background dot structure.

**Perf. 14x15, 15x14**
**1995, Nov. 15** **Litho.**
777a A297 20p Type II 3.50 3.50
779c A297 28p Type II 3.50 3.50
790a A297 52p Type II 5.00 5.00
791a A298 £1 Type IV 6.00 6.00
792a A298 £2 Type IV 12.50 12.50
793a A298 £5 Type IV 30.00 30.00
*Nos. 777a-793a (6)* 60.50 60.50

A299

A300

**1990, Mar. 22** **Litho.** **Perf. 14x15**
**Booklet Stamps**
795 A299 26p Gift boxes 3.50 3.50
796 A299 26p Nosegay 3.50 3.50
797 A299 30p Horseshoe 3.50 3.50
798 A299 30p Balloons 3.50 3.50
*a.* Bklt. pane of 4, #795-798 English labels 14.00
*b.* As "a," 4 English, 4 Gaelic labels 14.00
Greetings. Available only in discount booklets containing #798a, 798b. Bklts. sold for
£1.98.

**1990, Apr. 5　　Litho.　　Perf. 14x15**
799 A300 30p Tackle　　　　　1.75　2.00
800 A300 30p Heading the ball　1.75　2.00
　a.　Pair, #799-800　　　　4.00　4.00
1990 World Cup Soccer Championships, Italy.
　Printed in sheets of 8 plus label. Value $15.

Williamite Wars, 300th Anniv. — A301

**1990, Apr. 5　　Litho.　　Perf. 13½**
801 A301 30p Siege of Limerick　1.25　1.25
802 A301 30p Battle of the
　　　　　　　　Boyne　　　　1.25　1.25
　a.　Pair, #801-802　　　　3.00　3.00

Penny Black, 150th Anniv. A302

**1990, May 3　　Litho.　　Perf. 15x14**
803 A302 30p #780　　　　　1.25　.90
　a.　Bklt. pane, #803, 2 each
　　　#552a, 780a　　　　　8.00
804 A302 50p #68, 255, 550,
　　　　　　　780　　　　　1.75　1.75
　a.　Bklt. pane, 2 ea #803-804　10.00
　b.　Bklt. pane of 4, #552a, 780a,
　　　803-804　　　　　　8.00
　　See note following No. 584.

Europa
1990 — A303

Post offices.

**1990, May 3　　　　　　Perf. 14x15**
805 A303 30p GPO, Dublin　　1.25　1.00
806 A303 41p Westport P.O.,
　　　　　　　County Mayo　1.50　1.25
　Printed in sheets of 10+2 labels.　Value $27.50.

Statesman Type of 1986

**1990, June 21　　Litho.　　Perf. 14x15**
807 A240 30p Michael Collins　3.00　2.50

Irish Missionaries — A304

Design: 50p, Working at water pump.

**1990, June 21　　　　　　Perf. 15x14**
808 A304 26p multicolored　　.80　.80
809 A304 50p multicolored　　1.75　1.75

Garden Flowers — A305

**1990, Aug. 30　　Litho.　　Perf. 14x15**
810 A305 26p Narcissus　　　.80　.80
811 A305 30p Rosa x hibernica　1.00　1.00
　a.　Bklt. pane, 2 each #810-811　8.00
812 A305 41p Primula　　　　1.50　1.50
813 A305 50p Erica erigena　　1.75　1.75
　a.　Booklet pane of 4, #810-813　9.00
　　Nos. 810-813 (4)　　　5.05　5.05
　　See note following No. 584.

Theater A306

Designs: No. 814, Playboy of the Western World. No. 815, Juno and the Paycock. No. 816, The Field. No. 817, Waiting for Godot.

**1990, Oct. 18　　Litho.　　Perf. 13½**
814 A306 30p multicolored　　1.75　1.75
815 A306 30p multicolored　　1.75　1.75
816 A306 30p multicolored　　1.75　1.75
817 A306 30p multicolored　　1.75　1.75
　a.　Block or strip of 4, #814-817　7.00　7.00

A307

Christmas A308

**1990, Nov. 15　　Litho.　　Perf. 14x15**
818 A307 26p Child praying　　.90　.90
819 A308 26p Nativity scene　　.90　.90
820 A308 30p Madonna and
　　　　　　　Child　　　　1.10　1.10
821 A308 50p Adoration of the
　　　　　　　Magi　　　　1.75　1.75
　　Nos. 818-821 (4)　　　4.65　4.65
　No. 818 sold only in discount sheets of 12 for £2.86. Value $15.

Love — A309

Irish Cycles — A310

**1991, Jan. 29　　Litho.　　Perf. 14x15**
822 A309 26p shown　　　　1.00　1.00
823 A309 30p Boy, girl kissing　1.25　1.25

**1991, Mar. 5**
824 A310 26p Starley rover　　.90　.90
825 A310 30p Child's horse tricy-
　　　　　　　cle　　　　　1.10　1.10

826 A310 50p Penny farthing　1.75　1.75
　a.　Souvenir sheet of 3, #824-826　6.50　7.50
　　Nos. 824-826 (3)　　　3.75　3.75
　　See note following No. 584.

1916 Rising, 75th Anniv. A311

Design: Statue of Cuchulainn by Oliver Sheppard, 1916 Proclamation.

**1991, Apr. 3　　Litho.　　Perf. 15x14**
827 A311 32p multicolored　　1.75　1.75

Dublin, European City of Culture A312

Designs: 28p, La Traviata, performed by Dublin Grand Opera Society. 32p, Dublin City Hall. 44p, St. Patrick's Cathedral, 800th anniv. 52p, Custom House, 200th anniv.

**1991, Apr. 11　　　　　　Perf. 15x14**
828 A312 28p multicolored　　.90　.90
829 A312 32p multicolored　　1.10　1.10
830 A312 44p multicolored　　1.50　1.50
　a.　Booklet pane of 3, #828-830　5.50
　　　　Size: 41x25mm
　　　　Perf. 13½
831 A312 52p multicolored　　1.75　1.75
　a.　Booklet pane of 4, #828-831　5.50
　　　Complete booklet, #830a, 831a　12.50
　　Nos. 828-831 (4)　　　5.25　5.25
　50th anniv. of Dublin Grand Opera Soc. (No. 828).

Europa A313

**1991, May 14　　Litho.　　Perf. 15x14**
832 A313 32p Giotto probe　　1.00　.75
833 A313 44p Hubble telescope　1.75　1.75

Williamite Wars, 300th Anniv. A314

**1991, May 14**
834 A314 28p Siege of Athlone　1.75　1.75
835 A314 28p Treaty of Limerick　1.75　1.75
　a.　Pair, #834-835　　　　3.50　3.50

Statesman Type of 1986 and

Charles Stewart Parnell (1846-1891), Politician — A315

Society of United Irishmen, Bicent. A316

28p, John A. Costello (1891-1976), politician.

**Perf. 14x15, 15x14**

**1991, July 2　　　　　　Litho.**
836 A240 28p black　　　　　1.00　1.00
837 A315 32p multicolored　　1.10　1.10
838 A316 52p multicolored　　1.90　1.90
　　Nos. 836-838 (3)　　　4.00　4.00

A317

**Perf. 15x14, 14x15**

**1991, Sept. 3　　　　　　Litho.**
839 A317 28p Golfer putting,
　　　　　　　horiz.　　　　1.50　1.50
840 A317 32p shown　　　　2.25　2.25
　Walker Cup Competition, Portmarnock Golf Club (No. 839).

Irish Sheep — A318

**1991, Sept. 3　　Perf. 14x15, 15x14**
841 A318 32p Wicklow Cheviot　1.00　1.00
842 A318 38p Donegal Blackface　1.50　1.50
843 A318 52p Galway, horiz.　2.00　2.00
　　Nos. 841-843 (3)　　　4.50　4.50

Fishing Fleet A319

**1991, Oct. 17　　Litho.　　Perf. 15x14**
844 A319 28p Boatyard　　　.75　.75
845 A319 32p Inshore trawler　1.00　1.00
　a.　Bklt. pane of 5, #845, 2 each
　　　#768, 783　　　　　5.50
　b.　Bklt. pane, 2 each #844, 845　6.50
846 A319 44p Inshore potter　1.75　1.75
847 A319 52p Factory ship　　2.50　2.50
　a.　Booklet pane of 4, #844-847　9.00
　　Nos. 844-847 (4)　　　6.00　6.00
　　See note following No. 584.

Christmas A320

**1991, Nov. 14　　Litho.　　Perf. 14x15**
848 A320 28p Wise men, star　.85　.85
849 A321 28p Annunciation　　.95　.95
850 A321 32p Nativity　　　　1.00　1.00

851 A321 52p Adoration of the
　　　　　Magi　　　　　　　　2.50 2.50
　　　　　*Nos. 848-851 (4)*　　　　5.30 5.30
　　No. 848 issued only in discount sheets of
13+2 labels which sold for £3.36. Value $15.

Love
A322

　　Design: 32p, Rainbow over meadow, love
etched in stone, vert.

　　　　　　**Perf. 15x14, 14x15**
**1992, Jan. 28**　　　　　　　　**Litho.**
852 A322 28p shown　　　　　1.00 1.00
853 A322 32p multicolored　　　1.50 1.50

1992
Summer
Olympics,
Barcelona
A323

**1992, Feb. 25　Litho.　Perf. 15x14**
854 A323 32p Boxing　　　　　1.25 1.25
855 A323 44p Sailing　　　　　1.50 1.50
　　*a.*　Sheet of 4, 2 each #854-855　7.00 7.50
　　　　See note following No. 584.

Healthy
Lifestyle — A324

**1992, Feb. 25　　　Perf. 14x15**
856 A324 28p multicolored　　　1.10 1.10

Galway
Chamber
of
Commerce
and
Industry,
Bicent.
A325

**1992, Apr. 2　Litho.　Perf. 15x14**
857 A325 28p multicolored　　　1.25 1.25

Intl.
Maritime
Heritage
Year
A326

　　　　　　**Perf. 15x14, 14x15**
**1992, Apr. 2**　　　　　　　　**Litho.**
858 A326 32p Mari Cog　　　　1.50 1.50
859 A326 52p Ovoca, vert.　　　2.00 2.00

Greetings — A327

**1992, Apr. 2　　　　　Perf. 14x15**
860 A327 28p Coastline　　　　2.50 2.50
861 A327 28p Mountain　　　　2.50 2.50
862 A327 32p Flowers　　　　　2.50 2.50
863 A327 32p Pond　　　　　　2.50 2.50
　　*a.*　Bklt. pane of 4, #860-863, 8
　　　　English labels　　　　　10.00
　　*b.*　Bklt. pane of 4, #860-863, 4
　　　　English labels + 4 Gaelic
　　　　labels　　　　　　　　10.00
　　　　*Nos. 860-863 (4)*　10.00 10.00

　　#863a contains #860-863 in order. #863b
contains #862, 863, 860 and 861 in order.

Discovery
of America,
500th
Anniv.
A328

　　Europa: 44p, Landing in New World.

**1992, May 14　Litho.　Perf. 15x14**
864 A328 32p multicolored　　　*1.25 1.00*
865 A328 44p multicolored　　　*1.50 1.25*

Irish in the Americas — A329

　　Design: No. 867, The White House, bridge,
railroad workers, musicians, workers.

**1992, May 14　　　Perf. 13½**
866 A329 52p multicolored　　　1.75 1.75
867 A329 52p multicolored　　　1.75 1.75
　　*a.*　Pair, #866-867　　　　3.50 3.50

Pine
Marten
A330

**1992, July 9　Litho.　Perf. 15x14**
868 A330 28p shown　　　　　1.50 1.50
869 A330 32p In tree　　　　　1.75 1.75
870 A330 44p With young　　　2.50 2.50
871 A330 52p Holding bird　　　3.00 3.00
　　　　*Nos. 868-871 (4)*　　8.75 8.75
　　　　World Wildlife Fund.

Trinity College,
Dublin, 400th
Anniv. — A331

**1992, Sept. 2　Litho.　Perf. 13½**
872 A331 32p Library　　　　　1.10 1.10
873 A331 52p Main entrance　　1.75 1.75

Views of
Dublin by
James
Malton,
Bicent.
A332

**1992, Sept. 2　　　Perf. 15x14**
874 A332 28p Rotunda, Assem-
　　　　　　bly rooms　　　　1.00 1.00
875 A332 44p Charlemont House　1.50 1.50

Single
European
Market
A333

**1992, Oct. 15　Litho.　Perf. 15x14**
876 A333 32p multicolored　　　1.40 1.40
　　*a.*　Bklt. pane of 3　　　　4.50
　　*b.*　Bklt. pane of 4　　　　6.00
　　No. 876b comes with stamps in three formats: four singles, two pairs, and block of four.
See note following No. 584.

Food and
Farming — A334

**1992, Oct. 15　　　Perf. 14x15**
877 A334 32p Fresh food　　　1.50 1.50
878 A334 32p Cattle　　　　　1.50 1.50
879 A334 32p Combine harvest-
　　　　　　ing grain　　　　1.50 1.50
880 A334 32p Growing vegeta-
　　　　　　bles　　　　　　1.50 1.50
　　*a.*　Strip of 4, #877-880　6.00 6.00

A335

Christmas
A336

　　Designs: No. 881, Rural churchyard. No.
882, The Annunciation, manuscript illustration,
Chester Beatty Library, Dublin. 32p, Adoration
of the Shepherds, by Jocopo da Empoli. 52p,
Adoration of the Magi, by Johann
Rottenhammer.

**1992, Nov. 19**
881 A335 28p multicolored　　　.90 .90
882 A336 28p multicolored　　　1.00 1.00
883 A336 32p multicolored　　　1.10 1.00
884 A336 52p multicolored　　　1.75 1.75
　　　　*Nos. 881-884 (4)*　　4.75 4.65

　　No. 881 issued only in discount sheets of
13+2 labels which sold for £3.36. Value
$13.50.

Love
A337

　　Design: 28p, Queen of Hearts, vert.

　　　　　**Perf. 14x15, 15x14**
**1993, Jan. 26**　　　　　　　**Litho.**
885 A337 28p multicolored　　　1.00 1.00
886 A337 32p multicolored　　　1.25 1.25

Irish Impressionist Paintings — A338

　　Designs: 28p, Evening at Tangier, by Sir
John Lavery. 32p, The Goose Girl, by William
J. Leech. 44p, La Jeune Bretonne, by Roderic
O'Conor, vert. 52p, Lustre Jug, by Walter
Osborne, vert.

**1993, Mar. 4　　　　Perf. 13**
887 A338 28p multicolored　　　1.00 1.00
888 A338 32p multicolored　　　1.25 1.25
　　*a.*　Booklet pane of 2, #887-888　3.00
889 A338 44p multicolored　　　1.50 1.50
890 A338 52p multicolored　　　2.00 2.00
　　*a.*　Booklet pane of 2, #889-890　4.00
　　*b.*　Booklet pane of 4, #887-890　6.00
　　　　*Nos. 887-890 (4)*　　5.75 5.75

　　No. 890b exists in two formats with different
margin inscriptions.

Orchids — A339

**1993, Apr. 20　Litho.　Perf. 14x15**
891 A339 28p Bee orchid　　　.80 .80
892 A339 32p O'Kelly's orchid　1.00 1.00
893 A339 38p Dark red hel-
　　　　　　leborine　　　　1.75 1.75
894 A339 52p Irish lady's
　　　　　　tresses　　　　2.00 2.00
　　*a.*　Souvenir sheet of 4, #891-
　　　　894　　　　　　7.00 7.00
　　*b.*　As "a," with blue inscription　11.00 11.00
　　　　*Nos. 891-894 (4)*　　5.55 5.55

　　No. 894b has a larger top margin than No.
894a. Added Inscription includes text and flags
of Ireland and Thailand.

Contemporary Paintings — A340

　　Europa: 32p, Pears in a Copper Pan, by
Hilda van Stockum. 44p, Arrieta Orzola, by
Tony O'Malley.

**1993, May 18　Litho.　Perf. 13x13½**
895 A340 32p multicolored　　　1.25 1.25
896 A340 44p multicolored　　　*1.75 1.75*

　　Issued in sheets of 10 + 2 labels.

Gaelic
League,
Cent.
A341

　　Design: 52p, Illuminated manuscript
presented to founder Douglas Hyde, vert.

　　　　　　**Perf. 15x14, 14x15**
**1993, July 8**　　　　　　　　**Litho.**
897 A341 32p multicolored　　　1.25 1.25
898 A341 52p multicolored　　　2.00 2.00

Irish Amateur Swimming Assoc., Cent. A342

Designs: No. 899, Swimmer diving into water. No. 900, Woman swimming.

**1993, July 8**          **Perf. 15x14**
899 A342 32p multicolored          1.60 1.60
900 A342 32p multicolored          1.60 1.60
  a.   Pair, #899-900          3.25 3.25

Royal Hospital Donnybrook, 250th Anniv. — A343

Ceide Fields, County Mayo A345

Carlow College, Bicent. — A344

Edward Bunting (1773-1843), Composer — A346

**Perf. 15x14, 14x15, 13½ (52p)**
**1993, Sept. 2**          **Litho.**
901 A343 28p multicolored          .90 .90
902 A344 32p multicolored          1.00 1.00
903 A345 44p multicolored          1.40 1.40
904 A346 52p multicolored          1.75 1.75
  *Nos. 901-904 (4)*          5.05 5.05

Irish Buses A347

Designs: 28p, Great Northern Railways Gardner. 32p, CIE Leyland Titan. No. 907, Horse-drawn omnibus. No. 908, Char-a-banc.

**1993, Oct. 12     Litho.     Perf. 15x14**
905 A347 28p multicolored          1.00 1.00
906 A347 32p multicolored          1.00 1.00
  a.   Booklet pane, 2 each #905-906          5.00
907 A347 52p multicolored          2.00 2.00
908 A347 52p multicolored          2.00 2.00
  a.   Pair, #907-908          4.00 4.00
  b.   Booklet pane of 4, #905-908          6.00
  *Nos. 905-908 (4)*          6.00 6.00

Christmas A349

Designs: 32p, Mary placing infant Jesus in manger. 52p, Adoration of the shepherds.

**1993, Nov. 16          Litho.**
909 A348 28p multicolored          .90 .90
910 A349 28p multicolored          .90 .90
911 A349 32p multicolored          1.00 1.00
912 A349 52p multicolored          2.00 2.00
  *Nos. 909-912 (4)*          4.80 4.80

No. 909 issued only in discount sheets of 13+2 labels which sold for £3.36. Value $13.50.

Love A350

32p, Man, woman in shape of heart, vert.

**Perf. 15x14, 14x15**
**1994, Jan. 27          Litho.**
913 A350 28p multicolored          .90 .90
914 A350 32p multicolored          1.25 1.25

Greetings Stamps — A351

**1994, Jan. 27          Perf. 14x15**
915 A351 32p Face in sun          2.00 2.00
916 A351 32p Face in flower          2.00 2.00
917 A351 32p Face in heart          2.00 2.00
  a.   Souv. sheet of 3, #915-917          10.00 10.00
918 A351 32p Face in rose          2.00 2.00
  a.   Booklet pane of 4, #915-918,
       4 English + 4 Gaelic labels          8.00
  b.   As "a," 8 English labels          8.00
  *Nos. 915-918 (4)*          8.00 8.00

New Year 1994 (Year of the Dog), Hong Kong '94 (#917a).
#918a contains 915-918 in order. #918b contains 917, 918, 915, 916 in order.

Macra na Feirme, 50th Anniv. A352

The Taking of Christ, by Caravaggio A353

Irish Co-operative Organization Society, Cent. — A354

Irish Congress of Trade Unions, Cent. A355

**1994, Mar. 2     Litho.     Perf. 15x14**
919 A352 28p blue & gold          .80 .80
920 A353 32p multicolored          1.00 1.00
921 A354 38p multicolored          1.25 1.25
922 A355 52p blue, blk & lt blue          1.50 1.50
  *Nos. 919-922 (4)*          4.55 4.55

Voyages of St. Brendan (484-577) — A356

Europa: 32p, St. Brendan, Irish monks sailing past volcano. 44p, St. Brendan on island with sheep, monks in boat.

**1994, Apr. 18     Litho.     Perf. 15x14**
923 A356 32p multicolored          1.25 1.25
924 A356 44p multicolored          1.75 1.75
  a.   Miniature sheet of 2, #923-924          3.00 3.00

See Faroe Islands Nos. 264-265; Iceland Nos. 780-781.

Parliamentary Anniversaries — A357

#925, 1st meeting of the Dail, 1919. #926, 4th direct elections to European Parliament.

**1994, Apr. 27**
925 A357 32p multicolored          1.25 1.25
926 A357 32p multicolored          1.25 1.25
  a.   Booklet pane, 1 each #925-926          3.00
  b.   Booklet pane, 2 each #925-926          6.00
       Complete booklet, #926a, 926b          9.00

1994 World Cup Soccer Championships, US — A358

Players from: No. 927, Argentina in striped shirt, Ireland in green. No. 928, Ireland, Germany.

**1994, May 31          Perf. 14x15**
927 A358 32p multicolored          1.75 1.75
928 A358 32p multicolored          1.75 1.75
  a.   Pair, #927-928          3.50 3.50

Women's Hockey A359

32p, 1994 Women's Hockey World Cup, Dublin. 52p, Irish Ladies' Hockey Union, cent.

**1994, May 31          Perf. 13x13½**
929 A359 32p multicolored          1.25 1.25
930 A359 52p multicolored          1.50 1.50

Moths A360

**1994, July 12     Litho.     Perf. 14½x14**
931 A360 28p Garden tiger          .90 .90
932 A360 32p Burren green          1.00 1.00
933 A360 38p Emperor          1.25 1.25
934 A360 52p Elephant
           hawkmoth          1.60 1.60
  a.   Souvenir sheet of 4, #931-
       934          6.50 6.50
  b.   As "a," overprinted          10.00 10.00
       *Nos. 931-934 (4)*          4.75 4.75

**Size: 34x23mm**
**Self-Adhesive**
**Die Cut Perf. 11½**
935 A360 32p like #932          2.25 2.25
936 A360 32p like #931          2.25 2.25
937 A360 32p like #934          2.25 2.25
938 A360 32p like #933          2.25 2.25
  a.   Strip of 4, #935-938          9.00 9.00

Overprint on #934b shows PHILAKOREA '94 exhibition emblem and Chinese inscription.

A361

A362

A363

Anniversaries and Events — A364

28p, Medieval view of Drogheda. #940, Edmund Ignatius Rice (1762-1844), philantropist. #941, Edmund Burke (1729-97), political commentator. #942, Eamonn Andrews (1922-87), broadcaster. #943, Vickers Vimy aircraft.

**1994, Sept. 6     Litho.     Perf. 13½**
939 A361 28p multicolored          .90 .90
**Perf. 14x14½**
940 A362 32p multicolored          1.00 1.00
**Perf. 14x13½**
941 A363 32p multicolored          1.00 1.00
942 A363 52p multicolored          1.60 1.60

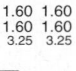

## Perf. 15x14

| | | | |
|---|---|---|---|
| 943 | A364 52p multicolored | 1.60 | 1.60 |
| | *Nos. 939-943 (5)* | 6.10 | 6.10 |

Drogheda, 800th anniv. (#939). First New-foundland-Ireland transatlantic flight, 75th anniv. (#943).

Nobel Prize Winners A365

#944, George Bernard Shaw (1856-1950), dramatist, essayist. #945, Samuel Beckett (1906-89), playwright. 32p, Sean McBride (1904-88), statesman. 52p, William Butler Yeats (1865-1939), poet.

### 1994, Oct. 18    Litho.    Perf. 15x14

| | | | |
|---|---|---|---|
| 944 | A365 28p multicolored | 1.00 | 1.00 |
| 945 | A365 28p multicolored | 1.00 | 1.00 |
| a. | Pair, #944-945 | 2.00 | 2.00 |
| 946 | A365 32p multicolored | 1.10 | 1.10 |
| a. | Booklet pane of 3, #944-946 | 3.00 | |
| b. | Bklt. pane, #944-945, 2 #946 | 4.00 | |
| 947 | A365 52p multicolored | 1.60 | 1.60 |
| a. | Booklet pane, 1 #946, 2 #947 | 4.50 | |
| b. | Booklet pane of 4, #944-947 | 5.00 | |
| | Prestige bklt., #946a-946b, 947a-947b | 20.00 | |
| | *Nos. 944-947 (4)* | 4.70 | 4.70 |

A366

Christmas A367

#948, Stained glass nativity scene. #949, Annunciation, detail, 11th cent. ivory plaque. 32p, Flight Into Egypt, 15th cent. wood carving. 52p, Nativity, detail, 11th cent. ivory plaque.

### 1994, Nov. 17    Litho.    Perf. 14x15

| | | | |
|---|---|---|---|
| 948 | A366 28p multicolored | .90 | .90 |
| 949 | A367 28p multicolored | 1.00 | 1.00 |
| 950 | A367 32p multicolored | 1.10 | 1.10 |
| 951 | A367 52p multicolored | 1.75 | 1.75 |
| | *Nos. 948-951 (4)* | 4.75 | 4.75 |

No. 948 issued only in discount sheets of 13+2 labels which sold for £3.36. Value $12.50.

Greetings Stamps — A368

### 1995, Jan. 24    Litho.    Perf. 14x15

| | | | |
|---|---|---|---|
| 952 | A368 32p Tree of hearts | 1.75 | 1.75 |
| | **Booklet Stamps** | | |
| 953 | A368 32p Teddy bear, balloon | 1.75 | 1.75 |
| 954 | A368 32p Clown juggling hearts | 1.75 | 1.75 |
| 955 | A368 32p Bouquet of flowers | 1.75 | 1.75 |
| a. | Booklet pane, #952-955 + 4 English, 4 Gaelic labels | 7.00 | |
| b. | As "a," 8 English labels | 7.00 | |

| | | | |
|---|---|---|---|
| c. | Souvenir sheet, #952, 954-955 + 3 English, 3 Gaelic labels | 9.00 | 9.00 |

New Year 1995 (Year of the Boar) (#955c). No. 955a contains #953-954, 952, 955 in order. No. 955b contains #952, 955, 953-954 in order.

Narrow Gauge Railways A369

### 1995, Feb. 28    Litho.    Perf. 15x14

| | | | |
|---|---|---|---|
| 956 | A369 28p West Clare | .90 | .90 |
| 957 | A369 32p Co. Donegal | 1.10 | 1.10 |
| 958 | A369 38p Cork & Muskerry | 1.25 | 1.25 |
| 959 | A369 52p Cavan & Leitrim | 1.75 | 1.75 |
| a. | Souvenir sheet of 4, #956-959 | 7.00 | 7.00 |
| | *Nos. 956-959 (4)* | 5.00 | 5.00 |

No. 959a exists with Singapore '95 overprint in sheet margin. Value $10.

Peace & Freedom A370

Europa: Nos. 960, 962, Stylized dove, reconstructed city. 44p, No. 963, Stylized dove, map of Europe.

### 1995, Apr. 6    Litho.    Perf. 15x14

| | | | |
|---|---|---|---|
| 960 | A370 32p multicolored | 1.00 | 1.00 |
| 961 | A370 44p multicolored | 1.75 | 1.75 |

#### Size: 34½x23mm
#### Self-Adhesive Coil Stamps
#### Die Cut Perf. 11½

| | | | |
|---|---|---|---|
| 962 | A370 32p multicolored | 3.00 | 3.00 |
| 963 | A370 32p multicolored | 3.00 | 3.00 |

Nos. 962-963 are coil stamps, printed in horizontal rolls of 100, with 50 of each design alternating.

1995 Rugby World Cup A371

### 1995, Apr. 6    Perf. 14

| | | | |
|---|---|---|---|
| 964 | A371 32p shown | 1.25 | 1.25 |
| 965 | A371 52p Player being tackled | 1.75 | 1.75 |

#### Souvenir Sheet

| | | | |
|---|---|---|---|
| 966 | A371 £1 like #964 | 5.50 | 6.50 |

No. 966 has a continuous design.

A372          A373

32p, Irish soldiers, Cross of Fontenoy.

### 1995, May 15    Photo.    Perf. 11½

| | | | |
|---|---|---|---|
| 967 | A372 32p multicolored | 1.40 | 1.40 |

Battle of Fontenoy, 250th Anniv. See Belgium No. 1583.

### 1995, May 15    Litho.    Perf. 14x15

Military uniforms: 28p, Irish Brigade, French Army, 1745. No. 969, Tercio Irlanda, Army of Flanders, 1605. No. 970, Royal Dublin Fusiliers, 1914. 38p, St. Patrick's Battalion, Papal Army, 1860. 52p, The Fighting 69th, Army of Potomac, 1861.

| | | | |
|---|---|---|---|
| 968 | A373 28p multicolored | 1.00 | 1.00 |
| 969 | A373 32p multicolored | 1.10 | 1.10 |
| a. | Bklt. pane, 2 ea #968-969 | 4.00 | |
| 970 | A373 32p multicolored | 1.10 | 1.10 |
| 971 | A373 38p multicolored | 1.40 | 1.40 |
| a. | Bklt. pane of 3, #968-969, #971 | 3.50 | |
| 972 | A373 52p multicolored | 2.25 | 2.25 |
| a. | Bklt. pane of 3, #968-969, 972 | 3.00 | |
| b. | Bklt. pane of 4, #968-969, 971-972 | 3.75 | |
| | Prestige booklet, #969a, 971a, 972a, 972b | 17.00 | |
| | *Nos. 968-972 (5)* | 6.85 | 6.85 |

Radio, Cent. A374

Designs: No. 973, Guglielmo Marconi, transmitting equipment. No. 974, Radio channel dial.

### 1995, June 8    Litho.    Perf. 13½

| | | | |
|---|---|---|---|
| 973 | A374 32p multicolored | 1.75 | 1.75 |
| 974 | A374 32p multicolored | 1.75 | 1.75 |
| a. | Pair, #973-974 | 3.50 | 3.50 |

See Germany #1900, Italy #2038-2039, San Marino #1336-1337, Vatican City #978-979.

A375

A376

A377

Anniversaries & Events A378

Designs: 28p, Dr. Bartholomew Mosse, Rotunda Hospital. No. 976, Piper, laurel wreath over map of Europe. No. 977, St. Patrick's College. 52p, Geological map of Ireland.

### 1995, July 27    Litho.    Perf. 14½x14

| | | | |
|---|---|---|---|
| 975 | A375 28p multicolored | .90 | .90 |
| 976 | A376 32p multicolored | 1.00 | 1.00 |
| | **Perf. 14½** | | |
| 977 | A377 32p multicolored | 1.00 | 1.00 |
| | **Perf. 13½** | | |
| 978 | A378 52p multicolored | 1.60 | 1.60 |
| | *Nos. 975-978 (4)* | 4.50 | 4.50 |

Rotunda Hospital, 250th anniv. (#975). End of World War II, 50th anniv. (#976). St. Patrick's College, Maynooth, bicent. (#977). Geological survey of Ireland, 150th anniv. (#978).

Reptiles & Amphibians — A379

### 1995, Sept. 1    Litho.    Perf. 15x14

| | | | |
|---|---|---|---|
| 979 | A379 32p Natterjack toad | 1.25 | 1.25 |
| 980 | A379 32p Common lizard | 1.25 | 1.25 |
| 981 | A379 32p Smooth newt | 1.25 | 1.25 |
| 982 | A379 32p Common frog | 1.25 | 1.25 |
| a. | Strip of 4, #979-982 | 12.50 | 12.50 |

#### Die Cut Perf. 9¼
#### Size: 34½x22½mm
#### Self-Adhesive

| | | | |
|---|---|---|---|
| 982B | A379 32p like No. 979 | 3.00 | 3.00 |
| 982C | A379 32p like No. 980 | 3.00 | 3.00 |
| 982D | A379 32p like No. 981 | 3.00 | 3.00 |
| 982E | A379 32p like No. 982 | 3.00 | 3.00 |
| f. | Strip of 4, Nos. 982B-982E | 12.50 | 12.50 |

Natl. Botanic Gardens, Bicent. — A380

Designs: 32p, Crinum moorei. 38p, Sarracenia x moorei. 44p, Solanum crispum "glasnevin."

### 1995, Oct. 9    Litho.    Perf. 14x15

| | | | |
|---|---|---|---|
| 983 | A380 32p multicolored | 1.00 | 1.00 |
| 984 | A380 38p multicolored | 1.10 | 1.10 |
| 985 | A380 44p multicolored | 1.40 | 1.40 |
| a. | Booklet pane of 3, #983-985 | 5.00 | |
| b. | Bklt. pane of 4, #984-985, 2 #983 | 6.00 | |
| | Complete booklet, #985a-985b | 11.00 | |
| | *Nos. 983-985 (3)* | 3.50 | 3.50 |

UN, 50th Anniv. A381

### 1995, Oct. 19    Perf. 13x13½

| | | | |
|---|---|---|---|
| 986 | A381 32p shown | 1.00 | 1.00 |
| 987 | A381 52p UN, "50" emblem | 1.75 | 1.75 |

A382

Christmas A383

Designs: No. 988, Adoration of the Magi. No. 989, Adoration of the Shepherds. 32p, Adoration of the Magi. 52p, Nativity.

### 1995, Nov. 16    Litho.    Perf. 14½x14

| | | | |
|---|---|---|---|
| 988 | A383 28p multicolored | .90 | .90 |
| 989 | A383 28p multicolored | .90 | .90 |
| 990 | A383 32p multicolored | 1.25 | 1.25 |
| 991 | A383 52p multicolored | 1.75 | 1.75 |
| | *Nos. 988-991 (4)* | 4.80 | 4.80 |

No. 988 issued only in discount sheets of 13+2 labels, which sold for £3.36. Value $12.00.

Greetings/Love Stamps — A384

Television cartoon characters from "Zog, Zig and Zag:" No. 992, With hearts. No. 993, Waving hands. No. 994, In car, wearing space helmets. No. 995, Holding out hands, wearing hats.

**1996, Jan. 23    Litho.    Perf. 14x15**
992  A384  32p multicolored                          3.25  3.25
**Booklet Stamps**
993  A384  32p multicolored                          3.25  3.25
994  A384  32p multicolored                          3.25  3.25
995  A384  32p multicolored                          3.25  3.25
a.  Booklet pane, Nos. 992-995, 5 English, 3 Gaelic labels                        12.50
b.  As "a," 7 English, 1 Gaelic label          12.50
     Complete booklet, #995a-995b             25.00
c.  Souvenir sheet, Nos. 992, 994-995 + 4 English, 2 Gaelic labels, 1 large label with Chinese inscription              10.00  10.00

No. 995a contains Nos. 993-995, 992 in order. No. 995b contains Nos. 995, 992-994 in order.
New Year 1996 (Year of the Rat) (#995c).

A385

1996 Summer/Paralympic Games, Atlanta — A386

**1996, Feb. 1**
996  A385  28p show                                  1.25  1.25
997  A386  32p Discus                                1.25  1.25
998  A386  32p Canoeing                              1.25  1.25
999  A386  32p Running                               1.25  1.25
a.  Strip of 3, Nos. 997-999                  5.00  5.00

No. 999a printed in sheets of 9 stamps. Value $15.00.

L'Imaginaire Irlandais — A387

**1996, Mar. 12    Litho.    Perf. 15x14**
1000  A387  32p multicolored                         1.10  1.10

Irish Horse Racing A388

**1996, Mar. 12    Litho.    Perf. 15x14**
1001  A388  28p Fairyhouse                            .90   .90
1002  A388  32p Punchestown                          1.00  1.00
1003  A388  32p The Curragh                          1.00  1.00
a.  Pair, #1002-1003                          2.00  2.00
b.  Booklet pane, 2 #1001, 1 each #1002-1003                           4.00
c.  Souv. sheet, #1002-1003              15.00  15.00
1004  A388  38p Galway                               1.25  1.25
a.  Booklet pane, 2 #1002, 1 #1004                                     3.75
1005  A388  52p Leopardstown                         1.60  1.60
a.  Bklt. pane, #1005, 2 #1003                        3.75
b.  Bklt. pane, 1 ea #1002-1005                       4.75
     Prestige booklet, Nos. 1003b, 1004a, 1005a, 1005b                           15.60
Nos. 1001-1005 (5)                           5.75  5.75

No. 1003c for China '96.

UNESCO World Heritage Site A389

UNICEF, 50th Anniv. A390

Designs: 28p, Passage tombs, Bru na Bóinne National Monument, Boyne Valley. 32p, Children.

**1996, Apr. 2    Litho.    Perf. 14**
1006  A389  28p sepia & black                        1.00  1.00
1007  A390  32p multicolored                         1.50  1.50

Europa A391

32p, Louie Bennett (1870-1956), Suffragette, trade unionist. 44p, Lady Augusta Gregory (1852-1932), playwright, co-founder of Abbey Theatre.

**1996, Apr. 2    Perf. 15x14**
1008  A391  32p violet                               1.00  1.00
1009  A391  44p green                                1.50  1.50
**Die Cut 9¼**
**Self-Adhesive Coil Stamps**
1009A  A391  32p like #1008                          1.50  1.50
1009B  A391  32p like #1009                          1.50  1.50

Nos. 962-963 are coil stamps, printed in horizontal rolls with each value alternating.

Irish Winners of Tourist Trophy Motorcycle Races — A392

32p, Stanley Woods. 44p, Artie Bell. No. 1012, Alec Bennett. 52p, No. 1014, Robert & Joey Dunlop.

**1996, May 30    Perf. 14**
1010  A392  32p multicolored                          .85   .85
1011  A392  44p multicolored                         1.25  1.25
1012  A392  50p multicolored                         1.75  1.75
1013  A392  52p multicolored                         1.75  1.75
Nos. 1010-1013 (4)                           5.60  5.60
**Souvenir Sheet**
1014  A392  50p multicolored                         3.00  3.00
See Isle of Man Nos. 701-705.

Michael Davitt (1846-1906), Nationalist Leader — A393

**1996, July 4    Litho.    Perf. 13½x13**
1015  A393  28p multicolored                          .90   .90

Ireland's Presidency of the European Union A394

**1996, July 4    Perf. 13x13½**
1016  A394  32p multicolored                         1.00  1.00

Thomas A. McLaughlin (1896-1971), Designer of Ardnacrusha Hydroelectric Power Station — A395

**1996, July 4**
1017  A395  38p multicolored                         1.25  1.25

Bord na Móna (Irish Peat Corp.), 50th Anniv. A396

**1996, July 4**
1018  A396  52p multicolored                         1.60  1.60

Irish Naval Service, 50th Anniv. A397

Designs: 32p, Coastal patrol vessel. 44p, Corvette. 52p, Motor torpedo boat, vert.

**1996, July 18    Perf. 15x14**
1019  A397  32p multicolored                         1.00  1.00
a.  Booklet pane, 3 #1019                             3.75
1020  A397  44p multicolored                         1.50  1.50
1021  A397  52p multicolored                         2.00  2.00
a.  Booklet pane of 3, #1019-1021                     7.00
     Complete booklet, #1019a, 1021a                 11.00
Nos. 1019-1021 (3)                           4.50  4.50

People with Disabilities A398

**1996, Sept. 3    Litho.    Perf. 14x15**
1022  A398  28p Man in wheelchair                    1.10  1.10
1023  A398  28p Blind woman, child                   1.10  1.10
a.  Pair, #1022-1023                          2.25  2.25

Freshwater Ducks A399

Designs: 32p, Anas crecca. 38p, Anas clypeata. 44p, Anas penelope. 52p, Anas platyrhynchos.

**1996, Sept. 24    Perf. 15x14**
1024  A399  32p multicolored                         1.00  1.00
1025  A399  38p multicolored                         1.25  1.25
1026  A399  44p multicolored                         1.50  1.50
1027  A399  52p multicolored                         2.00  2.00
a.  Souvenir sheet, #1024-1027               6.50  6.50
Nos. 1024-1027 (4)                           5.75  5.75

No. 1027a is a continuous design.

Motion Pictures, Cent. A400

**1996, Oct. 17    Litho.    Perf. 13½**
1028  A400  32p Man of Aran                          1.40  1.40
1029  A400  32p My Left Foot                         1.40  1.40
1030  A400  32p The Commitments                      1.40  1.40
1031  A400  32p The Field                            1.40  1.40
a.  Strip of 4, #1028-1031                    5.50  5.50

A401

Christmas A402

#1032, Stained glass scene of Holy Family. #1033, Adoration of the Magi. 32p, The Annunciation. 52p, Shepherds receive news of Christ's birth.

**1996, Nov. 19    Perf. 14**
1032  A401  28p multicolored                         1.00  1.00
1033  A402  28p multicolored                         1.00  1.00
1034  A402  32p multicolored                         1.10  1.10
1035  A402  52p multicolored                         2.00  2.00
Nos. 1032-1035 (4)                           5.10  5.10

No. 1032 sold only in discount sheets of 15 for £3.92. Value $15.

Spideog Robin — A403

Greenland Whitefronted Goose — A404

**Perf. 15x14, 14x15**
**1997, Jan. 16    Litho.**
1036  A403  28p Blue tit. horiz.                     1.00   .90
1037  A403  32p shown                                1.25  1.25
b.  Perf. 14                                  1.25  1.25

| | | | |
|---|---|---|---|
| **1038** | A403 | 44p Puffin | 1.75 1.75 |
| **1039** | A403 | 52p Barn owl | 2.00 2.00 |
| **1040** | A404 | £1 shown | 3.25 3.25 |

**Booklet Stamp**
**Size: 18x21mm, 21x18mm**

| | | | |
|---|---|---|---|
| **1040A** | A403 | 32p Like #1037 | 1.50 1.50 |
| *b.* | | Booklet pane, 3 #1040A, 1 #770 | 3.50 |
| | | Complete booklet, #1040b | 3.50 |

**Size: 20x23mm**
**Perf. 14x15**

| | | | |
|---|---|---|---|
| **1040C** | A403 | 32p Like #1037, "Eire" 8½mm wide ('99) | 1.50 1.50 |
| *d.* | | Bklt. pane of 5 + 5 labels | 7.50 |
| | | Complete booklet | 7.50 |
| | | Nos. 1036-1040C (7) | 12.25 12.15 |

On Nos. 1037,1037b "Eire" is 9mm wide, and size of design is 21x24mm.
See Nos. 1053-1054, 1067, 1076-1081A, 1094, 1105-1115C.
Compare with Nos. 1353-1373.
Issued: No. 1040C, 6/30/99.

Greetings
Stamps — A405

Designs: No. 1041, Doves on tree limb. No. 1042, Cow jumping over moon. No. 1043, Pig going to market. No. 1044, Rooster on fence.

**1997, Jan. 28    Litho.    Perf. 14x15**

| | | | |
|---|---|---|---|
| **1041** | A405 | 32p multicolored | 2.00 2.00 |

**Booklet Stamps**

| | | | |
|---|---|---|---|
| **1042** | A405 | 32p multicolored | 2.00 2.00 |
| **1043** | A405 | 32p multicolored | 2.00 2.00 |
| **1044** | A405 | 32p multicolored | 2.00 2.00 |
| *a.* | | Booklet pane, #1041-1044, 5 English, 3 Gaelic labels | 8.00 |
| *b.* | | As "a," #1041-1044, 7 English, 1 Gaelic label | 8.00 |
| | | Complete booklet, #1044a, 1044b | 16.00 |
| *c.* | | Souvenir sheet, 1042-1044, 3 English, 3 Gaelic labels + 1 large label with "Year of the Ox," Hong Kong '97 | 10.00 10.00 |

#1044a contains #1042, 1041, 1043-1044 in order. #1044b contains #1043-1044, 1041-1042 in order.

Irish State, 75th Anniv. A406

Designs: No. 1045, Dáil, national flag, constitution. No. 1046, Defense forces, badges, UN flag. No. 1047, Four Courts, scales of justice. No. 1048, Garda badge, Garda Siochána.

**1997, Feb. 18    Perf. 15x14**

| | | | |
|---|---|---|---|
| **1045** | A406 | 32p multicolored | 1.00 1.00 |
| **1046** | A406 | 32p multicolored | 1.00 1.00 |
| *a.* | | Pair, #1045-1046 | 2.00 2.00 |
| **1047** | A406 | 52p multicolored | 1.50 1.50 |
| **1048** | A406 | 52p multicolored | 1.50 1.50 |
| *a.* | | Pair, #1047-1048 | 3.00 3.00 |

See #1055-1058, 1082-1084, 1095-1096.

Marine
Mammals
A407

Designs: 28p, Halichoerus grypus, vert. 32p, Tursiops truncatus, vert. 44p, Phocaena phocaena. 52p, Orcinus orca.

**Perf. 14x15, 15x14**
**1997, Mar. 6    Litho.**

| | | | |
|---|---|---|---|
| **1049** | A407 | 28p multicolored | .85 .85 |
| **1050** | A407 | 32p multicolored | 1.00 1.00 |
| **1051** | A407 | 44p multicolored | 1.40 1.40 |

| | | | |
|---|---|---|---|
| **1052** | A407 | 52p multicolored | 1.75 1.75 |
| *a.* | | Souvenir sheet, #1049-1052 | 6.00 6.00 |
| | | Nos. 1049-1052 (4) | 5.00 5.00 |

**Bird Type of 1997**
**Die Cut Perf. 9x9½**

**1997, Mar. 6    Litho.**
**Self-Adhesive Coil Stamps**

| | | | |
|---|---|---|---|
| **1053** | A403 | 32p Peregrine falcon | 7.50 7.50 |
| **1054** | A403 | 32p like #1037 | 7.50 7.50 |
| *a.* | | Pair, #1053-1054 | 17.50 |

**Die Cut Perf. 11x11¼**

| | | | |
|---|---|---|---|
| **1054B** | A403 | 32p Like #1053 | 10.00 10.00 |
| **1054C** | A403 | 32p Like #1037 | 10.00 10.00 |
| *d.* | | Pair, #1054B-1054C | 20.00 |
| | | Nos. 1053-1054C (4) | 35.00 35.00 |

Issued: #1053-1054, 3/6/97; #1054B-1054C, 4/97.

**Irish State, 75th Anniv. Type of 1997**

#1055, Singer, violinist, bodhran player. #1056, Athlete, soccer and hurling players. #1057, Irish currency, blueprint, food processing plant. #1058, Abbey Theatre emblem, books, palette, paintbrushes, Séamus Heaney manuscript.

**1997, Apr. 3    Perf. 15x14**

| | | | |
|---|---|---|---|
| **1055** | A406 | 32p multicolored | 1.00 1.00 |
| **1056** | A406 | 32p multicolored | 1.00 1.00 |
| *a.* | | Pair, #1055-1056 | 2.00 2.00 |
| **1057** | A406 | 52p multicolored | 1.75 1.75 |
| **1058** | A406 | 52p multicolored | 1.75 1.75 |
| *a.* | | Pair, #1057-1058 | 3.40 3.40 |

Irish
Coinage,
Millennium
A408

**1997, Apr. 3    Perf. 15x14**

| | | | |
|---|---|---|---|
| **1059** | A408 | 32p First Irish coin | 1.00 1.00 |

Stories and
Legends
A409

Europa: 32p, "The Children of Lir" flying as swans. 44p, "Oisin & Niamh" on horse.

**1997, May 14    Litho.    Perf. 14**

| | | | |
|---|---|---|---|
| **1060** | A409 | 32p multicolored | 1.00 1.00 |
| **1061** | A409 | 44p multicolored | 1.50 1.50 |

**Die Cut Perf. 9x9½**
**Self-Adhesive Coil Stamps**

| | | | |
|---|---|---|---|
| **1062** | A409 | 32p like #1060 | 1.25 1.25 |
| **1063** | A409 | 32p like #1061 | 1.25 1.25 |
| *a.* | | Pair, #1062-1063 | 2.50 |

The Great
Famine,
150th
Anniv.
A410

Designs: 28p, Passengers waiting to board emigrant ship. 32p, Family group attending dying child. 52p, Irish Society of Friends soup kitchen.

**1997, May 14    Litho.    Perf. 15x14**

| | | | |
|---|---|---|---|
| **1064** | A410 | 28p multicolored | .90 .90 |
| **1065** | A410 | 32p multicolored | 1.00 1.00 |
| **1066** | A410 | 52p multicolored | 1.75 1.75 |
| | | Nos. 1064-1066 (3) | 3.65 3.65 |

**Bird Type of 1997**
**Souvenir Sheet**

**1997, May 29    Perf. 14**

| | | | |
|---|---|---|---|
| **1067** | A404 | £2 Pintail, horiz. | 15.00 15.00 |

PACIFIC 97.
No. 1067 shows the duck's head in brown. See #1111 for stamp with duck's head in black.

Kate O'Brien
(1897-1974),
Novelist — A411

**1997, July 1    Litho.    Perf. 14**

| | | | |
|---|---|---|---|
| **1068** | A411 | 28p multicolored | 1.00 1.00 |

St. Columba
(521-97), Irish
Patron
Saint — A412

**1997, July 1    Perf. 14x15**

| | | | |
|---|---|---|---|
| **1069** | A412 | 28p multicolored | 1.00 1.00 |

A413

A414

Designs: 32p, Daniel O'Connell (1775-1847), politician. 52p, John Wesley (1703-91), founder of Methodism, first visit to Ireland, 250th anniv.

**1997, July 1    Perf. 14x14½**

| | | | |
|---|---|---|---|
| **1070** | A413 | 32p multicolored | 1.25 1.25 |
| **1071** | A414 | 52p multicolored | 1.75 1.75 |

Lighthouses — A415

Designs: No. 1072, Baily. No. 1073, Tarbert. 38p, Hook Head, vert. 50p, Fastnet.

**1997, July 1    Perf. 15x14, 14x15**

| | | | |
|---|---|---|---|
| **1072** | A415 | 32p multicolored | 1.25 1.25 |
| **1073** | A415 | 32p multicolored | 1.25 1.25 |
| *a.* | | Pair, #1072-1073 | 2.50 2.50 |
| *b.* | | Bklt. pane, #1073, 2 #1072 | 3.00 |
| *c.* | | Bklt. pane, 2 ea #1072-1073 | 4.00 |
| **1074** | A415 | 38p multicolored | 1.25 1.25 |
| **1075** | A415 | 50p multicolored | 1.60 1.60 |
| *a.* | | Booklet pane, #1074-1075 | 3.00 |
| *b.* | | Bklt. pane of 4, #1073a, 1074-1075 | 5.00 |
| | | Complete booklet, #1073b, 1073c, 1075a, 1075b | 17.50 |

**Bird Types of 1997**
**Perf. 14x15, 15x14**

**1997, Aug. 27    Litho.**

| | | | |
|---|---|---|---|
| **1076** | A403 | 1p Magpie | .20 .20 |
| **1077** | A403 | 2p Gannet | .20 .20 |
| **1078** | A403 | 4p Corncrake | .20 .20 |
| **1079** | A403 | 10p Kingfisher | .20 .20 |
| **1080** | A403 | 20p Lapwing | .30 .20 |
| **1081** | A404 | £5 Shelduck | 15.00 12.50 |

**Booklet Stamp**
**Size: 18x21mm**

| | | | |
|---|---|---|---|
| **1081A** | A403 | 4p Like #1078 | 1.50 1.50 |
| | | Nos. 1076-1081A (7) | 17.60 15.00 |

**Irish State, 75th Anniv. Type of 1997**

28p, Quill, page from Annals of Four Masters, #128. 32p, Stained glass window, #82. 52p, Aer Lingus airplane, letter, #C7.

**1997, Aug. 27    Perf. 15x14**

| | | | |
|---|---|---|---|
| **1082** | A406 | 28p multicolored | .90 .90 |
| **1083** | A406 | 32p multicolored | 1.00 1.00 |
| **1084** | A406 | 52p multicolored | 1.75 1.75 |
| | | Nos. 1082-1084 (3) | 3.65 3.65 |

St. Patrick's
Battalion, 150th
Anniv. — A416

**1997, Sept. 12    Litho.    Perf. 14x13½**

| | | | |
|---|---|---|---|
| **1085** | A416 | 32p multicolored | 1.00 1.00 |

See Mexico No. 2049.

Bram
Stoker's
"Dracula"
A417

Scenes of Dracula: 28p, Being transformed into a bat, vert. 32p, With potential victim, vert. 38p, Emerging from coffin. 52p, With wolf.

**1997, Oct. 1    Perf. 14x15, 15x14**

| | | | |
|---|---|---|---|
| **1086** | A417 | 28p multicolored | .80 .80 |
| **1087** | A417 | 32p multicolored | 1.00 1.00 |
| *a.* | | Souvenir sheet of 1 | 2.50 2.50 |
| **1088** | A417 | 38p multicolored | 1.25 1.25 |
| **1089** | A417 | 52p multicolored | 1.50 1.50 |
| *a.* | | Souv. sheet of 4, #1086-1089 | 7.00 7.00 |
| | | Nos. 1086-1089 (4) | 4.55 4.55 |

Stamps from Nos. 1087a, 1089a have souvenir sheet background framing vignette.

A418

Christmas — A419

#1090-1092: Different images of Holy Family in stained glass. #1093, Christmas tree.

**1997, Nov. 18    Litho.    Perf. 14x15**

| | | | |
|---|---|---|---|
| **1090** | A418 | 28p multicolored | 1.00 1.00 |
| **1091** | A418 | 32p multicolored | 1.25 1.25 |
| **1092** | A418 | 52p multicolored | 1.75 1.75 |
| | | Nos. 1090-1092 (3) | 4.00 4.00 |

**Self-Adhesive**
**Serpentine Die Cut 9x9½**

| | | | |
|---|---|---|---|
| **1093** | A419 | 28p multicolored | .80 .80 |
| *a.* | | Booklet pane, 20 #1093 | 16.00 |

By its nature, No. 1093a is a complete booklet. The peelable paper backing serves as a booklet cover.
No. 1093 sold only in discount booklets for £5.32.

## Bird Type of 1997
**Perf. 15x14 (on 3 Sides)**

| 1997, Dec. 6 | | Litho. |
|---|---|---|
| **Booklet Stamp** | | |
| **1094** A403 32p like #1053 | 1.25 | 1.25 |
| a. Bkit. pane, #1081A, 3 #1094 | 5.25 | |
| Complete booklet, #1094a | 6.00 | |

### Irish State, 75th Anniv. Type of 1997

No. 1095, General Post Office, #68.
No. 1096: a, like #1048. b, like #1047. c, like #1057. d, like #1058. e, like #1082. f, like #1084.

| 1997, Dec. 6 | Litho. | Perf. 15x14 |
|---|---|---|
| **1095** A406 32p multicolored | 1.25 | 1.25 |

**Sheet of 12**

| **1096** A406 32p #a.-f. + #1045-1046, 1055-1056, 1083, 1095 | 17.50 | 18.00 |
|---|---|---|

Greetings
Stamps — A420

Love is: No. 1097, "...from my heart." No. 1098, "...a birthday wish." No. 1099, "...thinking of you." No. 1100, "...keeping in touch."

| 1998, Jan. 26 | Litho. | Perf. 14x15 |
|---|---|---|
| **1097** A420 32p multicolored | 1.50 | 1.50 |
| **1098** A420 32p multicolored | 1.50 | 1.50 |
| **1099** A420 32p multicolored | 1.50 | 1.50 |
| **1100** A420 32p multicolored | 1.50 | 1.50 |
| a. Bkit. pane, #1097-1100 + 8 labels | 6.00 | |
| Complete booklet, 2 #1100a | 12.00 | |
| b. Souv. sheet, #1098-1100 + 7 labels | 6.00 | 6.00 |

No. 1100a exists with stamps in two different orders. No. 1100b has 1 English, 4 Chinese, 1 Gaelic labels + 1 large label with "Year of the Tiger," in English and Chinese. Same value.
See Nos. 1120-1123.

Aviation
Pioneers
A421

28p, Lady Mary Heath (Sophie Catherine Pierce), 1st solo flight, Capetown-Croydon via Cairo, 1928. 32p, Col. James Fitzmaurice, navigator on "Bremen," 1st east-west Atlantic flight, 1928. 44p, Capt. J.P. (Paddy) Saul, navigator aboard Southern Cross, Dublin-Newfoundland, 1930. 52p, Capt. Charles Blair, 1st non-stop commercial flight Foynes-NYC, 1942.

| 1998, Feb. 24 | | Perf. 15x14 |
|---|---|---|
| **1101** A421 28p multicolored | .80 | .80 |
| **1102** A421 32p multicolored | 1.10 | 1.10 |
| a. Bkit. pane, 2 ea #1101-1102 | 3.00 | |
| **1103** A421 44p multicolored | 1.25 | 1.25 |
| a. Bkit. pane, #1103, 2 #1102 | 3.00 | |
| **1104** A421 52p multicolored | 1.50 | 1.50 |
| a. Bkit. pane, #1102, 2 #1104 | 3.50 | |
| b. Bkit. pane of 4, #1101-1104 | 3.75 | |
| Complete booklet, #1102a, 1103a, 1104a, 1104b | 17.00 | |
| Nos. 1101-1104 (4) | 4.65 | 4.65 |

### Bird Types of 1997

No. 1111A: b, Like #1107. c, Like #1080. d, Like #1077. e, Like #1078. f, Like #1076. g, Like #1106B, "Eire" 8½mm wide. h, Like #1079. i, Like #1053. j, Like #1039. k, Like #1037. l, Like #1109. m, Like #1106B, "Eire" 8½mm wide. n, Wren. o, Pied wagtail. p, Like #1038.

| 1998-99 | Litho. | Perf. 15x14, 14x15 |
|---|---|---|
| **1105** A403 5p Woodpigeon, horiz. | .60 | .50 |
| **1106** A403 30p Blackbird | 1.00 | .75 |
| d. Perf. 14 | 1.25 | .75 |
| **1106B** A403 30p Goldcrest, bkit. stamp | 1.25 | 1.25 |
| c. Booklet pane, 5 each #1106, 1106B | 12.00 | |
| Complete booklet, #1106Bc | 12.00 | |
| **1107** A403 35p Stonechat | 1.25 | 1.25 |
| a. Perf. 14 | 1.50 | 1.50 |

---

| **1108** A403 40p Ringed plover, horiz. | 1.50 | 1.50 |
|---|---|---|
| a. Perf. 14 | 1.75 | 1.75 |
| **1109** A403 45p Song thrush | 2.25 | 2.25 |
| a. Perf. 14 | 2.50 | 2.50 |
| **1110** A403 50p Sparrowhawk, horiz. | 2.50 | 2.50 |
| a. Perf. 14 | 2.75 | 2.75 |
| **1111** A404 £2 Pintail | 6.00 | 6.00 |

**Sheet of 15**

| **1111A** A403 30p #b.-p. | 17.50 | 17.50 |
|---|---|---|

See note under #1067.

### Booklet Stamps
**Size: 18x21mm, 21x18mm**

| **1112** A403 5p Like #1105 | 1.00 | 1.00 |
|---|---|---|
| **1113** A403 30p Like #1106 | 1.25 | 1.25 |
| a. Booklet pane, 2 #1112, 3 #1113 | 6.00 | |
| Complete booklet, #1113a | 6.00 | |
| **1113B** A403 30p like #1106B | .75 | .75 |
| c. Bkit. pane, 2 #1112, 3 #1113B + label | 3.00 | |
| Complete booklet, #1113c | 3.00 | |

**Size: 20x23mm**

| **1113D** A403 45p Like #1109, "Eire" 8½mm wide | 2.00 | 2.00 |
|---|---|---|
| e. Booklet pane of 4 + 4 labels | 8.00 | |
| Complete booklet | 8.00 | |

**Size: 21x24mm**
**Perf. 10¾x13 on 3 sides**

| **1113F** A403 30p Like #1106, "Eire" 8½mm wide | 1.25 | 1.25 |
|---|---|---|
| i. Like #1113F, perf. 14¼x14¾ on 3 sides ('99) | 1.25 | 1.25 |
| **1113G** A403 30p Like #1106B, "Eire" 8½mm wide | 1.25 | 1.25 |
| h. Booklet pane, 5 each #1113F-1113G | 12.50 | — |
| Booklet, #1113Gh | 12.50 | |
| j. Like #1113G, perf. 14¼x14¾ on 3 sides ('99) | 1.25 | 1.25 |

**Die Cut Perf. 9x9½**
**Self-Adhesive**

| **1114** A403 30p like #1106 | 3.75 | 3.75 |
|---|---|---|
| **1115** A403 30p like #1106B | 3.75 | 3.75 |
| a. Pair, #1114-1115 | 7.50 | 7.50 |

**Litho.**
**Die Cut Perf. 11x11¼**
**Self-Adhesive Coil Stamps**

| **1115B** A403 30p Like #1114 | 3.75 | 3.75 |
|---|---|---|
| **1115C** A403 30p Like #1115 | 3.75 | 3.75 |
| d. Pair, #1115B-1115C | 7.50 | 7.50 |

Issued: #1115B-1115C, 5/98; #1106B, 1113B, 9/4/98; #1111A, 2/16/99; #1113D, 6/30/99; #1113F, 1113G, 5/3/01.

Equestrian
Sports
A422

30p, Show jumping. 32p, Three-day event. 40p, Gymkhana. 45p, Dressage, vert.

| 1998, Apr. 2 | | |
|---|---|---|
| **1116** A422 30p multicolored | .90 | .75 |
| **1117** A422 32p multicolored | .95 | .75 |
| **1118** A422 40p multicolored | 1.25 | 1.25 |
| **1119** A422 45p multicolored | 1.40 | 1.40 |
| a. Souvenir sheet, #1116-1119 | 5.00 | 5.50 |
| Nos. 1116-1119 (4) | 4.50 | 4.15 |

### Greetings Type of 1998

| 1998, May 6 | Litho. | Perf. 14x15 |
|---|---|---|
| **Booklet Stamps** | | |
| **1120** A420 30p like #1098 | 1.40 | 1.40 |
| **1121** A420 30p like #1099 | 1.40 | 1.40 |
| **1122** A420 30p like #1100 | 1.40 | 1.40 |
| **1123** A420 30p like #1097 | 1.40 | 1.40 |
| a. Bkit. pane, #1120-1123 + 8 labels | 5.50 | |
| Complete booklet, 2 #1123a | 11.00 | |

No. 1123a exists with stamps in different order. Complete booklet contains two different panes.

---

Festivals
A423

Europa: 30p, Crinniú na mBáid, Kinvara (sailboats). 40p, Puck Fair, Killorglin.

| 1998, May 6 | | Perf. 15x14 |
|---|---|---|
| **1124** A423 30p multicolored | .80 | .80 |
| **1125** A423 40p multicolored | 1.25 | 1.25 |

**Serpentine Die Cut Perf 9x9½**
**Self-Adhesive**

| **1126** A423 30p like #1124 | 1.10 | 1.10 |
|---|---|---|
| **1127** A423 30p like #1125 | 1.10 | 1.10 |
| a. Pair, #1126-1127 | 2.25 | 2.25 |
| Nos. 1124-1127 (4) | 4.25 | 4.25 |

1798
Rebellion,
Bicent.
A424

Battle scene and: No. 1128, "Liberty." No. 1129, Pikeman. No. 1130, French soldier. No. 1131, Wolfe Tone. No. 1132, Henry Joy McCracken.

| 1998, May 6 | | |
|---|---|---|
| **1128** A424 30p multicolored | .90 | .90 |
| **1129** A424 30p multicolored | .90 | .90 |
| **1130** A424 30p multicolored | .90 | .90 |
| a. Strip of 3, #1128-1130 | 2.75 | 2.75 |
| **1131** A424 45p multicolored | 1.40 | 1.40 |
| **1132** A424 45p multicolored | 1.40 | 1.40 |
| a. Pair, #1131-1132 | 3.00 | 3.00 |

Tour de
France
Bicycle
Race
A425

#1133, 4 cyclists. #1134, 2 cyclists, 1 wearing dark glasses. #1135, 2 cyclists, 1 wearing hat. #1136, Leading rider in yellow jersey.

| 1998, June 2 | Litho. | Perf. 15x14 |
|---|---|---|
| **1133** A425 30p multicolored | 1.25 | 1.25 |
| **1134** A425 30p multicolored | 1.25 | 1.25 |
| **1135** A425 30p multicolored | 1.25 | 1.25 |
| **1136** A425 30p multicolored | 1.25 | 1.25 |
| a. Strip of 4, #1133-1136 | 5.50 | 5.50 |

Democracy
Stamps
A426

Designs: 30p, Local government (Ireland Act), cent. 32p, Entrance into European Union, 25th anniv. 35p, Women's vote in local elections, cent. 45c, Republic of Ireland Act, 50th anniv.

| 1998, June 2 | | |
|---|---|---|
| **1137** A426 30p multicolored | .85 | .85 |
| **1138** A426 32p multicolored | .90 | .90 |
| **1139** A426 35p multicolored | 1.00 | 1.00 |
| **1140** A426 45p multicolored | 1.25 | 1.25 |
| Nos. 1137-1140 (4) | 4.00 | 4.00 |

1998 Tall Ships
Race — A427

---

| **Perf. 14x15, 15x14** | | |
|---|---|---|
| 1998, July 20 | | Litho. |
| **1141** A427 30p Asgard II | .75 | .75 |
| a. Perf. 15 | 1.00 | 1.00 |
| **1142** A427 30p Eagle | 1.00 | 1.00 |
| a. Pair, #1141-1142 | 1.75 | 1.75 |
| b. Perf. 15 | 2.50 | 2.50 |
| c. Bkit. pane, #1142b, 2 #1141a | 2.25 | |
| **1143** A427 45p Boa Esperanza, horiz. | 1.25 | 1.25 |
| a. Perf. 15 | 1.50 | 1.50 |
| **1144** A427 £1 T.S. Royalist, horiz. | 3.00 | 3.00 |
| a. Perf. 15 | 5.00 | 5.00 |
| b. Bkit. pane of 3, #1142b, 1143a, 1144a | 9.00 | |
| Complete booklet, #1142c, 1144b | 11.50 | |
| Nos. 1141-1144 (4) | 6.00 | 6.00 |

**Souvenir Sheet**

| **1145** A427 £2 like #1143 | 8.00 | 8.00 |
|---|---|---|

**Die Cut Perf. 9x9½, 9½x9**
**Self-Adhesive**

| **1145A** A427 30p like #1143 | 3.00 | 3.00 |
|---|---|---|
| **1145B** A427 30p like #1141 | 3.00 | 3.00 |
| **1145C** A427 30p like #1142 | 3.00 | 3.00 |
| **1145D** A427 30p like #1144 | 3.00 | 3.00 |
| e. Strip of 4, #1145A-1145D | 12.50 | 12.50 |

Portugal '98 (#1145).
Issued: £2, 9/4; others, 7/20.

Postboxes — A428

### 1998, Sept. 3

No. 1146, Ashworth, 1856. No. 1147, Wallbox, 1922. No. 1148, Double Pillarbox, 1899. No. 1149, Penfold, 1866.

| **1146** A428 30p multicolored | 1.25 | 1.25 |
|---|---|---|
| **1147** A428 30p multicolored | 1.25 | 1.25 |
| **1148** A428 30p multicolored | 1.25 | 1.25 |
| **1149** A428 30p multicolored | 1.25 | 1.25 |
| a. Strip of 4, #1146-1149 | 5.00 | 5.00 |

Mary Immaculate College, Limerick,
Cent. — A429

Newton School,
Waterford,
Bicent. — A430

| 1998, Sept. 3 | Perf. 15x14, 14x15 |
|---|---|
| **1150** A429 30p multicolored | .80 | .80 |
| **1151** A430 40p multicolored | 1.25 | 1.25 |

Universal
Declaration
of Human
Rights,
50th Anniv.
A431

| 1998, Sept. 3 | | Perf. 15x14 |
|---|---|---|
| **1152** A431 45p multicolored | 1.25 | 1.25 |

Endangered Animals — A432

#1153, Cheetah. #1154, Scimitar-horned oryx. 40p, Golden lion tamarin. 45p, Tiger.

| 1998, Oct. 8 | Litho. | Perf. 14 | |
|---|---|---|---|
| 1153 A432 30p multi | | 1.10 | 1.10 |
| 1154 A432 30p multi | | 1.10 | 1.10 |
| a. Pair, #1153-1154 | | 2.25 | 2.25 |
| 1155 A432 40p multi, vert. | | 1.10 | 1.10 |
| 1156 A432 45p multi, vert. | | 1.25 | 1.25 |
| a. Souvenir sheet, #1153-1156, perf. 15 | | 5.50 | 5.50 |
| b. As "a" inscription on extended margin | | 9.00 | 9.00 |
| Nos. 1153-1156 (4) | | 4.55 | 4.55 |

Stamps on Nos. 1156a, 1156b have a white border. No. 1156b contains exhibition logo and "National Stamp Exhibition RDS-Dublin-6-8 November 1998" in sheet margin.

A433

Christmas — A434

#1157, Holy family. 32p, Adoration of the Shepherds. 45p, Adoration of the Magi. No. 1160, Choir singers.

| 1998, Nov. 17 | Litho. | Perf. 14x15 | |
|---|---|---|---|
| 1157 A433 30p multicolored | | .80 | .80 |
| 1158 A433 32p multicolored | | 1.00 | 1.00 |
| 1159 A433 45p multicolored | | 1.75 | 1.75 |
| Nos. 1157-1159 (3) | | 3.55 | 3.55 |

Booklet Stamp
Self-Adhesive
Serpentine Die Cut Perf. 11x11½

| 1160 A434 30p multicolored | 1.00 | 1.00 |
|---|---|---|
| a. Booklet pane of 20 | 20.00 | |

No. 1160a is a complete booklet. The Peelable paper backing serves as a booklet cover. No. 1160 sold only in discount booklets at £5.40.

A435

Pets greetings stamps.

| 1999, Jan. 26 | Litho. | Perf. 14x15 | |
|---|---|---|---|
| 1161 A435 30p Dog | | 1.25 | 1.25 |

Booklet Stamps

| 1162 A435 30p Cat | 1.25 | 1.25 |
|---|---|---|
| 1163 A435 30p Fish | 1.25 | 1.25 |
| 1164 A435 30p Rabbit | 1.25 | 1.25 |
| a. Booklet pane, #1161-1164 + 5 English, 3 Gaelic labels | 5.00 | |
| b. Booklet pane, #1161-1164 + 7 English, 1 Gaelic label | 5.00 | |
| Complete booklet, #1164a-1164b | 10.00 | |
| c. Souvenir sheet, #1162-1164 (see footnote) | 6.00 | 6.00 |

No. 1164a contains Nos. 1161-1164 in order. No. 1164b contains stamps in reverse order. No. 1164c has 1 English, 2 Chinese, 3 Gaelic labels + 1 large label with "Year of the Rabbit" in English and Chinese.

New Year 1999 (Year of the Rabbit) (#1164c).

A436

Irish Actors: 30p, Micheál Mac Liammóir (1899-1978). 45p, Siobhán McKenna (1923-86). 50p, Noel Purcell (1900-85).

| 1999, Feb. 16 | Litho. | Perf. 14x15 | |
|---|---|---|---|
| 1165 A436 30p brown | | 1.00 | 1.00 |
| 1166 A436 45p green | | 1.75 | 1.75 |
| 1167 A436 50p blue | | 2.25 | 2.25 |
| Nos. 1165-1167 (3) | | 5.00 | 5.00 |

Irish Emigration A437

| 1999, Feb. 26 | Litho. | Perf. 15x14 | |
|---|---|---|---|
| 1168 A437 45p multicolored | | 2.00 | 2.00 |

See US No. 3286.

Maritime Heritage A438

30p, Polly Woodside. 35p, Ilen. 45p, Royal Natl. Lifeboat Institution. £1, Titanic.

| 1999, Mar. 19 | Litho. | Perf. 14 | |
|---|---|---|---|
| 1169 A438 30p multi, vert. | | .80 | .80 |
| 1170 A438 35p multi, vert. | | .95 | .95 |
| 1171 A438 45p multi | | 1.25 | 1.25 |
| 1172 A438 £1 multi | | 2.75 | 2.75 |
| a. Souvenir sheet of 2 | | 6.50 | 6.50 |
| b. As "a" ovptd. in sheet margin | | 7.50 | 8.00 |
| Nos. 1169-1172 (4) | | 5.75 | 5.75 |

Souvenir Sheet
Perf. 14x14½

| 1173 Sheet of 2, #1173a, Australia #1729 | 6.00 | 6.00 |
|---|---|---|
| a. A438 30p like #1169 | 2.75 | .80 |

Australia '99, World Stamp Expo. (#1172b, #1173). See Australia No. 1729a. No. 1172b is overprinted in gold in sheet margin with Australia '99, World Stamp Expo exhibition emblem.
Sky is gray blue, country and denomination are 3mm high on #1169. Sky is blue, country and denomination are 4mm high on #1173a.

Natl. Parks A438a

Europa: #1174, 1176, Whooping swans, Kilcolman Nature Reserve. 40p, #1177, Fallow deer, Wellington Memorial Obelisk, Phoenix Park.

| 1999, Apr. 29 | Litho. | Perf. 15x14 | |
|---|---|---|---|
| 1174 A438a 30p multicolored | | 1.00 | 1.00 |
| 1175 A438a 40p multicolored | | 1.25 | 1.25 |

Die Cut Perf. 9x9½
Self-adhesive

| 1176 A438a 30p Like #1174 | 1.10 | 1.10 |
|---|---|---|
| 1177 A438a 30p Like #1175 | 1.10 | 1.10 |
| a. Pair, #1176-1177 | 2.25 | 2.25 |

A439

Prime Minister Sean Lemass (1899-1971).

| 1999, Apr. 29 | Litho. | Perf. 14x15 | |
|---|---|---|---|
| 1178 A439 30p green & black | | 2.00 | 2.00 |

A441

A440

| 1999, Apr. 29 | Litho. | Perf. 15x14 | |
|---|---|---|---|
| 1179 A440 30p multicolored | | 6.00 | 6.00 |

Introduction of the Euro. No. 1179 is denominated in both pence and euros.

| 1999, Apr. 29 | Litho. | Perf. 14x15 | |
|---|---|---|---|
| 1180 A441 45p multicolored | | 2.00 | 2.00 |

Council of Europe, 50th anniv.

Intl. Year of Older Persons A442

| 1999, June 15 | | Perf. 15x14 | |
|---|---|---|---|
| 1181 A442 30p multicolored | | 1.50 | 1.50 |

UPU, 125th Anniv. A443

| 1999, June 15 | | | |
|---|---|---|---|
| 1182 A443 30p Modern mail truck | | 1.00 | 1.00 |
| 1183 A443 30p Early mail truck | | 1.00 | 1.00 |
| a. Pair, #1182-1183 | | 2.00 | 2.00 |

Pioneer Total Abstinence Assoc., Cent. — A444

| 1999, June 15 | | Perf. 14x15 | |
|---|---|---|---|
| 1184 A444 32p Fr. James Cullen | | 2.00 | 2.00 |

Gaelic Football Team of the Millennium A445

No. 1185: a, Danno Keeffe. b, Enda Colleran. c, Joe Keohane. d, Seán Flanagan. e, Seán Murphy. f, John Joe Reilly. g, Martin O'Connell. h, Mick O'Connell. i, Tommy Murphy. j, Seán O'Neill. k, Seán Purcell. l, Pat Spillane. m, Mikey Sheehy. n, Tom Langan. o, Kevin Heffernan.

| 1999, Aug. 17 | Perf. 14¾x14¼ | Litho. | |
|---|---|---|---|
| 1185 Sheet of 15 + label | | 20.00 | 20.00 |
| a.-o. A445 30p any single | | 1.00 | 1.00 |

Booklet Stamps
Size: 33x22mm
Self-Adhesive
Serpentine Die Cut Perf. 11¼x11½

| 1186 A445 30p like #1185a | 1.25 | 1.25 |
|---|---|---|
| 1187 A445 30p like #1185c | 1.25 | 1.25 |
| 1188 A445 30p like #1185e | 1.25 | 1.25 |
| 1189 A445 30p like #1185h | 1.25 | 1.25 |
| 1190 A445 30p like #1185l | 1.25 | 1.25 |
| 1191 A445 30p like #1185m | 1.25 | 1.25 |
| a. Bklt. pane, #1186-1189, 2 each #1190-1191 | 10.00 | |
| 1192 A445 30p like #1185d | 1.25 | 1.25 |
| 1193 A445 30p like #1185b | 1.25 | 1.25 |
| 1194 A445 30p like #1185n | 1.25 | 1.25 |
| 1195 A445 30p like #1185k | 1.25 | 1.25 |
| a. Bklt. pane, 2 ea #1192-1195 | 10.00 | |
| 1196 A445 30p like #1185o | 1.25 | 1.25 |
| 1197 A445 30p like #1185g | 1.25 | 1.25 |
| 1198 A445 30p like #1185i | 1.25 | 1.25 |
| a. Bklt. pane, 3 ea #1196-1197, 2 #1198 | 10.00 | |
| 1199 A445 30p like #1185f | 1.25 | 1.25 |
| 1200 A445 30p like #1185j | 1.25 | 1.25 |
| a. Bklt. pane, 4 ea #1199-1200 | 10.00 | |

Nos. 1191a, 1195a, 1198a, 1200a are each complete booklets. The peelable paper backing serves as a booklet cover. #1185 exists imperf.

Airplanes A446

Designs: 30p, Douglas DC-3. 32p, Britten Norman Islander. 40p, Boeing 707. 45p, Lockheed Constellation.

| 1999, Sept. 9 | Litho. | Perf. 14¾x14¼ | |
|---|---|---|---|
| 1201 A446 30p multicolored | | 1.00 | 1.00 |
| a. Booklet pane of 4 | | 4.00 | |
| 1202 A446 32p multicolored | | 1.10 | 1.10 |
| a. Bklt. pane, 2 ea #1201, 1202 | | 4.50 | |
| 1203 A446 40p multicolored | | 1.40 | 1.40 |
| a. Bklt. pane, #1203, 2 #1201 | | 5.50 | |
| 1204 A446 45p multicolored | | 1.50 | 1.50 |
| a. Booklet pane, #1201-1204 | | 5.00 | |
| Complete bkt., #1201a-1204a | | 19.00 | |
| Nos. 1201-1204 (4) | | 5.00 | 5.00 |

Extinct Irish Animals A447

| | Perf. 14¼x14¾, 14¾x14¼ | | |
|---|---|---|---|
| 1999, Oct. 11 | | Litho. | |
| 1205 A447 30p Mammoth, vert. | | 1.00 | 1.00 |
| 1206 A447 30p Giant deer, vert. | | 1.00 | 1.00 |
| a. Pair, #1205-1206 | | 2.00 | 2.00 |
| 1207 A447 45p Wolf | | 1.50 | 1.50 |
| 1208 A447 45p Brown bear | | 1.50 | 1.50 |
| a. Pair, #1207-1208 | | 3.00 | 3.00 |
| b. Souvenir sheet, #1205-1208, perf. 14¾ | | 6.00 | 6.00 |

Stamps from No. 1208b do not have white border.

Die Cut Perf. 9¼x9½, 9½x9¼

| 1999, Oct. 11 | | Litho. | |
|---|---|---|---|
| | Self-Adhesive | | |
| 1209 A447 30p Like #1208 | | 2.50 | 2.50 |
| 1210 A447 30p Like #1205 | | 2.50 | 2.50 |
| 1211 A447 30p Like #1207 | | 2.50 | 2.50 |
| 1212 A447 30p Like #1206 | | 2.50 | 2.50 |
| a. Strip, #1209-1212 | | 10.00 | |

Christmas
A448

**1999, Nov. 4    Litho.    Perf. 14¾x14¼**
| | | | |
|---|---|---|---|
| 1213 | A448 30p Holy Family | .80 | .80 |
| 1214 | A448 32p Shepherds | 1.25 | 1.25 |
| 1215 | A448 45p Magi | 1.75 | 1.75 |
| | Nos. 1213-1215 (3) | 3.80 | 3.80 |

**Self-Adhesive Booklet Stamp**
**Size: 19x27mm**
*Die Cut 11x11¼*

| | | | |
|---|---|---|---|
| 1216 | A448 30p Angel, vert. | 1.00 | 1.00 |
| a. | Booklet pane of 20 | | 20.00 |

No. 1216a sold for £5.40 and is a complete
booklet.

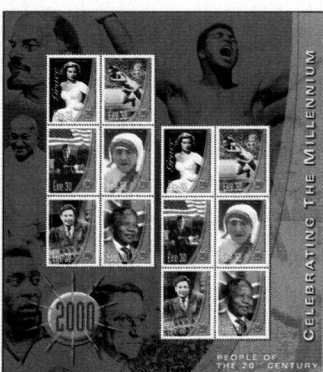

Millennium — A449

People of the 20th Century — No. 1217: a,
Grace Kelly. b, Jesse Owens. c, John F. Kennedy. d, Mother Teresa. e, John McCormack.
f, Nelson Mandela.

Irish Historic Events — No. 1218, horiz.: a,
Norman invasion, 1169. b, Flight of the Earls,
1607. c, Irish Parliament, 1782. d, Land
league. e, Irish independence. f, UN
peacekeeping.

Discoveries — No. 1219: a, Rev. Nicholas
Callan, electrical scientist. b, Birr Telescope. c,
Thomas Edison. d, Albert Einstein. e, Marie
Curie. f, Galileo.

The Arts — No. 1220: a, Ludwig van Beethoven. b, Dame Ninette de Valois, ballet
director. c, James Joyce. d, Mona Lisa, by
Leonardo da Vinci. e, Painting by Sir John
Lavery. f, William Shakespeare.

World Events — No. 1221, horiz.: a, French
Revolution, 1789. b, Industrial Revolution. c,
Peace, 1945. d, Women's liberation. e, Fall of
the Berlin Wall, 1989. f, Modern
communications.

Epic Journeys — No. 1222, horiz.: a, Marco
Polo. b, Capt. James Cook. c, Australian
explorers Robert O'Hara Burke and William
Wills. d, Antarctic explorer Ernest Shackleton.
e, Charles Lindbergh. f, Astronaut on moon.

**Perf. 14¼x14¾, 14¾x14¼**
**1999-2001    Litho.**
| | | | |
|---|---|---|---|
| 1217 | Sheet of 12, 2 | | |
| | ea #a.-f. | 20.00 | 20.00 |
| a.-f. | A449 30p Any single | 1.50 | 1.50 |
| 1218 | Sheet of 12, 2 | | |
| | ea #a.-f. | 20.00 | 20.00 |
| a.-f. | A449 30p Any single | 1.50 | 1.50 |
| 1219 | Sheet of 12, 2 | | |
| | each #a.-f. | 20.00 | 20.00 |
| a.-f. | A449 30p Any single | 1.50 | 1.50 |
| 1220 | Sheet of 12, 2 | | |
| | each #a.-f. | 20.00 | 20.00 |
| a.-f. | A449 30p Any single | 1.50 | 1.50 |
| 1221 | A449 Sheet of 12, 2 | | |
| | each #a-f | 20.00 | 20.00 |
| a.-f. | 30p Any single | 1.50 | 1.50 |
| 1222 | A449 Sheet of 12, 2 | | |
| | each #a-f | 20.00 | 20.00 |
| a.-f. | 30p Any single | 1.50 | 1.50 |

Issued: #1217, 12/31; #1218, 1/1/00; #1219,
2/29/00; #1220, 6/16/00; #1221, 12/31/00;
#1222, 1/1/01.

Mythical
Creatures — A450

**2000, Jan. 26    Litho.    Perf. 14¼x14¾**
| | | | |
|---|---|---|---|
| 1223 | A450 30p Frog Prince | 1.25 | 1.25 |
| 1224 | A450 30p Pegasus | 1.25 | 1.25 |
| 1225 | A450 30p Unicorn | 1.25 | 1.25 |
| 1226 | A450 30p Dragon | 1.25 | 1.25 |
| a. | Booklet pane, #1223-1226, + 3 Gaelic, 5 English labels | | 5.00 |
| b. | Booklet pane, #1223-1226, + 2 Gaelic, 6 English labels | | 5.00 |
| c. | Booklet pane, #1223, 1226, + 14 labels | | 2.50 |
| | Complete booklet, #1226a-1226c | | 12.50 |
| d. | Souvenir sheet, #1224-1226, + 7 labels | 6.00 | 6.00 |
| | Nos. 1223-1226 (4) | 5.00 | 5.00 |

New Year 2000 (Year of the Dragon), No.
1226d.

Emigrant
Ship Jeanie
Johnston
A451

**2000, Mar. 9    Litho.    Perf. 14¾x14¼**
| | | | |
|---|---|---|---|
| 1227 | A451 30p multi | 1.50 | 1.50 |

Europa, 2000

**Common Design Type**
**2000, May 9    Litho.    Perf. 14¼x14¾**
| | | | |
|---|---|---|---|
| 1230 | CD17 32p multi | 1.25 | 1.25 |

*Die Cut Perf 9½x9¼*
**Self-Adhesive**
**Size: 22x34mm**
| | | | |
|---|---|---|---|
| 1231 | CD17 30p multi | 1.10 | 1.10 |

Oscar Wilde (1854-
1900),
Playwright — A453

#1232, Portrait. #1233, The Happy Prince.
#1234, The Importance of Being Earnest.
#1235, The Picture of Dorian Gray. #1236, £2,
Like #1232, signature at left.

**Perf. 14¼x14¾, 14¼x14 (#1236)**
**2000, May 22    Litho.**
| | | | |
|---|---|---|---|
| 1232 | A453 30p multi | 1.25 | 1.25 |
| 1233 | A453 30p multi | 1.25 | 1.25 |
| 1234 | A453 30p multi | 1.25 | 1.25 |
| 1235 | A453 30p multi | 1.25 | 1.25 |
| a. | Block, #1232-1235 | 5.00 | 5.00 |

**Size: 27x27mm**
| | | | |
|---|---|---|---|
| 1236 | A453 30p multi + label | 10.00 | 10.00 |
| | Sheet of 20 | 200.00 | |
| | Nos. 1232-1236 (5) | 15.00 | 15.00 |

**Souvenir Sheet**
| | | | |
|---|---|---|---|
| 1237 | A453 £2 multi | 8.00 | 9.00 |
| a. | With Stamp Show 2000 emblem in margin | 6.00 | 6.00 |

No. 1237 contains one 30x40mm stamp.
No. 1236 was printed in sheets of 20
stamps and 20 labels for £10. These sheets
were not available at Irish post offices, but
were sold at the Irish Post booths at The
Stamp Show 2000 in London and World

Stamp Expo in Ahaheim, California. Labels
were blank, but purchasers could provide Irish
Post with photographic images or other artwork that would be reproduced on the labels.

2000
Summer
Olympics,
Sydney
A454

**2000, July 7    Litho.    Perf. 13¼**
| | | | |
|---|---|---|---|
| 1238 | A454 30p Running | 1.00 | 1.00 |
| 1239 | A454 30p Javelin | 2.00 | 2.00 |
| a. | Pair, #1238-1239 | 2.00 | 2.00 |
| 1240 | A454 50p Long jump | 1.50 | 1.50 |
| 1241 | A454 50p High jump | 1.50 | 1.50 |
| a. | Pair, #1240-1241 | 3.00 | 3.00 |

Stampin'
the Future
A455

Children's Stamp Design Contest Winners:
30p, Marguerite Nyhan (rocket and flowers),
vert. 32p, Kyle Staunton (2000). No. 1244,
Jennifer Branagan (Earth, sun and moon). No.
1245, Diarmuid O'Ceochain (rocket, building
on moon).

**Perf. 14¼x14¾, 14¾x14¼**
**2000, July 7**
| | | | |
|---|---|---|---|
| 1242 | A455 30p multi | .75 | .75 |
| 1243 | A455 32p multi | .75 | .75 |
| 1244 | A455 45p multi | 1.25 | 1.25 |
| 1245 | A455 45p multi | 1.25 | 1.25 |
| a. | Pair, #1244-1245 | 2.50 | 2.50 |
| | Nos. 1242-1245 (4) | 4.00 | 4.00 |

**Team of the Millennium Type of
1999**

Hurling — No. 1246: a, Tony Reddin. b,
Bobby Rackard. c, Nick O'Donnell. d, John
Doyle. e, Brian Whelahan. f, John Keane. g,
Paddy Phelan. h, Lory Meagher. i, Jack Lynch.
j, Jim Langton. k, Mick Mackey. l, Christy Ring.
m, Jimmy Doyle. n, Ray Cummins. o, Eddie
Keher.

**2000, Aug. 2    Litho.    Perf. 14¾x14¼**
| | | | |
|---|---|---|---|
| 1246 | Sheet of 15 + label | 20.00 | 20.00 |
| a.-o. | A455 30p Any single | 1.25 | 1.25 |

**Booklet Stamps**
**Self-Adhesive**
**Size: 33x22mm**
*Serpentine Die Cut 11¼x11½*
| | | | |
|---|---|---|---|
| 1247 | A445 30p Like #1246a | 1.25 | 1.25 |
| 1248 | A445 30p Like #1246m | 1.25 | 1.25 |
| 1249 | A445 30p Like #1246d | 1.25 | 1.25 |
| a. | Booklet, 3 each #1247-1248, 4 #1249 | | 10.00 |
| 1250 | A445 30p Like #1246b | 1.25 | 1.25 |
| 1251 | A445 30p Like #1246c | 1.25 | 1.25 |
| a. | Booklet, 5 each #1250-1251 | | 10.00 |
| 1252 | A445 30p Like #1246k | 1.25 | 1.25 |
| 1253 | A445 30p Like #1246e | 1.25 | 1.25 |
| 1254 | A445 30p Like #1246f | 1.25 | 1.25 |
| a. | Booklet, 4 #1252, 3 each #1253-1254 | | 10.00 |
| 1255 | A445 30p Like #1246g | 1.25 | 1.25 |
| 1256 | A445 30p Like #1246j | 1.25 | 1.25 |
| 1257 | A445 30p Like #1246h | 1.25 | 1.25 |
| 1258 | A445 30p Like #1246o | 1.25 | 1.25 |
| a. | Booklet, 2 each #1255-1256, 3 each #1257-1258 | | 10.00 |
| 1259 | A445 30p Like #1246i | 1.25 | 1.25 |
| 1260 | A445 30p Like #1246n | 1.25 | 1.25 |
| 1261 | A445 30p Like #1246l | 1.25 | 1.25 |
| a. | Booklet, 3 each #1259-1260, 4 #1261 | | 10.00 |
| | Nos. 1247-1261 (15) | 18.75 | 18.75 |

No. 1246 exists imperf.

Butterflies
A456

Designs: 30p, Peacock. 32p, Small tortoiseshell. 45p, Silver-washed fritillary. 50p,
Orange-tip.

**2000, Sept. 6    Perf. 13¼x12¾**
| | | | |
|---|---|---|---|
| 1262 | A456 30p multi | .75 | .75 |
| 1263 | A456 32p multi | 1.00 | 1.00 |
| 1264 | A456 45p multi | 1.50 | 1.50 |
| 1265 | A456 50p multi | 1.75 | 1.75 |
| a. | Souvenir sheet, #1262-1265 | 6.00 | 6.00 |

Stamps from No. 1265a lack year date.

Military
Aircraft
A457

Designs: No. 1266, Bristol F.2b Mk II fighter.
No. 1267, Hawker Hurricane Mk IIc. No. 1268,
Alouette III helicopter. No. 1269, De Havilland
DH.115 Vampire T.55.

**2000, Oct. 9    Litho.    Perf. 14¾x14¼**
| | | | |
|---|---|---|---|
| 1266 | A457 30p multi | .75 | .75 |
| 1267 | A457 30p multi | .75 | .75 |
| a. | Pair, #1266-1267 | 1.50 | 1.50 |
| b. | Booklet pane, 2 each #1266-1267 | | 3.00 |
| 1268 | A457 45p multi | 1.50 | 1.50 |
| a. | Booklet pane, #1266-1268 | | 3.00 |
| 1269 | A457 45p multi | 1.50 | 1.50 |
| a. | Pair, #1268-1269 | 3.00 | 3.00 |
| b. | Booklet pane, 2 each #1268-1269 | | 6.00 |
| c. | Booklet pane, #1266-1269 | | 4.50 |
| | Booklet, #1267b, 1268a, 1269b, 1269c | | 15.00 |
| | Nos. 1266-1269 (4) | 4.50 | 4.50 |

**Coil Stamps**
**Self-Adhesive**
*Die Cut Perf. 9¼x9½*
| | | | |
|---|---|---|---|
| 1270 | A457 30p Like #1266 | 2.25 | 2.25 |
| 1271 | A457 30p Like #1267 | 2.25 | 2.25 |
| 1272 | A457 30p Like #1269 | 2.25 | 2.25 |
| 1273 | A457 30p Like #1268 | 2.25 | 2.25 |
| a. | Strip, #1270-1273 | | 9.00 |

Dept. of
Agriculture,
Cent.
A458

**2000, Nov. 14    Litho.    Perf. 13½**
| | | | |
|---|---|---|---|
| 1274 | A458 50p multi | 1.50 | 1.50 |

Christmas
A459

Designs: No. 1275, Nativity. 32p, Adoration
of the Magi. 45p, Adoration of the Shepherds.
No. 1278, Flight to Egypt.

**2000, Nov. 14    Perf. 14¼x14¾**
| | | | |
|---|---|---|---|
| 1275 | A459 30p multi | .75 | .75 |
| 1276 | A459 32p multi | 1.25 | 1.25 |
| 1277 | A459 45p multi | 1.75 | 1.75 |

## Booklet Stamp
### Self-Adhesive
### Size: 21x26mm
### *Serpentine Die Cut 11¼*

| | | | |
|---|---|---|---|
| **1278** | A459 30p multi | 1.00 | 1.00 |
| *a.* | Booklet of 24 | 24.00 | |
| | *Nos. 1275-1278 (4)* | 4.75 | 4.75 |

No. 1278 sold for £6.60.

Pets — A460

Designs: Nos. 1279, 1283, Goldfish, hearts. Nos. 1280a, 1284, Snake. Nos. 1280b, 1282, Frog, four-leaf clover. Nos. 1280c, 1285, Turtle, stars. No. 1281, Lizard, daisy.

### 2001, Jan. 24 Litho. Perf. 14¼x14¾
| | | | |
|---|---|---|---|
| **1279** | A460 30p multi | 1.25 | 1.25 |

### Souvenir Sheet
| | | | |
|---|---|---|---|
| **1280** | Sheet of 3 | 5.00 | 5.00 |
| *a.-c.* | A460 30p Any single | 1.60 | 1.60 |

### Booklet Stamps
### Size: 25x30mm
### Self-Adhesive
### *Serpentine Die Cut 12*
| | | | |
|---|---|---|---|
| **1281** | A460 30p multi | 1.50 | 1.50 |
| **1282** | A460 30p multi | 1.50 | 1.50 |
| **1283** | A460 30p multi | 1.50 | 1.50 |
| **1284** | A460 30p multi | 1.50 | 1.50 |
| **1285** | A460 30p multi | 1.50 | 1.50 |
| *a.* | Booklet, 2 each #1281-1285 | | |
| | + 10 labels | 15.00 | |
| | *Nos. 1281-1285 (5)* | 7.50 | 7.50 |

New Year 2001 (Year of the Snake), No. 1280.

Broadcasting in Ireland — A461

Designs: 30p, Camera, audience, man. 32p, Microphone, announcers. 45p, People listening to radio. 50p, Television.

### 2001, Feb. 27 Perf. 14¾x14¼
| | | | |
|---|---|---|---|
| **1286** | A461 30p multi | .75 | .75 |
| **1287** | A461 32p multi | 1.00 | 1.00 |
| **1288** | A461 45p multi | 1.50 | 1.50 |
| **1289** | A461 50p multi | 1.75 | 1.75 |
| | *Nos. 1286-1289 (4)* | 5.00 | 5.00 |

Literary Anniversaries A462

Designs: 30p, Marsh's Library, first public library in Ireland, 300th anniv. 32p, Book of Common Prayer, first book printed in Ireland, 450th anniv.

### 2001, Mar. 14 Perf. 14¼x14¾
| | | | |
|---|---|---|---|
| **1290** | A462 30p multi | .70 | .70 |
| **1291** | A462 32p multi | .75 | .75 |

Comhaltas Ceoltóirí Eirann, 50th Anniv. — A463

Musician with: No. 1292, Bagpipes. No. 1293, Tambourine. No. 1294, Flute, horiz. No. 1295, Violin, horiz.

### *Perf. 14¼x14¾, 14¾x14¼*
### 2001, Mar. 14
| | | | |
|---|---|---|---|
| **1292** | A463 30p multi | .70 | .70 |
| **1293** | A463 30p multi | .70 | .70 |
| *a.* | Pair, #1292-1293 | 1.40 | 1.40 |
| **1294** | A463 45p multi | 1.00 | 1.00 |
| **1295** | A463 45p multi | 1.00 | 1.00 |
| *a.* | Pair, #1294-1295 | 2.00 | 1.00 |
| | *Nos. 1292-1295 (4)* | 3.40 | 3.40 |

Race Cars A464

Designs: Nos. 1296, 1300, 1301, Jordan Grand Prix Formula 1. Nos. 1297, 1304, Hillman Imp, Tulip Rally. Nos. 1298, 1303, Mini Cooper S, Monte Carlo Rally. Nos. 1299, 1302, Mercedes SSK, Irish Grand Prix.

### 2001, Apr. 26 Perf. 13¾x14¼
| | | | |
|---|---|---|---|
| **1296** | A464 30p multi | .75 | .75 |
| **1297** | A464 32p multi | 1.00 | 1.00 |
| **1298** | A464 45p multi | 1.50 | 1.50 |
| **1299** | A464 £1 multi | 3.25 | 3.25 |
| | *Nos. 1296-1299 (4)* | 6.50 | 6.50 |

### Souvenir Sheet
| | | | |
|---|---|---|---|
| **1300** | A464 £2 multi | 7.00 | 7.00 |
| *a.* | With Belgica show emblem in margin | 9.00 | 9.00 |

### Booklet Stamps
### Size: 36x24mm
### Self-Adhesive
### *Serpentine Die Cut 11¾*
| | | | |
|---|---|---|---|
| **1301** | A464 30p multi | 3.25 | 3.25 |
| **1302** | A464 30p multi | 3.25 | 3.25 |
| **1303** | A464 30p multi | 3.25 | 3.25 |
| **1304** | A464 30p multi | 3.25 | 3.25 |
| *a.* | Booklet, 4 #1301, 2 each #1302-1304 | 20.00 | |
| | *Nos. 1301-1304 (4)* | 13.00 | 13.00 |

Issued: No. 1300a, 6/9/01.

Irish Heriatge in Australia A465

### 2001, May 3 Perf. 14¾x14¼
| | | | |
|---|---|---|---|
| **1305** | A465 30p Ned Kelly | 1.00 | 1.00 |
| **1306** | A465 30p Peter Lalor | 1.00 | 1.00 |
| *a.* | Pair, #1305-1306 | 2.00 | 2.00 |
| **1307** | A465 45p Settlers | 1.25 | 1.25 |
| **1308** | A465 45p Emigrants | 1.25 | 1.25 |
| *a.* | Pair, #1307-1308 | 2.50 | 2.50 |
| | *Nos. 1305-1308 (4)* | 4.50 | 4.50 |

### Souvenir Sheet
| | | | |
|---|---|---|---|
| **1309** | A465 £1 Like #1305 | 4.50 | *4.50* |

Europa A466

### 2001, May 16 Litho. Perf. 14¾x14¼
| | | | |
|---|---|---|---|
| **1310** | A466 30p Wading | .75 | .75 |
| **1311** | A466 32p Fishing | 1.25 | 1.25 |

## Europa Type of 2001
### Die Cut Perf. 9¼x9½
### 2001, May 16 Litho.
### Coil Stamps
### Self-Adhesive
| | | | |
|---|---|---|---|
| **1312** | A466 30p Wading | 1.10 | 1.10 |
| **1313** | A466 30p Fishing | 1.10 | 1.10 |
| *a.* | Strip, #1312-1313 | 2.25 | |

### Bird Types of 1997 With Added Euro Denominations
Designs: Nos. 1314, 1319A, Blackbird. 1319B, Goldcrest. 32p, Robin. 35p, Puffin. 40p, Wren. 45p, Song thrush. £1, Greenland white-fronted goose.

### *Perf. 14¼x14¾*
### 2001, June 11 Litho.
| | | | |
|---|---|---|---|
| **1314** | A403 30p multi | 1.25 | 1.25 |
| **1315** | A403 32p multi | 1.75 | 1.75 |
| **1316** | A403 35p multi | 2.00 | 2.00 |
| **1317** | A403 40p multi | 2.50 | 2.50 |
| **1318** | A403 45p multi | 3.00 | 3.00 |

### *Perf. 14¾x14¼*
| | | | |
|---|---|---|---|
| **1319** | A404 £1 multi | 4.50 | 4.50 |
| | *Nos. 1314-1319 (6)* | 15.00 | 15.00 |

### Self-Adhesive
### Coil Stamps
### Size: 21x26mm
| | | | |
|---|---|---|---|
| **1319A** | A403 30p multi | 3.75 | 3.75 |
| **1319B** | A403 30p multi | 3.75 | 3.75 |
| *c.* | Pair, #1319A-1319B | 7.50 | |

Battle of Kinsale, 400th Anniv. A467

Designs: No. 1320, Soldiers on horseback. No. 1321, Soldiers in stream. 32p, Soldiers and ramparts. 45p, View of Kinsale.

### 2001, July 10 Perf. 13½
| | | | |
|---|---|---|---|
| **1320** | A467 30p multi | .75 | .75 |
| **1321** | A467 30p multi | .75 | .75 |
| *a.* | Pair, #1320-1321 | 1.50 | 1.50 |
| **1322** | A467 32p multi | 1.25 | 1.25 |
| **1323** | A467 45p multi | 1.50 | 1.50 |
| | *Nos. 1320-1323 (4)* | 4.25 | 4.25 |

Hall of Fame Athletes A468

Designs: Nos. 1324, 1328, Padraic Carney, soccer player. Nos. 1325, 1329, Frank Cummins, hurler. Nos. 1326, 1330, Jack O'Shea, soccer player. Nos. 1327, 1331, Nicky Rackard, hurler.

### 2001, Sept. 5 Litho. Perf. 14¾x14
| | | | |
|---|---|---|---|
| **1324** | A468 30p multi | 1.00 | 1.00 |
| **1325** | A468 30p multi | 1.00 | 1.00 |
| **1326** | A468 30p multi | 1.00 | 1.00 |
| **1327** | A468 30p multi | 1.00 | 1.00 |
| *a.* | Horiz. strip, #1324-1327 | 4.00 | 4.00 |

### Booklet Stamps
### Size: 33x22mm
### Self-Adhesive
### *Serpentine Die Cut 11x11½*
| | | | |
|---|---|---|---|
| **1328** | A468 30p multi | 2.25 | 2.25 |
| **1329** | A468 30p multi | 2.25 | 2.25 |
| **1330** | A468 30p multi | 2.25 | 2.25 |
| **1331** | A468 30p multi | 2.25 | 2.25 |
| *a.* | Booklet, 2 each #1328, 1331, 3 each #1329-1330 | 22.50 | |
| | *Nos. 1324-1331 (8)* | 13.00 | 13.00 |

Sailboats — A469

Designs: No. 1332, Ruffian 23. No. 1333, Howth 17. No. 1334, 1720 Sportsboat. No. 1335, The Glen. No. 1336, Ruffian 23. No. 1337, Howth 17. No. 1338, The Glen. No. 1339, 1720 Sportsboat.

### 2001, Sept. 5 Perf. 14x14¾
| | | | |
|---|---|---|---|
| **1332** | A469 30p multi | 1.00 | 1.00 |
| **1333** | A469 32p multi | 1.00 | 1.00 |
| **1334** | A469 45p multi | 1.50 | 1.50 |
| **1335** | A469 45p multi | 1.50 | 1.50 |
| *a.* | Horiz. pair, #1334-1335 | 3.00 | 3.00 |
| | *Nos. 1332-1335 (4)* | 5.00 | 5.00 |

### Coil Stamps
### Self-Adhesive
### *Serpentine Die Cut 9½x9¼*
| | | | |
|---|---|---|---|
| **1336** | A469 30p multi | 2.25 | 2.25 |
| **1337** | A469 30p multi | 2.25 | 2.25 |
| **1338** | A469 30p multi | 2.25 | 2.25 |
| **1339** | A469 30p multi | 2.25 | 2.25 |
| *a.* | Strip of 4, #1336-1339 | 9.00 | |

### Bird Type of 1997
### *Serpentine Die Cut 11¼*
### 2001, Oct. 9 Litho.
### Booklet Stamps
### Self-Adhesive
| | | | |
|---|---|---|---|
| **1340** | A403 N Blackbird | 1.50 | 1.50 |
| **1341** | A403 N Goldcrest | 1.50 | 1.50 |
| *a.* | Booklet, 5 each #1340-1341 | 15.00 | |
| **1342** | A403 E Robin | 1.50 | 1.50 |
| *a.* | Booklet of 10 + 10 etiquettes | 15.00 | |
| **1343** | A403 W Song thrush | 3.00 | 3.00 |
| *a.* | Booklet of 10 + 10 etiquettes | 30.00 | |
| | *Nos. 1340-1343 (4)* | 7.50 | 7.50 |

Fish A470

Designs: 30p, Perch. No. 1345, Arctic char. No. 1346, Pike. 45p, Common bream.

### 2001, Oct. 9 Perf. 14¾x14
| | | | |
|---|---|---|---|
| **1344** | A470 30p multi | 1.00 | 1.00 |
| **1345** | A470 32p multi | 1.50 | 1.50 |
| **1346** | A470 32p multi | 1.50 | 1.50 |
| *a.* | Horiz. pair, #1345-1346 | 3.00 | 3.00 |
| **1347** | A470 45p multi | 2.00 | 2.00 |
| *a.* | Booklet pane, #1344-1347 | 5.00 | — |
| *b.* | Booklet pane, #1345, 1346, 2 #1347 | 7.00 | — |
| *c.* | Booklet pane, 2 each #1344, 1347 | 6.00 | — |
| | Booklet, #1347b, 1347c, 2 #1347a | 23.00 | |

No. 1347a exists with stamps in different order. The booklet contains the two different panes.

Governmental Support of Arts, 50th Anniv. — A471

### 2001, Nov. 5 Perf. 14x14¾
| | | | |
|---|---|---|---|
| **1348** | A471 50p multi | 1.50 | 1.50 |

Christmas — A472

Designs: No. 1349, Nativity. 32p, Annunciation. 45p, Presentation in the Temple. No. 1352, Madonna and Child.

### 2001, Nov. 5 Perf. 14x14¾
| | | | |
|---|---|---|---|
| **1349** | A472 30p multi | .75 | .75 |
| **1350** | A472 32p multi | 1.00 | 1.00 |
| **1351** | A472 45p multi | 1.75 | 1.75 |

## Booklet Stamp
### Size: 21x27mm
### Self-Adhesive
#### Serpentine Die Cut 11x11¼

| | | | |
|---|---|---|---|
| 1352 | A472 30p multi | 1.00 | 1.00 |
| a. | Booklet of 24 | 24.00 | |
| | Nos. 1349-1352 (4) | 4.50 | 4.50 |

No. 1352a sold for £6.60.

### 100 Cents = 1 Euro (€)

A473

### Birds (With Euro Denominations Only) — A474

Designs: 1c, Magpie. 2c, Gannet. 3c, Blue tit, horiz. 4c, Corncrake. 5c, Wood pigeon, horiz. Nos. 1358, 1370, 10c, Kingfisher. 20c, Lapwing. Nos. 1360, 1371, 1372, 38c, Blackbird. No. 1373, 38c, Goldcrest. 41c, Chaffinch. 44c, Robin. 50c, Gray heron, horiz. 51c, Roseate tern, horiz. 57c, Curlew. €1, Barnacle goose. €2, Greenland white-fronted goose, vert. €5, Pintail. €10, Shelduck, vert.

#### Perf. 14x14¾, 14¾x14

**2002, Jan. 1**     **Litho.**

| | | | |
|---|---|---|---|
| 1353 | A473 1c multi | .20 | .20 |
| 1354 | A473 2c multi | .20 | .20 |
| 1355 | A473 3c multi | .20 | .20 |
| 1356 | A473 4c multi | .20 | .20 |
| 1357 | A473 5c multi | .20 | .20 |
| 1358 | A473 10c multi | .30 | .25 |
| 1359 | A473 20c multi | .60 | .50 |
| 1360 | A473 38c multi | 1.10 | 1.00 |
| 1361 | A473 41c multi | 1.25 | 1.10 |
| 1362 | A473 44c multi | 1.40 | 1.25 |
| 1363 | A473 50c multi | 1.50 | 1.40 |
| 1364 | A473 51c multi | 1.50 | 1.40 |
| 1365 | A473 57c multi | 1.75 | 1.50 |
| 1366 | A474 €1 multi | 3.00 | 2.75 |
| 1367 | A474 €2 multi | 6.00 | 5.50 |
| 1368 | A474 €5 multi | 15.00 | 14.00 |
| 1369 | A474 €10 multi | 30.00 | 27.50 |

### Booklet Stamps
#### Size: 18x20mm
#### Perf. 14¾x14¼ on 3 Sides

| | | | |
|---|---|---|---|
| 1370 | A473 10c multi | .75 | .75 |
| 1371 | A473 38c multi | 1.75 | 1.75 |
| a. | Booklet pane, #1370, 5 #1371 | 8.75 | — |
| | Booklet, #1371a | 8.75 | |

### Coil Stamps
#### Size: 21x26mm
#### Self-Adhesive
#### Serpentine Die Cut 11x11¼

| | | | |
|---|---|---|---|
| 1372 | A473 38c multi | 5.00 | 5.00 |
| 1373 | A473 38c multi | 5.00 | 5.00 |
| a. | Pair, #1372-1373 | 12.50 | 12.50 |
| | Nos. 1353-1373 (21) | 76.90 | 71.65 |

### Introduction of the Euro A475

Designs: 38c, 1 euro coin introduced in 2002. 41c, 50p coin used from 1971-2001. 57c, 1p coin used from 1928-71.

**2002, Jan. 1**   **Litho.**   **Perf. 14¾x14¼**

| | | | |
|---|---|---|---|
| 1374 | A475 38c multi | 1.10 | 1.10 |
| 1375 | A475 41c multi | 1.25 | 1.25 |
| 1376 | A475 57c multi | 1.75 | 1.75 |
| | Nos. 1374-1376 (3) | 4.10 | 4.10 |

### Toys — A476

Designs: Nos. 1377, 1379, Teddy bear. Nos. 1378a, 1381, Rocking horse. Nos. 1378b, 1382, Wooden locomotive. Nos. 1378c, 1380, Doll. No. 1383, Blocks.

**2002, Jan. 22**     **Perf. 14¼x14¾**

| | | | |
|---|---|---|---|
| 1377 | A476 38c multi | 1.25 | 1.25 |

### Souvenir Sheet
#### Perf. 14¼x14¾ on 3 or 4 Sides

| | | | |
|---|---|---|---|
| 1378 | Sheet of 3 | 6.00 | 6.00 |
| a.-c. | A476 38c Any single | 2.00 | 2.00 |

### Booklet Stamps
#### Self-Adhesive
#### Size: 21x27mm
#### Serpentine Die Cut 11¼

| | | | |
|---|---|---|---|
| 1379 | A476 38c multi | 1.10 | 1.10 |
| 1380 | A476 38c multi | 1.10 | 1.10 |
| 1381 | A476 38c multi | 1.10 | 1.10 |
| 1382 | A476 38c multi | 1.10 | 1.10 |
| 1383 | A476 38c multi | 1.10 | 1.10 |
| a. | Booklet of 10, 2 each #1379-1383, + 10 labels | 11.00 | |

New Year 2002 (Year of the Horse), No. 1378.

Nos. 1379-1383 (5)    5.50   5.50

### Steeplechasing in Ireland, 250th Anniv. — A477

**2002, Mar. 12**     **Perf. 14¾x14¼**

| | | | |
|---|---|---|---|
| 1384 | A477 38c Arkle | 1.25 | 1.25 |
| 1385 | A477 38c L'Escargot | 1.25 | 1.25 |
| 1386 | A477 38c Dawn Run | 1.25 | 1.25 |
| 1387 | A477 38c Istabraq | 1.25 | 1.25 |
| a. | Horiz. strip of 4, #1384-1387 | 5.00 | 5.00 |

### Scouting A478

Designs: No. 1388, Scout with peg and mallet. No. 1389, Scouts and leader around campfire. No. 1390, Scouts on hike. No. 1391, Scouts kayaking.

**2002, Mar. 12**

| | | | |
|---|---|---|---|
| 1388 | A478 41c multi | 1.25 | 1.25 |
| 1389 | A478 41c multi | 1.25 | 1.25 |
| a. | Horiz. pair, #1388-1389 | 2.50 | 2.50 |
| 1390 | A478 57c multi | 1.75 | 1.75 |
| 1391 | A478 57c multi | 1.75 | 1.75 |
| a. | Horiz. pair, #1390-1391 | 3.50 | 3.50 |
| | Nos. 1388-1391 (4) | 6.00 | 6.00 |

### Bird Type of 2002

Designs: No. 1395, Chaffinch. No. 1396, Goldcrest. 44c, Robin. 47c, Kestrel, horiz. 55c, Oystercatcher. 57c, Song thrush. 60c, Jay, horiz.

**2002**   **Litho.**   **Perf. 14¾x14**

| | | | |
|---|---|---|---|
| 1392 | A473 47c multi | 1.40 | 1.40 |
| 1393 | A473 55c multi | 1.60 | 1.60 |
| 1394 | A473 60c multi | 2.00 | 2.00 |

### Self-Adhesive
#### Serpentine Die Cut 11x11¼
#### Size: 21x26mm

| | | | |
|---|---|---|---|
| 1395 | A473 41c multi | 3.00 | 3.00 |
| 1396 | A473 41c multi | 3.00 | 3.00 |
| a. | Coil pair, #1395-1396 | 6.00 | |
| b. | Booklet of 10, 5 each #1395-1396 | 30.00 | |

### Booklet Stamps

| | | | |
|---|---|---|---|
| 1397 | A473 44c multi | 1.40 | 1.40 |
| a. | Booklet of 10 | 14.00 | |

| | | | |
|---|---|---|---|
| 1398 | A473 57c multi | 1.75 | 1.75 |
| a. | Booklet of 10 | 17.50 | |
| | Nos. 1392-1398 (7) | 14.15 | 14.15 |

Issued: Nos. 1395-1398, 4/2. Nos. 1392-1394, 6/17.
Compare Nos. 1395-1396 with Nos. 1433-1434.

### Mammals A479

Designs: 41c, Meles meles. 50c, €5, Lutra lutra. 57c, Sciurus vulgaris, vert. €1, Erinaceus europaeus, vert.

#### Perf. 14¾x14¼, 14¼x14¾

**2002, Apr. 23**     **Litho.**

| | | | |
|---|---|---|---|
| 1399 | A479 41c multi | 1.25 | 1.25 |
| 1400 | A479 50c multi | 1.50 | 1.50 |
| 1401 | A479 57c multi | 1.75 | 1.75 |
| 1402 | A479 €1 multi | 3.00 | 3.00 |
| | Nos. 1399-1402 (4) | 7.50 | 7.50 |

### Souvenir Sheet

| | | | |
|---|---|---|---|
| 1403 | A479 €5 multi | 15.00 | 15.00 |

### Europa A480

Designs: Nos. 1404, 1406, Clown. Nos. 1405, 1407, Equestrian act.

**2002, May 14**   **Litho.**   **Perf. 14¾x14**

| | | | |
|---|---|---|---|
| 1404 | A480 41c multi | 1.25 | 1.25 |
| 1405 | A480 44c multi | 1.40 | 1.40 |

### Coil Stamps
#### Size: 34x23mm
#### Self-Adhesive
#### Die Cut Perf. 9¼x9½

| | | | |
|---|---|---|---|
| 1406 | A480 41c multi | 1.25 | 1.25 |
| 1407 | A480 41c multi | 1.25 | 1.25 |
| a. | Horiz. pair, #1406-1407 | 2.50 | 2.50 |
| | Nos. 1404-1407 (4) | 5.15 | 5.15 |

### Soccer Stars A481

Designs: Nos. 1408, 1415, Packie Bonner. Nos. 1409, 1412, Roy Keane, vert. Nos. 1410, 1413, Paul McGrath, vert. Nos. 1411, 1414, David O'Leary, vert.

**2002, May 14**   **Perf. 14¾x14, 14x14¾**

| | | | |
|---|---|---|---|
| 1408 | A481 41c multi | 1.25 | 1.25 |
| 1409 | A481 41c multi | 1.25 | 1.25 |
| 1410 | A481 41c multi | 1.25 | 1.25 |
| 1411 | A481 41c multi | 1.25 | 1.25 |
| b. | Vert. strip of 3, #1409-1411 | 5.00 | 5.00 |

### Booklet Stamps
#### Sizes: 23x34, 34x23mm
#### Self-Adhesive
#### Serpentine Die Cut 11½x11¾, 11¾x11½

| | | | |
|---|---|---|---|
| 1412 | A481 41c multi | 1.50 | 1.50 |
| 1413 | A481 41c multi | 1.50 | 1.50 |
| 1414 | A481 41c multi | 1.50 | 1.50 |
| 1415 | A481 41c multi | 1.50 | 1.50 |
| a. | Booklet, 3 #1412-1413, 2 #1414-1415 | 15.00 | |

### Canonization of St. Pio of Pietrelcina (1887-1968) A482

**2002, June 17**   **Litho.**   **Perf. 14x14¾**

| | | | |
|---|---|---|---|
| 1416 | A482 41c multi | 2.00 | 2.00 |

### Brian Ború, 1000th Anniv of High Kingship A483

Designs: 41c, Leading troops into battle. 44c, Commanding ships. 57c, On throne. €1, Decreeing Armagh as the primacy of the Irish church.

**2002, July 9**     **Perf. 14¾x14**

| | | | |
|---|---|---|---|
| 1417 | A483 41c multi | 1.25 | 1.25 |
| 1418 | A483 44c multi | 1.50 | 1.50 |
| 1419 | A483 57c multi | 1.75 | 1.75 |
| 1420 | A483 €1 multi | 3.00 | 3.00 |
| | Nos. 1417-1420 (4) | 7.50 | 7.50 |

### Bird Type of 2002

Designs: No. 1421, Goldcrest. No. 1422, 36c, Wren. No. 1423, Chaffinch.

#### Perf. 14x14¾ on 3 Sides

**2002, Aug. 6**     **Litho.**

### Booklet Stamps

| | | | |
|---|---|---|---|
| 1421 | A473 41c multi | 1.25 | 1.25 |
| a. | Booklet pane of 10, 5 each #1361, 1421 | 12.50 | — |
| | Booklet, #1421a | 12.50 | |

#### Size: 18x21mm
#### Perf. 14¾x14¼ on 3 Sides

| | | | |
|---|---|---|---|
| 1422 | A473 36c multi | 1.25 | 1.25 |
| 1423 | A473 41c multi | 1.50 | 1.50 |
| a. | Booklet pane of 5, #1422, 4 #1423 + label | 11.50 | — |
| | Booklet, #1423a | 11.50 | |

### Paintings in National Gallery A484

Designs: No. 1424, Before the Start, by Jack B. Yeats. No. 1425, The Conjuror, by Nathaniel Hone. No. 1426, The Colosseum and Arch of Constantine, Rome, by Giovanni Paolo Panini. No. 1427, The Gleaners, by Jules Breton.

**2002, Aug. 29**     **Perf. 14¾x14**

| | | | |
|---|---|---|---|
| 1424 | A484 41c multi | 1.25 | 1.25 |
| a. | Booklet pane of 4 | 5.00 | |
| 1425 | A484 41c multi | 1.25 | 1.25 |
| a. | Booklet pane of 4 | 5.00 | |
| 1426 | A484 41c multi | 1.25 | 1.25 |
| a. | Booklet pane of 4 | 5.00 | |
| 1427 | A484 41c multi | 1.25 | 1.25 |
| a. | Horiz. strip, #1424-1427 | 5.00 | 4.00 |
| b. | Booklet pane of 4 | 5.00 | |
| | Booklet, #1424a, 1425a, 1426a, 1427b | 20.00 | |

### Archbishop Thomas Croke (1823-1902) A485

**2002, Sept. 17**     **Perf. 14x14¾**

| | | | |
|---|---|---|---|
| 1428 | A485 44c multi | 1.50 | 1.50 |

### Hall of Fame Athletes Type of 2001

Designs: No. 1429, Peter McDermott, soccer player. No. 1430, Jimmy Smyth, hurler.

No. 1431, Matt Connor, soccer player. No. 1432, Seanie Duggan, hurler.

**2002, Sept. 17**     *Perf. 14¾x14*
| | | | |
|---|---|---|---|
| 1429 | A468 41c multi | 1.25 | 1.25 |
| 1430 | A468 41c multi | 1.25 | 1.25 |
| 1431 | A468 41c multi | 1.25 | 1.25 |
| 1432 | A468 41c multi | 1.25 | 1.25 |
| a. | Horiz. strip, #1429-1432 | 5.00 | 5.00 |

### Bird Type of 2002 Redrawn

Designs: No. 1433, Chaffinch. No. 1434, Goldcrest

*Serpentine Die Cut 11x11¼*
**2002, Oct. 17**     *Photo.*

#### Coil Stamps
#### Self-Adhesive
| | | | |
|---|---|---|---|
| 1433 | A473 41c multi | 3.75 | 3.75 |
| 1434 | A473 41c multi | 3.75 | 3.75 |
| a. | Coil pair, #1433-1434 | 7.50 | |

Text appears grayer on Nos. 1433-1434 than on Nos. 1395-1396. On No. 1433, the second "h" of "Chaffinch" touches the branch, while it does not touch on No. 1395. On No. 1434, the points of the pine needles at the bottom of the stamp are shown, while they are cut off on No. 1396.

Irish Rock Musicians A486

Designs: Nos. 1435, 1439, U2. Nos. 1436, 1440, Phil Lynott. Nos. 1437, 1441, Van Morrison. Nos. 1438, 1442, Rory Gallagher.

**2002, Oct. 17**   *Litho.*   *Perf. 13¼x12¾*
| | | | |
|---|---|---|---|
| 1435 | A486 41c multi | 1.25 | 1.25 |
| 1436 | A486 41c multi | 1.25 | 1.25 |
| a. | Horiz. pair, #1435-1436 | 2.50 | 2.50 |
| 1437 | A486 57c multi | 1.75 | 1.75 |
| 1438 | A486 57c multi | 1.75 | 1.75 |
| a. | Horiz. pair, #1437-1438 | 3.50 | 3.50 |
| | Nos. 1435-1438 (4) | 6.00 | 6.00 |

#### Souvenir Sheets
#### Perf. 12¾x13¼
| | | | |
|---|---|---|---|
| 1439 | A486 €2 multi | 6.00 | 6.00 |
| 1440 | A486 €2 multi | 6.00 | 6.00 |
| 1441 | A486 €2 multi | 6.00 | 6.00 |
| 1442 | A486 €2 multi | 6.00 | 6.00 |

Christmas — A487

Scenes from *Les Très Riches Heures du Duc de Berry*: No. 1443, Adoration of the Magi. 44c, The Annunciation. 57c, Angels Announcing Birth to Shepherds. No. 1446, Adoration of the Shepherds.

**2002, Nov. 7**   *Litho.*   *Perf. 14¼x14¾*
| | | | |
|---|---|---|---|
| 1443 | A487 41c multi | 1.25 | 1.25 |
| 1444 | A487 44c multi | 1.40 | 1.40 |
| 1445 | A487 57c multi | 1.90 | 1.90 |

#### Booklet Stamp
#### Self-Adhesive
#### Size: 21x27mm
*Serpentine Die Cut 11x11¼*
| | | | |
|---|---|---|---|
| 1446 | A487 41c multi | 2.00 | 2.00 |
| a. | Booklet pane of 24 | 47.50 | |
| | Nos. 1443-1446 (4) | 6.55 | 6.55 |

No. 1446a sold for €9.43.

### Bird Type of 2002

Designs: 50c, Puffin. 75c, Ringed plover, horiz.. 95c, Sparrowhawk, horiz.

**2003, Jan. 6**   *Litho.*   *Perf. 14¾x14*
| | | | |
|---|---|---|---|
| 1447 | A473 75c multi | 2.25 | 2.25 |
| 1448 | A473 95c multi | 3.00 | 3.00 |

---

#### Booklet Stamp
#### Self-Adhesive
#### Size: 21x27mm
*Serpentine Die Cut 11x11¼*
| | | | |
|---|---|---|---|
| 1449 | A473 50c multi | 1.50 | 1.50 |
| a. | Booklet pane of 10 + 10 etiquettes | 15.00 | |

Baby Animals — A488

Designs: Nos. 1450, 1452, Puppies. Nos. 1451a, 1454, Goats. Nos. 1451b, 1453, Chicks. Nos. 1451c, 1455, Kittens. No. 1456, Rabbits.

**2003, Jan. 28**     *Perf. 14x14¾*
| | | | |
|---|---|---|---|
| 1450 | A488 41c multi | 1.25 | 1.25 |

#### Souvenir Sheet
#### Perf. 14x14¾ on 3 or 4 Sides
| | | | |
|---|---|---|---|
| 1451 | Sheet of 3 | 4.50 | 4.50 |
| a.-c. | A488 50c Any single | 1.50 | 1.50 |

#### Booklet Stamps
#### Size: 22x28mm
#### Self-Adhesive
*Serpentine Die Cut 11x11¼*
| | | | |
|---|---|---|---|
| 1452 | A488 41c multi | 1.25 | 1.25 |
| 1453 | A488 41c multi | 1.25 | 1.25 |
| 1454 | A488 41c multi | 1.25 | 1.25 |
| 1455 | A488 41c multi | 1.25 | 1.25 |
| 1456 | A488 41c multi | 1.25 | 1.25 |
| a. | Booklet pane of 10, 2 each #1452-1456 + 10 labels | 12.50 | |
| | Nos. 1452-1456 (5) | 6.25 | 6.25 |

New Year 2003 (Year of the Goat), No. 1451.

St. Patrick's Day — A489

Designs: Nos. 1457, 1460, St. Patrick. Nos. 1458, 1461, St. Patrick's Day Parade, Dublin. Nos. 1459, 1462, St. Patrick's Day Parade, New York.

**2003, Feb. 28**     *Perf. 14x14¾*
| | | | |
|---|---|---|---|
| 1457 | A489 41c multi | 1.25 | 1.25 |
| a. | Booklet pane of 4 | 5.00 | |
| 1458 | A489 50c multi | 1.50 | 1.50 |
| a. | Booklet pane of 4 | 6.00 | |
| 1459 | A489 57c multi | 1.75 | 1.75 |
| a. | Booklet pane of 4 | 7.00 | |
| b. | Booklet pane of 3, #1457-1459 | 4.50 | |
| | Complete booklet, #1457a, 1458a, 1459a, 1459b | 22.50 | |
| | Nos. 1457-1459 (3) | 4.50 | 4.50 |

#### Booklet Stamps
#### Self-Adhesive
#### Size: 22x32mm
*Serpentine Die Cut 11¼*
| | | | |
|---|---|---|---|
| 1460 | A489 41c multi | 1.25 | 1.25 |
| a. | Booklet pane of 10 | 12.50 | |
| 1461 | A489 50c multi | 1.50 | 1.50 |
| a. | Booklet pane of 10 | 15.00 | |
| 1462 | A489 57c multi | 1.75 | 1.75 |
| a. | Booklet pane of 10 | 17.50 | |
| | Nos. 1460-1462 (3) | 4.50 | 4.50 |

Beetles A490

Designs: 41c, €2, Seven-spotted ladybug. 50c, Great diving beetle. 57c, Leaf beetle. €1, Green tiger beetle.

---

**2003, Apr. 1**     *Perf. 13¾x14*
| | | | |
|---|---|---|---|
| 1463 | A490 41c multi | 1.25 | 1.25 |
| 1464 | A490 50c multi | 1.50 | 1.50 |
| 1465 | A490 57c multi | 1.75 | 1.75 |
| 1466 | A490 €1 multi | 3.00 | 3.00 |
| | Nos. 1463-1466 (4) | 7.50 | 7.50 |

#### Souvenir Sheet
| | | | |
|---|---|---|---|
| 1467 | A490 €2 multi | 6.00 | 6.00 |

European Year of People With Disabilities A491

**2003, May 9**     *Perf. 14¾x14*
| | | | |
|---|---|---|---|
| 1468 | A491 41c multi | 1.25 | 1.25 |

Europa — A492

Posters by Paul Henry: 41c, Dingle Peninsula (Ireland for Holidays). 57c, Connemara (Ireland This Year).

**2003, May 9**     *Perf. 14x14¾*
| | | | |
|---|---|---|---|
| 1469 | A492 41c multi | 1.25 | 1.25 |
| 1470 | A492 57c multi | 1.75 | 1.75 |

11th Special Olympics World Summer Games A493

Designs: 41c, Competitors waving. 50c, Swimmer. 57c, Sprinter. €1, Shot put.

**2003, May 20**     *Perf. 13¾x14*
| | | | |
|---|---|---|---|
| 1471 | A493 41c multi | 1.25 | 1.25 |
| 1472 | A493 50c multi | 1.50 | 1.50 |
| 1473 | A493 57c multi | 1.75 | 1.75 |
| 1474 | A493 €1 multi | 3.00 | 3.00 |
| | Nos. 1471-1474 (4) | 7.50 | 7.50 |

Ford Motor Company, Cent. A494

**2003, June 30**   *Litho.*   *Perf. 14¼x14*
| | | | |
|---|---|---|---|
| 1475 | A494 41c multi | 1.25 | 1.25 |

Gordon Bennett Race in Ireland, Cent. A495

Race map and 1903 automobiles: Nos. 1476, 1483, Napier. Nos. 1477, 1482, Mercedes. Nos. 1478, 1481, Mors. Nos. 1479, 1480, Winton.

**2003, June 30**     *Perf. 14¼x14*
| | | | |
|---|---|---|---|
| 1476 | A495 41c multi | 1.25 | 1.25 |
| 1477 | A495 41c multi | 1.25 | 1.25 |
| 1478 | A495 41c multi | 1.25 | 1.25 |
| 1479 | A495 41c multi | 1.25 | 1.25 |
| a. | Horiz. strip of 4, #1476-1479 | 5.00 | 5.00 |

---

#### Coil Stamps
#### Size: 33x22mm
#### Self-Adhesive
*Serpentine Die Cut 11¼*
| | | | |
|---|---|---|---|
| 1480 | A495 41c multi | 1.25 | 1.25 |
| 1481 | A495 41c multi | 1.25 | 1.25 |
| 1482 | A495 41c multi | 1.25 | 1.25 |
| 1483 | A495 41c multi | 1.25 | 1.25 |
| a. | Strip of 4, #1480-1483 | 5.00 | |

Rebellion of 1803, Bicent. A496

Designs: 41c, Robert Emmet (1778-1803), rebellion leader. 50c, Thomas Russell (1767-1803), rebellion leader. 57c, Anne Devlin (1780-1851), assistant to Emmet.

**2003, July 29**   *Litho.*   *Perf. 14¾x14*
| | | | |
|---|---|---|---|
| 1484 | A496 41c multi | 1.25 | 1.25 |
| 1485 | A496 50c multi | 1.50 | 1.50 |
| 1486 | A496 57c multi | 1.75 | 1.75 |
| | Nos. 1484-1486 (3) | 4.50 | 4.50 |

Powered Flight, Cent. A497

Designs: 41c, First Irish-built monoplane, built by Harry Ferguson, 1909. 50c, John Alcock & Arthur Brown's non-stop transatlantic flight, 1919. No. 1489, Lillian Bland, first female aircraft designer, 1910. Nos. 1490, 1491, Wright Flyer.

**2003, July 29**
| | | | |
|---|---|---|---|
| 1487 | A497 41c multi | 1.25 | 1.25 |
| 1488 | A497 50c multi | 1.50 | 1.50 |
| 1489 | A497 57c multi | 1.75 | 1.75 |
| 1490 | A497 57c multi | 1.75 | 1.75 |
| a. | Horiz. pair, #1489-1490 | 3.50 | 3.50 |

#### Souvenir Sheet
| | | | |
|---|---|---|---|
| 1491 | A497 €5 multi | 15.00 | 15.00 |

### Bird Type of 2002

Designs: 7c, Stonechat. 48c, No. 1494, Peregrine falcon. No. 1495, Pied wagtail.

**2003, Aug. 25**   *Litho.*   *Perf. 14x14¾*
| | | | |
|---|---|---|---|
| 1492 | A473 7c multi | .20 | .20 |
| 1493 | A473 48c multi | 1.50 | 1.50 |

#### Self-Adhesive
*Serpentine Die Cut 11x11¼*
| | | | |
|---|---|---|---|
| 1494 | A473 N multi | 1.50 | 1.50 |
| 1495 | A473 N multi | 1.50 | 1.50 |
| a. | Coil pair, #1494-1495 | 3.00 | |
| b. | Booklet pane, 5 each #1494-1495 | 15.00 | |

Nos. 1494-1495 each sold for 48c on day of issue.

### National Gallery Paintings Type of 2002

Designs: No. 1496, Self-portrait as Timanthes, by James Barry. No. 1497, Man Writing a Letter, by Gabriel Metsu. No. 1498, Woman Reading a Letter, by Metsu. No. 1499, Woman Seen From the Back, by Antoine Watteau.

**2003, Sept. 9**     *Perf. 14x14¾*
| | | | |
|---|---|---|---|
| 1496 | A484 48c multi | 1.50 | 1.50 |
| a. | Booklet pane of 4 | 6.00 | — |
| 1497 | A484 48c multi | 1.50 | 1.50 |
| 1498 | A484 48c multi | 1.50 | 1.50 |
| a. | Booklet pane, 2 each #1497-1498 | 6.00 | — |
| 1499 | A484 48c multi | 1.50 | 1.50 |
| a. | Horiz. strip, #1496-1499 | 6.00 | 6.00 |
| b. | Booklet pane of 4 | 6.00 | — |
| | Complete booklet, #1496a, 1499b, 2 #1498a | 20.00 | |

Frank O'Connor (1903-66), Writer — A498

**2003, Sept. 16   Litho.   Perf. 14x14¼**
1500  A498  50c multi          1.50  1.50

Ernest Thomas Sinton Walton (1903-95), 1951 Nobel Laureate in Physics — A499

**2003, Sept. 16**
1501  A499  57c multi          1.75  1.75

Mariners A500

Designs: Nos. 1502, 1507, Argentine Admiral William (Guillermo) Brown (1777-1857). Nos. 1503, 1506, 1510, American Commodore John Barry (1745-1803). Nos. 1504, 1508, Captain Robert Halpin (1836-94). Nos. 1505, 1509, Captain Richard Roberts (1803-41).

**Perf. 14¼x14 (#1502-1505, 1510)**
**2003, Sept. 30**
1502  A500  48c multi          1.50  1.50
1503  A500  48c multi          1.50  1.50
  a.    Horiz. pair, #1502-1503   3.00  3.00
1504  A500  57c multi          1.75  1.75
1505  A500  57c multi          1.75  1.75
  a.    Horiz. pair, #1504-1505   3.50  3.50

**Coil Stamps**
**Self-Adhesive (#1506-1509)**
**Size: 33x22mm (#1506-1509)**
**Serpentine Die Cut 11x11¼ (#1506-1509)**
1506  A500  48c multi          1.50  1.50
1507  A500  48c multi          1.50  1.50
1508  A500  48c multi          1.50  1.50
1509  A500  48c multi          1.50  1.50
  a.    Horiz. strip, #1506-1509   6.00  6.00
      Nos. 1502-1509 (8)       12.50 12.50

**Souvenir Sheet**
1510  A500  €5 multi          15.00 15.00

**Bird Type of 2002**

Designs: 4c, Corncrake. Nos. 1511, 1515, Pied wagtail. Nos. 1513, 1514, Peregrine falcon.

**Perf. 14x14¾ on 3 Sides**
**2003, Sept. 30                  Litho.**
**Booklet Stamps (#1511-1513)**
1511  A473  48c multi          1.50  1.50
  a.    Booklet pane, 5 each #1493,
        1511                    15.00   —
      Complete booklet, #1511a  15.00

**Size: 18x20mm**
**Perf. 15x14 on 3 Sides**
1512  A473  4c multi           .20   .20
1513  A473  48c multi          1.50  1.50
  a.    Booklet pane, 2 #1512, 4
        #1513                   6.50
      Complete booklet, #1513a  6.50
      Nos. 1511-1513 (3)        3.20  3.20

**Self-Adhesive**
**Size: 20x25mm**
**Serpentine Die Cut 11x11¼**
1514  A473  48c multi          1.50  1.50
1515  A473  48c multi          1.50  1.50
  a.    Coil pair, #1514-1515   3.00
  b.    Booklet pane, 5 each #1514-
        1515                    15.00

Examples of Nos. 1514-1515 from booklets are on a heavy, opaque paper, while those from coils are on a thinner, semi-transparent paper.

Election of Pope John Paul II, 25th Anniv. — A501

Pope John Paul II: 48c, In Ireland, 1979. 50c, At Vatican. 57c, At United Nations.

**2003, Oct. 16                  Perf. 14x14¾**
1516  A501  48c multi          1.50  1.50
1517  A501  50c multi          1.50  1.50
1518  A501  57c multi          1.75  1.75
      Nos. 1516-1518 (3)        4.75  4.75

Christmas A502

Designs: No. 1519, Flight into Egypt. 50c, Angel. 57c, Three Kings. No. 1522, Nativity.

**2003, Nov. 10                  Perf. 13¼**
1519  A502  48c multi          1.50  1.50
**Size: 37x27mm**
**Perf. 14¾x14**
1520  A502  50c multi          1.50  1.50
1521  A502  57c multi          1.75  1.75
      Nos. 1519-1521 (3)        4.75  4.75

**Booklet Stamp**
**Self-Adhesive**
**Size: 26x21mm**
**Serpentine Die Cut 11¼**
1522  A502  48c multi          1.50  1.50
  a.    Booklet pane of 24      36.00

No. 1522a sold for €11.04.

**Bird Type of 2002**

Designs: Nos. 1523, 1525, Puffin. Nos. 1524, 1526, Song thrush.

**2004, Jan. 5   Litho.   Perf. 14x14¾**
1523  A473  60c multi          1.90  1.90
1524  A473  65c multi          2.00  2.00

**Booklet Stamps**
**Self-Adhesive**
**Size: 21x26mm**
**Serpentine Die Cut 11x11¼**
1525  A473  60c multi          1.90  1.90
  a.    Booklet pane of 10      19.00
1526  A473  65c multi          2.00  2.00
  a.    Booklet pane of 10      20.00

Irish Presidency of the European Union — A503

**2004, Jan. 15                  Perf. 14x14¾**
1527  A503  48c multi          1.50  1.50

Love — A504

Designs: Nos. 1528, 1529a, 1530, Chimpanzees. Nos. 1529b, 1531, Panda. Nos. 1529c, 1532, Koala. No. 1533, Hippopotamus.

**2004, Jan. 30                  Perf. 14x14¾**
1528  A504  48c multi          1.50  1.50

**Souvenir Sheet**
**Perf. 14x14¾ on 3 or 4 Sides**
1529  Sheet of 3              6.00  6.00
  a.-c.  A504 60c Any single    1.90  1.90

**Booklet Stamps**
**Self-Adhesive**
**Size: 21x26mm**
**Serpentine Die Cut 11x11¼**
1530  A504  48c multi          1.50  1.50
1531  A504  48c multi          1.50  1.50
1532  A504  48c multi          1.50  1.50
1533  A504  48c multi          1.50  1.50
  a.    Booklet pane, 3 each #1530-
        1531, 2 each #1532-1533 +
        10 labels               15.00
      Nos. 1530-1533 (4)        6.00  6.00

New Year 2004 (Year of the Monkey), No. 1529.

Abbey Theater, Dublin, Cent. — A505

**2004, Feb. 27                  Perf. 14x14¾**
1534  A505  48c multi          1.50  1.50

St. Patrick's Day — A506

**2004, Feb. 27**
1535  A506  65c multi          2.00  2.00

Antarctic Expedition of Ernest Shackleton, 90th Anniv. A507

Designs: No. 1536, Ship's stern, expedition members, dogs. No. 1537, Ship's bow, expedition members, dogs. Nos. 1538, 1540a, Man emerging from tent. Nos. 1539, 1540b, Tents, expedition members.

**2004, Mar. 19                  Perf. 13½**
1536  A507  48c multi          1.50  1.50
1537  A507  48c multi          1.50  1.50
  a.    Horiz. pair, #1536-1537   3.00  3.00
  b.    Booklet pane, 2 #1537a   6.00
1538  A507  65c multi          2.00  2.00
1539  A507  65c multi          2.00  2.00
  a.    Horiz. pair, #1538-1539   4.00  4.00
  b.    Booklet pane, 2 #1539a   8.00
  c.    Booklet pane, #1537a, 1539a   7.00   —
      Complete booklet, #1537b,
      1539b, 2 #1539c           28.00
      Nos. 1536-1539 (4)        7.00  7.00

**Souvenir Sheet**
**Perf. 13½ on 2 or 3 Sides**
1540  Sheet of 2              6.25  6.25
  a.-b.  A507 €1 Either single   3.00  3.00

No. 1539c exists with two different margins, both of which are in complete booklet.

FIFA (Fédération Internationale de Football Association), Cent. A508

**2004, Mar. 31                  Perf. 13½x13**
1541  A508  60c multi          1.90  1.90

Expansion of the European Union A509

**2004, May 1   Litho.   Perf. 14¾x14**
1542  A509  65c multi          4.00  4.00

Europa — A510

Designs: 48c, Ross Castle. 65c, Cliffs of Moher.

**2004, May 11                  Perf. 14x13¾**
1543  A510  48c multi          1.50  1.50
1544  A510  65c multi          2.00  2.00

Ducks A511

Designs: 48c, Tufted duck. 60c, Red-breasted merganser. 65c, Gadwall. €1, Garganey.

**2004, May 11                  Perf. 13x13¼**
1545  A511  48c multi          1.50  1.50
1546  A511  60c multi          1.90  1.90
1547  A511  65c multi          2.00  2.00
1548  A511  €1 multi           3.00  3.00
  a.    Souvenir sheet, #1545-1548   8.75  8.75
      Nos. 1545-1548 (4)        8.40  8.40

Intl. Year of the Family, 10th Anniv. — A512

**2004, May 15   Litho.   Perf. 13¼x13**
1549  A512  65c multi          2.00  2.00

Winning Artwork in Texaco Children's Art Competition A513

Designs: 48c, Untitled work (Frog), by Daire Lee. 60c, Marmalade Cat, by Cian Colman.

65c, Ralleshin Dipditch, by Daire O'Rourke.
€1, Fish on a Dish, by Ailish Fitzpatrick, horiz.

| | | | |
|---|---|---|---|
| **2004, May 19** | | **Perf. 14x14¾** | |
| 1550 | A513 48c multi | 1.50 | 1.50 |
| 1551 | A513 60c multi | 1.90 | 1.90 |
| 1552 | A513 65c multi | 2.00 | 2.00 |
| | **Perf. 14¾x14** | | |
| 1553 | A513 €1 multi | 3.00 | 3.00 |
| | *Nos. 1550-1553 (4)* | 8.40 | 8.40 |

Publication of *Ulysses*, by James Joyce, Cent. — A514

Designs: 48c, Caricature of Joyce, by Tullio Percoli. 65c, Photograph of Joyce.

| | | | |
|---|---|---|---|
| **2004, June 16** | **Litho.** | **Perf. 13¼** | |
| 1554 | A514 48c multi | 1.50 | 1.50 |
| 1555 | A514 65c multi | 2.00 | 2.00 |

Irish College, Paris, France — A515

| | | | |
|---|---|---|---|
| **2004, June 26** | | **Perf. 14x14¾** | |
| 1556 | A515 65c multi | 2.00 | 2.00 |

Inauguration of LUAS Tram System, Dublin A516

| | | | |
|---|---|---|---|
| **2004, June 30** | | **Perf. 13¼** | |
| 1557 | A516 48c Environment | 1.50 | 1.50 |
| 1558 | A516 48c Accessibility | 1.50 | 1.50 |
| *a.* | Horiz. pair, #1557-1558 | 3.00 | 3.00 |

2004 Summer Olympics, Athens A517

Olympic flame, rings and: 48c, Javelin thrower. 60c, Myron's Discobolus.

| | | | |
|---|---|---|---|
| **2004, July 22** | | **Perf. 13¾x14** | |
| 1559 | A517 48c multi | 1.50 | 1.50 |
| 1560 | A517 60c multi | 1.90 | 1.90 |

Camogie, Cent. A518

Camogie players and: No. 1561, Camogie Association emblem. No. 1562, Cup.

| | | | |
|---|---|---|---|
| **2004, July 22** | | **Perf. 14¾x14** | |
| 1561 | A518 48c multi | 1.50 | 1.50 |
| 1562 | A518 48c multi | 1.50 | 1.50 |
| *a.* | Horiz. pair, #1561-1562 | 3.00 | 3.00 |

Flowers — A519

Designs: 4c, Common dog-violet. 5c, Dandelion. Nos. 1565, 1571, Primrose. Nos. 1569A, 1570, Daisy. 60c, Hawthorn. 65c, Bluebell. €2, Lords-and-ladies. €5, Dog-rose, horiz.

| | | | |
|---|---|---|---|
| | **Perf. 14x14¾, 14¾x14** | | |
| **2004, Sept. 9** | | **Litho.** | |
| 1563 | A519 4c multi | .20 | .20 |
| 1564 | A519 5c multi | .20 | .20 |
| 1565 | A519 48c multi | 1.50 | 1.50 |
| 1566 | A519 60c multi | 1.90 | 1.90 |
| 1567 | A519 65c multi | 2.00 | 2.00 |
| | **Size: 23x44mm** | | |
| 1568 | A519 €2 multi | 6.00 | 6.00 |
| | **Size: 44x23mm** | | |
| 1569 | A519 €5 multi | 15.00 | 15.00 |
| | *Nos. 1563-1569 (7)* | 26.80 | 26.80 |
| | **Booklet Stamp** | | |
| | **Perf. 14x14¾ on 3 Sides** | | |
| 1569A | A519 48c multi | 1.50 | 1.50 |
| *b.* | Booklet pane 5 each #1565, 1569A | 15.00 | — |
| | Complete booklet, #1569Ab | 15.00 | |
| | **Self-Adhesive** | | |
| | **Size: 20x25mm** | | |
| | **Serpentine Die Cut 11x11¼** | | |
| 1570 | A519 48c multi | 1.50 | 1.50 |
| 1571 | A519 48c multi | 1.50 | 1.50 |
| *a.* | Vert. coil pair, #1570-1571 | 3.00 | 3.00 |
| *b.* | Booklet pane, 5 each #1570-1571 | 15.00 | |

No. 1571 is on the left side of No. 1571b.

### National Gallery Paintings Type of 2002

Designs: No. 1572, The House Builders, by Walter Osborne. No. 1573, Kitchen Maid with the Supper at Emmaus, by Diego Velázquez. No. 1574, The Lamentation Over the Dead Christ, by Nicolas Poussin. No. 1575, The Taking of Christ, by Caravaggio.

| | | | |
|---|---|---|---|
| **2004, Sept. 16** | | **Perf. 14¾x14** | |
| 1572 | A484 48c multi | 1.50 | 1.50 |
| *a.* | Booklet pane of 4 | 6.00 | — |
| 1573 | A484 48c multi | 1.50 | 1.50 |
| *a.* | Booklet pane of 4 | 6.00 | — |
| 1574 | A484 48c multi | 1.50 | 1.50 |
| *a.* | Booklet pane of 4 | 6.00 | — |
| 1575 | A484 48c multi | 1.50 | 1.50 |
| *a.* | Horiz. strip of 4, #1572-1575 | 6.00 | 6.00 |
| *b.* | Booklet pane of 4 | 6.00 | — |
| | Complete booklet, #1572a, 1573a, 1574a, 1575b | 24.00 | |

Complete booklet sold for €8.

Nobel Prize Winners for Literature — A520

Designs: No. 1576, William Butler Yeats (1865-1939), 1923 winner. No. 1577, George Bernard Shaw (1856-1950), 1925 winner. No. 1578, Samuel Beckett (1906-89), 1969 winner. No. 1579, Seamus Heaney (b. 1939), 1995 winner.

| | | | |
|---|---|---|---|
| | **Perf. 12½x13½** | | |
| **2004, Oct. 1** | | **Litho. & Engr.** | |
| 1576 | A520 N multi | 1.50 | 1.50 |
| 1577 | A520 N multi | 1.50 | 1.50 |
| 1578 | A520 N multi | 1.50 | 1.50 |
| 1579 | A520 N multi | 1.50 | 1.50 |
| *a.* | Block of 4, #1576-1579 | 6.00 | 6.00 |
| *b.* | Booklet pane of 4, #1576-1579 | 6.00 | — |
| | Complete booklet, #1579b | 6.00 | |

Nos. 1576-1579 each sold for 48c on day of issue. See Sweden No. 2492.

Patrick Kavanagh (1904-67), Poet A521

| | | | |
|---|---|---|---|
| **2004, Oct. 21** | **Litho.** | **Perf. 13x13¼** | |
| 1580 | A521 48c green & black | 1.50 | 1.50 |

Quakerism in Ireland, 350th Anniv. A522

| | | | |
|---|---|---|---|
| **2004, Oct. 21** | | | |
| 1581 | A522 60c multi | 1.90 | 1.90 |

Christmas A523

Designs: 48c, Holy Family. 60c, Flight into Egypt. 65c, Adoration of the Magi.

| | | | |
|---|---|---|---|
| **2004, Nov. 10** | **Litho.** | **Perf. 14x14¾** | |
| 1582 | A523 48c multi | 1.50 | 1.50 |
| 1583 | A523 60c multi | 1.90 | 1.90 |
| 1584 | A523 65c multi | 2.00 | 2.00 |
| | *Nos. 1582-1584 (3)* | 5.40 | 5.40 |
| | **Booklet Stamp** | | |
| | **Self-Adhesive** | | |
| | **Serpentine Die Cut 11x11¼** | | |
| | **Size: 21x27mm** | | |
| 1585 | A523 48c multi | 1.50 | 1.50 |
| *a.* | Booklet pane of 24 | 36.00 | |

No. 1585a sold for €11.04.

Love A524

Birds: Nos. 1586, 1587b, 1590, Parrots. Nos. 1587a, 1588, Rooster. Nos. 1587c, 1591, Owl. No. 1589, Storks.

| | | | |
|---|---|---|---|
| **2005, Jan. 28** | | **Perf. 14¾x14** | |
| 1586 | A524 48c multi | 1.50 | 1.50 |
| 1587 | Sheet of 3 | 6.00 | 6.00 |
| *a.-c.* | A524 60c Any single | 2.00 | 2.00 |
| | **Booklet Stamps** | | |
| | **Self-Adhesive** | | |
| | **Serpentine Die Cut 11¼x11** | | |
| | **Size: 27x21mm** | | |
| 1588 | A524 48c multi | 1.50 | 1.50 |
| 1589 | A524 48c multi | 1.50 | 1.50 |
| 1590 | A524 48c multi | 1.50 | 1.50 |
| 1591 | A524 48c multi | 1.50 | 1.50 |
| *a.* | Booklet pane, 3 each #1588, 1590, 2 each #1589, 1591 + 10 labels | 15.00 | |

New Year 2005 (Year of the Rooster).

St. Patrick's Day — A525

| | | | |
|---|---|---|---|
| **2005, Feb. 17** | **Litho.** | **Perf. 14x14¾** | |
| 1592 | A525 65c multi | 2.00 | 2.00 |

Works of Women Artists A526

Designs: No. 1593, Landscape, Co. Wicklow, by Evie Hone (1894-1955). No. 1594, Seabird and Landmarks, by Nano Reid (1905-81). No. 1595, Threshing, by Mildred Anne Butler (1858-1941), vert. No. 1596, Three Graces, by Gabriel Hayes (1909-78), vert.

| | | | |
|---|---|---|---|
| **2005, Feb. 24** | | **Perf. 14¾x14, 14x14¾** | |
| 1593 | A526 48c multi | 1.50 | 1.50 |
| 1594 | A526 48c multi | 1.50 | 1.50 |
| *a.* | Horiz. pair, #1593-1594 | 3.00 | 3.00 |
| 1595 | A526 65c multi | 2.00 | 2.00 |
| 1596 | A526 65c multi | 2.00 | 2.00 |
| *a.* | Horiz. pair, #1595-1596 | 4.00 | 4.00 |

Cork, 2005 European Cultural Capital A527

| | | | |
|---|---|---|---|
| **2005, Mar. 7** | **Litho.** | **Perf. 13¼** | |
| 1597 | A527 48c shown | 1.50 | 1.50 |
| 1598 | A527 48c Buildings, bridge | 1.50 | 1.50 |
| *a.* | Horiz. pair, #1597-1598 | 3.00 | 3.00 |

Intl. Year of Physics — A528

Designs: 48c, William Rowan Hamilton (1805-65), mathematician and astronomer. 60c, UNESCO Headquarters, Paris. 65c, Albert Einstein (1879-1955), physicist.

| | | | |
|---|---|---|---|
| **2005, Mar. 14** | | | |
| 1599 | A528 48c multi | 1.50 | 1.50 |
| 1600 | A528 60c multi | 1.90 | 1.90 |
| 1601 | A528 65c multi | 2.00 | 2.00 |
| | *Nos. 1599-1601 (3)* | 5.40 | 5.40 |

Dublin-Belfast Railway, 150th Anniv. — A529

Designs: No. 1602, Modern train. No. 1603, Steam locomotive at Connolly Station, Dublin. 60c, Steam locomotive on Boyne Valley Viaduct. 65c, Modern train at station platform.

| | | | |
|---|---|---|---|
| **2005, Apr. 5** | **Litho.** | **Perf. 14¾x14** | |
| 1602 | A529 48c multi | 1.50 | 1.50 |
| *a.* | Booklet pane of 4 | 6.00 | — |
| 1603 | A529 48c multi | 1.50 | 1.50 |
| *a.* | Booklet pane of 4 | 6.00 | — |
| *b.* | Horiz. pair, #1602-1603 | 3.00 | 3.00 |
| 1604 | A529 60c multi | 1.90 | 1.90 |
| *a.* | Booklet pane of 4 | 7.75 | — |

**1605** A529 65c multi                 2.00 2.00
   a.  Booklet pane of 4          8.00
      Complete booklet, #1602a,
      1603a, 1604a, 1605a          27.75
   b.  Souvenir sheet, #1602-1605   8.50 8.50
      Nos. 1602-1605 (4)          6.90 6.90

     Complete booklet sold for €9.

### Flowers Type of 2004

Designs: 1c, Bloody crane's-bill. 2c, Irish orchid. 7c, Fly orchid. 10c, Mountain avens. €10, Spring gentian, horiz.

**2005, Apr. 12**              *Perf. 14x14¾*
**1606** A519 1c multi                  .20   .20
**1607** A519 2c multi                  .20   .20
**1608** A519 7c multi                  .20   .20
**1609** A519 10c multi                 .30   .30

       **Size: 44x23mm**
**1610** A519 €10 multi               30.00 30.00
      Nos. 1606-1610 (5)         30.90 30.90

Biosphere Reserves in Ireland and Canada — A530

Designs: 48c, Deer, Killarney National Park, Ireland. 65c, Saskatoon berries, Waterton Lakes National Park, Canada.

**2005, Apr. 22**              *Perf. 13¼x13*
**1611** A530 48c multi                1.50 1.50
**1612** A530 65c multi                2.00 2.00
   a.  Souvenir sheet, #1611-1612   3.75 3.75

     See Canada Nos. 2105-2106.

Europa
A531

**2005, May 9   Litho.**       *Perf. 14¼x14*
**1613** A531 48c Irish stew           1.50 1.50
**1614** A531 65c Oysters              2.00 2.00

Worldwide Fund for Nature (WWF) A532

Butterflies: 48c, Small copper. 60c, Green hairstreak. 65c, €5, Painted lady. €1, Pearl-bordered fritillary.

**2005, May 24**              *Perf. 13¼*
**1615** A532 48c multi                1.50 1.50
**1616** A532 60c multi                1.90 1.90
**1617** A532 65c multi                2.00 2.00
**1618** A532 €1 multi                 3.00 3.00
      Nos. 1615-1618 (4)          8.40 8.40

### Souvenir Sheet

**1619** A532 €5 multi               15.00 15.00

Tall Ships
A533

**2005, July 4   Litho.**      *Perf. 13½*
**1620** A533 48c Dunbrody             1.50 1.50
**1621** A533 60c Tenacious            1.90 1.90
**1622** A533 65c Eagle                2.00 2.00
      Nos. 1620-1622 (3)          5.40 5.40

---

Round Towers — A534

**2005, July 27   Litho.**     *Perf. 13¼*
**1623** A534 48c Glendalough          1.50 1.50
**1624** A534 48c Ardmore              1.50 1.50
**1625** A534 48c Clones               1.50 1.50
**1626** A534 48c Kilmacduagh          1.50 1.50
   a.  Horiz. strip of 4, #1623-1626   6.00 6.00

Apimondia 2005 Apriarists Congress, Dublin — A535

**2005, Aug. 19**             *Perf. 13½x13*
**1627** A535 65c multi                2.00 2.00

2006 Ryder Cup Golf Tournament, K Club, Straffan — A536

Designs: No. 1628, Golfers Darren Clark, Paul McGinley, and Pádraig Harrington. No. 1629, Golfers Eamonn Darcy, Christy O'Connor, Jr., and Philip Walton. 60c, Golfers Harry Bradshaw, Ronan Rafferty, and Christy O'Connor, Sr. 65c, K Club.

**2005, Sept. 27   Litho.**    *Perf. 14¾x14*
**1628** A536 48c multi                1.50 1.50
   a.  Booklet pane of 4          6.00   —
**1629** A536 48c multi                1.50 1.50
   a.  Pair, #1628-1629           3.00 3.00
   b.  Booklet pane of 4          6.00
**1630** A536 60c multi                2.00 2.00
   a.  Booklet pane of 4          8.00   —
   b.  Booklet pane, 2 each #1628-
      1630 ('06)                10.00   —
**1631** A536 65c multi                2.00 2.00
   a.  Booklet pane of 4          8.00   —
   b.  Booklet pane, 2 #1631 ('06)   4.00   —
      Complete booklet, #1628a,
      1629b, 1630a, 1631a       28.00
      Nos. 1628-1631 (4)         7.00 7.00

   Nos. 1630b, 1631b issued 9/14/06.

Pres. Erskine Childers (1905-74) A537

**2005, Oct. 10**             *Perf. 14x14¾*
**1632** A537 48c multi                1.50 1.50

Ireland in the United Nations A538

---

Designs: No. 1633, Irish Defense Force member assisting man in East Timor. No. 1634, Medical worker aiding child in East Timor. 60c, F. H. Boland, Ireland's signer of United Nations Charter. 65c, Irish Defense Force member in classroom in Lebanon.

**2005, Oct. 14**             *Perf. 14¾x14*
**1633** A538 48c multi                1.50 1.50
**1634** A538 48c multi                1.50 1.50
   a.  Horiz. pair, #1633-1634    3.00 3.00
**1635** A538 60c multi                1.90 1.90
**1636** A538 65c multi                2.00 2.00
      Nos. 1633-1636 (4)         6.90 6.90

Arthur Griffith's Policy Establishing Sinn Féin, Cent. — A539

**2005, Nov. 10**             *Perf. 13½*
**1637** A539 48c multi                1.50 1.50

Christmas A540

Designs: 48c, Nativity. 60c, Choir of angels. 65c, Choir of angels, diff.

**2005, Nov. 10**             *Perf. 14x14¾*
**1638** A540 48c multi                1.50 1.50
**1639** A540 60c multi                1.90 1.90
**1640** A540 65c multi                2.00 2.00
      Nos. 1638-1640 (3)         5.40 5.40

### Booklet Stamp
### Self-Adhesive
**Size: 21x27mm**
*Serpentine Die Cut 11x11¼*

**1641** A540 48c multi                1.50 1.50
   a.  Booklet pane of 26        39.00 39.00

   No. 1641a sold for €12.

Patrick Gallagher and Templecrone Cooperative Store — A541

**2006, Jan. 16   Litho.**     *Perf. 14¾x14*
**1642** A541 48c sepia                1.50 1.50

Templecrone Cooperative Agricultural Society, cent.

New Year 2006 (Year of the Dog) A542

Designs: Nos. 1643, 1644b, 1647, Dog, man and woman. Nos. 1644a, 1645, Two dogs, man. Nos. 1644c, 1646, Dog on leash, woman. No. 1648, Dog biting sneaker.

**2006, Jan. 16**             *Perf. 14¾x14*
**1643** A542 48c multi                1.50 1.50

### Souvenir Sheet

**1644**  Sheet of 3             6.50 6.50
  a.-c.  A542 65c Any single       2.00 2.00

---

### Booklet Stamps
### Self-Adhesive
**Size: 26x21mm**
*Serpentine Die Cut 11¼x11*

**1645** A542 48c multi                1.50 1.50
**1646** A542 48c multi                1.50 1.50
**1647** A542 48c multi                1.50 1.50
**1648** A542 48c multi                1.50 1.50
   a.  Booklet pane, 3 each #1645-
      1646, 2 each #1647-1648,
      + 10 labels               15.00
      Nos. 1645-1648 (4)         6.00 6.00

St. Patrick Lights the Paschal Fire at Slane, by Sean Keating A543

**2006, Feb. 16**             *Perf. 14¾x14*
**1649** A543 65c multi                2.00 2.00

     St. Patrick's Day.

### Flowers Type of 2004

Designs: 12c, Autumn gorse. 25c, Common knapweed. 75c, Navelwort. 90c, Viper's bugloss. €1, Foxglove.

**2006, Feb. 20**             *Perf. 14x14¾*
**1650** A519 12c multi                .40   .40
**1651** A519 25c multi                .75   .75
**1652** A519 75c multi                2.25 2.25
**1653** A519 90c multi                2.75 2.75

       **Size: 23x44mm**
**1654** A519 €1 multi                 3.00 3.00
      Nos. 1650-1654 (5)         9.15 9.15

### Booklet Stamp
### Self-Adhesive
**Size: 21x27mm**
*Serpentine Die Cut 11x11¼*

**1655** A519 75c multi                2.25 2.25
   a.  Booklet pane of 10        22.50

Trees A544

**2006, Mar. 7**              *Perf. 13¼*
**1656** A544 48c Sessile oak          1.50 1.50
**1657** A544 60c Yew                  1.90 1.90
**1658** A544 75c Ash                  2.25 2.25
**1659** A544 €1 Strawberry tree       3.00 3.00
   a.  Souvenir sheet, #1656-1659   9.00 9.00
   b.  As "a," with Washington
      2006 World Philatelic Ex-
      hibition emblem in margin  10.00 10.00
      Nos. 1656-1659 (4)         8.65 8.65

   No. 1659b issued in June. No. 1659b sold for €3.

St. Hubert, Stained Glass Window by Harry Clarke (1889-1931) A545

**2006, Mar. 21**             *Perf. 13¼*
**1660** A545 48c multi                1.50 1.50

Easter Rebellion, 90th Anniv. — A546

**2006, Apr. 12**     *Perf. 13½*
1661 A546 48c multi     1.50 1.50

Adoption of European Union Flag, 20th Anniv. A547

**2006, May 9**     *Perf. 14¼x14*
1662 A547 48c multi     1.50 1.50

Europa — A548

Winning art in children's stamp design contest: 48c, People holding Irish and European Union flags, by Katie McMillan. 75c, Flowers with flags, by Sarah Naughter.

**2006, May 9**     *Perf. 14x14¼*
1663 A548 48c multi     1.50 1.50
1664 A548 75c multi     2.25 2.25

University Church, Dublin, 150th Anniv. — A549

**2006, May 25 Litho.**     *Perf. 14x14¾*
1665 A549 48c multi     1.50 1.50

Department of the Gaeltacht, 50th Anniv. — A550

**2006, June 6**     *Perf. 13¼*
1666 A550 48c multi     1.50 1.50

TG4 Television Channel, 10th Anniv. A551

**2006, June 6**
1667 A551 48c multi     1.50 1.50

Celtic Scholars — A552

Designs: No. 1668, Máirtín O Cadhain (1906-70), writer. No. 1669, Johann Caspar Zeuss (1806-56), philologist.

**2006, June 6**     *Perf. 14x14¾*
1668 A552 48c multi     1.50 1.50
1669 A552 48c multi     1.50 1.50
    a.    Pair, #1668-1669     3.00 3.00

Rosslare-Fishguard Ferry Service, Cent. — A553

Designs: No. 1670, Steam ferry. No. 1671, Modern ferry.

**2006, June 20**     *Perf. 14¾x14*
1670 A553 48c multi     1.50 1.50
1671 A553 48c multi     1.50 1.50
    a.    Pair, #1670-1671     3.00 3.00
    b.    Souvenir sheet, #1670-1671     3.25 3.25

Battle of the Somme, 90th Anniv. A554

**2006, June 26**     *Perf. 13½x13¾*
1672 A554 75c multi     2.25 2.25

Guide Dog — A555

**Litho. & Embossed**
**2006, July 7**     *Perf. 13¼x13*
1673 A555 48c multi     1.50 1.50

A556

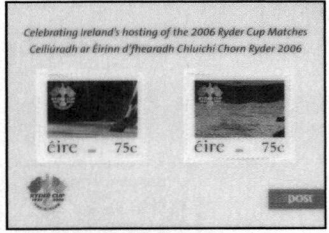

2006 Ryder Cup Golf Tournament, K Club, Straffan — A557

Golf ball: Nos. 1674, 1678, On tee. Nos. 1675, 1679, In rough. Nos. 1676, 1680, In sand trap. Nos. 1677, 1681, Near green. No. 1682: a, Tee shot. b, Sand trap shot.

**2006**     **Litho.**     *Perf. 14x14¾*
1674 A556 48c multi     1.50 1.50
1675 A556 48c multi     1.50 1.50
1676 A556 48c multi     1.50 1.50
1677 A556 48c multi     1.50 1.50
    a.    Horiz. strip, #1674-1677     6.00 6.00
    b.    Souvenir sheet #1674-1677     6.50 6.50
    c.    Booklet pane, 2 each #1674-1677     12.00 —
    d.    Booklet pane #1674-1677     6.00 —

**Coil Stamps**
**Self-Adhesive**
**Size: 21x27mm**
*Serpentine Die Cut 11x11¼*
1678 A556 48c multi     1.50 1.50
1679 A556 48c multi     1.50 1.50
1680 A556 48c multi     1.50 1.50
1681 A556 48c multi     1.50 1.50
    a.    Vert. strip, #1678-1681     6.00

**Souvenir Sheet**
**Self-Adhesive**
**Litho. With Three-Dimensional Plastic Affixed**
*Serpentine Die Cut 9¼*
1682 A557   Sheet of 2     4.75
    a.-b.   75c Either single     2.25 2.25
    Complete booklet, #1630b, 1631b, 1677c, 1677d, and unbound #1682     37.00

Issued: Nos. 1674-1678, 7/25; No. 1682, 9/14. Complete booklet sold for €12. No. 1677b has Ryder Cup emblem in margin while No. 1677d does not.

Winning of Olympic 1500-Meter Running Gold Medal by Ronnie Delany, 50th Anniv. — A558

*Perf. 13¾x13½*
**2006, Aug. 16**     **Litho.**
1683 A558 48c multi     1.50 1.50

Michael Cusack (1847-1906), Sports Journalist A559

**2006, Aug. 23**     *Perf. 14x14¾*
1684 A559 48c multi     1.50 1.50

Michael Davitt (1846-1906), Founder of National Land League — A560

**2006, Sept. 5**
1685 A560 48c multi     1.50 1.50

National Concert Hall, Dublin, 25th Anniv. — A561

**2006, Sept. 8**
1686 A561 48c multi     1.50 1.50

Inland Waterways — A562

Designs: No. 1687, Barrow River at Graiguenamanagh. No. 1688, Belturbet Marina, Erne River. No. 1689, Grand Canal at Cornalaur. No. 1690, Meelick Pier, Shannon River.

**2006, Oct. 20 Litho.**     *Perf. 13½x13¾*
1687 A562 75c multi     2.25 2.25
    a.    Booklet pane of 4     9.00
1688 A562 75c multi     2.25 2.25
    a.    Booklet pane of 4     9.00
1689 A562 75c multi     2.25 2.25
    a.    Booklet pane of 4     9.00
1690 A562 75c multi     2.25 2.25
    a.    Booklet pane of 4     9.00 —
    Complete booklet, #1687a-1690a     36.00

Traditional Irish Music Groups — A563

Designs: No. 1691, The Chieftains. No. 1692, The Dubliners. No. 1693, The Clancy Brothers and Tommy Makem. No. 1694, Altan.

**2006, Nov. 7 Litho.**     *Perf. 13½x13¾*
1691 A563 48c multi     1.50 1.50
    a.    Booklet pane of 4     6.00 —
1692 A563 48c multi     1.50 1.50
    a.    Booklet pane of 4     6.00 —
1693 A563 75c multi     2.25 2.25
    a.    Booklet pane of 4     9.00 —
1694 A563 75c multi     2.25 2.25
    a.    Booklet pane of 4     9.00 —
    Complete booklet, #1691a, 1692a, 1693a, 1694a     30.00
    b.    Souvenir sheet, #1691-1694     6.80 6.80
    c.    As "b," with Belgica '06 emblem added in margin     6.75 6.75
    d.    As "b," with MonacoPhil 2006 emblem added in margin     6.75 6.75

Complete booklet sold for €10. No. 1694c issued 11/16; No. 1694d, 12/1.

Christmas
A564        A565

Designs: No. 1695, Madonna and Child. 75c, Shepherd and lamb. No. 1697, Nativity.

**2006, Nov. 9**     *Perf. 14x14¾*
1695 A564 48c multi     1.50 1.50
1696 A564 75c multi     2.25 2.25

**Booklet Stamp**
**Self-Adhesive**
*Serpentine Die Cut 11x11¼*
1697 A565 48c multi     1.50 1.50
    a.    Booklet pane of 26     39.00
    Nos. 1695-1697 (3)     5.25 5.25

No. 1697a sold for €12.

Father Luke Wadding (1588-1657)
A566

Irish Franciscan College, Louvain, 400th Anniv. — A567

**2007, Jan. 24  Litho.  Perf. 14x14¾**
| 1698 | A566 | 75c multi | 2.25 | 2.25 |
| 1699 | A567 | 75c multi | 2.25 | 2.25 |

Hands With Wedding Rings
A568

Greetings
A569

Designs: No. 1701, Stamp with hat, heart balloon. No. 1702, Birthday cake.

**Serpentine Die Cut 11¼**
**2007, Jan. 26**
**Booklet Stamps**
**Self-Adhesive**
| 1700 | A568 | N multi | 1.50 | 1.50 |
| a. | | Booklet pane of 10 | 15.00 | |
| 1701 | A569 | N multi | 1.50 | 1.50 |
| 1702 | A569 | N multi | 1.50 | 1.50 |
| a. | | Booklet pane of 10, 5 each #1701-1702 | 15.00 | |
| | | Nos. 1700-1702 (3) | 4.50 | 4.50 |

Nos. 1700-1702 each sold for 48c on day of issue.

New Year 2007 (Year of the Pig)
A570

**2007, Feb. 9  Litho.  Perf. 14¾x14**
| 1703 | A570 | 75c grn & multi | 2.00 | 2.00 |

**Souvenir Sheet**
| 1704 | | Sheet of 3, #1704a, 2 #1703 | 6.00 | 6.00 |
| a. | | A570 75c red & multi | 2.00 | 2.00 |

St. Patrick's Day — A571

**2007, Feb. 9  Perf. 13½**
| 1705 | A571 | 75c multi | 2.00 | 2.00 |

Flight of the Earls, 400th Anniv. — A572

Designs: No. 1706, Hugh O'Neill, Earl of Tyrone, and ship at right. No. 1707, Rory O'Donnell, Earl of Tyrconnell, and rowboat at left.

**2007, Feb. 23  Perf. 14x14¾**
| 1706 | A572 | 48c multi | 1.25 | 1.25 |
| 1707 | A572 | 48c multi | 1.25 | 1.25 |
| a. | | Horiz. pair, #1706-1707 | 2.50 | 2.50 |
| b. | | Souvenir sheet, #1707a | 2.50 | 2.50 |

**Flowers Type of 2004**
Designs: 3c, Yellow flag. 55c, No. 1712, Large-flowered butterwort. 78c, Black bog-rush. 95c, Purple loosestrife. No. 1713, Blue-eyed grass.

**2007, Mar. 1  Litho.  Perf. 14x14¾**
| 1708 | A519 | 3c multi | .20 | .20 |
| 1709 | A519 | 55c multi | 1.50 | 1.50 |
| 1710 | A519 | 78c multi | 2.10 | 2.10 |
| 1711 | A519 | 95c multi | 2.50 | 2.50 |
| | | Nos. 1708-1711 (4) | 6.30 | 6.30 |

**Self-Adhesive**
**Size: 21x26mm**
**Serpentine Die Cut 11x11¼**
| 1712 | A519 | N multi | 1.50 | 1.50 |
| 1713 | A519 | N multi | 1.50 | 1.50 |
| a. | | Booklet pane, 5 each #1712-1713 | 15.00 | |
| b. | | Vert. coil pair, #1712-1713 | 3.00 | |

Nos. 1712-1713 each sold for 55c on day of issue.

Castles
A573

Designs: No. 1714, Trim Castle. No. 1715, Dunluce Castle. No. 1716, Lismore Castle. No. 1717, Portumna Castle.

**2007, Mar. 9  Perf. 14¾x14**
| 1714 | A573 | 55c multi | 1.50 | 1.50 |
| 1715 | A573 | 55c multi | 1.50 | 1.50 |
| 1716 | A573 | 55c multi | 1.50 | 1.50 |
| 1717 | A573 | 55c multi | 1.50 | 1.50 |
| a. | | Block of 4, #1714-1717 | 6.00 | 6.00 |
| b. | | Souvenir sheet, #1714-1717 | 6.00 | 6.00 |

Treaty of Rome, 50th Anniv. — A574

**2007, Mar. 28  Perf. 14x14¾**
| 1718 | A574 | 55c multi | 1.50 | 1.50 |

Planets — A575

Earth and: No. 1719, Jupiter. No. 1720, Neptune. No. 1721, Saturn. No. 1722, Uranus.

**2007, Apr. 20  Litho.  Perf. 13¼**
| 1719 | A575 | 55c multi | 1.50 | 1.50 |
| 1720 | A575 | 55c multi | 1.50 | 1.50 |
| a. | | Horiz. pair, #1719-1720 | 3.00 | 3.00 |

| 1721 | A575 | 78c multi | 2.25 | 2.25 |
| 1722 | A575 | 78c multi | 2.25 | 2.25 |
| a. | | Horiz. pair, #1721-1722 | 4.50 | 4.50 |
| b. | | Souvenir sheet, #1719-1722 | 7.50 | 7.50 |
| c. | | Booklet pane, #1719-1722 | 7.50 | — |
| | | Complete booklet, 4 #1722c | 30.00 | |
| | | Nos. 1719-1722 (4) | 7.50 | 7.50 |

No. 1722c has stamps with straight edges at right. Complete booklet contains four examples of No. 1722c with different margins.

**Flower Type of 2004**
Designs: 5c, Dandelion. 25c, Common knapweed. 55c, Large-flowered butterwort. 78c, Black bog-rush.

**Die Cut Perf. 12¾**
**2007, Apr. 20  Litho.**
**Coil Stamp**
**Self-Adhesive (#1723, 1728-1729)**
**Size: 21x26mm**
| 1723 | A519 | 55c multi | 1.50 | 1.50 |

**Booklet Stamps**
**Size: 17x20mm**
**Perf. 14¾x14 on 3 Sides**
| 1724 | A519 | 5c multi | .20 | .20 |
| 1725 | A519 | 25c multi | .70 | .70 |
| 1726 | A519 | 55c multi | 1.50 | 1.50 |
| a. | | Booklet pane of 6, #1725, 2 #1724, 3 #1726 | 5.75 | |
| | | Complete booklet, #1726a | 5.75 | |

**Size: 20x23mm**
**Perf. 14x14¾ on 3 Sides**
| 1727 | A519 | 55c multi | 1.50 | 1.50 |
| a. | | Booklet pane of 10 | 15.00 | |
| | | Complete booklet, #1727a | 15.00 | |

**Size: 21x26mm**
**Serpentine Die Cut 11x11¼**
| 1728 | A519 | 55c multi | 1.50 | 1.50 |
| a. | | Booklet pane of 10 | 15.00 | |
| 1729 | A519 | 78c multi | 2.25 | 2.25 |
| a. | | Booklet pane of 10 | 22.50 | |
| | | Nos. 1723-1729 (7) | 9.15 | 9.15 |

Europa
A576

**2007, May 9  Perf. 14¼x14**
| 1730 | A576 | 5c Female Scout | 1.50 | 1.50 |
| 1731 | A576 | 78c Male Scout | 2.10 | 2.10 |

Scouting, cent.

Canonization of St. Charles of Mount Argus (1821-93)
A577

**2007, June 5  Perf. 13¼**
| 1732 | A577 | 55c multi | 1.50 | 1.50 |

Institute of Public Administration, 50th Anniv. — A578

**2007, June 13**
| 1733 | A578 | 55c multi | 1.50 | 1.50 |

RTE Performing Groups
A579

Designs: Nos. 1734, 1742, National Symphony Orchestra (Ceolfhoireann Shiansach Náisiúnta). Nos. 1735, 1740, Concert Orchestra (Ceolfhoireann Cheolchoirme). Nos. 1736, 1743, Vanbrugh Quartet (Ceathairéad Vanbrugh). Nos. 1737, 1741, Philharmonic Choir (Cór Fiolarmónach). Nos. 1738, 1739, Children's Choir (Cór na nOg).

**2007, June 19  Perf. 13¼x13½**
| 1734 | A579 | 55c multi | 1.50 | 1.50 |
| 1735 | A579 | 55c multi | 1.50 | 1.50 |
| 1736 | A579 | 55c multi | 1.50 | 1.50 |
| a. | | Booklet pane, 2 each #1734-1736 | 9.00 | — |
| 1737 | A579 | 55c multi | 1.50 | 1.50 |
| 1738 | A579 | 55c multi | 1.50 | 1.50 |
| a. | | Horiz. strip of 5, #1734-1738 | 7.50 | 7.50 |
| b. | | Booklet pane, 2 each #1737-1738 | 6.00 | — |
| | | Complete booklet, 2 each #1736a, 1738b | 30.00 | |

**Booklet Stamps**
**Self-Adhesive**
**Serpentine Die Cut 11¼x11½**
| 1739 | A579 | 55c multi | 1.50 | 1.50 |
| 1740 | A579 | 55c multi | 1.50 | 1.50 |
| 1741 | A579 | 55c multi | 1.50 | 1.50 |
| 1742 | A579 | 55c multi | 1.50 | 1.50 |
| 1743 | A579 | 55c multi | 1.50 | 1.50 |
| a. | | Booklet pane of 10, 2 each #1739-1743 | 15.00 | |
| | | Nos. 1734-1743 (10) | 15.00 | 15.00 |

Revival of Honorable Society of King's Inns, 400th Anniv. — A580

**2007, July 10  Perf. 13¼**
| 1744 | A580 | 55c multi | 1.50 | 1.50 |

Registry of Deeds Act, 300th Anniv. A581

**2007, July 10  Perf. 14¾x14**
| 1745 | A581 | 78c multi | 2.25 | 2.25 |

National Anthem, Cent. A582

**2007, July 17  Litho.  Perf. 13½**
| 1746 | A582 | 55c multi | 1.50 | 1.50 |

**Weddings Type of 2007**
**Serpentine Die Cut 11¼**
**2007, July 25**
**Booklet Stamp**
**Self-Adhesive**
| 1747 | A568 | 55c multi | 1.50 | 1.50 |
| a. | | Booklet pane of 10 | 15.00 | |

Viking Ship Skuldelev 2 — A583

Designs: 55c, Ship. €3, Ship on water.

**2007, Aug. 7  Litho.  Perf. 14¾x14**
| 1748 | A583 | 55c multi | 1.50 | 1.50 |

**Souvenir Sheet**
| 1749 | A583 | €3 multi | 8.25 | 8.25 |

2007 Rugby World Cup, France — A584

Designs: 55c, Player carrying ball. 78c, Player catching ball.

**2007, Aug. 20**     *Perf. 13¼*
1750 A584 55c multi   1.50 1.50
a.   Souvenir sheet of 1   1.50 1.50
1751 A584 78c multi   2.25 2.25
a.   Souvenir sheet of 1   2.25 2.25

Cat Caricatures by Martyn Turner — A585

Designs: Nos. 1752, 1756a, Fat Cat. Nos. 1753, 1756b, Celtic Tigress. Nos. 1754, 1756c, Cool Cats. Nos. 1755, 1756d, Kilkenny Cat.

**2007, Sept. 6**     *Perf. 14x14¾*
1752 A585 55c multi   1.50 1.50
1753 A585 55c multi   1.50 1.50
a.   Horiz. pair, #1752-1753   3.00 3.00
1754 A585 78c multi   2.25 2.25
1755 A585 78c multi   2.25 2.25
a.   Horiz. pair, #1754-1755   4.50 4.50
**Souvenir Sheet**
*Perf. 13¼*
1756   Sheet of 4   7.50 7.50
a.-b.   A585 55c Either single, 16x16mm   1.50 1.50
c.-d.   A585 78c Either single, 16x16mm   2.25 2.25

Excavations of San Clemente Basilica, Rome, 150th Anniv. — A586

**2007, Sept. 12**     *Perf. 14¾x14*
1757 A586 55c multi   1.60 1.60

James Fintan Lalor (1807-49), Political Writer — A587

**2007, Sept. 18**     *Perf. 14x14¾*
1758 A587 55c multi   1.60 1.60

Natural History Museum, Dublin, 150th Anniv. — A588

**2007, Oct. 25**   Litho.   *Perf. 13¼*
1759 A588 55c multi   1.60 1.60

Christmas A589

Designs: No. 1760, Presentation in the Temple. No. 1761, Three Magi. No. 1762, Adoration of the Shepherds.

**2007, Nov. 8**     *Perf. 14¾x14*
1760 A589 55c multi   1.60 1.60
1761 A589 78c multi   2.40 2.40
**Self-Adhesive**
**Booklet Stamp**
**Size: 21x27mm**
*Serpentine Die Cut 11x11¼*
1762 A589 55c multi   1.60 1.60
a.   Booklet pane of 26   42.50
No. 1762a sold for €13.75.

Charles Wesley (1707-88), Hymn Writer — A590

**2007, Nov. 15**     *Perf. 14x14¾*
1763 A590 78c multi   2.40 2.40

Bride and Groom A591

*Serpentine Die Cut 11¼*
**2008, Jan. 16**     Litho.
**Booklet Stamp**
**Self-Adhesive**
1764 A591 55c multi   1.60 1.60
a.   Booklet pane of 10   16.00

Greetings — A592

*Serpentine Die Cut 11¼*
**2008, Jan. 16**
**Booklet Stamps**
**Self-Adhesive**
1765 A592 55c Frog   1.60 1.60
1766 A592 55c Elephant   1.60 1.60
a.   Booklet pane of 10, 5 each #1765-1766   16.00

New Year 2008 (Year of the Rat) A593

**2008, Jan. 23**     *Perf. 14¾x14*
1767 A593 78c multi   2.40 2.40
a.   Souvenir sheet of 3   7.25 7.25

Liam Whelan (1935-58), Soccer Player Killed in Airplane Crash — A594

**2008, Feb. 4**     *Perf. 13½x13¾*
1768 A594 55c multi   1.75 1.75

St. Patrick's Day — A595

**2008, Feb. 11**     *Perf. 13¼x13*
1769 A595 78c multi   2.40 2.40

**Flower Type of 2004**
Designs: 20c, Thrift. 50c, Biting stonecrop. 82c, Sea aster.

**2008, Mar. 3**   Litho.   *Perf. 14x14¾*
**Size: 20x23mm**
1770 A519 20c multi   .65 .65
1771 A519 50c multi   1.60 1.60
1772 A519 82c multi   2.50 2.50
a.   Booklet pane of 10   25.00
  Complete booklet, #1772a   25.00
Nos. 1770-1772 (3)   4.75 4.75
**Booklet Stamp**
**Self-Adhesive**
**Size: 21x25mm**
*Serpentine Die Cut 11x11¼*
1773 A519 82c multi   2.50 2.50
a.   Booklet pane of 10   25.00

European Year of Intercultural Dialogue — A596

**2008, Mar. 7**     *Perf. 13¼*
1774 A596 55c multi   1.75 1.75

Hugh Lane, by Antonio Mancini — A597

**2008, Mar. 28**   Litho.   *Perf. 13½*
1775 A597 55c multi   1.75 1.75
Dublin City Gallery, cent. (founded by Lane).

Paintings by Paul Henry (1876-1958) A598

Designs: No. 1776, A Connemara Village (left half, "Paul Henry" in blue). No. 1777, A Connemara Village (right half, "Paul Henry" in white). No. 1778, West of Ireland Landscape (left half, "Paul Henry" in gray at left). No. 1779, West of Ireland Landscape (right half, "Paul Henry" in gray at right).

**2008, Apr. 17**     *Perf. 13¼*
1776 A598 55c multi   1.75 1.75
1777 A598 55c multi   1.75 1.75
1778 A598 55c multi   1.75 1.75
1779 A598 55c multi   1.75 1.75
a.   Horiz. strip of 4, #1776-1779   7.00 7.00
b.   Booklet pane of 4, #1776-1779   7.00 —
  Complete booklet, 4 #1779b   28.00

No. 1779b has example of No. 1779 with straight edge at right. The four examples of No. 1779b in the complete booklet have different margins. The complete booklet sold for €9.

Credit Union Movement, 50th Anniv. A599

**2008, Apr. 23**     *Perf. 14¾x14*
1780 A599 55c multi   1.75 1.75

Intl. Year of Planet Earth A600

Plasticine sculptures of Earth created by children: No. 1781, Africa and Europe, by Mohammed Rahman. No. 1782, South and North America, by Conor Reid.

**2008, Apr. 28**     *Die Cut Perf.*
**Self-Adhesive**
1781 A600 55c red & multi   1.75 1.75
1782 A600 55c blue & multi   1.75 1.75
a.   Horiz. pair, #1781-1782   3.50
b.   Booklet pane of 10, 5 each #1781-1782   17.50

Institute of Creative Advertising and Design, 50th Anniv. A601

**2008, May 23**     *Perf. 13¼*
1783 A601 55c multi   1.75 1.75

R. M. S. Leinster, 90th Anniv. of Sinking A602

**2008, May 30**     *Perf. 14¾x14*
1784 A602 55c multi   1.75 1.75

Europa — A603

Designs: 55c, Boy writing letter. 82c, Girl writing letter.

**2008, June 9**     **Perf. 14x14¾**
1785 A603 55c multi     1.75 1.75
1786 A603 82c multi     2.50 2.50

Tidy Towns Competition, 50th Anniv. — A604

**2008, June 19**
1787 A604 55c multi     1.75 1.75

Participation of Irish Defense Forces in UN Missions, 50th Anniv. — A605

**2008, June 26**     **Perf. 14¾x14**
1788 A605 55c multi     1.75 1.75

Movies Filmed in Ireland — A606

Designs: No. 1789, Kings. No. 1790, Cré na Cille. No. 1791, The Wind that Shakes the Barley. No. 1792, Garage.

**2008, July 8**    **Litho.**    **Perf. 14¾x14**
1789 A606 55c multi     1.75 1.75
1790 A606 55c multi     1.75 1.75
1791 A606 82c multi     2.60 2.60
1792 A606 82c multi     2.60 2.60
   a.   Booklet pane of 4, #1789-
      1792     9.25 —
      Complete booklet, 4 #1792a    37.50
   b.   Souvenir sheet of 4, #1789-
      1792     8.75 8.75
     Nos. 1789-1792 (4)    8.70 8.70

No. 1792b has a printed margin. The complete booklet, which sold for €12, contains 4 examples of No. 1792a, each with a different order of stamps and without a printed margin.

2008 Summer Olympics, Beijing A607

Designs: 52c, Rowing. 82c, Shot put.

**2008, July 15**
1793 A607 55c multi     1.75 1.75
1794 A607 82c multi     2.60 2.60
    **Souvenir Sheet**
   **Stamps Inscribed "Olympex 2008"**
1795   Sheet of 2     4.50 4.50
   a.   A607 55c multi     1.75 1.75
   b.   A607 82c multi     2.60 2.60

Mushrooms A608

Designs: No. 1796, Parasol. No. 1797, Orange birch bolete. 82c, Pink waxcap. 95c, Scarlet elfcup.

**2008, Aug. 1**    **Litho.**    **Perf. 14x14¾**
1796 A608 55c multi     1.75 1.75
1797 A608 55c multi     1.75 1.75
   a.   Horiz. pair, #1796-1797    3.50 3.50
1798 A608 82c multi     2.60 2.60
     Nos. 1796-1798 (3)    6.10 6.10
    **Souvenir Sheet**
1799 A608 95c multi     3.00 3.00

First Transatlantic Cable Message From Europe to US, 150th Anniv. — A609

**2008, Aug. 15**     **Perf. 13¼**
1800 A609 82c multi     2.40 2.40

Old Age Pensions Act, Cent. — A610

**2008, Sept. 19**    **Litho.**    **Perf. 13¼**
1801 A610 55c multi     1.50 1.50

National University of Ireland, Cent. — A611

**2008, Sept. 19**     **Perf. 13½**
1802 A611 55c multi     1.50 1.50

Patrick Pearse (1879-1916), Patriot, and Founder of St. Enda's School — A612

Pearse and school buildings: No. 1803, Cullenswood House. No. 1804, The Hermitage.

**2008, Sept. 25**     **Perf. 14¾x14¼**
1803 A612 55c multi     1.50 1.50
1804 A612 55c multi     1.50 1.50

Irish Bands A613

**2008, Oct. 10**    **Litho.**    **Perf. 13½**
1805 A613 55c Planxty     1.50 1.50
1806 A613 55c De Danann     1.50 1.50
1807 A613 82c Tulla Ceili Band     2.25 2.25
1808 A613 82c Bothy Band     2.25 2.25
   a.   Souvenir sheet, #1805-1808    7.50 7.50
     Nos. 1805-1808 (4)    7.50 7.50

Dancers — A614

**2008, Nov. 7**    **Litho.**    **Perf. 13½**
1809 A614 55c Irish dancer     1.40 1.40
    **Souvenir Sheet**
1810   Sheet of 2, #1809,
     1810a     3.50 3.50
   a.   A614 82c Flamenco dancer    2.10 2.10
     See Spain Nos.

A615

Christmas — A616

Creche figures: No. 1811, Flight into Egypt. 82c, Annunciation. No. 1813, Infant Jesus.

**2008, Nov. 7**     **Perf. 14¾x14**
1811 A615 55c multi     1.40 1.40
1812 A615 82c multi     2.10 2.10
    **Booklet Stamp**
    **Self-Adhesive**
   **Serpentine Die Cut 11x11¼**
1813 A616 55c multi     1.40 1.40
   a.   Booklet pane of 26    37.50

No. 1813a sold for €13.75.

---

**AIR POST STAMPS**

Catalogue values for unused stamps in this section are for Never Hinged items.

Angel over Rock of Cashel AP1

Designs: 1p, 1sh3p, 1sh5p, Rock of Cashel. 3p, 8p, Lough Derg. 6p, Croagh Patrick. 1sh, Glendalough.

    **Perf. 15x14**
**1948-65**    **Wmk. 262**    **Engr.**
C1 AP1 1p dk brown ('49)    6.00 7.00
C2 AP1 3p blue    10.00 10.00
C3 AP1 6p rose lilac    1.00 1.00
C4 AP1 8p red brown ('54)    4.00 3.75

C5 AP1 1sh green ('49)    2.00 1.25
C6 AP1 1sh3p ver ('54)    5.00 1.25
     **Perf. 15**
C7 AP1 1sh5p dark blue ('65)    4.00 .90
     Nos. C1-C7 (7)    32.00 25.15

---

**POSTAGE DUE STAMPS**

D1

**1925**   **Typo.**   **Wmk. 44**   **Perf. 14x15**
J1 D1 ½p emerald    20.00 30.00
     Never hinged    90.00
J2 D1 1p carmine    12.00 9.00
     Never hinged    40.00
J3 D1 2p dark green    22.50 11.00
     Never hinged    80.00
J4 D1 6p plum    7.50 10.00
     Never hinged    30.00
     Nos. J1-J4 (4)    62.00 60.00

Catalogue values for unused stamps in this section, from this point to the end of the section, are for Never Hinged items.

**1940-70**      **Wmk. 262**
J5 D1 ½p emerald ('43)    27.50 22.50
J6 D1 1p brt carmine ('41)    1.10 .50
J7 D1 1½p vermilion ('52)    2.25 5.00
J8 D1 2p dark green    1.25 .55
J9 D1 3p blue ('52)    2.25 2.00
J10 D1 5p royal purple ('43)    3.50 7.50
J11 D1 6p plum ('60)    4.00 1.75
J12 D1 8p orange ('62)    7.50 4.00
J13 D1 10p red lilac ('65)    8.50 7.00
J14 D1 1sh lt yel grn ('69)    25.00 9.00
     Nos. J5-J14 (10)    82.85 63.30

**1971, Feb. 15**    **Typo.**    **Wmk. 262**
J15 D1 1p sepia    .20 .40
J16 D1 1½p bright green    .20 .40
J17 D1 3p gray green    .90 1.10
J18 D1 4p orange    1.25 1.60
J19 D1 5p bright blue    2.25 2.75
J20 D1 7p yellow    .30 .50
J21 D1 8p scarlet    .30 .50
     Nos. J15-J21 (7)    5.40 7.15

**1978**      **Unwmk.**
J25 D1 3p gray green    2.50 3.50
J26 D1 4p orange    4.00 10.50
J27 D1 5p bright blue    2.50 3.50
     Nos. J25-J27 (3)    9.00 17.50

Celtic Knot — D2      D3

**1980-85**    **Photo.**    **Perf. 15**
J28 D2 1p brt yel green    .75 1.00
J29 D2 2p ultramarine    .75 1.00
J30 D2 4p dark green    .75 1.00
J31 D2 6p yel orange    .75 1.00
J32 D2 8p violet blue    1.00 1.25
J33 D2 18p green    1.60 2.00
J33A D2 20p org brown ('85)    3.50 4.50
J34 D2 24p emerald    2.25 1.90
J35 D2 30p violet blue ('85)    7.00 7.00
J36 D2 50p rose pink ('85)    4.00 4.00
     Nos. J28-J36 (10)    22.35 24.65

Issue dates: 1p, 2p, 4p, 6p, 8p, 18p, 24p, June 11; 20p, 30p, 50p, Aug. 22.

**1988, Oct. 6**    **Litho.**    **Perf. 14x15**
J37 D3 1p blk, dp yel & brt
     red    .55 .80
J38 D3 2p blk, vio brn & brt
     red    .55 .80
J39 D3 3p blk, dull vio & brt
     red    .55 .80
J40 D3 4p blk, vio & brt red    .55 .80
J41 D3 5p blk, vio bl & brt
     red    .55 .80
J42 D3 17p blk, brt ol grn & brt
     red    1.10 1.60
J43 D3 20p blk, bluish gray &
     brt red    1.40 1.90
J44 D3 24p blk, bl grn & brt
     red    1.60 2.25
J45 D3 30p blk & brt red    1.60 2.25
J46 D3 50p blk, gray & brt red    2.25 2.75

| J47 | D3 | £1 blk, dk ol brn & brt red | 4.50 | 5.50 |
|---|---|---|---|---|
| | | Nos. J37-J47 (11) | 15.20 | 20.25 |

## ISRAEL

ˈiz-rē-əl

LOCATION — Western Asia, bordering on the Mediterranean Sea
GOVT. — Republic
AREA — 8,017 sq. mi.
POP. — 5,749,760 (1999 est.)
CAPITAL — Jerusalem

When the British mandate of Palestine ended in May 1948, the Jewish state of Israel was proclaimed by the Jewish National Council in Palestine.

1000 Mils = 1 Pound
1000 Prutot = 1 Pound (1949)
100 Agorot = 1 Pound (1960)
100 Agorot = 1 Shekel (1980)

**Catalogue values for all unused stamps in this country are for Never Hinged items.**

### Tabs

Stamps of Israel are printed in sheets with tabs (labels) usually attached below the bottom row, sometimes at the sides.

Tabs of the following numbers are in two parts, perforated between: 9, 15, 23-37, 44, 46-47, 50, 55, 62-65, 70-72, 74-77, 86-91, 94-99, 104-118, 123-126, 133-136B, 138-141, 143-151, 160-161, 165-167, 178-179, 182, 187-189, 203, 211-213, 222-223, 228-237, 243-244, 246-250, 256-258, 269-270, 272-273, 275, 294-295, 312, 337-339, 341-344, 346-347, 353-354, C1-C13, C22-C30. Both parts must be present to qualify for with tab value. Stamps with only one part sell for about one-quarter to one-third full tab prices.

### Watermarks

Wmk. 301 — ISRAEL in Hebrew

Wmk. 302 — Multiple Stag

Ancient Judean Coins
A1        A2

Designs: Nos. 1-6, Various coins.

---

**Perf. 10, 11 and Compound**

| | | 1948, May 16 | Typo. | Unwmk. |
|---|---|---|---|---|
| 1 | A1 | 3m orange | .30 | .20 |
| 2 | A1 | 5m yellow grn | .30 | .20 |
| 3 | A1 | 10m red violet | .50 | .20 |
| 4 | A1 | 15m red | .75 | .25 |
| 5 | A1 | 20m bright ultra | 2.50 | .35 |
| 6 | A1 | 50m orange brown | 9.50 | 1.00 |
| | | Nos. 1-6 (6) | 13.85 | 2.20 |
| | | Nos. 1-6 (6) with tabs | 275.00 | |
| | | Set, hinged tabs | 110.00 | |

**Size: 34½x22mm**

| 7 | A2 | 250m dark sl grn | 35.00 | 11.00 |
|---|---|---|---|---|
| 8 | A2 | 500m red brn, cr | 150.00 | 55.00 |

**Size: 36½x24mm**

| 9 | A2 | 1000m blk bl, pale bl | 225.00 | 110.00 |
|---|---|---|---|---|
| | | Nos. 7-9 (3) | 410.00 | 176.00 |
| | | Nos. 7-9 with tabs | 7,500. | |
| | | Set, hinged | 190.00 | |

Nos. 1-9 exist imperf.
See design A6. For overprints see #J1-J5.

**Rouletted**

| 1a | A1 | 3m | .50 | .20 |
|---|---|---|---|---|
| 2b | A1 | 5m | .65 | .25 |
| 3b | A1 | 10m | 11.00 | .90 |
| | | Nos. 1a-3b (3) | 12.15 | 1.35 |
| | | Set, with tabs | 265.00 | |
| | | Set with tabs, hinged | 125.00 | |

Flying Scroll — A3

| | | 1948, Sept. 26 | Litho. | Perf. 11½ |
|---|---|---|---|---|
| 10 | A3 | 3m brn red & ultra | .40 | .20 |
| 11 | A3 | 5m dl grn & ultra | .40 | .20 |
| 12 | A3 | 10m dp car & ultra | .40 | .20 |
| 13 | A3 | 20m dp ultra & ultra | | |
| 14 | A3 | 65m brown & red | 1.50 | .85 |
| | | | 12.00 | 3.75 |
| | | Nos. 10-14 (5) | 14.70 | 5.20 |
| | | With tabs | 250.00 | |
| | | With tabs, hinged | 110.00 | |

Jewish New Year, 5709.

Flag of Israel — A4

**1949, Mar. 31**

| 15 | A4 | 20m bright blue | .50 | .25 |
|---|---|---|---|---|
| | | With tab | 50.00 | |

Appointment of the government by the Knesset.

### Souvenir Sheet

A5

| | | 1949, May 1 | | Imperf. |
|---|---|---|---|---|
| 16 | A5 | Sheet of 4 | 90.00 | 27.50 |
| a. | | 10m dark carmine rose | 17.50 | 4.00 |

1st anniv. of Israeli postage stamps. The sheet was sold at "TABUL," First National Stamp Exhibition, in Tel Aviv, May 1-6, 1949. Tickets, costing 100 mils, covered the entrance fee and one sheet.

---

Bronze Half-Shekel of 67 A.D. — A6

Approach to Jerusalem — A8

Hebrew University, Jerusalem A7

"The Negev" by Reuven Rubin — A9

| | | 1949-50 | Unwmk. | Perf. 11½, 14 |
|---|---|---|---|---|
| 17 | A6 | 3p gray black | .25 | .20 |
| 18 | A6 | 5p purple | .20 | .20 |
| 19 | A6 | 10p green | .20 | .20 |
| 20 | A6 | 15p deep rose | .25 | .20 |
| 21 | A6 | 30p dark blue | .30 | .20 |
| 22 | A6 | 50p brown | 1.25 | .20 |
| 23 | A7 | 100p Prus grn | .40 | .20 |
| | | With tab | 20.00 | |
| 24 | A8 | 250p org brn & gray | 1.25 | .65 |
| | | With tab | 37.50 | |
| 25 | A9 | 500p dp org & brown | 7.50 | 5.50 |
| | | With tab | 240.00 | |
| | | Nos. 17-25 (9) | 11.60 | 7.55 |
| | | Nos. 17-22 with tabs (6) | 75.00 | |
| | | Tete beche pairs, Nos. 18-21 | 80.00 | 80.00 |

Each of Nos. 17-22 portrays a different coin. 25th anniv. of the Hebrew University in Jerusalem (No. 23).
Issued: 250p, 2/16; 3p-50p, 12/18; 100p, 5/9/50; 500p, 12/26/50.
See Nos. 38-43, 56-61, 80-83, and design A1. For overprints see Nos. O1-O4.

Well at Petah Tikva — A10

**1949, Aug. 10**      **Perf. 11**

| 27 | A10 | 40p dk grn & brn | 8.50 | .30 |
|---|---|---|---|---|
| | | With tab | 90.00 | |

70th anniv. of Petah Tikva.

Arms and Service Insignia A11

| | | 1949, Sept. 20 | | Perf. 11½ |
|---|---|---|---|---|
| 28 | A11 | 5p Air Force | .35 | .25 |
| 29 | A11 | 10p Navy | .95 | .40 |
| 30 | A11 | 35p Army | 4.25 | 2.75 |
| | | Nos. 28-30 (3) | 5.55 | 3.40 |
| | | With tabs | 675.00 | |

Jewish New Year, 5710.

---

Running Stag — A12

**1950, Mar. 26**

| 31 | A12 | 40p purple | .55 | .30 |
|---|---|---|---|---|
| a. | | Booklet pane of 4 | 3.75 | |
| 32 | A12 | 80p rose red | .70 | .35 |
| a. | | Booklet pane of 4 | 7.50 | |
| | | Complete booklet, 1 ea. #31a, 32a | 25.00 | |
| b. | | Nos. 31 and 32 tête bêche | 45.00 | 25.00 |
| | | With tabs | 72.50 | |

75th anniv. (in 1949) of the UPU.

Struggle for Free Immigration A13

Arrival of Immigrants A14

**1950, Apr. 23**

| 33 | A13 | 20p dull brown | 2.50 | 1.50 |
|---|---|---|---|---|
| 34 | A14 | 40p dull green | 5.25 | 3.50 |
| | | With tabs | 575.00 | |

Independence Day, Apr. 22, 1950.

---

Fruit and Star of David — A15

**1950, Aug. 31        Litho.        Perf. 14**
35  A15  5p  vio blue & org          .20  .20
36  A15  15p  red brn & grn          .35  .20
       With tabs                     45.00

Jewish New Year, 5711.

Runner and Track
A16

**1950, Oct. 1**
37  A16  80p  olive & sl blk         1.60  .60
       With tab                      70.00

3rd Maccabiah, Ramat Gan, Sept. 27, 1950.

**Coin Type of 1949 Redrawn**

Designs: Various coins.

**1950**
38  A6   3p  gray black              .20  .20
39  A6   5p  purple                  .20  .20
   a.  Tête bêche pair               3.00  3.00
40  A6  10p  green                   .20  .20
   a.  Tête bêche pair               1.25  1.00
41  A6  15p  deep rose               .20  .20
   a.  Tête bêche pair               2.00  1.75
42  A6  30p  dark blue               .20  .20
   a.  Tête bêche pair               4.00  4.00
43  A6  50p  brown                   .20  .20
       Nos. 38-43 (6)                1.20  1.20
       With tabs                     2.90

Inscription at left measures 11mm on Nos. 38-43; 9mm on Nos. 17-22.

Detail from Tablet, "Founding of Tel Aviv"
A17

**1951, Mar. 22**
44  A17  40p  dark brown             .30  .20
       With tab                      20.00

40th anniversary of Tel Aviv.

Young Man Holding Outline Map of Israel — A18

**1951, Apr. 30        Litho.**
45  A18  80p  red brown              .20  .20
       With tab                      3.75

Issued to promote the sale of Independence Bonds.

Metsudat Yesha
A19

Hakastel
A20

**1951, May 9        Unwmk.**
46  A19  15p  red brown              .30  .20
47  A20  40p  deep blue              .60  .20
       With tabs                     45.00

Proclamation of State of Israel, 3rd anniv.

Tractor and Wheat — A21

Tree — A22

Plower and National Fund Stamp of 1902 — A23

**1951, June 24        Perf. 14**
48  A21  15p  red brown              .20  .20
49  A22  25p  Prussian green         .20  .20
50  A23  80p  dull blue              .35  .20
       Nos. 48-50 (3)                .75  .60
       With tabs                     90.00

Jewish National Fund, 50th anniversary.

Theodor Zeev Herzl — A24

Carrier Pigeons — A25

**1951, Aug. 14**
51  A24  80p  gray green             .20  .20
       With tab                      4.00

23rd Zionist Congress, Jerusalem.

**1951, Sept. 16**

Designs: 15p, Girl holding dove and fruit. 40p, Scrolls of the law.

52  A25  5p  blue                    .20  .20
53  A25  15p  cerise                 .20  .20
54  A25  40p  rose violet            .20  .20
       Nos. 52-54 (3)                .60  .60
       With tabs                     3.25

Jewish New Year, 5712.

Menorah and Emblems of Twelve Tribes — A26

**1952, Feb. 27**
55  A26  1000p  dk bl & gray         16.00  7.00
       With tab                      250.00

**Redrawn Coin Type of 1950**

Designs: Various coins.

**1952, Mar. 30**
56  A6  20p  orange                  .20  .20
   a.  Tête bêche pair               2.50  2.50
57  A6  35p  olive green             .20  .20
58  A6  40p  orange brown            .20  .20
59  A6  45p  red violet              .20  .20
   a.  Tête bêche pair               4.50  4.50
60  A6  60p  carmine                 .20  .20
61  A6  85p  aquamarine              .20  .20
       Nos. 56-61 (6)                1.20  1.20
       With tabs                     12.00

Thistle and Yad Mordecai Battlefield
A27

Battlefields: 60p, Cornflower and Deganya. 110p, Anemone and Safed.

**1952, Apr. 29**
62  A27  30p  lil rose & vio brn     .20  .20
63  A27  60p  ultra & gray blk       .20  .20
64  A27  110p  crimson & gray        .35  .25
       Nos. 62-64 (3)                .75  .65
       With tabs                     20.00

Proclamation of State of Israel, 4th anniv.

Manhattan Skyline and American Zionists' House
A28

**1952, May 13**
65  A28  220p  dark blue & gray      .35  .20
       With tab                      11.00

Opening of American Zionists' House, Tel Aviv.

Figs — A29

**Unwmk.**
**1952, Sept. 3        Litho.        Perf. 14**
66  A29  15p  shown                  .30  .20
67  A29  40p  Lily                   .30  .20
68  A29  110p  Dove                  .30  .20
69  A29  220p  Nut cluster           .50  .20
       Nos. 66-69 (4)                1.40  .80
       With tabs                     24.50

Jewish New Year, 5713.

Pres. Chaim Weizmann (1874-1952) and Presidential Standard — A30

**1952, Dec. 9**
70  A30  30p  slate                  .20  .20
71  A30  110p  black                 .25  .20
       With tab                      9.00

Weizmann, president of Israel 1948-52.

Numeral Incorporating Agricultural Scenes — A31

**1952, Dec. 31**
72  A31  110p  brown, buff & emer    .40  .20
       With tab                      8.50

70th anniversary of B.I.L.U. (Bet Yaakov Lechu Venelcha) immigration.

Five Anemones and State Emblem — A32

**1953, Apr. 19**
73  A32  110p  grnsh bl, bl blk & red   .20  .20
       With tab                      4.25

5th anniversary of State of Israel.

Rabbi Moshe ben Maimon (Maimonides)
A33

Holy Ark, Jerusalem
A34

**1953, Aug. 3  Wmk. 301  Perf. 14x13**
74  A33  110p  brown                 .35  .35
       With tab                      8.25

7th International Congress of History of Science, Jerusalem, Aug. 4-11.

**1953, Aug. 11**

Holy Arks: 45p, Petah Tikva. 200p, Safed.

75  A34  20p  sapphire               .20  .20
76  A34  45p  brown red              .20  .20
77  A34  200p  purple                .20  .20
       Nos. 75-77 (3)                .60  .60
       With tabs                     9.75

Jewish New Year, 5714.

Combined Ball-Globe
A35

Desert Rose
A36

**Unwmk.**
**1953, Sept. 20        Litho.        Perf. 14**
78  A35  110p  blue & dark brn       .20  .20
       With tab                      4.25

4th Maccabiah, Sept. 20-29, 1953.

**1953, Sept. 22**
79  A36  200p  multicolored          .20  .20
       With tab                      4.50

Conquest of the Desert Exhib., 9/22-10/14.

**Redrawn Type of 1950**

Designs: Various coins.

**1954, Jan. 5**
80  A6  80p  olive bister            .20  .20
81  A6  95p  blue green              .20  .20
82  A6  100p  fawn                   .20  .20
83  A6  125p  violet blue            .20  .20
       Nos. 80-83 (4)                .80  .80
       With tabs                     3.00

Marigold and Ruins at Yehiam — A37

350p, Narcissus and bridge at Gesher.

**1954, May 5**               **Litho.**
84  A37  60p dk bl, mag & ol
              gray             .20   .20
85  A37  350p dk brn, grn & yel  .20   .20
   With tabs                 2.25
   Memorial Day and 6th anniversary of proclamation of State of Israel.

Theodor Zeev Herzl (1860-1904), Founder of Zionist Movement — A38

**1954, July 21**           **Wmk. 302**
86  A38  160p dk bl, dk brn & cr  .20   .20
   With tab                 .85

Bearers with Grape Cluster A39

**1954, Sept. 8**         **Perf. 13x14**
87  A39  25p dark brown     .20   .20
   With tab                 .20
   Jewish New Year, 5715.

19th Century Mail Coach and Jerusalem Post Office A40

   200p, Mail truck & present G.P.O., Jerusalem.

**1954, Oct. 13**            **Perf. 14**
88  A40  60p blue, blk & yel   .20   .20
89  A40  200p dk grn, blk & red  .20   .20
   With tabs               3.00
   TABIM, National Stamp Exhibition, Jerusalem, Oct. 13-18.

Baron Edmond de Rothschild (1845-1934) and Grape Cluster — A41

**1954, Nov. 23**         **Perf. 13x14**
90  A41  300p dark blue green  .20   .20
   With tab                 .85

Lighted Oil Lamp A42

**1955, Jan. 13**          **Perf. 13x14**
91  A42  250p dark blue     .20   .20
   With tab                 .75
   Teachers' Association, 50th anniversary.

---

Parachutist and Barbed Wire — A43

**1955, Mar. 31**      **Litho.**   **Perf. 14**
92  A43  120p dk Prus green   .20   .20
   With tab                 .45
   Jewish volunteers from Palestine who
served in British army in World War II.

Lighted Menorah A44

**1955, Apr. 26**
93  A44  150p dk grn, blk & org  .20   .20
   With tab                 .35
   Proclamation of State of Israel, 7th anniv.

Immigration by Ship — A45

   Designs: 10p, Immigration by plane. 25p,
Agricultural training. 30p, Gardening. 60p,
Vocational training. 750p, Scientific education.

**1955, May 10**    **Unwmk.**   **Perf. 14**
94  A45  5p brt blue & black   .20   .20
95  A45  10p red & black      .20   .20
96  A45  25p deep grn & black  .20   .20
97  A45  30p orange & black   .20   .20
98  A45  60p lilac rose & blk   .20   .20
99  A45  750p olive bis & blk   .25   .20
     Nos. 94-99 (6)     1.25  1.20
     With tabs              1.75
   Israel's Youth Immigration Institution, 20th
anniv.

Musicians with Tambourine and Cymbals A46      Mandrake, Reuben A48

Ambulance A47

   Musician with: 60p, Ram's Horn. 120p, Loud
Trumpet. 250p, Harp.

**1955, Aug. 25**    **Photo.**   **Wmk. 302**
100  A46  25p dark green & org  .20   .20
             **Unwmk.**
101  A46  60p dk gray & orange  .20   .20
102  A46  120p dark blue & yel   .20   .20
103  A46  250p red brn & org    .20   .20
    #100-103, with tabs         .50
   Jewish New Year, 5716.
   See Nos. 121-123.

---

**1955, Nov. 1**    **Wmk. 301**   **Perf. 14**
104  A47  160p grn, red & blk   .20   .20
   With tab                 .30
   Magen David Adom (Israeli Red Cross),
25th anniv.

**1955-57**    **Wmk. 302**   **Perf. 13x14**
   Twelve Tribes: 20p, Gates of Sechem,
Simeon. 30p, Ephod, Levi. 40p, Lion, Judah.
50p, Scales, Dan. 60p, Stag, Naphtali. 80p,
Tents, Gad. 100p, Tree, Asher. 120p, Sun and
stars, Issachar. 180p, Ship, Zebulon. 200p,
Sheaf of wheat, Joseph. 250p, Wolf,
Benjamin.
105  A48  10p bright green    .20   .20
106  A48  20p red lilac ('56)   .20   .20
107  A48  30p bright ultra     .20   .20
108  A48  40p brown ('56)    .20   .20
109  A48  50p grnsh bl ('56)   .20   .20
110  A48  60p lemon        .20   .20
111  A48  80p deep vio ('56)  .20   .20
112  A48  100p vermilion     .20   .20
113  A48  120p olive ('56)    .20   .20
114  A48  180p lil rose ('56)  .20   .20
115  A48  200p green ('56)    .20   .20
116  A48  250p gray ('56)     .20   .20
    #105-116, with tabs      2.00
     See Nos. 133-136B.

Albert Einstein (1879-1955) and Equation of his Relativity Theory — A49

**1956, Jan. 3**         **Perf. 13x14**
117  A49  350p brown      .20   .20
   With tab                 .60

Technion, Haifa A50

**1956, Jan. 3**          **Wmk. 302**
118  A50  350p lt ol grn & blk   .20   .20
   With tab                 .20
   Israel Institute of Technology, 30th anniv.

"Eight Years of Israel" — A51     Jaffa Oranges — A52

**1956, Apr. 12**    **Litho.**   **Perf. 14**
119  A51  150p multicolored   .20   .20
   With tab                 .20
   Proclamation of State of Israel, 8th anniv.

**1956, May 20**   **Wmk. 302**  **Perf. 14**
120  A52  300p bl grn & orange  .20   .20
   With tab                 .20
   4th Intl. Congress of Mediterranean Citrus
Growers.

     **New Year Type of 1955**
   Musician with: 30p, Lyre. 50p, Cymbals.
150p, Double oboe, horiz.

**1956, Aug. 14**   **Photo.**  **Perf. 14x13**
121  A46  30p brown & brt blue  .20   .20
           **Perf. 14**
122  A46  50p purple & orange   .20   .20
123  A46  150p dk bl grn & org   .20   .20
    #121-123, with tabs         .25
   Jewish New Year, 5717.

---

Haganah Insignia A54     Bezalel Museum and Antique Lamp A55

**1957, Jan. 1**         **Perf. 13x14**
124  A54  20p + 80p brt grn   .20   .20
125  A54  50p + 150p car rose  .20   .20
126  A54  50p + 350p ultra    .20   .20
    #124-126, with tabs         .25
   Defense issue. Divided denomination used
to show increased postal rate.

**1957, Apr. 29**    **Litho.**   **Perf. 14**
127  A55  400p multicolored   .20   .20
   With tab                 .20
   Bezalel Natl. Museum, Jerusalem, 50th
anniv.

Jet Plane and "9" — A56     Horse and Seal — A57

**1957, Apr. 29**

| 128 | A56 | 250p deep bl & blk | .20 | .20 |
|---|---|---|---|---|
| | | With tab | | .20 |

Proclamation of State of Israel, 9th anniv.

**1957, Sept. 4    Wmk. 302    Perf. 14**

Ancient Seals: 160p, Lion. 300p, Gazelle.

| 129 | A57 | 50p ocher & blk, *lt bl* | .20 | .20 |
|---|---|---|---|---|

**Perf. 14x13**

| | | **Photo.** | **Unwmk.** |
|---|---|---|---|

| 130 | A57 | 160p grn & blk, *bis brn* | .20 | .20 |
|---|---|---|---|---|
| 131 | A57 | 300p dp car & blk, *pink* | .20 | .20 |
| | | #130-131, with tabs | | .25 |

Jewish New Year, 5718.

### TABIL
### Souvenir Sheet

Bet Alpha Synagogue Mosaic — A58

**1957, Sept. 17    Litho.    Roulette 13**

| 132 | A58 | Sheet of 4 | .30 | .30 |
|---|---|---|---|---|
| a. | | 100p multicolored | .20 | .20 |
| b. | | 200p multicolored | .20 | .20 |
| c. | | 300p multicolored | .20 | .20 |
| d. | | 400p multicolored | .20 | .20 |

1st Intl. stamp exhib. in Israel, Tel Aviv, 9/17-23.

### Tribes Type of 1955-57
### Perf. 13x14

| **1957-59** | | **Unwmk.** | **Photo.** |
|---|---|---|---|
| 133 | A48 | 10p brt grn ('58) | .20 | .20 |
| 133A | A48 | 20p red lilac | .20 | .20 |
| 133C | A48 | 40p brown ('59) | .55 | .45 |
| 134 | A48 | 50p greenish blue | .20 | .20 |
| 135 | A48 | 60p lemon | .20 | .20 |
| 136 | A48 | 100p vermilion | .20 | .20 |
| 136B | A48 | 120p olive ('58) | .20 | .20 |
| | | Nos. 133-136B (7) | 1.75 | 1.65 |
| | | With tabs | 42.50 | |

Hammer Thrower — A59

**1958, Jan. 20    Perf. 14x13**

| 137 | A59 | 500p bister & car | .20 | .20 |
|---|---|---|---|---|
| | | With tab | | .25 |

Maccabiah Games, 25th anniversary.

Ancient Ship — A60

Ships: 20p, Three-master used for "illegal immigration." 30p, Cargo ship "Shomron." 1000p, Passenger ship "Zion."

**Wmk. 302**

**1958, Jan. 27    Litho.    Perf. 14**
**Size: 36½x22½mm**

| 138 | A60 | 10p ocher, red & blk | .20 | .20 |
|---|---|---|---|---|

**Perf. 13x14**
**Photo.**

| 139 | A60 | 20p brt grn, blk & brn | .20 | .20 |
|---|---|---|---|---|
| 140 | A60 | 30p red, blk & grnsh bl | .20 | .20 |

**Size: 56½x22½mm**

| 141 | A60 | 400p brt bl, blk & grn | .20 | .20 |
|---|---|---|---|---|
| | | #138-141, with tabs | | .35 |

Issued to honor Israel's merchant fleet.

Menorah and Olive Branch — A61

**Unwmk.**

**1958, Apr. 21    Litho.    Perf. 14**

| 142 | A61 | 400p gold, blk & grn | .20 | .20 |
|---|---|---|---|---|
| | | With tab | | .20 |

Memorial Day and 10th anniversary of proclamation of State of Israel.

Dancing Youths Forming "10" — A62

**1958, July 2**

| 143 | A62 | 200p dk org & dk grn | .20 | .20 |
|---|---|---|---|---|
| | | With tab | | .20 |

First World Conference of Jewish Youth, Jerusalem, July 28-Aug. 1.

Convention Center, Jerusalem A63

**1958, July 2**

| 144 | A63 | 400p vio & org, *yellow* | .20 | .20 |
|---|---|---|---|---|
| | | With tab | | .20 |

10th Anniversary of Independence Exhibition, Jerusalem, June 5-Aug. 21.

Wheat — A64

**1958, Aug. 27    Photo.    Perf. 14x13**

| 145 | A64 | 50p shown | .20 | .20 |
|---|---|---|---|---|
| 146 | A64 | 60p Barley | .20 | .20 |
| 147 | A64 | 160p Grapes | .20 | .20 |
| 148 | A64 | 300p Figs | .20 | .20 |
| | | #145-148, with tabs | | .30 |

Jewish New Year, 5719.

"Love Thy Neighbor . . ." — A65

**1958, Dec. 10    Litho.    Perf. 14**

| 149 | A65 | 750p yel, gray & grn | .20 | .20 |
|---|---|---|---|---|
| | | With tab | | .90 |

Universal Declaration of Human Rights, 10th anniversary.

Designing and Printing Stamps A66

Radio and Telephone — A67

120p, Mobile post office. 500p, Teletype.

**1959, Feb. 25    Wmk. 302    Perf. 14**

| 150 | A66 | 60p olive, blk & red | .20 | .20 |
|---|---|---|---|---|
| 151 | A66 | 120p olive, blk & red | .20 | .20 |
| 152 | A67 | 250p olive, blk & red | .20 | .20 |
| 153 | A67 | 500p olive, blk & red | .20 | .20 |
| | | #150-153, with tabs | | .45 |

Decade of postal activities in Israel.

Shalom Aleichem A68        Cyclamen A69

Portraits: No. 155, Chaim Nachman Bialik. No. 156, Eliezer Ben-Yehuda.

**1959    Unwmk.    Photo.    Perf. 14x13**

| 154 | A68 | 250p yel grn & red brn | .20 | .20 |
|---|---|---|---|---|
| 155 | A68 | 250p ocher & ol gray | .20 | .20 |
| | | #154-155, with tabs | | .35 |

**Perf. 14**
**Litho.**

| 156 | A68 | 250p bl & vio bl | .20 | .20 |
|---|---|---|---|---|
| | | With tab | | .40 |

Birth cent. of Aleichem (Solomon Rabinowitz), Yiddish writer (No. 154); 25th death anniv. of Bialik, Hebrew poet (No. 155); birth cent. of Ben-Yehuda, father of modern Hebrew (No. 156).

Issued: #154, 3/30; #155, 7/22; #156, 11/25.

**1959, May 11    Wmk. 302    Perf. 14**

Flowers: 60p, Anemone. 300p, Narcissus.

### Flowers in Natural Colors

| 157 | A69 | 60p deep green | .20 | .20 |
|---|---|---|---|---|
| 158 | A69 | 120p deep plum | .20 | .20 |
| 159 | A69 | 300p blue | .20 | .20 |
| | | #157-159, with tabs | | .35 |

Memorial Day and 11th anniversary of proclamation of State of Israel.

Buildings, Tel Aviv — A70

**1959, May 4**

| 160 | A70 | 120p multicolored | .20 | .20 |
|---|---|---|---|---|
| | | With tab | | .20 |

50th anniversary of Tel Aviv.

Bristol Britannia and Windsock A71

**1959, July 22**

| 161 | A71 | 500p multicolored | .20 | .20 |
|---|---|---|---|---|
| | | With tab | | .30 |

Civil Aviation in Israel, 10th anniversary.

Pomegranates A72

**Perf. 14x13**

**1959, Sept. 9    Photo.    Unwmk.**

| 162 | A72 | 60p shown | .20 | .20 |
|---|---|---|---|---|
| 163 | A72 | 200p Olives | .20 | .20 |
| 164 | A72 | 350p Dates | .20 | .20 |
| | | Nos. 162-164 (3) | .60 | .60 |
| | | With tabs | 1.50 | |

Jewish New Year, 5720.

Merhavya A73

Settlements: 120p, Yesud Ha-Maala. 180p, Deganya.

**1959, Nov. 25    Photo.    Perf. 13x14**

| 165 | A73 | 60p citron & dk grn | .20 | .20 |
|---|---|---|---|---|
| 166 | A73 | 120p red brn & ocher | .20 | .20 |
| 167 | A73 | 180p blue & dk grn | .20 | .20 |
| | | Nos. 165-167 (3) | .60 | .60 |
| | | With tabs | 1.90 | |

Settlements of Merhavya and Deganya, 50th anniv.; Yesud Ha-Maala, 75th anniv.

Judean Coin (66-70 A.D.) — A74

**1960    Unwmk.    Perf. 13x14**
**Denominations in Black**

| 168 | A74 | 1a brn, *pinkish* | .20 | .20 |
|---|---|---|---|---|
| a. | | On surface colored paper | .20 | .20 |
| | | As "a," with tab | .75 | |
| b. | | Black overprint omitted | | |
| 169 | A74 | 3a brt red, *pinkish* | .20 | .20 |
| 170 | A74 | 5a gray, *pinkish* | .20 | .20 |
| 171 | A74 | 6a brt grn, *lt bl* | .20 | .20 |
| 171A | A74 | 7a gray, *bluish* | .20 | .20 |
| 172 | A74 | 8a mag, *lt blue* | .20 | .20 |
| 173 | A74 | 12a grnsh bl, *lt bl* | .20 | .20 |
| a. | | Black overprint omitted | | |
| 174 | A74 | 18a orange | .20 | .20 |
| 175 | A74 | 25a blue | .20 | .20 |
| 176 | A74 | 30a carmine | .20 | .20 |
| 177 | A74 | 50a bright lilac | .20 | .20 |
| | | #168-177, with tabs | 2.00 | |

Issue dates: 7a, July 6; others, Jan. 6.

Operation "Magic Carpet" A75

Design: 50a, Resettled family in front of house, grapes and figs.

**1960, Apr. 7    Unwmk.    Perf. 13x14**

| 178 | A75 | 25a red brown | .20 | .20 |
|---|---|---|---|---|
| 179 | A75 | 50a green | .20 | .20 |
| | | #178-179, with tabs | | .35 |

World Refugee Year, July 1, 1959-June 30, 1960.

Sand Lily — A76

Design: 32a, Evening primrose.

**1960, Apr. 27    Litho.    Perf. 14**
180  A76  12a multicolored          .20    .20
181  A76  32a brn, yel & grn        .20    .20
    #180-181, with tabs               .55

Memorial Day; proclamation of State of Israel, 12th anniv. See #204-206, 238-240.

Atom Diagram and Atomic Reactor A77

**1960, July 6    Wmk. 302    Perf. 14**
182  A77  50a blue, red & blk       .20    .20
    With tab                          .60

Installation of Israel's first atomic reactor.

Theodor Herzl and Rhine at Basel — A78

King Saul — A79

**1960, Aug. 31    Litho.    Perf. 14**
183  A78  25a gray brown            .20    .20
    With tab                          .40

**1960, Aug. 31    Wmk. 302**
Designs: 25a, King David. 40a, King Solomon.

**Kings in Multicolor**
184  A79  7a emerald                .20    .20

**Unwmk.**
185  A79  25a brown                 .20    .20
186  A79  40a blue                  .25    .20
    Nos. 185-186 (2)             .45    .40
    With tabs                        1.25

Jewish New Year, 5721. See Nos. 208-210.

Jewish Postal Courier, Prague, 18th Century A80

**Perf. 13x14**
**1960, Oct. 9    Photo.    Unwmk.**
187  A80  25a olive blk, gray       .25    .20
    With tab                         2.50
  a.  Souvenir sheet          13.00   8.00

TAVIV Natl. Stamp Exhib., Tel Aviv, Oct. 9-19.
No. 187a sold only at Exhibition for 50a.

Henrietta Szold and Hadassah Medical Center A81

**1960, Dec. 14    Perf. 13x14**
188  A81  25a turq bl & vio gray    .20    .20
    With tab                          .30

Birth cent. of Henrietta Szold, founder of Hadassah, American Jewish women's organization.

Shields of Jerusalem and First Zionist Congress A82

**1960, Dec. 14    Unwmk.    Perf. 14**
189  A82  50a vio bl & turq blue    .20    .20
    With tab                         1.10

25th Zionist Congress, Jerusalem, 1960.

Ram — A83

Signs of Zodiac — A84

**1961, Feb. 27    Photo.    Perf. 13x14**
190  A83  1a Ram                    .20    .20
191  A83  2a Bull                   .20    .20
192  A83  6a Twins                  .20    .20
193  A83  7a Crab                   .20    .20
194  A83  8a Lion                   .20    .20
  a.  Booklet pane of 6 ('65)          .45
195  A83  10a Virgin                .20    .20
196  A83  12a Scales                .20    .20
  a.  Booklet pane of 6 ('65)          .45
197  A83  18a Scorion               .20    .20
198  A83  20a Archer                .20    .20
199  A83  25a Goat                  .20    .20
200  A83  32a Water bearer          .20    .20
201  A83  50a Fishes                .20    .20

**Perf. 14**
**Litho.**
202  A84  £1 dk bl, gold & lt bl    .25    .20
    Nos. 190-202 (13)            2.65   2.60
    With tabs                        5.25

Booklet pane sheets (Nos. 194a, 196a) of 36 (9x4) contain 6 panes of 6, with gutters dividing the sheet in four sections. Each sheet yields 4 tete beche pairs and 4 tete beche gutter pairs, or strips. See Nos. 215-217.
Vertical strips of 6 of the 1a, 10a and No. 216 (5a) are from larger sheets from which coils were produced. Regular sheets of 50 are arranged 10x5.

Javelin Thrower and "7" — A85

**1961, Apr. 18    Litho.    Perf. 14**
203  A85  25a multicolored          .20    .20
    With tab                          .45

7th Intl. Congress of the Hapoel Sports Org., Ramat Gan, May 1961.

**Flower Type of 1960**
7a, Myrtle. 12a, Sea onion. 32a, Oleander.

**1961, Apr. 18    Unwmk.**
**Flowers in Natural Colors**
204  A76  7a green                  .20    .20
205  A76  12a rose carmine          .20    .20
206  A76  32a brt greenish bl       .20    .20
    Nos. 204-206 (3)             .60    .60
    With tabs                        1.00

Memorial Day; proclamation of State of Israel, 13th anniv.

Scaffold Around "10" and Sapling — A86

**1961, June 14    Photo.    Perf. 14**
207  A86  50a Prussian blue         .20    .20
    With tab                          .55

Israel bond issue 10th anniv.

**Type of 1960**
Designs: 7a, Samson. 25a, Judas Maccabaeus. 40a, Bar Cocheba.

**1961, Aug. 21    Litho.    Perf. 14**
**Multicolored Designs**
208  A79  7a red orange             .20    .20
209  A79  25a gray                  .20    .20
210  A79  40a lilac                 .20    .20
    Nos. 208-210 (3)             .60    .60
    With tabs                        1.25

Jewish New Year, 5722.

Bet Hamidrash Synagogue, Medzibozh A87

**1961, Aug. 21    Photo.    Perf. 13x14**
211  A87  25a dk brn & yel          .20    .20
    With tab                          .40

Bicentenary of death of Rabbi Israel Baal-Shem-Tov, founder of Hasidism.

Pine Cone A88

Design: 30a, Symbolic trees.

**1961, Dec. 26    Unwmk.    Perf. 13x14**
212  A88  25a green, yel & blk      .20    .20
213  A88  30a org, green & ind      .20    .20
    #212-213, with tabs              2.00

Achievements of afforestation program.

Cello, Harp, French Horn and Kettle Drum — A89

**1961, Dec. 26    Litho.    Perf. 14**
214  A89  50a multicolored          .25    .25
    With tab                         2.00

Israel Philharmonic Orchestra, 25th anniv.

**Zodiac Type of 1961 Surcharged with New Value**
**1962, Mar. 18    Photo.    Perf. 13x14**
215  A83  3a on 1a lt lilac         .20    .20
  a.  Without overprint           80.00
216  A83  5a on 7a gray             .20    .20
217  A83  30a on 32a emerald        .20    .20
  a.  Without overprint           32.50
    #215-217, with tabs               .25

See note after No. 202.

Anopheles Maculipennis and Chart Showing Decline of Malaria in Israel — A90

View of Rosh Pinna — A91

**1962, Apr. 30    Perf. 14x13**
218  A90  25a ocher, red & blk      .20    .20
    With tab                          .50

WHO drive to eradicate malaria.

**1962, Apr. 30    Unwmk.**
219  A91  20a yel, green & brn      .20    .20
    With tab                          .50

Rosh Pinna agricultural settlement, 80th anniv.

Flame ("Hear, O Israel . . .") A92

Yellow Star of David and Six Candles A93

**1962, Apr. 30    Photo.**
220  A92  12a black, org & red      .20    .20

**Perf. 14**
221  A93  55a multicolored          .20    .20
    #220-221, with tabs              1.40

Heroes and Martyrs Day, in memory of the 6,000,000 Jewish victims of Nazi persecution.

Vautour Fighter-Bomber — A94

Design: 30a, Fighter-Bombers in formation.

**1962, Apr. 30    Perf. 13x14**
222  A94  12a blue                  .20    .20
223  A94  30a olive green           .20    .20
    #222-223, with tabs              1.75

Memorial Day; proclamation of the state of Israel, 14th anniv.

Symbolic Flags — A95

Wolf and Lamb, Isaiah 11:6 — A96

**1962, June 5    Perf. 14**
224  A95  55a multicolored          .20    .20
    With tab                         1.00

Near East Intl. Fair, Tel Aviv, June 5-July 5.

## 1962, Sept. 5

Designs: 28a, Leopard and kid, Isaiah 11:6. 43a, Child and asp, Isaiah 11:8.

| | | | |
|---|---|---|---|
| 225 | A96 | 8a buff, red & black | .20 .20 |
| 226 | A96 | 28a buff, lilac & black | .20 .20 |
| 227 | A96 | 43a buff, org & black | .20 .20 |
| | | *Nos. 225-227 (3)* | .60 .60 |
| | | With tab | 3.00 |

Jewish New Year, 5723.

Boeing
707 — A97

## 1962, Nov. 7     *Perf. 13x14*

| | | | |
|---|---|---|---|
| 228 | A97 | 55a bl, dk bl & rose lil | .30 .20 |
| | | With tab | 1.25 |
| a. | | Souvenir sheet | 2.25 1.75 |

El Al Airlines; El Al Philatelic Exhibition, Tel Aviv, Nov. 7-14. Issued in sheets of 15.

No. 228a contains one stamp in greenish blue, dark blue & rose lilac with greenish blue color continuing into margin design (No. 228 has white perforations). Sold for £1 for one day at philatelic counters in Jerusalem, Haifa and Tel Aviv and for one week at the El Al Exhibition.

Cogwheel
Symbols of
UJA
Activities
A98

## 1962, Dec. 26   Unwmk.   *Perf. 13x14*

| | | | |
|---|---|---|---|
| 229 | A98 | 20a org red, sil & bl | .20 .20 |
| | | With tab | .50 |

25th anniv. of the United Jewish Appeal (United States) and its support of immigration, settlement, agriculture and care of the aged and sick.

Janusz
Korczak
A99

## 1962, Dec. 26      Photo.

| | | | |
|---|---|---|---|
| 230 | A99 | 30a olive grn & blk | .20 .20 |
| | | With tab | .45 |

Dr. Janusz Korczak (Henryk Goldszmit, 1879-1942), physician, teacher and writer, killed in Treblinka concentration camp.

Orange
butterflyfish
A100

Red Sea fish: 3a, Pennant Coral Fish. 8a, Lionfish. 12a, Zebra-striped angelfish.

## 1962, Dec. 26   Litho.   *Perf. 14*
### Fish in Natural Colors

| | | | |
|---|---|---|---|
| 231 | A100 | 3a green | .20 .20 |
| 232 | A100 | 6a purple | .20 .20 |
| 233 | A100 | 8a brown | .20 .20 |
| 234 | A100 | 12a dark blue | .20 .20 |
| | | #231-234, with tabs | .60 |

See Nos. 246-249.

Stockade at
Dawn
A101

Design: 30a, Completed stockade at night.

## 1963, Mar. 21   Unwmk.   *Perf. 14*

| | | | |
|---|---|---|---|
| 235 | A101 | 12a yel brn, blk & yel | .20 .20 |
| 236 | A101 | 30a dp plum, blk & lt bl | .20 .20 |
| | | #235-236, with tabs | .85 |

25th anniv. of the "Stockade and Tower" villages.

Hand
Offering
Food to
Bird
A102

## 1963, Mar. 21   Photo.   *Perf. 13x14*

| | | | |
|---|---|---|---|
| 237 | A102 | 55a gray & black | .25 .20 |
| | | With tab | .80 |
| a. | | Booklet pane of 4 | 32.50 |

FAO "Freedom from Hunger" campaign. Issued in sheets of 15 (5x3) with 5 tabs. The booklet pane sheet of 16 (4x4) is divided into 2 panes of 8 (4x2) by horizontal gutter. The 4 stamps at left in each pane are inverted in relation to the 4 at right, making 4 horizontal tete beche pairs down the center of the sheet.

### Flower Type of 1960

8a, White lily. 30a, Hollyhock. 37a, Tulips.

## 1963, Apr. 25   Litho.   *Perf. 14*
### Flowers in Natural Colors

| | | | |
|---|---|---|---|
| 238 | A76 | 8a slate | .20 .20 |
| 239 | A76 | 30a yellow green | .20 .20 |
| 240 | A76 | 37a sepia | .20 .20 |
| | | *Nos. 238-240 (3)* | .60 .60 |
| | | With tabs | 3.00 |

Memorial Day; proclamation of the State of Israel, 15th anniv.

Typesetter, 19th
Century — A103

## 1963, June 19   Photo.   *Perf. 14x13*

| | | | |
|---|---|---|---|
| 241 | A103 | 12a tan & vio brn | .50 .40 |
| | | With tab | 1.60 |
| a. | | Sheet of 16 | 45.00 65.00 |

Hebrew press in Palestine, cent. The background of the sheet shows page of 1st issue of "Halbanon" newspaper, giving each stamp a different background.

"The Sun Beat
upon the Head
of
Jonah" — A104

Hoe Clearing
Thistles — A105

Designs: 30a, "There was a mighty tempest in the sea." 55a, "Jonah was in the belly of the fish." 30a, 55a horiz.

## 1963, Aug. 21     *Perf. 14x13, 13x14*

| | | | |
|---|---|---|---|
| 242 | A104 | 8a org, lil & blk | .20 .20 |
| 243 | A104 | 30a multicolored | .20 .20 |
| 244 | A104 | 55a multicolored | .20 .20 |
| | | *Nos. 242-244 (3)* | .60 .60 |
| | | With tabs | 2.75 |

Jewish New Year, 5724.

## 1963, Aug. 21      *Perf. 14*

| | | | |
|---|---|---|---|
| 245 | A105 | 37a multicolored | .20 .20 |
| | | With tab | .90 |

80 years of agricultural settlements in Israel; "Year of the Pioneers."

### Fish Type of 1962

Red Sea Fish: 2a, Undulate triggerfish. 6a, Radiate turkeyfish. 8a, Bigeye. 12a, Imperial angelfish.

## 1963, Dec. 16   Litho.   *Perf. 14*
### Fish in Natural Colors

| | | | |
|---|---|---|---|
| 246 | A100 | 2a violet blue | .20 .20 |
| 247 | A100 | 6a green | .20 .20 |
| 248 | A100 | 8a orange | .20 .20 |
| 249 | A100 | 12a olive green | .20 .20 |
| | | *Nos. 246-249 (4)* | .80 .80 |
| | | With tabs | .90 |

S.S. Shalom, Sailing Vessel and
Ancient Map of Coast Line — A106

## 1963, Dec. 16   Photo.   *Perf. 13x14*

| | | | |
|---|---|---|---|
| 250 | A106 | £1 ultra, brt grn & lil | .85 .45 |
| | | With tab | 8.00 |

Maiden voyage of S.S. Shalom.

"Old Age and
Survivors
Insurance"
A107

Pres. Izhak Ben-
Zvi (1884-1963)
A108

Designs (Insurance): 25a, Maternity. 37a, Large family. 50a, Workers' compensation.

## 1964, Feb. 24   Litho.   *Perf. 14*

| | | | |
|---|---|---|---|
| 251 | A107 | 12a multicolored | .20 .20 |
| 252 | A107 | 25a multicolored | .20 .20 |
| 253 | A107 | 37a multicolored | .20 .20 |
| 254 | A107 | 50a multicolored | .30 .30 |
| | | *Nos. 251-254 (4)* | .90 .90 |
| | | With tabs | 7.75 |

Natl. Insurance Institute 10th anniv.

## 1964, Apr. 13   Photo.   *Perf. 14x13*

| | | | |
|---|---|---|---|
| 255 | A108 | 12a dark brown | .20 .20 |
| | | With tab | .20 |

Terrestrial Spectroscopy — A109

Designs: 35a, Macromolecules of the living cell. 70a, Electronic computer.

## 1964, Apr. 13      *Perf. 14*

| | | | |
|---|---|---|---|
| 256 | A109 | 8a multicolored | .20 .20 |
| 257 | A109 | 35a multicolored | .20 .20 |
| 258 | A109 | 70a multicolored | .20 .20 |
| | | *Nos. 256-258 (3)* | .60 .60 |
| | | With tabs | 3.50 |

Proclamation of the State of Israel, 16th anniv.; Israel's contribution to science.

Basketball
Players
A110

Serpent of
Aesculapius and
Menorah
A111

8a, Runner. 12a, Discus thrower. 50a, Soccer.

## 1964, June 24     *Perf. 14x13*

| | | | |
|---|---|---|---|
| 259 | A110 | 8a brt brick red & dk brown | .20 .20 |
| 260 | A110 | 12a rose lil & dk brn | .20 .20 |
| 261 | A110 | 30a bl, car & dk brn | .20 .20 |
| 262 | A110 | 50a yel grn, org red & dk brown | .20 .20 |
| | | *Nos. 259-262 (4)* | .80 .80 |
| | | With tabs | .90 |

Israel's participation in the 18th Olympic Games, Tokyo, Oct. 10-25.

## 1964, Aug. 5      Unwmk.

| | | | |
|---|---|---|---|
| 263 | A111 | £1 ol bis & slate grn | .40 .30 |
| | | With tab | .75 |

6th World Congress of the Israel Medical Association, Haifa, Aug. 3-13.

Ancient Glass
Vase — A112

Different glass vessels, 1st-3rd centuries.

## 1964, Aug. 5      Litho.

| | | | |
|---|---|---|---|
| 264 | A112 | 8a vio, brn & org | .20 .20 |
| 265 | A112 | 35a ol, grn & bl grn | .20 .20 |
| 266 | A112 | 70a brt car rose, blue & violet blue | .20 .20 |
| | | *Nos. 264-266 (3)* | .60 .60 |
| | | With tabs | .85 |

Jewish New Year, 5725.

Steamer
Bringing
Immigrants
A113

Eleanor
Roosevelt
(1884-1962)
A114

## 1964, Nov. 2   Litho.   *Perf. 14*

| | | | |
|---|---|---|---|
| 267 | A113 | 25a slate bl, bl grn & blk | .20 .20 |
| | | With tab | .35 |

30th anniv. of the blockade runners bringing immigrants to Israel.

## 1964, Nov. 2   Photo.   *Perf. 14x13*

| | | | |
|---|---|---|---|
| 268 | A114 | 70a dull purple | .20 .20 |
| | | With tab | .45 |

Chess Board, Knight and Emblem of
Chess Olympics — A115

## 1964, Nov. 2     *Perf. 13x14*

| | | | |
|---|---|---|---|
| 269 | A115 | 12a shown | .20 .20 |
| 270 | A115 | 70a Rook | .35 .30 |
| | | With tabs | 1.90 |

16th Chess Olympics, Tel Aviv, Nov. 1964.

"Africa-Israel
Friendship" — A116

## 1964, Nov. 30    Photo.    *Perf. 14x13*
271 A116 57a ol, blk, gold & red
        brown       .35   .20
     With tab     2.00
   *a.*  Souvenir sheet   1.40  1.40
TABAI, Natl. Stamp Exhibition, dedicated to African-Israel friendship, Haifa, Nov. 30-Dec. 6. No. 271a contains one imperf. stamp. Sold for £1.

View of Masada from West A117

Designs: 36a, Northern Palace, lower terrace. £1, View of Northern Palace, vert.

## 1965, Feb. 3    Photo.    *Perf. 13x14*
272 A117 25a dull green   .20  .20
273 A117 36a bright blue   .20  .20
274 A117 £1 dark red brn   .20  .20
   *Nos. 272-274 (3)*   .60  .60
   With tabs   1.75
Ruins of Masada, the last stronghold in the war against the Romans, 66-73 A.D.

Book Fair Emblem A118

## 1965, Mar. 24    Photo.    *Perf. 13x14*
275 A118 70a gray ol, brt bl & blk  .20  .20
   With tab   .30
2nd Intl. Book Fair, Jerusalem, April.

Arms of Ashdod — A119

## 1965-66    *Perf. 13x14*
Town Emblems: 1a, Lydda (Lod). 2a, Qiryat Shemona. 5a, Petah Tikva. 6a, Nazareth. 8a, Beersheba. 10a Bet Shean. 12a, Tiberias. 20a, Elat. 25a, Acre (Akko). 35a, Dimona. 37a, Zefat. 50a, Rishon Leziyyon. 70a, Jerusalem. £1, Tel Aviv-Jaffa. £3, Haifa.

### Size: 17x22½mm
276 A119 1a brown   .20  .20
277 A119 2a lilac rose   .20  .20
278 A119 5a gray   .20  .20
279 A119 6a violet   .20  .20
280 A119 8a orange   .20  .20
  *a.*  Booklet pane of 6   .45
281 A119 10a emerald   .20  .20
282 A119 12a dark purple   .20  .20
  *a.*  Booklet pane of 6   .50
283 A119 15a green   .20  .20
284 A119 20a rose red   .20  .20
285 A119 25a ultramarine   .20  .20
286 A119 35a magenta   .20  .20
287 A119 37a olive   .20  .20
288 A119 50a greenish bl   .20  .20

### *Perf. 14x13*
### Size: 22x27mm
289 A119 70a dark brown   .20  .20
290 A119 £1 dark green   .25  .20
291 A119 £3 dk carmine rose   .55  .20
   *Nos. 276-291 (16)*   3.60  3.20
   With tabs   10.00

Issued: #283-286, 3/24/65; #290, 11/24/65; #291, 3/14/66; others, 2/2/66.
The uncut booklet pane sheets of 36 are divided into 4 panes (2 of 6 stamps, 2 of 12) by horizontal and vertical gutters. alf of the stamps in the 2 panes of 12 are inverted, causing 4 horizontal tête bêche pairs and 4 horizontal tête bêche gutter pairs.
Vertical strips of 6 of the 1a, 5a and 10a are from larger sheets, released Jan. 10, 1967, from which coils were produced. Regular sheets of 50 are arranged 10x5.
No. 290 also comes tagged (1975).
See Nos. 334-336, 386-393.

---

Hands Reaching for Hope, and Star of David — A120

"Irrigation of the Desert" — A121

## 1965, Apr. 27    Unwmk.    *Perf. 14x13*
292 A120 25a gray, black & yel   .20  .20
   With tab   .40
Liberation of Nazi concentration camps, 20th anniv.

## 1965, Apr. 27    Photo.
293 A121 37a olive bister & blue   .20  .20
   With tab   .20
Memorial Day; proclamation of the state of Israel, 17th anniv.

Telegraph Pole and Syncom Satellite A122

## 1965, July 21    Unwmk.    *Perf. 13x14*
294 A122 70a vio, blk & grnsh bl   .20  .20
   With tab   .45
ITU, centenary.

Symbol of Cooperation and UN Emblem A123

## 1965, July 21    Litho.    *Perf. 14*
295 A123 36a gray, dp claret, bl,
        red & bis   .20  .20
   With tab   .30
International Cooperation Year.

Dead Sea Extraction Plant A124

"Let There be Light . . ." A125

## 1965, July 21
296 A124 12a Crane   .20  .20
297 A124 50a shown   .20  .20
   #296-297, with tabs   .70
Dead Sea chemical industry.

## 1965, Sept. 7    Photo.    *Perf. 13x14*
Genesis 1, The Creation: 8a, Firmament and Waters. 12a, Dry land and vegetation. 25a, Heavenly lights. 35a, Fish and fowl. 70a, Man.
298 A125 6a dk pur, lil & gold   .20  .20
299 A125 8a brt grn, dk bl &
        gold   .20  .20
300 A125 12a red brn, blk & gold  .20  .20
301 A125 25a dk pur, pink & gold  .20  .20
302 A125 35a lt & dk bl & gold   .20  .20
303 A125 70a dp cl, car & gold   .35  .25
   *Nos. 298-303 (6)*   1.35  1.25
   With tabs   1.50
Jewish New Year, 5726. Sheets of 20 (10x2).

---

Charaxes Jasius A126

Flags over Rooftops A127

Butterflies & Moths: 6a, Papilio alexanor maccabaeus. 8a, Daphnis nerii. 12a, Zegris eupheme uarda.

## 1965, Dec. 15    Litho.    *Perf. 14*
### Butterflies in Natural Colors
304 A126 2a lt olive green   .20  .20
305 A126 6a lilac   .20  .20
306 A126 8a ocher   .20  .20
307 A126 12a blue   .20  .20
   #304-307, with tabs   .60

## 1966, Apr. 20    Litho.    *Perf. 14*
Designs: 30a, Fireworks over Tel Aviv. 80a, Warships and Super Mirage jets, Haifa.
308 A127 12a multi   .20  .20
309 A127 30a multi   .20  .20
310 A127 80a multi   .20  .20
   #308-310, with tabs   .45
Proclamation of state of Israel, 18th anniv.

Memorial, Upper Galilee — A128

## 1966, Apr. 20    Photo.    *Perf. 14x13*
311 A128 40a olive gray   .20  .20
   With tab   .20
Issued for Memorial Day.

Knesset Building, Jerusalem — A129

## 1966, June 22    Photo.    *Perf. 13x14*
312 A129 £1 deep blue   .25  .20
   With tab   .50
Inauguration of the Knesset Building (Parliament). Sheets of 12.

Road Sign and Motorcyclist A130

Spice Box A131

Road Signs and: 5a, Bicyclist. 10a, Pedestrian. 12a, Child playing ball. 15a, Automobile.

## 1966, June 22    *Perf. 14*
313 A130 2a sl, red brn & lil
        rose   .20  .20
314 A130 5a ol bis, sl & lil rose   .20  .20
315 A130 10a vio, lt bl & lil rose   .20  .20

---

316 A130 12a bl, grn & lil rose   .20  .20
317 A130 15a grn, red & lil rose   .20  .20
   #313-317, with tabs   .25
Issued to publicize traffic safety.

## 1966, Aug. 24    Photo.    *Perf. 13x14*
Ritual Art Objects: 15a, Candlesticks. 35a, Kiddush cup. 40a, Torah pointer. 80a, Hanging lamp.
318 A131 12a sil, gold, blk & bl   .20  .20
319 A131 15a sil, gold, blk & lil   .20  .20
320 A131 35a sil, gold, blk & em-
        er   .20  .20
321 A131 40a sil, gold, blk & vio
        bl   .20  .20
322 A131 80a sil, gold, blk & red   .20  .20
   #318-322, with tabs   .75
Jewish New Year, 5727.

Bronze Panther, Avdat, 1st Century, B.C. — A132

30a, Stone menorah, Tiberias, 2nd Cent. 40a, Phoenician ivory sphinx, 9th cent., B.C. 55a, Gold earring (calf's head), Ashdod, 6th-4th cents. B.C. 80a, Miniature gold capital, Persia, 5th cent., B.C. £1.15, Gold drinking horn (ram's head), Persia, 5th cent., B.C., vert.

## 1966, Oct. 26    Litho.    *Perf. 14*
323 A132 15a dp bl & yel brn   .20  .20
324 A132 30a vio brn & bister   .25  .20
325 A132 40a sepia & yel bis   .30  .20
326 A132 55a Prus grn, dp
        yel & brown   .35  .20
327 A132 80a lake, dp yel &
        brown   .55  .25
### *Perf. 13x14*
328 A132 £1.15 vio, gold & brn   1.25  .70
   *Nos. 323-328 (6)*   2.90  1.75
   With tabs   6.00
Israel Museum, Jerusalem. Sheets of 12.

Coach and Mailman of Austrian Levant — A133

Microscope and Cells — A134

Designs: 15a, Turkish mailman and caravan. 40a, Palestinian mailman and locomotive. £1, Israeli mailman and jet liner.

## 1966, Dec. 14    Photo.    *Perf. 14*
329 A133 12a ocher & green   .20  .20
330 A133 15a lt grn, brn & dp
        car   .20  .20
331 A133 40a brt rose & dk
        blue   .20  .20
332 A133 £1 grnsh bl & brown   .20  .20
   *Nos. 329-332 (4)*   .80  .80
   With tabs   .80
Issued for Stamp Day.

## 1966, Dec. 14    *Perf. 14x13*
333 A134 15a red & dark slate
        grn   .20  .20
   With tab   .20
Campaign against cancer.

### Arms Type of 1965-66
Town Emblems: 40a, Mizpe Ramon. 55a, Ashkelon. 80a, Rosh Pinna.

## 1967, Feb. 8    Unwmk.    *Perf. 13x14*
334 A119 40a dark olive   .20  .20
335 A119 55a dk carmine rose   .20  .20
336 A119 80a red brown   .20  .20
   *Nos. 334-336 (3)*   .60  .60
   With tabs   1.75

Port of Acre
A135

Ancient Ports: 40a, Caesarea. 80a, Jaffa.

**1967, Mar. 22   Photo.   Perf. 13x14**
337  A135  15a dark brown            .20  .20
338  A135  40a dark blue grn         .20  .20
339  A135  80a deep blue             .20  .20
       Nos. 337-339 (3)              .60  .60
       With tabs                    1.00

Page of Shulhan Aruk and Crowns — A136

**1967, Mar. 22          Perf. 13½x13**
340  A136  40a dk & lt bl, gray &
                        gold         .20  .20
       With tab                           .25

400th anniv. of the publication (in 1565) of the Shulhan Aruk, a compendium of Jewish religious and civil law, by Joseph Karo (1488-1575).

War of Independence Memorial — A137

**1967, May 10  Unwmk.  Perf. 13x14**
341  A137  55a lt bl, indigo & sil  .20  .20
       With tab                           .40

Issued for Memorial Day, 1967.

Auster Plane over Convoy on Jerusalem Road
A138

Military Aircraft: 30a, Mystère IV jet fighter over Dead Sea area. 80a, Mirage jet fighters over Masada.

**1967, May 10                Photo.**
342  A138  15a lt ol grn & dk bl
                        grn          .20  .20
343  A138  30a ocher & dark brn      .20  .20
344  A138  80a grnsh bl & vio bl     .20  .20
       Nos. 342-344 (3)              .60  .60
       With tabs                          .80

Issued for Independence Day, 1967.

Israeli Ships in Straits of Tiran
A139

15a, Star of David, sword & olive branch, vert. 80a, Wailing (Western) Wall, Jerusalem.

**1967, Aug. 16      Perf. 14x13, 13x14**
345  A139  15a dk red, blk & yel     .20  .20
346  A139  40a Prussian green        .20  .20
347  A139  80a deep violet           .20  .20
       #345-347, with tabs                .25

Victory of the Israeli forces, June, 1967.

Torah, Scroll of the Law — A140

Various ancient, decorated Scrolls of the Law.

**1967, Sept. 13              Perf. 13x14**
348  A140  12a gold & multi          .20  .20
349  A140  15a silver & multi        .20  .20
350  A140  35a gold & multi          .20  .20
351  A140  40a silver & multi        .20  .20
352  A140  80a gold & multi          .20  .20
       #348-352, with tabs                .70

Jewish New Year, 5728. Sheets of 20 (10x2).

Chaim Weizmann
A141

Design: 40a, Lord Balfour.

**1967, Nov. 2   Photo.   Perf. 13x14**
353  A141  15a dark green            .20  .20
354  A141  40a brown                 .20  .20
       #353-354, with tabs                .25

50th anniv. of the Balfour Declaration, which established the right to a Jewish natl. home in Palestine. Issued in sheets of 15.

Emblem and Doll — A142      Nubian Ibex — A143

Inscriptions: 30a, Hebrew. 40a, French.

**1967, Nov. 2      Litho.      Perf. 14**
355  A142  30a yellow & multi        .20  .20
356  A142  40a brt bl & multi        .20  .20
357  A142  80a brt grn & multi       .20  .20
       #355-357, with tabs                .45

Intl. Tourist Year. Issued in sheets of 15.

**1967, Dec. 27     Litho.      Perf. 13**

18a, Caracal lynx. 60a, Dorcas gazelles.

**Animal in Ocher & Brown**
358  A143  12a dull purple           .20  .20
359  A143  18a bright green          .20  .20
360  A143  60a bright blue           .20  .20
       #358-360, with tabs                .40

Flags Forming Soccer Ball — A144

**1968, Mar. 11     Photo.      Perf. 13**
361  A144  80a ocher & multi         .20  .20
       With tab                           .25

Pre-Olympic soccer tournament.

Welcoming Immigrants      Resistance Fighter
A145                      A146

Design: 80a, Happy farm family.

**1968, Apr. 24     Litho.      Perf. 14**
362  A145  15a lt green & multi      .20  .20
363  A145  80a cream & multi         .20  .20
       #362-363, with tabs                .25

Issued for Independence Day, 1968.

**1968, Apr. 24     Photo.    Perf. 14x13**
364  A146  60a brown olive           .20  .20
       With tab                           .20

Warsaw Ghetto Uprising, 25th anniv. Design from Warsaw Ghetto Memorial.

Sword and Laurel      Rifles and Helmet
A147                  A148

**1968, Apr. 24     Litho.      Perf. 14**
365  A147  40a gold & multi          .20  .20
366  A148  55a black & multi         .20  .20
       #365-366, with tabs                .30

Zahal defense army, Independence Day (No. 365); Memorial Day (No. 366).

Candle and Prison Window      Prime Minister Moshe Sharett
A149                          (1894-1965)
                              A150

**1968, June 5     Photo.    Perf. 14x13**
367  A149  80a blk, gray & sepia     .20  .20
       With tab                           .20

Issued to honor those who died for freedom.

**1968, June 5                Unwmk.**
368  A150  £1 deep brown             .20  .20
       With tab                           .20

27th Zionist Congress.

Knot Forming Star of David — A151      Dome of the Rock and Absalom's Tomb — A152

**1968, Aug. 21     Litho.      Perf. 13**
369  A151  30a multi                 .20  .20
       With tab                           .20

50 years of Jewish Scouting. Sheets of 15.

**1968, Aug. 21     Photo.    Perf. 14x13**

Views of Jerusalem: 15a, Church of the Resurrection. 35a, Tower of David and City Wall. 40a, Yemin Moshe District and Mount of Olives. 60a, Israel Museum and "Shrine of the Book."

370  A152  12a gold & multi          .20  .20
371  A152  15a gold & multi          .20  .20
372  A152  35a gold & multi          .20  .20
373  A152  40a gold & multi          .20  .20
374  A152  60a gold & multi          .20  .20
       #370-374, with tabs                .50

Jewish New Year, 5729. Sheets of 15.

Detail from Lions' Gate, Jerusalem (St. Stephen's Gate)
A153

**1968, Oct. 8   Unwmk.   Perf. 13x14**
375  A153  £1 brown org             .20  .20
       With tab                           .20
  a.    Souvenir sheet         .35  .30

TABIRA Natl. Philatelic Exhibition. No. 375a contains one imperf. stamp. Sold only at exhibition for £1.50. No. 375 issued in sheets of 15.

Abraham Mapu      Wheelchair Basketball
A154              A155

**1968, Oct. 8    Photo.    Perf. 14x13**
376  A154  30a dark olive grn        .20  .20
       With tab                           .20

Mapu (1808-1867), novelist and historian.

**1968, Nov. 6    Photo.    Perf. 14x13**
377  A155  40a green & yel grn       .20  .20
       With tab                           .20

17th Stoke-Mandeville Games for the Paralyzed, Nov. 4-13. Sheets of 15.

Port of Elat — A156

Ports of Israel: 60a, Ashdod. £1, Haifa.

**1969, Feb. 19   Unwmk.   Perf. 13x14**
378  A156  30a deep magenta          .20  .20
379  A156  60a brown                 .20  .20
380  A156  £1 dull green             .20  .20
       Nos. 378-380 (3)              .60  .60
       With tabs                    2.00

Tank
A157

**1969, Apr. 16   Photo.   Perf. 13x14**
381  A157  15a shown                 .20  .20
382  A157  80a Destroyer             .20  .20
       #381-382, with tabs                .40

Issued for Independence Day 1969.

Israel's Flag at Half-mast — A158

**1969, Apr. 16**
383 A158 55a vio, gold & bl .20 .20
With tab .25
Issued for Memorial Day.

Worker and ILO Emblem A159

**1969, Apr. 16**
384 A159 80a dark blue grn .20 .20
With tab .25
ILO, 50th anniversary.

Hand Holding Torch A160

Arms of Hadera A161

**1969, July 9    Photo.    Perf. 14x13**
385 A160 60a gold & multi .20 .20
With tab .60
Issued to publicize the 8th Maccabiah.

**1969-73    Perf. 13x14**
Town Emblems: 3a, Hertseliya. 5a, Holon. 15a, Bat Yam. 18a, Ramla. 20a, Kefar Sava. 25a, Giv'atayim. 30a, Rehovot. 40a, Netanya. 50a, Bene Beraq. 60a, Nahariyya. 80a, Ramat Gan.

386 A161 2a green .20 .20
387 A161 3a deep magenta .20 .20
388 A161 5a orange .20 .20
389 A161 15a bright rose .20 .20
  c. Bklt. pane of 6 (2 #389 + 4 #389A) ('71) .65
389A A161 18a ultra ('70) .20 .20
  d. Bklt. pane of 6 ('71) .70
  e. Bklt. pane of 6 (1 #281 + 5 #389A) ('73) .65
389B A161 20a brown ('70) .20 .20
  f. Bklt. pane of 5 + label ('73) .90
390 A161 25a dark blue .20 .20
390A A161 30a brt pink ('70) .20 .20
391 A161 40a purple .20 .20
392 A161 50a greenish bl .20 .20
392A A161 60a olive ('70) .20 .20
393 A161 80a dark green .20 .20
  Nos. 386-393 (12) 2.40 2.40
  With tabs 3.75

Nos. 389c and 389d were also sold in uncut sheets of 36, No. 389e in uncut sheet of 18. See note after No. 291 about similar sheets.

Noah Building the Ark — A162

The Story of the Flood: 15a, Animals boarding the Ark. 35a, The Ark during the flood. 40a, Noah sending out the dove. 60a, Noah and the rainbow.

**1969, Aug. 13    Unwmk.    Perf. 14**
394 A162 12a multicolored .20 .20
395 A162 15a multicolored .20 .20
396 A162 35a multicolored .20 .20
397 A162 40a multicolored .20 .20
398 A162 60a multicolored .20 .20
  #394-398, with tabs .70
  Jewish New Year, 5730. Sheets of 15.

King David by Marc Chagall A163

**1969, Sept. 24    Photo.    Perf. 14**
399 A163 £3 multicolored .65 .55
With tab 1.25

Atom Diagram and Test Tube — A164

**1969, Nov. 3    Perf. 14x13**
400 A164 £1.15 vio bl & multi .70 .45
With tab 2.25
Weizmann Institute of Science, 25th anniv.

Joseph Trumpeldor A165

Dum Palms, Emeq Ha-Arava A166

**1970, Jan. 21    Photo.    Perf. 14x13**
401 A165 £1 dark purple .25 .20
With tab .60
50th anniv. of the defense of Tel Hay under the leadership of Joseph Trumpeldor.

**1970, Jan. 21**
Views: 3a, Tahana Waterfall. 5a, Nahal Baraq Canyon, Negev. 6a, Cedars in Judean Hills. 30a, Soreq Cave, Judean Hills.

402 A166 2a olive .20 .20
403 A166 3a deep blue .20 .20
404 A166 5a orange red .20 .20
405 A166 6a slate green .20 .20
406 A166 30a brt purple .20 .20
  #402-406, with tabs .35
  Issued to publicize nature reserves.

Magic Carpet Shaped as Airplane A167

Prime Minister Levi Eshkol (1895-1969) A168

**1970, Jan. 21    Litho.    Perf. 13**
407 A167 30a multicolored .20 .20
With tab .20
20th anniv. of "Operation Magic Carpet" which airlifted the Yemeni Jews to Israel.

**1970, Mar. 11    Litho.    Perf. 14**
408 A168 15a bl & multi .20 .20
With tab .20

Mania Shochat — A169

Camel and Train — A170

Portrait: 80a, Ze'ev Jabotinsky (1880-1940), writer and Zionist leader.

**1970, Mar. 11    Photo.    Perf. 14x13**
409 A169 40a dp plum & buff .20 .20
410 A169 80a green & cream .20 .20
  #409-410, with tabs 1.10
Ha-Shomer (Watchmen defense organization), 60th anniv. (No. 409); defense of Jerusalem, 50th anniv. (No. 410).

**1970, Mar. 11    Litho.    Perf. 13**
411 A170 80a orange & multi .40 .25
With tab .75
Opening of Dimona-Oron Railroad.

Scene from "The Dibbuk" — A171

**1970, Mar. 11    Photo.    Perf. 14x13**
412 A171 £1 multicolored .20 .20
With tab .60
Habimah Natl. Theater, 50th anniv.

Memorial Flame A172

Orchis Laxiflorus A173

**1970, May 6    Photo.    Perf. 13x14**
413 A172 55a vio, pink & blk .20 .20
With tab .25
Issued for Memorial Day, 1970.

**1970, May 6    Litho.    Perf. 14**
Flowers: 15a, Iris mariae. 80a, Lupinus pilosus.

414 A173 12a pale gray, plum & grn .20 .20
415 A173 15a multicolored .20 .20
416 A173 80a pale bl & multi .30 .30
  Nos. 414-416 (3) .70 .70
  With tabs .95
Issued for Independence Day, 1970.

Charles Netter — A174

420 Class Yachts — A175

80a, Agricultural College (Mikwe Israel) & garden.

**1970, May 6    Photo.    Perf. 14x13**
417 A174 40a lt grn, dk brn & gold .20 .20
418 A174 80a gold & multi .20 .20
With tabs 1.25
Centenary of first agricultural college in Israel; its founder, Charles Netter.

**1970, July 8    Photo.    Perf. 14x13**
Designs: Various 420 Class yachts.

419 A175 15a grnsh bl, blk & sil .20 .20
420 A175 30a ol, red, blk & sil .20 .20
421 A175 80a ultra, blk & silver .25 .20
  Nos. 419-421 (3) .65 .60
  With tabs 1.10
World "420" Class Sailing Championships.

Hebrew Letters Shaped Like Ship and Buildings A176

**1970, July 8    Perf. 13x14**
422 A176 40a gold & multi .20 .20
With tab .20
Keren Hayesod, a Zionist Fund to maintain schools and hospitals in Palestine, 50th anniv.

Arava Plane A177

**1970, July 8**
423 A177 £1 brt blue, blk & sil .20 .20
With tab .35
First Israeli designed and built aircraft.

Bird (Exiles) and Sun (Israel) A178

**1970, Sept. 7    Litho.    Perf. 14**
424 A178 80a yel & multi .20 .20
With tab .25
"Operation Ezra and Nehemiah," the exodus of Iraqi Jews.

Old Synagogue, Cracow — A179

Historic Synagogues: 15a, Great Synagogue, Tunis. 35a, Portuguese Synagogue, Amsterdam. 40a, Great Synagogue, Moscow. 60a, Shearith Israel Synagogue, New York.

**Perf. 14, 13 (15a)**
**1970, Sept. 7    Photo.**
425 A179 12a gold & multi .20 .20
426 A179 15a gold & multi .20 .20
427 A179 35a gold & multi .20 .20

| | | | | |
|---|---|---|---|---|
| 428 | A179 | 40a gold & multi | .20 | .20 |
| 429 | A179 | 60a gold & multi | .20 | .20 |
| | | #425-429, with tabs | | .40 |

Jewish New Year, 5731.

Tel Aviv Post Office, 1920 — A180

**1970, Oct. 18    Photo.    Perf. 14**

| | | | | |
|---|---|---|---|---|
| 430 | A180 | £1 multicolored | .20 | .20 |
| | | With tab | | .25 |
| a. | | Souvenir sheet | 1.25 | 1.50 |

TABIT Natl. Stamp Exhibition, Tel Aviv, Oct. 18-29. No. 430a contains an imperf. stamp similar to No. 430. Sold for £1.50.

Mother and Child A181

**1970, Oct. 18        Perf. 13x14**

| | | | | |
|---|---|---|---|---|
| 431 | A181 | 80a dp grn, yel & gray | .20 | .20 |
| | | With tab | | .45 |

WIZO, Women's Intl. Zionist Org., 50th anniv.

Paris Quai, by Camille Pissarro — A182

Paintings from Tel Aviv Museum: 85a, The Jewish Wedding, by Josef Israels. £2, Flowers in a Vase, by Fernand Leger.

**1970, Dec. 22    Litho.    Perf. 14**

| | | | | |
|---|---|---|---|---|
| 432 | A182 | 85a black & multi | .20 | .20 |
| 433 | A182 | £1 black & multi | .20 | .20 |
| 434 | A182 | £2 black & multi | .50 | .30 |
| | | Nos. 432-434 (3) | .90 | .70 |
| | | With tabs | | 1.75 |

Hammer and Menorah Emblem — A183

Persian Fallow Deer — A184

**1970, Dec. 22**

| | | | | |
|---|---|---|---|---|
| 435 | A183 | 35a gold & multi | .20 | .20 |
| | | With tab | | .20 |

General Federation of Labor in Israel (Histadrut), 50th anniversary.

**1971, Feb. 16    Litho.    Perf. 13**

Animals of the Bible: 3a, Asiatic wild ass. 5a, White oryx. 78a, Cheetah.

| | | | | |
|---|---|---|---|---|
| 436 | A184 | 2a multicolored | .20 | .20 |
| 437 | A184 | 3a multicolored | .20 | .20 |
| 438 | A184 | 5a multicolored | .20 | .20 |
| 439 | A184 | 78a multicolored | .20 | .20 |
| | | #436-439, with tabs | | .45 |

"Samson and Dalila," Israel National Opera — A185

Theater Art in Israel: No. 441, Inn of the Ghosts, Cameri Theater. No. 442, A Psalm of David, Inbal Dance Theater.

**1971, Feb. 16        Perf. 14x13**

| | | | | |
|---|---|---|---|---|
| 440 | A185 | 50a bister & multi | .20 | .20 |
| 441 | A185 | 50a lt grn & multi | .20 | .20 |
| 442 | A185 | 50a blue & multi | .20 | .20 |
| | | Nos. 440-442 (3) | .60 | .60 |
| | | With tabs | | .60 |

Basketball A186

Defense Forces Emblem A187

No. 444, Runner. No. 445, Athlete on rings.

**1971, Apr. 13    Litho.    Perf. 14**

| | | | | |
|---|---|---|---|---|
| 443 | A186 | 50a green & multi | .20 | .20 |
| 444 | A186 | 50a ocher & multi | .20 | .20 |
| 445 | A186 | 50a lt vio & multi | .20 | .20 |
| | | #443-445, with tabs | | .50 |

9th Hapoel Games.

**1971, Apr. 13    Photo.    Perf. 14x13**

| | | | | |
|---|---|---|---|---|
| 446 | A187 | 78a multicolored | .20 | .20 |
| | | With tab | | .25 |

Memorial Day, 1971, and the war dead.

Jaffa Gate, Jerusalem — A188

Gates of Jerusalem: 18c, New Gate. 35c, Damascus Gate. 85c, Herod's Gate.

**1971, Apr. 13        Perf. 14**
**Size: 41x41mm**

| | | | | |
|---|---|---|---|---|
| 447 | A188 | 15a gold & multi | .20 | .20 |
| 448 | A188 | 18a gold & multi | .20 | .20 |
| 449 | A188 | 35a gold & multi | .25 | .20 |
| 450 | A188 | 85a gold & multi | .60 | .40 |
| a. | | Souvenir sheet of 4 | 3.50 | 3.50 |
| | | Nos. 447-450 (4) | 1.25 | 1.00 |
| | | With tabs | | 2.00 |

Independence Day, 1971. No. 450a contains 4 stamps similar to Nos. 447-450, but smaller (27x27mm). Sold at the Jerusalem Exhibition for £2.

See Nos. 488-491.

"He Wrote . . . Words of the Covenant" A189

"You shall rejoice in your feast" A190

85a, "First Fruits . . ." Exodus 23:19. £1.50, ". . . Feast of Weeks" Exodus 34:22. The quotation on 50a is from Exodus 34:28. The quotations are in English on the tabs.

**1971, May 25    Photo.    Perf. 14x13**

| | | | | |
|---|---|---|---|---|
| 451 | A189 | 50a yellow & multi | .20 | .20 |
| 452 | A189 | 85a yellow & multi | .25 | .20 |
| 453 | A189 | £1.50 yellow & multi | .45 | .30 |
| | | Nos. 451-453 (3) | .90 | .70 |
| | | With tabs | | 1.75 |

For the Feast of Weeks (Shabuoth).

**1971, Aug. 24    Photo.    Perf. 14x13**

Designs: 18a, "You shall dwell in booths for seven days . . ." Leviticus 23:42. 20a, "That I made the people of Israel dwell in booths . . ." Lev. 23:43. 40a, ". . . when you have gathered in the produce of the land" Lev. 23:39. 65a, ". . . then I will give you your rains in their season" Lev. 26:4. The quotation on 15a is from Deuteronomy 16:14. The quotations are in English on tabs.

| | | | | |
|---|---|---|---|---|
| 454 | A190 | 15a yellow & multi | .20 | .20 |
| 455 | A190 | 18a yellow & multi | .20 | .20 |
| 456 | A190 | 20a yellow & multi | .20 | .20 |
| 457 | A190 | 40a yellow & multi | .20 | .20 |
| 458 | A190 | 65a yellow & multi | .20 | .20 |
| | | #454-458, with tabs | | .75 |

For the Feast of Tabernacles (Sukkoth).

Sun Shining on Fields A191

**1971, Aug. 24        Perf. 14**

| | | | | |
|---|---|---|---|---|
| 459 | A191 | 40a gold & multi | .20 | .20 |
| | | With tab | | .20 |

1st cooperative settlement in Israel, at Emeq (Valley of Israel), 50th anniv.

Retort and Grain — A192

**1971, Oct. 25    Litho.    Perf. 14**

| | | | | |
|---|---|---|---|---|
| 460 | A192 | £1 green & multi | .20 | .20 |
| | | With tab | | .20 |

50th anniversary of Volcani Institute of Agricultural Research.

---

**Tagging**

Starting in 1975, vertical luminescent bands were overprinted on various regular and commemorative stamps.

In the 1971-75 regular series, values issued both untagged and tagged are: 20a, 25a, 30a, 35a, 45a, 50a, 65a, £1.10, £1.30, £2 and £3. Also No. 290 was re-issued with tagging in 1975.

Regular issues from 1975 onward, including the £1.70, are tagged unless otherwise noted.

Tagged commemoratives include Nos. 562-563 and all from Nos. 567-569 onward unless otherwise noted.

---

Negev — A193

**1971-75    Photo.    Perf. 13x14**

Landscapes: 3a, Judean desert. 5a, Gan Ha-Shelosha. 18a, Kinneret. 20a, Tel Dan. 22a, Fishermen, Yafo. 25a, Arava. 30a, En Avedat. 35a, Brekhat Ram, Golan Heights. 45a, Grazing sheep, Mt. Hermon. 50a, Rosh Pinna. 55a, Beach and park, Netanya. 65a, Plain of Zebulun. 70a, Shore, Engedi. 80a, Beach at Elat. 88a, Boats in Akko harbor. 95a, Hamifratz Hane'elam. £1.10, Aqueduct near Akko. £1.30, Zefat. £1.70, Upper Nazareth. £2, Coral Island. £3, Haifa.

| | | | | |
|---|---|---|---|---|
| 461 | A193 | 3a deep blue | .20 | .20 |
| 462 | A193 | 5a green | .20 | .20 |
| 463 | A193 | 15a deep org | .20 | .20 |
| 464 | A193 | 18a bright mag | .65 | .20 |
| 464A | A193 | 20a dark green | .20 | .20 |
| 465 | A193 | 22a brt blue | 1.00 | .25 |
| 465A | A193 | 25a orange red | .20 | .20 |
| 466 | A193 | 30a brt rose | .20 | .20 |
| 466A | A193 | 35a plum | .20 | .20 |
| 467 | A193 | 45a dull vio blue | .20 | .20 |
| 468 | A193 | 50a green | .20 | .20 |
| 469 | A193 | 55a olive | .20 | .20 |
| 469A | A193 | 65a black | .20 | .20 |
| 470 | A193 | 70a deep car | .20 | .20 |
| 470A | A193 | 80a deep ultra | .20 | .20 |
| 471 | A193 | 88a greenish blue | 1.00 | .20 |
| 472 | A193 | 95a org ver | .80 | .20 |
| 472A | A193 | £1.10 olive | .20 | .20 |
| 472B | A193 | £1.30 deep blue | .20 | .20 |
| 472C | A193 | £1.70 dark brown | .40 | .20 |
| 473 | A193 | £2 brown | .40 | .20 |
| 474 | A193 | £3 deep violet | .55 | .20 |
| | | Nos. 461-474 (22) | 7.80 | 4.45 |
| | | With tabs | 12.00 | |

Issued: 15a, 18a, 50a, 88a, 10/25; 22a, 55a, 70a, 1/4/72; 3a, 5a, 30a, £3, 11/7/72; 45a, 95a, £2, 1/16/73; 20a, 65a, 10/23/73; 35a, £1.10, 12/20/73; 25a, 80a, £1.30, 11/5/74; £1.70, 6/17/75.

See No. 592.

"Get Wisdom" Proverbs 4:7 — A194

Abstract Designs: 18a, Mathematical and scientific formula. 20a, Tools and engineering symbols. 40a, Abbreviations of various college degrees.

**1972, Jan. 4    Litho.    Perf. 14**

| | | | | |
|---|---|---|---|---|
| 475 | A194 | 15a brt grn & multi | .20 | .20 |
| 476 | A194 | 18a multicolored | .20 | .20 |
| 477 | A194 | 20a multicolored | .20 | .20 |
| 478 | A194 | 40a red, blk & gold | .20 | .20 |
| | | #475-478, with tabs | | .30 |

The Scribe, Sculpture by Boris Schatz A195

Works by Israeli Artists: 55a, Young Girl (Sarah), by Abel Pann. 70a, Zefat (landscape), by Menahem Shemi, horiz. 85a, Old Jerusalem, by Jacob Steinhardt. £1, Resurrection (abstract), by Aharon Kahana.

**Perf. 13x14 (40a, 85a), 14**
**1972, Mar. 7**

| | | | | |
|---|---|---|---|---|
| 479 | A195 | 40a black & tan | .20 | .20 |
| 480 | A195 | 55a red brn & multi | .20 | .20 |
| 481 | A195 | 70a lt grn & multi | .20 | .20 |
| 482 | A195 | 85a blk & yellow | .25 | .20 |
| 483 | A195 | £1 blk & multi | .30 | .25 |
| | | Nos. 479-483 (5) | 1.15 | 1.05 |
| | | With tabs | | 1.40 |

Exodus — A196

Passover: 45a, Baking unleavened bread.
95a, Seder.

**1972, Mar. 7    Litho.    Perf. 13**
484  A196  18a buff & multi          .20    .20
485  A196  45a buff & multi          .20    .20
486  A196  95a buff & multi          .30    .20
     *Nos. 484-486 (3)*              .70    .60
     With tabs                      1.25

"Let My People
Go" — A197

**1972, Mar. 7    Perf. 14**
487  A197  55a blk, bl & yel grn     .45    .30
     With tab                       3.00

No. 487 inscribed in Hebrew, Arabic, Russian and English.

**Gate Type of 1971**

Gates of Jerusalem: 15a, Lions' Gate. 18a,
Golden Gate. 45a, Dung Gate. 55a, Zion
Gate.

**1972, Apr. 17    Photo.    Perf. 14**
**Size: 40x40mm**
488  A188  15a gold & multi          .20    .20
489  A188  18a gold & multi          .20    .20
490  A188  45a gold & multi          .25    .25
491  A188  55a gold & multi          .35    .35
  a.  Souvenir sheet of 4           2.60   2.60
     *Nos. 488-491 (4)*             1.00   1.00
     With tabs                      2.25

Independence Day. #491a contains 4
27x27mm stamps similar to #488-491. Sold for
£2.

Jethro's
Tomb — A198

**1972, Apr. 17    Litho.    Perf. 13**
492  A198  55a multicolored          .20    .20
     With tab                         .25

Memorial
Day — A199

**1972, Apr. 17    Perf. 14**
493  A199  55a Flowers               .20    .20
     With tab                         .25

Hebrew Words
Emerging from
Opened
Ghetto — A200

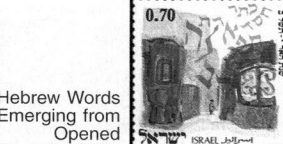

**1972, June 6    Perf. 13**
494  A200  70a blue & multi          .45    .35
     With tab                       2.00

Rabbi Isaac ben Solomon Ashkenazi Luria
("Ari") (1534-72), Palestinian cabalist.

International Book
Year — A201

**1972, June 6    Perf. 14x13**
495  A201  95a Printed page          .25    .20
     With tab                         .35

Satellite Earth
Station, Satellite
and
Rainbow — A202

**1972, June 6    Perf. 13**
496  A202  £1 tan & multi            .20    .20
     With tab                         .30

Opening of satellite earth station in Israel.

17th Cent. Ark,     Menorah and
Ancona — A203       "25" — A204

Holy Arks from: 45a, Padua, 1729. 70a,
Parma, 17th century. 95a, Reggio Emilia,
1756. Arks moved to Israel from Italian
synagogues.

**1972, Aug. 8    Photo.    Perf. 14x13**
497  A203  15a deep brn & yel        .20    .20
498  A203  45a dp grn, yel grn &
           gold                      .20    .20
499  A203  70a brn red, yel & bl     .20    .20
500  A203  95a magenta & gold        .20    .20
     *Nos. 497-500 (4)*              .80    .80
     With tabs                      1.50

Jewish New Year, 5733.

**1972, Aug. 8**
501  A204  £1 silver, bl & mag       .20    .20
     With tab                         .25

25th anniversary of the State of Israel.

Brass
Menorah,
Morocco,
18th-19th
Century
A205

Menorahs: 25a, Brass, Poland, 18th century. 70a, Silver, Germany, 17th century.

**1972, Nov. 7    Litho.    Perf. 14x13**
502  A205  12a emer, blk & bl grn    .20    .20
503  A205  25a lil rose, blk & org   .20    .20
504  A205  70a blue, blk & vio       .20    .20
     *#502-504, with tabs*           .55

Hanukkah (Festival of Lights), 1972.

Child's              Pendant — A207
Drawing — A206

Designs: Children's drawings.

**1973, Jan. 16    Litho.    Perf. 14**
**Sizes: 22½x37mm (2a, 55a);
17x48mm (3a)**
505  A206  2a blk & multi            .20    .20
506  A206  3a multicolored           .20    .20
507  A206  55a multicolored          .20    .20
     *#505-507, with tabs*           .30

Youth Wing of Israel Museum, Jerusalem
(2a, 3a) and Youth Workshops, Tel Aviv
Museum (55a).

**1973, Jan. 16    Photo.    Perf. 14x13**
508  A207  18a silver & multi        .20    .20
     With tab                         .20

Immigration of North African Jews.

Levi, by
Marc
Chagall
A208

Tribes of Israel: #510, Simeon. #511, Reuben. #512, Issachar. #513, Zebulun. #514,
Judah. #515, Dan. #516, Gad. #517, Asher.
#518, Naphtali. #519, Joseph. No.520,
Benjamin.

**1973    Litho.    Perf. 14**
509  A208  £1 multicolored           .40    .40
510  A208  £1 gray grn & multi       .40    .40
511  A208  £1 olive & multi          .40    .40
512  A208  £1 gray bl & multi        .40    .40
513  A208  £1 lemon & multi          .40    .40
514  A208  £1 gray & multi           .40    .40
515  A208  £1 bl grn & multi         .40    .40
516  A208  £1 gray & multi           .40    .40
517  A208  £1 yel grn & multi        .40    .40
518  A208  £1 sepia & multi          .40    .40
519  A208  £1 olive & multi          .40    .40
520  A208  £1 tan & multi            .40    .40
     *Nos. 509-520 (12)*            4.80   4.80
     With tabs                      8.50

Designs from stained glass windows by
Marc Chagall, Hadassah-Hebrew University
Medical Center Synagogue, Jerusalem.
Issued: #509-514, 3/26; #515-520, 8/21.

Israel's Declaration of
Independence — A209

**1973, May 3    Photo.    Perf. 14**
521  A209  £1 ocher & multi          .20    .20
     With tab                         .25
  a.  Souvenir sheet                 .65    .75

25 years of Independence. No. 521a sold
for £1.50.

Star of
David and
Runners
A210

**1973, May 3    Litho.**
522  A210  £1.10 multicolored        .20    .20
     With tab                         .25

9th Maccabiah.

Prison-cloth
Hand — A211

**1973, May 3    Photo.**
523  A211  55a blue black            .20    .20
     With tab                         .20

Heroes and martyrs of the Holocaust, 1933-1945.

Flame               Prophets
A212                A213

**1973, May 3    Litho.**
524  A212  65a multicolored          .20    .20
     With tab                         .25

Memorial Day.

**1973, Aug. 21    Photo.    Perf. 13x14**
525  A213  18a Isaiah               .20    .20
526  A213  65a Jeremiah             .20    .20
527  A213  £1.10 Ezekiel            .20    .20
     *#525-527, with tabs*           .25

Jewish New Year, 5734.

Torch of Learning,
Cogwheel — A214

**1973, Oct. 23    Perf. 14x13**
528  A214  £1.25 slate & multi       .20    .20
     With tab                         .25

50th anniversary of the Technion, Israel
Institute of Technology.

Rescue Boat and
Danish
Flag — A215

**1973, Oct. 23**     **Perf. 13x14**
529 A215 £5 bister, red & blk    .40   .30
    With tab       .50

30th anniversary of the rescue by the Danes of the Jews in Denmark.

Spectators at Stamp Show — A216

Design: £1, Spectators, different design.

**1973, Dec. 20**   **Litho.**   **Perf. 13**
530 A216   20a brown & multi    .20   .20
531 A216   £1 brown & multi    .20   .20
    #530-531, with tabs      .20

JERUSALEM '73 Philatelic Exhibition, Mar. 25-Apr. 2, 1974.

### Souvenir Sheets

Israel No. 7 — A217

Designs: £2, No. 8. £3, No. 9.

**1974, Mar. 25**   **Photo.**   **Perf. 14x13**
532 A217 £1 silver & dk slate grn    .20   .20
533 A217 £2 silver & red brn    .20   .20
534 A217 £3 silver & blk blue    .20   .20
    Nos. 532-534 (3)      .60   .60

Jerusalem '73 Philatelic Exhibition, Mar. 25-Apr. 2, 1974 (postponed from Dec. 1973), 25th anniv. of State of Israel. Each sheet was sold with a 50 per cent surcharge.

Soldier with Prayer Shawl A218

Quill and Inkwell with Hebrew Letters A219

**1974, Apr. 23**     **Perf. 13x14**
535 A218 £1 blk & light bl    .20   .20
    With tab      .20

Memorial Day.

**1974, Apr. 23**     **Perf. 14x13**
536 A219 £2 gold & black    .20   .20
    With tab      .25

50th anniversary of Hebrew Writers Assn.

Lady in Blue, by Moshe Kisling A220

---

Designs: £2, Mother and Child, Sculpture by Chana Orloff. £3, Girl in Blue, by Chaim Soutine.

**1974, June 11**   **Litho.**   **Perf. 14**
537 A220 £1.25 multicolored    .20   .20
538 A220 £2 multicolored    .20   .20
539 A220 £3 multicolored    .30   .30
    #537-539, with tabs     1.00

Art works from Tel Aviv, En Harod and Jerusalem Museums.

Wrench A221

**1974, June 11**
540 A221 25a multicolored    .20   .20
    With tab      .20

50th anniv. of Working Youth Movement.

Istanbuli Synagogue, Jerusalem — A222

Designs: Interiors of restored synagogues in Jerusalem's Old City.

**1974, Aug. 6**   **Photo.**   **Perf. 13x14**
541 A222 25a shown    .20   .20
542 A222 70a Emtzai Synagogue    .20   .20
543 A222 £1 Rabbi Yohanan Synagogue    .20   .20
    #541-543, with tabs      .25

Jewish New Year, 5735.

Lady Davis Technical Center "AMAL," Tel Aviv — A223

60a, Elias Sourasky Library, Tel Aviv University. £1.45, Mivtahim Rest Home, Zikhron Yaaqov.

**1974, Aug. 6**     **Perf. 13½x14**
544 A223 25a violet black    .20   .20
545 A223 60a dark blue    .20   .20
546 A223 £1.45 maroon    .20   .20
    #544-546, with tabs      .25

Modern Israeli architecture.

David Ben-Gurion — A224

**1974, Nov. 5**     **Perf. 14**
547 A224 25a brown    .20   .20
548 A224 £1.30 slate green    .20   .20
    #547-549, with tabs      .25

David Ben-Gurion (1886-1973), first Prime Minister and Minister of Defense of Israel.

---

Arrows on Globe — A225

Dove Delivering Letter — A226

**1974, Nov. 5**   **Litho.**   **Perf. 14**
549 A225 25a black & multi    .20   .20
       **Photo.**
550 A226 £1.30 gold & multi    .20   .20
    #549-550, with tabs      .25

Centenary of Universal Postal Union.

Hebrew University, Mount Scopus, Jerusalem — A227

**1975, Jan. 14**   **Litho.**   **Perf. 13**
551 A227 £2.50 multicolored    .20   .20
    With tab      .25

Hebrew University, 50th anniv.

Girl Carrying Plant — A228

Welder — A229

Arbor Day: 35a, Bird singing in tree. £2, Boy carrying potted plant.

**1975, Jan. 14**     **Perf. 14**
552 A228 1a multicolored    .20   .20
553 A228 35a multicolored    .20   .20
554 A228 £2 multicolored    .20   .20
    #552-554, with tabs      .25

**1975, Jan. 14**   **Photo.**   **Perf. 14x13**
80a, Tractor driver. £1.20, Electrical lineman.
555 A229 30a multicolored    .20   .20
556 A229 80a multicolored    .20   .20
557 A229 £1.20 ultra & multi    .20   .20
    #555-557, with tabs      .25

Occupational safety and publicity for the Institute for Safety and Hygiene.

Hebrew University Synagogue, Jerusalem — A230

Modern Israeli architecture: £1.30, Yad Mordecai Museum. £1.70, Bat Yam City Hall.

**Perf. 14, 13½x14 (#559)**
**1975, Mar. 4**     **Photo.**
558 A230 80a brown    .20   .20
559 A230 £1.30 slate green    .20   .20
560 A230 £1.70 brown olive    .20   .20
    #558-560, with tabs      .40

---

US President Harry S Truman (1884-1972) — A231

**1975, Mar. 4**   **Engr.**   **Perf. 14**
561 A231 £5 dark brown    .35   .20
    With tab      .40

Eternal Flame over Soldier's Grave — A232

Memorial Tablet — A233

**1975, Apr. 10**   **Photo.**   **Perf. 14x13**
562 A232 £1.45 black & multi    .20   .20
    With tab      .25

Memorial Day.

**1975, Apr. 10**
563 A233 £1.45 blk, red & gray    .20   .20
    With tab      .25

In memory of soldiers missing in action.

Hurdling A234

**1975, Apr. 10**     **Perf. 13x14**
564 A234 25a shown    .20   .20
565 A234 £1.70 Bicycling    .20   .20
566 A234 £3 Volleyball    .20   .20
    #564-566, with tabs      .40

10th Hapoel Games; 50th anniv. of Hapoel Org.

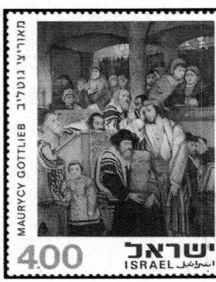

Yom Kippur, by Maurycy Gottlieb A235

Paintings of religious holidays: £1.00 Hanukkah, by Mortiz D. Oppenheim. 1.40, The Purim Players, by Jankel Adler, horiz.

**1975, June 17**   **Litho.**   **Perf. 14**
567 A235 £1 multicolored    .20   .20
568 A235 £1.40 multicolored    .20   .20
569 A235 £4 multicolored    .20   .20
    #567-569, with tabs      .50

Old Couple A236

**1975, June 17**   **Photo.**   **Perf. 13x14**
570 A236 £1.85 multicolored    .20   .20
    With tab      .25

International Gerontological Association, 10th triennial conference, Jerusalem.

Pres. Zalman Shazar (1889-1974) — A237

**1975, Aug. 5    Photo.    Perf. 14x13**
571 A237  35a silver & blk        .20   .20
          With tab                      .20

Pioneer Women, 50th Anniv. — A238

**1975, Aug. 5              Perf. 14½**
572 A238  £5 Emblem               .30   .20
          With tab                      .35

Judges of Israel — A239

**1975, Aug. 5              Perf. 13x14**
573 A239  35a Gideon              .20   .20
574 A239  £1 Deborah              .20   .20
575 A239  £1.40 Jephthah          .20   .20
          #573-575, with tabs           .35

Jewish New Year, 5736.

Hebrew University, Mt. Scopus — A240

**1975, Oct. 14   Photo.   Perf. 14x13**
576 A240  £4 multicolored         .20   .20
          With tab                      .25

Return of Hadassah to Mt. Scopus, Jerusalem.

Collared Pratincoles A241

Protected Birds: £1.70, Spur-winged plover. £2, Black-winged stilts.

**1975, Oct. 14   Litho.   Perf. 13**
577 A241  £1.10 pink & multi      .20   .20
578 A241  £1.70 lemon & multi     .20   .20
579 A241  £2 multicolored         .20   .20
          #577-579, with tabs           .40

Butterfly and Factory (Air Pollution) — A242

Designs: 80a, Fish and tanker (water pollution). £1.70, Ear and jet (noise pollution).

**1975, Dec. 9    Photo.    Perf. 14**
580 A242  50a car & multi         .20   .20
581 A242  80a green & multi       .20   .20
582 A242  £1.70 orange & multi    .20   .20
          Nos. 580-582 (3)        .60   .60
          With tabs                     .45

Environmental protection.

Star of David — A243

**1975-80                   Perf. 13x14**
583 A243  75a vio bl & car        .20   .20
584 A243  £1.80 violet bl & gray  .20   .20
585 A243  £1.85 vio bl & lt brn   .20   .20
586 A243  £2.45 vio bl & brt
                green             .20   .20
587 A243  £2.70 vio bl & purple   .20   .20
588 A243  £4.30 ultra & red       .20   .20
589 A243  £5.40 vio bl & ol       .30   .20
590 A243  £8 vio bl & bl          .40   .20
          Nos. 583-590 (8)       1.90  1.60
          With tabs               2.75

Issued: £1.85, 12/9; £2.45, 6/22/76; 75a, 12/77; £5.40, 5/23/78; £1.80, £8, 5/22/79; £2.70, 12/25/79; £4.30, 5/26/80.

**Landscape Type of 1971-75**

Design: £10, View of Elat and harbor.

**1976, Aug. 17  Photo.  Perf. 14x14½**
592 A193  £10 Prussian blue       .85   .20
          With tab                1.00

No. 592 issued both tagged and untagged.

"In the days of Ahasuerus." — A247

Designs (from Book of Esther): 80a, "He set the royal crown on her head." £1.60, "Thus shall it be done to the man whom the king delights to honor."

**1976, Feb. 17   Photo.   Perf. 14**
593 A247  40a multicolored        .20   .20
594 A247  80a multicolored        .20   .20
595 A247  £1.60 multicolored      .20   .20
  a.  Souv. sheet of 3, #593-595, perf
      13x14                       .35   .35
      #593-595, with tabs              .30

Purim Festival. No. 595a sold for £4.

Border Settlement, Barbed Wire — A248

**1976, Feb. 17**
596 A248  £1.50 olive & multi     .20   .20
          With tab                      .25

Border settlements, part of Jewish colonization of Holy Land.

Symbolic Key — A249

**1976, Feb. 17**
597 A249  £1.85 multicolored      .20   .20
          With tab                      .25

Bezalel Academy of Arts and Design, Jerusalem, 70th anniv.

"200" US Flag A250

**1976, Apr. 25   Photo.   Perf. 13x14**
598 A250  £4 gold & multi         .25   .20
          With tab                      .30

American Bicentennial.

Dancers of Meron, by Reuven Rubin A251

**1976, Apr. 25   Litho.   Perf. 14**
599 A251  £1.30 multicolored      .20   .20
          With tab                      .25

Lag Ba-Omer festival.

8th Brigade Monument, Ben-Gurion Airport — A252

**1976, Apr. 25   Photo.   Perf. 14x13**
600 A252  £1.85 multicolored      .20   .20
          With tab                      .25

Memorial Day.

**Souvenir Sheet**

Tourism, Sport and Industry — A253

**1976, Apr. 25**
601 A253  Sheet of 3             .60   .50
  a.  £1 multicolored            .20   .20
  b.  £2 multicolored            .20   .20
  c.  £4 multicolored            .35   .25

No. 601 sold for £10.

High Jump A254

**1976, June 22            Perf. 13x14**
602 A254  £1.60 shown            .20   .20
603 A254  £2.40 Diving          .20   .20
604 A254  £4.40 Gymnastics      .30   .25
          #602-604, with tabs          .65

21st Olympic Games, Montreal, Canada, July 17-Aug. 1.

Tents and Suns — A255

**1976, June 22            Perf. 14**
605 A255  £1.50 green & multi    .20   .20
          With tab                     .25

Israel Camping Union.

"Truth"            Pawn
A256              A257

Design: £1.50, "Judgment" (scales). £1.90, "Peace" (dove and olive branch).

**1976, Aug. 17   Photo.   Perf. 14x13**
**Tagged**
606 A256  45a gold & multi       .20   .20
607 A256  £1.50 gold & multi     .20   .20
608 A256  £1.90 gold & multi     .20   .20
          #606-608, with tabs          .30

Festivals 5737.

**1976, Oct. 19   Litho.   Perf. 14**
609 A257  £1.30 shown           .20   .20
610 A257  £1.60 Rook           .20   .20
          #609-610, with tabs         .35

22nd Men's and 7th Women's Chess Olympiad, Haifa, Oct. 24-Nov. 11.

Byzantine Building, 6th Century A258

70a, City wall, 7th cent. B.C. £2.40, Robinson's Arch. £2.80, Steps to Gate of Hulda. Both from area leading to 2nd Temple, 1st cent. B.C. £5, Wall, Omayyad Palace, 8th cent. A.D.

**1976                Litho.   Perf. 14**
611 A258  70a multicolored       .20   .20
612 A258  £1.30 multicolored     .20   .20
613 A258  £2.40 multicolored     .20   .20
614 A258  £2.80 multicolored     .35   .20
615 A258  £5 multicolored        .45   .40
          Nos. 611-615 (5)      1.40  1.20
          With tabs              1.75

Excavations in Old Jerusalem.

Issued: #612-614, 10/19; #611, 615, 12/23.

Clearing the Land, 1890 A259

Designs: 10a, Building harbor wall. 60a, Road building, vert. £1.40, Plower and horse-drawn plow. £1.80, Planting trees.

**1976, Dec. 23   Photo.   Perf. 13**
616 A259  5a brown & gold        .20   .20
617 A259  10a purple & gold      .20   .20
618 A259  60a gold & car         .20   .20

| | | | |
|---|---|---|---|
| 619 | A259 | £1.40 gold & blue | .20 .20 |
| 620 | A259 | £1.80 green & gold | .20 .20 |

#616-620, with tabs    .40

Work of the pioneers.

"Let's Pull up Grandfather's Carrot" — A260

**1977, Feb. 15    Litho.    Perf. 14**

621  A260  £2.60 multicolored   .25 .20
With tab   .30

Voluntary service.

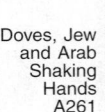

Doves, Jew and Arab Shaking Hands A261

£1.40, Arab & Jew holding hands, and flowers. £2.70, Peace dove, Arab and Jew dancing. Illustrations for the book "My Shalom-My Peace."

**1977, Feb. 15**

| | | | |
|---|---|---|---|
| 622 | A261 | 50a multicolored | .20 .20 |
| 623 | A261 | £1.40 multicolored | .20 .20 |
| 624 | A261 | £2.70 multicolored | .25 .25 |

622-#624, with tabs   .55

Children's drawings for peace.

"By the Rivers of Babylon . . ." — A262

Drawings by Efraim Moshe Lilien: £1.80, Abraham, vert. £2.10, "May our eyes behold thee when thou returnest to Zion in compassion."

**Perf. 14x13, 13x14**

**1977, Feb. 15    Photo.**

| | | | |
|---|---|---|---|
| 625 | A262 | £1.70 gray, brn & blk | .20 .20 |
| 626 | A262 | £1.80 yel, blk & brn | .20 .20 |
| 627 | A262 | £2.10 lt grn & dk grn | .25 .20 |

Nos. 625-627 (3)   .65 .60
With tabs   .75

Souvenirs for 5th Zionist Congress, 1902.

Trumpet A263

Embroidered Sabbath Cloth A264

**1977, Apr. 19    Litho.    Perf. 14**

| | | | |
|---|---|---|---|
| 628 | A263 | £1.50 shown | .20 .20 |
| 629 | A263 | £2 Lyre | .20 .20 |
| 630 | A263 | £5 Cymbals | .25 .20 |

#628-630, with tabs   .55

Ancient musical instruments, Haifa Music Museum and Amli Library.

**1977, Apr. 19    Perf. 13x14**

631  A264  £3 buff & multi   .25 .20
With tab   .30

Importance of Sabbath observation in Jewish life.

Parachutists' Memorial, Bilu-Gedera, Tel Aviv — A265

**1977, Apr. 19    Perf. 13x14**

632  A265  £3.30 gray, blk & grn   .30 .25
With tab   .40

Memorial Day.

10th Maccabiah — A266

**1977, June 23    Photo.    Perf. 14x13**

| | | | |
|---|---|---|---|
| 633 | A266 | £1 Fencing | .20 .20 |
| 634 | A266 | £2.50 Shot put | .20 .20 |
| 635 | A266 | £3.50 Judo | .25 .20 |

Nos. 633-635 (3)   .65 .60
With tabs   .70

ZOA Convention Emblem — A267

**1977, June 23    Perf. 14**

636  A267  £4 silver & multi   .30 .20
With tab   .40

Convention of Zionist Organization of America (ZOA), Jerusalem, June 1977.

Petah Tikva Centenary — A268

**1977, June 23    Perf. 14x13**

637  A268  £1.50 multicolored   .20 .20
With tab   .20

Matriarchs of the Bible — A269

**1977, Aug. 16    Photo.    Perf. 14**

| | | | |
|---|---|---|---|
| 638 | A269 | 70a Sarah | .20 .20 |
| 639 | A269 | £1.50 Rebekah | .20 .20 |
| 640 | A269 | £2 Rachel | .20 .20 |
| 641 | A269 | £3 Leah | .20 .20 |

#638-641, with tabs   .75

Jewish New Year, 5738.

Frontier Guard — A270

Illuminated Page — A271

**1977, Aug. 16    Litho.    Perf. 14**

| | | | |
|---|---|---|---|
| 642 | A270 | £1 shown | .20 .20 |
| 643 | A270 | £1 Police | .20 .20 |
| 644 | A270 | £1 Civil Guard | .20 .20 |

#642-644, with tabs   .35

Israel Police Force, established Mar. 26, 1948.

**1977, July 21    Photo.    Perf. 14x13**

645  A271  £4 multicolored   .20 .20
With tab   .25

4th cent. of Hebrew printing at Safad.

Farm Growing from Steel Helmet A272

Koffler Accelerator A273

**1977, Oct. 18    Litho.    Perf. 14**

646  A272  £3.50 multicolored   .20 .20
With tab   .25

Fighting Pioneer Youth (NAHAL), established 1949.

**1977, Oct. 18    Photo.    Perf. 14x13**

647  A273  £8 black & blue   .60 .40

Inauguration of Koffler accelerator at Weizmann Institute of Science, Rehovot. Untagged.

Caesarea — A274

Scenes: £1, Arava on the Dead Sea. £20, Rosh Pinna.

**1977-78    Perf. 13½x14**

**Size: 27x22mm**

| | | | |
|---|---|---|---|
| 649 | A274 | 10a violet blue | .20 .20 |
| 664 | A274 | £1 olive bister | .20 .20 |

**Perf. 14½x14**

**Size: 27½x26½mm**

672  A274  £20 org & dk grn ('78)   .80 .20
#(649-672), with tabs   1.50

The 10a is untagged. The £1, £20 issued tagged and untagged.
Issued: 10a, £1, 10/18/77; £20, 7/4/78.

First Holy Land Locomotive A276

Locomotives: £1.50, Jezreel Valley train. £2, British Mandate period. £2.50, Israel Railways.

**1977, Dec. 13    Photo.    Perf. 13x14**

| | | | |
|---|---|---|---|
| 674 | A276 | 65a multicolored | .20 .20 |
| 675 | A276 | £1.50 multicolored | .20 .20 |
| 676 | A276 | £2 multicolored | .20 .20 |
| 677 | A276 | £2.50 multicolored | .25 .25 |
| a. | | Souvenir sheet of 4, #674-677 | 1.50 1.25 |

#674-677, with tabs   .90

Railways in the Holy Land. #677a sold for £10.

Cypraea Isabella — A277

Designs: Red Sea shells.

**1977, Dec. 13    Litho.    Perf. 14**

| | | | |
|---|---|---|---|
| 678 | A277 | £2 shown | .20 .20 |
| 679 | A277 | £2 Lioconcha castrensis | .20 .20 |
| 680 | A277 | £2 Gloripallium pallium | .20 .20 |
| 681 | A277 | £2 Malea pomum | .20 .20 |

#678-681, with tabs   .50

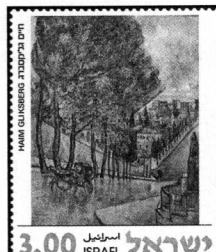

Street in Jerusalem, by Haim Glicksberg (1904-1970) A278

Paintings: £3.80, Thistles, by Leopold Krakauer (1890-1954). £4.40, An Alley in Zefat, by Mordekhai Levanon (1901-1968).

**1978, Feb. 14**

| | | | |
|---|---|---|---|
| 682 | A278 | £3 multicolored | .20 .20 |
| 683 | A278 | £3.80 multicolored | .20 .20 |
| 684 | A278 | £4.40 multicolored | .25 .25 |

Nos. 682-684 (3)   .65 .65
With tabs   .65

Marriage Contract, Netherlands, 1648 — A279

Marriage Contracts (Ketubah): £3.90, Morocco, 1897. £6, Jerusalem, 1846.

**1978, Feb. 14**

| | | | |
|---|---|---|---|
| 685 | A279 | 75a multicolored | .20 .20 |
| 686 | A279 | £3.90 multicolored | .20 .20 |
| 687 | A279 | £6 multicolored | .30 .20 |

#685-687, with tabs   .65

Eliyahu Golomb — A280

Designs: Portraits.

**1978, Apr. 23    Photo.    Perf. 14x13**

| | | | |
|---|---|---|---|
| 688 | A280 | £2 shown | .20 .20 |
| 689 | A280 | £2 Dr. Moshe Sneh | .20 .20 |
| 690 | A280 | £2 David Raziel | .20 .20 |
| 691 | A280 | £2 Yitzhak Sadeh | .20 .20 |
| 692 | A280 | £2 Abraham Stern | .20 .20 |

#688-692, with tabs   .60

Heroes of underground movement. Nos. 688-692 issued in sheets of 15.
See Nos. 695-696, 699-700, 705-706, 712-714, 740-742.

## Souvenir Sheet

Jerusalem, Mosaic, from Madaba
Map — A281

**1978, Apr. 23    Litho.    Perf. 14**
693 A281   Sheet of 4           1.40  1.40
  a.   £1 multicolored      .20   .20
  b.   £2 multicolored      .25   .20
  c.   £3 multicolored      .40   .35
  d.   £4 multicolored      .50   .45

Tabir '78 National Stamp Exhibition, Jerusalem, Apr. 23. No. 693 sold for $15.

Flowers
A282

Design: Flowers, after children's paintings on Memorial Wall in Yad-Lebanim Museum, Petah Tikva. Each stamp shows different flowers.

**1978, Apr. 23              Perf. 14**
694       Sheet of 15          1.40  1.25
  a.-o.  A282 £1.50 single stamp  .20  .20

Memorial Day.

### Heroes Type

Designs: No. 695, Theodor Herzl. No. 696, Chaim Weizmann.

**1978, July 5    Photo.    Perf. 14x13**
695 A280  £2 gray & gray ol    .20   .20
696 A280  £2 buff & vio bl     .20   .20
  #695-696, with tabs       .25

Herzl, founder of Zionism; Weizmann, 1st President of Israel.

Hatiqwa, 1st Verse
A285

YMCA Building, Jerusalem
A286

**1978, July 4              Perf. 13x14**
697 A285  £8.40 multicolored   .45   .35
  With tab                    .50

Centenary of Israeli National Anthem, Hatiqwa, by poet Naftali Herz Imber.

**1978, July 4    Litho.    Perf. 13**
698 A286  £5.40 multicolored   .25   .20
  With tab                    .35

Centenary of YMCA in Jerusalem.

### Heroes Type

Designs: No. 699, Rabbi Kook (1865-1935). No. 700, Rabbi Ouziel (1880-1963).

**1978, Aug. 22    Photo.    Perf. 14x13**
699 A280  £2 pale gray & slate
         grn          .20   .20
700 A280  £2 pale gray & dk pur  .20  .20
  #699-700, with tabs       .25

Patriarchs
A288

**1978, Aug. 22              Perf. 14**
701 A288  £1.10 Abraham & Isaac  .20  .20
702 A288  £5.20 Isaac           .25   .25
703 A288  £6.60 Jacob           .30   .30
  #701-703, with tabs       .70

Festivals 5739.

Families and Houses
A289

**1978, Aug. 22              Perf. 13x14**
704 A289  £5.10 multicolored    .30   .20
  With tab                    .35

Social welfare.

### Heroes Type

Designs: No. 705, David Ben-Gurion. No. 706, Ze'ev Jabotinsky.

**1978, Oct. 31    Photo.    Perf. 14x13**
705 A280  £2 buff & vio brn     .20   .20
706 A280  £2 gray & indigo      .20   .20
  #705-706, with tabs       .25

30 years of independence. Ben-Gurion, first Prime Minister, and Ze'ev Vladimir Jabotinsky (1880-1940), leader of World Union of Zionist Revisionists.

Star of David and Growing Tree — A291

**1978, Oct. 31    Litho.    Perf. 14**
707 A291  £8.40 multicolored    .45   .35
  With tab                    .50

United Jewish Appeal, established 1939 in US to help Israel.

Old and New Hospital Buildings
A292

**1978, Oct. 31**
708 A292  £5.40 multicolored    .25   .20
  With tab                    .30

Opening of new Shaare Zedek Medical Center, Jerusalem.

Silver and Enamel Vase, India — A293

Iris Lortetii — A295

£3, Elephant with howdah, Persia, 13th cent. £4, Mosque lamp, glass and enamel, Syria, 14th cent.

**1978, Oct. 31**
709 A293  £2.40 multicolored    .20   .20
710 A293  £3 multicolored       .20   .20
711 A293  £4 multicolored       .20   .20
  Nos. 709-711 (3)      .60   .60
  With tabs                   .65

Leo Arie Mayer Memorial Museum for Islamic Art, Jerusalem.

### Heroes Type

#712, Menachem Ussishkin (1863-1941). #713, Berl Katzenelson (1878-1944). #714, Max Nordau (1849-1923).

**1978, Dec. 26    Photo.    Perf. 14x13**
712 A280  £2 citron & sl grn    .20   .20
713 A280  £2 gray & vio blue    .20   .20
714 A280  £2 buff & black       .20   .20
  #712-714, with tabs       .45

30th anniversary of independence.

**1978, Dec. 26    Litho.    Perf. 14**
Protected Wild Flowers: £5.40, Iris haynei. £8.40, Iris nazarena.

715 A295  £1.10 multicolored    .20   .20
716 A295  £5.40 multicolored    .30   .25
717 A295  £8.40 multicolored    .45   .35
  Nos. 715-717 (3)      .95   .80
  With tabs                   .95

Agricultural Mechanization
A296

Symbolic Designs: £2.40, Seawater desalination. £4.30, Electronics. £5, Chemical fertilizers.

**1979, Feb. 13    Litho.    Perf. 13**
718 A296  £1.10 multicolored    .20   .20
719 A296  £2.40 multicolored    .20   .20
720 A296  £4.30 multicolored    .20   .20
721 A296  £5 multicolored       .20   .20
  #718-721, with tabs       .70

Technological Achievements.

"Hope from Darkness"
A297

**1979, Feb. 13**
722 A297  £5.40 multicolored    .30   .25
  With tab                    .35

Salute to "the Righteous among Nations," an award to those who helped during Nazi period.

Jewish Brigade Flag — A298

**1979, Feb. 13    Photo.    Perf. 14**
723 A298  £5.10 blue, yel & blk  .25  .25
  With tab                    .30

Jewish Brigade served with British Armed Forces during WWII.

Paper (Prayer for Peace) in Crevice of Western Wall — A299

**1979, Mar. 26    Photo.    Perf. 14x13**
724 A299  £10 multicolored      .35   .25
  With tab                    .40
  a.   Souv. sheet of 1, imperf.  .40  .45

Signing of peace treaty between Israel and Egypt, Mar. 26.

11th Hapoel Games — A300

**1979, Apr. 23    Litho.    Perf. 13**
725 A300  £1.50 Weightlifting   .20   .20
726 A300  £6 Tennis             .30   .20
727 A300  £11 Gymnastics        .50   .40
  Nos. 725-727 (3)     1.00   .80
  With tabs                  1.00

"50" and Rotary Emblem — A301

**1979, Apr. 23    Photo.    Perf. 14x13**
728 A301  £7 multicolored       .35   .25
  With tab                    .40

Rotary Intl. in Israel, 50th anniv.

Navy Memorial, Ashdod
A302

**1979, Apr. 23**
729 A302  £5.10 multicolored    .25   .20
  With tab                    .30

Memorial Day.

Rabbi Yehoshua ben Hananya
A303

Flag Colors as Search Light
A304

Craftsmen-Sages: £8.50, Rabbi Meir Baal Ha-Ness, scribe. £13, Rabbi Johanan, sandal maker.

**1979, Sept. 4    Photo.    Perf. 14x13**
730 A303  £1.80 multicolored    .20   .20
731 A303  £8.50 multicolored    .20   .20
732 A303  £13 multicolored      .35   .30
  Nos. 730-732 (3)      .75   .70
  With tabs                   .75

Jewish New Year 5740.

**1979, Sept. 4**
733 A304  £10 multicolored      .25   .20
  With tab                    .30

Jewish Agency, 50th anniversary.

Hot Springs,
Tiberias
A305

Boy Riding
Rainbow
A306

Design: £12, Dead Sea health resorts.

**1979, Sept. 4    Litho.    Perf. 14**
734 A305    £8 multicolored    .20    .20
735 A305    £12 multicolored    .30    .25
 #734-735, with tabs    .55

**1979, Nov. 13    Photo.    Perf. 13x14**
736 A306    £8.50 multicolored    .20    .20
 With tab    .25

International Year of the Child.

Jerusalem — A307

Children's Drawings of Jerusalem: £4, People of different nationalities, horiz. £5, Praying at the Western Wall, horiz.

**1979, Nov. 13    Perf. 14**
737 A307    £1.80 multicolored    .20    .20
738 A307    £4 multicolored    .20    .20
739 A307    £5 multicolored    .20    .20
 #737-739, with tabs    .30

**Heroes Type**

Designs: £7, Arthur Ruppin (1876-1943). £9, Joseph Trumpeldor (1880-1920). £13, Aaron Aaronsohn (1876-1919).

**1979, Nov. 13    Photo.    Perf. 14x13**
740 A280    £7 gray & magenta    .20    .20
741 A280    £9 pale grn & Prus bl    .25    .25
742 A280    £13 pale yel & dk ol    .35    .35
 Nos. 740-742 (3)    .80    .80
 With tabs    1.10

Sorek
Cave — A308

**1980, Jan. 15    Litho.    Perf. 13x14**
743 A308    £50 multicolored    1.00    .50
 With tab    1.25

Star of David in
Cogwheel
A309

Scolymus
Maculatus
A310

**1980, Jan. 15    Perf. 14**
744 A309    £13 multicolored    .40    .40
 With tab    .45

Organization for Rehabilitation through Training (ORT), centenary.

**1980, Jan. 15**

Thistles: £5.50, Echinops viscosus. £8.50, Cynara syriaca.

745 A310    50a multicolored    .20    .20
746 A310    £5.50 multicolored    .20    .20
747 A310    £8.50 multicolored    .25    .20
 #745-747, with tabs    .50

Men and Drop of
Blood — A311

Mobile Intensive
Care
Unit — A312

**1980, Apr. 15    Photo.    Perf. 14x13**
748 A311    £2.70 multicolored    .20    .20
749 A312    £13 multicolored    .30    .30
a.    Souv. sheet, 2 each #748-749    1.00    1.00
 #748-749, with tabs    .45

Magen David Adom (Red Star of David), 50th anniv.

Road of
Courage
Monument
A313

Sabbath
Lamp,
Netherlands,
18th Century
A314

**1980, Apr. 15    Litho.    Perf. 14**
750 A313    £12 multicolored    .30    .25
 With tab    .35

Memorial Day.

**1980, Aug. 5    Photo.    Perf. 13x14**

Sabbath Lamps: £20, Germany, 18th century. £30, Morocco, 19th century.

751 A314    £4.30 multicolored    .20    .20
752 A314    £20 multicolored    .30    .30
753 A314    £30 multicolored    .50    .50
 Nos. 751-753 (3)    1.00    1.00
 With tabs    1.10

Yizhak
Gruenbaum
A315

Renewal of
Jewish
Settlement in
Gush Etzion
A316

**1980, Aug. 5    Perf. 14x13**
754 A315    £32 sepia    .80    .70
 With tab    .85

Yizhak Gruenbaum (1879-1970), first minister of the interior.

**1980, Aug. 5**
755 A316    £19 multicolored    .35    .30
 With tab    .40

NATIONAL STAMP EXHIBITION HAIFA 80

View of Haifa and Mt. Carmel, 17th
Century — A317

**1980, Sept. 28    Litho.    Perf. 14x13**
756 A317    Sheet of 2    2.00    2.25
a.    2s multicolored    .75    .85
b.    3s multicolored    1.00    1.10

Haifa 80 National Stamp Exhibition, Haifa, Sept. 28-Oct. 7.

A318

**1980-81    Photo.    Perf. 13x14**
757 A318    5a brt yel grn & green    .20    .20
758 A318    10a red & brt mag    .20    .20
759 A318    20a grnsh bl & dk blue    .20    .20
760 A318    30a lil & dp vio    .20    .20
761 A318    50a red org & red brown    .20    .20
762 A318    60a brt yel grn & dk brown    .20    .20
762A A318    70a Prus bl & black    .20    .20
763 A318    1s brt mag & dk green    .20    .20
764 A318    2s dk bl grn & brn red    .25
765 A318    2.80s brown & grn    .30    .20
766 A318    3.20s gray & red    .35    .20
767 A318    4.20s ultra & dk pur    .40    .20
768 A318    5s green & blk    .55    .20
769 A318    10s brn org & brn    1.25    .20
 #757-769, with tabs    5.00

Issued: 70a, 5/5/81; others, 12/16/80.
See Nos. 784-786, 807-808

Prime Minister Golda
Meir (1898-
1978) — A319

**1981, Feb. 10    Photo.    Perf. 14x13**
770 A319    2.60s rose violet    .40    .40
 With tab    .45

View of Jerusalem, by Mordechai
Ardon — A320

**1981, Feb. 10    Litho.    Perf. 14**

Paintings of Jerusalem by: 50a, Anna Ticho. 1.50s, Joseph Zaritsky, vert.

771 A320    50a multicolored    .20    .20
772 A320    1.50s multicolored    .25    .20
773 A320    2.50s multicolored    .40    .35
 Nos. 771-773 (3)    .85    .75
 With tabs    .95

Hand Putting
Coin in Light
Bulb — A321

**1981, Mar. 17    Photo.    Perf. 14**
774 A321    2.60s shown    .25    .25
775 A321    4.20s Hand squeezing solar energy    .40    .35
 #774-775, with tabs    .80

Shmuel Yosef
Agnon (1880-
1970),
Writer — A322

Wind
Surfing — A323

Designs: 2.80s, Moses Montefiore (1784-1885), first knighted English Jew. 3.20s, Abba Hillel Silver (1893-1963), statesman.

**Perf. 14x13, 14 (3.20s)**
**1981, Mar. 17**
776 A322    2s dk blue & blk    .25    .25
777 A322    2.80s dk bl grn & blk    .30    .30
778 A322    3.20s deep bis & blk    .35    .30
 Nos. 776-778 (3)    .90    .85
 With tabs    1.00

**1981, May 5    Perf. 14x13**
779 A323    80a shown    .20    .20
780 A323    4s Basketball    .55    .55
781 A323    6s High jump    .75    .75
 Nos. 779-781 (3)    1.50    1.50
 With tabs    1.50

11th Maccabiah Games, July 8-16.

Biq'at
Hayarden
Memorial
A324

Jewish Family
Heritage
A325

**1981, May 5    Perf. 13x14**
782 A324    1s red & black    .20    .20
 With tab    .25

**1981, May 5    Litho.    Perf. 14**
783 A325    3s multicolored    .40    .35
 With tab    .45

**Type of 1980**
**1981, Aug. 25    Photo.    Perf. 13x14**
784 A318    90a dp vio & brn org    .20    .20
785 A318    3s red & dk blue    .45    .30
786 A318    4s dk brn vio & dp lil rose    .50    .35
 Nos. 784-786 (3)    1.15    .85
 With tabs    1.25

The Burning Bush
A326

Roses
A327

Festivals 5742 (Book of Exodus): 1s "Let my people go . . ." 3s, Crossing of the Red Sea. 4s, Moses with Tablets.

**1981, Aug. 25**
| | | | |
|---|---|---|---|
| 787 | A326 70a multicolored | .20 | .20 |
| 788 | A326 1s multicolored | .20 | .20 |
| 789 | A326 3s multicolored | .35 | .35 |
| 790 | A326 4s multicolored | .45 | .40 |
| | Nos. 787-790 (4) | 1.20 | 1.15 |
| | With tabs | 1.25 | |

**1981, Oct. 22       Litho.       Perf. 14**
| | | | |
|---|---|---|---|
| 791 | A327 90a Rosa damas-cena | .20 | .20 |
| 792 | A327 3.50s Rosa phoenicia | .40 | .35 |
| 793 | A327 4.50s Rosa hybrida | .50 | .45 |
| | Nos. 791-793 (3) | 1.10 | 1.00 |
| | With tabs | 1.50 | |

Ha-Shiv'a Interchange, Morasha-Ashod Highway — A328

**1981, Oct. 22       Photo.       Perf. 14x13**
| | | | |
|---|---|---|---|
| 794 | A328 8s multicolored | .70 | .65 |
| | With tab | .75 | |

Elat Stone
A329

Arbutus Andrachne
A330

**1981, Dec. 29       Litho.       Perf. 14**
| | | | |
|---|---|---|---|
| 795 | A329 2.50s shown | .25 | .25 |
| 796 | A329 5.50s Star sapphire | .55 | .55 |
| 797 | A329 7s Emerald | .70 | .70 |
| | Nos. 795-797 (3) | 1.50 | 1.50 |
| | With tabs | 2.25 | |

**1981, Dec. 29**
| | | | |
|---|---|---|---|
| 798 | A330 3s shown | .30 | .30 |
| 799 | A330 3s Cercis siliquastrum | .30 | .30 |
| 800 | A330 3s Quercus ithaburensis | .30 | .30 |
| a. | Vert. or horiz. strip of 3, #798-800 | 1.00 | 1.00 |
| | #800a, horiz. strip of 3 with tabs | 1.25 | |
| | Sheets of 9. | | |

Road Safety — A331

**1982, Mar. 2       Photo.       Perf. 14x13**
| | | | |
|---|---|---|---|
| 801 | A331 7s multicolored | .70 | .70 |
| | With tab | 1.00 | |
| a. | Souvenir sheet | 1.25 | 1.25 |
| | No. 801a sold for 10s. | | |

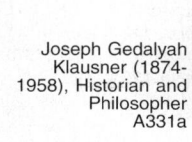

Joseph Gedalyah Klausner (1874-1958), Historian and Philosopher A331a

7s, Perez Bernstein (1890-1971), writer and editor. 8s, Rabbi Arys Levin (1885-1969).

**1982, Mar. 2**
| | | | |
|---|---|---|---|
| 802 | A331a 7s multi | .50 | .50 |
| 803 | A331a 8s multi | .55 | .55 |
| 804 | A331a 9s cream & dk bl | .65 | .65 |
| | Nos. 802-804 (3) | 1.70 | 1.70 |
| | With tabs | 1.90 | |

**Type of 1980 and**

Produce — A332

**1982-83       Photo.       Perf. 13 x 14**
| | | | |
|---|---|---|---|
| 805 | A332 40a Prus bl & grn | .20 | .20 |
| 806 | A332 80a lt bl & pur | .20 | .20 |
| 807 | A318 1.10s ol & red | .20 | .20 |
| 808 | A318 1.20s bl & red | .20 | .20 |
| 809 | A332 1.40s ol grn & red | .20 | .20 |
| 810 | A332 6s red vio & brn org | .25 | .20 |
| 811 | A332 7s brn org & ol | .20 | .20 |
| 812 | A332 8s brt grn & red brn | .20 | .20 |
| 813 | A332 9s ol & brn | .25 | .20 |
| 814 | A332 15s ver & brt grn | .40 | .20 |
| | Nos. 805-814 (10) | 2.30 | 2.00 |
| | With tabs | 5.00 | |

Issued: 1.10s, 2/11; 1.20s, 3/16; 1.40s, 6/22/82; 40a, 80a, 6s, 1/11/83; 7s-15s, 10/11/83.
See Nos. 876-879.

Tel Aviv Landscape, by Aryeh Lubin (d. 1980) — A333

Landscapes by: 8s, Sionah Tagger, vert. 15s, Israel Paldi (1892-1979).

**1982, Apr. 22       Litho.       Perf. 14**
| | | | |
|---|---|---|---|
| 815 | A333 7s multicolored | .50 | .50 |
| 816 | A333 8s multicolored | .50 | .50 |
| 817 | A333 15s multicolored | 1.00 | 1.00 |
| | Nos. 815-817 (3) | 2.00 | 2.00 |
| | With tabs | 3.00 | |

Gedudei Nouar Youth Corps
A334

Armour Memorial, En Zetim
A335

**1982, Apr. 22       Photo.       Perf. 14x13**
| | | | |
|---|---|---|---|
| 818 | A334 5s multicolored | .40 | .35 |
| | With tab | .55 | |

**1982, Apr. 22       Litho.       Perf. 14**
| | | | |
|---|---|---|---|
| 819 | A335 1.50s multicolored | .20 | .20 |
| | With tab | .20 | |

Memorial Day.

Joshua Addressing Crowd — A336

Festivals 5743 (Book of Joshua): 5.50s, Crossing River Jordan. 7.50s, Blowing down walls of Jericho. 9.50s, Battle with five kings of Amorites.

**1982, Aug. 10       Perf. 14**
| | | | |
|---|---|---|---|
| 820 | A336 1.50s multicolored | .20 | .20 |
| 821 | A336 5.50s multicolored | .30 | .30 |
| 822 | A336 7.50s multicolored | .45 | .45 |
| 823 | A336 9.50s multicolored | .55 | .55 |
| | Nos. 820-823 (4) | 1.50 | 1.50 |
| | With tabs | 1.50 | |

Hadassah, 70th Anniv. — A337

**1982, Aug. 10       Litho.**
| | | | |
|---|---|---|---|
| 824 | A337 12s multicolored | .85 | .70 |
| | With tab | 1.25 | |

Rosh Pinna Settlement Centenary A338

**1982       Photo.       Perf. 13x14**
| | | | |
|---|---|---|---|
| 825 | A338 2.50s shown | .20 | .20 |
| 826 | A338 3.50s Rishon Leziyyon | .20 | .20 |
| 827 | A338 6s Zikhron Yaaqov | .35 | .30 |
| 828 | A338 9s Mazkeret Batya | .65 | .60 |
| | Nos. 825-828 (4) | 1.40 | 1.30 |
| | With tabs | 1.50 | |

Issued: 2.50s, 3.50s, Aug. 10; others, Oct. 5.
See Nos. 849-850.

Olive Branch
A339

Emblem of Council for a Beautiful Israel
A340

**1982, Sept. 12**
| | | | |
|---|---|---|---|
| 829 | A339 multicolored | .20 | .20 |
| | With tab | .40 | |
| a. | Booklet pane of 8 + 8 ('84) | 3.00 | |
| | Sold at various values. | | |

**1982, Oct. 5       Litho.       Perf. 14**
| | | | |
|---|---|---|---|
| 830 | A340 17s multicolored | .90 | .75 |
| | With tab | 1.00 | |
| a. | Souv. sheet of 1, imperf. | 2.25 | 2.25 |

No. 830a was for Beer Sheva '82 National Stamp Exhibition. Sold for 25s.

Eliahu Bet Tzuri — A341

Independence Martyrs: b, Hannah Szenes. c, Shlomo Ben Yosef. d, Yosef Lishanski. e, Naaman Belkind. f, Eliezer Kashani. g, Yechiel Dresner. h, Dov Gruner. i, Mordechai Alkachi. j, Eliahu Hakim. k, Meir Nakar. l, Avshalom Haviv. m, Yaakov Weiss. n, Meir Feinstein. o, Moshe Barazani. p, Eli Cohen. q, Samuel

Azaar. r, Moshe Marzouk. s, Shalom Salih. t, Yosef Basri.

**1982, Dec.       Perf. 14x13½**
| | | | |
|---|---|---|---|
| 831 | Sheet of 20 | 5.50 | 5.50 |
| a.-t. | A341 3s multicolored | .20 | .20 |

Anti-Smoking Campaign
A342

**1983, Feb. 15       Litho.       Perf. 13**
| | | | |
|---|---|---|---|
| 832 | A342 7s Candy in ash tray | .35 | .25 |
| | With tab | .50 | |

Beekeeping
A343

**1983, Feb. 15       Photo.       Perf. 13x14**
| | | | |
|---|---|---|---|
| 833 | A343 30s multi | 1.60 | 1.50 |
| | With tab | 1.75 | |

A343a

**1983, Feb. 15       Litho.       Perf. 14**
| | | | |
|---|---|---|---|
| 834 | A343a 8s Golan | .30 | .30 |
| 835 | A343a 15s Galil | .65 | .55 |
| 836 | A343a 20s Yehuda and Shomeron | .95 | .70 |
| | Nos. 834-836 (3) | 1.90 | 1.55 |
| | With tabs | 3.00 | |

Memorial Day (Apr. 17) — A344

**1983, Apr. 12       Perf. 13**
| | | | |
|---|---|---|---|
| 837 | A344 3s Division of Steel Memorial, Besor Region | .20 | .20 |
| | With tab | .20 | |

Independence Day — A345

**1983, Apr. 12       Perf. 14**
| | | | |
|---|---|---|---|
| 838 | A345 25s multicolored | 1.25 | 1.00 |
| | With tab | 1.40 | |
| a. | Souvenir sheet, imperf. | 2.50 | 2.25 |

No. 838a sold for 35s.

12th Hapoel Games — A346

**1983, Apr. 12       Perf. 14x13**
| | | | |
|---|---|---|---|
| 839 | A346 6s multicolored | .25 | .25 |
| | With tab | .35 | |

50th Anniv. of Israel Military Industries — A347

**1983, Apr. 12**
840 A347 12s multicolored .55 .55
With tab .60

**Souvenir Sheet**

WWII Uprising Leaders — A348

Designs: a, Yosef Glazman (1908-1943), Founder of United Partisans Org. b, Text. 1 c, Mordechai Anilewicz (1919-1943), leader of Warsaw Ghetto revolt. No. 841 sold for 45s.

**1983, June 7**    **Perf. 14**
841 A348 Sheet of 3 2.75 2.75
a.   10s multicolored .75 .60
b.   10s multicolored .75 .60
c.   10s multicolored .75 .60

Raoul Wallenberg (1912-1945), Swedish Diplomat — A349

**1983, June 7**    **Perf. 14x13**
842 A349 14s multicolored .65 .45
With tab 1.00

The Last Way, by Yosef Kuzkovski — A350

**1983, June 7**    **Perf. 14**
843 A350 35s multicolored 1.10 1.10
With tab 1.25

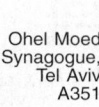

Ohel Moed Synagogue, Tel Aviv A351

**1983, Aug. 23**
844 A351 3s shown .20 .20
845 A351 12s Yeshurun Society, Jerusalem .35 .35
846 A351 16s Ohel Aharon, Haifa .50 .50
847 A351 20s Eliyahu Khakascni, Beer Sheva .60 .60
   Nos. 844-847 (4) 1.65 1.65
With tabs 1.90

View of Afula, Jezreel Valley — A352

**1983, Aug. 23**
848 A352 15s multicolored .65 .55
With tab .80

**Settlement Type of 1982**
**1983, Aug. 23**
849 A338 11s Yesud Ha-Maala .45 .40
850 A338 13s Nes Ziyyona .50 .45
   #849-850, with tabs 1.25

**Souvenir Sheet**

Tel Aviv Seashore Promenade — A353

**1983, Sept. 25**    **Perf. 14x13**
851 A353 Sheet of 2 8.00 8.00
a.   30s multicolored 2.50 2.25
b.   50s multicolored 4.00 3.75

Tel Aviv '83, 13th Natl. Stamp Show, Sept. Sold for 120s.

KFIR-C2 Tactical Fighter — A354

**1983, Dec. 13**    **Photo.**    **Perf. 14**
852 A354 8s shown .20 .20
853 A354 18s Reshef class missile boat .25 .25
854 A354 30s Merkava-MK1 battle tank .45 .45
   Nos. 852-854 (3) .90 .90
With tab .90

Rabbi Meir Bar-Ilan (1880-1949), Founder of Mizrachi Movement — A355

**1983, Dec. 13**    **Photo.**    **Perf. 14x13**
855 A355 9s multicolored .20 .20
With tab .20

Jewish Immigration from Germany, 50th Anniv. A356

**1983, Dec. 13**    **Photo.**    **Perf. 13x14**
856 A356 14s multicolored .40 .35
With tab .45

Michael Halperin (1860-1919), Zionist — A357

Uri Zvi Grinberg (1896-1981), Poet — A358

15s, Yigal Allon (1918-1980), military commander, founder of Israel Labor Party.

**1984, Mar. 15**    **Photo.**    **Perf. 14x13**
857 A357 7s multicolored .20 .20
**Litho.**
**Perf. 14**
858 A357 15s multicolored .25 .25
**Perf. 13**
859 A358 16s multicolored .30 .30
   Nos. 857-859 (3) .75 .75
With tabs 1.00

Hevel Ha-Besor Settlement — A359

**1984, Mar. 15**    **Perf. 14**
860 A359 12s shown .20 .20
861 A359 17s Arava .30 .25
862 A359 40s Gaza Strip .75 .50
   Nos. 860-862 (3) 1.25 .95
With tabs 1.50

Monument of Alexander Zaid, by David Polus A360

Monuments: No. 864, Tel Hay Defenders (seated lion), by Abraham Melnikov (1892-1960). No. 865, Dov Gruner, by Chana Orloff (1888-1968).

**1984, Mar. 15**    **Perf. 13x14**
863 A360 15s multicolored .35 .25
864 A360 15s multicolored .35 .25
865 A360 15s multicolored .35 .25
   Nos. 863-865 (3) 1.05 .75
With tabs 1.35

Memorial Day — A361

Natl. Labor Fed., 50th Anniv. — A362

Design: Oliphant House (Druse military memorial), Dalyat Al Karmil.

**1984, Apr. 26**    **Photo.**    **Perf. 14x13**
866 A361 10s multicolored .20 .20
With tab .20

**1984, Apr. 26**
867 A362 35s multicolored .35 .25
.40

**Produce Type of 1982-83**
**1984**    **Photo.**    **Perf. 13x14**
876 A332 30s vio brn & red .35 .25
877 A332 50s dp bis & rose mag .65 .40
878 A332 100s gray & green 1.25 .80
879 A332 500s dp org & bl blk 1.10 .90
   Nos. 876-879 (4) 3.35 2.35
With tabs 7.00

Issued: 500s, 11/27; others 4/26.

Leon Pinsker (1821-91), A363

Gen. Charles O. Wingate (1903-44) A364

**1984, July 3**    **Perf. 14x13**
880 A363 20s Hovevei Zion founder .20 .20
881 A364 20s British soldier .20 .20
   #880-881, with tabs .50

Hearts, Stars — A365

**1984, July 3**
882 A365 30s multicolored .25 .25
With tab .30

70th anniv. of American Jewish Joint Distribution Committee (philanthropic org. created during World War I).

1984 Summer Olympics A366

**1984, July 3**    **Litho.**    **Perf. 14**
883 A366 80s Dove .70 .70
With tab .90

**Souvenir Sheet**
**Perf. 14x13**
884 A366 240s like 80s 5.00 4.25

No. 884 contains one 23x32mm stamp. Sold for 350s.

Biblical Women A367

David Wolffsohn (1856-1914), Jewish Colonial Trust Founder A368

**1984, Sept. 4**    **Photo.**    **Perf. 13x14**
885 A367 15s Hannah .20 .20
886 A367 70s Ruth .35 .35
887 A367 100s Huldah .60 .60
   Nos. 885-887 (3) 1.15 1.15
With tabs 1.25

**1984, Sept. 4**    **Perf. 14x14½**
888 A368 150s multicolored .90 .60
With tab 1.25

Nahalal Settlement (Founded 1921) A369

**1984, Sept. 4**        **Perf. 14**
889 A369 80s multicolored    .50   .45
    With tab              .60

World Food Day, Oct. 16 — A370

**1984, Nov. 27**        **Litho.**
891 A370 200s Bread, wheat   1.00   .65
    With tab            1.10

Rabbi Isaac Herzog (1888-1959), Statesman, Scholar — A371

**1984, Nov. 27**   **Photo.**   **Perf. 14½**
892 A371 400s multicolored   1.60   1.40
    With tab            1.75

A372

**Perf. 14, 13 (30s)**

**1984, Nov. 27**         **Litho.**
Children's Book Illustrations (Authors and their books): 20s, Apartment to Let, by Leah Goldberg (1911-70). 30s, Why is the Zebra Wearing Pajamas, by Omer Hillel (b. 1926) (30x30mm). 50s, Across the Sea, by Haim Nahman Bialik (1873-1934).

893 A372 20s multicolored    .20   .20
894 A372 30s multicolored    .20   .20
895 A372 50s multicolored    .30   .20
    Nos. 893-895 (3)     .70   .60
    With tab            .80

Birds of Prey — A373

**1985, Feb. 5**    **Litho.**    **Perf. 14**
896 A373 100s Lappet faced
          vulture        .35   .35
897 A373 200s Bonelli's eagle   .60   .60
898 A373 300s Sooty falcon    .80   .80
899 A373 500s Griffon vulture   1.50   1.50
    Nos. 896-899 (4)    3.25   3.25
    With tabs          6.00

**Souvenir Sheet**

899A      Sheet of 4    8.00   5.00
   b.   A373 100s like #896   .50   .40
   c.   A373 200s like #897   .90   .80
   d.   A373 300s like #898   1.25   1.10
   e.   A373 500s like #899   1.75   1.60

No. 899A sold for 1650s. Nos. 899Ab-899Ad do not have inscriptions below the design.

---

Aviation in the Holy Land A374

**1985, Apr. 2**    **Litho.**    **Perf. 14**
900 A374 50s Bleriot XI, 1913   .20   .20
901 A374 150s Scipio-Short S-17
          Kent, 1931      .50   .40
902 A374 250s Tiger Moth DH-
          82, 1934       .80   .70
903 A374 300s Scion-Short S-16,
          1937         .85   1.00
    Nos. 900-903 (4)    2.35   2.30
    With tabs          2.75

Natl. Assoc. of Nurses — A375

**1985, Apr. 2**    **Litho.**    **Perf. 14**
904 A375 400s multicolored   1.00   .95
    With tab            1.50

Golani Brigade Memorial and Museum — A376

**1985, Apr. 2**   **Photo.**   **Perf. 14x13**
905 A376 50s multicolored    .25   .20
    With tab            .45

Zivia (1914-1978) and Yitzhak (1915-1981) Zuckerman, Resistance Heroes, Warsaw Ghetto — A377

**1985, Apr. 2**   **Photo.**   **Perf. 13x14**
906 A377 200s multicolored    .65   .50
    With tab            .80

Souvenir Sheets

Dome of the Rock A378

16th Cent. Bas-relief, Ottoman Period A379

---

Adam, Eve and the Serpent (detail) — A380

#907b, The Western Wall. #907c, Church of the Holy Sepulchre. #908b, Hand, 18th cent. bas-relief, Jewish Quarter. #908c, Rosette carving, 12th-13th cent. Crusader capital. #909, Frontispiece and detail, Schocken Bible, South Germany, ca. 1290.

**1985, May 14**   **Litho.**   **Perf. 13x14**
907     Sheet of 3     3.00   3.00
   a.-c.   A378 200s any single   .80   .75
        Sold for 900s.

        **Perf. 14x13**
908     Sheet of 3     4.00   4.00
   a.-c.   A379 350s any single   1.25   1.10
        Sold for 1500s.

        **Perf. 14**
909 A380 800s multi     3.75   3.75
    Nos. 907-909 (3)   10.75   10.75
        Sold for 1200s.

The Israeli postal administration authorized the Intl. Philatelic Federation (FIP) to overprint a limited number of these souvenir sheets for sale exclusively at ISRAPHIL '85 to raise funds. The FIP overprints have control numbers and are inscribed "Under the Patronage of the Philatelic Federation" in the sheet margin. The sheets remained valid for postage but were not sold by the post office. Value for set of sheets $40.

12th Maccabiah Games A381

1985 Festivals A382

**1985, July 16**    **Litho.**    **Perf. 14**
910 A381 400s Basketball    .75   .75
911 A381 500s Tennis       .90   .90
912 A381 600s Windsurfing   1.10   1.10
    Nos. 910-912 (3)    2.75   2.75
    With tabs          4.00

**1985, July 16**    **Litho.**    **Perf. 14**
Tabernacle utensils: 100sh, Ark of the Covenant. 150sh, Acacia showbread table. 200sh, Menora. 300sh, Incense altar.

913 A382 100s multi      .20   .20
914 A382 150s multi      .30   .30
915 A382 200s multi      .35   .35
916 A382 300s multi      .55   .55
    Nos. 913-916 (4)    1.40   1.40
    With tabs          2.25

---

A383

A384

**1985, July 16**    **Litho.**    **Perf. 14**
917 A383 150s Emblem, badges   .40   .25
    With tab            .55

Intl. Youth Year.

**1985, Nov. 5**    **Litho.**    **Perf. 14**
918 A384 200s multi      .80   .25
    With tab            .95

Leon Yehuda Recanati (1890-1945), financier and philanthropist.

Meir Dizengoff (1861-1936), Founder and Mayor of Tel Aviv — A385

**1985, Nov. 5**
919 A385 500s multi     1.00   .65
    With tab           1.25

Gedera Settlement, Cent. A386

**1985, Nov. 5**   **Photo.**   **Perf. 13x14**
920 A386 600s multi     1.10   .80
    With tab           1.40

The Kibbutz — A387

**1985, Nov. 5**    **Litho.**    **Perf. 14**
921 A387 900s multi     1.25   1.10
    With tab           1.50

Theodor Herzl A388

Capital, Second Temple, Jerusalem A389

Designs: 1s, Corinthian, A.D. 1st cent. 3s, Ionic, 1st cent. B.C.

**1986, Jan. 1**   **Photo.**   **Perf. 13x14**
922 A388 1a red & ultra     .20   .20
923 A388 2a green & ultra    .20   .20
924 A388 3a brown & ultra    .20   .20
925 A388 5a blue & ultra     .20   .20
926 A388 10a org & ultra     .20   .20
927 A388 20a pink & ultra    .20   .20
928 A388 30a lemon & ultra   .25   .25
929 A388 50a pur & ultra     .45   .40
930 A389 1s multi         1.00   .95
931 A389 3s multi         2.75   2.75
    Nos. 922-931 (10)   5.65   5.55
    With tabs          6.25

1s and 3s designs with 1000a and 1500a values were not issued.

See Nos. 1014-1020.

Red Sea
Coral
A390

**1986, Mar. 4**     **Litho.**     **Perf. 14**
932 A390 30a Balanophyllia .35 .35
933 A390 40a Goniopora .50 .50
934 A390 50a Dendronephthya .65 .65
    Nos. 932-934 (3) 1.50 1.50
    With tabs 3.00

Arthur Rubinstein (1887-1982),
Pianist — A391

**1986, Mar. 4**     **Photo.**     **Perf. 13x14**
935 A391 60a Picasso portraits .90 .80
    With tab 1.25

Broadcasting from
Jerusalem, 50th
Anniv. — A392

**1986, Mar. 4**     **Litho.**     **Perf. 14**
936 A392 70a Map and
    microphone, 1936 .90 .90
    With tab 1.10

Negev Brigade
Memorial, Beer
Sheva — A393

**1986, May 4**     **Litho.**     **Perf. 13**
937 A393 20a multicolored .30 .30
    With tab .40

Memorial Day.

Al Jazzar Mosque,
Akko — A394

**1986, May 4**     **Photo.**     **Perf. 14x13**
938 A394 30a multicolored .40 .40
    With tab .50

Id Al-Fitr Feast.

Institutes of Higher Learning in the
US — A395

Designs: No. 939, 942a, Hebrew Union College, Jewish Institute of Religion, 1875, Cincinnati. No. 940, 942b, Yeshiva University,

---

1886, NYC. No. 941, 942c, Jewish Theological
Seminary of America, 1886, NYC.

**1986, May 4**     **Litho.**     **Perf. 14**
939 A395 50a multicolored .60 .60
940 A395 50a multicolored .60 .60
941 A395 50a multicolored .60 .60
    Nos. 939-941 (3) 1.80 1.80
    With tabs 2.75

**Souvenir Sheet**

942     Sheet of 3 + label 4.00 4.00
a.-c. A395 75a any single 1.25 1.25

AMERIPEX '86. Size of Nos. 942a-942c:
36x23mm. No. 942 sold for 3s.

Ben Gurion
Airport,
50th Anniv.
A396

**1986, July 22**       **Perf. 14x13**
943 A396 90a Terminal from air-
    craft 1.25 1.25
    With tab 1.50

"No to Racism" in Graffiti — A397

**1986, July 22**       **Perf. 14**
944 A397 60a multicolored .90 .80
    With tab 1.10

Druze
Feast of
Prophet
Nabi
Sabalan
A398

**1986, July 22**       **Photo.**     **Perf. 14**
945 A398 40a Tomb, Hurfeish .50 .50
    With tab .60

Joseph Sprinzak
(1885-1959), 1st
Speaker of
Knesset — A399

**1986, July 22**       **Litho.**     **Perf. 13**
946 A399 80a multicolored 1.00 1.00
    With tab 1.10

Worms
Illuminated
Mahzor, 13th
Cent. — A400

**1986, Sept. 23**     **Litho.**     **Perf. 13x14**
947 A400 20a Gates of Heaven .25 .25
948 A400 40a Sheqalim, prayer .50 .50
949 A400 90a Rose flower prayer
    introduction 1.10 1.10
    Nos. 947-949 (3) 1.85 1.85
    With tabs 2.25

... 

David Ben-Gurion (1886-
1973) — A401

---

**1986, Oct. 19**     **Litho.**     **Perf. 14x13**
950 A401 1s multicolored 1.25 1.25
    With tab 1.40

**Souvenir Sheet**

Map of the Holyland, by Gerard de
Jode, 1578 — A402

**1986, Oct. 19**       **Perf. 14½**
951 A402 2s multicolored 4.00 3.50

NATANYA '86 Stamp Exhibition; Organized
philately in Natanya, 50th anniv. Sold for 3s.

Israel
Meteorological
Service, 50th
Anniv. — A403

**1986, Dec. 18**     **Litho.**     **Perf. 13**
952 A403 50a multicolored .70 .70
    With tab 1.25

Basilica of the
Annunciation,
Nazareth — A404

**1986, Dec. 18**     **Litho.**     **Perf. 14**
953 A404 70a multicolored .90 .90
    With tab 1.60

Israel Philharmonic Orchestra, 50th
Anniv. — A405

**1986, Dec. 18**
954 A405 1.50s Bronislaw Huber-
    man, violinist 2.25 2.00
955 A405 1.50s Arturo Toscanini,
    conductor 2.25 2.00
a.     Pair, #954-955 4.50 4.00
    With tabs 6.75

Owls
A406

**1987, Feb. 24**     **Litho.**     **Perf. 14x13**
956 A406 30a Bubo bubo .55 .55
957 A406 40a Otus brucei .70 .70
958 A406 50a Tyto alba .90 .90
959 A406 80a Strix butleri 1.50 1.50
    Nos. 956-959 (4) 3.65 3.65
    With tabs 8.00

**Souvenir Sheet**

960     Sheet of 4 10.00 10.00
a.     A406 30a like #956 1.40 1.40
b.     A406 40a like #957 1.75 1.75
c.     A406 50a like #958 2.25 2.25
d.     A406 80a like #959 3.50 3.50

Sold for 3s. Nos. 960a-960d do not have
inscriptions below the design.

---

Ammunition
Hill
Memorial,
Jerusalem
A407

**1987, Apr. 16**     **Litho.**     **Perf. 14**
961 A407 30a multicolored .40 .40
    With tab .65

Memorial Day.

13th
Hapoel
Games
A408

**1987, Apr. 16**
962 A408 90a multicolored 1.10 1.10
    With tab 1.60

**Souvenir Sheet**

HAIFA '87 Stamp Exhibition — A409

**1987, Apr. 16**       **Perf. 14x13**
963 A409 2.70s No. C8 6.00 6.00
    Sold for 4s.

Amateur Radio Operators — A410

**1987, June 14**     **Litho.**     **Perf. 14**
964 A410 2.50s multi 3.75 3.75
    With tab 4.50

World Dog Show,
June 23-27 — A411

**1987, June 14**
965 A411 40a Saluki .90 .70
966 A411 50a Sloughi 1.10 .90
967 A411 2s Canaan 5.00 4.00
    Nos. 965-967 (3) 7.00 5.60
    With tabs 9.00

Clean
Environment
A412

**1987, June 14**       **Perf. 13**
968 A412 40a multicolored .75 .45
    With tab .85

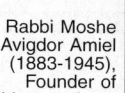

Rabbi Moshe
Avigdor Amiel
(1883-1945),
Founder of
Yeshivas — A413

**1987, Sept. 10          Litho.          Perf. 14**
969  A413  1.40s multi                    1.40  1.40
   With tab                          1.50

Synagogue Models,
Nahum Goldmann
Museum, Tel Aviv
A414

Kupat Holim
Health
Insurance
Institute,
75th Anniv.
A415

**1987, Sept. 10          Perf. 13x14**
970  A414  30a  Altneuschul,
     Prague, 13th
     cent.                    .40  .40
971  A414  50a  Aleppo, Syria, 9th
     cent.                    .60  .60
972  A414  60a  Florence, Italy,
     19th cent.               .75  .75
   Nos. 970-972 (3)            1.75  1.75
   With tabs                         1.90

See Nos. 996-998.

**1987, Sept. 10          Perf. 14**
973  A415  1.50s multi                    1.50  1.50
   With tab                          1.75

Pinhas Rosen
(1887-1978), First
Minister of
Justice — A416

**1987, Nov. 24          Litho.          Perf. 13**
974  A416  80a multicolored              .90  .90
   With tab                          1.25

A417

**1987, Nov. 24          Perf. 14**
Exploration of the Holy Land, 19th cent.:
30a, Thomas Howard Molyneux (1847) and
Christopher Costigan (1835). 50a, William
Francis Lynch (1848). 60a, John MacGregor
(1868-1869).

975  A417  30a multi                     .45  .45
976  A417  50a multi                     .70  .70
977  A417  60a multi                     .85  .55
   Nos. 975-977 (3)            2.00  1.70
   With tabs                         2.50

**Souvenir Sheet**
978    Sheet of 3              4.00  4.00
a.  A417  40a like #975                  .85  .85
b.  A417  50a like #976                 1.25  1.25
c.  A417  80a like #977                 1.75  1.75

No. 978 sold for 2.50s.

A418

A419

**1988, Jan. 26**
979  A418  10a  Computer tech-
     nology                   .20  .20
980  A418  80a  Genetic engi-
     neering                  .95  .95
981  A418  1.40s  Medical engi-
     neering                 1.60  1.60
   Nos. 979-981 (3)            2.75  2.75
   With tabs                         3.00

Industrialization of Israel, cent.

**1988, Jan. 26**
982  A419  40a multicolored              .50  .50
   With tab                          .60

Water conservation.

Australia Bicentennial — A420

**1988, Jan. 26          Perf. 14**
983  A420  1s multi                     1.25  1.25
   With tab                          1.50

Sunflower — A421

**1988, Mar. 9          Photo.          Perf. 13x14**
984  A421  (30a)  dk yel grn & yel       .25  .25
   With tab                          .35

A422

Design: Anne Frank (1929-45), Amsterdam
house where she hid.

**1988, Apr. 19          Litho.**
985  A422  60a multicolored              .50  .50
   With tab                          .60

Independence 40
Stamp Exhibition,
Jerusalem
A423

**1988, Apr. 19**
Design: Modern Jerusalem.

986  A423  1s shown                      .90  .90
   With tab                          1.00

**Souvenir Sheet**
987  A423  2s detail from 1s           3.50  3.50

No. 987 sold for 3s.

Memorial
Day
A424

**1988, Apr. 19          Perf. 14x13**
988  A424  40a multicolored              .35  .35
   With tab                          .45
a.    Souvenir sheet of 1           .75  .75

Natl. independence, 40th anniv. No. 988a
contains one stamp like No. 988 but without
copyright inscription LR. Sold for 60a.

**Souvenir Sheet**

Israel's 40th
Anniv.
Exhibition, Tel
Aviv — A425

Stamps on stamps: a, No. 245. b, No. 297.
c, No. 120. d, No. 96. e, Like No. 794. f, No.
252. g, No. 333. h, No. 478.

**1988, June 9          Litho.          Perf. 14**
989    Sheet of 8 + label       2.75  2.75
a.-h.  A425  20a any single              .30  .30

Sold for 2.40s. Center label pictures Israel
40 emblem.

B'nai B'rith in
Jerusalem,
Cent. — A426

**1988, June 27          Perf. 14**
990  A426  70a multicolored              .70  .70
   With tab                          .75

Nature
Reserves in
the Negev
A427

**1988, June 27**
991  A427  40a  Ein Zin                  .50  .40
992  A427  60a  She'Zaf                  .70  .60
993  A427  70a  Ramon                    .90  .75
   Nos. 991-993 (3)            2.10  1.75
   With tabs                         2.40

See Nos. 1052-1054, 1154-1156.

Agents
Executed
During
World War
II — A428

Portraits: 40a, Havivah Reik (1914-1944).
1.65s, Enzo Hayyim Sereni (1905-1944).

**1988, Sept. 1          Litho.**
994  A428  40a multicolored              .35  .35
995  A428  1.65s multicolored           1.40  1.40
   #994-995, with tabs               1.90

**Synagogue Models Type of 1987**

Models in the Nahum Goldmann Museum,
Tel Aviv: 35a, Kai-Feng Fu Synagogue, 12th
cent., China. 60a, Zabludow Synagogue, 17th
cent., Poland. 70a, Touro Synagogue, 1763,
Newport, Rhode Island, designed by Peter
Harrison.

**1988, Sept. 1          Perf. 13x14**
996  A414  35a multicolored              .30  .30
997  A414  60a multicolored              .55  .55
998  A414  70a multicolored              .65  .65
   Nos. 996-998 (3)            1.50  1.50
   With tabs                         1.60

A429

**1988, Nov. 9          Perf. 14**
999  A429  80a multicolored              .85  .85
   With tab                          1.00

Kristallnacht, Nazi pogrom in Germany, 50th
anniv.

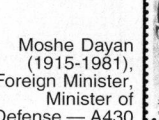

Moshe Dayan
(1915-1981),
Foreign Minister,
Minister of
Defense — A430

**1988, Nov. 9          Perf. 13**
1000  A430  40a multicolored             .40  .40
   With tab                          .50

Jewish
Legion,
70th Anniv.
A431

**1988, Nov. 9          Perf. 14**
1001  A431  2s  yel brn, sepia &
     lem                    1.60  1.60
   With tab                          1.75

Agricultural Achievements — A433

50a, Avocado (fruit-growing). 60a, Lilium
longiflorum (horticulture). 90a, Irrigation.

**1988, Dec. 22          Perf. 14**
1004  A433  50a multicolored             .45  .45
1005  A433  60a multicolored             .55  .55
1006  A433  90a multicolored             .85  .85
   Nos. 1004-1006 (3)          1.85  1.85
   With tabs                         2.00

Natl.
Tourism — A434

**1989, Mar. 12          Litho.          Perf. 13**
1007  A434  40a  Red Sea                 .45  .35
1008  A434  60a  Dead Sea                .60  .50
1009  A434  70a  Mediterranean
     Sea                     .75  .55
1010  A434  1.70s  Sea of Galilee       1.75  1.40
   Nos. 1007-1010 (4)          3.55  2.80
   With tabs                         3.75

Rabbi Judah Leib
Maimon (1875-
1962) — A435

**1989, Mar. 12          Perf. 14**
1011  A435  1.70s multi                 1.75  1.25
   With tab                          2.00

Rashi, Rabbi Solomon Ben Isaac (b. 1039), Talmudic Commentator — A436

**1989, Mar. 12**
1012 A436 4s buff & black     4.25 3.00
   With tab     4.50

Memorial Day — A437     UNICEF — A438

Fallen Airmen's Memorial at Har Tayassim.

**1989, Apr. 30**    **Litho.**    **Perf. 14**
1013 A437 50a multi     .50 .45
   With tab     .60

**Archaeology Type of 1986**

Gates of Huldah, Temple Compound, Mt. Moriah: 40a, Rosettes and rhomboids, frieze and columns, facade of the eastern gate, 1st cent. B.C. 60a, Corinthian capital, 6th cent.

70a, Bas-relief from the Palace of Umayade Caliphs, 8th cent. 80a, Corinthian capital from the Church of Ascension on the Mount of Olives, 12-13th cent. 90a, Star of David, limestone relief, northern wall, near the new gate, Suleiman's Wall. 2s, Mamluk relief, 14th century. 10s, Carved frieze from a sepulcher entrance, end of the Second Temple Period.

**1988-90**    **Litho.**    **Perf. 14**
1014 A389 40a multi     .35 .30
1015 A389 60a multi     .50 .40
1016 A389 70a multi     .55 .40
1017 A389 80a multi     .65 .45
1018 A389 90a multi     .65 .45
1019 A389 2s multi     1.40 .95
1020 A389 10s multi     8.75 5.75
   Nos. 1014-1020 (7)     12.85 8.70
   With tabs     14.00

Issued: 40a, 60a, 12/22/88; 70a, 80a, 6/11/89; 10s, 4/30/89; 90a, 10/17/89; 2s, 6/12/90.

**1989, Apr. 30**     **Perf. 14**
1022 A438 90a multicolored     .80 .65
   With tab     .90

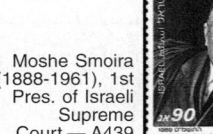

Moshe Smoira (1888-1961), 1st Pres. of Israeli Supreme Court — A439

**1989, June 11**    **Litho.**    **Perf. 13**
1023 A439 90a deep blue     .80 .65
   With tab     .90

13th Maccabiah Games, July 3-13 A440

**1989, June 11**     **Perf. 13x14**
1024 A440 80a multi     .80 .65
   With tab     .90

Ducks — A441

---

Designs: a, Garganey. b, Mallard. c, Teal. d, Shelduck.

**1989, July 18**    **Litho.**    **Perf. 14**
1025    Strip of 4     5.75 5.75
   With tabs     9.00
a.-d.    A441 80a any single     1.25 .85

**Souvenir Sheet**
1025E    Sheet of 4     7.00 7.00
f.    A441 80a like No. 1025d     1.60 1.60
g.    A441 80a like No. 1025b     1.60 1.60
h.    A441 80a like No. 1025a     1.60 1.60
i.    A441 80a like No. 1025c     1.60 1.60

World Stamp Expo '89. No. 1025E contains four 29x33mm stamps. Sold for 5s.

Graphic Design Industry — A442

**1989, July 18**
1026 A442 1s multi     1.00 .75
   With tab     1.10

**Souvenir Sheet**

French Revolution, Bicent. — A443

**1989, July 7**
1027 A443 3.50s multi     8.50 8.50

Sold for 5s.

Hebrew Language Council, Cent. — A444

**1989, Sept. 3**    **Litho.**    **Perf. 13x14**
1028 A444 1s multi     .95 .70
   With tab     1.10

Rabbi Yehuda Hai Alkalai (1798-1878), Zionist — A445

**1989, Sept. 3**     **Perf. 14**
1029 A445 2.50s multi     5.00 1.75
   With tab     6.50

Mizrah Festival A446

Paper cutouts: 50a, Menorah and lions, by Gadoliahu Neminsky, Holbenisk, Ukraine, 1921. 70a, Menorah and hands, Morocco, 19th-20th cent. 80a, "Misrah," hunting scene and deer, Germany, 1818.

---

**1989, Sept. 3**     **Perf. 14x13**
1030 A446 50a multi     .45 .35
1031 A446 70a multi     .65 .50
1032 A446 80a multi     .75 .55
   Nos. 1030-1032 (3)     1.85 1.40
   With tabs     2.00

Tevel '89 Youth Stamp Exhibition, Oct. 15-21 A447

**1989, Oct. 12**    **Photo.**    **Perf. 13x14**
1033 A447 50a multi     .45 .30
   With tab     .60

1st Israeli Stamp Day — A448

**1989, Oct. 17**    **Litho.**    **Perf. 14**
1034 A448 1s multi     .85 .75
   With tab     .95

Special Occasions A449

**1989, Nov. 17**    **Photo.**    **Perf. 13½x14**
1035 A449 (50a) Good luck     .45 .35
1036 A449 (50a) With love     .45 .35
   a.    Booklet pane of 10     5.00
1037 A449 (50a) See you again     .45 .35
   a.    Booklet pane of 10 + 2 labels     5.75
   b.    Sheet of 20 + 5 labels     11.50
   Nos. 1035-1037 (3)     1.35 1.05
   With tabs     1.75

Nos. 1036a, 1037a contain 5 tete-beche pairs, No. 1037b contains 10 tete-beche pairs. #1037a-1037b had value of 80a when released.

Issued: No. 1036a, Aug. 7, 1990. Nos. 1037a-1037b, June 22, 1993.

See Nos. 1059-1061, 1073-1075.

A450

Design: Tapestry and Rebab, a Stringed Instrument, from the Museum of Bedouin Culture.

**1990, Feb. 13**    **Litho.**    **Perf. 13**
1038 A450 1.50s multicolored     1.25 .95
   With tab     1.50

The Circassians in Israel — A451

**1990, Feb. 13**    **Photo.**    **Perf. 14x13**

Designs: Circassian folk dancers.

1039 A451 1.50s multicolored     1.25 .95
   With tab     1.50

---

Rehovot City, Cent. A452

**1990, Feb. 13**     **Perf. 14**
1040 A452 2s multicolored     1.90 1.40
   With tab     2.25

**Souvenir Sheet**

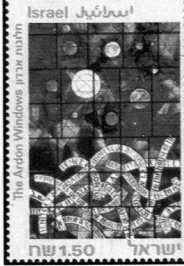

Isaiah's Vision of Eternal Peace, by Mordecai Ardon — A453

Series of 3 stained-glass windows, The Hall of Eternal Jewishness and Humanism, Hebrew University Library, Jerusalem: a, "Roads to Jerusalem" (inscription at L). b, Isaiah's prophecy of broken guns beaten into ploughshares (inscription at R).

**1990, Apr. 17**    **Litho.**    **Perf. 14**
1041    Sheet of 2     7.00 7.00
a.-b.    A453 1.50s any single     3.00 3.00

Stamp World London '90. Sold for 4.50s. Also exists imperf. Value $85.

Architecture — A454

Design: 75a, School, Deganya Kibbutz, 1930. 1.10s, Dining hall, Kibbutz Tel Yosef by Leopold Krakauer, 1933. 1.20s, Engel House by Ze'ev Rechter, 1933. 1.40s, Home of Dr. Chaim Weizmann, Rehovot by Erich Mendelsohn, 1936. 1.60s, Jewish Agency for Palestine, Jerusalem, by Yohanan Ratner, 1932.

**1990-92**    **Photo.**    **Perf. 14x13½**
1044 A454 75a black, pale grn
       & buff     .60 .55
1045 A454 1.10s blk, yel & grn     .95 .95
1046 A454 1.20s blk, bl & yel     1.10 1.10
1047 A454 1.40s blk, lt lil & buff     1.25 1.25
1048 A454 1.60s multicolored     1.10 1.10
   a.    Dotted rose lilac background     1.10 1.10
   Nos. 1044-1048 (5)     5.00 4.95
   With tabs     5.25

No. 1051 has a solid bluish lilac background. Issued: 75a, 4/17; 1.10s, 1.20s, 12/12; 1.40s, 4/9/91; 1.60s, 4/26/92; #1048a, 7/14/96.

**Nature Reserves Type of 1988**

**1990, Apr. 17**    **Litho.**    **Perf. 14**
1052 A427 60a Gamla,
       Yehudiyya     .55 .45
1053 A427 80a Huleh     .75 .55
1054 A427 90a Mt. Meron     .90 .65
   Nos. 1052-1054 (3)     2.20 1.65
   With tabs     2.50

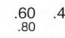

Memorial Day A456

**1990, Apr. 17**    **Photo.**    **Perf. 13x14**
1055 A456 60a Artillery Corps
       Memorial     .60 .45
   With tab     .80

Intl. Folklore Festival, Haifa — A457

**1990, June 12     Litho.     Perf. 14**
1056  1.90s Denom at UL     2.50 2.50
1057  1.90s Denom at UR     2.50 2.50
  *a.* A457 Pair, #1056-1057     5.00 5.00
     With tabs     6.00

Hagana, 70th
Anniv. — A459

**1990, June 12**
1058 A459 1.50s multicolored     1.40 1.40
     With tab     1.50

**Special Occasions Type of 1989**
**1990, June 12     Perf. 13½x14**
1059 A449 55a Good luck     .50 .35
1060 A449 80a See you again     .75 .50
1061 A449 1s With love     .95 .60
     Nos. 1059-1061 (3)     2.20 1.45
     With tabs     2.50

Spice
Boxes — A460

55a, Austro-Hungarian spice box, 19th cent.
80a, Italian, 19th cent. 1s, German, 18th cent.

**1990, Sept. 4     Litho.     Perf. 13½x14**
1062 A460 55a sil, gray & blk     .40 .40
1063 A460 80a sil, gray & blk     .60 .60
1064 A460 1s multicolored     .75 .75
  *a.* Bklt. pane of 6 (3 #1062, 2
     #1063, #1064)     7.50 7.50
     Nos. 1062-1064 (3)     1.75 1.75
     With tabs     1.90

A461

**1990, Sept. 4     Perf. 13**
1065 A461 1.10s Aliya absorption     .85 .85
     With tab     .90

Electronic
Mail — A462

**1990, Sept. 4     Perf. 14x13**
1066 A462 1.20s black & grn     .90 .90
     With tab     1.00

Souvenir Sheet

Beersheba '90 Stamp
Exhibition — A463

**1990, Sept. 4     Perf. 13x14**
1067 A463 3s multicolored     5.50 5.50
     Sold for 4s.

Computer
Games — A464

**1990, Dec. 12     Litho.     Perf. 13x14**
1068 A464 60a Basketball     .45 .45
1069 A464 60a Chess     .45 .45
1070 A464 60a Auto racing     .45 .45
     Nos. 1068-1070 (3)     1.35 1.35
     With tabs     1.50

Ze'ev Jabotinsky
(1880-1940),
Zionist
Leader — A465

**1990, Dec. 12     Litho.     Perf. 13x14**
1071 A465 1.90s multicolored     1.40 1.40
     With tab     1.50

Philately
Day — A466

**1990, Dec. 12     Perf. 14**
1072 A466 1.20s P.O., Yafo, #5     .90 .90
     With tab     1.00

**Special Occasions Type of 1989**
**1991, Feb. 19     Photo.     Perf. 13½x14**
1073 A449 (60a) Happy birthday     .45 .35
1074 A449 (60a) Keep in touch     .45 .35
  *a.* Booklet pane of 10 + 2 labels     5.75
  *b.* Sheet of 20 + 5 labels     11.50
1075 A449 (60a) Greetings     .45 .35
     Nos. 1073-1075 (3)     1.35 1.05
     With tabs     1.50

No. 1074a contains 5 tete-beche pairs. No.
1074b contains 10 tete-beche pairs.
Nos. 1074a-1074b had value of 85a when
released.
Issued: Nos. 1074a-1074b, 4/18/94.

Famous
Women
A467

Designs: No. 1076, Sarah Aaronsohn
(1890-1917), World War I heroine. No. 1077,
Rahel Bluwstein (1890-1931), poet. No. 1078,
Lea Goldberg (1911-1970), poet.

**1991, Feb. 19     Perf. 14**
1076 A467 1.30s multicolored     1.10 1.10
1077 A467 1.30s multicolored     1.10 1.10
1078 A467 1.30s multicolored     1.10 1.10
     Nos. 1076-1078 (3)     3.30 3.30
     With tabs     3.50

See Nos. 1096-1097, 1102-1103.

Hadera,
Cent. — A468

**1991, Feb. 19     Perf. 13**
1079 A468 2.50s multicolored     2.00 2.00
     With tab     2.25

Intelligence
Services
Memorial,
G'lilot
A469

**1991, Apr. 9     Litho.     Perf. 14**
1080 A469 65a multicolored     .60 .60
     With tab     .70

14th
Hapoel
Games
A470

**1991, Apr. 9**
1081 A470 60a multicolored     .55 .50
1082 A470 90a multicolored     .75 .70
1083 A470 1.10s multicolored     .95 .90
     Nos. 1081-1083 (3)     2.25 2.10
     With tabs     2.50

Electrification
A471

Designs: 70a, First power station, Tel Aviv,
1923. 90a, Yarden Power Station, Naharayim,
1932. 1.20s, Rutenberg Power Station,
Ashqelon, 1991.

**1991, June 11     Litho.     Perf. 13**
1084 A471 70a multicolored     .65 .60
1085 A471 90a multicolored     .80 .75
1086 A471 1.20s multicolored     1.10 1.00
     Nos. 1084-1086 (3)     2.55 2.35
     With tabs     2.75

Rabbi Shimon
Hakham (1843-
1910)
A472

**1991, June 11**
1087 A472 2.10s multicolored     1.90 1.50
     With tab     2.00

Souvenir Sheet

Postal and Philatelic Museum, Tel
Aviv — A473

Israel #5, Palestine #70, Turkey #133.

**1991, June 11     Perf. 14x13**
1088 A473 3.40s multicolored     7.00 7.00

No. 1088 sold for 5s. Exists imperf. Value
$90.

A474

Jewish Festivals: 65a, Man blowing ram's
horn, Rosh Hashanah. 1s, Father blessing
children, Yom Kippur. 1.20s, Family seated at
harvest table, Sukkoth.

**1991, Aug. 27     Litho.     Perf. 14**
1089 A474 65a multicolored     .50 .50
1090 A474 1s multicolored     .75 .75
1091 A474 1.20s multicolored     .90 .90
     Nos. 1089-1091 (3)     2.15 2.15
     With tabs     2.50

Jewish Chronicle,
150th
Anniv. — A475

**1991, Aug. 27**
1092 A475 1.50s multicolored     1.10 1.10
     With tab     1.25

Baron Maurice De Hirsch (1831-1896),
Founder of Jewish Colonization
Assoc. — A476

**1991, Aug. 27     Perf. 14**
1093 A476 1.60s multicolored     1.25 1.25
     With tab     1.40

Souvenir Sheet

Haifa, by Gustav Bauernfeind — A477

**1991, Aug. 27     Perf. 14x13**
1094 A477 3s multicolored     6.25 5.00

Haifa '91, Israeli-Polish Philatelic Exhibition.
Sold for 4s.

Philately
Day — A478

**1991, Dec. 2　　　Litho.　　Perf. 13**
1095 A478 70a #2 on piece　　.50　.50
　　　With tab　　　　　　　　　　　.60

**Famous Women Type of 1991**

Designs: 1s, Rahel Yanait Ben-Zvi (1886-1979), politician. 1.10s, Dona Gracia (Nasi, 1510?-1569), philanthropist.

**1991, Dec. 2　　　Litho.　　Perf. 14**
1096 A467　1s multicolored　　.70　.70
1097 A467 1.10s multicolored　.75　.75
　　　#1096-1097, with tabs　　　　1.60

1992 Summer
Olympics,
Barcelona — A479

**1991, Dec. 2**
1098 A479 1.10s multicolored　　.85　.85
　　　With tab　　　　　　　　　　　1.40

Lehi — A480　　　　Etzel — A481

**1991, Dec. 2　　　　　　　Perf. 14**
1099 A480 1.50s multicolored　1.00 1.00
　　　With tab　　　　　　　　　　　1.25

**1991, Dec. 2**
1100 A481 1.50s blk & red　　1.00 1.00
　　　With tab　　　　　　　　　　　1.25

Wolfgang
Amadeus Mozart,
Death
Bicent. — A482

**1991, Dec. 2　　　　　　　Perf. 13**
1101 A482 2s multicolored　　2.75 1.75
　　　With tab　　　　　　　　　　　3.25
　　a. Booklet pane of 4　　　　　11.00

One pair in No. 1101a is tete beche.

**Famous Women Type of 1991**

80a, Hanna Rovina (1889-1980), actress. 1.30s, Rivka Guber (1902-81), educator.

**1992, Feb. 18　　Litho.　　Perf. 14**
1102 A467 80a multicolored　　.50　.50
1103 A467 1.30s multicolored　.90　.90
　　　#1102-1103, with tabs　　　　1.50

Sea of Galilee
A483

Anemone
A483a

**1992, Feb. 18**
1104 A483 85a Trees　　　　1.50　.70
1105 A483 85a Sailboat　　　1.50　.70
1106 A483 85a Fish　　　　　1.50　.70
　　a. Strip of 3, #1104-1106　4.50 2.10
　　　With tabs　　　　　　　　　　5.00

**1992, Feb. 18　Photo.　Perf. 13x14**
1107 A483a (75a) multi　　　.50　.45
　　　With tab　　　　　　　　　　　.60

PALMAH, 50th
Anniv.
A484

The Samaritans
A485

**1992, Feb. 18　　Litho.　　Perf. 14**
1108 A484 1.50s multicolored　1.00 1.00
　　　With tab　　　　　　　　　　　1.25

**1992, Feb. 18**
1109 A485 2.60s multicolored　1.75 1.75
　　　With tab　　　　　　　　　　　2.25

Rabbi Hayyim
Joseph David
Azulai (1724-1806)
A486

Rabbi Joseph
Hayyim Ben
Elijah (1834-
1909)
A487

**1992, Apr. 26　　　　　　Perf. 13**
1110 A486 85a multicolored　　.60　.60
　　　　　　　　　　　　　　Perf. 14
1111 A487 1.20s multicolored　.80　.80
　　　#1110-1111, with tabs　　　1.75

Discovery
of America,
500th
Anniv.
A488

**1992, Apr. 26　　　　　　Perf. 14**
1112 A488 1.60s multicolored　1.25 1.25
　　　　　　　　　　　　　　　　1.40

Memorial
Day — A488a

**1992, Apr. 26　　Litho.　　Perf. 13**
1113 A488a 85a multicolored　　.55　.55
　　　With tab　　　　　　　　　　　.60

**Souvenir Sheet**

Expulsion
of Jews
from Spain,
500th
Anniv.
A489

Designs: No. 1114a, 80a, Map of Palestine. b, 1.10s, Map of Italy, Sicily, Greece and central Mediterranean. c, 1.40s, Map of Spain and Portugal.

**1992, Apr. 26　　　　　　Perf. 14**
1114 A489 Sheet of 3, #a.-c.　3.75 3.75

Jaffa-Jerusalem Railway,
Cent. — A490

Different train and four scenes on each stamp showing railroad equipment and memorabilia.

**1992**
1115 A490　85a multicolored　　.65　.60
1116 A490　1s multicolored　　.80　.75
1117 A490 1.30s multicolored　1.00　.95
1118 A490 1.60s multicolored　1.25 1.10
　　　#1115-1118, with tabs　　　4.00
　　a. Bklt. pane of 4, #1115-1118　4.00

**Souvenir Sheet**
1118B　Sheet of 4 + 4 labels　4.75 4.75
　　c. A490 50a like #1118　　1.00 1.00
　　d. A490 50a like #1117　　1.00 1.00
　　e. A490 50a like #1115　　1.00 1.00
　　f. A490 50a like #1116　　1.00 1.00

Nos. 1115 and 1118, 1116 and 1117 are tete beche in No. 1118a. Nos. 1118c and 1118d, 1118d and 1118e are tete beche in No. 1118B.

Issued: #1118B, Sept. 17; others June 16.

Rabbi Hayyim
Benatar (1696-
1743)
A491

Rabbi Shalom
Sharabi (1720-
1777)
A492

**1992, June 16　　　　　　Perf. 13**
1119 A491 1.30s multicolored　　.90　.90
1120 A492　3s multicolored　　2.00 2.00
　　　#1119-1120, with tabs　　　3.25

Jewish Natl. &
University Library,
Jerusalem,
Cent. — A493

85a, Parables, 1491. 1s, Italian manuscript, 15th cent. 1.20s, Bible translation by Martin Buber.

**1992, Sept. 17　　Litho.　Perf. 13x14**
1121 A493 85a multicolored　　.55　.55
1122 A493　1s multicolored　　.65　.65
1123 A493 1.20s multicolored　.80　.80
　　　Nos. 1121-1123 (3)　　　　2.00 2.00
　　　With tabs　　　　　　　　　　2.25

Supreme
Court
A494

**1992, Sept. 17　　　　　　Perf. 14**
1124 A494 3.60s multicolored　2.10 2.10
　　　With tab　　　　　　　　　　　2.25

Wild Animals
A495

#1125, Panthera pardus saxicolor. #1126, Elephas maximus. #1127, Pan troglodytes. #1128, Panthera leo persica.

**1992, Sept. 17**
1125 A495 50a multicolored　　.50　.50
1126 A495 50a multicolored　　.50　.50
1127 A495 50a multicolored　　.50　.50
1128 A495 50a multicolored　　.50　.50
　　a. Strip of 4, #1125-1128　2.25 2.25
　　　With tabs　　　　　　　　　　2.50

European
Unification
A496

**1992, Dec. 8　　Litho.　　Perf. 13**
1129 A496 1.50s multicolored　　.90　.90
　　　　　　　　　　　　　　　　1.00

Stamp Day.

First Hebrew
Film, 75th
Anniv. — A497

Films: 80a, Liberation of the Jews, 1918. 2.70s, Oded, the Vagabond, 1932, first Hebrew feature film. 3.50s, The Promised Land, 1935, first Hebrew talkie.

**1992, Dec. 8**
1130 A497　80a multicolored　　.60　.60
1131 A497 2.70s multicolored　1.90 1.90
1132 A497 3.50s multicolored　2.50 2.50
　　　Nos. 1130-1132 (3)　　　　5.00 5.00
　　　With tabs　　　　　　　　　　5.25

Birds — A498

**1992-98　　Photo.　　Perf. 13x14**
1133 A498 10a Wallcreeper　　.20　.20
1134 A498 20a Tristram's
　　　　　　　grackle　　　　　.20　.20
1135 A498 30a White wagtail　.20　.20
1137 A498 50a Palestine sun-
　　　　　　　bird　　　　　　　.30　.20
1141 A498 85a Sinai
　　　　　　　rosefinch　　　　.45　.30
1142 A498 90a Swallow　　　.60　.60
1142A A498　1s Trumpeter
　　　　　　　finch　　　　　　.65　.65
　　b. Violet background　　　　.65　.65
1143 A498 1.30s Graceful war-
　　　　　　　bler　　　　　　　.70　.45
1144 A498 1.50s Black-eared
　　　　　　　wheatear　　　　.85　.55
1146 A498 1.70s Common bul-
　　　　　　　bul　　　　　　　.85　.55
　　　Nos. 1133-1146 (10)　　　5.00 3.90
　　　With tabs　　　　　　　　　　5.25

No. 1142A has a gray background.

**Souvenir Sheet**

Designs: a, like #1133. b, like #1137. c, like #1135. d, like #1134. e, like #1141. f, like #1144. g, like #1146. h, like #1142A. i, like #1143. j, like #1142.

**Litho.　　　　　Perf. 14**
1152　Sheet of 10　　　　　6.00 6.00
　a.-j. A498 30a Any single　　.50　.50

Nos. 1152a-1152j, issued for China '96, 9th Asian Intl. Philatelic Exhibition, have color variations and a gray border.

Issued: 10a, 20a, 30a, 90a, 12/8; 1.30s, 1.70s, 12/9/93; 50a, 1.50s, 2/16/93; 85a, 2/8/94; 1s, 6/7/95; #1152, 4/17/96; #1142Ab, 11/22/98.

This is an expanding set. Numbers may change.

Menachem Begin (1913-92), Prime Minister 1977-83 — A499

**1993, Feb. 16    Litho.    Perf. 13**
1153  A499  80a multicolored            .45   .45
With tab                                     .50

**Nature Reserves Type of 1988**
**1993, Feb. 16                    Perf. 14**
1154  A427  1.20s Hof Dor               .70   .70
1155  A427  1.50s Nahal Ammud           .90   .90
1156  A427  1.70s Nahal Ayun            .95   .95
Nos. 1154-1156 (3)             2.55  2.55
With tabs                             2.75

Baha'i World Center, Haifa — A500

**1993, Feb. 16                    Perf. 13**
1157  A500  3.50s multicolored        3.25  2.25
With tab                              5.25

Medical Corps Memorial — A501

**1993, Apr. 18    Litho.    Perf. 13**
1158  A501  80a multicolored            .45   .45
With tab                                     .55

Scientific Concepts A502          Warsaw Ghetto Uprising, 50th Anniv. A503

**1993, Apr. 18                    Perf. 14**
1159  A502  80a Principle of lift       .50   .50
1160  A502  80a Waves                   .50   .50
1161  A502  80a Color mixing            .50   .50
1162  A502  80a Eye's memory            .50   .50
a.    Strip of 4, #1159-1162          2.00  2.00
With tabs                             2.25

**1993, Apr. 18                    Perf. 14**
1163  A503  1.20s gray, black & yel     .80   .80
With tab                                     .85

See Poland No. 3151.

Independence, 45th Anniv. — A504

**1993, Apr. 18                    Perf. 14**
1164  A504  3.60s multicolored        2.25  2.25
With tab                              2.50

Giulio Racah (1909-1965), Physicist — A505

1.20s, Aharon Katchalsky-Katzi (1913-72), chemist.

**1993, June 29   Photo.   Perf. 13x14**
1165  A505  80a magenta, bister
& blue              .45   .45
1166  A505  1.20s magenta, bister
& blue              .65   .65
#1165-1166, with tabs          1.25

Traffic Safety — A506          Fight Against Drugs — A507

Children's drawings: 80a, Family crossing street. 1.20s, Traffic signs. 1.50s, Traffic director with hand as face.

**1993, June 29   Litho.    Perf. 14**
1167  A506  80a multicolored           .50   .50
1168  A506  1.20s multicolored         .80   .80
1169  A506  1.50s multicolored         .95   .95
Nos. 1167-1169 (3)             2.25  2.25
With tabs                             2.50

**1993, June 29                    Perf. 14**
1170  A507  2.80s multicolored        1.75  1.75
With tab                              1.90

14th Maccabiah Games A508

**1993, June 29                    Perf. 14**
1171  A508  3.60s multicolored        2.25  2.25
With tab                              2.50

Respect for the Elderly A509          Festivals A510

**1993, Aug. 22    Litho.    Perf. 14**
1172  A509  80a multicolored           .50   .50
With tab                                     .55

**1993, Aug. 22                    Perf. 14**
1173  A510  80a Wheat                  .55   .55
1174  A510  1.20s Grapes               .75   .75
1175  A510  1.50s Olives               .95   .95
Nos. 1173-1175 (3)             2.25  2.25
With tabs                             2.50

Environmental Protection — A511

**1993, Aug. 22**
1176  A511  1.20s multicolored         .80   .80
With tab                                     .85

B'nai B'rith, 150th Anniv. — A512

**1993, Aug. 22                    Perf. 13**
1177  A512  1.50s multicolored         .90   .90
With tab                              1.00

**Souvenir Sheet**

Expoziție Filatelică Binațională

Telafila '93, Israel-Romania Philatelic Exhibition — A513

3.60s, Immigrant Ship, by Marcel Janco.

**1993, Aug. 21   Litho.   Perf. 14x13**
1178  A513  3.60s multicolored        2.50  2.50

Hebrew Magazines for Children, Cent. A514

**1993, Dec. 9    Litho.    Perf. 14**
1179  A514  1.50s multicolored         .90   .90
With tab                              1.00

Philately Day.

Hanukkah A515

Hanukkah lamp with candles lit and: 90a, Oil lamp, Talmudic Period. 1.30s, Hanukkah Lamp, Eretz Israel carved stone, 20th cent. 2s, Lighting the Hanukkah Lamp, Rothschild Miscellany illuminated manuscript, c. 1470. #1183, Moroccan lamp, Mazagan. #1184: Folding Hanukkah Lamp, Lodz Ghetto, 1944. 2.10s, Coin of the Bar-Kokhba War. 1.80s, Cubic copper savivon (dreidel). 2.15s, Hanukkah lamp "Mattathias the Hasmonean," by Boris Schatz.

**1993-99**
1180  A515  90a multicolored           .55   .55
1181  A515  1.30s multicolored         .80   .80
1182  A515  2s multicolored           1.25  1.25
1183  A515  1.50s multicolored         .90   .90
1184  A515  1.50s multicolored        1.00  1.00
1185  A515  2.10s multicolored        1.25  1.25
1186  A515  1.80s multicolored        1.00  1.00
1187  A515  2.15s multicolored        1.10  1.10
Nos. 1180-1187 (8)             7.85  7.85
With tabs                             8.75

The numbering of this set reflects the lighting of the candles on the Menorah.
Issued: 90a, 1.30s, 2s, 12/9/93; #1183, 11/27/94; #1184, 12/14/95; #1185-1186, 12/23/97; 2.15s, 1/5/99.
This is an expanding set. Numbers have been reserved for additional values.

Beetles A516

#1189, Graphopterus serrator. #1190, Potosia cuprea. #1191, Coccinella septempunctata. #1192, Chlorophorus varius.

**1994, Feb. 8    Litho.    Perf. 14**
1189  A516  85a multicolored           .45   .40
1190  A516  85a multicolored           .45   .40
1191  A516  85a multicolored           .45   .40
1192  A516  85a multicolored           .45   .40
a.    Bkt. pane, 2 each #1189-1192    4.25
Nos. 1189-1192 (4)             1.80  1.60
With tabs                             1.90

Health — A517

**1994, Feb. 8                     Perf. 13**
1193  A517  85a Exercise               .55   .40
1194  A517  1.30s Don't smoke          .75   .60
1195  A517  1.60s Eat sensibly         .95   .75
Nos. 1193-1195 (3)             2.25  1.75
With tabs                             2.50

Mordecai Haffkine (1860-1930), Developer of Cholera Vaccine — A518

**1994, Feb. 8                     Perf. 14**
1196  A518  3.85s multicolored        2.25  1.75
With tab                              2.50

Intl. Style Architecture in Tel Aviv, 1930-39 A519

#1197, Citrus House, by Karl Rubin, 1936-38. #1198, Assuta Hospital, by Yosef Neufeld, 1934-35. #1199, Cooperative Workers' Housing, by Arieh Sharon, 1934-36.

**1994, Apr. 5    Litho.    Perf. 14**
1197  A519  85a multicolored           .50   .50
1198  A519  85a multicolored           .50   .50
1199  A519  85a multicolored           .50   .50
Nos. 1197-1199 (3)             1.50  1.50
With tabs                             1.60

Memorial Day — A520

85a, Monument to fallen soldiers of Communications, Electronics & Computer Corps, Yehud.

**1994, Apr. 5    Litho.    Perf. 14**
1200  A520  85a multicolored           .50   .50
With tab                                     .55

Prevent Violence — A521

**1994, Apr. 5**      **Perf. 13**
1201 A521 3.85s black & red   2.10 2.10
    With tab      2.25

Saul Adler (1895-1966),
Scientist — A522

**1994, Apr. 5**      **Perf. 14**
1202 A522 4.50s multicolored   2.60 2.60
    With tab      2.75

Hot Air
Ballooning
A523

#1203, Filling balloon. #1204, Balloons in flight. #1205, Marking target.

**1994, June 21**   **Litho.**   **Perf. 14**
1203 A523 85a multicolored   .50 .50
1204 A523 85a multicolored   .50 .50
1205 A523 85a multicolored   .50 .50
    Nos. 1203-1205 (3)   1.50 1.50
    With tabs      1.60

Tarbut
Elementary
Schools,
75th Anniv.
A524

**1994, June 21**
1206 A524 1.30s multicolored   .80 .80
           .90

Antoine de
St. Exupery
(1900-44)
A525

**1994, June 21**
1207 A525 5s multicolored   3.00 3.00
    With tab      3.25

Intl. Olympic
Committee,
Cent. — A526

Peace — A527

**1994, June 21**
1208 A526 2.25s multicolored   1.40 1.40
    With tab      1.50

**1994, Aug. 23**   **Litho.**   **Perf. 14**
1209 A527 90a multicolored   .55 .55
    With tab      .60

Peace Between Arabs and Israelis.

Children's
Drawings of
Bible
Stories
A528

Designs: 85a, Adam and Eve. 1.30s, Jacob's Dream. 1.60s, Moses in the Bulrushes. 4s, Parting of the Red Sea.

**1994, Aug. 23**
1210 A528 85a multicolored   .50 .50
1211 A528 1.30s multicolored   .80 .80
1212 A528 1.60s multicolored   .95 .95
    Nos. 1210-1212 (3)   2.25 2.25
    With tabs      2.50

**Souvenir Sheet**
**Perf. 13x14**
1213 A528   4s multicolored   2.75 2.75

No. 1213 contains one 40x51mm stamp.

Immigration to
Israel — A529

**1994, Aug. 23**      **Perf. 13**
1214 A529 1.40s Third Aliya   .80 .80
1215 A529 1.70s Fourth Aliya   .95 .95
    #1214-1215, with tabs   1.90

Israel-Jordan Peace
Treaty — A530

**1994, Oct. 26**   **Litho.**   **Perf. 14**
1216 A530 3.50s multicolored   2.00 2.00
    With tab      2.25

Public Transportation — A531

Designs: 90a, Ford Model T's, 1920's. 1.40s, White Super buses, 1940's. 1.70s, Leyland Royal Tiger buses, 1960's.

**1994, Nov. 27**
1217 A531 90a multicolored   .55 .55
1218 A531 1.40s multicolored   .90 .90
1219 A531 1.70s multicolored   1.00 1.00
    Nos. 1217-1219 (3)   2.45 2.45
    With tabs      2.75

Computerization of Post
Offices — A532

**1994, Nov. 27**
1220 A532 3s multicolored   1.90 1.90
           2.00

Dreyfus
Affair, Cent.
A533

**1994, Nov. 27**
1221 A533 4.10s multicolored   2.50 2.50
    With tab      2.75

Outdoor
Sculpture
A534

Designs: 90a, Serpentine, by Itzhak Danziger (1916-77), Yarkon Park, Tel Aviv. 1.40s, Stabile, by Alexander Calder (1898-1976), Mount Herzl, Jerusalem. 1.70s, Gate to the Hall of Remembrance, by David Palombo (1920-66), Yad Vashem, Jerusalem.

**1995, Feb. 7**   **Litho.**   **Perf. 14x13**
1222 A534 90a multicolored   .55 .55
1223 A534 1.40s multicolored   .90 .90
1224 A534 1.70s multicolored   1.00 1.00
    Nos. 1222-1224 (3)   2.45 2.45
    With tabs      2.75

Jewish
Composers
A535

Title of work, composer: No. 1225, Schelomo, by Ernest Bloch (1880-1959). No. 1226, Symphony No. 1 - Jeremiah, by Leonard Bernstein (1918-90).

**1995, Feb. 7**
1225 A535 4.10s multicolored   2.50 2.50
1226 A535 4.10s multicolored   2.50 2.50
    #1225-1226, with tabs   5.50

See Nos. 1231-1232, 1274-1275.

Ordnance Corps
Monument,
Netanya — A536

**1995, Apr. 25**   **Litho.**   **Perf. 13**
1227 A536 1s multicolored   .65 .65
    With tab      .70

End of World War II, Liberation of
Concentration Camps, 50th
Anniv. — A537

**1995, Apr. 25**      **Perf. 14x13**
1228 A537   1s multicolored   .65 .65
    With tab      .70

**Souvenir Sheet**
1229 A537 2.50s like #1228   1.60 1.60

No. 1229 contains one 51x40mm stamp.

UN, 50th
Anniv.
A538

**1995, Apr. 25**      **Perf. 14**
1230 A538 1.50s multicolored   .90 .90
    With tab      1.00

**Composer Type of 1995**

#1231, Arnold Schoenberg (1874-1951). #1232, Darius Milhaud (1892-1974).

**1995, Apr. 25**
1231 A535 2.40s multicolored   1.50 1.50
1232 A535 2.40s multicolored   1.50 1.50
    #1231-1232, with tabs   3.25

**Souvenir Sheet**

Jewish Volunteers to British Army in
World War II — A539

Illustration reduced.

**1995, Apr. 25**
1233 A539 2.50s multicolored   1.75 1.75
    With tab      2.00

15th
Hapoel
Games,
Ramat Gan
A540

**1995, June 7**   **Litho.**   **Perf. 14**
1234 A540 1s Kayak   .65 .65
    With tab      .70

Kites — A541

Designs: No. 1235, Hexagonal "Tiara" kite, bird-shaped kite, rhombic Eddy kite. No. 1236, Drawing of kite glider, "Cody War Kite," box kite. No. 1237, Rhombic aerobatic kites, aerobatic "Delta" kite, drawing by Otto Lilienthal.

**1995, June 7**
1235   1s multicolored   .65 .65
1236   1s multicolored   .65 .65
1237   1s multicolored   .65 .65
    **a.** A541 Strip of 3, #1235-1237   2.00 2.00
    With tabs      2.25

Children's
Books
A542

Designs: 1s, Stars in a Bucket, by Anda Amir-Pinkerfeld. 1.50s, Hurry, Run, Dwarfs, by Miriam Yallan-Stekelis. 1.80s, Daddy's Big Umbrella, by Levin Kipnis.

**1995, June 7**
1238 A542   1s multicolored   .65 .65
1239 A542 1.50s multicolored   1.00 1.00
1240 A542 1.80s multicolored   1.25 1.25
    Nos. 1238-1240 (3)   2.90 2.90
    With tabs      3.25

Zim Israel
Navigation
Co. Ltd.,
50th Anniv.
A543

**1995, June 7**
1241 A543 4.40s multicolored   3.00 3.00
    With tab      3.25

Festivals
A544

Designs: 1s, Elijah's Chair for circumcision, linen cloth. 1.50s, Tallit bag, usually a Bar-

Mitzvah gift. 1.80s, Marriage Stone for breaking glass at wedding, cloth.

**1995, Sept. 4**     **Litho.**     *Perf. 14*
| | | | |
|---|---|---|---|
| 1242 | A544 | 1s multicolored | .65 .65 |
| 1243 | A544 | 1.50s multicolored | 1.00 1.00 |
| 1244 | A544 | 1.80s multicolored | 1.25 1.25 |
| | *Nos. 1242-1244 (3)* | | 2.90 2.90 |
| | With tabs | | 3.25 |

Jerusalem, 3000th Anniv. A545

Designs: 1s, 6th Cent. mosaic pavement, Gaza Synagogue. 1.50s, 19th Cent. illustration of city from map of Eretz Israel, by Rabbi Pinie of Safed. 1.80s, Aerial photograph of Knesset, Supreme Court.

**1995, Sept. 4**
| | | | |
|---|---|---|---|
| 1245 | A545 | 1s multicolored | .65 .65 |
| 1246 | A545 | 1.50s multicolored | 1.00 1.00 |
| 1247 | A545 | 1.80s multicolored | 1.25 1.25 |
| | *Nos. 1245-1247 (3)* | | 2.90 2.90 |
| | With tabs | | 3.25 |

Veterinary Services, 75th Anniv. A546

**1995, Sept. 4**
| | | | |
|---|---|---|---|
| 1248 | A546 | 4.40s multicolored | 3.00 3.00 |
| | With tab | | 3.25 |

Yitzhak Rabin (1922-95), Prime Minister A547

**1995, Dec. 5**
| | | | |
|---|---|---|---|
| 1249 | A547 | 5s multicolored | 3.25 3.25 |
| | | | 3.50 |

Fire Fighting and Rescue Service, 70th Anniv. A548

Designs: No. 1250, Fighting fire. No. 1251, Rescue vehicle, fireman beside car.

**1995, Dec. 14**
| | | | |
|---|---|---|---|
| 1250 | A548 | 1s multicolored | .65 .65 |
| 1251 | A548 | 1s multicolored | .65 .65 |
| | #1250-1251, with tabs | | 1.50 |

Model Planes A549

**1995, Dec. 14**
| | | | |
|---|---|---|---|
| 1252 | A549 | 1.80s multicolored | 1.25 1.25 |
| | With tab | | 1.40 |

Philately Day.

Motion Pictures, Cent. A550

Silhouettes of people in theater viewing: 4.40s, Marx Brothers, Simone Signoret, Peter Sellers, Danny Kaye, Al Jolson.

**1995, Dec. 14**
| | | | |
|---|---|---|---|
| 1253 | A550 | 4.40s multicolored | 3.00 3.00 |
| | With tab | | 3.25 |

**Souvenir Sheet**

Jerusalem, City of David, 3000th Anniv. A551

Designs: a, Mosaic pavement of King David playing harp, Gaza Synagogue, 6th cent. CE. b, Map of Eretz Israel drawn by Rabbi Pinie, 19th cent. c, Present day aerial view of Knesset and Supreme Court.

**1995, Dec. 16**
| | | | |
|---|---|---|---|
| 1254 | | Sheet of 3 | 2.75 2.75 |
| **a.** | A551 | 1s multicolored | .60 .60 |
| **b.** | A551 | 1.50s multicolored | .90 .90 |
| **c.** | A551 | 1.80s multicolored | 1.25 1.25 |

Sports — A552

**1996-98**     **Photo.**     *Perf. 13x14*
| | | | |
|---|---|---|---|
| 1256 | A552 | 1.05s Mountain cycling | .65 .65 |
| 1257 | A552 | 1.10s Horseback riding | .65 .65 |
| **a.** | | Booklet pane of 20 | 13.00 |
| | | Complete booklet, #1257a | 13.00 |
| 1258 | A552 | 1.80s Water skiing | 1.00 1.00 |
| 1259 | A552 | 1.90s Paragliding | 1.25 1.25 |
| 1260 | A552 | 2s Women's volleyball | 1.25 1.25 |
| 1261 | A552 | 2.20s Whitewater rafting | 1.25 1.25 |
| 1262 | A552 | 3s Beach bat & ball | 1.75 1.75 |
| 1263 | A552 | 5s Archery | 3.00 3.00 |
| 1264 | A552 | 10s Rappelling | 5.75 5.75 |
| | *Nos. 1256-1264 (9)* | | 16.55 16.55 |
| | With tabs | | 18.50 |

Issued: 1.05s, 1.90s, 2s, 2/20/96; 1.10s, 5s, 2/13/97; 10s, 7/8/97; 3s, 9/23/97; 1258, 1261, 2/17/98.

**Souvenir Sheet**

Synagogue, Dura-Europos, Syria, 3rd Century A.D. — A553

Murals from synagogue walls: a, Temple, walls of Jerusalem. b, Torah Ark niche. c, Anointing of David as king by Prophet Samuel.

**1996, Feb. 20**     **Litho.**     *Perf. 14x13*
| | | | |
|---|---|---|---|
| 1266 | A553 | Sheet of 3 | 2.75 2.75 |
| **a.** | | 1.05s multicolored | .60 .60 |
| **b.** | | 1.60s multicolored | .90 .90 |
| **c.** | | 1.90s multicolored | 1.25 1.25 |

Jerusalem, 3000th anniv.

Israel Cattle Breeders' Assoc., 70th Anniv. A554

**1996, Feb. 20**          *Perf. 14*
| | | | |
|---|---|---|---|
| 1267 | A554 | 4.65s multicolored | 3.00 3.00 |
| | | | 3.25 |

Hebrew Writers' Assoc., 75th Anniv. — A555

No. 1269: a, M.J. Berdyczewski. b, Yehuda Burla. c, Devorah Baron. d, Haim Hazaz. e,

J.L. Gordon. f, Joseph Hayyim Brenner. g, Abraham Shlonsky. h, Yaakov Shabtai. i, I.L. Peretz. j, Nathan Alterman. k, Saul Tchernichowsky. l, Amir Gilboa. m, Yokheved Bat-Miriam. n, Mendele Mokher Sefarim.

**1996, Apr. 17**     **Litho.**     *Perf. 14*
| | | | |
|---|---|---|---|
| 1269 | | Pane of 14 | 3.50 3.50 |
| **a.-n.** | A555 | 40a Any single | .25 .25 |

Manufacturers Assoc. of Israel, 75th Anniv. — A556

**1996, Apr. 17**
| | | | |
|---|---|---|---|
| 1271 | A556 | 1.05s multicolored | .65 .65 |
| | With tab | | .75 |

Monument to the Fallen Israel Police A557

**1996, Apr. 17**
| | | | |
|---|---|---|---|
| 1272 | A557 | 1.05s multicolored | .65 .65 |
| | With tab | | .75 |

Settlement of Metulla, Cent. — A558

**1996, Apr. 17**
| | | | |
|---|---|---|---|
| 1273 | A558 | 1.90s multicolored | 1.25 1.25 |
| | With tab | | 1.40 |

**Composer Type of 1995**

Designs: No. 1274, Felix Mendelssohn (1809-47). No. 1275, Gustav Mahler (1860-1911).

**1996**     **Litho.**     *Perf. 14*
| | | | |
|---|---|---|---|
| 1274 | A535 | 4.65s multicolored | 3.00 3.00 |
| 1275 | A535 | 4.65s multicolored | 3.00 3.00 |
| | #1274-1275, with tabs | | 6.50 |

Issued: #1275, 4/17/96; #1274, 6/25/96.

A559          A560

**1996, June 25**
| | | | |
|---|---|---|---|
| 1276 | A559 | 1.05s multicolored | .65 .65 |
| | With tab | | .75 |

Eleven Jewish settlements in Negev Desert, 50th Anniv.

**1996, June 25**
| | | | |
|---|---|---|---|
| 1277 | A560 | 1.05s Fencing | .65 .65 |
| 1278 | A560 | 1.60s Pole vault | 1.00 1.00 |
| 1279 | A560 | 1.90s Wrestling | 1.25 1.25 |
| **a.** | | Booklet pane of 6, 1 #1277, 2 #1278, 3 #1279 | 6.50 |
| | | Complete booklet, #1279a | 6.50 |
| | *Nos. 1277-1279 (3)* | | 2.90 2.90 |
| | With tabs | | 3.25 |

1996 Summer Olympics, Atlanta.

Fruit A561

1.05s, Orange, "sweety", kumquat, lemon. 1.60s, Avocado, persimmon, date, mango, grapes. 1.90s, Carambola, lychee, papaya.

**1996, June 25**
| | | | |
|---|---|---|---|
| 1280 | A561 | 1.05s multicolored | .65 .65 |
| 1281 | A561 | 1.60s multicolored | 1.00 1.00 |
| 1282 | A561 | 1.90s multicolored | 1.25 1.25 |
| | *Nos. 1280-1282 (3)* | | 2.90 2.90 |
| | With tabs | | 3.25 |

Public Works Department, 75th Anniv. — A562

**1996, Sept. 3**     **Litho.**     *Perf. 14*
| | | | |
|---|---|---|---|
| 1283 | A562 | 1.05s multicolored | .65 .65 |
| | With tab | | .75 |

Festivals A563

Stylized designs: 1.05s, Bowl of honey, two lighted candles, Rosh Hashanah. 1.60s, Sukka booth, Sukkot. 1.90s, Inside of synagogue during Torah reading, Simchat Torah.

**1996, Sept. 3**
| | | | |
|---|---|---|---|
| 1284 | A563 | 1.05s multicolored | .65 .65 |
| 1285 | A563 | 1.60s multicolored | 1.00 1.00 |
| 1286 | A563 | 1.90s multicolored | 1.25 1.25 |
| | *Nos. 1284-1286 (3)* | | 2.90 2.90 |
| | With tabs | | 3.25 |

1st Zionist Congress, Cent. — A564

Designs: 4.65s, Tapestry of Theodore Herzl, David's Tower, shining sun. 5s, Casino building, Basel, site of first congress.

**1996, Sept. 3**
| | | | |
|---|---|---|---|
| 1287 | A564 | 4.65s multicolored | 3.00 3.00 |
| | With tab | | 3.25 |

**Souvenir Sheet**
| | | | |
|---|---|---|---|
| 1288 | A564 | 5s multicolored | 3.00 3.00 |

No. 1288 contains one 40x51mm stamp.

Hanukkah A565

**Serpentine Die Cut 11**
**1996, Oct. 22**          **Photo.**
| | | | |
|---|---|---|---|
| 1289 | A565 | 2.50s multicolored | 1.50 1.50 |
| | With tab | | 1.60 |

See US No. 3118.

Ha-Shilo'ah, Cent., edited by Ahad Ha'am (1856-1927) — A566

**1996, Dec. 5　　Litho.　　Perf. 14**
1290　A566　1.15s multicolored　　.70　.70
　　With tab　　　　　　　　　　　　.80

Coexistence: Man and Animals — A567

**1996, Dec. 5**
1291　A567　1.10s Birds, aircraft　　.65　.65
1292　A567　1.75s Pets　　　　　　1.10　1.10
1293　A567　2s Dolphins　　　　　1.25　1.25
　　Nos. 1291-1293 (3)　　　　　3.00　3.00
　　With tabs　　　　　　　　　　3.25

Space Research in Israel A568

**1996, Dec. 5**
1294　A568　2.05s multicolored　　1.25　1.25
　　With tab　　　　　　　　　　1.40

Philately Day.

UOAD (Umbrella Organization of Associations for the Disabled) — A569

**1996, Dec. 5**
1295　A569　5s multicolored　　3.00　3.00
　　With tab　　　　　　　　　　3.25

Souvenir Sheet

Inventors — A570

Designs: a, 1.50s, Alexander Graham Bell (1847-1922). b, 2s, Thomas Alva Edison (1847-1931).

**1997, Feb. 13　　Litho.　　Perf. 13**
1296　A570　Sheet of 2, #a.-b.　2.25　2.25

Hong Kong '97.

Ethnic Costumes A571

1.10s, Ethiopia. 1.70s, Kurdistan. 2s, Salonica.

**1997, Feb. 13　　　　　　　Perf. 14**
1297　A571　1.10s multicolored　　.65　.65
1298　A571　1.70s multicolored　1.00　1.00
1299　A571　2s multicolored　　　1.25　1.25
　　Nos. 1297-1299 (3)　　　　　2.90　2.90
　　With tabs　　　　　　　　　3.25

Miguel de Cervantes (1547-1616), Writer — A572

**1997, Feb. 13**
1300　A572　3s multicolored　　　1.75　1.75
　　With tab　　　　　　　　　　2.00

Mounument to the Fallen Soldiers of the Logistics Corps A573

**1997, Apr. 30　　Litho.　　Perf. 14**
1301　A573　1.10s multicolored　　.65　.65
　　With tab　　　　　　　　　　.70

A574　　　　　　　　A575

Jewish monuments in Prague: No. 1302, Tombstone of Rabbi Judah Loew MaHaRal. No. 1303, Altneuschul Synagogue.

**1997, Apr. 30**
1302　A574　1.70s blue & multi　1.00　1.00
1303　A574　1.70s red & multi　　1.00　1.00
　a.　Sheet, 4 each, #1302-1303　8.00　8.00
　　　#1302-1303, with tabs　　　2.25

Stamps in No. 1303a do not have tabs. See Czech Republic Nos. 3009-3010.

**1997, Apr. 30**
Design: "The Vilna Gaon," Rabbi Elijah Ben Solomon Zalman (1720-97).
1304　A575　2s multicolored　　　1.25　1.25
　　With tab　　　　　　　　　　1.40

Organized Clandestine Immigration (1934-48) — A576

**1997, Apr. 30**
1305　A576　5s multicolored　　　3.00　3.00
　　With tab　　　　　　　　　　3.25

Souvenir Sheet

Discovery of the Cairo Geniza, Cent., Discovery of Dead Sea Scrolls, 50th Anniv. — A577

Designs: a, 2s, Ben Ezra Synagogue, Cairo. b, 3s, Cliffs, Dead Sea, Prof. Sukenik examining scrolls.

**1997, May 29　　Litho.　　Perf. 13**
1306　A577　Sheet of 2, #a.-b.　3.00　3.00

Pacific '97.

Hello First Grade A578

**1997, July 8　　Litho.　　Perf. 14**
1307　A578　1.10s multicolored　　.65　.65
　　With tab　　　　　　　　　　.70

Road Safety — A579

#1308, "Keep in Lane," car sinking into lake, fish. #1309, "Keep Your Distance," car with bird on front grille. #1310, "Don't Drink and Drive," man holding drink, car balanced on edge of cliff.

**1997, July 8　　　　　　　Perf. 13**
1308　A579　1.10s multicolored　　.65　.65
1309　A579　1.10s multicolored　　.65　.65
1310　A579　1.10s multicolored　　.65　.65
　　Nos. 1308-1310 (3)　　　　　1.95　1.95
　　With tabs　　　　　　　　　2.25

15th Maccabiah Games A580

**1997, July 8**
1311　A580　5s Ice skating　　　3.00　3.00
　　With tab　　　　　　　　　　3.25

Festival Stamps — A581

The Visiting Patriarchs, Sukkot: 1.10s, Abraham. 1.70s, Isaac. 2s, Jacob.

**1997, Sept. 23　　Litho.　　Perf. 14**
1312　A581　1.10s multicolored　　.60　.60
1313　A581　1.70s multicolored　　.95　.95
1314　A581　2s multicolored　　　1.10　1.10
　a.　Booklet pane, 1 #1312, 2
　　　#1313, 3 #1314　　　　　　5.75
　　　Complete booklet, #1314a　5.75
　　Nos. 1312-1314 (3)　　　　　2.65　2.65
　　With tabs　　　　　　　　　3.00

Compare with Nos. 1375-1378.

Music and Dance in Israel — A582

Designs: 1.10s, Zimriya, World assembly of choirs. 2s, Karmiel Dance Festival. 3s, Festival of Klezmers (musical instruments).

**1997, Sept. 23　　　　　　Perf. 13**
1315　A582　1.10s multicolored　　.60　.60
1316　A582　2s multicolored　　1.10　1.10
1317　A582　3s multicolored　　1.75　1.75
　　Nos. 1315-1317 (3)　　　　3.45　3.45
　　With tabs　　　　　　　　3.75

UN Resolution on Creation of Jewish State, 50th Anniv. — A583

**1997, Sept. 23　　　　　Perf. 13x14**
1318　A583　5s multicolored　　2.75　2.75
　　With tab　　　　　　　　　3.00

Souvenir Sheet

Pushkin's "Eugene Onegin," Translated by Abraham Shlonsky — A584

Illustration reduced.

**1997, Nov. 19　　　　　　Perf. 14x13**
1319　A584　5s multicolored　　2.75　2.75

See Russia No. 6418.

State of Israel, 50th Anniv. in 1998 — A585

**1997, Dec. 23　　　　　　　Perf. 14**
1320　A585　(1.10s) multicolored　　.60　.60
　　With tab　　　　　　　　　　.65
　a.　Size: 17x22mm　　　　　　.60　.60
　　　With tab　　　　　　　　　.65
　b.　Booklet pane, 20 #1320a　12.00
　　　Complete booklet, #1320b　12.00
　c.　As "a," perf. 13x14, photo.　.60　.60
　　　With tab　　　　　　　　　.65

No. 1320b consists of two blocks of 10 stamps, tete-beche in relationship to each other. No. 1320 is 18x23mm. No. 1320a has brighter blue stripes in flag.
　Issued: #1320a, 2/17/98; #1320c, 5/3/98.

"MACHAL," Overseas Volunteers A586

Designs: 1.80s, "GACHAL," recruitment in the Diaspora.

**1997, Dec. 23**
1321　A586　1.15s multicolored　　.65　.65
1322　A586　1.80s multicolored　1.00　1.00
　　#1321-1322, with tabs　　　1.75

Chabad's Children of Chernobyl
A587

**1997, Dec. 23**
1323 A587 2.10s multicolored    1.10 1.10
With tab    1.25

A588      A589

**1997, Dec. 23**
1324 A588 2.50s Julia Set Fractal   1.40 1.40
With tab    1.50

Philately Day.

**1998, Feb. 17    Litho.    Perf. 14x13**

Three battle fronts during war: Nos. 1325, 1328a (1.50s), Northern Front, photograph of people, Zefat, 1948. Nos. 1326, 1328b (2.50s), Central Front, drawing over photograph of vehicles coming down mountain, outskirts of Jerusalem, 1948. Nos. 1327, 1328c (3s), Southern Front, raising Israeli flag, Elat, 1949.

1325 A589 1.15s multicolored   .65 .65
1326 A589 1.15s multicolored   .65 .65
1327 A589 1.15s multicolored   .65 .65
Nos. 1325-1327 (3)   1.95 1.95
With tabs   2.25

**Souvenir Sheet**
1328 A589   Sheet of 3, #a.-c.   3.90 3.90

War of Independence, 1947-49. No. 1328b is 51x40mm.

Chaim Herzog (1918-97), President of Israel
A590

**1998, Feb. 17     Perf. 14**
1329 A590 5.35s multicolored   3.00 3.00
With tab   3.25

A591      A592

Jewish Contributions to Modern World Culture: a, Franz Kafka (1883-1924), writer. b, George Gershwin. c, Lev Davidovich Landau (1908-68), physicist. d, Albert Einstein. e, Leon Blum (1872-1950), statesman. f, Elizabeth Rachel Felix (1821-58), actress.

**1998, Apr. 27    Litho.    Perf. 14**
1330   Sheet of 6 + 6 labels   3.00 3.00
a.-f. A591 90a Any single   .50 .50

**1998, Apr. 27**
1331 A592 1.15s multicolored   .60 .60
With tab   .65

Memorial Day.

A593      A594

**1998, Apr. 27**
1332 A593 1.15s multicolored   .60 .60
With tab   .65

Declaration of the Establishment of the State of Israel, 50th anniv.

**1998, Apr. 27**
1333 A594 5.35s multicolored   3.00 3.00
With tab   3.25

Israel Defense Forces, 50th anniv.

Holocaust Memorial Day — A595

Non-Jews who risked their lives to save Jews during Holocaust: Giorgio Perlasca, Aristides de Sousa Mendes, Carl Lutz, Sempo Sugihara, Selahattin Ulkumen. Illustration reduced.

**1998, Apr. 27     Perf. 13**
1334 A595 6s multicolored   3.25 3.25
With tab   3.50

Children's Pets — A596

Israel '98: a, Cat. b, Dog. c, Bird. d, Goldfish. e, Hamster. f, Rabbit.

**1998, May 13**
1335   Sheet of 6   2.00 2.00
a.-f. A596 60a Any single   .35 .35

No. 1335 contains diagonal perforations so that lower left corner of each stamp can be removed leaving denominated portion in shape of a pentagon.

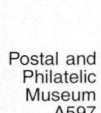

Postal and Philatelic Museum
A597

Illustrations by Kariel Gardosh featuring cartoon character, "Srulik:" a, At post office counter. b, Looking at stamp with magnifying glass. c, Putting mail into post box.

**1998, May 13     Perf. 14**
1336   Sheet of 3   3.75 3.75
a. A597 1.50s multicolored   .80 .80
b. A597 2.50s multicolored   1.25 1.25
c. A597 3s multicolored   1.60 1.60

Aircraft Used in War of Independence, 1948 — A598

**1998, May 3    Litho.    Perf. 14**
1337 A598 2.20s Dragon Rapide   1.25 1.25
1338 A598 2.20s Spitfire   1.25 1.25
1339 A598 2.20s B-17 Flying Fortress   1.25 1.25
a.   Strip of 3, #1337-1339   3.75 3.75
With tabs   4.00 4.00

Israel '98.

No. 1339a was issued in sheets containing 2 strips printed tete beche separated by strip of three labels.

A limited edition booklet exist. It contained the following panes: 1 #1305, 1 #1318, 1 #1320, 1 #1320b, 1 each #1321-1322, 1 each #1325-1327, 1 #1332, 1 #1333, 1 #1339a.

**Souvenir Sheet**

Mosaic of a Young Woman, Zippori — A599

Illustration reduced.

**1998, May 13**
1340 A599 5s multicolored   3.25 3.25

Israel '98. Sold for 6s

**Souvenir Sheet**

King Solomon's Temple — A600

a, Drawing of the temple. b, Inscribed ivory pomegranate. Illustration reduced.

**1998, May 13**
1341 A600   Sheet of 2   4.00 4.00
a.   2s multicolored   1.60 1.60
b.   3s multicolored   2.40 2.40

Israel '98. Sold for 7s

Israel Jubilee Exhibition
A601

**1998, Aug. 3    Litho.    Perf. 14x13**
1342 A601 5.35s multicolored   2.50 2.50
With tab   2.75

Child's Drawing "Living in a World of Mutual Respect"
A602

**1998, Sept. 8     Perf. 14**
1343 A602 1.15s multicolored   .55 .55
With tab   .60

Holy Cities
A603

**1998, Sept. 8**
1344 A603 1.80s Hebron   .85 .85
1345 A603 2.20s Jerusalem   1.00 1.00
#1344-1345, with tabs   2.10

**1999**
1346 A603 1.15s Zefat   .60 .60
1347 A603 5.35s Tiberias   2.75 2.75
#1346-1347, with tabs   3.75

Festival Stamps
A604

Holy ark curtains: 1.15s, Peacocks on both sides of menorah, text, Star of David. 1.80s, Menorah, text, two lions. 2.20s, Text surrounded by ornate floral pattern.

**1998, Sept. 8**
1348 A604 1.15s multicolored   .55 .55
1349 A604 1.80s multicolored   .85 .85
1350 A604 2.20s multicolored   1.00 1.00
Nos. 1348-1350 (3)   2.40 2.40
With tabs   2.75

Natl. Flag      Hyacinth
A605      A606

**1998, Dec. 17    Litho.    Die Cut**
**Self-Adhesive**
1351 A605 1.15s dk bl & bl   .55 .55
1352 A605 2.15s dk bl & grn   1.00 1.00
1353 A605 3.25s dk bl & rose red   1.60 1.60
1354 A605 5.35s dk bl & yel org   2.75 2.75
Nos. 1351-1354 (4)   5.90 5.90

**1999, Feb. 1    Photo.    Perf. 15**
1355 A606 (1.15s) multicolored   .60 .60
With tab   .65

Knesset, 50th Anniv.
A607

**1999, Feb. 1    Litho.    Perf. 14**
1356 A607 1.80s multicolored   .90 .90
With tab   1.00

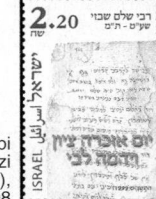

Manuscript of Rabbi Shalem Shabazi (1619-80), Poet — A608

**1999, Feb. 1**
1357 A608 2.20s multicolored   1.10 1.10
With tab   1.25

Jewish Colonial Trust, Cent.
A609

Drawings from one pound sterling share.

**1999, Feb. 16**
1358 A609 1.80s multicolored   .90 .90
With tab   1.00

Ethnic Costumes
A610

Designs: 2.15s, Yemenite Jewry, Yemen. 3.25s, Bene Israel Community, India.

**1999, Feb. 16**
1359 A610 2.15s multicolored   1.10 1.10
1360 A610 3.25s multicolored   1.60 1.60
#1359-1360, with tabs   3.00

## Souvenir Sheet

Ancient Boat from Sea of Galilee — A611

a, 3s, Reconstructed boat. b, 5s, Ancient boat.

**1999, Mar. 19**    **Litho.**    *Perf. 13*
1361   A611   Sheet of 2, #a.-b.    4.00   4.00

Australia '99, World Stamp Expo.

### Jewish Contributions to Modern World Culture Type of 1998

Designs: a, Emile Durkheim (1858-1917), social scientist. b, Paul Erlich (1854-1915), medical researcher. c, Rosa Luxemburg (1870-1919), politician. d, Norbert Wiener (1894-1964), mathematician, developer of computer science. e, Sigmund Freud (1856-1939), psychologist, founder of psychoanalysis. f, Martin Buber (1878-1965), religious philosopher.

**1999, Apr. 18**    **Litho.**    *Perf. 14*
1362     Sheet of 6 + 6 labels   2.75   2.75
a.-f.   A591 90a Any single    .45   .45

Monument for Fallen Bedouin Soldiers A612

**1999, Apr. 18**
1363   A612   1.20s multicolored    .60   .60
    With tab       .65

Israel's Admission to UN, 50th Anniv. A613

**1999, Apr. 18**
1364   A613   2.30s multicolored   1.10   1.10
    With tab       1.25

Simcha Holtzberg (1924-94), Holocaust Survivor, "Father of Wounded Soldiers" A614

**1999, Apr. 18**
1365   A614   2.50s multicolored   1.25   1.25
    With tab       1.40

Painting, "My Favorite Room," by James Ensor (1860-1949) — A614a

**1999, May 16**    **Photo.**    *Perf. 11½*
1365A   A614a 2.30s multi    1.10   1.10
    With tab       1.25

See Belgium No. 1738.

"Lovely Butterfly," Children's Television Show A615

Puppets: No. 1366, Ouza, the goose. No. 1367, Nooly, the chick & Shabi, the snail. No. 1368, Batz, the tortoise, and Pingi, the penguin.

**1999, June 22**    **Litho.**    *Perf. 14*
1366   A615   1.20s multicolored   .60   .60
1367   A615   1.20s multicolored   .60   .60
1368   A615   1.20s multicolored   .60   .60
a.     Strip of 3, #1366-1368   1.80   1.80
    With tabs       2.00

Pilgrimage to the Holy Land A616

**1999, June 22**
1369   A616   3s Nazareth    1.50   1.50
1370   A616   3s River Jordan   1.50   1.50
1371   A616   3s Jerusalem    1.50   1.50
    Nos. 1369-1371 (3)    4.50   4.50
    With tabs       5.00

Rabbi Or Sharga (?-1794) — A617

Illustration from Musa-Nameh manuscript, by Shahin, depicting battle of Isreal over Amalek.

**1999, June 22**
1372   A617   5.60s multicolored   2.75   2.75
    With tab       3.00

### Ethnic Costumes Type of 1999

Designs: 2.30s, Jewish woman in traditional Moroccan costume. 3.40s, Jewish man in traditional costume of Bukhara.

**1999, Sept. 1**    **Litho.**    *Perf. 14*
1373   A610   2.30s multicolored   1.10   1.10
1374   A610   3.40s multicolored   1.60   1.60
    #1373-1374, with tab    3.00

"Ushpizin," Guests in the Sukkah, Festival of Sukkoth — A619

**1999, Sept. 1**
1375   A619   1.20s Joseph    .60   .60
1376   A619   1.90s Moses    .90   .90
1377   A619   2.30s Aaron    1.10   1.10
1378   A619   5.60s David    2.75   2.75
a.     Bklt. pane, #1376-1378, 3
    #1375      6.75   6.75
    Complete booklet, #1378a   6.75
    Nos. 1375-1378 (4)    5.35   5.35
    With tabs       6.00

Stamp Day A620

**1999, Sept. 1**
1379   A620   5.35s multicolored   2.50   2.50
    With tab       2.75

Ceramic Urns, Museum of Jewish Culture, Bratislava, Slovakia — A621

Designs: No. 1380, Urn from 1776 showing man on sick bed, denomination at UL. No. 1381, Urn from 1734 showing funeral procession, denomination at UR.

**1999, Nov. 23**    **Litho.**    *Perf. 14*
1380   A621   1.90s multi    .95   .95
1381   A621   1.90s multi    .95   .95
    #1380-1381, with tabs    2.10

See Slovakia Nos. 344-345.

Kiryat Shemona, 50th Anniv. A622

**1999, Dec. 7**
1382   A622   1.20s multicolored   .60   .60
    With tab       .65

Proclamation of Jerusalem as Israel's Capital, 50th Anniv. — A623

**1999, Dec. 7**      *Perf. 13x14*
1383   A623   3.40s multicolored   1.60   1.60
    With tab       1.75

Sidna "Baba Sali" The Admor, Israel Abihssira (1890-1984) A624

**1999, Dec. 7**      *Perf. 13*
1384   A624   4.40s multi    2.25   2.25
    With tab       2.50

Millennium A625

Designs: 1.40s, Joggers in park. 1.90s, Researcher with flask. 2.30s, Man at computer. 2.80s, Astronaut in space.

**2000, Jan. 1**
1385   A625   1.40s multi    .70   .70
1386   A625   1.90s multi    .95   .95
1387   A625   2.30s multi    1.10   1.10
1388   A625   2.80s multi    1.40   1.40
    Nos. 1385-1388 (4)    4.15   4.15
    With tabs       4.75

Stampin' the Future Children's Stamp Design Contest Winners A626

Various children's drawings.

**2000, Jan. 1**      *Perf. 13x13½*
### Background Colors
1389   A626   1.20s blue    .60   .60
1390   A626   1.90s yel org   .95   .95
1391   A626   2.30s red    1.10   1.10
1392   A626   3.40s green    1.60   1.60
    Nos. 1389-1392 (4)    4.25   4.25
    With tabs       4.75

Fairy Tales of Hans Christian Andersen (1805-75) A627

1.20s, The Little Mermaid. 1.90s, The Emperor's New Clothes. 2.30s, The Ugly Duckling.

**2000, Feb. 15**    **Litho.**    *Perf. 13x14*
1393   A627   1.20s multi    .60   .60
1394   A627   1.90s multi    .95   .95
1395   A627   2.30s multi    1.10   1.10
    Nos. 1393-1395 (3)    2.65   2.65
    With tabs       3.00

Pilgrimage to the Holy Land A628

Churches: 1.40s, All Apostles, Capernaum. 1.90s, St. Andrew's, Jerusalem. 2.30s, Church of the Visitation, Ein Kerem.

**2000, Feb. 15**      *Perf. 14x13*
1396   A628   1.40s multi    .70   .70
1397   A628   1.90s multi    .95   .95
1398   A628   2.30s multi    1.10   1.10
    Nos. 1396-1398 (3)    2.75   2.75
    With tabs       3.00

King Hussein of Jordan (1935-99) A629

Shuni Historic Site A630

**2000, Feb. 15**    **Litho.**    *Perf. 14*
1399   A629   4.40s multi    2.25   2.25
    With tab       2.50

*Perf. 14 Syncopated*

**2000, Feb. 15**      **Photo.**
1400   A630   2.30s multi    1.10   1.10
    With tab       1.25

See #1409, 1427.

A631           A632

Worldwide Fund for Nature: Various depictions of Blanford's fox.

**2000, May 3**    **Litho.**    *Perf. 14*
### Denomination Color
1401   A631   1.20s red violet   .75   .75
1402   A631   1.20s green    .75   .75
1403   A631   1.20s blue    .75   .75

| 1404 A631 1.20s yellow | .75 | .75 |
|---|---|---|
| a. Strip, #1401-1404 + central label | 4.00 | 4.00 |
| With tabs | 4.00 | |

**2000, May 3**

| 1405 A632 1.20s multi | .60 | .60 |
|---|---|---|
| With tab | .65 | |

Memorial Day.

Intl. Communications Day — A633

**2000, May 3**      **Perf. 13**

| 1406 A633 2.30s multi | 1.10 | 1.10 |
|---|---|---|
| With tab | 1.25 | |

Land of Three Religions A634

**2000, May 3**

| 1407 A634 3.40s multi | 1.60 | 1.60 |
|---|---|---|
| With tab | 1.75 | |

Johann Sebastian Bach (1685-1750) A635

**2000, May 3**

| 1408 A635 5.60s multi | 2.75 | 2.75 |
|---|---|---|
| With tab | 3.00 | |

**Historic Site Type of 2000**
**Perf. 14 Syncopated**

**2000, July 25**      **Photo.**

| 1409 A630 1.20s Juara | .60 | .60 |
|---|---|---|
| With tab | .70 | |
| a. Perf. 14¾x15 Syncopated | .60 | .60 |
| With tab | .70 | |

The line containing the country name in English and Arabic is 10mm long on No. 1409, 11 mm long on No. 1409a. Issued: #1409a, 2001.

2000 Summer Olympics, Sydney — A636

**2000, July 25**    **Litho.**    **Perf. 13**

| 1410 A636 2.80s multi | 1.40 | 1.40 |
|---|---|---|
| With tab | 1.50 | |

A637             A638

**2000, July 25**      **Perf. 14**

| 1411 A637 4.40s multi | 2.25 | 2.25 |
|---|---|---|
| With tab | 2.50 | |

King Hassan II of Morocco (1929-99).

---

**2000, June 25**      **Perf. 13½x13**

Israeli food.

| 1412 A638 1.40s Couscous | .70 | .70 |
|---|---|---|
| 1413 A638 1.90s Gefilte fish | .95 | .95 |
| 1414 A638 2.30s Falafel | 1.10 | 1.10 |
| a. Booklet pane, #1412, 2 #1413, 3 #1414 | 6.00 | |
| Booklet, #1414a | 6.00 | |
| Nos. 1412-1414 (3) | 2.75 | 2.75 |
| With tabs | 3.00 | |

Dental Health A639

**2000, Sept. 19**    **Litho.**    **Perf. 14**

| 1415 A639 2.20s multi | 1.10 | 1.10 |
|---|---|---|
| With tab | 1.25 | |

Dohany Synagogue, Budapest A640

**2000, Sept. 19**      **Perf. 13x14**

| 1416 A640 5.60s multi | 2.75 | 2.75 |
|---|---|---|
| With tab | 3.00 | |

See Hungary No. 3710.

Jewish New Year Cards — A641

Designs: 1.20s, Boy giving girl a gift. 1.90s, Girl holding Zionist flag. 2.30s, Man giving flowers and greetings to woman.

**2000, Sept. 19**      **Perf. 14**

| 1417 A641 1.20s multi | .60 | .60 |
|---|---|---|
| 1418 A641 1.90s multi | .95 | .95 |
| 1419 A641 2.30s multi | 1.10 | 1.10 |
| Nos. 1417-1419 (3) | 2.65 | 2.65 |
| With tabs | 3.00 | |

Aleppo Codex — A642

**2000, Dec. 5**      **Perf. 13**

| 1420 A642 4.40s multi | 2.10 | 2.10 |
|---|---|---|
| With tab | 2.40 | |

Dinosaurs A643

Designs: No. 1421, Struthiomimuses on beach. No. 1422, Struthiomimuses in forest. No. 1423, Struthiomimus on hill.

**2000, Dec. 5**    **Litho.**    **Perf. 13**

| 1421 A643 2.20s multi | 1.10 | 1.10 |
|---|---|---|
| 1422 A643 2.20s multi | 1.10 | 1.10 |
| 1423 A643 2.20s multi | 1.10 | 1.10 |
| a. Strip of 3, #1421-1423 | 3.30 | 3.30 |
| With tabs | 3.50 | |

---

Science Fiction A644

Designs: 2.80s, Robot. 3.40s, Time travel. 5.60s, Space flight.

**2000, Dec. 5**      **Perf. 14**

| 1424 A644 2.80s multi | 1.40 | 1.40 |
|---|---|---|
| 1425 A644 3.40s multi | 1.75 | 1.75 |
| 1426 A644 5.60s multi | 2.75 | 2.75 |
| Nos. 1424-1426 (3) | 5.90 | 5.90 |
| With tabs | 6.50 | |

**Historic Sites Type of 2000**
**Perf. 14 Syncopated**

**2000-2001**      **Photo.**

| 1427 A630 2.20s Mitzpe Revivim | 1.10 | 1.10 |
|---|---|---|
| With tab | 1.25 | |
| 1428 A630 3.40s Ilaniyya | 1.75 | 1.75 |
| With tab | 1.90 | |

Issued: 2.20s, 12/5; 3.40s, 2/13/01.

Settlements, Cent. — A645

**2001, Feb. 13**    **Litho.**    **Perf. 14**

| 1429 A645 2.50s Yavne'el | 1.25 | 1.25 |
|---|---|---|
| 1430 A645 4.70s Menahamia | 2.25 | 2.25 |
| 1431 A645 5.90s Kefar Tavor | 3.00 | 3.00 |
| Nos. 1429-1431 (3) | 6.50 | 6.50 |
| With tabs | 7.25 | |

Hebrew Letters Aleph and Beth — A646

No. 1432: a, Aleph. b, Beth. c, Gimel. d, Daleth. e, He. f, Waw. g, Zayin. h, Heth. i, Teth. j, Yod. k, Kaph. l, Lamed. m, Mem. n, Nun. o, Samekh. p, Ayin. q, Pe. r, Sadhe. s, Qoph. t, Resh. u, Sin. v, Taw.

No. 1433 — End-of-word letters: a, Kaph. b, Mem. c, Nun. d, Pe. e, Sadhe.

**2001, Feb. 13**    **Photo.**    **Perf. 15**

| 1432 | Sheet of 22 | 1.10 | 1.10 |
|---|---|---|---|
| a.-v. | A646 10a Any single | .20 | .20 |

**Litho.**
**Perf. 14**

| 1433 | Horiz. strip of 5 | .25 | .25 |
|---|---|---|---|
| a.-e. | A646 10a Any single | .20 | .20 |
| 1434 | A646 1s shown | .50 | .50 |
| | With tab | .55 | |

No. 1433 issued in sheets of two tete-beche strips. The horizontal strips of stamps in No. 1432 are printed tete-beche.

**Worldwide Fund for Nature Type of 2000 Without WWF Emblem**

Designs: 1.20s, Lesser kestrel. 1.70s, Kuhl's pipistrelle. 2.10s, Roe deer. 2.50s, Greek tortoise.

**2001, Mar. 18**    **Litho.**    **Perf. 14**

| 1435 A631 1.20s multi | .65 | .65 |
|---|---|---|
| 1436 A631 1.70s multi | .85 | .85 |
| 1437 A631 2.10s multi | 1.10 | 1.10 |
| 1438 A631 2.50s multi | 1.40 | 1.40 |
| a. Booklet pane, 2 each #1435-1438 | 8.00 | |
| Nos. 1435-1438 (4) | 4.00 | 4.00 |
| With tabs | 4.25 | |

Flowers — A647

---

No. 1439: a, Prairie gentian (purple). b, Barberton daisy (yellow) c, Star of Bethlehem (orange). d, Calla lily (white).

**2001, Mar. 18**

| 1439 | Horiz. strip of 4 + 6 labels | 2.40 | 2.40 |
|---|---|---|---|
| a.-d. | A647 1.20s Any single | .60 | .60 |

No. 1439 was printed in sheets of four strips. The second and fourth strips in the sheet have the stamps in reverse order. Sheets sold at the Jerusalem 2001 Stamp Exhibition could have their labels personalized by the purchaser.

**Souvenir Sheet**

Jerusalem 2001 Stamp Exhibition — A648

**2001, Mar. 18**

| 1440 A648 10s multi | 5.00 | 5.00 |
|---|---|---|

Monument to Fallen Nahal Soldiers — A649

**2001, Apr. 18**    **Litho.**    **Perf. 13**

| 1441 A649 1.20s multi | .55 | .55 |
|---|---|---|
| With tab | .60 | |

Memorial Day.

**Historic Sites Type of 2000**
**Perf. 14 Syncopated**

**2001, May 23**      **Photo.**

| 1442 A630 2s Sha'ar HaGay Inn | .95 | .95 |
|---|---|---|
| With tab | 1.10 | |

Shrine of the Báb Terraces, Haifa — A650

**2001, May 23**      **Perf. 13x13¼**

| 1443 A650 3s multi | 1.40 | 1.40 |
|---|---|---|
| With tab | 1.60 | |

Karaite Jews — A651

**2001, May 23**    **Litho.**    **Perf. 14**

| 1444 A651 5.60s multi | 2.75 | 2.75 |
|---|---|---|
| With tab | 3.00 | |

## Souvenir Sheet

Belgica 2001 Intl. Stamp Exhibition, Brussels — A652

Cut diamonds: a, 1.40s, Marquise. b, 1.70s, Round. c, 4.70s, Square.

**2001, May 23**     *Perf. 14¾x14½*
| 1445 | A652 | Sheet of 3 | 4.75 | 4.75 |
|---|---|---|---|---|
| a. | | 1.40s multi | .85 | .85 |
| b. | | 1.70s multi | 1.00 | 1.00 |
| c. | | 4.70s multi | 2.75 | 2.75 |

No. 1445 sold for 10s.

Youth Movements — A653

**2001, July 17**     *Perf. 14*
| 1446 | A653 | 5.60s multi | 2.75 | 2.75 |
|---|---|---|---|---|
| | With tab | | 3.00 | |

Bezalel School of Art Ceramic Facade Tiles — A654

Landscapes of: 1.20s, Hebron. 1.40s, Jaffa. 1.90s, Haifa. 2.30s, Tiberias.

**2001, July 17**     *Perf. 13x14*
| 1447 | A654 | 1.20s multi | .55 | .55 |
|---|---|---|---|---|
| 1448 | A654 | 1.40s multi | .65 | .65 |
| 1449 | A654 | 1.90s multi | .90 | .90 |
| 1450 | A654 | 2.30s multi | 1.10 | 1.10 |
| | *Nos. 1447-1450 (4)* | | 3.20 | 3.20 |
| | With tabs | | 3.50 | |

## Souvenir Sheet

Phila Nippon '01, Japan — A655

Children's stamp design contest winners: a, 1.20s, Balloons. b, 1.40s, Cat. c, 2.50s, Veterinarian with dog. d, 4.70s, Dolphins.

**2001, July 17**     *Perf. 14¾*
| 1451 | A655 | Sheet of 4 | 4.75 | 4.75 |
|---|---|---|---|---|
| a. | | 1.20s multi | .55 | .55 |
| b. | | 1.40s multi | .70 | .70 |
| c. | | 2.50s multi | 1.25 | 1.25 |
| d. | | 4.70s multi | 2.25 | 2.25 |

No. 1451 sold for 10s.

Shota Rustaveli (c. 1172-c. 1216), Georgian Poet — A656

**2001, Sept. 3**   *Litho.*    *Perf. 13x14*
| 1452 | A656 | 3.40s multi | 1.60 | 1.60 |
|---|---|---|---|---|
| | With tab | | 1.75 | |

Yehuda Amichai (1924-2000), Poet — A657

**2001, Sept. 3**
| 1453 | A657 | 5.60s multi | 2.60 | 2.60 |
|---|---|---|---|---|
| | | | 2.75 | |

Jewish National Fund, Cent A658

**2001, Sept. 3**     *Perf. 14*
| 1454 | A658 | 5.60s multi | 2.60 | 2.60 |
|---|---|---|---|---|
| | With tab | | 2.75 | |

## Jewish New Year Cards Type of 2000

Designs: 1.20s, Soldier, dove with olive branch. 1.90s, Two women. 2.30s, Boy with flowers.

**2001, Sept. 3**
| 1455 | A641 | 1.20s multi | .55 | .55 |
|---|---|---|---|---|
| 1456 | A641 | 1.90s multi | .90 | .90 |
| 1457 | A641 | 2.30s multi | 1.10 | 1.10 |
| | *Nos. 1455-1457 (3)* | | 2.55 | 2.55 |
| | With tabs | | 2.75 | |

Selection of Col. Ilan Ramon as Israel's First Astronaut — A659

**2001, Dec. 11**   *Litho.*    *Perf. 13*
| 1458 | A659 | 1.20s multi | .55 | .55 |
|---|---|---|---|---|
| | With tab | | .65 | |

Akim Association for the Rehabilitation of the Mentally Handicapped, 50th Anniv. — A660

**2001, Dec. 11**     *Perf. 13x14*
| 1459 | A660 | 2.20s multi | 1.00 | 1.00 |
|---|---|---|---|---|
| | With tab | | 1.10 | |

Heinrich Heine (1797-1856), Poet — A661

**2001, Dec. 11**
| 1460 | A661 | 4.40s multi | 2.10 | 2.10 |
|---|---|---|---|---|
| | With tab | | 2.40 | |

Institute for the Blind, Jerusalem, Cent. A662

## Litho. & Embossed

**2001, Dec. 11**     *Perf. 14¾*
| 1461 | A662 | 5.60s multi | 2.60 | 2.60 |
|---|---|---|---|---|
| | With tab | | 3.00 | |

Coastal Conservation A663

**2001, Dec. 11**   *Litho.*    *Perf. 13*
| 1462 | A663 | 10s multi | 4.75 | 4.75 |
|---|---|---|---|---|
| | With tab | | 5.25 | |

## Flower Type of 2001

**2002, Feb. 24**   *Litho.*    *Perf. 14*
| 1463 | A647 | 1.20s Yellow lily | .55 | .55 |
|---|---|---|---|---|
| | With tab | | .60 | |

No. 1463 has small picture of flower at left, while No. 1439b has small picture of flower at right.

Languages A664

**2002, Feb. 24**     *Perf. 13x14*
| 1464 | A664 | 2.10s Yiddish | .90 | .90 |
|---|---|---|---|---|
| 1465 | A664 | 2.10s Ladino | .90 | .90 |
| | With tabs | | 2.00 | |

Mushrooms A665

Designs: 1.90s, Agaricus campester. 2.20s, Amanita muscaria. 2.80s, Suillus granulatus.

**2002, Feb. 24**
| 1466 | A665 | 1.90s multi | .80 | .80 |
|---|---|---|---|---|
| 1467 | A665 | 2.20s multi | .95 | .95 |
| 1468 | A665 | 2.80s multi | 1.25 | 1.25 |
| | *Nos. 1466-1468 (3)* | | 3.00 | 3.00 |
| | With tabs | | 3.50 | |

Months of the Year — A666

Designs: a, Tishrei (shofar, pomegranates). b, Heshvan (dried leaves). c, Kislev (dreidel, Hanukkah candles). d, Tevet (orange, flowers). e, Shevat (seedling, flowers, seeds). f, Adar (party hat, noisemaker, hamentashen). g, Nisan (cup, matzoh, flowers). h, Iyyar (bow and arrows, seeds). i, Sivan (wheat, sickle). j, Tammuz (flower, shells). k, Av (bride, groom, grapes). l, Elul, (cotton, dates, prayer book).

**2002, Feb. 24**   *Photo.*    *Perf. 14x14¼*
| 1469 | A666 | Sheet of 12 | 6.25 | 6.25 |
|---|---|---|---|---|
| a.-l. | | 1.20s Any single | .50 | .50 |

### Self-Adhesive
*Serpentine Die Cut 16*

| 1470 | A666 | Booklet of 12 | 6.25 | |
|---|---|---|---|---|
| a.-l. | | 1.20s Any single | .50 | .50 |

Monument to Fallen Military Police A667

**2002, Apr. 10**   *Litho.*    *Perf. 14*
| 1471 | A667 | 1.20s multi | .50 | .50 |
|---|---|---|---|---|
| | With tab | | .60 | |

Hakhel Le Yisrael — A668

**2002, Apr. 10**     *Perf. 13x14*
| 1472 | A668 | 4.70s multi | 2.00 | 2.00 |
|---|---|---|---|---|
| | With tab | | 2.25 | |

Israel Foundation for Handicapped Children, 50th Anniv. — A669

**2002, Apr. 10**
| 1473 | A669 | 5.90s multi | 2.50 | 2.50 |
|---|---|---|---|---|
| | | | 2.75 | |

Historians — A670

Designs: No. 1474, Heinrich Graetz (1817-91). No. 1475, Simon Dubnow (1860-1941). No. 1476, Benzion Dinur (1884-1973). No. 1477, Yitzhak Baer (1888-1980).

**2002, Apr. 10**     *Perf. 14*
| 1474 | A670 | 2.20s multi | .90 | .90 |
|---|---|---|---|---|
| 1475 | A670 | 2.20s multi | .90 | .90 |
| 1476 | A670 | 2.20s multi | .90 | .90 |
| 1477 | A670 | 2.20s multi | .90 | .90 |
| | *Nos. 1474-1477 (4)* | | 3.60 | 3.60 |
| | With tabs | | 4.00 | |

## Historic Sites Type of 2000
*Perf. 14 Syncopated*

**2002, June 18**     *Photo.*
| 1478 | A630 | 3.30s Hatsar Kinneret | 1.40 | 1.40 |
|---|---|---|---|---|
| | With tab | | 1.60 | |

Cable Cars — A671

**2002, June 18**   *Litho.*    *Perf. 14*
| 1479 | A671 | 2.20s Haifa | .95 | .95 |
|---|---|---|---|---|
| 1480 | A671 | 2.20s Massada | .95 | .95 |
| 1481 | A671 | 2.20s Menara | .95 | .95 |
| 1482 | A671 | 2.20s Rosh Haniqra | .95 | .95 |
| | *Nos. 1479-1482 (4)* | | 3.80 | 3.80 |
| | With tabs | | 4.25 | |

## Souvenir Sheet

Geology — A672

**2002, June 18**

| | | | | |
|---|---|---|---|---|
| 1483 | A672 | Sheet of 3 | 5.00 | 5.00 |
| *a.* | | 2.20s Fish fossil | 1.10 | 1.10 |
| *b.* | | 3.40s Copper minerals | 1.75 | 1.75 |
| *c.* | | 4.40s Ammonite | 2.10 | 2.10 |

No. 1483 sold for 12s.

Rechavam Ze'evy (1926-2001), Assassinated Tourism Minister A673

Baruch Spinoza (1632-77), Philosopher A674

**2002, Aug. 27      Litho.      Perf. 14**

| | | | | |
|---|---|---|---|---|
| 1484 | A673 | 1.20s multi | .50 | .50 |
| | With tab | | | .60 |

**2002, Aug. 27               Perf. 13x14**

| | | | | |
|---|---|---|---|---|
| 1485 | A674 | 5.90s multi | 2.50 | 2.50 |
| | With tab | | | 2.75 | 2.75 |

Wine — A675

Designs: 1.20s, Clippers, bunch of grapes. 1.90s, Corkscrew, cork. 2.30s, Wine glass, bottle.

**2002, Aug. 27                       Perf. 14**

| | | | | |
|---|---|---|---|---|
| 1486 | A675 | 1.20s multi | .50 | .50 |
| 1487 | A675 | 1.90s multi | .80 | .80 |
| 1488 | A675 | 2.30s multi | 1.00 | 1.00 |
| | Nos. 1486-1488 (3) | | 2.30 | 2.30 |
| | With tabs | | | 2.60 |

Birds of the Jordan Valley A676

**2002, Aug. 27              Perf. 14½x14**

| | | | | |
|---|---|---|---|---|
| 1489 | A676 | 2.20s Golden eagle | .95 | .95 |
| 1490 | A676 | 2.20s Black stork | .95 | .95 |
| 1491 | A676 | 2.20s Common crane | .95 | .95 |
| | Nos. 1489-1491 (3) | | 2.85 | 2.85 |
| | With tabs | | | 3.25 |

### Historic Sites Type of 2000
**Perf. 14 Syncopated**

**2002, Aug. 27                       Photo.**

| | | | | |
|---|---|---|---|---|
| 1492 | A630 | 4.60s Kadoorie School | 2.00 | 2.00 |
| | With tab | | | 2.25 |

### Hyacinth Type of 1999
**Perf. 14 Syncopated**

**2002, Oct. 21                       Photo.**

| | | | | |
|---|---|---|---|---|
| 1492A | A606 | (1.20s) multi | .55 | .55 |
| | With tab | | | .60 |

---

Political Journalists A677

Designs: 1.20s, Abba Ahimeir (1897-1962). 3.30s, Israel Eldad (1910-96). 4.70s, Moshe Beilinson (1890-1936). 5.90s, Rabbi Binyamin (1880-1957).

**2002, Nov. 26      Litho.      Perf. 14**

| | | | | |
|---|---|---|---|---|
| 1493 | A677 | 1.20s multi | .50 | .50 |
| 1494 | A677 | 3.30s multi | 1.40 | 1.40 |
| 1495 | A677 | 4.70s multi | 2.00 | 2.00 |
| 1496 | A677 | 5.90s multi | 2.50 | 2.50 |
| | Nos. 1493-1496 (4) | | 6.40 | 6.40 |
| | With tabs | | | 7.25 |

Toys A678

Menorah A679

**2002, Nov. 26**

| | | | | |
|---|---|---|---|---|
| 1497 | A678 | 2.20s Five Stones | .95 | .95 |
| 1498 | A678 | 2.20s Marbles | .95 | .95 |
| 1499 | A678 | 2.20s Spinning top | .95 | .95 |
| 1500 | A678 | 2.20s Yo-yo | .95 | .95 |
| | Nos. 1497-1500 (4) | | 3.80 | 3.80 |
| | With tabs | | | 4.25 |

**2002-03      Photo.      Perf. 15x14¾**

| | | | | |
|---|---|---|---|---|
| 1501 | A679 | 20a red | .20 | .20 |
| 1502 | A679 | 30a gray olive | .20 | .20 |
| 1503 | A679 | 40a gray green | .20 | .20 |
| 1504 | A679 | 50a gray brown | .20 | .20 |
| 1505 | A679 | 1s purple | .40 | .40 |
| | With tabs | | | .65 |
| 1506 | A679 | 1.30s blue | .50 | .50 |
| | Nos. 1501-1506 (6) | | 1.70 | 1.70 |
| | With tabs | | | 1.25 |

Issued: 30a, 1s, 11/26/02; 20a, 40a, 50a, 1.30s, 2/11/03.

Yeshivot Hahesder, 50th Anniv. (in 2004) A680

**2003, Feb. 11      Litho.      Perf. 14**

| | | | | |
|---|---|---|---|---|
| 1507 | A680 | 1.20s multi | .50 | .50 |
| | With tab | | | .60 |

11 September 2001, by Michael Gross — A681

**2003, Feb. 11                    Perf. 13x14**

| | | | | |
|---|---|---|---|---|
| 1508 | A681 | 2.30s multi | .95 | .95 |
| | With tab | | | 1.10 |

Monument for the Victims of Hostile Acts, Jerusalem A682

**2003, Feb. 11                    Perf. 14x13**

| | | | | |
|---|---|---|---|---|
| 1509 | A682 | 4.70s multi | 1.90 | 1.90 |
| | With tab | | | 2.25 |

---

Powered Flight, Cent. A683

Designs: 2.30s, Wright Flyer in flight. 3.30s, Engine, propeller, Wright brothers. 5.90s, Orville Wright piloting Wright Flyer.

**2003, Feb. 11                       Perf. 14**

| | | | | |
|---|---|---|---|---|
| 1510 | A683 | 2.30s multi | .95 | .95 |
| 1511 | A683 | 3.30s multi | 1.40 | 1.40 |
| 1512 | A683 | 5.90s multi | 2.40 | 2.40 |
| | Nos. 1510-1512 (3) | | 4.75 | 4.75 |
| | With tabs | | | 5.25 |

Memorial Day — A684

**2003, Apr. 27      Litho.      Perf. 14**

| | | | | |
|---|---|---|---|---|
| 1513 | A684 | 1.20s multi | .55 | .55 |
| | With tab | | | .65 |

Holocaust Memorial Day — A685

**2003, Apr. 27                       Perf. 13**

| | | | | |
|---|---|---|---|---|
| 1514 | A685 | 2.20s multi | 1.00 | 1.00 |
| | With tab | | | 1.10 |

Yemeni Jewish Immigration A686

**2003, Apr. 27                       Perf. 14**

| | | | | |
|---|---|---|---|---|
| 1515 | A686 | 3.30s multi | 1.50 | 1.50 |
| | With tab | | | 1.60 |

Israeli Aircraft Industries, 50th Anniv. A687

**2003, Apr. 27**

| | | | | |
|---|---|---|---|---|
| 1516 | A687 | 3.30s multi | 1.50 | 1.50 |
| | With tab | | | 1.60 |

Independence, 55th Anniv. — A688

**2002, Apr. 27**

| | | | | |
|---|---|---|---|---|
| 1517 | A688 | 5.90s multi | 2.75 | 2.75 |
| | With tab | | | 3.00 |

Famous Men — A689

Designs: 1.90s, Ya'akov Meridor (1913-95), government minister. 2.20s, Ya'akov Dori (1899-1973), first chief of staff of the Israel Defense Forces. 2.80s, Sheikh Ameen Tarif

---

(1898-1993), President of Druse Religious Court.

**2003, Apr. 27                       Perf. 13**

| | | | | |
|---|---|---|---|---|
| 1518 | A689 | 1.90s multi | .85 | .85 |
| 1519 | A689 | 2.20s multi | 1.00 | 1.00 |
| 1520 | A689 | 2.80s multi | 1.25 | 1.25 |
| | Nos. 1518-1520 (3) | | 3.10 | 3.10 |
| | With tabs | | | 3.50 |

Greetings — A690

Designs: No. 1521, Open box, Hebrew letters. No. 1522, Bride and groom. No. 1523, Heart as flower.

**2003, Apr. 27                       Perf. 14**

| | | | | |
|---|---|---|---|---|
| 1521 | A690 | (1.20s) multi | .55 | .55 |
| *a.* | | Sheet of 12 + 12 labels | 9.50 | 9.50 |
| 1522 | A690 | (1.20s) multi | .55 | .55 |
| *a.* | | Sheet of 12 + 12 labels | 9.50 | 9.50 |
| 1523 | A690 | (1.20s) multi | .55 | .55 |
| *a.* | | Sheet of 12 + 12 labels | 9.50 | 9.50 |
| | Nos. 1521-1523 (3) | | 1.65 | 1.65 |
| | | | | 1.90 |

Nos. 1521a-1523a issued 10/19. Each sold for 21.20s. Labels could be personalized.

### Greetings Type of 2003

Designs: No. 1524, Hot air balloon, flowers. No. 1525, Flowers and ladybug. No. 1526, Boy and teddy bear.

**2003, June 24      Litho.      Perf. 14**

| | | | | |
|---|---|---|---|---|
| 1524 | A690 | (1.20s) multi | .55 | .55 |
| *a.* | | Sheet of 12 + 12 labels | 9.50 | 9.50 |
| 1525 | A690 | (1.20s) multi | .55 | .55 |
| *a.* | | Sheet of 12 + 12 labels | 9.50 | 9.50 |
| 1526 | A690 | (1.20s) multi | .55 | .55 |
| *a.* | | Sheet of 12 + 12 labels | 9.50 | 9.50 |
| | Nos. 1524-1526 (3) | | 1.65 | 1.65 |
| | | | | 1.90 |

Nos. 1524a-1526a issued 10/19. Each sold for 21.20s. Labels could be personalized.

Village Centenaries A691

**2003, June 24      Litho.      Perf. 14**

| | | | | |
|---|---|---|---|---|
| 1527 | A691 | 3.30s Atlit | 1.50 | 1.50 |
| 1528 | A691 | 3.30s Givat-Ada | 1.50 | 1.50 |
| 1529 | A691 | 3.30s Kfar-Saba | 1.50 | 1.50 |
| | Nos. 1527-1529 (3) | | 4.50 | 4.50 |
| | With tabs | | | 5.00 |

Evolution of the Israeli Flag A692

Designs: 1.90s, Flag of the Prague Jewish community, 15th cent. 2.30s, Ness Ziona flag, 1891. 4.70s, Theodor Herzl's "Der Judenstaat" flag design, 1896. 5.90s, Israeli flag, 1948.

**2003, June 24**

| | | | | |
|---|---|---|---|---|
| 1530 | A692 | 1.90s multi | .90 | .90 |
| 1531 | A692 | 2.30s multi | 1.10 | 1.10 |
| 1532 | A692 | 4.70s multi | 2.10 | 2.10 |
| 1533 | A692 | 5.90s multi | 2.75 | 2.75 |
| | Nos. 1530-1533 (4) | | 6.85 | 6.85 |
| | With tabs | | | 7.50 |

Yad Vashem, 50th Anniv. — A693

Stars of David and: No. 1534, List of Jewish forced laborers. No. 1535, Teddy bear, page of testimony.

## 2003, Sept. 9    Litho.    *Perf. 14*

| | | | |
|---|---|---|---|
| 1534 | A693 | 2.20s multi | 1.00 1.00 |
| 1535 | A693 | 2.20s multi | 1.00 1.00 |
| a. | | Pair, #1534-1535 | 2.00 2.00 |
| | | Pair with tabs | 2.25 |
| b. | | Miniature sheet, 3 #1535a | 6.00 6.00 |

No. 1535b issued 2004.

Olive Oil — A694

Designs: 1.30s, Olives. 1.90s, Olive press. 2.30s, Jars of oil.

## 2003, Sept. 9

| | | | |
|---|---|---|---|
| 1536 | A694 | 1.30s multi | .55 .55 |
| 1537 | A694 | 1.90s multi | .85 .85 |
| 1538 | A694 | 2.30s multi | 1.00 1.00 |
| a. | | Booklet pane, #1536, 2 #1537, 3 #1538 | 5.25 — |
| | | Complete booklet, #1538a | 5.25 |
| | | *Nos. 1536-1538 (3)* | 2.40 2.40 |
| | | With tabs | 2.75 |

### Souvenir Sheet

Armenian Ceramics in Jerusalem — A695

No. 1539: a, Deer, by Karakashian-Balian Studio, 1930s-1940s. b, Bird, by Stepan Karakashian, 1980s. c, Tree of Life, by Marie Balian, 1990s.

## 2003, Sept. 9    *Perf.*

| | | | |
|---|---|---|---|
| 1539 | A695 | Sheet of 3 | 6.50 6.50 |
| a. | | 2.30s multi | 1.40 1.40 |
| b. | | 3.30s multi | 2.10 2.10 |
| c. | | 4.70s multi | 3.00 3.00 |

No. 1539 contains three 31mm diameter stamps and sold for 15s.

### Hyacinth Type of 1999

*Serpentine Die Cut 13½x14*

## 2003, Dec. 4    Photo.

### Booklet Stamp

### Self-Adhesive

| | | | |
|---|---|---|---|
| 1540 | A606 | (1.30s) multi | .60 .60 |
| a. | | Booklet pane of 20 | 12.00 |

Immigrants to Israel — A696

Designs: 2.10s, Leibowitch family, clerical house, Zikhron Ya'acov. 6.20s, Second Aliya immigrants, Rothschild Ave., Tel Aviv.

## 2003, Dec. 9    Litho.    *Perf. 13*

| | | | |
|---|---|---|---|
| 1541 | A696 | 2.10s multi | .95 .95 |
| 1542 | A696 | 6.20s multi | 3.00 3.00 |
| | | With tabs | 4.50 |

Famous Men — A697

Designs: 3.30s, Aharon David Gordon (1856-1922), laborer. 4.90s, Emile Habiby (1921-96), journalist, politician. 6.20s, Yehoshua Hankin (1865-1945), land developer.

## 2003, Dec. 9    *Perf. 14*

| | | | |
|---|---|---|---|
| 1543 | A697 | 3.30s multi | 1.50 1.50 |
| 1544 | A697 | 4.90s multi | 2.25 2.25 |
| 1545 | A697 | 6.20s multi | 3.00 3.00 |
| | | *Nos. 1543-1545 (3)* | 6.75 6.75 |
| | | With tabs | 7.50 |

Children on Wheels — A698

No. 1546: a, Boy on bicycle. b, Girl on roller blades. c, Girl on scooter. d, Boy on skateboard.

## 2003, Dec. 9    *Perf. 13¾*

| | | | |
|---|---|---|---|
| 1546 | | Horiz. strip of 4 | 2.40 2.40 |
| a.-d. | | Souvenir sheet, Any single | .60 .60 |
| | | Strip with tabs | 2.75 |

Philately Day.

Red Sea Fish A699

Designs: No. 1547, Amphiprion bicinctus. No. 1548, Pseudanthias squamipinnis. No. 1549, Pseudochromis fridmani. No. 1550, Chaetodon paucifasciatus.

## 2004, Jan. 30    Litho.    *Perf. 14*

| | | | |
|---|---|---|---|
| 1547 | A699 | 1.30s multi | .60 .60 |
| 1548 | A699 | 1.30s multi | .60 .60 |
| 1549 | A699 | 1.30s multi | .60 .60 |
| 1550 | A699 | 1.30s multi | .60 .60 |
| a. | | Souvenir sheet, #1547-1550 | 3.50 3.50 |
| | | *Nos. 1547-1550 (4)* | 2.40 2.40 |
| | | With tabs | 2.75 |

2004 Hong Kong Stamp Expo (#1550a). No. 1550a sold for 7.50s.

Menachem Begin Heritage Center, Jerusalem A700

## 2004, Feb. 24    *Perf. 13*

| | | | |
|---|---|---|---|
| 1551 | A700 | 2.50s multi | 1.10 1.10 |
| | | With tab | 1.25 |

Col. Ilan Ramon (1954-2003), First Israeli Astronaut — A701

## 2004, Feb. 24

| | | | |
|---|---|---|---|
| 1552 | A701 | 2.60s multi | 1.25 1.25 |
| | | With tab | 1.40 |

### Historians Type of 2002

Designs: 2.40s, Emanuel Ringelblum (1900-44). 3.70s, Jacob Talmon (1916-80). 6.20s, Jacob Herzog (1921-72).

## 2004, Feb. 24    *Perf. 14*

| | | | |
|---|---|---|---|
| 1553 | A670 | 2.40s multi | 1.10 1.10 |
| 1554 | A670 | 3.70s multi | 1.60 1.60 |
| 1555 | A670 | 6.20s multi | 2.75 2.75 |
| | | *Nos. 1553-1555 (3)* | 5.45 5.45 |
| | | With tabs | 6.00 |

Memorial Day A702

## 2004, Apr. 20    Litho.    *Perf. 14*

| | | | |
|---|---|---|---|
| 1556 | A702 | 1.30s multi | .60 .60 |
| | | With tab | .65 |

FIFA (Fédération Internationale de Football Association), Cent. — A703

## 2004, May 3    *Perf. 13*

| | | | |
|---|---|---|---|
| 1557 | A703 | 2.10s multi | .95 .95 |
| | | With tab | 1.10 |

Printed in sheets of 12 + 4 central labels.

UEFA (European Football Union), 50th Anniv. A704

## 2004, May 3    *Perf. 14*

| | | | |
|---|---|---|---|
| 1558 | A704 | 6.20s multi | 2.75 2.75 |
| | | With tab | 3.00 |

Ottoman Clock Towers — A705

## 2004, May 3    *Perf. 13x14*

| | | | |
|---|---|---|---|
| 1559 | A705 | 1.30s Acre | .60 .60 |
| 1560 | A705 | 1.30s Safed | .60 .60 |
| 1561 | A705 | 1.30s Jaffa | .60 .60 |
| 1562 | A705 | 1.30s Jerusalem | .60 .60 |
| 1563 | A705 | 1.30s Haifa | .60 .60 |
| | | *Nos. 1559-1563 (5)* | 3.00 3.00 |
| | | With tabs | 3.25 |

### Booklet Stamps

| | | | |
|---|---|---|---|
| 1563A | A705 | 3.10s Safed | 1.40 1.40 |
| f. | | Booklet pane of 1 | 1.40 |
| 1563B | A705 | 3.70s Acre | 1.60 1.60 |
| g. | | Booklet pane of 1 | 1.60 |
| 1563C | A705 | 5.20s Haifa | 2.25 2.25 |
| h. | | Booklet pane of 1 | 2.25 |
| 1563D | A705 | 5.50s Jerusalem | 2.40 2.40 |
| i. | | Booklet pane of 1 | 2.40 |
| 1563E | A705 | 7s Jaffa | 3.00 3.00 |
| j. | | Booklet pane of 1 | 3.40 |
| k. | | Booklet pane, #1563A-1563E | 11.00 — |
| | | Complete booklet, #1563Af, 1563Bg, 1563Ch, 1563Di, 1563Ej, 1563Ek | 22.00 |
| | | *Nos. 1563A-1563E (5)* | 10.65 10.65 |

A706

Great Synagogue of Rome — A707

## 2004, May 20    Litho.    *Perf. 13x14*

| | | | |
|---|---|---|---|
| 1564 | A706 | 2.10s multi | .95 .95 |
| 1565 | A707 | 2.10s multi | .95 .95 |
| | | With tabs | 2.25 |

See Italy Nos. 2607-2608.

Theodor Herzl (1860-1904), Zionist Leader — A708

## 2004, July 6    *Perf. 13*

| | | | |
|---|---|---|---|
| 1566 | A708 | 2.50s multi | 1.10 1.10 |
| | | With tab | 1.25 |

See Austria No. 1960, Hungary No. 3903.

National Insurance Institute, 50th Anniv. — A709

## 2004, July 6

| | | | |
|---|---|---|---|
| 1567 | A709 | 7s multi | 3.25 3.25 |
| | | With tab | 3.75 |

2004 Summer Olympics, Athens A710

Medals won by Israeli athletes in previous Olympics: 1.50s, 1992 Silver medal, Judo. 2.40s, 1996 Bronze medal, Men's Mistral (windsurfing). 6.90s, 2000 Bronze medal, Kayaking.

## 2004, July 6    *Perf. 14*

| | | | |
|---|---|---|---|
| 1568 | A710 | 1.50s multi | .65 .65 |
| 1569 | A710 | 2.40s multi | 1.10 1.10 |
| 1570 | A710 | 6.90s multi | 3.25 3.25 |
| | | *Nos. 1568-1570 (3)* | 5.00 5.00 |
| | | With tabs | 5.50 |

Founding of Herzliya Hebrew High School, Tel Aviv, Cent. (in 2005) — A711

## 2004, Aug. 31    Litho.    *Perf. 13x14*

| | | | |
|---|---|---|---|
| 1571 | A711 | 2.20s multi | 1.00 1.00 |
| | | With tab | 1.10 |

Ben-Gurion Heritage Institute — A712

## 2004, Aug. 31    *Perf. 13*

| | | | |
|---|---|---|---|
| 1572 | A712 | 2.50s multi | 1.10 1.10 |
| | | With tab | 1.25 |

Adventure Stories — A713

Designs: 2.20s, Eight on the Trail of One, by Yemima Avidar-Tchernovitz (parachutist). 2.50s, The "Hasamba" Series, by Igal Mossin-sohn (children, donkey). 2.60s, Our Gang, by Pucho (four people).

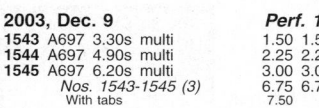

## 2004, Aug. 31
| | | | | |
|---|---|---|---|---|
| **1573** | A713 | 2.20s | multi | 1.00 1.00 |
| **1574** | A713 | 2.50s | multi | 1.10 1.10 |
| **1575** | A713 | 2.60s | multi | 1.25 1.25 |
| | *Nos. 1573-1575 (3)* | | | 3.35 3.35 |
| | With tabs | | | 3.75 |

Festivals
A714

Bread making: 1.50s, Wheat ears, sickle. 2.40s, Mill, wooden fork. 2.70s, Oven, bread shovel.

## 2004, Aug. 31        Perf. 14x13
| | | | | |
|---|---|---|---|---|
| **1576** | A714 | 1.50s | multi | .65 .65 |
| **1577** | A714 | 2.40s | multi | 1.10 1.10 |
| **1578** | A714 | 2.70s | multi | 1.25 1.25 |
| | *Nos. 1576-1578 (3)* | | | 3.00 3.00 |
| | With tabs | | | 3.25 |

Opening of Third Terminal at Ben-Gurion Airport
A715

## 2004, Nov. 2    Litho.    Perf. 14x13
| | | | | |
|---|---|---|---|---|
| **1579** | A715 | 2.70s | multi | 1.25 1.25 |
| | With tab | | | 1.40 |

Winning Design of Telabul 2004 Stamp Designing Contest
A716

## 2004, Dec. 14
| | | | | |
|---|---|---|---|---|
| **1580** | A716 | 1.30s | multi | .60 .60 |
| | With tab | | | .70 |

Bank of Israel, 50th Anniv.
A717

## 2004, Dec. 14
| | | | | |
|---|---|---|---|---|
| **1581** | A717 | 6.20s | multi | 3.00 3.00 |
| | With tab | | | 3.25 |

Philately Day
A718

Designs: 2.10s, Mailbox of Austrian Postal Services, Jerusalem Post Office. 2.20s, Mailbox of British Mandate era, Lilienblum St. Post Office, Tel Aviv. 3.30s, Modern mailbox, Main Post Office, Tel Aviv.

## 2004, Dec. 14
| | | | | |
|---|---|---|---|---|
| **1582** | A718 | 2.10s | multi | .95 .95 |
| **1583** | A718 | 2.20s | multi | 1.00 1.00 |
| **1584** | A718 | 3.30s | multi | 1.60 1.60 |
| | *Nos. 1582-1584 (3)* | | | 3.55 3.55 |
| | With tabs | | | 4.00 |

Ancient Water Systems
A719

Designs: 2.10s, Hazor water tunnel and ivory cosmetics spoon. 2.20s, Megiddo water system and seal. 3.30s, Caesarea Aqueduct, coin from Caesarea. 6.20s, Hezekiah's tunnel, pool of Siloam, Jerusalem, and imprinted piece of clay.

## 2005, Feb. 22    Litho.    Perf. 14x13
| | | | | |
|---|---|---|---|---|
| **1585** | A719 | 2.10s | multi | .95 .95 |
| **1586** | A719 | 2.20s | multi | 1.00 1.00 |
| **1587** | A719 | 3.30s | multi | 1.50 1.50 |
| **1588** | A719 | 6.20s | multi | 3.00 3.00 |
| | *Nos. 1585-1588 (4)* | | | 6.45 6.45 |
| | With tabs | | | 7.25 |

Animals in the Bible
A720

Designs: Nos. 1589, 1593a, Ostrich. Nos. 1590, 1593b, Brown bear. Nos. 1591, 1593c, Wolf. Nos. 1592, 1592d, Nile crocodile.

## 2005, Feb. 22        Perf. 14x13
| | | | | |
|---|---|---|---|---|
| **1589** | A720 | 1.30s | yel & multi | .60 .60 |
| **1590** | A720 | 1.30s | blue & multi | .60 .60 |
| **1591** | A720 | 2.20s | org & multi | 1.00 1.00 |
| **1592** | A720 | 2.20s | pink & multi | 1.00 1.00 |
| | *Nos. 1589-1592 (4)* | | | 3.20 3.20 |
| | With tabs | | | 3.50 |

### Souvenir Sheet
### Perf. 14
| | | | | |
|---|---|---|---|---|
| **1593** | | Sheet of 4 | | 5.50 5.50 |
| **a.** | A720 | 1.30s yel & multi | | .85 .85 |
| **b.** | A720 | 2.10s blue & multi | | 1.40 1.40 |
| **c.** | A720 | 2.30s org & multi | | 1.50 1.50 |
| **d.** | A720 | 2.80s pink & multi | | 1.75 1.75 |

No. 1593 sold for 12s and contains four 40x25mm stamps.

Memorial Day
A721

## 2005, May 3    Litho.    Perf. 14x13½
| | | | | |
|---|---|---|---|---|
| **1594** | A721 | 1.50s | multi | .70 .70 |
| | With tab | | | .80 |

Reserve Force
A722

## 2005, May 3
| | | | | |
|---|---|---|---|---|
| **1595** | A722 | 2.20s | multi | 1.00 1.00 |
| | With tab | | | 1.10 |

Bar-Ilan University, 50th Anniv.
A723

## 2005, May 3
| | | | | |
|---|---|---|---|---|
| **1596** | A723 | 2.20s | multi | 1.00 1.00 |
| | With tab | | | 1.10 |

End of World War II, 60th Anniv. — A724

No. 1597: a, Jewish partisan and underground fighters. b, Jewish soldiers in Allied forces.
Illustration reduced.

## 2005, May 3
| | | | | |
|---|---|---|---|---|
| **1597** | A724 | Horiz. pair | | 3.00 3.00 |
| **a.-b.** | | 3.30s Either single | | 1.50 1.50 |
| | With tab | | | 3.25 |

Schools — A725

Designs: 2.10s, Hebrew kindergarden, Rishon Le-Zion. 6.20s, Lemel Elementary School, Jerusalem.

## 2005, May 3        Perf. 13½x14
| | | | | |
|---|---|---|---|---|
| **1598** | A725 | 2.10s | multi | 1.00 1.00 |
| **1599** | A725 | 6.20s | multi | 3.00 3.00 |
| | With tabs | | | 4.50 4.50 |

Pope John Paul II (1920-2005)
A726

## 2005, May 18    Litho.    Perf. 13¾x14
| | | | | |
|---|---|---|---|---|
| **1600** | A726 | 3.30s | multi | 1.50 1.50 |
| | With tab | | | 1.75 |

### Historic Sites Type of 2000
### Serpentine Die Cut 11¼x11
## 2005, June 7                Litho.
### Booklet Stamp
### Self-Adhesive
| | | | | |
|---|---|---|---|---|
| **1601** | A630 | 2.20s | Mitzpe Revimim | 1.00 1.00 |
| **a.** | | Booklet pane of 12 | | 12.00 |

2005 Maccabiah Games — A727

## 2005, July 11        Perf. 13¾x14
| | | | | |
|---|---|---|---|---|
| **1602** | A727 | 3.30s | multi | 1.50 1.50 |
| | With tab | | | 1.75 |

Gagea Commutate — A728

### Perf. 14 Syncopated
## 2005, July 26            Photo.
| | | | | |
|---|---|---|---|---|
| **1603** | A728 | (1.30s) | multi | .60 .60 |
| | With tab | | | .70 |

See No. 1618.

Maimonides (1138-1204), Rabbi, Philosopher
A729

## 2005, July 26    Litho.    Perf. 13¾x14
| | | | | |
|---|---|---|---|---|
| **1604** | A729 | 8.20s | multi | 3.75 3.75 |
| | | | | 4.25 |

Paintings — A730

Designs: 2.20s, Agrippas Street, by Arie Aroch. 4.90s, Tablets of the Covenant, by Moshe Castel. 6.20s, The Rift in Time, No. 7, by Moshe Kupferman.

## 2005, July 26            Perf. 13¾x14
| | | | | |
|---|---|---|---|---|
| **1605** | A730 | 2.20s | multi | 1.00 1.00 |
| **1606** | A730 | 4.90s | multi | 2.25 2.25 |
| **1607** | A730 | 6.20s | multi | 2.75 2.75 |
| | *Nos. 1605-1607 (3)* | | | 6.00 6.00 |
| | With tabs | | | 6.75 |

Prime Minister Yitzhak Rabin (1922-95) and Yitzhak Rabin Center, Tel Aviv — A731

## 2005, Sept. 27    Litho.    Perf. 13
| | | | | |
|---|---|---|---|---|
| **1608** | A731 | 2.20s | multi | .95 .95 |
| | With tab | | | 1.10 |

Albert Einstein (1879-1955), Physicist — A732

## 2005, Sept. 27
| | | | | |
|---|---|---|---|---|
| **1609** | A732 | 3.30s | multi | 1.50 1.50 |
| | With tab | | | 1.60 |

Intl. Year of Physics.
See No. 1620.

Priestly Blessing at Western Wall — A733

## 2005, Sept. 27        Perf. 13½x14
| | | | | |
|---|---|---|---|---|
| **1610** | A733 | 6.20s | multi | 2.75 2.75 |
| | | | | 3.00 |

Medicine in Israel
A734

## 2005, Sept. 27        Perf. 14x13½
| | | | | |
|---|---|---|---|---|
| **1611** | A734 | 1.40s | Geriatrics | .65 .65 |
| **1612** | A734 | 2.20s | Pediatrics | .95 .95 |
| **1613** | A734 | 2.20s | Rehabilitation | .95 .95 |
| **1614** | A734 | 6.20s | Mental Health | 2.75 2.75 |
| | *Nos. 1611-1614 (4)* | | | 5.30 5.30 |
| | With tabs | | | 6.00 |

Orders of the Mishnah
A735

## 2005, Sept. 27

| | | | | |
|---|---|---|---|---|
| **1615** | A735 | 1.30s Zeraim | .60 | .60 |
| **1616** | A735 | 2.10s Moed | .90 | .90 |
| **1617** | A735 | 2.30s Nashim | 1.00 | 1.00 |
| | | *Nos. 1615-1617 (3)* | 2.50 | 2.50 |
| | | With tabs | 2.75 | |

### Gagea Commutate Type of 2005
*Serpentine Die Cut 13½x14*

| 2005, Nov. 3 | | | | Photo. |
|---|---|---|---|---|
| **1618** | A728 | (1.30s) multi | .60 | .60 |
| **a.** | | Booklet pane of 20 | 12.00 | |

Diplomatic Relations With Germany, 40th Anniv. — A736

| 2005, Nov. 3 | | Litho. | | Perf. 13 |
|---|---|---|---|---|
| **1619** | A736 | 2.10s multi | .90 | .90 |
| | | With tab | 1.00 | |

See Germany No. 2359.

### Einstein Type of 2005
Souvenir Sheet

| 2005, Dec. 27 | | | | |
|---|---|---|---|---|
| **1620** | A732 | 8.20s multi | 5.25 | 5.25 |

Philately Day, Jerusalem 2006 National Stamp Exhibition. No. 1620 sold for 12s.

Children's Rights — A737

Inscriptions: No. 1621, Childhood is happiness. No. 1622, Indifference hurts. No. 1623, A warm home.

| 2005, Dec. 27 | | | Perf. 13½x14 |
|---|---|---|---|---|
| **1621** | A737 | 1.30s multi | .60 | .60 |
| **1622** | A737 | 1.30s multi | .60 | .60 |
| **1623** | A737 | 1.30s multi | .60 | .60 |
| | | *Nos. 1621-1623 (3)* | 1.80 | 1.80 |
| | | With tabs | 2.00 | |

Theater Personalities A738

Designs: No. 1624, Joseph Millo (1916-97), director. No. 1625, Moshe Halevy (1895-1974), director. No. 1626, Shai K. Ophir (1928-87), actor. No. 1627, Nissim Aloni (1926-88), playwright.

| 2005, Dec. 27 | | | | |
|---|---|---|---|---|
| **1624** | A738 | 2.20s multi | .95 | .95 |
| **1625** | A738 | 2.20s multi | .95 | .95 |
| **1626** | A738 | 6.20s multi | 2.75 | 2.75 |
| **1627** | A738 | 6.20s multi | 2.75 | 2.75 |
| | | *Nos. 1624-1627 (4)* | 7.40 | 7.40 |
| | | With tabs | 8.25 | |

Manufacturers Association of Israel, 85th Anniv. — A739

| 2005, Dec. 29 | | Litho. | | Perf. 13¾x14 |
|---|---|---|---|---|
| **1628** | A739 | 1.50s multi | .65 | .65 |
| | | With tab | .75 | |

Emblem of Israel Post A740

| 2006 | | | | Perf. 14x13¾ |
|---|---|---|---|---|
| **1629** | A740 | 1.50s multi | .65 | .65 |
| | | With tab | .75 | |

### Souvenir Sheet
*Imperf*

| | | | | |
|---|---|---|---|---|
| **1630** | A740 | 5.90s multi | 3.50 | 3.50 |

Issued: 1.50s, 2/28; 5.90s, 5/8. Jerusalem 2006 National Stamp Exhibition (#1630). No. 1630 sold for 7.50s. Embossed and numbered examples of No. 1630 were given as gifts and were not available for sale.

Headquarters of Chabad Lubavitch Hasidism, Brooklyn, NY — A741

| 2006, Feb. 28 | | | | Perf. 14x13¾ |
|---|---|---|---|---|
| **1631** | A741 | 2.50s multi | 1.10 | 1.10 |
| | | With tab | 1.25 | |

Pres. Ezer Weizman (1924-2005) A742

| 2005, Feb. 28 | | | | Perf. 13¾x14 |
|---|---|---|---|---|
| **1632** | A742 | 7.40s multi | 3.25 | 3.25 |
| | | With tab | 3.50 | |

Children's Art A743

Contest-winning art by Jewish children in US: Nos. 1633, 1637a, Desert Bloom, by Yael Bildner. Nos. 1634, 1637c, Harmony, by Michela T. Janower. Nos. 1635, 1637d, Together in Israel, by Jessica Deutsch. Nos. 1636, 1637b, Colors of Israel, by Marissa Galin.

| 2006 | | | | Perf. 14x13¾ |
|---|---|---|---|---|
| **1633** | A743 | 1.50s multi | .65 | .65 |
| **1634** | A743 | 2.40s multi | 1.00 | 1.00 |
| **1635** | A743 | 3.60s multi | 1.60 | 1.60 |
| **1636** | A743 | 7.40s multi | 3.25 | 3.25 |
| | | *Nos. 1633-1636 (4)* | 6.50 | 6.50 |
| | | With tabs | 7.25 | |

### Souvenir Sheet
*Perf. 14*

| | | | | |
|---|---|---|---|---|
| **1637** | | Sheet of 4 | 6.75 | 6.75 |
| **a.** | A743 | 2.20s multi | 1.10 | 1.10 |
| **b.** | A743 | 2.40s multi | 1.25 | 1.25 |
| **c.** | A743 | 3.60s multi | 1.75 | 1.75 |
| **d.** | A743 | 5.10s multi | 2.60 | 2.60 |

Issued: Nos. 1633-1636, 2/28; No. 1637, 5/28. Washington 2006 World Philatelic Exhibition (#1637). No. 1637 sold for 15s and contains four 40x35mm stamps.

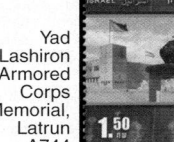

Yad Lashiron Armored Corps Memorial, Latrun A744

| 2006, Apr. 11 | | | | Perf. 14x13¾ |
|---|---|---|---|---|
| **1638** | A744 | 1.50s multi | .70 | .70 |
| | | With tab | .80 | |

Memorial Day.

Tel Aviv University, 50th Anniv. A745

| 2006, May 8 | | | | |
|---|---|---|---|---|
| **1639** | A745 | 3.60s multi | 1.60 | 1.60 |
| | | With tab | 1.75 | |

Tulips — A746

| 2006, May 8 | | | | Perf. 14x14¼ |
|---|---|---|---|---|
| **1640** | A746 | 1.50s shown | .70 | .70 |
| **a.** | | Sheet of 12 + 12 labels | 12.50 | 12.50 |
| **1641** | A746 | 1.50s Columbines | .70 | .70 |
| | | With tabs | 1.60 | |
| **a.** | | Sheet of 12 + 12 labels | 12.50 | 12.50 |

Nos. 1640a and 1641a each sold for 27s. Labels could be personalized.
Compare with type A647.

### Souvenir Sheet

Jerusalem 2006 National Stamp Exhibition — A747

| 2006, May 8 | | | | Perf. 14 |
|---|---|---|---|---|
| **1642** | A747 | 10s multi | 6.75 | 6.75 |

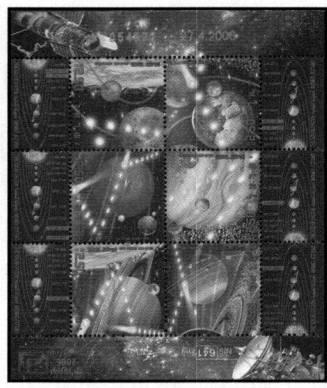

The Solar System — A748

Designs: Nos. 1643a, 1644d, Sun, Mercury and Venus. Nos. 1643b, 1644c, Earth, Moon and Mars. Nos. 1643c, 1644e, Neptune, Pluto, and moons. Nos. 1643d, 1644b, Jupiter, moons and asteroids. Nos. 1643e, 1644f, Saturn, moon, Sun and asteroids. Nos. 1643f, 1644a, Uranus, moons, asteroids, part of Saturn.

| 2006, May 8 | | | | Perf. 13 |
|---|---|---|---|---|
| **1643** | A748 | Sheet of 6 | 6.75 | 6.75 |
| **a.-f.** | | 2.50s Any single | 1.10 | 1.10 |

### Self-Adhesive
*Serpentine Die Cut 11*

| | | | | |
|---|---|---|---|---|
| **1644** | A748 | Booklet pane of 6 | 6.75 | |
| **a.-f.** | | 2.50s Any single | 1.10 | 1.10 |

Jerusalem 2006 National Stamp Exhibition. The six individual stamps, when separated, could be rearranged to produce a Star of David over the planets.

Religious Zionist Education, Cent. — A749

| 2006, July 25 | | | | Perf. 13¾x14 |
|---|---|---|---|---|
| **1645** | A749 | 3.60s multi | 1.60 | 1.60 |
| | | With tab | 1.75 | |

Rabbis of Jerusalem A750

Rabbis: 1.50s, Jacob Saul Eliachar (1817-1906). 2.20s, Samuel Salant (1816-1909). 2.40s, Jacob Meir (1856-1939).

| 2006, July 25 | | | | |
|---|---|---|---|---|
| **1646** | A750 | 1.50s multi | .70 | .70 |
| **1647** | A750 | 2.20s multi | 1.00 | 1.00 |
| **1648** | A750 | 2.40s multi | 1.10 | 1.10 |
| | | *Nos. 1646-1648 (3)* | 2.80 | 2.80 |
| | | With tabs | 3.00 | |

Silver Khamsas A751

Khamsa from: 1.50s, Morocco, 1920. 2.50s, Tunisia, 1930. 7.40s, Iran, 1925.

**2006, July 26**
| | | | |
|---|---|---|---|
| 1649 | A751 1.50s multi | .70 | .70 |
| 1650 | A751 2.50s multi | 1.10 | 1.10 |
| 1651 | A751 7.40s multi | 3.50 | 3.50 |
| | Nos. 1649-1651 (3) | 5.30 | 5.30 |
| | With tabs | 5.75 | |

Abba Eban (1915-2002), Foreign Minister — A752

**2006, Sept. 12**     **Perf. 14x13¾**
| | | | |
|---|---|---|---|
| 1652 | A752 7.30s multi | 3.50 | 3.50 |
| | With tab | 4.00 | |

**Orders of the Mishnah Type of 2005**
**2006, Sept. 12**
| | | | |
|---|---|---|---|
| 1653 | A735 1.50s Nezikin | .70 | .70 |
| 1654 | A735 2.20s Kodashim | 1.00 | 1.00 |
| 1655 | A735 2.40s Tohorot | 1.10 | 1.10 |
| | Nos. 1653-1655 (3) | 2.80 | 2.80 |
| | With tabs | 3.00 | |

Bezalel Academy of Arts and Design, Cent. — A753

**2006, Sept. 12**     **Perf. 13**
| | | | |
|---|---|---|---|
| 1656 | Horiz. strip of 3 | 3.50 | 3.50 |
| a. | A753 2.50s green | 1.10 | 1.10 |
| b. | A753 2.50s blue | 1.10 | 1.10 |
| c. | A753 2.50s orange | 1.10 | 1.10 |
| | Strip with tabs | 4.00 | |

Medicinal Herbs and Spices — A754

Designs: 1.50s, Coriandrum sativum. 2.50s, Micromeria fruticosa. 3.30s, Mentha piperita.

**2006, Dec. 17**   **Litho.**   **Perf. 14¼x14**
| | | | |
|---|---|---|---|
| 1657 | A754 1.50s multi | .70 | .70 |
| 1658 | A754 2.50s multi | 1.25 | 1.25 |
| 1659 | A754 3.30s multi | 1.60 | 1.60 |
| | Nos. 1657-1659 (3) | 3.55 | 3.55 |
| | With tabs | 4.00 | |

Creation of Esperanto Language, 120th Anniv. A755

**2006, Dec. 17**     **Perf. 14x13¾**
| | | | |
|---|---|---|---|
| 1660 | A755 3.30s multi | 1.60 | 1.60 |
| | With tab | 1.75 | |

Israeli Fashions A756

Women's fashions from: 1.50s, 1882-1948. 2.50s, 1948-73. 3.30s, 1973-90. 7.30s, 1990-2005.

**2006, Dec. 17**     **Perf. 13**
| | | | |
|---|---|---|---|
| 1661 | A756 1.50s multi | .70 | .70 |
| 1662 | A756 2.50s multi | 1.25 | 1.25 |
| 1663 | A756 3.30s multi | 1.60 | 1.60 |
| 1664 | A756 7.30s multi | 3.50 | 3.50 |
| | Nos. 1661-1664 (4) | 7.05 | 7.05 |
| | With tabs | 7.75 | |

Crusader Sites in Israel A757

**2006, Dec. 17**   **Litho.**   **Perf. 14x13¾**
| | | | |
|---|---|---|---|
| 1665 | A757 2.50s Atlit | 1.25 | 1.25 |
| 1666 | A757 2.50s Caesarea | 1.25 | 1.25 |
| 1667 | A757 2.50s Montfort | 1.25 | 1.25 |
| 1668 | A757 2.50s Belvoir | 1.25 | 1.25 |
| | Nos. 1665-1668 (4) | 5.00 | 5.00 |
| | With tabs | 5.50 | |

Development — A758

Development of the: 2.50s, Negev. 3.30s, Galilee.

**2007, Feb. 20**   **Litho.**   **Perf. 14x13¾**
| | | | |
|---|---|---|---|
| 1669 | A758 2.50s multi | 1.25 | 1.25 |
| 1670 | A758 3.30s multi | 1.60 | 1.60 |
| | With tabs | 3.25 | |

Sports and Physical Education A759

Inscriptions: 2.90s, Physical education in schools. 3s, Wingate Institute. 7.30s, Sport for all.

**2007, Feb. 20**
| | | | |
|---|---|---|---|
| 1671 | A759 2.90s multi | 1.40 | 1.40 |
| 1672 | A759 3s multi | 1.50 | 1.50 |
| 1673 | A759 7.30s multi | 3.50 | 3.50 |
| | Nos. 1671-1673 (3) | 6.40 | 6.40 |
| | With tabs | 7.25 | |

Educational Television A760

Designs: Nos. 1674a, 1675, Ma Pit'om (green panel). Nos. 1674b, 1676, Krovim Krovim (blue panel). Nos. 1674c, 1677, No Secrets (orange panel).

**2007, Feb. 20**     **Perf. 13¾x14**
| | | | |
|---|---|---|---|
| 1674 | Strip of 3 | 3.75 | 3.75 |
| a.-c. | A760 2.50s Any single | 1.25 | 1.25 |
| | Strip with tabs | 4.25 | |

**Booklet Stamps**
**Self-Adhesive**
**Serpentine Die Cut 10¾x11**
| | | | |
|---|---|---|---|
| 1675 | A760 2.50s multi | 1.25 | 1.25 |
| 1676 | A760 2.50s multi | 1.25 | 1.25 |
| 1677 | A760 2.50s multi | 1.25 | 1.25 |
| a. | Booklet pane, 2 each #1675-1677 | 7.50 | |

Memorial Day A761

**2007, Apr. 17**   **Litho.**   **Perf. 14x13¾**
| | | | |
|---|---|---|---|
| 1678 | A761 1.50s multi | .75 | .75 |
| | With tab | .85 | |

Scouting, Cent. A762

**2007, Apr. 17**
| | | | |
|---|---|---|---|
| 1679 | A762 2.50s multi | 1.25 | 1.25 |
| | With tab | 1.40 | |

Regional Development Towns — A763

Towns in: 2.50s, Northern region. 3.30s, Central region. 7.30s, Southern region.

**2007, Apr. 17**
| | | | |
|---|---|---|---|
| 1680 | A763 2.50s multi | 1.25 | 1.25 |
| 1681 | A763 3.30s multi | 1.75 | 1.75 |
| 1682 | A763 7.30s multi | 3.75 | 3.75 |
| | Nos. 1680-1682 (3) | 6.75 | 6.75 |
| | With tabs | 7.50 | |

**Souvenir Sheet**

Neve-Tzedek Neighborhood of Tel Aviv, 120th Anniv. — A764

**2007, Apr. 17**     **Perf. 13¾x14**
| | | | |
|---|---|---|---|
| 1683 | A764 Sheet of 3 | 7.50 | 7.50 |
| a. | 2.20s Founders | 1.50 | 1.50 |
| b. | 3.30s Neve-Tzedek | 2.25 | 2.25 |
| c. | 5.80s Intellectuals | 3.75 | 3.75 |

No. 1683 sold for 15s.

Reunification of Jerusalem, 40th Anniv. — A765

**2007, May 16**
| | | | |
|---|---|---|---|
| 1684 | A765 1.50s multi | .75 | .75 |
| | With tab | .85 | |

Volunteer Organizations A766

**2007, June 20**     **Perf. 13**
| | | | |
|---|---|---|---|
| 1685 | A766 1.50s multi | .75 | .75 |
| | With tab | .85 | |

Israel Prison Service — A767

**2007, June 20**     **Perf. 13¾x14**
| | | | |
|---|---|---|---|
| 1686 | A767 2.50s multi | 1.25 | 1.25 |
| | | 1.40 | |

Dance — A768

No. 1687: a, Ballet. b, Ethnic dance. c, Israeli folk dance. d, Modern dance.

**2007, June 20**
| | | | |
|---|---|---|---|
| 1687 | Horiz. strip of 4 | 4.25 | 4.25 |
| a.-d. | A768 2.20s Any single | 1.00 | 1.00 |
| | Strip with tabs | 4.75 | |

UNESCO World Heritage Sites A769

Designs: 3.30s, Akko (Acre). 5s, 10s, Tel Aviv. 5.80s, Masada.

**2007**     **Perf. 14x13¾**
| | | | |
|---|---|---|---|
| 1688 | A769 3.30s multi | 1.60 | 1.60 |
| 1689 | A769 5s multi | 2.40 | 2.40 |
| 1690 | A769 5.80s multi | 2.75 | 2.75 |
| | Nos. 1688-1690 (3) | 6.75 | 6.75 |
| | With tabs | 7.50 | |

**Souvenir Sheet**
| | | | |
|---|---|---|---|
| 1691 | A769 10s multi | 7.25 | 7.25 |

Issued: 3.30s, 5s, 5.80s, 6/20; 10s, 8/27. Tel Aviv, cent. (#1691). No. 1691 sold for 15s.

Beach — A770

**2007, Aug. 27**     **Perf. 14**
| | | | |
|---|---|---|---|
| 1692 | A770 (1.50s) multi | .75 | .75 |
| | With tab | .85 | |

Hashomer A771

**2007, Aug. 27**     **Perf. 14x13¾**
| | | | |
|---|---|---|---|
| 1693 | A771 3.30s multi | 1.60 | 1.60 |
| | With tab | 1.75 | |

Israel Reserve Forces — A772

**2007, Aug. 27**     **Perf. 13¾x14**
| | | | |
|---|---|---|---|
| 1694 | A772 7.30s multi | 3.75 | 3.75 |
| | With tab | 4.25 | |

Chalom Messas (1909-2003), Chief Rabbi of Morocco and Jerusalem A773

**2007, Aug. 27**
1695 A773 7.30s multi 3.75 3.75
    With tab 4.25

Women of the Bible — A774

**2007, Aug. 27**
1696 A774 1.50s Jael .75 .75
1697 A774 2.20s Esther 1.10 1.10
1698 A774 2.40s Miriam 1.25 1.25
    Nos. 1696-1698 (3) 3.10 3.10
    With tabs 3.50

**Theodor Herzl Type of 1986**
*Serpentine Die Cut 13½x13¾*
**2007, Nov. 1** **Litho.**
**Self-Adhesive**
1699 A388 5a blue & ultra .20 .20

**Medicinal Herbs and Spices Type of 2006**
Designs: 1.55s, Laurus nobilis. 2.25s, Coridothymus capitatus.

**2007, Nov. 5** **Perf. 14**
1700 A754 1.55s multi .80 .80
1701 A754 2.25s multi 1.25 1.25
    With tabs 2.25

Rabbi Itzhak Kaduri (1902-2006) A775

**2007, Dec. 5** **Perf. 13½x14**
1702 A775 8.15s multi 4.25 4.25
    With tab 4.75

Tel Aviv Movie Theaters A776

Designs: 4.50s, Eden Cinema. 4.60s, Mograbi Cinema.

**2007, Dec. 5** **Perf. 14x13½**
1703 A776 4.50s multi 2.40 2.40
1704 A776 4.60s multi 2.40 2.40
    With tabs 5.25

Family Love — A777

Designs: 1.55s, Boy giving flower to mother. 2.25s, Girl with baby brother. 3.55s. Father and son.

**2007, Dec. 5** **Perf. 13½x14**
1705 A777 1.55s multi .80 .80
1706 A777 2.25s multi 1.25 1.25
1707 A777 3.55s multi 1.90 1.90
    Nos. 1705-1707 (3) 3.95 3.95
    With tabs 4.50

Hula Nature Reserve A778

Designs: Nos. 1708a, 1710, Pelicans, Caspian terrapins, iris (denomination in yellow). Nos. 1708b, 1709, Water buffalos, marbled duck, reed warbler, wildcat, wild raspberry (denomination in red violet). Nos. 1708c, 1711, Otter, catfish, cranes, willow herb (denomination in orange).

**2007, Dec. 5** **Perf. 14x13½**
1708 Strip of 3 3.75 3.75
  a.-c. A778 2.25s Any single 1.25 1.25
    Strip with tabs 4.25

**Booklet Stamps**
**Self-Adhesive**
*Serpentine Die Cut 11x10¼*
1709 A778 2.25s multi 1.25 1.25
1710 A778 2.25s multi 1.25 1.25
1711 A778 2.25s multi 1.25 1.25
  a. Booklet pane, 2 each #1709-1711 7.50
    Nos. 1709-1711 (3) 3.75 3.75

**Miniature Sheet**

Noah's Ark — A779

No. 1712: a, Dove and olive branch. b, Noah and family, animals, leaving ark. c, Camels, giraffes, zebra, elephants, whale. d, Peafowl, bears, tiger. e, Lions, wolf. f, Wolf, leopards, goats, kangaroos.

**2007, Dec. 5** **Perf. 14**
1712 A779 Sheet of 6 8.50 8.50
  a.-f. 2.25s Any single 1.40 1.40
World Stamp Championship Israel 2008. No. 1712 sold for 16s.

Israel Rokach (1896-1959), Mayor of Tel Aviv — A780

**2008, Jan. 27** **Litho.** **Perf. 14x13¾**
1713 A780 2.25s multi 1.25 1.25
    With tab 1.40

Tel Aviv Land Lottery, Cent. (in 2009) — A781

**2008, Jan. 27** **Perf. 13**
1714 A781 4.50s multi 2.50 2.50
    With tab 2.75

Intl. Holocaust Remembrance Day — A782

**2008, Jan. 27** **Perf. 14**
1715 A782 4.60s multi 2.60 2.60
    With tab 3.00

See United Nations No.948, United Nations Offices in Geneva No.479, United Nations Offices in Vienna No. 412.

Mekorot, National Water System, 70th Anniv. — A783

**2008, Jan. 27** **Perf. 13¾x14**
1716 A783 5.80s multi 3.25 3.25
    With tab 3.75

Akiva Aryeh Weiss (1868-1947), Tel Aviv Builder and Developer — A784

**2008, Jan. 27** **Perf. 14x13¾**
1717 A784 8.15s multi 4.75 4.75
    With tab 5.25

UNESCO World Heritage Sites A785

Designs: 2.25s, Biblical Tels. 3.40s, Incense Route.

**2008, Jan. 27**
1718 A785 2.25s multi 1.25 1.25
1719 A785 3.40s multi 1.90 1.90
    With tabs 3.50

Israeli Boy and Flag — A786

Flowers — A787

**2008, Apr. 28** **Litho.** **Perf. 14**
1720 A786 (1.55s) multi .90 .90
    With tab 1.00

**Booklet Stamp**
**Self-Adhesive**
*Serpentine Die Cut 13½x14*
1721 A786 (1.55s) multi .90 .90
  a. Booklet pane of 20 18.00

**2008, Apr. 28** **Perf. 14**
1722 A787 (1.55s) White roses .90 .90
1723 A787 (1.55s) Cyclamen persicum .90 .90
    With tabs 2.00

Independence, 60th Anniv. — A788

**2008, Apr. 28** **Perf. 14x13¾**
1724 A788 1.55s multi .90 .90
    With tab 1.00

Memorial Day — A789

**2008, Apr. 28** **Perf. 13¾x14**
1725 A789 1.55s multi .90 .90
    With tab 1.00

Israel Export Institute, 50th Anniv. A790

**2008, Apr. 28** **Perf. 14x13¾**
1726 A790 2.80s multi 1.60 1.60
    With tab 1.75

**Souvenir Sheet**

Hatikva (National Anthem), 120th Anniv. — A791

**2008, Apr. 28** **Perf. 13¾**
1727 A791 10s multi 8.75 8.75
No. 1727 sold for 15s.

**Miniature Sheet**

Independence Day Posters — A792

No. 1728 — Poster from: a, 1981 (green panel). b, 1991 (brown panel). c, 2006 (blue panel). d, 1971 (purple panel). e, 1965 (dark red panel). f, 1952 (orange panel).

**2008, Apr. 28** **Perf. 13¾x14**
1728 A792 Sheet of 6 8.00 8.00
  a.-f. 2.25s Any single 1.25 1.25

Children's Art — A793

Designs: No. 1729, I Love Israel (numbers, symbols, Hebrew and Roman letters), by Etai Epstein. No. 1730, Israel is My Home (Hebrew letters, house and map of Israel), by Yuval Sulema and Eden Vilker. No. 1731, Israel's 60th, (girl, telescope, cat, butterflies, flowers and "60"), by Daniel Hazan.

**2008, May 14**     **Perf. 13½x14**
| | | | | |
|---|---|---|---|---|
| 1729 | A793 | 2.25s multi | 1.40 | 1.40 |
| 1730 | A793 | 2.25s multi | 1.40 | 1.40 |
| 1731 | A793 | 2.25s multi | 1.40 | 1.40 |
| | | Nos. 1729-1731 (3) | 4.20 | 4.20 |
| | | With tabs | 4.75 | |

Souvenir Sheet

Jerusalem of Gold — A794

**Litho. & Embossed With Foil Application**
**2008, May 14**     **Perf. 14½x14¼**
| | | | | |
|---|---|---|---|---|
| 1732 | A794 | 18s multi | 13.50 | 13.50 |

No. 1732 sold for 22.50s.

Souvenir Sheet

Tel Aviv, Cent. (in 2009) — A795

No. 1733 — Sketches of Tel Aviv life by Nahum Gutman: a, The First Concert. b, The First Lamp Post. c, Dr. Hisin.

**2008, May 14**   **Litho.**   **Perf. 14x13¾**
| | | | | |
|---|---|---|---|---|
| 1733 | A795 | Sheet of 3 | 11.00 | 11.00 |
| a. | | 3.50s multi | 2.75 | 2.75 |
| b. | | 4.50s multi | 3.75 | 3.75 |
| c. | | 5.50s multi | 4.50 | 4.50 |

2008 World Stamp Championships, Israel. No. 1733 sold for 18s.

Gush Katif, 1970-2005 Gaza Strip Settlement A796

**2008, July 14**   **Litho.**   **Perf. 14x13**
| | | | | |
|---|---|---|---|---|
| 1734 | A796 | 1.55s multi | .90 | .90 |
| | | With tab | 1.00 | |

Promenades — A797

Designs: 4.50s, Tabgha Promenade (on Sea of Galilee), Capernaum. 4.60s, Armon

Hanatziv Promenade, Jerusalem. 8.15s, Rishonim Promenade, Netanya.

**2008, July 14**
| | | | | |
|---|---|---|---|---|
| 1735 | A797 | 4.50s multi | 2.60 | 2.60 |
| 1736 | A797 | 4.60s multi | 2.75 | 2.75 |
| 1737 | A797 | 8.15s multi | 4.75 | 4.75 |
| | | Nos. 1735-1737 (3) | 10.10 | 10.10 |
| | | With tabs | 11.00 | |

2008 Summer Olympics, Beijing A798

**2008, July 14**
| | | | | |
|---|---|---|---|---|
| 1738 | A798 | 1.55s Swimming | .90 | .90 |
| 1739 | A798 | 1.55s Gymnastics | .90 | .90 |
| 1740 | A798 | 2.25s Sailing | 1.40 | 1.40 |
| 1741 | A798 | 2.25s Tennis | 1.40 | 1.40 |
| | | Nos. 1738-1741 (4) | 4.60 | 4.60 |
| | | With tabs | 5.00 | |

Rabbis A799

Designs: 2.30s, Rabbi Samuel Mohilewer (1824-98). 8.50s, Rabbi Zvi Hirsch Kalischer (1795-1874).

**2008, Sept. 17**     **Perf. 12½x13**
| | | | | |
|---|---|---|---|---|
| 1742 | A799 | 2.30s multi | 1.40 | 1.40 |
| 1743 | A799 | 8.50s multi | 5.00 | 5.00 |
| | | With tabs | 7.00 | |

Torah Crowns A800

Torah crown from: 1.60s, Aden, late 19th cent. No. 1737, Turkey, 19th cent. No. 1738, Poland, 1729.

**2008, Sept. 17**     **Perf. 14x13**
| | | | | |
|---|---|---|---|---|
| 1744 | A800 | 1.60s multi | .95 | .95 |
| 1745 | A800 | 3.80s multi | 2.25 | 2.25 |
| 1746 | A800 | 3.80s multi | 2.25 | 2.25 |
| | | Nos. 1744-1746 (3) | 5.45 | 5.45 |
| | | With tabs | 6.00 | |

**Herbs and Spices Type of 2006 and**

Salvia Fruticosa — A801

Design: 1.60s, Artemisia arborescens.

**2008, Sept. 17**     **Perf. 13**
| | | | | |
|---|---|---|---|---|
| 1747 | A754 | 1.60s multi | .95 | .95 |
| 1748 | A801 | (2.90s) multi | 1.75 | 1.75 |
| | | With tabs | 3.00 | |

**Self-Adhesive**
**Booklet Stamp**
**Serpentine Die Cut 11x10¾**
| | | | | |
|---|---|---|---|---|
| 1749 | A801 | (2.90s) multi | 1.75 | 1.75 |
| a. | | Booklet pane of 10 + 10 eti-quettes | 17.50 | |

Landmarks of France and Israel — A802

Airplane, stamped first flight cover and: 1.60s, Haifa waterfront, Israel. 3.80s, Eiffel Tower, Paris.

**2008, Nov. 6**   **Litho.**   **Perf. 14**
| | | | | |
|---|---|---|---|---|
| 1750 | A802 | 1.60s multi | .85 | .85 |
| 1751 | A802 | 3.80s multi | 2.00 | 2.00 |
| | | With tabs | 3.25 | |

First flight between France and Israel, 60th anniv. See France Nos. 3533-3534.

2008 Census A803

**2008, Dec. 17**     **Perf. 14x13**
| | | | | |
|---|---|---|---|---|
| 1752 | A803 | 1.60s multi | .85 | .85 |
| | | With tab | .95 | |

Israeli Defense Forces Radio A804

**2008, Dec. 17**     **Perf. 14x13¾**
| | | | | |
|---|---|---|---|---|
| 1753 | A804 | 2.30s multi | 1.25 | 1.25 |
| | | With tab | 1.40 | |

Taglit-Birthright Israel — A805

**2008, Dec. 17**     **Perf. 14x13**
| | | | | |
|---|---|---|---|---|
| 1754 | A805 | 5.60s multi | 3.00 | 3.00 |
| | | With tab | 3.25 | |

Ancient Letters A806

Designs: 1.60s, Bar Kokhba letters, A.D. 134. 2.30s, Lachish letters, 589 B.C. 8.50s, Letter from Ugarit, 1230 B.C.

**2008, Dec. 17**
| | | | | |
|---|---|---|---|---|
| 1755 | A806 | 1.60s multi | .85 | .85 |
| 1756 | A806 | 2.30s multi | 1.25 | 1.25 |
| 1757 | A806 | 8.50s multi | 4.50 | 4.50 |
| | | Nos. 1755-1757 (3) | 6.60 | 6.60 |
| | | With tabs | 7.25 | |

---

**AIR POST STAMPS**

Doves Pecking at Grapes — AP1

Marisa Eagle — AP2

Designs: 30p, Beth Shearim eagle. 40p, Mosaic bird. 50p, Stylized dove. 250p, Mosaic dove and olive branch.

**Perf. 11½**
**1950, June 25**   **Unwmk.**   **Litho.**
| | | | | |
|---|---|---|---|---|
| C1 | AP1 | 5p brt grnsh bl | .60 | .20 |
| C2 | AP1 | 30p gray | .30 | .20 |
| C3 | AP1 | 40p dark green | .30 | .20 |
| C4 | AP1 | 50p henna brown | .30 | .20 |
| C5 | AP2 | 100p rose car | 11.00 | 11.00 |
| C6 | AP2 | 250p dk gray bl | 1.50 | .50 |
| | | Nos. C1-C6 (6) | 14.00 | 12.30 |
| | | With tabs | 275.00 | |

Haifa Bay and City Seal AP3

120p, Haifa, Mt. Carmel and city seal.

**1952, Apr. 13**     **Perf. 14**
**Seal in Gray**
| | | | | |
|---|---|---|---|---|
| C7 | AP3 | 100p ultramarine | .30 | .20 |
| C8 | AP3 | 120p purple | .20 | .20 |
| | | #C7-C8, with tabs | 15.00 | |

Stamps were available only on purchase of a ticket to the National Stamp Exhibition, Haifa. Price, including ticket, 340p.

Olive Tree — AP4

Tanur Cascade AP5      Coast at Tel Aviv-Jaffa AP6

70p, En Gev, Sea of Galilee. 100p, Road to Jerusalem. 150p, Lion Rock. 350p, Bay of Elat, Red Sea. 750p, Lake Hule. 3000p, Tomb of Rabbi Meir Baal Haness, Tiberias.

**1953-56**      **Litho.**

| | | | | |
|---|---|---|---|---|
| C9 | AP4 | 10p olive grn | .20 | .20 |
| C10 | AP4 | 70p violet | .20 | .20 |
| C11 | AP4 | 100p green | .20 | .20 |
| C12 | AP4 | 150p orange brn | .20 | .20 |
| C13 | AP4 | 350p car rose | .20 | .20 |
| C14 | AP5 | 500p dull & dk bl | .20 | .20 |
| C15 | AP6 | 750p brown | .20 | .20 |
| C16 | AP6 | 1000p deep bl grn | 4.50 | .75 |
| | | With tab | 95.00 | |
| C17 | AP6 | 3000p claret | 6.10 | 2.35 |
| | | Nos. C9-C17 (9) | | |
| | | Nos. C9-C15, C17 with tabs | 5.00 | |

Issued: 1000p, 3/16/53; 10p, 100p, 500p, 3/2/54; 70p, 150p, 350p, 4/6/54; 750p, 8/21/56; 3000p, 11/13/56.

Old Town, Zefat — AP7      Houbara Bustard — AP9

Port of Elat ('Aqaba) — AP8

Designs: 20a, Ashkelon, Afridar Center. 25a, Acre, tower and boats. 30a, Haifa, view from Mt. Carmel. 35a, Capernaum, ancient synagogue, horiz. 40a, Jethro's tomb, horiz. 50a, Jerusalem, horiz. 65a, Tiberias, tower and lake, horiz. £1, Jaffa, horiz.

**1960-61**      **Photo.**      **Perf. 13x14, 14x13**

| | | | | |
|---|---|---|---|---|
| C18 | AP7 | 15a light lil & blk | .20 | .20 |
| C19 | AP7 | 20a brt yel grn & blk | .20 | .20 |
| C20 | AP7 | 25a orange & blk ('61) | .20 | .20 |
| C21 | AP7 | 30a grnsh bl & blk ('61) | .20 | .20 |
| C22 | AP7 | 35a yel grn & blk ('61) | .20 | .20 |
| C23 | AP7 | 40a lt vio & blk ('61) | .20 | .20 |
| C24 | AP7 | 50a olive & blk ('61) | .20 | .20 |
| C25 | AP7 | 65a lt ultra & black | .20 | .20 |
| C26 | AP7 | £1 pink & blk ('61) | .40 | .30 |
| | | Nos. C18-C26 (9) | 2.00 | 1.90 |
| | | With tabs | 11.00 | |

Issued: #C18, C19, C25, 2/24/60; #C20-C22, 6/14/61; #C23, C24, C26, 10/26/61.

**Wmk. 302**

**1962, Feb. 21**      **Litho.**      **Perf. 14**

| | | | | |
|---|---|---|---|---|
| C27 | AP8 | £3 multicolored | 1.60 | 1.00 |
| | | With tab | 9.00 | |

**Perf. 13x14, 14x13**

**1963**      **Unwmk.**      **Photo.**

Birds: 5a, Sinai rose finch, horiz. 20a, White-breasted kingfisher, horiz. 28a, Mourning wheatear, horiz. 30a, Blue-cheeked bee

---

eater. 40a, Graceful prinia. 45a, Palestine sunbird. 70a, Scops owl. £1, Purple heron. £3, White-tailed Sea eagle.

| | | | | |
|---|---|---|---|---|
| C28 | AP9 | 5a dp vio & multi | .20 | .20 |
| C29 | AP9 | 20a red & multi | .20 | .20 |
| C30 | AP9 | 28a emerald & multi | .20 | .20 |
| C31 | AP9 | 30a orange & multi | .20 | .20 |
| C32 | AP9 | 40a multicolored | .20 | .20 |
| C33 | AP9 | 45a yellow & multi | .20 | .20 |
| C34 | AP9 | 55a multicolored | .20 | .20 |
| C35 | AP9 | 70a black & multi | .20 | .20 |
| C36 | AP9 | £1 multicolored | .35 | .35 |
| C37 | AP9 | £3 ultra & multi | .85 | .70 |
| | | Nos. C28-C37 (10) | 2.80 | 2.65 |
| | | With tabs | 5.75 | |

Issue dates: #C28-C30, Apr. 15; #C31-C33, June 19; #C34-C36, Feb. 13; #C37, Oct. 23.

Diamond and Boeing 707 AP10

Boeing 707 and: 10a, Textiles. 30a, Symbolic stamps. 40a, Vase, jewelry. 50a, Chick, egg. 55a, Melon, avocado, strawberries. 60a, Gladioli. 80a, Electronic equipment, chart. £1, Heavy oxygen isotopes (chemical apparatus). £1.50, Women's fashions.

**1968**      **Photo.**      **Perf. 13x14**

| | | | | |
|---|---|---|---|---|
| C38 | AP10 | 10a ultra & multi | .20 | .20 |
| C39 | AP10 | 30a gray & multi | .20 | .20 |
| C40 | AP10 | 40a multicolored | .20 | .20 |
| C41 | AP10 | 50a multicolored | .20 | .20 |
| C42 | AP10 | 55a multicolored | .20 | .20 |
| C43 | AP10 | 60a sl grn, lt grn & red | .20 | .20 |
| C44 | AP10 | 80a yel, brn & lt bl | .20 | .20 |
| C45 | AP10 | £1 dark bl & org | .20 | .20 |
| C46 | AP10 | £1.50 multicolored | .25 | .25 |
| C47 | AP10 | £3 pur & lt bl | .30 | .25 |
| | | Nos. C38-C47 (10) | 2.15 | 2.05 |
| | | With tabs | 3.00 | |

Israeli exports. Sheets of 15 (5x3).
Issued: #C38-C41, 3/11; #C47, 2/7; #C42-C43, C45, 11/6; #C44, C46, 12/23.

---

**POSTAGE DUE STAMPS**

Types of Regular Issue Overprinted in Black

Various coins, as on postage denominations.

**Unwmk.**

**1948, May 28**      **Typo.**      **Perf. 11**

**Yellow Paper**

| | | | | |
|---|---|---|---|---|
| J1 | A1 | 3m orange | 3.00 | 1.25 |
| J2 | A1 | 5m yellow green | 4.00 | 1.75 |
| J3 | A1 | 10m red violet | 7.00 | 4.00 |
| J4 | A1 | 20m ultramarine | 13.00 | 8.00 |
| J5 | A1 | 50m orange brown | 52.50 | 47.50 |
| | | Nos. J1-J5 (5) | 79.50 | 62.50 |
| | | With tabs (blank) | | 2,750. |

The 3m, 20m and 50m are known with overprint omitted.
Nos. J1-J5 exist imperf.

D1      Running Stag — D2

**1949, Dec. 18**      **Litho.**      **Perf. 11½**

| | | | | |
|---|---|---|---|---|
| J6 | D1 | 2p orange | .20 | .20 |
| J7 | D1 | 5p purple | .20 | .20 |
| J8 | D1 | 10p yellow green | .20 | .20 |
| J9 | D1 | 20p vermilion | .20 | .20 |
| J10 | D1 | 30p violet blue | .25 | .20 |
| J11 | D1 | 50p orange brown | .45 | .25 |
| | | Nos. J6-J11 (6) | 1.50 | 1.25 |
| | | With tabs (blank) | 125.00 | |

---

**1952, Nov. 30**      **Unwmk.**      **Perf. 14**

| | | | | |
|---|---|---|---|---|
| J12 | D2 | 5p orange brown | .20 | .20 |
| J13 | D2 | 10p Prussian blue | .20 | .20 |
| J14 | D2 | 20p magenta | .20 | .20 |
| J15 | D2 | 30p gray black | .20 | .20 |
| J16 | D2 | 40p green | .20 | .20 |
| J17 | D2 | 50p brown | .20 | .20 |
| J18 | D2 | 60p purple | .20 | .20 |
| J19 | D2 | 100p red | .20 | .20 |
| J20 | D2 | 250p blue | .20 | .20 |
| | | Nos. J12-J20 (9) | 1.80 | 1.80 |
| | | With tabs (blank) | 5.00 | |

---

**OFFICIAL STAMPS**

Redrawn Type of 1950 Overprinted in Black

**1951, Feb. 1**      **Unwmk.**      **Perf. 14**

| | | | | |
|---|---|---|---|---|
| O1 | A6 | 5p bright red violet | .20 | .20 |
| O2 | A6 | 15p vermilion | .20 | .20 |
| O3 | A6 | 30p ultramarine | .20 | .20 |
| O4 | A6 | 40p orange brown | .20 | .20 |
| | | Nos. O1-O4 (4) | .80 | .80 |
| | | With tabs | 20.00 | |

---

# ITALIAN COLONIES

ə-ˈtal-yən ˈkä-lə-nēz

## General Issues for all Colonies

100 Centesimi = 1 Lira

**Used values in italics are for postaly used stamps. Cancelled-to-order copies sell for about the same as unused, hinged stamps.**

**Watermark**

Wmk. 140

---

Type of Italy, Dante Alighieri Society Issue, in New Colors and Overprinted in Red or Black

**1932, July 11**      **Wmk. 140**      **Perf. 14**

| | | | | |
|---|---|---|---|---|
| 1 | A126 | 10c gray blk | .85 | 2.50 |
| 2 | A126 | 15c olive brn | .85 | 2.50 |
| 3 | A126 | 20c slate grn | .85 | 1.75 |
| 4 | A126 | 25c dk grn | .85 | 1.75 |
| 5 | A126 | 30c red brn (Bk) | .85 | 1.75 |
| 6 | A126 | 50c bl blk | .85 | .85 |
| 7 | A126 | 75c car rose (Bk) | 1.75 | 4.25 |
| 8 | A126 | 1.25 l dk bl | 1.75 | 6.75 |
| 9 | A126 | 1.75 l violet | 1.75 | 10.00 |
| 10 | A126 | 2.75 l org (Bk) | 1.75 | 21.00 |
| 11 | A126 | 5 l + 2 l ol grn | 1.75 | 25.00 |
| 12 | A126 | 10 l + 2.50 l dp bl | 1.75 | 37.50 |
| | | Nos. 1-12, C1-C6 (18) | 29.10 | 214.60 |

**Types of Italy, Garibaldi Issue, in New Colors and Inscribed: "POSTE COLONIALI ITALIANE"**

**1932, July 1**      **Photo.**

| | | | | |
|---|---|---|---|---|
| 13 | A138 | 10c green | 3.40 | 12.50 |
| 14 | A138 | 20c car rose | 3.40 | 6.75 |
| 15 | A138 | 25c green | 3.40 | 6.75 |

---

| | | | | |
|---|---|---|---|---|
| 16 | A138 | 30c green | 3.40 | 12.50 |
| 17 | A138 | 50c car rose | 3.40 | 6.75 |
| 18 | A141 | 75c car rose | 3.40 | 15.00 |
| 19 | A141 | 1.25 l deep blue | 3.40 | 15.00 |
| 20 | A141 | 1.75 l + 25c dp bl | 6.00 | 21.00 |
| 21 | A144 | 2.55 l + 50c ol brn | 6.00 | 37.50 |
| 22 | A145 | 5 l + 1 l dp bl | 6.00 | 45.00 |
| | | Nos. 13-22, C8-C12 (15) | 69.05 | 296.25 |

See Nos. CE1-CE2.

Plowing with Oxen — A1      Pack Camel — A2

Lioness — A3

**1933, Mar. 27**      **Wmk. 140**

| | | | | |
|---|---|---|---|---|
| 23 | A1 | 10c ol brn | 11.50 | 16.00 |
| 24 | A2 | 20c dl vio | 11.50 | 16.00 |
| 25 | A3 | 25c green | 11.50 | 16.00 |
| 26 | A1 | 50c purple | 11.50 | 16.00 |
| 27 | A2 | 75c carmine | 11.50 | 19.50 |
| 28 | A3 | 1.25 l blue | 11.50 | 19.50 |
| 29 | A1 | 2.75 l red orange | 17.50 | 32.50 |
| 30 | A2 | 5 l + 2 l gray grn | 22.50 | 72.50 |
| 31 | A3 | 10 l + 2.50 l org brn | 22.50 | 95.00 |
| | | Nos. 23-31, C13-C19 (16) | 258.50 | 617.50 |

Annexation of Eritrea by Italy, 50th anniv.

Agricultural Implements A4

Arab and Camel — A5      "Eager with New Life" — A7

Steam Roller — A6

**1933**      **Photo.**      **Perf. 14**

| | | | | |
|---|---|---|---|---|
| 32 | A4 | 5c orange | 8.00 | 11.50 |
| 33 | A5 | 25c green | 8.00 | 11.50 |
| 34 | A6 | 50c purple | 8.00 | 8.00 |
| 35 | A4 | 75c carmine | 8.00 | 19.50 |
| 36 | A5 | 1.25 l deep blue | 8.00 | 19.50 |
| 37 | A6 | 1.75 l rose red | 8.00 | 19.50 |
| 38 | A4 | 2.75 l dark blue | 8.00 | 27.50 |
| 39 | A5 | 5 l brnsh blk | 12.00 | 36.00 |
| 40 | A6 | 10 l bluish blk | 12.00 | 47.50 |
| 41 | A7 | 25 l gray black | 17.50 | 72.50 |
| | | Nos. 32-41, C20-C27 (18) | 193.00 | 548.50 |

10th anniversary of Fascism. Each denomination bears a different inscription.
Issue dates: 25 l, Dec. 26; others, Oct. 5.

Mercury and Fasces — A8

Soccer Kickoff — A10

Scoring a Goal — A9

**1934, Apr. 18**

| | | | | |
|---|---|---|---|---|
| 42 | A8 | 20c red orange | 1.75 | 6.00 |
| 43 | A8 | 30c slate green | 1.75 | 6.00 |
| 44 | A8 | 50c indigo | 1.75 | 6.00 |
| 45 | A8 | 1.25 l blue | 1.75 | 6.00 |
| | | Nos. 42-45 (4) | 7.00 | 24.00 |

15th annual Trade Fair, Milan.

**1934, June 5**

| | | | | |
|---|---|---|---|---|
| 46 | A9 | 10c olive green | 25.00 | 40.00 |
| 47 | A9 | 50c purple | 50.00 | 27.50 |
| 48 | A9 | 1.25 l blue | 50.00 | 100.00 |
| 49 | A10 | 5 l brown | 67.50 | 300.00 |
| 50 | A10 | 10 l gray blue | 67.50 | 300.00 |
| | | Nos. 46-50,C29-C35 (12) | 515.00 | 1,532. |

2nd World Soccer Championship.

**SEMI-POSTAL STAMPS**

Many issues of Italy and Italian Colonies include one or more semi-postal denominations. To avoid splitting sets, these issues are generally listed as regular postage, airmail, etc., unless all values carry a surtax.

**AIR POST STAMPS**

**Italian Air Post Stamps for Dante Alighieri Society Issue in New Colors and Overprinted in Red or Black Like #1-12**

**1932, July 11    Wmk. 140    Perf. 14**

| | | | | |
|---|---|---|---|---|
| C1 | AP10 | 50c gray blk (R) | 1.75 | 6.75 |
| C2 | AP11 | 1 l indigo (R) | 1.75 | 6.75 |
| C3 | AP11 | 3 l gray (R) | 2.50 | 10.00 |
| C4 | AP11 | 5 l ol brn (R) | 2.50 | 17.00 |
| C5 | AP10 | 7.70 l + 2 l car rose | 2.50 | 21.00 |
| C6 | AP11 | 10 l + 2.50 l org | 2.50 | 37.50 |
| | | Nos. C1-C6 (6) | 13.50 | 99.00 |

Leonardo da Vinci — AP1

**1932, Sept. 7    Photo.    Perf. 14½**

| | | | | |
|---|---|---|---|---|
| C7 | AP1 | 100 l dp grn & brn | 13.50 | 110.00 |

**Types of Italian Air Post Stamps, Garibaldi Issue, in New Colors and Inscribed: "POSTE AEREA COLONIALE ITALIANA"**

**1932, July 1**

| | | | | |
|---|---|---|---|---|
| C8 | AP13 | 50c car rose | 3.50 | 15.00 |
| C9 | AP14 | 80c green | 3.50 | 15.00 |
| C10 | AP13 | 1 l + 25c ol brn | 6.75 | 25.00 |
| C11 | AP13 | 2 l + 50c ol brn | 6.75 | 25.00 |
| C12 | AP14 | 5 l + 1 l ol brn | 6.75 | 37.50 |
| | | Nos. C8-C12 (5) | 27.25 | 117.50 |

Eagle AP2

Savoia Marchetti 55 — AP3

Savoia Marchetti 55 Over Map of Eritrea AP4

**1933    Perf. 14**

| | | | | |
|---|---|---|---|---|
| C13 | AP2 | 50c org brn | 9.50 | 16.00 |
| C14 | AP2 | 1 l blk vio | 9.50 | 16.00 |
| C15 | AP3 | 3 l carmine | 19.50 | 32.50 |
| C16 | AP3 | 5 l olive brn | 19.50 | 32.50 |
| C17 | AP2 | 7.70 l + 2 l slate | 24.00 | 72.50 |
| C18 | AP3 | 10 l + 2.50 l dp bl | 24.00 | 72.50 |
| C19 | AP4 | 50 l dk vio | 21.00 | 72.50 |
| | | Nos. C13-C19 (7) | 127.00 | 314.50 |

50th anniv. of Italian Government of Eritrea. Issue dates: 50 l, June 1; others, Mar. 27.

Macchi-Costoldi Seaplane — AP5

Savoia S73 — AP6

Winding Propeller AP7

"More Efficient Machinery" AP8

**1933-34**

| | | | | |
|---|---|---|---|---|
| C20 | AP5 | 50c org brn | 9.50 | 16.00 |
| C21 | AP6 | 75c red vio | 9.50 | 16.00 |
| C22 | AP5 | 1 l bis brn | 9.50 | 16.00 |
| C23 | AP6 | 3 l olive gray | 9.50 | 32.50 |
| C24 | AP5 | 10 l dp vio | 9.50 | 32.50 |
| C25 | AP6 | 12 l bl grn | 9.50 | 47.50 |
| C26 | AP7 | 20 l gray blk | 14.50 | 60.00 |
| C27 | AP8 | 50 l blue ('34) | 24.00 | 55.00 |
| | | Nos. C20-C27 (8) | 95.50 | 275.50 |

Tenth anniversary of Fascism. Issue dates: 50 l, Dec. 26; others, Oct. 5.

Natives Hailing Dornier Wal — AP9

**1934, Apr. 24**

| | | | | |
|---|---|---|---|---|
| C28 | AP9 | 25 l brown olive | 25.00 | 175.00 |

Issued in honor of Luigi Amadeo, Duke of the Abruzzi (1873-1933).

Airplane over Stadium AP10

Goalkeeper Leaping — AP11

Seaplane and Soccer Ball AP12

**1934, June**

| | | | | |
|---|---|---|---|---|
| C29 | AP10 | 50c yel brn | 15.00 | 40.00 |
| C30 | AP10 | 75c dp vio | 15.00 | 40.00 |
| C31 | AP11 | 5 l brn blk | 45.00 | 95.00 |
| C32 | AP11 | 10 l red org | 45.00 | 95.00 |
| C33 | AP11 | 15 l car rose | 45.00 | 95.00 |
| C34 | AP11 | 25 l green | 45.00 | 200.00 |
| C35 | AP12 | 50 l bl grn | 45.00 | 200.00 |
| | | Nos. C29-C35 (7) | 255.00 | 765.00 |

World Soccer Championship Games, Rome. Issued: 50 l, June 21; others, June 5.

**AIR POST SPECIAL DELIVERY STAMPS**

**Garibaldi Type of Italy Wmk. 140**

**1932, Oct. 6    Photo.    Perf. 14**

| | | | | |
|---|---|---|---|---|
| CE1 | APSD1 | 2.25 l + 1 l dk vio & sl | 6.75 | 25.00 |
| CE2 | APSD1 | 4.50 l + 1.50 l dk brn & grn | 6.75 | 37.50 |

# ITALIAN E. AFRICA

ə-'tal-yən 'ēst 'a-fri-kə

LOCATION — In eastern Africa, bordering on the Red Sea and Indian Ocean
GOVT. — Italian Colony
AREA — 665,977 sq. mi. (estimated)
POP. — 12,100,000 (estimated)
CAPITAL — Asmara

This colony was formed in 1936 and included Ethiopia and the former colonies of Eritrea and Italian Somaliland. For previous issues see listings under these headings.

100 Centesimi = 1 Lira

**Used values in italics are for postally used stamps. Cancelled-to-order copies sell for about the same as unused, hinged stamps.**

Grant's Gazelle — A1

Eagle and Lion — A2

Victor Emmanuel III — A3

Fascist Legionary — A5

Statue of the Nile — A4

Desert Road — A6

**Wmk. 140**

**1938, Feb. 7    Photo.    Perf. 14**

| | | | | |
|---|---|---|---|---|
| 1 | A1 | 2c red orange | 1.25 | 1.10 |
| 2 | A2 | 5c brown | 1.25 | .20 |
| 3 | A3 | 7½c dk violet | 1.75 | 3.25 |
| 4 | A4 | 10c olive brown | 2.40 | .20 |
| 5 | A5 | 15c slate green | 1.25 | .40 |
| 6 | A3 | 20c crimson | 1.25 | .20 |
| 7 | A6 | 25c green | 2.40 | .20 |
| 8 | A1 | 30c olive brown | 1.75 | .80 |
| 9 | A2 | 35c sapphire | 2.50 | 8.50 |
| 10 | A3 | 50c purple | 1.25 | .20 |

**Engr.**

| | | | | |
|---|---|---|---|---|
| 11 | A5 | 75c carmine lake | 2.50 | .40 |
| 12 | A6 | 1 l olive green | 1.75 | .20 |
| 13 | A3 | 1.25 l deep blue | 2.50 | .40 |
| 14 | A4 | 1.75 l orange | 17.00 | .20 |
| 15 | A2 | 2 l cerise | 2.50 | .40 |
| 16 | A6 | 2.55 l dark brown | 12.50 | 25.00 |
| 17 | A3 | 3.70 l purple | 42.50 | 42.50 |
| 18 | A5 | 5 l purple | 10.00 | 4.25 |
| 19 | A2 | 10 l henna brown | 15.00 | 17.00 |
| 20 | A4 | 20 l dull green | 25.00 | 25.00 |
| | | Nos. 1-20,C1-C11,CE1-CE2 (33) | 303.05 | 237.45 |

Augustus Caesar (Octavianus) A7

Goddess Abundantia A8

**1938, Apr. 25    Photo.    Perf. 14**

| | | | | |
|---|---|---|---|---|
| 21 | A7 | 5c bister brn | .85 | 2.00 |
| 22 | A8 | 10c copper red | .85 | 1.25 |
| 23 | A7 | 25c deep green | 1.25 | 1.25 |
| 24 | A8 | 50c purple | 1.25 | .85 |
| 25 | A7 | 75c crimson | 1.25 | 3.00 |
| 26 | A8 | 1.25 l deep blue | 1.25 | 8.50 |
| | | Nos. 21-26,C12-C13 (8) | 9.20 | 26.85 |

Bimillenary of the birth of Augustus Caesar (Octavianus), first Roman emperor.

Rome-Berlin Axis.
Four stamps of type AP8, without "Posta Aerea," were prepared in 1941, but not issued. Value, each $1,900.

Native Boat — A9

Native Soldier — A10

Statue Suggesting Italy's Conquest of Ethiopia — A11

**1940, May 11**      **Wmk. 140**

| | | | | |
|---|---|---|---|---|
| 27 | A9 | 5c olive brown | .85 | .85 |
| 28 | A10 | 10c red orange | .85 | .85 |
| 29 | A11 | 25c green | 1.25 | 1.75 |
| 30 | A9 | 50c purple | 1.25 | .85 |
| 31 | A10 | 75c rose red | 1.25 | 4.25 |
| 32 | A11 | 1.25 l dark blue | 1.25 | 3.25 |
| 33 | A10 | 2 l + 75c carmine | 1.25 | 17.00 |
| | | *Nos. 27-33,C14-C17 (11)* | 13.95 | 38.80 |

Issued in connection with the first Triennial Overseas Exposition held at Naples.

Hitler and Mussolini ("Two Peoples, One War") A12

**1941, June 19**

| | | | |
|---|---|---|---|
| 34 | A12 | 5c ocher | 2.50 |
| 35 | A12 | 10c chestnut | 2.50 |
| 36 | A12 | 20c black | 3.25 |
| 37 | A12 | 25c turquoise grn | 3.25 |
| 38 | A12 | 50c rose lilac | 3.25 |
| 39 | A12 | 75c rose car | 3.25 |
| 40 | A12 | 1.25 l brt ultra | 3.25 |
| | | *Nos. 34-40,C18-C19 (9)* | 108.00 |

### SEMI-POSTAL STAMPS

Many issues of Italy and Italian Colonies include one or more semi-postal denominations. To avoid splitting sets, these issues are generally listed as regular postage, airmail, etc., unless all values carry a surtax.

### AIR POST STAMPS

Plane Flying over Mountains AP1

Mussolini Carved in Stone Cliff — AP2

Airplane over Lake Tsana AP3

Bataleur Eagle — AP4

Eagle Attacking Serpent — AP5

---

**Wmk. Crowns (140)**

**1938, Feb. 7**    **Photo.**    *Perf. 14*

| | | | | |
|---|---|---|---|---|
| C1 | AP1 | 25c slate green | 3.25 | 4.25 |
| C2 | AP2 | 50c olive brown | 60.00 | .20 |
| C3 | AP3 | 60c red orange | 2.50 | 10.00 |
| C4 | AP1 | 75c orange brn | 3.25 | 2.50 |
| C5 | AP4 | 1 l slate blue | 1.25 | .20 |

**Engr.**

| | | | | |
|---|---|---|---|---|
| C6 | AP2 | 1.50 l violet | 1.75 | .40 |
| C7 | AP3 | 2 l slate blue | 1.75 | 1.75 |
| C8 | AP1 | 3 l carmine lake | 2.50 | 6.75 |
| C9 | AP4 | 5 l red brown | 40.00 | 25.00 |
| C10 | AP2 | 10 l violet brn | 10.00 | 10.00 |
| C11 | AP1 | 25 l slate blue | 20.00 | 25.00 |
| | | *Nos. C1-C11 (11)* | 146.25 | 86.05 |

**1938, Apr. 25**      **Photo.**

| | | | | |
|---|---|---|---|---|
| C12 | AP5 | 50c bister brown | 1.25 | 5.00 |
| C13 | AP5 | 1 l purple | 1.25 | 5.00 |

Bimillenary of the birth of Augustus Caesar (Octavianus), first Roman emperor.

### Triennial Overseas Exposition Type

#C14, C16, Tractor. #C15, C17, Plane over city.

**1940, May 11**

| | | | | |
|---|---|---|---|---|
| C14 | A10 | 50c olive gray | 1.25 | 5.00 |
| C15 | A9 | 1 l purple | 1.25 | 5.00 |
| C16 | A10 | 2 l + 75c gray blue | 1.75 | — |
| C17 | A9 | 5 l + 2.50 l red brn | 1.75 | — |
| | | *Nos. C14-C17 (4)* | 6.00 | 10.00 |

Hitler and Mussolini ("Two Peoples, One War") AP8

AP9

**1941, Apr. 24**

| | | | |
|---|---|---|---|
| C18 | AP8 | 1 l slate blue | 80.00 |
| C19 | AP9 | 1 l slate blue | 6.75 |

Rome-Berlin Axis.

### AIR POST SPECIAL DELIVERY STAMPS

Plow and Airplane — APSD1

**Wmk. 140**

**1938, Feb. 7**    **Engr.**    *Perf. 14*

| | | | | |
|---|---|---|---|---|
| CE1 | APSD1 | 2 l slate blue | 4.25 | 8.50 |
| CE2 | APSD1 | 2.50 l dark brown | 4.25 | 12.50 |

### SPECIAL DELIVERY STAMPS

Victor Emmanuel III — SD1

**Wmk. 140**

**1938, Apr. 16**    **Engr.**    *Perf. 14*

| | | | | |
|---|---|---|---|---|
| E1 | SD1 | 1.25 l dark green | 4.25 | 6.75 |
| E2 | SD1 | 2.50 l dark carmine | 4.25 | 17.00 |

---

### POSTAGE DUE STAMPS

Italy, Nos. J28 to J40, Overprinted in Black

**1941**    **Wmk. 140**    *Perf. 14*

| | | | |
|---|---|---|---|
| J1 | D6 | 5c brown | 1.60 |
| J2 | D6 | 10c blue | 1.60 |
| J3 | D6 | 20c rose red | 3.25 |
| J4 | D6 | 25c green | 3.25 |
| J5 | D6 | 30c red orange | 6.75 |
| J6 | D6 | 40c black brown | 6.75 |
| J7 | D6 | 50c violet | 6.75 |
| J8 | D6 | 60c slate black | 10.00 |
| J9 | D7 | 1 l red orange | 20.00 |
| J10 | D7 | 2 l green | 20.00 |
| J11 | D7 | 5 l violet | 32.50 |
| J12 | D7 | 10 l blue | 20.00 |
| J13 | D7 | 20 l carmine rose | 20.00 |
| | | *Nos. J1-J13 (13)* | 152.45 |

In 1943 a set of 11 "Segnatasse" stamps, picturing a horse and rider and inscribed "A. O. I.," was prepared but not issued. Value, $12.50.

---

# ITALIAN STATES

ə-'tal-yən 'stāts

## Watermarks

Wmk. 157 —
Large Letter "A"

Wmk. 184 —
Interlaced Wavy
Lines

Wmk. 184 has double lined letters diagonally across the sheet reading: "II R R POSTE TOSCANE."

Wmk. 185 — Crowns in the sheet

The watermark consists of twelve crowns, arranged in four rows of three, with horizontal and vertical lines between them. Only parts of the watermark appear on each stamp. (Reduced illustration.)

Wmk. 186 —
Fleurs-de-Lis in
Sheet

## MODENA

LOCATION — In northern Italy
GOVT. — Duchy
AREA — 1,003 sq. mi.
POP. — 448,000 (approx.)
CAPITAL — Modena

In 1852, when the first postage stamps were issued, Modena was under the rule of Duke Francis V of the House of Este-Lorraine. In June, 1859, he was overthrown and the Duchy was annexed to the Kingdom of Sardinia

which on March 17, 1861, became the Kingdom of Italy.

100 Centesimi = 1 Lira

Values of Modena stamps vary tremendously according to condition. Values are for very fine examples, and values for unused stamps are for examples with original gum as defined in the catalogue introduction. Extremely fine or superb copies sell at much higher prices, and fine or poor copies sell at greatly reduced prices. In addition, very fine unused copies without gum sell for about 20% of the values shown.

Coat of Arms
A1    A2

**1852    Unwmk.    Typo.    Imperf.**

### Without Period After Figures of Value

| | | | | |
|---|---|---|---|---|
| 1 | A1 | 5c blk, *green* | 2,300. | 140.00 |
| a. | | Pair, #1, 6 | 2,750. | 2,000. |
| 2 | A1 | 10c blk, *rose* | 575.00 | 90.00 |
| a. | | "EENT. 10" | 7,250. | 2,500. |
| b. | | "1" of "10" inverted | 7,250. | 2,500. |
| c. | | "CNET" | 1,450. | 1,800. |
| d. | | No period after "CENT" | 2,175. | 875.00 |
| e. | | Pair, #2, 7 | 1,200. | 2,500. |
| 3 | A1 | 15c blk, *yellow* | 57.50 | 35.00 |
| a. | | "CETN 15." | 7,250. | 1,100. |
| b. | | No period after "CENT" | 290.00 | 575.00 |
| 4 | A1 | 25c blk, *buff* | 72.50 | 42.50 |
| a. | | No period after "CENT" | 650.00 | 1,100. |
| b. | | "ENT.25" omitted | 1,000. | |
| c. | | 25c black, *green* (error) | 2,900. | 2,000. |
| d. | | "N" of "CENT" omitted | 725.00 | 1,800. |
| 5 | A1 | 40c blk, *blue* | 440.00 | 125.00 |
| a. | | 40c black, *pale blue* | 14,500. | 1,350. |
| b. | | No period after "CENT" | 1,800. | 1,800. |
| c. | | As "a," no period after "CENT" | — | — |
| d. | | Pair, #5, 8 | 725.00 | 2,500. |

Unused examples of No. 5a lack gum.
See Nos. PR3-PR4.

### With Period After Figures of Value

| | | | | |
|---|---|---|---|---|
| 6 | A1 | 5c blk, *green* | 35.00 | 47.50 |
| a. | | 5c black, *olive green* | 440.00 | 140.00 |
| | | As "a," without gum | 30.00 | |
| b. | | "ENT" | — | 2,500. |
| c. | | "CNET" | 4,250. | 3,600. |
| d. | | As "a," "CNET" | 2,200. | 2,200. |
| e. | | "E" of "CENT" sideways | — | 5,750. |
| f. | | As "a," "CEN1" | 2,500. | 2,500. |
| g. | | As "a," no period after "5" | 650.00 | 575.00 |
| h. | | Double impression | 1,200. | — |
| i. | | As "a," double impression | 1,200. | |
| j. | | Pair, #6a, 6g | 1,200. | 2,350. |
| 7 | A1 | 10c blk, *rose* | 440.00 | 325.00 |
| a. | | "CENE" | 1,450. | 1,800. |
| b. | | "CNET" | 650.00 | 900.00 |
| c. | | "CE6T" | 1,450. | 1,800. |
| d. | | "N" of "CENT" sideways | 10,000. | 4,350. |
| e. | | Double impression | 1,500. | 4,400. |
| 8 | A1 | 40c blk, *blue* | 50.00 | 125.00 |
| a. | | "CNET" | 290.00 | 900.00 |
| b. | | "CENE" | 650.00 | 1,800. |
| c. | | "CE6T" | 650.00 | 1,800. |
| d. | | "49" | 290.00 | 900.00 |
| e. | | "4C" | 650.00 | 1,800. |
| f. | | "CEN.T" | 32,500. | |

Unused examples of No. 6h lack gum.

### Wmk. 157

| | | | | |
|---|---|---|---|---|
| 9 | A1 | 1 l black | 57.50 | 2,150. |
| a. | | Period after "LIRA" | 160.00 | 4,000. |
| b. | | No period after "1" | 150.00 | 3,250. |

### Provisional Government

**1859          Unwmk.**

| | | | | |
|---|---|---|---|---|
| 10 | A2 | 5c green | 1,450. | 700.00 |
| a. | | 5c emerald | 1,525. | 800.00 |
| b. | | 5c dark green | 1,525. | 800.00 |
| 11 | A2 | 15c brown | 2,350. | 4,000. |
| a. | | 15c gray brown | 325.00 | |
| b. | | 15c black brown | 2,600. | 5,000. |
| c. | | No period after "15" | 2,900. | 4,750. |
| d. | | Period before "CENT" | 4,000. | 6,500. |
| e. | | Double impression (#11a) | | 1,450. |
| 12 | A2 | 20c lilac | 65.00 | 1,200. |
| a. | | 20c violet | 4,000. | 160.00 |
| b. | | 20c blue violet | 2,200. | 160.00 |
| c. | | No period after "20" | 100.00 | 1,450. |
| d. | | "ECNT" | 250.00 | 3,100. |
| e. | | "N" inverted | 200.00 | 2,200. |
| f. | | Double impression (#12b) | | 5,750. |
| 13 | A2 | 40c carmine | 190.00 | 1,275. |
| a. | | 40c brown rose | 190.00 | 1,275. |
| b. | | No period after "40" | 360.00 | 2,275. |
| c. | | Period before "CENT" | 360.00 | 2,275. |
| d. | | Inverted "5" before the "C" | 32,500. | 44,000. |
| 14 | A2 | 80c buff | 190.00 | 19,000. |
| a. | | 80c brown orange | 190.00 | 19,000. |
| b. | | "CENT 8" | 360.00 | |

| | | | | |
|---|---|---|---|---|
| c. | | "CENT 0" | 1,200. | — |
| d. | | No period after "80" | 360.00 | — |
| e. | | "N" inverted | 360.00 | — |

The reprints of the 1859 issue have the word "CENT" and the figures of value in different type from the originals. There is no frame line at the bottom of the small square in the lower right corner.

## NEWSPAPER TAX STAMPS

NT1          NT2

| B. G. CEN. 9 | | B. G. CEN. 9. |
|---|---|---|
| Type I | | Type II |

**1853    Unwmk.    Typo.    Imperf.**

| | | | | |
|---|---|---|---|---|
| PR1 | NT1 | 9c blk, *violet* (I) | — | 3,100. |
| PR2 | NT1 | 9c blk, *violet* (II) | 725.00 | 80.00 |
| a. | | No period after "9" | 1,100. | 275.00 |

All known unused examples of #PR1 lack gum.

**1855-57**

| | | | | |
|---|---|---|---|---|
| PR3 | A1 | 9c blk, *violet* | | 3.65 |
| a. | | No period after "9" | | 7.25 |
| b. | | No period after "CENT" | | 11.00 |
| PR4 | A1 | 10c blk, *gray vio* ('57) | 72.50 | 250.00 |
| a. | | "CEN1" | 360.00 | 1,450. |

No. PR3 was never placed in use.

**1859**

| | | | | |
|---|---|---|---|---|
| PR5 | NT2 | 10c black | 1,150. | 2,200. |
| a. | | Double impression | 16,500. | 20,000. |
| b. | | Vert. guidelines between stamps | | 1,000. |

No. PR5 has horizontal guide lines between stamps. No. PR5b is a second printing, which was not issued.

These stamps did not pay postage, but were a fiscal tax collected by the postal authorities on newspapers arriving from foreign countries.
The stamps of Modena were superseded by those of Sardinia in February, 1860.

## PARMA

LOCATION — Comprising the present provinces of Parma and Piacenza in northern Italy.
GOVT. — Independent Duchy
AREA — 2,750 sq. mi. (1860)
POP. — 500,000 (1860)
CAPITAL — Parma

Parma was annexed to Sardinia in 1860.

100 Centesimi = 1 Lira

Values of Parma stamps vary tremendously according to condition. Values are for very fine examples, and values for unused stamps are for examples with original gum as defined in the catalogue introduction except for No. 8 which is known only without gum. Extremely fine or superb copies sell at much higher prices, and fine or poor copies sell at greatly reduced prices. In addition, very fine unused copies without gum sell for about 20% of the values shown.

Crown and Fleur-de-lis
A1    A2

**1852    Unwmk.    Typo.    Imperf.**

| | | | | |
|---|---|---|---|---|
| 1 | A1 | 5c blk, *yellow* | 125.00 | 140.00 |
| 2 | A1 | 10c blk, *white* | 125.00 | 140.00 |
| 3 | A1 | 15c blk, *pink* | 3,600. | 72.50 |
| a. | | Tête bêche pair | | 100,000. |
| b. | | Double impression | | 4,250. |
| 4 | A1 | 25c blk, *violet* | 14,500. | 215.00 |
| 5 | A1 | 40c blk, *blue* | 2,900. | 400.00 |
| a. | | 40c black, *pale blue* | — | 525.00 |

**1854-55**

| | | | | |
|---|---|---|---|---|
| 6 | A1 | 5c org yel | 8,600. | 875.00 |
| a. | | 5c lemon yellow | 11,500. | 1,100. |
| b. | | Double impression | | 18,000. |
| 7 | A1 | 15c red | 10,000. | 215.00 |
| 8 | A1 | 25c red brn ('55) | — | 425.00 |
| a. | | Double impression | | 32,500. |

No. 8 unused is without gum.

**1857-59**

| | | | | |
|---|---|---|---|---|
| 9 | A2 | 15c red ('59) | 360.00 | 360.00 |
| 10 | A2 | 25c red brown | 575.00 | 215.00 |
| 11 | A2 | 40c bl, wide "0" ('58) | 80.00 | 500.00 |
| a. | | Narrow "0" in "40" | 85.00 | 550.00 |

### Provisional Government

A3

**1859**

| | | | | |
|---|---|---|---|---|
| 12 | A3 | 5c yel grn | 650.00 | 23,000. |
| a. | | 5c blue green | 2,900. | 4,250. |
| 13 | A3 | 10c brown | 1,325. | 650.00 |
| a. | | 10c deep brown | 1,325. | 650.00 |
| b. | | "1" of "10" inverted | 2,700. | 5,400. |
| c. | | Thick "0" in "10" | 2,700. | 5,500. |
| 14 | A3 | 20c pale blue | 1,325. | 200.00 |
| a. | | 20c deep blue | 1,325. | 240.00 |
| b. | | Thick "0" in "20" | 1,550. | 250.00 |
| 15 | A3 | 40c red | 8,750. | |
| a. | | 40c brown red | 23,000. | 12,500. |
| b. | | Thick "0" in "40," (#15) | 825.00 | 10,500. |
| c. | | Thick "0" in "40," (#15a) | 25,000. | 14,500. |

| | | | |
|---|---|---|---|
| **16** | A3 80c olive yellow | 8,000. | 230,000. |
| *a.* | 80c org yel | 11,000. | |
| *d.* | Thick "0" in "80," (#16) | 8,500. | |
| *e.* | Thick "0" in "80," (#16a) | | 11,500. |

Nos. 12-16 exist in two other varieties: with spelling "CFNTESIMI" and with small "A" in"STATI." These are valued about 50 per cent more than normal stamps.
See Nos. PR1-PR2.

### NEWSPAPER TAX STAMPS

#### Type of 1859
**1853-57 Unwmk. Typo. Imperf.**
**Normal Paper ('53)**

| | | | |
|---|---|---|---|
| **PR1** | A3 6c black, *deep rose* | | 325.00 |
| **PR2** | A3 9c black, *blue* | 2,300. | |
| | | 1,275. | 15,500. |

Full margins = 1¼mm.

**Thin, Semitransparent Paper ('57)**

| | | | |
|---|---|---|---|
| *PR1a* | A3 6c black, *rose* ('57) | 125.00 | |
| *PR2a* | A3 9c black, *blue* | 72.50 | |

These stamps belong to the same class as the Newspaper Tax Stamps of Modena, Austria, etc.
Nos. PR1a-PR2a were not issued.
Note following #16 also applies to #PR1-PR2.
The stamps of Parma were superseded by those of Sardinia in 1860.

### ROMAGNA

LOCATION — Comprised the present Italian provinces of Forli, Ravenna, Ferrara and Bologna.
GOVT. — Formerly one of the Roman States
AREA — 5,626 sq. mi.
POP. — 1,341,091 (1853)
CAPITAL — Ravenna

Postage stamps were issued when a provisional government was formed pending the unification of Italy. In 1860 Romagna was annexed to Sardinia and since 1862 the postage stamps of Italy have been used.

100 Bajocchi = 1 Scudo

Values of Romagna stamps vary tremendously according to condition. Values are for very fine examples, and values for unused stamps are for examples with original gum as defined in the catalogue introduction. Extremely fine or superb copies sell at much higher prices, and fine or poor copies sell at greatly reduced prices. In addition, very fine unused copies without gum sell for about 20% of the values shown.

A1

**1859 Unwmk. Typo. Imperf.**

| | | | |
|---|---|---|---|
| **1** | A1 ½b blk, *straw* | 35.00 | 325.00 |
| *a.* | Half used as ¼b on cover | | 13,250. |
| **2** | A1 1b blk, *drab* | 35.00 | 160.00 |
| **3** | A1 2b blk, *buff* | 50.00 | 175.00 |
| *a.* | Half used as 1b on cover | | 5,000. |
| **4** | A1 3b blk, *dk grn* | 57.50 | 350.00 |
| **5** | A1 4b blk, *fawn* | 650.00 | 160.00 |
| *a.* | Half used as 2b on cover | | 28,500. |
| **6** | A1 5b blk, *gray vio* | 72.50 | 400.00 |
| **7** | A1 6b blk, *yel grn* | 475.00 | 8,000. |
| *a.* | Half used as 3b on cover | | 125,000. |
| **8** | A1 8b blk, *rose* | 115.00 | 1,800. |
| *a.* | Half used as 4b on cover | | 125,000. |
| **9** | A1 20b blk, *gray grn* | 115.00 | 2,500. |

These stamps have been reprinted several times. The reprints usually resemble the originals in the color of the paper but there are impressions on incorrect colors and also in colors on white paper. They often show broken letters and other injuries. The Y shaped ornaments between the small circles in the corners are broken and blurred and the dots outside the circles are often missing or joined to the circles.
Forged cancellations are plentiful.
Bisects used Oct. 12, 1859 to Mar. 1, 1860.

---

The stamps of Romagna were superseded by those of Sardinia in February, 1860.

### ROMAN STATES

LOCATION — Comprised most of the central Italian Peninsula, bounded by the former Kingdom of Lombardy-Venetia and Modena on the north, Tuscany on the west, and the Kingdom of Naples on the southeast.
GOVT. — Under the direct government of the See of Rome.
AREA — 16,000 sq. mi.
POP. — 3,124,758 (1853)
CAPITAL — Rome

Upon the formation of the Kingdom of Italy, the area of the Roman States was greatly reduced and in 1870 they disappeared from the political map of Europe. Postage stamps of Italy have been used since that time.

100 Bajocchi = 1 Scudo
100 Centesimi = 1 Lira (1867)

Values of Roman States stamps vary tremendously according to condition. Values are for very fine examples, and values for unused stamps are for examples with original gum as defined in the catalogue introduction. Extremely fine or superb copies sell at much higher prices, and fine or poor copies sell at greatly reduced prices. In addition, very fine unused copies without gum sell for about 20% of the values shown.

Papal Arms
A1      A2

A3      A4

A5      A6

A7      A8

A9      A10

A11

**1852 Unwmk. Typo. Imperf.**

| | | | |
|---|---|---|---|
| **1** | A1 ½b blk, *dl vio* | 57.50 | 125.00 |
| *a.* | ½b black, *gray blue* | 725.00 | 95.00 |
| *b.* | ½b black, *gray lilac* | 725.00 | 325.00 |
| *c.* | ½b black, *gray* | 725.00 | 97.50 |
| *d.* | ½b black, *reddish violet* | 3,600. | 1,800. |
| *e.* | ½b black, *dark violet* | 275.00 | 275.00 |
| *f.* | Tête bêche pair | | 32,500. |

---

| | | | |
|---|---|---|---|
| *h.* | As "a," half used as ¼b on wrapper | | 65,000. |
| | Pen cancel | | 11,500. |
| *i.* | Double impression | — | 5,750. |
| *j.* | Impression on both sides | | 13,000. |
| **2** | A2 1b blk, *gray grn* | 290.00 | 11.00 |
| *a.* | 1b black, *bl green* | 850.00 | 57.50 |
| *b.* | Half used as ½b on cover | | 550.00 |
| *c.* | Grayish oily ink | 1,075. | 40.00 |
| *d.* | Double impression | | 6,000. |
| *e.* | Impression on both sides | — | 13,000. |
| **3** | A3 2b blk, *grnsh white* | 14.00 | 72.50 |
| *a.* | 2b black, *yellow green* | 215.00 | 15.00 |
| *b.* | As #3, half used as 1b on cover | | 6,500. |
| *c.* | As "a," half used as 1b on cover | | 475.00 |
| *d.* | Grayish oily ink | 1,075. | 40.00 |
| *e.* | No period after "BAJ" | 150.00 | 42.50 |
| *f.* | As "a" and "e" | 425.00 | 27.50 |
| *g.* | Double impression | | 5,500. |
| **4** | A4 3b blk, *brown* | 175.00 | 65.00 |
| *a.* | 3b black, *light brown* | 5,250. | 125.00 |
| *b.* | 3b black, *yellow brown* | 2,500. | 50.00 |
| *c.* | 3b black, *yellow buff* | 2,500. | 50.00 |
| *d.* | 3b black, *chrome yellow* | 42.50 | 200.00 |
| *e.* | One-third used as 1b on circular | | 3,600. |
| *f.* | Two-thirds used as 2b on circular | | 11,500. |
| *g.* | Grayish oily ink | 5,250. | 215.00 |
| *h.* | Impression on both sides | — | 13,000. |
| *i.* | Double impression | — | 6,000. |
| *j.* | Half used as 1 ½b on cover | | 14,250. |
| **5** | A5 4b blk, *lemon* | 250.00 | 85.00 |
| *a.* | 4b black, *yellow* | 250.00 | 85.00 |
| *b.* | 4b black, *rose brown* | 10,000. | 125.00 |
| *c.* | 4b black, *gray brown* | 7,750. | 87.50 |
| *d.* | Half used as 2b on cover | | 2,700. |
| *e.* | One-quarter used as 1b on cover | | 25,000. |
| *f.* | Impression on both sides | | 13,000. |
| *g.* | Ribbed paper | 300.00 | 75.00 |
| *h.* | Grayish oily ink | 16,000. | 350.00 |
| *i.* | As "a," half used as 2b on cover | | 4,250. |
| *j.* | As "a," one-quarter used as 1b on cover | | 23,500. |
| **6** | A6 5b blk, *rose* | 250.00 | 16.00 |
| *a.* | 5b black, *pale rose* | 260.00 | 18.00 |
| *c.* | Impression on both sides | | 13,000. |
| *d.* | Double impression | | 6,000. |
| *e.* | Grayish oily ink | 1,500. | 47.50 |
| *f.* | Half used as 2 ½b on cover | | 72,500. |
| **7** | A7 6b blk, *grnsh gray* | 1,000. | 85.00 |
| *a.* | 6b black, *gray* | 1,600. | 92.50 |
| *b.* | 6b black, *grayish lilac* | 1,400. | 225.00 |
| *c.* | Grayish oily ink | 4,250. | 250.00 |
| *d.* | Double impression | — | 6,000. |
| *e.* | Half used as 3b on cover | | 5,750. |
| *f.* | One-third used as 2b on cover | | 21,500. |
| **8** | A8 7b blk, *blue* | 1,425. | 80.00 |
| *a.* | Half used as 3 ½b on cover | | 36,000. |
| *b.* | Double impression | | 5,500. |
| *c.* | Grayish oily ink | 4,300. | 160.00 |
| **9** | A9 8b black | 650.00 | 47.50 |
| *a.* | Half used as 4b on cover | | 9,500. |
| *b.* | Quarter used as 2b on cover | | 90,000. |
| *c.* | Double impression | | 250.00 |
| *d.* | Grayish oily ink | 2,650. | 250.00 |
| **10** | A10 50b dull blue | 16,000. | 1,800. |
| *a.* | 50b deep blue (worn impression) | 23,000. | 2,900. |
| **11** | A11 1sc rose | 4,000. | 3,600. |

Counterfeits exist of Nos. 10-11. Fraudulent cancellations are found on No. 11.

A12      A13

A14      A15

A16      A17

---

A18

**1867 Imperf.**
**Glazed Paper**

| | | | |
|---|---|---|---|
| **12** | A12 2c blk, *green* | 115.00 | 275.00 |
| *a.* | No period after "Cent" | 125.00 | 290.00 |
| **13** | A13 3c blk, *gray* | 1,275. | 7,750. |
| *a.* | 3c black, *lilac gray* | 3,200. | 2,500. |
| **14** | A14 5c blk, *lt bl* | 175.00 | 250.00 |
| *a.* | No period after "5" | 350.00 | 500.00 |
| **15** | A15 10c blk, *vermilion* | 1,575. | 92.50 |
| *a.* | Double impression | | 7,250. |
| **16** | A16 20c blk, *cop red* (unglazed) | 200.00 | 115.00 |
| *a.* | No period after "20" | 650.00 | 325.00 |
| *b.* | No period after "CENT" | 650.00 | 315.00 |
| **17** | A17 40c blk, *lil rose* | 225.00 | 215.00 |
| *a.* | No period after "40" | 275.00 | 275.00 |
| **18** | A18 80c blk, *lil rose* | 200.00 | 525.00 |
| *a.* | No period after "80" | 350.00 | 850.00 |
| | Nos. 12-18 (7) | 3,765. | 9,222. |

Imperforate stamps on unglazed paper, or in colors other than listed, are unfinished remainders of the 1868 issue.
Fraudulent cancellations are found on Nos. 13, 14, 17, 18.

**1868 Glazed Paper Perf. 13**

| | | | |
|---|---|---|---|
| **19** | A12 2c blk, *green* | 10.50 | 72.50 |
| *a.* | No period after "CENT" | 12.50 | 90.00 |
| **20** | A13 3c blk, *gray* | 47.50 | 3,200. |
| *a.* | 3c black, *lilac gray* | 9,000. | 20,000. |
| **21** | A14 5c blk, *lt bl* | 29.00 | 57.50 |
| *a.* | No period after "5" | 30.00 | 72.50 |
| *b.* | No period after "Cent" | 110.00 | 275.00 |
| *c.* | 5c black, *lt bl* (unglazed, imperf., without gum) | 90.00 | |
| **22** | A15 10c blk, *org ver* | 3.50 | 12.50 |
| *a.* | 10c black, *vermilion* | 72.50 | 14.00 |
| *b.* | 10c black, *ver* (unglazed) | 1.00 | — |
| *c.* | 10c black, *ver* (unglazed, imperf., without gum) | 1.00 | — |
| **23** | A16 20c blk, *dp crim* | 5.75 | 26.50 |
| *a.* | 20c black, *magenta* | 7.25 | 42.50 |
| *b.* | 20c blk, *mag* (unglazed) | 350.00 | 35.00 |
| *c.* | 20c blk, *mag* (imperf., without gum) | 2.75 | — |
| *d.* | 20c blk, *cop red* (unglazed) | 1,800. | 50.00 |
| *e.* | 20c blk, *dp crim* (imperf., without gum) | 2.75 | — |
| *f.* | No period after "20" (copper red) | 2,500. | 350.00 |
| *g.* | No period after "20" (mag) | 29.00 | 215.00 |
| *h.* | No period after "20" (deep crimson) | 29.00 | 215.00 |
| *i.* | No period after "CENT" (copper red) | 2,500. | 350.00 |
| *j.* | No period after "CENT" (magenta) | 29.00 | 215.00 |
| *k.* | No period after "CENT" (deep crimson) | 29.00 | 215.00 |
| **24** | A17 40c blk, *grnsh yel* | 10.00 | 140.00 |
| *a.* | 40c black, *yellow* | 250.00 | 90.00 |
| *b.* | 40c black, *orange yellow* | 110.00 | 900.00 |
| *c.* | No period after "40" | 14.50 | 115.00 |
| **25** | A18 80c blk, *rose lilac* | 250.00 | 360.00 |
| *a.* | 80c black, *bright rose* | 5,750. | 45,000. |
| *b.* | 80c black, *rose lilac* (unglazed) | 57.50 | — |
| *c.* | No period after "80" *rose lilac*(unglazed) | 110.00 | 500.00 |
| *d.* | 80c black, *pale rose lilac* (unglazed) | 85.00 | — |
| *e.* | 80c black, *pale rose* (unglazed) | 50.00 | 350.00 |
| *f.* | As "e," no period after "80" | 65.00 | 600.00 |
| *g.* | As "a," no period after "80" | 6,750. | — |
| *h.* | As "e," double impression | — | — |
| | Nos. 19-25 (7) | 356.25 | 3,869. |

All values except the 3c exist imperforate vertically or horizontally and in vertical and horizontal pairs, imperf between. See the *Scott Specialized Catalogue of Stamps and Covers* for detailed listings.
Double impressions are known of the 5c, 10c, 20c (all three colors), 40c and 80c.
Fraudulent cancellations are found on Nos. 20, 24 and 25.
The stamps of the 1867 and 1868 issues have been privately reprinted; many of these reprints are well executed and it is difficult to distinguish them from the originals. Most reprints show more or less pronounced defects of the design. On the originals the horizontal lines between stamps are unbroken, while on most of the reprints these lines are broken. Most of the perforated reprints gauge 11½.

Roman States stamps were replaced by those of Italy in 1870.

# SARDINIA

LOCATION — An island in the Mediterranean Sea off the west coast of Italy and a large area in northwestern Italy, including the cities of Genoa, Turin and Nice.

GOVT. — Kingdom

As a result of war and revolution, most of the former independent Italian States were joined to the Kingdom of Sardinia in 1859 and 1860. On March 17, 1861, the name was changed to the Kingdom of Italy.

100 Centesimi = 1 Lira

Values of Sardinia stamps vary tremendously according to condition. Values are for very fine examples, and values for unused stamps are for examples with original gum as defined in the catalogue introduction. Extremely fine or superb copies sell at much higher prices, and fine or poor copies sell at greatly reduced prices. In addition, very fine unused copies without gum sell for about 20-30% of the values shown.

A1

A2

A3

King Victor Emmanuel II — A4

## 1851 Unwmk. Litho. Imperf.

| | | | | |
|---|---|---|---|---|
| 1 | A1 | 5c gray blk | 10,000. | 2,150. |
| a. | | 5c black | 10,000. | 2,150. |
| 2 | A1 | 20c blue | 8,250. | 215. |
| a. | | 20c deep blue | 8,250. | 215. |
| b. | | 20c pale blue | 8,250. | 360. |
| 3 | A1 | 40c rose | 17,250. | 4,250. |
| | | 40c violet rose | 17,250. | 7,250. |

## Vignette & Inscriptions Embossed
### 1853

| | | | | |
|---|---|---|---|---|
| 4 | A2 | 5c bl grn | 16,000. | 1,325. |
| a. | | Double embossing | | 3,250. |
| 5 | A2 | 20c dl bl | 17,250. | 175. |
| a. | | Double embossing | | 1,400. |
| 6 | A2 | 40c pale rose | 10,750. | 1,100. |
| b. | | Double embossing | | 2,500. |

## Lithographed Frame in Color, Colorless Embossed Vignette
### 1854

| | | | | |
|---|---|---|---|---|
| 7 | A3 | 5c yellow grn | 32,500. | 650. |
| a. | | Double embossing | | 1,450. |
| b. | | 5c grayish green | 3,250. | |
| 8 | A3 | 20c blue | 18,000. | 140. |
| a. | | Double embossing | | 550. |
| b. | | 20c indigo | 900. | |
| 9 | A3 | 40c rose | 90,000. | 3,250. |
| a. | | Double embossing | | 5,750. |
| b. | | 40c brown rose | 215. | |

Nos. 7b, 8b and 9b, differing in shade from the original stamps, were prepared but not issued.

## Typographed Frame in Color, Colorless Embossed Vignette
### 1855-63 Unwmk. Imperf.

Stamps of this issue vary greatly in color, paper and sharpness of embossing as between the early (1855-59) printings and the later (1860-63) ones. Year dates after each color name indicate whether the stamp falls into the Early or Late printing group.

As a rule, early printings are on smooth thick paper with sharp embossing, while later printings are usually on paper varying from thick to thin and of inferior quality with embossing less distinct and printing blurred. The outer frame shows a distinct design on the early printings, while this design is more or

less blurred or even a solid line on the later printings.

| | | | | |
|---|---|---|---|---|
| 10 | A4 | 5c green ('62-63) | 5.75 | 14.50 |
| a. | | 5c yellow green ('62-63) | 35.00 | 21.00 |
| b. | | 5c olive green ('60-61) | 425.00 | 275.00 |
| c. | | 5c yellow green ('55-59) | 1,000. | 200.00 |
| d. | | 5c myrtle green ('57) | 5,000. | 500.00 |
| e. | | 5c emerald ('55-57) | 3,600. | 425.00 |
| f. | | Head inverted | — | 3,250. |
| g. | | Double head, one inverted | — | 3,250. |
| 11 | A4 | 10c bis ('63) | 5.75 | 21.00 |
| a. | | 10c ocher ('62) | 105.00 | 21.00 |
| b. | | 10c olive bister ('62) | 175.00 | 27.50 |
| c. | | 10c olive green ('61) | 250.00 | 37.50 |
| d. | | 10c reddish brown ('61) | 1,250. | 140.00 |
| e. | | 10c gray brown ('61) | 175.00 | 50.00 |
| f. | | 10c olive gray ('60-61) | 350.00 | 72.50 |
| g. | | 10c gray ('60) | 1,275. | 225.00 |
| h. | | 10c grayish brown ('59) | 125.00 | 215.00 |
| i. | | 10c violet brown ('59) | 650.00 | 275.00 |
| j. | | 10c dark brown ('58) | 775.00 | 400.00 |
| k. | | Head inverted | — | 4,000. |
| l. | | Double head, one inverted | — | 4,000. |
| m. | | Pair, one without embossing | 2,500. | — |
| n. | | Half used as 5c on cover | | 100,000. |
| 12 | A4 | 20c indigo ('62) | 115.00 | 50.00 |
| a. | | 20c blue ('61) | 215.00 | 21.00 |
| b. | | 20c light blue ('60-61) | 215.00 | 21.00 |
| c. | | 20c Prussian bl ('59-60) | 725.00 | 35.00 |
| d. | | 20c indigo ('57-58) | 540.00 | 50.00 |
| e. | | 20c sky blue ('55-56) | 5,000. | 215.00 |
| f. | | 20c cobalt ('55) | 2,850. | 125.00 |
| g. | | Head inverted | 2,850. | 1,425. |
| h. | | Double head, one inverted | | — |
| i. | | Pair, one without embossing | 1,425. | — |
| j. | | Half used as 10c on cover | | 125,000. |
| 13 | A4 | 40c red ('63) | 22.50 | 50.00 |
| a. | | 40c rose ('61-62) | 180.00 | 72.50 |
| b. | | 40c carmine ('60) | 725.00 | 425.00 |
| c. | | 40c light red ('57) | 3,250. | 140.00 |
| d. | | 40c vermilion ('55-57) | 5,000. | 425.00 |
| e. | | Head inverted | — | 5,500. |
| f. | | Double head, one inverted | — | 5,500. |
| g. | | Pair, one without embossing | 2,150. | — |
| h. | | Half used as 20c on cover | | 72,500. |
| 14 | A4 | 80c org yel ('62) | 27.50 | 500.00 |
| a. | | 80c yellow ('60-61) | 32.50 | 400.00 |
| b. | | 80c yellow ocher ('59) | 900.00 | 725.00 |
| c. | | 80c ocher ('58) | 225.00 | 575.00 |
| d. | | 80c brown orange ('58) | 225.00 | 575.00 |
| e. | | Head inverted | — | 20,000. |
| f. | | Half used as 40c on cover | | — |
| 15 | A4 | 3 l bronze ('61) | 500.00 | 3,250. |
| | | Nos. 10-15 (6) | 676.50 | 3,885. |

Forgeries of the inverted and double head varieties have been made by applying a faked head embossing to printer's waste without head. These forgeries are plentiful.

Fraudulent cancellations are found on #13-15.

The 5c, 20c and 40c have been reprinted; the embossing of the reprints is not as sharp as that of the originals, the colors are dull and blurred.

## NEWSPAPER STAMPS

N1

### Typographed and Embossed
#### 1861 Unwmk. Imperf.

| | | | | |
|---|---|---|---|---|
| P1 | N1 | 1c black | 8.00 | 14.00 |
| a. | | Numeral "2" | 725.00 | 2,500. |
| b. | | Figure of value inverted | 2,150. | 34,000. |
| c. | | Double impression | | |
| P2 | N1 | 2c black | 160.00 | 115.00 |
| a. | | Numeral "1" | 11,000. | 32,500. |
| b. | | Figure of value inverted | 2,150. | 34,000. |

Forgeries of the varieties of the embossed numerals have been made from printer's waste without numerals.

See Italy No. P1 for 2c buff.

The stamps of Sardinia were superseded in 1862 by those of Italy, which were identical with the 1855 issue of Sardinia, but perforated. Until 1863, imperforate and perforated stamps were issued simultaneously.

# TUSCANY

LOCATION — In the north central part of the Apennine Peninsula.

GOVT. — Grand Duchy
AREA — 8,890 sq. mi.
POP. — 2,892,000 (approx.)
CAPITAL — Florence

Tuscany was annexed to Sardinia in 1860.

60 Quattrini = 20 Soldi = 12 Crazie = 1 Lira

100 Centesimi = 1 Lira (1860)

Values of Tuscany stamps vary tremendously according to condition. Values are for very fine examples, and values for unused stamps are for examples with original gum as defined in the catalogue introduction. Extremely fine or superb copies sell at much higher prices, and fine or poor copies sell at greatly reduced prices. In addition, very fine unused copies without gum sell for about 20% of the values shown.

Lion of Tuscany — A1

### 1851-52 Typo. Wmk. 185 Imperf.
### Blue, Grayish Blue or Gray Paper

| | | | | |
|---|---|---|---|---|
| 1 | A1 | 1q black ('52) | 17,500. | 2,500. |
| 2 | A1 | 1s ocher, grayish | 22,000. | 2,750. |
| a. | | 1s orange, grayish | 25,000. | 2,750. |
| b. | | 1s yellow, bluish | 27,500. | 3,000. |
| 3 | A1 | 2s scarlet | 72,500. | 10,000. |
| 4 | A1 | 1cr carmine | 12,000. | 175. |
| a. | | 1cr brown carmine | 15,000. | 175. |
| 5 | A1 | 2cr blue | 7,250. | 190. |
| a. | | 2cr greenish blue | 7,750. | 200. |
| 6 | A1 | 4cr green | 12,000. | 250. |
| a. | | 4cr bluish green | 12,000. | 250. |
| 7 | A1 | 6cr slate blue | 13,250. | 375. |
| a. | | 6cr blue | 12,000. | 400. |
| b. | | 6cr indigo | 12,000. | 400. |
| 8 | A1 | 9cr gray lilac | 27,500. | 375. |
| a. | | 9cr deep violet | 27,500. | 400. |
| 9 | A1 | 60cr red ('52) | 120,000. | 33,000. |

The first paper was blue, later paper more and more grayish. Stamps on distinctly blue paper sell about 20 percent higher, except Nos. 3 and 9 which were issued on blue paper only. Examples without watermark are proofs.

Reprints of Nos. 3 and 9 have re-engraved value labels, color is too brown and impressions blurred and heavy. Paper same as originals.

### 1857-59 Wmk. 184
### White Paper

| | | | | |
|---|---|---|---|---|
| 10 | A1 | 1q black | 2,400. | 1,325. |
| 11 | A1 | 1s yellow | 66,000. | 7,750. |
| 12 | A1 | 1cr carmine | 16,500. | 825. |
| 13 | A1 | 2cr blue | 5,000. | 190. |
| 14 | A1 | 4cr blue green | 12,000. | 250. |
| 15 | A1 | 6cr deep blue | 15,500. | 375. |
| 16 | A1 | 9cr gray lilac ('59) | 60,000. | 7,750. |

### Provisional Government

Coat of Arms — A2

#### 1860

| | | | | |
|---|---|---|---|---|
| 17 | A2 | 1c brn lilac | 4,250. | 1,400. |
| a. | | 1c red lilac | 5,500. | 1,550. |
| b. | | 1c gray lilac | 4,250. | 1,400. |
| 18 | A2 | 5c green | 17,500. | 325.00 |
| a. | | 5c olive green | 20,000. | 350.00 |
| b. | | 5c yellow green | 24,000. | 500.00 |
| 19 | A2 | 10c deep brn | 5,000. | 82.50 |
| a. | | 10c gray brown | 6,000. | 82.50 |
| b. | | 10c purple brown | 5,000. | 82.50 |
| 20 | A2 | 20c blue | 15,000. | 250.00 |
| a. | | 20c deep blue | 15,000. | 300.00 |
| b. | | 20c gray blue | 16,500. | 300.00 |
| 21 | A2 | 40c rose | 22,000. | 425.00 |
| a. | | 40c carmine | 22,000. | 425.00 |
| b. | | Half used as 20c on cover | | 300.00 |
| 22 | A2 | 80c pale red brn | 42,500. | 2,000. |
| a. | | 80c brown orange | 42,500. | 2,000. |
| 23 | A2 | 3 l ocher | 300,000. | 135,000. |

Dangerous counterfeits exist of #1-PR1c.

See Italy No. P1 for 2c buff.

## NEWSPAPER TAX STAMP

NT1

### 1854 Unwmk. Typo. Imperf.
### Yellowish Pelure Paper

| | | | | |
|---|---|---|---|---|
| PR1 | NT1 | 2s black | | 120.00 |
| a. | | Tête bêche pair | | 1,100. |
| b. | | as "a," one stamp on back | | 1,100. |
| c. | | Double impression | | 825.00 |

This stamp represented a fiscal tax on newspapers coming from foreign countries. It was not canceled when used.

The stamps of Tuscany were superseded by those of Sardinia in 1861.

# TWO SICILIES

LOCATION — Formerly comprised the island of Sicily and the lower half of the Apennine Peninsula.

GOVT. — Independent Kingdom
CAPITAL — Naples

The Kingdom was annexed to Sardinia in 1860.

200 Tornesi = 100 Grana = 1 Ducat

Values of Two Sicilies stamps vary tremendously according to condition. Values are for very fine examples, and values for unused stamps are for examples with original gum as defined in the catalogue introduction. Extremely fine or superb copies sell at much higher prices, and fine or poor copies sell at greatly reduced prices. In addition, very fine unused copies without gum sell for about 20-30% of the values shown.

## Naples

Coat of Arms
A1        A2

A3            A4

A5            A6

A7

### 1858 Engr. Wmk. 186 Imperf.

| | | | | |
|---|---|---|---|---|
| 1 | A1 | ½g pale lake | 2,000. | 360.00 |
| a. | | ½g rose lake | 2,000. | 360.00 |
| b. | | ½g lake | 2,600. | 550.00 |
| c. | | ½g carmine lake | 3,250. | 800.00 |
| d. | | Half used as ¼g on newspaper | | 215,000. |
| 2 | A2 | 1g pale lake | 1,000. | 50.00 |
| a. | | 1g rose lake | 575.00 | 50.00 |
| b. | | 1g brown lake | 1,450. | 110.00 |
| c. | | 1g carmine lake | 900.00 | 87.50 |
| d. | | Printed on both sides | | 2,000. |

| | | | | |
|---|---|---|---|---|
| e. | Printed on both sides,<br>one inverted | | | 900.00 |
| 3 | A3 | 2g pale lake | 400.00 | 16.00 |
| a. | 2g rose lake | | 400.00 | 16.00 |
| b. | 2g lake | | 650.00 | 29.00 |
| c. | 2g carmine lake | | 900.00 | 25.00 |
| d. | Impression of 1g on<br>reverse | | | 1,800. |
| e. | Double impression | | | 11,000. |
| f. | Impression on both sides | | | 2,000. |
| 4 | A4 | 5g brown lake | 3,100. | 60.00 |
| a. | 5g rose lake | | 2,600. | 60.00 |
| b. | 5g carmine lake | | 4,000. | 65.00 |
| d. | Impression on both sides | | | 5,000. |
| e. | 5g rose carmine | | 5,500. | 175.00 |
| f. | 5g bright carmine | | 6,000. | 215.00 |
| g. | 5g dark carmine | | 7,000. | 325.00 |
| 5 | A5 | 10g rose lake | 5,750. | 215.00 |
| a. | 10g lake | | 6,200. | 290.00 |
| b. | 10g carmine lake | | 6,100. | 290.00 |
| c. | Printed on both sides | | | 16,000. |
| d. | Double impression | | | 18,000. |
| 6 | A6 | 20g rose lake | 5,100. | 650.00 |
| a. | 20g lake | | 5,100. | 725.00 |
| b. | Double impression | | 72,500. | |
| c. | 20g pale rose | | 7,250. | 1,500. |
| d. | 20g rose car rose | | 8,500. | 1,750. |
| 7 | A7 | 50g rose lake | 11,500. | 2,900. |
| a. | 50g lake | | 11,500. | 2,900. |

As a secret mark, the engraver, G. Masini, placed a minute letter of his name just above the lower outer line of each stamp. There were three plates of the 2g, one plate of the 50g, and two plates of each of the other values.

Only one example of No. 6b is known.
Nos. 1-2, 4-7 have been reprinted in bright rose and Nos. 1 and 7 in dull brown. The reprints are on thick unwatermarked paper. Value $8 each.

### Provisional Government

A8

A9

**1860**

| | | | | |
|---|---|---|---|---|
| 8 | A8 | ½t deep blue | 180,000. | 11,500. |
| 9 | A9 | ½t blue | 44,000. | 3,800. |
| a. | ½t deep blue | | 44,000. | 3,800. |

100 varieties of each.
No. 8 was made from the plate of No. 1, which was altered by changing the "G" to "T."
No. 9 was made from the same plate after a second alteration erasing the coat of arms and inserting the Cross of Savoy. Dangerous counterfeits exist of Nos. 8-9.

### Sicily

Ferdinand II — A10

**1859    Unwmk.    Engr.    Imperf.**

| | | | | |
|---|---|---|---|---|
| 10 | A10 | ½g orange | 575.00 | 4,000. |
| c. | Printed on both sides | | | 40,000. |
| 11 | A10 | 1g dk brn | 17,500. | 700.00 |
| 12h | A10 | 1g pale ol grn<br>(III) | 200.00 | 180.00 |
| c. | Double impression | | 4,400. | 4,400. |
| 13g | A10 | 2g blue | 180.00 | 120.00 |
| b. | Printed on both sides | | — | 26,000. |
| 14 | A10 | 5g deep rose | 725.00 | 600.00 |
| 15 | A10 | 5g vermilion | 600.00 | 1,600. |
| 16 | A10 | 10g dark blue | 800.00 | 375.00 |
| 17 | A10 | 20g dk gray vio | 800.00 | 625.00 |
| 18 | A10 | 50g dk brn red | 800.00 | 4,750. |

There were three plates each for the 1g and 2g, two each for the ½g and 5g and one plate each for the other values.
Nos. 10a, 10b, 11, 11a, 14, 14a, 14b and 15 are printed from Plate I on which the stamps are 2 to 2½mm apart. On almost all stamps from Plate I, the S and T of POSTA touch.
Nos. 12a, and 15a are from Plate II and No. 12 is from Plate III. On both Plates II and III stamps are spaced 1½mm apart. Most stamps

from Plate II have a white line about 1mm long below the beard.
Nos. 10-18 are on soft, porous paper with brownish gum, while Nos. 10, 12 and 13 exist also on hard white paper, with white gum. Color shades exist, some on both types of paper. For detailed listings, see the *Scott Classic Specialized Catalogue of Stamps and Covers.*
The ½g blue is stated to be a proof of which two copies are known used on cover.
Fraudulent cancellations are known on Nos. 10, 15, 15a and 18.

### Neapolitan Provinces

King Victor
Emmanuel II — A11

### Lithographed, Center Embossed

**1861    Unwmk.     Imperf.**

| | | | | |
|---|---|---|---|---|
| 19 | A11 | ½t green | 18.00 | 225.00 |
| a. | ½t yellow green | | 500.00 | 290.00 |
| b. | ½t emerald | | 5,750. | 900.00 |
| c. | ½t black (error) | | 47,500. | 57,500. |
| d. | Head inverted (green) | | 240.00 | |
| e. | Head inverted (yel grn) | | | 11,500. |
| f. | Printed on both sides | | | 29,000. |
| 20 | A11 | ½g bister | 175.00 | 225.00 |
| a. | ½g brown | | 175.00 | 250.00 |
| b. | ½g gray brown | | 215.00 | 225.00 |
| c. | Head inverted | | 1,800. | |
| 21 | A11 | 1g black | 350.00 | 32.50 |
| a. | Head inverted | | | 1,800. |
| 22 | A11 | 2g blue | 115.00 | 12.50 |
| a. | 2g deep blue | | 115.00 | 12.50 |
| b. | Head inverted | | 400.00 | 900.00 |
| c. | 2g black (error) | | | 60,000. |
| 23 | A11 | 5g car rose | 215.00 | 125.00 |
| a. | 5g vermilion | | 215.00 | 175.00 |
| b. | 5g lilac rose | | 250.00 | 290.00 |
| c. | Head inverted | | 1,100. | 8,000. |
| e. | Printed on both sides | | | 18,000. |
| 25 | A11 | 10g orange | 110.00 | 275.00 |
| a. | 10g ocher | | 1,300. | 725.00 |
| b. | 10g bister | | 125.00 | 275.00 |
| 26 | A11 | 20g yellow | 500.00 | 2,500. |
| c. | Head inverted | | | 36,000. |
| 27 | A11 | 50g gray | 35.00 | 9,000. |
| a. | 50g slate | | 42.50 | 9,000. |
| b. | 50g slate blue | | 50.00 | 11,500. |
| | Nos. 19-27 (8) | | 1,518. | 12,395. |

Counterfeits of the inverted head varieties of this issue are plentiful. See note on forgeries after Sardinia No. 15.
Fraudulent cancellations are found on Nos. 19-20, 23-27.
Stamps similar to those of Sardinia 1855-61, type A4 but with inscriptions in larger, clearer lettering, were prepared in 1861 for the Neapolitan Provinces. They were not officially issued although a few are known postally used. Denominations: 5c, 10c, 20c, 40c and 80c.

Stamps of Two Sicilies were replaced by those of Italy in 1862.

---

### ITALY

'i-t&#601;l-&#275;

LOCATION — Southern Europe
GOVT. — Republic
AREA — 119,764 sq. mi.
POP. — 56,735,130 (1999 est.)
CAPITAL — Rome

Formerly a kingdom, Italy became a republic in June 1946

100 Centesimi = 1 Lira
100 Cents = 1 Euro (2002)

> **Catalogue values for unused stamps in this country are for Never Hinged items, beginning with Scott 691 in the regular postage section, Scott B47 in the semipostal section, Scott C129 in the airpost section, Scott D21 in the pneumatic post section, Scott E32 in the special delivery section, Scott EY11 in the authorized delivery section, Scott J83 in the postage due section, Scott Q77 in the parcel post section, Scott QY5 in the parcel post authorized delivery section, Scott 1N1 in the A.M.G. section, Scott 1LN1 in the Venezia Giulia section, 1LNC1 in the occupation air post section, 1LNE1 in the occupation special delivery section, and all of the items in the Italian Social Republic area.**

### Watermarks

Wmk. 87 —
Honeycomb

Wmk. 140 —
Crown

Wmk. 277 —
Winged Wheel

Wmk. 303 —
Multiple Stars

Values of Italy stamps vary tremendously according to condition. Quotations are for very fine examples, and values for unused stamps are for examples with original gum as defined in the catalogue introduction. Extremely fine or superb copies sell at much higher prices, and fine or poor copies sell at greatly reduced prices. In addition, unused copies without gum are discounted severely.
Very fine examples of Nos. 17-21, 24-75, J2-J27, O1-O8 and Q1-Q6 will have perforations barely clear of the frameline or design due to the narrow spacing of the stamps on the plates.

King Victor Emmanuel II
A4      A5

### Typographed; Head Embossed

**1862    Unwmk.     Perf. 11½x12**

| | | | | |
|---|---|---|---|---|
| 17 | A4 | 10c bister | 8,000. | 325.00 |
| g. | Vert. half used as 5c on<br>cover | | | 125,000. |
| 19 | A4 | 20c dark blue | 24.00 | 40.00 |
| k. | Vert. half used as 10c on<br>cover | | | 175,000. |
| 20 | A4 | 40c red | 325.00 | 200.00 |
| 21 | A4 | 80c orange | 72.50 | 2,000. |

The outer frame shows a distinct design on the early printings, while this design is more or less blurred, or even a solid line, on the later printings.
Numerous shades of Nos. 17-21 exist. Some are very expensive. For listings, see the *Scott Classic Catalogue.*
The 20c and 40c exist perf. 11½. These are remainders of Sardinia with forged perforations.
Counterfeit cancellations are often found on No. 21.

### Lithographed; Head Embossed

**1863      Imperf.**

| | | | | |
|---|---|---|---|---|
| 22 | A4 | 15c blue | 95.00 | 55.00 |
| a. | Head inverted | | | 80,000. |
| b. | Double head | | 140.00 | 85.00 |
| c. | Head omitted | | 650.00 | 47,500. |
| j. | Triple head | | 350.00 | 550.00 |

See note after Sardinia No. 15.
No. 22c is valued with original gum only.

Two types of No. 23:
Type I — First "C" in bottom line nearly closed.
Type II — "C" open. Line broken below "Q."

**1863      Litho.**

| | | | | |
|---|---|---|---|---|
| 23 | A5 | 15c blue, Type II | 8.00 | 14.50 |
| a. | Type I | | 400.00 | 27.50 |
| | Without gum, type I | | 47.50 | |
| c. | As "a," double impression | | | 5,250. |
| f. | As "a," printed on both<br>sides | | | 22,500. |

One example of No. 23f is known used, cancelled "Milano, 25-VII-1863." Unused examples always lack gum and are from printer's waste. They are of little value.

A6

A7

A8

A13

## 1863-77 Typo. Wmk. 140 Perf. 14

| | | | | |
|---|---|---|---|---|
| 24 | A6 | 1c gray green | 8.00 | 4.00 |
| a. | | Imperf., pair | | 12,000. |
| 25 | A7 | 2c org brn ('65) | 32.50 | 2.75 |
| a. | | Imperf., pair | 225.00 | 325.00 |
| 26 | A8 | 5c slate grn | 2,000. | 4.50 |
| 27 | A8 | 10c buff | 3,500. | 5.50 |
| a. | | 10c orange brown | 3,500. | 5.50 |
| 28 | A8 | 10c blue ('77) | 6,500. | 6.50 |
| 29 | A8 | 15c blue | 3,000. | 4.00 |
| a. | | Imperf., single | | 5,500. |
| 30 | A8 | 30c brown | 12.00 | 12.00 |
| a. | | Imperf., single | | — |
| 31 | A8 | 40c carmine | 7,250. | 8.00 |
| a. | | 40c rose | 7,250. | 8.00 |
| 32 | A8 | 60c lilac | 12.00 | 19.00 |
| 33 | A13 | 2 l vermilion | 32.50 | 125.00 |

Nos. 26 to 32 have the head of type A8 but with different corner designs for each value.
Early printings of Nos. 24-27, 29-33 were made in London, later printings in Turin. Values are for Turin printings. London printings of 1c, 2c, 30c, 60c and 2 l sell for more.
For overprints see Italian Offices Abroad Nos. 1-5, 8-11.

No. 29 Surcharged in Brown

## 1865

Type I — Dots flanking stars in oval, and dot in eight check-mark ornaments in corners.
Type II — Dots in oval, none in corners.
Type III — No dots.

| | | | | |
|---|---|---|---|---|
| 34 | A8 | 20c on 15c bl (I) | 750.00 | 4.75 |
| a. | | Type II | 9,500. | 20.00 |
| b. | | Type III | 2,000. | 8.00 |
| c. | | Inverted surcharge (I) | | 72,500. |

A15

## 1867-77 Typo.

| | | | | |
|---|---|---|---|---|
| 35 | A15 | 20c blue | 800.00 | 1.60 |
| 36 | A15 | 20c orange ('77) | 4,750. | 4.00 |

For overprints see Italian Offices Abroad #9-10.

Official Stamps Surcharged in Blue

## 1877

| | | | | |
|---|---|---|---|---|
| 37 | O1 | 2c on 2c lake | 225.00 | 32.50 |
| 38 | O1 | 2c on 5c lake | 275.00 | 40.00 |
| 39 | O1 | 2c on 20c lake | 1,000. | 4.75 |
| 40 | O1 | 2c on 30c lake | 875.00 | 16.00 |
| 41 | O1 | 2c on 1 l lake | 675.00 | 4.75 |
| 42 | O1 | 2c on 2 l lake | 675.00 | 12.00 |
| 43 | O1 | 2c on 5 l lake | 1,000. | 16.00 |
| 44 | O1 | 2c on 10 l lake | 675.00 | 20.00 |
| | | Nos. 37-44 (8) | 5,400. | 146.00 |

### Inverted Surcharge

| | | | | |
|---|---|---|---|---|
| 37a | O1 | 2c on 2c | | 1,800. |
| 38a | O1 | 2c on 5c | | 1,450. |
| 39a | O1 | 2c on 20c | 45,000. | 1,000. |
| 40a | O1 | 2c on 30c | | 1,450. |
| 41a | O1 | 2c on 1 l | 52,500. | 1,300. |
| 42a | O1 | 2c on 2 l | 52,500. | 1,450. |
| 43a | O1 | 2c on 5 l | | 1,450. |
| 44a | O1 | 2c on 10 l | | 1,450. |

King Humbert I — A17

## 1879 Typo. Perf. 14

| | | | | |
|---|---|---|---|---|
| 45 | A17 | 5c blue green | 9.50 | 1.60 |
| 46 | A17 | 10c claret | 550.00 | 1.75 |
| 47 | A17 | 20c orange | 525.00 | 1.60 |
| 48 | A17 | 25c blue | 950.00 | 8.00 |
| 49 | A17 | 30c brown | 190.00 | 2,400. |
| 50 | A17 | 50c violet | 22.50 | 22.50 |
| 51 | A17 | 2 l vermilion | 65.00 | 350.00 |

Nos. 45-51 have the head of type A17 with different corner designs for each value.
Beware of forged cancels on No. 49, both off and on cover.
For surcharges and overprints see Nos. 64-66, Italian Offices Abroad 12-17.

Arms of Savoy — A24

Humbert I — A25

A26

A27

A28

A29

## 1889

| | | | | |
|---|---|---|---|---|
| 52 | A24 | 5c dark green | 1,000. | 3.25 |
| 53 | A25 | 40c brown | 14.50 | 20.00 |
| 54 | A26 | 45c gray green | 2,250. | 9.50 |
| 55 | A27 | 60c violet | 19.00 | 47.50 |
| 56 | A28 | 1 l brown & yel | 19.00 | 24.00 |
| a. | | 1 l brown & orange | 21.00 | 30.00 |
| 57 | A29 | 5 l grn & claret | 30.00 | 800.00 |

Forged cancellations exist on #51, 57.

Parcel Post Stamps of 1884-86 Surcharged in Black

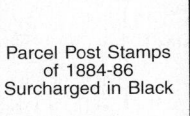

## 1890

| | | | | |
|---|---|---|---|---|
| 58 | PP1 | 2c on 10c ol gray | 6.00 | 8.00 |
| a. | | Inverted surcharge | 525.00 | 3,250. |
| 59 | PP1 | 2c on 20c blue | 6.00 | 8.00 |
| 60 | PP1 | 2c on 50c claret | 65.00 | 47.50 |
| a. | | Inverted surcharge | | 45,000. |
| 61 | PP1 | 2c on 75c blue grn | 6.00 | 8.00 |
| 62 | PP1 | 2c on 1.25 l org | 55.00 | 40.00 |
| a. | | Inverted surcharge | 80,000. | 40.00 |
| 63 | PP1 | 2c on 1.75 l brn | 24.00 | 60.00 |
| | | Nos. 58-63 (6) | 162.00 | 171.50 |

Stamps of 1879 Surcharged

## 1890-91

| | | | | |
|---|---|---|---|---|
| 64 | A17 | 2c on 5c bl grn ('91) | 22.50 | 55.00 |
| a. | | "2" with thin tail | 140.00 | 325.00 |
| 65 | A17 | 20c on 30c brown | 475.00 | 10.00 |
| 66 | A17 | 20c on 50c violet | 550.00 | 47.50 |
| | | Nos. 64-66 (3) | 1,047. | 112.50 |

On Nos. 65-66 the period is omitted in the surcharge.

Arms of Savoy — A33

Humbert I — A34

A35

A36

A37

A38

## 1891-96 Typo.

| | | | | |
|---|---|---|---|---|
| 67 | A33 | 5c green | 650.00 | 2.40 |
| 68 | A34 | 10c claret ('96) | 9.50 | 2.40 |
| 69 | A35 | 20c orange ('95) | 9.50 | 2.40 |
| 70 | A36 | 25c blue | 9.50 | 10.00 |
| 71 | A37 | 45c ol grn ('95) | 9.50 | 10.00 |
| 72 | A38 | 5 l blue & rose | 95.00 | 240.00 |

Arms of Savoy — A39

A40

A41

## 1896-97

| | | | | |
|---|---|---|---|---|
| 73 | A39 | 1c brown | 11.00 | 8.00 |
| a. | | Half used as ½c on postal card | | 1,600. |
| 74 | A40 | 2c orange brown | 11.00 | 2.00 |
| 75 | A41 | 5c green ('97) | 40.00 | 2.00 |
| | | Nos. 73-75 (3) | 62.00 | 12.00 |

A42

Coat of Arms
A43  A44

Victor Emmanuel III
A45  A46

## 1901-26

| | | | | |
|---|---|---|---|---|
| 76 | A42 | 1c brown | 1.60 | .40 |
| a. | | Imperf, single | 400.00 | 650.00 |
| 77 | A43 | 2c org brn | 1.60 | .40 |
| a. | | Double impression | 125.00 | 225.00 |
| b. | | Imperf, single | 125.00 | 160.00 |
| 78 | A44 | 5c blue grn | 80.00 | .60 |
| a. | | Imperf, single | 1,900. | |
| 79 | A45 | 10c claret | 110.00 | 1.25 |
| a. | | Imperf, single | — | 9,500. |
| 80 | A45 | 20c orange | 24.00 | 1.25 |
| 81 | A45 | 25c ultra | 225.00 | 4.00 |
| | | 25c dp blue | 225.00 | 4.00 |

| | | | | |
|---|---|---|---|---|
| 82 | A46 | 25c grn & pale grn ('26) | 82.50 | .35 |
| 83 | A45 | 40c brown | 725.00 | 9.50 |
| 84 | A45 | 45c olive grn | 11.00 | .40 |
| a. | | Imperf, single | 140.00 | 210.00 |
| 85 | A46 | 50c violet | 875.00 | 17.50 |
| 86 | A46 | 75c dk red & rose ('26) | 4.75 | .35 |
| 87 | A46 | 1 l brown & grn | 4.75 | .40 |
| a. | | Imperf, single | 72.50 | 110.00 |
| b. | | Floral design (green) omitted | 160.00 | |
| c. | | Double impression of vignette (brown) | 72.50 | 100.00 |
| 88 | A46 | 1.25 l bl & ultra ('26) | 12.00 | .35 |
| 89 | A46 | 2 l dk grn & org ('23) | 24.00 | 6.50 |
| 90 | A46 | 2.50 l dk grn & org ('26) | 55.00 | 8.00 |
| 91 | A46 | 5 l blue & rose | 32.50 | 7.25 |
| | | Nos. 76-91 (16) | 2,268. | 58.50 |

Nos. 83, 85, unused, are valued in fine condition.
The borders of Nos. 79-81, 83-85, 87, 89 and 91 differ slightly for each denomination.
On Nos. 82, 86, 88 and 90, the value is expressed as "Cent. 25," etc.
See No. 87d in set following No. 174G.
For surcharges and overprints see Nos. 148-149, 152, 158, 174F-174G, B16; Austria N20-N21, N27, N30, N52-N53, N58, N60, N64-N65, N71, N74; Dalmatia 1, 6-7.

## Overprints & Surcharges

See Offices in China, Crete, Africa, Turkish Empire (Albania to Valona) and Aegean Islands for types A36-A58 overprinted or surcharged.

No. 80 Surcharged in Black

C. 15

## 1905

| | | | | |
|---|---|---|---|---|
| 92 | A45 | 15c on 20c org | 72.50 | 2.00 |
| a. | | Double surcharge | | 4,500. |

No. 93    No. 111    No. 123

A47

**1906   Unwmk.   Engr.   Perf. 12**

| | | | | |
|---|---|---|---|---|
| 93 | A47 | 15c slate | 72.50 | 1.00 |
| *a.* | | Vert. pair, imperf horiz. | 175.00 | 200.00 |
| *b.* | | Horiz. pair, imperf vert. | 175.00 | 200.00 |
| *c.* | | Booklet pane of 6 | — | |
| | | Complete booklet, 4 #93c | 13,000. | |

A48      A49

**1906-19   Wmk. 140   Typo.   Perf. 14**

| | | | | |
|---|---|---|---|---|
| 94 | A48 | 5c green | 1.25 | .35 |
| *a.* | | Imperf, single | 40.00 | 40.00 |
| *b.* | | Printed on both sides | 240.00 | |
| 95 | A48 | 10c claret | 2.75 | .35 |
| *a.* | | Imperf, single | 40.00 | 40.00 |
| 96 | A48 | 15c slate ('19) | 1.60 | .40 |
| *a.* | | Imperf, single | 140.00 | 225.00 |
| | | Nos. 94-96 (3) | 5.60 | 1.10 |

The frame of #95 differs in several details.
See Nos. 96b-96d following No. 174G.
For overprints and surcharge see Nos. 142A-142B, 150, 174A, B5, B9-B10; Austria N22-N23, N31, N54-N55, N61-N62, N66-N67; Dalmatia 2-5.

**1908-27**

| | | | | |
|---|---|---|---|---|
| 97 | A49 | 20c brn org ('25) | 1.60 | 1.00 |
| 98 | A49 | 20c green ('25) | .20 | .20 |
| 99 | A49 | 20c lil brn ('26) | 2.40 | .35 |
| 100 | A49 | 25c blue | 2.40 | .35 |
| *a.* | | Imperf, single | 72.50 | 72.50 |
| *b.* | | Printed on both sides | 200.00 | 325.00 |
| 101 | A49 | 25c lt grn ('27) | 6.50 | 16.00 |
| 102 | A49 | 30c org brn ('22) | 2.40 | .80 |
| *a.* | | Imperf, single | 240.00 | |
| 103 | A49 | 30c gray ('25) | 4.75 | .20 |
| 104 | A49 | 40c brown | 4.00 | .35 |
| *a.* | | Imperf, single | 95.00 | 95.00 |
| 105 | A49 | 50c violet | 1.60 | .35 |
| *a.* | | Imperf, single | 87.50 | 87.50 |
| 106 | A49 | 55c dl vio ('20) | 9.50 | 20.00 |
| 107 | A49 | 60c car ('17) | 2.40 | .40 |
| 108 | A49 | 60c blue ('23) | 6.50 | 65.00 |
| 109 | A49 | 60c brn org ('26) | 9.50 | .60 |
| 110 | A49 | 85c red brn ('20) | 16.00 | 16.00 |
| | | Nos. 97-110 (14) | 69.75 | 121.60 |

The upper panels of Nos. 104 and 105 are in solid color with white letters. A body of water has been added to the background.
See Nos. 100c-105j following No. 174G.
For overprints & surcharges see #142C-142D,147, 151, 153-157, 174B-174E, B7-B8, B12-B15A; Austria N24-N26, N28-N29, N32, N56-N57, N59, N63, N68-N70, N72-N73.

A50      A51

**Redrawn**
***Perf. 13x13½, 13½x14***

**1909-17   Typo.   Unwmk.**

| | | | | |
|---|---|---|---|---|
| 111 | A50 | 15c slate black | 275.00 | 2.40 |
| 112 | A50 | 20c brown org ('16) | 65.00 | 4.75 |

No. 111 is similar to No. 93, but the design has been redrawn and the stamp is 23mm high instead of 25mm. There is a star at each side of the coat collar, but one is not distinct.
See illustrations next to A47.
For overprints see Nos. B6, B11.

---

**Wmk. 140    Perf. 14**

| | | | | |
|---|---|---|---|---|
| 113 | A50 | 20c brn org ('17) | 8.00 | .40 |
| *a.* | | Imperf, single | 32.50 | 40.00 |

Stamps overprinted "Prestito Nazionale, 1917," or later dates, are Thrift or Postal Savings Stamps.

**1910, Nov. 1**

| | | | | |
|---|---|---|---|---|
| 114 | A51 | 10 l gray grn & red | 80.00 | 32.50 |
| *a.* | | Red inverted | 5,500. | |

For surcharge see Dalmatia No. 8.

Giuseppe Garibaldi
A52      A53

***Perf. 14x13½***

**1910, Apr. 15    Unwmk.**

| | | | | |
|---|---|---|---|---|
| 115 | A52 | 5c green | 27.50 | 27.50 |
| 116 | A52 | 15c claret | 55.00 | 55.00 |

50th anniversary of freedom of Sicily.

**1910, Dec. 1**

| | | | | |
|---|---|---|---|---|
| 117 | A53 | 5c claret | 140.00 | 140.00 |
| 118 | A53 | 15c green | 250.00 | 200.00 |

50th anniversary of the plebiscite of the southern Italian provinces in 1860.

**Used values in italics are for postally used stamps. CTO's sell for about the same as unused, hinged stamps.**

Symbols of Rome and Turin — A54      Symbol of Valor — A55

Genius of Italy — A56      Glory of Rome — A57

**1911, May 1   Engr.   Perf. 14x13½**

| | | | | |
|---|---|---|---|---|
| 119 | A54 | 2c brown | 3.25 | 6.50 |
| *a.* | | Vert. pair, imperf horiz. | 95.00 | 95.00 |
| *b.* | | Horiz. pair, imperf vert. | 95.00 | 95.00 |
| 120 | A55 | 5c deep green | 40.00 | 35.00 |
| 121 | A56 | 10c carmine | 32.50 | 47.50 |
| *a.* | | Vert. pair, imperf horiz. | | |
| *b.* | | Horiz. pair, imperf vert. | 200.00 | 200.00 |
| 122 | A57 | 15c slate | 35.00 | 72.50 |
| | | Nos. 119-122 (4) | 110.75 | 161.50 |

50th anniv. of the union of Italian States to form the Kingdom of Italy.
Nos. 115 to 122 were sold at a premium over their face value.
For surcharges see Nos. 126-128.

---

Victor Emmanuel III — A58      Campanile, Venice — A59

**1911, Oct.   Re-engraved   Perf. 13½**

| | | | | |
|---|---|---|---|---|
| 123 | A58 | 15c slate | 32.50 | 1.25 |
| *a.* | | Imperf, single | 95.00 | 125.00 |
| *b.* | | Printed on both sides | 350.00 | 525.00 |
| *c.* | | Bklt. pane of 6 | | |

The re-engraved stamp is 24mm high. The stars at each side of the coat collar show plainly and the "C" of "Cent" is nearer the frame than in No. 93. See illustrations next to A47.
For surcharge see No. 129.

**1912, Apr. 25    Perf. 14x13½**

| | | | | |
|---|---|---|---|---|
| 124 | A59 | 5c indigo | 9.50 | 14.50 |
| 125 | A59 | 15c dk brn | 50.00 | 60.00 |

Re-erection of the Campanile at Venice.

Nos. 120-121 Surcharged in Black

**1913, Mar. 1**

| | | | | |
|---|---|---|---|---|
| 126 | A55 | 2c on 5c dp grn | 2.40 | 6.75 |
| 127 | A56 | 2c on 10c car | 2.40 | 6.75 |

No. 122 Surcharged in Violet

| | | | | |
|---|---|---|---|---|
| 128 | A57 | 2c on 15c slate | 2.40 | 6.75 |
| | | Nos. 126-128 (3) | 7.20 | 20.25 |
| | | Set, never hinged | 16.00 | |

No. 123 Surcharged

**1916**

| | | | | |
|---|---|---|---|---|
| 129 | A58 | 20c on 15c slate | 17.50 | 1.25 |
| | | Never hinged | 45.00 | |
| *a.* | | Bklt. pane of 6 | — | |
| *b.* | | Inverted surcharge | 325.00 | 325.00 |
| *c.* | | Double surcharge | 210.00 | 210.00 |
| *e.* | | Vert. pair, one without surcharge | 1,200. | |
| *g.* | | Imperf, single | 160.00 | 200.00 |

Old Seal of Republic of Trieste
A60      Allegory of Dante's Divine Comedy
A61

---

Italy Holding Laurels for Dante — A62      Dante Alighieri — A63

**Wmk. 140**

**1921, June 5   Litho.   Perf. 14**

| | | | | |
|---|---|---|---|---|
| 130 | A60 | 15c blk & rose | 7.25 | 55.00 |
| *a.* | | Horiz. pair, imperf btwn. | 725.00 | |
| 131 | A60 | 25c bl & rose | 7.25 | 55.00 |
| 132 | A60 | 40c brn & rose | 7.25 | 55.00 |
| | | Nos. 130-132 (3) | 21.75 | 165.00 |
| | | Set, never hinged | 50.00 | |

Reunion of Venezia Giulia with Italy.

**1921, Sept. 28    Typo.**

| | | | | |
|---|---|---|---|---|
| 133 | A61 | 15c vio brn | 7.25 | 27.50 |
| *a.* | | Imperf, single | 40.00 | 40.00 |
| 134 | A62 | 25c gray grn | 7.25 | 27.50 |
| *a.* | | Imperf, single | 40.00 | 40.00 |
| 135 | A63 | 40c brown | 7.25 | 27.50 |
| *a.* | | Imperf, single | 40.00 | 40.00 |
| | | Nos. 133-135 (3) | 21.75 | 82.50 |
| | | Set, never hinged | 43.50 | |

600th anniversary of the death of Dante.
A 15c gray was not issued. Value, $72.50.

"Victory" — A64

***Perf. 14, 14x13½***

**1921, Nov. 1    Engr.**

| | | | | |
|---|---|---|---|---|
| 136 | A64 | 5c olive green | 1.25 | 2.00 |
| *c.* | | Imperf, single | 240.00 | 240.00 |
| 137 | A64 | 10c red | 1.60 | 2.40 |
| *c.* | | Imperf, single | 240.00 | 475.00 |
| 138 | A64 | 15c slate green | 3.25 | 9.50 |
| 139 | A64 | 25c ultra | 1.60 | 6.50 |
| *c.* | | Imperf, single | 175.00 | 175.00 |
| *d.* | | As "c," double impression | 600.00 | |
| | | Nos. 136-139 (4) | 7.70 | 20.40 |
| | | Set, never hinged | 16.00 | |

3rd anniv. of the victory on the Piave.
For surcharges see Nos. 171-174.

Flame of Patriotism Tempering Sword of Justice — A65      Giuseppe Mazzini — A66

Mazzini's Tomb
A67

**1922, Sept. 20   Typo.   Perf. 14**

| | | | | |
|---|---|---|---|---|
| 140 | A65 | 25c maroon | 13.00 | 32.50 |
| 141 | A66 | 40c vio brn | 22.50 | 37.50 |
| 142 | A67 | 80c dk bl | 13.00 | 52.50 |
| | | Nos. 140-142 (3) | 48.50 | 122.50 |
| | | Set, never hinged | 120.00 | |

Mazzini (1805-1872), patriot and writer.

Nos. 95, 96, 100 and 104 Overprinted in Black

**1922, June 4    Wmk. 140    Perf. 14**

| | | | | |
|---|---|---|---|---|
| 142A | A48 | 10c claret | 450.00 | 375.00 |
| 142B | A48 | 15c slate | 250.00 | 300.00 |
| 142C | A49 | 25c blue | 250.00 | 300.00 |
| 142D | A49 | 40c brown | 400.00 | 350.00 |
| | | Nos. 142A-142D (4) | 1,350. | 1,325. |
| | | Set, never hinged | 3,200. | |

9th Italian Philatelic Congress, Trieste. Counterfeits exist.

Christ Preaching The Gospel — A68

Portrait at upper right and badge at lower right differ on each value. Portrait at upper left is of Pope Gregory XV. Others: 20c, St. Theresa. 30c, St. Dominic. 50c, St. Francis of Assisi. 1 l, St. Francis Xavier.

**1923, June 11**

| | | | | |
|---|---|---|---|---|
| 143 | A68 | 20c ol grn & brn org | 6.50 | 140.00 |
| a. | | Imperf., single | 400.00 | 550.00 |
| b. | | Vert. pair, imperf btwn. | 875.00 | 1,200. |
| 144 | A68 | 30c claret & brn org | 6.50 | 140.00 |
| a. | | Imperf., single | 400.00 | 550.00 |
| c. | | Horiz. pair, imperf btwn. | 875.00 | 1,200. |
| 145 | A68 | 50c vio & brn org | 6.50 | 140.00 |
| a. | | Imperf., single | 400.00 | 550.00 |
| c. | | Horiz. pair, imperf btwn. | 1,200. | 1,600. |
| d. | | Vert. pair, imperf btwn. | 875.00 | 1,200. |
| 146 | A68 | 1 l bl & brn org | 6.50 | 140.00 |
| a. | | Imperf., single | 400.00 | 550.00 |
| c. | | Horiz. pair, imperf btwn. | 875.00 | 1,200. |
| d. | | Vert. pair, imperf btwn. | 875.00 | 1,200. |
| | | Nos. 143-146 (4) | 26.00 | 560.00 |
| | | Set, never hinged | 60.00 | |

300th anniv. of the Propagation of the Faith. Practically the entire issue was delivered to speculators.

Stamps of Previous Issues, Surcharged:

a

b

c

d

e

**1923-25**

| | | | | |
|---|---|---|---|---|
| 147 | A49(a) | 7½c on 85c | .20 | 1.25 |
| a. | | Double surcharge | — | 1,500. |
| 148 | A42(b) | 10c on 1c | .20 | .35 |
| a. | | Inverted surcharge | 24.00 | 40.00 |
| 149 | A43(b) | 10c on 2c | .20 | .35 |
| a. | | Inverted surcharge | 60.00 | 95.00 |
| 150 | A48(c) | 10c on 15c | .20 | .35 |
| 151 | A49(a) | 20c on 25c | .20 | .35 |
| 152 | A45(d) | 25c on 45c | .40 | 14.50 |
| 153 | A49(a) | 25c on 60c | 1.60 | 1.00 |
| 154 | A49(a) | 30c on 50c | .20 | .35 |
| 155 | A49(a) | 30c on 55c | .80 | .35 |
| 156 | A49(a) | 50c on 40c | 4.75 | .40 |
| a. | | Inverted surcharge | 225.00 | 325.00 |
| b. | | Double surcharge | 125.00 | 140.00 |

| | | | | |
|---|---|---|---|---|
| 157 | A49(a) | 50c on 55c | 22.50 | 12.00 |
| a. | | Inverted surcharge | 1,000. | 2,000. |
| 158 | A51(e) | 1.75 l on 10 l | 11.00 | 27.50 |
| | | Nos. 147-158 (12) | 42.25 | 58.75 |
| | | Set, never hinged | 110.00 | |

Years of issue: Nos. 148-149, 156-157, 1923; Nos. 147, 152-153, 1924; others, 1925.

Emblem of the New Government A69

Wreath of Victory, Eagle and Fasces A70

Symbolical of Fascism and Italy — A71

**Unwmk.**

**1923, Oct. 24    Engr.    Perf. 14**

| | | | | |
|---|---|---|---|---|
| 159 | A69 | 10c dark green | 4.75 | 9.50 |
| a. | | Imperf., single | 800.00 | 800.00 |
| 160 | A69 | 30c dark violet | 4.75 | 9.50 |
| 161 | A69 | 50c brown carmine | 8.00 | 16.00 |

**Wmk. 140    Typo.**

| | | | | |
|---|---|---|---|---|
| 162 | A70 | 1 l blue | 12.00 | 16.00 |
| 163 | A70 | 2 l brown | 16.00 | 20.00 |
| 164 | A71 | 5 l blk & bl | 24.00 | 55.00 |
| a. | | Imperf., single | 325.00 | — |
| | | Nos. 159-164 (6) | 69.50 | 126.00 |
| | | Set, never hinged | 175.00 | |

Anniv. of the March of the Fascisti on Rome.

Fishing Scene A72

Designs: 15c, Mt. Resegone. 30c, Fugitives bidding farewell to native mountains. 50c, Part of Lake Como. 1 l, Manzoni's home, Milan. 5 l, Alessandro Manzoni. The first four designs show scenes from Manzoni's work "I Promessi Sposi."

**1923, Dec. 29    Perf. 14**

| | | | | |
|---|---|---|---|---|
| 165 | A72 | 10c brn red & blk | 20.00 | 140.00 |
| 166 | A72 | 15c bl grn & blk | 20.00 | 140.00 |
| 167 | A72 | 30c blk & slate | 20.00 | 140.00 |
| a. | | Imperf., single | 2,500. | |
| | | Never hinged | 3,000. | |
| 168 | A72 | 50c org brn & blk | 20.00 | 140.00 |
| 169 | A72 | 1 l blue & blk | 140.00 | 650.00 |
| a. | | Imperf., single, no gum | 160.00 | 725.00 |
| 170 | A72 | 5 l vio & blk | 725.00 | — |
| a. | | Imperf., single | 875.00 | 3,500. |
| | | Never hinged | 2,250. | |
| | | Nos. 165-170 (6) | 945.00 | 4,710. |
| | | Set, never hinged | 3,000. | |

50th anniv. of the death of Alessandro Manzoni.

Nos. 136-139 Surcharged

**1924, Feb.**

| | | | | |
|---|---|---|---|---|
| 171 | A64 | 1 l on 5c ol grn | 17.50 | 210.00 |
| 172 | A64 | 1 l on 10c red | 11.00 | 210.00 |
| 173 | A64 | 1 l on 15c slate grn | 17.50 | 210.00 |
| 174 | A64 | 1 l on 25c ultra | 11.00 | 210.00 |
| | | Nos. 171-174 (4) | 57.00 | 840.00 |
| | | Set, never hinged | 140.00 | |

Surcharge forgeries exist.

**Perf. 14x13½**

| | | | | |
|---|---|---|---|---|
| 171a | A64 | 1 l on 5c | 35.00 | 250.00 |
| 172a | A64 | 1 l on 10c | 20.00 | 250.00 |
| 173a | A64 | 1 l on 15c | 35.00 | 250.00 |
| 174h | A64 | 1 l on 25c | 20.00 | 250.00 |
| | | Nos. 171a-174h (4) | 110.00 | 1,000. |
| | | Set, never hinged | 220.00 | |

Nos. 95, 102, 105, 108, 110, 87 and 89 Overprinted in Black or Red

**1924, Feb. 16**

| | | | | |
|---|---|---|---|---|
| 174A | A48 | 10c claret | 1.60 | 40.00 |
| 174B | A49 | 30c org brn | 1.60 | 40.00 |
| 174C | A49 | 50c violet | 1.60 | 40.00 |
| 174D | A49 | 60c bl (R) | 13.00 | 110.00 |
| 174E | A49 | 85c choc (R) | 6.50 | 110.00 |
| 174F | A46 | 1 l brn & grn | 45.00 | 400.00 |
| 174G | A46 | 2 l dk grn & org | 32.50 | 400.00 |
| | | Nos. 174A-174G (7) | 101.80 | 1,140. |
| | | Set, never hinged | 250.00 | |

These stamps were sold on an Italian warship which made a cruise to South American ports in 1924.

Overprint forgeries exist of #174D-174G.

Stamps of 1901-22 with Advertising Labels Attached

**Perf. 14 all around, Imperf. between 1924-25**

| | | | | |
|---|---|---|---|---|
| 96b | A48 | 15c + Bitter Campari | 4.00 | 24.00 |
| 96c | A48 | 15c + Cordial Campari | 4.00 | 20.00 |
| 96d | A48 | 15c + Columbia | 65.00 | 47.50 |
| 100c | A49 | 25c + Abrador | 125.00 | 125.00 |
| 100d | A49 | 25c + Coen | 250.00 | 55.00 |
| 100e | A49 | 25c + Piperno | 1,900. | 875.00 |
| 100f | A49 | 25c + Reinach | 125.00 | 80.00 |
| 100g | A49 | 25c + Tagliacozzo | 875.00 | 875.00 |
| 102b | A49 | 30c + Columbia | 35.00 | 40.00 |
| 105b | A49 | 50c + Coen | 1,900. | 80.00 |
| 105c | A49 | 50c + Columbia | 24.00 | 16.00 |
| 105d | A49 | 50c + De Montel | 4.00 | 16.00 |
| 105e | A49 | 50c + Piperno | 2,400. | 300.00 |
| 105f | A49 | 50c + Reinach | 250.00 | 65.00 |
| 105g | A49 | 50c + Siero Casali | 27.50 | 47.50 |
| 105h | A49 | 50c + Singer | 4.00 | 9.50 |
| 105i | A49 | 50c + Tagliacozzo | 2,750. | 550.00 |
| 105j | A49 | 50c + Tantal | 400.00 | 150.00 |
| 87d | A46 | 1 l + Columbia | 875.00 | 875.00 |
| | | Nos. 96b-87d (19) | 12,017. | 4,250. |
| | | Set, never hinged | 19,750. | |

No. 113 with Columbia label and No. E3 with Cioccolato Perugina label were prepared but not issued. Values $55, $20.

King Victor Emmanuel III — A78

**Perf. 11, 13½ (No. 177)**

| | | **1925-26** | **Engr.** | **Unwmk.** |
|---|---|---|---|---|
| 175 | A78 | 60c brn car | .80 | .80 |
| a. | | Perf. 13½ | 6.50 | 2.40 |
| b. | | Imperf., pair | 275.00 | |
| 176 | A78 | 1 l dk bl | .80 | .80 |
| a. | | Perf. 13½ | 14.50 | 8.00 |
| b. | | Imperf., pair | 275.00 | |
| 177 | A78 | 1.25 l dk bl ('26) | 4.00 | 2.40 |
| a. | | Perf. 11 | 95.00 | 95.00 |
| b. | | Imperf., pair | 600.00 | |
| | | Nos. 175-177 (3) | 5.60 | 4.00 |
| | | Set, never hinged | 14.00 | |

25th year of the reign of Victor Emmanuel III.

Nos. 175 to 177 exist with sideways watermark of fragments of letters or a crown, which are normally on the sheet margin.

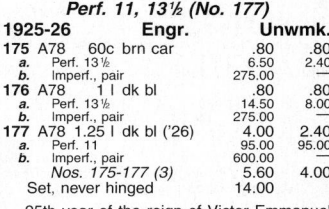

St. Francis and His Vision A79

Monastery of St. Damien A80

Assisi Monastery A81

St. Francis' Death A82

St. Francis — A83

**1926, Jan. 30    Wmk. 140    Perf. 14**

| | | | | |
|---|---|---|---|---|
| 178 | A79 | 20c gray grn | .80 | 1.00 |
| 179 | A80 | 40c dk vio | .80 | 1.00 |
| 180 | A81 | 60c red brn | .80 | 1.00 |
| a. | | Imperf., pair | 450.00 | 450.00 |

Unwmk. Perf. 11
181 A83 30c slate blk .80 1.00
a. Perf. 13½ 24.00 16.00
Never hinged 60.00
182 A82 1.25 l dark blue 4.00 1.00
a. Perf. 13½ 475.00 32.50
Never hinged 1,200.

Perf. 13½
183 A83 5 l + 2.50 l dk brn 11.00 100.00
Nos. 178-183 (6) 18.20 105.00
Set, never hinged 45.00

St. Francis of Assisi, 700th death anniv.

Alessandro Volta — A84

1927 Wmk. 140 Typo. Perf. 14
188 A84 20c dk car 1.60 1.25
189 A84 50c grnsh blk 2.40 .80
190 A84 60c chocolate 4.75 4.75
191 A84 1.25 l ultra 11.00 8.00
Nos. 188-191 (4) 19.75 14.80
Set, never hinged 50.00

Cent. of the death of Alessandro Volta.
The 20c in purple is Cyrenaica No. 25 with overprint omitted. Value, $3,850.

A85   A86

1927-29 Size: 17½x22mm Perf. 14
192 A85 50c brn & slate 2.40 .40
a. Imperf., pair — —

Unwmk.
Engr. Perf. 11
Size: 19x23mm
193 A85 1.75 l dp brn 3.25 .35
a. Perf. 13½ ('29) 35,000. 2,750.
Never hinged 55,000.
b. Perf. 11x13½ ('29) — 2,250.
c. Perf. 13½x11 ('29) — 2,250.
194 A85 1.85 l black 1.60 .70
195 A85 2.55 l brn car 3.50 9.50
196 A85 2.65 l dp vio 4.50 72.50
Nos. 192-196 (5) 15.25 83.45
Set, never hinged 37.50

1928-29 Wmk. 140 Typo. Perf. 14
197 A86 7½c lt brown 3.25 12.00
198 A86 15c brown org ('29) 2.40 .35
199 A86 35c gray blk ('29) 6.00 12.00
200 A86 50c dull violet 13.00 .35
Nos. 197-200 (4) 24.65 24.70
Set, never hinged 60.00

Emmanuel Philibert, Duke of Savoy — A87

Statue of Philibert, Turin — A88

Philibert and Italian Soldier of 1918 — A89

1928 Perf. 11, 14
201 A87 20c red brn & ultra 8.00 12.00
a. Perf. 13½ 200.00 200.00
202 A87 25c dp red & bl grn 8.00 12.00
a. Perf. 13½ 65.00 47.50

203 A87 30c bl grn & red brn 16.00 24.00
a. Center inverted 50,000. 6,750.
b. Perf. 13½ 32.50 32.50
204 A89 50c org brn & bl 4.00 1.25
205 A89 75c dp red 4.75 4.00
206 A88 1.25 l bl & blk 4.75 4.00
207 A89 1.75 l bl grn 32.50 24.00
208 A87 5 l vio & bl grn 27.50 100.00
209 A89 10 l blk & pink 35.00 200.00
210 A88 20 l vio & blk 70.00 675.00
Nos. 201-210 (10) 210.50 1,056.
Set, never hinged 525.00

400th anniv. of the birth of Emmanuel Philibert, Duke of Savoy; 10th anniv. of the victory of 1918; Turin Exhibition.

She-wolf Suckling Romulus and Remus
A90   A95a

Julius Caesar A91

Augustus Caesar A92

"Italia" — A93

A94   A95

1929-42 Wmk. 140 Photo. Perf. 14
213 A90 5c olive brn .20 .20
214 A91 7½c deep vio 1.60 .20
215 A92 10c dark brn .20 .20
216 A93 15c slate grn .20 .20
217 A91 20c rose red .20 .20
218 A94 25c dp green .20 .20
219 A95 30c olive brn .20 .20
a. Imperf., pair 950.00
220 A93 35c dp blue .20 .20
221 A95 50c purple .20 .20
a. Imperf., pair 550.00 725.00
222 A94 75c rose red .20 .20
222A A91 1 l dk pur ('42) .20 .20
223 A94 1.25 l dp blue .20 .20
224 A92 1.75 l red org .20 .20
225 A93 2 l car lake .20 .20
226 A95a 2.55 l slate grn .20 .80
226A A95a 3.70 l pur ('30) .20 .80
227 A95a 5 l rose red .20 .20
228 A93 10 l purple 4.00 4.00
229 A91 20 l lt green 4.75 12.00
230 A92 25 l bluish sl 11.00 35.00
231 A94 50 l dp violet 13.00 92.50
Nos. 213-231 (21) 37.55 148.10
Set, never hinged 92.50

Stamps of the 1929-42 issue overprinted "G.N.R." are 1943 local issues of the Guardia Nazionale Republicana.
See Nos. 427-438, 441-459.
For surcharge and overprints see Nos. 460, M1-M13, 1N10-1N13, 1LN1-1LN1A, 1LN10; Italian Social Republic 1-5A; Yugoslavia-Ljubljana N36-N54.

Courtyard of Monte Cassino A96

Monks Laying Cornerstone — A98

St. Benedict of Nursia — A100

Designs: 25c, Fresco, "Death of St. Benedict." 75c+15c, 5 l+1 l, Monte Cassino Abbey.

1929, Aug. 1 Photo. Wmk. 140
232 A96 20c red orange 1.60 1.60
233 A96 25c dk green 1.60 1.60
234 A98 50c + 10c ol brn 4.00 24.00
235 A98 75c + 15c crim 4.75 32.50
236 A96 1.25 l + 25c saph 6.50 35.00
237 A98 5 l + 1 l dk vio 9.50 100.00

Unwmk.
Engr.
238 A100 10 l + 2 l slate grn 14.50 225.00
Nos. 232-238 (7) 42.45 419.70
Set, never hinged 105.00

14th cent. of the founding of the Abbey of Monte Cassino by St. Benedict in 529 A.D. The premium on some of the stamps was given to the committee for the celebration of the centenary.

Prince Humbert and Princess Marie José A101

1930, Jan. 8 Photo. Wmk. 140
239 A101 20c orange red .80 .60
240 A101 50c + 10c ol brn 2.40 4.00
241 A101 1.25 l + 25c dp bl 5.50 13.00
Nos. 239-241 (3) 8.70 17.60
Set, never hinged 22.50

Marriage of Prince Humbert of Savoy with Princess Marie José of Belgium.
The surtax on Nos. 240 and 241 was for the benefit of the Italian Red Cross Society.
The 20c in green is Cyrenaica No. 35 with overprint omitted. Value, $30,000.

Ferrucci Leading His Army A102

Fabrizio Maramaldo Killing Ferrucci A103

Francesco Ferrucci — A104

1930, July 10
242 A102 20c rose red .80 .80
243 A103 25c deep green 1.40 .80
244 A103 50c purple .80 .40
245 A103 1.25 l deep blue 11.00 4.75

246 A104 5 l + 2 l org red 22.50 140.00
Nos. 242-246 (5) 36.50 146.75
Set, never hinged 91.50
Nos. 242-246,C20-C22 (8) 60.50 314.75
Set, never hinged 151.50

4th cent. of the death of Francesco Ferrucci, Tuscan warrior.

### Overprints
### See Aegean Islands for types A103-A145 Overprinted.

Helenus and Aeneas A106

Designs: 20c, Anchises and Aeneas watch passing of Roman Legions. 25c, Aeneas feasting in shade of Albunea. 30c, Ceres and her children with fruits of Earth. 50c, Harvesters at work. 75c, Woman at loom, children and calf. 1.25 l, Anchises and his sailors in sight of Italy. 5 l+1.50 l, Shepherd piping by fireside. 10 l+2.50 l, Aeneas leading his army.

1930, Oct. 21 Photo. Perf. 14
248 A106 15c olive brn 2.40 2.40
249 A106 20c orange 2.40 1.60
250 A106 25c green 3.20 1.60
251 A106 30c dull vio 9.50 4.00
252 A106 50c violet 16.00 .80
253 A106 75c rose red 4.00 12.00
254 A106 1.25 l blue 4.00 12.00

Unwmk. Engr.
255 A106 5 l +1.50 l red brn 60.00 325.00
256 A106 10 l +2.50 l gray grn 60.00 450.00
Nos. 248-256 (9) 161.50 809.40
Set, never hinged 405.00
Nos. 248-256,C23-C26 (13) 332.00 1,634.
Set, never hinged 835.00

Bimillenary of the birth of Virgil. Surtax on Nos. 255-256 was for the National Institute Figli del Littorio.

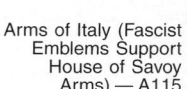

Arms of Italy (Fascist Emblems Support House of Savoy Arms) — A115

1930, Dec. 16 Photo. Wmk. 140
257 A115 2c deep orange 1.60 .20
Never hinged 4.00

St. Anthony being Installed as a Franciscan A116

Olivares Hermitage, Portugal A118

St. Anthony Freeing Prisoners A120

St. Anthony's Death A121

St. Anthony Succoring the Poor — A122

Designs: 25c, St. Anthony preaching to the fishes. 50c, Basilica of St. Anthony, Padua.

**Wmk. 140**

| | | | | |
|---|---|---|---|---|
| **1931, Mar. 9** | | **Photo.** | | **Perf. 14** |
| 258 | A116 | 20c dull violet | 4.00 | 1.25 |
| 259 | A116 | 25c gray green | 2.40 | 1.25 |
| 260 | A118 | 30c brown | 6.50 | 2.40 |
| 261 | A118 | 50c violet | 2.00 | .80 |
| 262 | A120 | 1.25 l blue | 20.00 | 9.50 |

| | | **Unwmk.** | | **Engr.** |
|---|---|---|---|---|
| 263 | A121 | 75c brown red | 9.50 | 16.00 |
| a. | | Perf. 12 | 100.00 | 250.00 |
| | | Never hinged, #263a | 200.00 | |
| 264 | A122 | 5 l + 2.50 l ol grn | 40.00 | 210.00 |
| | | Nos. 258-264 (7) | 84.40 | 241.20 |
| | | Set, never hinged | 210.00 | |

7th centenary of the death of Saint Anthony of Padua.

Tower of Meloria — A123

Training Ship "Amerigo Vespucci" A124

Cruiser "Trento" A125

| | | | | |
|---|---|---|---|---|
| **1931, Nov. 29** | | **Photo.** | | **Wmk. 140** |
| 265 | A123 | 20c rose red | 8.75 | 2.00 |
| 266 | A124 | 50c purple | 8.75 | 4.00 |
| 267 | A125 | 1.25 l dk bl | 24.00 | 4.75 |
| | | Nos. 265-267 (3) | 41.50 | 8.35 |
| | | Set, never hinged | 160.00 | |

Royal Naval Academy at Leghorn (Livorno), 50th anniv.

Giovanni Boccaccio A126

Designs: 15c, Niccolo Machiavelli. 20c, Paolo Sarpi. 25c, Count Vittorio Alfieri. 30c, Ugo Foscolo. 50c, Count Giacomo Leopardi. 75c, Giosue Carducci. 1.25 l, Carlo Giuseppe Botta. 1.75 l, Torquato Tasso. 2.75 l, Francesco Petrarca. 5 l+2.50 l, Ludovico Ariosto. 10 l+2.50 l, Dante Alighieri.

| | | | | |
|---|---|---|---|---|
| **1932, Mar. 14** | | | | **Perf. 14** |
| 268 | A126 | 10c olive brn | 3.25 | 1.60 |
| 269 | A126 | 15c slate green | 3.25 | 2.00 |
| 270 | A126 | 20c rose red | 3.25 | 1.60 |
| 271 | A126 | 25c dp green | 3.25 | 1.25 |
| 272 | A126 | 30c olive brn | 4.00 | 1.60 |
| 273 | A126 | 50c violet | 2.40 | .80 |
| 274 | A126 | 75c car rose | 16.00 | 8.00 |
| 275 | A126 | 1.25 l dp blue | 4.75 | 4.00 |
| 276 | A126 | 1.75 l orange | 12.00 | 8.00 |
| 277 | A126 | 2.75 l gray | 24.00 | 40.00 |
| 278 | A126 | 5 l + 2 l car rose | 29.00 | 175.00 |

| | | | | |
|---|---|---|---|---|
| 279 | A126 | 10 l + 2.50 l ol grn | 35.00 | 275.00 |
| | | Nos. 268-279 (12) | 140.15 | 518.85 |
| | | Set, never hinged | 360.00 | |
| | | Nos. 268-279,C28-C33,C34 (19) | 239.15 | 1,491. |
| | | Set, never hinged | 600.00 | |

Dante Alighieri Society, a natl. literary association founded to promote development of the Italian language and culture. The surtax was added to the Society funds to help in its work.

View of Caprera A138

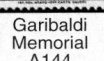

Garibaldi Carrying His Dying Wife A141

Garibaldi Memorial A144

Giuseppe Garibaldi A145

Designs: 20c, 30c, Garibaldi meeting Victor Emmanuel II. 25c, 50c, Garibaldi at Battle of Calatafimi. 1.25 l, Garibaldi's tomb. 1.75 l+25c, Rock of Quarto.

| | | | | |
|---|---|---|---|---|
| **1932, Apr. 6** | | | | |
| 280 | A138 | 10c gray blk | 2.40 | 1.60 |
| 281 | A138 | 20c olive brn | 2.40 | 1.25 |
| 282 | A138 | 25c dull grn | 3.20 | 1.60 |
| 283 | A138 | 30c orange | 3.25 | 2.40 |
| 284 | A138 | 50c violet | 1.60 | .40 |
| 285 | A141 | 75c rose red | 16.00 | 9.50 |
| 286 | A141 | 1.25 l dp blue | 32.50 | 4.00 |
| 287 | A141 | 1.75 l + 25c bl gray | 40.00 | 87.50 |
| 288 | A144 | 2.55 l + 50c red brn | 32.50 | 125.00 |
| 289 | A145 | 5 l + 1 l cop red | 32.50 | 130.00 |
| | | Nos. 280-289 (10) | 166.35 | 363.25 |
| | | Set, never hinged | 410.00 | |
| | | Nos. 280-289,C35-C39,CE1-CE2 (17) | 242.35 | 619.25 |
| | | Set, never hinged | 600.00 | |

50th anniv. of the death of Giuseppe Garibaldi, patriot.

Plowing with Oxen and Tractor A146

10c, Soldier guarding mountain pass. 15c, Marine, battleship & seaplane. 20c, Head of Fascist youth. 25c, Hands of workers & tools. 30c, Flags, Bible & altar. 35c, "New roads for the new Legions." 50c, Mussolini statue, Bologna. 60c, Hands with spades. 75c, Excavating ruins. 1 l, Steamers & galleons. 1.25 l, Italian flag, map & points of compass. 1.75 l, Flag, athlete & stadium. 2.55 l, Mother & child. 2.75 l, Emblems of drama, music, art & sport. 5 l+2.50 l, Roman emperor.

| | | | | |
|---|---|---|---|---|
| **1932, Oct. 27** | | | | **Photo.** |
| 290 | A146 | 5c dk brown | 2.40 | 1.25 |
| 291 | A146 | 10c dk brown | 2.40 | .80 |
| 292 | A146 | 15c dk gray grn | 2.40 | 1.25 |
| 293 | A146 | 20c car rose | 2.40 | .60 |
| 294 | A146 | 25c dp green | 2.40 | .40 |
| 295 | A146 | 30c dk brown | 3.25 | 2.40 |
| 296 | A146 | 35c dk blue | 8.00 | 9.50 |
| 297 | A146 | 50c purple | 1.60 | .40 |
| 298 | A146 | 60c orange brn | 12.00 | 8.00 |
| 299 | A146 | 75c car rose | 4.00 | 4.00 |
| 300 | A146 | 1 l black vio | 16.00 | 6.50 |
| 301 | A146 | 1.25 l dp blue | 4.00 | 1.60 |
| 302 | A146 | 1.75 l orange | 24.00 | 2.00 |
| 303 | A146 | 2.55 l dk gray | 29.00 | 40.00 |
| 304 | A146 | 2.75 l slate grn | 29.00 | 40.00 |

| | | | | |
|---|---|---|---|---|
| 305 | A146 | 5 l + 2.50 l car rose | 40.00 | 300.00 |
| | | Nos. 290-305 (16) | 182.85 | 418.70 |
| | | Set, never hinged | 445.00 | |
| | | Nos. 290-305,C40-C41,E16-E17 (20) | 206.50 | 622.95 |
| | | Set, never hinged | 495.50 | |

10th anniv. of the Fascist government and the March on Rome.

Statue of Athlete — A162

Cross in Halo, St. Peter's Dome — A163

| | | | | |
|---|---|---|---|---|
| **1933, Aug. 16** | | | | **Perf. 14** |
| 306 | A162 | 10c dk brown | .80 | .80 |
| 307 | A162 | 20c rose red | .80 | .80 |
| 308 | A162 | 50c purple | .80 | .40 |
| 309 | A162 | 1.25 l blue | 4.75 | 6.50 |
| | | Nos. 306-309 (4) | 7.15 | 8.50 |
| | | Set, never hinged | 18.00 | |

Intl. University Games at Turin, Sept., 1933.

**1933, Oct. 23**

Designs: 25c, 50c, Angel with cross. 1.25 l, as 20c. 2.55 l, + 2.50 l, Cross with doves.

| | | | | |
|---|---|---|---|---|
| 310 | A163 | 20c rose red | 4.75 | 1.25 |
| 311 | A163 | 25c green | 12.00 | 1.60 |
| 312 | A163 | 50c purple | 4.75 | .40 |
| 313 | A163 | 1.25 l dp blue | 12.00 | 4.75 |
| 314 | A163 | 2.55 l + 2.50 l blk | 8.00 | 140.00 |
| | | Nos. 310-314 (5) | 41.50 | 148.00 |
| | | Set, never hinged | 105.00 | |
| | | Nos. 310-314,CB1-CB2 (7) | 47.90 | 209.00 |
| | | Set, never hinged | 121.00 | |

Issued at the solicitation of the Order of the Holy Sepulchre of Jerusalem to mark the Holy Year.

Anchor of the "Emanuele Filiberto" A166

Antonio Pacinotti A172

Designs: 20c, Anchor. 50c, Gabriele d'Annunzio. 1.25 l, St. Vito's Tower. 1.75 l, Symbolizing Fiume's annexation. 2.55 l+2 l,

Victor Emmanuel III arriving aboard "Brindisi." 2.75 l+2.50 l, Galley, gondola and battleship.

| | | | | |
|---|---|---|---|---|
| **1934, Mar. 12** | | | | |
| 315 | A166 | 10c dk brown | 6.50 | 4.00 |
| 316 | A166 | 20c rose red | 1.60 | 1.60 |
| 317 | A166 | 50c purple | 1.60 | 1.60 |
| 318 | A166 | 1.25 l blue | 1.60 | 6.50 |
| 319 | A166 | 1.75 l + 1 l indigo | 1.60 | 35.00 |
| 320 | A166 | 2.55 l + 2 l dull vio | 1.60 | 55.00 |
| 321 | A166 | 2.75 l + 2.50 l ol grn | 1.60 | 55.00 |
| | | Nos. 315-321 (7) | 16.10 | 158.70 |
| | | Set, never hinged | 40.00 | |
| | | Nos. 315-321,C56-C61,CE5-CE7 (16) | 26.50 | 312.10 |
| | | Set, never hinged | 66.50 | |

10th anniversary of the annexation of Fiume.

| | | | | |
|---|---|---|---|---|
| **1934, May 23** | | | | |
| 322 | A172 | 50c purple | .80 | .40 |
| 323 | A172 | 1.25 l sapphire | 1.25 | 2.75 |
| | | Set, never hinged | 5.00 | |

75th anniv. of invention of the dynamo by Antonio Pacinotti (1841-1912), scientist.

Guarding the Goal — A173

Players — A175

Soccer Players A174

| | | | | |
|---|---|---|---|---|
| **1934, May 23** | | | | |
| 324 | A173 | 20c red orange | 6.50 | 8.00 |
| 325 | A174 | 25c green | 6.50 | 2.40 |
| 326 | A174 | 50c purple | 6.50 | 1.25 |
| 327 | A174 | 1.25 l blue | 16.00 | 16.00 |
| 328 | A175 | 5 l + 2.50 l brn | 87.50 | 475.00 |
| | | Nos. 324-328 (5) | 123.00 | 502.65 |
| | | Set, never hinged | 310.00 | |
| | | Nos. 324-328,C62-C65 (9) | 249.00 | 1,250. |
| | | Set, never hinged | 610.00 | |

2nd World Soccer Championship.
For overprints see Aegean Islands #31-35.

Luigi Galvani — A176

**1934, Aug. 16**

| | | | | |
|---|---|---|---|---|
| 329 | A176 | 30c brown, *buff* | 1.00 | .80 |
| 330 | A176 | 75c carmine, *rose* | 1.40 | 3.25 |
| | | Set, never hinged | 6.00 | |

Intl. Congress of Electro-Radio-Biology.

Carabinieri Emblem — A177

Cutting Barbed Wire A178

Designs: 20c, Sardinian Grenadier and soldier throwing grenade. 25c, Alpine Infantry. 30c, Military courage. 75c, Artillery. 1.25 l, Acclaiming the Service. 1.75 l+1 l, Cavalry. 2.55 l+2 l, Sapping Detail. 2.75 l+2 l, First aid.

**1934, Sept. 6**  **Photo.**  **Wmk. 140**

| | | | | |
|---|---|---|---|---|
| 331 | A177 | 10c dk brown | 2.40 | 2.40 |
| 332 | A178 | 15c olive grn | 2.40 | *4.00* |
| 333 | A178 | 20c rose red | 2.40 | 1.60 |
| 334 | A177 | 25c green | 4.00 | 1.60 |
| 335 | A178 | 30c dk brown | 4.00 | *8.00* |
| 336 | A178 | 50c purple | 2.40 | .80 |
| 337 | A178 | 75c car rose | 40.00 | 12.00 |
| 338 | A178 | 1.25 l dk blue | 40.00 | 8.00 |
| 339 | A177 | 1.75 l + 1 l red org | 17.50 | 52.50 |
| 340 | A178 | 2.55 l + 2 l dp cl | 17.50 | 67.50 |
| 341 | A178 | 2.75 l + 2 l vio | 40.00 | 72.50 |
| | | Nos. 331-341 (11) | 153.60 | 230.90 |
| | | Set, never hinged | 385.00 | |
| | | Nos. 331-341,C66-C72 (18) | 202.10 | 379.90 |
| | | Set, never hinged | 505.00 | |

Centenary of Military Medal of Valor.
For overprints see Aegean Islands #36-46.

Man Holding Fasces A187

Standard Bearer, Bayonet Attack A188

Design: 30c, Eagle and soldier.

**1935, Apr. 23**  **Perf. 14**

| | | | | |
|---|---|---|---|---|
| 342 | A187 | 20c rose red | .80 | .80 |
| 343 | A187 | 30c dk brown | 6.50 | 6.50 |
| 344 | A188 | 50c purple | .80 | .40 |
| | | Nos. 342-344 (3) | 8.10 | 7.70 |
| | | Set, never hinged | 20.00 | |

Issued in honor of the University Contests.

Fascist Flight Symbolism A190

Leonardo da Vinci — A191

**1935, Oct. 1**

| | | | | |
|---|---|---|---|---|
| 345 | A190 | 20c rose red | 16.00 | 2.00 |
| 346 | A190 | 30c brown | 32.50 | 6.50 |
| 347 | A191 | 50c purple | 65.00 | 1.25 |
| 348 | A191 | 1.25 l dk blue | 72.50 | 7.25 |
| | | Nos. 345-348 (4) | 186.00 | 17.00 |
| | | Set, never hinged | 735.00 | |

International Aeronautical Salon, Milan.

Vincenzo Bellini — A192

Bellini's Villa — A194

Bellini's Piano A193

**1935, Oct. 15**

| | | | | |
|---|---|---|---|---|
| 349 | A192 | 20c rose red | 16.00 | 4.00 |
| 350 | A192 | 30c brown | 24.00 | 12.00 |
| 351 | A192 | 50c violet | 24.00 | 1.60 |
| 352 | A192 | 1.25 l dk blue | 40.00 | 16.00 |
| 353 | A193 | 1.75 l + 1 l red org | 35.00 | 200.00 |
| 354 | A194 | 2.75 l + 2 l ol blk | 65.00 | 225.00 |
| | | Nos. 349-354 (6) | 204.00 | 458.60 |
| | | Set, never hinged | 510.00 | |
| | | Nos. 349-354,C79-C83 (11) | 287.00 | 868.10 |
| | | Set, never hinged | 710.00 | |

Bellini (1801-35), operatic composer.

Map of Italian Industries A195

Designs: 20c, 1.25 l, Map of Italian Industries. 30c, 50c, Cogwheel and plow.

**1936, Mar. 23**

| | | | | |
|---|---|---|---|---|
| 355 | A195 | 20c red | .80 | .40 |
| 356 | A195 | 30c brown | .80 | *1.25* |
| 357 | A195 | 50c purple | .80 | .35 |
| 358 | A195 | 1.25 l blue | 4.75 | 3.00 |
| | | Nos. 355-358 (4) | 7.15 | 5.00 |
| | | Set, never hinged | 18.00 | |

The 17th Milan Trade Fair.

Flock of Sheep A197

Ajax Defying the Lightning A199

Bust of Horace A200

Designs: 20c, 1.25 l+1 l, Countryside in Spring. 75c, Capitol. 1.75 l+1 l, Pan piping. 2.55 l+1 l, Dying warrior.

**Wmk. Crowns (140)**

**1936, July 1**  **Photo.**  **Perf. 14**

| | | | | |
|---|---|---|---|---|
| 359 | A197 | 10c dp green | 6.50 | 1.25 |
| 360 | A197 | 20c rose red | 4.75 | .80 |
| 361 | A199 | 30c olive brn | 6.50 | 2.25 |
| 362 | A200 | 50c purple | 6.50 | .40 |
| 363 | A197 | 75c rose red | 16.00 | 9.50 |
| 364 | A197 | 1.25 l + 1 l dk bl | 27.50 | 125.00 |
| 365 | A199 | 1.75 l + 1 l car rose | 32.50 | 200.00 |
| 366 | A197 | 2.55 l + 1 l sl blk | 40.00 | 225.00 |
| | | Nos. 359-366 (8) | 140.25 | 564.20 |
| | | Set, never hinged | 350.00 | |
| | | Nos. 359-366,C84-C88 (13) | 201.50 | 980.20 |
| | | Set, never hinged | 500.00 | |

2000th anniv. of the birth of Quintus Horatius Flaccus (Horace), Roman poet.

Child Holding Wheat — A204

Child Giving Salute — A205

Child and Fasces — A206

"Il Bambino" by della Robbia — A207

**1937, June 28**

| | | | | |
|---|---|---|---|---|
| 367 | A204 | 10c yellow brn | 3.25 | 1.60 |
| 368 | A205 | 20c car rose | 3.25 | 1.25 |
| 369 | A204 | 25c green | 3.25 | 2.00 |
| 370 | A206 | 30c dk brown | 4.75 | 4.00 |
| 371 | A205 | 50c purple | 3.25 | .40 |
| 372 | A207 | 75c rose red | 16.00 | 17.50 |
| 373 | A205 | 1.25 l dk blue | 20.00 | 17.50 |
| 374 | A206 | 1.75 l + 75c org | 40.00 | 140.00 |
| 375 | A207 | 2.75 l + 1.25 l dk bl grn | 32.50 | 160.00 |
| 376 | A205 | 5 l + 3 l bl gray | 40.00 | 225.00 |
| | | Nos. 367-376 (10) | 166.25 | 569.25 |
| | | Set, never hinged | 415.00 | |
| | | Nos. 367-376,C89-C94 (16) | 262.25 | 1,143. |
| | | Set, never hinged | 655.00 | |

Summer Exhibition for Child Welfare. The surtax on Nos. 374-376 was used to support summer camps for children.

Rostral Column — A208

15c, Army Trophies. 20c, Augustus Caesar (Octavianus) offering sacrifice. 25c, Cross Roman Standards. 30c, Julius Caesar and Julian Star. 50c, Augustus receiving acclaim. 75c, Augustus Caesar. 1.25 l, Symbolizing maritime glory of Rome. 1.75 l+1 l, Sacrificial Altar. 2.55 l+2 l, Capitol.

**1937, Sept. 23**

| | | | | |
|---|---|---|---|---|
| 377 | A208 | 10c myrtle grn | 3.25 | .80 |
| 378 | A208 | 15c olive grn | 3.25 | 1.25 |
| 379 | A208 | 20c red | 3.25 | .60 |
| 380 | A208 | 25c green | 3.25 | .60 |
| 381 | A208 | 30c olive bis | 4.00 | .80 |
| 382 | A208 | 50c purple | 3.25 | .35 |
| 383 | A208 | 75c scarlet | 3.25 | *4.75* |
| 384 | A208 | 1.25 l dk blue | 8.00 | 5.50 |
| 385 | A208 | 1.75 l + 1 l plum | 40.00 | *125.00* |
| 386 | A208 | 2.55 l + 2 sl blk | 52.50 | *175.00* |
| | | Nos. 377-386 (10) | 124.00 | 314.65 |
| | | Set, never hinged | 300.00 | |
| | | Nos. 377-386,C95-C99 (15) | 259.00 | 662.65 |
| | | Set, never hinged | 625.00 | |

Bimillenary of the birth of Emperor Augustus Caesar (Octavianus) on the occasion of the exhibition opened in Rome by Mussolini, Sept. 22, 1937.
For overprints see Aegean Islands #47-56.

Gasparo Luigi Pacifico Spontini A218

Antonius Stradivarius A219

Count Giacomo Leopardi A220

Giovanni Battista Pergolesi A221

Giotto di Bondone — A222

**1937, Oct. 25**

| | | | | |
|---|---|---|---|---|
| 387 | A218 | 10c dk brown | 1.60 | .80 |
| 388 | A219 | 20c rose red | 1.60 | .80 |
| 389 | A220 | 25c dk green | 1.60 | .80 |
| 390 | A221 | 30c dk brown | 1.60 | 1.60 |
| 391 | A220 | 50c purple | 1.60 | .80 |
| 392 | A221 | 75c crimson | 2.25 | 4.75 |
| 393 | A222 | 1.25 l dp blue | 3.25 | 4.75 |
| 394 | A218 | 1.75 l dp orange | 3.25 | 4.75 |
| 395 | A219 | 2.55 l + 2 l gray grn | 16.00 | *160.00* |
| 396 | A222 | 2.75 l + 2 l red brn | 16.00 | *200.00* |
| | | Nos. 387-396 (10) | 48.75 | 379.05 |
| | | Set, never hinged | 125.00 | |

Centennials of Spontini, Stradivarius, Leopardi, Pergolesi and Giotto.
For overprints see Aegean Islands #57-58.

Guglielmo Marconi A223

Augustus Caesar (Octavianus) A224

**1938, Jan. 24**

| | | | | |
|---|---|---|---|---|
| 397 | A223 | 20c rose pink | 3.25 | .80 |
| 398 | A223 | 50c purple | .80 | .35 |
| 399 | A223 | 1.25 l blue | 3.25 | 5.50 |
| | | Nos. 397-399 (3) | 7.30 | 6.65 |
| | | Set, never hinged | 18.00 | |

Guglielmo Marconi (1874-1937), electrical engineer, inventor of wireless telegraphy.

**1938, Oct. 28**

10c, Romulus Plowing. 25c, Dante. 30c, Columbus. 50c, Leonardo da Vinci. 75c, Victor Emmanuel II and Garibaldi. 1.25 l, Tomb of

Unknown Soldier, Rome. 1.75 l, Blackshirts' March on Rome, 1922. 2.75 l, Map of Italian East Africa and Iron Crown of Monza. 5 l, Victor Emmanuel III.

| | | | | |
|---|---|---|---|---|
| 400 | A224 | 10c brown | 2.40 | .90 |
| 401 | A224 | 20c car rose | 2.40 | .90 |
| 402 | A224 | 25c dk green | 2.40 | .90 |
| 403 | A224 | 30c olive brn | 2.40 | 2.00 |
| 404 | A224 | 50c lt violet | 2.40 | .90 |
| 405 | A224 | 75c rose red | 3.25 | 3.25 |
| 406 | A224 | 1.25 l dp blue | 6.50 | 3.25 |
| 407 | A224 | 1.75 l vio blk | 8.00 | 4.00 |
| 408 | A224 | 2.75 l slate grn | 26.00 | 47.50 |
| 409 | A224 | 5 l lt red brn | 32.50 | 52.50 |
| | Nos. 400-409 (10) | | 88.25 | 116.10 |
| | Set, never hinged | | 215.00 | |
| | Nos. 400-409,C100-C105 (16) | | 142.25 | 286.60 |
| | Set, never hinged | | 350.00 | |

Proclamation of the Empire.

Wood-burning Engine and Streamlined Electric Engine — A234

| 1939, Dec. 15 | Photo. | Perf. 14 | |
|---|---|---|---|
| 410 A234 | 20c rose red | .80 | .60 |
| 411 A234 | 50c brt violet | 1.60 | .80 |
| 412 A234 | 1.25 l dp blue | 3.25 | 4.00 |
| Nos. 410-412 (3) | | 5.65 | 5.40 |
| Set, never hinged | | 14.00 | |

Centenary of Italian railroads.

Adolf Hitler and Benito Mussolini A235

Hitler and Mussolini A236

| 1941 | | Wmk. 140 | |
|---|---|---|---|
| 413 A235 | 10c dp brown | 2.40 | 2.40 |
| 414 A235 | 20c red orange | 2.40 | 2.40 |
| 415 A235 | 25c dp green | 8.00 | 2.40 |
| 416 A236 | 50c violet | 6.50 | 2.40 |
| 417 A236 | 75c rose red | 8.00 | 6.50 |
| 418 A236 | 1.25 l deep blue | 9.50 | 9.50 |
| Nos. 413-418 (6) | | 36.80 | 25.20 |
| Set, never hinged | | 80.00 | |

Rome-Berlin Axis.
Stamps of type A236 in the denominations and colors of Nos. 413-415 were prepared but not issued. They were sold for charitable purposes in 1948. Value $32.50 each.

Galileo Teaching Mathematics at Padua — A237

Designs: 25c, Galileo presenting telescope to Doge of Venice. 50c, Galileo Galilei (1564-1642). 1.25 l, Galileo studying at Arcetri.

| 1942, Sept. 28 | | | |
|---|---|---|---|
| 419 A237 | 10c dk org & lake | .80 | .60 |
| 420 A237 | 25c gray grn & grn | .80 | .60 |
| 421 A237 | 50c brn vio & vio | .80 | .60 |
| a. | Frame missing | 650.00 | |
| 422 A237 | 1.25 l Prus bl & ultra | .75 | 2.75 |
| Nos. 419-422 (4) | | 3.15 | 4.55 |
| Set, never hinged | | 6.00 | |

Statue of Rossini — A241

Gioacchino Rossini — A242

| 1942, Nov. 23 | | Photo. | |
|---|---|---|---|
| 423 A241 | 25c deep green | .80 | .80 |
| 424 A241 | 30c brown | .80 | .80 |
| 425 A242 | 50c violet | .80 | .80 |
| 426 A242 | 1 l blue | .80 | 2.00 |
| Nos. 423-426 (4) | | 3.20 | 4.40 |
| Set, never hinged | | 6.00 | |

Gioacchino Antonio Rossini (1792-1868), operatic composer.

"Victory for the Axis" A243

"Discipline is the Weapon of Victory" A244

"Everything and Everyone for Victory" A245

"Arms and Hearts Must Be Stretched Out Towards the Goal" A246

| Perf. 14 all around, Imperf. between | | | |
|---|---|---|---|
| 1942 | Photo. | Wmk. 140 | |
| 427 A243 | 25c deep green | .40 | 1.25 |
| 428 A244 | 25c deep green | .40 | 1.25 |
| 429 A245 | 25c deep green | .40 | 1.25 |
| 430 A246 | 25c deep green | .40 | 1.25 |
| 431 A243 | 30c olive brown | .40 | 4.00 |
| 432 A244 | 30c olive brown | .40 | 4.00 |
| 433 A245 | 30c olive brown | .40 | 4.00 |
| 434 A246 | 30c olive brown | .40 | 4.00 |
| 435 A243 | 50c purple | .40 | 1.25 |
| 436 A244 | 50c purple | .40 | 1.25 |
| 437 A245 | 50c purple | .40 | 1.25 |
| 438 A246 | 50c purple | .40 | 1.25 |
| Nos. 427-438 (12) | | 4.80 | 26.00 |
| Set, never hinged | | 12.00 | |

Issued in honor of the Italian Army.
The left halves of #431-438 are type A95.
For overprints see Italian Socal Republic #6-17.

She-Wolf Suckling Romulus and Remus — A247

| Perf. 10½x11½, 11x11½, 11½, 14 | | | |
|---|---|---|---|
| 1944, Jan. | Litho. | Wmk. 87 | |
| | Without Gum | | |
| 439 A247 | 50c rose vio & bis rose | 2.40 | 4.00 |
| | Unwmk. | | |
| 440 A247 | 50c rose vio & pale rose | .40 | 1.60 |

Nos. 439-440 exist imperf., part perf.

**Types of 1929**

| 1945, May | Unwmk. | Perf. 14 | |
|---|---|---|---|
| 441 A93 | 15c slate green | .20 | .20 |
| 442 A93 | 35c deep blue | .20 | .40 |
| 443 A91 | 1 l deep violet | .50 | .20 |
| Nos. 441-443 (3) | | .90 | .80 |
| Set, never hinged | | 2.00 | |

**Types of 1929 Redrawn Fasces Removed**

Victor Emmanuel III A248

Julius Caesar A249

Augustus Caesar A250

"Italia" A251

A252

| 1944-45 | Wmk. 140 Photo. | Perf. 14 | |
|---|---|---|---|
| 444 A248 | 30c dk brown | .20 | .20 |
| 445 A248 | 50c purple | 2.75 | 4.00 |
| 446 A248 | 60c slate grn ('45) | .20 | 1.25 |
| 447 A249 | 1 l dp violet ('45) | .20 | .20 |
| Nos. 444-447 (4) | | 3.35 | 5.65 |
| Set, never hinged | | 7.25 | |

| 1945 | Unwmk. | Perf. 14 | |
|---|---|---|---|
| 448 A250 | 10c dk brown | .20 | 1.60 |
| 448A A249 | 20c rose red | .20 | .20 |
| 449 A251 | 50c dk violet | .20 | .20 |
| 450 A248 | 60c slate grn | .20 | .20 |
| 451 A251 | 60c red org | .20 | .20 |
| 452 A251 | 1 l dp violet | .20 | .20 |
| 452A A249 | 1 l dp vio, redrawn | .20 | .20 |
| 452B A251 | 2 l dp car | 1.60 | 1.25 |
| 452C A251 | 10 l purple | 4.75 | 7.25 |
| Nos. 448-452C (9) | | 7.75 | 11.30 |
| Set, never hinged | | 19.00 | |

| 1945 | | Wmk. 277 | |
|---|---|---|---|
| 453 A249 | 20c rose red | .20 | .80 |
| 454 A248 | 60c slate grn | .20 | .80 |
| 455 A249 | 1 l dp violet | .20 | .20 |
| 456 A251 | 1.20 l dk brown | .20 | .80 |
| 457 A251 | 2 l dk red | .20 | .20 |
| 458 A252 | 5 l dk red | .20 | .80 |
| 459 A251 | 10 l purple | 5.50 | 8.00 |
| Nos. 453-459 (7) | | 6.70 | 11.60 |
| Set, never hinged | | 17.00 | |

Nos. 452A and 457 are redrawings of types A249 and A251. In the redrawn 1 l, the "L" of "LIRE" extends under the "IRE" and the letters of "POSTE ITALIANE" are larger. In the original the "L" extends only under the "I."
In the redrawn 2 l, the "2" is smaller and thinner, and the design is less distinct.
For overprints see Nos. 1LN2-1LN8.

No. 224 Surcharged in Black

| 1945, Mar. | | Wmk. 140 | |
|---|---|---|---|
| 460 A92 | 2.50 l on 1.75 l red org | .20 | .50 |
| | Never hinged | .20 | |
| a. | Six bars at left | 1.50 | 1.50 |

Loggia dei Mercanti, Bologna A253

Basilica of San Lorenzo, Rome A254

**Stamps of Italian Social Republic Surcharged in Black**

| 1945, May 2 | Photo. | Perf. 14 | |
|---|---|---|---|
| 461 A253 | 1.20 l on 20c crim | .20 | .25 |
| 462 A254 | 2 l on 25c green | .20 | .25 |
| a. | 2½ mm between "2" and "LIRE" | 1.50 | 1.50 |
| | Set, never hinged | .80 | |

Breaking Chain A255

United Family and Scales A256

Planting Tree — A257

Tying Tree — A258

Torch A259

"Italia" and Sprouting Oak Stump A260

| 1945-47 | Wmk. 277 Photo. | Perf. 14 | |
|---|---|---|---|
| 463 A255 | 10c rose brown | .20 | .20 |
| 464 A256 | 20c dk brown | .20 | .20 |
| 464A A259 | 25c brt bl grn ('46) | .20 | .20 |
| 465 A257 | 40c slate | .20 | .20 |
| 465A A255 | 50c dp vio ('46) | .20 | .20 |
| 466 A258 | 60c dk green | .20 | .40 |
| 467 A255 | 80c car rose | .20 | .20 |
| 468 A257 | 1 l dk green | .20 | .20 |
| 469 A259 | 1.20 l chestnut | .20 | 1.25 |
| 470 A258 | 2 l dk claret brn | .20 | .40 |
| 471 A259 | 3 l red | .20 | .20 |
| 471A A256 | 4 l red org ('46) | .25 | .20 |
| 472 A259 | 5 l deep blue | .30 | .20 |
| 472A A257 | 6 l dp vio ('47) | 6.50 | .20 |
| 473 A255 | 10 l slate | .80 | .20 |
| 473A A257 | 15 l dp bl ('46) | 8.00 | .20 |
| 474 A259 | 20 l dk red vio | 2.50 | .20 |
| 475 A260 | 25 l dk grn | 24.00 | .20 |
| 476 A260 | 50 l dk vio brn | 8.00 | .20 |
| Nos. 463-476 (19) | | 52.55 | 5.25 |
| Set, never hinged | | 200.00 | |

See Nos. 486-488.
For overprints see Nos. 1LN11-1LN12, 1LN14-1LN19, Trieste 1-13, 15-17, 30-32, 58-68, 82-83.

United Family and Scales A261

| 1946 | Engr. | Perf. 14 | |
|---|---|---|---|
| 477 A261 | 100 l car lake | 175.00 | 2.00 |
| | Never hinged | 450.00 | |
| a. | Perf. 14x13½ | 190.00 | 2.50 |
| | Never hinged | 475.00 | |

For overprints see #1LN13, Trieste 14, 69.

Cathedral of St. Andrea, Amalfi — A262

Church of St. Michael, Lucca — A263

"Peace" from Fresco at Siena A264

Signoria Palace, Florence A265

View of Cathedral Domes, Pisa A266

Republic of Genoa A267

"Venice Crowned by Glory," by Paolo Veronese A268

Oath of Pontida A269

**1946, Oct. 30**

| | | | | |
|---|---|---|---|---|
| 478 | A262 | 1 l brown | .20 | .20 |
| 479 | A263 | 2 l dk blue | .20 | .20 |
| 480 | A264 | 3 l dk bl grn | .20 | .20 |
| 481 | A265 | 4 l dp org | .20 | .20 |
| 482 | A266 | 5 l dp violet | .20 | .20 |
| 483 | A267 | 10 l car rose | .20 | .20 |
| 484 | A268 | 15 l dp ultra | .65 | .65 |
| 485 | A269 | 20 l red brown | .20 | .20 |
| | *Nos. 478-485 (8)* | | 2.05 | 2.05 |
| | Set, never hinged | | 3.25 | |

Proclamation of the Republic.

**Types of 1945**
**1947-48   Wmk. 277   Photo.   Perf. 14**

| | | | | |
|---|---|---|---|---|
| 486 | A255 | 8 l dk green ('48) | 2.50 | .20 |
| 487 | A256 | 10 l red orange | 29.00 | .20 |
| 488 | A259 | 30 l dk blue ('48) | 175.00 | .25 |
| | *Nos. 486-488 (3)* | | 206.50 | .65 |
| | Set, never hinged | | 515.00 | |

St. Catherine Giving Mantle to Beggar — A270

5 l, St. Catherine carrying cross. 10 l, St. Catherine, arms outstretched. 30 l, St. Catherine & scribe.

**1948, Mar. 1**   **Photo.**

| | | | | |
|---|---|---|---|---|
| 489 | A270 | 3 l yel grn & gray grn | .20 | .20 |
| 490 | A270 | 5 l vio & bl | .30 | .35 |
| 491 | A270 | 10 l red brn & vio | 1.60 | 4.00 |
| 492 | A270 | 30 l bis & gray brn | 11.00 | 27.50 |
| | *Nos. 489-492 (4)* | | 13.10 | 32.05 |
| | Set, never hinged | | 32.50 | |
| | *Nos. 489-492,C127-C128 (6)* | | 86.60 | 97.05 |
| | Set, never hinged | | 182.50 | |

600th anniv. of the birth of St. Catherine of Siena, Patroness of Italy.

"Constitutional Government" — A271

**1948, Apr. 12**

| | | | | |
|---|---|---|---|---|
| 493 | A271 | 10 l rose vio | .80 | 1.00 |
| 494 | A271 | 30 l blue | 1.75 | 3.00 |
| | Set, never hinged | | 6.50 | |

Proclamation of the constitution of 1/1/48.

Uprising at Palermo, Jan. 12, 1848 A272

Designs (Revolutionary scenes): 4 l, Rebellion at Padua. 5 l, Proclamation of statute, Turin. 6 l, "Five Days of Milan." 8 l, Daniele Manin proclaming the Republic of Venice. 10 l, Defense of Vicenza. 12 l, Battle of Curtatone. 15 l, Battle of Gioto. 20 l, Insurrection at Bologna. 30 l, "Ten Days of Brescia." 50 l, Garibaldi in Rome fighting. 100 l, Death of Goffredo Mameli.

**1948, May 3**

| | | | | |
|---|---|---|---|---|
| 495 | A272 | 3 l dk brown | .50 | 1.25 |
| 496 | A272 | 4 l red violet | .50 | 1.25 |
| 497 | A272 | 5 l dp blue | 3.25 | 1.25 |
| 498 | A272 | 6 l dp yel grn | 1.60 | 1.25 |
| 499 | A272 | 8 l brown | 1.60 | 1.25 |
| 500 | A272 | 10 l orange red | 1.25 | 1.25 |
| 501 | A272 | 12 l dk gray grn | 3.75 | 3.25 |
| 502 | A272 | 15 l gray blk | 9.00 | 2.00 |
| 503 | A272 | 20 l car rose | 21.00 | 14.50 |
| 504 | A272 | 30 l brt ultra | 4.50 | 2.00 |
| 505 | A272 | 50 l violet | 45.00 | 5.50 |
| 506 | A272 | 100 l blue blk | 82.50 | 27.50 |
| | *Nos. 495-506 (12)* | | 174.45 | 62.25 |
| | Set, never hinged | | 430.00 | |
| | *Nos. 495-506,E26 (13)* | | 249.45 | 82.25 |
| | Set, never hinged | | 580.00 | |

Centenary of the Risorgimento, uprisings of 1848-49 which led to Italian unification.
For overprints see Trieste Nos. 18-29, E5.

Alpine Soldier and Bassano Bridge A273

**1948, Oct. 1   Wmk. 277   Perf. 14**

| | | | | |
|---|---|---|---|---|
| 507 | A273 | 15 l dark green | 1.60 | 2.40 |
| | Never hinged | | 3.25 | |

Bridge of Bassano, re-opening, Oct. 3, 1948.
For overprint see Trieste No. 33.

Gaetano Donizetti — A274

**1948, Oct. 23**   **Photo.**

| | | | | |
|---|---|---|---|---|
| 508 | A274 | 15 l dark brown | 1.25 | 2.25 |

Death cent. of Gaetano Donizetti, composer.
For overprint see Trieste No. 34.

Fair Buildings A275

**1949, Apr. 12**

| | | | | |
|---|---|---|---|---|
| 509 | A275 | 20 l dark brown | 3.25 | 4.00 |
| | Never hinged | | 9.50 | |

27th Milan Trade Fair, April 1949.
For overprint see Trieste No. 35.

Standard of Doges of Venice — A276

15 l, Clock strikers, Lion Tower and Campanile of St. Mark's. 20 l, Lion standard and Venetian galley. 50 l, Lion tower and gulls.

**1949, Apr. 12**
**Buff Background**

| | | | | |
|---|---|---|---|---|
| 510 | A276 | 5 l red brown | .20 | .20 |
| 511 | A276 | 15 l dk green | 2.40 | 2.40 |
| 512 | A276 | 20 l dp red brn | 4.75 | 2.40 |
| 513 | A276 | 50 l dk blue | 26.00 | 2.40 |
| | *Nos. 510-513 (4)* | | 33.35 | 5.20 |
| | Set, never hinged | | 85.00 | |

Biennial Art Exhibition of Venice, 50th anniv.
For overprints see Trieste Nos. 36-39.

"Transportation" and Globes — A277

**1949, May 2   Wmk. 277   Perf. 14**

| | | | | |
|---|---|---|---|---|
| 514 | A277 | 50 l brt ultra | 27.50 | 9.50 |
| | Never hinged | | 60.00 | |

75th anniv. of the UPU.
For overprint see Trieste No. 40.

Workman and Ship — A278

**1949, May 30**   **Photo.**

| | | | | |
|---|---|---|---|---|
| 515 | A278 | 5 l dk green | 4.75 | 8.00 |
| 516 | A278 | 15 l violet | 12.00 | 24.00 |
| 517 | A278 | 20 l brown | 22.50 | 24.00 |
| | *Nos. 515-517 (3)* | | 39.25 | 56.00 |
| | Set, never hinged | | 100.00 | |

European Recovery Program.
For overprints see Trieste Nos. 42-44.

The Vascello, Rome A279

**1949, May 18**

| | | | | |
|---|---|---|---|---|
| 518 | A279 | 100 l brown | 140.00 | 125.00 |
| | Never hinged | | 275.00 | |

Centenary of Roman Republic.
For overprint see Trieste No. 41.

Giuseppe Mazzini — A280

Vittorio Alfieri — A281

**1949, June 1**

| | | | | |
|---|---|---|---|---|
| 519 | A280 | 20 l gray | 4.00 | 4.75 |
| | Never hinged | | 12.00 | |

Erection of a monument to Giuseppe Mazzini (1805-72), Italian patriot and revolutionary.
For overprint see Trieste No. 45.

**1949, June 4**   **Photo.**

| | | | | |
|---|---|---|---|---|
| 520 | A281 | 20 l brown | 3.25 | 3.50 |
| | Never hinged | | 9.50 | |

200th anniv. of the birth of Vittorio Alfieri, tragic dramatist.
For overprint see Trieste No. 46.

Basilica of St. Just, Trieste A282

**1949, June 8**

| | | | | |
|---|---|---|---|---|
| 521 | A282 | 20 l brown red | 9.50 | 20.00 |
| | Never hinged | | 14.50 | |

Trieste election, June 12, 1949.
For overprint see Trieste No. 47.

Staff of Aesculapius, Globe — A283

**1949, June 13   Wmk. 277   Perf. 14**

| | | | | |
|---|---|---|---|---|
| 522 | A283 | 20 l violet | 16.00 | 16.00 |
| | Never hinged | | 40.00 | |

2nd World Health Cong., Rome, 1949.
For overprint see Trieste No. 49.

Lorenzo de Medici A284

Andrea Palladio A285

**1949, Aug. 4**

| | | | | |
|---|---|---|---|---|
| 523 | A284 | 20 l violet blue | 4.00 | 4.00 |
| | Never hinged | | 12.00 | |

Birth of Lorenzo de Medici, 500th anniv.
For overprint see Trieste No. 50.

**1949, Aug. 4**

| | | | | |
|---|---|---|---|---|
| 524 | A285 | 20 l violet | 6.50 | 9.50 |
| | Never hinged | | 16.00 | |

Andrea Palladio (1518-1580), architect.
For overprint see Trieste No. 51.

Tartan and Fair Buildings A286

**1949, Aug. 16**
**525** A286 20 l red    2.75 *3.25*
Never hinged    8.00

133th Levant Fair, Bari, September, 1949.
For overprint see Trieste No. 52.

Voltaic Pile — A287    Alessandro Volta — A288

**1949, Sept. 14**    **Engr.**    **Perf. 14**
**526** A287 20 l rose car    3.25   3.25
   **a.** Perf. 13x14    13.00   10.00
**527** A288 50 l deep blue    37.50   37.50
   **a.** Perf. 13x14    160.00   67.50
   Set, never hinged    105.00

Invention of the Voltaic Pile, 150th anniv.
For overprints see Trieste Nos. 53-54.

Holy Trinity Bridge — A289

**1949, Sept. 19**    **Photo.**
**528** A289 20 l deep green    4.00   3.50
Never hinged    9.50

Issued to publicize plans to reconstruct Holy Trinity Bridge, Florence.
For overprint see Trieste No. 55.

Gaius Valerius Catullus A290    Domenico Cimarosa A291

**1949, Sept. 19**    **Wmk. 277**    **Perf. 14**
**529** A290 20 l brt blue    4.75   3.50
Never hinged    12.00

2000th anniversary of the death of Gaius Valerius Catullus, Lyric poet.
For overprint see Trieste No. 56.

**1949, Dec. 28**
**530** A291 20 l violet blk    4.00   3.25
Never hinged    11.50

Bicentenary of the birth of Domenico Cimarosa, composer.
For overprint see Trieste No. 57.

Milan Fair Scene A292

**1950, Apr. 12**    **Photo.**
**531** A292 20 l brown    2.40   3.25
Never hinged    4.75

The 28th Milan Trade Fair.
For overprint see Trieste No. 70.

Flags and Italian Automobile A293

**1950, Apr. 29**
**532** A293 20 l vio gray    4.50   2.75
Never hinged    12.00

32nd Intl. Auto Show, Turin, May 4-14, 1950.

---

For overprint see Trieste No. 71.

Pitti Palace, Florence A294

"Perseus" by Cellini — A295    Composite of Italian Cathedrals and Churches — A296

**1950, May 22**
**533** A294 20 l olive grn    3.25   3.25
**534** A295 55 l blue    30.00   17.50
   Set, never hinged    85.00

5th General Conf. of UNESCO.
For overprints see Trieste Nos. 72-73.

**1950, May 29**
**535** A296 20 l violet    6.50   .80
**536** A296 55 l blue    32.50   3.25
   Set, never hinged    100.00

Holy Year, 1950.
For overprints see Trieste Nos. 74-75.

Gaudenzio Ferrari A297    Radio Mast and Tower of Florence A298

**1950, July 1**    **Wmk. 277**    **Perf. 14**
**537** A297 20 l gray grn    8.00   3.50
Never hinged    20.00

Issued to honor Gaudenzio Ferrari.
For overprint see Trieste No. 76.

**1950, July 15**    **Photo.**
**538** A298 20 l purple    9.50   10.00
**539** A298 55 l blue    75.00   *160.00*
   Set, never hinged    240.00

Intl. Shortwave Radio Conf., Florence, 1950.
For overprints Trieste see Nos. 77-78.

Ludovico A. Muratori A299    Guido d'Arezzo A300

**1950, July 22**
**540** A299 20 l brown    2.40   2.75
Never hinged    7.25

200th anniv. of the death of Ludovico A. Muratori, writer.
For overprint see Trieste No. 79.

**1950, July 29**
**541** A300 20 l dark green    8.00   3.25
Never hinged    24.00

900th anniv. of the death of Guido d'Arezzo, music teacher and composer.
For overprint see Trieste No. 80.

---

Tartan and Fair Buildings A301

**1950, Aug. 21**
**542** A301 20 l chestnut brown    4.00   2.75
Never hinged

Levant Fair, Bari, September, 1950.
For overprint see Trieste No. 81.

G. Marzotto and A. Rossi — A302    Tobacco Plant — A303

**1950, Sept. 11**
**543** A302 20 l indigo    2.40   2.00
Never hinged    4.75

Pioneers of the Italian wool industry.
For overprint see Trieste No. 84.

**1950, Sept. 11**

Designs: 20 l, Mature plant, different background. 55 l, Girl holding tobacco plant.

**544** A303 5 l dp claret & grn    1.60   *4.00*
**545** A303 20 l brown & grn    2.50   1.25
**546** A303 55 l dp ultra & brn    35.00   32.50
   Nos. 544-546 (3)    39.10   37.75
   Set, never hinged    100.00

Issued to publicize the European Tobacco Conference, Rome, 1950.
For overprints see Trieste Nos. 85-87.

Arms of the Academy of Fine Arts — A304    Augusto Righi — A305

**1950, Sept. 16**
**547** A304 20 l ol brn & red brn    2.75   2.75
Never hinged    6.50

200th anniv. of the founding of the Academy of Fine Arts, Venice.
For overprint see Trieste No. 88.

**1950, Sept. 16**
**548** A305 20 l cream & gray blk    2.75   2.75
Never hinged    6.50

Centenary of the birth of Augusto Righi, physicist.
For overprint see Trieste No. 89.

Blacksmith, Aosta Valley — A306    1851 Stamp of Tuscany — A307

Designs: 1 l, Auto mechanic. 2 l, Mason. 5 l, Potter. 6 l, Lace-making. 10 l, Weaving. 12 l, Sailor steering boat. 15 l, Shipbuilding. 20 l, Fisherman. 25 l, Sorting oranges. 30 l,

---

Woman carrying grapes. 35 l, Olive picking. 40 l, Wine cart. 50 l, Shepherd and flock. 55 l, Plowing. 60 l, Grain cart. 65 l, Girl worker in hemp field. 100 l, Husking corn. 200 l, Woodcutter.

**1950, Oct. 20**    **Wmk. 277**    **Perf. 14**
**549** A306 50c vio blue    .20   .20
**550** A306 1 l dk bl vio    .20   .20
**551** A306 2 l sepia    .20   .20
**552** A306 5 l dk gray    .20   .20
**553** A306 6 l chocolate    .20   .20
**554** A306 10 l dp green    3.75   .20
**555** A306 12 l dp blue grn    1.90   .20
**556** A306 15 l dk gray bl    1.25   .20
**557** A306 20 l blue vio    9.50   .20
**558** A306 25 l brn org    1.60   .20
**559** A306 30 l magenta    1.25   .20
**560** A306 35 l crimson    8.00   1.25
**561** A306 40 l brown    .30   .20
**562** A306 50 l violet    11.50   .20
**563** A306 55 l dp blue    .65   .20
**564** A306 60 l red    2.25   .20
**565** A306 65 l dk grn    .65   .20

**Perf. 13x14, 14x13**
**Engr.**

**566** A306 100 l brn org    32.50   .20
   **a.** Perf. 13    32.50   .20
   **b.** Perf. 14    35.00   .20
**567** A306 200 l ol brn    9.50   3.25
   **a.** Perf. 14    9.50   3.25
   Nos. 549-567 (19)    85.60   7.90
   Set, never hinged    210.00

See Nos. 668-673A. For overprints see Trieste Nos. 90-108, 122-124, 178-180.

**1951, Mar. 27**    **Photo.**    **Perf. 14**

Design: 55 l, Tuscany 6cr.

**568** A307 20 l red vio & red    1.60   1.10
**569** A307 55 l ultra & blue    19.00   40.00
   Set, never hinged    52.50

Centenary of Tuscany's first stamps.
For overprints see Trieste Nos. 109-110.

Italian Automobile A308

**1951, Apr. 2**
**570** A308 20 l dk green    5.50   3.50
Never hinged    16.00

33rd Intl. Automobile Exhib., Turin, Apr. 4-15, 1951.
For overprint see Trieste No. 111.

Altar of Peace, Medea A309

**1951, Apr. 11**
**571** A309 20 l blue vio    3.25   3.25
Never hinged    11.00

Consecration of the Altar of Peace at Redipuglia Cemetery, Medea.
For overprint see Trieste No. 112.

Helicopter over Leonardo da Vinci Heliport — A310    P. T. T. Building, Milan Fair — A311

**1951, Apr. 12**    **Photo.**
**572** A310 20 l brown    9.50   2.00
**573** A311 55 l dp blue    32.50   *70.00*
   Set, never hinged    105.00

29th Milan Trade Fair.
For overprints see Trieste Nos. 113-114.

Symbols of the
International
Gymnastic
Festival
A312

Statue of
Diana, Spindle
and Turin
Tower
A313

**Wmk. 277**

**1951, May 18    Photo.    Perf. 14**
**Fleur-de-lis in Red**
574  A312  5 l dk brown       20.00  *600.00*
575  A312  10 l Prus green    20.00  *600.00*
576  A312  15 l vio blue      20.00  *600.00*
      Nos. 574-576 (3)        60.00  *1,800.*
      Set, never hinged      100.00

International Gymnastic Festival and Meet,
Florence, 1951.
Fake cancellations exist on Nos. 574-576.
For overprints see Trieste Nos. 115-117.

**1951, Apr. 26**
577  A313  20 l purple        10.00  4.50
      Never hinged                   30.00

Tenth International Exhibition of Textile Art
and Fashion, Turin, May 2-16.
For overprint see Trieste No. 118.

Landing of
Columbus
A314

**1951, May 5**
578  A314  20 l Prus green     5.00  4.00
      Never hinged                   22.50

500th anniversary of birth of Columbus.
For overprint see Trieste No. 119.

Reconstructed Abbey of
Montecassino — A315

Design: 55 l, Montecassino Ruins.

**1951, June 18**
579  A315  20 l violet         4.00  2.00
580  A315  55 l brt blue      40.00  55.00
      Set, never hinged        90.00

Issued to commemorate the reconstruction
of the Abbey of Montecassino.
For overprints see Trieste Nos. 120-121.

Pietro Vannucci
(Il Perugino)
A316

Stylized Vase
A317

Cartouche
of
Amenhotep
III and
Pitcher
A318

**1951, July 23**
581  A316  20 l brn & red brn   2.75  *4.00*
      Never hinged                    5.00

500th anniversary (in 1950) of the birth of
Pietro Vannucci, painter.
For overprint see Trieste No. 125.

**1951, July 23**
582  A317  20 l grnsh gray & blk  6.00  4.00
583  A318  55 l vio bl & pale sal 22.50 52.50
      Set, never hinged             60.00

Triennial Art Exhibition, Milan, 1951.
For overprints see Trieste Nos. 126-127.

Cyclist — A319

**1951, Aug. 23**
584  A319  25 l gray black      5.50  5.50
      Never hinged                   12.00

World Bicycle Championship Races, Milan,
Aug.-Sept. 1951.
For overprint see Trieste No. 128.

Tartan and
Globes
A320

**1951, Sept. 8**                  **Photo.**
585  A320  25 l deep blue       3.25  3.25
      Never hinged                   12.00

15th Levant Fair, Bari, September 1951.
For overprint see Trieste No. 129.

"La Figlia di
Jorio" by
Michetti
A321

**1951, Sept. 15    Wmk. 277    Perf. 14**
586  A321  25 l dk brown       3.25  3.25
      Never hinged                    9.00

Centenary of the birth of Francesco Paolo
Michetti, painter.
For overprint see Trieste No. 130.

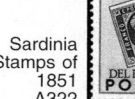

Sardinia
Stamps of
1851
A322

**1951, Oct. 5**
587  A322  10 l shown          1.25  3.25
588  A322  25 l 20c stamp      1.60  1.60
589  A322  60 l 40c stamp      8.00  15.00
      Nos. 587-589 (3)        10.85  19.85
      Set, never hinged        26.00

Centenary of Sardinia's 1st postage stamp.
For overprints see Trieste Nos. 131-133.

Mercury — A323

Roman
Census
A324

**1951, Oct. 31**
590  A323  10 l green          1.00  2.00
591  A324  25 l vio gray       3.00  2.00
      Set, never hinged         8.50

3rd Industrial and the 9th General Italian
Census.
For overprints see Trieste Nos. 134-135.

Winter Scene — A325

Trees
A326

**1951, Nov. 21**
592  A325  10 l ol & dl grn    1.25  *4.50*
593  A326  25 l dull grn       3.50  1.25
      Set, never hinged        10.00

Issued to publicize the Festival of Trees.
For overprints see Trieste Nos. 136-137.

Giuseppe
Verdi
A327

Portraits of Verdi, various backgrounds.

**1951, Nov. 19**                  **Engr.**
594  A327  10 l vio brn & dk grn  2.40  *4.00*
595  A327  25 l red brn & dk
                brn               6.00  1.60
596  A327  60 l dp grn & indigo  24.00  20.00
      Nos. 594-596 (3)           32.40  25.60
      Set, never hinged          65.00

50th anniversary of the death of Giuseppe
Verdi, composer.
For overprints see Trieste Nos. 138-140.

Vincenzo
Bellini — A328

**Wmk. 277**

**1952, Jan. 28    Photo.    Perf. 14**
597  A328  25 l gray & gray blk  2.00  1.60
      Never hinged                     6.00

150th anniversary of the birth of Vincenzo
Bellini, composer.
For overprint see Trieste No. 141.

Palace of
Caserta
and
Statuary
A329

**1952, Feb. 1**
598  A329  25 l dl grn & ol bis  1.60  1.25
      Never hinged                     5.00

Issued to honor Luigi Vanvitelli, architect.

For overprint see Trieste No. 142.

Statues of Athlete
and River God
Tiber — A330

**1952, Mar. 22**
599  A330  25 l brn & sl blk    1.00  1.10
      Never hinged                    2.00

Issued on the occasion of the first International Exhibition of Sports Stamps.
For overprint see Trieste No. 143.

Milan Fair
Buildings
A331

**1952, Apr. 12**                  **Engr.**
600  A331  60 l ultra          27.50  24.00
      Never hinged                   55.00

30th Milan Trade Fair.
For overprint see Trieste No. 144.

Leonardo da
Vinci — A332

Virgin of the
Rocks — A332a

**1952    Wmk. 277    Photo.    Perf. 14**
601  A332  25 l deep orange     .20   .20

**Unwmk.**
**Engr.**                      **Perf. 13**
601A  A332a  60 l ultra        2.40  9.25

**Wmk. 277**
601B  A332  80 l brn car      12.00   .40
   c.    Perf. 14x13          10.00   .40
      Set, never hinged        40.00

Leonardo da Vinci, 500th birth anniv.
For overprints see Trieste #145, 163-164.

First Stamps and Cathedral Bell
Towers of Modena and Parma
A333

**1952, May 29**                   **Perf. 14**
602  A333  25 l blk & red brn   1.00  1.25
603  A333  60 l blk & ultra     4.00  *15.00*
      Set, never hinged         12.00

Cent. of the 1st postage stamps of Modena
and Parma.
For overprints see Trieste Nos. 146-147.

Globe and
Torch — A334

Lion of St.
Mark — A335

**1952, June 7**
**604** A334 25 l bright blue ... 1.00 1.25
Never hinged ... 2.75

Issued to honor the Overseas Fair at Naples and Italian labor throughout the world.
For overprint see Trieste No. 148.

**1952, June 14**
**605** A335 25 l black & yellow ... 1.25 1.25

26th Biennial Art Exhibition, Venice.
For overprint see Trieste No. 149.

"P" and Basilica of St. Anthony A336

Flag and Basilica of St. Just A337

**1952, June 19**
**606** A336 25 l bl gray, red & dk bl ... 2.00 1.60
Never hinged ... 6.00

30th International Sample Fair of Padua.
For overprint see Trieste No. 150.

**1952, June 28**
**607** A337 25 l dp grn, dk brn & red ... 1.40 1.40
Never hinged ... 3.25

4th International Sample Fair of Trieste.
For overprint see Trieste No. 151.

Fair Entrance and Tartan A338

**1952, Sept. 6    Wmk. 277    Perf. 14**
**608** A338 25 l dark green ... 1.00 1.25
Never hinged ... 2.25

16th Levant Fair, Bari, Sept. 1952.
For overprint see Trieste No. 152.

Girolamo Savonarola A339

Mountain Peak and Climbing Equipment A340

**1952, Sept. 20**
**609** A339 25 l purple ... 1.60 1.00
Never hinged ... 4.50

500th anniversary of the birth of Girolamo Savonarola.
For overprint see Trieste No. 153.

**1952, Oct. 4**
**610** A340 25 l gray ... .60 .60
Never hinged ... 1.25

Issued to publicize the National Exhibition of the Alpine troops, Oct. 4, 1952.
For overprint see Trieste No. 154.

Colosseum and Plane A341

**1952, Sept. 29**
**611** A341 60 l vio bl & dk bl ... 9.00 12.00
Never hinged ... 16.00

Issued to publicize the first International Civil Aviation Conference, Rome, Sept. 1952.
For overprint see Trieste No. 155.

Guglielmo Cardinal Massaia and Map A342

**1952, Nov. 21    Engr.    Perf. 13**
**612** A342 25 l brn & dk brn ... 1.25 1.75
Never hinged ... 1.75

Centenary of the establishment of the first Catholic mission in Ethiopia.
For overprint see Trieste No. 156.

Symbols of Army, Navy and Air Force A343

Sailor, Soldier and Aviator A344

Design: 60 l, Boat, plane and tank.

**1952, Nov. 3    Photo.    Perf. 14**
**613** A343 10 l dk green ... .20 .20
**614** A344 25 l blk & dk brn ... .40 .20
**615** A344 60 l black & blue ... 3.50 7.00
Nos. 613-615 (3) ... 4.10 7.40
Set, never hinged ... 9.50

Armed Forces Day, Nov. 4, 1952.
For overprints see Trieste Nos. 157-159.

Antonio Mancini — A345

Vincenzo Gemito — A346

**1952, Dec. 6**
**616** A345 25 l dark green ... .60 1.00
**617** A346 25 l brown ... .60 1.00
Set, never hinged ... 2.50

Birth centenaries of Antonio Mancini, painter, and Vincenzo Gemito, sculptor.
For overprints see Trieste Nos. 160-161.

Martyrs, Jailer and Artist Boldini A347

**1952, Dec. 31**
**618** A347 25 l gray blk & dk blue ... .80 .80
Never hinged ... 3.00

Centenary of the deaths of the five Martyrs of Belfiore.
For overprint see Trieste No. 162.

Antonello da Messina — A349

**1953, Feb. 21    Photo.    Perf. 14**
**621** A349 25 l car lake ... .85 .85
Never hinged ... 2.75

Messina Exhibition of the paintings of Antonello and his 15th cent. contemporaries.
For overprint see Trieste No. 165.

Racing Cars A350

**1953, Apr. 24**
**622** A350 25 l violet ... .85 .85
Never hinged ... 1.25

20th 1,000-mile auto race.
For overprint see Trieste No. 166.

Decoration "Knights of Labor" Bee and Honeycomb A351

Arcangelo Corelli A352

**1953, Apr. 30**
**623** A351 25 l violet ... .60 .80
Never hinged ... 1.25

For overprint see Trieste No. 167.

**1953, May 30**
**624** A352 25 l dark brown ... .60 .80
Never hinged ... 1.25

300th anniv. of the birth of Arcangelo Corelli, composer.
For overprint see Trieste No. 168.

St. Clare of Assisi and Convent of St. Damien A353

"Italia" after Syracusean Coin A354

**1953, June 27**
**625** A353 25 l brown & dull red ... .40 .50
Never hinged ... .85

St. Clare of Assisi, 700th death anniv.
For overprint see Trieste No. 169.

**1953-54    Wmk. 277    Perf. 14**
**Size: 17x21mm**
**626** A354 5 l gray ... .20 .20
**627** A354 10 l org ver ... .20 .20
**628** A354 12 l dull green ... .20 .20
**628A** A354 13 l brt lil rose ('54) ... .20 .20
**629** A354 20 l brown ... 1.90 .20
**630** A354 25 l purple ... 2.50 .20
**631** A354 35 l rose car ... .30 .20
**632** A354 60 l blue ... 16.00 7.25
**633** A354 80 l orange brn ... 32.50 .80
Nos. 626-633 (9) ... 54.00 9.45
Set, never hinged ... 150.00

See Nos. 661-662, 673B-689, 785-788, 998A-998W, 1288-1290. For overprints see Trieste Nos. 170-177.

Mountain Peaks — A355

Tyche, Goddess of Fortune — A356

**1953, July 11**
**634** A355 25 l blue green ... .60 .60
Never hinged ... 1.75

Festival of the Mountain.
For overprint see Trieste No. 181.

**1953, July 16**
**635** A356 25 l dark brown ... .50 .20
**636** A356 60 l deep blue ... 2.50 3.50
Set, never hinged ... 7.25

Intl. Exposition of Agriculture, Rome, 1953.
For overprints see Trieste Nos. 182-183.

Continents Joined by Rainbow A357

**1953, Aug. 6**
**637** A357 25 l org & Prus bl ... 2.75 .20
**638** A357 60 l lil rose & dk vio bl ... 6.00 1.40
Set, never hinged ... 18.00

Signing of the North Atlantic Treaty, 4th anniv.
For overprints see Trieste Nos. 184-185.

Luca Signorelli A358

Agostino Bassi A359

**1953, Aug. 13**
**639** A358 25 l dk brn & dull grn ... .40 .40
Never hinged ... 1.10

Issued to publicize the opening of an exhibition of the works of Luca Signorelli, painter.
For overprint see Trieste No. 186.

**1953, Sept. 5**
**640** A359 25 l dk gray & brown ... .35 .35
Never hinged ... .80

6th International Microbiology Congress, Rome, Sept. 6-12, 1953.
For overprint see Trieste No. 187.

Siena — A360

Rapallo A361

Views: 20 l, Seaside at Gardone. 25 l, Mountain, Cortina d'Ampezzo. 35 l, Roman ruins, Taormina. 60 l, Rocks and sea, Capri.

**1953, Dec. 31**     *Perf. 14*
| | | | | |
|---|---|---|---|---|
| 641 | A360 | 10 l dk brn & red brn | .20 | .20 |
| 642 | A361 | 12 l lt blue & gray | .20 | .20 |
| 643 | A361 | 20 l brn org & dk brn | .25 | .20 |
| 644 | A360 | 25 l dk grn & pale bl | .60 | .20 |
| 645 | A361 | 35 l cream & brn | .65 | .40 |
| 646 | A361 | 60 l bl grn & ind | 1.60 | 1.75 |
| | *Nos. 641-646 (6)* | | 3.50 | 2.95 |
| | Set, never hinged | | 10.00 | |

For overprints see Trieste Nos. 188-193, 204-205.

Lateran Palace, Rome — A362

Television Screen and Aerial — A363

**1954, Feb. 11**
| | | | | |
|---|---|---|---|---|
| 647 | A362 | 25 l dk brown & choc | .30 | .20 |
| 648 | A362 | 60 l blue & ultra | 1.60 | 3.00 |
| | Set, never hinged | | 5.00 | |

Signing of the Lateran Pacts, 25th anniv.
For overprints see Trieste Nos. 194-195.

**1954, Feb. 25**
| | | | | |
|---|---|---|---|---|
| 649 | A363 | 25 l purple | .65 | .20 |
| 650 | A363 | 60 l dp blue grn | 2.75 | 4.50 |
| | Set, never hinged | | 9.00 | |

Introduction of regular natl. television service.
For overprints see Trieste Nos. 196-197.

"Italia" and Quotation from Constitution A364

**1954, Mar. 20**
| | | | | |
|---|---|---|---|---|
| 651 | A364 | 25 l purple | .70 | .20 |
| | Never hinged | | 2.00 | |

Propaganda for the payment of taxes.
For overprint see Trieste No. 198.

Vertical Flight Trophy — A365

Eagle Perched on Ruins — A366

**1954, Apr. 24**
| | | | | |
|---|---|---|---|---|
| 652 | A365 | 25 l gray black | .40 | .70 |
| | Never hinged | | .90 | |

Issued to publicize the experimental transportation of mail by helicopter, April 1954.
For overprint see Trieste No. 199.

**1954, June 1**
| | | | | |
|---|---|---|---|---|
| 653 | A366 | 25 l gray, org brn & blk | .20 | .35 |
| | Never hinged | | .40 | |

10th anniv. of Italy's resistance movement.
For overprint see Trieste No. 200.

Alfredo Catalani, Composer, Birth Centenary — A367

**1954, June 19**     *Perf. 14*
| | | | | |
|---|---|---|---|---|
| 654 | A367 | 25 l dk grnsh gray | .20 | .30 |
| | Never hinged | | .40 | |

For overprint see Trieste No. 201.

Marco Polo, Lion of St. Mark and Dragon A368

**1954, July 8**     *Engr.*     *Perf. 14*
| | | | | |
|---|---|---|---|---|
| 655 | A368 | 25 l red brown | .25 | .20 |

*Perf. 13*
| | | | | |
|---|---|---|---|---|
| 656 | A368 | 60 l gray green | 1.75 | 5.50 |
| a. | Perf. 13x12 | | 6.00 | 6.00 |
| | Set, never hinged | | 5.25 | |

700th anniv. of the birth of Marco Polo.
For overprints see Trieste Nos. 202-203.

Automobile and Cyclist A369

**1954, Sept. 6**     *Photo.*     *Perf. 14*
| | | | | |
|---|---|---|---|---|
| 657 | A369 | 25 l dp green & red | .30 | .30 |
| | Never hinged | | .60 | |

Italian Touring Club, 60th anniv.
For overprint see Trieste No. 206.

St. Michael Overpowering the Devil — A370

**1954, Oct. 9**
| | | | | |
|---|---|---|---|---|
| 658 | A370 | 25 l rose red | .25 | .20 |
| 659 | A370 | 60 l blue | .85 | 1.10 |
| | Set, never hinged | | 1.90 | |

23rd general assembly of the International Criminal Police, Rome 1954.
For overprints see Trieste Nos. 207-208.

Pinocchio and Group of Children — A371

**1954, Oct. 26**
| | | | | |
|---|---|---|---|---|
| 660 | A371 | 25 l rose red | .40 | .30 |
| | Never hinged | | .80 | |

Carlo Lorenzini, creator of Pinocchio.

### Italia Type of 1953-54

**1954, Dec. 28**     *Engr.*     *Perf. 13*
**Size: 22½x27½mm**
| | | | | |
|---|---|---|---|---|
| 661 | A354 | 100 l brown | 55.00 | .30 |
| 662 | A354 | 200 l dp blue | 5.00 | .50 |
| | Set, never hinged | | 190.00 | |

Madonna, Perugino A372

Amerigo Vespucci and Map A373

60 l, Madonna of the Pieta, Michelangelo.

**1954, Dec. 31**     *Photo.*     *Perf. 14*
| | | | | |
|---|---|---|---|---|
| 663 | A372 | 25 l brown & bister | .25 | .20 |
| 664 | A372 | 60 l black & cream | 1.10 | 2.75 |
| | Set, never hinged | | 3.00 | |

Issued to mark the end of the Marian Year.

**1954, Dec. 31**     *Engr.*     *Perf. 13*
| | | | | |
|---|---|---|---|---|
| 665 | A373 | 25 l dp plum | .25 | .20 |
| a. | Perf. 13x14 | | 5.75 | .80 |
| 666 | A373 | 60 l blue blk | 1.25 | 2.75 |
| a. | Perf. 13x14 | | 1.25 | 2.75 |
| | Set, never hinged | | 3.50 | |

500th anniv. of the birth of Amerigo Vespucci, explorer, 1454-1512.

Silvio Pellico (1789-1854), Dramatist — A374

**Wmk. 277**

**1955, Jan. 24**     *Photo.*     *Perf. 14*
| | | | | |
|---|---|---|---|---|
| 667 | A374 | 25 l brt blue & vio | .30 | .20 |
| | Never hinged | | .40 | |

### Italy at Work Type of 1950

**1955-57**     **Wmk. 303**
| | | | | |
|---|---|---|---|---|
| 668 | A306 | 50c vio bl | .20 | .20 |
| 669 | A306 | 1 l dk bl vio | .20 | .20 |
| 670 | A306 | 2 l sepia | .20 | .20 |
| 671 | A306 | 15 l dk gray bl | .65 | .25 |
| 672 | A306 | 30 l magenta | 27.50 | .50 |
| 673 | A306 | 50 l violet | 12.00 | .20 |
| 673A | A306 | 65 l dk grn ('57) | 14.00 | 45.00 |
| | *Nos. 668-673A (7)* | | 54.75 | 46.60 |
| | Set, never hinged | | 140.00 | |

### Italia Type of 1953-54 and

St. George, by Donatello — A374a

**1955-58**     **Wmk. 303**     **Photo.**     *Perf. 14*
**Size: 17x21mm**
| | | | | |
|---|---|---|---|---|
| 673B | A354 | 1 l gray ('58) | .20 | .20 |
| 674 | A354 | 5 l slate | .20 | .20 |
| 675 | A354 | 6 l ocher ('57) | .20 | .20 |
| 676 | A354 | 10 l org ver | .20 | .20 |
| 677 | A354 | 12 l dull green | .20 | .20 |
| 678 | A354 | 13 l brt lil rose | .20 | .20 |
| 679 | A354 | 15 l gray vio ('56) | .20 | .20 |
| 680 | A354 | 20 l brown | .20 | .20 |
| 681 | A354 | 25 l purple | .20 | .20 |
| 682 | A354 | 35 l rose car | .20 | .20 |
| 683 | A354 | 50 l olive ('58) | .25 | .20 |
| 685 | A354 | 60 l blue | .20 | .20 |
| 686 | A354 | 80 l brown org | .20 | .20 |
| 687 | A354 | 90 l lt red brn ('58) | .20 | .20 |

**Engr.**     *Perf. 13½*
**Size: 22½x28mm**
| | | | | |
|---|---|---|---|---|
| 688 | A354 | 100 l brn ('56) | 4.50 | .20 |
| a. | Perf. 13½x12 | | 4.50 | .20 |
| b. | Perf. 13½x14 | | 1,300. | 24.00 |
| 689 | A354 | 200 l gray bl ('57) | 3.75 | .20 |
| 690 | A374a | 500 l grn ('57) | 1.25 | .20 |
| b. | Perf. 14x13½ | | .65 | .20 |
| 690A | A374a | 1000 l rose car ('57) | 2.25 | .60 |
| c. | Perf. 14x13½ | | 1.25 | .20 |
| | *Nos. 673B-690A (18)* | | 14.60 | 4.00 |
| | Set, never hinged | | 45.00 | |

Nos. 690-690A were printed on ordinary and fluorescent paper.
See Nos. 785-788. See Nos. 998A-998W for small-size set.

> **Catalogue values for unused stamps in this section, from this point to the end of the section, are for Never Hinged items.**

"Italia" A375

Oil Derrick and Old Roman Aqueduct A376

**1955, Mar. 15**     *Photo.*     *Perf. 14*
| | | | | |
|---|---|---|---|---|
| 691 | A375 | 25 l rose vio | 2.00 | .20 |

Issued as propaganda for the payment of taxes.

**1955, June 6**
60 l, Marble columns and oil field on globe.
| | | | | |
|---|---|---|---|---|
| 692 | A376 | 25 l olive green | .40 | .20 |
| 693 | A376 | 60 l henna brown | 1.40 | 1.50 |

4th World Petroleum Cong., Rome, June 6-15, 1955.

Antonio Rosmini, Philosopher, Death Centenary — A377

**1955, July 1**     **Wmk. 303**     *Perf. 14*
| | | | | |
|---|---|---|---|---|
| 694 | A377 | 25 l sepia | 1.00 | .20 |

Girolamo Fracastoro and Stadium at Verona A378

**1955, Sept. 1**
| | | | | |
|---|---|---|---|---|
| 695 | A378 | 25 l gray blk & brn | .70 | .20 |

Intl. Medical Congress, Verona, Sept. 1-4.

Basilica of St. Francis, Assisi A379

**1955, Oct. 4**
| | | | | |
|---|---|---|---|---|
| 696 | A379 | 25 l black & cream | .40 | .20 |

Issued in honor of St. Francis and for the 7th centenary (in 1953) of the Basilica in Assisi.

Young Man at Drawing Board — A380

**1955, Oct. 15**
| | | | | |
|---|---|---|---|---|
| 697 | A380 | 25 l Prus green | .40 | .20 |

Centenary of technical education in Italy.

Harvester — A381

FAO Headquarters, Rome — A382

**1955, Nov. 3**
698 A381 25 l rose red & brn .30 .25
699 A382 60 l blk & brt pur 1.60 1.25

Intl. Institute of Agriculture, 50th anniv. and FAO, successor to the Institute, 10th anniv.

A383     A384

**1955, Nov. 10**
700 A383 25 l rose brown 1.10 .20

70th anniversary of the birth of Giacomo Matteotti, Italian socialist leader.

**1955, Nov. 19**
701 A384 25 l dark green .35 .20

Death of Battista Grassi, zoologist, 30th anniv.

"St. Stephen Giving Alms" — A385

"St. Lorenzo Giving Alms" A386

**1955, Nov. 26**
702 A385 10 l black & cream .20 .20
703 A386 25 l ultra & cream .40 .20

Death of Fra Angelico, painter, 500th anniv.

Giovanni Pascoli A387

**1955, Dec. 31**
704 A387 25 l gray black .30 .20

Centenary of the birth of Giovanni Pascoli, poet.

Ski Jump "Italia" A388

Stadiums at Cortina: 12 l, Skiing. 25 l, Ice skating. 60 l, Ice racing, Lake Misurina.

**1956, Jan. 26**    **Photo.**
705 A388 10 l blue grn & org .20 .20
706 A388 12 l yellow & blk .20 .20
707 A388 25 l vio blk & org brn .35 .20
708 A388 60 l sapphire & org 2.25 2.50
Nos. 705-708 (4) 3.00 3.10

VII Winter Olympic Games at Cortina d'Ampezzo, Jan. 26-Feb. 5, 1956.

Mail Coach and Tunnel Exit A389

**1956, May 19**   **Wmk. 303**   *Perf. 14*
709 A389 25 l dk blue grn 6.00 .80

50th anniv. of the Simplon Tunnel.

Arms of Republic and Symbols of Industry A390

**1956, June 2**
710 A390 10 l gray & slate bl .30 .20
711 A390 25 l pink & rose red .45 .20
712 A390 60 l lt bl & brt bl 4.75 5.50
713 A390 80 l orange & brn 7.00 .20
Nos. 710-713 (4) 12.50 6.10

Tenth anniversary of the Republic.

Amedeo Avogadro A391

**1956, Sept. 8**
714 A391 25 l black vio .25 .20

Centenary of the death of Amedeo Avogadro, physicist.

**Europa Issue**

"Rebuilding Europe" — A392

**1956, Sept. 15**
715 A392 25 l dark green 1.50 .20
716 A392 60 l blue 10.00 1.00

Issued to symbolize the cooperation among the six countries comprising the Coal and Steel Community.

Globe and Satellites A393

**1956, Sept. 22**
717 A393 25 l intense blue .25 .20

7th Intl. Astronautical Cong., Rome, Sept. 17-22.

Globe — A394

**1956, Dec. 29**   **Litho.**   **Unwmk.**
718 A394 25 l red & bl grn, *pink* .30 .20
719 A394 60 l bl grn & red, *pale bl grn* .40 .20

Italy's admission to the United Nations. The design, viewed through red and green glasses, becomes three-dimensional.

Postal Savings Bank and Notes A395

**1956, Dec. 31**   **Photo.**   **Wmk. 303**
720 A395 25 l sl bl & dp ultra .25 .20

80th anniversary of Postal Savings.

Ovid A396     Antonio Canova A397

Paulina Borghese as Venus A398

**1957, June 10**    *Perf. 14*
721 A396 25 l ol grn & blk .30 .20

2000th anniversary of the birth of the poet Ovid (Publius Ovidius Naso).

**1957, July 15**    **Engr.**
60 l, Sculpture: Hercules and Lichas.
722 A397 25 l brown .20 .20
723 A397 60 l gray .25 .60
724 A398 80 l vio blue .25 .20
Nos. 722-724 (3) .70 1.00

Birth of Antonio Canova, sculptor, 200th anniv.

Traffic Light A399    "United Europe" A400

**Wmk. 303**

**1957, Aug. 7**   **Photo.**   *Perf. 14*
725 A399 25 l green, blk & red .35 .20

Campaign for careful driving.

**1957, Sept. 16**   **Litho.**   *Perf. 14*
**Flags in Original Colors**
726 A400 25 l light blue .75 .20
    *Perf. 13*
727 A400 60 l violet blue 5.50 .60

United Europe for peace and prosperity.

Giosue Carducci A401    Filippino Lippi A402

**1957, Oct. 14**    **Engr.**    *Perf. 14*
728 A401 25 l brown .30 .20

Death of the poet Giosue Carducci, 50th anniv.

**1957, Nov. 25**   **Wmk. 303**   *Perf. 14*
729 A402 25 l reddish brown .30 .20

Birth of Filippino Lippi, painter, 500th anniv.

2000th Anniv. of the Death of Marcus Tullius Cicero, Roman Statesman and Writer — A403

**1957, Nov. 30**    **Photo.**
730 A403 25 l brown red .25 .20

St. Domenico Savio and Students of Various Races A404

**1957, Dec. 14**
731 A404 15 l brt lil & blk .25 .20

Cent. of the death of St. Domenico Savio.

St. Francis of Paola A405    Giuseppe Garibaldi A406

**1957, Dec. 21**    **Engr.**
732 A405 25 l black .25 .20

450th anniv. of the death of St. Francis of Paola, patron saint of seafaring men.

**1957, Dec. 14**   *Perf. 14x13, 13x14*
Design: 110 l, Garibaldi monument, horiz.
733 A406 15 l slate green .25 .20
734 A406 110 l dull purple .35 .20

150th anniv. of the birth of Giuseppe Garibaldi.

Peasant, Dams and Map of Sardinia A407

**1958, Feb. 1**    **Engr.**    *Perf. 14*
738 A407 25 l bluish grn .25 .20

Completion of the Flumendosa-Mulargia irrigation system.

Immaculate Conception Statue, Rome, and Lourdes Basilica — A408

**1958, Apr. 16**    **Wmk. 303**    *Perf. 14*
739 A408 15 l rose claret    .25  .20
740 A408 60 l blue    .25  .20
Apparition of the Virgin Mary at Lourdes, cent.

Book and Symbols of Labor Industry and Agriculture A409

Designs: 60 l, "Tree of Freedom," vert. 110 l, Montecitorio Palace.

**1958, May 9**    **Photo.**    *Perf. 14*
741 A409  25 l bl grn & ocher    .25  .20
742 A409  60 l blk brn & bl    .25  .20
743 A409 110 l ol bis & blk brn    .25  .20
   Nos. 741-743 (3)    .75  .60
10th anniversary of the constitution.

Brussels Fair Emblem A410

Prologue from Pagliacci A411

**1958, June 12**
744 A410 60 l blue & yellow    .25  .20
Intl. and Universal Exposition at Brussels.

**1958, July 10**
745 A411 25 l dk bl & dk red    .25  .20
Birth of Ruggiero Leoncavallo, composer, cent.

Scene from La Bohème A412

**1958, July 10**    **Engr.**    **Unwmk.**
746 A412 25 l dark blue    .25  .20
Birth of Giacomo Puccini, composer, cent.

Giovanni Fattori, Self-portrait A413

"Ave Maria on the Lake" by Giovanni Segantini A414

**1958, Aug. 7**    **Wmk. 303**    *Perf. 13x14*
747 A413 110 l redsh brown    .40  .30
Death of Giovanni Fattori, painter, 50th anniv.

**1958, Aug. 7**    *Perf. 14*
748 A414 110 l slate, *buff*    .40  .30
Birth of Giovanni Segantini, painter, cent.

Map of Brazil, Plane and Arch of Titus A415

**1958, Aug. 23**    **Photo.**    *Perf. 14*
749 A415 175 l Prus green    .80  *1.25*
Italo-Brazilian friendship on the occasion of Pres. Giovanni Gronchi's visit to Brazil.

---

**Common Design Types**
pictured following the introduction.

---

**Europa Issue, 1958**
Common Design Type
**1958, Sept. 13**
   **Size: 20½x35½mm**
750 CD1 25 l red & blue    .60  .20
751 CD1 60 l blue & red    *1.25*  .35
Issued to show the European Postal Union at the service of European integration.

½g Stamp of Naples A416

Evangelista Torricelli A417

Design: 60 l, 1g Stamp of Naples.

   *Perf. 14x13½, 13½*
**1958, Oct. 4**    **Engr.**    **Unwmk.**
752 A416 25 l brown red    .20  .20
753 A416 60 l blk & red brn    .20  .20
Centenary of the stamps of Naples.

**1958, Oct. 20**    **Wmk. 303**    *Perf. 14*
754 A417 25 l rose claret    .65  .20
350th anniv. of the birth of Evangelista Torricelli, mathematician and physicist.

"The Triumph of Caesar," Montegna A418

Persian Style Bas-relief, Sorrento A419

25 l, Coats of Arms of Trieste, Rome & Trento, horiz. 60 l, War memorial bell of Rovereto.

**1958, Nov. 3**    **Engr.**    *Perf. 14x13½*
755 A418 15 l green    .20  .20
756 A418 25 l gray    .20  .20
757 A418 60 l rose claret    .20  .20
   Nos. 755-757 (3)    .60  .60
40th anniv. of Italy's victory in World War I.

**1958, Nov. 27**    **Photo.**
758 A419 25 l sepia, *bluish*    .25  .20
759 A419 60 l vio bl, *bluish*    .45  .60
Visit of the Shah of Iran to Italy.

Eleonora Duse — A420

Dancers and Antenna — A421

**Unwmk.**
**1958, Dec. 11**    **Engr.**    *Perf. 14*
760 A420 25 l brt ultra    .25  .20
Cent. of the birth of Eleonora Duse, actress.

**1958, Dec. 29**    **Photo.**    **Wmk. 303**
Design: 60 l, Piano, dove and antenna.
761 A421 25 l red, bl & blk    .20  .20
762 A421 60 l ultra & blk    .20  .20
10th anniv. of the Prix Italia (International Radio and Television Competitions).

Stamp of Sicily — A422

Design: 60 l, Stamp of Sicily, 5g.

   *Perf. 14x13½*
**1959, Jan. 2**    **Engr.**    **Unwmk.**
763 A422 25 l Prus green    .20  .20
764 A422 60 l dp orange    .20  .20
Centenary of the stamps of Sicily.

Dome of St. Peter's and Tower of Lateran Palace A423

**Wmk. 303**
**1959, Feb. 11**    **Photo.**    *Perf. 14*
765 A423 25 l ultra    .25  .20
30th anniversary of the Lateran Pacts.

Map of North Atlantic and NATO Emblem A424

**1959, Apr. 4**
766 A424 25 l dk bl & ocher    .20  .20
767 A424 60 l dk bl & green    .20  .20
10th anniv. of NATO.

Arms of Paris and Rome A425

**1959, Apr. 9**
768 A425 15 l blue & red    .20  .20
769 A425 25 l blue & red    .20  .20
Cultural ties between Rome and Paris.

"A Gentle Peace Has Come" — A426

Statue of Lord Byron — A427

**1959, Apr. 13**    **Engr.**    **Unwmk.**
770 A426 25 l olive green    .20  .20
International War Veterans Association convention, Rome.

**1959, Apr. 21**
771 A427 15 l black    .20  .20
Unveiling in Rome of a statue of Lord Byron by Bertel Thorvaldson, Danish sculptor.

Camillo Prampolini — A428

**1959, Apr. 27**    **Unwmk.**    *Perf. 14*
772 A428 15 l car rose    3.50  .40
Camillo Prampolini, socialist leader and reformer, birth centenary.

Fountain of Dioscuri and Olympic Rings — A429

Baths of Carcalla A430

Designs: 25 l, Capitoline tower. 60 l, Arch of Constantine. 110 l, Ruins of Basilica of Massentius.

## 1959, June 23    Photo.    Wmk. 303
### Designs in Dark Sepia
| | | | | |
|---|---|---|---|---|
| 773 | A429 | 15 l red orange | .20 | .20 |
| 774 | A429 | 25 l blue | .20 | .20 |
| 775 | A430 | 35 l bister | .20 | .20 |
| 776 | A430 | 60 l rose lilac | .25 | .30 |
| 777 | A430 | 110 l yellow | .30 | .20 |
| | | Nos. 773-777 (5) | 1.15 | 1.10 |

1960 Olympic Games in Rome.

Victor Emanuel II, Garibaldi, Cavour, Mazzini
A431

Battle of San Fermo
A432

25 l, "After the Battle of Magenta" by Fattori and Red Cross, vert. 60 l, Battle of Palestro. 110 l, "Battle of Magenta" by Induno, vert.

### Engr., Cross Photo. on 25 l
## 1959, June 27    Unwmk.
| | | | | |
|---|---|---|---|---|
| 778 | A431 | 15 l gray | .20 | .20 |
| 779 | A431 | 25 l brn & red | .20 | .20 |
| 780 | A432 | 35 l dk violet | .20 | .20 |
| 781 | A432 | 60 l ultra | .20 | .20 |
| 782 | A432 | 110 l magenta | .20 | .20 |
| | | Nos. 778-782 (5) | 1.00 | 1.00 |

Cent. of the war of independence. No. 779 for the centenary of the Red Cross idea.

Labor Monument, Geneva
A433

Stamp of Romagna
A434

## 1959, July 20    Perf. 14x13, 14
| | | | | |
|---|---|---|---|---|
| 783 | A433 | 25 l violet | .20 | .20 |
| 784 | A433 | 60 l brown | .30 | .20 |

40th anniv. of the ILO.

### Italia Type of 1953-54
### Photo.; Engr. (100 l, 200 l)
## 1959-66    Wmk. 303    Perf. 14
### Size: 17x21mm
| | | | | |
|---|---|---|---|---|
| 785 | A354 | 30 l bis brn ('60) | .25 | .20 |
| 786 | A354 | 40 l lil rose ('60) | 1.25 | .20 |
| 786A | A354 | 70 l Prus grn ('60) | .35 | .20 |
| 787 | A354 | 100 l brown | .65 | .20 |
| 787A | A354 | 130 l gray & dl red ('66) | .25 | .20 |
| 788 | A354 | 200 l dp blue | .65 | .20 |
| | | Nos. 785-788 (6) | 3.40 | 1.20 |

## 1959, Sept. 1    Photo.
Design: 60 l, Stamp of Romagna, 20b.
| | | | | |
|---|---|---|---|---|
| 789 | A434 | 25 l pale brn & blk | .20 | .20 |
| 790 | A434 | 60 l gray grn & blk | .20 | .20 |

Centenary of the stamps of Romagna.

### Europa Issue, 1959
### Common Design Type
## 1959, Sept. 19
### Size: 22x27½mm
| | | | | |
|---|---|---|---|---|
| 791 | CD2 | 25 l olive green | .40 | .20 |
| 792 | CD2 | 60 l blue | .40 | .20 |

Stamp of 1953 with Facsimile Cancellation
A435

Aeneas Fleeing with Father and Son, by Raphael
A436

## 1959, Dec. 20    Wmk. 303    Perf. 14
| | | | | |
|---|---|---|---|---|
| 793 | A435 | 15 l gray, rose car & blk | .20 | .20 |

Italy's first Stamp Day, Dec. 20, 1959.

## 1960, Apr. 7    Engr.    Unwmk.
| | | | | |
|---|---|---|---|---|
| 794 | A436 | 25 l lake | .20 | .20 |
| 795 | A436 | 60 l gray violet | .20 | .20 |

World Refugee Year, 7/1/59-6/30/60. Design is detail from "The Fire in the Borgo."

Garibaldi's Proclamation to the Sicilians — A437

King Victor Emmanuel and Garibaldi Meeting at Teano — A438

60 l, Volunteers embarking, Quarto, Genoa.

### Wmk. 303
## 1960, May 5    Photo.    Perf. 14
| | | | | |
|---|---|---|---|---|
| 796 | A437 | 15 l brown | .20 | .20 |

### Perf. 13x14, 14x13
### Engr.    Unwmk.
| | | | | |
|---|---|---|---|---|
| 797 | A438 | 25 l rose claret | .20 | .20 |
| 798 | A437 | 60 l ultramarine | .20 | .20 |

Cent. of the liberation of Southern Italy (Kingdom of the Two Sicilies) by Garibaldi.

Emblem of 17th Olympic Games — A439

Olympic Stadium A440

Statues: 15 l, Roman Consul on way to the games. 35 l, Myron's Discobolus. 110 l, Seated boxer. 200 l, Apoxyomenos by Lysippus.
Stadia: 25 l, Velodrome. 60 l, Sports palace. 150 l, Small sports palace.

### Photogravure, Engraved
### Perf. 14x13½, 13½x14
## 1960    Wmk. 303, Unwmk.
| | | | | |
|---|---|---|---|---|
| 799 | A439 | 5 l yellow brn | .20 | .20 |
| 800 | A440 | 10 l dp org & dk bl | .20 | .20 |
| 801 | A439 | 15 l ultra | .20 | .20 |
| 802 | A440 | 25 l lt vio & brn | .20 | .20 |
| 803 | A439 | 35 l rose cl | .20 | .20 |
| 804 | A440 | 60 l bluish grn & brn | .20 | .20 |
| 805 | A439 | 110 l plum | .20 | .20 |
| 806 | A440 | 150 l blue & brn | 1.60 | 2.75 |
| 807 | A439 | 200 l green | .80 | .20 |
| | | Nos. 799-807 (9) | 3.80 | 4.35 |

17th Olympic Games, Rome, 8/25-9/11. The photo. denominations (5-10, 25, 60, 150 l) are wmkd.; the engraved (15, 35, 110, 200 l) are unwmkd.

Bottego Statue, Parma
A441

Michelangelo da Caravaggio
A442

## 1960    Unwmk.    Engr.    Perf. 14
| | | | | |
|---|---|---|---|---|
| 808 | A441 | 30 l brown | .20 | .20 |

Birth cent. of Vittorio Bottego, explorer.

### Europa Issue, 1960
### Common Design Type
## 1960    Photo.    Wmk. 303
### Size: 37x27mm
| | | | | |
|---|---|---|---|---|
| 809 | CD3 | 30 l dk grn & bis brn | .30 | .20 |
| 810 | CD3 | 70 l dk bl & salmon | .40 | .25 |

## 1960    Unwmk.    Engr.    Perf. 13x13½
| | | | | |
|---|---|---|---|---|
| 811 | A442 | 25 l orange brn | .20 | .20 |

350th anniv. of the death of Michelangelo da Caravaggio (Merisi), painter.

Mail Coach and Post Horn
A443

## 1960    Wmk. 303    Photo.    Perf. 14
| | | | | |
|---|---|---|---|---|
| 812 | A443 | 15 l blk brn & org brn | .20 | .20 |

Issued for Stamp Day, Dec. 20.

Slave, by Michelangelo — A444

Designs from Sistine Chapel by Michelangelo: 5 l, 10 l, 115 l, 150 l, Heads of various "slaves." 15 l, Joel. 20 l, Libyan Sybil. 25 l, Isaiah. 30 l, Eritrean Sybil. 40 l, Daniel. 50 l, Delphic Sybil. 55 l, Cumaean Sybil. 70 l, Zachariah. 85 l, Jonah. 90 l, Jeremiah. 100 l, Ezekiel. 200 l, Self-portrait. 500 l, Adam. 1000 l, Eve.

### Wmk. 303
## 1961, Mar. 6    Photo.    Perf. 14
### Size: 17x21mm
| | | | | |
|---|---|---|---|---|
| 813 | A444 | 1 l gray | .20 | .20 |
| 814 | A444 | 5 l brown org | .20 | .20 |
| 815 | A444 | 10 l red org | .20 | .20 |
| 816 | A444 | 15 l brt lil | .20 | .20 |
| 817 | A444 | 20 l Prus grn | .20 | .20 |
| 818 | A444 | 25 l brown | .30 | .20 |
| 819 | A444 | 30 l purple | .20 | .20 |
| 820 | A444 | 40 l rose red | .20 | .20 |
| 821 | A444 | 50 l olive | .45 | .20 |
| 822 | A444 | 55 l red brn | .20 | .20 |
| 823 | A444 | 70 l blue | .20 | .20 |
| 824 | A444 | 85 l slate grn | .20 | .20 |
| 825 | A444 | 90 l lil rose | .40 | .20 |
| 826 | A444 | 100 l vio gray | .75 | .20 |
| 827 | A444 | 115 l ultra | .25 | .20 |

### Engr.
| | | | | |
|---|---|---|---|---|
| 828 | A444 | 150 l chocolate | 1.10 | .20 |
| 829 | A444 | 200 l dark blue | 1.75 | .20 |
| a. | | Perf. 13½ | 1.75 | .20 |

### Perf. 13½
### Size: 22x27mm
| | | | | |
|---|---|---|---|---|
| 830 | A444 | 500 l blue grn | 3.50 | .20 |
| 831 | A444 | 1000 l brown red | 3.25 | .50 |
| | | Nos. 813-831 (19) | 13.75 | 4.10 |

Map Showing Flight from Italy to Argentina
A445

185 l, Italy to Uruguay. 205 l, Italy to Peru.

## 1961, Apr.    Photo.    Perf. 14
| | | | | |
|---|---|---|---|---|
| 832 | A445 | 170 l ultra | 4.50 | 4.50 |
| 833 | A445 | 185 l dull green | 4.50 | 4.50 |
| 834 | A445 | 205 l violet blk | 9.00 | 9.00 |
| a. | | 205 l rose lilac | 1,650. | |
| | | Nos. 832-834 (3) | 18.00 | 18.00 |

Visit of Pres. Gronchi to South America, 4/61.

Nos. 832-833 and 834a were issued Apr. 4, to become valid on Apr. 6. The map of Peru on No. 834a was drawn incorrectly and the stamp was therefore withdrawn on Apr. 4. A corrected design in new color (No. 834) was issued Apr. 6. Forgeries of No. 834a exist.

Statue of Pliny, Como Cathedral
A446

Ippolito Nievo (1831-61), Writer
A447

## 1961, May 27
| | | | | |
|---|---|---|---|---|
| 835 | A446 | 30 l brown | .20 | .20 |

1900th anniversary of the birth of Pliny the Younger, Roman consul and writer.

## 1961, June 8    Wmk. 303    Perf. 14
| | | | | |
|---|---|---|---|---|
| 836 | A447 | 30 l multi | .20 | .20 |

St. Paul Aboard Ship
A448

## 1961, June 28
| | | | | |
|---|---|---|---|---|
| 837 | A448 | 30 l multi | .20 | .20 |
| 838 | A448 | 70 l multi | .30 | .30 |

1,900th anniversary of St. Paul's arrival in Rome. The design is after a miniature from the Bible of Borso D'Este.

Cavalli Gun and Gaeta Fortress
A449

Cent. of Italian unity: 30 l, Carignano palace, Turin. 40 l, Montecitorio palace, Rome. 70 l, Palazzo Vecchio, Florence. 115 l, Villa Madama, Rome. 300 l, Steel construction, Italia '61 Exhibition, Turin.

## 1961, Aug. 12    Photo.
| | | | | |
|---|---|---|---|---|
| 839 | A449 | 15 l dk bl & redsh brn | .20 | .20 |
| 840 | A449 | 30 l dk bl & red brn | .20 | .20 |
| 841 | A449 | 40 l bl & brn | .35 | .20 |
| 842 | A449 | 70 l brn & pink | .50 | .20 |
| 843 | A449 | 115 l org brn & dk bl | 1.75 | .20 |
| 844 | A449 | 300 l brt grn & red | 5.00 | 4.00 |
| | | Nos. 839-844 (6) | 8.00 | 5.00 |

### Europa Issue, 1961
### Common Design Type
## 1961, Sept. 18    Wmk. 303    Perf. 14
### Size: 36½x21mm
| | | | | |
|---|---|---|---|---|
| 845 | CD4 | 30 l carmine | .25 | .20 |
| 846 | CD4 | 70 l yel grn | .30 | .25 |

Giandomenico
Romagnosi — A450

**Perf. 13½**

**1961, Nov. 28　　Unwmk.　　Engr.**
847　A450　30 l green　　　　　.20　.20
Bicentenary of the birth of Giandomenico Romagnosi, jurist and philosopher.

Design from 1820 Sardinia Letter Sheet
A451

**Wmk. 303**

**1961, Dec. 3　　Photo.　　Perf. 14**
848　A451　15 l lil rose & blk　.20　.20
Issued for Stamp Day 1961.

Family Scene "I am the Lamp that Glows so Gently . . ."
A452

**1962, Apr. 6　　Wmk. 303　　Perf. 14**
849　A452　30 l red　　　　　　.20　.20
850　A452　70 l blue　　　　　.25　.30
Death of Giovanni Pascoli, poet, 50th anniv.

Pacinotti's Dynamo
A453

**1962, June 12**
851　A453　30 l rose & blk　　.20　.20
852　A453　70 l ultra & blk　　.25　.30
Antonio Pacinotti (1841-1912), physicist and inventor of the ring winding dynamo.

St. Catherine of Siena, by Andrea Vanni — A454　　Lion of St. Mark — A455

70 l, St. Catherine, 15th century woodcut.

**1962, June 26　　　　　　Photo.**
853　A454　30 l black　　　　.20　.20
**Engraved and Photogravure**
854　A454　70 l red & blk　　.25　.40
500th anniversary of the canonization of St. Catherine of Siena, Patroness of Italy.

**1962, Aug. 25　　　　　　Photo.**
Design: 30 l, Stylized camera eye.
855　A455　30 l bl & blk　　　.20　.20
856　A455　70 l red org & blk　.20　.20
Intl. Film Festival in Venice, 30th anniv.

Motorcyclist and Bicyclist
A456

70 l, Group of cyclists.　300 l, Bicyclist.

**1962, Aug. 30**
857　A456　30 l grn & blk　　.20　.20
858　A456　70 l bl & blk　　　.20　.20
859　A456　300 l dp org & blk　4.00　2.50
　　Nos. 857-859 (3)　　　　4.40　2.90
World Bicycle Championship Races.

**Europa Issue, 1962**
Common Design Type

**1962, Sept. 17**
**Size: 37x21mm**
860　CD5　30 l carmine　　　.45　.20
861　CD5　70 l blue　　　　　.90　.30

Swiss and Italian Flags, Eugenio and Angela Lina Balzan Medal
A457

**1962, Oct. 25　　Wmk. 303　　Perf. 14**
862　A457　70 l rose red, grn &
　　　　　brn　　　　　　　.30　.20
1st distribution of the Balzan Prize by the Intl. Balzan Foundation for Italian-Swiss Cooperation.

Malaria Eradication Emblem — A458　　Stamps of 1862 and 1961 — A459

**1962, Oct. 31　　　　　　Photo.**
863　A458　30 l light violet　　.20　.20
864　A458　70 l light blue　　.25　.25
WHO drive to eradicate malaria.

**1962, Dec. 2**
865　A459　15 l pur, buff & bister　.20　.20
Stamp Day and cent. of Italian postage stamps.

A460　　　　　　　　　A461

Holy Spirit Descending on Apostles.

**1962, Dec. 8**
866　A460　30 l org & dk bl grn,
　　　　　buff　　　　　　.20　.20
867　A460　70 l dk bl grn & org,
　　　　　buff　　　　　　.20　.20
21st Ecumenical Council of the Roman Catholic Church, Vatican II. The design is an illumination from the Codex Syriacus.

**1962, Dec. 10　　Engr.　　Unwmk.**
Statue of Count Camillo Bensi di Cavour.
868　A461　30 l dk grn　　　.20　.20
Centenary of Court of Accounts.

Count Giovanni Pico della Mirandola
A462　　Gabriele D'Annunzio
A463

**Wmk. 303**
**1963, Feb. 25　　Photo.　　Perf. 14**
869　A462　30 l gray blk　　.20　.20
Mirandola (1463-94), Renaissance scholar.

**1963, Mar. 12　　Engr.　　Unwmk.**
870　A463　30 l dk grn　　　.20　.20
Issued to commemorate the centenary of the birth of Gabriele d'Annunzio, author and soldier.

Sower — A464

Design: 70 l, Harvester tying sheaf, sculpture from Maggiore Fountain, Perugia.

**1963, Mar. 21　　Photo.　　Wmk. 303**
871　A464　30 l rose car & brn　.20　.20
872　A464　70 l bl & brn　　　.30　.30
FAO "Freedom from Hunger" campaign.

Mt. Viso, Alpine Club Emblem, Ax and Rope — A465

Map of Italy and "INA" Initials — A466

**1963, Mar. 30　　Wmk. 303　　Perf. 14**
873　A465　115 l dk brn & brt bl　.20　.20
Italian Alpine Club founding, cent.

**1963, Apr. 4**
874　A466　30 l grn & blk　　.20　.20
50th anniv. of the Natl. Insurance Institute.

Globe and Stamp
A467

**1963, May 7　　Photo.　　Perf. 14**
875　A467　70 l bl & grn　　　.20　.20
1st Intl. Postal Conf., Paris, 1863.

Crosses and Centenary Emblem on Globe — A468

**1963, June 8　　Wmk. 303　　Perf. 14**
876　A468　30 l dk gray & red　.20　.20
877　A468　70 l dl bl & red　　.25　.25
International Red Cross founding, cent.

Roman Column, Globe and Highways
A469

**1963, Aug. 21　　Wmk. 303　　Perf. 14**
878　A469　15 l gray ol & dk bl　.20　.20
879　A469　70 l dl bl & brn　　.20　.20
UN Tourist Conf., Rome, Aug. 21-Sept. 5.

**Europa Issue, 1963**
Common Design Type
**1963, Sept. 16**
**Size: 27½x23mm**
880　CD6　30 l rose & brn　　.30　.20
881　CD6　70 l brn & grn　　.35　.25

Bay of Naples, Vesuvius and Sailboats
A470　　Athlete on Greek Vase
A471

**1963, Sept. 21　　Wmk. 303　　Perf. 14**
882　A470　15 l bl & org　　　.20　.20
883　A471　70 l dk grn & org brn　.20　.20
4th Mediterranean Games, Naples, Sept. 21-29.

Giuseppe Gioachino Belli (1791-1863), Poet — A472　　Stamps Forming Flower — A473

**1963, Nov. 14　　Wmk. 303　　Perf. 14**
884　A472　30 l red brn　　　.20　.20

**1963, Dec. 1**
885　A473　15 l bl & car　　　.20　.20
Issued for Stamp Day.

Pietro Mascagni and Old Costanzi Theater, Rome — A474

#886, Giuseppe Verdi & La Scala, Milan.

## 1963 Photo.

886 A474 30 l gray grn & yel brn .20 .20
887 A474 30 l yel brn & gray grn .20 .20

Verdi (1813-1901), and Mascagni (1863-1945), composers. Issued: #886, Oct. 10; #887, Dec. 7.

Galileo Galilei
A475

Nicodemus by Michelangelo
A476

## 1964, Feb. 15 Wmk. 303 Perf. 14

888 A475 30 l org brn .20 .20
889 A475 70 l black .20 .20

Galilei (1564-1642), astronomer & physicist.

## 1964, Feb. 18 Photo.

890 A476 30 l brown .20 .20

Michelangelo Buonarroti (1475-1564), artist. Head of Nicodemus (self-portrait?) from the Pieta, Florence Cathedral. See No. C137.

Carabinieri
A477

70 l, Charge of Pastrengo, 1848, by De Albertis.

## 1964, June 5 Wmk. 303 Perf. 14

891 A477 30 l vio bl & red .20 .20
892 A477 70 l brown .20 .20

150th anniv. of the Carabinieri (police corps).

Giambattista Bodoni — A478

### Perf. 14x13

## 1964, July 30 Engr. Unwmk.

893 A478 30 l carmine .20 .20
a. Perf. 13 .20 .20

Death of Giambattista Bodoni (1740-1813), printer & type designer (Bodoni type), 150th anniv.

### Europa Issue, 1964
Common Design Type
Wmk. 303

## 1964, Sept. 14 Photo. Perf. 14
Size: 21x37mm

894 CD7 30 l brt rose lilac .25 .20
895 CD7 70 l blue green .30 .25

Walled City — A479

Left Arch of Victor Emmanuel Monument, Rome — A480

## 1964, Oct. 15 Photo. Perf. 14

896 A479 30 l emer & dk brn .20 .20
897 A479 70 l bl & dk brn .20 .20

## Unwmk. Engr.

898 A479 500 l red 1.00 .50
Nos. 896-898 (3) 1.40 .90

7th Congress of European Towns. The buildings in design are: Big Ben, London; Campodoglio, Rome; Town Hall, Bruges; Römer, Frankfurt; Town Hall, Paris; Belfry, Zurich; Gate, Kampen (Holland).

## 1964, Nov. 4 Photo. Wmk. 303

899 A480 30 l dk red brn .20 .20
900 A480 70 l blue .20 .20

Pilgrimage to Rome of veterans living abroad.

Giovanni da Verrazano and Verrazano-Narrows Bridge, New York Bay — A481

## 1964, Nov. 21 Wmk. 303 Perf. 14

901 A481 30 l blk & brn .20 .20

Opening of the Verrazano-Narrows Bridge connecting Staten Island and Brooklyn, NY, and to honor Giovanni da Verrazano (1485-1528), discoverer of New York Bay. See No. C138.

Italian Sports Stamps, 1934-63 — A482

## 1964, Dec. 6 Photo. Perf. 14

902 A482 15 l gldn brn & dk brn .20 .20

Issued for Stamp Day.

Italian Soldiers in Concentration Camp — A483

Victims Trapped by Swastika A484

15 l, Italian soldier, sailor and airman fighting for the Allies. 70 l, Guerrilla fighters in the mountains. 115 l, Marchers with Italian flag. 130 l, Ruins of city and torn Italian flag.

## 1965, Apr. 24 Photo. Wmk. 303

903 A483 10 l black .20 .20
904 A483 15 l grn & rose car .20 .20
905 A484 30 l plum .20 .20
906 A483 70 l deep blue .20 .20
907 A484 115 l rose car .20 .20
908 A484 130 l grn, sepia & red .20 .20
Nos. 903-908 (6) 1.20 1.20

Italian resistance movement during World War II, 20th anniv.

Antonio Meucci, Guglielmo Marconi and ITU Emblem A485

## 1965, May 17 Perf. 14

909 A485 70 l red & dk grn .20 .20

Cent. of the ITU.

Sailboats of Flying Dutchman Class
A486

Designs: 70 l, Sailboats of 5.5-meter class, vert. 500 l, Sailboats, Lightning class.

## 1965, May 31 Photo. Wmk. 303

910 A486 30 l blk & dl rose .20 .20
911 A486 70 l blk & ultra .20 .20
912 A486 500 l blk & gray bl .40 .30
Nos. 910-912 (3) .80 .70

Issued to publicize the World Yachting Championships, Naples and Alassio.

Mont Blanc and Tunnel
A487

## 1965, June 16 Wmk. 303 Perf. 14

913 A487 30 l black .20 .20

Opening of the Mont Blanc Tunnel connecting Entrayes, Italy, and Le Polerins, France.

Alessandro Tassoni and Scene from "Seccia Rapita" — A488

## Unwmk.

## 1965, Sept. 20 Photo. Perf. 14

914 A488 40 l blk & multi .20 .20

Tassoni (1565-1635), poet. Design is from 1744 engraving by Bartolomeo Soliani.

### Europa Issue, 1965
Common Design Type

## 1965, Sept. 27 Wmk. 303
Size: 36½x27mm

915 CD8 40 l ocher & ol grn .20 .20
916 CD8 90 l ultra & ol grn .25 .20

Dante, 15th Century Bust — A489

Designs (from old Manuscripts): 40 l, Dante in Hell. 90 l, Dante in Purgatory led by Angel of Chastity. 130 l, Dante in Paradise interrogated by St. Peter on faith, horiz.

### Perf. 13½x14, 14x13½

## 1965, Oct. 21 Photo. Unwmk.

917 A489 40 l multi .20 .20
918 A489 90 l multi .20 .20
919 A489 130 l multi .20 .20

## Wmk. 303 Perf. 14

920 A489 500 l slate grn .40 .30
Nos. 917-920 (4) 1.00 .90

Dante Alighieri (1265-1321), poet.

House under Construction — A490

## 1965, Oct. 31 Wmk. 303 Perf. 14

921 A490 40 l buff, blk & org brn .20 .20

Issued for Savings Day.

Jet Plane, Moon and Airletter Border
A491

Design: 40 l, Control tower and plane.

## 1965, Nov. 3

922 A491 40 l dk Prus bl & red .20 .20

## Unwmk.

923 A491 90 l red, grn, dp bl & buff .20 .20

Night air postal network.

Map of Italy with Milan-Rome Highway — A492

Two-Man Bobsled — A493

## 1965, Dec. 5 Photo. Perf. 13x14

924 A492 20 l bl, blk, ocher & gray .20 .20

Issued for Stamp Day.

## 1966, Jan. 24 Wmk. 303 Perf. 14

Design: 90 l, Four-man bobsled.

925 A493 40 l dl bl, gray & red .20 .20
926 A493 90 l vio & bl .20 .20

Intl. Bobsled Championships, Cortina d'Ampezzo.

Woman Skater — A494

Benedetto Croce — A495

Winter University Games: 40 l, Skier holding torch, horiz. 500 l, Ice hockey.

**1966, Feb. 5**       Photo.
| 927 | A494 | 40 l blk & red | .20 | .20 |
| 928 | A494 | 90 l vio & red | .20 | .20 |
| 929 | A494 | 500 l brn & red | .40 | .30 |
| | *Nos. 927-929 (3)* | | .80 | .70 |

**1966, Feb. 25**    Wmk. 303    *Perf. 14*
| 930 | A495 | 40 l brown | .20 | .20 |

Benedetto Croce (1866-1952), philosopher, statesman and historian.

Arms of Venice and Other Cities in Venezia — A496

**1966, Mar. 22**    Photo.    Unwmk.
| 932 | A496 | 40 l gray & multi | .20 | .20 |

Centenary of Venezia's union with Italy.

Battle of Bezzecca — A497

**1966, July 21**    Wmk. 303    *Perf. 14*
| 933 | A497 | 90 l ol grn | .20 | .20 |

Centenary of the unification of Italy and of the Battle of Bezzecca.

Umbrella Pine — A498

Carnations62 A499

25 l, Apples. 50 l, Florentine iris. 55 l, Cypresses. 90 l, Daisies. 170 l, Olive tree. 180 l, Juniper.

**1966-68**    Unwmk.    *Perf. 13½x14*
| 934 | A498 | 20 l multi | .20 | .20 |
| **934A** | A498 | 25 l multi ('67) | .20 | .20 |
| 935 | A498 | 40 l multi | .20 | .20 |
| **935A** | A498 | 50 l multi ('67) | .20 | .20 |
| **935B** | A498 | 55 l multi ('68) | .20 | .20 |
| 936 | A499 | 90 l multi | .20 | .20 |
| 937 | A498 | 170 l multi | .25 | .20 |
| **937A** | A498 | 180 l multi ('68) | .25 | .20 |
| | *Nos. 934-937A (8)* | | 1.70 | 1.60 |

Tourist Attractions A500

"I" in Flag Colors — A501

**1966, May 28**    Wmk. 303    *Perf. 14*
| 938 | A500 | 20 l yel, org & blk | .20 | .20 |

Issued for tourist publicity and in connection with the National Conference on Tourism, Rome.

*Perf. 13½x14*
**1966, June 2**    Photo.    Unwmk.
| 939 | A501 | 40 l multi | .20 | .20 |
| 940 | A501 | 90 l multi | .20 | .20 |

20th anniversary of the Republic of Italy.

Singing Angels, by Donatello — A502

Madonna, by Giotto — A503

**1966, Sept. 24**    Photo.    Unwmk.
| 941 | A502 | 40 l multi | .20 | .20 |

Donatello (1386-1466), sculptor.

**Europa Issue, 1966**
**Common Design Type**
**1966, Sept. 26**    Wmk. 303    *Perf. 14*
**Size: 22x38mm**
| 942 | CD9 | 40 l brt pur | .20 | .20 |
| 943 | CD9 | 90 l brt bl | .25 | .20 |

*Perf. 13½x14*
**1966, Oct. 20**    Photo.    Unwmk.
| 944 | A503 | 40 l multi | .20 | .20 |

700th anniversary of the birth of Giotto di Bondone (1266?-1337), Florentine painter.

Italian Patriots A504

**1966, Nov. 3**    Wmk. 303    *Perf. 14*
| 945 | A504 | 40 l gray & dl grn | .20 | .20 |

50th anniv. of the execution by Austrians of 4 Italian patriots: Fabio Filzi, Cesare Battisti, Damiano Chiesa and Nazario Sauro.

Postrider — A505

*Perf. 14x13½*
**1966, Dec. 4**    Photo.    Unwmk.
| 946 | A505 | 20 l multi | .20 | .20 |

Issued for Stamp Day.

Globe and Compass Rose A506

**1967, Mar. 20**    Photo.    Wmk. 303
| 947 | A506 | 40 l dull blue | .20 | .20 |

Centenary of Italian Geographical Society.

Arturo Toscanini (1867-1957), Conductor — A507

**1967, Mar. 25**      *Perf. 14*
| 948 | A507 | 40 l dp vio & cream | .20 | .20 |

Seat of Parliament on Capitoline Hill, Rome A508

**1967, Mar. 25**      *Perf. 14*
| 949 | A508 | 40 l sepia | .20 | .20 |
| 950 | A508 | 90 l rose lil & blk | .20 | .20 |

10th anniv. of the Treaty of Rome, establishing the European Common Market.

**Europa Issue, 1967**
**Common Design Type**
**1967, Apr. 10**    Wmk. 303    *Perf. 14*
**Size: 22x28mm**
| 951 | CD10 | 40 l plum & pink | .20 | .20 |
| 952 | CD10 | 90 l ultra & pale gray | .35 | .25 |

Alpine Ibex, Grand Paradiso Park — A509

National Parks: 40 l, Brown bear, Abruzzi Apennines, horiz. 90 l, Red deer, Stelvio Pass, Ortler Mountains, horiz. 170 l, Oak and deer, Circeo.

*Perf. 13½x14, 14x13½*
**1967, Apr. 22**      Photo.
| 953 | A509 | 20 l multi | .20 | .20 |
| 954 | A509 | 40 l multi | .20 | .20 |
| 955 | A509 | 90 l multi | .20 | .20 |
| 956 | A509 | 170 l multi | .30 | .30 |
| | *Nos. 953-956 (4)* | | .90 | .90 |

Claudio Monteverdi and Characters from "Orfeo" A510

**1967, May 15**      *Perf. 14*
| 957 | A510 | 40 l bis brn & brn | .20 | .20 |

Monteverdi (1567-1643), composer.

Bicyclists and Mountains A511

50th Bicycle Tour of Italy: 90 l. Three bicyclists on the road. 500 l, Group of bicyclists.

*Perf. 14x13½*
**1967, May 15**    Photo.    Unwmk.
| 958 | A511 | 40 l multi | .20 | .20 |
| 959 | A511 | 90 l brt bl & multi | .20 | .20 |
| 960 | A511 | 500 l yel grn & multi | .95 | .45 |
| | *Nos. 958-960 (3)* | | 1.35 | .85 |

Luigi Pirandello and Stage A512

**1967, June 28**      *Perf. 14x13*
| 961 | A512 | 40 l blk & multi | .20 | .20 |

Pirandello (1867-1936), novelist & dramatist.

Stylized Mask A513

**1967, June 30**    Wmk. 303    *Perf. 14*
| 962 | A513 | 20 l grn & blk | .20 | .20 |
| 963 | A513 | 40 l car rose & blk | .20 | .20 |

10th "Festival of Two Worlds," Spoleto.

Postal Card with Postal Zone Number A514

Design: 40 l, 50 l, Letter addressed with postal zone number.

**Wmk. 303, Unwmkd, (20 l, 40 l)**
**1967-68**
| 964 | A514 | 20 l multi | .20 | .20 |
| 965 | A514 | 25 l multi ('68) | .20 | .20 |
| 966 | A514 | 40 l multi | .20 | .20 |
| 967 | A514 | 50 l multi ('68) | .20 | .20 |
| | *Nos. 964-967 (4)* | | .80 | .80 |

Introduction of postal zone numbers, 7/1/67.

Pomilio PC-1 Biplane and 1917 Airmail Postmark A515

**1967, July 18**    Photo.    Wmk. 303
| 968 | A515 | 40 l blk & lt bl | .20 | .20 |

1st airmail stamp, Italy #C1, 50th anniv.

St. Ivo Church, Rome — A516

Umberto Giordano and "Improvisation" from Opera Andrea Chenier — A517

**1967, Aug. 2    Unwmk.    Perf. 14**
969  A516  90 l  multi                     .20   .20
Francesco Borromini (1599-1667), architect.

**1967, Aug. 28                 Wmk. 303**
970  A517  20 l  blk & org brn            .20   .20
Umberto Giordano (1867-1948), composer.

Oath of Pontida, by Adolfo Cao — A518

ITY Emblem — A519

**1967, Sept. 2**
971  A518  20 l  dk brn                    .20   .20
800th anniv. of the Oath of Pontida, which united the Lombard League against Emperor Frederick I.

**Perf. 13½x14**
**1967, Oct. 23    Photo.    Unwmk.**
972  A519  20 l  blk, cit & brt bl         .20   .20
973  A519  50 l  blk, org & brt bl         .20   .20
Issued for International Tourist Year, 1967.

Lions Emblem — A520

Soldier at the Piave — A521

**1967, Oct. 30                 Perf. 14x13½**
974  A520  50 l  multi                     .20   .20
50th anniversary of Lions International.

**1967, Nov. 9                  Perf. 13x14**
975  A521  50 l  multi                     .20   .20
50th anniversary of Battle of the Piave.

Enrico Fermi at Los Alamos and Model of 1st Atomic Reactor — A522

"Day and Night" and Pigeon Carrying Italy No. 924 — A523

**Wmk. 303**
**1967, Dec. 2    Photo.    Perf. 14**
976  A522  50 l  org brn & blk            .20   .20
25th anniv. of the 1st atomic chain reaction under Enrico Fermi (1901-54), Chicago, IL.

**1967, Dec. 3    Unwmk.    Perf. 13½x14**
977  A523  25 l  multi                     .20   .20
Issued for Stamp Day, 1967.

Scouts at Campfire — A524

St. Aloysius Gonzaga, by Pierre Legros — A525

**1968, Apr. 23                 Perf. 13x14**
978  A524  50 l  multi                     .20   .20
Issued to honor the Boy Scouts.

**Europa Issue, 1968**
**Common Design Type**
**Perf. 14x13**
**1968, Apr. 23                 Wmk. 303**
**Size:  36½x26mm**
979  CD11  50 l  blk, rose & sl grn        .20   .20
980  CD11  90 l  blk, bl & brn             .25   .20

**Perf. 13½x14**
**1968, May 28    Photo.    Wmk. 303**
981  A525  25 l  red brn & dl vio          .20   .20
Aloysius Gonzaga (1568-1591), Jesuit priest who ministered to victims of the plague.

Arrigo Boito and Mephistopheles — A526

**1968, June 10    Unwmk.    Perf. 14**
982  A526  50 l  multi                     .20   .20
Boito (1842-1918), composer and librettist.

Francesco Baracca and "Planes," by Giacomo Balla A527

**1968, June 19**
983  A527  25 l  multi                     .20   .20
Major Francesco Baracca (1888-1918), World War I aviator.

Giambattista Vico — A528

Bicycle Wheel and Velodrome, Rome — A529

Designs: No. 985, Tommaso Campanella. No. 986, Gioacchino Rossini.

**Perf. 14x13½**
**1968        Engr.        Wmk. 303**
984  A528  50 l  ultra                     .20   .20
985  A528  50 l  black                     .20   .20
a.    Perf. 13½                            .90   .20
986  A528  50 l  car rose                  .20   .20
    Nos. 984-986 (3)                       .60   .60
Vico (1668-1744), philosopher; Campanella (1568-1639), Dominican monk, philosopher poet and teacher; Rossini (1792-1868), composer.
Issued: #984, 6/24; #985, 9/5; #986, 10/25.

**Perf. 13x14**
**1968, Aug. 26    Photo.    Unwmk.**
987  A529  25 l  slate, rose & brown       .20   .20
988  A529  90 l  slate, blue & ver         .20   .20
Bicycling World Championships: 25 l for the track championships at the Velodrome in Rome; 90 l, the road championships at Imola.

"The Small St. Mark's Place," by Canaletto — A531

**1968, Sept. 30    Unwmk.    Perf. 14**
989  A531  50 l  pink & multi              .20   .20
Canaletto (Antonio Canale, 1697-1768), Venetian painter.

"Mobilization" — A533

Symbolic Designs: 25 l, Trench war. 40 l, The Navy. 50 l, The Air Force. 90 l, The Battle of Vittorio Veneto. 180 l, The Unknown Soldier.

**1968, Nov. 2    Photo.    Unwmk.**
990  A533  20 l  brn & multi               .20   .20
991  A533  25 l  bl & multi                .20   .20
992  A533  40 l  multi                     .20   .20
993  A533  50 l  multi                     .20   .20
994  A533  90 l  grn & multi               .20   .20
995  A533  180 l  bl & multi               .30   .30
    Nos. 990-995 (6)                      1.30  1.30
50th anniv. of the Allies' Victory in WW I.

Emblem — A534

**1968, Nov. 20                 Perf. 14x13½**
996  A534  50 l  blk, bl grn & red         .20   .20
50th anniv. of the Postal Checking Service.

Parabolic Antenna, Fucino A535

**1968, Nov. 25    Photo.    Perf. 14**
997  A535  50 l  multi                     .20   .20
Issued to publicize the expansion of the space communications center at Fucino.

Development of Postal Service — A536

**1968, Dec. 1                  Wmk. 303**
998  A536  25 l  car & yel                 .20   .20
Issued for the 10th Stamp Day.

**Fluorescent Paper**
was introduced in 1968 for regular and special delivery issues. These stamps are about 1mm. smaller each way than the non-fluorescent ones they replaced, except Nos. 690-690A which remained the same size.
Commemorative or nonregular stamps issued only on fluorescent paper are Nos. 935B, 937A, 965, 967 and from 981 onward unless otherwise noted.

**Italia Type of 1953-54**
Small Size:  16x19½-20mm
**Photo.; Engr. (100, 150, 200-400 l)**

| | | | | | |
|---|---|---|---|---|---|
| **1968-76** | | **Wmk. 303** | | **Perf. 14** | |
| 998A | A354 | 1 l | dk gray | .20 | .20 |
| 998B | A354 | 5 l | slate | .20 | .20 |
| 998C | A354 | 6 l | ocher | .20 | .20 |
| 998D | A354 | 10 l | org ver | .20 | .20 |
| 998E | A354 | 15 l | gray vio | .20 | .20 |
| 998F | A354 | 20 l | brown | .20 | .20 |
| 998G | A354 | 25 l | purple | .20 | .20 |
| 998H | A354 | 30 l | bis brn | .20 | .20 |
| 998I | A354 | 40 l | lil rose | .20 | .20 |
| 998J | A354 | 50 l | olive | .20 | .20 |
| 998K | A354 | 55 l | vio ('69) | .20 | .20 |
| 998L | A354 | 60 l | blue | .20 | .20 |
| 998M | A354 | 70 l | Prus grn | .20 | .20 |
| 998N | A354 | 80 l | brn org | .20 | .20 |
| 998O | A354 | 90 l | lt red brn | .20 | .20 |
| 998P | A354 | 100 l | redsh brn | .20 | .20 |
| 998Q | A354 | 125 l | ocher & lil ('74) | .20 | .20 |
| 998R | A354 | 130 l | gray & dl red | .20 | .20 |
| 998S | A354 | 150 l | vio ('76) | .25 | .20 |
| 998T | A354 | 180 l | gray & vio brn ('71) | .30 | .20 |
| 998U | A354 | 200 l | slate blue | .35 | .20 |
| 998V | A354 | 300 l | Prus grn ('72) | .50 | .20 |
| 998W | A354 | 400 l | dull red ('76) | .65 | .20 |
| | | *Nos. 998A-998W (23)* | | 5.65 | 4.60 |

Memorial Medal — A537

**Unwmk.**
**1969, Apr. 22**    **Photo.**    **Perf. 14**
999 A537 50 l pink & blk    .20   .20
Centenary of the State Audit Bureau.

**Europa Issue, 1969**
Common Design Type
**1969, Apr. 28**      **Perf. 14x13**
**Size: 35½x25½mm**
1000 CD12 50 l mag & multi    .25   .20
1001 CD12 90 l bl & multi    .45   .20

Niccolo Machiavelli A538      ILO Emblem A539

**1969, May 3**      **Perf. 14x13½**
1002 A538 50 l blue & multi    .20   .20
Niccolo Machiavelli (1469-1527), statesman and political philosopher.

**Wmk. 303**
**1969, June 7**    **Photo.**    **Perf. 14**
1003 A539 50 l grn & blk    .20   .20
1004 A539 90 l car & blk    .20   .20
50th anniv. of the ILO.

Federation Emblem, Tower of Superga Basilica and Matterhorn A540

**1969, June 26**    **Unwmk.**    **Perf. 14**
1005 A540 50 l gold, bl & car    .20   .20
Federation of Italian Philatelic Societies, 50th anniv.

Sondrio-Tirano Stagecoach, 1903 — A541

**1969, Dec. 7**    **Engr.**    **Wmk. 303**
1006 A541 25 l violet blue    .20   .20
Issued for the 11th Stamp Day.

Downhill Skier — A542

90 l, Sassolungo & Sella Group, Dolomite Alps.

---

**Perf. 13x14**
**1970, Feb. 6**    **Unwmk.**    **Photo.**
1007 A542 50 l blue & multi    .20   .20
1008 A542 90 l blue & multi    .20   .20
World Alpine Ski Championships, Val Gardena, Bolzano Province, Feb. 6-15.

Galatea, by Raphael A543

Painting: 50 l, Madonna with the Goldfinch (detail), by Raphael, 1483-1520.

**1970, Apr. 6**    **Photo.**    **Perf. 14x13**
1009 A543 20 l multi    .20   .20
1010 A543 50 l multi    .20   .20

Symbol of Flight, Colors of Italy and Japan A544

**1970, May 2**    **Unwmk.**    **Perf. 14**
1011 A544 50 l multi    .20   .20
1012 A544 90 l multi    .20   .20
50th anniv. of Arturo Ferrarin's flight from Rome to Tokyo, Feb. 14-May 31, 1920.

**Europa Issue, 1970**
Common Design Type
**1970, May 4**      **Wmk. 303**
**Size: 36x20mm**
1013 CD13 50 l red & org    .25   .20
1014 CD13 90 l bl grn & org    .40   .20

Gattamelata, Bust by Donatello — A545

**1970, May 30**    **Engr.**    **Perf. 14x13**
1015 A545 50 l slate green    .20   .20
Erasmo de' Narni, called Il Gattamelata (1370-1443), condottiere.

Runner A546

**Unwmk.**
**1970, Aug. 26**    **Photo.**    **Perf. 14**
1016 A546 20 l shown    .20   .20
1017 A546 180 l Swimmer    .30   .20
1970 World University Games, Turin, 8/26-9/6.

Dr. Maria Montessori and Children A547

**1970, Aug. 31**      **Perf. 14x13**
1018 A547 50 l multi    .20   .20
Montessori (1870-1952), educator & physician.

---

Map of Italy and Quotation of Count Camillo Cavour — A548

**1970, Sept. 19**    **Unwmk.**    **Perf. 14**
1019 A548 50 l multi    .20   .20
Union of the Roman States with Italy, cent.

Loggia of St. Mark's Campanile, Venice A549

**Perf. 14x13½**
**1970, Sept. 26**    **Engr.**    **Wmk. 303**
1020 A549 50 l red brown    .20   .20
Iacopo Tatti "Il Sansovino" (1486-1570), architect.

Garibaldi at Battle of Dijon A550

**1970, Oct. 15**    **Photo.**    **Perf. 14**
1021 A550 20 l gray & dk bl    .20   .20
1022 A550 50 l brt rose lil & dk bl    .20   .20
Cent. of Garibaldi's participation in the Franco-Prussian War during Battle of Dijon.

Tree and UN Emblem — A551

**1970, Oct. 24**    **Unwmk.**    **Perf. 13x14**
1023 A551 25 l blk, sep & grn    .20   .20
1024 A551 90 l blk, brt bl & yel grn    .20   .20
25th anniversary of the United Nations.

Rotary Emblem A552

**1970, Nov. 12**    **Wmk. 303**    **Perf. 14**
1025 A552 25 l bluish vio & org    .20   .20
1026 A552 90 l bluish vio & org    .20   .20
Rotary International, 65th anniversary.

Telephone Dial and Trunk Lines A553

---

**1970, Nov. 24**
1027 A553 25 l yel grn & dk red    .20   .20
1028 A553 90 l ultra & dk red    .20   .20
Issued to publicize the completion of the automatic trunk telephone dialing system.

"Man Damaging Nature" — A554      Virgin and Child, by Fra Filippo Lippi — A556

Mail Train A555

**1970, Nov. 28**    **Wmk. 303**    **Perf. 14**
1029 A554 20 l car lake & grn    .20   .20
1030 A554 25 l dk bl & emer    .20   .20
For European Nature Conservation Year.

**1970, Dec. 6**      **Engr.**
1031 A555 25 l black    .20   .20
For the 12th Stamp Day.

**1970, Dec. 12**    **Photo.**    **Unwmk.**
1032 A556 25 l multi    .20   .20
Christmas 1970. See No. C139.

Saverio Mercadante (1795-1870), Composer — A557

**1970, Dec. 17**      **Wmk. 303**
1033 A557 25 l vio & gray    .20   .20

Mercury, by Benvenuto Cellini — A558      Bramante's Temple, St. Peter in Montorio — A559

**1971, Mar. 20**    **Photo.**    **Perf. 14**
1034 A558 50 l Prussian blue    .20   .20
Benvenuto Cellini (1500-1571), sculptor.

**Photogravure and Engraved**
**1971, Apr. 8**      **Perf. 13x14**
1035 A559 50 l ocher & blk    .20   .20
Honoring Bramante (Donato di Angelo di Antonio, 1444-1514), architect.

Adenauer, Schuman, De Gasperi A560

## Perf. 14x13½
### 1971, Apr. 28     Photo.     Wmk. 303
1036 A560 50 l blk & lt grnsh bl    .20   .20
1037 A560 90 l blk & lil rose    .20   .20

European Coal & Steel Community, 20th anniv.

### Europa Issue, 1971
### Common Design Type
### 1971, May 3       Perf. 14
1038 CD14 50 l ver & dk red    .25   .20
1039 CD14 90 l brt rose lil & dk lil    .40   .20

Giuseppe Mazzini, Italian Flag — A561

### Perf. 14x13½
### 1971, June 12       Unwmk.
1040 A561 50 l multi    .20   .20
1041 A561 90 l multi    .20   .20

25th anniversary of the Italian Republic.

Kayak Passing Between Poles A562

Design: 90 l, Kayak in free descent.

### 1971, June 16     Photo.     Perf. 14
1042 A562 25 l multi    .20   .20
1043 A562 50 l multi    .20   .20

Canoe Slalom World Championships, Merano.

Skiing, Basketball, Volleyball — A563

50 l, Gymnastics, cycling, track and swimming.

### Perf. 13½x14
### 1971, June 26     Photo.     Unwmk.
1044 A563 20 l emer, ocher & blk    .20   .20
1045 A563 50 l dl bl, org & blk    .20   .20

Youth Games.

Plane Circling Globe and "A" — A564

Designs: 50 l, Ornamental "A." 150 l, Tail of B747 in shape of "A."

### 1971, Sept. 16       Perf. 14x13½
1046 A564 50 l multi    .20   .20
1047 A564 90 l multi    .20   .20
1048 A564 150 l multi    .25   .20
    Nos. 1046-1048 (3)    .65   .60

ALITALIA, Italian airlines founding, 25th anniv.

---

Grazia Deledda (1871-1936), Novelist — A565

### Photogravure and Engraved
### Perf. 13½x14
### 1971, Sept. 28       Wmk. 303
1049 A565 50 l blk & salmon    .20   .20

Child in Barrel Made of Banknote — A566

### Perf. 13x14
### 1971, Oct. 27     Photo.     Unwmk.
1050 A566 25 l blk & multi    .20   .20
1051 A566 50 l multi    .20   .20

Publicity for postal savings bank.

UNICEF Emblem and Children A567

90 l, Children hailing UNICEF emblem.

### 1971, Nov. 26       Perf. 14x13
1052 A567 25 l pink & multi    .20   .20
1053 A567 90 l multi    .20   .20

25th anniv. of UNICEF.

Packet Tirrenia and Postal Ensign A568

### 1971, Dec. 5     Wmk. 303     Perf. 14
1054 A568 25 l slate green    .20   .20

Stamp Day.

Nativity A569

Christmas: 90 l, Adoration of the Kings. Both designs are from miniatures in Evangelistary of Matilda in Nonantola Abbey, 12th-13th centuries.

### Perf. 14x13
### 1971, Dec. 10     Photo.     Unwmk.
1055 A569 25 l gray & multi    .20   .20
1056 A569 90 l gray & multi    .20   .20

Giovanni Verga and Sicilian Cart — A570

---

### 1972, Jan. 27
1057 A570 25 l org & multi    .20   .20
1058 A570 50 l multi    .20   .20

Verga (1840-1922), writer & playwright.

Giuseppe Mazzini (1805-1872), Patriot and Writer — A571

### Wmk. 303
### 1972, Mar. 10     Engr.     Perf. 13
1059 A571 25 l blk & Prus grn    .20   .20
1060 A571 90 l black    .20   .20
1061 A571 150 l blk & rose red    .25   .20
    Nos. 1059-1061 (3)    .65   .60

Flags, Milan Fair A572

Designs: 50 l, 90 l, Different abstract views.

### Perf. 14x13½
### 1972, Apr. 14     Photo.     Unwmk.
1062 A572 25 l emer & blk    .20   .20
1063 A572 50 l dp org & blk    .20   .20
1064 A572 90 l bl & blk    .20   .20
    Nos. 1062-1064 (3)    .60   .60

50th anniversary of the Milan Sample Fair.

### Europa Issue 1972
### Common Design Type
### 1972, May 2       Perf. 13x14
### Size: 26x36mm
1065 CD15 50 l multi    .25   .20
1066 CD15 90 l multi    .40   .20

Alpine Soldier and Pack Mule A573

50 l, Mountains, Alpinist's hat, pick & laurel. 90 l, Alpine soldier & mountains.

### 1972, May 10       Perf. 14x13
1067 A573 25 l ol & multi    .20   .20
1068 A573 50 l bl & multi    .20   .20
1069 A573 90 l grn & multi    .20   .20
    Nos. 1067-1069 (3)    .60   .60

Centenary of the Alpine Corps.

Brenta Mountains, Society Emblem A574

Emblem and: 50 l, Mountain climber & Brenta Mountains. 180 l, Sunset over Mt. Crozzon.

### Perf. 14x13
### 1972, Sept. 2     Photo.     Unwmk.
1070 A574 25 l multi    .20   .20
1071 A574 50 l multi    .20   .20
1072 A574 180 l multi    .30   .20
    Nos. 1070-1072 (3)    .70   .60

Tridentine Alpinist Society centenary.

---

Conference Emblem, Seating Diagram A575

### 1972, Sept. 21
1073 A575 50 l multi    .20   .20
1074 A575 90 l multi    .20   .20

60th Conference of the Inter-Parliamentary Union, Montecitorio Hall, Rome.

St. Peter Damian, by Giovanni di Paoli, c. 1445 A576

### 1972, Sept. 21       Photo.
1075 A576 50 l multi    .20   .20

St. Peter Damian (1007-72), church reformer, cardinal, papal legate.

The Three Graces, by Antonio Canova (1757-1822), Sculptor — A577

### 1972, Oct. 13     Engr.     Wmk. 303
1076 A577 50 l black    .20   .20

Page from Divine Comedy, Foligno Edition A578

Designs (Illuminated First Pages): 90 l, Mantua edition, vert. 180 l, Jesina edition.

### Perf. 14x13½, 13½x14
### 1972, Nov. 23     Photo.     Unwmk.
1077 A578 50 l ocher & multi    .20   .20
1078 A578 90 l multi    .20   .20
1079 A578 180 l multi    .30   .20
    Nos. 1077-1079 (3)    .70   .60

500th anniversary of three illuminated editions of Dante's Divine Comedy.

Angel — A579

Christmas: 25 l, Christ Child in cradle, horiz. 150 l, Angel. All designs from 18th century Neapolitan crèche.

### Perf. 13x14, 14x13
### 1972, Dec. 6       Photo.
1080 A579 20 l multi    .20   .20
1081 A579 25 l multi    .20   .20
1082 A579 150 l multi    .25   .20
    Nos. 1080-1082 (3)    .65   .60

Passenger and Mail Autobus A580

**1972, Dec. 16   Engr.   Wmk. 303**
1083 A580 25 l magenta   .20 .20
Stamp Day.

Leòn Battista Alberti — A581

Lorenzo Perosi — A582

**1972, Dec. 16   Perf. 14**
1084 A581 50 l ultra & ocher   .20 .20
Leòn Battista Alberti (1404-1472), architect, painter, organist and writer.

**1972, Dec. 20   Photo.   Unwmk.**
1085 A582 50 l dk vio brn & org   .20 .20
1086 A582 90 l blk & yel grn   .20 .20
Lorenzo Perosi (1872-1956), priest & composer.

Luigi Orione and Boys — A583

Ship Exploring Ocean Floor — A584

**1972, Dec. 30**
1087 A583 50 l lt bl & dk bl   .20 .20
1088 A583 90 l ocher & slate grn   .20 .20
Orione (1872-1940), founder of CARITAS; Catholic Welfare Organization.

**1973, Feb. 15   Photo.   Perf. 13x14**
1089 A584 50 l multi   .20 .20
Cent. of the Naval Hydrographic Institute.

Palace Staircase, Caserta A585

**1973, Mar. 1   Engr.   Perf. 14x13½**
1090 A585 25 l gray olive   .20 .20
Luigi Vanvitelli (1700-1773), architect.

Schiavoni Shore — A586

---

The Tetrarchs, 4th Century Sculpture — A587

50 l, "Triumph of Venice," by Vittore Carpaccio. 90 l, Bronze horses from St. Mark's. 300 l, St. Mark's Square covered by flood.

**1973   Photo.   Perf. 14**
1091 A586 20 l ultra & multi   .20 .20
1092 A587 25 l ultra & multi   .20 .20
1093 A586 50 l ultra & multi   .20 .20
1094 A587 90 l ultra & multi   .20 .20
1095 A586 300 l ultra & multi   .50 .30
Nos. 1091-1095 (5)   1.30 1.10
Save Venice campaign. Issued: #1091, 3/5; others 4/10.

Verona Fair Emblem — A588

Title Page for Book about Rosa — A589

**1973, Mar. 10   Perf. 13x14**
1096 A588 50 l multi   .20 .20
75th International Fair, Verona.

**1973, Mar. 15   Perf. 14**
1097 A589 25 l org & blk   .20 .20
Salvator Rosa (1615-1673), painter & poet.

G-91 Jet Fighters A590

Designs: 25 l, Formation of S-55 seaplanes. 50 l, G-91Y fighters. 90 l, Fiat CR-32's flying figure 8. 180 l, Camprini-Caproni jet, 1940.

**1973, Mar. 28   Perf. 14x13½**
1098 A590 20 l multi   .20 .20
1099 A590 25 l multi   .20 .20
1100 A590 50 l multi   .20 .20
1101 A590 90 l multi   .20 .20
1102 A590 180 l multi   .30 .20
Nos. 1098-1102,C140 (6)   1.40 1.20
50th anniversary of military aviation.

Soccer Field and Ball A591

Design: 90 l, Soccer players and goal.

**1973, May 19   Photo.   Perf. 14x13½**
1103 A591 25 l ol, blk & lt grn   .20 .20
1104 A591 90 l grn & multi   .60 .20
75th anniv. of Italian Soccer Federation.

---

Alessandro Manzoni, by Francisco Hayez — A592

Villa Rotunda, by Andrea Palladio (1508-80), Architect. — A593

**1973, May 22   Engr.**
1105 A592 25 l blk & brn   .20 .20
Manzoni (1785-1873), novelist and poet.

**1973, May 30   Photo.   Unwmk.**
**Perf. 13x14**
1106 A593 90 l blk, yel & lem   .20 .20

Spiral and Cogwheels A594

**1973, June 20   Perf. 14x13**
1107 A594 50 l gold & multi   .20 .20
50th anniversary of the State Supply Office.

**Europa Issue 1973**
**Common Design Type**
**1973, June 30   Litho.   Perf. 14**
**Size: 36x20mm**
1108 CD16 50 l lil, gold & yel   .25 .20
1109 CD16 90 l lt bl grn, gold & yel   .40 .25

Catcher and Diamond A595

Design: 90 l, Diamond and batter.

**1973, July 21   Photo.   Perf. 14x13½**
1110 A595 25 l multi   .20 .20
1111 A595 90 l multi   .20 .20
International Baseball Cup.

Viareggio by Night — A596

**1973, Aug. 10   Photo.   Perf. 13x14**
1112 A596 25 l blk & multi   .20 .20
Viareggio Carnival.

Assassination of Giovanni Minzoni — A597

**1973, Aug. 23   Perf. 14x13**
1113 A597 50 l multi   .20 .20
Minzoni (1885-1923), priest & social worker.

---

Gaetano Salvemini (1873-1957), Historian, Anti-Fascist — A598

**1973, Sept. 8   Perf. 14x13½**
1114 A598 50 l pink & multi   .20 .20

Palazzo Farnese, Caprarola, by Vignola A599

**1973, Sept. 21   Engr.   Perf. 14x13½**
1115 A599 90 l choc & yel   .20 .20
Giacomo da Vignola (real name, Giacomo Barocchio), 1507-1573, architect.

St. John the Baptist, by Caravaggio A600

**Lithographed & Engraved**
**1973, Sept. 28   Perf. 14**
1116 A600 25 l blk & dl yel   .20 .20
400th anniversary of the birth of Michelangelo da Caravaggio (1573-1610?), painter.

Tower of Pisa — A601

**1973, Oct. 8   Photo.**
1117 A601 50 l multi   .20 .20
8th century of Leaning Tower of Pisa.

Sandro Botticelli — A602

**1973-74   Photo.   Perf. 14x13½**
1118 A602 50 l shown   .20 .20
1119 A602 50 l Giambattista Piranesi   .20 .20
1120 A602 50 l Paolo Veronese   .20 .20
1121 A602 50 l Andrea del Verrocchio   .20 .20
1122 A602 50 l Giovanni Battista Tiepolo   .20 .20
1123 A602 50 l Francesco Borromini   .20 .20
1124 A602 50 l Rosalba Carriera   .20 .20
1125 A602 50 l Giovanni Bellini   .20 .20
1126 A602 50 l Andrea Mantegna   .20 .20
1127 A602 50 l Raphael   .20 .20
Nos. 1118-1127 (10)   2.00 2.00
Famous artists.
Issued: #1118-1122, 11/5; #1123-1127, 5/25/74.
See #1204-1209, 1243-1247, 1266-1270.

Trevi Fountain, Rome — A603

Designs: No. 1129, Immacolatella Fountain, Naples. No. 1130, Pretoria Fountain, Palermo.

**Photogravure and Engraved**
**1973, Nov. 10**          *Perf. 13½x14*
1128  A603  25 l  blk & multi          .20   .20
1129  A603  25 l  blk & multi          .20   .20
1130  A603  25 l  blk & multi          .20   .20
      Nos. 1128-1130 (3)               .60   .60
See Nos. 1166-1168, 1201-1203, 1251-1253, 1277-1279, 1341-1343, 1379-1381.

Angels, by Agostino di Duccio — A604

Sculptures by Agostino di Duccio: 25 l, Virgin and Child.  150 l, Angels with flute and trumpet.

**1973, Nov. 26**
1131  A604   20 l  yel grn & blk       .20   .20
1132  A604   25 l  lt bl & blk         .20   .20
1133  A604  150 l  yel & blk           .25   .20
      Nos. 1131-1133 (3)               .65   .60
Christmas 1973.

Map of Italy, Rotary Emblems — A605

**1973, Nov. 28**          **Photo.**
1134  A605  50 l  red, grn & dk bl     .20   .20
50th anniv. of Rotary International of Italy.

Caravelle A606

**Wmk. 303**
**1973, Dec. 2**  **Engr.**     *Perf. 14*
1135  A606  25 l  Prussian blue        .20   .20
15th Stamp Day.

Gold Medal of Valor, 50th Anniv. — A607

*Perf. 13½x14*
**1973, Dec. 10**  **Photo.**  **Unwmk.**
1136  A607  50 l  gold & multi         .20   .20

Enrico Caruso (1873-1921), Operatic Tenor — A608

**1973, Dec. 15**          **Engr.**
Design: 50 l, Caruso as Duke in Rigoletto.
1137  A608  50 l  magenta              .20   .20

Christ Crowning King Roger — A609

Norman art in Sicily: 50 l, King William II offering model of church to the Virgin, mosaic from Monreale Cathedral. The design of 20 l, is from a mosaic in Martorana Church, Palermo.

**Lithographed and Engraved**
**1974, Mar. 4**          *Perf. 13½x14*
1138  A609  20 l  ind & buff           .20   .20
1139  A609  50 l  red & lt grn         .20   .20

Luigi Einaudi (1874-1961), Pres. of Italy — A610

**1974, Mar. 23**  **Engr.**  *Perf. 14x13½*
1140  A610  50 l  green                .20   .20

Guglielmo Marconi (1874-1937), Italian Inventor and Physicist — A611

Design: 90 l, Marconi and world map.

**1974, Apr. 24**  **Photo.**  *Perf. 14x13½*
1141  A611  50 l  bl grn & gray        .20   .20
1142  A611  90 l  vio & multi          .20   .20

David, by Giovanni L. Bernini — A612

Europa: 90 l, David, by Michelangelo.

**1974, Apr. 29**  **Photo.**  *Perf. 13½x14*
1143  A612  50 l  sal, ultra & gray    .50   .20
1144  A612  90 l  grn, ultra & buff    .50   .20

Customs Frontier Guards, 1774, 1795, 1817 — A613

Uniforms of Customs Service: 50 l, Lombardy Venetia, 1848, Sardinia, 1815, Tebro Battalion, 1849. 90 l, Customs Guards, 1866, 1880 and Naval Marshal, 1892. 180 l, Helicopter pilot, Naval and Alpine Guards, 1974. All bordered with Italian flag colors.

**1974, June 21**  **Photo.**  *Perf. 14*
1145  A613   40 l  multi               .20   .20
1146  A613   50 l  multi               .20   .20
1147  A613   90 l  multi               .20   .20
1148  A613  180 l  multi               .30   .20
      Nos. 1145-1148 (4)               .90   .80
Customs Frontier Guards bicentenary.

Sprinter A614

**1974, June 28  Photo.  *Perf. 14x13***
1149  A614  40 l  shown                .20   .20
1150  A614  50 l  Pole vault           .20   .20
European Athletic Championships, Rome.

Sharpshooter — A615

Design: 50 l, Bersaglieri emblem.

**1974, June 27**
1151  A615  40 l  multi                .20   .20
1152  A615  50 l  grn & multi          .20   .20
Bersaglieri Veterans Association, 50th anniv.

View of Portofino — A616

**1974, July 10**          *Perf. 14*
1153  A616  40 l  shown                .20   .20
1154  A616  40 l  View of Gradara      .20   .20
Tourist publicity.
See Nos. 1190-1192, 1221-1223, 1261-1265, 1314-1316, 1357-1360, 1402-1405, 1466-1469, 1520-1523, 1563A-1563D, 1599-1602, 1630-1633, 1708-1711, 1737-1740, 1776-1779, 1803-1806, 1830-1833, 1901-1904.

Petrarch (1304-74), Poet — A617

50 l, Petrarch at his desk (from medieval manuscript).

**Lithographed and Engraved**
**1974, July 19**          *Perf. 13½x14*
1155  A617  40 l  ocher & multi        .20   .20
1156  A617  50 l  ocher, yel & bl      .20   .20

Niccolo Tommaseo (1802-1874), Writer, Venetian Education Minister — A618

Tommaseo Statue, by Ettore Ximenes, Shibenik.

**1974, July 19**
1157  A618  50 l  grn & pink           .20   .20

Giacomo Puccini (1858-1924), Composer A619

**1974, Aug. 16**          **Photo.**
1158  A619  40 l  multi                .20   .20

Lodovico Ariosto (1474-1533), Poet — A620

**1974, Sept. 9  Engr.  *Perf. 14x13½***
1159  A620  50 l  King Roland, woodcut      .20   .20
The design is from a contemporary illustration of Ariosto's poem "Orlando Furioso."

Quotation from Menippean Satire by Varro A621

**1974, Sept. 21**
1160  A621  50 l  ocher & dk red       .20   .20
Marcus Terentius Varro (116-27 BC), Roman scholar and writer.

"October," 15th Century Mural A622

**1974, Sept. 28**  **Photo.**  *Perf. 14*
1161  A622  50 l  multi                .20   .20
14th International Wine Congress, Trento.

"UPU" and Emblem
A623

Design: 90 l, Letters, "UPU" and emblem.

**1974, Oct. 19    Photo.    Perf. 14**
1162  A623  50 l multi              .20   .20
1163  A623  90 l multi              .20   .20

Centenary of Universal Postal Union.

St. Thomas Aquinas, by Francesco Traini — A624

**1974, Oct. 25                      Perf. 13x14**
1164  A624  50 l multi              .20   .20

St. Thomas Aquinas (1225-1274), scholastic philosopher, 700th death anniversary.

Bas-relief from Ara Pacis — A625

**1974, Oct. 26**
1165  A625  50 l multi              .20   .20

Centenary of the Ordini Forensi (Bar Association).

**Fountain Type of 1973**

Designs: No. 1166, Oceanus Fountain, Florence. No. 1167, Neptune Fountain, Bologna. No. 1168, Fontana Maggiore, Perugia.

**Photogravure and Engraved**
**1974, Nov. 9              Perf. 13x14**
1166  A603  40 l blk & multi        .20   .20
1167  A603  40 l blk & multi        .20   .20
1168  A603  40 l blk & multi        .20   .20
     Nos. 1166-1168 (3)             .60   .60

St. Francis Adoring Christ Child, Anonymous — A626

**Photogravure and Engraved**
**1974, Nov. 26          Perf. 14x13½**
1169  A626  40 l multi              .20   .20

Christmas 1974.

Masked Dancers — A627

**1974, Dec. 1    Photo.    Perf. 13½x14**
1170  A627  40 l Pulcinella         .20   .20
1171  A627  50 l shown              .20   .20
1172  A627  50 l Pantaloon          .20   .20
     Nos. 1170-1172 (3)             .60   .60

16th Stamp Day 1974.

God Admonishing Adam, by Jacopo della Quercia — A628

Courtyard, Uffizi Gallery, Florence, by Giorgio Vasari A629

**1974, Dec. 20    Engr.    Perf. 14**
1173  A628  90 l dk vio bl          .20   .20
**Lithographed and Engraved**
1174  A629  90 l multi              .20   .20

Italian artists: Jacopo della Quercia (1374-c. 1438), sculptor, and Giorgio Vasari (1511-1574), architect, painter and writer.

Angel with Tablet — A630

Angel with Cross — A632

Angels' Bridge, Rome — A631

Holy Year 1975: 50 l, Angel holding column. 150 l, Angel holding Crown of Thorns. The angels are statues by Giovanni Bernini on the Angels' Bridge (San Angelo).

**1975, Mar. 25    Photo.    Perf. 14**
1175  A630   40 l multi             .20   .20
1176  A630   50 l bl & multi        .20   .20
1177  A631   90 l bl & multi        .20   .20
1178  A630  150 l vio & multi       .25   .20
1179  A632  180 l multi             .30   .20
     Nos. 1175-1179 (5)            1.15  1.00

Pitti Madonna, by Michelangelo A633

Works of Michelangelo: 50 l, Niche in Vatican Palace. 90 l, The Flood, detail from Sistine Chapel.

**1975, Apr. 18    Engr.    Perf. 13½x14**
1180  A633  40 l dl grn             .20   .20
1181  A633  50 l sepia              .20   .20
1182  A633  90 l red brn            .20   .20
     Nos. 1180-1182 (3)             .60   .60

Michelangelo Buonarroti (1475-1564), sculptor, painter and architect.

Flagellation of Jesus, by Caravaggio A634

Europa: 150 l, Apparition of Angel to Hagar and Ishmael, by Tiepolo (detail).

**1975, Apr. 29    Photo.    Perf. 13x14**
1183  A634  100 l multi             .30   .25
1184  A634  150 l multi             .30   .25

Four Days of Naples, by Marino Mazzacurati A635

Resistance Fighters of Cuneo, by Umberto Mastroianni A636

Design: 100 l, Martyrs of Ardeatine Caves, by Francesco Coccia.

**1975, Apr. 23**
1185  A635   70 l multi             .20   .20
1186  A636  100 l ol & multi        .20   .20
1187  A636  150 l multi             .25   .20
     Nos. 1185-1187 (3)             .65   .60

Resistance movement victory, 30th anniv.

Globe and IWY Emblem A637

**1975, May                Perf. 14x13½**
1188  A637  70 l multi              .20   .20

International Women's Year 1975.

Satellite, San Rita Launching Platform — A638

**1975, May 28            Perf. 13½x14**
1189  A638  70 l multi              .20   .20

San Marco satellite project.

**Tourist Type of 1974**

Paintings: No. 1190, View of Isola Bella. No. 1191, Baths of Montecatini. No. 1192, View of Cefalù.

**1975, June 16    Photo.    Perf. 14**
1190  A616  150 l grn & multi       .25   .20
1191  A616  150 l bl grn & multi    .25   .20
1192  A616  150 l red brn & multi   .25   .20
     Nos. 1190-1192 (3)             .75   .60

Artist and Model, Armando Spadini A640

Painting: No. 1194, Flora, by Guido Reni.

**1975, June 20    Engr.    Perf. 14**
1193  A640  90 l blk & multi        .20   .20
1194  A640  90 l multi              .20   .20

50th death anniv. of Armando Spadini and 400th birth anniv. of Guido Reni.

Giovanni Pierluigi da Palestrina (1525-94), Composer of Sacred Music — A641

**1975, June 27    Engr.    Perf. 13½x14**
1195  A641  100 l magenta & tan     .20   .20

Emmigrants and Ship A642

**1975, June 30    Photo.    Perf. 14x13½**
1196  A642  70 l multi              .20   .20

Italian emigration centenary.

Emblem of United Legal Groups A643

**and Perf. 14x13½**
**1975, July 25    Photo.    Engr.**
1197  A643  100 l yel, grn & red    .20   .20

Unification of Italian legal organizations, cent.

Locomotive Wheels A644

**1975, Sept. 15    Photo.    Perf. 14x13½**
1198  A644  70 l multi              .20   .20

Intl. Railroad Union, 21st cong., Bologna.

Salvo D'Acquisto, by Vittorio Pisano A645

**1975, Sept. 23**
1199 A645 100 l multi .20 .20
D'Acquisto died in 1943 saving 22 people.

Stylized Syracusean Italia — A646

**1975, Sept. 26 Photo. Perf. 13½x14**
1200 A646 100 l org & multi .20 .20
Cent. of unification of the State Archives.

**Fountain Type of 1973**
Designs: No. 1201, Rosello Fountain, Sassari. No. 1202, Fountain of the 99 Faucets, Aquila. No. 1203, Piazza Fontana, Milan.

**Photogravure and Engraved**
**1975, Oct. 30 Perf. 13x14**
1201 A603 70 l blk & multi .20 .20
1202 A603 70 l blk & multi .20 .20
1203 A603 70 l blk & multi .20 .20
Nos. 1201-1203 (3) .60 .60

**Botticelli Type of 1973-74**
**1975, Nov. 14 Photo. Perf. 14x13½**
1204 A602 100 l Alessandro Scarlatti .20 .20
1205 A602 100 l Antonio Vivaldi .20 .20
1206 A602 100 l Gaspare Spontini .20 .15
1207 A602 100 l F. B. Busoni .20 .20
1208 A602 100 l Francesco Cilea .20 .20
1209 A602 100 l Franco Alfano .20 .20
Nos. 1204-1209 (6) 1.20 1.15

Famous musicians.

Annunciation to the Shepherds A648

Christmas: 100 l, Nativity. 150 l, Annunciation to the Kings. Designs from painted wood panels, portal of Alatri Cathedral, 14th century.

**Lithographed and Engraved**
**1975, Nov. 25 Perf. 13½x14**
1210 A648 70 l grn & multi .20 .20
1211 A648 100 l ultra & multi .20 .20
1212 A648 150 l brn & multi .20 .20
Nos. 1210-1212 (3) .60 .60

"The Magic Orchard" — A649

Children's Drawings: 70 l, Children on Horseback, horiz. 150 l, Village and procession, horiz.

**Perf. 14x13½, 13½x14**
**1975, Dec. 7 Photo.**
1213 A649 70 l multi .20 .20
1214 A649 100 l multi .20 .20
1215 A649 150 l multi .25 .20
Nos. 1213-1215 (3) .65 .60
17th Stamp Day.

Boccaccio, by Andrea del Castagno — A650

Design: 150 l, Frontispiece for "Fiammetta," 15th century woodcut.

**Engraved and Lithographed**
**1975, Dec. 22 Perf. 13½x14**
1216 A650 100 l yel grn & blk .20 .20
1217 A650 150 l buff & multi .25 .20
Giovanni Boccaccio (1313-1375), writer.

State Advocate's Office, Rome — A651

**1976, Jan. 30 Photo. Perf. 13½x14**
1218 A651 150 l multi .25 .20
State Advocate's Office, centenary.

ITALIA 76 Emblem — A652

Design: 180 l, Milan Fair pavilion.

**1976, Mar. 27 Photo. Perf. 13½x14**
1219 A652 150 l blk, red & grn .35 .20
1220 A652 180 l blk, red, grn & bl .45 .20
ITALIA 76 International Philatelic Exhibition, Milan, Oct. 14-24.

**Tourist Type of 1974**
Tourist publicity: #1221, Fenis Castle. #1222, View of Ischia. #1223, Itria Valley.

**1976, May 21 Photo. Perf. 14**
1221 A616 150 l grn & multi .25 .20
1222 A616 150 l plum & multi .25 .20
1223 A616 150 l yel & multi .25 .20
Nos. 1221-1223 (3) .75 .60

Majolica Plate, Deruta — A653

Europa: 180 l, Ceramic vase in shape of woman's head, Caltagirone.

**1976, May 22 Perf. 13½x14**
1224 A653 150 l multi .25 .20
1225 A653 180 l brn & multi .30 .20

Italian Flags — A654

Italian Presidents A655

**1976, June 1**
1226 A654 100 l multi .20 .20
1227 A655 150 l multi .25 .20
30th anniversary of Italian Republic.

Fortitude, by Giacomo Serpotta, 1656-1732 A656

Paintings: No. 1229, Woman at Table, by Umberto Boccioni, 1882-1916. No. 1230, The Gunner's Letter, by F. T. Marinetti, 1876-1944.

**1976, July 26 Engr. Perf. 14**
1228 A656 150 l blue .25 .20

**Lithographed and Engraved**
1229 A656 150 l multi .25 .20
1230 A656 150 l blk & red .25 .20
Nos. 1228-1230 (3) .75 .60
Italian art.

Paintings by Vittore Carpaccio (1460-1526), Venetian Painter — A657

#1230, St. George. #1231, Dragon, after painting in Church of St. George Schiavoni, Venice.

**1976, July 30 Engr. Perf. 14x13½**
1231 A657 150 l rose lake .25 .20
1232 A657 150 l rose lake .25 .20
a. Pair, #1231-1232 + label .50 .20

Flora, by Titian A658

**1976, Sept. 15 Engr. Perf. 14**
1233 A658 150 l carmine .25 .20
Titian (1477-1576), Venetian painter.

St. Francis, 13th Century Fresco — A659

**1976, Oct. 2 Engr. Perf. 14**
1234 A659 150 l brown .25 .20
St. Francis of Assisi, 750th death anniv.

Cart, from Trajan's Column A660

100 l, Emblem of Kingdom of Sardinia. 150 l, Marble mask, 19th cent. mail box. 200 l, Hand canceler, 19th cent. 400 l, Automatic letter sorting machine.

**1976, Oct. 14 Photo. Perf. 14x13½**
1235 A660 70 l multi .20 .20
1236 A660 100 l multi .20 .20
1237 A660 150 l multi .25 .20
1238 A660 200 l multi .30 .20
1239 A660 400 l multi .65 .20
Nos. 1235-1239 (5) 1.60 1.00
ITALIA 76 International Philatelic Exhibition, Milan, Oct. 14-24.

Girl and Animals — A661

Designs (Children' Drawings): 100 l, Trees, rabbit and flowers. 150 l, Boy healing tree.

**1976, Oct. 17 Perf. 13½x14**
1240 A661 40 l multi .20 .20
1241 A661 100 l multi .20 .20
1242 A661 150 l multi .25 .20
Nos. 1240-1242 (3) .65 .60
18th Stamp Day and nature protection.

**Botticelli Type of 1973-74**
**1976, Nov. 22 Photo. Perf. 14x13½**
1243 A602 170 l Lorenzo Ghiberti .25 .20
1244 A602 170 l Domenico Ghirlandaio .25 .20
1245 A602 170 l Sassoferrato .25 .20
1246 A602 170 l Carlo Dolci .25 .20
1247 A602 170 l Giovanni Piazzetta .25 .20
Nos. 1243-1247 (5) 1.25 1.00

Famous painters.

The Visit, by Silvestro Lega A662

**1976, Dec. 7 Photo. Perf. 14x13½**
1248 A662 170 l multi .25 .20
Silvestro Lega (1826-1895), painter.

Adoration of the Kings, by Bartolo di Fredi — A663

Christmas: 120 l, Nativity, by Taddeo Gaddi.

**1976, Dec. 11**     *Perf. 13½x14*
| | | | |
|---|---|---|---|
| 1249 | A663 70 l multi | .20 | .20 |
| 1250 | A663 120 l multi | .20 | .20 |

**Fountain Type of 1973**

Designs: No. 1251, Antique Fountain, Gallipoli. No. 1252, Madonna Fountain, Verona. No. 1253, Silvio Cosini Fountain, Palazzo Doria, Genoa.

**Lithographed and Engraved**

**1976, Dec. 21**     *Perf. 13½x14*
| | | | |
|---|---|---|---|
| 1251 | A603 170 l blk & multi | .25 | .20 |
| 1252 | A603 170 l blk & multi | .25 | .20 |
| 1253 | A603 170 l blk & multi | .25 | .20 |
| | Nos. 1251-1253 (3) | .75 | .60 |

Snakes Forming Net A664

Design: 170 l, Drug addict and poppy.

**1977, Feb. 28 Photo.**   *Perf. 14x13½*
| | | | |
|---|---|---|---|
| 1254 | A664 120 l multi | .20 | .20 |
| 1255 | A664 170 l multi | .25 | .20 |

Fight against drug abuse.

Micca Setting Fire A665

**1977, Mar. 5**
| | | | |
|---|---|---|---|
| 1256 | A665 170 l multi | .25 | .20 |

Pietro Micca (1677-1706), patriot who set fire to the powder magazine of Turin Citadel.

Globe with Cross in Center — A666

Design: 120 l, People of the World united as brothers by St. John Bosco.

**1977, Mar. 29 Photo.**   *Perf. 13x13½*
| | | | |
|---|---|---|---|
| 1257 | A666 70 l multi | .20 | .20 |
| 1258 | A666 120 l multi | .20 | .20 |

Honoring the Salesian missionaries.

Italian Constitution, Article 53 — A667

**1977, Apr. 14 Photo.**   *Perf. 14*
| | | | |
|---|---|---|---|
| 1259 | A667 120 l bis, brn & blk | .20 | .20 |
| 1260 | A667 170 l lt grn, grn & blk | .25 | .20 |

"Pay your taxes."

---

**Tourist Type of 1974**

Europa (Europa Emblem and): 170 l, Taormina. 200 l, Castle del Monte.

**1977, May 2**
| | | | |
|---|---|---|---|
| 1261 | A616 170 l multi | .65 | .20 |
| 1262 | A616 200 l multi | .85 | .25 |

**Tourist Type of 1974**

Paintings: No. 1263, Canossa Castle. No. 1264, Fermo. No. 1265, Castellana Caves.

**1977, May 30 Photo.**   *Perf. 14*
| | | | |
|---|---|---|---|
| 1263 | A616 170 l brn & multi | .25 | .20 |
| 1264 | A616 170 l vio & multi | .25 | .20 |
| 1265 | A616 170 l gray & multi | .25 | .20 |
| | Nos. 1263-1265 (3) | .75 | .60 |

**Botticelli Type of 1973-74**

**1977, June 27**    *Perf. 14x13½*
| | | | |
|---|---|---|---|
| 1266 | A602 70 l Filippo Brunelleschi | .20 | .20 |
| 1267 | A602 70 l Pietro Aretino | .20 | .20 |
| 1268 | A602 70 l Carlo Goldoni | .20 | .20 |
| 1269 | A602 70 l Luigi Cherubini | .20 | .20 |
| 1270 | A602 70 l Eduardo Bassini | .20 | .20 |
| | Nos. 1266-1270 (5) | 1.00 | 1.00 |

Famous artists, writers and scientists.

Justice, by Andrea Delitio A669

Painting: No. 1272, Winter, by Giuseppe Arcimboldi, 1527-c.1593.

**Engraved and Lithographed**

**1977, Sept. 5**    *Perf. 14*
| | | | |
|---|---|---|---|
| 1271 | A669 170 l multi | .25 | .20 |
| 1272 | A669 170 l multi | .25 | .20 |

Corvette Caracciolo — A670

Italian Ships: No. 1274, Hydrofoil gunboat Sparviero. No. 1275, Paddle steamer Ferdinando Primo. No. 1276, Passenger liner Saturnia.

**Photogravure and Engraved**

**1977, Sept. 23**    *Perf. 14x13½*
| | | | |
|---|---|---|---|
| 1273 | 170 l multi | .25 | .20 |
| 1274 | 170 l multi | .25 | .20 |
| 1275 | 170 l multi | .25 | .20 |
| 1276 | 170 l multi | .25 | .20 |
| a. | A670 Block or strip of 4, #1273-1276 + 2 labels | 1.00 | .50 |

See #1323-1326, 1382-1385, 1435-1438.

**Fountain Type of 1973**

Designs: No. 1277, Pacassi Fountain, Gorizia. No. 1278, Fraterna Fountain, Isernia. No. 1279, Palm Fountain, Palmi.

**Lithographed and Engraved**

**1977, Oct. 18**    *Perf. 13x14*
| | | | |
|---|---|---|---|
| 1277 | A603 120 l blk & multi | .20 | .20 |
| 1278 | A603 120 l blk & multi | .20 | .20 |
| 1279 | A603 120 l blk & multi | .20 | .20 |
| | Nos. 1277-1279 (3) | .60 | .60 |

Volleyball — A671

---

Designs (Children's Drawings): No. 1281, Butterflies and net. No. 1282, Flying kites.

**1977, Oct. 23 Photo.**   *Perf. 13x14*
| | | | |
|---|---|---|---|
| 1280 | A671 120 l multi | .20 | .20 |
| 1281 | A671 120 l multi | .20 | .20 |
| 1282 | A671 120 l multi | .20 | .20 |
| a. | Block of 3, #1280-1282 + label | .50 | .30 |

19th Stamp Day.

Symbolic Blood Donation A672

Design: 70 l, Blood donation symbolized.

**1977, Oct. 26**    *Perf. 14x13½*
| | | | |
|---|---|---|---|
| 1283 | A672 70 l multi | .20 | .20 |
| 1284 | A672 120 l multi | .30 | .20 |

Blood donors.

Quintino Sella and Italy No. 24 — A673

**1977, Oct. 23**    *Perf. 13½x14*
| | | | |
|---|---|---|---|
| 1285 | A673 170 l olive & blk brn | .30 | .20 |

Quintino Sella (1827-1884), statesman, engineer, mineralogist, birth sesquicentenary.

**Italia Type of 1953-54 and**

Italia — A674

**1977-87**    **Wmk. 303**    *Perf. 14*
   **Size: 16x20mm**
    **Photo.**
| | | | |
|---|---|---|---|
| 1288 | A354 120 l dk bl & emer | .20 | .20 |

    **Photo. & Engr.**
| | | | |
|---|---|---|---|
| 1289 | A354 170 l grn & ocher | .25 | .20 |

    **Litho. & Engr.**
| | | | |
|---|---|---|---|
| 1290 | A354 350 l red, ocher & pur | .55 | .20 |

    *Perf. 14x13½*
| | | Engr. | Unwmk. |
|---|---|---|---|
| 1291 | A674 1500 l multi | 2.40 | .20 |
| 1292 | A674 2000 l multi | 3.25 | .20 |
| 1293 | A674 3000 l multi | 5.00 | .20 |
| 1294 | A674 4000 l multi | 6.50 | .20 |
| 1295 | A674 5000 l multi | 8.25 | .65 |
| 1296 | A674 10,000 l multi | 16.00 | 2.40 |
| 1297 | A674 20,000 l multi | 32.50 | 17.00 |
| | Nos. 1288-1297 (10) | 74.90 | 21.45 |

Issued: 120 l, 170 l, 350l, 11/22/77; 5,000 l, 12/4/78; 4,000 l, 2/12/79; 3,000 l, 3/12/79; 2,000 l, 4/12/79; 1,500 l, 5/14/79; 10,000 l, 6/27/83; 20,000 l, 1/5/87.

Dina Galli (1877-1951), Actress — A675

    *Perf. 13½x14*
**1977, Dec. 2 Photo.**   **Unwmk.**
| | | | |
|---|---|---|---|
| 1309 | A675 170 l multi | .25 | .20 |

---

Adoration of the Shepherds, by Pietro Testa — A676

Christmas: 120 l, Adoration of the Shepherds, by Gian Jacopo Caraglio.

**Lithographed and Engraved**

**1977, Dec. 13**    *Perf. 14*
| | | | |
|---|---|---|---|
| 1310 | A676 70 l blk & ol | .20 | .20 |
| 1311 | A676 120 l blk & bl grn | .20 | .20 |

La Scala Opera House, Milan, Bicent. — A677

Designs: 170 l, Facade. 200 l, Auditorium.

**1978, Mar. 15 Litho.**   *Perf. 13½x14*
| | | | |
|---|---|---|---|
| 1312 | A677 170 l multi | .25 | .20 |
| 1313 | A677 200 l multi | .30 | .20 |

**Tourist Type of 1974**

Paintings: 70 l, Gubbio. 200 l, Udine. 600 l, Paestum.

**1978, Mar. 30 Photo.**   *Perf. 14*
| | | | |
|---|---|---|---|
| 1314 | A616 70 l multi | .20 | .20 |
| 1315 | A616 200 l multi | .30 | .20 |
| 1316 | A616 600 l multi | 1.00 | .55 |
| | Nos. 1314-1316 (3) | 1.50 | .95 |

Giant Grouper — A678

Designs (outline of "Amerigo Vespucci" in background): No. 1318, Leatherback turtle. No. 1319, Mediterranean monk seal. No. 1320, Audouin's gull.

**1978, Apr. 3**    *Perf. 14x13*
| | | | |
|---|---|---|---|
| 1317 | A678 170 l multi | .45 | .20 |
| 1318 | A678 170 l multi | .45 | .20 |
| 1319 | A678 170 l multi | .45 | .20 |
| 1320 | A678 170 l multi | .45 | .20 |
| a. | Strip of 4, #1317-1320 + label | 1.90 | 1.00 |

Endangered species in Mediterranean.

Castel Nuovo, Angevin Fortifications, Naples — A679

Europa: 200 l, Pantheon, Rome.

**1978, Apr. 29 Litho.**   *Perf. 14x13½*
| | | | |
|---|---|---|---|
| 1321 | A679 170 l multi | .45 | .25 |
| 1322 | A679 200 l multi | .55 | .25 |

**Ship Type of 1977**

Designs: No. 1323, Cruiser Benedetto Brin. No. 1324, Cruiser Benedetto Brin. No. 1325, Ligurian brigantine Fortuna. No. 1326, Container ship Africa.

**1978, May 8**    **Litho. & Engr.**
| | | | |
|---|---|---|---|
| 1323 | 170 l multi | .55 | .20 |
| 1324 | 170 l multi | .55 | .20 |
| 1325 | 170 l multi | .55 | .20 |

| | | | |
|---|---|---|---|
| **1326** | 170 l multi | .55 | .20 |
| *a.* | A670 Block of 4, #1323-1326 + 2 labels | 2.25 | .75 |

Matilde Serao — A680

Designs: Portraits of famous Italians.

**1978, May 10**    **Engr.**    **Perf. 14x13½**

| | | | |
|---|---|---|---|
| **1327** | A680 170 l shown | .25 | .20 |
| **1328** | A680 170 l Vittorino da Feltre | .25 | .20 |
| **1329** | A680 170 l Victor Emmanuel II | .25 | .20 |
| **1330** | A680 170 l Pope Pius IX | .25 | .20 |
| **1331** | A680 170 l Marcello Malpighi | .25 | .20 |
| **1332** | A680 170 l Antonio Meucci | .25 | .20 |
| *a.* | Block of 6, #1327-1332 | 1.50 | .75 |

Constitution, 30th Anniv. — A681

**1978, June 2**    **Litho.**    **Perf. 13½x14**

| | | | |
|---|---|---|---|
| **1333** | A681 170 l multi | .25 | .20 |

Telegraph Wires and Lens — A682

**1978, June 30**    **Photo.**

| | | | |
|---|---|---|---|
| **1334** | A682 120 l lt bl & gray | .20 | .20 |

Photographic information.

The Lovers, by Tranquillo Cremona (1837-1878) — A683

Design: 520 l, The Cook (woman with goose), by Bernardo Strozzi (1581-1644).

**Engraved and Lithographed**

**1978, July 12**    **Perf. 14**

| | | | |
|---|---|---|---|
| **1335** | A683 170 l multi | .55 | .20 |
| **1336** | A683 520 l multi | 2.25 | .75 |

Holy Shroud of Turin, by Giovanni Testa, 1578 — A684

**1978, Sept. 8**    **Photo.**    **Perf. 14**

| | | | |
|---|---|---|---|
| **1337** | A684 220 l yel, red & blk | .35 | .20 |

400th anniversary of the transfer of the Holy Shroud from Savoy to Turin.

Volleyball — A685

Design: 120 l, Volleyball, diff.

**1978, Sept. 20**

| | | | |
|---|---|---|---|
| **1338** | A685 80 l multi | .45 | .20 |
| **1339** | A685 120 l multi | .45 | .20 |

Men's Volleyball World Championship.

Mother and Child, by Masaccio — A686

**1978, Oct. 18**    **Engr.**    **Perf. 13½x14**

| | | | |
|---|---|---|---|
| **1340** | A686 170 l indigo | .25 | .20 |

Masaccio (real name Tommaso Guidi; 1401-28), painter.

**Fountain Type of 1973**

Designs: No 1341, Neptune Fountain, Trent. No. 1342, Fortuna Fountain, Fano. No. 1343, Cavallina Fountain, Genzano di Lucania.

**1978, Oct. 25**    **Litho. & Engr.**

| | | | |
|---|---|---|---|
| **1341** | A603 120 l blk & multi | .20 | .20 |
| **1342** | A603 120 l blk & multi | .20 | .20 |
| **1343** | A603 120 l blk & multi | .20 | .20 |
| | Nos. 1341-1343 (3) | .60 | .60 |

Virgin and Child, by Giorgione — A687

Adoration of the Kings, by Giorgione — A688

**1978, Nov. 8**    **Engr.**    **Perf. 13x14**

| | | | |
|---|---|---|---|
| **1344** | A687 80 l dark red | .20 | .20 |

     **Photo.**    **Perf. 14x13½**

| | | | |
|---|---|---|---|
| **1345** | A688 120 l multi | .20 | .20 |

Christmas 1978.

Flags as Flowers — A689

Designs: No. 1347, European flags. No. 1348, "People hailing Europe."

**1978, Nov. 26**    **Photo.**    **Perf. 13x14**

| | | | |
|---|---|---|---|
| **1346** | A689 120 l multi | .20 | .20 |
| **1347** | A689 120 l multi | .20 | .20 |
| **1348** | A689 120 l multi | .20 | .20 |
| | Nos. 1346-1348 (3) | .60 | .60 |

20th Stamp Day on theme "United Europe."

State Printing Office, Stamps A690

Design: 220 l, Printing press and stamps.

**1979, Jan. 6**    **Photo.**    **Perf. 14x13½**

| | | | |
|---|---|---|---|
| **1349** | A690 170 l multi | .25 | .20 |
| **1350** | A690 220 l multi | .35 | .20 |

1st stamps printed by State Printing Office, 50 anniv.

St. Francis Washing Lepers, 13th Century Painting A691

**1979, Jan. 22**

| | | | |
|---|---|---|---|
| **1351** | A691 80 l multi | .20 | .20 |

Leprosy relief.

Bicyclist Carrying Bike — A692

**1979, Jan. 27**    **Perf. 13½x14**

| | | | |
|---|---|---|---|
| **1352** | A692 170 l multi | .25 | .20 |
| **1353** | A692 220 l multi | .35 | .20 |

World Crosscountry Bicycle Championships.

Virgin Mary, by Antonello da Messina A693

Painting: 520 l, Haystack, by Ardengo Soffici (1879-1964).

**1979, Feb. 15**    **Engr.**    **Perf. 14**

| | | | |
|---|---|---|---|
| **1354** | A693 170 l multi | .30 | .20 |
| **1355** | A693 520 l multi | .85 | .50 |

Albert Einstein (1879-1955), Theoretical Physicist and His Equation. — A694

**Lithographed and Engraved**

**1979, Mar. 14**    **Perf. 13x14**

| | | | |
|---|---|---|---|
| **1356** | A694 120 l multi | .20 | .20 |

**Tourist Type of 1974**

Paintings: 70 l, Asiago. 90 l, Castelsardo. 170 l, Orvieto. 220 l, Scilla.

**1979, Mar. 30**    **Photo.**    **Perf. 14**

| | | | |
|---|---|---|---|
| **1357** | A616 70 l grn & multi | .20 | .20 |
| **1358** | A616 90 l car & multi | .20 | .20 |
| **1359** | A616 170 l ultra & multi | .25 | .20 |
| **1360** | A616 220 l gray & multi | .35 | .20 |
| | Nos. 1357-1360 (4) | 1.00 | .80 |

Famous Italians — A695

No. 1361, Carlo Maderno (1556-1629), architect. No. 1362, Lazzaro Spallanzani (1729-1799), physiologist. No. 1363, Ugo Foscolo (1778-1827), writer. No. 1364 Massimo Bontempelli (1878-1960), journalist. No. 1365, Francesco Severi (1879-1961), mathematician.

**1979, Apr. 23**    **Engr.**    **Perf. 14x13½**

| | | | |
|---|---|---|---|
| **1361** | A695 170 l multi | .25 | .20 |
| **1362** | A695 170 l multi | .25 | .20 |
| **1363** | A695 170 l multi | .25 | .20 |
| **1364** | A695 170 l multi | .25 | .20 |
| **1365** | A695 170 l multi | .25 | .20 |
| | Nos. 1361-1365 (5) | 1.25 | 1.00 |

Telegraph A696

Europa: 220 l, Carrier pigeons.

**1979, Apr. 30**    **Photo.**    **Perf. 14**

| | | | |
|---|---|---|---|
| **1366** | A696 170 l multi | .65 | .20 |
| **1367** | A696 220 l multi | .65 | .30 |

Flags and "E" — A697

**1979, May 5**    **Perf. 14x13½**

| | | | |
|---|---|---|---|
| **1368** | A697 170 l multi | .25 | .20 |
| **1369** | A697 220 l multi | .35 | .20 |

European Parliament, first direct elections, June 7-10.

Exhibition Emblem, Dome of Milan A698

**1979, June 22**    **Photo.**    **Perf. 14**

| | | | |
|---|---|---|---|
| **1370** | A698 170 l multi | .25 | .20 |
| **1371** | A698 220 l multi | .35 | .20 |

3rd World Machine Tool Exhib., Milan, Oct. 10-18.

Aeneas and Rotary Emblem — A699

**1979, June 9**     **Perf. 13½x14**
1372 A699 220 l multi    .35   .20
70th World Rotary Cong., Rome, June 1979.

Basket — A700

**1979, June 13**     **Perf. 14**
1373 A700 80 l shown    .20   .20
1374 A700 120 l Basketball players    .30   .20
21st European Basketball Championship, June 9-20.

A701

Patient & Physician, 16th cent. woodcut.

**1979, June 16**     **Photo. & Engr.**
1375 A701 120 l multi    .20   .20
Digestive Ailments Study Week.

A702

**Lithographed and Engraved**
**1979, July 9**     **Perf. 13x14**
Design: Ottorino Respighi (1879-1936), composer, Roman landscape.
1376 A702 120 l multi    .20   .20

Woman Making Phone Call A703

200 l, Woman with old-fashioned phone.

**1979, Sept. 20**   **Photo.**    **Perf. 14**
1377 A703 170 l red & gray    .25   .20
1378 A703 220 l grn & slate    .35   .20
3rd World Telecommunications Exhibition, Geneva, Sept. 20-26.

**Fountain Type of 1973**
Designs: No. 1379, Great Fountain, Viterbo. No. 1380, Hot Springs, Acqui Terme. No. 1381, Pomegranate Fountain, Issogne Castle.

**Lithographed and Engraved**
**1979, Sept. 22**     **Perf. 13x14**
1379 A603 120 l multi    .30   .20
1380 A603 120 l multi    .30   .20
1381 A603 120 l multi    .30   .20
   Nos. 1379-1381 (3)    .90   .60

**Ship Type of 1977**
Designs: No. 1382, Cruiser Enrico Dandolo. No. 1383, Submarine Carlo Fecia. No. 1384, Freighter Cosmos. No. 1385, Ferry Deledda.

**1979, Oct. 12**     **Perf. 14x13½**
1382 170 l multi    .30   .20
1383 170 l multi    .30   .20
1384 170 l multi    .30   .20
1385 170 l multi    .30   .20
  a. A670 Block of 4, #1382-1385 + 2 labels    1.60   .75

Penny Black, Rowland Hill A704

**1979, Oct. 25**     **Photo.**
1386 A704 220 l multi    .35   .20

Minstrels and Church A705

**1979, Nov. 7**   **Photo.**    **Perf. 14x13½**
1387 A705 120 l multi    .20   .20
Christmas 1979.

Black and White Boys Holding Hands A706

Children's Drawings: 120 l, Children of various races under umbrella map, vert. 150 l, Children and red balloons.

**Perf. 14x13½, 13½x14**
**1979, Nov. 25**     **Photo.**
1388 A706 70 l multi    .20   .20
1389 A706 120 l multi    .20   .20
1390 A706 150 l multi    .25   .20
   Nos. 1388-1390 (3)    .65   .60
21st Stamp Day.

Solar Energy Panels A707

Energy Conservation: 170 l, Sun & pylon.

**1980, Feb. 25**   **Photo.**    **Perf. 14x13½**
1391 A707 120 l multi    .20   .20
1392 A707 170 l multi    .25   .20

St. Benedict of Nursia, 1500th Birth Anniv. — A708

**1980, Mar. 21**   **Engr.**    **Perf. 13½x14**
1393 A708 220 l dark blue    .35   .20

Royal Palace, Naples — A709

**Lithographed and Engraved**
**1980, Apr. 16**     **Perf. 13½x14**
1394 A709 220 l multi    .35   .20
20th International Philatelic Exhibition, Europa '80, Naples, Apr. 26-May 4.

Antonio Pigafetta, Caravel A710

Europa: 220 l, Antonio Lo Surdo (1880-1949) geophysicist.

**1980, Apr. 28**   **Litho.**    **Perf. 14x13½**
1395 A710 170 l multi    .40   .20
1396 A710 220 l multi    .70   .30

St. Catherine, Reliquary Bust — A711

**1980, Apr. 29**     **Photo.**
1397 A711 170 l multi    .25   .20
St. Catherine of Siena (1347-1380).

Italian Red Cross A712

**1980, May 15**   **Photo.**    **Perf. 14x13½**
1398 A712 70 l multi    .20   .20
1399 A712 80 l multi    .20   .20

Temples of Philae, Egypt — A713

**1980, May 20**
1400   Pair + label    .70   .20
  a. A713 220 l shown    .35   .20
  b. A713 220 l Temple of Philae, diff.    .35   .20
Italian civil engineering achievements (Temples of Philae saved from ruin by Italian engineers).

Soccer Player A714

**1980, June 11**
1401 A714 80 l multi    1.75   .75
European Soccer Championships, Milan, Turin, Rome, Naples, June 9-22.

**Tourist Type of 1974**
Paintings: 80 l, Erice. 150 l, Villa Rufolo, Ravello. 200 l, Roseto degli Abruzzi. 670 l, Public Baths, Salsomaggiore Terme.

**1980, June 28**     **Perf. 14**
1402 A616 80 l multi    .20   .20
1403 A616 150 l multi    .30   .20
1404 A616 200 l multi    .35   .20
1405 A616 670 l multi    1.10   .60
   Nos. 1402-1405 (4)    1.95   1.20

Cosimo I with his Artists, by Giorgio Vasari, and Armillary sphere — A715

**1980, July 2**     **Perf. 13½x14**
1406 A715   Pair + label    .50   .50
  a.   170 l Cosimo I    .25   .20
  b.   170 l Armillary sphere    .25   .20
The Medici in Europe of the 16th Century Exhibition, Florence.

Fonte Avellana Monastery Millennium A716

**1980, Sept. 3**   **Engr.**    **Perf. 14x13½**
1407 A716 200 l grn & brn    .30   .20

St. Angelo Castle, Rome — A717

Designs: Castles.
Photo (#1408-1417), Litho and Engr. (#1418-1422, 1425, 1427-1428), Engr. (#1423-1424, 1426, 1429-1434)**Perf. 14x13½**
**1980, Sept. 22**     **Wmk. 303**
1408   5 l shown    .20   .20
1409   10 l Sforzesco, Milan    .20   .20
1410   20 l Del Monte, Andria    .20   .20
1411   40 l Ursino, Catania    .20   .20
1412   50 l Rocca di Calascio    .20   .20
1413   60 l Norman Tower, St. Mauro Fort    .20   .20
1414   90 l Isola Capo Rizzuto    .20   .20
1415   100 l Aragonese, Ischia    .20   .20
1416   120 l Estense, Ferrara    .20   .20
1417   150 l Miramare, Trieste    .25   .20
1418   170 l Ostia, Rome    .25   .20
1419   180 l Gavone, Savona    .25   1.00
1420   200 l Cerro al Volturno, Isernia    .30   .20
1421   250 l Rocca di Mondavio    .40   .20
1422   300 l Svevo, Bari    .50   .20
1423   350 l Mussomeli, Caltanissetta    .55   .20

| | | | | |
|---|---|---|---|---|
| 1424 | 400 l | Imperatore-Prato, Florence | .65 | .20 |
| 1425 | 450 l | Bosa, Nuoro | .70 | .20 |
| 1426 | 500 l | Rovereto, Trento | .80 | .20 |
| 1427 | 600 l | Scaligero, Sirmione | 1.00 | .20 |
| 1428 | 700 l | Ivrea, Turin | 1.10 | .20 |
| 1429 | 800 l | Rocca Maggiore, Assisi | 1.25 | .20 |
| 1430 | 900 l | St. Pierre, Aosta | 1.50 | .20 |
| 1431 | 1000 l | Montagnana, Padua | 1.60 | .20 |
| | | Nos. 1408-1431 (24) | 12.90 | 5.60 |

### Coil Stamps
### Perf. 14 Vert.
### Size: 16x21mm

| | | | | |
|---|---|---|---|---|
| 1432 | 30 l | St. Severna, Rome | .20 | .20 |
| 1433 | 120 l | Lombardia, Enna | .25 | .20 |
| a. | | Pair, Nos. 1432-1433 | .40 | .20 |
| 1434 | 170 l | Serralunga d'Alba, Cuneo | .30 | .20 |
| a. | | Pair, Nos. 1432, 1434 | .75 | .75 |
| | | Nos. 1432-1434 (3) | .75 | .60 |

No. 1412 exists dated "1980."
See #1475-1484, 1657-1666, 1862-1866.

### Ship Type of 1977

#1435, Corvette Gabbiano. #1436, Torpedo boat Audace. #1437, Sailing ship Italia. #1438, Floating dock Castoro Sei.

### Lithographed and Engraved

| | | | | |
|---|---|---|---|---|
| 1980, Oct. 11 | | | Perf. 14x13½ | |
| 1435 | 200 l | multi | 1.25 | .20 |
| 1436 | 200 l | multi | 1.25 | .20 |
| 1437 | 200 l | multi | 1.25 | .20 |
| 1438 | 200 l | multi | 1.25 | .20 |
| a. | | A670 Block of 4, #1435-1438 + 2 labels | 7.00 | 1.00 |

Philip Mazzei (1730-1816), Political Writer in US — A718

| | | | | |
|---|---|---|---|---|
| 1980, Oct. 18 | Photo. | | Perf. 13½x14 | |
| 1439 | A718 | 320 l multi | .50 | .20 |

Villa Foscari Malcontenta, Venezia — A719

Villas: 150 l, Barbaro Maser, Treviso. 170 l, Godi Valmarana, Vicenza.

### Lithographed and Engraved

| | | | | |
|---|---|---|---|---|
| 1980, Oct. 31 | | | Perf. 14x13½ | |
| 1440 | A719 | 80 l multi | .40 | .20 |
| 1441 | A719 | 150 l multi | .40 | .20 |
| 1442 | A719 | 170 l multi | .40 | .20 |
| | | Nos. 1440-1442 (3) | 1.20 | .60 |

See Nos. 1493-1495, 1528-1530, 1565-1568, 1606-1609, 1646-1649, 1691-1695.

St. Barbara, by Palma the Elder (1480-1528) — A720

Design: No. 1444, Apollo and Daphne, by Gian Lorenzo Bernini (1598-1680).

| | | | | |
|---|---|---|---|---|
| 1980, Nov. 20 | | | Perf. 14 | |
| 1443 | A720 | 520 l multi | .85 | .55 |
| 1444 | A720 | 520 l multi | .85 | .55 |

Nativity Sculpture by Federico Brandini, 16th Cent. — A721

| | | | | |
|---|---|---|---|---|
| 1980, Nov. 22 | | | Engr. | |
| 1445 | A721 | 120 l brn org & blk | .20 | .20 |

Christmas 1980.

View of Verona A722

22nd Stamp Day: Views of Verona drawings by school children.

| | | | | |
|---|---|---|---|---|
| 1980, Nov. 30 | Photo. | | Perf. 14x13½ | |
| 1446 | A722 | 70 l multi | .20 | .20 |
| 1447 | A722 | 120 l multi | .20 | .20 |
| 1448 | A722 | 170 l multi | .25 | .20 |
| | | Nos. 1446-1448 (3) | .65 | .60 |

Daniele Comboni (1831-1881), Savior of the Africans — A723

| | | | | |
|---|---|---|---|---|
| 1981, Mar. 14 | | | Engr. | |
| 1449 | A723 | 80 l multi | .20 | .20 |

Alcide de Gasperi (1881-1954), Statesman A724

| | | | | |
|---|---|---|---|---|
| 1981, Apr. 3 | | | Perf. 13½x14 | |
| 1450 | A724 | 200 l olive green | .30 | .20 |

International Year of the Disabled — A725

| | | | | |
|---|---|---|---|---|
| 1981, Apr. 11 | | | Photo. | |
| 1451 | A725 | 300 l multi | .50 | .20 |

A726

| | | | | |
|---|---|---|---|---|
| 1981, Apr. 27 | Photo. | | Perf. 13½x14 | |
| 1452 | A726 | 200 l Roses | .30 | .20 |
| 1453 | A726 | 200 l Anemones | .30 | .20 |
| 1454 | A726 | 200 l Oleanders | .30 | .20 |
| | | Nos. 1452-1454 (3) | .90 | .60 |

See Nos. 1510-1512, 1555-1557.

Europa — A727

Designs: No. 1455, Chess game with human pieces, Marostica. No. 1456, Horse race, Siena.

| | | | | |
|---|---|---|---|---|
| 1981, May 4 | | | | |
| 1455 | A727 | 300 l shown | 1.00 | .40 |
| 1456 | A727 | 300 l multicolored | 1.00 | .40 |

St. Rita Offering Thorn — A728

| | | | | |
|---|---|---|---|---|
| 1981, May 22 | | | | |
| 1457 | A728 | 600 l multi | 1.00 | .60 |

St. Rita of Cascia, 600th birth anniversary.

Ciro Menotti (1798-1831), Patriot — A729

| | | | | |
|---|---|---|---|---|
| 1981, May 26 | Engr. | | Perf. 14x13½ | |
| 1458 | A729 | 80 l brn & blk | .20 | .20 |

G-222 Aeritalia Transport Plane — A730

| | | | | |
|---|---|---|---|---|
| 1981, June 1 | | | Photo. | |
| 1459 | | 200 l shown | .30 | .20 |
| 1460 | | 200 l MB-339 Aermacchi jet | .30 | .20 |
| 1461 | | 200 l A-109 Agusta helicopter | .30 | .20 |
| 1462 | | 200 l P-68 Partenavia transport plane | .30 | .20 |
| a. | | A730 Block of 4, #1459-1462 + 2 labels | 1.35 | .65 |

See Nos. 1505-1508, 1550-1553.

Hydro-geological Research — A731

| | | | | |
|---|---|---|---|---|
| 1981, June 8 | | | Perf. 13½x14 | |
| 1463 | A731 | 80 l multi | .20 | .20 |

Sao Simao Dam and Power Station, Brazil — A732

Civil Engineering Works Abroad: No. 1465, High Island Power Station, Hong Kong.

| | | | | |
|---|---|---|---|---|
| 1981, June 26 | Engr. | | Perf. 14x13½ | |
| 1464 | A732 | 300 l dark blue | .50 | .20 |
| 1465 | A732 | 300 l red | .50 | .20 |
| a. | | Pair, #1464-1465 + label | 1.00 | .35 |

See Nos. 1516-1517, 1538-1539.

### Tourist Type of 1974

| | | | | |
|---|---|---|---|---|
| 1981, July 4 | Photo. | | Perf. 14 | |
| 1466 | A616 | 80 l View of Matera | .20 | .20 |
| 1467 | A616 | 150 l Lake Garda | .20 | .20 |
| 1468 | A616 | 300 l St. Teresa di Gallura beach | .60 | .20 |
| 1469 | A616 | 900 l Tarquinia | 1.75 | .40 |
| | | Nos. 1466-1469 (4) | 2.75 | 1.00 |

Naval Academy, Livorno and Navy Emblem A735

Naval Academy of Livorno Centenary: 150 l, View. 200 l, Cadet with sextant, training ship Amerigo Vespucci.

| | | | | |
|---|---|---|---|---|
| 1981, July 24 | | | Perf. 14x13½ | |
| 1472 | A735 | 80 l multi | .20 | .20 |
| 1473 | A735 | 150 l multi | .25 | .20 |
| 1474 | A735 | 200 l multi | .30 | .20 |
| | | Nos. 1472-1474 (3) | .75 | .60 |

### Castle Type of 1980
### Perf. 14x13½

| | | | | |
|---|---|---|---|---|
| 1981-84 | Photo. | | Wmk. 303 | |
| 1475 | A717 | 30 l Aquila | .20 | .20 |
| 1476 | A717 | 70 l Aragonese, Reggio Calabria | .20 | .20 |
| 1477 | A717 | 80 l Sabbionara, Avio | .20 | .20 |

### Perf. 13½

| | | | | |
|---|---|---|---|---|
| 1478 | A717 | 550 l Rocca Sinibalda | .90 | .20 |
| 1479 | A717 | 1400 l Caldoresco, Vasto | 2.25 | .65 |
| | | Nos. 1475-1479 (5) | 3.75 | 1.45 |

Issue dates: Nos. 1475-1477, Aug. 20, 1981; Nos. 1478-1479, Feb. 14, 1984.

### Coil Stamps

| | | | | |
|---|---|---|---|---|
| 1981-88 | Engr. | | Perf. 14 Vert. | |
| | | Size: 16x21mm | | |
| 1480 | A717 | 50 l Scilla | .20 | .20 |
| 1481 | A717 | 200 l Angionia, Lucera | 2.75 | 2.00 |
| 1482 | A717 | 300 l Norman Castle, Melfi | .60 | .20 |
| 1483 | A717 | 400 l Venafro | .65 | .20 |
| 1484 | A717 | 450 l Piobbico Pesaro | .75 | .20 |
| a. | | Pair, #1480, 1484 | .95 | .40 |
| | | Nos. 1480-1484 (5) | 4.95 | 2.80 |

Issued: #1481-1482, 9/30; #1483, 6/25/83; #1480, 1484, 7/25/85; #1484a, 3/1/88.

Palazzo Spada, Rome (Council Seat) A736

| | | | | |
|---|---|---|---|---|
| 1981, Aug. 31 | Engr. | | Unwmk. | |
| 1485 | A736 | 200 l multi | .30 | .20 |

State Council sesquicentennial.

World Cup
Races — A737

**1981, Sept. 4   Photo.   Perf. 13½x14**
1486  A737  300 l  multi                    .50  .20

Harbor View, by Carlo Carra (1881-
1966) — A738

#1488, Castle, by Guiseppe Ugonia (1881-
1944).

**Lithographed and Engraved**
**1981, Sept. 7                       Perf. 14**
1487  A738  200 l  multi                    .30  .20
1488  A738  200 l  multi                    .30  .20
   See #1532-1533, 1638-1639, 1697-1698,
1732.

Riace Bronze, 4th Cent. B.C. — A739

**1981, Sept. 9   Photo.   Perf. 13½x14**
1489      200 l  Statue                     .30  .20
1490      200 l  Statue, diff.              .30  .20
   a.  A739 Pair, #1489-1490               .65  .30
   Greek statues found in 1972 in sea near
Reggio di Calabria.

Virgil,
Mosaic,
Treviri
A740

**1981, Sept. 19                      Perf. 14**
1491  A740  600 l  multi                   1.00  .60
   Virgil's death bimillennium.

Food and
Wine, by
Gregorio
Sciltian
A741

**1981, Oct. 16   Litho.   Perf. 14**
1492  A741  150 l  multi                    .30  .20
   World Food Day.

**Villa Type of 1980**
**Lithographed and Engraved**
**1981, Oct. 17                  Perf. 14x13½**
1493  A719  100 l  Villa Campolieto,
                     Ercolano              .20  .20
1494  A719  200 l  Cimbrone, Ravel-
                     lo                     .30  .20
1495  A719  300 l  Pignatelli, Naples      .50  .20
   Nos. 1493-1495 (3)                      1.00  .60

Adoration of the Magi, by Giovanni de
Campione d'Italia (Christmas
1981) — A743

**1981, Nov. 21   Engr.   Perf. 14**
1496  A743  200 l  multi                    .35  .20

Pope John XXIII
(1881-1963)
A744

**1981, Nov. 25  Photo.  Perf. 13½x14**
1497  A744  200 l  multi                    .30  .20

Stamp
Day — A745

**Photogravure, Photogravure and
Engraved (200 l)**
**Perf. 14x13½, 13½x14**
**1981, Nov. 29**
1498  A745  120 l  Letters, horiz.         .20  .20
1499  A745  200 l  Angel, letter
                     chest                 .35  .20
1500  A745  300 l  Letter seal             .55  .20
   Nos. 1498-1500 (3)                      1.10  .60

St. Francis of
Assisi, 800th Birth
Anniv. — A746

Design: St. Francis Receiving the Stigmata,
by Pietro Cavaro.

**1982, Jan. 6                  Perf. 13½x14**
1501  A746  300 l  dk bl & brn             .50  .20

Niccolo Paganini
(1782-1840),
Composer,
Violinist — A748

**1982, Feb. 19   Photo.   Perf. 13½x14**
1503  A748  900 l  multi                   1.50  .85

Anti-smoking Campaign — A749

**1982, Mar. 2   Photo.   Perf. 14x13½**
1504  A749  300 l  multi                    .50  .20

**Aircraft Type of 1981**
**1982, Mar. 27   Litho.   Perf. 14x13½**
1505      300 l  Aeritalia MRCA            .50  .20
1506      300 l  SIAI 260 Turbo            .50  .20
1507      300 l  Piaggio 166-dl3 Tur-
                   bo                       .50  .20
1508      300 l  Nardi NH-500              .50  .20
   a.  A730 Block of 4, #1505-1508 + 2
        labels                             4.25

Sicilian Vespers,
700th
Anniv. — A750

**1982, Mar. 31   Engr.   Perf. 13½x14**
1509  A750  120 l  multi                    .20  .20

**Flower Type of 1981**
**1982, Apr. 10                       Photo.**
1510  A726  300 l  Cyclamens               .55  .20
1511  A726  300 l  Camellias               .55  .20
1512  A726  300 l  Carnations              .55  .20
   Nos. 1510-1512 (3)                      1.65  .60

Europa — A751

**Photogravure and Engraved**
**1982, May 3                   Perf. 13½x14**
1513  A751  200 l  Coronation of
                     Charlemagne,
                     799              .85   .45
1514  A751  450 l  Treaty of Rome
                     signatures,
                     1957           1.00   .55

**Engineering Type of 1981**
**1982, May 29   Photo.   Perf. 14x13½**
1516  A732  450 l  Microwaves
                     across Red
                     Sea                   .75  .20
1517  A732  450 l  Automatic letter
                     sorting               .75  .20
   a.  Pair, #1516-1517 + label           1.50  .65

Giuseppe
Garibaldi (1807-
82)
A753

**1982, June 2                  Perf. 13½x14**
1518  A753  200 l  multi                    .65  .20

Game of the
Bridge,
Pisa — A754

**1982, June 5**
1519  A754  200 l  multi                    .35  .20
   See Nos. 1562, 1603, 1628-1629, 1655,
1717, 1749, 1775, 1807.

**Tourist Type of 1974**
**1982, June 28                       Perf. 14**
1520  A616  200 l  Frasassi Caves          .40  .20
1521  A616  200 l  Paganella Valley        .40  .20
1522  A616  450 l  Temple of Agri-
                     gento                 .75  .20
1523  A616  450 l  Rodi Garganico
                     Beach                 .75  .20
   Nos. 1520-1523 (4)                      2.30  .80

World Junior Canoeing
Championship — A755

**1982, Aug. 4   Photo.   Perf. 14**
1524  A755  200 l  multi                    .40  .20

Duke Federico da Montefeltro (1422-
1482) — A756

**Photogravure and Engraved**
**1982, Sept. 10                  Perf. 14x13½**
1525  A756  200 l  Urbino Palace,
                     Gubbio Council
                     House                 .30  .20

Italy's
Victory in
1982 World
Cup
A757

**1982, Sept. 12   Photo.   Perf. 14**
1526  A757  1000 l  World Cup             1.75  .75

69th Inter-Parliamentary Conference,
Rome — A758

**1982, Sept. 14**     *Perf. 14x13½*
1527 A758 450 l multi     .75 .20

**Villa Type of 1980**

Designs: 150 l, Temple of Aesculapius, Villa
Borghese, Rome. 250 l, Villa D'Este, Tivoli,
Rome. 350 l, Villa Lante, Bagnaia, Viterbo.

**Photogravure and Engraved**
**1982, Oct. 1**     *Perf. 14x13½*
1528 A719 150 l multi     .25 .20
1529 A719 250 l multi     .40 .20
1530 A719 350 l multi     1.75 .20
    Nos. 1528-1530 (3)     2.40 .60

Thurn and Taxis
Family Postal
Service — A759

**1982, Oct. 23**     *Engr.*     *Perf. 13½x14*
1531 A759 300 l Franz von Taxis
(1450-1517)     .50 .20

**Art Type of 1981**

Paintings: No. 1532, The Fortune Teller by
G.B. Piazzetta (1682-1754). No. 1533, Anto-
nietta Negroni Prati Morosini as a Little Girl by
Francesco Hayez (1791-1882).

**Lithographed and Engraved**
**1982, Nov. 3**     *Perf. 14*
1532 A738 300 l multi     .60 .20
1533 A738 300 l multi     .60 .20

24th Stamp
Day
A761

Children's Drawings.

**1982, Nov. 28**     *Photo.*     *Perf. 14x13½*
1534 A761 150 l multi     .25 .20
1535 A761 250 l multi     .40 .20
1536 A761 350 l multi     .55 .20
    Nos. 1534-1536 (3)     1.20 .60

Cancer
Research — A762

**1983, Jan. 14**     *Photo.*     *Perf. 13½x14*
1537 A762 400 l multi     .65 .20

**Engineering Type of 1981**

**1983, Jan. 20**     *Perf. 13½*
1538 A732 400 l Globe, factories     .65 .20
1539 A732 400 l Automated as-
    sembly line     .65 .20
    a.    Pair, #1538-1539     1.40 .65

Crusca Academy,
400th Anniv. — A763

**1983, Jan. 25**     *Engr.*     *Perf. 14x13½*
1540 A763 400 l Emblem     .65 .20

World Biathlon Championship — A764

**1983, Feb. 5**     *Photo.*     *Perf. 14*
1541 A764 200 l multi     .30 .20

Gabriele Rossetti
(1783-1854),
Writer — A765

**1983, Feb. 28**     *Engr.*     *Perf. 14x13½*
1542 A765 300 l dk brn & dk bl     .50 .20

Francesco
Guicciardini
(1483-1540),
Historian — A766

**1983, Mar. 5**     *Engr.*     *Perf. 13½x14*
1543 A766 450 l sepia     .75 .20

Umberto Saba (1883-1957),
Poet — A767

**1983, Mar. 9**     *Photo.*     *Perf. 14x13½*
1544 A767 600 l multi     1.00 .20

Pope Pius XII
(1876-1958)
A768

**1983, Mar. 21**     *Engr.*     *Perf. 13½x14*
1545 A768 1400 l dark blue     2.25 .40

Holy Year — A769

**1983, Mar. 25**     *Photo.*     *Perf. 14*
1546 A769 250 l St. Paul's Basili-
    ca     .40 .20
1547 A769 300 l St. Maria Mag-
    giore Church     .50 .20
1548 A769 400 l San Giovanni
    Church     .65 .20
1549 A769 500 l St. Peter's
    Church     1.10 .20
    Nos. 1546-1549 (4)     2.65 .80

**Aircraft Type of 1981**

**1983, Mar. 28**     *Litho.*     *Perf. 14x13½*
1550    400 l Caproni C22J glider     .65 .20
1551    400 l Aeritalia Macchi jet
    fighter     .65 .20
1552    400 l SIAI-211 jet trainer     .65 .20
1553    400 l A-129 Agusta heli-
    copter     .65 .20
    a.    A730   Block or strip of 4, #1550-
      1553 + 2 labels     4.00

Intl. Workers' Day
(May 1) — A770

**1983, Apr. 29**     *Engr.*     *Perf. 14x13½*
1554 A770 1200 l blue     2.00 .50

**Flower Type of 1981**

**1983, Apr. 30**     *Photo.*     *Perf. 13½x14*
1555 A726 200 l Mimosa     .60 .20
1556 A726 200 l Rhododendron     1.00 .20
1557 A726 200 l Gladiolus     1.00 .20
    Nos. 1555-1557 (3)     2.60 .60

Europa
1983
A771

**Litho. & Engr.**
**1983, May 2**     *Perf. 14x13½*
1558 A771 400 l Galileo, tele-
    scope, 160l     4.00 1.00
1559 A771 500 l Archimedes and
    his screw     4.00 .40

Ernesto T. Moneta (1833-1918), Nobel
Peace Prize Winner, 1907 — A772

**1983, May 5**     *Engr.*     *Perf. 14x13½*
1560 A772 500 l multi     .80 .20

Monument, Globe,
Computer Screen
A773

20th Natl.
Eucharistic
Congress
A775

**1983, May 9**     *Photo.*     *Perf. 13½x14*
1561 A773 500 l multi     .80 .20
3rd Intl. Congress of Jurisdicial Information.

**Folk Celebration Type of 1982**

#1562, La Corsa Dei Ceri Procession,
Gubbio.

**1983, May 13**     *Perf. 13½*
1562 A754 300 l multi     .55 .20

**1983, May 14**     *Perf. 14*
1563 A775 300 l multi     .50 .20

**Tourist Type of 1974**

**1983, July 30**     *Photo.*     *Perf. 14*
1563A A616 250 l Alghero     .40 .20
1563B A616 300 l Bardonecchia     .80 .25
1563C A616 400 l Riccione     1.40 .35
1563D A616 500 l Taranto     2.00 .40
    Nos. 1563A-1563D (4)     4.60 1.20

Girolamo
Frescobaldi
(1583-1643),
Composer
A776

**1983, Sept. 14**     *Engr.*     *Perf. 13½x14*
1564 A776 400 l brn & grn     .65 .30

**Villa Type of 1980**

Designs: 250 l, Fidelia, Spello. 300 l,
Imperiale, Pesaro. 400 l, Michetti Convent,
Francavilla al Mare. 500 l, Riccia.

**Photogravure and Engraved**
**1983, Oct. 10**     *Perf. 14x13½*
1565 A719 250 l multi     .75 .20
1566 A719 300 l multi     .60 .20
1567 A719 400 l multi     1.25 .25
1568 A719 500 l multi     1.40 .35
    Nos. 1565-1568 (4)     4.00 1.00

Francesco de Sanctis (1817-1883),
Writer — A777

**1983, Oct. 28**     *Photo.*
1569 A777 300 l multi     .50 .20

Christmas
1983 — A778

Raphael Paintings: 250 l, Madonna of the
Chair. 400 l, Sistine Madonna. 500 l, Madonna
of the Candelabra.

**1983, Nov. 10**     *Perf. 13½x14*
1570 A778 250 l multi     .40 .20
1571 A778 400 l multi     .65 .25
1572 A778 500 l multi     1.40 .30
    Nos. 1570-1572 (3)     2.45 .75

25th Stamp Day,
World
Communications
Year — A779

Children's Drawings. 200 l, 400 l horiz.

## Perf. 14x13½, 13½x14

**1983, Nov. 27**
| | | | |
|---|---|---|---|
| 1573 | A779 | 200 l | Letters holding hands | .30 | .20 |
| 1574 | A779 | 300 l | Spaceman | .60 | .20 |
| 1575 | A779 | 400 l | Flag train, globe | 1.00 | .25 |
| | | Nos. 1573-1575 (3) | | 1.90 | .65 |

Road Safety
A780

## Perf. 13½x14, 14x13½

**1984, Jan. 20**     **Photo.**
| | | | | | |
|---|---|---|---|---|---|
| 1576 | A780 | 300 l | Bent road sign, vert. | .50 | .20 |
| 1577 | A780 | 400 l | Accident | .65 | .35 |

Promenade in Bois de Boulogne, by Giuseppe de Nittis (1846-1884) — A781

Design: 400 l, Portrait of Paul Guillaume, 1916, by Amedeo Modigliani (1884-1920).

## Lithographed and Engraved
**1984, Jan. 25**     **Perf. 14**
| | | | | | |
|---|---|---|---|---|---|
| 1578 | A781 | 300 l | multi | .60 | .20 |
| 1579 | A781 | 400 l | multi | .65 | .30 |

Galaxy-Same Tractor — A782

Italian-made vehicles.

**1984, Mar. 10**     **Photo.**     **Perf. 14x13½**
| | | | | | |
|---|---|---|---|---|---|
| 1580 | A782 | 450 l | shown | .70 | .40 |
| 1581 | A782 | 450 l | Alfa-33 car | .70 | .40 |
| 1582 | A782 | 450 l | Maserati Biturbo car | .70 | .40 |
| 1583 | A782 | 450 l | Iveco 190-38 truck | .70 | .40 |
| a. | | Block of 4, #1580-1583 + 2 labels | | 6.00 | 1.90 |

See Nos. 1620-1623, 1681-1684.

A783

**1984, Apr. 10**
| | | | | | |
|---|---|---|---|---|---|
| 1584 | A783 | 300 l | Mosaic, furnace | .50 | .20 |
| 1585 | A783 | 300 l | Glass Blower | .50 | .20 |
| a. | | Pair, #1584-1585 + label | | 1.25 | .55 |

2nd European Parliament Elections — A784

**1984, Apr. 16**
| | | | | | |
|---|---|---|---|---|---|
| 1586 | A784 | 400 l | Parliament Strasbourg | .55 | .25 |

Forest Preservation — A785

**1984, Apr. 24**     **Photo.**     **Perf. 14x13½**
| | | | | | |
|---|---|---|---|---|---|
| 1587 | A785 | 450 l | Helicopter fire patrol | .70 | .40 |
| 1588 | A785 | 450 l | Hedgehog, squirrel, badger | .70 | .40 |
| 1589 | A785 | 450 l | Riverside waste dump | .70 | .40 |
| 1590 | A785 | 450 l | Plant life, animals | .70 | .40 |
| a. | | Block of 4, #1587-1590 | | 9.50 | 1.90 |

Italia '85
A786

**1984, Apr. 26**     **Perf. 14**
| | | | | | |
|---|---|---|---|---|---|
| 1591 | A786 | 450 l | Ministry of Posts, Rome | .80 | .30 |
| 1592 | A786 | 550 l | Via Appia Antiqua, Rome | 1.00 | .35 |

Rome Pacts, 40th Anniv. A787

Trade Unionists: Giuseppe di Vittorio, Bruno Buozzi, Achille Grandi.

**1984, Apr. 30**     **Perf. 14x13½**
| | | | | | |
|---|---|---|---|---|---|
| 1593 | A787 | 450 l | multi | .70 | .30 |

Europa (1959-84) A788

**1984, May 5**
| | | | | | |
|---|---|---|---|---|---|
| 1594 | A788 | 450 l | multi | 5.00 | .90 |
| 1595 | A788 | 550 l | multi | 8.50 | 3.25 |

Intl. Telecommunications Symposium, Florence, May — A789

**1984, May 7**     **Perf. 14**
| | | | | | |
|---|---|---|---|---|---|
| 1596 | A789 | 550 l | multi | .90 | .35 |

Italian Derby Centenary A790

## Lithographed and Engraved
**1984, May 12**     **Perf. 14x13½**
| | | | | | |
|---|---|---|---|---|---|
| 1597 | A790 | 250 l | Racing | 1.40 | .20 |
| 1598 | A790 | 400 l | Racing, diff. | 1.75 | .25 |

## Tourist Type of 1974
**1984, May 19**     **Photo.**     **Perf. 14**
| | | | | | |
|---|---|---|---|---|---|
| 1599 | A616 | 350 l | Campione d'Italia | .80 | .25 |
| 1600 | A616 | 400 l | Chianciano Terme baths | .80 | .25 |
| 1601 | A616 | 450 l | Padula | 1.60 | .30 |
| 1602 | A616 | 550 l | Greek ampitheater, Syracuse | 1.60 | .35 |
| | | Nos. 1599-1602 (4) | | 4.80 | 1.15 |

## Folk Celebration Type of 1982
Design: La Macchina Di Santa Rosa.

**1984, Sept. 3**     **Photo.**     **Perf. 13½x14**
| | | | | | |
|---|---|---|---|---|---|
| 1603 | A754 | 400 l | multi | .70 | .25 |

Peasant Farming A792

**1984, Oct. 1**     **Photo.**     **Perf. 14x13½**
| | | | | | |
|---|---|---|---|---|---|
| 1604 | A792 | 250 l | Grain harvester, thresher | .40 | .20 |
| 1605 | A792 | 350 l | Cart, hand press | .55 | .20 |

## Villa Type of 1980
Designs: 250 l, Villa Caristo, Stignano. 350 l, Villa Doria Pamphili, Genoa. 400 l, Villa Reale, Stupinigi. 450 l, Villa Mellone, Lecce.

## Lithographed and Engraved
**1984, Oct. 6**     **Perf. 14x13½**
| | | | | | |
|---|---|---|---|---|---|
| 1606 | A719 | 250 l | multi | .75 | .20 |
| 1607 | A719 | 350 l | multi | .75 | .20 |
| 1608 | A719 | 400 l | multi | 1.50 | .25 |
| 1609 | A719 | 450 l | multi | 1.50 | .25 |
| | | Nos. 1606-1609 (4) | | 4.50 | .90 |

Italia '85 — A793

**1984, Nov. 9**     **Perf. 13½x14**
| | | | | | |
|---|---|---|---|---|---|
| 1610 | A793 | 550 l | Etruscan bronze statue | .90 | .30 |
| 1611 | A793 | 550 l | Italia '85 emblem | .90 | .30 |
| 1612 | A793 | 550 l | Etruscan silver mirror | .90 | .30 |
| a. | | Strip of 3, #1610-1612 | | 4.00 | 1.50 |

Journalistic Information A794

**1985, Jan. 15**     **Photo.**     **Perf. 13½x14**
| | | | | | |
|---|---|---|---|---|---|
| 1613 | A794 | 350 l | Globe, paper tape, microwave dish | .55 | .20 |

Modern Problems — A795

**1985, Jan. 23**     **Photo.**     **Perf. 13½x14**
| | | | | | |
|---|---|---|---|---|---|
| 1614 | A795 | 250 l | Aging | .40 | .20 |

A796

Italia '85. No. 1615, The Hunt, by Raphael (1483-1520). No. 1616, Emblem. No. 1617, Detail from fresco by Baldassare Peruzzi (1481-1536) in Bishop's Palace, Ostia Antica.

## Photo. and Engr., Photo. (#1616)
**1985, Feb. 13**     **Perf. 13½x14**
| | | | | | |
|---|---|---|---|---|---|
| 1615 | A796 | 600 l | multi | 1.00 | .30 |
| 1616 | A796 | 600 l | multi | 1.00 | .30 |
| 1617 | A796 | 600 l | multi | 1.00 | .30 |
| a. | | Strip of 3, #1615-1617 | | 5.00 | 1.50 |

Faience Tiles, Plate, Flask and Covered Bowl — A797

Italian ceramics: No. 1619, Tile mural, gladiators in combat.

**1985, Mar. 2**     **Photo.**     **Perf. 14x13½**
| | | | | | |
|---|---|---|---|---|---|
| 1618 | A797 | 600 l | multi | 1.00 | .30 |
| 1619 | A797 | 600 l | multi | 1.00 | .30 |
| a. | | Pair, #1618-1619 + label | | 3.25 | .75 |

## Italian Vehicle Type of 1984
**1985, Mar. 21**
| | | | | | |
|---|---|---|---|---|---|
| 1620 | A782 | 450 l | Lancia Thema | .75 | .25 |
| 1621 | A782 | 450 l | Fiat Abarth | .75 | .25 |
| 1622 | A782 | 450 l | Fiat Uno | .75 | .25 |
| 1623 | A782 | 450 l | Lamborghini | .75 | .25 |
| a. | | Block of 4, #1620-1623 + 2 labels | | 15.00 | 1.50 |

A799

Italia '85: No. 1624, Church of St. Mary of Peace, Rome, by Pietro de Cortona (1596-1669). No. 1625, Exhibition emblem. No. 1626, Church of St. Agnes, Rome, fountain and obelisk.

## Photo. and Engr., Photo. (#1625)
**1985, Mar. 30**     **Perf. 13½x14**
| | | | | | |
|---|---|---|---|---|---|
| 1624 | A799 | 250 l | multi | .40 | .20 |
| 1625 | A799 | 250 l | multi | .40 | .20 |
| 1626 | A799 | 250 l | multi | .40 | .20 |
| a. | | Strip of 3, #1624-1626 | | 1.50 | .50 |

Pope Sixtus V, (1520-1590), 400th Anniv. of Papacy — A800

Sixtus V, dome of St. Peter's Basilica, Rome.

**1985, Apr. 24**     **Litho. and Engr.**
| | | | | | |
|---|---|---|---|---|---|
| 1627 | A800 | 1500 l | multi | 2.40 | 1.25 |

## Folk Celebration Type of 1982
Folktales: No. 1628, The March of the Turks, Potenza. No. 1629, San Marino Republican Regatta, Amalti.

**1985, May 29**     **Photo.**
1628 A754 250 l multi    .70 .20
1629 A754 350 l multi    1.10 .20

## Tourist Type of 1974

Scenic views: 350 l, Bormio town center. 400 l, Mt. Vesuvius from Castellamare di Stabia. 450 l, Stromboli Volcano from the sea. 600 l, Beach, old town at Termoli.

**1985, June 1**     **Perf. 14**
1630 A616 350 l multi    .55 .20
1631 A616 400 l multi    .80 .20
1632 A616 450 l multi    1.00 .30
1633 A616 600 l multi    2.25 .35
    Nos. 1630-1633 (4)    4.60 1.10

Nature Conservation A803

**1985, June 5**     **Perf. 13½x14**
1634 A803 500 l European beaver    .80 .30
1635 A803 500 l Primula    .80 .30
1636 A803 500 l Nebrodi pine    .80 .30
1637 A803 500 l Italian sandpiper    .80 .30
a.   Block of 4, #1634-1637    13.00 1.50

## Art Type of 1981

Designs: No. 1638, Madonna bu Il Sassoferrato, G.B. Salvi, 1609-1685. No. 1639, Pride of the Work by Mario Sironi, 1885-1961.

**Lithographed and Engraved**
**1985, June 15**     **Perf. 14**
1638 A738 350 l multi    .80 .20
1639 A738 400 l multi    1.10 .25

Europa — A805

Tenors and Composers: 500 l, Aureliano Pertile (1885-1969) and Giovanni Martinelli (1885-1962). 600 l, Johann Sebastian Bach (1685-1750) and Vincenzo Bellini (1801-1835).

**1985, June 20**   **Photo.**   **Perf. 13½x14**
1640 A805 500 l multi    4.50 .60
1641 A805 600 l multi    8.00 1.10

San Salvatore Abbey, Monte Amiata, 950th Anniv. A806

**Lithographed and Engraved**
**1985, Aug. 1**     **Perf. 14x13½**
1642 A806 450 l multi    .75 .30

World Cycling Championships — A807

**1985, Aug. 21**     **Photo.**
1643 A807 400 l multi    1.10 .25

7th Intl. Congress for Crime Prevention, Milan, Aug. 26-Sept. 6 — A808

**1985, Aug. 26**
1644 A808 600 l multi    1.00 .35

Intl. Youth Year A809

**1985, Sept. 3**
1645 A809 600 l multi    1.00 .35

## Villa Type of 1980

Designs: 300 l, Nitti, Maratea. 400 l, Aldrovandi Mazzacorati, Bologna. 500 l, Santa Maria, Pula. 600 l, De Mersi, Villazzano.

**Lithographed and Engraved**
**1985, Oct. 1**     **Perf. 14x13½**
1646 A719 300 l multi    .90 .20
1647 A719 400 l multi    1.10 .25
1648 A719 500 l multi    1.75 .30
1649 A719 600 l multi    2.25 .35
    Nos. 1646-1649 (4)    6.00 1.10

Natl. and Papal Arms, Treaty Document A810

**1985, Oct. 15**     **Photo.**
1650 A810 400 l multi    .75 .25

Ratification of new Concordat with the Vatican.

### Souvenir Sheets

Parma #10, View of Parma A812

Switzerland #3L1 A813

Sardinia #1, Great Britain #1 — A814

No. 1651: b, Two Sicilies #3, Naples. c, Two Sicilies #10, Palermo. d, Modena #3, Modena. e, Roman States #8, Rome. f, Tuscany #5, Florence. g, Sardinia #15, Turin. h, Romagna #7, Bologna. i, Lombardy-Venetia #4, Milan.
No. 1652b, Japan #1. c, US #2. d, Western Australia #1. e, Mauritius #4.
Illustration A814 reduced.

**Lithographed and Engraved**
**1985, Oct. 25**     **Perf. 14**
1651   Sheet of 9    6.00 2.75
  a.-i.   A812 300 l, any single    .50 .20
    **Perf. 14x13½**
1652   Sheet of 5 + label    5.50 1.90
  a.-e.   A813 500 l, any single    .80 .30
    **Imperf**
1653 A814 4000 l multi    6.50 3.25

Italia '85, Rome, Oct. 25-Nov. 3.

Long-distance Skiing — A815

**1986, Jan. 25**   **Photo.**   **Perf. 14x13½**
1654 A815 450 l multi    .75 .30

## Folk Celebration Type of 1982

Design: Procession of St. Agnes, Le Candelore Folk Festival, Catania.

**1986, Feb. 3**     **Perf. 13½x14**
1655 A754 450 l multi    .75 .30

Amilcare Ponchielli (1834-1886), Composer — A816

**Photogravure and Engraved**
**1986, Mar. 8**     **Perf. 14x13½**
1656 A816 2000 l Scene from La Gioconda    3.25 1.75

## Castle Type of 1980

Designs: 380 l, Vignola, Modena. 650 l, Montecchio Castle, Castiglion Fiorentino. 750 l, Rocca di Urbisaglia.

    **Perf. 14x13½**
**1986-90**   **Photo.**   **Wmk. 303**
1657 A717 380 l multi ('87)    .60 .30
1658 A717 650 l multi    1.10 .30
    **Engr.**
1659 A717 750 l multi ('90)    1.25 .75
    Nos. 1657-1659 (3)    2.95 1.35

Issue date: 750 l, Sept. 20.

### Coil Stamps
    **Perf. 14 Vert.**
**1988-91**   **Engr.**   **Wmk. 303**
    **Size: 16x21mm**
1661 A717 100 l St. Severa    .20 .20
1662 A717 500 l Norman Castle, Melfi    .80 .40
1663 A717 600 l Scaligero, Sirmione    1.10 .55
1664 A717 650 l Serralunga D'Alba    1.10 .50
1665 A717 750 l Venafro    1.25 .60
1666 A717 800 l Rocca Maggiore, Assisi    1.50 .75
    Nos. 1661-1666 (6)    5.95 3.00

Issued: 600 l, 800 l, 2/20/91; others, 3/1/88.

Giovanni Battista Pergolesi (1710-1736), Musician — A817

    **Perf. 13½x14**
**1986, Mar. 15**   **Photo.**   **Unwmk.**
1667 A817 2000 l multi    3.25 1.25

The Bay, Acitrezza — A818

**1986, Mar. 24**     **Perf. 14**
1668 A818 350 l shown    .65 .25
1669 A818 450 l Piazzetta, Capri    .90 .30
1670 A818 550 l Kursaal, Merano    1.00 .35
1671 A818 650 l Lighthouse, San Benedetto del Tronto    1.25 .45
    Nos. 1668-1671 (4)    3.80 1.35

Europa 1986 — A819

Trees in special shapes: a, Heart (life). b, Star (poetry). c, Butterfly (color). d, Sun (energy).

**1986, Apr. 28**   **Photo.**   **Perf. 13x14**
1672   Block of 4    12.00 12.00
  a.-d.   A819 650 l, any single    1.10 .45

25th Intl. Opthalmological Congress, Rome, May 4-10 — A820

**1986, May 3**   **Photo.**   **Perf. 14**
1673 A820 550 l multi    .90 .40

Police in Uniform — A821

**1986, May 10**
1674 A821 550 l multi    1.60 .40
1675 A821 650 l multi    1.90 .45

European Police Conference, Chianciano Terme, May 10-12. Nos. 1674-1675 printed se-tenant with labels picturing male or female police.

Battle of Bezzecca, 120th Anniv. A822

**1986, May 31**     **Perf. 14x13½**
1676 A822 550 l multi    .90 .35

Memorial Day for Independence Martyrs — A823

**1986, May 31** **Perf. 14**
1677 A823 2000 l multi 3.25 1.40

Bersaglieri Corps of Mountain Troops, 150th Anniv. — A824

**1986, June 1** **Perf. 13½x14**
1678 A824 450 l multi .75 .30

Telecommunications — A825

**1986, June 16** **Perf. 14x13½**
1679 A825 350 l multi .55 .25

Sacro Monte di Varallo Monastery — A826

**1986, June 28** **Engr.** **Perf. 14**
1680 A826 2000 l Prus bl & sage grn 3.00 1.40

**Italian Vehicle Type of 1984**

**1986, July 4** **Photo.** **Perf. 14x13½**
1681 A782 450 l Alfa Romeo AR8 Turbo .75 .30
1682 A782 450 l Innocenti 650 SE .75 .30
1683 A782 450 l Ferrari Testarossa .75 .30
1684 A782 450 l Fiatallis FR 10B .75 .30
a. Block of 4, #1681-1684 + 2 labels 12.00

Ladies' Fashions — A827

Breda Heavy Industry — A828

Olivetti Computer Technology — A829

**1986, July 14**
1685 A827 450 l shown .75 .30
1686 A827 450 l Men's fashions .75 .30
a. Pair, #1685-1686 + label 3.50 .75
1687 A828 650 l shown 3.00 .45
1688 A829 650 l shown 3.00 .45
Nos. 1685-1688 (4) 7.50 1.50

Alitalia, Italian Airlines, 40th Anniv. A830

**1986, Sept. 16** **Photo.** **Perf. 14x13½**
1689 A830 550 l Anniv. emblem 1.00 .40
1690 A830 650 l Jet, runway lights 1.25 .50

**Villa Type of 1980**

**1986, Oct. 1** **Photo. & Engr.**
1691 A719 350 l Necker, Trieste .65 .25
1692 A719 350 l Borromeo, Cassano D'Adda .65 .25
1693 A719 450 l Palagonia, Bagheria .85 .35
1694 A719 550 l Medicea, Poggio a Caiano 1.00 .40
1695 A719 650 l Castello d'Issogne, Issogne 1.25 .50
Nos. 1691-1695 (5) 4.40 1.75

Christmas — A831

Madonna and Child, bronze sculpture by Donatello, Basilica del Santo, Padua.

**1986, Oct. 10** **Engr.** **Perf. 14**
1696 A831 450 l brown olive .75 .35

**Art Type of 1981**
Designs: 450 l, Seated Woman Holding a Book, drawing by Andrea del Sarto, Uffizi, Florence, vert. 550 l, Daphne at Pavarola, painting by Felice Casorati, Museum of Modern Art, Turin, vert.

**1986, Oct. 11** **Litho. & Engr.**
1697 A738 450 l blk & pale org 1.75 .35
1698 A738 550 l multi 2.25 .40

Memorial, Globe, Plane — A832

Plane, Cross, Men — A833

Stamp Day A834

**1986, Nov. 29** **Perf. 14x13½**
1701 A834 550 l Die of Sardinia No. 2 1.50 .45
Francesco Matraire, printer of first Sardinian stamps.

A835

Industries — A836

**Perf. 14½x13½**
**1987, Feb. 27** **Photo.**
1702 A835 700 l Marzotto Textile, 1836 1.10 .55
1703 A836 700 l Italgas Energy Corp., 1837 1.10 .55

Environmental Protection — A837

Designs: a, Volturno River. b, Garda Lake. c, Trasimeno Lake. d, Tirso River.

**1987, Mar. 6** **Litho.** **Perf. 14x13½**
1704 Block of 4 8.00 2.00
a.-d. A837 500 l, any single .80 .40

Antonio Gramsci (1891-1937), Author and Artist — A838

**1987, Apr. 27** **Litho.** **Perf. 14x13½**
1705 A838 600 l scar & gray black 1.00 .50

Europa 1987 A839

Modern architecture: 600 l, Church of Sun Motorway, Florence, designed by Michelucci. 700 l, Railway station, Rome, designed by Nervi.

**1987, May 4** **Photo.**
1706 A839 600 l multi 2.50 .60
1707 A839 700 l multi 3.25 .60

**1986, Nov. 11** **Photo.**
1699 A832 550 l multi .90 .45
1700 A833 650 l multi 1.10 .55
Intl. Peace Year, memorial to Italian airmen who died at Kindu, Zaire, while on a peace mission.

**Tourist Type of 1974**
**1987, May 9** **Perf. 14**
1708 A616 380 l Verbania Pallanza .75 .30
1709 A616 400 l Palmi .80 .35
1710 A616 500 l Vasto 1.00 .40
1711 A616 600 l Villacidro 1.25 .50
Nos. 1708-1711 (4) 3.80 1.55

Naples Soccer Club, Nat'l. Champions A840

**1987, May 18** **Litho.** **Perf. 13½x14**
1712 A840 500 l multi 1.90 .40

The Absinthe Drinkers, by Degas — A841

**1987, May 29**
1713 A841 380 l multi .80 .30
Fight against alcoholism.

St. Alfonso M. de Liguori (1696-1787) and Gulf of Naples — A842

**1987, Aug. 1** **Perf. 14x13½**
1714 A842 400 l multi .65 .30

Events A843

Emblems and natl. landmarks: No. 1715, OLYMPHILEX '87, Intl. Olympic Committee Building, Foro Italico, Rome. No. 1716, World Athletics Championships, Olympic Stadium, Rome.

**1987, Aug. 29** **Photo.** **Perf. 14x14½**
1715 A843 700 l multi 1.10 .55
1716 A843 700 l multi 1.10 .55

**Folk Celebration Type of 1982**
Design: Quintana Joust, Foligno.

**Perf. 13½x14½**
**1987, Sept. 12** **Photo.**
1717 A754 380 l multi .70 .30

Piazzas A844

380 l, Piazza del Popolo, Ascoli Piceno. 500 l, Piazza Giuseppe Verdi, Palermo. 600 l, Piazza San Carlo, Turin. 700 l, Piazza dei Signori, Verona.

## Litho. & Engr.
**1987, Oct. 10**      *Perf. 14x13½*
| | | | | |
|---|---|---|---|---|
| **1718** | A844 | 380 l | multi | .75 | .30 |
| **1719** | A844 | 500 l | multi | 1.00 | .40 |
| **1720** | A844 | 600 l | multi | 1.25 | .50 |
| **1721** | A844 | 700 l | multi | 1.40 | .55 |

*Nos. 1718-1721 (4)*    4.40 1.75

See Nos. 1747-1748, 1765-1766.

Christmas
A845

Paintings by Giotto: 500 l, Adoration in the Manger, Basilica of St. Francis, Assisi. 600 l, The Epiphany, Scrovegni Chapel, Padua.

**1987, Oct. 15**   Photo.   *Perf. 13½x14*
| | | | | |
|---|---|---|---|---|
| **1722** | A845 | 500 l | multi | .90 | .40 |
| **1723** | A845 | 600 l | multi | 1.10 | .50 |

Battle of Mentana, 120th Anniv. A846

## Litho. & Engr.
**1987, Nov. 3**      *Perf. 14x13½*
| | | | | |
|---|---|---|---|---|
| **1724** | A846 | 380 l | multi | .70 | .35 |

Il Pantocrator (Christ), Mosaic, Monreale Cathedral — A847

Coat of Arms and San Carlo Theater, Naples, from an 18th Cent. Engraving — A848

**1987, Nov. 4**       *Perf. 14*
| | | | | |
|---|---|---|---|---|
| **1725** | A847 | 500 l | multi | 1.50 | .45 |
| **1726** | A848 | 500 l | multi | 1.50 | .45 |

Artistic heritage. See Nos. 1768-1769.

Nunziatella Military School, 200th Anniv. A849

**1987, Nov. 14**      *Perf. 14x13½*
| | | | | |
|---|---|---|---|---|
| **1727** | A849 | 600 l | multi | 1.00 | .50 |

Stamp Day — A850

Philatelist Marco DeMarchi (d. 1936) holding magnifying glass and stamp album, Milan Cathedral.

**1987, Nov. 20**   Photo.   *Perf. 13½x14*
| | | | | |
|---|---|---|---|---|
| **1728** | A850 | 500 l | multi | 1.60 | .45 |

Homo Aeserniensis (Flint Knapper) — A851

## Photo. & Engr.
**1988, Feb. 6**      *Perf. 13½x14*
| | | | | |
|---|---|---|---|---|
| **1729** | A851 | 500 l | multi | .80 | .40 |

Remains of Isernia Man, c. 736,000 years-old, discovered near Isernia.

E. Quirino Visconti School, Rome A852

## Litho. & Engr.
**1988, Mar. 1**   Unwmk.   *Perf. 14x13½*
| | | | | |
|---|---|---|---|---|
| **1730** | A852 | 500 l | multi | .80 | .40 |

See Nos. 1764, 1824, 1842.

St. John Bosco (1815-1888), Educator — A853

**1988, Apr. 2**   Photo.   *Perf. 13½x14*
| | | | | |
|---|---|---|---|---|
| **1731** | A853 | 500 l | multi | .80 | .40 |

## Art Type of 1981

Painting: *The Archaeologists,* by Giorgio de Chirico (1888-1978).

**1988, Apr. 7**   Engr.      *Perf. 14*
| | | | | |
|---|---|---|---|---|
| **1732** | A738 | 650 l | multi, vert. | 1.90 | .55 |

1st Printed Hebrew Bible, 500th Anniv. A854

Soncino Bible excerpt, 15th cent.

**1988, Apr. 22**   Photo.   *Perf. 13½x14*
| | | | | |
|---|---|---|---|---|
| **1733** | A854 | 550 l | multi | .90 | .45 |

Epilepsy Foundation A855

Design: St. Valentine, electroencephalograph readout, epileptic in seizure and medieval crest.

**1988, Apr. 23**
| | | | | |
|---|---|---|---|---|
| **1734** | A855 | 500 l | multi | .80 | .40 |

Europa 1988 A856

Transport and communication: 650 l, ETR 450 locomotive. 750 l, Electronic mail, map of Italy.

**1988, May 2**
| | | | | |
|---|---|---|---|---|
| **1735** | A856 | 650 l | multi | 1.75 | .60 |
| **1736** | A856 | 750 l | multi | 2.25 | .85 |

## Tourist Type of 1974

Scenic views: 400 l, Castiglione della Pescaia. 500 l, Lignano Sabbiadoro. 650 l, Noto. 750 l, Vieste.

**1988, May 7**   Photo.     *Perf. 14*
| | | | | |
|---|---|---|---|---|
| **1737** | A616 | 400 l | multi | .65 | .30 |
| **1738** | A616 | 500 l | multi | .80 | .40 |
| **1739** | A616 | 650 l | multi | 1.10 | .55 |
| **1740** | A616 | 750 l | multi | 1.25 | .60 |

*Nos. 1737-1740 (4)*    3.80 1.85

A858

**1988, May 16**
| | | | | |
|---|---|---|---|---|
| **1741** | A858 | 500 l | Golf | .80 | .40 |

1990 World Cup Soccer Championships — A859

**1988, May 16**   Litho.   *Perf. 14x13½*
| | | | | |
|---|---|---|---|---|
| **1742** | A859 | 3150 l | blk, grn & dark red | 5.25 | 3.25 |

1988 Natl. Soccer Championships, Milan — A860

**1988, May 23**      *Perf. 13½x14*
| | | | | |
|---|---|---|---|---|
| **1743** | A860 | 650 l | multi | 1.10 | .55 |

Bronze Sculpture, Pergola — A861

**1988, June 4**   Engr.     *Perf. 14*
| | | | | |
|---|---|---|---|---|
| **1744** | A861 | 500 l | Horse | .80 | .40 |
| **1745** | A861 | 650 l | Woman | 1.10 | .55 |

Bologna University, 900th Anniv. — A862

**1988, June 10**   Engr.   *Perf. 13½x14*
| | | | | |
|---|---|---|---|---|
| **1746** | A862 | 500 l | violet | .80 | .40 |

## Piazza Type of 1987

Designs: 400 l, Piazza del Duomo, Pistoia. 550 l, Piazza del Unita d'Italia, Trieste.

## Litho. & Engr.
**1988, July 2**      *Perf. 14x13½*
| | | | | |
|---|---|---|---|---|
| **1747** | A844 | 400 l | multi | .70 | .30 |
| **1748** | A844 | 550 l | multi | .95 | .40 |

## Folk Celebration Type of 1982

Discesa Dei Candelieri, Sassari: Man wearing period costume, column and bearers.

**1988, Aug. 13**   Photo.   *Perf. 13½x14*
| | | | | |
|---|---|---|---|---|
| **1749** | A754 | 550 l | multi | 1.40 | .40 |

Intl. Gastroenterology and Digestive Endoscopy Congress, Rome — A863

**1988, Sept. 5**
| | | | | |
|---|---|---|---|---|
| **1750** | A863 | 750 l | multi | 1.25 | .60 |

Neorealistic Films — A864

Italian films amd directors: 500 l, *Ossessione,* 1942, by Luchino Visconti. 650 l, *Ladri di Biciclette,* 1948, by Vittorio DeSica. 2400 l, *Roma Citta Aperta,* 1945, by Roberto Rossellini. 3050 l, *Riso Amaro,* 1949, by Giuseppe DeSantis.

**1988, Oct. 13**   Litho.   *Perf. 14x13½*
| | | | | |
|---|---|---|---|---|
| **1751** | A864 | 500 l | multi | .80 | .40 |
| **1752** | A864 | 650 l | multi | 1.10 | .55 |
| **1753** | A864 | 2400 l | multi | 4.00 | 2.00 |
| **1754** | A864 | 3050 l | multi | 5.00 | 2.50 |

*Nos. 1751-1754 (4)*    10.90 5.45

Elsag — A865

Aluminia — A866

State Mint and Polygraphic
Insitute — A867

Italian Industries.

**1988, Oct. 19　　　　Photo.**
1755　A865　750 l multi　　　1.25　.65
1756　A866　750 l multi　　　1.25　.65

**Photo. & Engr.**
1757　A867　750 l multi　　　1.25　.65
　　　*Nos. 1755-1757 (3)*　　3.75　1.95

Christmas:
*Nativity,* by
Pasquale
Celommi, Church
of the Virgin's
Assumption
A868

**1988, Oct. 29　Photo.　Perf. 13½x14**
1758　A868　650 l multi　　　1.40　.55

Christmas
A869

**Photo. & Engr.**
**1988, Nov. 12　　　Perf. 14x13½**
1759　A869　500 l dark blue grn &
　　　　　　　chest brn　　1.40　.40

St. Charles Borromeo (1538-1584),
Ecclesiastical Reformer — A870

**1988, Nov. 4　　　Litho. & Engr.**
1760　A870　2400 l multi　　　4.00　2.25

Stamp
Day — A871

Japan #69 & stamp designer Edoardo
Chiossone.

**1988, Dec. 9　Photo.　Perf. 13½x14**
1761　A871　500 l multi　　　.80　.40

Campaign
Against
AIDS — A872

**1989, Jan. 13**
1762　A872　650 l multi　　　1.10　.55

Paris-Peking Rally — A873

**1989, Jan. 21　　　Perf. 14½x13½**
1763　A873　3150 l Map, Itala race
　　　　　　　car　　　5.25　2.50

**School Type of 1988**
**1989　Photo. & Engr.　Perf. 14x13½**
1764　A852　650 l multi　　　1.10　.55

**Piazza Type of 1987**
No. 1765, Piazza Del Duomo, Catanzaro.
No. 1766, Piazza Di Spagna, Rome.

**Litho. & Engr.**
**1989, Apr. 10　　　Perf. 14x13½**
1765　A844　400 l multi　　　.85　.30
1766　A844　400 l multi　　　.85　.30

Velo World Yachting
Championships
A875

**1989, Apr. 8　Photo.　Perf. 14**
1767　A875　3050 l multi　　　5.00　2.50

**Artistic Heritage Type of 1987**
Art and architecture: 500 l, King with scepter
and orb, Palazzo Della Ragione, Padova, vert.
650 l, Crypt of St. Nicolas, St. Nicolas Basilica,
Bari, vert.

**1989, Apr. 8　Litho. & Engr., Engr.**
1768　A847　500 l multi　　　.80　.40
1769　A847　650 l indigo　　　1.10　.55

Europa
1989 — A876

Children's games.

**Perf. 14x13½, 13½x14**
**1989, May 8　　　　　　Photo.**
1770　A876　500 l Leapfrog, horiz.　1.10　.50
1771　A876　650 l shown　　　1.60　.50
1772　A876　750 l Sack race,
　　　　　　　horiz.　　　1.60　.50
　　　*Nos. 1770-1772 (3)*　4.30　1.50

European
Parliament 3rd
Elections — A877

**1989, June 3　　　Perf. 13½x14**
1773　A877　500 l multi　　　1.00　.35
No. 1773 also inscribed in European Currency Units "ECU 0,31."

Pisa University — A878

**1989, May 29　Engr.　Perf. 14x13½**
1774　A878　500 l violet　　　.80　.40

**Folk Celebration Type of 1982**
Priest and Flower Feast street scene.

**1989, May 27　Photo.　Perf. 13½x14**
1775　A754　400 l multi　　　.60　.30

**Landscape Type of 1974**
**1989, June 10　Photo.　Perf. 14**
1776　A616　500 l Naxos Gardens　1.00　.35
1777　A616　500 l Spotorno　　1.00　.35
1778　A616　500 l Pompei　　　1.00　.35
1779　A616　500 l Grottammare　1.00　.35
　　　*Nos. 1776-1779 (4)*　4.00　1.40

Ministry of
Posts,
Cent.
A879

**1989, June 24　　　Perf. 14x13½**
1780　A879　500 l Posthorn, No.
　　　　　　　52　　　　.80　.40
1781　A879　2400 l Posthorn,
　　　　　　　Earth　　4.00　2.00

INTER Soccer Championships — A880

**1989, June 26**
1782　A880　650 l multi　　　1.10　.55

Interparliamentary Union,
Cent. — A881

**1989, June 28**
1783　A881　750 l multi　　　1.25　.60

French Revolution, Bicent. — A882

**1989, July 7　Photo.　Perf. 14**
1784　A882　3150 l multi　　　5.00　2.25

*Fortified Walls of Corinaldo,* by
Francesco di Giorgio Martini (1439-
1502) — A883

**Litho. & Engr.**
**1989, Sept. 2　　　Perf. 14**
1785　A883　500 l multi　　　.90　.40

Charlie Chaplin (1889-1977) — A884

**1989, Sept. 23　Engr.　Perf. 14x13½**
1786　A884　750 l black & sepia　1.40　.55

Naples-Portici Railway, 150th
Anniv. — A885

Illustration reduced.

**1989, Oct. 3　　　Litho. & Engr.**
1787　　550 l Denom at UL　　.90　.45
1788　　550 l Denom at UR　　.90　.45
　　*a.* A885 Pair, #1787-1788　2.00　1.10

*Adoration of the Kings,* by
Correggio — A887

**1989, Oct. 21　Photo.　Perf. 13½x14**
1789　　500 l multicolored　　.80　.40
1790　　500 l multicolored　　.80　.40
　　*a.* A887 Pair, #1789-1790　2.00　.90

Christmas.

Fidardo Castle, the Stradella, Accordion — A889

Industries.

**1989, Oct. 14  Photo.  Perf. 14x13½**
1791 A889 450 l Music  .75 .35
1792 A889 450 l Arnoldo World Publishing  .75 .35

Stamp Day — A890

**1989, Nov. 24  Perf. 13½x14**
1793 A890 500 l Emilio Diena  1.00 .40

1990 World Soccer Championships, Italy — A891

**1989, Dec. 9  Engr.  Perf. 13½x14**
1794 A891 450 l multicolored  .75 .35

Columbus's First Voyage, 1474-1484 — A892

**1990, Feb. 24  Photo.**
1795 700 l Denom at UL  1.10 .55
1796 700 l Denom at UR  1.10 .55
  a. A892 Pair, #1795-1796  2.25 1.50

**Souvenir Sheets**

1990 World Cup Soccer Championships, Italy — A894

Soccer club emblems and stadiums in Italy.
No. 1797: a, Italy. b, US. c, Olympic Stadium, Rome. d, Municipal Stadium, Florence. e, Austria. f, Czechoslovakia.
No. 1798: a, Argentina. b, Russia. c, St. Paul Stadium, Naples. d, New Stadium, Bari. e, Cameroun. f, Romania.
No. 1799: a, Brazil. b, Costa Rica. c, Alps Stadium, Turin. d, Ferraris Stadium, Genoa. e, Sweden. f, Scotland.
No. 1800: a, UAE. b, West Germany. c, Dall'ara Stadium, Bologna. d, Meazza Stadium, Milan. e, Colombia. f, Yugoslavia.
No. 1801: a, Belgium. b, Uruguay. c, Bentegodi Stadium, Verona. d, Friuli Stadium, Udine. e, South Korea. f, Spain.
No. 1802: a, England. b, Netherlands. c, Sant'elia Stadium, Cagliari. d, La Favorita Stadium, Palermo. e, Ireland. f, Egypt.

**1990, Mar. 24  Perf. 14x13½**
1797  Sheet of 6  4.50 2.25
  a.-f. A894 450 l any single  .75 .35
1798  Sheet of 6  6.00 3.00
  a.-f. A894 600 l any single  1.00 .50
1799  Sheet of 6  6.50 3.25
  a.-f. A894 650 l any single  1.10 .55
1800  Sheet of 6  6.50 3.25
  a.-f. A894 700 l any single  1.10 .55
1801  Sheet of 6  7.50 3.75
  a.-f. A894 800 l any single  1.25 .60
1802  Sheet of 6  12.00 6.00
  a.-f. A894 1200 l any single  2.00 1.00
  Nos. 1797-1802 (6)  43.00 21.50

See No. 1819.

**Tourist Type of 1974**

**1990, Mar. 30  Photo.  Perf. 14**
1803 A616 600 l Sabbioneta  1.00 .50
1804 A616 600 l Montepulciano  1.00 .50
1805 A616 600 l Castellammare del Golfo  1.00 .50
1806 A616 600 l San Felice Circeo  1.00 .50
  Nos. 1803-1806 (4)  4.00 2.00

**Folk Celebration Type of 1982**

Design: Horse race, Merano.

**1990, Apr. 9  Perf. 13½x14**
1807 A754 600 l multicolored  1.00 .50

Aurelio Saffi, Death Cent. A895

**1990, Apr. 10  Perf. 14**
1808 A895 700 l multicolored  1.10 .55

Giovanni Giorgi (1871-1950) — A896

**1990, Apr. 23  Perf. 14x13½**
1809 A896 600 l multicolored  1.00 .55

Metric System in Italy, 55th. anniv.

Labor Day, Cent. — A897

**1990, Apr. 28  Photo.  Perf. 13½x14**
1810 A897 600 l multicolored  1.00 .55

Naples Soccer Club, Italian Champions A898

**1990, Apr. 30  Perf. 13½x14**
1811 A898 700 l multicolored  1.25 .65

Europa A899

Post Offices: 700 l, San Silvestro Piazza, Rome. 800 l, Fondaco Tedeschi, Venice.

**1990, May 7  Perf. 14x13½**
1812 A899 700 l multicolored  1.50 .60
1813 A899 800 l multicolored  2.25 .75

Giovanni Paisiello (1740-1816), Composer A900

**1990, May 9  Perf. 14x13½**
1814 A900 450 l multicolored  .75 .40

Dante Alighieri (1265-1321), Poet — A901

**1990, May 12  Perf. 14x13½**
1815 A901 700 l multicolored  1.10 .60

Dante Alighieri Soc., cent.

Mosaic (Detail) — A902

Sculpture — A903

**Photo. (#1816), Litho. & Engr. (#1817)**
**1990, May 19  Perf. 13½x14**
1816 A902 450 l multicolored  .75 .40
1817 A903 700 l multicolored  1.10 .60

Malatestiana Music Festival, Rimini, 40th Anniv. — A904

**1990, June 15  Photo.  Perf. 14**
1818 A904 600 l multicolored  1.00 .60

**World Cup Soccer Type of 1990**
**Inscribed "Campione Del Mondo"**
**1990, July 9  Litho.  Perf. 14x13½**
1819 A894 like No. 1800b  1.50 .60

Still Life, by Giorgio Morandi (1890-1964) — A905

**1990, July 20  Engr.  Perf. 14**
1820 A905 750 l black  1.25 .60

Greco-Roman Wrestling, World Championships — A906

**1990, Oct. 11  Litho.  Perf. 14x13½**
1821 A906 3200 l multicolored  5.25 2.50

Christmas — A907

Paintings of the Nativity by: 600 l, Emidio Vangelli. 750 l, Pellegrino.

**1990, Oct. 26  Perf. 14**
1822 A907 600 l multicolored  1.00 .50
1823 A907 750 l multicolored  1.25 .60

**School Type of 1988 and**

Italian Schools — A908

Designs: 600 l, Bernardino Telesio gymnasium, Cosenza. 750 l, University of Catania.

**Litho. & Engr.**
**1990, Nov. 5  Perf. 14x13½**
1824 A852 600 l multicolored  1.00 .50

**Engr.**
1825 A908 750 l multicolored  1.25 .60

Stamp Day — A909

Self-portrait, Corrado Mezzana (1890-1952).

**1990, Nov. 16  Litho.  Perf. 13½x14**
1826 A909 600 l multicolored  1.10 .55

A910

**1991, Jan. 5    Litho.    Perf. 13½x14**
1827  A910  600 l  The Nativity          1.00    .50

Genoa Flower
Show — A911

**1991, Jan. 10                     Perf. 14**
1828  A911  750 l  multicolored          1.25    .60

Seal of the Univ.
of Siena — A912

**1991, Jan. 15    Photo.    Perf. 13½x14**
1829  A912  750 l  multicolored          1.25    .60

**Tourist Type of 1974**

| **1991** | | | **Photo.** | |
|---|---|---|---|---|
| 1830 | A616 | 600 l | San Remo | 1.00 | .50 |
| 1831 | A616 | 600 l | Roccaraso | 1.00 | .50 |
| 1832 | A616 | 600 l | La Maddalena | 1.00 | .50 |
| 1833 | A616 | 600 l | Calgi | 1.00 | .50 |
| | | | Nos. 1830-1833 (4) | 4.00 | 2.00 |

United Europe — A913

**Perf. 14x13½**
**1991, Mar. 12    Photo.    Unwmk.**
1834  A913  750 l  multi                 1.25    .60

#1834 also carries .48 ECU denomination.

Discovery of America, 500th Anniv. (in
1992) — A914

**1991, Mar. 22                    Litho.**
1835     750 l  Ships leaving port       1.25    .60
1836     750 l  Columbus, Queen's
                court                     1.25    .60
  a.  A914 Pair, #1835-1836              2.50    1.25

Giuseppe Gioachino Belli (1791-1863),
Poet — A916

**1991, Apr. 15    Litho.    Perf. 14x13½**
1837  A916  600 l  bl & gray blk         1.00    .50

Church of St. Gregory, Rome — A917

**1991, Apr. 20    Photo.    Perf. 14x13½**
1838  A917  3200 l  multicolored         5.25    2.50

Europa
A918

**1991, Apr. 29    Photo.    Perf. 14x13½**
1839  A918  750 l  DRS satellite         1.60    .70
1840  A918  800 l  Hermes space
                  shuttle                1.60    .70

Santa Maria
Maggiore Church,
Lanciano — A919

**1991, May 2    Engr.    Perf. 13½x14**
1841  A919  600 l  brown                 1.00    .50

**Schools Type of 1988**

Design: D. A. Azuni school, Sassari.

**Litho. & Engr.**
**1991, May 3                     Perf. 14x13½**
1842  A852  600 l  multicolored          1.00    .50

Team Genoa,
Italian Soccer
Champions,
1990-91 — A920

**1991, May 27    Photo.    Perf. 13½x14**
1843  A920  3000 l  multicolored         5.00    3.25

Basketball,
Cent. — A921

**1991, June 5**
1844  A921  500 l  multicolored          .80    .40

Children's
Rights — A922

**1991, June 14**
1845  A922  600 l  shown                 1.00    .50
1846  A922  750 l  Man, child with
                  balloon                1.25    .60

Art and
Culture
A923

Designs: 600 l, Sculpture by Pericle Fazzini
(b. 1913). 3200 l, Exhibition Hall, Turin,
designed by Pier Luigi Nervi (1891-1979).

**Litho. & Engr.**
**1991, June 21                   Perf. 14**
1847  A923  600 l  multicolored          1.00    .50
1848  A923  3200 l  multicolored         5.25    2.50

Egyptian
Museum,
Turin — A924

**1991, Aug. 31    Litho.    Perf. 13½x14**
1849  A924  750 l  grn, yel & gold       1.25    .60

Luigi Galvani (1737-1798),
Electrophysicist — A925

**1991, Sept. 24                   Perf. 14x13½**
1850  A925  750 l  multicolored          1.25    .60
Radio, cent. (in 1995). See Nos. 1873,
1928, 1964.

Nature
Protection
A926

**1991, Oct. 10    Photo.    Perf. 14x13½**
1851  A926  500 l  Marevivo
                  posidonia              .90    .45
1852  A926  500 l  Falco pellegrino      .90    .45
1853  A926  500 l  Cervo sardo           .90    .45
1854  A926  500 l  Orso marsicano        .90    .45
       Nos. 1851-1854 (4)               3.60    1.80

World Wildlife Fund.

Wolfgang
Amadeus Mozart,
Death
Bicent. — A927

**1991, Oct. 7                     Perf. 13½x14**
1855  A927  800 l  multicolored          1.25    .60

Christmas
A928

**1991, Oct. 18**
1856  A928  600 l  multicolored          1.00    .50

Giulio and Alberto Bolaffi,
Philatelists — A929

**1991, Oct. 25                    Perf. 14**
1857  A929  750 l  multicolored          1.25    .60
Stamp Day.

Pietro Nenni (1891-1980),
Politician — A930

**1991, Oct. 30**
1858  A930  750 l  multicolored          1.25    .60

Fountain of
Neptune,
Florence, by
Bartolomeo
Ammannati
(1511-1592)
A931

**1992, Feb. 6    Photo.    Perf. 13½x14**
1859  A931  750 l  multicolored          1.25    .60

22nd European Indoor Track
Championships — A932

**1992, Jan. 30                    Perf. 14x13½**
1860  A932  600 l  multicolored          1.00    .50

University of Ferrara, 600th Anniv. — A933

**1992, Mar. 4   Photo.   Perf. 13½x14**
1861  A933  750 l  multicolored       1.25   .60

**Castle Type of 1980**
**Perf. 14x13½**

**1992-94   Photo.   Wmk. 303**
1862  A717  200 l  Cerro al Vol-
                    turno                .30   .20
1863  A717  250 l  Mondavio              .40   .20
1864  A717  300 l  Bari                  .50   .20
1865  A717  450 l  Bosa                  .75   .35
1866  A717  850 l  Arechi, Salerno      1.50   .75
        Nos. 1862-1866 (5)              3.45  1.70

Issued: 200 l, 250 l, 300 l, 450 l, 2/24/94; 850 l, 3/7/92.
This is an expanding set. Numbers will change if necessary.

University of Naples — A934

**1992, Mar. 9   Unwmk.   Perf. 14x13½**
1872  A934  750 l  multicolored       1.25   .60

**Radio Cent. Type of 1991**

Alessandro Volta (1745-1827), Italian physicist.

**1992, Mar. 26**
1873  A925  750 l  multicolored       1.25   .60
        Radio, cent. (in 1995).

Genoa '92 Intl. Philatelic Exhibition — A935

**1992, Mar. 27   Perf. 13½x14**
1874  A935  750 l  multicolored       1.25   .60

Lorenzo de Medici (1449-1492) A936

**1992, Apr. 8   Perf. 14**
1875  A936  750 l  bl & org brn       1.25   .60

Filippini Institute, 300th Anniv. — A937

**1992, May 2   Photo.   Perf. 13½x14**
1876  A937  750 l  multicolored       1.25   .60

Discovery of America, 500th Anniv. A938

#1877, Columbus seeking Queen Isabella's support. #1878, Columbus' fleet. #1879, Sighting land. #1880, Landing in New World.

**1992, Apr. 24   Photo.   Perf. 14x13½**
1877  A938  500 l  multicolored       .90   .45
1878  A938  500 l  multicolored       .90   .45
1879  A938  500 l  multicolored       .90   .45
1880  A938  500 l  multicolored       .90   .45
   a.    Block of 4, #1877-1880       3.75  1.90

See US Nos. 2620-2623.

Discovery of America, 500th Anniv. — A939

Designs: 750 l, Monument to Columbus, Genoa. 850 l, Globe, Genoa '92 Exhibition emblem.

**1992, May 2   Perf. 13½x14**
1881  A939  750 l  multicolored       1.40   .65
1882  A939  850 l  multicolored       1.75   .75
        Europa.

**Miniature Sheets**

Voyages of Columbus — A940

Columbus: #1883: a, Presenting natives. b, Announcing his discovery. c, In chains.
   #1884: a, Welcomed at Barcelona. b, Restored to favor. c, Describing his 3rd voyage.
   #1885: a, In sight of land. b, Fleet. c, Queen Isabella pledging her jewels.
   #1886: a, Soliciting aid from Isabella. b, At La Rabida. c, Recall.
   #1887: a, Landing. b, Santa Maria. c, Queen Isabella and Columbus. #1888, Columbus.
   #1883-1888 are similar in design to US #230-245.

**1992, May 22   Engr.   Perf. 10½**
1883  A940       Sheet of 3          7.25  3.75
   a.    50 l olive black             .20   .20
   b.    300 l dark blue green        .50   .25
   c.    4000 l red violet           6.50  3.00
1884  A940       Sheet of 3          6.25  3.00
   a.    100 l brown violet           .20   .20
   b.    800 l magenta               1.25   .80
   c.    3000 l green                5.00  2.40

1885  A940       Sheet of 3          4.25  2.00
   a.    200 l dark blue              .30   .20
   b.    900 l ultra                 1.50   .75
   c.    1500 l orange               2.50  1.25
1886  A940       Sheet of 3          3.50  1.75
   a.    400 l chocolate              .65   .30
   b.    700 l vermillion            1.10   .55
   c.    1000 l slate blue           1.60   .80
1887  A940       Sheet of 3          5.00  2.40
   a.    500 l brown violet           .80   .40
   b.    600 l dark green            1.00   .50
   c.    2000 l crimson lake         3.25  1.50
1888  A940  5000 l Sheet of 1        8.25  4.00
        Nos. 1883-1888 (6)          34.50 16.90

See US Nos. 2624-2629, Portugal Nos. 1918-1923 and Spain Nos. 2677-2682.

Tour of Italy Bicycle Race A941

**1992, May 23   Photo.   Perf. 14x13½**
1889  A941  750 l  Ocean            1.50   .75
1890  A941  750 l  Mountains        1.50   .75
   a.    Pair, #1889-1890           3.00  1.50

No. 1890a printed in continuous design.

Milan, Italian Soccer Champions A942

**1992, May 25   Perf. 13½x14**
1891  A942  750 l  black, red & grn 1.50   .75

Beach Resorts A943

**1992   Perf. 14x13½**
1892  A943  750 l  Viareggio        1.25   .60
1893  A943  750 l  Rimini           1.25   .60

Issued: #1892, May 30; #1893, June 13.

Tazio Nuvolari (1892-1953), Race Car Driver — A944

**1992, June 5   Perf. 14x13½**
1900  A944  3200 l  multicolored    5.25  2.75

**Tourism Type of 1974**
**1992, June 30   Perf. 14**
1901  A616  600 l  Arcevia          1.00   .50
1902  A616  600 l  Maratea          1.00   .50
1903  A616  600 l  Braies           1.00   .50
1904  A616  600 l  Pantelleria      1.00   .50
        Nos. 1901-1904 (4)          4.00  2.00

The Shepherds, by Jacopo da Ponte — A945

Discovery of America, 500th Anniv. — A946

**Litho. & Engr.**
**1992, Sept. 5   Perf. 14**
1905  A945  750 l  multicolored     1.25   .60

500 l, Columbus' house, Genoa. 600 l, Columbus' fleet. 750 l, Map. 850 l, Columbus pointing to land. 1200 l, Coming ashore. 3200 l, Columbus, art by Michelangelo.

**1992, Sept. 18   Photo.   Perf. 13½x14**
1906  A946   500 l  multicolored     .80   .40
1907  A946   600 l  multicolored    1.00   .50
1908  A946   750 l  multicolored    1.25   .60
1909  A946   850 l  multicolored    1.40   .70
1910  A946  1200 l  multicolored    2.00  1.00
1911  A946  3200 l  multicolored    5.25  2.50
        Nos. 1906-1911 (6)         11.70  5.70

Genoa '92.

Stamp Day — A947

**1992, Sept. 22   Perf. 14**
1912  A947  750 l  multicolored     1.25   .70

**Self-Adhesive**
**Perf. 13½**
1913  A947  750 l  multicolored     2.25   .70

Lions Intl., 75th Anniv. — A948

**1992, Sept. 24   Perf. 14x13½**
1914  A948  3000 l  multicolored    5.00  2.50

Single European Market A949

**1992, Oct. 5   Photo.   Perf. 14x13½**
1915  A949  600 l  multicolored     1.00   .50

Intl. Conference on Nutrition, Rome A950

**1992, Oct. 16   Photo.   Perf. 14x13½**
1916  A950  500 l  multicolored     .80   .40

Christmas
A951

**1992, Oct. 31**
1917   A951   600 l   multicolored    1.00   .50

Miniature Sheet

United Europe — A952

Buildings on natl. flags, inscriptions in native language: a, Italy (Benvenuta). b, Belgium (Vienvenue, Welkom). c, Denmark (Velkommen). d, France (Bienvenue L'Europe). e, Germany (Willkommen). f, Greece. g, Ireland (Failte). h, Luxembourg (Bienvenue Europe). i, Netherlands (Welkom). j, Portugal (Bem-Vinda). k, United Kingdom (Welcome). l, Spain (Bienvenida).

**1993, Jan. 20   Photo.   Perf. 13½x14**
**Sheet of 12**
1918   A952   750 l   #a.-l.    15.00   15.00

Meeting of Veterans of 1943 Battle of Nikolajewka, Russia — A953

**1993, Jan. 23   Litho.   Perf. 14x13½**
1919   A953   600 l   multicolored    1.00   .50

Carlo Goldoni
(1707-93),
Playwright
A954

Paintings depicting scenes from plays: No. 1920, Man in harlequin costume leaning on picture. No. 1921, Woman seated in front of harlequins.

**1993, Feb. 6   Photo.   Perf. 13½x14**
1920   A954   500 l   multicolored    .80   .40
1921   A954   500 l   multicolored    .80   .40

Mosaic
from the
Piazza
Armerina
A955

**1993, Feb. 20   Photo. & Engr.   Perf. 14**
1922   A955   750 l   multicolored    1.25   .60

Natl. Health
Day
Promoting
a Healthy
Heart
A956

**1993, Mar. 5   Photo.   Perf. 14x13½**
1923   A956   750 l   multicolored    1.25   .60

Cats
A957

**1993, Mar. 6   Perf. 14x13½, 13½x14**
1924   A957   600 l   European    1.00   .50
1925   A957   600 l   Maine coon, vert.    1.00   .50
1926   A957   600 l   Devon Rex, vert.    1.00   .50
1927   A957   600 l   White Persian    1.00   .50
   *Nos. 1924-1927 (4)*    4.00   2.00

**Radio Cent. Type of 1991**

Design: 750 l, Temistocle Calzecchi Onesti.

**1993, Mar. 26   Litho.   Perf. 14x13½**
1928   A925   750 l   multicolored    1.25   .60
   Radio cent. (in 1995).

City Scene, by Francesco Guardi
(1712-1793) — A958

**Photo. & Engr.**
**1993, Apr. 6    Perf. 14**
1929   A958   3200 l   multicolored    5.25   2.50

Horace (Quintus
Horatius Flaccus),
Poet and Satirist,
2000th Anniv. of
Death — A959

**1993, Apr. 19   Photo.   Perf. 13½x14**
1930   A959   600 l   multicolored    1.00   .50

Contemporary
Paintings — A960

Europa: 750 l, Carousel Animals, by Lino Bianchi Barriviera. 850 l, Abstract, by Gino Severini.

**1993, May 3**
1931   A960   750 l   multicolored    1.25   .60
1932   A960   850 l   multicolored    1.40   .70

Natl. Soccer
Champions,
Milan — A961

**1993, May 24**
1933   A961   750 l   multicolored    1.25   .60

Natl. Academy of
St. Luke, 400th
Anniv. — A962

**1993, May 31    Photo.**
1934   A962   750 l   multicolored    1.25   .60

St. Giuseppe
Benedetto
Cottolengo (1786-
1842)
A963

**1993, May    Photo. & Engr.**
1935   A963   750 l   multicolored    1.25   .60

Family Fest
'93 — A964

**1993, June 5   Photo.   Perf. 14x13½**
1936   A964   750 l   multicolored    1.25   .60

Tourism
A965

**1993, June 28   Photo.   Perf. 14x13½**
1937   A965   600 l   Palmanova    1.00   .50
1938   A965   600 l   Senigallia    1.00   .50
1939   A965   600 l   Carloforte    1.00   .50
1940   A965   600 l   Sorrento    1.00   .50
   *Nos. 1937-1940 (4)*    4.00   2.00
   See Nos. 1972-1975, 2032-2035.

1993 World
Kayaking
Championships,
Trentino — A966

**1993, July 1    Perf. 13½x14**
1941   A966   750 l   multicolored    1.25   .60

Regina Margherita Observatory,
Cent. — A967

**1993, Sept. 4   Photo.   Perf. 14x13½**
1942   A967   500 l   multicolored    1.00   .50

Museum
Treasures
A968

Designs: No. 1943, Concert, by Bartolomeo Manfredi. No. 1944, Ancient map of Foggia. 750 l, Illuminated page with "S," vert. 850 l, The Death of Adonis, by Sebastiano Del Piombo.

**Perf. 14x13½, 13½x14**
**1993, Nov. 27    Litho.**
1943   A968   600 l   multicolored    1.00   .50
1944   A968   600 l   multicolored    1.00   .50
1945   A968   750 l   multicolored    1.25   .60
1946   A968   850 l   multicolored    1.40   .70
   *Nos. 1943-1946 (4)*    4.65   2.30

Holy Stairway,
Veroli — A969

**1993, Sept. 25   Photo.   Perf. 13½x14**
1947   A969   750 l   multicolored    1.25   .60

World War
II — A970

Events of 1943: No. 1948, Deportation of Jews from Italy, Oct. 16, 1943. No. 1949, Soldiers, helmet (Battle of Naples). No. 1950, Execution of the Cervi Brothers.

**1993, Sept. 25**
1948   A970   750 l   multicolored    1.25   .60
1949   A970   750 l   multicolored    1.25   .60
1950   A970   750 l   multicolored    1.25   .60
   *Nos. 1948-1950 (3)*    3.75   1.80
   See Nos. 1984-1986.

Thurn and
Taxis Postal
History
A971

#1951, Coach. #1952, Coat of arms. #1953, Cart. #1954, Post rider on galloping horse. #1955, Post rider on walking horse.

**1993, Oct. 2    Perf. 14x13½**
1951   A971   750 l   multicolored    1.25   .60
1952   A971   750 l   multicolored    1.25   .60
1953   A971   750 l   multicolored    1.25   .60
1954   A971   750 l   multicolored    1.25   .60
1955   A971   750 l   multicolored    1.25   .60
   *Nos. 1951-1955 (5)*    6.25   3.00

| | | | | |
|---|---|---|---|---|
| 1951a | A971 | 750 l | 1.25 | .60 |
| 1952a | A971 | 750 l | 1.25 | .60 |
| 1953a | A971 | 750 l | 1.25 | .60 |
| 1954a | A971 | 750 l | 1.25 | .60 |
| 1955a | A971 | 750 l | 1.25 | .60 |
| b. | Booklet pane of 5, #1951a-1955a | | 5.00 | |

Bank of Italy, Cent. A972

**1993, Oct. 15**     *Perf. 14x13½*
| | | | | |
|---|---|---|---|---|
| 1956 | A972 | 750 l | Bank exterior | 1.25 .60 |
| 1957 | A972 | 1000 l | 1000 Lire note | 1.60 .80 |

Christmas A973

Designs: 600 l, Living Creche in the town of Corchiano. 750 l, Detail of The Annunciation, by Piero Della Francesca.

**1993, Oct. 26**   **Litho.**   *Perf. 13½x14*
| | | | | |
|---|---|---|---|---|
| 1958 | A973 | 600 l | multicolored | 1.00 .50 |
| 1959 | A973 | 750 l | multicolored | 1.25 .60 |

Stamp Day A974

**1993, Nov. 12**   **Photo.**   *Perf. 14*
| | | | | |
|---|---|---|---|---|
| 1960 | A974 | 600 l | blue & red | 1.00 .50 |

First Italian colonial postage stamps, cent.

Circus — A975

**1994, Jan. 8**   **Litho.**   *Perf. 13½x14*
| | | | | |
|---|---|---|---|---|
| 1961 | A975 | 600 l | Acrobat, horses | 1.00 .50 |
| 1962 | A975 | 750 l | Clown performing | 1.25 .60 |

Presence of Women in the Home A976

**1994, Feb. 14**   **Photo.**   *Perf. 14*
| | | | | |
|---|---|---|---|---|
| 1963 | A976 | 750 l | multicolored | 1.25 .60 |

**Radio Cent. Type of 1991**

750 l, Augusto Righi (1850-1920), physicist.

*Perf. 14x13½*
**1994, Mar. 11**   **Photo.**   **Unwmk.**
| | | | | |
|---|---|---|---|---|
| 1964 | A925 | 750 l | multicolored | 1.25 .60 |

Radio cent. (in 1995).

---

Dogs A977

**1994, Mar. 12**     *Perf. 14x13*
| | | | | |
|---|---|---|---|---|
| 1965 | A977 | 600 l | German shepherd | 1.00 .50 |
| 1966 | A977 | 600 l | Abruzzi sheep-dog | 1.00 .50 |
| 1967 | A977 | 600 l | Boxer | 1.00 .50 |
| 1968 | A977 | 600 l | Dalmatian | 1.00 .50 |
| | | *Nos. 1965-1968 (4)* | | 4.00 2.00 |

Italian Cuisine — A978

**1994, Mar. 24**     *Perf. 13x14*
| | | | | |
|---|---|---|---|---|
| 1969 | A978 | 500 l | Breads | .80 .40 |
| 1970 | A978 | 600 l | Pasta | 1.00 .50 |

Procession Honoring Apparition of Christ, Tarquinia — A979

**1994, Apr. 2**     *Perf. 13½*
| | | | | |
|---|---|---|---|---|
| 1971 | A979 | 750 l | multicolored | 1.25 .60 |

**Tourism Type of 1993**

**1994, Apr. 23**   **Photo.**   *Perf. 14x13½*
| | | | | |
|---|---|---|---|---|
| 1972 | A965 | 600 l | Orta San Giulio | 1.00 .50 |
| 1973 | A965 | 600 l | Santa Marinella | 1.00 .50 |
| 1974 | A965 | 600 l | Messina | 1.00 .50 |
| 1975 | A965 | 600 l | Monticchio, Potenza | 1.00 .50 |
| | | *Nos. 1972-1975 (4)* | | 4.00 2.00 |

A981

Nobel Prize Winners: 750 l, Camillo Golgi (1844-1926), Physician, Medicine, 1906. 850 l, Guilio Natta (1903-), Chemistry, 1963.

**1994, May 2**   **Photo.**   *Perf. 13½x14*
| | | | | |
|---|---|---|---|---|
| 1976 | A981 | 750 l | multicolored | 1.25 .60 |
| 1977 | A981 | 850 l | multicolored | 1.40 .70 |

Publication of "Summa de Arithemtica, Geometria, Proportioni et Proportionalita," 500th Anniv. — A982

Fra Luca Pacioli (c. 1445-1514), mathematician.

**1994, May 2**   **Photo.**   *Perf. 14x13*
| | | | | |
|---|---|---|---|---|
| 1978 | A982 | 750 l | multicolored | 1.25 .60 |

---

Lajos Kossuth (1802-94) — A983

**1994, Apr. 30**   **Photo.**   *Perf. 13½x14*
| | | | | |
|---|---|---|---|---|
| 1979 | A983 | 3750 l | multicolored | 6.00 3.00 |

Milan, Winners of 1993-94 Italian Soccer Championships — A984

**1994, May 2**     *Perf. 14x13½*
| | | | | |
|---|---|---|---|---|
| 1980 | A984 | 750 l | multicolored | 1.25 .60 |

World Swimming Championships A985

**1994, May 2**   **Photo.**   *Perf. 14x13½*
| | | | | |
|---|---|---|---|---|
| 1981 | A985 | 600 l | Diving | 1.00 .50 |
| 1982 | A985 | 750 l | Water polo | 1.25 .60 |

Archaeology Exhibition, Rimini — A986

**1994, May 6**
| | | | | |
|---|---|---|---|---|
| 1983 | A986 | 750 l | multicolored | 1.25 .60 |

**World War II Type of 1993**

Events of 1944: No. 1984, Destruction of Monte Cassino. No. 1985, Massacre of the Ardeatine Caves. No. 1986, Massacre at Marzabotto.

**1994, May 18**
| | | | | |
|---|---|---|---|---|
| 1984 | A970 | 750 l | multicolored | 1.25 .60 |
| 1985 | A970 | 750 l | multicolored | 1.25 .60 |
| 1986 | A970 | 750 l | multicolored | 1.25 .60 |
| | | *Nos. 1984-1986 (3)* | | 3.75 1.80 |

22nd Natl. Eucharistic Congress, Siena — A987

**1994, May 28**   **Photo.**   *Perf. 13½x14*
| | | | | |
|---|---|---|---|---|
| 1987 | A987 | 600 l | multicolored | 1.00 .50 |

---

Ariadne, Venus and Bacchus, by Tintoretto (1518-94) — A988

**1994, May 31**     *Perf. 14*
| | | | | |
|---|---|---|---|---|
| 1988 | A988 | 750 l | multicolored | 1.25 .60 |

Brotherhood of Mercy, Florence, 700th Anniv. — A989

**1994, June 4**     *Perf. 14x13½*
| | | | | |
|---|---|---|---|---|
| 1989 | A989 | 750 l | multicolored | 1.25 .60 |

European Parliamentary Elections — A990

**1994, June 11**   **Photo.**   *Perf. 13½x14*
| | | | | |
|---|---|---|---|---|
| 1990 | A990 | 600 l | multicolored | 1.00 .50 |

Natl. Museums — A991

#1991, Attic Krater, Natl. Archaeological Museum. #1992, Ancient drawing, Natl. Archives. 750 l, Statue, Natl. Roman Museum. 850 l, Medallion, Natl. Archives.

**1994, June 16**
| | | | | |
|---|---|---|---|---|
| 1991 | A991 | 600 l | multicolored | 1.00 .50 |
| 1992 | A991 | 600 l | multicolored | 1.00 .50 |
| 1993 | A991 | 750 l | multicolored | 1.25 .60 |
| 1994 | A991 | 850 l | multicolored | 1.40 .70 |
| | | *Nos. 1991-1994 (4)* | | 4.65 2.30 |

Intl. Olympic Committee, Cent. — A992

**1994, June 23**
| | | | | |
|---|---|---|---|---|
| 1995 | A992 | 850 l | multicolored | 1.40 .70 |

G-7 Summit, Naples — A993

**1994, July 8**
1996 A993 600 l multicolored 1.00 .50

A 750 l in this this design was printed but not issued.

A995

A996

**1994, Sept. 8 Photo. Perf. 14**
1998 A995 500 l multicolored .80 .40

Basilica of Loreto, 500th anniv.

**1994, Sept. 19**
1999 A996 750 l multicolored 1.25 .60

Frederick II (1194-1250), Holy Roman Emperor.

Stamp Day — A998

Designs: 600 l, Pietro Miliani (1744-1817), paper manufacturer. 750 l, Convent of San Domenico.

**1994, Sept. 16 Photo. Perf. 13½x14**
2001 A998 600 l multicolored 1.00 .50
2002 A998 750 l multicolored 1.25 .60

Basilica of St. Mark, 900th Anniv. A999

**1994, Oct. 8 Photo. Perf. 13½x13**
2003 A999 750 l multicolored 1.25 .60
*a.* Souvenir sheet of 2, tete beche 2.50 2.50

No. 2003 printed with se-tenant label. No. 2003a contains one each No. 2003 and San Marino No. 1314. Only No. 2003 was valid for postage in Italy. See San Marino No. 1314.

Christmas A1000

600 l, The Annunciation, by Melozzo da Forli. 750 l, Madonna and Child, by Lattanzio da Rimini.

**1994, Nov. 5 Photo. Perf. 13½x14**
2004 A1000 600 l multicolored 1.00 .50
2005 A1000 750 l multicolored 1.25 .60

Italian Touring Club, Cent. — A1001

**1994, Nov. 8**
2006 A1001 600 l multicolored 1.00 .50

CREDIOP, 75th Anniv. — A1002

**1994, Nov. 11**
2007 A1002 750 l multicolored 1.25 .60

Giovanni Gentile (1875-1944), Philosopher A1003

**1994, Nov. 21**
2008 A1003 750 l multicolored 1.25 .60

Querini Dubois Palace, Venice — A1004

**1994 Perf. 13½x14**
2009 A1004 600 l red & silver 1.00 .50

New Italian Postal Emblem A1005

**1994 Perf. 14x13½**
2010 A1005 750 l red, black & green 1.25 .60
2011 A1005 750 l red brown 1.25 .60
*a.* Pair, #2010-2011 2.50 1.25

See Nos. 2059-2060.

World Speed Skating Championships — A1006

**1995, Feb. 6 Photo. Perf. 14x13½**
2012 A1006 750 l multicolored 1.25 .60

Achille Beltrame (1871-1945) A1007

Design: 500 l, Cover of first issue of LA DOMENICA DEL CORRIERE.

**1995, Feb. 18 Photo. Perf. 13½x14**
2013 A1007 500 l multicolored .80 .40

Italian Food — A1008

**1995, Mar. 4**
2014 A1008 500 l Rice .80 .40
2015 A1008 750 l Olives, olive oil 1.25 .60

See Nos. 2068-2069.

Birds A1009

**1995, Mar. 11 Photo. Perf. 14x13½**
2016 A1009 600 l Heron 1.00 .50
2017 A1009 600 l Vulture 1.00 .50
2018 A1009 600 l Royal eagle 1.00 .50
2019 A1009 600 l Alpine chaffinch 1.00 .50
Nos. 2016-2019 (4) 4.00 2.00

UN, 50th Anniv. A1010

**1995, Mar. 24 Photo. Perf. 14x13½**
2020 A1010 850 l multicolored 1.40 .70

Fifth Day of Milan War Memorial, by Giuseppe Grandi, Cent. A1011

**1995, Mar. 25 Photo. Perf. 14x13½**
2021 A1011 750 l gold, black & blue 1.25 .60

Miniature Sheet

End of World War II, 50th Anniv. — A1012

Designs: a, Mafalda de Savoy, concentration camp, barbed wire. b, Allied DUKW, Battles of Anzio and Nettuno. c, Women in World War II, Teresa Gullace. d, Gold Medal of Valor, Palazzo Vecchio, Florence. e, Gold Medal of Valor, building, Vittorio Veneto. f, Gold Medal of Valor, Cathedral, Cagliari. g. Mountain Battalion. h, Air dropping supplies, Balkans. i, Atlantic fleet.

**1995, Mar. 31 Photo. Perf. 14x13½**
2022 A1012 750 l Sheet of 9, #a.-i. 11.00 5.50

Natl. Treasures A1013

Designs: No. 2023, Illuminated manuscript with "P," State Archives, Rome. No. 2024, Painting of Port of Naples, by Tavola Strozzi, Natl. Museum of San Martino, horiz. No. 2025, Illuminated manuscript with "I," Christ, State Archives, Mantua. No. 2026, Painting, Sacred and Profane Love, by Titian, Borghese Gallery and Museum, Rome, horiz.

*Perf. 13½x14, 14x13½*
**1995, Apr. 28 Photo.**
2023 A1013 500 l multicolored .80 .40
2024 A1013 500 l multicolored .80 .40
2025 A1013 750 l multicolored 1.25 .60
2026 A1013 850 l multicolored 1.40 .70
Nos. 2023-2026 (4) 4.25 2.10

Venice Biennial, Cent. — A1014

**1995, Apr. 29 Perf. 13½x14**
2027 A1014 750 l multicolored 1.25 .60

Basilica of Santa Croce, Florence A1015

**1995, May 3 Engr.**
2028 A1015 750 l deep brn blk 1.25 .60

Peace & Freedom A1016

Europa: 750 l, Family, liberating soldiers, Italian flag. 850 l, Stars of European flag, church, mosque.

**1995, May 5 Photo. Perf. 13½x14**
2029 A1016 750 l multicolored 1.25 .60
2030 A1016 850 l multicolored 1.40 .70

Volleyball, Cent. — A1017

**1995, May 8**
2031 A1017 750 l multicolored 1.25 .60

**Tourism Type of 1993**
**1995, May 12 Photo. Perf. 14x13½**
2032 A965 750 l Nuoro 1.25 .60
2033 A965 750 l Susa 1.25 .60
2034 A965 750 l Alatri 1.25 .60
2035 A965 750 l Venosa 1.25 .60
Nos. 2032-2035 (4) 5.00 2.40

Discovery of the X-Ray, Cent. A1018

**1995, June 2**
2036 A1018 750 l multicolored 1.25 .60

1994-95 Natl. Soccer Championship Team, Juventus A1019

**1995, June 5 Perf. 13½x14**
2037 A1019 750 l multicolored 1.25 .60

Radio, Cent. A1020

Designs: 750 l, Griffone House. 850 l, Guglielmo Marconi, transmitting equipment.

**1995, June 8 Perf. 14x13½**
2038 A1020 750 l multicolored 1.25 .60
**Perf. 14**
2039 A1020 850 l multicolored 1.40 .70
No. 2039 is 36x21mm. See Germany No. 1900, Ireland No. 974a, San Marino Nos. 1336-1337, Vatican City Nos. 978-979.

A1021

St. Anthony of Padua (1195-1231) — A1022

**Perf. 13½x14, 14x13½**
**1995, June 13**
2040 A1021 750 l multicolored 1.25 .60
2041 A1022 850 l multicolored 1.40 .70
See Brazil No. 2539 and Portugal Nos. 2054-2057.

Historical Public Gardens A1023

Designs: No. 2042, Durazzo Pallavicini, Pegli. No. 2043, Boboli, Firenze. No. 2044, Ninfa, Cisterna di Latina. No. 2045, Royal Park, Caserta.

**Litho. & Engr.**
**1995, June 24 Perf. 14x13½**
2042 A1023 750 l multicolored 1.25 .60
2043 A1023 750 l multicolored 1.25 .60
2044 A1023 750 l multicolored 1.25 .60
2045 A1023 750 l multicolored 1.25 .60
Nos. 2042-2045 (4) 5.00 2.40

Congress of European Society of Ophthalmology A1024

**1995, June 24 Litho. Perf. 13½x14**
2046 A1024 750 l multicolored 1.25 .60

The Sailors' Wives, by Massimo Campigli (1895-1971) — A1025

**1995, July 4 Photo. Perf. 14**
2047 A1025 750 l multicolored 1.25 .60

14th World Conference on Relativity, Florence A1026

**1995, Aug. 7 Litho. Perf. 14x13**
2048 A1026 750 l Galileo, Einstein 1.25 .60

Motion Pictures, Cent. — A1027

#2049, Son of the Shiek, Rudolph Valentino. #2050, L'oro Di Napoli, Toto. #2051, Le Notti Di Cabiria, F. Fellini. #2052, Cinecitta '95.

**Litho. & Engr.**
**1995, Aug. 29 Perf. 13½x14**
2049 A1027 750 l multicolored 1.25 .60
2050 A1027 750 l multicolored 1.25 .60
2051 A1027 750 l multicolored 1.25 .60
2052 A1027 750 l multicolored 1.25 .60
Nos. 2049-2052 (4) 5.00 2.40
See #2099-2101, 2170-2172, 2269-2271.

FAO, 50th Anniv. A1028

**1995, Sept. 1 Photo. Perf. 14x13½**
2053 A1028 850 l multicolored 1.25 .60

Basilica of Pontida & Death of St. Albert of Prezzate, 900th Anniv. A1029

**1995, Sept. 2 Engr.**
2054 A1029 1000 l blue & brown 1.60 .80

ROMA '95, First World Military Games — A1030

**1995, Sept. 6 Photo. Perf. 13½x14**
2055 A1030 850 l multicolored 1.40 .70

Italian News Agency (ANSA), 50th Anniv. A1031

**1995, Oct. 27 Photo. Perf. 14x13½**
2056 A1031 750 l multicolored 1.25 .60

Christmas A1032

Designs: 750 l, Nativity figurines, Cathedral of Polignano a Mare, by Stefano da Putignano. 850 l, Adoration of the Magi, by Fra Angelico.

**1995, Nov. 18**
2057 A1032 750 l multicolored 1.25 .60
2058 A1032 850 l multicolored 1.40 .70

**New Italian Postal Emblem Type of 1994**
**1995, Dec. 9 Photo. Perf. 13½x14**
**Size: 26x18mm**
2059 A1005 750 l like No. 2011 1.25 .60
a. Booklet pane of 8 10.00
Complete booklet, #2059a 10.00
2060 A1005 850 l like No. 2010 1.40 .70
a. Booklet pane of 8 11.50
Complete booklet, #2060a 11.50

Renato Mondolfo A1033

**1995, Dec. 9 Photo. Perf. 14x13½**
2061 A1033 750 l multicolored 1.25 .60
Philately Day.

F.T. Marinetti (1876-1944), Poet and Ideologue — A1034

**1996, Jan. 19 Photo. Perf. 14**
2062 A1034 750 l multicolored 1.25 .60

Collections from Natl. Museum and Archives A1035

#2063, Arms of the Academy of Georgofili, Florence. #2064, Illuminated manuscript from Lucca (1372), vert. #2065, Manuscript of Gabriele D'Annunzio (1863-1938), author, soldier, political leader. #2066, French miniature, c. 1486.

**1996, Feb. 26 Perf. 14x13½, 13½x14**
2063 A1035 750 l multicolored 1.25 .60
2064 A1035 750 l multicolored 1.25 .60
2065 A1035 850 l multicolored 1.40 .70
2066 A1035 850 l multicolored 1.40 .70
Nos. 2063-2066 (4) 5.30 2.60

Sarah and the Angel, by Tiepolo (1696-1770) — A1036

**1996, Mar. 5 Perf. 14**
2067 A1036 1000 l multicolored 1.60 .80

**Italian Food Type of 1995**
**1996, Mar. 20 Perf. 13½x14**
2068 A1008 500 l White wine, grapes .80 .40
2069 A1008 750 l Red wine, grapes 1.25 .60

CHINA '96, 9th Asian Intl. Philatelic Exhibition A1037

**1996, Mar. 22 Perf. 14x13½**
2070 A1037 1250 l multicolored 2.00 1.00
Marco Polo's return from China, 700th anniv. (in 1995).
See San Marino No. 1350.

Cathedral of Milan — A1038

No. 2071, Front entrance. No. 2072, Corner, side view.

**1996, Mar. 23**      *Perf. 13½x14*
| | | | | |
|---|---|---|---|---|
| 2071 | A1038 | 750 l multicolored | 1.25 | .60 |
| 2072 | A1038 | 750 l multicolored | 1.25 | .60 |
| a. | | Pair, #2071-2072 | 2.50 | 1.25 |
| b. | | Booklet pane, 4 #2072a | 11.50 | |
| | | Complete booklet, #2072b | 11.50 | |

No. 2072a is a continuous design.
ITALIA '98, Intl. Philatelic Exhibition, Milan.

A1039

**1996, Apr. 3**      *Perf. 13½x14, 14x13½*
| | | | | |
|---|---|---|---|---|
| 2073 | A1039 | 750 l shown | 1.25 | .60 |
| 2074 | A1039 | 750 l Globe, "100" | 1.25 | .60 |

Natl. Press Federation, 50th anniv. (#2073). "La Gazzetta dello Sport," cent. (#2074), horiz.

Intl. Museum of Postal Images, Belvedere Ostrense A1040

**1996, Apr. 13 Photo.**    *Perf. 13½x14*
| | | | | |
|---|---|---|---|---|
| 2075 | A1040 | 500 l multicolored | .80 | .40 |

Academy of Finance Police, Cent. — A1040a

**1996, Apr. 13**
| | | | | |
|---|---|---|---|---|
| 2076 | A1040a | 750 l multicolored | 1.25 | .60 |

RAMOGE Agreement Between France, Italy, Monaco, 20th Anniv. A1041

**Photo. & Engr.**
**1996, May 14**     *Perf. 14x13½*
| | | | | |
|---|---|---|---|---|
| 2077 | A1041 | 750 l multicolored | 1.25 | .60 |

See France No. 2524, Monaco No. 1998.

Rome-New York Trans-Continental Drive — A1042

**1996, Apr. 13 Photo.**    *Perf. 13½x14*
| | | | | |
|---|---|---|---|---|
| 2078 | A1042 | 4650 l multicolored | 7.50 | 3.75 |

Europa (Famous Women) A1043

750 l, Carina Negrone, pilot. 850 l, Adelaide Ristori, actress.

**1996, Apr. 29 Photo.**    *Perf. 13½x14*
| | | | | |
|---|---|---|---|---|
| 2079 | A1043 | 750 l multicolored | 1.25 | .60 |
| 2080 | A1043 | 850 l multicolored | 1.40 | .70 |

St. Celestine V (1215-96) A1044

**Litho. & Engr.**
**1996, May 18**     *Perf. 14x13½*
| | | | | |
|---|---|---|---|---|
| 2081 | A1044 | 750 l multicolored | 1.25 | .60 |

Tourism A1045

#2082, Pienza Cathedral. #2083, St. Anthony's Church, Diano Marina. #2084, Belltower of Church of St. Michael the Archangel, Monte Sant'Angelo. #2085, Prehistoric stone dwelling, Lampedusa.

**1996, May 18 Photo.**    *Perf. 14x13½*
| | | | | |
|---|---|---|---|---|
| 2082 | A1045 | 750 l multicolored | 1.25 | .60 |
| 2083 | A1045 | 750 l multicolored | 1.25 | .60 |
| 2084 | A1045 | 750 l multicolored | 1.25 | .60 |
| 2085 | A1045 | 750 l multicolored | 1.25 | .60 |
| | | Nos. 2082-2085 (4) | 5.00 | 2.40 |

Consecration of Reconstructed Farfa Abbey, 500th Anniv. — A1046

**1996, May 18 Photo.**    *Perf. 13½x14*
| | | | | |
|---|---|---|---|---|
| 2086 | A1046 | 1000 l multicolored | 1.60 | .80 |

Mediterranean Fair, Palermo — A1047

**1996, May 25**      *Perf. 14x13½*
| | | | | |
|---|---|---|---|---|
| 2087 | A1047 | 750 l multicolored | 1.25 | .60 |

Italian Republic, 50th Anniv. — A1048

**1996, June 1**      *Perf. 13½x14*
| | | | | |
|---|---|---|---|---|
| 2088 | A1048 | 750 l multicolored | 1.25 | .60 |

Production of Vespa Motor Scooters, 50th Anniv. — A1049

**1996, June 20**
| | | | | |
|---|---|---|---|---|
| 2089 | A1049 | 750 l multicolored | 1.25 | .60 |

First Meeting of European Economic Community, Messina and Venice, 40th Anniv. — A1050

**1996, June 21**      *Perf. 14*
| | | | | |
|---|---|---|---|---|
| 2090 | A1050 | 750 l multicolored | 1.25 | .60 |

Modern Olympic Games, Cent. A1051

Designs: 500 l, Runners, 1896. 750 l, Discus, Atlanta skyline, vert. 850 l, Gymnast on rings, basketball, Atlanta stadium. 1250 l, 1896 stadium, Athens, 1996 stadium, Atlanta, vert.

     *Perf. 14x13½, 13½x14*
**1996, July 1**      **Photo.**
| | | | | |
|---|---|---|---|---|
| 2091 | A1051 | 500 l multicolored | .80 | .40 |
| 2092 | A1051 | 750 l multicolored | 1.25 | .60 |
| 2093 | A1051 | 850 l multicolored | 1.40 | .70 |
| 2094 | A1051 | 1250 l multicolored | 2.00 | 1.00 |
| | | Nos. 2091-2094 (4) | 5.45 | 2.70 |

Butterflies A1052

#2095, Melanargia arge. #2096, Papilio hospiton. #2097, Zygaena rubicundus. #2098, Acanthobrahmaea europaea.

**1996, Aug. 26**      *Perf. 14x13½*
| | | | | |
|---|---|---|---|---|
| 2095 | A1052 | 750 l multicolored | 1.25 | .60 |
| 2096 | A1052 | 750 l multicolored | 1.25 | .60 |
| 2097 | A1052 | 750 l multicolored | 1.25 | .60 |
| 2098 | A1052 | 750 l multicolored | 1.25 | .60 |
| | | Nos. 2095-2098 (4) | 5.00 | 2.40 |

**Motion Picture Type of 1995**

#2099, Massimo Troisi in "Scusate Il Ritardo." #2100, Aldo Fabrizi in "Prima Comunione." #2101, Bartolomeo Pagano as Maciste in "Cabiria."

**Photo. & Engr.**
**1996, Aug. 30**     *Perf. 13½x14*
| | | | | |
|---|---|---|---|---|
| 2099 | A1027 | 750 l multicolored | 1.25 | .60 |
| 2100 | A1027 | 750 l multicolored | 1.25 | .60 |
| 2101 | A1027 | 750 l multicolored | 1.25 | .60 |
| | | Nos. 2099-2101 (3) | 3.75 | 1.80 |

A1054

**1996, Sept. 7 Photo.**    *Perf. 13½x14*
| | | | | |
|---|---|---|---|---|
| 2102 | A1054 | 750 l multicolored | 1.25 | .60 |

Milan, 1995-96 national soccer champions.

The Duomo, Cathedral of Santa Maria del Fiore, Florence, 700th Anniv. A1055

**1996, Sept. 7 Engr.**     *Perf. 14x13½*
| | | | | |
|---|---|---|---|---|
| 2103 | A1055 | 750 l dark blue | 1.25 | .60 |

13th Intl. Congress of Prehistoric Science — A1056

**1996, Sept. 9 Photo.**    *Perf. 13½x14*
| | | | | |
|---|---|---|---|---|
| 2104 | A1056 | 850 l multicolored | 1.40 | .70 |

Levant Fair, Bari A1057

**1996, Sept. 13 Photo.**    *Perf. 14x13½*
| | | | | |
|---|---|---|---|---|
| 2105 | A1057 | 750 l multicolored | 1.25 | .60 |

1997 Mediterranean Games, Bari — A1058

**1996, Sept. 13**      *Perf. 13½x14*
| | | | | |
|---|---|---|---|---|
| 2106 | A1058 | 750 l multicolored | 1.25 | .60 |

Juventus, 1995-96 European Soccer Champions A1059

**1996, Sept. 14**
2107 A1059 750 l multicolored 1.25 .60

Alessandro Pertini (1896-1990), Former President A1060

**1996, Sept. 25 Photo. Perf. 13½x14**
2108 A1060 750 l multicolored 1.25 .60

Eugenio Montale (1896-1981), Poet — A1061

**1996, Oct. 12 Litho. & Engr.**
2109 A1061 750 l blue & brown 1.25 .60

Annunciation, by Pietro da Cortona (1596-1669) A1062

**1996, Oct. 31 Photo.**
2110 A1062 500 l multicolored .80 .40

Invitation to Philately A1063

Designs: 750 l, Tex Willer, western scene. 850 l, Seagulls, gondola, city, Corto Maltese.

**Litho. & Engr.**
**1996, Oct. 31 Perf. 14x13½**
2111 A1063 750 l multicolored 1.25 .60
2112 A1063 850 l multicolored 1.40 .70

Stamp Day — A1064

**1996, Nov. 8 Photo. Perf. 13½x14**
2113 A1064 750 l multicolored 1.25 .60

Universities of Italy — A1065

**Perf. 13½x14, 14x13½**
**1996, Nov. 9 Engr.**
Designs: No. 2114, Agrarian School, cent., University of Perugia. No. 2115, University of Sassari (1562-1996), horiz. No. 2116, University of Salerno

2114 A1065 750 l brown 1.25 .60
2115 A1065 750 l green 1.25 .60
2116 A1065 750 l blue 1.25 .60
Nos. 2114-2116 (3) 3.75 1.80

World Food Day — A1066

**1996, Nov. 13 Photo. Perf. 14x13½**
2117 A1066 850 l green & black 1.40 .70

Christmas A1067

Designs: 750 l, Madonna and Child, by Pisanello. 850 l, Santa, toys, horiz.

**Perf. 13½x14, 14x13½**
**1996, Nov. 15**
2118 A1067 750 l multicolored 1.25 .60
2119 A1067 850 l multicolored 1.40 .70

UNESCO, 50th Anniv. — A1068

850 l, UNICEF 50th Anniv., baby, globe, emblem.

**1996, Nov. 20 Perf. 13½x14**
2120 A1068 750 l multicolored 1.25 .60
2121 A1068 850 l multicolored 1.40 .70

Natl. Institute of Statistics, 70th Anniv. — A1069

**1996, Nov. 26**
2122 A1069 750 l multicolored 1.25 .60

"Strega" Literary Award 50th Anniv. — A1070

**1996, Nov. 29**
2123 A1070 3400 l multicolored 5.50 2.75

First Natl. Flag, Bicent. — A1071

**1997, Jan. 7 Photo. Perf. 13½x14**
2124 A1071 750 l multicolored 1.25 .60

Sestrieres '97, World Alpine Skiing Championships A1072

**1997, Feb. 1 Photo. Perf. 13½x14**
2125 A1072 750 l shown 1.25 .60
2126 A1072 850 l Ski of colors 1.40 .70

Galileo Ferraris (1847-97), Physicist, Electrical Engineer A1073

**1997, Feb. 7 Perf. 14x13½**
2127 A1073 750 l multicolored 1.25 .60

Emanuela Loi (1967-92),Police Woman Killed by Mafia — A1074

**1997, Mar. 8**
2128 A1074 750 l multicolored 1.25 .60

Italia '98, World Philatelic Exhibition, Milan — A1075

Designs: a, Airmail philately. b, Topical philately. c, Postal history. d, Philatelic literature.

**1997, Mar. 21 Litho. Perf. 13½x14**
2129 Sheet of 4 5.00 2.50
a.-d. A1075 750 l any single 1.25 .60

Statue of Marcus Aurelius (121-180), Roman Emperor A1076

**1997, Mar. 25 Photo.**
2130 A1076 750 l multicolored 1.25 .60
Treaty of Rome, 40th anniv.

St. Ambrose (339-397), Bishop of Milan — A1077

**Litho. & Engr.**
**1997, Apr. 4 Perf. 14**
2131 A1077 1000 l multicolored 1.60 .80

St. Geminian, 1600th Death Anniv. — A1078

**1997, Apr. 4 Photo. Perf. 13½x14**
2132 A1078 750 l multicolored 1.25 .60

University of Rome A1079

Design: No. 2134, University of Padua.

**1997, Apr. 14 Engr. Perf. 14x13½**
2133 A1079 750 l claret 1.25 .60
2134 A1079 750 l blue 1.25 .60

Founding of Rome, 2750th Anniv. A1080

**1997, Apr. 21 Photo. Perf. 14x13½**
2135 A1080 850 l multicolored 1.40 .70

Timoleontee Wall, Gela — A1081

**1997, Apr. 24**
2136 A1081 750 l multicolored 1.25 .60

Antonio Gramsci (1891-1937), Politician — A1082

**1997, Apr. 26 Photo. Perf. 14**
2137 A1082 850 l multicolored 1.40 .70

Monastery Church, Pavia, 500th Anniv. — A1083

**1997, May 3 Perf. 13½x14**
2138 A1083 1000 l multicolored 1.60 .80

Stories and Legends A1084

Europa: 800 l, Cobbler's workshop. 900 l, Street singer, vert.

**Perf. 14x13, 13x14**
**1997, May 5 Photo.**
2139 A1084 800 l multicolored 1.25 .60
2140 A1084 900 l multicolored 1.50 .75

Massimo Theatre, Palermo, Cent. — A1085

**1997, May 16 Photo. Perf. 13½x14**
2141 A1085 800 l multicolored 1.25 .60

Tourism A1086

Designs: No. 2142, St. Vitalian Basilica, Ravenna. No. 2143, Tomb of Marcus Tullius Cicero (106-43BC), Formia. No. 2144, College of Assumption of the Holy Mary, Positano. No. 2145, St. Sebastian Church, Acireale.

**1997, May 17 Photo. Perf. 14x13**
2142 A1086 800 l multicolored 1.25 .60
2143 A1086 800 l multicolored 1.25 .60
2144 A1086 800 l multicolored 1.25 .60
2145 A1086 800 l multicolored 1.25 .60
Nos. 2142-2145 (4) 5.00 2.40

Book Fair, Turin — A1087

**1997, May 22 Perf. 13½x14**
2146 A1087 800 l multicolored 1.25 .60

Queen Paola of Belgium, 60th Birthday A1088

**1997, May 23 Photo. Perf. 14x13½**
2147 A1088 750 l San Angelo Castle 1.25 .60
See Belgium No. 1652.

Rome Fair A1089

**1997, May 24 Photo. Perf. 14x13½**
2148 A1089 800 l multicolored 1.25 .60

Cathedral of Orvieto — A1090

**1997, May 31 Engr. Perf. 13x14**
2149 A1090 450 l deep violet .75 .35

Fr. Giuseppe Morosini (1913-44) A1091

**1997, June 4 Photo.**
2150 A1091 800 l multicolored 1.25 .60

Bologna Fair A1092

**1997, June 7 Perf. 14x13**
2151 A1092 800 l multicolored 1.25 .60

Juventus, 1996-97 Italian Soccer Champions A1093

**1997, June 7 Perf. 13½x14**
2152 A1093 800 l multicolored 1.25 .60

Abruzzo Natl. Park, 75th Anniv. — A1094

**1997, June 7 Photo. Perf. 13½x14**
2153 A1094 800 l multicolored 1.25 .60

Italian Naval League, Cent. — A1095

**1997, June 10 Photo. Perf. 13½x14**
2154 A1095 800 l multicolored 1.25 .60

13th Mediterranean Games, Bari — A1096

**1997, June 13 Perf. 14x13½**
2155 A1096 900 l multicolored 1.50 .75

Public Gardens A1097

Designs: No. 2156, Miramare-Trieste Park. No. 2157, Cavour-Santena. No. 2158, Villa Sciarra, Rome. No. 2159, Orto Botanical Gardens, Palermo.

**Photo. & Engr.**
**1997, June 14 Perf. 14x13½**
2156 A1097 800 l multicolored 1.25 .60
2157 A1097 800 l multicolored 1.25 .60
2158 A1097 800 l multicolored 1.25 .60
2159 A1097 800 l multicolored 1.25 .60
Nos. 2156-2159 (4) 5.00 2.40

Italian Labor Force — A1098

**Perf. 13½x14, 14x13½**
**1997, June 20**
2160 A1098 800 l Industry 1.25 .60
2161 A1098 900 l Agriculture, horiz. 1.50 .75

John Cabot's Voyage to Canada, 500th Anniv. A1099

**1997, June 24 Litho. Perf. 14**
2162 A1099 1300 l multicolored 2.10 1.00
See Canada No. 1649.

Pietro Verri (1728-97), Economist, Journalist A1100

**1997, June 28 Perf. 13½x14**
2163 A1100 3600 l multicolored 6.00 3.00

Madonna of the Rosary by Pomarancio il Vecchio (Niccolo Cercignani)(d. 1597) — A1101

650 l, The Miracle of Ostia, by Paolo de Dono Uccello (1397-1475).

**1997, July 19 Photo. Perf. 13½x14**
2164 A1101 450 l multicolored .75 .35
**Size: 26x37mm**
2165 A1101 650 l multicolored 1.00 .50

Varia di Palmi Festival — A1102

**1997, Aug. 2 Perf. 13½x14**
2166 A1102 800 l multicolored 1.25 .60

Universiade 97, Sicily A1103

**1997, Aug. 19 Photo. Perf. 14x13½**
2167 A1103 450 l Basketball .75 .35
2168 A1103 800 l High jump 1.25 .60

Antonio Rosmini (1797-1855), Priest, Philosopher — A1104

**1997, Aug. 26**
2169 A1104 800 l multicolored 1.25 .60

**Motion Picture Type of 1995**
#2170, Pietro Germi in "The Railway Man."
#2171, Anna Magnani in "Mamma Roma."
#2172, Ugo Tognazzi in "My Dear Friends."

**Photo. & Engr.**
**1997, Aug. 27** *Perf. 13½x14*
2170 A1027 800 l multicolored 1.25 .60
2171 A1027 800 l multicolored 1.25 .60
2172 A1027 800 l multicolored 1.25 .60
*Nos. 2170-2172 (3)* 3.75 1.80

Viareggio Literary Prize A1106

**1997, Aug. 30 Photo.** *Perf. 14x13½*
2173 A1106 4000 l multicolored 6.50 3.25

Intl. Fair, Bolzano A1107

**1997, Sept. 1**
2174 A1107 800 l multicolored 1.25 .60

A1108

Artifacts and Paintings from Natl. Museums and Galleries: 450 l, Bronze head, 500BC, National Museum, Reggio Calabria. 650 l, Madonna and Child with Two Vases of Roses, by Ercole di Roberti, Natl. Picture Gallery, Ferrara. 800 l, Miniature of troubadour, Sordello da Goito, Arco Palace Museum, Manta. 900 l, St. George and the Dragon, Vitale da Bologna, Natl. Picture Gallery, Bologna.

**1997, Sept. 13 Photo.** *Perf. 13½x14*
2175 A1108 450 l multicolored .75 .35
2176 A1108 650 l multicolored 1.00 .50
2177 A1108 800 l multicolored 1.25 .60
2178 A1108 900 l multicolored 1.50 .75
*Nos. 2175-2178 (4)* 4.50 2.20

Pope Paul VI (1897-1978) A1109

**1997, Sept. 26 Engr.** *Perf. 13x14*
2179 A1109 4000 l dark blue 6.50 3.25

Milan Fair A1110

**1997, Sept. 30 Photo.** *Perf. 14x13*
2180 A1110 800 l multicolored 1.25 .60

Marshall Plan, 50th Anniv. — A1111

**1997, Oct. 17**
2181 A1111 800 l multicolored 1.25 .60

Christmas A1112

Nativity scenes: 800 l, Molded polychrome, from Church of St. Francis, Leonessa. 900 l, Fresco, from Baglioni Chapel, St. Mother Mary Church, Spello.

**1997, Oct. 18**
2183 A1112 800 l multicolored 1.25 .60
2184 A1112 900 l multicolored 1.50 .25

Aristide Merloni (1897-1970) A1113

**1997, Oct. 24** *Perf. 13x14*
2185 A1113 800 l multicolored 1.25 .60

Giovanni Battista Cavalcaselle (1819-97), Art Historian A1114

**Litho. & Engr.**
**1997, Oct. 31** *Perf. 13½x14*
2186 A1114 800 l multicolored 1.25 .60

Philately Day — A1115

**1997, Dec. 5 Photo.**
2187 A1115 800 l multicolored 1.25 .60

Emigration of Italian Population of Dalmatia, Istria & Fiume, 50th Anniv. A1116

**1997, Dec. 6** *Perf. 14x13½*
2188 A1116 800 l multicolored 1.25 .60

State Highway Police, 50th Anniv. A1117

**1997, Dec. 12**
2189 A1117 800 l multicolored 1.25 .60

Constitution, 50th Anniv. — A1118

**1998, Jan. 2 Photo.** *Perf. 13½x14*
2190 A1118 800 l multicolored 1.25 .60

Hercules and the Hydra, by Antonio Del Pollaiolo (1429-98) A1119

**1998, Jan. 3** *Perf. 14*
2191 A1119 800 l multicolored 1.25 .60
See Nos. 2278, 2319.

Famous Writers A1120

450 l, Bertolt Brecht (1898-1956), playwright. 650 l, Federico Garcia Lorca (1898-1936), poet, dramatist. 800 l, Curzio Malaparte (Kurt Suckert) (1898-1957), journalist, writer. 900 l, Leonida Repaci (1898-1985), writer.

**1998, Feb. 2** *Perf. 14x13½*
2192 A1120 450 l multi .75 .35
2193 A1120 650 l multi 1.00 .50
2194 A1120 800 l multi 1.25 .60
2195 A1120 900 l multi, vert. 1.50 .75
*Nos. 2192-2195 (4)* 4.50 2.20

Verona Fair, Cent. A1121

**1998, Feb. 11 Photo.** *Perf. 14x13½*
2196 A1121 800 l multicolored 1.25 .60

Jewish Emancipation, 150th Anniv. — A1122

**1998, Mar. 28** *Perf. 14*
2197 A1122 800 l multicolored 1.25 .60

National Festivals A1123

**1998, Apr. 3 Litho.** *Perf. 13½x14*
2198 A1123 800 l Umbria Jazz 1.25 .60
2199 A1123 900 l Giffoni Film 1.50 .75

Europa.

Completion of "The Last Supper," by Leonardo da Vinci (1452-1519), 500th Anniv. — A1124

**1998, Apr. 4 Engr.** *Perf. 14x13½*
2200 A1124 800 l red brown 1.25 .60

Gaetano Donizetti (1797-1848), Composer — A1125

**1998, Apr. 8 Photo.**
2201 A1125 800 l multicolored 1.25 .60

Italian Opera, 400th Anniv. — A1126

**1998, Apr. 8** *Perf. 13½x14*
2202 A1126 800 l multicolored 1.25 .60

Cathedral of Turin, 500th anniv., and Shroud of Turin — A1127

**1998, Apr. 18 Photo. Perf. 13½x14**
2203 A1127 800 l multicolored 1.25 .60

Tourism A1128

#2204, Castle, Otranto. #2205, Mori Fountain and Castle, Marino. #2206, Village and chapel, Livigno. #2207, Marciana Marina, Elba Island.

**1998, Apr. 18 Litho. Perf. 14x13½**
2204 A1128 800 l multicolored 1.25 .60
2205 A1128 800 l multicolored 1.25 .60
2206 A1128 800 l multicolored 1.25 .60
2207 A1128 800 l multicolored 1.25 .60
Nos. 2204-2207 (4) 5.00 2.40

See Nos. 2283-2286.

Sardinia Intl. Fair A1129

**1998, Apr. 23 Photo. Perf. 14x13½**
2208 A1129 800 l multicolored 1.25 .60

The Charge of Carabinieri at Pastrengo, by Sebastiano de Albertis (1828-97) A1130

**1998, Apr. 30 Perf. 13½x14**
2209 A1130 800 l multicolored 1.25 .60

A1131

**1998, May 11 Photo. Perf. 13½x14**
2210 A1131 800 l Padua Fair 1.25 .60

Juventus, 1997-98 Italian Soccer Champions A1132

**1998, May 18**
2211 A1132 800 l multicolored 1.25 .60

Polytechnical School, Turin — A1133

**1998, May 18 Engr. Perf. 14x13½**
2212 A1133 800 l dark blue 1.25 .60

World Food Program — A1134

**1998, May 22 Photo.**
2213 A1134 900 l multicolored 1.50 .75

4th Intl. Convention on Fossils, Evolution, and Environment, Pergola — A1135

**1998, May 30 Photo. Perf. 14x13½**
2214 A1135 800 l multicolored 1.25 .60

Carthusian Monastery of Santa Maria di Pesio, 825th Anniv. A1136

**1998, May 30**
2215 A1136 800 l multicolored 1.25 .60

A1137

**1998, June 2 Perf. 13½x14**
2216 A1137 800 l multicolored 1.25 .60
Honoring the fallen of the Italian police corps.

6th World Congress of Endoscopic Surgery — A1138

**1998, June 3**
2217 A1138 900 l multicolored 1.50 .75

Italian Museums A1139

#2218, Regional Archeological Museum, Agrigento. #2219, Natl. Museum of the Risorgimento, Turin. #2220, Peggy Guggenheim Collection, Venier Dei Leoni Palace, Venice.

**1998, June 6 Perf. 13½x14, 14x13½**
2218 A1139 800 l multi 1.25 .60
2219 A1139 800 l multi, horiz. 1.25 .60
2220 A1139 800 l multi, horiz. 1.25 .60
Nos. 2218-2220 (3) 3.75 1.80

A1140

**1998, June 13 Perf. 13½x14**
2221 A1140 800 l Vicenza Fair 1.25 .60

Giacomo Leopardi (1798-1837), Poet — A1141

**1998, June 29 Photo. Perf. 14x13½**
2222 A1141 800 l dark brn & sep 1.25 .60

Women in Art — A1142

Paintings: 100 l, "Young Velca," Etruscan tomb. 450 l, Detail from, "Herod's Feast," by Filippo Lippi. 650 l, Woman in profile, by Fra Benci. 800 l, "Lady with the Unicorn," by Raphael. 1000 l, sculpture of Constanza Buonarelli, by Gian Lorenzo Bernini.

**1998, July 8 Photo. Perf. 14x13½**
2223 A1142 100 l blk & multi .20 .20
2224 A1142 450 l vio & multi .75 .35
2225 A1142 650 l gray grn & multi 1.00 .50

**Engr.**
**Wmk. 303**
2226 A1142 800 l red brn & multi 1.25 .60
2227 A1142 1000 l grn bl & multi 1.60 .80
Nos. 2223-2227 (5) 4.80 2.45

**Denominated in Lira and Euros**
**1999, Jan. 28 Photo. Perf. 14x13½**
2228 A1142 100 l blk & multi .20 .20
2229 A1142 450 l vio & multi .70 .35
2230 A1142 650 l gray grn & multi .95 .45

**Engr.**
**Wmk. 303**
2231 A1142 800 l red brn & multi 1.10 .55
2232 A1142 1000 l grn bl & multi 1.50 .75
Nos. 2228-2232 (5) 4.45 2.30

See Nos. 2436-2453.

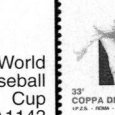

33rd World Baseball Cup A1143

**Perf. 14x13½**
**1998, July 21 Photo. Unwmk.**
2251 A1143 900 l multicolored 1.50 .75

Columbus' Landing in Venezuela and Exploration of Amerigo Vespucci, 500th Anniv. A1144

**1998, Aug. 12**
2252 A1144 1300 l multicolored 2.10 1.00
See Venezuela No. 1595.

Riccione Intl. Stamp Fair, 50th Anniv. — A1145

**1998, Aug. 28 Perf. 13½x14**
2253 A1145 800 l multicolored 1.25 .60

Mother Teresa (1910-97) A1146

**1998, Sept. 5 Perf. 14x13½, 13½x14**
2254 A1146 800 l shown 1.25 .60
2255 A1146 900 l Portrait, vert. 1.50 .75
See Albania Nos. 2578-2579.

Father Pio da Pietrelcina (1887-1968) — A1147

**1998, Sept. 23 Engr. Perf. 14x13½**
2256 A1147 800 l deep blue 1.25 .60

1998 World Equestrian Championships, Rome — A1148

**1998, Oct. 2 Photo. Perf. 14x13½**
2257 A1148 4000 l multicolored 6.50 3.25

School of Higher Education in Telecommunications, Rome — A1149

**1998, Oct. 9    Engr.    Perf. 14x13½**
2258  A1149  800 l  deep blue    1.25   .60

Italia '98, Intl. Philatelic Exhibition — A1150

**1998, Oct. 23    Photo.    Perf. 14**
2259  A1150  800 l  Pope John Paul II    1.25   .60

See San Marino No. 1430 and Vatican City No. 1085.

Armed Forces Day A1151

Emblem from branch of the military and: No. 2260, Aircraft carrier "Giuseppe Garibaldi," Navy. No. 2261, Eurofighter 2000, Air Force. No. 2262, Officer, Carabinieri (police force), vert. No. 2263, Italian monument, El Alamein battlefield, vert.

**Perf. 14x13½, 13½x14**
**1998, Oct. 24    Photo.**
2260  A1151  800 l  multicolored    1.25   .60
2261  A1151  800 l  multicolored    1.25   .60
2262  A1151  800 l  multicolored    1.25   .60
2263  A1151  800 l  multicolored    1.25   .60
      Nos. 2260-2263 (4)    5.00  2.40

Nos. 2260-2263 were printed se-tenant with Italia '98 label. Air Force, 75th anniv. (#2261).

Art Day — A1152

**1998, Oct. 25    Perf. 13½x14**
2264  A1152  800 l  Dionysus    1.25   .60
      Italia '98.

Enzo Ferrari (1898-1988) Automobile Manufacturer — A1153

a, 1931 Bobbio-Passo del Penice. b, 1952 Ferrari F1. c, 1963 Ferrari GTO. d, 1998 Ferrari F1.

**1998, Oct. 26    Litho.    Perf. 13½**
2265  A1153  800 l  Sheet of 4, #a.-d.    5.25  2.50
      Italia '98.

Universal Declaration of Human Rights, 50th Anniv. — A1154

**1998, Oct. 27    Photo.    Perf. 14x13½**
2266  A1154  1400 l  multicolored    2.25  1.10
Printed se-tenant with a label. Italia '98.

Europe Day — A1155

**1998, Oct. 28    Perf. 13½x14**
2267  A1155  800 l  multicolored    1.25   .60

**Die Cut Perf. 11**
**Self-Adhesive**
**Booklet Stamp**
2268  A1155  800 l  multicolored    1.25   .60
  a.  Booklet pane of 6    7.50
      Complete booklet, #2268a    7.50

**Motion Picture Type of 1995**

Motion pictures, stars: 450 l, "Ti Conosco Mascherina," Eduardo de Filippo. 800 l, "Fantasmi a Roma," Antonio Pietrangeli. 900 l, "Il Signor Max," Mario Camerini.

**1998, Oct. 29    Litho. & Engr.**
2269  A1027  450 l  multicolored    .75   .35
2270  A1027  800 l  multicolored    1.25   .60
2271  A1027  900 l  multicolored    1.50   .75
      Nos. 2269-2271 (3)    3.50  1.70

Nos. 2269-2271 each printed se-tenant with label. Italia '98.

Communications Day — A1156

**1998, Oct. 31    Photo.**
2272  A1156  800 l  multicolored    1.25   .60

Souvenir Sheet

Stamp Day — A1157

Illustration reduced.

**1998, Nov. 1    Litho.**
2273  A1157  4000 l  multicolored    6.50  3.25
      Italia '98.

Christmas A1158

800 l, Sculpture, "The Epiphany," Church of St. Mark, Seminara, vert. 900 l, Adoration of the shepherds, drawing by Giulio Romano.

**Perf. 13½x14, 14x13½**
**1998, Nov. 28    Engr.**
2274  A1158  800 l  deep blue    1.25   .60
2275  A1158  900 l  brown    1.50   .75

The Ecstasy of St. Teresa, Sculpture by Gian Lorenzo Bernini — A1159

**1998, Dec. 1    Photo.    Perf. 13½x14**
2276  A1159  900 l  multicolored    1.50   .75

Emancipation of Valdesi, 150th Anniv. — A1160

**1998, Dec. 4    Perf. 14**
2277  A1160  800 l  multicolored    1.25   .60

**Art Type of 1998**

Conception of Space, by Lucio Fontana (1899-1968).

**1999, Feb. 19    Photo.    Perf. 14**
2278  A1119  450 l  multicolored    .75   .35

National Parks A1162

Europa: 800 l, Wolf, Calabria, vert. 900 l, Birds, Tuscan Archipelago.

**Perf. 13¼x14, 14x13¼**
**1999, Mar. 12    Photo.**
2279  A1162  800 l  multicolored    1.25   .60
2280  A1162  900 l  multicolored    1.50   .75

Holy Year 2000 — A1163

**1999, Mar. 13    Perf. 13¼x13¾**
2281  A1163  1400 l  Holy Door    2.25  1.10

St. Egidio Church, Cellere A1164

**1999, Apr. 10    Engr.    Perf. 13¾x13½**
2282  A1164  800 l  brown lake    1.25   .60

**Tourism Type of 1998**

#2283, Earthen pyramids, Segonzano. #2284, Waterfalls, river, Terni. #2285, Buildings, Lecce. #2286, Walls around Lipari.

**1999, Apr. 17    Photo.    Perf. 14x13¼**
2283  A1128  800 l  multicolored    1.25   .60
2284  A1128  800 l  multicolored    1.25   .60
2285  A1128  800 l  multicolored    1.25   .60
2286  A1128  800 l  multicolored    1.25   .60
      Nos. 2283-2286 (4)    5.00  2.40

Museums A1165

#2287, Swan on Lake, Casina della Civette, Rome. #2288, "Iulia Bela," International Ceramics Museum, Faenza, vert. #2289, Bells, Marinelli Historic Bell Museum, Agnone.

**Perf. 14x13¼, 13¼x14**
**1999, Apr. 17    Photo.**
2287  A1165  800 l  multicolored    1.25   .60
2288  A1165  800 l  multicolored    1.25   .60
2289  A1165  800 l  multicolored    1.25   .60
      Nos. 2287-2289 (3)    3.75  1.80

Constitutional Court — A1166

**Perf. 13¾x13¼**
**1999, Apr. 23    Photo.**
2290  A1166  800 l  multicolored    1.25   .60

Natl. Firefighting Service A1167

**1999, Apr. 29**
2291  A1167  800 l  multicolored    1.25   .60

Military Academy of Modena — A1168

**1999, May 3    Photo.    Perf. 13¼x14**
2292  A1168  800 l  multicolored    1.25   .60

50th Anniv. of Death of Grande Torino Soccer Team in Airplane Crash
A1169

**1999, May 4    Photo.    Perf. 14x13¼**
2293 A1169 800 l Plane, team members    1.25    .60
2294 A1169 900 l Superga Basili-ca, names    1.50    .75

Council of Europe, 50th Anniv. A1170

**1999, May 5    Photo.    Perf. 14x13¼**
2295 A1170 800 l multicolored    1.25    .60

Milan, 1998-99 Italian Soccer Champions A1171

**1999, June 7    Photo.    Perf. 13¼x14**
2296 A1171 800 l multicolored    1.25    .60

Elections for European Parliament, 20th Anniv. A1172

**1999, June 10    Photo.    Perf. 14x13¼**
2297 A1172 800 l multicolored    1.25    .60

Priority Mail A1173

**Typo. & Silk-screened**
**1999, June 14    Die Cut 11¼**
**Self-Adhesive**
2298 A1173 1200 l multicolored    2.00    1.00
a.    Bklt. pane of 4 + 4 etiquettes    8.00
    Complete booklet, #2298a    8.00
b.    Bklt. pane of 8, no etiquettes    16.00
    Complete booklet, #2298b    16.00

No. 2298 was intended for Priority Mail service. Self-adhesive blue etiquettes to be used with each stamp on mail were provided on the sheets and in booklets of 4 stamps.
    The backing paper from the sheet stamps is rouletted, while the backing paper in the booklets is not.
    See No. 2324.

Fausto Coppi (1919-60), Cyclist A1174

**1999, June 12    Photo.    Perf. 14x13¼**
2299 A1174 800 l multi    1.25    .60

Fiat Automobile Co., Cent. — A1175

**1999, July 10    Photo.    Perf. 13¼x14**
2300 A1175 4800 l multi    7.75    3.75

Statue of Our Lady of the Snows, Mt. Rocciamelone, Cent. — A1176

**1999, July 19**
2301 A1176 800 l multi    1.25    .60

Eleonora de Fonseca Pimentel (1752-1799), Writer — A1177

**1999, Aug. 20    Perf. 14x13¼**
2302 A1177 800 l multi    1.25    .60

30th World Canoe Championships — A1178

**1999, Aug. 26**
2303 A1178 900 l multi    1.50    .75

Johann Wolfgang von Goethe (1749-1832), German Poet — A1179

**1999, Aug. 28**
2304 A1179 4000 l multi    6.50    3.00

World Cycling Championships A1180

**1999, Sept. 15    Photo.    Perf. 13¼x14**
2305 A1180 1400 l multi    2.25    1.10

Stamp Day — A1181

**1999, Sept. 25    Photo.    Perf. 13¼x14**
2306 A1181 800 l multi    1.25    .60

Basilica of St. Francis, Assisi — A1182

**Litho. & Engr.**
**1999, Sept. 25    Perf. 14x13¼**
2307 A1182 800 l multi    1.25    .60

Giuseppe Parini (1729-99), Poet — A1183

**1999, Oct. 2    Engr.    Perf. 13¼x14**
2308 A1183 800 l blue gray    1.25    .60

Alessandro Volta's Pile, Bicent. — A1184

**1999, Oct. 11    Photo.**
2309 A1184 3000 l multi    5.00    2.25

UPU, 125th Anniv. A1185

**1999, Oct. 18    Perf. 14x13¼**
2310 A1185 900 l multi    1.50    .70

Goffredo Mameli (1827-49), Lyricist of Natl. Anthem, Nos. 506, 518 — A1186

**1999, Oct. 22    Perf. 14**
2311 A1186 1500 l multi    2.40    1.10

"Stamps, Our Friends" — A1187

Various abstract designs: a, 450 l. b, 650 l. c, 800 l. d, 1000 l.

**1999, Oct. 23    Perf. 13¼x14**
2312 A1187 Sheet of 4, #a.-d.    4.75    2.25

A1188

**1999, Nov. 4**
2313 A1188 900 l 1899 Military Conscript    1.50    .70

Christmas A1189

Designs: 800 l, Santa Claus, reindeer and sleigh. 1000 l, Nativity, By Dosso Dossi.

**1999, Nov. 5    Photo.**
2314 A1189 800 l multi    1.25    .60
2315 A1189 1000 l multi    1.60    .75
    See Finland Nos. 1117-1119.

Holy Year 2000 A1190

#2316, Map by Conrad Peutinger, 1507. #2317, 18th cent. print of pilgrims in Rome. #2318, Bas-relief, facade of Fidenza Duomo.

**1999, Nov. 24    Photo.    Perf. 14x13¼**
2316 A1190 1000 l multi    1.60    .75
2317 A1190 1000 l multi    1.60    .75
2318 A1190 1000 l multi    1.60    .75
    Nos. 2316-2318 (3)    4.80    2.25

**Art Type of 1998**

Design: Restless Leopard, by Antonio Ligabue (1899-1965), horiz.

**1999, Nov. 27    Photo.    Perf. 14**
2319 A1119 1000 l multi    1.60    .75

Schools A1191

Designs: 450 l, State Institute of Art, Urbino. 650 l, Normal Superior School, Pisa.

**1999, Nov. 27    Engr.    Perf. 14x13¼**
2320 A1191 450 l black    .75    .35
2321 A1191 650 l brown    1.00    .45

Year 2000
A1192

**1999, Nov. 27** Photo.
2322 A1192 4800 l multi 7.75 3.50

**Souvenir Sheet**

Millennium — A1193

Designs: a, The past. b, The future.

**2000, Jan. 1** Litho. Perf. 14x13¼
2323 A1193 Sheet of 2 6.50 6.50
a.-b. A1193 2000 l Any single 3.25 1.50

See #2330-2332, 2365.

**Priority Mail Type of 1999 Redrawn
With Yellow Rectangle at Center
Typo. & Silk-Screened**
**2000, Jan. 10** Die Cut 11¼
**Self-Adhesive**
2324 A1173 1200 l multi 2.00 .90

No. 2324 was intended for Priority Mail service. A self-adhesive blue etiquette is adjacent to the stamp. See No. 2393 for similar stamp with Posta Prioritaria in lower case letters.

First Performance of Opera "Tosca,"
Cent. — A1194

**Litho. & Engr.**
**2000, Jan. 14** Perf. 14x13¼
2325 A1194 800 l multi 1.25 .50

Basilica of St.
Paul — A1195

**2000, Jan. 18** Photo. Perf. 13¼x14
2326 A1195 1000 l multi 1.60 .70

Holy Year 2000.

Six Nation Rugby
Tournament — A1196

**2000, Feb. 5** Perf. 14x13¼
2327 A1196 800 l multi 1.25 .50

5th Symposium
on Breast
Diseases
A1197

**2000, Feb. 12** Perf. 13¼x14
2328 A1197 800 l shown 1.25 .50
2329 A1197 1000 l Woman holding rose 1.60 .70

**Millennium Type of 2000**
**Souvenir Sheet**

No. 2330: a, Art. b, Science.
No. 2331: a, Nature. b, The city.
No. 2332: a, Generations. b, Space.

**2000** Litho. Perf. 14x13¼
2330 Sheet of 2 2.50 2.50
a.-b. A1193 800 l Any single 1.25 .50
2331 Sheet of 2 2.50 2.50
a.-b. A1193 800 l Any single 1.25 .50
2332 Sheet of 2 2.50 2.50
a.-b. A1193 800 l Any single 1.25 .50

Issued: #2330, 3/4; #2331, 5/4; #2332, 7/4.

Skiing World
Cup — A1198

**2000, Mar. 7** Photo. Perf. 13¼x14
2333 A1198 4800 l multi 7.75 3.50

**Souvenir Sheet**

Italian Design — A1199

Household furnishings designed by:
a, Achille & Pier Giacomo Castiglioni, Ettore Sottsass, Jr. Carlo Bartoli, Aldo Rossi. b, Mario Bellini, Alessandro Mendini, Vico Magistretti, Alberto Meda & Paolo Rizzatto. c, Gio Ponti, Gatti Paolini Teodoro, Massimo Morozzi, Tobia Scarpa. d, Pietro Chiesa, Joe Colombo, Cini Boeri & Tomu Katayanagi, Lodovico Acerbis & Giotto Stoppino. e, Gaetano Pesce, Antonio Citterio & Oliver Loew, Enzo Mari, De Pas D'Urbino Lomazzi. f, Marco Zanuso, Anna Castelli Ferrieri, Michele de Lucchi & Giancarlo Fassina, Bruno Munari.

**2000, Mar. 9** Litho. Perf. 13¼
2334 Sheet of 6 7.50 7.50
a.-f. A1199 800 l Any single 1.25 .50

Holy Year
2000
A1200

Paintings depicting the life of Jesus:
450 l, The Adoration of the Shepherds, by Ghirlandaio. 650 l, The Baptism and Temptation of Christ, by Veronese, vert. 800 l, The Last Supper, by Ghirlandaio, vert. 1000 l, Fresco from Episodes of the Life of the Virgin Mary and Christ, by Giotto. 1200 l, The Resurrection of Christ, by Piero della Francesca, vert.

Perf. 14x13¼, 13¼x14
**2000, Mar. 10** Litho.
2335 A1200 450 l multi .75 .35
2336 A1200 650 l multi 1.00 .40
2337 A1200 800 l multi 1.25 .50
2338 A1200 1000 l multi 1.60 .70
2339 A1200 1200 l multi 2.00 .90
Nos. 2335-2339 (5) 6.60 2.85

La Civiltá
Cattolica,
150th
Anniv.
A1201

**2000, Apr. 6** Photo. Perf. 14x13¼
2340 A1201 800 l multi 1.25 .55

San
Giuseppe
de
Merode
College,
Rome,
150th
Anniv.
A1202

**2000, Apr. 8**
2341 A1202 800 l multi 1.25 .55

Intl. Cycling
Union,
Cent. — A1203

**2000, Apr. 14** Photo. Perf. 13¼x14
2342 A1203 1500 l multi 2.40 1.00

Tourism — A1204

Designs: No. 2343, Terre di Franciacorta, Brescia. No. 2344, Dunarobba Petrified Forest, Avigliano Umbro. No. 2345, Ercolano. No. 2346, Bella di Taormina Island.

**2000, Apr. 14** Perf. 14x13¼
2343 A1204 800 l multi 1.25 .50
2344 A1204 800 l multi 1.25 .50
2345 A1204 800 l multi 1.25 .50
2346 A1204 800 l multi 1.25 .50
Nos. 2343-2346 (4) 5.00 2.00

Little Holy Society,
Caltanissetta — A1205

**2000, Apr. 19**
2347 A1205 800 l multi 1.25 .50

Niccolò Piccinni
(1728-1800),
Opera Composer
A1206

**2000, May 6** Perf. 13¼x14
2348 A1206 4000 l multi 6.50 2.75

**Europa, 2000**
**Common Design Type**
**2000, May 9**
2349 CD17 800 l multi 1.25 .50

Post and Telecommunications
Historical Museum — A1207

No. 2350, Ship, telecommunications equipment. No. 2351, #19, 20.

**2000, May 9** Litho. Perf. 14x13¼
2350 A1207 800 l multi 1.25 .50
2351 A1207 800 l multi 1.25 .50

Lazio, 1999-2000
Soccer
Champions
A1208

**2000, May 20** Photo. Perf. 13¼x14
2352 A1208 800 l multi 1.25 .50

Monza
Cathedral
A1209

**2000, May 31**
2353 A1209 800 l multi 1.25 .50

Rome,
Headquarters of
UN Food and
Agriculture
Agencies
A1210

**2000, June 17** Photo. Perf. 13¼x14
2354 A1210 1000 l multi 1.60 .70

Jesus the Redeemer Monument, Nuoro, Cent. — A1211

**2000, June 24**
2355 A1211 800 l multi — 1.25 .50

Società Italiana per Condotte d'Acqua, Construction Company, 120th Anniv. — A1212

**2000, June 28** — *Perf. 14x13¼*
2356 A1212 800 l multi — 1.25 .50

Stampin' the Future Children's Stamp Design Contest Winner — A1213

**2000, July 7** — *Perf. 13¼x14*
2357 A1213 1000 l multi — 1.60 .70

Archery World Championships, Campagna A1214

**2000, July 8**
2358 A1214 1500 l multi — 2.40 1.00

World Cycling Championships A1215

**2000, July 31 Photo.** *Perf. 13¼x14*
2359 A1215 800 l multi — 1.25 .50

Madonna and Child, by Carlo Crivelli A1216

**Litho. & Engr.**
**2000, Aug. 8** — *Perf. 14*
2360 A1216 800 l multi — 1.25 .50

Sant'Orso Fair, 1000th Anniv. A1217

**2000, Aug. 8 Photo.** *Perf. 14x13¼*
2361 A1217 1000 l multi — 1.60 .70

18th World Congress of Transplantation Society A1218

**2000, Aug. 26 Photo.** *Perf. 13¼x14*
2362 A1218 1000 l multi — 1.60 .70

2000 Summer Olympics, Sydney — A1219

Designs: 800 l, Celebrating athlete, Olympic stadium, Sydney. 1000 l, Myron's Discobolus, Sydney skyline.

**2000, Sept. 1**
2363 A1219 800 l multi — 1.25 .50
2364 A1219 1000 l multi — 1.60 .70

**Millennium Type of 2000**
Souvenir Sheet

No. 2365, vert.: a, War. b, Peace.

**2000** — *Litho.* *Perf. 13¼x14*
2365 Sheet of 2 — 2.50 2.50
a.-b. A1193 800 l Any single — 1.25 .50
Issued: No. 2365, 9/4.

**Millennium Type of 2000**

No. 2366: a, Meditation. b, Expression.

**2000, Nov. 4 Litho.** *Perf. 14x13¼*
2366 Sheet of 2 — 2.50 2.50
a.-b. A1193 800 l Any single — 1.25 .50
Issued: No. 2366, 11/4.

Battle of Marengo, Bicent. — A1220

**2000, Sept. 8 Photo.** *Perf. 13¼x14*
2367 A1220 800 l multi — 1.25 .50

Fellini Film Year — A1221

**2000, Sept. 20 Photo.** *Perf. 13¼x14*
2368 A1221 800 l multi — 1.25 .50

Philately Day A1222

**2000, Sept. 23 Photo.** *Perf. 14x13¼*
2369 A1222 800 l multi — 1.25 .50

Father Luigi Maria Monti (1825-1900) — A1223

**2000, Sept. 30 Photo.** *Perf. 14x13¼*
2370 A1223 800 l multi — 1.25 .50

Antonio Salieri (1750-1825), Composer A1224

**2000, Sept. 30** — *Perf. 13¼x14*
2371 A1224 4800 l multi — 7.75 3.25

2000 Paralympics, Sydney — A1225

**2000, Oct. 2 Photo.** *Perf. 13¼x14*
2372 A1225 1500 l multi — 2.40 1.10

World Mathematics Year — A1226

**2000, Oct. 14 Photo.** *Perf. 14x13¼*
2373 A1226 800 l multi — 1.25 .50

Voluntarism A1227

**2000, Oct. 18** — *Perf. 13¼x14*
2374 A1227 800 l multi — 1.25 .50

Giordano Bruno (1548-1600), Philosopher — A1228

**2000, Oct. 20** — *Perf. 14x13¼*
2375 A1228 800 l multi — 1.25 .50

Madonna and Child, by Luca Della Robbia A1229

**Litho. & Engr.**
**2000, Oct. 25** — *Perf. 14*
2376 A1229 800 l multi — 1.25 .50

Accademia Roveretana Degli Agiati, 250th Anniv. — A1230

**2000, Oct. 26 Photo.** *Perf. 13¼x14*
2377 A1230 800 l multi — 1.25 .50

Gaetano Martino (1900-67), Statesman — A1231

**2000, Nov. 3 Photo.** *Perf. 14*
2378 A1231 800 l multi — 1.25 .50

Perseus, by Benvenuto Cellini (1500-71), Sculptor — A1232

**Litho. & Engr.**

**2000, Nov. 3**      **Perf. 14**
2379 A1232 1200 l multi    2.00 .85

Schools A1233

Designs: 800 l, Camerino University. 1000 l, Calabria University, Cosenza.

**2000, Nov. 6**   **Engr.**   **Perf. 14x13¼**
2380 A1233 800 l blue    1.25 .50
2381 A1233 1000 l blue    1.60 .70

Christmas A1234

Designs: 800 l, Snowflakes. 1000 l, Creche, Matera Cathedral, horiz.

**Perf. 13¼x14, 14x13¼**
            **Photo.**
**2000, Nov. 6**
2382 A1234 800 l multi    1.25 .50
2383 A1234 1000 l multi    1.60 .70

World Snowboarding Championships A1235

**2001, Jan. 15**   **Photo.**   **Perf. 13¼x14**
2384 A1235 1000 l multi    1.60 .70

The Annunciation, by Botticelli — A1236

**2001, Jan. 18**      **Perf. 14**
2385 A1236 1000 l multi    1.60 .70
Exhibit of Italian art at Natl. Museum of Western Art, Tokyo.

Souvenir Sheet

Opera Composers — A1237

No. 2386: a, Vincenzo Bellini (1801-35). b, Domenico Cimarosa (1749-1801). c, Gaspare Luigi Pacifico Spontini (1774-1851). d, Giuseppe Verdi (1813-1901).

**2001, Jan. 27**   **Litho.**   **Perf. 13¼x14**
2386 A1237   Sheet of 4    5.00 5.00
 a.-d.   800 l Any single    1.25 .50

St. Rose of Viterbo (1235-1252) A1238

**2001, Mar. 6**   **Photo.**   **Perf. 13¼x14**
2387 A1238 800 l multi    1.25 .50

Souvenir Sheet

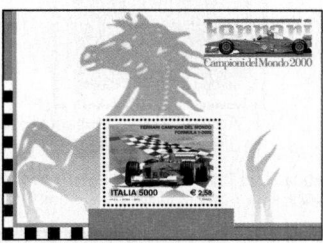

Ferrari, 2000 Formula 1 World Champions — A1239

**2001, Mar. 9**   **Litho.**   **Perf. 14x13¼**
2388 A1239 5000 l multi    8.25 8.25

Santa Maria Abbey, Sylvis — A1240

**2001, Mar. 10**      **Engr.**    **Perf. 14**
2389 A1240 800 l blue    1.25 .50

Postage Stamp Sesquicentennials — A1241

Designs: No. 2390, Tuscany #1. No. 2391, Sardinia #1. No. 2392, Lombardy-Venetia #1.

**2001, Mar. 31**   **Photo.**   **Perf. 13¼x14**
2390 A1241 800 l multi    1.25 .50
2391 A1241 800 l multi    1.25 .50
2392 A1241 800 l multi    1.25 .50
  Nos. 2390-2392 (3)    3.75 1.50

Priority Mail A1242

**Serpentine Die Cut 11**
**Typo & Silk Screened**
**2001, Apr. 10**
        **Self-Adhesive**
2393 A1242 1200 l multi    2.00 .85
 a.   Booklet pane of 4 + 4 eti-
      quettes    8.00
     Booklet #2393a    8.00
Compare with No. 2324. No. 2393 was intended for Priority Mail service. A self-adhesive blue etiquette is adjacent to the stamp. See Nos. 2466-2471.

Tourism A1243

**2001, Apr. 14**   **Photo.**   **Perf. 14x13¼**
2394 A1243 800 l Stintino    1.25 .50
2395 A1243 800 l Comacchio    1.25 .50
2396 A1243 800 l Diamante    1.25 .50
2397 A1243 800 l Pioraco    1.25 .50
  Nos. 2394-2397 (4)    5.00 2.00

Nature and the Environment A1244

Designs: 450 l, Campanula. 650 l, Marmots. 800 l, Storks. 1000 l, World Day Against Desertification.

**2001, Apr. 21**      **Perf. 13¼x14**
2398 A1244 450 l multi    .75 .35
2399 A1244 650 l multi    1.00 .40
2400 A1244 800 l multi    1.25 .50
2401 A1244 1000 l multi    1.60 .70
  Nos. 2398-2401 (4)    4.60 1.95

General Agricultural Confederation A1245

**2001, Apr. 24**   **Photo.**   **Perf. 13¼x14**
2402 A1245 800 l multi    1.25 .50

Gorizia, 1000th Anniv. A1246

**2001, Apr. 28**
2403 A1246 800 l multi    1.25 .50

Europa A1247

**2001, May 4**   **Photo.**   **Perf. 14x13¼**
2404 A1247 800 l multi    1.25 .50

European Union's Charter of Fundamental Rights — A1248

**2001, May 9**   **Photo.**   **Perf. 14x13¼**
2405 A1248 800 l multi    1.25 .50

Order of the Knights of Labor, Cent. — A1249

**2001, May 9**   **Photo.**   **Perf. 13¼x14**
2406 A1249 800 l multi    1.25 .50

Workplace Injury Memorial Day — A1250

**2001, May 19**
2407 A1250 800 l multi    1.25 .50

Art and Student Creativity Day A1251

Children's art by: No. 2408, Lucia Catena. No. 2409, Luigi Di Cristo. No. 2410, Barbara Grilli. No. 2411, Rita Vergari, vert.

**2001, May 26**   **Perf. 13¼x14, 14x13¼**
2408 A1251 800 l multi    1.25 .50
2409 A1251 800 l multi    1.25 .50
2410 A1251 800 l multi    1.25 .50
2411 A1251 800 l multi    1.25 .50
  Nos. 2408-2411 (4)    5.00 2.00

Masaccio (1401-28), Painter — A1252

**2001, June 1**              *Perf. 13¼x14*
2412  A1252  800 l multi          1.25   .50

Madonna of Senigallia, by Piero della Francesca A1253

**Litho. & Engr.**
**2001, June 9**              *Perf. 14*
2413  A1253  800 l multi          1.25   .50

Panathlon International, 50th Anniv. — A1254

**2001, June 12  Photo.  Perf. 13¼x14**
2414  A1254  800 l multi          1.25   .50

Republic of San Marino, 1700th Anniv. — A1255

**2001, June 23**
2415  A1255  800 l multi          1.25   .50

Rome, 2000-2001 Soccer Champions A1256

**2001, June 23  Photo.  Perf. 13¼x14**
2416  A1256  800 l multi          1.25   .50

Harbormaster's Corps and Coast Guard — A1257

**2001, July 20  Photo.  Perf. 14x13¼**
2417  A1257  800 l multi          1.25   .50

Salvatore Quasimodo (1901-68), Writer — A1258

**2001, Aug. 20**              *Perf. 13¼x14*
2418  A1258  1500 l multi         2.40  1.00

Octagonal Room, Domus Aurea (Golden House of Nero), Rome — A1259

**2001, Aug. 31  Engr.  Perf. 14**
2419  A1259  1000 l multi         1.60   .70

Italian Design A1260

Household furnishings designed by: a, Piero Lissoni, Patricia Urquiola and Anna Bartoli. b, Monica Graffeo and Rodolfo Dordoni. c, Ferruccio Laviani and Massimo Iosa Ghini. d, Anna Gili and Miki Astori. e, Marco Ferreri, M. Cananzi and R. Semprini. f, Stefano Giovannoni and Massimiliano Datti.

**2001, Sept. 1  Litho.  Perf. 13¼**
2420        Sheet of 6            7.50  7.50
   *a.-f.*  A1260 800 l Any single   1.25   .50

Cent. of Il Quarto Stato, Painting by Giuseppe Pellizza da Volpedo — A1261

**2001, Sept. 15  Engr.  Perf. 14x13¼**
2421  A1261  1000 l brown         1.60   .70

Discovery of Mummified Man "Otzi" in Melting Glacier, 10th Anniv. — A1262

**2001, Sept. 19  Photo.  Perf. 13¼x14**
2422  A1262  800 l multi          1.25   .50

Stamp Day A1263

**2001, Sept. 22**              *Perf. 14x13¼*
2423  A1263  800 l multi          1.25   .50

Enrico Fermi (1901-54), Physicist — A1264

**2001, Sept. 29**              *Perf. 13¼x14*
2424  A1264  800 l multi          1.25   .50

Schools A1265

Designs: No. 2425, Pavia University. No. 2426, Bari University, vert. No. 2427, Camilo Cavour State Science High School, Rome.

**Perf. 14x13¼, 13¼x14**
**2001, Sept. 29**              **Engr.**
2425  A1265  800 l blue           1.25   .50
2426  A1265  800 l red brown      1.25   .50
2427  A1265  800 l Prus blue      1.25   .50
   Nos. 2425-2427 (3)             3.75  1.50

Latin Union A1266

**2001, Oct. 12  Photo.  Perf. 14x13¼**
2428  A1266  800 l multi          1.25   .50

Natl. Archaeological Museum, Taranto — A1267

**2001, Oct. 12  Photo.  Perf. 14x13¼**
2429  A1267  1000 l multi         1.60   .70

Intl. Food and Agriculture Organizations A1268

Wheat and emblem of: a, Intl. Fund for Agricultural Development. b, Food and Agriculture Organization and farmer (49x27mm). c, World Food Program.

**2001, Oct. 16  Photo.  Perf. 14x13¼**
2430        Horiz. strip of 3     3.75  3.75
   *a.-c.*  A1268 800 l Any single  1.25   .50

Enthroned Christ and Angels, Sancta Sanctorum, St. John Lateran Basilica A1269

**Litho. & Engr.**
**2001, Oct. 19**              *Perf. 14*
2431  A1269  800 l multi          1.25   .50

Madonna and Child, by Macrino d'Alba A1270

**2001, Oct. 20**
2432  A1270  800 l multi          1.25   .50

A1271

Christmas A1272

**2001, Oct. 30  Photo.  Perf. 14x13¼**
2433  A1271  800 l multi          1.25   .50
2434  A1272  1000 l multi         1.60   .70

Souvenir Sheet

Italian Silk Industry — A1273

**Silk-screened on Silk**
**2001, Nov. 29**              *Imperf.*
2435  A1273  5000 l multi         8.25  8.25

100 Cents = 1 Euro (€)
**Women in Art Type of 1998 With Denominations in Euros Only**

Designs: 1c, Hebe, sculpture by Antonio Canova. 2c, Profile of woman from Syracuse tetradrachm. 3c, Queen of Sheba from "The Meeting of King Solomon and the Queen of Sheba," painting by Piero della Francesa. 5c, "Young Velca," Etruscan tomb. 10c, Head of terra cotta statue, 3rd cent. BC. 20c, Danae, painting by Correggio. 23c, Detail from "Herod's Feast," by Fra Filippo Lippi. 41c, "Lady with the Unicorn," by Raphael. 45c, "Venus of Urbina," by Titian. 50c, "Antea," by Parmigianino. 65c, "Princess of Trebizonde," by Antonio Pisano. 77c, "Primavera," by Botticelli. 85c, "Courtesan," by Vittore Carpaccio.

**Perf. 14x13¼, 13¼x13½ (#2447, 2449, 2450, 2452, 2453)**
**2002-04**                    **Photo.**
2436  A1142  1c multi            .20   .20
   *a.*     Perf. 13¼x13½        .20   .20

| | | | | |
|---|---|---|---|---|
| **2437** | A1142 | 2c multi | .20 | .20 |
| **a.** | | Perf. 13¼x13½ | .20 | .20 |
| **2438** | A1142 | 3c multi | .20 | .20 |
| **a.** | | Perf. 13¼x13½ | .20 | .20 |
| **2440** | A1142 | 5c multi | .20 | .20 |
| **2441** | A1142 | 10c multi | .25 | .20 |
| **a.** | | Perf. 13¼x13½ ('04) | .30 | .20 |
| **2443** | A1142 | 20c multi | .60 | .20 |
| **a.** | | Perf. 13¼x13½ | .60 | .20 |
| **2444** | A1142 | 23c multi | .70 | .20 |

**Engr.**
**Wmk. 303**

| | | | | |
|---|---|---|---|---|
| **2446** | A1142 | 41c multi | 1.25 | .45 |
| **a.** | | Perf. 13¼x13½ | 1.00 | .35 |
| **2447** | A1142 | 45c multi | 1.40 | .50 |
| **2448** | A1142 | 50c multi | 1.50 | .55 |
| **a.** | | Perf. 13¼x13½ | 1.50 | .55 |
| **2449** | A1142 | 65c multi | 1.90 | .70 |
| **2450** | A1142 | 70c multi | 2.10 | .75 |
| **2451** | A1142 | 77c multi | 2.25 | .80 |
| **a.** | | Perf. 13¼x13½ | 2.25 | .80 |
| **2452** | A1142 | 85c multi | 2.50 | .90 |
| **2453** | A1142 | 90c multi | 2.75 | 1.00 |
| | *Nos. 2436-2453 (15)* | | 18.00 | 7.05 |

Issued: 2c, 5c, 10c, 23c, 41c, 50c, No. 2451, 1/1. 1c, 3c, 20c, 3/1; Nos. 2437a, 2438a, 2004; No. 2446a, 2003. No. 2451a, 2004 (?); Nos. 2436a, 2440a, 2448a, 2004; 45c, 1/27/04; 65c, 3/20/04; 85c, 2/17/04; No. 2443a, 2004; 70c, 7/31/04; 90c, 6/26/04; No. 2441a, 2004. This is an expanding set.
No. 2446 was reprinted in 2003 with imprint "I.P.Z.S. S.p.A.-Roma."

Italia — A1274

***Perf. 14x13¼, 13¼x13½ (#2460, 2461A, 2462)***

| **2002** | | **Engr.** | | **Unwmk.** |
|---|---|---|---|---|
| **2454** | A1274 | €1 multi | 3.00 | 1.50 |
| **2455** | A1274 | €1.24 multi | 3.75 | 1.75 |
| **2457** | A1274 | €1.55 multi | 4.50 | 2.25 |
| **2459** | A1274 | €2.17 multi | 6.50 | 3.25 |
| **2460** | A1274 | €2.35 multi | 7.00 | 3.50 |
| **2461** | A1274 | €2.58 multi | 7.75 | 3.75 |
| **2461A** | A1274 | €2.80 multi | 8.50 | 4.25 |
| **2462** | A1274 | €3 multi | 9.00 | 4.50 |
| **2463** | A1274 | €3.62 multi | 10.50 | 5.25 |
| **2465** | A1274 | €6.20 multi | 18.00 | 9.00 |
| | *Nos. 2454-2465 (10)* | | 78.50 | 39.00 |

Issued: €1, €1.24, €1.55, €2.17, €2.58, €3.62, 1/2. €6.20, 3/1. Nos. 2436a, 2440a, 2448a, 2004; 45c, 1/27/04; 65c, 3/20/04; 85c, 2/17/04.
Compare Type A1274 with Type A1407.

**Priority Mail Type of 2001 with Euro Denominations Only**
**Typo. & Silk Screened**
**2002, Jan. 2** *Serpentine Die Cut 11*
**Self-Adhesive**
**Background Color**

| | | | | |
|---|---|---|---|---|
| **2466** | A1242 | 62c yellow | 1.90 | .95 |
| | Booklet, 4 #2466 | | 7.50 | |
| **2467** | A1242 | 77c blue green | 2.25 | 1.10 |
| **2468** | A1242 | €1 blue | 3.00 | 1.50 |
| **2469** | A1242 | €1.24 yel green | 3.75 | 1.75 |
| **2470** | A1242 | €1.86 rose | 5.50 | 2.75 |
| **2471** | A1242 | €4.13 lilac | 12.00 | 6.00 |
| | *Nos. 2466-2471 (6)* | | 28.40 | 14.05 |

A self-adhesive etiquette is adjacent to each stamp.
No. 2466-2471 were reprinted in 2003 with imprint "I.P.Z.S. S.p.A.-Roma-2003." No. 2468 was reprinted in 2004 with imprint "I.P.Z.S. S.p.A. - Roma - 2004."

Introduction of the Euro — A1275

No. 2472: a, 1285 Venetian ducat. b, 1252 Genoan genovino and Florentine florin.
No. 2473: a, Euro symbol and flags. b, 1946 Italian 1-lira coin and new 1-euro coin.
Illustration reduced.

**2002, Jan. 2   Photo.   Perf. 14x13¼**

| | | | | |
|---|---|---|---|---|
| **2472** | A1275 | Horiz. pair | 2.50 | .90 |
| **a.-b.** | | 41c Either single | 1.25 | .45 |
| **2473** | A1275 | Horiz. pair | 2.50 | .90 |
| **a.-b.** | | 41c Either single | 1.25 | .45 |

Blessed Josemaría Escrivá (1902-75), Founder of Opus Dei A1276

**2002, Jan. 9**
| | | | | |
|---|---|---|---|---|
| **2474** | A1276 | 41c multi | 1.25 | .45 |

Luigi Bocconi and Luigi Bocconi Commercial University, Milan A1277

**2002, Jan. 24**
| | | | | |
|---|---|---|---|---|
| **2475** | A1277 | 41c multi | 1.25 | .45 |

Parma Stamps, 150th Anniv. — A1278

**2002, Jan. 26       Perf. 13¼x14**
| | | | | |
|---|---|---|---|---|
| **2476** | A1278 | 41c No. 1 | 1.25 | .45 |

Intl. Year of Mountains A1279

**2001, Feb. 1**
| | | | | |
|---|---|---|---|---|
| **2477** | A1279 | 41c multi | 1.25 | .45 |

2006 Winter Olympics, Turin — A1280

**2002, Feb. 23**
| | | | | |
|---|---|---|---|---|
| **2478** | A1280 | 41c multi | 1.25 | .45 |

Malato Alla Fonte, Sculpture by Arnolfo de Cambio — A1281

**2002, Mar. 8       Engr.       Perf. 14**
| | | | | |
|---|---|---|---|---|
| **2479** | A1281 | 41c red lilac | 1.25 | .45 |

Tourism A1282

Designs: No. 2480, Venaria Reale. No. 2481, San Gimignano. No. 2482, Sannicandro di Bari. No. 2483, Capo d'Orlando.

**2002, Mar. 23   Photo.   Perf. 14x13¼**
| | | | | |
|---|---|---|---|---|
| **2480** | A1282 | 41c multi | 1.25 | .45 |
| **2481** | A1282 | 41c multi | 1.25 | .45 |
| **2482** | A1282 | 41c multi | 1.25 | .45 |
| **2483** | A1282 | 41c multi | 1.25 | .45 |
| | *Nos. 2480-2483 (4)* | | 5.00 | 1.80 |

Santa Maria Della Grazie Sanctuary, Spezzano Albanese — A1283

**2002, Apr. 3       Engr.       Perf. 14**
| | | | | |
|---|---|---|---|---|
| **2484** | A1283 | 41c red brown | 1.25 | .45 |

State Police, 150th Anniv. A1284

**2002, Apr. 12   Photo.   Perf. 14x13¼**
| | | | | |
|---|---|---|---|---|
| **2485** | A1284 | 41c multi | 1.25 | .45 |

Fr. Matteo Ricci (1552-1610), Missionary in China, Geographer — A1285

**2002, Apr. 20**
| | | | | |
|---|---|---|---|---|
| **2486** | A1285 | 41c multi | 1.25 | .45 |

Europa A1286

**2002, May 4   Photo.   Perf. 14x13¼**
| | | | | |
|---|---|---|---|---|
| **2487** | A1286 | 41c multi | 1.25 | .45 |

Francesco Morosini Naval School, Venice A1287

**2002, May 4**
| | | | | |
|---|---|---|---|---|
| **2488** | A1287 | 41c multi | 1.25 | .45 |

Italian Cinema — A1288

Designs: No. 2489, Umberto D., directed by Vittorio De Sica. No. 2490, Miracle in Milan, written by Cesare Zavattini.

**Litho. & Engr.**

**2002, May 10       Perf. 13¼x14**
| | | | | |
|---|---|---|---|---|
| **2489** | A1288 | 41c multi | 1.25 | .45 |
| **2490** | A1288 | 41c multi | 1.25 | .45 |

Juventus, 2001-02 Italian Soccer Champions A1289

**2002, May 18       Photo.**
| | | | | |
|---|---|---|---|---|
| **2491** | A1289 | 41c multi | 1.25 | .45 |

Giovanni Falcone (1939-92) and Paolo Borsellino (1940-92), Judges Assassinated by Mafia — A1290

**2002, May 23       Perf. 14x13¼**
| | | | | |
|---|---|---|---|---|
| **2492** | A1290 | 62c multi | 1.90 | .75 |

NATO-Russia Summit Meeting, Rome — A1291

**2002, May 28   Photo.   Perf. 14x13¼**
| | | | | |
|---|---|---|---|---|
| **2493** | A1291 | 41c multi | 1.25 | .45 |

World Kayak Championships, Valsesia — A1292

**2002, May 30       Perf. 13¼x14**
| | | | | |
|---|---|---|---|---|
| **2494** | A1292 | 52c multi | 1.50 | .60 |

Italian Military Forces in Peace Missions — A1293

**2002, June 1**
| | | | | |
|---|---|---|---|---|
| **2495** | A1293 | 41c multi | 1.25 | .45 |

Modena Stamps, 150th Anniv. — A1294

**2002, June 1   Photo.   Perf. 13¼x14**
| | | | | |
|---|---|---|---|---|
| **2496** | A1294 | 41c multi | 1.25 | .45 |

Alfredo Binda (1902-86), Cyclist — A1295

**2002, June 14   Photo.   *Perf. 13¼x14***
2497  A1295  41c multi          1.25   .45

St. Pio of Pietrelcina (1887-1968) — A1296

**2002, June 16          *Perf. 14***
2498  A1296  41c multi          1.25   .45

Monument to the Massacre of the Acqui Division — A1297

**2002, June 21          *Perf. 13¼x14***
2499  A1297  41c multi          1.25   .45

The Crucifixion, by Cimabue A1298

**Litho. & Engr.**
**2002, June 22          *Perf. 14***
2500  A1298  €2.58 multi        7.75  3.00

Prefectural Institute, Bicent. A1299

**2002, June 24   Photo.   *Perf. 14x13¼***
2501  A1299  41c multi          1.25   .45

St. Maria Goretti (1890-1902) A1300

**2002, July 6          *Perf. 13¼x14***
2502  A1300  41c multi          1.25   .45

Jules Cardinal Mazarin (1602-61), and Birthplace A1301

**2002, July 13   Photo.   *Perf. 14x13¼***
2503  A1301  41c multi          1.25   .45

Italians Around the World — A1302

**2002, Aug. 8          *Perf. 13¼x14***
2504  A1302  52c multi          1.50   .60

Monument to Sant'Anna di Stazzema Massacre A1303

**2002, Aug. 17**
2505  A1303  41c multi          1.25   .45

UNESCO World Heritage Sites — A1304

Designs: 41c, Pisa. 52c, Aeolian Islands. Illustration reduced.

**2002, Aug. 30          *Perf. 14***
2506  A1304  41c multi + label  1.25   .45
2507  A1304  52c multi + label  1.50   .60

Italian Design A1305

Apparel by: a, Krizia. b, Dolce e Gabbana. c, Gianfranco Ferre. d, Giorgio Armani. e, Laura Biagiotti. f, Prada.

**2002, Aug. 30          Litho.**
2508       Sheet of 6           7.50  7.50
  a.-f.  A1305  41c Any single   1.25   .45

Carlo Alberto Dalla Chiesa (1920-82), Prefect of Palermo Assassinated by Mafia — A1306

**2002. Sept. 3   Photo.   *Perf. 13¼x14***
2509  A1306  41c multi          1.25   .45

Concordia Theater, Monte Castello de Vibio — A1307

**Litho. & Engr.**
**2002, Sept. 7          *Perf. 14***
2510  A1307  41c multi          1.25   .45

Sailboat Gathering, Imperia A1308

**2002, Sept. 11   Photo.   *Perf. 14x13¼***
2511  A1308  41c multi          1.25   .45

Santa Giulia Museum, Brescia — A1309

Palazzo Altemps, Roman Natl. Museum A1310

***Perf. 13¼x14, 14x13¼***
**2002, Oct. 4          Photo.**
2512  A1309  41c multi          1.25   .45
2513  A1310  41c multi          1.25   .45

Roman States Postage Stamps, 150th Anniv. — A1311

**2002, Oct. 4   Photo.   *Perf. 13¼x14***
2514  A1311  41c Roman States
                 #6             1.25   .45

Flora and Fauna — A1312

**2002, Oct. 11**
2515  A1312  23c Orchid          .70   .30
2516  A1312  52c Lynx           1.50   .60
2517  A1312  77c Stag beetle    2.25   .90
  Nos. 2515-2517 (3)            4.45  1.80

World Food Day — A1313

**2002, Oct. 16   Photo.   *Perf. 13¼x14***
2518  A1313  41c multi          1.25   .45

Forestry Corps — A1314

**2002, Oct. 22**
2519  A1314  41c multi          1.25   .45

Father Carlo Gnocchi (1902-56), Founder of Fondazione Pro Juventute A1315

**2002, Oct. 25**
2520  A1315  41c multi          1.25   .45

2002 Muscular Dystrophy Telethon A1316

**2002, Oct. 31          *Perf. 14x13¼***
2521  A1316  41c multi          1.25   .45

Christmas A1317

Designs: 41c, Nativity. 62c, Child with candle, Christmas tree, vert.

***Perf. 14x13¼, 13¼x14***
**2002, Oct. 31          Photo.**
2522  A1317  41c multi          1.25   .45
2523  A1317  62c multi          1.90   .75

Women's Sports — A1318

**2002, Nov. 20   Photo.   *Perf. 13¼x14***
2524  A1318  41c multi          1.25   .45

Stamp Day
A1319

**2002, Nov. 29**     *Perf. 14x13¼*
2525 A1319 62c multi     1.90  .75

2002 World Cup Soccer
Championships, Japan and
Korea — A1320

No. 2526: a, Flags, soccer ball and field
(33mm diameter). b, Soccer player, years of
Italian championships.
Illustration reduced.

**2002, Nov. 29**   Litho.    *Perf. 14*
2526 A1320   Horiz. pair    3.00 1.50
*a.-b.*    52c Either single    1.50  .60

See Argentina No. 2184, Brazil No. 2840,
France No. 2891, Germany No. 2163 and Uruguay No. 1946.

Vittorio Emanuele
Orlando (1860-
1952),
Politician — A1321

**2002, Dec. 4**   Photo.    *Perf. 13¼x14*
2527 A1321 41c multi     1.25  .45

2003 Winter
Universiade
Games,
Tarvisio — A1322

**2003, Jan. 16**   Photo.   *Perf. 13½x14*
2528 A1322 52c multi     1.50  .60

"La Repubblica Italiana" Philatelic
Exhibition, Rome
A1323

**2003, Jan. 16**     *Perf. 14*
2529 A1323 62c multi     1.90  .75
*a.*    Booklet pane of 5    9.50 —
    Complete booklet, #2529a   9.50

World Cyclocross
Championships,
Monopoli — A1324

**2003, Feb. 1**   Photo.   *Perf. 13¼x14*
2530 A1324 41c multi     1.25  .60

Alinari Brothers Photographic Studio,
150th Anniv. — A1325

Illustration reduced.

**2003, Feb. 1**     *Perf. 14x13¼*
2531 A1325 77c multi + label    2.25 1.10

European
Year of the
Disabled
A1326

**2003, Feb. 14**
2532 A1326 41c multi     1.25  .60

World Nordic Skiing Championships,
Val di Fiemme — A1327

**2003, Feb. 18**   Photo.   *Perf. 14x13¼*
2533 A1327 41c multi     1.25  .60

National Civil Service — A1328

**2003, Feb. 25**   Photo.   *Perf. 14x13¼*
2534 A1328 62c multi + label    1.90  .75

Duel of
Barletta,
500th Anniv.
A1329

**2003, Mar. 6**
2535 A1329 41c multi     1.25  .60

Torquato Tasso High School,
Rome — A1330

**2003, Mar. 11**   Photo.    *Perf. 14*
2536 A1330 41c multi     1.25  .60

Encounter
at the
Golden
Door, by
Giotto
A1331

**2003, Mar. 20**     Litho. & Engr.
2537 A1331 41c multi     1.25  .60

Gian Rinaldo Carli High School, Pisino
d'Istria — A1332

**2003, Mar. 24**     Photo.
2538 A1332 41c multi     1.25  .60

Lincei Academy,
400th
Anniv. — A1333

**2003, Mar. 26**     Litho. & Engr.
             *Perf. 13¼x14*
2539 A1333 41c multi     1.25  .60

World Junior Fencing Championships,
Trapani — A1334

**2003, Apr. 4**   Photo.   *Perf. 14x13¼*
2540 A1334 41c multi     1.25  .60

Acquasanta
Golf Club,
Rome,
Cent.
A1335

**2003, Apr. 5**
2541 A1335 77c multi     2.25 1.10

### Tourism Type of 2002

**2003, Apr. 5**
2542 A1282 41c Sestri Levante   1.25  .60
2543 A1282 41c Lanciano    1.25  .60
2544 A1282 41c Procida    1.25  .60
   Nos. 2542-2544 (3)    3.75 1.80

La Sapienza University, Rome, 700th
Anniv. — A1336

**2003, Apr. 10**   Photo.    *Perf. 14*
2545 A1336 41c multi     1.25  .60

Natl. Pasta
Museum,
Rome — A1337

**2003, Apr. 17**     *Perf. 13¼x14*
2546 A1337 41c multi     1.25  .60

Guido Carli Free Intl. University for
Social Studies — A1338

**2003, Apr. 23**   Photo.    *Perf. 14*
2547 A1338 €2.58 multi     7.75 3.75

Europa — A1339

Poster art by Marcello Dudovich: 41c,
Woman in blue dress. 52c, Women in white
dresses.

**2003, May 5**   Photo.   *Perf. 13¼x14*
2548 A1339 41c multi     1.25  .60
2549 A1339 52c multi     1.50  .75

Central
State
Archives,
50th Anniv.
A1340

**2003, May 8**     *Perf. 14x13¼*
2550 A1340 41c multi     1.25  .60

Veronafil
Philatelic
Exhibition,
Verona
A1341

**2003, May 9**
2551 A1341 41c multi     1.25  .60

Aldo Moro (1916-78), Premier — A1342

**2003, May 9** Perf. 13¼x14
2552 A1342 62c multi 1.90 .95

Souvenir Sheet

Antonio Meucci (1808-96), Telephone Pioneer — A1343

**2003, May 28** Litho.
2553 A1343 52c multi 1.50 .75

Father Eugenio Barsanti and Felice Matteucci, Internal Combustion Engine Pioneers A1344

**2003, May 31 Photo.** Perf. 14x13¼
2554 A1344 52c multi 1.50 .75

Post Office, Latina A1345

**2003, June 30 Engr.** Perf. 14
2555 A1345 41c blue 1.25 .60

City of Latina, 70th anniv.

Italian Presidency of the Council of the European Union A1346

**2003, July 1 Photo.** Perf. 14x13¼
2556 A1346 41c multi 1.25 .60

Ezio Vanoni (1903-56), Economist A1347

**2003, July 1** Perf. 13¼x14
2557 A1347 €2.58 multi 7.75 3.75

The Assumption, by Corrado Giaquinto (c. 1694-1765) A1348

**2003, July 2** Perf. 14
2558 A1348 77c multi 2.25 1.10

Eugenio Balzan (1874-1953), Journalist — A1349

**2003, July 15 Photo.** Perf. 14x13¼
2559 A1349 41c multi 1.25 .60

Francesco Mazzola "Il Parmigianino," (1503-40), Painter — A1350

**2003, Aug. 23 Photo.** Perf. 14x14¼
2560 A1350 41c multi 1.25 .60

Juventus, 2002-03 Italian Soccer Champions A1351

**2003, Aug. 30** Perf. 13¼x14
2561 A1351 41c multi 1.25 .60

Abbey of St. Sylvester I, Nonantola — A1352

**Litho. & Engr.**
**2003, Sept. 6** Perf. 14
2562 A1352 41c multi 1.25 .60

Italian Aviation Pioneers A1353

**2003, Sept. 12 Photo.** Perf. 13x13¼
2563 A1353 52c Mario Calderara 1.50 .75
2564 A1353 52c Mario Cobianchi 1.50 .75
2565 A1353 52c Gianni Caproni 1.50 .75
2566 A1353 52c Alessandro
 Marchetti 1.50 .75
a. Souvenir sheet, #2563-2566 6.00 6.00

Giovanni Giolitti (1842-1928), Premier — A1354

**2003, Sept. 13 Photo.** Perf. 14x13¼
2567 A1354 41c multi 1.25 .60

Europalia Italia Festival, Belgium A1355

Designs: 41c, Still Life, by Giorgio Morandi. 52c, 1947 Cisitalia 202, designed by Battista Pininfarina.

**2003, Sept. 13**
2568 A1355 41c multi 1.25 .60
2569 A1355 52c multi 1.50 .75

See Belgium Nos. 1980-1981.

Cent. of First Publication of Leonardo Magazine, by Attilio Vallecchi (1880-1946) A1356

**2003, Sept. 27 Photo.** Perf. 13x13¼
2570 A1356 41c multi 1.25 .60

The Family — A1357

**2003, Oct. 3** Perf. 13¼x13
2571 A1357 77c multi 2.25 1.10

Maestà, by Duccio di Buoninsegna A1358

**2003, Oct. 4**
2572 A1358 41c multi 1.25 .60

Exhibition of paintings by Duccio di Buoninsegna, Siena.

Vittorio Alfieri (1749-1803), Poet — A1359

**2003, Oct. 8** Perf. 13x13¼
2573 A1359 41c multi 1.25 .60

Ugo La Malfa (1903-79), Government Minister — A1360

**2003, Oct. 13** Perf. 13¼x13
2574 A1360 62c multi 1.90 .95

Bernardino Ramazzini (1633-1714), Physician — A1361

**2003, Oct. 15** Perf. 13x13¼
2575 A1361 41c multi 1.25 .60

Confedilizia Property Owner's Organization, 120th Anniv. — A1362

**2003, Oct. 15** Perf. 13¼x13
2576 A1362 €2.58 multi 7.75 3.75

Nativity, by Gian Paolo Cavagna — A1363

Poinsettia A1364

**2003, Oct. 24**
2577 A1363 41c multi 1.25 .60
2578 A1364 62c multi 1.90 .95

Christmas.

Futurist Art by Giacomo Balla A1365

Designs: 41c, Forme Grido Viva L'Italia. 52c, Linee-Forza del Pugno di Boccioni.

**2003, Nov. 26  Photo.  Perf. 13x13¼**
2579  A1365  41c multi            1.25   .60
2580  A1365  52c multi            1.50   .75

Philately Day
A1366

**2003, Nov. 28  Photo.  Perf. 13x13¼**
2581  A1366  41c multi            1.25   .60

**Priority Mail Type of 2001 With Euro Denominations Only**

**Typo. & Silk Screened**
2004            *Serpentine Die Cut 11*
**Self-Adhesive**
**Background Color**
2582  A1242  60c orange
                   (gold
                   frame)         1.75   .85
2583  A1242  80c yellow
                   brown          2.40  1.25
2584  A1242  €1.40 green          4.25  2.00
2585  A1242  €1.50 gray           4.50  2.25
**Photo.**
2585A A1242  60c dull or-
                   ange
                   (bronze
                   frame)         1.75   .85
2585B A1242  80c dull brn
                   (bronze
                   frame)         2.40  1.25
        *Nos. 2582-2585B (6)*    17.05  8.45

Issued: 60c, 1/2; €1.40, 1/10; 80c, €1.50, No. 2585A, 3/19/04. A self-adhesive etiquette is adjacent to each stamp.
The frame has a splotchy appearance on Nos. 2585A and 2585B.
No. 2585A exists dated 2005. Undated examples of No. 2585B were issued in 2008. See No. 2613A.

A1367

Television Transmissions in Italy, 50th Anniv. — A1368

**2004, Jan. 3  Photo.  Perf. 13x13¼**
2586  A1367  41c multi            1.25   .60
2587  A1368  62c multi            1.90   .95

Giorgio La Pira (1904-77), Judge
A1369

**2004, Jan. 9  Photo.  Perf. 13x13¼**
2588  A1369  41c multi            1.25   .60

Genoa, 2004 European Cultural Capital — A1370

**2004, Feb. 12  Photo.  Perf. 13¼x13**
2589  A1370  45c multi            1.25   .60

2006 Winter Olympics, Turin — A1371

Designs: 23c, Santa Maria Assunta Church, Pragelato. 45c, San Pietro Apostolo Church, Bardonecchia. 62c, Mole Antonelliana, Turin. 65c, Fountain, Sauze d'Oulx.

**2004, Mar. 9**
2590  A1371  23c multi             .70   .35
2591  A1371  45c multi            1.25   .60
2592  A1371  62c multi            1.90   .95
2593  A1371  65c multi            1.90   .95
        *Nos. 2590-2593 (4)*       5.75  2.85

Petrarch (1304-74), Poet — A1372

**2004, Mar. 18**
2594  A1372  45c multi            1.25   .60

Giorgio Amarelli Licorice Museum, Rossano — A1373

**2004, Apr. 3                   Perf. 14**
2595  A1373  45c multi            1.25   .60

Road Safety
A1374

Designs: 60c, Car dashboard, traffic signs. 62c, Seat belt, map of Italy, vert.

**2004, Apr. 7   Perf. 13x13¼, 13¼x13**
2596  A1374  60c multi            1.75   .85
2597  A1374  62c multi            1.90   .95

**Tourism Type of 2002**
**2004, Apr. 10  Photo.  Perf. 13x13¼**
2598  A1282  45c Vignola          1.25   .60
2599  A1282  45c Viterbo          1.25   .60
2600  A1282  45c Isole Egadi      1.25   .60
        *Nos. 2598-2600 (3)*       3.75  1.80

Casa del Fascio, Como, Designed by Giuseppe Terragni (1904-43), Architect
A1375

**2004, Apr. 17                 Perf. 13x13¼**
2601  A1375  85c multi            2.50  1.25

**Souvenir Sheet**

Rome-Bangkok Foundation — A1376

No. 2602: a, Wat Saket, Bangkok. b, Colosseum, Rome.

**2004, Apr. 21  Litho.  Perf. 14x13¼**
2602  A1376  Sheet of 2          3.75  3.75
*a.-b.*      65c Either single   1.90   .95
        See Thailand No. 2125.

Martyrdom of St. George, 1700th Anniv. — A1377

**2004, Apr. 23  Photo.  Perf. 14**
2603  A1377  €2.80 multi         8.50  4.25

Europa
A1378

Map of Europe and: 45c, Closed suitcase. 62c, Open suitcase.

**2004, May 7                   Perf. 13x13¼**
2604  A1378  45c multi            1.25   .60
2605  A1378  62c multi            1.90   .95

**Souvenir Sheet**

L'Aquila - Foggia Livestock Trail — A1379

**2004, May 8  Litho.  Perf. 14x13¼**
2606  A1379  45c multi            1.25   .60

Great Synagogue, Rome — A1380

**2004, May 20  Photo.  Perf. 13¼x14**
2607  A1380  60c shown           1.75   .85
2608  A1380  62c Synagogue, diff. 1.90   .95

See Israel Nos. 1564-1565.

Milan, 2003-04 Italian Soccer Champions
A1381

**2004, May 22                  Perf. 13x13¼**
2609  A1381  45c multi            1.25   .60

50th Puccini Festival — A1382

**2004, May 28  Photo.  Perf. 13¼x13**
2610  A1382  60c multi            1.75   .85

University of Turin, 600th Anniv. — A1383

**2004, June 3  Engr.  Perf. 14**
2611  A1383  45c brown           1.25   .60

Achille Varzi (1904-48), Automobile and Motorcycle Racer
A1384

**2004, June 5  Photo.  Perf. 13x13¼**
2612  A1384  45c multi            1.25   .60

Penitentiary Police Corps — A1385

**2004, June 16  Photo.  Perf. 13x13¼**
2613  A1385  45c multi            1.25   .60

## Priority Mail Type of 2001 With Euro Denominations Only
### *Serpentine Die Cut 11*
**2004, June 16**    **Photo.**

**Self-Adhesive**
**Background Color**

| | | | | |
|---|---|---|---|---|
| 2613A | A1242 | €1.40 blue green | 4.25 | 2.00 |
| 2614 | A1242 | €2 slate grn (bronze frame) | 6.00 | 3.00 |
| 2615 | A1242 | €2.20 rose | 6.50 | 3.25 |
| | *Nos. 2613A-2615 (3)* | | 16.75 | 8.25 |

Issued: €2, 6/16; €1.40, July; €2.20, 6/26.
A self-adhesive etiquette is adjacent to each stamp.
No. 2613A has a less obvious coating over the circled "P" that shines most when viewed from an oblique angle. No. 2613A exists dated 2006. Undated examples of No. 2613A were issued in 2007. Undated examples of Nos. 2614 and 2615 were issued in 2008.

Ascent of K2 By Italian Mountaineers, 50th Anniv. — A1386

**2004, July 31**   **Photo.**   *Perf. 13¼x13*
2616   A1386   65c multi    1.90   .95

Italian Regions A1387

**2004, Aug. 27**    *Perf. 14x13¼*

| | | | | |
|---|---|---|---|---|
| 2617 | A1387 | 45c Liguria | 1.25 | .60 |
| 2618 | A1387 | 45c Emilia Romagna | 1.25 | .60 |
| 2619 | A1387 | 45c Abruzzo | 1.25 | .60 |
| 2620 | A1387 | 45c Basilicata | 1.25 | .60 |
| | *Nos. 2617-2620 (4)* | | 5.00 | 2.40 |

Apparition of Madonna of Tirano, 500th Anniv. — A1388

**2004, Sept. 4**    *Perf. 13¼x13*
2621   A1388   45c multi    1.25   .60

St. Nilus of Rossano (c. 905-1005), Abbot — A1389

**2004, Sept. 25**   **Photo.**   *Perf. 14¼x14*
2622   A1389   45c multi    1.25   .60

State Archives, Florence — A1390

**2004, Sept. 30**   **Photo.**   *Perf. 14¼x14*
2623   A1390   45c multi    1.25   .60

Lacemaking — A1391

**2004, Oct. 8**   **Embroidered**   *Imperf.*
**Self-Adhesive**
2624   A1391   €2.80 blue & gray    8.50   4.25

Filo d'Oro Society — A1392

**2004, Oct. 9**   **Photo.**   *Perf. 13¼x13*
2625   A1392   45c multi    1.25   .60

Victor Emmanuel III State Technical Institute, Lucera A1393

**2004, Oct. 16**    *Perf. 14x14¼*
2626   A1393   45c multi    1.25   .60

Father Luigi Guanella (1842-1915) A1394

**2004, Oct. 19**   **Photo.**   *Perf. 13¼x13*
2627   A1394   45c multi    1.25   .60

Return of Trieste to Italy, 50th Anniv. A1395

**2004, Oct. 26**    *Perf. 13x13¼*
2628   A1395   45c multi    1.25   .60
   a.    Booklet pane of 4    5.00   —
     Complete booklet, #2628a    5.00

Military Information and Security Service A1396

**2004, Oct. 27**   **Photo.**   *Perf. 13x13¼*
2629   A1396   60c multi    1.75   .85

European Constitution — A1397

**2004, Oct. 29**
2630   A1397   62c multi    1.90   .95

Venice Dockyards, 900th Anniv. A1398

**2004, Oct. 30**   **Photo.**   *Perf. 13x13¼*
2631   A1398   €2.80 multi    8.50   4.25

Live Nativity Scene, Tricase A1399

**2004, Oct. 30**   **Photo.**   *Perf. 13x13¼*
2632   A1399   45c multi    1.25   .60

Christmas Tree — A1400

**Photo. & Embossed**
*Perf. 13¼x13*
2633   A1400   62c multi    1.90   .95

Hands and Braille Book — A1401

**Photo. & Embossed**
**2004, Nov. 6**    *Perf. 14*
2634   A1401   45c multi    1.25   .60

Martyrdom of St. Lucy, 1700th Anniv. — A1402

**2004, Nov. 6**   **Photo.**   *Perf. 13¼x13*
2635   A1402   45c multi    1.25   .60

Philately Day — A1403

**2004, Nov. 12**    *Perf. 13¼x14*
2636   A1403   45c multi    1.25   .60

Tenth "Sport For All" World Congress A1404

**2004, Nov. 12**   **Photo.**   *Perf. 13¼x13*
2637   A1404   65c multi    1.90   .95

Maria Santissima Assunta Free University, Rome — A1405

**2004, Nov. 15**    *Perf. 14*
2638   A1405   45c multi    1.25   .60

**Souvenir Sheet**

Italian-made Footwear — A1406

No. 2639: a, Woman's shoe by Casadei. b, Men's shoes by Moreschi. c, Men's shoe by Fratelli Rosetti. d, Athletic shoe by Superga.

**2004, Nov. 27**   **Photo.**   *Perf. 13¼x13*
2639   A1406   Sheet of 4    5.00   5.00
   a.-d.    45c Any single    1.25   .60

Italia With Large Numerals — A1407

**Perf. 13¼x13½**
**2005, Jan. 21    Engr.    Unwmk.**
2640 A1407 €1 multi          3.00  1.50
Compare type A1407 with type A1274.

Italian Auto Club, Cent. — A1408

**2005, Jan. 21  Photo.   Perf. 13¼x13**
2648 A1408 45c multi          1.25   .60

Luigi Calabresi (1937-72), Assassinated Police Commissioner A1409

**2005, Jan. 26**
2649 A1409 45c multi  .       1.25   .60

Exodus of Italians From Istria, Fiume and Dalmazia, 60th Anniv. A1410

**2005, Feb. 10  Photo.   Perf. 14x13¼**
2650 A1410 45c multi          1.25   .60

Rotary International, Cent. — A1411

**2005, Feb. 23         Perf. 13¼x14**
2651 A1411 65c multi          1.90   .95

Sassari Brigade A1412

**2005, Mar. 1          Perf. 14x13¼**
2652 A1412 45c multi          1.25   .60

14th Art Quadrennial, Rome — A1413

**2005, Mar. 4**
2653 A1413 45c multi          1.25   .60

**Italian Regions Type of 2004**
**2005, Mar. 18         Perf. 13x13¼**
2654 A1387 45c Lombardy       1.25   .60
2655 A1387 45c Friuli-Venezia
                 Giulia       1.25   .60
2656 A1387 45c Campania       1.25   .60
2657 A1387 45c Calabria       1.25   .60
      Nos. 2654-2657 (4)      5.00  2.40

2006 Winter Olympics, Turin — A1414

Turin Olympics emblem and: 23c, Pinerolo. 45c, Cesana Torinese. 60c, Mascots Neve and Gliz. 62c, Sestriere.

**2005, Mar. 21         Perf. 13¼x13**
2658 A1414 23c multi           .70   .35
2659 A1414 45c multi          1.25   .60
2660 A1414 60c multi          1.75   .85
2661 A1414 62c multi          1.90   .95
      Nos. 2658-2661 (4)      5.60  2.75

Intl. Year of Physics A1415

**2005, Mar. 29         Perf. 14x13¼**
2662 A1415 85c multi          2.50  1.25

Opening of New Milan Fair Complex A1416

**2005, Mar. 31**
2663 A1416 45c multi          1.25   .60

State Railways, Cent. A1417

**2005, Apr. 22  Photo.   Perf. 13x13¼**
2664 A1417 45c multi          1.25   .60

Italian Army — A1418

**2005, Apr. 29         Perf. 13¼x13**
2665 A1418 45c multi          1.25   .60

Europa — A1419

**2005, May 9   Photo.   Perf. 13¼x13**
2666 A1419 45c Wheat          1.10   .55
2667 A1419 62c Grapes         1.90   .95

St. Ignatius of Làconi (1701-81) A1420

**2005, May 11  Photo.   Perf. 13¼x13**
2668 A1420 45c multi          1.25   .60

Commercial Confederation, 60th Anniv. — A1421

**2005, May 18**
2669 A1421 60c multi          1.75   .85

Tommaso Campanella High School, Reggio Calabria — A1422

**2005, May 20  Photo.   Perf. 13x13¼**
2670 A1422 45c multi          1.25   .60

San Giuseppe da Copertino Basilica A1423

**2005, May 21    Engr.    Perf. 14**
2671 A1423 45c blue gray      1.25   .60

Tourism — A1424

**2005, May 26                Photo.**
2672 A1424 45c Asolo          1.25   .60
2673 A1424 45c Rocchetta a Vol-
                 turno        1.25   .60
2674 A1424 45c Amalfi         1.25   .60
      Nos. 2672-2674 (3)      3.75  1.80
See Nos. 2734-2736, 2803-2806, 2887-2890.

St. Gerardo Maiella (1726-55) A1425

**2005, May 28         Perf. 13x13¼**
2675 A1425 45c multi          1.25   .60

Juventus, 2004-05 Italian Soccer Champions A1426

**2005, June 6         Perf. 13¼x13**
2676 A1426 45c multi          1.25   .60

Ratification of Modifications to Italy-Vatican Concordat, 20th Anniv. — A1427

Arms of Vatican City and Italy and: 45c, Map. €2.80, Pen.

**2005, June 9         Perf. 13x13¼**
2677 A1427   45c multi        1.25   .60
2678 A1427 €2.80 multi        8.50  4.25
     See Vatican City Nos. 1301-1302.

First Italian Dirigible Flight by Almerico da Schio, Cent. A1428

**2005, June 17  Photo.  *Perf. 13x13¼***
2679 A1428 €3 multi                          9.00  4.75

European Youth Olympic Festival, Lignano Sabbiadoro — A1429

**2005, June 20  Photo.  *Perf. 13¼x13***
2680 A1429 62c multi                         1.90  .95

Intl. Day Against Illegal Drugs A1430

**2005, June 25  Photo.  *Perf. 13x13¼***
2681 A1430 45c multi                         1.25  .60

Institute for Maritime Trades Social Insurance A1431

**2005, June 28**
2682 A1431 45c multi                         1.25  .60

Leo Longanesi (1905-57), Writer — A1432

**2005, Aug. 26  Engr.  *Perf. 13¼x14***
2683 A1432 45c dark blue                     1.25  .60

Alberto Ascari (1918-55), Race Car Driver A1433

**2005, Sept. 2  Photo.  *Perf. 13x13¼***
2684 A1433 €2.80 multi                       8.50  4.25

A1434

National Military Aerobatic Team A1435

**2005, Sept. 3  Photo.  *Perf. 13x13¼***
2685 A1434 45c multi                         1.25  .60
2686 A1435 60c multi                         1.75  .85

Pietro Savorgnan di Brazzà (1852-1905), Explorer of Africa — A1436

**2005, Sept. 14  Photo.  *Perf. 13¼x13***
2687 A1436 45c multi                         1.25  .60

Guido Gonella (1905-82), Politician, Journalist A1437

**2005, Sept. 17**
2688 A1437 45c multi                         1.25  .60

Italian Participation in Exploration of Mars — A1438

**Photo. With Hologram Applied**
**2005, Sept. 21             *Die Cut***
**Self-Adhesive**
2689 A1438 80c multi                         2.40  1.25
Printed in sheets of 4.

Intercultura, 50th Anniv. — A1439

**2005, Sept. 23  Photo.  *Perf. 13x13¼***
2690 A1439 60c multi                         1.75  .85

Louis Vuitton Cup Acts 8 & 9 (Races to Determine America's Cup Challenger), Trapani — A1440

**2005, Sept. 28  Photo.  *Perf. 13¼x13***
2691 A1440 €2.80 multi                       8.50  4.25

**Priority Mail Type of 2001 With Euro Denominations Only**
**2005  Photo.  *Serpentine Die Cut 11***
**Self-Adhesive**
**Inscribed "I. P. Z. S.  S. p. A. - ROMA 2005" at Bottom**
**Background Color**
2691A A1242      62c yellow         1.90  .95
2691B A1242      €1.50 gray         4.50  2.25
  Issued: 62c, Oct.; €1.50, Dec.
  Nos. 2466 and 2585 have different printer's inscriptions and have a more easily seen coating over the circled "P" than on Nos. 2691A and 2691B. The coating over the circled "P" on Nos. 2691A and 2691B shines most when viewed from an oblique angle. A self-adhesive etiquette is adjacent to each stamp. Nos. 2691A and 2691B have self-adhesive selvage surrounding the stamp and etiquette. This selvage is not found on Nos. 2466 and 2585.
  Mo. 2691B exists without year date and without etiquette, issued in 2007.

Stamp Day — A1441

**2005, Oct. 7  Photo.  *Perf. 13¼x13***
2692 A1441 45c multi                         1.25  .60

Italian Organ Donation Association A1442

**2005, Oct. 7  Photo.  *Perf. 13¼x13***
2693 A1442 60c multi                         1.75  .85

National Association of Communities A1443

**2005, Oct. 19**
2694 A1443 45c multi                         1.25  .60

Story of Sts. Stephan and John The Baptist, by Fra Filippo Lippi A1444

**2005, Oct. 25            *Perf. 13x13¼***
2695 A1444 45c shown           1.25  .60
2696 A1444 €1.50 Four men      4.50  2.25

A1445

Christmas A1446

**2005, Oct. 31  Photo.  *Perf. 13x13¼***
2697 A1445 45c multi                         1.25  .60
              ***Perf. 13¼x13***
2698 A1446 62c multi                         1.90  .95

Alcide De Gasperi (1881-1954), Prime Minister — A1447

**2005, Nov. 9  Photo.  *Perf. 13¼x13***
2699 A1447 62c multi                         1.90  .95

Giuseppe Mazzini (1805-72), Revolution Leader A1448

**2005, Nov. 10  Photo.  *Perf. 13x13¼***
2700 A1448 45c multi                         1.25  .60

National Civil Protection A1449

**2005, Nov. 16  Photo.  *Perf. 13¼x13***
2701 A1449 45c multi                         1.25  .60

Italian Red Cross — A1450

2005, Nov. 16
2702 A1450 45c multi          1.25   .60

Admission to United Nations, 50th Anniv. A1451

2005, Nov. 23          Perf. 13x13¼
2703 A1451 70c multi          2.10  1.00

Popes Reigning in 2005 A1452

Designs: 45c, Pope John Paul II (1920-2005). 65c, Pope Benedict XVI.

2005, Nov. 26  Photo.  Perf. 13x13¼
2704 A1452 45c multi          1.25   .60
2705 A1452 65c multi          1.90   .95

Reconstitution of Caserta Province, 60th Anniv. — A1453

2005, Dec. 5  Photo.  Perf. 13x13¼
2706 A1453 45c .multi          1.25   .60

Opening of Enrico Toti Submarine Exhibit at Natl. Museum of Science and Technology, Milan A1454

2005, Dec. 7
2707 A1454 82c multi          2.40  1.25

Eighteenth Birthday Greetings A1455

2006, Jan. 1  Photo.  Perf. 13½x13
2708 A1455 45c blue & multi   1.25   .60
2709 A1455 45c pink & multi   1.25   .60
Souvenir sheets of 1 of redrawn stamps similar to Nos. 2708-2709 exist from a limited printing.

Panini, Soccer Card and Sticker Creators A1456

2006, Jan. 30  Photo.  Perf. 13x13¼
2710 A1456 €2.80 multi          8.50  4.25

Quattroruote Magazine, 50th Anniv. — A1457

2006, Feb. 1          Perf. 13¼x13
2711 A1457 62c multi          1.90   .95

Carlo Bo University, Urbino, 500th Anniv. — A1458

Ernesto Cairoli State High School, Varese — A1459

Alessandron Tassoni State Science High School, Modena — A1460

Agostino Nifo State High School, Sessa Aurunca — A1461

2006, Feb. 6
2712 A1458 45c multi          1.25   .60
2713 A1459 45c multi          1.25   .60
2714 A1460 45c multi          1.25   .60
2715 A1461 45c multi          1.25   .60
    Nos. 2712-2715 (4)        5.00  2.40

2006 Winter Olympics, Turin A1462

2006, Feb. 8          Perf. 13x13¼
2716 A1462 23c Biathlon        .70   .35
2717 A1462 45c Figure
               skating       1.25   .60
2718 A1462 65c Ice hockey     1.90   .95
2719 A1462 70c Curling        2.10  1.00
2720 A1462 85c Bobsled        2.50  1.25
2721 A1462 90c Alpine ski-
               ing           2.75  1.90
2722 A1462 €1 Torch          3.00  1.50
2723 A1462 €1.30 Luge        4.00  2.00
2724 A1462 €1.70 Medals      5.00  2.50
  a.    Souvenir sheet, #2716-
         2724                24.00 12.00
    Nos. 2716-2724 (9)       23.20 12.05

Nos. 23, 45, 79 and 239 — A1463

2006, Feb. 9  Photo.  Perf. 13¼x13
2725 A1463 60c multi          1.75   .85
  a.    Booklet pane of 4    7.00   —
         Complete booklet, #2725a  7.00
    Kingdom of Italy Stamp Show, Rome.

Dalmatian Historical Society, 80th Anniv. A1464

2006, Feb. 10  Engr.  Perf. 13x13¼
2726 A1464 45c red vio & dk bl  1.25   .60

Detail of Fresco From Mantua Castle Bridal Chamber, by Andrea Mantegna (1431-1506) — A1465

2006, Feb. 25  Photo.  Perf. 13x13¼
2727 A1465 45c multi          1.25   .60

2006 Winter Paralympics, Turin — A1466

2006, Mar. 9          Perf. 13¼x13
2728 A1466 60c multi          1.75   .85

Items Made in Italy A1467

2006, Mar. 11          Perf. 13x13¼
2729 A1467 60c Gelato         1.75   .85
2730 A1467 €2.80 Carrara mar-
               ble           8.50  4.25

National Singers Association, 25th Anniv. — A1468

2006, Mar. 17
2731 A1468 45c multi          1.25   .60

Aircraft Carrier "Cavour" A1469

2006, Mar. 17
2732 A1469 60c multi          1.75   .85

Opening of Sempione Tunnel — A1470

2006, Mar. 18          Perf. 13¼x13
2733 A1470 62c multi          1.90   .95

Tourism Type of 2005
2006, Mar. 24
2734 A1424 45c Lago di Como   1.25   .60
2735 A1424 45c Marina di Pie-
               trasanta       1.25   .60
2736 A1424 45c Pozzuoli       1.25   .60
    Nos. 2734-2736 (3)        3.75  1.80

Intl. Day of Mountains A1471

**2006, Mar. 30**
2737 A1471 60c multi      1.75 .85

Madonna and Child Icon, Mondragone Basilica — A1472

**2006, Apr. 1**
2738 A1472 45c multi      1.25 .60

First Vote for Italian Citizens Abroad — A1473

**2006, Apr. 3**    *Perf. 13¼x13*
2739 A1473 62c multi      1.90 .95

"Two Republics" Philatelic Exhibition A1474

**2006, Apr. 5 Photo.**   *Perf. 13x13¼*
2740 A1474 62c multi      1.90 .95
    **a.**    Souvenir sheet, #2740, San
        Marino #1676a     4.00 4.00

See San Marino No. 1676. On No. 2740a, the Italian stamp is on the left. On San Marino No. 1676, the Italian stamp is on the right. Both stamps in No. 2740a have text printed on reverse.

Matterhorn Ski School, 70th Anniv. — A1475

**2006, Apr. 13 Photo.**   *Perf. 13¼x13*
2741 A1475 45c multi      1.25 .60

Madonna of Humility, by Gentile da Fabriano A1476

**2006, Apr. 20 Photo.**   *Perf. 13x13¼*
2742 A1476 €2.80 multi      8.50 4.50

Il Giorno Newspaper, 50th Anniv. — A1477

**2006, Apr. 21**    *Perf. 13¼x13*
2743 A1477 45c multi      1.25 .60

Constitutional Court, 50th Anniv. — A1478

**2006, Apr. 22**         **Engr.**
2744 A1478 45c blue      1.25 .60

Enrico Mattei (1906-62), Public Administrator A1479

**2006, Apr. 29 Photo.**   *Perf. 13¼x13*
2745 A1479 45c multi      1.25 .60

**Italian Regions Type of 2004**

**2006, Apr. 29**      *Perf. 13x13¼*
2746 A1387 45c Piedmont    1.25 .60
2747 A1387 45c Tuscany    1.25 .60
2748 A1387 45c Lazio    1.25 .60
2749 A1387 45c Puglia    1.25 .60
    *Nos. 2746-2749 (4)*    5.00 2.40

Targa Floria Automobile Race Track, Cent. — A1480

**2006, May 6 Photo.**   *Perf. 13¼x13*
2750 A1480 60c multi      1.75 .85

Christopher Columbus (1451-1506), Explorer — A1481

**2006, May 6 Photo.**   *Perf. 13x13¼*
2751 A1481 62c multi      1.90 .95

Europa A1482

People sitting on wall: 45c, View of faces. 62c, View of backs.

**2006, May 8**
2752 A1482 45c multi      1.25 .60
2753 A1482 62c multi      1.90 .95

General Assembly of Intl. Military Sport Council, Rome A1483

**2006, May 9**
2754 A1483 45c multi      1.25 .60

2006 World Team Chess Championships, Turin — A1484

**2006, May 20 Photo.**   *Perf. 13¼x13*
2755 A1484 62c multi      1.90 .95

Constituent Assembly, 60th Anniv. A1485

**2006, June 1**      *Perf. 13x13¼*
2756 A1485 60c multi      1.75 .85

Woman Suffrage, 60th Anniv. — A1486

**2006, June 1**      *Perf. 13¼x13*
2757 A1486 60c multi      1.75 .85

2006 World Bridge Championships, Verona — A1487

**2006, June 9**      *Perf. 13x13¼*
2758 A1487 65c multi      1.90 .95

Salto di Quirra Proving Grounds, 50th Anniv. — A1488

**2006, June 13**      *Perf. 13¼x13*
2759 A1488 60c multi      1.75 .85

Customs Department General Headquarters, Cent. — A1489

Customs Cadet Legion, Cent. A1490

**2006, June 21**      *Perf. 13¼x13*
2760 A1489 60c multi      1.75 .85
            *Perf. 13x13¼*
2761 A1490 60c multi      1.75 .85

Reopening of Greek Theater, Tindari, 50th Anniv. — A1491

**2006, July 6**      *Perf. 13¼x13*
2762 A1491 €1.50 multi      4.50 2.25

Autostrada del Sole, 50th Anniv. A1492

**2006, July 10**      *Perf. 13x13¼*
2763 A1492 60c multi      1.75 .85

Terrorist Bombing in Bologna, 26th Anniv. — A1493

**2006, Aug. 2**     **Perf. 13¼x13**
2764 A1493 60c multi    1.75 .85

Italian Philatelic Union, 40th Anniv. — A1494

Illustration reduced.

**2006, Sept. 1**     **Perf. 13x13¼**
2765 A1494 60c multi + label    1.75 .85

St. Gregory the Great (540-604) A1495

**2006, Sept. 2**     **Perf. 13¼x13**
2766 A1495 60c multi    1.75 .85

Victory of Italian 2006 World Cup Soccer Team A1496

**2006, Sept. 9**   **Photo.**   **Perf. 13x13¼**
2767 A1496 €1 multi    3.00 1.50

Victims of Terrorism A1497

**2006, Sept. 16**
2768 A1497 60c multi    1.75 .85

Ettore Majorana (1906-38?), Physicist A1498

**2006, Sept. 18**     **Perf. 13¼x13**
2769 A1498 60c multi    1.75 .85

Saints A1499

Designs: No. 2770, St. Ignatius of Loyola (1491-1556). No. 2771, St. Francis Xavier (1506-52).

**2006, Sept. 27**     **Perf. 13x13¼**
2770 A1499 60c multi    1.75 .85
2771 A1499 60c multi    1.75 .85

World Fencing Championships, Turin — A1500

**2006, Sept. 29**
2772 A1500 65c multi    1.90 .95

Lottery, 500th Anniv. A1501

**2006, Oct. 6**   **Photo.**   **Perf. 13x13¼**
2773 A1501 60c multi    1.75 .85

Philately Day A1502

**2006, Oct. 6**
2774 A1502 60c multi    1.75 .85

Land and Marine Area Protection System A1503

**2006, Oct. 6**
2775 A1503 65c multi    1.90 .95

Luchino Visconti (1906-76), Film Director — A1504

**2006, Oct. 13**     **Perf. 13¼x13**
2776 A1504 60c multi    1.75 .85

Dino Buzzati (1906-72), Writer A1505

**2006, Oct. 16**     **Perf. 13x13¼**
2777 A1505 60c multi    1.50 .75

Adoration of the Magi, by Jacopo Bassano A1506

Christmas Tree — A1507

**2006, Oct. 28**   **Engr.**   **Perf. 13x13¼**
2778 A1506 60c rose    1.60 .80
         **Photo.**
      **Perf. 13¼x13**
2779 A1507 65c multi    1.75 .85

Vittoriano Building, Tomb of the Unknown Soldier, Rome A1508

**2006, Nov. 11**   **Photo.**   **Perf. 13x13¼**
2780 A1508 60c multi    1.60 .80

Cathedral of St. Evasius, Casale Monteferrato — A1509

**2007, Jan. 4**   **Engr.**   **Perf. 13x13¼**
2781 A1509 60c rose    1.60 .80

First Montessori School, Cent. — A1510

**2007, Jan. 5**   **Photo.**   **Perf. 13¼x13**
2782 A1510 60c multi    1.60 .80

School for Public Administration, 50th Anniv. — A1511

**2007, Jan. 10**   **Photo.**   **Perf. 13x13¼**
2783 A1511 65c multi    1.75 .85

Parma Cathedral — A1512

**2007, Jan. 13**   **Engr.**   **Perf. 13¼x13**
2784 A1512 60c green    1.60 .80

Arturo Toscanini (1867-1957), Conductor A1513

**2007, Jan. 16**     **Photo.**
2785 A1513 60c multi    1.60 .80

St. Francis of Paola (1416-1507) — A1514

**2007, Jan. 27**     **Perf. 13x13¼**
2786 A1514 60c multi    1.60 .80

Ferrante Gonzaga (1507-57), Soldier A1515

**2007, Jan. 27**
2787 A1515 €1 multi    2.60 1.40

Antonio Genovesi Salerno Foundation, 20th Anniv. — A1516

**2007, Jan. 29**   **Photo.**   **Perf. 13¼x13**
2788 A1516 60c multi    1.60 .80

Relocation of Istrian Area Refugees to Giuliana di Fertilia District, Sardinia, 60th Anniv.
A1517

**2007, Feb. 10** **Photo.** **Perf. 13x13¼**
2789 A1517 60c multi 1.60 .80

Father Lodovico Acernese (1835-1916)
A1518

**2007, Feb. 16** **Photo.** **Perf. 13¼x13**
2790 A1518 23c multi .60 .30

Giosuè Carducci (1835-1907), 1906 Nobel Laureate in Literature — A1519

**2007, Feb. 16** **Photo.** **Perf. 13x13¼**
2791 A1519 60c multi 1.60 .80

University of Brescia — A1520

**2007, Feb. 26** **Perf. 13¼x13**
2792 A1520 60c multi 1.60 .80

European Equal Opportunity Year — A1521

**2007, Mar. 1** **Photo.** **Perf. 13¼x13**
2793 A1521 60c multi 1.60 .80

Scipione Maffei State High School, Verona — A1522

**2007, Mar. 14** **Photo.** **Perf. 13¼x13**
2794 A1522 60c multi 1.60 .80

Nicolò Carosio (1907-84), Radio Sportscaster — A1523

**2007, Mar. 15** **Perf. 13x13¼**
2795 A1523 65c multi 1.75 .85

### Italian Regions Type of 2004

**2007, Mar. 16** **Photo.** **Perf. 13x13¼**
2796 A1387 60c Trentino-Alto Adige 1.60 .80
2797 A1387 60c Marche 1.60 .80
2798 A1387 60c Umbria 1.60 .80
2799 A1387 60c Sardinia 1.60 .80
Nos. 2796-2799 (4) 6.40 3.20

Venice, UNESCO World Heritage Site — A1524

**2007, Mar. 16** **Engr.** **Perf. 13¼x13**
2800 A1524 60c black 1.60 .80

Intl. Electrotechnical Commission A1525

**2007, Mar. 16** **Photo.** **Perf. 13x13¼**
2801 A1525 €1.50 multi 4.00 2.00

Souvenir Sheet

Treaty of Rome, 50th Anniv. — A1526

**2007, Mar. 25** **Photo.** **Perf. 13x13¼**
2802 A1526 Sheet of 2 3.50 3.50
a. 60c Stars and "50" 1.60 .80
b. 65c "Insieme dal 1957" 1.75 .85

### Tourism Type of 2005

**2005, Apr. 13** **Perf. 13¼x13**
2803 A1424 60c Brunico-Bruneck 1.75 .85
2804 A1424 60c Gaeta 1.75 .85
2805 A1424 60c Massafra 1.75 .85
2806 A1424 60c Cattolica Er-aclea 1.75 .85
Nos. 2803-2806 (4) 7.00 3.40

Giuseppe Tomasi di Lampedusa (1896-1957), Writer — A1527

**2007, Apr. 14** **Photo.** **Perf. 13¼x13**
2807 A1527 60c multi 1.75 .85

Forum, Rome A1528

**2007, Apr. 21** **Perf. 13x13¼**
2808 A1528 60c multi 1.75 .85

Europa — A1529

Scouts: 60c, In canoe. 65c, At campfire.

**2007, Apr. 23** **Perf. 13¼x13**
2809 A1529 60c multi 1.75 .85
2810 A1529 65c multi 1.90 .95
a. Souvenir sheet, #2809-2810 3.75 1.90

Duccio Galamberti (1906-44), World War II Resistance Leader — A1530

**2007, Apr. 24**
2811 A1530 60c multi 1.75 .85

School of Economics and Finance, Rome, 50th Anniv. A1531

**2007, Apr. 27** **Perf. 13x13¼**
2812 A1531 €2.80 multi 7.75 3.75

Cinecittà Film Studios, Rome, 70th Anniv. A1532

**2007, Apr. 28**
2813 A1532 65c multi 1.75 .85

Polirone Monastery, San Benedetto Po, 1000th Anniv. — A1533

**2007, May 5** **Engr.** **Perf. 13¼x13**
2814 A1533 60c blue & blk 1.60 .80

Malatesta Castle, Montefiore Conca — A1534

**2007, May 12**
2815 A1534 60c brown 1.60 .80

Bancarella Musica Folk Music Project — A1535

**2007, May 23** **Photo.**
2816 A1535 60c multi 1.60 .80

Emblem of Lamborghini Automobiles A1536

**2007, May 23**
2817 A1536 85c multi 2.40 1.25

F. C. Internazionale, 2006-07 Italian Soccer Champions A1537

**2007, June 4** **Photo.** **Perf. 13¼**
2818 A1537 60c multi 1.60 .80

Chianca Dolmen — A1538

**2007, June 9   Engr.   Perf. 13¼x13**
2819 A1538 60c brown          1.75   .85

Luigi Ganna, (1883-1957), Cyclist — A1539

**2007, June 9   Photo.   Perf. 13¼x13**
2820 A1539 60c multi          1.60   .80

Altiero Spinelli (1907-86), Writer and Politician A1540

**2007, June 21          Perf. 13x13¼**
2821 A1540 60c multi          1.60   .80

Two Worlds Festival, 50th Anniv. A1541

**2007, June 29   Photo.   Perf. 13x13¼**
2822 A1541 60c multi          1.75   .85

San Vincenzo Basilica, Galliano — A1542

**2007, July 2   Litho.   Rouleted 7**
**On Wood Veneer**
**Self-Adhesive**
2823 A1542 €2.80 black        7.75  3.75

Fiat 500 Automobile A1543

**2007, July 4   Photo.   Perf. 13x13¼**
2824 A1543 60c multi          1.75   .85

Giuseppe Garibaldi (1807-82), Patriot A1544

**2007, July 4**
2825 A1544 65c multi          1.90   .95

Capt. Maurizio Poggiali (1965-97), Pilot A1545

**2007, July 6**
2826 A1545 60c multi          1.75   .85

Roman Speleology Club A1546

**2007, July 9**
2827 A1546 €1.40 multi        4.00  2.00

Primo Carnera (1906-67), Boxer A1547

**2007, July 13**
2828 A1547 60c multi          1.75   .85

Marco Foscarini School, Venice — A1548

St. Pius V Institute for Political Studies, Rome — A1549

Salerno Medical College — A1550

**2007, Sept. 17   Photo.   Perf. 13¼x13**
2829 A1548 60c multi          1.75   .85
2830 A1549 60c multi          1.75   .85
2831 A1550 60c multi          1.75   .85
    Nos. 2829-2831 (3)        5.25  2.55

Protected Donkey Breeds A1551

**2007, Sept. 22          Perf. 13x13¼**
2832 A1551 60c multi          1.75   .85

31st European Women's Basketball Championships A1552

**2007, Sept. 22          Perf. 13¼x13**
2833 A1552 65c multi          1.90   .95

Sacra di San Michele Abbey, Sant'Ambroglio di Torino — A1553

**2007, Sept. 29          Engr.**
2834 A1553 60c red brown      1.75   .85

Concetto Marchesi (1878-1957), Historian A1554

**2007, Oct. 1          Photo.**
2835 A1554 60c multi          1.75   .85

Jacopo Barozzi (Il Vignola) (1507-73), Architect A1555

**2007, Oct. 1          Perf. 13x13¼**
2836 A1555 €2.80 multi        8.00  4.00

Grandparent's Day — A1556

**2007, Oct. 2**
2837 A1556 60c multi          1.75   .85

Philately Day — A1557

**2007, Oct. 12          Perf. 13¼x13**
2838 A1557 60c multi          1.75   .85

Cupid and Psyche, Sculpture by Antonio Canova (1757-1822) — A1558

**2007, Oct. 12   Engr.   Perf. 13x13¼**
2839 A1558 €1.50 black        4.25  2.10

Miniature Sheet

Entertainers — A1559

No. 2840: a, Beniamino Gigli (1890-1957), opera singer. b, Maria Callas (1923-77), opera singer. c, Amedeo Nazzari (1907-79), actor.

**2007, Oct. 18   Photo.   Perf. 13¼x13**
2840 A1559   Sheet of 3       5.25  2.60
a.-c.        60c Any single   1.75   .85

Giuseppe Di Vittorio (1892-1957), Union Leader — A1560

**2007, Nov. 3          Perf. 13x13¼**
2841 A1560 60c multi          1.75   .85

Mondadori Publishing House, Cent. A1561

**2007, Nov. 12**
2842 A1561 60c multi     1.75 .85

Madonna and Child, by Giovan Battista Cima da Conegliano A1562

Snow-covered House and Trees — A1563

**2007, Nov. 20 Engr. Perf. 13¼x13**
2843 A1562 60c green     1.75 .85
    **Photo.**
2844 A1563 65c multi     1.90 .95
    Christmas.

Italian 2007-08 Term on UN Security Council A1564

**2007, Dec. 1 Photo. Perf. 13x13¼**
2845 A1564 85c multi     2.50 1.25

Governor's Palace, Fiume (Rijeka, Croatia) A1565

**2007, Dec. 10**
2846 A1565 65c multi     1.90 .95

Italian Constitution, 60th Anniv. — A1566

**2008, Jan. 2 Perf. 13¼x13**
2847 A1566 60c multi     1.75 .90

Italian Red Cross Volunteer Nursing Corps, Cent. — A1567

**2008, Jan. 29**
2848 A1567 60c multi     1.75 .90

Amintore Fanfani (1908-99), Politician A1568

**2008, Feb. 6 Perf. 13x13¼**
2849 A1568 €1 multi     3.00 1.50

Italian Stock Exchange, Bicent. — A1569

**2008, Feb. 8 Perf. 13¼x13**
2850 A1569 65c multi     2.00 1.00

Olivetti Typewriter and First Olivetti Factory A1570

**2008, Feb. 12 Perf. 13¼x13**
2851 A1570 60c multi     1.90 .95
    Olivetti Corporation, Cent.

Villa Reale, Monza, Designed by Giuseppe Piermarini A1571

**2008, Feb. 18 Engr. Perf. 13¼x13**
2852 A1571 €1.40 black & blue     4.25 2.10

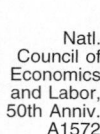

Natl. Council of Economics and Labor, 50th Anniv. A1572

**2008, Feb. 20 Photo.**
2853 A1572 €1.50 multi     4.75 2.40

Dorando Pietri (1885-1942), Marathon Runner — A1573

**2008, Feb. 23**
2854 A1573 60c multi     1.90 .95

    Souvenir Sheet

Song, "Nel Blu, Dipinto di Blu," 50th Anniv. — A1574

**2008, Feb. 25 Perf. 13¼x13**
2855 A1574 60c multi     1.90 .95

Anna Magnani (1908-73), Actress — A1575

**2008, Mar. 7**
2856 A1575 60c multi     1.90 .95

Emblem of Ricordi Publishing House and La Scala Theater, Milan A1576

**2008, Mar. 7 Photo. Perf. 13¼x13**
2857 A1576 60c indigo & gray     1.90 .95
    Ricordi Music Publishing House, bicent.

Italia 2009 Intl. Philatelic Exhibition, Rome — A1577

Exhibition emblem and: 60c, Congress Center. 65c, Colosseum.

**2008, Mar. 7 Photo. Perf. 13¼x13**
2858 A1577 60c multi     1.90 .95
2859 A1577 65c multi     2.00 1.00

Carlo Combi High School, Capodistria — A1578,

**2008, Mar. 8**
2860 A1578 60c multi     1.90 .95

Edmondo de Amicis (1846-1908), Writer — A1579

**2008, Mar. 11 Photo. Perf. 13¼x13**
2861 A1579 60c multi     1.90 .95

Self-portrait, by Bernardino di Betto (Pintoricchio, c. 1454-1513) — A1580

**2008, Mar. 14 Perf. 13x13¼**
2862 A1580 60c multi     1.90 .95

Running of the Madonna, Sulmona — A1581

**2008, Mar. 15 Perf. 13¼x13**
2863 A1581 60c multi     1.90 .95

Italian Rowing Federation, 120th Anniv. A1582

**2008, Mar. 31 Photo. Perf. 13¼x13**
2864 A1582 65c multi     2.10 1.10

Confirmation of the Rule, by
Giotto — A1583

**2008, Apr. 16  Photo.  Perf. 13x13¼**
2865 A1583 60c multi  1.90 .95
Rule of life of St. Francis of Assisi, 700th
anniv.

Rome
A1584

**2008, Apr. 21**
2866 A1584 60c multi  1.90 .95

Italian National
Press Federation,
Cent. — A1585

**2008, Apr. 23  Perf. 13¼x13**
2867 A1585 60c multi  1.90 .95

Flight,
Sculpture
by
Pasquale
Basile
A1586

**2008, Apr. 23  Perf. 13x13¼**
2868 A1586 €1.40 multi  4.50 2.25
Intl. Decade of Education for Sustainable
Development.

Giovannino
Guareschi (1908-
68), Journalist
A1587

**2008, May 1  Photo.  Perf. 13¼x13**
2869 A1587 60c multi  1.90 .95

Ludovico Geymonat (1908-91),
Philosopher — A1588

**2008, May 8  Perf. 13x13¼**
2870 A1588 60c multi  1.90 .95

Europa — A1589

Designs: 60c, Red mailbox. 65c, Brown
mailbox.

**2008, May 9  Photo.  Perf. 13¼x13**
2871 A1589 60c multi  1.90 .95
2872 A1589 65c multi  2.00 1.00

Works of
Andrea
Palladio
(1508-80),
Architect
A1590

Designs: 60c, Alpini Bridge, Bassano. 65c,
Palladian Basilica, Vicenza.

**2008, May 10  Engr.  Perf. 13x13¼**
2873 A1590 60c multi  1.90 .95
2874 A1590 65c multi  2.10 1.10

St. Francis Caracciolo (1563-
1608) — A1591

**2008, May 23  Photo.  Perf. 13x13¼**
2875 A1591 60c multi  1.90 .95

**Italian Regions Type of 2004**
**2008, May 23  Photo.  Perf. 13x13¼**
2876 A1387 60c Valle d'Aosta  1.90 .95
2877 A1387 60c Veneto  1.90 .95
2878 A1387 60c Molise  1.90 .95
2879 A1387 60c Sicily  1.90 .95
  Nos. 2876-2879 (4)  7.60 3.80

Guastalla School, Monza — A1592

**2008, May 24  Photo.  Perf. 13¼x13**
2880 A1592 60c dk & lt blue  1.90 .95

Ducati Desmosedici GP7
Motorcycle — A1593

**2008, May 31  Perf. 13x13¼**
2881 A1593 60c multi  1.90 .95

Giacomo Puccini
(1858-1924),
Composer
A1594

**2008, June 21  Photo.  Perf. 13¼x13**
2882 A1594 €1.50 multi  4.75 2.40

F. C. Internazionale, 2007-08 Italian
Soccer Champions — A1595

**2008, July 4  Photo.  Perf. 13x13¼**
2883 A1595 60c multi  1.90 .95

2008
Summer
Olympics,
Beijing
A1596

Olympic rings and: 60c, Torch bearer and
map. 85c, Greek and Chinese athletes.

**2008, July 7  Photo.  Perf. 13x13¼**
2884 A1596 60c multi  1.90 .95
2885 A1596 85c multi  2.75 1.40

Tommaso
Landolfi
(1908-79),
Writer
A1597

**2008, July 19  Photo.  Perf. 13x13¼**
2886 A1597 60c multi  1.90 .95

**Tourism Type of 2005**
**2008, July 24  Photo.  Perf. 13¼x13**
2887 A1424 60c Tre Cime di
  Lavaredo  1.90 .95
2888 A1424 60c Introdacqua  1.90 .95
2889 A1424 60c Casamicciola
  Terme  1.90 .95
2890 A1424 60c Mamoiada  1.90 .95
  Nos. 2887-2890 (4)  7.60 3.80

Bowl of Saffron and
Crocuses — A1598

Ingredients for Spaghetti
all'Amatriciana — A1599

**2008  Photo.  Perf. 13¼x13**
2891 A1598 60c multi  1.90 .95
**Perf. 13x13¼**
2892 A1599 60c multi  1.90 .95
Issued: No. 2891, 7/26; No. 2892, 8/29.

Bell Tower,
Treviglio
A1600

**2008, Aug. 30  Engr.  Perf. 13x13¼**
2893 A1600 60c multi  1.75 .85

Dante Alighieri High School,
Gorizia — A1601

Seal of the University of
Perugia — A1602

**2008, Sept. 8  Photo.  Perf. 13¼x13**
2894 A1601 60c multi  1.75 .85
2895 A1602 60c multi  1.75 .85

Cesare Pavese
(1908-50),
Writer — A1603

**2008, Sept. 9**
2896 A1603 65c multi  1.90 .95

Alberico Gentili (1552-1608), Jurist — A1604

**2008, Sept. 13**    *Perf. 13x13¼*
2897 A1604 65c multi    1.90   .95

Malatestiana Library, Cesena — A1605

**2008, Sept. 19 Engr.**    *Perf. 13¼x13*
2898 A1605 60c black    1.75   .85

World Road Cycling Championships, Varese — A1606

**2008, Sept. 22 Photo.**    *Perf. 13x13¼*
2899 A1606 60c multi    1.75   .85

Philately Day — A1607

**2008, Oct. 10**    *Perf. 13¼x13*
2900 A1607 60c multi    1.60   .80

Italia 2009 Intl. Philatelic Exhibition, Rome A1608

**2008, Oct. 10 Photo.**    *Perf. 13x13¼*
2901 A1608 85c multi    2.40 1.25

**Litho. on Gold Foil**
**Self-Adhesive**
***Rouletted 8***
2902 A1608 €2.80 multi    7.50 3.75

Local Police — A1609

**2008, Oct. 23 Photo.**    *Perf. 13¼x13¼*
2903 A1609 60c multi    1.60   .80

---

Oath of the Plebian Tribune, 2500th Anniv. A1610

**2008, Oct. 24**    *Perf. 13x13¼*
2904 A1610 60c multi    1.60   .80

Madonna and Child Enthroned with Two Angels, by Lorenzo di Credi — A1611

Wreath — A1612

**2008, Oct. 30 Photo.**    *Perf. 13¼x13*
2905 A1611 60c multi    1.60   .80

**Litho. on Gold Foil**
**Self-Adhesive**
***Rouletted 8***
2906 A1612 €2.80 multi    7.25 3.75

Christmas.

UNESCO World Heritage Sites — A1613

Designs: 60c, Val d'Orcia. €2.80, Historic Center of Urbino.

**2008, Oct. 31 Engr.**    *Perf. 13¼x13*
2907 A1613 60c multi    1.60   .80
2908 A1613 €2.80 blue & black    7.25 3.75

## SEMI-POSTAL STAMPS

Many issues of Italy and Italian Colonies include one or more semi-postal denominations. To avoid splitting sets, these issues are generally listed as regular postage, airmail, etc., unless all values carry a surtax.

Italian Flag — SP1

Italian Eagle Bearing Arms of Savoy — SP2

---

**1915-16 Typo. Wmk. 140 Perf. 14**
| | | | |
|---|---|---|---|
| B1 | SP1 10c + 5c rose | 8.50 | 10.00 |
| B2 | SP2 15c + 5c slate | 6.75 | 8.50 |
| B3 | SP2 20c + 5c orange | 32.50 | 60.00 |
| | *Nos. B1-B3 (3)* | 47.75 | 78.50 |
| | Set, never hinged | 115.00 | |

No. B2 Surcharged

**1916**
| | | | |
|---|---|---|---|
| B4 | SP2 20c on 15c + 5c | 21.00 | 50.00 |
| | Never hinged | 52.50 | |
| a. | Double overprint | 600.00 | — |
| | Never hinged | | |
| b. | Inverted overprint | 600.00 | 1,000. |
| | Never hinged | 250.00 | |

Regular Issues of 1906-16 Overprinted in Blue or Red

**1921**
| | | | |
|---|---|---|---|
| B5 | A48 10c claret (Bl) | *1,275.* | 1,350. |
| B6 | A50 20c brn org (Bl) | *1,875.* | 425.00 |
| B7 | A49 25c blue (R) | 250.00 | 150.00 |
| B8 | A49 40c brn (Bl) | 100.00 | 21.00 |
| a. | Inverted overprint | 160.00 | 150.00 |
| | *Nos. B5-B8 (4)* | *3,500.* | 1,946. |
| | Set, never hinged | 5,500. | |

Regular Issues of 1901-22 Overprinted in Red, Black, Blue, Brown or Orange

**1922-23**
| | | | |
|---|---|---|---|
| B9 | A48 10c cl ('23) (Bk) | 105.00 | 75.00 |
| a. | Blue overprint | 105.00 | 75.00 |
| | Never hinged | 200.00 | |
| b. | Brown overprint | 105.00 | 75.00 |
| | Never hinged | 200.00 | |
| B10 | A48 15c slate (Org) | 375.00 | 450.00 |
| a. | Blue overprint | 1,000. | 925.00 |
| | Never hinged | 2,000. | |
| B11 | A50 20c brn org (Bk) | 425.00 | 450.00 |
| a. | Blue overprint | 850.00 | 450.00 |
| | Never hinged | 1,700. | |
| B12 | A49 25c blue (Bk; '23) | 140.00 | 110.00 |
| b. | Red overprint | 375.00 | *450.00* |
| | Never hinged | 750.00 | |
| B12A | A49 30c org brn (Bk) | 275.00 | 190.00 |
| B13 | A49 40c brn (Bl) | 200.00 | 110.00 |
| a. | Black overprint | 210.00 | 110.00 |
| | Never hinged | 425.00 | |
| b. | As "a," invtd. ovpt. | — | — |
| B14 | A49 50c vio ('23) (Bk) | 750.00 | 675.00 |
| a. | Double overprint | | |
| B15 | A49 60c car (Bk) | 2,700. | 2,375. |
| B15A | A49 85c choc (Bk) | 375.00 | *450.00* |
| B16 | A46 1 l brn & grn ('23) (Bk) | 4,650. | 2,750. |
| a. | Inverted overprint | 5,250. | |
| | *Nos. B9-B16 (10)* | 9,995. | 7,635. |
| | Set, never hinged | 14,250. | |

The stamps overprinted "B. L. P." were sold by the Government below face value to the National Federation for Assisting War Invalids. Most of them were affixed to special envelopes (Buste Lettere Postali) which bore advertisements. The Federation was permitted to sell these envelopes at a reduction of 5c from the face value of each stamp. The profits for the war invalids were derived from the advertisements.

Values of Nos. B5-B16 unused are for stamps with original gum. Most copies without gum or with part gum sell for about a quarter of values quoted. Uncanceled stamps affixed to the special envelopes usually sell for about half value.

The overprint on Nos. B9-B16 is wider (13½mm) than that on Nos. B5-B8 (11mm). The 1922-23 overprint exists both typo. and litho. on 10c, 15c, 20c and 25c; only litho. on 40c, 50c, 60c and 1 l; and only typo. on 30c and 85c.

Counterfeits of the B.L.P. overprints exist.

---

Administering Fascist Oath — SP3

**1923, Oct. 29**    *Perf. 14x14½*
| | | | |
|---|---|---|---|
| B17 | SP3 30c + 30c brown | 32.50 | *115.00* |
| B18 | SP3 50c + 50c violet | 32.50 | *115.00* |
| a. | Horiz. pair, imperf between | | 1,100. |
| B19 | SP3 1 l + 1 l gray | 32.50 | *115.00* |
| | *Nos. B17-B19 (3)* | 97.50 | 345.00 |
| | Set, never hinged | 250.00 | |

The surtax was given to the Benevolent Fund of the Black Shirts (the Italian National Militia).

Anniv. of the March of the Fascisti on Rome.

St. Maria Maggiore SP4

Pope Opening Holy Door SP8

Designs: 30c+15c, St. John Lateran. 50c+25c, St. Paul's Church. 60c+30c, St. Peter's Basilica. 5 l+2.50 l, Pope closing Holy Door.

**1924, Dec. 24**    *Perf. 12*
| | | | |
|---|---|---|---|
| B20 | SP4 20c + 10c dk grn & brn | 4.25 | 12.50 |
| B21 | SP4 30c + 15c dk brn & brn | 4.25 | 12.50 |
| B22 | SP4 50c + 25c vio & brn | 4.25 | 12.50 |
| B23 | SP4 60c + 30c dp rose & brn | 4.25 | 37.50 |
| B24 | SP8 1 l + 50c dp bl & vio | 6.75 | 37.50 |
| B25 | SP8 5 l + 2.50 l org brn & vio | 8.50 | 75.00 |
| | *Nos. B20-B25 (6)* | 32.25 | 187.50 |
| | Set, never hinged | 80.00 | |

The surtax was contributed toward the Holy Year expenses.

Castle of St. Angelo SP10

Victor Emmanuel II — SP14

50c+20c, 60c+30c, Aqueduct of Claudius. 1.25 l+50c, 1.25 l+60c, Capitol, Roman Forum. 5 l+2 l, 5 l+2.50 l, People's Gate.

**Unwmk.**
**1926, Oct. 26 Engr.**    *Perf. 11*
| | | | |
|---|---|---|---|
| B26 | SP10 40c + 20c dk brn & blk | 3.50 | 18.00 |
| B27 | SP10 60c + 30c brn red & ol brn | 3.50 | 18.00 |
| B28 | SP10 1.25 l + 60c bl grn & blk | 3.50 | 55.00 |
| B29 | SP10 5 l + 2.50 l dk bl & blk | 5.00 | 160.00 |
| | *Nos. B26-B29 (4)* | 15.50 | 251.00 |
| | Set, never hinged | 37.50 | |

**Stamps inscribed "Poste Italiane" and "Fiere Campionaria di Tripoli" are listed in Libya.**

## 1928, Mar. 1

| | | | | |
|---|---|---|---|---|
| B30 | SP10 | 30c + 10c dl vio & blk | 11.50 | 37.50 |
| B31 | SP10 | 50c + 20c ol grn & sl | 20.00 | 37.50 |
| B32 | SP10 | 1.25 l + 50c dp bl & blk | 25.00 | 75.00 |
| B33 | SP10 | 5 l + 2 l brn red & blk | 55.00 | 300.00 |
| | | Nos. B30-B33 (4) | 111.50 | 450.00 |
| | | Set, never hinged | 275.00 | |

The tax on Nos. B26 to B33 was devoted to the charitable work of the Voluntary Militia for National Defense.
See Nos. B35-B38.

## 1929, Jan. 4    Photo.    Perf. 14

| | | | | |
|---|---|---|---|---|
| B34 | SP14 | 50c + 10c olive green | 4.25 | 9.25 |
| | | Never hinged | | 10.50 |

50th anniv. of the death of King Victor Emmanuel II. The surtax was for veterans.

### Type of 1926 Issue

Designs in same order.

## 1930, July 1                     Engr.

| | | | | |
|---|---|---|---|---|
| B35 | SP10 | 30c + 10c dk grn & vio | 2.50 | 27.50 |
| B36 | SP10 | 50c + 10c dk grn & bl grn | 3.50 | 22.50 |
| B37 | SP10 | 1.25 l + 30c ind & grn | 8.50 | 60.00 |
| B38 | SP10 | 5 l + 1.50 l blk brn & ol brn | 17.00 | 225.00 |
| | | Nos. B35-B38 (4) | 31.50 | 335.00 |
| | | Set, never hinged | 77.50 | |

The surtax was for the charitable work of the Voluntary Militia for National Defense.

Militiamen at Ceremonial Fire with Quotation from Leonardo da Vinci — SP15

Symbolical of Pride for Militia — SP16

Symbolical of Militia Guarding Immortality of Italy SP17

Militia Passing Through Arch of Constantine SP18

## 1935, July 1    Photo.    Wmk. 140

| | | | | |
|---|---|---|---|---|
| B39 | SP15 | 20c + 10c rose red | 10.00 | 12.00 |
| B40 | SP16 | 25c + 15c green | 10.00 | 18.00 |
| B41 | SP17 | 50c + 30c purple | 10.00 | 22.50 |
| B42 | SP18 | 1.25 l + 75c blue | 10.00 | 35.00 |
| | | Nos. B39-B42 (4) | 40.00 | 87.50 |
| | | Set, never hinged | 100.00 | |
| | | Nos. B39-B42,CB3 (5) | 50.00 | 125.00 |
| | | Set, never hinged | 117.50 | |

The surtax was for the Militia.

Roman Battle
SP19

Roman Warriors
SP20

## 1941, Dec. 13

| | | | | |
|---|---|---|---|---|
| B43 | SP19 | 20c + 10c rose red | .20 | .55 |
| B44 | SP19 | 30c + 15c brown | .20 | .70 |
| B45 | SP20 | 50c + 25c violet | .25 | .85 |
| B46 | SP20 | 1.25 l + 1 l blue | .30 | .90 |
| | | Nos. B43-B46 (4) | .95 | 3.00 |
| | | Set, never hinged | 4.50 | |

2,000th anniv. of the birth of Livy (59 B.C.-17 A.D.), Roman historian.

> **Catalogue values for unused stamps in this section, from this point to the end of the section, are for Never Hinged items.**

Aid for Flood Victims — SP21

## 1995, Jan. 2    Photo.    Perf. 13½x14

| | | | | |
|---|---|---|---|---|
| B47 | SP21 | 750 l +2250 l multi | 4.00 | 3.50 |

Queen Helen (1873-1952) SP22

## 2002, Mar. 2    Photo.    Perf. 13¼x14

| | | | | |
|---|---|---|---|---|
| B48 | SP22 | 41c + 21c multi | 1.10 | 1.10 |

Surtax for breast cancer research and prevention.

Intl. Commission on Occupational Health, 28th Congress — SP23

## 2006, Mar. 8    Photo.    Perf. 13x13¼

| | | | | |
|---|---|---|---|---|
| B49 | SP23 | 60c +30c multi | 2.25 | 2.25 |

Surtax for breast cancer research.

---

## AIR POST STAMPS

Used values for Nos. C1-C105 are for postally used stamps with legible cancellations. Forged cancels on these issues abound, and expertization is srongly recommended.

Special Delivery Stamp No. E1 Overprinted

## 1917, May    Wmk. 140    Perf. 14

| | | | | |
|---|---|---|---|---|
| C1 | SD1 | 25c rose red | 18.00 | 42.50 |
| | | Never hinged | 45.00 | |

Type of SD3 Surcharged in Black

## 1917, June 27

| | | | | |
|---|---|---|---|---|
| C2 | SD3 | 25c on 40c violet | 21.00 | 50.00 |
| | | Never hinged | 55.00 | |

Type SD3 was not issued without surcharge.

AP2

## 1926-28                     Typo.

| | | | | |
|---|---|---|---|---|
| C3 | AP2 | 50c rose red ('28) | 18.00 | 12.50 |
| C4 | AP2 | 60c gray | 5.00 | 12.50 |
| C5 | AP2 | 80c brn vio & brn ('28) | 32.50 | 125.00 |
| C6 | AP2 | 1 l blue | 12.00 | 12.50 |
| C7 | AP2 | 1.20 l brn ('27) | 29.00 | 125.00 |
| C8 | AP2 | 1.50 l buff | 18.00 | 32.50 |
| C9 | AP2 | 5 l gray grn | 42.50 | 115.00 |
| | | Nos. C3-C9 (7) | 157.00 | 435.00 |
| | | Set, never hinged | 375.00 | |

Nos. C4 and C6 Surcharged

## 1927, Sept. 16

| | | | | |
|---|---|---|---|---|
| C10 | AP2 | 50c on 60c gray | 20.00 | 60.00 |
| a. | | Pair, one without surcharge | 1,500. | |
| C11 | AP2 | 80c on 1 l blue | 57.50 | 250.00 |
| | | Set, never hinged | 190.00 | |

Pegasus
AP3

Wings
AP4

Spirit of Flight — AP5

Arrows
AP6

## 1930-32    Photo.    Wmk. 140

| | | | | |
|---|---|---|---|---|
| C12 | AP4 | 25c dk grn ('32) | .20 | .20 |
| C13 | AP3 | 50c olive brn | .20 | .20 |
| C14 | AP5 | 75c org brn ('32) | .40 | .20 |
| C15 | AP4 | 80c org red | .20 | .70 |
| C16 | AP5 | 1 l purple | .20 | .20 |

| | | | | |
|---|---|---|---|---|
| C17 | AP6 | 2 l deep blue | .40 | .20 |
| C18 | AP3 | 5 l dk green | .80 | 1.60 |
| C19 | AP3 | 10 l dp car | 1.60 | 6.50 |
| | | Nos. C12-C19 (8) | 4.00 | 9.80 |
| | | Set, never hinged | 10.00 | |

The 50c, 1 l and 2 l were reprinted in 1942 with labels similar to those of Nos. 427-438, but were not issued. Value, set of 3: unused $550; never hinged, $1,100.
For overprints see Nos. MC1-MC5. For overprints and surcharges on design AP6 see Nos. C52-C55; Yugoslavia-Ljubljana NB9-NB20, NC11-NC17.

### Ferrucci Type of Postage

Statue of Ferrucci.

## 1930, July 10

| | | | | |
|---|---|---|---|---|
| C20 | A104 | 50c purple | 4.00 | 18.00 |
| C21 | A104 | 1 l orange brn | 4.00 | 20.00 |
| C22 | A104 | 5 l + 2 l brn vio | 16.00 | 130.00 |
| | | Nos. C20-C22 (3) | 24.00 | 168.00 |
| | | Set, never hinged | 60.00 | |

For overprinted types see Aegean Islands Nos. C1-C3.

### Virgil Type of Postage

Jupiter sending forth his eagle.

## 1930, Oct. 21    Photo.    Wmk. 140

| | | | | |
|---|---|---|---|---|
| C23 | A106 | 50c lt brown | 24.00 | 35.00 |
| C24 | A106 | 1 l orange | 24.00 | 40.00 |

### Engr.
### Unwmk.

| | | | | |
|---|---|---|---|---|
| C25 | A106 | 7.70 l + 1.30 l vio brn | 57.50 | 350.00 |
| C26 | A106 | 9 l + 2 l indigo | 65.00 | 400.00 |
| | | Nos. C23-C26 (4) | 170.50 | 825.00 |
| | | Set, never hinged | 430.00 | |

The surtax on Nos. C25-C26 was for the National Institute Figli del Littorio.
For overprinted types see Aegean Islands Nos. C4-C7.

Trans-Atlantic Squadron — AP9

**1930, Dec. 15    Photo.    Wmk. 140**

| | | | | |
|---|---|---|---|---|
| C27 | AP9 | 7.70 l | Prus bl & gray | 450.00   *1,350.* |
| | | Never hinged | | 900.00 |
| a. | | Seven stars instead of six | | 1,500.   — |
| | | Never hinged | | 3,000. |

Flight by Italian aviators from Rome to Rio de Janeiro, Dec. 1930-Jan. 12, 1931.

Leonardo da Vinci's Flying Machine AP10

Leonardo da Vinci AP11

Leonardo da Vinci — AP12

**1932**

| | | | | |
|---|---|---|---|---|
| C28 | AP10 | 50c | olive brn | 5.00   *9.00* |
| C29 | AP11 | 1 l | violet | 6.50   *11.50* |
| C30 | AP11 | 3 l | brown red | 8.00   *30.00* |
| C31 | AP11 | 5 l | dp green | 13.00   *37.50* |
| C32 | AP10 | 7.70 l | + 2 l dk bl | 10.00   *120.00* |
| C33 | AP11 | 10 l | + 2.50 l blk brn | 11.50   *190.00* |
| | | *Nos. C28-C33 (6)* | | 54.00   *398.00* |
| | | Set, never hinged | | 130.00 |

**Engr.**
**Unwmk.**

| | | | | |
|---|---|---|---|---|
| C34 | AP12 | 100 l | brt bl & grnsh blk | 45.00   *575.00* |
| | | Never hinged | | 110.00 |
| a. | | Thin paper | | 200.00   *1,000.* |

Dante Alighieri Soc. and especially Leonardo da Vinci, to whom the invention of a flying machine has been attributed. Surtax was for the benefit of the Society.

Inscription on No. C34: "Man with his large wings by beating against the air will be able to dominate it and lift himself above it".

Issued: #C28-C33, Mar. 14; #C34, Aug. 6.

For overprinted types see Aegean Islands Nos. C8-C13.

Garibaldi's Home at Caprera AP13

Farmhouse where Anita Garibaldi Died AP14

50c, 1 l+25c, Garibaldi's home, Caprera. 2 l+50c, Anita Garibaldi. 5 l+1 l, Giuseppe Garibaldi.

**1932, Apr. 6    Photo.    Wmk. 140**

| | | | | |
|---|---|---|---|---|
| C35 | AP13 | 50c | copper red | 5.00   *8.00* |
| C36 | AP14 | 80c | deep green | 5.00   *13.00* |
| C37 | AP13 | 1 l | + 25c red brn | 8.00   *32.50* |

---

| | | | | |
|---|---|---|---|---|
| C38 | AP13 | 2 l | + 50c dp bl | 13.00   *45.00* |
| C39 | AP14 | 5 l | + 1 l dp grn | 13.00   *52.50* |
| | | *Nos. C35-C39 (5)* | | 44.00   *151.00* |
| | | Set, never hinged | | 110.00 |

50th anniv. of the death of Giuseppe Garibaldi, patriot. The surtax was for the benefit of the Garibaldi Volunteers.

For overprinted types see Aegean Islands Nos. C15-C19.

### March on Rome Type of Postage

50c, Eagle sculpture and airplane. 75c, Italian buildings from the air.

**1932, Oct. 27       Perf. 14**

| | | | | |
|---|---|---|---|---|
| C40 | A146 | 50c | dark brown | 3.25   *10.00* |
| C41 | A146 | 75c | orange brn | 10.00   *32.50* |
| | | Set, never hinged | | 32.50 |

### Graf Zeppelin Issue

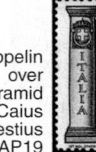

Zeppelin over Pyramid of Caius Cestius AP19

Designs: 5 l, Tomb of Cecilia Metella. 10 l, Stadium of Mussolini. 12 l, St. Angelo Castle and Bridge. 15 l, Roman Forum. 20 l, Imperial Avenue.

**1933, Apr. 24**

| | | | | |
|---|---|---|---|---|
| C42 | AP19 | 3 l | black & grn | 23.00   *100.00* |
| C43 | AP19 | 5 l | green & brn | 23.00   *110.00* |
| C44 | AP19 | 10 l | car & dl bl | 23.00   *260.00* |
| C45 | AP19 | 12 l | dk bl & red org | 23.00   *450.00* |
| C46 | AP19 | 15 l | dk brn & gray | 23.00   *525.00* |
| C47 | AP19 | 20 l | org brn & bl | 23.00   *575.00* |
| a. | | Vertical pair, imperf. between | | 9,000. |
| | | Never hinged | | 14,000. |
| | | *Nos. C42-C47 (6)* | | 138.00   *2,020.* |
| | | Set, never hinged | | 325.00 |

### Balbo's Trans-Atlantic Flight Issue

Italian Flag

King Victor Emmanuel III

Allegory "Flight" — AP25

#C49, Colosseum at Rome, Chicago skyline. #C48-C49 consist of 3 parts; Italian flag, Victor Emmanuel III, & scene arranged horizontally.

**1933, May 20**

| | | | | |
|---|---|---|---|---|
| C48 | AP25 | 5.25 l | + 19.75 l red, grn & ultra | 125.00   *1,800.* |
| | | Never hinged | | 250.00 |
| a. | | Left stamp without ovpt. | | 25,000. |
| | | Never hinged | | 37,500. |
| C49 | AP25 | 5.25 l | + 44.75 l grn, red & ultra | 160.00   *1,800.* |
| | | Never hinged | | 325.00 |

Transatlantic Flight, Rome-Chicago, of 24-seaplane squadron led by Gen. Italo Balbo. Center and right sections paid postage. At left is registered air express label overprinted "APPARECCHIO" and abbreviated pilot's name. Twenty triptychs of each value differ in name overprint.

---

No. C49 overprinted "VOLO DI RITORNO/ NEW YORK-ROMA" was not issued; flight canceled. Value, unused: $29,000; never hinged, $43,000.

For overprints see Nos. CO1, Aegean Islands C26-C27.

### Type of Air Post Stamp of 1930 Surcharged in Black

**1934, Jan. 18**

| | | | | |
|---|---|---|---|---|
| C52 | AP6 | 2 l on 2 l | yel | 7.25   *75.00* |
| C53 | AP6 | 3 l on 2 l | yel grn | 7.25   *105.00* |
| C54 | AP6 | 5 l on 2 l | rose | 7.25   *210.00* |
| C55 | AP6 | 10 l on 2 l | vio | 7.25   *300.00* |
| | | *Nos. C52-C55 (4)* | | 29.00   *690.00* |
| | | Set, never hinged | | 72.50 |

For use on mail carried on a special flight from Rome to Buenos Aires.

### Annexation of Fiume Type of Postage

25c, 75c, View of Fiume Harbor. 50c, 1 l+50c, Monument to the Dead. 2 l+1.50 l, Venetian Lions. 3 l+2 l, Julian wall.

**1934, Mar. 12**

| | | | | |
|---|---|---|---|---|
| C56 | A166 | 25c | green | .80   *4.00* |
| C57 | A166 | 50c | brown | .80   *2.40* |
| C58 | A166 | 75c | org brn | .80   *10.00* |
| C59 | A166 | 1 l | + 50c dl vio | .80   *16.00* |
| C60 | A166 | 2 l | + 1.50 l dl bl | .80   *21.00* |
| C61 | A166 | 3 l | + 2 l blk brn | .80   *23.00* |
| | | *Nos. C56-C61 (6)* | | 4.80   *76.40* |
| | | Set, never hinged | | 12.50 |

Airplane and View of Stadium AP32

Soccer Player and Plane AP33

Airplane and Stadium Entrance AP35

Airplane over Stadium AP34

**1934, May 24**

| | | | | |
|---|---|---|---|---|
| C62 | AP32 | 50c | car rose | 10.00   *32.50* |
| C63 | AP33 | 75c | gray blue | 16.00   *40.00* |
| C64 | AP34 | 5 l | + 2.50 l ol grn | 50.00   *275.00* |
| C65 | AP35 | 10 l | + 5 l brn blk | 50.00   *400.00* |
| | | *Nos. C62-C65 (4)* | | 126.00   *747.50* |
| | | Set, never hinged | | 300.00 |

2nd World Soccer Championships.

For overprinted types see Aegean Islands Nos. C28-C31.

Zeppelin under Fire AP36

---

Air Force Memorial — AP40

Designs: 25c, 80c, Zeppelin under fire. 50c, 75c, Motorboat patrol. 1 l+50c, Desert infantry. 2 l+1 l, Plane attacking troops.

**1934, Apr. 24**

| | | | | |
|---|---|---|---|---|
| C66 | AP36 | 25c | dk green | 3.25   *6.50* |
| C67 | AP36 | 50c | gray | 3.25   *8.00* |
| C68 | AP36 | 75c | dk brown | 3.25   *10.00* |
| C69 | AP36 | 80c | slate blue | 3.25   *12.00* |
| C70 | AP36 | 1 l | + 50c red brn | 8.00   *30.00* |
| C71 | AP36 | 2 l | + 1 l brt bl | 11.50   *37.50* |
| C72 | AP40 | 3 l | + 2 l brn blk | 16.00   *45.00* |
| | | *Nos. C66-C72 (7)* | | 48.50   *149.00* |
| | | Set, never hinged | | 120.00 |

Cent. of the institution of the Military Medal of Valor.

For overprinted types see Aegean Islands Nos. C32-C38.

King Victor Emmanuel III — AP41

**1934, Nov. 5**

| | | | | |
|---|---|---|---|---|
| C73 | AP41 | 1 l | purple | 3.25   *60.00* |
| C74 | AP41 | 2 l | brt blue | 3.25   *70.00* |
| C75 | AP41 | 4 l | red brown | 7.50   *225.00* |
| C76 | AP41 | 5 l | dull green | 7.50   *300.00* |
| C77 | AP41 | 8 l | rose red | 23.00   *400.00* |
| C78 | AP41 | 10 l | brown | 25.00   *550.00* |
| | | *Nos. C73-C78 (6)* | | 69.50   *1,605.* |
| | | Set, never hinged | | 160.00 |

65th birthday of King Victor Emmanuel III and the nonstop flight from Rome to Mogadiscio.

For overprint see No. CO2.

Muse Playing Harp AP42

Angelic Dirge for Bellini AP43

Scene from Bellini Opera, La Sonnambula — AP44

**1935, Sept. 24**

| | | | | |
|---|---|---|---|---|
| C79 | AP42 | 25c | dull yellow | 4.75   *11.00* |
| C80 | AP42 | 50c | brown | 4.75   *9.50* |
| C81 | AP42 | 60c | rose carmine | 16.00   *24.00* |
| C82 | AP43 | 1 l | + 1 l purple | 25.00   *140.00* |
| C83 | AP44 | 5 l | + 2 l green | 32.50   *225.00* |
| | | *Nos. C79-C83 (5)* | | 83.00   *409.50* |
| | | Set, never hinged | | 200.00 |

Vincenzo Bellini, (1801-35), operatic composer.

### Quintus Horatius Flaccus Type of Postage

25c, Seaplane in Flight. 50c, 1 l+1 l, Monoplane over valley. 60c, Oak and eagle. 5 l+2 l, Ruins of ancient Rome.

**1936, July 1**

| | | | | |
|---|---|---|---|---|
| C84 | A197 | 25c | dp green | 3.25   *8.00* |
| C85 | A197 | 50c | dk brown | 5.00   *8.00* |
| C86 | A197 | 60c | scarlet | 8.00   *20.00* |

| | | | | | |
|---|---|---|---|---|---|
| C87 | A197 | 1 l + 1 l vio | 20.00 | 140.00 |
| C88 | A197 | 5 l + 2 l slate bl | 25.00 | 240.00 |
| | *Nos. C84-C88 (5)* | | 61.25 | *416.00* |
| | Set, never hinged | | 150.00 | |

Child of the Balilla AP49

Heads of Children AP50

**1937, June 28**

| | | | | |
|---|---|---|---|---|
| C89 | AP49 | 25c dk bl grn | 8.00 | 17.50 |
| C90 | AP50 | 50c brown | 16.00 | 12.00 |
| C91 | AP49 | 1 l purple | 12.00 | 20.00 |
| C92 | AP50 | 2 l + 1 l dk bl | 16.00 | 125.00 |
| C93 | AP49 | 3 l + 2 l org | 20.00 | 175.00 |
| C94 | AP50 | 5 l + 3 l rose lake | 24.00 | 225.00 |
| | *Nos. C89-C94 (6)* | | 96.00 | *574.50* |
| | Set, never hinged | | 240.00 | |

Summer Exhibition for Child Welfare. The surtax on Nos. C92-C94 was used to support summer camps for poor children.

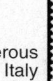
Prosperous Italy AP51

50c, Prolific Italy. 80c, Apollo's steeds. 1 l+1 l, Map & Roman Standard. 5 l+1 l, Augustus Caesar.

**1937, Sept. 23**

| | | | | |
|---|---|---|---|---|
| C95 | AP51 | 25c red vio | 8.00 | 12.00 |
| C96 | AP51 | 50c olive brn | 8.00 | 10.00 |
| C97 | AP51 | 80c orange brn | 24.00 | 16.00 |
| C98 | AP51 | 1 l + 1 l dk bl | 30.00 | 110.00 |
| C99 | AP51 | 5 l + 1 l dl vio | 65.00 | 200.00 |
| | *Nos. C95-C99 (5)* | | 135.00 | *348.00* |
| | Set, never hinged | | 325.00 | |

Bimillenary of the birth of Augustus Caesar (Octavianus) on the occasion of the exhibition opened in Rome by Mussolini on Sept. 22nd, 1937.

For overprinted types see Aegean Islands Nos. C39-C43.

King Victor Emmanuel III — AP56

25c, 3 l, King Victor Emmanuel III. 50c, 1 l, Dante Alighieri. 2 l, 5 l, Leonardo da Vinci.

**1938, Oct. 28**

| | | | | |
|---|---|---|---|---|
| C100 | AP56 | 25c dull green | 5.00 | 6.50 |
| C101 | AP56 | 50c dk yel brn | 5.00 | 6.50 |
| C102 | AP56 | 1 l violet | 8.00 | 10.00 |
| C103 | AP56 | 2 l royal blue | 8.00 | 37.50 |
| C104 | AP56 | 3 l brown car | 13.00 | 45.00 |
| C105 | AP56 | 5 l dp green | 15.00 | 65.00 |
| | *Nos. C100-C105 (6)* | | 54.00 | *170.50* |
| | Set, never hinged | | 135.00 | |

Proclamation of the Empire.

Plane and Clasped Hands AP59

Swallows in Flight AP60

**1945-47  Wmk. 277  Photo.  Perf. 14**

| | | | | |
|---|---|---|---|---|
| C106 | AP59 | 1 l slate bl | .20 | .20 |
| C107 | AP60 | 2 l dk blue | .20 | .20 |
| C108 | AP59 | 3.20 l red org | .20 | .20 |
| C109 | AP60 | 5 l dk green | .20 | .20 |
| C110 | AP59 | 10 l car rose | .20 | .20 |
| C111 | AP60 | 25 l dk bl ('46) | 6.50 | 13.00 |
| C112 | AP59 | 25 l brown ('47) | .20 | .20 |
| C113 | AP60 | 50 l dk grn ('46) | 14.00 | 20.00 |
| C114 | AP59 | 50 l violet ('47) | .20 | .20 |
| | *Nos. C106-C114 (9)* | | 21.90 | *34.40* |
| | Set, never hinged | | 40.00 | |

Issued: #C111, C113, 7/13/46; #C112, C114, 4/21/47.

See Nos. C130-C131. For surcharges and overprints see Nos. C115, C136, 1LNC1-1LNC7, Trieste C1-C6, C17-C22.

No. C108 Surcharged in Black

**1947, July 1**

| | | | | |
|---|---|---|---|---|
| C115 | AP59 | 6 l on 3.20 l | .20 | .20 |
| | Never hinged | | .20 | |
| a. | Pair, one without surcharge | | 1,200. | |
| b. | Inverted surcharge | | 22,500. | |

Radio on Land — AP61

Plane over Capitol Bell Tower — AP65

Designs: 6 l, 25 l, Radio on land. 10 l, 35 l, Radio at sea. 20 l, 50 l, Radio in the skies.

**1947, Aug. 1  Photo.  Perf. 14**

| | | | | |
|---|---|---|---|---|
| C116 | AP61 | 6 l dp violet | .20 | .20 |
| C117 | AP61 | 10 l dk car rose | .20 | .20 |
| C118 | AP61 | 20 l dp orange | .75 | .75 |
| C119 | AP61 | 25 l aqua | 1.10 | 1.60 |
| C120 | AP61 | 35 l brt blue | 1.10 | 2.40 |
| C121 | AP61 | 50 l lilac rose | 3.00 | 5.00 |
| | *Nos. C116-C121 (6)* | | 6.35 | *10.15* |
| | Set, never hinged | | 10.00 | |

50th anniv. of radio.
For overprints see Trieste Nos. C7-C12.

**1948**

| | | | | |
|---|---|---|---|---|
| C123 | AP65 | 100 l green | 1.10 | .20 |
| C124 | AP65 | 300 l lilac rose | .20 | .60 |
| C125 | AP65 | 500 l ultra | .40 | 1.20 |

**Engr.**

| | | | | |
|---|---|---|---|---|
| C126 | AP65 | 1000 l dk brown | .65 | 2.40 |
| a. | Vert. pair, imperf. btwn. | | 275.00 | 275.00 |
| b. | Perf. 14x13 | | .75 | 2.40 |
| | *Nos. C123-C126 (4)* | | 2.35 | *4.40* |
| | Set, never hinged | | 11.00 | |

See No. C132-C135. For overprints see Trieste Nos. C13-C16, C23-C26.

St. Catherine Carrying Cross AP66

200 l, St. Catherine with outstretched arms.

**1948, Mar. 1  Photo.**

| | | | | |
|---|---|---|---|---|
| C127 | AP66 | 100 l bl vio & brn org | 47.50 | 40.00 |
| C128 | AP66 | 200 l dp blue & bis | 26.00 | 25.00 |
| | Set, never hinged | | 150.00 | |

600th anniversary of the birth of St. Catherine of Siena, patroness of Italy.

Catalogue values for unused stamps in this section, from this point to the end of the section, are for Never Hinged items.

Giuseppe Mazzini (1805-1872), Patriot — AP67

**1955, Dec. 31  Wmk. 303  Perf. 14**

| | | | | |
|---|---|---|---|---|
| C129 | AP67 | 100 l Prus green | 1.60 | 1.40 |

**Types of 1945-46, 1948**

**1955-62  Wmk. 303  Perf. 14**

| | | | | |
|---|---|---|---|---|
| C130 | AP60 | 5 l green ('62) | .20 | .20 |
| C131 | AP59 | 50 l vio ('57) | .20 | .20 |
| C132 | AP65 | 100 l green | .75 | .20 |
| C133 | AP65 | 300 l lil rose | .85 | .55 |
| C134 | AP65 | 500 l ultra ('56) | 1.00 | .90 |

**Engr.**
**Perf. 13½**

| | | | | |
|---|---|---|---|---|
| C135 | AP65 | 1000 l maroon ('59) | 2.00 | 2.00 |
| | *Nos. C130-C135 (6)* | | 5.00 | *4.05* |

**Fluorescent Paper**
See note below No. 998.
No. C132 was issued on both ordinary and fluorescent paper. The design of the fluorescent stamp is smaller.
Airmail stamps issued only on fluorescent paper are Nos. C139-C140.

Type of 1945-46 Surcharged in Ultramarine

**1956, Feb. 24**

| | | | | |
|---|---|---|---|---|
| C136 | AP59 | 120 l on 50 l mag | 1.25 | 1.60 |

Visit of Pres. Giovanni Gronchi to the US and Canada.

Madonna of Bruges, by Michelangelo AP68

**Wmk. 303**

**1964, Feb. 18  Photo.  Perf. 14**

| | | | | |
|---|---|---|---|---|
| C137 | AP68 | 185 l black | .30 | .30 |

Michelangelo Buonarroti (1475-1564), artist.

**Verrazano Type of Regular Issue**

**1964, Nov. 21  Wmk. 303  Perf. 14**

| | | | | |
|---|---|---|---|---|
| C138 | A481 | 130 l blk & dull grn | .20 | .20 |

See note after No. 901.

Adoration of the Kings, by Gentile da Fabriano — AP69

**1970, Dec. 12  Photo.  Unwmk.**

| | | | | |
|---|---|---|---|---|
| C139 | AP69 | 150 l multicolored | .30 | .20 |

Christmas 1970.

**Aviation Type of Regular Issue**

Design: F-140S Starfighter over Aeronautical Academy, Pozzuoli.

**1973, Mar. 28  Photo.  Perf. 14x13½**

| | | | | |
|---|---|---|---|---|
| C140 | A590 | 150 l multicolored | .30 | .20 |

**AIR POST SEMI-POSTAL STAMPS**

**Holy Year Type of Postage**

Dome of St. Peter's, dove with olive branch, Church of the Holy Sepulcher.

**Wmk. 140**

**1933, Oct. 23  Photo.  Perf. 14**

| | | | | |
|---|---|---|---|---|
| CB1 | A163 | 50c + 25c org brn | 2.40 | 16.00 |
| CB2 | A163 | 75c + 50c brn vio | 4.00 | 45.00 |
| | Set, never hinged | | 16.00 | |

Symbolical of Military Air Force — SPAP2

**1935, July 1**

| | | | | |
|---|---|---|---|---|
| CB3 | SPAP2 | 50c + 50c brown | 10.00 | 37.50 |
| | Never hinged | | 25.00 | |

The surtax was for the Militia.

**AIR POST SPECIAL DELIVERY STAMPS**

Garibaldi, Anita Garibaldi, Plane APSD1

**Wmk. 140**

**1932, June 2  Photo.  Perf. 14**

| | | | | |
|---|---|---|---|---|
| CE1 | APSD1 | 2.25 l + 1 l | 16.00 | 52.50 |
| CE2 | APSD1 | 4.50 l + 1.50 l | 16.00 | 52.50 |
| | Set, never hinged | | 80.00 | |

Death of Giuseppe Garibaldi, 50th anniv.
For overprinted types see Aegean Islands Nos. CE1-CE2.

Airplane and Sunburst APSD2

**1933-34**

| | | | | |
|---|---|---|---|---|
| CE3 | APSD2 | 2 l gray blk ('34) | .20 | 2.40 |
| CE4 | APSD2 | 2.25 l gray blk | 6.50 | 180.00 |
| | Set, never hinged | | 17.00 | |

For overprint and surcharge see Nos. MCE1; Yugoslavia-Ljubljana NCE1.

**Annexation of Fiume Type**

Flag raising before Fascist headquarters.

**1934, Mar. 12**

| | | | | |
|---|---|---|---|---|
| CE5 | A166 | 2 l + 1.25 l | 4.00 | 29.00 |
| CE6 | A166 | 2.25 l + 1.25 l | .80 | 23.00 |
| CE7 | A166 | 4.50 l + 2 l | .80 | 25.00 |
| | *Nos. CE5-CE7 (3)* | | 5.60 | *77.00* |
| | Set, never hinged | | 14.00 | |

Triumphal Arch in Rome APSD4

**1934, Aug. 31**

| | | | | |
|---|---|---|---|---|
| CE8 | APSD4 | 2 l + 1.25 l brown | 16.00 | 40.00 |
| CE9 | APSD4 | 4.50 l + 2 l cop red | 20.00 | 40.00 |
| | | Set, never hinged | 90.00 | |

Centenary of the institution of the Military Medal of Valor.

For overprinted types see Aegean Islands Nos. CE3-CE4.

### AIR POST OFFICIAL STAMPS

**Balbo Flight Type of Air Post Stamp of 1933 Overprinted**

| **1933** | | **Wmk. 140** | | *Perf. 14* |
|---|---|---|---|---|
| CO1 | AP25 | 5.25 l + 44.75 l red, grn & red vio | 3,100. | 12,500. |
| | | Never hinged | 4,750. | |

**Type of Air Post Stamp of 1934 Overprinted in Gold**

| **1934** | | | | |
|---|---|---|---|---|
| CO2 | AP41 | 10 l blue blk | 825.00 | 12,500. |
| | | Never hinged | 1,600. | |

65th birthday of King Victor Emmanuel III and the non-stop flight from Rome to Mogadiscio.

### PNEUMATIC POST STAMPS

Regno d'Italia Posta Pneumatica — PN1

| **1913-28** | | **Wmk. 140 Typo.** | | *Perf. 14* |
|---|---|---|---|---|
| D1 | PN1 | 10c brown | 2.75 | 22.50 |
| D2 | PN1 | 15c brn vio ('28) | 2.40 | 12.50 |
| a. | | 15c dull violet ('21) | 3.25 | 22.50 |
| D3 | PN1 | 15c rose red ('28) | 8.00 | 20.00 |
| D4 | PN1 | 15c claret ('28) | 2.40 | 12.50 |
| D5 | PN1 | 20c brn vio ('25) | 18.00 | 40.00 |
| D6 | PN1 | 30c blue ('23) | 8.00 | 125.00 |
| D7 | PN1 | 35c rose red ('27) | 20.00 | 200.00 |
| D8 | PN1 | 40c dp red ('26) | 24.00 | 290.00 |
| | | Nos. D1-D8 (8) | 85.55 | 722.50 |

**Nos. D1, D2a, D5-D6, D8 Surcharged Like Nos. C10-C11**

| **1924-27** | | | | |
|---|---|---|---|---|
| D9 | PN1 | 15c on 10c | 4.00 | 27.00 |
| D10 | PN1 | 15c on 20c ('27) | 8.00 | 50.00 |
| D11 | PN1 | 20c on 10c ('25) | 8.00 | 52.50 |
| D12 | PN1 | 20c on 15c ('25) | 10.00 | 32.50 |
| D13 | PN1 | 35c on 20c ('27) | 21.00 | 225.00 |
| D14 | PN1 | 40c on 30c ('25) | 10.00 | 250.00 |
| | | Nos. D9-D14 (6) | 61.00 | 637.00 |

Dante Alighieri PN2

Galileo Galilei PN3

**1933, Mar. 29**      **Photo.**

| | | | | |
|---|---|---|---|---|
| D15 | PN2 | 15c dark violet | .30 | 1.60 |
| D16 | PN3 | 35c rose red | .30 | 5.00 |

**Similar to Types of 1933, Without "REGNO"**

**1945, Oct. 22**      **Wmk. 277**

| | | | | |
|---|---|---|---|---|
| D17 | PN2 | 60c dull brown | .20 | 3.25 |
| D18 | PN3 | 1.40 l dull blue | .20 | 3.25 |

Minerva — PN6

**1947, Nov. 15**

| | | | | |
|---|---|---|---|---|
| D19 | PN6 | 3 l rose lilac | 6.50 | 10.50 |
| D20 | PN6 | 5 l aqua | .20 | .20 |
| | | Set, never hinged | 8.50 | |

**Catalogue values for unused stamps in this section, from this point to the end of the section, are for Never Hinged items.**

**1958-66**      **Wmk. 303**

| | | | | |
|---|---|---|---|---|
| D21 | PN6 | 10 l rose red | .20 | .20 |
| D22 | PN6 | 20 l sapphire ('66) | .20 | .20 |

### SPECIAL DELIVERY STAMPS

Victor Emmanuel III — SD1

| **1903-26** | | **Typo. Wmk. 140** | | *Perf. 14* |
|---|---|---|---|---|
| E1 | SD1 | 25c rose red | 50.00 | 1.20 |
| a. | | Imperf., pair | 500.00 | 625.00 |
| E2 | SD1 | 50c dl red ('20) | 5.00 | 1.75 |
| E3 | SD1 | 60c dl red ('22) | 8.00 | 1.20 |
| E4 | SD1 | 70c dl red ('25) | .80 | .35 |
| E5 | SD1 | 1.25 l dp bl ('26) | .25 | .20 |
| | | Nos. E1-E5 (5) | 64.05 | 4.70 |

No. E1 is almost always found poorly centered, and it is valued thus.

For overprints and surcharges see Nos. C1, E11, E13, Austria NE1-NE2, Dalmatia E1, Offices in Crete, Offices in Africa, Offices in Turkish Empire.

Victor Emmanuel III — SD2

| **1908-26** | | | | |
|---|---|---|---|---|
| E6 | SD2 | 30c blue & rose | 1.60 | 4.00 |
| E7 | SD2 | 2 l bl & red ('25) | 8.00 | 90.00 |
| E8 | SD2 | 2.50 l bl & red ('26) | 2.75 | 8.00 |
| | | Nos. E6-E8 (3) | 12.35 | 102.00 |

The 1.20 lire blue and red (see No. E12) was prepared in 1922, but not issued. Value: unused $200; never hinged $400.

For surcharges and overprints see Nos. E10, E12, Austria MNE3, Dalmatia E2, Offices in China, Offices in Africa, Offices in Turkish Empire.

SD3

**1917, Nov.**

| | | | | |
|---|---|---|---|---|
| E9 | SD3 | 25c on 40c violet | 32.50 | 100.00 |

Type SD3 not issued without surcharge. For surcharge see No. C2.

No. E6 Surcharged

**1921, Oct.**

| | | | | |
|---|---|---|---|---|
| E10 | SD2 | 1.20 l on 30c | 2.00 | 16.00 |
| a. | | Comma in value omitted | 12.50 | 50.00 |
| b. | | Double surcharge | 325.00 | |

No. E2 Surcharged

**1922, Jan. 9**

| | | | | |
|---|---|---|---|---|
| E11 | SD1 | 60c on 50c dull red | 40.00 | 2.00 |
| a. | | Inverted surcharge | 290.00 | 290.00 |
| b. | | Double surcharge | | 1,300. |
| c. | | Imperf., pair | 500.00 | 625.00 |

Type of 1908 Surcharged

**1924, May**

| | | | | |
|---|---|---|---|---|
| E12 | SD2 | 1.60 l on 1.20 l bl & red | 1.60 | 80.00 |
| a. | | Double surch., one inverted | 310.00 | |

**No. E3 Surcharged like No. E11**

**1925, Apr. 11**

| | | | | |
|---|---|---|---|---|
| E13 | SD1 | 70c on 60c dull red | .90 | 1.20 |
| a. | | Inverted surcharge | 325.00 | 400.00 |

Victor Emmanuel III — SD4

**1932-33**      **Photo.**

| | | | | |
|---|---|---|---|---|
| E14 | SD4 | 1.25 l green | .20 | .20 |
| E15 | SD4 | 2.50 l deep org ('33) | .25 | 5.75 |

For overprints and surcharges see Nos. ME1, Italian Social Republic E1-E2, Yugoslavia-Ljubljana NB5-NB8, NE1.

**March on Rome Type of Postage**

1.25 l Ancient Pillars and Entrenchments. 2.50 l, Head of Mussolini, trophies of flags, etc.

**1932, Oct. 27**

| | | | | |
|---|---|---|---|---|
| E16 | A146 | 1.25 l deep green | 2.40 | 1.75 |
| E17 | A146 | 2.50 l deep orange | 8.00 | 160.00 |
| | | Set, never hinged | 18.00 | |

"Italia" SD7

**1945, Aug.**      **Wmk. 277**      *Perf. 14*

| | | | | |
|---|---|---|---|---|
| E18 | SD7 | 5 l rose carmine | .20 | 1.00 |

Winged Foot SD8

Rearing Horse and Torch-Bearer — SD9

| **1945-51** | | | | |
|---|---|---|---|---|
| E19 | SD8 | 5 l henna brn | .20 | .20 |
| E20 | SD9 | 10 l deep blue | .20 | .20 |
| E21 | SD9 | 15 l dk car rose ('47) | 1.60 | .20 |
| E22 | SD8 | 25 l brt red org ('47) | 22.50 | .20 |
| E23 | SD8 | 30 l dp vio ('46) | 3.00 | 3.25 |
| E24 | SD8 | 50 l lil rose ('51) | 22.50 | .20 |
| E25 | SD9 | 60 l car rose ('48) | 35.00 | .20 |
| | | Nos. E19-E25 (7) | 85.00 | 4.45 |
| | | Set, never hinged | 160.00 | |

See No. E32. For overprints see Nos. 1LNE1-1LNE2, Trieste E1-E4, E6-E7.

**Type of Regular Issue of 1948 Inscribed: "Espresso"**

**1948, Sept. 18**    **Photo.**    *Perf. 14*

| | | | | |
|---|---|---|---|---|
| E26 | A272 | 35 l violet (*Naples*) | 75.00 | 20.00 |
| | | Never hinged | 150.00 | |

**Catalogue values for unused stamps in this section, from this point to the end of the section, are for Never Hinged items.**

**Type of 1945-51**

**1955, July 7**    **Wmk. 303**    *Perf. 14*

| | | | | |
|---|---|---|---|---|
| E32 | SD8 | 50 l lilac rose | 5.75 | .20 |

Etruscan Winged Horses SD10

**1958-76**      **Photo.**

**Size: 36½x20¼mm**

| | | | | |
|---|---|---|---|---|
| E33 | SD10 | 75 l magenta | .20 | .20 |

**Size: 36x20mm**

| | | | | |
|---|---|---|---|---|
| E34 | SD10 | 150 l dl bl grn ('68) | .25 | .20 |
| a. | | Size: 36½x20¼mm ('66) | .40 | .20 |
| E35 | SD10 | 250 l blue ('74) | .30 | .20 |
| E36 | SD10 | 300 l brown ('76) | .40 | .20 |
| | | Nos. E33-E36 (4) | 1.15 | .80 |

Nos. E34-E36 are fluorescent.

### AUTHORIZED DELIVERY STAMPS

For the payment of a special tax for the authorized delivery of correspondence privately instead of through the post office.

AD1

**1928**    **Wmk. 140 Typo.**    *Perf. 14*

| | | | | |
|---|---|---|---|---|
| EY1 | AD1 | 10c dull blue | 6.50 | .60 |
| a. | | Perf. 11 | 28.00 | 3.25 |

Coat of Arms — AD2

**1930**      **Photo.**      *Perf. 14*

| | | | | |
|---|---|---|---|---|
| EY2 | AD2 | 10c dark brown | .20 | .20 |

For surcharge and overprint see Nos. EY3, Italian Social Republic EY1.

**No. EY2 Surcharged in Black**

**1945**
EY3  AD2  40c on 10c dark brown  .50 1.20

Coat of Arms — AD3          "Italia" — AD4

**1945-46       Photo.      Wmk. 277**
| | | | | |
|---|---|---|---|---|
| EY4 | AD3 | 40c dark brown | .25 | 1.00 |
| EY5 | AD3 | 1 l dk brown ('46) | 3.25 | 5.00 |

For overprint see Trieste No. EY1.

**1947-52       Size: 27½x22½mm**
| | | | | |
|---|---|---|---|---|
| EY6 | AD4 | 1 l brt grnsh bl | .20 | .20 |
| EY7 | AD4 | 8 l brt red ('48) | 10.00 | .20 |
| | | **Size: 20½x16½mm** | | |
| EY8 | AD4 | 15 l violet ('49) | 27.50 | .20 |
| EY9 | AD4 | 20 l rose vio ('52) | 2.00 | .20 |
| | | *Nos. EY6-EY9 (4)* | 39.70 | .80 |
| | | Set, never hinged | 125.00 | |

For overprints see Trieste Nos. EY2-EY5.

> **Catalogue values for unused stamps in this section, from this point to the end of the section, are for Never Hinged items.**

Italia Type of 1947

**1955-90  Wmk. 303  Photo.  Perf. 14**
**Size: 20½x16½mm**
| | | | | |
|---|---|---|---|---|
| EY11 | AD4 | 20 l rose vio | .20 | .20 |
| EY12 | AD4 | 30 l Prus grn ('65) | .20 | .20 |
| EY13 | AD4 | 35 l ocher ('74) | .20 | .20 |
| EY14 | AD4 | 110 l lt ultra ('77) | .20 | .20 |
| EY15 | AD4 | 270 l brt pink ('84) | .75 | .25 |
| | | **Size: 19½x16½mm** | | |
| EY16 | AD4 | 300 l rose & grn ('87) | .60 | .40 |
| EY17 | AD4 | 370 l tan & brn vio | .65 | .40 |
| | | *Nos. EY11-EY17 (7)* | 2.80 | 1.85 |

Issue date: 370 l, Sept. 24, 1990.

### POSTAGE DUE STAMPS

Unused values for Postage Due stamps are for examples with full original gum. Stamps without gum, with part gum or privately gummed sell for much less.

D1          D2

**1863      Unwmk.      Litho.      Imperf.**
| | | | | |
|---|---|---|---|---|
| J1 | D1 | 10c yellow | 2,000. | 225.00 |
| *a.* | | 10c yellow orange | 2,100. | 250.00 |
| | | Without gum | 80.00 | |

**1869      Wmk. 140      Typo.      Perf. 14**
| | | | | |
|---|---|---|---|---|
| J2 | D2 | 10c buff | 5,000. | 65.00 |

D3          D4

**1870-1925**
| | | | | |
|---|---|---|---|---|
| J3 | D3 | 1c buff & mag | 4.00 | 12.50 |
| J4 | D3 | 2c buff & mag | 13.00 | 25.00 |
| J5 | D3 | 5c buff & mag | 1.60 | .80 |
| J6 | D3 | 10c buff & mag | 1.60 | .80 |
| *b.* | | Imperf. ('71) | | 2,000. |
| J7 | D3 | 20c buff & mag | 16.00 | .80 |
| *a.* | | Imperf., pair ('94) | 250.00 | 250.00 |
| J8 | D3 | 30c buff & mag | 5.00 | 1.25 |
| *b.* | | Imperf. | 2,900. | 1,600. |
| J9 | D3 | 40c buff & mag | 5.00 | 2.40 |
| J10 | D3 | 50c buff & mag | 5.00 | 1.25 |
| *b.* | | Imperf. | | 1,800. |
| J11 | D3 | 60c buff & mag | 250.00 | 4.00 |
| J12 | D3 | 60c buff & brn ('25) | 40.00 | 15.00 |
| J13 | D3 | 1 l lt brn & brn | 5,300. | 20.00 |
| J14 | D3 | 1 l bl & mag ('94) | 40.00 | 1.25 |
| *a.* | | Imperf., pair | 160.00 | 180.00 |
| J15 | D3 | 2 l lt brn & brn | 5,300. | 32.50 |
| J16 | D3 | 2 l bl & mag ('03) | 57.50 | 6.50 |
| J17 | D3 | 5 l brn & brn ('74) | 540.00 | 37.50 |
| J18 | D3 | 5 l bl & mag ('03) | 200.00 | 32.50 |
| J19 | D3 | 10 l brn & brn ('74) | 6,500. | 37.50 |
| J20 | D3 | 10 l bl & mag ('94) | 200.00 | 6.50 |

Early printings of 5c, 10c, 30c, 40c, 50c and 60c were in buff and magenta, later ones (1890-94) in stronger shades. The earlier, paler shades and their inverted-numeral varieties sell for considerably more than those of the later shades. Values are for the later shades.

For surcharges and overprints see Nos. J25-J27, Austria NJ1-NJ16, Dalmatia J1-J4, Offices in China, Offices in Turkish Empire.

**Numeral Inverted**
| | | | | |
|---|---|---|---|---|
| J3a | D3 | 1c | 4,500. | 2,900. |
| J4a | D3 | 2c | 11,500. | 4,000. |
| J5a | D3 | 5c | 6.50 | 12.50 |
| J6a | D3 | 10c | 8.00 | 16.00 |
| J7b | D3 | 20c | 65.00 | 60.00 |
| J8a | D3 | 30c | 12.50 | 25.00 |
| J9a | D3 | 40c | 540.00 | 650.00 |
| J10a | D3 | 50c | 60.00 | 80.00 |
| J11a | D3 | 60c | 540.00 | 400.00 |
| J13a | D3 | 1 l | | — |
| J14b | D3 | 1 l | 4,500. | 3,250. |
| J15a | D3 | 2 l | | 2,900. |
| J16a | D3 | 2 l | 3,750. | 3,750. |
| J17a | D3 | 5 l | | 1,450. |
| J19a | D3 | 10 l | | 325.00 |

**1884-1903**
| | | | | |
|---|---|---|---|---|
| J21 | D4 | 50 l green | 90.00 | 80.00 |
| J22 | D4 | 50 l yellow ('03) | 100.00 | 50.00 |
| J23 | D4 | 100 l claret | 90.00 | 40.00 |
| J24 | D4 | 100 l blue ('03) | 80.00 | 20.00 |
| | | *Nos. J21-J24 (4)* | 360.00 | 190.00 |

**Nos. J3 & J4 Surcharged in Black**

**1890-91**
| | | | | |
|---|---|---|---|---|
| J25 | D3 | 10c on 2c | 130.00 | 37.50 |
| J26 | D3 | 20c on 1c | 540.00 | 29.00 |
| *a.* | | Inverted surcharge | | 10,000. |
| J27 | D3 | 30c on 2c | 1,800. | 12.50 |
| *a.* | | Inverted surcharge | | 2,700. |
| | | *Nos. J25-J27 (3)* | 2,470. | 79.00 |

Coat of Arms
D6          D7

**1934**                          **Photo.**
| | | | | |
|---|---|---|---|---|
| J28 | D6 | 5c brown | .80 | .40 |
| J29 | D6 | 10c blue | .80 | .40 |
| J30 | D6 | 20c rose red | .80 | .40 |
| J31 | D6 | 25c green | .80 | .40 |
| J32 | D6 | 30c red org | .80 | .40 |
| J33 | D6 | 40c blk brn | .80 | 3.25 |
| J34 | D6 | 50c violet | .80 | .40 |
| J35 | D6 | 60c slate blk | .80 | 8.00 |
| J36 | D7 | 1 l red org | .80 | .40 |
| J37 | D7 | 2 l green | .80 | .40 |
| J38 | D7 | 5 l violet | 1.60 | .80 |

| | | | | |
|---|---|---|---|---|
| J39 | D7 | 10 l blue | 6.50 | 5.75 |
| J40 | D7 | 20 l car rose | 12.50 | 21.00 |
| | | *Nos. J28-J40 (13)* | 28.60 | 42.00 |

For overprints and surcharges see Italian Social Republic #J1-J13, Yugoslavia-Ljubljana NJ14-NJ22.

D8          D9

**1945-46      Unwmk.      Perf. 14**
| | | | | |
|---|---|---|---|---|
| J41 | D8 | 5c brn, *grayish* ('46) | 2.40 | 5.00 |
| J42 | D8 | 10c blue | .45 | 1.00 |
| J43 | D8 | 20c rose red, *grayish* ('46) | 2.00 | 1.00 |
| J44 | D8 | 25c dk grn | .45 | 1.00 |
| J45 | D8 | 30c red org | .45 | 1.00 |
| J46 | D8 | 40c blk brn | .45 | 1.00 |
| J47 | D8 | 50c violet | .45 | 1.00 |
| J48 | D8 | 60c black | .45 | 5.00 |
| J49 | D9 | 1 l red org | .45 | 1.00 |
| J50 | D9 | 2 l green | .45 | 1.00 |
| J51 | D9 | 5 l violet | .45 | 1.00 |
| J52 | D9 | 10 l blue | .45 | 1.00 |
| J53 | D9 | 20 l car rose | .45 | 5.00 |
| | | *Nos. J41-J53 (13)* | 9.35 | 25.00 |

Nos. J41 and J43 have yellow gum.

**Wmk. 277**
| | | | | |
|---|---|---|---|---|
| J54 | D8 | 10c dark blue | .20 | 5.00 |
| J55 | D8 | 25c dk grn | 1.25 | 5.75 |
| J56 | D8 | 30c red org | 1.25 | 10.00 |
| J57 | D8 | 40c blk brn | .20 | .20 |
| J58 | D8 | 50c vio ('46) | 5.75 | 5.75 |
| J59 | D8 | 60c bl blk ('46) | 7.50 | 20.00 |
| J60 | D9 | 1 l red org | .20 | .20 |
| J61 | D9 | 2 l dk grn | .20 | .20 |
| J62 | D9 | 5 l violet | 12.00 | 7.50 |
| J63 | D9 | 10 l dark blue | 18.00 | 10.00 |
| J64 | D9 | 20 l car rose | 29.00 | 25.00 |
| | | *Nos. J54-J64 (11)* | 75.55 | 89.60 |
| | | Set, never hinged | 190.00 | |

For overprints see Trieste Nos. J1, J3-J5.

D10

**1947-54          Photo.      Perf. 14**
| | | | | |
|---|---|---|---|---|
| J65 | D10 | 1 l red orange | .20 | .20 |
| J66 | D10 | 2 l dk green | .20 | .20 |
| J67 | D10 | 3 l carmine | .50 | 2.40 |
| J68 | D10 | 4 l brown | .30 | 1.25 |
| J69 | D10 | 5 l violet | .65 | .20 |
| J70 | D10 | 6 l vio blue | 2.00 | 3.25 |
| J71 | D10 | 8 l rose vio | 8.50 | 4.00 |
| J72 | D10 | 10 l deep blue | .75 | .20 |
| J73 | D10 | 12 l golden brn | 3.25 | 3.25 |
| J74 | D10 | 20 l lil rose | 35.00 | .20 |
| J75 | D10 | 25 l dk red ('54) | 35.00 | .80 |
| J76 | D10 | 50 l aqua | 25.00 | .20 |
| J77 | D10 | 100 l org yel ('52) | 8.00 | .20 |

**Engr.          Perf. 13½x14**
| | | | | |
|---|---|---|---|---|
| J78 | D10 | 500 l dp bl & dk car ('52) | 8.50 | .40 |
| *a.* | | Perf. 11x13 | 10.00 | .40 |
| *b.* | | Perf. 13 | 10.00 | .40 |
| | | *Nos. J65-J78 (14)* | 127.85 | 16.75 |
| | | Set, never hinged | 325.00 | |

For overprints see Trieste Nos. J2, J6-J29.

> **Catalogue values for unused stamps in this section, from this point to the end of the section, are for Never Hinged items.**

**1955-91  Wmk. 303  Photo.  Perf. 14**
| | | | | |
|---|---|---|---|---|
| J83 | D10 | 5 l violet | .20 | .20 |
| J85 | D10 | 8 l rose vio | 200.00 | 225.00 |
| J86 | D10 | 10 l deep blue | .20 | .20 |
| J87 | D10 | 20 l lil rose | .20 | .20 |
| J88 | D10 | 25 l dk red | .20 | .20 |
| J89 | D10 | 30 l gray brn ('61) | .30 | .20 |
| J90 | D10 | 40 l dl brn ('66) | .20 | .20 |
| J91 | D10 | 50 l aqua | .30 | .20 |
| *a.* | | Type II | .30 | .20 |
| J92 | D10 | 100 l org yel ('58) | .25 | .20 |

**Engr.**
| | | | | |
|---|---|---|---|---|
| J93 | D10 | 500 l dp bl & dk car ('61) | 3.25 | .20 |
| J94 | D10 | 900 l dp car & gray grn ('84) | 1.20 | .25 |

| | | | | |
|---|---|---|---|---|
| J95 | D10 | 1500 l brown & orange | 3.00 | 1.60 |
| | | *Nos. J83,J86-J95 (11)* | 9.30 | 3.65 |

Type I imprint on No. J91 reads: "1ST POL. STATO OFF. CARET VALORI". Type II imprint reads: "I.P.Z.S. OFF. CARTE VALORI" (1992). No. J91 has lighter background with more distinguishable lettering and design.

No. J92 exists with both Type I & Type II imprints.

Nos. J92 and J93 exist with "I. P. Z. S. ROMA" imprint.

Issue date: 1500 l, Feb. 20, 1991.

### MILITARY STAMPS

Regular Stamps, 1929-42, Overprinted

**1943       Wmk. 140       Perf. 14**
| | | | | |
|---|---|---|---|---|
| M1 | A90 | 5c ol brn | .50 | .80 |
| M2 | A92 | 10c dk brn | .50 | .80 |
| M3 | A93 | 15c slate grn | .50 | .80 |
| M4 | A91 | 20c rose red | .50 | .80 |
| M5 | A94 | 25c dp grn | .50 | .80 |
| M6 | A95 | 30c ol grn | .50 | .80 |
| M7 | A95 | 50c purple | .50 | .40 |
| M8 | A91 | 1 l dk pur | 3.25 | 20.00 |
| M9 | A94 | 1.25 l deep blue | .50 | 1.00 |
| M10 | A92 | 1.75 l red org | .50 | .80 |
| M11 | A93 | 2 l car lake | .50 | 1.00 |
| M12 | A95a | 5 l rose red | .50 | 3.25 |
| M13 | A93 | 10 l purple | 3.25 | 29.00 |
| | | *Nos. M1-M13 (13)* | 12.00 | 60.25 |

Due to a shortage of regular postage stamps during 1944-45, this issue was used for ordinary mail. "P. M." stands for "Posta Militare."

### MILITARY AIR POST STAMPS

Air Post Stamps, 1930 Overprinted Like Nos. M1-M13 in Black

**1943       Wmk. 140       Perf. 14**
| | | | | |
|---|---|---|---|---|
| MC1 | AP3 | 50c olive brown | .50 | .80 |
| MC2 | AP5 | 1 l purple | .50 | .80 |
| MC3 | AP6 | 2 l deep blue | .50 | 15.00 |
| MC4 | AP3 | 3 l dark green | 3.25 | 25.00 |
| MC5 | AP3 | 5 l deep carmine | 3.25 | 32.50 |
| | | *Nos. MC1-MC5 (5)* | 8.00 | 74.10 |

### MILITARY AIR POST SPECIAL DELIVERY STAMPS

**#CE3 Overprinted Like #M1-M13**

**1943       Wmk. 140       Perf. 14**
| | | | | |
|---|---|---|---|---|
| MCE1 | APSD2 | 2 l gray black | 3.25 | 29.00 |

### MILITARY SPECIAL DELIVERY STAMP

**#E14 Overprinted Like #M1-M13**

**1943       Wmk. 140       Perf. 14**
| | | | | |
|---|---|---|---|---|
| ME1 | SD4 | 1.25 l green | .50 | 1.60 |

### OFFICIAL STAMPS

O1

**1875       Wmk. 140       Typo.       Perf. 14**
| | | | | |
|---|---|---|---|---|
| O1 | O1 | 2c lake | 4.00 | 5.00 |
| O2 | O1 | 5c lake | 4.00 | 5.00 |
| O3 | O1 | 20c lake | 3.25 | 1.60 |
| O4 | O1 | 30c lake | 3.25 | 3.25 |
| O5 | O1 | 1 l lake | 6.50 | 16.00 |
| O6 | O1 | 2 l lake | 20.00 | 50.00 |
| O7 | O1 | 5 l lake | 80.00 | 160.00 |
| O8 | O1 | 10 l lake | 150.00 | 135.00 |
| | | *Nos. O1-O8 (8)* | 271.00 | 375.85 |

For surcharges see Nos. 37-44.

Stamps inscribed "Servizio Commissioni" were used in connection with the postal service but not for the payment of postage.

### NEWSPAPER STAMP

N1

**Typographed, Numeral Embossed**
**1862**     **Unwmk.**     *Imperf.*
P1   N1   2c buff    52.50   *110.00*
   a.   Numeral double    475.00   *1,600.*

Black 1c and 2c stamps of similar type are listed under Sardinia.

### PARCEL POST STAMPS

King Humbert
I — PP1

**1884-86**   **Wmk. 140**   **Typo.**   *Perf. 14*
**Various Frames**
| | | | | |
|---|---|---|---|---|
| Q1 | PP1 | 10c olive gray | 125.00 | 100.00 |
| Q2 | PP1 | 20c blue | 250.00 | 160.00 |
| Q3 | PP1 | 50c claret | 10.00 | 15.00 |
| Q4 | PP1 | 75c blue grn | 10.00 | 15.00 |
| Q5 | PP1 | 1.25 l orange | 20.00 | 32.50 |
| Q6 | PP1 | 1.75 l brown | 25.00 | 125.00 |
| | *Nos. Q1-Q6 (6)* | | 440.00 | *447.50* |

For surcharges see Nos. 58-63.

Parcel Post stamps from No. Q7 onward were used by affixing them to the waybill so that one half remained on it following the parcel, the other half staying on the receipt given the sender. Most used halves are right halves. Complete stamps were and are obtainable canceled, probably to order.

Both unused and used values are for complete stamps.

PP2

**1914-22**    **Wmk. 140**    *Perf. 13*
| | | | | |
|---|---|---|---|---|
| Q7 | PP2 | 5c brown | 5.00 | 11.50 |
| Q8 | PP2 | 10c deep blue | 5.00 | 11.50 |
| Q9 | PP2 | 20c black ('17) | 20.00 | 11.50 |
| Q10 | PP2 | 25c red | 25.00 | 11.50 |
| Q11 | PP2 | 50c orange | 32.50 | 25.00 |
| Q12 | PP2 | 1 l violet | 37.50 | 10.00 |
| Q13 | PP2 | 2 l green | 40.00 | 10.00 |
| Q14 | PP2 | 3 l bistre | 50.00 | 32.50 |
| Q15 | PP2 | 4 l slate | 57.50 | 50.00 |
| Q16 | PP2 | 10 l rose lil ('22) | 100.00 | 50.00 |
| Q17 | PP2 | 12 l red brn ('22) | 160.00 | 310.00 |
| Q18 | PP2 | 15 l ol grn ('22) | 150.00 | 310.00 |
| Q19 | PP2 | 20 l brn vio ('22) | 125.00 | 310.00 |
| | *Nos. Q7-Q19 (13)* | | 807.50 | *1,153.* |

**Halves Used**
| | |
|---|---|
| Q7-Q14, each | .40 |
| Q15 | .80 |
| Q16 | 1.60 |
| Q17 | 4.00 |
| Q18 | 4.00 |
| Q19 | 6.50 |

Imperfs exist. Value per pair: 20c, 25c, 50c, 2 l, 3l, 4 l: $50 each; 10l $225.

### No. Q7 Surcharged

| | | | | |
|---|---|---|---|---|
| Q20 | PP2 | 30c on 5c brown | 1.60 | *16.00* |
| | Half stamp | | | *3.25* |
| Q21 | PP2 | 60c on 5c brown | 1.60 | *16.00* |
| | Half stamp | | | *3.25* |
| Q22 | PP2 | 1.50 l on 5c brown | 5.50 | *140.00* |
| | Half stamp | | | *6.50* |
|   a. | Double surcharge | | 250.00 | |

### No. Q16 Surcharged

| | | | | |
|---|---|---|---|---|
| Q23 | PP2 | 3 l on 10 l rose lilac | 5.50 | *55.00* |
| | Half stamp | | | *3.25* |
| | *Nos. Q20-Q23 (4)* | | 14.20 | *227.00* |

PP3

**1927-39**          **Wmk. 140**
| | | | | |
|---|---|---|---|---|
| Q24 | PP3 | 5c brn ('38) | .80 | *2.00* |
| Q25 | PP3 | 10c dp bl ('39) | .80 | *2.00* |
| Q26 | PP3 | 25c red ('32) | .80 | *2.00* |
| Q27 | PP3 | 30c ultra | .80 | *2.90* |
| Q28 | PP3 | 50c org ('32) | .80 | *2.00* |
| Q29 | PP3 | 60c red | .80 | *2.90* |
| Q30 | PP3 | 1 l lilac ('31) | .80 | *2.90* |
| Q31 | PP3 | 1 l brn vio ('36) | 24.00 | *72.50* |
| Q32 | PP3 | 2 l grn ('32) | .80 | *2.90* |
| Q33 | PP3 | 3 l bister | .80 | *6.50* |
|   a. | Printed on both sides | | 65.00 | |
| Q34 | PP3 | 4 l gray | .80 | *6.50* |
| Q35 | PP3 | 10 l rose lil ('34) | 2.40 | *40.00* |
| Q36 | PP3 | 20 l lil brn ('33) | 3.25 | *57.50* |
| | *Nos. Q24-Q36 (13)* | | 37.65 | *202.60* |

Value of used halves: Nos. Q24-Q34, each 40c; Q35 80c; Q36 $4.
For overprints see Italian Social Republic Nos. Q1-Q12.

Nos. Q24-Q30, Q32-Q36 Overprinted Between Halves in Black

**1945**       **Wmk. 140**      *Perf. 13*
| | | | | |
|---|---|---|---|---|
| Q37 | PP3 | 5c brown | 1.30 | *8.00* |
| Q38 | PP3 | 10c dp blue | 1.30 | *8.00* |
| Q39 | PP3 | 25c red | .90 | *8.00* |
| Q40 | PP3 | 30c ultra | 15.00 | *32.50* |
| Q41 | PP3 | 50c orange | 1.30 | *8.00* |
| Q42 | PP3 | 60c red | 1.30 | *8.00* |
| Q43 | PP3 | 1 l lilac | 1.30 | *8.00* |
| Q44 | PP3 | 2 l green | 1.30 | *8.00* |
| Q45 | PP3 | 3 l bister | 1.30 | *8.00* |
| Q46 | PP3 | 4 l gray | 1.30 | *8.00* |
| Q47 | PP3 | 10 l rose lilac | 16.00 | *65.00* |
| Q48 | PP3 | 20 l lilac brn | 24.00 | *140.00* |
| | *Nos. Q37-Q48 (12)* | | 66.30 | *309.50* |
| | Set, never hinged | | 160.00 | |

**Halves Used**
| | |
|---|---|
| Q37-48, each | .20 |

### Type of 1927
### With Fasces Removed
**1946**            **Typo.**
| | | | | |
|---|---|---|---|---|
| Q55 | PP3 | 1 l lilac | 1.90 | *5.00* |
| Q56 | PP3 | 2 l green | 1.40 | *5.00* |
| Q57 | PP3 | 3 l yellow org | 1.90 | *8.00* |
| Q58 | PP3 | 4 l gray | 4.00 | *8.00* |
| Q59 | PP3 | 10 l rose lilac | 42.50 | *75.00* |
| Q60 | PP3 | 20 l lilac brn | 57.50 | *250.00* |
| | *Nos. Q55-Q60 (6)* | | 109.20 | *351.00* |
| | Set, never hinged | | 260.00 | |

**Halves Used**
| | |
|---|---|
| Q55-Q58 | .20 |
| Q59 | .80 |
| Q60 | 1.25 |

PP4

PP5

**Perf. 13, 13x14, 12½x13**
**1946-54**     **Photo.**     **Wmk. 277**
| | | | | |
|---|---|---|---|---|
| Q61 | PP4 | 25c dl vio bl ('48) | .20 | .20 |
| Q62 | PP4 | 50c brown ('47) | .40 | .20 |
| Q63 | PP4 | 1 l golden brn ('47) | .40 | .20 |
| Q64 | PP4 | 2 l lt bl grn ('47) | .80 | .20 |
| Q65 | PP4 | 3 l red org ('47) | .40 | .20 |
| Q66 | PP4 | 4 l gray blk ('47) | 6.50 | 10.00 |
| Q67 | PP4 | 5 l lil rose ('47) | .40 | .20 |
|   a. | Perf. 13 | | .40 | .20 |
| Q68 | PP4 | 10 l violet | 8.00 | .40 |
|   a. | Perf. 13 | | 8.00 | 2.00 |
| Q69 | PP4 | 20 l lilac brn | 3.25 | .60 |
|   a. | Perf. 13 | | 5.00 | 1.00 |
| Q70 | PP4 | 30 l plum ('52) | 4.00 | 5.00 |
|   a. | Perf. 13 | | 4.00 | *5.00* |
| Q71 | PP4 | 50 l rose red | 16.00 | 2.40 |
|   a. | Perf. 13 | | 16.00 | 2.40 |
| Q72 | PP4 | 100 l sapphire | 40.00 | 45.00 |
|   a. | Perf. 13 | | 140.00 | 45.00 |
| Q73 | PP4 | 200 l green ('48) | 55.00 | 80.00 |
|   a. | Perf. 13 | | 55.00 | 80.00 |
| Q74 | PP4 | 300 l brn car ('48) | 725.00 | 1,050. |
|   a. | Perf. 13 | | 725.00 | 1,050. |
| Q75 | PP4 | 500 l brown ('48) | 40.00 | 35.00 |

**Engr.**
**Perf. 13**
| | | | | |
|---|---|---|---|---|
| Q76 | PP5 | 1000 l ultra ('54) | 2,800. | 3,100. |
| | *Nos. Q61-Q76 (16)* | | 3,700. | 4,329. |
| | Set, never hinged | | 5,500. | |

**Halves Used**
| | |
|---|---|
| Q61-Q73 | .20 |
| Q74 | 8.00 |
| Q75 | 3.25 |
| Q76 | 20.00 |

For overprints see Trieste Nos. Q1-Q26.

Catalogue values for unused stamps in this section, from this point to the end of the section, are for Never Hinged items.

**Perf. 12½x13**
**1955-59**    **Wmk. 303**    **Photo.**
**Without Imprint**
| | | | | |
|---|---|---|---|---|
| Q77 | PP4 | 25c vio bl | .20 | .20 |
| Q77A | PP4 | 50c brn ('56) | 3.00 | 3.00 |
| Q78 | PP4 | 5 l lil rose ('59) | .20 | .20 |
| Q79 | PP4 | 10 l violet | .20 | .20 |
| Q80 | PP4 | 20 l lil brn | .20 | .20 |
| Q81 | PP4 | 30 l plum ('56) | .20 | .20 |
| Q82 | PP4 | 40 l dl vio ('57) | .20 | .20 |
| Q83 | PP4 | 50 l rose red | .20 | .20 |
| Q84 | PP4 | 100 l sapphire | .20 | .20 |
| Q85 | PP4 | 150 l org brn ('57) | .20 | .20 |
| Q86 | PP4 | 200 l grn ('56) | .30 | .20 |
| Q87 | PP4 | 300 l brn car ('58) | .45 | .40 |
| Q88 | PP4 | 400 l gray blk ('57) | .55 | .45 |
| Q89 | PP4 | 500 l brn ('57) | 1.00 | .60 |

**Engr.**
**Perf. 13**
| | | | | |
|---|---|---|---|---|
| Q90 | PP5 | 1000 l ultra ('57) | 1.25 | .95 |
| Q91 | PP5 | 2000 l red brn & car ('57) | 4.50 | 4.50 |
| | *Nos. Q77-Q91 (16)* | | 12.85 | *11.90* |

**Halves Used**
| | |
|---|---|
| Q77-Q89 | .20 |
| Q90-Q91 | .40 |

**1960-66**    **Photo.**    *Perf. 12½x13*
| | | | | |
|---|---|---|---|---|
| Q92 | PP4 | 60 l bright lilac | .20 | .20 |
| Q93 | PP4 | 140 l dull red | .25 | .30 |
| Q94 | PP4 | 280 l yellow | .60 | .45 |
| Q95 | PP4 | 600 l olive bister | .70 | .75 |
| Q96 | PP4 | 700 l blue ('66) | 1.75 | .75 |
| Q97 | PP4 | 800 l dp org ('66) | 2.10 | .95 |
| | *Nos. Q92-Q97 (6)* | | 5.60 | 3.40 |

**Halves Used**
| | |
|---|---|
| Q92-Q93 | .20 |
| Q94 | .20 |
| Q95 | .40 |
| Q96-Q97 | .25 |

Imprint: "I.P.S.-Off. Carte Valori-Roma"

**1973, Mar.**    **Photo.**    **Wmk. 303**
| | | | | |
|---|---|---|---|---|
| Q98 | PP4 | 20 l lilac brown | .20 | .20 |
| Q99 | PP4 | 30 l plum | .20 | .20 |

### PARCEL POST AUTHORIZED DELIVERY STAMPS

For the payment of a special tax for the authorized delivery of parcels privately instead of through the post office.

Both unused and used values are for complete stamps.

PAD1

**1953**   **Wmk. 277**   **Photo.**   *Perf. 13*
| | | | | |
|---|---|---|---|---|
| QY1 | PAD1 | 40 l orange red | 12.50 | *12.50* |
| QY2 | PAD1 | 50 l ultra | 160.00 | *160.00* |
| QY3 | PAD1 | 75 l brown | 80.00 | *80.00* |
| QY4 | PAD1 | 110 l lil rose | 80.00 | *80.00* |
| | *Nos. QY1-QY4 (4)* | | 332.50 | *332.50* |
| | Set, never hinged | | 450.00 | |

**Halves Used**
| | |
|---|---|
| QY1 | .35 |
| QY2 | 1.25 |
| QY3 | 3.25 |
| QY4 | 3.25 |

For overprints see Trieste Nos. QY1-QY4.

Catalogue values for unused stamps in this section, from this point to the end of the section, are for Never Hinged items.

**1956-58**   **Wmk. 303**   *Perf. 12½x13*
| | | | | |
|---|---|---|---|---|
| QY5 | PAD1 | 40 l orange red | 1.60 | .90 |
| QY6 | PAD1 | 50 l ultra | 3.25 | 2.25 |
| QY7 | PAD1 | 60 l brt vio bl ('58) | 9.00 | 5.25 |
| QY8 | PAD1 | 75 l brown | 375.00 | 160.00 |
| QY9 | PAD1 | 90 l lil ('58) | .35 | .75 |
| QY10 | PAD1 | 110 l lil rose | 375.00 | 140.00 |
| QY11 | PAD1 | 120 l grnsh bl ('58) | .35 | .75 |
| | *Nos. QY5-QY11 (7)* | | 764.55 | 309.90 |

**Halves Used**
| | |
|---|---|
| QY5-QY6 | .20 |
| QY7 | .90 |
| QY8,QY10 | 8.00 |
| QY9 | .30 |
| QY11 | .25 |

**1960-81**
| | | | | |
|---|---|---|---|---|
| QY12 | PAD1 | 70 l green ('66) | 45.00 | 9.00 |
| QY13 | PAD1 | 80 l brown | .40 | .40 |
| QY14 | PAD1 | 110 l org yel | .40 | .40 |
| QY15 | PAD1 | 140 l black | .45 | .50 |
| QY16 | PAD1 | 150 l car rose ('68) | .30 | .50 |
| QY17 | PAD1 | 180 l red ('66) | .40 | .60 |
| QY18 | PAD1 | 240 l dk bl ('66) | .45 | .70 |

**Engr.**      *Perf. 13½*
| | | | | |
|---|---|---|---|---|
| QY19 | PAD1 | 500 l ocher ('76) | 1.40 | 1.40 |
| QY20 | PAD1 | 600 l bl grn ('79) | 1.40 | 1.40 |
| QY21 | PAD1 | 900 l ultra ('81) | 1.10 | 1.40 |
| | *Nos. QY12-QY21 (10)* | | 51.30 | 16.30 |

**Halves Used**
| | |
|---|---|
| QY12 | 4.00 |
| QY13-QY15, QY18, QY21 | .20 |
| QY16, QY17, QY19 | .25 |
| QY20 | .35 |

PAD2

*Perf. 14x13½*
**1984**   **Photo.**   **Wmk. 303**
| | | | | |
|---|---|---|---|---|
| QY22 | PAD2 | 3000 l multi | | 3.50 | 2.50 |

### OCCUPATION STAMPS

**Issued under Austrian Occupation**

Emperor Karl of Austria
OS1           OS2

## Austria #M49-M67 Surcharged in Black

### 1918 Unwmk. Perf. 12½

| | | | | |
|---|---|---|---|---|
| N1 | OS1 | 2c on 1h grnsh bl | .35 | .70 |
| N2 | OS1 | 3c on 2h red org | .35 | .70 |
| N3 | OS1 | 4c on 3h ol gray | .35 | .70 |
| N4 | OS1 | 6c on 5h ol grn | .35 | .70 |
| N5 | OS1 | 7c on 6h vio | .35 | .70 |
| a. | | Perf. 12½x11½ | 28.00 | 65.00 |
| N6 | OS1 | 11c on 10h org brn | .35 | .70 |
| N7 | OS1 | 13c on 12h blue | .35 | .70 |
| N8 | OS1 | 16c on 15h brt rose | .35 | .70 |
| N9 | OS1 | 22c on 20h red brn | .35 | .70 |
| a. | | Perf. 11½ | 14.00 | 30.00 |
| N10 | OS1 | 27c on 25h ultra | .50 | 1.00 |
| N11 | OS1 | 32c on 30h slate | .35 | .70 |
| N12 | OS1 | 43c on 40h ol bis | .35 | .70 |
| a. | | Perf. 11½ | 14.00 | 30.00 |
| N13 | OS1 | 53c on 50h dp grn | .35 | .70 |
| N14 | OS1 | 64c on 60h rose | .35 | .70 |
| N15 | OS1 | 85c on 80h dl bl | .35 | .70 |
| N16 | OS1 | 95c on 90h dk vio | .35 | .70 |
| N17 | OS2 | 2 l 11c on 2k rose, straw | .35 | .70 |
| N18 | OS2 | 3 l 16c on 3k grn, bl | 1.00 | 2.00 |
| N19 | OS2 | 4 l 22c on 4k rose, grn | 1.00 | 2.00 |
| | | Nos. N1-N19 (19) | 8.10 | 16.20 |

Emperor Karl — OS3

## Austria #M69-M81 Surcharged in Black

### 1918

| | | | |
|---|---|---|---|
| N20 | OS3 | 2c on 1h grnsh bl | 6.00 |
| N21 | OS3 | 3c on 2h orange | 6.00 |
| N22 | OS3 | 4c on 3h ol gray | 6.00 |
| N23 | OS3 | 6c on 5h yel grn | 6.00 |
| N24 | OS3 | 11c on 10h dk brn | 6.00 |
| N25 | OS3 | 22c on 20h red | 6.00 |
| N26 | OS3 | 27c on 25h blue | 6.00 |
| N27 | OS3 | 32c on 30h bister | 6.00 |
| N28 | OS3 | 48c on 45h dk sl | 6.00 |
| N29 | OS3 | 53c on 50h dp grn | 6.00 |
| N30 | OS3 | 64c on 60h violet | 6.00 |
| N31 | OS3 | 85c on 80h rose | 6.00 |
| N32 | OS3 | 95c on 90h brn vio | 6.00 |
| N33 | OS3 | 1 l 6c on 1k ol grn, grrnish | 6.00 |
| | | Nos. N20-N33 (14) | 84.00 |

Nos. N20 to N33 inclusive were never placed in use in the occupied territory. They were, however, on sale at the Post Office in Vienna for a few days before the Armistice.

## OCCUPATION SPECIAL DELIVERY STAMPS

Bosnia #QE1-QE2 Surcharged

### 1918 Unwmk. Perf. 12½

| | | | | |
|---|---|---|---|---|
| NE1 | SH1 | 3c on 2h ver | 5.50 | 12.00 |
| NE2 | SH1 | 6c on 5h dp grn | 5.50 | 12.00 |

Nos. NE1-NE2 are on yellowish paper. Reprints on white paper sell for about 70 cents a set.

## OCCUPATION POSTAGE DUE STAMP

### Bosnia #J16, J18-J19, J21-J24 Surcharged Like Nos. NE1-NE2

### 1918 Unwmk. Perf. 12½

| | | | | |
|---|---|---|---|---|
| NJ1 | D2 | 6c on 5h red | 1.90 | 3.75 |
| a. | | Perf. 11½ | 5.50 | 12.00 |
| NJ2 | D2 | 11c on 10h red | 1.90 | 3.75 |
| a. | | Perf. 11½ | 5.50 | 12.00 |
| NJ3 | D2 | 16c on 15h red | .90 | 1.90 |
| NJ4 | D2 | 27c on 25h red | .90 | 1.90 |
| NJ5 | D2 | 32c on 30h red | .90 | 1.90 |
| NJ6 | D2 | 43c on 40h red | .90 | 1.90 |
| NJ7 | D2 | 53c on 50h red | .90 | 1.90 |
| | | Nos. NJ1-NJ7 (7) | 8.30 | 17.00 |

## OCCUPATION NEWSPAPER STAMPS

Austrian #MP1-MP4 Surcharged

### 1918 Unwmk. Perf. 12½

| | | | | |
|---|---|---|---|---|
| NP1 | MN1 | 3c on 2h blue | .20 | .25 |
| a. | | Perf. 11½ | 2.75 | 6.00 |
| NP2 | MN1 | 7c on 6h org | .45 | .90 |
| NP3 | MN1 | 11c on 10h car | .45 | .90 |
| NP4 | MN1 | 22c on 20h brn | .35 | .70 |
| a. | | Perf. 11½ | 15.00 | 32.50 |
| | | Nos. NP1-NP4 (4) | 1.45 | 2.75 |

## A.M.G.

Issued jointly by the Allied Military Government of the United States and Great Britain, for civilian use in areas under Allied occupation.

> **Catalogue values for unused stamps in this section are for Never Hinged items.**

OS4

Offset Printing
"Italy Centesimi" (or "Lira") in Black

### 1943 Unwmk. Perf. 11

| | | | | |
|---|---|---|---|---|
| 1N1 | OS4 | 15c pale orange | 1.00 | .80 |
| 1N2 | OS4 | 25c pale citron | 1.00 | .80 |
| 1N3 | OS4 | 30c light gray | 1.00 | .80 |
| 1N4 | OS4 | 50c light violet | 1.00 | .80 |
| 1N5 | OS4 | 60c orange yellow | 1.00 | 1.90 |
| 1N6 | OS4 | 1 l lt yel green | 1.00 | .80 |
| 1N7 | OS4 | 2 l deep rose | 2.25 | 1.60 |
| 1N8 | OS4 | 5 l light blue | 3.25 | 2.75 |
| 1N9 | OS4 | 10 l buff | 3.25 | 4.00 |
| | | Nos. 1N1-1N9 (9) | 14.75 | 14.25 |

Italy Nos. 217, 220 and 221 Overprinted in Blue, Vermilion, Carmine or Orange

### 1943, Dec. 10 Wmk. 140 Perf. 14

| | | | | |
|---|---|---|---|---|
| 1N10 | A91 | 20c rose red (Bl) | 1.50 | 3.00 |
| 1N11 | A93 | 35c dp blue (C) | 17.50 | 19.00 |
| a. | | 35c deep blue (V) | 35.00 | 60.00 |
| 1N13 | A95 | 50c purple (C) | .75 | 1.10 |
| a. | | 50c purple (O) | .90 | 2.00 |
| | | Nos. 1N10-1N13 (3) | 19.75 | 23.10 |

Nos. 1N1-1N9 were for use in Sicily, Nos. 1N10-1N13 for use in Naples.

## VENEZIA GIULIA

> **Catalogue values for unused stamps in this section are for Never Hinged items.**

Stamps of Italy, 1929 to 1945 Overprinted in Black:

a b

### On Stamps of 1929

### 1945-47 Wmk. 140 Perf. 14

| | | | | |
|---|---|---|---|---|
| 1LN1 | A92 (a) | 10c dk brown | .30 | .35 |
| 1LN1A | A91 (a) | 20c rose red ('47) | .40 | .50 |

### On Stamps of 1945

### 1945 Wmk. 277 Perf. 14

| | | | | |
|---|---|---|---|---|
| 1LN2 | A249 (a) | 20c rose red | .35 | .50 |
| 1LN3 | A248 (a) | 60c sl grn | .45 | .35 |
| 1LN4 | A249 (a) | 1 l dp vio | .30 | .35 |
| 1LN5 | A251 (a) | 2 l dk red | .35 | .35 |
| 1LN6 | A252 (b) | 5 l dk red | .65 | .50 |
| 1LN7 | A251 (a) | 10 l purple | .90 | 1.25 |
| | | Nos. 1LN2-1LN7 (6) | 3.00 | 3.30 |

### On Stamps of 1945

### 1945-46 Unwmk.

| | | | | |
|---|---|---|---|---|
| 1LN7A | A250(a) | 10c dk brn ('46) | .30 | .25 |
| 1LN7B | A249(a) | 20c rose red ('46) | .25 | .50 |
| 1LN8 | A251(a) | 60c red org | .25 | .25 |
| | | Nos. 1LN7A-1LN8 (3) | .80 | 1.00 |

### On Air Post Stamp of 1930

### 1945 Wmk. 140 Perf. 14

| | | | | |
|---|---|---|---|---|
| 1LN9 | AP3 (a) | 50c olive brn | .25 | .50 |

### On Stamp of 1929

### 1946

| | | | | |
|---|---|---|---|---|
| 1LN10 | A91 (a) | 20 l lt green | 2.25 | 6.50 |

### On Stamps of 1945

### Wmk. 277

| | | | | |
|---|---|---|---|---|
| 1LN11 | A260 (a) | 25 l dk green | 8.00 | 8.00 |
| 1LN12 | A260 (a) | 50 l dk vio brn | 8.00 | 15.00 |

Italy No. 477 Overprinted in Black

| | | | | |
|---|---|---|---|---|
| 1LN13 | A261 | 100 l car lake | 29.00 | 65.00 |
| | | Nos. 1LN10-1LN13 (4) | 47.25 | 94.50 |

## Stamps of Italy, 1945-47 Overprinted Type "a" in Black

### 1947

| | | | | |
|---|---|---|---|---|
| 1LN14 | A259 | 25c brt bl grn | .25 | 1.00 |
| 1LN15 | A258 | 2 l dk claret brn | .60 | .35 |
| 1LN16 | A259 | 3 l red | .45 | .25 |
| 1LN17 | A259 | 4 l red org | .70 | .25 |
| 1LN18 | A257 | 6 l deep violet | 2.00 | 1.90 |
| 1LN19 | A259 | 20 l dk red vio | 55.00 | 4.00 |
| | | Nos. 1LN14-1LN19 (6) | 59.00 | 7.75 |

Some denominations of the Venezia Giulia A.M.G. issues exist with inverted overprint; several values exist in horizontal and vertical pairs, one stamp without overprint.

## OCCUPATION AIR POST STAMPS

> **Catalogue values for unused stamps in this section are for Never Hinged items.**

### Italy Nos. C106-C107 and C109-C113 Overprinted Like 1LN13 in Black

### 1946-47 Wmk. 277 Perf. 14

| | | | | |
|---|---|---|---|---|
| 1LNC1 | AP59 | 1 l sl blue ('47) | .40 | 5.00 |
| 1LNC2 | AP60 | 2 l dk blue ('47) | .40 | 2.50 |
| 1LNC3 | AP60 | 5 l dk green ('47) | 3.00 | 1.50 |
| 1LNC4 | AP59 | 10 l car rose ('47) | 3.00 | 1.50 |
| 1LNC5 | AP60 | 25 l dk blue | 3.00 | 1.50 |
| 1LNC6 | AP60 | 25 l brown ('47) | 35.00 | 35.00 |
| 1LNC7 | AP59 | 50 l dk green | 6.50 | 10.00 |
| | | Nos. 1LNC1-1LNC7 (7) | 51.30 | 57.00 |

Nos. 1LNC5 and 1LNC7 exist with inverted overprint; No. 1LNC5 with double overprint, one inverted.

## OCCUPATION SPECIAL DELIVERY STAMPS

> **Catalogue values for unused stamps in this section are for Never Hinged items.**

### Italy Nos. E20 and E23 Overprinted Like 1LN13 in Black

### 1946 Wmk. 277 Perf. 14

| | | | | |
|---|---|---|---|---|
| 1LNE1 | SD9 | 10 l deep blue | 4.00 | 1.60 |
| 1LNE2 | SD8 | 30 l deep violet | 8.75 | 19.00 |

## ITALIAN SOCIALIST REPUBLIC

On Sept. 15, 1943, Mussolini proclaimed the establishment of a Republican fascist party and a new fascist government. This government's authority covered only the Northern Italy area occupied by the Germans.

> **Catalogue values for unused stamps in this section are for hinged stamps. Never hinged examples are valued at 2-2.5 times the values shown.**

Italy Nos. 218, 219, 221 to 223 and 231 Overprinted in Black or Red:

a b

c

### 1944 Wmk. 140 Perf. 14

| | | | | |
|---|---|---|---|---|
| 1 | A94(a) | 25c deep grn | .30 | 2.00 |
| 2 | A95(b) | 30c ol brn (R) | .30 | 2.00 |
| 3 | A95(c) | 50c pur (R) | .30 | 2.00 |
| 4 | A94(a) | 75c rose red (R) | .30 | 2.00 |
| 5 | A94(b) | 1.25 l dp bl (R) | .30 | 2.00 |
| 5A | A94(b) | 50 l dp vio (R) | 250.00 | 3,100. |
| | | Nos. 1-5 (5) | 1.50 | 10.00 |

Nos. 1 to 5 exist with overprint inverted. Value, each: unused $40; used $25.
No. 1 exists with overprint "b." Value: unused, $55; used $550.
Counterfeits of No. 5A exist.

### Italy Nos. 427 to 438 Overprinted Same in Black or Red

| | | | | |
|---|---|---|---|---|
| 6 | A243(a) | 25c deep green | .45 | 3.25 |
| 7 | A244(a) | 25c deep green | .45 | 3.25 |
| 8 | A245(a) | 25c deep green | .45 | 3.25 |
| 9 | A246(a) | 25c deep green | .45 | 3.25 |
| 10 | A243(b) | 30c olive brown (R) | .45 | — |
| 11 | A244(b) | 30c olive brown (R) | .45 | — |
| 12 | A245(b) | 30c olive brown (R) | .45 | — |
| 13 | A246(b) | 30c olive brown (R) | .45 | — |
| 14 | A243(c) | 50c purple (R) | .45 | 3.25 |
| 15 | A244(c) | 50c purple (R) | .45 | 3.25 |
| 16 | A245(c) | 50c purple (R) | .45 | 3.25 |
| 17 | A246(c) | 50c purple (R) | .45 | 3.25 |
| | | Nos. 6-17 (12) | 5.40 | 26.00 |

Loggia dei Mercanti, Bologna — A1

Basilica of San Lorenzo, Rome — A2

Drummer Boy — A3

### 1944 Photo. Perf. 14

| | | | | |
|---|---|---|---|---|
| 18 | A1 | 20c crimson | .20 | .60 |
| 19 | A2 | 25c green | .20 | .60 |
| 20 | A3 | 30c brown | .20 | .60 |
| 21 | A3 | 75c dark red | .20 | 1.60 |
| | | Nos. 18-21 (4) | .80 | 3.40 |

For surcharges see Italy Nos. 461-462.

Church of St. Ciriaco, Ancona
A4

Monte Cassino Abbey
A5

Loggia dei Mercanti, Bologna
A6

Basilica of San Lorenzo, Rome
A7

Statue of "Rome"
A8

Basilica of St. Maria delle Grazie, Milan
A9

**1944**            **Unwmk.**

| | | | | |
|---|---|---|---|---|
| 22 | A4 | 5c brown | .20 | .35 |
| 23 | A5 | 10c brown | .20 | .20 |
| 24 | A6 | 20c rose red | .20 | .20 |
| 25 | A7 | 25c deep green | .20 | .20 |
| 26 | A3 | 30c brown | .20 | .20 |
| 27 | A8 | 50c purple | .20 | .20 |
| 28 | A8 | 75c dark red | 1.25 | 25.00 |
| 29 | A5 | 1 l purple | .20 | .20 |
| 30 | A9 | 1.25 l blue | .80 | 16.00 |
| 31 | A9 | 3 l deep green | .80 | 50.00 |
| | | Nos. 22-31 (10) | 4.25 | 92.55 |

Bandiera Brothers — A10

**1944, Dec. 6**

| | | | | |
|---|---|---|---|---|
| 32 | A10 | 25c deep green | .35 | .55 |
| 33 | A10 | 1 l purple | .35 | .55 |
| 34 | A10 | 2.50 l rose red | .35 | 7.50 |
| | | Nos. 32-34 (3) | 1.05 | 8.60 |

Cent. of the execution of Attilio (1811-44) and Emilio Bandiera (1819-44), revolutionary patriots who were shot at Cosenza, July 23, 1844, by Neapolitan authorities after an unsuccessful raid.

This set was overprinted in 1945 by the committee of the National Philatelic Convention to publicize that gathering at Venice.

---

### SPECIAL DELIVERY STAMPS

Italy Nos. E14 and E15 Overprinted in Red or Black

**1944**     **Wmk. 140**     **Perf. 14**

| | | | | |
|---|---|---|---|---|
| E1 | SD4 | 1.25 l green (R) | .25 | .60 |
| E2 | SD4 | 2.50 l deep orange | .25 | 25.00 |

---

Cathedral, Palermo
SD1

**1944**           **Photo.**

| | | | | |
|---|---|---|---|---|
| E3 | SD1 | 1.25 l green | .25 | 1.00 |

### AUTHORIZED DELIVERY STAMP

> Catalogue values for unused stamps in this section are for Never Hinged items.

Italy No. EY2 Overprinted

**1944**     **Wmk. 140**     **Perf. 14**

| | | | | |
|---|---|---|---|---|
| EY1 | AD2 | 10c dark brown | .25 | .80 |

### POSTAGE DUE STAMPS

Italy #J28-J40 Overprinted Like #EY1

**1944**     **Wmk. 140**     **Perf. 14**

| | | | | |
|---|---|---|---|---|
| J1 | D6 | 5c brown | 5.00 | 8.00 |
| J2 | D6 | 10c blue | 5.00 | 6.50 |
| J3 | D6 | 20c rose red | 5.00 | 6.50 |
| J4 | D6 | 25c green | 5.00 | 6.50 |
| J5 | D6 | 30c red org | 5.00 | 12.50 |
| J6 | D6 | 40c blk brn | 5.00 | 16.00 |
| J7 | D6 | 50c violet | 5.00 | 5.75 |
| J8 | D6 | 60c slate blk | 25.00 | 50.00 |
| J9 | D7 | 1 l red org | 5.00 | 5.75 |
| J10 | D7 | 2 l green | 16.00 | 29.00 |
| J11 | D7 | 5 l violet | 45.00 | 250.00 |
| J12 | D7 | 10 l blue | 80.00 | 400.00 |
| J13 | D7 | 20 l car rose | 80.00 | 450.00 |
| | | Nos. J1-J13 (13) | 286.00 | 1,246. |

### PARCEL POST STAMPS

Both unused and used values are for complete stamps.

Italian Parcel Post Stamps and Types of 1927-39 Overprinted Like No. EY1

**1944**     **Wmk. 140**     **Perf. 13**

| | | | | |
|---|---|---|---|---|
| Q1 | PP3 | 5c brown | 6.50 | 75.00 |
| Q2 | PP3 | 10c deep blue | 6.50 | 75.00 |
| Q3 | PP3 | 25c carmine | 6.50 | 80.00 |
| Q4 | PP3 | 30c ultra | 6.50 | 80.00 |
| Q5 | PP3 | 50c orange | 6.50 | 75.00 |
| Q6 | PP3 | 60c red | 6.50 | 290.00 |
| Q7 | PP3 | 1 l lilac | 6.50 | 75.00 |
| Q8 | PP3 | 2 l green | 375.00 | 1,800. |
| Q9 | PP3 | 3 l yel grn | 50.00 | 550.00 |
| Q10 | PP3 | 4 l gray | 90.00 | 650.00 |
| Q11 | PP3 | 10 l rose lilac | 190.00 | 250.00 |
| Q12 | PP3 | 20 l lilac brn | 500.00 | 3,750. |
| | | Nos. Q1-Q12 (12) | 1,250. | 7,750. |

No parcel post service existed in 1944. Nos. Q1-Q12 were used undivided, for regular postage.

---

## ITALIAN OFFICES ABROAD

Stamps listed under this heading were issued for use in the Italian Post Offices which, for various reasons, were maintained from time to time in foreign countries.

100 Centesimi = 1 Lira

---

### GENERAL ISSUE

Values of Italian Offices Abroad stamps vary tremendously according to condition. Quotations are for very fine examples, and values for unused stamps are for examples with original gum as defined in the catalogue introduction. Extremely fine or superb copies sell at much higher prices, and fine or poor copies sell at greatly reduced prices. In addition, unused copies without gum are discounted severely.

Very fine examples of Nos. 1-17 will have perforations barely clear of the frameline or design due to the narrow spacing of the stamps on the plates.

Italian Stamps with Corner Designs Slightly Altered and Overprinted

| | | | | |
|---|---|---|---|---|
| **1874-78** | | **Wmk. 140** | | **Perf. 14** |
| 1 | A6 | 1c olive green | 29.00 | 77.50 |
| a. | | Inverted overprint | 30,000. | |
| c. | | 2 dots in lower right corner | 80.00 | 260.00 |
| d. | | Three dots in upper right corner | 350.00 | 1,600. |
| e. | | Without overprint | 60,000. | |
| 2 | A7 | 2c orange brn | 32.50 | 45.00 |
| a. | | Without overprint | 60,000. | 80,000. |
| 3 | A8 | 5c slate grn | 950.00 | 47.50 |
| a. | | Lower right corner not altered | 17,500. | 2,250. |
| 4 | A8 | 10c buff | 2,400. | 45.00 |
| a. | | Upper left corner not altered | 17,500. | 2,250. |
| b. | | None of the corners altered | — | 55,000. |
| c. | | Lower corners not altered | — | 8,750. |
| 5 | A8 | 10c blue ('78) | 525.00 | 32.50 |
| 6 | A15 | 20c blue | 2,250. | 47.50 |
| 7 | A15 | 20c org ('78) | 8,750. | 27.50 |
| 8 | A8 | 30c brown | 8.00 | 24.00 |
| a. | | None of the corners altered | — | 35,000. |
| b. | | Right lower corner not altered | — | — |
| c. | | Double overprint | — | — |
| 9 | A8 | 40c rose | 8.00 | 32.50 |
| 10 | A8 | 60c lilac | 19.00 | 200.00 |
| 11 | A13 | 2 l vermilion | 240.00 | 725.00 |

| | | | | |
|---|---|---|---|---|
| **1881** | | | | |
| 12 | A17 | 5c green | 24.00 | 20.00 |
| 13 | A17 | 10c claret | 8.00 | 16.00 |
| 14 | A17 | 20c orange | 8.00 | 9.50 |
| a. | | Double overprint, on piece | — | — |
| 15 | A17 | 25c blue | 8.00 | 24.00 |
| 16 | A17 | 50c violet | 20.00 | 80.00 |
| 17 | A17 | 2 l vermilion | 24.00 | — |
| | | Nos. 12-17 (6) | 92.00 | |
| | | Nos. 12-16 (5) | | 149.50 |

The "Estero" stamps were used in various parts of the world, South America, Africa, Turkey, etc.

Forged cancellations exist on Nos. 1-2, 9-11, 16.

---

### OFFICES IN CHINA

100 Cents = 1 Dollar

**PEKING**

**PECHINO**
**2 CENTS**

Italian Stamps of 1901-16 Handstamped

**Wmk. 140, Unwmk.**

| | | | | |
|---|---|---|---|---|
| **1917** | | | **Perf. 12, 13½, 14** | |
| 1 | A48 | 2c on 5c green | 225.00 | 160.00 |
| c. | | 4c on 5c green | 5,600. | |
| 3 | A48 | 4c on 10c claret (No. 95) | 450.00 | 250.00 |
| c. | | 4c on 10c claret (No. 79) | — | |
| 5 | A58 | 6c on 15c slate | 875.00 | 600.00 |
| b. | | 8c on 15c slate | 3,500. | 3,000. |
| 7 | A58 | 8c on 20c on 15c slate | 4,000. | 2,400. |
| 8 | A50 | 8c on 20c brn org (No. 112) | 8,000. | 2,600. |

| | | | | |
|---|---|---|---|---|
| 9 | A49 | 20c on 50c vio | 45,000. | 24,000. |
| b. | | 40c on 50c violet | 16,000. | 12,500. |
| 11 | A46 | 40c on 1 l brn & grn | 260,000. | 35,000. |

Inverted surcharges are found on Nos. 1, 3, 3c, 5, 7-9; values same. Double surcharge one inverted exist on Nos. 1, 3; value about double.

Excellent forgeries exist of the higher valued stamps of Offices in China.

Italian Stamps of 1901-16 Overprinted

| | | | | |
|---|---|---|---|---|
| **1917-18** | | | | |
| 12 | A42 | 1c brown | 20.00 | 32.50 |
| 13 | A43 | 2c orange brown | 20.00 | 32.50 |
| a. | | Double overprint | 275.00 | |
| 14 | A48 | 5c green | 4.75 | 11.00 |
| a. | | Double overprint | 175.00 | |
| 15 | A48 | 10c claret | 4.75 | 11.00 |
| 16 | A50 | 20c brn org (No. 112) | 160.00 | 175.00 |
| 17 | A49 | 25c blue | 4.75 | 16.00 |
| 18 | A49 | 50c violet | 4.75 | 16.00 |
| 19 | A46 | 1 l brown & grn | 14.00 | 27.50 |
| 20 | A46 | 5 l blue & rose | 20.00 | 47.50 |
| 21 | A51 | 10 l gray grn & red | 160.00 | 375.00 |
| | | Nos. 12-21 (10) | 413.00 | 744.00 |

Italy No. 113, the watermarked 20c brown orange, was also overprinted "Pechino," but not issued. Value $20.

Italian Stamps of 1901-16 Surcharged:

a             b

TWO DOLLARS:
Type I — Surcharged "2 dollari" as illustration "b."
Type II — Surcharged "2 DOLLARI."
Type III — Surcharged "2 dollari." "Pechino" measures 11½mm wide, instead of 13mm.

| | | | | |
|---|---|---|---|---|
| **1918-19** | | | **Perf. 14** | |
| 22 | A42 | ½c on 1c brown | 140.00 | 140.00 |
| a. | | Surcharged "1 cents" | 800.00 | 800.00 |
| 23 | A43 | 1c on 2c org brn | 4.75 | 11.00 |
| a. | | Surcharged "1 cents" | 400.00 | 400.00 |
| 24 | A48 | 2c on 5c green | 4.75 | 11.00 |
| 25 | A48 | 4c on 10c claret | 4.75 | 11.00 |
| 26 | A50 | 8c on 20c brn org (No. 112) | 22.50 | 24.00 |
| 27 | A49 | 10c on 25c blue | 11.00 | 24.00 |
| 28 | A49 | 20c on 50c violet | 14.00 | 24.00 |
| 29 | A46 | 40c on 1 l brown & green | 200.00 | 250.00 |
| 30 | A46 | $2 on 5 l bl & rose (type I) | 325.00 | 600.00 |
| a. | | Type II | 87,500. | 67,500. |
| b. | | Type III | 12,500. | 8,750. |
| | | Nos. 22-30 (9) | 726.75 | 1,095. |

Italy No. 100 Surcharged

| | | | | |
|---|---|---|---|---|
| **1919** | | | | |
| 32 | A49 | 10c on 25c blue | 4.75 | 14.00 |

---

### PEKING SPECIAL DELIVERY STAMPS

Italian Special Delivery Stamp 1908 Overprinted Like Nos. 12-21

| | | | | |
|---|---|---|---|---|
| **1917** | | **Wmk. 140** | | **Perf. 14** |
| E1 | SD2 | 30c blue & rose | 9.50 | 32.50 |

No. E1 Surcharged

## 1918

| | | | | |
|---|---|---|---|---|
| E2 | SD2 | 12c on 30c bl & rose | 72.50 | 260.00 |

## PEKING POSTAGE DUE STAMPS

### Italian Postage Due Stamps Overprinted Like Nos. 12-21

| 1917 | | Wmk. 140 | Perf. 14 | |
|---|---|---|---|---|
| J1 | D3 | 10c buff & magenta | 3.25 | 10.00 |
| J2 | D3 | 20c buff & magenta | 3.25 | 10.00 |
| J3 | D3 | 30c buff & magenta | 3.25 | 10.00 |
| J4 | D3 | 40c buff & magenta | 6.50 | 10.00 |
| | | Nos. J1-J4 (4) | 16.25 | 40.00 |

### Nos. J1-J4 Surcharged Like No. E2

| 1918 | | | | |
|---|---|---|---|---|
| J5 | D3 | 4c on 10c | 87,500. | 67,500. |
| J6 | D3 | 8c on 20c | 32.50 | 52.50 |
| J7 | D3 | 12c on 30c | 87.50 | 160.00 |
| J8 | D3 | 16c on 40c | 325.00 | 800.00 |

In 1919, the same new values were surcharged on Italy Nos. J6-J9 in a different style: four lines to cancel the denomination, and "-PECHINO- 4 CENTS." These were not issued. Value $1.10 each.

---

## TIENTSIN

### TIENTSIN 2 CENTS

Italian Stamps of 1906 Handstamped

| | | Wmk. 140, Unwmk. | | |
|---|---|---|---|---|
| 1917 | | Perf. 12, 13½, 14 | | |
| 1 | A48 | 2c on 5c green | 400.00 | 400.00 |
| c. | | 4c on 5c green | 11,000. | |
| 2 | A48 | 4c on 10c claret | 725.00 | 550.00 |
| 4 | A58 | 6c on 15c slate | 1,750. | 1,200. |
| b. | | 4c on 15c slate | 4,750. | 4,400. |
| | | Nos. 1-4 (3) | 2,875. | 2,150. |

Italian Stamps of 1901-16 Overprinted

| 1917-18 | | | | |
|---|---|---|---|---|
| 5 | A42 | 1c brown | 20.00 | 32.50 |
| a. | | Inverted overprint | 325.00 | 325.00 |
| 6 | A43 | 2c orange brn | 20.00 | 32.50 |
| 7 | A48 | 5c green | 4.75 | 11.00 |
| 8 | A48 | 10c claret | 4.75 | 11.00 |
| 9 | A50 | 20c brn org (#112) | 160.00 | 175.00 |
| 10 | A49 | 25c blue | 4.75 | 16.00 |
| 11 | A49 | 50c violet | 4.75 | 16.00 |
| 12 | A46 | 1 l brown & grn | 14.00 | 27.50 |
| 13 | A46 | 5 l blue & rose | 20.00 | 47.50 |
| 14 | A51 | 10 l gray grn & red | 160.00 | 375.00 |
| | | Nos. 5-14 (10) | 413.00 | 744.00 |

Italy No. 113, the watermarked 20c brown orange was also overprinted "Tientsin," but not issued. Value $20.

Italian Stamps of 1901-16 Surcharged:

a  b

TWO DOLLARS:
Type I — Surcharged "2 Dollari" as illustration "b".
Type II — Surcharged "2 dollari".
Type III — Surcharged "2 Dollari". "Tientsin" measures 10mm wide instead of 13mm.

| 1918-21 | | | Perf. 14 | |
|---|---|---|---|---|
| 15 | A42 | ½c on 1c brown | 140.00 | 140.00 |
| a. | | Inverted surcharge | 400.00 | 400.00 |
| b. | | Surcharged "1 cents" | 800.00 | 800.00 |
| 16 | A43 | 1c on 2c org brn | 4.75 | 11.00 |
| a. | | Surcharged "1 cents" | 400.00 | 400.00 |
| b. | | Inverted surcharge | 400.00 | 400.00 |
| 17 | A48 | 2c on 5c green | 4.75 | 11.00 |
| 18 | A48 | 4c on 10c claret | 4.75 | 11.00 |

| 19 | A50 | 8c on 20c brn org (#112) | 22.50 | 24.00 |
|---|---|---|---|---|
| 20 | A49 | 10c on 25c blue | 11.00 | 24.00 |
| 21 | A49 | 20c on 50c violet | 14.00 | 24.00 |
| 22 | A46 | 40c on 1 l brn & grn | 200.00 | 250.00 |
| 23 | A46 | $2 on 5 l bl & rose (type I) | 325.00 | 600.00 |
| a. | | Type II | 13,000. | 8,750. |
| b. | | Type III ('21) | 11,500. | 8,750. |
| | | Nos. 15-23 (9) | 726.75 | 1,095. |

## SPECIAL DELIVERY STAMPS

Italian Special Delivery Stamp of 1908 Overprinted

| 1917 | | Wmk. 140 | Perf. 14 | |
|---|---|---|---|---|
| E1 | SD2 | 30c blue & rose | 9.50 | 32.50 |

No. E1 Surcharged

| 1918 | | | | |
|---|---|---|---|---|
| E2 | SD2 | 12c on 30c bl & rose | 72.50 | 250.00 |

## POSTAGE DUE STAMPS

Italian Postage Due Stamps Overprinted

| 1917 | | Wmk. 140 | Perf. 14 | |
|---|---|---|---|---|
| J1 | D3 | 10c buff & magenta | 3.25 | 10.00 |
| a. | | Double overprint | 275.00 | |
| J2 | D3 | 20c buff & magenta | 3.25 | 10.00 |
| J3 | D3 | 30c buff & magenta | 3.25 | 10.00 |
| a. | | Double overprint | 275.00 | |
| J4 | D3 | 40c buff & magenta | 6.50 | 10.00 |
| | | Nos. J1-J4 (4) | 20.00 | 27.50 |

Nos. J1-J4 Surcharged

| 1918 | | | | |
|---|---|---|---|---|
| J5 | D3 | 4c on 10c | 4,750. | 5,500. |
| J6 | D3 | 8c on 20c | 32.50 | 52.50 |
| J7 | D3 | 12c on 30c | 87.50 | 160.00 |
| J8 | D3 | 16c on 40c | 325.00 | 600.00 |

In 1919, the same new values were surcharged on Italy Nos. J6-J9 in a different style: four lines to cancel the denomination, and "-TIENTSIN- 4 CENTS." These were not issued. Value $8.00 each.

## OFFICES IN CRETE

40 Paras = 1 Piaster
100 Centesimi = 1 Piaster (1906)
Italy Nos. 70 and 81 Surcharged in Red or Black

a  b

| 1900-01 | | Wmk. 140 | Perf. 14 | |
|---|---|---|---|---|
| 1 | A36(a) | 1pi on 25c blue | 12.00 | 80.00 |
| 2 | A45(b) | 1pi on 25c dp bl (Bk) ('01) | 4.00 | 100.00 |

Italian Stamps Overprinted

### 1906
### On Nos. 76-79, 92, 81, 83-85, 87, 91

| 3 | A42 | 1c brown | 1.60 | 2.40 |
|---|---|---|---|---|
| a. | | Pair, one without ovpt. | 1,050. | |
| 4 | A43 | 2c org brn | 1.60 | 2.40 |
| a. | | Imperf., pair | 1,050. | |
| b. | | Double overprint | 300.00 | |
| 5 | A44 | 5c bl grn | 2.40 | 3.25 |
| 6 | A45 | 10c claret | 240.00 | 175.00 |
| 7 | A45 | 15c on 20c org | 2.40 | 3.25 |
| 8 | A45 | 25c blue | 8.00 | 12.00 |
| 9 | A45 | 40c brown | 8.00 | 12.00 |
| 10 | A45 | 45c ol grn | 6.50 | 12.00 |
| 11 | A45 | 50c violet | 8.00 | 16.00 |
| 12 | A46 | 1 l brn & grn | 52.50 | 67.50 |
| 13 | A46 | 5 l bl & rose | 325.00 | 350.00 |
| | | Nos. 3-13 (11) | 656.00 | 655.80 |

### On Nos. 94-95, 100, 104-105

| 1907-10 | | | | |
|---|---|---|---|---|
| 14 | A48 | 5c green | 1.60 | 1.60 |
| a. | | Inverted overprint | 300.00 | |
| 15 | A48 | 10c claret | 1.60 | 1.60 |
| 16 | A49 | 25c blue | 2.40 | 10.00 |
| 17 | A49 | 40c brown | 27.50 | 32.50 |
| 18 | A49 | 50c violet | 2.40 | 10.00 |
| | | Nos. 14-18 (5) | 35.50 | 55.70 |

### On No. 111 in Violet

| 1912 | | Unwmk. | Perf. 13x13½ | |
|---|---|---|---|---|
| 19 | A50 | 15c slate black | 2.40 | 4.00 |

## SPECIAL DELIVERY STAMP

Special Delivery Stamp of Italy Overprinted

| 1906 | | Wmk. 140 | Perf. 14 | |
|---|---|---|---|---|
| E1 | SD1 | 25c rose red | 8.00 | 16.00 |

## OFFICES IN AFRICA

40 Paras = 1 Piaster
100 Centesimi = 1 Lira (1910)

### BENGASI

Italy No. 81 Surcharged in Black

| 1901 | | Wmk. 140 | Perf. 14 | |
|---|---|---|---|---|
| 1 | A45 | 1pi on 25c dp bl | 47.50 | 160.00 |

### Same Surcharge on Italy No. 100

| 1911 | | | | |
|---|---|---|---|---|
| 1A | A49 | 1pi on 25c blue | 47.50 | 160.00 |

## TRIPOLI

Italian Stamps of 1901-09 Overprinted in Black or Violet

| 1909 | | | Wmk. 140 | |
|---|---|---|---|---|
| 2 | A42 | 1c brown | 4.00 | 3.25 |
| a. | | Inverted overprint | 275.00 | |
| 3 | A43 | 2c orange brn | 2.40 | 3.25 |
| 4 | A48 | 5c green | 125.00 | 9.50 |
| a. | | Double overprint | 275.00 | |
| 5 | A48 | 10c claret | 3.25 | 3.25 |
| a. | | Double overprint | 225.00 | 225.00 |
| 6 | A49 | 25c blue | 2.40 | 3.25 |
| 7 | A49 | 40c brown | 6.50 | 8.00 |
| 8 | A49 | 50c violet | 8.00 | 9.50 |
| | | Perf. 13½x14 | | |
| | | Unwmk. | | |
| 9 | A50 | 15c slate blk (V) | 4.00 | 4.75 |
| | | Nos. 2-9 (8) | 155.55 | 44.75 |

Italian Stamps of 1901 Overprinted

| 1909 | | Wmk. 140 | Perf. 14 | |
|---|---|---|---|---|
| 10 | A46 | 1 l brown & grn | 125.00 | 87.50 |
| 11 | A46 | 5 l blue & rose | 40.00 | 240.00 |

### Same Overprint on Italy Nos. 76-77

| 1915 | | | | |
|---|---|---|---|---|
| 12 | A42 | 1c brown | 2.40 | |
| 13 | A43 | 2c orange brown | 2.40 | |

Nos. 12-13 were prepared but not issued.

---

## SPECIAL DELIVERY STAMPS

### Italy Nos. E1, E6 Overprinted Like Nos. 10-11

**1909**    **Wmk. 140**    *Perf. 14*

| | | | | |
|---|---|---|---|---|
| E1 | SD1 | 25c rose red | 13.00 | 9.50 |
| E2 | SD2 | 30c blue & rose | 4.75 | 14.00 |

Tripoli was ceded by Turkey to Italy in Oct., 1912, and became known as the Colony of Libia. Later issues will be found under Libya.

---

### OFFICES IN TURKISH EMPIRE

**40 Paras = 1 Piaster**

Various powers maintained post offices in the Turkish Empire before World War I by authority of treaties which ended with the signing of the Treaty of Lausanne in 1923. The foreign post offices were closed Oct. 27, 1923.

### GENERAL ISSUE

Italian Stamps of 1906-08 Surcharged

### Printed at Turin

**1908**       **Wmk. 140**

| | | | | |
|---|---|---|---|---|
| 1 | A48 | 10pa on 5c green | 4.00 | 4.00 |
| 2 | A48 | 20pa on 10c claret | 4.00 | 4.00 |
| 3 | A49 | 40pa on 25c blue | 2.40 | 2.40 |
| 4 | A49 | 80pa on 50c violet | 4.00 | 4.00 |

See Janina Nos. 1-4.

Surcharged in Violet

**Unwmk.**

| | | | | |
|---|---|---|---|---|
| 5 | A47 | 30pa on 15c slate | 1.60 | 2.40 |
| | | *Nos. 1-5 (5)* | 16.00 | 16.80 |

Nos. 1, 2, 3 and 5 were first issued in Janina, Albania, and subsequently for general use. They can only be distinguished by the cancellations.

Italian Stamps of 1901-08 Surcharged:

Nos. 6-8       No. 9

Nos. 10-12

### Printed at Constantinople

**1908**       **First Printing**

| | | | | |
|---|---|---|---|---|
| 6 | A48 | 10pa on 5c green | 240. | 260. |
| a. | | Vert. pair, one without surcharge | | 2,400. |
| 7 | A48 | 20pa on 10c claret | 240. | 260. |
| 8 | A47 | 30pa on 15c slate | 800. | 800. |
| 9 | A49 | 1pi on 25c blue | 800. | 800. |
| a. | | "PIASTRE" | 1,200. | 1,200. |
| 10 | A49 | 2pi on 50c violet | 2,400. | 2,250. |
| 11 | A46 | 4pi on 1 l brn & grn | 11,000. | 7,500. |
| 12 | A46 | 20pi on 5 l bl & rose | 30,000. | 22,000. |

On Nos. 8, 9 and 10 the surcharge is at the top of the stamp. No. 11 has the "4" closed at the top. No. 12 has the "20" wide.

### Second Printing
Surcharged:

Nos. 13-15      No. 16

Nos. 17-19

| | | | | |
|---|---|---|---|---|
| 13 | A48 | 10pa on 5c green | 12.00 | 18.00 |
| 14 | A48 | 20pa on 10c claret | 12.00 | 18.00 |
| 15 | A47 | 30pa on 15c slate | 47.50 | 47.50 |
| a. | | Double surcharge | 190.00 | 190.00 |
| b. | | Triple surcharge | 450.00 | 450.00 |
| 16 | A49 | 1pi on 25c blue | 12.00 | 18.00 |
| a. | | "PIPSTRA" | 160.00 | 160.00 |
| b. | | "1" omitted | 160.00 | 160.00 |
| 17 | A49 | 2pi on 50c violet | 95.00 | 105.00 |
| a. | | Surcharged "20 PIASTRE" | 1,600. | 1,600. |
| b. | | "20" with "0" scratched out | 525.00 | 525.00 |
| c. | | "2" 5mm from "PIASTRE" | 190.00 | 190.00 |
| 18 | A46 | 4pi on 1 l brn & grn | 1,100. | 950.00 |
| 19 | A46 | 20pi on 5 l bl & rose | 5,500. | 2,800. |
| | | *Nos. 13-19 (7)* | 6,778. | 3,956. |

On No. 18 the "4" is open at the top.

### Third Printing

Surcharged in Red

| | | | | |
|---|---|---|---|---|
| 20 | A47 | 30pa on 15c slate | 8.00 | 8.00 |
| a. | | Double surcharge | 225.00 | 225.00 |

### Fourth Printing
Surcharged:

| | | | | |
|---|---|---|---|---|
| 20B | A46 | 4pi on 1 l brn & grn | 55.00 | 72.50 |
| c. | | Inverted "S" | 175.00 | 175.00 |
| 20D | A46 | 20pi on 5 l bl & rose | 160.00 | 200.00 |
| i. | | Inverted "S" | 450.00 | 450.00 |

### Fifth Printing
Surcharged

| | | | | |
|---|---|---|---|---|
| 20E | A46 | 4pi on 1 l brn & grn | 47.50 | 65.00 |
| f. | | Surch. "20 PIASTRE" | 1,900. | |
| 20G | A46 | 20pi on 5 l bl & rose | 47.50 | 65.00 |
| h. | | Double surcharge | 1,200. | 1,200. |

Italian Stamps of 1906-19 Surcharged

**1921**

| | | | | |
|---|---|---|---|---|
| 21 | A48 | 1pi on 5c green | 190.00 | 325.00 |
| 22 | A48 | 2pi on 15c slate | 6.50 | 9.50 |
| 23 | A50 | 4pi on 20c brn org (No. 113) | 65.00 | 75.00 |

| | | | | |
|---|---|---|---|---|
| 24 | A49 | 5pi on 25c blue | 65.00 | 75.00 |
| a. | | Double surcharge | 275.00 | |
| 25 | A49 | 10pi on 60c carmine | 4.00 | 6.50 |
| | | *Nos. 21-25 (5)* | 330.50 | 491.00 |

No. 21 is almost always found poorly centered, and it is valued thus.
On No. 25 the "10" is placed above "PIASTRE."

### Italian Stamps of 1901-19 Surcharged

n      o

**1922**

| | | | | |
|---|---|---|---|---|
| 26 | A42(n) | 10pa on 1c brown | 1.60 | 2.75 |
| 27 | A43(n) | 20pa on 2c org brn | 1.60 | 2.75 |
| 28 | A48(n) | 30pa on 5c green | 4.00 | 4.75 |
| 29 | A48(o) | 1pi20pa on 10c slate | 5.50 | 2.75 |
| 30 | A50(n) | 3pi on 20c brn org (#113) | 8.00 | 16.00 |
| 31 | A49(o) | 3pi30pa on 25c blue | 3.25 | 2.75 |
| 32 | A49(o) | 7pi20pa on 60c carmine | 6.50 | 4.75 |
| 33 | A46(n) | 15pi on 1 l brn & grn | 24.00 | 45.00 |
| | | *Nos. 26-33 (8)* | 54.45 | 81.50 |

No No. 32, the distance between the two lines is 2mm. See note after No. 58A.

### Italy No. 100 Surcharged

| | | | | |
|---|---|---|---|---|
| 34 | A49 | 3.75pi on 25c blue | 2.40 | 2.75 |

### Italian Stamps of 1901-20 Surcharged:

q      r

**1922**

| | | | | |
|---|---|---|---|---|
| 35 | A48 | 30pi on 5c green | 4.00 | 18.00 |
| 36 | A49 | 1.50pi on 25c blue | 2.40 | 8.00 |
| 37 | A49 | 3.75pi on 40c brown | 3.25 | 9.50 |
| 38 | A49 | 4.50pi on 50c violet | 8.00 | 20.00 |
| 39 | A49 | 7.50pi on 60c carmine | 6.50 | 14.00 |
| 40 | A49 | 15pi on 85c red brn | 12.00 | 28.00 |
| 41 | A46 | 18.75pi on 1 l brn & grn | 5.50 | 24.00 |

On No. 40 the numerals of the surcharge are above "PIASTRE."
On No. 42 the figure "4" is open at top. See note after No. 61.
On No. 43 the figure "9" has a curved or arched bottom. See note after No. 62.

Surcharged

| | | | | |
|---|---|---|---|---|
| 42 | A46 | 45pa on 5 l bl & rose | 400.00 | 550.00 |
| 43 | A51 | 90pa on 10 l gray grn & red | 400.00 | 725.00 |

### Italian Stamps of 1901-17 Surcharged Type "q" or:

| | | | | |
|---|---|---|---|---|
| 44 | A43 | 30pa on 2c org brn | 2.40 | 4.75 |
| 45 | A50 | 1.50pi on 20c brn org (#113) | 1.75 | 4.75 |
| | | *Nos. 35-45 (11)* | 845.80 | 1,406. |

### Italian Stamps of 1901-20 Surcharged in Black or Red

| | | | | |
|---|---|---|---|---|
| 46 | A48 | 30pa on 5c green | 1.60 | 2.40 |
| 47 | A48 | 1½pi on 10c claret | 1.60 | 2.40 |
| 48 | A49 | 3pi on 25c blue | 16.00 | 6.00 |
| 49 | A49 | 3¾pi on 40c brown | 2.40 | 2.40 |
| 50 | A49 | 4½pi on 50c violet | 40.00 | 35.00 |
| 51 | A49 | 7½pi on 85c red brn | 6.50 | 8.00 |
| a. | | "PIASIRE" | 40.00 | 40.00 |
| 52 | A46 | 7½pi on 1 l brn & grn (R) | 8.00 | 10.00 |
| a. | | Double surcharge | 160.00 | 160.00 |
| b. | | "PIASIRE" | 47.50 | 47.50 |
| 53 | A46 | 15pi on 1 l brn & grn | 60.00 | 130.00 |
| 54 | A46 | 45pi on 5 l blue & rose | 105.00 | 87.50 |
| 55 | A51 | 90pi on 10 l gray grn & red | 80.00 | 160.00 |
| | | *Nos. 46-55 (10)* | 321.10 | 443.70 |

### Italian Stamps of 1901-20 Surcharged Type "o" or:

No. 58      No. 59

Nos. 61-62

**1923**

| | | | | |
|---|---|---|---|---|
| 56 | A49 | 1pi20pa on 25c blue | 11.00 | |
| 57 | A49 | 3pi30pa on 40c brown | 11.00 | |
| 58 | A49 | 4pi20pa on 50c violet | 11.00 | |
| 58A | A49 | 7pi20pa on 60c car | 32.50 | |
| 59 | A49 | 15pi on 85c red brn | 11.00 | |
| 60 | A46 | 18pi30pa on 1 l brn & grn | 11.00 | |
| a. | | Double surcharge | 275.00 | |
| 61 | A46 | 45pi on 5 l bl & rose | 32.50 | |
| 62 | A51 | 90pi on 10 l gray grn & red | 27.50 | |
| | | *Nos. 56-62 (8)* | 147.50 | |

On No. 58A the distance between the lines is 1.5mm. On No. 61 the figure "4" is closed at top. On No. 62 the figure "9" is nearly rectilinear at bottom.
Nos. 56-62 were not issued.

---

### SPECIAL DELIVERY STAMPS

Italian Special Delivery Stamps Surcharged

Surcharged

**1908**    **Wmk. 140**    *Perf. 14*

| | | | | |
|---|---|---|---|---|
| E1 | SD1 | 1pi on 25c rose red | 2.40 | 4.00 |

Surcharged

**1910**

| | | | | |
|---|---|---|---|---|
| E2 | SD2 | 60pa on 30c blue & rose | 4.00 | 5.50 |

Surcharged

**1922**

| E3 | SD2 | 15pi on 1.20 l on 30c bl & rose | 24.00 | 65.00 |
|---|---|---|---|---|

On No. E3, lines obliterate the first two denominations.

15 PIASTRE

Surcharged

**1922**

| E4 | SD2 | 15pi on 30c bl & rose | 350.00 | 750.00 |
|---|---|---|---|---|

Surcharged

**1923**

| E5 | SD2 | 15pi on 1.20 l blue & red | | 13.00 |
|---|---|---|---|---|

No. E5 was not regularly issued.

## ALBANIA

Stamps of Italy Surcharged in Black

| | | **1902** | **Wmk. 140** | **Perf. 14** |
|---|---|---|---|---|
| 1 | A44 | 10pa on 5c green | 4.00 | 2.40 |
| 2 | A45 | 35pa on 20c orange | 5.50 | 6.50 |
| 3 | A45 | 40pa on 25c blue | 11.00 | 6.50 |
| | | Nos. 1-3 (3) | 20.50 | 15.40 |

Nos. 1-3 with red surcharges are proofs.

| | | **1907** | | |
|---|---|---|---|---|
| 4 | A48 | 10pa on 5c green | 40.00 | 52.50 |
| 5 | A48 | 20pa on 10c claret | 24.00 | 22.50 |
| 6 | A45 | 80pa on 50c violet | 24.00 | 22.50 |
| | | Nos. 4-6 (3) | 88.00 | 97.50 |

No. 5 is almost always found poorly centered, and it is valued thus.

## CONSTANTINOPLE

Stamps of Italy Surcharged in Black or Violet

| | | **Wmk. 140, Unwmk. (#3)** | | |
|---|---|---|---|---|
| | | **1909-11** | **Perf. 14, 12** | |
| 1 | A48 | 10pa on 5c green | 1.60 | 2.00 |
| 2 | A48 | 20pa on 10c claret | 1.60 | 2.00 |
| 3 | A47 | 30pa on 15c slate (V) | 1.60 | 2.00 |
| 4 | A49 | 1pi on 25c blue | 1.60 | 2.00 |
| a. | | Double surcharge | 210.00 | 210.00 |
| 5 | A49 | 2pi on 50c violet | 2.40 | 2.75 |

Surcharged

| 6 | A46 | 4pi on 1 l brn & grn | 2.40 | 3.25 |
|---|---|---|---|---|
| 7 | A46 | 20pi on 5 l bl & rose | 50.00 | 55.00 |
| 8 | A51 | 40pi on 10 l gray grn & red | 4.00 | 26.00 |
| | | Nos. 1-8 (8) | 65.20 | 95.00 |

Italian Stamps of 1901-19 Surcharged:

Nos. 10, 12-13 | Nos. 9, 11

| | | **1922** | | |
|---|---|---|---|---|
| 9 | A48 | 20pa on 5c green | 16.00 | 28.00 |
| 10 | A48 | 1pi20pa on 15c slate | 1.60 | 2.40 |
| 11 | A49 | 3pi on 30c org brn | 1.60 | 2.40 |
| 12 | A49 | 3pi30pa on 40c brown | 1.60 | 2.40 |
| 13 | A46 | 7pi20pa on 1 l brn & grn | 1.60 | 2.40 |
| | | Nos. 9-13 (5) | 22.40 | 37.60 |

Italian Stamps of 1901-20 Surcharged

| | | **1923** | | |
|---|---|---|---|---|
| 14 | A48 | 30pa on 5c green | 2.00 | 2.40 |
| 15 | A49 | 1pi20pa on 25c blue | 2.00 | 2.40 |
| 16 | A49 | 3pi30pa on 40c brown | 2.00 | 2.00 |
| 17 | A49 | 4pi20pa on 50c violet | 2.00 | 2.00 |
| 18 | A49 | 7pi20pa on 60c car | 2.00 | 2.00 |
| 19 | A49 | 15pi on 85c red brn | 2.00 | 3.25 |
| 20 | A46 | 18pi30pa on 1 l brn & grn | 2.00 | 3.25 |
| 21 | A46 | 45pi on 5 l bl & rose | 3.25 | 7.25 |
| 22 | A51 | 90pi on 10 l gray grn & red | 3.25 | 8.00 |
| | | Nos. 14-22 (9) | 20.50 | 32.55 |

## CONSTANTINOPLE SPECIAL DELIVERY STAMP

Unissued Italian Special Delivery Stamp of 1922 Surcharged in Black

| | | **1923** | **Wmk. 140** | **Perf. 14** |
|---|---|---|---|---|
| E1 | SD2 | 15pi on 1.20 l bl & red | 6.50 | 32.50 |

## CONSTANTINOPLE POSTAGE DUE STAMPS

Italian Postage Due Stamps of 1870-1903 Overprinted

| | | **1922** | **Wmk. 140** | **Perf. 14** |
|---|---|---|---|---|
| J1 | D3 | 10c buff & mag | 95.00 | 110.00 |
| J2 | D3 | 30c buff & mag | 95.00 | 110.00 |
| J3 | D3 | 60c buff & mag | 95.00 | 110.00 |
| J4 | D3 | 1 l blue & mag | 95.00 | 110.00 |
| J5 | D3 | 2 l blue & mag | 1,450. | 2,200. |
| J6 | D3 | 5 l blue & mag | 550.00 | 725.00 |
| | | Nos. J1-J6 (6) | 2,380. | 3,365. |

A circular control mark with the inscription "Poste Italiane Constantinopoli" and with the arms of the Kingdom of Italy (Savoy Cross) in the center was applied to each block of four of these stamps in black.

## DURAZZO

Stamps of Italy Surcharged in Black or Violet

| | | **Wmk. 140, Unwmk. (#3)** | | |
|---|---|---|---|---|
| | | **1909-11** | **Perf. 14, 12** | |
| 1 | A48 | 10pa on 5c green | 1.60 | 3.25 |
| 2 | A48 | 20pa on 10c claret | 1.60 | 3.25 |
| 3 | A47 | 30pa on 15c slate (V) | 47.50 | 4.00 |
| 4 | A49 | 1pi on 25c blue | 3.25 | 4.00 |
| 5 | A49 | 2pi on 50c violet | 3.25 | 4.00 |

Surcharged

| 6 | A46 | 4pi on 1 l brn & grn | 4.00 | 4.75 |
|---|---|---|---|---|
| 7 | A46 | 20pi on 5 l bl & rose | 210.00 | 225.00 |
| 8 | A51 | 40pi on 10 l gray grn & red | 20.00 | 95.00 |
| | | Nos. 1-8 (8) | 291.20 | 343.25 |

No. 3 Surcharged

| | | **1916** | **Unwmk.** | **Perf. 12** |
|---|---|---|---|---|
| 9 | A47 | 20c on 30pa on 15c slate | 4.00 | 20.00 |

## JANINA

Stamps of Italy Surcharged

| | | **1902-07** | **Wmk. 140** | **Perf. 14** |
|---|---|---|---|---|
| 1 | A44 | 10pa on 5c green | 8.00 | 3.25 |
| 2 | A45 | 35pa on 20c orange | 4.75 | 4.00 |
| 3 | A45 | 40pa on 25c blue | 28.00 | 9.50 |
| 4 | A45 | 80pa on 50c vio ('07) | 47.50 | 40.00 |
| | | Nos. 1-4 (4) | 88.25 | 56.75 |

Surcharged in Black or Violet

| | | **Wmk. 140, Unwmk. (#7)** | | |
|---|---|---|---|---|
| | | **1909-11** | **Perf. 14, 12** | |
| 5 | A48 | 10pa on 5c green | 1.60 | 3.25 |
| 6 | A48 | 20pa on 10c claret | 1.60 | 3.25 |
| 7 | A47 | 30pa on 15c slate (V) | 1.60 | 3.25 |
| 8 | A49 | 1pi on 25c blue | 1.60 | 3.25 |
| 9 | A49 | 2pi on 50c violet | 1.60 | 4.00 |

Surcharged

| 10 | A46 | 4pi on 1 l brn & grn | 4.00 | 4.75 |
|---|---|---|---|---|
| 11 | A46 | 20pi on 5 l bl & rose | 260.00 | 290.00 |
| 12 | A51 | 40pi on 10 l gray grn & red | 16.00 | 95.00 |
| | | Nos. 5-12 (8) | 288.00 | 406.75 |

## JERUSALEM

Stamps of Italy Surcharged in Black or Violet

| | | **Wmk. 140, Unwmk. (#3)** | | |
|---|---|---|---|---|
| | | **1909-11** | **Perf. 14, 12** | |
| 1 | A48 | 10pa on 5c green | 6.50 | 12.00 |
| 2 | A48 | 20pa on 10c claret | 6.50 | 12.00 |
| 3 | A47 | 30pa on 15c slate (V) | 6.50 | 17.50 |
| 4 | A49 | 1pi on 25c blue | 6.50 | 12.00 |
| 5 | A49 | 2pi on 50c violet | 24.00 | 40.00 |

Surcharged

| 6 | A46 | 4pi on 1 l brn & grn | 32.50 | 60.00 |
|---|---|---|---|---|
| 7 | A46 | 20pi on 5 l bl & rose | 1,100. | 950.00 |
| 8 | A51 | 40pi on 10 l gray grn & red | 47.50 | 450.00 |
| | | Nos. 1-8 (8) | 1,230. | 1,553. |

Forged cancellations exist on Nos. 1-8.

## SALONIKA

Stamps of Italy Surcharged in Black or Violet

| | | **Wmk. 140, Unwmk. (#3)** | | |
|---|---|---|---|---|
| | | **1909-11** | **Perf. 14, 12** | |
| 1 | A48 | 10pa on 5c green | 1.60 | 3.25 |
| 2 | A48 | 20pa on 10c claret | 1.60 | 3.25 |
| 3 | A47 | 30pa on 15c slate (V) | 2.40 | 3.25 |
| 4 | A49 | 1pi on 25c blue | 2.40 | 3.25 |
| 5 | A49 | 2pi on 50c violet | 2.40 | 4.00 |

Surcharged

| 6 | A46 | 4pi on 1 l brn & grn | 4.00 | 5.00 |
|---|---|---|---|---|
| 7 | A46 | 20pi on 5 l bl & rose | 450.00 | 575.00 |
| 8 | A51 | 40pi on 10 l gray grn & red | 15.00 | 11.50 |
| | | Nos. 1-8 (8) | 479.40 | 608.50 |

## SCUTARI

Stamps of Italy Surcharged in Black or Violet

| | | **Wmk. 140, Unwmk. (#3)** | | |
|---|---|---|---|---|
| | | **1909-11** | **Perf. 14, 12** | |
| 1 | A48 | 10pa on 5c green | 1.60 | 3.25 |
| 2 | A48 | 20pa on 10c claret | 1.60 | 3.25 |
| 3 | A47 | 30pa on 15c slate (V) | 25.00 | 6.50 |
| 4 | A49 | 1pi on 25c blue | 1.60 | 3.25 |
| 5 | A49 | 2pi on 50c violet | 1.60 | 5.00 |

Surcharged

| | | | | |
|---|---|---|---|---|
| 6 | A46 | 4pi on 1 l brn & grn | 3.25 | 5.00 |
| 7 | A46 | 20pi on 5 l bl & rose | 29.00 | 45.00 |
| 8 | A51 | 40pi on 10 l gray grn & red | 65.00 | 150.00 |
| | | Nos. 1-8 (8) | 128.65 | 221.25 |

**Surcharged like Nos. 1-5**

**1915**

| | | | | |
|---|---|---|---|---|
| 9 | A43 | 4pa on 2c orange brn | 2.40 | 5.00 |

No. 3 Surcharged

**1916    Unwmk.    Perf. 12**

| | | | | |
|---|---|---|---|---|
| 10 | A47 | 20c on 30pa on 15c slate | 5.00 | 25.00 |

### SMYRNA

Stamps of Italy
Surcharged in Black or
Violet

**Wmk. 140, Unwmk. (#3)**

**1909-11    Perf. 14, 12**

| | | | | |
|---|---|---|---|---|
| 1 | A48 | 10pa on 5c green | 1.60 | 1.60 |
| 2 | A48 | 20pa on 10c claret | 1.60 | 1.60 |
| 3 | A47 | 30pa on 15c slate (V) | 3.25 | 5.00 |
| 4 | A49 | 1pi on 25c blue | 3.25 | 5.00 |
| 5 | A49 | 2pi on 50c violet | 4.00 | 6.50 |

Surcharged

| | | | | |
|---|---|---|---|---|
| 6 | A46 | 4pi on 1 l brn & grn | 5.00 | 8.00 |
| 7 | A46 | 20pi on 5 l bl & rose | 150.00 | 180.00 |
| 8 | A51 | 40pi on 10 l gray grn & red | 20.00 | 100.00 |
| | | Nos. 1-8 (8) | 188.70 | 307.70 |

Italian Stamps of 1901-22 Surcharged:

Nos. 10, 12-13    Nos. 9, 11

**1922**

| | | | | |
|---|---|---|---|---|
| 9 | A48 | 20pa on 5c green | 25.00 | |
| 10 | A48 | 1pi20pa on 15c slate | 1.60 | |
| 11 | A49 | 3pi on 30c org brn | 1.60 | |
| 12 | A49 | 3pi30pa on 40c brown | 3.25 | |
| 13 | A46 | 7pi20pa on 1 l brn & grn | 3.25 | |
| | | Nos. 9-13 (5) | 34.70 | |

Nos. 9-13 were not issued.

### VALONA

Stamps of Italy
Surcharged in Black or
Violet

**Wmk. 140, Unwmk. (#3)**

**1909-11    Perf. 14, 12**

| | | | | |
|---|---|---|---|---|
| 1 | A48 | 10pa on 5c green | 1.60 | 3.25 |
| 2 | A48 | 20pa on 10c claret | 1.60 | 3.25 |
| 3 | A47 | 30pa on 15c slate (V) | 16.00 | 6.50 |
| 4 | A49 | 1pi on 25c blue | 2.40 | 3.25 |
| 5 | A49 | 2pi on 50c violet | 2.40 | 4.00 |

Surcharged

| | | | | |
|---|---|---|---|---|
| 6 | A46 | 4pi on 1 l brn & grn | 2.40 | 4.00 |
| 7 | A46 | 20pi on 5 l bl & rose | 50.00 | 57.50 |
| 8 | A51 | 40pi on 10 l gray grn & red | 52.50 | 150.00 |
| | | Nos. 1-8 (8) | 128.90 | 231.75 |

Italy No. 123
Surcharged in Violet
or Red Violet

**1916**

| | | | | |
|---|---|---|---|---|
| 9 | A58 | 30pa on 15c slate (V) | 4.00 | 12.50 |
| a. | | Red violet surcharge | 8.00 | 25.00 |

No. 9 Surcharged

| | | | | |
|---|---|---|---|---|
| 10 | A58 | 20c on 30pa on 15c slate | 1.60 | 16.00 |

### AEGEAN ISLANDS
#### (Dodecanese)

A group of islands in the Aegean Sea
off the coast of Turkey. They were occupied by Italy during the Tripoli War and
were ceded to Italy by Turkey in 1924 by
the Treaty of Lausanne. Stamps of Italy
overprinted with the name of the island
were in use at the post offices maintained in the various islands.

Rhodes, on the island of the same
name, was capital of the entire group.

100 Centesimi = 1 Lira

#### GENERAL ISSUE

Italian Stamps of 1907-
08 Overprinted

**1912    Wmk. 140    Perf. 14**

| | | | | |
|---|---|---|---|---|
| 1 | A49 | 25c blue | 42.50 | 30.00 |
| a. | | Inverted overprint | 250.00 | 250.00 |
| 2 | A49 | 50c violet | 42.50 | 30.00 |
| a. | | Inverted overprint | 250.00 | 250.00 |

**Virgil Issue**
Types of Italian Stamps of 1930
Overprinted in Red or Blue

**1930    Photo.    Wmk. 140    Perf. 14**

| | | | | |
|---|---|---|---|---|
| 3 | A106 | 15c vio blk | 1.25 | 17.00 |
| 4 | A106 | 20c org brn | 1.25 | 17.00 |
| 5 | A106 | 25c dk green | 1.25 | 6.75 |
| 6 | A106 | 30c lt brown | 1.25 | 6.75 |
| 7 | A106 | 50c dull vio | 1.25 | 6.75 |
| 8 | A106 | 75c rose red | 1.25 | 17.00 |
| 9 | A106 | 1.25 l gray bl | 1.25 | 21.00 |

**Engr.**
**Unwmk.**

| | | | | |
|---|---|---|---|---|
| 10 | A106 | 5 l + 1.50 l dk vio | 4.25 | 42.50 |
| 11 | A106 | 10 l + 2.50 l ol brn | 4.25 | 42.50 |
| | | Nos. 3-11,C4-C7 (13) | 30.75 | 352.25 |

**St. Anthony of Padua Issue**
Types of Italian Stamps of 1931
Overprinted in Blue or Red

**1932    Photo.    Wmk. 140    Perf. 14**

| | | | | |
|---|---|---|---|---|
| 12 | A116 | 20c black brn | 25.00 | 18.00 |
| 13 | A116 | 25c dull grn | 25.00 | 18.00 |
| 14 | A118 | 30c brown org | 25.00 | 21.00 |
| 15 | A118 | 50c dull vio | 25.00 | 17.00 |
| 16 | A120 | 1.25 l gray bl | 25.00 | 25.00 |

**Engr.**
**Unwmk.**

| | | | | |
|---|---|---|---|---|
| 17 | A121 | 75c lt red | 25.00 | 30.00 |
| 18 | A122 | 5 l + 2.50 l dp org | 25.00 | 110.00 |
| | | Nos. 12-18 (7) | 175.00 | 239.00 |

**Dante Alighieri Society Issue**
Types of Italian Stamps of 1932
Overprinted

**1932    Photo.    Wmk. 140**

| | | | | |
|---|---|---|---|---|
| 19 | A126 | 10c grnsh gray | 1.25 | 5.00 |
| 20 | A126 | 15c black vio | 1.25 | 5.00 |
| 21 | A126 | 20c brown org | 1.25 | 5.00 |
| 22 | A126 | 25c dp green | 1.25 | 5.00 |
| 23 | A126 | 30c dp org | 1.25 | 5.00 |
| 24 | A126 | 50c dull vio | 1.25 | 2.50 |
| 25 | A126 | 75c rose red | 1.25 | 8.50 |
| 26 | A126 | 1.25 l blue | 1.25 | 6.75 |
| 27 | A126 | 1.75 l ol brn | 1.60 | 8.50 |
| 28 | A126 | 2.75 l car rose | 1.60 | 8.50 |
| 29 | A126 | 5 l + 2 l dp vio | 2.10 | 21.00 |
| 30 | A126 | 10 l + 2.50 l dk brn | 2.10 | 32.50 |
| | | Nos. 19-30 (12) | 17.40 | 113.25 |

See Nos. C8-C14.

**Soccer Issue**
Types of Italy, "Soccer" Issue,
Overprinted in Black or Red

**1934**

| | | | | |
|---|---|---|---|---|
| 31 | A173 | 20c brn rose (Bk) | 67.50 | 75.00 |
| 32 | A174 | 25c green (R) | 67.50 | 75.00 |
| 33 | A174 | 50c violet (R) | 250.00 | 45.00 |
| 34 | A174 | 1.25 l gray bl (R) | 67.50 | 115.00 |
| 35 | A175 | 5 l +2.50 l bl (R) | 67.50 | 300.00 |
| | | Nos. 31-35 (5) | 520.00 | 610.00 |

See Nos. C28-C31.

**Same Overprint on Types of Medal
of Valor Issue of Italy, in Red or
Black**

**1935**

| | | | | |
|---|---|---|---|---|
| 36 | A177 | 10c sl gray (R) | 42.50 | 75.00 |
| 37 | A178 | 15c brn (Bk) | 42.50 | 75.00 |
| 38 | A178 | 20c red org (Bk) | 42.50 | 75.00 |
| 39 | A177 | 25c dp grn (R) | 42.50 | 75.00 |
| 40 | A178 | 30c lake (Bk) | 42.50 | 75.00 |
| 41 | A178 | 50c ol grn (Bk) | 42.50 | 75.00 |
| 42 | A178 | 75c rose red (Bk) | 42.50 | 75.00 |
| 43 | A178 | 1.25 l dp bl (R) | 42.50 | 75.00 |
| 44 | A177 | 1.75 l + 1 l pur (R) | 32.50 | 75.00 |
| 45 | A178 | 2.55 l + 2 l dk car (Bk) | 32.50 | 75.00 |
| 46 | A178 | 2.75 l + 2 l org brn (Bk) | 32.50 | 75.00 |
| | | Nos. 36-46 (11) | 437.50 | 825.00 |

See Nos. C32-C38, CE3-CE4.

Types of Italy, 1937,
Overprinted in Blue
or Red

**1938    Wmk. 140    Perf. 14**

| | | | | |
|---|---|---|---|---|
| 47 | A208 | 10c dk brn (Bl) | 3.00 | 6.75 |
| 48 | A208 | 15c pur (R) | 3.00 | 6.75 |
| 49 | A208 | 20c yel bis (Bl) | 3.00 | 6.75 |
| 50 | A208 | 25c myr grn (R) | 3.00 | 6.75 |
| 51 | A208 | 30c dp cl (Bl) | 3.00 | 6.75 |
| 52 | A208 | 50c sl grn (R) | 3.00 | 12.50 |
| 53 | A208 | 75c rose red (Bl) | 3.00 | 12.50 |
| 54 | A208 | 1.25 l dk bl (R) | 3.00 | 12.50 |
| 55 | A208 | 1.75 l + 1 l dp org (Bl) | 4.25 | 22.50 |
| 56 | A208 | 2.55 l + 2 l ol brn (R) | 4.25 | 22.50 |
| | | Nos. 47-56 (10) | 32.50 | 116.25 |

Bimillenary of birth of Augustus Caesar
(Octavianus), first Roman emperor.
See Nos. C39-C43.

**Same Overprint of Type of Italy,
1937, in Red**

**1938**

| | | | | |
|---|---|---|---|---|
| 57 | A222 | 1.25 l deep blue | 1.10 | 2.10 |
| 58 | A222 | 2.75 l + 2 l brown | 1.40 | 8.50 |

600th anniversary of the death of Giotto di
Bondone, Italian painter.

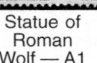

Statue of
Roman
Wolf — A1

Arms of
Rhodes — A2

Dante's
House,
Rhodes
A3

**1940    Photo.**

| | | | | |
|---|---|---|---|---|
| 59 | A1 | 5c lt brown | .40 | 1.25 |
| 60 | A2 | 10c pale org | .40 | 1.25 |
| 61 | A3 | 25c blue grn | 1.00 | 2.10 |
| 62 | A1 | 50c rose vio | 1.00 | 2.10 |
| 63 | A2 | 75c dull ver | 1.00 | 4.25 |

| | | | | |
|---|---|---|---|---|
| 64 | A3 | 1.25 l dull blue | 1.00 | 4.25 |
| 65 | A2 | 2 l + 75c rose | 1.00 | 21.00 |
| | | Nos. 59-65,C44-C47 (11) | 10.80 | 67.20 |

Triennial Overseas Exposition, Naples.

---

### AIR POST STAMPS

#### Ferrucci Issue

Types of Italian Air Post Stamps
of 1930 Overprinted in Blue or Red
Like Nos. 12-18

**1930**    **Wmk. 140**    *Perf. 14*

| | | | | |
|---|---|---|---|---|
| C1 | A104 | 50c brn vio (Bl) | 8.50 | 21.00 |
| C2 | A104 | 1 l dk bl (R) | 8.50 | 21.00 |
| C3 | A104 | 5 l + 2 l dp car (Bl) | 17.00 | 55.00 |
| | | Nos. C1-C3 (3) | 34.00 | 97.00 |

Nos. C1-C3 were sold at Rhodes only.

#### Virgil Issue

Types of Italian Air Post Stamps of
1930 Overprinted in Red or Blue Like
Nos. 3-11

**1930**        *Photo.*

| | | | | |
|---|---|---|---|---|
| C4 | A106 | 50c dp grn (R) | 2.50 | 32.50 |
| C5 | A106 | 1 l rose red (Bl) | 2.50 | 32.50 |

**Engr.**
**Unwmk.**

| | | | | |
|---|---|---|---|---|
| C6 | A106 | 7.70 l + 1.30 l dk brn (R) | 4.25 | 42.50 |
| C7 | A106 | 9 l + 2 l gray (R) | 4.25 | 67.50 |
| | | Nos. C4-C7 (4) | 13.50 | 175.00 |

#### Dante Alighieri Society Issue

Types of Italian Air Post Stamps of
1932 Overprinted Like Nos. 19-30

**1932**    **Wmk. 140**

| | | | | |
|---|---|---|---|---|
| C8 | AP10 | 50c car rose | 1.25 | 5.00 |
| C9 | AP11 | 1 l dp grn | 1.25 | 5.00 |
| C10 | AP11 | 3 l dl vio | 1.25 | 6.75 |
| C11 | AP11 | 5 l dp org | 1.25 | 6.75 |
| C12 | AP10 | 7.70 l + 2 l ol brn | 2.50 | 17.00 |
| C13 | AP11 | 10 l + 2.50 l dk bl | 2.50 | 25.00 |
| | | Nos. C8-C13 (6) | 10.00 | 65.50 |

Leonardo da
Vinci — AP12

**1932**    **Photo.**    *Perf. 14½*

| | | | | |
|---|---|---|---|---|
| C14 | AP12 | 100 l dp bl & grnsh gray | 19.00 | 120.00 |

Garibaldi Types of Italian Air Post
Stamps of 1932 Overprinted in Red
or Blue Like Nos. 12-18

**1932**

| | | | | |
|---|---|---|---|---|
| C15 | AP13 | 50c deep green | 42.50 | 105.00 |
| C16 | AP14 | 80c copper red | 42.50 | 105.00 |
| C17 | AP13 | 1 l + 25c dl bl | 42.50 | 105.00 |
| C18 | AP13 | 2 l + 50c red brn | 42.50 | 105.00 |
| C19 | AP14 | 5 l + 1 l bluish sl | 42.50 | 105.00 |
| | | Nos. C15-C19 (5) | 212.50 | 525.00 |

See Nos. CE1-CE2.

Graf
Zeppelin
over
Rhodes
AP17

**1933**        *Perf. 14*

| | | | | |
|---|---|---|---|---|
| C20 | AP17 | 3 l olive brn | 60.00 | 200.00 |
| C21 | AP17 | 5 l dp vio | 60.00 | 250.00 |
| C22 | AP17 | 10 l dk green | 60.00 | 375.00 |
| C23 | AP17 | 12 l dk blue | 60.00 | 425.00 |
| C24 | AP17 | 15 l car rose | 60.00 | 425.00 |
| C25 | AP17 | 20 l gray blk | 60.00 | 425.00 |
| | | Nos. C20-C25 (6) | 360.00 | 2,100. |

#### Balbo Flight Issue

Types of Italian Air Post Stamps of
1933 Overprinted

**1933**    **Wmk. 140**    *Perf. 14*

| | | | | |
|---|---|---|---|---|
| C26 | AP25 | 5.25 l + 19.75 l grn, red & bl gray | 45.00 | 135.00 |
| C27 | AP25 | 5.25 l + 44.75 l red, grn & bl gray | 45.00 | 135.00 |

#### Soccer Issue

Types of Italian Air Post Stamps of
1934 Overprinted in Black or Red Like
#31-35

**1934**

| | | | | |
|---|---|---|---|---|
| C28 | AP32 | 50c brown (R) | 8.50 | 50.00 |
| C29 | AP33 | 75c rose red) | 8.50 | 50.00 |
| C30 | AP34 | 5 l + 2.50 l red org | 21.00 | 110.00 |
| C31 | AP35 | 10 l + 5 l grn (R) | 21.00 | 135.00 |
| | | Nos. C28-C31 (4) | 59.00 | 345.00 |

#### Types of Medal of Valor Issue of Italy Overprinted in Red or Black Like #31-35

**1935**

| | | | | |
|---|---|---|---|---|
| C32 | AP36 | 25c dp grn | 60.00 | 92.50 |
| C33 | AP36 | 50c blk brn (R) | 60.00 | 92.50 |
| C34 | AP36 | 75c rose | 60.00 | 92.50 |
| C35 | AP36 | 80c dk brn | 60.00 | 92.50 |
| C36 | AP36 | 1 l + 50c ol grn | 42.50 | 92.50 |
| C37 | AP36 | 2 l + 1 l dp bl (R) | 42.50 | 92.50 |
| C38 | AP40 | 3 l + 2 l vio (R) | 42.50 | 92.50 |
| | | Nos. C32-C38 (7) | 367.50 | 647.50 |

#### Types of Italy Air Post Stamps, 1937,

Overprinted in Blue or Red Like #47-56

**1938**    **Wmk. 140**    *Perf. 14*

| | | | | |
|---|---|---|---|---|
| C39 | AP51 | 25c dl gray vio (R) | 3.25 | 6.75 |
| C40 | AP51 | 50c grn (R) | 3.25 | 6.75 |
| C41 | AP51 | 80c brt bl (R) | 3.25 | 21.00 |
| C42 | AP51 | 1 l + 1 l rose lake | 5.00 | 25.00 |
| C43 | AP51 | 5 l + 1 l rose red | 8.50 | 50.00 |
| | | Nos. C39-C43 (5) | 23.25 | 109.50 |

Bimillenary of the birth of Augustus Caesar
(Octavianus).

Statues of
Stag and
Roman
Wolf
AP18

Plane over Government Palace,
Rhodes — AP19

**1940**        *Photo.*

| | | | | |
|---|---|---|---|---|
| C44 | AP18 | 50c olive blk | 1.25 | 3.75 |
| C45 | AP19 | 1 l dk vio | 1.25 | 3.75 |
| C46 | AP18 | 2 l + 75c dk bl | 1.25 | 8.50 |
| C47 | AP19 | 5 l + 2.50 l cop brn | 1.25 | 15.00 |
| | | Nos. C44-C47 (4) | 5.00 | 31.00 |

Triennial Overseas Exposition, Naples.

---

### AIR POST SPECIAL DELIVERY STAMPS

Type of Italian Garibaldi Air Post
Special Delivery Stamps
Overprinted in Blue or Ocher Like
Nos. 12-18

**1932**    **Wmk. 140**    *Perf. 14*

| | | | | |
|---|---|---|---|---|
| CE1 | APSD1 | 2.25 l + 1 l bl & rose & (Bl) | 62.50 | 170.00 |

| | | | | |
|---|---|---|---|---|
| CE2 | APSD1 | 4.50 l + 1.50 l ocher & gray (O) | 62.50 | 170.00 |

#### Type of Medal of Valor Issue of Italy, Overprinted in Black Like Nos. 31-35

**1935**

| | | | | |
|---|---|---|---|---|
| CE3 | APSD4 | 2 l + 1.25 l dp bl | 42.50 | 92.50 |
| CE4 | APSD4 | 4.50 l + 2 l grn | 42.50 | 92.50 |

---

### ISSUES FOR THE INDIVIDUAL ISLANDS

#### Italian Stamps of 1901-20 Overprinted with Names of Various Islands as

a

b

c

The 1912-22 issues of each island
have type "a" overprint in black on all
values except 15c (type A58) and 20c
on 15c, which have type "b" overprint in
violet.

The 1930-32 Ferruci and Garibaldi
issues are types of the Italian issues,
printed in different colors or shades,
overprinted type "c."

---

### CALCHI

#### Overprinted "Karki" in Black or Violet

**1912-22**    **Wmk. 140**    *Perf. 13½, 14*

| | | | | |
|---|---|---|---|---|
| 1 | A43 | 2c orange brn | 6.00 | 6.75 |
| a. | | Double overprint | 300.00 | |
| 2 | A48 | 5c green | 2.50 | 6.75 |
| 3 | A48 | 10c claret | .40 | 6.75 |
| 4 | A48 | 15c slate ('22) | 3.25 | 32.50 |
| a. | | Double overprint | 300.00 | |
| 5 | A50 | 20c brn org ('21) | 3.25 | 30.00 |
| 6 | A49 | 25c blue | .40 | 6.75 |
| 7 | A49 | 40c brown | .40 | 6.75 |
| 8 | A49 | 50c violet | .40 | 12.00 |

**Unwmk.**

| | | | | |
|---|---|---|---|---|
| 9 | A58 | 15c slate (V) | 29.00 | 13.50 |
| 10 | A50 | 20c brn org ('17) | 92.50 | 125.00 |
| | | Nos. 1-10 (10) | 138.10 | 246.75 |

No. 9 Surcharged

**1916**        *Perf. 13½*

| | | | | |
|---|---|---|---|---|
| 11 | A58 | 20c on 15c slate | 1.60 | 21.00 |

#### Ferrucci Issue

Types of Italy
Overprinted in Red or Blue

**1930**    **Wmk. 140**    *Perf. 14*

| | | | | |
|---|---|---|---|---|
| 12 | A102 | 20c vio (R) | 3.25 | 6.75 |
| 13 | A103 | 25c dk grn (R) | 3.25 | 6.75 |
| 14 | A103 | 50c blk (R) | 3.25 | 6.75 |
| 15 | A103 | 1.25 l dp bl (R) | 3.25 | 6.75 |
| 16 | A104 | 5 l + 2 l dp car (Bl) | 6.75 | 22.50 |
| | | Nos. 12-16 (5) | 19.75 | 49.50 |

#### Garibaldi Issue

Types of Italy
Overprinted "CARCHI" in Red or Blue

**1932**

| | | | | |
|---|---|---|---|---|
| 17 | A138 | 10c brown | 17.00 | 30.00 |
| 18 | A138 | 20c red brn (Bl) | 17.00 | 30.00 |
| 19 | A138 | 25c dp grn | 17.00 | 30.00 |
| 20 | A138 | 30c bluish sl | 17.00 | 30.00 |
| 21 | A138 | 50c red vio (Bl) | 17.00 | 30.00 |
| 22 | A141 | 75c cop red (Bl) | 17.00 | 30.00 |
| 23 | A141 | 1.25 l dl bl | 17.00 | 30.00 |
| 24 | A141 | 1.75 l + 25c brn | 17.00 | 30.00 |
| 25 | A144 | 2.55 l + 50c org (Bl) | 17.00 | 30.00 |
| 26 | A145 | 5 l + 1 l dl vio | 17.00 | 30.00 |
| | | Nos. 17-26 (10) | 170.00 | 300.00 |

---

### CALINO

#### Overprinted "Calimno" in Black or Violet

**1912-21**    **Wmk. 140**    *Perf. 13½, 14*

| | | | | |
|---|---|---|---|---|
| 1 | A43 | 2c orange brn | 6.00 | 6.75 |
| 2 | A48 | 5c green | 1.60 | 6.75 |
| 3 | A48 | 10c claret | .40 | 6.75 |
| 4 | A48 | 15c slate ('21) | 3.25 | 32.50 |
| 5 | A50 | 20c brn org ('21) | 3.25 | 32.50 |
| 6 | A49 | 25c blue | 6.00 | 6.75 |
| 7 | A49 | 40c brown | .40 | 6.75 |
| 8 | A49 | 50c violet | .40 | 12.50 |

**Unwmk.**

| | | | | |
|---|---|---|---|---|
| 9 | A58 | 15c slate (V) | 22.50 | 13.50 |
| 10 | A50 | 20c brn org ('17) | 67.50 | 125.00 |
| | | Nos. 1-10 (10) | 111.30 | 249.75 |

No. 9 Surcharged Like Calchi No. 11

**1916**        *Perf. 13½*

| | | | | |
|---|---|---|---|---|
| 11 | A58 | 20c on 15c slate | 13.50 | 25.00 |

#### Ferrucci Issue

Types of Italy
Overprinted in Red or Blue

**1930**    **Wmk. 140**    *Perf. 14*

| | | | | |
|---|---|---|---|---|
| 12 | A102 | 20c violet (R) | 3.25 | 6.75 |
| 13 | A103 | 25c dk green (R) | 3.25 | 6.75 |
| 14 | A103 | 50c black (R) | 3.25 | 6.75 |
| 15 | A103 | 1.25 l dp bl (R) | 3.25 | 6.75 |
| 16 | A104 | 5 l + 2 l dp car (Bl) | 6.75 | 22.50 |
| | | Nos. 12-16 (5) | 19.75 | 49.50 |

#### Garibaldi Issue

Types of Italy
Overprinted in Red or Blue

**1932**

| | | | | |
|---|---|---|---|---|
| 17 | A138 | 10c brown | 17.00 | 30.00 |
| 18 | A138 | 20c red brn (Bl) | 17.00 | 30.00 |
| 19 | A138 | 25c dp grn | 17.00 | 30.00 |
| 20 | A138 | 30c bluish sl | 17.00 | 30.00 |
| 21 | A138 | 50c red vio (Bl) | 17.00 | 30.00 |
| 22 | A141 | 75c cop red (Bl) | 17.00 | 30.00 |
| 23 | A141 | 1.25 l dull blue | 17.00 | 30.00 |
| 24 | A141 | 1.75 l + 25c brn | 17.00 | 30.00 |
| 25 | A144 | 2.55 l + 50c org (Bl) | 17.00 | 30.00 |
| 26 | A145 | 5 l + 1 l dl vio | 17.00 | 30.00 |
| | | Nos. 17-26 (10) | 170.00 | 300.00 |

---

### CASO

#### Overprinted "Caso" in Black or Violet

**1912-21**    **Wmk. 140**    *Perf. 13½, 14*

| | | | | |
|---|---|---|---|---|
| 1 | A43 | 2c orange brn | 6.00 | 6.75 |
| 2 | A48 | 5c green | 2.50 | 6.75 |
| 3 | A48 | 10c claret | .40 | 6.75 |
| 4 | A48 | 15c slate ('21) | 3.25 | 32.50 |
| 5 | A50 | 20c brn org ('20) | 3.25 | 30.00 |
| 6 | A49 | 25c blue | .40 | 6.75 |
| 7 | A49 | 40c brown | .40 | 6.75 |
| 8 | A49 | 50c violet | .40 | 12.50 |

**Unwmk.**

| | | | | |
|---|---|---|---|---|
| 9 | A58 | 15c slate (V) | 29.00 | 13.50 |
| 10 | A50 | 20c brn org ('17) | 92.50 | 125.00 |
| | | Nos. 1-10 (10) | 138.10 | 247.25 |

No. 9 Surcharged Like Calchi No. 11

**1916**        *Perf. 13½*

| | | | | |
|---|---|---|---|---|
| 11 | A58 | 20c on 15c slate | .85 | 17.00 |

#### Ferrucci Issue

Types of Italy
Overprinted in Red or Blue

**1930**    **Wmk. 140**    *Perf. 14*

| | | | | |
|---|---|---|---|---|
| 12 | A102 | 20c vio (R) | 3.25 | 6.75 |
| 13 | A103 | 25c dk grn (R) | 3.25 | 6.75 |
| 14 | A103 | 50c blk (R) | 3.25 | 6.75 |
| 15 | A103 | 1.25 l dp bl (R) | 3.25 | 6.75 |

| 16 | A104 | 5 l + 2 l dp car (Bl) | 6.75 | 22.50 |
|---|---|---|---|---|
| | | Nos. 12-16 (5) | 19.75 | 49.50 |

### Garibaldi Issue
Types of Italy
Overprinted in Red or Blue

**1932**

| 17 | A138 | 10c brown | 17.00 | 30.00 |
|---|---|---|---|---|
| 18 | A138 | 20c red brn (Bl) | 17.00 | 30.00 |
| 19 | A138 | 25c dp grn | 17.00 | 30.00 |
| 20 | A138 | 30c bluish sl | 17.00 | 30.00 |
| 21 | A138 | 50c red vio (Bl) | 17.00 | 30.00 |
| 22 | A141 | 75c cop red (Bl) | 17.00 | 30.00 |
| 23 | A141 | 1.25 l dl bl | 17.00 | 30.00 |
| 24 | A141 | 1.75 l + 25c brn | 17.00 | 30.00 |
| 25 | A144 | 2.55 l + 50c org (Bl) | 17.00 | 30.00 |
| 26 | A145 | 5 l + 1 l dl vio | 17.00 | 30.00 |
| | | Nos. 17-26 (10) | 170.00 | 300.00 |

### COO

### (Cos, Kos)

### Overprinted "Cos" in Black or Violet

| 1912-22 | | Wmk. 140 | Perf. 13½, 14 | |
|---|---|---|---|---|
| 1 | A43 | 2c orange brn | 6.00 | 6.75 |
| 2 | A48 | 5c green | 62.50 | 6.75 |
| 3 | A48 | 10c claret | 2.50 | 6.75 |
| 4 | A48 | 15c slate ('22) | 3.25 | 45.00 |
| 5 | A50 | 20c brn org ('21) | 2.50 | 27.50 |
| 6 | A49 | 25c blue | 27.50 | 6.75 |
| 7 | A49 | 40c brown | .40 | 6.75 |
| 8 | A49 | 50c violet | .40 | 12.50 |

### Unwmk.

| 9 | A58 | 15c slate (V) | 32.50 | 13.50 |
|---|---|---|---|---|
| 10 | A50 | 20c brn org ('17) | 37.50 | 125.00 |
| | | Nos. 1-10 (10) | 175.05 | 257.25 |

### No. 9 Surcharged Like Calchi No. 11

**1916** — **Perf. 13½**

| 11 | A58 | 20c on 15c slate | 13.50 | 30.00 |
|---|---|---|---|---|

### Ferrucci Issue
Types of Italy
Overprinted in Red or Blue

| 1930 | | Wmk. 140 | Perf. 14 | |
|---|---|---|---|---|
| 12 | A102 | 20c vio (R) | 3.25 | 6.75 |
| 13 | A103 | 25c dk green (R) | 3.25 | 6.75 |
| 14 | A103 | 50c blk (R) | 3.25 | 6.75 |
| 15 | A103 | 1.25 l dp bl (R) | 3.25 | 6.75 |
| 16 | A104 | 5 l + 2 l dp car (Bl) | 6.75 | 22.50 |
| | | Nos. 12-16 (5) | 19.75 | 49.50 |

### Garibaldi Issue
Types of Italy
Overprinted in Red or Blue

**1932**

| 17 | A138 | 10c brown | 17.00 | 30.00 |
|---|---|---|---|---|
| 18 | A138 | 20c red brn (Bl) | 17.00 | 30.00 |
| 19 | A138 | 25c dp grn | 17.00 | 30.00 |
| 20 | A138 | 30c bluish sl | 17.00 | 30.00 |
| 21 | A138 | 50c red vio (Bl) | 17.00 | 30.00 |
| 22 | A141 | 75c cop red (Bl) | 17.00 | 30.00 |
| 23 | A141 | 1.25 l dl bl | 17.00 | 30.00 |
| 24 | A141 | 1.75 l + 25c brn | 17.00 | 30.00 |
| 25 | A144 | 2.55 l + 50c org (Bl) | 17.00 | 30.00 |
| 26 | A145 | 5 l + 1 l dl vio | 17.00 | 30.00 |
| | | Nos. 17-26 (10) | 170.00 | 300.00 |

### LERO

### Overprinted "Leros" in Black or Violet

| 1912-22 | | Wmk. 140 | Perf. 13½, 14 | |
|---|---|---|---|---|
| 1 | A43 | 2c orange brn | 6.75 | 6.75 |
| 2 | A48 | 5c green | 5.00 | 6.75 |
| 3 | A48 | 10c claret | 1.60 | 6.75 |
| 4 | A48 | 15c slate ('22) | 3.25 | 6.75 |
| 5 | A50 | 20c brn org ('21) | 110.00 | 85.00 |
| 6 | A49 | 25c blue | 32.50 | 6.75 |
| 7 | A49 | 40c brown | 3.25 | 6.75 |
| 8 | A49 | 50c violet | .40 | 12.50 |

### Unwmk.

| 9 | A58 | 15c slate (V) | 50.00 | 13.50 |
|---|---|---|---|---|
| 10 | A50 | 20c brn org ('17) | 37.50 | 125.00 |
| | | Nos. 1-10 (10) | 250.25 | 299.75 |

### No. 9 Surcharged Like Calchi No. 11

**1916** — **Perf. 13½**

| 11 | A58 | 20c on 15c slate | 13.50 | 25.00 |
|---|---|---|---|---|

### Ferrucci Issue
Types of Italy
Overprinted in Red or Blue

| 1930 | | | Perf. 14 | |
|---|---|---|---|---|
| 12 | A102 | 20c violet (R) | 3.25 | 6.75 |
| 13 | A103 | 25c dk green (R) | 3.25 | 6.75 |
| 14 | A103 | 50c black (R) | 3.25 | 6.75 |
| 15 | A103 | 1.25 l dp bl (R) | 3.25 | 6.75 |
| 16 | A104 | 5 l + 2 l dp car (Bl) | 6.75 | 22.50 |
| | | Nos. 12-16 (5) | 19.75 | 49.50 |

### Garibaldi Issue
Types of Italy
Overprinted in Red or Blue

**1932**

| 17 | A138 | 10c brown | 17.00 | 30.00 |
|---|---|---|---|---|
| 18 | A138 | 20c red brn (Bl) | 17.00 | 30.00 |
| 19 | A138 | 25c dp grn | 17.00 | 30.00 |
| 20 | A138 | 30c bluish sl | 17.00 | 30.00 |
| 21 | A138 | 50c red vio (Bl) | 17.00 | 30.00 |
| 22 | A141 | 75c cop red (Bl) | 17.00 | 30.00 |
| 23 | A141 | 1.25 l dl bl | 17.00 | 30.00 |
| 24 | A141 | 1.75 l + 25c brn | 17.00 | 30.00 |
| 25 | A144 | 2.55 l + 50c org (Bl) | 17.00 | 30.00 |
| 26 | A145 | 5 l + 1 l dl vio | 17.00 | 30.00 |
| | | Nos. 17-26 (10) | 170.00 | 300.00 |

### LISSO

### Overprinted "Lipso" in Black or Violet

| 1912-22 | | Wmk. 140 | Perf. 13½, 14 | |
|---|---|---|---|---|
| 1 | A43 | 2c orange brn | 6.00 | 6.75 |
| 2 | A48 | 5c green | 2.50 | 6.75 |
| 3 | A48 | 10c claret | 1.60 | 6.75 |
| 4 | A48 | 15c slate ('22) | 3.25 | 30.00 |
| 5 | A50 | 20c brn org ('21) | 3.25 | 32.50 |
| 6 | A49 | 25c blue | .40 | 6.75 |
| 7 | A49 | 40c brown | 1.60 | 6.75 |
| 8 | A49 | 50c violet | .40 | 12.50 |

### Unwmk.

| 9 | A58 | 15c slate (V) | 26.50 | 13.50 |
|---|---|---|---|---|
| 10 | A50 | 20c brn org ('17) | 60.00 | 125.00 |
| | | Nos. 1-10 (10) | 105.50 | 247.25 |

### No. 9 Surcharged Like Calchi No. 11

**1916** — **Perf. 13½**

| 11 | A58 | 20c on 15c slate | .85 | 20.00 |
|---|---|---|---|---|

### Ferrucci Issue
Types of Italy
Overprinted in Red or Blue

| 1930 | | Wmk. 140 | Perf. 14 | |
|---|---|---|---|---|
| 12 | A102 | 20c vio (R) | 3.25 | 6.75 |
| 13 | A103 | 25c dk grn (R) | 3.25 | 6.75 |
| 14 | A103 | 50c blk (R) | 3.25 | 6.75 |
| 15 | A103 | 1.25 l dp bl (R) | 3.25 | 6.75 |
| 16 | A104 | 5 l + 2 l dp car (Bl) | 6.75 | 22.50 |
| | | Nos. 12-16 (5) | 19.75 | 49.50 |

### Garibaldi Issue
Types of Italy
Overprinted "LIPSO" in Red or Blue

**1932**

| 17 | A138 | 10c brown | 17.00 | 30.00 |
|---|---|---|---|---|
| 18 | A138 | 20c red brn (bl) | 17.00 | 30.00 |
| 19 | A138 | 25c dp grn | 17.00 | 30.00 |
| 20 | A138 | 30c bluish sl | 17.00 | 30.00 |
| 21 | A138 | 50c red vio (Bl) | 17.00 | 30.00 |
| 22 | A141 | 75c cop red (Bl) | 17.00 | 30.00 |
| 23 | A141 | 1.25 l dl bl | 17.00 | 30.00 |
| 24 | A141 | 1.75 l + 25c brn | 17.00 | 30.00 |
| 25 | A144 | 2.55 l + 50c org (Bl) | 17.00 | 30.00 |
| 26 | A145 | 5 l + 1 l dl vio | 17.00 | 30.00 |
| | | Nos. 17-26 (10) | 170.00 | 300.00 |

### NISIRO

### Overprinted "Nisiros" in Black or Violet

| 1912-22 | | Wmk. 140 | Perf. 13½, 14 | |
|---|---|---|---|---|
| 1 | A43 | 2c orange brn | 6.00 | 6.75 |
| 2 | A48 | 5c green | 2.50 | 6.75 |
| 3 | A48 | 10c claret | .40 | 6.75 |
| 4 | A48 | 15c slate ('22) | 18.00 | 32.50 |
| 5 | A50 | 20c brn org ('21) | 75.00 | 92.50 |
| 6 | A49 | 25c blue | 1.60 | 6.75 |
| 7 | A49 | 40c brown | .40 | 6.75 |
| 8 | A49 | 50c violet | 3.25 | 12.50 |

### Unwmk.

| 9 | A58 | 15c slate (V) | 25.00 | 13.50 |
|---|---|---|---|---|
| 10 | A50 | 20c brn org ('17) | 92.50 | 125.00 |
| | | Nos. 1-10 (10) | 224.65 | 309.75 |

### No. 9 Surcharged Like Calchi No. 11

**1916** — **Perf. 13½**

| 11 | A58 | 20c on 15c slate | .85 | 21.00 |
|---|---|---|---|---|

### Ferrucci Issue
Types of Italy
Overprinted in Red or Blue

| 1930 | | Wmk. 140 | Perf. 14 | |
|---|---|---|---|---|
| 12 | A102 | 20c vio (R) | 3.25 | 6.75 |
| 13 | A103 | 25c dp grn (R) | 3.25 | 6.75 |
| 14 | A103 | 50c blk (R) | 3.25 | 6.75 |
| 15 | A103 | 1.25 l dp bl (R) | 3.25 | 6.75 |
| 16 | A104 | 5 l + 2 l dp car (Bl) | 6.75 | 22.50 |
| | | Nos. 12-16 (5) | 19.75 | 49.50 |

### Garibaldi Issue
Types of Italy
Overprinted in Red or Blue

**1932**

| 17 | A138 | 10c brown | 17.00 | 30.00 |
|---|---|---|---|---|
| 18 | A138 | 20c red brn (Bl) | 17.00 | 30.00 |
| 19 | A138 | 25c dp grn | 17.00 | 30.00 |
| 20 | A138 | 30c bluish slate | 17.00 | 30.00 |
| 21 | A138 | 50c red vio (Bl) | 17.00 | 30.00 |
| 22 | A141 | 75c cop red (Bl) | 17.00 | 30.00 |
| 23 | A141 | 1.25 l dull blue | 17.00 | 30.00 |
| 24 | A141 | 1.75 l + 25c brn | 17.00 | 30.00 |
| 25 | A144 | 2.55 l + 50c org (Bl) | 17.00 | 30.00 |
| 26 | A145 | 5 l + 1 l dl vio | 17.00 | 30.00 |
| | | Nos. 17-26 (10) | 170.00 | 300.00 |

### PATMO

### Overprinted "Patmos" in Black or Violet

| 1912-22 | | Wmk. 140 | Perf. 13½, 14 | |
|---|---|---|---|---|
| 1 | A43 | 2c orange brn | 6.00 | 6.75 |
| 2 | A48 | 5c green | 2.50 | 6.75 |
| 3 | A48 | 10c claret | 1.60 | 6.75 |
| 4 | A48 | 15c slate ('22) | 3.25 | 32.50 |
| 5 | A50 | 20c brn org ('21) | 110.00 | 125.00 |
| 6 | A49 | 25c blue | .65 | 6.75 |
| 7 | A49 | 40c brown | 3.25 | 6.75 |
| 8 | A49 | 50c violet | .40 | 12.50 |

### Unwmk.

| 9 | A58 | 15c slate (V) | 25.00 | 13.50 |
|---|---|---|---|---|
| 10 | A50 | 20c brn org ('17) | 60.00 | 125.00 |
| | | Nos. 1-10 (10) | 212.65 | 342.25 |

### No. 9 Surcharged Like Calchi No. 11

**1916** — **Perf. 13½**

| 11 | A58 | 20c on 15c slate | 13.50 | 30.00 |
|---|---|---|---|---|

### Ferrucci Issue
Types of Italy
Overprinted in Red or Blue

| 1930 | | Wmk. 140 | Perf. 14 | |
|---|---|---|---|---|
| 12 | A102 | 20c vio (R) | 3.25 | 6.75 |
| 13 | A103 | 25c dk grn (R) | 3.25 | 6.75 |
| 14 | A103 | 50c blk (R) | 3.25 | 6.75 |
| 15 | A103 | 1.25 l dp bl (R) | 3.25 | 6.75 |
| 16 | A104 | 5 l + 2 l dp car (Bl) | 6.75 | 22.50 |
| | | Nos. 12-16 (5) | 19.75 | 49.50 |

### Garibaldi Issue
Types of Italy
Overprinted in Red or Blue

**1932**

| 17 | A138 | 10c brown | 17.00 | 30.00 |
|---|---|---|---|---|
| 18 | A138 | 20c red brn (Bl) | 17.00 | 30.00 |
| 19 | A138 | 25c dp grn | 17.00 | 30.00 |
| 20 | A138 | 30c bluish slate | 17.00 | 30.00 |
| 21 | A138 | 50c red vio (Bl) | 17.00 | 30.00 |
| 22 | A141 | 75c cop red (Bl) | 17.00 | 30.00 |
| 23 | A141 | 1.25 l dl bl | 17.00 | 30.00 |
| 24 | A141 | 1.75 l + 25c brn | 17.00 | 30.00 |
| 25 | A144 | 2.55 l + 50c org (Bl) | 17.00 | 30.00 |
| 26 | A145 | 5 l + 1 l dl vio | 17.00 | 30.00 |
| | | Nos. 17-26 (10) | 170.00 | 300.00 |

### PISCOPI

### Overprinted "Piscopi" in Black or Violet

| 1912-21 | | Wmk. 140 | Perf. 13½, 14 | |
|---|---|---|---|---|
| 1 | A43 | 2c orange brn | 6.00 | 6.75 |
| 2 | A48 | 5c green | 2.50 | 6.75 |
| 3 | A48 | 10c claret | .40 | 6.75 |
| 4 | A48 | 15c slate ('21) | 13.50 | 32.50 |
| 5 | A50 | 20c brn org ('21) | 37.50 | 55.00 |
| 6 | A49 | 25c blue | .40 | 6.75 |
| 7 | A49 | 40c brown | .40 | 6.75 |
| 8 | A49 | 50c violet | .40 | 12.50 |

### Unwmk.

| 9 | A58 | 15c slate (V) | 29.00 | 13.50 |
|---|---|---|---|---|
| 10 | A50 | 20c brn org ('17) | 60.00 | 100.00 |
| | | Nos. 1-10 (10) | 150.10 | 247.25 |

### No. 9 Surcharged Like Calchi No. 11

**1916** — **Perf. 13½**

| 11 | A58 | 20c on 15c slate | .85 | 21.00 |
|---|---|---|---|---|

### Ferrucci Issue
Types of Italy
Overprinted in Red or Blue

| 1930 | | Wmk. 140 | Perf. 14 | |
|---|---|---|---|---|
| 12 | A102 | 20c vio (R) | 3.25 | 6.75 |
| 13 | A103 | 25c dk grn (R) | 3.25 | 6.75 |
| 14 | A103 | 50c blk (R) | 3.25 | 6.75 |
| 15 | A103 | 1.25 l dp bl (R) | 3.25 | 6.75 |
| 16 | A104 | 5 l + 2 l dp car (Bl) | 6.75 | 22.50 |
| | | Nos. 12-16 (5) | 19.75 | 49.50 |

### Garibaldi Issue
Types of Italy
Overprinted in Red or Blue

**1932**

| 17 | A138 | 10c brown | 17.00 | 30.00 |
|---|---|---|---|---|
| 18 | A138 | 20c red brn (Bl) | 17.00 | 30.00 |
| 19 | A138 | 25c dp grn | 17.00 | 30.00 |
| 20 | A138 | 30c bluish sl | 17.00 | 30.00 |
| 21 | A138 | 50c red vio (Bl) | 17.00 | 30.00 |
| 22 | A141 | 75c cop red (Bl) | 17.00 | 30.00 |
| 23 | A141 | 1.25 l dl bl | 17.00 | 30.00 |
| 24 | A141 | 1.75 l + 25c brn | 17.00 | 30.00 |
| 25 | A144 | 2.55 l + 50c org (Bl) | 17.00 | 30.00 |
| 26 | A145 | 5 l + 1 l dl vio | 17.00 | 30.00 |
| | | Nos. 17-26 (10) | 170.00 | 300.00 |

### RHODES

### (Rodi)

### Overprinted "Rodi" in Black or Violet

| 1912-24 | | Wmk. 140 | Perf. 13½, 14 | |
|---|---|---|---|---|
| 1 | A43 | 2c org brn | .40 | 6.75 |
| 2 | A48 | 5c green | 2.50 | 6.75 |
| a. | | Double overprint | 300.00 | |
| 3 | A48 | 10c claret | .40 | 6.75 |
| 4 | A48 | 15c slate ('21) | 110.00 | 55.00 |
| 5 | A45 | 20c org ('16) | 2.50 | 6.00 |
| 6 | A50 | 20c brn org ('19) | 5.00 | 14.00 |
| a. | | Double overprint | 85.00 | |
| 7 | A49 | 25c blue | 2.50 | 6.75 |
| 8 | A49 | 40c brown | 3.25 | 6.75 |
| 9 | A49 | 50c violet | .40 | 12.50 |
| 10 | A49 | 85c red brn ('22) | 60.00 | 92.50 |
| 11 | A46 | 1 l brn & grn ('24) | 1.75 | |

No. 11 was not regularly issued.

### Unwmk.

| 12 | A58 | 15c slate (V) | 30.00 | 13.50 |
|---|---|---|---|---|
| 13 | A50 | 20c brn org ('17) | 125.00 | 125.00 |
| | | Nos. 1-13 (13) | 343.70 | 352.25 |

### No. 12 Surcharged Like Calchi No. 11

**1916** — **Perf. 13½**

| 14 | A58 | 20c on 15c slate | 92.50 | 115.00 |
|---|---|---|---|---|

Windmill, Rhodes — A1

Medieval Galley — A2

Christian Knight — A3

Crusader Kneeling in Prayer — A4

Crusader's
Tomb — A5

### No Imprint

**1929     Unwmk.     Litho.     Perf. 11**

| 15 | A1 | 5c magenta | 10.00 | 1.60 |
|----|----|-----------|-------|------|
| 16 | A2 | 10c olive brn | 10.00 | 1.25 |
| 17 | A3 | 20c rose red | 10.00 | .40 |
| 18 | A3 | 25c green | 10.00 | .40 |
| 19 | A4 | 30c dk blue | 42.50 | .85 |
| 20 | A5 | 50c dk brown | 10.00 | .35 |
| 21 | A5 | 1.25 l dk blue | 10.00 | 1.60 |
| 22 | A4 | 5 l magenta | 67.50 | 92.50 |
| 23 | A4 | 10 l olive brn | 175.00 | 250.00 |
| | | Nos. 15-23 (9) | 345.00 | 348.95 |

Visit of the King and Queen of Italy to the
Aegean Islands. The stamps are inscribed
"Rodi" but were available for use in all the
Aegean Islands.
Nos. 15-23 and C1-C4 were used in eastern
Crete in 1941-42 with Greek postmarks.
See Nos. 55-63.

### Ferrucci Issue

Types of Italy
Overprinted in Red or Blue

**1930     Wmk. 140     Perf. 14**

| 24 | A102 | 20c violet (R) | 3.25 | 6.75 |
|----|------|---------------|------|------|
| 25 | A103 | 25c dk green (R) | 3.25 | 6.75 |
| 26 | A103 | 50c black (R) | 3.25 | 6.75 |
| 27 | A103 | 1.25 l dp blue (R) | 3.25 | 6.75 |
| 28 | A104 | 5 l + 2 l dp car | | |
| | | (Bl) | 6.75 | 22.50 |
| | | Nos. 24-28 (5) | 19.75 | 49.50 |

### Hydrological Congress Issue

Rhodes Issue of 1929 Overprinted

**1930     Unwmk.     Perf. 11**

| 29 | A1 | 5c magenta | 32.50 | 30.00 |
|----|----|-----------|-------|-------|
| 30 | A2 | 10c olive brn | 32.50 | 30.00 |
| 31 | A3 | 20c rose red | 40.00 | 30.00 |
| 32 | A3 | 25c green | 50.00 | 6.00 |
| 33 | A4 | 30c dk blue | 32.50 | 6.75 |
| 34 | A5 | 50c dk brown | 600.00 | 22.50 |
| 35 | A5 | 1.25 l dk blue | 425.00 | 115.00 |
| 36 | A4 | 5 l magenta | 275.00 | 500.00 |
| 37 | A4 | 10 l olive grn | 275.00 | 525.00 |
| | | Nos. 29-37 (9) | 1,762. | 1,265. |

Rhodes Issue of 1929 Overprinted in
Blue or Red

**1931**

| 38 | A1 | 5c magenta (Bl) | 6.75 | 15.00 |
|----|----|-----------|------|-------|
| 39 | A2 | 10c olive brn (R) | 6.75 | 15.00 |
| 40 | A3 | 20c rose red (Bl) | 6.75 | 25.00 |
| 41 | A3 | 25c green (R) | 6.75 | 25.00 |
| 42 | A4 | 30c dk blue (R) | 6.75 | 25.00 |
| 43 | A5 | 50c dk brown (R) | 50.00 | 50.00 |
| 44 | A5 | 1.25 l dk bl (R) | 42.50 | 85.00 |
| | | Nos. 38-44 (7) | 126.25 | 240.00 |

Italian Eucharistic Congress, 1931.

### Garibaldi Issue

Types of Italy
Overprinted in Red or Blue

**1932     Wmk. 140     Perf. 14**

| 45 | A138 | 10c brown | 17.00 | 30.00 |
|----|------|-----------|-------|-------|
| 46 | A138 | 20c red brn (Bl) | 17.00 | 30.00 |
| 47 | A138 | 25c dp grn (R) | 17.00 | 30.00 |
| 48 | A138 | 30c bluish sl | 17.00 | 30.00 |
| 49 | A138 | 50c red vio (Bl) | 17.00 | 30.00 |
| 50 | A141 | 75c cop red (Bl) | 17.00 | 30.00 |
| 51 | A141 | 1.25 l dl bl | 17.00 | 30.00 |
| 52 | A141 | 1.75 l + 25c brn | 17.00 | 30.00 |

| 53 | A144 | 2.55 l + 50c org | | |
|----|------|-----------|------|-------|
| | | (Bl) | 17.00 | 30.00 |
| 54 | A145 | 5 l + 1 l dl vio | 17.00 | 30.00 |
| | | Nos. 45-54 (10) | 170.00 | 300.00 |

### Types of Rhodes Issue of 1929

Imprint: "Officina Carte-Valori Roma"

**1932**

| 55 | A1 | 5c rose lake | 1.00 | .20 |
|----|----|-----------|------|-----|
| 56 | A1 | 10c dk brn | 1.00 | .20 |
| 57 | A3 | 20c red | 1.00 | .20 |
| 58 | A3 | 25c dl grn | 1.00 | .20 |
| 59 | A4 | 30c dl bl | 1.00 | .20 |
| 60 | A5 | 50c blk brn | 1.00 | .20 |
| 61 | A5 | 1.25 l dp bl | 1.00 | .20 |
| 62 | A4 | 5 l rose lake | 1.00 | 1.50 |
| 63 | A4 | 10 l ol brn | 2.10 | 3.75 |
| | | Nos. 55-63 (9) | 10.10 | 6.65 |

Aerial
View of
Rhodes
A6

Map of
Rhodes — A7

**1932     Wmk. 140     Litho.     Perf. 11**

**Shield in Red**

| 64 | A6 | 5c blk & grn | 8.50 | 17.00 |
|----|----|-----------|------|-------|
| 65 | A6 | 10c blk & vio bl | 8.50 | 12.50 |
| 66 | A6 | 20c blk & dl yel | 8.50 | 12.50 |
| 67 | A6 | 25c lil & blk | 8.50 | 12.50 |
| 68 | A6 | 30c blk & pink | 8.50 | 12.50 |

**Shield and Map Dots in Red**

| 69 | A7 | 50c blk & gray | 8.50 | 12.50 |
|----|----|-----------|------|-------|
| 70 | A7 | 1.25 l red brn & | | |
| | | gray | 8.50 | 25.00 |
| 71 | A7 | 5 l dk bl & gray | 21.00 | 67.50 |
| 72 | A7 | 10 l dk grn & | | |
| | | gray | 60.00 | 115.00 |
| 73 | A7 | 25 l choc & gray | 325.00 | 1,000. |
| | | Nos. 64-73 (10) | 465.50 | 1,287. |

20th anniv. of the Italian occupation and
10th anniv. of Fascist rule.

Deer and Palm — A8

**1935, Apr.     Photo.     Wmk. 140**

| 74 | A8 | 5c orange | 20.00 | 25.00 |
|----|----|-----------|-------|-------|
| 75 | A8 | 10c brown | 20.00 | 25.00 |
| 76 | A8 | 20c car rose | 20.00 | 30.00 |
| 77 | A8 | 25c green | 20.00 | 30.00 |
| 78 | A8 | 30c purple | 20.00 | 32.50 |
| 79 | A8 | 50c red brn | 20.00 | 32.50 |
| 80 | A8 | 1.25l blue | 20.00 | 85.00 |
| 81 | A8 | 5 l yellow | 150.00 | 300.00 |
| | | Nos. 74-81 (8) | 290.00 | 560.00 |

Holy Year.

## WEIHNACHTEN  WEIHNACHTEN
## 1944   1944

The above overprints on No. 55 are
stated to have been prepared locally for
use on German military correspondence, but banned by postal authorities
in Berlin.

### RHODES SEMI-POSTAL STAMPS

Rhodes Nos. 55-62 Surcharged in
Black or Red

**1943     Wmk. 140     Perf. 14**

| B1 | A1 | 5c + 5c rose lake | 2.50 | 2.50 |
|----|----|-----------|------|------|
| B2 | A2 | 10c + 10c dk brn | 2.50 | 2.50 |
| B3 | A3 | 20c + 20c red | 2.50 | 2.50 |
| B4 | A3 | 25c + 25c dl grn | 2.50 | 2.50 |
| B5 | A4 | 30c + 30c dl bl (R) | 4.25 | 3.25 |
| B6 | A5 | 50c + 50c blk brn | 4.25 | 3.25 |
| B7 | A5 | 1.25 l + 1.25 l dp bl | | |
| | | (R) | 5.00 | 5.00 |
| B8 | A4 | 5 l + 5 l rose lake | 100.00 | 150.00 |
| | | Nos. B1-B8 (8) | 123.50 | 171.50 |

The surtax was for general relief.

Rhodes Nos. 55 to 58, 60 and 61
Surcharged in Black or Red

**1944**

| B9 | A1 | 5c + 3 l rose lake | 2.50 | 5.75 |
|----|----|-----------|------|------|
| B10 | A2 | 10c + 3 l dk brn (R) | 2.50 | 5.75 |
| B11 | A3 | 20c + 3 l red | 2.50 | 5.75 |
| B12 | A3 | 25c + 3 l dl grn (R) | 2.50 | 5.75 |
| B13 | A5 | 50c + 3 l blk brn (R) | 2.50 | 5.75 |
| B14 | A5 | 1.25 l + 5 l dp bl (R) | 30.00 | 45.00 |
| | | Nos. B9-B14 (6) | 42.50 | 73.75 |

The surtax was for war victims.

Rhodes Nos. 62 and 63 Surcharged in
Red

**1945**

| B17 | A4 | 5 l + 10 l rose lake | 10.00 | 21.00 |
|-----|----|-----------|-------|-------|
| B18 | A4 | 10 l + 10 l ol brn | 10.00 | 21.00 |

The surtax was for the Red Cross.

### RHODES AIR POST STAMPS

Symbolical of
Flight — AP18

**1935-38     Typo.     Wmk. 140     Perf. 14**

| C1a | AP18 | 50c black & yellow | .85 | .40 |
|-----|------|-----------|-----|-----|
| C2a | AP18 | 80c black & mag | .85 | 2.50 |
| C3a | AP18 | 1 l black & green | .85 | .40 |
| C4a | AP18 | 5 l black & red vio | 4.25 | 4.50 |
| | | Nos. C1a-C4a (4) | 6.80 | 8.30 |

Nos. C1a-C4a were issued in 1937-38, on
paper with sideways watermark. The 1935
first printing is on paper within which the watermark is upright. For detailed listings, see the
*Scott Classic Specialized Catalogue.*

### RHODES AIR POST SEMI-POSTAL STAMPS

Rhodes Nos. C1-
C4 Surcharged in
Silver

**1944     Wmk. 140     Perf. 14**

| CB1 | AP18 | 50c + 2 l | 10.00 | 3.25 |
|-----|------|-----------|-------|------|
| CB2 | AP18 | 80c + 2 l | 10.00 | 6.75 |
| CB3 | AP18 | 1 l + 2 l | 15.00 | 8.50 |
| CB4 | AP18 | 5 l + 2 l | 100.00 | 110.00 |
| | | Nos. CB1-CB4 (4) | 135.00 | 128.50 |

The surtax was for war victims.

### RHODES SPECIAL DELIVERY STAMPS

Stag — SD1

**1936     Photo.     Wmk. 140     Perf. 14**

| E1 | SD1 | 1.25 l green | 2.50 | 3.25 |
|----|-----|-----------|------|------|
| E2 | SD1 | 2.50 l vermilion | 4.25 | 5.00 |

Nos. 58 and 57
Surcharged in Black

**1943**

| E3 | A3 | 1.25 l on 25c dl grn | .35 | 1.10 |
|----|----|-----------|-----|------|
| E4 | A3 | 2.50 l on 20c red | .35 | 1.10 |

### RHODES SEMI-POSTAL SPECIAL DELIVERY STAMPS

Rhodes Nos. E1
and E2
Surcharged in Red
or Black

**1943     Wmk. 140     Perf. 14**

| EB1 | SD1 | 1.25 l + 1.25 l (R) | 26.00 | 17.50 |
|-----|-----|-----------|-------|-------|
| EB2 | SD1 | 2.50 l + 2.50 l | 32.50 | 22.50 |

The surtax was for general relief.

### RHODES POSTAGE DUE STAMPS

Maltese
Cross
PD1

Immortelle
PD2

**1934     Photo.     Wmk. 140     Perf. 13**

| J1 | PD1 | 5c vermilion | 3.25 | 4.25 |
|----|-----|-----------|------|------|
| J2 | PD1 | 10c carmine | 3.25 | 4.25 |
| J3 | PD1 | 20c dk green | 3.25 | 2.50 |
| J4 | PD1 | 30c purple | 3.25 | 3.25 |
| J5 | PD1 | 40c dk blue | 3.25 | 6.75 |
| J6 | PD2 | 50c vermilion | 3.25 | 2.50 |
| J7 | PD2 | 60c carmine | 3.25 | 12.50 |
| J8 | PD2 | 1 l dk green | 3.25 | 12.50 |
| J9 | PD2 | 2 l purple | 3.25 | 6.75 |
| | | Nos. J1-J9 (9) | 29.25 | 55.25 |

## RHODES PARCEL POST STAMPS

Both unused and used values are for complete stamps.

PP1

PP2

**1934    Photo.    Wmk. 140    Perf. 13**

| Q1 | PP1 | 5c vermilion | 4.25 | 5.00 |
|---|---|---|---|---|
| Q2 | PP1 | 10c carmine | 4.25 | 5.00 |
| Q3 | PP1 | 20c dk green | 4.25 | 5.00 |
| Q4 | PP1 | 25c purple | 4.25 | 5.00 |
| Q5 | PP1 | 50c dk blue | 4.25 | 5.00 |
| Q6 | PP1 | 60c black | 4.25 | 5.00 |
| Q7 | PP2 | 1 l vermilion | 4.25 | 5.00 |
| Q8 | PP2 | 2 l carmine | 4.25 | 5.00 |
| Q9 | PP2 | 3 l dk green | 4.25 | 5.00 |
| Q10 | PP2 | 4 l purple | 4.25 | 5.00 |
| Q11 | PP2 | 10 l dk blue | 4.25 | 5.00 |
| | | Nos. Q1-Q11 (11) | 46.75 | 55.00 |

Value of used halves, Nos. Q1-Q11, each 20 cents.

See note preceding No. Q7 of Italy.

---

### SCARPANTO

**Overprinted "Scarpanto" in Black or Violet**

**1912-22    Wmk. 140    Perf. 13½, 14**

| 1 | A43 | 2c orange brn | 6.75 | 6.75 |
|---|---|---|---|---|
| 2 | A48 | 5c green | 1.60 | 6.75 |
| 3 | A48 | 10c claret | .40 | 6.75 |
| 4 | A48 | 15c slate ('22) | 13.50 | 25.00 |
| 5 | A50 | 20c brown org ('21) | 37.50 | 37.50 |
| 6 | A49 | 25c blue | 6.00 | 6.75 |
| 7 | A49 | 40c brown | .40 | 6.75 |
| 8 | A49 | 50c violet | 1.60 | 12.50 |

**Unwmk.**

| 9 | A58 | 15c slate (V) | 21.00 | 13.50 |
|---|---|---|---|---|
| 10 | A50 | 20c brown org ('17) | 92.50 | 125.00 |
| | | Nos. 1-10 (10) | 181.25 | 247.25 |

**No 9 Surcharged Like Calchi No. 11**

**1916    Perf. 13½**

| 11 | A58 | 20c on 15c slate | .85 | 25.00 |
|---|---|---|---|---|

**Ferrucci Issue**

Overprinted in Red or Blue

**1930    Wmk. 140    Perf. 14**

| 12 | A102 | 20c violet (R) | 3.25 | 6.75 |
|---|---|---|---|---|
| 13 | A103 | 25c dk green (R) | 3.25 | 6.75 |
| 14 | A103 | 50c black (R) | 3.25 | 6.75 |
| 15 | A103 | 1.25 l dp blue (R) | 3.25 | 6.75 |
| 16 | A104 | 5 l + 2 l dp car (Bl) | 6.75 | 22.50 |
| | | Nos. 12-16 (5) | 19.75 | 49.50 |

**Garibaldi Issue**

Types of Italy
Overprinted in Red or Blue

**1932**

| 17 | A138 | 10c brown | 17.00 | 30.00 |
|---|---|---|---|---|
| 18 | A138 | 20c red brown (Bl) | 17.00 | 30.00 |
| 19 | A138 | 25c dp green | 17.00 | 30.00 |
| 20 | A138 | 30c bluish slate | 17.00 | 30.00 |
| 21 | A138 | 50c red vio (Bl) | 17.00 | 30.00 |
| 22 | A141 | 75c cop red (Bl) | 17.00 | 30.00 |
| 23 | A141 | 1.25 l dull blue | 17.00 | 30.00 |
| 24 | A141 | 1.75 l + 25c brown | 17.00 | 30.00 |
| 25 | A144 | 2.55 l + 50c org (Bl) | 17.00 | 30.00 |
| 26 | A145 | 5 l + 1 l dl vio | 17.00 | 30.00 |
| | | Nos. 17-26 (10) | 170.00 | 300.00 |

---

### SIMI

**Overprinted "Simi" in Black or Violet**

**1912-21    Wmk. 140    Perf. 13½, 14**

| 1 | A43 | 2c orange brn | 11.50 | 6.75 |
|---|---|---|---|---|
| 2 | A48 | 5c green | 21.00 | 6.75 |
| 3 | A48 | 10c claret | .40 | 6.75 |
| 4 | A48 | 15c slate ('21) | 92.50 | 55.00 |
| 5 | A50 | 20c brown org ('21) | 45.00 | 30.00 |
| 6 | A49 | 25c blue | 5.00 | 6.75 |
| 7 | A49 | 40c brown | .40 | 6.75 |
| 8 | A49 | 50c violet | .40 | 12.50 |

---

**Unwmk.**

| 9 | A58 | 15c slate (V) | 45.00 | 13.50 |
|---|---|---|---|---|
| 10 | A50 | 20c brn org ('17) | 47.50 | 85.00 |
| | | Nos. 1-10 (10) | 268.70 | 229.75 |

**No. 9 Surcharged Like Calchi No. 11**

**1916    Perf. 13½**

| 11 | A58 | 20c on 15c slate | 6.50 | 18.00 |
|---|---|---|---|---|

**Ferrucci Issue**

Types of Italy
Overprinted in Red or Blue

**1930    Wmk. 140    Perf. 14**

| 12 | A102 | 20c violet (R) | 3.25 | 6.75 |
|---|---|---|---|---|
| 13 | A103 | 25c dk green (R) | 3.25 | 6.75 |
| 14 | A103 | 50c blk (R) | 3.25 | 6.75 |
| 15 | A103 | 1.25 l dp blue (R) | 3.25 | 6.75 |
| 16 | A104 | 5 l + 2 l dp car (Bl) | 6.75 | 22.50 |
| | | Nos. 12-16 (5) | 19.75 | 49.50 |

**Garibaldi Issue**

Types of Italy
Overprinted in Red or Blue

**1932**

| 17 | A138 | 10c brown | 17.00 | 30.00 |
|---|---|---|---|---|
| 18 | A138 | 20c red brn (Bl) | 17.00 | 30.00 |
| 19 | A138 | 25c deep green | 17.00 | 30.00 |
| 20 | A138 | 30c bluish slate | 17.00 | 30.00 |
| 21 | A138 | 50c red vio (Bl) | 17.00 | 30.00 |
| 22 | A141 | 75c cop red (Bl) | 17.00 | 30.00 |
| 23 | A141 | 1.25 l dl bl | 17.00 | 30.00 |
| 24 | A141 | 1.75 l + 25c brn | 17.00 | 30.00 |
| 25 | A144 | 2.55 l + 50c org (Bl) | 17.00 | 30.00 |
| 26 | A145 | 5 l + 1 l dl vio | 17.00 | 30.00 |
| | | Nos. 17-26 (10) | 170.00 | 300.00 |

---

### STAMPALIA

**Overprinted "Stampalia" in Black or Violet**

**1912-21    Wmk. 140    Perf. 13½, 14**

| 1 | A43 | 2c org brn | 6.75 | 6.75 |
|---|---|---|---|---|
| 2 | A48 | 5c green | .40 | 6.75 |
| 3 | A48 | 10c claret | .40 | 6.75 |
| 4 | A48 | 15c slate ('21) | 8.50 | 25.00 |
| 5 | A50 | 20c brn org ('21) | 32.50 | 42.50 |
| 6 | A49 | 25c blue | .65 | 6.75 |
| 7 | A49 | 40c brown | 2.50 | 6.75 |
| 8 | A49 | 50c violet | .45 | 12.50 |

**Unwmk.**

| 9 | A58 | 15c slate (V) | 26.00 | 13.50 |
|---|---|---|---|---|
| 10 | A50 | 20c brn org ('17) | 67.50 | 85.00 |
| | | Nos. 1-10 (10) | 145.65 | 212.25 |

**No. 9 Surcharged Like Calchi No. 11**

**1916    Perf. 13½**

| 11 | A58 | 20c on 15c slate | .85 | 17.00 |
|---|---|---|---|---|

**Ferrucci Issue**

Types of Italy
Overprinted in Red or Blue

**1930    Wmk. 140    Perf. 14**

| 12 | A102 | 20c violet (R) | 3.25 | 6.75 |
|---|---|---|---|---|
| 13 | A103 | 25c dk green (R) | 3.25 | 6.75 |
| 14 | A103 | 50c black (R) | 3.25 | 6.75 |
| 15 | A103 | 1.25 l dp blue (R) | 3.25 | 6.75 |
| 16 | A104 | 5 l + 2 l dp car (Bl) | 6.75 | 22.50 |
| | | Nos. 12-16 (5) | 19.75 | 49.50 |

**Garibaldi Issue**

Types of Italy
Overprinted in Red or Blue

**1932**

| 17 | A138 | 10c brown | 17.00 | 30.00 |
|---|---|---|---|---|
| 18 | A138 | 20c red brn (Bl) | 17.00 | 30.00 |
| 19 | A138 | 25c dp green | 17.00 | 30.00 |
| 20 | A138 | 30c bluish slate | 17.00 | 30.00 |
| 21 | A138 | 50c red vio (Bl) | 17.00 | 30.00 |
| 22 | A141 | 75c cop red (Bl) | 17.00 | 30.00 |
| 23 | A141 | 1.25 l dull blue | 17.00 | 30.00 |
| 24 | A141 | 1.75 l + 25c brn | 17.00 | 30.00 |
| 25 | A144 | 2.55 l + 50c org (Bl) | 17.00 | 30.00 |
| 26 | A145 | 5 l + 1 l dl vio | 17.00 | 30.00 |
| | | Nos. 17-26 (10) | 170.00 | 300.00 |

---

## TRIESTE

A free territory (1947-1954) on the Adriatic Sea between Italy and Yugoslavia. In 1954 the territory was divided, Italy acquiring the northern section and seaport, Yugoslavia the southern section (Zone B).

> Catalogue values for all unused stamps in this country are for Never Hinged items.

### ZONE A

**Issued jointly by the Allied Military Government of the United States and Great Britain**
Stamps of Italy 1945-47 Overprinted:

a

b

c

**1947, Oct. 1    Wmk. 277    Perf. 14**

| 1 | A259(a) | 25c brt bl grn | .20 | 1.50 |
|---|---|---|---|---|
| 2 | A255(a) | 50c dp vio | .20 | 1.50 |
| 3 | A257(a) | 1 l dk grn | .20 | .20 |
| 4 | A258(a) | 2 l dk cl brn | .20 | .20 |
| 5 | A259(a) | 3 l red | .20 | .20 |
| 6 | A259(a) | 4 l red org | .20 | .20 |
| 7 | A256(a) | 5 l deep blue | .20 | .20 |
| 8 | A257(a) | 6 l dp vio | .20 | .20 |
| 9 | A255(a) | 10 l slate | .20 | .20 |
| 10 | A257(a) | 15 l deep blue | 2.00 | .20 |
| 11 | A259(a) | 20 l dk red vio | 3.25 | .20 |
| 12 | A260(b) | 25 l dk grn | 4.75 | 8.00 |
| 13 | A260(b) | 50 l dk vio brn | 6.00 | 4.00 |

**    Perf. 14x13½**

| 14 | A261(c) | 100 l car lake | 36.00 | 27.50 |
|---|---|---|---|---|
| | | Nos. 1-14 (14) | 53.80 | 44.30 |

The letters "F. T. T." are the initials of "Free Territory of Trieste."

**Italy Nos. 486-488 Ovptd. Type "a"**

**1948, Mar. 1    Perf. 14**

| 15 | A255 | 8 l dk green | 3.25 | 4.75 |
|---|---|---|---|---|
| 16 | A256 | 10 l red org | 9.50 | .25 |
| 17 | A259 | 30 l dk blue | 200.00 | 9.50 |
| | | Nos. 15-17 (3) | 212.75 | 14.50 |

**Italy Nos. 495 to 506 Overprinted**

d

**1948, July 1**

| 18 | A272 | 3 l dk brn | .40 | .40 |
|---|---|---|---|---|
| 19 | A272 | 4 l red vio | .40 | .40 |
| 20 | A272 | 5 l deep blue | .40 | .40 |
| 21 | A272 | 6 l dp yel grn | .80 | .40 |
| 22 | A272 | 8 l brown | .40 | .40 |
| 23 | A272 | 10 l org red | .80 | .40 |
| 24 | A272 | 12 l dk gray grn | .40 | 1.25 |
| 25 | A272 | 15 l gray blk | 13.00 | 12.00 |
| 26 | A272 | 20 l car rose | 20.00 | 12.00 |
| 27 | A272 | 30 l brt ultra | 2.50 | 2.50 |
| 28 | A272 | 50 l violet | 12.00 | 12.00 |
| 29 | A272 | 100 l bl blk | 35.00 | 35.00 |
| | | Nos. 18-29 (12) | 86.10 | 77.15 |

Italy, Nos. 486 to 488, Overprinted in Carmine

---

**1948, Sept. 8**

| 30 | A255 | 8 l dk green | .30 | .25 |
|---|---|---|---|---|
| 31 | A256 | 10 l red org | .30 | .25 |
| 32 | A259 | 30 l dk blue | 1.75 | 1.75 |
| | | Nos. 30-32,C17-C19 (6) | 4.10 | 4.40 |

The overprint is embossed.

**Italy, No. 507, Overprinted Type "d" in Carmine**

**1948, Oct. 15**

| 33 | A273 | 15 l dk green | 2.00 | 2.00 |
|---|---|---|---|---|

**Italy, No. 508, Overprinted in Green**

e

**1948, Nov. 15**

| 34 | A274 | 15 l dk brown | 10.00 | 2.00 |
|---|---|---|---|---|

**Italy, No. 509, Overprinted Type "d" in Red**

**1949, May 2    Wmk. 277    Perf. 14**

| 35 | A275 | 20 l dk brown | 10.00 | 2.75 |
|---|---|---|---|---|

**Italy, Nos. 510 to 513, Overprinted**

f

**1949, May 2    Buff Background**

| 36 | A276 | 5 l red brown | .80 | 1.40 |
|---|---|---|---|---|
| 37 | A276 | 15 l dk green | 9.50 | 14.00 |
| 38 | A276 | 20 l dp red brn | 6.00 | 1.40 |
| 39 | A276 | 50 l dk blue | 12.50 | 7.25 |
| | | Nos. 36-39 (4) | 28.80 | 24.05 |

**Italy, No. 514, Overprinted Type "d" in Red**

**1949, May 2**

| 40 | A277 | 50 l brt ultra | 4.50 | 4.00 |
|---|---|---|---|---|

**Italy, No. 518, Overprinted Type "d" in Red**

**1949, May 30**

| 41 | A279 | 100 l brown | 62.50 | 100.00 |
|---|---|---|---|---|

**Italy, Nos. 515-517, Ovptd. Type "f"**

**1949, June 15**

| 42 | A278 | 5 l dk green | 11.00 | 7.25 |
|---|---|---|---|---|
| 43 | A278 | 15 l violet | 11.00 | 14.00 |
| 44 | A278 | 20 l brown | 11.00 | 11.00 |
| | | Nos. 42-44 (3) | 33.00 | 32.25 |

**Italy, Nos. 519 and 520, Overprinted Type "e" in Carmine**

**1949, July 16**

| 45 | A280 | 20 l gray | 10.00 | 11.75 |
|---|---|---|---|---|
| 46 | A281 | 20 l brown | 10.00 | 11.75 |

**Italy, No. 521 Overprinted in Green**

g

**1949, June 8**

| 47 | A282 | 20 l brown red | 6.50 | 3.00 |
|---|---|---|---|---|

**Italy, No. 522, Overprinted Type "f" in Carmine**

**1949, July 8**

| 49 | A283 | 20 l violet | 16.00 | 5.00 |
|---|---|---|---|---|

**Italy, No. 523 Overprinted Type "e", without Periods, in Black**

**1949, Aug. 27**

| 50 | A284 | 20 l violet blue | 9.00 | 4.50 |
|---|---|---|---|---|

## Italy, No. 524 Ovptd. Type "f"

**1949, Aug. 27**
51 A285  20 l violet          17.50 13.00

## Italy, No. 525, Overprinted Type "d" in Green

**1949, Sept. 10**
52 A286  20 l red             10.00  3.75

## Italy Nos. 526 and 527 Overprinted

h

**Wmk. 277**
**1949, Nov. 7      Photo.      Perf. 14**
53 A287  20 l rose car         4.50  4.00
54 A288  50 l deep blue       16.50 14.00

## Same Overprint on No. 528

**1949, Nov. 7**
55 A289  20 l dp grn           5.00  3.00

## Same Overprint on No. 529

**1949, Nov. 7**
56 A290  20 l brt blue         4.00  3.00

## Same Overprint in Red on No. 530

**1949, Dec. 28**
57 A291  20 l violet blk       4.50  2.00

## Same Overprint in Black on Italian Stamps of 1945-48

**1949-50                         Photo.**
58 A257   1 l dk green    .20    .80
59 A258   2 l dk cl brn   .20    .20
60 A259   3 l red         .20    .20
61 A256   5 l deep blue   .20    .20
62 A257   6 l dp violet   .20    .20
63 A255   8 l dk green  35.00  20.00
64 A256  10 l red org     .20    .20
65 A257  15 l deep blue  3.25    .80
66 A259  20 l dk red vio 1.60   1.60
67 A260  25 l dk grn ('50) 27.50 3.00
68 A260  50 l dk vio brn
              ('50)      42.50   2.25

**Engr.**
69 A261 100 l car lake   95.00  15.00
     Nos. 58-69 (12)    206.05  43.05

Issued: 3 l, 20 l, 10/21; 5 l, 11/5; 10 l, 11/7;
100 l, 11/23; 15 l, 11/28; 1 l, 2 l, 6 l, 8 l, 12/28;
50 l, 1/19; 25 l, 2/25.

## Italy, No. 531, Overprinted Type "g" in Carmine

**1950, Apr. 12**
70 A292  20 l brown            5.00  2.00

## Same Overprint in Carmine on Italy, No. 532

**1950, Apr. 29**
71 A293  20 l vio gray         1.75  2.00

## Same Overprint in Carmine on Italy, Nos. 533 and 534

**1950, May 22**
72 A294  20 l olive green      3.00  1.60
73 A295  55 l blue            12.00 13.00

## Italy, Nos. 535 and 536, Overprinted Type "h" in Black

**1950, May 29**
74 A296  20 l violet          4.25   1.60
75 A296  55 l blue           14.50  13.00

## Italy, No. 537, Overprinted Type "g" in Carmine

**1950, July 10**
76 A297  20 l gray grn         3.00  2.25

## Same Overprint in Carmine on Italy, Nos. 538-539

**1950, July 15**
77 A298  20 l purple           6.50  4.50
78 A298  55 l blue            22.50 22.50

## Italy, No. 540, Overprinted Type "h"

**1950, July 22**
79 A299  20 l brown            4.75  2.25

---

## Italy, No. 541 Overprinted in Carmine

i

**1950, July 29**
80 A300  20 l dk grn           4.75  2.25

## Italy, No. 542, Overprinted Type "g"

**1950, Aug. 21**
81 A301  20 l chnt brn         2.50  2.00

## Italy, Nos. 473A and 474, Overprinted

**1950, Aug. 27**
82 A257  15 l deep blue        3.00  2.25
83 A259  20 l dk red vio       3.00   .75
       Trieste Fair.

## Italy, No. 543, Overprinted Type "i" in Carmine

**1950, Sept. 11**
84 A302  20 l indigo           1.25  1.70

## Italy Nos. 544-546, Ovptd. Type "h"

**1950, Sept. 16  Wmk. 277  Perf. 14**
85 A303   5 l dp cl & grn   .50   2.00
86 A303  20 l brn & grn    2.40   2.00
87 A303  55 l dp ultra & brn 25.00 25.00
      Nos. 85-87 (3)      27.90  29.00

## Same, in Black, on Italy No. 547

**1950, Sept. 16**
88 A304  20 l ol brn & red brn  3.00  1.75

## Same, in Black, on Italy No. 548

**1950, Sept. 16**
89 A305  20 l cr & gray blk    5.00  1.75

## Italy, Nos. 549 to 565, Overprinted Type "g" in Black

**1950, Oct. 20**
90 A306  50c violet blue   .20    .20
91 A306   1 l dk blue vio  .20    .20
92 A306   2 l sepia        .20    .20
93 A306   5 l dk gray      .20    .20
94 A306   6 l chocolate    .25    .20
95 A306  10 l deep green   .40    .20
96 A306  12 l dp blue grn  .80   1.00
97 A306  15 l dk gray bl  1.25    .20
98 A306  20 l blue vio    1.25    .20
99 A306  25 l brown org   2.75    .20
100 A306 30 l magenta     1.00    .60
101 A306 35 l crimson     2.75   1.50
102 A306 40 l brown       1.75    .80
103 A306 50 l violet       .25    .30
104 A306 55 l deep blue    .25    .60
105 A306 60 l red         7.75   5.00
106 A306 65 l dk green     .25    .55

## Italy Nos. 566 and 567 Overprinted

k

**Perf. 14, 14x13½**
**Engr.**
107 A306 100 l brown org   4.50    .45
108 A306 200 l olive brn   3.50   5.50
      Nos. 90-108 (19)    29.50  18.10

---

## Italy Nos. 568 and 569 Overprinted Type "k" in Black

**1951, Mar. 27   Photo.   Perf. 14**
109 A307 20 l red vio & red    2.75  2.00
110 A307 55 l ultra & bl      40.00 35.00

## Italy No. 570 Overprinted Type "g"

**1951, Apr. 2**
111 A308 20 l dk grn           1.75  1.75

## Same, on Italy No. 571

**1951, Apr. 11**
112 A309 20 l bl vio           2.00  1.75

## Italy Nos. 572 and 573 Overprinted

**1951, Apr. 12**
113 A310(h) 20 l brown         1.60  1.25
114 A311(g) 55 l deep blue     3.25  3.50

## Italy Nos. 574 to 576 Overprinted Type "h" in Black

**1951, May 18   Fleur-de-Lis in Red**
115 A312   5 l dk brown        6.50 17.50
116 A312  10 l Prus grn        6.50 17.50
117 A312  15 l vio bl          6.50 17.50
      Nos. 115-117 (3)        19.50 52.50

## Italy No. 577 Overprinted

m

**1951, Apr. 26**
118 A313  20 l purple          2.00  2.00

## Italy No. 578 Overprinted Type "h"

**1951, May 5**
119 A314  20 l Prus green       3.00  3.25

## Italy Nos. 579-580 Ovptd. Type "g"

**1951, June 18**
120 A315  20 l violet          1.00  1.25
121 A315  55 l brt blue        2.75  3.50

Nos. 94, 98 and 104
Overprinted

**1951, June 24**
122 A306   6 l chocolate      .60    .75
123 A306  20 l blue violet   1.00    .60
124 A306  55 l deep blue     1.40   1.25
      Nos. 122-124 (3)       3.00   2.60

Issued to publicize the Trieste Fair, 1951.

## Italy No. 581 Overprinted

n

**1951, July 23**
125 A316  20 l brn & red brn   1.00  1.10

## Italy Nos. 582 and 583 Overprinted Types "n" and "h" in Red

**1951, July 23**
126 A317(n) 20 l grnsh gray &
                 blk          1.10  1.25
127 A318(h) 55 l vio bl & pale
                 sal          2.50  3.75

---

## Italy No. 584 Overprinted Type "g" in Carmine

**1951, Aug. 23**
128 A319  25 l gray blk        9.00  3.25

## Overprint "g" on Italy No. 585

**1951, Sept. 8**
129 A320  25 l deep blue       1.10  1.10

## Italy No. 586 Overprinted Type "h" in Red

**1951, Sept. 15**
130 A321  25 l dk brn          1.10  1.10

## Italy Nos. 587-589 Overprinted in Blue

o

**1951, Oct. 11**
131 A322  10 l dk brn & gray   .45    .90
132 A322  25 l rose red & bl grn .80  .80
133 A322  60 l vio bl & red org 1.25 1.50
      Nos. 131-133 (3)        2.50   3.20

## Italy Nos. 590-591 Overprinted

p

**1951, Oct. 31            Photo.**
**Overprint Spaced to Fit Design**
134 A323  10 l green           .75    .90
135 A324  25 l vio gray        .75    .90

## Italy Nos. 592-593 Ovptd. Type "k"

**1951, Nov. 21**
136 A325  10 l ol & dull grn   .80   1.25
137 A326  25 l dull green     1.00    .80

## Italy Nos. 594-596 Overprinted Types "k" or "p" in Black

**1951, Nov. 23**
**Overprint "p" Spaced to Fit Design**
138 A327(p) 10 l vio brn & dk
                 grn          1.00   1.00
139 A327(k) 25 l red brn & dk
                 brn          1.00   1.00
140 A327(p) 60 l dp grn & ind 2.00   2.00
      Nos. 138-140 (3)        4.00   4.00

## Italy No. 597 Overprinted Type "p"

**1952, Jan. 28   Wmk. 277   Perf. 14**
**Overprint Spaced to Fit Design**
141 A328  25 l gray & gray blk 1.00   .70

## Italy No. 598 Overprinted Type "k"

**1952, Feb. 2**
142 A329  25 l dl grn & ol bis 1.00   .70

## Same on Italy No. 599

**1952, Mar. 26**
143 A330  25 l brn & sl blk    .85    .70

## Same on Italy No. 600

**1952, Apr. 12**
144 A331  60 l ultra           2.50  3.25

## Same on Italy No. 601

**1952, Apr. 16**
145 A332  25 l dp orange       .75    .20

## Stamps of Italy Overprinted "AMG FTT" in Various Sizes and Arrangements On Nos. 602-603

**1952, June 14   Wmk. 277   Perf. 14**
146 A333  25 l blk & red brn   .65    .60
147 A333  60 l blk & ultra    1.10   1.75

## On No. 604

**1952, June 7**
148 A334  25 l bright blue     .90    .70

**On No. 605**

**1952, June 14**
| | | | |
|---|---|---|---|
| 149 | A335 | 25 l black & yellow | .90 .70 |

**On No. 606**

**1952, June 19**
| | | | |
|---|---|---|---|
| 150 | A336 | 25 l bl gray, red & dk bl (R) | .90 .70 |

**On No. 607**

**1952, June 28**
| | | | |
|---|---|---|---|
| 151 | A337 | 25 l dp grn, dk brn & red | .90 .70 |

**On No. 608**

**1952, Sept. 6**
| | | | |
|---|---|---|---|
| 152 | A338 | 25 l dark green | .90 .70 |

**On No. 609 in Bronze**

**1952, Sept. 20**
| | | | |
|---|---|---|---|
| 153 | A339 | 25 l purple | .90 .70 |

**On No. 610**

**1952, Oct. 4**
| | | | |
|---|---|---|---|
| 154 | A340 | 25 l gray | .90 .70 |

**On No. 611**

**1952, Oct. 1**
| | | | |
|---|---|---|---|
| 155 | A341 | 60 l vio bl & dk bl | 2.25 3.25 |

**On No. 612**

**1952, Nov. 21**    *Perf. 13*
| | | | |
|---|---|---|---|
| 156 | A342 | 25 l brn & dk brn | 1.00 .70 |

**On Nos. 613-615**

**1952, Nov. 3**    *Perf. 14*
| | | | |
|---|---|---|---|
| 157 | A343 | 10 l dk green | .20 .35 |
| 158 | A344 | 25 l blk & dk brn | .80 .30 |
| 159 | A344 | 60 l blk & blue | .80 1.50 |
| | | *Nos. 157-159 (3)* | 1.80 2.15 |

**On Nos. 616-617**

**1952, Dec. 6**
| | | | |
|---|---|---|---|
| 160 | A345 | 25 l dk green | .90 .70 |
| 161 | A346 | 25 l brown | .90 .70 |

**On No. 618**

**1953, Jan. 5**
| | | | |
|---|---|---|---|
| 162 | A347 | 25 l gray blk & dk bl (Bl) | .90 .70 |

**On Nos. 601A-601B**

**1952, Dec. 31**
| | | | |
|---|---|---|---|
| 163 | A332a | 60 l ultra (G) | .75 1.25 |
| 164 | A332 | 80 l brown car | 1.60 .50 |

**On No. 621**

**1953, Feb. 21**
| | | | |
|---|---|---|---|
| 165 | A349 | 25 l car lake | .90 .70 |

**On No. 622**

**1953, Apr. 24**
| | | | |
|---|---|---|---|
| 166 | A350 | 25 l violet | .90 .70 |

**On No. 623**

**1953, Apr. 30**
| | | | |
|---|---|---|---|
| 167 | A351 | 25 l violet | .90 .70 |

**On No. 624**

**1953, May 30**
| | | | |
|---|---|---|---|
| 168 | A352 | 25 l dark brown | .90 .70 |

**On No. 625**

**1953, June 27**
| | | | |
|---|---|---|---|
| 169 | A353 | 25 l brn & dull red | .90 .70 |

**On Nos. 626-633**

**1953-54**
| | | | |
|---|---|---|---|
| 170 | A354 | 5 l gray | .20 .20 |
| 171 | A354 | 10 l org ver | .25 .20 |
| 172 | A354 | 12 l dull grn | .25 .20 |
| 172A | A354 | 13 l brt lil rose ('54) | .25 .20 |
| 173 | A354 | 20 l brown | .25 .20 |
| 174 | A354 | 25 l purple | .25 .20 |
| 175 | A354 | 35 l rose car | 1.00 1.00 |
| 176 | A354 | 60 l blue | 1.00 1.00 |
| 177 | A354 | 80 l org brn | 2.50 2.75 |
| | | *Nos. 170-177 (9)* | 5.95 6.95 |

Issue dates: 13 l, Feb. 1. Others, June 16.

Italy, Nos. 554, 558 and 564 Overprinted in Red or Green

**1953, June 27**
| | | | |
|---|---|---|---|
| 178 | A306 | 10 l dp green (R) | .40 .60 |
| 179 | A306 | 25 l brown org | .50 .40 |
| 180 | A306 | 60 l red | .60 1.00 |
| | | *Nos. 178-180 (3)* | 1.50 2.00 |

5th International Sample Fair of Trieste.

**On No. 634**

**1953, July 11**
| | | | |
|---|---|---|---|
| 181 | A355 | 25 l blue green | 1.10 .70 |

**On Nos. 635-636**

**1953, July 16**
| | | | |
|---|---|---|---|
| 182 | A356 | 25 l dark brown | .45 .50 |
| 183 | A356 | 60 l deep blue | .70 1.00 |

**On Nos. 637-638**

**1953, Aug. 6**
| | | | |
|---|---|---|---|
| 184 | A357 | 25 l org & Prus bl | 1.00 1.00 |
| 185 | A357 | 60 l lil rose & dk vio bl | 3.00 3.25 |

**On No. 639**

**1953, Aug. 13**
| | | | |
|---|---|---|---|
| 186 | A358 | 25 l dk brn & dl grn | .90 .70 |

**On No. 640**

**1953, Sept. 5**
| | | | |
|---|---|---|---|
| 187 | A359 | 25 l dk gray & brn | .90 .70 |

**On Nos. 641-646**

**1954, Jan. 26**
| | | | |
|---|---|---|---|
| 188 | A360 | 10 l dk brn & red brn | .25 .30 |
| 189 | A361 | 12 l lt bl & gray | .30 .50 |
| 190 | A361 | 20 l brn org & dk brn | .40 .35 |
| 191 | A361 | 25 l dk grn & pale bl | .40 .20 |
| 192 | A361 | 35 l cream & brn | .40 .80 |
| 193 | A361 | 60 l bl grn & ind | .55 1.00 |
| | | *Nos. 188-193 (6)* | 2.30 3.15 |

**On Nos. 647-648**

**1954, Feb. 11**
| | | | |
|---|---|---|---|
| 194 | A362 | 25 l dk brn & choc | .45 .50 |
| 195 | A362 | 60 l bl & ultra | .65 1.00 |

**On Nos. 649-650**

**1954, Feb. 25**
| | | | |
|---|---|---|---|
| 196 | A363 | 25 l purple | .45 .35 |
| 197 | A363 | 60 l dp bl grn | .95 1.50 |

**On No. 651**

**1954, Mar. 20**
| | | | |
|---|---|---|---|
| 198 | A364 | 25 l purple | 1.00 .50 |

**On No. 652**

**1954, Apr. 24**
| | | | |
|---|---|---|---|
| 199 | A365 | 25 l gray blk | .90 .70 |

**On No. 653**

**1954, June 1**
| | | | |
|---|---|---|---|
| 200 | A366 | 25 l gray, org brn & blk | .90 .70 |

**On No. 654**

**1954, June 19**
| | | | |
|---|---|---|---|
| 201 | A367 | 25 l dk grnsh gray | .90 .70 |

**On Nos. 655-656**

**1954, July 8**
| | | | |
|---|---|---|---|
| 202 | A368 | 25 l red brown | .40 .55 |
| 203 | A368 | 60 l gray green | .95 1.25 |

**FIERA DI TRIESTE 1954**

Nos. 644, 646 With Additional Overprint

**1954, June 17**
| | | | |
|---|---|---|---|
| 204 | A360 | 25 l dk grn & pale bl | .55 .60 |
| 205 | A361 | 60 l bl grn & indigo | .75 1.00 |

International Sample Fair of Trieste.

**On No. 657**

**1954, Sept. 6**
| | | | |
|---|---|---|---|
| 206 | A369 | 25 l dp grn & red | .90 .70 |

**On Nos. 658-659**

**1954, Oct. 30**
| | | | |
|---|---|---|---|
| 207 | A370 | 25 l rose red | .30 .40 |
| 208 | A370 | 60 l blue | .55 .65 |

### OCCUPATION AIR POST STAMPS

**Air Post Stamps of Italy, 1945-47, Overprinted Type "c" in Black**

**1947, Oct. 1**    **Wmk. 277**    *Perf. 14*
| | | | |
|---|---|---|---|
| C1 | AP59 | 1 l slate bl | .20 .20 |
| C2 | AP60 | 2 l dk blue | .20 .20 |
| C3 | AP60 | 5 l dk green | 3.25 2.25 |
| C4 | AP59 | 10 l car rose | 3.25 2.25 |
| C5 | AP60 | 25 l brown | 7.25 3.50 |
| C6 | AP59 | 50 l violet | 45.00 5.50 |
| | | *Nos. C1-C6 (6)* | 59.15 13.90 |

**Italy, Nos. C116 to C121, Overprinted Type "b" in Black**

**1947, Nov. 19**
| | | | |
|---|---|---|---|
| C7 | AP61 | 6 l dp violet | 1.25 1.75 |
| C8 | AP61 | 10 l dk car rose | 1.25 1.75 |
| C9 | AP61 | 20 l dp org | 9.50 4.25 |
| C10 | AP61 | 25 l aqua | 1.75 2.00 |
| C11 | AP61 | 35 l brt blue | 1.75 2.50 |
| C12 | AP61 | 50 l lilac rose | 9.50 2.50 |
| | | *Nos. C7-C12 (6)* | 25.00 14.75 |

**Italy, Nos. C123 to C126, Overprinted Type "f" in Black**

**1948**
| | | | |
|---|---|---|---|
| C13 | AP65 | 100 l green | 90.00 2.25 |
| C14 | AP65 | 300 l lil rose | 11.50 13.00 |
| C15 | AP65 | 500 l ultra | 13.50 19.00 |
| C16 | AP65 | 1000 l dk brown | 150.00 175.00 |
| | | *Nos. C13-C16 (4)* | 265.00 209.25 |

Issue date: Nos. C13-C15, Mar. 1.

**Italy, No. C110, C113 and C114, Overprinted in Black**

(Reduced Illustration)

**1948, Sept. 8**
| | | | |
|---|---|---|---|
| C17 | AP59 | 10 l carmine rose | .35 .35 |
| C18 | AP60 | 25 l brown | .70 .90 |
| C19 | AP59 | 50 l violet | .70 .90 |
| | | *Nos. C17-C19 (3)* | 1.75 2.15 |

The overprint is embossed.

**Italy Air Post Stamps of 1945-48 Overprinted Type "h" in Black**

**1949-52**
| | | | |
|---|---|---|---|
| C20 | AP59 | 10 l car rose | .20 .20 |
| C21 | AP60 | 25 l brown ('50) | .20 .20 |
| C22 | AP59 | 50 l violet | .20 .20 |
| C23 | AP65 | 100 l green | .75 .20 |
| C24 | AP65 | 300 l lil rose ('50) | 11.50 16.50 |
| C25 | AP65 | 500 l ultra ('50) | 25.00 20.00 |
| C26 | AP65 | 1000 l dk brn ('52) | 38.00 38.00 |
| | | *Nos. C20-C26 (7)* | 75.85 75.30 |

No. C26 is found in two perforations: 14 and 14x13.

Issued: 100 l, 11/7; 50 l, 12/5; 10 l, 12/28; 25 l, 1/23; 300 l, 500 l, 11/25; 1000 l, 2/18.

### OCCUPATION SPECIAL DELIVERY STAMPS

**Special Delivery Stamps of Italy 1946-48 Overprinted Type "c"**

**1947-48**    **Wmk. 277**    *Perf. 14*
| | | | |
|---|---|---|---|
| E1 | SD9 | 15 l dk car rose | .20 .20 |
| E2 | SD8 | 25 l brt red org ('48) | 40.00 10.00 |
| E3 | SD8 | 30 l dp vio | .40 .30 |
| E4 | SD9 | 60 l car rose ('48) | 35.00 16.00 |
| | | *Nos. E1-E4 (4)* | 75.60 26.50 |

Issue dates: Oct. 1, 1947. Mar. 1, 1948.

**Italy No. E26, Overprinted Type "d"**

**1948, Sept. 24**
| | | | |
|---|---|---|---|
| E5 | A272 | 35 l violet | 2.75 3.00 |

**Italy No. E25, Overprinted Type "h"**

**1950, Sept. 27**
| | | | |
|---|---|---|---|
| E6 | SD9 | 60 l car rose | 6.25 1.50 |

**Italy No. E32 Overprinted Type "k"**

**1952, Feb. 4**
| | | | |
|---|---|---|---|
| E7 | SD8 | 50 l lilac rose | 6.25 1.50 |

### OCCUPATION AUTHORIZED DELIVERY STAMPS

**Authorized Delivery Stamp of Italy, 1946 Overprinted Type "a" in Black**

**1947, Oct. 1**    **Wmk. 277**    *Perf. 14*
| | | | |
|---|---|---|---|
| EY1 | AD3 | 1 l dark brown | .25 .25 |

Italy, No. EY7 Overprinted in Black

**1947, Oct. 29**
| | | | |
|---|---|---|---|
| EY2 | AD4 | 8 l bright red | 9.75 1.75 |

**Italy, No. EY8, Overprinted Type "a" in Black**

**1949, July 30**
| | | | |
|---|---|---|---|
| EY3 | AD4 | 15 l violet | 55.00 11.00 |

**Same, Overprinted Type "h" in Black**

**1949, Nov. 7**
| | | | |
|---|---|---|---|
| EY4 | AD4 | 15 l violet | 1.25 .50 |

**Italy No. EY9 Overprinted Type "h" in Black**

**1952, Feb. 4**
| | | | |
|---|---|---|---|
| EY5 | AD4 | 20 l rose violet | 8.75 .50 |

### OCCUPATION POSTAGE DUE STAMPS

**Postage Due Stamps of Italy, 1945-47, Overprinted Type "a"**

**1947, Oct. 1**    **Wmk. 277**    *Perf. 14*
| | | | |
|---|---|---|---|
| J1 | D9 | 1 l red orange | .20 .25 |
| J2 | D10 | 2 l dk green | .20 .35 |
| J3 | D9 | 5 l violet | 6.00 .25 |
| J4 | D9 | 10 l dk blue | 8.75 1.75 |
| J5 | D9 | 20 l car rose | 24.00 1.75 |
| J6 | D10 | 50 l aqua | 1.40 .50 |
| | | *Nos. J1-J6 (6)* | 40.55 4.85 |

**Same Overprint on Postage Due Stamps of Italy, 1947**

**1949**
| | | | |
|---|---|---|---|
| J7 | D10 | 1 l red orange | .20 .50 |
| J8 | D10 | 3 l carmine | .55 1.25 |
| J9 | D10 | 4 l brown | 7.50 11.00 |
| J10 | D10 | 5 l violet | 90.00 15.00 |
| J11 | D10 | 6 l vio blue | 22.50 21.00 |
| J12 | D10 | 8 l rose vio | 47.50 55.00 |
| J13 | D10 | 10 l deep blue | 125.00 15.00 |
| J14 | D10 | 12 l golden brn | 17.00 18.00 |
| J15 | D10 | 20 l lilac rose | 17.00 4.50 |
| | | *Nos. J7-J15 (9)* | 327.25 141.25 |

Issued: 3 l, 4 l, 6 l, 8 l, 12 l, 1/24; others, 4/15.

**Postage Due Stamps of Italy, 1947-54, Overprinted Type "h"**

**1949-54**
| | | | |
|---|---|---|---|
| J16 | D10 | 1 l red orange | .25 .20 |
| J17 | D10 | 2 l dk green | .25 .20 |
| J18 | D10 | 3 l ('54) | .35 .70 |
| J20 | D10 | 5 l violet | .45 .20 |
| J21 | D10 | 6 l vio bl ('50) | .35 .20 |
| J22 | D10 | 8 l rose vio ('50) | .35 .20 |
| J23 | D10 | 10 l deep blue | .50 .20 |
| J24 | D10 | 12 l gldn brn ('50) | 1.10 .70 |
| J25 | D10 | 20 l lilac rose | 1.90 .50 |
| J26 | D10 | 25 l dk red ('54) | 4.75 6.50 |
| J27 | D10 | 50 l aqua ('50) | 3.25 .20 |
| J28 | D10 | 100 l org yel ('52) | 5.25 .50 |
| J29 | D10 | 500 l dp bl & dk car ('52) | 30.00 12.00 |
| | | *Nos. J16-J29 (13)* | 48.75 22.30 |

Issued: 5 l, 10 l, 11/7; 1 l, 11/22; 2 l, 20 l, 12/28; 6 l, 8 l, 12 l, 5/16; 50 l, 11/25; 100 l, 11/11; 500 l, 6/19; 3 l, 1/24; 25 l, 2/1.

### OCCUPATION PARCEL POST STAMPS

See note preceding Italy No. Q7.

## Parcel Post Stamps of Italy, 1946-48, Overprinted:

### 1947-48　　Wmk. 277　　Perf. 13½

| | | | | |
|---|---|---|---|---|
| Q1 | PP4 | 1 l golden brn | .25 | .40 |
| Q2 | PP4 | 2 l lt bl grn | .35 | .50 |
| Q3 | PP4 | 3 l red org | .40 | .60 |
| Q4 | PP4 | 4 l gray blk | .50 | .75 |
| Q5 | PP4 | 5 l lil rose ('48) | 1.40 | 2.00 |
| Q6 | PP4 | 10 l violet | 2.75 | 4.00 |
| Q7 | PP4 | 20 l lilac brn | 4.00 | 6.00 |
| Q8 | PP4 | 50 l rose red | 6.50 | 9.00 |
| Q9 | PP4 | 100 l sapphire | 8.00 | 12.00 |
| Q10 | PP4 | 200 l grn ('48) | 350.00 | 500.00 |
| Q11 | PP4 | 300 l brn car ('48) | 175.00 | 250.00 |
| Q12 | PP4 | 500 l brn ('48) | 100.00 | 150.00 |
| | | Nos. Q1-Q12 (12) | 649.15 | 935.25 |

**Halves Used**

| | |
|---|---|
| Q1-Q4 | .20 |
| Q5 | .20 |
| Q6-Q7 | .20 |
| Q8 | .20 |
| Q9 | .25 |
| Q10 | 5.75 |
| Q11 | 4.50 |
| Q12 | 1.90 |

Issued: #Q1-Q4, Q6-Q9, Oct. 1; others, Mar. 1.

## Parcel Post Stamps of Italy, 1946-54, Overprinted:

### 1949-54

| | | | | |
|---|---|---|---|---|
| Q13 | PP4 | 1 l gldn brn ('50) | 1.50 | 1.50 |
| Q14 | PP4 | 2 l lt bl grn ('51) | .50 | 1.00 |
| Q15 | PP4 | 3 l red org ('51) | .50 | 1.00 |
| Q16 | PP4 | 4 l gray blk ('51) | .75 | .75 |
| Q17 | PP4 | 5 l lilac rose | .75 | 1.00 |
| Q18 | PP4 | 10 l violet | 1.50 | 1.50 |
| Q19 | PP4 | 20 l lil brn | 1.75 | 1.75 |
| Q20 | PP4 | 30 l plum ('52) | .75 | .90 |
| Q21 | PP4 | 50 l rose red ('50) | 1.50 | 1.50 |
| Q22 | PP4 | 100 l saph ('50) | 3.50 | 5.00 |
| Q23 | PP4 | 200 l green | 25.00 | 50.00 |
| Q24 | PP4 | 300 l brn car ('50) | 100.00 | 140.00 |
| Q25 | PP4 | 500 l brn ('51) | 60.00 | 80.00 |

### Perf. 13x13½

| | | | | |
|---|---|---|---|---|
| Q26 | PP5 | 1000 l ultra ('54) | 175.00 | 175.00 |
| | | Nos. Q13-Q26 (14) | 373.00 | 460.90 |

**Halves Used**

| | |
|---|---|
| Q13-Q18, Q20 | .20 |
| Q19, Q22 | .30 |
| Q21 | .30 |
| Q23 | .75 |
| Q24 | .80 |
| Q25 | .80 |
| Q26 | 2.00 |

Pairs of Q18 exist with 5mm between overprints instead of 11mm. Value $800.

Issued: 20 l, 200 l, 11/22; 5 l, 10 l, 11/28; 300 l, 1/19; 50 l, 3/10; 1 l, 10/7; 100 l, 11/9; 500 l, 11/25; 2 l, 3 l, 4 l, 8/1; 30 l, 3/6; 1000 l, 8/12.

---

## PARCEL POST AUTHORIZED DELIVERY STAMPS

For the payment of a special tax for the authorized delivery of parcels privately instead of through the post office. Both unused and used values are for complete stamps.

### Parcel Post Authorized Delivery Stamps of Italy 1953 Overprinted in Black like Nos. Q13-Q26

#### 1953, July 8　　Wmk. 277

| | | | | |
|---|---|---|---|---|
| QY1 | PAD1 | 40 l org red | 10.00 | 3.00 |
| QY2 | PAD1 | 50 l ultra | 10.00 | 3.00 |
| QY3 | PAD1 | 75 l brown | 10.00 | 7.00 |
| QY4 | PAD1 | 110 l lilac rose | 10.00 | 7.00 |
| | | Nos. QY1-QY4 (4) | 40.00 | 20.00 |

**Halves Used**

| | |
|---|---|
| QY1 | .20 |
| QY2 | .20 |
| QY3-QY4 | .35 |

---

# IVORY COAST

ˈīv-rē ˈkōst

LOCATION — West coast of Africa, bordering on Gulf of Guinea
GOVT. — Republic
AREA — 127,520 sq. mi.
POP. — 15,818,068 (1999 est.)
CAPITAL — Yamoussoukro

The former French colony of Ivory Coast became part of French West Africa and used its stamps, starting in 1945. On December 4, 1958, Ivory Coast became a republic, with full independence on August 7, 1960.

100 Centimes = 1 Franc

Catalogue values for unused stamps in this country are for Never Hinged items, beginning with Scott 167 in the regular postage section, Scott B15 in the semipostal section, Scott C14 in the airpost section, Scott J19 in the postage due section, Scott M1 in the military section, and Scott O1 in the official section.

Navigation and Commerce — A1

### Perf. 14x13½

#### 1892-1900　　Typo.　　Unwmk.
#### Colony Name in Blue or Carmine

| | | | | |
|---|---|---|---|---|
| 1 | A1 | 1c black, lil bl | 1.80 | 2.00 |
| 2 | A1 | 2c brown, buff | 2.75 | 2.90 |
| 3 | A1 | 4c claret, lav | 4.50 | 4.00 |
| 4 | A1 | 5c green, grnsh | 12.50 | 9.00 |
| 5 | A1 | 10c black, lavender | 18.00 | 12.50 |
| 6 | A1 | 10c red ('00) | 130.00 | 100.00 |
| 7 | A1 | 15c blue, quadrille paper | 29.00 | 13.00 |
| 8 | A1 | 15c gray ('00) | 20.00 | 5.75 |
| 9 | A1 | 20c red, green | 20.00 | 15.00 |
| 10 | A1 | 25c black, rose | 22.50 | 6.50 |
| 11 | A1 | 25c blue ('00) | 37.50 | 30.00 |
| 12 | A1 | 30c brown, bister | 32.50 | 25.00 |
| 13 | A1 | 40c red, straw | 25.00 | 16.00 |
| 14 | A1 | 50c car, rose | 77.50 | 65.00 |
| 15 | A1 | 50c brn, azure ('00) | 37.50 | 32.50 |
| 16 | A1 | 75c deep vio, org | 32.50 | 32.50 |
| 17 | A1 | 1fr brnz grn, straw | 52.50 | 40.00 |
| | | Nos. 1-17 (17) | 556.05 | 411.65 |

Perf. 13½x14 stamps are counterfeits.
For surcharges see Nos. 18-20, 37-41.

Nos. 12, 16-17
Surcharged in Black

#### 1904

| | | | | |
|---|---|---|---|---|
| 18 | A1 | 0,05c on 30c brn, bis | 82.50 | 82.50 |
| 19 | A1 | 0,10c on 75c vio, org | 18.00 | 18.00 |
| 20 | A1 | 0,15c on 1fr brnz grn, straw | 22.50 | 22.50 |
| | | Nos. 18-20 (3) | 123.00 | 123.00 |

Gen. Louis Faidherbe
A2

Oil Palm — A3

Dr. N. Eugène Ballay
A4

#### 1906-07
#### Name of Colony in Red or Blue

| | | | | |
|---|---|---|---|---|
| 21 | A2 | 1c slate | 1.80 | 1.80 |
| 22 | A2 | 2c chocolate | 1.90 | 1.90 |
| 23 | A2 | 4c choc, gray bl | 2.25 | 2.25 |
| a. | | Name double | 200.00 | |
| 24 | A2 | 5c green | 4.00 | 2.75 |
| 25 | A2 | 10c carmine (B) | 9.00 | 6.00 |
| 26 | A3 | 20c black, azure | 10.00 | 9.00 |
| 27 | A3 | 25c bl, pinkish | 9.00 | 5.75 |
| 28 | A3 | 30c choc, pnksh | 11.50 | 8.25 |
| 29 | A3 | 35c black, yel | 12.50 | 5.75 |
| 30 | A3 | 45c choc, grnsh | 18.00 | 11.50 |
| 31 | A3 | 50c deep violet | 15.00 | 11.50 |
| 32 | A3 | 75c blue, org | 15.00 | 11.50 |
| 33 | A4 | 1fr black, azure | 40.00 | 32.50 |
| 34 | A4 | 2fr blue, pink | 52.50 | 50.00 |
| 35 | A4 | 5fr car, straw (B) | 100.00 | 95.00 |
| 36 | | Nos. 21-36 (15) | 302.45 | 255.45 |

### Stamps of 1892-1900 Surcharged in Carmine or Black

#### 1912

| | | | | |
|---|---|---|---|---|
| 37 | A1 | 5c on 15c gray (C) | 1.25 | 1.25 |
| 38 | A1 | 5c on 30c brn, bis (C) | 2.00 | 2.00 |
| 39 | A1 | 10c on 40c red, straw | 1.90 | 2.00 |
| a. | | Pair, one without surcharge | 75.00 | |
| 40 | A1 | 10c on 50c brn, az (C) | 3.25 | 3.75 |
| 41 | A1 | 10c on 75c dp vio, org | 9.00 | 10.00 |
| | | Nos. 37-41 (5) | 17.40 | 19.00 |

Two spacings between the surcharged numerals are found on Nos. 37 to 41. For detailed listings, see the *Scott Classic Specialized Catalogue of Stamps and Covers.*

River Scene
A5

#### 1913-35

| | | | | |
|---|---|---|---|---|
| 42 | A5 | 1c vio brn & vio | .25 | .25 |
| 43 | A5 | 2c brown & blk | .25 | .25 |
| 44 | A5 | 4c vio & vio brn | .30 | .30 |
| 45 | A5 | 5c yel grn & bl grn | 1.10 | .50 |
| 46 | A5 | 5c choc & ol brn ('22) | .25 | .50 |
| 47 | A5 | 10c red org & rose | 1.80 | .90 |
| 48 | A5 | 10c yel grn & bl grn ('22) | .55 | .55 |
| 49 | A5 | 10c car rose, bluish ('26) | .30 | .30 |
| 50 | A5 | 15c org & rose ('17) | 1.00 | .55 |
| 51 | A5 | 20c black & gray | .65 | .50 |
| 52 | A5 | 25c ultra & bl | 10.00 | 6.50 |
| 53 | A5 | 25c blk & vio ('22) | .50 | .50 |
| 54 | A5 | 30c choc & brn | 2.00 | 1.80 |
| 55 | A5 | 30c red org & rose ('22) | 2.50 | 2.50 |
| 56 | A5 | 30c lt bl & rose red ('26) | .50 | .50 |
| 57 | A5 | 30c dl grn & grn ('27) | .50 | .50 |
| 58 | A5 | 35c vio & org | .90 | .75 |
| 59 | A5 | 40c gray & bl grn | 1.60 | .80 |
| 60 | A5 | 45c red org & choc | 1.00 | .75 |
| 61 | A5 | 45c dp rose & mar ('34) | 5.75 | 5.00 |
| 62 | A5 | 50c black & vio | 4.50 | 3.25 |
| 63 | A5 | 50c ultra & bl ('22) | 1.50 | 1.50 |
| 64 | A5 | 50c org & bl ('25) | .65 | .65 |
| 65 | A5 | 60c vio, pnksh ('25) | .75 | .75 |
| 66 | A5 | 65c car rose & ol grn ('26) | 1.60 | 1.60 |
| 67 | A5 | 75c brn & rose | 1.00 | .80 |
| 68 | A5 | 75c ind & ultra ('34) | 4.00 | 4.00 |
| 69 | A5 | 85c red vio & blk ('26) | 1.60 | 1.60 |
| 70 | A5 | 90c brn red & rose ('30) | 14.00 | 13.00 |
| 71 | A5 | 1fr org & black | 1.10 | 1.00 |
| 72 | A5 | 1.10fr dl grn & dk brn ('28) | 7.00 | 7.00 |
| 73 | A5 | 1.50fr lt bl & dp bl ('30) | 9.00 | 7.50 |
| 74 | A5 | 1.75fr lt ultra & mag ('35) | 14.00 | 9.00 |
| 75 | A5 | 2fr brn & blue | 5.00 | 2.90 |
| 76 | A5 | 3fr red vio ('30) | 9.00 | 7.50 |
| 77 | A5 | 5fr dk bl & choc | 7.50 | 5.75 |
| | | Nos. 42-77 (36) | 113.90 | 91.75 |

Nos. 45, 47, 50 and 58 exist on both ordinary and chalky paper.
For surcharges see Nos. 78-91, B1.
Nos. 45, 47 and 52, pasted on cardboard and overprinted "Valeur d'echange" and value of basic stamp, were used as emergency currency in 1920.

### Stamps and Type of 1913-34 Surcharged

#### 1922-34

| | | | | |
|---|---|---|---|---|
| 78 | A5 | 50c on 45c dp rose & maroon ('34) | 3.75 | 2.60 |
| 79 | A5 | 50c on 75c indigo & ultra ('34) | 2.25 | 1.75 |
| 80 | A5 | 50c on 90c brn red & rose ('34) | 2.25 | 2.25 |
| 81 | A5 | 60c on 75c vio, pnksh | .55 | .55 |
| 82 | A5 | 65c on 15c orange & rose ('25) | 1.10 | 1.10 |
| 83 | A5 | 85c on 75c brown & rose ('25) | 1.50 | 1.25 |
| | | Nos. 78-83 (6) | 11.40 | 9.50 |

### Stamps and Type of 1913 Surcharged with New Value and Bars

#### 1924-27

| | | | | |
|---|---|---|---|---|
| 84 | A5 | 25c on 2fr (R) | 1.10 | 1.10 |
| 85 | A5 | 25c on 5fr | 1.10 | 1.10 |
| 86 | A5 | 90c on 75c brn red & cer ('27) | 1.75 | 1.50 |
| 87 | A5 | 1.25fr on 1fr dk bl & ultra (R) ('26) | 1.25 | 1.25 |
| 88 | A5 | 1.50fr on 1fr lt bl & dk blue ('27) | 1.75 | 1.75 |
| 89 | A5 | 3fr on 5fr brn red & bl grn ('27) | 5.50 | 5.25 |
| 90 | A5 | 10fr on 5fr dl red & rose lil ('27) | 17.50 | 16.00 |
| 91 | A5 | 20fr on 5fr bl grn & ver ('27) | 20.00 | 18.00 |
| | | Nos. 84-91 (8) | 49.95 | 45.95 |

Common Design Types pictured following the introduction.

### Colonial Exposition Issue
Common Design Types
Name of Country in Black

#### 1931　　Engr.　　Perf. 12½

| | | | | |
|---|---|---|---|---|
| 92 | CD70 | 40c deep green | 3.75 | 3.75 |
| 93 | CD71 | 50c violet | 5.75 | 5.75 |
| 94 | CD72 | 90c red orange | 5.50 | 5.50 |
| 95 | CD73 | 1.50fr dull blue | 5.75 | 5.75 |
| | | Nos. 92-95 (4) | 20.75 | 20.75 |

Stamps of Upper Volta 1928, Overprinted

#### 1933　　Perf. 13½x14

| | | | | |
|---|---|---|---|---|
| 96 | A5 | 2c brown & lilac | .25 | .25 |
| 97 | A5 | 4c blk & yellow | .35 | .35 |
| 98 | A5 | 5c ind & gray bl | .65 | .50 |
| 99 | A5 | 10c indigo & pink | .50 | .50 |
| 100 | A5 | 15c brown & blue | 1.25 | 1.00 |

| | | | | |
|---|---|---|---|---|
| 101 | A5 | 20c brown & green | 1.25 | 1.00 |
| 102 | A6 | 25c brn & yellow | 2.10 | 1.90 |
| 103 | A6 | 30c dp grn & brn | 2.40 | 2.00 |
| 104 | A6 | 45c brown & blue | 8.25 | 6.50 |
| 105 | A6 | 65c indigo & bl | 3.25 | 2.90 |
| 106 | A6 | 75c black & lilac | 4.00 | 2.50 |
| 107 | A6 | 90c brn red & lil | 3.25 | 2.90 |

### Overprinted

| | | | | |
|---|---|---|---|---|
| 108 | A7 | 1fr brown & green | 4.00 | 2.90 |
| 109 | A7 | 1.50fr ultra & grysh | 3.75 | 2.90 |

### Surcharged

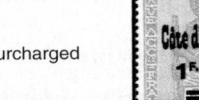

| | | | | |
|---|---|---|---|---|
| 110 | A6 | 1.25fr on 40c blk & pink | 2.50 | 2.25 |
| 111 | A6 | 1.75fr on 50c blk & green | 4.25 | 3.25 |
| | | *Nos. 96-111 (16)* | 42.00 | 33.60 |

Baoulé Woman — A6

Rapids on Comoe River — A9

Mosque at Bobo-Dioulasso — A7

Coastal Scene A8

### 1936-44      Perf. 13

| | | | | |
|---|---|---|---|---|
| 112 | A6 | 1c carmine rose | .25 | .25 |
| 113 | A6 | 2c ultramarine | .25 | .25 |
| 114 | A6 | 3c dp grn ('40) | .25 | .25 |
| 115 | A6 | 4c chocolate | .25 | .25 |
| 116 | A6 | 5c violet | .25 | .25 |
| 117 | A6 | 10c Prussian bl | .25 | .25 |
| 118 | A6 | 15c copper red | .25 | .25 |
| 119 | A7 | 20c ultramarine | .35 | .25 |
| 120 | A7 | 25c copper red | .40 | .25 |
| 121 | A7 | 30c blue green | .35 | .35 |
| 122 | A6 | 30c brown ('40) | .25 | .25 |
| 123 | A6 | 35c dp grn ('38) | .85 | .60 |
| 124 | A7 | 40c carmine rose | .40 | .35 |
| 125 | A7 | 45c brown | .65 | .65 |
| 126 | A7 | 45c blue grn ('40) | .35 | .35 |
| 127 | A7 | 50c plum | .50 | .50 |
| 128 | A7 | 55c dark vio ('38) | .60 | .60 |
| 129 | A7 | 60c car rose ('40) | .40 | .40 |
| 130 | A8 | 65c red brown | .65 | .50 |
| 131 | A8 | 70c red brn ('40) | .60 | .60 |
| 132 | A8 | 75c dark violet | 1.10 | .75 |
| 133 | A8 | 80c blk brn ('38) | 1.25 | .90 |
| 134 | A8 | 90c carmine rose | 8.50 | 5.50 |
| 135 | A8 | 90c dk grn ('39) | .75 | .75 |
| 136 | A8 | 1fr dark green | 4.00 | 2.75 |
| 137 | A8 | 1fr car rose ('38) | 1.30 | .85 |
| 138 | A8 | 1fr dk vio ('40) | .60 | .60 |
| 139 | A8 | 1.25fr copper red | .50 | .40 |
| 140 | A8 | 1.40fr ultra ('40) | .60 | .60 |
| 141 | A8 | 1.50fr ultramarine | .50 | .40 |
| 141A | A8 | 1.50fr grnsh blk ('44) | 1.80 | 1.80 |
| 142 | A8 | 1.60fr blk brn ('40) | 1.00 | 1.00 |

| | | | | |
|---|---|---|---|---|
| 143 | A9 | 1.75fr carmine rose | .50 | .40 |
| 144 | A9 | 1.75fr dull bl ('38) | 1.00 | .85 |
| 145 | A9 | 2fr ultramarine | .75 | .60 |
| 146 | A9 | 2.25fr dark bl ('39) | 1.10 | 1.10 |
| 147 | A9 | 2.50fr rose red ('40) | 1.40 | 1.40 |
| 148 | A9 | 3fr green | .75 | .60 |
| 149 | A9 | 5fr chocolate | .85 | .65 |
| 150 | A9 | 10fr violet | 1.25 | 1.00 |
| 151 | A9 | 20fr copper red | 2.10 | 1.80 |
| | | *Nos. 112-151 (41)* | 39.70 | 32.10 |

Stamps of types A7-A9 without "RF," see Nos. 166A-166D.
For surcharges see Nos. B8-B11.

### Paris International Exposition Issue
Common Design Types

#### 1937      Perf. 13

| | | | | |
|---|---|---|---|---|
| 152 | CD74 | 20c deep violet | 1.80 | 1.80 |
| 153 | CD75 | 30c dark green | 1.80 | 1.80 |
| 154 | CD76 | 40c carmine rose | 1.80 | 1.80 |
| 155 | CD77 | 50c dk brn & bl | 1.50 | 1.50 |
| 156 | CD78 | 90c red | 1.50 | 1.50 |
| 157 | CD79 | 1.50fr ultra | 1.90 | 1.90 |
| | | *Nos. 152-157 (6)* | 10.30 | 10.30 |

### Colonial Arts Exhibition Issue
Souvenir Sheet
Common Design Type

#### 1937      Imperf.

| | | | | |
|---|---|---|---|---|
| 158 | CD76 | 3fr sepia | 8.50 | 10.00 |

Louis Gustave Binger A10

#### 1937      Perf. 13

| | | | | |
|---|---|---|---|---|
| 159 | A10 | 65c red brown | .60 | .60 |

Death of Governor General Binger; 50th anniv. of his exploration of the Niger.

### Caillie Issue
Common Design Type

#### 1939   Engr.   Perf. 12½x12

| | | | | |
|---|---|---|---|---|
| 160 | CD81 | 90c org brn & org | .75 | .75 |
| 161 | CD81 | 2fr bright violet | 1.20 | 1.20 |
| 162 | CD81 | 2.25fr ultra & dk bl | 1.20 | 1.20 |
| | | *Nos. 160-162 (3)* | 3.15 | 3.15 |

### New York World's Fair Issue
Common Design Type

#### 1939

| | | | | |
|---|---|---|---|---|
| 163 | CD82 | 1.25fr carmine lake | 1.50 | 1.50 |
| 164 | CD82 | 2.25fr ultramarine | 1.50 | 1.50 |

Ebrié Lagoon and Marshal Pétain A11

#### 1941

| | | | | |
|---|---|---|---|---|
| 165 | A11 | 1fr green | .75 | — |
| 166 | A11 | 2.50fr deep blue | .85 | — |

For surcharges, see Nos. B14A-B14B.

### Types of 1936-40 Without "RF"

#### 1944      Perf. 13

| | | | |
|---|---|---|---|
| 166A | A7 | 30c brown | 1.60 |
| 166B | A8 | 60c car rose | 1.75 |
| 166C | A8 | 1fr dark violet | 1.75 |
| 166D | A9 | 20fr copper red | 3.75 |
| | | *Nos. 166A-166D (4)* | 8.85 |

Nos. 166A-166D were issued by the Vichy government in France, but were not placed on sale in Ivory Coast.

For other stamps inscribed Cote d'Ivoire and Afrique Occidental Francaise see French West Africa Nos. 58, 72, 77.

**Catalogue values for unused stamps in this section, from this point to the end of the section, are for Never Hinged items.**

### Republic

Elephant A12

President Felix Houphouet-Boigny A13

#### 1959, Oct. 1   Engr.   Perf. 13

| | | | | |
|---|---|---|---|---|
| 167 | A12 | 10fr black & emerald | .75 | .30 |
| 168 | A12 | 25fr vio brn & olive | 1.25 | .50 |
| 169 | A12 | 30fr ol blk & grnsh bl | 1.50 | .95 |
| | | *Nos. 167-169 (3)* | 3.50 | 1.75 |

### Imperforates
Most Ivory Coast stamps from 1959 onward exist imperforate in issued and trial colors, and also in small presentation sheets in issued colors.

#### 1959, Dec. 4      Unwmk.

| | | | | |
|---|---|---|---|---|
| 170 | A13 | 25fr violet brown | 1.00 | .60 |

Proclamation of the Republic, 1st anniv.

Bété Mask — A14

Designs: Masks of 5 tribes: Bété, Gueré, Baoulé, Senufo and Guro. #174-176 horiz.

#### 1960      Perf. 13

| | | | | |
|---|---|---|---|---|
| 171 | A14 | 50c pale brn & vio brn | .20 | .20 |
| 172 | A14 | 1fr violet & mag | .20 | .20 |
| 173 | A14 | 2fr ultra & bl grn | .25 | .20 |
| 174 | A14 | 4fr dk grn & org | .25 | .20 |
| 175 | A14 | 5fr ver & brown | .40 | .30 |
| 176 | A14 | 6fr dark brn & vio | .50 | .40 |
| 177 | A14 | 45fr dk grn & brn vio | 1.80 | 1.00 |
| 178 | A14 | 50fr dk brn & grnsh bl | 2.75 | 1.20 |
| 179 | A14 | 85fr car & slate grn | 5.00 | 2.25 |
| | | *Nos. 171-179 (9)* | 11.35 | 5.95 |

### C.C.T.A. Issue
Common Design Type

#### 1960, May 16   Engr.   Perf. 13

| | | | | |
|---|---|---|---|---|
| 180 | CD106 | 25fr grnsh bl & vio | 1.10 | .50 |

Emblem of the Entente A14a

Blood Lilies A16

Young Couple with Olive Branch and Globe — A15

#### 1960, May 29   Photo.   Perf. 13x13½

| | | | | |
|---|---|---|---|---|
| 181 | A14a | 25fr multicolored | 1.40 | 1.00 |

1st anniv. of the Entente (Dahomey, Ivory Coast, Niger and Upper Volta).

#### 1961, Aug. 7   Engr.   Perf. 13

| | | | | |
|---|---|---|---|---|
| 182 | A15 | 25fr emer, bister & blk | 1.00 | .50 |

First anniversary of Independence.

#### 1961-62

Designs: Various Local Plants & Orchids.

| | | | | |
|---|---|---|---|---|
| 183 | A16 | 5fr dk grn, red & orange ('62) | 1.10 | .35 |
| 184 | A16 | 10fr ultra, claret & yel | .65 | .35 |
| 185 | A16 | 15fr org, rose lil & green ('62) | 2.10 | .50 |
| 186 | A16 | 20fr brn, dk red & yel | 1.25 | .50 |
| 187 | A16 | 25fr grn, red brn & yel | 4.00 | 1.60 |
| 188 | A16 | 30fr blk, car & green | 1.50 | .75 |
| 189 | A16 | 70fr green, ver & yel | 4.00 | 1.60 |
| 190 | A16 | 85fr brn, lil, yel & grn | 6.00 | 2.00 |
| | | *Nos. 183-190 (8)* | 17.70 | 6.55 |

Early Letter Carrier and Modern Mailman — A17

#### 1961, Oct. 14      Unwmk.   Perf. 13

| | | | | |
|---|---|---|---|---|
| 191 | A17 | 25fr choc, emer & bl | 1.00 | .70 |

Issued for Stamp Day.

Ayamé Dam — A18

#### 1961, Nov. 18      Engr.

| | | | | |
|---|---|---|---|---|
| 192 | A18 | 25fr grnsh bl, blk & grn | 1.25 | .50 |

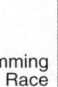

Swimming Race A19

#### 1961, Dec. 23      Unwmk.   Perf. 13

| | | | | |
|---|---|---|---|---|
| 193 | A19 | 5fr shown | .45 | .20 |
| 194 | A19 | 20fr Basketball | .65 | .30 |
| 195 | A19 | 5fr Soccer | 1.10 | .45 |
| | | *Nos. 193-195 (3)* | 2.20 | .95 |

Abidjan Games, Dec. 24-31. See No. C17.

Palms — A20

#### 1962, Feb. 5   Photo.   Perf. 12x12½

| | | | | |
|---|---|---|---|---|
| 196 | A20 | 25fr brn, blue & org | 1.10 | .45 |

Commission for Technical Co-operation in Africa South of the Sahara, 17th session, Abidjan, 2/5-16.

Fort Assinie and Assinie River — A21

**1962, May 26    Engr.    Perf. 13**
197 A21 85fr Prus grn, grn & dl
        red brn                    3.25  1.50
  Centenary of the Ivory Coast post.

**African and Malagasy Union Issue**
**Common Design Type**
**1962, Sept. 8   Photo.   Perf. 12½x12**
198 CD110 30fr multicolored    2.10  .75
  African and Malagasy Union, 1st anniv.

Fair Emblem, Cotton and
Spindles — A22

**1963, Jan. 26    Engr.    Perf. 13**
199 A22 50fr grn, brn org & se-
        pia                        3.00  1.10
  Bouake Fair, Jan. 26-Feb. 4.

Stylized
Map of
Africa
A23

**1963, May 25   Photo.   Perf. 12½x12**
200 A23 30fr ultra & emerald   1.40  1.00
  Conference of African heads of state for
African unity, Addis Ababa.

Hartebeest          UNESCO
A24              Emblem, Scales
               and Globe
                    A25

Designs: 1fr, Yellow-backed duiker, horiz.
2fr, Potto. 4fr, Beecroft's hyrax, horiz. 5fr,
Water chevrotain. 15fr, Forest hog, horiz.
20fr, Wart hog, horiz. 25fr, Bongo (antelope).
45fr, Cape hunting dogs, or hyenas, horiz.
50fr, Black-and-white colobus (monkey).

**1963-64           Engr.        Perf. 13**
201 A24  1fr choc, grn & yel-
         low ('64)              .75   .20
202 A24  2fr blk, dk bl, gray ol
         & brown ('64)          .75   .20
203 A24  4fr red brn, dk bl,
         brn & black ('64)      .65   .30
204 A24  5fr sl grn, brn & cit-
         ron ('64)             .65   .30
205 A24 10fr ol grn & ocher    .85   .30
206 A24 15fr red brn, grn &
         black ('64)           1.40  .45
207 A24 20fr red org grn & blk 1.75  .45
208 A24 25fr red brn & green   2.40  .60
209 A24 45fr choc, bl grn & yel
         green                 5.00  1.50

210 A24 50fr red brn, grn & blk 7.00  2.00
  a.   Min. sheet of 4, #205, 207,
       209-210                 35.00 35.00
       Nos. 201-210 (10)       21.20  6.30
       See Nos. 218-220.

**1963, Dec. 10              Unwmk.**
211 A25 85fr dk bl, blk & org   2.25  .80
  Universal Declaration of Human Rights,
15th anniv.

Sun Radiating        Weather
from Ivory Coast     Station and
over Africa          Balloon
A26                  A27

**1964, Mar. 17   Photo.   Perf. 12x12½**
212 A26 30fr grn, dl vio & red  1.10  .45
  Inter-African Conference of Natl. Education
Ministers.

**1964, Mar. 23          Perf. 13x12½**
213 A27 25fr multicolored      1.25  .60
  World Meteorological Day, Mar. 23.

Physician
Vaccinating
Child — A28

**1964, May 8     Engr.    Perf. 13**
214 A28 50fr dk brn, bl & red   1.90  .70
  Issued to honor the National Red Cross.

Wrestlers, Globe and Torch — A29

**1964, June 27   Unwmk.   Perf. 13**
215 A29 35fr Globe, torch, ath-
        letes, vert.            1.75  .60
216 A29 65fr shown              3.25  1.20
  18th Olympic Games, Tokyo, Oct. 10-25.

**Europafrica Issue, 1964**
**Common Design Type**

Design: 30fr, White man and black man
beneath tree of industrial symbols.

**1964, July 20   Photo.   Perf. 12x13**
217 CD116 30fr multicolored    1.30  .35

**Animal Type of 1963-64**

Designs: 5fr, Manatee, horiz. 10fr, Pygmy
hippopotamus, horiz. 15fr, Royal antelope.

**1964, Oct. 17    Engr.    Perf. 13**
218 A24  5fr yel grn, sl grn & brn 1.00  .30
219 A24 10fr sep, Prus grn & dp
         cl                     2.40  .45
220 A24 15fr lil rose, grn & org
         brn                    3.50  .45
       Nos. 218-220 (3)        6.90  1.20

**Co-operation Issue**
**Common Design Type**
**1964, Nov. 7    Unwmk.    Perf. 13**
221 CD119 25fr grn, dk brn & red 1.10  .35

Korhogo
Mail
Carriers
with Guard,
1914 — A30

**1964, Nov. 28              Engr.**
222 A30 85fr blk, brn, bl & brn
        red                     3.25  1.40
  Issued for Stamp Day.

Potter
A31

Artisans: 10fr, Wood carvers. 20fr, Ivory
carver. 25fr, Weaver.

**1965, Mar. 27    Engr.    Perf. 13**
223 A31  5fr mag, green & blk   .45   .25
224 A31 10fr red lil, grn & blk .55   .25
225 A31 20fr bis, dp bl & dk brn 1.00  .30
226 A31 25fr brn, olive & car   1.25  .45
       Nos. 223-226 (4)        3.25  1.25

Unloading
Mail, 1900
A32

**1965, Apr. 24   Unwmk.   Perf. 13**
227 A32 30fr multicolored      1.40  .70
  Issued for Stamp Day.

A32a

ITU emblem, old and new telecommunication equipment.

**1965, May 17**
228 A32a 85fr mar, brt grn & dk
         bl                     2.75  .70
  ITU, centenary.

Abidjan
Railroad
Station
A33

**1965, June 12    Engr.    Perf. 13**
229 A33 30fr magenta, bl & brn
        ol                      1.75  .80

Pres. Felix Houphouet-Boigny and
Map of Ivory Coast — A34

**1965, Aug. 7    Photo.   Perf. 12½x13**
230 A34 30fr multicolored      1.10  .45
  Fifth anniversary of Independence.

Hammerhead        Baoulé Mother
Stork — A35       and Child,
                  Carved in
                  Wood — A37

Mail Train,
1906 — A36

Birds: 1fr, Bruce's green pigeon, horiz. 2fr,
Spur-winged goose, horiz. 5fr, Stone par-
tridge. 15fr, White-breasted guinea fowl. 30fr,
Namaqua dove, horiz. 50fr, Lizard buzzard,
horiz. 75fr, Yellow-billed stork. 90fr, Forest (or
Latham's) francolin.

**1965-66            Engr.       Perf. 13**
231 A35  1fr yel grn, pur & yel-
         low ('66)             1.00  .30
232 A35  2fr slate grn, blk &
         red ('66)             1.00  .40
233 A35  5fr dk ol, dk brn & brn
         red ('66)             1.25  .45
234 A35 10fr red lil, blk & red
         brown                 1.40  .30
235 A35 15fr sl grn, gray & ver 1.50  .40
236 A35 30fr sl grn, mar & red
         brown                 2.10  .65
237 A35 50fr brn, blk & chlky bl 3.75  1.00
238 A35 75fr org, mar & sl grn 6.50  1.60
239 A35 90fr emerald, blk &
         brown ('66)           7.50  3.25
       Nos. 231-239 (9)        26.00  8.35

**1966, Mar. 26    Engr.    Perf. 13**
240 A36 30fr grn, blk & mar    2.75  1.00
  Issued for Stamp Day.

**1966, Apr. 9              Unwmk.**

Designs: 10fr, Unguent vessel, Wamougo
mask lid, 20fr, Atié carved drums. 30fr, Bété
female ancestral figure.

241 A37  5fr blk & emerald     .50   .25
242 A37 10fr purple & blk      .80   .30
243 A37 20fr orange & blk      2.25  .80
244 A37 30fr red & black       2.60  1.10
       Nos. 241-244 (4)        6.15  2.45

  Intl. Negro Arts Festival, Dakar, Senegal,
4/1-24.

Hotel Ivoire
A38

**1966, Apr. 30    Engr.    Perf. 13**
245 A38 15fr bl, grn, red & olive  .90  .40

Farm
Tractor
A39

**1966, Aug. 7    Photo.   Perf. 12½x12**
246 A39 30fr multicolored      1.10  .55
  6th anniversary of independence.

Uniformed
Teacher
and
Villagers
A40

**1966, Sept. 1**    Engr.    *Perf. 13*
247 A40 30fr dk red, indigo & dk
      brn      1.10   .50
    National School of Administration.

Veterinarian
Treating
Cattle
A41

**1966, Oct. 22**    Engr.    *Perf. 13*
248 A41 30fr ol, bl & dp brn    1.10   .50
    Campaign against cattle plague.

Man, Waves,     Delivery of Gift
UNESCO           Parcels — A43
Emblem — A42

**1966, Nov. 14**    Engr.    *Perf. 13*
249 A42 30fr dp bl & vio brn    1.10   .55
    UNESCO, 20th anniv.

**1966, Dec. 11**    Engr.    *Perf. 13*
250 A43 30fr dk bl, brn & blk    1.10   .55
    UNICEF, 20th anniv.

Bouaké
Hospital
and Red
Cross
A44

**1966, Dec. 20**
251 A44 30fr red brn, red & lilac   1.10   .55

Sikorsky S-43 Seaplane and
Boats — A45

**1967, Mar. 25**    Engr.    *Perf. 13*
252 A45 30fr indigo, bl grn & brn   3.50 1.20
    Stamp Day. 30th anniv. of the Sikorsky S-43
flying boat route.

Pineapple
Harvest
A46

**1967**        Engr.      *Perf. 13*
253 A46 20fr shown         .65   .40
254 A46 30fr Cabbage tree     .90   .50
255 A46 100fr Bananas     3.75 1.20
    *Nos. 253-255 (3)*    5.30 2.10
    Issue dates: 30fr, June 24; others, Mar. 25.

---

Genie, Protector of
Assamlangangan
A47

**1967, July 31**    Engr.    *Perf. 13*
256 A47 30fr grn, blk & maroon   1.10   .55
    Intl. PEN Club (writers' organization), 25th
Congress, Abidjan, July 31-Aug. 5.

Old and
New
Houses
A48

**1967, Aug. 7**    Photo.    *Perf. 12½x12*
257 A48 30fr multicolored    1.10   .55
    7th anniversary of independence.

Lions
Emblem
and
Elephant's
Head
A49

**1967, Sept. 2**    Photo.    *Perf. 12½x13*
258 A49 30fr lt bl & multi    1.50   .60
    50th anniversary of Lions International.

### Monetary Union Issue
#### Common Design Type

**1967, Nov. 4**    Engr.    *Perf. 13*
259 CD125 30fr car, slate grn &
      blk        .90   .40

Allegory of     Tabou Radio
French         Station — A51
Recognition of
Ivory
Coast — A50

**1967, Nov. 17**    Photo.    *Perf. 13x12½*
260 A50 90fr multicolored    3.00   .95
    Days of Recognition, 20th anniv. See No.
298.

**1968, Mar. 9**    Engr.    *Perf. 13*
261 A51 30fr dk grn, brn & brt
      grn       1.25   .55
    Issued for Stamp Day.

Cotton
Mill — A52

    Designs: 5fr, Palm oil extraction plant. 15fr,
Abidjan oil refinery. 20fr, Unloading raw cotton and spinning machine, vert. 30fr, Flour
mill. 50fr, Cacao butter extractor. 70fr, Instant
coffee factory, vert. 90fr, Saw mill and timber.

---

**1968**        Engr.      *Perf. 13*
262 A52 5fr ver, slate grn & blk    .45   .20
263 A52 10fr dk grn, gray & ol
      bis         .75   .20
264 A52 15fr ver, lt ultra & blk   1.60   .65
265 A52 20fr Prus blue & choc   1.25   .55
266 A52 30fr dk grn, brt bl &
      brown      1.25   .65
267 A52 50fr red, brt grn & blk   2.00   .90
268 A52 70fr dk brn, bl & brn   2.75 1.00
269 A52 90fr dp bl, blk & brn   3.50 1.60
    *Nos. 262-269 (8)*    13.55 5.75
    Issued: 5fr, 15fr, June 8; 10fr, 20fr, 90fr,
Mar. 23; others, Oct. 5.

Canoe
Race
A53

**1968, Apr. 6**    Engr.    *Perf. 13*
270 A53   30fr shown       1.10   .50
271 A53 100fr Runners     3.00   .90
    19th Olympic Games, Mexico City, 10/12-27.

Queen
Pokou
Sacrificing
her
Son — A54

**1968, Aug. 7**    Photo.    *Perf. 12½x12*
272 A54 30fr multicolored    1.10   .50
    8th anniversary of independence.

Vaccination,
WHO
Emblem
and
Elephant's
Head
A55

**1968, Sept. 28**    Engr.    *Perf. 13*
273 A55 30fr choc, brt bl & ma-
      roon      1.10   .50
    WHO, 20th anniversary.

Antelope in
Forest — A56

**1968, Oct. 26**    Engr.    *Perf. 13*
274 A56 30fr ultra, brn & olive   6.00 1.25
    Protection of fauna and flora.

Abidjan Anthropological Museum and
Carved Screen — A57

**1968, Nov. 2**
275 A57 30fr vio bl, ol & rose
      mag      1.10   .50

---

Human
Rights
Flame and
Statues of
"Justitia"
A58

**1968, Nov. 9**    Engr.    *Perf. 13*
276 A58 30fr slate, org & dk brn   1.10   .50
    International Human Rights Year.

"Ville de
Maranhao"
at Grand
Bassam
A59

**1969, Mar. 8**    Engr.    *Perf. 13*
277 A59 30fr brn, brt bl & grn   1.75   .55
    Issued for Stamp Day.

Opening of Hotel Ivoire,
Abidjan — A60

**1969, Mar. 29**
278 A60 30fr ver, bl & grn   1.25   .50

Carved      Mountains and
Figure — A61    Radio Tower,
            Man — A62

**1969, July 5**    Engr.    *Perf. 13*
279 A61 30fr red lil, blk & red org   1.20   .60
    Ivory Coast art exhibition, Fine Arts
Museum, Vevey, Switzerland, 7/12-9/22.

**1969, Aug. 7**    Engr.    *Perf. 13*
280 A62 30fr dl brn, sl & grn   1.40   .50
    9th anniversary of independence.

### Development Bank Issue
#### Common Design Type

    Design: Development Bank emblem and
Ivory Coast coat of arms.

**1969, Sept. 6**
281 CD130 30fr ocher, grn & mar   .85   .40

Arms of Bouake — A63

Sport
Fishing and
SKAL
Emblem
A64

    Coats of Arms: 15fr, Abidjan. 30fr, Ivory
Coast.

**1969** **Photo.** **Perf. 13**
282 A63 10fr multicolored .45 .20
283 A63 15fr multicolored .55 .25
284 A63 30fr multicolored .90 .25
*Nos. 282-284 (3)* 1.90 .70

Issued: 10fr, 10/25; 15fr, 12/27; 30fr, 12/20.
See Nos. 335-336, 378-382, design A297.

**1969, Nov. 22** **Engr.** **Perf. 13**
285 A64 30fr shown 4.00 .55
286 A64 100fr Vacation village,
SKAL emblem 5.00 1.40

1st Intl. Congress in Africa of the SKAL
Tourist Assoc., Abidjan, Nov. 23-28.

**ASECNA Issue**
**Common Design Type**
**1969, Dec. 13** **Engr.** **Perf. 13**
287 CD132 30fr vermilion 1.00 .40

University Center, Abidjan — A65

**1970, Feb. 26** **Engr.** **Perf. 13**
288 A65 30fr indigo & yel grn 1.00 .50

Higher education in Ivory Coast, 10th anniv.

Gabriel
Dadié and
Telegraph
Operator
A66

**1970, Mar. 7** **Engr.** **Perf. 13**
289 A66 30fr dk red, sl grn & blk .80 .40

Stamp Day; Gabriel Dadié (1891-1953) 1st
native-born postal administrator.

University of Abidjan — A67

**1970, Mar. 21** **Photo.**
290 A67 30fr Prus bl, dk pur & dk
yel grn 1.00 .50

3rd General Assembly of the Assoc. of
French-language Universities (A.U.P.E.L.F.).

Safety Match
Production — A68

**1970, May 9** **Engr.** **Perf. 13**
291 A68 5fr shown .45 .45
292 A68 20fr Textile industry .65 .40
293 A68 50fr Shipbuilding 1.75 .50
*Nos. 291-293 (3)* 2.85 1.35

Radar, Classroom with
Television — A69

**1970, May 17**
294 A69 40fr red, grn & gray olive 1.20 .55

Issued for World Telecommunications Day.

**UPU Headquarters Issue**
**Common Design Type**
**1970, May 20**
295 CD133 30fr lil, brt grn & olive 1.20 .50

UN
Emblem,
Lion,
Antelopes
and Plane
A70

**1970, June 27** **Engr.** **Perf. 13**
296 A70 30fr dk red brn, ultra &
dk green 3.50 1.25

25th anniversary of the United Nations.

Coffee Branch
and Bags
Showing
Increased
Production
A71

**1970, Aug. 7** **Engr.** **Perf. 13**
297 A71 30fr org, bluish grn &
gray 1.50 .50

Tenth anniversary of independence.

**Type of 1967**
**1970, Oct. 29 Photo.** **Perf. 12x12½**
298 A50 40fr multicolored 1.20 .50

Ivory Coast Democratic Party, 5th Congress.

Power Plant
at
Uridi — A73

**1970, Nov. 21** **Engr.** **Perf. 13**
299 A73 40fr multicolored 2.25 .40

Independence, 10th Anniv. — A73a

Designs: Nos. 299A, 299D, Pres.
Houphouet-Boigny, Gen. Charles DeGaulle.
Nos. 299B, 299F, Pres. Houphouet-Boigny,
elephants. Nos. 299C, 299E, Coat of arms.

**1970, Nov. 27 Embossed** **Perf. 10½**
**Die Cut**
299A A73a 300fr Silver 15.00 15.00
299B A73a 300fr Silver 15.00 15.00
299C A73a 300fr Silver 15.00 15.00
g. Pair, #299B-299C 35.00 35.00
299D A73a 1000fr Gold 45.00 45.00
299E A73a 1000fr Gold 45.00 45.00
**Litho. & Embossed**
299F A73a 1200fr Gold &
multi 45.00 45.00
h. Pair, #299E-299F 100.00 100.00

Nos. 299B, 299F are airmail.

Postal
Service
Autobus,
1925
A74

**1971, Mar. 6** **Engr.** **Perf. 13**
300 A74 40fr dp grn, dk brn &
gldn brn 2.75 .50

Stamp Day.

Marginella
Desjardini
A75

Marine Life: 1fr, Aporrhaispes gallinae. 5fr,
Neptunus validus. 10fr, Hermodice caruncu-
lata, vert. No. 305, Natica fanel, vert. No.
306, Goniaster cuspidatus, vert. No. 307,
Xenorhora digitata. 25fr, Conus prometheus.
35fr, Polycheles typhlops, vert. No. 310,
Conus genuanus. No. 311, Chlamys flabellum.
45fr, Strombus bubonius. 50fr,
Enoplometopus callistus, vert. 65fr, Cypraea
stercoraria.

**1971-72** **Engr.** **Perf. 13**
301 A75 1fr olive & multi .50 .20
302 A75 5fr red & multi .50 .30
303 A75 10fr emer & multi 1.00 .30
304 A75 15fr brt bl & multi 1.00 .35
305 A75 15fr dp car & multi 1.50 .40
306 A75 20fr ocher & car 1.90 .50
307 A75 20fr ver & multi 2.25 .65
308 A75 25fr dk car, rose brn
& black 1.25 .35
309 A75 35fr yel & multi 2.50 .75
310 A75 40fr emer & multi 4.00 1.25
311 A75 40fr brown & multi 3.25 1.10
312 A75 45fr multi 4.50 1.50
313 A75 50fr green & multi 5.00 1.60
314 A75 65fr bl, rose brn & sl
grn 3.50 1.50
*Nos. 301-314 (14)* 32.65 10.75

Issued: #304, 306, 310, 4/24/71; 5fr, 35fr,
50fr, 6/5/71; 1fr, 10fr, #311, 10/23/71; 25fr,
65fr, 1/29/72; #305, 307, 45fr, 4/3/72.

Submarine
Cable
Station,
1891
A76

**1971, May 17**
315 A76 100fr bl, ocher & olive 2.50 .85

3rd World Telecommunications Day.

Apprentice and
Lathe — A77

**1971, June 19** **Engr.** **Perf. 13**
316 A77 35fr grn, slate & org brn 1.00 .40

Technical instruction and professional
training.

Map of Africa and Telecommunications
System — A78

**1971, June 26** **Perf. 13x12½**
317 A78 45fr magenta & multi 1.00 .40

Pan-African Telecommunications system.

Bondoukou Market — A79

**1971, Aug. 7** **Engr.** **Perf. 13**
**Size: 48x27mm**
318 A79 35fr ultra, brn & slate 1.00 .45

11th anniv. of independence. See No. C46.

White,
Black and
Yellow
Girls — A80

**1971, Oct. 10** **Photo.** **Perf. 13**
319 A80 40fr shown .80 .25
320 A80 45fr Boys around globe .80 .25

Intl. Year Against Racial Discrimination.

Gaming
Table and
Lottery
Tickets
A81

**1971, Nov. 13** **Perf. 12½**
321 A81 35fr green & multi 1.25 .50

National lottery.

Electric Power
Installations — A82

**1971, Dec. 18** **Perf. 13**
322 A82 35fr red brn & multi 2.25 .50

Cogwheel
and
Workers
A83

**1972, Mar. 18** **Engr.** **Perf. 13**
323 A83 35fr org, bl & dk brn .75 .40

Technical Cooperation Week.

"Your Heart is
Your
Health" — A84

Girls Reading,
Book Year
Emblem — A85

**1972, Apr. 7**   **Photo.**   **Perf. 12½x13**
324   A84   40fr blue, olive & red    1.00   .50
World Health Day.

*Perf. 12½x13, 13x12½*
**1972, Apr. 22**      **Engr.**
325   A85   35fr Boys reading, horiz.   .75   .25
326   A85   40fr shown    1.00   .40
International Book Year.

Postal
Sorting
Center,
Abidjan
A86

**1972, May 13**        **Perf. 13**
327   A86   40fr dk grn, rose lil & bis   1.25   .40
Stamp Day.

Radio Tower,
Abobo, and ITU
Emblem — A87

**1972, May 17**   **Engr.**    **Perf. 13**
328   A87   40fr blue, red & grn    2.25   .75
4th World Telecommunications Day.

Computer
Operator,
Punch Card
A88

**1972, June 24**
329   A88   40fr brt grn, bl & red    2.25   .60
Development of computerized information.

View of Odienné — A89

**1972, Aug. 7**   **Engr.**    **Perf. 13**
330   A89   35fr bl, grn & brn    1.00   .60
12th anniversary of independence.

---

### West African Monetary Union Issue
### Common Design Type

**1972, Nov. 2**   **Engr.**    **Perf. 13**
331   CD136   40fr brn, gray & red
         lilac    1.00   .50

Diamond and Diamond Mine — A90

**1972, Nov. 4**
332   A90   40fr Prus bl, slate & org
         brn    3.50   1.75

Pasteur
Institute,
Louis
Pasteur
A91

**1972, Nov. 21**
333   A91   35fr vio bl, grn & brn    1.25   .50
Pasteur (1822-1895), chemist and
bacteriologist.

Children at
Village
Pump
A92

**1972, Dec. 9**   **Engr.**    **Perf. 13**
334   A92   35fr dk red, grn & blk    1.25   .40
Water campaign. See No. 360.

### Arms Type of 1969
**1973**      **Photo.**    **Perf. 12**
335   A63   5fr Daloa    .50   .25
336   A63   10fr Gagnoa    .50   .25

Nos. 335-336 are 16½-17x22mm and have
"DELRIEU" below design at right. Nos. 282-
284 are 17x23mm and have no name at lower
right.

Dr. Armauer G.
Hansen — A93

**1973, Feb. 3**   **Engr.**    **Perf. 13**
342   A93   35fr lil, dp bl & brn    1.25   .40
Centenary of the discovery of the Hansen
bacillus, the cause of leprosy.

Lake Village Bletankoro — A94

**1973, Mar. 10**   **Engr.**    **Perf. 13**
343   A94   200fr choc, bl & grn    5.00   2.00

Balistes
Capriscus
A95

---

Fish: 20fr, Pseudupeneus prayensis. 25fr,
Cephalopholis taeniops. 35fr, Priacanthus
arenatus. 50fr, Xyrichthys novacula.

**1973-74**      **Engr.**    **Perf. 13**
344   A95   15fr ind & slate grn    1.75   .60
345   A95   20fr lilac & multi    3.00   .75
346   A95   25fr slate grn & rose
         ('74)    4.50   .75
347   A95   35fr rose red & slate
         grn    3.25   .90
348   A95   50fr blk, ultra & rose
         red    4.50   1.10
     Nos. 344-348 (5)    17.00   4.10
Issued: 50fr, 3/24; 15fr, 20fr, 7/7; 35fr, 12/1;
25fr, 3/2.

Children
A96

**1973, Apr. 7**   **Engr.**    **Perf. 13**
354   A96   40fr grn, blk & dl red    1.25   .45
Establishment of first children's village in
Africa (SOS villages for homeless children).

Parliament, Abidjan — A97

**1973, Apr. 24**   **Photo.**    **Perf. 13x12½**
355   A97   100fr multicolored    1.40   .45
112th session of the Inter-parliamentary
Council.

Teacher
and PAC
Store
A98

**1973, May 12**   **Photo.**    **Perf. 13x12½**
356   A98   40fr multicolored    .75   .25
Commercial Action Program (PAC).

Mother, Typist,
Dress Form and
Pot — A99

**1973, May 26**
357   A99   35fr multicolored    1.00   .40
Technical instruction for women.

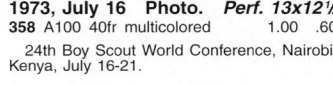

Farmers,
African
Scout
Emblem
A100

**1973, July 16**   **Photo.**    **Perf. 13x12½**
358   A100   40fr multicolored    1.00   .60
24th Boy Scout World Conference, Nairobi,
Kenya, July 16-21.

---

Party Headquarters,
Yamoussokro — A101

**1973, Aug. 7**   **Photo.**    **Perf. 13**
359   A101   35fr multicolored    1.00   .50

Children at
Dry Pump
A102

**1973, Aug. 16**        **Engr.**
360   A102   40fr multicolored    1.25   .45
African solidarity in drought emergency.

### African Postal Union Issue
### Common Design Type
**1973, Sept. 12**   **Engr.**    **Perf. 13**
361   CD137   100fr pur, blk & red    2.50   1.00

Decorated Arrow
Heads, Abidjan
Museum — A103

**1973, Sept. 15**   **Photo.**   **Perf. 12½x13**
362   A103   5fr blk, brn red & brn    .60   .25

Ivory Coast No. 1 — A104

**1973, Oct. 9**   **Engr.**    **Perf. 13**
363   A104   40fr emer, blk & org    1.30   .60
Stamp Day.

Highway
Intersection
A105

**1973, Oct. 13**
364   A105   35fr blue, blk & grn    1.00   .45
Indenie-Abidjan intersection.

Map of Africa,
Federation
Emblem — A106

Elephant
Emblem — A107

**1973, Oct. 26    Photo.    Perf. 13**
365  A106  40fr ultra, red brn & vio bl    .85    .30
Intl. Social Security Federation, 18th General Assembly, Abidjan, Oct. 26-Nov. 3.

**1973, Nov. 19**
366  A107  40fr blk & bister    .85    .30
7th World Congress of the Universal Federation of World Travel Agents' Associations, Abidjan.

Kong Mosque — A108

**1974, Mar. 9**
367  A108  35fr bl, grn & brn    1.25    .60

People and Sun A109

**1974, Apr. 20    Photo.    Perf. 13**
368  A109  35fr multicolored    .85    .40
Permanent Mission to UN.

Grand Lahou Post Office — A110

**1974, May 17    Engr.    Perf. 13**
369  A110  35fr multicolored    1.00    .60
Stamp Day.

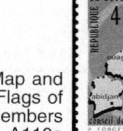
Map and Flags of Members A110a

**1974, May 29    Photo.    Perf. 13x12½**
370  A110a  40fr blue & multi    .75    .25
15th anniversary of the Council of Accord.

Pres. Houphouet-Boigny
A111        A112

**1974-76    Engr.    Perf. 13**
371  A111  25fr grn, org & brn    .65    .25
a.    Booklet pane of 10    6.50
b.    Booklet pane of 20    13.00
373  A112  35fr org, grn & brn    1.00    .20
a.    Booklet pane of 10    10.00
b.    Booklet pane of 20    20.00
374  A112  40fr grn, org & brn    1.00    .20
a.    Booklet pane of 10    10.00
375  A112  60fr bl, car & brn ('76)    .90    .40
376  A112  65fr car, bl & brn ('76)    .90    .40
Nos. 371-376 (5)    4.45    1.45
See Nos. 783-792.

Ivory Coast Arms Type of 1969 with smaller "P" and "s" in "Postes"

**1974, June 29    Photo.    Perf. 12**
378  A63  35fr brn, emer & gold    .70    .20
a.    Booklet pane of 10    7.50
b.    Booklet pane of 20    15.00
379  A63  40fr vio, bl, emer & gold    .90    .20
a.    Booklet pane of 10    10.00
b.    Booklet pane of 20    20.00

**1976, Jan.**
Inscribed: "COTE D'IVOIRE"
380  A63  60fr car, gold & emer    .90    .25
381  A63  65fr grn, gold & emer    .90    .30
382  A63  70fr bl, gold & emer    1.00    .40
Nos. 378-382 (5)    4.40    1.35
See design A297.

WPY Emblem — A114

**1974, Aug. 19    Engr.    Perf. 13**
383  A114  40fr emerald & blue    1.00    .30
World Population Year.

Cotton Harvest — A115

**1974, Sept. 21    Litho.    Perf. 12½x13**
384  A115  50fr multicolored    1.25    .50

UPU Centenary A116

**1974, Oct. 9    Engr.    Perf. 13**
385  A116  40fr multicolored    .90    .30
See Nos. C59-C60.

Plowing Farmer, Service Emblem A117

**1974, Dec. 7    Photo.    Perf. 13**
386  A117  35fr multicolored    .75    .30
14th anniversary of independence.

National Library, First Anniv. — A118

**1975, Jan. 9    Photo.    Perf. 13**
387  A118  40fr multicolored    .75    .30

Raoul Follereau and Blind Students — A119

**1975, Jan. 26    Engr.    Perf. 13**
388  A119  35fr multicolored    2.00    .80
Follereau, educator of the blind and lepers.

Congress Emblem — A120

Coffee Cultivation A121

**1975, Mar. 4    Photo.    Perf. 12½x13**
389  A120  40fr blk & emerald    .75    .30
52nd Congress of the Intl. Assoc. of Seed Crushers, Abidjan, Mar. 2-7.

**1975, Mar. 15    Perf. 13½x13**
390  A121  5fr Flowering branch    .40    .20
391  A121  10fr Branch with beans    .70    .20

Sassandra Wharf — A122

**1975, Apr. 19    Engr.    Perf. 13**
392  A122  100fr multicolored    2.50    1.50

Letter Sorting A123

**1975, Apr. 26    Photo.    Perf. 13**
393  A123  40fr multicolored    1.25    .60
Stamp Day.

Cotton Flower — A124

Cotton Bolls — A125

**1975, May 3    Photo.    Perf. 13**
394  A124  5fr multicolored    .45    .45
395  A125  10fr multicolored    .80    .45
Cotton cultivation.

Marie Kore, Women's Year Emblem — A126

**1975, May 19    Engr.    Perf. 13**
396  A126  45fr lt bl, yel grn & brn    1.00    .50
International Women's Year.

Fort Dabou — A127

**1975, June 7    Engr.    Perf. 13**
397  A127  50fr multicolored    1.00    .65

Abidjan Harbor — A128

40fr, Grand Bassam wharf, 1906. 100fr, Planned harbor expansion on Locodjro.

**1975, July 1    Photo.    Perf. 13**
398  A128  35fr multicolored    1.25    .60
**Miniature Sheet**
399    Sheet of 3    10.00    10.00
a.    A128 40fr multi, vert.    4.00    4.00
b.    A128 100fr multi    4.00    4.00
25th anniversary of Abidjan Harbor. No. 399 contains Nos. 398, 399a, 399b.

Cacao Pods on Tree — A129

**1975, Aug. 2**
400  A129  35fr multicolored    2.25    .65

Farm Workers A130

**1975, Oct. 4   Photo.   *Perf. 13x12½***
401 A130 50fr multicolored   1.00   .60
    Natl. Org. for Rural Development.

Railroad Bridge, N'zi River — A131

**1975, Dec. 7   Photo.   *Perf. 13***
402 A131 60fr multicolored   6.00   1.50
    15th anniversary of independence.

Baoulé Mother and Child, Carved in Wood — A132

**1976, Jan. 24   Litho.   *Perf. 13***
403 A132 65fr black & multi   2.25   .75

Baoulé Mask A133

Chief Abron's Chair A133a

**1976, Feb. 7   Photo.   *Perf. 12½***
404 A133 20fr multicolored   .65   .25
405 A133a 150fr multicolored   3.25   1.25

Senufo Statuette — A134

**1976, Feb. 21   *Perf. 13x13½***
406 A134 25fr ocher & multi   1.25   .60

Telephones 1876 and 1976 — A135

**1976, Mar. 10   Litho.   *Perf. 12***
407 A135 70fr multicolored   1.25   .65
    Centenary of first telephone call by Alexander Graham Bell, Mar. 10, 1876.

Ivory Coast Map, Pigeon, Carving A136

**1976, Apr. 10   Photo.   *Perf. 12½***
408 A136 65fr multicolored   1.00   .50
    20th Stamp Day.

Smiling Trees and Cat — A137

**1976, June 5   Litho.   *Perf. 12½***
409 A137 65fr multicolored   1.25   .60
    Nature protection.

Children with Books — A138

**1976, July 3   Photo.   *Perf. 12½x13***
410 A138 65fr multicolored   1.30   .60

Runner, Maple Leaf, Olympic Rings — A139

**1976, July 17   Litho.   *Perf. 12***
411 A139 60fr Javelin, vert.   1.25   .60
412 A139 65fr shown   1.25   .60
    21st Olympic Games, Montreal, Canada, July 17-Aug. 1.

Mohammad Ali Jinnah — A139a

**1976, Aug. 14   Litho.   *Perf. 13***
412A A139a 50fr multicolored   65.00   15.00
    1st Governor-General of Pakistan.

Cashew A140

**1976, Sept. 18   *Perf. 12½***
413 A140 65fr blue & multi   2.25   .80

Highway and Conference Emblem — A141

**1976, Oct. 25   Litho.   *Perf. 12½x12***
414 A141 60fr multicolored   1.00   .50
    3rd African Highway Conference, Abidjan, July 25-30.

Pres. Houphouet-Boigny A142

**1976-77   Photo.   *Perf. 13½x12½***
415 A142 35fr brn, red lil & blk ('77)   225.00   —
416 A142 40fr brt grn, ocher & brn blk   4.50   .75
    a.   Bklt. pane of 12 (8#416, 4#417)   55.00
417 A142 45fr ocher, brt grn & brn blk   4.50   1.00
418 A142 60fr brn, mag & brn blk   6.00   1.00
419 A142 65fr grn, org & brn blk   7.00   1.50
    Nos. 416-419 (4)   22.00   4.25

The 40fr and 45fr issued in booklet and coil; 35fr, 60fr and 65fr in coil only. Stamps from booklets are imperf. on one side or two adjoining sides. Coils have control number on back of every 10th stamp.

John Paul Jones, American Marine and Ship — A143

American Bicentennial: 125fr, Count de Rochambeau and grenadier of Touraine Regiment. 150fr, Admiral Count Jean Baptiste d'Estaing and French marine. 175fr, Lafayette and grenadier of Soissons Regiment. 200fr, Jefferson, American soldier, Declaration of Independence. 500fr, Washington, US flag, Continental officer.

**1976, Nov. 27   Litho.   *Perf. 11***
421 A143 100fr multicolored   1.50   .30
422 A143 125fr multicolored   1.90   .50
423 A143 150fr multicolored   2.25   .60
424 A143 175fr multicolored   2.25   .75
425 A143 200fr multicolored   2.40   .75
    Nos. 421-425 (5)   10.30   2.90

**Souvenir Sheet**
426 A143 500fr multicolored   7.00   2.50

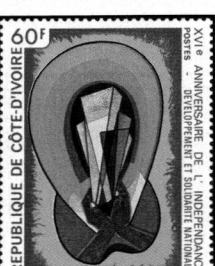

"Development and Solidarity" — A144

**1976, Dec. 7   Photo.   *Perf. 13***
427 A144 60fr multicolored   1.00   .60
    16th anniversary of independence.

Benin Head, Ivory Coast Arms — A145

**1977, Jan. 15   Photo.   *Perf. 13***
428 A145 65fr gold, dk brn & grn   1.25   .75
    2nd World Black and African Festival, Lagos, Nigeria, Jan. 15-Feb. 12.

Musical Instruments — A146

**1977, Mar. 5   Engr.   *Perf. 13***
429 A146 5fr Baoule bells   .35   .25
430 A146 10fr Senufo balafon   .35   .25
431 A146 20fr Dida drum   .55   .25
    Nos. 429-431 (3)   1.25   .75

Air Afrique Plane Unloading Mail A147

**1977, Apr. 9   Litho.   *Perf. 13***
432 A147 60fr multicolored   1.25   .60
    Stamp Day.

Sassenage Castle, Grenoble — A148

**1977, May 21    Litho.    Perf. 12½**
433  A148  100fr multicolored        2.25   .75
Intl. French Language Council, 10th anniv.

Orville and Wilbur Wright, "Wright Flyer," 1903 — A149

History of Aviation: 75fr, Louis Bleriot crossing English Channel, 1909. 100fr, Ross Smith and Vickers-Vimy (flew England-Australia, 1919). 200fr, Charles A. Lindbergh and "Spirit of St. Louis" (flew New York-Paris, 1927). 300fr, Supersonic jet Concorde, 1976. 500fr, Lindbergh in flying suit and "Spirit of St. Louis."

**1977, June 27    Litho.    Perf. 14**
434  A149  60fr multi        1.10   .30
435  A149  75fr multi        1.25   .30
436  A149  100fr multi       1.50   .30
437  A149  200fr multi       3.25   .75
438  A149  300fr multi       5.00  1.25
    Nos. 434-438 (5)        12.10  2.90
**Souvenir Sheet**
439  A149  500fr multi       6.50  2.00

Santos Dumont's "Ville de Paris," 1907 — A150

65fr, LZ1 at takeoff. 150fr, "Schwaben" LZ10 over Germany. 200fr, "Bodensee" LZ120, 1919. 300fr, LZ127 over Sphinx & pyramids.

**1977, Sept. 3    Litho.    Perf. 11**
440  A150  60fr multi        1.00   .25
441  A150  65fr multi        1.00   .25
442  A150  150fr multi       2.25   .50
443  A150  200fr multi       3.25   .75
444  A150  300fr multi       4.00  1.00
    Nos. 440-444 (5)        11.50  2.75
History of the Zeppelin. Exist imperf. See No. C63.

Congress Emblem — A151

**1977, Sept. 12    Photo.    Perf. 12½**
445  A151  60fr lt & dk grn       .90   .50
17th Intl. Congress of Administrative Sciences in Africa, Abidjan, Sept. 12-16.

A152

**1977, Nov. 12    Photo.    Perf. 13½x14**
446  A152  65fr multicolored      3.50   .75
Yamoussoukro, 1st Ivory Coast container ship.

Butterflies A152a

Designs: 30fr, Epiphora rectifascia boolana. 60fr, Charaxes jasius epijasius. 65fr, Imbrasia arata. 100fr, Palla decius.

**1977, Nov.    Photo.    Perf. 14x13**
446A  A152a  30fr multi       —    2.25
446B  A152a  60fr multi       —   17.50
446C  A152a  65fr multi       —    4.00
446D  A152a  100fr multi      —    6.00
    Nos. 446A-446D (4)            29.75
Set, unused                    280.00

A153

Hand Holding Produce, Generators, Factories.

**1977, Dec. 7    Photo.    Perf. 13½**
447  A153  60fr multicolored      1.00   .50
17th anniversary of independence.

Flowers — A153a

**1977    Photo.    Perf. 13x14**
447A  A153a  5fr Strophanthus hispidus    —    —
447B  A153a  20fr Anthurium cultorum      —    —
447C  A153a  60fr Arachnis flos-aeris     —    —
447D  A153a  65fr Renanthera storiei      —    —
Set, unused                      500.00

Presidents Giscard d'Estaing and Houphouet-Boigny — A154

**1978, Jan. 11    Perf. 13**
448  A154  60fr multicolored      1.25   .35
449  A154  65fr multicolored      1.40   .35
450  A154  100fr multicolored     1.75   .75
    a.  Souvenir sheet, 500fr   10.00 10.00
    Nos. 448-450 (3)             4.40  1.45
Visit of Pres. Valery Giscard d'Estaing. No. 450a contains one stamp.

St. George and the Dragon, by Rubens — A155

Paintings by Peter Paul Rubens (1577-1640): 150fr, Child's head. 250fr, Annunciation. 300fr, The Birth of Louis XIII. 500fr, Virgin & Child.

**1978, Mar. 4    Litho.    Perf. 13½**
451  A155  65fr gold & multi       .90   .25
452  A155  150fr gold & multi     2.25   .60
453  A155  250fr gold & multi     3.25   .80
454  A155  300fr gold & multi     4.50  1.00
    Nos. 451-454 (4)             10.90  2.65
**Souvenir Sheet**
455  A155  500fr gold & multi     6.00  2.25

Royal Guards — A156

**1978, Apr. 1    Litho.    Perf. 12½**
456  A156  60fr shown            1.25   .35
457  A156  65fr Cosmological figures   1.25   .35

Rural Postal Center — A157

**1978, Apr. 8**
458  A157  60fr multicolored      1.00   .50
Stamp Day.

Antenna, ITU Emblem A158

**1978, May 17    Perf. 13**
459  A158  60fr multicolored      1.00   .50
10th World Telecommunications Day.

Svante August Arrhenius, Electrolytic Apparatus — A159

Nobel Prize Winners: 75fr, Jules Bordet, child, mountains, eagle and Petri dish. 100fr, André Gide, and St. Peter's, Rome. 200fr, John Steinbeck and horse farm. 300fr, Children with flowers and UNICEF emblem. 500fr, Max Planck, rockets and earth.

**1978, May 27    Litho.    Perf. 13½**
460  A159  60fr multi         .75   .20
461  A159  75fr multi        1.00   .25
462  A159  100fr multi       1.25   .30
463  A159  200fr multi       2.50   .60
464  A159  300fr multi       4.25   .90
    Nos. 460-464 (5)         9.75  2.25
**Souvenir Sheet**
465  A159  500fr multi       5.50  1.50

Soccer Ball, Player and Argentina '78 Emblem — A160

Soccer Ball, Argentina '78 Emblem and: 65fr, Player, vert. 100fr, Player, diff. 150fr, Goalkeeper. 300fr, Ball as sun, and player, vert. 500fr, Ball as globe with Argentina on map of South America.

**1978, June 17**
466  A160  60fr multi         .75   .20
467  A160  65fr multi        1.00   .25
468  A160  100fr multi       1.25   .50
469  A160  150fr multi       1.75   .50
470  A160  300fr multi       3.50   .90
    Nos. 466-470 (5)         8.25  2.35
**Souvenir Sheet**
471  A160  500fr multi       5.00  1.50
11th World Cup Soccer Championship, Argentina, June 1-25.

Miniodes Discolor A161

Butterflies: 65fr, Charaxes lactetinctus. 100fr, Papilio zalmoxis. 200fr, Papilio antimachus.

**1978, July 8    Photo.    Perf. 14x13**
472  A161  60fr multicolored      3.75  1.00
473  A161  65fr multicolored      3.75  1.00
474  A161  100fr multicolored     5.50  1.75
475  A161  200fr multicolored    10.00  4.00
    Nos. 472-475 (4)            23.00  7.75

Cricket A162

Insects: 20fr, 60fr, Various hemiptera. 65fr, Goliath beetle.

**1978, Aug. 26    Litho.    Perf. 12½**
476  A162  10fr multicolored      1.10   .40
477  A162  20fr multicolored      1.75   .40
478  A162  60fr multicolored      3.50  1.00
479  A162  65fr multicolored      5.00  1.25
    Nos. 476-479 (4)            11.35  3.05

Stylized Figures Emerging from TV Screen A163

65fr, Passengers on train made up of TV sets.

**1978, Sept. 18**                        *Perf. 13*
480  A163  60fr multicolored         1.10   .30
481  A163  65fr multicolored         1.10   .30

Educational television programs.

Map of Ivory Coast, Mobile Drill Platform Ship A164

Map of Ivory Coast, Ram at Discovery Site and: 65fr, Gold goblets. 500fr, Pres. Houphouet-Boigny holding gold goblets.

**1978, Oct. 18   Litho.   *Perf. 12½x12***
482  A164  60fr multicolored         1.50   .50
483  A164  65fr multicolored         1.50   .50

**Souvenir Sheet**

484  A164  500fr multicolored       12.00  12.00

Announcement of oil discovery off the coast of Ivory Coast, 1st anniv.

National Assembly, Paris, UPU Emblem A165

**1978, Dec. 2   Litho.   *Perf. 13½***
485  A165  200fr multicolored        2.25   1.00

Congress of Paris, centenary.

Drummer A166

**1978, Dec. 7   Photo.   *Perf. 12½x13***
486  A166  60fr multicolored         1.25   .50

18th anniversary of independence.

Poster — A167

Design: 65fr, Arrows made of flags, and television screen.

**1978, Dec. 12**
487  A167  60fr multicolored         1.00   .40
488  A167  65fr multicolored         1.00   .40

Technical cooperation among developing countries with the help of educational television.

Plowing — A168

**1979, Jan. 27   Photo.   *Perf. 13***
489  A168  100fr multicolored        2.25   .50

King Hassan II, Pres. Houphouet-Boigny, Flags and Map of Morocco and Ivory Coast — A169

**1979, Jan. 27   Photo.   *Perf. 13***
490  A169  60fr multicolored         3.00   1.00
491  A169  65fr multicolored         4.00   1.25
492  A169  500fr multicolored       20.00   8.50
        Nos. 490-492 (3)            27.00

Visit of King Hassan of Morocco to Ivory Coast. The visit never took place and the stamps were not issued. To recover the printing costs the stamps were sold in Paris for one day.

Horus — A170

**1979, Feb. 17   Litho.   *Perf. 12½***
493  A170  200fr multi              3.00   1.50
494  A170  500fr Vulture with
            ankh, car-
            touches                  6.50   3.50

UNESCO drive to save Temples of Philae.

Flowers — A171

**1979, Feb. 24**
495  A171  30fr Locranthus          1.25   .50
496  A171  60fr Vanda Josephine      1.75   .60
497  A171  65fr Renanthera storiei   2.00   .90
        Nos. 495-497 (3)            5.00   2.00

Wildlife Protection A172

**1979, Mar. 24   Photo.   *Perf. 13x13½***
498  A172  50fr Hippopotamus         2.50   .80

Globe and Emblem — A173            Child Riding Dove — A174

**1979, Apr. 1   Litho.   *Perf. 12x12½***
499  A173  60fr multicolored          .75   .50
500  A174  65fr multicolored          .85   .50
501  A173  100fr multicolored        1.60   1.00
502  A174  500fr multicolored        6.25   3.50
        Nos. 499-502 (4)            9.45   5.50

International Year of the Child.

Rural Mail Delivery — A175

**1979, Apr. 7**                        *Perf. 12½*
503  A175  60fr multicolored         1.25   .35

Stamp Day.

Korhogo Cathedral — A176

**1979, Apr. 9**                        *Perf. 13*
504  A176  60fr multicolored         1.00   .45

Arrival of Catholic missionaries, 75th anniv.

Crying Child — A177

**1979, May 17   Litho.   *Perf. 12½***
505  A177  65fr multicolored         1.00   .50

10th anniv. of SOS Village (for homeless children).

Euphaedra Xypete A178

Butterflies: 65fr, Pseudacraea bois duvali. 70fr, Auchenisa schausi.

**1979, May 26**                        *Perf. 13x13½*
506  A178  60fr multicolored         2.50   1.00
507  A178  65fr multicolored         3.00   1.00
508  A178  70fr multicolored         4.50   1.50
        Nos. 506-508 (3)           10.00   3.50

Endangered Animals — A179

**1979, June 2**
509  A179  5fr Antelopes            1.00   .40
510  A179  20fr Duikerbok           1.50   .50
511  A179  60fr Aardvark            4.50   1.50
        Nos. 509-511 (3)            7.00   2.40

UPU Emblem, Radar, Truck and Ship — A180

#513, Ancestral figure & antelope, vert.

**1979, June 8   Engr.   *Perf. 13***
512  A180  70fr multi               3.50   2.50

**Photo.**

513  A180  70fr multi               3.50   2.50

Philexafrique II, Libreville, Gabon, June 8-17. Nos. 512, 513 each printed in sheets of 10 with 5 labels showing exhibition emblem.

Rowland Hill, Steam Locomotive, Great Britain No. 75 — A181

Rowland Hill, Locomotives and: 75fr, Ivory Coast #125. 100fr, Hawaii #4. 150fr, Japan #30, syll. 3. 300fr, France #2. 500fr, Ivory Coast #123.

## 1979, July 7     Litho.     *Perf. 13½*
| | | | | |
|---|---|---|---|---|
| 514 | A181 | 60fr multi | .75 | .25 |
| 515 | A181 | 75fr multi | .90 | .25 |
| 516 | A181 | 100fr multi | 1.50 | .40 |
| 517 | A181 | 150fr multi | 1.75 | .50 |
| 518 | A181 | 300fr multi | 3.75 | .75 |
| | *Nos. 514-518 (5)* | | 8.65 | 2.15 |

**Souvenir Sheet**
| | | | | |
|---|---|---|---|---|
| 519 | A181 | 500fr multi | 7.00 | 2.00 |

Sir Rowland Hill (1795-1879), originator of penny postage.

Insects — A181a

A181b

## 1979     Photo.     *Perf. 14x13, 13x14*
| | | | | |
|---|---|---|---|---|
| 519A | A181a | 30fr Wasp | 15.00 | 2.50 |
| 519B | A181a | 60fr Praying mantis, vert. | 30.00 | 4.00 |
| 519C | A181a | 65fr Cricket | 40.00 | 4.00 |
| | *Nos. 519A-519C (3)* | | 85.00 | 10.50 |

## 1979     Photo.     *Perf. 13x14*
Musical instruments.
| | | | | |
|---|---|---|---|---|
| 519D | A181b | 100fr Harp | 35.00 | 14.00 |
| 519E | A181b | 150fr Whistles | 50.00 | 20.00 |

"TELECOM 79" — A182     Culture Day — A183

## 1979, Sept. 20     Litho.     *Perf. 13x12½*
| | | | | |
|---|---|---|---|---|
| 520 | A182 | 60fr multicolored | 1.00 | .40 |

3rd World Telecommunications Exhibition, Geneva, Sept. 20-26.

## 1979, Oct. 13     *Perf. 12½*
| | | | | |
|---|---|---|---|---|
| 521 | A183 | 65fr multicolored | 1.00 | .40 |

Fish — A183a

## 1979     Photo.     *Perf. 14x13*
| | | | | |
|---|---|---|---|---|
| 521A | A183a | 60fr Pterois volitans | 150.00 | — |
| 521B | A183a | 65fr Coelacanth | 150.00 | — |

Boxing — A184

## 1979, Oct. 27     Litho.     *Perf. 14x13½*
| | | | | |
|---|---|---|---|---|
| 522 | A184 | 60fr shown | .75 | .25 |
| 523 | A184 | 65fr Running | .75 | .25 |
| 524 | A184 | 100fr Soccer | 1.25 | .30 |
| 525 | A184 | 150fr Bicycling | 1.75 | .50 |
| 526 | A184 | 300fr Wrestling | 3.50 | 1.25 |
| | *Nos. 522-526 (5)* | | 8.00 | 2.55 |

**Souvenir Sheet**
| | | | | |
|---|---|---|---|---|
| 527 | A184 | 500fr Gymnastics | 6.00 | 2.00 |

Pre-Olympic Year.

Wildlife Fund Emblem and Jentink's Duiker — A185

Wildlife Protection: 60fr, Colobus Monkey. 75fr, Manatees. 100fr, Epixerus ebii. 150fr, Hippopotamus. 300fr, Chimpanzee.

## 1979, Nov. 3     Litho.     *Perf. 14½*
| | | | | |
|---|---|---|---|---|
| 528 | A185 | 40fr multi | 3.25 | .30 |
| 529 | A185 | 60fr multi | 3.50 | .50 |
| 530 | A185 | 75fr multi | 5.00 | .50 |
| 531 | A185 | 100fr multi | 7.00 | .75 |
| 532 | A185 | 150fr multi | 10.50 | 1.00 |
| 533 | A185 | 300fr multi | 21.00 | 2.00 |
| | *Nos. 528-533 (6)* | | 50.25 | 5.05 |

Raoul Follerau Institute, Adzope — A186

## 1979, Dec. 6     Litho.     *Perf. 12½*
| | | | | |
|---|---|---|---|---|
| 534 | A186 | 60fr multi | 1.50 | .50 |

Independence, 19th Anniversary A187

## 1979, Dec. 7     Litho.     *Perf. 14x13½*
| | | | | |
|---|---|---|---|---|
| 535 | A187 | 60fr multicolored | 1.25 | .25 |

Fireball A188

Local Flora: 5fr, Clerodendron thomsonae, vert. 50fr, Costus incanusiamus, vert. 60fr, Ficus elastica abidjan, vert.

## 1980     Litho.     *Perf. 12½*
| | | | | |
|---|---|---|---|---|
| 536 | A188 | 5fr multicolored | .30 | .20 |
| 537 | A188 | 10fr multicolored | .40 | .20 |
| 538 | A188 | 50fr multicolored | 1.25 | .30 |
| 539 | A188 | 60fr multicolored | 1.40 | .30 |
| | *Nos. 536-539 (4)* | | 3.35 | 1.00 |

Issued: 5fr, 10fr, Jan. 26; 50fr, 60fr, Feb. 16.

Rotary Intl., 75th Anniv. — A189

## 1980, Feb. 23     Photo.     *Perf. 13½*
| | | | | |
|---|---|---|---|---|
| 540 | A189 | 65fr multicolored | 1.00 | .40 |

International Archives Day — A190

## 1980, Feb. 26     Litho.
| | | | | |
|---|---|---|---|---|
| 541 | A190 | 65fr multicolored | 1.00 | .45 |

Astronaut Shaking Hands with Boy — A191

Path of Apollo 11 — A192

## 1980, July 6     Photo.
| | | | | |
|---|---|---|---|---|
| 542 | A191 | 60fr multicolored | .90 | .50 |
| 543 | A192 | 65fr multicolored | .90 | .50 |
| 544 | A191 | 70fr multicolored | 1.75 | .75 |
| 545 | A192 | 150fr multicolored | 3.00 | 1.75 |
| | *Nos. 542-545 (4)* | | 6.55 | 3.50 |

Apollo 11 moon landing, 10th anniv. (1979).

Jet and Map of Africa A193

## 1980, Mar. 22     *Perf. 12½*
| | | | | |
|---|---|---|---|---|
| 546 | A193 | 60fr multicolored | 1.00 | .35 |

ASECNA (Air Safety Board), 20th anniv.

Boys and Stamp Album, Globe — A194

## 1980, Apr. 12     Litho.     *Perf. 12½*
| | | | | |
|---|---|---|---|---|
| 547 | A194 | 65fr bl grn & red brn | 1.25 | .30 |

Stamp Day; Youth philately.

Missionary and Church, Aboisso A195

## 1980, Apr. 26     Photo.     *Perf. 13x13½*
| | | | | |
|---|---|---|---|---|
| 548 | A195 | 60fr multicolored | 1.25 | .50 |

Settlement of the Holy Fathers at Aboisso, 75th anniversary.

Fight Against Cigarette Smoking A196

## 1980, May 3     *Perf. 12½*
| | | | | |
|---|---|---|---|---|
| 549 | A196 | 60fr multicolored | 1.25 | .30 |

Pope John Paul II, Pres. Houphouet-Boigny — A197

## 1980, May 10     Photo.     *Perf. 13*
| | | | | |
|---|---|---|---|---|
| 550 | A197 | 65fr multicolored | 3.50 | 1.25 |

Visit of Pope John Paul II to Ivory Coast.

Le Belier Locomotive A198

## 1980, May 17     Litho.     *Perf. 13*
| | | | | |
|---|---|---|---|---|
| 551 | A198 | 60fr shown | .75 | .35 |
| 552 | A198 | 65fr Abidjan Railroad Station, 1904 | .85 | .35 |
| 553 | A198 | 100fr Passenger car, 1908 | 1.75 | .70 |
| 554 | A198 | 150fr Steam locomotive, 1940 | 2.25 | 1.00 |
| | *Nos. 551-554 (4)* | | 5.60 | 2.40 |

Central Bank of West African States, 1st Anniversary A199

## 1980, May 26     Litho.     *Perf. 12x12½*
| | | | | |
|---|---|---|---|---|
| 555 | A199 | 60fr multicolored | 1.00 | .40 |

Lujtanus Sebae A200

**1980, Apr. 19    Photo.    *Perf. 14***
556 A200  60fr  shown                      3.50   .75
557 A200  65fr  Monodactylus
                sebae, vert.               3.75  1.25
558 A200 100fr  Colisa fasciata            4.50  1.50
       *Nos. 556-558 (3)*                 11.75  3.50

Snake — A201

**1980, July 12    Litho.    *Perf. 12½***
559 A201  60fr  shown                      2.25   .75
560 A201 150fr  Toad                       5.00  1.75

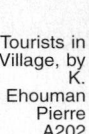

Tourists in
Village, by
K.
Ehouman
Pierre
A202

Conference
Emblem — A203

**1980, Aug. 9**
561 A202  60fr  multicolored               .75   .30
562 A203  65fr  multicolored               .75   .30
  National Tourist Office, Abidjan; World Tourism Conference, Manila.

Forticula
Auricularia
A204

**  *Perf. 14x13, 13x14***
**1980, Sept. 6                          Photo.**
563 A204  60fr  shown                      5.00  2.25
564 A204  65fr  Praying mantis,
                vert.                      5.00  2.25

**  *Perf. 13½x13, 13x13½***
**1980, Oct. 11                          Photo.**
  Designs: 60fr, 200fr, Various grasshoppers.
565 A204  60fr  multi, vert.               2.50  1.50
566 A204 200fr  multi                      7.50  3.50

Hands Free from Chain, Map of Ivory
Coast, Pres. Houphouet-
Boigny — A205

Pres. Houphouet-Boigny, Symbols of
Development — A206

---

**  *Perf. 12½x13, 14x14½ (A206)***
**1980, Oct. 18**
567 A205  60fr  shown                      1.40   .75
568 A206  65fr  shown                      1.40   .75
569 A205  70fr  Map, colors,
                document                   2.00  1.00
570 A205 150fr  like #567                  4.50  2.75
571 A206 300fr  like #568                  8.00  4.50
       *Nos. 567-571 (5)*                 17.30  9.75
  Pres. Houphouet-Boigny, 75th birthday.

7th PDCI
and RDA
Congress
A207

**1980, Oct. 25                          *Perf. 12½***
572 A207  60fr  multicolored               1.00   .30
573 A207  65fr  multicolored               1.00   .30

River
Cruise Boat
Sotra
A208

**1980, Dec. 6    Litho.    *Perf. 13x13½***
574 A208  60fr  multicolored               1.25   .50

View of Abidjan — A209

**1980, Dec. 7                           *Perf. 13x12½***
575 A209  60fr  multicolored               1.00   .30
  20th anniversary of independence.

Universities
Association
Emblem — A210

African Postal
Union, 5th
Anniversary
A211

**1980, Dec. 16                          *Perf. 12½***
576 A210  60fr  multicolored               1.00   .50
  African Universities Assoc., 5th General
Conf.

**1980, Dec. 24    Photo.    *Perf. 13½***
577 A211 150fr  multi                      1.75   .50

---

Herichtys Cyanoguttatum — A212

**1981, Mar. 14    Litho.    *Perf. 12½***
578 A212  60fr  shown                      1.25   .75
579 A212  65fr  Labeo bicolor              1.25   .75
580 A212 200fr  Tetraodon fluvia-
                tilis                      3.50  2.00
       *Nos. 578-580 (3)*                  6.00  3.50

Birds — A212a

**1980, Dec. 30    Photo.    *Perf. 14½x14***
580A A212a  60fr  Spreo
                  superbus        65.00  15.00
580B A212a  65fr  Tockus
                  camurus         65.00  15.00
580C A212a  65fr  Balearica
                  pavonina        70.00  16.00
580D A212a 100fr  Ephippi-
                  orhyn-
                  chus          200.00 175.00
       *Nos. 580A-580D (4)*     400.00 221.00

Post Office,
Grand
Lahou
A213

25th Anniv.
of Ivory
Coast
Philatelic
Club
A214

**1981, May 2    Litho.    *Perf. 12½***
581 A213  60fr  multicolored               1.00   .30
582 A214  65fr  multicolored               1.00   .30

  Stamp Day.

13th World Telecommunications
Day — A215

**1981, May 17**
583 A215  30fr  multicolored                .50   .20
584 A215  60fr  multicolored               1.00   .35

Viking Satellite Landing, 1976 — A216

  Space Conquest: Columbia space shuttle.

---

**1981, June 13    Litho.    *Perf. 13½***
585 A216  60fr  multi                       .75   .25
586 A216  75fr  multi                       .90   .30
587 A216 125fr  multi                      1.40   .60
588 A216 300fr  multi                      3.50  1.25
       *Nos. 585-588 (4)*                   6.55  2.40

**Souvenir Sheet**
589 A216 500fr  multi                      5.25  1.25

Local
Flowers — A217

Prince Charles and Lady Diana,
Coach — A218

**1981, July 4    Photo.    *Perf. 14½x14***
590 A217  50fr  Amorphophallus            1.75   .60
591 A217  60fr  Sugar Cane                2.25  1.25
592 A217 100fr  Heliconia ivoirea         4.00  1.75
       *Nos. 590-592 (3)*                  8.00  3.60

**1981, Aug. 8    Litho.    *Perf. 12½***
  Royal Wedding: Couple and coaches.
593 A218  80fr  multi                       .90   .25
594 A218 100fr  multi                      1.25   .50
595 A218 125fr  multi                      1.75   .85
       *Nos. 593-595 (3)*                  3.90  1.60
**Souvenir Sheet**
596 A218 500fr  multi                      6.00  2.00

  For overprints see Nos. 642-645.

Elephant on Flag
and Map — A219

**1981, Sept.    Litho.    *Perf. 12½***
597 A219  80fr  multicolored                .75   .25
598 A219 100fr  multicolored               1.00   .50
599 A219 125fr  multicolored               1.50   .60
       *Nos. 597-599 (3)*                   3.25  1.35

  See Nos. 662-666, 833.

Soccer
Players
A220

  Soccer players.

**1981, Sept. 19                         *Perf. 14***
600 A220  70fr  multi, horiz.               .75   .40
601 A220  80fr  multi, horiz.               .80   .50
602 A220 100fr  multi                      1.00   .60

603 A220 150fr multi 1.50 .90
604 A220 350fr multi 3.75 1.75
Nos. 600-604 (5) 7.80 4.15

**Souvenir Sheet**

605 A220 500fr multi, horz. 5.00 2.00
ESPANA '82 World Cup Soccer
Championship.
For overprints see Nos. 651-656.

West African Rice Development
Assoc., 10th Anniv. — A221

**1981, Oct. 3** **Perf. 12½**
606 A221 80fr multicolored 1.25 .50

World Food
Day
A222

**1981, Oct. 18**
607 A222 100fr multicolored 1.25 .60

Post Day — A223

**1981, Oct. 9** **Litho.** **Perf. 12½**
608 A223 70fr multicolored .75 .30
609 A223 80fr multicolored .85 .50
610 A223 100fr multicolored 1.25 .60
Nos. 608-610 (3) 2.85 1.40

75th Anniv. of Grand Prix — A224

Designs: Winners and their cars.

**1981, Nov. 21** **Perf. 14**
611 A224 15fr Felice Nazarro,
1907 .25 .20
612 A224 40fr Jim Clark, 1962 .50 .20
613 A224 80fr Fiat, 1907 1.00 .45
614 A224 100fr Auto Union, 1936 1.25 .50
615 A224 125fr Ferrari, 1961 1.75 .60
Nos. 611-615 (5) 4.75 1.95

**Souvenir Sheet**

616 A224 500fr 1933 car 6.00 2.25

21st Anniv. of Independence — A225

---

**1981, Dec. 7** **Perf. 13x12½**
617 A225 50fr multicolored .60 .30
618 A225 80fr multicolored 1.10 .50

Traditional
Hairstyle — A226

Rotary Emblem
on Map
of — A228

Stamp Day Africa — A227

Designs: Various hairstyles.

**1981, Dec. 19** **Photo.** **Perf. 14½x14**
619 A226 80fr multicolored 1.75 .85
620 A226 100fr multicolored 2.75 1.25
621 A226 125fr multicolored 3.50 1.75
Nos. 619-621 (3) 8.00 3.85

**1982, Apr. 3** **Litho.** **Perf. 12½x12**
622 A227 100fr Bingerville P.O.,
1902 1.25 .60

**1982, Apr. 13** **Perf. 12½**
623 A228 100fr ultra & gold 1.25 .60
Pres. Houphouet-Boigny's Rotary Goodwill
Conference, Abidjan, Apr. 13-15.

250th Birth Anniv. of George
Washington — A229

Anniversaries: 100fr, Auguste Piccard
(1884-1962), Swiss physicist. 350fr, Goethe
(1749-1832). 450fr, 500fr, Princess Diana,
21st birthday (portraits).

**1982, May 15** **Litho.** **Perf. 13**
624 A229 80fr multi .75 .35
625 A229 100fr multi 1.00 .50
626 A229 350fr multi 4.00 1.25
627 A229 450fr multi 5.00 1.50
Nos. 624-627 (4) 10.75 3.60

**Souvenir Sheet**

628 A229 500fr multi 4.50 1.25

---

Visit of French Pres. Mitterand, May
21-24 — A230

**1982, May 21** **Photo.** **Perf. 13½**
629 A230 100fr multicolored 1.00 .40

14th World Telecommunications
Day — A231

**1982, May 29** **Litho.** **Perf. 13**
630 A231 80fr multicolored .90 .25

Scouting
Year — A232

Scouts sailing, diff. 80fr, 150fr, 350fr, 500fr
vert.

**1982, May 29** **Perf. 12½**
631 A232 80fr multi .90 .30
632 A232 100fr multi 1.50 .35
633 A232 150fr multi 1.90 .60
634 A232 350fr multi 4.00 1.25
Nos. 631-634 (4) 8.30 2.50

**Souvenir Sheet**

635 A232 500fr multi 7.00 2.50

TB Bacillus
Centenary
A233

**1982, June 5** **Photo.** **Perf. 13x13½**
636 A233 30fr brown & multi .75 .35
637 A233 80fr lt grn & multi 1.25 .65

UN Conference
on Human
Environment, 10th
Anniv. — A234

**1982, July** **Photo.** **Perf. 13½x13**
638 A234 40fr multicolored .70 .30
639 A234 80fr multicolored 1.25 .50

League of Ivory
Coast
Secretaries, First
Congress — A235

---

**1982, Aug. 9** **Litho.** **Perf. 12½x13**
640 A235 80fr tan & multi 1.00 .40
641 A235 100fr silver & multi 1.25 .50

593-596 Overprinted in Blue:
"NAISSANCE / ROYALE 1982"
**1982, Aug. 21** **Perf. 12½**
642 A218 80fr multi 1.20 .50
643 A218 100fr multi 1.25 .60
644 A218 125fr multi 1.50 .75
Nos. 642-644 (3) 3.95 1.85

**Souvenir Sheet**

645 A218 500fr multi 5.00 5.00
Birth of Prince William of Wales, June 21.

La Colombe de l'Avenir, 1962, by
Pablo Picasso (1881-1973) — A236

Picasso Paintings: 80fr, Child with Dove,
1901. 100fr, Self-portrait, 1901. 185fr, Les
Demoiselles d'Avignon, 1907. 350fr, The
Dream, 1932. Nos. 646-649 vert.

**1982, Sept. 4** **Litho.** **Perf. 13**
646 A236 80fr multi 1.00 .40
647 A236 100fr multi 1.25 .40
648 A236 185fr multi 3.00 .75
649 A236 350fr multi 4.50 1.75
650 A236 500fr multi 6.50 2.00
Nos. 646-650 (5) 16.25 5.30

Nos. 600-605 Overprinted with World
Cup Winners 1966-1982 in Black on
Silver
**1982, Oct. 9** **Litho.** **Perf. 14**
651 A220 70fr multi .75 .30
652 A220 80fr multi .90 .60
653 A220 100fr multi 1.20 .60
654 A220 150fr multi 1.75 1.00
655 A220 350fr multi 4.00 2.00
Nos. 651-655 (5) 8.60 4.50

**Souvenir Sheet**

656 A220 500fr multi 6.50 6.50
Italy's victory in 1982 World Cup.

13th World UPU Day — A237

Designs: 80fr, P.O. counter. 100fr, Postel-
2001 building, Abidjan, vert. 350fr, Postal
workers. 500fr, Postel-2001 interior.

**1982, Oct. 23** **Perf. 12½**
657 A237 80fr multi .80 .50
658 A237 100fr multi 1.40 .50
659 A237 350fr multi 4.00 1.75

**Size: 48x37mm**
**Perf. 13**
660 A237 500fr multi 4.75 2.25
Nos. 657-660 (4) 10.95 5.00

22nd Anniv. of Independence — A238

**1982, Dec. 7** **Perf. 13**
661 A238 100fr multicolored 1.25 .60

## Elephant Type of 1981

**1982-84**
| | | | | | |
|---|---|---|---|---|---|
| **662** | A219 | 5fr | multicolored | .20 | .20 |
| **662A** | A219 | 10fr | multi ('84) | .45 | .20 |
| **662B** | A219 | 20fr | multi | .45 | .20 |
| **663** | A219 | 25fr | multicolored | .40 | .20 |
| **664** | A219 | 30fr | multicolored | .40 | .20 |
| **665** | A219 | 40fr | multicolored | .60 | .20 |
| **666** | A219 | 50fr | multicolored | .60 | .20 |
| | | *Nos. 662-666 (7)* | | 3.10 | 1.40 |

Man
Waterfall
A238a

**1982      Photo.      Perf. 15x14**
| | | | | | |
|---|---|---|---|---|---|
| **666A** | A238a | 80fr | shown | 20.00 | 2.00 |
| **666B** | A238a | 80fr | Boisee Sa-vanna | 30.00 | 1.75 |
| **666C** | A238a | 500fr | like #666A | 65.00 | 7.00 |
| | | *Nos. 666A-666C (3)* | | 115.00 | 10.75 |

Issued: #666B, Dec. 18; others, Nov. 27.

20th Anniv.
of West
African
Monetary
Union
A239

**1982, Dec. 21      Litho.      Perf. 12½**
| | | | | | |
|---|---|---|---|---|---|
| **667** | A239 | 100fr | Emblem | 1.25 | .50 |

Abouissa
Children's
Village
A240

**1983, Mar. 5      Photo.      Perf. 13½x13**
| | | | | | |
|---|---|---|---|---|---|
| **668** | A240 | 125fr | multicolored | 1.75 | .75 |

Anteater
A241

**1983, Mar. 12      Litho.      Perf. 12½x13**
| | | | | | |
|---|---|---|---|---|---|
| **669** | A241 | 35fr | Pangolin, vert. | .60 | .20 |
| **670** | A241 | 90fr | shown | 1.20 | .50 |
| **671** | A241 | 100fr | Colobus monkey, vert. | 1.50 | .60 |
| **672** | A241 | 125fr | Buffalo | 1.75 | .75 |
| | | *Nos. 669-672 (4)* | | 5.05 | 2.05 |

Stamp Day — A242

**1983, Mar. 19      Litho.      Perf. 12½**
| | | | | | |
|---|---|---|---|---|---|
| **673** | A242 | 100fr | Grand Bassam P.O., 1903 | 1.25 | .60 |

Easter
1983
A243

Paintings by Rubens (1577-1640). 100fr, 400fr, 500fr vert.

**1983, Apr. 9      Perf. 13**
| | | | | | |
|---|---|---|---|---|---|
| **674** | A243 | 100fr | Descent from the Cross | 1.10 | .30 |
| **675** | A243 | 125fr | Resurrection | 1.30 | .50 |
| **676** | A243 | 350fr | Crucifixion | 3.50 | 1.25 |
| **677** | A243 | 400fr | Piercing of the Sword | 4.50 | 1.50 |
| **678** | A243 | 500fr | Descent, diff. | 5.00 | 2.00 |
| | | *Nos. 674-678 (5)* | | 15.40 | 5.55 |

25th Anniv. of UN Economic
Commission for Africa — A244

**1983, Apr. 29      Litho.      Perf. 13x12½**
| | | | | | |
|---|---|---|---|---|---|
| **679** | A244 | 100fr | multicolored | 1.25 | .60 |

Gray
Parakeet
A245

**1983, June 11**
| | | | | | |
|---|---|---|---|---|---|
| **680** | A245 | 100fr | Fish eagle, vert. | 2.00 | 1.00 |
| **681** | A245 | 125fr | shown | 2.75 | .75 |
| **682** | A245 | 150fr | Touracoes | 4.25 | 1.00 |
| | | *Nos. 680-682 (3)* | | 9.00 | 2.75 |

World Communications Year — A245a

**1983, July 16      Perf. 12½x13**
| | | | | | |
|---|---|---|---|---|---|
| **682A** | A245a | 100fr | shown | 125.00 | — |
| **682B** | A245a | 125fr | diff. | 125.00 | — |

A246

**1983, Sept. 3      Litho.      Perf. 12½**
| | | | | | |
|---|---|---|---|---|---|
| **683** | A246 | 50fr | Flali, Gouro | .50 | .30 |
| **684** | A246 | 100fr | Masked dancer, Guere | 1.10 | .50 |
| **685** | A246 | 125fr | Stilt dancer, Yacouba | 1.50 | .60 |
| | | *Nos. 683-685 (3)* | | 3.10 | 1.40 |

20th Anniv. of the Ivory Hotel,
Abidjan — A249

**1983, Sept. 7      Perf. 13**
| | | | | | |
|---|---|---|---|---|---|
| **693** | A249 | 100fr | multicolored | 1.25 | .60 |

Ecology in
Action
A250

**1983, Oct. 24      Litho.**
| | | | | | |
|---|---|---|---|---|---|
| **694** | A250 | 25fr | Forest after fire | .75 | .40 |
| **695** | A250 | 100fr | Animals fleeing | 2.00 | .80 |
| **696** | A250 | 125fr | Animals grazing | 2.75 | 2.10 |
| | | *Nos. 694-696 (3)* | | 5.50 | 3.30 |

Raphael (1483-1520), 500th Birth
Anniv. — A252

Paintings:    100fr, Christ and St. Peter. 125fr, Study for St. Joseph, vert. 350fr, Virgin of the House of Orleans, vert. 500fr, Virgin with the Blue Diadem, vert.

**1983, Nov. 5      Litho.      Perf. 13**
| | | | | | |
|---|---|---|---|---|---|
| **698** | A252 | 100fr | multi | 1.20 | .35 |
| **699** | A252 | 125fr | multi | 1.50 | .50 |
| **700** | A252 | 350fr | multi | 3.75 | 1.50 |
| **701** | A252 | 500fr | multi | 5.00 | 2.00 |
| | | *Nos. 698-701 (4)* | | 11.45 | 4.35 |

Auto Race
A253

**1983, Oct. 24      Litho.      Perf. 12½**
| | | | | | |
|---|---|---|---|---|---|
| **702** | A253 | 100fr | Car, map | 1.50 | .60 |

Flowers — A254

**1983, Nov. 26      Photo.      Perf. 14x15**
| | | | | | |
|---|---|---|---|---|---|
| **703** | A254 | 100fr | Fleurs d'Ananas | 150.00 | — |
| **704** | A254 | 125fr | Heliconia Rostrata | 10.00 | 2.50 |
| **705** | A254 | 150fr | Rose de Porcelaine | 10.00 | 2.50 |
| | | *Nos. 703-705 (3)* | | 170.00 | |

23rd Anniv. of Independence — A255

**1983, Dec. 7**
| | | | | | |
|---|---|---|---|---|---|
| **706** | A255 | 100fr | multicolored | 1.25 | .50 |

First Audio-visual Forum,
Abidjan — A256

**1984, Jan. 25      Litho.      Perf. 13x12½**
| | | | | | |
|---|---|---|---|---|---|
| **707** | A256 | 100fr | Screen, arrow | 1.25 | .50 |

14th African
Soccer
Cup — A257

**1984, Mar. 4      Photo.      Perf. 12½**
| | | | | | |
|---|---|---|---|---|---|
| **708** | A257 | 100fr | Emblem | 1.00 | .40 |
| **709** | A257 | 200fr | Maps shaking hands | 2.00 | 1.00 |

Local Insects
A258

**1984, Mar. 24      Litho.      Perf. 13**
| | | | | | |
|---|---|---|---|---|---|
| **710** | A258 | 100fr | Argiope, vert. | 2.00 | .75 |
| **711** | A258 | 125fr | Polistes gallicus | 2.25 | 1.00 |

Stamp Day — A259

**1984, Apr. 7      Litho.      Perf. 12½**
| | | | | | |
|---|---|---|---|---|---|
| **712** | A259 | 100fr | Abidjan P.O., 1934 | 1.25 | .50 |

Lions
Emblem
A260

**1984, Apr. 27      Perf. 13½x13**
| | | | | | |
|---|---|---|---|---|---|
| **713** | A260 | 100fr | multicolored | 1.00 | .50 |
| **714** | A260 | 125fr | multicolored | 1.75 | .75 |

3rd Convention of Multi-district 403, Abidjan, Apr. 27-29.

16th World Telecommunications Day — A261

**1984, May 17**      *Perf. 12½*
715   A261   100fr multi     1.25   .50

Council of Unity, 25th Anniv. — A262

**1984, May 29**
716   A262   100fr multicolored    1.25   .40
717   A262   125fr multicolored    1.50   .50

First Governmental Palace, Grand-Bassam — A263

**1984, July 14**    **Litho.**    *Perf. 12½*
718   A263   100fr shown      1.25   .40
719   A263   125fr Palace of Justice,
              Grand-Bassam    1.50   .60

Men Playing Eklan — A264

**1984, Aug. 11**      *Perf. 13*
720   A264   100fr Board     1.40   .40
721   A264   125fr shown     1.50   .60

Locomotive "Gazelle" — A265

**1984**                *Perf. 12½*
722   A265   100fr shown     1.25   .50
723   A265   100fr Cargo ship    1.25   .50
724   A265   125fr Superpacific    2.00   .60
725   A265   125fr Cargo ship, diff.   1.50   .60
726   A265   350fr Pacific type 10   4.50   1.50
727   A265   350fr Ocean liner    4.00   1.50
728   A265   500fr Mallet class
               GT2      6.50   2.25
729   A265   500fr Ocean liner, diff.   6.50   2.25
       Nos. 722-729 (8)     27.50   9.70

Issue dates: trains, Aug. 25; ships, Sept. 1.

Stamp Day
A266

**1984, Oct. 20**    **Litho.**    *Perf. 12½*
730   A266   100fr Map, post offices   1.50   .50

10th Anniv., West African Union A267

**1984, Oct. 27**    **Litho.**    *Perf. 13½*
731   A267   100fr Map, member
              nations     1.00   .50

Wildlife — A267a

**1984, Nov. 3**    **Photo.**    *Perf. 14½x15*
731A   A267a   100fr Tragelaphus
              scriptus    75.00   12.00
731B   A267a   150fr Felis serval   75.00   12.00

Tourism
A267b

**1984, Nov. 10**    **Photo.**    *Perf. 15x14½*
731C   A267b   50fr Le Club Val-
             tur     65.00   11.00
731D   A267b   100fr Grand
             Lahou    65.00   11.00

Flowers — A267c

**1984, Nov. 17**    **Photo.**    *Perf. 14½x15*
731E   A267c   100fr Allamanda
             carthartica   75.00   12.00
731F   A267c   125fr Baobob   75.00   12.00

90th Anniv., Ivory Coast Postage Stamps A268

**1984, Nov. 23**    **Litho.**    *Perf. 12½*
732   A268   125fr Book cover   1.50   .75

24th Anniv. of Independence — A269

**1984, Dec. 7**    **Litho.**    *Perf. 12½*
733   A269   100fr Citizens, outline
             map     1.00   .50

Rotary Intl. Conf. — A270

**1985, Jan. 16**    **Litho.**    *Perf. 12½x13*
734   A270   100fr multicolored   1.00   .50
735   A270   125fr multicolored   1.25   .60

Traditional Costumes
A271

**1985, Feb. 16**    **Litho.**    *Perf. 13½*
736   A271   90fr Dan le Babou   1.50   .50
737   A271   100fr Post-natal gown   1.50   .60

Birds — A271a

**1985**      **Photo.**    *Perf. 14½x15*
737A   A271a   25fr Marabout   150.00   17.50
737B   A271a   100fr Jacana   150.00   17.50
737C   A271a   350fr Ibis   150.00   17.50
       Nos. 737A-737C (3)    450.00

Issued: Nos. 737A, 737B, Mar. No. 737C, 8/17.

Stamp Day — A272

**1985, Apr. 13**    **Litho.**    *Perf. 12½*
738   A272   100fr Riverboat Adjame   2.25   1.00

18th District of Zonta Intl., 7th Conference, Abidjan, Apr. 25-27 — A273

**1985, Apr. 25**    **Litho.**    *Perf. 13½*
739   A273   125fr Zonta Intl. em-
             blem     1.40   .75

Bondoukou — A273a

100fr, Marche de Bondoukou. 125fr, Mosque, Samatiguila.

**1985**      **Litho.**    *Perf. 14½x13½*
739A   A273a   100fr mul-
             ticolored   140.00   9.00
739B   A273a   125fr mul-
             ticolored   140.00   9.00
739C   A273a   200fr mul-
             ticolored   140.00   9.00
       Nos. 739A-739C (3)    420.00   27.00

PHILEXAFRICA '85, Lome — A274

**1985, May 15**      *Perf. 13*
740   A274   200fr Factory, jet, van   2.25   1.10
741   A274   200fr Youth sports,
             farming    2.25   1.10
   *a.*    Pair, Nos. 740-741 + label   6.00   6.00

African Development Bank, 20th Anniv. — A275

**1985, June 18**
742   A275   100fr Senegal chemical
             industry    1.00   .50
743   A275   125fr Gambian tree
             nursery    1.25   .75

Intl. Youth Year — A276

**1985, July 20**      *Perf. 12½*
744   A276   125fr Map, profiles,
             dove     1.40   .60

Natl. Armed Forces, 25th Anniv. — A277

Emblems: No. 745, Presidential Guard. No. 746, F.A.N.C.I. 125fr, Air Transport & Liaison Group, G.A.T.L. 200fr, National Marines. 350fr, National Gendarmerie.

**1985, July 27**      *Perf. 12½x13*

| | | | | |
|---|---|---|---|---|
| 745 | A277 | 100fr dp rose lil & gold | 1.00 | .50 |
| 746 | A277 | 100fr dark bl & gold | 1.00 | .50 |
| 747 | A277 | 125fr blk brn & gold | 1.50 | .60 |
| 748 | A277 | 200fr blk brn & gold | 2.25 | 1.00 |
| 749 | A277 | 350fr brt ultra & sil | 3.50 | 2.00 |
| | | *Nos. 745-749 (5)* | 9.25 | 4.60 |

1986 World Cup Soccer Preliminaries, Mexico — A279

**1985, Aug.**      *Perf. 13*

| | | | | |
|---|---|---|---|---|
| 751 | A279 | 100fr Heading the ball | 1.00 | .50 |
| 752 | A279 | 150fr Tackle | 1.50 | .90 |
| 753 | A279 | 200fr Dribbling | 1.75 | 1.20 |
| 754 | A279 | 350fr Passing | 3.75 | 2.00 |
| | | *Nos. 751-754 (4)* | 8.00 | 4.60 |

**Souvenir Sheet**

| | | | | |
|---|---|---|---|---|
| 755 | A279 | 500fr Power shot | 5.00 | 2.00 |

Ivory Coast — Sovereign Military Order of Malta Postal Convention, Dec. 19, 1984 — A280

**1985, Aug. 31**      *Perf. 13x12½*

| | | | | |
|---|---|---|---|---|
| 756 | A280 | 125fr Natl. arms | 1.25 | .75 |
| 757 | A280 | 350fr S.M.O.M. arms | 3.50 | 2.00 |

Visit of Pope John Paul II — A281

**1985, Sept. 24**      *Perf. 13*
**Overprint in Black**

| | | | | |
|---|---|---|---|---|
| 758 | A281 | 100fr Portrait, St. Paul's Cathedral, Abidjan | 2.25 | 1.00 |

The overprint, "Consecration de la Cathedrale Saint Paul d'Abidjon," was added to explain the reason for the visit of the Pope. Copies without overprint exist but were not issued.

UN Child Survival Campaign A282

**1985, Oct. 5**    **Litho.**    *Perf. 13½x14*

| | | | | |
|---|---|---|---|---|
| 759 | A282 | 100fr Breast-feeding | 1.00 | .50 |
| 760 | A282 | 100fr Oral rehydration therapy | 1.00 | .50 |
| 761 | A282 | 100fr Mother and child | 1.00 | .50 |
| 762 | A282 | 100fr Vaccination | 1.00 | .50 |
| | | *Nos. 759-762 (4)* | 4.00 | 2.00 |

UN 40th Anniv. — A283

**1985, Oct. 31**      *Perf. 13*

| | | | | |
|---|---|---|---|---|
| 763 | A283 | 100fr multicolored | 1.25 | .50 |

Admission to UN, 25th anniv.

World Wildlife Fund — A284

Striped antelopes.

**1985, Nov. 30**

| | | | | |
|---|---|---|---|---|
| 764 | A284 | 50fr multicolored | 7.00 | 1.00 |
| 765 | A284 | 60fr multicolored | 9.00 | 2.00 |
| 766 | A284 | 75fr multicolored | 18.00 | 3.00 |
| 767 | A284 | 100fr multicolored | 27.50 | 5.00 |
| | | *Nos. 764-767 (4)* | 61.50 | 11.00 |

City Skyline — A285

**1985, Nov. 21**    **Litho.**    *Perf. 13*

| | | | | |
|---|---|---|---|---|
| 768 | A285 | 125fr multicolored | 1.50 | .75 |

Expo '85 national industrial exhibition.

Return to the Land Campaign A286

Handicrafts A287

**1985, Dec. 7**      *Perf. 12½*

| | | | | |
|---|---|---|---|---|
| 769 | A286 | 125fr multicolored | 1.50 | .75 |

Natl. independence, 25th anniv.

Flowers — A286a

100fr, L'Amorphophallus staudtii. 125fr, Crinum scillifolium. 200fr, Triphyophyllum peltatum.

**1985, Dec. 28**    **Litho.**    *Perf. 14x15*

| | | | | |
|---|---|---|---|---|
| 769A | A286a | 100fr multi | 140.00 | 10.00 |
| 769B | A286a | 125fr multi | 140.00 | 10.00 |
| 769C | A286a | 200fr multi | 140.00 | 10.00 |
| | | *Nos. 769A-769C (3)* | 420.00 | 30.00 |

**1986, Jan.**      *Perf. 13½*

| | | | | |
|---|---|---|---|---|
| 770 | A287 | 125fr Spinning thread | 1.50 | .75 |
| 771 | A287 | 155fr Painting | 2.00 | 1.00 |

Flora — A288

Cooking Utensils, Natl. Museum, Abidjan — A289

**1986, Feb. 22**    **Litho.**    *Perf. 13½*

| | | | | |
|---|---|---|---|---|
| 772 | A288 | 40fr Omphalocarpum elatum | .50 | .20 |
| 773 | A288 | 50fr Momordica charantia | .60 | .25 |
| 774 | A288 | 125fr Millettia takou | 1.50 | 1.00 |
| 775 | A288 | 200fr Costus afer | 2.25 | 1.25 |
| | | *Nos. 772-775 (4)* | 4.85 | 2.70 |

**1986, Mar. 6**      *Perf. 13x12½, 12½x13*

| | | | | |
|---|---|---|---|---|
| 776 | A289 | 20fr We bowl | .20 | .20 |
| 777 | A289 | 30fr Baoule bowl | .30 | .20 |
| 778 | A289 | 90fr Baoule platter | 1.25 | .50 |
| 779 | A289 | 125fr Dan scoop | 1.40 | .75 |
| 780 | A289 | 440fr Baoule lidded pot | 5.00 | 2.50 |
| | | *Nos. 776-780 (5)* | 8.15 | 4.15 |

Nos. 776-778 horiz.

Natl. Pedagogic and Vocational School, 10th Anniv. — A290

**1986, Mar. 20**      *Perf. 13½*

| | | | | |
|---|---|---|---|---|
| 781 | A290 | 125fr multicolored | 1.50 | .60 |

Cable Ship Stephan, 1910 — A291

**1986, Apr. 12**    **Litho.**    *Perf. 12½*

| | | | | |
|---|---|---|---|---|
| 782 | A291 | 125fr multicolored | 2.25 | .60 |

Stamp Day.

**Houphouet-Boigny Type of 1974-76**

**1986, Apr.**    **Engr.**    *Perf. 13*

| | | | | |
|---|---|---|---|---|
| 783 | A112 | 5fr dk red, dp rose lil & brn | .20 | .20 |
| 784 | A112 | 10fr gray grn, brt bl & brn | .20 | .20 |
| 785 | A112 | 20fr brt ver, blk brn & brn | .20 | .20 |
| 786 | A112 | 25fr bl, dp rose lil & brn | .25 | .20 |
| 787 | A112 | 30fr brt ver, blk brn & brn | .25 | .20 |
| 789 | A112 | 50fr lake, dk vio & brn | .50 | .25 |
| 790 | A112 | 90fr dk brn vio, rose lake & brn | .90 | .40 |
| 791 | A112 | 125fr brt lil rose, brt ver & brn | 1.50 | .50 |
| 792 | A112 | 155fr dk brn vio, Prus bl & brn | 1.50 | .60 |
| | | *Nos. 783-792 (9)* | 5.50 | 2.75 |

The 1986 printing of the 40fr is in slightly darker colors than No. 374.

Natl. Youth and Sports Institute, 25th Anniv. — A293

**1986, May 9**    **Litho.**    *Perf. 12½*

| | | | | |
|---|---|---|---|---|
| 793 | A293 | 125fr brt org & dk yel grn | 1.50 | .60 |

Fish A294

5fr, Polypterus endlicheri. 125fr, Synodontis punctifer. 150fr, Protopterus annectens. 155fr, Synodontis koensis. 440fr, Malapterurus electricus.

**1986, July 5**    **Litho.**    *Perf. 14½x13½*

| | | | | |
|---|---|---|---|---|
| 794 | A294 | 5fr multi | .20 | .20 |
| 795 | A294 | 125fr multi | 1.50 | .60 |
| 796 | A294 | 150fr multi | 2.00 | .75 |
| 797 | A294 | 155fr multi | 2.10 | .75 |
| 798 | A294 | 440fr multi | 6.00 | 2.25 |
| | | *Nos. 794-798 (5)* | 11.80 | 4.55 |

Enthronement of a Chief, Agni District — A295

**1986, July 19**      *Perf. 13½x14½*

| | | | | |
|---|---|---|---|---|
| 799 | A295 | 50fr Drummer, vert. | .50 | .40 |
| 800 | A295 | 350fr Chief in litter | 4.00 | 2.00 |
| 801 | A295 | 440fr Royal entourage | 5.00 | 3.00 |
| | | *Nos. 799-801 (3)* | 9.50 | 5.40 |

Rural Houses — A296

**1986, Aug. 2**    **Litho.**    *Perf. 14x15*

| | | | | |
|---|---|---|---|---|
| 802 | A296 | 125fr Baoule aoulo | 1.40 | .60 |
| 803 | A296 | 155fr Upper Antiam eva | 1.75 | 1.00 |
| 804 | A296 | 350fr Lobi soukala | 3.75 | 1.75 |
| | | *Nos. 802-804 (3)* | 6.90 | 3.35 |

Coat of
Arms
A297

Coastal
Landscapes
A298

**1986-87      Engr.      Perf. 13**
807 A297 50fr bright org         .50 .25
808 A297 125fr dark green       1.50 .40
809 A297 155fr crimson          1.75 .40
810 A297 195fr blue ('87)       2.00 .40
   *Nos. 807-810 (4)*           5.75 1.45

Issue dates: 50fr, 125fr, 155fr, Aug. 23.

**Perf. 14x15, 15x14**
**1986, Aug. 30                Litho.**
820 A298 125fr Grand Bereby     1.75 .75
821 A298 155fr Sableux Boubele,
                horiz.          2.25 1.25

Oceanographic Research
Center — A299

**Perf. 14½x13½**
**1986, Sept. 13              Litho.**
822 A299 125fr Fishing grounds  1.40 .60
823 A299 155fr Net fishing      1.75 1.00

Intl. Peace
Year — A300

**1986, Oct. 16   Litho.   Perf. 14x13½**
824 A300 155fr multicolored     1.75 .75

Research and Development — A301

**1986, Nov. 15              Perf. 13½x14**
825 A301 125fr Bull            1.75 1.00
826 A301 155fr Wheat           1.75 1.00

Natl. Independence, 26th
Anniv. — A302

**1986, Dec. 6    Litho.    Perf. 13½x14**
827 A302 155fr multicolored    1.75 .75

Rural
Housing
A303

**1987, Mar. 14   Litho.   Perf. 13½x14**
828 A303 190fr Guesseple Dan    2.25 1.25
829 A303 550fr M'Bagui Senoufo  6.50 3.50

Stamp
Day — A304

Jean Mermoz
College, 25th
Anniv. — A305

**1987, Apr. 4              Perf. 13x13½**
830 A304 155fr Mailman, 1918    1.75 1.00

**1987, Apr. 9              Perf. 13**
831 A305 40fr Cock, elephant    .50 .25
832 A305 155fr Dove, children   1.75 .75

**Elephant Type of 1981**
**1987, Apr. 9**
833 A219 35fr multicolored      .50 .20

Fouilles, by Krah
N'Guessan
A306

Paintings by local artists: 500fr, Cortege
Ceremonial, by Santoni Gerard.

**1987, Aug. 14   Litho.   Perf. 14½x15**
841 A306 195fr multi           2.25 1.25
842 A306 500fr multi           5.50 3.50

World Post
Day,
Express
Mail
Service
A307

**1987, Oct. 9              Perf. 13½**
843 A307 155fr multi           1.75 1.00
844 A307 195fr multi           2.25 1.25

Intl. Trade
Cent.
A308

**1987, Oct. 24**
845 A308 155fr multi           1.75 1.00

A309

**1987, Dec. 5   Litho.   Perf. 14x13½**
846 A309 155fr multicolored    1.75 1.00
   Natl. Independence, 27th anniv.

A310

**1988, Feb. 20   Litho.   Perf. 14x13½**
847 A310 155fr multicolored    1.75 1.00
   Lions Club for child survival.

The
Modest
Canary,
by Monne
Bou
A311

Paintings by local artists: 20fr, The Couple,
by K.J. Houra, vert. 150fr, The Eternal Dance,
by Bou, vert. 155fr, La Termitiere, by Mathilde
Moro, vert. 195fr, The Sun of Independence,
by Michel Kodjo, vert.

**1988, Jan. 30   Perf. 12½x13, 13x12½**
848 A311 20fr multi            .30 .20
849 A311 30fr shown            .30 .20
850 A311 150fr multi           1.75 .75
851 A311 155fr multi           1.75 .75
852 A311 195fr multi           2.50 1.00
   *Nos. 848-852 (5)*          6.60 2.90

Stamp Day
A312

**1988, Apr. 4    Litho.    Perf. 13**
853 A312 155fr Bereby P.O., c.
                1900           1.75 1.00

A313

**1988, Apr. 18   Litho.   Perf. 15x14**
854 A313 195fr blk & dark red  2.75 1.75
   15th French-Language Nations Cardiology
Congress, Abidjan, Apr. 18-20.

A314

**1988, May 21   Litho.   Perf. 12x13**
855 A314 195fr multicolored    2.25 1.25
   Intl. Fund for Agricultural Development
(IFAD), 10th anniv.

1st Intl.
Day for the
Campaign
Against
Drug Abuse
and Drug
Trafficking
A315

**1988, Aug. 27   Litho.   Perf. 13½**
856 A315 155fr multi           2.00 1.25

Stone
Heads — A316

Natl.
Independence
28th
Anniv. — A318

World Post Day — A317

Various stone heads from the Niangoran-
Bouah Archaeological Collection.

**Litho. & Engr.**
**1988, July 9              Perf. 13x14½**
857 A316 5fr beige & sep       .25 .20
858 A316 10fr buff & sep       .25 .20
859 A316 30fr pale grn & sep   .30 .20
860 A316 155fr pale yel & sep  2.00 1.00
861 A316 195fr pale yel grn &
                sep            2.75 1.25
   *Nos. 857-861 (5)*          5.55 2.85

**1988, Oct. 15   Litho.   Perf. 14**
862 A317 155fr multi           1.75 1.00

**1988, Dec. 6              Perf. 11½x12**
Year of the Forest: 40fr, Healthy trees. No.
864, Stop forest fires. No. 865, Planting trees.

863 A318 40fr multi            .60 .25
864 A318 155fr multi           2.25 .90
865 A318 155fr multi           2.25 .90
   *Nos. 863-865 (3)*          5.10 2.05

History of
Money
A319

**1989, Feb. 25　Litho.　*Perf. 12x11½***
**Granite Paper**
866　A319　50fr shown　　　　　1.00　.25
867　A319　195fr Senegal bank
　　　　　　notes, 1854,
　　　　　　1901　　　　　　　2.75　1.25
　See Nos. 885-886, 896-898, 915. For surcharges see Nos. 904-905.

"Valeur
d'echange
0fr.25" on
25c Type
A5, 1920
A320

**1989, Apr.　　　　　　*Perf. 12½***
868　A320　155fr multi　　　　2.00　1.00
　　　　Stamp Day.

Jewelry
from the
National
Museum
Collection
A321

**1989, Mar. 25　Litho.　*Perf. 14***
869　A321　90fr Voltaic bracelets　1.25　.60
870　A321　155fr Anklets　　　　2.25　1.25

Sculptures
by
Christian
Lattier
A322

**　*Perf. 11½x12, 12x11½***
**1989, May 13　　　Granite Paper**
871　A322　40fr The Old Man and
　　　　　　the Infant, vert.　.50　.25
872　A322　155fr The Saxophone
　　　　　　Player, vert.　　2.00　1.00
873　A322　550fr The Panther　6.00　3.25
　　　Nos. 871-873 (3)　　　8.50　4.50

　For surcharge see No. 903.

Council for Rural Development, 30th
Anniv. — A323

**1989, May 29　　　　　*Perf. 15x14***
874　A323　75fr Flags, well, tractor,
　　　　　　field　　　　　1.25　.40
　　See Togo No. 1526.

Intl. Peace Congress — A324

**1989, June　Litho.　*Perf. 13***
875　A324　195fr multi　　　　2.25　1.00

Rural
Habitat
A325

**1989, June 10　Litho.　*Perf. 14***
876　A325　155fr Hut, Sirikukube
　　　　　　Dida　　　　　1.75　1.00
　For surcharge see No. 902.

Sekou Watara, King of Kong (1710-
1745) — A326

　Designs: No. 878, Bastille, Declaration of Human Rights and Citizenship.

**1989, July 7　Litho.　*Perf. 13***
877　A326　200fr shown　　　3.50　1.75
878　A326　200fr multi　　　　3.50　1.75
　a.　Pair, Nos. 877-878 + label　8.00　6.00

　PHILEXFRANCE '89, French revolution bicent.

Endangered Species — A327

**1989, Sept. 16　　　*Perf. 12x11½***
**Granite Paper**
879　A327　25fr Varanus niloticus　.50　.30
880　A327　100fr Crocodylus
　　　　　　niloticus　　　2.00　1.25

World Post
Day
A328

**1989, Oct. 9　Litho.　*Perf. 12½x13***
881　A328　195fr multi　　　　2.25　1.00

CAPTEAO,
30th Anniv.
A329

**1989, Oct. 28　Litho.　*Perf. 12½***
882　A329　155fr multicolored　2.00　1.00
　Conference of Postal and Telecommunication Administrations of West African Nations.

A330

A331

**1989, Dec. 7　　　　　*Perf. 13***
883　A330　155fr multicolored　1.75　1.00
　　Natl. independence, 29th anniv.

**1990, Jan. 18　Litho.　*Perf. 13***
884　A331　155fr multicolored　1.75　1.00
　　Pan-African Union, 10th anniv.

　History of Money Type of 1989
**1990, Mar. 17　Litho.　*Perf. 12x11½***
**Granite Paper**
885　A319　155fr 1923 25fr note　1.75　1.00
886　A319　195fr 1, 2, 5fr notes　3.00　1.50

Stamp Day
A332

**1990, Apr. 21　Litho.　*Perf. 13x12½***
887　A332　155fr Packet Africa　2.25　1.00

Multinational
Postal School,
20th
Anniv. — A333

**1990, May 31　　　　*Perf. 12½***
888　A333　155fr multicolored　1.75　.90

Rural
Village
A334

**1990, June 30　　　　*Perf. 14***
889　A334　155fr multicolored　1.75　.60

Intl.
Literacy
Year
A335

**1990, July 28　　　　*Perf. 15x14***
890　A335　195fr multicolored　2.25　1.00

Dedication of Basilica of Notre Dame
of Peace, Yamoussoukro — A336

**1990, Sept. 8　　　*Perf. 14½x13½***
891　A336　155fr shown　　　1.75　.80
892　A336　195fr Basilica, diff.　2.75　1.25

Visit of Pope John Paul II — A337

**1990, Sept. 9　　　　　*Perf. 13***
893　A337　500fr multicolored　6.00　3.00

World Post
Day — A338

**1990, Oct. 9　Litho.　*Perf. 14x15***
894　A338　195fr multicolored　4.00　1.50

Independence, 30th Anniv. — A339

**1990, Dec. 6　Litho.　*Perf. 13½x14½***
895　A339　155fr multicolored　2.25　.90

　History of Money Type of 1989
**1991, Mar. 1　Litho.　*Perf. 11½***
**Granite Paper**
896　A319　40fr French West Afri-
　　　　　　ca 1942 5fr,
　　　　　　100fr notes　　.55　.25
897　A319　155fr like #896　1.75　.85
898　A319　195fr French West Afri-
　　　　　　ca & Togo 50fr,
　　　　　　500fr notes　2.40　1.25
　　　Nos. 896-898 (3)　4.70　2.35
　For surcharges see Nos. 904-905.

Stamp Day
A340

**1991, May 18　Litho.　*Perf. 13½***
899　A340　150fr multicolored　1.75　.55

## Miniature Sheets of 9

French Open Tennis Championships, Cent. — A341

Tennis Players: No. 900a, Henri Cochet. b, Rene Lacoste. c, Jean Borotra. d, Don Budge. e, Marcel Bernard. f, Ken Rosewall. g, Rod Laver. h, Bjorn Borg. i, Yannick Noah.

No. 901a, Suzanne Lenglen. b, Helen Wills Moody. c, Simone Mathieu. d, Maureen Connolly. e, Francoise Durr. f, Margaret Court. g, Chris Evert. h, Martina Navratilova. i, Steffi Graf.

**1991, May 24   Litho.   Perf. 13½**
900 A341 200fr #a.-i.        22.50 22.50
901 A341 200fr #a.-i.        22.50 22.50

### Nos. 872, 876, 897-898 Surcharged

#### Perfs. as Before
**1991, July 15          Litho.**
902 A325 150fr on 155fr #876   1.75  .55
**Granite Paper**
903 A322 150fr on 155fr #897   1.75  .55
904 A319 150fr on 155fr #897   1.75  .65
905 A319 200fr on 195fr #898   2.25  .80
   Nos. 902-905 (4)            7.50 2.55

Location of obliterator and surcharge varies.

Packet Boats
A342

**1991, June 28   Litho.   Perf. 12x11½**
**Granite Paper**
906 A342 50fr Europe           .65  .25
907 A342 550fr Asia           6.00 3.00

World Post Day
A343

**1991, Oct. 9           Perf. 13**
908 A343 50fr shown            .65  .25
909 A343 100fr SIPE, globe    1.25  .50

Tribal Drums — A344

**1991      Litho.      Perf. 14x15**
910 A344 5fr We                .20  .20
911 A344 25fr Krou, Soubre region
                               .20  .20
912 A344 150fr Sinematiali    2.00 1.10
913 A344 200fr Akye, Alepe region
                              2.50 1.25
   Nos. 910-913 (4)           4.90 2.75

Independence, 31st Anniv. — A345

**1991, Dec. 7   Litho.   Perf. 13½x14½**
914 A345 150fr multicolored   2.25  .80

#### History of Money Type of 1989
**1991, Dec. 8          Perf. 12x11½**
**Granite Paper**
915 A319 100fr like #898      1.25  .70

Flowers
A346

Various flowers.

**1991, Dec. 20   Engr.   Perf. 13**
916 A346 150fr grn, blk & mag, vert.
                              1.75  .65
917 A346 200fr grn, olive & rose car
                              2.25  .85

African Soccer Championships — A347

Designs: 150fr, Elephants holding trophy, map, soccer ball, vert.

**1992, Apr. 22   Litho.   Perf. 13**
918 A347 20fr multicolored     .35  .25
919 A347 150fr multicolored   2.00 1.25

Animals
A348

**1992, May 5   Engr.   Perf. 13x12½**
920 A348 5fr Viverra civetta   .20  .20
921 A348 40fr Nandinia binotata .55  .20
922 A348 150fr Tragelaphus euryceros
                              2.25  .80
923 A348 500fr Panthera pardus 5.50 3.25
   Nos. 920-923 (4)           8.50 4.45

World Post Day — A349

**1992, Oct. 7          Litho.   Perf. 13**
924 A349 150fr black & blue   1.75  .80

First Ivory Coast Postage Stamp, Cent. — A350

Designs: a, #3. b, #197. b, #182, #909 with mail trucks, post office boxes.

**1992, Oct. 7**
925 A350 150fr Pair, #a.-b. + label
                              5.00 3.50

Funeral Monuments
A351

Various grave site monuments.

**1992, Dec. 30   Engr.   Perf. 13**
926 A351 5fr multicolored      .20  .20
927 A351 50fr multicolored     .75  .25
928 A351 150fr multicolored   1.75  .80
929 A351 400fr multicolored   4.25 1.75
   Nos. 926-929 (4)           6.95 3.00

Intl. Abidjan Marathon
A351a

**1992, Nov. 20   Litho.   Perf. 11½**
**Granite Paper**
929A A351a 150fr Flags, runners
                              1.25  .50
929B A351a 200fr Runners      2.50  .75
   Nos. 929A-929B were not available in the philatelic market until Apr. 1994.

Gold Mine of Ity, 1st Anniv. — A351b

32nd Anniv. of Independence
A351c

**1992, Nov. 8   Litho.   Perf. 14x15**
929C A351b 200fr multicolored 3.00 1.20
   No. 929C was not available in the philatelic market until Apr. 1994.

**1992, Dec. 4**
150fr, People, flag, Statue of Liberty, map.
929D A351c 30fr shown          .50  .35
929E A351c 150fr multicolored 2.25  .75
   Nos. 929D-929E were not available in the philatelic market until Apr. 1994.

Tourist Attractions — A351d

Environmental Summit — A351e

**Perf. 14x15, 15x14**
**1992, Sept. 4          Litho.**
929F A351d 10fr Modern hotel, horiz.  —  —
929G A351d 25fr Dent de Man    35.00  —
929H A351d 100fr Resort, horiz. 45.00  —
929I A351d 200fr Map of tourist sites
                               65.00  —

**Perf. 11½x12, 12x11½**
**1992, June 5          Litho.**
200fr, Prevent water pollution, horiz.
**Granite Paper**
929J A351e 150fr multicolored 70.00  —
929K A351e 200fr multicolored 70.00  —

Stamp Day
A352

Designs showing children interested in philately: No. 930, Girl, stamp collection, #169. No. 931, Girl, #431, #446B, #186, and #920. 150fr, Boy sitting under tree, stamp exhibition.

**1993, Apr. 17   Litho.   Perf. 13½**
930 A352 50fr multicolored     .55  .25
931 A352 50fr multicolored     .55  .25
932 A352 150fr multicolored   2.00  .75
   Nos. 930-932 (3)           3.10 1.25

A353                    A354

Medicinal plants.

**1993, May 14   Litho.   Perf. 11½x12**
**Granite Paper**
933 A353 5fr Argemone mexicana .35  .20
934 A353 20fr Hibiscus esculentus
                               .45  .20
935 A353 200fr Cassia alata   2.50 1.25
   Nos. 933-935 (3)           3.30 1.65

**1993, Aug. 27   Photo.   Perf. 12x11½**

Orchids: 10fr, Calyptrochilum emarginatum. 50fr, Plectrelminthus caudathus. 150fr, Eulophia guineensis.

**Granite Paper**
936 A354 10fr multicolored     .20  .20
937 A354 50fr multicolored     .40  .25
938 A354 150fr multicolored   1.75  .90
   Nos. 936-938 (3)           2.35 1.35

Ivory Coast Colony, Cent.
A355

25fr, Organization charter. 100fr, Colonial Governor Louis Gustave Binger, Pres. F. Houphouet-Boigny. 500fr, Natives selecting goods for trade.

**1993, Sept. 17**      *Perf. 13x12½*
| | | | | |
|---|---|---|---|---|
| 939 | A355 | 25fr green & black | .35 | .20 |
| 940 | A355 | 100fr blue & black | 1.25 | .75 |
| 941 | A355 | 500fr brown & black | 6.00 | 3.50 |
| | | *Nos. 939-941 (3)* | 7.60 | 4.45 |

Elimination Round of 1994 World Cup Soccer Championships, US — A356

Designs: 150fr, Cartoon soccer players. 200fr, Three players. 300fr, Two players. 400fr, Cartoon players, diff.

**1993, Sept. 24**    **Litho.**    *Perf. 14x15*
| | | | | |
|---|---|---|---|---|
| 942 | A356 | 150fr multicolored | 1.25 | .55 |
| 943 | A356 | 200fr multicolored | 2.25 | .85 |
| 944 | A356 | 300fr multicolored | 3.50 | 1.75 |
| 945 | A356 | 400fr multicolored | 4.50 | 2.50 |
| | | *Nos. 942-945 (4)* | 11.50 | 5.65 |

World Post Day
A357

Designs: 30fr, Map of Ivory Coast. 200fr, Post office, Bouake.

**1993, Oct. 9**      *Perf. 13x13½*
| | | | | |
|---|---|---|---|---|
| 946 | A357 | 30fr multicolored | .35 | .20 |
| 947 | A357 | 200fr multicolored | 2.40 | 1.25 |

African Biennial of Plastic Arts, Abidjan
A358

*Perf. 14½x13½*

**1993, Nov. 24**      **Litho.**
| | | | | |
|---|---|---|---|---|
| 948 | A358 | 200fr multicolored | 2.00 | 1.00 |

Independence, 33rd Anniv. — A359

**1993, Dec. 7**    **Litho.**    *Perf. 13½x13*
| | | | | |
|---|---|---|---|---|
| 950 | A359 | 200fr multicolored | 2.50 | 1.00 |

Pres. Felix Houphouet-Boigny (1905-93) — A360

Pres. Houphouet-Boigny and: Nos. 951a, 952a, 953a, Modern buildings, technology. Nos. 951b, 952b, 953b, Agriculture, shipping. Nos. 951c, 952c, 953c, Dove, rainbow, Presidential palace.

**1994, Feb. 5**    **Litho.**    *Perf. 13*
| | | | | |
|---|---|---|---|---|
| 951 | A360 | 150fr Strip of 3, #a.-c. | | |
| | | | 3.00 | 2.00 |
| 952 | A360 | 200fr Strip of 3, #a.-c. | | |
| | | | 4.00 | 3.00 |

**Souvenir Sheet**
**Perf. 12**
| | | | | |
|---|---|---|---|---|
| 953 | A360 | 500fr Sheet of 3, #a.-c. | | |
| | | | 12.00 | 12.00 |

Raoul Follereau, Campaign Against Leprosy
A361

**1994, Feb. 20**    **Litho.**    *Perf. 13*
| | | | | |
|---|---|---|---|---|
| 954 | A361 | 150fr multicolored | 1.25 | .50 |

RASCOM (Regional African Satellite Communications Organization), 1st Meeting, Abidjan — A362

**1994, Jan. 19**    **Litho.**    *Perf. 14x13*
| | | | | |
|---|---|---|---|---|
| 955 | A362 | 150fr multicolored | 1.25 | .40 |

Woman Carrying Basket — A363

**Litho. & Engr.**
**1994-95**      *Perf. 13½x13*
**Color of Border**
| | | | | |
|---|---|---|---|---|
| 956 | A363 | 5fr orange | .20 | .20 |
| 956A | A363 | 10fr green | .20 | .20 |
| 956B | A363 | 20fr red | .20 | .20 |
| 957 | A363 | 25fr blue | .20 | .20 |
| 957A | A363 | 30fr olive bister | .20 | .20 |
| 958 | A363 | 40fr yellow green | .20 | .20 |
| 959 | A363 | 50fr brown | .25 | .20 |
| 960 | A363 | 75fr lilac rose | .30 | .20 |
| 961 | A363 | 150fr bright green | .70 | .35 |
| 961A | A363 | 180fr pale lake | .95 | .50 |
| 961B | A363 | 280fr gray | 1.40 | .70 |
| 962 | A363 | 300fr violet | 1.40 | .70 |
| | | *Nos. 956-962 (12)* | 6.20 | 3.85 |

Issued: 30fr, 180fr, 280fr, 5/16/95, dated 1994; others, 11/4/94.

Stained Glass Windows, Basilica of Notre Dame of Peace, Yamoussoukro
A364

Designs: 25fr, Christ, world map. 150fr, Christ, fishermen. 200fr, Madonna and Child. 600fr, Aerial view of Cathedral, Yamoussoukro.

**1994, Nov. 18**    **Litho.**    *Perf. 14*
| | | | | |
|---|---|---|---|---|
| 963 | A364 | 25fr lilac rose & multi | .35 | .20 |
| 964 | A364 | 150fr pale orange & multi | 1.25 | .60 |
| 965 | A364 | 200fr yellow & mulit | 1.40 | .80 |
| | | *Nos. 963-965 (3)* | 3.00 | 1.60 |

**Souvenir Sheet**
| | | | | |
|---|---|---|---|---|
| 966 | A364 | 600fr multicolored | 5.00 | 5.00 |

Natl. Independence, 34th Anniv. — A365

**1994, Dec. 6**    **Litho.**    *Perf. 12*
| | | | | |
|---|---|---|---|---|
| 967 | A365 | 150fr multicolored | 1.00 | .40 |

Snakes
A366

Designs: 10fr, Python regius. 20fr, Philothamnus semivariegatus. 100fr, Dendroaspis veridis. 180fr, Bitis arietans. 500fr, Bitis nasicornis.

**1995, June 23**    **Litho.**    *Perf. 13*
| | | | | |
|---|---|---|---|---|
| 968 | A366 | 10fr multicolored | .20 | .20 |
| 969 | A366 | 20fr multicolored | .20 | .20 |
| 970 | A366 | 100fr multicolored | .65 | .25 |
| 971 | A366 | 180fr multicolored | 1.40 | .75 |
| 972 | A366 | 500fr multicolored | 3.00 | 1.50 |
| | | *Nos. 968-972 (5)* | 5.45 | 2.90 |

FAO, 50th Anniv. — A367      UN, 50th Anniv. — A368

**1995, Aug. 4**    **Litho.**    *Perf. 11½*
| | | | | |
|---|---|---|---|---|
| 973 | A367 | 100fr multicolored | 1.00 | .35 |
| 974 | A368 | 280fr multicolored | 2.75 | .75 |

Mushrooms
A369

Designs: 30fr, Lentinus tuber-regium. 50fr, Volvariella volvacea. 180fr, Dictyophora indusiata. 250fr, Termitomyces schimperi.

**1995, Sept. 8**      *Perf. 14x13½*
| | | | | |
|---|---|---|---|---|
| 975 | A369 | 30fr multicolored | .50 | .35 |
| 976 | A369 | 50fr multicolored | .90 | .70 |
| 977 | A369 | 180fr multicolored | 2.75 | 1.00 |
| 978 | A369 | 250fr multicolored | 3.00 | 2.00 |
| a. | | Block of 4, #975-978 | 8.50 | 6.00 |

#978a was issued in sheets of 16 stamps.

Louis Pasteur (1822-95)
A370

**1995, Sept. 28**      *Perf. 11½*
| | | | | |
|---|---|---|---|---|
| 979 | A370 | 280fr multicolored | 1.75 | .75 |

School Philatelic Clubs
A371

**1995, Oct. 6**      *Perf. 13½*
| | | | | |
|---|---|---|---|---|
| 980 | A371 | 50fr GSR | .65 | .20 |
| 981 | A371 | 180fr LBP | 2.00 | .80 |

Butterflies
A371a

180fr, Pala decius. 280fr, Papilio dardanus. 550fr, Papilio menestheus.

**1995**    **Litho.**    *Perf. 15x14*
| | | | | |
|---|---|---|---|---|
| 981A | A371a | 180fr multicolored | 12.00 | 1.00 |
| 981B | A371a | 280fr multicolored | 17.50 | 1.50 |
| 981C | A371a | 550fr multicolored | 22.50 | 2.50 |
| | | *Nos. 981A-981C (3)* | 52.00 | 5.00 |

Transportation in Abidjan — A372

Designs: 180fr, People pushing, pulling cart of grain, automobiles, bus on street. 280fr, People getting into bus in middle of traffic.

**1996, May 24**      *Perf. 13½*
| | | | | |
|---|---|---|---|---|
| 982 | A372 | 180fr multicolored | 1.25 | .60 |
| 983 | A372 | 280fr multicolored | 2.00 | 1.00 |

Fish
A373

Designs: 50fr, Heterotis niloticus. 180fr, Auchenoglanis occidentalis. 700fr, Schilbe mandibularis.

**1996, June**
| | | | | |
|---|---|---|---|---|
| 984 | A373 | 50fr multicolored | .40 | .30 |
| 985 | A373 | 180fr multicolored | 1.25 | .75 |
| 986 | A373 | 700fr multicolored | 5.00 | 2.50 |
| | | *Nos. 984-986 (3)* | 6.65 | 3.55 |

A374

A375

Orchids: 40fr, Cyrtorchis arcuata. 100fr, Eulophia horsfalii. 180fr, Eulophidium maculatum. 200fr, Ansellia africana.

**1996, July 12    Litho.    Perf. 13½x13**
| | | | | |
|---|---|---|---|---|
| 987 | A374 | 40fr multicolored | .40 | .30 |
| 988 | A374 | 100fr multicolored | 1.00 | .75 |
| 989 | A374 | 180fr multicolored | 2.00 | 1.25 |
| 990 | A374 | 200fr multicolored | 2.00 | 1.25 |
| | | Nos. 987-990 (4) | 5.40 | 3.55 |

**1996, Nov. 19**
| | | | | |
|---|---|---|---|---|
| 991 | A375 | 200fr Boxing | 1.25 | .60 |
| 992 | A375 | 280fr Running | 2.00 | 1.00 |
| 993 | A375 | 400fr Long jump | 2.50 | 1.25 |
| 994 | A375 | 500fr Natl. Olympic Committee emblem | 3.25 | 1.75 |
| | | Nos. 991-994 (4) | 9.00 | 4.60 |

1996 Summer Olympic Games, Atlanta.

Carved Canes
A376

180fr, Cane of Birifor hunter. 200fr, Cane of Chief Lobi. 280fr, Cane of Chief Lobi (Gbobéri).

**1996, Sept. 20    Litho.    Perf. 11½**
| | | | | |
|---|---|---|---|---|
| 995 | A376 | 180fr black & green | 1.25 | .60 |
| 996 | A376 | 200fr black & org yel | 1.25 | .70 |
| 997 | A376 | 280fr black & lilac | 2.00 | 1.00 |
| | | Nos. 995-997 (3) | 4.50 | 2.30 |

Water Flowers
A377

Designs: 50fr, Nelumbo nucifera. 180fr, Nymphea lotus. 280fr, Nymphea capensis. 700fr, Nymphea alba.

**1997, June 20    Litho.    Perf. 13½x14**
| | | | | |
|---|---|---|---|---|
| 998 | A377 | 50fr multicolored | .30 | .25 |
| 999 | A377 | 180fr multicolored | 1.25 | .60 |
| 1000 | A377 | 280fr multicolored | 2.00 | 1.00 |
| 1001 | A377 | 700fr multicolored | 4.50 | 2.50 |
| | | Nos. 998-1001 (4) | 8.05 | 4.35 |

Basilica of Our Lady of Peace, Yamoussoukro — A378

a, 180fr, Pres. Felix Houphouet-Boigny, exterior view of basilica. b, 200fr, Interior view. c, 280fr, Aerial view, Pope John Paul II.

**1997, July 8    Litho.    Perf. 13**
| | | | | |
|---|---|---|---|---|
| 1002 | A378 | Strip of 3, #a.-c. | 5.00 | 4.00 |

Traditional Jewelry — A379

Various beaded necklaces.

**1997, Aug. 22    Perf. 11½**
| | | | | |
|---|---|---|---|---|
| 1003 | A379 | 50fr plum & black | .35 | .25 |
| 1004 | A379 | 100fr plum & black | .75 | .50 |
| 1005 | A379 | 180fr plum & black | 1.25 | .75 |
| | | Nos. 1003-1005 (3) | 2.35 | 1.50 |

A379a

**1997, Oct. 10    Litho.    Perf. 11½**
**Granite Paper**
| | | | | |
|---|---|---|---|---|
| 1006 | A379a | 100fr red & multi | .65 | .25 |
| 1007 | A379a | 180fr blue & multi | 1.25 | .75 |
| 1008 | A379a | 500fr green & multi | 3.00 | 1.50 |
| | | Nos. 1006-1008 (3) | 4.90 | 2.50 |

A380

Various stone heads of Gohitafla.

**1997, Nov. 28    Perf. 13½**
Work tools: 180fr, Pulley. 280fr, Comb. 300fr, Navette, horiz.
| | | | | |
|---|---|---|---|---|
| 1009 | A380 | 180fr orange & multi | 1.25 | .50 |
| 1010 | A380 | 280fr green & multi | 1.75 | .75 |
| 1011 | A380 | 300fr blue & multi | 1.75 | .75 |
| | | Nos. 1009-1011 (3) | 4.75 | 2.00 |

Endangered Species
A381

Designs: 180fr, African manatee. 280fr, Jentink's duiker. 400fr, Kob antelope.

**1997, Dec. 19    Photo.    Perf. 11½**
| | | | | |
|---|---|---|---|---|
| 1012 | A381 | 180fr multicolored | 1.75 | 1.00 |
| 1013 | A381 | 280fr multicolored | 1.75 | 1.00 |
| 1014 | A381 | 400fr multicolored | 2.50 | 1.25 |
| | | Nos. 1012-1014 (3) | 6.00 | 3.25 |

1998 World Cup Soccer Championships, France — A382

Paris landmarks in background and: 180fr, Player, ball depicted with angry face. 280fr, Flags of nations inside outline of player. 400fr, Player taking shot on goal. 500fr, Two players, mascot, vert.

**Perf. 13x13½, 13½x13**
**1998, June 5    Litho.**
| | | | | |
|---|---|---|---|---|
| 1015 | A382 | 180fr multicolored | 1.25 | .60 |
| 1016 | A382 | 280fr multicolored | 1.75 | 1.00 |
| 1017 | A382 | 400fr multicolored | 2.50 | 1.25 |
| 1018 | A382 | 500fr multicolored | 3.00 | 1.25 |
| | | Nos. 1015-1018 (4) | 8.50 | 4.10 |

Mushrooms
A383

Endemic Plants — A384

50fr, Agaricus bingensis. 180fr, Lactarius gymnocarpus. 280fr, Termitomyces le testui.

**1998, June 26    Litho.    Perf. 13½x13**
| | | | | |
|---|---|---|---|---|
| 1019 | A383 | 50fr multicolored | .65 | .40 |
| 1020 | A383 | 180fr multicolored | 1.50 | 1.00 |
| 1021 | A383 | 280fr multicolored | 2.25 | 1.25 |
| | | Nos. 1019-1021 (3) | 4.40 | 2.65 |

See No. B20A.

**1998, July 10    Perf. 12**
Designs: 40fr, Hutchinsonia barbata. 100fr, Synsepalum aubrevillei. 180fr, Cola lorougnonis.

**Granite Paper**
| | | | | |
|---|---|---|---|---|
| 1022 | A384 | 40fr multicolored | .45 | .20 |
| 1023 | A384 | 100fr multicolored | .90 | .50 |
| 1024 | A384 | 180fr multicolored | 1.25 | .75 |
| | | Nos. 1022-1024 (3) | 2.60 | 1.45 |

Traditional Costumes from Grand-Bassam Museum — A385

**1998, Nov. 13    Litho.    Perf. 13½x13**
| | | | | |
|---|---|---|---|---|
| 1025 | A385 | 180fr Tapa | 1.25 | .75 |
| 1026 | A385 | 280fr Raffia | 1.75 | 1.25 |

Trains of Africa
A386

180fr, South African Railway, 1918. 280fr, Garret 2-8-2+2-8-2 Beyer Peacock, 1925. 500fr, Cecil Rhodes.

**1999, Feb. 26    Litho.    Perf. 13½**
| | | | | |
|---|---|---|---|---|
| 1027 | A386 | 180fr multicolored | 1.25 | .75 |
| 1028 | A386 | 280fr multicolored | 2.00 | 1.25 |
| | **Souvenir Sheet** | | | |
| 1029 | A386 | 500fr multicolored | 2.50 | 2.50 |

See No. B20B.

PhilexFrance '99, World Philatelic Exhibition — A387

Animals: 180fr+20fr, Loxodonta africana. 250fr, Syncerus caffer. 280fr, Pan troglodytes. 400fr, Cercopithecus aethiops.

**1999, July 2    Litho.    Perf. 13x13¼**
| | | | | |
|---|---|---|---|---|
| 1030 | A387 | 180fr +20fr multi | 1.75 | 1.25 |
| 1031 | A387 | 250fr multicolored | 1.75 | 1.25 |
| 1032 | A387 | 280fr multicolored | 1.90 | 1.25 |
| 1033 | A387 | 400fr multicolored | 2.50 | 1.75 |
| | | Nos. 1030-1033 (4) | 7.90 | 5.50 |

UPU, 125th Anniv. A388

UPU emblem and: 180fr+20fr, Carved heads. 280fr, Methods of delivering mail.

**1999, June 25    Perf. 11¾x11½**
| | | | | |
|---|---|---|---|---|
| 1034 | A388 | 180fr +20fr multi | 1.25 | .75 |
| 1035 | A388 | 280fr multicolored | 1.75 | 1.25 |

Flowers
A389

Ahouakro Rock Formations
A390

Designs: 100fr, Ancistrochilus rothschilianus. 180fr+20fr, Brachycorythis pubescens. 200fr, Bulbophyllum barbigerum. 280fr, Habenaria macrandra.

**1999, July 27    Litho.    Perf. 13¼x13**
| | | | | |
|---|---|---|---|---|
| 1036 | A389 | 100fr multicolored | .60 | .35 |
| 1037 | A389 | 180fr +20fr multi | 1.60 | 1.25 |
| 1038 | A389 | 200fr multicolored | 1.60 | 1.25 |
| 1039 | A389 | 280fr multicolored | 2.00 | 1.25 |
| | | Nos. 1036-1039 (4) | 5.80 | 4.10 |

**Perf. 13¼x14, 14x13¼**
**1999, Aug. 6    Litho.**
Various rock formations.
| | | | | |
|---|---|---|---|---|
| 1040 | A390 | 180fr +20fr multi, horiz. | 1.75 | .75 |
| 1041 | A390 | 280fr multi, horiz. | 1.75 | 1.00 |
| 1042 | A390 | 400fr multi | 2.50 | 1.75 |
| | | Nos. 1040-1042 (3) | 6.00 | 3.50 |

PhilexFrance 99 — A391

**1999, July 2    Litho.    Perf. 13**
| | | | | |
|---|---|---|---|---|
| 1043 | A391 | 280fr multicolored | 4.00 | 4.00 |

No. 1043 has a holographic image. Soaking in water may affect hologram.

Birds — A392

Designs: 50fr, Oriolus auratus. 180fr + 20fr, Nectarinia cinnyris venusta. 280fr, Trenon vinago australis. 300fr, Psittacus eithacus.

**1999, Oct. 29　Litho.　Perf. 13¼x13**
| | | | |
|---|---|---|---|
| 1044 | A392 | 50fr multi | .45 | .25 |
| 1045 | A392 | 180fr + 20fr multi | 1.50 | 1.00 |
| 1046 | A392 | 280fr multi | 2.25 | 1.25 |
| 1047 | A392 | 300fr multi | 2.25 | 1.25 |
| | | Nos. 1044-1047 (4) | 6.45 | 3.75 |

Fish A393

Designs: 100fr, Synodontis schall. 180fr + 20fr, Chromidotilapia guntheri. 280fr, Distichodus rostratus.

**1999, Nov. 19　　　　Perf. 13½x13¼**
| | | | |
|---|---|---|---|
| 1048 | A393 | 100fr multi | .75 | .35 |
| 1049 | A393 | 180fr +20fr multi | 1.50 | 1.00 |
| 1050 | A393 | 280fr multi | 2.25 | 1.50 |
| | | Nos. 1048-1050 (3) | 4.50 | 2.85 |

Challenges for Ivory Coast in Third Millennium — A394

Designs: 100fr, Education. 180fr +20fr, Agriculture. 200fr, Industry. 250fr, Information. 280fr, Peace. 400fr, Culture.

**1999, Dec. 10　　　　Perf. 13½x13¾**
| | | | |
|---|---|---|---|
| 1051 | A394 | 100fr multi | .65 | .35 |
| 1052 | A394 | 180fr +20fr multi | 1.25 | .75 |
| 1053 | A394 | 200fr multi | 1.25 | .75 |
| 1054 | A394 | 250fr multi | 1.50 | 1.00 |
| 1055 | A394 | 280fr multi | 1.50 | 1.00 |
| 1056 | A394 | 400fr multi | 1.75 | 1.75 |
| | | Nos. 1051-1056 (6) | 7.90 | 5.60 |

Native Masks A395

**Perf. 13½x13¼, 13¼x13½**
**2000, June 30　　　　　　　　Litho.**
| | | | |
|---|---|---|---|
| 1057 | A395 | 30fr Wambélé | .35 | .20 |
| 1058 | A395 | 180fr +20fr Djè | 1.25 | .80 |
| 1059 | A395 | 400fr Korobla, vert. | 2.25 | 1.75 |
| | | Nos. 1057-1059 (3) | 3.85 | 2.75 |

Edible Plants — A396

Designs: 30fr, Blighia sapida. 180fr+20fr, Ricinodendron heudelotii. 300fr, Telfaira occidentalis. 400fr, Napoleonaea vogelii.

**2000, July 14　　　Perf. 13¼x13½**
| | | | |
|---|---|---|---|
| 1060 | A396 | 30fr multi | .35 | .20 |
| 1061 | A396 | 180fr +20fr multi | 1.40 | .80 |
| 1062 | A396 | 300fr multi | 1.75 | 1.25 |
| 1063 | A396 | 400fr multi | 2.25 | 2.00 |
| | | Nos. 1060-1063 (4) | 5.75 | 4.25 |

Pres. Robert Guei, Elephant, Map and Dove — A397

**2000, Aug. 4　　　　Perf. 13¾x13¼**
| | | | |
|---|---|---|---|
| 1064 | A397 | 180fr +20fr red & multi | 1.25 | .80 |
| 1065 | A397 | 400fr yel & multi | 2.50 | 1.75 |

Independence, 40th anniv., coup d'etat of Robert Guei.

Cacao — A398

Frame colors: 5fr, Dark blue green. 10fr, Light brown. 20fr, Claret. 25fr, Blue. 30fr, Greenish black. 40fr, Cerise. 50fr, Golden brown. 100fr, Brown. 180fr+20fr, Orange. 300fr, Blue violet. 350fr, Prussian blue. 400fr, Emerald. 600fr, Olive green.

**Perf. 11½x11¾**
**2000, Aug. 25　　　　　　　　Photo.**
**Granite Paper**
| | | | |
|---|---|---|---|
| 1066-1078 | A398 | Set of 13 | 10.00 | 7.00 |

National Lottery, 30th Anniv. — A399

Denominations: 180fr+20fr, 400fr.

**2000, Aug. 30　Litho.　Perf. 13¼x13**
| | | | |
|---|---|---|---|
| 1079-1080 | A399 | Set of 2 | 3.50 | 2.50 |

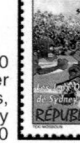

2000 Summer Olympics, Sydney A400

Designs: 180fr+20fr, Soccer. 400fr, Kangaroo. 600fr, Runners. 750fr, Bird over stadium.

**2000, Sept. 8　　　　Perf. 13½x13¼**
| | | | |
|---|---|---|---|
| 1081-1084 | A400 | Set of 4 | 12.00 | 9.00 |

Hairstyles — A401

Various hairstyles: 180fr+20fr, 300fr, 400fr, 500fr.

**2000, Sept. 22　　　Perf. 13¾x13¼**
| | | | |
|---|---|---|---|
| 1085-1088 | A401 | Set of 4 | 8.50 | 6.50 |

Release of Nelson Mandela, 10th Anniv. — A402

**2000, Oct. 6　Photo.　Perf. 12x11¾**
| | | | |
|---|---|---|---|
| 1089 | A402 | 300fr multi | 1.75 | 1.25 |

Historic Monuments A403

Designs: 180fr+20fr, Queen Pokou. 400fr, Akwaba. 600fr, Invocation of the Spirits.

**2000, Nov. 10　Litho.　Perf. 13½x13**
| | | | |
|---|---|---|---|
| 1090-1092 | A403 | Set of 3 | 7.00 | 6.00 |

UN High Commisioner for Refugees, 50th Anniv. — A404

**2000, Dec. 8　Photo.　Perf. 11¾x12**
| | | | |
|---|---|---|---|
| 1093 | A404 | 400fr multi | 2.50 | 1.75 |

Abokouamekro Animal Park — A405

Designs: 50fr, Cattle. 100fr, Rhinoceroses. 180fr+20fr, Rhinoceros. 400fr+20fr, Cattle.

**2001, May 14　Litho.　Perf. 13½x13¼**
| | | | |
|---|---|---|---|
| 1094-1097 | A405 | Set of 4 | 5.00 | 3.00 |

Sculpted Columns in National Museum — A406

Designs: 100fr, Alingué, Wouo Anouman. 180fr+20fr, Blolo Bian, Blolo B1a. 300fr+20fr, Botoumo. 400fr+20fr, Odi Oka.

**2001, June 18　　　　Perf. 13¼x13**
| | | | |
|---|---|---|---|
| 1098-1101 | A406 | Set of 4 | 5.00 | 5.00 |

Elimination Rounds for World Cup Soccer Championships — A407

Various soccer plays: 180fr + 20fr, 400fr + 20fr, 600fr + 20fr, 700fr.

**2001, Aug. 21　Litho.　Perf. 13x13¼**
| | | | |
|---|---|---|---|
| 1102-1105 | A407 | Set of 4 | 10.00 | 10.00 |

The following items inscribed "Republique de Cote d'Ivoire" have been declared "illegal" by Ivory Coast postal authorities:

Sheets of nine 100fr stamps: Marilyn Monroe (2 different).

Sheets of six 100fr stamps: Shells and Rotary emblem (2 different), Dogs and Scouting emblem (2 different), Butterflies and Scouting emblem (2 different), Orchids (2 different), Motorbike races and Rotary emblem (2 different), Table tennis players (2 different), Old fire engines (2 different), Elvis Presley (2 different), Marilyn Monroe, Pope John Paul II.

Sheets of six stamps: Trains (4 different).

Souvenir sheets of one stamp: Trains (4 different).

Sheet of ten 200fr Stamps: Birds.

Sheets of nine stamps of various denominations: Japanese Women, Earle K. Bergey, Julie Bell, Michael Möbius, Nudes.

Sheet of eight stamps of various denominations: Nature Conservancy.

Sheets of eight 300fr stamps: Owls and Mushrooms, Lighthouses and Penguins.

Sheets of eight 100fr stamps: Anthony Hopkins, Ben Affleck, Eminem.

Sheets of six stamps of various denominations: Spirited Away, Nature Conservancy, Nudes

Sheets of six 500fr stamps: History of World Aircraft (5 different), Red Cross and Rotary emblem, Japanese Women, Actresses, Women Tennis Players, Marilyn Monroe.

Sheet of six 450fr stamps: The Lord of the Rings.

Sheets of six 400fr stamps: Beatles (2 different).

Sheets of six 350fr stamps: Uniforms of World War II (5 different).

Sheets of Six 300fr stamps: Harry Potter (3 different), Fire Engines (2 different), Owls and Mushrooms.

Sheets of six 200fr stamps: Dogs and Scouting emblem, Lighthouses and Rotary emblem.

Sheets of six 100fr stamps: Pope John Paul II, Celine Dion, Pierce Brosnan, Classic Automobiles.

Sheets of four 100fr stamps: AC/DC, Backstreet Boys, Bee Gees, Beatles, Doors, Freddie Mercury, KISS, Madonna, Metallica, Queen, Rolling Stones.

Sheets of three stamps of various denominations: Nature Conservancy (2 different), Fairy Tales, Fantasy Tales, Dinosaurs, Steam Railways.

Sheet of two 1000fr stamps: Pope John Paul II.

Sheets of Two 500fr stamps: Nature Conservancy, Mother Teresa and Pope John Paul II.

Sheets of two 250fr stamps: Pope John Paul II (3 different).

Souvenir sheets of one 1000fr stamp: Dinosaurs, Fish, Owl and Scouting emblem.

Souvenir sheets of one 500fr stamp: Snow White, Nature Conservancy, Pope John Paul II.

Souvenir sheets of one 300fr stamp: Harry Potter (2 different).

Souvenir sheets of one 250fr stamp: Disney Cartoons and Scouting emblem (10 different).

Souvenir sheets of one 150fr stamp: Fire Engines and Scouting emblem (5 different).

Souvenir sheets of one 100fr stamp: Sorayama (5 different), Locomotives (2 different).

Korhogo Art
A408

Designs: 100fr, Shown. 180fr+20fr, Hunters and wildlife. 400fr+20fr, Painter, vert.

**2001, Nov. 27   Litho.   Perf. 14**
1106-1108  A408   Set of 3   4.00 4.00

A409

2002 World Cup Soccer Championships, Japan and Korea — A410

Design: 300fr+20fr, Caricatures of soccer players in action, horiz.

**Perf. 13¾, 13x13¼ (#1110), 13¼x13 (#1112)**

**2002, June 6   Litho.**
1109  A409  180fr +20fr grn &
              multi        1.25 1.25
1110  A410  300fr +20fr multi  2.25 2.25
1111  A409  400fr + 20fr red &
              multi        2.75 2.75
       Complete booklet, 10 #1111  30.00 30.00
1112  A410  600fr +20fr shown  4.00 4.00

**Souvenir Sheet**
1113  A409  500fr red & multi  3.50 3.50

Ivory Coast — People's Republic of China Diplomatic Relations, 20th Anniv.
A411

**2003, July 9   Litho.   Perf. 12**
1114  A411  180fr grn & multi  1.00 1.00
1115  A411  400fr org & multi  2.00 2.00
1116  A411  650fr red & multi  3.50 3.50
       Nos. 1114-1116 (3)        6.50

Sculpted Columns in Museum of Civilizations
A412

Designs: 20fr, Alinguè Bia column. 100fr, Laliè column. 180fr+20fr, Tre Ni Tre column. 300fr+20fr, Golikplé-Kplé column.

**2003, Nov. 27   Litho.   Perf. 13½x13**
1117  A412  20fr multi      .20   .20
1118  A412  100fr multi     .50   .50
1119  A412  180fr +20fr shown  1.00 1.00
1120  A412  300fr +20fr multi  1.50 1.50
       Nos. 1117-1120 (4)        3.20

Paintings by Unknown Artists — A413

Designs: 50fr, Au Revoir. 100fr, Ballet. 250fr, Le Chef, horiz. 500fr, Ligne de Main, horiz. 825fr, Appel, horiz.

**Perf. 13¼x13, 13x13¼**

**2004, June 15   Litho.**
1121-1125  A413  Set of 5   — —

Independence, 44th Anniv. — A414

Denominations: 100fr, 250fr.

**2004, Aug. 7   Perf. 13¼x13**
1126-1127  A414  Set of 2   — —

2004 Summer Olympics, Athens
A415

Designs: 50fr, Sprint race. 100fr, Greco-Roman wrestling, vert. 250fr, Torch bearer, vert. 825fr, Discus throw, vert.

**Perf. 13x13¼, 13¼x13**

**2004, Aug. 13**
1128-1131  A415   Set of 4   — —

National Reconciliation
A416

**2004, Sept. 28   Litho.   Perf. 13¼x13**
1132  A416  50fr shown   — —
   An additional stamp was released in this set. The editors would like to examine it.

Promotion of Women
A417

**2004, Nov. 26   Litho.   Perf. 14x13½**
1134  A417  250fr multi   — —

Molothrus Bonariensis
A418

**Perf. 14¼x13½**

**2004, Dec. 22   Litho.**
1135  A418  50fr multi   —

Tenth General Assembly of African Organization of Supreme Audit Institutions
A421

Frame color: 250fr, Blue. 350fr, Purple.

**2005, July 18   Litho.   Perf. 13¼**
1139-1140  A421  Set of 2   — —

"Culture and Excellence" — A422

Designs: 100fr, Dan spoon. 250fr, Sénoufo cane, vert.

**2005, July 25   Perf. 13x13½, 13½x13**
1141-1142  A422  Set of 2   — —

World Summit on the Information Society, Tunis — A423

Frame color: 30fr, Red. 220fr, Green.

**2005, Sept. 28   Perf. 13¼**
1143-1144  A423  Set of 2   — —

Women's Hairstyles
A424

Various hairstyles: 70fr, 100fr, 250fr, 350fr.

**2005, Nov. 3**
1145-1148  A424  Set of 4   — —

Kings and Chiefs — A425

Designs: 30fr, Tchaman chief standing. 70fr, Tchaman chief, diff. 80fr, Yacouba, Baoulé

and Abron chiefs, horiz. 250fr, Akan king and staff-bearer, horiz.

**2005, Nov. 22**
1149-1152  A425  Set of 4   —

Masks — A426

Designs: 70fr, Dan. 220fr, Gu. 250fr, Zamblé.

**2005, Dec. 22**
1153-1155  A426  Set of 3   — —

Europa Stamps, 50th Anniv. (in 2006) — A427

Map of Ivory Coast and: 30fr, Corn and map of Ireland. 70fr, Rubber tree and map of Germany. 80fr, Cotton plant and map of Poland. 220fr, Bananas and map of Netherlands. 250fr, Pineapple and map of Czech Republic. 350fr, Cacao and map of Belgium. 400fr, Sweet potatoes and map of Great Britain. 650fr, Coffee beans and map of Italy. 1000fr, Peanuts and map of Portugal. 2775fr, Palm nut and map of Spain.

**2005, Dec. 23   Litho.   Perf. 13¼**
1156-1165  A427  Set of 10  22.00 22.00
1160a       Miniature sheet, #1156-
              1160          2.40 2.40
1165a       Miniature sheet, #1161-
              1165          19.50 19.50
1165b       Miniature sheet, #1156-
              1165          22.00 22.00

Coffee Branches, Flowers and Cherries — A428

Designs: 220fr, Coffea arabusta. 250fr, Coffea liberica.

**2005, Dec. 28   Litho.   Perf. 13¼**
1166-1167  A428  Set of 2   — —

Endangered Plants — A430

Designs: 70fr, Monosalpinx guillaumetii. 80fr, Monanthotaxis capea. 100fr, Okoubaka aubrevillei.

**2005, Dec. 28   Litho.   Perf. 13¼**
1171  A430  70fr multi    — —
1172  A430  80fr multi    — —
1173  A430  100fr multi   — —

   An additional stamp was released in this set. The editors would like to examine any examples.

Urban Transportation — A431

Designs: 30fr, Buses, automobiles, ferry. 80fr, Buses, automobiles, ferry, diff.

**2005, Dec. 29**    Litho.    **Perf. 13¼**
1174-1175 A431 Set of 2    — —

Léopold Sédar Senghor (1906-2001), First President of Senegal — A432

Denominations: 50fr, 250fr.

**2006, Mar. 20**    Litho.    **Perf. 13½**
1176-1177 A432 Set of 2    2.40 2.40

## SEMI-POSTAL STAMPS

No. 47 Surcharged in Red

**1915**    Unwmk.    **Perf. 14x13½**
B1   A5   10c + 5c    1.60   1.60
   *a.*   Double surcharge    75.00 75.00

Issued on ordinary and chalky paper.

### Curie Issue
Common Design Type
**1938**    **Perf. 13**
B2   CD80   1.75fr + 50c brt ultra    10.00 9.00

### French Revolution Issue
Common Design Type
**1939**    **Photo.**
**Name and Value Typo. in Black**
B3   CD83   45c + 25c grn    8.00 8.00
B4   CD83   70c + 30c brn    8.00 8.00
B5   CD83   90c + 35c red org    8.00 8.00
B6   CD83   1.25fr + 1fr rose
        pink    8.00 8.00
B7   CD83   2.25fr + 2fr blue    8.00 8.00
   *Nos. B3-B7 (5)*    40.00 40.00

Stamps of 1936-38 Surcharged in Red or Black

**1941**
B8   A7   50c + 1fr plum (Bk)    2.50 2.50
B9   A8   80c + 2fr blk brn (R)    10.50 10.50
B10   A8   1.50fr + 2fr ultra (R)    11.50 11.50
B11   A9   2fr + 3fr ultra (Bk)    12.50 12.50
   *Nos. B8-B11 (4)*    37.00 37.00

Common Design Type and

Native Engineer SP1

---

Senegalese Light Artillery SP2

**1941**    **Photo.**    **Perf. 13½**
B12   SP1   1fr + 1fr red    1.25
B13   CD86   1.50fr + 3fr claret    1.25
B14   SP2   2.50fr + 1fr blue    1.25
   *Nos. B12-B14 (3)*    3.75

Nos. B12-B14 were issued by the Vichy government in France, but were not placed on sale in Ivory Coast.

Nos. 165-166 Surcharged in Black or Red

**1944**    **Engr.**    **Perf. 12½x12**
B14A   50c + 1.50fr on 2.50fr
     deep blue (R)    .75
B14B   + 2.50fr on 1fr green    .75
Colonial Development Fund.

Nos. B14A-B14B were issued by the Vichy government in France, but were not placed on sale in Ivory Coast.

> Catalogue values for unused stamps in this section, from this point to the end of the section, are for Never Hinged items.

### Republic
#### Anti-Malaria Issue
Common Design Type
**1962, Apr. 7**    **Engr.**    **Perf. 12½x12**
B15   CD108   25fr + 5fr ol grn    1.25 1.25

#### Freedom from Hunger Issue
Common Design Type
**1963, Mar. 21**    **Perf. 13**
B16   CD112   25fr + 5fr red lil, dk
       vio & brn    1.50 1.50

Red Cross - Red Crescent Soc., Child Survival Campaign — SP3

**1987, May 8**    Litho.    **Perf. 13½**
B17   SP3   195fr +5fr multi    2.50 2.50

No. B17 surcharged "+5fr" in red. Not issued without surcharge. Surtax for the Red Cross - Red Crescent Soc.

Organization of African Unity, 25th Anniv. — SP4

**1988, Nov. 19**    Litho.    **Perf. 12½x13**
B18   SP4   195fr +5fr multi    2.25 2.25

---

Marie Therese Houphouet-Boigny and N'Daya Intl. Emblem — SP5

**1988, Dec. 9**    Litho.    **Perf. 13**
B19   SP5   195fr +5fr multi    2.50 2.25
   N'Daya Intl., 1st anniv.

See postage issues, beginning with #1030, for semi-postal stamps that are part of sets with regular postage stamps.

Council of Understanding, Solidarity & Rural Development, 40th Anniv. — SP6

**1999, May 29**    Litho.    **Perf. 13x13½**
B20   SP6   180fr +20fr multi    1.20 1.20

### Postage Types of 1998-99 With Added Surtax
**1999 ?**    Litho.    **Perf. 12**
**Granite Paper (#B20A)**
B20A   A383   180fr +20fr Like
       #1024    —
   **Perf. 13½**
B20B   A386   180fr +20fr Like
       #1027    —
Nos. B20A-B20B apparently were not issued with Nos. 1022-1024 and 1027-1029.

Independence, 41st Anniv. — SP7

**2001, Aug. 7**    Litho.    **Perf. 13¼x13½**
B21   SP7   180fr +20fr multi    1.10 1.10

Year of Dialogue Among Civilizations SP8

**2001, Oct. 9**    **Perf. 13x13¼**
B22   SP8   400fr +20fr multi    2.25 2.25

---

Second Republic, 1st Anniv. SP9

**2001, Oct. 26**
B23   SP9   180fr +20fr multi    1.10 1.10

Planned 2004 Universal Postal Union Congress, Abidjan — SP10

Vignette size: 180fr+20fr, 23x37mm. 400fr+20fr, 26x37mm. 600fr+20fr, 36x49mm.

   **Perf. 13, 13¼x13 (#B25)**
**2001, Dec. 21**    **Litho.**
B24   SP10   180fr +20fr multi    1.00 1.00
   *a.*   Souvenir sheet of 1    5.00 5.00
B25   SP10   400fr +20fr multi    2.25 2.25
B26   SP10   600fr +20fr multi    3.25 3.25

On Nos. B24-B26 and B24a portions of the design were applied by a thermographic process producing a shiny raised effect. No. B24a sold for 1000fr and contains imperforate examples of Nos. B25 and B26 in the margin, which are surmised to be invalid for postage as the face value of these two stamps exceeds the selling price of the sheet. The 2004 UPU Congress was moved from Abidjan to Bucharest, Romania due to political unrest in the Ivory Coast.

St. Valentine's Day — SP11

   *Serpentine Die Cut*
**2002, Feb. 14**    **Litho.**
**Booklet Stamp**
**Self-Adhesive**
B27   SP11   180fr +20fr multi    1.10 1.10
   *a.*   Booklet pane of 8    9.00

Jean Mermoz Intl. College, Abidjan, 40th Anniv. SP12

Panel color: 180fr+20fr, Tan. 400fr+20fr, Red.

**2002, Apr. 19**    **Perf. 13½x13¼**
B28-B29   SP12   Set of 2    3.00 3.00

Decentralization SP14

Denomination color: 180fr+20fr, Green. 400fr+20fr, Blue.

**2002, Dec. 4**    Litho.    **Perf. 13¼x13**
B34-B35   SP14   Set of 2    3.00 3.00

SP15

Campaign Against AIDS — SP16

Illustration SP15 reduced.

**2003, Dec. 22    Litho.    Perf. 13¼**
B36 SP15 180fr +20fr multi          1.00  1.00
**Perf. 13¾**
B37 SP16 400fr +20fr multi          2.00  2.00
Values for No. B37 are for stamps with surrounding selvage.

---

### AIR POST STAMPS

Common Design Type

**1940 Unwmk. Engr. Perf. 12½x12**
C1 CD85 1.90fr ultramarine          .40   .40
C2 CD85 2.90fr dark red             .40   .40
C3 CD85 4.50fr dk gray grn          .75   .75
C4 CD85 4.90fr yel bister          1.00  1.00
C5 CD85 6.90fr deep orange         1.50  1.50
   Nos. C1-C5 (5)                  4.05  4.05

Common Design Types

**1942**
C6  CD88 50c car & blue                 .25
C7  CD88 1fr brn & black                .50
C8  CD88 2fr dk grn & red brn           .75
C9  CD88 3fr dk blue & scar             .75
C10 CD88 5fr vio & dk red               .75
**Frame Engraved, Center Typographed**
C11 CD89 10fr multicolored             1.00
C12 CD89 20fr multicolored             1.50
C13 CD89 50fr multicolored       2.00  4.00
   Nos. C6-C13 (8)               7.50  4.00

There is doubt whether Nos. C6-C12 were officially placed in use.

| Catalogue values for unused stamps in this section, from this point to the end of the section, are for Never Hinged items. |
|---|

### Republic

Lapalud Place and Post Office, Abidjan — AP1

Designs: 200fr, Houphouet-Boigny Bridge. 500fr, Ayamé dam.

**1959, Oct. 1    Engr.    Perf. 13**
C14 AP1 100fr multicolored      4.00   .80
C15 AP1 200fr multicolored      6.00  2.50
C16 AP1 500fr multicolored     13.00  5.00
   Nos. C14-C16 (3)            23.00  8.30

Sports Type of 1961

**1961, Dec. 23**
C17 A19 100fr High jump         4.50  2.25

---

### Air Afrique Issue
Common Design Type
**1962, Feb. 17    Unwmk.    Perf. 13**
C18 CD107 50fr Prus bl, choc &
          org brn               2.00  1.25

Village in Man Region — AP2

**1962, June 23    Engr.    Perf. 13**
C19 AP2 200fr Street in
          Odienne, vert.        7.50  3.00
C20 AP2 500fr shown            13.00  5.00

UN Headquarters, New York — AP3

**1962, Sept. 20    Perf. 13**
C21 AP3 100fr multi             3.00  1.25
   Admission to the UN, 2nd anniv.

Sassandra Bay — AP4

**1963    Unwmk.    Perf. 13**
C22 AP4 50fr Moossou bridge     2.25   .75
C23 AP4 100fr shown             3.25  1.75
C24 AP4 200fr Comoe River       6.00  2.75
   Nos. C22-C24 (3)            11.50  5.25

### African Postal Union Issue
Common Design Type
**1963, Sept. 8    Photo.    Perf. 12½**
C25 CD114 85fr org brn, ocher &
          red                   2.50  1.50

### 1963 Air Afrique Issue
Common Design Type
**1963, Nov. 19    Unwmk.    Perf. 13x12**
C26 CD115 25fr crim, gray, blk &
          grn                   1.00   .50

Ramses II and Queen Nefertari — AP5

President John F. Kennedy (1917-63) — AP7

---

Arms of Republic — AP6

**1964, Mar. 7    Engr.    Perf. 13**
C27 AP5 60fr car, blk & red brn  3.00  1.50
   UNESCO campaign to save historic monuments in Nubia.

**1964, June 13    Photo.**
C28 AP6 200fr ultra, yel grn &
          gold                  5.00  2.25

**1964, Nov. 14    Unwmk.    Perf. 12½**
C29 AP7 100fr gray, cl brn &
          blk                   3.00  1.50
a.   Souvenir sheet of 4       15.00 15.00

Liana Bridge, Lieupleu — AP8

**1965, Dec. 4    Engr.    Perf. 13**
C30 AP8 100fr ol grn, dk grn &
          dk red brn           3.50  1.75

Street in Kong — AP9

**1966, Mar. 5    Engr.    Perf. 13**
C31 AP9 300fr brt bl, bis brn &
          vio brn              9.00  5.00

### Air Afrique Issue, 1966
Common Design Type
**1966, Aug. 20    Photo.    Perf. 13**
C32 CD123 30fr dk grn, blk &
          gray                 1.00   .60

Air Afrique Headquarters AP10

**1967, Feb. 4    Engr.    Perf. 13**
C33 AP10 500fr emer, ind &
          ocher               12.50  6.00
   Opening of Air Afrique headquarters in Abidjan.

### African Postal Union Issue, 1967
Common Design Type
**1967, Sept. 9    Engr.    Perf. 13**
C34 CD124 100fr blk, vio & car
          lake                 3.50  1.50

---

Senufo Village — AP11

**1968    Engr.    Perf. 13**
C35 AP11 100fr shown            3.50  1.25
C36 AP11 500fr Tiegba village  12.50  4.50
Issue dates: 100fr, Feb. 17; 500fr, Apr. 27.

### PHILEXAFRIQUE Issue

Street in Grand Bassam, by Achalme — AP12

**1969, Jan. 11    Photo.    Perf. 12x12½**
C37 AP12 100fr grn & multi      5.00  5.00
   PHILEXAFRIQUE Phil. Exhib., Abidjan, Feb. 14-23. Printed with alternating green label. Value, single with attached label, $6.

### 2nd PHILEXAFRIQUE Issue
Common Design Type
50fr, Ivory Coast #130 & view of San Pedro. 100fr, Ivory Coast #149 & man wearing chief's garments, vert. 200fr, Ivory Coast #77 # Exhibition Hall, Abidjan.

**1969, Feb. 14    Engr.    Perf. 13**
C38 CD128 50fr grn, brn red
          & deep bl            3.25  3.25
C39 CD128 100fr brn, org &
          dp blue              5.00  5.00
C40 CD128 200fr brn, gray &
          dp blue              7.50  7.50
a.   Min. sheet of 3, #C38-C40 20.00 20.00
   Nos. C38-C40 (3)           15.75 15.75
   Opening of PHILEXAFRIQUE.

Man Waterfall — AP13

Mount Niangbo — AP14

**1970    Engr.    Perf. 13**
C41 AP13 100fr multicolored     3.50  1.50
C42 AP14 200fr multicolored     4.50  2.00
Issue dates: 100fr, Jan. 6; 200fr, July 18.

San Pedro Harbor — AP15

**1971, Mar. 21    Engr.    Perf. 13**
C43 AP15 100fr multicolored     2.25  1.00

Treichville Swimming Pool — AP16

**1971, May 29　Photo.　Perf. 12½**
C44　AP16　100fr multicolored　3.00　1.50

Aerial View of Coast Line — AP17

**1971, July 3　Engr.　Perf. 13**
C45　AP17　500fr multi　12.00　6.00
Tourist publicity for the African Riviera.

**Bondoukou Market Type of Regular Issue**
Design: 200fr, Similar to No. 318, but without people at left and in center.

**Embossed on Gold Paper**
**1971, Aug. 7　Perf. 12½**
**Size: 36x26mm**
C46　A79　200fr gold, ultra & blk　5.00　2.50

**African Postal Union Issue, 1971**
**Common Design Type**
Design: 100fr, Ivory Coast coat of arms and UAMPT building, Brazzaville, Congo.

**1971, Nov. 13　Photo.　Perf. 13x13½**
C47　CD135　100fr bl & multi　2.00　1.00

Lion of St. Mark AP18

**1972, Feb. 5　Photo.　Perf. 12½**
C48　AP18　100fr shown　3.50　1.75
C49　AP18　200fr Waves, St.
　　　　　　Mark's Basilica,
　　　　　　Venice　6.00　3.25
UNESCO campaign to save Venice.

Kawara Mosque — AP19

**1972, Apr. 29　Engr.　Perf. 13**
C50　AP19　500fr bl, brn & ocher　12.50　6.50

View of Gouessesso — AP20

**1972　Engr.　Perf. 13**
C51　AP20　100fr shown　3.25　1.25
C52　AP20　200fr Jacqueville
　　　　　　Lake　4.75　1.75
C53　AP20　500fr Kossou Dam　10.00　6.00
　　　Nos. C51-C53 (3)　18.00　9.00
Issued: 100fr, 6/10; 200fr, 1/8; 500fr, 11/17.

Akakro Radar Earth Station — AP21

**1972, Nov. 27　Engr.　Perf. 13**
C54　AP21　200fr brt bl, sl grn &
　　　　　　choc　4.50　1.75

The Judgment of Solomon, by Nandjui Legue — AP22

**1973, Aug. 26　Photo.　Perf. 13**
C55　AP22　500fr multi　12.50　6.00
6th World Peace Conference for Justice.

Sassandra River Bridge — AP23

**1974, May 4　Engr.　Perf. 13**
C56　AP23　100fr blk & yel grn　2.25　.75
C57　AP23　500fr slate grn & brn　12.00　4.25

Vridi Soap Factory, Abidjan — AP24

**1974, July 6　Photo.　Perf. 13**
C58　AP24　200fr multi　3.50　1.75

UPU Emblem, Ivory Coast Flag, Post Runner and Jet — AP25

**1974, Oct. 9　Photo.　Perf. 13**
C59　AP25　200fr multi　5.00　3.00
C60　AP25　300fr multi　6.00　4.00
Centenary of Universal Postal Union.

Fly Whisk and Panga Knife, Symbols of Akans Royal Family — AP26

**1976, Apr. 3　Photo.　Perf. 12½x13**
C61　AP26　200fr brt bl & multi　5.00　2.00

Tingrela Mosque — AP27

**1977, May 7　Engr.　Perf. 13**
C62　AP27　500fr multi　7.50　4.50

**Zeppelin Type of 1977**
**Souvenir Sheet**
"Graf Zeppelin" LZ 127 over New York.

**1977, Sept. 3　Litho.　Perf. 11**
C63　A150　500fr multi　6.25　1.90
Exists imperf.

**Philexafrique II - Essen Issue**
**Common Design Types**
#C64, Elephant and Ivory Coast No. 239.
#C65, Pheasant and Bavaria No. 1.

**1978, Nov. 1　Litho.　Perf. 13x12½**
C64　CD138　100fr multi　3.50　2.50
C65　CD139　100fr multi　3.50　2.50
　a.　Pair, #C64-C65 + label　8.00　8.00

Gymnast, Olympic Rings — AP28

Various gymnasts. 75fr, 150fr, 350fr, vert.

**1980, July 24　Litho.　Perf. 14½**
C66　AP28　75fr multi　1.25　.25
C67　AP28　150fr multi　1.75　.45
C68　AP28　250fr multi　3.25　1.00
C69　AP28　350fr multi　3.75　1.25
　　　Nos. C66-C69 (4)　10.00　2.95

**Souvenir Sheet**
C70　AP28　500fr multi　6.00　2.00
22nd Summer Olympic Games, Moscow, July 19-Aug. 3.

President Houphouet-Boigny, 75th Birthday AP28a

**Embossed Die Cut**
**1980, Oct. 18　Perf. 10½**
C70A　AP28a　2000fr Silver　22.50　22.50
C70B　AP28a　3000fr Gold　37.50　37.50

Manned Flight Bicentenary — AP29

Various balloons. 100fr, 125fr, 350fr vert.

**1983, Apr. 2　Litho.　Perf. 13**
C71　AP29　100fr Montgolfier,
　　　　　　1783　1.00　.35
C72　AP29　125fr Hydrogen,
　　　　　　1783　1.50　.45
C73　AP29　150fr Mail transport,
　　　　　　1870　1.75　.50
C74　AP29　350fr Double Eagle
　　　　　　II, 1978　4.50　1.00
C75　AP29　500fr Dirigible　6.50　1.75
　　　Nos. C71-C75 (5)　15.25　4.05

Pre-Olympic Year — AP30

Various swimming events.

**1983, July 9　Litho.　Perf. 14**
C76　AP30　100fr Crawl　1.00　.35
C77　AP30　125fr Diving　1.25　.50
C78　AP30　350fr Backstroke　3.50　1.25
C79　AP30　400fr Butterfly　4.25　1.50
　　　Nos. C76-C79 (4)　10.00　3.60

**Souvenir Sheet**
C80　AP30　500fr Water polo　6.50　2.00

1984 Summer Olympics — AP31

Pentathlon.

**1984, Mar.　Perf. 12½**
C81　AP31　100fr Swimming　1.00　.30
C82　AP31　125fr Running　1.25　.40
C83　AP31　185fr Shooting　1.75　.60
C84　AP31　350fr Fencing　3.75　1.25
　　　Nos. C81-C84 (4)　7.75　2.55

**Souvenir Sheet**
C85　AP31　500fr Equestrian　6.00　1.50

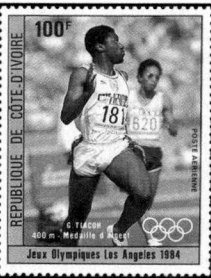

Los Angeles Olympics Winners AP32

**1984, Dec. 15　Litho.　Perf. 13**
C86　AP32　100fr Tiacoh, silver　1.25　.25
C87　AP32　150fr Lewis, gold　1.75　.40
C88　AP32　200fr Babers, gold　2.50　.75
C89　AP32　500fr Cruz, gold　5.00　1.50
　　　Nos. C86-C89 (4)　10.50　2.90

Christmas
AP33

Paintings: 100fr, Virgin and Child, by Correggio. 200fr, Holy Family with Angels, by Andrea del Sarto. 400fr, Virgin and Child, by Bellini.

| 1985, Jan. 12 | | | Perf. 13 | |
|---|---|---|---|---|
| C90 | AP33 | 100fr multi | 1.20 | .40 |
| C91 | AP33 | 200fr multi | 2.25 | .90 |
| C92 | AP33 | 400fr multi | 4.00 | 2.00 |
| | | Nos. C90-C92 (3) | 7.45 | 3.30 |

Nos. C91-C92 have incorrect frame inscriptions.

Audubon Birth Bicentenary — AP34

Birds: 100fr, Mergus serrator. 150fr, Pelecanus erythrorhynchos. 200fr, Mycteria americana. 350fr, Melanitta deglandi.

| 1985, June 8 | | Litho. | Perf. 13 | |
|---|---|---|---|---|
| C93 | AP34 | 100fr multi | 1.20 | .45 |
| C94 | AP34 | 150fr multi, vert. | 1.75 | .70 |
| C95 | AP34 | 200fr multi, vert. | 3.00 | 1.00 |
| C96 | AP34 | 350fr multi | 4.25 | 2.00 |
| | | Nos. C93-C96 (4) | 10.20 | 4.15 |

PHILEXAFRICA '85, Lome, Togo — AP35

| 1985, Nov. 16 | | Litho. | Perf. 13 | |
|---|---|---|---|---|
| C97 | AP35 | 250fr shown | 3.75 | 2.00 |
| C98 | AP35 | 250fr Soccer, boys and deer | 3.75 | 2.00 |
| a. | | Pair, #C97-C98 + label | 9.00 | 6.00 |

Edmond Halley, Computer Drawing of Comet — AP36

Return of Halley's Comet: 155fr, Sir William Herschel, Uranus. 190fr, Space probe, comet. 350fr, MS T-5 probe, comet. 440fr, Skylab, Kohoutek comet.

| 1986, Jan. | | Litho. | Perf. 13 | |
|---|---|---|---|---|
| C99 | AP36 | 125fr shown | 1.25 | .50 |
| C100 | AP36 | 155fr multi | 1.50 | .75 |
| C101 | AP36 | 190fr multi | 1.90 | .90 |
| C102 | AP36 | 350fr multi | 3.50 | 1.75 |
| C103 | AP36 | 440fr multi | 4.25 | 2.25 |
| | | Nos. C99-C103 (5) | 12.40 | 6.15 |

1986 World Cup Soccer Championships, Mexico — AP37

Various soccer plays.

| 1986, Apr. 26 | | Litho. | Perf. 13 | |
|---|---|---|---|---|
| C104 | AP37 | 90fr multi | .90 | .35 |
| C105 | AP37 | 125fr multi | 1.25 | .60 |
| C106 | AP37 | 155fr multi | 1.75 | .75 |
| C107 | AP37 | 440fr multi | 4.50 | 2.25 |
| C108 | AP37 | 500fr multi | 5.00 | 2.50 |
| | | Nos. C104-C108 (5) | 13.40 | 6.45 |

**Souvenir Sheet**
**Perf. 13½x13**

| C109 | AP37 | 600fr multi | 6.50 | 2.00 |
|---|---|---|---|---|

AP38

1988 Summer Olympics, Seoul — AP39

Sailing sports.

| 1987, May 23 | | Litho. | Perf. 12½ | |
|---|---|---|---|---|
| C110 | AP38 | 155fr Soling Class | 1.50 | .60 |
| C111 | AP38 | 195fr Windsurfing | 2.25 | .75 |
| C112 | AP38 | 250fr 470 Class | 3.00 | 1.00 |
| C113 | AP38 | 550fr Windsurfing, diff. | 6.00 | 2.50 |
| | | Nos. C110-C113 (4) | 12.75 | 4.85 |

**Souvenir Sheet**

| C114 | AP39 | 650fr 470 Class, diff. | 7.00 | 2.25 |
|---|---|---|---|---|

1988 Summer Olympics, Seoul — AP40

| 1988, June 18 | | Litho. | Perf. 13 | |
|---|---|---|---|---|
| C115 | AP40 | 100fr Gymnastic rings | .90 | .40 |
| C116 | AP40 | 155fr Women's handball | 1.25 | .60 |
| C117 | AP40 | 195fr Boxing | 2.00 | .75 |
| C118 | AP40 | 500fr Parallel bars | 5.00 | 2.00 |
| | | Nos. C115-C118 (4) | 9.15 | 3.75 |

**Souvenir Sheet**

| C119 | AP40 | 500fr Horizontal bar | 14.00 | 1.60 |
|---|---|---|---|---|

1990 World Cup Soccer Championships, Italy — AP41

Italian monuments and various athletes.

| 1989, Nov. 25 | | Litho. | Perf. 13 | |
|---|---|---|---|---|
| C120 | AP41 | 195fr Milan Cathedral | 2.00 | .75 |
| C121 | AP41 | 300fr Columbus Monument, Genoa | 3.00 | 1.25 |
| C122 | AP41 | 450fr Turin | 4.25 | 1.75 |
| C123 | AP41 | 550fr Bologna | 6.00 | 2.00 |
| | | Nos. C120-C123 (4) | 15.25 | 5.75 |

World Cup Soccer Championships, Italy — AP42

Various plays.

| 1990, May 31 | | Litho. | Perf. 13 | |
|---|---|---|---|---|
| C124 | AP42 | 155fr multicolored | 1.60 | .60 |
| C125 | AP42 | 195fr multicolored | 2.00 | .75 |
| C126 | AP42 | 500fr multicolored | 5.00 | 2.00 |
| C127 | AP42 | 600fr multicolored | 7.00 | 2.50 |
| | | Nos. C124-C127 (4) | 15.60 | 5.85 |

## AIR POST SEMI-POSTAL STAMPS

Types of Dahomey Air Post Semi-Postal Issue
**Perf. 13½x12½, 13 (#CB3)**
**Photo, Engr. (#CB3)**

**1942, June 22**

| CB1 | SPAP1 | 1.50fr + 3.50fr green | 1.00 | 5.50 |
|---|---|---|---|---|
| CB2 | SPAP2 | 2fr + 6fr brown | 1.00 | 5.50 |
| CB3 | SPAP2 | 3fr + 9fr car red | 1.00 | 5.50 |
| | | Nos. CB1-CB3 (3) | 3.00 | 16.50 |

Native children's welfare fund.

**Colonial Education Fund**
Common Design Type
**Perf. 12½x13½**

| 1942, June 22 | | | | Engr. |
|---|---|---|---|---|
| CB4 | CD86a | 1.20fr + 1.80fr blue & red | 1.00 | 5.50 |

## POSTAGE DUE STAMPS

Natives — D1

D2

**Perf. 14x13½**

| 1906-07 | | Unwmk. | | Typo. |
|---|---|---|---|---|
| J1 | D1 | 5c grn, greenish | 4.00 | 4.00 |
| J2 | D1 | 10c red brown | 4.00 | 4.00 |
| J3 | D1 | 15c dark blue | 6.00 | 6.00 |
| J4 | D1 | 20c blk, yellow | 9.00 | 9.00 |
| J5 | D1 | 30c red, straw | 9.00 | 9.00 |
| J6 | D1 | 50c violet | 7.00 | 7.00 |
| J7 | D1 | 60c black, buff | 32.50 | 32.50 |
| J8 | D1 | 1fr blk, pinkish | 35.00 | 35.00 |
| | | Nos. J1-J8 (8) | 106.50 | 106.50 |

**1914**

| J9 | D2 | 5c green | .25 | .25 |
|---|---|---|---|---|
| J10 | D2 | 10c rose | .30 | .30 |
| J11 | D2 | 15c gray | .30 | .30 |
| J12 | D2 | 20c brown | .55 | .55 |
| J13 | D2 | 30c blue | .55 | .55 |
| J14 | D2 | 50c black | .90 | .90 |
| J15 | D2 | 60c orange | 1.25 | 1.25 |
| J16 | D2 | 1fr violet | 1.50 | 1.50 |
| | | Nos. J9-J16 (8) | 5.60 | 5.60 |

Type of 1914 Issue Surcharged

**1927**

| J17 | D2 | 2fr on 1fr lilac rose | 2.50 | 2.50 |
|---|---|---|---|---|
| J18 | D2 | 3fr on 1fr org brown | 2.50 | 2.50 |

> Catalogue values for unused stamps in this section, from this point to the end of the section, are for Never Hinged items.

**Republic**

Guéré
Mask — D3

Mask — D4

| 1960 | | Engr. | Perf. 14x13 | |
|---|---|---|---|---|

**Denomination Typographed in Black**

| J19 | D3 | 1fr purple | .20 | .20 |
|---|---|---|---|---|
| J20 | D3 | 2fr bright green | .20 | .20 |
| J21 | D3 | 5fr orange yellow | .50 | .50 |
| J22 | D3 | 10fr ultramarine | .90 | .90 |
| J23 | D3 | 20fr lilac rose | 1.60 | 1.60 |
| | | Nos. J19-J23 (5) | 3.40 | 3.40 |

| 1962, Nov. 3 | | Typo. | Perf. 13½x14 | |
|---|---|---|---|---|

Designs: Various masks and heads, Bingerville school of art.

| J24 | D4 | 1fr org & brt blue | .20 | .20 |
|---|---|---|---|---|
| J25 | D4 | 2fr black & red | .30 | .30 |
| J26 | D4 | 5fr red & dark grn | .40 | .40 |
| J27 | D4 | 10fr green & lilac | .90 | .90 |
| J28 | D4 | 20fr dark pur & blk | 1.60 | 1.60 |
| | | Nos. J24-J28 (5) | 3.40 | 3.40 |

Baoulé
Weight — D5

Gold
Weight — D6

Designs: Various Baoulé weights.

| 1968, May 18 | | Photo. | Perf. 13 | |
|---|---|---|---|---|
| J29 | D5 | 5fr cit, brn & bl grn | .20 | .20 |
| J30 | D5 | 10fr lt bl, brn & bl grn | .30 | .30 |
| J31 | D5 | 15fr sal, brn & bl grn | .80 | .80 |
| J32 | D5 | 20fr gray, car & bl grn | 1.10 | 1.10 |
| J33 | D5 | 30fr bis, brn & bl grn | 1.50 | 1.50 |
| | | Nos. J29-J33 (5) | 3.90 | 3.90 |

| 1972, May 27 | | | | Engr. |
|---|---|---|---|---|

Designs: Various gold weights.

| J34 | D6 | 20fr vio bl & org red | .90 | .90 |
|---|---|---|---|---|
| J35 | D6 | 40fr ver & ocher | 1.50 | 1.50 |
| J36 | D6 | 50fr orange & chocolate | 2.00 | 2.00 |
| J37 | D6 | 100fr slate grn & ocher | 4.00 | 4.00 |
| | | Nos. J34-J37 (4) | 8.40 | 8.40 |

It has been reported that Nos. J34-J37 were used briefly as regular postage for domestic use. Examples of use as postage to foreign addresses exists.

## MILITARY STAMP

> The catalogue value for the unused stamp in this section is for Never Hinged.

Coat of Arms — M1

**Perf. 13x14**

**1967, Jan. 1**    **Unwmk.**    **Typo.**
M1   M1   multi             3.50   3.50

## OFFICIAL STAMPS

> Catalogue values for unused stamps in this section are for Never Hinged items.

Ivory Coast Coat of Arms — O1

**1974, Jan. 1**    **Photo.**    **Perf. 12**
| | | | | |
|---|---|---|---|---|
| O1 | O1 | (35fr) green & multi | .75 | .25 |
| O2 | O1 | (75fr) orange & multi | 1.20 | .45 |
| O3 | O1 | (100fr) lil rose & multi | 1.50 | .80 |
| O4 | O1 | (250fr) violet & multi | 4.00 | 1.50 |
| | | Nos. O1-O4 (4) | 7.45 | 3.00 |

## PARCEL POST STAMPS

Postage Due Stamps of French Colonies Overprinted

Overprinted in Black

**1903**    **Unwmk.**    **Imperf.**
| | | | | |
|---|---|---|---|---|
| Q1 | D1 | 50c lilac | 42.50 | 40.00 |
| Q2 | D1 | 1fr rose, *buff* | 42.50 | 40.00 |

Overprinted in Black

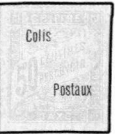

| | | | | |
|---|---|---|---|---|
| Q3 | D1 | 50c lilac | 3,100. | 3,200. |
| Q4 | D1 | 1fr rose, *buff* | 3,100. | 3,200. |

**Accents on "O" of "COTE"**
Nos. Q7-Q8, Q11-Q12, Q15, Q17-Q18, Q21-Q22, Q24-Q25 exist with or without accent.

Overprinted

---

**Red Overprint**
| | | | | |
|---|---|---|---|---|
| Q5 | D1 | 50c lilac | 110.00 | 110.00 |
| *a.* | | Inverted overprint | 400.00 | 400.00 |

**Blue Black Overprint**
| | | | | |
|---|---|---|---|---|
| Q6 | D1 | 1fr rose, *buff* | 80.00 | 80.00 |
| *a.* | | Inverted overprint | 350.00 | 350.00 |

Surcharged in Black

a           b

c           d

e           f

g           h

**1903**
| | | | | |
|---|---|---|---|---|
| Q7 | D1 | 50c on 15c pale grn | 15.00 | 14.00 |
| *a.* | | Inverted surcharge | 200.00 | 200.00 |
| Q8 | D1 | 50c on 60c brn, *buff* | 35.00 | 32.50 |
| *a.* | | Inverted surcharge | 225.00 | 225.00 |
| Q9 | (a) | 1fr on 5c blue | 4,000. | 3,250. |
| Q10 | (b) | 1fr on 5c blue | 4,000. | 2,700. |
| Q11 | (c) | 1fr on 5c blue | 18.00 | 14.00 |
| *a.* | | Inverted surcharge | 900.00 | 900.00 |
| Q12 | (d) | 1fr on 5c blue | 26.00 | 22.50 |
| Q13 | (e) | 1fr on 5c blue | 4,300. | 3,800. |
| Q14 | (f) | 1fr on 5c blue | 10,750. | 9,000. |
| Q15 | (g) | 1fr on 5c blue | 100.00 | 100.00 |
| Q16 | (h) | 1fr on 5c blue | 3,500. | 3,600. |
| Q17 | (c) | 1fr on 10c gray brn | 25.00 | 21.50 |
| *a.* | | Inverted surcharge | 325.00 | 325.00 |
| Q18 | (d) | 1fr on 10c gray brn | 40.00 | 36.00 |
| *a.* | | Inverted surcharge | 450.00 | 450.00 |
| Q19 | (g) | 1fr on 10c gray brn | 3,700. | 3,500. |
| Q20 | (h) | 1fr on 10c gray brn | 43,000. | |

Some authorities regard Nos. Q9 and Q10 as essays. A sub-type of type "a" has smaller, bold "XX" without serifs.

Surcharged in Black:

j           k

---

i

| | | | | |
|---|---|---|---|---|
| Q21 | (i) | 4fr on 60c brn, *buff* | 120.00 | 120.00 |
| *a.* | | Double surcharge | | 5,500. |
| Q22 | (k) | 4fr on 60c brn, *buff* | 325.00 | 325.00 |
| Q23 | (l) | 4fr on 60c brn, *buff* | 1,200. | 1,000. |

Surcharged in Black

| | | | | |
|---|---|---|---|---|
| Q24 | D1 | 4fr on 15c green | 110.00 | 110.00 |
| *a.* | | One large star | 500.00 | 500.00 |
| *b.* | | Two large stars | 300.00 | 300.00 |
| Q25 | D1 | 4fr on 30c rose | 110.00 | 110.00 |
| *a.* | | One large star | 500.00 | 500.00 |
| *b.* | | Two large stars | 300.00 | 300.00 |

Overprinted in Black

**1904**
| | | | | |
|---|---|---|---|---|
| Q26 | D1 | 50c lilac | 35.00 | 35.00 |
| *a.* | | Inverted overprint | | |
| Q27 | D1 | 1fr rose, *buff* | 35.00 | 35.00 |
| *a.* | | Inverted overprint | | |

Overprinted in Black

| | | | | |
|---|---|---|---|---|
| Q28 | D1 | 50c lilac | 35.00 | 35.00 |
| *a.* | | Inverted overprint | 225.00 | 225.00 |
| Q29 | D1 | 1fr rose, *buff* | 35.00 | 35.00 |
| *a.* | | Inverted overprint | 225.00 | 225.00 |

Surcharged in Black

| | | | | |
|---|---|---|---|---|
| Q30 | D1 | 4fr on 5c blue | 240.00 | 240.00 |
| Q31 | D1 | 8fr on 15c green | 240.00 | 240.00 |

Overprinted in Black

**1905**
| | | | | |
|---|---|---|---|---|
| Q32 | D1 | 50c lilac | 80.00 | 80.00 |
| Q33 | D1 | 1fr rose, *buff* | 80.00 | 80.00 |

Surcharged in Black

| | | | | |
|---|---|---|---|---|
| Q34 | D1 | 2fr on 1fr rose, *buff* | 225.00 | 225.00 |
| Q35 | D1 | 4fr on 1fr rose, *buff* | 225.00 | 225.00 |
| *a.* | | Italic "4" | 2,200. | 2,200. |
| Q36 | D1 | 8fr on 1fr rose, *buff* | 650.00 | 650.00 |

---

# album accessories

## ADVANTAGE STOCK SHEETS

Advantage stock sheets fit directly in your 2-post or 3-ring National or Specialty album. Available with 1 to 8 pockets.

**Sheets are sold in packages of 10.**

- Stock sheets match album pages in every respect, including size, border, and color.
- Punched to fit perfectly in binder.
- Ideal for storing minor varieties and collateral material. A great place to keep new issues until the next supplement is available.
- Provides the protection of clear acetate pockets on heavyweight pages.

### NATIONAL BORDER

| Item | | | Retail | AA* |
|------|--|--|--------|-----|
| AD11 | 1 Pocket | 242mm | $19.99 | $17.99 |
| AD12 | 2 Pockets | 119mm | $19.99 | $17.99 |
| AD13 | 3 Pockets | 79mm | $19.99 | $17.99 |
| AD14 | 4 Pockets | 58mm | $19.99 | $17.99 |
| AD15 | 5 Pockets | 45mm | $19.99 | $17.99 |
| AD16 | 6 Pockets | 37mm | $19.99 | $17.99 |
| AD17 | 7 Pockets | 34mm | $19.99 | $17.99 |
| AD18 | 8 Pockets | 31mm | $19.99 | $17.99 |

### SPECIALTY BORDER

| Item | | | Retail | AA* |
|------|--|--|--------|-----|
| AD21 | 1 Pocket | 242mm | $19.99 | $17.99 |
| AD22 | 2 Pockets | 119mm | $19.99 | $17.99 |
| AD23 | 3 Pockets | 79mm | $19.99 | $17.99 |
| AD24 | 4 Pockets | 58mm | $19.99 | $17.99 |
| AD25 | 5 Pockets | 45mm | $19.99 | $17.99 |
| AD26 | 6 Pockets | 37mm | $19.99 | $17.99 |
| AD27 | 7 Pockets | 34mm | $19.99 | $17.99 |
| AD28 | 8 Pockets | 31mm | $19.99 | $17.99 |

### BLANK PAGES

Ideal for developing your own album pages to be integrated with your album.

### SPECIALTY SERIES PAGES (BORDER A)
(20 per pack)

| Item | | Retail | AA* |
|------|--|--------|-----|
| ACC110 | | $7.74 | $5.99 |
| ACC111 | Quadrille* | $7.74 | $5.99 |

*Graph pattern printed on page.*

## SPECIALTY/NATIONAL SERIES BINDERS

National series pages are punched for 3-ring and 2-post binders. The 3-ring binder is available in two sizes. The 2-post binder comes in one size. All Scott binders are covered with a tough green leatherette material that is washable and reinforced at stress points for long wear.

### 3-RING BINDERS & SLIPCASES

With the three ring binder, pages lay flat and the rings make turning the pages easy. The locking mechanism insure that the rings won't pop open even when the binder is full.

| Item | | | Retail | AA* |
|------|--|--|--------|-----|
| ACBR01 | Small 3-Ring Binder | Holds up to 100 pages | $36.74 | $29.99 |
| ACBR03 | Large 3-Ring Binder | Holds up to 250 pages | $36.74 | $29.99 |
| ACSR01 | Small 3-Ring Slipcase. | | $29.99 | $24.99 |
| ACSR03 | Large 3-Ring Slipcase. | | $29.99 | $24.99 |

### LARGE 2-POST BINDER & SLIPCASE

For the traditional Scott collector, we offer the standard hinge post binder. Scott album pages are punched with rectangular holes that fit on rectangular posts. The posts and pages are held by a rod that slides down from the top. With the post binder pages do not lie flat. However, filler strips are available for a minimal cost.

| Item | | | Retail | AA* |
|------|--|--|--------|-----|
| ACBS03 | Large 2-Post Binder | Holds up to 250 pages | $52.99 | $45.99 |
| ACSS03 | Large 2-Post Slipcase | | $29.99 | $24.99 |

## ALBUM PAGE DIVIDERS

Postage, air post, semi-postals; they're all right at your fingertips with National/Specialty Album Page Dividers. The dividers are a great way to keep your albums organized and save wear and tear on your pages.

| Item | | Retail | AA* |
|------|--|--------|-----|
| ACC145 | Package of 10 | $4.49 | $3.49 |

## NATIONAL SERIES PAGES (BORDER B)
(20 per pack)

| Item | | Retail | AA* |
|------|--|--------|-----|
| ACC120 | | $7.74 | $5.99 |
| ACC121 | Quadrille* | $7.74 | $5.99 |

## PAGE PROTECTORS

Protect your stamps and album pages with a clear archival quality plastic sleeve. Sleeves fits over the entire page and protects pages from creases, fingerprints and tears. Scott Page protectors are pvc free and thin enough that they won't make your binder bulge. Page Protectors are available in two sizes. Sold in packages of 25.

### 2-Post Minuteman/International Pg Protectors

| Item | Retail | AA* |
|------|--------|-----|
| ACC165 | $13.99 | $11.75 |

### National/Specialty Series Pg Protectors*

| Item | Retail | AA* |
|------|--------|-----|
| ACC166 | $13.99 | $11.75 |

*Punched to fit 2-post and 3-ring binder.*

# Illustrated Identifier

This section pictures stamps or parts of stamp designs that will help identify postage stamps that do not have English words on them.

Many of the symbols that identify stamps of countries are shown here as well as typical examples of their stamps.

See the Index and Identifier on the previous pages for stamps with inscriptions such as "sen," "posta," "Baja Porto," "Helvetia," "K.S.A.," etc.

*Linn's Stamp Identifier* is now available. The 144 pages include more 2,000 inscriptions and over 500 large stamp illustrations. Available from Linn's Stamp News, P.O. Box 29, Sidney, OH 45365-0029.

## 1. HEADS, PICTURES AND NUMERALS

### GREAT BRITAIN

Great Britain stamps never show the country name, but, except for postage dues, show a picture of the reigning monarch.

Victoria

Edward VII    George V    Edward VIII

George VI

Elizabeth II

Some George VI and Elizabeth II stamps are surcharged in annas, new paisa or rupees. These are listed under Oman.

---

Silhouette (sometimes facing right, generally at the top of stamp)

The silhouette indicates this is a British stamp. It is not a U.S. stamp.

### VICTORIA

Queen Victoria

### INDIA

Other stamps of India show this portrait of Queen Victoria and the words "Service" and "Annas."

### AUSTRIA

---

### YUGOSLAVIA

(Also BOSNIA & HERZEGOVINA if imperf.)

### BOSNIA & HERZEGOVINA

Denominations also appear in top corners instead of bottom corners.

### HUNGARY

Another stamp has posthorn facing left

### BRAZIL

### AUSTRALIA

Kangaroo and Emu

### GERMANY

**Mecklenburg-Vorpommern**

## SWITZERLAND

## PALAU

# 2. ORIENTAL INSCRIPTIONS

## CHINA

Any stamp with this one character is from China (Imperial, Republic or People's Republic).
This character appears in a four-character overprint on stamps of Manchukuo. These stamps are local provisionals, which are unlisted. Other overprinted Manchukuo stamps show this character, but have more than four characters in the overprints. These are listed in People's Republic of China.

Some Chinese stamps show the Sun.

Most stamps of Republic of China show this series of characters.

Stamps with the China character and this character are from People's Republic of China.

Calligraphic form of People's Republic of China

| (一) | (二) | (三) | (四) | (五) | (六) |
|------|------|------|------|------|------|
| 1 | 2 | 3 | 4 | 5 | 6 |
| (七) | (八) | (九) | (十) | (一十) | (二十) |
| 7 | 8 | 9 | 10 | 11 | 12 |

## Chinese stamps without China character

## REPUBLIC OF CHINA

## PEOPLE'S REPUBLIC OF CHINA

Mao Tse-tung

## MANCHUKUO

Temple          Emperor Pu-Yi

The first 3 characters are common to many Manchukuo stamps.

The last 3 characters are common to other Manchukuo stamps.

Orchid Crest

Manchukuo stamp without these elements

## JAPAN

Chrysanthemum Crest    Country Name

Japanese stamps without these elements

The number of characters in the center and the design of dragons on the sides will vary.

## RYUKYU ISLANDS

Country Name

## PHILIPPINES

### (Japanese Occupation)

Country Name

## NORTH BORNEO
### (Japanese Occupation)

Indicates Japanese     Country
Occupation            Name

## MALAYA
### (Japanese Occupation)

Indicates Japanese Occupation     Country Name

## BURMA

### Union of Myanmar

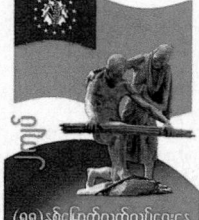

Union of Myanmar

### (Japanese Occupation)

Indicates Japanese Occupation     Country Name

Other Burma Japanese Occupation stamps without these elements

Burmese Script

## KOREA

These two characters, in any order, are common to stamps from the Republic of Korea (South Korea) or of the People's Democratic Republic of Korea (North Korea).

This series of four characters can be found on the stamps of both Koreas.
Most stamps of the Democratic People's Republic of Korea (North Korea) have just this inscription.

Indicates Republic of Korea (South Korea)

South Korean postage stamps issed after 1952 do not show currency expressed in Latin letters. Stamps wiith "HW," "HWAN," "WON," "WN," "W" or "W" with two lines through it, if not illustrated in listings of stamps before this date, are revenues.
North Korean postage stamps do not have currency expressed in Latin letters.

Yin Yang appears on some stamps.

THAILAND

Country Name

King Chulalongkorn

King Prajadhipok and Chao P'ya Chakri

## 3. CENTRAL AND EASTERN ASIAN INSCRIPTIONS

### INDIA - FEUDATORY STATES

**Alwar**          **Bhor**

**Bundi**

Similar stamps come with different designs in corners and differently drawn daggers (at center of circle).

**Dhar**          **Faridkot**

**Hyderabad**

Similar stamps exist with straight line frame around stamp, and also with different central design which is inscribed "Postage" or "Post & Receipt."

**Indore**          **Jhalawar**

A similar stamp has the central figure in an oval.

### Nandgaon

### Nowanuggur

### Poonch

Similar stamps exist
in various sizes

### Rajpeepla          ### Soruth

### BANGLADESH

Country Name

## NEPAL

Similar stamps are smaller, have squares in
upper corners and have five or nine
characters in central bottom panel.

### TANNU TUVA          ### ISRAEL

### GEORGIA

This inscription is found on
other pictorial stamps.

Country Name

### ARMENIA

The four characters are found somewhere
on pictorial stamps. On some stamps only
the middle two are found.

## 4. AFRICAN INSCRIPTIONS

### ETHIOPIA

## 5. ARABIC INSCRIPTIONS

١ ٢ ٣ ٤ ٥
1  2  3  4  5

٦ ٧ ٨ ٩ ٠
6  7  8  9  0

## AFGHANISTAN

Many early Afghanistan stamps show Tiger's head, many of these have ornaments protruding from outer ring, others show inscriptions in black.

Arabic Script

Mosque Gate & Crossed Cannons
The four characters are found somewhere on pictorial stamps. On some stamps only the middle two are found.

## BAHRAIN

## EGYPT

Postage

# INDIA - FEUDATORY STATES

## Jammu & Kashmir

Text and thickness of ovals vary. Some stamps have flower devices in corners.

## India-Hyderabad

## IRAN

Country Name

Royal Crown

Lion with Sword

Symbol

## IRAQ

## JORDAN

## LEBANON

Similar types have denominations at top and slightly different design.

# LIBYA

Country Name in various styles

Other Libya stamps show Eagle and Shield (head facing either direction) or Red, White and Black Shield (with or without eagle in center).

Without Country Name

## SAUDI ARABIA

Tughra (Central design)

Palm Tree and Swords

### SYRIA

### THRACE          YEMEN

### PAKISTAN

### PAKISTAN - BAHAWALPUR

Country Name in top panel, star and crescent

### TURKEY

Star & Crescent is a device found on many Turkish stamps, but is also found on stamps from other Arabic areas (see Pakistan-Bahawalpur)

Tughra (similar tughras can be found on stamps of Turkey in Asia, Afghanistan and Saudi Arabia)

Mohammed V

Mustafa Kemal

Plane, Star and Crescent

## TURKEY IN ASIA

Other Turkey in Asia pictorials show star & crescent.
Other stamps show tughra shown under Turkey.

## 6. GREEK INSCRIPTIONS

### GREECE

Country Name in various styles
(Some Crete stamps overprinted with the Greece country name are listed in Crete.)

Lepta

Drachma    Drachmas      Lepton

Abbreviated Country Name

Other forms of Country Name

No country name

### CRETE

Country Name

These words are on other stamps

Grosion

Crete stamps with a surcharge that have the year "1922" are listed under Greece.

## EPIRUS          IONIAN IS.

Country Name

## 7. CYRILLIC INSCRIPTIONS

## RUSSIA

Postage Stamp

Imperial Eagle

Postage in various styles

Abbreviation for Kopeck

Abbreviation for Ruble

Russian

Abbreviation for Russian Soviet Federated Socialist Republic

RSFSR stamps were overprinted (see below)

Abbreviation for Union of Soviet Socialist Republics

This item is footnoted in Latvia

## RUSSIA - Army of the North

"OKCA"

## RUSSIA - Wenden

## RUSSIAN OFFICES IN THE TURKISH EMPIRE

   These letters appear on other stamps of the Russian offices.

The unoverprinted version of this stamp and a similar stamp were overprinted by various countries (see below).

## ARMENIA

## BELARUS

## FAR EASTERN REPUBLIC

Country Name

## SOUTH RUSSIA

Country Name

## FINLAND

Circles and Dots
on stamps similar
to Imperial
Russia issues

## BATUM

Forms of Country Name

## TRANSCAUCASIAN FEDERATED REPUBLICS

 Abbreviation for
Country Name

## KAZAKHSTAN

Country Name

## KYRGYZSTAN

  Country Name

## ROMANIA

## TADJIKISTAN

Country Name & Abbreviation

## UKRAINE

Country Name in various forms

The trident appears
on many stamps,
usually as an overprint.

Abbreviation for
Ukrainian Soviet
Socialist Republic

## WESTERN UKRAINE

Abbreviation for
Country Name

## AZERBAIJAN

Country Name

**А.С.С.Р.**

Abbreviation for Azerbaijan
Soviet Socialist Republic

## MONTENEGRO

**ЦРНЕГОРЕ**

# ЦРНА ГОРА

Country Name in various forms

**ЦР.ГОРЕ**

Abbreviation
for country
name

No country name
(A similar Montenegro
stamp without country
name has same vignette.)

## SERBIA

**СРПСКА** **СРБИЈА**

Country Name in various forms

**СРП** **К.С.**

Abbreviation for country name

No country name

## SERBIA & MONTENEGRO

## YUGOSLAVIA

**ЈУГОСЛАВИЈА**

Showing country name

 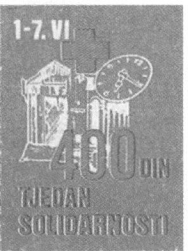

No Country Name

## MACEDONIA

**МАКЕДОНИЈА**

Country Name

**МАКЕДОНСКИ**
1997

Different form of Country Name

## BOSNIA & HERZEGOVINA
## (Serb Administration)

# РЕПУБЛИКА СРПСКА

Country Name

**РЕПУБЛИКЕ СРПСКЕ**

Different form of Country Name

No Country Name

## BULGARIA

Country Name    Postage

Stotinka

Stotinki (plural)    Abbreviation for
Stotinki

Country Name in various forms and styles

No country name

 Abbreviation for
Lev, leva

## MONGOLIA

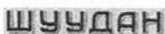

Country name in    Tugrik in Cyrillic
one word

Country name in    Mung in Cyrillic
two words

 Mung
in Mongolian

 Tugrik
in Mongolian

Arms

No Country Name

# Cover Supplies

## COVER SLEEVES
Protect your covers with clear polyethylene sleeves.
**Sold in packages of 100.**

### U.S. POSTAL CARD

3¾"

5⅞"

| Item | Retail | AA* |
|------|--------|-----|
| CV005 | $3.95 | $2.99 |

### U.S. FIRST DAY COVER #6

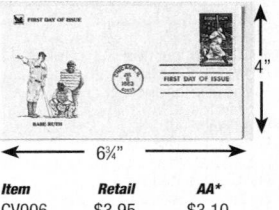

4"

6¾"

| Item | Retail | AA* |
|------|--------|-----|
| CV006 | $3.95 | $3.10 |

### CONTINENTAL POSTCARD

4¼"

6¼"

| Item | Retail | AA* |
|------|--------|-----|
| CV007 | $4.95 | $3.74 |

### EUROPEAN FIRST DAY COVER

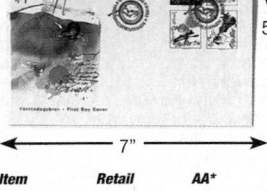

5⅜"

7"

| Item | Retail | AA* |
|------|--------|-----|
| CV009 | $4.95 | $3.74 |

### #10 BUSINESS ENVELOPE

4¾"

10"

| Item | Retail | AA* |
|------|--------|-----|
| CV010 | $5.95 | $4.49 |

## COVER BINDERS AND PAGES
Padded, durable, 3-ring binders will hold up to 100 covers. Features the "D" ring mechanism on the right hand side of album so you don't have to worry about creasing or wrinkling covers when opening or closing binder. Cover pages sold separately. Available in black with 1 or 2 pockets. Sold in packages of 10.

| Item | | Retail | AA* |
|------|--|--------|-----|
| CBRD | Red | $11.99 | $9.59 |
| CBBL | Blue | $11.99 | $9.59 |
| CBGY | Gray | $11.99 | $9.59 |
| CBBK | Black | $11.99 | $9.59 |
| SS2PGB | Pgs. 2-Pock. | $4.50 | $3.75 |
| SS2PG1B | Pgs. 1-Pock. | $4.50 | $3.75 |

## COVER BOX
Box measures 10½" x 7⅜" x 4¼" and will hold hundreds of covers.

| Item | Retail | AA* |
|------|--------|-----|
| CVBOX | $7.74 | $6.24 |

## U.S. POSTAL HISTORY SAMPLER
An entertaining and informative introduction to the many different U.S. postal history topics cover collections can be built. Topics covered include train wreck covers, fancy cancels, APO markings, campaign covers, flag cancels and many more. Available in either hardbound or softcover format.

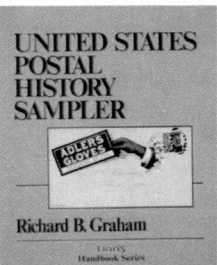

| Item | | Retail | AA* |
|------|--|--------|-----|
| LIN36 | Softcover | $14.95 | **$6.99** |

## AMOS ADVANTAGE

## To Order Call
# 1-800-572-6885
## www.amosadvantage.com

## INDEX AND IDENTIFIER

**All page numbers shown are those in this Volume 3.**

Postage stamps that do not have English words on them are shown in the Identifier which begins on page 1314.

# Vol. 3 Number Additions, Deletions & Changes

| Number in 2009 Catalogue | Number in 2010 Catalogue |
|---|---|

**German East Africa**
21 .......................................... deleted
new ...................................... 21a

**German States**
**North German Confederation**
new ...................................... 12d

**Great Britain**
new ...................................... 1088a
new ...................................... MH80e
MH93a ................................. MH92a
MH93b ................................. MH92b

**Guernsey**
488a ...................................... 488b
488b ...................................... 488c
488c ...................................... 488a
new ...................................... 925m
new ...................................... 925n

**Isle of Man**
new ...................................... 1110a
new ...................................... 1111a
new ...................................... 1112a
new ...................................... 1113a
new ...................................... 1114b
new ...................................... 1114c
new ...................................... 1115a
new ...................................... 1116a
new ...................................... 1117a
new ...................................... 1118a
new ...................................... 1119b
new ...................................... 1119c
new ...................................... 1173a
new ...................................... 1175a
new ...................................... 1183a
new ...................................... 1183b
new ...................................... 1242a
new ...................................... 1245a

**Greece**
new ...................................... 160a

**Greenland**
new ...................................... 226a

**Griqualand West**
new ...................................... 64a

**Guadeloupe**
new ...................................... 12a
new ...................................... 23a

**Guatemala**
new ...................................... 533a
new ...................................... 545a

**Hungary**
new ...................................... 962a-967a
new ...................................... 1004a-1011a
new ...................................... 1048a-1056Ca
new ...................................... 1585a

**Iceland**
new ...................................... 32c
new ...................................... 32d

**Iceland**
new ...................................... 62a
new ...................................... 65Ca
new ...................................... 132a

**Ifni**
new ...................................... 36
new ...................................... 45

**India – Convention States**

**Jind**
67a ........................................ deleted
69a ........................................ deleted
O29a ..................................... deleted

**Nabha**
O20a ..................................... deleted

**India - Feudatory States**

**Alwar**
1b .......................................... deleted
2c .......................................... deleted
new ........................................ 3a
new ........................................ 3b
new ........................................ 4b
4b ........................................... 4c
4c ........................................... 4d
new ........................................ 4e
new ........................................ 4f
new ........................................ 4g
new ........................................ 4h

**Bamra**
3b .......................................... deleted
8c .......................................... deleted
15b ........................................ deleted
15c ........................................ deleted

**Bhopal**
3a .......................................... deleted
19e ........................................ deleted
68 .......................................... deleted
68a ........................................ deleted
69 .......................................... deleted
70 .......................................... deleted
71 .......................................... deleted
75a ........................................ deleted
76c ........................................ deleted
new ........................................ 84a-90a
new ........................................ O14a
O30a ..................................... deleted
new ........................................ O31b
new ........................................ O31c
new ........................................ O31d
new ........................................ O31e
O32a ..................................... O32d
O32c ..................................... O32a
O32d ..................................... O32e
new ........................................ O32b
new ........................................ O32c
new ........................................ O32f
new ........................................ O33a
new ........................................ O33b
new ........................................ O33c
new ........................................ O33d

**Bhopal**
new ...................................... O34b
new ...................................... O34c
new ...................................... O34d
new ...................................... O35b
new ...................................... O35c
new ...................................... O36a
new ...................................... O36b
new ...................................... O36c
new ...................................... O36d
new ...................................... O39a
new ...................................... O40d
new ...................................... O40e
O41d ..................................... deleted
new ...................................... O41d
new ...................................... O42a
new ...................................... O42b
new ...................................... O42c
new ...................................... O42d
new ...................................... O45a
O58a ..................................... deleted
O58b ..................................... deleted
new ...................................... O59a

**Cochin**
new ........................................ 8a
11a ........................................ deleted
new ........................................ 12
new ........................................ 12d
new ........................................ 12A
new ........................................ 12Ae
new ........................................ 12Af
new ........................................ 12B
new ........................................ 12Bg
new ........................................ 12C
new ........................................ 12Ch
new ........................................ 90a
O2a ....................................... deleted

**Hyderabad**
new ........................................ 5c
5c ........................................... 5d

**Indore**
new ........................................ 20a
new ........................................ 22a
new ........................................ 24a

**Jaipur**
new ........................................ 16b
new ........................................ 18c
23 .......................................... deleted
23A ......................................... 23

**Jind**
11 .......................................... deleted

**Kishangarh**
new ........................................ 4a
new ........................................ 25Bc
new ........................................ 37a
54b ........................................ deleted
new ........................................ 59a
new ........................................ 60b

**Nowanuggur**
2b .......................................... deleted

**Rajasthan**
1-7b ...................................... deleted
new ........................................ 1b-7
new ........................................ 2c
new ........................................ 3b
new ........................................ 1c-7a
new ........................................ 11
new ........................................ 11a
new ........................................ 12a
new ........................................ 13a
new ........................................ 13b

**Sirmoor**
new ........................................ 12a
O7a ....................................... deleted

**Soruth**
14c ......................................... 14d
new ........................................ 14c
15a ........................................ deleted
new ........................................ 15a
new ........................................ 15b
23a ........................................ deleted
39c ........................................ deleted
new ........................................ 42a

**Travancore-Cochin**
19 .......................................... deleted

**Italy**
new ........................................ 23f

# INDEX TO ADVERTISERS
## 2010 VOLUME 3

# National Album Series

The National series offers a panoramic view of our country's heritage through postage stamps. It is the most complete and comprehensive U.S. album series you can buy. There are spaces for every major U.S. stamp listed in the Scott Catalogue, including Special Printings, Newspaper stamps and much more.

- Pages printed on one side.

- All spaces identified by Scott numbers.

- All major variety of stamps are either illustrated or described.

- Chemically neutral paper protects stamps.

- Sold as page units only. Binders, slipcases and labels sold separately.

| Item | | | Retail |
|------|------|---------|--------|
| 100NTL1 | 1845-1934 | 108 pgs | $64.99 |
| 100NTL2 | 1935-1976 | 108 pgs | $64.99 |
| 100NTL3 | 1977-1993 | 114 pgs | $64.99 |
| 100NTL4 | 1994-1999 | 96 pgs | $64.99 |
| 100NTL5 | 2000-2005 | 126 pgs | $64.99 |

Supplemented in March.

# U.S. National Kit

The most complete and comprehensive U.S. stamp album is now available in a money-saving complete kit package! This kit contains all five National album parts, 4 large National Series 3-ring binders, slipcases, protector sheets and National album labels, pre-cut value pack of black ScottMounts and the *U.S. Specialized Catalogue*.

| Item | Retail |
|------|--------|
| NATLKIT | $649.99 |

What ever your collecting specialty Scott Publishing has an album for you. For more information on the entire line of Scott albums and products visit your local stamp dealer or online at:
**www.amosadvantage.com**

**SCOTT®**

**1-800-572-6885**
P.O. BOX 828
Sidney OH 45365
**www.amosadvantage.com**

**AMOS**
PUBLISHING

# 2010
# VOLUME 3
# DEALER DIRECTORY
# YELLOW PAGE LISTINGS

**This section of your Scott Catalogue contains advertisements to help you conveniently find what you need, when you need it...!**

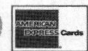

## China

**THE STAMP ACT**
PO Box 1136
Belmont, CA 94002
PH: 650-703-2342
PH: 650-592-3315
FAX: 650-508-8104
thestampact@sbcglobal.net
www.thestampact.com

## Ducks

**MICHAEL JAFFE**
PO Box 61484
Vancouver, WA 98666
PH: 360-695-6161
PH: 800-782-6770
FAX: 360-695-1616
mjaffe@brookmanstamps.com
www.brookmanstamps.com

## Egypt

**KAMAL SHALABY**
3, Aly Basha Fahmy St.
8th Floor, Gleem
Alexandria
EGYPT
PH/FAX: +203-5840254
Cell: +2-0105838213
alexstamplover@yahoo.com
www.stampsofegypt.com

## German Colonies

**COLONIAL STAMP COMPANY**
5757 Wilshire Blvd. PH #8
Los Angeles, CA 90036
PH: 323-933-9435
FAX: 323-939-9930
Toll Free in North America
PH: 877-272-6693
FAX: 877-272-6694
info@colonialstampcompany.com
www.colonialstampcompany.com

## German E. Africa (B & G)

**COLONIAL STAMP COMPANY**
5757 Wilshire Blvd. PH #8
Los Angeles, CA 90036
PH: 323-933-9435
FAX: 323-939-9930
Toll Free in North America
PH: 877-272-6693
FAX: 877-272-6694
info@colonialstampcompany.com
www.colonialstampcompany.com

## German New Guinea (B & G)

**COLONIAL STAMP COMPANY**
5757 Wilshire Blvd. PH #8
Los Angeles, CA 90036
PH: 323-933-9435
FAX: 323-939-9930
Toll Free in North America
PH: 877-272-6693
FAX: 877-272-6694
info@colonialstampcompany.com
www.colonialstampcompany.com

## German So. West Africa

**COLONIAL STAMP COMPANY**
5757 Wilshire Blvd. PH #8
Los Angeles, CA 90036
PH: 323-933-9435
FAX: 323-939-9930
Toll Free in North America
PH: 877-272-6693
FAX: 877-272-6694
info@colonialstampcompany.com
www.colonialstampcompany.com

## German States

**COLONIAL STAMP COMPANY**
5757 Wilshire Blvd. PH #8
Los Angeles, CA 90036
PH: 323-933-9435
FAX: 323-939-9930
Toll Free in North America
PH: 877-272-6693
FAX: 877-272-6694
info@colonialstampcompany.com
www.colonialstampcompany.com

**TILL NEUMANN CLASSIC PHILATELY**
PO Box 10 29 40
28029 Bremen
GERMANY
PH: +49.421.79 40 260
FAX: +49.421.79 40 261
tn@klassische-philatelie.de
www.klassische-philatelie.de

## Germany

**HENRY GITNER PHILATELISTS, INC.**
PO Box 3077-S
Middletown, NY 10940
PH: 845-343-5151
PH: 800-947-8267
FAX: 845-343-0068
hgitner@hgitner.com
www.hgitner.com

## Germany

**WWW.WORLDSTAMPS.COM**
242 West Saddle River Road
Suite C
Upper Saddle River, NJ 07458
PH: 201-236-8122
FAX: 201-236-8133 Fax
by mail:
Frank Geiger Philatelists
info@WorldStamps.com
www.WorldStamps.com

## Gold Coast

**COLONIAL STAMP COMPANY**
5757 Wilshire Blvd. PH #8
Los Angeles, CA 90036
PH: 323-933-9435
FAX: 323-939-9930
Toll Free in North America
PH: 877-272-6693
FAX: 877-272-6694
info@colonialstampcompany.com
www.colonialstampcompany.com

## Great Britain

**ARON R. HALBERSTAM PHILATELISTS, LTD.**
PO Box 150168
Van Brunt Station
Brooklyn, NY 11215-0168
PH: 718-788-3978
FAX: 718-965-3099
arh@arhstamps.com
www.arhstamps.com

**COLONIAL STAMP COMPANY**
5757 Wilshire Blvd. PH #8
Los Angeles, CA 90036
PH: 323-933-9435
FAX: 323-939-9930
Toll Free in North America
PH: 877-272-6693
FAX: 877-272-6694
info@colonialstampcompany.com
www.colonialstampcompany.com

## Hong Kong

**ARON R. HALBERSTAM PHILATELISTS, LTD.**
PO Box 150168
Van Brunt Station
Brooklyn, NY 11215-0168
PH: 718-788-3978
FAX: 718-965-3099
arh@arhstamps.com
www.arhstamps.com

## Hong Kong

**COLONIAL STAMP COMPANY**
5757 Wilshire Blvd. PH #8
Los Angeles, CA 90036
PH: 323-933-9435
FAX: 323-939-9930
Toll Free in North America
PH: 877-272-6693
FAX: 877-272-6694
info@colonialstampcompany.com
www.colonialstampcompany.com

**THE STAMP ACT**
PO Box 1136
Belmont, CA 94002
PH: 650-703-2342
PH: 650-592-3315
FAX: 650-508-8104
thestampact@sbcglobal.net
www.thestampact.com

## India & States

**COLONIAL STAMP COMPANY**
5757 Wilshire Blvd. PH #8
Los Angeles, CA 90036
PH: 323-933-9435
FAX: 323-939-9930
Toll Free in North America
PH: 877-272-6693
FAX: 877-272-6694
info@colonialstampcompany.com
www.colonialstampcompany.com

## Iraq

**COLONIAL STAMP COMPANY**
5757 Wilshire Blvd. PH #8
Los Angeles, CA 90036
PH: 323-933-9435
FAX: 323-939-9930
Toll Free in North America
PH: 877-272-6693
FAX: 877-272-6694
info@colonialstampcompany.com
www.colonialstampcompany.com

## Israel

**HENRY GITNER PHILATELISTS, INC.**
PO Box 3077-S
Middletown, NY 10940
PH: 845-343-5151
PH: 800-947-8267
FAX: 845-343-0068
hgitner@hgitner.com
www.hgitner.com

## Italy

**HENRY GITNER
PHILATELISTS, INC.**
PO Box 3077-S
Middletown, NY 10940
PH: 845-343-5151
PH: 800-947-8267
FAX: 845-343-0068
hgitner@hgitner.com
www.hgitner.com

**WWW.WORLDSTAMPS.COM**
242 West Saddle River Road
Suite C
Upper Saddle River, NJ 07458
PH: 201-236-8122
FAX: 201-236-8133 Fax
by mail:
Frank Geiger Philatelists
info@WorldStamps.com
www.WorldStamps.com

**ZANARIA FILATELICI**
Via Santa Margherita 6
20121 Milano
ITALY
PH: +39 02 805 24 27
FAX: +39 02 805 11 86
info@zanaria.com
www.zanaria.com

## Japan

**MICHAEL ROGERS, INC.**
415 S. Orlando Ave.
Winter Park, FL 32789-3683
PH: 407-644-2290
PH: 800-843-3751
FAX: 407-645-4434
Stamps@michaelrogersinc.com
www.michaelrogersinc.com

**WWW.WORLDSTAMPS.COM**
242 West Saddle River Road
Suite C
Upper Saddle River, NJ 07458
PH: 201-236-8122
FAX: 201-236-8133 Fax
by mail:
Frank Geiger Philatelists
info@WorldStamps.com
www.WorldStamps.com

## Korea

**MICHAEL ROGERS, INC.**
415 S. Orlando Ave.
Winter Park, FL 32789-3683
PH: 407-644-2290
PH: 800-843-3751
FAX: 407-645-4434
Stamps@michaelrogersinc.com
www.michaelrogersinc.com

## Latin America

**GUY SHAW**
PO Box 27138
San Diego, CA 92198
PH/FAX: 858-485-8269
guyshaw@guyshaw.com
www.guyshaw.com

## Manchukuo

**MICHAEL ROGERS, INC.**
415 S. Orlando Ave.
Winter Park, FL 32789-3683
PH: 407-644-2290
PH: 800-843-3751
FAX: 407-645-4434
Stamps@michaelrogersinc.com
www.michaelrogersinc.com

## Middle East-Arab

**MICHAEL ROGERS, INC.**
415 S. Orlando Ave.
Winter Park, FL 32789-3683
PH: 407-644-2290
PH: 800-843-3751
FAX: 407-645-4434
Stamps@michaelrogersinc.com
www.michaelrogersinc.com

## New Issues

**DAVIDSON'S STAMP
SERVICE**
PO Box 36355
Indianapolis, IN 46236-0355
PH: 317-826-2620
ed-davidson@earthlink.net
www.newstampissues.com

## New Issues - Retail

**BOMBAY PHILATELIC INC.**
PO Box 90937
Raleigh, NC 27675
PH: 561-499-7990
FAX: 561-499-7553
sales@bombaystamps.com
www.bombaystamps.com

## Postal History

**TILL NEUMANN CLASSIC
PHILATELY**
PO Box 10 29 40
28029 Bremen
GERMANY
PH: +49.421.79 40 260
FAX: +49.421.79 40 261
tn@klassische-philatelie.de
www.klassische-philatelie.de

## South America

**GUY SHAW**
PO Box 27138
San Diego, CA 92198
PH/FAX: 858-485-8269
guyshaw@guyshaw.com
www.guyshaw.com

## STAMP STORES

### California

**BROSIUS STAMP, COIN &
SUPPLIES**
2105 Main St.
Santa Monica, CA 90405
PH: 310-396-7480
FAX: 310-396-7455

**COLONIAL STAMP CO./
BRITISH EMPIRE
SPECIALIST**
5757 Wilshire Blvd. PH #8
(by appt.)
Los Angeles, CA 90036
PH: 323-933-9435
FAX: 323-939-9930
Toll Free in North America
PH: 877-272-6693
FAX: 877-272-6694
info@colonialstampcompany.com
www.colonialstampcompany.com

**FISCHER-WOLK
PHILATELICS**
22762 Aspan St.
Suite 211
Lake Forest, CA 92630
PH: 949-837-2932
fw@occoxmail.com

**NATICK STAMPS & HOBBIES**
411 E. Huntington Dr.
Suite 209
Arcadia, CA 91006
PH: 626-445-2185
natickco@att.net

## STAMP STORES

### Colorado

**SHOWCASE STAMPS**
3865 Wadsworth
Wheat Ridge, CO 80033
PH: 303-425-9252
kbeiner@colbi.net
www.showcasestamps.com

### Connecticut

**SILVER CITY COIN & STAMP**
41 Colony St.
Meriden, CT 06451
PH: 203-235-7634
FAX: 203-237-4915

### Georgia

**STAMPS UNLIMITED OF
GEORGIA, INC.**
100 Peachtree St.
Suite 1460
Atlanta, GA 30303
PH: 404-688-9161
tonyroozen@yahoo.com

### Illinois

**DR. ROBERT FRIEDMAN &
SONS**
2029 W. 75th St.
Woodridge, IL 60517
PH: 800-588-8100
FAX: 630-985-1588
drbobstamps@yahoo.com
www.drbobfriedmanstamps.com

**SIDMORE STAMPS**
145 E. Lincoln Hwy.
DeKalb, IL 60115
PH: 815-787-7000
sidmorestamps@verizon.net
www.sidmorestamps.net
Authorized APS Dealer

### Indiana

**KNIGHT STAMP & COIN CO.**
237 Main St.
Hobart, IN 46342
PH: 219-942-4341
PH: 800-634-2646
knight@knightcoin.com
www.knightcoin.com

---

## STAMP STORES

### Massachusetts

**KAPPY'S COINS & STAMPS**
534 Washington St.
Norwood, MA 02062
PH: 781-762-5552
kappyscoins@aol.com

### New Jersey

**BERGEN STAMPS & COLLECTIBLES**
306 Queen Anne Rd.
Teaneck, NJ 07666
PH: 201-836-8987

**PHILLY STAMP & COIN CO., INC.**
683 Haddon Ave.
Collingswood, NJ 08108
PH: 856-854-5333
FAX: 856-854-5377
phillysc@verizon.net
www.phillystampandcoin.com

**TRENTON STAMP & COIN CO.**
Thomas DeLuca
Store: Forest Glen Plaza
1804 Route 33
Hamilton Square, NJ 08690
Mail: PO Box 8574
Trenton, NJ 08650
PH: 800-446-8664
PH: 609-584-8100
FAX: 609-587-8664
TOMD4TSC@aol.com

### New York

**CHAMPION STAMP CO., INC.**
432 W. 54th St.
New York, NY 10019
PH: 212-489-8130
FAX: 212-581-8130
championstamp@aol.com
www.championstamp.com

### Ohio

**HILLTOP STAMP SERVICE**
Richard A. Peterson
PO Box 626
Wooster, OH 44691
PH: 330-262-8907
PH: 330-262-5378
hilltop@bright.net

**THE LINK STAMP CO.**
3461 E. Livingston Ave.
Columbus, OH 43227
PH/FAX: 614-237-4125
PH/FAX: 800-546-5726

### Texas

**HERITAGE AUCTION GALLERIES**
3500 Maple Ave, 17th Floor
Dallas, TX 75219
PH: 800-872-6467
FAX: 214-409-1425
Stamps@HA.com
HA.com

### Virginia

**KENNEDY'S STAMPS & COINS, INC.**
7059 Brookfield Plaza
Springfield, VA 22150
PH: 703-569-7300
FAX: 703-569-7644
j.w.kennedy@verizon.net

**LATHEROW & CO., INC.**
5054 Lee Hwy.
Arlington, VA 22207
PH: 703-538-2727
PH: 800-647-4624
FAX: 703-538-5210
latherow@filatco.com

### Topicals

**E. JOSEPH MCCONNELL**
PO Box 683
Monroe, NY 10949
PH: 845-783-9791
FAX: 845-782-0347
ejstamps@gmail.com
www.EJMcConnell.com

### Topicals-Columbus

**MR. COLUMBUS**
PO Box 1492
Fennville, MI 49408
PH: 269-543-4755
columbus@accn.org

### United States

**ACS STAMP COMPANY**
10831 Chambers Way
Commerce City, CO 80022
PH: 303-841-8666
ACS@ACSStamp.com
www.acsstamp.com

**BROOKMAN STAMP CO.**
PO Box 90
Vancouver, WA 98666
PH: 360-695-1391
PH: 800-545-4871
FAX: 360-695-1616
larry@brookmanstamps.com
www.brookmanstamps.com

### U.S.-Collections Wanted

**DR. ROBERT FRIEDMAN & SONS**
2029 W. 75th St.
Woodridge, IL 60517
PH: 800-588-8100
FAX: 630-985-1588
drbobstamps@yahoo.com
www.drbobfriedmanstamps.com

### U.S.-Rare Stamps

**HERITAGE AUCTION GALLERIES**
3500 Maple Ave, 17th Floor
Dallas, TX 75219
PH: 800-872-6467
FAX: 214-409-1425
Stamps@HA.com
HA.com

### Want Lists

**CHARLES P. SCHWARTZ**
PO Box 165
Mora, MN 55051
PH: 320-679-4705
charlesp@ecenet.com

### Want Lists-British Empire 1840-1935 German Cols./Offices

**COLONIAL STAMP COMPANY**
5757 Wilshire Blvd. PH #8
Los Angeles, CA 90036
PH: 323-933-9435
FAX: 323-939-9930
Toll Free in North America
PH: 877-272-6693
FAX: 877-272-6694
info@colonialstampcompany.com
www.colonialstampcompany.com

### Wanted-Estates

**HERITAGE AUCTION GALLERIES**
3500 Maple Ave, 17th Floor
Dallas, TX 75219
PH: 800-872-6467
FAX: 214-409-1425
Stamps@HA.com
HA.com

### Wanted to Buy

**HERITAGE AUCTION GALLERIES**
3500 Maple Ave, 17th Floor
Dallas, TX 75219
PH: 800-872-6467
FAX: 214-409-1425
Stamps@HA.com
HA.com

### Wanted-U.S.

**HERITAGE AUCTION GALLERIES**
3500 Maple Ave, 17th Floor
Dallas, TX 75219
PH: 800-872-6467
FAX: 214-409-1425
Stamps@HA.com
HA.com

### Wanted-U.S. Collections

**BROOKMAN STAMP CO.**
PO Box 90
Vancouver, WA 98666
PH: 360-695-1391
PH: 800-545-4871
FAX: 360-695-1616
larry@brookmanstamps.com
www.brookmanstamps.com

### Wanted-Worldwide Collections

**DR. ROBERT FRIEDMAN & SONS**
2029 W. 75th St.
Woodridge, IL 60517
PH: 800-588-8100
FAX: 630-985-1588
drbobstamps@yahoo.com
www.drbobfriedmanstamps.com

**THE STAMP CENTER DUTCH COUNTRY AUCTIONS**
4115 Concord Pike
Wilmington, DE 19803
PH: 302-478-8740
FAX: 302-478-8779
auctions@thestampcenter.com
www.thestampcenter.com

### Websites

**ACS STAMP COMPANY**
10831 Chambers Way
Commerce City, CO 80022
PH: 303-841-8666
ACS@ACSStamp.com
www.acsstamp.com

**HERITAGE AUCTION GALLERIES**
3500 Maple Ave, 17th Floor
Dallas, TX 75219
PH: 800-872-6467
FAX: 214-409-1425
Stamps@HA.com
HA.com

### Worldwide-Year Sets

**WWW.WORLDSTAMPS.COM**
242 West Saddle River Road
Suite C
Upper Saddle River, NJ 07458
PH: 201-236-8122
FAX: 201-236-8133 Fax
by mail:
Frank Geiger Philatelists
info@WorldStamps.com
www.WorldStamps.com

### Worldwide